*Profiling 10,183 New Jersey manufacturing, processing, & wholesale distribution establishments...*

# New Jersey Manufacturers Register®

Published by

(847) 864-7000 • Fax: (847) 332-1100

1633 Central Street • Evanston, IL 60201

info@manufacturersnews.com • manufacturersnews.com

No listing, page or other part of this publication may be reproduced, scanned, keypunched, stored in a retrieval system or transmitted in any form or by any means without the prior written consent of the publisher.

The information in this publication is for the confidential use of the purchaser only. This information is not to be distributed, sold or otherwise provided to a third party in any form. This information is not to be used illegally.

This publication contains copyrighted information. The companies included and many of the data elements listed were selected and formulated based on educated and creative judgments by MNI editors. Any unauthorized usage, reproduction or appropriation of this information, including representing any of the information as set to appear in non-MNI publications (printed or electronic) is strictly prohibited, and will be prosecuted to the fullest extent of the law. This directory also contains seeded information to detect unauthorized usage.

This information is provided for use in accordance with all applicable federal, state and local laws. Companies herein have not opted in to receive unsolicited advertisements via fax or e-mail.

While every effort has been made to ensure the completeness and accuracy of the listings herein, the publisher cannot and does not guarantee that every one of the hundreds of thousands of facts contained is correct. The publisher waives any responsibility for liability arising from errors or omissions.

Copyright 2015
Printed in U.S.A.

ISSN 1094-1010
ISBN 978-1-58202-875-0

PATERSON FREE PUBLIC LIBRARY
250 Broadway
Paterson, New Jersey 07501

# How To Use The
# NEW JERSEY MANUFACTURERS REGISTER®

This directory is divided into seven sections, each of which serves as a different guide to useful company information. Refer to the Table of Contents page to find the beginning of each section.

## INDUSTRY

Lists companies by product or industrial service. Use this section for purchasing or finding suppliers of a particular product or service.

### DIE CASTINGS

**ABCO Die Casters, Inc.**
Email: jvitollo@abcodiecasters.com
Founded in 1971, serving numerous industries throughout North America by supplying quality zinc die castings & powder coated components
Phone—(973) 624-7030
Fax—(973) 624-7425
Web—www.abcodiecasters.com
**39 Tompkins Point Rd., Newark 07114**

Carteret Die Casting Corp.
Phone—(732) 246-0070
74 Veronica Ave., P.O. Box 5610, Somerset 08875

Premier Die Casting Co., Inc.
Phone—(732) 634-3000
1177 Rahway Ave., Avenel 07001

## U.S. INDUSTRIAL EXPANSION & RELOCATION GUIDE

A state by state breakdown of facts and figures to aid companies in their site and facility planning decisions. Contains relevant information about each state's manufacturing climate, industries, tax rates and business incentives. Also features listings of organizations that can assist companies seeking to relocate or expand.

## ALPHABETICAL

Each company is listed in its proper alphabetical sequence, followed by its address and phone number.

A & A Co., Inc., 2700 S. Clinton Ave., South Plainfield, 07080 .................. (908) 561-2378
A & A Concrete Products, Inc.,
  2 S. Corporate Dr., P.O. Box 108, Riverdale, 07457 ....................... (973) 835-2239
† A & A Iron & Metal Co., LLC, 2006 40th St., North Bergen, 07047 ......... (201) 865-1370
A & A Ironworks, Inc., 955 Burnt Meadow Rd., Hewitt 07421 ................ (973) 728-4300
A & A Soft Pretzel Co., 1100 N. 32nd St., Camden, 08105 .................... (856) 338-0208
A & C Catalysts, Inc., 1600 W. Blancke St., Linden, 07036 ................... (908) 474-9393
A & D Industrial & Marine Repair,
  900 Port Reading Ave., Ste. B-2, Port Reading, 07064 .................... (732) 541-1481
A & F Electroplating, Inc., 106 Ashland Ave., West Orange, 07052 ......... (973) 736-4344
A & F Sign Company LLC, 28 E. Railway Ave., Paterson, 07503 ............. (973) 278-3707
A & F Tool, 930 Magnolia Ave., Elizabeth, 07201 ........................... (973) 262-1792
A & J Canvas Co., Inc., Maple Spruce St., P.O. Box 30, Rosenhayn, 08352 .... (856) 451-5606
A & J Tool Specialties, Inc., 235 Morris Ave., Summit, 07901 .............. (908) 277-0550
A & L Plastics Co., Inc., 2 Municipal Rd., P.O. Box 160, Newton, 07860 ...... (973) 383-2221
A & R Recycling Co.,
  1004 Union Landing Rd., P.O. Box 2440, Cinnaminson, 08077 .......... (856) 829-1712
A & R Sewing Co., Inc., 451 Communipaw Ave., Jersey City, 07304 ....... (201) 332-0622
A & S Packaging & Display Corp., 120 Kero Rd., Carlstadt, 07072 ......... (201) 531-1900
★ A & S Screen Printing, LP, 2305-B Garry Rd., Riverton, 08077 .......... (609) 267-4830
A A A Pharmaceutical, Inc., 157-160 W. Jefferson St., Paulsboro, 08066 ... (609) 288-6060
A A A Stamp & Seal Mfg. Co., 361 N. Midland Ave., Saddle Brook, 07663 .. (201) 796-1500
A A Graphics, Inc. 431 N. Midland Ave., Unit C, Saddle Brook. 07663 ...... (201) 398-0710

## GEOGRAPHICAL

Each company is listed alphabetically by city and contains as many as 30 different facts per company listing such as:
- key executive names
- employee counts
- years in business
- product descriptions

and much more.

**Florham Park**
(Morris—N.W.)

BASF CORPORATION (H Q)
100 Park Ave. (07932)
Phone—**(973) 245-6000**
National—(800) 526-1072
Fax—(973) 245-6714
www.basf.us
Email—kelley.white@basf.com
Chrm., CEO—Hans Engel
Pres., Ex. V-P. & CFO—Andre Becker
Pres. & Ex. V-P., Cust. & Market Dev.—Beate Ehle
Pres. & Ex. V-P., Catalysts Div.—Kenneth Lane
Sr. V-P., Gen. Counsel & CCO—Matthew Lepore
V-P., Chief Comms. Officer—Robin Rotenberg
Sr. V-P., Hum. Res.—Judy Zagorski
Corp. Media Rels. Mgr.—Kelley P. White
SIC—2899; Corporate headquarters; industrial chemicals; Brand name— Ecovio; Elastopave; Luquafleece; Soluplus; Glysantin; Basotect; Green Sense; Sonneborn; Headline; Termidor; Phantom; Tonalin CLA
Employs—1400; Estab.—1958
Worldwide: 112,000
Sales—$99Bil
325,000 sq ft site, Distrib.—Intl.
Publicly owned corporation

## S.I.C.

Each company is listed under its U.S. Govt. Standard Industrial Classification Number; including complete address, phone, name and title of decision maker, number of employees, and product description.

### 33 PRIMARY METAL INDUSTRIES

**3312 Blast furnaces & steel mills**

47 Industries, LLC, 59 2nd Ave., Raritan 08869
  Owner—Mike Palazzo, 1 emp., *Aluminum & stainless steel fabrication* ............. (908) 526-8865
A & A Ironworks, Inc., 955 Burnt Meadow Rd., Hewitt 07421
  Pres.—Adam G. Muzer, 15 emp., *Ironwork & structural steel fabrication* ............. (973) 728-4300
A & R Recycling Co., 1004 Union Landing Rd., P.O. Box 2440, Cinnaminson 08077
  Pres.—Anthony Tognini, 14 emp., *Metal recycling* ............. (856) 829-1712
A R J Custom Fabrication, Inc., 151 Taylor St., Trenton 08638
  Pres.—Anthony Jones, 10 emp., *Stainless steel fabrication* ............. (609) 695-6227
Airmet, Inc., 671 N. 3rd St., Newark 07107
  Pres.—Stephen A. Yavorski, Sr., 6 emp., *Metal fences, gates, railings, steel* ............. (973) 481-5550
Alloy Welding Co., Inc., 6-A Culnen Dr., Somerville 08876
  Pres.—Leonard F. Schaffenberger, 10 emp., *Structural steel & steel fabrication* ............. (908) 218-1551

## PARENT COMPANY

Each parent company/home office is listed alphabetically followed by its subsidiaries among the state's manufacturers, processors, wholesalers and distributors.

**JOHNSON & JOHNSON**
1 Johnson & Johnson Plz., New Brunswick NJ 08933 ................. (732) 524-0400
  Worldwide Chrm., Consumer Div.—Jesse Wu; CEO—Alex Gorsky;
  V-P., Fin. & CFO—Dominic J. Caruso; V-P., Inv. Rels.—Louise Mehrotra
Ethicon, Inc., 737 U.S. Highway 22 W., P.O. Box 151, Somerville, 08876 ....... (908) 218-0707
Janssen Pharmaceuticals, Inc.,
  1125 Trenton-Harbourton Rd., P.O. Box 200, Titusville, 08560 ............. (908) 218-6000
Janssen Research & Development, LLC, A Div. of Johnson & Johnson,
  920 U.S. Highway 202, P.O. Box 300, Raritan, 08869 ................. (908) 704-4000
Johnson & Johnson Consumer Companies, Inc. (H Q),
  199 Grandview Rd., Skillman, 08558 ................. (908) 874-1000

## COUNTY BREAKDOWNS & GROWTH CHARTS

A useful tool to establish sales territories. Counties are divided into sections alphabetically followed by the name of each city. Our 5 year growth charts show manufacturing and distribution locations by county, city and industry.

**Manufacturers' News, Inc.**
Identify & Contact U.S. Manufacturers

1633 Central St. • Evanston, IL 60201
847-864-7000 • Fax: 847-332-1100
info@manufacturersnews.com
manufacturersnews.com

Chairman.................................Howard S. Dubin
President/CEO...........................Thomas G. Dubin
Chief Operating Officer.......................George Kartsounes
Chief Technology Officer ..................Scott G. Kartsounes

**Editorial**
Executive Editor ...............................Steven J. Garland
Senior Editors......................Stephen Fowler, Laura Saaf
Editors.................................... Monica Kinchen
Assistant Editor.............Vanessa Brown, Michelle Smith,
Savan Poeut
Senior Researchers........................ Mabel Burton, Allan Zeitlin
Researchers......................... Mitchell Aronov, Wendy Braun,
Violet Espinoza, Sandra Gardner, John Hardrick,
Charles Hesketh, Melissa Hitson, Melanie Hooper,
George Ikhtari, Thomas Lang, Gwen Lester, Robert Kwitek,
Steve Mattingly, Derek Murga, Bobbi Sue Reilly,
Joell Todd, Louise Wilson
Senior Copy Editor ............Nancy Garland, Dajuan Harmon,
Adam Parrilli
Copy Editors.................................Dwanna Adams,
Trina Billups-Jones, Vanessa Garvy, Thi Navi Thach
Advertising Copy Editor................................. Liliana Martinez

**Production**
Production Manager...................... Jennifer Gorman
Asst. Production Manager ...........................Erik Nanstiel
Graphic Artist........................................Carrie Bernstein
QC Coord. .............................................. Becki Lane
Production Assistant ......................... Trish Rivera-Ostapowicz

**Operations**
Mailroom Manager.......................Adrian Guerrero
Public Relations Manager..........................Jennifer Ratcliff
Shipping Department Manager............Amilcar Ivan Rayo

**Information Technology**
Technical Support Manager ................... Anthony Benitez
Technical Support Specialist....................... Steve Andraws
Software Developer........................ Karam ShamasYousif
Sales Support ....................................... Kati Hungerford
Data Research Intern.............................. Ivan Kavanagh

**Customer Service**
Manager...............................................Lori Henry
Customer Service Representatives ..............Cornelia Bora,
Annie O'Connor, Jack Kessie, Karen Weissmuller
**Advertising Contracts**
Supervisor................................................Marina Turcinovic

**Sales**
Product Sales Executives................... Robert Burke, Jr.,
Stephen Deutser, Micah Jackson, Barbara Levin
Advertising Sales Executives..........Michael Carney, Mike Casper,
Denice Chiles, Mark Huskins, Stacie Jarecki, Bernard Levin,
Jeffrey Mash, Ira Rosenbaum, Barbara Savini, Sherri Salomon,
Charles Scherer, Kathy Shorr, Jon Shulman, Brian Weber
Advertising Administrator............................Dave Valenta

# NEW JERSEY MANUFACTURERS REGISTER®
# Table of Contents

# STAND OUT
## from the competition!
### with a display ad or bold-type telephone listing in next year's edition!

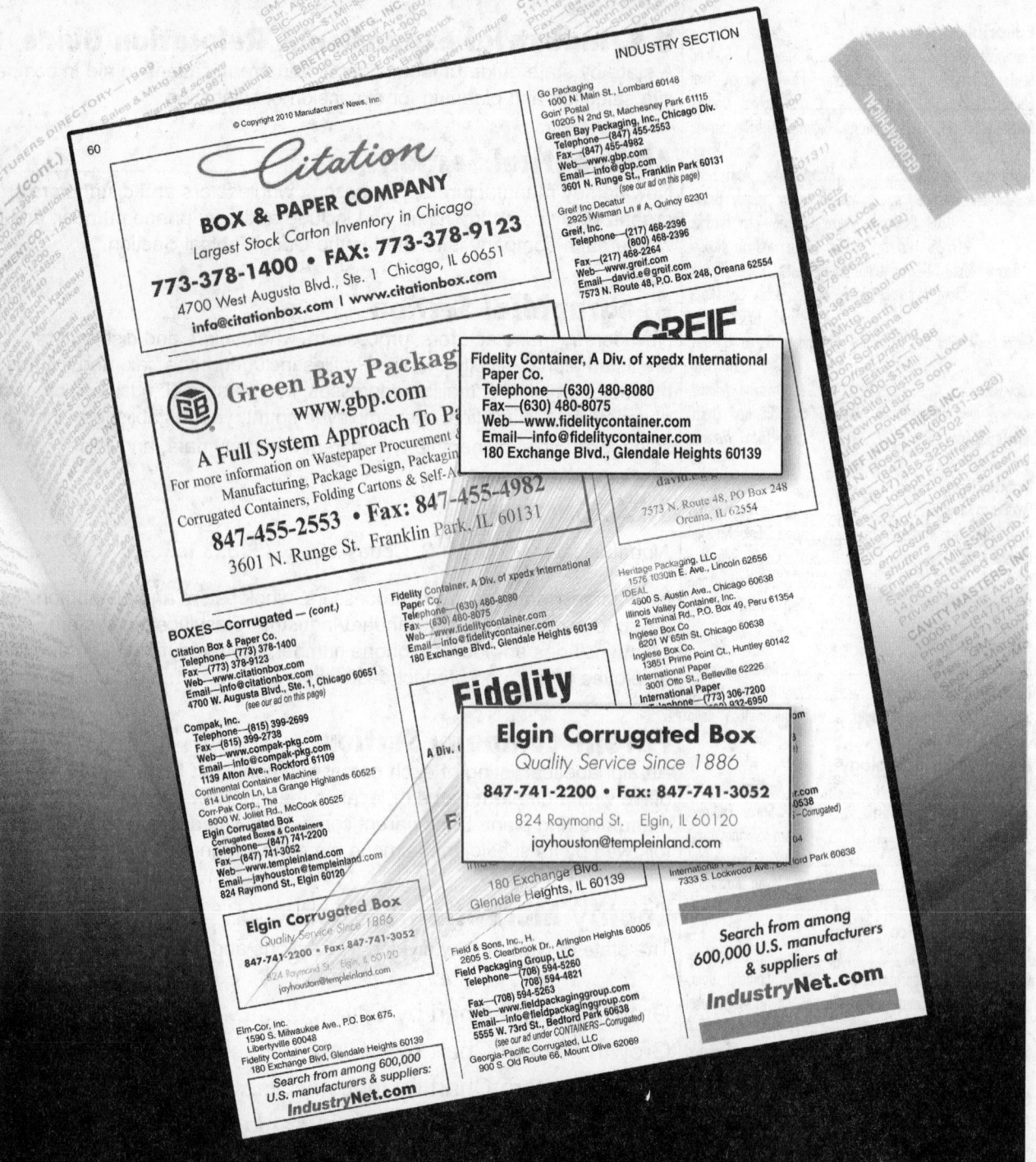

Many buyers use the **INDUSTRY SECTION** to find in-state suppliers and services. Only display advertisers can supply the detailed product information needed to make these purchasing decisions. Buyers call advertisers first!

## Call 847-864-7590 to reserve your ad or bold-type listing in next year's edition!

# Industry Section

## ABRASIVE GRINDING WHEELS

Noritake Co., Inc. (H Q)
Phone—(201) 796-2222
15-22 Fair Lawn Ave., Fair Lawn 07410
Sample Marshall Laboratories, Inc.
Phone—(201) 933-0570
63 Park Ave., Lyndhurst 07071
Web Industries, Inc.
Phone—(973) 335-1200
5 Mars Ct., P.O. Box 237, Montville 07045

## ABRASIVES

Beacut Abrasives Corp.
Phone—(973) 249-1420
788 Paterson Ave., East Rutherford 07073
Chamberlain's VACU-Blast Sales
Phone—(856) 829-6444
1200 Bannard St., P.O. Box 225, Cinnaminson 08077
Easy Abrasives, LLC (H Q)
Phone—(973) 575-7879
16 Passaic Ave., Unit 8, Fairfield 07004
Hall Co. Abrasives, William R.
Phone—(856) 784-6700
901 E. Gibbsboro Rd., Lindenwold 08021
**Indasa U.S.A., Inc.**
**Phone—(800) 326-5909 / (973) 916-0090**
**Fax—(973) 227-1144**
**Web—www.indasa-abrasives.com**
**Email—salesusa@indasausa.com**
**23 Madison Rd., Fairfield 07004**
Muenz Engineered Sales Co.
Phone—(908) 273-6755
21 Chatham Rd., Summit 07901
Robinson Tech International Corp.
Phone—(973) 287-6458
310 Fairfield Rd., Fairfield 07004

## ABRASIVES — Coated

Indasa U. S. A., Inc.
Phone—(800) 916-0090
23 Madison Rd., Fairfield 07004
**Indasa U.S.A., Inc.**
**Phone—(800) 326-5909 / (973) 916-0090**
**Fax—(973) 227-1144**
**Web—www.indasa-abrasives.com**
**Email—salesusa@indasausa.com**
**23 Madison Rd., Fairfield 07004**

## ABRASIVES — Diamond

Advanced Abrasives Corp.
Phone—(856) 665-9300
7980 National Hwy., Pennsauken 08110

## ABSORBENT PRODUCTS

SPC Sorbent Products Co., Inc.
Phone—(732) 302-0080
645 Howard Ave., Somerset 08873

## ACCOUNTANTS

**ATA CPA Group LLC**
**Phone—(732) 777-9330**
**Fax—(732) 777-9331**
**Web—www.atacpa.com**
**Email—info@atacpa.com**
**1918 State Route 27, Edison 08817**
Bott & Co., Charles G.
Phone—(973) 618-1886
Fax—(973) 618-0118
Web—www.cbottcpa.com
Email—bottcpa@gmail.com
90 Eagle Rock Ave., Roseland 07068

Botwinick & Co. LLC
Phone—(201) 909-0090
Fax—(201) 909-8533
Web—www.botwinick.com
201 W. Passaic St., Ste. 206, Rochelle Park 07662
Demetrius Berkower LLC
Phone—(973) 812-0100
Fax—(973) 812-0750
Web—www.demetriusberkower.com
Email—john@demetriusberkower.com
155 US Highway 46, Ste. 301, Wayne 07470

## Demetrius Berkower LLC
*Accountants*
**(973) 812-0100**
**www.demetriusberkower.com**
155 U.S. Highway 46 Ste. 301 Wayne, NJ 07470

Howard Komendant, CPA P.C.
Phone—(973) 471-1919
Fax—(973) 471-0933
Web—www.hkcpapc.com
Email—hk@hkcpapc.com
1005 Clifton Ave., Ste. 205, Clifton 07013

## Howard Komendant, CPA P.C.
*Quality accountants*
**www.hkcpapc.com**
**973-471-1919**
1005 Clifton Ave., Ste. 205 Clifton, NJ 07013

Lembo & Assoc. PA
Phone—(973) 427-6332
535 High Mountain Rd., Ste. 203, North Haledon 07508
Maggioncalda, Austin B.
Phone—(856) 696-2200
Fax—(856) 794-9798
Web—www.abmpa.com
Email—abmpa@comcast.net
5546 Chestnut Ave., P.O. Box 606, Buena 08310
Murphy & Co. LLC
Phone—(973) 579-7775
Fax—(973) 579-9316
Web—www.murphycpas.com
Email—murphy@murphycpas.com
94 Main St., Newton 07860
Nisonoff & Quadrel, LLC
Phone—(732) 254-3000
Fax—(732) 254-3001
Email—jamesquadrel@yahoo.com
P.O. Box 358, South River 08882
Samuel Klein And Company
Phone—(973) 624-6100
Fax—(973) 624-6101
Web—www.sklein-cpa.com
Email—contact@sklein-cpa.com
550 Broad St., Ste. 1100, Newark 07102
Toscano Consulting
Phone—(732) 442-2954
Fax—(732) 414-7688
Web—www.toscanocorp.com
Email—mtoscano@toscanocorp.com
389 Smith St., Perth Amboy 08861

*Do nationwide searches for products & services at:*
**IndustryNet.com**

WithumSmith+Brown, PC
Jim Hannah, CPA, Partner
Phone—(973) 898-9494
Fax—(973) 898-0686
Web—www.withum.com
Email—jhannah@withum.com
465 South St., Ste. 200, Morristown 07960

## ACCOUNTANTS — Certified Public

Demetrius Berkower LLC
Phone—(973) 812-0100
Fax—(973) 812-0750
Web—www.demetriusberkower.com
Email—john@demetriusberkower.com
155 US Highway 46, Ste. 301, Wayne 07470
*(see our ad under ACCOUNTANTS)*

## ACOUSTICAL CONTRACTORS

Proform Acoustic Surfaces LLC
Phone—(201) 553-9614
Fax—(201) 553-0193
Web—www.proformacoustic.com
Email—info@proformacoustic.com
P.O. Box 1363, Secaucus 07096

## Proform Acoustic Surfaces LLC
*Quality Acoustical Contractors*
**www.proformacoustic.com**
**info@proformacoustic.com**
**(201) 553-9614**
PO Box 1363 • Secaucus, NJ 07096

## ACRYLIC FABRICATORS

Emco Industrial Plastics, Inc.
Supplier of Plastic Sheet, Rod, Tube, Films & Prototyping
Phone—(973) 559-5610
Fax—(973) 239-1595
Web—www.emcoplastics.com
Email—mailbox@emcoplastics.com
99 Commerce Rd., P.O. Box 2503, Cedar Grove 07009
*(see our ad Outside Front Cover)*
KB Acrylics, Inc.
Phone—(856) 589-3110
I-295 Industrial Ctr., Bldg. B, Box 47, Westville 08093

## ACTUATORS

Lehigh Fluid Power, Inc.
Phone—(609) 397-3487
1413 Route 179, Lambertville 08530
Moran Power Dynamics
Phone—(732) 544-8443
263 Route 537 E., Colts Neck 07722
Motion Systems Corp.
Phone—(732) 222-1800
600 Industrial Way W., Eatontown 07724

## ADAPTERS — AC-DC

Americor Electronics, Ltd.
Phone—(847) 956-6200 / (800) 830-5337
Fax—(847) 956-0300
Web—www.americor-usa.com
Email—info@americor-usa.com
675 S. Lively Blvd., Elk Grove Village, IL 60007
*(see our ads under CABLE ASSEMBLIES & CORD SETS)*

**MASTERBOND®**
ADHESIVES | SEALANTS | COATINGS
*Helping engineers meet specific requirements*

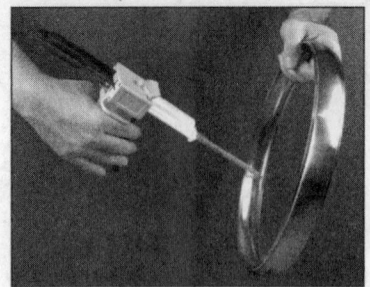

- Over 3,000 products
- Custom formulations
- Personal one on one customer support
- Latest technological developments

154 Hobart Street, Hackensack, NJ 07601 USA     +201.343.8983 • main@masterbond.com

## ADDITIVES

**Munzing**
1455 Broad St., Bloomfield 07003
Formulators of Specialty Additive Defoamers for over 180 years
Phone—(973) 279-1306 / (800) 524-0055
Fax—(973) 338-0420
Web—www.munzing.com
Email—info@munzing.us
975 Ultra Dr., Clover, SC 29710

Shamrock Technologies, Inc.
Phone—(973) 242-2999
255 Pacific St., Newark 07114

Troy Corp.
Phone—(973) 443-4200
8 Vreeland Rd., Florham Park 07932

## ADDITIVES — Plastic

Amfine Chemical Corp.
Phone—(201) 818-0159
10 Mountainview Rd., Ste. N-215, Upper Saddle River 07458

Glitterex Corp.
Phone—(908) 272-9121
7 Commerce Dr., Cranford 07016

Polyvel, Inc.
Phone—(609) 567-0080
100 9th St., Hammonton 08037

Reedy International Corp.
Phone—(732) 264-1777
25 E. Front St., Ste. 200, Keyport 07735

**Technick Products, Inc.**
Additives for rubber & plastic; mold release agents, halogenated & non-halogenated flame retardants & green cleaning agents
Phone—(908) 791-0400
Fax—(908) 791-9991
Web—www.technickproducts.com
Email—info@technickproducts.com
238 Saint Nicholas Ave., South Plainfield 07080

## ADHESIVE APPLICATION MACHINERY

Potdevin Machine Co.
Phone—(201) 288-1941
26 Fairfield Pl., West Caldwell 07006

## ADHESIVE DISPENSING EQUIPMENT

Albion Engineering Co.
Phone—(856) 235-6688
1250 N. Church St., Moorestown 08057

Fisnar, Inc.
Phone—(973) 646-5044
19-C Chapin Rd. Ste. 307, Pine Brook 07058

## ADHESIVE FILM

Adhesive Films, Inc.
Phone—(973) 882-4944
4 Barnet Rd., P.O. Box 651, Pine Brook 07058

Maintape, Inc.
Phone—(609) 395-1704
1 Capital Dr., Ste. 101, Bldg. 1, Cranbury 08512

## ADHESIVES

AMB Enterprises, LLC
Phone—(973) 225-1070
25 Lake St., Paterson 07501

American Adhesives & Coatings, Inc.
Phone—(973) 623-7070
470 Mulberry St., Newark 07114

**Baker-Titan Adhesives**
Phone—(973) 225-1070
Fax—(973) 225-1079
Web—www.bakertitan.com
Email—info@bakertitan.com
25 Lake St., Paterson 07501

Bostik, Inc.
Phone—(856) 848-8669
2000 Nolte Dr., West Deptford 08066

Compounders, Inc.
Phone—(732) 938-5007
15 Marl Rd., P.O. Box 413, Farmingdale 07727

**E & H Laminating & Slitting Co.**
Phone—(973) 345-1725
Fax—(973) 345-3224
Web—www.ehlam.com
Email—info@ehlam.com
138 Grand St., Paterson 07501

**E & H Laminating & Slitting Co.**

Adhesives

**973-345-1725**
**Fax: 973-345-3224**

138 Grand St.
Paterson, NJ 07501

**www.ehlam.com**
**info@ehlam.com**

Hudson Industries Corp.
Phone—(973) 402-0100
271 U.S. Highway 46, Ste. F-207, Fairfield 07004

*Search from among*
**430,000 U.S. manufacturers**
**& suppliers at**

**IndustryNet.com**

Innovative Resin Systems, Inc.
Emails: spatel@rez-cure.com & manny@rez-cure.com
Structural adhesives, coatings, pottings & encapsulating compounds
Phone—(973) 465-6887
Fax—(973) 465-0592
Web—www.rez-cure.com
Email—info@rez-cure.com
257 Wilson Ave., Newark 07105

**Innovative Resin Systems, Inc.**

**973-465-6887**
**Fax:**
**973-465-0592**

www.rez-cure.com

Email: spatel@rez-cure.com
Email: manny@rez-cure.com

**257 Wilson Ave.**
**Newark, NJ 07105**

Jedco Adhesives Co., Div. Of Morre-Tec Industries, Inc.
Phone—(908) 688-9009
1 Gary Rd., Union 07083

**Master Bond, Inc.**
Manufacturer of custom formulated adhesives for advanced applications
Phone—(201) 343-8983
Fax—(201) 343-2132
Web—www.masterbond.com
Email—main@masterbond.com
154 Hobart St., Hackensack 07601
*(see our ad on this page)*

Mercury Adhesives, Inc.
Phone—(973) 472-3307
140 Dayton Ave., Passaic 07055

Mon-Eco Industries, Inc.
Phone—(732) 257-7942
5 Joanna Ct., East Brunswick 08816

National Casein Of New Jersey
Phone—(856) 829-1880
401 Martha's Ln., P.O. Box 226, Riverton 08077

Palmetto Adhesives Co., Inc.
Phone—(856) 451-0405
1785 Burlington Rd., Bridgeton 08302

Permabond, LLC (H Q)
Phone—(732) 868-1372
223 Churchill Ave., Somerset 08873

Signature Marketing & Mfg.
Phone—(973) 427-3700
301 Wagaraw Rd., Hawthorne 07506

Sika Corp.
Phone—(973) 473-3330
995 Towbin Ave., Lakewood 08701

Synthetic Surfaces Inc.
Phone—(908) 233-6803
P.O. Box 241, Scotch Plains 07076

Zymet, Inc.
Phone—(973) 428-5245
7 Great Meadow Ln., East Hanover 07936

## ADHESIVES — Epoxy

**Innovative Resin Systems, Inc.**
Emails: spatel@rez-cure.com & manny@rez-cure.com
Structural adhesives, coatings, pottings & encapsulating compounds
Phone—(973) 465-6887
Fax—(973) 465-0592
Web—www.rez-cure.com
257 Wilson Ave., Newark 07105
*(see our ad under ADHESIVES)*

## ADHESIVES — Epoxy — (cont.)

**Kelken Construction Systems**
Manufacturer & distributor of various types of concrete/masonry anchoring systems, including chemical adhesive, epoxy, mechanical anchors (wedge), as well as, cast-in-place, hook & anchor bolts
Phone—(732) 416-6730
Fax—(732) 416-6733
Web—www.kelken.com
Email—sales@kelken.com
550 Hartle St., Ste. C, Sayreville 08872

**Master Bond, Inc.**
Manufacturer of custom formulated adhesives for advanced applications
Phone—(201) 343-8983
Fax—(201) 343-2132
Web—www.masterbond.com
Email—main@masterbond.com
154 Hobart St., Hackensack 07601
*(see our ad under ADHESIVES)*

## ADHESIVES — Industrial

DriTac Flooring Products, LLC
Phone—(973) 614-9000
60 Webro Rd., Clifton 07012

**Master Bond, Inc.**
Manufacturer of custom formulated adhesives for advanced applications
Phone—(201) 343-8983
Fax—(201) 343-2132
Web—www.masterbond.com
Email—main@masterbond.com
154 Hobart St., Hackensack 07601
*(see our ad under ADHESIVES)*

Royal Adhesive, Inc.
Phone—(973) 694-0845
48 Burgess Pl., Wayne 07470

W. W. Grainger, Inc.
Phone—(973) 777-7700
308 Allwood Rd., Clifton 07012

## ADHESIVES — Medical

**Master Bond, Inc.**
Manufacturer of custom formulated adhesives for advanced applications
Phone—(201) 343-8983
Fax—(201) 343-2132
Web—www.masterbond.com
Email—main@masterbond.com
154 Hobart St., Hackensack 07601
*(see our ad under ADHESIVES)*

## ADHESIVES — Pressure Sensitive

Quality Coatings
Phone—(908) 637-4556
Island Dragway Rd., P.O. Box 13, Great Meadows 07838

## ADHESIVES — Ultraviolet

**Master Bond, Inc.**
Manufacturer of custom formulated adhesives for advanced applications
Phone—(201) 343-8983
Fax—(201) 343-2132
Web—www.masterbond.com
Email—main@masterbond.com
154 Hobart St., Hackensack 07601
*(see our ad under ADHESIVES)*

## ADULT INCONTINENCE PRODUCTS

Griffin Care, LLC
Phone—(856) 455-6870
80 Manheim Ave., Bridgeton 08302

## ADVERTISING — Direct Mail

Colortec Printing & Mailing LLC
Phone—(856) 767-0108
424 Kelley Dr., Ste. A, West Berlin 08091

## ADVERTISING SPECIALTIES

J K A Specialties Mfg., Inc.
Phone—(609) 859-2090
157 Eayrestown Rd., Southampton 08088
Red Feather Marketing Group
Phone—(973) 966-1399
332 Main St., Madison 07940

## AERATION EQUIPMENT

Woodward Jogger Aerators, Inc.
Phone—(201) 933-6800
45 Carlton Ave., East Rutherford 07073

## AEROSPACE ASSEMBLIES

**Concept Group, Inc.**
Glass to metal seals (hermetic packages) & Vacuum insulated components
Phone—(856) 767-5506
Fax—(856) 768-3981
Web—www.conceptgroupinc.com
Email—applications@conceptgroupinc.com
380 Cooper Rd., West Berlin 08091
*(see our ad under MACHINE PARTS — Precision)*

## AEROSPACE COMPONENTS

Alpine Corp.
Phone—(201) 666-0959
42 Bergenline Ave., Westwood 07675
H & W Tool Co., Inc.
Phone—(973) 366-0131
22 Lee Ave., Dover 07801
Moser Jewel Co.
Phone—(908) 454-1155
518 Route 57, Phillipsburg 08865
PHT Aerospace, LLC
Phone—(973) 831-1230
230 West Pkwy., Ste. 2, Pompton Plains 07444
Pioneer Machine & Tool Co.
Phone—(856) 779-8800
425 E. Broadway, P.O. Box 8, Maple Shade 08052
Vulcan Tool Co., Inc.
Phone—(908) 686-0550
1080-C Garden State Rd., Union 07083

## AEROSPACE FASTENERS

B/E Consumables Management
Phone—(201) 265-8770
650 From Rd., Paramus 07652
**Wm. H. Brewster Jr., Inc.**
Email: sales@brewster-washers.com
Manufacturing Precision Parts Since 1919; Made in U.S.A.
Phone—(973) 227-1050
Fax—(973) 227-2363
Web—www.brewster-washers.com
16 Kulick Rd., Fairfield 07004
*(see our ad Outside Front Cover)*

## AEROSPACE PRODUCTS

Arde, Inc.
Phone—(201) 784-9880
875 Washington Ave., Carlstadt 07072
Ho-Ho-Kus, Inc.
Phone—(973) 278-2274
189-201 Lyon St., Paterson 07524
Whippany Actuation System
Phone—(973) 428-9898
110 Algonquin Pkwy., Whippany 07981

## AGGREGATES

Weldon Materials, Inc. (H Q)
Phone—(908) 233-4444
141 Central Ave., Westfield 07090

**Need an IndustrySection for another state?**

Call us... 847-864-7590

## AGITATORS

**Warwick Mfg. & Equipment Co., LLC**
Buy & sell used: Chemical, food, cosmetic, packaging & pharmaceutical equipment
Phone—(732) 729-0400 / (732) 241-9263
Fax—(732) 729-1235
Web—www.warwickequipment.com
Email—sales@warwickequipment.com
1112 12th St., North Brunswick 08902
*(see our ad Outside Back Cover)*

## AGRICULTURAL EQUIPMENT — Wholesale

Rodio Tractor Sales, Inc.
Phone—(609) 561-0141
717 White Horse Pike, Hammonton 08037

## AIR CARGO SERVICES

Thor Xpress Transport LLC
Phone—(973) 361-3900
Fax—(908) 368-8660
Web—www.thorxpress.com
Email—info@thorxpress.com
750 Walnut Ave., Ste. 4, Cranford 07016

## AIR COMPRESSORS — Rebuilt

Air Center, Inc.
Phone—(908) 276-1992
270 Monroe Ave., Kenilworth 07033

## AIR CONDITIONERS

ABCO Refrigeration Supply Corp.
Phone—(908) 931-0700
395 N. 14th St., Kenilworth 07033
Kooltronic, Inc.
Phone—(609) 466-3400
30 Pennington-Hopewell Rd., P.O. Box 240, Pennington 08534
Task U. S. A.
Phone—(732) 739-0377
3 Cass St., Keyport 07735
Trane Co.
Phone—(609) 587-3400
2231 E. State St., Trenton 08619

## AIR CONDITIONING CONTRACTORS

**Kilpatrick, Inc., B. J.**
Specializing in commercial HVAC service; We offer preventive maintenance contracts
Phone—(856) 768-4747
Fax—(856) 768-5782
Web—www.bjkilpatrick.com
Email—info@bjkilpatrick.com
136 S. White Horse Pike, Berlin 08009

## AIR CONDITIONING EQUIPMENT

**Nutley Heating & Cooling Supply, Inc.**
Phone—(973) 667-6880
Fax—(973) 667-4602
Web—www.nutleysupply.com
Email—ralpholiver@nutleysupply.com
156 Chestnut St., Nutley 07110
*(see our ad under BOILERS)*

## AIR FILTRATION SYSTEMS

**General Carbon Corporation**
Activated Carbon Equipment & Services for Liquid & Vapor Applications
Phone—(973) 523-2223
Fax—(973) 523-1494
Web—www.generalcarbon.com
Email—sales@generalcarbon.com
33 Paterson St., Paterson 07501
*(see our ad under CARBON — Activated)*
Mitsubishi Hitachi Power Systems America - Energy & Environment
Phone—(908) 605-2800
645 Martinsville Rd., Basking Ridge 07920

## AIR FRESHENERS

Chemspa Industries, Inc.
Phone—(973) 386-1158
22 Deforest Ave., East Hanover 07936
**Housechem, A Div. of Menshen Packaging U.S.A., Inc.**
Phone—(201) 445-8808
Fax—(201) 445-2810
Web—www.housechem.com
Email—info@housechem.com
25 Industrial Park, Waldwick 07463

## AIR HANDLING EQUIPMENT

Mainstream Custom Air Handling Units
Phone—(908) 931-1010
47 Russo Pl., Berkeley Heights 07922

## AIR MONITORING SYSTEMS

Trace Environmental Systems, Inc.
Phone—(973) 383-3550
7 Park Lake Rd., Unit 9, Sparta 07871

## AIR POLLUTION CONTROL EQUIPMENT

Air Clean Co., Inc.
Phone—(908) 355-1515
1135 Chestnut St., Elizabeth 07201
**Bionomic Industries, Inc.**
Phone—(201) 529-1094
Fax—(201) 529-0252
Web—www.bionomicind.com
Email—info@bionomicind.com
777 Corporate Dr., Mahwah 07430
**CSM Worldwide, Inc.**
Air pollution control, catalytic oxidizers, VOC & NOX abatement, SCR, RTO
Phone—(908) 233-2882
Fax—(908) 233-1064
Web—www.csmworldwide.com
Email—mtorstrup@csmworldwide.com
1100 Globe Ave., Mountainside 07092
Datatest, Inc.
Phone—(908) 369-1590
300 Valley Rd., Hillsborough 08844

## AIR POLLUTION CONTROL SYSTEMS

Belco Technologies Corp.
Phone—(973) 884-4700
9 Entin Rd., Parsippany 07054

## AIR PURIFICATION EQUIPMENT

Bioclimatic Air Systems
Phone—(856) 764-4300
600 Delran Pkwy., Ste. D, Delran 08075
Spartan Air Purification
Phone—(856) 768-2929
150 Cooper Rd., Ste. E-14, West Berlin 08091
Vitaire Corp.
Phone—(973) 473-2244
141 Lanza Ave., 4th Fl., Garfield 07026

## AIR PURIFICATION SOLUTIONS

Biological Controls, Inc.
Phone—(732) 542-5822
749 Hope Rd., Eatontown 07724

## AIRCRAFT

Dassault Falcon Jet Corp. (H Q)
Phone—(201) 440-6700
Teterboro Airport, 200 Riser Rd., Little Ferry 07643

find additional suppliers at IndustryNet.com

## AIRCRAFT COMPONENTS & SUPPLIES

**Aeropanel Corp.**
Phone—(973) 335-9636
Fax—(973) 263-6304
Web—www.aeropanel.com
Email—lfix@aeropanel.com
661 Myrtle Ave., Boonton 07005

## AEROPANEL CORP.

www.aeropanel.com

lfix@aeropanel.com

(973) 335-9636
FAX: (973) 263-6304

661 Myrtle Ave.
Boonton, NJ 07005

**Day Tool & Mfg., Inc.**
ISO 9001:2008, AS9100 Rev. C
Phone—(908) 439-3800
Fax—(908) 439-3955
Web—www.daytool.com
Email—juddcallahan@daytool.com
6 Carman Ln., P.O. Box 466, Whitehouse 08888
J A Machine & Tool Co., Inc.
Phone—(201) 767-1308
84 Herbert Ave., Closter 07624
McWilliams Forge Co.
Phone—(973) 627-0200
387 Franklin Ave., Rockaway 07866
**R. A. Johnson Inc.**
Phone—(973) 575-3353
Fax—(973) 575-2620
Email—gg4parts@aol.com
339 Changebridge Rd., Pine Brook 07058
Sun Dial & Panel Corp.
Phone—(973) 226-4334
2 Daniel Rd., Fairfield 07004

## AIRCRAFT CONTROLS

Panelcraft, Inc.
Phone—(973) 895-2700
105 W. Dewey Ave., Bldg. C, Unit 16, Wharton 07885

## AIRCRAFT ENGINE PARTS

**R. A. Johnson Inc.**
Phone—(973) 575-3353
Fax—(973) 575-2620
Email—gg4parts@aol.com
339 Changebridge Rd., Pine Brook 07058

## AIRCRAFT ENGINES

Alcoa
Phone—(973) 361-2310
9 Roy St., Dover 07801

## AIRCRAFT GROUND SUPPORT EQUIPMENT

**R. A. Johnson Inc.**
Phone—(973) 575-3353
Fax—(973) 575-2620
Email—gg4parts@aol.com
339 Changebridge Rd., Pine Brook 07058

## AIRCRAFT PARTS

Aerosource, Inc.
Phone—(732) 469-9300
390 Campus Dr., Somerset 08873
Export Consultants Corp.
Phone—(732) 469-0700
250 Lackland Dr., Ste. 6, P.O. Box 308, Middlesex 08846
Zodiac Arresting Systems America - Logan
Phone—(856) 241-8620
2239 High Hill Rd., Swedesboro 08085

## ALLOYS

VDM Metals USA, LLC
Phone—(973) 437-1664
306 Columbia Tpke., Florham Park 07932
Victory White Metal Co., Inc.
Phone—(201) 585-0747
129 Victoria Pl. W., Fort Lee 07024
Wheeler Industrial Corp.
Phone—(973) 926-0551
485 Lyons Ave., Irvington 07111

## ALTERNATORS

J & R Rebuilders, Inc.
Phone—(856) 627-1414
330 Washington Ave., Laurel Springs 08021

## J & R Rebuilders, Inc.
Rebuilt alternators & starters
(856) 627-1414
330 Washington Ave.
Laurel Springs, NJ 08021

Mobile Power, Inc.
Phone—(908) 852-3117
392 Watters Rd., Hackettstown 07840

## ALUMINUM

**Bristol Aluminum Company**
Email: info@bristolaluminum.com
Phone—(215) 946-3160 / (800) 338-5532
Fax—(215) 946-3302
Web—www.bristolaluminum.com
5514 Bristol Emilie Rd., Levittown, PA 19057
(see our ad under ALUMINUM EXTRUSIONS)
**Rancocas Metals Corp.**
A full service metals center, stocking a vast inventory of almost every non-ferrous metal in a wide array of sizes & shapes
Phone—(609) 267-4120 / (800) 762-6382
Fax—(609) 267-5690
Web—www.rancocasmetals.com
Email—sales@rancocasmetals.com
35 Indel Ave., P.O. Box 223, Rancocas 08073
(see our ad under METAL SERVICE CENTERS)

## ALUMINUM EXTRUDED SHAPES

Coltwell Industries, Inc.
Phone—(908) 276-7600
55 Winans Ave., Cranford 07016

## ALUMINUM EXTRUSIONS

Aluminum Shapes, LLC
Phone—(800) 242-7512
9000 River Rd., Delair 08110

Is your company properly represented in the IndustrySection?
If not, call... 847-864-7590

## ALUMINUM EXTRUSIONS — (cont.)

**Bristol Aluminum Company**
Email: info@bristolaluminum.com
Phone—(215) 946-3160 / (800) 338-5532
Fax—(215) 946-3302
Web—www.bristolaluminum.com
Email—sales@bristolaluminum.com
5514 Bristol Emilie Rd., Levittown, PA 19057

# Bristol
## Aluminum Company
*Mfr. of Aluminum Extrusions*
### Since 1949
*Offering Anodizing, Fabrication,
Powder Coating, Precision Sawing*
**Prototypes < 100 lb to Multi
Truckload Quantities Available.
Buy Mill Direct & Save**
## (800) 338-5532
**FAX: (215) 946-3302
5514 Bristol Emilie Rd.
Levittown, PA 19057**
www.bristolaluminum.com
info@bristolaluminum.com

**Minalex Corp.**
Phone—(908) 534-4044
25 Coddington Rd., P.O. Box 247, Whitehouse Station 08889
**Unique Aluminum Extrusion, LLC**
Phone—(732) 271-0006
333 Cedar Ave., Ste. 6, Middlesex 08846

## ALUMINUM FABRICATING

**Academy Fence Co., Inc.**
Phone—(973) 674-0600
119 N. Day St., Orange 07050
**Bluewater Welding & Fabrication, LLC**
Phone—(609) 522-7352
1089 Route 47, P.O. Box 206, Dennisville 08214
**Bristol Aluminum Company**
Email: info@bristolaluminum.com
Phone—(215) 946-3160 / (800) 338-5532
Fax—(215) 946-3302
Web—www.bristolaluminum.com
5514 Bristol Emilie Rd., Levittown, PA 19057
*(see our ad under ALUMINUM EXTRUSIONS)*
**Bush Tank Fabricators, Inc.**
Phone—(973) 596-1121
222 Thomas St., Newark 07114
**Center Metal Fabricators, Inc.**
Phone—(609) 567-1808
1026 Black Horse Pike, P.O. Box 29, Hammonton 08037
**Durex, Inc.**
Email: custserv@durexinc.com
ISO 9001 Registered Contract Metal Fabrication Facility
Phone—(908) 688-0800
Fax—(908) 688-0718
Web—www.durexinc.com
5 Stahuber Ave., Union 07083
*(see our ad under METAL FABRICATING)*
**Helidex, LLC (H Q)**
Phone—(201) 636-2546
186 Paterson Ave., Ste. 303, East Rutherford 07073
**Heritage Towers, Inc.**
Phone—(609) 884-5999
910 Shunpike Rd., Ste. B, Cape May 08204
**Stefano Fence Systems, Inc.**
Phone—(732) 321-5050
737 New Durham Rd., Edison 08817

*Search from among 430,000
U.S. manufacturers & suppliers:*
**IndustryNet.com**

**Versatile Welding Group, LLC**
Steel & Aluminum
Phone—(908) 298-8900 / (877) 939-5348
Fax—(908) 298-9550
Web—www.versatile-us.com
Email—jimd@versatile-us.com
340 Cox St., Roselle 07203
*(see our ad under STEEL FABRICATING)*

## ALUMINUM OXIDE

**Summit Chemical Specialty Products**
Phone—(908) 782-9500
45 River Rd., Ste. 300, Flemington 08822

## ALUMINUM POWDER

**United States Metal Powders, Inc.**
Phone—(908) 782-5454
408 U.S. Highway 202, Flemington 08822

## ALUMINUM PRODUCTS

**Empire Resources**
Phone—(201) 944-2200
1 Parker Plz., Fort Lee 07024
**Versatile Welding Group, LLC**
Steel & Aluminum
Phone—(908) 298-8900 / (877) 939-5348
Fax—(908) 298-9550
Web—www.versatile-us.com
Email—jimd@versatile-us.com
340 Cox St., Roselle 07203
*(see our ad under STEEL FABRICATING)*

## ALUMINUM SULFATE

**Chemtrade**
Phone—(973) 589-5300
330 Doremus Ave., Newark 07105
**Universal Chemicals Inc.**
Phone—(973) 589-1525
Fax—(973) 589-8013
Web—www.universalchem.com
Email—info@universalchem.com
100 N. Hackensack Ave., Kearny 07032

## AMBULANCES

**PL Custom Body & Equipment Co.**
Phone—(732) 223-1411
2201 Atlantic Ave., Manasquan 08736

## AMMONIA

**W.D. Service Company, Inc.**
780 Creek Rd., Bellmawr 08031
Phone—(856) 931-6100 / (800) 366-9326
Fax—(856) 931-4505
Web—www.wdserviceco.com
Email—sales@wdserviceco.com
P.O. Box 147, Bellmawr 08099

## AMMONIA — Anhydrous

**W.D. Service Company, Inc.**
780 Creek Rd., Bellmawr 08031
Anhydrous Ammonia Cylinders-150 lb., also 2 lb., 4 lb., 10 lb. Cartridges
Phone—(856) 931-6100 / (800) 366-9326
Fax—(856) 931-4505
Web—www.wdserviceco.com
Email—sales@wdserviceco.com
P.O. Box 147, Bellmawr 08099

## AMMONIA — Aqua

**W.D. Service Company, Inc.**
780 Creek Rd., Bellmawr 08031
Reagent Grade ammonia solutions in all size containers, including 1 gal, 5 gal, 15 gal, 50 gal, totes & bulk. Any concentration available. We are a leading manufacturer
Phone—(856) 931-6100 / (800) 366-9326
Fax—(856) 931-4505
Web—www.wdserviceco.com
Email—sales@wdserviceco.com
P.O. Box 147, Bellmawr 08099

## AMMUNITION

**Lightfield Ammunition Corp.**
Phone—(732) 462-9200
912 Highway 33, Freehold 07728
**Metalico, Inc. (H Q)**
Phone—(908) 497-9610
186 North Ave. E., Cranford 07016
**Ultimate Training Munitions**
Phone—(908) 725-9000
55 Readington Rd., North Branch 08876

## AMPLIFIERS

**Adcomm, Inc.**
Phone—(201) 342-6349
89 Leuning St., 1st Fl., South Hackensack 07606
**Apogee Sound International, LLC**
Phone—(201) 995-2001
50 Spring St., Ramsey 07446
**Euphonic Audio, Inc.**
Phone—(888) 894-3790
18 Newtown Blvd., Robbinsville 08691
**Fuchs Audio Technology, LLC**
Phone—(973) 772-4420
407 Getty Ave., 2nd Fl., Clifton 07011
**PatchAmp, Inc.**
Phone—(201) 457-1504
20 E. Kennedy St., Hackensack 07601
**T/Mac, Inc.**
Phone—(732) 247-0022
100 Jersey Ave., Bldg. D-6, New Brunswick 08901

## AMUSEMENT GAMES

**Coastal Amusements, Inc.**
Phone—(732) 905-6662
1950 Swarthmore Ave., Lakewood 08701
**Shooting Star, Inc.**
Phone—(908) 789-2500
2500 Plainfield Ave., Scotch Plains 07076

## AMUSEMENT PARK RIDES & EQUIPMENT

**Maxflight Corp.**
Phone—(732) 281-2007
1 Executive Dr., Toms River 08755
**Rides4U, Inc.**
Phone—(908) 526-8009
221 Evans Way, Ste. E, Somerville 08876

## ANALYTICAL INSTRUMENTS

**Assem-Pak, Inc.**
Phone—(856) 692-3355
1649 Castpa Pl., Vineland 08360
**BioTillion, LLC**
Phone—(609) 454-3523
30 Vreeland Dr., Ste. 7, Skillman 08558
**Distek, Inc.**
Phone—(732) 422-7585
121 N. Center Dr., North Brunswick 08902
**HORIBA Scientific**
Phone—(732) 494-8660
3880 Park Ave., Edison 08820
**Rudolph Instruments, Inc.**
Phone—(973) 983-6700
400 Morris Ave., Ste. 120, Denville 07834
**Spark Holland, Inc.**
Phone—(609) 799-7250
816 Delsea Dr. N., Glassboro 08028
**V. Tech Instruments, Inc.**
Phone—(973) 546-7635
171 Burns Ave., Lodi 07644
**Waltron, Bull & Roberts, LLC**
Phone—(908) 534-5100
50 Tannery Rd., P.O. Box 70, Whitehouse 08888

## ANALYTICAL LABORATORIES

**Loricon Testing Service, Inc.**
Analytical Testing-Microbiology
Phone—(732) 787-4131
Fax—(732) 264-4585
Web—www.loricontesting.com
Email—loricon55@optonline.net
55 State Route 36, Keyport 07735

## ANALYTICAL TESTING SERVICES

Koslow Scientific Co.
Phone—(201) 541-9100
172 Walkers Ln., Englewood 07631

Loricon Testing Service, Inc.
Analytical Testing-Microbiology
Phone—(732) 787-4131
Fax—(732) 264-4585
Web—www.loricontesting.com
Email—loricon55@optonline.net
55 State Route 36, Keyport 07735

LORICON
Testing Service, Inc.

Meeting All Your
Microbiological & Analytical
Testing Requirements

Loricon Testing Service, Inc.
Loricon Analytical Testing Laboratory, LLC
(732) 787-4131   loricon55@optonline.net
55 State Route 36   Keyport, NJ 07735

## ANCHORS — Concrete

Kelken Construction Systems
Manufacturer & distributor of various types of
concrete/masonry anchoring systems, including
chemical adhesive, epoxy, mechanical anchors
(wedge), as well as, cast-in-place, hook & anchor
bolts
Phone—(732) 416-6730
Fax—(732) 416-6733
Web—www.kelken.com
Email—sales@kelken.com
550 Hartle St., Ste. C, Sayreville 08872

Kelken-Gold, Inc.
Phone—(732) 416-6730
550 Hartle St., Ste. C, Sayreville 08872

## ANCHORS — Marine

Good Automatic Windlass, Inc.
Phone—(609) 698-4402
357 Route 72, Barnegat 08005

## ANIMAL GROOMING PRODUCTS

Madison Feed & Grooming
Phone—(973) 377-8885
Fax—(973) 377-5036
Web—www.vcahospitals.com/madison
262 Main St., Madison 07940

## ANIMAL HEALTH PRODUCTS

Hartz Mountain Corp., The
Phone—(201) 271-4800
400 Plaza Dr., Secaucus 07094

Madison Feed & Grooming
Phone—(973) 377-8885
Fax—(973) 377-5036
Web—www.vcahospitals.com/madison
262 Main St., Madison 07940

Nutri Pet Research, Inc./NUPRO Supplements
Phone—(732) 786-8822
227 State Route 33 E., Manalapan 07726

## ANNEALING SERVICES

Magnetic Metals Corp.
State of the Art Annealing Process
Phone—(856) 964-7842
Fax—(856) 365-8723
Web—www.magmet.com
Email—khaley@magmet.com
1900 Hayes Ave., Camden 08105

## ANODES

Stuart Steel Protection Corp.
Phone—(732) 469-5544
411 Elizabeth Ave., Somerset 08873

Do nationwide searches for
products & services at:
IndustryNet.com

## ANODIZING

Miller & Sons, Inc.
Celebrating over 100 years in Business
Phone—(973) 759-6445 / (973) 759-6446
Fax—(973) 759-1625
Web—www.millerplatingnj.com
Email—millerplating@aol.com
24 Belleville Ave., Belleville 07109
(see our ad under ELECTROPLATING)

## ANODIZING — Aluminum

Andarn Electro Service, Inc.
Phone—(973) 523-6334
72 Michigan Ave., Paterson 07503

B & M Finishers, Inc.
Phone—(908) 241-5640
201 S. 31st St., Kenilworth 07033

## ANODIZING — Hard Coat

Miller & Sons, Inc.
Celebrating over 100 years in Business
Phone—(973) 759-6445 / (973) 759-6446
Fax—(973) 759-1625
Web—www.millerplatingnj.com
Email—millerplating@aol.com
24 Belleville Ave., Belleville 07109
(see our ad under ELECTROPLATING)

## ANTIFREEZE

Houghton Chemical Corp.
Phone—(800) 777-2466
Fax—(617) 254-2713
Web—www.houghton.com
Email—bhoughton@houghton.com
30 Amor Ave., Carlstadt 07072

## APPAREL

(also see 'Clothing' headings)

Alfred's Sport Shop
Phone—(973) 377-0051
32 Main St., Madison 07940

Delta Galil USA, Inc.
Established in 1975, Delta Galil industries is a global
manufacturer & marketer of private label apparel
products for men, women & children
Phone—(201) 902-0055
Fax—(201) 902-0070
Web—www.deltagalil.com
Email—delta.us@deltagalil.com
1 Harmon Plz., 5th Fl., Secaucus 07094

Scaasis Originals, Inc./Oceanic Trading Co.
Phone—(732) 775-7474
1006 11th Ave., Neptune 07753

Tony Jones Apparel, Inc.
Phone—(973) 773-6200
300-1 Route 17 S., Unit C, Lodi 07644

Vantage Apparel
Phone—(732) 340-3000
100 Vantage Dr., Avenel 07001

## APPLIANCE PARTS

Marcone Supplies
Phone—(973) 371-8800
870 Boulevard, Ste. 4, Kenilworth 07033

Marcone Supply
Phone—(201) 489-6444
180 Main St., Hackensack 07601

## APPLIANCES

Haier America Trading, LLC (H Q)
Phone—(973) 617-1800
1800 Valley Rd., Wayne 07470

Oberg & Lindquist Corp.
Phone—(201) 664-1300
671 Broadway, Westwood 07675

find additional suppliers at
IndustryNet.com

## APPLIANCES — Household

Aspen Mfg. Co., Inc.
Phone—(609) 871-6400
703 Van Rossum Ave., Unit 5, Beverly 08010

Eastern Marketing Corp.
Phone—(973) 403-8900
24 Eisenhower Pkwy., Roseland 07068

Gotham Sales Co.
Phone—(973) 912-8412
302 Main St., Millburn 07041

HYSO, LLC
Phone—(201) 635-9555
430 Gotham Pkwy., 2nd Fl., Carlstadt 07072

Johnson's Appliances & Bedding
Phone—(609) 399-1598
930 Asbury Ave., P.O. Box 95, Ocean City 08226

Johnson's Appliances & Bedding
Phone—(609) 522-1421
2510 New York Ave., Wildwood 08260

Karl's Appliance, LLC
Phone—(973) 227-1777
65 Passaic Ave., Fairfield 07004

Maverick Industries, Inc.
Phone—(732) 417-9666
94 Mayfield Ave., Edison 08837

Reno's Appliance
Addtl. Web: www.buyrenos.com
Toll Free Ph: (866)88-RENOS
Phone—(973) 247-1860 / (866) 887-3667
Fax—(973) 247-1865
Web—www.renosappliance.com
Email—sales@renosappliance.net
235 McLean Blvd., Route 20 N., Paterson 07504

Reno's Appliance
Toll Free: (866) 88-RENOS
(973) 247-1860 / FAX: (973) 247-1865
235 McLean Blvd., Rte. 20 N., Paterson, NJ 07504
www.renosappliance.com
www.buyrenos.com

## APPRAISERS

Forest Jewelers
Phone—(609) 924-1363
Fax—(609) 924-1505
Web—www.forestjewelers.com
104 Nassau St., Princeton 08542

George Olmezer Appraisal Services Inc.
Phone—(732) 634-9000
Fax—(732) 634-9252
Web—www.golmezer.com
Email—olmezer@comcast.net
283 Prospect Ave., Avenel 07001

Max Vantage LLC
Phone—(732) 556-4000
Web—www.maxvantageamc.com
Email—info@maxvantageamc.com
606 Main St., Belmar 07719

Tighue Appraisal Group
Phone—(609) 581-0100
Fax—(609) 581-8435
Web—www.Tighueappraisal.com
Email—Tighueappraisal@verizon.net
100 White Horse Ave., Hamilton Township 08610

## AQUARIUMS & SUPPLIES

Estes Co., Inc., Clifford W.
Phone—(973) 575-4400
182 Fairfield Rd., Ste. 8, Fairfield 07004

## ARCHITECTURAL CAST STONE

Continental Cast Stone East
Phone—(856) 753-4000
400 Cooper Rd., West Berlin 08091

Search from among 430,000
U.S. manufacturers & suppliers:
IndustryNet.com

## ARCHITECTURAL DESIGN

**Infinite Manufacturing Group, Inc.**
Email: a.moses@infinitegroupusa.com
**Phone—(973) 649-9950**
**Web—www.infinitegroupusa.com**
**171 Coit St., Irvington 07111**

## ARCHITECTURAL METAL WORK

All Action Architectural Metal & Glass
Phone—(732) 738-6655
146 Sylvania Pl., Ste. G, South Plainfield 07080
Artistic Metal Works Corp.
Phone—(973) 304-0600
199 7th Ave., Hawthorne 07506
B & B Iron Works
Phone—(973) 375-9000
300 Coit St., Irvington 07111
Beta Iron Works, Inc.
Phone—(973) 815-2730
31 Pasadena Ave., Lodi 07644
Bolt Welding & Iron Works
Phone—(609) 393-3993
78 Wall St., Trenton 08609
Carfaro, Inc.
Phone—(609) 890-6600
2075 E. State Street Ext., Trenton 08619
City Glass Co.
Phone—(201) 436-8400
282 Broadway, P.O. Box 178, Bayonne 07002
Clem's Ornamental Iron Works, Inc.
Phone—(732) 968-7200
110 11th St., Piscataway 08854
Columbian Iron Works, Inc.
Phone—(973) 684-2303
332 Vreeland Ave., Paterson 07513
Coordinated Metals Co., Inc.
Phone—(201) 460-7280
626 16th St., Carlstadt 07072
Dave's Architectural Iron, LLC
Phone—(973) 523-6323
121 McBride Ave., Ste. C, Paterson 07501
Decorative Iron Works
Phone—(973) 595-8517
7383 Belmont Ave., Paterson 07522
Fast Weld Co.
Phone—(908) 213-0155
502 New Brunswick Ave., Phillipsburg 08865
Interstate Architectural & Iron, Inc.
Phone—(201) 941-0393
243 Laird Ave., Cliffside Park 07010
Kruysman Co., Ron
Phone—(856) 327-0605
7100 W. Buckshutem Rd., Millville 08332
L M C Corp.
Phone—(973) 279-3573
23 E. 23rd St., Paterson 07514
Louis Iron Works
Phone—(973) 624-2700
218 Lackawanna Ave., Newark 07103
Majka Railing, Inc.
Phone—(973) 247-7603
125 McBride Ave., Paterson 07501
Mazmet
Phone—(908) 654-7686
1050 Bristol Rd., Mountainside 07092
**Merchant & Evans, Inc.**
**Phone—(609) 387-3033 / (800) 257-6215**
**Fax—(609) 387-4838**
**Web—www.ziprib.com**
**Email—rjaconelli@ziprib.com**
**308 Connecticut Dr., Burlington 08016**
*(see our ad under ROOFING—Metal)*
Post To Post, LLC
Phone—(609) 646-9300
2545 Fire Rd., Ste. 1, Egg Harbor Township 08234
Runtak Rails, LLC
Phone—(201) 391-0380
174 Kinderkamack Rd., Ste. A, Park Ridge 07656
S & S Mfg., Inc.
Phone—(732) 698-2400
115 Fieldcrest Ave., Edison 08837
Schtiller & Plevy, Inc.
Phone—(973) 242-4600
695 S. 12th St., Newark 07103
Two Brothers Iron Works
Phone—(201) 866-7970
3709 Liberty Ave., North Bergen 07047

Willow Iron Works
Phone—(201) 659-7266
67 Pollock Ave., Jersey City 07305

## ARCHITECTURAL MODELS

Radii, Inc.
Phone—(201) 420-4700
66 Willow Ave., 3rd Fl., Hoboken 07030

## ARCHITECTURAL PRODUCTS

Metropole, Inc.
Phone—(973) 473-2727
214 Clifton Blvd., Clifton 07011
Outwater Plastics/Industries, Inc.
Phone—(201) 498-8750
24 River Rd., P.O. Box 500, Bogota 07603

## ART SUPPLIES

Cra-Z-Art
Phone—(973) 543-2037
1578 Sussex Tpke., Bldg. 5, Randolph 07869
Daler-Rowney U. S. A., Ltd.
Phone—(609) 655-5252
7 Corporate Dr., Cranbury 08512
S & R Sales, Inc.
Phone—(732) 905-0278
1 Sandart Plz., Jackson 08527
Steiner Paper Corp.
Phone—(732) 651-6009
4000 Borden Town Ave., Sayreville 08872

## ARTWORK

Ascalon Studios, Inc.
Phone—(856) 768-3779
430 Cooper Rd., West Berlin 08091
Rizzo Fine Arts Inc., Nicholas F.
Phone—(973) 635-7278
32 Watchung Ave., Chatham 07928

## ASBESTOS ABATEMENT PRODUCTS

ARAMSCO
Phone—(856) 686-7700
1480 Grandview Ave., P.O. Box 29, Thorofare 08086

## ASBESTOS CONSULTANTS

**Certified Health & Safety Services, LLC**
**Safe Today-Here Tomorrow**
**Phone—(856) 829-4463 / (800) 423-0137**
**Fax—(856) 786-3101**
**Web—www.certified-health-and-safety.com**
**Email—chss1@comcast.net**
**1902 Taylors Ln., Ste. A, Cinnaminson 08077**
*(see our ad under ENVIRONMENTAL CONSULTANTS)*
**Environmental Health Investigations**
**Phone—(973) 729-5649**
**Fax—(973) 729-5649**
**Web—www.ehi-inc.com**
**Email—bkerbel@ehi-inc.com**
**655 W. Shore Trl., Sparta 07871**
*(see our ad under ENVIRONMENTAL CONSULTANTS)*

## ASBESTOS REMOVAL

**Shade Environmental, LLC**
**Phone—(856) 755-0099**
**Fax—(856) 482-5879**
**Web—www.shadeenvironmental.com**
**Email—bill@shadellc.com**
**623 Cutler Ave., Maple Shade 08052**

## ASPHALT EMULSIONS

Dosch King Emulsions, Inc.
Phone—(973) 887-0145
16 Troy Hills Rd., Whippany 07981

*Do nationwide searches for products & services at:*
**IndustryNet.com**

## ASPHALT PAVING MATERIALS

American Asphalt Co., Inc.
Phone—(856) 456-2899
116 Main St., West Collingswood Heights 08059
American Asphalt Company, Inc.
Phone—(856) 456-2899
1701 River Rd., Burlington 08016
Asphalt Paving Systems
Phone—(609) 561-4161
500 N. Egg Harbor Rd., P.O. Box 530, Hammonton 08037
Colas, Inc. (H Q)
Phone—(973) 290-9082
163 Madison Ave., Ste. 500, Morristown 07960
South State, Inc.
Phone—(856) 881-6030
1340 Glassboro Rd., Williamstown 08094
Weldon Asphalt Co.
Phone—(908) 233-9440
1 New Providence Rd., Watchung 07060
Weldon Asphalt Corp.
Phone—(908) 862-0646
2000 Marshes Dock Rd., Linden 07036

## ASPHALT PRODUCTS

Arawak Paving Company
Phone—(609) 561-4100
7503 Weymouth Rd., Hammonton 08037
Barrett Paving Materials Inc. (H Q)
Phone—(973) 533-1001
3 Becker Farm Rd., Ste. 307, Roseland 07068
Beaver Run Farms
Phone—(973) 875-5555
300 Beaver Run Rd., Lafayette 07848
Blueknight Energy Partners L. P.
Phone—(856) 456-6673
King & Jersey St., P.O. Box 31, Gloucester City 08030
Brick-Wall Corp.
Phone—(732) 787-0226
25 1st Ave., Ste. 200, Atlantic Highlands 07716
Brick-Wall Corp.
Phone—(609) 693-6223
2215 Lacey Rd., Forked River 08731
**Earle Asphalt Company**
**1800 Route 34, Bldg. 2, Ste. 205, Wall 07719**
**Phone—(732) 308-1113**
**Web—www.earleco.com**
**Email—info@earleco.com**
**P.O. Box 556, Farmingdale 07727**
Flemington Bituminous Corp.
Phone—(908) 782-2722
205 Pennsylvania Ave., Flemington 08822
Meredith Paving Corp.
Phone—(856) 829-4343
1300 Union Landing Rd., Cinnaminson 08077
National Paving Co., Inc.
Phone—(856) 767-1950
148 Williamstown Rd., P.O. Box 5, Berlin 08009
Newark Asphalt Corp.
Phone—(973) 268-3636
30 Passaic St., Newark 07104
Owens Corning
Phone—(201) 998-5666
1249 Newark Tpke., Kearny 07032
Pierson Construction Co., Inc., R. E. (H Q)
Phone—(856) 769-8244
426 Swedesboro Rd., Pilesgrove 08098
Pierson Materials Inc., R. E.
Phone—(856) 467-4199
860 Oak Grove Rd., P.O. Box 704, Bridgeport 08014
**South State Materials, LLC**
**Phone—(856) 451-5300**
**Fax—(856) 455-3461**
**Web—www.southstateinc.com**
**Email—kfrancis@southstateinc.com**
**202 Reeves Rd., P.O. Box 68, Bridgeton 08302**
Sta-Seal, Inc.
Phone—(609) 924-0300
5205 Route 130 S., Bordentown 08505
Stavola Contracting Co., Inc.
Phone—(732) 542-2328
120 Old Bergen Mill Rd., Englishtown 07726
Stavola Contracting Co., Inc.
Phone—(732) 542-2328
175 Drift Rd., Tinton Falls 07724
Stavola Old Bridge Materials
Phone—(732) 721-6900
85 Waterworks Rd., Old Bridge 08857

## ASPHALT PRODUCTS — (cont.)

Stone Industries, Inc.
Phone—(973) 595-6250
400-402 Central Ave., Haledon 07508

**Stone, Inc., A. E.**
Progressive, community-minded paving co. operating
hot mix asphalt facilities at Egg Harbor Twp. &
Winslow Twp., NJ. Providing public agencies, dev. &
contrs. w/high quality hot mix asphalt, crushed stone,
recycled aggregate products & svcs
**Phone—(609) 641-2781**
**Fax—(609) 641-0374**
**Web—www.aestone.com**
**1435 Doughty Rd., Egg Harbor Township
08234**

Tilcon New York, Inc.
Phone—(973) 366-7741
625 Mount Hope Rd., Wharton 07885

Tilcon Totowa Asphalt
Phone—(973) 256-8300
859 Riverview Dr., Totowa 07512

Trap Rock
Phone—(609) 265-8500
27 Maple Ave., Mount Holly 08060

Trap Rock Ind., LLC
Phone—(609) 924-0300
4415 Route 27, P.O. Box 419, Kingston 08528

Trap Rock Industries
Phone—(732) 738-4222
Foot of Crows Mill Rd., Keasbey 08832

**Walter R. Earle Corporation**
655 S. Hope Chapel Rd., Jackson 08527
**Phone—(732) 657-8551**
**Web—www.earleco.com**
**Email—info@earleco.com**
**P.O. Box 757, Farmingdale 07727**

Warren Materials
Phone—(908) 859-3333
703 Route 57, Stewartsville 08886

Weldon Asphalt Co.
Phone—(201) 991-3200
1100 Harrison Ave., Kearny 07032

Weldon Asphalt Co.
Phone—(973) 627-7500
311 W. Main St., Rockaway 07866

Weldon Asphalt Co.
Phone—(973) 228-7473
1 Eisenhower Pkwy., Roseland 07068

Weldon Materials, Inc.
Phone—(973) 663-1800
181 Route 181, Lake Hopatcong 07849

Winslow Hot Mix, LLC
Phone—(609) 561-2100
784 Piney Hollow Rd., Hammonton 08037

Young Asphalt Paving Materials, Robert
Phone—(973) 728-8133
830 Burnt Meadow Rd., Hewitt 07421

Ziegler Chemical & Mineral Corp.
Phone—(732) 752-4111
600 Prospect Ave., Piscataway 08854

Ziegler Chemical & Mineral Corp.
Phone—(732) 752-4111
600 Prospect Ave., Bldg. A, Piscataway 08854

## ASSEMBLIES — Mechanical

**Bergen Cable Technology, LLC**
Cable Assemblies, Wire Rope & Lockwire
Replacement Safety Cable
**Phone—(973) 276-9596 / (800) 237-4369**
**Fax—(973) 276-9566**
**Web—www.bergencable.com**
**Email—sales@bergencable.com**
**343 Kaplan Dr., Fairfield 07004**
*(see our ad under WIRE ROPE)*

**Carl Stahl Sava Industries, Inc.**
Mechanical Assemblies, Cable Assemblies, Idler
Pulleys, Push & Pull Controls; ISO Certified
**Phone—(973) 835-0882**
**Fax—(973) 835-0877**
**Web—www.savacable.com**
**Email—sales@savacable.com**
**4 N. Corporate Dr., P.O. Box 30, Riverdale
07457**
*(see our ad under CABLE ASSEMBLIES)*

## ASSEMBLY — Electromechanical

Techflex
Phone—(973) 300-9242
29 Brookfield Dr., Sparta 07871

## ASSEMBLY AND FABRICATING SERVICES

**Merchant & Evans, Inc.**
**Phone—(609) 387-3033 / (800) 257-6215**
**Fax—(609) 387-4838**
**Web—www.ziprib.com**
**Email—rjaconelli@ziprib.com**
**308 Connecticut Dr., Burlington 08016**
*(see our ad under ROOFING—Metal)*

## ASSEMBLY MACHINERY

Kahle Automation
Phone—(973) 993-1850
89 Headquarters Plz., Ste. 355, Morristown
07960

## ASSET MANAGEMENT

RPR Graphics, Inc.
Phone—(908) 654-8080
1136 U.S. Highway 22, P.O. Box 1159,
Mountainside 07092

## AUCTIONEERS

**Dutch Auction Sales**
**Phone—(856) 423-6800**
**Web—www.dutchauctionsales.com**
**Email—dutchauctionsales@gmail.com**
**356 Swedesboro Ave., Mickleton 08056**

## AUDIO BOOKS

Learning Ally
Phone—(609) 452-0606
20 Roszel Rd., Princeton 08540

## AUDIO DEVICES

**Americor Electronics, Ltd.**
**Phone—(847) 956-6200 / (800) 830-5337**
**Fax—(847) 956-0300**
**Web—www.americor-usa.com**
**Email—info@americor-usa.com**
**675 S. Lively Blvd., Elk Grove Village, IL 60007**
*(see our ads under CABLE ASSEMBLIES & CORD SETS)*

APB-DynaSonics, Inc.
Phone—(973) 785-1101
20 W. End Rd., Totowa 07512

Empirical Labs, Inc.
Phone—(973) 541-9446
41 N. Beverwyck Rd., Lake Hiawatha 07034

Musical Distributors Group, LLC
Phone—(973) 335-7888
9 Mars Ct., Unit C-3, Boonton 07005

S D I Technologies, Inc.
Phone—(877) 895-8324
1299 Main St., Rahway 07065

Sony Electronics, Inc.
Phone—(201) 930-1000
1 Sony Dr., Park Ridge 07656

## AUDIO VISUAL EQUIPMENT & SYSTEMS

A. V. Bluebook
Phone—(800) 631-0868
80 Little Falls Rd., Fairfield 07004

Aurora Multimedia Corp.
Phone—(732) 591-5800
205 Commercial Ct., Morganville 07751

FSR, Inc.
Phone—(973) 785-4347
244 Bergen Blvd., West Paterson 07424

Hamilton Buhl
Phone—(201) 229-9800
80 Little Falls Rd., Fairfield 07004

Kingwood Industrial Products, Inc.
Phone—(908) 852-8655
261 Main St., Unit 1 & 2, Hackettstown 07840

Phoenix Systems, LLC
Phone—(201) 857-3901
39 Morningside Ave., North Haledon 07508

Verrex Corp.
Phone—(908) 232-7000
1130 Route 22, Mountainside 07092

Washington Professional Systems, Inc.
Phone—(856) 273-8688
109 Gaither Dr., Ste. 301, Mount Laurel 08054

## AUTOMATIC TELLER MACHINES (ATMs)

Heartland Payment Systems, Inc. (H Q)
Phone—(609) 683-3831
90 Nassau St., 2nd Fl., Princeton 08542

## AUTOMATION COMPONENTS

**Cuny & Guerber, Inc.**
Special counter available for contractors
**Phone—(201) 617-5800**
**Fax—(201) 617-5557**
**Web—www.cuny.biz**
**Email—sales@cuny.biz**
**2100 Kerrigan Ave., P.O. Box 1192, Union City
07087**
*(see our ad under ELECTRICAL EQUIPMENT AND SUPPLIES
— Wholesale)*

Norstat, Inc.
Phone—(973) 586-2500
300 Round Hill Dr., Ste. 4, Rockaway 07866

## AUTOMATION EQUIPMENT

Axis, Inc.
Phone—(908) 429-0090
210 Meister Ave., Somerville 08876

CTC International, Inc.
Phone—(973) 228-2300
11 York Ave., West Caldwell 07006

Intelligrated
Phone—(732) 302-2590
265 Davidson Ave., Ste. 219, Somerset 08873

Shingle & Gibb Company
Phone—(856) 234-8500
845 Lancer Dr., Moorestown 08057

Stelron Cam Co.
Phone—(201) 529-5450
1495 MacArthur Blvd., Mahwah 07430

V.S. Systematics, Inc.
Phone—(908) 241-5110
300 S. Michigan Ave., 1st Fl., Kenilworth 07033

## AUTOMATION MACHINERY

Alfa Production Systems
Phone—(908) 654-0255
522 Boulevard, Westfield 07090

Automation Sales Co.
Phone—(908) 832-7040
226 Beacon Hill Rd., Califon 07830

Eastern Automation Systems
Phone—(732) 938-2002
1151 New Jersey Route 33, P.O. Box 2394,
Farmingdale 07727

HAYNES Corp.
Phone—(908) 439-4600
6 Carman Ln., P.O. Box 467, Whitehouse 08888

## AUTOMATION SYSTEMS

**Connell Industries, Inc.**
Premier Control Systems Integrator/Custom Control
Solutions Provider
**Phone—(877) 926-6635**
**Fax—(305) 675-2612**
**Web—www.connell-ind.com**
**Email—vincent.digangi@connell-ind.com**
**13 Fairfield Ave., West Caldwell 07006**
*(see our ad under CONTROL SYSTEMS)*

Cuny & Guerber, Inc.
Phone—(201) 617-5800
2100 Kerrigan Ave., P.O. Box 1192, Union City
07087

*find additional suppliers at*
**IndustryNet.com**

## AUTOMATION SYSTEMS — (cont.)

**FlexLink Systems, Inc.**
FlexLink conveying to assemble, fill, machine & package
Phone—(610) 973-8200 / (800) 782-1399
Fax—(610) 973-8345
Web—www.flexlink.com
Email—info.us@flexlink.com
6580 Snowdrift Rd., Allentown, PA 18106
    *(see our ad under CONVEYOR SYSTEMS)*

Library Automation Technologies
    Phone—(856) 566-4121
    2 E. Atlantic Ave., Somerdale 08083

LRC Associates, Inc.
    Phone—(215) 244-1150
    328 S. 2nd St., Millville 08332

Precision Automation Company, Inc.
    Phone—(856) 428-7400
    1841 Old Cuthbert Rd., Cherry Hill 08034

Robotunits, Inc.
    Phone—(732) 438-0500
    5 Chris Ct., Ste. G, Dayton 08810

Teknics Industries, Inc.
    Phone—(973) 633-7575
    170 Beaver Brook Rd., Lincoln Park 07035

## AUTOMOBILE AUCTIONS

**Auto Exchange**
Founded in 1979, providing personal service & security in the salvage recovery industry to insurance cos., financial institutions & leasing cos., offering a central market place to efficiently & reliably dispose of their salvage vehicles
Phone—(732) 238-4006 / (800) 222-0829
Fax—(732) 238-9821
Web—www.autoexchangenj.com
Email—cpalfrey@autoexchangenj.com
580 Jernee Mill Rd., Sayreville 08872

## Auto Exchange
*Quality Automobile Auctions*
www.autoexchangenj.com
**(732) 238-4006**
580 Jernee Mill Rd. • Sayreville, NJ 08872

## AUTOMOBILE RADIO & STEREO SYSTEMS

Blitz Safe Of America, Inc.
    Phone—(201) 569-5000
    33 Honeck St., Englewood 07631

## AUTOMOBILE REPAIR & SERVICE

**Dario's Imported Car Service**
Phone—(609) 396-5538
Fax—(609) 278-0969
Web—www.dariosimportcarsnj.com
Email—dariosimportcars@juno.com
299 Hillcrest Ave., Trenton 08618

## AUTOMOBILE SALVAGE

**Auto Exchange**
Founded in 1979, providing personal service & security in the salvage recovery industry to insurance cos., financial institutions & leasing cos., offering a central market place to efficiently & reliably dispose of their salvage vehicles
Phone—(732) 238-4006 / (800) 222-0829
Fax—(732) 238-9821
Web—www.autoexchangenj.com
Email—cpalfrey@autoexchangenj.com
580 Jernee Mill Rd., Sayreville 08872
    *(see our ad under AUTOMOBILE AUCTIONS)*

Search from among 430,000 U.S. manufacturers & suppliers:
**IndustryNet.com**

**Perone's Auto Service & Salvage**
We Buy All Metals & Iron. 10-40 Yard Container Service For Demolition & Clean Ups
Phone—(732) 563-1630
Fax—(732) 563-1774
Web—www.peronesauto.com
Email—peronesauto@yahoo.com
371 US Highway 22, Green Brook 08812
    *(see our ad under SCRAP IRON & METAL RECYCLING)*

## AUTOMOBILE SEAT COVERS

Atlas Auto Trim, Inc.
    Phone—(732) 985-6800
    81 Highway 1, Edison 08817

**E.W.E. Auto Seat Cover Co.**
Phone—(201) 869-6470
Fax—(201) 868-8491
Email—eweauto@yahoo.com
8431 Kennedy Blvd., North Bergen 07047

## AUTOMOBILE TOPS

Auto Sun Roof, Inc. (H Q)
    Phone—(856) 786-0600
    1305 Industrial Hwy., P.O. Box 2321, Cinnaminson 08077

**E.W.E. Auto Seat Cover Co.**
Phone—(201) 869-6470
Fax—(201) 868-8491
Email—eweauto@yahoo.com
8431 Kennedy Blvd., North Bergen 07047

## AUTOMOBILE WRECKING

**Perone's Auto Service & Salvage**
We Buy All Metals & Iron. 10-40 Yard Container Service For Demolition & Clean Ups
Phone—(732) 563-1630
Fax—(732) 563-1774
Web—www.peronesauto.com
Email—peronesauto@yahoo.com
371 US Highway 22, Green Brook 08812
    *(see our ad under SCRAP IRON & METAL RECYCLING)*

## AUTOMOBILES — Passenger Cars

BMW Of North America, LLC (H Q)
    Phone—(201) 307-4000
    300 Chestnut Ridge Rd., Woodcliff Lake 07677

Subaru Of America, Inc. (H Q)
    Phone—(856) 488-8500
    2235 Route 70 W., Subaru Plz., Cherry Hill 08002

## AUTOMOBILES — Wholesale

Jaguar Land Rover North America
    Phone—(201) 818-8500
    555 MacArthur Blvd., Mahwah 07430

## AUTOMOTIVE ACCESSORIES

Modern Technologies Group, Inc.
    Phone—(609) 714-8900
    3 Reeves Station Rd., Medford 08055

MPT Industries
    Phone—(973) 989-9220
    85 Franklin Rd., Hamilton Bus. Park, Ste. 6-B, Dover 07801

Olde Granddad Industries
    Phone—(201) 997-1899
    1 Market St., Passaic 07055

StreetGlow, Inc. (H Q)
    Phone—(973) 709-9000
    57 Oak St., Norwood 07648

## AUTOMOTIVE AFTERMARKET

Odyssey Specialty Vehicles
    Phone—(973) 328-2667
    317 Richard Mine Rd., Wharton 07885

Do nationwide searches for products & services at:
**IndustryNet.com**

## AUTOMOTIVE BODY SHOP EQUIPMENT

Kemperle, Inc., Albert
    Phone—(908) 925-6133
    626 E. Elizabeth Ave., Linden 07036

W & E Sales Co., Inc.
    Phone—(973) 824-2000
    370 Elizabeth Ave., Newark 07112

## AUTOMOTIVE ENGINE REBUILDING

Houpert Truck Service
    Phone—(856) 767-0145
    115 Atlantic Ave., P.O. Box 8, Berlin 08009

K & K Automotive, Inc.
    Phone—(973) 777-2235
    979 Main Ave., Passaic 07055

Shoemaker's Automotive Machine
    Phone—(609) 624-0847
    176 Kings Hwy., Cape May Court House 08210

## AUTOMOTIVE INTERIORS

**E.W.E. Auto Seat Cover Co.**
Phone—(201) 869-6470
Fax—(201) 868-8491
Email—eweauto@yahoo.com
8431 Kennedy Blvd., North Bergen 07047

## AUTOMOTIVE PARTS

**American Auto II, Inc.**
New & Used Auto Glass
Phone—(609) 965-6700 / (866) 883-4799
Fax—(609) 965-6501
Web—www.americanauto2.com
Email—parts@americanauto2.com
3135 Route 50, Mays Landing 08330
    *(see our ad on next page)*

Felco Products, LLC
    Phone—(973) 890-7979
    18 Furler St., Totowa 07512

Gnutti Carlo
    Phone—(201) 768-8200
    140 Ludlow Ave., Northvale 07647

Gren Machinery Co.
    Phone—(732) 356-5118
    70 School House Rd., Somerset 08873

JDM Engineering
    Phone—(732) 780-0770
    60 Jerseyville Ave., Freehold 07728

JJ Products, Inc.
    Phone—(973) 228-3460
    133 Mountain Ave., West Caldwell 07006

Kramer Electronics USA, Inc./Sierra Video Systems (H Q)
    Phone—(908) 735-0018
    6 State Route 173 W., Clinton 08809

Neptune Auto Supply, Inc.
    Phone—(732) 774-0002
    51 TFH Plz., Neptune City 07753

Phoenix Friction Products, Inc.
    Phone—(732) 667-7937
    276-278 Lincoln Blvd., Middlesex 08846

## AUTOMOTIVE PARTS — Rebuilt

Last Chance Rebuilt Corp.
    Phone—(908) 245-4421
    340 W. 1st Ave., Roselle 07203

Part-Rite, Inc.
    Phone—(732) 269-5000
    19 Butler Ave., Bayville 08721

Rudy's & Vitor's V. A. S. Co., Inc.
    Phone—(732) 388-0334
    521 W. Hazelwood Ave., P.O. Box 1544, Rahway 07065

## AUTOMOTIVE PARTS — Used

**Carlyn Transmission, Inc.**
Phone—(856) 582-0224
Fax—(856) 582-5554
Email—carlyn5@verizon.net
509 Beechwood Ave., Pitman 08071

© Copyright 2015 Manufacturers' News, Inc.

American Auto II, Inc.
**AMERICAN II, Inc.**
*New & Used Auto Parts*
*New & Used Auto Glass With Installation*
**609.965.6700 • FAX: 609.965.6501**
Email: *parts@americanauto2.com*
**1-866.883.4799** • www.americanauto2.com
3135 Route 50  Mays Landing, NJ 08330

## AUTOMOTIVE PARTS — Used — (cont.)

**DC Starting & Charging Systems, Inc., DBA: Generator & Starter Exchange**
Phone—(609) 396-2661
Fax—(609) 396-2633
Web—www.generatorstarterexchange.com
Email—generatorstarternj@gmail.com
117 Mulberry St., Trenton 08638

**Lacey Used Auto Parts**
Phone—(973) 465-7553
Fax—(973) 465-1849
Web—www.laceyusedautoparts.com
305 Wilson Ave., Newark 07105

## AUTOMOTIVE PARTS — Wholesale

Ace Auto Salvage
Phone—(201) 997-6178
34 Stover Ave., Kearny 07032
Auto King Parts & Supplies
Phone—(732) 521-0474
67 E. Railroad Ave., Jamesburg 08831
Autopart International, Inc.
Phone—(201) 488-4187
260 Hudson St., Hackensack 07601
Autopart International, Inc.
Phone—(856) 405-0346
1773 Pine Ave., Unit A, Vineland 08360
Dreyco, Inc.
Phone—(201) 896-9000
263 Veterans Blvd., Carlstadt 07072
K. S. I. Trading Corp.
Phone—(908) 668-1380
100 Wade Ave., Ste. A, South Plainfield 07080
Knopf Automotive, LLC
Phone—(732) 212-0444
93 Shrewsbury Ave., Apt. 1, Red Bank 07701
National Parts Supply Co., Inc.
Phone—(908) 782-3530
56 State Route 31, Flemington 08822
National Parts Supply Co., Inc.
Phone—(732) 247-5171
535 Milltown Rd., North Brunswick 08902
P & A Auto Parts, Inc.
Phone—(973) 405-6068
396 Midland Ave., Garfield 07026
P & A Auto Parts, Inc.
Phone—(201) 843-7156
530 River St., Hackensack 07601

Parts Distributors, LLC
Phone—(856) 778-1400
901 N. Lenola Rd., P.O. Box 832, Moorestown 08057
Strauss Discount Auto
Phone—(732) 390-9000
7-C Brick Plant Rd., South River 08882
Suburban Auto Seat Co., Inc.
Phone—(973) 778-9227
35 Industrial Rd., Lodi 07644
Worldwide Parts & Accessories Corp.
Phone—(732) 230-5000
300 Herrod Blvd., Dayton 08810

## AUTOMOTIVE PRODUCTS

**American Auto II, Inc.**
New & Used Auto Glass
Phone—(609) 965-6700 / (866) 883-4799
Fax—(609) 965-6501
Web—www.americanauto2.com
Email—parts@americanauto2.com
3135 Route 50, Mays Landing 08330
*(see our ad on this page)*
Solv-Tec, Inc.
Phone—(609) 261-4242
3860 Sylon Blvd., Hainesport 08036

## AUTOMOTIVE REFINISHING PRODUCTS

Clausen Co., The
Phone—(732) 738-1165
1055 King George Post Rd., Edison 08817

## AUTOMOTIVE SERVICE

S & G Tool Aid Corp.
Phone—(973) 824-7730
43 E. Alpine St., Newark 07114

## AUTOMOTIVE SERVICE EQUIPMENT

Mastercool, Inc.
Phone—(973) 252-9119
1 Aspen Dr., Randolph 07869

**find additional suppliers at IndustryNet.com**

## AUTOMOTIVE TRIM

Wowtrim
Phone—(732) 340-0766
178 W. Westfield Ave., Roselle Park 07204

## AVIATION ELECTRONICS

EMS Aviation
Phone—(856) 234-5020
121 Whittendale Dr., Ste. A, Moorestown 08057
L-3 Communications Corp., Space & Navigation Systems
Phone—(973) 446-4000
450 Clark Dr., Budd Lake 07828

## AWARD RIBBONS

Denali Co., LLC, The (H Q)
Phone—(732) 219-7771
43 W. Front St., Ste. 11, Red Bank 07701

## AWARDS

Crown Trophy-River Edge, NJ
Phone—(201) 261-3933
488 Kinderkamack Rd., River Edge 07661
Picture-It, Inc.
Phone—(732) 819-0420
1703 State Route 27, Edison 08817
Stewart-Morris, Inc.
Phone—(973) 822-2777
71 Kings Rd., Madison 07940
T J's Sportwide Trophy & Awards
Phone—(973) 989-8775
236 S. Salem St., Randolph 07869

## AWARDS — Corporate Recognition

B&D Marketing, Inc.
Phone—(856) 354-2004
1879 Old Cuthbert Rd., Ste. 21, Cherry Hill 08034
Ironbound Trophy Center
Phone—(973) 344-3872
289 Lafayette St., Ste. A, Newark 07105

## AWNINGS — Aluminum

Clark Home Supply
Phone—(732) 388-5447
205 Westfield Ave., Clark 07066
Tuers Aluminum, LLC
Phone—(732) 458-2031
2562 Lakewood-Allenwood Rd., Howell 07731
Weather Tek Aluminum Corp.
Phone—(732) 752-0313
123 N. Washington Ave., P.O. Box 405, Dunellen 08812
Weathercraft Mfg. Co.
Phone—(201) 262-0055
13 Emerson Plz. E., Emerson 07630

## AWNINGS — Fabric

Artisan Awning Co.
Phone—(973) 383-5608
17 Jefferson St., P.O. Box 387, Newton 07860
Hansen Awning Co.
Phone—(609) 886-1685
18 Church Rd., Rio Grande 08242

## AWNINGS — Retractable

Huggins Aluminum Products
Phone—(856) 767-0506
576 N. Route 73, West Berlin 08091

## AWNINGS AND CANOPIES

ACS Canvas & Awnings
Phone—(609) 953-9700
83 Union St., Medford 08055
Awning Concepts & Design, Inc.
Phone—(732) 462-1131
916 Route 33, Freehold 07728
Awning Shoppe, The
Phone—(732) 787-4246
190 Highway 36, Keansburg 07734

INDUSTRY

## AWNINGS AND CANOPIES —
### *(cont.)*

Berges Trenton Awning Co., Inc.
Phone—(609) 641-7861
12 W. Washington Ave., Pleasantville 08232

Blacher Canvas Products, Inc.
Phone—(732) 968-3666
604 Bound Brook Rd., Dunellen 08812

Brown's Awning Co.
Phone—(609) 398-6262
628 West Ave., Ocean City 08226

Capitol City Aluminum Products
Phone—(609) 587-3653
407 Rutgers Ave., Hamilton 08619

DSM Enterprises, Inc.
Phone—(732) 380-9779
132 Lewis St., Unit B-5, Eatontown 07724

Fiber-Lite Mfg. Co., Inc.
Phone—(973) 208-1300
1152 Greenpond Rd., Newfoundland 07435

G & J Solutions, Inc.
Phone—(609) 861-9838
419 Madison Ave., Woodbine 08270

Laggren's, LLC
Phone—(609) 235-9883
P.O. Box 7173, Monroe Township 08831

Lloyd's Of Millville, Inc.
Phone—(856) 825-0345
208 S. Wade Blvd., Millville 08332

Marshall, Inc., G. E.
Phone—(609) 392-2464
810 S. Broad St., Trenton 08611

McBride Awning Co.
Phone—(732) 892-6256
304 Richmond Ave., Point Pleasant Beach 08742

Monmouth & Ocean County Awning Co.
Phone—(732) 775-4881
508 Main St., Asbury Park 07712

Opdyke Awning, Inc.
Phone—(732) 449-5940
2036 State Route 35, Wall Township 07719

**Shore Awning Co., Inc.**
**Email: sales@shoreawning.com**
**Phone—(732) 578-1882**
**Fax—(732) 578-1885**
**Web—www.shoreawning.com**
**P.O. Box 38, Avon by the Sea 07717**

Stetsers J.D. Canvas Products, Inc.
Phone—(856) 423-4901
644 Billings Ave., Paulsboro 08066

## AXLES

Quality Rebuilders, Inc.
Phone—(973) 523-8800
969 Market St., Paterson 07513

Rebuilt Parts Co.
Phone—(856) 662-3252
7929 River Rd., Pennsauken 08110

## BABY ACCESSORIES

ABAA, Inc. (H Q)
Phone—(908) 766-4900
P.O. Box 26, Bernardsville 07924

Dream On Me Industries, Inc.
Phone—(908) 791-0555
125 Helen St., South Plainfield 07080

## BACKPACKS

Wheelchair Gear
Phone—(609) 653-6787
126 Cindy Dr., Egg Harbor Township 08234

## BACTERIOLOGICAL PRODUCTS

Monmouth BioProducts
Phone—(732) 863-0300
3 Industrial Ct., Ste. 4, Freehold 07728

## BADGES

Badge Company Of New Jersey
Phone—(908) 735-7700
223 Hamden Rd., P.O. Box 100, Annandale 08801

## All Size Poly Bags
*Nationwide Distributor of Plastic Bags*

**800-635-9959 • 732-828-3400**
**FAX: 732-828-7703**

**www.allsizepolybags.com**

**Email: info@rksplastics.com**

P.O. Box 836 • New Brunswick, NJ 08903

## BAGELS

Bylada Foods, LLC
Phone—(201) 933-7474
140 W. Commercial Ave., Moonachie 07074

D & C Bagel Boys, Inc.
Phone—(732) 566-4523
1055-C Highway 34, Matawan 07747

Original Bagel & Bialy Co.
Phone—(973) 227-5777
2 Fairfield Crescent, West Caldwell 07006

Plaza 70 Bagels
Phone—(856) 983-5151
65 Highway 70 E., Marlton 08053

## BAGS

**Dana Poly Inc.**
**The Home of Quality Film & Bags**
**Phone—(908) 474-0600 / (800) 474-1020**
**Fax—(908) 474-0604**
**Web—www.danapoly.com**
**Email—sales@danapoly.com**
**1301 W. Elizabeth Ave., Linden 07036**
*(see our ad under BAGS—Plastic)*

**Forem Packaging, Inc.**
**In Business for 25 Years; Laminated Materials**
**Phone—(973) 589-0402**
**Fax—(973) 589-0453**
**Email—sales@forempackaging.com**
**2-44 Cornelia St., P.O. Box 50090, Newark 07105**
*(see our ad under PACKAGING—Flexible)*

LBU, Inc.
Phone—(973) 773-4800
217 Brook Ave., Ste. 6, Passaic 07055

NYP Corp.
Phone—(908) 351-6550
805 E. Grand St., Elizabeth 07201

## BAGS — Anti-Static

**Dana Poly Inc.**
**The Home of Quality Film & Bags**
**Phone—(908) 474-0600 / (800) 474-1020**
**Fax—(908) 474-0604**
**Web—www.danapoly.com**
**Email—sales@danapoly.com**
**1301 W. Elizabeth Ave., Linden 07036**
*(see our ad under BAGS—Plastic)*

## BAGS — Canvas

DiMilo Industries
Phone—(973) 955-0460
90 Dayton Ave., Ste. 38, Passaic 07055

## BAGS — Duffel

TerraCycle, Inc.
Phone—(609) 393-4252
121 New York Ave., Trenton 08638

## BAGS — Food

**Forem Packaging, Inc.**
**In Business for 25 Years; Laminated Materials**
**Phone—(973) 589-0402**
**Fax—(973) 589-0453**
**Email—sales@forempackaging.com**
**2-44 Cornelia St., P.O. Box 50090, Newark 07105**
*(see our ad under PACKAGING—Flexible)*

## BAGS — Laundry

Object Design, Inc.
Phone—(973) 442-5790
105 W. Dewey Ave., Bldg. C, Unit 5, Wharton 07885

Tingue, Brown & Co. (H Q)
Phone—(201) 796-4490
535 N. Midland Ave., Saddle Brook 07663

## BAGS — Paper

Duro Bag Mfg. Co.
Phone—(908) 351-2400
750 Dowd Ave., Elizabeth 07201

Ronpak, Inc.
Phone—(732) 968-8000
4301 New Brunswick Ave., South Plainfield 07080

## BAGS — Plastic

A N S Plastics Corp.
Phone—(732) 247-2776
625 Jersey Ave., Ste. 11, New Brunswick 08901

A-1 Plastics
Phone—(973) 344-4441
136 Tichenor St., Newark 07105

Absolute Packaging & Supply, Inc.
Phone—(973) 278-0202
456 E. 22nd St., Paterson 07514

**All Size Poly Bags**
**Leaders in supplying plastic bags, packaging, shipping & warehouse supplies nationwide**
**Phone—(800) 635-9959 / (732) 828-3400**
**Fax—(732) 828-7703**
**Web—www.allsizepolybags.com**
**Email—info@rksplastics.com**
**P.O. Box 836, New Brunswick 08903**
*(see our ad on this page)*

Alpha Industries Corp. (H Q)
Phone—(201) 933-6000
P.O. Box 808, Lyndhurst 07071

Bag Factory, Inc., The
Phone—(908) 925-7122
726 N. Stiles St., Linden 07036

Beta Plastics Corp.
Phone—(201) 933-1400
120 Amor Ave., Carlstadt 07072

Central Poly Corp.
Phone—(908) 862-7570
2400 Bedle Pl., Linden 07036

D C Plastic Products
Phone—(201) 339-0111
12 E. 2nd St., P.O. Box 353, Bayonne 07002

*Search from among 430,000 U.S. manufacturers & suppliers:*
**IndustryNet.com**

*Do nationwide searches for products & services at:*
**IndustryNet.com**

© Copyright 2015 Manufacturers' News, Inc.

## BAGS — Plastic — *(cont.)*

**Dana Poly Inc.**
The Home of Quality Film & Bags
Phone—(908) 474-0600 / (800) 474-1020
Fax—(908) 474-0604
Web—www.danapoly.com
Email—sales@danapoly.com
1301 W. Elizabeth Ave., Linden 07036

**DANAPOLY** Inc.
The Home of Quality Film & Bags

Plastic Bags & Film
Tubing & Sheeting
**908-474-0600**
**800-474-1020**
**FAX: 908-474-0604**
sales@danapoly.com
www.danapoly.com
**1301 W. Elizabeth Ave.**
**Linden, NJ 07036**

Dash Industries, Inc.
Phone—(732) 364-5850
639 5th St., Lakewood 08701
Eastar Plastics, Inc.
Phone—(732) 564-1899
250 Circle Dr. N., Piscataway 08854
Encore Poly Corp.
Phone—(201) 845-4510
240 W. Passaic St., Ste. 7, Maywood 07607
Fordion Packaging Ltd.
Phone—(201) 692-1344
185 Linden St., Hackensack 07601
Gemini Plastic Films Corp.
Phone—(973) 340-0700
535 Midland Ave., P.O. Box 360, Garfield 07026
Golden Plastics, Inc.
Phone—(201) 393-9833
510-A Industrial Ave., Teterboro 07608
Heritage Bag Co., Inc.
Phone—(856) 467-2247
2321 High Hill Rd., Swedesboro 08085
Keystone Packaging Service, Inc.
Phone—(908) 454-8567
555 Warren St., Phillipsburg 08865
KNF Flexpak Corporation.
Phone—(201) 656-4012
44 Howell St., Jersey City 07306
Lally-Pak, Inc.
Phone—(908) 353-3344
1209 Central Ave., Hillside 07205
Mercury Plastic Bag Co., Inc.
Phone—(973) 778-7200
168 7th St., Passaic 07055
Omega Plastics Corp.
Phone—(201) 933-5353
Page & Schuyler Ave., Bldg. 3, P.O. Box 808, Lyndhurst 07071
Primepak Company
Phone—(201) 836-5060
133 Cedar Ln., Ste. 104, Teaneck 07666
Robyn Packaging Co., Inc.
Phone—(973) 696-2059
31 Augusta Dr., Wayne 07470
Royal Slide Sales Co., Inc.
Phone—(973) 777-1177
42 Hepworth Pl., Garfield 07026
**Rutan Poly Industries, Inc.**
Quality custom plastic bags & film
Phone—(201) 529-1474 / (800) 872-1474
Fax—(201) 529-4440
Web—www.rutanpoly.com
Email—sales@rutanpoly.com
39 Siding Pl., Mahwah 07430
Shiprite Packaging, Inc.
Phone—(201) 385-4747
161 Woodbine St., Bergenfield 07621

Sierra Packaging, Inc.
Phone—(732) 571-2900
60 State Route 36, Ste. C, West Long Branch 07764
Southeastern Plastics Corp.
Phone—(732) 846-8500
15 Home News Row, New Brunswick 08901
Steelson Packaging
Phone—(201) 909-0011
190 W. Passaic St., Rochelle Park 07662
Tee Pee Packaging Corp.
Phone—(973) 328-6500
85 Harrison St., Dover 07801
Top Notch Plastics
Phone—(732) 946-0049
217 Bradwick Way, Marlboro 07746
**X-L Plastics, Inc.**
Phone—(973) 777-1888
Fax—(973) 777-1275
Web—www.x-lplastics.com
Email—sales@x-lplastics.com
220 Clifton Blvd., Clifton 07011

## BAGS — Polyethylene

Champion Plastics Corp.
Phone—(973) 777-9400
220 Clifton Blvd., Clifton 07011
**Dana Poly Inc.**
The Home of Quality Film & Bags
Phone—(908) 474-0600 / (800) 474-1020
Fax—(908) 474-0604
Web—www.danapoly.com
Email—sales@danapoly.com
1301 W. Elizabeth Ave., Linden 07036
*(see our ad under BAGS—Plastic)*
**Phoenix Industries, LLC**
Phone—(973) 366-4199
Fax—(973) 366-5288
Web—www.phoenixpkgind.com
Email—vnorcia@phoenixpkgind.com
105 W. Dewey Ave., P.O. Box 416, Wharton 07885
Poly Express, LLC
Phone—(800) 843-7659
318 McLean Blvd., Bldg. 5, Paterson 07504
**Rutan Poly Industries, Inc.**
Quality custom plastic bags & film
Phone—(201) 529-1474 / (800) 872-1474
Fax—(201) 529-4440
Web—www.rutanpoly.com
Email—sales@rutanpoly.com
39 Siding Pl., Mahwah 07430

## BAGS — Polypropylene

**All Size Poly Bags**
Leaders in supplying plastic bags, packaging, shipping & warehouse supplies nationwide
Phone—(800) 635-9959 / (732) 828-3400
Fax—(732) 828-7703
Web—www.allsizepolybags.com
Email—info@rksplastics.com
P.O. Box 836, New Brunswick 08903
*(see our ad under BAGS—Plastic)*
Halsted Corp.
Phone—(201) 433-3323
78 Halladay St., Jersey City 07304

## BAGS — Specialty

Accurate Flannel Bag Co., Inc.
Phone—(973) 720-1800
468 Totowa Ave., Ste. 3, Paterson 07522

## BAKERY MIXES

**Corbion Caravan**
Corporate Headquarters Lenexa, KS; Regional Office & Bakery
Phone—(973) 256-8886 / (800) 526-5261
Fax—(973) 256-5789
Web—www.corbion.com
Email—bakery@corbion.com
100 Adams Dr., Totowa 07512
Puratos Corp.
Phone—(856) 428-4300
1941 Old Cuthbert Rd., Cherry Hill 08034

## BAKERY PRODUCTS

AHB Foods International
Phone—(856) 642-9955
823 E. Gate Dr., Unit 3, Mount Laurel 08054
Americas Bakery
Phone—(973) 372-0700
32-50 Buffington St., P.O. Box 5099, Irvington 07111
Antique Bakery & Pizzeria, Inc.
Phone—(201) 714-9323
122 Willow Ave., Hoboken 07030
Aryzta/La Brea Bakery
Phone—(856) 417-8100
11 Technology Dr., Swedesboro 08085
Automatic Rolls Of New Jersey, Inc.
Phone—(732) 549-2243
1 Gourmet Ln., Edison 08837
Bakers Bounty
Phone—(908) 587-1602
7 Maple Ave., Linden 07036
Baker's Perfection, Inc.
Phone—(973) 983-0700
198 Green Pond Rd., Rockaway 07866
Bakers Puff Pastry
Phone—(973) 977-2255
1 Industrial Plz., Paterson 07503
Bakery, The
Phone—(201) 384-1456
99 N. Washington Ave., Bergenfield 07621
Balthazar Bakery
Phone—(201) 503-9717
214 S. Dean St., Englewood 07631
Bread & Bagels
Phone—(856) 667-2333
1600 Church Rd., Cherry Hill 08002
Bridor USA
Phone—(856) 691-8000
2260 Industrial Way, Vineland 08360
Brother's Quality Bakery
Phone—(201) 991-4364
365 Kearny Ave., Kearny 07032
Brothers Quality Bakery Of Allwood
Phone—(973) 473-1467
70 Market St., Clifton 07012
Cacia's Bakery
Phone—(856) 228-5986
1010 S. Black Horse Pike, Blackwood 08012
Cake Specialty, Inc.
Phone—(973) 238-0500
255 Goffle Rd., Hawthorne 07506
Calandra's Italian & French Bakery
Phone—(973) 484-5598
204 1st Ave. W., Newark 07107
Certified Bakery, Inc.
Phone—(201) 635-9245
20 Universal Pl., Carlstadt 07072
Classic Cake Co., The
Phone—(856) 751-5448
480 Evesham Rd., Cherry Hill 08003
Columbus Bakery, Inc.
Phone—(973) 429-1697
197 Bloomfield Ave., Bloomfield 07003
Del Buono Baking Co.
Phone—(856) 546-9585
319 Black Horse Pike, Haddon Heights 08035
Deluxe Italian Bakery, Inc.
Phone—(856) 939-5000
680 E. Clements Bridge Rd., Runnemede 08078
Ecce Panis
Phone—(732) 254-1770
3-B Brick Plant Rd., East Brunswick 08816
Elegant Desserts
Phone—(201) 933-0770
275 Warren St., Lyndhurst 07071
Farinhas Bakery, Inc.
Phone—(973) 482-5640
301 Harrison Ave., Harrison 07029
Food & Beverage, Inc.
Phone—(201) 288-8881
100 Hollister Rd., Unit 5, Teterboro 07608
Formica Bros. Bakery
Phone—(609) 348-8934
2310 Arctic Ave., Atlantic City 08401
Fragale's Baking Co.
Phone—(973) 546-0327
68-74 Gaston Ave., Garfield 07026
Gelbstein Bakery
Phone—(732) 363-3636
415 Clifton Ave., Lakewood 08701

## BAKERY PRODUCTS — *(cont.)*

**Gianella Baking Co.**
Phone—(973) 523-9258
298 21st Ave., Paterson 07501

**Ginsburg Bakery, Inc.**
Phone—(609) 345-2265
300 N. Tennessee Ave., Atlantic City 08401

**Gourmet Dessert Outlet, LLC**
Phone—(973) 815-1111
851 Van Houten Ave., Clifton 07013

**Hudson Bread**
Phone—(201) 422-7900
5601-5711 Tonnelle Ave., North Bergen 07047

**International Delights Bakery Co.**
Phone—(973) 928-5582
230 Brighton Rd., Clifton 07012

**Italian Peoples Bakery, Inc.**
Phone—(609) 396-9869
307 Hudson St., Trenton 08611

**Joey's Fine Foods, Inc.**
Phone—(973) 482-1400
135 Manchester Pl., Newark 07104

**John Wm. Macy CheeseSticks, Inc.**
Phone—(201) 791-8036
80 Kipp Ave., Elmwood Park 07407

**Kashmir Crown Bakery**
Phone—(908) 474-1470
710 W. Linden Ave., Linden 07036

**Kashmir Crown Baking, LLC**
Phone—(908) 474-0970
1030 W. Linden Ave., Linden 07036

**La Esperanza Baking**
Phone—(201) 871-1934
148 W. Forest Ave., Englewood 07631

**Liberty Brand Pastries & Foods**
Phone—(201) 863-3350
2409 Central Ave., Union City 07087

**Lithuanian Bakery, Inc., T. J.**
Phone—(908) 354-0970
131 Inslee Pl., Elizabeth 07206

**Manischewitz Co., The (H Q)**
Phone—(201) 553-1100
80 Avenue K, Newark 07105

**Mendoker's Quality Bakery, Inc.**
Phone—(732) 521-0056
34 W. Railroad Ave., Jamesburg 08831

**Mother's Kitchen, Inc.**
Phone—(609) 589-3033
499 Veterans Dr., Burlington 08016

**Muffins & Stuff**
Phone—(973) 881-9900
53 Jersey St., Paterson 07501

**Natale's Summit Bakery**
Phone—(908) 277-2074
185 Broad St., Summit 07901

**Nicolos Italian Bakery & Deli, Inc.**
Phone—(973) 746-1398
6 Baldwin St., Montclair 07042

**Oliveri & Sons, Inc., A.**
Baking Flour & Ingredients
Phone—(201) 319-9112
Fax—(201) 319-9720
Web—www.aoliveriandsons.com
Email—nickd@aoliveriandsons.com
4401 Dell Ave., P.O. Box 88, North Bergen 07047

"SERVING BAKERS FOR OVER 100 YEARS"
A. Oliveri & Sons Inc.
Baking Flour and Ingredients
www.aoliveriandsons.com / (201) 319-9112
4401 Dell Ave., PO Box 88 • North Bergen, NJ 07047

**Omni Baking Co.**
Phone—(856) 205-1485
2621 Freddy Ln., Vineland 08360

**Orlando Bakery**
Phone—(973) 772-8883
236 Harrison Ave., Lodi 07644

**Orthodox Baking Co., Inc.**
Phone—(973) 844-9393
555 Cortlandt St., Belleville 07109

**Panera Bread Co., LLC**
Phone—(973) 276-0250
5 E. Evans St., Fairfield 07004

**Paramount Bakeries, Inc.**
Phone—(973) 482-6638
61 Davenport Ave., Newark 07107

**Pride Gourmet Bakers, Inc.**
Phone—(973) 340-3200
450 Getty Ave., Clifton 07011

**Prince Donut Co., Inc.**
Phone—(908) 925-2262
2345 E. Linden Ave., Linden 07036

**Quality Bakery Products Of New Jersey, Inc.**
Phone—(609) 871-7393
24 Ironside Ct., Willingboro 08046

**R. P. Baking Co.**
Phone—(973) 483-3374
840 Jersey St., Harrison 07029

**Ronic, Inc.**
Phone—(973) 772-2217
173 Ray St., Garfield 07026

**Royal Baking Co.**
Phone—(201) 296-0888
8 Empire Blvd., Moonachie 07074

**Santos Bakery**
Phone—(973) 732-7200
123 Hudson St., Newark 07103

**Scala Pastry**
Phone—(732) 398-9808
1896 U.S. Highway 130, North Brunswick 08902

**Schripps European Bread, Inc.**
Phone—(201) 867-0909
5410 Tonnelle Ave., North Bergen 07047

**Serrani's Bakery**
Phone—(973) 678-1777
114 S. Essex Ave., Orange 07050

**Sweet Potato Pie, Inc.**
Phone—(973) 279-3405
140 Auburn St., Paterson 07501

**Teixeira's Bakery**
Phone—(973) 589-8875
113-129 Kossuth St., P.O. Box 5550, Newark 07105

**Terrigno's Bakery**
Phone—(856) 451-6368
632 N. Pearl St., Bridgeton 08302

**Toufayan Bakery, Inc.**
Phone—(201) 941-2000
175 Railroad Ave., Ridgefield 07657

**Uptown Bakeries/J & J Snack Foods**
Phone—(856) 467-9552
300 Eagle Ct., P.O. Box 257, Bridgeport 08014

**Vieira's Bakery**
Phone—(973) 589-7719
34-48 Avenue K, Newark 07105

**Vieiras Bakery, Inc.**
Phone—(973) 465-1212
34 Avenue K, Ste. 48, Newark 07105

**Zaiya, Inc.**
Phone—(201) 343-3988
185 Kenneth St., Hackensack 07601

**Zinicola Baking Co.**
Phone—(973) 667-1306
127 King St., Nutley 07110

## BAKERY PRODUCTS — Custom Blend

**Tatz Industries, Inc., William**
Phone—(973) 751-0720
11 Railroad Pl., Belleville 07109

## BAKERY PRODUCTS — Specialty

**Anthony & Sons Italian Bakery**
Phone—(973) 625-2323
20 Luger Rd., Denville 07834

**Bella Palermo Pastry Shop, Inc.**
Phone—(908) 354-8610
619 Elizabeth Ave., Elizabeth 07206

## BAKERY PRODUCTS — Wholesale

**J & K Ingredients, Inc.**
Sausville Foods
Phone—(973) 340-8700
Fax—(973) 340-4994
Web—www.jkingredients.net
Email—sales@jkingredients.net
160 E. 5th St., Paterson 07524

**Puratos Corp.**
Phone—(856) 661-3112
945 Sherman Ave., Pennsauken 08110

## BAKEWARE

**Sasa Demarle, Inc.**
Phone—(609) 395-0219
8 Corporate Dr., Cranbury 08512

## BAKING EQUIPMENT & MACHINERY

**Coastal Imports, Inc.**
Phone—(732) 223-4356
31 Mulberry Ct., Unit B, Brielle 08730

**Erika Record, LLC**
Phone—(973) 614-8500
37 Atlantic Way, Clifton 07012

**Excalibur Bagel & Bakery Equipment, Inc.**
Phone—(201) 797-2788
4-01 Banta Pl., Fair Lawn 07410

**Excellent Bakery Equipment Co.**
Phone—(973) 244-1664
315 Fairfield Rd., Fairfield 07004

**Magna Industries, Inc.**
Phone—(732) 905-0957
Fax—(732) 367-2989
Web—www.magnaindustries.com
Email—sales@magnaindustries.com
1825 Swarthmore Ave., Ste. 1, Lakewood 08701

**RONDO Inc. USA**
Phone—(201) 229-9700
51 Joseph St., Moonachie 07074

**Warwick Mfg. & Equipment Co., LLC**
Buy & sell used: Chemical, food, cosmetic, packaging & pharmaceutical equipment
Phone—(732) 729-0400 / (732) 241-9263
Fax—(732) 729-1235
Web—www.warwickequipment.com
Email—sales@warwickequipment.com
1112 12th St., North Brunswick 08902
*(see our ad Outside Back Cover)*

## BAKING INGREDIENTS

**BakeMark USA, LLC**
Phone—(609) 747-9000
1815 Route 130 N., Burlington 08016

**Church & Dwight Co., Inc.**
Phone—(732) 730-3100
800 Airport Rd., Lakewood 08701

**Corbion Caravan**
Corporate Headquarters Lenexa, KS; Regional Office & Bakery
Phone—(973) 256-8886 / (800) 526-5261
Fax—(973) 256-5789
Web—www.corbion.com
Email—bakery@corbion.com
100 Adams Dr., Totowa 07512

**IFC Products, Inc.**
Email: joe@ifcproducts.com
Phone—(908) 587-1221
Fax—(908) 587-1661
Web—www.ifcproducts.com
568 E. Elizabeth Ave., P.O. Box 2175, Linden 07036

**J & K Ingredients, Inc.**
Sausville Foods
Phone—(973) 340-8700
Fax—(973) 340-4994
Web—www.jkingredients.net
Email—sales@jkingredients.net
160 E. 5th St., Paterson 07524

**Malt Products Corp.**
Phone—(201) 845-4420
88 Market St., P.O. Box 898, Saddle Brook 07663

## BALANCES

**Ohaus Corp.**
Phone—(973) 377-9000
7 Campus Dr., Ste. 310, Parsippany 07054

*find additional suppliers at*
**IndustryNet.com**

INDUSTRY

## BALANCING SERVICES

**Vibration Associates**
Phone—(732) 671-7182
Fax—(732) 671-7183
Email—office@vibrationassociates.com
19 Shephard Dr., P.O. Box 4123, Middletown 07748
_____

## BALLS

**Scientific Alloys Corp.**
Spheres, Solders, Metal Powder Balls, Precious Metals
Phone—(973) 478-8323
Fax—(973) 478-6780
Web—www.bgaspheres.com
Email—bgaspheres@aol.com
5 Troast Ct., Clifton 07011
*(see our ad Outside Front Cover)*
_____

## BANK SUPPLIES

E. Greene Of North Carolina, Inc.
Phone—(973) 838-5200
P.O. Box 1017, West Caldwell 07007
_____

## BANKS

**Gibraltar Bank**
Phone—(973) 515-0885
Web—www.gibraltarbanknj.com
2 Railroad Plz., Ste. 2, Whippany 07981
**NVE Bank**
Phone—(201) 816-2810
Fax—(201) 816-7379
Web—www.nvebank.com
76 Engle St., Englewood 07631
_____

## BANNERS

Screen-Trans Development Corp.
Phone—(201) 933-7800
100 Grand St., Moonachie 07074
Tandem Graphics, Inc.
Phone—(973) 513-9779
207 Wanaque Ave., Pompton Lakes 07442
_____

## BAR CODE SYSTEMS

BarCodeAmerica.com
Phone—(973) 377-8182
144 Shunpike Rd., P.O. Box 506, Madison 07940
Rack Design Group Inc. / BarCodeAmerica.com
Phone—(973) 377-8182
81 Clinton Rd., Fairfield 07004
_____

## BAR CODING EQUIPMENT

Symbology Enterprises, Inc.
Phone—(908) 725-1699
185 Industrial Pkwy., Ste. H, Somerville 08876
_____

## BAR STOOLS

Top Line Seating, Inc.
Phone—(908) 241-9051
540 S. 31st St., Kenilworth 07033
_____

## BAR SUPPLIES

Kraftware Corp.
Phone—(908) 259-8883
270 Cox St., Roselle 07203
Krowne Metal Corp.
Phone—(973) 305-3300
100 Haul Rd., Wayne 07470

*Do nationwide searches for products & services at:*
**IndustryNet.com**

## BARBECUE GRILLS

**Big Green Egg, Inc.**
Phone—(770) 938-9394 / (800) 793-2292
Fax—(770) 938-9395
Web—www.BigGreenEgg.com
Email—manufacturing@biggreenegg.com
3417 Lawrenceville Hwy., Atlanta, GA 30084

GRILL | ROAST | SMOKE | BAKE
**Big Green Egg**
The Ultimate Cooking Experience®
BigGreenEgg.com

LazyMan Mfg.
Phone—(908) 475-5315
616 Hardwick St., P.O. Box 327, Belvidere 07823
_____

## BARS

Wood & Laminates, Inc.
Phone—(973) 773-7475
102 Route 46 E., Lodi 07644
_____

## BASKETS — Metal

Hillside Wire Cloth, Inc.
Phone—(973) 751-3131
109 Roosevelt Ave., Belleville 07109
_____

## BATHROOM ACCESSORIES

Bath Connection, The
Phone—(973) 467-7888
183 Millburn Ave., Millburn 07041
Ginsey Industries, Inc.
Phone—(856) 933-1300
2078 Center Square Rd., Swedesboro 08085
_____

## BATTERIES

**Dantona Industries**
Phone—(516) 783-5050 / (800) 326-8662
Fax—(516) 783-1145
Web—www.dantona.com
Email—sales@dantona.com
3051 Burns Ave., Wantagh, NY 11793
Eos Energy Storage, LLC
Phone—(732) 225-8400
214 Fernwood Ave., Bldg. B, Edison 08837
Interstate Battery System Of America, Inc.
Phone—(856) 767-3903
408 Commerce Ln., West Berlin 08091
_____

## BATTERIES — Automotive

**Dantona Industries**
Phone—(516) 783-5050 / (800) 326-8662
Fax—(516) 783-1145
Web—www.dantona.com
Email—sales@dantona.com
3051 Burns Ave., Wantagh, NY 11793
_____

## BATTERIES — Storage

Hoppecke Batterys, Inc.
Phone—(856) 616-0032
1960 Old Cuthbert Rd., Ste. 130, Cherry Hill 08034
_____

## BATTERY ASSEMBLIES

**Dantona Industries**
Phone—(516) 783-5050 / (800) 326-8662
Fax—(516) 783-1145
Web—www.dantona.com
Email—sales@dantona.com
3051 Burns Ave., Wantagh, NY 11793

*Search from among 430,000 U.S. manufacturers & suppliers:*
**IndustryNet.com**

## BATTERY CHARGERS

Data Technologies, Inc.
Phone—(201) 784-3225
224 N. Pegasus Ave., Ste. A, Northvale 07647
_____

## BATTERY HOLDERS

Acme Model Engineering Co.
Phone—(973) 379-4193
115 Victory Rd., Springfield 07081
_____

## BATTERY MONITORING DEVICES

**BTECH, Inc.**
Email: sales@btechinc.com
Stationary Battery Monitors & Systems
Phone—(973) 983-1120
Fax—(973) 983-1125
Web—www.btechinc.com
10 Astro Pl., Rockaway 07866
*(see our ad under WIRELESS COMMUNICATION SYSTEMS)*
_____

## BATTERY PACKS

**Dantona Industries**
Phone—(516) 783-5050 / (800) 326-8662
Fax—(516) 783-1145
Web—www.dantona.com
Email—sales@dantona.com
3051 Burns Ave., Wantagh, NY 11793
_____

## BATTERY TEST EQUIPMENT

**BTECH, Inc.**
Email: sales@btechinc.com
Stationary Battery Monitors & Systems
Phone—(973) 983-1120
Fax—(973) 983-1125
Web—www.btechinc.com
10 Astro Pl., Rockaway 07866
*(see our ad under WIRELESS COMMUNICATION SYSTEMS)*
_____

## BATTING

Chasen & Sons, Inc., M.
Phone—(973) 374-8956
117 S. 20th St., Irvington 07111
Chasen & Sons, Inc., M.
Phone—(973) 589-8700
123 S. 20th St., Irvington 07111
_____

## BEARINGS

Accurate Bushing Co., Inc./Smith Bearing Div.
Phone—(908) 789-1121
443 North Ave., 1st Fl., Garwood 07027
Amscot Structural Products Corp.
Phone—(973) 989-8800
241 E. Blackwell St., Dover 07801
Ardom Bearing Group
Phone—(732) 370-2310
1000 Bennett Blvd., Ste. 7, Lakewood 08701
Ardom Bearing Group
Phone—(908) 755-3000
3377 S. Clinton Ave., Unit 15, South Plainfield 07080
Bearing Depot & Supply, Inc.
Phone—(732) 563-2225
819 Lincoln Blvd., Ste. 1, Middlesex 08846
DGB Bearing & Technology
Phone—(856) 848-3200
700 Mid Atlantic Pkwy., P.O. Box 189, Thorofare 08086
George A. Mathewson Co.
Phone—(973) 344-0081
9-11 Foundry St., Newark 07105
King Engine Bearings
Phone—(973) 857-0705
371 Little Falls Rd., Ste. 5, Cedar Grove 07009
Motion Industries, Inc.
Phone—(908) 241-1047
141 Market St., Ste. 8, Kenilworth 07033
Motion Industries, Inc.
Phone—(732) 828-8711
12-D Jules Ln., New Brunswick 08901
Motion Industries, Inc.
Phone—(201) 288-8111
600 Hollister Rd., Teterboro 07608

## BEARINGS — (cont.)

Motion Industries, Inc.
Phone—(609) 588-0555
9A S. Gold Dr., Trenton 08691

**PBM Supply Co., Inc.**
**Phone—(973) 839-0050**
**Fax—(973) 839-4886**
**Email—pbmsupply@verizon.net**
**88 Cannonball Rd., P.O. Box 351, Pompton Lakes 07442**

Pioneer Bearing Corp.
Phone—(973) 325-9095
623 Eagle Rock Ave., Ste. 135, West Orange 07052

RBC Bearings, Inc.
Phone—(609) 882-5050
400 Sullivan Way, West Trenton 08628

## BEARINGS — Aircraft

Oavco Ltd., LLC
Phone—(609) 454-5340
103 Carnegie Ctr., Princeton 08540

## BEARINGS — Ball

AST Bearings, LLC
Phone—(973) 335-2230
115 Main Rd., Montville 07045

Emmco Development Corp.
Phone—(732) 469-6464
243 Belmont Dr., Somerset 08873

## BEARINGS — Bronze

Accurate Bronze Bearing Co.
Phone—(973) 345-2304
64 Illinois Ave., Paterson 07503

## BEARINGS — Linear

**Rollon Corp.**
**Phone—(973) 300-5492**
**Fax—(908) 852-2714**
**Web—www.rolloncorp.com**
**Email—info@rolloncorp.com**
**101 Bilby Rd., Ste. B, Hackettstown 07840**

## BEARINGS — Precision

Consolidated Bearings Company
Phone—(973) 539-8300
10 Wing Dr., Cedar Knolls 07927

## BEARINGS — Roller

Berliss Bearing Co.
Phone—(973) 992-4242
644 W. Mount Pleasant Ave., P.O. Box 45, Livingston 07039

IKO International, Inc.
Phone—(973) 402-0254
91 Walsh Dr., Parsippany 07054

## BEAUTY CARE PRODUCTS

3lab, Inc. (H Q)
Phone—(201) 567-9100
100 W. Sheffield Ave., Englewood 07631

American Spraytech, LLC
Phone—(908) 725-6060
205 Meister Ave., Branchburg 08876

CCA Industries, Inc. (H Q)
Phone—(201) 935-3232
200 Murray Hill Pkwy., East Rutherford 07073

Cococare Products, Inc.
Phone—(973) 989-8880
85 Franklin Rd., Dover 07801

Cosmetic Essence, Inc.
Phone—(609) 395-1271
1248 S. River Rd., Cranbury 08512

Emiliani Enterprises
Phone—(908) 964-6340
600 Green Ln., Union 07083

Energizer Personal Care
Phone—(973) 753-3000
240 Cedar Knolls Rd., Ste. 401, Cedar Knolls 07927

Finger Mates, Inc.
Phone—(732) 681-4411
707 10th Ave., Belmar 07719

Genesis Pharmaceutical, Inc. (H Q)
Phone—(800) 459-8663
8 Campus Dr., Parsippany 07054

International Beauty Products
Phone—(973) 575-6400
26 Chapin Rd., Ste. 1108, P.O. Box 708, Pine Brook 07058

Omega Packaging Corp.
Phone—(973) 890-9505
55 Kings Rd., Totowa 07512

Pooka, Inc.
Phone—(973) 954-2471
87 Halsey St., Newark 07102

Precious Cosmetics Corp.
Phone—(973) 478-4633
296 Midland Ave., Saddle Brook 07663

Promeko, Inc.
Phone—(201) 861-6446
543 59th St., West New York 07093

R&R Cosmetics, LLC
Phone—(732) 340-1000
1140 Randolph Ave., Rahway 07065

Shira Esthetics, Inc.
Phone—(908) 497-9497
65 S. 21st St., Ste. 2, Kenilworth 07033

**World Wide Packaging, LLC**
**Fax: (973) 805-6510**
**Phone—(973) 805-6500**
**Web—www.wwpinc.com**
**Email—sales@wwpinc.com**
**15 Vreeland Rd., Florham Park 07932**

## BEAUTY SALON EQUIPMENT & SUPPLIES

De Pasquale Salon Systems, Inc.
Phone—(201) 797-9101
21-21 Broadway, Fair Lawn 07410

Takara Belmont U. S. A., Inc.
Phone—(732) 469-5000
101 Belmont Dr., Somerset 08873

## BED FRAMES

Knickerbocker Bed Co.
Phone—(201) 933-3100
770 Commercial Ave., Carlstadt 07072

## BEDDING

Bananafish
Phone—(212) 686-4666
250 Passaic St., Newark 07104

Bebe Chic
Phone—(201) 941-5414
530 Church St., Ridgefield 07657

**Phoenix Down Corp.**
**Web: www.downhomeoutlet.com**
**Toll Free Ph: (800) ALLDOWN; Feather Beds, Comforters & Covers**
**Phone—(973) 812-8100 / (800) 255-3696**
**Fax—(973) 812-9077**
**Web—www.phoenixdown.com**
**Email—phod@phoenixdown.com**
**85 US Highway 46, Totowa 07512**

**Phoenix Down Corp.**
Bedding
**800-255-3696 • 973-812-8100**
**FAX: 973-812-9077**
**85 US Highway 46 Totowa, NJ 07512**
www.downhomeoutlet.com
Email: phod@phoenixdown.com

## BEDDING COMPONENTS

Alway, Inc. (H Q)
Phone—(908) 788-7220
440 U.S. Highway 202, Flemington 08822

## BEDSPREADS

Beatrice Home Fashions, Inc.
Phone—(908) 561-7370
151 Helen St., P.O. Box 86, South Plainfield 07080

**Phoenix Down Corp.**
**Web: www.downhomeoutlet.com**
**Toll Free Ph: (800) ALLDOWN; Feather Beds, Comforters & Covers**
**Phone—(973) 812-8100 / (800) 255-3696**
**Fax—(973) 812-9077**
**Email—phod@phoenixdown.com**
**85 US Highway 46, Totowa 07512**
*(see our ad under BEDDING)*

## BEER & ALE

Anheuser-Busch Cos., Inc.
Phone—(973) 645-7700
200 U.S. Highway 1 & 9, Newark 07114

Basil T's Brew Pub & Italian Grill
Phone—(732) 842-5990
183 Riverside Ave., Red Bank 07701

Cape May Brewing Co.
Phone—(609) 849-9933
1288 Hornet Rd., Rio Grande 08242

Climax Brewing Co., Inc.
Phone—(908) 620-9585
112 Valley Rd., Roselle Park 07204

Cricket Hill Brewing Co., Inc.
Phone—(973) 276-9415
24 Kulick Rd., Fairfield 07004

Flying Fish Brewing Co.
Phone—(856) 504-3442
900 Kennedy Blvd., Somerdale 08083

High Point Brewing Co., Inc.
Phone—(973) 838-7400
22 Park Pl., Butler 07405

New Jersey Beer Co., LLC
Phone—(201) 758-8342
4201 Tonnelle Ave., North Bergen 07047

River Horse
Phone—(609) 883-0890
2 Graphics Dr., Trenton 08628

**Shore Point Distributing Co.**
**100 Shore Point Dr., Freehold 07728**
**Addtl. Web: www.njcoors.com**
**Craft Beer Division**
**Phone—(732) 308-3334**
**Fax—(732) 308-1610**
**Web—www.shorepoint.com**
**P.O. Box 275, Adelphia 07710**
*(also see our ad under DISTILLED SPIRITS)*

**Shore Point Distributing Co.**
*Beer & Ale*
*Craft Beer Division, Wine & Spirits Division*
www.shorepoint.com / www.njcoors.com
**(732) 308-3334 • Fax: (732) 308-1610**
100 Shore Point Drive, Freehold, NJ 07728

Tun Tavern Restaurant & Brewery
Phone—(609) 347-7800
2 Convention Blvd., Atlantic City 08401

## BEER BREWING EQUIPMENT & SUPPLIES

**Corrado's Family Affair**
**There is a difference**
**Phone—(973) 340-0628**
**Fax—(973) 340-2052**
**Web—www.corradosmarket.com**
**Email—gerrycorradojr@corradosmarket.com**
**1578 Main Ave., Clifton 07011**

## BELLOWS

**Servometer-PMG, LLC**
**Contacts & Assemblies**
**Phone—(973) 785-4630**
**Fax—(973) 785-0756**
**Web—www.servometer.com**
**Email—info@servometer.com**
**501 Little Falls Rd., Cedar Grove 07009**

## BELLOWS — Metal

Servometer-PMG, LLC
Phone—(973) 785-4630
501 Little Falls Rd., Cedar Grove 07009

## BELTING

**BRECOflex Co., L.L.C.**
**Phone—(732) 460-9500 / (888) 463-1400**
**Fax—(732) 542-6725**
**Web—www.brecoflex.com**
**Email—info@brecoflex.com**
**222 Industrial Way W., Eatontown 07724**

## BELTING — Conveyor

BRECOflex Co., L.L.C.
Phone—(732) 460-9500
222 Industrial Way W., Eatontown 07724
Forbo Siegling, LLC
Phone—(201) 567-6100
130 Coolidge Ave., Englewood 07631
Mulhern Belting, Inc.
Phone—(201) 337-5700
148 Bauer Dr., P.O. Box 620, Oakland 07436
Sparks Belting Co.
Phone—(973) 227-4100
5 Spielman Rd., Fairfield 07004
Stiles Enterprises, Inc.
Phone—(973) 625-9660
114 Beach St., P.O. Box 92, Rockaway 07866
**Volta Belting Technology**
**Phone—(973) 276-7905**
**Fax—(973) 276-7908**
**Web—www.voltabelting.com**
**Email—sales@voltabelting.com**
**11 Chapin Rd., Pine Brook 07058**
Watson Assocs., Inc.
Phone—(856) 845-8800
800 Grove Rd., Thorofare 08086

## BELTING — Industrial

Belting Industries Co., Inc.
Phone—(908) 272-8591
20 Boright Ave., P.O. Box 310, Kenilworth 07033

## BELTING — Rubber

**Jason Industrial Inc.**
**Phone—(973) 227-4904**
**Fax—(973) 227-1651**
**Web—www.jasonindustrial.com**
**Email—inquiries@jasonindustrial.com**
**340 Kaplan Dr., P.O. Box 10004, Fairfield 07004**

Polytech Design, Inc.
Phone—(973) 340-1390
26 W. 1st St., Clifton 07011

## BELTING — Teflon®

**(Teflon® is a registered trademark of DuPont)**

Emco Industrial Plastics, Inc.
Supplier of Plastic Sheet, Rod, Tube, Films &
Prototyping
Phone—(973) 559-5610
Fax—(973) 239-1595
Web—www.emcoplastics.com
Email—mailbox@emcoplastics.com
99 Commerce Rd., P.O. Box 2503, Cedar
Grove 07009
*(see our ad Outside Front Cover)*

## BELTS — Timing

**BRECOflex Co., L.L.C.**
**Phone—(732) 460-9500 / (888) 463-1400**
**Fax—(732) 542-6725**
**Web—www.brecoflex.com**
**Email—info@brecoflex.com**
**222 Industrial Way W., Eatontown 07724**
*(see our ads under BELTING & PULLEYS)*

## BENDING — Pipe & Tube

**Arntzen Corp.**
**Mfr. Of Rolled & Welded Steel Cylinders-Cones-Pipe-Shapes-Fittings**
**Phone—(815) 334-0788 / (800) 957-7655**
**Fax—(815) 334-0778**
**Web—www.ArntzenRolling.com**
**Email—Sales@ArntzenCorp.com**
**14600 Washington St., Woodstock, IL 60098**

## BENDING MACHINES

Pedrick Tool & Machine Co.
Phone—(856) 829-8900
1518 Bannard St., P.O. Box 190, Riverton 08077

## BEVERAGE CONCENTRATES & SYRUPS

Drink Atoast Co., Inc.
Phone—(856) 461-1000
603 Harrison St., P.O. Box 204, Riverside 08075
**Flavor Development Corp.**
**Phone—(201) 784-8188**
**Fax—(201) 784-5501**
**Web—www.flavordev.com**
**Email—sales@flavordev.com**
**388 Chestnut St., Norwood 07648**
*(see our ad under FLAVORINGS & FLAVORS)*
Sea Breeze Fruit Flavors, Inc.
Phone—(973) 334-7777
441 Route 202, Towaco 07082
Supreme Mfg. Co., Inc.
Phone—(732) 254-0087
5 Connerty Ct., East Brunswick 08816
Vineland Syrup, Inc.
Phone—(856) 691-5772
723 Southeast Blvd., Vineland 08360

## BEVERAGE DISPENSERS

Bridy Sales & Leasing Co., Inc.
Phone—(973) 345-4311
115 Madison Ave., Paterson 07524

## BEVERAGE FLAVORINGS

**Allen Flavors, Inc.**
**Phone—(908) 561-5995**
**Fax—(908) 561-4164**
**Web—www.allenflavors.com**
**Email—info@allenflavors.com**
**23 Progress St., Edison 08820**

*Do nationwide searches for products & services at:*
**IndustryNet.com**

**Flavor Development Corp.**
**Phone—(201) 784-8188**
**Fax—(201) 784-5501**
**Web—www.flavordev.com**
**Email—sales@flavordev.com**
**388 Chestnut St., Norwood 07648**
*(see our ad under FLAVORINGS & FLAVORS)*
**Mafco Worldwide Corp.**
**Phone—(856) 964-8840**
**Fax—(856) 964-6029**
**Web—www.magnasweet.com**
**Email—magnasweet@mafcolicorice.com**
**300 Jefferson St., Camden 08104**
*(see our ad under FLAVORINGS & FLAVORS)*

## BEVERAGES

Beverage Distribution Center, Inc.
Phone—(856) 665-6200
8275 Route 130, Pennsauken 08110
Crystal Beverage Corp.
Phone—(201) 991-2342
174 Sanford Ave., P.O. Box 393, Kearny 07032
H2m Beverages
Phone—(973) 831-2010
223 Wanaque Ave., POMPTON LAKES 07442
Hillside Bottling Corp.
Phone—(908) 353-6773
1 Evans Terminal, Hillside 07205
LiDestri Foods, Inc.
Phone—(856) 662-1800
1550 John Tipton Blvd., Pennsauken 08110
Pepsi Beverages Company
Phone—(732) 424-3000
2200 New Brunswick Ave., Piscataway 08854
Pepsi-Cola & National Brand Beverages Ltd.
Phone—(856) 665-6200
8191 N. U.S. Route 130, Pennsauken 08110
Regale, Inc., Kristian
Phone—(201) 587-9800
4 Forest Ave., Ste. 202, Paramus 07652
**Sunny Delight Beverages Co.**
**Leading producer of juice-based drinks in N. America; producing & marketing 7 brands: SunnyD, Elations glucosamine & chondroitin dietary supplement, Fruit2O flavored waters, Veryfine juices, Fruit smoothies & Crystal Light bottled beverages**
**Phone—(732) 329-2391**
**Web—www.sunnyd.com**
**Email—sales@sunnyd.com**
**10 Corn Rd., Dayton 08810**
*(see our ad under FRUIT JUICES)*
Union Beverage Packers, LLC
Phone—(908) 206-9111
600 N. Union Ave., Hillside 07205
Whitlock Packaging Corp.
Phone—(973) 361-9794
92 N. Main St., Wharton 07885
Yoo-Hoo Chocolate Beverage Corp.
Phone—(201) 933-0070
600 Commercial Ave., Carlstadt 07072

## BEVERAGES — Health

**Sunny Delight Beverages Co.**
**Leading producer of juice-based drinks in N. America; producing & marketing 7 brands: SunnyD, Elations glucosamine & chondroitin dietary supplement, Fruit2O flavored waters, Veryfine juices, Fruit smoothies & Crystal Light bottled beverages**
**Phone—(732) 329-2391**
**Web—www.sunnyd.com**
**Email—sales@sunnyd.com**
**10 Corn Rd., Dayton 08810**
*(see our ad under FRUIT JUICES)*

## BEVERAGES — Wholesale

High Grade Beverage
Phone—(732) 821-7600
891 Georges Rd., Monmouth Junction 08852
High Grade Beverage
Phone—(973) 927-1400
86 Canfield Ave., Randolph 07869
J.D. Beverage Co.
Phone—(973) 344-8149
10 Richards St., Newark 07105

## BICYCLE RACKS

**Versatile Welding Group, LLC**
Steel & Aluminum
Phone—(908) 298-8900 / (877) 939-5348
Fax—(908) 298-9550
Web—www.versatile-us.com
Email—jimd@versatile-us.com
340 Cox St., Roselle 07203
*(see our ad under STEEL FABRICATING)*

## BICYCLES

Joannou Cycle Co., Inc., G.
Phone—(201) 768-9050
151 Ludlow Ave., Northvale 07647
Kent International Inc.
Phone—(973) 434-8181
60 E. Halsey Rd., Parsippany 07054
Van Dessel Sports, LLC
Phone—(973) 543-2599
15 W. Main St., Ste. 2, Mendham 07945

## BILLIARD EQUIPMENT & SUPPLIES

Best Billiards
Phone—(908) 730-0933
393 Pittstown Rd., Pittstown 08867
Imperial Billiards Corp.
Phone—(908) 459-4825
2 Sandy Ln., Hardwick 07825

## BILLING SERVICES

**Ambulance Billing Co., LLC**
Phone—(908) 479-4921
Web—www.ambulancebillingco.com
1 Rapp Rd., Milford 08848

## BINDERIES

Bellia Business Products & Services, Inc.
Phone—(856) 845-2234
1047 N. Broad St., Woodbury 08096
Nu E-Z Custom Bindery, LLC
Phone—(201) 488-4140
111 Essex St., Hackensack 07601
Postalogic, LLC
Phone—(973) 546-1400
64 Outwater Ln., Ste. 1, Garfield 07026

## BINDERS

**Spiral James Burn (Spiral Binding Co., Inc.)**
A manufacturer and worldwide distributor of a diverse line of binding and laminating equipment and supplies
Phone—(800) 631-3572
Fax—(973) 256-5981
Web—www.spiralbinding.com
Email—info@spiralbinding.com
1 Maltese Dr., Totowa 07512

## BINDERS — Loose Leaf

Jonathan Leasing Corp.
Phone—(908) 226-3434
17 Water St., Lebanon 08833

## BINDERY EQUIPMENT

Equipment Solutions Corp.
Phone—(973) 887-9277
622 State Route 10, Ste. 20, Whippany 07981

## BINDING EQUIPMENT & SUPPLIES

Executive Binding Systems, Inc.
Phone—(201) 642-0011
330 Franklin Tpke., Mahwah 07430
Spiral Binding Co., Inc.
Phone—(973) 256-0666
1 Maltese Dr., Totowa 07512

**Spiral James Burn (Spiral Binding Co., Inc.)**
A manufacturer and worldwide distributor of a diverse line of binding and laminating equipment and supplies
Phone—(800) 631-3572
Fax—(973) 256-5981
Web—www.spiralbinding.com
Email—info@spiralbinding.com
1 Maltese Dr., Totowa 07512

## BINDINGS — Plastic Spiral

**Spiral James Burn (Spiral Binding Co., Inc.)**
A manufacturer and worldwide distributor of a diverse line of binding and laminating equipment and supplies
Phone—(800) 631-3572
Fax—(973) 256-5981
Web—www.spiralbinding.com
Email—info@spiralbinding.com
1 Maltese Dr., Totowa 07512

## BIOFUELS

American By-Products Recyclers, LLC
Phone—(973) 267-0109
301 Roycefield Rd., Hillsborough 08844
Unity Fuels, LLC
Phone—(201) 641-5000
225 Industrial Ave., Ridgefield Park 07660

## BIOLOGICAL PRODUCTS

Collagen Matrix, Inc.
Phone—(201) 405-1477
509 Commerce St., Franklin 07417
Collagen Matrix, Inc.
Phone—(201) 405-1477
15 Thornton Rd., Oakland 07436
Progenitor Cell Therapy, LLC
Phone—(201) 883-5300
4 Pearl Ct., Ste. C, Allendale 07401

## BIOMEDICAL PRODUCTS

3D Biotek, LLC
Phone—(732) 729-6270
1 Ilene Ct., Hillsborough 08844
ABSCO, Inc.
Phone—(973) 635-9040
101 Eisenhower Pkwy., Ste. 402, Roseland 07068
PBL Assay Science
Phone—(732) 777-9123
131 Ethel Rd. W., Ste. 6, Piscataway 08854

## BIOPHARMACEUTICALS

Bristol-Myers Squibb Company
Phone—(609) 897-2000
777 Scudders Mill Rd., Plainsboro 08536
Insmed, Inc.
Phone—(908) 977-9900
10 Finderne Ave., Bridgewater 08807
Ipsen Biopharmaceuticals, Inc.
Phone—(866) 837-2422
106 Allen Rd., 3rd Fl., Basking Ridge 07920
Medicines Co., The
Phone—(973) 290-6000
8 Sylvan Way, Parsippany 07054
Soligenix, Inc.
Phone—(609) 538-8200
29 Emmons Dr., Ste. C-10, Princeton 08540

## BIOTECHNOLOGY PRODUCTS & SERVICES

Genzyme Corp., Biosurgery Div.
Phone—(201) 945-9550
1125 Pleasant View Ter., Ridgefield 07657
Primary Systems, Inc.
Phone—(732) 679-2200
30 State Route 18, Ste. 1, Old Bridge 08857
Princeton Separation, Inc.
Phone—(732) 431-3338
100 Commerce Dr., Freehold 07728

## BLACK OXIDIZING

**Metlab**
Heat Treating & Black Oxide Specialists
Phone—(215) 233-2600 / (800) 319-7359
Fax—(215) 233-5653
Web—www.metlabheattreat.com
Email—mpodob@metlabheattreat.com
1000 E. Mermaid Ln., Glenside, PA 19038
*(see our ad under HEAT TREATING)*

## BLADES — Knife

IDL TechniEdge, LLC
Phone—(908) 497-9818
30 Boright Ave., Kenilworth 07033
U. S. Blade Mfg.
Phone—(908) 272-2898
90 Myrtle St., Cranford 07016

## BLANKETS

Logo Knits, Inc.
Phone—(732) 382-6961
42-A Cindy Ln., Ocean 07712
Photothrow, Inc.
Phone—(855) 645-4438
280 N. Midland Ave., Bldg. J-1, Saddle Brook 07663

## BLASTING

**Dynamic Sodablasting LLC**
Phone—(732) 367-0102
Web—www.dynamicsodablastingllc.com
Email—sodablastingd@hotmail.com
333 New Central Ave., Lakewood 08701

## BLEACHES

Kuehne Co.
Phone—(973) 589-0700
86 Hackensack Ave., Kearny 07032
**Universal Chemicals Inc.**
Phone—(973) 589-1525
Fax—(973) 589-8013
Web—www.universalchem.com
Email—info@universalchem.com
100 N. Hackensack Ave., Kearny 07032

## BLENDING SYSTEMS

**Warwick Mfg. & Equipment Co., LLC**
Buy & sell used: Chemical, food, cosmetic, packaging & pharmaceutical equipment
Phone—(732) 729-0400 / (732) 241-9263
Fax—(732) 729-1235
Web—www.warwickequipment.com
Email—sales@warwickequipment.com
1112 12th St., North Brunswick 08902
*(see our ad Outside Back Cover)*

## BLINDS — Window

Blinds To Go, Inc.
Phone—(732) 901-2001
1800 Cedar Bridge Ave., Lakewood 08701
Blinds To Go, Inc.
Phone—(732) 321-5000
101 E. State Route 4, Paramus 07652

## BLISTER PACKAGING

**Abilities Of Northwest Jersey, Inc.**
Fulfillment/Contract Packaging/Assembly
Phone—(908) 689-1118
Fax—(908) 689-6363
Web—www.abilitiesnw.com
Email—info@abilitiesnw.com
264 Route 31 N., P.O. Box 251, Washington 07882
*(see our ad under CONTRACT PACKAGING SERVICES)*

*find additional suppliers at* **IndustryNet.com**

*Search from among 430,000 U.S. manufacturers & suppliers:* **IndustryNet.com**

© Copyright 2015 Manufacturers' News, Inc.

## BLOOD BANK EQUIPMENT & SUPPLIES

Terumo Medical Corp. (H Q)
Phone—(732) 302-4900
2101 Cottontail Ln., Somerset 08873

## BLOWERS

Aer-X-Dust Corp.
Phone—(732) 946-9462
P.O. Box 93, Tennent 07763

## BLUEPRINTING

Ace Reprographic Service, Inc.
Phone—(973) 684-5945
74 E. 30th St., Paterson 07514

Ahern's Printing & Graphics
Phone—(732) 223-1476
231 Parker Ave., Manasquan 08736

ARC Document Solutions
Phone—(973) 372-5200
844 Fairfield Ave., Kenilworth 07033

Arc Reprographics, Inc.
Phone—(609) 646-9324
1110 New Rd., Absecon 08201

Deleon Printing & Supply, Inc.
Phone—(201) 798-8440
311 Palisade Ave., Jersey City 07307

KDF Reprographics, Inc.
Phone—(201) 784-9991
10 Volvo Dr., Rockleigh 07647

**Quality Repro Centers, Inc.**
**Phone—(201) 794-3905**
**Fax—(201) 794-3909**
**Web—www.qrepro.com**
**Email—qrepro@optonline.net**
**296 Route 46 E., P.O. Box 111, Elmwood Park 07407**
*(see our ad under PRINTING – Digital)*

Rethink Color, a division of NRI
Phone—(609) 896-4100
3175 Princeton Pike, Lawrenceville 08648

## BOARDS — Cutting Block

Cutting Board Co.
Phone—(908) 725-0187
291 Highway 22, Lebanon 08833

## BOAT & MARINE EQUIPMENT

Monarch Moor Whips
Phone—(732) 244-4584
1104 Tiller Ave., Beachwood 08722

Raritan Engineering Co., Inc.
Phone—(856) 825-4900
530 Orange St., Millville 08332

Tower Systems, Inc.- Atlantic Towers & St. Croix Marine Products
Phone—(732) 237-8800
235 Hickory Ln., P.O. Box D, Bayville 08721

Viking Marine Products, Inc.
Phone—(732) 826-4559
1160 State St., Ste. 17, Perth Amboy 08861

## BOAT & MARINE INTERIORS

**Costa Marine Canvas & Enclosures, LLC**
**Phone—(609) 965-1538**
**Fax—(609) 965-2625**
**Web—www.costamarinecanvas.com**
**Email—info@costamarinecanvas.com**
**1324 Moss Mill Rd., Egg Harbor City 08215**

**E.W.E. Auto Seat Cover Co.**
Boat Seats
**Phone—(201) 869-6470**
**Fax—(201) 868-8491**
**Email—eweauto@yahoo.com**
**8431 Kennedy Blvd., North Bergen 07047**

## BOAT COVERS

Archie's Boat Tops, LLC
Phone—(732) 721-7566
1800 Route 35, South Amboy 08879

Batten The Hatches
Phone—(973) 663-1910
70 State Route 181, Lake Hopatcong 07849

Canvas Lady, The
Phone—(609) 628-3257
19 Killdeer Hill Rd., Woodbine 08270

Canvas Shop Of Avon, Inc.
Phone—(732) 988-5775
504 Main St., Avon by the Sea 07717

Colie Sailmakers, Inc.
Phone—(732) 892-4344
1649 Bay Ave., Point Pleasant Beach 08742

**Costa Marine Canvas & Enclosures, LLC**
**Phone—(609) 965-1538**
**Fax—(609) 965-2625**
**Web—www.costamarinecanvas.com**
**Email—info@costamarinecanvas.com**
**1324 Moss Mill Rd., Egg Harbor City 08215**

Custom Designers, LLC
Phone—(201) 652-5219
80 Greenwood Ave., Ste. 14, Midland Park 07432

Fisher Canvas Products, Inc.
Phone—(609) 239-2733
415 Saint Mary St., Burlington 08016

Garden State Canvas Products Co.
Phone—(732) 892-7021
1671 Beaver Dam Rd., Point Pleasant Boro 08742

Gioia Sails Inc.
Phone—(732) 901-6770
1951 Rutgers University Blvd., Lakewood 08701

Lippincott Marine
Phone—(856) 764-8282
74 Norman Ave., Delran 08075

Nautical Canvas Designs
Phone—(732) 892-7677
506 Elizabeth Ave., Point Pleasant Beach 08742

Ries Co., Inc., R. E.
Phone—(732) 892-1842
107 Lake Ave., Brielle 08730

S & S Custom Covers LLC
Phone—(732) 903-7518
2034 Bridge Ave., Point Pleasant 08742

## BOATS

Allen Steel Co.
Phone—(856) 785-1171
202 High St., Leesburg 08327

Forsberg's Boat Works, Inc.
Phone—(732) 892-4246
1692 W. End Dr., Point Pleasant Boro 08742

Grant Boat Works
Phone—(609) 971-1075
120 Lakeside Dr., Ste. E, P.O. Box 597, Forked River 08731

Henriques Yachts, Inc.
Phone—(732) 269-1180
198 Hilton Ave., Bayville 08721

Ocean Rockets, Inc.
Phone—(609) 628-4445
5 Mosquito Landing Rd., Tuckahoe 08250

Ocean Yachts, Inc.
Phone—(609) 965-4616
2713 Green Bank Rd., Egg Harbor City 08215

Patriot Marine Fabricating
Phone—(609) 693-5542
708-4 Old Shore Rd., Forked River 08731

Roseman's Boat Yard & Charter
Phone—(609) 884-3370
5 Roseman Ln., Cape May 08204

True World Group, LLC (H Q)
Phone—(201) 750-0024
24 Link Dr., Rockleigh 07647

Yank Marine, Inc.
Phone—(609) 628-2928
Mosquito Landing Rd., P.O. Box 569, Tuckahoe 08250

## BOATS — Custom Built Fiberglass

**Commercial Water Sports, Inc.**
**Phone—(609) 624-3404**
**Fax—(609) 624-3402**
**Web—www.cwsboats.com**
**Email—sales@cwsboats.com**
**28 Clermont Dr., Cape May Court House 08210**

Out Island Sport Yachts, Inc.
Phone—(609) 861-4000
107 Edgewood Ave., West Berlin 08091

## BOATS — Rebuilt

Gordon's Marine Service
Phone—(609) 296-5817
454 S. Green St., Tuckerton 08087

## BOILER CONTROLS

BGS, Inc.
Phone—(732) 442-5000
910 E. County Line Rd., Ste. 101, Lakewood 08701

## BOILER FEED PUMPS

**Allied Pump Corporation**
**Phone—(201) 798-3277**
**Fax—(201) 798-8781**
**Web—www.allied-pump.com**
**Email—alliedpumps@gmail.com**
**1109 Grand Ave., Bldg. 5, North Bergen 07047**
*(see our ad under PUMPS)*

## BOILER RENTAL

**Powerhouse Equipment**
**Phone—(856) 764-3333**
**Web—www.powerhouse.com**
**240 Creek Rd., Delanco 08075**

## BOILER REPAIRING

**Manhattan Welding**
Boilers, burners, mech. contracting, steel fabrication, cert. welding, 24 hours
**Phone—(908) 687-4494**
**Fax—(908) 688-6684**
**Web—www.manhattanwelding.com**
**Email—info@manhattanwelding.com**
**1434 Chestnut Ave., Hillside 07205**

**MANHATTAN WELDING**
Boiler & Burner Repair,
Service & Install • ASME Welding
**SINCE 1914**
**(908) 687-4494**
www.manhattanwelding.com
1434 Chestnut Ave. • Hillside, NJ 07205

Supreme Energy, Inc.
**Phone—(973) 678-1800**
**Fax—(973) 672-0148**
**Web—www.supremeenergyinc.com**
**Email—info@supremeenergyinc.com**
**532 Freeman St., Orange 07050**

## BOILERS

Edwards Hydronic Parts, LLC
Phone—(973) 835-7754
101 Alexander Ave., Pompton Plains 07444

Energy Kinetics, Inc.
Phone—(908) 735-2066
51 Molasses Hill Rd., Lebanon 08833

**Nutley Heating & Cooling Supply, Inc.**
**Phone—(973) 667-6880**
**Fax—(973) 667-4602**
**Web—www.nutleysupply.com**
**Email—ralpholiver@nutleysupply.com**
**156 Chestnut St., Nutley 07110**
*(see our ad on next page)*

**Wallace Eannace Associates, Inc.**
**Phone—(201) 891-9550 / (800) 932-4891**
**Fax—(201) 891-4298**
**Web—www.wea-inc.com**
**779 Susquehanna Ave., Franklin Lakes 07417**

**Warwick Mfg. & Equipment Co., LLC**
Buy & sell used: Chemical, food, cosmetic, packaging & pharmaceutical equipment
**Phone—(732) 729-0400 / (732) 241-9263**
**Fax—(732) 729-1235**
**Web—www.warwickequipment.com**
**Email—sales@warwickequipment.com**
**1112 12th St., North Brunswick 08902**
*(see our ad Outside Back Cover)*

## BOILERS — *(cont.)*

Weil-McLain
Phone—(856) 866-7400
17000 Commerce Pkwy., Ste. B, Mount Laurel
08054

## BOILERS — Industrial

Foster Wheeler Corp. (H Q)
Phone—(908) 730-4000
53 Frontage Rd., P.O. Box 9000, Hampton 08827

## BOLLARDS

Pipe Guards Bollards, LLC
Phone—(908) 354-2259
478 Schiller St., Elizabeth 07206

## BOLTS

**(also see 'Nuts & Bolts' and 'Fasteners')**

Shallcross Bolt & Specialties Co.
The complete source for all your fastener needs
Phone—(908) 925-4700
Fax—(908) 925-8451
Web—www.shallcrossbolt.com
Email—info@shallcrossbolt.com
1 McCandless St., Linden 07036

## Shallcross
Bolt & Specialties Co.

Complete source for all
your fastener needs

908-925-4700
FAX: 908-925-8451

www.shallcrossbolt.com
info@shallcrossbolt.com

1 McCandless St.
Linden, NJ 07036

## BOLTS — Anchor

Kelken Construction Systems
Manufacturer & distributor of various types of
concrete/masonry anchoring systems, including
chemical adhesive, epoxy, mechanical anchors
(wedge), as well as, cast-in-place, hook & anchor
bolts
Phone—(732) 416-6730
Fax—(732) 416-6733
Web—www.kelken.com
Email—sales@kelken.com
550 Hartle St., Ste. C, Sayreville 08872

## BONDING COMPOUNDS

USG Corp., Port Reading Plt.
Phone—(732) 636-7900
300 Markley St., Port Reading 07064

## BOOK COVERS

Kimco Products, LLC
Phone—(201) 265-6800
64 E. Midland Ave., Ste. 5, Paramus 07652

## BOOKBINDING

Abby Bindery, LLC
Phone—(973) 690-5509
121 Christie St., Newark 07105

## Nutley Heating & Cooling Supply, Inc.

*Quality Boilers*

### (973) 667-6880
### FAX: (973) 667-4602

www.nutleysupply.com | ralpholiver@nutleysupply.com

156 Chestnut Street  Nutley, NJ 07110

Bassil Bookbinding & Finishing, Inc.
Phone—(201) 440-4925
2 Alsan Way, Little Ferry 07643
Bethel Bindery, Inc.
Phone—(609) 296-5043
1500 Route 539, Tuckerton 08087
Bindgraphics Co., Inc.
Phone—(908) 245-1110
490 W. 1st Ave., Roselle 07203
Bind-Rite Services, Inc.
Phone—(201) 440-5585
16 Horizon Blvd., South Hackensack 07606
Bound To Last
Phone—(732) 942-0423
144 E. 9th St., Lakewood 08701
Colorful Story Books, Inc.
Phone—(908) 561-3333
2 Hollywood Ct., South Plainfield 07080
Custom & Wasmund Bindery
Phone—(973) 815-1400
9 Sheridan Ave., Clifton 07011
Delaware Valley Bindery, Inc.
Phone—(609) 771-1550
18 Graphics Dr., Trenton 08628
E & M Bindery, Inc.
Phone—(973) 777-9300
11 Peekay Dr., Clifton 07014
Everbind Marco Book Co., Inc.
Phone—(973) 458-0485
60 Industrial Rd., P.O. Box 695, Lodi 07644
Gilosa Bindery, Inc., Joseph A.
Phone—(973) 279-8006
555 20th Ave., Paterson 07504
LB Book Bindery, LLC
Phone—(973) 244-0442
19 Gardner Rd., Ste. I, Fairfield 07004
LoGatto Bookbinding, Inc.
Phone—(201) 438-4344
390 Paterson Ave., P.O. Box 7483, East
Rutherford 07073
McCormicks Bindery, Inc.
Phone—(856) 663-8035
5815 Magnolia Ave., Pennsauken 08109
**Meadowlands Bindery, Inc.**
Small saddle stitch, die cutting, fugitive glue, re-moist
glue & tipping Pl's & office folders, shrink wrapping
Phone—(201) 935-6161
Fax—(201) 935-9014
Web—www.meadowlandsbindery.com
Email—frank@mbibindery.com
146 W. Commercial Ave., Moonachie 07074

## Meadowlands Bindery, Inc.
*Bookbinding*
### 201-935-6161
www.meadowlandsbindery.com
146 W. Commercial Ave.  Moonachie, NJ 07074

Mid State Bindery
Phone—(908) 755-9388
148 Sylvania Pl., South Plainfield 07080

Northeast Bindery, Inc.
Phone—(908) 436-3737
419 Trumbull St., Elizabeth 07206
O&T-Suter Conservation, LLC
Phone—(201) 265-0262
96 Hillside Ave., Emerson 07630
Reid Book Binding, D.
Phone—(732) 494-9589
543 New Durham Rd., Metuchen 08840
Spink & Gabor, Inc.
Phone—(973) 478-4551
11 Troast Ct., Clifton 07011
Trentypo, Inc.
Phone—(609) 883-5971
312 Stokes Ave., P.O. Box 304, Trenton 08638
Turul Bookbindery, Inc.
Phone—(973) 361-2810
60 Route 15 S., Wharton 07885

## BOOKBINDING MACHINERY

On Demand Machinery, LLC
Phone—(908) 351-6906
150 Broadway, Elizabeth 07206
Schaefer, Inc., Ernest
Phone—(908) 964-1280
731 Lehigh Ave., Union 07083

## BOOKBINDING MATERIALS & SUPPLIES

Schaefer, Inc., Ernest
Bookbinders board
Phone—(908) 964-1280
Fax—(908) 964-6787
Web—www.ernestschaeferinc.com
Email—eschaeferinc@aol.com
731 Lehigh Ave., Union 07083
Spiral James Burn (Spiral Binding Co., Inc.)
A manufacturer and worldwide distributor of a diverse
line of binding and laminating equipment and
supplies
Phone—(800) 631-3572
Fax—(973) 256-5981
Web—www.spiralbinding.com
Email—info@spiralbinding.com
1 Maltese Dr., Totowa 07512

## BOOTS

Pro Line Mfg. Co., LLC
Phone—(973) 692-9696
186 Parish Dr., Wayne 07470

## BORING TOOLS

Triple D Enterprises, Inc.
Phone—(609) 859-3000
135 Eayrestown Rd., Southampton 08088

*Do nationwide searches for
products & services at:*
**IndustryNet.com**

## BOTTLE CAPS

Newark Liner & Washer, Inc.
Phone—(973) 482-5400
819 Broadway, Newark 07104

## BOTTLE CAPS — Plastic

Novembal U. S. A., A Tetra Pak Co.
Phone—(732) 287-4949
3 Greek Ln., Edison 08817

## BOTTLES — Glass

Gerresheimer, Inc.
Phone—(856) 506-0501
1300 Wheaton Ave., Millville 08332

## BOTTLES — Plastic

Abbott Industries
Phone—(973) 345-1116
1-11 Morris St., Paterson 07501
Berry Plastics
Phone—(609) 655-4600
34 Engelhard Dr., Monroe Township 08831
Berry Plastics, Inc.
Phone—(908) 454-0900
190 Strykers Rd., Phillipsburg 08865
Consolidated Container Co.
Phone—(908) 351-7919
28-36 Slater Dr., Elizabeth 07206
Container Mfg., Inc.
Phone—(732) 563-0100
50 Baekeland Ave., P.O. Box 428, Middlesex 08846
Graham Packaging Co. L. P.
Phone—(908) 475-2181
600 5th St., Belvidere 07823
Q-Pak, Inc.
Phone—(973) 483-4404
2145 McCarter Hwy., Newark 07104
Qualipac America Corp.
Phone—(973) 389-7730
1 Garret Mountain Plz., 5th Fl., West Paterson 07424
Tri-Delta Plastics, Inc.
Phone—(908) 722-6021
208 Cougar Ct., Hillsborough 08844

## BOTTLING MACHINERY

Lazar Technologies, Inc.
Phone—(732) 739-9622
39 Evergreen St., Hazlet 07730

## BOTTLING PLANTS

Maplewood Beverage Packers, LLC
Phone—(973) 416-4582
45 Camptown Rd., Maplewood 07040

## BOXES

Century Packaging, Inc.
Phone—(732) 249-6600
42 Edgeboro Rd., East Brunswick 08816
McLean Packaging Corp.
Phone—(856) 359-2600
1504 Glen Ave., Moorestown 08057
United States Box Corp.
Phone—(973) 481-2000
1296 McCarter Hwy., Newark 07104

## BOXES — Corrugated

Albert Paper Products Co.
Phone—(973) 373-0330
464 Coit St., Irvington 07111
Balsco Corrugated Box & Display, LLC
Phone—(973) 546-0500
160 Union Ave., East Rutherford 07073

find additional suppliers at
IndustryNet.com

Beacon Container Corp.
Phone—(610) 582-2222 / (800) 422-8383
Fax—(610) 582-3992
Web—www.beaconcontainer.com
Email—customerservice@
beaconcontainer.com
700 W. 1st St., Birdsboro, PA 19508

Beacon Container
Custom Corrugated Boxes
Beacon Container Corporation
700 West First Street, Birdsboro, PA 19508
800-422-8383 • (610) 582-2222
Fax: (610) 582-3992
www.beaconcontainer.com

Beisler Weidmann Co., Inc.
Phone—(973) 759-5020
233 Cortlandt St., Belleville 07109
Bell Container Corp.
Phone—(973) 344-4400
615 Ferry St., P.O. Box 5728, Newark 07105
Creoh U. S. A.
Phone—(718) 821-0570
910 E. County Line Rd., Ste. 202-A, Lakewood 08701
Delaware Valley Box & Lumber Co.
Phone—(856) 939-1900
14 Austin Ave., Glendora 08029
Enterprise Corrugated Container, LLC
Phone—(201) 797-7200
575 N. Midland Ave., P.O. Box 857, Saddle Brook 07663
Ferguson Containers
Phone—(908) 454-9755
20 Industrial Rd., Phillipsburg 08865
G & S Feldman, Inc.
Phone—(732) 918-8838
P.O. Box 1136, Oakhurst 07755
Hillside Paper Products, Inc.
Phone—(908) 352-3300
20 Butler St., Elizabeth 07206
International Paper Co.
Phone—(856) 546-7000
100 E. Gloucester Pike, Barrington 08007
International Paper Co.
Phone—(856) 931-8000
370 Benigno Blvd., Bellmawr 08031
International Paper Co.
Phone—(732) 828-1700
101 Ford Ave., Milltown 08850
International Paper Co.
Phone—(732) 251-2000
140 Summerhill Rd., Spotswood 08884
International Paper Co.
Phone—(856) 853-7000
33 Phoenix Dr., Thorofare 08086
Interstate Container Brunswick, LLC
Phone—(732) 821-8100
501 Finnegan Ln., North Brunswick 08902
Kampack, Inc.
Phone—(973) 589-7400
100 Frontage Rd., Newark 07114
Levine Industries
Phone—(973) 742-1000
86 Levine St., South Paterson Sta., Paterson 07503
Levine Packaging Supply Corp.
Phone—(973) 575-5383
400 U.S. Highway 46 E., Fairfield 07004
New York Corrugated Box Co., LLC
Phone—(973) 742-5000
239 Lindberg Pl., Ste. 1, Paterson 07503

New York Corrugated Box, LLC
Phone—(973) 742-5000
239 Lindbergh Pl., Ste. Ll, Paterson 07503
Packaging Corp. Of America, Cranbury Creative Design Center
Phone—(856) 596-5020
8 E. Stow Rd., Ste. 100, Marlton 08053
Packaging Unlimited, Inc.
Phone—(609) 394-9400
17 Chelten Way, Bldg. A, Trenton 08638
Paige Packaging
Phone—(973) 483-0505
1 Paul Kohner Pl., Elmwood Park 07407
Paige Packaging/Bradley Corrugated
Phone—(973) 458-9600
Web—www.paigepackaging.com
Email—jchazin@paigepackaging.com
1 Paul Kohner Pl., Elmwood Park 07407
Raritan Packaging Industries, Inc.
Phone—(732) 246-7200
570 Jersey Ave., New Brunswick 08901
RHE Container Co.
Phone—(201) 804-8300
Fax—(201) 804-8484
Web—www.rhecontainer.com
Email—rhecoinc@aol.com
25 Amor Ave., Carlstadt 07072

RHE
Container Co.
www.rhecontainer.com
Email: rhecoinc@aol.com
(201) 804-8300
FAX: (201) 804-8484
25 Amor Ave.
Carlstadt, NJ 07072

Robessa Enterprises, Inc.
Phone—(856) 251-0055
1030 Delsea Dr., P.O. Box 72, Westville 08093
Rock-Tenn Co.
Phone—(732) 274-2500
1 Corn Rd., P.O. Box 440, Dayton 08810
Rock-Tenn Co.
Phone—(973) 268-4938
2013 McCarter Hwy., Newark 07104
State Container Corp.
Phone—(201) 933-5200
111 W. Commercial Ave., Moonachie 07074
Sunshine Metal & Sign, Inc.
Phone—(973) 676-4432
467 Maryland St., Orange 07050
SupplyOne, Inc.
Phone—(856) 727-1010
1090 Thomas Busch Memorial Hwy., Pennsauken 08110
Sutherland Packaging, Inc.
Phone—(973) 786-5141
254 Brighton Ave., P.O. Box 1429, Andover 07821

Send an RFQ (request for quote)
to multiple suppliers at
IndustryNet.com

## BOXES — Corrugated — *(cont.)*

**Trent Corp., The**
Phone—(609) 587-7515
Fax—(609) 586-9710
Web—www.trentbox.com
Email—trentboxmfgco@aol.com
1384 Yardville Hamilton Square Rd., P.O. Box 2650, Trenton 08690

---

# The Trent Corp.
*Corrugated & bulk boxes*

### www.trentbox.com
### (609) 587-7515
PO Box 2650 Trenton, NJ 08690

---

**Trenton Corrugated Products, Inc.**
Phone—(609) 695-0808
17 Cheltan Way, Trenton 08638
**Victory Box Corp.**
Phone—(908) 245-5100
645 W. 1st Ave., Roselle 07203
**Woodland Mfg. Co., Inc.**
Phone—(609) 587-4180
1936 E. State St., Hamilton 08619

## BOXES — Folding

**Coastal Packaging**
Phone—(201) 955-4414
48 Sellers St., Kearny 07032
**Cross Country Box Co., Inc.**
Manufacturers of Setup Boxes
Phone—(973) 673-8349
Fax—(973) 673-8351
Web—www.crosscountrybox.com
Email—dan@crosscountrybox.com
2-8 Central Ave., East Orange 07018
**Miniature Folding**
Phone—(201) 773-6477
300 9th Ave., Hawthorne 07506
**Specialty Paper Box Co.**
Rigid, Corrugated, Folding & Plastic Boxes
Phone—(973) 396-8556
Fax—(973) 396-8557
Email—specialty201@aol.com
14 Highland Dr., North Caldwell 07006

---

# Specialty Paper Box Co.
*Rigid, Corrugated, Folding & Plastic Boxes*
**(973) 396-8556 • Fax: (973) 396-8557**
specialty201@aol.com
14 Highland Dr.
North Caldwell, NJ 07006

---

## BOXES — Gift

**Capitol Box Corp.**
Phone—(201) 867-6018
Fax—(201) 867-4159
Web—www.capitolbox.com
Email—capitolbox@verizon.net
1300 6th St., North Bergen 07047
*(see our ad under BOXES—Set-Up)*

## BOXES — Jewelry

**RaGar Co., Inc.**
Phone—(732) 493-1416
2106 Kings Hwy., Asbury Park 07712
**Vikolya Corp.**
Phone—(732) 529-5540
140 Ethel Rd. W., Unit J, Piscataway 08854

## BOXES — Paper: Folding

**Cultech, Inc.**
Phone—(732) 225-2722
3500 Hatley Rd., South Plainfield 07080

---

**Gilt Edge Folding Boxes, Inc.**
Phone—(201) 843-1450
P.O. Box 544, Saddle Brook 07663
**Keystone Folding Box Co., Inc.**
Phone—(973) 483-1054
367 Verona Ave., Newark 07104
**MultiPackaging Solutions**
Phone—(908) 757-6000
901 Durham Ave., South Plainfield 07080
**New York Folding Box Co.**
Phone—(973) 347-6932
20 Continental Dr., Stanhope 07874
**Pin Point Container Corp.**
Phone—(856) 848-2115
669 Tanyard Rd., Deptford 08096
**Shure-Pak Corp.**
Phone—(856) 825-0808
1500 N. 10th St., P.O. Box 105, Millville 08332

## BOXES — Paperboard

**Capitol Box Corp.**
Phone—(201) 867-6018
Fax—(201) 867-4159
Web—www.capitolbox.com
Email—capitolbox@verizon.net
1300 6th St., North Bergen 07047
*(see our ad under BOXES—Set-Up)*

## BOXES — Plastic

**Specialty Paper Box Co.**
Rigid, Corrugated, Folding & Plastic Boxes
Phone—(973) 396-8556
Fax—(973) 396-8557
Email—specialty201@aol.com
14 Highland Dr., North Caldwell 07006

---

# Specialty Paper Box Co.
*Rigid, Corrugated, Folding & Plastic Boxes*
**(973) 396-8556 • Fax: (973) 396-8557**
specialty201@aol.com
14 Highland Dr.
North Caldwell, NJ 07006

---

**Visual Packaging Corp.**
Phone—(973) 835-7055
91 4th Ave., Haskell 07420

## BOXES — Rigid

**Capitol Box Corp.**
Phone—(201) 867-6018
Fax—(201) 867-4159
Web—www.capitolbox.com
Email—capitolbox@verizon.net
1300 6th St., North Bergen 07047
*(see our ad under BOXES—Set-Up)*
**Cross Country Box Co., Inc.**
Manufacturers of Setup Boxes
Phone—(973) 673-8349
Fax—(973) 673-8351
Web—www.crosscountrybox.com
Email—dan@crosscountrybox.com
2-8 Central Ave., East Orange 07018
**North Jersey Paper Box Corp.**
Phone—(201) 348-4233
132 32nd St., P.O. Box 700, Union City 07087
**Oppenheim Plastics Co., Inc.**
Phone—(201) 391-3811
90 Broadway, Woodcliff Lake 07677

## BOXES — Set-Up

**Allstate Paper Box Co., Inc.**
Phone—(973) 589-2600
223 Raymond Blvd., Newark 07105

---

*Search from among 430,000 U.S. manufacturers & suppliers:*
**IndustryNet.com**

---

**Capitol Box Corp.**
Phone—(201) 867-6018
Fax—(201) 867-4159
Web—www.capitolbox.com
Email—capitolbox@verizon.net
1300 6th St., North Bergen 07047

---

# Capitol Box Corp.
### Since 1936
*Rigid Set-Up
Paper Board Boxes*

### www.capitolbox.com
Email: capitolbox@verizon.net
### (201) 867-6018
### FAX: (201) 867-4159
1300 6th Street
North Bergen, NJ 07047

---

**Specialty Paper Box Co.**
Rigid, Corrugated, Folding & Plastic Boxes
Phone—(973) 396-8556
Fax—(973) 396-8557
Email—specialty201@aol.com
14 Highland Dr., North Caldwell 07006

---

# Specialty Paper Box Co.
*Rigid, Corrugated, Folding & Plastic Boxes*
**(973) 396-8556 • Fax: (973) 396-8557**
specialty201@aol.com
14 Highland Dr.
North Caldwell, NJ 07006

---

## BOXES — Wooden

**Delaware Valley Box & Lumber Co.**
Phone—(609) 890-2900
2651 E. State St. Ext., Trenton 08619
**Tri-State Crating & Pallet Co.**
Phone—(973) 357-8293 / (888) 845-0050
Fax—(973) 357-8296
Web—www.tristatecrating.com
Email—sales@tristatecrating.com
85 Fulton St., Paterson 07501
*(see our ad under CRATES—Wooden)*
**Vandereems Mfg. Co., Inc.**
Phone—(973) 427-2355
40 Schoon Ave., Hawthorne 07506

## BRAKE LININGS

**Reddaway Mfg. Co., Inc.**
Phone—(973) 589-1410
32 Euclid Ave., Newark 07105

## BRAKES

**Hi-Per Tech Brake Products, Inc.**
Phone—(856) 881-0900
100 Delsea Dr., P.O. Box 770, Glassboro 08028
**Industrial Brake & Clutch Exchange**
Phone—(732) 970-0090
2 U.S. Highway 9, Ste. 4, Morganville 07751

## BRAKES — Air

**ClearDrain**
Phone—(856) 461-0091
219 Saint Mihiel Dr., Riverside 08075

© Copyright 2015 Manufacturers' News, Inc.

## BRAKES — Automotive

ABS Brake Systems Ltd.
  Phone—(201) 689-6893
  445 Godwin Ave., Midland Park 07432

## BRASS PRODUCTS

Benchmark
  Phone—(609) 397-1131
  Cane Farm, Bldg. 7, P.O. Box 214, Rosemont
  08556
Brass Shop, Inc.
  Phone—(908) 232-2161
  611 Central Ave., Westfield 07090
Summit Brass & Bronze Works, Inc.
  Phone—(201) 861-2080
  112 71st St., Guttenberg 07093

## BRAZING

**(also see 'Welding')**

**Bennett Heat Treating & Brazing Co., Inc.**
  **Complete metallurgical consulting & heat treating
  service**
  **Phone—(215) 674-8120**
  **Fax—(215) 674-1312**
  **Web—www.bennettheat.co**
  **Email—pciulla@bennettheat.com**
  **82 Richard Rd., Ivyland, PA 18974**
**Bennett Heat Treating & Brazing Co., Inc.**
  **Complete metallurgical consulting & heat treating
  service**
  **Phone—(973) 589-0590**
  **Fax—(973) 589-6518**
  **Web—www.bennettheat.com**
  **Email—pciulla@bennettheat.com**
  **690 Ferry St., Newark 07105**

**Bennett Heat Treating &
Brazing Co., Inc.**

*Complete Metalluragical Consulting
& Heat Treating Service*

Any Questions Go To: www.bennettheat.com
**973-589-0590 • Fax: 973-589-6518**
**690 Ferry St. Newark, NJ 07105**

Kenney Steel Treating Corp.
  Phone—(201) 998-4420
  100 Quincy Pl., Kearny 07032

## BRAZING ALLOYS

Krohn Industries, Inc.
  Phone—(201) 933-9696
  303 Veterans Blvd., P.O. Box 98, Carlstadt 07072

## BRAZING EQUIPMENT

**AGF Burner, Inc.**
  **Phone—(732) 730-8090**
  **Fax—(732) 730-8060**
  **Web—www.agfburner.com**
  **Email—sales@agfburner.com**
  **1955 Swarthmore Ave., Unit 2, Lakewood
  08701**

  *(see our ad under GAS BURNERS)*

## BRAZING PASTE

Turbobraze Corp.
  Phone—(908) 687-1030
  687 Lehigh Ave., P.O. Box 897, Union 07083

## BREAD CRUMBS

New Crushed Toast Corp.
  Phone—(908) 925-2920
  625 Pennsylvania Ave., Linden 07036

*Do nationwide searches for
products & services at:*
**IndustryNet.com**

## BRIDGE CRANES

**Cranez, Inc.**
  **For more than 20 yrs., serving the Tri-State area.
  Offering free no-obligation est.; providing svc. 24 hrs.,
  7 days a week & no-cost site checks. Operators are
  CCO/Natnl. Commission certified, have TWIC
  credentials & O.S.H.A 30-hrs trained**
  **Phone—(856) 262-0288 / (877) 262-0288**
  **Fax—(856) 262-2654**
  **Web—www.cranezincnj.com**
  **Email—cranez06@aol.com**
  **2610 S. Black Horse Pike, Williamstown 08094**

## BRIDGES — Steel

Bauer, Inc., Susan R.
  Phone—(973) 657-1590
  427 Margaret King Ave., Ringwood 07456

## BROADCASTING EQUIPMENT

ATI Audio
  Phone—(856) 719-9900
  154 Cooper Road S-902, West Berlin 08091
Eventide, Inc.
  Phone—(201) 641-1200
  1 Alsan Way, Little Ferry 07643
QEI Corp.
  Phone—(856) 728-2020
  1 Airport Dr., P.O. Box 805, Williamstown 08094
Radio Systems Design, Inc.
  Phone—(856) 467-8000
  601 Heron Dr., Logan Township 08085
Zaxcom, Inc.
  Phone—(973) 835-5000
  230 West Pkwy., Unit 9, Pompton Plains 07444

## BROOMS

**Keystone Plastics, Inc.**
  **Fax: (908) 561-3404**
  **Web: Web: www.keystonesweeperbrushes.com**
  **Phone—(908) 561-1300 / (800) 635-5238**
  **Email—jackaroe1954@yahoo.com**
  **3451 S. Clinton Ave., South Plainfield 07080**

## BRUSHES

Andon Brush Co., Inc.
  Phone—(973) 256-6611
  1 Merrit Ave., Little Falls 07424
Manufacturers' Brush Corp.
  Phone—(973) 882-6966
  69 King St., Dover 07801
Silver Brush Ltd.
  Phone—(609) 443-4900
  92 N. Main St., Bldg. 18-E, P.O. Box 414, Windsor
  08561
The Fifty/Fifty Group, Inc
  Phone—(201) 343-1243
  343 S. River St., Hackensack 07601
Trim Brush Co., Inc.
  Phone—(973) 887-2525
  22 Littell Rd., East Hanover 07936

## BRUSHES — Carbon

Mersen USA BN Corp.
  Phone—(973) 334-0700
  400 Myrtle Ave., Boonton 07005

## BRUSHES — Industrial

Custom Brush Co. Inc.
  Phone—(856) 354-1673
  1933 Owl Ct., Cherry Hill 08003
Industrial Brush Co., Inc.
  Phone—(973) 575-0455
  105 Clinton Rd., Fairfield 07004
Jenkins & Sons, Inc., M. W.
  Phone—(973) 239-5150
  444 Pompton Ave., P.O. Box 303, Cedar Grove
  07009
Newark Brush Company
  Phone—(973) 376-1000
  1 Silver Ct., Springfield 07081

Ward & Sons, Inc., J. B.
  Phone—(973) 827-4600
  1434 Route 565, Wantage 07461

## BUFFING & POLISHING WHEELS

Garfield Industries, Inc.
  Phone—(973) 575-8800
  62 Clinton Rd., Fairfield 07004

## BUILDING AUTOMATION SYSTEMS

Harrison Electro Mechanical Corp.
  Phone—(732) 382-6008
  1607 Coach St., Rahway 07065

## BUILDING MAINTENANCE SERVICES

**Shades Of Green**
  **Specializing in Quality Indoor Plants, Design, Install
  & Maintenance at Affordable Prices in Central &
  Northern New Jersey**
  **Phone—(908) 769-9522 / (800) 564-9435**
  **Fax—(908) 769-9455**
  **Web—www.shadesofgreenplants.com**
  **Email—shadesofgreen@optonline.net**
  **P.O. Box 150, Berkeley Heights 07922**

## BUILDING MATERIALS

**Behnke's Paramus Building Supply Co.**
  **General Framing Lumber & Engineered Lumber**
  **Phone—(201) 262-1818 / (800) 354-1818**
  **Fax—(201) 262-9250**
  **Web—www.paramusbuildingsupply.com**
  **Email—kevinb@paramusbuildingsupply.com**
  **P.O. Box 587, Paramus 07653**

**Behnke's Paramus
Building Supply Co.**

*General Framing Lumber
Engineered Lumber*
**800-354-1818**
**201-262-1818**
**Fax: 201-262-9250**
www.paramusbuildingsupply.com
kevinb@paramusbuildingsupply.com
**PO Box 587
Paramus, NJ 07653**

Construction Specialties, Inc.
  Phone—(908) 236-0800
  3 Werner Way, Lebanon 08833
Gentek Building Products, Inc.
  Phone—(732) 381-0900
  11 Craigwood Rd., Avenel 07001
Heath Lumber Co.
  Phone—(609) 392-1166
  1580 N. Olden Avenue Ext., Ewing 08638
Homasote Co.
  Phone—(609) 883-3300
  932 Lower Ferry Rd., P.O. Box 7240, Trenton
  08628
Huber Corp., J.M. (H Q)
  Phone—(732) 549-8600
  499 Thornall St., 8th Fl., Edison 08837
Kuiken Brothers Company, Inc.
  Phone—(973) 584-2444
  31 State Route 10 E., Succasunna 07876
PrimeSource Building Products, Inc.
  Phone—(732) 296-0600
  20 Van Dyke Ave, New Brunswick 08901

## BUILDING MATERIALS — (cont.)

Vinylast, Inc.
Phone—(732) 367-7200
1830 Swarthmore Ave., Lakewood 08701

## BUILDING MATERIALS — Wholesale

ABC Supply Co., Inc.
Phone—(856) 461-5252
5004 Route 130, Riverside 08075
ABC Supply Co., Inc., Bradco Div.
Phone—(609) 484-9100
725 W. Delilah Rd., Pleasantville 08232
ABC Supply Co., Inc., Bradco Div.
Phone—(609) 393-7000
301 Brunswick Ave., Trenton 08618
Allied Building Products Corp.
Phone—(908) 820-9790
850 Flora St., Elizabeth 07201
Allied Building Products Corp.
Phone—(973) 827-4113
406 State Route 23 N., Franklin 07416
Allied Building Products Corp.
Phone—(201) 529-3300
27-33 Franklin Tpke., Mahwah 07430
Allied Building Products Corp.
Phone—(973) 357-1600
27 Kentucky Ave., Paterson 07503
Allied Building Products Corp.
Phone—(732) 341-4767
320 W. Water St., Toms River 08753
Allied Building Products Corp.
Phone—(973) 790-5500
595 Union Blvd., Totowa 07512
Allied Building Products Corp.
Phone—(732) 449-3355
2065 State Route 34, Wall Township 07719
Arzee Supply
Phone—(201) 935-0800
1905 Swarthmore Ave., Lakewood 08701
Arzee Supply Corp. Of New Jersey
Phone—(973) 267-1576
15 E. Frederick Pl., Cedar Knolls 07927
ATAK Trucking, Inc.
Phone—(917) 912-2900
1341 Route 34, Matawan 07747
Dubell Lumber Co.
Phone—(856) 665-9100
731 Cuthbert Blvd., Cherry Hill 08002
Dubell Lumber Co.
Phone—(609) 654-4143
148 Route 70 E., P.O. Box 1449, Medford 08055
Extech Building Materials, Inc.
Phone—(973) 274-3340
61-89 Ave. K, Newark 07105
L & W Supply Corp.
Phone—(908) 362-6103
126 Route 94, Blairstown 07825
L & W Supply Corp.
Phone—(732) 341-3737
1351 Route 37 W., Toms River 08755
MarJam Supply Co.
Phone—(973) 491-6030
6 International Way, Newark 07114
MarJam Supply Co.
Phone—(609) 407-1234
615 W. Delilah Rd., Pleasantville 08232
Mid-State Lumber Corp.
Phone—(908) 725-4900
200 Industrial Pkwy., Branchburg 08876
Rugby ABP Corp.
Phone—(201) 807-9701
60 Joseph St., Moonachie 07074
Tri-County Building Supplies, Inc.
Phone—(609) 465-7839
211 Stites & Railroad Aves., Cape May Court House 08210
Tri-County Building Supplies, Inc.
Phone—(609) 646-0950
1001 Doughty Rd., Pleasantville 08232
Woodhaven Lumber & Millwork, Inc.
Phone—(609) 597-1118
725 E. Bay Ave., Manahawkin 08050

*find additional suppliers at* **IndustryNet.com**

## BUILDING PANELS

American Panel Tec
Phone—(732) 968-0555
1640 New Market Ave., Bldg. 1-A, South Plainfield 07080

## BUILDING SUPPLIES

Allied Building Products Corp.
Phone—(201) 507-8400
15 E. Union Ave., East Rutherford 07073
Arzee Supply Corp. Of New Jersey
Phone—(908) 820-3700
450 York St., Elizabeth 07201
Kuiken Brothers Commercial
Phone—(973) 772-0044
485 River Dr., Garfield 07026
Randall Mfg. Co., Inc.
Phone—(973) 484-7600
200 Sylvan Ave., Newark 07104
Rocket Building Supply Co., Inc.
Phone—(201) 652-8884
13 Hewson Ave., Waldwick 07463
Tri-County Building Supplies, Inc.
Phone—(609) 465-5021
14 Reading Ave., Cape May Court House 08210

## BUILDINGS — Insulated

**Johnson Building Systems, Inc.**
**Classified rating-1,2 & 3 hour fire wall & ceiling assemblies**
**Phone—(215) 673-6050 / (800) 445-7249**
**Fax—(215) 322-2076**
**Web—www.johnsonenergygroup.com**
**Email—rsears@johnsonenergygroup.com**
**975 Jaymor Rd., Southampton, PA 18966**

## BUILDINGS — Metal

**Iorio Construction Co.**
**Phone—(732) 364-4588**
**Fax—(732) 905-6993**
**Web—www.iorioconstructioncompany.com**
**Email—info@iorioconstructioncompany.com**
**700 Vassar Ave., Ste. 4, Lakewood 08701**

## BUILDINGS — Modular

Williams Scotsman, Inc.
Phone—(973) 589-1234
35 Ford Ln., Kearny 07032

## BUILDINGS — Prefabricated

**Johnson Building Systems, Inc.**
**Classified rating-1,2 & 3 hour fire wall & ceiling assemblies**
**Phone—(215) 673-6050 / (800) 445-7249**
**Fax—(215) 322-2076**
**Web—www.johnsonenergygroup.com**
**Email—rsears@johnsonenergygroup.com**
**975 Jaymor Rd., Southampton, PA 18966**
Pre-Fab Structures, Inc.
Phone—(856) 768-4257
907 Wedgewood Way, Atco 08004
**Stanker & Galetto, Inc.**
**Phone—(856) 692-8098**
**Fax—(856) 692-3058**
**Web—www.stankergaletto.com**
**Email—rkadlac@stankergaletto.com**
**317 W. Elmer Rd., Vineland 08360**
*(see our ad under DESIGN & BUILD CONTRACTORS)*

## BUILDINGS — Prefabricated Metal

P M C Diners, Inc.
Phone—(201) 337-6146
56 Spruce St., Oakland 07436
Twin Modular Services, Inc.
Phone—(856) 227-0057
1001 Lower Landing Rd., Ste. 607, Blackwood 08012

## BUILDINGS — Storage

Kempton Wood Products, LLC
Phone—(732) 449-8673
2800 Ridgewood Rd., Wall 07719

## BUILDINGS — Wood

Medford Cedar Products, Inc.
Phone—(609) 859-1400
59 Old Red Lion Rd., Vincentown 08088

## BULKHEADS

**Rice Associates, Inc.**
**Phone—(732) 530-2009**
**Fax—(732) 530-1351**
**Email—riceassociatesnj@verizon.net**
**569 River Rd., Ste. 10, Fair Haven 07704**

**Rice Associates, Inc.**
*Quality Bulkheads*
**(732) 530-2009**
Fax: (732) 530-1351
Email: riceassociatesnj@verizon.net
569 River Rd., Ste. 10 • Fair Haven, NJ 07704

## BULLETS

Hawk Precision, Inc.
Phone—(856) 299-2800
849 Hawks Bridge Rd., Salem 08079

## BURGLAR ALARM SYSTEMS

**Diamond Electronics**
**Phone—(609) 371-9500**
**Web—www.diamondelectronicsnj.com**
**299 Ward St., Ste. A, Hightstown 08520**
**Ocean Security Systems, Inc.**
**Phone—(732) 270-1784**
**Fax—(732) 270-4486**
**Web—www.oceansecurity.com**
**Email—info@oceansecurity.com**
**P.O. Box 1349, Island Heights 08732**
Protection One, Inc.
Phone—(973) 227-3421
50 Williams Pkwy., Ste. L, East Hanover 07936

## BURIAL MONUMENTS & MEMORIALS

Burns Bros. & McCabe, Inc.
Phone—(201) 795-0800
787 Tonnele Ave., Jersey City 07307
Cumberland Marble & Monument, Inc.
Phone—(856) 691-3334
2858 S. West Blvd., Vineland 08360
Memorial Arts, Inc.
Phone—(201) 652-4301
1172 E. Ridgewood Ave., Ridgewood 07450
Paterson Monuments Co., Inc.
Phone—(973) 942-0727
317 Totowa Ave., Paterson 07502
Saracino Monuments, LLC, Frank
Phone—(201) 945-1266
359 Bergen Blvd., Fairview 07022
U. S. Artistic Monument Co., Inc.
Phone—(973) 777-7786
262 Main Ave., Clifton 07014
White Eagle Monumental Co., Inc.
Phone—(201) 991-0094
257 Ridge Rd., North Arlington 07031

## BURIAL VAULTS

Kenny Wilbert Vault Co.
Phone—(908) 637-4736
40 Shades of Death Rd., Great Meadows 07838

**INDUSTRY**

## BURIAL VAULTS — Cement

Bradbury Burial Vault Co., Inc.
Phone—(856) 227-2555
761 Lower Landing Rd., Blackwood 08012
Brewster Vaults & Monuments, Inc.
Phone—(856) 785-1412
1017 Steeprun Rd., Millville 08332
Cooper Wilbert Burial Vault Co., Inc.
Phone—(856) 547-8405
621 E. Atlantic Ave., Barrington 08007
Creter Vault Corp.
Phone—(908) 782-7771
417 Highway 202, Flemington 08822
Dodson Vault Co., E.
Phone—(856) 728-7660
P.O. Box 966, Williamstown 08094

## BURNERS

**Manhattan Welding**
Boilers, burners, mech. contracting, steel fabrication,
cert. welding, 24 hours
**Phone—(908) 687-4494**
**Fax—(908) 688-6684**
**Web—www.manhattanwelding.com**
**Email—info@manhattanwelding.com**
**1434 Chestnut Ave., Hillside 07205**
*(see our ad under BOILER REPAIRING)*
**Nutley Heating & Cooling Supply, Inc.**
**Phone—(973) 667-6880**
**Fax—(973) 667-4602**
**Web—www.nutleysupply.com**
**Email—ralpholiver@nutleysupply.com**
**156 Chestnut St., Nutley 07110**
*(see our ad under BOILERS)*

## BURNERS — Industrial

**AGF Burner, Inc.**
**Phone—(732) 730-8090**
**Fax—(732) 730-8060**
**Web—www.agfburner.com**
**Email—sales@agfburner.com**
**1955 Swarthmore Ave., Unit 2, Lakewood
08701**
*(see our ad under GAS BURNERS)*

## BUSES

**Atlantic Detroit Diesel-Allison, LLC**
**Phone—(201) 489-5800**
**Fax—(201) 368-1071**
**Web—www.atlanticdda.com**
**180 Route 17 S., P.O. Box 950, Lodi 07644**
*(see our ad under ENGINES—Diesel)*
Van-Con, Inc.
Phone—(732) 356-8484
123 William St., Middlesex 08846

## BUSHINGS

**(also see 'Bearings')**

Boneham Metal Products, Inc.
Phone—(908) 272-1200
327 N. 14th St., Kenilworth 07033

## BUSINESS CONSULTANTS

**ac2 Solutions, Inc.**
**Phone—(732) 264-2920**
**Web—www.ac2solutions.com**
**Email—ac2@ac2solutions.com**
**12 Crown Plz., Hazlet 07730**
**American Business Systems, Inc.**
**Phone—(201) 521-9200**
**Fax—(201) 521-9298**
**155 Sterling Ave., Jersey City 07305**
**Digipulse Tech**
**Phone—(609) 265-1666**
**Web—www.digipulsetech.com**
**811 Church Rd., Ste. 169, Cherry Hill 08002**
**Kepner-Tregoe Inc.**
**Phone—(609) 921-2806**
**Web—www.kepner-tregoe.com**
**116 Village Blvd., Ste. 304, Princeton 08540**

New Jersey Mfg. Extension Program, Inc.
**Phone—(973) 998-9801**
**Fax—(973) 860-4637**
**Web—www.njmep.org**
**Email—info@njmep.org**
**2 Ridgedale Ave., Ste. 305, Cedar Knolls
07927**
*(see our ad under MANUFACTURING CONSULTANTS)*

## BUSINESS EQUIPMENT

Automated Business Products, Inc. (H Q)
Phone—(201) 489-1440
50 Clinton Pl., Mail Slot 1, Hackensack 07601

## BUSINESS FORMS

Acu-Data Business Products, Inc.
Phone—(973) 838-5678
1572 State Route 23, Ste. D, Butler 07405
County Graphics Forms Management Co.
Phone—(908) 474-9797
2 Stercho Rd., Linden 07036
Degree Day Systems, Inc.
Phone—(973) 239-7900
33 Village Park Rd., P.O. Box 510, Cedar Grove
07009
Hygrade Business Group, Inc.
Phone—(973) 249-6700
232 Entin Rd., P.O. Box 1099, Clifton 07014
J Z D, LLC
Phone—(732) 257-2727
733 Route 18, East Brunswick 08816
Maggio Data Forms Printing Ltd.
Phone—(856) 931-7805
171 Heller Pl., Bellmawr 08031
Master Business Forms Co.
Phone—(973) 594-8743
195 Allwood Rd., Clifton 07012
New Jersey Business Forms Mfg. Corp.
Phone—(201) 569-4500
55 W. Sheffield Ave., Englewood 07631
Proforma Spectrum Graphics
Phone—(973) 882-8666
373 Route 46 W., Bldg. D, Ste. 130, Fairfield
07004
Roelyn Litho, Inc.
Phone—(732) 942-9650
687 Propect St., Unit 410, Lakewood 08701
S & S Printing
Phone—(856) 784-2718
610 S. White Horse Pike, Somerdale 08083
Stewart Business Forms, Inc.
Phone—(856) 768-2011
28 Redstone Ridge, P.O. Box 715, Voorhees
08043

## BUSINESS MACHINES

Image Systems For Business
Phone—(732) 302-1500
22 Worlds Fair Dr., Ste. E, Somerset 08873

## BUSINESS MANAGEMENT SOFTWARE

Millennium Systems International
Phone—(973) 402-9500
28 Eastmans Rd., Parsippany 07054
Systems House, Inc., The
Phone—(973) 777-8050
1033 U.S. Highway 46, Clifton 07013

## BUSINESS SERVICES

**JK Management LLC**
**Phone—(973) 591-5255**
**P.O. Box 1276, Clifton 07012**

## BUTTONS

Eagle Button Co., Inc.
Phone—(201) 652-4063
700-76 Broadway, Westwood 07675
Nu-Style Embroidery & Button Co., Inc.
Phone—(201) 864-1808
5212 Polk St., West New York 07093

## CABINET MAKERS

SandKamp Woodworks, LLC
Phone—(201) 200-0101
430 Communipaw Ave., Jersey City 07304
**Spaulding Fabricators Inc.**
**Custom Wholesale Countertops for the Style of Your
Life**
**Phone—(732) 840-4433**
**Fax—(732) 840-4970**
**Web—www.spauldingfabricators.com**
**Email—spauldingfabricators@verizon.net**
**1136 Industrial Pkwy., Brick 08724**
*(see our ad under COUNTERTOPS)*

## CABINETS

Cabinet Works Corp.
Phone—(856) 931-7289
511 W. Kings Hwy., Mount Ephraim 08059
Canary Closets & Cabinetry
Phone—(908) 851-2894
697 Rahway Ave., Union 07083
Gafgen Cabinetmakers, Thomas P.
Phone—(609) 448-2060
5 Truman Ct., Robbinsville 08691
Hansen's Cabinet Shop, Inc.
Phone—(973) 377-2444
42 Park Ave., Madison 07940
Hester Bros., Inc.
Phone—(862) 432-5183
114 Beach St., Ste. 5, Rockaway 07866
Hutchinson Cabinets, LLC
Phone—(856) 468-5500
244 Bark Bridge Rd., Sewell 08080
Kobolak & Son, Inc.
Phone—(856) 829-6106
1818 Bannard St., Cinnaminson 08077
Mitchell's Woodworking, LLC
Phone—(609) 261-7500
780 Jacksonville Mount Holly Rd., Westampton
08060
Newark Dental Pemco
Phone—(973) 564-9622
35 Stern Ave., P.O. Box 249, Springfield 07081

## CABINETS — Commercial

J M J Woodworking, Inc.
Phone—(973) 471-6449
100 8th St., Bldg. 300, Passaic 07055
Other Orthodontic Co., Inc.
Phone—(973) 383-8662
22 Gail Ct., Sparta 07871

## CABINETS — Electronic

H & H Industrial Corp.
Phone—(856) 663-4444
7612 N. Crescent Blvd., Pennsauken 08110

## CABINETS — Kitchen

Advanced Cabinets
Phone—(973) 481-3441
654 4th St., Newark 07107
Alex's Custom Kitchens, LLC
Phone—(201) 933-9359
824 Paterson Ave., East Rutherford 07073
Atlas Woodwork
Phone—(973) 621-9595
212 Wright St., Newark 07114
**Behnke's Building Supply**
**Phone—(201) 384-1450**
**Fax—(201) 384-8304**
**Email—kevinb@paramusbuildingsupply.com**
**42 Portland Ave., Bergenfield 07621**
Bennett Cabinets, Inc.
Phone—(732) 548-1616
1251 Highway 1, Edison 08837
Bothers Woodworking, Inc., A. R.
Phone—(908) 725-2891
236 Dukes Pkwy., P.O. Box 127, Somerville 08876
Britton Cabinets
Phone—(732) 222-2232
199 Westwood Ave., Long Branch 07740
Choice Cabinetry, LLC
Phone—(908) 707-8801
61 5th St., Somerville 08876

© Copyright 2015 Manufacturers' News, Inc.

## CABINETS — Kitchen — (cont.)

Costas Architectural Woodworking
Phone—(973) 429-7004
248 Montgomery St., Bloomfield 07003

Custom Cabinets By Jim Bucko, Inc.
Phone—(609) 889-7666
135 W. Burk Ave., Wildwood 08260

Custom Creations By M. D.
Phone—(609) 294-1321
52 Ishmael Rd., Tuckerton 08087

Finest Enterprises, Inc.
Phone—(732) 892-1121
2107 Herbertsville Rd., Point Pleasant 08742

Forino Kitchen Cabinets, Inc.
Phone—(201) 573-0990
33 S. Maple Ave., Park Ridge 07656

Kitchen Kraftsman, The
Phone—(732) 583-3321
343 State Route 34, Matawan 07747

Lutjens Co., Inc., G.
Phone—(973) 278-9639
80 George St., Paterson 07503

Masda Corp.
Phone—(973) 386-1100
22 Troy Rd., P.O. Box D, Whippany 07981

Narva Kitchens & Closets, Inc.
Phone—(718) 735-7722
101 Victory Rd., Springfield 07081

On The Level Counter Top, Inc.
Phone—(732) 370-4186
825 Brook Rd., Lakewood 08701

Parsons Cabinetry, Inc.
Phone—(973) 279-4954
80 George St., Paterson 07503

Precision Cabinets
Phone—(732) 462-3342
410 E. Freehold Rd., Freehold 07728

R & T Custom Cabinets
Phone—(856) 728-1979
1311 Herbert Blvd., Williamstown 08094

Red Bank Cabinet Co.
Phone—(732) 741-8080
548 Shrewsbury Ave., Tinton Falls 07701

Royal Cabinet Co., Inc.
Phone—(908) 203-8000
152 U.S. Highway 206, Unit 14-D, Hillsborough 08844

Ruedi Kuhns Wood Shop
Phone—(908) 755-6947
509 Berckman St., Plainfield 07062

Salerno's Kitchen Cabinets, Inc.
Phone—(201) 794-1990
599 N. Midland Ave., Saddle Brook 07663

Wood Shop
Phone—(732) 446-3377
24 Water St., Englishtown 07726

Woodwork 4 U, LLC
Phone—(973) 643-3044
205 Frelinghuysen Ave., Newark 07114

## CABINETS — Kitchen & Bathroom

Borst Cabinet Co.
Phone—(201) 825-4220
15 Schierloh Ct., Ramsey 07446

Empire Industries, Inc.
Phone—(973) 279-2050
40 Warren St., Paterson 07524

Hanssem Corp.
Phone—(908) 754-4949
155 Helen St., South Plainfield 07080

KBM Kitchen & Bath
Phone—(973) 890-4900
75 Harrison St., Little Falls 07424

Mr. Paul's Custom Cabinets
Phone—(732) 528-9427
2416 Highway 35, Manasquan 08736

**Paramount Fixture Corp.**
Distributing Armstrong & Homecrest cabinets & a variety of imported kitchen cabinets; offering custom-made granite & stone counter tops
**Phone—(973) 485-1585 / (973) 485-8261**
**Fax—(973) 485-3366**
**Web—www.paramountfixturecorp.com**
**Email—fixtureman175@aol.com**
**175 Mount Pleasant Ave., Newark 07104**

T J Mfg., Inc.
Phone—(732) 938-7325
Allaire Airport, Bldg. 25, P.O. Box 2361, Farmingdale 07727

Terzano Cabinetry, Inc.
**Phone—(201) 373-9500**
**Fax—(201) 373-9510**
**Web—www.terzanocabinetry.com**
**Email—info@terzanocabinetry.com**
**111 Leuning St., Unit G, South Hackensack 07606**

## CABINETS — Medicine

**Century Bathworks, Inc.**
Luxury glass shower enclosures & medicine cabinets
**Phone—(973) 785-4290 / (800) 524-2578**
**Fax—(973) 785-0777**
**Web—www.centurybathworks.com**
**Email—info@centurybathworks.com**
**250 Lackawanna Ave., Woodland Park 07424**

## CABINETS — Metal

Falstrom Co.
Phone—(973) 777-0013
1 Falstrom Ct., P.O. Box 118, Passaic 07055

United Hospital Supply Corp.
Phone—(609) 387-7580
4422 Route 130 S., Burlington 08016

## CABINETS — Plastic Laminate

Integrated Laminate Systems
Phone—(856) 786-6500
1301 Industrial Hwy., Riverton 08077

Jafco Industries, LLC
Phone—(732) 356-1502
136 Lincoln Blvd., Middlesex 08846

Napco Cabinets, Inc.
Phone—(856) 665-0253
6938 Westfield Ave., Pennsauken 08110

## CABINETS — Wooden

Acro Display
Phone—(856) 488-9710
2250-A Sherman Ave., Pennsauken 08110

Architectural Cabinetry
Phone—(908) 689-1600
51 Willow St., Washington 07882

Artisan Kitchen Studio, LLC
Phone—(908) 236-7233
26 Cokesbury Rd., P.O. Box 151, Lebanon 08833

Beech Woodworks, Inc.
Phone—(973) 225-0111
9 Kentucky Ave., Paterson 07503

Bozzone Custom Woodwork, Inc.
Phone—(973) 334-5598
77 N. Beverwyck Rd., Lake Hiawatha 07034

Buzz-Bee Cabinetry Co.
Phone—(856) 691-5474
589 N. East Ave., Vineland 08360

Castle Woodcraft Assocs.
Phone—(732) 349-1519
161 Route 9, P.O. Box 426, Pine Beach 08741

CNC Associates
Phone—(718) 416-3853
101 Kentile Rd., South Plainfield 07080

Codfish Park Design, LLC
Phone—(646) 298-4050
39 Commerce St., Chatham 07928

Colfax Cabinet Co., Inc.
Phone—(973) 546-5422
86 Ackerman Ave., Clifton 07011

Corporate Woodworking, Inc.
Phone—(973) 227-2211
368 Passaic Ave., P.O. Box 10362, Fairfield 07004

Creations By Jeffrey, Inc.
Phone—(732) 506-0051
1522 Route 37 E., Toms River 08753

Creative Cabinet Designs, Inc.
Phone—(973) 402-5886
301 Main St., Boonton 07005

Creative Innovations, Inc.
Phone—(973) 636-9060
20-21 Wagaraw Rd., Ste. 31-B, Fair Lawn 07410

Custom Interiors, Inc.
Phone—(201) 573-9702
47 W. Grand Ave., Montvale 07645

Custom Wood Furniture, Inc.
Phone—(973) 579-4880
37 E. Clinton St., P.O. Box 3034, Newton 07860

Custom Wood, LLC
Phone—(609) 758-8288
400 Goldman Dr., Cream Ridge 08514

Custom Woodcraft Co.
Phone—(973) 472-0824
81 Park Pl., Passaic 07055

Custom Woodworking
Phone—(908) 232-9525
813 Jerusalem Rd., Scotch Plains 07076

Darkstar Woodworking
Phone—(201) 248-1575
123 Woodland Ave., Westwood 07675

Downtown Interiors, LLC
Phone—(201) 798-4728
629 Grove St., 8th Fl., Jersey City 07310

Eastern Millwork, Inc.
Phone—(201) 451-9510
18 Chapel Ave., Jersey City 07305

Eppley Building & Design, Inc.
Phone—(973) 636-9499
220-B Goffle Rd., Hawthorne 07506

Feldman Assocs., Inc., F. L.
Phone—(732) 776-8544
811 Memorial Dr., Asbury Park 07712

Frank's Cabinet Shop, Inc.
Phone—(908) 658-4396
1992 Burnt Mills Rd., P.O. Box 78, Pluckemin 07978

Franley Products, Inc.
Phone—(732) 244-1496
89 Riverwood Dr., Ste. 4, Toms River 08755

Garfield Cabinets & Millwork, Inc.
Phone—(973) 340-0507
22 Garfield Ave., Garfield 07026

Handmade Furniture Co.
Phone—(609) 597-2708
612 Main St., West Creek 08092

J D M Woodworking & Cabinetry
Phone—(201) 646-1480
226 Huyler St., South Hackensack 07606

Joti Kitchens
Phone—(609) 383-1350
413 S. Main St., Pleasantville 08232

K W, Inc.
Phone—(609) 882-6363
1536 Lower Ferry Rd., Ewing 08618

Keator Bilt Custom Cabinets
Phone—(732) 776-5133
805 2nd Ave., Asbury Park 07712

Kentucky Cabinet Corp.
Phone—(347) 452-5797
601 Lehigh Ave., Union 07083

Laminate Creations, LLC
Phone—(856) 232-8323
1235 Hurffville Rd., Deptford 08096

Lauderdale Millwork, Inc.
Phone—(908) 508-9550
77 Industrial Rd., Berkeley Heights 07922

Lawler Woodwork, LLC
Phone—(732) 942-7204
938 Lakewood Farmingdale Rd., Howell 07731

Longo's Cabinet Shop
Phone—(973) 472-3567
101 Monroe St., Garfield 07026

Mastercrafts
Phone—(201) 641-6555
152 Louis St., South Hackensack 07606

Miceli Cabinet Corp.
Phone—(201) 933-4004
128 Madison Ave., Englewood 07631

Millner Kitchens, Inc.
Phone—(609) 890-7300
200-B Whitehead Rd., Ste. 108, Hamilton 08619

Miter Box, LLC
Phone—(201) 773-6209
4-21 Banta Pl., Ste. B, Fair Lawn 07410

Modern Equipment Co., Inc.
Phone—(609) 298-2100
19 Ann St., Bordentown 08505

Prinz Woodworking, Inc.
Phone—(973) 977-2345
381 E. 22nd St., Paterson 07514

Ramsay Cabinetmakers, Inc., David
Phone—(856) 234-7776
310 Mill St., Moorestown 08057

Rivers Edge Woodworks & Design
Phone—(973) 337-2288
90 Dayton Ave., Passaic 07055

Ross, Inc., A. W.
Phone—(973) 471-5900
297 Monroe St., Passaic 07055

**AMERICOR**®
CONNECTING THE WORLD

675 S. Lively Blvd., Elk Grove Village, IL 60007
**847.956.6200 • 800.830.5337**
fax 847.956.0300 • www.americor-usa.com
E-mail: info@americor-usa.com

## CABINETS — Wooden — *(cont.)*

Sam's Custom Woodworking
Phone—(609) 267-4962
14 Dunham Ln., Mount Holly 08060
Shearman Cabinets, Inc.
Phone—(973) 677-0071
195 N. Munn Ave., East Orange 07017
Shekia Group, LLC, The
Phone—(732) 372-7668
1130 King Georges Post Rd., Edison 08837
Showtech, Inc.
Phone—(973) 249-6336
40 Entin Rd., Clifton 07014
Stelton Cabinet & Supply
Phone—(732) 985-1035
1358 Stelton Rd., Piscataway 08854
Stevens Cabinet & Millwork
Phone—(908) 996-6290
776 Frenchtown Rd., Milford 08848
Superior Custom Kitchens, LLC
Phone—(908) 753-6005
126 Mount Bethel Rd., Warren 07059
Taylor Made Cabinets
Phone—(609) 978-6900
516 E. Bay Ave., Manahawkin 08050
Taylor Made Custom Cabinetry, Inc.
Phone—(856) 786-5433
7035 Central Hwy., Ste. 200, Pennsauken 08109
Vanco Millwork, Inc.
Phone—(973) 992-3061
18 Microlab Rd., Livingston 07039
West Hudson Millwork, Inc.
Phone—(201) 991-7191
60 Arlington Ave., Kearny 07032
Will's Custom Displays & Woodwork
Phone—(908) 925-0008
1202 E. Elizabeth Ave., Linden 07036
Wood Artisans, Inc.
Phone—(201) 768-1663
49 Oak St., Norwood 07648
Wood Works
Phone—(856) 728-4520
1111 N. Black Horse Pike, Williamstown 08094
Wood-O-Rama, Inc.
Phone—(201) 768-1180
100 67th St., Closter 07624

## CABLE

Antronix, Inc. (H Q)
Phone—(609) 395-1390
440 Forsgate Dr., Cranbury 08512
Canare Corp. Of America
Phone—(973) 837-0070
45 Commerce Way, Unit C, Totowa 07512
IBOCO Corp.
Phone—(732) 417-0066
26 Northfield Ave., Edison 08837

## CABLE — Aircraft Control

**Bergen Cable Technology, LLC**
Cable Assemblies, Wire Rope & Lockwire
Replacement Safety Cable
**Phone—(973) 276-9596 / (800) 237-4369**
**Fax—(973) 276-9566**
**Web—www.bergencable.com**
**Email—sales@bergencable.com**
**343 Kaplan Dr., Fairfield 07004**
*(see our ad under WIRE ROPE)*

## CABLE — Electronic

E C Tronics, Inc.
Phone—(856) 829-7161
855 Industrial Hwy., Unit 5, Riverton 08077
Flexco Microwave, Inc.
Phone—(908) 835-1720
17 Karville Rd., P.O. Box 115, Port Murray 07865

## CABLE — Fiber Optic

C Technologies, Inc.
Phone—(908) 707-1009
757 U.S. Highway 202/206, Bridgewater 08807
Multimode Fiber Optics, Inc.
Phone—(908) 684-5802
432 Sand Shore Rd., Unit 1, Hackettstown 07840
OFS Fitel, LLC, Specialty Photonics Div.
Phone—(732) 748-7400
25 Schoolhouse Rd., Somerset 08873
Tyco Electronics Subsea Communications, LLC (H Q)
Phone—(732) 578-7000
250 Industrial Way W., Eatontown 07724

## CABLE ACCESSORIES

**Lapp USA**
Cables, accessories & connectors. Everything from one source
**Phone—(973) 660-9700 / (800) 774-3539**
**Fax—(973) 660-9330**
**Web—www.lappusa.com**
**Email—sales@lappusa.com**
**29 Hanover Rd., Florham Park 07932**
*(see our ad under CONNECTORS—Electric Wire & Cable)*

## CABLE AND WIRE HARNESSES

Alta Technologies, Inc.
Phone—(609) 538-9500
1545 Reed Rd., P.O. Box 100, Pennington 08534
Electronic Subassemblies, Inc.
Phone—(856) 629-2492
1541 New Brooklyn Rd., Sicklerville 08081
Trek Connect
Phone—(856) 608-0901
120 Mount Holly Bypass, Lumberton 08048

## CABLE ASSEMBLIES

**Ace Electronics, Inc.**
Cable assemblies, bulk wire & cable connectors
**Phone—(732) 603-9800**
**Fax—(732) 603-9767**
**Web—www.aceelectronics.com**
**235 Liberty St., Metuchen 08840**
Ameral International, Inc.
Phone—(856) 456-9000
7 Railroad Ln., Brooklawn 08030
**Americor Electronics, Ltd.**
**Phone—(847) 956-6200 / (800) 830-5337**
**Fax—(847) 956-0300**
**Web—www.americor-usa.com**
**Email—info@americor-usa.com**
**675 S. Lively Blvd., Elk Grove Village, IL 60007**
*(see our ad on this page)*

Archtech Electronics Corp.
Phone—(732) 355-1288
117 Docks Corner Rd., Ste. A, Dayton 08810
**Bergen Cable Technology, LLC**
Cable Assemblies, Wire Rope & Lockwire
Replacement Safety Cable
**Phone—(973) 276-9596 / (800) 237-4369**
**Fax—(973) 276-9566**
**Web—www.bergencable.com**
**Email—sales@bergencable.com**
**343 Kaplan Dr., Fairfield 07004**
*(see our ad under WIRE ROPE)*
Carl Stahl Sava Industries, Inc.
Mechanical Assemblies, Cable Assemblies, Idler Pulleys, Push & Pull Controls; ISO Certified
**Phone—(973) 835-0882**
**Fax—(973) 835-0877**
**Web—www.savacable.com**
**Email—sales@savacable.com**
4 N. Corporate Dr., P.O. Box 30, Riverdale 07457

**Carl Stahl Sava Industries, Inc.**

*Mechanical Cable, Cable Assemblies, Idler Pulleys, Push & Pull Contols; ISO Certified*

**973-835-0882**
**Fax: 973-835-0877**
**www.savacable.com**

4 N. Corporate Dr.
Riverdale, NJ 07457

Custom Cable Crafters, Inc.
Phone—(856) 696-3151
1830 Gallagher Dr., Ste. 103, Vineland 08360
Delaire U. S. A., Inc.
Phone—(732) 528-4520
1913 Atlantic Ave., Ste. R-1, Manasquan 08736
Gray Contract Assembly
Phone—(856) 589-3263
102 Columbia Ave., Pitman 08071
Key Joy USA, LLC
Phone—(732) 339-0450
3 Kellogg Ct., Ste. 12, Edison 08817
**Lapp USA**
Cables, accessories & connectors. Everything from one source
**Phone—(973) 660-9700 / (800) 774-3539**
**Fax—(973) 660-9330**
**Web—www.lappusa.com**
**Email—sales@lappusa.com**
**29 Hanover Rd., Florham Park 07932**
*(see our ad under CONNECTORS—Electric Wire & Cable)*
National Communication, Inc.
Phone—(973) 325-3151
69 Washington St., West Orange 07052
Quadrangle Products
Phone—(732) 792-1234
28 Harrison Ave., Bldg. 16-D, Englishtown 07726
**Ram Electronic Industries Inc.**
Web: www.ramoem.com
Email: steve@ramelectronics.net
**Phone—(856) 864-0999**
**Fax—(856) 786-2244**
**1704 Taylors Ln., Ste. 7, Cinnaminson 08077**
Valconn Electronics, Inc.
Phone—(908) 687-1600
909 Rahway Ave., Union 07083
Wireworks Corp.
Phone—(908) 686-7400
380 Hillside Ave., Hillside 07205
Y.C. Cable East, Inc.
Phone—(732) 868-0800
240 Circle Dr. N., Piscataway 08854

## CABLE ASSEMBLIES — Computer

Computer Crafts, Inc.
Phone—(973) 423-3500
57 Thomas Rd., Hawthorne 07506
J M L Computer Products, Inc.
Phone—(856) 753-8500
9 Wheelwright Ln., Cherry Hill 08003

## CABLE ASSEMBLIES — Electric

Jettron Products, Inc.
Phone—(973) 887-0571
56 Route 10 W., P.O. Box 337, East Hanover 07936

## CABLE ASSEMBLIES — Electronic

Ccard, Inc.
Phone—(732) 303-8264
17 Belleterre Dr., Manalapan 07726
Francis Metals Co., Inc.
Phone—(732) 761-0500
687 Prospect St., Ste. 430, Lakewood 08701
General Reliance Corp.
Phone—(973) 361-1400
88 Ford Rd., Ste. 20, Denville 07834

## CABLE ASSEMBLIES — Medical

**Bergen Cable Technology, LLC**
**Cable Assemblies, Wire Rope & Lockwire**
**Replacement Safety Cable**
**Phone—(973) 276-9596 / (800) 237-4369**
**Fax—(973) 276-9566**
**Web—www.bergencable.com**
**Email—sales@bergencable.com**
**343 Kaplan Dr., Fairfield 07004**
*(see our ad under WIRE ROPE)*
**Carl Stahl Sava Industries, Inc.**
**Mechanical Assemblies, Cable Assemblies, Idler**
**Pulleys, Push & Pull Controls; ISO Certified**
**Phone—(973) 835-0882**
**Fax—(973) 835-0877**
**Web—www.savacable.com**
**Email—sales@savacable.com**
**4 N. Corporate Dr., P.O. Box 30, Riverdale 07457**
*(see our ad under CABLE ASSEMBLIES)*

## CABLE HANDLING EQUIPMENT

Utility Industries, Inc.
Phone—(856) 435-6969
500 Springdale Rd., Ste. K-1, Somerdale 08083

## CABLE MANAGEMENT SYSTEMS

**Lapp USA**
**Cables, accessories & connectors. Everything from**
**one source**
**Phone—(973) 660-9700 / (800) 774-3539**
**Fax—(973) 660-9330**
**Web—www.lappusa.com**
**Email—sales@lappusa.com**
**29 Hanover Rd., Florham Park 07932**
*(see our ad under CONNECTORS—Electric Wire & Cable)*

## CABLE TELEVISION EQUIPMENT

B-Tron Corp.
Phone—(856) 719-8485
154 Cooper Rd., Ste. 1203, West Berlin 08091
Gamco Industries, Inc.
Phone—(732) 381-0700
7 Walnut Ave., Clark 07066

## CABLES — Computer

Data Access Datapatch, Inc.
Phone—(201) 843-5468
40 Eisenhower Dr., Ste. 101, Paramus 07652

*Search from among 430,000 U.S. manufacturers & suppliers:*
**IndustryNet.com**

## CABLES — Electric

Okonite Co., Inc., The (H Q)
Email: seltsam@okonite.com
Setting The Standard Since 1868
Phone—(201) 825-0300
Fax—(201) 825-9026
Web—www.okonite.com
102 Hilltop Rd., P.O. Box 340, Ramsey 07446
*(see our ad under WIRE AND CABLE)*
Prysmian Power Cables & Systems, LLC
Phone—(908) 791-2828
5 Hollywood Ct., South Plainfield 07080

## CABLES — Push-Pull

**Bergen Cable Technology, LLC**
**Cable Assemblies, Wire Rope & Lockwire**
**Replacement Safety Cable**
**Phone—(973) 276-9596 / (800) 237-4369**
**Fax—(973) 276-9566**
**Web—www.bergencable.com**
**Email—sales@bergencable.com**
**343 Kaplan Dr., Fairfield 07004**
*(see our ad under WIRE ROPE)*

## CABLING — Voice & Data

Liberty Electronics
Phone—(973) 625-7966
465 Route 53, Denville 07834

## CAKES

Mara's Gourmet Cheesecake
Phone—(973) 682-9200
281 Speedwell Ave., Morristown 07960

## CALCULATORS

Lane Bond Traders
Phone—(973) 586-2720
27 Cedar Lake Rd., Denville 07834

## CALENDARS

Roth Studio Collection, LLC, The Judith
Phone—(973) 543-4455
3 Stone House Rd., Mendham 07945

## CALIBRATION EQUIPMENT

**Gaston Sales & Service**
**Phone—(609) 462-0201**
**Fax—(609) 588-5428**
**Email—lengaston@aol.com**
**P.O. Box 3121, Trenton 08619**
Woyshner Service Co., Inc.
Phone—(856) 461-9196
813 Edgewood Ave., Riverside 08075

## CALIBRATION SERVICES

**Fizzarotti Instrumentation Service**
**Process Control Instrumentation & Calibration**
**Control**
**Phone—(732) 833-4505**
**Fax—(732) 833-4507**
**Web—www.fizzinstrumentation.com**
**Email—mail@fizzinstrumentation.com**
**436 W. Commodore Blvd., Ste. 4, Jackson 08527**

**Fizzarotti Instrumentation Service**
Quality calibration services
www.fizzinstrumentation.com
**(732) 833-4505**
436 W. Commodore Blvd. Ste. 4
Jackson, NJ 08527

*Do nationwide searches for products & services at:*
**IndustryNet.com**

Pyrometer Equipment Co. Inc.
Phone—(201) 998-0904
Fax—(908) 439-3880
Web—www.pyrometerequipment.com
Email—sbugglin@pyrometerequipment.com
15 Lance Rd., Lebanon 08833

## CAMERAS

Oxberry, LLC
Phone—(201) 935-3000
180 Broad St., Carlstadt 07072
SightLogix, Inc.
Phone—(609) 951-0008
745 Alexander Rd., Ste. 5 & 6, Princeton 08540
Telemetrics, Inc.
Robotic television camera systems
Phone—(201) 848-9818
Fax—(201) 848-9819
Web—www.telemetricsinc.com
6 Leighton Pl., Ste. 4, Mahwah 07430
Vision Research, Inc.
High Speed Digital Imaging Systems
Phone—(973) 696-4500
Fax—(973) 696-0560
Web—www.visionresearch.com
Email—phantom@visionresearch.com
100 Dey Rd., Wayne 07470

**Vision Research, Inc.**
*High Speed Digital Imaging Systems*
973-696-4500 • FAX: 973-696-0560
100 Dey Road  Wayne, NJ 07470
www.visionresearch.com
phantom@visionresearch.com

## CAMERAS — Underwater

Pioneer Research Co.
Phone—(856) 866-9191
97 Foster Rd., Ste. 5, Moorestown 08057

## CANDLES

Ana Design Corp.
Phone—(609) 394-0300
1 Ott St., Trenton 08638
Candle Artisans, Inc.
Phone—(908) 689-2000
253 E. Washington Ave., P.O. Box 190, Washington 07882
Little House Candles
Phone—(609) 758-2996
20 Province Line Rd., New Egypt 08533
Star Soap & Candle, LLC
Phone—(201) 690-9090
300 Industrial Ave., Ridgefield Park 07660
USA Tealight, LLC
Phone—(732) 943-2408
4 Craigwood Rd., Avenel 07001
Wick It, LLC
Phone—(973) 249-2970
1 Gregory Ave., Passaic 07055

## CANDY

**(also see 'Confectionery')**

Al's Home Made Candies
Phone—(856) 691-4536
1133 Fairmount Ave., Vineland 08360
Au'some Inc. (H Q)
Phone—(732) 951-8818
2031 Highway 130, Ste. E., Bldg. A, Monmouth Junction 08852
Bayard's Chocolate Co., Inc.
Phone—(856) 663-2565
2325 Marlton Pike West, Cherry Hill 08002
Bergen Marzipan & Chocolate
Phone—(201) 385-8343
205 S. Washington Ave., Bergenfield 07621
Bromilow's Chocolates, Inc.
Phone—(973) 684-1496
350 Rifle Camp Rd., Woodland Park 07424

## CANDY — (cont.)

**Brummer's Handmade Chocolates**
Phone—(908) 232-1904
125 E. Broad St., Westfield 07090

**Capco Enterprises, Inc.**
34 DeForest Ave., Ste. 3, East Hanover 07936
Email: clapone@capcoenterprisesinc.com
**Phone—(973) 884-0044 / (800) 252-1011**
**Fax—(973) 884-8711**
**Web—www.capcoenterprisesinc.com**
**Email—sales@capcoenterprisesinc.com**
**P.O. Box 335, Florham Park 07932**

### Capco Enterprises Inc.

*Jordan Almonds, Sugar Free Jordan Almonds,
Roasted Flavored Almonds, Sundae Flavored Almonds,
Sugar Coated Pistachios, Peanuts, Licorice and Chic Peas*

**www.capcoenterprisesinc.com**

**973-884-0044**    Fax: **973-884-8711**

34 De Forest Avenue, East Hanover, NJ 07936

**Ce De Candy, Inc.**
Phone—(908) 964-0660
1091 Lousons Rd., Union 07083

**Chilton Laboratories**
Phone—(973) 575-1990
299-B Fairfield Ave., Fairfield 07004

**Chocolate Belles**
Phone—(732) 920-2266
249 Chamber Bridge Rd., Brick 08723

**Critchley's Candies**
Phone—(201) 967-1800
812 Kinderkamack Rd., River Edge 07661

**Criterion Chocolates, Inc.**
Phone—(732) 542-7847
125 Lewis St., Eatontown 07724

**Damask's Candies, Inc.**
Phone—(856) 467-1661
2255 Highway 322, Woolwich Township 08085

**Duffys Delicious Candies Co., Inc.**
Phone—(856) 456-2955
29 N. Broadway, Gloucester City 08030

**Enjou Chocolate, Inc.**
Phone—(973) 993-9090
8 Dehart St., Morristown 07960

**Genevieve's, Inc.**
Phone—(973) 772-8816
174 Ray St., Garfield 07026

**Giambri's Quality Sweets**
Phone—(856) 783-1099
26 Brand Ave., Clementon 08021

**Hillside Candy Co.**
**Phone—(973) 926-2300**
**Fax—(973) 926-4440**
**Web—www.hillsidecandy.com**
**Email—info@hillsidecandy.com**
**35 Hillside Ave., Hillside 07205**

**Jagielky's Home Made Candy**
Phone—(609) 823-6501
5115 Ventnor Ave., Ventnor City 08406

**James Candy Company**
**Phone—(609) 344-1519 / (800) 441-1404**
**Fax—(609) 344-0246**
**Web—www.jamescandy.com**
**Email—sales@jamescandy.com**
**1519 Boardwalk, Atlantic City 08401**

**Kings Candy Co., Inc.**
Phone—(201) 791-4444
55 Bank St., P.O. Box 264, Elmwood Park 07407

**Krause's Homemade Candy Co.**
**Phone—(201) 943-4790**
**Fax—(201) 943-4790**
**Web—www.krausescandies.com**
**Email—krausescandies@gmail.com**
**50 Bergen Blvd., Fairview 07022**

**Lucille's Own Made Candy Co.**
Phone—(609) 597-7300
156 E. Route 72, Manahawkin 08050

**Mars Chocolate North America**
Phone—(908) 852-1000
800 High St., Hackettstown 07840

**Morinaga America, Inc.**
Phone—(201) 947-0408
400 Kelby St., 14th Fl., Fort Lee 07024

**Old Monmouth Peanut Brittle Co.**
Phone—(732) 462-1311
627 Park Ave., Freehold 07728

---

**PIM Brands, LLC**
Phone—(732) 560-8300
500 Pierce St., Somerset 08873

**Promotion In Motion Cos., Inc., The (H Q)**
Phone—(201) 784-5800
25 Commerce Dr., Allendale 07401

**Rauhauser's Candy**
Phone—(609) 399-1465
721 Asbury Ave., Ocean City 08226

**Richards Chocolates Co., Inc., Al**
Phone—(201) 436-0915
851 Broadway, Bayonne 07002

**Shriver's Salt Water Taffy & Fudge**
Phone—(609) 399-0100
9th St. & Boardwalk, P.O. Box 899, Ocean City 08226

**Sophisticated Chocolates Mfg., Inc.**
Phone—(609) 443-4747
92 N. Main St., Windsor 08561

**Steel's Fudge, Inc.**
Phone—(609) 345-4051
1928 E. Riverside Dr., Atlantic City 08401

**Thomas Sweet Chocolates, Inc.**
Phone—(609) 924-7222
29 Palmer Sq. W., Princeton 08542

**Varda International Corp.**
Phone—(908) 354-9090
41 S. Spring St., Elizabeth 07201

---

## CANOPIES — Metal

**Handi-Hut, Inc.**
Smoking shelters, bus stop passenger shelters, entry canopies & bicycle shelters & racks
**Phone—(973) 614-1800 / (800) 603-6635**
**Fax—(973) 614-8011**
**Web—www.handi-hut.com**
**Email—staff@handi-hut.com**
**3 Grunwald St., Clifton 07013**
*(also see our ad under SHELTERS)*

### Handi-Hut, Inc.

*Smoking Shelters, Bus Stop Passenger
Shelters & Entry Canopies*

**www.handi-hut.com**

**973-614-1800 • Fax: 973-614-8011**

3 Grunwald Street   Clifton, NJ 07013

---

## CANS — Metal

**Allstate Can Corp.**
**Phone—(973) 560-9030**
**Fax—(973) 560-9217**
**Web—www.allstatecan.com**
**Email—tincans@allstatecan.com**
**1 Woodhollow Rd., Parsippany 07054**

### Allstate Can Corp.

*Decorative & custom
metal containers*

**(973) 560-9030**

**www.allstatecan.com**

1 Woodhollow Rd.   Parsippany, NJ 07054

**Silgan Containers Mfg. Corp.**
Phone—(732) 287-0300
135 National Rd., Edison 08817

**Stamplus Mfg., Inc.**
Phone—(908) 241-8844
654 W. 1st Ave., Roselle 07203

---

## CANS — Paper & Fibre

**Sonoco Products Co.**
Phone—(609) 655-0300
5 Stults Rd., Dayton 08810

*find additional suppliers at*
**IndustryNet.com**

---

## CANVAS — Marine

**Bay Shore Canvas**
Phone—(732) 477-8520
310 Firehouse Rd., Brick 08723

**Superior Marine Canvas Corp.**
Phone—(856) 241-1724
75 Belfiore Dr., Swedesboro 08085

**Vannote Custom Canvas**
Phone—(732) 830-6555
1904 Grand Central Ave., Lavallette 08735

---

## CANVAS PRODUCTS

**A & J Canvas Co., Inc.**
Phone—(856) 451-5606
Maple Spruce St., P.O. Box 30, Rosenhayn 08352

**Beachwood Canvas Works, LLC**
Phone—(732) 929-3168
39 Lake Ave., P.O. Box 137, Island Heights 08732

**Fisher & Sons, Inc., Harold F.**
Phone—(856) 461-2883
200 Ash St., Delanco 08075

**J & L Boat Canvas**
Phone—(732) 262-1535
190 Drum Point Rd., Brick 08723

**Jean's Canvas Products**
**Phone—(732) 787-0070**
**Fax—(732) 787-0591**
**Web—www.jeanscanvas.com**
**Email—manager@jeanscanvas.com**
**780 State Highway 36, Belford 07718**

**Kerry Wilkens, Inc.**
Phone—(732) 787-0070
780 State Route 36, Belford 07718

**Main Attractions, Inc.**
Phone—(732) 225-3500
85 Newfield Ave., Edison 08837

**Ridgewood Awning Co., Inc.**
Phone—(201) 847-0909
445 W. Main St., Ste. 6, Wyckoff 07481

**Texas Canvas Co.**
Phone—(973) 278-3802
266 Union Blvd., Totowa 07512

---

## CAPACITORS

**Americor Electronics, Ltd.**
**Phone—(847) 956-6200 / (800) 830-5337**
**Fax—(847) 956-0300**
**Web—www.americor-usa.com**
**Email—info@americor-usa.com**
**675 S. Lively Blvd., Elk Grove Village, IL 60007**
*(see our ads under CABLE ASSEMBLIES & CORD SETS)*

**Electronic Concepts, Inc.**
Phone—(732) 542-7880
526 Industrial Way W., Eatontown 07724

---

## CAPPING EQUIPMENT

**UAC Packaging, LLC**
New Cappers, Rebuilt & Reconditioned Resina Cappers
**Phone—(908) 595-6890**
**Fax—(908) 595-6893**
**Web—www.uacpackaging.com**
**Email—cappers@uacpackaging.com**
**330 Roycefield Rd., Unit C, Hillsborough 08844**
*(see our ad under PACKAGING MACHINERY)*

**Warwick Mfg. & Equipment Co., LLC**
Buy & sell used: Chemical, food, cosmetic, packaging & pharmaceutical equipment
**Phone—(732) 729-0400 / (732) 241-9263**
**Fax—(732) 729-1235**
**Web—www.warwickequipment.com**
**Email—sales@warwickequipment.com**
**1112 12th St., North Brunswick 08902**
*(see our ad Outside Back Cover)*

---

## CAPS — Plastic

**Amcor Rigid Plastics**
Phone—(856) 327-1540
625 Sharp St., Millville 08332

**Sap Seal Products**
Phone—(201) 385-5553
52 Woodbine St., Bergenfield 07621

© Copyright 2015 Manufacturers' News, Inc.

A29

## CAPS AND HATS

Alboum Hat Co., Inc., W.
  Phone—(973) 371-9100
  1439 Springfield Ave., Irvington 07111
Castellane Mfg. Co.
  Phone—(609) 625-3427
  1405 Cantillion Blvd., P.O. Box 921, Mays Landing 08330
Headwear Creations, Inc.
  Phone—(973) 622-1144
  200 Wright St., Newark 07114
Unionwear/New Jersey Headwear Corp.
  Phone—(973) 497-0102
  305 3rd Ave. W., Ste. 5, Newark 07107

## CAR WASH DETERGENTS

Styles Mfg. Co., Inc., A. E.
  Phone—(732) 899-0872
  416 Richmond Ave., P.O. Box 1306, Point Pleasant Beach 08742

## CARBON — Activated

**General Carbon Corporation**
  **Activated Carbon Equipment & Services for Liquid & Vapor Applications**
  **Phone—(973) 523-2223**
  **Fax—(973) 523-1494**
  **Web—www.generalcarbon.com**
  **Email—sales@generalcarbon.com**
  **33 Paterson St., Paterson 07501**
    *(see our ad on this page)*

## CARD READERS

Koamtac, Inc.
  Phone—(609) 256-4700
  116 Village Blvd., Ste. 305, Princeton 08540

## CARDIOLOGY EQUIPMENT

Mednet Healthcare Technologies, Inc.
  Phone—(609) 671-1790
  275 Phillips Blvd., Ewing 08618
VectraCor, Inc.
  Phone—(973) 904-0444
  785 Totowa Rd., Ste. 100, Totowa 07512

## CARDS — Greeting, Holiday

CustomShots
  Phone—(609) 296-1811
  189 Silver Lake Dr., West Creek 08092
GINN Co.
  Phone—(201) 216-1660
  812 Jersey Ave., Jersey City 07310
Greetingtap, LLC
  Phone—(347) 731-4263
  832 Spicer Ave., South Plainfield 07080
Lydia's Land, LLC
  Phone—(856) 983-7258
  P.O. Box 852, Marlton 08053
Nobleworks, Inc.
  Phone—(201) 420-0095
  500 Patterson Plank Rd., Union City 07087
Prudent Publishing Co.
  Phone—(973) 347-4554
  400 N. Frontage Rd., Landing 07850
Prudent Publishing Co. (H Q)
  Phone—(201) 641-7900
  65 Challenger Rd., Ridgefield Park 07660
Quadriga Art, Inc.
  Phone—(856) 663-2500
  825 Hylton Rd., Pennsauken 08110

## CARDS — Plastic

Valid USA, Inc.
  Phone—(908) 668-0999
  800 Montrose Ave., South Plainfield 07080

## CARGO CONTROL EQUIPMENT

Kinedyne Corp. (H Q)
  Phone—(908) 231-1800
  151 Industrial Pkwy., Branchburg 08876

# General Carbon Corp.
### Cleaning The World With Activated Carbon

GENERAL CARBON CORP.

## Activated Carbon Equipment and Services
## For Liquid and Vapor Applications
## Manufacturer and Supplier Since 1958

33 Paterson St., Paterson, NJ 07501
T (973) 523-2223 F (973) 523-1494

www.GeneralCarbon.com
sales@generalcarbon.com

## CARPENTERS

Raging Bull Carpentry
  Phone—(973) 249-1832
  58 Wallington Ave., Wallington 07057

## CARPET & RUG DISTRIBUTORS

Gardner Industries, Inc.
  Phone—(862) 210-8906
  Fax—(973) 521-7004
  Web—www.gardnerindustries.com
  Email—ggarner@garnerindustries.com
  12 Commerce Rd., Fairfield 07004

## CARPET LAYING EQUIPMENT & SUPPLIES

R.A.H. Carpet Supplies, Inc.
  Phone—(973) 778-4759
  80 Willow St., East Rutherford 07073

## CARPET MACHINERY

N-C Carpet Binding & Equipment Corp.
  Phone—(973) 481-3500
  858 Summer Ave., Newark 07104

## CARPETS

Couristan, Inc.
  Phone—(201) 585-8500
  2 Executive Dr., Ste. 400, Fort Lee 07024
Edison Foam Processing Corp.
  Phone—(732) 225-2440
  157 Helen St., South Plainfield 07080
Innovative Carpets
  Phone—(201) 894-1008
  45 Legion Dr., Cresskill 07626

## CARPETS — Wholesale

Momeni, Inc.
  Phone—(212) 532-9577
  60 Broad St., Carlstadt 07072

## CARTONING MACHINERY

**Warwick Mfg. & Equipment Co., LLC**
  **Buy & sell used: Chemical, food, cosmetic, packaging & pharmaceutical equipment**
  **Phone—(732) 729-0400 / (732) 241-9263**
  **Fax—(732) 729-1235**
  **Web—www.warwickequipment.com**
  **Email—sales@warwickequipment.com**
  **1112 12th St., North Brunswick 08902**
    *(see our ad Outside Back Cover)*

*Search from among 430,000 U.S. manufacturers & suppliers:*
**IndustryNet.com**

## CARTONS — Corrugated

(also see 'Boxes—Corrugated')
National Packaging Corp.
  Phone—(973) 344-0100
  Fax—(973) 344-0220
  Web—www.nationalpack.com
  Email—info@nationalpack.com
  14 Campus Dr., Kearny 07032
Stickel Packaging Supply
  Packaging & material handling equipment
  Phone—(732) 905-2811
  Fax—(732) 364-6909
  Web—www.stickelpackaging.com
  1991 Rutgers University Blvd., Lakewood Industrial Pk., Lakewood 08701
    *(see our ad under PACKAGING MACHINERY—Wholesale)*

## CARTONS — Folding

(also see 'Boxes' categories)
Accurate Box Co., Inc.
  Phone—(973) 345-2000
  86 5th Ave., Paterson 07524
Graphic Packaging International, Inc.
  Phone—(732) 424-2100
  4100 New Brunswick Ave., Piscataway 08854
Ruffino Packaging, Inc.
  Phone—(201) 487-1260
  63 Green St., Hackensack 07601

## CARTRIDGE HEATERS

**Dalton Electric Heating Co., Inc.**
  **The Leader in Cartridge Heater Technology**
  **Phone—(978) 356-9844**
  **Fax—(978) 356-9846**
  **Web—www.daltonelectric.com**
  **Email—dalton@daltonelectric.com**
  **28 Hayward St., Ipswich, MA 01938**

## CASE GOODS — Metal

Arnold Desks, Inc.
  Phone—(908) 686-5656
  1409 Chestnut Ave., P.O. Box 842, Hillside 07205

## CASEIN

American Casein Co., Inc.
  Phone—(609) 387-3130
  109 Elbow Ln., Burlington 08016

## CASES

Cases By Source, Inc.
  Phone—(201) 831-0005
  215 Island Rd., Mahwah 07430
Nelson Custom Case Co.
  Phone—(908) 479-6902
  1014 State Route 173, Bloomsbury 08804

**All Quality ALUMINUM FOUNDRY**

**Precision Sand Castings in Aluminum and Zinc**

## COMPLETE MACHINING & FINISHING
### (717) 299-5651 • FAX: (717) 299-2318

2485 Old Philadelphia Pike
Smoketown, PA 17576

**www.allqaf.com • Email: sales@allqaf.com**

## CASES — Carrying

C & D Cases, Inc.
Phone—(973) 473-4800
407 River Rd., Unit 9, Clifton 07014
Case-It
Phone—(201) 804-5556
1050 Valley Brook Ave., Lyndhurst 07071
Century Service Affiliates, Inc.
Phone—(973) 742-8118
22 Mercer St., Ste. 1, Paterson 07524
Colemax Group, LLC / Prima Cases
Phone—(201) 489-1080
P.O. Box 103, Glen Rock 07452
Ivyskin, LLC
Phone—(201) 266-5555
282 Grand Ave., Englewood 07631
Princeton Case Co., Inc.
Phone—(908) 687-1750
615 Sherwood Pkwy., Mountainside 07092

## CASES — Display

AMKO Displays, LLC (H Q)
Phone—(201) 460-7199
4 Barrett Ave., Moonachie 07074
Specialty Fabricators, LLC
Phone—(609) 758-6995
118 Meany Rd., Wrightstown 08562

## CASES — Plastic

Accessory Workshop (H Q)
Phone—(888) 691-3047
16 Arcadian Ave., Ste. C-7, Paramus 07652

## CASEWORK

Capra Custom Cabinetry & Millwork, LLC
Phone—(908) 797-9848
259 E. Washington Ave., Washington 07882
Casework Design
Phone—(908) 722-7401
10 County Line Rd., Ste 26, Branchburg 08876
Design Of Tomorrow, Inc.
Phone—(973) 227-5676
24 Sherwood Ln., Fairfield 07004

## CASEWORK — Plastic Clad

R & M Mfg., Inc.
Phone—(609) 495-8032
20 Abeel Rd., Monroe 08831

## CASH REGISTERS

Comtrex Systems Corp.
Phone—(856) 778-0090
1247 N. Church St., Ste. 7, Moorestown 08057

## CASKET INTERIORS

Berry & Sons, Inc., Miller
Phone—(856) 785-1420
Robbinstown Rd., P.O. Box 174, Port Norris 08349

*Do nationwide searches for products & services at:*
**IndustryNet.com**

## CASTERS

Federal Casters Corp.
Phone—(973) 483-6700
785 Harrison Ave., Harrison 07029
Fortuna Enterprise USA, Inc.
Phone—(856) 778-7588
235 Country Club Dr., Moorestown 08057

## CASTINGS

**All Quality Aluminum Foundry**
2485 Old Philadelphia Pike, Smoketown 17576
Precision sand castings in aluminum & zinc
Phone—(717) 299-5651
Fax—(717) 299-2318
Web—www.allqaf.com
Email—sales@allqaf.com
PO Box 46128, Philadelphia, PA 19160
*(see our ad on this page)*
Bierman Everett Foundry Co.
Phone—(973) 373-8800
133 S. 20th St., Irvington 07111
Cutting Edge Casting, Inc.
Phone—(908) 925-7500
1233 W. Saint Georges Ave., Linden 07036
D & S Castings, Inc.
Phone—(609) 689-0100
300 Whitehead Rd., Trenton 08619
Industrial Ferguson Foundry
Phone—(908) 686-8888
2365 Route 22 W., P.O. Box 531, Union 07083
Specialty Castings, Inc.
Phone—(856) 845-3105
42 Curtis Ave., Woodbury 08096

## CASTINGS — Alloy

Alloy Cast Products, Inc.
Phone—(908) 245-2255
700 Swenson Dr., Kenilworth 07033
Biomet, Inc.
Phone—(201) 797-7300
20-01 Pollitt Dr., Fair Lawn 07410

## CASTINGS — Aluminum

**All Quality Aluminum Foundry**
2485 Old Philadelphia Pike, Smoketown 17576
Precision sand castings in aluminum & zinc
Phone—(717) 299-5651
Fax—(717) 299-2318
Web—www.allqaf.com
Email—sales@allqaf.com
PO Box 46128, Philadelphia, PA 19160
*(see our ad on this page)*
American Aluminum Casting Co.
Phone—(973) 372-3200
324 Coit St., Irvington 07111
B & R Industries, Inc.
Phone—(732) 752-3022
196 12th St., Piscataway 08854

## CASTINGS — Art

Johnson Atelier
Phone—(609) 890-7777
60 Sculptors Way, Mercerville 08619

## CASTINGS — Brass

Dornan, Inc.
Phone—(732) 295-4491
333 Cedarcroft Dr., Brick 08724

## CASTINGS — Brass, Bronze & Aluminum

Federal Bronze Casting Industries
Phone—(973) 589-7575
9 Backus St., Newark 07105
Flemington Aluminum & Brass, Inc.
Phone—(908) 782-6317
24 Junction Rd., Flemington 08822
Richmond Industries, Inc.
Phone—(732) 355-1616
1 Chris Ct., Dayton 08810

## CASTINGS — Investment

Atlantic Casting & Engineering
Phone—(973) 779-2450
810 Bloomfield Ave., Clifton 07012
Engineered Precision Casting Co.
Phone—(732) 671-2424
952 Palmer Ave., Middletown 07748
Tec Cast, Inc.
Phone—(201) 935-3885
440 Meadow Ln., Carlstadt 07072
Wheaton Co., R. W.
Phone—(908) 241-4955
215 W. Clay Ave., P.O. Box 4017, Roselle Park 07204

## CASTINGS — Iron

General Foundries, Inc.
Phone—(732) 697-9000
1 Progress Rd., North Brunswick 08902

## CASTINGS — Machined

**All Quality Aluminum Foundry**
2485 Old Philadelphia Pike, Smoketown 17576
Precision sand castings in aluminum & zinc
Phone—(717) 299-5651
Fax—(717) 299-2318
Web—www.allqaf.com
Email—sales@allqaf.com
PO Box 46128, Philadelphia, PA 19160
*(see our ad on this page)*

## CASTINGS — Sand

**All Quality Aluminum Foundry**
2485 Old Philadelphia Pike, Smoketown 17576
Precision sand castings in aluminum & zinc
Phone—(717) 299-5651
Fax—(717) 299-2318
Web—www.allqaf.com
Email—sales@allqaf.com
PO Box 46128, Philadelphia, PA 19160
*(see our ad on this page)*

## CASTINGS — Steel

S H P C, Inc.
Phone—(973) 589-5242
187 Christie St., P.O. Box 5328, Newark 07105
Talbot Assocs., Inc.
Phone—(973) 376-9570
11 Cleveland Pl., Springfield 07081

## CASTINGS — Urethane

Precision Escalators
Phone—(908) 259-9017
147 N. Michigan Ave., Kenilworth 07033

*Search from among*
*430,000 U.S. manufacturers*
*& suppliers at*

**IndustryNet.com**

**INDUSTRY**

## CASTINGS — Zinc

**All Quality Aluminum Foundry**
2485 Old Philadelphia Pike, Smoketown 17576
Precision sand castings in aluminum & zinc
Phone—(717) 299-5651
Fax—(717) 299-2318
Web—www.allqaf.com
Email—sales@allqaf.com
PO Box 46128, Philadelphia, PA 19160
*(see our ad under CASTINGS)*

## CATALYSTS

Scientific Design Co., Inc.
Phone—(201) 641-0500
49 Industrial Ave., Little Ferry 07643

## CATERING SERVICES

**Corrado's Family Affair**
There is a difference
Phone—(973) 340-0628
Fax—(973) 340-2052
Web—www.corradosmarket.com
Email—gerrycorradojr@corradosmarket.com
1578 Main Ave., Clifton 07011

## CAULKS

**Specified Technologies Inc.**
Firestopping Products
Phone—(908) 526-8000 / (800) 992-1180
Fax—(908) 526-9623
Web—www.stifirestop.com
Email—sales@stifirestop.com
210 Evans Way, Somerville 08876
*(see our ad under FIRE PROTECTION SYSTEMS)*

## CAUSTIC SODA

**Universal Chemicals Inc.**
Phone—(973) 589-1525
Fax—(973) 589-8013
Web—www.universalchem.com
Email—info@universalchem.com
100 N. Hackensack Ave., Kearny 07032

## CD & AUDIO DUPLICATION

Audio Dynamix, Inc.
Phone—(201) 567-5488
170 Coolidge Ave., Englewood 07631
Mardee Co., Inc.
Phone—(908) 753-4343
242 Saint Nicholas Ave., South Plainfield 07080
Oasis Recording, Inc.
Phone—(888) 296-2747
7905 N. Crescent Blvd., Delair 08110

## CEILING SYSTEMS

**Erco Ceilings, Blinds & Division 10**
Phone—(800) 327-8066
Fax—(856) 881-7330
Web—www.ercoonline.com
Email—esther.s@ercoonline.com
32 N. Delsea Dr., Glassboro 08028

## CELLULAR COMMUNICATION TOWERS

G-Way Microwave
Phone—(201) 343-6388
38 Leuning St., South Hackensack 07606

## CELLULAR PHONE ACCESSORIES

South Mill Design, LLC
Phone—(877) 466-0273
131 S. Mill Rd., Princeton Junction 08550

## CELLULOSE PRODUCTS

Ashland Aqualon, Inc.
Phone—(732) 254-1234
50 S. Minnisink Ave., Parlin 08859

## CEMENT

Holcim U.S.
Phone—(856) 964-2555
595 Morgan Blvd., Camden 08104
Lehigh Cement Co.
Phone—(973) 579-2111
66 Demarest Rd., Sparta 07871

## CEMENT BLENDING

Ace Crete Products, Inc.
Phone—(732) 269-1400
250 Hickory Ln., Bayville 08721

## CEMETERIES

G & C Fab Con, LLC
Phone—(908) 782-0526
5 Foster Ln., Bldg. A, Flemington 08822

## CENTRIFUGES

GEA Mechanical Equipment US, Inc.
Phone—(201) 767-3900
100 Fairway Ct., Northvale 07647
Hamilton Bell Co., Inc.
Phone—(201) 391-4100
30 Craig Rd., Montvale 07645
Heinkel Filtering Systems, Inc.
Phone—(856) 467-3399
520 Sharptown Rd., Swedesboro 08085
**Warwick Mfg. & Equipment Co., LLC**
Buy & sell used: Chemical, food, cosmetic, packaging & pharmaceutical equipment
Phone—(732) 729-0400 / (732) 241-9263
Fax—(732) 729-1235
Web—www.warwickequipment.com
Email—sales@warwickequipment.com
1112 12th St., North Brunswick 08902
*(see our ad Outside Back Cover)*

## CERAMIC PRODUCTS

Accuratus Corporation
Phone—(908) 213-7070
35 Howard St., Phillipsburg 08865
American Beryllia, Inc.
Phone—(973) 248-8080
16 1st Ave., Haskell 07420
Curran Pfeiff Corp.
Phone—(732) 225-0555
Liddle Ave., Edison 08837
Eigen Arts, Inc.
Phone—(201) 798-7310
150 Bay St., Jersey City 07302
Morgan Advanced Ceramics, Inc.
Phone—(973) 227-8877
26 Madison Rd., Fairfield 07004
Shedd Designs, LLC, John
Phone—(609) 924-6394
200 Washington St., P.O. Box 276, Rocky Hill 08553

## CERAMICS — Electronic

Ceramic Products, Inc.
Phone—(201) 342-8200
221 Park St., Hackensack 07601
Isolantite Mfg. Co., Inc.
Phone—(908) 647-3333
337 Warren Ave., Stirling 07980
L S P Industrial Ceramics
Phone—(609) 397-8330
34 Mount Airy Village Rd., P.O. Box 302, Lambertville 08530
National Ceramic Co., Inc.
Phone—(609) 394-5373
500 Southard St., Trenton 08638

**EZ Select®.com**
**REAL-TIME** Access to Industrial Leads!

**Pekay Industries, Inc.**
Ceramics Metalized For The Electronic & Medical Industries
Phone—(732) 938-2722
Fax—(732) 919-0224
Southard Ave., P.O. Box 559, Farmingdale 07727

**Pekay Industries, Inc.**

*Electronics Ceramic Terminals*

**(732) 938-2722**
**FAX: (732) 919-0224**

Southard Avenue
P.O. Box 559
Farmingdale, NJ 07727

## CERAMICS — Industrial

Certech, Inc.
Phone—(201) 939-7400
1 Park Pl. W., Wood Ridge 07075

## CERAMICS — Piezoelectric

TBT Group, Inc.
Phone—(856) 753-4500
191 Heller Pl., Bellmawr 08031

## CESIUM CHLORIDE

VAR-LAC-OID Chemical Co., Inc.
Phone—(201) 236-8800
24 Industrial Ave., P.O. Box 181, Upper Saddle River 07458

## CHAINS — Roller

HKK Chain Corp. Of America
Phone—(973) 575-7860
9 Riverside Dr., P.O. Box 604, Pine Brook 07058

## CHAINS — Welded

**Modern International Corp.**
Phone—(732) 696-9100
Fax—(732) 696-9111
Web—www.moderninternational.net
Email—dstern@moderninternational.net
145 Cliffwood Ave., Cliffwood 07721

## CHAIRS

Dauphin North America
Phone—(973) 263-1100
100 Fulton St., Boonton 07005
**E.W.E. Auto Seat Cover Co.**
Office Chairs
Phone—(201) 869-6470
Fax—(201) 868-8491
Email—eweauto@yahoo.com
8431 Kennedy Blvd., North Bergen 07047

## CHARTS

Leneta Co., Inc.
Phone—(201) 847-9300
15 Whitney Rd., Mahwah 07430

© Copyright 2015 Manufacturers' News, Inc.

**Arthur Schuman**
Heritage • Leadership • Innovation

Unrivaled Market Leader in the Imported & Domestic Cheese Industry

**(973) 227-0030**
FAX: (973) 227-1525

www.arthurschuman.com
info@arthurschuman.com

40 New Dutch Ln. • Fairfield, NJ 07004

## CHASSIS

**Hercules Enterprises, LLC**
Phone—(908) 369-0000
321 Valley Rd., Hillsborough 08844

## CHEESE & CHEESE SPECIALTIES

**Anderson International Foods, Inc.**
Phone—(516) 747-2210
95 Burma Rd., Jersey City 07305

**Antonio Mozzarella Factory, Inc.**
Phone—(973) 353-9411
631 Frelinghuysen Ave., Newark 07114

**Arthur Schuman, Inc.**
Unrivaled market leader in the imported & domestic cheese industry
Phone—(973) 227-0030
Fax—(973) 227-1525
Web—www.arthurschuman.com
Email—info@arthurschuman.com
40 New Dutch Ln., Fairfield 07004
*(see our ad on this page)*

**Biazzo Dairy Products, Inc.**
Phone—(201) 941-6800
1145 Edgewater Ave., Ridgefield 07657

**Capital Foods, Inc.**
Phone—(908) 587-9050
1701 E. Elizabeth Ave., Linden 07036

**Cognati Cheese Co., Inc.**
Phone—(201) 807-9100
205 Moonachie Rd., 2nd Fl., Moonachie 07074

**DCI Cheese Co.**
Phone—(201) 807-0999
861 Washington Ave., Carlstadt 07072

**Finlandia Cheese, Inc.**
Phone—(973) 316-6699
2001 U.S. Highway 46, Ste. 303, Parsippany 07054

**No Registration.**
**No Password.**
**No Hassle!**

*Source quickly & easily at*
**IndustryNet.com**

**J.V.M. Sales, Inc.**
Phone—(908) 862-4866
Fax—(908) 862-4867
Web—www.gratedcheeseusa.com
Email—jsales.jvm@verizon.net
3401-A Tremley Point Rd., Linden 07036

**J.V.M. Sales, Inc.**

Grated & Shredded Cheese & Cheese Specialties

**908-862-4866**

**Fax: 908-862-4867**

www.gratedcheeseusa.com
jsales.jvm@verizon.net

**3401-A Tremley Point Rd.**
**Linden, NJ 07036**

**Lebanon Cheese Co., Inc.**
Phone—(908) 236-2611
3 Railroad Ave., P.O. Box 63, Lebanon 08833

**Lioni Latticini, Inc.**
Phone—(908) 686-6061
Fax—(908) 686-3449
Web—www.lionimozzarella.com
Email—info@lionimozzarella.com
555 Lehigh Ave., Union 07083

**Losurdo Foods, Inc.**
Phone—(201) 343-6680
20 Owens Rd., Hackensack 07601

**Lotito Foods, Inc.**
Phone—(973) 684-2900
510 E. 35th St., Paterson 07504

*Search from among 430,000 U.S. manufacturers & suppliers at*
**IndustryNet.com**

**Lotito Foods, Inc./Mrs. Mazzula Foods**
Email: tgallina@lotitofoods.com
Specializing in gourmet Italian food products
Phone—(732) 248-0222
Fax—(732) 248-0442
Web—www.lotitofoods.com
Email—info@lotitofoods.com
240 Carter Dr., Edison 08817

**Lotito Foods, Inc./Mrs. Mazzula Foods**

*Cheese & sun-dried tomato products*

**www.lotitofoods.com**

**732-248-0222**

240 Carter Dr.  Edison, NJ 08817

**Montena Taranto Foods, Inc.**
Phone—(201) 943-8484 / (800) 809-3336
Fax—(201) 943-6037
Email—montenataranto@aol.com
400 Victoria Ter., Ridgefield 07657

**Sankar Assocs., Inc.**
Phone—(201) 994-1700
14 Empire Blvd., Moonachie 07074

**Schratter Foods, Inc. (H Q)**
Phone—(973) 575-3226
333 Fairfield Rd., Fairfield 07004

**Tipico Products, Inc.**
Phone—(732) 942-8820
490 Oberlin Ave. S., Lakewood 08701

**Toscana Cheese Co., Inc.**
Phone—(201) 617-1500
575 Windsor Dr., Secaucus 07094

**Tropical Cheese Industries, Inc.**
Phone—(732) 442-4898
450 Fayette St., Perth Amboy 08861

**Valley Shepherd Creamery**
Phone—(908) 876-3200
50 Fairmount Rd., Long Valley 07853

## CHEESECAKES

**Catering By The Maddalenas, Inc.**
Phone—(609) 466-7510
415 Route 31 N., Ringoes 08551

**Cinderella Cheesecake Co., Inc.**
Phone—(856) 461-6302
208 N. Fairview St., P.O. Box 36, Riverside 08075

## CHEMICAL ADDITIVES

**E. I. du Pont de Nemours & Co., Chambers Works Plt.**
Phone—(856) 299-5000
67 Canal St., Deepwater 08023

**Kenrich Petrochemicals, Inc.**
Phone—(201) 823-9000
140 E. 22nd St., P.O. Box 32, Bayonne 07002

## CHEMICAL ANALYSIS EQUIPMENT

**ECI Technology, Inc.**
Phone—(973) 890-1114
60 Gordon Dr., Totowa 07512

## CHEMICAL BLENDING

**Caled Industries, Inc.**
Phone—(973) 696-7575
26 Hanes Dr., Wayne 07470

**Cogesco Water Technologies Corp.**
Phone—(973) 249-9711
Fax—(973) 249-6911
Web—www.cogescointl.com
Email—greche@cogescointl.com
891 Bloomfield Ave., Clifton 07012

*find additional suppliers at*
**IndustryNet.com**

INDUSTRY

## CHEMICAL CLEANING SERVICES

**Veolia ES Technical Solutions, LLC**
Recycling Industrial Solvents
Phone—(732) 469-5100
Fax—(732) 469-1957
Web—www.veoliaes.com
Email—ray.clark@veolia.com
125 Factory Ln., Middlesex 08846
*(see our ad under SOLVENT RECYCLING)*

## CHEMICAL DISTRIBUTORS

**Brenntag Specialties, Inc.**
Phone—(908) 561-6100 / (800) 732-0562
Fax—(800) 543-1484
Web—www.brenntagspecialties.com
Email—specialties@brenntag.com
1000 Coolidge St., South Plainfield 07080

**Supplier of Chemical Products Since 1974**

**GJCHEMICAL.COM**

Email: **Marketing@GJChemical.com**

Phone **973.589.1450** • Fax **732.249.0082**

G.J. CHEMICAL CO., INC. • 40 Veronica Ave • Somerset NJ 08873

---

## BRENNTAG
### SPECIALTIES

Chemical Distributors

**(908) 561-6100**
**Fax: (800) 543-1484**

1000 Coolidge St.
South Plainfield, NJ 07080

**www.brenntagspecialties.com**

**specialties@brenntag.com**

---

**G.J. Chemical Co., Inc.**
An ISO 9001:2008 Registered Company
Phone—(973) 589-1450
Fax—(732) 249-0082
Web—www.gjchemical.com
Email—marketing@gjchemical.com
40 Veronica Ave., Somerset 08873
*(see our ad on this page)*

**Protameen Chemicals, Inc.**
Phone—(973) 256-4374
375 Minnisink Rd., Totowa 07512

**Seidler Chemical & Supply Co.**
Chemicals & Chemical Re-Packaging & Distribution
Phone—(973) 465-1122
Fax—(973) 465-4469
Web—www.seidlerchem.com
Email—sales@seidlerchem.com
537 Raymond Blvd., Newark 07105

## CHEMICAL FEED SYSTEMS

**Chemquip Corp.**
Phone—(973) 684-3009
258-262 Atlantic St., Paterson 07503

## CHEMICAL HANDLING SYSTEMS

**United Energy Corp.**
Phone—(732) 994-5225
3526 U.S. Highway 9 S., Ste. 103, Howell 07731

## CHEMICAL PLANT EQUIPMENT & SUPPLIES

**EcReCon, Inc.**
Used Chemical Processing Equipment
Phone—(856) 299-4500
Fax—(856) 299-4446
Web—www.EcReCon.com
Email—sales@ecrecon.com
62 N. Broad St., Penns Grove 08069
*(see our ad under CHEMICAL PROCESSING EQUIPMENT)*

---

**Warwick Mfg. & Equipment Co., LLC**
Buy & sell used: Chemical, food, cosmetic, packaging
& pharmaceutical equipment
Phone—(732) 729-0400 / (732) 241-9263
Fax—(732) 729-1235
Web—www.warwickequipment.com
Email—sales@warwickequipment.com
1112 12th St., North Brunswick 08902
*(see our ad Outside Back Cover)*

## CHEMICAL PROCESSING & PACKAGING

**A. L. Wilson Chemical Co.**
Phone—(201) 997-3300
1050 Harrison Ave., P.O. Box 207, Kearny 07032

## CHEMICAL PROCESSING EQUIPMENT

**EcReCon, Inc.**
Used Chemical Processing Equipment
Phone—(856) 299-4500
Fax—(856) 299-4446
Web—www.EcReCon.com
Email—sales@ecrecon.com
62 N. Broad St., Penns Grove 08069

---

### EcReCon INC.

Buy/Sell Quality Used Process Equipment
Buy/Sell Complete Plants/Dismantling

**(856) 299-4500**

**sales@ecrecon.com**

**www.EcReCon.com**

**We Want to Buy
Your Surplus Equipment**

---

## CHEMICAL PRODUCTS

**Baumar Industries, Inc.**
Phone—(973) 667-5490
29 E. Centre St., Nutley 07110

*Search from among 430,000
U.S. manufacturers & suppliers:*
**IndustryNet.com**

---

## CHEMICAL REPACKAGING

**Seidler Chemical & Supply Co.**
Chemicals & Chemical Re-Packaging & Distribution
Phone—(973) 465-1122
Fax—(973) 465-4469
Web—www.seidlerchem.com
Email—sales@seidlerchem.com
537 Raymond Blvd., Newark 07105

## CHEMICAL SURFACTANTS

**Ardmore, Inc.**
Phone—(973) 481-2406
29 Riverside Ave., Bldg. 14, Newark 07104
**BASF Corp.**
Phone—(908) 689-7540
2 Pleasant View Ave., Washington 07882
**HYCHEM Corporation**
Phone—(732) 280-8803
611 Main St., Ste. B-2, Belmar 07719
**Pilot Chemical Co.**
Phone—(732) 634-6613
267 Homestead Ave., Avenel 07001
**Stepan Co.**
Phone—(609) 298-1222
220 4th St., Fieldsboro 08505
**Universal Preserv-A-Chem, Inc.**
Phone—(732) 568-1266
60 Jiffy Rd., Somerset 08873

## CHEMICALS

**Alan Chemical Corp., Inc.**
Phone—(732) 855-6828
843 Rahway Ave., Ste. 400, Woodbridge 07095
**Bergen International, LLC**
Phone—(201) 299-4499
411 Route 17 S., Ste. 100, Hasbrouck Heights 07604
**Croda, Inc. (H Q)**
Phone—(732) 417-0800
300 Columbus Cir., Ste. A, Edison 08837
**Dallas Group Of America, Inc., The (H Q)**
Phone—(908) 534-7800
374 Route 22, P.O. Box 489, Whitehouse 08888
**Evonik Corporation (H Q)**
Phone—(973) 929-8000
299 Jefferson Rd., Parsippany 07054
**Ferro Corp., Delaware River Plt.**
Email: knightonjr@ferro.com
Commodity chemicals
Phone—(856) 467-8216 / (800) 321-9942
Fax—(856) 467-8308
Web—www.ferro.com
170 U.S. Route 130 S., P.O. Box 309, Bridgeport 08014

Find Suppliers
Nationally FREE!

## CHEMICALS — *(cont.)*

**G.J. Chemical Co., Inc.**
**An ISO 9001:2008 Registered Company**
**Phone—(973) 589-1450**
**Fax—(732) 249-0082**
**Web—www.gjchemical.com**
**Email—marketing@gjchemical.com**
**40 Veronica Ave., Somerset 08873**

**GJ CHEMICAL**
THE WORLD'S LEADING SOURCE OF CHEMICALS FOR TECHNOLOGIES
**Supplier of Chemical Products Since 1974**
GJCHEMICAL.COM
Email: Marketing@GJChemical.com
Phone 973.589.1450 • Fax 732.249.0082
G.J. CHEMICAL CO., INC. • 40 Veronica Ave • Somerset NJ 08873

GEO Specialty Chemicals, Inc.
Phone—(973) 484-8400
1st & Essex St., Harrison 07029

**Hummel Croton, Inc.**
**Phone—(908) 754-1800**
**Fax—(908) 754-1815**
**Web—www.hummelcroton.com**
**Email—sales@hummelcroton.com**
**10 Harmich Rd., South Plainfield 07080**
 *(see our ad under CHEMICALS—Industrial)*

Indofine Chemical Co., Inc.
Phone—(908) 359-6778
121 Stryker Ln., Hillsborough 08844

J & J Materials, Inc.
Phone—(732) 988-3300
49 Laurel Ave., P.O. Box 2128, Neptune City 07753

Lubrizol Advanced Materials, Inc.
Phone—(973) 471-1300
1 Industrial W., Clifton 07012

LyondellBasell Industries
Phone—(732) 777-2272
340 Meadow Rd., Edison 08817

MEL Chemicals
Phone—(908) 782-5800
500 Barbertown Point Breeze Rd., Flemington 08822

Parts Cleaning Technologies, LLC
Phone—(856) 786-8686
835 Industrial Hwy., Ste. 1, Cinnaminson 08077

**Phibro-Tech, Inc.**
**The Copper Chemical Company™**
**Phone—(201) 329-7300 / (800) 357-6840**
**Fax—(201) 329-7035**
**Web—www.phibro-tech.com**
**Email—phibro-tech@pahc.com**
**300 Frank W. Burr Blvd., Ste. 21, Glenpointe Center East, 3rd Fl., Teaneck 07666**

Seidler Chemical & Supply Co.
Phone—(973) 465-1122
537 Raymond Blvd., Newark 07105

TATA Chemicals North America, Inc. (H Q)
Phone—(973) 599-5500
100 Enterprise Dr., 7th Fl., Rockaway 07866

Vinchem, Inc.
Phone—(973) 635-4841
301 Main. St., P.O. Box 639, Chatham 07928

Water Mark Technologies, Inc.
Phone—(973) 663-3438
762 State Route 15 S., Ste. 2-B, Lake Hopatcong 07849

## CHEMICALS — Agricultural

Aquatrols Corp. Of America
Phone—(856) 537-6003
1273 Imperial Way, Paulsboro 08066

Mitchell Products, LLC
Phone—(856) 327-2005
1205 W. Main St., Millville 08332

## CHEMICALS — Cleaning

Banner Chemical Corp.
Phone—(973) 676-2900
111 Hill St., Orange 07050

Biofusion, Inc.
Phone—(201) 447-6241
310 Godwin Ave., Ridgewood 07450

ClorDiSys Solutions, Inc.
Phone—(908) 236-4100
291 Route 22 E., Salem Industrial Park 5, Lebanon 08833

NCH Corp.
Phone—(732) 329-8111
34 Stouts Ln., P.O. Box 25, Monmouth Junction 08852

## CHEMICALS — Coating

**Brenntag Specialties, Inc.**
**Phone—(908) 561-6100 / (800) 732-0562**
**Fax—(800) 543-1484**
**Web—www.brenntagspecialties.com**
**Email—specialties@brenntag.com**
**1000 Coolidge St., South Plainfield 07080**
 *(see our ad under CHEMICAL DISTRIBUTORS)*

## CHEMICALS — Construction

**Brenntag Specialties, Inc.**
**Phone—(908) 561-6100 / (800) 732-0562**
**Fax—(800) 543-1484**
**Web—www.brenntagspecialties.com**
**Email—specialties@brenntag.com**
**1000 Coolidge St., South Plainfield 07080**
 *(see our ad under CHEMICAL DISTRIBUTORS)*

Sika Corporation
Phone—(201) 933-8800
201 Polito Ave., Lyndhurst 07071

US Concrete Materials, LLC
Phone—(201) 385-6470
189 Berkley Pl., Dumont 07628

## CHEMICALS — Contract Manufacturing

Chem-Is-Try, Inc.
Phone—(732) 372-7311
160-1 Liberty St., Metuchen 08840

## CHEMICALS — Cosmetic

Aromor Flavors & Fragrances, Inc.
Phone—(201) 503-1662
560 Sylvan Ave., Ste. 60, Englewood Cliffs 07632

**Brenntag Specialties, Inc.**
**Phone—(908) 561-6100 / (800) 732-0562**
**Fax—(800) 543-1484**
**Web—www.brenntagspecialties.com**
**Email—specialties@brenntag.com**
**1000 Coolidge St., South Plainfield 07080**
 *(see our ad under CHEMICAL DISTRIBUTORS)*

**Evans Chemetics LP (H Q)**
**Phone—(201) 992-3100**
**Fax—(201) 992-3101**
**Web—www.evans-chemetics.com**
**Email—info@evans-chemetics.com**
**500 Frank W. Burr Blvd., 4th Fl., Glenpointe Center West, Teaneck 07666**
 *(see our ad under SULFUR)*

Global Seven, Inc.
Phone—(973) 664-1900
198 Green Pond Rd., P.O. Box 696, Rockaway 07866

KOBO Products, Inc.
Phone—(908) 757-0033
3474 S. Clinton Ave., South Plainfield 07080

Lipo Chemicals, Inc.
Phone—(973) 345-8600
207 19th Ave., Paterson 07504

Lonza, Inc.
Phone—(908) 561-5200
70 Tyler Pl., South Plainfield 07080

Sensient Cosmetic & Pharmaceutical Technologies
Phone—(908) 757-4500
107 Wade Ave., South Plainfield 07080

## CHEMICALS — Custom Blending

Cargille TAB-PRO Corp.
Phone—(973) 267-8888
4 E. Frederick Pl., Cedar Knolls 07927

Colonial Chemical
Phone—(609) 268-1200
78 Carranza Rd., Tabernacle 08088

**G.J. Chemical Co., Inc.**
**An ISO 9001:2008 Registered Company**
**Phone—(973) 589-1450**
**Fax—(732) 249-0082**
**Web—www.gjchemical.com**
**Email—marketing@gjchemical.com**
**40 Veronica Ave., Somerset 08873**
 *(see our ads under CHEMICAL DISTRIBUTORS & CHEMICALS)*

Indco, Inc.
Phone—(856) 456-6100
511 Essex St., P.O. Box 109, Gloucester City 08030

**Seidler Chemical & Supply Co.**
**Chemicals & Chemical Re-Packaging & Distribution**
**Phone—(973) 465-1122**
**Fax—(973) 465-4469**
**Web—www.seidlerchem.com**
**Email—sales@seidlerchem.com**
**537 Raymond Blvd., Newark 07105**

## CHEMICALS — Electronic

**Seidler Chemical & Supply Co.**
**Chemicals & Chemical Re-Packaging & Distribution**
**Phone—(973) 465-1122**
**Fax—(973) 465-4469**
**Web—www.seidlerchem.com**
**Email—sales@seidlerchem.com**
**537 Raymond Blvd., Newark 07105**

Voltaix, LLC (H Q)
Phone—(908) 231-9060
3121 U.S. Highway 22, P.O. Box 5357, Branchburg 08876

## CHEMICALS — Flame Retardant

Firefreeze Worldwide, Inc.
Phone—(973) 394-1335
429 Rockaway Valley Rd., Boonton 07005

## CHEMICALS — Household

**Brenntag Specialties, Inc.**
**Phone—(908) 561-6100 / (800) 732-0562**
**Fax—(800) 543-1484**
**Web—www.brenntagspecialties.com**
**Email—specialties@brenntag.com**
**1000 Coolidge St., South Plainfield 07080**
 *(see our ad under CHEMICAL DISTRIBUTORS)*

## CHEMICALS — Industrial

Air Products & Chemicals, Inc.
Phone—(732) 446-5676
405 State Route 33, Englishtown 07726

BASF Corporation (H Q)
Phone—(973) 245-6000
100 Park Ave., Florham Park 07932

Bluestar Silicones U.S.A. Corp. (H Q)
Phone—(732) 227-2060
2 Tower Center Blvd., Ste. 1601, East Brunswick 08816

Bracco Diagnostics, Inc.
Phone—(609) 514-2200
259 Prospect Plains Rd., Bldg. H, Monroe Township 08831

Cal-Chlor Corp.
Phone—(732) 271-3500
141 Baekeland Ave., Piscataway 08854

Chemetall
Phone—(908) 464-6900
675 Central Ave., New Providence 07974

Chemtrade Chemical, LLC
Phone—(973) 515-0900
90 E. Halsey Rd., 3rd Fl., Parsippany 07054

**Evans Chemetics LP (H Q)**
**Phone—(201) 992-3100**
**Fax—(201) 992-3101**
**Web—www.evans-chemetics.com**
**Email—info@evans-chemetics.com**
**500 Frank W. Burr Blvd., 4th Fl., Glenpointe Center West, Teaneck 07666**
 *(see our ad under SULFUR)*

*Do nationwide searches for products & services at:*
**IndustryNet.com**

INDUSTRY

## CHEMICALS — Industrial — (cont.)

**G.J. Chemical Co., Inc.**
An ISO 9001:2008 Registered Company
**Phone—(973) 589-1450**
**Fax—(732) 249-0082**
**Web—www.gjchemical.com**
**Email—marketing@gjchemical.com**
**40 Veronica Ave., Somerset 08873**
*(see our ads under CHEMICAL DISTRIBUTORS & CHEMICALS)*

Halocarbon Products Corp. (H Q)
Phone—(201) 262-8899
887 Kinderkamack Rd., 2nd Fl., River Edge 07661

Hisco, Inc.
Phone—(732) 745-2828
55 Veronica Ave., Somerset 08873

**Hummel Croton, Inc.**
**Phone—(908) 754-1800**
**Fax—(908) 754-1815**
**Web—www.hummelcroton.com**
**Email—sales@hummelcroton.com**
**10 Harmich Rd., South Plainfield 07080**
*(see our ad on this page)*

Lonza, Inc.
Phone—(201) 316-9200
90 Boroline Rd., Allendale 07401

LyondellBasell Industries
Phone—(973) 578-2200
300 Doremus Ave., Newark 07105

**Phibro-Tech, Inc.**
The Copper Chemical Company™
**Phone—(201) 329-7300 / (800) 357-6840**
**Fax—(201) 329-7035**
**Web—www.phibro-tech.com**
**Email—phibro-tech@pahc.com**
**300 Frank W. Burr Blvd., Ste. 21, Glenpointe Center East, 3rd Fl., Teaneck 07666**

PMC Group, Inc. (H Q)
Phone—(856) 533-1866
1288 Route 73, Mount Laurel 08054

Pride Solvents & Chemical Co.
Phone—(732) 499-0125
211 Randolph Ave., Avenel 07001

Sekisui America Corp. (H Q)
Phone—(201) 423-7960
333 Meadowlands Pkwy., 4th Fl., Secaucus 07094

Veckridge Chemical Co., Inc.
Phone—(973) 344-1818
60 Central Ave., Kearny 07032

## CHEMICALS — Inorganic

Elementis Chromium, Inc. (H Q)
Phone—(609) 443-2000
469 Old Trenton Rd., East Windsor 08512

General Chemical Corp.
Phone—(908) 464-1500
235 Snyder Ave., Berkeley Heights 07922

**Hummel Croton, Inc.**
**Phone—(908) 754-1800**
**Fax—(908) 754-1815**
**Web—www.hummelcroton.com**
**Email—sales@hummelcroton.com**
**10 Harmich Rd., South Plainfield 07080**
*(see our ad on this page)*

Madison Industries, Inc.
Phone—(732) 727-2225
554 Waterworks Rd., Old Bridge 08857

MORRE-TEC Industries, Inc.
Phone—(908) 688-9009
1 Gary Rd., Union 07083

Old Bridge Chemical, Inc.
Phone—(732) 727-2225
554 Waterworks Rd., Old Bridge 08857

## CHEMICALS — Laboratory

Fabric Chemical Corp.
Phone—(201) 432-0440
61 Cornelison Ave., Jersey City 07304

G.J. Chemical Co., Inc.
Phone—(973) 589-4176
128 Doremus Ave., Newark 07105

*find additional suppliers at*
**IndustryNet.com**

---

# Hummel Croton, Inc.
*Industrial Chemicals*
**www.hummelcroton.com**
**908-754-1800  FAX: 908-754-1815**
10 Harmich Rd.  South Plainfield, NJ 07080

**G.J. Chemical Co., Inc.**
An ISO 9001:2008 Registered Company
**Phone—(973) 589-1450**
**Fax—(732) 249-0082**
**Web—www.gjchemical.com**
**Email—marketing@gjchemical.com**
**40 Veronica Ave., Somerset 08873**
*(see our ads under CHEMICAL DISTRIBUTORS & CHEMICALS)*

**Seidler Chemical & Supply Co.**
Chemicals & Chemical Re-Packaging & Distribution
**Phone—(973) 465-1122**
**Fax—(973) 465-4469**
**Web—www.seidlerchem.com**
**Email—sales@seidlerchem.com**
**537 Raymond Blvd., Newark 07105**

Spectrum Chemical Mfg. Corp.
Phone—(732) 214-1300
769 Jersey Ave., New Brunswick 08901

## CHEMICALS — Oil Field

**Evans Chemetics LP (H Q)**
**Phone—(201) 992-3100**
**Fax—(201) 992-3101**
**Web—www.evans-chemetics.com**
**Email—info@evans-chemetics.com**
**500 Frank W. Burr Blvd., 4th Fl., Glenpointe Center West, Teaneck 07666**
*(see our ad under SULFUR)*

## CHEMICALS — Organic

**Evans Chemetics LP (H Q)**
**Phone—(201) 992-3100**
**Fax—(201) 992-3101**
**Web—www.evans-chemetics.com**
**Email—info@evans-chemetics.com**
**500 Frank W. Burr Blvd., 4th Fl., Glenpointe Center West, Teaneck 07666**
*(see our ad under SULFUR)*

**Hummel Croton, Inc.**
**Phone—(908) 754-1800**
**Fax—(908) 754-1815**
**Web—www.hummelcroton.com**
**Email—sales@hummelcroton.com**
**10 Harmich Rd., South Plainfield 07080**
*(see our ad on this page)*

## CHEMICALS — Pharmaceutical

Capsugel (H Q)
Phone—(862) 242-1700
412 Mount Kemble Ave., Ste. 200-C, Morristown 07960

Chemo Dynamics, Inc.
Phone—(732) 721-4700
3 Crossman Rd. S., Sayreville 08872

Cyalume Specialty Products
Phone—(732) 469-7760
100 W. Main St., P.O. Box 669, Bound Brook 08805

**Excellentia International**
**Phone—(732) 749-9840**
**Fax—(732) 200-3791**
**Web—www.excellentiaint.com**
**Email—info@excellentiaint.com**
**19 Progress St., Edison 08820**

---

**Noramco, Inc.**
Leading Supplier of Opiate-Derived API; 2 U.S. Manufacturing Locations
**Phone—(302) 761-2909 / (302) 761-2940**
**Fax—(302) 761-2913**
**Web—www.noramco.com**
**Email—noramcoAPI@its.jnj.com**
**500 Swedes Landing Rd., Wilmington, DE 19801**

Sabinsa Corp.
Phone—(732) 777-1111
20 Lake Dr., East Windsor 08520

**Seidler Chemical & Supply Co.**
Chemicals & Chemical Re-Packaging & Distribution
**Phone—(973) 465-1122**
**Fax—(973) 465-4469**
**Web—www.seidlerchem.com**
**Email—sales@seidlerchem.com**
**537 Raymond Blvd., Newark 07105**

**Siegfried USA, LLC**
We develop & produce active pharmaceutical substances
**Phone—(856) 678-3601 / (877) 763-8630**
**Fax—(856) 678-4008**
**Web—www.siegfried-usa.com**
**Email—rita.vaneck@siegfried-usa.com**
**33 Industrial Park Rd., Pennsville 08070**
*(see our ad under PHARMACEUTICALS)*

## CHEMICALS — Plating

**Seidler Chemical & Supply Co.**
Chemicals & Chemical Re-Packaging & Distribution
**Phone—(973) 465-1122**
**Fax—(973) 465-4469**
**Web—www.seidlerchem.com**
**Email—sales@seidlerchem.com**
**537 Raymond Blvd., Newark 07105**

Surface Technology, Inc.
Phone—(609) 259-0099
105 N. Gold Dr., Robbinsville 08691

## CHEMICALS — Reagent

Cooper Chemical Co.
Phone—(908) 876-3231
20 Parker Rd., Long Valley 07853

**G.J. Chemical Co., Inc.**
An ISO 9001:2008 Registered Company
**Phone—(973) 589-1450**
**Fax—(732) 249-0082**
**Web—www.gjchemical.com**
**Email—marketing@gjchemical.com**
**40 Veronica Ave., Somerset 08873**
*(see our ads under CHEMICAL DISTRIBUTORS & CHEMICALS)*

Plenum Scientific Research, Inc.
Phone—(201) 489-2771
210 Lee Pl., Hackensack 07601

**Seidler Chemical & Supply Co.**
Chemicals & Chemical Re-Packaging & Distribution
**Phone—(973) 465-1122**
**Fax—(973) 465-4469**
**Web—www.seidlerchem.com**
**Email—sales@seidlerchem.com**
**537 Raymond Blvd., Newark 07105**

*Search from among 430,000 U.S. manufacturers & suppliers:*
**IndustryNet.com**

## CHEMICALS — Reagent — (cont.)

**SPEX CertiPrep, Inc.**
**Toll Free 800-LAB-SPEX; Organic & Inorganic**
**Certified Reference Materials**
**Phone—(732) 549-7144 / (800) 522-7739**
**Fax—(732) 603-9647**
**Web—www.spexcertiprep.com**
**Email—crmsales@spexcsp.com**
**203 Norcross Ave., Metuchen 08840**

## CHEMICALS — Rubber Makers'

Technical Processing, Inc.
Phone—(973) 278-4950
81 Dale Ave., Paterson 07501

## CHEMICALS — Specialty

Adam, Gates & Co., LLC
Phone—(908) 829-3386
249 Homestead Rd., Hillsborough 08844
Ajinomoto North America, Inc. (H Q)
Phone—(201) 292-3200
400 Kelby St., Ste. 18, Fort Lee 07024
Ashland, Inc.
Phone—(973) 635-1551
116 Summit Ave., Chatham 07928
Ashland, Inc., International Specialty Products (H Q)
Phone—(973) 533-5400
56 Livingston Ave., Ste. 400, Roseland 07068
Cytec Industries, Inc. (H Q)
Phone—(973) 357-3100
5 Garret Mountain Plz., Woodland Park 07424
**Deltech Resin Co.**
**Phone—(973) 589-0880 / (973) 589-3331**
**(800) 785-4415**
**Fax—(973) 589-7231**
**Web—www.deltechcorp.com**
**Email—danderson@deltechresins.com**
**49 Rutherford St., Newark 07105**
*(see our ad under RESINS)*
Elementis Specialties, Inc.
Phone—(201) 395-5108
400 Claremont Ave., Jersey City 07304
**Evans Chemetics LP (H Q)**
**Phone—(201) 992-3100**
**Fax—(201) 992-3101**
**Web—www.evans-chemetics.com**
**Email—info@evans-chemetics.com**
**500 Frank W. Burr Blvd., 4th Fl., Glenpointe**
**Center West, Teaneck 07666**
*(see our ad under SULFUR)*
FUJIFILM Hunt Chemicals U.S.A., Inc. (H Q)
Phone—(201) 995-2200
40 Boroline Rd., Allendale 07401
GP Chemicals, Inc. (H Q)
Phone—(201) 869-2200
7225 Bergenline Ave., North Bergen 07047
Industrial Water Technologies, Inc.
Phone—(732) 888-1233
6 Village Ct., Hazlet 07730
**Innovative Resin Systems, Inc.**
**Emails: spatel@rez-cure.com & manny@rez-**
**cure.com**
**Structural adhesives, coatings, pottings &**
**encapsulating compounds**
**Phone—(973) 465-6887**
**Fax—(973) 465-0592**
**Web—www.rez-cure.com**
**257 Wilson Ave., Newark 07105**
*(see our ad under ADHESIVES)*
Jarchem Industries, Inc.
Phone—(973) 344-0600
414 Wilson Ave., Newark 07105
Johnson Matthey, Inc.
Phone—(856) 384-7000
2001 Nolte Dr., West Deptford 08066
OMG Electronic Chemicals, LLC
Phone—(908) 222-5800
400 Corporate Ct., Ste. A, South Plainfield 07080
Pflaumer Bros.
Phone—(609) 883-4610
1008 Whitehead Road Ext., Ewing 08638

**Phibro-Tech, Inc.**
**The Copper Chemical Company™**
**Phone—(201) 329-7300 / (800) 357-6840**
**Fax—(201) 329-7035**
**Web—www.phibro-tech.com**
**Email—phibro-tech@pahc.com**
**300 Frank W. Burr Blvd., Ste. 21, Glenpointe**
**Center East, 3rd Fl., Teaneck 07666**
Solvay U. S. A., Inc.
Phone—(609) 860-4000
8 Cedar Brook Dr., CN-7500, Cranbury 08512
Thermo Fisher Scientific
Phone—(908) 526-1800
755 U.S. Highway 202, Bridgewater 08807
Tyger Scientific, Inc.
Phone—(609) 434-0144
324 Stokes Ave., Ewing 08638

## CHEMICALS — Textile

Arol Chemical Products Co.
Phone—(973) 344-1510
649 Ferry St., Newark 07105
Grant Industries, Inc.
Phone—(201) 791-6700
125 Main Ave., Elmwood Park 07407

## CHEMICALS — Wholesale

**G.J. Chemical Co., Inc.**
**An ISO 9001:2008 Registered Company**
**Phone—(973) 589-1450**
**Fax—(732) 249-0082**
**Web—www.gjchemical.com**
**Email—marketing@gjchemical.com**
**40 Veronica Ave., Somerset 08873**
*(see our ads under CHEMICAL DISTRIBUTORS &*
*CHEMICALS)*
Thermo Fisher Scientific Inc.
Phone—(201) 796-7100
1 Reagent Ln., Fair Lawn 07410

## CHILD CARE ACCESSORIES

Childcare Supply Co. Inc.
Phone—(732) 786-9888
77 Pension Rd., Ste. 13, Englishtown 07726

## CHILLERS

**Warwick Mfg. & Equipment Co., LLC**
**Buy & sell used: Chemical, food, cosmetic, packaging**
**& pharmaceutical equipment**
**Phone—(732) 729-0400 / (732) 241-9263**
**Fax—(732) 729-1235**
**Web—www.warwickequipment.com**
**Email—sales@warwickequipment.com**
**1112 12th St., North Brunswick 08902**
*(see our ad Outside Back Cover)*

## CHIMNEY MAINTENANCE & REPAIR

**David The Village Sweep**
**Phone—(908) 756-1807**
**Fax—(908) 325-1807**
**Web—www.villagesweepnj.com**
**651 Jerusalem Rd., Scotch Plains 07076**

## CHINA

CAC International
Phone—(973) 371-4300
30 Camptown Rd., Maplewood 07040
Nikko Ceramics, Inc.
Phone—(201) 840-5200
815 Fairview Ave., Ste. 9, Fairview 07022

## CHOCOLATE PRODUCTS

Barry Callebaut USA, LLC
Phone—(856) 663-2260
1500 Suckle Hwy., Pennsauken 08110
Cocoa Processing Corp.
Phone—(201) 792-5866
650 Ramsey Ave., Hillside 07205

Conrad's Confectionery, Inc.
Phone—(201) 664-2895
107 Westwood Ave., Westwood 07675
Ferrero U.S.A., Inc.
Phone—(732) 764-9300
600 Cottontail Ln., Somerset 08873
J. Emanuel Chocolatier
Phone—(908) 955-7591
461-B Main St., Chester 07930
Krause Candy, Inc., Mrs. Hanna
Phone—(201) 843-0337
89 Westview Ave., Paramus 07652
Mecca & Sons Trucking Corp. (H Q)
Phone—(201) 792-5866
580 Luis Munoz Marin Blvd., Jersey City 07310
Nouveautes, Inc.
Phone—(973) 882-8850
70 Clinton Rd., Fairfield 07004
Savita Naturals Ltd.
Phone—(856) 467-4949
617 Heron Dr., Swedesboro 08085
Van Holten's Homemade Candy, Inc.
Phone—(732) 840-0888
1893 Route 88, Brick 08724

## CHOKES

**Metal Associates, Inc.**
**Phone—(973) 835-8480 / (800) 838-1978**
**Fax—(973) 835-7981**
**Web—www.metalassociates.com**
**Email—metals@rcn.com**
**230 W. Parkway, Unit 3-2, Pompton Plains**
**07444**

## CHRISTMAS DECORATIONS

Garden State Foliage, LLC
Phone—(732) 751-0075
600 Central Ave., Farmingdale 07727

## CHRISTMAS TREES — Artificial

National Christmas Products
Phone—(908) 709-4141
2 Commerce Dr., Cranford 07016

## CHROMATOGRAPHIC EQUIPMENT

ES Industries
Phone—(856) 753-8400
701 S. Route 73, West Berlin 08091
Princeton Chromatography, Inc.
Phone—(609) 860-1803
1206 Cranbury-S. River Rd., Cranbury 08512
Sonntek, Inc.
Phone—(201) 236-9300
125 Pleasant Ave., Upper Saddle River 07458

## CIGARETTES

Eonsmoke, LLC (H Q)
Phone—(800) 616-3711
1500 Main Ave., Ste. 2, Clifton 07011
United Candy & Tobacco Co.
Phone—(201) 943-8675
7408 Tonnelle Ave., North Bergen 07047

## CIGARS

Zucca, Inc., L. J.
Phone—(856) 692-7425
760 S. Delsea Dr., P.O. Box 1447, Vineland 08362

## CIRCUIT BOARDS

Altior
Phone—(732) 440-1280
444 Route 35 S., Bldg. B, Eatontown 07724
Thomas Instrumentation, Inc.
Phone—(609) 624-7777
118 Kings Hwy., Cape May Court House 08210

*Do nationwide searches for products & services at:*
**IndustryNet.com**

*find additional suppliers at*
**IndustryNet.com**

## CIRCUIT BREAKERS

**Cuny & Guerber, Inc.**
Special counter available for contractors
**Phone—(201) 617-5800**
**Fax—(201) 617-5557**
**Web—www.cuny.biz**
**Email—sales@cuny.biz**
**2100 Kerrigan Ave., P.O. Box 1192, Union City 07087**
*(see our ad under ELECTRICAL EQUIPMENT AND SUPPLIES — Wholesale)*

Federal Pacific Equipment, Inc.
Phone—(732) 840-4800
1133 Industrial Pkwy., Ste. A, Brick 08724

Snap Action, Inc.
Phone—(908) 654-4380
1260 Route 22 W., Mountainside 07092

## CIRCUITS — Integrated

Anadigics, Inc.
Phone—(908) 668-5000
141 Mount Bethel Rd., Warren 07059

## CLAMPS

Behringer Corp.
Phone—(973) 948-0226
17 Ridge Rd., Branchville 07826

**BRECOflex Co., L.L.C.**
**Phone—(732) 460-9500 / (888) 463-1400**
**Fax—(732) 542-6725**
**Web—www.brecoflex.com**
**Email—info@brecoflex.com**
**222 Industrial Way W., Eatontown 07724**
*(see our ads under BELTING & PULLEYS)*

Stauff Corp.
Phone—(201) 444-7800
7 William Demarest Pl., Waldwick 07463

## CLAY PRODUCTS

**(also see 'Refractories')**

Chavant, Inc.
Phone—(732) 751-0003
5043 Industrial Rd., Farmingdale 07727

Sculpture House, Inc.
Phone—(609) 466-2986
405 Skillman Rd., P.O. Box 69, Skillman 08558

## CLEANERS

International Products Corp.
Phone—(609) 386-8770
201 Connecticut Dr., Burlington 08016

## CLEANERS — Household

**Brenntag Specialties, Inc.**
**Phone—(908) 561-6100 / (800) 732-0562**
**Fax—(800) 543-1484**
**Web—www.brenntagspecialties.com**
**Email—specialties@brenntag.com**
**1000 Coolidge St., South Plainfield 07080**
*(see our ad under CHEMICAL DISTRIBUTORS)*

Church & Dwight Co., Inc. (H Q)
Phone—(609) 683-5900
500 Charles Ewing Blvd., Ewing 08628

Edwards Creative Products, Inc.
Phone—(856) 665-3200
910 Beechwood Ave., Cherry Hill 08002

**Housechem, A Div. of Menshen Packaging U.S.A., Inc.**
**Phone—(201) 445-8808**
**Fax—(201) 445-2810**
**Web—www.housechem.com**
**Email—info@housechem.com**
**25 Industrial Park, Waldwick 07463**

Stanson Corp.
Phone—(973) 344-8666
2 N. Hackensack Ave., Kearny 07032

## CLEANERS — Industrial

Ultra Clean Technologies Corp.
Phone—(856) 451-2176
1274 Highway 77, Bridgeton 08302

## CLEANING COMPOUNDS

Advanced Safety Products, Inc.
Phone—(856) 691-1700
37 S. Valley Ave., Vineland 08360

Cadie Products Corp.
Phone—(973) 278-8300
151 E. 11th St., Paterson 07524

Chemique, Inc.
Phone—(856) 235-4161
315 N. Washington Ave., Moorestown 08057

Earth Friendly Products, Inc.
Phone—(201) 750-7701
380 Chestnut St., Norwood 07648

Epic Industries
Phone—(732) 249-6867
1007 Jersey Ave., New Brunswick 08901

Housechem, A Div. of Menshen Packaging U.S.A., Inc.
Phone—(201) 445-8808
25 Industrial Park, Waldwick 07463

**InventeK Colloidal Cleaners, LLC (USA)**
Colloidal Cleaners for EVERY CLEANING NEED.
Degreasers, Carpet Cleaners
**Phone—(856) 206-0058**
**Fax—(856) 206-0094**
**Web—www.inventekcleaners.com**
**Email—info@inventekcleaners.com**
**106 Gaither Dr., Mount Laurel 08054**

---

**InventeK Colloidal Cleaners, LLC (USA)**
*Colloidal Cleaners for EVERY CLEANING NEED.*
*Degreasers, Carpet Cleaners*
**(856) 206-0058**
**www.inventekcleaners.com**
106 Gaither Dr. • Mount Laurel, NJ 08054

---

Penetone Corp. (H Q)
Phone—(609) 921-0501
1000 Herrontown Rd., Ste. 2, Princeton 08540

Petronio Shoe Products Corp.
Phone—(973) 751-7579
305 Cortlandt St., Belleville 07109

Swisher Hygiene Inc.
Phone—(800) 221-0806
1805 Lower Rd., Linden 07036

## CLEANING COMPOUNDS — Automobile

Consolidated Chemex Corp.
Phone—(732) 828-7676
235 Jersey Ave., New Brunswick 08901

## CLEANING COMPOUNDS — Environmental

InventeK Colloidal Cleaners, LLC (USA)
Colloidal Cleaners for EVERY CLEANING NEED.
Degreasers, Carpet Cleaners
Phone—(856) 206-0058
Fax—(856) 206-0094
Web—www.inventekcleaners.com
Email—info@inventekcleaners.com
106 Gaither Dr., Mount Laurel 08054
*(see our ad under CLEANING COMPOUNDS)*

## CLEANING COMPOUNDS — Industrial

Federal Mining & Mfg. Co.
Phone—(908) 241-9355
288 E. 12th Ave., Roselle 07203

**Fine Organics Corp.**
Email: fosales@aol.com
Since 1939, manufacturing organic chemical intermediaries and specialty chemicals for transportation, manufacturing, printing, metalworking, aviation, power utilities, automotive & electronics
**Phone—(973) 478-1000**
**Fax—(973) 478-6120**
**Web—www.fineorganicscorp.com**
**420 Kuller Rd., P.O. Box 2277, Clifton 07015**

Foster & Co., Inc.
Phone—(973) 267-4100
15 Wing Dr., Cedar Knolls 07927

Global Specialty Products USA, Inc.
Phone—(609) 518-7577
10 Eagle Ave., Ste. 500, Mount Holly 08060

**InventeK Colloidal Cleaners, LLC (USA)**
Colloidal Cleaners for EVERY CLEANING NEED.
Degreasers, Carpet Cleaners
**Phone—(856) 206-0058**
**Fax—(856) 206-0094**
**Web—www.inventekcleaners.com**
**Email—info@inventekcleaners.com**
**106 Gaither Dr., Mount Laurel 08054**
*(see our ad under CLEANING COMPOUNDS)*

Pariser Industries, Inc.
Phone—(973) 569-9090
91 Michigan Ave., Paterson 07503

Penetone Corp.
Phone—(201) 567-3000
700 Gotham Pkwy., Ste. 2, Carlstadt 07072

## CLEANING COMPOUNDS — Pipe & Drain

Trap-Zap Environmental Systems, Inc.
Phone—(201) 251-9970
255 Braen Ave., Wyckoff 07481

## CLEANING COMPOUNDS — Wholesale

Bio-Ox International, Inc.
Phone—(732) 650-9779
140 Ethel Rd. W., Ste. U, Piscataway 08854

## CLEANING EQUIPMENT — Industrial

FCS Fluidaire Cleaning Services, Inc.
Phone—(732) 964-1700
11 Industrial Dr., New Brunswick 08901

Plasmatic Systems, Inc.
Phone—(732) 297-9107
1327 Aaron Rd., North Brunswick 08902

**Taylor Northeast**
Providing of a broad range of services for Material Handling & Industrial Cleaning Equipment in the eastern-PA area since 1985. Services range from new & used lift truck sales, leasing & rentals to service, parts & remanufacturing
**Phone—(610) 286-8080 / (800) 762-2500**
**Fax—(610) 286-8099**
**Web—www.taylornortheast.com**
**Email—kkoch@taylornortheast.com**
**931 Hemlock Rd., Morgantown, PA 19543**

## CLEANING SERVICES

**Barbara's Homecare Inc.**
**Phone—(973) 748-4761**
**Fax—(973) 748-2944**
**Web—www.barbarashomecare.com**
**Email—barbarashomecare@comcast.net**
**23 Pitt St., Bloomfield 07003**

**Foulke Family Property Services**
**Phone—(609) 722-3409**
**6308 Palmer Ave., Mays Landing 08330**

## CLEANING SUPPLIES

Arden Sales
Phone—(732) 730-1418
128 14th St., Lakewood 08701

Reckitt Benckiser, LLC
Phone—(908) 533-2000
799 U.S. Highway 206, P.O. Box 5817, Hillsborough 08844

## CLEANING SYSTEMS — High Pressure

Firehawk Industries, LLC
Phone—(609) 393-0007
309 N. Willow St., Trenton 08618

## CLEANING SYSTEMS — Industrial

Applied Surface Technologies
Phone—(908) 464-6675
15 Hawthorne Dr., New Providence 07974

## CLEANROOM EQUIPMENT

CleanZones, LLC
Phone—(732) 534-5590
640 Herman Rd., Ste. 2, Jackson 08527

## CLIPS

J.R.M. Products, Inc.
Phone—(732) 495-3092
701 Locust St., Keyport 07735

## CLOCKS

Arcadian Clock Co.
Phone—(908) 276-0276
189 North Ave. E., Cranford 07016
Garrett Clocks
Phone—(908) 231-9231
35 N. Middaugh St., Unit 3-C, Somerville 08876

## CLOSETS

California Closet Co.
Phone—(609) 655-1899
2666 U.S. Highway 130, Cranbury 08512
California Closets
Phone—(973) 882-3800
4 Gardner Rd., Ste. 5, Fairfield 07004
Closet Butler
Phone—(973) 729-9222
3 Spielman Rd., Fairfield 07004
Closettech
Phone—(732) 792-0088
203 Woodward Rd., Englishtown 07726
Direct Cabinet Sales
Phone—(732) 382-8080
265 Central Ave., Clark 07066
Sophisticated Storage Solutions, LLC
Phone—(732) 356-4200
7-W Chimney Rock Rd., Bridgewater 08807

## CLOSURES — Plastic

Stull Technologies, Inc.
Phone—(732) 873-5000
17 Veronica Ave., Somerset 08873

## CLOTHING

Bethel Industries, Inc.
Phone—(201) 656-8222
3423 John F. Kennedy Blvd., Jersey City 07307
Black Universities Supply Shop, The
Phone—(908) 754-8088
410 Leland Ave., Plainfield 07062
Gold Attachments Sewing Supply, Inc.
Phone—(201) 854-0320
7051 Kennedy Blvd., North Bergen 07047
Knick-Knack, Inc.
Phone—(201) 727-9339
20 Henry St., Teterboro 07608
Link Theory
Phone—(201) 728-5700
165 Polito Ave., Lyndhurst 07071
Monarch Towel Co., Inc.
Phone—(732) 442-0442
737 Cortlandt St., Perth Amboy 08861
Onwards, Inc. (H Q)
Phone—(732) 309-7348
10 Connor Dr., Manalapan 07726
Schott Bros., Inc.
Phone—(908) 527-0011
735 Rahway Ave., Union 07083
Unicor Federal Prison Industries, Inc.
Phone—(609) 723-1100
5835 Doughboy Loop, P.O. Box 38, Fort Dix 08640

## CLOTHING — Bridal

Gibson Designs, Inc., Kathy
Phone—(201) 420-0088
1416 Willow Ave., Hoboken 07030
Merry Modes 2000
Phone—(973) 773-2501
61 Willet St., Ste. 2, Passaic 07055
Textiles By Anthony, Inc.
Phone—(973) 773-2501
61 Willett St., Bldg. 12, 2nd Fl., Passaic 07055

## CLOTHING — Children's & Infants'

8 To 20 Partners, LLC
Phone—(732) 855-1400
5 Paddock St., Avenel 07001
Carter Co., The William
Phone—(201) 313-1783
17 The Promenade, Edgewater 07020
Celebrity International, Inc. (H Q)
Phone—(732) 476-2999
51 Saw Mill Pond Rd., Edison 08817
Children's Apparel Network Ltd.
Phone—(908) 351-4477
77 S. 1st St., Elizabeth 07206
Franco Apparel Group
Phone—(732) 438-5170
231 Docks Corner Rd., Dayton 08810
LT Apparel Group
Phone—(732) 438-5500
301 Herrod Blvd., P.O. Box 1001, Dayton 08810
Miller, LLC, Sally (H Q)
Phone—(732) 729-4840
30 N. Main St., Milltown 08850
Nano's, LLC
Phone—(973) 616-1515
22 Park Pl., P.O. Box 41, Butler 07405

## CLOTHING — Fur

Lea Furs, Inc. Ltd.
Phone—(201) 444-5554
45 S. Broad St., Ridgewood 07450

## CLOTHING — Knit

Artex Knitting Mills, Inc.
Phone—(856) 456-2800
300 Harvard Ave., P.O. Box 183, Westville 08093

## CLOTHING — Leather

Cockpit USA, Inc.
Phone—(908) 558-9704
725 New Point Rd., Elizabeth 07201
Unik International, Inc.
Phone—(201) 531-1777
40 Triangle Blvd., Carlstadt 07072

## CLOTHING — Maternity

Lilo Maternity, LLC
Phone—(732) 370-5456
1526 Laguna Ln., Lakewood 08701

## CLOTHING — Men's

Cleve Shirtmakers, Inc. (H Q)
Phone—(201) 825-6122
P.O. Box 678, Saddle River 07458
Ermenegildo Zegna Corp. (H Q)
Phone—(201) 816-0921
100 W. Forest Ave., Ste. A, Englewood 07631
Fabian Couture Group International
Phone—(201) 460-7776
205 Chubb Ave., Ste. 1, Lyndhurst 07071
Jade Eastern Trading, Inc.
Phone—(201) 440-8500
245 Moonachie Rd., Moonachie 07074
Merc USA, Inc.
Phone—(201) 489-3527
41 Newman St., Hackensack 07601
Omavi Clothing Co. (H Q)
Phone—(973) 642-2000
701-703 McCarter Hwy., Ste. 102, Newark 07102

Shelton, LLC, Todd
Phone—(551) 655-4106
450 Murray Hill Pkwy., Ste. C-2, East Rutherford 07073

## CLOTHING — Protective

Ansell Healthcare Products, LLC (H Q)
Ansell Protects
Phone—(732) 345-5400 / (800) 800-0444
Fax—(732) 219-5114
Web—www.ansell.com
Email—info@ansell.com
111 Wood Ave. S., Ste. 210, Iselin 08830

**Ansell**

**Ansell Healthcare Products, LLC**
**(732) 345-5400**
*www.ansell.com*
111 Wood Ave. S., Ste. 210, Iselin, NJ 08830

## CLOTHING — Religious

Church Vestment Mfg. Co., Inc.
Phone—(973) 942-2833
41-43 Paterson Ave., Paterson 07522
Gaiser, Inc., Robert F.
Phone—(973) 838-0696
292 Main St., P.O. Box 807, Butler 07405
Peach Boutique, The
Phone—(908) 351-0739
1139 E. Jersey St., Ste. 319, Elizabeth 07201

## CLOTHING — Safety

Loveline Industries, Inc.
Phone—(973) 928-3427
90 Dayton Ave., Ste. 33, Passaic 07055

## CLOTHING — Sports

Aladen Athletic Wear, LLC
Phone—(973) 838-2425
53 Cannonball Rd., Pompton Lakes 07442
United Sport Apparel
Phone—(973) 575-7840
20 Gloria Ln., Fairfield 07004

## CLOTHING — Women's

Attitudes In Dressing, Inc.
Phone—(908) 354-7218
107 Trumbull St., Bldg. B-8, Elizabeth 07206
Calvaruso Clothing, G. & F.
Phone—(201) 945-7118
345 Palisade Ave., Cliffside Park 07010
CS Apparel, Inc. (H Q)
Phone—(732) 906-9666
3910 Park Ave., Ste. 2, Edison 08820
Jackie Evans, Inc.
Phone—(973) 471-6991
1823 3rd St., Passaic 07055
Jump Apparel
Phone—(201) 558-9191
350 Secaucus Rd., Secaucus 07094
M&S Canada Corp.
Phone—(732) 901-6636
8 Arosa Hill, Lakewood 08701
Metropolitan Mfg., Inc.
Phone—(201) 933-8111
450 Murray Hill Pkwy., East Rutherford 07073
RAZA-Designs, Inc.
Phone—(201) 430-8590
220 61st St., Ste. 2-C, West New York 07093
Silkhouse International, Inc.
Phone—(201) 945-4569
28 Garden Pl., Ste. 128, Edgewater 07020
Swisstex Co.
Phone—(201) 861-8000
220 61st St., 2nd Fl., West New York 07093

## CLOTHING — Women's — (cont.)

Zaralo, LLC
Phone—(862) 902-5220
Fax—(862) 902-5291
1 Cape May St., Harrison 07029

## CLUTCHES

Electroid Co.
Phone—(973) 467-8100
45 Fadem Rd., Springfield 07081

## CLUTCHES — Industrial

Ogura Industrial Corp.
Phone—(732) 271-7361
100 Randolph Rd., 2nd Fl., Somerset 08873

## COAL — Anthracite

Transition Metals Technology
Phone—(856) 468-6747
314 N. West Ave., Wenonah 08090

## COATING MACHINERY

Kraemer Koating, Inc.
Phone—(732) 886-6315
1925 Swarthmore Ave., Lakewood 08701
New Era Converting Machinery
Phone—(201) 670-4848
235 Route 20, Paterson 07504

## COATING SERVICES — Industrial

Majestic Optical Coatings
Phone—(732) 388-5604
152 Willow Way, Clark 07066

## COATINGS

ACTEGA Kelstar, Inc.
Phone—(856) 829-6300
950 S. Chester Ave., Ste. B-2, Delran 08075
ALT Global, LLC
Phone—(973) 287-6158
3 Edison Pl., Ste. 2, Fairfield 07004
**American Chemical & Adhesive LLC**
**Phone—(908) 353-2260**
**Fax—(908) 353-3641**
**Email—qzaman17@yahoo.com**
**410 Division St., Elizabeth 07201**
Chris Industries, Inc.
Phone—(732) 431-1800
98 Industrial Ct., Freehold 07728
COTE-L Industries, Inc.
Phone—(201) 836-0733
1542 Jefferson St., Teaneck 07666
Hydromer, Inc.
Phone—(908) 722-5000
35 Industrial Pkwy., Branchburg 08876
**Innovative Resin Systems, Inc.**
**Emails: spatel@rez-cure.com & manny@rez-cure.com**
**Structural adhesives, coatings, pottings & encapsulating compounds**
**Phone—(973) 465-6887**
**Fax—(973) 465-0592**
**Web—www.rez-cure.com**
**257 Wilson Ave., Newark 07105**
*(see our ad under ADHESIVES)*
Kefa Northeast
Phone—(201) 664-5487
P.O. Box 88, Budd Lake 07828
**Master Bond, Inc.**
**Manufacturer of custom formulated adhesives for advanced applications**
**Phone—(201) 343-8983**
**Fax—(201) 343-2132**
**Web—www.masterbond.com**
**Email—main@masterbond.com**
**154 Hobart St., Hackensack 07601**
*(see our ad under ADHESIVES)*
Monster Coatings, Inc.
Phone—(973) 983-7662
306-A Capitol St., Saddle Brook 07663
Norton & Son, Inc.
Phone—(201) 437-0770
148 E. 5th St., Bayonne 07002

**Peerless Coatings, LLC**
**Providing Powder Coating, Sandblasting, Assembling & Packaging Services, Teflon® finishes along with Traditional Wet Paint finishes, and all types of Metalizing.**
**Phone—(973) 427-8771**
**Fax—(973) 427-8779**
**Web—www.peerlesscoatings.com**
**Email—peerless1@verizon.net**
**220-A Goffle Rd., Hawthorne 07506**
Quantum Coating, Inc.
Phone—(856) 231-0706
1259 N. Church St., Bldg. 1, Moorestown 08057
Spray Coat Finishing Co., Inc.
Phone—(856) 541-0950
1125 Kaighn Ave., Camden 08103
Thermo Cote, Inc.
Phone—(973) 464-3575
198 Green Pond Rd., Ste. 5, Rockaway 07866
Verseidag Seemee US, Inc. (H Q)
Phone—(973) 252-1189
4 Aspen Dr., Randolph 07869
Vertellus Performance Materials, Inc.
Phone—(201) 858-8810
40 Avenue A, Bayonne 07002

## COATINGS — Ceramic

Ceronics, Inc.
Phone—(732) 566-5600
5 Dock St., P.O. Box 75, Matawan 07747
IHI Ionbond
Phone—(973) 586-4700
200 Roundhill Dr., Rockaway 07866

## COATINGS — Conductive

Antistatic Industries, A Div. of ADM Tronics, Inc.
Phone—(201) 767-6040
224 Pegasus Ave., Northvale 07647

## COATINGS — Industrial

Seagrave Coatings Corp.
Phone—(201) 933-1000
209 N. Michigan Ave., Kenilworth 07033

## COATINGS — Protective

Andek Corporation
Phone—(856) 786-6900
850 Glen Ave., P.O. Box 392, Moorestown 08057
Biosearch Medical Products, Inc.
Phone—(908) 722-5000
35 Industrial Pkwy., Branchburg 08876
General Plastics Corp.
Phone—(973) 748-5500
55 La France Ave., Bloomfield 07003

## COATINGS — Specialty

InMat Inc.
Phone—(908) 874-7788
216 U.S. Highway 206, Ste. 7, Hillsborough 08844
Jema-American, Inc.
Phone—(732) 968-5333
824 South Ave., Middlesex 08846
Meadowbrook Inventions, Inc.
Phone—(908) 766-0606
260 Mine Brook Rd., P.O. Box 960, Bernardsville 07924

## COATINGS — Teflon®

**(Teflon® is a registered trademark of DuPont)**
Plastics Consulting & Mfg. Co.
Phone—(856) 963-7700
1431 Ferry Ave., Camden 08104

## COATINGS — Textile

The CLI Group
Phone—(973) 279-9174
932 Market St., Paterson 07513

*Search from among 430,000 U.S. manufacturers & suppliers:*
**IndustryNet.com**

## COATINGS — Thermal Spray

A & A Co., Inc.
Phone—(908) 561-2378
2700 S. Clinton Ave., South Plainfield 07080
Parkway-Kew Corp.
Phone—(732) 398-2100
2095 Excelsior Ave., North Brunswick 08902
Safas Corp.
Phone—(973) 772-5252
2 Ackerman Ave., Clifton 07011

## COATINGS — Thin Film

Thinfilms, Inc.
Phone—(908) 359-7014
15 Ilene Ct., Ste. 6, Hillsborough 08844

## COATS — Fur

Antonovich Furs, Inc.
Phone—(973) 785-0077
125 Route 46 W., Totowa 07512
Blaustein, Inc., M.
Phone—(973) 379-1080
516 Millburn Ave., Short Hills 07078

## COCONUT PRODUCTS

CNS Confectionery Products, LLC
Phone—(201) 823-1400
33 Hook Rd., Bayonne 07002
International Coconut Corp.
Phone—(908) 289-1555
225 W. Grand St., Elizabeth 07202

## CODE DATING EQUIPMENT

Bell-Mark Sales Co., Inc.
Phone—(973) 882-0202
331 Changebridge Rd., P.O. Box 2007, Pine Brook 07058
Carteret Coding, Inc.
Phone—(732) 574-0900
1431 Raritan Rd., Clark 07066

## COFFEE — Wholesale

Kaffe Magnum Opus
Phone—(856) 327-9962
500 S. Wade Blvd., Millville 08332

## COFFEE ROASTING & PACKING

Caffe Borbone USA
Phone—(973) 227-7799
19 Commerce Rd., Ste. G, Fairfield 07004
Coffee Assocs., Inc.
Phone—(201) 945-1060
178 Old River Rd., P.O. Box 240, Edgewater 07020
Coffee Co., LLC, The
Phone—(609) 399-5533
928 Boardwalk, Ocean City 08226
Corim Industries
Phone—(732) 840-1670
1112 Industrial Pkwy., Brick 08724
Greene Bros. Specialty Coffee Roasters, Inc.
Phone—(908) 979-0022
313 High St., Hackettstown 07840
Jersey Shore Coffee Roasters, LLC
Phone—(732) 291-0505
64 Thompson Ave., Ste. B, Leonardo 07737
Kobrick Coffee Co., Inc.
Phone—(201) 656-6313
693 Luis Marin Blvd., Jersey City 07310
La Sierra Coffee Roasters, LLC
Phone—(973) 927-9595
42 Bartley Rd., Flanders 07836
Lacas Coffee Co.
Phone—(856) 910-8662
7950 National Hwy., Pennsauken 08110
Melitta U. S. A.
Phone—(856) 428-7202
1401 Berlin Rd., Cherry Hill 08034
Nestle' USA, Inc., Beverage Div.
Phone—(732) 462-1300
61 Jerseyville Ave., Freehold 07728

## COFFEE ROASTING & PACKING
### — (cont.)

Pan American Coffee Co., LLC
Phone—(201) 963-2329
500 16th St., Hoboken 07030
Tata Global Beverages (H Q)
Phone—(201) 571-0300
155 Chestnut Ridge Rd., 2nd Fl., Montvale 07645
W.B. Law & Son, Inc.
Phone—(973) 344-2270
280 Wilson Ave., Unit B, Newark 07105

## COLLECTION AGENCIES

**Abrams, Davis & Keller, Inc.**
Phone—(973) 895-4700
Fax—(973) 895-4702
Web—www.adkcollections.com
Email—markg@adkcollections.com
1201 Sussex Tpke., Randolph 07869
**Grip Collection Services**
Phone—(908) 755-1595
963 Park Ave., Apt. 1, Plainfield 07060
**Kramer & Assocs.**
Phone—(201) 968-0327
Fax—(201) 646-0060
Web—www.kramercollects.com
Email—info@kramercollects.com
401 Hackensack Ave., 9th Fl., Hackensack 07601
**Nationwide Tracers**
Phone—(732) 974-9710
P.O. Box 257, Spring Lake 07762

## COLOR CONCENTRATES

Breen Color Concentrates, Inc.
Phone—(609) 397-8200
11 Kari Dr., Lambertville 08530
IFC Solutions
Phone—(908) 862-8810
1601 E. Linden Ave., Linden 07036

## COLOR SEPARATIONS

New Life Color Reproduction, Inc.
Phone—(201) 943-7005
610 Broad Ave., Ridgefield 07657
Pressto Graphics, Inc.
Phone—(732) 286-9300
467 Lakehurst Rd., P.O. Box 467, Toms River 08755

## COLOR STANDARDS

**Pantone LLC**
Phone—(201) 935-5500 / (888) 726-8663
Fax—(201) 896-0242
Web—www.pantone.com
590 Commerce Blvd., Carlstadt 07072

## COLORANTS FOR PLASTICS

Colorco, Inc.
Phone—(908) 862-3010
1261 W. Elizabeth Ave., Linden 07036
Riverdale Color Mfg., Inc.
Phone—(732) 376-9300
1 Walnut St., Perth Amboy 08861

## COLORS & PIGMENTS

**Brenntag Specialties, Inc.**
Phone—(908) 561-6100 / (800) 732-0562
Fax—(800) 543-1484
Web—www.brenntagspecialties.com
Email—specialties@brenntag.com
1000 Coolidge St., South Plainfield 07080
(see our ad under CHEMICAL DISTRIBUTORS)
O'Neil Color & Compounding Corp.
Phone—(973) 777-8999
61 River Dr., Garfield 07026

Do nationwide searches for products & services at: IndustryNet.com

## COLORS — Food

Food Ingredient Solutions, LLC
Phone—(201) 440-4377
10 Malcolm Ave., Unit 1, Teterboro 07608

## COMMODITIES BROKERS

**Heraeus Precious Metals North America, LLC**
Refining, trading, jewelry sweeps, karat gold, polishing sweeps & platinum scrap
Phone—(973) 817-7878
Fax—(973) 578-2786
Web—www.heraeus.com
Email—refiningnj@heraeus.com
65 Euclid Ave., Newark 07105

## COMMUNICATION EQUIPMENT

Avaya, Inc. (H Q)
Phone—(908) 953-6000
211 Mount Airy Rd., Basking Ridge 07920
Cellebrite USA Corp.
Phone—(201) 848-8552
7 Campus Dr., Ste. 210, Parsippany 07054
Communications Supply Corp.
Phone—(732) 346-1550
104 Sunfield Ave., Edison 08837
Conolog Corp.
Phone—(908) 722-8081
5 Columbia Rd., Somerville 08876
Iniven, A Div. Of Conolog Corp.
Phone—(908) 722-8081
5 Columbia Rd., Somerville 08876
Sonetronics, Inc.
Phone—(732) 681-5016
1718 State Route 71, P.O. Box L, Belmar 07719
Sycamore Networks, Inc.
Phone—(856) 359-9301
100 Century Pkwy, Ste. 120, Mount Laurel 08054
Wide Band Systems, Inc.
Phone—(973) 586-6500
389 Franklin Ave., Rockaway 07866

## COMMUNICATION EQUIPMENT — Medical

Lingraphicare America, Inc.
Phone—(609) 275-1300
103 Carnegie Ctr., Ste. 204, Princeton 08540

## COMMUNICATION EQUIPMENT — Satellite

**ORBCOMM, Inc. (H Q)**
Satellite modems & wireless remote monitoring & control systems integration for refrigerated & temperature-controlled transportation
Phone—(703) 433-6300 / (800) 672-2666
Fax—(703) 433-6400
Web—www.orbcomm.com
395 W. Passaic St., Ste. 325, Rochelle Park 07662

## COMMUNICATION SYSTEMS

East Coast Security Products
Phone—(973) 625-3277
53 Green Pond Rd., Ste. 1, Rockaway 07866
L-3 Communications Corp.
Phone—(856) 338-3000
1 Federal St., Camden 08102
Mikros Systems Corp.
Phone—(609) 987-1513
707 Alexander Rd., Princeton 08540
Teknicom Sales Co.
Phone—(201) 327-4500
470 Commercial Ave., Palisades Park 07650

Need an **IndustrySection** for another state?

Call us... 847-864-7590

## COMMUNICATIONS TESTING EQUIPMENT

**Wireless Telecom Group, Inc.**
Phone—(973) 386-9696
Fax—(973) 386-9191
Web—www.wtcom.com
Email—info@wtcom.com
25 Eastmans Rd., Parsippany 07054

## COMPACT DISC DUPLICATION

Synergem
Phone—(732) 225-0001
2323 Randolph Ave., Avenel 07001

## COMPACT DISCS

Disc Makers
Phone—(856) 663-9030
7905 N. Route 130, Pennsauken 08110

## COMPACTORS — Refuse

**Arrow Steel, Inc.**
Email: mario@arrowcompactor.com
Manufacturing Industrial Refuse Compactors for High Rise Apartment Complexes since 1977. Made in USA
Phone—(973) 523-1122
Fax—(973) 977-9490
Web—www.arrowcompactor.com
629 E. 19th St., Paterson 07514
Multi-Pak Corp.
Phone—(201) 342-7474
180 Atlantic St., Hackensack 07601
**Premier Compaction Systems**
Fax: (973) 305-5502
Web: www.premiercompactionsystems.com
Manufacturing Industrial Refuse Compactors & Fabricated Chutes for High Rise Apartment Complexes since 1977. Made in the USA
Phone—(973) 305-6646 / (800) 877-7475 / (201) 819-9564
Email—john@pfmgreen.com
264 Lackawanna Ave., Woodland Park 07424

## COMPOSITES

**Technick Products, Inc.**
Additives for rubber & plastic; mold release agents, halogenated & non-halogenated flame retardants & green cleaning agents
Phone—(908) 791-0400
Fax—(908) 791-9991
Web—www.technickproducts.com
Email—info@technickproducts.com
238 Saint Nicholas Ave., South Plainfield 07080

## COMPOST

Nature's Choice Corp.
Phone—(908) 475-1804
40 Foul Rift Rd., Belvidere 07823
Rotondi & Sons, Inc., S.
Phone—(908) 475-1916
139 Reeder Rd., Phillipsburg 08865

## COMPRESSOR PARTS

**ARMCO Compressor Products Corp.**
Phone—(201) 866-6766
Fax—(201) 866-0360
Web—www.armcocompressor.com
Email—sales@armcocompressor.com
2042 46th St., North Bergen 07047

## COMPRESSOR REPAIR SERVICES

**Comairco Equipment, Inc.**
Compressor Rental
Phone—(732) 331-1100 / (908) 756-1900
Fax—(908) 756-1909
Web—www.comairco.com
Email—sales@comairco.com
17 Progress St., Edison 08820

© Copyright 2015 Manufacturers' News, Inc.

A41

## COMPRESSORS

Aavolyn Corp.
Phone—(856) 327-8040
207 Bogden Blvd., P.O. Box 1097, Millville 08332
Atlas Copco North America, LLC (H Q)
Phone—(973) 397-3400
7 Campus Dr., Ste. 200, Parsippany 07054

## COMPRESSORS — Air

**Air & Gas Technologies, Inc.**
**Sales/Service of Air, CNG & Breathing Air Systems**
**Phone—(732) 566-7227 / (800) 716-5550**
**Fax—(732) 566-0535**
**Web—www.airgastech.com**
**Email—bkeelen@airgastech.com**
**42 Industrial Dr., Keyport 07735**
Airmatic Compressor Systems, Inc.
Phone—(201) 342-1300
700 Washington Ave., Carlstadt 07072
**Comairco Equipment, Inc.**
**Compressor Rental**
**Phone—(732) 331-1100 / (908) 756-1900**
**Fax—(908) 756-1909**
**Web—www.comairco.com**
**Email—sales@comairco.com**
**17 Progress St., Edison 08820**
Gas Drying, Inc.
Phone—(973) 361-2212
355 W. Dewey Ave., P.O. Box 504, Wharton 07885
International Compressor Co., Inc.
Phone—(973) 824-7170
361 Jelliff Ave., Newark 07108
Scales Industrial Technologies, Inc of NJ
Phone—(973) 890-1010
185 Lackawanna Ave., Woodland Park 07424
**Warwick Mfg. & Equipment Co., LLC**
**Buy & sell used: Chemical, food, cosmetic, packaging & pharmaceutical equipment**
**Phone—(732) 729-0400 / (732) 241-9263**
**Fax—(732) 729-1235**
**Web—www.warwickequipment.com**
**Email—sales@warwickequipment.com**
**1112 12th St., North Brunswick 08902**
*(see our ad Outside Back Cover)*

## COMPRESSORS — Breathing Air

**Air & Gas Technologies, Inc.**
**Sales/Service of Air, CNG & Breathing Air Systems**
**Phone—(732) 566-7227 / (800) 716-5550**
**Fax—(732) 566-0535**
**Web—www.airgastech.com**
**Email—bkeelen@airgastech.com**
**42 Industrial Dr., Keyport 07735**

## COMPRESSORS — Gas

Parenta & Sons Enterprises, Inc.
Phone—(973) 334-9266
85 Fulton St., Unit 9-B, Boonton 07005

## COMPRESSORS — Natural Gas

**Air & Gas Technologies, Inc.**
**Sales/Service of Air, CNG & Breathing Air Systems**
**Phone—(732) 566-7227 / (800) 716-5550**
**Fax—(732) 566-0535**
**Web—www.airgastech.com**
**Email—bkeelen@airgastech.com**
**42 Industrial Dr., Keyport 07735**
Corban Energy Group
Phone—(201) 509-8555
418 Falmouth Ave., Elmwood Park 07407

## COMPUTER CONSULTANTS

**Computer Solutions**
**Phone—(609) 514-0100**
**Fax—(609) 514-0707**
**Web—www.welinku.com**
**Email—info@welinku.com**
**2630 Nottingham Way, Trenton 08619**

*find additional suppliers at*
**IndustryNet.com**

eMazzanti Technologies
Computer network systems integration
Phone—(201) 360-4400
Fax—(201) 360-4500
Web—www.emazzanti.net
Email—info@emazzanti.net
701 Grand St., Hoboken 07030
**Front Source Technologies LLC**
**Phone—(973) 772-1616**
**Fax—(973) 772-1611**
**Web—www.frontsourcetech.com**
**Email—support@front-source.com**
**5 E. 1st St., Clifton 07011**
**Global Technical Software**
**Phone—(609) 890-0316**
**Fax—(732) 862-1103**
**Web—www.gtssminds.com**
**3705 Quakerbridge Rd., Ste. 212, Trenton 08619**
**JEMS Software & Consulting, Inc.**
**Phone—(609) 585-8530**
**Fax—(609) 585-5539**
**Web—www.jemssoco.com**
**Email—jem@jemssoco.com**
**P.O. Box 10070, Trenton 08650**

## COMPUTER EQUIPMENT & SUPPLIES

Asset Recovery Specialists, Inc.
Phone—(856) 467-9822
3 Killdeer Ct., Ste. 303, Swedesboro 08085
Computer Wholesalers, Inc.
Phone—(908) 684-0802
715 Willow Grove St., Ste. 5, Hackettstown 07840
Falcon Safety Products, Inc.
Phone—(908) 707-4900
25 Imclone Dr., P.O. Box 1299, Branchburg 08876
SHI International Corp.
Phone—(732) 477-6479
290 Davidson Ave., Somerset 08873
Storage Engine, Inc.
Phone—(732) 747-6995
1 Sheila Dr., Eatontown 07724

## COMPUTER NETWORKING SYSTEMS

I.D. Systems, Inc.
Phone—(201) 996-9000
123 Tice Blvd., Ste. 101, Woodcliff Lake 07677
**Integrated Business Systems, Inc.**
**Phone—(973) 575-4950**
**Fax—(973) 575-4953**
**Web—www.ibsre.com**
**Email—sales@ibsre.com**
**999 Riverview Dr., Ste. 280, Totowa 07512**
**JEMS Software & Consulting, Inc.**
**Phone—(609) 585-8530**
**Fax—(609) 585-5539**
**Web—www.jemssoco.com**
**Email—jem@jemssoco.com**
**P.O. Box 10070, Trenton 08650**
Shore Microsystems, Inc.
Phone—(732) 870-0800
45 Memorial Pkwy., Long Branch 07740
**Yorktel**
**Managed Services, Cloud, Mobility, Interoperability**
**Phone—(732) 413-6000 / (866) 836-8463**
**Fax—(732) 413-6060**
**Web—www.yorktel.com**
**Email—sosowski@yorktel.com**
**81 Corbett Way, Eatontown 07724**

## COMPUTER PARTS

Comp-Solutions & Services
Phone—(856) 863-1137
621 N. Delsea Dr., Clayton 08312

## COMPUTER PARTS & SUPPLIES — Wholesale

Thanks For Being Green, LLC
Phone—(856) 333-0991
5070-B Central Hwy., Merchantville 08109

## COMPUTER PERIPHERALS

Dataram Corp.
Phone—(609) 799-0071
777 Alexander Rd., Princeton 08540
Index Security, Inc. (H Q)
Phone—(732) 531-9209
500 Parker Ave., Ste. G, Deal 07723
RAD Data Communications, Inc.
Phone—(201) 529-1100
900 Corporate Dr., Ste. 1, Mahwah 07430
Xceedium, Inc.
Phone—(201) 536-1000
30 Montgomery St., Ste. 1020, Jersey City 07302

## COMPUTERS

AAEON Electronics, Inc. (H Q)
Phone—(732) 203-9300
11 Crown Plz., Ste. 208, Hazlet 07730
Alphatec Computer Communications
Phone—(973) 344-8736
41 Merchant St., Newark 07105
BIG Client, LLC
Phone—(732) 918-8221
1 Industrial Way W., Bldg. E, Eatontown 07724
Blue Sage Software
Phone—(973) 366-1900
35 Lord William Penn Dr., Morristown 07960
Casio America, Inc. (H Q)
Phone—(973) 361-5400
570 Mount Pleasant Ave., Dover 07801
Computerist, Inc.
Phone—(973) 226-0100
15 Smull Ave., Ste. A, Caldwell 07006
DAX Systems, Inc.
Phone—(973) 227-8111
343 New Rd., Ste. 4, Parsippany 07054
Dialogic Corp.
Phone—(973) 967-6000
1515 State Route 10 E., Parsippany 07054
Dynamic Decisions, Inc.
Phone—(908) 755-5000
2709 Hamilton Blvd., South Plainfield 07080
Franklin Electronic Publishers, Inc.
Phone—(609) 386-2500
8 Terri Ln., Burlington 08016
Futuretech Systems, Inc.
Phone—(732) 777-7355
515 Plainfield Ave., Ste. 101, Edison 08817
Global Business Dimensions Inc.
Phone—(973) 831-5866
220 W. Parkway, Ste. 8, Pompton Plains 07444
I T O X, LLC
Phone—(732) 390-2815
15 Corporate Pl. S., Ste. 201, Piscataway 08854
J W S Computers, Inc.
Phone—(908) 730-6628
20 S. Main St., Lambertville 08530
**JEMS Software & Consulting, Inc.**
**Phone—(609) 585-8530**
**Fax—(609) 585-5539**
**Web—www.jemssoco.com**
**Email—jem@jemssoco.com**
**P.O. Box 10070, Trenton 08650**
Network Access Systems
Phone—(732) 355-9770
19 Isaac Dr., Dayton 08810
PlanITROI Inc
Phone—(973) 664-0700
100-10 Ford Rd., Denville 07834
R T I, Inc.
Phone—(201) 261-5852
401 Hasbrouck Blvd., Oradell 07649

## COMPUTERS — Micro

Touch Dynamic, Inc.
Phone—(732) 382-5701
17 Camptown Rd., Irvington 07111

## COMPUTING SYSTEMS

Telegence Corp.
Phone—(856) 755-1717
383 Kings Hwy. N., Ste. B-1, Cherry Hill 08034

*Search from among 430,000 U.S. manufacturers & suppliers:*
**IndustryNet.com**

# CONCRETE

Capitol Pavers & Retaining Wall, Inc.
  Phone—(732) 727-5460
  90 Main St., P.O. Box 3249, South Amboy 08879
Harsco Corp.
  Phone—(732) 396-1269
  1800 Lower Rd., Linden 07036

## CONCRETE — Decorative

**Concrete Impressions, Inc.**
  **Color, Release, Sealer, Stamps, Stains, Overlays, Saw**
  **Blades & Stegmeier Forms**
  **Phone—(609) 298-8949**
  **Fax—(609) 298-8770**
  **Web—www.concrete-impressions.com**
  **Email—conslab8@comcast.net**
  **24059 W. Main St., Columbus 08022**
JM Lifestyles, LLC
  Phone—(973) 668-5057
  215 State Route 10, Ste. 3, Randolph 07869

## CONCRETE — Dry Mix

Gifford & Co., Brian L.
  Phone—(856) 327-0011
  514 Bogden Blvd., Millville 08332

## CONCRETE — Precast

Conti Group, The (H Q)
  Phone—(732) 520-5000
  2045 State Route 27, Edison 08817

## CONCRETE — Precast & Prestressed

Boccella Precast, LLC
  Phone—(856) 767-3861
  324 New Brooklyn Rd., Berlin 08009
Franklin Precast
  Phone—(973) 827-7563
  20 Park Dr., Franklin 07416

## CONCRETE — Ready-Mixed

Action Supply, Inc.
  Phone—(609) 390-0663
  1413 Stagecoach Rd., Ocean View 08230
Allied Concrete Co., Inc.
  Phone—(973) 627-6150
  205 Franklin Ave., Rockaway 07866
Benanti, Inc., D. F.
  Phone—(732) 422-3102
  420 Quarry Ln., North Brunswick 08902
Clayton & Sons, LLC, Ralph
  Phone—(609) 758-6900
  58 Goldman Dr., Cookstown 08511
Clayton & Sons, Ralph
  Phone—(609) 383-1818
  103 Chestnut Ave., Egg Harbor Township 08234
Clayton & Sons, Ralph
  Phone—(609) 597-2233
  125 Cox Crossing Rd., West Creek 08092
Clayton & Sons, Ralph (H Q)
  Phone—(732) 751-7600
  1355 Campus Pkwy., Neptune 07753
Clayton Block Co., Inc.
  Phone—(732) 751-7600
  1355 Campus Pkwy., Neptune 07753
Colonial Concrete Co.
  Phone—(973) 482-1920
  1196 McCarter Hwy., Newark 07104
Colonial Concrete Co.
  Phone—(201) 435-9200
  9301 Railroad Ave., North Bergen 07047
Concrete On Demand, Inc.
  Phone—(201) 337-0005
  45 Edison Ave., Ste. 1, Oakland 07436
County Concrete Corp.
  Phone—(973) 538-3113
  145 Ridgedale Ave., Morristown 07960
Eastern Concrete Materials, Inc. (H Q)
  Phone—(201) 797-7979
  475 Market St., 3rd Fl., Elmwood Park 07407
Erial Concrete, Inc.
  Phone—(856) 784-8884
  965 Hickstown Rd., Sicklerville 08081

Fazzio & Sons, Inc., Frank J.
  Phone—(856) 589-3760
  458 Elwood Ave., Pitman 08071
Hinchman & Son, Inc., Herbert J.
  Phone—(973) 942-2063
  26 Pike Dr., Wayne 07470
Kennedy Concrete
  Phone—(856) 692-8650
  1969 S. East Ave., Vineland 08360
L & L Redi-Mix, Inc.
  Phone—(800) 696-2271
  1939 U.S. Highway 206, Southampton 08088
Penn Jersey Building Materials, Inc.
  Phone—(856) 467-0400
  247 Cedar Swamp Rd., Bridgeport 08014
Penn Jersey Building Materials, Inc.
  Phone—(609) 485-0068
  2819 Fire Rd., Egg Harbor Township 08234
Pierson Materials Co., Inc., R. E.
  Phone—(856) 467-1421
  860 Oak Grove Rd., P.O. Box 704, Bridgeport 08014
Pierson Materials Corp., R. E.
  Phone—(856) 696-2901
  184 W. Sherman Ave., Vineland 08360
Pierson Materials, Inc., R. E.
  Phone—(609) 267-2257
  1550 Route 38, Mount Holly 08060
Pierson Materials, Inc., R. E.
  Phone—(856) 740-2400
  151 Industrial Dr., Williamstown 08094
Ralph Clayton & Sons
  Phone—(609) 695-0767
  1144 New York Ave., Trenton 08638
S C C Concrete
  Phone—(908) 859-2172
  1051 River Rd., P.O. Box 47, Phillipsburg 08865
Service Concrete Co.
  Phone—(973) 697-4040
  173 Oak Ridge Rd., P.O. Box 235, Oak Ridge 07438
Silvi Concrete Products, Inc.
  Phone—(267) 907-9150
  470 State Highway 33, Englishtown 07726
Sparta Sand & Gravel Co., Inc.
  Phone—(973) 383-4651
  33 Demarest Rd., Sparta 07871
Tanis & Sons, Inc., Joel
  Phone—(201) 796-1556
  17-68 River Rd., Fair Lawn 07410

## CONCRETE ADMIXTURES

Anti-Hydro International, Inc.
  Phone—(908) 284-9000
  45 River Rd., Ste. 200, Flemington 08822
**Hycrete, Inc.**
  **Phone—(201) 386-8110 / (866) 492-7383**
  **Fax—(201) 386-8155**
  **Web—www.hycrete.com**
  **Email—info@hycrete.com**
  **462 Barell Ave., Carlstadt 07072**
W. R. Grace & Co.
  Phone—(201) 869-5220
  2133 85th St., North Bergen 07047

## CONCRETE AGGREGATES

**Concrete Impressions, Inc.**
  **Color, Release, Sealer, Stamps, Stains, Overlays, Saw**
  **Blades & Stegmeier Forms**
  **Phone—(609) 298-8949**
  **Fax—(609) 298-8770**
  **Web—www.concrete-impressions.com**
  **Email—conslab8@comcast.net**
  **24059 W. Main St., Columbus 08022**

## CONCRETE BLOCKS

Clayton Block Co., Inc
  Phone—(201) 955-6292
  2 Porete Ave., North Arlington 07031
Oliver Mfg. Supply Co.
  Phone—(732) 634-8100
  730 Port Reading Ave., P.O. Box 274, Port Reading 07064
Reuther Material Co., Inc.
  Phone—(201) 863-3550
  5303 Tonnelle Ave., North Bergen 07047

Smith & Son, Inc., R. P.
  Phone—(973) 584-4063
  Main St., P.O. Box 209, Succasunna 07876

## CONCRETE COATINGS

Shared Systems Technology, Inc.
  Phone—(856) 218-7900
  127 Salem Ave., Thorofare 08086

## CONCRETE COLORING

**Concrete Impressions, Inc.**
  **Color, Release, Sealer, Stamps, Stains, Overlays, Saw**
  **Blades & Stegmeier Forms**
  **Phone—(609) 298-8949**
  **Fax—(609) 298-8770**
  **Web—www.concrete-impressions.com**
  **Email—conslab8@comcast.net**
  **24059 W. Main St., Columbus 08022**

## CONCRETE CUTTING

A & L Concrete Cutting Inc.
  **Phone—(973) 296-8274**
  **Fax—(973) 234-5054**
  **Email—zimkim@optonline.com**
  **P.O. Box 922, Hopatcong 07843**
Affordable Concrete Cutter
  **Phone—(973) 452-4945**
  **Fax—(973) 252-1937**
  **Web—www.affordableconcretecutter.com**
  **Email—larrybakerconstruction@yahoo.com**
  **8 Corvair Ct., Flanders 07836**
American Coring & Supply, Inc.
  **Phone—(732) 255-8787 / (732) 513-8642**
  **Fax—(732) 255-5559**
  **Email—amcoring@aol.com**
  **89 Susan St., Toms River 08753**

## CONCRETE CUTTING MACHINERY

Marindus Co., Inc
  Phone—(201) 567-8383
  P.O. Box 663, Englewood 07631

## CONCRETE FORMS

**Concrete Impressions, Inc.**
  **Color, Release, Sealer, Stamps, Stains, Overlays, Saw**
  **Blades & Stegmeier Forms**
  **Phone—(609) 298-8949**
  **Fax—(609) 298-8770**
  **Web—www.concrete-impressions.com**
  **Email—conslab8@comcast.net**
  **24059 W. Main St., Columbus 08022**
EFCO Forms
  Phone—(732) 308-1010
  77 Vanderburg Rd., Marlboro 07746
Ulma Form Works, Inc.
  Phone—(973) 636-2040
  58 5th Ave., Hawthorne 07506

## CONCRETE PAVERS

CST Pavers a division of Pavestone
  Phone—(973) 948-7193
  23 Ridge Rd., P.O. Box 2736, Branchville 07826
CST Products, LLC
  Phone—(856) 299-5339
  345 Route 130, P.O. Box 402, Pedricktown 08067

## CONCRETE PIPE

Alva-Tech, Inc.
  **Intumescent Firestop Products & Joint Fillers For**
  **Underground Steel & Concrete Pipe**
  **Phone—(609) 747-1133**
  **Fax—(609) 747-1136**
  **Web—www.alva-tech.com**
  **Email—info@alva-tech.com**
  **1208 Columbus Rd., Ste. G, Burlington 08016**
Oldcastle Precast, Inc.
  Phone—(609) 561-3400
  1920 12th St., Williamstown 08094

INDUSTRY

## CONCRETE PIPE — (cont.)

Vianini Pipe, Inc.
Phone—(908) 534-4021
39 County Line Rd., Whitehouse Station 08889

## CONCRETE PRODUCTS

Anchor Concrete Products, Inc. (H Q)
Phone—(732) 292-2500
331 Newman Springs Rd., Bldg. 2, 3rd Fl., Ste. 236, Red Bank 07701

**Concrete Impressions, Inc.**
Color, Release, Sealer, Stamps, Stains, Overlays, Saw Blades & Stegmeier Forms
**Phone—(609) 298-8949**
**Fax—(609) 298-8770**
**Web—www.concrete-impressions.com**
**Email—conslab8@comcast.net**
**24059 W. Main St., Columbus 08022**

County Concrete Corp.
Phone—(973) 584-7122
50 Railroad Ave., P.O. Box F, Kenvil 07847

Empire Blended Products, Inc.
Phone—(732) 269-4949
250 Hickory Ln., Bayville 08721

Grinnell Concrete Pavingstones, Inc.
Phone—(973) 383-9300
482 Houses Corner Rd., Sparta 07871

Henry Corp., E. P.
Phone—(856) 845-6200
201 Park Ave., P.O. Box 615, Woodbury 08096

Northeast Concrete Products, LLC
Phone—(973) 728-1667
937 Burnt Meadow Rd., P.O. Box 963, Hewitt 07421

QUIKRETE Cos., Inc, The
Phone—(856) 768-6642
22 Union Ave., Berlin 08009

Tri-State QUIKRETE
Phone—(973) 347-4569
150 Gold Mine Rd., Flanders 07836

## CONCRETE PRODUCTS — Precast

A & A Concrete Products, Inc.
Phone—(973) 835-2239
2 S. Corporate Dr., P.O. Box 108, Riverdale 07457

Di Ferraro, Inc.
Phone—(973) 694-7200
28 Burgess Pl., Wayne 07470

Flemington Precast & Supply, LLC
Phone—(908) 782-3246
18 Allen St., Flemington 08822

Gambale Precast, Inc.
Phone—(856) 784-3399
1 Erial Rd., Clementon 08021

Garden State Precast, Inc.
Phone—(732) 938-4436
1630 Wyckoff Rd., Wall Township 07719

Gillespie, Inc., Paul J.
Phone—(856) 839-0891
2565 Brunetta Dr., Vineland 08360

Hunterdon Ornamental Concrete, Inc.
Phone—(908) 534-4556
440 Highway 22, Whitehouse Station 08889

J. B. & Sons Concrete Products Co.
Phone—(856) 767-4140
358 New Brooklyn Rd., Berlin 08009

Jersey Precast Corporation
Phone—(609) 689-3700
853 Nottingham Way, Trenton 08638

Medford Concrete Co.
Phone—(609) 654-2200
4 Tidswell Ave., P.O. Box 273, Medford 08055

Mershon Concrete, LLC
Phone—(609) 298-2150
Route 130 S., P.O. Box 254, Bordentown 08505

Mid State Filigree Systems, Inc.
Phone—(609) 448-8700
22 Brickyard Rd., P.O. Box 435, Cranbury 08512

Peerless Concrete Products, Inc.
Phone—(973) 838-3060
246 Main St., Butler 07405

Precast Mfg. Co., LLC
Phone—(908) 454-2122
187 Strykers Rd., Phillipsburg 08865

Precast Systems, Inc.
Phone—(609) 208-1987
57 Sharon Station Rd., Allentown 08501

Smith's Concrete Products
Phone—(856) 696-3102
3504 S. West Blvd., Vineland 08360

Stag Bros. Cast Stone
Phone—(732) 363-6582
720 Vassar Ave., Lakewood 08701

## CONCRETE REINFORCING STEEL

Ahle Co., Inc., J. M.
Phone—(732) 238-1700
190 William St., Ste. 2-D, South River 08882

**Bayshore Rebar Inc.**
Reinforcing steel erection post tension specialist
**Phone—(609) 484-8900**
**Fax—(609) 484-8969**
**Web—www.bayshorerebar.com**
**Email—info@bayshorerebar.com**
**1509 S. New Rd., Pleasantville 08232**

**Bayshore Rebar Inc.**
*Reinforcing Steel Erection*
*Post Tension Specialist*
**www.bayshorerebar.com**
**609-484-8900 / FAX: 609-484-8969**
1509 S. New Rd. • Pleasantville, NJ 08232

HarMac Rebar & Steel Corp.
Phone—(732) 651-7822
301 Hartle St., Sayreville 08872

## CONCRETE RESTORATION PRODUCTS

Strongwall Industries, Inc.
Phone—(201) 445-4633
107 Chestnut St., Ridgewood 07450

## CONCRETE SAWING

**A & L Concrete Cutting Inc.**
**Phone—(973) 296-8274**
**Fax—(973) 234-5054**
**Email—zimkim@optonline.com**
**P.O. Box 922, Hopatcong 07843**

## CONCRETE TOOLS

**Concrete Impressions, Inc.**
Color, Release, Sealer, Stamps, Stains, Overlays, Saw Blades & Stegmeier Forms
**Phone—(609) 298-8949**
**Fax—(609) 298-8770**
**Web—www.concrete-impressions.com**
**Email—conslab8@comcast.net**
**24059 W. Main St., Columbus 08022**

## CONDIMENTS

C & E Canners, Inc.
Phone—(609) 561-1078
1249 Mays Landing Rd., P.O. Box 229, Hammonton 08037

Muirhead Of Ringoes New Jersey, Inc.
Phone—(908) 782-7803
43 U.S. Highway 202, Ringoes 08551

## CONDUIT — Electrical

Andrex, Inc.
Phone—(908) 852-4377
101 Bilby Rd., Ste. E, Hackettstown 07840

## CONES — Steel

**Arntzen Corp.**
Mfr. Of Rolled & Welded Steel Cylinders-Cones-Pipe-Shapes-Fittings
**Phone—(815) 334-0788 / (800) 957-7655**
**Fax—(815) 334-0778**
**Web—www.ArntzenRolling.com**
**Email—Sales@ArntzenCorp.com**
**14600 Washington St., Woodstock, IL 60098**

## CONFECTIONERY
(also see 'Candy')

Astor Chocolate Corp.
Phone—(732) 901-1001
651 New Hampshire Ave., Lakewood 08701

Birnn Chocolates, Inc.
Phone—(732) 545-4400
314 Cleveland Ave., Highland Park 08904

**Capco Enterprises, Inc.**
34 DeForest Ave., Ste. 3, East Hanover 07936
Email: clapone@capcoenterprisesinc.com
**Phone—(973) 884-0044 / (800) 252-1011**
**Fax—(973) 884-8711**
**Web—www.capcoenterprisesinc.com**
P.O. Box 335, Florham Park 07932
*(see our ad under CANDY)*

Confection Collection
Phone—(732) 905-3039
6754 Route 9, Howell 07731

**James Candy Company**
**Phone—(609) 344-1519 / (800) 441-1404**
**Fax—(609) 344-0246**
**Web—www.jamescandy.com**
**Email—sales@jamescandy.com**
**1519 Boardwalk, Atlantic City 08401**

Krause's Homemade Candy Co.
**Phone—(201) 943-4790**
**Fax—(201) 943-4790**
**Web—www.krausescandies.com**
**Email—krausescandies@gmail.com**
50 Bergen Blvd., Fairview 07022

Laura's Fudge, Inc.
Phone—(609) 729-1555
357 E. Wildwood Ave., P.O. Box 871, Wildwood 08260

**Laura's Fudge, Inc.**
*Fudge, candy, macaroon cookies*
**(609) 729-1555**
**www.laurasfudge.com**
357 E. Wildwood Ave., PO Box 871
Wildwood, NJ 08260

Lee Sims Chocolates
Phone—(201) 433-1308
743 Bergen Ave., Jersey City 07306

Manhattan Chocolates Co.
Phone—(201) 339-6886
186 E. 22nd St., Bayonne 07002

Metro Candy Apple Corp.
Phone—(973) 772-0837
203 Paterson Ave., Ste. 1, Wallington 07057

Steel's Fudge, Inc.
Phone—(609) 398-2383
1000 Boardwalk, Ocean City 08226

Steel's Fudge, Inc. (H Q)
Phone—(609) 345-4051
2719 Boardwalk, Atlantic City 08401

## CONFECTIONERY INGREDIENTS

**Mafco Worldwide Corp.**
**Phone—(856) 964-8840**
**Fax—(856) 964-6029**
**Web—www.magnasweet.com**
**Email—magnasweet@mafcolicorice.com**
**300 Jefferson St., Camden 08104**
*(see our ad under FLAVORINGS & FLAVORS)*

## CONNECTORS

Central Connectors, Inc.
Phone—(732) 972-3456
4 Bridge Plaza Dr., Ste. 1, Manalapan 07726

Connector Technology, Inc.
Phone—(732) 745-2880
5 Walter E. Foran Blvd., Ste. 4005, Flemington 08822

Elgen Mfg. Co.
Phone—(201) 964-0008
10 Railroad Ave., Closter 07624

Interstate Connecting Components, Inc.
Phone—(856) 722-5535
120 Mount Holly Byp., Lumberton 08048

## CONNECTORS — *(cont.)*

Robert Technologies, Inc.
Phone—(732) 254-6389
37 Main St., South River 08882

Teesing USA, LLC
Phone—(973) 383-0691
10 Millpond Dr., Unit 7, Lafayette 07848

Thomas & Betts Corp., Elastimold Div.
Phone—(908) 852-1122
1 Esna Pk., Hackettstown 07840

## CONNECTORS — Electric Wire & Cable

**Lapp USA**
**Cables, accessories & connectors. Everything from one source**
**Phone—(973) 660-9700 / (800) 774-3539**
**Fax—(973) 660-9330**
**Web—www.lappusa.com**
**Email—sales@lappusa.com**
**29 Hanover Rd., Florham Park 07932**

**LAPP USA**

Cables, Connectors, Strain Relief & Cable Management

**973-660-9700**

**800-774-3539**

**FAX: 973-660-9330**

29 Hanover Rd.
Florham Park, NJ 07932

www.lappusa.com

sales@lappusa.com

## CONNECTORS — Signal & Power

**Lapp USA**
**Cables, accessories & connectors. Everything from one source**
**Phone—(973) 660-9700 / (800) 774-3539**
**Fax—(973) 660-9330**
**Web—www.lappusa.com**
**Email—sales@lappusa.com**
**29 Hanover Rd., Florham Park 07932**
*(see our ad under CONNECTORS—Electric Wire & Cable)*

## CONSTRUCTION — Highway

**Green Construction Inc.**
**Specializing in heavy highway construction**
**Phone—(732) 238-9370**
**Fax—(732) 613-0838**
**P.O. Box 550, South River 08882**

## CONSTRUCTION CONSULTANTS

**PC Construction & Management**
**Construction & Management**
**Phone—(856) 933-7899**
**Fax—(856) 933-0003**
**Web—www.pcconstructionmgmt.com**
**Email—carl@pcconstructionmgmt.com**
**505 W. Kings Hwy., Mount Ephraim 08059**

*Is your company properly represented in the* **Industry**Section?

If not, call... 847-864-7590

## CONSTRUCTION COST ESTIMATING

**Scozzari Builders, Inc.**
**Phone—(609) 882-5730**
**Fax—(609) 989-1262**
**Web—www.scozzari.com**
**Email—nscozzari@scozzari.com**
**1891 N. Olden Avenue Ext., Ewing 08638**
*(see our ad under CONTRACTORS — General)*

## CONSTRUCTION EQUIPMENT

A. H. Harris & Sons, Inc.
Phone—(973) 227-1600
160 Fairfield Rd., Fairfield 07004

Binder Machinery Co., Inc.
Phone—(856) 767-5900
201 N. Route 73, Winslow 08095

Hoffman Equipment, Inc.
Phone—(732) 752-3600
300 S. Randolphville Rd., Piscataway 08854

Mabey Inc.
Phone—(732) 752-6600
218 N. Randolphville Rd., Piscataway 08854

**Rodio Tractor Sales, Inc.**
**Phone—(609) 561-0141**
**Fax—(609) 561-4344**
**Web—www.rodiotractor.com**
**Email—sales@rodiotractor.com**
**717 White Horse Pike, Hammonton 08037**

**Warwick Mfg. & Equipment Co., LLC**
**Buy & sell used: Chemical, food, cosmetic, packaging & pharmaceutical equipment**
**Phone—(732) 729-0400 / (732) 241-9263**
**Fax—(732) 729-1235**
**Web—www.warwickequipment.com**
**Email—sales@warwickequipment.com**
**1112 12th St., North Brunswick 08902**
*(see our ad Outside Back Cover)*

## CONSTRUCTION EQUIPMENT — Wholesale

Modern Group Ltd.
Phone—(800) 846-5840
75 New St., Edison 08837

Modern Group Ltd.
Phone—(201) 288-1441
112-128 Route 17 N., Hasbrouck Heights 07604

## CONSTRUCTION EQUIPMENT ATTACHMENTS

Long Reach High Reach, LLC
Phone—(856) 797-6999
890 E. Rte. 70, Ste. B, Marlton 08053

## CONSTRUCTION MANAGEMENT

**Ingrassia Construction Co. Inc.**
**Phone—(908) 222-1787**
**Fax—(908) 222-1449**
**Web—www.ingrassiaconstruction.com**
**Email—estimating@ingrassiaconstruction.com**
**40 Stirling Rd., Ste. 214, Watchung 07069**

**Scozzari Builders, Inc.**
**Phone—(609) 882-5730**
**Fax—(609) 989-1262**
**Web—www.scozzari.com**
**Email—nscozzari@scozzari.com**
**1891 N. Olden Avenue Ext., Ewing 08638**
*(see our ad under CONTRACTORS — General)*

**Stanker & Galetto, Inc.**
**Phone—(856) 692-8098**
**Fax—(856) 692-3058**
**Web—www.stankergaletto.com**
**Email—rkadlac@stankergaletto.com**
**317 W. Elmer Rd., Vineland 08360**
*(see our ad under DESIGN & BUILD CONTRACTORS)*

## CONSTRUCTION SUPPLIES

Numax, Inc.
Phone—(856) 910-0088
7251-B Browning Rd., Pennsauken 08109

## CONSTRUCTION TOOLS

Grabber Northeast
Phone—(856) 662-2525
1125 Thomas Busch Memorial Hwy., Pennsauken 08110

## CONSULTANTS — Industrial Hygiene

**Environmental Health Investigations**
**Phone—(973) 729-5649**
**Fax—(973) 729-5649**
**Web—www.ehi-inc.com**
**Email—bkerbel@ehi-inc.com**
**655 W. Shore Trl., Sparta 07871**
*(see our ad under ENVIRONMENTAL CONSULTANTS)*

## CONSUMER PRODUCTS

Reckitt Benckiser, Inc.
Phone—(973) 404-2600
399 Interpace Pkwy., P.O. Box 225, Parsippany 07054

Unilever North America
Phone—(201) 567-8000
700 Sylvan Ave., Englewood Cliffs 07632

## CONTACT LENSES

Lens Mode, Inc.
Phone—(973) 467-2000
150 Main St., Ste. 1, Millburn 07041

The Lifestyle Company, Inc.
Phone—(732) 303-7849
6 Paragon Way, Ste. 112, Freehold 07728

## CONTACTS — Electrical

Hoyt Corp.
Phone—(201) 894-0707
520 S. Dean St., Englewood 07631

**Repco, Inc.**
**Replacement contact sets for AC & DC motor starters**
**Phone—(800) 822-9190**
**Fax—(800) 424-9224**
**Web—www.repcoinc.com**
**Email—sales@repcoinc.com**
**6 Eves Dr., Marlton 08053**

**Servometer-PMG, LLC**
**Contacts & Assemblies**
**Phone—(973) 785-4630**
**Fax—(973) 785-0756**
**Web—www.servometer.com**
**Email—info@servometer.com**
**501 Little Falls Rd., Cedar Grove 07009**

## CONTAINERS

Kearny Steel Container Corp.
Phone—(973) 589-2070
401 South St., Newark 07105

MAUSER USA LLC
Phone—(732) 353-7000
35 Cotters Ln., Ste. C, East Brunswick 08816

Paperboard Products Co.
Phone—(201) 440-1600
21 Shafer Pl., Hackensack 07601

## CONTAINERS — Aluminum Foil

Penny Plate, LLC (H Q)
Phone—(856) 429-7583
14000 Horizon Way, Ste. 300, Mount Laurel 08054

## CONTAINERS — Bulk

**MAUSER USA LLC**
**Industrial**
**Phone—(732) 353-7000 / (732) 353-7100**
**Fax—(732) 651-9777**
**Web—www.mausergroup.com**
**Email—info.us@mausergroup.com**
**35 Cotters Ln., Ste. C, East Brunswick 08816**

## CONTAINERS — Cargo

Atlantic Coast Container Brokerage & Sales, Inc.
Phone—(908) 755-2898
906 Oak Tree Rd., Ste. P, South Plainfield 07080

## CONTAINERS — Corrugated

**(also see 'Boxes—Corrugated')**

President Container Group
Phone—(201) 933-7500
200 W. Commercial Ave., Moonachie 07074
RFC Container Co.
Phone—(856) 692-0404
2066 S. East Ave., Vineland 08360

## CONTAINERS — Fibre

**American Tube & Paper**
80 Furler St., Totowa 07512
**Phone—(973) 256-3600**
**Fax—(973) 785-3341**
**Web—www.AmericanPaperProducts.com**
**Email—sales@americanpaperproducts.com**
**P.O. Box 68, Totowa 07511**
*(see our ad under MAILING TUBES)*

## CONTAINERS — Glass

Ardagh Group
Phone—(856) 455-2000
443 S. East Ave., P.O. Box 400, Bridgeton 08302
Ardagh Group
Phone—(856) 935-4000
83 Griffith St., Salem 08079
Piramal Glass USA, Inc.
Phone—(856) 728-9300
918 E. Malaga Rd., Williamstown 08094
Piramal Glass-USA, Inc. (H Q)
Phone—(856) 293-6400
401 Route 73 N., Bldg. 10, Ste. 202, Lake Center
Executive Pk., Marlton 08053
Scientific Laboratory Supplies, Inc.
Phone—(856) 327-4410
1401 Wade Blvd., Millville 08332

## CONTAINERS — Hazardous Materials

**MAUSER USA LLC**
MAUSER is a global leader in industrial packaging-
drums & IBCs
**Phone—(732) 353-7000 / (732) 353-7100**
**Fax—(732) 651-9777**
**Web—www.mausergroup.com**
**Email—info.us@mausergroup.com**
**35 Cotters Ln., Ste. C, East Brunswick 08816**

## CONTAINERS — Plastic

Andler South Corp.
Phone—(609) 485-2000
102 E. Parkway Dr., Egg Harbor Township 08234
BE & K Plastics
Phone—(609) 386-3200
340 E. Broad St., Burlington 08016
Consolidated Container Co., LLC
Phone—(609) 655-0855
4 Pleasant Hill Rd., Monroe Township 08831
Parkway Plastics, Inc.
Phone—(732) 752-3636
561 Stelton Rd., Piscataway 08854
Power Container Corp.
Phone—(732) 560-3655
33 Schoolhouse Rd., Somerset 08873
Ring Container Technologies
Phone—(973) 258-0707
50 Fadem Rd., Ste. 1, Springfield 07081
S L M Mfg. Corp.
Phone—(732) 469-7500
47 Langstaff Ave., Edison 08817
Schutz Container Systems, Inc.
Phone—(908) 526-6161
200 Aspen Hill Rd., P.O. Box 5950, North Branch
08876
Stephen Plastics, Inc., Douglas
Phone—(973) 523-3030
22-36 Green St., Paterson 07501

TricorBraun
Phone—(201) 556-4800
250 Pehle Ave., Ste. 100, Saddle Brook 07663
Unette Corp.
Phone—(973) 328-6800
1578 Sussex Tpke., Randolph 07869
Unit Pack Co., Inc.
Phone—(973) 239-4112
7 Lewis Rd., Cedar Grove 07009

## CONTAINERS — Steel

Portable Container Services
Phone—(973) 515-4721
101 Eisenhower Pkwy., Ste. 300, Roseland 07068
Rudco Products, Inc.
Phone—(856) 691-0800
114 E. Oak Rd., Vineland 08360
Wastequip, Inc.
Phone—(856) 629-9222
460 New Brooklyn Rd., Williamstown 08094

## CONTAINERS — Storage

Flexcon Products Corp.
Phone—(908) 871-7000
200 Connell Dr., Ste. 1200, Berkeley Heights
07922

## CONTAINERS — Wholesale

Keith Industries, Inc.
Phone—(973) 642-3332
248 Astor St., Newark 07114

## CONTRACT ASSEMBLY

Easter Seals New Jersey (H Q)
Phone—(732) 257-6662
9 Terminal Rd., New Brunswick 08901
Mercer Occupational Training
Phone—(609) 393-2483
600 New York Ave., Trenton 08638
Miniature Folding, Inc.
Phone—(201) 773-6477
14 Wenzel St., Elmwood Park 07407
**North American Sterilization & Packaging
Company, Inc.**
**Email: rogerm@naspco.com**
**Phone—(973) 209-4388 / (800) 392-6310**
**Fax—(973) 209-6374**
**Web—www.naspco.com**
**19 Park Dr., Franklin 07416**
*(see our ad under CONTRACT MANUFACTURING—Medical)*
Northwest Essex Community Healthcare Network,
Inc.
Phone—(973) 744-7733
83 Walnut St., Montclair 07042
Occupational Training Center
Phone—(856) 768-0845
215 W. White Horse Pike, Berlin 08009
Pafa Training Center, Inc.
Phone—(856) 696-1414
1301 W. Forest Grove Rd., Bldg. 3-C, Vineland
08360
Pride Products, Inc.
Phone—(908) 353-6800
5 Slater Dr., Elizabeth 07206
Raritan Valley Workshop
Phone—(732) 828-8080
9 Terminal Rd., New Brunswick 08901
Reed-Lane, Inc.
Phone—(973) 709-1090
359 Newark Pompton Tpke., Wayne 07470

## CONTRACT MACHINING

Triple S Industries
Phone—(908) 862-0110
1108 E. Linden Ave., P.O. Box 1293, Linden
07036

## CONTRACT MANUFACTURING

Alliance Technologies Group, Inc.
Phone—(973) 664-1151
3 Luger Rd., Ste. 4, Denville 07834
**Comtron, Inc.**
Electromechanical Assy., testing, antennas,
duplexers & combline filters.
**Phone—(732) 446-7571**
**Fax—(732) 446-5768**
**Web—www.comtroninc.com**
**Email—dlacross@comtroninc.com**
**391 State Route 33 E., Englishtown 07726**
**Durex, Inc.**
Email: custserv@durexinc.com
ISO 9001 Registered Contract Metal Fabrication
Facility
**Phone—(908) 688-0800**
**Fax—(908) 688-0718**
**Web—www.durexinc.com**
**5 Stahuber Ave., Union 07083**
*(see our ad under METAL FABRICATING)*
Jade Apparel, Inc.
Phone—(973) 522-1003
133 Kossuth St., Newark 07105
**Menshen Packaging U.S.A., Inc.**
**Phone—(201) 445-7436**
**Fax—(201) 445-3473**
**Web—www.menshenusa.com**
**Email—info@menshenusa.com**
**21 Industrial Park, Waldwick 07463**
NEAC, Inc.
Phone—(908) 903-9100
526 Pacific Ave., #2202, Atlantic City 08401

## CONTRACT MANUFACTURING — Electronic

C & C Jetronic, Inc.
Phone—(609) 758-3553
126 Evergreen Rd., New Egypt 08533
Ellenby Technologies, Inc.
Phone—(856) 848-2020
412 Grandview Ave., Woodbury Heights 08097
K-Tron Electronics
Phone—(856) 232-2300
590 Woodbury Glassboro Rd., Sewell 08080
Motek Industries, LLC
Phone—(201) 836-4167
250 Park Ave., Teaneck 07666
Panurgy OEM
Phone—(973) 625-4056
701 Ford Rd., Rockaway 07866
Patriot American Solutions, LLC
Phone—(973) 586-2717
5 Astro Pl., Rockaway 07866
Powerspec, Inc.
Phone—(732) 494-9490
1 Linsley Pl., Metuchen 08840
PPI-Time Zero, Inc.
Phone—(973) 278-6500
11 Madison Rd., Fairfield 07004
SAK Technologies, Inc.
Phone—(973) 340-8300
134 Gaston Ave., Garfield 07026
SPEM Corp.
Phone—(732) 356-3366
403 Bell St., Piscataway 08854

## CONTRACT MANUFACTURING — Medical

Merton Tech, LLC
Phone—(201) 881-0555
168 Central Ave., Rochelle Park 07662

IndustryNet.com
Find Suppliers Nationally FREE!

*Do nationwide searches for
products & services at:*
**IndustryNet.com**

## CONTRACT MANUFACTURING — Medical — *(cont.)*

**North American Sterilization & Packaging Company, Inc.**
Email: rogerm@naspco.com
Phone—(973) 209-4388 / (800) 392-6310
Fax—(973) 209-6374
Web—www.naspco.com
Email—sales@naspco.com
19 Park Dr., Franklin 07416

### NASP
North American Sterilization & Packaging Company, Inc.
973-209-4388 • 800-392-6310
www.naspco.com rogerm@naspco.com
19 Park Dr. Franklin, NJ 07416

## CONTRACT MANUFACTURING — Pharmaceuticals

**I G I Laboratories, Inc.**
Phone—(856) 697-1441
105 Lincoln Ave., P.O. Box 687, Buena 08310

**Reed-Lane, Inc.**
Email: jluke@reedlane.com
Phone—(973) 709-1090
Fax—(973) 709-1091
Web—www.reedlane.com
359 Newark Pompton Tpke., Wayne 07470

## CONTRACT MANUFACTURING AND PACKAGING

**American Instants, Inc.**
Phone—(973) 584-8811
117 Bartley Flanders Rd., P.O. Box 817, Flanders 07836

**Cosmetics & Perfume Filling & Packaging, Inc.**
Phone—(973) 680-8900
30 Engelhard Dr., Monroe 08831

**Dimensional Merchandising, Inc.**
Fax: (973) 328-4598
Phone—(973) 328-1600
Web—www.dminj.com
Email—info@dminj.com
86 N. Main St., Wharton 07885

**Multi-Pak Packaging**
Phone—(973) 439-1182
19 Spielman Rd., Fairfield 07004

**World Wide Packaging, LLC**
Fax: (973) 805-6510
Phone—(973) 805-6500
Web—www.wwpinc.com
Email—sales@wwpinc.com
15 Vreeland Rd., Florham Park 07932

Steer traffic to your web site and leads to your inbox...
*with a preferred listing at*
**IndustryNet.com**

## CONTRACT PACKAGING SERVICES

**Abilities Of Northwest Jersey, Inc.**
Fulfillment/Contract Packaging/Assembly
Phone—(908) 689-1118
Fax—(908) 689-6363
Web—www.abilitiesnw.com
Email—info@abilitiesnw.com
264 Route 31 N., P.O. Box 251, Washington 07882

### Abilities
of Northwest Jersey Inc.

**Fulfillment/Contract Packaging/Assembly**

**908.689.1118**
**Fax 908.689.6363**

**www.abilitiesnw.com**
**info@abilitiesnw.com**

264 Route 31 N., P.O. Box 251
Washington, NJ 07882

**Aphena Pharma Solutions-NJ, Inc.**
Phone—(973) 887-4440
Fax—(973) 887-9098
Web—www.aphenapharma.com
Email—sales@aphenapharma.com
125 Algonquin Pkwy., Whippany 07981

**Assemblies Unlimited, Inc.**
Phone—(877) 273-6259
530 N. Michigan Ave., Kenilworth 07033

**Berkeley Contract Packaging, LLC**
Phone—(908) 810-4000
530 N. Michigan Ave., Kenilworth 07033

**Center For Educational Advancement**
Phone—(908) 782-1480
11 Minneakoning Rd., Flemington 08822

**Center Vocational Rehabilitation**
Phone—(732) 544-1800
15 Meridian Rd., Ste. 1, Eatontown 07724

**ElviPharma, LLC**
Phone—(732) 433-5591
60 Ethel Rd. W., Piscataway 08854

**Gloucester City Box Works, LLC**
Phone—(856) 456-9032
775 Charles St., Gloucester City 08030

**Hudson Community Enterprises**
Phone—(201) 432-5959
780 Montgomery St., Jersey City 07306

**LRM Packaging, Inc.**
Phone—(201) 342-2530
41 James St., South Hackensack 07606

**Marlow Candy & Nut Co.**
Phone—(201) 569-7606
65 Honeck St., Englewood 07631

**Rimmel Rogers, Inc.**
Phone—(201) 998-4700
250 Passaic St., Newark 07104

**SPT Packaging LLC**
Phone—(973) 246-5635
Fax—(973) 246-5636
Web—www.sptpkg.com
Email—jdefelice@sptpkg.com
489 Clifton Ave., Clifton 07011

**Tech Art, Inc.**
Phone—(201) 525-0044
12 E. 5th St., Paterson 07524

*find additional suppliers at*
**IndustryNet.com**

## CONTRACTORS

**Beck Contracting**
Commercial & Residential
Phone—(732) 840-1080
Fax—(732) 840-9492
Web—www.beckcontracting.com
Email—beckcontracting@aol.com
431 20th Ave., Brick 08724

**Curb Appeal General Contracting LLC**
Phone—(201) 970-0022
Fax—(201) 476-0114
Web—www.curbappealgcllc.com
68 Montvale Ave., Montvale 07645

## CONTRACTORS — Building

**Burke Builders Inc.**
Phone—(609) 886-4049
Fax—(609) 886-5199
Web—www.burke-builders.com
Email—mcb0119@yahoo.com
358 Crescent Dr., Cape May 08204

**Capoano Contractors, Inc.**
Phone—(732) 244-5595
Fax—(732) 505-3235
Web—www.capoanobuilt.com
Email—dcapoano@capoanocontractors.com
1889 Route 9, Ste. 103, Toms River 08755

**John Paul Builders**
Phone—(732) 202-6386
Web—www.johnpaulbuilders.net
Email—info@johnpaulbuilders.com
1999 Route 88, Brick 08724

## CONTRACTORS — Concrete

**Crete Concrete Construction**
Phone—(201) 445-3500
Fax—(201) 445-5808
Web—www.creteconcrete.com
Email—peter@creteconcrete.com
835 Ringwood Ave., Haskell 07420

**Custom Craft Concrete**
Phone—(609) 859-8110
Web—www.customcraftconcrete.net
168 Red Lion Rd., Southampton 08088

**Zomparelli Contractors LLC, t/a Ripi Concrete**
Phone—(609) 587-1784
Fax—(609) 587-6079
Email—zomparellicontractorsllc@gmail.com
11 Michael McCorristin Rd., Trenton 08690

## CONTRACTORS — Gas Stations

**Michael Marra, Inc.**
Petroleum Contractors
Phone—(732) 566-0444
Fax—(732) 566-9698
Web—www.marraconstruction.com
Email—mmi@marraconstruction.com
30-32 Industrial Dr., Keyport 07735

**Michael Marra, Inc.**
*Quality Service Station Contractors*
**(732) 566-0444**
FAX: (732) 566-9698
www.marraconstruction.com
mmi@marraconstruction.com
30-32 Industrial Drive
Keyport, NJ 07735

## CONTRACTORS — General

**Ingrassia Construction Co. Inc.**
Phone—(908) 222-1787
Fax—(908) 222-1449
Web—www.ingrassiaconstruction.com
Email—estimating@
ingrassiaconstruction.com
40 Stirling Rd., Ste. 214, Watchung 07069

**Scozzari Builders, Inc.**
Phone—(609) 882-5730
Fax—(609) 989-1262
Web—www.scozzari.com
Email—nscozzari@scozzari.com
1891 N. Olden Avenue Ext., Ewing 08638

## Scozzari Builders, Inc.
General Contractors
Commercial / Industrial / Institutional
609-882-5730 / www.scozzari.com
1891 N. Olden Avenue Ext.
Ewing, NJ 08638

**Stanker & Galetto, Inc.**
Phone—(856) 692-8098
Fax—(856) 692-3058
Web—www.stankergaletto.com
Email—rkadlac@stankergaletto.com
317 W. Elmer Rd., Vineland 08360
*(see our ad under DESIGN & BUILD CONTRACTORS)*

## CONTRACTORS — Remodeling

**Divine Energy Solutions**
Basement, sump pump, crawl space & foundation specialists
Phone—(800) 436-6535
Web—www.nwjerseyenergy.com
414 E. Blackwell St., Dover 07801

**Quality 1st Basement Systems**
Basement, sump pump, crawl space & foundation specialists
Phone—(888) 680-3830
Web—www.quality1stbasementsystems.com
1160 State St., Perth Amboy 08861

## CONTRACTORS' EQUIPMENT & SUPPLIES

**Cuny & Guerber, Inc.**
Special counter available for contractors
Phone—(201) 617-5800
Fax—(201) 617-5557
Web—www.cuny.biz
Email—sales@cuny.biz
2100 Kerrigan Ave., P.O. Box 1192, Union City 07087
*(see our ad under ELECTRICAL EQUIPMENT AND SUPPLIES – Wholesale)*

**GAMS Power Tools & Supplies, Inc.**
Phone—(201) 955-0222
133-135 Schuyler Ave., Kearny 07032

**Pipeline Supply Co.**
Phone—(732) 560-1509 / (800) 354-4244
Fax—(732) 560-0064
Web—www.pipelinesupplynj.com
Email—office@pipelinesupplynj.com
203 Egel Ave., Middlesex 08846

## CONTROL PANELS

**Automation & Control, Inc.**
Phone—(856) 234-2300
1491 Lancer Dr., Moorestown 08057

**Buchmann Control Panels Mfg., Inc.**
Phone—(201) 791-3161
5-18 Banta Pl., Fair Lawn 07410

**Etta Controls, Inc.**
Phone—(973) 731-6552
31 Belgrade Ter., West Orange 07052

**Howman Assocs., Inc.**
Phone—(732) 985-7474
12 Garden St., Edison 08817

**Lincoln Electric Products Co., Inc.**
Phone—(908) 688-2900
947 Lehigh Ave., Union 07083

**MAC Products, Inc.**
Phone—(973) 344-0700
60 Pennsylvania Ave., P.O. Box 469, Kearny 07032

**P K M Panel Systems Corp.**
Phone—(732) 238-6760
43 Ferry St., P.O. Box 272, South River 08882

## CONTROL PANELS — Electric

**Mid State Controls, Inc.**
Phone—(732) 335-0500
8 Crown Plz., Ste. 102, Hazlet 07730

**Powertronic, Inc.**
Phone—(732) 643-1500
3092 Shafto Rd., Unit 7, Tinton Falls 07753

## CONTROL SYSTEMS

**Connell Industries, Inc.**
Premier Control Systems Integrator/Custom Control Solutions Provider
Phone—(877) 926-6635
Fax—(305) 675-2612
Web—www.connell-ind.com
Email—vincent.digangi@connell-ind.com
13 Fairfield Ave., West Caldwell 07006

**CONNELL INDUSTRIES**

*Premier Control Systems Integrator/Custom Control Solutions Provider*

**(877) 926-6635**
**Fax: (305) 675-2612**

*email: vincent.digangi@connell-ind.com*

**www.connell-ind.com**

13 Fairfield Ave., West Caldwell, NJ 07006

**Crestron Electronics, Inc.**
Phone—(201) 767-3400
15 Volvo Dr., Rockleigh 07647

**Electronic Marine Systems**
Phone—(732) 382-4344
800 Ferndale Pl., Rahway 07065

**Fizzarotti Instrumentation Service**
Process Control Instrumentation & Calibration Control
Phone—(732) 833-4505
Fax—(732) 833-4507
Web—www.fizzinstrumentation.com
Email—mail@fizzinstrumentation.com
436 W. Commodore Blvd., Ste. 4, Jackson 08527

**Fizzarotti Instrumentation Service**
Quality calibration services
www.fizzinstrumentation.com
**(732) 833-4505**
436 W. Commodore Blvd. Ste. 4
Jackson, NJ 08527

**Fleetwash, Inc. (H Q)**
Phone—(800) 847-3735
26 Law Dr., Unit E, Fairfield 07004

**Flow Safe, Inc.**
Phone—(973) 627-8553
30 Broad St., Denville 07834

*Search from among 430,000 U.S. manufacturers & suppliers:*
**IndustryNet.com**

**Hayes Pump, Inc.**
Pumps, filters, seals, control systems
Phone—(973) 808-0606 / (800) 343-5020
Fax—(973) 808-7311
Web—www.hayespump.com
Email—Customerservice@hayespump.com
295 Fairfield Ave., Fairfield 07004

**HPI**
Flow solutions since 1898
**Hayes Pump, Inc.**
*Quality Pumps*
**800-343-5020**
973-808-0606 • FAX: 973-808-7311
295 Fairfield Ave. Fairfield, NJ 07004
www.hayespump.com Customerservice@hayespump.com

**Industrial Environmental**
Phone—(908) 241-3830
176 W. Westfield Ave., Elizabeth 07201

**Matrix Controls Co., Inc.**
Phone—(732) 469-5551
330 Elizabeth Ave., Somerset 08873

**Nova Systems**
Phone—(973) 697-3281
246 Cozy Lake Rd., Oak Ridge 07438

**Radwell International, Inc.**
Stocking, Selling, Repairing New & Surplus Industrial Automation, MRO, Pneumatic, Motion, Electronic, Hydraulic, HVAC & Electrical Control Equipment for plant floor & facilities maintenance machinery. Also buying Surplus Industrial Controls
Phone—(609) 288-9393 / (800) 332-4336
Fax—(609) 288-9417
Web—www.plccenter.com
Email—ahorner@plccenter.com
111 Mount Holly Bypass, Lumberton 08048

**Sienna Systems Corporation**
Providing open systems integration solutions for building controls to Construction Managers, Mechanical Contractors & Facility Managers
Phone—(973) 736-2155
Fax—(973) 736-1753
Web—www.sienna.net
Email—plambrou@sienna.net
22 Colonial Woods Dr., West Orange 07052
*(see our ad under CONTROL SYSTEMS INTEGRATORS)*

**Thermo Systems, LLC (H Q)**
Phone—(609) 371-3300
84 Twin Rivers Dr., East Windsor 08520

## CONTROL SYSTEMS — Industrial

**A.K. De Rama Industrial Control Systems, Inc.**
Phone—(908) 789-1600
253 Sheffield St., Mountainside 07092

**Advanced Industrial Controls Corp.**
Phone—(908) 725-7575
10 County Line Rd., Ste. 30, Somerville 08876

## CONTROL SYSTEMS — Programmable

**Connell Industries, Inc.**
Premier Control Systems Integrator/Custom Control Solutions Provider
Phone—(877) 926-6635
Fax—(305) 675-2612
Web—www.connell-ind.com
Email—vincent.digangi@connell-ind.com
13 Fairfield Ave., West Caldwell 07006
*(see our ad under CONTROL SYSTEMS)*

*Send an RFQ (request for quote) to multiple suppliers at*
**IndustryNet.com**

# Sienna Systems Corporation
## Schneider Control Systems
# 973-736-2155
## FAX: 973-736-1753

22 Colonial Woods Dr. West Orange, NJ 07052

**www.sienna.net • plambrou@sienna.net**

## CONTROL SYSTEMS INTEGRATORS

**Sienna Systems Corporation**
Providing open systems integration solutions for building controls to Construction Managers, Mechanical Contractors & Facility Managers
Phone—(973) 736-2155
Fax—(973) 736-1753
Web—www.sienna.net
Email—plambrou@sienna.net
22 Colonial Woods Dr., West Orange 07052
*(see our ad on this page)*

## CONTROLLERS — Programmable

A Mat Control Technologies, LLC
Phone—(908) 756-1699
70 Mount Bethel Rd., Warren 07059
Thomas Instrumentation, Inc. (H Q)
Phone—(609) 624-2630
133 Landing Rd., Cape May Court House 08210

## CONTROLS

Mechanical Ingenuity Corp.
Phone—(732) 842-8889
61 Riordan Pl., Shrewsbury 07702
Westlock Controls Corp.
Phone—(201) 794-7650
280 N. Midland Ave., Ste. 258, Saddle Brook 07663

## CONTROLS — Electric

East Coast Panelboard, Inc.
Phone—(732) 739-6400
101 Tornillo Way, Tinton Falls 07712
Sico Systems Control, Inc.
Phone—(973) 831-9110
1263 Ringwood Ave., Haskell 07420

## CONTROLS — Flow

Curtiss-Wright Corp. (H Q)
Phone—(973) 541-3700
10 Waterview Blvd., 2nd Fl., Parsippany 07054
McIntosh Controls Corp.
Phone—(973) 433-4700
218 Little Falls Rd., Unit 1, Cedar Grove 07009
Process Components
Phone—(732) 786-1500
301 John Wall Rd., Monroe Township 08831

## CONTROLS — Industrial

Artisan Controls Corp.
Phone—(973) 598-9400
111 Canfield Ave., Ste. B-15-18, Randolph 07869
Circonix Technologies, LLC
Phone—(973) 962-6160
29 Executive Pkwy., Ringwood 07456
Electronika For Industry, Inc.
Phone—(973) 575-4994
3599 Route 46, Parsippany 07054
Ellis Kuhnke Controls, Inc.
Phone—(732) 291-3334
132 Lewis St., Unit A-2, Eatontown 07724
H A Z Laboratories
Phone—(908) 453-3300
39 Hartmans Corner Rd., Washington 07882

Howman Electronics
Phone—(908) 534-2247
Route 22 E., Salem Industrial Pk., Whitehouse 08888
Industrial Controls Distributors, LLC
Phone—(732) 918-9000
17 Christopher Way, Eatontown 07724

## CONTROLS — Motor Speed

Allied Pump Corporation
Phone—(201) 798-3277
Fax—(201) 798-8781
Web—www.allied-pump.com
Email—alliedpumps@gmail.com
1109 Grand Ave., Bldg. 5, North Bergen 07047
*(see our ad under PUMPS)*

## CONTROLS — Programmable

Control & Power Systems, Inc.
Phone—(973) 575-3300
17 Spielman Rd., Fairfield 07004
West Electronics, Inc.
Phone—(609) 387-4300
5 Terri Ln., Ste. 15, P.O. Box 366, Burlington 08016

## CONTROLS — Temperature

Burling Instruments, Inc.
Phone—(973) 635-9481
16 River Rd., P.O. Box 298, Chatham 07928
General Electronic Enterprises, Inc.
Phone—(732) 381-1144
132 W. Main St., Rahway 07065
Heat-Timer Corp.
Phone—(973) 575-4004
20 New Dutch Ln., Fairfield 07004
Quantem Corp.
Phone—(609) 883-9191
1457 Lower Ferry Rd., Trenton 08618
Zytron Control Products, Inc.
Phone—(609) 771-0101
20 Lexington Ave., Trenton 08618

## CONVERTERS — Packaging

**American Tube & Paper**
80 Furler St., Totowa 07512
Phone—(973) 256-3600
Fax—(973) 785-3341
Web—www.AmericanPaperProducts.com
Email—sales@americanpaperproducts.com
P.O. Box 68, Totowa 07511
*(see our ad under MAILING TUBES)*
Tremont Co., Inc., I. W.
Phone—(973) 427-3800
18 Utter Ave., Hawthorne 07506

## CONVERTING EQUIPMENT

Davis-Standard, LLC
Phone—(908) 722-6000
220 Davidson Ave., Ste. 401, Somerset 08873
International Converting Machinery, Inc.
Phone—(973) 728-2600
45 Camelot Dr., West Milford 07480
Princeton Power Systems, Inc.
Phone—(609) 955-5390
3175 Princeton Pike, Ste. C, Lawrenceville 08648

## CONVEYOR CHAINS

DYNA-Veyor, Inc.
Phone—(973) 484-1119
10 Hudson St., Newark 07103

## CONVEYOR SYSTEMS

Caddy Corp.
Phone—(856) 467-4222
509 Sharptown Rd., P.O. Box 345, Bridgeport 08014
Coperion K-Tron Pitman, Inc.
Phone—(856) 589-0500
590 Woodbury Glassboro Rd., Sewell 08080
FlexLink Systems, Inc.
FlexLink conveying to assemble, fill, machine & package
Phone—(610) 973-8200 / (800) 782-1399
Fax—(610) 973-8345
Web—www.flexlink.com
Email—info.us@flexlink.com
6580 Snowdrift Rd., Allentown, PA 18106

## FlexLink Systems, Inc.
www.flexlink.com
Email: info.us@flexlink.com
Toll Free: (800) 782-1399
(610) 973-8200 • Fax: (610) 973-8345
6580 Snowdrift Rd. Allentown, PA 18106

JG Machine Works
Also, mechanical crimping of pumps onto fragrance glass bottles
Phone—(732) 203-2077
Fax—(732) 203-2078
Web—www.jgmachine.com
Email—dnelson@jgmachine.com
2182 State Route 35, Holmdel 07733
*(see our ad under FILLING MACHINERY)*
Lamson Airtubes, LLC
Phone—(973) 300-4267
10 Millpond Dr., Unit 4, Lafayette 07848
Sandvik Process Systems, LLC
Phone—(973) 790-1600
21 Campus Rd., Totowa 07512
Tec Installations, Inc.
Phone—(973) 684-0503
375 E. 22nd St., Paterson 07514
Traycon Manufacturing Company
Phone—(201) 939-5555
555 Barell Ave., Carlstadt 07072

## CONVEYORS

BEUMER Corporation
Phone—(732) 893-2800
800 Apgar Dr., Somerset 08873
Century Conveyor Service, Inc.
Phone—(908) 205-0625
4301 S. Clinton Ave., South Plainfield 07080
Conveyor Systems & Components
Phone—(856) 461-8084
21 Norman Ave., P.O. Box 343, Delran 08075
ECS, LLC
Phone—(732) 462-5530
1827 U.S. Highway 9, Howell 07731
Equipment Erectors, Inc.
Phone—(732) 846-1212
110 Garden St., Somerset 08873
FlexLink Systems, Inc.
FlexLink conveying to assemble, fill, machine & package
Phone—(610) 973-8200 / (800) 782-1399
Fax—(610) 973-8345
Web—www.flexlink.com
Email—info.us@flexlink.com
6580 Snowdrift Rd., Allentown, PA 18106
*(see our ad under CONVEYOR SYSTEMS)*
Garvey Corp.
Phone—(609) 561-2450
208 S. Route 73, Hammonton 08037
Lynn Mechanical Contractors
Phone—(856) 829-1717
1810 Rowland St., Riverton 08077

INDUSTRY

## CONVEYORS — (cont.)

**Nedco Conveyor Technology Co.**
Toll Free Ph: (888)-AT-NEDCO
Phone—(908) 964-9400
Fax—(908) 964-9411
Web—www.nedcoconveyor.com
Email—nedconvey@aol.com
967 Lehigh Ave., Union 07083

Teledynamics, LLC
Phone—(973) 248-3360
45 Indian Ln. E., Ste. 1, Towaco 07082

**Warwick Mfg. & Equipment Co., LLC**
Buy & sell used: Chemical, food, cosmetic, packaging
& pharmaceutical equipment
Phone—(732) 729-0400 / (732) 241-9263
Fax—(732) 729-1235
Web—www.warwickequipment.com
Email—sales@warwickequipment.com
1112 12th St., North Brunswick 08902
*(see our ad Outside Back Cover)*

## CONVEYORS — Belt

**BRECOflex Co., L.L.C.**
Phone—(732) 460-9500 / (888) 463-1400
Fax—(732) 542-6725
Web—www.brecoflex.com
Email—info@brecoflex.com
222 Industrial Way W., Eatontown 07724
*(see our ads under BELTING & PULLEYS)*

D A S Installations, Inc.
Phone—(973) 473-6858
176 Saddle River Rd., Bldg. D, Garfield 07026

Flow-Turn, Inc.
Phone—(908) 687-3225
1050 Commerce Ave., Ste. 1, Union 07083

**PBM Supply Co., Inc.**
Vulcanizing of conveyor belts
Phone—(973) 839-0050
Fax—(973) 839-4886
Email—pbmsupply@verizon.net
88 Cannonball Rd., P.O. Box 351, Pompton
Lakes 07442

## CONVEYORS — Food Handling & Processing

**Jason Industrial Inc.**
PVC & Polyurethane Light Weight Conveyor Belting
Phone—(973) 227-4904
Fax—(973) 227-1651
Web—www.jasonindustrial.com
Email—inquiries@jasonindustrial.com
340 Kaplan Dr., P.O. Box 10004, Fairfield
07004

## CONVEYORS — Gravity

Conveyors By North American
Phone—(973) 777-6600
156 Huron Ave., Clifton 07013

## CONVEYORS — Power Turn

**White Conveyors, Inc.**
Email: mark.speckhart@white-conveyors.com
Phone—(800) 524-0273
Fax—(908) 686-9317
Web—www.white-conveyors.com
10 Boright Ave., Kenilworth 07033

## CONVEYORS — Spiral

Automated Flexible Conveyors, Inc.
Phone—(973) 340-1695
55 Walman Ave., 2nd Fl., Clifton 07011

## CONVEYORS — Stainless Steel

**FlexLink Systems, Inc.**
FlexLink conveying to assemble, fill, machine &
package
Phone—(610) 973-8200 / (800) 782-1399
Fax—(610) 973-8345
Web—www.flexlink.com
Email—info.us@flexlink.com
6580 Snowdrift Rd., Allentown, PA 18106
*(see our ad under CONVEYOR SYSTEMS)*

## CONVEYORS — Vertical Reciprocating

**Lightning Lift Products**
Also hydraulic lift equipment; Designing, providing &
installing drive on, drive off car lifts, freight lifts, pallet
lifts, vertical reciprocating conveyors & high speed
lifts
Phone—(856) 824-0022
Fax—(856) 824-0868
Web—www.lightningliftproducts.com
Email—tweldon@lightningliftproducts.com
P.O. Box 5493, Delanco 08075

## COOKIES

Continental Cookies, Inc.
Phone—(201) 498-1966
185 S. Newman St., Hackensack 07601

Direct Sales & Services
Phone—(973) 340-4480
141 Lanza Ave., Bldg. 8, Garfield 07026

Jimmy's Cookies, LLC
Phone—(201) 797-8900
18-01 River Rd., Fair Lawn 07410

Mondelez International, Inc.
Phone—(201) 794-4000
22-11 State Route 208, Fair Lawn 07410

Tripician Macaroons
Phone—(609) 645-1546
640 White Horse Pike, Absecon 08201

## COOKING OIL REMOVAL

**Darling Ingredients, Inc.**
Email: bfrish@darlingii.com
Phone—(973) 465-1900 / (800) 842-5927
Fax—(973) 465-9247
Web—www.darlingii.com
825 Wilson Ave., Newark 07105

## COOKWARE

Bon Chef, Inc.
Phone—(973) 383-8848
205 State Route 94, Lafayette 07848

Ceramcor, LLC
Phone—(732) 929-2833
1026 Samantha Way, Toms River 08753

Groupe SEB USA
Phone—(856) 825-6300
2121 Eden Rd., Millville 08332

## COOLANTS

**Hangsterfer's Laboratories, Inc.**
Phone—(856) 468-0216
Fax—(856) 468-0200
Web—www.hangsterfers.com
Email—sales@hangsterfers.com
175 Ogden Rd., Mantua 08051
*(see our ad under LUBRICANTS—Metalworking)*

## COOLING SYSTEMS

Electric Fan Engineering Co.
Phone—(732) 203-0320
8 Crown Plz., Unit 105, Hazlet 07730

Electro Impulse Laboratory, Inc.
Phone—(732) 776-5800
1805 Route 33, Neptune 07753

**Midland Radiator Service Co.**
Phone—(973) 340-0533 / (800) 605-8001
Fax—(973) 340-5941
Web—www.midlandradiator.com
Email—midlandrad@aol.com
420 Midland Ave., Garfield 07026
*(see our ad under RADIATORS)*

## COOLING TOWERS

Delta Cooling Towers, Inc.
Phone—(973) 586-2201
185 U.S. Highway 206, Roxbury Township 07836

**find additional suppliers at IndustryNet.com**

## COPIERS

General Reproduction Products
Phone—(201) 934-0027
23 McKee Dr., Mahwah 07430

Integrated Document Technologies
Phone—(973) 237-1200
1 Cardinal Dr., Little Falls 07424

## COPPER

**Freeport-McMoran Copper & Gold**
Phone—(908) 558-4318 / (800) 522-9929
Fax—(908) 351-9475
Web—www.fcx.com/metals/bayway.htm
Email—william_geissel@fmi.com
48-94 Bayway Ave., Elizabeth 07202

**FREEPORT-McMoRan COPPER & GOLD**
Copper, Copper Alloys & Extruded Metals
www.fcx.com/metals/bayway.htm
(800) 522-9929
48-94 Bayway Ave. • Elizabeth, NJ 07202

## COPPER FABRICATORS

**Freeport-McMoran Copper & Gold**
Phone—(908) 558-4318 / (800) 522-9929
Fax—(908) 351-9475
Web—www.fcx.com/metals/bayway.htm
Email—william_geissel@fmi.com
48-94 Bayway Ave., Elizabeth 07202
*(see our ad under COPPER)*

## COPPER PRODUCTS

**Phibro-Tech, Inc.**
The Copper Chemical Company™
Phone—(201) 329-7300 / (800) 357-6840
Fax—(201) 329-7035
Web—www.phibro-tech.com
Email—phibro-tech@pahc.com
300 Frank W. Burr Blvd., Ste. 21, Glenpointe
Center East, 3rd Fl., Teaneck 07666

## CORD — Braided & Twisted

American Power Cord Corp.
Phone—(973) 574-8301
217 Brook Ave., 3rd Fl., Passaic 07055

*Need a database
of manufacturers
for a telemarketing
or mail campaign?*

*Call mni at 800-221-2172
for database solutions!*

**Manufacturers' News, Inc.**
*the industrial information source since 1912*

**AMERICOR** ®
CONNECTING THE WORLD

675 S. Lively Blvd., Elk Grove Village, IL 60007
**847.956.6200 • 800.830.5337**
fax 847.956.0300 • www.americor-usa.com
E-mail: info@americor-usa.com

## CORD SETS

**Americor Electronics, Ltd.**
  Phone—(847) 956-6200 / (800) 830-5337
  Fax—(847) 956-0300
  Web—www.americor-usa.com
  Email—info@americor-usa.com
  **675 S. Lively Blvd., Elk Grove Village, IL 60007**
    (see our ad on this page)
International Cord Sets, Inc.
  Phone—(973) 227-2118
  6 Spielman Rd., Fairfield 07004

## CORES

**American Tube & Paper**
  80 Furler St., Totowa 07512
  **Phone—(973) 256-3600**
  Fax—(973) 785-3341
  Web—www.AmericanPaperProducts.com
  Email—sales@americanpaperproducts.com
  **P.O. Box 68, Totowa 07511**
    (see our ad under MAILING TUBES)

## CORROSION MONITORS

CorrView International, LLC
  Phone—(973) 770-7764
  P.O. Box 8513, Landing 07850

## CORRUGATED PRODUCTS

**(also see specific product)**
TimBar Corp.
  Phone—(201) 568-7300
  15-01 Pollitt Dr., Unit 9, Fair Lawn 07410

## CORRUGATED SHEETS

Georgia Pacific, Inc.
  Phone—(908) 995-2228
  623 Riegelsville Rd., Milford 08848
Philcorr, LLC
  Phone—(856) 205-0557
  2317 Almond Rd., Vineland 08360

## COSMETIC INGREDIENTS

**Brenntag Specialties, Inc.**
  **Phone—(908) 561-6100 / (800) 732-0562**
  Fax—(800) 543-1484
  Web—www.brenntagspecialties.com
  Email—specialties@brenntag.com
  **1000 Coolidge St., South Plainfield 07080**
    (see our ad under CHEMICAL DISTRIBUTORS)
Extracts & Ingredients Ltd., Div. Of MORRE-TEC
  Industries, Inc.
  Phone—(908) 688-9009
  1 Gary Rd., Union 07083
Lipo Chemicals, Inc.
  Phone—(973) 926-0331
  1515 W. Blancke St., Linden 07036
**Mafco Worldwide Corp.**
  **Phone—(856) 964-8840**
  Fax—(856) 964-6029
  Web—www.magnasweet.com
  Email—magnasweet@mafcolicorice.com
  **300 Jefferson St., Camden 08104**
    (see our ad under FLAVORINGS & FLAVORS)

MMP, Inc.
  Email: sales.us@mmpinc.com
  Phone—(908) 561-4435
  Fax—(908) 561-4780
  Web—www.mmpinc.com
  Email—inquiry@mmpinc.com
  3470 S. Clinton Ave., South Plainfield 07080

**MMP**

Raw Materials and Specialty
Products for the Cosmetic and
Personal Care Industries

**www.mmpinc.com**

**(908) 561-4435**

3470 S. Clinton Ave. • South Plainfield, NJ 07080

Phoenix Chemical, Inc.
  Phone—(908) 707-0232
  60 4th St., Somerville 08876
TRI-K Industries, Inc.
  Phone—(973) 298-8850
  2 Stewart Ct., P.O. Box 10, Denville 07834
Ultra Chemical, Inc.
  Phone—(732) 224-0200
  2 Bridge Ave., Ste. 630, Red Bank 07701

## COSMETICS

Ambix Laboratories
  Phone—(973) 890-9002
  55 W. End Rd., Totowa 07512
Beilis Development, LLC (H Q)
  Phone—(973) 559-5670
  20-21 Wagaraw Rd., Bldg. 31-B, Fair Lawn 07410
Bentley Laboratories, LLC
  Phone—(732) 512-0200
  111 Fieldcrest Ave., Edison 08837
Christine Valmy Inc.
  Phone—(973) 575-1050
  285 Changebridge Rd., Ste. 1, Pine Brook 07058
Cosmetic Coatings, Inc.
  Phone—(201) 438-7150
  219 Broad St., P.O. Box 95, Carlstadt 07072
Cosmetic Essence, Inc.
  Phone—(201) 941-9800
  1135 Pleasantview Ter. W., Ridgefield 07657
Davion, Inc.
  Phone—(973) 485-0793
  29-75 Riverside Ave., Bldg. 10, Newark 07104
Davlyn Industries, Inc.
  Phone—(609) 860-5100
  7 Fitzgerald Ave., Monroe Township 08831

Fiabila, Inc.
  Phone—(973) 659-9510
  114 Iron Mountain Rd., Mine Hill 07803
Gallant Laboratories, Inc.
  Phone—(609) 268-0953
  142 Stockes Rd., Vincentown 08088
Global Colorants, Inc.
  Phone—(973) 751-2227
  83 Roosevelt Ave., Belleville 07109
**Grant Industries, Inc.**
  **Phone—(201) 791-6700**
  **Fax—(201) 791-0038**
  **Web—www.grantinc.com**
  **Email—info@grantinc.com**
  **125 Main Ave., Elmwood Park 07407**

**GRANT INDUSTRIES**
*Where Performance Matters*

*Textile chemicals & cosmetics*
**201-791-6700 • www.grantinc.com**
125 Main Ave. • Elmwood Park, NJ 07407

Guest Packaging, LLC
  Phone—(732) 382-7270
  414 E. Inman Ave., Rahway 07065
Innovative Cosmetics, Inc.
  Phone—(973) 773-7700
  270 Clifton Blvd., Clifton 07011
Interfashion Cosmetics Corp.
  Phone—(201) 288-5858
  32 Henry St., Teterboro 07608
Irving Rice & Co.
  Phone—(609) 655-6890
  161 Docks Corner Rd., Dayton 08810
Kirker Enterprises, Inc.
  Phone—(973) 754-9000
  55 E. 6th St., Paterson 07524
Lasting Impression, Inc.
  Phone—(201) 871-7388
  333 S. Dean St., Englewood 07631
L'Oreal U S A, Inc.
  Phone—(732) 562-5000
  81 New England Ave., Piscataway 08854
Mona Lisa Cosmetics, Inc.
  Phone—(201) 791-5644
  280 N. Midland Ave., Ste. 520, Saddle Brook
  07663
Novapac Laboratories, Inc.
  Phone—(973) 414-8800
  545 N. Arlington Ave., East Orange 07017
Nu-World Corp.
  Phone—(732) 541-6300
  300 Milik St., Carteret 07008
Pantina Cosmetics, Inc.
  Phone—(201) 288-7767
  30 Henry St., Teterboro 07608
Paramount Cosmetics, Inc.
  Phone—(973) 472-2323
  93 Entin Rd., Ste. 4, Clifton 07014
**QRS Beauty Corp.**
  **Phone—(201) 313-0305**
  **Fax—(201) 313-0316**
  **Web—www.qrsbeauty.com**
  **Email—info@qrsbeauty.com**
  **11 Commercial Ave., Fairview 07022**
Quality Cosmetics Mfg.
  Phone—(908) 755-9588
  4455 S. Clinton Ave., South Plainfield 07080
Royale Cosmetics Corp.
  Phone—(732) 246-7275
  4-A Jules Ln., New Brunswick 08901
Sarkli Repechage Ltd.
  Phone—(201) 549-4200
  300 Castle Rd., Secaucus 07094
Schwan Cosmetics U.S.A., Inc.
  Phone—(732) 777-6800
  21 Gordon Rd., Piscataway 08854
**Shiseido America, Inc.**
  **Phone—(609) 371-5800**
  **Web—www.shiseido.com**
  **366 Princeton Hightstown Rd., East Windsor
  08520**
Sysco Guest Supply (H Q)
  Phone—(609) 514-9696
  4301 Highway 1, P.O. Box 902, Monmouth
  Junction 08852

© Copyright 2015 Manufacturers' News, Inc.

A51

INDUSTRY

## COSMETICS — (cont.)

Tevco Enterprises, Inc.
Phone—(908) 754-7306
110 Pomponio Ave., South Plainfield 07080
Topline Products Co., Inc.
Phone—(973) 785-1600
155 Route 46 W., 2nd Fl., Wayne 07470
Tru-Form Cosmetics, Inc.
Phone—(973) 564-9111
50 Springfield Ave., Springfield 07081

## COSTUMES

Costume Gallery
Phone—(609) 386-6601
4451 Route 130 S., Burlington 08016
Creative Costume Co.
Phone—(212) 564-5552
61 Wilk Rd., Edison 08837
Silvertop Assocs., Inc.
Phone—(856) 939-9599
600 E. Clements Bridge Rd., Runnemede 08078

## COTTON GOODS

Comfort Concepts, Inc.
Phone—(201) 941-6700
501 Broad Ave., Ste. 7, Ridgefield 07657

## COUNTERTOPS

Accent Kitchen & Bath Center & Countertops
Phone—(732) 786-1001
510 Englishtown Rd., Monroe 08831
All Granite & Marble Corp.
Phone—(201) 440-6779
1 Mount Vernon St., Ste. A, Ridgefield Park 07660
Allen Cabinets & Millwork, Inc.
Phone—(973) 694-0665
60 Newark Pompton Tpk., Pequannock 07440
**Artistic Marble & Granite Surfaces, Inc.**
Web: www.NJMarble.com
**Phone—(973) 304-2001**
**Fax—(973) 427-9142**
**Email—artistic269@aol.com**
**269 Goffle Rd., Hawthorne 07506**
Bedrock Granite, Inc.
Phone—(732) 741-0010
803 Shrewsbury Ave., Shrewsbury 07702
Better Plastics, Inc.
Phone—(201) 332-6777
1 Mallory Ave., Jersey City 07305
Caputo International, Inc.
Phone—(732) 225-5777
112 Northfield Ave., Edison 08837
Counterfit
Phone—(609) 871-8888
1 Ironside Ct., Willingboro 08046
Countertops Plus, Inc.
Phone—(973) 365-2232
61 Willet St., Bldg. T, Passaic 07055
Custom Counters By Precision
Phone—(973) 773-0111
11-17 Linden St., Passaic 07055
East Coast Counter Tops, Inc.
Phone—(732) 363-7734
166 Main St., P.O. Box 645, Lakewood 08701
G & M Custom Formica Work
Phone—(732) 888-0360
120 Francis St., Bldg. C, Keyport 07735
Imperial Design
Phone—(856) 742-8480
729 Charles St., Gloucester City 08030
Industrial Consulting & Marketing
Phone—(973) 427-2474
20-21 Wagaraw Rd., Bldg. 38, Fair Lawn 07410
Laminetics, Inc.
Phone—(732) 367-1116
1263 River Ave., Lakewood 08701
Marmo Enterprises, Inc.
Phone—(908) 486-4421
468 Elizabeth Ave., Somerset 08873
Meridian Surfaces
Phone—(201) 337-7888
677 Ramapo Valley Rd., Oakland 07436
Merlino Marble & Granite, Inc.
Phone—(609) 624-9500
92 Route 50, Ocean View 08230

Miller Fabricators
Phone—(856) 541-9499
1135 Mount Ephraim Ave., Camden 08103
North Bergen Marble & Granite Corp.
Phone—(201) 945-9988
217 Palisade Ave., Cliffside Park 07010
Rich's Kitchens, Inc.
Phone—(973) 838-4026
309 Hamburg Tpke., Butler 07405
S M Counter Tops, LLC
Phone—(609) 926-9301
432 Boston Ave., Egg Harbor Township 08234
**Spaulding Fabricators Inc.**
**Custom Wholesale Countertops for the Style of Your Life**
**Phone—(732) 840-4433**
**Fax—(732) 840-4970**
**Web—www.spauldingfabricators.com**
**Email—spauldingfabricators@verizon.net**
**1136 Industrial Pkwy., Brick 08724**

**SPAULDING FABRICATORS INC.**
*Corian • Granite • Quartz • Marble*
www.spauldingfabricators.com
(732) 840-4433 / Fax: (732) 840-4970
1136 Industrial Pkwy. • Brick, NJ 08724

Stone Crafters, LLC
Phone—(609) 646-0406
6084 Reega Ave., Egg Harbor Township 08234
Stone Systems Of NJ
Phone—(973) 778-5525
95 8th St., P.O. Box 4207, Passaic 07055
Top Line Co.
Phone—(856) 662-6400
2131 Bethel Ave., Pennsauken 08110

## COUNTERTOPS — Custom

Marvic Corp./A.J.D. Stone
Phone—(908) 686-4340
2450 Iorio St., Union 07083
**Spaulding Fabricators Inc.**
**Custom Wholesale Countertops for the Style of Your Life**
**Phone—(732) 840-4433**
**Fax—(732) 840-4970**
**Web—www.spauldingfabricators.com**
**Email—spauldingfabricators@verizon.net**
**1136 Industrial Pkwy., Brick 08724**
*(see our ad under COUNTERTOPS)*

## COUNTERTOPS — Granite

Abruzzi Stone & Flooring, LLC
Phone—(856) 616-0800
1641 Marlton Pike E., Cherry Hill 08034
**ACD Custom Granite, Inc.**
**Phone—(732) 695-2400**
**Fax—(732) 695-2401**
**Web—www.acdcustomgranite.com**
**Email—cynthia@acdcustomgranite.com**
**1304 Roller Rd., Ocean 07712**
Apex Marble & Granite, Inc.
Phone—(973) 857-3655
998 Pompton Ave., Cedar Grove 07009
Atlantic Stone II, LLC
Phone—(973) 928-1458
98 Somerset St., Garfield 07026
Atlas Marble & Granite
Phone—(973) 491-5454
44 Fadem Rd., Springfield 07081
Colossus Granite & Marble, Inc.
Phone—(856) 742-0090
416 Crescent Blvd., Brooklawn 08030
Father & Son Design Center, LLC
Phone—(973) 575-8635
111 Clinton Rd., Ste. 1, Fairfield 07004
Ilkem Marble & Granite
Phone—(856) 433-8714
2010 Springdale Rd., Ste. 200, Cherry Hill 08003
J & J Corp., Inc.
Phone—(201) 313-0900
8607 River Rd., North Bergen 07047

Jersey Granite & Tile, LLC
Phone—(732) 683-1600
234 Boundary Rd., Ste. 4, Marlboro 07746
Lincoln Marble Works
Phone—(732) 381-9098
785 Martin St., P.O. Box 111, Rahway 07065
Marble & Granite Fabricators
Phone—(609) 392-2792
950 Pennsylvania Ave., Trenton 08638
Marble & Stone Crafters, LLC
Phone—(201) 343-2840
50 Johnson Ave., Ste. F, Hackensack 07601
**Marmo Enterprises, Inc.**
**Phone—(908) 486-4421**
**Fax—(732) 649-3072**
**Web—www.marmoenterprises.net**
**Email—drmarmo@marmoenterprises.net**
**468 Elizabeth Ave., Somerset 08873**
New Jersey Granite & Marble Corp.
Phone—(973) 266-8952
50 S. Center St., Unit 3, Orange 07050
**Oceana Designs, Inc.**
**Email: george.gavallas@oceanadesigns.net**
**Phone—(732) 987-6944**
**Fax—(732) 987-6947**
**Web—www.oceanadesigns.net**
**Email—sales@oceanadesigns.net**
**450 Oberlin Ave. S., Lakewood 08701**

**Oceana Designs, Inc.**
*Granite & marble countertops*
www.oceanadesigns.net
(732) 987-6944
450 Oberlin Ave. S. Lakewood, NJ 08701

Ozer International, LLC
Phone—(973) 497-5656
145 Manchester Pl., Newark 07104
Progressive Dimensions, Inc.
Phone—(732) 244-0109
44 Flint Rd., Toms River 08757
Romano & Son, Inc.
Phone—(973) 472-3240
501 Baldwin Ave., Lodi 07644
**Spaulding Fabricators Inc.**
**Custom Wholesale Countertops for the Style of Your Life**
**Phone—(732) 840-4433**
**Fax—(732) 840-4970**
**Web—www.spauldingfabricators.com**
**Email—spauldingfabricators@verizon.net**
**1136 Industrial Pkwy., Brick 08724**
*(see our ad under COUNTERTOPS)*
Stone King, Inc.
Phone—(732) 868-8687
900 Lincoln Blvd., Ste. 1, Middlesex 08846
Stone Surfaces Of Central Jersey, Inc.
Phone—(732) 745-1727
690 Jersey Ave., Unit 13, New Brunswick 08901
Top Shops, LLC
Phone—(973) 442-0050
361 W. Dewey Ave., Ste. 8, Wharton 07885
Urvesh Granite (USA), Inc.
Phone—(201) 369-3934
1777 Route 130 S., North Brunswick 08902
Workshop Stone
Phone—(973) 230-9212
281 Mount Pleasant Ave., Newark 07104

## COUNTERTOPS — Quartz

Kitchen King, Inc.
Phone—(732) 341-9660
1561 Route 9, Toms River 08755

## COUNTERTOPS — Solid Surface

ALPS Technologies, Inc.
Phone—(732) 764-0777
500 Memorial Dr., Ste. 1, Somerset 08873
Gengaro Stone, LLC
Phone—(732) 776-6000
90 S. Main St., Ocean Grove 07756
Intelco Of Delaware Valley
Phone—(856) 456-6755
250 Harvard Ave., P.O. Box 9, Westville 08093

## COUNTERTOPS — Solid Surface — *(cont.)*

Quality Solid Surface, Inc.
 Phone—(973) 357-9770
 333 Vreeland Ave., Paterson 07513

SolidSurface Designs, Inc.
 Phone—(856) 910-7720
 1651 Sherman Ave., Pennsauken 08110

Statewide Granite & Marble
 Phone—(201) 653-1700
 3257 Kennedy Blvd., Jersey City 07306

Stone Surfaces, Inc.
 Phone—(201) 935-8803
 890 Paterson Plank Rd., East Rutherford 07073

## COUPLINGS

John Crane, Inc.
 Phone—(856) 241-3507
 Fax—(856) 241-3531
 Web—www.johncrane.com
 Email—broot@johncrane.com
 301 Berkeley Dr., Swedesboro 08085

Servometer-PMG, LLC
 Contacts & Assemblies
 Phone—(973) 785-4630
 Fax—(973) 785-0756
 Web—www.servometer.com
 Email—info@servometer.com
 501 Little Falls Rd., Cedar Grove 07009

## COURT REPORTING SERVICES

Guy J. Renzi & Assocs., Inc.
 Phone—(609) 989-9199
 Fax—(609) 581-2424
 Web—www.renziassociates.com
 Email—info@renziassociates.com
 2277 State Highway 33, Ste. 410, Trenton 08690

Jersey Shore Reporting
 Phone—(732) 282-0704
 Fax—(732) 282-0714
 Web—www.jerseyshorereporting.com
 Email—info@jerseyshorereporting.com
 517 Passaic Ave., Ste. A, Spring Lake 07762

John F. Trainor Inc.
 Phone—(609) 581-1330
 Fax—(609) 581-3844
 Email—trottoj@optonline.net
 4573 S. Broad St., Ste. 110, Trenton 08620

Quick Court Reporting, LLC
 Phone—(973) 618-0872
 Fax—(973) 618-0871
 Web—www.quickreporters.com
 Email—office@quickreporters.com
 47 Brian Rd., West Caldwell 07006

Schulman, Wiegmann & Associates
 Phone—(732) 752-7800
 Fax—(732) 752-7166
 Email—bwiegmann@swreporters.com
 216 Stelton Rd., Ste. C-1, Piscataway 08854

Taylor & Friedberg, LLC
 Certified Shorthand Reporters
 Phone—(973) 285-0411
 Fax—(973) 285-9569
 Web—www.taylorfriedberg.com
 Email—csr@taylorfriedberg.com
 60 Washington St., Ste.105, Morristown 07960

## COVERS — Machinery

Air World, Inc.
 Phone—(201) 831-0700
 126 Christie Ave., Mahwah 07430

## COVERS — Plastic

Broadway Industries
 Phone—(609) 662-3970
 1 S. Middlesex Ave., Monroe 08831

Search from among 430,000 U.S. manufacturers & suppliers: IndustryNet.com

Dana Poly Inc.
 The Home of Quality Film & Bags
 Phone—(908) 474-0600 / (800) 474-1020
 Fax—(908) 474-0604
 Web—www.danapoly.com
 Email—sales@danapoly.com
 1301 W. Elizabeth Ave., Linden 07036
 *(see our ad under BAGS—Plastic)*

## COVERS — Protective

E.W.E. Auto Seat Cover Co.
 Leather, Fabric & Vinyl Automotive Seat Covers
 Phone—(201) 869-6470
 Fax—(201) 868-8491
 Email—eweauto@yahoo.com
 8431 Kennedy Blvd., North Bergen 07047

In-Pak Services, Inc.
 Phone—(973) 595-5250
 474 Getty Ave., Clifton 07011

## CRACKERS

The Snack Factory, LLC
 Phone—(609) 683-5400
 11 Tamarack Cir., Skillman 08558

## CRAFTS & SUPPLIES

Hygloss Products, Inc.
 Phone—(973) 458-1700
 45 Hathaway St., Wallington 07057

## CRANE RENTAL

Bruce R. Koerner Cranes & Equipment, Inc.
 Phone—(973) 989-7990
 Fax—(973) 989-1991
 Web—www.koernercranes.com
 Email—sales@koernercranes.com
 400 Franklin Ave., Rockaway 07866

**Bruce R. Koerner Cranes & Equipment, Inc.**
Quality Crane Rental
**973-989-7990**
FAX: 973-989-1991
**400 Franklin Avenue Rockaway, NJ 07866**
**www.koernercranes.com**
Email: sales@koernercranes.com

Shinn Cranes, LLC
 Crane Rentals, Sales, Inspection, Training & NCCCO Certification
 Phone—(732) 458-2800
 Fax—(732) 458-2833
 Web—www.shinncranes.com
 Email—info@shinncranes.com
 1600 Ocean Ave., Lakewood 08701
 *(see our ad under CRANES)*

## CRANE SERVICES

Shinn Cranes, LLC
 Crane Rentals, Sales, Inspection, Training & NCCCO Certification
 Phone—(732) 458-2800
 Fax—(732) 458-2833
 Web—www.shinncranes.com
 Email—info@shinncranes.com
 1600 Ocean Ave., Lakewood 08701
 *(see our ad under CRANES)*

## CRANES

Atlantic Equipment Construction Co.
 In business over 50 years. Modular sets and hydraulic lifts.
 Phone—(609) 494-5321 / (609) 597-9690
 Fax—(609) 494-2702
 Email—atlanticequip@msn.com
 8101 Bay Ter., Harvey Cedars 08008

Cranez, Inc.
 For more than 20 yrs., serving the Tri-State area. Offering free no-obligation est.; providing svc. 24 hrs., 7 days a week & no-cost site checks. Operators are CCO/Natnl. Commission certified, have TWIC credentials & O.S.H.A 30-hrs trained
 Phone—(856) 262-0288 / (877) 262-0288
 Fax—(856) 262-2654
 Web—www.cranezincnj.com
 Email—cranez06@aol.com
 2610 S. Black Horse Pike, Williamstown 08094

Garden State Engine & Equipment Co., Inc.
 Phone—(908) 534-5444
 3509 U.S. Highway 22, Branchburg 08876

Hoffman Equipment, Inc.
 Phone—(856) 875-0036
 2610 S. Black Horse Pike, Williamstown 08094

P & A Crane & Hoist Co.
 Phone—(908) 527-6990
 369 Reuter Ave., Elizabeth 07202

Shinn Cranes, LLC
 Crane Rentals, Sales, Inspection, Training & NCCCO Certification
 Phone—(732) 458-2800
 Fax—(732) 458-2833
 Web—www.shinncranes.com
 Email—info@shinncranes.com
 1600 Ocean Ave., Lakewood 08701

**Shinn Cranes, LLC**
Crane Rentals, Sales, Inspection, Training & NCCCO Certification
**Thomas J. Shinn, Operations Manager**
**(732) 458-2800**
**www.shinncranes.com**
1600 Ocean Ave. Lakewood, NJ 08701

## CRANES — Truck & Trailer

Dunbar Mfg., LLC
 Phone—(856) 346-0666
 2400 Egg Harbor Rd., Lindenwold 08021

## CRATES — Wooden

A B C Crating & Rigging Co.
 Phone—(973) 684-0046
 1-21 Erie St., Paterson 07524

Jan Packaging, Inc.
 100 Harrison St., Dover 07801
 Email—kcaristia@janpackaging.com
 Toll Free Ph: (888)4-JANPAK
 Phone—(973) 361-7200
 Fax—(973) 361-3306
 Web—www.janpackaging.com
 P.O. Box 448, Dover 07802
 *(see our ad under PACKAGING—Industrial)*

Rectico, Inc.
 Phone—(973) 575-0009
 12 Gloria Ln., Unit 1, Fairfield 07004

Tri-State Crating & Pallet Co.
 Phone—(973) 357-8293 / (888) 845-0050
 Fax—(973) 357-8296
 Web—www.tristatecrating.com
 Email—sales@tristatecrating.com
 85 Fulton St., Paterson 07501

**Tri-State Crating & Pallet Co.**
*Wooden Crates*
973-357-8293 • 888-845-0050
FAX: 973-357-8296
www.tristatecrating.com sales@tristatecrating.com
85 Fulton Street • Paterson, NJ 07501

## CREDIT UNIONS

**Garden Savings Federal Credit Union**
　Phone—(973) 576-2000 / (888) 554-9328
　Fax—(973) 316-0317
　Web—www.gardensavings.org
　Email—memberservices@
　gardensavingsfcu.com
　129 Littleton Rd., Ste. 101, Parsippany 07054

**Jersey Central Federal Credit Union**
　Phone—(908) 272-3040
　Web—www.jerseycentralfcu.com
　23 North Ave. E., Cranford 07016

## CRUCIBLES

Bartley Crucible Refractories
　Phone—(609) 393-0066
　15 Muirhead Ave., P.O. Box 5464, Trenton 08638

## CRUSHERS

Atlantic Coast Crushers, Inc.
　Phone—(908) 259-9292
　128 Market St., Kenilworth 07033

**Franklin Miller, Inc.**
　Phone—(973) 535-9200
　Fax—(973) 535-6269
　Web—www.franklinmiller.com
　Email—info@franklinmiller.com
　60 Okner Pkwy., P.O. Box 070663, Livingston
　07039

# Franklin Miller, Inc.

*Size Reduction Processors*

## (973) 535-9200
## Fax: 973-535-6269

www.franklinmiller.com

info@franklinmiller.com

60 Okner Pkwy.

Livingston, NJ 07039

International Process Equipment Co.
　Phone—(856) 665-4007
　9300 Route 130 N., Pennsauken 08110

## CRYOGENIC EQUIPMENT

Cryofab, Inc.
　Phone—(908) 686-3636
　540 N. Michigan Ave., P.O. Box 485, Kenilworth
　07033
Cryogenic Equipment & Repair Co., Inc. (Cerco)
　Phone—(732) 727-1555
　3143 Bordentown Ave., Bldg. 4, Parlin 08859

*Send an RFQ (request for quote)*
*to multiple suppliers at*

**IndustryNet.com**

Independence Cryogenic Engineering, LLC
　Phone—(609) 294-0012
　Fax—(609) 294-0163
　Web—www.cryopumper.com
　Email—frankhughes@cryopumper.com
　891 Route 9 N., P.O. Box 527, Little Egg Harbor
　08087

**INDEPENDENCE**
CRYOGENIC ENGINEERING, LLC
MRI REFRIGERATION SPECIALIST

*MRI Refrigeration Specialist*
**609-294-0012**
**www.cryopumper.com**
891 Route 9 N PO Box 527  Little Egg Harbor, NJ 08087

## CRYSTALS — Laser

Deltronic Crystal Industries
　Phone—(973) 328-7000
　60 Harding Ave., Dover 07801

## CRYSTALS — Optical

Reflex Analytical Corporation
　Phone—(201) 444-8958
　643 Albert Pl., Ridgewood 07450

## CRYSTALS — Oscillator

Cardinal Components, Inc.
　Phone—(973) 785-1333
　145 U.S. Highway 46 W., Wayne Interchange I,
　Wayne 07470

## CURTAIN PARTITIONS

**Beltor Mfg. Corp.**
　**Cubicle Curtains & Curtain Tracks**
　Phone—(856) 768-5570 / (856) 424-1900
　Fax—(856) 768-5723
　Web—www.beltormfg.com
　Email—beltormfginc@hotmail.com
　50 Union Ave., Ste. 12, Berlin 08009

## CURTAINS

Ackerson Drapery & Decorating Services, Inc.
　Phone—(732) 905-4433
　500 James St., Ste. 14, Lakewood 08701

## CURTAINS — Cubicle

**Beltor Mfg. Corp.**
　**Cubicle Curtains & Curtain Tracks**
　Phone—(856) 768-5570 / (856) 424-1900
　Fax—(856) 768-5723
　Web—www.beltormfg.com
　Email—beltormfginc@hotmail.com
　50 Union Ave., Ste. 12, Berlin 08009
Ka-Lor Cubicle & Supply Co., Inc.
　Phone—(201) 891-8077
　P.O. Box 804, Fair Lawn 07410

## CURTAINS — Shower

Hospi-Tel Mfg. Co., Inc.
　Phone—(973) 678-7100
　545 N. Arlington Ave., East Orange 07017

## CURTAINS — Stage

Hansen Co., Inc., Joseph C.
　Phone—(201) 222-1677
　629 Grove St., Ste. 26, Jersey City 07310

## CUTLERY

Lifetime Brands, Inc., Distribution Center
　Phone—(609) 208-1500
　12 Applegate Dr., Robbinsville 08691
Master Cutlery, Inc.
　Phone—(201) 271-7600
　700 Penhorn Ave., Secaucus 07094

## CUTTING FLUIDS — Metal

**Hangsterfer's Laboratories, Inc.**
　Phone—(856) 468-0216
　Fax—(856) 468-0200
　Web—www.hangsterfers.com
　Email—sales@hangsterfers.com
　175 Ogden Rd., Mantua 08051
　*(see our ad under LUBRICANTS—Metalworking)*

## CUTTING MACHINERY

ABOX Automation Corp.
　Phone—(973) 659-9611
　2 Frassetto Way, Unit 2, Lincoln Park 07035
Forthmann Machines, Inc.
　Phone—(201) 818-1221
　1495 MacArthur Blvd., Mahwah 07430

## CUTTING TOOLS — Carbide

BlackHawk Industrial, Atlantic Tool Systems Div.
　Phone—(973) 238-0009
　170 5th Ave., Hawthorne 07506
Sandvik, Inc. (H Q)
　Phone—(201) 794-5000
　1702 Nevins Rd., P.O. Box 428, Fair Lawn 07410
Triple-T Cutting Tools, Inc.
　Phone—(856) 768-0800
　135 Edgewood Ave., West Berlin 08091

## CUTTING TOOLS — Screw Machine

Tool Shop, Inc.
　Phone—(856) 767-8077
　335 Chestnut Ave., P.O. Box 36, West Berlin
　08091

## CYBERSECURITY RISK MANAGEMENT

**Direct Computer Resources, Inc.**
　**Protecting personally identifiable information (PII)**
　Phone—(201) 848-0018 / (800) 878-4211
　Fax—(201) 848-0064
　Web—www.datavantage.com
　Email—info@datavantage.com
　120 Birch Rd., Franklin Lakes 07417
　*(see our ad under DATA MASKING SOFTWARE)*

## CYLINDER HEADS — Rebuilt

Delta Sales Co., Inc.
　Phone—(973) 838-0371
　1355 State Route 23, Butler 07405
R A M Hydraulics
　Phone—(732) 237-0904
　215 B. Hickory Ln., P.O. Box 416, Bayville 08721

## CYLINDERS

Pamarco Global Graphics, Imaging Div.
　Phone—(856) 829-4585
　1 Roto Ave., Palmyra 08065
**Van Hydraulics**
　Phone—(732) 442-5500
　Fax—(732) 442-5443
　Web—www.vanhydraulics.com
　Email—admin@vanhydraulics.com
　643 Sayre Ave., Perth Amboy 08861

## CYLINDERS — Gas

Kaplan Industries, Inc.
　Phone—(856) 779-8181
　10 Morris Ave., Route 73, Maple Shade 08052
Leland Ltd., Inc.
　Phone—(908) 561-2000
　2614 S. Clinton Ave., P.O. Box 466, South
　Plainfield 07080

## CYLINDERS — Hydraulic

Industrial Hydraulics & Rubber, LLC
　Phone—(856) 966-2600
　458 Atlantic Ave., Camden 08104

## CYLINDERS — Steel

**Arntzen Corp.**
Mfr. Of Rolled & Welded Steel Cylinders-Cones-Pipe-Shapes-Fittings
Phone—(815) 334-0788 / (800) 957-7655
Fax—(815) 334-0778
Web—www.ArntzenRolling.com
Email—Sales@ArntzenCorp.com
14600 Washington St., Woodstock, IL 60098

## DAIRY EQUIPMENT & MACHINERY

Grand Equipment Of America
Phone—(201) 784-1101
267 Livingston St., Northvale 07647
WCB Ice Cream
Phone—(201) 784-1101
Fax—(201) 784-1116
Web—www.wcbicecream.com
Email—nwhite@wcbicecream.com
267 Livingston St., Northvale 07647

## DAIRY PRODUCTS

Amish Dairy Products, LLC
Phone—(973) 256-7676
41 Vreeland Ave., Ste. 101, Totowa 07512
Clofine Dairy & Food Products, Inc.
Phone—(609) 653-1000
1407 New Rd., P.O. Box 335, Linwood 08221
Cumberland Dairy, Inc.
Phone—(856) 451-1300
80 Edward Ave., Bridgeton 08302
Dairy Delight, LLC
Phone—(201) 939-7878
1 Industrial Dr., Rutherford 07070
Halo Farm, Inc.
Phone—(609) 695-3311
970 Spruce St., Lawrenceville 08648
Maglione's Italian Ices
Phone—(732) 283-0705
111 Madison St., Iselin 08830
Tuscan Dairy, Inc.
Phone—(609) 499-2600
117 Cumberland Blvd., Burlington 08016

## DAIRY PRODUCTS — Wholesale

Cumberland Dairy, Inc.
Phone—(856) 451-1300
899 Landis Ave., P.O. Box 308, Rosenhayn 08352
Hunter Walton & Co., Inc.
Phone—(732) 805-0808
120 Circle Dr. N., Piscataway 08854
MCT Dairies, Inc.
Phone—(973) 258-9600
15 Bleeker St., Millburn 07041

## DAMPERS

D.E.B. Mfg., Inc.
Phone—(732) 364-7007
850 Towbin Ave., Lakewood 08701

## DAMPERS — Ventilation System

Trolex Corp.
Phone—(201) 794-8004
20 Bushes Ln., Elmwood Park 07407

## DANCEWEAR

Bal Togs Industries
Phone—(201) 866-0201
6605-09 Smith Ave., North Bergen 07047
Ballet Makers, Inc. (H Q)
Phone—(973) 595-9000
1 Campus Rd., Totowa 07512

## DATA ACQUISITION SYSTEMS

CG Automation Solutions USA
Phone—(973) 379-7400
60 Fadem Rd., Springfield 07081
Phillips Scientific
Phone—(201) 934-8015
31 Industrial Ave., Ste. 1, Mahwah 07430

## DATA COMMUNICATION EQUIPMENT

Walk The Technology Solution
Phone—(856) 222-0643
9000 Commerce Pkwy., Ste. H, Mount Laurel 08054

## DATA MASKING SOFTWARE

**Direct Computer Resources, Inc.**
Protecting personally identifiable information (PII)
Phone—(201) 848-0018 / (800) 878-4211
Fax—(201) 848-0064
Web—www.datavantage.com
Email—info@datavantage.com
120 Birch Rd., Franklin Lakes 07417

Direct Computer Resources, Inc.
DataVantage®
Protecting Personally Identifiable Information (PII)
www.datavantage.com / (800) 878-4211
120 Birch Rd. • Franklin Lakes, NJ 07417

## DAVITS

St. Croix Marine Products, Inc.
Phone—(732) 237-8800
235 Hickory Ln., Bayville 08721

## DEAERATORS

Cornell Machine Co., The
Phone—(973) 379-6860
45 Brown Ave., Springfield 07081
Enpro, Inc.
Phone—(908) 236-2137
1401 U.S. Highway 22, P.O. Box 418, Lebanon 08833

## DEBURRING MACHINERY

Century Engineering Co., Inc.
Phone—(973) 779-3900
4 Orono St., Clifton 07013
Falls Products, Inc.
Phone—(973) 537-6464
220 Franklin Rd., 1st Fl., Randolph 07869

## DECALS

Johnson & Mayer, Inc.
Phone—(201) 646-1717
58 Hobart St., Hackensack 07601
Superior Graphics & Signs, Inc.
Phone—(732) 625-0101
576 Casino Dr., Howell 07731

## DECKS

**Canam Steel Corp.**
Steel decks
Phone—(908) 561-3484 / (800) 526-7518
Fax—(908) 561-6772
Web—www.canam-construction.com
14 Harmich Rd., South Plainfield 07080

## DECKS — Metal

Roof Deck, Inc.
Phone—(609) 448-6666
80 Twin Rivers Dr., P.O. Box 295, Hightstown 08520

## DECORATING SERVICES

Decor, Inc.
Phone—(201) 569-1900
60 Cedar Ln., Englewood 07631

## DECORATIONS — Seasonal

Blackwell Assocs., Inc.
Phone—(732) 238-8000
15 Kimberly Rd., East Brunswick 08816

## DEFOAMING AGENTS

**Munzing**
1455 Broad St., Bloomfield 07003
Formulators of Specialty Additive Defoamers for over 180 years
Phone—(973) 279-1306 / (800) 524-0055
Fax—(973) 338-0420
Web—www.munzing.com
Email—info@munzing.us
975 Ultra Dr., Clover, SC 29710

## DEHYDRATING EQUIPMENT

Drytech, Inc.
Phone—(609) 758-1794
54 Wrightstown Cookstown Rd., P.O. Box 249, Cookstown 08511

## DELIVERY SERVICES

**Mercury Mail & Messenger Service**
Phone—(973) 227-9315
Fax—(973) 227-6110
Web—www.mercurydelivery.com
Email—joe@mercurydelivery.com
P.O. Box 1241, Caldwell 07007

## DEMOLITION CONTRACTORS

**American Coring & Supply, Inc.**
Phone—(732) 255-8787 / (732) 513-8642
Fax—(732) 255-5559
Email—amcoring@aol.com
89 Susan St., Toms River 08753

## DENTAL EQUIPMENT & SUPPLIES

**Acteon, Inc.**
Phone—(856) 222-9988
Fax—(856) 222-4726
Web—www.acteongroup.com
Email—info@us.acteongroup.com
124 Gaither Dr., Ste. 140, Mount Laurel 08054
George Taub Products
Phone—(201) 798-5353
277 New York Ave., Jersey City 07307
Keystone Industries
Phone—(856) 663-4700
616 Hollywood Ave., Cherry Hill 08002
M T I Precision Products, LLC
Phone—(732) 905-7440
730 Airport Rd., Lakewood 08701
Palisades Dental, LLC
Phone—(201) 569-0050
111 Cedar Ln., P.O. Box 5419, Englewood 07631
Titan Implants, Inc.
Phone—(201) 439-0027
18 Columbia Ave., Bergenfield 07621

## DENTAL EQUIPMENT & SUPPLIES — Wholesale

Sullivan Dental Products, Inc.
Phone—(973) 227-3533
45 U.S. Highway 46, Montville 07058

Search from among 430,000 U.S. manufacturers & suppliers at
IndustryNet.com

© Copyright 2015 Manufacturers' News, Inc.

**A55**

## DENTAL INSTRUMENTS

Essential Dental Systems, Inc.
Phone—(201) 487-9090
89 Leuning St., Ste. 2, South Hackensack 07606
Handler Mfg. Co., Inc.
Phone—(908) 233-7796
612 North Ave. E., Westfield 07090
SS White Burs, Inc.
Phone—(800) 535-2877
1145 Towbin Ave., Lakewood 08701

## DENTAL MATERIALS

DMG America, LLC
Phone—(201) 894-5505
242 S. Dean St., Englewood 07631

## DENTAL PRODUCTS

Dental Models & Designs, Inc.
Phone—(973) 472-8009
20 Passaic St., Ste. 3, Garfield 07026
Ivoclar Vivadent Mfg., Inc.
Phone—(732) 563-4755
500 Memorial Dr., Somerset 08873
Lincoln Dental Supply, Inc.
Phone—(856) 488-1333
616 Hollywood Ave., Cherry Hill 08002
Natural Dental Studios, Inc.
Phone—(908) 281-0089
216 U.S. Highway 206, Ste. 23, Hillsborough 08844

## DENTAL PROSTHETICS

Amory A & E Campian Dental Art, Inc.
Phone—(732) 240-0323
803 Main St., Ste. 2, Toms River 08753
E M Orthodontic Labs, Inc.
Phone—(201) 652-4411
6 Lafayette Pl., P.O. Box 112, Waldwick 07463
Fields, Inc., Samuel H.
Phone—(201) 343-4626
197 Union St., Hackensack 07601
Garden State Dental Prosthetics, Inc.
Phone—(732) 922-6650
805 4th Ave., Asbury Park 07712
Helm Dental, Inc.
Phone—(201) 342-2915
111 Troast St., Hackensack 07601
Malin Corp., James S.
Phone—(973) 831-9135
3 Victoria Ln., Ringwood 07456

## DESIGN & BUILD CONTRACTORS

**Stanker & Galetto, Inc.**
**Phone—(856) 692-8098**
**Fax—(856) 692-3058**
**Web—www.stankergaletto.com**
**Email—rkadlac@stankergaletto.com**
**317 W. Elmer Rd., Vineland 08360**
*(see our ad on this page)*

## DESIGNERS — Industrial

**Insync Design**
**Phone—(973) 428-9090**
**Fax—(973) 428-8884**
**Web—www.insyncdesign.com**
**Email—zambelli@insyncdesign.com**
**114 Algonquin Pkwy., Whippany 07981**

## DESSERTS

Bindi North America, Inc.
Phone—(973) 751-1754
507 Main St., Belleville 07109
Bindi North America, Inc. (H Q)
Phone—(973) 812-8118
630 Belleville Tpke., Kearny 07032
RW Delights, Inc.
Phone—(718) 683-1038
50 Division Ave., Ste. 44, Millington 07946
Taste It Presents, Inc.
Phone—(908) 241-9191
200 Sumner Ave., Kenilworth 07033

## STANKER & GALETTO
### Turning Visions Into Reality!
Design/Build • Construction Managers • General Contractors
317 W. Elmer Rd., Vineland, NJ 08360
856-692-8098   rkadlac@stankergaletto.com
www.stankergaletto.com

Tofutti Brands, Inc.
Phone—(908) 272-2400
50 Jackson Dr., Cranford 07016

## DETERGENTS

Aqua Products, Inc.
Phone—(856) 829-8444
2703 River Rd., P.O. Box 231, Cinnaminson 08077
Cavalier Chemical Co.
Phone—(908) 558-0110
26 Papetti Plz., Elizabeth 07206
Diamond Chemical Company, Inc.
Phone—(201) 935-4300
Union Ave. & DuBois St., P.O. Box 7428, East Rutherford 07073
Dynamic Blending Co., Inc.
Phone—(856) 541-6626
1475 S. 6th St., Camden 08104
Envirochem, Inc.
Phone—(732) 238-6700
425 Whitehead Ave., South River 08882
Metro-Chem, Inc.
Phone—(973) 589-2800
24 Pennsylvania Ave., P.O. Box 401, Kearny 07032
Polycracker, Inc.
Phone—(973) 335-2828
487 Division St., Boonton 07005
SWI International, Inc.
Phone—(973) 334-2525
487 Division St., Boonton 07005
Tessie's Soap Box
Phone—(201) 533-8337
65 South St., Jersey City 07307

## DEWATERING EQUIPMENT

**Komline-Sanderson Engineering**
**Phone—(908) 234-1000 / (800) 225-5457**
**Fax—(908) 234-9487**
**Web—www.komline.com**
**Email—info@komline.com**
**12 Holland Ave., Peapack 07977**

## DIAGNOSTIC EQUIPMENT

**Diopsys, Inc.**
**Visual evoked potential (VEP) vision testing & medical devices**
**Phone—(973) 244-0622**
**Fax—(973) 244-0670**
**Web—www.diopsys.com**
**16 Chapin Rd., Ste. 912, P.O. Box 672, Pine Brook 07058**
Ortho-Clinical Diagnostics, Inc. (H Q)
Phone—(908) 218-1300
1001 U.S. Highway 202, P.O. Box 350, Raritan 08869

## DIAGNOSTIC REAGENTS

E N G Scientific, Inc.
Phone—(973) 472-7200
82 Industrial St. E., Clifton 07012
Origio, Inc.
Phone—(856) 762-2000
77 Elbo Ln., Mount Laurel 08054

Pharmaseq, Inc.
Phone—(732) 355-0100
11 Deerpark Dr., Ste. 104, Monmouth Junction 08852
Zeus Scientific, Inc.
Phone—(908) 526-3744
200 Evans Way, Somerville 08876

## DIAGNOSTIC TEST KITS

AIRMED Biotech, LLC
Phone—(215) 378-9114
510 Titus Rd., Lambertville 08530
Akers Biosciences, Inc.
Phone—(856) 848-8698
201 Grove Rd., Thorofare 08086
American Bionostica, Inc.
Phone—(856) 467-7070
510 Heron Dr., Ste. 203, Swedesboro 08085
AP Diagnostic Laboratories, Inc.
Phone—(732) 906-7800
1692 Oak Tree Rd., Ste. 17, Edison 08820
Cenogenics Corp.
Phone—(732) 536-6457
100 Route 520, P.O. Box 308, Morganville 07751
Church & Dwight Co., Inc.
Phone—(609) 655-6000
326 Half Acre Rd., Cranbury 08512
Diagnostic Specialties
Phone—(732) 549-4011
4 Leonard St., Metuchen 08840
**DRG International, Inc.**
**Phone—(973) 564-7555**
**Fax—(973) 564-7556**
**Web—www.drg-international.com**
**Email—corp@drg-international.com**
**841 Mountain Ave., Springfield 07081**
Enterix, Inc.
Phone—(732) 429-1899
236 Fernwood Ave., Edison 08837
Euroimmun US, Inc.
Phone—(973) 656-1000
1100 The American Rd., Ste. 1, Morris Plains 07950
**Hilin Life Products, Inc.**
**Phone—(973) 648-0265**
**Fax—(973) 648-0267**
**Web—www.knowhen.com**
**Email—info@hilinlife.com**
**211 Warren St., Ste. 211, Newark 07103**
Immunostics, Inc.
Phone—(732) 918-0770
3505 Sunset Ave., Ocean 07712
Laboratory Diagnostics Co., Inc.
Phone—(732) 536-6300
100 Route 520, P.O. Box 160, Morganville 07751
Princeton BioMeditech Corp.
Phone—(732) 274-1000
4242 U.S. Highway 1, Monmouth Junction 08852
Roche Molecular Systems, Inc.
Phone—(908) 253-7200
1080 U.S. Highway 202 S., Branchburg 08876
Scimedx Corp.
Phone—(973) 625-8822
53 Richboynton Rd., Dover 07801
Sensonics, Inc.
Phone—(800) 547-8838
125 White Horse Pike, P.O. Box 112, Haddon Heights 08035

## DIAPERS

Bentley Mfg., Inc.
Phone—(732) 572-5933
41 Ethel Rd., Piscataway 08854

## DIE CASTINGS

**ABCO Die Casters, Inc.**
Email: jvitollo@abcodiecasters.com
Founded in 1971, serving numerous industries
throughout North America by supplying quality zinc
die castings & powder coated components
Phone—(973) 624-7030
Fax—(973) 624-7425
Web—www.abcodiecasters.com
39 Tompkins Point Rd., Newark 07114

Carteret Die Casting Corp.
Phone—(732) 246-0070
74 Veronica Ave., P.O. Box 5610, Somerset 08875

Premier Die Casting Co., Inc.
Phone—(732) 634-3000
1177 Rahway Ave., Avenel 07001

## DIE CASTINGS — Zinc

**Carteret Die Casting Corp.**
Email: jmudrak@carteretdiecasting.com
Phone—(732) 246-0070
Fax—(732) 246-0196
Web—www.carteretdiecasting.com
74 Veronica Ave., P.O. Box 5610, Somerset
08875

## DIE COMPONENTS

Dura-Carb, Inc.
Phone—(973) 697-6665
204 Chamberlain Rd., P.O. Box 407, Oak Ridge
07438

Precision Ball Specialties, Inc.
Phone—(856) 881-5646
1451 Glassboro Rd., Williamstown 08094

## DIE CUTTING

Bielen Graphic Arts, R. J.
Phone—(732) 545-3501
6 Jules Ln., New Brunswick 08901

BOBST North America, Inc.
Phone—(973) 226-8000
146 Harrison Ave., Roseland 07068

Danielle Die Cut Products, Inc.
Phone—(973) 278-3000
238 Lindbergh Pl., Paterson 07503

Davis Paper Dimensions, Inc.
Phone—(856) 931-6040
400 Benigno Blvd., Bellmawr 08031

Dynamic Die Cutting & Finishings
Phone—(973) 589-8338
104-110 South St., Newark 07114

Gleicher Mfg. Corp.
Phone—(908) 233-2211
851 Jerusalem Rd., Scotch Plains 07076

Grand Displays, Inc.
Phone—(201) 994-1500
12 Empire Blvd., Moonachie 07074

Nal-Pak Paper Specialties, LLC
Phone—(732) 462-5196
18 Monterey Ln., Englishtown 07726

O & C Die Cutters & Finishers
Phone—(973) 890-7778
16 Andrews Dr., West Paterson 07424

Prestige Assocs., Inc.
Phone—(609) 393-1509
39 Mead St., Trenton 08638

Quick Cut Stamping & Embossing, Inc.
Phone—(856) 321-0050
815 E. Main St., Maple Shade 08052

Raybold Mfg., Inc.
Phone—(856) 327-7733
102 S. 8th St., Millville 08332

Sabre Die Cutting Co., Inc.
Phone—(973) 357-9800
68 Mill St., Paterson 07501

*find additional suppliers at*
**IndustryNet.com**

**Specialty Rubber, Inc.**
A Veteran Owned Company
Phone—(609) 704-2555 / (800) 249-5848
Fax—(609) 704-8020
Web—www.specialtyrubber.com
Email—specrub@yahoo.com
4500 White Horse Pike, P.O. Box 483, Elwood
08217
*(also see our ads under GASKETS — Rubber & SHIELDING —
EMI/RFI)*

**Speciality Rubber, Inc.**
*A Veteran Owned Company*
**(800) 249-5848**
**(609) 704-2555 • Fax (609) 704-8020**
**www.specialtyrubber.com**
**specrub@yahoo.com**
4500 White Horse Pike, P.O. Box 483 • Elwood, NJ 08217

V M C Die Cutting Corp.
Phone—(973) 450-4655
357 Cortlandt St., Belleville 07109

Valenta & Sons, Inc., Jerry
Phone—(973) 423-2220
40 Schoon Ave., Hawthorne 07506

Valley Die-Cutting Co., Inc.
Phone—(973) 731-8884
10 Park Ave., West Orange 07052

## DIES — Cutting

Container Graphics Corp.
Phone—(732) 922-1180
3535 Highway 66, Parkway 100, Bldg. 2, Neptune
07753

**Unity Graphics & Engraving/Unity Steel Rule
Die**
Rubber Printing, Plate Engraving & Steel Rule Dies
Phone—(201) 569-6400
Fax—(201) 569-2956
Web—www.gounity.com
Email—unitypres@gounity.com
210 S. Van Brunt St., P.O. Box 88, Englewood
07631

US Magic Box, Inc.
Phone—(973) 772-2070
221 McArthur Ave., Garfield 07026

## DIES — Precision

**Graybill's Tool & Die, Inc.**
Email: geoff@graybills.com
Phone—(717) 665-5546
Fax—(717) 665-3107
Web—www.graybills.com
147 W. High St., Manheim, PA 17545
*(see our ads under MACHINE BUILDERS—Custom &
MACHINING — Precision)*

## DIES — Stamping

F & G Tool & Die, Inc.
Phone—(908) 241-5880
195 Sumner Ave., Kenilworth 07033

## DIES — Steel Rule

Ace Steel Rule Die Co.
Phone—(609) 654-4161
251 Atsion Rd., Medford 08055

Barcus Co., Inc., Edgar C.
Phone—(856) 456-0204
Route 45 & Park Ave., P.O. Box 128, Westville
08093

Die Tech, LLC
Phone—(201) 343-8324
58 McKinley St., Hackensack 07601

Golden Rule, Inc.
Phone—(856) 663-3074
7150 N. Park Dr., Ste. 620, Pennsauken 08109

Kessler Steel Rule Die, Inc.
Phone—(856) 767-0231
1004 Industrial Dr., Ste. 10, West Berlin 08091

Lasercam, Inc.
Phone—(201) 941-1262
1039 Hoyt Ave., Ridgefield 07657

Master Craft Steel Rule Die
Phone—(973) 674-7662
84 Bell St., Orange 07050

MMC Steel Rule Dies
Phone—(973) 760-3286
864 New Brunswick Ave., Piscataway 08854

Peterson Steel Rule Die Corp.
Phone—(201) 935-6180
35 Broad St., Carlstadt 07072

Precision Steel Rule Die
Phone—(856) 931-2548
400 Benigno Blvd., Rear, Bellmawr 08031

Redkeys Dies, Inc.
Phone—(856) 456-7890
1307 Market St., Gloucester City 08030

Rule One, Inc.
Phone—(973) 661-4563
68 E. Centre St., Nutley 07110

Smith Steel Rule Die, Michael
Phone—(856) 692-5510
2479 S. Main Rd., Vineland 08360

Spec Steel Rule Dies, Inc.
Phone—(609) 443-9200
92 N. Main St., Bldg. 1-B, P.O. Box 33, Windsor
08561

Supreme Steel Rule Dies, Inc.
Phone—(973) 345-9474
985 Madison Ave., Paterson 07501

**Unity Graphics & Engraving/Unity Steel Rule
Die**
Rubber Printing, Plate Engraving & Steel Rule Dies
Phone—(201) 569-6400
Fax—(201) 569-2956
Web—www.gounity.com
Email—unitypres@gounity.com
210 S. Van Brunt St., P.O. Box 88, Englewood
07631

Zin-Tech
Phone—(856) 661-0900
1416 Union Ave., Pennsauken 08110

## DIESEL ENGINES — Sales & Service

**Atlantic Detroit Diesel-Allison, LLC**
Phone—(201) 291-8415
Fax—(201) 845-3288
Web—www.atlanticdda.com
33 Gregg St., Lodi 07644

Stewart & Stevenson Power Products, LLC- ADDA
Div.
Phone—(201) 489-5800
180 Route 17 S., P.O. Box 950, Lodi 07644

## DIETARY SUPPLEMENTS

ABRAZIL, LLC
Phone—(732) 658-5191
1 Jacques Ave., Kendall Park 08824

AkPharma, Inc.
Phone—(609) 645-5100
6840 Old Egg Harbor Rd., Egg Harbor Township
08234

Ethical Alternative Products, LLC
Phone—(201) 251-7771
525 Cedar Hill Ave., Wyckoff 07481

Garden State Nutritionals, LLC
Phone—(973) 575-9200
8 Henderson Dr., West Caldwell 07006

Prime Pack, LLC
Phone—(732) 253-7734
262 Old New Brunswick Rd., Ste. N, Piscataway
08854

R-Kane Products, Inc.
Phone—(856) 663-0644
8351 National Hwy., Pennsauken 08110

Tomer Laboratories
Phone—(732) 560-1885
350 Campus Dr., Somerset 08873

Triarco Industries, Inc. (H Q)
Phone—(973) 942-5100
2 Brighton Rd., Ste. 404, Clifton 07012

*Search from among 430,000
U.S. manufacturers & suppliers:*
**IndustryNet.com**

INDUSTRY

## DIGITAL RECORDING SYSTEMS

**Vision Research, Inc.**
**High Speed Digital Imaging Systems**
Phone—(973) 696-4500
Fax—(973) 696-0560
Web—www.visionresearch.com
Email—phantom@visionresearch.com
100 Dey Rd., Wayne 07470
*(see our ad under CAMERAS)*

## DIGITAL SIGNAL PROCESSING

Pentek, Inc.
Phone—(201) 818-5900
1 Park Way, 2nd Fl., Upper Saddle River 07458

## DIODES

Dean Technology, Inc.
Phone—(732) 938-4499
5027 Industrial Rd., Unit 4, P.O. Box 848,
Farmingdale 07727
**New Jersey Semiconductor Products, Inc.**
**We are your source for all your semiconductor needs**
**& requirements**
Phone—(973) 376-2922 / (212) 227-6005
Fax—(973) 376-8960
Web—www.njsemi.com
Email—sales@njsemi.com
20 Stern Ave., Springfield 07081
Thorlabs, Inc.
Phone—(973) 300-3000
56 Sparta Ave., Newton 07860

## DIRECT MARKETING SERVICES

Federal Direct (H Q)
Phone—(973) 667-9800
95 Main Ave., Ste. 2, Clifton 07014

## DISASTER RECOVERY SERVICES

**GWS Contractors, Inc.**
**Since 1977, specializing in Environmental**
**Remediation, Tank Removals, Emergency Response**
**Services & Vapor Intrusion Mitigation. Providing a 24**
**hour, 7 day a week customer response network**
Phone—(732) 297-4847
Fax—(732) 297-4389
Web—www.gwscontractors.com
Email—contact@gwscontractors.com
105 Fresh Ponds Rd., Jamesburg 08831

## DISC JOCKEY EQUIPMENT

Gemini DJ & Pro Audio
Phone—(732) 346-0061
107 Trumbull St., Ste. F-8, Elizabeth 07206

## DISINFECTANTS

**(also see 'Cleaners—Household')**

Microgen, Inc.
Phone—(973) 575-9025
33 Clinton Rd., Ste. 102, West Caldwell 07006

## DISINFECTING EQUIPMENT & DISINFECTORS

Glasco UV, LLC
Phone—(201) 934-3348
126 Christie Ave., Ste. 1, Mahwah 07430

## DISPENSING EQUIPMENT

Autobar Systems Corp.
Phone—(732) 922-3355
1 Meridian Rd., Eatontown 07724
Mega Pumps, L. P.
Phone—(732) 578-9100
611 Industrial Way W., Eatontown 07724

*Do nationwide searches for*
*products & services at:*
**IndustryNet.com**

## DISPENSING PUMPS

**Multiforce Systems Corp.**
**Automated fuel management integrated systems for**
**the transportation industry**
Phone—(609) 683-4242
Fax—(609) 683-4835
Web—www.fuelforce.com
Email—sales@fuelforce.com
101 Wall St., Princeton 08540
*(see our ad under PUMPS — Gasoline Dispensing)*

## DISPLAY MATERIALS

10-31, Inc.
Phone—(908) 496-4946
2 W. Crisman Rd., Columbia 07832
**American Tube & Paper**
**80 Furler St., Totowa 07512**
Phone—(973) 256-3600
Fax—(973) 785-3341
Web—www.AmericanPaperProducts.com
Email—sales@americanpaperproducts.com
P.O. Box 68, Totowa 07511
*(see our ad under MAILING TUBES)*
Pharmakon Corp.
Phone—(856) 829-3161
2200 Wallace Blvd., Unit C, P.O. Box 217,
Cinnaminson 08077

## DISPLAY RACKS

Fixturecraft Corp.
Phone—(908) 272-8145
1457 Raritan Rd., Ste. 201, Clark 07066
RB & A, Inc.
Phone—(973) 726-0830
350 Sparta Ave., Bldg. C, Sparta 07871
Spark Wire Products Co., Inc.
Phone—(973) 773-6945
158 River Rd., Clifton 07014
Wagner Rack, Inc.
Phone—(973) 278-6966
2 Broad St., Clifton 07013
**Wire Displays, Inc.**
Phone—(973) 537-0090
Fax—(973) 537-0906
Web—www.blancind.com
Email—bschwarz@blancind.com
88 King St., Ste. 1, Dover 07801

## DISPLAY SYSTEMS

Hannecke Display Systems, Inc.
Phone—(973) 335-0434
91 Fulton St., Unit 4, Boonton 07005
Testrite Instrument Co.
Phone—(201) 543-0240
216 S. Newman St., Hackensack 07601

## DISPLAYS

Blanc Industries, Inc.
Phone—(973) 678-1200
88 King St., Dover 07801
City Diecutting, Inc.
Phone—(973) 270-0370
1 Cory Rd., Ste. C, Morristown 07960
Compass Display & Promotion Co., Inc.
Phone—(609) 695-5300
1659 Calhoun St., Trenton 08638
**Infinite Manufacturing Group, Inc.**
Email—a.moses@infinitegroupusa.com
Phone—(973) 649-9950
Web—www.infinitegroupusa.com
171 Coit St., Irvington 07111
National Display Group, Inc.
Phone—(856) 661-1212
6850 River Rd., Pennsauken 08110
Parker3d
Phone—(908) 322-5552
1325 Terrill Rd., Scotch Plains 07076
Parkway Wire Frame Co., Inc.
Phone—(973) 242-5220
249 Astor St., Newark 07114
Preferred Display, Inc.
Phone—(973) 405-5137
310 Brighton Rd., Clifton 07012

Props, Displays & Interiors, Inc.
Phone—(862) 704-6463
45 Glenwood Pl., East Orange 07017
Trans World Marketing Corp.
Phone—(201) 935-5565
360 Murray Hill Pkwy., East Rutherford 07073

## DISPLAYS — Corrugated

Progress Display, Inc.
Phone—(908) 757-6650
39 Progress St., Edison 08820
Taurus Display Corp.
Phone—(856) 793-3500
1249 Glen Ave., Moorestown 08057
Tech-Pak, Inc.
Phone—(201) 935-3800
100 Blum, P.O. Box 51, Wood Ridge 07075

## DISPLAYS — Electronic

**Tally Display Corp.**
**Toll Free Ph: (800)75-TALLY; Manufacturing LED**
**signs & systems for large companies. Specializing in**
**custom & one-of-a-kind projects. Offering extensive**
**experience in broadcasting, video, advertising,**
**signage & software creation**
Phone—(973) 777-7760 / (800) 758-2559
Fax—(973) 777-6220
Web—www.tallydisplay.com
Email—info@tallydisplay.com
19 Gardner Rd., Ste. A, Fairfield 07004

## DISPLAYS — Jewelry

Jewelry Tray & Pad Co., Inc.
Phone—(201) 941-4300
1150 Edgewater Ave., Ridgefield 07657
Ovadia Corp.
Phone—(973) 256-9200
101 E. Main St., 2nd Fl., Little Falls 07424

## DISPLAYS — LED

**Tally Display Corp.**
**Toll Free Ph: (800)75-TALLY; Manufacturing LED**
**signs & systems for large companies. Specializing in**
**custom & one-of-a-kind projects. Offering extensive**
**experience in broadcasting, video, advertising,**
**signage & software creation**
Phone—(973) 777-7760 / (800) 758-2559
Fax—(973) 777-6220
Web—www.tallydisplay.com
Email—info@tallydisplay.com
19 Gardner Rd., Ste. A, Fairfield 07004

## DISPLAYS — Multimedia

**Immersive Realities, A Div. Of Dimensional**
**Communications Inc.**
Phone—(201) 767-1500
Fax—(201) 767-9696
Web—www.immersive-realities.com
Email—bobs@immersive-realities.com
1595 MacArthur Blvd., Mahwah 07430

## DISPLAYS — Plastic

Clip Strip Corp.
Phone—(201) 342-9155
343 S. River St., Hackensack 07601
Da Vinci Displays, LLC
Phone—(732) 730-3001
123 Taft Dr., Brick 08724
Hudson Display Corp.
Phone—(973) 623-8255
831 Frelinghuysen Ave., Newark 07114

## DISPLAYS — Point of Purchase

Algar-The Display Connection Inc.
Phone—(201) 438-1000
131 W. Commercial Ave., Moonachie 07074
Alpak Display Group
Phone—(201) 797-1411
575 N. Midland Ave., Saddle Brook 07663
Blanc Display Group, The
Phone—(973) 537-0090
88 King St., Ste. 1, Dover 07801

## DISPLAYS — Point of Purchase — (cont.)

C C & D Capital Contracting & Design, Inc.
Phone—(908) 561-8411
640 North Ave., Plainfield 07060

Chatham Container Display Corp.
Phone—(800) 266-4848
6 Northridge Way, Warren 07059

Datascan Graphics, Inc.
Phone—(973) 543-4800
55 Madison Ave., Ste. 400, Morristown 07960

Design Display Group, Inc.
Phone—(201) 438-6000
105 Amor Ave., Carlstadt 07072

Design Production, Inc.
Phone—(201) 447-5656
9 Industrial Pk., Waldwick 07463

**Emco Industrial Plastics, Inc.**
**Supplier of Plastic Sheet, Rod, Tube, Films & Prototyping**
**Phone—(973) 559-5610**
**Fax—(973) 239-1595**
**Web—www.emcoplastics.com**
**Email—mailbox@emcoplastics.com**
**99 Commerce Rd., P.O. Box 2503, Cedar Grove 07009**
*(see our ad Outside Front Cover)*

Hathaway Plastics, Inc.
Phone—(908) 688-9494
911 Springfield Rd., Union 07083

Henschel-Steinau, Inc.
Phone—(201) 760-4100
50 Commerce Dr., Allendale 07401

Impact Displays Group, LLC
Phone—(212) 842-1800
310 13th St., Carlstadt 07072

Intermarket Technology, Inc.
Phone—(973) 872-9090
92 Newark Pompton Tpke., Wayne 07470

JED Display, LLC
Phone—(201) 340-2329
55 Arlington Ave., Kearny 07032

Metaline Products Co., Inc.
Phone—(732) 721-1373
101 N. Feltus St. & 241 Raritan St., South Amboy 08879

**MPM Display, Inc.**
**Phone—(973) 374-3477**
**Fax—(973) 374-0078**
**Email—michaelmpm@mac.com**
**74 Woolsey St., Irvington 07111**

Rand Diversified
Phone—(732) 287-2525
3 Ethel Rd., Ste. 301, Edison 08817

**SPT Packaging LLC**
**Phone—(973) 246-5635**
**Fax—(973) 246-5636**
**Web—www.sptpkg.com**
**Email—jdefelice@sptpkg.com**
**489 Clifton Ave., Clifton 07011**

Strive Group, LLC, The
Phone—(973) 893-1300
160 Chubb Ave., Ste. 101, Lyndhurst 07071

Unified Resources In Display, Inc./Display Pro Manufacturing
Phone—(908) 272-1112
40 Boright Ave., Kenilworth 07033

Zaller Studios, Inc.
Phone—(973) 743-5175
265 Watsessing Ave., Bloomfield 07003

## DISPLAYS — Portable

Nomadic Display
Phone—(862) 210-8120
4-6 Just Rd., Fairfield 07004

## DISPLAYS — Trade Show & Convention

Art Guild, Inc.
Phone—(856) 853-7500
300 Wolf Dr., West Deptford 08086

**Dimensional Communications Inc.**
**Trade show displays & booths**
**Phone—(201) 767-1500**
**Fax—(201) 767-9696**
**Web—www.dimcom.com**
**Email—info@dimcom.com**
**1595 MacArthur Blvd., Mahwah 07430**

Fiber Optic Systems, Inc.
Phone—(908) 534-5500
P.O. Box 62, Whitehouse Station 08889

Graphic Presentation Systems, Inc.
Phone—(732) 981-1120
262 Old New Brunswick Rd., Ste. F, Piscataway 08854

Klose Assocs., Inc.
Phone—(732) 229-8950
804 Broadway, West Long Branch 07764

Lynch Exhibits
Phone—(609) 387-1600
7 Campus Dr., Burlington 08016

## DISTILLED SPIRITS

Allied Beverage Group, LLC
Phone—(201) 842-6200
600 Washington Ave., P.O. Box 838, Carlstadt 07072

Dozortsev & Sons Enterprises
Phone—(908) 353-1234
411-415 John St., Elizabeth 07202

Jersey Artisan Distilling
Phone—(973) 521-7623
32 Pier Ln. W., Bldg. C, Fairfield 07004

**Shore Point Distributing Co.**
**100 Shore Point Dr., Freehold 07728**
**Addtl. Web: www.njcoors.com**
**Craft Beer Division**
**Phone—(732) 308-3334**
**Fax—(732) 308-1610**
**Web—www.shorepoint.com**
**P.O. Box 275, Adelphia 07710**
*(also see our ad under BEER & ALE)*

**Shore Point Distributing Co.**
*Beer & Ale*
*Craft Beer Division, Wine & Spirits Division*
www.shorepoint.com / www.njcoors.com
**(732) 308-3334 • Fax: (732) 308-1610**
100 Shore Point Drive, Freehold, NJ 07728

## DOCKS

Custom Docks, Inc.
Phone—(973) 948-3732
234 Route 206, Branchville 07826

## DOCUMENT IMAGING

**Morris County Duplicating Corp.**
**Phone—(973) 993-8484**
**Fax—(973) 605-8828**
**Web—www.mcdsolutions.com**
**Email—copies@mcdsolutions.com**
**1 Lafayette Ave., Morristown 07960**

## DOCUMENT SHREDDING SERVICES

**DocuVault Delaware Valley LLC**
**Phone—(856) 853-5160**
**Fax—(856) 853-5164**
**Web—www.docuvaultdv.com**
**Email—customerservice@docuvaultdv.com**
**1240 Forest Pkwy., Ste. 100, West Deptford 08066**

## DOG & CAT FOODS

**(also see 'Pet Food')**

Innovation Concepts, Inc. (H Q)
Phone—(973) 853-5300
870 Warwick Tpke., Hewitt 07421

Menu Foods, Inc.
Phone—(856) 662-7412
9130 Griffith Morgan Ln., Pennsauken 08110

## DOLL CLOTHING

Chriselles Dolls
Phone—(201) 488-1905
216 Hillbrook Dr., River Edge 07661

Oshko International Corp.
Phone—(732) 821-8222
115 Riverbend Dr., North Brunswick 08902

## DOLLIES

Hilman Rollers
Phone—(732) 462-6277
12 Timber Ln., P.O. Box 45, Marlboro 07746

## DONUTS

Jersey Shore CPL, Inc.
Phone—(732) 308-9990
301-C Commerce Dr., Freehold 07728

## DOOR COMPONENTS

Foremost Wood Products
Phone—(718) 447-5836
191 Vineyard Rd., Edison 08817

## DOORS

**Bildisco Door Mfg., Inc.**
**Wooden & metal doors**
**Phone—(973) 673-2400**
**Fax—(973) 673-2236**
**Web—www.bildisco.com**
**Email—bildiscomfg@comcast.net**
**21 Central Ave., West Orange 07052**
*(see our ad on next page)*

DCI Metro, Inc.
Phone—(201) 340-4329
1 Maple St., Unit 1, East Rutherford 07073

GPS Specialty Doors, Inc.
Phone—(973) 778-6200
90 Dayton Ave., Unit 4-B, Passaic 07055

Hahn's Woodworking Co., Inc.
Phone—(908) 722-2742
181 Meister Ave., Somerville 08876

Tri State Hardware, Inc.
Phone—(856) 810-0990
5 Perina Blvd., Cherry Hill 08003

## DOORS — Aluminum

Five Star Building Products, Inc.
Phone—(201) 869-4181
2012 86th St., North Bergen 07047

Rebco, Inc.
Phone—(973) 684-0200
1171 Madison Ave., Ste. 1, Paterson 07503

## DOORS — Cabinet

Pazera Cabinets Door
Phone—(732) 727-1600
3160 Bordentown Ave., Old Bridge 08857

## DOORS — Commercial

Door Jockey, Inc.
Phone—(732) 942-6099
915 18th Ave., Wall 07719

## DOORS — Overhead

Arm-R-Lite Door Mfg. Co., Inc.
Phone—(908) 754-2600
2700 Hamilton Blvd., South Plainfield 07080

Burlington County Overhead Door Co., Inc.
Phone—(609) 387-9092
444 Logan Ave., P.O. Box 127, Burlington 08016

Gray Overhead Door Co.
Phone—(908) 355-3889
439 Third Ave., Elizabeth 07206

**Independent Overhead Door Co., Inc.**
**Phone—(732) 356-5522**
**Fax—(732) 356-2885**
**Web—www.independentdoor.com**
**Email—paul@independentdoor.com**
**176 US Highway 206, Hillsborough 08844**

*find additional suppliers at*
**IndustryNet.com**

INDUSTRY

## DOORS — Overhead, Garage

Amarr Garage Doors
 Phone—(908) 534-4112
 12 Coddington Rd., Whitehouse Station 08889
Fimbel Architectural Door Specialties
 Phone—(908) 534-1732
 8 Coddington Rd., Whitehouse Station 08889
**Independent Overhead Door Co., Inc.**
 **Phone—(732) 356-5522**
 **Fax—(732) 356-2885**
 **Web—www.independentdoor.com**
 **Email—paul@independentdoor.com**
 **176 US Highway 206, Hillsborough 08844**
Ridge Doors
 Phone—(732) 329-2311
 335 New Rd., P.O. Box 180, Monmouth Junction
 08852

## DOORS — Rolling

Acme Rolling Steel Door Corp.
 Phone—(201) 943-7070
 1099 Linden Ave., P.O. Box 33, Ridgefield 07657
Fast Doors, LLC
 Phone—(856) 966-3278
 1800 Copewood St., Camden 08103
Guardrite Steel Door Corp.
 Phone—(973) 481-4424
 81 Springdale Ave., Newark 07107
**Independent Overhead Door Co., Inc.**
 **Phone—(732) 356-5522**
 **Fax—(732) 356-2885**
 **Web—www.independentdoor.com**
 **Email—paul@independentdoor.com**
 **176 US Highway 206, Hillsborough 08844**
Jersey Steel Doors, Inc.
 Phone—(973) 482-4020
 95 N. 11th St., Newark 07107
Phil-Mar Industries
 Phone—(856) 966-0931
 1800 Copewood St., Camden 08103

## DOORS — Security

Stanley Access Technologies, LLC
 Phone—(609) 890-0877
 17 Marlen Dr., Ste. C, Trenton 08691
**SW Lock & Door Check Co.**
 **Phone—(201) 863-2234**
 **Fax—(201) 863-1511**
 **Email—swlock3701@yahoo.com**
 **3701 Kennedy Blvd., Union City 07087**

## DOORS — Shower

American Glass Crafters, Inc.
 Phone—(201) 525-1116
 193 Veterans Blvd., Carlstadt 07072
**Century Bathworks, Inc.**
 **Luxury glass shower enclosures & medicine cabinets**
 **Phone—(973) 785-4290 / (800) 524-2578**
 **Fax—(973) 785-0777**
 **Web—www.centurybathworks.com**
 **Email—info@centurybathworks.com**
 **250 Lackawanna Ave., Woodland Park 07424**
 *(see our ad on this page)*
Easco Shower Doors Co.
 Phone—(973) 209-4141
 3 Industrial Dr., Vernon 07462
Nelson Glass & Aluminum Co., Inc.
 Phone—(609) 924-2880
 45 Spring St., Princeton 08542
Somerset Glass Co., Inc.
 Phone—(732) 297-7444
 2086 U.S. Highway 130, North Brunswick 08902
Style Rite Of America, Inc.
 Phone—(973) 478-1100
 118 Seger Ave., Clifton 07011

## DOORS — Steel

Accurate Door & Hardware, Inc.
 Phone—(973) 812-2266
 10 W. End Rd., Totowa 07512
Miele Iron Works, Inc.
 Phone—(908) 686-0943
 2340 Route 22 E., Union 07083

# Bildisco Door Mfg., Inc.
*Wooden & Metal Doors*
## www.bildisco.com
## bildiscomfg@comcast.net
## (973) 673-2400 / Fax: (973) 673-2236
## 21 Central Ave., West Orange, NJ 07052

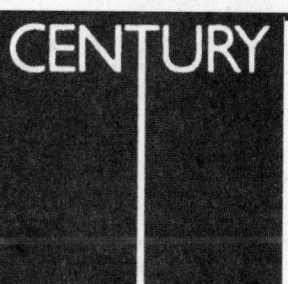

# CENTURY
## CENTURY
### BATHWORKS, INC.
Framed & Frameless Glass Showers
Medicine Cabinets
## (973) 785-4290 / FAX: (973) 785-0777
250 Lackawanna Avenue
Woodland Park, NJ 07424

Pioneer Industries, Inc.
 Phone—(201) 933-1900
 171 S. Newman St., Hackensack 07601

## DOORS — Strip

Tuckahoe Mfg.
 Phone—(856) 696-4100
 327 Tuckahoe Rd., Vineland 08360

## DOORS — Wooden

B & B Millwork
 Phone—(973) 249-0300
 333 Monroe Ave., Kenilworth 07033
**Bildisco Door Mfg., Inc.**
 **Wooden & metal doors**
 **Phone—(973) 673-2400**
 **Fax—(973) 673-2236**
 **Web—www.bildisco.com**
 **Email—bildiscomfg@comcast.net**
 **21 Central Ave., West Orange 07052**
 *(see our ad on this page)*
DiNaso Building Supplies
 Phone—(732) 886-6666
 133 Ocean Ave., Lakewood 08701
F T Millwork
 Phone—(732) 741-1216
 9-B Catherine St., Red Bank 07701
Manhattan Door Corp.
 Phone—(718) 963-1111
 109 Kero Rd., Carlstadt 07072
Urban Millwork & Supply Corp.
 Phone—(973) 278-7072
 90 2nd Ave., Paterson 07514
Woodhut, LLC
 Phone—(732) 414-6440
 339 Fairfield Rd., Freehold 07728

Yonkers Plywood Mfg.
 Phone—(732) 727-1200
 3130 Bordentown Ave., P.O. Box 152, Old Bridge
 08857

## DOUGH — Frozen

Guttenplan's Frozen Dough Specialists, Inc.
 Phone—(732) 495-9480
 100 Highway 36, Middletown 07748
J & J Snack Foods Corp.
 Phone—(856) 933-3597
 361 Benigno Blvd., Ste. A, Bellmawr 08031

## DRAINS

Reliance Plastic & Chemical Corp.
 Phone—(201) 797-8014
 38-27 Wilson St., P.O. Box 395, Fair Lawn 07410
**We Do Floor Drains**
 **Floor Drains**
 **Phone—(973) 452-4945**
 **Fax—(973) 252-1937**
 **Web—www.affordableconcretecutter.com**
 **Email—larrybakerconstruction@yahoo.com**
 **8 Corvair Ct., Flanders 07836**

## DRAPERIES

Alan Schatzberg & Assoc., Inc.
 Phone—(201) 440-8855
 45 Ruta Ct., South Hackensack 07606
Altina's Custom Interiors
 Phone—(609) 924-3367
 Princeton Shopping Ctr., 301 N. Harrison,
 Princeton 08540
Baum Draperies
 Phone—(973) 661-1841
 666 Passaic Ave., Nutley 07110

## DRAPERIES — *(cont.)*

Best Drapery & Blind Mfg. Co.
Phone—(856) 429-2242
1 Kresson Rd., Cherry Hill 08034

Bloomfield Drapery Co., Inc.
Phone—(973) 777-3566
948 Paterson Ave., East Rutherford 07073

Crown Custom Cleaners
Phone—(856) 310-0710
27 E. Kings Hwy., Audubon 08106

Daniel's Custom Draperies, Inc.
Phone—(856) 939-2212
620 W. Clements Bridge Rd., Runnemede 08078

Don's Drapery Mfg. Co.
Phone—(973) 751-1544
145 Heckel St., Belleville 07109

Drapery Corp. Of America, Inc.
Phone—(973) 925-1200
12-16 1st Ave., Paterson 07524

Kay Window Fashions, Inc.
Phone—(862) 591-1555
271 2nd St., Saddle Brook 07663

Kushner Draperies Mfg., LLC
Phone—(856) 317-9696
5305 Route 70, Pennsauken 08109

Lawrence Custom Drapery Shop
Phone—(609) 695-3877
323 4th St., Ewing 08638

Master Drapery Workroom, Inc.
Phone—(908) 272-4404
220 N. 14th St., Kenilworth 07033

McKnight Drapery Services
Phone—(732) 741-3655
126 Majestic S., Lincroft 07738

Metropolitan Window Fashions
Phone—(201) 689-6030
799 Route 17 S., Paramus 07652

North Jersey Window Treatments, LLC
Phone—(201) 487-2121
164 South St., Hackensack 07601

Silberstein, Inc., M.
Phone—(732) 741-1762
428 Broad St., Shrewsbury 07702

Superior Drapery Co. & Harbor Linen Co
Phone—(856) 435-2000
2 Foster Ave., Gibbsboro 08026

Weiss & Sons, Inc., I.
Phone—(201) 402-6500
815 Fairview Ave., Ste. 10, Fairview 07022

Window Covering Concepts
Phone—(609) 261-1181
29 Bella Rd., Lumberton 08048

Windowscapes
Phone—(908) 850-0678
5 Winay Ter., Long Valley 07853

## DRESSES

Arecia's Creations
Phone—(201) 864-7388
3704 Park Ave., Weehawken 07086

## DRILL HEADS — Multiple Spindle

AutoDrill, LLC
Phone—(908) 542-0244
50 Division Ave., Ste. 18, Millington 07946

## DRILLING — Laser

**Ackley Machine Corp.**
**Email: pgulotta@ackleymachine.com**
**Laser Drilling & Inspection of Pharmaceutical Tablets**
**Phone—(856) 234-3626**
**Fax—(856) 234-8657**
**Web—www.ackleymachine.com**
**1273 N. Church St., Ste. 106, Moorestown 08057**

## DRILLING FLUIDS

**Hangsterfer's Laboratories, Inc.**
**Phone—(856) 468-0216**
**Fax—(856) 468-0200**
**Web—www.hangsterfers.com**
**Email—sales@hangsterfers.com**
**175 Ogden Rd., Mantua 08051**
*(see our ad under LUBRICANTS—Metalworking)*

## DRILLS

Hutchinson Co., William T.
Phone—(908) 688-0533
453 Lehigh Ave., Union 07083

## DRINK MIXES

C B Food, Inc.
Phone—(973) 773-9224
1 Madison St., Bldg. B, East Rutherford 07073

## DRIVE SHAFTS

Drive Line Service Of New Jersey, Inc.
Phone—(973) 473-7900
622 U.S. Highway 46, Clifton 07013

Mr. Drive Shaft
Phone—(732) 938-4118
5134-A Hurley Pond Rd., Farmingdale 07727

## DRIVE SYSTEMS

Atlanta Drive Systems, Inc.
Phone—(732) 282-0480
1775 State Route 34, Ste. D-10, Farmingdale 07727

## DRIVES

Electronic Drives & Controls, Inc.
Phone—(973) 428-0500
17 Eastmans Rd., Parsippany 07054

## DRIVES — Variable Speed

Rockwell Automation, Inc.
Phone—(732) 225-1360
165 Fieldcrest Ave., Raritan Ctr., Edison 08837

## DRUG DELIVERY SYSTEMS

LTS Lohmann Therapy Systems Corp.
Phone—(973) 244-2026
21 Henderson Dr., West Caldwell 07006

Torpac, Inc.
Phone—(973) 244-1125
333 U.S. Highway 46, Fairfield 07004

## DRUMS

**(also see 'Containers')**

**MAUSER USA LLC**
**MAUSER is a global leader in industrial packaging-drums & IBCs**
**Phone—(732) 353-7000 / (732) 353-7100**
**Fax—(732) 651-9777**
**Web—www.mausergroup.com**
**Email—info.us@mausergroup.com**
**35 Cotters Ln., Ste. C, East Brunswick 08816**

**Patrick J. Kelly Drums, Inc.**
**New & reconditioned industrial steel, plastic & fiber drums, IBCs & totes**
**Phone—(856) 963-1795 / (800) 963-1795**
**Fax—(856) 963-1788**
**Web—www.kellydrums.com**
**Email—sales@kellydrums.com**
**1810 River Ave., Camden 08105**

**PKD**
PATRICK J. KELLY DRUMS, INC.
*New & Reconditioned Steel & Plastic Drums & Totes*
www.kellydrums.com / (856) 963-1795
1810 River Avenue • Camden, NJ 08105

Tunnel Barrel & Drum Co., Inc.
Phone—(201) 933-1444
Fax—(201) 933-3423
Web—www.tunnelbarrel.com
Email—anthony@tunnelbarrel.com
85 Triangle Blvd., Carlstadt 07072

## DRUMS — Fibre

Enviro-Pak, Inc.
Phone—(732) 248-1600
125 National Rd., Edison 08817

Greif, Inc.
Phone—(609) 448-5300
200 Rike Dr., Millstone Township 08535

## DRUMS — Plastic

Bergen Barrel & Drum Co.
Phone—(201) 998-3500
43 O'Brien St., Ste. 45, Kearny 07032

## DRUMS — Steel

Industrial Drum Co.
Phone—(856) 881-2000
784 New Jersey Ave., P.O. Box 586, Glassboro 08028

Jones & Son, Inc., William
Phone—(856) 963-1199
238 Liberty St., Camden 08104

KTK Corp.
Phone—(732) 985-0447
65 Midvale Rd., Edison 08817

Mauser USA LLC
Phone—(732) 634-6000
14 Convery Blvd., Woodbridge 07095

Rahway Steel Drum Co. (H Q)
Phone—(732) 382-0113
202 Elliot St., Avenel 07001

## DRY CLEANING EQUIPMENT

Multimatic
Phone—(201) 767-9660
162 Veterans Dr., P.O. Box 156, Northvale 07647

## DRYERS — Compressed Air

**Gas Drying, Inc.**
**Phone—(973) 361-2212**
**Fax—(973) 361-4215**
**Web—www.gasdrying.com**
**Email—gasdrying@nac.net**
**355 W. Dewey Ave., P.O. Box 504, Wharton 07885**

## DRYERS — Industrial

**Komline-Sanderson Engineering**
**Phone—(908) 234-1000 / (800) 225-5457**
**Fax—(908) 234-9487**
**Web—www.komline.com**
**Email—info@komline.com**
**12 Holland Ave., Peapack 07977**

**Warwick Mfg. & Equipment Co., LLC**
**Buy & sell used: Chemical, food, cosmetic, packaging & pharmaceutical equipment**
**Phone—(732) 729-0400 / (732) 241-9263**
**Fax—(732) 729-1235**
**Web—www.warwickequipment.com**
**Email—sales@warwickequipment.com**
**1112 12th St., North Brunswick 08902**
*(see our ad Outside Back Cover)*

## DRYERS — Sludge

**Komline-Sanderson Engineering**
**Phone—(908) 234-1000 / (800) 225-5457**
**Fax—(908) 234-9487**
**Web—www.komline.com**
**Email—info@komline.com**
**12 Holland Ave., Peapack 07977**

## DRYING EQUIPMENT — Industrial

**Komline-Sanderson Engineering**
**Phone—(908) 234-1000 / (800) 225-5457**
**Fax—(908) 234-9487**
**Web—www.komline.com**
**Email—info@komline.com**
**12 Holland Ave., Peapack 07977**

R Welding
Phone—(609) 971-6017
97 Main St., Waretown 08758

© Copyright 2015 Manufacturers' News, Inc.   **A61**

## DRYING EQUIPMENT — Industrial — *(cont.)*

Witte Co., Inc., The
Phone—(908) 689-6500
507 Route 31 S., P.O. Box 47, Washington 07882

## DRYING EQUIPMENT — Infrared

Radiant Energy Systems, Inc.
Phone—(973) 423-5220
175 N. Ethel Ave., Hawthorne 07506

## DUCTS

D & M Sheet Metal Co., Inc.
Phone—(201) 939-6300
430 Central Ave., East Rutherford 07073
Duct Mate, Inc.
Phone—(201) 488-8002
190 Lexington Ave., Hackensack 07601
WP Ducts
Phone—(973) 786-7179
219 U.S. Highway 206, P.O. Box 547, Andover 07821

## DUCTS — Flexible

ATCO Rubber Products, Inc.
Phone—(856) 794-3393
1480 N. West Blvd., Vineland 08360
DU Technologies, Inc.
Phone—(201) 729-0070
300 W. Commercial Ave., Moonachie 07074

## DUCTS — HVAC

Air & Specialties Sheet Metal
Phone—(908) 233-8306
276 Sheffield St., Mountainside 07092
Air Distribution Systems, Inc.
Phone—(856) 874-1100
1000 Astoria Blvd., Cherry Hill 08003
**Atlantic Air Enterprises**
**Phone—(732) 381-4000 / (800) 899-4279 / (732) 381-4016**
**Fax—(732) 499-0122**
**Web—www.atlanticairent.com**
**Email—contactus@atlanticairent.com**
**856 Elston St., Rahway 07065**
Dan's Heating & Air Conditioning, Inc.
Phone—(732) 297-9162
1007 Eastpark Blvd., Cranbury 08512
Environmental Air Systems
Phone—(732) 681-0856
801 11th Ave., P.O. Box 508, Belmar 07719
Hays Sheet Metal, Inc.
Phone—(856) 662-7722
7070 Kaighns Ave., Bldg. B, Pennsauken 08109
Homiek Sheet Metal Fabrication & HVAC Supplies, Inc.
Phone—(732) 364-7644
1352 Route 9, Lakewood 08701
Professional Environment Systems
Phone—(201) 991-3000
49 O'Brien Rd., Kearny 07032
**Waage Electric, Inc.**
**Melting Pots & Duct Heaters & Immersion Heaters**
**Phone—(908) 245-9363 / (800) 922-4365**
**Fax—(908) 245-8477**
**Web—www.waage.com**
**Email—info@waage.com**
**720 Colfax Ave., P.O. Box 337, Kenilworth 07033**
*(see our ad under FURNACES—Industrial)*
Woodroof Metal Shop
Phone—(856) 455-1111
73 Water St., Bridgeton 08302

## DUCTS — Metal

Comfort Mechanical Corp.
Phone—(732) 870-2292
420 Division St., P.O. Box 4135, Long Branch 07740
Ducts Sheet Metal, LLC
Phone—(732) 727-8781
6200 Main St., South Amboy 08879

## DUST COLLECTING SYSTEMS

Sternvent
Phone—(908) 688-0807
5 Stahuber Ave., Union 07083
**Warwick Mfg. & Equipment Co., LLC**
**Buy & sell used: Chemical, food, cosmetic, packaging & pharmaceutical equipment**
**Phone—(732) 729-0400 / (732) 241-9263**
**Fax—(732) 729-1235**
**Web—www.warwickequipment.com**
**Email—sales@warwickequipment.com**
**1112 12th St., North Brunswick 08902**
*(see our ad Outside Back Cover)*

## DUST CONTROL EQUIPMENT

C D M Dust Control Of New Jersey
Phone—(732) 222-3694
15-17 S. 7th Ave., Long Branch 07740
National Environmental Service Co. (H Q)
Phone—(973) 543-4586
7 Hampshire Dr., Mendham 07945
National Environmental Services Co.
Phone—(908) 813-1195
700 Grand Ave., Hackettstown 07840

## DVD REPLICATION

Post Office Digital, Inc.
Phone—(201) 945-8119
33 Hilliard Ave., Edgewater 07020

## DYES

Epolin
Phone—(973) 465-9495
358-364 Adams St., Newark 07105
Fabricolor Holdings, Inc.
Phone—(973) 742-5800
24 1/2 Van Houten St., P.O. Box 1856, Paterson 07505
Narad Marketing Corporation
Phone—(973) 881-0206
200 Piaget Ave., Clifton 07011
**Nova Specialty Chemicals, LLC**
**Phone—(973) 586-2147**
**Fax—(973) 215-2975**
**Web—www.novaspecialties.com**
**Email—sales@novaspecialties.com**
**404 E. Main St., Rockaway 07866**
Orient Corp. Of America (H Q)
Phone—(908) 298-0990
6 Commerce Dr., Ste. 301, Cranford 07016
Rainbow Specialty Colors, Inc.
Phone—(973) 304-0912
27 Utter Ave., Ste. B, Hawthorne 07506
Resolv Corporation
Phone—(973) 676-5141
410 Division St., Elizabeth 07201
Royce Assocs., L. P.
Phone—(973) 279-0400
28-36 Paterson St., Paterson 07501
Royce Assocs., L. P. (H Q)
Phone—(201) 438-5200
35 Carlton Ave., East Rutherford 07073
**Spectra Colors Corp.**
**Phone—(201) 997-0606**
**Fax—(201) 997-0504**
**Web—www.SpectraColors.com**
**Email—Dyes@SpectraColors.com**
**25 Rizzolo Rd., Kearny 07032**

**Spectra** Colors Corporation
You'll Know Us By Our Colors
**(201) 997-0606 / FAX: (201) 997-0504**
25 Rizzolo Rd. • Kearny, NJ 07032
**www.SpectraColors.com**
Email: Dyes@SpectraColors.com

Sunbelt Corp.
Phone—(803) 329-9787
63 Atwood Pl., Wayne 07470

## EARTH MOVING EQUIPMENT

**Hainesport Tool & Maintenance**
**Manufacturer of machine parts & assemblies**
**Phone—(609) 261-0016**
**Fax—(609) 261-2105**
**Web—www.hainesporttool.com**
**Email—rich@hainesporttool.com**
**1924 Ark Rd., Hainesport 08036**

## EDUCATIONAL AIDS

Festo Didactic Inc.
Phone—(732) 938-2000
1710 Highway 34, P.O. Box 686, Farmingdale 07727

## EGG PROCESSORS

I S E Farms, Inc.
Phone—(908) 454-4148
110 Goodspring Rd., P.O. Box 567, Broadway 08808
Michael Foods, Inc.
Phone—(908) 282-7140
847 North Ave., Elizabeth 07201
Papetti's Hygrade Egg Products, Inc.
Phone—(908) 282-7140
877 North Ave. E., Elizabeth 07201
Puglisi Egg Farms, Inc.
Phone—(732) 938-2373
75 Easy St., Howell 07731

## ELASTOMERS

**Brenntag Specialties, Inc.**
**Phone—(908) 561-6100 / (800) 732-0562**
**Fax—(800) 543-1484**
**Web—www.brenntagspecialties.com**
**Email—specialties@brenntag.com**
**1000 Coolidge St., South Plainfield 07080**
*(see our ad under CHEMICAL DISTRIBUTORS)*

## ELECTRIC CONVERTERS

Ocean Power Technologies, Inc.
Phone—(609) 730-0400
1590 Reed Rd., Pennington 08534

## ELECTRIC MOTORS

Atlantic Kenmark Electric, Inc.
Phone—(201) 991-2117
11 Ewing Ave., North Arlington 07031
Bogue Systems, Inc.
Phone—(973) 523-2200
100 Pennsylvania Ave., Paterson 07503
D Electric Motors, Inc.
Phone—(856) 696-5959
94 W. Sherman Ave., Vineland 08360
Hansome Energy Systems, Inc.
Phone—(908) 862-9044
365 Dalziel Rd., Linden 07036
Quality Electric Motor Service, Inc.
Phone—(732) 257-6655
396 State Route 18, East Brunswick 08816
Reliable Electric Motor Repair, Inc.
Phone—(973) 278-8122
19 California Ave., Paterson 07503
Universal Electric Motor Service, Inc.
Phone—(201) 968-1000
131 S. Newman St., Hackensack 07601
**Warwick Mfg. & Equipment Co., LLC**
**Buy & sell used: Chemical, food, cosmetic, packaging & pharmaceutical equipment**
**Phone—(732) 729-0400 / (732) 241-9263**
**Fax—(732) 729-1235**
**Web—www.warwickequipment.com**
**Email—sales@warwickequipment.com**
**1112 12th St., North Brunswick 08902**
*(see our ad Outside Back Cover)*
Willier Electric Motor Repair Co., Inc.
Phone—(856) 627-3535
1 Linden Ave., P.O. Box 98, Gibbsboro 08026

*Search from among 430,000 U.S. manufacturers & suppliers:*
**IndustryNet.com**

## ELECTRIC MOTORS — Rebuilt & Repaired

Electrical Motor Repair Co.
  Phone—(609) 392-6149
  809 E. State St., Trenton 08609
Lockwood's Electric Motor Service, Inc.
  Phone—(609) 587-2333
  2239 Nottingham Way, Trenton 08619

## ELECTRICAL COMPONENTS

American Fittings Corp.
  Phone—(201) 664-0027
  17-10 Willow St., Fair Lawn 07410
Castle Industries, Inc.
  Phone—(201) 585-8400
  120 Sylvan Ave., Ste. 107, Englewood Cliffs 07632
Douglas Electrical Components, Inc.
  Phone—(973) 627-8230
  5 Middlebury Blvd., Randolph 07869
Palmer Electronics, Inc.
  Phone—(973) 772-5900
  156 Belmont Ave., Garfield 07026
Panel Components & Systems, Inc.
  Phone—(973) 448-9400
  149 Main St., Stanhope 07874

## ELECTRICAL CONNECTORS

Hofer Machine & Tool Co., Inc.
  Phone—(973) 427-1195
  126 Linda Vista Ave., North Haledon 07508
Richards Mfg.
  Phone—(973) 371-1771
  517 Lyons Ave., Irvington 07111
Walther Electric Corp., F.
  Phone—(732) 537-9201
  12 Worlds Fair Dr., Ste. F, Somerset 08873

## ELECTRICAL CONTRACTORS

**Accent Electric Corp.**
  **Phone—(908) 353-6649**
  **Fax—(908) 233-2246**
  **Web—www.accentelectric.net**
  **Email—accentelectric@att.net**
  **232 Hemlock Ave., Garwood 07027**
**Advanced Electric Design and Service, LLC**
  Full service residential, commercial & industrial
  electrical contractors
  **Phone—(732) 396-0033**
  **Fax—(908) 789-9659**
  **Web—www.aedsllc.com**
  **Email—info@advancedelectricdesign.net**
  **P.O. Box 126, Rahway 07065**
**Americor Electronics, Ltd.**
  **Phone—(847) 956-6200 / (800) 830-5337**
  **Fax—(847) 956-0300**
  **Web—www.americor-usa.com**
  **Email—info@americor-usa.com**
  **675 S. Lively Blvd., Elk Grove Village, IL 60007**
  *(see our ads under CABLE ASSEMBLIES & CORD SETS)*
**Como Electric, Inc.**
  **Phone—(732) 449-7625**
  **Fax—(732) 449-6896**
  **Email—comoelect@aol.com**
  **909 Wall Rd., Spring Lake 07762**
  *(see our ad under GENERATORS—Electric)*
**Elite Electric Inc.**
  **Phone—(973) 694-1342**
  **Web—www.elite-electric-inc.com**
  **Email—elite_electric_inc@yahoo.com**
**HBC Company Inc.**
  **Phone—(973) 777-4472**
  **Fax—(973) 777-4822**
  **Web—www.hbcco.com**
  **Email—jhoogendoorn@hbcco.com**
  **131 Washington St., Lodi 07644**

*Do nationwide searches for products & services at:*
**IndustryNet.com**

Joseph Battaglio Electrical Contractors LLC
  Phone—(732) 616-1800
  Fax—(732) 899-3525
  Web—www.josephbattaglioelectricians.com
  P.O. Box 764, Point Pleasant 08742

Quality Electrical Contractors
**(732) 616-1800**
Fax (732) 899-3525
**www.josephbattaglioelectricians.com**
P.O. Box 764 • Point Pleasant, NJ 08742

**MDC Electrical Contractor, LLC**
  **Phone—(973) 483-2828**
  **13 New York Ave., Newark 07105**
Rene Gadoury Electrical Contracting L.L.C.
  Phone—(609) 387-1399
  7 Coronet Ter., Burlington 08016

**Rene Gadoury Electrical Contracting L.L.C.**
*NJ Lic #7511A*
**(609) 387-1399**
www.renegadouryelectricalcontracting.com
7 Coronet Ter. • Burlington, NJ 08016

Santonastaso Electric
  Quality Electrical Contractors
  Phone—(908) 359-4269
  Fax—(908) 359-5402
  Email—santonastasoelectric@yahoo.com
  1 Cumberland Rd., Hillsborough 08844

**Santonastaso Electric**
*Quality electrical contractors*
**(908) 359-4269**
1 Cumberland Rd. Hillsborough, NJ 08844

Skylands Electric LLC
  Phone—(908) 894-5657
  Fax—(908) 894-5660
  Email—skylands1@comcast.net
  11 Quakertown Rd., Pittstown 08867
Speedy Electric
  Phone—(609) 443-1428
  92 Conover Rd., East Windsor 08520
Warrenville Electrical
  Phone—(908) 510-8201
  Fax—(908) 242-3619
  Web—www.warrenvilleelectrical.com
  Email—peter.warrenville@gmail.com
  7 Forest Dr., Warren 07059

## ELECTRICAL DISCHARGE MACHINERY

Single Source Technologies
  Phone—(973) 227-6601
  30 Chapin Rd., Ste. 1208, P.O. Box 655, Pine Brook 07058

## ELECTRICAL DISCHARGE MACHINING (EDM)

Advanced Precision, Inc.
  Phone—(973) 383-2296
  15 Wilson Dr., Sparta 07871
**Advantage EDM**
  **Phone—(973) 786-0177**
  **Fax—(973) 786-0277**
  **Web—www.advantageedm.com**
  **Email—info@advantageedm.com**
  **38 Main St., Route 206, Andover 07821**

FIMS Mfg. Corp.
  **Phone—(201) 845-7088**
  **Fax—(201) 845-8287**
  **Web—www.fimsmfg.com**
  **Email—fimsmfg@optonline.net**
  **8 Allerman Rd., Oakland 07436**
New Jersey Precision Technologies, Inc.
  Phone—(908) 232-8847
  1081 Bristol Rd., Mountainside 07092
Olympic EDM & Waterjet, Inc.
  Phone—(973) 492-0664
  20 Kiel Ave., Butler 07405

## ELECTRICAL DISTRIBUTION EQUIPMENT

American Modular Power Solution
  Phone—(973) 588-4026
  429 Rockaway Rd., Bldg. 10, Boonton 07005
Schneider Electric
  Phone—(973) 263-6100
  2001 Highway 46, Ste. 402, Parsippany 07054

## ELECTRICAL EQUIPMENT AND SUPPLIES

Edgewater Mfg. Co., Inc
  Phone—(201) 664-0022
  17-10 Willow St., Fair Lawn 07410
MJG Technologies, Inc.
  Phone—(856) 228-6118
  832 Camden Ave., Blackwood 08012
Power Dynamics, Inc.
  Phone—(973) 560-0019
  145 Algonquin Pkwy., Whippany 07981
Swanson Assocs.
  Phone—(973) 984-5930
  P.O. Box 151, Wayne 07470
Turtle & Hughes, Inc.
  Phone—(732) 560-5575
  188 Foothill Rd., Bridgewater 08807
Turtle & Hughes, Inc.
  Phone—(732) 574-3600
  1900 Lower Rd., Linden 07036

## ELECTRICAL EQUIPMENT AND SUPPLIES — Wholesale

**AA Electric, Inc.**
  Quality Electrical Equipment & Supplies
  **Phone—(800) 237-8274 / (973) 777-5477**
  **Fax—(973) 773-1193**
  **Web—www.a-aelectric.com**
  **Email—njsales@a-aelectric.com**
  **1 Madison St., Ste. D, East Rutherford 07073**

**AA Electric, Inc.**
*Electric Controls In Stock*
**800-237-8274**
**973-777-5477**
Fax: 973-773-1193
**www.A-Aelectric.com**
njsales@a-aelectric.com
1 Madison St., Ste. D
East Rutherford, NJ 07073

Allied Electronics, Inc.
  Phone—(732) 846-4271
  197 State Hwy. N-18, East Brunswick 08816
Billows Electric Supply Co., Inc.
  Phone—(609) 345-6154
  301 N. New Rd., Pleasantville 08232

## ELECTRICAL EQUIPMENT AND SUPPLIES — Wholesale — (cont.)

Chiswick Electric Co., Inc.
Phone—(973) 824-9600
40 Brown Ave., Springfield 07081

Colonial Electric Supply Co., The
Phone—(609) 465-7144
1143 S. Route 9, Cape May Court House 08210

Colonial Electric Supply Co., The
Phone—(609) 704-9950
469 S. White Horse Pike, Hammonton 08037

Cooper Electric Supply Co.
Phone—(973) 940-8905
17 Route 206 S., Unit 3, Augusta 07822

Cooper Electric Supply Co.
Phone—(732) 920-3130
933 Cedarbridge Ave., Brick 08723

Cooper Electric Supply Co.
Phone—(201) 945-5900
217 Broad Ave., Fairview 07022

Cooper Electric Supply Co.
Phone—(732) 462-2424
3477 U.S. Highway 9, Freehold 07728

Cooper Electric Supply Co.
Phone—(201) 434-8575
1521 John F. Kennedy Blvd., Jersey City 07305

Cooper Electric Supply Co.
Phone—(732) 340-0346
1805 Lower Rd., Linden 07036

Cooper Electric Supply Co.
Phone—(609) 978-4666
317 E. Bay Ave., Manahawkin 08050

Cooper Electric Supply Co.
Phone—(732) 671-5000
666 State Route 35, Middletown 07748

Cooper Electric Supply Co.
Phone—(856) 853-9922
1251 Metropolitan Ave., West Deptford 08066

**Cuny & Guerber, Inc.**
Special counter available for contractors
**Phone—(201) 617-5800**
**Fax—(201) 617-5557**
**Web—www.cuny.biz**
**Email—sales@cuny.biz**
**2100 Kerrigan Ave., P.O. Box 1192, Union City 07087**
*(see our ad on this page)*

Farmer Electrical Supply
Phone—(973) 887-0510
16 Littell Rd., East Hanover 07936

Longo Electrical-Mechanical
Phone—(973) 537-0400
1 Harry Shupe Blvd., Wharton 07885

Swift Electrical Supply Co., Inc.
Phone—(201) 462-0900
100 Hollister Rd., Teterboro 07608

United Electric Supply Co.
Phone—(856) 691-6668
1150 W. Garden Rd., Vineland 08360

W. W. Grainger, Inc.
Phone—(908) 272-7156
55 Jackson Dr., Cranford 07016

## ELECTRICAL PANELS

Eaton Corp., Electrical Div.
Phone—(609) 835-4230
96 Stemmers Ln., Westampton 08060

Olson Motor & Control Co., Inc.
Phone—(908) 231-1500
100 Old Camplain Rd., Hillsborough 08844

## ELECTRICAL PARTS

Heyco Products, Inc.
Phone—(732) 286-4336
1800 Industrial Way N., Toms River 08755

## ELECTRICAL POWER EQUIPMENT & SYSTEMS

U.S. Tech, Inc.
Phone—(800) 783-8187
P.O. Box 152, Franklin Lakes 07417

*Do nationwide searches for products & services at:*
**IndustryNet.com**

## Cuny & Guerber, Inc.

Electrical Equipment & Supplies

**201-617-5800** • FAX: 201-617-5557

**www.cuny.biz** • Email: sales@cuny.biz

2100 Kerrigan Ave., PO Box 1192 Union City, NJ 07087

## ELECTRICAL REPAIR & SERVICE

**Radwell International, Inc.**
Stocking, Selling, Repairing New & Surplus Industrial Automation, MRO, Pneumatic, Motion, Electronic, Hydraulic, HVAC & Electrical Control Equipment for plant floor & facilities maintenance machinery. Also buying Surplus Industrial Controls
**Phone—(609) 288-9393 / (800) 332-4336**
**Fax—(609) 288-9417**
**Web—www.plccenter.com**
**Email—ahorner@plccenter.com**
**111 Mount Holly Bypass, Lumberton 08048**

## ELECTRICAL SUPPLIES

Precision Filaments
Phone—(732) 462-3755
17 Bannard St., Ste. 30, Freehold 07728

## ELECTRICAL SUPPLIES — Wholesale

**AA Electric, Inc.**
Quality Electrical Equipment & Supplies
**Phone—(800) 237-8274 / (973) 777-5477**
**Fax—(973) 773-1193**
**Web—www.a-aelectric.com**
**Email—njsales@a-aelectric.com**
**1 Madison St., Ste. D, East Rutherford 07073**
*(see our ad under ELECTRICAL EQUIPMENT AND SUPPLIES—Wholesale)*

American Distributors, Inc.
Phone—(973) 328-1181
2 Emery Ave., Ste. 1, Randolph 07869

Billows Electric Supply Co., Inc.
Phone—(609) 890-2822
1719 Nottingham Way, Trenton 08619

Billows Electric Supply Co., Inc.
Phone—(609) 522-7736
3901 New Jersey Ave., Wildwood 08260

Colonial Electric Supply Co., The
Phone—(609) 645-8110
701 W. Delilah Rd., Pleasantville 08232

Colonial Electric Supply Co., The
Phone—(856) 462-6300
64 W. Landis Ave., Vineland 08360

Cooper Electric Supply Co.
Phone—(201) 385-7777
72 N. Washington Ave., Bergenfield 07621

Cooper Electric Supply Co.
Phone—(609) 833-2115
2727 Fire Rd., Egg Harbor Township 08234

Cooper Electric Supply Co.
Phone—(908) 782-3200
19 Royal Rd., Flemington 08822

Cooper Electric Supply Co.
Phone—(732) 747-2233
1 Matrix Dr., Monroe 08831

Cooper Electric Supply Co.
Phone—(908) 454-8500
225 Stockton St., Phillipsburg 08865

Cooper Electric Supply Co.
Phone—(908) 756-4090
412 W. 2nd St., Plainfield 07060

Cooper Electric Supply Corp.
Phone—(973) 278-8400
444 Route 46 E., Fairfield 07004

Fox Electric Supply Co., Inc.
Phone—(973) 227-4151
1 Dodge Dr., West Caldwell 07006

Gexpro
Phone—(856) 241-4700
522 Pedricktown Rd., Swedesboro 08085

Graybar Electric Co., Inc.
Phone—(973) 404-5555
105 E. Crest Ave., Ste. 207, Edison 08837

Griffith Electric Supply Co., Inc.
Phone—(908) 203-1601
4-W Chimney Rock Rd., Bridgewater 08807

Griffith Electric Supply Co., Inc.
Phone—(609) 695-6121
5 2nd St., Trenton 08611

Main Electric Supply Co., Inc.
Phone—(609) 860-8500
24 Public Rd., P.O. Box 7323, Monroe Township 08831

Monarch Electric Co., Inc.
Phone—(973) 227-4151
1 Dodge Dr., West Caldwell 07006

Monarch Electric Supply Co.
Phone—(732) 249-1616
1527 Livingston Ave., North Brunswick 08902

Rahway Electric Supply, Inc.
Phone—(732) 381-6060
1684 Essex St., Rahway 07065

RSR Electronics, Inc.
Phone—(732) 381-8777
900 Hart St., Rahway 07065

Rumsey Electric Co.
Phone—(609) 989-9400
311 N. Clinton Ave., Trenton 08638

Wayne Electrical Supply Co.
Phone—(973) 839-6500
255 W. Parkway, Pompton Plains 07444

## ELECTRICAL TERMINALS

Connector Products, Inc.
Phone—(856) 829-9190
1300 John Tipton Blvd., Pennsauken 08110

## ELECTRICAL WIRING HARNESSES

**Ram Electronic Industries Inc.**
Web: www.ramoem.com
Email: steve@ramelectronics.net
**Phone—(856) 864-0999**
**Fax—(856) 786-2244**
**1704 Taylors Ln., Ste. 7, Cinnaminson 08077**

## ELECTRO MAGNETICS

APW Company
Phone—(973) 627-0643
5 Astro Pl., Ste. B, Rockaway 07866

## ELECTRODES

BASF Fuel Cell, Inc.
Phone—(732) 545-5100
39 Veronica Ave., Somerset 08873

*find additional suppliers at*
**IndustryNet.com**

## ELECTROMECHANICAL ASSEMBLIES

Symcon, Inc.
Phone—(201) 967-7378
47 Cedar Ln., West Milford 07480

## ELECTRON TUBES

Schlumberger-Princeton Technology Center
Phone—(609) 799-1000
20 Wallace Rd., Princeton Junction 08550
Troy-Onic, Inc.
Phone—(973) 584-6830
90 Dell Ave., P.O. Box 494, Kenvil 07847

## ELECTRONIC ASSEMBLIES

Mars International, Inc.
Phone—(908) 233-0044
60 Kingsbridge Rd., Piscataway 08854

## ELECTRONIC ASSEMBLY

Access Control Group, LLC
Phone—(908) 789-8700
2555 U.S. Highway 130 S., Ste. 2, Cranbury 08512

## ELECTRONIC ASSEMBLY — Contract

LC Engineers, Inc.
Phone—(732) 340-9190
1471 Pinewood St., Rahway 07065
Medco West
Phone—(201) 457-9260
25-21 Di Carolis Ct., Hackensack 07601

## ELECTRONIC ASSEMBLY EQUIPMENT

inTEST Corp.
Phone—(856) 505-8800
804 E. Gate Dr., Ste. 200, Mount Laurel 08054

## ELECTRONIC COILS

Stonite Coil Corp.
Phone—(609) 585-6600
476 Route 156, P.O. Box 11036, Yardville 08620

## ELECTRONIC COMPONENTS

Advanced Technology Group, Inc.
Phone—(973) 627-6955
101 Round Hill Dr., Rockaway 07866
Anatech Electronics, Inc.
Phone—(973) 772-4242
70 Outwater Ln., Ste. 3, P.O. Box 2217, Garfield 07026
Armel Electronics, Inc.
Phone—(201) 869-4300
1601 75th St., North Bergen 07047
Ballantine Laboratories, Inc.
Phone—(908) 713-7742
312 Old Allerton Rd., Annandale 08801
Bel Fuse, Inc. (H Q)
Phone—(201) 432-0463
206 Van Vorst St., Jersey City 07302
Celco, Inc.
Phone—(201) 327-1123
14 Industrial Ave., 3rd Fl., Mahwah 07430
Clantech, Inc.
Phone—(908) 281-7667
198 Highway 206 S., Hillsborough 08844
Compex Corp.
Phone—(856) 335-2277
439 Commerce Ln., Ste. 1, West Berlin 08091
Conta-Clip, Inc.
Phone—(732) 564-0705
400 Apgar Dr., Ste. D, P.O. Box 6510, Somerset 08873
Data Delay Devices, Inc.
Phone—(973) 773-2299
3 Mount Prospect Ave., Clifton 07013

Dewey Electronics Corp.
Phone—(201) 337-4700
27 Muller Rd., Oakland 07436
Dtrovision, LLC
Phone—(201) 488-3232
535 E. Crescent Ave., Ste. 1, Ramsey 07446
Fujipoly America Corp.
Phone—(732) 969-0100
900 Milik St., P.O. Box 119, Carteret 07008
Future Electronics Corp.
Phone—(973) 299-0400
959 Route 46 E., Ste. 303, Parsippany Pl, Parsippany 07054
**Hamamatsu Corporation**
**Phone—(908) 231-0960**
**Fax—(908) 231-1539**
**Web—www.hamamatsu.com**
**Email—usa@hamamatsu.com**
**360 Foothill Rd., P.O. Box 6910, Bridgewater 08807**
Innodyne Engineering
Phone—(646) 240-0200
1711 Ginesi Dr., Unit 2, Freehold 07728
Johanson Mfg. Corp.
Phone—(973) 334-2676
301 Rockaway Valley Rd., Boonton 07005
JP Rotella Co., Inc.
Phone—(973) 942-2559
20 E. Barbour St., Haledon 07508
K R Electronics, Inc.
Phone—(732) 636-1900
91 Avenel St., Avenel 07001
Lantek Corporation
Phone—(973) 579-8100
29 Brookfield Dr., Sparta 07871
Linearizer Technology, Inc.
Phone—(609) 584-8424
3 Nami Ln., Ste. 9-C, Hamilton 08619
Lockheed Martin
Phone—(856) 722-4100
199 Borton Landing Rd., Rm. 108-108, P.O. Box 1027, Moorestown 08057
Mercury Commercial Electronics
Phone—(973) 244-1040
2 Henderson Dr., Ste. B, Caldwell 07006
Merrimac Industries, Inc.
Phone—(973) 575-1300
41 Fairfield Pl., West Caldwell 07006
Metuchen Capacitors, Inc.
Phone—(732) 888-9700
2139 Highway 35, Ste. 2, P.O. Box 399, Holmdel 07733
Microelettrica-USA, LLC
Phone—(973) 598-0806
4 Middlebury Blvd., Ste. 12, Randolph 07869
Microlab/FXR
Phone—(973) 386-9696
25 Eastmans Rd., Parsippany 07054
**New Jersey Semiconductor Products, Inc.**
**We are your source for all your semiconductor needs & requirements**
**Phone—(973) 376-2922 / (212) 227-6005**
**Fax—(973) 376-8960**
**Web—www.njsemi.com**
**Email—sales@njsemi.com**
**20 Stern Ave., Springfield 07081**
Panasonic Industrial Devices Sales Co. Of America (H Q)
Phone—(908) 464-3550
2 River Front Plz., 7th Fl., Newark 07102
**PNY Technologies, Inc.**
**Phone—(973) 515-9700**
**Fax—(973) 560-5590**
**Web—www.pny.com**
**Email—info@pny.com**
**100 Jefferson Rd., Parsippany 07054**

**PNY** PNY Technologies, Inc.
Make Life Simple™
USB Flash Drives, Flash Memory Cards, Video Cards, Power Packs/Mobile Accessories, Solid State Drives, PC Memory
973-515-9700 • www.pny.com
100 Jefferson Rd. Parsippany, NJ 07054

Pulsar Microwave Corp.
Phone—(973) 779-6262
48 Industrial St. W., Clifton 07012

R F L Electronics, Inc.
Phone—(973) 334-3100
353 Powerville Rd., Boonton 07005
Samsung Electronics America, Inc.
Phone—(201) 229-4000
85 Challenger Rd., Ridgefield Park 07660
Schaffner EMC, Inc.
Phone—(732) 225-9533
52 Mayfield Ave., Edison 08837
Silver Cloud Mfg. Co.
Phone—(856) 825-8900
525 Orange St., Millville 08332
**Solid State, Inc.**
**Email: andrewl@solidstateinc.com**
**Your total solution source for electronic components**
**Phone—(973) 429-8700 / (800) 631-2075**
**Fax—(973) 429-1499**
**Web—www.solidstateinc.com**
**Email—sales@solidstateinc.com**
**46 Farrand St., Bloomfield 07003**

**Solid State, Inc.**
Your Total Solution Source for Electronic Components
www.solidstateinc.com / 800-631-2075
973-429-8700 / Fax: 973-429-1499
46 Farrand St. • Bloomfield, NJ 07003

T & E Industries, Inc.
Phone—(973) 672-5454
215 Watchung Ave., Orange 07050
Union City Filament Corp.
Phone—(201) 945-3366
1039-A Hoyt Ave., P.O. Box 777, Ridgefield 07657
Waveline, Inc.
Phone—(973) 808-9113
160 Passaic Ave., Fairfield 07004

## ELECTRONIC COMPONENTS — Wholesale

ARCO, INC.
Phone—(201) 828-9808
300 State Route 17, Unit K, Mahwah 07430
**New Jersey Semiconductor Products, Inc.**
**We are your source for all your semiconductor needs & requirements**
**Phone—(973) 376-2922 / (212) 227-6005**
**Fax—(973) 376-8960**
**Web—www.njsemi.com**
**Email—sales@njsemi.com**
**20 Stern Ave., Springfield 07081**
Powell Electronics, Inc.
Phone—(856) 241-8000
200 Commodore Dr., Logan Township 08085

## ELECTRONIC CONNECTORS

Adapter Technologies, Inc.
Phone—(856) 767-3930
154 Cooper Rd., Unit 1303, West Berlin 08091
Central Components Mfg., LLC (H Q)
Phone—(732) 469-5720
440 Lincoln Blvd., Middlesex 08846
Da-Green Electronics, Inc.
Phone—(732) 254-2735
37 Main St., P.O. Box 486, South River 08882
Volta Corp.
Phone—(732) 583-3300
11 Industrial Dr., P.O. Box 1027, Laurence Harbor 08879

## ELECTRONIC CONTROL SYSTEMS

CTI Motor Drives, Inc.
Phone—(732) 613-8390
105 Jackson St., South River 08882
FMDK Technologies, Inc.
Phone—(201) 828-9822
63 Ramapo Valley Rd., Lobby 4, Mahwah 07430

Search from among 430,000 U.S. manufacturers & suppliers:
IndustryNet.com

## ELECTRONIC CONTROLS

Barantec, Inc.
Phone—(973) 779-8774
777 Passaic Ave., Ste. 345, Clifton 07012
Electronic Technology, Inc.
Phone—(973) 371-5160
511 Lyons Ave., Irvington 07111

## ELECTRONIC ENCLOSURES

GAW Associates, Inc.
Phone—(856) 608-1428
670 Deer Rd., Unit A, Cherry Hill 08034

## ELECTRONIC EQUIPMENT & SUPPLIES

Blonder Tongue Laboratories, Inc.
Phone—(732) 679-4000
1 Jake Brown Rd., P.O. Box 1000, Old Bridge 08857
Comtron, Inc.
Phone—(732) 446-7571
391 State Route 33 E., Englishtown 07726
Dataprobe, Inc.
Phone—(201) 934-9944
1-B Pearl Ct., Allendale 07401
JACE Systems, Inc.
Phone—(800) 800-4276
5 Rockhill Rd., Ste. 2, Cherry Hill 08003
Lacey Cash Registers & Business Machines Co.
Phone—(609) 971-9494
2180 Llewellyn Pkwy., P.O. Box 1151, Forked River 08731
Mennekes Electronics, Inc.
Phone—(973) 882-8333
277 Fairfield Rd., Fairfield 07004
MYAT, Inc.
Phone—(201) 684-0100
360 Franklin Tpke., Mahwah 07430
Panasonic Corp. Of North America (H Q)
Phone—(201) 348-7500
2 River Front Plz., Newark 07102
Sakar International, Inc. (H Q)
Phone—(732) 248-1306
195 Carter Dr., Edison 08817
Star Micronics America, Inc. (H Q)
Phone—(732) 623-5500
1150 King Georges Post Rd., Edison 08837

## ELECTRONIC EQUIPMENT & SUPPLIES — Wholesale

**Hamamatsu Corporation**
**Phone—(908) 231-0960**
**Fax—(908) 231-1539**
**Web—www.hamamatsu.com**
**Email—usa@hamamatsu.com**
**360 Foothill Rd., P.O. Box 6910, Bridgewater 08807**
PTC Electronics, Inc.
Phone—(201) 847-0500
45 Whitney Rd., Ste. B-9, Mahwah 07430
Relay Specialties, Inc.
Phone—(201) 337-1000
17 Raritan Rd., P.O. Box 7000, Oakland 07436

## ELECTRONIC HARDWARE

Garan Electronics, Inc.
Phone—(908) 484-7100
223 Stirling Rd., Unit C, Warren 07059

## ELECTRONIC HARNESSES

**Ram Electronic Industries Inc.**
**Web: www.ramoem.com**
**Email: steve@ramelectronics.net**
**Phone—(856) 864-0999**
**Fax—(856) 786-2244**
**1704 Taylors Ln., Ste. 7, Cinnaminson 08077**

## ELECTRONIC SYSTEMS

General Dynamics Advanced Information Systems
Phone—(973) 514-4000
7-9 Vreeland Rd., Florham Park 07932

V G Controls, Inc.
Phone—(973) 764-6500
11 Butternut Dr., Vernon 07462

## ELECTRONIC TEST EQUIPMENT

Empire Telecommunications, Inc.
Phone—(201) 569-3339
15 S. Van Brunt St., Englewood 07631
In-Phase Technologies, Inc.
Phone—(609) 298-9555
401 Bordentown Hedding Rd., Bldg. 4, Ste. A, Bordentown 08505
Signalcrafters Tech, Inc.
Phone—(973) 781-0880
57 Eagle Rock Ave., East Hanover 07936
Tel-Instrument Electronics Corp.
Phone—(201) 933-1600
1 Branca Rd., East Rutherford 07073

## ELECTRONIC TRANSFORMERS

Bey Electronics Corp.
Phone—(973) 225-9494
39 Kentucky Ave., Paterson 07503
Hunterdon Transformer Co.
Phone—(908) 454-2400
75 Industrial Rd., Alpha 08865
Mech-Tronics
Phone—(609) 267-0680
100 Campus Dr., Mount Holly 08060
Torelco, Inc.
Phone—(908) 387-0814
55 Industrial Dr., Alpha 08865

## ELECTRONIC TUBES

ITW Thielex
Phone—(732) 873-5500
95 Commerce Dr., Somerset 08873

## ELECTRONIC WIRE & CABLE

**Okonite Co., Inc., The (H Q)**
**Email: seltsam@okonite.com**
**Setting The Standard Since 1868**
**Phone—(201) 825-0300**
**Fax—(201) 825-9026**
**Web—www.okonite.com**
**102 Hilltop Rd., P.O. Box 340, Ramsey 07446**
*(see our ad under WIRE AND CABLE)*

## ELECTRONICS — Consumer

CVE, Inc.
Phone—(201) 770-0005
5 N. Corporate Dr., Riverdale 07457
LG Electronics USA, Inc. (H Q)
Phone—(201) 816-2000
1000 Sylvan Ave., Englewood Cliffs 07632
Sharp Electronics Corp. (H Q)
Phone—(201) 529-8200
1 Sharp Plz., Mahwah 07430

## ELECTRONICS — Industrial

Technical Systems Group, Inc.
Phone—(973) 785-1118
28 Muller Pl., Little Falls 07424
TomPat Technologies, Inc.
Phone—(973) 785-1118
28 Muller Pl., Little Falls 07424

## ELECTRONICS MANUFACTURING SERVICES (EMS)

Precision Graphics, Inc.
Phone—(908) 707-8880
21 County Line Rd., Somerville 08876

## ELECTRO-OPTICAL EQUIPMENT

Chromatic Control, LLC (H Q)
Phone—(973) 944-3996
63 Fox Trail Rd., P.O. Box 374, Sparta 07871

Fastpulse Technology, Inc.
Phone—(973) 478-5757
220 Midland Ave., Saddle Brook 07663

## ELECTROPLATING

**(also see 'Plating—Electro')**
**B & B Electroplating Co.**
**Electroplating, including Tin, Silver, Nickel, Barrel & Rack**
**Phone—(908) 925-5044**
**Fax—(908) 925-1936**
**Web—www.bbplating.com**
**Email—r2thistle@aol.com**
**559 Pennsylvania Ave., Linden 07036**
Hunter Products, Inc.
Phone—(908) 526-8440
792 Partridge Dr., P.O. Box 6795, Bridgewater 08807
**Miller & Sons, Inc.**
**Celebrating over 100 years in Business**
**Phone—(973) 759-6445 / (973) 759-6446**
**Fax—(973) 759-1625**
**Web—www.millerplatingnj.com**
**Email—millerplating@aol.com**
**24 Belleville Ave., Belleville 07109**

Since 1913　QUALITY SERVICE　4 Generations
Miller & Sons, Inc.
Electroplating
Anodize
973-759-6445
Fax: 973-759-1625
24 Belleville Ave.
Belleville, NJ 07109
www.millerplatingnj.com
millerplating@aol.com

## ELEVATOR PARTS & SUPPLIES

Elevator Doors, Inc./Elevator Cabs, Inc.
Phone—(973) 790-9100
15 Jane St., Paterson 07522
Elevator Products Corp.
Phone—(973) 341-8000
100 Dermarest Dr., Wayne 07470
Elevator Technology Corp.
Phone—(973) 523-7760
337 Market St., Paterson 07501
Regency Elevator Products
Phone—(973) 481-1400
870 Mount Prospect Ave., Newark 07104
Schindler Elevator Corp. (H Q)
Phone—(973) 397-6500
20 Whippany Rd., Morristown 07960
Woerner Machine & Tool Co.
Phone—(908) 979-0042
700 Grand Ave., Bldg. 7, Hackettstown 07840

## ELEVATORS

**CESCO Elevator**
**Phone—(908) 561-7077**
**Web—www.cescoelevator.com**
**4401 S. Clifton Ave., South Plainfield 07080**
**Morris County Elevator, Inc.**
**Phone—(973) 252-1700**
**Fax—(973) 252-1817**
**Web—www.morriscountyelevator.com**
**Email—jenni.copen@morriscountyelevator.com**
**227 US Highway 206, Ste. 13, Flanders 07836**

## ELEVATORS — *(cont.)*

North American Elevator, Inc.
Phone—(908) 523-1234
609 W. Elizabeth Ave., Linden 07036

**On The Level Elevator & Escalator**
**Phone—(732) 708-0782**
**Fax—(732) 708-0012**
**Web—www.onthelevelelevator.com**
**Email—on.the.level.elevator@gmail.com**
**P.O. Box 18, Atlantic Highlands 07716**

**South Jersey Elevator**
**Phone—(609) 545-8512**
**Fax—(609) 545-8502**
**Web—www.SJElevator.com**
**Email—SJElevator@live.com**
**652 West Ave., Ocean City 08226**

## ELEVATORS — Freight & Passenger

Fujitec America Inc., New York Region
Phone—(973) 330-0100
215 Entin Rd., Clifton 07014

## ELEVATORS — Invalid

Florlift Of New Jersey, Inc.
Phone—(973) 484-1717
19 Gardner Rd., Ste. M, Fairfield 07004

## EMBLEMS

C & P Embroidery, LLC
Phone—(201) 854-0388
6602 Smith Ave., North Bergen 07047

Eastern Emblem Mfg. Corp.
Phone—(201) 867-3159
509 18th St., P.O. Box 828, Union City 07087

Golden Rule Creations
Phone—(201) 337-4050
250 Terrace Rd., Franklin Lakes 07417

Jarco U. S. Casting Corp.
Phone—(201) 271-0003
109 45th St., Union City 07087

New Rose, Inc.
Phone—(856) 812-0509
1500 Almonesson Rd., Ste. 8, Woodbury 08096

## EMBOSSING

Holographic Finishing, Inc.
Phone—(201) 941-4651
501 Hendricks Cswy., P.O. Box 597, Ridgefield 07657

**Regal Stamp & Sign Co., Inc.**
**Making Our Mark Since 1970. Rubber Stamps, Embossing, Seals & Signage**
**Phone—(201) 939-0400**
**Fax—(201) 939-5203**
**Web—www.regalstampnj.com**
**Email—regalstamp@verizon.net**
**240 Park Ave., P.O. Box 342, East Rutherford 07073**

*(see our ad under RUBBER STAMPS)*

## EMBROIDERY

A A Patchworks, Inc. (H Q)
Phone—(973) 810-2121
311 Mechanic St., Boonton 07005

Accent Apparel LLC
Phone—(732) 341-7576
405 Atlantic City Blvd., Beachwood 08722

All-Star Pro & Sport Store
Phone—(732) 774-3444
642 State Route 35 N., Neptune 07753

Apparel Zone, Inc.
Phone—(732) 441-7780
165 Amboy Rd., Ste. 505, Morganville 07751

Aristocrat Embroidery Corp.
Phone—(201) 869-9126
7014 Jackson St., Guttenberg 07093

Art's Embroidery, LLC
Phone—(732) 870-1155
175 Monmouth Rd., West Long Branch 07764

Athletic Imprinters, Inc.
Phone—(856) 346-4545
775 Ashbourne Ave., Lindenwold 08021

Bon-Jour Group, LLC
Phone—(201) 646-1070
1100 Blanch Ave., Norwood 07648

Boy On A Dolphin Corp.
Phone—(732) 495-2200
308 State Route 36, Port Monmouth 07758

Carol's Creations, LLC
Phone—(856) 428-0621
112 Kipling Rd., Cherry Hill 08003

Cobyco, Inc.
Phone—(732) 446-4448
65 Wilson Ave., Manalapan 07726

Continental Cap Co.
Phone—(973) 778-2628
64 Passaic St., Wood Ridge 07075

Cox Merchandising, LLC, Fred
Phone—(201) 310-0740
34 Radburn Rd., Glen Rock 07452

Custom Embroidery
Phone—(609) 383-9292
73 E. New Jersey Ave., P.O. Box 1489, Pleasantville 08232

Dearbrook Fabrics, Inc.
Phone—(201) 945-4141
430 Walker St., P.O. Box 338, Fairview 07022

Embroider This Co.
Phone—(973) 663-5551
7 Duck Point Trl., Wharton 07885

Embroidery By Cozy, Inc.
Phone—(973) 661-9781
695 Passaic Ave., Nutley 07110

Embroidery Concept & Design, LLC
Phone—(732) 926-9400
201 Pond Ave., Middlesex 08846

Embroidery Technologies, Inc.
Phone—(732) 295-1300
737 Howe St., Point Pleasant Boro 08742

Embroidme
Phone—(732) 752-1871
215 U.S. Highway 22, Green Brook 08812

Empire Designs, Inc.
Phone—(732) 446-6447
7 Main St., Englishtown 07726

ERL Embroidery & Screen Printing
Phone—(973) 633-7428
8 Evergreen Dr., Lincoln Park 07035

Fancy Threads
Phone—(609) 466-0050
31 Railroad Pl., Hopewell 08525

Faraj, Inc.
Phone—(201) 313-4480
422 Cliff St., Fairview 07022

Finesse & Lucas
Phone—(732) 367-0839
40 Chestnut St., Ste. 14, Lakewood 08701

Gallery Monograms
Phone—(201) 569-0189
360 Sherman Ave., Teaneck 07666

Garden State Embroidery
Phone—(856) 616-9490
1879 Old Cuthbert Rd., Unit 10, Cherry Hill 08034

Hamilton Embroidery, Inc.
Phone—(201) 867-4084
907-909 21st St., Union City 07087

Imagery Embroidery Corporation
Phone—(201) 343-9333
2907-2911 Jeannette St., Union City 07087

In Stitches Embroidery, Inc.
Phone—(732) 460-2660
1020 Campus Dr., Morganville 07751

J & G Enterprises, Inc.
Phone—(973) 667-7673
182 High St., Nutley 07110

J & S Finishing, Inc.
Phone—(201) 854-0338
443 62nd St., West New York 07093

J S Designs
Phone—(609) 268-3018
321 Oakshade Rd., Shamong 08088

K & C Fund Raising & Embroidery
Phone—(856) 881-6019
101 S. Delsea Dr., Clayton 08312

Landsman Uniforms, Inc.
Phone—(609) 909-1000
4450 Black Horse Pike, Ste. 3958, Mays Landing 08330

Life A Stitch
Phone—(732) 969-0232
37 Jackson Ave., Carteret 07008

Li'l Inspirations, LLC
Phone—(908) 369-5840
P.O. Box 5754, Hillsborough 08844

Monogram Madness
Phone—(973) 927-5278
50 Main St., Succasunna 07876

Nu-Style Embroidery & Trimming
Phone—(201) 864-1808
5212 Polk St., West New York 07093

Personalized Paraphernalia
Phone—(908) 526-0602
22 Division St., Somerville 08876

ProImage Apparel, LLC
Phone—(201) 773-9292
280 N. Midland Ave., Bldg. H, Saddle Brook 07663

Promotion Works
Phone—(201) 842-1107
45 Wadsworth St., Wallington 07057

R & R Graphics, Inc.
Phone—(856) 751-7671
1724 Route 70 E., Unit B, Cherry Hill 08003

R K E Athletic Lettering
Phone—(732) 280-1111
1901 State Route 71, Ste. 1-C, Belmar 07719

Schreyer Embroidery Co., Inc.
Phone—(201) 943-6221
50 Industrial Ave., Fairview 07022

Sequins City
Phone—(201) 348-8111
1302 13th St., North Bergen 07047

Sew Ann Sew Thomas Enterprises
Phone—(973) 742-2664
153 Pearl St., Paterson 07501

Sew Many Gifts, Inc.
Phone—(609) 275-4532
6 Cranston Ct., Princeton Junction 08550

Shangri La Farm, LLC
Phone—(732) 901-8777
1055 Maxim Southard Rd., Howell 07731

**Smith Enterprises**
**Phone—(215) 416-9881**
**Fax—(856) 608-9588**
**Web—www.smithentpromos.com**
**Email—dstees@comcast.net**
**100 Hillside Ln., P.O. Box 1433, Mount Laurel 08054**

Southern Ocean Marine Sportswear
Phone—(609) 698-8868
79 S. Main St., Ste. 2, Barnegat 08005

Sparkle Embroidery Monograms
Phone—(856) 468-0304
550 Bridgeton Pike, Ste. 12, Mantua 08051

Star Embroidery Corp.
Phone—(973) 481-4300
305 3rd Ave. W., Newark 07107

Stitch-It-Up Embroidery
Phone—(201) 512-9881
151 Fisher Rd., Mahwah 07430

Stylus Custom Apparel, Inc.
Phone—(908) 587-0800
729 E. Elizabeth Ave., Linden 07036

Tone Embroidery, Inc.
Phone—(201) 943-1082
333 Bergen Blvd., Fairview 07022

Toni Embroidery Co.
Phone—(201) 664-6909
475 Broadway, Westwood 07675

Trenton Joe's Embroidery
Phone—(609) 538-9450
4 Scotch Rd., Ewing 08628

Unique Embroidery, Inc.
Phone—(201) 943-9191
1030 Pleasantview Ter., Ridgefield 07657

University Apparel, Inc.
Phone—(609) 871-3601
2501 Mount Holly Rd., Ste. 262, Burlington 08016

Weber & Doebrich, Inc.
Phone—(201) 867-1540
119 61st St., West New York 07093

Wisco Promo & Uniform, Inc.
Phone—(973) 767-2022
160 Route 46 E., Saddle Brook 07663

World's Finest, Inc.
Phone—(609) 394-8001
267 Hamilton Ave., Trenton 08609

Wostbrock Embroidery, Inc.
Phone—(201) 445-3074
11 Paterson Ave., Midland Park 07432

*Do nationwide searches for products & services at:*
**IndustryNet.com**

## EMBROIDERY SUPPLIES

Sandpiper Embroidery, Inc.
Phone—(609) 522-4560
5905 New Jersey Ave., Wildwood Crest 08260

## EMERGENCY VEHICLE EQUIPMENT

KALDOR Emergency Lights, LLC
Phone—(732) 780-6707
19 Vanderburg Rd., Marlboro 07746

## EMISSIONS MONITORS

Monitoring Solutions, Inc.
Phone—(908) 713-0172
78 Route 173, Ste. 7, Hampton 08827

## EMPLOYEE BENEFIT PLANS

Sanford Insurance Group
Phone—(973) 783-6600
Fax—(973) 783-2904
Web—www.sanfordinsnj.com
Email—bsanford@sanfordinsure.com
210 Bellevue Ave., Montclair 07043

## EMPLOYMENT AGENCIES

AmeriTemps, Inc.
Phone—(856) 966-0999
Fax—(856) 966-1114
Web—www.ameritempsinc.com
Email—nj@ameritempsinc.com
608 S. Broadway, Camden 08103
Diamond Staffing Service Inc.
Phone—(201) 974-8831
Web—www.diamondstaffinginc.com
404 43rd St., Union City 07087
Labor Ready
Phone—(609) 538-9330
Fax—(609) 538-9335
Web—www.laborready.com
Email—1806-br@laborready.com
1470 Prospect St., Ewing 08638

## EMPLOYMENT CONTRACTORS — Temporary Help

Labor Ready
Phone—(609) 538-9330
Fax—(609) 538-9335
Web—www.laborready.com
Email—1806-br@laborready.com
1470 Prospect St., Ewing 08638

## EMULSIFIERS

Corbion Caravan
Corporate Headquarters Lenexa, KS; Regional Office & Bakery
Phone—(973) 256-8886 / (800) 526-5261
Fax—(973) 256-5789
Web—www.corbion.com
Email—bakery@corbion.com
100 Adams Dr., Totowa 07512

## ENCLOSURES

Gavan Graham Electrical Products
Phone—(908) 729-9000
751 Rahway Ave., Union 07083
Lux Entertainment, LLC
Phone—(888) 282-8425
629 E. 19th St., Paterson 07514

## ENCLOSURES — Bathtub & Shower

Century Bathworks, Inc.
Luxury glass shower enclosures & medicine cabinets
Phone—(973) 785-4290 / (800) 524-2578
Fax—(973) 785-0777
Web—www.centurybathworks.com
Email—info@centurybathworks.com
250 Lackawanna Ave., Woodland Park 07424

Precision Shower Doors, Inc.
Phone—(732) 389-8175
359 Essex Rd., Tinton Falls 07753

## ENCLOSURES — Screen, Porch & Patio

Disco Aluminum
Phone—(908) 754-2699
518 South Ave., Plainfield 07060

## ENCLOSURES — Sheet Metal

Par-Metal, Inc.
Phone—(201) 955-0800
29 Ewing Ave., North Arlington 07031
Pepco Mfg. Co.
Phone—(856) 783-3700
210 E. Evergreen Ave., P.O. Box 160, Somerdale 08083

## ENCODERS

Communication Devices, Inc.
Phone—(973) 334-1980
85 Fulton St., Unit 2, Boonton 07005

## ENDOSCOPES

Fuji Film Medical Systems U.S.A., Inc.
Phone—(973) 633-5600
10 Highpoint Dr., Wayne 07470
PENTAX Of America, Inc.
Phone—(201) 571-2300
3 Paragon Dr., Ste. 1, Montvale 07645

## ENERGY MANAGEMENT SYSTEMS

Honeywell International, Inc. (H Q)
Phone—(973) 455-2000
101 Columbia Rd., Morristown 07962

## ENGINE COMPONENTS

L E C Electronics, Inc.
Phone—(856) 227-3953
814 Warsaw Ave., Blackwood 08012
Manley Performance Products, Inc.
Phone—(732) 905-3366
1960 Swarthmore Ave., Lakewood 08701

## ENGINE PARTS

NRG Energy, Inc. (H Q)
Phone—(609) 524-4500
211 Carnegie Ctr., Princeton 08540

## ENGINE REBUILDING & REPAIR

American Crankshaft Grinding Co., Inc.
Phone—(908) 352-5558
851-861 Fairmount Ave., Elizabeth 07201
Arrow Machine Co.
Phone—(973) 642-2430
117 Norfolk St., Newark 07103
Cast Technology, Inc.
Phone—(908) 753-5155
161 West St., South Plainfield 07080
Ceralli Competition Engines, Inc.
Phone—(973) 742-4972
395 E. 18th St., Paterson 07524
D & F Performance
Phone—(856) 767-4095
417 N. Grove St., Berlin 08009
Medford Speed & Machine, Inc.
Phone—(609) 801-0808
132 Red Lion Rd., Southampton 08088

## ENGINEERING EQUIPMENT & SUPPLIES

Brewer Assocs.
Phone—(732) 564-9070
400 Apgar Dr., Unit G, Somerset 08873

## ENGINEERING SERVICES

BRECOflex Co., L.L.C.
Phone—(732) 460-9500 / (888) 463-1400
Fax—(732) 542-6725
Web—www.brecoflex.com
Email—info@brecoflex.com
222 Industrial Way W., Eatontown 07724
*(see our ads under BELTING & PULLEYS)*
TMG Engineering Inc.
Phone—(732) 738-9670
Fax—(732) 738-9672
Web—www.tmg-engr.com
Email—fmosher@tmg-engr.com
1090 King Georges Post Rd., Ste. 903, Edison 08837

## ENGINEERS — Civil

Herbert J. Neilio LLC
Phone—(856) 468-2000
P.O. Box 127, Mantua 08051

## ENGINEERS — Consulting

AMEC Environment & Infrastructure
Phone—(732) 302-9500
Fax—(732) 302-9504
Web—www.amec.com
285 Davidson Ave., Ste. 405, Somerset 08873
Commsult Communications LP
Phone—(201) 792-2008
Fax—(212) 208-2416
Web—www.commsult.com
Email—hprestia@commsult.com
111 Town Square Pl., Ste. 620, Jersey City 07310
GEI Consultants, Inc.
Phone—(973) 873-7110
Fax—(973) 509-9625
Web—www.geiconsultants.com
Email—mlevinson@geiconsultants.com
1 Greenwood Ave., Ste. 210, Montclair 07042
*(see our ad under ENVIRONMENTAL SERVICES)*
Hoffmark Industries Ltd.
Phone—(973) 337-0837
Fax—(973) 773-9807
247 Speer Ave., Ste. 1, Clifton 07013
M. V. Engineering, LLC
Diverse experience, training and certifications of M.V. Engineering's staff provides support for licensed proffesional engineers; serving engineering needs of municipal government, local and State utilities and authorities
Phone—(609) 465-7080
Fax—(609) 465-3973
Web—www.mvengllc.com
Email—b.murphy.mve@comcast.net
P.O. Box 484, Cape May Court House 08210
Storm Water Compliance Solutions LLC
Phone—(908) 879-1145
Fax—(908) 879-0564
Web—
www.stormwatercompliancesolutions.com
Email—dflynn@
stormwatercompliancesolutions.com
P.O. Box 572, Chester 07930

## ENGINEERS — Electrical

Total Comfort Mechanical
Phone—(732) 527-0091
Fax—(732) 527-0100
Web—www.total-cg.com
Email—sales@total-cg.com
295 Kimball St., Woodbridge 07095

## ENGINEERS — Environmental

Sadat Associates
Phone—(609) 826-9600
Fax—(609) 826-9601
1545 Lamberton Rd., Trenton 08611

*find additional suppliers at*
**IndustryNet.com**

# Atlantic Detroit Diesel-Allison, LLC

## Corporate Headquarters & Diesel Engines

### 201-489-5800 • FAX: 201-368-1071

### www.atlanticdda.com

### 180 Route 17 South  Lodi, NJ 07644

**KRAFTPOWER**
*The power of performance.*

241 West Parkway
Pompton Plains, NJ 07444

## Tel: 973-835-9800  Fax: 973-835-5246

### Please visit us at www.kraftpower.com

## Power Systems Specialists since 1965

## ENGINES — Gas

**Kraft Power Corp.**
Email: njsales@kraftpower.com
Phone—(973) 835-9800 / (800) 221-3284
Fax—(973) 835-5246
Web—www.kraftpower.com
Email—njinfo@kraftpower.com
241 W. Parkway, Pompton Plains 07444
*(see our ad on this page)*

**Lake Small Engine Repair, LLC**
Service, Sales & Parts
Phone—(732) 873-9047
Fax—(732) 873-3395
Web—www.lakesmallengine.com
Email—lakesmallenginerepair@verizon.net
283 Cedar Grove Ln., Somerset 08873

## Lake Small Engine Repair, LLC

### Service, Sales & Parts

## (732) 873-9047
## FAX: (732) 873-3395

www.lakesmallengine.com

lakesmallenginerepair@verizon.net

283 Cedar Grove Ln.
Somerset, NJ 08873

## ENGINEERS — Geotechnical

**GEI Consultants, Inc.**
Phone—(973) 873-7110
Fax—(973) 509-9625
Web—www.geiconsultants.com
Email—mlevinson@geiconsultants.com
1 Greenwood Ave., Ste. 210, Montclair 07042
*(see our ad under ENVIRONMENTAL SERVICES)*

## ENGINEERS — Mechanical

**Total Comfort Mechanical**
Phone—(732) 527-0091
Fax—(732) 527-0100
Web—www.total-cg.com
Email—sales@total-cg.com
295 Kimball St., Woodbridge 07095

## ENGINEERS — Safety

**FallProof Systems LLC**
Specialists in Engineered Fall Protection Systems
Phone—(609) 325-5555
Fax—(609) 584-8882
Web—www.fallproof.com
Email—solutions@fallproof.com
61 2nd Ave., Trenton 08619

## ENGINES

Coates International Ltd.
Phone—(732) 449-7717
2100 Highway 34 & Ridgewood Rd., Wall 07719
Engine Distributors, Inc.
Phone—(856) 228-7298
400 University Ct., Blackwood 08012

## ENGINES — Automotive

Coates Precision Engineering Ltd.
Phone—(732) 449-7717
2100 Highway 34 & Ridgewood Rd., Wall 07719
Jackson Racing Engines, Inc., Henry
Phone—(609) 758-7476
787 Route 537, Cream Ridge 08514

## ENGINES — Diesel

**Atlantic Detroit Diesel-Allison, LLC**
Corporate Headquarters & Diesel Engines
Phone—(201) 489-5800
Fax—(201) 368-1071
Web—www.atlanticdda.com
180 Route 17 S., P.O. Box 950, Lodi 07644
*(see our ad on this page)*
**Atlantic Detroit Diesel-Allison, LLC**
Phone—(732) 752-7100
Fax—(732) 752-8380
Web—www.atlanticdda.com
169 Old New Brunswick Rd., Piscataway 08854
Jersey Diesel
Phone—(856) 785-8810
487 Main St., Dorchester 08316
**Johnson & Towers, Inc.**
Detroit Diesel, Allison, MTU; Marine & Generator Services
Phone—(609) 272-1415
Fax—(609) 272-1868
Web—www.johnsontowers.com
Email—pprior@johnsontowers.com
2701 Fire Rd., Egg Harbor Township 08234
**Kraft Power Corp.**
Email: njsales@kraftpower.com
Quality Engines
Phone—(973) 835-9800 / (800) 221-3284
Fax—(973) 835-5246
Web—www.kraftpower.com
241 W. Parkway, Pompton Plains 07444
*(see our ad on this page)*
Mack Boring & Parts Co.
Phone—(908) 964-0700
2365 U.S. Highway 22 W., P.O. Box 3116, Union 07083
Mid-Atlantic Engine Supply
Phone—(856) 829-7798
Route 130 S. & Pennsauken St., P.O. Box 2270, Cinnaminson 08077

*Search from among 430,000 U.S. manufacturers & suppliers:*
**IndustryNet.com**

## ENGINES — High Performance

LRB Performance Machine Co.
Phone—(973) 209-7770
22-B Lasinski Rd., Franklin 07416
Pro-Motion Engines, LLC
Phone—(973) 884-5936
2 Great Meadow Ln., Apt. B, East Hanover 07936

## ENGINES — Rebuilt

Jetek Enterprises, LLC
Phone—(609) 266-4700
4329 Atlantic Brigantine Blvd., Brigantine 08203
Lake Small Engine Repair, LLC
Phone—(732) 873-9047
283 Cedar Grove Ln., Somerset 08873

## ENGINES — Rebuilt Diesel

**Atlantic Detroit Diesel-Allison, LLC**
Phone—(732) 752-7100
Fax—(732) 752-8380
Web—www.atlanticdda.com
169 Old New Brunswick Rd., Piscataway 08854
Melton Sales & Service, Inc.
Phone—(609) 699-4800
511 Elbow Ln., Burlington 08016

## ENGINES — Truck

**Johnson & Towers, Inc.**
Detroit Diesel, Allison, MTU; Marine & Generator Services
Phone—(609) 272-1415
Fax—(609) 272-1868
Web—www.johnsontowers.com
Email—pprior@johnsontowers.com
2701 Fire Rd., Egg Harbor Township 08234
Johnson & Towers, Inc.
Phone—(856) 234-6990
2021 Briggs Rd., P.O. Box 4000, Mount Laurel 08054

© Copyright 2015 Manufacturers' News, Inc.

A69

INDUSTRY

# ENGRAVING

A-1 J D K Specialties
Phone—(732) 928-9495
1 Millstream Rd., Cream Ridge 08514

Acme Engraving Co., Inc.
Phone—(973) 778-0885
19-37 Delaware Ave., P.O. Box 1657, Passaic 07055

All State Medal Co., Inc.
Phone—(973) 458-1458
16 Adams Pl., Lodi 07644

All-Star Pro Trophy
Phone—(732) 364-1188
1012 Cox Cro Rd., Ste. 10, Toms River 08755

American Image
Phone—(201) 384-9200
45 W. Broad St., Bergenfield 07621

Bannister Co., Inc.
Phone—(732) 828-1353
126 N. Main St., Milltown 08850

Brown's Engraving, LLC
Phone—(609) 894-4443
12 Fort Dix Rd., Pemberton 08068

Cumberland Engraving Service
Phone—(856) 451-5052
127 W. Broad St., Bridgeton 08302

Custom Engraving
Phone—(732) 574-1901
29 Highland Rd., Colonia 07067

Engraver's Bench & Greek Unique, Inc.
Phone—(973) 297-1810
1212 Raymond Blvd., Newark 07102

Engraving Services Of New Jersey
Phone—(732) 341-0170
804 Columbia Rd., Toms River 08753

Foster Engraving and Laser Co.
Phone—(201) 489-5979
174 S. Main St., Ste. B, Hackensack 07601

Garden State Awards
Phone—(201) 795-9420
3516 John F. Kennedy Blvd., Jersey City 07307

Garden State Engraving
Phone—(732) 463-0060
126 Perrine Ave., Piscataway 08854

Hap Engraving Ltd.
Phone—(732) 223-4800
106 Windsor Way, Berkeley Heights 07922

Hero's Salute Awards Co.
Phone—(973) 696-5085
1875 State Route 23, Wayne 07470

Illusion Engraved
Phone—(732) 442-4488
311 Fayette St., Perth Amboy 08861

J & J Engraving
Phone—(201) 342-0798
45 Worth St., South Hackensack 07606

Jory Engravers, Inc.
Phone—(201) 939-1546
23 W. Erie Ave., Rutherford 07070

Lincoln Monument Co., Inc.
Phone—(973) 744-1800
405 Orange Rd., Montclair 07042

Main Street Awards, Inc.
Phone—(609) 448-6324
55 N. Main St., P.O. Box 323, Windsor 08561

Metro Bowl
Phone—(201) 791-2995
37-02 Broadway, Fair Lawn 07410

Nash Engraving, Inc.
Phone—(856) 456-5656
528 Nicholson Rd., Gloucester City 08030

Paul's Custom Awards & Trophy, Inc.
Phone—(856) 547-7777
200 White Horse Pike, Barrington 08007

Perry's
Phone—(732) 222-5040
11 N. 5th Ave., Long Branch 07740

Rios Engraving
Phone—(973) 539-5749
1 Maple Ave., Morristown 07960

Rubber Stamp Engraving
Phone—(732) 726-5664
386 Avenel St., Avenel 07001

Trophies Unlimited
Phone—(609) 298-3544
122 Fernwood Ave., Trenton 08610

West Hudson Industries
Phone—(732) 381-6800
1687 Saint Georges Ave., Rahway 07065

Woodbridge Monument Factory, Inc.
Phone—(732) 634-1521
10 Main St., Ste. K, Woodbridge 07095

# ENGRAVING — Industrial

Precision Engraving II, Inc.
Phone—(973) 887-3350
13 Ridgedale Ave., P.O. Box 243, East Hanover 07936

Westside Engravers
Phone—(856) 455-4790
76 N. West Ave., Bridgeton 08302

# ENGRAVING — Laser

Arista Trophies & Awards
Phone—(201) 387-2165
25 Portland Ave., Bergenfield 07621

Fischer Laser Marking, Inc.
Phone—(973) 616-4696
384 Otterhole Rd., West Milford 07480

Gecko Graphics, Inc.
Phone—(856) 740-9042
128 Berlin Cross Keys Rd., Williamstown 08094

Laser Xpressions, Inc.
Phone—(732) 303-9530
3710 Route 9 S., 2nd Fl., Freehold 07728

Merit Trophies & Engraving, Inc.
Phone—(201) 487-5780
184 Main St., Hackensack 07601

# ENGRAVING — Mechanical

N. B. C. Engraving Co., Inc.
Phone—(201) 387-8011
228 Park St., Hackensack 07601

# ENGRAVING — Photo

**Globe Photoengraving Co., LLC**
**Phone—(201) 489-2300**
**Fax—(201) 641-7682**
**Web—www.globeengraving.com**
**Email—magdies1@verizon.net**
**19 N. Washington Ave., Little Ferry 07643**

# ENGRAVING — Plastic

Gough Engraving & Advertising Specialties
Phone—(609) 882-8700
1745 N. Olden Avenue Ext., Ewing 08638

# ENGRAVING — Stationery

Precise Continental
Phone—(973) 350-0330
1 Cape May St., Harrison 07029

# ENGRAVING — Trophy

Crown Trophy Co., Inc.
Phone—(908) 789-0460
86 North Ave., Garwood 07027

# ENGRAVING EQUIPMENT & SUPPLIES

Cronite Co., Inc.
Phone—(973) 887-7900
120 E. Halsey Rd., P.O. Box 6330, Parsippany 07054

# ENVELOPES

**ADM Corp.**
**Phone—(732) 469-0900**
**Fax—(732) 469-0785**
**Web—www.admcorporation.com**
**Email—info@admcorporation.com**
**100 Lincoln Blvd., Middlesex 08846**

American Envelope & Printing Co.
Phone—(908) 241-9900
212 Columbus Ave., Roselle 07203

Atlantic Envelope Co.
Phone—(973) 882-0436
16 Passaic Ave., Unit 7, Fairfield 07004

Clinton Envelope
Phone—(856) 314-3636
9130 Pennsauken Hwy., Ste. C, Pennsauken 08110

KD Envelopes & Printing, LLC
Phone—(908) 686-1798
7 Mark Rd., Kenilworth 07033

Reliable Envelope & Graphics, Inc.
Phone—(201) 794-7756
85 Main Ave., Elmwood Park 07407

**Tension Envelope Corp.**
**Fax: (201) 488-1216**
**Phone—(201) 487-1880**
**Fax—(201) 498-0341**
**Web—www.tension.com**
**Email—info@tensionenvelope.com**
**19 Wesley St., South Hackensack 07606**

## Tension Envelope Corp.
### Envelopes
www.tension.com / (201) 487-1880
info@tensionenvelope.com
19 Wesley St. South Hackensack, NJ 07606

# ENVELOPES — Lithographed

Cenveo, Inc.
Phone—(201) 434-2100
25 Linden Ave. E., Jersey City 07305

# ENVIRONMENTAL CONSULTANTS

**Certified Health & Safety Services, LLC**
Safe Today-Here Tomorrow
**Phone—(856) 829-4463 / (800) 423-0137**
**Fax—(856) 786-3101**
**Web—www.certified-health-and-safety.com**
**Email—chss1@comcast.net**
**1902 Taylors Ln., Ste. A, Cinnaminson 08077**

**Certified Health & Safety Services, LLC**
Safe Today-Here Tomorrow
856-829-4463   800-423-0137
Fax: 856-786-3101
www.certified-health-and-safety.com
1902 Taylors Lane, Suite A
Cinnaminson, NJ 08077

Environmental Health Investigations
Phone—(973) 729-5649
Fax—(973) 729-5649
Web—www.ehi-inc.com
Email—bkerbel@ehi-inc.com
655 W. Shore Trl., Sparta 07871

## EHI

### ENVIRONMENTAL HEALTH INVESTIGATIONS

Environmental Consulting

**973-729-5649**
**Fax: 973-729-5649**

www.ehi-inc.com • bkerbel@ehi-inc.com

655 West Shore Trail
Sparta, NJ 07871

# PSC

### Environmental Services, LLC

## 800-365-9295

## 215-822-2676 • FAX: 215-997-8219

2337 N. Penn Rd., Hatfield, PA 19440

www.pscnow.com • info@pscnow.com

## ENVIRONMENTAL HEALTH & SAFETY SERVICES

**Certified Health & Safety Services, LLC**
Safe Today-Here Tomorrow
Phone—(856) 829-4463 / (800) 423-0137
Fax—(856) 786-3101
Web—www.certified-health-and-safety.com
Email—chss1@comcast.net
1902 Taylors Ln., Ste. A, Cinnaminson 08077
*(see our ad on this page)*

## ENVIRONMENTAL MANAGEMENT

**PSC Environmental Services, LLC**
Phone—(215) 822-2676 / (800) 365-9295
Fax—(215) 997-8219
Web—www.pscnow.com
Email—info@pscnow.com
2337 N. Penn Rd., Hatfield, PA 19440
*(see our ad on this page)*

## ENVIRONMENTAL MONITORING EQUIPMENT

**Pine Environmental Services, LLC**
Phone—(609) 371-9663
92 N. Main St., Bldg. 20, Windsor 08561

## ENVIRONMENTAL REMEDIATION SERVICES

**Dover Environmental Sciences**
Phone—(973) 328-1909
Fax—(973) 361-0909
Web—www.dover-environmental.com
Email—carol@dover-environmental.com
311 E. Blackwell St., Ste. B, Dover 07801

**General Carbon Corporation**
Activated Carbon Equipment & Services for Liquid & Vapor Applications
Phone—(973) 523-2223
Fax—(973) 523-1494
Web—www.generalcarbon.com
Email—sales@generalcarbon.com
33 Paterson St., Paterson 07501
*(see our ad under CARBON—Activated)*

**GWS Contractors, Inc.**
Since 1977, specializing in Environmental Remediation, Tank Removals, Emergency Response Services & Vapor Intrusion Mitigation. Providing a 24 hour, 7 day a week customer response network
Phone—(732) 297-4847
Fax—(732) 297-4389
Web—www.gwscontractors.com
Email—contact@gwscontractors.com
105 Fresh Ponds Rd., Jamesburg 08831

*Search from among*
*430,000 U.S. manufacturers*
*& suppliers at*

**IndustryNet.com**

**State Environmental Services, Inc.**
Addtl. Web: www.pumpnj.com
Phone—(609) 298-8838
Fax—(609) 324-4386
Web—www.sescor.net
Email—bmd@sescor.net
P.O. Box 186, Bordentown 08505

**State Environmental Services, Inc.**

www.sescor.net (609) 298-8838

PO Box 186 Bordentown, NJ 08505

## ENVIRONMENTAL SERVICES

**Accutech Environmental Service Inc.**
Full Service Environmental Consulting, Servicing the Tri-State Area.
Phone—(732) 739-6444
Fax—(732) 739-0451
Web—www.accutechenvironmental.com
Email—jim@accutechenvironmental.com
43 W. Front St., Ste. D, Keyport 07735

**Act Technologies Inc.**
Phone—(973) 300-4818
286 Houses Corner Rd., Ste. C, Sparta 07871

**Angelo Morresi**
Phone—(973) 239-5626
Fax—(973) 857-9778
Email—amorresi@aol.com
43 Bennett Ave., Cedar Grove 07009

**Brinkerhoff Environmental Services, Inc.**
Phone—(732) 223-2225
Fax—(732) 223-3666
Web—www.brinkenv.com
Email—lbrinkerhoff@brinkenv.com
1805 Atlantic Ave., Manasquan 08736

**BRINKERHOFF**

ENVIRONMENTAL SERVICES, INC.

## 732-223-2225

1805 Atlantic Ave. Manasquan, NJ 08736

www.brinkenv.com

**Brinkerhoff Environmental Services, Inc.**
Phone—(609) 714-2141
Fax—(609) 714-2143
133 Jackson Rd., Ste. D, Medford 08055

**BRINKERHOFF**

ENVIRONMENTAL SERVICES, INC.

## 609-714-2141

133 Jackson Rd., Ste. D Medford, NJ 08055

www.brinkenv.com

**Certified Health & Safety Services, LLC**
Safe Today-Here Tomorrow
Phone—(856) 829-4463 / (800) 423-0137
Fax—(856) 786-3101
Web—www.certified-health-and-safety.com
Email—chss1@comcast.net
1902 Taylors Ln., Ste. A, Cinnaminson 08077
*(see our ad under ENVIRONMENTAL CONSULTANTS)*

**Dover Environmental Sciences**
Phone—(973) 328-1909
Fax—(973) 361-0909
Web—www.dover-environmental.com
Email—carol@dover-environmental.com
311 E. Blackwell St., Ste. B, Dover 07801

**GEI Consultants, Inc.**
Phone—(973) 873-7110
Fax—(973) 509-9625
Web—www.geiconsultants.com
Email—mlevinson@geiconsultants.com
1 Greenwood Ave., Ste. 210, Montclair 07042

# GEI Consultants

## *Quality Environmental Services*

www.geiconsultants.com

## (973) 873-7110

1 Greenwood Avenue • Suite 210
Montclair, NJ 07042

**PSC Environmental Services, LLC**
Phone—(215) 822-2676 / (800) 365-9295
Fax—(215) 997-8219
Web—www.pscnow.com
Email—info@pscnow.com
2337 N. Penn Rd., Hatfield, PA 19440
*(see our ad on this page)*

**Sandstone Environmental Assocs., Inc.**
Phone—(732) 494-1100
Fax—(732) 494-1107
Web—www.sandstoneairnoise.com
505 Main St., Metuchen 08840

**State Environmental Services, Inc.**
Addtl. Web: www.pumpnj.com
Phone—(609) 298-8838
Fax—(609) 324-4386
Web—www.sescor.net
Email—bmd@sescor.net
P.O. Box 186, Bordentown 08505
*(see our ad under ENVIRONMENTAL REMEDIATION SERVICES)*

**T. Slack Environmental Services, Inc.**
Tank Solutions-Oil Tank Experts
Phone—(908) 964-2717
Fax—(908) 964-4244
Web—www.oiltanksolutions.com
Email—info@oiltanksolutions.com
180 Market St., Kenilworth 07033
*(also see our ad under TANK REMOVAL)*

**Tank Solutions**
Oil Tank Experts

908.964.2717
Fax: 908.964.4244

**T. Slack Environmental Services, Inc.**
Tank Solutions — Oil Tank Experts
180 Market St. • Kenilworth, NJ 07033
www.oiltanksolutions.com

## ENVIRONMENTAL SERVICES —
### (cont.)

Val Associates Laboratory Inc.
Phone—(856) 354-1337
600 Deer Rd., Ste. 7, Cherry Hill 08034

---

**Val Associates Laboratory Inc.**
*Quality environmental services*
**www.vallabs.com**
**(856) 354-1337**
600 Deer Rd., Ste. 7 Cherry Hill, NJ 08034

---

## ENVIRONMENTAL SYSTEMS

BASF Corporation, Catalysts Div.
Phone—(732) 205-5000
25 Middlesex-Essex Tpke., P.O. Box 770, Iselin 08830

## ENVIRONMENTAL TEST EQUIPMENT

Enviropore, Inc.
Phone—(609) 261-1588
P.O. Box 443, Lumberton 08048

## ENVIRONMENTAL TESTING SERVICES

**Dover Environmental Sciences**
**Phone—(973) 328-1909**
**Fax—(973) 361-0909**
**Web—www.dover-environmental.com**
**Email—carol@dover-environmental.com**
**311 E. Blackwell St., Ste. B, Dover 07801**

## ENZYMES

Worthington Biochemical Corp.
Phone—(732) 942-1660
730 Vassar Ave., Lakewood 08701

## EPOXIES

**Master Bond, Inc.**
Manufacturer of custom formulated adhesives for advanced applications
**Phone—(201) 343-8983**
**Fax—(201) 343-2132**
**Web—www.masterbond.com**
**Email—main@masterbond.com**
**154 Hobart St., Hackensack 07601**
*(see our ad under ADHESIVES)*

## EPOXY COATINGS

Armorpoxy, Inc.
Phone—(908) 810-9613
805 Lehigh Ave., Union 07083
Duraamen Engineered Products, Inc.
Phone—(973) 230-1301
457 Frelinghuysen Ave., Newark 07114

## EQUIPMENT RENTAL

**A Rent All Center**
**Phone—(973) 227-6990**
**Fax—(973) 227-6991**
**Web—www.arentallcenter.com**
**Email—arentallcenter@me.com**
**67 US Highway 46 East, Pine Brook 07058**
**Bruce R. Koerner Cranes & Equipment, Inc.**
**Phone—(973) 989-7990**
**Fax—(973) 989-1991**
**Web—www.koernercranes.com**
**Email—sales@koernercranes.com**
**400 Franklin Ave., Rockaway 07866**
*(see our ad under CRANE RENTAL)*

---

**Taylor Northeast**
Providing of a broad range of services for Material Handling & Industrial Cleaning Equipment in the eastern-PA area since 1985. Services range from new & used lift truck sales, leasing & rentals to service, parts & remanufacturing
**Phone—(610) 286-8080 / (800) 762-2500**
**Fax—(610) 286-8099**
**Web—www.taylornortheast.com**
**Email—kkoch@taylornortheast.com**
**931 Hemlock Rd., Morgantown, PA 19543**

## ERGONOMICS

Humanscale Corp.
Phone—(732) 537-2944
220 Circle Dr. N., Piscataway 08854

## ESCALATORS

Schindler Elevator Corp.
Phone—(856) 234-2220
840 N. Lenola Rd., Ste. 4, Moorestown 08057

## ETCHING — Metal

Towne Technologies, Inc.
Phone—(908) 722-9500
6-10 Bell Ave., P.O. Box 460, Somerville 08876

## EVENT MANAGEMENT

**O'Mealia Special Events**
**Phone—(908) 781-8418**
**Web—www.omealia.com**
**Email—info@omealia.com**
**P.O. Box 710, Peapack 07977**

## EXERCISE EQUIPMENT

CAP Barbell, Inc.
Phone—(908) 624-1133
625 Rahway Ave., Union 07083
Landice, Inc.
Phone—(973) 927-9010
111 Canfield Ave., Unit A-1, Randolph 07869

## EXHAUST SYSTEMS

East Performance Exhaust
Phone—(908) 236-2820
1050 U.S. Highway 22, Bldg. B, Lebanon 08833

## EXHIBITS — Museum

Peoplevision, Inc.
Phone—(973) 509-2056
311 E. 1st Ave., Bldg. A, Roselle 07203

## EXHIBITS — Trade Show

Apple Exhibits
Phone—(201) 943-2775
730 Grand Ave., Unit 1-A, Ridgefield 07657
**CDI Group, Inc.**
**Email: richard@cdigroupinc.com**
**Phone—(908) 862-1493 / (800) 339-8246**
**Fax—(908) 862-9018**
**Web—www.cdigroupinc.com**
**1135 W. Elizabeth Ave., Linden 07036**
Creating Your Design, LLC
Phone—(973) 357-1080
45 Wood St., Paterson 07524
Exhibit Co., Inc., The
Phone—(732) 465-1070
239 Old New Brunswick Rd., Piscataway 08854
ExhibitCraft, Inc.
Phone—(973) 686-9393
22 Riverview Dr., Ste. 103, Wayne 07470
Impact Unlimited, Inc.
Phone—(732) 274-2000
250 Ridge Rd., P.O. Box 558, Dayton 08810
Ostlund, Inc., Cal
Phone—(908) 688-4466
555 N. Michigan Ave., Kenilworth 07033
Porta-Display, Inc.
Phone—(973) 574-0057
790 Bloomfield Ave., Ste. B-2, Clifton 07012

---

Presentation Solutions, Inc.
Phone—(732) 961-1960
432 Clearstream Rd., Jackson 08527
SYMA Systems, Inc.
Phone—(856) 686-4190
300 Wolf Dr., West Deptford 08086

## EXPANSION JOINTS

A P S Supply Co.
Phone—(609) 877-7900
711 Cooper St., Beverly 08010
La Favorite Industries, Inc.
Phone—(973) 279-1266
33 Shady St., Paterson 07524
Papco Industries, Inc.
Phone—(201) 767-9051
245 Pegasus Ave., Northvale 07647

## EXTRUSION EQUIPMENT

RANDCASTLE Extrusion Systems, Inc.
Phone—(973) 239-1150
220 Little Falls Rd., Unit 6, Cedar Grove 07009
Techline Extrusion Systems
Phone—(973) 831-0317
89 4th Ave., Haskell 07420

## EXTRUSIONS

Brentrick, Inc.
Phone—(973) 357-3579
527 E. 39th St., Paterson 07504
Hoffman Extrusions, Inc.
Phone—(732) 774-2728
103 1/2 Mount Tabor Way, P.O. Box 397, Ocean Grove 07756
Mac Metals, Inc.
Phone—(201) 997-8001
936 Harrison Ave., CN 670, Kearny 07032

## EXTRUSIONS — Fluoropolymer

**Altaflo**
**Phone—(973) 300-3344**
**Fax—(973) 300-3345**
**Web—www.altaflo.com**
**Email—sales@altaflo.com**
**23 Wilson Dr., Sparta 07871**

---

*Fluoropolymer & Fluoroplastic Tubing & Pipe*
**altaflo** www.altaflo.com
973-300-3344 • sales@altaflo.com
23 Wilson Dr. Sparta, NJ 07871

---

## EXTRUSIONS — PVC

Proform Acoustic Surfaces LLC
Phone—(201) 553-9614
307 Julianne Ter., Secaucus 07094

## EYEGLASSES
### (also see 'Optical Lenses')

Charmant Group, Inc.
Phone—(973) 538-1511
400 American Rd., Morris Plains 07950
Liberty Sport, Inc.
Phone—(973) 882-0986
107 Fairfield Rd., Fairfield 07004
Manasquan Sight Saver Optical
Phone—(732) 223-4242
1407 W. Atlantic Ave., Manasquan 08736
Marfori Family Eye Care
Phone—(732) 920-1775
20 Brick Plz., Brick 08723
Optical Insight, LLC
Phone—(732) 828-3937
778 Highway 1, North Brunswick 08902
Pearle Vision, Inc.
Phone—(732) 505-0533
1278 Hooper Ave., Toms River 08753

## EYEGLASSES — (cont.)

Value Eyewear, Inc.
Phone—(973) 478-6500
1454 Main Ave., Clifton 07011

## EYEWEAR — Safety

Mancine Optical Co.
Phone—(856) 764-0200
2910 Route 130, Ste. 1, Delran 08075

## FABRIC FINISHING

EFX Tex, LLC
Phone—(973) 345-7601
555 E. 31st St., Paterson 07513

## FABRIC STRUCTURES

Hudson Awning & Sign Co., Inc.
Phone—(201) 339-7171
27 Cottage St., Bayonne 07002
Membrane Structure Solutions, Inc.
Phone—(908) 520-0112
340 N. Wyoming Ave., South Orange 07079

## FABRICATORS

**Arntzen Corp.**
Mfr. Of Rolled & Welded Steel Cylinders-Cones-Pipe-Shapes-Fittings
**Phone—(815) 334-0788 / (800) 957-7655**
**Fax—(815) 334-0778**
**Web—www.ArntzenRolling.com**
**Email—Sales@ArntzenCorp.com**
**14600 Washington St., Woodstock, IL 60098**
**DIHCO, Inc.**
**Phone—(201) 327-0518**
**Fax—(201) 327-8759**
**Email—DIHCO-INC@hotmail.com**
**612 E. Crescent Ave., Upper Saddle River 07458**

DIHCO Inc.
612 Crescent Avenue
Upper Saddle River, NJ 07458
**(201) 327-0518**

**Durex, Inc.**
Email: custserv@durexinc.com
ISO 9001 Registered Contract Metal Fabrication Facility
**Phone—(908) 688-0800**
**Fax—(908) 688-0718**
**Web—www.durexinc.com**
**5 Stahuber Ave., Union 07083**
*(see our ad under METAL FABRICATING)*
Metalfab, Inc.
Phone—(973) 764-2000
11 Prices Switch Rd., P.O. Box 9, Vernon 07462
Selco Mfg. Corp.
Phone—(973) 244-1177
3 Fairfield Crescent, West Caldwell 07006

## FABRICS

Interspec
Phone—(732) 938-4114
5025 Industrial Rd., Farmingdale 07727

## FABRICS — Coated

Sommers Plastic Products, Inc.
Phone—(973) 777-7888
31 Styertowne Rd., Clifton 07012

## FABRICS — Knit

Royal Lace Co., Inc.
Phone—(718) 495-9327
902 E. Hazelwood Ave., Rahway 07065

## FABRICS — Nonwoven

Avanti
Phone—(609) 655-5333
2650 U.S. Highway 130., Ste. I, Cranbury 08512

## FABRICS — Wholesale

Tri Vantage, LLC
Phone—(732) 868-8400
16 Worlds Fair Dr., Somerset 08873

## FABRICS — Woven

Central Shippee, Inc.
Phone—(973) 838-1616
46 Star Lake Rd., Bloomingdale 07403
Mactex, LLC
Phone—(973) 340-3131
489-A Getty Ave., Clifton 07011

## FALL PROTECTION PRODUCTS

**FallProof Systems LLC**
Specialists in Engineered Fall Protection Systems
**Phone—(609) 325-5555**
**Fax—(609) 584-8882**
**Web—www.fallproof.com**
**Email—solutions@fallproof.com**
**61 2nd Ave., Trenton 08619**

## FANS — Axial

**Americor Electronics, Ltd.**
**Phone—(847) 956-6200 / (800) 830-5337**
**Fax—(847) 956-0300**
**Web—www.americor-usa.com**
**Email—info@americor-usa.com**
**675 S. Lively Blvd., Elk Grove Village, IL 60007**
*(see our ads under CABLE ASSEMBLIES & CORD SETS)*

## FANS — Industrial

Glocon, Inc. (Swifter Fans)
Phone—(973) 463-7300
3-1 Luger Rd., Denville 07834

## FANS AND BLOWERS

United Blower Co., Inc.
Phone—(201) 601-5700
22 Westbrook Dr., Morganville 07751

## FASTENERS

**AALL American Fasteners**
**Phone—(856) 786-7799**
**Fax—(856) 786-8063**
**Email—sales@aallamericanfasteners.com**
**2303 Garry Rd., Ste. 1, Cinnaminson 08077**
Accurate Precision Fasteners Corp.
Phone—(201) 567-9700
20 Honeck St., Englewood 07631
Aerospace Manufacturing Corporation
Phone—(973) 472-2300
80 Van Winkle Ave., P.O. Box 3398, Wallington 07057
Amerifast Corp.
Phone—(908) 754-8989
104 Sylvania Pl., South Plainfield 07080
C & G Screws Unlimited
Phone—(732) 892-8400
2150 Route 88, Brick 08724
Captive Fastener Corp.
Phone—(201) 337-6800
19 Thornton Rd., Oakland 07436
Champion Fasteners, Inc.
Phone—(609) 267-5222
707 Smithville Rd., Lumberton 08048
Cold Headed Fasteners, Inc.
Phone—(856) 461-3244
401 Creek Rd., P.O. Box 5488, Delanco 08075
Columbia Nut & Bolt, LLC
Phone—(201) 641-7600
50 Graphic Pl., Moonachie 07074

Enfasco
Rivet Nuts
**Phone—(856) 662-7660**
**Fax—(856) 662-6172**
**Web—www.enfasco.com**
**Email—sales@enfasco.com**
**1675 Hylton Rd., Pennsauken 08110**

# Enfasco

Rivet Nuts

www.enfasco.com
sales@enfasco.com

**(856) 662-7660**
**FAX: (856) 662-6172**

1675 Hylton Road
Pennsauken, NJ 08110

Fastenal Co.
Phone—(609) 239-3016
921 Route 130 N., Burlington 08016
Fastenal Co.
Phone—(732) 254-1117
500 Hartle St., Ste. D, Sayreville 08872
Ford Atlantic Fastener Co., Inc.
Phone—(973) 882-1191
341 Changebridge Rd., P.O. Box 733, Pine Brook 07058
**GKY Industries**
Fasteners*Hardware*Tools for All Industries
**Phone—(201) 656-2377**
**Fax—(201) 656-0566**
**Web—www.gkyindustries.com**
**Email—sales@gkyindustries.com**
**383 8th St., Jersey City 07302**
Integrity Precision Products
Phone—(201) 767-0700
7 Reuten Dr., Closter 07624
Micron Fastener, Inc.
Phone—(973) 278-4100
85-99 Hazel St., Paterson 07503
P & R Fasteners, Inc.
Phone—(732) 302-3600
325 Pierce St., Somerset 08873
Porteous Fastener Co., Inc.
Phone—(732) 376-8420
1000 Amboy Ave., Ste. 1, Perth Amboy 08861
**Protex Latches & Band Clamps Ltd.**
Handles, Hinges, Clamps & Fasteners Made in England for over 90 years
**Phone—(314) 436-0080**
**Fax—(314) 436-0481**
**Web—www.protex.com**
**Email—terry.barber@protex.com**
**34 Benton Pl., St. Louis, MO 63104**
Schadler & Sons, Inc., John
Phone—(973) 777-5620
242 S. Parkway, P.O. Box 1068, Clifton 07014

*Search from among*
*430,000 U.S. manufacturers*
*& suppliers at*

**IndustryNet.com**

## FASTENERS — (cont.)

**Shallcross Bolt & Specialties Co.**
The complete source for all your fastener needs
Phone—(908) 925-4700
Fax—(908) 925-8451
Web—www.shallcrossbolt.com
Email—info@shallcrossbolt.com
1 McCandless St., Linden 07036

**Shallcross**
Bolt & Specialties Co.

Complete source for all
your fastener needs

**908-925-4700**
**FAX: 908-925-8451**

www.shallcrossbolt.com
info@shallcrossbolt.com

**1 McCandless St.**
**Linden, NJ 07036**

Unicorp, Inc.
Phone—(973) 674-1700
291 Cleveland St., Orange 07050
WingIt Innovations, LLC
Phone—(732) 869-4466
714 5th Ave., Bradley Beach 07720

## FASTENERS — Apparel

Kane-M, Inc.
Phone—(973) 777-2797
1 Madison St., Ste. F-9, East Rutherford 07073
Yale Hook & Eye Co., Inc.
Phone—(973) 824-1440
33 Race St., Hillside 07205

## FASTENERS — Automotive

Precision Fasteners, Inc.
Phone—(732) 627-0032
24 Worlds Fair Dr., Ste. D, Somerset 08873

## FASTENERS — Hook & Loop

FASTENation, Inc.
Phone—(973) 591-1277
120 Brighton Rd., Ste. 2, Clifton 07012
W B C Industries, Inc.
Phone—(908) 789-1234
625 Central Ave., Westfield 07090

## FASTENERS — Industrial

**AALL American Fasteners**
Phone—(856) 786-7799
Fax—(856) 786-8063
Email—sales@aallamericanfasteners.com
2303 Garry Rd., Ste. 1, Cinnaminson 08077
**Enfasco**
Rivet Nuts
Phone—(856) 662-7660
Fax—(856) 662-6172
Web—www.enfasco.com
Email—sales@enfasco.com
1675 Hylton Rd., Pennsauken 08110
*(see our ad under FASTENERS)*
Kanebridge Corp.
Phone—(201) 337-3200
153 Bauer Dr., Oakland 07436
TICO Mfg., Inc.
Phone—(856) 767-8430
1044 Industrial Dr., Unit 9, West Berlin 08091

## FASTENERS — Self-Locking

Aerospace Nylok
Phone—(973) 427-8555
11 Thomas Rd. S., Hawthorne 07506
ZaGO Mfg. Co., Inc.
Phone—(973) 643-6700
21 E. Runyon St., Newark 07114

## FASTENERS — Wholesale

Fastenal Co.
Phone—(609) 813-2356
1115 N. New Rd., Absecon 08201
Fastenal Co.
Phone—(856) 768-3657
421 Route 73 & Cushman Ave., Unit 11, Berlin 08009
Fastenal Co.
Phone—(201) 804-2228
33 Route 17 S., East Rutherford 07073
Fastenal Co.
Phone—(732) 542-7533
22 Meridian Rd., Unit 2, Eatontown 07724
Fastenal Co.
Phone—(732) 777-1029
55 Carter Dr., Edison 08817
Fastenal Co.
Phone—(973) 244-0540
68-A Clinton Rd., Fairfield 07004
Fastenal Co.
Phone—(973) 691-0547
186 Gold Mine Rd., Unit 1, Flanders 07836
Fastenal Co.
Phone—(856) 939-2500
316 Black Horse Pike, Unit C, Glendora 08029
Fastenal Co.
Phone—(908) 862-8880
1026 W. Elizabeth Ave., Unit 2, Linden 07036
Fastenal Co.
Phone—(732) 748-0140
550 Lincoln Blvd., Middlesex 08846
Fastenal Co.
Phone—(732) 246-0248
987 Jersey Ave., Ste. C, New Brunswick 08901
Fastenal Co.
Phone—(973) 278-5509
443 Madison Ave., Paterson 07524
Fastenal Co.
Phone—(609) 259-4290
1163 Route 130, Robbinsville 08691
Fastenal Co.
Phone—(609) 530-0456
1875 N. Olden Ave., Trenton 08638
Fastenal Co.
Phone—(973) 428-3300
53 S. Jefferson Rd., Ste. K, Whippany 07981
**Shallcross Bolt & Specialties Co.**
The complete source for all your fastener needs
Phone—(908) 925-4700
Fax—(908) 925-8451
Web—www.shallcrossbolt.com
Email—info@shallcrossbolt.com
1 McCandless St., Linden 07036
*(see our ad under BOLTS)*

## FASTENING SYSTEMS

**Enfasco**
Rivet Nuts
Phone—(856) 662-7660
Fax—(856) 662-6172
Web—www.enfasco.com
Email—sales@enfasco.com
1675 Hylton Rd., Pennsauken 08110
*(see our ad under FASTENERS)*
U. S. A. Tolerance Rings
Phone—(609) 745-5000
85 Route 31 N., Pennington 08534

## FEED

Abba Products Corp.
Phone—(908) 353-0669
1301 Central Ave., Hillside 07205
Epicore Networks U.S.A., Inc.
Phone—(609) 267-9118
4 Lina Ln., Eastampton 08060

Phibro Animal Health Corp.
Phone—(201) 329-7300
300 Frank W. Burr Blvd., Stn. 21, Glenpointe Center East, 3rd Fl., Teaneck 07666
ReConserve, Inc.
Phone—(732) 826-4240
1250 Amboy Ave., Perth Amboy 08861
Research Diets, Inc.
Phone—(732) 247-2390
20 Jules Ln., New Brunswick 08901
**Wilenta Feed, Inc.**
Animal feed from recycled bakery by-products
Phone—(201) 863-3035 / (201) 325-0044
Fax—(201) 863-2705
Web—www.wilenta.com
46 Henry St., Secaucus 07094

**Wilenta Feed, Inc.**
*Animal feed from recycled bakery by-products*
**www.wilenta.com**
**(201) 863-3035**
46 Henry St. Secaucus, NJ 07094

Woodstown Ice & Coal Co.
Phone—(856) 769-0069
50 E. Grant St., P.O. Box 285, Woodstown 08098

## FENCE CONTRACTORS

**Hapco Fence Contractors**
Phone—(732) 747-7552
Fax—(732) 747-9686
Email—hfences@verizon.net
P.O. Box 2085, Red Bank 07701

## FENCES — Chain Link

Artistic Fence
Phone—(973) 779-4540
757 River Dr., Passaic 07055
Consolidated Steel & Aluminum Fence
Phone—(908) 272-6262
316 N. 12th St., P.O. Box 643, Kenilworth 07033
Security Fabricators, Inc.
Phone—(908) 272-9171
316 N. 12th St., P.O. Box 643, Kenilworth 07033

## FENCES AND FENCE POSTS

A-Able Fence Builders
Phone—(973) 325-1900
28 Lakeside Ave., West Orange 07052

## FENCING

Abate Fence, Inc.
Phone—(973) 827-4167
3619 Route 23, Hamburg 07419
All Quality Fence
Phone—(973) 927-0722
1266 Route 46, P.O. Box 85, Ledgewood 07852
All-State Fence, Inc.
Phone—(732) 431-4944
1389 Route 9 N., Howell 07731
**American Discount Fence Co.**
Residential & Commercial Fence Railings
Phone—(856) 939-3022
Fax—(856) 939-8388
Web—www.americandiscountfence.com
Email—adfc@verizon.net
777 W. Clements Bridge Rd., Runnemede 08078
American Fence Co.
Phone—(973) 546-4373
326 U.S. Highway 46, Saddle Brook 07663
Anello Fence, LLC
Phone—(973) 839-4100
50 State Route 23, Pequannock 07440
Burger & Son, Inc., Edwin R.
Phone—(856) 468-2300
732 Main St., P.O. Box 184, Sewell 08080
DiPasquale Fence Co.
Phone—(732) 536-0660
196 Route 9 N., Englishtown 07726

INDUSTRY

# FENCING — (cont.)

**Emerson Fence, Inc.**
Phone—(201) 265-5150
10 Lincoln Blvd., P.O. Box 306, Emerson 07630

**Essex Fence Co.**
Phone—(973) 625-4122
132 U.S. Highway 46, Rockaway 07866

**Fence Max**
Phone—(609) 646-2430
6514 Black Horse Pike, Egg Harbor Township 08234

**Guardian Fence Co., Inc.**
Phone—(973) 824-1850
180 Wright St., P.O. Box 2009, Newark 07114

**Homestead Fence Contractors, LLC**
General fence, PVC, sheds & railings
**Phone—(609) 296-1829**
**Fax—(609) 597-0090**
**Web—www.homesteadfence.com**
**Email—info@homesteadfence.com**
**637 Main St., West Creek 08092**

**Jan Fence Co., Inc.**
Phone—(973) 694-4055
4 Industrial Rd., Pompton Plains 07444

**Majestic Fence Co., Inc.**
Phone—(732) 363-8181
6839 US Highway 9, Howell 07731

**Master Wire Mfg. & Fence Co.**
Phone—(609) 567-1616
Fax—(609) 561-0673
Web—www.masterwirefence.com
Email—mwmfginc@msn.com
1019 Black Horse Pike, Route 322, P.O. Box 328, Hammonton 08037

## Master Wire Mfg. & Fence Co.

*Wholesale / Retail, Installations*
*Residential / Industrial*

**(609) 567-1616**

Certified SBE/WBE

www.masterwirefence.com

mwmfginc@msn.com

1019 Black Horse Pike, Route 322
Hammonton, NJ 08037

**Master Wire Mfg., Inc.**
Phone—(609) 567-1616
1019 Black Horse Pike, Route 322, P.O. Box 328, Hammonton 08037

**Mr. B. Fence Co.**
Phone—(609) 882-1896
325 Stokes Ave., Trenton 08638

**Mr. Fence**
Specializing in fences and patio furniture, gazebos, wishing wells, swing-sets, arbors, lighthouses and many custom yard accessories
**Phone—(732) 303-1614**
**Fax—(732) 303-0358**
**Web—www.cmrfence.com**
**Email—cmrfence@aol.com**
**3468 U.S. Highway 9, Ste. 2, Freehold 07728**

**Murphy Fence Co., Inc.**
Phone—(609) 886-1635
507 Seashore Rd., Cape May 08204

**Taylor Fence Co.**
Phone—(732) 747-5498
1246 Route 33, Farmingdale 07727

**Walpole Woodworkers, Inc.**
Phone—(973) 539-3555
540 Tabor Rd., Morris Plains 07950

*Do nationwide searches for products & services at:*
**IndustryNet.com**

# FENCING — Aluminum

**OnGuard Fence Systems**
Phone—(908) 429-5522
18 Culnen Dr., Branchburg 08876

# FENCING — Vinyl

**Belmont Wholesale Fence Mfg.**
Phone—(973) 472-5121
112-114 Monroe St., Garfield 07026

**Freedom Fence & Building Products**
Phone—(973) 345-0911
168 Wabash Ave., Paterson 07503

**LMT Mercer Group, Inc.**
Phone—(609) 989-0399
690 Puritan Ave., Lawrence Township 08648

**Master Wire Mfg. & Fence Co.**
Phone—(609) 567-1616
Fax—(609) 561-0673
Web—www.masterwirefence.com
Email—mwmfginc@msn.com
1019 Black Horse Pike, Route 322, P.O. Box 328, Hammonton 08037
*(see our ad under FENCING)*

**Ninsa Vinyl Fence, LLC**
Phone—(609) 561-5397
125 Lincoln St., Hammonton 08037

**Ocean City Vinyl Fence Co., Inc.**
Phone—(609) 399-8288
719 Haven Ave., Ocean City 08226

**Phoenix Mfg., Inc.**
Phone—(732) 380-1666
1306 Brielle Ave., Ocean 07712

# FENCING — Wholesale

**Master Wire Mfg. & Fence Co.**
Phone—(609) 567-1616
Fax—(609) 561-0673
Web—www.masterwirefence.com
Email—mwmfginc@msn.com
1019 Black Horse Pike, Route 322, P.O. Box 328, Hammonton 08037
*(see our ad under FENCING)*

**Modern Fence & Construction, LLC**
Phone—(732) 238-5588
1527 Livingston Ave., North Brunswick 08902

# FENCING — Wooden

**Accent Fence, Inc.**
Phone—(609) 965-6400
1450 Bremen Ave., P.O. Box 656, Egg Harbor City 08215

**Alenco Fence & Supply Corp.**
Phone—(609) 654-6060
167 Route 70, Bldg. B, Medford 08055

**All-State Fence, Inc.**
Phone—(732) 431-4944
1389 Highway 9 N., Howell 07731

**Amechi Fence**
Phone—(856) 227-6691
5950 Route 42, Turnersville 08012

**Bergen Fence, Inc.**
Phone—(201) 641-2111
279 Bergen Tpke., Ridgefield Park 07660

**Blue Anchor Fence, LLC**
Phone—(609) 561-1874
314 Arrowood Ave., Hammonton 08037

**Delta Fence Co.**
Phone—(908) 355-9066
541 Spring St., Elizabeth 07201

**Fences By Taylor, Inc.**
Phone—(732) 349-8626
1246 Highway 33, Howell 07731

**Haddon Fence Co., Inc.**
Phone—(609) 261-1286
1460 Route 38, Hainesport 08036

**Homestead Fence Contractors, LLC**
Phone—(609) 296-1829
637 Main St., West Creek 08092

**P & S Blizzard Corp.**
Phone—(973) 523-1700
722 Madison Ave., Paterson 07501

**Suburban Fence Co.**
Phone—(609) 452-2630
532 Mulberry St., Trenton 08638

**Tri-State Fences & Supply, Inc.**
Phone—(973) 875-3213
806 Route 23, Sussex 07461

# FERTILIZERS

**Crop Production Services, Inc.**
Phone—(908) 735-5545
127 Perryville Rd., Pittstown 08867

**Doggett Corp., The**
**Phone—(908) 236-6335 / (800) 448-1862**
**Fax—(908) 236-7716**
**Web—www.doggettcorp.com**
**Email—mellickr@cs.com**
**30 Cherry St., Lebanon 08833**

**Espoma Co.**
Phone—(856) 825-0542
6 Espoma Rd., Millville 08332

**Plant Food Co., Inc.**
**Phone—(609) 448-0935**
**Fax—(609) 443-8038**
**Web—www.plantfoodco.com**
**Email—pfc@plantfoodco.com**
**38 Hightstown Cranbury Station Rd., Cranbury 08512**

# FERTILIZERS — Blended

**Chamberlin & Barclay, Inc.**
Phone—(609) 655-0700
2 Hightstown Cranbury Station Rd., Cranbury 08512

**Growmark FS, LLC**
Phone—(908) 479-4500
60 Lehigh Ave., P.O. Box 116, Bloomsbury 08804

**Plant Food Co., Inc.**
**Phone—(609) 448-0935**
**Fax—(609) 443-8038**
**Web—www.plantfoodco.com**
**Email—pfc@plantfoodco.com**
**38 Hightstown Cranbury Station Rd., Cranbury 08512**

**Reed & Perrine Sales, Inc.**
Phone—(732) 446-6363
396 Main St., P.O. Box 100, Tennent 07763

**South Jersey Farmers Exchange, Inc.**
Phone—(856) 769-0062
101 East Ave., Woodstown 08098

# FERTILIZERS — Farm

**Plant Food Co., Inc.**
**Phone—(609) 448-0935**
**Fax—(609) 443-8038**
**Web—www.plantfoodco.com**
**Email—pfc@plantfoodco.com**
**38 Hightstown Cranbury Station Rd., Cranbury 08512**

# FIBER OPTIC COMPONENTS

**American Fibertek, Inc.**
Phone—(732) 302-0660
120 Belmont Dr., Somerset 08873

**Ascentta, Inc.**
Phone—(732) 868-1766
370 Campus Drive, Ste. 105, Somerset 08873

**Chiral Photonics, Inc.**
Phone—(973) 732-0030
26 Chapin Rd., Unit 1104, P.O. Box 694, Pine Brook 07058

**Database Access Systems, Inc.**
Phone—(973) 335-0800
60 Midvale Rd., Ste. 206, P.O. Box 126, Mountain Lakes 07046

**FibroLAN, Inc.**
Phone—(201) 843-1626
350 W. Passaic St., Ste. 23, Rochelle Park 07662

**Go Foton**
Phone—(732) 469-9650
28 Worlds Fair Dr., Somerset 08873

**Nistica, Inc.**
Phone—(908) 707-9500
745 U.S. Highway 202-206, Ste. 201, Bridgewater 08807

© Copyright 2015 Manufacturers' News, Inc. A75

## FIBER OPTIC COMPONENTS —
**(cont.)**

Princetel, Inc.
  Phone—(609) 588-8801
  2560 E. State Street Ext., Hamilton 08619

**Princetel, Inc.**
*Fiber Optic Components*
**(609) 895-9890**
**www.princetel.com**
2560 E. State St. Ext. • Hamilton, NJ 08619

Radiant Communications Corp.
  Phone—(908) 757-7444
  5001 Hadley Rd., P.O. Box 867, South Plainfield 07080
VitroCom, Inc.
  Phone—(973) 402-1443
  8 Morris Ave., P.O. Box 125, Mountain Lakes 07046

## FIBER OPTIC DETECTORS

Linear Photonics, LLC
  Phone—(609) 584-5747
  3 Nami Ln., Ste. 7-C, Hamilton 08619

## FIBER OPTICS

Chromis Fiberoptics, Inc.
  Phone—(732) 764-0900
  6 Powderhorn Dr., Warren 07059
Fiberguide Industries, Inc.
  Phone—(908) 647-6601
  1 Bay St., Stirling 07980
Fiber-Span
  Phone—(908) 253-9080
  3434 U.S. Highway 22, Ste. 120, Branchburg 08876
Norland Products, Inc.
  Phone—(609) 395-1966
  2540 Route 130, Ste. 100, Cranbury 08512
PD-LD, Inc.
  Phone—(609) 564-7900
  30-B Pennington-Hopewell Rd., Pennington 08534
Tielmann, Inc., D. R.
  Phone—(732) 332-1860
  1208 State Route 34, Ste. 1, Matawan 07747

## FIBERGLASS FABRICATING

DR Fiberglass
  Phone—(732) 929-8448
  2027 Route 37 E., Toms River 08753
Fibrenetics, Inc.
  Phone—(732) 636-5670
  2 Cutters Dock Rd., Woodbridge 07095

## FIBERGLASS MATERIALS

Cervinis, Inc.
  Phone—(856) 691-1744
  3656 N. Mill Rd., Vineland 08360
Molded Fiberglass Products
  Phone—(609) 538-8822
  3 Industry Ct., Trenton 08638

## FIBERGLASS MOLDING

Hamilton Transit Corporate Center
  Phone—(609) 587-1188
  572 Whitehead Rd., Trenton 08619

## FIBERGLASS REINFORCED PLASTIC PRODUCTS

FRP Corp.
  Phone—(973) 763-5496
  15 Hoskier Rd., South Orange 07079
Imco Reinforced Plastics, Inc.
  Phone—(856) 235-7254
  858 N. Lenola Rd., Moorestown 08057

## JG Machine Works

*Filling Machinery*

**(732) 203-2077 • FAX: (732) 203-2078**

**www.jgmachine.com** • *Email: dnelson@jgmachine.com*

2182 State Route 35  Holmdel, NJ 07733

**Technick Products, Inc.**
  Additives for rubber & plastic; mold release agents, halogenated & non-halogenated flame retardants & green cleaning agents
  **Phone—(908) 791-0400**
  **Fax—(908) 791-9991**
  **Web—www.technickproducts.com**
  **Email—info@technickproducts.com**
  **238 Saint Nicholas Ave., South Plainfield 07080**

## FIGURINES

TMP International, Inc.
  Phone—(973) 838-7072
  15 Hamburg Tpke., Bloomingdale 07403

## FILE FOLDERS

Redwallet Connection, LLC
  Phone—(201) 223-2644
  907 21st St., Union City 07087

## FILLING CONTRACTORS

Contract Filling, Inc.
  Phone—(973) 239-6608
  10 Cliffside Dr., Cedar Grove 07009

## FILLING MACHINERY

Am Jet Enterprises
  Phone—(973) 627-5690
  11 1/2 Elm St., Rockaway 07866
CryoVation, LLC
  Phone—(609) 914-4792
  9-B Mary Way, Hainesport 08036
**JG Machine Works**
  Also, mechanical crimping of pumps onto fragrance glass bottles
  **Phone—(732) 203-2077**
  **Fax—(732) 203-2078**
  **Web—www.jgmachine.com**
  **Email—dnelson@jgmachine.com**
  **2182 State Route 35, Holmdel 07733**
      *(see our ad on this page)*
Per-Fil Industries, Inc.
  Phone—(856) 461-5700
  407 Adams St., P.O. Box 9, Riverside 08075
Romar Machine & Tool Co.
  Phone—(201) 337-7111
  521 Commerce St., Franklin Lakes 07417
**Warwick Mfg. & Equipment Co., LLC**
  Buy & sell used: Chemical, food, cosmetic, packaging & pharmaceutical equipment
  **Phone—(732) 729-0400 / (732) 241-9263**
  **Fax—(732) 729-1235**
  **Web—www.warwickequipment.com**
  **Email—sales@warwickequipment.com**
  **1112 12th St., North Brunswick 08902**
      *(see our ad Outside Back Cover)*

## FILM

General Film Products
  Phone—(908) 351-0454
  107 Trumbull St., Bldg. R-2, Elizabeth 07206

## FILM EXTRUSION

CET Films, Inc.
  Phone—(732) 367-5511
  1650 Corporate Rd. W., Lakewood 08701

## FILTER BAGS

General Filter Corp.
  Phone—(973) 584-9220
  14 Constitution Ave., Succasunna 07876
Kavon Filter Products Co., Inc.
  Phone—(732) 938-3135
  5022 Industrial Rd., P.O. Box 1166, Wall Township 07719
Summit Filter Corporation
  Phone—(908) 687-3500
  20 Milltown Rd., P.O. Box 427, Union 07083

## FILTER ELEMENTS

Allied Group, Inc.
  Phone—(973) 543-5404
  5 Coldhill Rd., Bldg. 19, P.O. Box 209, Mendham 07945

## FILTER MEDIA

**General Carbon Corporation**
  Activated Carbon Equipment & Services for Liquid & Vapor Applications
  **Phone—(973) 523-2223**
  **Fax—(973) 523-1494**
  **Web—www.generalcarbon.com**
  **Email—sales@generalcarbon.com**
  **33 Paterson St., Paterson 07501**
      *(see our ad under CARBON—Activated)*
Inversand Co.
  Phone—(856) 881-2345
  226 N. Atlantic Ave., P.O. Box 650, Clayton 08312

## FILTER PAPER

**Avery Filter Co., Inc.**
  **Phone—(201) 666-9664**
  **Fax—(201) 666-3802**
  **Web—www.averyfilter.com**
  **Email—ken@averyfilter.com**
  **99 Kinderkamack Rd., Ste. 209, Westwood 07675**

## FILTER PRESSES

**Avery Filter Co., Inc.**
  **Phone—(201) 666-9664**
  **Fax—(201) 666-3802**
  **Web—www.averyfilter.com**
  **Email—ken@averyfilter.com**
  **99 Kinderkamack Rd., Ste. 209, Westwood 07675**
**Warwick Mfg. & Equipment Co., LLC**
  Buy & sell used: Chemical, food, cosmetic, packaging & pharmaceutical equipment
  **Phone—(732) 729-0400 / (732) 241-9263**
  **Fax—(732) 729-1235**
  **Web—www.warwickequipment.com**
  **Email—sales@warwickequipment.com**
  **1112 12th St., North Brunswick 08902**
      *(see our ad Outside Back Cover)*

**INDUSTRY**

## FILTERING MATERIALS

Gusmer Enterprises, Inc. (H Q)
Phone—(908) 301-1811
1165 Globe Ave., Mountainside 07092
TransWeb, LLC
Phone—(856) 205-1313
1473 W. Forest Grove Rd., Vineland 08360

## FILTERING SYSTEMS

**John Crane, Inc.**
**Phone—(856) 241-3507**
**Fax—(856) 241-3531**
**Web—www.johncrane.com**
**Email—broot@johncrane.com**
**301 Berkeley Dr., Swedesboro 08085**

## FILTERS

Advanced Filtration Co.
Phone—(732) 901-6676
25-A Arnold Blvd., P.O. Box 324, Howell 07731
**Hayes Pump, Inc.**
Pumps, filters, seals, control systems
**Phone—(973) 808-0606 / (800) 343-5020**
**Fax—(973) 808-7311**
**Web—www.hayespump.com**
**Email—Customerservice@hayespump.com**
**295 Fairfield Ave., Fairfield 07004**

**Hayes Pump, Inc.**
*Quality Pumps*
**800-343-5020**
Flow solutions since 1898
**973-808-0606 • FAX: 973-808-7311**
295 Fairfield Ave. Fairfield, NJ 07004
www.hayespump.com Customerservice@hayespump.com

Liquiflo, Inc.
Phone—(732) 271-4600
7 Wilpert Rd., Bridgewater 08807
**Warwick Mfg. & Equipment Co., LLC**
Buy & sell used: Chemical, food, cosmetic, packaging & pharmaceutical equipment
**Phone—(732) 729-0400 / (732) 241-9263**
**Fax—(732) 729-1235**
**Web—www.warwickequipment.com**
**Email—sales@warwickequipment.com**
**1112 12th St., North Brunswick 08902**
*(see our ad Outside Back Cover)*

## FILTERS — Air

BioAir Solutions, LLC
Phone—(856) 258-6969
110 Kresson-Gibbsboro Rd., Ste. 303, Voorhees 08043
Camfil USA, Inc.
Phone—(973) 616-7300
1 N. Corporate Dr., Riverdale 07457
Columbia Filters, Inc.
Phone—(201) 438-3883
255 Highland Cross, Rutherford 07070
Smith Filter Corp.
Phone—(732) 745-2600
16 Van Dyke Ave., New Brunswick 08901

## FILTERS — EMI/RFI

**Americor Electronics, Ltd.**
**Phone—(847) 956-6200 / (800) 830-5337**
**Fax—(847) 956-0300**
**Web—www.americor-usa.com**
**Email—info@americor-usa.com**
**675 S. Lively Blvd., Elk Grove Village, IL 60007**
*(see our ads under CABLE ASSEMBLIES & CORD SETS)*

## FILTERS — Industrial

**Atmos Tech Industries**
**Phone—(732) 493-8400**
**1108 Pollack Ave., Ocean 07712**
Filter Technologies, Inc.
Phone—(732) 329-2500
45 Stouts Ln., Unit 3, Monmouth Junction 08852

Komline-Sanderson Engineering
**Phone—(908) 234-1000 / (800) 225-5457**
**Fax—(908) 234-9487**
**Web—www.komline.com**
**Email—info@komline.com**
**12 Holland Ave., Peapack 07977**
Technical Fabricators, Inc.
Phone—(732) 469-7373
203 Wood Ave., Ste. A, Middlesex 08846

## FILTERS — Liquid

**General Carbon Corporation**
Activated Carbon Equipment & Services for Liquid & Vapor Applications
**Phone—(973) 523-2223**
**Fax—(973) 523-1494**
**Web—www.generalcarbon.com**
**Email—sales@generalcarbon.com**
**33 Paterson St., Paterson 07501**
*(see our ad under CARBON—Activated)*
Universal Filters, Inc.
Phone—(732) 774-8555
1207 Main St., Asbury Park 07712

## FILTERS — Water

Filtrex, Inc.
Phone—(973) 595-0400
450 Hamburg Tpke., Wayne 07470
**General Carbon Corporation**
Activated Carbon Equipment & Services for Liquid & Vapor Applications
**Phone—(973) 523-2223**
**Fax—(973) 523-1494**
**Web—www.generalcarbon.com**
**Email—sales@generalcarbon.com**
**33 Paterson St., Paterson 07501**
*(see our ad under CARBON—Activated)*
Industrial Filters Co., Inc.
Phone—(973) 575-0533
9 Industrial Rd., Fairfield 07004
**Orival Water Filters**
Automatic self-cleaning line pressure powered water filters
**Phone—(201) 568-3311**
**Fax—(201) 568-1916**
**Web—www.orival.com**
**Email—filters@orival.com**
**213 S. Van Brunt St., Englewood 07631**

## FILTRATION EQUIPMENT

Avery Filter Co., Inc.
Phone—(201) 666-9664
99 Kinderkamack Rd., Ste. 209, Westwood 07675
Filtration Solutions, Inc.
Phone—(908) 684-4000
432 Sand Shore Rd., Ste. 8, Hackettstown 07840
Summit International Filtration Systems
Phone—(201) 847-2370
500 W. Main St., Ste. 10, Wyckoff 07481

## FILTRATION PRODUCTS & SERVICES

Shaffer Products, Inc.
Phone—(908) 206-1980
20 Milltown Rd., P.O. Box 427, Union 07083

## FILTRATION SYSTEMS

Eaton Filtration, LLC
Phone—(732) 767-4200
44 Apple St., Tinton Falls 07724
**Leem/LSS Filtration**
The one stop source for your filtration needs
**Phone—(201) 236-4833**
**Fax—(201) 236-2004**
**Web—www.leemfiltration.com**
**Email—info@leemfiltration.com**
**25 Arrow Rd., Ramsey 07446**

## FINANCIAL ADVISORS

**Financial Principles**
**Phone—(973) 582-1000**
**Web—www.financialprinciples.com**
**310 Passaic Ave., Ste. 203, Fairfield 07004**

Massey Morgan Financial Solutions, LLC
Phone—(609) 975-8020
Email—ljm@masseymorgan.com
89 N. Main St., Medford 08055
MB Consultants
Phone—(973) 672-1300
Fax—(973) 672-1312
Email—info@mbconsultants.biz
55 Washington St., Ste. 609, East Orange 07017

## FINANCIAL SERVICES

NVE Bank
Phone—(201) 816-2810
Fax—(201) 816-7379
Web—www.nvebank.com
76 Engle St., Englewood 07631
Thrift Investment Corp.
Phone—(732) 738-9100
Web—www.thriftinvestment.com
P.O. Box 538, Fords 08863

## FINISHING — Print

21st Century Finishing, Inc.
Phone—(201) 797-0212
280 N. Midland Ave., Ste. 414, Saddle Brook 07663
Globe Die Cutting Products
Phone—(732) 494-7744
76 Liberty St., P.O. Box 4339, Metuchen 08840
Glue-Fold, Inc., Div. Of Perfect Finishing, Inc.
Phone—(973) 575-8400
40 Webro Rd., Clifton 07012
Perfect Finishing, Inc.
Phone—(973) 472-7400
40 Webro Rd., Clifton 07012
Poplar Bindery, Inc.
Phone—(856) 727-8030
300 Mill St., Moorestown 08057

## FINISHING EQUIPMENT

Nova Finishing Systems, Inc.
Phone—(215) 444-9981
P.O. Box 185, Hatboro, PA 19040

**Nova Finishing Systems, Inc.**
*Manufacturers of small industrial mass finishing equipment*
**www.novafinishing.com**
**800-444-4159**
P.O. Box 185 Hatboro, PA 19040

## FIRE ALARM SYSTEM INSTALLATION

**Como Electric, Inc.**
**Phone—(732) 449-7625**
**Fax—(732) 449-6896**
**Email—comoelect@aol.com**
**909 Wall Rd., Spring Lake 07762**
*(see our ad under GENERATORS—Electric)*

## FIRE ALARM SYSTEMS

Cooper Notification
Phone—(732) 222-6880
273 Branchport Ave., Long Branch 07740
Systems Sales Corp.
Phone—(732) 751-0600
1345 Campus Pkwy., Neptune 07753

## FIRE EXTINGUISHERS

Amerex Corp.
Phone—(201) 337-1616
128 Bauer Dr., Ste. 4, Oakland 07436
Cintas Fire Protection
Phone—(973) 347-3901
1705 U.S. Route 46 W., Ledgewood 07852

INDUSTRY

## FIRE EXTINGUISHERS — (cont.)

Pem All Fire Extinguisher Corp.
Phone—(908) 276-0211
39-A Myrtle St., P.O. Box 586, Cranford 07016

## FIRE FIGHTING EQUIPMENT

All Hands Fire Equipment, LLC
Phone—(732) 502-8060
7 3rd Ave., Neptune City 07753
Fire Hooks Unlimited
Phone—(732) 280-7737
1827 Old Mill Rd., Wall 07719

## FIRE PROTECTION CONSULTANTS

U.S. Mineral Products Company, DBA: Isolatek International
Leader in Advancing Passive Fire Protection Technology. The leading single source mfr. of passive fireproofing materials for steel construction, known for their exceptional thermal performance, superior durability & ease of application
Phone—(973) 347-1200
Fax—(973) 347-9170
Web—www.isolatek.com
Email—sales@isolatek.com
41 Furnace St., Stanhope 07874

## FIRE PROTECTION EQUIPMENT

Foremost Fire Protection, LLC
Sprinklers
Phone—(908) 753-8244
Fax—(908) 753-8850
Email—foremostfire@msn.com
P.O. Box 434, South Plainfield 07080
(see our ad under SPRINKLERS—Fire)
Rotating Equipment Specialist Inc.
Testing/Troubleshooting/Repairing Fire Pumps
Phone—(908) 876-5460
Fax—(908) 876-9453
Email—respumps@comcast.net
4 Valley View Rd., Long Valley 07853

## FIRE PROTECTION SYSTEMS

Alison Control, Inc.
Phone—(973) 575-7100
35 Daniel Rd. W., Fairfield 07004
Siemens Infrastructure & Cities, Building Technologies
Phone—(973) 593-2600
8 Fernwood Rd., Florham Park 07932
Specified Technologies Inc.
Firestopping Products
Phone—(908) 526-8000 / (800) 992-1180
Fax—(908) 526-9623
Web—www.stifirestop.com
Email—sales@stifirestop.com
210 Evans Way, Somerville 08876
(see our ad on this page)
Tyco (H Q)
Phone—(609) 720-4200
9 Roszel Rd., Princeton 08540

## FIRE RESTORATION

Servpro Of Northwest Bergen
Fire & Water Damage
Phone—(201) 236-2400 / (800) 497-7179
Fax—(201) 670-1011
Web—www.servpronorthwestbergen.com
Email—servpro8204@aol.com
151 Crescent Ave., Waldwick 07463

## FIRE RETARDANTS

Firefreeze Worldwide, Inc. (H Q)
Phone—(973) 627-0722
272 Highway 46, Rockaway 07866
Nofire Technologies, Inc.
Phone—(201) 818-1616
5 James St., South Hackensack 07606

## SPECIFIED TECHNOLOGIES INC.

Firestopping Products

**800-992-1180 • 908-526-8000**

**Fax: 908-526-9623**

www.stifirestop.com  sales@stifirestop.com

210 Evans Way • Somerville, NJ 08876

## Fire Guard Sprinkler Corp.

*Quality Fire Suppression Systems*

**www.fireguardsprinkler.com**

**(201) 440-1777**
FAX: (201) 440-5485

1-A Mount Vernon Street
Ridgefield Park, NJ 07660

## FIRE SPRINKLERS — Automatic

Capitol Fire Protection Co., Inc.
Phone—(609) 393-3936
56 N. Logan Ave., Trenton 08609
Fire Guard Sprinkler Corp.
Phone—(201) 440-1777
Fax—(201) 440-5485
Web—www.fireguardsprinkler.com
Email—ric@fireguardsprinkler.com
1-A Mount Vernon St., Ridgefield Park 07660
(see our ad on this page)
Foremost Fire Protection, LLC
Phone—(908) 753-8244
Fax—(908) 753-8850
Email—foremostfire@msn.com
P.O. Box 434, South Plainfield 07080
(see our ad under SPRINKLERS—Fire)
Neill Supply Co., Inc.
Phone—(201) 939-1100
700 Schuyler Ave., Lyndhurst 07071

## FIRE SUPPRESSION SYSTEMS

Fire Guard Sprinkler Corp.
Phone—(201) 440-1777
Fax—(201) 440-5485
Web—www.fireguardsprinkler.com
Email—ric@fireguardsprinkler.com
1-A Mount Vernon St., Ridgefield Park 07660
(see our ad on this page)

## FIRE TRUCKS

Ward LaFrance, Inc.
Phone—(609) 922-8383
37 W. Broad St., Paulsboro 08066

## FIREARMS

Faber Precision, Inc.
Phone—(973) 983-1844
198 Green Pond Rd., Unit D, Rockaway 07866

## FIREPLACES & ACCESSORIES

The Fireplace Place
Phone—(973) 227-8540
264 U.S. Highway 46 E., Fairfield 07004

## FIREPROOFING CONTRACTORS

NFI Co. Inc.
Phone—(973) 478-3486
Fax—(973) 478-0463
Email—lou@nationalfireproofing.net
105 Plauderville Ave., Garfield 07026
U.S. Mineral Products Company, DBA: Isolatek International
Leader in Advancing Passive Fire Protection Technology. The leading single source mfr. of passive fireproofing materials for steel construction, known for their exceptional thermal performance, superior durability & ease of application
Phone—(973) 347-1200
Fax—(973) 347-9170
Web—www.isolatek.com
Email—sales@isolatek.com
41 Furnace St., Stanhope 07874

## FIREPROOFING MATERIALS

Isolatek International (H Q)
Phone—(973) 347-1200
41 Furnace St., Stanhope 07874

## FIREPROOFING MATERIALS —
*(cont.)*

**U.S. Mineral Products Company, DBA: Isolatek International**
Leader in Advancing Passive Fire Protection Technology. The leading single source mfr. of passive fireproofing materials for steel construction, known for their exceptional thermal performance, superior durability & ease of application
Phone—(973) 347-1200
Fax—(973) 347-9170
Web—www.isolatek.com
Email—sales@isolatek.com
41 Furnace St., Stanhope 07874

## FIRESTOP PRODUCTS

**Alva-Tech, Inc.**
Intumescent Firestop Products & Joint Fillers For Underground Steel & Concrete Pipe
Phone—(609) 747-1133
Fax—(609) 747-1136
Web—www.alva-tech.com
Email—info@alva-tech.com
1208 Columbus Rd., Ste. G, Burlington 08016

**Specified Technologies Inc.**
Firestopping Products
Phone—(908) 526-8000 / (800) 992-1180
Fax—(908) 526-9623
Web—www.stifirestop.com
Email—sales@stifirestop.com
210 Evans Way, Somerville 08876
*(see our ad under FIRE PROTECTION SYSTEMS)*

## FIREWORKS

Cartridge Actuated Devices, Inc.
Phone—(973) 347-2281
40 Old Indian Spring Rd., Andover 07821
Cartridge Actuated Devices, Inc. (H Q)
Phone—(973) 575-1312
51 Dwight Pl., Fairfield 07004
Garden State Fireworks, Inc.
Phone—(908) 647-1086
383 Carlton Rd., P.O. Box 403, Millington 07946
Pyrotechnic Industries, Inc.
Phone—(856) 697-1023
1640 Garden Rd., Vineland 08360

## FIRST AID SUPPLIES & EQUIPMENT

PeaPodz, LLC
Phone—(201) 362-8883
79 S. Central Ave., Ramsey 07446
Top Safety Products Co.
Phone—(908) 707-8680
160 Meister Ave., Ste. 16, Branchburg 08876
Water-Jel Technologies
Phone—(201) 507-8300
50 Broad St., Carlstadt 07072

## FISHING EQUIPMENT

T G Mfg., Inc.
Phone—(609) 561-0022
299 Old Forks Rd., Hammonton 08037

## FISHING TACKLE & LURES

Aqua Clear Tackle
Phone—(609) 861-1088
P.O. Box 8454, Turnersville 08012
Folsom Corp. (H Q)
Phone—(201) 529-3550
43 McKee Dr., Ste. 1, P.O. Box 6660, Mahwah 07430
MegaStrike, Inc.
Phone—(732) 780-7383
331 Fairfield Rd., Ste. B-1, Freehold 07728

## FITNESS EQUIPMENT

TechnoGym U. S. A. Corp.
Phone—(206) 623-1488
700 U.S. Highway 46 E., Fairfield 07004

## FITTINGS

SIGMA Corp. (H Q)
Phone—(609) 758-0800
700 Goldman Dr., P.O. Box 300, Cream Ridge 08514

## FITTINGS — Conduit & Cable

**Lapp USA**
Cables, accessories & connectors. Everything from one source
Phone—(973) 660-9700 / (800) 774-3539
Fax—(973) 660-9330
Web—www.lappusa.com
Email—sales@lappusa.com
29 Hanover Rd., Florham Park 07932
*(see our ad under CONNECTORS—Electric Wire & Cable)*

## FIXTURES — Bathroom

Afina Corp.
Phone—(973) 684-7650
40 Warren St., Paterson 07524
Lenape Products, Inc.
Phone—(609) 394-5376
600 Plum St., Trenton 08638
Lineaaqua, LLC
Phone—(908) 226-1199
2216 Hamilton Blvd., South Plainfield 07080

## FIXTURES — Custom

**Infinite Manufacturing Group, Inc.**
Email: a.moses@infinitegroupusa.com
Phone—(973) 649-9950
Web—www.infinitegroupusa.com
171 Coit St., Irvington 07111

## FIXTURES — Display

Display Sales, Inc.
Phone—(732) 251-8981
P.O. Box 115, Spotswood 08884
Regal-Pinnacle Mfg., Inc.
Phone—(609) 714-2330
220 Route 70, Ste. A, Medford 08055
Sama Plastics Corp.
Phone—(973) 239-7200
20 Sand Park Rd., Cedar Grove 07009

## FLAGS AND BANNERS

Annin Flagmakers
Phone—(973) 228-9400
105 Eisenhower Pkwy., Ste. 203, Roseland 07068
**Apollo Flags LLC**
Phone—(973) 256-8362
Fax—(973) 256-1049
Web—www.apolloflags.com
Email—apolloflags@optonline.net
594 Union Blvd., Totowa 07512
Metro Flag Co.
Phone—(973) 366-1776
353 Richard Mine Rd., Unit 100, Wharton 07885
Raritan Printing Plus Flags & Banners, Inc.
Phone—(732) 721-2121
109 N. Feltus St., South Amboy 08879

## FLAME HARDENING

**AGF Burner, Inc.**
Phone—(732) 730-8090
Fax—(732) 730-8060
Web—www.agfburner.com
Email—sales@agfburner.com
1955 Swarthmore Ave., Unit 2, Lakewood 08701
*(see our ad under GAS BURNERS)*

## FLAME RETARDANTS

Anhydrides & Chemicals, Inc.
Phone—(973) 465-0077
7-33 Amsterdam St., Newark 07105

## FLANGES

**Metal Associates, Inc.**
Phone—(973) 835-8480 / (800) 838-1978
Fax—(973) 835-7981
Web—www.metalassociates.com
Email—metals@rcn.com
230 W. Parkway, Unit 3-2, Pompton Plains 07444

## FLANGES — Plate

**Arntzen Corp.**
Mfr. Of Rolled & Welded Steel Cylinders-Cones-Pipe-Shapes-Fittings
Phone—(815) 334-0788 / (800) 957-7655
Fax—(815) 334-0778
Web—www.ArntzenRolling.com
Email—Sales@ArntzenCorp.com
14600 Washington St., Woodstock, IL 60098

## FLASHLIGHTS

Princeton Tec
Phone—(609) 298-9331
5198 Route 130 N., Bordentown 08505
Tektite Industries, Inc.
Phone—(609) 656-0600
309 N. Clinton Ave., Trenton 08638

## FLATWARE

Hampton Forge, Ltd.
Phone—(732) 389-5507
442 State Route 35, Eatontown 07724

## FLAVORING EXTRACTS

**Citromax USA**
Beverages, Confection, Dairy & Baked Goods
Phone—(201) 933-8405
Fax—(201) 933-8217
Web—www.citromax.com
Email—cgonzabay@citroil.com
444 Washington Ave., Carlstadt 07072

## Citromax USA
*Beverages, Confection, Dairy & Baked Goods*
**www.citromax.com**
(201) 933-8405 • FAX: (201) 933-8217
444 Washington Ave. Carlstadt, NJ 07072

Excellentia International
Phone—(732) 749-9840
Fax—(732) 200-3791
Web—www.excellentiaint.com
Email—info@excellentiaint.com
19 Progress St., Edison 08820
IFC Products, Inc.
Email: joe@ifcproducts.com
Phone—(908) 587-1221
Fax—(908) 587-1661
Web—www.ifcproducts.com
568 E. Elizabeth Ave., P.O. Box 2175, Linden 07036
Savoury Systems International, Inc.
Phone—(908) 526-2524
230 Industrial Pkwy., Ste. C, P.O. Box 5487, Branchburg 08876
Sentrex Ingredients, LLC
Phone—(908) 862-4440
350 Cantor Ave., Linden 07036

## FLAVORINGS & FLAVORS

Adron, Inc.
Phone—(973) 334-1600
94 Fanny Rd., P.O. Box 270, Boonton 07005
Advanced Biotech, Inc.
Phone—(973) 339-6242
10 Taft Rd., Totowa 07512

## FLAVORINGS & FLAVORS — (cont.)

**Allen Flavors, Inc.**
Phone—(908) 561-5995
Fax—(908) 561-4164
Web—www.allenflavors.com
Email—info@allenflavors.com
23 Progress St., Edison 08820

Brand Aromatics, Inc.
Phone—(732) 363-8080
1600 Oak St., P.O. Box 3033, Lakewood 08701

Campbell Soup Supply Co.
Phone—(908) 561-1660
3500 S. Clinton Ave., South Plainfield 07080

**Citroil Enterprises, Inc.**
Fruit, Juices, Oils
Phone—(201) 933-8405
Fax—(201) 933-8217
Web—www.citromax.com
Email—cgonzabay@citroil.com
444 Washington Ave., Carlstadt 07072

**Citroil** enterprises
*Quality Flavorings & Flavors*
**www.citromax.com**
**(201) 933-8405 • FAX: (201) 933-8217**
444 Washington Ave. Carlstadt, NJ 07072

**Citromax USA**
Beverages, Confection, Dairy & Baked Goods
Phone—(201) 933-8405
Fax—(201) 933-8217
Web—www.citromax.com
Email—cgonzabay@citroil.com
444 Washington Ave., Carlstadt 07072

## Citromax USA
*Beverages, Confection, Dairy & Baked Goods*
**www.citromax.com**
**(201) 933-8405 • FAX: (201) 933-8217**
444 Washington Ave. Carlstadt, NJ 07072

Creation Flavors International LLC
Phone—(732) 763-8622
1 Richmond St., Ste. 3038, New Brunswick 08901

**Elan Chemical Company, Inc.**
Producing natural aromatic chemical intermediates
for the flavor & fragrance industry
Phone—(973) 344-8014
Fax—(973) 344-1948
Web—www.elan-chemical.com
Email—sales@elan-chemical.com
268 Doremus Ave., Newark 07105

**Excellentia International**
Phone—(732) 749-9840
Fax—(732) 200-3791
Web—www.excellentiaint.com
Email—info@excellentiaint.com
19 Progress St., Edison 08820

**Firmenich, Inc.**
A Passion for Smell and Taste. The largest privately-
owned company in the perfume and flavor business,
creating many of the world's favorite perfumes for
over 100 years.
Phone—(973) 589-3443
Web—www.firmenich.com
Email—ron.kurtz@firmenich.com
150 Firmenich Way, Newark 07114

Firmenich, Inc.
Phone—(609) 452-1000
250 Plainsboro Rd., Plainsboro 08536

Flaroma, Inc.
Phone—(973) 316-8185
96 Fanny Rd., P.O. Box 325, Mountain Lakes
07046

Flavor & Fragrance Specialties, Inc. (H Q)
Phone—(201) 825-2025
3 Industrial Ave., Mahwah 07430

*find additional suppliers at*
**IndustryNet.com**

**Flavor Development Corp.**
Phone—(201) 784-8188
Fax—(201) 784-5501
Web—www.flavordev.com
Email—sales@flavordev.com
388 Chestnut St., Norwood 07648

## Flavor Development Corp.
*Flavors*
**(201) 784-8188**
FAX: (201) 784-5501

388 Chestnut Street
Norwood, NJ 07648

**www.flavordev.com**

**sales@flavordev.com**

Flavor Dynamics, Inc.
Phone—(908) 822-8855
640 Montrose Ave., South Plainfield 07080

Flavor Solutions, Inc.
Phone—(732) 354-1931
120 New England Ave., Piscataway 08854

Flavors Materials International, Inc.
Phone—(732) 499-9700
10-D Englehard Ave., Avenel 07001

Foote & Jenks Corp.
Phone—(856) 966-0700
1420 Crestmont Ave., Camden 08103

Frutarom USA, Inc.
Phone—(201) 861-9500
9500 Railroad Ave., North Bergen 07047

Givaudan Flavors Corp.
Phone—(973) 386-9800
245 Merry Ln., East Hanover 07936

Hagelin Flavor Technologies
Phone—(908) 707-4400
200 Meister Ave., Branchburg 08876

International Flavors & Fragrances, Inc.
Phone—(732) 329-4600
150 Docks Corner Rd., Dayton 08810

International Flavors & Fragrances, Inc.
Phone—(732) 264-4500
600 Highway 36, Hazlet 07730

**Mafco Worldwide Corp.**
Phone—(856) 964-8840
Fax—(856) 964-6029
Web—www.magnasweet.com
Email—magnasweet@mafcolicorice.com
300 Jefferson St., Camden 08104

 **mafco** Worldwide Corporation
*Flavorings & Flavors*
**(856) 964-8840** • www.magnasweet.com
magnasweet@mafcolicorice.com
300 Jefferson St. Camden, NJ 08104

Medallion International, Inc.
Phone—(973) 616-3401
233 W. Parkway, Pompton Plains 07444

Natural Flavors, Inc.
Phone—(973) 589-1230
268 Doremus Ave., Newark 07105

Prime Ingredients, Inc.
Phone—(201) 791-6655
280 N. Midland Ave., Bldg. U, Saddle Brook
07663

Robertet Flavors, Inc.
Phone—(732) 981-8300
10 Colonial Dr., Piscataway 08854

Spray-Tek, Inc.
Phone—(732) 469-0050
344 Cedar Ave., Middlesex 08846

Summit Hill Flavors
Phone—(732) 805-0335
253 Lackland Dr. W., Middlesex 08846

Symrise, Inc.
Phone—(201) 288-3200
300 North St., Teterboro 07608

Whittle & Mutch, Inc.
Phone—(856) 235-1165
712 Fellowship Rd., Mount Laurel 08054

## FLEECE PRODUCTS

Bear Hands Ltd.
Phone—(201) 807-9898
38 Main St., Little Ferry 07643

## FLEET MANAGEMENT SYSTEMS — GPS

**Multiforce Systems Corp.**
Automated fuel management integrated systems for
the transportation industry
Phone—(609) 683-4242
Fax—(609) 683-4835
Web—www.fuelforce.com
Email—sales@fuelforce.com
101 Wall St., Princeton 08540
*(see our ad under PUMPS — Gasoline Dispensing)*

## FLIGHT SIMULATORS

Malwin Electronics Corp.
Phone—(973) 881-1500
52 E. 22nd St., Paterson 07514

## FLOOR CLEANING EQUIPMENT

Mercury Floor Machines, Inc.
Phone—(201) 568-4606
110 S. Van Brunt St., Englewood 07631

**Taylor Northeast**
Providing of a broad range of services for Material
Handling & Industrial Cleaning Equipment in the
eastern-PA area since 1985. Services range from new
& used lift truck sales, leasing & rentals to service,
parts & remanufacturing
Phone—(610) 286-8080 / (800) 762-2500
Fax—(610) 286-8099
Web—www.taylornortheast.com
Email—kkoch@taylornortheast.com
931 Hemlock Rd., Morgantown, PA 19543

## FLOOR COATINGS

Garon Products, Inc.
Phone—(732) 828-6400
256 Maxim Rd., Howell 07731

Garon Products, Inc.
Phone—(732) 223-2500
2430 Route 34, Ste. B-12, Manasquan 08736

## FLOOR COVERINGS

Congoleum Corp., Plt. 2
Phone—(609) 584-3000
3500 Quakerbridge Rd., P.O. Box 3127,
Mercerville 08619

Fishman Flooring Solutions
Phone—(856) 857-1141
621 Chapel Ave. E., Ste. A, Cherry Hill 08034

Mannington Mills, Inc.
Phone—(856) 935-3000
75 Mannington Mills Rd., P.O. Box 30, Salem
08079

Michael Halebian & Co., Inc.
Phone—(201) 935-3535
557 Washington Ave., Carlstadt 07072

## FLOOR SYSTEMS

**Compu-Struct, Inc.**
Phone—(973) 839-9525
Fax—(973) 839-1686
Email—compustructinc@aol.com
328 Boulevard, Pompton Plains 07444

## FLOOR TRUSSES

**UFP Berlin, LLC**
Email: dgoldman@ufpi.com
**Phone—(856) 767-0043**
**Fax—(856) 767-1526**
Web—www.ufpi.com
Email—info@ufpi.com
159 Jackson Rd., Berlin 08009

# UFP Berlin, LLC

## Wooden Trusses & Wall Panels

# (856) 767-0043

## Fax: (856) 767-1526

159 Jackson Rd.
Berlin, NJ 08009

# www.ufpi.com

## Email: dgoldman@ufpi.com

## FLOOR UNDERLAYMENTS

**Diversified Industries, Inc.**
**Phone—(856) 662-1981**
**Fax—(856) 662-5708**
Web—www.diversifiedindustries.com
Email—sales@diversifiedindustries.com
121 High Hill Rd., Swedesboro 08085

## FLOORING — Epoxy

Crossfield Products Corp.
Phone—(908) 245-2800
140 Valley Rd., Roselle Park 07204
Palma, Inc.
Phone—(800) 336-7256
14 Salter Pl., P.O. Box 2539, Bloomfield 07003
Stonhard, A Div. Of StonCor Group
Phone—(856) 779-7500
1000 E. Park Ave., P.O. Box 308, Maple Shade 08052

## FLOORING — Hardwood

**European Flooring Co.**
**Phone—(973) 783-3900**
**Fax—(973) 783-4385**
Web—www.europeanfloor.com
Email—abilio@europeanfloor.com
1 Preston Pl., Montclair 07043
GV Floors
Phone—(201) 558-7889
701 Penhorn Ave., Ste. 6, Secaucus 07094
Log Power, Inc.
Phone—(609) 259-9709
646 Route 524, P.O. Box 597, Allentown 08501

## FLOORING — Plastic

Evertile Flooring Co., Inc.
Phone—(973) 242-7474
127 Frelinghuysen Ave., Newark 07114
Scientific Materials Corp.
Phone—(908) 218-0010
30 Vail Ter., P.O. Box 5298, Somerville 08876

## FLOORING — Resilient

Congoleum Corp.
Phone—(609) 584-3000
3500 Quakerbridge Rd., P.O. Box 3127, Mercerville 08619

## FLOORING — Wholesale

Classic Tile, Inc.
Phone—(908) 289-8400
325 Pine St., P.O. Box 1066, Elizabeth 07207
**Gardner Industries, Inc.**
**Phone—(862) 210-8906**
**Fax—(973) 521-7004**
Web—www.gardnerindustries.com
Email—ggarner@garnerindustries.com
**12 Commerce Rd., Fairfield 07004**
General Floor Industries
Phone—(856) 931-0012
190 Benigno Blvd., Bellmawr 08031
General Floor, Inc.
Phone—(856) 424-0111
2 Pin Oak Ln., Cherry Hill 08003
General Floor, Inc.
Phone—(732) 603-6100
777 New Durham Rd., Edison 08817
General Floor, Inc.
Phone—(908) 241-4888
125 Market St., Kenilworth 07033
General Floor, Inc.
Phone—(856) 663-4750
815 Hylton Rd., Pennsauken 08110

## FLOORING CONTRACTORS

**European Flooring Co.**
**Phone—(973) 783-3900**
**Fax—(973) 783-4385**
Web—www.europeanfloor.com
Email—abilio@europeanfloor.com
1 Preston Pl., Montclair 07043
**Heritage Hardwood Flooring**
**Phone—(201) 684-1075**
**Fax—(201) 684-1073**
98 N. Railroad Ave., Mahwah 07430

## FLORIST SUPPLIES

Pennock Co.
Phone—(215) 492-7900
7135 Colonial Ln., Pennsauken 08109

## FLORISTS — Wholesale

**Delaware Valley Wholesale Florist, Inc.**
**Phone—(856) 468-7000**
**Fax—(856) 464-2753**
Web—www.dvflora.com
**520 Mantua Blvd., Sewell 08080**
Sunshine Bouquet Co.
Phone—(732) 274-2900
3 Chris Ct., Ste. A, P.O. Box 892, Dayton 08810

## FLOUR

Oliveri & Sons, Inc., A.
Phone—(201) 319-9112
4401 Dell Ave., P.O. Box 88, North Bergen 07047

## FLOUR MILLING & PROCESSING

Bay State Milling Co.
Phone—(973) 772-1000
404 Getty Ave., Clifton 07011

## FLOW RACKS

Keneco, Inc.
Phone—(908) 241-3700
123 N. 8th St., P.O. Box 121, Kenilworth 07033

## FLOWER POTS

Koba Corp.
Phone—(732) 469-0110
60 Baekeland Ave., Middlesex 08846

## FLOWERS — Artificial

Sunset Florist, LLC
Phone—(201) 941-5411
470 Bergen Blvd., Ridgefield 07657

## FLUID HANDLING SYSTEMS

Marotta Controls, Inc.
Phone—(973) 334-7800
78 Boonton Ave., P.O. Box 427, Montville 07045

## FLUIDS — Hydraulic

Hytek Industries Corp.
Phone—(732) 229-5730
215 Comanche Dr., P.O. Box 56, Oceanport 07757

## FLUORESCENT LIGHTING FIXTURES

Bliss Electrical Supply Co.
Phone—(908) 289-9719
207 South St., Elizabeth 07202

## FLUOROPOLYMERS

Solvay Specialty Polymers USA, Inc.
Phone—(856) 853-8119
10 Leonard Ln., West Deptford 08086

## FLUXES

**(also see 'Soldering Fluxes')**
American Flux & Metals Corp.
Phone—(609) 561-7500
352 E. Fleming Pike, P.O. Box 74, Winslow 08095

## FOAM — Polyurethane

F X I, Foamex Innovations Div.
Phone—(201) 933-8540
13 Manor Rd., East Rutherford 07073
Inoac - Crest Foam
Phone—(201) 807-0809
100 Carol Pl., Moonachie 07074
**Stanley Foam Rubber Corp.**
**Phone—(973) 778-1660**
**Fax—(973) 778-9014**
Web—www.stanleyfoam.com
Email—stanleyfoam@yahoo.com
14 Orchard St., Wallington 07057

## FOAM FABRICATION

**A & S Packaging & Display Corp.**
**Custom Foam Fabrication, Your Design or Ours**
**Phone—(201) 531-1900**
Web—www.aspkg.com
Email—customer.service@aspkg.com
**120 Kero Rd., Carlstadt 07072**
Capital Foam Products, Inc.
Phone—(201) 933-5277
75 E. Union Ave., P.O. Box 7564, East Rutherford 07073
**Diversified Industries, Inc.**
**Phone—(856) 662-1981**
**Fax—(856) 662-5708**
Web—www.diversifiedindustries.com
Email—sales@diversifiedindustries.com
**121 High Hill Rd., Swedesboro 08085**
DV8 Enterprises, LLC
Phone—(201) 641-4944
141 W. Commercial Ave., Moonachie 07074
Foam Rubber Fabricators, Inc.
Phone—(973) 751-1445
740 Washington Ave., Ste. 1, Belleville 07109
Monmouth Rubber & Plastics Corp.
Phone—(732) 229-3444
75 Long Branch Ave., Long Branch 07740
New Industrial Foam Corp.
Phone—(908) 561-4010
1355 W. Front St., P.O. Box 3120, Plainfield 07063
Rempac Foam, LLC (H Q)
Phone—(973) 881-8880
370 W. Passaic St., Rochelle Park 07662
Robertson Industries
Phone—(973) 293-8666
19 State Route 23, Montague 07827

*Search from among 430,000 U.S. manufacturers & suppliers:*
**IndustryNet.com**

## FOAM FABRICATION — (cont.)

**Stickel Packaging Supply**
Packaging & material handling equipment
**Phone—(732) 905-2811**
**Fax—(732) 364-6909**
**Web—www.stickelpackaging.com**
**1991 Rutgers University Blvd., Lakewood**
**Industrial Pk., Lakewood 08701**
*(see our ad under PACKAGING MACHINERY—Wholesale)*
TCP Reliable, Inc.
  Phone—(732) 346-9200
  551 Raritan Center Pkwy., Edison 08837

## FOAM INSULATION

Dow Chemical Co., The
  Phone—(856) 910-4900
  1500 John Tipton Blvd., Pennsauken 08110

## FOAM MOLDERS

Polycel Structural Foam, Inc.
  Phone—(908) 722-5254
  68 County Line Rd., Somerville 08876

## FOAM PACKAGING

**A & S Packaging & Display Corp.**
Custom Foam Fabrication, Your Design or Ours
**Phone—(201) 531-1900**
**Web—www.aspkg.com**
**Email—customer.service@aspkg.com**
**120 Kero Rd., Carlstadt 07072**
Foam Pack Industries Div. Of Patis, Inc.
  Phone—(973) 376-3700
  72 Fadem Rd., Springfield 07081

## FOAM PRODUCTS

A & S Packaging & Display Corp.
  Phone—(201) 531-1900
  120 Kero Rd., Carlstadt 07072
Tekni-Plex, Inc.
  Phone—(908) 722-4800
  201 Industrial Pkwy., Somerville 08876
Utility Development Corp.
  Phone—(973) 994-4334
  112 Naylon Ave., Livingston 07039

## FOAM RUBBER PRODUCTS

RAK Foam Sales, Inc.
  Phone—(908) 668-1122
  1355 W. Front St., P.O. Box 3248, Plainfield 07063

## FOIL — Aluminum

Aleris Mfg.
  Phone—(856) 881-3600
  838 N. Delsea Dr., Clayton 08312

## FOIL — Hot Stamping

C W C Industries, Inc.
  Phone—(973) 344-1434
  185 Foundry St., Newark 07105
**Crown Roll Leaf, Inc.**
  **Phone—(973) 742-4000 / (800) 631-3831**
  **Fax—(973) 742-0219**
  **Web—www.crownrollleaf.com**
  **Email—info@crownrollleaf.com**
  **91 Illinois Ave., Paterson 07503**
    *(see our ad on this page)*
Spectrum Foils, Inc.
  Phone—(973) 481-0808
  68 Ivy Creek Dr., Little Egg Harbor 08087

## FOIL STAMPING & EMBOSSING

All American Graphic Arts
  Phone—(908) 686-1479
  763 Ramsey Ave., Hillside 07205

*Do nationwide searches for products & services at:*
**IndustryNet.com**

# Crown Roll Leaf, Inc.®

- Metallized & Pigment Hot Stamping Foils
- Textile Foils
- Heat Transfer Products
- Woodgrain Products
- Holographic Diffraction Patterns
- Dazzling Pixellated Patterns
- Holograms
- Holographic Laminating Films
- Holographic Security Products
- Scratch-off Products

## 800-631-3831
### Tel: 973-742-4000 • Fax: 973-742-0219
### www.crownrollleaf.com
### info@crownrollleaf.com
## 91 Illinois Ave. Paterson, NJ 07503

Crown Roll Leaf, Inc.
  Phone—(973) 742-4000 / (800) 631-3831
  Fax—(973) 742-0219
  Web—www.crownrollleaf.com
  Email—info@crownrollleaf.com
  91 Illinois Ave., Paterson 07503
    *(See our ad on this page)*
House Of Gold, Inc.
  Phone—(856) 665-0020
  1505 Suckle Hwy., Pennsauken 08110
IDP Films
  Phone—(973) 227-1661
  24 Commerce Rd., Ste. P, Fairfield 07004

## FOOD BLENDING

Farbest-Tallman Foods Corp. (H Q)
  Phone—(201) 573-4900
  160 Summit Ave., Ste. 200, Montvale 07645
Toll Compaction Group, LLC
  Phone—(732) 776-8225
  14 Memorial Dr., Neptune 07753

## FOOD GRADE CHEMICALS

Stepan Co.
  Phone—(201) 845-3030
  100 W. Hunter Ave., Maywood 07607

## FOOD INGREDIENTS

Advanced Food Systems, Inc.
  Phone—(732) 873-6776
  21 Roosevelt Ave., Somerset 08873
Asiamerica Ingredients, Inc.
  Phone—(201) 497-5993
  245 Old Hook Rd., Ste. 3, Westwood 07675
**Bioactive Resources, LLC**
  **Phone—(908) 561-3114**
  **Fax—(908) 561-3115**
  **Web—www.bioactiveresources.com**
  **Email—info@bioactiveresources.com**
  **138 Sylvania Pl., South Plainfield 07080**

**Brenntag Specialties, Inc.**
  **Phone—(908) 561-6100 / (800) 732-0562**
  **Fax—(800) 543-1484**
  **Web—www.brenntagspecialties.com**
  **Email—specialties@brenntag.com**
  **1000 Coolidge St., South Plainfield 07080**
    *(see our ad under CHEMICAL DISTRIBUTORS)*
Certified Processing Corp.
  Phone—(973) 923-5200
  184 Route 22 E., Hillside 07205
**Excellentia International**
  **Phone—(732) 749-9840**
  **Fax—(732) 200-3791**
  **Web—www.excellentiaint.com**
  **Email—info@excellentiaint.com**
  **19 Progress St., Edison 08820**
Global Ingredients, Inc.
  Phone—(973) 278-6677
  317 9th Ave., Paterson 07514
Importers Service Corp.
  Phone—(732) 248-1946
  65 Brunswick Ave., Edison 08817
**LycoRed Corp.**
  **377 Crane St., Orange 07050**
  **Email: customerservices@us.lycored.com**
  **Phone—(877) 592-6733**
  **Fax—(973) 882-0323**
  **Web—www.lycored.com**
  **P.O. Box 759, Orange 07051**
Marcor Development Corp.
  Phone—(201) 935-2111
  341 Michele Pl., Carlstadt 07072
Northeast Pro-Tech, Inc.
  Phone—(973) 777-5654
  61 Willet St., Bldg. L, Passaic 07055

EZSelect®.com
REAL-TIME Access to
Industrial Leads!

## FOOD INGREDIENTS — (cont.)

**Paulaur Corp.**
Phone—(609) 395-8844
Fax—(609) 395-8850
Web—www.paulaur.com
Email—sales@paulaur.com
105 Melrich Rd., Cranbury 08512

**Paulaur Corp.**
Food Ingredients

www.paulaur.com
Email: sales@paulaur.com

609-395-8844
Fax: 609-395-8850

105 Melrich Road
Cranbury, NJ 08512

## FOOD MIXES

RC Fine Foods, Inc.
Phone—(908) 359-5500
139 Stryker Ln., Hillsborough 08844

## FOOD PACKAGING

Sealed Air Corp.
Phone—(201) 712-7000
301 Mayhill St., Saddle Brook 07663
Sealed Air Corp. (H Q)
Phone—(201) 791-7600
200 Riverfront Blvd., 3rd Fl., Elmwood Park 07407

## FOOD PROCESSING EQUIPMENT

AM-MAC, Inc.
Phone—(973) 575-7567
311 Route 46 W., Fairfield 07004
Ashton Food Machinery Co., Inc.
Phone—(973) 521-7603
P.O. Box 60, Montville 07045
Bridge Rotary Machine Co., LLC
Phone—(856) 829-3110
614 Kennedy St., P.O. Box 45, Palmyra 08065
Custom Sales & Service, Inc.
Phone—(609) 561-6900
275 S. 2nd Rd., P.O. Box 635, Hammonton 08037
**EcReCon, Inc.**
Used Chemical Processing Equipment
Phone—(856) 299-4500
Fax—(856) 299-4446
Web—www.EcReCon.com
Email—sales@ecrecon.com
62 N. Broad St., Penns Grove 08069
*(see our ad under CHEMICAL PROCESSING EQUIPMENT)*
E-Z Edge, Inc.
Phone—(201) 295-1171
6119 Adams St., West New York 07093
Gray Star, Inc.
Phone—(973) 398-3331
200 Valley Rd., Ste. 200, Mount Arlington 07856
Hill Machine, Inc.
Phone—(973) 684-2808
295 Governor St., Paterson 07501
**Key International, Inc.**
Phone—(609) 619-3685
Fax—(609) 619-3686
Web—keyinternational.com
Email—sales@keyinternational.com
4 Corporate Dr., Cranbury 08512

**Kuhl Corp.**
Over 100 Years in Business
Phone—(908) 782-5696
Fax—(908) 782-2751
Web—www.kuhlcorp.com
Email—mjv@kuhlcorp.com
39 Kuhl Rd., P.O. Box 26, Flemington 08822

**KUHL CORP.**
908.782.5696
Fax: 908.782.2751
*Over 100 Years in Business*
www.kuhlcorp.com/mjv@kuhlcorp.com
Washers • Dryers • Coolers

Linker Machines
Phone—(973) 983-0001
20 Pine St., Rockaway 07866
M B C Food Machinery Corp.
Phone—(201) 489-7000
78 McKinley St., Hackensack 07601
Patty-O-Matic, Inc.
Phone—(732) 938-2757
Route 547, P.O. Box 404, Farmingdale 07727
R S R Food Service Equipment Corp.
Phone—(609) 646-5158
6574 Delilah Rd., Egg Harbor Township 08234
Solbern
Phone—(973) 227-3030
8 Kulick Rd., Fairfield 07004
T M U, Inc.
Phone—(609) 884-7656
910 Shunpike Rd., Cape May 08204
Techno Design, Inc.
Phone—(973) 478-0930
11 Erie St., Front, Garfield 07026
Winter Scale & Equipment
Phone—(888) 808-3611
20-A Kulick Rd., Fairfield 07004

## FOOD PRODUCTS

Abraham's Natural Foods
Phone—(732) 229-5799
9 Long Branch Ave., P.O. Box 89, Long Branch 07740
Amboy Group
Phone—(732) 510-5600
1 Amboy Ave., Woodbridge 07095
**Arthur Schuman, Inc.**
Unrivaled market leader in the imported & domestic cheese industry
Phone—(973) 227-0030
Fax—(973) 227-1525
Web—www.arthurschuman.com
Email—info@arthurschuman.com
40 New Dutch Ln., Fairfield 07004
*(see our ad under CHEESE & CHEESE SPECIALTIES)*
Dee & L, LLC
Phone—(201) 858-0131
67 Lefante Way, P.O. Box 3431, Bayonne 07002
Interstate Sales New of Jersey, LLC
Phone—(856) 433-8692
1226 Haddonfield-Berlin Rd., Unit C-2, Voorhees 08043
Lucy's Ravioli Kitchen & Market
Phone—(609) 924-3623
830 State Rd., Princeton 08540
Malincho Inc
Phone—(609) 677-6090
2545 Fire Rd., Ste. 3, Egg Harbor Township 08234
Mitsui Foods, Inc.
Phone—(201) 750-0500
35 Maple St., Norwood 07648
Oasis Foods Co.
Phone—(908) 964-0477
635 Ramsey Ave., P.O. Box 697, Hillside 07205
Pinnacle Foods Group, LLC (H Q)
Phone—(856) 969-7100
121 Woodcrest Rd., Cherry Hill 08003
Ready Pac
Phone—(856) 241-0900
101 Arlington Blvd., Swedesboro 08085
Sussex Innovations, LLC
Phone—(917) 699-9489
137 Libertyville Rd., Wantage 07461

## FOOD PRODUCTS — Asian

Summit Import Corp.
Phone—(201) 985-9800
100 Summit Pl., Jersey City 07305

## FOOD PRODUCTS — Canned

General Mills Progresso
Phone—(856) 691-1565
500 W. Elmer Rd., Vineland 08360
Goya Foods, Inc. (H Q)
Phone—(201) 348-4900
100 Seaview Dr., Secaucus 07094

## FOOD PRODUCTS — Dehydrated

Deb-El Food Products, LLC
Phone—(908) 351-0330
2 Papetti Plz., P.O. Box 876, Elizabeth 07206
**Kalustyan Corp.**
Spices, herbs & seasonings
Phone—(908) 688-6111
Fax—(908) 688-4415
Web—www.kalustyan.com
Email—kerri@kalustyan.com
855 Rahway Ave., Union 07083

## FOOD PRODUCTS — Dry

Goya Foods, Inc.
Phone—(201) 865-3470
650 New County Rd., Secaucus 07094

## FOOD PRODUCTS — Ethnic

M & G Food, Inc.
Phone—(973) 340-0340
1295 Main Ave., Clifton 07011

## FOOD PRODUCTS — Frozen

Camerican International
Phone—(201) 587-0101
45 Eisenhower Dr., Ste. 310, Paramus 07652
Dewy Meadow Foods, Inc.
Phone—(908) 218-5655
1018 Rector Rd., Bridgewater 08807
Fairfield Gourmet Food Corp.
Phone—(973) 227-2800
11 Cliffside Dr., Cedar Grove 07009
Fillo Factory, Inc.
Phone—(201) 439-1036
10 Fairway Ct., Northvale 07647
Gourmet Kitchen, Inc.
Phone—(732) 775-5222
1238 State Route 33, Neptune 07753
Miami Onion Roll Co.
Phone—(973) 389-2202
111 Berkshire Ave., Paterson 07502
Old Fashioned Kitchen, Inc.
Phone—(732) 364-4100
1045 Towbin Ave., Lakewood 08701
Surfside Products, Inc.
Phone—(856) 785-2115
1733 Main St., P.O. Box 692, Port Norris 08349
Tovli, Inc.
Phone—(718) 417-6677
49 Hunter St., Newark 07114

## FOOD PRODUCTS — Gourmet

**Delicious Orchards**
Mail Order
Phone—(732) 462-1989 / (800) 624-1893
Fax—(732) 409-4993
Web—www.deliciousorchardsnj.com
Email—frank0517m@aol.com
320 State Route 34, Colts Neck 07722
Gourmet Foods, Inc.
Phone—(973) 237-1776
25 Andrews Dr., Woodland Park 07424
Groezinger Provision, Inc.
Phone—(732) 775-3220
1200 7th Ave., Neptune 07753
Haddon House Food Products, Inc.
Phone—(732) 367-7901
433 Oak Glen Rd., Howell 07731

INDUSTRY

## FOOD PRODUCTS — Gourmet —
**(cont.)**

Haddon House Food Products, Inc. (H Q)
Phone—(609) 654-7901
250 Old Marlton Pike, Medford 08055

**Lotito Foods, Inc./Mrs. Mazzula Foods**
Specializing in gourmet Italian food products
**Phone—(732) 248-0222**
**Fax—(732) 248-0442**
**Web—www.lotitofoods.com**
**Email—tgallina@lotitofoods.com**
**240 Carter Dr., Edison 08817**
*(see our ad under CHEESE & CHEESE SPECIALTIES)*

## FOOD PRODUCTS — Hispanic

Rico Foods, Inc.
Phone—(973) 278-0589
527 E. 18th St., Paterson 07514

## FOOD PRODUCTS — Indian

Deep Foods, Inc.
Phone—(908) 810-7500
1090 Springfield Rd., Union 07083

## FOOD PRODUCTS — Infant

Nestle Healthcare Nutrition, Inc. (H Q)
Phone—(973) 593-7500
12 Vreeland Rd., 2nd Fl., P.O. Box 697, Florham
Park 07932

## FOOD PRODUCTS — Italian

Apple Food Sales Co., Inc.
Phone—(201) 592-0277
117 Fort Lee Rd., Ste. B-7, Leonia 07605
Cento Fine Foods
Phone—(856) 853-5445
100 Cento Blvd., West Deptford 08086
**Colonna Brothers, Inc.**
Email: lizcerenov@colonnabrothers.com
Grated & Shredded Cheese, Bread Crumbs, Spices,
Sprinkles & Italian Specialty
**Phone—(201) 864-1115 / (800) 626-8384**
**Fax—(201) 864-0144**
**Web—www.colonnabrothers.com**
**4102 Bergen Tpke., P.O. Box 808, North**
**Bergen 07047**
L & D's Sapore Ravioli & Cheese, Inc.
Phone—(732) 563-9190
429-B Lincoln Blvd., Middlesex 08846
LaRosa Bakery, Inc.
Phone—(732) 842-4324
79 Neuman Springs Rd. E., Shrewsbury 07702
**Lotito Foods, Inc./Mrs. Mazzula Foods**
Email: tgallina@lotitofoods.com
Specializing in gourmet Italian food products
**Phone—(732) 248-0222**
**Fax—(732) 248-0442**
**Web—www.lotitofoods.com**
**240 Carter Dr., Edison 08817**
*(see our ad under CHEESE & CHEESE SPECIALTIES)*
Rich Products
Phone—(856) 696-5600
1910 Gallagher Dr., Vineland 08360
Roma Food Enterprises, Inc.
Phone—(732) 463-7662
1 Roma Blvd., Piscataway 08854
Roma Of Mid-Atlantic
Phone—(856) 467-8100
301 Heron Dr., Swedesboro 08085
Star Ravioli Mfg. Co., Inc.
Phone—(201) 933-6427
2 Anderson Ave., Moonachie 07074

## FOOD PRODUCTS — Japanese

JFC International, Inc.
Phone—(908) 525-4400
55 Wildcat Way, Linden 07036

## FOOD PRODUCTS — Kosher

Abeles & Heymann Kosher Products
Phone—(908) 206-8886
739 Ramsey Ave., Hillside 07205

IFC Products, Inc.
Email: joe@ifcproducts.com
**Phone—(908) 587-1221**
**Fax—(908) 587-1661**
**Web—www.ifcproducts.com**
**568 E. Elizabeth Ave., P.O. Box 2175, Linden**
**07036**
R.A.B. Food Group, LLC
Phone—(201) 553-1100
80 Avenue K, Newark 07105
Real Kosher LLC
Phone—(973) 690-5394
146 Christie St., Newark 07105
Ungar's Food Products, Inc.
Phone—(201) 703-1300
9 Boumar Pl., Elmwood Park 07407

## FOOD PRODUCTS — Mediterranean

Kontos Foods, Inc.
Phone—(973) 278-2800
100 6th Ave., P.O. Box 628, Paterson 07544

## FOOD PRODUCTS — Mexican

Mayab Happy Tacos, Inc.
Phone—(732) 293-0400
450 Florida Grove Rd., Perth Amboy 08861
Viva Mexican Restaurant
Phone—(908) 788-0744
117 Broad St., Unit 1, Flemington 08822

## FOOD PRODUCTS — Polish

Delicious Fresh Pierogi, Inc.
Phone—(908) 245-0550
594 Chestnut St., Roselle Park 07204

## FOOD PRODUCTS — Private Label

Cameco, Inc.
**Phone—(973) 239-2700**
**Fax—(973) 239-5392**
**Web—www.camecoinc.com**
**Email—info@camecoinc.com**
**100 Pine St., Verona 07044**

## FOOD PRODUCTS — Vegetarian

J.P. Veggies, Inc.
Phone—(973) 808-1540
222 New Rd., Parsippany 07054

## FOOD PRODUCTS — Wholesale

Albert's Organics, Inc.
Phone—(856) 241-9090
200 Eagle Ct., P.O. Box 624, Bridgeport 08014
**Capco Enterprises, Inc.**
34 DeForest Ave., Ste. 3, East Hanover 07936
Email: clapone@capcoenterprisesinc.com
**Phone—(973) 884-0044 / (800) 252-1011**
**Fax—(973) 884-8711**
**Web—www.capcoenterprisesinc.com**
**P.O. Box 335, Florham Park 07932**
*(see our ad under CANDY)*
Ecuadorian Rainforest, LLC
Phone—(973) 759-2002
25 Main St., Bldg. 6, Belleville 07109
Ferraro Foods, Inc.
Phone—(732) 424-3400
287 S. Randolphville Rd., Piscataway 08854
Foods Galore, Inc.
Phone—(856) 488-1112
9246 Commerce Hwy., Pennsauken 08110
IFC Products, Inc.
Email: joe@ifcproducts.com
**Phone—(908) 587-1221**
**Fax—(908) 587-1661**
**Web—www.ifcproducts.com**
**568 E. Elizabeth Ave., P.O. Box 2175, Linden**
**07036**
Jetro Cash & Carry, Inc.
Phone—(201) 434-4334
1 Amity St., Jersey City 07304

Mivila Corp.
Phone—(973) 278-4148
226 Getty Ave., Paterson 07503
Nishimoto Trading Co. Ltd.
Phone—(201) 804-1600
602 Washington Ave., Carlstadt 07072
Performance Food Group-AFI Foodservice
Phone—(908) 629-1800
1 Ikea Dr., Elizabeth 07207
Restaurant Depot, LLC
Phone—(856) 488-4288
1050 Thomas Busch Memorial Hwy., Pennsauken
08110
US Foods, Inc.
Phone—(732) 934-3400
1051 Amboy Ave., Perth Amboy 08861

## FOOD SERVICE DISTRIBUTORS

Driscoll Foods
Phone—(973) 672-9400
174 Delawanna Ave., Clifton 07014
KeyImpact Sales & Systems, Inc.
Phone—(609) 265-8300
95 Connecticut Dr., Burlington 08016
SYSCO Food Services Of Metro New York, LLC
Phone—(201) 433-2000
20 Theodore Conrad Dr., Jersey City 07305

## FOOD SERVICE EQUIPMENT

Aero Mfg Co.
Phone—(973) 473-5300
310 Allwood Rd., P.O. Box 1250, Clifton 07012
American Showcase & Foodservice Equipment, Inc.
Phone—(973) 227-1277
19 Commerce Rd., Unit H, Fairfield 07004
Creative Industrial Kitchens
Phone—(973) 633-0420
8 Leo Pl., Wayne 07470
**Foremost Groups Inc.**
Commercial
**Phone—(973) 428-0400**
**Fax—(973) 428-6166**
**Web—www.foremostgroups.com**
**Email—marketing@foremostgroups.com**
**906 Murray Rd., East Hanover 07936**
Franklin Machine Products, Inc.
Phone—(609) 267-3700
101 Mount Holly By Pass, Lumberton 08048

## FOOD SERVICE EQUIPMENT — Wholesale

M&J Frank, Inc.
Phone—(973) 887-1040
29 Eagle Rock Ave., East Hanover 07936

## FOOD SERVICE SUPPLIES

Crystalware
Phone—(732) 367-4444
601 Prospect St., Lakewood 08701
Plastic Plus, Inc. (H Q)
Phone—(973) 614-0271
184 Willet St., Passaic 07055

## FOOD SUPPLEMENTS

Grow Co., Inc.
Phone—(201) 941-8777
55 Railroad Ave., Ridgefield 07657

## FOOTWEAR

Aetrex Worldwide, Inc.
Phone—(201) 833-2700
414 Alfred Ave., Teaneck 07666
Leif J. Ostberg, Inc. (H Q)
Phone—(973) 956-6990
401 Hamburg Tpke., Ste. 305, Wayne 07470

## FORGINGS

Taurus International, Inc.
Phone—(201) 825-2420
275 N. Franklin Tpke., Ste. 3, Ramsey 07446

## FORGINGS — Iron & Steel

U. S. Drop Forge Corp.
  Phone—(856) 467-0500
  Highway 551, P.O. Box 131, Swedesboro 08085

## FORGINGS — Steel

All Metals & Forge Group, LLC
  Phone—(973) 276-5000
  75 Lane Rd., Fairfield 07004

## FORKLIFT CERTIFICATION

Taylor Northeast
  Providing of a broad range of services for Material
  Handling & Industrial Cleaning Equipment in the
  eastern-PA area since 1985. Services range from new
  & used lift truck sales, leasing & rentals to service,
  parts & remanufacturing
  Phone—(610) 286-8080 / (800) 762-2500
  Fax—(610) 286-8099
  Web—www.taylornortheast.com
  Email—kkoch@taylornortheast.com
  931 Hemlock Rd., Morgantown, PA 19543

## FORKLIFT SERVICE & REPAIR

Taylor Northeast
  Providing of a broad range of services for Material
  Handling & Industrial Cleaning Equipment in the
  eastern-PA area since 1985. Services range from new
  & used lift truck sales, leasing & rentals to service,
  parts & remanufacturing
  Phone—(610) 286-8080 / (800) 762-2500
  Fax—(610) 286-8099
  Web—www.taylornortheast.com
  Email—kkoch@taylornortheast.com
  931 Hemlock Rd., Morgantown, PA 19543

## FORKLIFT TRUCK PARTS

Action Lift Trucks, Inc.
  Phone—(973) 589-2320
  Fax—(973) 824-4768
  Web—www.actionlifttrucks.com
  Email—actionlift@optonline.net
  35 Avenue C, Newark 07114

## FORKLIFTS

Action Lift Trucks, Inc.
  Phone—(973) 589-2320
  Fax—(973) 824-4768
  Web—www.actionlifttrucks.com
  Email—actionlift@optonline.net
  35 Avenue C, Newark 07114
Central Forklift, Inc.
  Phone—(732) 805-9494
  415 Bell St., Piscataway 08854
Crown Lift Trucks, Inc.
  Phone—(845) 753-5868
  680 River Dr., Elmwood Park 07407
Electric Forklift Repair Corp.
  Phone—(732) 249-7757
  837 Somerset St., P.O. Box 1126, Somerset
  08875
Forklift Headquarter, LLC
  Phone—(732) 821-1413
  975 Joyce Kilmer Ave., North Brunswick 08902
GAR Equipment
  Industrial forklifts
  Phone—(908) 756-9560
  Fax—(908) 753-0579
  Web—www.garequipment.com
  Email—cmolloy@garequipment.com
  2624 Hamilton Blvd., South Plainfield 07080
Raymond Of NJ, LLC
  Phone—(908) 624-9570 / (800) 800-2024
  Fax—(908) 624-9553
  Web—www.raymond-nj.com
  Email—info@raymond-nj.com
  1000 Brighton St., Union 07083
  (see our ad under MATERIAL HANDLING EQUIPMENT)
Rent-Rite Lift Truck Services
  Phone—(973) 586-4477
  73 Green Pond Rd., P.O. Box 349, Rockaway
  07866

Taylor Northeast
  Providing of a broad range of services for Material
  Handling & Industrial Cleaning Equipment in the
  eastern-PA area since 1985. Services range from new
  & used lift truck sales, leasing & rentals to service,
  parts & remanufacturing
  Phone—(610) 286-8080 / (800) 762-2500
  Fax—(610) 286-8099
  Web—www.taylornortheast.com
  Email—kkoch@taylornortheast.com
  931 Hemlock Rd., Morgantown, PA 19543
Warwick Mfg. & Equipment Co., LLC
  Buy & sell used: Chemical, food, cosmetic, packaging
  & pharmaceutical equipment
  Phone—(732) 729-0400 / (732) 241-9263
  Fax—(732) 729-1235
  Web—www.warwickequipment.com
  Email—sales@warwickequipment.com
  1112 12th St., North Brunswick 08902
  (see our ad Outside Back Cover)

## FORM, FILL & SEAL MACHINERY

Key-Pak Machines By Luciano Packaging
Technologies, Inc
  Phone—(908) 722-3222
  29 County Line Rd., Somerville 08876
Prodo-Pak Corp.
  The Real Leader in Pouch & Tube Filling & Sealing
  Machinery, ideal for all liquids, creams, pastes &
  semi-viscous products
  Phone—(973) 772-4500
  Fax—(973) 772-0471
  Web—www.prodo-pak.com
  Email—sales@prodo-pak.com
  77 Commerce St., P.O. Box 363, Garfield 07026

## FOUNDATION GARMENTS

Q-T Foundations Co., Inc.
  Phone—(201) 986-7800
  496 Kinderkamack Rd., Ste. 107, Oradell 07649

## FOUNDATIONS — Philanthropic, Educational, etc.

Freedom House Foundation
  Phone—(908) 617-5492
  Web—www.freedomhousenj.org
  Email—events@freedomhousenj.org
  2004 State Route 31, Ste. 1, Clinton 08809
Jewish Renaissance Foundation
  Phone—(732) 324-2114
  Fax—(732) 324-0256
  Web—www.jrfnt.org
  149 Kearny Ave., Ste. 2, Perth Amboy 08861

## FOUNDRY EQUIPMENT & MACHINERY

Hainesport Tool & Maintenance
  Manufacturer of machine parts & assemblies
  Phone—(609) 261-0016
  Fax—(609) 261-2105
  Web—www.hainesporttool.com
  Email—rich@hainesporttool.com
  1924 Ark Rd., Hainesport 08036

## FOUNTAINS — Decorative

Massarelli's Lawn Ornaments
  Phone—(609) 567-9700
  500 S. Egg Harbor Rd., Hammonton 08037

## FOURSLIDE PARTS

Flanner & Associates
  Since 1987, specializing in representing
  manufacturers of fourslide parts, wire, metal, plastic,
  and rubber for the Aerospace, Automotive,
  Electronics, and Medical industries
  Phone—(609) 588-0790 / (609) 647-7821
  Email—gflanner@optonline.net
  104 Caitlin Ln., Hamilton 08691

## FRAGRANCE INGREDIENTS

Cosmetic Essence, Inc.
  Phone—(732) 225-2031
  50 Clearview Rd., Edison 08837

Excellentia International
  Phone—(732) 749-9840
  Fax—(732) 200-3791
  Web—www.excellentiaint.com
  Email—info@excellentiaint.com
  19 Progress St., Edison 08820
Firmenich, Inc.
  A Passion for Smell and Taste. The largest privately-
  owned company in the perfume and flavor business,
  creating many of the world's favorite perfumes for
  over 100 years.
  Phone—(973) 589-3443
  Web—www.firmenich.com
  Email—ron.kurtz@firmenich.com
  150 Firmenich Way, Newark 07114
Flamingo Bay, Inc.
  Phone—(973) 726-8882
  10 Seneca Trl., Sparta 07871
Fragrance Resources, Inc.
  Phone—(732) 264-6767
  275 Clark St., P.O. Box 110, Keyport 07735
Mane USA, Inc.
  Phone—(973) 633-5533
  60 Demarest Dr., Wayne 07470
Sozio, Inc.
  Phone—(732) 572-5600
  51 Ethel Rd. W., Piscataway 08854

## FRAGRANCES

Andrea Aromatics, Inc.
  Phone—(609) 695-7710
  150 Enterprise Ave., Trenton 08638
Aromatic Innovations
  Phone—(732) 967-6346
  600 Hartle St., Sayreville 08872
Ascent Aromatics, Inc.
  Phone—(908) 755-0120
  120 Case Dr., South Plainfield 07080
Atlantis Aromatics, Inc.
  Phone—(732) 919-1112
  5047 Industrial Rd., Ste. 4, Farmingdale 07727
Berje Inc.
  Phone—(973) 748-8980
  700 Blair Rd., Carteret 07008
Colgate-Palmolive Co.
  Phone—(609) 239-2000
  400 Elbow Ln., Burlington 08016
Continental Aromatics
  Phone—(973) 238-9300
  1 Thomas Rd. S., Hawthorne 07506
Cosmetic Essence, Inc. (H Q)
  Phone—(732) 888-7788
  2182 Route 35 S., Holmdel 07733
Custom Essence, Inc.
  Phone—(732) 249-6405
  53 Veronica Ave., Somerset 08873
Dana Classic Fragrances, Inc. (H Q)
  Phone—(201) 881-8550
  400 Lyster Ave., Saddle Brook 07663
Drom Fragrances International, Inc.
  Phone—(973) 316-8400
  Fax—(973) 316-9039
  Web—www.drom.com
  Email—info@drom.com
  5 Jacksonville Rd., Towaco 07082
Elan Chemical Company, Inc.
  Producing natural aromatic chemical intermediates
  for the flavor & fragrance industry
  Phone—(973) 344-8014
  Fax—(973) 344-1948
  Web—www.elan-chemical.com
  Email—sales@elan-chemical.com
  268 Doremus Ave., Newark 07105
French Color & Fragrance Co.
  Phone—(201) 567-6883
  488 Grand Ave., Englewood 07631
Intarome Fragrance & Flavor Corp.
  Phone—(201) 767-8700
  370 Chestnut St., Norwood 07648
International Aromatics, Inc.
  Phone—(201) 964-0900
  200 Anderson Ave., Moonachie 07074
Kavango, Inc.
  Phone—(732) 424-2430
  544 Lincoln Blvd., Middlesex 08846
Kerry Ingredients & Flavors
  Phone—(732) 882-0202
  160 Terminal Ave., Clark 07066

## FRAGRANCES — (cont.)

**Oriental Aromatics, Inc.**
Phone—(973) 227-0400
21 Spielman Rd., Fairfield 07004
**Orpheus Ltd.**
Phone—(973) 983-1400
40 Woodland Ave., Rockaway 07866
**Premier Specialties, Inc.**
Phone—(732) 469-6615
236 Blackford Ave., Middlesex 08846

**Premier Specialties, Inc.**
*Fragrances & flavors*
www.premierfragrances.com
(732) 469-6615
236 Blackford Ave. Middlesex, NJ 08846

**Shiseido America, Inc.**
Phone—(609) 371-5800
Web—www.shiseido.com
366 Princeton Hightstown Rd., East Windsor 08520
**Symrise, Inc.**
Phone—(908) 429-6946
180 Industrial Pkwy., Branchburg 08876
**Takasago International Corp.**
Phone—(201) 767-9001
267 Union St., Northvale 07647
**Takasago International Corp.**
Phone—(201) 767-9001
4 Volvo Dr., P.O. Box 932, Rockleigh 07647
**Ungerer & Co.**
Phone—(973) 628-0600
4 Bridgewater Ln., P.O. Box U, Lincoln Park 07035

## FREIGHT FORWARDING

**American Export Lines**
Phone—(973) 824-2333
Fax—(973) 824-8319
Web—www.shipit.com
Email—info@aelshipping.com
161 Frelinghuysen Ave., Newark 07114
**Mill Wright LLC**
Quality freight forwarding
Phone—(908) 862-0061
Fax—(908) 862-8137
Web—www.millwrightexport.com
Email—support@millwrightexport.com
720 W. Edgar Rd., Linden 07036

**MILL WRIGHT LLC**
*Quality freight forwarding*
www.MillWrightExport.com
email: support@millwrightexport.com
(908) 862-0061
702 W. Edgar Rd. Linden, NJ 07036

**RCL Agencies, Inc.**
Phone—(973) 779-5900
Fax—(973) 779-6842
Web—www.oceanfreight.com
842 Clifton ave., Ste. 1, Clifton 07013
**Samrat Samrat**
Phone—(732) 640-0931
Fax—(732) 640-0932
Web—www.samratusa.com
Email—admin@samratusa.com
10 Corporate Place S., Ste. 104, Piscataway 08854

IndustryNet.com
**Find Suppliers Nationally FREE!**

## FREIGHT FORWARDING — International

**SGF Freight Service**
Phone—(908) 351-9000
Fax—(908) 351-9099
Web—www.sgffreight.com
Email—info@sgffreight.com
142 6th St., Elizabeth 07206

## FROZEN NOVELTIES

**Alice Corp.**
Phone—(201) 943-5877
815 Fairview Ave., Unit 9-A, Fairview 07022

## FRUIT JUICES

**Clement Pappas & Company, Inc.**
Phone—(856) 455-1001
1045 Parsonage Rd., Seabrook 08302
**Clement Pappas & Company, Inc. (H Q)**
Phone—(856) 455-1000
Web—www.clementpappas.com
1 Collins Dr., Ste. 200, Carneys Point 08069
**Gregory Packaging, Inc.**
Phone—(973) 465-1113
247 Rome St., P.O. Box 5188, Newark 07105
**Johanna Foods, Inc.**
Phone—(908) 788-2200
20 Johanna Farms Rd., P.O. Box 272, Flemington 08822
**Ocean Spray Cranberries, Inc.**
Phone—(609) 298-0905
104 E. Park St., Bordentown 08505
**Sunny Delight Beverages Co.**
Leading producer of juice-based drinks in N. America; producing & marketing 7 brands: SunnyD, Elations glucosamine & chondroitin dietary supplement, Fruit2O flavored waters, Veryfine juices, Fruit smoothies & Crystal Light bottled beverages
Phone—(732) 329-2391
Fax—(732) 329-6560
Web—www.sunnyd.com
Email—sales@sunnyd.com
10 Corn Rd., Dayton 08810

**Sunny Delight Beverages Co.**
Juice Drink Manufacturer
**732-329-2391**
10 Corn Rd.
Dayton, NJ 08810
www.sunnyd.com
sales@sunnyd.com

## FRUIT PROCESSING & PACKAGING

**Momma's Home Made, LLC**
Phone—(856) 753-3250
1225 Haddonfield Berlin Rd., Southgate Plz., Ste. 2, Voorhees 08043
**Springdale Farm Market, Inc.**
Phone—(856) 424-8674
1638 Springdale Rd., Cherry Hill 08003
**Sunny Slope Farms**
Phone—(856) 451-0022
400 Greenwich Rd., Bridgeton 08302

## FRUITS — Dried

**International Foodsource, LLC**
Phone—(973) 361-7044
52 Richboynton Rd., Dover 07801
**La Dominica**
Phone—(201) 348-4294
635 56th St., West New York 07093

## FRUITS — Frozen

**Townsend Farms, Inc.**
Phone—(856) 825-5240
3501 S. East Blvd., Vineland 08360

## FRUITS AND VEGETABLES — Wholesale

**ACB Produce, Inc.**
Phone—(973) 522-1141
Fax—(973) 522-1160
Email—acbproduce@aol.com
135-137 Pacific St., Newark 07105
**Capespan North America**
Phone—(856) 742-0242
701 N. Broadway., Ste. 102, Gloucester City 08030
**Corrado's Family Affair**
There is a difference
Phone—(973) 340-0628
Fax—(973) 340-2052
Web—www.corradosmarket.com
Email—gerrycorradojr@corradosmarket.com
1578 Main Ave., Clifton 07011
**Donio, Inc.,** Frank
Phone—(609) 561-2466
692 N. Egg Harbor Rd., P.O. Box 529, Hammonton 08037
**V.A. Tramontano & Son**
Phone—(908) 753-4944
Web—www.tramontanoproduce.com
P.O. Box 584, South Plainfield 07080

## FUEL — Diesel

**Nova Specialty Chemicals, LLC**
Phone—(973) 586-2147
Fax—(973) 215-2975
Web—www.novaspecialties.com
Email—sales@novaspecialties.com
404 E. Main St., Rockaway 07866
**Taylor Oil Co., Inc.**
The premier provider of on-site fueling services (highest quality gasoline, diesel fuel & other petroleum products) to construction crews, contractors, boats & marinas along the East Coast and beyond
Phone—(908) 725-7737
Fax—(908) 725-7746
Web—www.tayloroilco.com
Email—fbloom@tayloroilco.com
77 2nd St., P.O. Box 974, Somerville 08876

## FUEL — Military

**Nova Specialty Chemicals, LLC**
Phone—(973) 586-2147
Fax—(973) 215-2975
Web—www.novaspecialties.com
Email—sales@novaspecialties.com
404 E. Main St., Rockaway 07866

## FUEL ADDITIVES

**C & S Scientific Corp.**
Phone—(609) 448-7037
P.O. Box 1056, Hightstown 08520
**INTERCAT, Inc. (H Q)**
Phone—(732) 223-4644
2399 Highway 34, Ste. C-1, Manasquan 08736
**Technol Fuel Conditioners, Inc.**
Phone—(732) 542-0111
145 Wyckoff Rd., Ste. 300, Eatontown 07724

*find additional suppliers at*
**IndustryNet.com**

**WAAGE ELECTRIC, INC.**

*Melting Pots & Duct Heaters & Immersion Heaters*

www.waage.com • Email: info@waage.com

**800-922-4365 • 908-245-9363**

**FAX: 908-245-8477**

720 Colfax Avenue, PO Box 337 Kenilworth, NJ 07033

## FUEL INJECTION SYSTEMS — Diesel

Garden State Diesel
Phone—(856) 914-9797
97 Foster Rd., Ste. 4, Moorestown 08057

## FUEL SYSTEMS

**Multiforce Systems Corp.**
Automated fuel management integrated systems for the transportation industry
Phone—(609) 683-4242
Fax—(609) 683-4835
Web—www.fuelforce.com
Email—sales@fuelforce.com
101 Wall St., Princeton 08540
*(see our ad under PUMPS – Gasoline Dispensing)*

Orpak USA
Phone—(201) 441-9820
100 1st St., Ste. 200, Hackensack 07601

## FUEL TREATMENT PRODUCTS

**Nova Specialty Chemicals, LLC**
Phone—(973) 586-2147
Fax—(973) 215-2975
Web—www.novaspecialties.com
Email—sales@novaspecialties.com
404 E. Main St., Rockaway 07866

## FULFILLMENT SERVICES

**Abilities Of Northwest Jersey, Inc.**
Fulfillment/Contract Packaging/Assembly
Phone—(908) 689-1118
Fax—(908) 689-6363
Web—www.abilitiesnw.com
Email—info@abilitiesnw.com
264 Route 31 N., P.O. Box 251, Washington 07882
*(see our ad under CONTRACT PACKAGING SERVICES)*

## FUNERAL SUPPLIES

AG Peters & Son, Inc.
Phone—(856) 931-7476
1025 N. Black Horse Pike, Runnemede 08078

## FUR NOVELTIES

A. Hantman Inc
Phone—(212) 239-1358
309 Michaels Ct., Woodbridge 07095

## FURNACES — Heat Treating

Pennington Furnace Supply, Inc.
Phone—(609) 737-2500
6 Brookside Ave., Pennington 08534

**Need an**
***IndustrySection***
**for another state?**

Call us... 847-864-7590

## FURNACES — Heating

**Nutley Heating & Cooling Supply, Inc.**
Phone—(973) 667-6880
Fax—(973) 667-4602
Web—www.nutleysupply.com
Email—ralpholiver@nutleysupply.com
156 Chestnut St., Nutley 07110
*(see our ad under BOILERS)*

## FURNACES — High Temperature

CM Furnace, Inc.
Phone—(973) 338-6500
103 Dewey St., Bloomfield 07003

Elnik Systems, LLC
Email: cjoens@elnik.com
Specializing in process equipment for metal injection molding
Phone—(973) 239-6066
Fax—(973) 239-3272
Web—www.elnik.com
107 Commerce Rd., Cedar Grove 07009

Inductotherm Corp.
Phone—(609) 267-9000
10 Indel Ave., P.O. Box 157, Rancocas 08073

Procedyne Corp.
Phone—(732) 249-8347
11 Industrial Dr., New Brunswick 08901

## FURNACES — Industrial
### (also see 'Heating Eqpt.—Industrial')

H E D International, Inc.
Phone—(609) 466-1900
449 Route 31, P.O. Box 246, Ringoes 08551

Hankin Environmental Systems, Inc.
Phone—(908) 722-9595
1 Harvard Way, Ste. 6, P.O. Box 5759, Hillsborough 08844

**Waage Electric, Inc.**
Melting Pots & Duct Heaters & Immersion Heaters
Phone—(908) 245-9363 / (800) 922-4365
Fax—(908) 245-8477
Web—www.waage.com
Email—info@waage.com
720 Colfax Ave., P.O. Box 337, Kenilworth 07033
*(see our ad on this page)*

## FURNACES — Vacuum

**Consarc Corp.**
Phone—(609) 267-8000
Fax—(609) 267-1366
Web—www.consarc.com
Email—sales@consarc.com
100 Indel Ave., P.O. Box 156, Rancocas 08073

Elnik Systems, LLC
Email: cjoens@elnik.com
Specializing in process equipment for metal injection molding
Phone—(973) 239-6066
Fax—(973) 239-3272
Web—www.elnik.com
107 Commerce Rd., Cedar Grove 07009

PV/T, Inc.
Phone—(609) 267-3933
100 Indel Ave., P.O. Box 156, Rancocas 08073

T-M Vacuum Products, Inc.
Phone—(856) 829-2000
630 S. Warrington Ave., Cinnaminson 08077

## FURNITURE
### (also see following and specific product)

Arnold Furniture Mfrs., Inc.
Email: arnoldfurniture@gmail.com
Phone—(973) 399-0505
Fax—(973) 399-7638
Web—www.arnoldfurniture.com
400 Coit St., Irvington 07111

Creative Furniture, Inc. (H Q)
Phone—(732) 248-0255
240 Mill Rd., Edison 08817

Custom Decorators Workroom
Phone—(973) 625-0516
415 E. Main St., Denville 07834

Delform, LLC
Phone—(201) 438-3915
225 Highland Cross, Ste. 6, Rutherford 07070

**Foremost Groups Inc.**
Bath Furniture, Indoor & Outdoor Furniture
Phone—(973) 428-0400
Fax—(973) 428-6166
Web—www.foremostgroups.com
Email—marketing@foremostgroups.com
906 Murray Rd., East Hanover 07936

Gar Products
Phone—(732) 364-2100
170 Lehigh Ave., Lakewood 08701

**Greenbaum Interiors**
Phone—(973) 279-3000
Fax—(973) 279-3006
Web—www.greenbauminteriors.com
Email—susan@greenbauminteriors.com
101 Washington St., Paterson 07505

Hanover Direct, Inc. (H Q)
Phone—(201) 863-7300
1500 Harbor Blvd., 1st Fl., Weehawken 07086

Jenkins, Inc., Brad
Phone—(973) 331-1995
291 Mount Kemble Ave., Morristown 07960

Union City Mirror & Table Co.
Phone—(201) 867-1827
129 34th St., Union City 07087

## FURNITURE — Computer

CBT Supply, Inc. (H Q)
Phone—(973) 586-2783
Fax—(800) 770-7042
Web—www.smartdesks.com
Email—sales@smartdesks.com
P.O. Box 391, Hibernia 07842

## FURNITURE — Ergonomic

Ekornes, Inc. (H Q)
Phone—(732) 302-0097
615 Pierce St., Somerset 08873

## FURNITURE — Hospital

Blickman, Inc.
Phone—(973) 330-0557
500 U.S. Highway 46, Clifton 07011

## FURNITURE — Institutional

Academia Furniture Industries
Phone—(973) 472-0100
4 Passaic St., Wood Ridge 07075

## FURNITURE — Juvenile

Berg Furniture U. S. A., Inc.
Phone—(856) 310-0511
120 E. Gloucester Pike, Barrington 08007

Early Childhood Resources, LLC
Phone—(856) 638-1170
2165 Center Square Rd., Logan Township 08085

Search from among 430,000
U.S. manufacturers & suppliers:
**IndustryNet.com**

© Copyright 2015 Manufacturers' News, Inc. **A87**

## FURNITURE — Library

Arnold Kolax Furniture, Inc.
Phone—(973) 375-3344
146 Coit St., Irvington 07111

## FURNITURE — Metal

Extra Office, Inc.
Phone—(732) 381-9773
580 Leesville Ave., Rahway 07065

## FURNITURE — Outdoor, Lawn & Patio

Barlow Tyrie, Inc.
Phone—(856) 273-7878
1263 Glen Ave., Ste. 230, Moorestown 08057
Cast Classics, Inc.
Phone—(201) 896-1515
65 Railroad Ave., Ridgefield 07657
Modern Boat Works, Inc.
Phone—(609) 241-8916
P.O. Box 456, Oceanville 08231
**Mr. Fence**
Specializing in fences and patio furniture, gazebos, wishing wells, swing-sets, arbors, lighthouses and many custom yard accessories
**Phone—(732) 303-1614**
**Fax—(732) 303-0358**
**Web—www.cmrfence.com**
**Email—cmrfence@aol.com**
**3468 U.S. Highway 9, Ste. 2, Freehold 07728**

## FURNITURE — Plastic Laminate

Drake Corp.
Phone—(732) 254-1530
154 Tices Ln., East Brunswick 08816

## FURNITURE — Restaurant

Deitz & Sons, Inc., M.
Phone—(908) 686-8800
490 Hillside Ave., Hillside 07205
Domico Upholstery Co.
Phone—(856) 853-8181
1337 Delsea Dr., Woodbury 08096

## FURNITURE — Upholstered

Frank's Upholstery & Draperies
Phone—(856) 779-8585
49 S. Boulevard Ave., Maple Shade 08052
Masters Interiors, Inc.
Phone—(973) 253-0784
1500 Main Ave., Clifton 07011
Salto Decorators, LLC
Phone—(201) 261-2518
80-82 Kinderkamack Rd., Oradell 07649
Sleepable Sofas Ltd.
Phone—(973) 546-4502
6 Empire Blvd., Moonachie 07074

## FURNITURE — Wholesale

Business Furniture, Inc.
Phone—(908) 355-3400
133 Rahway Ave., Elizabeth 07202

## FURNITURE — Wood

Boomerang Used Office Furniture
Phone—(856) 582-0100
9155 River Rd., Pennsauken 08110
Carmel Furniture, Inc.
Phone—(201) 796-0099
404 N. Midland Ave., Saddle Brook 07663
Czar, Inc.
Phone—(973) 278-4002
51 Montgomery St., Belleville 07109
Danan Design Corp.
Phone—(201) 891-5342
599 Franklin Ave., Franklin Lakes 07417
Designs In Wood
Phone—(856) 546-8338
209 Williams Ave., Barrington 08007

Desiron
Phone—(908) 241-7776
820 Colfax Ave., Kenilworth 07033
Kismet Furniture, Inc.
Phone—(973) 278-3117
80 George St., Paterson 07503
Lee's Woodworking, Inc.
Phone—(732) 681-1002
726 Walling Ave., Belmar 07719
MossFauset Woodworking
Phone—(201) 714-9797
49 Harrison St., 13th Fl., Hoboken 07030
Munire Furniture, Inc.
Phone—(732) 339-6070
91 New England Ave., Piscataway 08854
Saco & Birnbaum Fine Woodworking
Phone—(973) 675-8999
71 Glenwood Pl., East Orange 07017
Salon Interiors
Phone—(201) 488-7888
62 Leuning St., South Hackensack 07606
Samuelson Furniture, Inc.
Phone—(973) 333-6090
11-13 Maryland Ave., Paterson 07503
Sherman & Son, Inc., W. F.
Phone—(732) 223-1505
84 Broad St., Manasquan 08736
SK Custom Creations, Inc.
Phone—(973) 754-9261
50 Furler St., Totowa 07512
T & T Cabinet Works, Inc.
Phone—(973) 279-0909
388 River St., Paterson 07524

## FURNITURE REPAIR & REFINISHING

Furniture Mill, Inc., The
Phone—(609) 771-0274
1536 Lower Ferry Rd., Ewing 08628

## FURNITURE SLIPCOVERS

Jason Furniture & Plastic Covers, Inc.
Phone—(732) 442-9700
334 State St., Perth Amboy 08861

## FUSES & ACCESSORIES

Fuseco, Inc.
Phone—(973) 894-3727
86 Lackawanna Ave., Ste. 240, Woodland Park 07424

## GAGES — Precision

Blanchette Tool & Gage Mfg.
Phone—(973) 471-2100
845 Bloomfield Ave., P.O. Box 1270, Clifton 07012

## GAGES — Pressure

Ernst Flow Industries
Phone—(732) 938-5641
116 Main St., Farmingdale 07727

## GAGES — Vacuum

**DigiVac Co.**
**Phone—(732) 765-0900**
**Fax—(732) 765-1800**
**Web—www.digivac.com**
**Email—sales@digivac.com**
**105-B Church St., Matawan 07747**

## GALVANIZING — Hot Dip

**American Galvanizing Co., Inc.**
**Phone—(609) 567-2090**
**Fax—(609) 567-2822**
**Web—www.amergalv.com**
**Email—jgregor@amergalv.com**
**P.O. Box 408, Hammonton 08037**
New Jersey Galvanizing & Tinning Works, Inc.
Phone—(973) 242-3200
139 Haynes Ave., 1st Fl., Newark 07114

V & S Amboy Galvanizing
Phone—(732) 442-7555
1190 Amboy Ave., Perth Amboy 08861

## GAMES

Bucci Management Co., Inc.
Phone—(609) 561-1888
603 N. 1st Rd., Hammonton 08037
Endless Games, Inc.
Phone—(732) 414-2213
35 Main St., Ste. B, Matawan 07747
Geebee Marketing, Inc.
Phone—(732) 777-6033
300 Raritan Ave., 2nd Fl., Highland Park 08904
Jersey Jack Pinball, Inc.
Phone—(732) 364-9900
1645 Oak St., Lakewood 08701
Park Sales
Phone—(732) 899-0684
P.O. Box 586, Point Pleasant Beach 08742

## GAMES — Computer & Video

P & E Technologies, Inc.
Phone—(732) 751-1515
5140 W. Hurley Pond Rd., Farmingdale 07727

## GAMING EQUIPMENT & SUPPLIES

Smartplay International, Inc.
Phone—(609) 880-1860
1550 Bridgeboro Rd., Edgewater Park 08010
WMS Gaming, Inc.
Phone—(609) 569-0100
2511 Fire Rd., Ste. A-10, Egg Harbor Township 08234

## GARAGE DOOR OPENERS — Automatic

Napoleon/Lynx
Phone—(973) 278-5588
25 Empire Blvd., South Hackensack 07606

## GAS ANALYZERS

Perma Pure, LLC
Phone—(732) 244-0010
8 Executive Dr., Toms River 08755
Tess-Com, Inc.
Phone—(732) 560-8100
400 South Ave., Ste. 11, Middlesex 08846

**Need a database
of manufacturers
for a telemarketing
or mail campaign?**

**Call mni at 800-221-2172
for database solutions!**

**Manufacturers' News, Inc.**
the industrial information source since 1912

**AGF Burner, Inc.**

1955 Swarthmore Avenue
Unit 2
Lakewood, NJ 08701

Gas Burners

**732-730-8090**
**FAX: 732-730-8060**

www.agfburner.com

sales@agfburner.com

## GAS BURNERS

**AGF Burner, Inc.**
   Phone—**(732) 730-8090**
   Fax—**(732) 730-8060**
   Web—www.agfburner.com
   Email—sales@agfburner.com
   **1955 Swarthmore Ave., Unit 2, Lakewood 08701**
      *(see our ad on this page)*
Carlisle Machine Works, Inc.
   Phone—(856) 825-0627
   412 S. Wade Blvd., Bldg. 5, P.O. Box 746, Millville 08332
N. M. Knight Co., Inc.
   Phone—(856) 327-4855
   1001 S. 2nd St., P.O. Box 1099, Millville 08332
**Nutley Heating & Cooling Supply, Inc.**
   Phone—**(973) 667-6880**
   Fax—**(973) 667-4602**
   Web—www.nutleysupply.com
   Email—ralpholiver@nutleysupply.com
   **156 Chestnut St., Nutley 07110**
      *(see our ad under BOILERS)*

## GAS DETECTION SYSTEMS

CEA Instrument, Inc.
   Phone—(201) 967-5660
   160 Tillman St., Westwood 07675

## GAS DETECTORS

Control Instruments Corp.
   Phone—(973) 575-9114
   25 Law Dr., Fairfield 07004
Electronic Measurement Laboratories, Inc.
   Phone—(732) 846-4029
   668 Easton Ave., Somerset 08873
Spectrex, Inc.
   Phone—(973) 239-8398
   218 Little Falls Rd., Unit 12, Cedar Grove 07009

## GAS DISTRIBUTORS

SOS Gases, Inc.
   Phone—(201) 998-7800
   1100 Harrison Ave., Kearny 07032

## GAS MONITORING SYSTEMS

Airscan, Inc.
   Phone—(908) 823-9425
   291 Route 22 E., Ste. 12, Lebanon 08833
American Gas & Chemical Co.
   Phone—(201) 767-7300
   220 Pegasus Ave., Northvale 07647

## GAS PROCESSING

Aeropres Corp.
   Phone—(908) 722-2571
   318 Valley Rd., Hillsborough 08844

## GAS PROCESSING EQUIPMENT

Cavagna North America, Inc.
   Phone—(732) 469-2100
   50 Napoleon Ct., Somerset 08873

## GAS PURIFICATION SYSTEMS

Advanced Specialty Gas Equipment
   Phone—(732) 271-9300
   241 Lackland Dr., Middlesex 08846
Resource Systems, Inc.
   Phone—(973) 884-0650
   7 Merry Ln., East Hanover 07936

## GASES — Acetylene

**Welco Acetylene Corp.**
   Phone—**(973) 465-1043**
   Fax—**(973) 589-7438**
   Email—john_j_smith@praxair.com
   **321 Roanoke Ave., Newark 07105**

**Welco Acetylene Corp.**

Acetylene Gas

**973-465-1043 / FAX: 973-589-7438**

john_j_smith@praxair.com

321 Roanoke Ave.  Newark, NJ 07105

## GASES — Calibration

Mesa Laboratories, Inc.
   Phone—(973) 492-8400
   10 Park Pl., Ste. 3, Butler 07405

## GASES — Compressed

Airgas Retail Solutions
   Phone—(732) 431-0288
   270 U.S. Highway 9, Manalapan 07726
**SOS Gases, Inc.**
   **Industrial & Laboratory Gas; Welding Eqpt., Rental & Repair Service**
   Phone—**(201) 998-7800 / (800) 626-7998**
   Fax—**(201) 998-5243**
   Web—www.sosgasesinc.com
   Email—sosgasesinc@msn.com
   **1100 Harrison Ave., Kearny 07032**
      *(see our ad under WELDING EQUIPMENT & SUPPLIES)*

## GASES — Industrial

Air Liquide America Specialty Gases, LLC
   Phone—(908) 754-7700
   2330 Hamilton Blvd., South Plainfield 07080
Linde Electronics & Specialty Gases
   Phone—(908) 454-7455
   80 Industrial Dr., Alpha 08865
Linde Gas North America, LLC
   Phone—(800) 755-9277
   1 Greenwich St., Ste. 200, Stewartsville 08886
Linde North America, Inc. (H Q)
   Phone—(908) 464-8100
   575 Mountain Ave., New Providence 07974
Matheson Tri-Gas, Inc.
   Phone—(908) 991-9200
   150 Allen Rd., Ste. 302, Basking Ridge 07920
**SOS Gases, Inc.**
   **Industrial & Laboratory Gas; Welding Eqpt., Rental & Repair Service**
   Phone—**(201) 998-7800 / (800) 626-7998**
   Fax—**(201) 998-5243**
   Web—www.sosgasesinc.com
   Email—sosgasesinc@msn.com
   **1100 Harrison Ave., Kearny 07032**
      *(see our ad under WELDING EQUIPMENT & SUPPLIES)*
Valley National Gases, WV LLC
   Phone—(856) 848-7321
   201 Crown Point Rd., West Deptford 08086

## GASES — Liquified Petroleum

**SOS Gases, Inc.**
   **Industrial & Laboratory Gas; Welding Eqpt., Rental & Repair Service**
   Phone—**(201) 998-7800 / (800) 626-7998**
   Fax—**(201) 998-5243**
   Web—www.sosgasesinc.com
   Email—sosgasesinc@msn.com
   **1100 Harrison Ave., Kearny 07032**
      *(see our ad under WELDING EQUIPMENT & SUPPLIES)*

## GASES — Medical

Airgas East, Inc.
   Phone—(856) 933-0544
   270 Benigno Blvd., Bellmawr 08031
**SOS Gases, Inc.**
   **Industrial & Laboratory Gas; Welding Eqpt., Rental & Repair Service**
   Phone—**(201) 998-7800 / (800) 626-7998**
   Fax—**(201) 998-5243**
   Web—www.sosgasesinc.com
   Email—sosgasesinc@msn.com
   **1100 Harrison Ave., Kearny 07032**
      *(see our ad under WELDING EQUIPMENT & SUPPLIES)*

## GASES — Propane

Airgas, Inc.
   Phone—(201) 337-5891
   5 Iron Horse Rd., Oakland 07436
Dry Ice Corp. (H Q)
   Phone—(201) 767-3200
   189 Central Ave., Old Tappan 07675
Praxair, Inc.
   Phone—(856) 299-3500
   554 Shell Rd., Penns Grove 08069
Propane Power Corporation, a Div. of Suburban Propane
   Phone—(973) 589-3030
   915 Delancy St., Newark 07105
**SOS Gases, Inc.**
   **Industrial & Laboratory Gas; Welding Eqpt., Rental & Repair Service**
   Phone—**(201) 998-7800 / (800) 626-7998**
   Fax—**(201) 998-5243**
   Web—www.sosgasesinc.com
   Email—sosgasesinc@msn.com
   **1100 Harrison Ave., Kearny 07032**
      *(see our ad under WELDING EQUIPMENT & SUPPLIES)*
Suburban Propane Partners, L.P. (H Q)
   Phone—(973) 887-5300
   240 Route 10 W., P.O. Box 206, Whippany 07981

## GASES — Specialty

Airgas East, Inc.
   Phone—(973) 633-9666
   1-D Frassetto Way, Lincoln Park 07035
Airgas Specialty Gases
   Phone—(856) 829-7878
   600 Union Landing Rd., Riverton 08077
**SOS Gases, Inc.**
   **Industrial & Laboratory Gas; Welding Eqpt., Rental & Repair Service**
   Phone—**(201) 998-7800 / (800) 626-7998**
   Fax—**(201) 998-5243**
   Web—www.sosgasesinc.com
   Email—sosgasesinc@msn.com
   **1100 Harrison Ave., Kearny 07032**
      *(see our ad under WELDING EQUIPMENT & SUPPLIES)*

INDUSTRY

## GASKET MATERIALS

**Ja-Bar Silicone Corp.**
Since 1965, mfg. specialty Silicone Elastomer Seals to Mil, Federal, AMS, SAF or customer specifications. Quality control system approved for Mil-I-45208. Serving the Automotive, Aerospace, Commercial & Medical Industries. ISO 9001:2008
Phone—(973) 786-5000
Fax—(973) 786-5546
Web—www.ja-bar.com
Email—info@ja-bar.com
252 Brighton Rd., P.O. Box 1249, Andover 07821
*(see our ad on this page)*

## GASKETS

**Alltite Gasket Co. Inc.**
Industrial metal, metal clad & composition sheet gaskets for heat exchangers
Phone—(732) 254-2154
Fax—(732) 254-7150
Web—www.alltitegasket.com
Email—sales@alltitegasket.com
323 William St., South River 08882

**AMP Custom Rubber, Inc.**
Phone—(732) 888-2714 / (888) 888-2714
Fax—(732) 739-2715
Web—www.ampcustomrubber.com
Email—amprubber@aol.com
P.O. Box 377, Hazlet 07730

**AMP Custom Rubber, Inc.**
Gaskets
888-888-2714 • 732-888-2714
FAX: 732-739-2715
P.O. Box 377 Hazlet, NJ 07730
Email: amprubber@aol.com

Arcy Mfg. Co., Inc.
Phone—(201) 635-1910
575 Industrial Rd., Carlstadt 07072

**Briggs Co., The**
Phone—(302) 328-9471 / (800) 435-7293
Fax—(302) 322-7707
Web—www.briggsco.net
Email—briggssales@briggsco.net
3 Bellecor Dr., New Castle, DE 19720

Capital Gasket & Rubber Corp.
Phone—(856) 939-3670
325 E. Clements Bridge Rd., Runnemede 08078

Coast Rubber & Gasket, Inc.
Phone—(609) 747-0110
1208 Columbus Rd., Ste. G, Burlington 08016

Lamatek, Inc.
Phone—(856) 599-6000
1226 Forest Pkwy., West Deptford 08066

Mercer Gasket & Shim, Inc.
Phone—(856) 931-5000
110 Benigno Blvd., Bellmawr 08031

Metal Textiles Corp.
Phone—(732) 287-0800
970 New Durham Rd., Edison 08818

**Metallo Gasket Co., Inc.**
Phone—(732) 545-7223
Fax—(732) 545-9848
Web—www.metallogasket.com
Email—info@metallogasket.com
16 Bethany St., New Brunswick 08901

Tri-Comp, Inc.
Phone—(973) 835-1110
230 West Pkwy., Unit 14, Pompton Plains 07444

## GASKETS — Rubber

Baxter Rubber Co.
Phone—(973) 227-1956
10 Spielman Rd., Fairfield 07004

Custom Gasket Mfg.
Phone—(201) 331-6363
640 E. Palisade Ave., Englewood Cliffs 07632

Rubber Fab Technologies Group
Phone—(973) 579-2959
26 Brookfield Dr., Sparta 07871

# Ja-Bar Silicone Corp.
### Mfrs. of Silicone & EMI/RFI Shielding Products
## ISO 9001:2008
### P.O. Box 1249 Andover, NJ 07821
# PH: 973-786-5000
# FAX: 973-786-5546
http://www.ja-bar.com • info@ja-bar.com

**Specialty Rubber, Inc.**
A Veteran Owned Company
Phone—(609) 704-2555 / (800) 249-5848
Fax—(609) 704-8020
Web—www.specialtyrubber.com
Email—specrub@yahoo.com
4500 White Horse Pike, P.O. Box 483, Elwood 08217
*(also see our ads under DIE CUTTING & SHIELDING—EMI/RFI)*

**Speciality Rubber, Inc.**
A Veteran Owned Company
**(800) 249-5848**
(609) 704-2555 • Fax (609) 704-8020
www.specialtyrubber.com
specrub@yahoo.com
4500 White Horse Pike, P.O. Box 483 • Elwood, NJ 08217

Trico Hose & Gasket Corp.
Phone—(609) 693-5301
700-2 Challenger Way, Lacey Business Pk., Forked River 08731

## GASOLINE

**Taylor Oil Co., Inc.**
The premier provider of on-site fueling services (highest quality gasoline, diesel fuel & other petroleum products) to construction crews, contractors, boats & marinas along the East Coast and beyond
Phone—(908) 725-7737
Fax—(908) 725-7746
Web—www.tayloroilco.com
Email—fbloom@tayloroilco.com
77 2nd St., P.O. Box 974, Somerville 08876

## GATES — Iron

T. S. Gates, Inc.
Phone—(973) 523-7323
202 12th Ave., Paterson 07501

## GAZEBOS

**Mr. Fence**
Specializing in fences and patio furniture, gazebos, wishing wells, swing-sets, arbors, lighthouses and many custom yard accessories
Phone—(732) 303-1614
Fax—(732) 303-0358
Web—www.cmrfence.com
Email—cmrfence@aol.com
3468 U.S. Highway 9, Ste. 2, Freehold 07728

## GEAR BOXES

Andantex U.S.A., Inc.
Phone—(732) 493-2812
1705 Valley Rd., Ocean 07712

**Chalmers & Kubeck, Inc.**
Phone—(610) 494-4300
Fax—(610) 485-1484
Web—www.candk.com
Email—jmoore@candk.com
150 Commerce Dr., P.O. Box 2447, Aston, PA 19014
*(see our ad under MACHINE WORK & MACHINING)*

Koll Machine & Tool Co., Frank G.
Phone—(732) 870-2966
390 Warburton Pl., P.O. Box 464, Long Branch 07740

## GEAR DRIVES

Walter Machine Co., Inc., The
Phone—(201) 656-5654
84-98 Cambridge Ave., P.O. Box 7700, Jersey City 07307

## GEAR MOTORS
**(also see 'Electric Motors')**

Bauer Gear Motor, LLC
Phone—(732) 469-8770
31 Schoolhouse Rd., Somerset 08873

## GEAR PUMPS

Dynaflow Engineering
Phone—(732) 356-9790
106 Egel Ave., Middlesex 08846

*Search from among 430,000 U.S. manufacturers & suppliers:*
**IndustryNet.com**

*Do nationwide searches for products & services at:*
**IndustryNet.com**

## GEAR REDUCERS

Koellmann Gear Corp.
Phone—(201) 447-0200
8 Industrial Pk., Waldwick 07463

## GEARS

Acme Gear Co., Inc.
Phone—(201) 568-2245
130 W. Forest Ave., P.O. Box 779, Englewood 07631
State Tool Gear Co., Inc.
Phone—(973) 642-6181
211 Camden St., Newark 07103

## GEARS — Plastic

Intech Corp.
Phone—(201) 767-8066
250 Herbert Ave., Closter 07624

## GEARS — Precision

Apex Gear & Machine Co.
Phone—(973) 482-5542
938 Lake St., Newark 07104
Halkias Gear & Machine Works
Phone—(973) 748-4901
14 Willow St., Bloomfield 07003
M J H Gear & Tool Co., Inc.
Phone—(212) 246-3800
15 Maple St., Norwood 07648

## GEL PACKS

Icy Cools, Inc.
Phone—(609) 448-0172
15 Oscar Dr., P.O. Box 686, Roosevelt 08555

## GELATINS

Poly-Gel, LLC
Phone—(973) 884-3300
30 Leslie Ct., Whippany 07981

## GENERATOR SETS

ENER-G Rudox, Inc.
Phone—(201) 438-0111
765 State Route 17 N., P.O. Box 467, Carlstadt 07072
Kraft Power Corp.
Email: njsales@kraftpower.com
Phone—(973) 835-9800 / (800) 221-3284
Fax—(973) 835-5246
Web—www.kraftpower.com
241 W. Parkway, Pompton Plains 07444
(see our ad under ENGINES—Gas)

## GENERATORS

Advanced Electric Design and Service, LLC
Sales & service for electric, gas, natural gas & portable generators
Phone—(732) 396-0033
Fax—(908) 789-9659
Web—www.aedsllc.com
Email—info@advancedelectricdesign.net
P.O. Box 126, Rahway 07065
D & W Diesel
Phone—(732) 566-4970
423 County Rd., Cliffwood 07721
Innovative Power Solutions, LLC
Phone—(732) 544-1075
373 South St., Eatontown 07724
Kraft Power Corp.
Email: njsales@kraftpower.com
Phone—(973) 835-9800 / (800) 221-3284
Fax—(973) 835-5246
Web—www.kraftpower.com
241 W. Parkway, Pompton Plains 07444
(see our ad under ENGINES—Gas)

find additional suppliers at IndustryNet.com

Midland Radiator Service Co.
Phone—(973) 340-0533 / (800) 605-8001
Fax—(973) 340-5941
Web—www.midlandradiator.com
Email—midlandrad@aol.com
420 Midland Ave., Garfield 07026
(see our ad under RADIATORS)
Warwick Mfg. & Equipment Co., LLC
Buy & sell used: Chemical, food, cosmetic, packaging & pharmaceutical equipment
Phone—(732) 729-0400 / (732) 241-9263
Fax—(732) 729-1235
Web—www.warwickequipment.com
Email—sales@warwickequipment.com
1112 12th St., North Brunswick 08902
(see our ad Outside Back Cover)

## GENERATORS — Diesel

Atlantic Detroit Diesel-Allison, LLC
Diesel & Gas Powered Generators, Transfer Switches, Switchgear Sales & Service
Phone—(201) 291-8415
Fax—(201) 845-3288
Web—www.atlanticdda.com
Email—msudia@atlanticdda.com
33 Gregg St., Lodi 07644

## GENERATORS — Electric

Como Electric, Inc.
Phone—(732) 449-7625
Fax—(732) 449-6896
Email—comoelect@aol.com
909 Wall Rd., Spring Lake 07762

## Como Electric, Inc.

*Generator Installations*

**(732) 449-7625**
**FAX: (732) 449-6896**

909 Wall Road
Spring Lake, NJ 07762

**Email: comoelect@aol.com**

Kraft Power Corp.
Email: njsales@kraftpower.com
Phone—(973) 835-9800 / (800) 221-3284
Fax—(973) 835-5246
Web—www.kraftpower.com
241 W. Parkway, Pompton Plains 07444
(see our ad under ENGINES—Gas)

## GENERATORS — Gas

R & J Control, Inc.
Phone—(973) 328-6880
58 Harding Ave., Dover 07801
Stewart & Stevenson Power Products, LLC, ADDA Div.
Phone—(201) 291-8415
33 Gregg St., Lodi 07644

## GIFT BASKETS

Delicious Orchards
Mail Order
Phone—(732) 462-1989 / (800) 624-1893
Fax—(732) 409-4993
Web—www.deliciousorchardsnj.com
Email—frank0517m@aol.com
320 State Route 34, Colts Neck 07722

Sweet Success
Phone—(908) 561-2997
14 Ellison Rd., Watchung 07069

## GIFT ITEMS

Artique, Inc.
Phone—(201) 444-8989
P.O. Box 44, Midland Park 07432
Custom Products Mfg., Inc.
Phone—(908) 852-2078
430 Sand Shore Rd., Ste. 4 & 5, Hackettstown 07840
LittleGifts, Inc. (H Q)
Phone—(212) 868-2559
600 Meadowlands Pkwy., Ste. 131, Secaucus 07094
Satterfield Originals
Phone—(908) 902-0290
130 Bodman Pl., Apt. 2, Red Bank 07701

## GIFTS — Corporate

Myron Corp.
Phone—(201) 843-6464
205 Maywood Ave., Maywood 07607

## GLASS

Atlantic International Technologies, Inc.
Phone—(973) 625-0053
114 Beach St., Bldg. 3, Rockaway 07866
Karr Glass, Inc., Peggy
Phone—(973) 659-1200
100 Washington St., Randolph 07869
Legacy Stairs & Millwork, Inc.
Phone—(732) 905-7705
Fax—(732) 905-7750
Web—www.legacystairs.com
Email—sales@legacystairs.com
1000 Airport Rd., Ste. 104, Lakewood 08701
(see our ad under STAIRS)
Union County Plate Glass Co. (H Q)
Phone—(908) 354-0380
1050 Elizabeth Ave., P.O. Box 9027, Elizabeth 07201

## GLASS — Architectural

Berkowitz, Inc., L.P., J. E.
Phone—(856) 456-7800
1 Gateway Blvd., P.O. Box 427, Pedricktown 08067
Galaxy Glass & Stone
Phone—(973) 575-3440
277 Fairfield Rd., P.O. Box 10154, Fairfield 07004
Mainland Plate Glass Co., Inc.
Phone—(609) 641-6553
53 E. West Jersey Ave., Pleasantville 08232
Solar Furnace Glass
Phone—(908) 362-9661
4 Camp Wasigan Rd., Blairstown 07825

## GLASS — Art, Cut

Crystal World, Inc.
Phone—(201) 488-0909
89 Leuning St., Ste. A-2, South Hackensack 07606
Victorian Glass Carver
Phone—(856) 662-1391
5515 Toms Ave., Pennsauken 08109

## GLASS — Automotive

American Auto II, Inc.
New & Used Auto Glass
Phone—(609) 965-6700 / (866) 883-4799
Fax—(609) 965-6501
Web—www.americanauto2.com
Email—parts@americanauto2.com
3135 Route 50, Mays Landing 08330
(see our ad under AUTOMOTIVE PARTS)
BK Classic Auto Glass, LLC
Phone—(973) 759-1485
441 Cortlandt St., Belleville 07109

## GLASS — Automotive — (cont.)

**Quality Auto Glass Inc.**
Phone—(908) 754-2652
Fax—(908) 754-3113
Web—www.qualityautoglassnj.com
2300 S. Clinton Ave., South Plainfield 07080

---

**Quality Auto Glass Inc.**
*Quality Glass*
www.qualityautoglassnj.com
908.754.2652 • Fax: 908.754.3113
2300 S. Clinton Avenue
South Plainfield, NJ 07080

---

## GLASS — Decorative

**Phoenix Glass, LLC**
Phone—(856) 692-0100
Fax—(856) 696-5155
Web—www.pxglass.com
Email—rohrmanf@pxglass.com
615 Alvine Rd., Pittsgrove 08318

---

**Phoenix Glass, LLC**
ISO 9001:2008 Certified
Vial Manufacturing & Decorating Services
856-692-0100 • www.pxglass.com
615 Alvine Rd. Pittsgrove, NJ 08318

---

## GLASS — Electronic

**Precision Electronic Glass, Inc.**
Glass Custom Components
Phone—(856) 691-2234 / (800) 982-4734
Fax—(856) 691-3090
Web—www.pegglass.com
Email—info@pegglass.com
1013 Hendee Rd., Vineland 08360

## GLASS — Etched

Seagull Stained Glass
Phone—(609) 345-3126
1917 Kuehnle Ave., Atlantic City 08401

## GLASS — Flat

Elco Glass Industries Co., Inc.
Phone—(732) 363-6550
1855 Swarthmore Ave., Lakewood 08701

## GLASS — Insulating

Eastern Glass Resources, Inc.
Phone—(973) 483-8411
770 Supor Blvd., Harrison 07029
Insulite, Inc.
Phone—(732) 255-1700
1890 Church Rd., Toms River 08753
RSL, Inc. (H Q)
Phone—(609) 484-1600
3092 English Creek Ave., Egg Harbor Township 08234

## GLASS — Sight

Ernst Co., Inc., John C.
Phone—(973) 940-1600
21 Gail Ct., Sparta 07871

## GLASS — Stained, Leaded

Artique Glass Studio
Phone—(201) 444-3500
483 S. Broad St., Glen Rock 07452

Creations In Glass
Phone—(201) 488-0229
344 Main St., Hackensack 07601
Feldman Stained Glass
Phone—(201) 434-2887
401 Halladay St., Jersey City 07304
Galossi Glass Design, Inc.
Phone—(908) 232-2111
12 Van Pelt Dr., Whitehouse Station 08889
Hiemer & Co., Edward W.
Phone—(973) 772-5081
141 Wabash Ave., Clifton 07011
**J & R Lamb Studios, Inc.**
Phone—(201) 891-8585
Fax—(201) 891-8855
Web—www.lambstudios.com
Email—lambstudios@optonline.net
190 Greenwood Ave., Midland Park 07432
Matawan Stained Glass
Phone—(732) 583-1030
77-A Main St., Matawan 07747
**Rambusch Company**
Family Owned Since 1898
Phone—(201) 333-2525
Fax—(201) 433-3355
Web—www.rambusch.com
Email—info@rambusch.com
160 Cornelison Ave., Jersey City 07304
*(see our ad under LIGHTING FIXTURES)*
Stained Glass Design, Inc.
Phone—(973) 772-5070
87 Dellglen Ave., Lodi 07644
Studio J/Architectural Glass Effects
Phone—(973) 569-0200
215 Pennsylvania Ave., Paterson 07503
Sunflower Glass Studio
Phone—(609) 397-1535
877 Sergeantsville Rd., Stockton 08559
Tracy's Stained Glass Studio
Phone—(908) 273-8040
11 New Providence Ave., Summit 07901

## GLASS — Tempered

**Blue Star Glass, Inc.**
Phone—(732) 422-1272
Fax—(732) 422-1274
Web—www.bluestarglass.net
Email—info@bluestarglass.net
2300 U.S. Highway 1, Bldg. 31, North Brunswick 08902
Jersey Tempered Glass, Inc.
Phone—(856) 273-8700
2035 Briggs Rd., P.O. Box 205, Mount Laurel 08054
Precision Mirror & Glass, Inc.
Phone—(732) 389-8175
89 Route 35 N., Eatontown 07724
Pride Tempered Glass Products, LLC
Phone—(856) 365-1200
2001 S. 6th St., Camden 08104

## GLASS — Wholesale

Bendheim
Phone—(973) 471-1733
61 Willett St., Bldg. PP, Passaic 07055

## GLASS AND MIRRORS

Frank's Aluminum Glass & Mirrors Co.
Phone—(732) 462-8141
588 Park Ave., Freehold 07728
Freehold Glass & Mirror, Inc.
Phone—(732) 462-6200
38 South St., Freehold 07728
Gorkin Glass Co., Inc.
Phone—(908) 756-0544
26 Race St., North Plainfield 07060
Innovative Glass & Mirror, Inc.
Phone—(732) 961-2267
15 Chambersbridge Rd., Lakewood 08701
Seashore Glass & Mirror
Phone—(609) 407-6032
2547 Fire Rd., Ste. 2-B, Egg Harbor Township 08234
Suburban Glass & Mirror, Inc.
Phone—(201) 447-0440
418 S. Broad St., Ridgewood 07450

Tri-State Glass & Mirror, Inc.
Phone—(732) 591-5545
11-A Jocama Blvd., Old Bridge 08857
Twin Glass Co.
Phone—(609) 645-8834
6422 Black Horse Pike, Egg Harbor Township 08234

## GLASS BEADS — Industrial

Potters Industries, Inc.
Phone—(201) 460-0666
600 Industrial Rd., Carlstadt 07072

## GLASS BLOCKS

Swift-Track, Inc. (H Q)
Phone—(201) 226-9537
58 Schlosser Dr., Rochelle Park 07662

## GLASS BLOWING EQUIPMENT

**AGF Burner, Inc.**
Phone—(732) 730-8090
Fax—(732) 730-8060
Web—www.agfburner.com
Email—sales@agfburner.com
1955 Swarthmore Ave., Unit 2, Lakewood 08701
*(see our ad under GAS BURNERS)*

## GLASS CUTTING

**AGF Burner, Inc.**
Phone—(732) 730-8090
Fax—(732) 730-8060
Web—www.agfburner.com
Email—sales@agfburner.com
1955 Swarthmore Ave., Unit 2, Lakewood 08701
*(see our ad under GAS BURNERS)*
Blue Star Glass, Inc.
Phone—(732) 422-1272
Fax—(732) 422-1274
Web—www.bluestarglass.net
Email—info@bluestarglass.net
2300 U.S. Highway 1, Bldg. 31, North Brunswick 08902
General Glass International
Phone—(201) 553-1850
101 Venture Way, Secaucus 07094
Triton Associated Industries, Inc.
Phone—(856) 697-3050
North Brewster Rd., P.O. Box 627, Buena 08310

## GLASS FABRICATING EQUIPMENT

Armour Products
Phone—(973) 427-8787
176-180 5th Ave., Hawthorne 07506
De Dietrich U. S. A., Inc. (H Q)
Phone—(908) 317-2585
244 Sheffield St., Mountainside 07092

## GLASS FABRICATION

21st Century Optical
Phone—(973) 379-2020
5 Powder Horn Dr., Warren 07059
Ad Plus
Phone—(609) 653-7007
111 Cambridge Ave., Linwood 08221
**AGF Burner, Inc.**
Phone—(732) 730-8090
Fax—(732) 730-8060
Web—www.agfburner.com
Email—sales@agfburner.com
1955 Swarthmore Ave., Unit 2, Lakewood 08701
*(see our ad under GAS BURNERS)*
**Blue Star Glass, Inc.**
Phone—(732) 422-1272
Fax—(732) 422-1274
Web—www.bluestarglass.net
Email—info@bluestarglass.net
2300 U.S. Highway 1, Bldg. 31, North Brunswick 08902

## GLASS FABRICATION — (cont.)

Camden Glass, Inc.
Phone—(856) 365-0142
111 Marlton Ave., Camden 08105
Clifton Mirror & Glass Co., Inc.
Phone—(973) 772-7770
188 Getty Ave., Clifton 07011
Creamer Glass, LLC
Phone—(856) 327-2023
411 N. 10th St., Millville 08332
Dynasil Corp. Of America
Phone—(856) 767-4600
385 Cooper Rd., West Berlin 08091
Elliott Glass Co., Inc.
Phone—(973) 256-8098
192 Lackawanna Ave., Ste. 103, Woodland Park 07424
Ewing Glass Co.
Phone—(609) 882-1818
1354 Parkside Ave., Trenton 08638
Friedrich & Dimmock, Inc.
Phone—(856) 825-0305
2127 Wheaton Ave., P.O. Box 230, Millville 08332
Glass Dynamics, LLC
Phone—(856) 205-1530
2662 Hance Bridge Rd., Vineland 08361
Glaston America, Inc.
Phone—(856) 786-1200
600-D Commerce Pkwy., Mount Laurel 08054
Hudson United Glass & Window Corp.
Phone—(201) 440-3937
476 Hudson St., Hackensack 07601
Lager Glass Co., Inc.
Phone—(732) 775-9220
1913 Heck Ave., P.O. Box 426, Neptune 07753
McGrory Glass, Inc.
Phone—(856) 579-3200
1400 Grandview Ave., Paulsboro 08066
Mullin Glass Co., Inc.
Phone—(973) 838-6767
268 Main St., Butler 07405
Norman's Glass & Auto Services, Inc.
Phone—(609) 386-7100
4482 Route 130 S., Burlington 08016
Oldcastle BuildingEnvelope®
Phone—(866) 653-2278
1500 Glen Ave., Moorestown 08057
Penta Glass Industries, Inc.
Phone—(973) 478-2110
71 Hepworth Pl., Garfield 07026
**Q Glass Co., Inc.**
**Phone—(973) 335-5191 / (800) 619-0069**
**Fax—(973) 335-2057**
**Web—www.qglass.com**
**Email—dan@qglass.com**
**624 Main Rd., Towaco 07082**
Richland Glass Co., Inc.
Phone—(856) 691-1697
1640 S. West Blvd., Vineland 08360
Suburban Glass & Mirror, Inc.
Phone—(201) 768-9586
231 Herbert Ave., Closter 07624
Thermoseal Industries, LLC
Phone—(856) 456-3109
400 Water St., Gloucester City 08030
Wheaton Glass Warehouse
Phone—(856) 327-5228
1501 N. 10th St., Millville 08332

## GLASS RECYCLING

Glass Cycle Systems, Inc.
Phone—(973) 838-0034
5 Mathews Ave., Riverdale 07457

## GLASSWARE

Cardinal International, Inc.
Phone—(973) 628-0900
43 Route 46 E., Ste. 709, P.O. Box 897, Pine Brook 07058
**Gerresheimer Glass, Inc.**
**Manufacturer of high-quality specialty products made of glass & plastic for the global pharma & healthcare industry**
**Phone—(856) 692-3600**
**Web—www.gerresheimer.com**
**Email—info-tubing-us@gerresheimer.com**
**537 Crystal Ave., Vineland 08360**

Glastron, Inc.
Phone—(856) 692-0500
510 N. West Blvd., Vineland 08360
Quest Industries, LLC
Phone—(908) 851-9070
480 Mundet Pl., Hillside 07205

## GLASSWARE — Laboratory

A M K Glass, Inc.
Phone—(856) 692-1488
2880 Industrial Way, Vineland 08360
Ace Glass, Inc.
Phone—(856) 692-3333
1430 N. West Blvd., Vineland 08360
AGC Acquisition, LLC
Phone—(856) 692-4435
3740 N. West Blvd., Vineland 08360
Finneran Assocs., J. G.
Phone—(856) 696-3605
3600 Reilly Ct., Vineland 08360
Hess Glass Products
Phone—(856) 691-1432
601 N. Orchard Rd., Vineland 08360
Martin, Inc., H. S.
Phone—(856) 692-8700
1149 Southeast Blvd., Vineland 08360
N D S Technologies, Inc.
Phone—(856) 691-0330
891 E. Oak Rd., Vineland 08360
**Q Glass Co., Inc.**
**Phone—(973) 335-5191 / (800) 619-0069**
**Fax—(973) 335-2057**
**Web—www.qglass.com**
**Email—dan@qglass.com**
**624 Main Rd., Towaco 07082**

## GLASSWARE — Scientific

Chemglass, Inc.
Phone—(856) 696-0014
3800 N. Mill Rd., Vineland 08360
Glassblowers.Com, Inc.
Phone—(856) 232-7898
P.O. Box 8089, Turnersville 08012
International Glass Work, Inc.
Phone—(856) 691-5628
723 E. Park Ave., P.O. Box 1015, Vineland 08360
New Era Enterprises, Inc.
Phone—(856) 794-2005
208 N. West Blvd., Rear, Newfield 08344
Norell, Inc.
Phone—(856) 697-0020
314 Arbor Ave., P.O. Box 307, Landisville 08326
**Q Glass Co., Inc.**
**Phone—(973) 335-5191 / (800) 619-0069**
**Fax—(973) 335-2057**
**Web—www.qglass.com**
**Email—dan@qglass.com**
**624 Main Rd., Towaco 07082**
Technical Glass Products, Inc.
Phone—(973) 989-5500
243 E. Blackwell St., Ste. B, Dover 07801
V M Glass Co.
Phone—(856) 794-9333
3231 N. Mill Rd., Vineland 08360
Wheaton Industries, Inc.
Phone—(856) 825-1100
1501 N. 10th St., Millville 08332
Wilmad-LabGlass
Phone—(856) 691-3200
1172 N. West Blvd., Vineland 08360

## GLOBAL POSITIONING SYSTEMS

GuardTrax, LLC
Phone—(908) 272-0114
11 Commerce Dr., Lobby, Cranford 07016

## GLOVES

Ansell Healthcare Products, LLC (H Q)
Phone—(732) 345-5400
111 Wood Ave. S., Ste. 210, Iselin 08830
POLY-Version, Inc.
Phone—(201) 451-0600
49 Fisk St., Jersey City 07305

## GLUE

Gluefast Co., Inc.
Phone—(732) 918-4600
3535 State Route 66, Ste. 1, Neptune 07753
Union Rubber, Inc.
Phone—(609) 396-9328
232 Allen St., Trenton 08618

## GOLF ACCESSORIES

Crown Products, Inc.
Phone—(732) 493-0022
1302 Roller Rd., Ocean 07712

## GOLF CARTS

JerseyCarts, LLC
Phone—(908) 806-6400
6 Whiskey Ln., Flemington 08822
Vic Gerard Golf Cars
Phone—(732) 938-4464
281 Squankum Rd., Farmingdale 07727

## GOLF COURSE EQUIPMENT & SUPPLIES

Fairway Products Co.
Phone—(856) 358-6016
265 Garden Rd., P.O. Box 611, Elmer 08318

## GOLF COURSE MANAGEMENT

Harris Miniature Golf Courses, Inc.
Phone—(609) 522-4200
141 W. Burk Ave., Wildwood 08260

## GRADUATION SUPPLIES

Trim & Tassels, LLC (H Q)
Phone—(973) 808-1566
204 Passaic Ave., Unit 3, Fairfield 07004

## GRANITE

**Artistic Marble & Granite Surfaces, Inc.**
**Web: www.NJMarble.com**
**Phone—(973) 304-2001**
**Fax—(973) 427-9142**
**Email—artistic269@aol.com**
**269 Goffle Rd., Hawthorne 07506**
**B & B Granite Block Sales, LLC**
**Phone—(732) 922-1810**
**Web—www.bbgraniteblock.com**
**1700 Bloomsbury Ave., Ocean 07712**
High Bridge Stone Co., Inc.
Phone—(973) 344-5522
187 Marsh St., Newark 07114
House Of Granite & Marble, Inc.
Phone—(732) 367-7211
1920 Swarthmore Ave., Ste. 4, Lakewood 08701
Lotus Exim International, Inc.
Phone—(201) 475-2810
16 Leliarts Ln., Elmwood Park 07407
Monuments Are Forever, Inc.
Phone—(908) 862-0220
200 E. Edgar Rd., Ste. 1-A, Linden 07036
Natural Stone Kitchen & Bath
Phone—(732) 297-5450
2280 U.S. Highway 130, North Brunswick 08902
**Reliance Granite & Marble**
**Phone—(908) 624-1995**
**Fax—(908) 624-1996**
**Email—rgmusa@gmail.com**
**2333 US Highway 22 W., Ste. 2, Union 07083**

## GRAPHIC ARTS EQUIPMENT

IBF Corp.
Phone—(973) 546-0055
44 Plauderville Ave., Garfield 07026
Kompac Technologies, LLC
Phone—(908) 534-8411
7 Commerce St., Ste. 1, Somerville 08876

Search from among 430,000 U.S. manufacturers & suppliers: IndustryNet.com

## GRAPHIC ARTS SERVICES

Hillman Graphic Products
Phone—(201) 487-6900
P.O. Box 5233, Somerset 08875

## GRAPHIC ARTS SUPPLIES

Agfa Corp.
Phone—(973) 812-0400
400 Heller Park Ct., Dayton 08810

## GRAPHITE & GRAPHITE PRODUCTS

**Asbury Graphite Mills, Inc. (H Q)**
Email: sales@asbury.com
Phone—(908) 537-2155
Fax—(908) 537-2908
Web—www.asbury.com
405 Old Main St., P.O. Box 144, Asbury 08802
Bar-Lo Carbon Products, Inc.
Phone—(973) 227-2717
31 W. Daniel Rd., P.O. Box 10031, Fairfield 07004

## GRAPHITE LUBRICANTS

**Asbury Graphite Mills, Inc. (H Q)**
Email: sales@asbury.com
Phone—(908) 537-2155
Fax—(908) 537-2908
Web—www.asbury.com
405 Old Main St., P.O. Box 144, Asbury 08802

## GREASE TRAP SERVICES

**Darling Ingredients, Inc.**
Email: bfrish@darlingii.com
Phone—(973) 465-1900 / (800) 842-5927
Fax—(973) 465-9247
Web—www.darlingii.com
825 Wilson Ave., Newark 07105

## GRINDERS — Centerless

Glebar Co.
Phone—(201) 337-1500
527 Commerce St., P.O. Box 623, Franklin Lakes 07417
Royal Masters Grinders, Inc.
Phone—(201) 337-8500
143 Bauer Dr., P.O Box 630, Oakland 07436

## GRINDING

**B & L Precision Grinding Corp.**
Specializing in centerless grinding
Phone—(973) 839-4141
Fax—(973) 839-4760
Email—blgrinding@verizon.net
7-B Ivy St., Pompton Lakes 07442
**B & M Grinding Co.**
Phone—(973) 564-7648
Fax—(973) 564-5298
50 Brown Ave., Springfield 07081
*(see our ad under GRINDING – Precision)*
**M & S Machine & Tool Corp.**
Phone—(973) 345-5847
Fax—(973) 345-0579
Web—www.mandsmachine.com
Email—nazim@mandsmachine.com
108 Maryland Ave., Paterson 07503

## GRINDING — Blanchard

**Gaum, Inc.**
AS9100C Certified
Phone—(609) 586-0132
Fax—(609) 586-9748
Web—www.gauminc.com
Email—mail@gauminc.com
1080 Route 130, P.O. Box 485, Robbinsville 08691
*(see our ads Outside Front Cover & under MACHINE WORK & MACHINING)*

## GRINDING — Centerless

A M A Centerless Grinding, Inc.
Phone—(973) 835-2919
88-C Cannonball Rd., P.O. Box 14, Pompton Lakes 07442
**B & L Precision Grinding Corp.**
Specializing in centerless grinding
Phone—(973) 839-4141
Fax—(973) 839-4760
Email—blgrinding@verizon.net
7-B Ivy St., Pompton Lakes 07442
F & R Grinding, Inc.
Phone—(908) 996-0440
138 County Road 513, Frenchtown 08825

## GRINDING — Crush Form

**M & M Grinding, LLC**
Also grinding-crush form
Phone—(732) 542-1157
Fax—(732) 542-1241
Email—mmgrinding@verizon.net
132 Lewis St., Eatontown 07724

## GRINDING — Cylindrical

**M & M Grinding, LLC**
Also grinding-crush form
Phone—(732) 542-1157
Fax—(732) 542-1241
Email—mmgrinding@verizon.net
132 Lewis St., Eatontown 07724

## GRINDING — Plastics

Allgrind Plastics, Inc.
Phone—(908) 479-4400
6 Vliet Farm Rd., Asbury 08802

## GRINDING — Precision

**B & M Grinding Co.**
Phone—(973) 564-7648
Fax—(973) 564-5298
Web—www.bandmgrinding.com
Email—fred10658@yahoo.com
50 Brown Ave., Springfield 07081

B & M GRINDING CO.
*Internal & External Metal Grinding*
(973) 564-7648
FAX: (973) 564-5298
50 Brown Ave., Springfield, NJ 07081

J & M Precision Enterprises, Inc.
Phone—(856) 661-9595
8103 River Rd., Pennsauken 08110
JOCO Precision, Inc.
Phone—(908) 862-1611
333 Dalziel Rd., Linden 07036
M & D Precision Centerless Grinding, Inc.
Phone—(856) 764-1616
120 Kossuth St., Riverside 08075
Ronald-Mark Assocs., Inc.
Phone—(856) 582-6766
150 N. Summit Ave., P.O. Box 355, Pitman 08071
S & S Precision
Phone—(856) 662-0006
2205 Sherman Ave., Pennsauken 08110

## GRINDING — Rail

**Orgo-Thermit, Inc.**
Email: georgeanne.tutunjian@orgothermit.com
Mfgr. & supplier of Aluminothermic welding prods & equipment for tee-rail, crane rail & grooved rail, as well as providing comprehensive training programs for the process of joining steel rails
Phone—(732) 657-5781
Fax—(732) 657-5899
Web—www.orgothermit.com
3500 Colonial Dr. N., Manchester 08759

## GRINDING EQUIPMENT & SUPPLIES

Everite Machine Products Co.
Phone—(856) 330-6700
6995 Airport Highway Ln., Pennsauken 08110
Themac, Inc.
Phone—(201) 438-2313
405 Railroad Ave., P.O. Box 44, East Rutherford 07073

## GRINDING MACHINERY

Pallmann Industries, Inc.
Phone—(973) 471-1450
820 Bloomfield Ave., Clifton 07012

## GRINDING WHEELS — Diamond

3M Co.
Phone—(973) 884-2500
140 Algonquin Pkwy., Whippany 07981
Alpex Wheel Co.
Phone—(201) 871-1700
29 Atwood Ave., P.O. Box 357, Tenafly 07670
New Jersey Diamond Products Co.
Phone—(973) 684-0949
108 Kentucky Ave., Paterson 07503

## GROCERIES — Wholesale

Atalanta Corporation
Phone—(908) 351-8000
1 Atalanta Plz., Elizabeth 07206
La Fe Foods, Inc.
Phone—(201) 329-6260
230 Moonachie Ave., Moonachie 07074
McLane Burlington
Phone—(609) 239-5000
600 Commerce Dr., Burlington 08016
McLane New Jersey
Phone—(856) 351-6200
742 Courses Landing Rd., Carneys Point 08069

## GROUT

Boiardi Products Corp.
Phone—(973) 256-1100
453 Main St., Ste. 4, Little Falls 07424
Custom Building Products, Inc.
Phone—(856) 467-9226
2115 High Hill Rd., Logan Township 08085
Fuller Construction Products, Inc., H.B.
Phone—(732) 287-8330
59 Brunswick Ave., Edison 08817

## GUITAR STRINGS

D R Handmade Strings, Inc.
Phone—(201) 599-0100
7 Palisade Ave., Emerson 07630

## GUM — Chewing

GumRunners, LLC
Phone—(201) 678-9300
333 Washington St., P.O. Box 392, Jersey City 07303

## GUTTER COVERS

R. K. Industries, Inc.
Phone—(732) 531-1123
259 Overbrook Ave., Oakhurst 07755

## GUTTERS & DOWNSPOUTS

American Seamless Gutter & Leader Corp.
Phone—(973) 838-4505
286 Hamburg Tpke., Riverdale 07457
**Dannucci Roofing Co. Inc.**
**Phone—(908) 996-6462**
**167 County Road 513, Frenchtown 08825**
Royal Seamless Corp.
Phone—(732) 901-9595
1000 Airport Rd., Ste. 202, Lakewood 08701

## GYPSUM & GYPSUM PRODUCTS

Georgia-Pacific Gypsum, LLC
Phone—(856) 966-7600
1101 S. Front St., Camden 08103
National Gypsum Co.
Phone—(609) 499-3300
1818 River Rd., Burlington 08016

## HAIR ACCESSORIES

AJ Tanner Ltd.
Phone—(973) 523-5204
93 Harrison St., 2nd Fl., Paterson 07501
Cellunet Mfg. Co., Inc.
Phone—(609) 386-3361
460 Veterans Dr., Burlington 08016

## HAIR CARE PRODUCTS

**Ambix Laboratories**
*Custom & Private Label Hair Care Products*
**Phone—(973) 890-9002**
**Fax—(973) 890-9778**
**Web—www.ambixlabs.com**
**Email—ambixlab@aol.com**
**55 W. End Rd., Totowa 07512**
*(see our ad under PROTEIN)*
American Comb Corp.
Phone—(973) 523-6551
22 Kentucky Ave., Paterson 07503
Bernard, Inc., Dennis
Phone—(800) 541-5456
142 Ely Harmony Rd., Freehold 07728
Carter Solution, Inc., The Jane
Phone—(973) 677-1008
45 S. 17th St., East Orange 07018
Colora Henna
Phone—(201) 939-0969
217 Washington Ave., Carlstadt 07072
**E. T. Browne Drug Company, Inc.**
Toll Free (877)PALMERS
**Phone—(201) 894-9020 / (877) 725-6377**
**Fax—(201) 894-5152**
**Web—www.palmers.com**
**440 Sylvan Ave., P.O. Box 1613, Englewood Cliffs 07632**
EC Hair Import, Inc.
Phone—(201) 933-8071
99 Murray Hill Pkwy., Ste. B, East Rutherford 07073
Fairy Tales Hair Care Corp.
Phone—(973) 473-8182
90-B Dayton Ave., Passaic 07055
Fantasia Industries Corp.
Phone—(201) 261-7070
20 Park Pl., Paramus 07652
Hair Systems, Inc.
Phone—(732) 446-2202
30 Park Ave., P.O. Box 449, Englishtown 07726
**Imperial DAX Co., Inc.**
**Phone—(973) 227-6105**
**Fax—(973) 808-8533**
**Web—www.daxhaircare.com**
**Email—lzawisha@imperialdax.com**
**120 New Dutch Ln., Fairfield 07004**
L'Oreal U S A, Inc.
Phone—(732) 499-2838
222 Terminal Ave., Clark 07066
Olla Beauty Supply, Inc.
Phone—(973) 575-5260
10 New Maple Ave., Unit 301-A, P.O. Box 898, Pine Brook 07058
Razac Products Co., Inc.
Phone—(973) 622-3700
25 Brenner St., Newark 07108
Scories, Inc.
Phone—(973) 923-1372
28 Vassar Ave., P.O. Box 4223, Newark 07112

## HAMMERMILLS

**Warwick Mfg. & Equipment Co., LLC**
Buy & sell used: Chemical, food, cosmetic, packaging & pharmaceutical equipment
**Phone—(732) 729-0400 / (732) 241-9263**
**Fax—(732) 729-1235**
**Web—www.warwickequipment.com**
**Email—sales@warwickequipment.com**
**1112 12th St., North Brunswick 08902**
*(see our ad Outside Back Cover)*

## HANDBAGS

Gio Vali Corp.
Phone—(973) 279-3032
463 Grand St., Paterson 07505
Jaclyn, Inc.
Phone—(201) 909-6000
197 W. Spring Valley Ave., Ste. 1, Maywood 07607
Latico Leather
Phone—(973) 442-9622
321 Palmer Rd., Ste. A, Denville 07834
Manolucci Designs
Phone—(201) 861-2259
220 61st St., Ste. 2-D, West New York 07093
Maple Leather Co.
Phone—(609) 397-1199
14 Raven Rock Rd., P.O. Box 319, Stockton 08559
Miller Corp., Carol S.
Phone—(201) 406-4578
98 Saddlewood Dr., Ste. A, Hillsdale 07642

## HANDICAPPED MOBILITY AIDS

**Drive-Master Co., Inc.**
Wheelchair Accessible, Rental
**Phone—(973) 808-9709**
**Fax—(973) 808-9713**
**Web—www.DriveMasterMobility.com**
**Email—info@DriveMasterMobility.com**
**37 Daniel Rd. West, Fairfield 07004**
*(see our ad under VEHICLES – Handicapped Accessible)*
Maddak Inc.
Phone—(973) 628-7600
661 State Route 23, Wayne 07470

## HANDLES — Leather

Leather Handle Mfg. Co.
Phone—(973) 485-2866
44 Dickerson St., Newark 07103

## HANDRAILS — Metal

Trylon Metal Works Inc.
Phone—(201) 939-8282
136 Park Ave., Lyndhurst 07071

## HANDRAILS — Wood

New Jersey Stair & Rail, Inc.
Phone—(732) 583-8400
746 Lloyd Rd., Matawan 07747

## HANGERS — Garment

American Hanger & Fixture Corp.
Phone—(908) 687-1776
687 Lehigh Ave., Union 07083
B & G International, Inc.
Phone—(973) 824-0334
1085 Morris Ave., Union 07083
Mainetti USA, Inc.
Phone—(201) 215-2900
300 Mac Ln., Keasbey 08832
MP Technologies, LLC (H Q)
Phone—(646) 366-1155
345 Claremont Ave., Ste. 26, Montclair 07042

## HARDWARE

### (also see following and specific product)

A+ Products, Inc.
Phone—(732) 866-9111
8 Timber Ln., Marlboro Industrial Pk., Marlboro 07746
Art Material Service Co., Inc.
Phone—(732) 545-8888
625 Joyce Kilmer Ave., New Brunswick 08901
AS America, Inc. (H Q)
Phone—(732) 980-3000
1 Centennial Ave., P.O. Box 6820, Piscataway 08855
Component Hardware Group, Inc.
Phone—(732) 363-4700
1890 Swarthmore Ave., P.O. Box 2020, Lakewood 08701

Hoboken Hearth Products, LLC
Phone—(551) 206-3350
46 Bi-State Plz., Westwood 07675
Omnia Industries, Inc.
Phone—(973) 239-7272
5 Cliffside Dr., P.O. Box 330, Cedar Grove 07009
S. Parker Hardware Mfg.
Phone—(201) 569-1600
1 Parker Dr., P.O. Box 9882, Englewood 07631
**Shallcross Bolt & Specialties Co.**
**The complete source for all your fastener needs**
**Phone—(908) 925-4700**
**Fax—(908) 925-8451**
**Web—www.shallcrossbolt.com**
**Email—info@shallcrossbolt.com**
**1 McCandless St., Linden 07036**
*(see our ad under BOLTS)*

## HARDWARE — Builders'

**Bildisco Door Mfg., Inc.**
Wooden & metal doors
**Phone—(973) 673-2400**
**Fax—(973) 673-2236**
**Web—www.bildisco.com**
**Email—bildiscomfg@comcast.net**
**21 Central Ave., West Orange 07052**
*(see our ad under DOORS)*

## HARDWARE — Decorative

AmerTac, Inc.
Phone—(201) 825-0388
1 Route 17 S., Saddle River Executive Center, Saddle River 07458
Moe Distributors, Inc.
Phone—(973) 539-8200
55 Abbett Ave., Morristown 07960

## HARDWARE — Door Opening

Schmidt Co., Inc., J. G.
Phone—(732) 563-9500
354 U.S. Highway 22, P.O. Box 880, Green Brook 08812

## HARDWARE — Specialty

C. R. Laurence Co., Inc.
Phone—(856) 727-1022
1511 Lancer Dr., Moorestown 08057

## HARDWARE — Wholesale

Accredited Lock Supply
Phone—(201) 865-5015
1161 Paterson Plank Rd., Secaucus 07094
Commercial Hardware, Inc.
Phone—(856) 810-0600
5 Perina Blvd., Cherry Hill 08003
Franzen International, Inc.
Phone—(201) 405-2228
23 Birch St., Ste. 1, Midland Park 07432
Melfast, Inc.
Phone—(973) 227-0045
18 Passaic Ave., Unit 4-5, Fairfield 07004
**Protex Latches & Band Clamps Ltd.**
Handles, Hinges, Clamps & Fasteners Made in England for over 90 years
**Phone—(314) 436-0080**
**Fax—(314) 436-0481**
**Web—www.protex.com**
**Email—terry.barber@protex.com**
**34 Benton Pl., St. Louis, MO 63104**

## HARDWOOD

Plywood & Door Mfrs. Corp. (H Q)
Phone—(908) 687-7890
1435 Morris Ave., 3rd Fl., P.O. Box 1212, Union 07083
Rex Lumber Co.
Phone—(732) 446-4200
1 Station St., P.O. Box 1776, Englishtown 07726

*Do nationwide searches for products & services at:*
**IndustryNet.com**

## HATS

Baik Kwang Corp.
Phone—(201) 507-9985
601 Commercial Ave., P.O. Box 7072, Carlstadt 07072
Colombino Headwear, Inc.
Phone—(973) 473-4733
61 Willet St., Passaic 07055
Kathy Jeanne, Inc.
Phone—(973) 575-9898
7 Industrial Rd., Fairfield 07004
Philadelphia Rapid Transit
Phone—(856) 488-0202
2650 Haddonfield Rd., Pennsauken 08110
Serratelli Hat Co., Inc.
Phone—(973) 623-4133
418-26 Central Ave., P.O. Box 7069, Newark 07107

## HATS — Men's

NES Enterprises, Inc.
Phone—(201) 964-1400
513 Washington Ave., Carlstadt 07072

## HAULING

**Bruce R. Koerner Cranes & Equipment, Inc.**
**Phone—(973) 989-7990**
**Fax—(973) 989-1991**
**Web—www.koernercranes.com**
**Email—sales@koernercranes.com**
**400 Franklin Ave., Rockaway 07866**
*(see our ad under CRANE RENTAL)*

## HEADPHONES & HEADSETS

Plastasonics, Inc.
Phone—(732) 938-7694
5031 Industrial Rd., Farmingdale 07727

## HEALTH CARE CONSULTANTS

**AdvantEdge Healthcare Solutions**
Billing services for specialty physicians & ASCs
**Phone—(908) 279-8120 / (877) 501-1611**
**Fax—(908) 791-3330**
**Web—www.ahsrcm.com**
**Email—info@ahsrcm.com**
**30 Technology Dr., Ste. 1N, Warren 07059**

## HEALTH CARE PRODUCTS

Caldwell Consumer Health, LLC (H Q)
Phone—(973) 360-1090
8 Elmer St., Ste. 1, Madison 07940
ConvaTec, Inc.
Phone—(732) 412-5500
CenterPoint II, Ste. 205, 1140 Route 22 E., Bridgewater 08807
Gel Concepts, LLC
Phone—(973) 884-8995
30 Leslie Ct., Whippany 07981
**Gerresheimer Glass, Inc.**
Manufacturer of high-quality specialty products made of glass & plastic for the global pharma & healthcare industry
**Phone—(856) 692-3600**
**Web—www.gerresheimer.com**
**Email—info-tubing-us@gerresheimer.com**
**537 Crystal Ave., Vineland 08360**
Imperial Drug & Spice Corp.
Phone—(201) 348-1551
5620 Kennedy Blvd. W., West New York 07093
**Jamol Laboratories, Inc.**
Manufacturer of OTC botanical nose drops for the treatment of allergies, congestion, nose bleeds and any type of sinus issues
**Phone—(201) 262-6363**
**Fax—(201) 262-2437**
**Web—www.ponaris.net**
**Email—jamollab@aol.com**
**13 Ackerman Ave., P.O. Box 313, Emerson 07630**
Nutrition North America
Phone—(973) 734-0023
10 Saddle Rd., Cedar Knolls 07927
Purest Colloids, Inc.
Phone—(609) 267-2112
600 Highland Dr., Ste. 602, Mount Holly 08060

## HEARING AIDS

**Bernafon, LLC**
2501 Cottontail Ln., Somerset 08873
**Phone—(732) 560-9996 / (888) 941-4203**
**Fax—(732) 560-4877**
**Web—www.bernafon-us.com**
**Email—info@bernafon-us.com**
**P.O. Box 6706, Somerset 08875**
Oticon, Inc.
Phone—(732) 560-1220
580 Howard Ave., Somerset 08873
**Penta Hearing Care**
**Phone—(973) 595-8811**
**Fax—(973) 595-8818**
**Web—www.pentahearingcarewayne.com**
**Email—kruf@aah.net**
**645 Hamburg Tpke., Wayne 07470**
Siemens Hearing Instruments, Inc.
Phone—(732) 562-6600
10 Constitution Ave., P.O. Box 1397, Piscataway 08855

## HEAT EXCHANGERS

Atlas Industrial Mfg. Co.
Phone—(973) 779-3970
81 Somerset Pl., Clifton 07012
D C Fabricators, Inc.
Phone—(609) 499-3000
801 W. Front St., Florence 08518
Edwards Coils Corp.
Phone—(973) 835-2815
101 Alexander Ave., Unit 6, Pompton Plains 07444
Fluorotherm Polymers, Inc.
Phone—(973) 575-0760
333 New Rd., Ste. 1, Parsippany 07054
Group Thermo, Inc. (H Q)
Phone—(908) 757-8955
137 S. Pemberton Ave., Oceanport 07757
Perry Products Corp.
Phone—(609) 267-1600
25 Hainesport-Mount Laurel Rd., Hainesport 08036
R A S Process Equipment
Phone—(609) 371-1000
324 Meadowbrook Rd., Robbinsville 08691
Voorheis Industries, Inc.
Phone—(973) 227-2446
369 Thornden St., South Orange 07079

## HEAT EXCHANGERS — Plate

Plate Concepts, Inc.
Phone—(908) 236-9570
1221 U.S. Highway 22, Ste. 3, Lebanon 08833
Polaris Plate Heat Exchangers
Phone—(732) 345-7188
106 Apple St., Ste. 106, Tinton Falls 07724

## HEAT SEALERS

**Dalton Electric Heating Co., Inc.**
The Leader in Cartridge Heater Technology
**Phone—(978) 356-9844**
**Fax—(978) 356-9846**
**Web—www.daltonelectric.com**
**Email—dalton@daltonelectric.com**
**28 Hayward St., Ipswich, MA 01938**

## HEAT SEALING — Plastic

**Dalton Electric Heating Co., Inc.**
The Leader in Cartridge Heater Technology
**Phone—(978) 356-9844**
**Fax—(978) 356-9846**
**Web—www.daltonelectric.com**
**Email—dalton@daltonelectric.com**
**28 Hayward St., Ipswich, MA 01938**

## *Is your company properly represented in the IndustrySection?*

If not, call... 847-864-7590

## HEAT SEALING — Vinyl

**Dalton Electric Heating Co., Inc.**
The Leader in Cartridge Heater Technology
**Phone—(978) 356-9844**
**Fax—(978) 356-9846**
**Web—www.daltonelectric.com**
**Email—dalton@daltonelectric.com**
**28 Hayward St., Ipswich, MA 01938**
E T Mfg., Inc.
Phone—(973) 777-6662
90 Dayton Ave., Bldg. 10-C, Ste. 89, Passaic 07055

## HEAT SINKS

AOS Thermal Compounds, LLC
Phone—(732) 389-5514
22 Meridian Rd., Ste. 6, Eatontown 07724

## HEAT TRACING

HTD Heat Trace, Inc.
Phone—(908) 788-5210
8 Bartles Corner Rd., Unit 104, Flemington 08822

## HEAT TRANSFER EQUIPMENT

Hamon Corp.
Phone—(908) 685-4000
58 E. Main St., P.O. Box 1500, Somerville 08876
Lummus Technology
Phone—(973) 893-3000
1515 Broad St., Bloomfield 07003
QLT.com
Phone—(732) 431-0740
238 Boundary Rd., Unit 304, Marlboro 07746

## HEAT TRANSFER FLUIDS

**Houghton Chemical Corp.**
**Phone—(800) 777-2466**
**Fax—(617) 254-2713**
**Web—www.houghton.com**
**Email—bhoughton@houghton.com**
**30 Amor Ave., Carlstadt 07072**

## HEAT TRANSFERS

**Crown Roll Leaf, Inc.**
**Phone—(973) 742-4000 / (800) 631-3831**
**Fax—(973) 742-0219**
**Web—www.crownrollleaf.com**
**Email—info@crownrollleaf.com**
**91 Illinois Ave., Paterson 07503**
*(See our ad under FOIL—Hot Stamping)*
F & M Expressions Unlimited
Phone—(201) 512-3338
211 Island Rd., Mahwah 07430

## HEAT TREATING

**Bennett Heat Treating & Brazing Co., Inc.**
Complete metallurgical consulting & heat treating service
**Phone—(215) 674-8120**
**Fax—(215) 674-1312**
**Web—www.bennetheat.co**
**Email—pciulla@bennetheat.com**
**82 Richard Rd., Ivyland, PA 18974**
**Bennett Heat Treating & Brazing Co., Inc.**
Complete metallurgical consulting & heat treating service
**Phone—(973) 589-0590**
**Fax—(973) 589-6518**
**Web—www.bennetheat.com**
**Email—pciulla@bennetheat.com**
**690 Ferry St., Newark 07105**

**Bennett Heat Treating & Brazing Co., Inc.**
*Complete Metalluragical Consulting & Heat Treating Service*
Any Questions Go To: www.bennetheat.com
973-589-0590 • Fax: 973-589-6518
690 Ferry St. Newark, NJ 07105

© Copyright 2015 Manufacturers' News, Inc.

# Metlab

Heat Treating & Black Oxide Specialists

## 800-319-7359

## 215-233-2600 • FAX: 215-233-5653

### www.metlabheattreat.com

## 1000 E. Mermaid Ln. Glenside, PA 19038

## HEAT TREATING — (cont.)

**Bolttech Mannings, Inc.**
Phone—(973) 537-1576
321 Richard Mine Rd., Ste. 300, Wharton 07885
**Braddock Heat Treating Co., Inc.**
Phone—(732) 356-2906
123 Chimney Rock Rd., Bridgewater 08807
**Metlab**
Heat Treating & Black Oxide Specialists
Phone—(215) 233-2600 / (800) 319-7359
Fax—(215) 233-5653
Web—www.metlabheattreat.com
Email—mpodob@metlabheattreat.com
1000 E. Mermaid Ln., Glenside, PA 19038
*(see our ad on this page)*

## HEAT TREATING — Metal

**Bennett Heat Treating & Brazing Co., Inc.**
Complete metallurgical consulting & heat treating service
Phone—(215) 674-8120
Fax—(215) 674-1312
Web—www.bennettheat.co
Email—pciulla@bennettheat.com
82 Richard Rd., Ivyland, PA 18974
**Bennett Heat Treating & Brazing Co., Inc.**
Complete metallurgical consulting & heat treating service
Phone—(973) 589-0590
Fax—(973) 589-6518
Web—www.bennettheat.com
Email—pciulla@bennettheat.com
690 Ferry St., Newark 07105

## Bennett Heat Treating & Brazing Co., Inc.

*Complete Metallurgical Consulting*
*& Heat Treating Service*
Any Questions Go To: www.bennettheat.com
**973-589-0590 • Fax: 973-589-6518**
690 Ferry St. Newark, NJ 07105

**Blue Blade Steel**
Phone—(908) 272-2620
123 N. 8th St., P.O. Box 40, Kenilworth 07033
**Bodycote**
Phone—(908) 245-0717
304 Cox St., Roselle 07203
**Delphi Engineering & Contracting, Inc.**
Phone—(856) 228-5700
131 Blackwood Barnsboro Rd., Sewell 08080
**Team Industrial Services**
Phone—(610) 859-7800
4 Killdeer Ct., Ste. 300, Swedesboro 08085
**Temperature Processing Co., Inc.**
Phone—(201) 991-8000
228 River Rd., North Arlington 07031

## HEATERS — Emergency

**Dalton Electric Heating Co., Inc.**
The Leader in Cartridge Heater Technology
Phone—(978) 356-9844
Fax—(978) 356-9846
Web—www.daltonelectric.com
Email—dalton@daltonelectric.com
28 Hayward St., Ipswich, MA 01938

## HEATERS — Enclosure

**Dalton Electric Heating Co., Inc.**
The Leader in Cartridge Heater Technology
Phone—(978) 356-9844
Fax—(978) 356-9846
Web—www.daltonelectric.com
Email—dalton@daltonelectric.com
28 Hayward St., Ipswich, MA 01938

## HEATERS — Immersion

**Dalton Electric Heating Co., Inc.**
The Leader in Cartridge Heater Technology
Phone—(978) 356-9844
Fax—(978) 356-9846
Web—www.daltonelectric.com
Email—dalton@daltonelectric.com
28 Hayward St., Ipswich, MA 01938

## HEATERS — Infrared

**Glenro, Inc.**
Phone—(973) 279-5900
39 McBride Avenue Ext., Paterson 07501
**Kinetics Infrared**
Phone—(973) 575-5332
40 Pier Ln. W., Fairfield 07004
**Radiation Systems, Inc.**
Phone—(201) 891-7515
455 W. Main St., Wyckoff 07481

## HEATERS — Water

**Diversified Heat Transfer, Inc.**
Phone—(718) 386-6666
439 Main Rd., Route 202, Towaco 07082
**Nutley Heating & Cooling Supply, Inc.**
Phone—(973) 667-6880
Fax—(973) 667-4602
Web—www.nutleysupply.com
Email—ralpholiver@nutleysupply.com
156 Chestnut St., Nutley 07110
*(see our ad under BOILERS)*
**Wallace Eannace Associates, Inc.**
Phone—(201) 891-9550 / (800) 932-4891
Fax—(201) 891-4298
Web—www.wea-inc.com
779 Susquehanna Ave., Franklin Lakes 07417

## HEATING & AIR CONDITIONING

**Kilpatrick, Inc., B. J.**
Specializing in commercial HVAC service; We offer preventive maintenance contracts
Phone—(856) 768-4747
Fax—(856) 768-5782
Web—www.bjkilpatrick.com
Email—info@bjkilpatrick.com
136 S. White Horse Pike, Berlin 08009
**Trane, Inc.** (H Q)
Phone—(732) 652-7100
1 Centennial Ave., P.O. Box 6820, Piscataway 08855

*find additional suppliers at*
**IndustryNet.com**

## HEATING ELEMENTS — Cartridge

**Dalton Electric Heating Co., Inc.**
The Leader in Cartridge Heater Technology
Phone—(978) 356-9844
Fax—(978) 356-9846
Web—www.daltonelectric.com
Email—dalton@daltonelectric.com
28 Hayward St., Ipswich, MA 01938

## HEATING ELEMENTS — Electric

**Dalton Electric Heating Co., Inc.**
The Leader in Cartridge Heater Technology
Phone—(978) 356-9844
Fax—(978) 356-9846
Web—www.daltonelectric.com
Email—dalton@daltonelectric.com
28 Hayward St., Ipswich, MA 01938
**Ulanet Co., George**
Phone—(973) 589-4876
413-415 Market St., Newark 07105
**Waage Electric, Inc.**
Melting Pots & Duct Heaters & Immersion Heaters
Phone—(908) 245-9363 / (800) 922-4365
Fax—(908) 245-8477
Web—www.waage.com
Email—info@waage.com
720 Colfax Ave., P.O. Box 337, Kenilworth 07033
*(see our ad under FURNACES–Industrial)*

## HEATING ELEMENTS — Industrial

**Dalton Electric Heating Co., Inc.**
The Leader in Cartridge Heater Technology
Phone—(978) 356-9844
Fax—(978) 356-9846
Web—www.daltonelectric.com
Email—dalton@daltonelectric.com
28 Hayward St., Ipswich, MA 01938

## HEATING EQUIPMENT

**Advanced Hydronics Sales, Inc.**
Phone—(201) 573-0606
Fax—(201) 573-0499
Web—www.ahreps.com
Email—sales@ahreps.com
500 N. Franklin Tpke., Ste. 102, Ramsey 07446
**Alabaster Supply, Inc.**
Phone—(732) 330-9242
2317 South St., Toms River 08753
**Corbett Industries, Inc.**
Phone—(201) 445-6311
39 Hewson Ave., Ste. B, P.O. Box 212, Waldwick 07463
**Dalton Electric Heating Co., Inc.**
The Leader in Cartridge Heater Technology
Phone—(978) 356-9844
Fax—(978) 356-9846
Web—www.daltonelectric.com
Email—dalton@daltonelectric.com
28 Hayward St., Ipswich, MA 01938
**Encur, Inc.**
Phone—(732) 264-2098
200 Division St., P.O. Box 92, Keyport 07735
**Nutley Heating & Cooling Supply, Inc.**
Phone—(973) 667-6880
Fax—(973) 667-4602
Web—www.nutleysupply.com
Email—ralpholiver@nutleysupply.com
156 Chestnut St., Nutley 07110
*(see our ad under BOILERS)*
**Triangle Tube Phase III, Inc.**
Phone—(856) 228-8881
1 Triangle Ln., Blackwood 08012
**Wallace Eannace Associates, Inc.**
Phone—(201) 891-9550 / (800) 932-4891
Fax—(201) 891-4298
Web—www.wea-inc.com
779 Susquehanna Ave., Franklin Lakes 07417

*Search from among 430,000*
*U.S. manufacturers & suppliers:*
**IndustryNet.com**

© Copyright 2015 Manufacturers' News, Inc.

## HEATING EQUIPMENT — Electric

**Dalton Electric Heating Co., Inc.**
The Leader in Cartridge Heater Technology
Phone—(978) 356-9844
Fax—(978) 356-9846
Web—www.daltonelectric.com
Email—dalton@daltonelectric.com
28 Hayward St., Ipswich, MA 01938

**Waage Electric, Inc.**
Melting Pots & Duct Heaters & Immersion Heaters
Phone—(908) 245-9363 / (800) 922-4365
Fax—(908) 245-8477
Web—www.waage.com
Email—info@waage.com
720 Colfax Ave., P.O. Box 337, Kenilworth 07033

*(see our ad under FURNACES—Industrial)*

## HEATING EQUIPMENT — Industrial

**Advanced Hydronics Sales, Inc.**
Phone—(201) 573-0606
Fax—(201) 573-0499
Web—www.ahreps.com
Email—sales@ahreps.com
500 N. Franklin Tpke., Ste. 102, Ramsey 07446

**Dalton Electric Heating Co., Inc.**
The Leader in Cartridge Heater Technology
Phone—(978) 356-9844
Fax—(978) 356-9846
Web—www.daltonelectric.com
Email—dalton@daltonelectric.com
28 Hayward St., Ipswich, MA 01938

Hotfoil-EHS, Inc.
Phone—(609) 588-0900
2960 E. State Street Ext., Hamilton 08619

Industrial Combustion Associates Inc.
Phone—(732) 271-0300
20 Worlds Fair Dr., Ste. C, Somerset 08873

Solar Products, Inc.
Phone—(973) 835-6581
228 Wanaque Ave., Pompton Lakes 07442

## HEATING EQUIPMENT — Industrial Process

**Dalton Electric Heating Co., Inc.**
The Leader in Cartridge Heater Technology
Phone—(978) 356-9844
Fax—(978) 356-9846
Web—www.daltonelectric.com
Email—dalton@daltonelectric.com
28 Hayward St., Ipswich, MA 01938

ECCO High Frequency
Phone—(973) 248-3366
2360 Hamburg Tpke., Wayne 07470

## HEATING SYSTEMS

Monitor Products, Inc.
Phone—(609) 584-0505
7-A Marlen Dr., Robbinsville 08691

Therma-Tech Corp.
Phone—(973) 345-0076
300 Dakota St., Paterson 07503

## HEATING, VENTILATION & AIR CONDITIONING

**Kilpatrick, Inc., B. J.**
Specializing in commercial HVAC service; We offer preventive maintenance contracts
Phone—(856) 768-4747
Fax—(856) 768-5782
Web—www.bjkilpatrick.com
Email—info@bjkilpatrick.com
136 S. White Horse Pike, Berlin 08009

Marlyn Sheet Metal, Inc.
Phone—(856) 863-6900
606 N. Delsea Dr., Clayton 08312

## HELMETS

International Riding Helmets, Inc.
Phone—(732) 290-3000
21 Industrial Dr., Old Bridge Township, Keyport 07735

## HERBAL PRODUCTS

Hamilltime Enterprises, Inc.
Phone—(732) 303-5998
1761 U.S. Highway 9, Howell 07731

## HERBS

Herbalist & Alchemist, Inc.
Phone—(908) 689-9020
51 S. Wandling Ave., Washington 07882

## HERBS — Medicinal

Navinta, LLC
Phone—(609) 883-1135
1499 Lower Ferry Rd., Trenton 08618

## HOBBY KITS & PRODUCTS

Beta Craft, Inc.
Phone—(609) 655-1940
2682 Route 130, P.O. Box 536, Cranbury 08512

EnvironMolds, LLC
Phone—(908) 273-5401
18 Bank St., Ste. 1, Summit 07901

Shadow Racing & Hobby Products, Inc.
Phone—(973) 684-7270
70 1st Ave., Paterson 07514

## HOISTS

Breeze-Eastern Corp.
Phone—(973) 602-1001
35 Melanie Ln., Whippany 07981

Permadur Industries, Inc.
Phone—(908) 359-9767
186 U.S. Highway 206 S., Hillsborough 08844

SISSCO Material Handling
Phone—(908) 359-9767
186 Route 206 S., Hillsborough 08844

## HOLDING COMPANIES

Alpine Group, Inc., The (H Q)
Phone—(201) 549-4400
1 Meadowlands Plz., Ste. 801, East Rutherford 07073

D&M Holdings US, Inc. (H Q)
Phone—(201) 762-6500
100 Corporate Dr., Mahwah 07430

Friend Skoler & Co., Inc. (H Q)
Phone—(201) 712-0075
160 Pehle Ave., Ste. 303, Saddle Brook 07663

Ikaria, Inc. (H Q)
Phone—(908) 238-6600
53 Frontage Rd., P.O. Box 9001, Hampton 08827

Stamm International Corp. (H Q)
Phone—(201) 947-1700
1530 Palisade Ave., P.O. Box 1929, Fort Lee 07024

## HOLOGRAMS

JDSU
Phone—(609) 632-0800
2 Applegate Dr., Robbinsville 08691

## HOLOGRAPHIC OPTICAL ELEMENTS

**ITW Covid Security Group**
Web: www.itwsbi.com
Phone—(609) 395-5600
Fax—(609) 860-6401
Email—info@itw.com
32 Commerce Dr., Ste. 1, Cranbury 08512

## HOME ACCESSORIES

Nourison Industries (H Q)
Phone—(201) 368-6900
5 Sampson St., Saddle Brook 07663

Pegasus Home Fashions, Inc.
Phone—(908) 965-1919
107 Trumbull St., Bldg. G-1, P.O. Box 9030, Elizabeth 07206

## HOME DECOR PRODUCTS

Creative Displays & Designs, Inc.
Phone—(732) 918-8010
349 Essex Rd., Neptune 07753

International Mercantile Agencies, Inc.
Phone—(732) 246-3900
18 Home News Row, New Brunswick 08901

Milltex Mfg. Co.
Phone—(732) 840-3021
1101 Industrial Pkwy., Brick 08724

## HOME IMPROVEMENT PRODUCTS

**Atlantic Window & Door, Inc.**
Fax: (732) 556-6496
Phone—(732) 793-2452
Web—www.exteriorsbyatlantic.com
Email—atlanticwindoor@aol.com
1608 Dubac Rd., Wall Township 07719

HBC Home & Hardware
Phone—(609) 860-9990
324-A Half Acre Rd., Cranbury 08512

## HOME THEATER SYSTEMS

Onkyo USA Corp. (H Q)
Phone—(201) 785-2600
18 Park Way, Upper Saddle River 07458

## HOMOGENIZERS

**Warwick Mfg. & Equipment Co., LLC**
Buy & sell used: Chemical, food, cosmetic, packaging & pharmaceutical equipment
Phone—(732) 729-0400 / (732) 241-9263
Fax—(732) 729-1235
Web—www.warwickequipment.com
Email—sales@warwickequipment.com
1112 12th St., North Brunswick 08902

*(see our ad Outside Back Cover)*

## HONEY

E&M Gold Beekeepers, LLC
Phone—(732) 542-6528
113 Hope Rd., Tinton Falls 07724

Hilltop Honey, LLC
Phone—(201) 953-0198
15 Hill St., North Caldwell 07006

## HOPPERS

**Arrow Steel, Inc.**
Email: mario@arrowcompactor.com
Hopper Door Repair. Manufacturing Industrial Refuse Compactors for High Rise Apartment Complexes since 1977. Made in USA
Phone—(973) 523-1122
Fax—(973) 977-9490
Web—www.arrowcompactor.com
629 E. 19th St., Paterson 07514

## HORSE EQUIPMENT

CDK Industry, LLC
Phone—(856) 488-5456
900 Haddonfield Rd., Cherry Hill 08002

Clothes Horse, Inc.
Phone—(856) 829-8460
2200 Wallace Blvd., Ste. A, Cinnaminson 08077

Curvon Corp.
Phone—(732) 747-3832
34 Apple St., Tinton Falls 07724

Union Hill Corp. (H Q)
Phone—(732) 786-9422
34 Water St., Englishtown 07726

Vac's Bandage Co.
Phone—(973) 345-3355
163 Pennsylvania Ave., Paterson 07503

## HORTICULTURAL SPECIALTIES

Brick Wholesale Flower Market
Phone—(732) 477-6765
570 Mantoloking Rd., Brick 08723

## HOSE — Flexible Metal

B & A Flex, Inc.
  Phone—(908) 722-2808
  34 Charlotte Dr., Bridgewater 08807
Components & Controls, Inc.
  Phone—(201) 438-9190
  495 Washington Ave., P.O. Box 437, Carlstadt 07072
**Hose Shop, Inc., The**
  **Phone—(732) 562-1000**
  **Fax—(732) 562-9222**
  **Web—www.hoseshopinc.com**
  **100 New England Ave., Ste. 2, Piscataway 08854**

## HOSE — Flexible Plastic

Saint-Gobain Performance Plastics
  Phone—(908) 218-8888
  460 Milltown Rd., Bridgewater 08807

## HOSE — Garden & Lawn

Flexon Industries Corp.
  Phone—(973) 824-5530
  1 Flexon Plz., Newark 07114

## HOSE — Industrial

Combined Supply Co., LLC
  Phone—(908) 353-8888
  640 S. Broad St., P.O. Box 9192, Elizabeth 07202
**Jason Industrial Inc.**
  **Phone—(973) 227-4904**
  **Fax—(973) 227-1651**
  **Web—www.jasonindustrial.com**
  **Email—inquiries@jasonindustrial.com**
  **340 Kaplan Dr., P.O. Box 10004, Fairfield 07004**
Novaflex Industries, Inc.
  Phone—(856) 768-2275
  1024 Industrial Dr., West Berlin 08091

## HOSE — Plastic

Harrison Hose & Tubing, Inc.
  Phone—(609) 631-8804
  2705 Kuser Rd., Trenton 08691

## HOSE — Rubber

**Briggs Co., The**
  **Phone—(302) 328-9471 / (800) 435-7293**
  **Fax—(302) 322-7707**
  **Web—www.briggsco.net**
  **Email—briggssales@briggsco.net**
  **3 Bellecor Dr., New Castle, DE 19720**
Goodyear Rubber Products Corp.
  Phone—(732) 448-1111
  1583 Livingston Ave., Ste. 4, North Brunswick 08902
Hart Industries, Inc.
  Phone—(856) 686-1455
  135 Crown Rd., Thorofare 08086
**Hose Shop, Inc., The**
  **Phone—(732) 562-1000**
  **Fax—(732) 562-9222**
  **Web—www.hoseshopinc.com**
  **100 New England Ave., Ste. 2, Piscataway 08854**
**Industrial Rubber Co.**
  Rubber hose, hydraulic fittings, sheets & gaskets
  **Phone—(908) 351-1550**
  **Fax—(908) 351-8350**
  **Web—www.indrubber.com**
  **Email—sales@indrubber.com**
  **P.O. Box 359, Elizabeth 07207**
Rubber Fabrication & Molding, Inc.
  Phone—(908) 852-7725
  1100 Route 519, P.O. Box 412, Johnsonburg 07846

*Do nationwide searches for products & services at:*
IndustryNet.com

## HOSE — Teflon®

**(Teflon® is a registered trademark of DuPont)**
**Briggs Co., The**
  **Phone—(302) 328-9471 / (800) 435-7293**
  **Fax—(302) 322-7707**
  **Web—www.briggsco.net**
  **Email—briggssales@briggsco.net**
  **3 Bellecor Dr., New Castle, DE 19720**

## HOSE ASSEMBLIES

Atlantic Rubber Enterprises
  Phone—(973) 697-5900
  35 Union Valley Rd., Newfoundland 07435
**Briggs Co., The**
  **Phone—(302) 328-9471 / (800) 435-7293**
  **Fax—(302) 322-7707**
  **Web—www.briggsco.net**
  **Email—briggssales@briggsco.net**
  **3 Bellecor Dr., New Castle, DE 19720**
**Certified Products Co.**
  Email: joe.f@cerprod.com
  Also hydraulic repairs & hoses
  **Phone—(201) 433-0013 / (800) 654-2436**
  **Fax—(201) 433-1482**
  **Web—www.cerprodnjhydraulics.com**
  **269 Kearney Ave., Jersey City 07305**
Couse & Bolten Co.
  Phone—(973) 344-6330
  90 South St., Dock 5, Newark 07114
Exitflex USA, Inc.
  Phone—(732) 512-9141
  254 Raritan Center Pkwy., Edison 08837
U. S. Brass & Copper, Corp.
  Phone—(908) 486-3322
  641 E. Elizabeth Ave., P.O. Box 1052, Linden 07036

## HOSIERY

Mayer/Berkshire Corp. (H Q)
  Phone—(973) 696-6200
  25 Edison Rd., P.O. Box 244, Wayne 07474
Sox Trot, Inc.
  Phone—(201) 944-5250
  373 Grand Ave., Palisades Park 07650
Standard Merchandising Co. (H Q)
  Phone—(856) 964-9700
  1125 Wright Ave., Camden 08103

## HOSPITAL EQUIPMENT

Biological Controls, Inc.
  Phone—(732) 389-8922
  749 Hope Rd., Ste. A, Tinton Falls 07724
**DRG International, Inc.**
  **Phone—(973) 564-7555**
  **Fax—(973) 564-7556**
  **Web—www.drg-international.com**
  **Email—corp@drg-international.com**
  **841 Mountain Ave., Springfield 07081**

## HOT STAMPING

API Foils, Inc.
  Phone—(732) 382-6800
  329 New Brunswick Ave., Rahway 07065

## HOT STAMPING EQUIPMENT

**Schaefer, Inc., Ernest**
  Bookbinders board
  **Phone—(908) 964-1280**
  **Fax—(908) 964-6787**
  **Web—www.ernestschaeferinc.com**
  **Email—eschaeferinc@aol.com**
  **731 Lehigh Ave., Union 07083**
Vansco, Inc.
  Phone—(973) 835-8423
  138-B Cannonball Rd., Pompton Lakes 07442

## HOTEL SUPPLIES

A D S Sale Co., Inc.
  Phone—(732) 591-0500
  1010 Campus Dr., Morganville 07751

## HOUSEWARES

E-Z Do, Inc.
  Phone—(732) 287-8111
  40 Executive Ave., Edison 08817

## HOUSEWARES — Plastic

Better Home Plastics Corp.
  Phone—(201) 592-0370
  439 Commercial Ave., Palisades Park 07650
Organize It All, Inc.
  Phone—(201) 488-0808
  24 River St., Ste. 201, Bogota 07603

## HOUSINGS — Industrial

Amherst Scientific, LLC
  Phone—(973) 770-7772
  112 Kings Hwy., Landing 07850
CRP Industries, Inc.
  Phone—(609) 578-4100
  35 Commerce Dr., Cranbury 08512

## HVAC CONTROLS

C & F Burner Co.
  Phone—(201) 998-8083
  39 River Rd., P.O. Box 7189, North Arlington 07031
EWC Controls, Inc.
  Phone—(732) 446-3110
  385 State Route 33, Manalapan 07726
Micro-Air, Inc.
  Phone—(609) 259-2636
  124 Route 526, Allentown 08501
**Supreme Energy, Inc.**
  **Phone—(973) 678-1800**
  **Fax—(973) 672-0148**
  **Web—www.supremeenergyinc.com**
  **Email—info@supremeenergyinc.com**
  **532 Freeman St., Orange 07050**

## HVAC EQUIPMENT

Dunphey-Smith Co.
  Phone—(908) 687-6292
  30 Progress St., Union 07083
**Enterprise HVAC Supply**
  **Phone—(973) 759-6900**
  **Fax—(973) 759-6400**
  **Web—www.enterprisehvacsupply.org**
  **701 Main St., Belleville 07109**
Ferguson Enterprises, Inc.
  Phone—(732) 530-7200
  207 Cooper Rd., Red Bank 07701
Ferguson Enterprises, Inc.
  Phone—(609) 466-5445
  404 Route 31 N., Ringoes 08551
Grove Supply, Inc.
  Phone—(856) 303-2310
  1818 Rowland St., Cinnaminson 08077
Grove Supply, Inc.
  Phone—(609) 522-1449
  3801 Park Blvd., Wildwood 08260
Harvey Industries, Inc., Sid
  Phone—(908) 245-8688
  159 E. 1st Ave., Roselle 07203
Harvey Industries, Inc., Sid
  Phone—(609) 882-1766
  1684 5th St., Trenton 08638
Honeywell HBS
  Phone—(856) 437-1832
  534 Fellowship Rd., Mount Laurel 08054
**Hudson Heating Wholesaler, Inc.**
  **Phone—(201) 348-6700**
  **Fax—(201) 348-8906**
  **Web—www.hudsonheatingwholesaler.com**
  **1109 Grand Ave., Ste. 1, North Bergen 07047**
Lyon, Conklin & Co., Inc.
  Phone—(856) 488-0191
  1165 Thomas Busch Memorial Hwy., Pennsauken 08110
Nutley Heating & Cooling Supply Co.
  Phone—(732) 919-1933
  5016 Industrial Rd., Wall Township 07727
Nutley Heating & Cooling Supply Co., Inc.
  Phone—(973) 470-8844
  50 Page Rd., Clifton 07012

© Copyright 2015 Manufacturers' News, Inc.

## HVAC EQUIPMENT — (cont.)

**Nutley Heating & Cooling Supply, Inc.**
**Phone—(973) 667-6880**
**Fax—(973) 667-4602**
**Web—www.nutleysupply.com**
**Email—ralpholiver@nutleysupply.com**
**156 Chestnut St., Nutley 07110**
*(see our ad under BOILERS)*

Penn Supply, Inc.
Phone—(609) 394-1151
618 E. State St., Trenton 08609

R. E. Michel Co., Inc.
Phone—(732) 886-3592
895 Towbin Ave., Lakewood 08701

R. E. Michel Co., Inc.
Phone—(732) 465-9700
262 Old New Brunswick Rd., Piscataway 08854

SISCO Mfg. Co., Inc.
Phone—(856) 486-7550
7930 National Hwy., Pennsauken 08110

**Supreme Energy, Inc.**
**Phone—(973) 678-1800**
**Fax—(973) 672-0148**
**Web—www.supremeenergyinc.com**
**Email—info@supremeenergyinc.com**
**532 Freeman St., Orange 07050**

United Supply Co., Inc.
Phone—(732) 329-6301
7 Chris Ct., Ste. A, Dayton 08810

United Supply Co., Inc.
Phone—(908) 757-3232
457 W. End Ave., Plainfield 07060

Z & Z Holding Co Inc
Phone—(908) 298-1212
370 Market St., P.O. Box 239, Kenilworth 07033

## HYBRID CIRCUITS — Thick Film

Hybrid-Tek, Inc.
Phone—(609) 259-3355
9 Trenton Lakewood Rd., Ste. 1, Clarksburg 08510

## HYDRAULIC EQUIPMENT

Clifton Fluid Power Machinery
Phone—(973) 778-3923
295 Allwood Rd., Clifton 07012

## HYDRAULIC EQUIPMENT — Rebuilt

American Custom Hydraulics, Inc.
Phone—(973) 751-1440
33 Roosevelt Ave., Belleville 07109

## HYDRAULIC FITTINGS

Frederiks Machine & Tool, Inc.
Phone—(609) 397-4991
99 Kingwood Stockton Rd., P.O. Box 247, Rosemont 08556

**Industrial Rubber Co.**
**Rubber hose, hydraulic fittings, sheets & gaskets**
**Phone—(908) 351-1550**
**Fax—(908) 351-8350**
**Web—www.indrubber.com**
**Email—sales@indrubber.com**
**P.O. Box 359, Elizabeth 07207**

## HYDRAULIC HOSE ASSEMBLIES

Cumberland Valve, Inc.
Phone—(856) 451-1324
746 Shiloh Pike, Bridgeton 08302

## HYDRAULIC SYSTEMS

Complete Hydraulic Works, Inc.
Phone—(201) 444-7877
140 Greenwood Ave., Midland Park 07432

## HYDRAULICS

Corrective Hydraulics
Phone—(973) 334-3792
731 Birch St., P.O. Box 850, Boonton 07005

## HYDROCHLORIC ACID

Reagent Chemical & Research, Inc.
Phone—(908) 284-2800
115 U.S. Highway 202, Ringoes 08551

**Universal Chemicals Inc.**
**Phone—(973) 589-1525**
**Fax—(973) 589-8013**
**Web—www.universalchem.com**
**Email—info@universalchem.com**
**100 N. Hackensack Ave., Kearny 07032**

## HYDROFORMING

Laeger Metal Spinning Co., Inc.
Phone—(908) 925-5530
1514 E. Elizabeth Ave., Linden 07036

## HYDRONICS

Ammark Corp.
Phone—(973) 616-2555
230 W. Parkway, Ste. 12, Pompton Plains 07444

## ICE

Air Liquide America L.P.
Phone—(856) 423-5220
A-Line Rd., P.O. Box 155, Gibbstown 08027

Angelo's Ice Co., Inc.
Phone—(908) 754-4091
100 Sylvania Pl., South Plainfield 07080

Arctic Glacier, Inc.
Phone—(908) 231-0100
2 Johnson Dr., Raritan 08869

Artic Ice Mfg. & Dry Ice Co.
Phone—(201) 370-3141
158 Semel Ave., Garfield 07026

Ice King & Cold Storage, Inc.
Phone—(732) 922-0852
4045 Route 33 W., Tinton Falls 07753

Sea Isle Ice Co., Inc.
Phone—(609) 263-8794
230 42nd St., Sea Isle City 08243

South Jersey Ice & Cold Storage LLC
Phone—(856) 692-3990
544 E. Pear St., Vineland 08360

## ICE ARENA PRODUCTS

CALMAC
Phone—(201) 797-1511
3-00 Banta Pl., Fair Lawn 07410

## ICE CREAM

All Seasons Ice Cream Corp.
Phone—(201) 878-6790
15 E.12th St., Paterson 07524

Applegate Farm Homemade Ice Cream, Inc.
Phone—(973) 744-5900
616 Grove St., Montclair 07043

Arctic Ice Cream
Phone—(609) 393-4264
22 Arctic Pkwy., Ewing 08638

Clyde's Ices & Ice Cream, Inc.
Phone—(973) 546-2760
48 Gaston Ave., Garfield 07026

Dairyland Ice Cream
Phone—(973) 923-7625
487 Chancellor Ave., Irvington 07111

Guernsey Crest Ice Cream Co.
Phone—(973) 742-4620
134 19th Ave., Paterson 07513

Kwality Foods, LLC
Phone—(732) 906-1941
1734 Oak Tree Rd., Edison 08820

Leo's Famous Yum Yum
Phone—(856) 797-8771
7 Tomlinson Mill Rd., Ste. 5, Medford 08055

Limpert Bros., Inc.
Phone—(856) 691-1353
202 N. West Blvd., Vineland 08360

Mister Cookie Face, LLC
Phone—(732) 370-5533
1989 Rutgers University Blvd., Lakewood 08701

Mr. Green Tea Ice Cream Co.
Phone—(732) 446-9800
25 Church St., Unit 104, Keyport 07735

Nasto's Ice Cream Co., Inc.
Phone—(973) 589-3333
236 Jefferson St., Newark 07105

Piece Of Cake Gourmet Ice Cream, Inc.
Phone—(732) 382-0281
62 W. Inman Ave., Rahway 07065

Water Ice Factory, Inc.
Phone—(856) 627-6831
15 Evergreen Rd, Chatham 08084

## ICE CREAM CONES

Novelty Cone Co., Inc.
Phone—(856) 665-9525
807 Sherman Ave., Pennsauken 08110

## ICE CREAM FREEZERS

Troy Hills Mfg., Inc.
Phone—(973) 263-1885
2 Como Ct., P.O. Box 98, Towaco 07082

## ICE CREAM MAKING EQUIPMENT

**WCB Ice Cream**
**Phone—(201) 784-1101**
**Fax—(201) 784-1116**
**Web—www.wcbicecream.com**
**Email—nwhite@wcbicecream.com**
**267 Livingston St., Northvale 07647**

## ICE CREAM MIXES

Panza & Sons, Ltd., A.
Phone—(732) 225-1314
141 Fieldcrest Ave., Edison 08837

## ICE SHAVING EQUIPMENT

Clawson Machine, Div. Of Technology General Corp.
Phone—(973) 827-8209
12 Cork Hill Rd., Franklin 07416

## IDENTIFICATION BADGES

CompoSecure, LLC
Phone—(908) 518-0500
500 Memorial Dr., Somerset 08873

K & A Industries, Inc.
Phone—(908) 226-7000
51 Cragwood Rd., Ste. 204, South Plainfield 07080

## IDENTIFICATION EQUIPMENT

Gill Assocs. Identification Systems, LLC
Phone—(973) 835-5456
2025 Hamburg Tpke., Ste. M, Wayne 07470

O'Brien Co., Inc., J.
Phone—(973) 379-8844
40 Commerce St., Springfield 07081

## IDENTIFICATION PRODUCTS — Biometric

ZK Software (H Q)
Phone—(732) 412-6007
201 Circle Dr. N., Ste. 116, Piscataway 08854

## IDENTIFICATION SYSTEMS — Radio Frequency

New Jersey Microsystems, Inc.
Phone—(973) 297-1450
211 Warren St., Ste. 31, Newark 07103

## IGNITORS — Oil & Gas Burner

Crown Engineering Corp.
Phone—(732) 938-3600
550 Squankum Yellowbrook Rd., Howell 07731

## IGNITORS — Oil & Gas Burner —
**(cont.)**

Westwood Products, Inc.
Phone—(732) 651-7700
330 William St., P.O. Box 610, South River 08882

## IMAGE PROCESSING EQUIPMENT

Advanced Imaging Assocs., Inc.
Phone—(973) 823-8999
190 Munsonhurst Rd., Ste. 6, Franklin 07416

## IMPORTERS

**Courier Systems, Inc.**
**Phone—(201) 432-0550**
**Fax—(201) 432-9686**
**Web—www.csweb.biz**
**Email—rick.murad@csweb.biz**
**180 Pulaski St., Bayonne 07002**
**Foremost Groups Inc.**
**Phone—(973) 428-0400**
**Fax—(973) 428-6166**
**Web—www.foremostgroups.com**
**Email—marketing@foremostgroups.com**
**906 Murray Rd., East Hanover 07936**

## IMPORTS

**J.V.M. Sales, Inc.**
**Phone—(908) 862-4866**
**Fax—(908) 862-4867**
**Web—www.gratedcheeseusa.com**
**Email—jsales.jvm@verizon.net**
**3401-A Tremley Point Rd., Linden 07036**
*(see our ad under CHEESE & CHEESE SPECIALTIES)*

## IMPRINTING — Letterpress

Clark's Hallmark Shop
Phone—(973) 584-5119
275 State Route 10 E., Ste. 31, Succasunna 07876

## INDEX TABS

Custom Index, Inc.
Phone—(973) 890-2414
8 Vreeland Ave., Totowa 07512
Rush Index Tabs, Inc.
Phone—(201) 531-1555
60 Willow St., East Rutherford 07073

## INDUCTION HEATING EQUIPMENT

ElectroHeat Induction
Phone—(908) 494-0726
9 Spruce St., Jersey City 07306
RDO Induction LLC
Phone—(908) 835-7222
2170 State Route 57 W., Washington 07882

## INDUCTION MELTING EQUIPMENT

Consarc Corp.
Phone—(609) 267-8000
100 Indel Ave., P.O. Box 156, Rancocas 08073

## INDUCTION MELTING FURNACES

ABP Induction, LLC
Phone—(732) 932-6400
1460 Livingston Ave., North Brunswick 08902

*Do nationwide searches for products & services at:*

**IndustryNet.com**

## INDUCTORS

**Power Magnetics, Inc.**
**A global provider of a wide range of custom transformers, inductors & reactors for the most demanding applications in a wide variety of industries**
**Phone—(609) 695-1170 / (800) 747-0845**
**Fax—(609) 695-5907**
**Web—www.powermagneticsinc.com**
**Email—sales@powermagneticsinc.com**
**377 Reservoir St., Trenton 08618**

## INDUSTRIAL EQUIPMENT & SUPPLIES

A&M Industrial, Inc.
Phone—(732) 574-1111
37 W. Cherry St., P.O. Box 1044, Rahway 07065
Ameridia
Phone—(732) 805-4001
20 Worlds Fair Dr., Ste. F, Somerset 08873
Durawear Glove & Safety, Inc.
Phone—(908) 284-0776
30 Royal Rd., Ste. 4, Flemington 08822
EIC Industry Group Corp. (H Q)
Phone—(973) 983-1988
53 Green Pond Rd., Ste. 3, Rockaway 07866

## INDUSTRIAL EQUIPMENT & SUPPLIES — Wholesale

A&M Industrial, Inc.
Phone—(908) 862-1800
325 Commerce Rd., Linden 07036
ABCO Systems, Inc.
Phone—(201) 507-0999
15 Willet St., Ste. 4, Bloomfield 07003
Applied Industrial Technologies, Inc.
Phone—(732) 356-0522
24-C Worlds Fair Dr., Somerset 08873
F & H Supply, Inc
Phone—(856) 451-7080
1315 Route 77, P.O. Box 379, Bridgeton 08302
**Fastenal**
**Phone—(609) 261-3111**
**Fax—(609) 261-1051**
**Web—www.fastenal.com**
**Email—noche@stores.fastenal.com**
**140 Mount Holly Bypass, Ste. 4, Lumberton 08048**
Gaffney-Kroese Supply Corp.
Phone—(732) 885-9000
50 Randolph Rd., Somerset 08873
**GKY Industries**
**Fasteners*Hardware*Tools for All Industries**
**Phone—(201) 656-2377**
**Fax—(201) 656-0566**
**Web—www.gkyindustries.com**
**Email—sales@gkyindustries.com**
**383 8th St., Jersey City 07302**
J & J Industrial Supply, Inc.
Phone—(973) 235-0100
113 E. Centre St., P.O. Box 110174, Nutley 07110
Jesco, Inc.
Phone—(908) 821-1400
118 Saint Nicholas Ave., South Plainfield 07080
Kaman Industrial Technologies Corp.
Phone—(908) 687-0004
502 Bloy St., Hillside 07205
Kaman Industrial Technologies Corp.
Phone—(856) 227-7000
195 Borelli Rd., Paulsboro 08066
Kaman Industrial Technologies Corp.
Phone—(856) 284-7400
195 Borrelli Blvd., Ste. B, Paulsboro 08066
Madsen & Howell, Inc.
Phone—(732) 826-4000
500 Market St., Ste. 1, Perth Amboy 08861
McMaster-Carr Supply Co.
Phone—(609) 259-8900
200 New Canton Way, Robbinsville 08691
Metro Industrial Supply, Inc.
Phone—(973) 546-5660
200 Charles St., Garfield 07026
MSC Industrial Supply Co.
Phone—(732) 512-9555
105 Newfield Ave., Ste. E, Edison 08837

Richards Co.
Phone—(201) 797-6300
437 Boulevard, P.O. Box 199, Elmwood Park 07407
Sanzo Ltd.
Phone—(908) 276-6654
35 Munsee Dr., Cranford 07016
T & B Specialties, Inc.
Phone—(732) 928-4500
479 Wright Debow Rd., Jackson 08527
**Taylor Northeast**
**Providing a broad range of services for Material Handling & Industrial Cleaning Equipment in the eastern-PA area since 1985. Services range from new & used lift truck sales, leasing & rentals to service, parts & remanufacturing**
**Phone—(610) 286-8080 / (800) 762-2500**
**Fax—(610) 286-8099**
**Web—www.taylornortheast.com**
**Email—kkoch@taylornortheast.com**
**931 Hemlock Rd., Morgantown, PA 19543**
W. W. Grainger, Inc.
Phone—(908) 787-1952
560-596 Bercik St., Ste. 1, Elizabeth 07201
W. W. Grainger, Inc.
Phone—(973) 227-7220
277 Route 46 W., Fairfield 07004
W. W. Grainger, Inc.
Phone—(856) 234-8550
819 E. Gate Dr., Mount Laurel 08054
W. W. Grainger, Inc.
Phone—(609) 394-2620
1585 N. Olden Ave., Trenton 08638
**Warwick Mfg. & Equipment Co., LLC**
**Buy & sell used: Chemical, food, cosmetic, packaging & pharmaceutical equipment**
**Phone—(732) 729-0400 / (732) 241-9263**
**Fax—(732) 729-1235**
**Web—www.warwickequipment.com**
**Email—sales@warwickequipment.com**
**1112 12th St., North Brunswick 08902**
*(see our ad Outside Back Cover)*
Wurth International Trading America
Phone—(201) 995-1111
91 Grant St., Ramsey 07446
Yecies, Inc., Herman W.
Phone—(973) 736-7362
11 Roosevelt Ave., P.O. Box 6186, West Orange 07052

## INDUSTRIAL HYGIENE SERVICES

**Detail Associates Inc.**
**Phone—(201) 569-6708**
**Fax—(201) 569-4378**
**Web—www.daienviro.com**
**Email—stephenj@daienviro.com**
**300 Grand Ave., Ste. 104, Englewood 07631**

## INFORMATION SECURITY SERVICES

**Direct Computer Resources, Inc.**
**Protecting personally identifiable information (PII)**
**Phone—(201) 848-0018 / (800) 878-4211**
**Fax—(201) 848-0064**
**Web—www.datavantage.com**
**Email—info@datavantage.com**
**120 Birch Rd., Franklin Lakes 07417**
*(see our ad under DATA MASKING SOFTWARE)*

## INFRARED DEVICES

Redfield Corp.
Phone—(201) 845-3990
336 W. Passaic St., Rochelle Park 07662

## INFRARED HEATING SYSTEMS

Marsden, Inc.
Phone—(856) 663-2227
6800 Westfield Ave., Pennsauken 08110

## INFRARED IMAGING SYSTEMS

Sofradir EC, Inc.
Phone—(973) 882-0211
373 U.S. Highway 46, Ste. E, Fairfield 07004

## INGOTS — Aluminum

State Metal Industries, Inc.
Phone—(856) 964-1510
941 S. 2nd St., Camden 08103

## INJECTION MOLDED PRODUCTS

Echo Molding, Inc.
Phone—(908) 688-0099
911 Springfield Rd., Union 07083

## INJECTION MOLDING — Custom

**(also see 'Plastic Injection Molding')**

Polymer Technologies, Inc.
Phone—(973) 778-9100
10 Clifton Blvd., Clifton 07011
Valley Plastic Molding Co., Inc.
Phone—(973) 334-2100
P.O. Box 30, Boonton 07005

## INJECTION MOLDING — Thermoplastic

**Wiggins Plastics, Inc.**
Est. 1948-ISO Certified; Custom Injection/
Thermoplastics/Thermosets/Compression/Transfer
Molding
**Phone—(973) 667-7200**
**Fax—(973) 667-3227**
**Web—www.wigginsplastics.com**
**Email—info@wigginsplastics.com**
**180 Kingsland Rd., P.O. Box 1077, Clifton**
**07014**
*(see our ad under PLASTIC INJECTION MOLDING)*

## INJECTION MOLDING MACHINERY

Projects, Inc.
Phone—(856) 825-7312
310 Orange St., Millville 08332

## INJECTION MOLDS

Accurate Mold, Inc.
Phone—(856) 784-8484
900 Chestnut Ave., Somerdale 08083
Big 3 Precision Mold Services
Phone—(856) 293-1400
30 Gorton Rd., Millville 08332
Hammonton Mold Co., Inc.
Phone—(856) 728-9112
4171 S. Black Horse Pike, Williamstown 08094
**L & Z Tool & Engineering, Inc.**
Email: fcooper@lztool.com
**Phone—(908) 322-2220**
**Fax—(908) 322-3758**
**Web—www.lztool.com**
**1691 U.S. Highway 22, Watchung 07069**
Newark Mold & Tool, Inc.
Phone—(973) 578-2881
147 New Jersey Railroad Ave., Newark 07104
Thal Precision Industries, Inc.
Phone—(732) 381-6106
19-A Walnut Ave., Clark 07066

## INKJET CARTRIDGES

Care Plus NJ, Inc.
Phone—(973) 553-1954
185 6th Ave., Paterson 07524
Cartridge World New Providence, LLC
Phone—(908) 771-9696
1310 Springfield Ave., New Providence 07974
Petitts Ink Corp.
Phone—(973) 984-2400
1745 State Route 10, Ste. 4, Morris Plains 07950

## INKJET CODING SYSTEMS

Digital Design, Inc.
Phone—(973) 857-0901
67 Sand Park Rd., Cedar Grove 07009

## INKS

Caloric Color Co., Inc.
Phone—(973) 471-4748
176 Saddle River Rd., Bldg. A, South Hackensack 07606
Faust, Inc., Rudolph
Phone—(908) 507-5104
542 South Ave. E., Cranford 07016
Ranger Industries, Inc.
Phone—(732) 389-1101
15 Park Rd., Tinton Falls 07724
Wilpak Industries, Inc.
Phone—(201) 997-7600
244 Dukes St., Kearny 07032
WYLD Grand Format Imaging, LLC
Phone—(908) 587-2995
1618 E. Elizabeth Ave., Linden 07036

## INKS — Inkjet

American Ink Jet Systems, Inc.
Phone—(201) 263-9177
34 Chestnut St., Emerson 07630
GSC Imaging, LLC
Phone—(856) 317-9301
7150 N. Park Dr., Ste. 540, Pennsauken 08109

## INKS — Marking

American Coding & Marking Ink Co.
Phone—(908) 756-0373
1220 North Ave., Plainfield 07062

## INKS — Printing

Central Ink Corp.
Phone—(856) 467-5562
2085 Center Square Rd., Unit A, Swedesboro 08085
Flint Group
Phone—(732) 329-4627
6 Corn Rd., Dayton 08810
J.M. Fry Co., Inc.
Phone—(732) 238-1060
124 Tices Ln., Ste. A, East Brunswick 08816
Monarch Color Corp.
Phone—(856) 662-0432
7247 Browning Rd., Pennsauken 08109
Pertech Inks Corp.
Phone—(908) 354-1700
140 Grand St., Carlstadt 07072
Prismacolor Corp.
Phone—(973) 887-7900
120 E. Halsey Rd., P.O. Box 6330, Parsippany 07054
Selective Coatings & Inks, Inc.
Phone—(732) 938-7677
5008 Industrial Rd., Farmingdale 07727
Sun Chemical Corp.
Phone—(201) 933-4500
631 Central Ave., Carlstadt 07072
Sun Chemical Corp.
Phone—(201) 438-4041
390 Central Ave., East Rutherford 07073
Sun Chemical Corp.
Phone—(973) 404-6000
35 Waterview Blvd., Ste. 100, Parsippany 07054
Superior Printing Ink Co., Inc.
Phone—(856) 482-9066
666 E. Linwood Ave., Maple Shade 08052
Superior Printing Ink Co., Inc.
Phone—(201) 478-5600
100 North St., Teterboro 07608
Supreme Ink Co., Inc.
Phone—(973) 344-2922
65 McWhorter St., Newark 07105
Toyo Ink America
Phone—(732) 752-5660
4301 New Brunswick Ave., Ste. A, South Plainfield 07080
Toyo Ink America, LLC
Phone—(201) 804-0616
30 Murray Hill Pkwy., Ste. 100, East Rutherford 07073
US Ink Corp.
Phone—(201) 438-4041
390 Central Ave., East Rutherford 07073

US Ink Corp. (H Q)
Phone—(201) 935-8666
631 Central Ave., Carlstadt 07072
Uvitec Printing Ink, Inc.
Phone—(973) 778-0737
14 Mill St., Lodi 07644

## INKS — Screen Print

Champion Ink Co., Inc.
Phone—(201) 868-4100
2045 88th St., North Bergen 07047
Nazdar Co.
Phone—(856) 663-7878
7055 Central Hwy., Pennsauken 08109
Solar Color Chemical Corp.
Phone—(201) 945-5775
180 River Rd., Edgewater 07020
**Total Ink Solutions**
Plastisol, Supplies, Screens, Mesh, Press Wash & Color Match
**Phone—(201) 487-9600 / (877) 937-6400**
**Fax—(201) 487-9620**
**Web—www.totalinksolutions.com**
**Email—marc@totalinksolutions.com**
**200 S. Newman St., Unit 4, Hackensack 07601**

**Total Ink Solutions**
*Plastisol, Supplies, Screens, Mesh,*
*Press Wash & Color Match*
**201-487-9600 • Fax: 201-487-9620**
www.totalinksolutions.com
marc@totalinksolutions.com
200 S. Newman St., Unit 4 • Hackensack, NJ 07601

Triangle Ink Co., Inc.
Phone—(201) 935-2777
53-57 Van Dyke St., Wallington 07057

## INSECT CONTROL EQUIPMENT

Vandermolen Corp.
Phone—(973) 992-8506
119 Dorsa Ave., Livingston 07039

## INSERT MOLDING

Weiss-Aug Co. Inc.
Phone—(973) 887-7600
220 Merry Ln., East Hanover 07936

## INSERTS

Precision Specialties
Phone—(973) 751-7588
120 Greylock Ave., Belleville 07109

## INSPECTION EQUIPMENT

**Ackley Machine Corp.**
Email: pgulotta@ackleymachine.com
**Phone—(856) 234-3626**
**Fax—(856) 234-8657**
**Web—www.ackleymachine.com**
**1273 N. Church St., Ste. 106, Moorestown**
**08057**
Glenbrook Technologies, Inc.
Phone—(973) 361-8866
11 Emery Ave., Randolph 07869
Operations Technology, Inc.
Phone—(908) 362-6200
30 Lambert Rd., P.O. Box 408, Blairstown 07825
Resec Systems, LLC
Phone—(201) 384-6960
93 S. Railroad Ave., Ste. A, Bergenfield 07621

## INSPECTION SERVICES

**General Information Services LLC**
Property Insurance Inspections
**Phone—(201) 797-4800**
**Web—www.geninfoserv.com**
**P.O. Box 487, Fair Lawn 07410**

## INSTALLATION SERVICES

**East Coast Kitchen Installations, Inc.**
Installation of commercial food service equipment
Phone—(732) 901-8609
Email—gerrylyle@optonline.net
2 Robert Ave., Howell 07731

**Portuguese Structural Steel, Inc.**
Phone—(973) 344-1342
Fax—(973) 344-1730
Web—www.portuguesesteel.com
Email—paula@portuguesesteel.com
255 South St., Newark 07114
*(see our ad under STRUCTURAL STEEL FABRICATION)*

**Right Way Heating & Cooling**
Phone—(856) 563-1283
Fax—(856) 690-0171
41-D Osborn Ave., P.O Box 1198, Vineland 08362

## INSTRUMENTATION

Industrial Instrumentation Services, Inc.
Phone—(732) 815-9090
1400 Rahway Ave., Ste. 4, Avenel 07001
Photon Technology International
Phone—(732) 494-8660
3880 Park Ave., Edison 08820
Powercomm Solutions, LLC
Phone—(908) 806-7025
15 Minneakoning Rd., Ste. 311, Flemington 08822
Willrich Precision Instrument, Inc.
Phone—(201) 567-1411
80 Broadway, Cresskill 07626

## INSTRUMENTS — Aircraft

Aeronautical Instrument & Radio, Inc.
Phone—(973) 473-0034
234 Garibaldi Ave., Lodi 07644
Avionic Instruments, LLC
Phone—(732) 388-3500
1414 Randolph Ave., P.O. Box 498, Avenel 07001
Avionix Corp.
Phone—(201) 343-1550
35 Ruta Ct., South Hackensack 07606
Consolidated Instrument, Avionics & Radio Sales & Service
Phone—(201) 288-1189
510 Industrial Ave., Teterboro 07608
**Instrument Specialties Co., Inc.**
Email: sabate@inscousa.com
Phone—(973) 335-2136
Fax—(973) 335-5740
Web—www.inscousa.com
Email—info@inscousa.com
661 Myrtle Ave., Boonton 07005

**Instrument Specialties Co., Inc.**
*Aircraft Instruments*
(973) 335-2136
Fax: (973) 335-5740
www.inscousa.com
sabate@inscousa.com
661 Myrtle Ave.
Boonton, NJ 07005

## INSTRUMENTS — Precision

Rame-Hart Instrument Co., LLC
Phone—(973) 448-0305
19 Route 10 E., Ste. 11, Succasunna 07876

## INSULATION — Electrical

Dolph Co., John C.
Phone—(732) 329-2333
320 New Rd., Monmouth Junction 08852
Stevens Products, Inc.
Phone—(973) 672-2140
128 N. Park St., East Orange 07017

## INSULATION — Fiberglass

Johns Manville
Phone—(856) 768-7000
437 North Grove St., Berlin 08009
Johns Manville
Phone—(732) 225-9190
1000 Liddle Ave., Edison 08837
Pacor, Inc.
Phone—(609) 324-1100
333 Rising Sun Rd., Bordentown 08505

## INSULATION — Industrial

**Jersey Firestop, LLC**
Phone—(732) 537-9156
Fax—(732) 537-9157
Email—jersey04@verizon.net
317 E. 2nd St., Bound Brook 08805

## INSULATION — Polystyrene

Poly Molding, LLC
Phone—(973) 835-7161
96 4th Ave., Haskell 07420

## INSULATION CONTRACTORS

**Jersey Firestop, LLC**
Phone—(732) 537-9156
Fax—(732) 537-9157
Email—jersey04@verizon.net
317 E. 2nd St., Bound Brook 08805

## INSURANCE

**Affordable Insurance Agency, LLC**
Phone—(856) 854-5665
Fax—(856) 854-4058
Web—www.affordableinsurancesnj.com
Email—lisa@aiaofnj.com
2910 Mount Ephraim Ave., Camden 08104
**Affordable Insurance Agency, LLC**
Phone—(856) 256-1033
Fax—(856) 256-1088
Web—www.affordableinsurancesnj.com
Email—lisa@aiaofnj.com
250 N. Woodbury Rd., Pitman 08071
Allen Freeman Insurance
Phone—(732) 634-7114
Fax—(732) 634-2583
Email—awfins8@aol.com
135 Green St., Ste. 2, Woodbridge 07095
Auto Insurance Store NJ
Phone—(609) 893-0500
Web—www.progressive.com
P.O. Box 739, Browns Mills 08015
Berkley Surety Group LLC
Phone—(973) 775-5021
Web—www.berkleysurety.com
412 Mount Kemble Ave., Ste. 310N, Morristown 07960
Business Insurance Consultants, Inc.
Phone—(732) 946-9300
Fax—(732) 946-7505
Web—www.businessinsure.com
Email—jwoodruff@businessinsure.com
34 W. Main St., Holmdel 07733

*Search from among 430,000 U.S. manufacturers & suppliers at*
**IndustryNet.com**

**Cedar Risk Management**
A full service insurance agency. Whether you are looking for yourself, your company, your great-aunt Jemima, or even your dog, we can tailor an insurance policy that is right for you. And we are licensed in multiple states
Phone—(908) 237-1800
Fax—(908) 788-7031
Web—www.cedarrisk.com
Email—vweir@cedarrisk.com
349 State Route 31, Ste. 201, Flemington 08822

Cereijo & Assocs. Inc.
Phone—(201) 894-8299
Web—www.progressiveagent.com
62 Engle St., Englewood 07631
Conover Beyer Assocs. Inc.
Phone—(732) 223-9700
Fax—(732) 223-6044
Web—www.conoverbeyer.com
Email—jechurch@conoverbeyer.com
2600 Highway 35, Manasquan 08736
Durkin Agency Inc.
Phone—(201) 567-3700
Fax—(201) 567-7472
Web—www.durkinagency.com
Email—info@durkinagency.com
106 Grand Ave., Ste. 360, Englewood 07631
Durkin Agency Inc.
Phone—(201) 567-3700
Fax—(201) 825-9143
Web—www.durkinagency.com
Email—info@dirkinagency.com
48 S. Franklin Tpke., Ramsey 07446
**Elias B. Cohen & Assocs.**
Insurance & Risk Management
Phone—(973) 403-9500
Fax—(973) 403-7755
Web—www.cohenins.com
Email—neil_owens@cohenins.com
101 Eisenhower Pkwy., Ste. 202, Roseland 07068

**E.B. COHEN**
Insurance and Risk Management • Since 1932
101 Eisenhower Parkway, Roseland, New Jersey 07068
(973) 403-9500
www.cohenins.com

Financial Insurance Services, LLC
Phone—(732) 316-4720
Fax—(732) 316-4725
Web—www.financialinservices.com
924 US Highway 9, 2nd Fl., South Amboy 08879
Insurance Office Of America
Phone—(856) 608-1000
Web—www.ioausa.com
220 Lake Dr. E., Ste. 304, Cherry Hill 08002
Ivan Agency Inc.
Phone—(201) 585-5155
Fax—(201) 585-7227
Email—ivanagency@hotmail.com
111 Grand Ave., Ste. 218, Palisades Park 07650
Omega Insurance LLC
Phone—(908) 355-8765
Web—www.omegainsagency.com
619 Westfield Ave., Apt. 3, Elizabeth 07208
Rettino Insurance Agency Inc.
Toll Free Ph: (877)702-SAVE; Service Beyond the Contract
Phone—(609) 625-2143
Fax—(609) 625-7926
Web—www.rettinoinsurance.com
P.O. Box 428, Mays Landing 08330
Sanford Insurance Group
Phone—(973) 783-6600
Fax—(973) 783-2904
Web—www.sanfordinsnj.com
Email—bsanford@sanfordinsure.com
210 Bellevue Ave., Montclair 07043
State Farm Insurance
Phone—(908) 522-8330
Fax—(908) 522-8320
Email—bert@bertsweeney.com
35 Beechwood Rd., Ste. 3D, Summit 07901

© Copyright 2015 Manufacturers' News, Inc. **A103**

## INSURANCE — (cont.)

**Strube Agency**
Phone—(856) 227-1426
Fax—(856) 227-0497
Email—hstrubejr@comcast.net
1612 Cooper St., Woodbury 08096

**Suburban Brokers, Inc.**
T/A Suburban
Phone—(201) 796-1881
Fax—(201) 797-6689
Web—www.suburbanins.net
Email—leightona@suburbanins.net
P.O. Box 400, Fair Lawn 07410

**Thomas Brackin Inc.**
Phone—(973) 334-1316
Fax—(973) 334-4672
Email—tsbrackin@optonline.net
P.O. Box 68, Mountain Lakes 07046

**Tri-State Insurance Adjusters, Inc.**
Phone—(856) 323-1001
Fax—(856) 323-1002
Web—www.tri-stateadjusters.com
606 S. White Horse Pike, Audubon 08106

---

**Tri-State Insurance Adjusters, Inc.**
*Multi-Line Claim Services*
www.tri-stateadjusters.com
(856) 323-1001 / Fax: (856) 323-1002
606 S. White House Pike
Audubon, NJ 08106

---

**VIA Insurance Agency, Incorporated**
Phone—(908) 862-4047
Fax—(908) 862-0308
Web—www.valvano.com
Email—mikev@valvano.com
16 W. Elizabeth Ave., P.O. Box 1100, Linden 07036

---

**(908) 862-4047**
Fax: (908) 862-0308
VIA INSURANCE & FINANCIAL SERVICES
**VALVANO INSURANCE AGENCY**
Web: valvano.com / Email: mikev@valvano.com
16 W. Elizabeth Ave., PO Box 1100 • Linden, NJ 07036

---

**Winant-Bomack Insurance**
Phone—(732) 918-7999
Fax—(732) 918-7970
Web—www.winantbomack.com
3318 State Route 33, Neptune 07753

## INSURANCE — Life & Health

**Cedar Risk Management**
A full service insurance agency. Whether you are looking for yourself, your company, your great-aunt Jemima, or even your dog, we can tailor an insurance policy that is right for you. And we are licensed in multiple states
Phone—(908) 237-1800
Fax—(908) 788-7031
Web—www.cedarrisk.com
Email—vweir@cedarrisk.com
349 State Route 31, Ste. 201, Flemington 08822

**Sanford Insurance Group**
Phone—(973) 783-6600
Fax—(973) 783-2904
Web—www.sanfordinsnj.com
Email—bsanford@sanfordinsure.com
210 Bellevue Ave., Montclair 07043

---

**EZSelect®.com**
**REAL-TIME** Access to Industrial Leads!

## INSURANCE — Property & Casualty

**Cedar Risk Management**
A full service insurance agency. Whether you are looking for yourself, your company, your great-aunt Jemima, or even your dog, we can tailor an insurance policy that is right for you. And we are licensed in multiple states
Phone—(908) 237-1800
Fax—(908) 788-7031
Web—www.cedarrisk.com
Email—vweir@cedarrisk.com
349 State Route 31, Ste. 201, Flemington 08822

## INSURANCE ADJUSTERS

**DPV Adjustment Service, Inc.**
Phone—(908) 782-4980
Fax—(908) 782-9951
Email—dpvadj@earthlink.net
260 US Highway 202/31, Ste. 300, Flemington 08822

**Tri-State Insurance Adjusters, Inc.**
Phone—(856) 323-1001
Fax—(856) 323-1002
Web—www.tri-stateadjusters.com
606 S. White Horse Pike, Audubon 08106
*(see our ad under INSURANCE)*

## INSURANCE CLAIMS PROCESSING

**GTA Electronic Med Billing Solutions**
Phone—(973) 616-7111
Fax—(973) 616-7338
Email—grace@gtamedicalbilling.com
75 Greenwood Lake Tpke., Ringwood 07456

## INSURANCE CONSULTANTS

**Winston Benefits**
Quality insurance consultants
Phone—(732) 899-0990 / (888) 579-4000
Fax—(732) 899-0994
Web—www.winstonbenefits.com
Email—sales@winstonbenefits.com
2399 Highway 34, Bldg. C2, Manasquan 08736

---

**Winston Benefits**
*Quality Insurance Consultants*
www.winstonbenefits.com
**(732) 899-0990**
2399 Highway 34 • Building C2
Manasquan, NJ 08736

---

## INSURANCE SOFTWARE

**Cover-All Technologies, Inc.**
Phone—(973) 461-5200
412 Mount Kemble Ave., Ste. 110-C, Morristown 07960

---

*find additional suppliers at*
**IndustryNet.com**

## INTERIOR DECORATING & DESIGN

**Diane Barabas**
Phone—(908) 233-7374
Email—dianebs@aol.com
22 Stoneleigh Park, Westfield 07090

## INVENTORY SERVICES

**Argent Associates Inc.**
Phone—(732) 512-9009
Fax—(732) 512-9549
Web—www.argentassociates.com
Email—sales@argentassociates.com
140 Fieldcrest Ave., Edison 08837

## INVERTERS

**Tekris Power Electronics, Inc.**
Phone—(732) 938-4996
1675 State Route 34, Farmingdale 07727

## INVESTIGATORS

**Global Investigative Concepts**
Phone—(732) 583-0377
Fax—(732) 583-8713
Email—gicpi@optonline.net
P.O. Box 322, Matawan 07747

**Sullivan & Sullivan**
Phone—(609) 584-7599
Fax—(609) 586-2402
P.O. Box 8401, Trenton 08650

## INVESTMENT ADVISORS

**Boston Investment Partners LLC**
Phone—(732) 449-0611
Fax—(857) 241-3129
Web—www.bostoninvestmentpartners.com
Email—rcody@bostoninvestmentpartners.com
1010 State Route 71, Ste. 2, Spring Lake 07762

## ION EXCHANGE RESINS

**Graver Technologies, LLC**
Phone—(973) 690-5290
72 Lockwood St., Newark 07105

## IRON — Scrap

**Perone's Auto Service & Salvage**
We Buy All Metals & Iron. 10-40 Yard Container Service For Demolition & Clean Ups
Phone—(732) 563-1630
Fax—(732) 563-1774
Web—www.peronesauto.com
Email—peronesauto@yahoo.com
371 US Highway 22, Green Brook 08812
*(see our ad under SCRAP IRON & METAL RECYCLING)*

## IRON FABRICATING

**Carfaro Railings Company, Frank**
Also iron & aluminum railing; East gate windows guards
Phone—(908) 879-7312
Fax—(908) 879-8870
70 Hacklebarney Rd., Long Valley 07853

**Kenco Wire & Iron Products, Inc.**
Phone—(732) 495-3000
425 Carr Ave., Keansburg 07734

**New Jersey Iron, Inc.**
Phone—(732) 928-7242
905 Patterson Rd., Jackson 08527

## IRONING BOARD COVERS & PADS

**Tanner Assocs.**
Phone—(201) 865-4500
600 Palisade Ave., Union City 07087

## IRONWORK — Ornamental & Architectural

A & A Ironworks, Inc.
Phone—(973) 728-4300
955 Burnt Meadow Rd., Hewitt 07421

Alberona Iron Work, Inc.
Phone—(973) 674-3375
452 Scotland Rd., Orange 07050

**Ciccone Custom Railing & Manufacturing, Inc.**
**Phone—(732) 349-7071**
**Fax—(732) 349-7079**
**Web—www.cicconerailing.com**
**Email—customrailing@gmail.com**
**2002 Route 9, Toms River 08755**

Collo Ornamental Iron, Inc.
Phone—(609) 926-8799
1723 Somers Point Rd., Egg Harbor Township 08234

Cusumano Perma-Rail Co.
Phone—(908) 245-9281
213 W. Westfield Ave., Roselle Park 07204

De Risi Iron Works Co.
Phone—(732) 774-6570
910 Asbury Ave., Asbury Park 07712

Fredon Welding & Iron Works Co.
Phone—(973) 383-6768
52 State Route 15, P.O. Box 260, Lafayette 07848

International Forge, LLC
Phone—(973) 729-0359
14 Doty Rd., Haskell 07420

Kaufman Iron Works, Inc., J.
Phone—(718) 991-5400
217 Godwin Ave., Paterson 07501

La Forge De Style
Phone—(201) 488-1955
57 Romanelli Ave., South Hackensack 07606

Polmar Iron Work, Inc.
Phone—(732) 882-0900
673 New Brunswick Ave., Rahway 07065

SRS, Inc.
Phone—(732) 548-6630
74 Liberty St., P.O. Box 4277, Metuchen 08840

Stout's Metal Products
Phone—(856) 854-7938
222 Lincoln Ave., Collingswood 08108

Ungarini Iron Works, LLC
Phone—(609) 392-0540
56 N. Logan Ave., Trenton 08609

Weldall Welding & Ironworks
Phone—(973) 674-8868
115-117 S. Day St., Orange 07050

Wolek's Ornamental Iron Works
Phone—(732) 681-5929
1719 H St., Route 71 W., Belmar 07719

## IRRIGATION PRODUCTS

Cutting Edge Grower Supply LLC
Phone—(732) 905-9220
5033 Industrial Rd., Farmingdale 07727

## JACKETS

Vertical Source, Inc. (H Q)
Phone—(732) 530-5330
812 Broad St., Shrewsbury 07702

## JACKETS — Leather

Passaic Leather Coat, Inc.
Phone—(973) 777-4026
51 Market St., Passaic 07055

Prime Fur & Leather, Inc.
Phone—(201) 941-9600
2931 Industrial Ave., Fairview 07022

*Search from among*
*430,000 U.S. manufacturers*
*& suppliers at*
**IndustryNet.com**

## JACKS — Hydraulic

Hilman Rollers
Phone—(732) 462-6277 / (888) 276-5548
Fax—(732) 462-6355
Web—www.hilmanrollers.com
Email—sales@hilmanrollers.com
12 Timber Ln., P.O. Box 45, Marlboro 07746

**TOE JACKS**   732-462-6277
**www.hilmanrollers.com**

Metro Hydraulic Jack Co.
Phone—(973) 350-0111
1271 McCarter Hwy., P.O. Box 9410, Newark 07104

## JANITOR SERVICES

**Always Immaculate Inc.**
**Phone—(732) 270-6556**
**Fax—(732) 270-6057**
**Web—www.alwaysimmaculate.com**
**Email—storres@alwaysimmaculate.com**
**1201 Route 37 E., Ste. 6, Toms River 08753**

**Atlantic Janitorial Services**
**Ext. 19**
**Phone—(908) 298-1666**
**Fax—(908) 298-0125**
**Email—atljanitorial@aol.com**
**23 N. Michigan Ave., Kenilworth 07033**

**CleanSafe Solutions Corp.**
**Phone—(732) 544-8500**
**Web—www.csspropertyservices.com**
**6 Industrial Way W., Ste. H, Eatontown 07724**

**Frank's Cleaning Service**
**Phone—(856) 914-1020**
**Fax—(856) 914-1020**
**Web—www.franks-cleaning.com**
**Email—corv2tt2031@comcast.net**
**25 Village Of Stoney Run, Apt. D, Maple Shade 08052**

**HMJ Cleaning**
**Phone—(732) 229-2577**
**385 Ocean Blvd., Apt. 1E, Long Branch 07740**

**QC Cleaning LLC**
**Phone—(732) 833-1500**
**Fax—(732) 833-1598**
**Web—www.qualitycarecleaning.com**
**Email—info@qualitycarecleaning.com**
**585 N. County Line Rd., Ste. 3, Jackson 08527**

## JANITORIAL EQUIPMENT & SUPPLIES

Ace Janitorial Supply, Inc.
Phone—(201) 529-1750
164 Franklin Tpke., Ste. 2, Mahwah 07430

American Paper & Supply Co., LLC
Phone—(201) 939-4200
10 Industrial Rd., P.O. Box 346, Carlstadt 07072

Amsan Eagle Maintenance Supply
Phone—(856) 317-9500
80 Twin Bridge Dr., Pennsauken 08110

Dade Paper Co.
Phone—(732) 254-3100
120 Tices Ln., East Brunswick 08816

Energy Recycling Co., LLC
Phone—(732) 545-6619
409 Joyce Kilmer Ave., New Brunswick 08901

**Jersey Paper Plus, Inc.**
**Phone—(732) 750-1900**
**Fax—(732) 750-2824**
**Web—www.jerseypaper.com**
**47 Brunswick Ave., Edison 08817**

Lerro Products, Inc.
Phone—(856) 203-3561
1321 Walnut St., Camden 08103

Supplyone, Inc.
Phone—(718) 392-7400
1200 Madison Ave., Paterson 07503

## JELLIES, JAMS & PRESERVES

Allied Old English, Inc.
Phone—(732) 636-2060
100 Markley St., Port Reading 07064

B & G Foods, Inc. (H Q)
Phone—(973) 401-6500
4 Gatehall Dr., Ste. 110, Parsippany 07054

## JEWELERS' TOOLS & SUPPLIES

Metro America Sales, Inc.
Phone—(908) 490-0001
137 South Ave., Fanwood 07023

Shor International Corp.
Phone—(973) 520-8777
77 Fairwood Rd., Madison 07940

## JEWELRY

Aabhushan Exports Private Ltd.
Phone—(732) 516-0800
155 Wood Ave., Edison 08820

Aires Jewelry Co.
Phone—(973) 292-0950
3 Harrison Ave., Morris Plains 07950

Aydin Jewelry, Inc.
Phone—(201) 818-1002
885 Route 17 S., Ramsey 07446

Barrasso & Blasi, Inc.
Phone—(973) 761-0595
1581 Springfield Ave., Maplewood 07040

Bhamra Chain Mfg. Co.
Phone—(908) 686-4555
1020 Springfield Rd., Union City 07087

Big Apple Jewelry Mfg.
Phone—(201) 531-1600
62 Railroad Ave., East Rutherford 07073

Calbar, LLC
Phone—(201) 246-1555
307 Bergen Ave., Kearny 07032

Calima Jewels
Phone—(973) 746-2976
215 Glen Ridge Ave., Montclair 07042

Callahan Jewelers, Inc.
Phone—(201) 768-6136
86 Vervalen St., Closter 07624

Castor Jewelry
Phone—(609) 397-0809
13 N. Union St., Lambertville 08530

Church & Co.
Phone—(732) 363-4949
2121 Whitesville Rd., Toms River 08755

Cinco Star, LLC
Phone—(732) 744-1617
2 Karnell Ct., Edison 08820

Corbo Jewelers, Inc.
Phone—(973) 777-1635
1055 Bloomfield Ave., Clifton 07012

Creations By Stefano, Inc.
Phone—(201) 863-5806
1261 Paterson Plank Rd., Secaucus 07094

Donsky Designs
Phone—(609) 345-4445
3851 Boardwalk, Apt. 2405, Atlantic City 08401

Eli Jewels, Inc.
Phone—(201) 291-4200
14 Wyckoff Ave., Ramsey 07446

Fisher Co., Inc., Robert
Phone—(908) 928-0002
280 Sheffield St., Mountainside 07092

## JEWELRY — (cont.)

**Gary's Gem Garden**
Phone—(856) 795-5077
404 Route 70 E., Cherry Hill 08034

**GlassRoots, Inc.**
Phone—(973) 353-9555
10 Bleeker St., Newark 07102

**Guida Setting Co.**
Phone—(973) 625-1225
124 E. Main St., Denville 07834

**Harris Kenya Gem Co., Tom**
Phone—(609) 823-3315
6504 Ventnor Ave., Ventnor City 08406

**I Did It Metal Art, Inc.**
Phone—(732) 866-8481
53 Gables Way, Jackson 08527

**Ilie's Eternally Flawless**
Phone—(201) 487-1991
275 E. State Route 4, Paramus 07652

**Jeweler's Gallery Corp.**
Phone—(973) 543-6117
9 W. Main St., Mendham 07945

**Jewelry Arts Mfg., Inc.**
Phone—(201) 864-5188
1701 Summit Ave., Union City 07087

**Jewelry Design Gallery, Inc.**
Phone—(732) 536-1184
357 U.S. Highway 9, Ste. 18, Englishtown 07726

**Jewelry Tool & Die Co.**
Phone—(908) 686-3500
4 Mark Rd., Ste. G, Kenilworth 07033

**Jocely, Inc.**
Phone—(800) 526-4597
280 Sheffield St., Mountainside 07092

**Jonart Metals, LLC**
Phone—(732) 382-0300
710 New Brunswick Ave., P.O. Box 333, Rahway 07065

**Kay, Inc., Scott**
Phone—(201) 287-0100
780 Palisape Ave., Teaneck 07666

**Kornspan Jewelry, Inc.**
Phone—(908) 925-1101
1131 W. Saint Georges Ave., Linden 07036

**Lamar Diamond Jewelry Corp.**
Phone—(201) 863-8683
5600 John F. Kennedy Blvd., Ste. 109, West New York 07093

**Le Monde Deluxe**
Phone—(856) 854-5440
232 White Horse Pike, Collingswood 08107

**Nadri Jewelry Group**
Phone—(201) 585-0088
2 Executive Dr., Ste. 500, Fort Lee 07024

**Novell Enterprises, Inc.**
Phone—(732) 428-8300
2100 Felver Ct., Rahway 07065

**Pacicco & Co. Jewelers**
Phone—(201) 947-1106
331 Broad Ave., Leonia 07605

**Paglia & Son, Inc., D.**
Phone—(908) 654-5999
280 Sheffield St., Mountainside 07092

**Provost Square Assocs.**
Phone—(973) 403-8755
6 Provost Sq., Caldwell 07006

**S & R Designs, Inc.**
Phone—(856) 985-0303
36 W. Route 70, Ste. 213, Marlton 08053

**Salkin's Jewel Case, Inc.**
Phone—(732) 462-3311
3585 Highway 9, South Freehold Shopping Ctr., Freehold 07728

**Samuel, Inc.**
Phone—(201) 439-1555
60 W. Englewood, Bergenfield 07621

**San Marel Designs, Inc.**
Phone—(973) 426-9554
98 U.S. Highway 46, Ste. 10, Budd Lake 07828

**SJA Jewelry, Inc.**
Phone—(201) 837-0990
44 Burlews Ct., Hackensack 07601

**Ski Jewelers Co.**
Phone—(732) 752-6446
299 Route 22, Green Brook 08812

**Star Creation, Inc. (H Q)**
Phone—(732) 819-7070
1506 Stelton Rd., Piscataway 08854

**Tomorrow's Heirlooms Handcrafted Gemstone Jewelry**
Phone—(609) 921-9440
2 Chambers St., Princeton 08542

**Trimarco Jewelers, Inc.**
Phone—(973) 762-7380
1847-1849 Springfield Ave., Maplewood 07040

**Ultimate Trading Corp.**
Phone—(973) 228-7700
4 Just Rd., Fairfield 07004

**Vincent & Co., Inc., J.**
Phone—(732) 256-4410
420 Route 34, Ste. 301, P.O. Box 448, Colts Neck 07722

## JEWELRY — Costume

**Atlas Fashions**
Phone—(732) 254-6090
148 Tices Ln., East Brunswick 08816

**David Aubrey, Inc**
Phone—(201) 653-2200
186 Griffith St., Jersey City 07307

**H M S Monaco, Inc.**
Phone—(201) 533-0007
629 Grove St., 5th Fl., Jersey City 07310

**InBeau, Inc.**
Phone—(201) 227-8875
101 W. Palisade, Englewood 07631

**Kole Design, LLC**
Phone—(732) 252-9365
35 Cedar Ct., Freehold 07728

**Lieberfarb, Inc.**
Phone—(973) 676-9090
2100 Felver Ct., Rahway 07065

**Making Waves, Inc.**
Phone—(856) 795-9311
1916 Old Cuthbert Rd., Ste. B-20, Cherry Hill 08034

**Oori Trading, Inc.**
Phone—(201) 367-3030
230 Union St., P.O. Box 154, Northvale 07647

**Perfect Pearl Co., Inc.**
Phone—(201) 705-5200
100 State St., Moonachie 07074

**Royal Deluxe Accessories, LLC**
Phone—(908) 523-0550
2563 Brunswick Ave., Bldg. O, Linden 07036

## JEWELRY — Gold

**Ayesha Studio & Gallery**
Phone—(201) 503-0073
21 N. Dean St., Englewood 07631

**Chavez Jewelry, Marie**
Phone—(973) 337-8551
642 Bloomfield Ave., Verona 07044

**Jost Brothers, Inc.**
Phone—(908) 453-2266
295 Jost Dr., Oxford 07863

**NEI Group, Inc.**
Phone—(201) 488-5858
44 Burlews Ct., Hackensack 07601

## JEWELRY — Silver

**925ny**
Phone—(732) 404-4400
200 Middlesex Tpke., Ste. 202, Iselin 08830

**Ann Carol Designs, Inc.**
Phone—(732) 469-7552
333 Mountain Ave., Bound Brook 08805

**Silver Stones International, LLC**
Phone—(732) 886-0011
902 E. County Line Rd., Ste. 200, Lakewood 08701

**Studio Feifish, Llc**
Phone—(973) 303-3287
54 Ironia Rd., Randolph 07869

## JEWELRY CASTING

**Joseph Castings, Inc.**
Phone—(201) 712-0717
25 Brook Ave., Maywood 07607

Search from among 430,000 U.S. manufacturers & suppliers:
**IndustryNet.com**

## JEWELRY FINDINGS

**E F Design Ltd.**
Phone—(201) 319-9075
600 Harbor Blvd., Unit 1022, Weehawken 07086

**Grassmann-Blake, Inc.**
Phone—(973) 379-6170
58 E. Willow St., Millburn 07041

**Metal City Findings Co.**
Phone—(201) 569-7300
456 Nordhoff Pl., P.O. Box 7300, Englewood 07631

**Solmor Mfg. Co., Inc.**
Phone—(973) 824-7203
164 Emmet St., Newark 07114

**Tessler & Weiss, Inc.**
Phone—(908) 686-0513
2389 Vauxhall Rd., P.O. Box 3414, Union 07083

## JEWELRY MOUNTINGS & SETTINGS

**Goldstein Setting Co Inc /TA DanMar Jewelers**
Phone—(908) 964-1034
2464 Morris Ave., Union 07083

**Victor's Three-D, Inc.**
Phone—(201) 845-4433
25 Brook Ave., Maywood 07607

## JEWELRY REPAIR

**Neves Jewelers**
Phone—(732) 741-7757
Fax—(732) 741-5175
Web—www.nevesjewelers.com
Email—nevesjewelers@aol.com
557 Broad St., Shrewsbury 07702

**Wolf Fine Jewelers**
Monmouth Mall, Ocean County Mall, Pier Shops at Caesars
Phone—(732) 460-9653
Web—www.wolffinejewelers.com
Email—info@wolffinejewelers.com
180 State Route 35, Ste. 1212, Eatontown 07724

## JOB SHOPS

**Bergen Cable Technology, LLC**
Cable Assemblies, Wire Rope & Lockwire Replacement Safety Cable
Phone—(973) 276-9596 / (800) 237-4369
Fax—(973) 276-9566
Web—www.bergencable.com
Email—sales@bergencable.com
343 Kaplan Dr., Fairfield 07004
(see our ad under WIRE ROPE)

**Durex, Inc.**
Email: custserv@durexinc.com
ISO 9001 Registered Contract Metal Fabrication Facility
Phone—(908) 688-0800
Fax—(908) 688-0718
Web—www.durexinc.com
5 Stahuber Ave., Union 07083
(see our ad under METAL FABRICATING)

**E & J Machine And Tool, LLC**
Phone—(973) 810-2312 / (973) 810-2313
Fax—(973) 601-7953
Web—www.ejmachine.com
Email—sales@ejmachine.com
12 Orben Dr., Unit 1, Landing 07850
(see our ad on next page)

**FIMS Mfg. Corp.**
Phone—(201) 845-7088
Fax—(201) 845-8287
Web—www.fimsmfg.com
Email—fimsmfg@optonline.net
8 Allerman Rd., Oakland 07436

INDUSTRYNET.com
THE INDUSTRIAL SEARCH ENGINE
**Find Suppliers Nationally FREE!**

# E & J Machine And Tool, LLC

## Job Shops

## (973) 810-2312

### FAX: (973) 601-7953

www.ejmachine.com   sales@ejmachine.com

12 Orben Dr., Unit 1 • Landing, NJ 07850

## JOB SHOPS — *(cont.)*

G. Cotter Enterprises, Inc.
  Phone—(973) 376-5840
  48 Brown Ave., Springfield 07081

**G. Cotter Enterprises, Inc.**
*Micro & laser micro welding job shop*
www.gcotter.com
**(973) 376-5840**
48 Brown Ave. Springfield, NJ 07081

International Tool & Mfg., Inc.
Precision machining job shop
Phone—(973) 227-6767
Fax—(973) 227-6711
Web—www.international-inc.com
Email—sales@international-inc.com
30 Sherwood Ln., Ste. 10, Fairfield 07004

**INTERNATIONAL TOOL & MFG., INC.**
*Precision machining job shop*
**(973) 227-6767**
www.international-inc.com
sales@international-inc.com
30 Sherwood Ln. Ste. 10 • Fairfield, NJ 07004

## JUICE EXTRACTORS

Citroil Enterprises, Inc.
  Fruit, Juices, Oils
  Phone—(201) 933-8405
  Fax—(201) 933-8217
  Web—www.citromax.com
  Email—cgonzabay@citroil.com
  444 Washington Ave., Carlstadt 07072

*Citroil* enterprises
*Quality Flavorings & Flavors*
**www.citromax.com**
**(201) 933-8405 • FAX: (201) 933-8217**
444 Washington Ave. Carlstadt, NJ 07072

## JUICES

Dr Pepper Snapple Group, Inc.
  Phone—(732) 969-1600
  1200 Milik St., Carteret 07008

---

Wayne County Foods, Inc.
  Phone—(973) 399-0101
  360 Coit St., Irvington 07111

## KETTLES — Stainless Steel

Warwick Mfg. & Equipment Co., LLC
  Buy & sell used: Chemical, food, cosmetic, packaging
  & pharmaceutical equipment
  Phone—(732) 729-0400 / (732) 241-9263
  Fax—(732) 729-1235
  Web—www.warwickequipment.com
  Email—sales@warwickequipment.com
  1112 12th St., North Brunswick 08902
  *(see our ad Outside Back Cover)*

## KEYBOARDS — Electronic

InduKey North America, LLC
  Phone—(877) 588-2172
  329 Moore Ave., Leonia 07605

## KILNS — Industrial

L & L Kiln Mfg. Co., Inc.
  Phone—(856) 294-0077
  505 Sharptown Rd., Swedesboro 08085

## KIOSKS

I & E Co.
  Phone—(973) 579-0009
  150 Main St., Ogdensburg 07439

## KITCHEN COUNTERTOPS

Artistic Marble & Granite Surfaces, Inc.
  Web: www.NJMarble.com
  Phone—(973) 304-2001
  Fax—(973) 427-9142
  Email—artistic269@aol.com
  269 Goffle Rd., Hawthorne 07506

## KITCHEN EQUIPMENT
### (also see specific headings)

South Jersey Metal, Inc.
  Phone—(856) 228-0642
  1651 Hurffville Rd., Route 41, P.O. Box 5148,
  Deptford 08096
T & A Metal Products, Inc.
  Phone—(856) 227-1700
  1671 Hurffville Rd., P.O. Box 1805, Deptford
  08096

## KITCHEN GADGETS & UTENSILS

Acme International Enterprises, Inc.
  Phone—(973) 416-0400
  400 Lyster Ave., Saddle Brook 07663

---

## KNIT PRODUCTS

Ameri-Tex, Inc.
  Phone—(973) 286-0102
  461 Frelinghuysen Ave., Newark 07114
Fleck Knitwear Co., Inc.
  Phone—(908) 754-8888
  400 Leland Ave., Plainfield 07062
Markbilt Technical Fabrics Corp.
  Phone—(973) 482-6400
  1875 McCarter Hwy., Newark 07104
Meadows Knitting Corp.
  Phone—(973) 482-6400
  1875 McCarter Hwy., Newark 07104

## KNIVES

Excel Hobby Blades Corp.
  Phone—(973) 278-4000
  481 Getty Ave., P.O. Box 1045, Paterson 07503
Stay Focused Marketing
  Phone—(201) 750-5050
  157 Veterans Dr., Northvale 07647

## KNIVES — Machine

Industrial Products Corp.
  Phone—(201) 652-5913
  1 Hollywood Ave., Ste. 30, Ho-Ho-Kus 07423

## KNIVES — Paper Cutting

Derma-Safe Co., LLC
  Phone—(973) 839-6383
  32 Juniper Rd., Wayne 07470

## KNOBS

Top Knobs USA, Inc.
  Phone—(908) 359-6174
  170 Township Line Rd., Bldg. D, Hillsborough
  08844

## LABEL TAPES

Web-Cote Industries, Inc.
  Phone—(973) 827-2299
  141 Wheatsworth Rd., P.O. Box 120, Hamburg
  07419

## LABELING EQUIPMENT

A T Information Products, Inc.
  Phone—(201) 529-0202
  575 Corporate Dr., Mahwah 07430
Harland America
  Phone—(856) 764-9622
  1803 Underwood Blvd., Delran 08075
Pro-Motion Industries, LLC
  Phone—(856) 809-0040
  102 Allied Pkwy., Sicklerville 08081

## LABELING MACHINES

Warwick Mfg. & Equipment Co., LLC
  Buy & sell used: Chemical, food, cosmetic, packaging
  & pharmaceutical equipment
  Phone—(732) 729-0400 / (732) 241-9263
  Fax—(732) 729-1235
  Web—www.warwickequipment.com
  Email—sales@warwickequipment.com
  1112 12th St., North Brunswick 08902
  *(see our ad Outside Back Cover)*

## LABELING SERVICES

Apparel Distribution, Inc.
  Phone—(732) 287-1110
  45 Saw Mill Pond Rd., Edison 08817

## LABELS

Brimar Industries, Inc.
  Phone—(973) 340-7889
  64 Outwater Ln., 3rd Fl., P.O. Box 467, Garfield
  07026
CCL Label, Inc.
  Phone—(609) 586-1332
  104 N. Gold Dr., Robbinsville 08691

INDUSTRY

## LABELS — (cont.)

Driscoll Label Co., Inc.
Phone—(973) 585-7295
19 West St., East Hanover 07936
Innovative Labeling, Inc.
Phone—(973) 227-4800
12 Gloria Ln., Ste. 4, Fairfield 07004
Trend Printing International Label, Inc.
Phone—(201) 941-6611
1183 Edgewater Ave., Ridgefield 07657

## LABELS — Bar Coded

Par Code Symbology, Inc.
Phone—(973) 618-0550
119 Harrison Ave., P.O. Box 87, Roseland 07068

## LABELS — Heat Transfer

Omega Heat Transfer Co., Inc.
Phone—(732) 340-0023
329 New Brunswick Ave., Rahway 07065
Superior Trademark, Inc.
Phone—(201) 652-1900
45 Zazzetti St., P.O. Box 35, Waldwick 07463
Webtech, Inc.
Phone—(609) 259-2800
108 N. Gold Dr., Robbinsville 08691

## LABELS — Pharmaceutical

Plymouth Printing Co., Inc. (H Q)
Phone—(908) 276-8100
450 North Ave., P.O. Box 68, Cranford 07016

## LABELS — Pressure Sensitive

Beau Label LLC
Phone—(973) 318-7800
385 Hillside Ave., Hillside 07205
Capital Label & Affixing Co.
Phone—(856) 786-1700
1100 Taylors Ln., Unit 5, Cinnaminson 08077
CCL Label TubeDec
Phone—(609) 953-5050
92 Ark Rd., Lumberton 08048
CCL Label, Inc.
Phone—(609) 443-3700
120 Stockton St., Hightstown 08520
Certified Labeling Solutions
Phone—(908) 704-9997
51 Old Camplain Rd., Hillsborough 08844
Classic Printers & Converters
Phone—(732) 985-1100
140 Ethel Rd. W., Ste. K, Piscataway 08854
Concord Paper Mfg., Inc.
Phone—(201) 567-2529
375 Sylvan Ave., Ste. 23, Englewood Cliffs 07632
Horizon Label, LLC
Phone—(856) 767-0777
1049 Industrial Dr., West Berlin 08091
Id Technology
Phone—(888) 405-4574
48 Spruce St., Oakland 07436
Label Graphics Mfg.
Phone—(973) 890-5665
315 Fairfield Rd., Unit 1, Fairfield 07004
Label Graphics Mfg., Inc.
Phone—(973) 890-5665
175 Paterson Ave., Little Falls 07424
Label Master, Inc.
Phone—(973) 546-3110
89 Dell Glen Ave., Lodi 07644
**Lizard Label, Inc.**
**Full scale, multi-press flexographic & digital print shop**
**Phone—(973) 808-0098 / (877) 807-0098**
**Fax—(973) 882-8829**
**Web—www.lizardlabel.com**
**Email—sales@lizardlabel.com**
**10-E Commerce Rd., Fairfield 07004**
Logotech, Inc.
Phone—(973) 882-9595
18 Madison Rd., Fairfield 07004

Do nationwide searches for products & services at:
IndustryNet.com

**Luminer Converting Group, Inc.**
**Email: info@luminer.com**
**A leading international pressure sensitive label printer & converter**
**Phone—(732) 886-6557**
**Fax—(732) 886-6692**
**Web—www.luminer.com**
**1925 Swarthmore Ave., Ste. 5, Lakewood 08701**
Mod-Tek Converting, LLC
Phone—(856) 662-6884
2550 Haddonfield Rd., Ste. E, Pennsauken 08110
Princeton Label Co.
Phone—(609) 490-0800
1226 U.S. Highway 130, Robbinsville 08691
Renell Label Print, Inc.
Phone—(201) 652-6544
15 Sunflower Ave., Paramus 07652
Scientific Labeling Systems, Inc.
Phone—(973) 722-8229
339 6th Ave. W., Newark 07107
**Tri-State Tape & Label Co., Inc.**
**Phone—(800) 682-7892 / (609) 387-4600**
**Fax—(609) 387-3691**
**Web—www.tristatelabel.com**
**Email—dwimer@tristatelabel.com**
**351 Railroad Ave., P.O. Box 377, Beverly 08010**
United Label Corp.
Phone—(973) 589-6500
65 Chambers St., Newark 07105
Wise Tag & Label Co., Inc.
Phone—(856) 663-2400
1077 Thomas Busch Memorial Hwy., Pennsauken 08110
Yellow Stone Distributing Co.
Phone—(973) 808-8188
50 Kulick Rd., Fairfield 07004

## LABELS — Thermal

Aeon Industries, Inc.
Phone—(732) 246-3224
76 Veronica Ave., Somerset 08873
TEMPTIME Corp.
Phone—(973) 984-6000
116 The American Rd., 2nd Fl., Morris Plains 07950

## LABELS — Woven

R-Pac International Corp.
Phone—(973) 916-1600
69 Kingsland Ave., Marino Plz. 1, Clifton 07014
Xpresa Labels Corp.
Phone—(973) 669-8444
681 Eagle Rock Ave., West Orange 07052

## LABOR MANAGEMENT SOFTWARE

Datamatics Management Services, Inc.
Phone—(732) 738-9600
330 New Brunswick Ave., Fords 08863
SumTotal Systems, LLC
Phone—(973) 364-0480
600 Parsippany Rd., Parsippany 07054

## LABORATORIES — Environmental

PSC Environmental Services, LLC
Phone—(215) 822-2676 / (800) 365-9295
Fax—(215) 997-8219
Web—www.pscnow.com
Email—info@pscnow.com
2337 N. Penn Rd., Hatfield, PA 19440
*(see our ad under ENVIRONMENTAL SERVICES)*

Need an
*Industry*Section
for another state?

Call us... 847-864-7590

## LABORATORIES — Testing & Inspection

Loricon Testing Service, Inc.
Analytical Testing-Microbiology
Phone—(732) 787-4131
Fax—(732) 264-4585
Web—www.loricontesting.com
Email—loricon55@optonline.net
55 State Route 36, Keyport 07735

LORICON
Testing Service, Inc.

Meeting All Your
Microbiological & Analytical
Testing Requirements
Loricon Testing Service, Inc.
Loricon Analytical Testing Laboratory, LLC
(732) 787-4131 loricon55@optonline.net
55 State Route 36 Keyport, NJ 07735

New Jersey Analyticals Labs
Also well certifications & environmental testing
Phone—(609) 737-3477
Fax—(609) 737-3052
Web—www.njal.com
Email—athomas@njal.com
380 Scotch Rd., Bldg. 2, Ste. 1B, Ewing 08628

## LABORATORY EQUIPMENT & SUPPLIES

Across International, LLC
Phone—(888) 988-0899
111 Dorsa Ave., Livingston 07039
Analytical Sales & Services, Inc.
Phone—(973) 616-0700
237 W. Parkway, Ste. 1, Pompton Plains 07444
Armfield, Inc.
Phone—(609) 208-2800
9 Trenton Lakewood Rd., Ste. 2, Millstone Township 08510
Arrow Engineering Co.
Phone—(908) 353-5233
260 Pennsylvania Ave., Hillside 07205
Azzota Corp.
Phone—(877) 649-2746
178 Franklin Rd., Randolph 07869
Belair Instrument Co., Inc.
Phone—(973) 912-8900
36 Commerce St., P.O. Box 619, Springfield 07081
Bel-Art Products, Inc.
Phone—(973) 694-0500
661 State Route 23, Wayne 07470
Bellco Glass, Inc.
Phone—(856) 691-1075
340 Edrudo Rd., Vineland 08360
Benchmark Scientific, Inc.
Phone—(908) 222-1712
116 Corporate Blvd., South Plainfield 07080
Cargille Laboratories
Phone—(973) 239-6633
55 Commerce Rd., Cedar Grove 07009
**DRG International, Inc.**
**Phone—(973) 564-7555**
**Fax—(973) 564-7556**
**Web—www.drg-international.com**
**Email—corp@drg-international.com**
**841 Mountain Ave., Springfield 07081**
Glen Mills Inc.
Phone—(973) 777-0777
220 Delawanna Ave., Clifton 07014
Globe Scientific, Inc.
Phone—(201) 599-1400
610 Winters Ave., Paramus 07652
Hematechnologies, Inc.
Phone—(908) 823-9430
291 U.S. Highway 22, Ste. 12, Lebanon 08833
Iron Mountain Plastics, Inc.
Phone—(201) 445-0063
112 Greenwood Ave., Midland Park 07432
J & H Berge, Inc.
Phone—(908) 561-1234
4111 S. Clinton Ave., South Plainfield 07080
L M Air Technology, Inc.
Phone—(732) 381-8200
1467 Pinewood St., Rahway 07065

## LABORATORY EQUIPMENT & SUPPLIES — (cont.)

Labnet International, Inc.
  Phone—(732) 417-0700
  31 Mayfield Ave., Edison 08837
Little Joe Industries
  Phone—(908) 359-5213
  10 Ilene Ct., Ste. 4, Hillsborough 08844
MEND Tech, Inc.
  Phone—(973) 340-9212
  38 Irving Pl., Garfield 07026
Microdata Instrument, Inc.
  Phone—(908) 222-1717
  1207 Hogan Dr., South Plainfield 07080
Omnitek, Inc.
  Phone—(908) 852-8500
  20 Newburgh Rd., Hackettstown 07840
OPS Diagnostics, LLC
  Phone—(908) 253-3444
  291 U.S. Highway 22 E., Bldg. 6, Lebanon 08833
Scientific Machine
  Phone—(732) 356-1553
  700 Cedar Ave., P.O. Box 67, Middlesex 08846
Spex Forensics
  Phone—(732) 549-7144
  203 Norcross Ave., Metuchen 08840
Troemner, LLC, Henry
  Phone—(856) 686-1600
  201 Wolf Dr., P.O. Box 87, Thorofare 08086
United Products & Instruments, Inc. (H Q)
  Phone—(732) 274-1155
  182 Ridge Rd., Ste. E, Dayton 08810
Xenopore Corp.
  Phone—(973) 423-2400
  299 Wagaraw Rd., Hawthorne 07506

## LABORATORY FURNITURE

Nulab Furniture Corp.
  Phone—(732) 792-0050
  11 Federal Rd., Monroe Township 08831

## LABORATORY REAGENTS

Perkins Co., Inc., P. W.
  Phone—(856) 769-3525
  221 Commissioners Pike, Woodstown 08098

## LACQUERS

Agate Lacquer Tri-Nat, LLC
  Phone—(732) 968-1080
  824 South Ave., Middlesex 08846

## LADDERS

A. L. Don
  Phone—(732) 574-1441
  1 Dock St., Matawan 07747

## LAKE & POND MANAGEMENT

Personalized Ponds Service
  Water pond & lake maintenance
  Phone—(856) 374-7888
  1342 Old Black Horse Pike, Blackwood 08012

## LAMINATES — Industrial

Thomson Lamination Co., Inc.
  Phone—(856) 779-8521
  504 E. Linwood Ave., Maple Shade 08052

## LAMINATING

Abbey/Watchung, LLC
  Phone—(908) 241-7717
  16 N. 26th St., Kenilworth 07033
Dikeman Laminating Corp.
  Phone—(973) 473-5696
  181 Sargeant Ave., Clifton 07013
E & H Laminating & Slitting Co.
  Phone—(973) 345-1725
  Fax—(973) 345-3224
  Web—www.ehlam.com
  Email—info@ehlam.com
  138 Grand St., Paterson 07501
    (see our ad under ADHESIVES)

International Foam Products, Inc.
  Phone—(201) 909-0950
  P.O. Box 545, Stanhope 07874
LACOA, Inc.
  Phone—(973) 754-1000
  34 Waite St., Paterson 07524

## LAMINATING — Paper Products

Butler Printing & Laminating
  Phone—(973) 838-8550
  250 Hamburg Tpke., P.O. Box 836, Butler 07405
Graph Corr, LLC
  Phone—(732) 355-0088
  4 Corn Rd., Dayton 08810
Lamitech, Inc.
  Phone—(609) 860-8037
  322 Half-Acre Rd., Cranbury 08512

## LAMINATING EQUIPMENT

Diamond Enterprise Group
  Phone—(908) 771-6777
  321 Snyder Ave., Berkeley Heights 07922
Royal Sovereign International, Inc.
  Phone—(201) 750-1020
  2 Volvo Dr., Rockleigh 07647

## LAMINATIONS — Fabric

Satesa Corp.
  Phone—(201) 871-8989
  154 W. Forest Ave., Englewood 07631

## LAMINATIONS — Foil

Unifoil Corp.
  Phone—(973) 244-9900
  12 Daniel Rd., Ste. 101, Fairfield 07004

## LAMINATIONS — Magnetic

Magnetic Metals Corp.
  Precision Motor Laminations
  Phone—(856) 964-7842
  Fax—(856) 365-8723
  Web—www.magmet.com
  Email—khaley@magmet.com
  1900 Hayes Ave., Camden 08105

## LAMP SHADES

Artistic Products, LLC
  Phone—(732) 382-4141
  1905 Elizabeth Ave., Rahway 07065
Jay-Bee Lamp & Shade Co., Inc.
  Phone—(973) 473-1569
  33 Hoover Ave., Passaic 07055
Monter Lite Co., Inc.
  Phone—(732) 748-1288
  560 Lincoln Blvd., Ste. 2, Middlesex 08846
New Brunswick Lamp Shade Co.
  Manufacturer of quality shades made in the USA. B2B only, since 1943
  Phone—(732) 545-0377
  Web—www.nbls.com
  Email—shades@nbls.com
  7 Terminal Rd., New Brunswick 08901
Sterling Products
  Phone—(973) 471-2858
  90 Dayton Ave., Bldg. 12-C, Ste. 77, Passaic 07055

## LAMPS

Big Eye Lamp, Inc.
  Phone—(732) 557-9400
  870 Route 530, Ste. 2, Whiting 08759

## LAMPS — Ultraviolet

Hanovia Specialty Lighting LLC
  Phone—(973) 651-5510
  6 Evans St., Fairfield 07004
TCS Technologies, Inc.
  Phone—(908) 852-7555
  430 Sand Shore Rd., Unit 1, Hackettstown 07840

## LANDSCAPE CONTRACTORS

John Mirza Landscaping Inc.
  Landscaping, Irrigation, Hydroseeding (Covering all your horticultural needs)
  Phone—(201) 476-9677
  Fax—(201) 265-1745
  Web—www.mirzalandscaping.com
  Email—mirzalandscaping@aol.com
  49 Spring Valley Rd., Ste. B, Montvale 07645

## LANDSCAPE EQUIPMENT

Reinco, Inc.
  Phone—(908) 755-0921
  520 North Ave., Plainfield 07060

## LANDSCAPE MATERIALS

Greenway Seed Co.
  Phone—(201) 791-1122
  Fax—(201) 791-6879
  Email—greenwayseed@verizon.net
  4-21 Banta Place, Fair Lawn 07410

## LANDSCAPE SUPPLIES

Schofield Co., Inc., George
  Phone—(732) 356-0858
  831 E. Main St., Bridgewater 08807

## LASER CUTTING

ADM Custom Metal Fabrication, Inc.
  Phone—(973) 284-0088
  Web—www.admmetal.com
  Email—info@admmetal.com
  263 Hillside Ave., Ste. 2, Nutley 07110

ADM CUSTOM METAL FABRICATION, INC.

LATEST CNC TECHNOLOGY
LASER CUTTING
LIGHTS OUT FABRICATION
ROBOTIC WELDING

GUARDS • PANELS • CONSOLES
CABINETS • TRANSITIONS • HOPPERS
FRAMEWORK • MACHINE BASES

973-284-0088

www.ADMmetal.com
info@admmetal.com

Airtec, Inc.
  Sheet metal fabrication, machining & laser cutting
  Phone—(732) 382-3700
  Fax—(732) 388-0084
  Email—airtecunique@aol.com
  17 W. Scott Ave., P.O. Box 1181, Rahway 07065
    (see our ad under SHEET METAL FABRICATION)
Durex, Inc.
  Email—custserv@durexinc.com
  ISO 9001 Registered Contract Metal Fabrication Facility
  Phone—(908) 688-0800
  Fax—(908) 688-0718
  Web—www.durexinc.com
  5 Stahuber Ave., Union 07083
    (see our ad under METAL FABRICATING)
GP Precision, Inc.
  ISO 9001:2000 Certified
  Phone—(908) 850-1940
  Fax—(908) 850-5926
  Web—www.gpsheetmetal.com
  Email—sales@gpsheetmetal.com
  434 Sand Shore Rd., Hackettstown 07840
TORNQVIST
  Phone—(973) 686-5999
  29 Hanes Dr., Wayne 07470

INDUSTRY

## LASER CUTTING — Plastic

**Emco Industrial Plastics, Inc.**
Supplier of Plastic Sheet, Rod, Tube, Films & Prototyping
Phone—(973) 559-5610
Fax—(973) 239-1595
Web—www.emcoplastics.com
Email—mailbox@emcoplastics.com
99 Commerce Rd., P.O. Box 2503, Cedar Grove 07009
*(see our ad Outside Front Cover)*

## LASERS

Applied Optronics
Phone—(908) 753-6300
111 Corporate Blvd., Bldg. J, South Plainfield 07080
Intense-US
Phone—(732) 249-2228
1200 Airport Rd., Ste. A, North Brunswick 08902
Light Age, Inc.
Phone—(732) 563-0600
500 Apgar Dr., Ste. 1, Somerset 08873
OSI Laser Diode, Inc.
Phone—(732) 549-9001
4 Olsen Ave., Edison 08820
Princeton Lightwave, Inc.
Phone—(609) 495-2600
2555 U.S. Highway 130, Ste. 1, Cranbury 08512
Swatch Group (U.S.), Inc. (H Q)
Phone—(201) 271-1400
1200 Harbor Blvd., 7th Fl., Weehawken 07086
**TRUMPF Photonics, Inc.**
Phone—(609) 925-8200
Fax—(609) 409-7021
Web—www.us.trumpf.com
Email—info@us.trumpf.com
2601 US Route 130 S., Cranbury 08512

**TRUMPF Photonics, Inc.**
*High-power semiconductor lasers*
**www.us.trumpf.com**
**(609) 925-8200**
2601 US Route 130 S. Cranbury, NJ 08512

## LASERS — Industrial

Haas Laser Technologies, Inc.
Phone—(973) 598-1150
37 Ironia Rd., Flanders 07836
Innovative Photonic Solutions
Phone—(732) 355-9300
4250 U.S. Highway 1, Ste. 1, Monmouth Junction 08852
Laser Energetics, Inc.
Phone—(609) 587-8250
3535 Quakerbridge Rd., Ste. 700, Mercerville 08619
PRC Laser
Phone—(973) 347-0100
350 N. Frontage Rd., Landing 07850
U.S. Laser Corp.
Phone—(201) 848-9200
825 Windham Ct. N., Ste. 2, Wyckoff 07481

## LATEX COMPOUNDS

**Deltech Resin Co.**
Phone—(973) 589-0880 / (973) 589-3331
(800) 785-4415
Fax—(973) 589-7231
Web—www.deltechcorp.com
Email—danderson@deltechresins.com
49 Rutherford St., Newark 07105
*(see our ad under RESINS)*

## LATEX SPECIALTY PRODUCTS

Lubrizol Advanced Materials, Inc.
Phone—(856) 351-2100
76 Porcupine Rd., Pedricktown 08067

## LAUNDRY EQUIPMENT

Hoffman/New Yorker, Inc. (H Q)
Phone—(201) 488-1800
46 Clinton Pl., Hackensack 07601
Reno's Appliance
Addtl. Web: www.buyrenos.com
Toll Free Ph: (866)88-RENOS
Phone—(973) 247-1860 / (866) 887-3667
Fax—(973) 247-1865
Web—www.renosappliance.com
Email—sales@renosappliance.net
235 McLean Blvd., Route 20 N., Paterson 07504
*(see our ad under APPLIANCES — Household)*

## LAUNDRY EQUIPMENT — Commercial

Equipment Marketers
Phone—(856) 428-3355
100 Melrose Ave., Cherry Hill 08003
Luca Laundry Equipment, Inc.
Phone—(908) 862-2200
1500 W. Blancke St., Linden 07036

## LAUNDRY SERVICES — Industrial

**Snow White Laundry Village**
Phone—(732) 222-3400
532 Broadway, Ste. 4, Long Branch 07740

**Snow White Laundry Village**
*Quality laundry services*
**(732) 222-3400**
532 Broadway, Ste. 4 Long Branch, NJ 07740

## LAWN & GARDEN EQUIPMENT

Arett Sales Corp.
Phone—(856) 751-1224
9285 Commerce Hwy., Pennsauken 08110
Keehn Power Products
Phone—(201) 489-4454
132 Johnson Ave., Hackensack 07601
Lake Small Engine Repair, LLC
Service, Sales & Parts
Phone—(732) 873-9047
Fax—(732) 873-3395
Web—www.lakesmallengine.com
Email—lakesmallenginerepair@verizon.net
283 Cedar Grove Ln., Somerset 08873
*(see our ad under ENGINES—Gas)*
**MacDonald, Inc., Wilfred**
Phone—(201) 931-1720
Fax—(201) 931-1730
Web—www.wilfredmacdonald.com
Email—mp@wilmac.biz
19 Central Blvd., South Hackensack 07606
Snow Joe, LLC
Phone—(866) 766-9563
86 Executive Ave., Edison 08817

## LAWN & GARDEN PRODUCTS

Garden Oaks Garden Center
Phone—(732) 356-7333
1921 U.S. Highway 22, Bound Brook 08805
Green & Sons, Inc., Jonathan
Phone—(732) 938-7007
48 Squankum-Yellowbrook Rd., Howell 07731
Haddonstone (USA) Ltd.
Phone—(856) 931-7011
201 Heller Pl., Bellmawr 08031
Missry Assocs., Inc.
Phone—(732) 752-7500
100 S. Washington Ave., Dunellen 08812

*find additional suppliers at*
**IndustryNet.com**

## LAWNMOWERS

Lake Small Engine Repair, LLC
Service, Sales & Parts
Phone—(732) 873-9047
Fax—(732) 873-3395
Web—www.lakesmallengine.com
Email—lakesmallenginerepair@verizon.net
283 Cedar Grove Ln., Somerset 08873
*(see our ad under ENGINES—Gas)*

## LAWNMOWERS — Riding

Lake Small Engine Repair, LLC
Service, Sales & Parts
Phone—(732) 873-9047
Fax—(732) 873-3395
Web—www.lakesmallengine.com
Email—lakesmallenginerepair@verizon.net
283 Cedar Grove Ln., Somerset 08873
*(see our ad under ENGINES—Gas)*

## LEAD TESTING

**Certified Health & Safety Services, LLC**
Safe Today-Here Tomorrow
Phone—(856) 829-4463 / (800) 423-0137
Fax—(856) 786-3101
Web—www.certified-health-and-safety.com
Email—chss1@comcast.net
1902 Taylors Ln., Ste. A, Cinnaminson 08077
*(see our ad under ENVIRONMENTAL CONSULTANTS)*

## LEAK DETECTORS

Leak Detection Associates, Inc.
Phone—(856) 405-6636
3003 N. Mill Rd., Vineland 08360
Superior Signal Company LLC
Phone—(732) 251-0800
178 W. Greystone Rd., Old Bridge 08857

## LEATHER

Coast To Coast Leather & Vinyl, Inc.
Phone—(732) 525-8877
1 Crossman Rd. S., Sayreville 08872
Dani Leather USA, Inc.
Phone—(973) 598-0890
37 Ironia Rd., Ste. 2, Flanders 07836

## LEATHER CARE PRODUCTS

Atlas Refinery, Inc.
Phone—(973) 589-2002
142 Lockwood St., Newark 07105

## LEATHER PRODUCTS

Browbands With Bling & Other Things
Phone—(732) 740-8300
985 Farmingdale Rd., Jackson 08527
Jack Georges, Inc.
Phone—(973) 777-6999
823 Main Ave., Passaic 07055
Pt Of Vu, LLC
Phone—(908) 979-1360
52 Edinborough Ct., Hackettstown 07840
Royce Leather
Phone—(201) 330-7720
501 Penhorn Ave., Ste. 9, Secaucus 07094

## LEATHER SEAT COVERS

**E.W.E. Auto Seat Cover Co.**
Phone—(201) 869-6470
Fax—(201) 868-8491
Email—eweauto@yahoo.com
8431 Kennedy Blvd., North Bergen 07047

## LEATHER TANNING

Myers Group, LLC, The
Phone—(973) 761-6414
74 Blanchard Rd., South Orange 07079

© Copyright 2015 Manufacturers' News, Inc.

## LENSES

Essilor Laboratories
Phone—(732) 563-9884
5 Powderhorn Dr., Warren 07059

I-See Optical Laboratories, Inc.
Phone—(856) 227-9300
44 W. Church St., Blackwood 08012

Sheridan Optical Co., Inc.
Phone—(856) 582-0963
108 Clinton Ave., Pitman 08071

## LETTERING

Educational Information & Resource Center
Phone—(856) 582-7000
107 Gilbreth Pkwy., Mullica Hill 08062

## LIFE SAVING EQUIPMENT

Air Cruisers, LLC
Phone—(732) 681-3527
1747 State Route 34, Wall Township 07727

Switlik Parachute Co., Inc.
Phone—(609) 587-3300
1325 E. State St., Trenton 08609

## LIFT TRUCK ATTACHMENTS

**Action Lift Trucks, Inc.**
**Phone—(973) 589-2320**
**Fax—(973) 824-4768**
**Web—www.actionlifttrucks.com**
**Email—actionlift@optonline.net**
**35 Avenue C, Newark 07114**

## LIFT TRUCK REPLACEMENT PARTS

**Raymond Of NJ, LLC**
**Phone—(908) 624-9570 / (800) 800-2024**
**Fax—(908) 624-9553**
**Web—www.raymond-nj.com**
**Email—info@raymond-nj.com**
**1000 Brighton St., Union 07083**
*(see our ad under MATERIAL HANDLING EQUIPMENT)*

## LIFT TRUCKS

**Action Lift Trucks, Inc.**
**Phone—(973) 589-2320**
**Fax—(973) 824-4768**
**Web—www.actionlifttrucks.com**
**Email—actionlift@optonline.net**
**35 Avenue C, Newark 07114**

Crown Lift Trucks
Phone—(201) 337-1211
104 Bauer Dr., Oakland 07436

## LIFTS

Trico Lift, Inc.
Phone—(800) 468-7426
418 Southgate Ct., Mickleton 08056

Trico Lift, Inc. (H Q)
Phone—(856) 776-2350
1101 Wheaton Ave., Millville 08332

## LIFTS — Aerial

**GAR Equipment**
**Also industrial forklifts**
**Phone—(908) 756-9560**
**Fax—(908) 753-0579**
**Web—www.garequipment.com**
**Email—cmolloy@garequipment.com**
**2624 Hamilton Blvd., South Plainfield 07080**

## LIFTS — Hydraulic

**Atlantic Equipment Construction Co.**
**In business over 50 years. Modular sets and hydraulic lifts.**
**Phone—(609) 494-5321 / (609) 597-9690**
**Fax—(609) 494-2702**
**Email—atlanticequip@msn.com**
**8101 Bay Ter., Harvey Cedars 08008**

**Lightning Lift Products**
**Also hydraulic lift equipment; Designing, providing & installing drive on, drive off car lifts, frieght lifts, pallet lifts, vertical reciprocating conveyors & high speed lifts**
**Phone—(856) 824-0022**
**Fax—(856) 824-0868**
**Web—www.lightningliftproducts.com**
**Email—tweldon@lightningliftproducts.com**
**P.O. Box 5493, Delanco 08075**

## LIGHT BOXES

**Infinite Manufacturing Group, Inc.**
**Email: a.moses@infinitegroupusa.com**
**Phone—(973) 649-9950**
**Web—www.infinitegroupusa.com**
**171 Coit St., Irvington 07111**

## LIGHT BULBS

Lumenarc, Inc.
Phone—(973) 227-8048
37 Fairfield Pl., West Caldwell 07006

Martek Industries, Inc.
Phone—(856) 427-9411
600 Deer Rd., Ste. 8, Cherry Hill 08034

Philips Lighting North America
Phone—(732) 563-3000
200 Franklin Square Dr., Somerset 08873

Unique Lighting, LLC
Phone—(609) 926-8966
555 7th St., Somers Point 08244

## LIGHTING — Commercial

Estrin Calabrese Sales Agency
Phone—(908) 722-9980
17 S. Main St., Ste. 3, Manville 08835

Illuminating Experiences, LLC
Phone—(732) 745-5858
625 Jersey Ave., Unit 7, New Brunswick 08901

Mercury Lighting Products Co.
Phone—(973) 244-9444
20 Audrey Pl., Fairfield 07004

New Horizon Lighting, Inc.
Phone—(732) 833-8086
632 Cedar Swamp Rd., Jackson 08527

Starfire Lighting, Inc.
Phone—(201) 438-9540
7 Donna Dr., Wood Ridge 07075

## LIGHTING — Decorative

Classic Coves
Phone—(908) 344-1776
P.O. Box 266, Garwood 07027

**Rambusch Company**
**Family Owned Since 1898**
**Phone—(201) 333-2525**
**Fax—(201) 433-3355**
**Web—www.rambusch.com**
**Email—info@rambusch.com**
**160 Cornelison Ave., Jersey City 07304**
*(see our ad under LIGHTING FIXTURES)*

## LIGHTING — Display & Exhibit

**CDI Group, Inc.**
**Email: richard@cdigroupinc.com**
**Phone—(908) 862-1493 / (800) 339-8246**
**Fax—(908) 862-9018**
**Web—www.cdigroupinc.com**
**1135 W. Elizabeth Ave., Linden 07036**

## LIGHTING — Electroluminescent

M K S, Inc.
Phone—(856) 451-5545
7 N. Industrial Blvd., Bridgeton 08302

## LIGHTING — Emergency

Carpenter Emergency Lighting, Inc.
Phone—(609) 689-3090
2 Marlen Dr., Hamilton 08691

## LIGHTING — Fluorescent

Coronet, Inc.
Phone—(973) 345-7660
77 Wood St., Paterson 07524

## LIGHTING — Industrial

Natale Machine & Tool Co., Inc.
Phone—(201) 933-5500
339 13th St., Carlstadt 07072

Vision Lighting, Inc.
Phone—(973) 720-1200
48 N. 2nd St., Paterson 07522

## LIGHTING — LED

Buhl Electric, Inc.
Phone—(201) 296-0600
80 Little Falls Rd., Fairfield 07004

Lightscape Materials, Inc.
Phone—(609) 734-2227
201 Washington Rd., Princeton 08540

Teledex, Inc. (H Q)
Phone—(908) 964-8109
1 Atlas St., Kenilworth 07033

## LIGHTING — Marine

Oceanic Electrical Mfg. Co.
Phone—(908) 355-1900
248-256 3rd St., Elizabeth 07206

## LIGHTING — Outdoor

RAB Lighting, Inc.
Phone—(201) 784-8600
170 Ludlow Ave., Northvale 07647

## LIGHTING — Specialty

Lumitron Corp., Inc.
Phone—(908) 273-8998
35 Russo Pl., Berkeley Heights 07922

**Rambusch Company**
**Family Owned Since 1898**
**Phone—(201) 333-2525**
**Fax—(201) 433-3355**
**Web—www.rambusch.com**
**Email—info@rambusch.com**
**160 Cornelison Ave., Jersey City 07304**
*(see our ad under LIGHTING FIXTURES)*

Smartlite, LLC
Phone—(973) 470-9400
25 Madison Ave., Clifton 07011

## LIGHTING — Theatrical

City Theatrical, Inc.
Phone—(201) 549-1160
475 Barell Ave., Carlstadt 07072

PRG Light, Inc.
Phone—(201) 758-4000
915 Secaucus Ave., Secaucus 07094

## LIGHTING EQUIPMENT

Dialight Corporation (H Q)
Phone—(732) 919-3119
1501 State Highway 34 S., Farmingdale 07727

Musco Sports Lighting, LLC
Phone—(732) 751-9114
5146 W. Hurley Pond Rd., Farmingdale 07727

Picasso Lighting Industries, LLC
Phone—(201) 246-8188
46 Sellers St., Kearny 07032

R & R Plastics, Inc.
Phone—(973) 365-8083
62-70 Myrtle Ave., Passaic 07055

Radiant Thermal Products Co.
Phone—(908) 241-7700
640 W. 1st Ave., Roselle 07203

Specialty Lighting Industries, Inc.
Phone—(732) 517-0800
1306 Doris Ave., Ocean 07712

## LIGHTING FIXTURE COMPONENTS

Mitronix, Inc.
Phone—(201) 263-0063
239 Old Tappan Rd., Old Tappan 07675

## LIGHTING FIXTURES

A.C.T. Lighting, Inc.
Phone—(201) 996-0884
122 John St., Hackensack 07601
Adam Metal Products
Phone—(973) 770-1100
7 Orben Dr., P.O. Box 450, Ledgewood 07852
American Brass & Crystal, Inc.
Phone—(908) 688-8611
835 Lehigh Ave., Union 07083
**Amerlux, LLC**
**Phone—(973) 882-5010**
**Fax—(973) 882-2605**
**Web—www.amerlux.com**
**Email—rferdico@amerlux.com**
**178 Bauer Dr., Oakland 07436**

amerlux
www.amerlux.com
Commercial
Lighting Fixtures
**973-882-5010**
FAX: 973-882-2605
**178 Bauer Dr.
Oakland, NJ 07436**

Belfer Group
Phone—(732) 493-2666
10 Ruckle Ave., Farmingdale 07727
Cast Lighting, LLC
Phone—(973) 423-2303
1120-A Goffle Rd., Hawthorne 07506
Compact Fluorescent Systems
Phone—(973) 729-5262
3 Adams St., Belvidere 07823
Design Plan Lighting, Inc.
Phone—(908) 996-7710
79 Trenton Ave., Frenchtown 08825
Fabbian USA Corp.
Phone—(973) 882-3824
161 Dwight Pl., Fairfield 07004
Gemini Cut Glass Co., Inc.
Phone—(201) 568-7722
4 E. Forest Ave., Englewood 07631
Genie House, Inc.
Phone—(609) 859-0600
139 Red Lion Rd., P.O. Box 2478, Vincentown 08088
Inner Spaces Lighting And Design, LLC
Phone—(201) 692-0702
98 Copley Ave., Teaneck 07666
It's Exciting Lighting, LLC
Phone—(856) 727-5200
1270 Glen Ave., Moorestown 08057
Kurt Versen Inc
Phone—(201) 664-8200
10 Charles St., Westwood 07675
Lucid Lighting, LLC
Phone—(609) 649-0596
811 Rosemont Ringoes Rd., Stockton 08559
Lum Tech Lighting, LLC
Phone—(856) 234-2211
201 Commerce Dr., Ste. 5, Moorestown 08057
Luminaire Lighting Corp.
Phone—(732) 549-0056
5 Sutton Pl., Edison 08817

Mark Architectural Lighting
Phone—(732) 985-2600
3 Kilmer Rd., Edison 08817
National Lighting Co., Inc.
Phone—(973) 751-1600
522 Cortlandt St., Belleville 07109
North American Illumination Co.
Phone—(973) 478-4700
79 Commerce St., Garfield 07026
Philips Luminaries NA
Phone—(908) 964-7000
2345 Vauxhall Rd., P.O. Box 129, Union 07083
R L E Industries, LLC
Phone—(973) 276-1444
35 Kulick Rd., Fairfield 07004
**Rambusch Company**
**Family Owned Since 1898**
**Phone—(201) 333-2525**
**Fax—(201) 433-3355**
**Web—www.rambusch.com**
**Email—info@rambusch.com**
**160 Cornelison Ave., Jersey City 07304**

**RAMBUSCH**
Standard & Custom Lighting Fixtures
(201) 333-2525 • info@rambusch.com
Fax: (201) 433-3355
160 Cornelison Ave. • Jersey City, NJ 07304

Reggiani Lighting USA, Inc.
Phone—(201) 372-1717
372 Starke Rd., Carlstadt 07072
Sea Gull Lighting Products, LLC.
Phone—(856) 764-0500
301 W. Washington St., P.O. Box 329, Riverside 08075
Service Lamp Corp.
Phone—(856) 768-0404
112 Route 73, Voorhees 08043
Voigt Lighting
Phone—(973) 928-2252
79 Commerce St., Garfield 07026
Zumtobel Lighting, Inc.
Phone—(973) 340-8900
17-09 Zink Pl., Unit 7, Fair Lawn 07410

## LIGHTNING PROTECTION EQUIPMENT

Lighting Prevention Systems, Inc.
Phone—(856) 767-7806
154 Cooper Rd., Unit 1201, P.O. Box 353, West Berlin 08091
Lightning Prevention Systems, Inc.
Phone—(856) 767-7209
154 Cooper Rd., Ste. 1201, West Berlin 08091
Warren Lightning Rod Co.
Phone—(856) 854-7000
2 Richey Ave., Collingswood 08107

## LIMESTONE PROCESSING

Chemlime N. J., Inc. (H Q)
Phone—(908) 389-1006
2350 South Ave., Scotch Plains 07076

## LINEAR MOTION COMPONENTS

Lee Linear
Phone—(732) 752-5200
727 South Ave., Piscataway 08854

## LINENS

Allen Linen Supply
Phone—(973) 742-6131
407 20th Ave., Paterson 07513
AMD Fine Linens, LLC
Phone—(201) 568-5255
18 W. Forest Ave., Englewood 07631
Elite Home Products
Phone—(201) 880-8292
95 Mayhill St., Ste. 3, Saddle Brook 07663

Home Essentials, Inc.
Phone—(732) 388-4008
1 Terminal Way, Avenel 07001
Pecata Enterprises, Inc.
Phone—(973) 523-5866
18 Market St., Paterson 07501

## LINERS

Dover Vinyl Products
Phone—(732) 244-1444
1746 Route 9, Toms River 08755
Kayden Mfg., Inc.
Phone—(201) 880-9898
83-A Burlews Ct., Hackensack 07601
Pegasus Products, Inc.
Phone—(908) 707-1122
19 Readington Rd., Somerville 08876

## LINERS — Drum

**Dana Poly Inc.**
**The Home of Quality Film & Bags**
**Phone—(908) 474-0600 / (800) 474-1020**
**Fax—(908) 474-0604**
**Web—www.danapoly.com**
**Email—sales@danapoly.com**
**1301 W. Elizabeth Ave., Linden 07036**
*(see our ad under BAGS—Plastic)*

## LINERS — Pond

The Liner Co., Inc.
Phone—(732) 761-0700
7 Meadows Run Dr., Colts Neck 07722

## LINGERIE

**Delta Galil USA, Inc.**
**Established in 1975, Delta Galil industries is a global manufacturer & marketer of private label apparel products for men, women & children**
**Phone—(201) 902-0055**
**Fax—(201) 902-0070**
**Web—www.deltagalil.com**
**Email—delta.us@deltagalil.com**
**1 Harmon Plz., 5th Fl., Secaucus 07094**
Maidenform Brands, Inc.
Phone—(732) 621-2500
485 U.S. Highway 1 S., Bldg. F, Iselin 08830
National Mill Industry, Inc. (H Q)
Phone—(908) 862-8400
22 Jackson Dr., Cranford 07016
Priamo Designs Ltd.
Phone—(201) 861-8808
6614 Broadway, West New York 07093
Wacoal America, Inc.
Phone—(201) 933-8400
1 Wacoal Plz., Lyndhurst 07071

## LININGS — Rubber

Mercer Coating & Lining Co., Inc.
Phone—(908) 925-5000
1410 E. Linden Ave., P.O. Box 1656, Linden 07036

## LIQUID CRYSTAL DISPLAYS (LCD)

Excel Display Corp.
Phone—(732) 246-3728
100 Jersey Ave., Ste. A206, New Brunswick 08901

## LIQUID FILLING MACHINES

Edhard Corp.
Phone—(908) 850-8444
279 Blau Rd., Hackettstown 07840
**JG Machine Works**
**Also, mechanical crimping of pumps onto fragrance glass bottles**
**Phone—(732) 203-2077**
**Fax—(732) 203-2078**
**Web—www.jgmachine.com**
**Email—dnelson@jgmachine.com**
**2182 State Route 35, Holmdel 07733**
*(see our ad under FILLING MACHINERY)*

© Copyright 2015 Manufacturers' News, Inc.

## LIQUID LEVEL CONTROLS

Valeur Corp., Oilco U. S. A. Div.
   Phone—(732) 329-4666
   596 Ridge Rd., P.O. Box 226, Monmouth Junction 08852

## LIQUORS

Black Prince Distillery, Inc.
   Phone—(973) 365-2050
   691 Clifton Ave., Clifton 07011
Federal Wine & Liquor Co.
   Phone—(973) 624-6444
   56 Hackensack Ave., P.O. Box 519, Kearny 07032
Grant & Sons, Inc., William
   Phone—(732) 225-9000
   130 Fieldcrest Ave., Edison 08837
Laird & Co., Inc.
   Phone—(732) 542-0312
   1 Laird Rd., Eatontown 07724
R & R Marketing, LLC
   Phone—(609) 587-6103
   2900 E. State Street Ext., Trenton 08619
R & R Marketing, LLC
   Phone—(973) 228-5100
   10 Patton Dr., West Caldwell 07006

## LOAD CELLS

PTC Electronics, Inc.
   Phone—(201) 847-0500
   Fax—(201) 847-1394
   Web—www.ptcelectronics.com
   Email—sales@ptcelectronics.com
   P.O. Box 72, Wyckoff 07481

## LOADING DOCK EQUIPMENT

Independent Overhead Door Co., Inc.
   Phone—(732) 356-5522
   Fax—(732) 356-2885
   Web—www.independentdoor.com
   Email—paul@independentdoor.com
   176 US Highway 206, Hillsborough 08844

## LOANS

American Mortgage Co.
   Phone—(973) 740-8866
   Fax—(206) 888-4518
   Web—www.americanmortgage.com
   Email—info@americanmortgage-usa.com
   154 S. Livingston Ave., Ste. 120, Livingston 07039
Maverick Funding Corp.
   Home Loans
   Phone—(973) 585-6500 / (888) 616-6866
   Fax—(973) 352-6064
   Web—www.maverickfunding.com
   Email—hr@maverickfunding.com
   9 Entin Rd., Parsippany 07054
Millennium Home Mortgage
   Phone—(908) 233-6610
   Fax—(908) 233-7036
   Web—www.mhmlender.com
   Email—jgalayda@mhmlender.com
   209 Central Ave., Westfield 07090

## LOANS — Commercial

NVE Bank
   Phone—(201) 816-2810
   Fax—(201) 816-7379
   Web—www.nvebank.com
   76 Engle St., Englewood 07631

## LOCKERS

Excelsior Metal Products, LLC
   Phone—(732) 651-9914
   151 State Route 33, Ste. 201, Manalapan 07726

## LOCKS

Caola & Co.
   Phone—(609) 890-7331
   2 Crossroads Dr., P.O. Box 8772, Hamilton 08691

KeyValet
   Phone—(732) 521-1394
   15 Industrial Dr., P.O. Box 1099, Laurence Harbor 08879
Mul-T-Lock USA, Inc.
   Phone—(973) 778-3222
   100 Commerce Way, Ste. 2, Hackensack 07601
Northeast Lock Corp.
   Phone—(973) 777-7509
   48 Oak St., Clifton 07014
Pit Bull Tire Lock Corp.
   Phone—(888) 304-5625
   205 W. Main St., 4th Fl., Somerville 08876

**Pit Bull Tire Lock Corp.**
*Tire locks*
www.tirelock.com
**(888) 304-5625**
205 W. Main St., 4th Fl. Somerville, NJ 08876

## LOCKS — Door

SW Lock & Door Check Co.
   Phone—(201) 863-2234
   Fax—(201) 863-1511
   Email—swlock3701@yahoo.com
   3701 Kennedy Blvd., Union City 07087

## LOCKS — Electric

Lee Electric, Inc.
   Phone—(201) 866-3656
   309-11 51st St., P.O. Box 238, West New York 07093

## LOCKSMITHS

SW Lock & Door Check Co.
   Phone—(201) 863-2234
   Fax—(201) 863-1511
   Email—swlock3701@yahoo.com
   3701 Kennedy Blvd., Union City 07087

## LOGGING

Kane Wood Fuel, LLC
   Phone—(856) 589-3292
   512 Cedar Ave., Pitman 08071
Mountain Top Logging, LLC
   Phone—(908) 413-2982
   P.O. Box 324, Lebanon 08833

## LUBRICANT ADDITIVES

Nova Specialty Chemicals, LLC
   Phone—(973) 586-2147
   Fax—(973) 215-2975
   Web—www.novaspecialties.com
   Email—sales@novaspecialties.com
   404 E. Main St., Rockaway 07866

## LUBRICANTS

FTI, Inc. (H Q)
   Phone—(973) 443-4200
   8 Vreeland Rd., Florham Park 07932
Stevens Industries, Inc.
   Phone—(201) 437-6500
   39 Avenue C, P.O. Box 8, Bayonne 07002
TC Petroleum
   Phone—(732) 367-2116
   575 Prospect St., Ste. 264, Lakewood 08701
Total Specialties USA, Inc.
   Phone—(908) 862-9300
   5 N. Stiles St., Linden 07036
Unique Technologies Assocs.
   Phone—(732) 882-0777
   42 Milled Way, Avenel 07001

*Search from among 430,000 U.S. manufacturers & suppliers:*
**IndustryNet.com**

## LUBRICANTS — Industrial

Anderol, Inc.
   Phone—(973) 887-7410
   215 Merry Ln., East Hanover 07936
BP Lubricants USA, Inc.
   Phone—(973) 633-2200
   1500 Valley Rd., Wayne 07470
Cumberland Vacuum Products
   Phone—(856) 691-9155
   720 S. West Blvd., Vineland 08360
Fluoramics, Inc.
   Phone—(201) 825-8110
   18 Industrial Ave., Mahwah 07430
Gordon Terminal Service Co. Of New Jersey, Inc.
   Phone—(201) 437-8300
   2 Hook Rd., P.O. Box 143, Bayonne 07002
Hangsterfer's Laboratories, Inc.
   Phone—(856) 468-0216
   Fax—(856) 468-0200
   Web—www.hangsterfers.com
   Email—sales@hangsterfers.com
   175 Ogden Rd., Mantua 08051
      *(see our ad under LUBRICANTS—Metalworking)*
Lockrey Company LLC
   Aerospace & industrial lubricants
   Phone—(856) 665-4794
   Fax—(856) 665-4166
   1280 Old York Rd., Burlington 08016
Lubriplate Lubricants Co.
   Phone—(973) 589-9150 / (800) 733-4755
   Fax—(973) 589-4432
   Web—www.lubriplate.com
   Email—info@lubriplate.com
   129 Lockwood St., Newark 07105
Magnalube, Inc.
   Phone—(718) 729-1000
   1331 W. Edgar Rd., P.O. Box 1250, Linden 07036

## LUBRICANTS — Metalworking

Hangsterfer's Laboratories, Inc.
   Phone—(856) 468-0216
   Fax—(856) 468-0200
   Web—www.hangsterfers.com
   Email—sales@hangsterfers.com
   175 Ogden Rd., Mantua 08051

**Hangsterfer's Laboratories, Inc.**
Metalworking Lubricants
www.hangsterfers.com
856-468-0216 • Fax: 856-468-0200
175 Ogden Rd.  Mantua, NJ 08051

## LUBRICANTS — Oil & Grease

Lubriplate Lubricants Co.
   Phone—(973) 589-9150 / (800) 733-4755
   Fax—(973) 589-4432
   Web—www.lubriplate.com
   Email—info@lubriplate.com
   129 Lockwood St., Newark 07105

## LUBRICANTS — Synthetic

Chemtura Corp., Hatco Div.
   Phone—(732) 738-1000
   1020 King George Post Rd., Fords 08863
Lubriplate Lubricants Co.
   Phone—(973) 589-9150 / (800) 733-4755
   Fax—(973) 589-4432
   Web—www.lubriplate.com
   Email—info@lubriplate.com
   129 Lockwood St., Newark 07105
Mil-Comm Products Co., Inc.
   Phone—(201) 935-8561
   2 Carlton Ave., East Rutherford 07073

## LUBRICATION EQUIPMENT

Devco Corp.
   Phone—(908) 630-0005
   131 Morristown Rd., Bldg. B, Basking Ridge 07920

INDUSTRY

## LUBRICATION SYSTEMS

T M Industries, Inc.
Phone—(908) 730-7674
729 Route 625 S., Hampton 08827

## LUGGAGE

Diamond Case Co.
Phone—(973) 227-8707
45 Fairfield Pl., West Caldwell 07006
Randa Luggage Co.
Phone—(973) 873-9050
200 Broadacres Dr., 2nd Fl., Bloomfield 07003
TUMI, Inc. (H Q)
Phone—(908) 756-4400
1001 Durham Ave., South Plainfield 07080

## LUMBER

Ackley's Sawmill
Phone—(856) 451-3704
98 W. Deerfield Rd., Bridgeton 08302
Agincourt Fine Wood
Phone—(908) 874-4737
212 E. Mountain Rd., Hillsborough 08844
Bayway Lumber
Phone—(201) 991-4200
43 Porete Ave., North Arlington 07031
Castner's Sawmill
Phone—(973) 383-5661
935 Fairview Lake Rd., P.O. Box 13, Stillwater 07875
Cutler Bros. Box & Lumber Co.
Phone—(201) 943-2535
711 W. Prospect Ave., P.O. Box 217, Fairview 07022
Delmont Sawmill
Phone—(856) 785-1018
4416 Route 47, Delmont 08314
Dreyer's Lumber & Hardware, Inc.
Phone—(732) 531-0220
348 Elberon Blvd., Oakhurst 07755
Edgewater Building Supply, Inc.
Phone—(609) 387-0136
704 Woodlane Rd., Beverly 08010
Garmar Industries, Inc.
Phone—(856) 241-9700
1625 Route 322, P.O. Box 460, Woolwich Township 08085
Jefferson Lumber & Millwork Corp.
Phone—(973) 663-3100
298 Espanong Rd., Lake Hopatcong 07849
Kuiken Brothers Company, Inc.
Phone—(201) 796-2082
6-02 Fair Lawn Ave., P.O. Box 1040, Fair Lawn 07410
Kuiken Brothers Company, Inc.
Phone—(201) 652-1000
145 Lake Ave., Midland Park 07432
Kuiken Brothers Company, Inc.
Phone—(973) 875-5106
175 Route 23, Wantage 07461
ProBuild Co., LLC
Phone—(856) 505-1100
817 Eastgate Dr., Ste. 101, Mount Laurel 08054

**No Registration.**
**No Password.**
**No Hassle!**

*Source quickly & easily at*
**IndustryNet.com**

Riephoff Sawmill, Inc.
Phone—(609) 259-7265
Fax—(609) 259-7267
Web—www.riephoffsawmill.com
Email—john@riephoffsawmill.com
763 Route 524, Allentown 08501

## Riephoff Sawmill, Inc.

www.riephoffsawmill.com

john@riephoffsawmill.com

**(609) 259-7265**

**FAX: (609) 259-7267**

763 Route 524
Allentown, NJ 08501

Schairer Bros.
Phone—(609) 965-0996
254 S. Bremen Ave., Egg Harbor City 08215

## LUMBER — Dimensional

Dubin Bros. Lumber Co., Inc.
Phone—(856) 854-4675
710 Newton Ave., P.O. Box 85, Oaklyn 08107

## LUMBER — Hardwood

Willard Bros. Lumber
Phone—(609) 890-1990
300 Basin Rd., Trenton 08619

## LUMBER — Wholesale

Garfield Lumber & Millwork Co.
Phone—(973) 478-2160
260 Lanza Ave., Garfield 07026
Tulnoy Lumber, Inc.
Phone—(732) 634-4000
9-D Raskulinecz Rd., Carteret 07008

## MACHINE BUILDERS — Custom

**Graybill's Tool & Die, Inc.**
Email: geoff@graybills.com
Phone—(717) 665-5546
Fax—(717) 665-3107
Web—www.graybills.com
Email—info@graybills.com
147 W. High St., Manheim, PA 17545

www.graybills.com

DESIGNERS · BUILDERS

**GRAYBILL'S TOOL & DIE, INC.**
A FULL SERVICE COMPANY
CONTROLS · LOGIC · PROGRAMMING
SPECIAL PRODUCTS
PROTOTYPES
CAD-CAM
WEDM
CNC

147 W. High St.
Manheim, PA 17545

MEMBER

Ph: (717) 665-5546

Zvonko Stulic & Son, Inc.
Phone—(973) 589-3773
21 Main St., Newark 07105

*Do nationwide searches for products & services at:*
**IndustryNet.com**

## MACHINE DESIGN

**Sigma Design Company**
Also engineered design build fabrication
Phone—(732) 629-7555
Fax—(732) 629-7556
Web—www.sigmadesign.net
Email—info@sigmadesign.net
200 Pond Ave., Middlesex 08846

*Design/Build Custom Mechanisms & Process Systems*
www.sigmadesign.net
info@sigmadesign.net
**(732) 629-7555**
200 Pond Ave. Middlesex, NJ 08846

**SIGMA DESIGN**

## MACHINE PARTS — Precision

C & S Precision Products, LLC
Phone—(973) 838-3644
22 Park Pl., Butler 07405
Central Safety Equipment, Inc.
Phone—(609) 386-6448
300 W. Broad St., P.O. Box 250, Burlington 08016
**Concept Group, Inc.**
Glass to metal seals (hermetic packages) & Vacuum insulated components
Phone—(856) 767-5506
Fax—(856) 768-3981
Web—www.conceptgroupinc.com
Email—applications@conceptgroupinc.com
380 Cooper Rd., West Berlin 08091

Hermetic Seals
Thermal Insulation
Vacuum Brazing

**CONCEPT** Group

www.conceptgroupinc.com
**856-767-5506/Fax: 856-768-3981**
380 Cooper Rd. West Berlin, NJ 08091

Dicar, Inc.
Phone—(973) 575-1174
10 Bloomfield Ave., P.O. Box 643, Pine Brook 07058
**E & J Machine And Tool, LLC**
Phone—(973) 810-2312 / (973) 810-2313
Fax—(973) 601-7953
Web—www.ejmachine.com
Email—sales@ejmachine.com
12 Orben Dr., Unit 1, Landing 07850
*(see our ad under JOB SHOPS)*
Eclipse Mfg., LLC
Phone—(973) 340-9939
438 Lanza Ave., Garfield 07026
Extruders International, Inc.
Phone—(908) 241-7750
181 W. Clay Ave., Roselle Park 07204
**FIMS Mfg. Corp.**
Phone—(201) 845-7088
Fax—(201) 845-8287
Web—www.fimsmfg.com
Email—fimsmfg@optonline.net
8 Allerman Rd., Oakland 07436
Foremost Machine Builders, Inc.
Phone—(973) 227-0700
23 Spielman Rd., Fairfield 07004
Galow Co., Inc., H.
Phone—(201) 768-0547
15 Maple St., Norwood 07648
**Gaum, Inc.**
AS9100C Certified
Phone—(609) 586-0132
Fax—(609) 586-9748
Web—www.gauminc.com
Email—mail@gauminc.com
1080 Route 130, P.O. Box 485, Robbinsville 08691
*(see our ads Outside Front Cover & under MACHINE WORK & MACHINING)*
General Polygon Systems, Inc.
Phone—(856) 825-3300
203 Peterson St., Millville 08332

## MACHINE PARTS — Precision —
### (cont.)

Gorsky, Inc., E.
Phone—(908) 322-8580
33 South Ave., Fanwood 07023

Greener Corp.
Phone—(732) 341-3880
4 Helmly St., Bayville 08721

**Hainesport Tool & Maintenance**
**Manufacturer of machine parts & assemblies**
**Phone—(609) 261-0016**
**Fax—(609) 261-2105**
**Web—www.hainesporttool.com**
**Email—rich@hainesporttool.com**
**1924 Ark Rd., Hainesport 08036**

**Hunter Mfg. Services, Inc.**
**Aerospace Quality Machine Parts & Pharmaceutical Change Parts**
**Phone—(973) 365-5880**
**Fax—(973) 365-0588**
**Web—www.huntermfg.net**
**Email—khunter@huntermfg.net**
**19 Just Rd., Fairfield 07004**
*(see our ad under MACHINE WORK & MACHINING—CNC)*

Indemax, Inc.
Phone—(973) 209-2424
1 Industrial Dr., Vernon 07462

J M T Design, Inc.
Phone—(732) 409-6661
914 Route 33, Fairfield Industrial Pk., Freehold 07728

J.D. Machine Parts, Inc.
Phone—(856) 691-8430
158 W. Weymouth Rd., Vineland 08360

LUSO Machine, Inc.
Phone—(973) 242-1717
29 Avenue C, Newark 07114

Machine Plus, Inc.
Phone—(973) 839-8884
97 4th Ave., Haskell 07420

Monick Mfg. Corp.
Phone—(609) 267-0777
2619 Route 206, Mount Holly 08060

Neuweiler, Inc., Karl H.
Phone—(908) 464-6532
23 Russo Pl., Berkeley Heights 07922

Olsen Machine, LLC
Phone—(856) 662-2121
2504 Route 73, Cinnaminson 08077

Qualiturn Corp.
Phone—(908) 241-4909
205 Columbus Ave., Roselle 07203

Ruoff & Sons, Inc.
Phone—(856) 931-2064
1030 Rose Ave., P.O. Box 320, Runnemede 08078

Stapling Machine Co., LLC
Phone—(973) 627-4400
41 Pine St., Rockaway 07866

V & L Machine Tool Co., Inc.
Phone—(973) 808-5858
30 Sherwood Ln., Ste. 11, Fairfield 07004

V H Machine Tool Co.
Phone—(973) 427-8666
29 Smith Ave., Fair Lawn 07410

Valle Precision Machine Co., Inc.
Phone—(973) 773-3037
58 Myrtle Ave., Passaic 07055

White Marine, Inc.
Phone—(732) 826-4491
500 Division St., Perth Amboy 08861

Zala Machine Co., Inc.
Phone—(908) 431-9106
109 Stryker Ln., Ste. 11, Hillsborough 08844

Zero Tolerance Machine
Phone—(856) 881-9072
1650 Glassboro Rd., Williamstown 08094

Ziezer Tool Co., Inc.
Phone—(908) 686-1332
960 Koehl Ave., Union 07083

## MACHINE SHOP SUPPLIES

PAC Tool & Supply Co., Inc.
Phone—(201) 933-8550
420 Paterson Ave., P.O. Box 7482, East Rutherford 07073

## MACHINE SHOPS
### (also see 'Machine Work & Machining')

A & D Industrial & Marine Repair
Phone—(732) 541-1481
900 Port Reading Ave., Ste. B-2, Port Reading 07064

**Advantage EDM**
**Phone—(973) 786-0177**
**Fax—(973) 786-0277**
**Web—www.advantageedm.com**
**Email—info@advantageedm.com**
**38 Main St., Route 206, Andover 07821**

**Aztech Mfg., LLC**
**Precision machining job shop**
**Phone—(609) 726-1212**
**Fax—(609) 726-0403**
**Web—www.aztechmfg.com**
**147 W. Hampton St., Pemberton 08068**

**Chalmers & Kubeck, Inc.**
**Phone—(610) 494-4300**
**Fax—(610) 485-1484**
**Web—www.candk.com**
**Email—jmoore@candk.com**
**150 Commerce Dr., P.O. Box 2447, Aston, PA 19014**
*(see our ad under MACHINE WORK & MACHINING)*

**Hunter Mfg. Services, Inc.**
**Aerospace Quality Machine Parts & Pharmaceutical Change Parts**
**Phone—(973) 365-5880**
**Fax—(973) 365-0588**
**Web—www.huntermfg.net**
**Email—khunter@huntermfg.net**
**19 Just Rd., Fairfield 07004**
*(see our ad under MACHINE WORK & MACHINING—CNC)*

**Unique Metal Products Co., Inc.**
**Metal products, fabrication, laser cutting & CNC machining job shop**
**Phone—(732) 388-1888**
**Fax—(732) 388-0084**
**Email—airtecunique@aol.com**
**17 W. Scott Ave., P.O. Box 1181, Rahway 07065**
*(see our ad under METAL PRODUCTS AND SPECIALTIES)*

## MACHINE TOOL REBUILDING

American Machine Tool Repair
Phone—(973) 927-0820
12 Middlebury Blvd., Randolph 07869

Jersey Machine Tool Repairing & Rebuilding Co.
Phone—(973) 575-1044
1275 Bloomfield Ave., Bldg. 2, Unit 10, Fairfield 07004

## MACHINE TOOLS

Jet Industrial Electronics Corp.
Phone—(973) 697-2300
104 Ridge Rd., Oak Ridge 07438

## MACHINE TOOLS — Precision

Astro Tool & Machine Co., Inc.
Phone—(732) 382-2450
810 Martin St., Rahway 07065

Nasa Machine Tools, Inc.
Phone—(973) 633-5200
1-B Frassetto Way, Lincoln Park 07035

## MACHINE TOOLS — Rebuilt

**Hainesport Tool & Maintenance**
**Manufacturer of machine parts & assemblies**
**Phone—(609) 261-0016**
**Fax—(609) 261-2105**
**Web—www.hainesporttool.com**
**Email—rich@hainesporttool.com**
**1924 Ark Rd., Hainesport 08036**

## MACHINE TOOLS — Wholesale

Indexing Technologies, Inc.
Phone—(201) 934-6333
37 Orchard St., Ramsey 07446

*find additional suppliers at* **IndustryNet.com**

## MACHINE WORK & MACHINING

Able Gear & Machine Co.
Phone—(973) 983-8055
91 Stickle Ave., Rockaway 07866

**Advantage EDM**
**Phone—(973) 786-0177**
**Fax—(973) 786-0277**
**Web—www.advantageedm.com**
**Email—info@advantageedm.com**
**38 Main St., Route 206, Andover 07821**

Aero Products Co.
Phone—(973) 759-0959
19-21 N. 8th St., Belleville 07109

Alex Machine Shop, Inc.
Phone—(201) 768-9110
267 Livingston St., P.O. Box 268, Northvale 07647

American Machine Specialties, Inc.
Phone—(201) 664-2100
51 Bergenline Ave., Westwood 07675

Anderson Machine Co.
Phone—(908) 281-7153
109 Stryker Ln., Unit 10, Hillsborough 08844

Arias Machine Tool & Die Co.
Phone—(732) 442-2398
645 Atlantic Ave., Perth Amboy 08861

Atlas Consolidated Machine Corp.
Phone—(973) 684-5803
53 Bleeker St., Paterson 07524

Automatic Machine Products
Phone—(973) 383-9929
56 Paterson Ave., Newton 07860

B & B Ultra-Sonic, Inc.
Phone—(908) 638-5775
10 E. Main St., High Bridge 08829

B & M Machine Co., Inc.
Phone—(973) 751-0789
67-69 Greylock Ave., Belleville 07109

B P Machine Co., Inc.
Phone—(732) 251-0449
10 American Way, Spotswood 08884

Barnett Machine Tool Corp.
Phone—(973) 482-6222
401 Supor Blvd., P.O. Box 189, Harrison 07029

BBK Machining, Inc.
Phone—(856) 358-8864
429 Garrison Rd., Elmer 08318

Berkshire Machine, Inc.
Phone—(973) 366-7710
390 Route 15 S., Wharton 07885

Bertot Industries, Inc.
Phone—(973) 267-0006
23 Malcolm St., Ste. 1, Morristown 07960

Betar, Inc.
Phone—(908) 359-4200
100 Randolph Rd., Ste. 4, Somerset 08873

Bisaga, Inc.
Phone—(856) 784-7966
212 Ashland Ave., Somerdale 08083

Biwal Mfg. Co., Inc.
Phone—(973) 778-0105
48 Industrial St. W., Clifton 07012

Blue Chip Industries, Inc.
Phone—(908) 704-1466
50 Old Camplain Rd., Hillsborough 08844

Blue Chip Technology
Phone—(856) 881-3133
267 Richwood Rd., P.O. Box 287, Richwood 08074

Bralen, LLC
Phone—(973) 948-6575
236 U.S. Highway 206 N., Branchville 07826

**Brodie System, Inc.**
**Phone—(908) 862-8620**
**Web—www.brodiesystem.com**
**1539 W. Elizabeth Ave., Linden 07036**

*Send an RFQ* (request for quote) *to multiple suppliers at* **IndustryNet.com**

## MACHINE WORK & MACHINING — (cont.)

**C & L Machining Co.**
General Machining Job Shop
Phone—(856) 456-1932
Fax—(856) 456-4401
Web—www.candlmachine.com
Email—candlmach@aol.com
110 S. New Broadway, P.O. Box 167, Brooklawn 08030

**C & L Machining Co.**
*General machining*
**www.candlmachine.com**
**(856) 456-1932**
110 S. New Broadway  Brooklawn, NJ 08030

C. J.'s Tool Mfg., Inc.
Phone—(856) 227-7342
620 Route 168, Turnersville 08012

C.A.M.E. Machine & Metal Works, Inc.
Phone—(201) 309-0005
181 Pacific Ave., Jersey City 07304

Carlen Machine Co.
Phone—(973) 808-1441
1275 Bloomfield Ave., Bldg. 10, Door 89, Fairfield 07004

Cartco, Inc.
Phone—(978) 692-7070
621 Grape St., Hammonton 08037

**Chalmers & Kubeck, Inc.**
Phone—(610) 494-4300
Fax—(610) 485-1484
Web—www.candk.com
Email—jmoore@candk.com
150 Commerce Dr., P.O. Box 2447, Aston, PA 19014
*(see our ad on this page)*

Charles Machine Shop Service, Rob
Phone—(908) 806-8512
24 Rake Rd., Flemington 08822

Class Tool Co.
Phone—(908) 561-6633
2500 S. Clinton Ave., P.O. Box 286, South Plainfield 07080

CMI-Promex, Inc.
Phone—(856) 351-1000
7 Benjamin Green Rd., Pedricktown 08067

**Concept Group, Inc.**
Glass to metal seals (hermetic packages) & Vacuum insulated components
Phone—(856) 767-5506
Fax—(856) 768-3981
Web—www.conceptgroupinc.com
Email—applications@conceptgroupinc.com
380 Cooper Rd., West Berlin 08091
*(see our ad under MACHINE PARTS — Precision)*

Cutting Techniques, Inc.
Phone—(201) 438-2222
651 Industrial Rd., Carlstadt 07072

DCM Industries LLC
Phone—(973) 675-3200
50 S. Center St., Unit 8, Orange 07050

Delta Machine Works, Inc.
Phone—(201) 935-7474
257 Division Ave., Carlstadt 07072

Deza Machine & Tool Co.
Phone—(973) 278-6654
938 E. 19th St., Paterson 07501

Diamond Machine Co., Inc.
Phone—(609) 490-8940
30 N. Valley Rd., P.O. Box 420, Roosevelt 08555

**DIHCO, Inc.**
Phone—(201) 327-0518
Fax—(201) 327-8759
Email—DIHCO-INC@hotmail.com
612 E. Crescent Ave., Upper Saddle River 07458
*(see our ad under FABRICATORS)*

Diversified Machine, LLC
Phone—(732) 251-6600
15 American Way, Ste. 12, Spotswood 08884

Drew-Wal Machine & Tool Corp.
Phone—(201) 641-3887
76 Monroe St., Little Ferry 07643

# CHALMERS & KUBECK, Inc.

*Machine Work & Machining*

**610-494-4300 • FAX: 610-485-1484**

www.candk.com

jmoore@candk.com

150 Commerce Dr. • PO Box 2447 • Aston, PA 19014

*Full Service Machine Shop*
*ISO 9001:2008 & AS9100C Certified*

- CNC Milling to 8' x 12'
- Turning to 30" x 15'
- Vertical Turning to 6' Diameter
- Welding Fabrication
- Blanchard Grinding to 6' Diameter
- Custom Machinery

**(609) 586-0132**
Fax (609) 586-9748
www.gauminc.com
e-mail:mail@gauminc.com
1080 Route 130
Robbinsville, NJ 08691

**E & J Machine And Tool, LLC**
Phone—(973) 810-2312 / (973) 810-2313
Fax—(973) 601-7953
Web—www.ejmachine.com
Email—sales@ejmachine.com
12 Orben Dr., Unit 1, Landing 07850
*(see our ad under JOB SHOPS)*

Edison Machine
Phone—(732) 494-5011
25 Liberty St., Metuchen 08840

Ed-Mar Industries, Inc.
Phone—(973) 808-9205
11 Ray Pl., Fairfield 07004

Edston Mfg. Co., Inc.
Phone—(908) 647-0116
321 Warren Ave., Stirling 07980

Elmi Machine & Tool Co., Inc.
Phone—(973) 882-1277
1275 Bloomfield Ave., Bldg. 5, Unit 2-B, Fairfield 07004

EMMC Co.
Phone—(973) 751-0100
1 Nicola Pl., Belleville 07109

Evans Machine & Tool Co.
Phone—(732) 442-1144
410 Summit Ave., Perth Amboy 08861

Exacta V & H Corp.
Phone—(856) 235-7379
107 Whittendale Dr., Moorestown 08057

Experimental Machine & Tool
Phone—(908) 534-4725
114 Pulaski Rd., Whitehouse Station 08889

**F & A Machine Co., Inc.**
Experts in short run production and prototyping of molybdenum and molybdenum alloys
Phone—(732) 356-5777
Fax—(732) 356-4102
Web—www.fandamachineco.com
Email—info@fandamachineco.com
133 Lincoln Blvd., Middlesex 08846

Famcam, Inc.
Phone—(973) 319-3033
3 Eastmans Rd., Parsippany 07054

Fano Machine & Tool Co.
Phone—(973) 773-9353
20 Passaic St., Garfield 07026

Farmer Co., Arthur E.
Phone—(609) 392-8722
47 Frazier St., Trenton 08618

Fazzio Machine & Steel
Phone—(856) 881-2832
3278 Glassboro Cross Keys Rd., P.O. Box 232, Glassboro 08028

Fischl Machine & Tool Co.
Phone—(973) 227-0767
79 Clinton Rd., Fairfield 07004

Frieri A Machine Tool Co., Inc.
Phone—(908) 753-7555
1112 Belmont Ave., South Plainfield 07080

Galicia Metal, Inc.
Phone—(973) 278-1058
573 E. 19th St., Paterson 07514

**Gaum, Inc.**
AS9100C Certified
Phone—(609) 586-0132
Fax—(609) 586-9748
Web—www.gauminc.com
Email—mail@gauminc.com
1080 Route 130, P.O. Box 485, Robbinsville 08691
*(also see our ad Outside Front Cover)*
*(see our ad on this page)*

General Machine & Experimental Works
Phone—(201) 843-9035
117 Gertrude Ave., Paramus 07652

Gibson, Inc., George
Phone—(856) 234-5502
801 S. Church St., Ste. 6, Mount Laurel 08054

H E K Machine, Inc.
Phone—(732) 442-8672
785 State St., Ste. 2, Perth Amboy 08861

H P Performance, Inc.
Phone—(973) 962-0800
8 Industrial Pkwy., Ringwood 07456

**Hainesport Tool & Maintenance**
Manufacturer of machine parts & assemblies
Phone—(609) 261-0016
Fax—(609) 261-2105
Web—www.hainesporttool.com
Email—rich@hainesporttool.com
1924 Ark Rd., Hainesport 08036

Hamelin Products, Inc.
Phone—(856) 451-2935
1616 Highway 77, P.O. Box 153, Deerfield Street 08313

*Is your company properly represented in the* **IndustrySection?**

If not, call... 847-864-7590

© Copyright 2015 Manufacturers' News, Inc.

## MACHINE WORK & MACHINING — (cont.)

**Hansen Machine & Tool Co., Inc.**
Also machine rebuilding & tooling for the cosmetic industry. Fill stem fabrication
Phone—(732) 340-0466
Fax—(732) 340-0467
Email—Bob@
hansenmachine.comcastbiz.net
27 Walnut Ave., Clark 07066

**HANSEN MACHINE AND TOOL CO. INC.**
TOOLS, FIXTURES & SPECIAL MACHINES

*Tooling & Machining of Parts*
Email: Bob@Hansenmachine.comcastbiz.net
**(732) 340-0466 / Fax: (732) 340-0467**
27 Walnut Avenue • Clark, NJ 07066

Harout Tool & Machine Corp.
Phone—(201) 646-0664
9-11 Dyatt Pl., Hackensack 07601
Head Masters, Inc.
Phone—(201) 843-6666
263 Route 46 W., Saddle Brook 07663
Heads Up Industries
Phone—(732) 846-3388
132 Van Liew Ave., Ste. 4, Milltown 08850
Hercules Welding & Machine Co.
Phone—(856) 829-1820
616 5th St., Palmyra 08065
Hun Machine Works, Inc.
Phone—(856) 461-7112
51 Whittaker St., P.O. Box 189, Riverside 08075
Hy-Tech Metal Works, Inc.
Phone—(908) 757-6754
1252 South Ave., Plainfield 07062
Industrial Machine & Engineering Co.
Phone—(908) 862-8874
1807 W. Elizabeth Ave., Linden 07036
Industrial Machine Corp.
Phone—(973) 345-1800
44 Lehigh Ave., Paterson 07503
Innovative Mfg., Inc.
Phone—(908) 904-1884
198 U.S. Highway 206, Ste. 4, Hillsborough 08844
Inventors Shop, The
Phone—(856) 303-8787
800 Industrial Hwy., Cinnaminson 08077
Iron Bound Metal, Inc.
Phone—(973) 242-5704
238 Emmet St., Newark 07114
J & D Tool, LLC
Phone—(908) 486-5353
5 Grant St., Linden 07036
J M Machine Co., LLC
Phone—(973) 253-2188
5 Central Ave., Ste. 2, P.O. Box 1863, Clifton 07011
Jo Bella Machine Mfg.
Phone—(732) 541-7076
232 Washington Ave., Carteret 07008
Joyrei Enterprises, Inc.
Phone—(732) 727-0742
3143 Bordentown Ave., Parlin 08859
K D Industries, Inc.
Phone—(973) 594-4800
18 Falstrom Ct., Passaic 07055
K H Machine Works
Phone—(201) 867-2338
4322 Grand Ave., North Bergen 07047
Kelles, Inc.
Phone—(908) 241-9300
20 Hoiles Dr., Kenilworth 07033
KPMC, Inc.
Phone—(609) 538-1100
113 Walters Ave., Trenton 08638
L & M Machine & Tool Co., Inc.
Phone—(973) 523-5288
105 Lehigh Ave., Paterson 07503
L.C. Machine Shop, Inc.
Phone—(856) 767-1111
249 S. White Horse Pike, Berlin 08009
Legend Machine & Grinding, LLC
Phone—(908) 685-1100
36 S. Adamsville Rd., Somerville 08876

Lehigh Precision Co., Inc.
Phone—(908) 351-6600
P.O. Box 214, Elizabeth 07207
Lentron Corp.
Phone—(973) 252-9668
24 Ironia Rd., Flanders 07836
**Livingston & W, Inc.**
973-B New Durham Rd., Edison 08817
CNC & general machining job shop
Phone—(732) 287-5790
Fax—(732) 287-5793
Email—livwil@optimum.net
P.O. Box 496, Edison 08818

**Livingston & W, Inc.**
CNC & General
Machining Job Shop

**732-287-5790**
Fax: 732-287-5793

Email: livwil@optimum.net

**973-B New Durham Road
PO Box 496 • Edison, NJ 08818**

Lucas & Son, H. N.
Phone—(856) 764-2400
211 Carriage Ln., Delran 08075
M & F Machine Works
Phone—(201) 433-4085
243-245 Custer Ave., Jersey City 07305
M & M Welding & Steel Fabricating
Phone—(908) 647-6060
344 Essex St., P.O. Box 168, Stirling 07980
**M & S Machine & Tool Corp.**
Phone—(973) 345-5847
Fax—(973) 345-0579
Web—www.mandsmachine.com
Email—nazim@mandsmachine.com
108 Maryland Ave., Paterson 07503
Mark I Industries, Inc.
Phone—(609) 884-0051
910 Shunpike Rd., Cape May 08204
Marshall Industrial Technologies
Phone—(609) 394-7153
529 S. Clinton Ave., Trenton 08611
**Martin Sprocket & Gear, Inc.**
Phone—(973) 633-5700
Fax—(973) 633-7196
7 Highpoint Dr., Wayne 07470
Master Tool Corp.
Phone—(732) 919-1010
342 Squankum Yellowbrook Rd., P.O. Box 7, Farmingdale 07727
Mechanical Components Corp.
Phone—(732) 938-3737
145 Yellowbrook Rd., Farmingdale 07727
Mercer Machine & Tool Products
Phone—(609) 587-1106
332 Darcy Ave., Trenton 08629
Metem Corp.
Phone—(973) 887-6635
700 Parsippany Rd., Parsippany 07054
Mid-Lantic Precision, Inc.
Phone—(856) 456-3810
940 Market St., Gloucester City 08030
Midway Machine Product Corp.
Phone—(609) 499-4377
763-A Railroad Ave., P.O. Box 129, Florence 08518
Mini Precision Devices, Inc.
Phone—(908) 351-7423
615 Pennsylvania Ave., Elizabeth 07201
Modern Metric Machine
Phone—(856) 547-4044
101 Nicholson Rd., Audubon 08106

N & J Machine Products Corp.
Phone—(973) 589-0031
52 Bruen St., Newark 07105
New Jersey Machine & Tool Co.
Phone—(973) 383-6102
257 Houses Corner Rd., Lafayette 07848
O.K. Tool Corp.
Phone—(908) 561-9920
1233 North Ave., Plainfield 07062
Phoenix Tool & Machine, Inc.
Phone—(856) 753-5565
1044 Industrial Dr., Unit 5, West Berlin 08091
Picut Manufacturing Company, Inc.
Phone—(908) 754-1333
140 Mount Bethel Rd., Warren 07059
Pine Hill Machine Shop & Welding
Phone—(856) 783-9842
44 W. 3rd Ave., Pine Hill 08021
Polo Machine, Inc.
Phone—(973) 340-9984
223 Banta Ave., P.O. Box 403, Garfield 07026
Precision Machined Products, LLC
Phone—(973) 227-9538
24 Kulick Rd., Fairfield 07004
Precision Metal Machining, Inc.
Phone—(201) 843-7427
800 Central Blvd., Ste. C, Carlstadt 07072
Precision Parts Unlimited, Inc.
Phone—(973) 659-3300
24 Patriot Crossing, Rockaway 07866
Precision Rollers, Inc.
Phone—(856) 768-7696
155 Cooper Rd., West Berlin 08091
Precision Specialists Machine, LLC
Phone—(856) 768-5990
1004 Industrial Dr., Ste. 5, West Berlin 08091
Progress Machine Shop, Inc.
Phone—(973) 278-4999
41 Kentucky Ave., Paterson 07503
Progressive Machine Co.
Phone—(201) 342-3636
293 Hudson St., Hackensack 07601
Pulcin Machine
Phone—(609) 387-3060
13 Cedar Ln., Bordentown 08505
Purves Marine Works
Phone—(609) 296-1263
197 Main St., West Creek 08092
Quality Industries, Inc.
Phone—(973) 478-4425
204 Getty Ave., Clifton 07011
Radco Enterprises, Inc.
Phone—(856) 691-3125
734 Oxford St., Vineland 08360
Rawco, Inc.
Phone—(908) 832-7700
452 Route 513, Califon 07830
Reuther Engineering & Machining Co., Inc.
Phone—(973) 485-5800
126 S. 14th St., Newark 07107
Robro Mfg., Inc.
Phone—(973) 279-7237
288 10th Ave., Paterson 07524
**Ruggieri Precision Machine, LLC**
Machining services, hydraulic & pump repairs, welding & fabricating
Phone—(609) 397-4378
Fax—(609) 397-3974
Web—www.ruggierimachine.com
Email—ruggierimachine@verizon.net
1404 Route 179, Lambertville 08530
R-Way Tooling & Metal Works
Phone—(856) 692-2218
224 S. Lincoln Ave., Vineland 08361
Ryan Industrial Service, Inc.
Phone—(732) 566-9538
80 Freneau Ave., Matawan 07747
Sandik Mfg., Inc.
Phone—(973) 779-0707
100 8th St., Bldg. 33-A, Passaic 07055
Sarlo Tool & Machine Co.
Phone—(856) 461-3206
62 Suburban Blvd., Delran 08075
Schall Mfg., Inc.
Phone—(732) 918-8800
3501 Rose Ave., Ocean 07712
Seibert Machine & Tool, Inc.
Phone—(908) 754-0774
4405 S. Clinton Ave., South Plainfield 07080
Service Machine Co.
Phone—(732) 356-9021
311 Lincoln Blvd., Middlesex 08846

© Copyright 2015 Manufacturers' News, Inc.

## MACHINE WORK & MACHINING —
### *(cont.)*

Sigma Engineering & Consulting Assocs.
Phone—(732) 356-3046
220 Lincoln Blvd., Middlesex 08846

Smith Tool & Mfg., R. G.
Phone—(973) 344-1395
245 South St., Newark 07114

Snyder Machine Co.
Phone—(908) 359-2745
214 Sunnymead Rd., Hillsborough 08844

Spectrum Tool
Phone—(973) 579-0087
56 Paterson Ave., Newton 07860

Steimling & Son, Inc.-Machinist
Phone—(732) 613-1550
7 Nickel Ave., Sayreville 08872

T P S Machining
Phone—(732) 223-9305
204 E. Main St., Manasquan 08736

TJK Machine, LLC
Phone—(856) 691-7811
870 E. Elmer Rd., Vineland 08360

Tomcel Machine, Inc.
Phone—(973) 256-8257
86 Lackawanna Ave., West Paterson 07424

Trend Machine, Inc.
Phone—(732) 382-4170
793 Martin St., P.O. Box 218, Rahway 07065

Tri Phase Tool Co.
Phone—(732) 370-4737
2345 Route 9, Ste. 10, Toms River 08755

Triangle Automatic, Inc.
Phone—(973) 625-3830
105 W. Dewey Ave., Ste. 305, Wharton 07885

Tur Machine, LLC
Phone—(908) 874-0235
198 U.S. Highway 206, Ste. 5, Hillsborough 08844

Unilite Co., Inc.
Phone—(973) 667-1674
151 River Rd., Nutley 07110

United Motor Parts, Inc.
Phone—(201) 837-6760
1130 Teaneck Rd., Teaneck 07666

Universal Metalcraft, Inc.
Phone—(973) 345-3284
24 Burgess Pl., Wayne 07470

Vertol Machine
Phone—(856) 327-2489
15 Burns Ave., Vineland 08360

Viking Yachting Center, Inc.
Phone—(609) 296-2388
5724 N. Route 9, New Gretna 08224

Vin-Law Machine & Tool Co., Inc.
Phone—(973) 227-5100
3 Kulick Rd., P.O. Box 10950, Fairfield 07004

Weldon Machine & Boring, Inc.
Phone—(732) 356-1887
134 Wood Ave., Middlesex 08846

Whitehouse Machine, LLC
Phone—(908) 534-4722
3585 U.S. Highway 22 E., Somerville 08876

Wortmann Machine Works, Inc., E.
Phone—(201) 288-1654
50 Hollister Rd., P.O. Box 1657, Teterboro 07608

Z & R Cutter Service, Inc.
Phone—(908) 647-6757
50 Division Ave., Ste. 21, Millington 07946

## MACHINE WORK & MACHINING — CNC

Accelerated CNC, LLC
Phone—(908) 561-8875
2500 S. Clinton Ave., Ste. A, South Plainfield 07080

American Machining Co., LLC
Phone—(856) 245-7801
110 Harmon Dr., Blackwood 08012

Arlington Machine & Tool Co.
Phone—(973) 276-1377
90 New Dutch Ln., Fairfield 07004

BCS Machine & Mfg. Corp.
Phone—(908) 561-1656
3575 Kennedy Rd., South Plainfield 07080

Bill Martin Machine, LLC
Phone—(973) 300-5052
56 Paterson Ave., Ste. 112, Newton 07860

C & C Tool & Machine Co., LLC
Phone—(856) 461-6090
38 W. Scott St., P.O. Box 407, Riverside 08075

Camtec Industries, Inc.
Phone—(732) 332-9800
28 Saddle Ridge Rd., Colts Neck 07722

Columbia Machine
Phone—(908) 475-4057
1 N. Riverview Ave., Columbia 07832

**Concept Group, Inc.**
Glass to metal seals (hermetic packages) & Vacuum insulated components
**Phone—(856) 767-5506**
**Fax—(856) 768-3981**
**Web—www.conceptgroupinc.com**
**Email—applications@conceptgroupinc.com**
**380 Cooper Rd., West Berlin 08091**
*(see our ad under MACHINE PARTS — Precision)*

CSI Fabricators
Phone—(973) 344-0955
15 Lexington St., Newark 07105

**Defined Pro Machining, LLC**
CNC machining: prototypes, production, reverse engineering & design
**Phone—(973) 941-2430**
**Fax—(973) 891-1039**
**Web—www.definedpro.com**
**Email—hf@definedpro.com**
**105 W. Dewey Ave., Ste. 205, Wharton 07885**

**Durex, Inc.**
Email: custserv@durexinc.com
ISO 9001 Registered Contract Metal Fabrication Facility
**Phone—(908) 688-0800**
**Fax—(908) 688-0718**
**Web—www.durexinc.com**
**5 Stahuber Ave., Union 07083**
*(see our ad under METAL FABRICATING)*

**E & J Machine And Tool, LLC**
**Phone—(973) 810-2312 / (973) 810-2313**
**Fax—(973) 601-7953**
**Web—www.ejmachine.com**
**Email—sales@ejmachine.com**
**12 Orben Dr., Unit 1, Landing 07850**
*(see our ad under JOB SHOPS)*

East Coast Steel, Inc.
Phone—(856) 582-6776
317 Salina Rd., Sewell 08080

Engineering Dynamics, LLC
Phone—(973) 794-4500
429 Rockaway Valley Rd., Ste. 1300, Boonton 07005

**F & A Machine Co., Inc.**
Experts in short run production and prototyping of molybdenum and molybdenum alloys
**Phone—(732) 356-5777**
**Fax—(732) 356-4102**
**Web—www.fandamachineco.com**
**Email—info@fandamachineco.com**
**133 Lincoln Blvd., Middlesex 08846**

G & B Machine, Inc.
Phone—(908) 722-7940
35 N. Middaugh St., Ste. 2-B, Somerville 08876

G B Industries II, Inc.
Phone—(973) 728-5900
341 Margaret King Ave., Ringwood 07456

Gadren Machine Co.
Phone—(856) 456-4329
108 Main St., P.O. Box 117, Mount Ephraim 08059

**Gaum, Inc.**
AS9100C Certified
**Phone—(609) 586-0132**
**Fax—(609) 586-9748**
**Web—www.gauminc.com**
**Email—mail@gauminc.com**
**1080 Route 130, P.O. Box 485, Robbinsville 08691**
*(see our ads Outside Front Cover & under MACHINE WORK & MACHINING)*

General Machine Kraft, Inc.
Phone—(908) 454-5955
216 Broad St., Phillipsburg 08865

Henry Machine Shop, Inc.
Phone—(908) 925-2218
345 Market St., Kenilworth 07033

Hummel Machine & Tool Co.
Phone—(201) 991-5200
580 Davis Ave., Kearny 07032

**Hunter Mfg. Services, Inc.**
Aerospace Quality Machine Parts & Pharmaceutical Change Parts
**Phone—(973) 365-5880**
**Fax—(973) 365-0588**
**Web—www.huntermfg.net**
**Email—khunter@huntermfg.net**
**19 Just Rd., Fairfield 07004**

**Hunter Manufacturing Services, Inc.**

*Aerospace Quality Machine Parts & Pharmaceutical Change Parts*

**973-365-5880**
**FAX: 973-365-0588**

19 Just Rd. • Fairfield, NJ 07004

**www.huntermfg.net**

**khunter@huntermfg.net**

Imperial Machine & Tool Co.
Phone—(908) 496-8100
8 W. Crisman Rd., Columbia 07832

JCW Rolling & Fabrication
Phone—(732) 548-7636
60 Liberty St., Metuchen 08840

Julius Machine & Tool Co.
Phone—(973) 515-8540
B-14 Merry Ln., East Hanover 07936

Kern & Szalai Machine, LLC
Phone—(856) 802-1500
351 Crider Ave., Moorestown 08057

Kinnery Metal
Phone—(973) 473-4664
11 Exchange Pl., Passaic 07055

L M C Precision, Inc.
Phone—(973) 522-0005
91 Rome St., Ste. 93, Newark 07105

Labern Machine Products
Phone—(908) 722-1970
3388 Highway 22 W., Branchburg 08876

**Livingston & W, Inc.**
973-B New Durham Rd., Edison 08817
CNC & general machining job shop
**Phone—(732) 287-5790**
**Fax—(732) 287-5793**
**Email—livwil@optimum.net**
**P.O. Box 496, Edison 08818**
*(see our ad under MACHINE WORK & MACHINING)*

Machine Corp., E. B.
Phone—(973) 442-7729
320 Richard Mine Rd., Wharton 07885

Machine Parts, Inc.
Phone—(973) 491-5444
17 Ferdon St., Newark 07105

Nodeco Machine Service
Phone—(908) 236-7996
5 Wayside Ln., Lebanon 08833

**Nova Precision Products, Inc.**
Precision CNC machining
**Phone—(973) 625-1586**
**Fax—(973) 586-2434**
**Web—www.novaprecisionproducts.com**
**Email—sales1@novaprecisionproducts.com**
**160 Franklin Ave., Rockaway 07866**

O M P Technologies, Inc.
Phone—(973) 808-5543
24-H Commerce Rd., Fairfield 07004

Precise Machine & Tool, Inc.
Phone—(201) 790-3320
369 Knickerbocker Ave., Paterson 07503

Quincas Corp.
Phone—(908) 850-3914
112 East Ave., Unit 7-A, Hackettstown 07840

R G I, Inc.
Phone—(973) 697-2624
27 Union Valley Rd., Newfoundland 07435

## MACHINE WORK & MACHINING — CNC — (cont.)

Rako Machine Products, Inc.
Phone—(609) 758-1200
845 Monmouth Rd., Cream Ridge 08514

Saturn Tool & Die, Inc.
Phone—(908) 964-0504
1064 Commerce Ave., Union 07083

Stollen Machine & Tool Co., Inc.
Phone—(908) 241-0622
761 Lexington Ave., Kenilworth 07033

Telemark CNC, LLC
Phone—(973) 794-4857
429 Rockaway Valley Rd., Bldg. 2200, Boonton 07005

**Unique Metal Products Co., Inc.**
Metal products, fabrication, laser cutting & CNC machining job shop
Phone—(732) 388-1888
Fax—(732) 388-0084
Email—airtecunique@aol.com
17 W. Scott Ave., P.O. Box 1181, Rahway 07065
(see our ad under METAL PRODUCTS AND SPECIALTIES)

V E P Manufacturing Inc.
Phone—(732) 657-0666
575 S. Hope Chapel Rd., Jackson 08527

Vermes Machine Co., Inc.
Phone—(856) 642-9300
351 Crider Ave., Moorestown 08057

## MACHINED PARTS

Accurate Machine, LLC.
Phone—(609) 758-1381
27 Arneytown Chesterfield Rd., Allentown 08501

Bright Machinery Mfg. Group, Inc.
Phone—(973) 345-7405
239 Lindbergh Pl., Bldg. 2-A, Paterson 07503

CADPRO, Inc.
Phone—(856) 435-0050
114 W. Atlantic Ave., Clementon 08021

Kumar & Kumar, Inc.
Phone—(732) 322-0435
57 Denise Dr., Edison 08820

T & P Machine Shop
Phone—(732) 424-9141
600 Prospect Ave., Piscataway 08854

Toth Inc.
Phone—(856) 662-8700
6970 Central Hwy., Pennsauken 08109

## MACHINERY — Automated

Spadix Technologies, Inc.
Phone—(732) 356-6906
110 Egel Ave., Middlesex 08846

## MACHINERY — CNC

Mid-Atlantic CNC, Inc.
Phone—(908) 809-1100
260 Evans Way, Branchburg 08876

## MACHINERY — Custom Designed

AZCO Corp.
Phone—(973) 439-1428
26 Just Rd., Fairfield 07004

**Day Tool & Mfg., Inc.**
ISO 9001:2008, AS9100 Rev. C
Phone—(908) 439-3800
Fax—(908) 439-3955
Web—www.daytool.com
Email—juddcallahan@daytool.com
6 Carman Ln., P.O. Box 466, Whitehouse 08888

Jersey Metalworks, LLC
Phone—(732) 565-1313
1022 Hamilton St., Ste. A, Somerset 08873

## MACHINERY — Industrial

Advanced Fastener Industries
Phone—(973) 283-1013
130 Main St., Butler 07405

AW Machinery, LLC
Phone—(973) 882-3223
7 Just Rd., Fairfield 07004

**Gaum, Inc.**
AS9100C Certified
Phone—(609) 586-0132
Fax—(609) 586-9748
Web—www.gauminc.com
Email—mail@gauminc.com
1080 Route 130, P.O. Box 485, Robbinsville 08691
(see our ads Outside Front Cover & under MACHINE WORK & MACHINING)

**Hainesport Tool & Maintenance**
Manufacturer of machine parts & assemblies
Phone—(609) 261-0016
Fax—(609) 261-2105
Web—www.hainesporttool.com
Email—rich@hainesporttool.com
1924 Ark Rd., Hainesport 08036

Independent Machine Co.
Phone—(973) 882-0060
2 Stewart Pl., Fairfield 07004

Kramer Industries, Inc.
Phone—(732) 650-9599
140 Ethel Rd. W., Ste. U, Piscataway 08854

M C Machinery Systems, Inc.
Phone—(973) 244-1501
16 Chapin Rd., P.O. Box 405, Pine Brook 07058

Progressive-Ruesch Machine Co., LLC
Phone—(973) 962-7700
21 Van Natta Dr., Ringwood 07456

Remington Industries, Inc., Cordes Machine Div.
Phone—(908) 233-2600
269 Sheffield St., Mountainside 07092

Syntex Group, Inc.
Phone—(856) 566-0058
1838 Downs Ave., Clementon 08021

**Warwick Mfg. & Equipment Co., LLC**
Buy & sell used: Chemical, food, cosmetic, packaging & pharmaceutical equipment
Phone—(732) 729-0400 / (732) 241-9263
Fax—(732) 729-1235
Web—www.warwickequipment.com
Email—sales@warwickequipment.com
1112 12th St., North Brunswick 08902
(see our ad Outside Back Cover)

WENCO Machinery Corp.
Phone—(973) 657-9660
355 Margaret King Ave., Ringwood 07456

Werko Machine Co., Inc.
Phone—(856) 662-0669
9200 Collins Ave., Pennsauken 08110

## MACHINERY — New & Used

American Machinery Liquidators, Inc.
Phone—(732) 390-0006
P.O. Box 6995, East Brunswick 08816

## MACHINERY — Rebuilt

Butensky Services Co., Inc.
Phone—(908) 707-0912
3380 Route 22, P.O. Box 5020, Somerville 08876

C & S Machinery Rebuilding Corp.
Phone—(973) 742-7302
636 E. 19th St., Paterson 07514

Wilson Reconditioning & Design Co., LLC
Phone—(973) 823-6317
117 S. Rutherford Ave., Franklin 07416

## MACHINERY — Special

Alfa Machine Co., Inc.
Phone—(732) 821-0044
2154 Highway 130 N., Monmouth Junction 08852

ESG, LLC
Phone—(973) 691-8517
3 Gold Mine Rd., Flanders 07836

## MACHINERY — Used

**EcReCon, Inc.**
Used Chemical Processing Equipment
Phone—(856) 299-4500
Fax—(856) 299-4446
Web—www.EcReCon.com
Email—sales@ecrecon.com
62 N. Broad St., Penns Grove 08069
(see our ad under CHEMICAL PROCESSING EQUIPMENT)

**Warwick Mfg. & Equipment Co., LLC**
Buy & sell used: Chemical, food, cosmetic, packaging & pharmaceutical equipment
Phone—(732) 729-0400 / (732) 241-9263
Fax—(732) 729-1235
Web—www.warwickequipment.com
Email—sales@warwickequipment.com
1112 12th St., North Brunswick 08902
(see our ad Outside Back Cover)

## MACHINERY MOVERS

**Hilman Rollers**
Phone—(732) 462-6277 / (888) 276-5548
Fax—(732) 462-6355
Web—www.hilmanrollers.com
Email—sales@hilmanrollers.com
12 Timber Ln., P.O. Box 45, Marlboro 07746
(see our ad under JACKS—Hydraulic)

## MACHINING

**Airtec, Inc.**
Sheet metal fabrication, machining & laser cutting
Phone—(732) 382-3700
Fax—(732) 388-0084
Email—airtecunique@aol.com
17 W. Scott Ave., P.O. Box 1181, Rahway 07065
(see our ad under SHEET METAL FABRICATION)

**B & L Precision Grinding Corp.**
Specializing in centerless grinding
Phone—(973) 839-4141
Fax—(973) 839-4760
Email—blgrinding@verizon.net
7-B Ivy St., Pompton Lakes 07442

**Defined Pro Machining, LLC**
CNC machining: prototypes, production, reverse engineering & design
Phone—(973) 941-2430
Fax—(973) 891-1039
Web—www.definedpro.com
Email—hf@definedpro.com
105 W. Dewey Ave., Ste. 205, Wharton 07885

**E & J Machine And Tool, LLC**
Phone—(973) 810-2312 / (973) 810-2313
Fax—(973) 601-7953
Web—www.ejmachine.com
Email—sales@ejmachine.com
12 Orben Dr., Unit 1, Landing 07850
(see our ad under JOB SHOPS)

**Megawatt Machine Services, LLC**
Phone—(732) 805-4000
Fax—(732) 805-4020
Web—www.megawattmachine.com
Email—sales@megawattmachine.com
417 Elizabeth Ave., Somerset 08873

## MACHINING — Aerospace

**Severna Operations, Inc.**
Phone—(973) 503-1600
Fax—(973) 503-1704
Web—www.severna.com
Email—nkoch@severna.com
3 Eastmans Rd., Parsippany 07054
(see our ad under PLASTIC MACHINING)

Stetz Machine Shop, John
Phone—(732) 495-0847
17 Highway 36, Middletown 07748

## MACHINING — Automotive

Dunn Fabrication
Phone—(856) 486-3866
8470 Remington Ave., Pennsauken 08110

Haledon Auto Parts
Phone—(973) 595-8200
269 Haledon Ave., Haledon 07508

Machine Shop At Engine Specialties, The
Phone—(856) 764-8701
203 Carriage Ln., Delran 08075

Tim's Automotive Machine Shop
Phone—(732) 573-0600
1760 Highway 37 E., Toms River 08753

Weston Machine
Phone—(732) 752-2711
161 11th St., Piscataway 08854

## MACHINING — CNC Large Scale

**ABCO Die Casters, Inc.**
Email: jvitollo@abcodiecasters.com
Founded in 1971, serving numerous industries
throughout North America by supplying quality zinc
die castings & powder coated components
**Phone—(973) 624-7030**
**Fax—(973) 624-7425**
**Web—www.abcodiecasters.com**
**39 Tompkins Point Rd., Newark 07114**

## MACHINING — Custom

**CADPRO, Inc.**
**Phone—(856) 435-0050**
**Fax—(856) 435-0600**
**Web—www.cadproinc.com**
**Email—elaine@cadproinc.com**
**114 W. Atlantic Ave., Clementon 08021**

## MACHINING — Medical

**Severna Operations, Inc.**
**Phone—(973) 503-1600**
**Fax—(973) 503-1704**
**Web—www.severna.com**
**Email—nkoch@severna.com**
**3 Eastmans Rd., Parsippany 07054**
*(see our ad under PLASTIC MACHINING)*

## MACHINING — Precision

A G Machine & Tool Co.
Phone—(908) 241-3205
147 E. 1st Ave., Roselle 07203
ABCO Metal, LLC
Phone—(973) 772-8160
138 3rd Ave., Paterson 07514
Actioneering Mfg. Engineers
Phone—(973) 299-1999
30 Plane St., Bldg. 12, P.O. Box 333, Boonton
07005
Advance Machine, Inc.
Phone—(908) 486-7244
531 Pennsylvania Ave., Linden 07036
Aerospace Precision Mfg. Co., Inc.
Phone—(973) 625-2100
6 Hinchman Ave., Denville 07834
**Airtec, Inc.**
Sheet metal fabrication, machining & laser cutting
**Phone—(732) 382-3700**
**Fax—(732) 388-0084**
**Email—airtecunique@aol.com**
**17 W. Scott Ave., P.O. Box 1181, Rahway 07065**
*(see our ad under SHEET METAL FABRICATION)*
All Tool Company, Inc.
Phone—(908) 687-3636
899 Rahway Ave., Union 07083
Almark Tool & Mfg. Co., Inc.
Phone—(908) 789-2440
27 South Ave., P.O. Box 189, Garwood 07027
Alpha Lehigh Tool & Machine Co., Inc.
Phone—(908) 454-6481
41 Industrial Rd., Alpha 08865
American Products Co., Inc.
Phone—(908) 687-4100
610 Rahway Ave., Union 07083
Ameritech Precision Machining Co.
Phone—(856) 767-1660
425 N. Grove St., Unit 3-A, Berlin 08009
Apostolico Machine
Phone—(973) 790-3351
144 Linwood Ave., Paterson 07502
Arch Custom Mfg Inc
Phone—(856) 966-3835
1215 S. 6th St., Camden 08104
Aries Precision Tool, Inc.
Phone—(201) 252-8550
300 State Route 17, Ste. H, Mahwah 07430
Atlantic Precision Technology, LLC
Phone—(732) 648-7786
432 Quarry Ln., North Brunswick 08902
**Aztech Mfg., LLC**
Precision machining job shop
**Phone—(609) 726-1212**
**Fax—(609) 726-0403**
**Web—www.aztechmfg.com**
**147 W. Hampton St., Pemberton 08068**

B & C Machine Co., Inc.
Phone—(973) 823-1120
22 Lasinski Rd., Franklin 07416
Bach Tool Precision, Inc.
Phone—(973) 962-6224
51 Executive Pkwy., Ringwood 07456
Bauer Precision, Inc.
Phone—(201) 307-0369
174 Kinderkamack Rd., Ste. D, Park Ridge 07656
C & S Tool Co., Inc.
Phone—(973) 887-6865
304 Ridgedale Ave., East Hanover 07936
Collinear Machine & Design
Phone—(973) 300-1681
7 Wilson Dr., Sparta 07871
Computa Base Machining, Inc.
Phone—(856) 767-9517
411 N. Grove St., P.O. Box 340, Berlin 08009
**Concept Group, Inc.**
Glass to metal seals (hermetic packages) & Vacuum
insulated components
**Phone—(856) 767-5506**
**Fax—(856) 768-3981**
**Web—www.conceptgroupinc.com**
**Email—applications@conceptgroupinc.com**
**380 Cooper Rd., West Berlin 08091**
*(see our ad under MACHINE PARTS — Precision)*
Creative Machining Systems, Inc.
Phone—(609) 586-3932
124 Youngs Rd., Mercerville 08619
Custom Cut Metal Products, Inc.
Phone—(973) 808-6803
7 Daniel Rd. E., Fairfield 07004
Cut Mark, Inc.
Phone—(856) 234-3428
801 S. Church St., Ste. 6, Mount Laurel 08054
D & G Precision
Phone—(908) 925-1578
709 Louis Ave., Linden 07036
DeJohn Machine Co.
Phone—(973) 478-1144
2 Elm St., Garfield 07026
Delva Tool & Machine Corp.
Phone—(856) 786-8700
1603 Industrial Hwy., P.O. Box 2249,
Cinnaminson 08077
Dependable Machining & Stone Co.
Phone—(732) 462-0262
53 Weaverville Rd., Freehold 07728
DeWalt Mfg. Co., Inc.
Phone—(856) 423-1207
88 W. Cohawkin Rd., Clarksboro 08020
Die-Tech, Inc.
Phone—(908) 369-6756
677 Amwell Rd., Hillsborough 08844
Diversitech, Inc.
Phone—(973) 835-2900
18 Hamburg Tpke., Riverdale 07457
Dynametric Tool Co.
Phone—(973) 471-8009
27 Somerset Pl., Clifton 07012
Dynamic Machining, Inc.
Phone—(856) 273-9830
876 N. Lenola Rd., Ste. 9-A, Moorestown 08057
**E & J Machine And Tool, LLC**
**Phone—(973) 810-2312 / (973) 810-2313**
**Fax—(973) 601-7953**
**Web—www.ejmachine.com**
**Email—sales@ejmachine.com**
**12 Orben Dr., Unit 1, Landing 07850**
*(see our ad under JOB SHOPS)*
ELC America Corp.
Phone—(732) 269-5274
235-B Hickory Ln., Bayville 08721
Elite Tool, Inc.
Phone—(732) 424-1126
1640 New Market Ave., P.O. Box 853, South
Plainfield 07080
**Ethylene Atlantic Corp.**
**Phone—(856) 467-0010**
**Fax—(856) 467-0610**
**Web—www.ethyleneatlantic.com**
**Email—sales@ethyleneatlantic.com**
**136 Church St., P.O. Box 430, Swedesboro
08085**
Ferry Machine Corp.
Phone—(201) 641-9191
75 Industrial Ave., Little Ferry 07643
Fluets Corp.
Phone—(908) 353-5229
260 Pennsylvania Ave., Hillside 07205

Form, Fit & Function, LLC
Phone—(973) 442-2290
25 McLean Blvd., Paterson 07514
Galaxy II, Inc.
Phone—(732) 828-2686
235 Jersey Ave., Unit A, New Brunswick 08901
Garvey Precision Machine, Inc.
Phone—(609) 835-4900
19 Ironside Ct., Willingboro 08046
**Gaum, Inc.**
AS9100C Certified
**Phone—(609) 586-0132**
**Fax—(609) 586-9748**
**Web—www.gauminc.com**
**Email—mail@gauminc.com**
**1080 Route 130, P.O. Box 485, Robbinsville
08691**
*(see our ads Outside Front Cover & under MACHINE WORK &
MACHINING)*
Geiger Tool & Mfg. Co., Inc.
Phone—(973) 777-2136
50 Liberty St., Passaic 07055
Globe Industries Corp.
Phone—(973) 992-8990
48 Industrial St. W., Clifton 07012
GMI
Phone—(732) 442-4572
599 State St., Perth Amboy 08861
GPR Co., Inc.
Phone—(973) 227-6160
22 Daniel Rd., Fairfield 07004
**Graybill's Tool & Die, Inc.**
Email: geoff@graybills.com
**Phone—(717) 665-5546**
**Fax—(717) 665-3107**
**Web—www.graybills.com**
**Email—info@graybills.com**
**147 W. High St., Manheim, PA 17545**

www.graybills.com
DESIGNERS • BUILDERS
GRAYBILL'S TOOL & DIE, INC.
A FULL SERVICE COMPANY
CONTROLS · LOGIC · PROGRAMMING
SPECIAL PRODUCTS
PROTOTYPES
CAD-CAM
WEDM
CNC
147 W. High St.
Manheim, PA 17545
MEMBER
Ph: (717) 665-5546

Great Notch Industries, Inc.
Phone—(201) 343-8110
140 Liberty St., Hackensack 07601
Guerard Co., J. D.
Phone—(609) 737-8892
43 Old Washington Crossing Rd., Titusville 08560
H.P. Machine Shop, Inc.
Phone—(856) 692-1192
415 Oxford St., Vineland 08360
**Hainesport Tool & Maintenance**
Manufacturer of machine parts & assemblies
**Phone—(609) 261-0016**
**Fax—(609) 261-2105**
**Web—www.hainesporttool.com**
**Email—rich@hainesporttool.com**
**1924 Ark Rd., Hainesport 08036**
Harrison Machine & Tool, Inc.
Phone—(609) 883-0800
21 Lexington Ave., Trenton 08618
High Precision Machine Shop, LLC
Phone—(973) 227-5110
1275 Bloomfield Ave., Ste. 63, Fairfield 07004
Howell Precision Tool Co.
Phone—(732) 919-7300
415 Cranberry Rd., Farmingdale 07727
I C Machine, Inc.
Phone—(973) 252-7083
199 U.S. Highway 46, Budd Lake 07828
IMCO, Inc.
Phone—(856) 499-2214
858 N. Lenola Rd., Bldg. 1, Moorestown 08057
International Tool & Machine, LLC
Phone—(908) 687-5580
446 Hillside Ave., Hillside 07205
**International Tool & Mfg., Inc.**
Precision machining job shop
**Phone—(973) 227-6767**
**Fax—(973) 227-6711**
**Web—www.international-inc.com**
**Email—sales@international-inc.com**
**30 Sherwood Ln., Ste. 10, Fairfield 07004**
*(see our ad under JOB SHOPS)*

© Copyright 2015 Manufacturers' News, Inc.

## MACHINING — Precision — (cont.)

**J & M Mfg., Inc.**
Phone—(908) 638-6727
54 Main St., P.O. Box 43, High Bridge 08829

**J N R Machine & Tool**
Phone—(908) 281-6603
12 Ilene Ct., Bldg. 12, Unit 2, Hillsborough 08844

**J.B.A.T., Inc.**
Phone—(856) 667-7307
28 Coles Ave., Cherry Hill 08002

**Jarco Industries, Inc.**
Phone—(973) 728-5012
1803 Union Valley Rd., West Milford 07480

**K & R Precision Machining**
Phone—(201) 385-8855
54 S. Front St., Bergenfield 07621

**K G M Precision Corp.**
Phone—(609) 801-0210
1875 Route 206, Southampton 08088

**Kaupp & Sons, Inc., C. B.**
Phone—(973) 761-4000
6 Newark Way, Maplewood 07040

**MDI Mfg., Inc.**
Phone—(732) 994-5599
100 Syracuse Ct., Lakewood 08701

**Mechanical Precision, Inc.**
Phone—(908) 782-2511
11 Hopewell Ave., Flemington 08822

**Metal Components**
Phone—(973) 247-1204
92 Maryland Ave., Paterson 07503

**Millson Precision Machining**
Phone—(732) 424-1700
145 11th St., Piscataway 08854

**Morris Tool & Machine Co.**
Phone—(973) 983-9209
80 Upper Hibernia Rd., Rockaway 07866

**MSD Precision**
Phone—(856) 262-8142
300 Thomas Ave., Bldg. 6, Williamstown 08094

**National Precision Tool Co., Inc.**
Phone—(973) 227-5005
24 Sherwood Ln., Fairfield 07004

**Nowak, Inc.**
Phone—(973) 366-7208
17 Robert St., Ste. B-5, Wharton 07885

**P & J Machine Co.**
Phone—(856) 767-8441
261 Crosskeys Rd., P.O. Box 178, Berlin 08009

**Parlin Precision Products, Inc.**
Phone—(732) 727-6111
999 Route 9, Parlin 08859

**Phelps Mfg., LLC**
Phone—(908) 453-2288
567 Brass Castle Rd., Oxford 07863

**Phoenix Precision, Inc.**
Phone—(973) 208-8877
2963 Route 23, Newfoundland 07435

**PK Precision Machining, Inc.**
Phone—(973) 925-2020
7 Mathews Ave., Riverdale 07457

**Precise Components & Tool Design, Inc.**
Phone—(973) 928-2928
10 Clifton Blvd., Unit A-4, Clifton 07011

**Precision Numerical Technology, Inc.**
Phone—(732) 591-4884
31 Ardsley Pl., Morganville 07751

**Precision Tool & Engineering, Inc.**
Phone—(609) 882-9223
123 Florence Ave., Trenton 08618

**Pro Machine Co.**
Phone—(973) 855-9935
5 Sicomac Rd., Haledon 07508

**Rabell Precision, Inc.**
Phone—(201) 473-7373
8 Queen Anne Rd., Bogota 07603

**Raue Screw Machine Product Co.**
Phone—(973) 697-7500
173 Oak Ridge Rd., P.O. Box 207, Oak Ridge 07438

**Rehtek Machine Co.**
Phone—(973) 365-2101
135 Monroe St., Passaic 07055

**Ridge Precision Products Inc.**
Phone—(973) 361-3508
288 U.S. Highway 46, Ste. D, Dover 07801

**RJD Machine Products, Inc.**
Phone—(609) 392-1515
1424 Heath Ave., Ewing 08638

**Rosco, Inc.**
Phone—(908) 789-1020
55 South Ave., P.O. Box 184, Garwood 07027

**S S Tool & Mfg. Co., Inc.**
Phone—(908) 486-5497
1 Garfield St., Linden 07036

**Select Machine Tool, Inc.**
Phone—(856) 933-2100
19 Thompson Ave., Mount Ephraim 08059

**Shore Precision Mfg., Inc.**
Phone—(732) 914-0949
1000 Industrial Way N., Unit D, Toms River 08755

**Sliker Machine Werkes, LLC**
Phone—(732) 238-0331
2 Maple St., P.O. Box 53, South River 08882

**Superior Tool & Mfg. Co., Inc.**
Phone—(908) 526-9011
42 Columbia Rd., Branchburg 08876

**T N R Tool & Machine Co.**
Phone—(908) 754-4010
2 Coddington Ave., North Plainfield 07060

**Taurus Precision, Inc.**
Phone—(973) 785-9254
129 Paterson Ave., Little Falls 07424

**Tech Products Co., Inc.**
Phone—(201) 444-7777
300 Greenwood Ave., Midland Park 07432

**Tru Mfg., Inc.**
Phone—(201) 768-4050
40 Oak St., Norwood 07648

**Unimade Metals, Inc.**
Phone—(201) 666-7747
115 Patterson St., Hillsdale 07642

**Utility Tool Co.**
Phone—(973) 743-8010
15 Orange St., Bloomfield 07003

**Vahl, Inc.**
Phone—(718) 492-6655
34 Kennedy Blvd., East Brunswick 08816

**Vector Precision Machining, Inc.**
Phone—(856) 740-5131
1558 Janvier Rd., Williamstown 08094

**Warren Mfg. Corp.**
Phone—(973) 227-4220
23 Bloomfield Ave., Pine Brook 07058

**West Machine Works, Inc.**
Phone—(732) 549-2183
101 Liberty St., Metuchen 08840

**West Side Precision Machine Products, Inc.**
Phone—(732) 560-9006
280 Lincoln Blvd., Middlesex 08846

**Woodbridge Machine & Tool Co., Inc.**
Phone—(732) 634-0179
259 Bergen St., Woodbridge 07095

**Zenex Precision Products Corp.**
Phone—(973) 523-6910
69 George St., Paterson 07503

---

## MACHINING — Precision & CNC

**ABCO Die Casters, Inc.**
Email: jvitollo@abcodiecasters.com
Founded in 1971, serving numerous industries throughout North America by supplying quality zinc die castings & powder coated components
Phone—(973) 624-7030
Fax—(973) 624-7425
Web—www.abcodiecasters.com
39 Tompkins Point Rd., Newark 07114

**Comtron, Inc.**
Swiss CNC turning, CNC turning, milling, brazing & turnkey assy. Mfg.
Phone—(732) 446-7571
Fax—(732) 446-5768
Web—www.comtroninc.com
Email—dlacross@comtroninc.com
391 State Route 33 E., Englishtown 07726

**Creter, Inc., Philip**
Phone—(908) 686-2910
20 Monroe St., Union 07083

**Custom Heliarc Welding & Machine, Inc.**
Phone—(908) 496-8190
49 Decatur St., P.O. Box 232, Columbia 07832

Search from among 430,000 U.S. manufacturers & suppliers:
IndustryNet.com

**E & J Machine And Tool, LLC**
Phone—(973) 810-2312 / (973) 810-2313
Fax—(973) 601-7953
Web—www.ejmachine.com
Email—sales@ejmachine.com
12 Orben Dr., Unit 1, Landing 07850
*(see our ad under JOB SHOPS)*

**Energy Beams, Inc.**
Phone—(973) 838-3037
185 Hamburg Tpke., Bloomingdale 07403

**G A F Machine Tool Co., Inc.**
Phone—(732) 264-8717
39 Maple Pl., P.O. Box 18, Keyport 07735

**Harley Tool & Machine, Inc.**
Phone—(201) 244-8899
24 McDermott Pl., Bergenfield 07621

**J M C Tool & Mfg. Co.**
Phone—(908) 241-8950
845 Fairfield Ave., Kenilworth 07033

**K T S Machine Shop**
Phone—(201) 791-2228
60 Bushes Ln., Elmwood Park 07407

**Lattimer USA**
Phone—(856) 691-2203
3603 N. Mill Rd., Vineland 08360

**Livingston & W, Inc.**
973-B New Durham Rd., Edison 08817
CNC & general machining job shop
Phone—(732) 287-5790
Fax—(732) 287-5793
Email—livwil@optimum.net
P.O. Box 496, Edison 08818
*(see our ad under MACHINE WORK & MACHINING)*

**M & S Machine & Tool Corp.**
Phone—(973) 345-5847
Fax—(973) 345-0579
Web—www.mandsmachine.com
Email—nazim@mandsmachine.com
108 Maryland Ave., Paterson 07503

**Machine Tech**
Phone—(732) 738-6810
3125 Woodbridge Ave., Ste. 4, Edison 08837

**P C R Technologies, Inc.**
Phone—(973) 882-0017
26 Chapin Rd., Unit 1111, Pine Brook 07058

**RJD Machine Products, Inc.**
Phone—(609) 392-1515
Fax—(609) 392-1098
Web—www.rjdmachineproducts.com
Email—admin@rjdmachineproducts.com
1424 Heath Ave., Ewing 08638

**Technatron, Inc.**
Phone—(908) 238-1122
78 Route 173 W., Ste. 9, Hampton 08827

**Tracer Tool & Machine Co., Inc.**
Phone—(201) 337-6184
32 Iron Horse Rd., Oakland 07436

**Unique Metal Products Co., Inc.**
Metal products, fabrication, laser cutting & CNC machining job shop
Phone—(732) 388-1888
Fax—(732) 388-0084
Email—airtecunique@aol.com
17 W. Scott Ave., P.O. Box 1181, Rahway 07065
*(see our ad under METAL PRODUCTS AND SPECIALTIES)*

**Zenith Precision, Inc.**
Phone—(201) 933-8640
536 Paterson Ave., East Rutherford 07073

---

## MACHINING — Production

**Defined Pro Machining, LLC**
CNC machining: prototypes, production, reverse engineering & design
Phone—(973) 941-2430
Fax—(973) 891-1039
Web—www.definedpro.com
Email—hf@definedpro.com
105 W. Dewey Ave., Ste. 205, Wharton 07885

**Precision Forms, Inc.**
Phone—(973) 838-3800
97 Decker Rd., Butler 07405

Do nationwide searches for products & services at:
IndustryNet.com

© Copyright 2015 Manufacturers' News, Inc.

A121

**INDUSTRY**

## MACHINING — Secondary Operations

Severna Operations, Inc.
Phone—(973) 503-1600
Fax—(973) 503-1704
Web—www.severna.com
Email—nkoch@severna.com
3 Eastmans Rd., Parsippany 07054
*(see our ad under PLASTIC MACHINING)*

## MACHINING CENTERS

Severna Operations, Inc.
Phone—(973) 503-1600
Fax—(973) 503-1704
Web—www.severna.com
Email—nkoch@severna.com
3 Eastmans Rd., Parsippany 07054
*(see our ad under PLASTIC MACHINING)*

## MAGAZINE DISTRIBUTORS

Hudson News Distributors, LLC
Phone—(201) 867-3600
5903 W. Side Ave., North Bergen 07047

## MAGICIAN PRODUCTS

D'Lite Products, Inc.
Phone—(201) 444-0822
540 Ravine Ct., Wyckoff 07481

## MAGNESIUM PROCESSING

Reade Manufacturing Co.
Phone—(732) 657-6451
2590 Ridgeway Blvd., Manchester 08759

## MAGNETIC MATERIALS

Fermag Technologies
Phone—(732) 985-7300
80 Executive Ave., Edison 08817

## MAGNETS

Dolan Creation, Inc.
Phone—(732) 938-6656
255 Squankum Rd., P.O. Box 693, Farmingdale 07727
Escadaus Magnetics
Phone—(973) 335-8888
2 Wood Glen Way, Boonton 07005
Prismatix Decal, Inc.
Phone—(201) 525-2800
324 Railroad Ave., Hackensack 07601

## MAGNIFIERS

Pike & Co., Inc., E. W.
Phone—(732) 396-0002
2149 Price St., Rahway 07065
Tech-Optics International
Phone—(856) 795-8585
600 Deer Rd., Cherry Hill 08034

## MAIL HANDLING EQUIPMENT

OPEX Corporation
OPEX Corporation is a recognized global technology leader in high speed mailroom automation, document imaging & material handling
Phone—(856) 727-1100
Fax—(856) 727-1955
Web—www.opex.com
Email—info@opex.com
305 Commerce Dr., Moorestown 08057

## MAILING EQUIPMENT & SUPPLIES

Neopost, Inc.
Phone—(973) 647-6700
2 Ridgedale Ave., 1st Fl., Cedar Knolls 07927

SELLING PRECISION INCORPORATED
CUSTOM HYDRAULIC MANIFOLDS

From circuit concept to finished manifold. Custom designed & manufactured hydraulic manifolds, or HIC (Hydraulic Integrated Circuits). Now offering Standard Manifolds & Subplates

800-676-2417 • Fax: (973) 728-9386
www.sellingprecision.com • sales@sellingprecision.com
264 Marshall Hill Rd.   West Milford, NJ 07480

## MAILING LISTS

Manufacturers' News, Inc.
Phone—(847) 864-7000
Fax—(847) 332-1100
Web—www.manufacturersnews.com
Email—sales@manufacturersnews.com
1633 Central St., Evanston, IL 60201

## MAILING MACHINES

Addressing Machine Supply
Phone—(908) 289-7900
1290 Central Ave., Hillside 07205

## MAILING TUBES

American Tube & Paper
80 Furler St., Totowa 07512
Phone—(973) 256-3600
Fax—(973) 785-3341
Web—www.AmericanPaperProducts.com
Email—sales@americanpaperproducts.com
P.O. Box 68, Totowa 07511

**American Tube & Paper**

*Paper Tubes & Cores*

**973-256-3600**
**Fax: 973-785-3341**

80 Furler St.
Totowa, NJ 07512

www.AmericanPaperProducts.com
sales@americanpaperproducts.com

## MAINTENANCE SUPPLIES

Interline Brands, Inc. (H Q)
Phone—(856) 439-1222
804 Eastgate Dr., Ste. 100, Mount Laurel 08054

## MALT EXTRACTS

Malt Products Corp.
Phone—(201) 845-9106
121 E. Hunter Ave., Maywood 07607

## MANAGEMENT SYSTEMS

Elemco Building Controls
Phone—(908) 281-2201
14 Ilene Ct., Bldg. 11, Unit 1, Hillsborough 08844

## MANHOLE COVERS

Campbell Foundry Co.
Phone—(973) 483-5480
800 Bergen St., Harrison 07029

## MANHOLES

Bridgestate Foundry Corp.
Phone—(856) 767-0400
175 Jackson Rd., Berlin 08009
Fairfield Industries, Inc.
Phone—(973) 483-0100
827 N. 6th St., Newark 07107

## MANIFOLDS — Hydraulic

Selling Precision, Inc.
From Circuit Concept To Finished Manifold. Custom designed & manufactured hydraulic manifolds, or HIC (Hydraulic Integrated Circuits). Now offering Standard Manifolds & Subplates
Phone—(973) 728-1214 / (800) 676-2417
Fax—(973) 728-9386
Web—www.sellingprecision.com
Email—sales@sellingprecision.com
264 Marshall Hill Rd., West Milford 07480
*(see our ad on this page)*

## MANUFACTURERS' REPRESENTATIVES

Flanner & Associates
Since 1987, specializing in representing manufacturers of fourslide parts, wire, metal, plastic, and rubber for the Aerospace, Automotive, Electronics, and Medical industries
Phone—(609) 588-0790 / (609) 647-7821
Email—gflanner@optonline.net
104 Caitlin Ln., Hamilton 08691
Maresco International
Phone—(908) 454-4770
7 Edge Rd., Phillipsburg 08865

## MANUFACTURING CONSULTANTS

New Jersey Mfg. Extension Program, Inc.
Phone—(973) 998-9801
Fax—(973) 860-4637
Web—www.njmep.org
Email—info@njmep.org
2 Ridgedale Ave., Ste. 305, Cedar Knolls 07927

**New Jersey Mfg. Extension Program, Inc.**

NJMEP  Quality Business Consultants

www.njmep.org • info@njmep.org
(973) 998-9801 • FAX: (973) 860-4637
2 Ridgedale Ave., Suite 305, Cedar Knolls, NJ 07927

*Do nationwide searches for products & services at:*
**IndustryNet.com**

## MAPS

Geographia Map Co., Inc.
Phone—(201) 488-4411
75 Moore St., Hackensack 07601

## MARBLE

Champion Marble & Granite, Inc.
Phone—(732) 409-3200
4 Kinney Rd., Manalapan 07726
Formia Marble & Stone, Inc.
Phone—(908) 259-0606
219 E. 11th Ave., Roselle 07203
Innovative Cutting Concepts, LLC
Phone—(609) 484-9960
203 Cates Rd., Egg Harbor Township 08234
Ocean Granite Marble, LLC
Phone—(609) 296-1800
140 7th Ave., Unit 9, Little Egg Harbor 08087
Unlimited Stone Designs
Phone—(973) 523-2224
7 McLean Blvd., Paterson 07514
Wilkstone, LLC
Phone—(973) 684-5100
128 19th Ave., Paterson 07513

## MARBLE — Cultured

Aphrodite Marble & Granite Co., Inc.
Phone—(609) 693-4450
700 Old Shore Rd., Forked River 08731

## MARBLE AND GRANITE PRODUCTS

A W Eurostile
Phone—(732) 493-1883
736 Route 35, Ocean 07712
**American Stone, Inc.**
**Cabinetry**
**Phone—(973) 318-7707**
**Fax—(973) 318-7667**
**Email—amerstone@aol.com**
**215 Route 22 W., Hillside 07205**
Arcade Tile & Marble Co.
Phone—(973) 678-4600
416 Central Ave., East Orange 07018
**Artistic Marble & Granite Surfaces, Inc.**
**Web: www.NJMarble.com**
**Phone—(973) 304-2001**
**Fax—(973) 427-9142**
**Email—artistic269@aol.com**
**269 Goffle Rd., Hawthorne 07506**
BCG Marble & Granite Co.
Phone—(732) 367-3788
370 Whitesville Rd., Jackson 08527
BCG Marble & Granite Fabricators Co., Inc.
Phone—(201) 343-8487
167 Sussex St., Hackensack 07601
C C S Stone
Phone—(201) 933-1515
9-11 Caesar Pl., Moonachie 07074
Classic Marble & Tile
Phone—(201) 440-8848
11 Main St., Little Ferry 07643
Cole Bros. Marble & Granite
Phone—(856) 455-7989
892 Parvins Mill Rd., Pittsgrove 08318
Hard Rock Marble & Granite, Inc.
Phone—(908) 620-9150
1101 Chestnut St., Roselle 07203
Marble Factory
Phone—(908) 353-2264
800 Magnolia Ave., Elizabeth 07201
New Granite & Marble, LLC
Phone—(973) 767-6216
35 8th St., Ste. 6, Passaic 07055
Phillipsburg Marble Co.
Phone—(908) 859-3435
1 Marble Hill Rd., P.O. Box 172, Phillipsburg 08865
Renaissance Marble & Granite
Phone—(856) 227-3535
107 Harmon Dr., Blackwood 08012
Robert Young & Sons, Inc.
Phone—(973) 483-0451
25 Grafton Ave., Newark 07104
Stone Tech Fabrication
Phone—(609) 984-8818
930 New York Ave., Trenton 08638

## MARINE EQUIPMENT & SUPPLIES

Marine Development & Research Corp.
Phone—(973) 754-7087
515 E. 41st St., Paterson 07504

## MARINE EQUIPMENT & SUPPLIES — Wholesale

W&O Supply, Inc.
Phone—(908) 486-5338
7 W. Baltimore Ave., Linden 07036

## MARKERBOARDS

New York Blackboard of NJ, Inc.
Phone—(973) 926-1600
83 U.S. Highway 22, Hillside 07205

## MARKETING CONSULTANTS

**Alcimed**
**Phone—(609) 514-0145**
**Email—princeton@alcimed.com**
**5 Vaughn Dr., Ste. 105, Princeton 08540**

## MARKING DEVICES

Arro-Mark Co., LLC
Phone—(201) 567-4112
158 W. Forest Ave., Englewood 07631
Trodat USA
Phone—(732) 529-8500
48 Hellar Pk., Somerset 08873

## MARKING EQUIPMENT — Industrial

Dalemark Industries, Inc.
Phone—(732) 367-3100
575 Prospect St., Ste. 211, Lakewood 08701

## MARKING SYSTEMS

Innovative Marking Systems, Inc.
Phone—(908) 322-2900
105 Forest Rd., Fanwood 07023

## MASKING PRODUCTS

Kinnarney Rubber Co., Inc.
Phone—(856) 468-1320
450 Main St., P.O. Box 37, Mantua 08051

## MASONRY & STONEWORK CONTRACTORS

**Green Acres Inc.**
**We also offer natural ponds & synthetic putting greens**
**Phone—(201) 941-5086**
**Fax—(201) 941-2228**
**Web—www.greenacresinc.com**
**Email—usaga1@aol.com**
**317 E. Columbia Ave., Palisades Park 07650**

## MASONRY MATERIALS & SUPPLIES

Athenia Mason Supply, Inc.
Phone—(973) 253-0570
72 Mina Ave., Clifton 07011
Clayton Block Co., Inc.
Phone—(732) 681-1414
1601 18th Ave., Belmar 07719
Clayton Block Co., Inc.
Phone—(732) 549-1234
1025 Route 1 S., Edison 08837
Clayton Block Co., Inc.
Phone—(732) 462-1860
225 Throckmorton St., Freehold 07728
Clayton Block Co., Inc.
Phone—(732) 349-3700
194 Chestnut St., Toms River 08753
Clayton Block Co., Inc.
Phone—(609) 693-3000
Route 9, Waretown 08758
Extech Building Materials, Inc.
Phone—(732) 919-3340
385 Asbury Rd., Farmingdale 07727
Richardson Co., J. B.
Phone—(609) 695-7474
1603 N. Olden Ave., Trenton 08638

## MATERIAL HANDLING EQUIPMENT

**(also see 'Conveyors' & 'Hoists')**

**Action Lift Trucks, Inc.**
**Phone—(973) 589-2320**
**Fax—(973) 824-4768**
**Web—www.actionlifttrucks.com**
**Email—actionlift@optonline.net**
**35 Avenue C, Newark 07114**
Barclay Brand Ferdon
Phone—(908) 561-2100
2401 S. Clinton Ave., P.O. Box 341, South Plainfield 07080
Capus Automation Services, Inc.
Phone—(908) 281-0227
856 Highway 206, Hillsborough 08844
Eastern Lift Truck Co., Inc.
Phone—(856) 779-8880
549 E. Linwood Ave., Route 73 N., P.O. Box 307, Maple Shade 08052
Electro Lift, Inc.
Phone—(973) 471-0204
204 Sargeant Ave., Clifton 07013
Essex Rise
Phone—(973) 575-7483
4 Fairfield Crescent, West Caldwell 07006
Jescraft
Phone—(201) 488-4545
201 W. Fort Lee Rd., Bogota 07603
Liftec, Inc.
Phone—(908) 769-0034
124 Sylvania Pl., South Plainfield 07080
Material Handling Supply, Inc.
Phone—(856) 541-1290
1 Old Salem Rd., Brooklawn 08030
Maximum Material Handling, LLC
Phone—(973) 227-1227
750 Edwards Rd., Parsippany 07054
Meto Lift, Inc.
Phone—(201) 405-0311
556 Commerce St., Franklin Lakes 07417
MHE, Inc.
Phone—(732) 571-6112
47 Atlantic Ave., Long Branch 07740
Middlesex Industrial Sales, Inc.
Phone—(732) 738-0537
522 New Brunswick Ave., Fords 08863
**OPEX Corporation**
**OPEX Corporation is a recognized global technology leader in high speed mailroom automation, document imaging & material handling**
**Phone—(856) 727-1100**
**Fax—(856) 727-1955**
**Web—www.opex.com**
**Email—info@opex.com**
**305 Commerce Dr., Moorestown 08057**
**Raymond Of NJ, LLC**
**Phone—(908) 624-9570 / (800) 800-2024**
**Fax—(908) 624-9553**
**Web—www.raymond-nj.com**
**Email—info@raymond-nj.com**
**1000 Brighton St., Union 07083**
*(see our ad on next page)*
Saturn Overhead Equipment, LLC
Phone—(732) 560-7210
100 Apgar Dr., Somerset 08873
Servolift, LLC
Phone—(973) 442-7878
35 Righter Rd., Randolph 07869
**Taylor Northeast**
**Providing of a broad range of services for Material Handling & Industrial Cleaning Equipment in the eastern-PA area since 1985. Services range from new & used lift truck sales, leasing & rentals to service, parts & remanufacturing**
**Phone—(610) 286-8080 / (800) 762-2500**
**Fax—(610) 286-8099**
**Web—www.taylornortheast.com**
**Email—kkoch@taylornortheast.com**
**931 Hemlock Rd., Morgantown, PA 19543**

INDUSTRY

## MATERIAL HANDLING EQUIPMENT — *(cont.)*

**UNEX Manufacturing, Inc.**
Phone—(732) 928-2800
Fax—(732) 928-2828
Web—www.unex.com
Email—span@unex.com
50 Progress Pl., Jackson 08527

W & H Systems, Inc.
Phone—(201) 933-7840
120 Asia Pl., Carlstadt 07072

**Warwick Mfg. & Equipment Co., LLC**
Buy & sell used: Chemical, food, cosmetic, packaging
& pharmaceutical equipment
Phone—(732) 729-0400 / (732) 241-9263
Fax—(732) 729-1235
Web—www.warwickequipment.com
Email—sales@warwickequipment.com
1112 12th St., North Brunswick 08902
*(see our ad Outside Back Cover)*

## MATERIAL HANDLING EQUIPMENT PARTS

Elkay Products Co., Inc.
Phone—(973) 376-7550
35 Brown Ave., P.O. Box 149, Springfield 07081

## MATERIAL HANDLING LIFTS

**Lightning Lift Products**
Also hydraulic lift equipment; Designing, providing &
installing drive on, drive off car lifts, frieght lifts, pallet
lifts, vertical reciprocating conveyors & high speed
lifts
Phone—(856) 824-0022
Fax—(856) 824-0868
Web—www.lightningliftproducts.com
Email—tweldon@lightningliftproducts.com
P.O. Box 5493, Delanco 08075

## MATERIAL HANDLING ROBOTS

**Resistance Welding Solutions, Inc.**
DBA: LORS Machinery
Phone—(908) 964-9100 / (800) 223-0909
Fax—(908) 964-4492
Web—www.lors.com
Email—sales@lors.com
1090 Lousons Rd., Union 07083
*(see our ads under WELDING ROBOTS & WELDING
EQUIPMENT & SUPPLIES)*

## MATERIAL HANDLING SYSTEMS — Bulk

Vibra Screw, Inc.
Phone—(973) 256-7410
755 Union Blvd., Totowa 07512

## MATERIALS TESTING EQUIPMENT

DEK-TRON International Corp.
Phone—(908) 226-1777
244 E. 3rd St., Plainfield 07060

## MATS

Matting World
Phone—(609) 641-4747
P.O. Box 43, Beverly 08010

## MATS — Automotive Floor

Newark Auto Top Co., Inc.
Phone—(973) 677-9935
23 Centerway, East Orange 07017

*Search from among*
*430,000 U.S. manufacturers*
*& suppliers at*
**IndustryNet.com**

## MATS — Crane

**Riephoff Sawmill, Inc.**
Phone—(609) 259-7265
Fax—(609) 259-7267
Web—www.riephoffsawmill.com
Email—john@riephoffsawmill.com
763 Route 524, Allentown 08501
*(see our ad under LUMBER)*

## MATS — Floor

G R Office Products, Inc.
Phone—(973) 345-2769
11 Kentucky Ave., Paterson 07503

## MATS — Safety

ASO Safety Solutions, Inc.
Phone—(973) 586-9600
300 Round Hill Dr., Ste. 6, Rockaway 07866

## MATTRESSES
**(also see Bedding)**

Bedding Industries Of America
Phone—(732) 628-0800
1375 Jersey Ave., North Brunswick 08902

Chiromatic, Inc.
Phone—(800) 526-5116
1375 Jersey Ave., North Brunswick 08902

Comfort Revolution (H Q)
Phone—(732) 272-9111
187 Route 36, Ste. 205, West Long Branch 07764

Drake Mills, LLC
Phone—(973) 345-0008
18 E. 5th St., Ste. B, Paterson 07524

Gerson Industries, Inc.
Phone—(973) 423-6100
20-21 Wagaraw Rd., Bldg. 37, P.O. Box 12, Fair
Lawn 07410

Innocor, Inc. (H Q)
Phone—(732) 263-0800
187 State Route 36, Ste. 101, West Long Branch
07764

M & R Diamond Quilting Co., Inc.
Phone—(908) 322-4178
35 South Ave., Fanwood 07023

New England Bedding Transport
Phone—(201) 997-2337
102 3rd Ave., Kearny 07032

Orange Mattress
Phone—(973) 761-1100
77 Central Ave., Clark 07066

Rex Bedding & Sleep Products
Phone—(908) 668-0220
300 W. 4th St., Plainfield 07060

Sealy Mattress Co. Of New Jersey
Phone—(973) 345-8800
697 River St., Paterson 07524

Spring Time Bedding Corp.
Phone—(973) 473-5400
25 Central Ave., Teterboro 07608

Therapedic International, Inc. (H Q)
Phone—(609) 720-0700
103 College Rd. E., 2nd Fl., Princeton 08540

White Lotus Home
Phone—(732) 828-2111
431 Raritan Ave., Highland Park 08904

## MEASURING EQUIPMENT

PulseTor, LLC
Phone—(609) 303-0578
1580 Reed Rd., Ste. C-2, Pennington 08534

## MEASURING INSTRUMENTS

Analytical Measurements
Phone—(908) 955-7170
22 Mountain View Dr., Chester 07930

DSPCon
Phone—(908) 722-5656
380 Foothill Rd., Ste. 101, Bridgewater 08807

Electronic Measuring Devices, Inc.
Phone—(973) 691-4755
15 Mill Rd., Flanders 07836

Flemington Instrument Co., Inc.
Phone—(908) 782-4229
55 Sandra Rd., P.O. Box 298, Ringoes 08551

Link Computer Graphics, Inc.
Phone—(973) 808-8990
17-A Daniel Rd., Fairfield 07004

Marine Electric Systems, Inc.
Phone—(201) 531-8600
80 Wesley St., South Hackensack 07606

Metricon Corp.
Phone—(609) 737-1052
12 N. Main St., P.O. Box 63, Pennington 08534

Schaedler Quinzel, Inc. (H Q)
Phone—(973) 263-4949
1259 U.S. Highway 46, Ste. 4, Parsippany 07054

Technical Products Co.
Phone—(973) 228-2258
264 Park Ave., Caldwell 07006

## MEAT — Wholesale

**Wotiz Meat Co.**
Phone—(973) 773-7556
Fax—(973) 773-7586
Web—www.wotiz.com
68 1st St., Passaic 07055

## MEAT CUTTING EQUIPMENT

J T D Sales, LLC (H Q)
Phone—(973) 482-5070
71 Bloomfield Ave., Newark 07104

## MEAT PACKING & PROCESSING

814 Americas
Phone—(908) 354-2674
814 2nd Ave., Elizabeth 07202

A R M National Foods, Inc.
Phone—(609) 394-0431
1546 Lamberton Rd., Trenton 08611

A. Gimenez Trading, LLC
Phone—(973) 697-2240
5 Wegmann Way, Oak Ridge 07438

Allied Specialty Foods, Inc.
Phone—(856) 507-1100
313 Hickory Pl., Vineland 08360

American Halal Slaughter House
Phone—(973) 817-8444
270 Raymond Blvd., Newark 07105

Applegate Farms (H Q)
Phone—(866) 587-5858
750 Route 202 S., Ste. 300, Bridgewater 08807

**Raymond of NJ, LLC**
*Material Handling Equipment*
800-800-2024 • FAX: 908-624-9553
1000 Brighton St. Union, NJ 07083
www.raymond-nj.com • info@raymond-nj.com

## MEAT PACKING & PROCESSING
### — (cont.)

Basha USA, LLC
  Phone—(201) 339-9770
  390 Broadway, Bayonne 07002
Beef International, Inc.
  Phone—(856) 663-6763
  7010 Central Hwy., Pennsauken 08109
Bergen Wholesale Meats Corp.
  Phone—(201) 342-2138
  154 Hackensack Ave., Hackensack 07601
Best Provision Co., Inc.
  Phone—(973) 242-5000
  144 Avon Ave., Newark 07108
Bierig Bros., Inc.
  Phone—(856) 691-9765
  3539 Reilly Ct., Vineland 08360
Brown & Co., C. W.
  Phone—(856) 423-3700
  161 Kings Hwy., Mount Royal 08061
Cameco, Inc.
  Phone—(973) 239-2700
  100 Pine St., Verona 07044
Catelli Bros. Veal & Lamb, Inc.
  Phone—(856) 869-9293
  50 Ferry Ave., Collingswood 08103
Catelli Bros. Veal & Lamb, Inc.
  Phone—(732) 741-3687
  776 Broad St., Shrewsbury 07702
Dealaman Enterprises, Inc.
  Phone—(908) 755-1780
  214 Mountain View Rd., Warren 07059
Delaware Food Market
  Phone—(609) 822-0222
  6506 Ventnor Ave., Ventnor City 08406
Dutch's Meats, Inc.
  Phone—(609) 882-6650
  30 Morse Ave., Ewing 08638
Foote's Slaughter House
  Phone—(856) 358-8550
  28 Swedesboro Rd., Monroeville 08343
Gaiser's European Style Provisions, Inc.
  Phone—(908) 686-3421
  2019 Morris Ave., Union 07083
Great American Veal Co., Inc.
  Phone—(973) 589-6363
  50 Avenue L, Ste. 5, Newark 07105
Green Tree Packing, Inc.
  Phone—(973) 473-1305
  65 Central Ave., P.O. Box 386, Passaic 07055
Ivo Delicious Meat Products, Inc.
  Phone—(973) 223-4044
  206 Dayton Ave., Passaic 07055
Kleemeyer & Merkel, Inc.
  Phone—(973) 377-0875
  68 Britten Rd., P.O. Box 204, Green Village 07935
Kupelian Foods, Inc.
  Phone—(201) 440-8055
  146 Bergen Tpke., Ridgefield Park 07660
**Lipari's Sausage, Inc.**
  **Phone—(973) 304-0137**
  **Fax—(973) 304-0728**
  **Web—www.liparisausage.com**
  **Email—lipsaus@aol.com**
  **220 6th Ave., Hawthorne 07506**
    *(see our ad under MEAT PRODUCTS—Sausage)*
Loeffler's Gourmet
  Phone—(609) 695-5068
  482 Whitehead Rd., Trenton 08619
Love Farms, LLC
  Phone—(973) 942-5683
  204 Albion Ave., Paterson 07502
Magnolia Beef Co., LLC
  Phone—(908) 352-9412
  1070 Magnolia Ave., Elizabeth 07201
Marcacci Meats, Inc.
  Phone—(856) 691-4848
  1853 Vine Rd., Vineland 08361
Mayabeque Products Corp.
  Phone—(201) 869-0531
  7424 Bergenline Ave., Ste. 1, North Bergen 07047
Megas Yeeros, LLC
  Phone—(212) 777-6342
  165 Chubb Ave., Lyndhurst 07071
New Jersey Halal Meat Packing
  Phone—(973) 684-3648
  841 Main St., Paterson 07503
Pulaski Meat Products Co.
  Phone—(908) 925-5380
  123 N. Wood Ave., Linden 07036

Rexell Foods Corp.
  Phone—(973) 741-0404
  120 Orchard St., Newark 07102
RobDav Distributors, Inc.
  Phone—(609) 259-6335
  1251 Yardville Allentown Rd., Allentown 08501
Senat Poultry, LLC
  Phone—(973) 742-4790
  28 Warren St., Paterson 07524
Streit & Son Co., Inc., Carl
  Phone—(732) 775-0803
  703 Atkins Ave., Neptune 07753
Sussex Meat Packing, Inc.
  Phone—(973) 875-5641
  205 Route 23, Sussex 07461
Thumann, Inc.
  Phone—(201) 935-3636
  670 Dell Rd., Carlstadt 07072
Trenton Steak Co.
  Phone—(609) 695-6776
  539 Chestnut Ave., Trenton 08611
Unity Brand Halal Products
  Phone—(973) 624-4847
  94 Orange St., Newark 07102
Wagner Provisions Co., Inc.
  Phone—(856) 423-1630
  54 E. Broad St., P.O. Box 169, Gibbstown 08027
Wayne Meat Corp.
  Phone—(973) 835-0211
  2234 Hamburg Tpke., Wayne 07470

## MEAT PROCESSING EQUIPMENT

New Brunswick Saw Service, Inc.
  Phone—(908) 755-2366
  400 Lincoln Blvd., Middlesex 08846
**Warwick Mfg. & Equipment Co., LLC**
  **Buy & sell used: Chemical, food, cosmetic, packaging**
  **& pharmaceutical equipment**
  **Phone—(732) 729-0400 / (732) 241-9263**
  **Fax—(732) 729-1235**
  **Web—www.warwickequipment.com**
  **Email—sales@warwickequipment.com**
  **1112 12th St., North Brunswick 08902**
    *(see our ad Outside Back Cover)*

## MEAT PRODUCTS — Beef

Buona Vita, Inc.
  Phone—(856) 453-7972
  1 S. Industrial Blvd., Bridgeton 08302
Burger Maker, Inc.
  Phone—(201) 939-4747
  666 16th St., Carlstadt 07072
Trenton Halal Packing Co.
  Phone—(609) 394-0331
  610 Roebling Ave., Trenton 08611

## MEAT PRODUCTS — Ham

Al & John, Inc.
  Phone—(973) 742-4990
  444 Marshall St., Paterson 07503
**Cameco, Inc.**
  **Phone—(973) 239-2700**
  **Fax—(973) 239-5392**
  **Web—www.camecoinc.com**
  **Email—info@camecoinc.com**
  **100 Pine St., Verona 07044**

## MEAT PRODUCTS — Poultry

**Cameco, Inc.**
  **Phone—(973) 239-2700**
  **Fax—(973) 239-5392**
  **Web—www.camecoinc.com**
  **Email—info@camecoinc.com**
  **100 Pine St., Verona 07044**

## MEAT PRODUCTS — Processed

Bringhurst Bros., Inc.
  Phone—(856) 767-0110
  38 W. Taunton Rd., Berlin 08009
Carnegie Deli, Inc.
  Phone—(201) 507-5557
  605 Washington Ave., Carlstadt 07072

Marathon Enterprises, Inc. (H Q)
  Phone—(201) 935-3330
  9 Smith St., Englewood 07631

## MEAT PRODUCTS — Sausage

**Lipari's Sausage, Inc.**
  **Phone—(973) 304-0137**
  **Fax—(973) 304-0728**
  **Web—www.liparisausage.com**
  **Email—lipsaus@aol.com**
  **220 6th Ave., Hawthorne 07506**

# Lipari's Sausage, Inc.
*Meat & Sausage Processing*

## 973-304-0137
## FAX: 973-304-0728

www.liparisausage.com
Email: lipsaus@aol.com

### 220 6th Ave.
### Hawthorne, NJ 07506

## MEAT PRODUCTS — Smoked

PRG Packing Corp. (H Q)
  Phone—(201) 242-5500
  2071 Lemoine Ave., Fort Lee 07024

## MEAT PRODUCTS — Wholesale

Buckhead Beef Co.
  Phone—(732) 661-4900
  220 Raritan Ctr., P.O. Box 6988, Edison 08837

## MEATS — Deli

**Cameco, Inc.**
  **Phone—(973) 239-2700**
  **Fax—(973) 239-5392**
  **Web—www.camecoinc.com**
  **Email—info@camecoinc.com**
  **100 Pine St., Verona 07044**
Red Square Foods, Inc.
  Phone—(732) 846-0190
  62 Berry St., Somerset 08873

## MECHANICAL COMPONENTS

Bright Lights USA, Inc.
  Phone—(856) 546-5656
  145 Shreve Ave., Barrington 08007

## MEDALS

Norco, Inc.
  Phone—(908) 789-1550
  237 South Ave., P.O. Box 186, Garwood 07027

## MEDICAL CENTERS

**Cobalt Medical Supply, Inc.**
  **Phone—(973) 305-0730 / (888) 350-3790**
  **Fax—(201) 465-3041**
  **Web—www.cobaltmed.com**
  **Email—sales@cobaltmed.com**
  **P.O. Box 367, Pequannock 07440**
    *(see our ad under MEDICAL EQUIPMENT & SUPPLIES)*

INDUSTRY

## MEDICAL CENTERS — *(cont.)*

**NJ Heart**
Phone—(908) 587-9300
Web—www.njheart.com
520 N. Wood Ave., Linden 07036

## MEDICAL CHAIRS

**Cobalt Medical Supply, Inc.**
**Phone—(973) 305-0730 / (888) 350-3790**
**Fax—(201) 465-3041**
**Web—www.cobaltmed.com**
**Email—sales@cobaltmed.com**
**P.O. Box 367, Pequannock 07440**
*(see our ad under MEDICAL EQUIPMENT & SUPPLIES)*

## MEDICAL DEVICES

Abbott Point Of Care
Phone—(609) 454-9000
400 College Rd. E., Princeton 08540
ADM Tronics Unlimited, Inc.
Phone—(201) 767-6040
224 Pegasus Ave., Northvale 07647
Baeta Corp.
Phone—(201) 471-0988
1 Bridge Plz., Ste. 275, Fort Lee 07024
**Bernafon, LLC**
**2501 Cottontail Ln., Somerset 08873**
**Phone—(732) 560-9996 / (888) 941-4203**
**Fax—(732) 560-4877**
**Web—www.bernafon-us.com**
**Email—info@bernafon-us.com**
**P.O. Box 6706, Somerset 08875**
Bipore, Inc.
Phone—(201) 767-1993
31 Industrial Pkwy., Northvale 07647
Burpee Material Technology, LLC
Phone—(732) 544-8900
15 Christopher Way, Eatontown 07724
C.R. Bard, Inc. (H Q)
Phone—(908) 277-8000
730 Central Ave., New Providence 07974
Catheter Robotics, Inc.
Phone—(973) 691-2000
500 International Dr., Ste. 255, Budd Lake 07828
CirculLite, Inc.
Phone—(201) 543-2430
250 Pehle Ave., Ste. 403, Saddle Brook 07663
**DRG International, Inc.**
**Phone—(973) 564-7555**
**Fax—(973) 564-7556**
**Web—www.drg-international.com**
**Email—corp@drg-international.com**
**841 Mountain Ave., Springfield 07081**
Elcam Medical, Inc.
Phone—(201) 457-1120
2 University Plz., Ste. 620, Hackensack 07601
Endo Pharmaceutical, Inc.
Phone—(609) 409-9010
8 Clarke Dr., Cranbury 08512
Flowonix
Phone—(973) 426-9229
500 International Dr., Ste. 200, Budd Lake 07828
Gore & Assocs., Inc., W. L.
Phone—(732) 681-7070
1746 State Route 34 N., Wall Township 07727
G-U Tek, Inc.
Phone—(908) 626-0012
266 King George Rd., Ste. B-2, Warren 07059
Martin Tool Co., Inc.
Phone—(973) 361-9212
60 Route 15 S., Wharton 07885
MICRO
Phone—(732) 302-0800
140 Belmont Dr., Somerset 08873
Nephros, Inc.
Phone—(201) 343-5202
41 Grand Ave., Ste. 201, River Edge 07661
Nexcore Technology, Inc.
Phone—(201) 968-9400
150 Hopper Ave., Waldwick 07463
**North American Sterilization & Packaging**
**Company, Inc.**
**Email—rogerm@naspco.com**
**Phone—(973) 209-4388 / (800) 392-6310**
**Fax—(973) 209-6374**
**Web—www.naspco.com**
**19 Park Dr., Franklin 07416**
*(see our ad under CONTRACT MANUFACTURING—Medical)*

Phil-Lu, Inc.
Phone—(732) 531-6338
1206 Herbert Ave., Ocean 07712
Triangle Mfg.
Phone—(201) 825-1212
116 Pleasant Ave., Upper Saddle River 07458
Vention Medical
Phone—(908) 561-0717
6 Century Rd., South Plainfield 07080

## MEDICAL ELECTRONICS

**Bloomex International, Inc.**
**Email: bloomex@aol.com**
**Phone—(201) 703-9799**
**Fax—(201) 703-9626**
**Web—www.bloomex.com**
**295 Molnar Dr., Elmwood Park 07407**
General Devices
Phone—(201) 313-7075
1000 River St., Ridgefield 07657

## MEDICAL EQUIPMENT — Durable

**Cobalt Medical Supply, Inc.**
**Phone—(973) 305-0730 / (888) 350-3790**
**Fax—(201) 465-3041**
**Web—www.cobaltmed.com**
**Email—sales@cobaltmed.com**
**P.O. Box 367, Pequannock 07440**
*(see our ad under MEDICAL EQUIPMENT & SUPPLIES)*
Stryker Corp.
Phone—(201) 760-8000
2 Pearl Ct., Allendale 07401

## MEDICAL EQUIPMENT — Emergency

**Cobalt Medical Supply, Inc.**
**Phone—(973) 305-0730 / (888) 350-3790**
**Fax—(201) 465-3041**
**Web—www.cobaltmed.com**
**Email—sales@cobaltmed.com**
**P.O. Box 367, Pequannock 07440**
*(see our ad under MEDICAL EQUIPMENT & SUPPLIES)*

## MEDICAL EQUIPMENT — Wholesale

Apria Healthcare, Inc.
Phone—(973) 305-0099
1 Frassetto Way, Ste. F, Lincoln Park 07035
Midwest Medical Supply Company, LLC
Phone—(201) 223-4602
200 Seaview Dr., Secaucus 07094
**Topcon Medical Systems, Inc.**
**Phone—(201) 599-5100**
**Fax—(201) 599-5250**
**Web—www.topcon.com**
**Email—tmsmarketing@topcon.com**
**111 Bauer Dr., Oakland 07436**

## MEDICAL EQUIPMENT AND SUPPLIES

Alkaline Corp.
Phone—(732) 531-7830
20 Meridian Rd., Eatontown 07724
Antares Pharma, Inc.
Phone—(609) 359-3020
100 Princeton S. Corporate Ctr., Ste. 300, Ewing 08628
Apria Healthcare, Inc.
Phone—(609) 265-2190
118 Burrs Rd., Ste. C, Mount Holly 08060
Becton, Dickinson & Co. (H Q)
Phone—(201) 847-6800
1 Becton Dr., Franklin Lakes 07417
**Bio Compression Systems, Inc.**
**Phone—(201) 939-0716**
**Fax—(201) 939-4503**
**Web—www.biocompression.com**
**Email—biosystems@biocompression.com**
**120 W. Commercial Ave., Moonachie 07074**
Brenner Metal Products Corp.
Phone—(973) 778-2466
16 Main Ave., P.O. Box 16, Wallington 07057

Cantel Medical Corp. (H Q)
Phone—(973) 890-7220
150 Clove Rd., 9th Fl., Little Falls 07424
Capintec, Inc.
Phone—(201) 825-9500
6 Arrow Rd., Ste. 101, Ramsey 07446
Cenmed Enterprises
Phone—(732) 447-1100
121 Jersey Ave., New Brunswick 08901
CH Technologies, Inc.
Phone—(201) 666-2335
263 Center Ave., Ste. 2, Westwood 07675
Clinical Image Retrieval, Inc.
Phone—(973) 862-6151
376 Lafayette Rd., Ste. 202, P.O. Box 899, Sparta 07871
**Cobalt Medical Supply, Inc.**
**Phone—(973) 305-0730 / (888) 350-3790**
**Fax—(201) 465-3041**
**Web—www.cobaltmed.com**
**Email—sales@cobaltmed.com**
**P.O. Box 367, Pequannock 07440**

**Cobalt Medical Supply, Inc.**

*Distributor of Medical Supplies & Equipment*

www.cobaltmed.com
sales@cobaltmed.com

**(888) 350-3790**
**Fax: (201) 465-3041**

PO Box 367
Pequannock, NJ 07440

Cross Medical Specialties, Inc.
Phone—(856) 589-3288
450 Andbro Dr., Unit 7, Pitman 08071
EBI
Phone—(973) 299-9300
399 Jefferson Rd., Parsippany 07054
Eurotek, Inc.
Phone—(732) 224-1300
Carlton Street 61, Unit 2, Rumson 07760
Impact Instrumentation, Inc.
Phone—(973) 882-1212
27 Fairfield Pl., West Caldwell 07006
Jan L, Inc.
Phone—(609) 261-1133
26 Mill St., Ste. 26, Mount Holly 08060
Ken-Mar Machine & Mfg.
Phone—(973) 278-5827
477 E. 30th St., Paterson 07504
Lymphedema Products, LLC
Phone—(732) 290-2888
750 State Route 34, Ste. 7, Matawan 07747
Mada Medical Products, Inc.
Phone—(201) 460-0454
625 Washington Ave., Carlstadt 07072
Maquet
Phone—(973) 244-6100
15 Law Dr., Fairfield 07004
McKesson Medical-Surgical
Phone—(856) 241-1709
1130 Commerce Blvd., Swedesboro 08085
MedConnection, LLC
Phone—(908) 213-7012
65 Howard St., Phillipsburg 08865
Medrecon, Inc.
Phone—(908) 789-2050
257 South Ave., Garwood 07027
Milestone Scientific, Inc. (H Q)
Phone—(973) 535-2717
220 S. Orange Ave., Ste. 102, Livingston 07039
Neurotron Medical
Phone—(609) 896-3444
800 Silvia St., West Trenton 08628

## MEDICAL EQUIPMENT AND SUPPLIES — *(cont.)*

O. R. Comfort, LLC
Phone—(973) 239-1950
28 Appleton Rd., Glen Ridge 07028

Owens & Minor, Inc.
Phone—(856) 423-9900
1220 Forest Pkwy., Paulsboro 08066

Pharmaceutical Innovations
Phone—(973) 242-2901
897 Frelinghuysen Ave., Newark 07114

Physitemp Instruments, Inc.
Phone—(973) 779-5577
154 Huron Ave., Clifton 07013

PSS/World Medical, Inc.
Phone—(973) 775-8600
208 Passaic Ave., Ste. 2, Fairfield 07004

Topcon Medical Systems, Inc.
Phone—(201) 599-5100
111 Bauer Dr., Oakland 07436

Tronex International, Inc.
Phone—(973) 335-2888
300 International Dr., Mount Olive 07828

V L V Assocs., Inc.
Phone—(973) 428-2884
30-C Ridgedale Ave., East Hanover 07936

Viscot Medical, LLC
Phone—(973) 887-9273
32 West St., P.O. Box 351, East Hanover 07936

Vital Signs, A CareFusion Co.
Phone—(973) 956-5300
20 Campus Rd., Totowa 07512

## MEDICAL IMAGING SYSTEMS

Diagnostic Services, Inc.
Phone—(732) 271-9199
220 Mountain Ave., Middlesex 08846

Diagnostix Plus, Inc.
Phone—(201) 530-5505
197 Cedar Ln., Ste. 1, Teaneck 07666

Independent Imaging
Phone—(856) 764-9729
1819 Underwood Blvd., Unit 1, Delran 08075

Jefferson Medical & Imaging, Inc.
Phone—(973) 697-5077
5470 Berkshire Valley Rd., P.O. Box 254, Oak Ridge 07438

## MEDICAL INSTRUMENTS

Alfa Wassermann, Inc.
Phone—(973) 882-8630
4 Henderson Dr., West Caldwell 07006

**Cobalt Medical Supply, Inc.**
**Phone—(973) 305-0730 / (888) 350-3790**
**Fax—(201) 465-3041**
**Web—www.cobaltmed.com**
**Email—sales@cobaltmed.com**
**P.O. Box 367, Pequannock 07440**
*(see our ad under MEDICAL EQUIPMENT & SUPPLIES)*

Custom Spine, Inc. (H Q)
Phone—(973) 808-0019
9 Campus Dr., Parsippany 07054

Endo Optiks, Inc.
Phone—(732) 530-6762
39 Sycamore Ave., Little Silver 07739

Katena Products, Inc.
Phone—(973) 989-1600
4 Stewart Ct., Denville 07834

KayPENTAX
Phone—(973) 628-6200
3 Paragon Dr., Montvale 07645

Quantum Concepts, Inc.
Phone—(201) 343-2008
24 River Rd., Ste. 12, Bogota 07603

Thoramet Surgical Products, Inc.
Phone—(973) 399-7792
301 Route 17-N, Ste. 800, Rutherford 07070

Totowa Precision Tooling, Inc.
Phone—(973) 256-2283
500 Riverview Dr., Totowa 07512

## MEDICAL MONITORS

Mindray North America
Phone—(201) 995-8000
800 MacArthur Blvd., Mahwah 07430

Peace Medical, Inc.
Phone—(973) 672-2120
50 S. Center St., Ste. 11, Orange 07050

Scivanta Medical Corp. (H Q)
Phone—(732) 282-1055
215 Morris Ave., Spring Lake 07762

## MEDICAL PRODUCTS

Bio-Medical Products Corp.
Phone—(973) 543-7434
10 Halstead Rd., Mendham 07945

**Cobalt Medical Supply, Inc.**
**Phone—(973) 305-0730 / (888) 350-3790**
**Fax—(201) 465-3041**
**Web—www.cobaltmed.com**
**Email—sales@cobaltmed.com**
**P.O. Box 367, Pequannock 07440**
*(see our ad under MEDICAL EQUIPMENT & SUPPLIES)*

CytoTherm
Phone—(609) 396-1456
110 Sewell Ave., Trenton 08610

Davol, Inc.
Phone—(856) 764-8158
1822 Underwood Blvd., Delran 08075

DDS, Inc.
Phone—(888) 495-7440
100 Commerce Way, Ste. 5, Hackensack 07601

Derma Sciences, Inc. (H Q)
Phone—(609) 514-4744
214 Carnegie Ctr., Ste. 300, Princeton 08540

LifeCell Corp.
Phone—(908) 947-1100
1 Millennium Way, Branchburg 08876

Med-X International, Inc.
Phone—(201) 387-8556
20 Foster St., Bergenfield 07621

Northeast Medical Systems Corp.
Phone—(856) 910-8111
901 Beechwood Ave., Cherry Hill 08002

Omnimed, Inc.
Phone—(856) 359-2231
800 Glen Ave., Moorestown 08057

TYRX, Inc.
Phone—(732) 246-8676
1 Deer Park Dr., Ste. G, Monmouth Junction 08852

## MEDICAL SOFT GOODS

Artegraft, Inc.
Phone—(732) 422-8333
220 N. Center Dr., North Brunswick 08902

## MEDICATION DISPENSERS

**Gerresheimer Glass, Inc.**
**Manufacturer of high-quality specialty products made of glass & plastic for the global pharma & healthcare industry**
**Phone—(856) 692-3600**
**Web—www.gerresheimer.com**
**Email—info-tubing-us@gerresheimer.com**
**537 Crystal Ave., Vineland 08360**

## MELTING POTS & TANKS

**Waage Electric, Inc.**
**Melting Pots & Duct Heaters & Immersion Heaters**
**Phone—(908) 245-9363 / (800) 922-4365**
**Fax—(908) 245-8477**
**Web—www.waage.com**
**Email—info@waage.com**
**720 Colfax Ave., P.O. Box 337, Kenilworth 07033**
*(see our ad under FURNACES—Industrial)*

## MENU COVERS

Graphic Express Menu Co., Inc.
Phone—(973) 685-0022
200 Clifton Blvd., Ste. 6, Clifton 07011

## METAL ART

Aram, Inc., Michael
Phone—(201) 758-2551
2102 83rd St., North Bergen 07047

## METAL COATING SERVICES

Aerocoat Source, LLC
Phone—(856) 428-8145
11 Morris Ave., Maple Shade 08052

Arrow Shed, LLC
Phone—(973) 835-3200
1 3rd Ave., Haskell 07420

Standard Tech Applied Resource
Phone—(732) 968-6776
824 South Ave., Middlesex 08846

## METAL CUTTING MACHINERY

Klingelhofer Corp.
Phone—(908) 232-7200
165 Mill Ln., Mountainside 07092

Maruka U.S.A., Inc.
Phone—(973) 487-3800
45 Route 46 E., Ste. 610, P.O. Box 747, Pine Brook 07058

## METAL CUTTING SERVICES

Altech Abrasives Services
Phone—(973) 305-1922
130 Ryerson Ave., Ste. 103, Wayne 07470

D & H Cutoff Co., Inc.
Phone—(908) 454-4961
412-I Trimmer Rd., Bldg. 11, Califon 07830

JSM Co.
Phone—(732) 695-9577
1052 Wayside Rd., Tinton Falls 07712

**M & B Waterjet Creations Inc.**
**Phone—(201) 403-5710**
**Web—www.mbwaterjet.com**
**Email—salesnj@mbwaterjet.com**
**650 Huyler St., Ste. 1, South Hackensack 07606**

Precision Shape Solutions
Phone—(973) 989-7199
243 E. Blackwell St., Dover 07801

## METAL DISTRIBUTORS

Atlas Bronze
Phone—(609) 599-1402
445 Bunting Ave., Trenton 08611

**Metal Associates, Inc.**
**Phone—(973) 835-8480 / (800) 838-1978**
**Fax—(973) 835-7981**
**Web—www.metalassociates.com**
**Email—metals@rcn.com**
**230 W. Parkway, Unit 3-2, Pompton Plains 07444**

## METAL FABRICATING

47 Industries, LLC
Phone—(908) 526-8865
59 2nd Ave., Raritan 08869

Ace Metal Kraft Co., Inc.
Phone—(973) 278-6605
815 McBride Ave., Woodland Park 07424

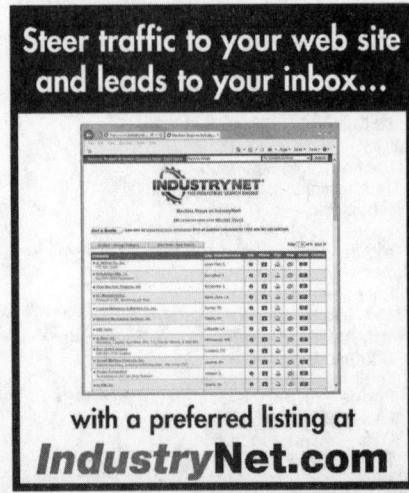

Steer traffic to your web site and leads to your inbox...

INDUSTRYNET

with a preferred listing at
**IndustryNet.com**

## METAL FABRICATING — (cont.)

**ADM Custom Metal Fabrication, Inc.**
Phone—(973) 284-0088
Web—www.admmetal.com
Email—info@admmetal.com
263 Hillside Ave., Ste. 2, Nutley 07110

## ADM CUSTOM METAL FABRICATION, INC.

LATEST CNC TECHNOLOGY
LASER CUTTING
LIGHTS OUT FABRICATION
ROBOTIC WELDING

GUARDS • PANELS • CONSOLES
CABINETS • TRANSITIONS • HOPPERS
FRAMEWORK • MACHINE BASES

### 973-284-0088

www.ADMmetal.com
info@admmetal.com

**All American Metal Fabricators**
Phone—(201) 567-2898
34 Harold St., Tenafly 07670
**American Aluminum Co. (AMALCO)**
Phone—(908) 233-3500
230 Sheffield St., Mountainside 07092

AMERICAN ALUMINUM COMPANY
*Metal Fabtication*
www.amalco.com / (908) 233-2500
230 Sheffield St. • Mountainside, NJ 07092

**American Custom Fabricators, Inc.**
Phone—(732) 237-0037
215-A Hickory Ln., Bayville 08721
**Arntzen Corp.**
Mfr. Of Rolled & Welded Steel Cylinders-Cones-Pipe-Shapes-Fittings
Phone—(815) 334-0788 / (800) 957-7655
Fax—(815) 334-0778
Web—www.ArntzenRolling.com
Email—Sales@ArntzenCorp.com
14600 Washington St., Woodstock, IL 60098
**BR Welding & Industrial Services, Inc.**
Phone—(732) 363-8253
3 Brook Rd., Howell 07731
**County Glass & Metal Installers, Inc.**
Phone—(201) 343-7417
80 Dewitt Pl., Hackensack 07601
**Curtiss-Wright Surface Technologies**
Phone—(201) 843-7800
80 Highway 4 E., Ste. 310, Paramus 07652
**Duffy, Inc., Andrew B.**
Phone—(856) 845-4900
322 Crown Point Rd., P.O. Box 569, Thorofare 08086

Search from among
430,000 U.S. manufacturers
& suppliers at
**IndustryNet.com**

**Durex, Inc.**
Email: custserv@durexinc.com
ISO 9001 Registered Contract Metal Fabrication Facility
Phone—(908) 688-0800
Fax—(908) 688-0718
Web—www.durexinc.com
Email—info@durexinc.com
5 Stahuber Ave., Union 07083

## Durex, Inc.

*ISO 9001 Registered Contract Metal Fabrication Facility*

(908) 688-0800 • Fax (908) 688-0718
www.durexinc.com
custserv@durexinc.com
5 Stahuber Ave. • Union, NJ 07083

**Dynamic Metals, Inc.**
Phone—(908) 769-5111
1713 S. 2nd St., Piscataway 08854
**Engineered Devices Corp.**
Phone—(201) 641-2880
25 Bergen Tpke., Ridgefield Park 07660
**G M Repair, Inc.**
Phone—(732) 350-0304
90 Millhurst Rd., Manalapan 07726
**Great Falls Metalworks, Inc.**
Phone—(973) 523-6811
301 E. 22nd St., Paterson 07514
**Henrich, Inc., Harold R.**
Phone—(732) 370-4455
300 Syracuse Ct., Lakewood 08701
**Holler Metal Fabricators, Inc.**
Phone—(732) 635-9050
215 Liberty St., Metuchen 08840
**Industrial Welding Co.**
Phone—(973) 589-3100
655 Ferry St., Newark 07105
**International Roll Forms, Inc.**
Phone—(856) 228-7333
8 International Ave., Sewell 08080
**J & J Custom Metal Fabricators, Inc.**
Phone—(973) 977-9373
85 5th Ave., Ste. 17, Paterson 07524
**Jersey Tank Fabricators, Inc.**
Phone—(908) 561-2865
1271 New Market Ave., South Plainfield 07080
**Kenvil Weldery & Machine, Inc.**
Phone—(973) 584-1729
15 Kings Pkwy., Ledgewood 07852
**Metal Cutting Corp.**
Phone—(973) 239-1101
89 Commerce Rd., Cedar Grove 07009
**Metal Masters**
Phone—(609) 332-3176
630 Laurel St., Beverly 08010
**Metfab Metals, LLC**
Phone—(973) 675-7676
560 Freeman St., Orange 07050
**Mozer, Inc., Theodore E.**
Phone—(856) 829-1432
601 W. 4th St., P.O. Box 25, Palmyra 08065
**North Jersey Metal Fabricators, Inc.**
Phone—(973) 305-9830
130 Ryerson Ave., Ste. 107, Wayne 07470
**Passaic County Welders, Inc.**
Two northern New Jersey plants, with 45,000 sq. ft. of manufacturing area, producing a wide range of custom products, including plate, structural, sheet & bar products in carbon steel, stainless steel & aluminum
Phone—(973) 696-1200
Fax—(973) 696-1411
Web—www.pcwfab.com
Email—robert@pcwfab.com
100 Parish Dr., Wayne 07470
*(see our ad under STEEL FABRICATING)*
**Perilstein Glass**
Phone—(973) 777-3610
285 Howe Ave., P.O. Box 84, Passaic 07055
**Precision Welding**
Phone—(973) 366-7316
845 Berkshire Valley Rd., Wharton 07885
**R M F Assocs., Inc.**
Phone—(908) 687-9355
202 Carolyn Rd., Union 07083
**R T B Fabricators, Inc.**
Phone—(732) 469-4127
220 Lincoln Blvd., Middlesex 08846

**R.S. Phillips Steel, LLC**
Phone—(973) 827-6464
128 Lake Pochung Rd., Sussex 07461
**SICA Metal Products**
Phone—(856) 227-6616
1775 Hurffville Rd., Route 41, P.O. Box 5525, Deptford 08096
**Skripak Metal Fabricators, Inc.**
Phone—(732) 364-9662
170 Oberlin Ave. N., Unit 17, Lakewood 08701
**Springfield Metal Products Co.**
Phone—(973) 379-4600
8 Commerce St., Springfield 07081
**Staloff Bros.**
Phone—(201) 653-6479
22 Lewis Ave., Jersey City 07306
**Stateline Fabricators, LLC**
Phone—(908) 387-8800
167 Bronico Way, Phillipsburg 08865
**Support Systems Specialties, Inc.**
Phone—(908) 510-4349
25 Ridge Rd., P.O. Box 269, South Plainfield 07080
**Swenson Welding & Fabrication, Bill**
Phone—(609) 653-1177
707 W. Duerer St., Egg Harbor City 08215
**TORNQVIST**
Phone—(973) 686-5999
29 Hanes Dr., Wayne 07470
**Unique Metal Products Co., Inc.**
Metal products, fabrication, laser cutting & CNC machining job shop
Phone—(732) 388-1888
Fax—(732) 388-0084
Email—airtecunique@aol.com
17 W. Scott Ave., P.O. Box 1181, Rahway 07065
*(see our ad under METAL PRODUCTS AND SPECIALTIES)*
**V & R Design Co.**
Phone—(732) 442-9249
941 State St., Perth Amboy 08861
**Versabar Corp.**
Phone—(973) 279-8400
100 Maltese Dr., Totowa 07512
**Versatile Welding Group, LLC**
Steel & Aluminum
Phone—(908) 298-8900 / (877) 939-5348
Fax—(908) 298-9550
Web—www.versatile-us.com
Email—jimd@versatile-us.com
340 Cox St., Roselle 07203
*(see our ad under STEEL FABRICATING)*
**Wellbilt Industries**
Phone—(908) 486-6002
2 Maple Ave., Linden 07036
**Z I Parts Co.**
Phone—(908) 241-0109
215 Cristiani St., Cranford 07016

## METAL FABRICATING MACHINERY

**Boro Supply Co., Inc.**
Phone—(201) 794-3111
2-21 Banta Pl., P.O. Box 1034, Fair Lawn 07410

## METAL FABRICATORS — Custom

**Arntzen Corp.**
Mfr. Of Rolled & Welded Steel Cylinders-Cones-Pipe-Shapes-Fittings
Phone—(815) 334-0788 / (800) 957-7655
Fax—(815) 334-0778
Web—www.ArntzenRolling.com
Email—Sales@ArntzenCorp.com
14600 Washington St., Woodstock, IL 60098
**Durex, Inc.**
Email: custserv@durexinc.com
ISO 9001 Registered Contract Metal Fabrication Facility
Phone—(908) 688-0800
Fax—(908) 688-0718
Web—www.durexinc.com
5 Stahuber Ave., Union 07083
*(see our ad under METAL FABRICATING)*
**Proof Productions, Inc.**
Phone—(856) 442-0700
599 Mantua Blvd., Sewell 08080
**Rhoads Metal Works, Inc.**
Phone—(856) 486-1551
1551 John Tipton Blvd., Pennsauken 08110

INDUSTRY

# METAL FINISHING

**All Bright Metal Finishing, LLC**
Phone—(908) 206-9411
760 Ramsey Ave., Hillside 07205

**All Metal Polishing & Plating, Inc.**
Phone—(973) 589-8070
23 George St., Newark 07105

**Automatic Plating, Inc.**
Phone—(856) 845-7323
3410 Jessup Rd., P.O. Box 54, West Deptford 08086

**Bridgeview Industrial Finishers, Inc.**
Serving Camden, Burlington, Gloucester Counties NJ & Philadelphia Areas
Phone—(856) 768-3624
Fax—(856) 768-2218
Web—www.bvfinishers.com
241 Terrace Blvd., Voorhees 08043
*(see our ad under POWDER COATING)*

**Cramer Plating, Inc.**
Phone—(908) 453-2887
4 Hoyt Ln., Belvidere 07823

**Dayton Grey Corp.**
Phone—(732) 869-0060
1008 1st Ave., Asbury Park 07712

**Diamond Brite Metal Processing**
Phone—(732) 564-1164
333 Cedar Ave., Ste. 1, Middlesex 08846

**Durex, Inc.**
Email: custserv@durexinc.com
ISO 9001 Registered Contract Metal Fabrication Facility
Phone—(908) 688-0800
Fax—(908) 688-0718
Web—www.durexinc.com
5 Stahuber Ave., Union 07083
*(see our ad under METAL FABRICATING)*

**Foley Co.**
Phone—(973) 575-8338
40 Pier Ln. W., Fairfield 07004

**Globe Plating, Inc.**
Phone—(973) 623-1116
220 Miller St., Newark 07114

**Haward Corporation**
Phone—(201) 991-8777
29 Porete Ave., North Arlington 07031

**Master Metal Polishing Corp.**
Phone—(973) 684-0119
57 Wood St., Paterson 07520

**Metal Graphics, Inc.**
Phone—(973) 242-0300
49 Empire St., Newark 07114

**Metal Masters**
Phone—(908) 996-2555
1 Lower Oak Grove Rd., Frenchtown 08825

**Miller & Sons, Inc.**
Celebrating over 100 years in Business
Phone—(973) 759-6445 / (973) 759-6446
Fax—(973) 759-1625
Web—www.millerplatingnj.com
Email—millerplating@aol.com
24 Belleville Ave., Belleville 07109
*(see our ad under ELECTROPLATING)*

**New Brunswick Plating, Inc.**
Phone—(732) 545-6522
1010 Jersey Ave., New Brunswick 08901

**Paramount Metal Finishing Co.**
Plating-Painting-Screen Printing-Assembly-Powder Coating-Certified ISO 9001:2008
Phone—(908) 862-0772
Fax—(908) 862-9477
Web—www.pmf1.com
Email—bnegrin@pmfnj.com
1515 W. Elizabeth Ave., Linden 07036

**Quality Metal Finishing Corp.**
Phone—(973) 345-0963
80 George St., 1st Fl., Paterson 07503

**Rennie Mfg. & Metal Finishing Co., Inc.**
Phone—(973) 773-9175
12-14 Rennie Pl., P.O. Box 285, Lodi 07644

**S & P Metal Finishing Corp.**
Phone—(609) 393-4833
185 Oakland St., Trenton 08618

**Superior Powder Coating, Inc.**
Phone—(908) 351-8707
600 Progress St., Elizabeth 07201

**United States Spray Finishing Co., Inc.**
Phone—(973) 589-3490
70 Blanchard St., Newark 07105

# METAL FORMING

**Hal-O Mfg. Co.**
Phone—(973) 824-6122
137 Meeker Ave., Newark 07114

# METAL PAINTING

**Bridgeview Industrial Finishers, Inc.**
Serving Camden, Burlington, Gloucester Counties NJ & Philadelphia Areas
Phone—(856) 768-3624
Fax—(856) 768-2218
Web—www.bvfinishers.com
241 Terrace Blvd., Voorhees 08043
*(see our ad under POWDER COATING)*

**Painting, Inc.**
Phone—(201) 489-6565
60 Luening St., South Hackensack 07606

**Penn Metal Finishing Co., Inc.**
Phone—(609) 387-3400
700 Jacksonville Rd., Burlington 08016

# METAL PARTS

**Bergen Metal Products, Inc.**
Phone—(973) 249-1500
120 Brighton Rd., Ste. 5, Clifton 07012

**Bigelow Components Corp.**
Phone—(973) 467-1200
74 Diamond Rd., Springfield 07081

**Cain Machine, Inc.**
Phone—(856) 825-7225
Fax—(856) 825-3126
Email—dcain124@comcast.net
1501 Oakland Ave., Millville 08332

**H & H Swiss Screw Machine Products Co., Inc.**
Phone—(908) 688-6390
1478 Chestnut Ave., Hillside 07205

# METAL POLISHING

**Polished Metals Ltd.**
Phone—(908) 688-1188
487 Hillside Ave., Ste. 5, Hillside 07205

# METAL POWDERS

**ACuPowder International, LLC**
Phone—(908) 851-4500
901 Lehigh Ave., Union 07083

**Ames Advanced Material**
Phone—(908) 561-1100
3900 S. Clinton Ave., South Plainfield 07080

**Atlantic Equipment Engineers, Inc.**
High purity metals, metal powders, compounds & fabricated forms. ISO Certified
Phone—(201) 828-9400
Fax—(201) 387-0291
Web—www.micronmetals.com
Email—info@micronmetals.com
24 Industrial Ave., P.O. Box 181, Upper Saddle River 07458

**Hoeganaes Corp. (H Q)**
Phone—(856) 829-2220
1001 Taylors Ln., Cinnaminson 08077

**Plasma Powders & Systems, Inc.**
Phone—(732) 431-0992
228 Boundary Rd., Ste. 2, P.O. Box 132, Marlboro 07746

**Scientific Alloys Corp.**
Spheres, Solders, Metal Powder Balls, Precious Metals
Phone—(973) 478-8323
Fax—(973) 478-6780
Web—www.bgaspheres.com
Email—bgaspheres@aol.com
5 Troast Ct., Clifton 07011
*(see our ad Outside Front Cover)*

**Winter, Inc. & Co., F. W.**
Phone—(856) 963-7490
Delaware Ave. & Elm St., Camden 08102

*find additional suppliers at* **IndustryNet.com**

# METAL PROCESSING MACHINERY

**Precious Metals Processing Consultants, Inc.**
Phone—(201) 944-8053
430 Bergen Blvd., Palisades Park 07650

# METAL PRODUCTS AND SPECIALTIES

(also see specific items)

**CADPRO, Inc.**
Phone—(856) 435-0050
Fax—(856) 435-0600
Web—www.cadproinc.com
Email—elaine@cadproinc.com
114 W. Atlantic Ave., Clementon 08021

**Flanner & Associates**
Since 1987, specializing in representing manufacturers of fourslide parts, wire, metal, plastic, and rubber for the Aerospace, Automotive, Electronics, and Medical industries
Phone—(609) 588-0790 / (609) 647-7821
Email—gflanner@optonline.net
104 Caitlin Ln., Hamilton 08691

**Gauer Metal Products, Inc.**
Phone—(908) 241-4080
175-179 N. Michigan Ave., Kenilworth 07033

**KWG Industries, LLC**
Phone—(908) 218-8900
330 Roycefield Rd., Unit B, Hillsborough 08844

**Moreng Metal Products**
Phone—(973) 256-2001
100 W. End Rd., Totowa 07512

**Mulberry Metal Products, Inc.**
Phone—(908) 688-8850
2199 Stanley Ter., Union 07083

**Titanium Industries, Inc.**
Phone—(973) 983-1185
18 Green Pond Rd., Rockaway 07866

**Unique Metal Products Co., Inc.**
Metal products, fabrication, laser cutting & CNC machining job shop
Phone—(732) 388-1888
Fax—(732) 388-0084
Email—airtecunique@aol.com
17 W. Scott Ave., P.O. Box 1181, Rahway 07065

**Unique Metal Products Co., Inc.**
CNC Laser, Fabricating & Machining
**(732) 388-1888**
**FAX: (732) 388-0084**
**airtecunique@aol.com**
17 W. Scott Ave. Rahway, NJ 07065

**Ware Industries, Inc.**
Phone—(908) 757-9000
400 Metuchen Rd., South Plainfield 07080

# METAL REFINING AND SMELTING

**Kearny Smelting & Refining, Inc.**
Phone—(201) 991-7276
936 Harrison Ave., Ste. 5, Kearny 07032

# METAL ROLL FORMING

**Arntzen Corp.**
Mfr. Of Rolled & Welded Steel Cylinders-Cones-Pipe-Shapes-Fittings
Phone—(815) 334-0788 / (800) 957-7655
Fax—(815) 334-0778
Web—www.ArntzenRolling.com
Email—Sales@ArntzenCorp.com
14600 Washington St., Woodstock, IL 60098

**H. Cross Co.**
Phone—(201) 964-9380
150 W. Commercial Ave., Moonachie 07074

# METAL SERVICE CENTERS

**Baosteel America, Inc.**
Phone—(201) 307-3355
85 Chestnut Ridge Rd., Ste. 210, Montvale 07645

## METAL SERVICE CENTERS —
### (cont.)

Capital Steel Service, LLC
Phone—(609) 882-6983
82 Stokes Ave., Trenton 08638

Flame-Cut Steel, Inc.
Phone—(201) 436-9300
97 E. 2nd St., Bayonne 07002

Metal Associates, Inc.
Phone—(973) 835-8480
230 W. Parkway, Unit 3-2, Pompton Plains 07444

National Electronic Alloys, Inc.
Phone—(201) 337-9400
3 Fir Ct., Oakland 07436

**Rancocas Metals Corp.**
A full service metals center, stocking a vast inventory of almost every non-ferrous metal in a wide array of sizes & shapes
**Phone—(609) 267-4120 / (800) 762-6382**
**Fax—(609) 267-5690**
**Web—www.rancocasmetals.com**
**Email—sales@rancocasmetals.com**
**35 Indel Ave., P.O. Box 223, Rancocas 08073**

**Rancocas Metals Corp.**
35 Indel Ave.
P.O. Box 223
Rancocas, NJ 08073
• Aluminum • Brass • Copper
• Stainless Steel • Bronze
Toll Free: 1.800.762.6382
609.267.4120 • Fax: 609.267.5690
www.rancocasmetals.com • sales@rancocasmetals.com

ThyssenKrupp Materials NA Copper & Brass Sales Div.
Phone—(610) 586-1800
800 Arlington Blvd., Ste. C, Swedesboro 08085

## METAL SPECIALTIES

**Metal Associates, Inc.**
**Phone—(973) 835-8480 / (800) 838-1978**
**Fax—(973) 835-7981**
**Web—www.metalassociates.com**
**Email—metals@rcn.com**
**230 W. Parkway, Unit 3-2, Pompton Plains 07444**

## METAL SPINNING

Clover Co., Inc., F. G.
Phone—(973) 625-1811
40 Stickle Ave., Rockaway 07866

Ultimate Spinning & Turning Corp.
Phone—(201) 372-9740
9 Willow St., Moonachie 07074

## METAL SPRAYING

**Chalmers & Kubeck, Inc.**
**Phone—(610) 494-4300**
**Fax—(610) 485-1484**
**Web—www.candk.com**
**Email—jmoore@candk.com**
**150 Commerce Dr., P.O. Box 2447, Aston, PA 19014**
*(see our ad under MACHINE WORK & MACHINING)*

## METAL STAMPINGS

A. K. Stamping Co., Inc.
Phone—(908) 232-7300
1159 Highway 22 E., Mountainside 07092

Accurate Forming
Phone—(973) 827-7155
24 Ames Blvd., Hamburg 07419

Array Mfg. Tech Corp.
Phone—(201) 997-1333
100 Arlington Ave., Kearny 07032

Basic Tool & Die Corp.
Phone—(908) 688-9155
752 Ramsey Ave., Hillside 07205

Bel-Tech Stamping, Inc.
Phone—(973) 728-8229
26 Industrial Rd., Ste. A, West Milford 07480

Bihler Of America, Inc.
Phone—(908) 213-9001
85 Industrial Dr., Phillipsburg 08865

C & C Metal Products Corp.
Phone—(201) 569-7300
456 Nordhoff Pl., P.O. Box 7300, Englewood 07631

**Carter Mfg. Co., Inc.**
**Phone—(201) 935-0770**
**Fax—(201) 935-2812**
**Web—www.carterstampings.com**
**Email—sales@carterstampings.com**
**55 Anderson Ave., Moonachie 07074**

Clover Stamping Co., Inc.
Phone—(973) 278-4888
60 Spruce St., Paterson 07501

Coining Mfg., LLC
Phone—(973) 253-0500
35 Monhegen, Clifton 07013

Co-Planar, Inc.
Phone—(973) 625-3500
88 Ford Rd, P.O. Box 1115, Denville 07834

Diamond Die Cutters & Embossers
Phone—(201) 876-8540
629 Grove St., 6th Fl., Jersey City 07310

**Durex, Inc.**
**Email: custserv@durexinc.com**
**ISO 9001 Registered Contract Metal Fabrication Facility**
**Phone—(908) 688-0800**
**Fax—(908) 688-0718**
**Web—www.durexinc.com**
**5 Stahuber Ave., Union 07083**
*(see our ad under METAL FABRICATING)*

Electro Magnetic Products, Inc.
Phone—(856) 235-3011
355 Crider Ave., Moorestown 08057

Electronic Mfg. Co.
Phone—(973) 762-1300
71 Newark Way, Maplewood 07040

Elray Mfg. Co., Inc.
Phone—(856) 881-1936
17 Liberty St., Glassboro 08028

Excel Die Corp.
Phone—(908) 587-2606
19 Grant St., Linden 07036

F & M Machine Co., Inc.
Phone—(908) 245-8830
751 Lexington Ave., Kenilworth 07033

Fairfield Stamping Co.
Phone—(201) 791-9888
374 Midland Ave., P.O. Box 8322, Saddle Brook 07663

General Stamping Co.
Phone—(973) 627-9500
451 E. Main St., Denville 07834

H T Stamping
Phone—(973) 227-4858
19 Gardner Rd., Ste. C, Fairfield 07004

**Hammer Mfg. Co., Inc.**
**Metal Stamping, Short/Medium Run**
**Phone—(908) 862-1730**
**Fax—(908) 862-1733**
**Web—www.hammermfg.com**
**Email—sales@hammermfg.us**
**417 Commerce Rd., P.O. Box 1340, Linden 07036**

**Hammer Mfg. Co., Inc.**
*Metal Stampings*
**www.hammermfg.com**
**(908) 862-1730**
417 Commerce Rd. P.O. Box 1340 • Linden, NJ 07036

Highland Metal Products, Inc.
Phone—(908) 245-4848
153 E. Highland Pkwy., Roselle 07203

Hillside Spinning & Stamping Co., Inc.
Phone—(973) 964-3080
1060 Commerce Ave., Union 07083

Infor Metal & Tooling Manufacturing Corporation
Phone—(973) 571-9520
16 Commerce Rd., Cedar Grove 07009

Interplex NAS Inc., Beta Div.
Phone—(201) 367-1300
232 Pegasus Ave., Northvale 07647

JMK Tool, Die & Mfg. Co., Inc.
Phone—(201) 845-4710
Fax—(201) 845-0240
Web—www.jmktool.com
Email—jkristofich@jmktool.com
19 W. Passaic St., Rochelle Park 07662

Jordan Mfg., LLC
Phone—(973) 383-8363
28 Randazzo Rd., P.O. Box 226, Lafayette 07848

**Magnetic Metals Corp.**
**Phone—(856) 964-7842**
**Fax—(856) 365-8723**
**Web—www.magmet.com**
**Email—khaley@magmet.com**
**1900 Hayes Ave., Camden 08105**

Manutech, Inc.
Phone—(856) 358-6136
29 State St., P.O.Box 758, Elmer 08318

Minitec Corp.
Phone—(973) 989-1426
158 W. Clinton St., Ste. V, Dover 07801

Omega Precision Corp.
Phone—(973) 256-3422
1384 Pompton Ave., Ste. 3, Cedar Grove 07009

P D Q Electronics Components Co., Inc.
Phone—(732) 281-0025
1113 Tiller Ave., Beachwood 08722

**Paramount Products, Inc.**
**Precision Metal Stamping**
**Phone—(732) 458-9200**
**Fax—(732) 458-3942**
**Web—www.paramountproductsco.com**
**Email—info@paramountproductsco.com**
**1104 Industrial Pkwy., Brick 08724**

Peterson Bros. Mfg.
Phone—(732) 271-8240
10 Baekeland Ave., Middlesex 08846

Peterson Stamping & Mfg. Co.
Phone—(908) 241-0900
75 N. Michigan Ave., P.O. Box 190, Kenilworth 07033

ProGasket Aerospace & Automotive, LLC
Phone—(973) 831-4533
14 Doty Rd., Haskell 07420

Progressive Tool & Mfg. Co.
Phone—(908) 245-7010
708 Fairfield Ave., Kenilworth 07033

Roseville Tool & Mfg.
Phone—(973) 992-5405
22 Okner Pkwy., Livingston 07039

**Semiconductor Mfg.**
**Metal Stampings of BGA & PGA Spheres & Wire Balls**
**Phone—(973) 478-2880**
**Fax—(973) 478-6780**
**Web—www.bgaspheres.com**
**Email—bgaspheres@aol.com**
**5 Troast Ct., Clifton 07011**

Short Run Stamping Co., Inc., The
Phone—(908) 862-1070
925 E. Linden Ave., Linden 07036

**smALL Quantities New Jersey, Inc.**
**Phone—(732) 248-9009**
**Fax—(732) 248-9559**
**Web—www.sqnji.com**
**Email—smallqnji@aol.com**
**P.O. Box 4167, Metuchen 08840**

Sofield Mfg. Co., Inc.
Phone—(201) 943-1118
2 Main St., Ridgefield Park 07660

Sowa Corp.
Phone—(973) 297-0008
223 Murray St., Newark 07114

**Stamping.com, Inc.**
**Phone—(732) 493-4697**
**Fax—(732) 493-3493**
**Web—www.stampinginc.com**
**Email—stamping@juno.com**
**3600 Sunset Ave., Asbury Park 07712**

**Stamping.com, Inc.**
*Metal Stampings*
732-493-4697 • Fax: 732-493-3493
www.stampinginc.com  stamping@juno.com
3600 Sunset Ave.  Asbury Park, NJ 07712

INDUSTRY

## METAL STAMPINGS — (cont.)

Stirrup Metal Products Corp.
  Phone—(973) 824-7086
  215 Emmet St., Newark 07114

Tekmet, LLC
  Phone—(973) 376-1700
  400 Myrtle Ave., Ste. A, Boonton 07005

Triform Products, Inc.
  Phone—(973) 278-2042
  219 Lafayette St., Paterson 07524

Tryco Tool & Mfg., Inc.
  Phone—(973) 674-6867
  363 S. Jefferson St., Orange 07050

## METAL STAMPINGS — Deep Drawn

J. J. Orly, Inc.
  Phone—(908) 276-9212
  20 Commerce Dr., Ste. 128, Cranford 07016

National Mfg. Co., Inc.
  Phone—(973) 635-8846
  12 River Rd., Chatham 07928

Topco, Inc.
  Phone—(908) 352-6720
  107 Trumbull St., Elizabeth 07206

## METAL STAMPINGS — Precision

BeCu Manufacturing Co., Inc.
  Phone—(908) 233-3343
  2347 Beryllium Rd., Scotch Plains 07076

**MICRO**
  Surgical devices, fabricated tube assemblies, insert/injection molding
  **Phone—(732) 302-0800**
  **Fax—(732) 302-0436**
  **Web—www.micro-co.com**
  **Email—sales@micro-co.com**
  **140 Belmont Dr., Somerset 08873**

Stampex Tool&Die, Inc.
  Phone—(973) 839-4040
  75 4th Ave., Haskell 07420

**Stamping.com, Inc.**
  **Phone—(732) 493-4697**
  **Fax—(732) 493-3493**
  **Web—www.stampinginc.com**
  **Email—stamping@juno.com**
  **3600 Sunset Ave., Asbury Park 07712**
    *(see our ad under METAL STAMPINGS)*

## METALLIZING

**Chalmers & Kubeck, Inc.**
  **Phone—(610) 494-4300**
  **Fax—(610) 485-1484**
  **Web—www.candk.com**
  **Email—jmoore@candk.com**
  **150 Commerce Dr., P.O. Box 2447, Aston, PA 19014**
    *(see our ad under MACHINE WORK & MACHINING)*

Miller & Sons, Inc., I. V.
  Phone—(732) 493-4040
  15 Cindy Ln., Ocean 07712

## METALS

Kaistar Research & Development, LLC
  Phone—(973) 362-1487
  15 Wilson Dr., Sparta 07871

**Metal Associates, Inc.**
  **Phone—(973) 835-8480 / (800) 838-1978**
  **Fax—(973) 835-7981**
  **Web—www.metalassociates.com**
  **Email—metals@rcn.com**
  **230 W. Parkway, Unit 3-2, Pompton Plains 07444**

**Scientific Alloys Corp.**
  Spheres, Solders, Metal Powder Balls, Precious Metals
  **Phone—(973) 478-8323**
  **Fax—(973) 478-6780**
  **Web—www.bgaspheres.com**
  **Email—bgaspheres@aol.com**
  **5 Troast Ct., Clifton 07011**
    *(see our ad Outside Front Cover)*

## METALS — Non-Ferrous

Global Metals Sales Corp.
  Phone—(212) 813-3100
  196 Inwood Ave., Montclair 07043

## METALS — Precious

**Scientific Alloys Corp.**
  Spheres, Solders, Metal Powder Balls, Precious Metals
  **Phone—(973) 478-8323**
  **Fax—(973) 478-6780**
  **Web—www.bgaspheres.com**
  **Email—bgaspheres@aol.com**
  **5 Troast Ct., Clifton 07011**
    *(see our ad Outside Front Cover)*

## METALS — Textured

Rimex Metals (USA) Inc
  Phone—(732) 549-3800
  2850 Woodbridge Ave., Edison 08837

## METALS — Wholesale

Fagan, Inc., Ed
  Phone—(201) 891-4003
  769 Susquehanna Ave., Franklin Lakes 07417

**Metal Associates, Inc.**
  **Phone—(973) 835-8480 / (800) 838-1978**
  **Fax—(973) 835-7981**
  **Web—www.metalassociates.com**
  **Email—metals@rcn.com**
  **230 W. Parkway, Unit 3-2, Pompton Plains 07444**

Minerais U. S., LLC
  Phone—(908) 874-7666
  105 Raider Blvd., Ste. 104, Hillsborough 08844

Rebuth Metal Services
  Phone—(908) 889-6400
  2262 Stocker Ln., P.O. Box 488, Scotch Plains 07076

TW Metals, Inc.
  Phone—(609) 655-4120
  27 Engelhard Dr., Monroe Township 08831

## METALWORKING FLUIDS

**Hangsterfer's Laboratories, Inc.**
  **Phone—(856) 468-0216**
  **Fax—(856) 468-0200**
  **Web—www.hangsterfers.com**
  **Email—sales@hangsterfers.com**
  **175 Ogden Rd., Mantua 08051**
    *(see our ad under LUBRICANTS—Metalworking)*

Process Research Products
  Phone—(609) 882-0400
  1013 Whitehead Road Ext., Trenton 08638

## METERS

Istec Corp.
  Phone—(973) 383-9888
  5 Park Lake Rd., Ste. 6, Sparta 07871

**Satec, Inc. (H Q)**
  **Phone—(908) 686-9510**
  **Fax—(908) 686-9520**
  **Web—www.satec-global.com**
  **Email—satec@oksatec.com**
  **10 Milltown Ct., Union 07083**

## METERS — Electric

Byram Laboratories, Inc.
  Phone—(908) 252-0852
  1 Columbia Rd., Branchburg 08876

## METERS — Flow

Kessler Ellis Products Co., Inc.
  Phone—(732) 935-1320
  10 Industrial Way E., Ste. 6, Eatontown 07724

Search from among 430,000 U.S. manufacturers & suppliers: IndustryNet.com

## METERS — Liquid

Advanced Marine Technology
  Phone—(732) 888-8248
  12 Crown Plz., Unit 204, Hazlet 07730

Blend-Rite Industries, Inc.
  Phone—(973) 395-3889
  585 Forest St., Unit 4, Orange 07050

## MICA

Crystex Composites, LLC
  Phone—(973) 779-8866
  125 Clifton Blvd., Clifton 07011

## MICROFILM EQUIPMENT & SUPPLIES

Zeta Products, Inc.
  Phone—(908) 688-0440
  1060 Garden State Rd., Union 07083

## MICROPHONES

Applied Microphone Technology
  Phone—(973) 729-9333
  104 Hillside Rd., Sparta 07871

Azden Corp.
  Phone—(973) 810-3070
  200 Valley Rd., Ste. 101, Mount Arlington 07856

## MICROSCOPES

Micron Optics
  Phone—(973) 267-5047
  14 Ridgedale Ave., Ste. 125, Cedar Knolls 07927

## MICROWAVE EQUIPMENT

Aeroflex Control Components, Inc.
  Phone—(732) 460-0212
  40 Industrial Way E., Eatontown 07724

American Radar Components, Inc.
  Phone—(973) 627-5530
  39 Front St., Denville 07834

Astrolab, Inc.
  Phone—(732) 560-3800
  4 Powderhorn Dr., Warren 07059

G T Microwave, Inc.
  Phone—(973) 361-5700
  2 Emery Ave., Ste. 2, Randolph 07869

Integrated Microwave Technologies, LLC
  Phone—(908) 852-3700
  200 International Dr., Mount Olive 07828

Jersey Microwave, LLC
  Phone—(908) 684-2390
  230 U.S. Highway 206, Ste. 407, Flanders 07836

Microwave Consulting Corp.
  Phone—(973) 523-6700
  150 Railroad Ave., Paterson 07501

Millimeter Wave Technology
  Phone—(845) 369-7808
  90 Dayton Ave., Ste. 6-E, Passaic 07055

Princeton Microwave Technology
  Phone—(609) 586-8140
  5 Nami Ln., Trenton 08619

Pro-Comm, Inc.
  Phone—(732) 206-0660
  1105 Industrial Pkwy., Brick 08724

R S Microwave Co., Inc.
  Phone—(973) 492-1207
  22 Park Pl., P.O. Box 273, Butler 07405

Synergy Microwave Corp.
  Phone—(973) 881-8800
  201 McLean Blvd., Paterson 07504

Taylor Microwave, Inc.
  Phone—(973) 890-7763
  48 Industrial W., Clifton 07012

UTE Microwave, Inc.
  Phone—(732) 922-1009
  3500 Sunset Ave., Ste. D-1, Ocean 07712

## MICROWAVE OVENS

M M T C, Inc.
  Phone—(609) 520-9699
  12 Roszel Rd., Ste. A-203, Princeton 08540

## MILITARY EQUIPMENT

Octal Corporation
   Phone—(201) 862-1010
   125 Galway Pl., Ste. B, Teaneck 07666

## MILITARY REPLACEMENT PARTS

Jarrdd.Co
   Phone—(856) 310-0100
   141 Shreve Ave., Barrington 08007
Spencer Industries, Inc.
   Phone—(973) 751-2200
   80 Holmes St., P.O. Box 128, Belleville 07109

## MILK

Farmland Dairies
   Phone—(973) 777-2500
   520 Main Ave., P.O. Box 3340, Wallington 07057
Readington Farms, Inc.
   Phone—(908) 534-2121
   12 Mill Rd., P.O. Box 164, Whitehouse 08888
Wakefern Food Corp. (H Q)
   Phone—(732) 906-5932
   5000 Riverside Dr., Keasbey 08832

## MILK — Powdered

Franklin Farms East, Inc.
   Phone—(908) 835-0016
   111 W. Washington Ave., Washington 07882

## MILLING — CNC

**Chalmers & Kubeck, Inc.**
   **Phone—(610) 494-4300**
   **Fax—(610) 485-1484**
   **Web—www.candk.com**
   **Email—jmoore@candk.com**
   **150 Commerce Dr., P.O. Box 2447, Aston, PA 19014**
      *(see our ad under MACHINE WORK & MACHINING)*
**E & J Machine And Tool, LLC**
   **Phone—(973) 810-2312 / (973) 810-2313**
   **Fax—(973) 601-7953**
   **Web—www.ejmachine.com**
   **Email—sales@ejmachine.com**
   **12 Orben Dr., Unit 1, Landing 07850**
      *(see our ad under JOB SHOPS)*
**FIMS Mfg. Corp.**
   **Phone—(201) 845-7088**
   **Fax—(201) 845-8287**
   **Web—www.fimsmfg.com**
   **Email—fimsmfg@optonline.net**
   **8 Allerman Rd., Oakland 07436**
**Gaum, Inc.**
   **AS9100C Certified**
   **Phone—(609) 586-0132**
   **Fax—(609) 586-9748**
   **Web—www.gauminc.com**
   **Email—mail@gauminc.com**
   **1080 Route 130, P.O. Box 485, Robbinsville 08691**
      *(see our ads Outside Front Cover & under MACHINE WORK & MACHINING)*
Stuart Mills, Inc.
   Phone—(973) 579-5717
   25 Stillwater Rd., Newton 07860

## MILLWORK

Black Millwork & Center Lumber Co.
   Phone—(201) 934-0100
   220 W. Crescent Ave., Allendale 07401
Boards & Beams Co., LLC
   Phone—(973) 299-6100
   1275 Bloomfield Ave., Ste. 92, Fairfield 07004
Bongiovanni Custom Cabinet & Furniture, LLC, Mario
   Phone—(609) 646-8488
   7 E. Pleasant Ave., Pleasantville 08232
Cabinet-Tronics, Inc.
   Phone—(609) 267-2625
   100 Birmingham Rd., P.O. Box 198, Birmingham 08011
Cobb's Mill, LLC
   Phone—(856) 451-0671
   146 Cobbs Mill Rd., Bridgeton 08302

Collingswood Architectural Millwork, Inc.
   Phone—(856) 854-0440
   715 Taylor Ave., Collingswood 08107
Creative Wood Products, Inc.
   Phone—(732) 370-0051
   370 Whiteville Rd., Jackson 08527
Custom Wood Creations, Inc.
   Phone—(908) 835-8999
   51 Willow St., Washington 07882
D & D Millwork Co., Inc.
   Phone—(973) 759-6336
   10-12 N. 7th St., Belleville 07109
Distinctive Wood Work, Inc.
   Phone—(609) 714-8505
   70 Stacy Haines Rd., Ste. D, Lumberton 08048
Diversified Millwork, Inc.
   Phone—(609) 270-7385
   420 N. 2nd Rd., Unit C, Hammonton 08037
Donnelly Industries, Inc.
   Phone—(973) 672-1800
   557 Route 23 S., Wayne 07470
Epic Management, Inc. (H Q)
   Phone—(732) 752-6100
   136 11th St., Ste. 1, Piscataway 08854
Epic Millwork
   Phone—(732) 296-0273
   1022 Hamilton St., Ste. G, Somerset 08873
Garden State Woodworking Co.
   Phone—(973) 748-2661
   344 Hoover Ave., Bloomfield 07003
**Infinite Manufacturing Group, Inc.**
   **Email: a.moses@infinitegroupusa.com**
   **Phone—(973) 649-9950**
   **Web—www.infinitegroupusa.com**
   **171 Coit St., Irvington 07111**
Jarahian Millwork, Inc.
   Phone—(732) 240-5151
   870 Route 530, Ste. 4, Whiting 08759
Kuehn Bevel, Inc.
   Phone—(973) 584-8282
   10 Furnace St., Stanhope 07874
New Century Wood Products
   Phone—(732) 271-2557
   131 Lincoln Blvd., Middlesex 08846
**Paramount Fixture Corp.**
   **A full service mfg. source for wood, laminate & steel fixtures for your retail, commercial & residential environments**
   **Phone—(973) 485-1585 / (973) 485-8261**
   **Fax—(973) 485-3366**
   **Web—www.paramountfixturecorp.com**
   **Email—fixtureman175@aol.com**
   **175 Mount Pleasant Ave., Newark 07104**
Peter Lumber Co.
   Phone—(609) 641-9000
   300 E. Washington Ave., P.O. Box 32, Pleasantville 08232
Pompton Millwork, Inc.
   Phone—(973) 835-0585
   1458 Ringwood Ave., Haskell 07420
Price Millwork
   Phone—(609) 652-0123
   305 Dennis Dr., Absecon 08201
Rhodes & Rhodes Millwork Co., Inc.
   Phone—(609) 653-3180
   3011 Ocean Heights Ave., Unit A, Egg Harbor Township 08234
Royal Lumber & Millwork Co., Inc.
   Phone—(201) 991-8550
   455 Schuyler Ave., P.O. Box 443, Kearny 07032
South Jersey Lumbermans, Inc.
   Phone—(609) 965-1411
   6268 Holly St., Mays Landing 08330
V-Custom Millwork, Inc.
   Phone—(732) 469-9600
   1480 Highway 22, P.O. Box 6842, Bridgewater 08807
Woodhaven Lumber & Millwork, Inc.
   Phone—(732) 901-0030
   200 James St., P.O. Box 870, Lakewood 08701
Woodshop, Inc., The
   Phone—(732) 349-8006
   58 Flint Rd., Toms River 08757
Woodtec, Inc.
   Phone—(908) 979-0180
   300 Stiger St., Hackettstown 07840

## MILLWORK — Architectural

Agresti Construction Co., Inc.
   Phone—(201) 825-8500
   356 Glenwood Ave., East Orange 07017

American Mica Corp.
   Phone—(908) 587-5237
   1015 Pennsylvania Ave., Linden 07036
Architectural Woodworking Assocs., LLC
   Phone—(908) 996-7866
   4 7th St., Frenchtown 08825
Blauth Millwork
   Phone—(609) 737-9502
   57 Pleasant Valley Rd., Titusville 08560
Bossen Architectural Millwork, Inc.
   Phone—(856) 786-1100
   1818 Bannard St., Cinnaminson 08077
Builders Architectural Millwork
   Phone—(732) 450-0056
   159 Newman Springs Rd. E., Shrewsbury 07702
Cozzolino Furniture Design, Inc.
   Phone—(973) 731-9292
   20 Standish Ave., West Orange 07052
CWI Architectural Millwork, LLC
   Phone—(856) 307-7900
   8 Deptford Rd., Dept. D, Glassboro 08028
D S F, Inc.
   Phone—(908) 218-5153
   401 U.S. Highway 202, Raritan 08869
Dubell Lumber Co.
   Phone—(609) 567-2467
   102 S. Route 73, Cedar Brook 08018
Empire Lumber & Millwork Co.
   Phone—(973) 242-2700
   377 Frelinghuysen Ave., Newark 07114
Foley-Waite Assocs., Inc.
   Phone—(973) 743-0700
   225 Belleville Ave., P.O. Box 164, Bloomfield 07003
K B Custom Interiors
   Phone—(856) 845-9112
   10-B Greenwood Ave., Woodbury 08096
Mango Custom Cabinets, Inc.
   Phone—(908) 813-3077
   216 W. Stiger St., Hackettstown 07840
Master Craftsman, LLC
   Phone—(856) 768-8088
   417 N. Grove St., Bldg. 2, Unit D, Berlin 08009
Midhattan Woodworking
   Phone—(732) 727-3020
   3130 Bordentown Ave., Old Bridge 08857
Mountain Millwork
   Phone—(732) 901-9400
   14 Clifton Ave. S., Lakewood 08701
New Jersey Hardwoods, Inc.
   Phone—(973) 754-0990
   1340 W. Front St., Plainfield 07063
Osborn's Mill
   Phone—(732) 751-0889
   149 Yellowbrook Rd., Farmingdale 07727
Poandl Brothers Woodworking, Inc.
   Phone—(732) 229-8585
   20 N. 7th Ave., P.O. Box 4015, Long Branch 07740
Sloan & Co., Inc.
   Phone—(973) 227-3555
   38 Fairfield Pl., West Caldwell 07006
Studio L Contracting, LLC
   Phone—(201) 837-1650
   1401 Palisade Ave., Teaneck 07666
Summit Millwork & Supply, Inc.
   Phone—(908) 277-0039
   235 Morris Ave., Summit 07901
Trade Images
   Phone—(856) 697-2700
   701 S. Harding Hwy., Buena 08310
Visual Architectural Designs, Inc.
   Phone—(908) 754-3000
   15 Harmich Rd., South Plainfield 07080
Zone Defense, Inc.
   Phone—(973) 328-0436
   4 Emery Ave., Randolph 07869

## MILLWORK — Custom

H2L, LLC
   Phone—(201) 864-0060
   4201 Tonnelle Ave., Ste. 2, North Bergen 07047
JM Custom Design Millwork
   Phone—(201) 487-8990
   101 Hobart St., Hackensack 07601
Terzano Cabinetry, Inc.
   Phone—(201) 373-9500
   111 Leuning St., Unit G, South Hackensack 07606

# Lawrence Mold and Tool Corp.
## *Molds*
**(609) 392-5422 • Fax: (609) 392-5861**
**www.lawrencemoldandtool.com**
**mboard@lmtproducts.com**
**1412 Ohio Ave. • Lawrenceville, NJ 08648**

## MINERAL PROCESSING EQUIPMENT

Quartz Technology, Inc.
 Phone—(908) 526-6362
 1355 Plymouth Rd., Bridgewater 08807

## MINING COMPANIES

Wantage Stone, LLC
 Phone—(973) 702-7866
 80 State Route 23, Hamburg 07419
Ward Sand & Materials
 Phone—(609) 859-2860
 223 Sooy Place Rd., Vincentown 08088

## MIRRORS

Floxite Company, Inc.
 Phone—(201) 529-2019
 31 Industrial Ave., Ste. 2, Mahwah 07430
Mirrotek International, LLC
 Phone—(973) 472-1400
 90 Dayton Ave., Bldg. 1-F, Passaic 07055

## MIST SYSTEMS

Atomizing Systems Inc.
 Phone—(201) 447-1222
 1 Hollywood Ave., Ste. 1, Ho-Ho-Kus 07423

## MIXING EQUIPMENT

Ekato Corp.
 Phone—(201) 825-4684
 48 Spruce St., Oakland 07436

## MIXING MACHINERY — Industrial

ARDE Barinco, Inc.
 Phone—(201) 768-6070
 875 Washington Ave., Carlstadt 07072
Hockmeyer Equipment Corp.
 Phone—(973) 482-0225
 610 Supor Blvd., Ste. 1, Harrison 07029
Jaygo, Inc.
 Phone—(908) 688-3600
 7 Emery Ave., Randolph 07869
Technology General Corp. (H Q)
 Phone—(973) 827-4143
 12 Cork Hill Rd., Franklin 07416
**Trico Poly Systems, LLC**
 **Polyurethane & epoxy processing machinery, including slinger degassers**
 **Phone—(973) 376-7770**
 **Fax—(973) 376-7779**
 **Web—www.tricopoly.com**
 **Email—tricopoly@verizon.net**
 **60 Brown Ave., Springfield 07081**
**Warwick Mfg. & Equipment Co., LLC**
 **Buy & sell used: Chemical, food, cosmetic, packaging & pharmaceutical equipment**
 **Phone—(732) 729-0400 / (732) 241-9263**
 **Fax—(732) 729-1235**
 **Web—www.warwickequipment.com**
 **Email—sales@warwickequipment.com**
 **1112 12th St., North Brunswick 08902**
 *(see our ad Outside Back Cover)*

## MODEL AIRPLANES

Dively Models, Inc., Bob
 Phone—(201) 310-2340
 540 Hudson St., Hackensack 07601

## MODELS — Plastic

Todd Architectural Models
 Phone—(973) 507-4072
 54 Mountainview Rd., P.O. Box 1002, Chatham 07928

## MODELS AND PROTOTYPES

Detail Model & Machine
 Phone—(856) 223-0184
 61 Woodstown Rd., Mullica Hill 08062
GAC Model Making, LLC
 Phone—(856) 857-9848
 1879 Old Cuthbert Rd., Unit 38, Cherry Hill 08034
Ramsey Model Design, David A.
 Phone—(609) 259-6757
 P.O. Box 87, Clarksburg 08510
Rapid Models & Prototypes, Inc.
 Phone—(856) 933-2929
 1311 Marlkress Rd., Cherry Hill 08003
Reeves International, Inc.
 Phone—(973) 956-9555
 34 Owens Dr., Wayne 07470

## MOLD BASES & COMPONENTS

Fredon Development Industries
 Phone—(973) 383-7576
 393 State Route 94 S., Newton 07860

## MOLD DESIGNING

**Shore Plastic Technologies, Inc.**
 **Specializing in comprehensive consulting engineering services for product development & testing, including 3D modeling, 2D drafting, FEA, moldflow & motion analysis**
 **Phone—(856) 327-5114**
 **Fax—(856) 825-9296**
 **Web—www.shoreplastictech.com**
 **Email—info@shoreplastictech.com**
 **215 Buck St., Millville 08332**

## MOLD POLISHING

Mold Polishing Co., Inc.
 Phone—(908) 518-9191
 45 North Ave., P. O. Box 96, Garwood 07027

## MOLD REMEDIATION SERVICES

**GWS Contractors, Inc.**
 **Since 1977, specializing in Environmental Remediation, Tank Removals, Emergency Response Services & Vapor Intrusion Mitigation. Providing a 24 hour, 7 day a week customer response network**
 **Phone—(732) 297-4847**
 **Fax—(732) 297-4389**
 **Web—www.gwscontractors.com**
 **Email—contact@gwscontractors.com**
 **105 Fresh Ponds Rd., Jamesburg 08831**

Servpro Of Northwest Bergen
 Fire & Water Damage
 Phone—(201) 236-2400 / (800) 497-7179
 Fax—(201) 670-1011
 Web—www.servpronorthwestbergen.com
 Email—servpro8204@aol.com
 151 Crescent Ave., Waldwick 07463

## MOLD REMOVAL

New Jersey Basement Waterproofing
 Phone—(732) 721-4900
 Web—www.njdrybasement.com
 Email—smendola@pdes-usa.net
 10 S. River Rd., Cranbury 08512

## MOLDING — Silicone

**Ja-Bar Silicone Corp.**
 **Since 1965, mfg. specialty Silicone Elastomer Seals to Mil, Federal, AMS, SAF or customer specifications. Quality control system approved for Mil-I-45208. Serving the Automotive, Aerospace, Commercial & Medical Industries. ISO 9001:2008**
 **Phone—(973) 786-5000**
 **Fax—(973) 786-5546**
 **Web—www.ja-bar.com**
 **Email—info@ja-bar.com**
 **252 Brighton Rd., P.O. Box 1249, Andover 07821**
 *(see our ad under GASKET MATERIALS)*

## MOLDS

**(also see following & 'Dies')**

Horizon Tool & Mold, Inc.
 Phone—(973) 300-0393
 56 Paterson Ave., Newton 07860
**Lawrence Mold and Tool Corp.**
 **Email: mboard@lmtproducts.com**
 **Phone—(609) 392-5422**
 **Fax—(609) 392-5861**
 **Web—www.lawrencemoldandtool.com**
 **Email—glesenskyj@lawrencemold.net**
 **1412 Ohio Ave., Lawrenceville 08648**
 *(see our ad on this page)*
TAF Tooling, LLC
 Phone—(908) 474-0294
 1100 E. Linden Ave., Linden 07036
Universal Mold & Tool, Inc.
 Phone—(856) 563-0488
 1200 S. West Blvd., Bldg. 4, Vineland 08360

## MOLDS — Investment Casting

Prentco Co.
 Phone—(908) 687-9518
 952 Koehl Ave., Union 07083

## MOLDS — Plastic

General Tool Specialties, Inc.
 Phone—(908) 874-3040
 284 Sunnymead Rd., Hillsborough 08844
Life Of The Party, LLC
 Phone—(732) 828-0886
 832 Ridgewood Ave., Ste. 4, North Brunswick 08902
Seajay Mfg. Co.
 Phone—(732) 774-0900
 9 Memorial Dr., Ste. 1, Neptune 07753

## MOLDS — Plastic Injection

Advance Tool & Die, Inc.
 Phone—(856) 854-6329
 1401 Bremen Ave., Egg Harbor City 08215
**Alpha Precision Mold**
 **3D Design-CAD-CAM, Mold Making-CNC Machining, Mold Polishing-Mold Repair, Plastic Injection-EDM Prototyping-Drill Press, Grinding Surface-Die Cast Reverse Engineering**
 **Phone—(908) 587-9090**
 **Fax—(908) 587-9020**
 **Web—www.alphaprecisionmold.com**
 **Email—info@alphaprecisionmold.com**
 **8 Roselle St., Linden 07036**

© Copyright 2015 Manufacturers' News, Inc.

## MOLDS — Plastic Injection —
### (cont.)

C & C Tool Co., LLC
Phone—(908) 431-0330
216 U.S. Highway 206, Ste. 2, Hillsborough 08844

CK Manufacturing, Inc.
Phone—(973) 808-3500
8 Gardner Rd., Fairfield 07004

Comet Tool Co., Inc.
Phone—(856) 256-1070
651 Lambs Rd., Pitman 08071

**Lawrence Mold and Tool Corp.**
Email—mboard@lmtproducts.com
Phone—(609) 392-5422
Fax—(609) 392-5861
Web—www.lawrencemoldandtool.com
1412 Ohio Ave., Lawrenceville 08648
*(see our ad under MOLDS)*

Lincoln Mold & Die Corp.
Phone—(908) 241-3344
225 E. 1st Ave., Roselle 07203

Linden Mold & Tool Corp.
Phone—(732) 381-1411
155 Wescott Dr., P.O. Box C, Rahway 07065

Precise Tool & Mold Co., Inc.
Phone—(732) 469-3062
240 E. Lackland Dr., Middlesex 08846

Preferred Plastics Corp.
Phone—(856) 662-6250
6512 Park Ave., Pennsauken 08109

Republic Mold & Tool Co., Inc.
Phone—(908) 862-3344
109 Bradford Ave., Linden 07036

Rotech Tool & Mold Co., Inc.
Phone—(908) 241-9669
824 Fairfield Ave., Kenilworth 07033

South Jersey Precision Tool & Mold, Inc.
Phone—(856) 327-0500
4375 S. Lincoln Ave., Vineland 08361

Viz Mold & Die Ltd.
Phone—(201) 784-8383
210 Industrial Pkwy., Northvale 07647

## MOLDS — Rubber

Perfectone Mold Co.
Phone—(201) 798-5353
277 New York Ave., Jersey City 07307

## MOLDS AND DIES

R. & M. Mold Mfg. Co., LLC
Phone—(908) 479-4444
1022 Route 173 E., P.O. Box 578, Bloomsbury 08804

Sedtek, Inc.
Phone—(201) 489-4040
113 Meadow St., Hackensack 07601

Union Tool & Mold Co.
Phone—(973) 763-6611
220 Rutgers St., Maplewood 07040

## MONITORING SYSTEMS

Digitize, Inc.
Phone—(973) 663-1011
158 Edison Rd., Lake Hopatcong 07849

Fluitec International (H Q)
Phone—(201) 946-4584
333 Washington St., Ste. 201, Jersey City 07302

Rees Scientific Corp.
Phone—(609) 530-1055
1007 Whitehead Road Ext., Trenton 08638

TX Technology Corp.
Phone—(973) 442-7500
100 Ford Rd., Unit 100-18, Denville 07834

## MONITORS — Video

Accuview, Inc.
Phone—(201) 440-2225
40-C Cotters Ln., Ste. F, East Brunswick 08816

Industrial Electronic Devices, Inc.
Phone—(908) 806-2255
8 Bartles Corner Rd., Bldg. 101, Flemington 08822

TBC Partners, LLC
Phone—(855) 937-6466
743 Alexander Rd., Ste. 15, Princeton 08540

## MONOGRAMMING

Anderson Monograms
Phone—(609) 652-5552
245 Fox Landing Rd., P.O. Box 163, Port Republic 08241

Monogram Shoppe
Phone—(856) 845-9299
5 S. Broad St., Woodbury 08096

## MONUMENTS

American Monument Co.
Phone—(201) 750-1000
50 Herbert Ave., Closter 07624

American Monument Co. (H Q)
Phone—(201) 569-4455
479 N. Dean St., Englewood 07631

Barre Monuments
Phone—(732) 240-2888
114 Atlantic City Blvd., Beachwood 08722

Suburban Monument & Vault
Phone—(973) 242-7007
203 Sherman Ave., P.O. Box 2370, Newark 07114

White Valley Memorials (H Q)
Phone—(856) 767-3030
292 W. White Horse Pike, Berlin 08009

William B. Snelbaker & Son
Phone—(856) 845-0634
43 Cooper St., Woodbury 08096

## MOPS

Quickie Mfg. Corp. (H Q)
Phone—(856) 829-7900
1150 Taylors Ln., P.O. Box 156, Cinnaminson 08077

## MORTAR

MAPEI Corp.
Phone—(732) 254-8001
Off White Head Ave., P.O. Box 105, South River 08882

## MORTGAGE BROKERING

**Commercial Mortgage Assoc., Inc.**
Real Estate Loans
Phone—(973) 316-5500
Web—www.commercialmortgagenj.com
Email—info@commercialmortgagenj.com
P.O. Box 5068, Parsippany 07054

## MORTGAGES

**Millennium Home Mortgage**
Loans
Phone—(908) 233-6610
Fax—(908) 233-7036
Web—www.mhmlender.com
Email—jgalayda@mhmlender.com
209 Central Ave., Westfield 07090

**NVE Bank**
Phone—(201) 816-2810
Fax—(201) 816-7379
Web—www.nvebank.com
76 Engle St., Englewood 07631

## MOTION CONTROL PRODUCTS

Van Air & Hydraulics, Inc.
Phone—(856) 779-7300
612 E. Woodlawn Ave., Maple Shade 08052

## MOTION CONTROLLERS

CDS Corp.
Phone—(973) 300-0090
27 Wilson Dr., Unit C, Sparta 07871

**Simple Step, LLC**
Phone—(973) 948-2938
Fax—(973) 948-0182
Web—www.simplestep.com
Email—sales@simplestep.com
12 W. Owassa Tpke., Newton 07860

**Simple Step, LLC**
*Motion Controllers for the Automation Industry*
www.simplestep.com
(973) 948-2938
12 W. Owassa Tpke., Newton, NJ 07860

## MOTOR CONTROLS

Eagle Engineering & Automation, Inc.
Phone—(732) 899-2292
2111 Herbertsville Rd., P.O. Box 924, Point Pleasant 08742

## MOTORCYCLES AND PARTS

Morris Magnetos, Inc.
Phone—(973) 540-9171
103 Washington St., Morristown 07960

## MOTORS AND CONTROLS

**Allied Pump Corporation**
Phone—(201) 798-3277
Fax—(201) 798-8781
Web—www.allied-pump.com
Email—alliedpumps@gmail.com
1109 Grand Ave., Bldg. 5, North Bergen 07047
*(see our ad under PUMPS)*

Hydro-Mechanical Systems, Inc.
Phone—(856) 848-8888
1030 Delsea Dr., P.O. Box 87, Westville 08093

Raz Performance Machine
Phone—(856) 697-4275
247 Harding Hwy., Vineland 08360

SEW-Eurodrive, Inc.
Phone—(856) 467-2277
2107 High Hill Rd., P.O. Box 481, Bridgeport 08014

**Somfy Systems, Inc.**
Motors & control systems for retractable awnings & rolling shutters
Phone—(609) 395-1300 / (800) 647-6639
Fax—(609) 395-1750
Web—www.somfysystems.com
Email—marketing_us@somfy.com
121 Herrod Blvd., Dayton 08810

## MOULDINGS

Flex Moulding, Inc.
Phone—(201) 360-3634
112 Wells Ave., Jersey City 07306

## MOULDINGS — Architectural

Bendix Architectural Products, Inc.
Phone—(973) 473-4780
90 Dayton Ave., Ste. 34, Passaic 07055

Designer Source, Inc.
Phone—(732) 264-7775
2139 State Route 35, Holmdel 07733

## MOULDINGS — Picture Frame

Roma Moulding, Inc.
Phone—(732) 346-0999
115 Northfield Ave., Edison 08837

## MOULDINGS — Wood

Monteath Moulding
Phone—(732) 727-4000
3150 Bordentown Ave., Old Bridge 08857

© Copyright 2015 Manufacturers' News, Inc.

## MOUNTING EQUIPMENT

SOLSTICE Mfg. Co.
 Phone—(908) 284-0096
 270 S. Main St., Ste. 102, Flemington 08822

## MOVERS

**All In One Moving**
 Phone—(201) 773-6960
 Fax—(201) 773-6961
 Web—www.allinonemoving.com
 Email—morgan@allinonemoving.com
 59 5th St., Saddle Brook 07663
**Ridgewood Moving Services Bekins**
 Phone—(201) 529-2211
 Web—www.ridgewoodmoving.com
 575 Corporate Dr., Ste. 405, Mahwah 07430

## MUDJACKING CONTRACTORS

Presscrete Co., Inc., The
 Phone—(908) 757-8600
 128 Oak Tree Ave., South Plainfield 07080

## MULCH

**Britton Industries, Inc.**
 Phone—(609) 588-8225 / (844) 274-8866
 Fax—(609) 588-8965
 Web—www.brittonindustries.com
 Email—sales@brittonindustries.com
 227 Bakers Basin Rd., P.O. Box 6499,
 Lawrenceville 08648
**Fairfield Pallet Co., Inc.**
 Phone—(856) 455-7999
 Web—www.fairfieldpallet.com
 282 Rockville Rd., P.O. Box 361, Fairton 08320
 *(see our ad under PALLETS)*
Nature's Choice Corp.
 Phone—(201) 333-5244
 482 Houses Corner Rd., Sparta 07871
Riverdale Environmental Recycling
 Phone—(973) 616-6654
 1 Riverdale Rd., Riverdale 07457

## MUSICAL INSTRUMENT ACCESSORIES

Jan-Mar Industries
 Phone—(201) 664-3930
 568 Hillsdale, P.O. Box 314, Hillsdale 07642

## MUSICAL INSTRUMENTS

Kratt Pitch Pipe Co., Wm
 Phone—(908) 709-8901
 40 Lafayette Pl., Kenilworth 07033
McNally Instruments, LLC
 Phone—(973) 983-9153
 11 Longview Rd., Rockaway 07866
Tech 21 USA, Inc.
 Phone—(973) 777-6996
 790 Bloomfield Ave., Ste. B-1, Clifton 07012
Trek II Products, Inc.
 Phone—(732) 214-9200
 570 Jersey Ave., New Brunswick 08901

## MUSICAL INSTRUMENTS — Percussion

Latin Percussion, Inc.
 Phone—(973) 330-9103
 160 Belmont Ave., Garfield 07026
**Malletech, LLC**
 **1107 11th Ave., Neptune 07753**
 **Phone—(732) 774-0011**
 **Fax—(732) 774-0033**
 **Web—www.mostlymarimba.com**
 **Email—malletech@mostlymarimba.com**
 **P.O. Box 467, Asbury Park 07712**
Vintage Vibe ltd.
 Phone—(973) 989-2178
 114 Beach St., Bldg. 5, Ground Fl., Rockaway 07866

## NAILS

BSTC Group, Inc.
 Phone—(973) 492-5220
 135 Kinnelon Rd., Rm. 201, Kinnelon 07405

## NAMEPLATES

Product Identification Co., Inc.
 Phone—(973) 955-4747
 141 Lanza Ave., Bldg. 19, Garfield 07026
Technical Name Plate Corp.
 Phone—(973) 773-4256
 92 1st St., Passaic 07055

## NATIVE AMERICAN PRODUCTS

Grey Owl Indian Craft Sales Corp.
 Phone—(732) 389-4626
 15 Meridian Rd., Ste. 5, Eatontown 07724

## NATURAL GAS

**Supreme Energy, Inc.**
 **Phone—(973) 678-1800**
 **Fax—(973) 672-0148**
 **Web—www.supremeenergyinc.com**
 **Email—info@supremeenergyinc.com**
 **532 Freeman St., Orange 07050**

## NAVIGATION AIDS

Kearfott Corporation, Guidance & Navigation Div.
 Phone—(973) 785-6000
 1150 McBride Ave., Little Falls 07424

## NECKTIES

Chipp II
 Phone—(212) 687-0850
 7 Spring Hill Cir., Wayne 07470
Goodman & Co., Inc., Bob
 Phone—(732) 446-0252
 2 Steward Ln., Englishtown 07726
K G Designs, Inc.
 Phone—(201) 692-1852
 581 Ogden Ave., Teaneck 07666
Stewart, Inc., Robert
 Phone—(973) 751-5151
 120 Little St., Belleville 07109

## NEON PRODUCTS

E G L Co., Inc.
 Phone—(908) 508-1111
 100 Industrial Rd., Berkeley Heights 07922

## NETTING

Endurance Net, Inc.
 Phone—(609) 499-3450
 763-B Railroad Ave., Florence 08518
Har-Tru Sports
 Phone—(434) 295-6167
 1715 Oak St., Ste. 1, Lakewood 08701
TEX-NET, Inc.
 Phone—(609) 499-9111
 763-B Railroad Ave., Florence 08518

## NETWORK INTEGRATION SERVICES

**JEMS Software & Consulting, Inc.**
 **Phone—(609) 585-8530**
 **Fax—(609) 585-5539**
 **Web—www.jemssoco.com**
 **Email—jem@jemssoco.com**
 **P.O. Box 10070, Trenton 08650**

## NETWORK MANAGEMENT PRODUCTS

Princeton Computer Support, Inc.
 Phone—(609) 520-0770
 3490 U.S. Highway 1, Ste. 15-E, Princeton 08540

Worldwide Supply, LLC
 Phone—(973) 823-6400
 1 Park Dr., Franklin 07416

## NETWORK SECURITY PRODUCTS

API Technologies Corp.
 Phone—(908) 546-3900
 120 Corporate Blvd., South Plainfield 07080

## NEWSPAPER PUBLISHERS

24 Horas-Portuguese Daily Newspaper
 Phone—(973) 817-7400
 68 Madison St., Newark 07105
About Our Town, Inc.
 Phone—(732) 968-1615
 2 Lakeview Ave., Ste. 312, Piscataway 08854
America OGGI
 Phone—(201) 358-6697
 475 Walnut St., Norwood 07648
Arab Voice Newspaper
 Phone—(973) 523-7815
 85-99 Hazel St., Paterson 07503
Area Auto Racing News, Inc.
 Phone—(609) 888-3618
 2829 S. Broad St., Trenton 08610
Argo Corp.
 Phone—(609) 652-4560
 Richard Stockton College, Ste. 202, Pomona 08240
Arts Weekly, Inc.
 Phone—(973) 812-6766
 52 Sindle Ave., P.O. Box 1140, Little Falls 07424
Asbury Park Press
 Phone—(732) 922-6000
 3600 Highway 66, Neptune 07753
Atlantic City Weekly, L. P.
 Phone—(609) 646-4848
 Bayport 1, 8025 Black Horse Pike, Ste. 3, Pleasantville 08232
Banda Oriental, Inc.
 Phone—(732) 388-8383
 777 W. Grand Ave., Rahway 07065
Bayonne Community News
 Phone—(201) 437-2460
 170 Broadway, Bayonne 07002
Beacon Publishing Co., Inc.
 Phone—(973) 279-8845
 775 Valley Rd., Clifton 07013
Brazilian Voice
 Phone—(973) 491-6200
 412 Chestnut St., P.O. Box 5686, Newark 07105
Bright Side Newspaper
 Phone—(609) 861-2034
 1560 Route 83, Cape May Court House 08210
Broad Street Media
 Phone—(856) 779-3800
 53 Haddonfield Rd., Ste. 306, Cherry Hill 08002
Burlington County Times, Inc.
 Phone—(609) 871-8000
 4284 Route 130, Willingboro 08046
Cambio Newspaper
 Phone—(201) 902-0811
 604 56th St., West New York 07093
Cape May Star & Wave
 Phone—(609) 884-3466
 600 Park Blvd., Ste. 28, West Cape May 08204
Catamaran Media Co., LLC
 Phone—(609) 383-8994
 3120 Fire Rd., Egg Harbor Township 08234
Catamaran Media Co., LLC
 Phone—(609) 624-8900
 507 S. Shore Rd., Marmora 08223
Catholic Star Herald
 Phone—(856) 583-6142
 15 N. 7th St., Camden 08102
Central Record Corp., The
 Phone—(609) 654-9221
 32 S. Main St., Ste. A, P.O. Box 1027, Medford 08055
Chinese Newsweek Corp.
 Phone—(732) 744-1000
 32 Bridge St., Metuchen 08840
Cindy Merckx Publications, LLC
 Phone—(856) 694-1600
 330 Oak Ave., Malaga 08328
Civil Service Leader
 Phone—(201) 941-6397
 313 Broad Ave., Ste. 203, Ridgefield 07657

© Copyright 2015 Manufacturers' News, Inc.

## NEWSPAPER PUBLISHERS —
### (cont.)

**CMD Media**
Phone—(732) 574-1200
P.O. Box 1061, Rahway 07065

**Coaster, The**
Phone—(732) 775-3010
1011 Main St., Asbury Park 07712

**Community News Service, LLC**
Phone—(609) 396-1511
15 Princess Rd., Ste. K, Lawrenceville 08648

**Community Newspapers & Magazines Of North Jersey Media Group**
Phone—(973) 569-7000
1 Garret Mountain Plz., P.O. Box 471, Woodland Park 07424

**County Seat, LLC**
Phone—(201) 488-5795
77 Hudson St., Hackensack 07601

**Courier News**
Phone—(908) 722-8800
92 E. Main St., Ste. 202, Somerville 08876

**Courier-Post Newspaper**
Phone—(856) 663-6000
301 Cuthbert Rd., Cherry Hill 08002

**Criterion Publishing Co.**
Phone—(732) 548-8300
87 Forrest St., P.O. Box 4278, Metuchen 08840

**Cumberland & Salem Guide**
Phone—(856) 451-1177
874 N. Pearl St., P.O. Box 735, Bridgeton 08302

**Daily Journal, The**
Phone—(856) 691-5000
891 E. Oak Rd., Vineland 08360

**Daily Princetonian Publishing Co., Inc.**
Phone—(609) 375-8553
48 University Pl., Princeton 08544

**Dow Jones & Co., Inc.**
Phone—(609) 520-4000
4300 N. Route 1, Monmouth Junction 08852

**Elmer Times Co., Inc.**
Phone—(856) 358-6171
21 State St., Elmer 08318

**Evergreen Printing**
Phone—(856) 933-0222
101 Haag Ave., Bellmawr 08031

**Exit Zero Publishing**
Phone—(609) 770-8479
109 Sunset Blvd., Ste. D, Cape May 08204

**Filipino Express Newspaper, Inc.**
Phone—(201) 434-1114
2711 John F. Kennedy Blvd., Jersey City 07306

**Forked River Gazette, Inc.**
Phone—(609) 693-7490
119 Voyager Rd., Manahawkin 08050

**Franklin Lakes Oakland**
Phone—(201) 612-5415
41 Oak St., Ridgewood 07450

**Gloucester City News, Inc.**
Phone—(856) 456-1199
34 S. Broadway, P.O. Box 151, Gloucester City 08030

**Gujarat Samachar**
Phone—(732) 452-1755
3 State Route 27, Ste. 307, Edison 08820

**Hammonton Gazette, Inc.**
Phone—(609) 704-1939
233 Bellevue Ave., P.O. Box 1228, Hammonton 08037

**Hammonton News & Atlantic County Newspaper Group**
Phone—(609) 561-2300
115 12th St., Hammonton 08037

**Hawthorne Press**
Phone—(973) 427-3330
463 Lafayette Ave., P.O. Box 1, Hawthorne 07507

**Hispano Publishing, LLC**
Phone—(908) 351-9390
437 Linden Ave., Elizabeth 07208

**Home News Tribune**
Phone—(908) 722-8800
92 E. Main St., Somerville 08876

**Hudson Reporter Assocs., LP**
Phone—(201) 798-7800
1400 Washington St., P.O. Box 3069, Hoboken 07030

**Info System**
Phone—(973) 777-4448
345 Main Ave., Wallington 07057

**Italian Tribune Publishing Co.**
Phone—(973) 860-0101
7 N. Willow St., Ste. 8-C, Montclair 07042

**Jersey Journal, The**
Phone—(201) 653-1000
1 Harmon Plz., Ste. 1010, Secaucus 07094

**Jersey Paw Prints**
Phone—(609) 909-5100
P.O. Box 26, Mays Landing 08330

**Jimcam Publishing, Inc.**
Phone—(201) 843-5700
19 W. Pleasant Ave., Maywood 07607

**Journal Register Co., The**
Phone—(609) 654-5000
32 S. Main St., Ste. A, Medford 08055

**Korea Daily, Inc.**
Phone—(201) 944-8299
10 E. Brinkerhoff Ave., Ste. 2-B, Palisades Park 07650

**Korean Bergen News**
Phone—(201) 894-9061
210 Sylvan Ave., Ste. 23, Englewood Cliffs 07632

**Lake Hopatcong News**
Phone—(973) 663-2800
37 Nolans Point Park Rd., Lake Hopatcong 07849

**Lavoz Spanish Newspapers**
Phone—(908) 352-6654
P.O. Box 899, Elizabeth 07207

**Legislative Index Of New Jersey**
Phone—(609) 393-2291
172 W. State St., Trenton 08608

**Life & Leisure, LLC**
Phone—(973) 696-8009
234 Main St., Ste. 2, Lincoln Park 07035

**Link News Inc., The**
Phone—(732) 222-4300
176 Broadway, P.O. Box 120, Long Branch 07740

**Luso-Americano Co., Inc.**
Phone—(973) 589-4600
88 Ferry St., Newark 07105

**Metropolitan Corporate Counsel**
Phone—(908) 654-4840
1180 Wychwood Rd., Mountainside 07092

**Micromedia Publications, Inc.**
Phone—(732) 657-7344
15 Union Ave., P.O. Box 521, Lakehurst 08733

**Monmouth Journal, The**
Phone—(732) 747-7007
212 Maple Ave., Red Bank 07701

**New Jersey Epoch Times**
Phone—(908) 548-8380
50 Cragwood Rd., South Plainfield 07080

**New Jersey Herald, The**
Phone—(973) 383-1500
2 Spring St., P.O. Box 10, Newton 07860

**New Jersey Jewish News**
Phone—(973) 887-3900
901 Route 10, Whippany 07981

**New York Daily News**
Phone—(201) 946-6000
125 Theodore Conrad Dr., Jersey City 07305

**Newark Morning Ledger Co.**
Phone—(973) 392-4141
1 Star Ledger Plz., Newark 07102

**News Of Cumberland County, The**
Phone—(856) 451-1000
93 5th St., Salem 08079

**NJN Publishing Independent Press, Inc.**
Phone—(908) 464-1025
309 South St., New Providence 07974

**NJN Publishing, Inc. (H Q)**
Phone—(908) 782-4747
8 Minneakoning Rd., Flemington 08822

**North Jersey Media Group Inc.**
Phone—(973) 586-8000
100 Commons Way, Rockaway 07866

**North Jersey Media Group, Inc.**
Phone—(973) 921-6451
181 Milburn Ave., Ste. 201, Millburn 07041

**North Jersey Media Group, Inc.**
Phone—(973) 569-7000
1 Garret Mountain Plz., P.O. Box 471, Woodland Park 07424

**Nosotros, News**
Phone—(732) 845-1911
P.O. Box 1337, Toms River 08754

**Observer**
Phone—(201) 288-0333
P.O. Box 445, Hasbrouck Heights 07604

**Ocean Star, The**
Phone—(732) 899-7606
421 River Ave., Point Pleasant Beach 08742

**Post Eagle Newspaper, Inc.**
Phone—(973) 473-5414
800 Van Houten Ave., Clifton 07013

**Princeton Packet, Inc.**
Phone—(609) 924-3244
300 Witherspoon St., P.O. Box 350, Princeton 08542

**Produce News, The**
Phone—(201) 986-7990
800 Kinderkamack Rd., Ste. 100, Oradell 07649

**Record, The**
Phone—(973) 569-7770
1 Garret Mountain Plz., P.O. Box 471, Woodland Park 07424

**Recorder Newspaper Co.**
Phone—(908) 766-3900
530 E. Main St., P.O. Box 600, Chester 07930

**Recorder Publishing Co. (H Q)**
Phone—(908) 766-3900
17-19 Morristown Rd., P.O. Box 687, Bernardsville 07924

**Retrospect, The**
Phone—(856) 854-1400
732 Haddon Ave., P.O. Box 296, Collingswood 08108

**Secaucus Home News**
Phone—(201) 867-2071
766 Irving Pl., Secaucus 07094

**South Bergenite**
Phone—(201) 933-1166
9 Lincoln Ave., Rutherford 07070

**South Jersey Publishing Co.**
Phone—(609) 272-7000
1000 W. Washington Ave., Pleasantville 08232

**South Jersey Times**
Phone—(856) 935-1500
93 5th St., Salem 08079

**Star Ledger**
Phone—(973) 882-6120
26 Riverside Dr., Pine Brook 07058

**Star News Group**
Phone—(732) 223-0076
13 Broad St., Manasquan 08736

**Targum Publishing Co.**
Phone—(732) 932-7051
126 College Ave., Ste. 431, New Brunswick 08901

**The New Town Press**
Phone—(856) 467-3113
421 Stone Meeting House Rd., Woolwich Township 08085

**The Observer**
Phone—(201) 991-1600
39 Seeley Ave., Kearny 07032

**Thomson Reuters Corp.**
Phone—(973) 662-3070
492 River Rd., Nutley 07110

**Times Of Trenton**
Phone—(609) 989-5454
413 River View Plz., Trenton 08611

**Treasure Hunt**
Phone—(908) 454-0880
1223 S. Main St., Phillipsburg 08865

**Trentonian, The**
Phone—(609) 989-7800
600 Perry St., Trenton 08618

**Two River Times**
Phone—(732) 219-5788
75 W. Front St., Ste. 2, Red Bank 07701

**U.S. 1 Publishing Co.**
Phone—(609) 452-7000
15 Princess Rd., Lawrenceville 08648

**Ukrainian National Affiliation, Inc.**
Phone—(973) 292-9800
2200 State Route 10, P.O. Box 280, Parsippany 07054

**Verona-Cedar Grove Times**
Phone—(973) 233-5048
130 Valley Rd., Montclair 07042

**Villadom Times, The**
Phone—(201) 652-0744
333 Godwin Ave., P.O. Box 96, Midland Park 07432

**Watchung Communications, Inc.**
Phone—(908) 232-4407
251 North Ave. W., Westfield 07090

**West Essex Tribune, Inc.**
Phone—(973) 992-1771
495 S. Livingston Ave., P.O. Box 65, Livingston 07039

**World Journal, Inc.**
Phone—(732) 632-8890
41-A Bridge St., Metuchen 08840

## NEWSPAPER PUBLISHERS —

*(cont.)*

World Media Enterprises, Inc.
Phone—(609) 272-7000
1000 W. Washington Ave., Pleasantville 08232
Worrall Community Newspapers, Inc.
Phone—(908) 686-7700
1291 Stuyvesant Ave., P.O. Box 1596, Union 07083

## NICKEL ALLOY SCRAP PROCESSING

Abbey Metal Corp.
Phone—(201) 438-0330
59 Grand St., Moonachie 07074

## NIGHTWEAR — Women's

Dolce Vita Intimates, LLC (H Q)
Phone—(973) 482-8400
1000 1st St., Harrison 07029

## NITROGEN

Praxair, Inc., Rairatan Bay, Plt. 907
Phone—(732) 738-4150
60 Crows Mill Rd., Keasbey 08832
**SOS Gases, Inc.**
**Industrial & Laboratory Gas; Welding Eqpt., Rental & Repair Service**
**Phone—(201) 998-7800 / (800) 626-7998**
**Fax—(201) 998-5243**
**Web—www.sosgasesinc.com**
**Email—sosgasesinc@msn.com**
**1100 Harrison Ave., Kearny 07032**
*(see our ad under WELDING EQUIPMENT & SUPPLIES)*

## NOISE ABATEMENT MATERIALS

Aeroacoustic Corp., The
Phone—(908) 241-8600
169 E. Highland Pkwy., Roselle 07203

## NOODLES

**H & U, Inc.**
**DBA: Sun Noodle Brand**
**Phone—(201) 530-1100**
**Fax—(201) 530-1101**
**Web—www.sunnoodle.com**
**Email—info@sunnoodle.com**
**375 North St., Ste. O, Teterboro 07608**

## NOTARY SERVICES

**JS Agency**
**Phone—(732) 324-8400**
**Fax—(732) 324-1838**
**Web—www.jsimmigration.com**
**418 State St., Perth Amboy 08861**

## NOZZLES

Sci-Bore, Inc.
Phone—(973) 414-9001
364 Glenwood Ave., Bldg. 18-E, East Orange 07017
Steinen Mfg. Co., Wm.
Phone—(973) 887-6400
29 E. Halsey Rd., Parsippany 07054

## NOZZLES — Automatic Gasoline

Danfoss Hago, Inc.
Phone—(908) 232-8687
1120 Globe Ave., Mountainside 07092
**Multiforce Systems Corp.**
**Automated fuel management integrated systems for the transportation industry**
**Phone—(609) 683-4242**
**Fax—(609) 683-4835**
**Web—www.fuelforce.com**
**Email—sales@fuelforce.com**
**101 Wall St., Princeton 08540**
*(see our ad under PUMPS – Gasoline Dispensing)*

## NOZZLES — Spray

American Filter & Tank Co., Inc.
Phone—(201) 857-5056
231 Greenwood Ave., Ste. 2, Midland Park 07432
Monarch Mfg. Works, Inc.
Phone—(856) 241-1500
7249-B Browning Rd., Merchantville 08109

## NUCLEAR FABRICATION

Joseph Oat Corp.
Phone—(856) 541-2900
2500 S. Broadway, Camden 08104

## NUCLEAR REPAIR

**Chalmers & Kubeck, Inc.**
**Phone—(610) 494-4300**
**Fax—(610) 485-1484**
**Web—www.candk.com**
**Email—jmoore@candk.com**
**150 Commerce Dr., P.O. Box 2447, Aston, PA 19014**
*(see our ad under MACHINE WORK & MACHINING)*

## NUMBERING MACHINES

Atlantic Zeiser, Inc.
Phone—(973) 228-0800
15 Patton Dr., West Caldwell 07006

## NUT PROCESSING

Nuts.Com
Phone—(908) 523-0333
125 Moen St., Cranford 07016
Nutsco, Inc.
Phone—(856) 966-6400
1115 S. 2nd St., Camden 08103
Star Snacks, LLC
Phone—(201) 200-9820
105 Harbor Dr., Jersey City 07305
Westco Fruit & Nut Products Co., Inc.
Phone—(973) 373-1866
93-97 Coit St., Irvington 07111

## NUTRACEUTICALS

DNE Nutraceuticals, Inc.
Phone—(732) 806-9538
700 Central Ave., Farmingdale 07719

## NUTRITIONAL SUPPLEMENTS

**Ambix Laboratories**
**Custom & P/L Liquid Nutritional Products**
**Phone—(973) 890-9002**
**Fax—(973) 890-9778**
**Web—www.ambixlabs.com**
**Email—ambixlab@aol.com**
**55 W. End Rd., Totowa 07512**
*(see our ad under PROTEIN)*
Aspire Pharmaceuticals, Inc.
Phone—(732) 447-1444
41 Veronica Ave., Somerset 08873
Command Nutritionals, LLC
Phone—(973) 227-8210
10 Washington Ave., Ste. 1, Fairfield 07004
Food Sciences Corporation
Phone—(856) 778-8080
821 E. Gate Dr., Mount Laurel 08054
Inergetics, Inc.
Phone—(908) 604-2500
550 Broad St., 12th Fl., Newark 07102
Life Science Laboratories, LLC
Phone—(732) 367-1900
170 Oberlin Ave. N., Ste. 26, Lakewood 08701
Life Science Labs Supplements, LLC
Phone—(732) 367-1749
170 Oberlin Ave., Lakewood 08701
Manhattan Drug Co., Inc.
Phone—(973) 926-0816
225 Long Ave., Bldg. 15, 3rd Fl., Hillside 07205
Mushroom Wisdom, Inc.
Phone—(973) 470-0010
1 Madison St., Bldg. F, East Rutherford 07073

MYOS Corp. (H Q)
Phone—(973) 509-0444
45 Horsehill Rd., Ste. 106, Cedar Knolls 07927
Naturex Inc.
Phone—(201) 440-5000
375 Huyler St., South Hackensack 07606
NVE, Inc.
Phone—(973) 786-7868
15 Whitehall Rd., Andover 07821
Rise-N-Shine, LLC (H Q)
Phone—(973) 729-4141
17 Woodport Rd., Ste. 1-E, Sparta 07871
Shanghai Freemen Americas, LLC (H Q)
Phone—(732) 981-1288
377 Hoes Ln., Ste. 240, Piscataway 08854
Solgar, Inc.
Phone—(201) 944-2311
500 Willow Tree Rd., Leonia 07605
Thomas & Co., Inc., P. L.
Phone—(973) 984-0900
119 Headquarters Plz., Morristown 07960
Vitamins for Life, LLC
Phone—(732) 663-1559
1806 Bellmore St., P.O. Box 853, Oakhurst 07755
Vitaquest International, LLC
Phone—(973) 575-9200
8 Henderson Dr., West Caldwell 07006

## NUTS (FOOD)

Monkey Joe's Big Nut Co.
Phone—(856) 627-4600
205 N. White Horse Pike, Laurel Springs 08021

## NUTS — Self Locking

Continental-Aero (H Q)
Phone—(973) 481-3000
530 Bergen St., P.O. Box 354, Harrison 07029

## NUTS AND BOLTS

**(also see 'Bolts' and 'Fasteners')**

M R L Mfg. Corp.
Phone—(973) 790-1744
59 Lee Ave., P.O. Box 8440, Haledon 07508
**National Standard Supply**
**Phone—(609) 693-7777**
**Fax—(609) 693-7277**
**Email—kpierson@nsstbb.com**
**706 Old Shore Rd., Ste. 4, Forked River 08731**

## OCCUPATIONAL HEALTH SERVICES

JFK Medical Center Occupational Health Services
Phone—(732) 321-7610
Fax—(732) 906-4928
Web—www.jfkmc.org
Email—jpascua@jfkhealth.org
65 James St., Parking Lot G, Edison 08818

## ODOR CONTROL PRODUCTS

**General Carbon Corporation**
**Activated Carbon Equipment & Services for Liquid & Vapor Applications**
**Phone—(973) 523-2223**
**Fax—(973) 523-1494**
**Web—www.generalcarbon.com**
**Email—sales@generalcarbon.com**
**33 Paterson St., Paterson 07501**
*(see our ad under CARBON–Activated)*

## ODOR CONTROL SYSTEMS

**General Carbon Corporation**
**Activated Carbon Equipment & Services for Liquid & Vapor Applications**
**Phone—(973) 523-2223**
**Fax—(973) 523-1494**
**Web—www.generalcarbon.com**
**Email—sales@generalcarbon.com**
**33 Paterson St., Paterson 07501**
*(see our ad under CARBON–Activated)*

INDUSTRY

## OFFICE EQUIPMENT

Brother International Corporation
Phone—(908) 704-1700
200 Crossing Blvd., Bridgewater 08807

Kyocera Document Solutions America, Inc. (H Q)
Phone—(973) 808-8444
225 Sand Rd., Fairfield 07004

Swintec East (H Q)
Phone—(201) 935-0115
320 W. Commercial Ave., Moonachie 07074

## OFFICE EQUIPMENT — Wholesale

Advanced Business Machines Co.
Phone—(732) 431-1464
230 Randolph Rd., Freehold 07728

Allister Business Systems, Inc.
Phone—(732) 972-8400
205 E. 1st Ave., Roselle 07203

Superior Office Systems, Inc.
Phone—(732) 738-0093
19 Gross Ave., Edison 08837

United Stationers Supply Co.
Phone—(609) 619-4000
100 Liberty Way, Cranbury 08512

## OFFICE FURNITURE

**Arnold Furniture Mfrs., Inc.**
**Email: arnoldfurniture@gmail.com**
**Phone—(973) 399-0505**
**Fax—(973) 399-7638**
**Web—www.arnoldfurniture.com**
**400 Coit St., Irvington 07111**

Arnold Reception Desks, Inc.
Phone—(973) 375-8101
120 Coit St., Irvington 07111

Atlas Desk & Office Equipment Corp.
Phone—(973) 242-8989
185-193 Central Ave., 2nd Fl., Newark 07103

BIF New York, Inc.
Phone—(201) 933-7777
465 Barell Ave., Carlstadt 07072

Business Furniture, Inc.
Phone—(973) 503-0730
10 Lanidex Plz. W., Ste. 202, Parsippany 07054

Casey's Executive Interiors
Phone—(732) 968-3236
152 Route 22 W., P.O. Box 7070, Green Brook 08812

Concord Products Co., Inc.
Phone—(856) 933-3000
251 Benigno Blvd., Bellmawr 08031

Design Line, Inc.
Phone—(908) 241-1911
283 Cox St., Roselle 07203

Ge-Ro Desk Co.
Phone—(973) 485-0505
334 N. 5th St., Newark 07107

Glenwood Office Furniture II, Inc.
Phone—(908) 687-3770
561 U.S. Highway 22, Hillside 07205

Global - The Total Office (H Q)
Phone—(856) 596-3390
17 W. Stow Rd., P.O. Box 562, Marlton 08053

Gordon International, Inc.
Phone—(732) 431-3361
6 Paragon Way, Freehold 07728

Hoppe Co., Inc., R. J.
Phone—(973) 485-5665
340 N. 5th St., Newark 07107

Jesper Office, LLC
Phone—(908) 218-4200
745 Route 202/206 S., Ste. 300, Somerville 08876

LaCour, Inc.
Phone—(973) 227-4755
36 Kulick Rd., Fairfield 07004

Stylex
Phone—(856) 461-5600
740 Coopertown Rd., P.O. Box 5038, Delanco 08075

Vaswani, Inc.
Phone—(973) 376-4425
18 Bernadette Ct., Springfield 07081

## OFFICE SUPPLIES

Officemate International Corp.
Phone—(732) 225-7422
90 Newfield Ave., Edison 08837

Supply Source
Phone—(201) 735-0232
64 Oak Ave., Tenafly 07670

## OIL & GAS EXPLORATION

Hess Corp.
Phone—(732) 940-3705
2800 U.S. Highway 1, North Brunswick 08902

Jay Bee Oil & Gas, Inc.
Phone—(908) 686-1493
1720 U.S. Highway 22 E., Union 07083

Woodruff Energy, Inc.
Phone—(856) 455-1111
73 Water St., P.O. Box 777, Bridgeton 08302

## OIL & GAS PROCESSING & REFINING

Hess Corp.
Phone—(732) 750-6000
1 Hess Plz., Woodbridge 07095

Paulsboro Refining Co.
Phone—(856) 224-6000
800 Billingsport Rd., Paulsboro 08066

Phillips 66 Bayway Refinery
Phone—(908) 523-5000
1400 Park Ave., Linden 07036

## OIL & GAS PRODUCTION

**K.W. Rastall Oil Co.**
**Phone—(732) 297-5600**
**Fax—(732) 297-4508**
**Web—www.rastalloil.com**
**P.O. Box 7174, North Brunswick 08902**

Majka & Sons Fuel Service, Joseph A.
Phone—(973) 777-8484
568 Paulison Ave., Clifton 07011

**Oil Tank Services**
**Phone—(908) 241-5011**
**Fax—(908) 241-5155**
**Web—www.oiltankservices.com**
**Email—oiltank05@yahoo.com**
**505 E. 1st Ave., Roselle 07203**

VGS Group, Inc.
Phone—(732) 887-5912
197 State Route 18, Ste. 235, East Brunswick 08816

## OIL BURNING SYSTEMS

**Mazzo Oil Co.**
**Phone—(973) 473-5181**
**Fax—(973) 478-2594**
**242 Palisades Ave., Garfield 07026**

**Mazzo Oil Co.**
*Quality Oil Burning Systems*
(973) 473-5181 / FAX: (973) 478-2594
242 Palisades Avenue
Garfield, NJ 07026

*Send an RFQ* (request for quote)
*to multiple suppliers at*
**IndustryNet.com**

Swanton Heating-Cooling-Fuel
Phone—(732) 708-0075
Fax—(732) 708-0171
Web—www.swantonheatcool.com
Email—info@swantonheatcool.com
37 Center Ave., Atlantic Highlands 07716

**Swanton Heating-Cooling-Fuel**
*Quality oil burning systems*
732-708-0075 • Fax: 732-708-0171
www.swantonheatcool.com
37 Center Ave. Atlantic Highlands, NJ 07716

## OIL FIELD EQUIPMENT

McJunkin Red Man Corporation
Phone—(856) 753-7690
305 Center Ave., Waterford Works 08089

## OIL FIELD SERVICES

Camin Cargo Control, Inc. (H Q)
Phone—(908) 523-0616
230 Marion Ave., Linden 07036

NMK Resources
Phone—(856) 686-4904
650 Grove Rd., Ste. 111, Paulsboro 08066

SGS North America, Inc. (H Q)
Phone—(201) 508-3000
201 Route 17 N., Rutherford 07070

## OIL FILTRATION EQUIPMENT

Renewable BioSystems, LLC
Phone—(973) 769-0600
20 Spielman Rd., Fairfield 07004

## OIL RECYCLING

Lorco Petroleum Services
Phone—(908) 820-8800
450 S. Front St., Elizabeth 07202

## OILS — Edible

Aarhus United USA, Inc.
Phone—(973) 344-1300
131 Marsh St., Newark 07114

Edesia Oil, LLC
Phone—(732) 851-7979
225 County Road 522, Unit B, Englishtown 07726

Oilmatic Systems, LLC
Phone—(732) 324-9890
155 Smith St., P.O. Box 185, Keasbey 08832

## OILS — Essential

Agilex Flavors & Fragrances, Inc.
Phone—(732) 393-7300
140 Centennial Ave., Piscataway 08854

**Citroil Enterprises, Inc.**
**Fruit, Juices, Oils**
**Phone—(201) 933-8405**
**Fax—(201) 933-8217**
**Web—www.citromax.com**
**Email—cgonzabay@citroil.com**
**444 Washington Ave., Carlstadt 07072**

*Citroil enterprises*
*Quality Flavorings & Flavors*
**www.citromax.com**
(201) 933-8405 • FAX: (201) 933-8217
444 Washington Ave. Carlstadt, NJ 07072

Elixens America, Inc.
Phone—(732) 388-3555
1443 Pinewood St., Rahway 07065

## Ferrell's Oil Service

## Quality Oils

## 856-299-0500 • FAX: 856-299-4959

### PO Box 130  Pedricktown, NJ 08067

### Email: bshaw@ferrellsoil.com

---

# J.W. Pierson Co.

*Fuel Oil — Diesel — Gasoline — Service*

## 973-673-5000 • FAX: 973-673-7385

## 888-459-4328

### 89 Dodd St. • East Orange, NJ 07017

## www.jwpierson.com

## OILS — Essential — *(cont.)*

**Excellentia International**
Phone—(732) 749-9840
Fax—(732) 200-3791
Web—www.excellentiaint.com
Email—info@excellentiaint.com
19 Progress St., Edison 08820

L.A. Champon & Co., Inc. (H Q)
Phone—(732) 923-0003
266 Broadway, Long Branch 07740

Symrise Purescents
Phone—(732) 922-2520
1715 Oak St., Ste. 3, Lakewood 08701

## OILS — Fuel

**Ferrell's Oil Service**
Phone—(856) 299-0500
Fax—(856) 299-4959
Email—bshaw@ferrellsoil.com
26 E. Mill St., P.O. Box 130, Pedricktown 08067
*(see our ad on this page)*

**J.W. Pierson Co.**
We Service Heating Equipment
Phone—(973) 673-5000 / (888) 459-4328
Fax—(973) 673-7385
Web—www.jwpierson.com
Email—shammond@jwpierson.com
89 Dodd St., East Orange 07017
*(see our ad on this page)*

**McElven Fuel Inc.**
Phone—(609) 894-8635
Fax—(609) 726-1586
Web—www.mcelvenfuelcompany.com
Email—sharon@mcelvenfuelcompany.com
4 Magnolia Rd., Pemberton 08068

**Petrotech, Inc.**
Dealer in Fuel Oils, #2 Diesel & Kerosene for the NJ Area
Phone—(201) 641-6466
Fax—(201) 440-6155
Email—petrotechfuel@verizon.net
381 Liberty St., Ste. 2, Little Ferry 07643

## OILS — Heating

**Supreme Energy, Inc.**
Phone—(973) 678-1800
Fax—(973) 672-0148
Web—www.supremeenergyinc.com
Email—info@supremeenergyinc.com
532 Freeman St., Orange 07050

## OILS — Industrial

H & B Petroleum Co., Inc.
Phone—(973) 664-0144
1 Wynding Way, Rockaway 07866

## OILS — Lubricating

Bel Ray Co., LLC
Phone—(732) 938-2421
1201 Bowman Ave., Wall 07719

**Certified Products Co.**
Email: joe.f@cerprod.com
Also hydraulic repairs & hoses
Phone—(201) 433-0013 / (800) 654-2436
Fax—(201) 433-1482
Web—www.cerprodnjhydraulics.com
269 Kearney Ave., Jersey City 07305

Clarkson & Ford Co.
Phone—(973) 777-0300
30 Industrial St. W., Clifton 07012

Exxon Mobil Corp.
Phone—(856) 224-5000
1001 Billingsport Rd., Paulsboro 08066

Grignard Co.
Phone—(732) 340-1111
505 Capobianco Plz., Rahway 07065

**Hangsterfer's Laboratories, Inc.**
Phone—(856) 468-0216
Fax—(856) 468-0200
Web—www.hangsterfers.com
Email—sales@hangsterfers.com
175 Ogden Rd., Mantua 08051
*(see our ad under LUBRICANTS—Metalworking)*

**Lockrey Company LLC**
Aerospace & industrial lubricants
Phone—(856) 665-4794
Fax—(856) 665-4166
1280 Old York Rd., Burlington 08016

**Lubriplate Lubricants Co.**
Phone—(973) 589-9150 / (800) 733-4755
Fax—(973) 589-4432
Web—www.lubriplate.com
Email—info@lubriplate.com
129 Lockwood St., Newark 07105

Power Mist Racing, LLC
Phone—(973) 383-1061
67 Stickles Pond Rd., Newton 07860

## OILS — Synthetic

**Lubriplate Lubricants Co.**
Phone—(973) 589-9150 / (800) 733-4755
Fax—(973) 589-4432
Web—www.lubriplate.com
Email—info@lubriplate.com
129 Lockwood St., Newark 07105

## OILS — Vegetable, Cooking

Supreme Oil Co., Inc.
Phone—(201) 567-3177
80 S. Dean St., Englewood 07631

## OILS — Wholesale

AMD Special Oil, LLC
Phone—(201) 327-0642
90 N. Franklin Tpke., Ramsey 07446

## OLIVES & OLIVE OIL

A Taste Of Olive, LLC
Phone—(856) 795-0043
106 Kings Hwy. E., Ste. A, Haddonfield 08033

**Kalustyan Corp.**
Spices, herbs & seasonings
Phone—(908) 688-6111
Fax—(908) 688-4415
Web—www.kalustyan.com
Email—kerri@kalustyan.com
855 Rahway Ave., Union 07083

Lionelli
Phone—(732) 826-7270
345 Florida Grove Rd., Perth Amboy 08861

## OPERATING ROOM EQUIPMENT

BioMediCon
Phone—(856) 778-1880
30 E. Central Ave., Moorestown 08057

## OPHTHALMIC INSTRUMENTS

Fortrad Instruments, LLC
Phone—(973) 543-2371
8 Franklin Rd., Mendham 07945

## OPHTHALMIC PRODUCTS

Lab-Tech, Inc.
Phone—(201) 784-1093
103 Stonehurst Ct., Northvale 07647

Motif Industries, Inc.
Phone—(973) 575-1800
8 Commerce Rd., Fairfield 07004

Schreiber, Inc., Earle C.
Phone—(732) 335-1424
1 Bethany Rd., Bldg. 1, Ste. 13, Hazlet 07730

Seiko Optical Products Of America, Inc. (H Q)
Phone—(201) 529-9099
575 Corporate Dr., Ste. 205, Mahwah 07430

## OPTICAL COMPONENTS

Anchor Optical Co.
Phone—(856) 573-6865
101 E. Gloucester Pike, Barrington 08007

Coherent Advanced Crystal Group
Phone—(973) 240-6800
31 Farinella Dr., East Hanover 07936

INDUSTRY

## OPTICAL COMPONENTS — (cont.)

Edmund Optics, Inc.
Phone—(856) 547-3488
101 E. Gloucester Pike, Barrington 08007
Esco Optics
Phone—(973) 697-3700
1 Tideland Rd., P.O. Box 308, Oak Ridge 07438

## OPTICAL FILTERS

O & S Research, Inc.
Phone—(856) 829-2800
1912 Bannard St., P.O. Box 221, Cinnaminson 08077

## OPTICAL GOODS

Shanghai Optics, Inc. (H Q)
Phone—(732) 321-6915
17 Brant Ave., Ste. 6, Clark 07066

## OPTICAL GOODS — Wholesale

Nassau Lens Co., Inc.
Phone—(201) 767-8033
160 LeGrand Ave., Northvale 07647
**Topcon Medical Systems, Inc.**
**Phone—(201) 599-5100**
**Fax—(201) 599-5250**
**Web—www.topcon.com**
**Email—tmsmarketing@topcon.com**
**111 Bauer Dr., Oakland 07436**

## OPTICAL LENSES

### (also see 'Eyeglasses' & 'Contact Lenses')

International Crystal Laboratories
Phone—(973) 478-8944
11 Erie St., Ste. 2, Garfield 07026
Kennedy Opticians
Phone—(908) 276-2020
552 Boulevard, Kenilworth 07033
Lens Co., Inc.
Phone—(973) 546-0866
700 Route 46 W., Unit 7, Clifton 07013
M H Optical Supplies, Inc.
Phone—(201) 489-1110
128 Leuning St., South Hackensack 07606
**Optic One Family Eye Care**
**Phone—(856) 786-1616**
**Fax—(856) 786-3565**
**Web—www.optic-one.com**
**Email—eyes@optic-one.com**
**2401 Route 130 S., Cinnaminson 08077**
Special Optics Manufacture & Design, Inc.
Phone—(973) 366-7289
315 Richard Mine Rd., Wharton 07885
Switch Vision
Phone—(973) 582-2304
103 Fairfield Rd., Fairfield 07004
Village Opticians
Phone—(732) 350-1900
550 Route 530, Whiting 08759
VIP Optical Laboratories, Inc.
Phone—(908) 523-1422
325 Dalziel Rd., Linden 07036

## OPTICAL MACHINERY

ISOWAVE
Phone—(973) 328-7000
64 Harding Ave., Dover 07801

## OPTICAL SUPPLIES & EQUIPMENT

Eagle Eyewear, Inc. (H Q)
Phone—(908) 236-9300
P.O. Box 486, Whitehouse 08888

## OPTICS — Industrial

Inrad Optics, Inc.
Phone—(201) 767-1910
181 Legrand Ave., Northvale 07647

---

**TRUMPF Photonics, Inc.**
**Phone—(609) 925-8200**
**Fax—(609) 409-7021**
**Web—www.us.trumpf.com**
**Email—info@us.trumpf.com**
**2601 US Route 130 S., Cranbury 08512**
*(see our ad under LASERS)*

## ORGANS — Pipe

Peragallo Pipe Organ Co.
Phone—(973) 684-3414
306 Buffalo Ave., Paterson 07503

## O-RINGS

**Captain O-Ring LLC**
**Phone—(215) 839-6565**
**Web—www.captainoring.com**
**Email—sales@captainoring.com**

## ORTHODONTIC EQUIPMENT & SUPPLIES

J.A.W. Products, Inc.
Phone—(856) 829-3210
835 Industrial Hwy., Unit 125, Cinnaminson 08077

## ORTHOPEDIC APPLIANCES — Artificial Limbs

AlliedOP, Inc.
Phone—(973) 328-3340
1 Emery Ave., Ste. 1, Randolph 07869
England Orthopedics, Inc.
Phone—(732) 286-4444
1002 Commons Way, Toms River 08755
Garden State Orthopaedic Center, Inc.
Phone—(201) 337-5566
9 Post Rd., Ste. OP-1, Oakland 07436
**Garden State Orthopedic, Inc.**
**Email: njgso@aol.com**
**Orthopedic**
**Phone—(973) 538-4948**
**Fax—(973) 605-8481**
**Web—www.gsortho.com**
**Email—gsoc@gsortho.com**
**95 Mount Kemble Ave., Morristown 07960**

## Garden State Orthopedic, Inc.

# (973) 538-4948
## FAX: (973) 605-8481

## www.gsortho.com
*Email: njgso@aol.com*

95 Mount Kemble Ave.
Morristown, NJ 07960

Hanger Prosthetics & Orthotics, Inc.
Phone—(732) 417-0480
265 Fernwood Ave., Edison 08837
Hanger Prosthetics & Orthotics, Inc.
Phone—(973) 736-0628
59 Main St., Ste. 111, West Orange 07052

*Do nationwide searches for products & services at:*
**IndustryNet.com**

---

Manfredi Orthotic & Prosthetic Affiliates, LLC
Phone—(732) 380-0366
749 Hope Rd., Eatontown 07724

# Manfredi Orthotic & Prosthetic Affiliates, LLC
*Orthopedic, Orthotic*
**www.manfredioandp.com**
## 732-380-0366
749 Hope Rd. Eatontown, NJ 07724

Next Step Orthopedics, Inc.
Phone—(973) 736-2244
331 Main St., West Orange 07052
North Jersey Prosthetics & Orthotics
Phone—(201) 943-4448
39 Broad Ave., Palisades Park 07650
Nouveau Prosthetics & Orthotics
Phone—(732) 739-0888
984 State Route 36, Hazlet 07730
Oertel Orthopedics, Inc.
Phone—(908) 688-1818
2095 U.S. Highway 22 W., Union 07083
Precision Shoe Brace & Limb, LLC
Phone—(908) 523-0026
618 W. Elizabeth Ave., P.O. Box 1213, Linden 07036
Somerset Prosthetic & Orthotics, Inc.
Phone—(732) 560-2830
56 W. Union Ave., Bound Brook 08805
Stryker Orthopaedics
Phone—(201) 831-5000
325 Corporate Dr., Mahwah 07430
Swiss Orthopedic Co., Inc.
Phone—(908) 874-5522
188 Highway 206, Hillsborough 08844

## ORTHOPEDIC BRACES

AlliedOP, Inc.
Phone—(201) 444-7750
579 Goffle Rd., Wyckoff 07481
Hanger Prosthetics & Orthotics
Phone—(856) 309-0709
201 White Horse Rd. E., Voorhees 08043
Ossur Americas, Inc.
Phone—(856) 345-6000
1414 Metropolitan Ave., Paulsboro 08066

## ORTHOPEDIC IMPLANTS

Extremity Medical, LLC
Phone—(973) 588-8980
300 Interpace Pkwy., Ste. 410, Parsippany 07054
Phillips Precision, Inc.
Phone—(201) 797-8820
7 Paul Kohner Pl., Elmwood Park 07407
Tyber Medical, LLC (H Q)
Phone—(866) 761-0933
89 Headquarters Plz. N., Ste. 1464, Morristown 07960
Zimmer Trabecular Metal Technology
Phone—(973) 576-0032
10 Pomerov Rd., Parsippany 07054
Zimmer Tri-State, Inc.
Phone—(856) 778-8300
1001 Briggs Rd., Ste. 275, Mount Laurel 08054

## ORTHOPEDIC INSTRUMENTS

Armac Assocs.
Phone—(888) 422-3044
71 Passaic Ave., Florham Park 07932
Westcon Orthopedics, Inc.
Phone—(908) 806-8981
4 Craig Rd., Neshanic Station 08853

## ORTHOPEDIC SUPPLIES

Precision Orthotic Lab International
Phone—(856) 848-6226
1595 Imperial Way, West Deptford 08066
Silipos, Inc.
Phone—(973) 928-5900
4 Brighton Rd., Ste. 320, Clifton 07012

## ORTHOTICS

**Allied Op**
Phone—(732) 341-9191
810 Hooper Ave., Toms River 08753

**AlliedOP**
Phone—(732) 545-2885
1527 Route 27, Somerset 08873

**Carlascio Inc.** Orthotics, Prosthetic, Custom Shoes
Phone—(201) 333-8716
283 Grove St., Jersey City 07302

**Diabetic & Athletic Foot Center, LLC, Cedarwood Plz.**
Toll Free Ph: 1-855-FIT-4YOU. Building Comfort from the Ground Up
Phone—(732) 281-3134 / (855) 348-4968
Fax—(732) 281-3137
Web—www.diabeticfootcenter.net
226 Route 37, Toms River 08753

**Diabetic & Athletic Foot Center, LLC, Fries Mill Plz.**
Toll Free Ph: 1-855-FIT-4YOU. Building Comfort from the Ground Up
Phone—(856) 582-3968 / (855) 348-4968
Fax—(856) 582-3967
Web—www.diabeticfootcenter.net
245 Fries Mill Rd., Turnersville 08012

**DIABETIC & ATHLETIC FOOT CENTER**
Fries Mill Plz.
**855-FIT-4YOU**
www.diabeticfootcenter.net
856-582-3968 • Fax: 856-582-3967
245 Fries Mill Rd. Turnersville, NJ 08012

**Edge Orthotics, Inc.**
Phone—(732) 549-3343
209 Pierson Ave., Edison 08837

**Lawall & Son, Inc., Harry J.**
Phone—(856) 691-7764
3071 E. Chestnut Ave., Ste. C-9, Vineland 08361

**Levy & Rappel, Inc.**
Phone—(973) 478-6511
339 10th St., Saddle Brook 07663

**Ortho Remedy, Inc., The**
Phone—(201) 943-3900
522 Anderson Ave., Cliffside Park 07010

**Ortho-Dynamics, Inc.**
Phone—(973) 742-4390
210 E. 16th St., Paterson 07524

**Orthofeet, Inc.**
Phone—(201) 767-6224
152-A Veterans Dr., Northvale 07647

**Orthologix, LLC**
Phone—(856) 651-1510
2301 E. Evesham Rd., Ste. 303, Voorhees 08043

**Pro-Fit Prosthetic & Orthotic, LLC**
Comprehensive Prosthetic & Orthotic Patient Care
Phone—(856) 809-9954 / (800) 996-7380
Web—www.profitlab.net
Email—pro.fit@comcast.net
76 W. Jimmie Leeds Rd., Ste. 103, Galloway 08205

**Pro-Fit Prosthetic & Orthotic, LLC**
Comprehensive Prosthetic & Orthotic Patient Care
Phone—(856) 809-9954 / (800) 996-7380
Web—www.profitlab.net
Email—pro.fit@comcast.net
10 Huron Ave., Ste. 1L, Jersey City 07306

**Pro-Fit Prosthetic & Orthotic, LLC**
Comprehensive Prosthetic & Orthotic Patient Care
Phone—(856) 809-9954 / (800) 996-7380
Web—www.profitlab.net
Email—pro.fit@comcast.net
409 Coventry Dr., Phillipsburg 08865

**Pro-Fit Prosthetic & Orthotic, LLC**
Comprehensive Prosthetic & Orthotic Patient Care
Phone—(856) 809-9910 / (800) 996-7380
Fax—(856) 809-9945
Web—www.profitlab.net
Email—pro.fit@comcast.net
215 Edgewood Ave., West Berlin 08091
*(see our ad under PROSTHETICS)*

*find additional suppliers at*
**IndustryNet.com**

## OSCILLATORS — Crystal

**Bomar Crystal Co.**
Phone—(732) 356-7787
201 Blackford Ave., P.O. Box 10, Middlesex 08846

**Kratos-CTI**
Phone—(973) 884-2580
9 Whippany Rd., Bldg. A-1, Whippany 07981

## OVENS — Bakery

**Revent, Inc.**
Phone—(732) 777-9433
Fax—(732) 777-1187
Web—www.revent.com
Email—info@revent.com
100 Ethel Rd. W., Piscataway 08854

## OVENS — Food Service

**Hickory Industries, Inc.**
Phone—(201) 223-0050
4900 W. Side Ave., North Bergen 07047

**Revent, Inc.**
Phone—(732) 777-9433
100 Ethel Rd. W., Piscataway 08854

## OVENS — Industrial

**Heller Industries, Inc.**
Phone—(973) 377-6800
4 Vreeland Rd., Ste. 1, Florham Park 07932

**Thermal Innovations Corp.**
Phone—(732) 223-1812
2220 Landmark Pl., Ste. 1, Manasquan 08736

## OXYGEN

**LifeGas, LLC**
Phone—(866) 543-3427
174 Ridge Rd., Ste. A, Dayton 08810

**SOS Gases, Inc.**
Industrial & Laboratory Gas; Welding Eqpt., Rental & Repair Service
Phone—(201) 998-7800 / (800) 626-7998
Fax—(201) 998-5243
Web—www.sosgasesinc.com
Email—sosgasesinc@msn.com
1100 Harrison Ave., Kearny 07032
*(see our ad under WELDING EQUIPMENT & SUPPLIES)*

## PACKAGING

**Acupac Packaging, Inc.**
Phone—(201) 529-3434
55 Ramapo Valley Rd., Mahwah 07430

**Beauty-Fill, LLC**
Phone—(732) 802-8200
170 Circle Dr. N., Piscataway 08854

**Brisar Industries, Inc.**
Phone—(973) 278-2500
150 E. 7th St., Paterson 07524

**Dirory Industries, Inc.**
Phone—(908) 757-6650
39 Progress St., Edison 08820

**Dixo Co., Inc.**
Phone—(201) 845-6000
158 Central Ave., P.O. Box 7038, Rochelle Park 07662

**Easter Seal Society Of New Jersey**
Phone—(973) 827-9066
133 Main St., Franklin 07416

**Easy Pak Services Of New Jersey**
Phone—(732) 274-2428
6 Nicholas Ct., P.O. Box 676, Dayton 08810

**Ever-Ready Media Packaging**
Phone—(973) 566-9333
P.O. Box 40, Haworth 07641

**IPAK, Inc**
Phone—(856) 486-0066
301 Grove Rd., West Deptford 08086

**J.I.T. Mfg., Inc.**
Phone—(973) 247-7300
50 Peel St., Paterson 07524

**Marleen, Inc.**
Phone—(856) 327-8281
1101 N. 10th St., P.O. Box 70, Millville 08332

**Method Assocs., Inc.**
Phone—(732) 888-0444
120 Francis St., Ste. 2, Keyport 07735

**Mfrs. Aid, Inc.**
Phone—(732) 613-6555
425 Whitehead Ave., South River 08882

**Mondo International, Inc.**
Phone—(973) 256-6123
464 Coit St., P.O. Box 894, Irvington 07111

**Package Development Co., Inc.**
Phone—(973) 983-8500
100 Round Hill Dr., Ste. 8, Rockaway 07866

**Paterson Packaging**
Phone—(201) 398-9693
269 Wilson St., Saddle Brook 07663

**Pioneer Packaging**
Phone—(973) 300-9300
31 Wilson Dr., Sparta 07871

**Qualis Packaging**
Phone—(908) 753-7300
550 Hadley Rd., South Plainfield 07080

**Quality Packaging Specialists International, LLC**
Phone—(609) 239-0503
5 Cooper St., Burlington 08016

## PACKAGING — Bakery & Confectionery

**Allstate Can Corp.**
Phone—(973) 560-9030
Fax—(973) 560-9217
Web—www.allstatecan.com
Email—tincans@allstatecan.com
1 Woodhollow Rd., Parsippany 07054
*(see our ad under CANS — Metal)*

**Healthy Food Brands, LLC**
Phone—(212) 444-9909
122 Quentin Ave., New Brunswick 08901

## PACKAGING — Chemical

**Bartlo Packaging, Inc.**
Phone—(973) 778-6900
61 Willet St., Bldg. Z, Passaic 07055

**Mid-Continent Packaging Co., Inc. (H Q)**
Phone—(973) 589-3544
55 Jacobus Ave., 1st Fl., Kearny 07032

**National Refrigerants, Inc.**
Phone—(856) 455-4555
661 Kenyon Ave., Bridgeton 08302

## PACKAGING — Corrugated

**General Partition Co., Inc.**
Email—abien@generalpartition.com
Designers & Manufacturers of Paperboard Partitions
Phone—(215) 785-1000
Fax—(215) 785-2160
Web—www.generalpartition.com
916 Washington Ave., P.O. Box 97, Croydon, PA 19021
*(see our ad under PARTITIONS—Box)*

**National Packaging Corp.**
Phone—(973) 344-0100
14 Campus Dr., Kearny 07032

**Vineland Packaging Corp.**
Phone—(856) 794-3300
3602 N. Mill Rd., Vineland 08360

## PACKAGING — Cosmetics

**Jerhel Plastics, Inc. (H Q)**
Phone—(201) 436-6662
63 New Hook Rd., Bayonne 07002

**MG America, Inc.**
Phone—(973) 808-8185
Fax—(973) 808-8421
Web—www.mgamerica.com
Email—sales@mgamerica.com
31 Kulick Rd., Fairfield 07004
*(see our ad under PACKAGING MACHINERY—Wholesale)*

**Pinnacle Cosmetics Packaging, LLC**
Phone—(908) 241-7777
80 Market St., P.O. Box 733, Kenilworth 07033

*Search from among 430,000 U.S. manufacturers & suppliers:*
**IndustryNet.com**

INDUSTRY

## PACKAGING — Flexible

Consolidated Packaging Group
Phone—(201) 440-4240
30 Bergen Tpke., P.O. Box 261, Ridgefield Park 07660

Datwyler, Inc.
Phone—(856) 663-2202
9012 Pennsauken Hwy., Pennsauken 08110

**Forem Packaging, Inc.**
In Business for 25 Years; Laminated Materials
**Phone—(973) 589-0402**
**Fax—(973) 589-0453**
**Email—sales@forempackaging.com**
**2-44 Cornelia St., P.O. Box 50090, Newark 07105**

*(see our ad on this page)*

Multi Plastics Extrusions
Phone—(732) 388-2300
30 Production Way, Avenel 07001

Plastic Plus Group, LLC
Phone—(201) 561-0404
600 Meadowlands Pkwy., Secaucus 07094

Plus Packaging, Inc.
Phone—(973) 538-2216
10 Mount Pleasant Rd., Morristown 07960

Power Bag & Film, LLC
Phone—(908) 832-6648
189 W. Valley Brook Rd., Califon 07830

Tri-Seal
Phone—(908) 782-4000
112 Church St., Flemington 08822

**Tri-State Tape & Label Co., Inc.**
**Phone—(800) 682-7892 / (609) 387-4600**
**Fax—(609) 387-3691**
**Web—www.tristatelabel.com**
**Email—dwimer@tristatelabel.com**
**351 Railroad Ave., P.O. Box 377, Beverly 08010**

## PACKAGING — Industrial

**Jan Packaging, Inc.**
100 Harrison St., Dover 07801
Email: kcaristia@janpackaging.com
Toll Free Ph: (888)4-JANPAK
Phone—(973) 361-7200
Fax—(973) 361-3306
Web—www.janpackaging.com
Email—janpkg@janpackaging.com
P.O. Box 448, Dover 07802

# Jan
# Packaging, Inc.

*Wooden Shipping Crates*
**www.janpackaging.com**
Email: kcaristia@janpackaging.com

# 973-361-7200
### FAX: 973-361-3306
### Toll Free: 888-4-JANPAK

100 Harrison St. • PO Box 448
Dover, NJ 07802

Tri-Cor Flexible Packaging, Inc.
Phone—(973) 940-1500
27 Brookfield Dr., Sparta 07871

## PACKAGING — Jewelry

Novel Box Co. Ltd.
Phone—(908) 686-7772
825 Lehigh Ave., Union 07083

Perfect Remedy Packaging, Inc.
Phone—(732) 697-0055
224 Washington St., Perth Amboy 08861

Suppliers of Flexible Packaging Materials
Bags, Rolls Laminations
**sales@forempackaging.com**

## ForemPACKAGING, inc.
# 973.589.0402 / Fax: 973.589.0453
2-44 Cornelia Street • Newark, NJ 07105

## PACKAGING — Liquids

Hy-Test Packaging Corp.
Phone—(973) 754-7000
515 E. 41st St., Paterson 07504

## PACKAGING — Medical

Amcor Flexibles, Inc.
Phone—(609) 267-5900
220 Shreve St., Mount Holly 08060

Beacon Converters, Inc.
Phone—(201) 797-2600
280 Midland Ave., P.O. Box 8208, Saddle Brook 07663

**North American Sterilization & Packaging Company, Inc.**
Email: rogerm@naspco.com
**Phone—(973) 209-4388 / (800) 392-6310**
**Fax—(973) 209-6374**
**Web—www.naspco.com**
**19 Park Dr., Franklin 07416**
*(see our ad under CONTRACT MANUFACTURING—Medical)*

Nutra-Med Packaging, Inc.
Phone—(973) 625-2274
385 Franklin Ave., Ste. E, Rockaway 07866

## PACKAGING — Personal Care Products

Cospack America Corp.
Phone—(732) 548-5858
3856 Park Ave., Edison 08820

## PACKAGING — Specialty

Telmark Packaging Corp.
Phone—(732) 739-9100
30 Freneau Ave., Ste. 2-B, Matawan 07747

## PACKAGING — Thermoformed

**MG America, Inc.**
**Phone—(973) 808-8185**
**Fax—(973) 808-8421**
**Web—www.mgamerica.com**
**Email—sales@mgamerica.com**
**31 Kulick Rd., Fairfield 07004**
*(see our ad under PACKAGING MACHINERY—Wholesale)*

## PACKAGING AND ASSEMBLY

**Abilities Of Northwest Jersey, Inc.**
Fulfillment/Contract Packaging/Assembly
**Phone—(908) 689-1118**
**Fax—(908) 689-6363**
**Web—www.abilitiesnw.com**
**Email—info@abilitiesnw.com**
**264 Route 31 N., P.O. Box 251, Washington 07882**
*(see our ad under CONTRACT PACKAGING SERVICES)*

Elite Packaging Corp.
Phone—(732) 651-9955
40 Cotters Ln., Ste. E, East Brunswick 08816

Occupational Center, The
Phone—(908) 241-7200
301 Cox St., Roselle 07203

**Peerless Coatings, LLC**
Providing Powder Coating, Sandblasting, Assembling & Packaging Services, Teflon® finishes along with Traditional Wet Paint finishes, and all types of Metalizing.
**Phone—(973) 427-8771**
**Fax—(973) 427-8779**
**Web—www.peerlesscoatings.com**
**Email—peerless1@verizon.net**
**220-A Goffle Rd., Hawthorne 07506**

Robalo Enterprises
Phone—(908) 753-1075
104 New Era Dr., South Plainfield 07080

## PACKAGING COMPONENTS

Lanco York, Inc.
Phone—(973) 278-7400
864 E. 25th St., Paterson 07513

## PACKAGING DISTRIBUTION

Dynaclear Packaging / Pro Pack, Inc.
Phone—(201) 337-1001
500 W. Main St., Wyckoff 07481

## PACKAGING EQUIPMENT

B.D. Briggs
Phone—(973) 989-1950
31 Richboynton Rd., Dover 07801

CAMPAK, Inc.
Phone—(973) 597-1414
119 Naylon Ave., Livingston 07039

Cavalla, Inc.
Phone—(201) 343-3338
111 Union St., Hackensack 07601

Clements Industries, Inc.
Phone—(201) 440-5500
50 Ruta Ct., South Hackensack 07606

Integrated Packaging Systems
Phone—(973) 664-0020
3 Luger Rd., Ste. 5, Denville 07834

Modular Packaging Systems, Inc.
Phone—(973) 970-9393
6 Aspen Dr., Randolph 07869

## PACKAGING MACHINERY

Action Packaging Automation, Inc.
Phone—(609) 448-9210
15 Oscar Dr., P.O. Box 190, Roosevelt 08555

Advantage Packaging Technologies, LLC
Phone—(201) 832-1858
P.O. Box 301, Carlstadt 07072

Applied Engineering, Corp.
Phone—(973) 772-6022
232 Palisade Ave., Garfield 07026

Cozzoli Machine Co.
Phone—(732) 564-0400
50 Schoolhouse Rd., Somerset 08873

F & L Machinery & Design, Inc.
Phone—(973) 218-6216
48 Commerce St., Springfield 07081

F P Developments, Inc.
Phone—(856) 875-7100
402 S. Main St., Williamstown 08094

**STICKEL**
**PACKAGING SUPPLY**

*Packaging & Material Handling Equipment*
# (732) 905-2811/ FAX: (732) 364-6909
## www.stickelpackaging.com
1991 Rutgers University Blvd. • Lakewood Industrial Park
Lakewood, NJ 08701

## PACKAGING MACHINERY — *(cont.)*

**Global Packaging Machinery, Inc.**
Cartoning & product handling machinery
Phone—(973) 279-2300
Fax—(973) 279-2301
Web—www.globalpackmachinery.com
36 Peel St., Paterson 07524

Gottscho Printing Systems, Inc.
Phone—(908) 688-2400
335 Chambers Brook Rd., Branchburg 08876

Heisler Industries, Inc.
Phone—(973) 227-6300
224 Passaic Ave., Fairfield 07004

**Hunter Mfg. Services, Inc.**
Aerospace Quality Machine Parts & Pharmaceutical
Change Parts
Phone—(973) 365-5880
Fax—(973) 365-0588
Web—www.huntermfg.net
Email—khunter@huntermfg.net
19 Just Rd., Fairfield 07004
*(see our ad under MACHINE WORK & MACHINING—CNC)*

Industrial Automation Systems Engineering Co., Inc.
Phone—(908) 218-1104
161 Industrial Pkwy., Unit 6, Branchburg 08876

**JG Machine Works**
Also, mechanical crimping of pumps onto fragrance
glass bottles
Phone—(732) 203-2077
Fax—(732) 203-2078
Web—www.jgmachine.com
Email—dnelson@jgmachine.com
2182 State Route 35, Holmdel 07733
*(see our ad under FILLING MACHINERY)*

Jo-De Machine Co., Inc.
Phone—(973) 427-9555
43 Ethel Ave., Hawthorne 07506

Kinesys Automation, Inc.
Phone—(201) 337-5000
5 Fir Ct., Unit 3, Oakland 07436

Monroe Machine & Design, Inc.
Phone—(732) 521-3434
566 Buckelew Ave., Monroe Township 08831

Norwalt Design, Inc.
Phone—(973) 927-3200
961 Route 10 E., Bldg. 2-A, Randolph 07869

Oystar USA, Inc.
Phone—(732) 343-7600
523 Raritan Centre S.W., Edison 08837

Pace Packaging Corp.
Phone—(973) 227-1040
3 Sperry Rd., Fairfield 07004

Packaging Consultants Assocs.
Phone—(856) 488-0277
7300 N. Crescent Blvd., Unit 14, Pennsauken
08110

Packaging Machinery & Equipment Co.
Phone—(973) 325-2418
181 Watson Ave., West Orange 07052

**Pester USA, Inc.**
Top performance & quality for film wrapping, case
packing & palletizing
Phone—(201) 327-7009
Fax—(201) 327-7824
Web—www.pester.com
Email—pester-usa@pester.com
80 Commerce Dr., Allendale 07401
*(see our ad under PACKAGING MACHINERY—Wholesale)*

**PMC Industries**
For more than 50 years, a leading supplier of
packaging machinery to consumer goods
manufacturers; specializing in capping machinery
Phone—(201) 342-3684
Fax—(201) 342-3568
Web—www.pmc-industries.com
Email—pmcindustries@verizon.net
275 Hudson St., Hackensack 07601

**Prodo-Pak Corp.**
The Real Leader in Pouch & Tube Filling & Sealing
Machinery, ideal for all liquids, creams, pastes &
semi-viscous products
Phone—(973) 772-4500
Fax—(973) 772-0471
Web—www.prodo-pak.com
Email—sales@prodo-pak.com
77 Commerce St., P.O. Box 363, Garfield 07026

Scandia Packaging Machinery Co.
Phone—(973) 473-6100
15 Industrial Rd., Fairfield 07004

Seal Spout Corp.
Phone—(908) 647-1900
50 Allen Rd., P.O. Box 74, Liberty Corner 07938

**UAC Packaging, LLC**
New Cappers, Rebuilt & Reconditioned Resina
Cappers
Phone—(908) 595-6890
Fax—(908) 595-6893
Web—www.uacpackaging.com
Email—cappers@uacpackaging.com
330 Roycefield Rd., Unit C, Hillsborough
08844

## UAC Packaging, LLC
*Specialists in Resina Capping
Parts and Machines (New and Old)*
**www.uacpackaging.com**
908-595-6890 • FAX: 908-595-6893
330 Roycefield Rd., Unit C • Hillsborough, NJ 08844
**Email: cappers@uacpackaging.com**

Uhlmann Packaging Systems
Phone—(973) 402-8855
44 Indian Ln. E., Towaco 07082

**Warwick Mfg. & Equipment Co., LLC**
Buy & sell used: Chemical, food, cosmetic, packaging
& pharmaceutical equipment
Phone—(732) 729-0400 / (732) 241-9263
Fax—(732) 729-1235
Web—www.warwickequipment.com
Email—sales@warwickequipment.com
1112 12th St., North Brunswick 08902
*(see our ad Outside Back Cover)*

Wrapade Packaging Systems, LLC
Phone—(973) 773-6150
27 Law Dr., Ste. B, Fairfield 07004

## PACKAGING MACHINERY — Wholesale

Marchesini Packaging Machinery
Phone—(973) 575-7445
43 Fairfield Pl., West Caldwell 07006

Mel-Pak Equipment Co.
Phone—(201) 825-2624
649 U.S. Highway 206, Ste. 9-303, Hillsborough
08844

**MG America, Inc.**
Phone—(973) 808-8185
Fax—(973) 808-8421
Web—www.mgamerica.com
Email—sales@mgamerica.com
31 Kulick Rd., Fairfield 07004

## MG America, Inc.
*Quality Packaging
Machinery*
### www.mgamerica.com
# (973) 808-8185
## FAX: (973) 808-8421
31 Kulick Rd.
Fairfield, NJ 07004

Pester USA, Inc.
Top performance & quality for film wrapping, case
packing & palletizing
Phone—(201) 327-7009
Fax—(201) 327-7824
Web—www.pester.com
Email—pester-usa@pester.com
80 Commerce Dr., Allendale 07401

## Pester USA, Inc.
Top performance & quality for film wrapping, case packing & palletizing
**201-327-7009 • FAX: 201-327-7824**
80 Commerce Dr. Allendale, NJ 07401
www.pester.com   pester-usa@pester.com

Pro-Pac Services, Inc.
Phone—(973) 962-8080
15 Van Natta Dr., Ringwood 07456

**Stickel Packaging Supply**
Packaging & material handling equipment
Phone—(732) 905-2811
Fax—(732) 364-6909
Web—www.stickelpackaging.com
Email—info@stickelpackaging.com
1991 Rutgers University Blvd., Lakewood
Industrial Pk., Lakewood 08701
*(see our ad on this page)*

## PACKAGING MATERIALS

All Poly Mfg., LLC
Phone—(732) 431-6630
200 Craig Rd., Ste. 201, Manalapan 07726

**All Size Poly Bags**
Leaders in supplying plastic bags, packaging,
shipping & warehouse supplies nationwide
Phone—(800) 635-9959 / (732) 828-3400
Fax—(732) 828-7703
Web—www.allsizepolybags.com
Email—info@rksplastics.com
P.O. Box 836, New Brunswick 08903
*(see our ad under BAGS—Plastic)*

Berlin Packaging, LLC
Phone—(201) 947-7744
2050 Center Ave., Ste. 400, Fort Lee 07024

Corman Bag Co.
Phone—(973) 729-2816
7 Evergreen Pl., Sparta 07871

Delta Paper Corp.
Phone—(856) 532-0333
8295 National Hwy., Pennsauken 08110

Fine Wrap Industry, Inc.
Phone—(732) 960-9602
123 Town Square Pl., Jersey City 07310

## PACKAGING MATERIALS — (cont.)

**General Partition Co., Inc.**
Email: abien@generalpartition.com
Designers & Manufacturers of Paperboard Partitions
Phone—(215) 785-1000
Fax—(215) 785-2160
Web—www.generalpartition.com
916 Washington Ave., P.O. Box 97, Croydon, PA 19021
*(see our ad under PARTITIONS—Box)*

Nexus Plastics, Inc.
Phone—(973) 427-3311
1 Loretto Ave., Hawthorne 07506

Plastiform Packaging, Inc.
Phone—(973) 983-8900
114 Beach St., Bldg. 6, P.O.Box 186, Rockaway 07866

Polyair North East
Phone—(201) 804-1700
495 Meadow Ln., Carlstadt 07072

Preferred Plastics & Packaging Co., Inc.
Phone—(973) 759-1510
681 Main St., Ste. 42, Belleville 07109

Signode Packaging Group
Phone—(800) 235-4066
151 Fabyan Pl., Newark 07112

Source Packaging, Inc.
Phone—(201) 831-0005
215 Island Rd., Mahwah 07430

Stephen Gould Corporation
Phone—(973) 428-1510
35 S. Jefferson Rd., Whippany 07981

**Stickel Packaging Supply**
Packaging & material handling equipment
Phone—(732) 905-2811
Fax—(732) 364-6909
Web—www.stickelpackaging.com
1991 Rutgers University Blvd., Lakewood Industrial Pk., Lakewood 08701
*(see our ad under PACKAGING MACHINERY—Wholesale)*

U.S. ProPack, Inc.
Phone—(732) 294-4500
341 Fairfield Rd., Freehold 07728

Vanguard Packaging, Inc.
Phone—(973) 391-9200
620 Ramsey Ave., Hillside 07205

## PACKAGING MATERIALS — Wholesale

Bailey Packaging Co., Inc.
Phone—(908) 759-0991
217 Prospect Ave., Ste. 8-3B, Cranford 07016

CPR Container
Phone—(973) 625-0664
94 Ford Rd., Ste. 5, Denville 07834

**Fidelity Paper & Supply Corp.**
Also Packaging Products & Corrugated Boxes
Phone—(973) 599-0222
Fax—(973) 599-0220
Web—www.fidelitypaper.com
Email—fpinfo@fidelitypaper.com
P.O. Box 376, East Hanover 07936

**Triangle Packaging, Inc.**
Phone—(973) 578-8989
Fax—(973) 578-8366
Web—www.trianglepackaging.com
Email—jfab@trianglepackaging.com
222 Pacific St., Newark 07114

Victory Packaging, Inc.
Phone—(732) 274-1745
8 Corn Rd., Ste. 2, Dayton 08810

## PACKAGING SERVICES

Econo-PAK
Phone—(973) 875-0990
1 Wiebel Plz., Sussex 07461

One Stop Packaging, LLC
Phone—(973) 272-0170
71-B Kingsland Ave., Clifton 07014

**Pabin Associates Inc.**
Phone—(201) 288-7216
Fax—(201) 288-4709
Email—pabinassociatesinc@gmail.com
281 Springfield Ave., Hasbrouck Heights 07604

SPT Packaging LLC
Phone—(973) 246-5635
Fax—(973) 246-5636
Web—www.sptpkg.com
Email—jdefelice@sptpkg.com
489 Clifton Ave., Clifton 07011

## PACKAGING SUPPLIES

Bacon & Graham, Inc.
Phone—(973) 684-1488
34 E. 25th St., Paterson 07514

Baxter Co., Inc., E. L.
Phone—(732) 229-8219
70 S. 7th Ave., P.O. Box 277, Long Branch 07740

CDS Packaging, LLC
Phone—(973) 219-1496
237 Vaile Rd., Parsippany 07054

Deluxe Packaging Co.
Phone—(856) 486-0006
1079 Thomas Busch Memorial Hwy., Pennsauken 08110

LPS Industries, Inc.
Phone—(201) 438-3515
10 Caesar Pl., Moonachie 07074

Siloa, Inc. (H Q)
Phone—(908) 234-9040
2493 Lamington Rd., Ste. C, Bedminster 07921

## PACKAGING SYSTEMS

Medical Packaging, Inc.
Phone—(609) 466-8991
470 Route 31, P.O. Box 500, Ringoes 08551

Systech Solutions, Inc.
Phone—(609) 395-8400
2540 U.S. Highway 130, Ste. 128, Cranbury 08512

## PACKING & CRATING SERVICES

**Tri-State Crating & Pallet Co.**
Phone—(973) 357-8293 / (888) 845-0050
Fax—(973) 357-8296
Web—www.tristatecrating.com
Email—sales@tristatecrating.com
85 Fulton St., Paterson 07501
*(see our ad under CRATES—Wooden)*

## PACKINGS — Mechanical

American Braiding & Mfg., Inc.
Phone—(732) 938-6333
247 Old Tavern Rd., Howell 07731

**John Crane, Inc.**
Phone—(856) 241-3507
Fax—(856) 241-3531
Web—www.johncrane.com
Email—broot@johncrane.com
301 Berkeley Dr., Swedesboro 08085

Lindstrom & King Co., Inc.
Phone—(973) 279-2511
108 McLean Blvd., Paterson 07514

## PADS — Mattress

**Phoenix Down Corp.**
Web: www.downhomeoutlet.com
Toll Free Ph: (800) ALLDOWN; Feather Beds, Comforters & Covers
Phone—(973) 812-8100 / (800) 255-3696
Fax—(973) 812-9077
Email—phod@phoenixdown.com
85 US Highway 46, Totowa 07512
*(see our ad under BEDDING)*

## PAILS — Metal

BWAY Corp.
Phone—(732) 247-6700
1202 Airport Rd., North Brunswick 08902

## PAILS — Plastic

MacAuley, Inc., James R.
Phone—(856) 767-3474
1 Industrial Dr., P.O. Box 704, Waterford Works 08089

North America Packaging Corp. (NAMPAC)
Phone—(732) 997-4100
7 Wheeling Rd., Dayton 08810

## PAINT

Benjamin Moore & Co.
Phone—(973) 344-1200
134 Lister Ave., Newark 07105

Benjamin Moore & Co. (H Q)
Phone—(201) 573-9600
101 Paragon Dr., Montvale 07645

Columbia Paint Lab, Inc.
Phone—(201) 435-4884
452 Communipaw Ave., Jersey City 07304

Dux Paints, Inc.
Phone—(973) 473-2376
18 Mill St., Lodi 07644

Epoplex
Phone—(856) 667-8399
1000 E. Park Ave., P.O. Box 308, Maple Shade 08052

Flexdel Corp.
Phone—(732) 901-7771
1969 Rutgers University Blvd., Lakewood 08701

Hartin Paint & Filler Corp.
Phone—(201) 438-3300
14th & Broad Sts., Carlstadt 07072

Hawthorne Paint Co., Inc.
Phone—(973) 423-2335
66 5th Ave., Hawthorne 07506

International Paint, LLC
Phone—(908) 686-1300
2270 Morris Ave., Union 07083

Landzettel & Sons, Inc.
Phone—(201) 796-3506
17-12 River Rd., Fair Lawn 07410

Milspray, LLC
Phone—(732) 886-2223
845 Towbin Ave., Lakewood 08701

Muralo Co., Inc.
Phone—(201) 437-0770
148 E. 5th St., Bayonne 07002

National Paint Industries
Phone—(732) 821-3200
1999 Elizabeth St., North Brunswick 08902

Penn Jersey Paint Co., Inc.
Phone—(973) 482-5430
1255 McCarter Hwy., Newark 07104

Performance Industries, Inc.
Phone—(609) 392-1450
51 Tucker St., Trenton 08618

Rust-Oleum Corp.
Phone—(732) 469-8100
480 Frelinghuysen Ave., Newark 07114

Rust-Oleum Corp., ZINSSER Brands
Phone—(732) 469-8100
173 Belmont Dr., Somerset 08873

Sherwin-Williams Co., The
Phone—(201) 933-3800
6 Currie Ave., Wallington 07057

Talon Paint Products, Inc.
Phone—(732) 821-3200
1999 Elizabeth St., North Brunswick 08902

Tenax Finishing Products Co.
Phone—(973) 589-9000
390 Adams St., Newark 07114

## PAINT — Automotive

FinishMaster, Inc.
Phone—(201) 435-1555
700 Garfield Ave., Jersey City 07305

## PAINT — Industrial

GFC Coatings & Chemicals
Phone—(973) 272-0257
18 Mill St., Lodi 07644

Pan Technology
Phone—(201) 438-7878
117 Moonachie Ave., Carlstadt 07072

R V Tech, Inc.
Phone—(908) 469-8701
801 Magnolia Ave., Bldg. 3-B, Elizabeth 07201

*Do nationwide searches for products & services at:*
**IndustryNet.com**

## PAINT — Marine

Flexabar Corp.
Phone—(732) 901-6500
1969 Rutgers Blvd., Lakewood 08701
International Paint, LLC
Phone—(908) 686-1300
Fax—(908) 686-8545
Web—www.yachtpaint.com
Email—interluxtechnicalservice@
yachtpaint.com
2270 Morris Ave., Union 07083
Kop-Coat, Inc.
Phone—(973) 625-3100
36 Pine St., Rockaway 07866

## PAINT — Water Based

Rich Art Color Co., Inc.
Phone—(201) 767-0009
202 Pegasus Ave., Northvale 07647
Tri-Chem, Inc.
Phone—(973) 751-9200
681 Main St., Ste. 27, Belleville 07109

## PAINT ADDITIVES

Elementis Specialties, Inc. (H Q)
Phone—(609) 443-2000
469 Old Trenton Rd., East Windsor 08512
Troy Chemicals
Phone—(973) 589-2500
1 Avenue L, Newark 07105

## PAINT BRUSHES

Elder & Jenks Co.
Phone—(201) 437-0770
148 E. 5th St., Bayonne 07002
Green & Son, Inc., Charles E.
Phone—(973) 485-3630
625 3rd St., Newark 07107

## PAINT FINISHING

CMF Limited, Inc.
Phone—(609) 695-3600
599 Ingham Ave., P.O. Box 5989, Trenton 08638

## PAINTBALL EQUIPMENT & SUPPLIES

Godforce Tactical, Inc.
Phone—(908) 561-2021
2614-B S. Clinton Ave., South Plainfield 07080

## PAINTING

All Season Painting Contractors
Phone—(908) 542-1100
Fax—(908) 542-1107
Web—www.allseasonpaintingnj.com
Email—fredste@verizon.net
320 Essex St., Ste. 6, Stirling 07980

**All Season Painting Contractors**
*Quality painting*
www.allseasonpaintingnj.com
**908-542-1100**
320 Essex St., Ste. 6  Stirling, NJ 07980

**EZ**Select®.com
REAL-TIME Access to Industrial Leads!

Julius H. Gross, Inc.
Phone—(609) 924-1474
220 Alexander St., Princeton 08540

**Julius H. Gross, Inc.**
*Quality Painting & Powerwashing*
**(609) 924-1474**
220 Alexander St. • Princeton, NJ 08540

Wilber's Painting & Carpentry
Phone—(973) 762-6333
Fax—(973) 762-6335
Web—www.wilberspainting.com
Email—info@wilberspainting.com
2087 Millburn Ave., Maplewood 07040

## PAINTING — Industrial

Atlantic Painting-Wallcovering Inc.
Phone—(973) 482-7996
Fax—(973) 482-7995
Email—atlanticpt@aol.com
26 Harrison Ave., Harrison 07029

## PAINTING EQUIPMENT & SUPPLIES

Deborah Sales, LLC
Phone—(973) 344-8466
109 Meeker Ave., Newark 07114

## PALLET RACKS — Steel

Frazier Industrial Co.
Phone—(908) 876-3001
91 Fairview Ave., P.O. Box F, Long Valley 07853

## PALLETS

Fairfield Pallet Co., Inc.
Phone—(856) 455-7999
Fax—(856) 451-9059
Web—www.fairfieldpallet.com
Email—pallets@fairfieldpallet.com
282 Rockville Rd., P.O. Box 361, Fairton 08320

**FAIRFIELD PALLET COMPANY, INC.**
www.fairfieldpallet.com
**(856) 455-7999**
282 Rockville Rd. Fairton, NJ 08320

General Pallet, LLC
Phone—(908) 238-1000
97 River Rd., Flemington 08822
Laurel Run Pallet, LLC
Custom built pallets and skids of any size and shape
Phone—(717) 436-5428
Fax—(717) 436-5575
Email—laurelrunpallet@hotmail.com
975 Billyville Rd., Mifflintown, PA 17059
*(see our ad under SKIDS)*
Triangle Packaging, Inc.
Phone—(973) 578-8989
Fax—(973) 578-8366
Web—www.trianglepackaging.com
Email—jfab@trianglepackaging.com
222 Pacific St., Newark 07114

## PALLETS — Export

PDQ Plastics, Inc.
Phone—(201) 823-0270
Fax—(201) 823-0345
Web—www.pdqplastics.com
Email—hartson@pdqplastics.com
7 Hook Rd., P.O. Box 1001, Bayonne 07002

## PALLETS — Heat Treated

ATCO Pallet Co.
Phone—(856) 461-8141
Fax—(856) 461-8146
Web—www.atcopallet.net
Email—atcopallet@comcast.net
1000 Creek Rd., P.O. Box 5115, Delanco 08075
Fairfield Pallet Co., Inc.
Phone—(856) 455-7999
Web—www.fairfieldpallet.com
282 Rockville Rd., P.O. Box 361, Fairton 08320
*(see our ad under PALLETS)*

## PALLETS — Plastic

PDQ Plastics, Inc.
Phone—(201) 823-0270
Fax—(201) 823-0345
Web—www.pdqplastics.com
Email—hartson@pdqplastics.com
7 Hook Rd., P.O. Box 1001, Bayonne 07002
Polymer Solutions International, Inc.
Phone—(609) 714-2899
9 Roxbury Dr., Medford 08055

## PALLETS — Recycled

Northeast Pallet Recycling, LLC
Phone—(732) 751-1919
133 Yellowbrook Rd., Farmingdale 07727

## PALLETS — Wooden

Ace Pallet Corp.
Phone—(856) 423-7277
215 E. Broad St., P.O. Box 228, Paulsboro 08066
ATCO Pallet Co.
Phone—(856) 461-8141
Fax—(856) 461-8146
Web—www.atcopallet.net
Email—atcopallet@comcast.net
1000 Creek Rd., P.O. Box 5115, Delanco 08075
Avenel Pallet Co., Inc.
Phone—(732) 752-0500
Foot Of S. 2nd St., P.O. Box 276, Dunellen 08812
Budget Pallet, Inc.
Phone—(201) 330-2800
3225 Dell Ave., North Bergen 07047
Coyote Pallet Co.
Phone—(973) 853-7266
13 Oradell Rd., Hewitt 07421
D & H Pallets, LLC
Phone—(973) 481-2981
45 Verona Ave., Newark 07104
Delisa Pallet Corp.
Phone—(973) 344-8600
91-97 Blanchard St., Newark 07105
Eagle Pallet
Phone—(856) 765-9444
108 S. Wade Blvd., Millville 08332
Extreme Pallet
Phone—(973) 596-1400
301-317 Astor St., Newark 07114
Extreme Pallet, Inc.
Phone—(973) 286-1717
315 Astor St., Newark 07114
F & R Pallets, Inc.
Phone—(856) 964-8516
1929 S. 4th St., Camden 08104
Fairfield Pallet Co., Inc.
Phone—(856) 455-7999
Web—www.fairfieldpallet.com
282 Rockville Rd., P.O. Box 361, Fairton 08320
*(see our ad under PALLETS)*
Forte Pallet, Inc.
Phone—(732) 727-3879
3 Water Works Rd., Old Bridge 08857
Gorgo Pallet Co.
Phone—(856) 692-0303
646 S. Delsea Dr., Vineland 08360
IFCO Systems
Phone—(609) 386-5200
320 Dulty's Ln., P.O. Box 1333, Burlington 08016
ISCO
Phone—(856) 672-9182
1 Commerce Dr., Bldg. 3, Barrington 08007
JUST Nation, LLC
Phone—(973) 485-5878
359 Central Ave., Newark 07103

## PALLETS — Wooden — *(cont.)*

**Laurel Run Pallet, LLC**
**Custom built pallets and skids of any size and shape**
**Phone—(717) 436-5428**
**Fax—(717) 436-5575**
**Email—laurelrunpallet@hotmail.com**
**975 Billyville Rd., Mifflintown, PA 17059**
*(see our ad under SKIDS)*

Love Pallet Company, LLC.
Phone—(908) 964-3385
460 Mundet Pl., P.O. Box 774, Hillside 07205

**LOVE**
**Pallet Company LLC.**
**Wooden Pallets**
**www.lovepallet.com**
**(908) 964-3385 / FAX: (908) 688-1525**
**460 Mundet Pl., PO Box 774 • Hillside, NJ 07205**

Millwood, Inc.
Phone—(732) 967-8818
7 Brick Plant Rd., Ste. C, South River 08882
Notie Corp.
Phone—(609) 259-3477
177-A Route 526, Allentown 08501
Pallet Express, Inc.
Phone—(973) 633-5858
70 Caroline Ave., Clifton 07011
Pedestal Pallet Co.
Phone—(732) 968-7488
777 N. Avenue Ext., P.O. Box 450, Dunellen 08812
Poor Boy Pallet, LLC
Phone—(856) 451-3771
45 Finley Rd., Bridgeton 08302
S & B Pallet Co.
Phone—(908) 756-3606
1348 S. 2nd St., Plainfield 07063
Select Enterprises, Inc.
Phone—(732) 287-8622
71 Executive Ave., Edison 08817
T & M Pallet Co., Inc.
Phone—(908) 454-3042
116 Edison Rd., Stewartsville 08886
Van Nick Pallet, Inc.
Phone—(908) 753-1800
104 Snyder Rd., South Plainfield 07080
Warren Pallet Co., Inc.
Phone—(908) 995-7172
601 County Road 627, Bloomsbury 08804

## PANELS

Lordon, Inc.
Phone—(908) 813-1143
453 Route 46, Ste. 1-A, Hackettstown 07840

## PANELS — Instrument

Instrumentation Design & Service Co.
Phone—(973) 728-3748
256 Bearfort Rd., West Milford 07480

## PANELS — Insulated

**Johnson Building Systems, Inc.**
**Classified rating-1,2 & 3 hour fire wall & ceiling assemblies**
**Phone—(215) 673-6050 / (800) 445-7249**
**Fax—(215) 322-2076**
**Web—www.johnsonenergygroup.com**
**Email—rsears@johnsonenergygroup.com**
**975 Jaymor Rd., Southampton, PA 18966**

## PANELS — Metal

Cooper Panels, LLC, John
Phone—(201) 487-4018
250 Maywood Ave., Ste. C, Maywood 07607

*find additional suppliers at*
**IndustryNet.com**

## PANELS — Prefabricated

**UFP Berlin, LLC**
**Email: dgoldman@ufpi.com**
**Phone—(856) 767-0043**
**Fax—(856) 767-1526**
**Web—www.ufpi.com**
**159 Jackson Rd., Berlin 08009**
*(see our ad under FLOOR TRUSSES)*

## PANTS

Palmyra Pants Co., Inc.
Phone—(856) 662-0398
9370 Route 130 N., Pennsauken 08110

## PAPER

Pengad, Inc.
Phone—(201) 436-5625
55 Oak St., P.O. Box 99, Bayonne 07002
**Roosevelt Paper Co.**
**Addtl. Fax: (856) 642-1950; Distributor Of Printing Papers**
**Phone—(856) 303-4100 / (800) 523-3470**
**Fax—(856) 642-1949**
**Web—www.rooseveltpaper.com**
**Email—degan@rooseveltpaper.com**
**1 Roosevelt Dr., Mount Laurel 08054**
xpedx
Phone—(973) 405-2310
261 River Rd., Clifton 07014
xpedx LLC A veritiv Company
Phone—(609) 518-9700
1200 Highland Dr., Ste. 1-B, Westampton 08060

## PAPER — Coated

Lamart Corp.
Phone—(973) 772-6262
16 Richmond St., Clifton 07011
Mondi
Phone—(201) 585-8875
1100 Slocum Ave., Ridgefield 07657
**Roosevelt Paper Co.**
**Addtl. Fax: (856) 642-1950; Distributor Of Printing Papers**
**Phone—(856) 303-4100 / (800) 523-3470**
**Fax—(856) 642-1949**
**Web—www.rooseveltpaper.com**
**Email—degan@rooseveltpaper.com**
**1 Roosevelt Dr., Mount Laurel 08054**
Tekkote Corp.
Phone—(201) 585-8875
580 Willow Tree Rd., Leonia 07605
Titan Converting
Phone—(732) 225-2080
150 Fieldcrest Ave., Ste. A, Edison 08837
Unifoil Corp.
Phone—(973) 244-9900
12 Vanil Rd. E., Fairfield 07004

## PAPER — Corrugated

Delta Corrugated Paper Products
Phone—(201) 941-1910
199 W. Ruby Ave., Palisades Park 07650

## PAPER — Gummed

L V Adhesive, Inc.
Phone—(212) 925-2600
341 Michele Pl., Carlstadt 07072

## PAPER — Printing

Ariva Distribution, Inc.
Phone—(856) 488-0800
1705 Suckle Hwy., Pennsauken 08110
**Roosevelt Paper Co.**
**Addtl. Fax: (856) 642-1950; Distributor Of Printing Papers**
**Phone—(856) 303-4100 / (800) 523-3470**
**Fax—(856) 642-1949**
**Web—www.rooseveltpaper.com**
**Email—degan@rooseveltpaper.com**
**1 Roosevelt Dr., Mount Laurel 08054**

xpedx
Phone—(973) 405-2300
261 River Rd., Clifton 07014

## PAPER — Tissue

Soundview Paper Co.
Phone—(201) 796-4000
1 Market St., Elmwood Park 07407

## PAPER — Waste

**Reliable Paper Recycling**
**Working for Resource Conservation & Recycling for over 27 years, a family owned company. Operating a fleet of 75+ trucks & trailers**
**Phone—(201) 333-5244**
**Fax—(201) 333-6712**
**Web—www.reliablepaperrecycling.com**
**1 Caven Point Ave., Jersey City 07305**

## PAPER — Waxed

**Seaboard Paper & Twine, LLC**
**Phone—(973) 413-8100**
**Fax—(775) 288-5329**
**Web—www.seaboardpaperandtwine.com**
**Email—bob.baretz@gmail.com**
**37 E. 6th St., Paterson 07524**

## PAPER — Wholesale

Bunzl New Jersey, Inc.
Phone—(732) 821-7000
27 Distribution Way, Monmouth Junction 08852
Ronstan Paper & Packaging
Phone—(732) 389-1040
72 James Way, Eatontown 07724

## PAPER BROKERS

U.S. Pulp & Paper Corp.
Phone—(856) 489-3500
1930 Marlton Pike E., Ste. N-73, Cherry Hill 08003

## PAPER CONVERTERS

Campbell Converting Corp.
Phone—(609) 835-2720
703 Van Rossum Ave., Unit 2, Beverly 08010
Consolidated Material Converters, Inc.
Phone—(732) 389-5973
74 Squankum Rd., Tinton Falls 07724
Custom Converters, Inc.
Phone—(973) 994-9000
115 Naylon Ave., Livingston 07039
Golden West Paper Converting
Phone—(908) 412-8889
121 Helen St., South Plainfield 07080
Laminated Industries, Inc.
Phone—(908) 862-5995
2000 Brunswick Ave., Linden 07036
Matthias Paper Corp.
Phone—(856) 467-6970
301 Arlington Blvd., P.O. Box 130, Swedesboro 08085
Newark Group, Inc., The (H Q)
Phone—(908) 276-4000
20 Jackson Dr., Cranford 07016
Norpak Corp.
Phone—(973) 589-4200
70 Blanchard St., Newark 07105
Papertec, Inc.
Phone—(862) 591-1100
141 Lanza Ave., Bldg. 29, Garfield 07026
Paris Business Products, Inc.
Phone—(609) 265-9200
800 Highland Dr., Westampton 08060
Quality Paper Converters Of New Jersey, Inc.
Phone—(973) 399-1200
673 S. 21st St., Irvington 07111
Ringel Bros., Inc.
Phone—(908) 688-9222
7 W. Shelton Ter., P.O. Box 727, Hillside 07205

**INDUSTRY**

## PAPER CONVERTERS — *(cont.)*

**Roosevelt Paper Co.**
Addtl. Fax: (856) 642-1950; Distributor Of Printing
Papers
Phone—(856) 303-4100 / (800) 523-3470
Fax—(856) 642-1949
Web—www.rooseveltpaper.com
Email—degan@rooseveltpaper.com
1 Roosevelt Dr., Mount Laurel 08054

William Usdan & Sons LLC
Phone—(973) 844-9988
140 Little St., Belleville 07109

## PAPER CONVERTING EQUIPMENT

Catbridge Machinery, LLC
Phone—(973) 808-0029
222 New Rd., Ste. 1, Parsippany 07054
Phoenix Machine
Phone—(973) 691-8029
4 Gold Mine Rd., Flanders 07836
Wagner Industries, Inc.
Phone—(973) 347-0800
51 Sparta Rd., Stanhope 07874

## PAPER CORES

**American Tube & Paper**
80 Furler St., Totowa 07512
Phone—(973) 256-3600
Fax—(973) 785-3341
Web—www.AmericanPaperProducts.com
Email—sales@americanpaperproducts.com
P.O. Box 68, Totowa 07511
*(see our ad under MAILING TUBES)*

## PAPER HANDLING EQUIPMENT

Colter & Peterson, Inc.
Phone—(973) 684-0901
414 E. 16th St., Paterson 07514

## PAPER MILL MACHINERY

Euler Industries, Inc.
Phone—(201) 666-9523
464 Old Tappan Rd., Old Tappan 07675

## PAPER PRODUCTS

**American Tube & Paper**
80 Furler St., Totowa 07512
Phone—(973) 256-3600
Fax—(973) 785-3341
Web—www.AmericanPaperProducts.com
Email—sales@americanpaperproducts.com
P.O. Box 68, Totowa 07511
*(see our ad under MAILING TUBES)*
Braco Mfg. Co. & Magic Safety Products, Inc.
Phone—(732) 968-0008
4301-B New Brunswick Ave., Ste. 2, South
Plainfield 07080
Diversified Display Products, LLC
Phone—(908) 686-2200
777 Ramsey Ave., P.O. Box 913, Hillside 07205
Flech Paper Products, Inc.
Phone—(973) 357-8111
55 1st Ave., Paterson 07514
Microfold, Inc.
Phone—(201) 641-5052
375 North St., Unit C, Teterboro 07608
Nosaj Disposables, Inc.
Phone—(800) 631-3809
3 Security Dr., Ste. 312, P.O. Box 355, Cranbury
08512
Rockline Industries, Inc.
Phone—(973) 257-9346
1 Kramer Dr., P.O. Box 189, Montville 07045
Schweitzer-Mauduit International, Inc.
Phone—(732) 723-6100
85 Main St., Spotswood 08884
Yerg Accounting Supplies
Phone—(973) 759-4041
85 Washington Ave., Belleville 07109

## PAPER TUBES

**American Tube & Paper**
80 Furler St., Totowa 07512
Phone—(973) 256-3600
Fax—(973) 785-3341
Web—www.AmericanPaperProducts.com
Email—sales@americanpaperproducts.com
P.O. Box 68, Totowa 07511
*(see our ad under MAILING TUBES)*
Paper Tube & Core, Inc.
Phone—(973) 977-8823
239 Lindbergh Pl., Paterson 07503
Ridgid Paper Tube Corp.
Phone—(973) 942-7000
10 Owens Dr., Wayne 07470

## PAPERBOARD

S. E. R. Diecutting
Phone—(856) 665-8805
7300 N. Crescent Blvd., Unit 5, Pennsauken
08110

## PARACHUTES

Airborne Systems North America Of New Jersey,
Inc.
Phone—(856) 663-1275
5800 Magnolia Ave., Pennsauken 08109

## PARADE FLOAT MATERIALS

Bond Parade Floats Displays, Inc.
Phone—(973) 778-3333
111 Clifton Blvd., Clifton 07011

## PARKING EQUIPMENT

Boomerang Systems, Inc.
Phone—(973) 538-1194
30-A Vreeland Rd., Ste. 150, Florham Park 07932
Park Plus, Inc.
Phone—(973) 574-8020
480 Main Ave., Ste. 1, Wallington 07057

## PARKING LOT EQUIPMENT & SUPPLIES

Amano McGann
Phone—(973) 618-4050
140 Harrison Ave., Roseland 07068

## PARKING METERS

Parkeon, Inc.
Phone—(856) 234-8000
40 Twosome Dr., Ste. 7, Moorestown 08057

## PARTITIONS — Box

**General Partition Co., Inc.**
Email: abien@generalpartition.com
Designers & Manufacturers of Paperboard Partitions
Phone—(215) 785-1000
Fax—(215) 785-2160
Web—www.generalpartition.com
Email—info@generalpartition.com
916 Washington Ave., P.O. Box 97, Croydon,
PA 19021

**General Partition Co., Inc.**
Designers & Mfrs. of Paperboard Partitions
215-785-1000 • Fax: 215-785-2160
www.generalpartition.com
916 Washington Ave., PO Box 97 Croydon, PA 19021

RTS Packaging, LLC
Phone—(908) 782-0505
869 State Highway 12, Frenchtown 08825

## PARTITIONS — Corrugated

Custom Liners, Inc.
Phone—(201) 569-1889
1555 Ruth Rd., Ste. 7, North Brunswick 08902

## PARTITIONS — Wire Mesh

Donaldson Co., Inc., R. J.
Phone—(856) 629-2737
1287 Glassboro Rd., Williamstown 08094

## PARTS WASHERS

Ramco Equipment Corp.
Phone—(908) 687-6700
32 Montgomery St., Hillside 07205
Safety-Kleen Systems, Inc.
Phone—(908) 791-9600
116 Skyline Dr., South Plainfield 07080

## PASTA PRODUCTS

Antonio's Pasta
Phone—(732) 442-1640
545 U.S. Highway 9 N., Woodbridge 07095
Bruno The King Of Ravioli Co.
Phone—(201) 646-0505
174 Union St., Hackensack 07601
Caesar's Pasta
Phone—(856) 227-2585
1001 Lower Landing Rd., Ste. 311, Blackwood
08012
Casa Di Trevi
Phone—(908) 259-9000
534 W. Westfield Ave., Roselle Park 07204
Conte's Pasta Co., Inc.
Phone—(856) 697-3400
310 Wheat Rd., Vineland 08360
DiPietro Foods, Inc.
Phone—(973) 762-4077
1701 Springfield Ave., Maplewood 07040
D'Orazio Foods, Inc.
Phone—(856) 931-1900
960 Creek Rd., Bellmawr 08031
Florence Ravioli Co.
Phone—(908) 322-7222
391 Park Ave., Scotch Plains 07076
M. A. R. Kit, Inc.
Phone—(856) 829-5992
1095 Cinnaminson Ave., Cinnaminson 08077
Mr. Pasta
Phone—(201) 991-5959
159 Ridge Rd., North Arlington 07031
North Jersey Ravioli Co.
Phone—(973) 772-5050
65 Pacific Ave., Garfield 07026
Portfirio Italian Food, Inc.
Phone—(609) 393-4116
320 Anderson St., Trenton 08611
Raffetto's Corp.
Phone—(201) 372-1222
62 W. Commercial Ave., Moonachie 07074
Rosa-Ly Pirogi
Phone—(973) 371-0650
256 Madison Ave., Irvington 07111
Roselli's Food Specialties, Inc., L. E.
Phone—(609) 654-4816
155 Church Rd., Medford 08055
San Marco Ravioli, Inc.
Phone—(973) 748-4545
38 Davey St., Bloomfield 07003
Savignano Foods Corp.
Phone—(973) 673-7537
107 S. Jefferson St., Orange 07050
Severino Pasta Mfg. Co.
Phone—(856) 854-7666
110 Haddon Ave., Westmont 08108
Vitamia & Sons
Phone—(973) 546-1140
206 Harrison Ave., Lodi 07644
Zeregas Sons, Inc., A.
Phone—(201) 797-1400
20-01 Broadway, P.O. Box 241, Fair Lawn 07410

## PASTRIES

Miel Patisserie, LLC
Phone—(856) 424-6435
1990 Route 70 E., Ste. 14, Cherry Hill 08003

**INDUSTRY**

## PASTRIES — *(cont.)*

Mini Frost Foods Corp.
  Phone—(973) 427-4258
  1237 Belmont Ave., Haledon 07508

## PATCHES — Embroidered

**A A Patchworks, Inc. (H Q)**
  **Emblems-Patches**
  **Phone—(973) 810-2121**
  **Fax—(973) 810-2122**
  **Web—www.aapatchworks.com**
  **Email—artwork@aapatchworks.com**
  **311 Mechanic St., Boonton 07005**
Tees & Novelties, Inc.
  Phone—(973) 574-7591
  P.O. Box 2059, Garfield 07026

## PATIO COVERS — Aluminum

Mid Jersey Building Supply
  Phone—(732) 657-2000
  2486 Ridgeway Blvd., Manchester 08759

## PATTERNS — Foundry

West Pattern Works, Inc.
  Phone—(609) 443-6241
  124 S. Main St., Cranbury 08512

## PAVILIONS

**Mr. Fence**
  Specializing in fences and patio furniture, gazebos,
  wishing wells, swing-sets, arbors, lighthouses and
  many custom yard accessories
  **Phone—(732) 303-1614**
  **Fax—(732) 303-0358**
  **Web—www.cmrfence.com**
  **Email—cmrfence@aol.com**
  **3468 U.S. Highway 9, Ste. 2, Freehold 07728**

## PAVING BRICK & STONES

Cambridge Pavers, Inc.
  Phone—(201) 933-5000
  Jerome Ave., P.O. Box 157, Lyndhurst 07071
Paverart, LLC
  Phone—(856) 783-7000
  2512 Egg Harbor Rd., Ste. C, Lindenwold 08021

## PAVING CONTRACTORS

**Green Construction Inc.**
  **Specializing in heavy highway construction**
  **Phone—(732) 238-9370**
  **Fax—(732) 613-0838**
  **P.O. Box 550, South River 08882**
**J. Alvino Paving, Inc.**
  **Phone—(973) 942-1112**
  **Fax—(973) 942-8930**
  **P.O. Box 3568, Wayne 07474**
      *(see our ad on this page)*

## PAVING MIXTURES — Bituminous

Mount Construction Co., Inc. (H Q)
  Phone—(856) 768-8493
  427 S. White Horse Pike, P.O. Box 619, Berlin
  08009

## PELLETS

**Cary Compounds, LLC**
  **Phone—(732) 274-2626**
  **Fax—(732) 274-9003**
  **Web—www.carycompounds.com**
  **Email—carycompounds@aol.com**
  **5 Nicholas Ct., Dayton 08810**
Coloron Plastics Corp.
  Phone—(908) 685-1210
  169 Meister Ave., Front, Somerville 08876
Polyfil Corp.
  Phone—(973) 627-4070
  74 Green Pond Rd., P.O. Box 130, Rockaway
  07866

---

# J. Alvino Paving, Inc.

*Quality Paving Contractors*

# 973-942-1112
## FAX: 973-942-8930

### P.O. Box 3568, Wayne, NJ 07474

## PENCILS

General Pencil Co.
  Phone—(201) 653-5351
  67 Fleet St., Jersey City 07306

## PENS

Bankers Pen Co., Inc.
  Phone—(718) 768-7107
  141 Lanza Rd., Garfield 07026

## PERFORMANCE TESTING

**Beacon Container Corp.**
  **ISTA Certified**
  **Phone—(610) 582-2222 / (800) 422-8383**
  **Fax—(610) 582-3992**
  **Web—www.beaconcontainer.com**
  **Email—customerservice@**
  **beaconcontainer.com**
  **700 W. 1st St., Birdsboro, PA 19508**
      *(see our ad under BOXES—Corrugated)*

## PERFUMES & COLOGNES

Chanel, Inc.
  Phone—(732) 885-5500
  876 Centennial Ave., Piscataway 08854
**Cookson & Hunt International**
  **Phone—(732) 212-9311**
  **Fax—(732) 212-9313**
  **Web—www.cooksonco.com**
  **Email—info@cooksonco.com**
  **227 E. Bergen Pl., Ste. 2, Red Bank 07701**
Creative Concepts Corp.
  Phone—(201) 750-1234
  70 Oak St., Ste. 202, Norwood 07648
**Firmenich, Inc.**
  A Passion for Smell and Taste. The largest privately-
  owned company in the perfume and flavor business,
  creating many of the world's favorite perfumes for
  over 100 years.
  **Phone—(973) 589-3443**
  **Web—www.firmenich.com**
  **Email—ron.kurtz@firmenich.com**
  **150 Firmenich Way, Newark 07114**
Fragrance Resources, Inc.
  Phone—(973) 777-2979
  620 Route 3 W., Clifton 07014
Givaudan Fragrances Corp.
  Phone—(973) 448-6500
  300 Waterloo Valley Rd., Mount Olive 07828
Lanman & Kemp-Barclay & Co., Inc.
  Phone—(201) 666-4990
  25 Woodland Ave., P.O. Box 421, Westwood
  07675
Procter & Gamble Mfg. Co.
  Phone—(732) 602-4500
  100 Essex Ave. E., Avenel 07001
Robertet-Novarome Fragrances, Inc.
  Phone—(973) 575-4550
  400 International Dr., Mount Olive 07828
Victory International U. S. A., LLC
  Phone—(732) 417-1040
  75 Newfield Ave., Edison 08837

## PERLITE

Schundler Co., Inc.
  Phone—(732) 287-2244
  150 Whitman Ave., Edison 08817

## PEST CONTROL SERVICES

**Ar-Dean Termite & Pest Control**
  **Phone—(908) 964-0108**
  **Fax—(908) 687-2725**
  **Web—www.ardeanpest.com**
  **Email—ardeanpest1@aol.com**
  **979 Suburban Rd., Union 07083**
**Cooper Pest Solutions**
  **Phone—(800) 949-2667**
  **Web—www.cooperpest.com**
  **Email—info@cooperpest.com**
  **351 Lawrence Station Rd., Lawrenceville**
  **08648**
**Emergency Pest Control, Inc.**
  **Phone—(973) 676-2847 / (800) 273-0278**
  **Fax—(973) 676-6808**
  **Web—www.apest.com**
  **Email—pestcontrol911@aol.com**
  **714 Scotland Rd., Orange 07050**
IPM Integrated Pest Management
  Phone—(609) 567-0100

## IPM Integrated Pest Management

*Quality Pest Control Services*

**(609) 567-0100 • www.ipmnj.com**

*"Serving South Jersey for 30 Years"*

## PESTICIDES

Growmark FS, LLC
  Phone—(856) 455-7688
  55 Silver Lake Rd., Bridgeton 08302
PIC Corp.
  Phone—(908) 862-7977
  1101 W. Elizabeth Ave., P.O. Box 4258, Linden
  07036

## PET FOOD

Bravo Packing
  Phone—(856) 299-1044
  59 N. Gothwood Ave., Carneys Point 08069
**Dr. Harvey's Healthy Formulations Inc.**
  **Phone—(732) 787-2400**
  **Fax—(732) 787-2445**
  **Web—www.drharveys.com**
  **Email—info@drharveys.com**
  **25 W. Highland Ave., Atlantic Highlands 07716**
Mid Jersey Pet Supply
  Phone—(732) 541-2807
  296 Pershing Ave., Carteret 07008

*Search from among 430,000
U.S. manufacturers & suppliers:*
**IndustryNet.com**

*Do nationwide searches for
products & services at:*
**IndustryNet.com**

© Copyright 2015 Manufacturers' News, Inc.

## PET FOOD INGREDIENTS

Daybrook Holdings, Inc. (H Q)
 Phone—(973) 538-6766
 161 Madison Ave., 2nd Fl., Morristown 07960
IMS Pet Industries
 Phone—(973) 249-0026
 34 Passaic St., Wood Ridge 07075

## PET PRODUCTS

Purple Pebble, LLC (H Q)
 Phone—(201) 444-7439
 58 Grand Ave., Waldwick 07463

## PET SERVICES

When Doody Calls
 Phone—(732) 495-7667
 Fax—(732) 495-7668
 Web—www.whendoodycalls.com
 Email—petpoop2001@yahoo.com
 20 Mills Ave., Port Monmouth 07758

## When Doody Calls
*Quality pet services*
www.whendoodycalls.com
(732) 495-7667
20 Mills Ave. Port Monmouth, NJ 07758

## PET SUPPLIES

Bird Toy Man
 Phone—(973) 584-0756
 197 S. Hillside Ave., Succasunna 07876
Central Pet
 Phone—(201) 529-5050
 301 Island Rd., Mahwah 07430
Crown Royale Ltd.
 Phone—(908) 859-1999
 99 Broad St., P.O. Box 5238, Phillipsburg 08865
Fab Dog, Inc.
 Phone—(973) 472-5555
 160 Gregg St., Unit 7, Lodi 07644
Nylabone Products
 Phone—(732) 988-8400
 1 TFH Plz., 3rd & Union Ave., P.O. Box 427, Neptune City 07753
Vo-Toys, Inc.
 Phone—(973) 484-0088
 400 S. 5th St., Harrison 07029

## PET TREATS

Fat Murray's Doggy Treats
 Phone—(973) 299-2968
 3 Deer Hill Dr., P.O. Box 32, Montville 07045
Loving Pets Corp.
 Phone—(609) 655-3700
 110 Melrich Rd., Ste. 1, Cranbury 08512

## PETROLEUM — Wholesale

Ferrell's Oil Service
 Phone—(856) 299-0500
 26 E. Mill St., P.O. Box 130, Pedricktown 08067
Hess Corp.
 Phone—(856) 663-5111
 123 Derousse Ave., Pennsauken 08110

## PETROLEUM PRODUCTS

Sonneborn, LLC
 Phone—(201) 760-2940
 Fax—(201) 760-2967
 Web—www.sonneborn.com
 Email—luther.jones@sonneborn.com
 600 Parsippany Rd., Ste. 100, Parsippany 07054

Taylor Oil Co., Inc.
 The premier provider of on-site fueling services (highest quality gasoline, diesel fuel & other petroleum products) to construction crews, contractors, boats & marinas along the East Coast and beyond
 Phone—(908) 725-7737
 Fax—(908) 725-7746
 Web—www.tayloroilco.com
 Email—fbloom@tayloroilco.com
 77 2nd St., P.O. Box 974, Somerville 08876

## PETROLEUM REFINERIES

PBF Energy Partners L. P. (H Q)
 Phone—(973) 455-7500
 1 Sylvan Way, Parsippany 07054

## PHARMACEUTICAL INGREDIENTS

Apicore US, LLC
 Phone—(732) 748-8882
 49 Napoleon Ct., Somerset 08873
Cambrex Corp.
 Phone—(201) 804-3000
 1 Meadowlands Plz., Ste. 1510, East Rutherford 07073
Hovione, LLC
 Phone—(609) 918-2600
 40 Lake Dr., East Windsor 08520
Johnson Matthey Pharmaceutical Materials
 Phone—(856) 384-7001
 2003 Nolte Dr., Paulsboro 08066
Mafco Worldwide Corp.
 Phone—(856) 964-8840
 Fax—(856) 964-6029
 Web—www.magnasweet.com
 Email—magnasweet@mafcolicorice.com
 300 Jefferson St., Camden 08104
 *(see our ad under FLAVORINGS & FLAVORS)*
Milestone PharmTech USA, Inc.
 Phone—(732) 579-8201
 100 Jersey Ave., Bldg. D, Box D-4, New Brunswick 08901
Noramco, Inc.
 Leading Supplier of Opiate-Derived API; 2 U.S. Manufacturing Locations
 Phone—(302) 761-2909 / (302) 761-2940
 Fax—(302) 761-2913
 Web—www.noramco.com
 Email—noramcoAPI@its.jnj.com
 500 Swedes Landing Rd., Wilmington, DE 19801
Paulaur Corp.
 Phone—(609) 395-8844
 Fax—(609) 395-8850
 Web—www.paulaur.com
 Email—sales@paulaur.com
 105 Melrich Rd., Cranbury 08512
 *(see our ad under FOOD INGREDIENTS)*
Siegfried USA, LLC
 We develop & produce active pharmaceutical substances
 Phone—(856) 678-3601 / (877) 763-8630
 Fax—(856) 678-4008
 Web—www.siegfried-usa.com
 Email—rita.vaneck@siegfried-usa.com
 33 Industrial Park Rd., Pennsville 08070
 *(see our ad under PHARMACEUTICALS)*
SST Corp.
 Phone—(973) 473-4300 / (800) 222-0921
 Fax—(973) 473-4326
 Web—www.sst-corp.com
 Email—info@sst-corp.com
 P.O. Box 1649, Clifton 07015

SST CORPORATION
*Distributor of Pharmaceutical Ingredients*
www.sst-corp.com
(973) 473-4300
PO Box 1649 • Clifton, NJ 07015

Suven Life Sciences Ltd.
 Phone—(732) 274-0037
 1100 Cornwall Rd., Monmouth Junction 08852

## PHARMACEUTICAL PACKAGING

Aphena Pharma Solutions-NJ, Inc.
 Phone—(973) 887-4440
 Fax—(973) 887-9098
 Web—www.aphenapharma.com
 Email—sales@aphenapharma.com
 125 Algonquin Pkwy., Whippany 07981
Comar, LLC
 Phone—(856) 692-6100
 Fax—(856) 692-9251
 Web—www.comar.com
 Email—info@comar.com
 1 Comar Pl., Buena 08310

Plastic Pharmaceutical Packaging
COMAR®
www.comar.com
(856) 692-6100
1 Comar Pl. Buena, NJ 08310

Deitz Co., Inc.
 Phone—(732) 681-0200
 1750 Highway 34, P.O. Box 1108, Wall 07719
DPT Lakewood, LLC
 Phone—(732) 367-9000
 1200 Paco Way, Bldg. 19, Lakewood 08701
James Alexander Corp.
 Phone—(908) 362-9266
 845 State Route 94, Blairstown 07825
Key International, Inc.
 Phone—(609) 619-3685
 Fax—(609) 619-3686
 Web—keyinternational.com
 Email—sales@keyinternational.com
 4 Corporate Dr., Cranbury 08512
Xerimis Inc.
 Phone—(856) 727-9940
 102 Executive Dr., Moorestown 08057

## PHARMACEUTICAL PROCESSING EQUIPMENT

AC Compacting, LLC
 Phone—(732) 249-6900
 1577 Livingston Ave., P.O. Box 7266, North Brunswick 08902
Dantco Mixers Corp.
 Phone—(973) 278-8776
 9 Oak St., Paterson 07501
EcReCon, Inc.
 Used Chemical Processing Equipment
 Phone—(856) 299-4500
 Fax—(856) 299-4446
 Web—www.EcReCon.com
 Email—sales@ecrecon.com
 62 N. Broad St., Penns Grove 08069
 *(see our ad under CHEMICAL PROCESSING EQUIPMENT)*
Glatt Air Techniques, Inc.
 Phone—(201) 825-8700
 20 Spear Rd., Ramsey 07446
GlobePharma, Inc.
 Phone—(732) 296-9700
 2-B Janine Pl., New Brunswick 08901
Key International, Inc.
 Phone—(609) 619-3685
 Fax—(609) 619-3686
 Web—keyinternational.com
 Email—sales@keyinternational.com
 4 Corporate Dr., Cranbury 08512
M. O. Industries, Inc.
 Phone—(973) 386-9228
 9 Whippany Rd., Bldg. B1-2, Whippany 07981
Mendel Co. (H Q)
 Phone—(973) 599-1300
 12-C Great Meadow Ln., East Hanover 07936
Rame-Hart, Inc.
 Phone—(973) 335-0560
 5 Emery Ave., Ste. 1, Randolph 07869
Scientific Industries, Inc.
 Phone—(973) 473-6900
 660 Kinderkamack Rd., Ste. 203, Oradell 07649
Sonar Products, Inc.
 Phone—(201) 729-1116
 609-611 Industrial Rd., Carlstadt 07072

INDUSTRY

## PHARMACEUTICAL PROCESSING EQUIPMENT — (cont.)

**Warwick Mfg. & Equipment Co., LLC**
Buy & sell used: Chemical, food, cosmetic, packaging & pharmaceutical equipment
Phone—(732) 729-0400 / (732) 241-9263
Fax—(732) 729-1235
Web—www.warwickequipment.com
Email—sales@warwickequipment.com
1112 12th St., North Brunswick 08902
*(see our ad Outside Back Cover)*

## PHARMACEUTICAL PRODUCTS — Disposable

**Gerresheimer Glass, Inc.**
Manufacturer of high-quality specialty products made of glass & plastic for the global pharma & healthcare industry
Phone—(856) 692-3600
Web—www.gerresheimer.com
Email—info-tubing-us@gerresheimer.com
537 Crystal Ave., Vineland 08360

Rexam Healthcare Packaging, Inc.
Phone—(908) 689-1660
14-B Brass Castle Rd., Washington 07882

## PHARMACEUTICAL SERVICES

**Siegfried USA, LLC**
We develop & produce active pharmaceutical substances
Phone—(856) 678-3601 / (877) 763-8630
Fax—(856) 678-4008
Web—www.siegfried-usa.com
Email—rita.vaneck@siegfried-usa.com
33 Industrial Park Rd., Pennsville 08070
*(see our ad under PHARMACEUTICALS)*

## PHARMACEUTICALS

A A A Pharmaceutical, Inc.
Phone—(609) 288-6060
157-160 W. Jefferson St., Paulsboro 08066
Acino Products, LLC
Phone—(609) 695-4300
9-B S. Gold Dr., Trenton 08691
Actavis, Inc.
Phone—(862) 261-7000
Morris Corporate Ctr. 3, 400 Interpace Pkwy., Parsippany 07054
Akorn, Inc.
Phone—(732) 846-8066
72 Veronica Ave., Somerset 08873
Akrimax Pharmaceuticals, LLC (H Q)
Phone—(908) 372-0506
11 Commerce Dr., 1st Fl., Ste. 100, Cranford 07016
Alpro, Inc.
Phone—(201) 342-4498
50 Romanelli Ave., South Hackensack 07606
Amneal Pharmaceuticals, LLC
Phone—(908) 947-3120
400 Crossing Blvd., 3rd Fl., Bridgewater 08807
Amneal Pharmaceuticals, LLC
Phone—(732) 645-3030
47 Colonial Dr., Piscataway 08854
Bayer HealthCare Pharmaceuticals (H Q)
Phone—(862) 404-3000
100 Bayer Blvd., Whippany 07981
Bayer Healthcare, Consumer Care Div.
Phone—(862) 404-3000
100 Bayer Blvd., P.O. Box 915, Whippany 07962
**Carecam International, Inc.**
Phone—(973) 227-0720
Fax—(973) 227-7395
10 Plog Rd., Fairfield 07004
Catalent Pharma Solutions, Inc. (H Q)
Phone—(732) 537-6200
14 Schoolhouse Rd., Somerset 08873
Celgene Corp.
Phone—(908) 673-9000
86 Morris Ave., Summit 07901
Celldex Therapeutics, Inc.
Phone—(908) 200-7500
53 Frontage Rd., Ste. 200, Hampton 08827
Central Admixture Pharmacy Services
Phone—(201) 541-0080
160 W. Forest Ave., Englewood 07631

**Cetylite, Inc.**
Phone—(856) 665-6111
9051 River Rd., Pennsauken 08110
CMIC CMO USA Corp.
Phone—(609) 395-9700
3 Cedarbrook Dr., Ste. 3, Cranbury 08512
Contract Coatings, Inc.
Phone—(201) 343-3131
161 Beech St., Hackensack 07601
Core Tech Solutions, Inc.
Phone—(609) 443-1400
50 Lake Dr. E. Windsor, Hightstown 08520
Covance, Inc. (H Q)
Phone—(609) 452-8550
210 Carnegie Ctr., Princeton 08540
Daiichi Sankyo, Inc. (H Q)
Phone—(973) 944-2600
2 Hilton Ct., Parsippany 07054
davAgen Pharmaceuticals, LLC
Phone—(732) 249-6363
68 Veronica Ave., Ste. 1, 2 & 10, Somerset 08873
Dr. Reddy's Laboratories, Inc. (H Q)
Phone—(609) 375-9900
107 College Rd. E., Princeton 08540
Eisai, Inc. (H Q)
Phone—(201) 692-1100
100 Tice Blvd., Woodcliff Lake 07677
Elite Pharmaceuticals, Inc.
Phone—(201) 750-2646
165 Ludlow Ave., Northvale 07647
Enzon Pharmaceuticals, Inc.
Phone—(732) 980-4500
20 Kingsbridge Rd., Piscataway 08854
Excellium Pharmaceutical, Inc.
Phone—(973) 276-9600
3 Oak Rd., Ste. G, Fairfield 07004
Exeltis
Phone—(973) 324-0200
1 Main St., Ste. 203, Chatham 07928
Frinton Laboratories, Inc.
Phone—(856) 722-7037
4204 Sylon Blvd., Hainesport 08036
**G & W Laboratories Inc.**
Email—jandrade@gwlabs.com
Phone—(908) 753-2000
Fax—(908) 753-5174
Web—www.gwlabs.com
111 Coolidge St., South Plainfield 07080
Gallus BioPharmaceuticals New Jersey, LLC
Phone—(609) 919-3300
201 College Rd. E., Princeton 08540
GE Healthcare
Phone—(908) 757-0500
900 Durham Ave., South Plainfield 07080
Genavite, LLC
Phone—(973) 779-1532
235 Clifton Blvd., Clifton 07011
Granulation Technology, Inc.
Phone—(973) 276-0740
12 Industrial Rd., Fairfield 07004
Guardian Drug Co., Inc.
Phone—(609) 860-2600
2 Charles Ct., Dayton 08810
Halo Pharmaceutical, Inc.
Phone—(973) 428-4000
30 N. Jefferson Rd., Whippany 07981
Hemispherx Biopharma, Inc.
Phone—(732) 249-3250
783 Jersey Ave., New Brunswick 08901
Immunomedics, Inc.
Phone—(973) 605-8200
300 The American Rd., Morris Plains 07950
InnoPharma, Inc.
Phone—(732) 885-2939
10 Knightsbridge Rd., Piscataway 08854
Intergel Vitamin Co.
Phone—(973) 371-4400
191 40th St., Irvington 07111
**Jacobus Pharmaceutical Co., Inc.**
37 Cleveland Ln., Princeton 08540
Phone—(609) 921-7447
Fax—(609) 799-1176
Email—LRJacobus@aol.com
P.O. Box 5290, Princeton 08543
Jacobus Pharmaceutical Co., Inc.
Phone—(609) 799-8221
P.O. Box 5290, Princeton 08540
Janssen Pharmaceuticals, Inc.
Phone—(908) 218-6000
1125 Trenton-Harbourton Rd., P.O. Box 200, Titusville 08560

Janssen Research & Development, LLC, A Div. of Johnson & Johnson
Phone—(908) 704-4000
920 U.S. Highway 202, P.O. Box 300, Raritan 08869
JHP Pharmaceuticals, LLC
Phone—(908) 658-3530
1 Upper Pond Rd., Bldg. D, Parsippany 07054
Matrix Distributors, Inc.
Phone—(732) 698-9991
110 Tices Ln., Ste. 5-B, East Brunswick 08816
**Meda Pharmaceuticals, Inc. (H Q)**
Phone—(732) 564-2200
Fax—(732) 564-2226
Web—www.meda.us
Email—info@meda.us
265 Davidson Ave., Somerset 08873
Merck & Co., Inc.
Phone—(908) 298-4000
2000 Galloping Hill Rd., Kenilworth 07033
Merck & Co., Inc.
Phone—(732) 594-4000
126 E. Lincoln Ave., P.O. Box 2000, Rahway 07065
Merck & Co., Inc. (H Q)
Phone—(908) 423-1000
1 Merck Dr., P.O. Box 100, Whitehouse Station 08889
Merial Ltd.
Phone—(732) 729-5700
631 U.S. Highway 1, North Brunswick 08902
MonoSol Rx, LLC (H Q)
Phone—(908) 941-1900
30 Technology Dr., Warren 07059
MPT Delivery Systems, Inc.
Phone—(973) 279-4132
95 Prince St., Paterson 07501
**Noramco, Inc.**
Leading Supplier of Opiate-Derived API; 2 U.S. Manufacturing Locations
Phone—(302) 761-2909 / (302) 761-2940
Fax—(302) 761-2913
Web—www.noramco.com
Email—noramcoAPI@its.jnj.com
500 Swedes Landing Rd., Wilmington, DE 19801
Novartis Consumer Health (H Q)
Phone—(973) 503-8000
200 Kimball Dr., Parsippany 07054
Novartis Pharmaceuticals Corp. (H Q)
Phone—(862) 778-8300
1 Health Plz., East Hanover 07936
Novel Laboratories, Inc.
Phone—(908) 603-6000
400 Campus Dr., Somerset 08873
Novo Nordisk, Inc. (H Q)
Phone—(609) 987-5800
800 Scudders Mill Rd., Plainsboro 08536
Nuclear Diagnostic Products, Inc.
Phone—(973) 664-9696
101 Round Hill Dr., Rockaway 07866
OHM Laboratories, Inc.
Phone—(732) 514-4380
14 Terminal Rd., New Brunswick 08901
OHM Laboratories, Inc.
Phone—(732) 418-2235
1385 Livingston Ave., P.O. Box 7397, North Brunswick 08902
P. F. Laboratories, Inc.
Phone—(973) 256-3100
700 Union Blvd., Totowa 07512
Pacira Pharmaceuticals, Inc. (H Q)
Phone—(973) 254-3560
5 Sylvan Way, Parsippany 07054
Par Pharmaceutical Cos., Inc.
Phone—(201) 802-4000
300 Tice Blvd., Woodcliff Lake 07677
PediatRx, Inc. (H Q)
Phone—(908) 975-0753
90 Fairmount Rd. W., P.O. Box 423, Califon 07830
PharMEDium
Phone—(732) 287-8655
43 Distribution Blvd., Edison 08817
Prolong Pharmaceuticals
Phone—(908) 444-4660
300 Corporate Ct., Ste. B, South Plainfield 07080
PuraCap Pharmaceutical, LLC
Phone—(908) 941-5456
1001 Durham Ave., South Plainfield 07080
Quantum Pharmaceuticals, Inc. (H Q)
Phone—(877) 873-3762
P.O. Box 244, Ogdensburg 07439

## PHARMACEUTICALS — (cont.)

Ranbaxy, Inc. (H Q)
  Phone—(609) 720-9200
  600 College Rd. E., Ste. 2100, Princeton 08540
Raritan Pharmaceuticals, Inc.
  Phone—(732) 432-8200
  8 Joanna Ct., East Brunswick 08816
Sandoz, Inc. (H Q)
  Phone—(609) 627-8500
  506 Carnegie Ctr., Ste. 400, Princeton 08540
Sanofi U. S. (H Q)
  Phone—(908) 981-5000
  55 Corporate Dr., Bridgewater 08807
Shionogi, Inc. (H Q)
  Phone—(973) 966-6900
  300 Campus Dr., Florham Park 07932
**Siegfried USA, LLC**
  **We develop & produce active pharmaceutical**
  **substances**
  **Phone—(856) 678-3601 / (877) 763-8630**
  **Fax—(856) 678-4008**
  **Web—www.siegfried-usa.com**
  **Email—rita.vaneck@siegfried-usa.com**
  **33 Industrial Park Rd., Pennsville 08070**

Siegfried | expect more
Pharmaceutical Contract Manufacturer
(856) 678-3601 • Fax: (856) 678-4008
www.siegfried-usa.com
33 Industrial Park Rd. • Pennsville, NJ 08070

Strativa Pharmaceuticals (H Q)
  Phone—(201) 802-4000
  300 Tice Blvd., Woodcliff Lake 07677
Sun Pharmaceutical Industries, Inc.
  Phone—(609) 495-2800
  270 Prospect Plains Rd., Cranbury 08512
Sunrise Pharmaceutical, Inc.
  Phone—(732) 382-6085
  665 E. Lincoln Ave., Rahway 07065
**Teva Pharmaceuticals U.S.A., Inc.**
  **Web: www.tevausa.com**
  **Phone—(973) 575-2775**
  **Fax—(973) 575-6089**
  **Email—tevahr@tevapharm.com**
  **8-10 Gloria Ln., Fairfield 07004**
Tris Pharma, Inc.
  Phone—(732) 940-2800
  2033 U.S. Highway 130, Ste. D, Monmouth
  Junction 08852
Validus Pharmaceuticals, LLC
  Phone—(973) 265-2777
  119 Cherry Hill Rd., Ste. 310, Parsippany 07054
Vertical Pharmaceuticals, Inc. (H Q)
  Phone—(732) 721-0070
  2500 Main St., Ste. 6, Sayreville 08872
Vils Pharma, Inc.
  Phone—(732) 777-6023
  135 Glendale Ave., Edison 08817
Warner Chilcott
  Phone—(973) 442-3200
  100 Enterprise Dr., Ste. 280, Rockaway 07866
Westward Pharmaceutical Corp.
  Phone—(856) 424-3700
  2 Esterbrook Ln., Cherry Hill 08003
West-Ward Pharmaceutical Corp.
  Phone—(732) 542-1191
  401 Industrial Way W., Eatontown 07724
Wockhardt USA, LLC (H Q)
  Phone—(973) 257-4960
  20 Waterview Blvd., Ste. 3, Parsippany 07054
Zydus Pharmaceuticals USA, Inc.
  Phone—(609) 730-1900
  73 Route 31 N., Pennington 08534

## PHARMACEUTICALS — Drug Candidates

Aerie Pharmaceuticals, Inc.
  Phone—(908) 470-4320
  135 U.S. Highway 206, Ste. 15, Bedminster
  07921
Cornerstone Pharmaceuticals, Inc.
  Phone—(609) 409-7050
  1 Duncan Dr., Cranbury 08512

Eli Lilly & Co.
  Phone—(908) 541-8100
  33 ImClone Dr., Branchburg 08876
Eli Lilly (H Q)
  Phone—(908) 541-8100
  440 Route 22 E., Bridgewater 08807
Mitsubishi Tanabe Pharma America, Inc. (H Q)
  Phone—(908) 607-1980
  525 Washington Blvd., Ste. 400, Jersey City
  07310
NPS Pharmaceuticals, Inc. (H Q)
  Phone—(908) 450-5300
  550 Hills Dr., Bedminster 07921
PTC Therapeutics, Inc.
  Phone—(908) 222-7000
  100 Corporate Ct., South Plainfield 07080
Roche Nutley
  Phone—(973) 235-5000
  340 Kingsland St., Nutley 07110
Tamir Biotechnology, Inc. (H Q)
  Phone—(732) 823-1003
  11 Deer Park Dr., Monmouth Junction 08852
ThromboGenics, Inc.
  Phone—(732) 590-2900
  101 Wood Ave. S., Ste. 600, Iselin 08830

## PHARMACEUTICALS — Generic

Actavis Elizabeth, LLC
  Phone—(908) 527-9100
  200 Elmora Ave., Elizabeth 07202
Amerigen Pharmaceuticals, Inc. (H Q)
  Phone—(732) 993-9827
  9 Polito Ave., Ste. 900, Lyndhurst 07071
CorePharma, LLC
  Phone—(732) 868-1090
  215 Wood Ave., Middlesex 08846
Glenmark Generics Inc., USA
  Phone—(201) 684-8000
  750 Corporate Dr., Mahwah 07430
Heritage Pharmaceuticals, Inc. (H Q)
  Phone—(732) 429-1000
  12 Christopher, Ste. 300, Eatontown 07724
Kremers Urban Pharmaceuticals, Inc. (H Q)
  Phone—(609) 936-5940
  902 Carnegie Ctr., Ste. 360, Princeton 08540
Nostrum Pharmaceuticals, LLC (H Q)
  Phone—(732) 543-2440
  1370 Hamilton St., Somerset 08873
Sciecure Pharma, Inc.
  Phone—(732) 329-8089
  11 Deerpark Dr., Ste. 120, Monmouth Junction
  08852

## PHARMACEUTICALS — Specialty

**Meda Pharmaceuticals, Inc. (H Q)**
  **Phone—(732) 564-2200**
  **Fax—(732) 564-2226**
  **Web—www.meda.us**
  **Email—info@meda.us**
  **265 Davidson Ave., Somerset 08873**

## PHARMACEUTICALS — Wholesale

**Aphena Pharma Solutions-NJ, Inc.**
  **Phone—(973) 887-4440**
  **Fax—(973) 887-9098**
  **Web—www.aphenapharma.com**
  **Email—sales@aphenapharma.com**
  **125 Algonquin Pkwy., Whippany 07981**
Caremark Rx, Inc.
  Phone—(973) 461-1550
  180 Passaic Ave., Ste. 5, Fairfield 07004
McKesson Corp.
  Phone—(856) 461-7800
  400 Delran Pkwy., Delran 08075
**Old Bridge Drugs & Surgicals**
  **Phone—(732) 525-2220**
  **Fax—(732) 525-2277**
  **200 Perrine Rd., Ste. 200B, Old Bridge 08857**

## PHOSPHATES

Innophos, Inc. (H Q)
  Phone—(609) 495-2495
  259 Prospect Plains Rd., Bldg. A, Cranbury
  08512

## PHOTOGRAPHERS — Commercial

**Janet Studios**
  **Phone—(732) 531-8848**
  **Fax—(732) 493-8841**
  **Web—www.janetstudios.com**
  **Email—info@janetstudios.com**
  **2104 Kings Hwy., Ocean 07712**

## PHOTOGRAPHIC EQUIPMENT & SUPPLIES

FUJIFILM U.S.A., Inc.
  Phone—(732) 857-3000
  1100 King Georges Post Rd., Edison 08837
Konica Minolta Business Solutions U. S. A., Inc. (H Q)
  Phone—(201) 825-4000
  100 Williams Dr., Ramsey 07446
Long Valley Equipment
  Phone—(908) 876-1022
  165 Fairview Ave., Long Valley 07853

## PHOTOGRAPHIC LIGHTING EQUIPMENT

**(also see 'Lighting Equipment')**
Dyna-Lite, Inc.
  Phone—(908) 687-8800
  1050 Commerce Ave., Union 07083

## PHOTONICS

Archcon Technology
  Phone—(908) 757-8817
  5000 Hadley Rd., South Plainfield 07080

## PHYSICAL THERAPY EQUIPMENT

Hausmann Industries, Inc.
  Phone—(201) 767-0255
  130 Union St., Northvale 07647

## PICKLES & PICKLE PRODUCTS

Ba-Tampte Pickle Products, Inc.
  Phone—(856) 697-9815
  2660 Main Rd., Franklinville 08322
Hengstenberg GmbH
  Phone—(201) 568-6596
  90 Pershing Pl., Cresskill 07626
**Kaplan & Zubrin, Inc.**
  **2nd & Kaighn Ave., Camden 08103**
  **Phone—(856) 964-1083**
  **Fax—(856) 964-0510**
  **Web—www.kzpickles.com**
  **Email—kz.pickles@verizon.net**
  **P.O. Box 1006, Camden 08101**
Paterson Pickle Co.
  Phone—(973) 523-1000
  285 4th Ave., Paterson 07514
Patriot Pickle
  Phone—(973) 709-9487
  20 Edison Dr., Wayne 07470
Pickle King
  Phone—(973) 977-2095
  220 Ellison St., Paterson 07505
Pickle-Licious
  Phone—(201) 833-0100
  384 Cedar Ln., Teaneck 07666

## PICTURE FRAMES

Beveled Edge
  Phone—(908) 754-6772
  51 Mount Bethel Rd., Warren 07059
Frame & Print
  Phone—(201) 358-0404
  778 Carver Ave., Westwood 07675
Helricks Picture Framing, Inc.
  Phone—(973) 361-1301
  158 W. Clinton St., Ste. G, Dover 07801
Hickok Matthews Co.
  Phone—(973) 335-3400
  337 Main Rd., Montville 07045

## PICTURE FRAMES — (cont.)

L & M Art Gallery, LLC
Phone—(908) 351-2633
126 Elmora Ave., Elizabeth 07202

Landsman Custom Picture Framing
Phone—(856) 784-2145
600 S. White Horse Pike, Somerdale 08083

Larson-Juhl, LLC
Phone—(973) 439-1801
165 Clinton Rd., Caldwell 07006

New Jersey Frame & Moulding Co.
Phone—(973) 684-6001
62 Kearney St., Paterson 07522

Nicholas Designs, R.
Phone—(201) 385-8713
41 Portland Ave., Bergenfield 07621

Shurts Frames & Molding, Don
Phone—(732) 363-1323
294 Lanes Mill Rd., Howell 07731

Sky Frame & Art, Inc.
Phone—(908) 354-5656
28 Evans Terminal, Hillside 07205

Stiefel Corp., George G. (H Q)
Phone—(201) 967-0868
364 N. Farview Ave., Paramus 07652

## PICTURE FRAMING

RAO Contract Sales, Inc.
Phone—(201) 652-1500
392 Atwood Pl., Wyckoff 07481

## PICTURE FRAMING EQUIPMENT & SUPPLIES

Callen Photo Mount Corp.
Phone—(973) 925-2390
185 6th Ave., Ste. 1, Paterson 07524

Frameware, Inc.
Phone—(973) 808-2022
8 Audrey Pl., Fairfield 07004

## PIGMENT DISPERSIONS

**Cardinal Color, Inc.**
**Phone—(973) 684-1919**
**Fax—(973) 684-0865**
**Web—www.cardinalcolor.com**
**Email—info@cardinalcolor.com**
**50-56 1st Ave., Paterson 07514**

Colorchem, Inc.
Phone—(973) 728-7731
1010 Greenwood Lake, Ringwood 07456

Dispersion Technology, Inc.
Phone—(732) 364-4488
1885 Swarthmore Ave., Lakewood 08701

Ferro Corp.
Phone—(732) 287-1930
54 Kellogg Ct., Edison 08817

K V K U. S. A., Inc.
Phone—(732) 846-2355
19-A Home News Row, New Brunswick 08901

Spectrachem
Phone—(973) 253-3553
10 Dell Glen Ave., Ste. 3-A, Lodi 07644

## PIGMENTS

Color Techniques, Inc.
Phone—(908) 412-9292
260 Ryan St., South Plainfield 07080

Greenville Colorants (H Q)
Phone—(201) 595-0200
20 Linden Ave. E., Jersey City 07305

Kronos Worldwide, Inc.
Phone—(609) 860-6200
5 Cedarbrook Dr., Ste. 2, Cranbury 08512

## PILLOWS

**(also see 'Bedding')**

American Home Mfg., LLC
Phone—(732) 465-1530
4 Corporate Pl., Piscataway 08854

Design Accents, LLC
Phone—(201) 660-2446
1330 Hamburg Tpke., Wayne 07470

Phoenix Down Corp.
Web: www.downhomeoutlet.com
Toll Free Ph: (800) ALLDOWN; Feather Beds,
Comforters & Covers
Phone—(973) 812-8100 / (800) 255-3696
Fax—(973) 812-9077
Email—phod@phoenixdown.com
85 US Highway 46, Totowa 07512
*(see our ad under BEDDING)*

## PINS

Main & Sons, Inc., Robert A.
Phone—(201) 447-3700
555 Goffle Rd., P.O. Box 159, Wyckoff 07481

Vogelsang Fastener Corp
Phone—(732) 364-0444
1790 Swarthmore Ave., Lakewood 08701

## PIPE

**Arntzen Corp.**
Mfr. of Large Diameter Steel Pipe 24 inches OD to 192 inches OD
**Phone—(815) 964-9413 / (800) 821-3475**
**Fax—(815) 964-0045**
**Web—www.ArntzenPipe.com**
**Email—PipeSales@ArntzenCorp.com**
**P.O. Box 898, Rockford, IL 61105**

**Campbell Foundry, Materials Div.**
**Phone—(732) 408-1111**
**Fax—(732) 408-1105**
**Email—sales@campbellfoundry.com**
**630 S. Hope Chapel Rd., Jackson 08527**

**Campbell Materials, A Div. of Campbell Foundry Co.**
**Phone—(201) 998-3765**
**Fax—(201) 998-3764**
**Email—sales@campbellfoundry.com**
**1235 Harrison Ave., Kearny 07032**

**East Coast Stainless, Inc.**
Stainless C-276, Alloy 20, 321, 347, 400, 410, 600, 625, 800, 825 & Chrome-Moly
**Phone—(302) 366-0675**
**Fax—(302) 366-0691**
**Web—www.eastcoaststainless.com**
**Email—sales@eastcoaststainless.com**
**30 Albe Dr., Ste. E, Newark, DE 19702**
*(see our ad under PIPE—Stainless Steel)*

## PIPE — Casing

**Arntzen Corp.**
Mfr. of Large Diameter Steel Pipe 24 inches OD to 192 inches OD
**Phone—(815) 964-9413 / (800) 821-3475**
**Fax—(815) 964-0045**
**Web—www.ArntzenPipe.com**
**Email—PipeSales@ArntzenCorp.com**
**P.O. Box 898, Rockford, IL 61105**

## PIPE — Ductile Iron

Atlantic States Cast Iron Pipe Co.
Phone—(908) 454-1161
183 Sitgreaves St., Phillipsburg 08865

## PIPE — High Density Polyethylene

Advanced Drainage Systems, Inc.
Phone—(856) 467-4779
300 Progress Ct., Logan Township 08085

## PIPE — Plastic

**Campbell Foundry, Materials Div.**
**Phone—(732) 408-1111**
**Fax—(732) 408-1105**
**Email—sales@campbellfoundry.com**
**630 S. Hope Chapel Rd., Jackson 08527**

**Campbell Materials, A Div. of Campbell Foundry Co.**
**Phone—(201) 998-3765**
**Fax—(201) 998-3764**
**Email—sales@campbellfoundry.com**
**1235 Harrison Ave., Kearny 07032**

Endot Industries, Inc.
Phone—(973) 625-8500
60 Green Pond Rd., Rockaway 07866

## PIPE — Stainless Steel

**East Coast Stainless, Inc.**
Stainless C-276, Alloy 20, 321, 347, 400, 410, 600, 625, 800, 825 & Chrome-Moly
**Phone—(302) 366-0675**
**Fax—(302) 366-0691**
**Web—www.eastcoaststainless.com**
**Email—sales@eastcoaststainless.com**
**30 Albe Dr., Ste. E, Newark, DE 19702**

**East Coast Stainless, Inc.**
*Stainless C-276, Alloy 20, 321, 347, 400, 410, 600, 625, 800, 825 & Chrome-Moly*
**302-366-0675**
**FAX: 302-366-0691**
30 Albe Dr., Ste. E
Newark, DE 19702
www.eastcoaststainless.com
sales@eastcoaststainless.com

Swepco Tube, LLC
Phone—(973) 778-3000
1 Clifton Blvd., Clifton 07011

## PIPE — Steel

**Arntzen Corp.**
Mfr. of Large Diameter Steel Pipe 24 inches OD to 192 inches OD
**Phone—(815) 964-9413 / (800) 821-3475**
**Fax—(815) 964-0045**
**Web—www.ArntzenPipe.com**
**Email—PipeSales@ArntzenCorp.com**
**P.O. Box 898, Rockford, IL 61105**

Kessler Industries, Inc.
Phone—(973) 684-2130
500 Green St., Woodbridge 07095

Morris Industries, Inc.
Phone—(973) 835-6600
777 Route 23, P.O. Box 278, Pompton Plains 07444

Salem Steel N.A., LLC (H Q)
Phone—(201) 843-1000
80 Route 4 E., Ste. 168, Paramus 07652

T K L Specialty Piping
Phone—(908) 454-0030
175 Broad St., P.O. Box 5149, Phillipsburg 08865

## PIPE — Teflon® Lined

**(Teflon® is a registered trademark of DuPont)**

**Briggs Co., The**
**Phone—(302) 328-9471 / (800) 435-7293**
**Fax—(302) 322-7707**
**Web—www.briggsco.net**
**Email—briggssales@briggsco.net**
**3 Bellecor Dr., New Castle, DE 19720**

## PIPE BENDING

American Railing Design
Phone—(732) 287-1122
191 Vineyard Rd., Edison 08817

**MP Tube Works, Inc.**
**Phone—(908) 317-2500**
**Fax—(908) 317-2969**
**Web—www.mptubeworksinc.com**
**Email—mptube@aol.com**
**237 Sheffield St., Mountainside 07092**

**Owner Operators**

W. Thomas    K. Parkin
R. Thomas

Bus    856-464-6820
Fax    856-464-6930
Cell    856-577-0245
Shop    856-415-0800

Mailing Address:
P.O. Box 278
Wenonah, N.J. 08090

www.cottermaninc.com
welders@cottermancorp.com

**ASME Code Certified**

**INDUSTRIAL**
CONTRACTORS

**COTTERMAN** INC

## PIPE FABRICATORS

Custom Fab Pipe Supply Corp.
Phone—(201) 343-3739
1-A Mount Vernon St., Ridgefield Park 07660

Ferguson Fire & Fabrication, Inc.
Phone—(973) 614-9292
151 Randolph St., Passaic 07055

Moretrench American Corp.
Phone—(973) 627-2100
100 Stickle Ave., Rockaway 07866

S & W Fabricators, Inc.
Phone—(856) 881-8068
100 S. Delsea Dr., Ste. 300, P.O. Box 664, Glassboro 08028

## PIPE FITTERS

**Cotterman, Inc.**
**Phone—(856) 464-6820 / (856) 577-0245**
**Fax—(856) 464-6930**
**Web—www.cottermaninc.com**
**Email—welders@cottermancorp.com**
**100 Hayes Ave., P.O. Box 278, Wenonah 08090**
*(see our ad on this page)*

Euro Mechanical, Inc.
Phone—(201) 313-8050
16 Industrial Ave., Fairview 07022

## PIPE FITTINGS

CB&I
Phone—(732) 435-0777
502-B Jersey Ave., New Brunswick 08901

Custom Alloy Corp.
Phone—(800) 453-1724
3 Washington Ave., Ste. 6, High Bridge 08829

**East Coast Stainless, Inc.**
Stainless C-276, Alloy 20, 321, 347, 400, 410, 600, 625, 800, 825 & Chrome-Moly
**Phone—(302) 366-0675**
**Fax—(302) 366-0691**
**Web—www.eastcoaststainless.com**
**Email—sales@eastcoaststainless.com**
**30 Albe Dr., Ste. E, Newark, DE 19702**
*(see our ad under PIPE—Stainless Steel)*

Esco Industrial Corp.
Phone—(973) 478-5888
141 Lanza Ave., Bldg. 3-B, Garfield 07026

Ramco Mfg. Co., Inc.
Phone—(908) 245-4500
365 Carnegie Ave., Kenilworth 07033

Standard Pipe Products, Inc.
Phone—(908) 264-8284
15 North Ave., Garwood 07027

*Search from among 430,000 U.S. manufacturers & suppliers at*
**IndustryNet.com**

## PIPE FITTINGS — Stainless Steel

**Alloy Stainless Products**
**In Business for over 60 Years**
**Phone—(973) 256-1616 / (800) 631-8372**
**Fax—(973) 256-5256**
**Web—www.alloystainless.com**
**Email—rich.norato@alloystainless.com**
**611 Union Blvd., Totowa 07512**

**Alloy Stainless Products**
*In Business for Over 60 Years*
**(800) 631-8372**
**(973) 256-1616 • Fax (973) 256-5256**
611 Union Blvd. • Totowa, NJ 07512
www.alloystainless.com
rich.norato@alloystainless.com

Dason Stainless Products Co.
Phone—(732) 382-7272
1773 Elizabeth Ave., Rahway 07065

**East Coast Stainless, Inc.**
Stainless C-276, Alloy 20, 321, 347, 400, 410, 600, 625, 800, 825 & Chrome-Moly
**Phone—(302) 366-0675**
**Fax—(302) 366-0691**
**Web—www.eastcoaststainless.com**
**Email—sales@eastcoaststainless.com**
**30 Albe Dr., Ste. E, Newark, DE 19702**
*(see our ad under PIPE—Stainless Steel)*

Knickerbocker Machine Shop, Inc.
Phone—(973) 256-1616
611 Union Blvd., Totowa 07512

## PIPE FLANGES

Tube Craft Of America
Phone—(856) 629-5626
667 Lebanon Ave., Williamstown 08094

## PIPE HANGERS

Blanco Assocs., Inc., J.
Phone—(973) 427-0619
280 9th Ave., Unit 1, Hawthorne 07506

Carpenter & Paterson, Inc.
Phone—(856) 488-1988
3900 River Rd., P.O. Box 556, Pennsauken 08110

Carpenter & Paterson, Inc.
Phone—(973) 772-1800
369 Jefferson St., Saddle Brook 07663

National Pipe Hanger Corp.
Phone—(609) 261-5353
200 Campus Dr., R.R. 30, Mount Holly 08060

## PIPE JOINT COMPOUNDS

X-Pando Products, Inc.
Phone—(609) 394-0150
Fax—(609) 989-4847
Web—www.xpando.com
Email—sales@xpando.com
500 Southard St., Trenton 08638

*find additional suppliers at*
**IndustryNet.com**

## PIPE THREADING MACHINERY

National Equipment Co.
Phone—(732) 938-5084
342 Squankum Yellowbrook Rd., P.O. Box 674, Farmingdale 07727

## PIPE, VALVES & FITTINGS — Wholesale

Canuso, Inc., Louis P.
Phone—(856) 845-2700
401 Crown Point Rd., P.O. Box 501, Thorofare 08086

Dodson Global, Inc.
Phone—(732) 238-7001
27 Cotters Ln., East Brunswick 08816

Duva, Inc., James
Phone—(908) 526-1222
66-B Columbia Rd., Branchburg 08876

Ferguson Enterprises, Inc.
Phone—(732) 905-1000
190 Oberlin Ave. N., Lakewood 08701

Kennedy Cos., The
Phone—(856) 813-5000
8000 Midlantic Dr., Ste. 200-N, Mount Laurel 08054

World Wide Metric, Inc.
Phone—(732) 247-2300
37 Readington Rd., P.O. Box 5267, Branchburg 08876

## PIPELINE EQUIPMENT & SUPPLIES

**Mulcare Pipeline Solutions**
**Phone—(973) 335-4800**
**Fax—(973) 402-1558**
**Web—www.mulcare.com**
**Email—mulcaremail@mulcare.com**
**9 Mars Ct., Ste. C-4, Boonton 07005**

Pipeline Supply Co.
Phone—(732) 560-1509
203 Egel Ave., Middlesex 08846

## PIPING — Industrial

Bayonne Plumbing Supply, Inc.
Phone—(201) 339-8000
250 Avenue E, Bayonne 07002

## PIPING CONTRACTORS

**L & L Mechanical Construction & Design Co., Inc.**
**Phone—(201) 460-1403**
**Fax—(201) 460-1394**
**325 Main St., East Rutherford 07073**

## PIPING SYSTEMS

Foodline Piping Products Co.
Phone—(856) 767-1177
225 Edgewood Ave., West Berlin 08091

Piping Solutions, Inc.
Phone—(732) 537-1009
81 Chimney Rock Rd., Ste. 3, Bridgewater 08807

## PIZZA

Panzarotti Tarantini Pizza, Inc.
Phone—(856) 489-0026
2060 Springdale Rd., Ste. 300, Cherry Hill 08003

## PIZZA — Frozen

Ko-Fro Foods, Inc.
Phone—(732) 499-8282
23 Mileed Way, Avenel 07001

McCain Foods USA, Inc.
Phone—(201) 368-0600
11 Gregg St., Lodi 07644

*Search from among 430,000 U.S. manufacturers & suppliers:*
**IndustryNet.com**

© Copyright 2015 Manufacturers' News, Inc. A153

## PLANNERS — City & Regional

**Ronald A. Sebrin Assocs. LLC**
Phone—(732) 701-9444
Fax—(732) 701-9919
Web—www.rasallc.com
Email—architechts@rasallc.com
405 Richmond Ave., Point Pleasant Beach 08742

## PLANTS

**Shades Of Green**
Specializing in Quality Indoor Plants, Design, Install & Maintenance at Affordable Prices in Central & Northern New Jersey
Phone—(908) 769-9522 / (800) 564-9435
Fax—(908) 769-9455
Web—www.shadesofgreenplants.com
Email—shadesofgreen@optonline.net
P.O. Box 150, Berkeley Heights 07922

## PLANTS — Artificial

**Shades Of Green**
Specializing in Quality Indoor Plants, Design, Install & Maintenance at Affordable Prices in Central & Northern New Jersey
Phone—(908) 769-9522 / (800) 564-9435
Fax—(908) 769-9455
Web—www.shadesofgreenplants.com
Email—shadesofgreen@optonline.net
P.O. Box 150, Berkeley Heights 07922

## PLANTS — Wholesale

**Kube-Pak Corp.**
Phone—(609) 259-3114
Fax—(609) 259-0487
Web—www.kubepak.com
Email—sales@kubepak.com
194 Route 526, Allentown 08501

## PLAQUES

Tropar Mfg. Co., Inc.
Phone—(973) 822-2400
5 Vreeland Rd., Florham Park 07932
W & E Baum, Inc.
Phone—(732) 866-1881
89 Bannard St., Freehold 07728

## PLASTER PRODUCTS — Ornamental

Plaque Art Creations Co.
Phone—(973) 482-2536
401 S. 2nd St., Harrison 07029

## PLASTIC ACRYLIC

Acrilex, Inc.
Phone—(201) 333-1500
230 Culver Ave., Jersey City 07305

## PLASTIC BLOW MOLDING

Flex Craft Co.
Phone—(732) 502-9500
814 Asbury Ave., Asbury Park 07712

## PLASTIC COLOR CONCENTRATES

**Brenntag Specialties, Inc.**
Phone—(908) 561-6100 / (800) 732-0562
Fax—(800) 543-1484
Web—www.brenntagspecialties.com
Email—specialties@brenntag.com
1000 Coolidge St., South Plainfield 07080
*(see our ad under CHEMICAL DISTRIBUTORS)*
Colorflo, Inc.
Phone—(908) 862-3010
1261 W. Elizabeth Ave., Linden 07036
Penn Color, Inc.
Phone—(201) 791-5100
30 Kohner Pl., Elmwood Park 07407

## PLASTIC COMPOUNDING

**Brenntag Specialties, Inc.**
Phone—(908) 561-6100 / (800) 732-0562
Fax—(800) 543-1484
Web—www.brenntagspecialties.com
Email—specialties@brenntag.com
1000 Coolidge St., South Plainfield 07080
*(see our ad under CHEMICAL DISTRIBUTORS)*
**Coastal Plastics, Inc.**
Specializing in small custom runs & quantities
Phone—(401) 539-2446
Fax—(401) 539-0055
Web—www.coastalplasticsinc.com
Email—coastalplastics@verizon.net
35 Mechanic St., P.O. Box 477, Hope Valley, RI 02832
Colorite, A Tekni-Plex Co.
Phone—(201) 941-2900
101 Railroad Ave., Ridgefield 07657
Compounding Engineering Solutions, Inc.
Phone—(973) 340-4000
473 Highway 46 W., Clifton 07011
Federal Plastics Corp.
Phone—(908) 272-5800
570 South Ave. E., Ste. F-1, Cranford 07016
**T & T Marketing, Inc.**
Phone—(973) 426-0453 / (800) 608-1577
Fax—(973) 426-0457
Web—www.ttmarketinginc.com
Email—info@ttmarketinginc.com
P.O. Box 120, Allamuchy 07820

**T & T MARKETING, INC.**
www.TTMARKETINGINC.com
**Toll Free:**
**800-608-1577**
**FAX: 973-426-0457**
P.O. Box 120
Allamuchy, NJ 07820

## PLASTIC COMPRESSION MOLDING

**Wiggins Plastics, Inc.**
Est. 1948-ISO Certified; Custom Injection/ Thermoplastics/Thermosets/Compression/Transfer Molding
Phone—(973) 667-7200
Fax—(973) 667-3227
Web—www.wigginsplastics.com
Email—info@wigginsplastics.com
180 Kingsland Rd., P.O. Box 1077, Clifton 07014
*(see our ad under PLASTIC INJECTION MOLDING)*

## PLASTIC CONVERTING

Paradigm Packaging, LLC (H Q)
Phone—(201) 507-0900
141 N. 5th St., Saddle Brook 07663

**EZSelect®.com**
**REAL-TIME** Access to Industrial Leads!

## PLASTIC CUSTOM COMPOUNDS

**Brenntag Specialties, Inc.**
Phone—(908) 561-6100 / (800) 732-0562
Fax—(800) 543-1484
Web—www.brenntagspecialties.com
Email—specialties@brenntag.com
1000 Coolidge St., South Plainfield 07080
*(see our ad under CHEMICAL DISTRIBUTORS)*

## PLASTIC DISTRIBUTORS

**Emco Industrial Plastics, Inc.**
Supplier of Plastic Sheet, Rod, Tube, Films & Prototyping
Phone—(973) 559-5610
Fax—(973) 239-1595
Web—www.emcoplastics.com
Email—mailbox@emcoplastics.com
99 Commerce Rd., P.O. Box 2503, Cedar Grove 07009
*(also see our ad Outside Front Cover)*

www.emcoplastics.com
**973-559-5610**
Fax: 973-239-1595
**Emco Industrial Plastics, Inc.**
Plastic Fabrication & Distributor

## PLASTIC EXTRUDED PRODUCTS

Aflex Extrusion Technologies, Inc.
Phone—(732) 752-0048
1600 Livingston Ave., North Brunswick 08902
Hyde Co., A. L.
Phone—(856) 227-0500
1 Main St., P.O. Box 62, Grenloch 08032

## PLASTIC EXTRUDING MACHINERY

Royle Systems Group, LLC
Phone—(201) 644-0345
111 Bauer Dr., Ste. 2, Oakland 07436

## PLASTIC EXTRUSIONS

A & L Plastics Co., Inc.
Phone—(973) 383-2221
2 Municipal Rd., P.O. Box 160, Newton 07860
Apco Extruders, Inc.
Phone—(732) 287-5555
180 National Rd., Edison 08817
**Coastal Plastics, Inc.**
Specializing in small custom runs & quantities
Phone—(401) 539-2446
Fax—(401) 539-0055
Web—www.coastalplasticsinc.com
Email—coastalplastics@verizon.net
35 Mechanic St., P.O. Box 477, Hope Valley, RI 02832
Coperion Corp.
Phone—(201) 327-6300
663 E. Crescent Ave., Ramsey 07446
Hall Mfg. Corp.
Phone—(973) 962-6022
297 Margaret King Ave., Ringwood 07456
**Hillside Plastics Corp.**
Phone—(800) 837-7731
Fax—(973) 923-2056
Web—www.hillsideplasticscorp.com
Email—maria@hillsideplastics.net
125 Long Ave., P.O. Box 609, Hillside 07205
Leco Plastics, Inc.
Phone—(201) 343-3330
130 Gamewell St., Hackensack 07601
Oliner Fibre Co., Inc.
Phone—(908) 688-5800
2391 Vauxhall Rd., P.O. Box 308, Union 07083
Patwin Plastics, Inc.
Phone—(908) 486-6600
2300 E. Linden Ave., Linden 07036

## PLASTIC EXTRUSIONS — *(cont.)*

Petro Extrusion Technologies, Inc.
Phone—(908) 789-3338
490 South Ave., Garwood 07027
Petro Plastics
Phone—(908) 789-1200
450 South Ave., P.O. Box 167, Garwood 07027
Rotuba Extruders, Inc.
Phone—(908) 486-1000
1401 S. Park Ave., Linden 07036

## PLASTIC EXTRUSIONS — Custom

Petro Packaging Co., Inc.
Phone—(908) 272-4054
16 Quine St., P.O. Box 546, Cranford 07016

## PLASTIC EXTRUSIONS — Profile

**Intek Plastics, Inc.**
Intek plastics is a premiere custom plastic extrusion company, known for providing high quality, precisely engineered, customer-specific products. We serve mid & large-sized OEM's in a wide variety of industries.
**Phone—(973) 427-7331**
**Fax—(973) 427-2616**
**Web—www.intekplastics.com**
**Email—sales@intekplastics.com**
**150 5th Ave., Hawthorne 07506**

Intek Plastics
(973) 427-7331 • Fax (973) 427-2616
www.intekplastics.com • sales@intekplastics.com
150 5th Ave. • Hawthorne, NJ 07506

## PLASTIC FABRICATED COMPONENTS

ASI Plastic, Inc.
Phone—(973) 345-7510
120 Getty Ave., Paterson 07503
Precision Technology, Inc.
Phone—(201) 767-1600
50 Maple St., P.O. Box 422, Norwood 07648
**Severna Operations, Inc.**
**Phone—(973) 503-1600**
**Fax—(973) 503-1704**
**Web—www.severna.com**
**Email—nkoch@severna.com**
**3 Eastmans Rd., Parsippany 07054**
*(see our ad under PLASTIC MACHINING)*

## PLASTIC FABRICATORS

ARC Plasmet Corp.
Phone—(201) 867-8533
4131 Bergen Tpke., North Bergen 07047
Complete Plastic Distributors, Inc.
Phone—(201) 666-8600
778 Carver Ave., Westwood 07675
Creative Patterns & Mfg., Inc.
Phone—(973) 589-1391
54 Freeman St., P.O. Box 5549, Newark 07105
Curbell, Inc., Plastics Div.
Phone—(856) 778-1100
844 N. Lenola Rd., Ste. 6, Moorestown 08057
E & T Plastics
Phone—(856) 787-0900
824 E. Gate Dr., Ste. E, Mount Laurel 08054
**Emco Industrial Plastics, Inc.**
Supplier of Plastic Sheet, Rod, Tube, Films & Prototyping
**Phone—(973) 559-5610**
**Fax—(973) 239-1595**
**Web—www.emcoplastics.com**
**Email—mailbox@emcoplastics.com**
**99 Commerce Rd., P.O. Box 2503, Cedar Grove 07009**
*(see our ad Outside Front Cover)*

Ethylene Atlantic Corp.
**Phone—(856) 467-0010**
**Fax—(856) 467-0610**
**Web—www.ethyleneatlantic.com**
**Email—sales@ethyleneatlantic.com**
**136 Church St., P.O. Box 430, Swedesboro 08085**
Grewe Plastics, Inc.
Phone—(973) 485-7602
123 S. 15th St., Newark 07107
J M J Profile, Inc.
Phone—(856) 767-3930
154 Copper Rd., Unit 1303, West Berlin 08091
Monarch Art Plastics, LLC
Phone—(856) 235-5151
3838 Church Rd., Mount Laurel 08054
Ronald-Mark Assocs., Inc.
Phone—(908) 558-0011
1227 Central Ave., P.O. Box 776, Hillside 07205
Rummel Industries, Inc.
Phone—(908) 688-6600
697 Rahway Ave., P.O. Box 1326, Union 07083
United Equipment & Fabricators
Phone—(973) 242-2737
175 Orange St., Newark 07103

## PLASTIC FILM

**Dana Poly Inc.**
The Home of Quality Film & Bags
**Phone—(908) 474-0600 / (800) 474-1020**
**Fax—(908) 474-0604**
**Web—www.danapoly.com**
**Email—sales@danapoly.com**
**1301 W. Elizabeth Ave., Linden 07036**
*(see our ad under BAGS — Plastic)*
**Emco Industrial Plastics, Inc.**
Supplier of Plastic Sheet, Rod, Tube, Films & Prototyping
**Phone—(973) 559-5610**
**Fax—(973) 239-1595**
**Web—www.emcoplastics.com**
**Email—mailbox@emcoplastics.com**
**99 Commerce Rd., P.O. Box 2503, Cedar Grove 07009**
*(see our ad Outside Front Cover)*
Griff Decorative Films Ltd.
Phone—(732) 367-2166
700 Vassar Ave., Lakewood 08701
Multi-Plastics, Inc.
Phone—(856) 241-9014
210 Commodore Dr., Swedesboro 08085
Polinas Plastics America, Inc.
Phone—(973) 777-8950
98 Scoles Ave., Clifton 07012
Poly One Corp.
Phone—(973) 522-2800
297 Ferry St., Newark 07105
Saint-Gobain Performance Plastics
Phone—(973) 696-4700
150 Dey Rd., Wayne 07470
Sigma Plastics Group (H Q)
Phone—(201) 933-6000
Page & Schuyler Aves., Bldg. 5, P.O. Box 808, Lyndhurst 07071
Sigma Stretch Film
Phone—(201) 507-9100
Page Ave., Bldg. 5 & 8, P.O. Box 808, Lyndhurst 07071
SunFlex Packagers, Inc.
Phone—(908) 709-1500
2 Commerce Dr., Cranford 07016

## PLASTIC FITTINGS

LNS Industries, Inc.
Phone—(609) 927-6656
P.O. Box 98, Somers Point 08244

## PLASTIC FOAM PACKAGING

CPI Packaging, Inc.
Phone—(732) 431-3500
50 Jiffy Rd., Somerset 08873

## PLASTIC FOAM PRODUCTS

Interfoam Fabricators, Inc.
Phone—(973) 633-8805
155 McBride Ave., Paterson 07501

WinCup
Phone—(732) 494-1999
190 Liberty St., Metuchen 08840

## PLASTIC INJECTION MOLDING

Ace Tool & Mfg. Co., Inc.
Phone—(973) 824-0222
532 Mulberry St., Ste. 1, Newark 07114
Creative Industries
Phone—(908) 561-5600
1409 Astor St., P.O. Box 313, South Plainfield 07080
Custom Craft Plastics
Phone—(732) 843-3000
100 King Arthurs Ct., P.O. Box 6029, North Brunswick 08902
Custom Molders Group
Phone—(908) 218-7997
160 Meister Ave., Ste. 1, Somerville 08876
Diversified Precision Tooling
Phone—(973) 361-8545
143 Baker St., Dover 07801
East Coast Plastics, Inc.
Phone—(856) 768-8700
427 Commerce Ln., Ste. 7, West Berlin 08091
**Emco Industrial Plastics, Inc.**
Supplier of Plastic Sheet, Rod, Tube, Films & Prototyping
**Phone—(973) 559-5610**
**Fax—(973) 239-1595**
**Web—www.emcoplastics.com**
**Email—mailbox@emcoplastics.com**
**99 Commerce Rd., P.O. Box 2503, Cedar Grove 07009**
*(see our ad Outside Front Cover)*
**Fram Trak Industries, Inc.**
Email: accounting@framtrak.com
**Phone—(732) 424-8400**
**Fax—(732) 424-8811**
**Web—www.framtrak.com**
**205 Hallock Ave., Middlesex 08846**
Frisch Plastics Corp.
Phone—(973) 685-5936
81 Windsor Dr., Pine Brook 07058
Genesis Biotechnology Group (H Q)
Phone—(609) 786-2800
1000 Waterview Dr., Hamilton 08691
Honeyware, Inc.
Phone—(201) 997-5900
244 Dukes St., Kearny 07032
Injection Works, Inc.
Phone—(856) 802-6444
104 Gaither Dr., Mount Laurel 08054
Injectron Corp.
Phone—(908) 753-1990
1000 S. 2nd St., P.O. Box 3012, Plainfield 07063
Inman Mold & Mfg. Co.
Phone—(732) 381-6229
815 Martin St., P.O. Box 1143, Rahway 07065
Interlink Products International, Inc.
Phone—(908) 862-8090
1315 E. Elizabeth Ave., Linden 07036
**J-Mac Plastics, Inc.**
**Phone—(908) 709-1111**
**Fax—(908) 709-8908**
**Email—service@jmacplastics.com**
**40 Lafayette Pl., Kenilworth 07033**
**Lawrence Mold and Tool Corp.**
Email: mboard@lmtproducts.com
**Phone—(609) 392-5422**
**Fax—(609) 392-5861**
**Web—www.lawrencemoldandtool.com**
**1412 Ohio Ave., Lawrenceville 08648**
*(see our ad under MOLDS)*
Madan Plastics, Inc.
Phone—(908) 276-8484
108 N. Union Ave., Ste. 3, Cranford 07016
MEC TECH, Inc.
Phone—(732) 505-0308
2200 Industrial Way S., Toms River 08755
**MedPlast Group**
**Phone—(856) 753-7600**
**Fax—(856) 768-1445**
**Web—www.medplastgroup.com**
**Email—dcain@medplastgroup.com**
**225 Old Egg Harbor Rd., West Berlin 08091**
Micro Molding, Inc.
Phone—(908) 454-1225
65 Howard St., Phillipsburg 08865

## PLASTIC INJECTION MOLDING —
(cont.)

**Montrose Molders Corp.**
Precision tooling & plastic injection molding
Phone—(908) 754-3030
Fax—(732) 529-4236
Web—www.montrosemolders.com
Email—bwilson@montrosemolders.com
25 Howard St., Piscataway 08854

**MONTROSE MOLDERS CORPORATION**

*Precision Tooling and Plastic Injection Molding*

www.montrosemolders.com

bwilson@montrosemolders.com

**(908) 754-3030**

FAX: (732) 529-4236

25 Howard St.
Piscataway, NJ 08854

Newton T & M Corp.
Phone—(973) 383-1232
119 Fredon Springdale Rd., Newton 07860
Pee Wee Molding Corp.
Phone—(732) 469-0200
240 Circle Dr. N., Piscataway 08854
Pierson Industries, Inc.
Phone—(973) 627-7945
7 Astro Pl., Rockaway 07866
Plastic Monofil Co. Ltd.
Phone—(732) 629-7701
25 Howard St., Piscataway 08854
Reiss Mfg., Inc.
Phone—(732) 446-6100
75 Mount Vernon Rd., P.O. Box 310, Englishtown 07726
Research & Mfg. Corp. Of America
Phone—(908) 862-6744
1130 W. Elizabeth, Linden 07036
Star-Glo Industries, LLC
Phone—(201) 939-6162
2 Carlton Ave., East Rutherford 07073
Technimold, Inc.
Phone—(908) 232-8331
715 Jerusalem Rd., Scotch Plains 07076
Technitool, Inc.
Phone—(856) 768-2707
1028 Industrial Dr., West Berlin 08091
Tri-Tech Tool & Design Co., Inc.
Phone—(732) 469-5433
30 Cherry St., South Bound Brook 08880
Van Ness Plastic Molding Co.
Phone—(973) 778-9500
400 Brighton Rd., Clifton 07012
Viking Mold & Tool, Inc.
Phone—(609) 476-9333
64 Tuckahoe Rd., Dorothy 08317

*Send an RFQ (request for quote) to multiple suppliers at*

**IndustryNet.com**

**Severna**

*Precision Machined and Molded Plastic Components*

3 Eastmans Road
Parsippany, NJ 07054
Ph 973-503-1600 Fax 973-503-1704

**www.severna.com**

Intertek

---

**Wiggins Plastics, Inc.**
Est. 1948-ISO Certified; Custom Injection/
Thermoplastics/Thermosets/Compression/Transfer
Molding
Phone—(973) 667-7200
Fax—(973) 667-3227
Web—www.wigginsplastics.com
Email—info@wigginsplastics.com
180 Kingsland Rd., P.O. Box 1077, Clifton 07014

**wigginsplastics, inc.**

*Since 1948*

**180 Kingsland Road
P.O. Box 1077
Clifton, NJ 07014**

Custom Injection • Thermoplastics &
Thermosets, Compression
& Transfer Molding

**Telephone: 973-667-7200**

**Fax: 973-667-3227**

email: info@wigginsplastics.com

Web: www.wigginsplastics.com

**ISO Certified**

Yuhl Products, Inc.
Phone—(908) 276-5180
15 N. 7th St., Kenilworth 07033

## PLASTIC INJECTION MOLDING —
Custom

Bennett Plastics, Inc.
Phone—(973) 684-1501
22 Kentucky Ave., Paterson 07503
Hoffman Precision Plastics, Inc.
Phone—(856) 228-3550
548 Almonesson Rd., P.O. Box 338, Blackwood 08012
**Lawrence Mold and Tool Corp.**
Email: mboard@lmtproducts.com
Phone—(609) 392-5422
Fax—(609) 392-5861
Web—www.lawrencemoldandtool.com
1412 Ohio Ave., Lawrenceville 08648
*(see our ad under MOLDS)*
LOR-TECH Plastics, LLC
Phone—(973) 503-1750
3 Eastmans Rd., Unit 3, Parsippany 07054

*Do nationwide searches for products & services at:*
**IndustryNet.com**

Menshen Packaging U.S.A., Inc.
Phone—(201) 445-7436
Fax—(201) 445-3473
Web—www.menshenusa.com
Email—info@menshenusa.com
21 Industrial Park, Waldwick 07463
Mira Plastics Co., Inc.
Phone—(973) 383-6380
1 Mira Ave., Fredon Twp., P. O. Box 399, Newton 07860
Severna Operations, Inc.
Phone—(973) 503-1600
Fax—(973) 503-1704
Web—www.severna.com
Email—nkoch@severna.com
3 Eastmans Rd., Parsippany 07054
*(see our ad on this page)*
Wiggins Plastics, Inc.
Est. 1948-ISO Certified; Custom Injection/
Thermoplastics/Thermosets/Compression/Transfer
Molding
Phone—(973) 667-7200
Fax—(973) 667-3227
Web—www.wigginsplastics.com
Email—info@wigginsplastics.com
180 Kingsland Rd., P.O. Box 1077, Clifton 07014
*(see our ad under PLASTIC INJECTION MOLDING)*

## PLASTIC INJECTION MOLDING —
Short Run

Severna Operations, Inc.
Phone—(973) 503-1600
Fax—(973) 503-1704
Web—www.severna.com
Email—nkoch@severna.com
3 Eastmans Rd., Parsippany 07054
*(see our ad on this page)*

## PLASTIC LAMINATING

Glenmore Plastic Industries, Inc.
Phone—(718) 649-7800
115 Newfield Ave., Edison 08837

## PLASTIC MACHINING

Emco Industrial Plastics, Inc.
Supplier of Plastic Sheet, Rod, Tube, Films &
Prototyping
Phone—(973) 559-5610
Fax—(973) 239-1595
Web—www.emcoplastics.com
Email—mailbox@emcoplastics.com
99 Commerce Rd., P.O. Box 2503, Cedar Grove 07009
*(see our ad Outside Front Cover)*
Severna Operations, Inc.
Phone—(973) 503-1600
Fax—(973) 503-1704
Web—www.severna.com
Email—nkoch@severna.com
3 Eastmans Rd., Parsippany 07054
*(see our ad on this page)*

## PLASTIC MATERIALS

Claude Bamberger Molding Compounds Corp.
Phone—(201) 933-6262
111 Paterson Plank Rd., P.O. Box 67, Carlstadt 07072
Heroflon USA Corp.
Phone—(908) 829-4949
Home State Road 249, Hillsborough 08844

## PLASTIC MOLDED PARTS

**Severna Operations, Inc.**
**Phone—(973) 503-1600**
**Fax—(973) 503-1704**
**Web—www.severna.com**
**Email—nkoch@severna.com**
**3 Eastmans Rd., Parsippany 07054**
*(see our ad under PLASTIC MACHINING)*

## PLASTIC MOLDING — Thermoset

**Wiggins Plastics, Inc.**
Est. 1948-ISO Certified; Custom Injection/
Thermoplastics/Thermosets/Compression/Transfer
Molding
**Phone—(973) 667-7200**
**Fax—(973) 667-3227**
**Web—www.wigginsplastics.com**
**Email—info@wigginsplastics.com**
**180 Kingsland Rd., P.O. Box 1077, Clifton 07014**
*(see our ad under PLASTIC INJECTION MOLDING)*

## PLASTIC MOLDING MACHINERY

Emabond Solutions, LLC
Phone—(201) 767-7400
49 Walnut St., Ste. 2, Norwood 07648
High Technology Corp.
Phone—(201) 488-0010
144 South St., Hackensack 07601
Jomar Corp.
Phone—(609) 646-8000
115 E. Parkway Dr., Egg Harbor Township 08234
Kautex Machines, Inc.
Phone—(908) 252-9350
201 Chambers Brook Rd., P.O. Box 5329, North Branch 08876
Orycon Control Technology, Inc.
Phone—(732) 922-2400
3407 Rose Ave., Ocean 07712

## PLASTIC PACKAGING

**All Size Poly Bags**
Leaders in supplying plastic bags, packaging,
shipping & warehouse supplies nationwide
**Phone—(800) 635-9959 / (732) 828-3400**
**Fax—(732) 828-7703**
**Web—www.allsizepolybags.com**
**Email—info@rksplastics.com**
**P.O. Box 836, New Brunswick 08903**
*(see our ad under BAGS—Plastic)*
B & W Plastics, Inc.
Phone—(973) 383-0020
20 Wilson Dr., Sparta 07871
Corbco, Inc.
Phone—(908) 239-3279
40 Canterbury Dr., Forked River 08731
M. S. Plastics Packaging Co., Inc.
Phone—(973) 492-2400
10 Park Pl., Bldg. 2-1A-2, Butler 07405
Reliant Group
Phone—(973) 977-8799
318 McLean Blvd., Paterson 07504

## PLASTIC PARTS

Princeton Tec
Phone—(609) 298-9331
110 Collings Ave., West Berlin 08091
Pro Plastics, Inc.
Phone—(908) 925-5555
1190 Sylvan St., P.O. Box 1489, Linden 07036

*find additional suppliers at*
**IndustryNet.com**

## PLASTIC PRODUCTS
(also see specific product)

Acme Plastics, Inc.
Phone—(973) 256-6666
222 Browertown Rd., P.O. Box 806, Woodland Park 07424
Associated Plastics, Inc.
Phone—(732) 574-2800
179 E. Inman Ave., Rahway 07065
Beauticraft Slipcover Co.
Phone—(215) 625-7979
9 Wynnewood Dr., Voorhees 08043
Bilfinger Water Technologies
Phone—(609) 693-9434
708 Challenger Way, Forked River 08731
Carpathian Industries, LLC
Phone—(201) 798-8883
51 Newark St., Ste. 508, Hoboken 07030
D & D Technology, Inc.
Phone—(908) 688-5154
254 Elmwood Ave., P.O. Box 3636, Union 07083
EMI Yoshi, Inc.
Phone—(732) 248-5533
1200 Jersey Ave., North Brunswick 08902
Engineered Plastic Products, Inc.
Phone—(908) 647-3500
269 Mercer St., P.O. Box 196, Stirling 07980
Engineering Laboratories, Inc.
Phone—(201) 337-8116
360 W. Oakland Ave., Oakland 07436
Frame-A-Coin Mfg.
Phone—(973) 822-0094
318 Front St., Ste. 1, Belvidere 07823
Imagine Corp., The
Phone—(973) 942-2888
320 N. 6th St., Prospect Park 07508
Inteplast Group Ltd. (H Q)
Phone—(973) 994-8000
9 Peach Tree Hill Rd., Livingston 07039
Kin Core
Phone—(908) 479-1188
70 North St., P.O. Box 485, Bloomsbury 08804
Laird Plastics, Inc.
Phone—(732) 593-2777
135 Fieldcrest Ave., Ste. 135-F, Edison 08837
Marlo Plastic Products, Inc.
Phone—(732) 792-1984
289 State Route 33, Manalapan 07726
Mr. Ice Bucket, LLC
Phone—(732) 545-0420
345 Sandford St., New Brunswick 08901
N.J. Plastics Machining & Fabricating, Inc.
Phone—(609) 965-1550
46 Liverpool Ave., P.O. Box 646, Egg Harbor City 08215
O K Tool & Die Co.
Phone—(856) 629-5757
603 Bluebell Rd., Williamstown 08094
Ryan Herco Flow Solutions Corp.
Phone—(908) 534-6111
50 Tannery Rd., Reading Industrial Ctr., Bldg. 3, Somerville 08876
**Severna Operations, Inc.**
**Phone—(973) 503-1600**
**Fax—(973) 503-1704**
**Web—www.severna.com**
**Email—nkoch@severna.com**
**3 Eastmans Rd., Parsippany 07054**
*(see our ad under PLASTIC MACHINING)*
ThermaFreeze Products Corp. (H Q)
Phone—(877) 777-8397
107 Maple Grange Rd., Vernon 07462
Thermo Plastics Technologies, Inc.
Phone—(908) 687-4833
1119 Morris Ave., Union 07083
Tyz-All Plastics, LLC
Phone—(201) 343-1200
130 Gamewell St., Hackensack 07601
United Plastics Group, Inc.
Phone—(732) 873-1848
30 Commerce Dr., Somerset 08873
Viz Plastic Products Ltd.
Phone—(201) 784-4442
210 Industrial Pkwy., Northvale 07647
W Y Plastic Industry, Inc.
Phone—(201) 617-8000
2500 Secaucus Rd., North Bergen 07047

## PLASTIC PRODUCTS —
## Protective

Transparent Office Products, LLC
Phone—(856) 488-5455
2550 Haddonfield Rd., Pennsauken 08110

## PLASTIC PROFILES & SHAPES

Interplast, Inc.
Phone—(609) 386-4990
100 Connecticut Dr., P.O. Box 1328, Burlington 08016
Jabat, Inc., K.
Phone—(732) 469-8177
342 Highway 22 W., Green Brook 08812

## PLASTIC RECYCLING

Plastic Services, Inc.
Phone—(201) 200-1200
200 Pacific Ave., Jersey City 07304

## PLASTIC RESINS

A & C Catalysts, Inc.
Phone—(908) 474-9393
1600 W. Blancke St., Linden 07036
Akcros Chemicals, Inc.
Phone—(732) 247-2202
500 Jersey Ave., New Brunswick 08901
American Infinity Compounding Corp.
Phone—(856) 467-3030
2079 Center Square Rd., Logan Township 08085
CVC Thermoset Specialties, Inc.
Phone—(856) 533-3000
844 N. Lenola Rd., Ste. 1, Moorestown 08057
Deltech Resin Co.
Phone—(973) 589-0880
49 Rutherford St., Newark 07105
Formosa Plastics Corp. U.S.A. (H Q)
Phone—(973) 992-2090
9 Peach Tree Hill Rd., Livingston 07039
OxyVinyls
Phone—(856) 299-8498
P.O. Box 411, Pedricktown 08067
Polymeric Resources Corporation, Inc.
Phone—(973) 694-4141
55 Haul Rd., Wayne 07470
Rimtec Corp.
Phone—(609) 387-0011
1702 Beverly Rd., Burlington 08016
ROWA Group USA, LLC
Phone—(609) 567-8600
100 9th St., Hammonton 08037
Sun Plastech Inc.
Phone—(973) 257-1999
1055 Parsippany Blvd., Ste. 405, Parsippany 07054

## PLASTIC SHEET, ROD & TUBE

Central Plastics Co.
Phone—(973) 808-0990
333 New Rd., Parsippany 07054
**Emco Industrial Plastics, Inc.**
Supplier of Plastic Sheet, Rod, Tube, Films &
Prototyping
**Phone—(973) 559-5610**
**Fax—(973) 239-1595**
**Web—www.emcoplastics.com**
**Email—mailbox@emcoplastics.com**
**99 Commerce Rd., P.O. Box 2503, Cedar Grove 07009**
*(also see our ad Outside Front Cover)*

www.emcoplastics.com
**973-559 -5610**
Fax: 973-239-1595
**Emco Industrial Plastics, Inc.**
Plastic Fabrication & Distributor

## PLASTIC SHEET, ROD & TUBE —
*(cont.)*

**Total Plastics, Inc.**
ISO 9001:2008 Certified
Phone—(609) 689-0990 / (888) 801-2006
Fax—(609) 689-1555
Web—www.totalplastics.com
Email—tpi_phi@totalplastics.com
299 Canal Rd., Fairless Hills, PA 19030
U. S. Cast
Phone—(856) 347-2342
321 Willow Grove Rd., Pittsgrove 08318

## PLASTIC SHEETING

**Emco Industrial Plastics, Inc.**
Supplier of Plastic Sheet, Rod, Tube, Films &
Prototyping
Phone—(973) 559-5610
Fax—(973) 239-1595
Web—www.emcoplastics.com
Email—mailbox@emcoplastics.com
99 Commerce Rd., P.O. Box 2503, Cedar
Grove 07009
        *(see our ad Outside Front Cover)*
Kappus Plastics Co., Inc.
Phone—(908) 537-2288
61-65 Route 31 S., P.O. Box 151, Hampton 08827
Primex Plastics Corp.
Phone—(973) 470-8000
65 River Dr., Garfield 07026

## PLASTIC SHEETING — Polyethylene

**Phoenix Industries, LLC**
Phone—(973) 366-4199
Fax—(973) 366-5288
Web—www.phoenixpkgind.com
Email—vnorcia@phoenixpkgind.com
105 W. Dewey Ave., P.O. Box 416, Wharton
07885

## PLASTIC THERMOFORMING

C & K Plastics, Inc.
Phone—(732) 549-0011
159 Liberty St., Metuchen 08840
Fitzpak, Inc.
Phone—(609) 860-0095
110 Melrich Rd., Ste. 2, Cranbury 08512
Trinity Mfg., LLC
Phone—(732) 549-2866
60 Leonard St., Metuchen 08840

## PLASTIC TRANSFER MOLDING

**Wiggins Plastics, Inc.**
Est. 1948-ISO Certified; Custom Injection/
Thermoplastics/Thermosets/Compression/Transfer
Molding
Phone—(973) 667-7200
Fax—(973) 667-3227
Web—www.wigginsplastics.com
Email—info@wigginsplastics.com
180 Kingsland Rd., P.O. Box 1077, Clifton
07014
        *(see our ad under PLASTIC INJECTION MOLDING)*

## PLASTIC TRIM

INTEX Millwork Solutions, LLC
Phone—(856) 293-4100
20 Bogden Blvd., Millville 08332

## PLASTICS

**AGF Burner, Inc.**
Phone—(732) 730-8090
Fax—(732) 730-8060
Web—www.agfburner.com
Email—sales@agfburner.com
1955 Swarthmore Ave., Unit 2, Lakewood
08701
        *(see our ad under GAS BURNERS)*

## PLASTIC HOUSINGS
### ENGINEERED PLASTIC PRODUCTS, INC.
269 Mercer St., PO Box 196 • Stirling, NJ 07980
www.engineeredplastic.com
eppi@engineeredplastic.com
**800-304-EPPI**
Tel: 908-647-3500   Fax: 908-647-1868

Central Art & Engineering, Inc.
Phone—(609) 758-5922
500 Goldman Dr., P.O. Box 289, Cream Ridge
08514
**Emco Industrial Plastics, Inc.**
Supplier of Plastic Sheet, Rod, Tube, Films &
Prototyping
Phone—(973) 559-5610
Fax—(973) 239-1595
Web—www.emcoplastics.com
Email—mailbox@emcoplastics.com
99 Commerce Rd., P.O. Box 2503, Cedar
Grove 07009
        *(also see our ad Outside Front Cover)*
**Hillside Plastics Corp.**
Phone—(800) 837-7731
Fax—(973) 923-2056
Web—www.hillsideplasticscorp.com
Email—maria@hillsideplastics.net
125 Long Ave., P.O. Box 609, Hillside 07205
Precision Mfg., LLC
Phone—(973) 278-6600
177 Gould Ave., Paterson 07503

## PLASTICS — Molded

**Montrose Molders Corp.**
Precision tooling & plastic injection molding
Phone—(908) 754-3030
Fax—(732) 529-4236
Web—www.montrosemolders.com
Email—bwilson@montrosemolders.com
25 Howard St., Piscataway 08854
        *(see our ad under PLASTIC INJECTION MOLDING)*

## PLASTICS — Reaction Injection Molded

Exothermic Molding, Inc.
Phone—(908) 272-2299
50 Lafayette Pl., Kenilworth 07033

## PLASTICS — Rotationally Molded

Meese Orbitron Dunne Co.
Phone—(201) 796-4667
535 N. Midland Ave., Saddle Brook 07663

## PLASTICS — Scrap

**Excel Plastics Recycling, Inc.**
Quality Plastics. Email: ed@excelrecycling.com
Phone—(201) 991-2500
Fax—(201) 991-2526
Web—www.excelrecycling.net
Email—brian@excelrecycling.net
996 Belleville Tpke., Kearny 07032

## PLASTICS — Thermoset

Owens Plastic Products, Inc.
Phone—(856) 447-3500
393 Main St., P.O. Box 118, Cedarville 08311

Search from among 430,000
U.S. manufacturers & suppliers:
**IndustryNet.com**

**Wiggins Plastics, Inc.**
Est. 1948-ISO Certified; Custom Injection/
Thermoplastics/Thermosets/Compression/Transfer
Molding
Phone—(973) 667-7200
Fax—(973) 667-3227
Web—www.wigginsplastics.com
Email—info@wigginsplastics.com
180 Kingsland Rd., P.O. Box 1077, Clifton
07014
        *(see our ad under PLASTIC INJECTION MOLDING)*

## PLASTICS — Vacuum Formed

Daysol Industries
Phone—(908) 272-5900
40 Boright Ave., Kenilworth 07033
**Engineered Plastic Products, Inc.**
Phone—(908) 647-3500 / (800) 304-3774
Fax—(908) 647-1868
Web—www.engineeredplastic.com
Email—eppi@engineeredplastic.com
269 Mercer St., P.O. Box 196, Stirling 07980
        *(see our ad on this page)*

## PLASTICS ENGINEERING

**Shore Plastic Technologies, Inc.**
Specializing in comprehensive consulting
engineering services for product development &
testing, including 3D modeling, 2D drafting, FEA,
moldflow & motion analysis
Phone—(856) 327-5114
Fax—(856) 825-9296
Web—www.shoreplastictech.com
Email—info@shoreplastictech.com
215 Buck St., Millville 08332

## PLASTICS MACHINERY & EQUIPMENT

Kuntz Co., Inc., R. T.
Phone—(732) 751-1770
5146 W. Hurley Pond Rd., P.O. Box 476,
Farmingdale 07727
Proven Technology, Inc.
Phone—(908) 359-7888
5 Woodshire Way, Hillsborough 08844
**Warwick Mfg. & Equipment Co., LLC**
Buy & sell used: Chemical, food, cosmetic, packaging
& pharmaceutical equipment
Phone—(732) 729-0400 / (732) 241-9263
Fax—(732) 729-1235
Web—www.warwickequipment.com
Email—sales@warwickequipment.com
1112 12th St., North Brunswick 08902
        *(see our ad Outside Back Cover)*

## PLASTICS RESEARCH & DEVELOPMENT

**Shore Plastic Technologies, Inc.**
Specializing in comprehensive consulting
engineering services for product development &
testing, including 3D modeling, 2D drafting, FEA,
moldflow & motion analysis
Phone—(856) 327-5114
Fax—(856) 825-9296
Web—www.shoreplastictech.com
Email—info@shoreplastictech.com
215 Buck St., Millville 08332

## PLATING

D. F. Enterprise, LLC
  Phone—(856) 875-1777
  3254 S. Black Horse Pike, Williamstown 08094

Ideal Plating & Polishing Co.
  **Phone—(973) 759-5559**
  **Fax—(973) 759-0277**
  **Email—rfknigge@gmail.com**
  **681 Main St., Bldg. 39, P.O. Box 100, Belleville 07109**

Independence Plating Corp.
  Phone—(973) 523-1776
  107 Alabama Ave., Paterson 07503

**Paramount Metal Finishing Co.**
  **Plating-Painting-Screen Printing-Assembly-Powder**
  **Coating-Certified ISO 9001:2008**
  **Phone—(908) 862-0772**
  **Fax—(908) 862-9477**
  **Web—www.pmf1.com**
  **Email—bnegrin@pmfnj.com**
  **1515 W. Elizabeth Ave., Linden 07036**

## PLATING — Aluminum

Ideal Plating & Polishing Co.
  **Phone—(973) 759-5559**
  **Fax—(973) 759-0277**
  **Email—rfknigge@gmail.com**
  **681 Main St., Bldg. 39, P.O. Box 100, Belleville 07109**

## PLATING — Chrome

**Industrial Hard Chromium Co.**
  **Phone—(973) 344-2265**
  **Fax—(973) 344-2812**
  **Web—www.ihcco.com**
  **Email—craig@ihcco.com**
  **7 Rome St., Newark 07105**

## PLATING — Electro

A & F Electroplating, Inc.
  Phone—(973) 736-4344
  106 Ashland Ave., West Orange 07052

Alcaro & Alcaro Plating Co., Inc.
  Phone—(973) 746-1200
  112 Pine St., P.O. Box 1215, Montclair 07042

American Electroplating Co.
  Phone—(973) 427-2300
  342 Lincoln Ave., Hawthorne 07506

**B & B Electroplating Co.**
  **Electroplating, including Tin, Silver, Nickel, Barrel & Rack**
  **Phone—(908) 925-5044**
  **Fax—(908) 925-1936**
  **Web—www.bbplating.com**
  **Email—r2thistle@aol.com**
  **559 Pennsylvania Ave., Linden 07036**

Becker Plating, Inc.
  Phone—(732) 775-8945
  121 Highway 35 N., Neptune 07753

Elkem, Inc.
  Phone—(732) 566-1700
  443 County Rd., Cliffwood 07721

Hill Cross Co., Inc.
  Phone—(201) 864-3393
  543 56th St., P.O. Box 60, West New York 07093

**Ideal Plating & Polishing Co.**
  **Phone—(973) 759-5559**
  **Fax—(973) 759-0277**
  **Email—rfknigge@gmail.com**
  **681 Main St., Bldg. 39, P.O. Box 100, Belleville 07109**

Imperial Electro Plating
  Phone—(201) 438-9450
  52 Park Ave., Lyndhurst 07071

Manco Plating, Inc.
  Phone—(973) 485-6800
  390 Park Ave., P.O. Box 7025, Newark 07107

Mastercraft Electroplating
  Phone—(908) 354-4404
  801 Magnolia Ave., Elizabeth 07201

Miller & Sons, Inc.
  Phone—(973) 759-6445
  24 Belleville Ave., Belleville 07109

Vanguard Research Industries
  Phone—(908) 753-2770
  239 Saint Nicholas Ave., South Plainfield 07080

## PLATING — Electroless Nickel

Ideal Plating & Polishing Co.
  **Phone—(973) 759-5559**
  **Fax—(973) 759-0277**
  **Email—rfknigge@gmail.com**
  **681 Main St., Bldg. 39, P.O. Box 100, Belleville 07109**

## PLATING — Gold

Ideal Plating & Polishing Co.
  **Phone—(973) 759-5559**
  **Fax—(973) 759-0277**
  **Email—rfknigge@gmail.com**
  **681 Main St., Bldg. 39, P.O. Box 100, Belleville 07109**

## PLATING — Hard Chrome

Diamond Hard Chromium Co., Inc.
  Phone—(973) 824-9412
  463 NJ Railroad Ave., Newark 07114

Tomken Plating Co., Inc.
  Phone—(856) 829-0607
  625 Pear St., P.O. Box 2323, Riverton 08077

## PLATING — Metal

Art Metalcraft Plating Co., Inc.
  Phone—(856) 365-0001
  529 S. 2nd St., Camden 08103

Deptford Plating
  Phone—(856) 227-1144
  Route 41 & Dein Ave., P.O. Box 5056, Deptford 08096

Duro Plating Co., Inc.
  Phone—(856) 963-4967
  273 Kaighns Ave., Camden 08103

General Magnaplate Corp.
  Phone—(908) 862-6200
  1331 U.S. Route 1, Linden 07036

**Mara Polishing & Plating Corp.**
  **Phone—(973) 242-0800**
  **Fax—(973) 242-5205**
  **Web—www.marametalpolishingplating.com**
  **Email—maraplater105@verizon.net**
  **105-107 W. Peddie St., Newark 07112**

Microcast Technologies Corp.
  Phone—(908) 523-9503
  1611 W. Elizabeth Ave., Linden 07036

Reflective Metals, Inc.
  Phone—(732) 918-7490
  1001 Hopewell Ave., Ocean 07712

Suffern Plating Co.
  Phone—(973) 473-4404
  210 Garibaldi Ave., P.O. Box 755, Lodi 07644

T R B Electro Corp.
  Phone—(973) 278-9014
  6 Morris St., P.O. Box 840, Paterson 07501

## PLATING EQUIPMENT & SUPPLIES

Galvanotech
  Phone—(908) 241-3900
  330-A Dalziel Rd., Linden 07036

International Micro Industries, Inc.
  Phone—(856) 616-0051
  1951 Old Cuthbert Rd., Bldg. 404, Cherry Hill 08034

## PLATING RACKS

Tilton Rack & Basket Corp.
  Phone—(973) 226-6010
  66 Passaic Ave., Fairfield 07004

## Need an *Industry*Section for another state?

Call us... 847-864-7590

## PLAYGROUND EQUIPMENT

**Mr. Fence**
  **Specializing in fences and patio furniture, gazebos, wishing wells, swing-sets, arbors, lighthouses and many custom yard accessories**
  **Phone—(732) 303-1614**
  **Fax—(732) 303-0358**
  **Web—www.cmrfence.com**
  **Email—cmrfence@aol.com**
  **3468 U.S. Highway 9, Ste. 2, Freehold 07728**

## PLEATING

Pleating Plus Ltd.
  Phone—(201) 863-2991
  527 40th St., Union City 07087

## PLUGS

**American Tube & Paper**
  **80 Furler St., Totowa 07512**
  **Phone—(973) 256-3600**
  **Fax—(973) 785-3341**
  **Web—www.AmericanPaperProducts.com**
  **Email—sales@americanpaperproducts.com**
  **P.O. Box 68, Totowa 07511**
  *(see our ad under MAILING TUBES)*

## PLUMBING AND HEATING EQUIPMENT — Wholesale

Aaron & Co.
  Phone—(732) 752-8200
  30 Turner Pl., Piscataway 08854

Blackman Plumbing Supply Co., Inc.
  Phone—(201) 529-5500
  270 Route 17 S., Mahwah 07430

Colonial Commercial Corp.
  Phone—(973) 427-8224
  275 Wagaraw Rd., Hawthorne 07506

Ferguson Enterprises, Inc.
  Phone—(732) 775-5270
  401 Main St., Avon By The Sea 07717

Ferguson Enterprises, Inc.
  Phone—(908) 725-0666
  830 Route 22, Bridgewater 08807

Ferguson Enterprises, Inc.
  Phone—(201) 945-3080
  369 Anderson Ave., Fairview 07022

Ferguson Enterprises, Inc.
  Phone—(609) 693-0077
  737 S. Main St., Forked River 08731

Ferguson Enterprises, Inc.
  Phone—(201) 369-5120
  1 Colony Rd., Jersey City 07305

General Plumbing Supply, Inc.
  Phone—(732) 248-1000
  980 New Durham Rd., Edison 08817

## PLUMBING FIXTURES

Chatham Brass, LLC
  Phone—(908) 668-0500
  1253 New Market Ave., Unit D, South Plainfield 07080

## PLUMBING SUPPLIES

D'Angelo Metal Products Co., Inc.
  Phone—(908) 862-8220
  360 Dalziel Rd., Linden 07036

Ferguson Enterprises, Inc.
  Phone—(201) 236-3111
  16 Arrow Rd., Ramsey 07446

Kissler & Co., Inc.
  Phone—(201) 896-9600
  770 Central Blvd., Carlstadt 07072

## PLUMBING SUPPLIES — Wholesale

Bergen Industrial Supply A division of F.W. Webb
  Phone—(201) 796-2600
  30 Stefanic Ave., Elmwood Park 07407

E & B Distributors, Inc.
  Phone—(732) 469-2266
  400 Route 22 E., Bridgewater 08807

## PLUMBING SUPPLIES —
### Wholesale — *(cont.)*

East Brunswick Supply, Inc.
Phone—(732) 254-1015
413 State Route 18, East Brunswick 08816

Ferguson Enterprises
Phone—(973) 614-9464
835 Bloomfield Ave., Clifton 07012

Ferguson Enterprises, Inc.
Phone—(609) 485-2266
2531 Tilton Rd., Egg Harbor Township 08234

Ferguson Enterprises, Inc.
Phone—(201) 768-6080
444 Livingston St., Norwood 07648

Ferguson Enterprises, Inc.
Phone—(973) 983-1177
100 U.S. Highway 46, Rockaway 07866

Grant Supply Co., Inc.
Phone—(732) 545-1018
901 Joyce Kilmer Ave., North Brunswick 08902

Grant Supply Co., Inc.
Phone—(609) 641-1114
755 W. Delilah Rd., Pleasantville 08232

New Jersey Plumbing, Heating & Industrial Supply, LLC
Phone—(973) 761-4567
91 Newark Way, Maplewood 07040

Palermo Supply
Phone—(609) 494-0343
1819 Central Ave., Ship Bottom 08008

Perrotti Sales
Phone—(908) 806-8899
19 Woodside Ln., Flemington 08822

Seashore Supply Of Wildwood
Phone—(609) 522-1491
306 Wildwood Ave., Wildwood 08260

Weinstein Supply Co.
Phone—(609) 677-0666
3187 Fire Rd., Egg Harbor Township 08234

Weinstein Supply Co.
Phone—(856) 825-1460
4019 S. Main Rd., Vineland 08360

Weinstein Supply Corp.
Phone—(856) 964-1700
1687 Haddon Ave., Camden 08103

## PLYWOOD — Wholesale

Fessenden Hall, Inc.
Phone—(856) 665-2210
1050 Sherman Ave., Pennsauken 08110

## PNEUMATIC COMPONENTS

Convertech, Inc.
Phone—(973) 328-1850
353 Richard Mine Rd., Wharton 07885

## PNEUMATIC CONTROL SYSTEMS

**Radwell International, Inc.**
**Stocking, Selling, Repairing New & Surplus Industrial Automation, MRO, Pneumatic, Motion, Electronic, Hydraulic, HVAC & Electrical Control Equipment for plant floor & facilities maintenance machinery. Also buying Surplus Industrial Controls**
**Phone—(609) 288-9393 / (800) 332-4336**
**Fax—(609) 288-9417**
**Web—www.plccenter.com**
**Email—ahorner@plccenter.com**
**111 Mount Holly Bypass, Lumberton 08048**

## POLISHES

Liquid Glass Enterprises, Inc.
Phone—(201) 387-6755
93 Railroad Ave., Bergenfield 07621

## POLISHES — Automotive

Harvey Westbury Corp. (H Q)
Phone—(201) 468-7779
160 Littleton Rd., Ste. 308, Parsippany 07054

## POLISHES — Metal

Matchless United Co.
Phone—(908) 862-7300
801 E. Linden Ave., Linden 07036

## POLISHING — Stainless Steel

GP Precision, Inc.
ISO 9001:2000 Certified
Phone—(908) 850-1940
Fax—(908) 850-5926
Web—www.gpsheetmetal.com
Email—sales@gpsheetmetal.com
434 Sand Shore Rd., Hackettstown 07840

## POLISHING EQUIPMENT

Delta Tool & Polishing Supplies Co., Inc.
Phone—(908) 518-7600
45 North Ave., P.O. Box 169, Garwood 07027

## POLLUTION CONTROL EQUIPMENT

Advanced Industrial Technology
Phone—(201) 265-1414
640 Cambridge Rd., Paramus 07652

D R Technology, Inc.
Phone—(732) 780-4664
73 South St., Freehold 07728

Redkoh Industries, Inc.
Phone—(908) 369-1590
300 Valley Rd., Hillsborough 08844

Town & Country Plastics, Inc.
Phone—(732) 780-5300
P.O. Box 269, Morganville 07751

## POLLUTION CONTROL SYSTEMS

Air Purifiers, Inc.
Phone—(973) 586-3988
1 Pine St., Rockaway 07866

Plymovent Corporation (H Q)
Phone—(609) 395-3500
115 Melrich Rd., Ste. 2, Cranbury 08512

## POLYESTER FIBERFILL

Carlee Corp.
Phone—(201) 768-6800
28 Piermont Rd., Rockleigh 07647

## POLYESTER FILM

Atlantic Protective Pouches
Phone—(732) 240-3871
1545 Route 37 W., Unit 6, Toms River 08755

Metal FX Films, LLC
Phone—(732) 560-1297
27 Kearney St., Unit B, Bridgewater 08807

## POLYETHYLENE FILM

AEP Industries Inc. (H Q)
Phone—(201) 641-6600
95 Chestnut Ridge Rd., Montvale 07645

B E R Plastic Corp.
Phone—(973) 839-2100
5 Curtis St., P.O. Box 2, Riverdale 07457

## POLYETHYLENE PRODUCTS

All American Poly Corp.
Phone—(732) 752-3200
40 Turner Pl., Piscataway 08854

Redi Packaging, Inc.
Phone—(732) 544-1480
265 Highway 36, Ste. 109, West Long Branch 07764

## POLYMERS

Borealis Compounds, Inc.
Phone—(908) 850-6200
176 Thomas Rd., Port Murray 07865

*Do nationwide searches for products & services at:* IndustryNet.com

Deltech Resin Co.
Phone—(973) 589-0880 / (973) 589-3331
(800) 785-4415
Fax—(973) 589-7231
Web—www.deltechcorp.com
Email—danderson@deltechresins.com
49 Rutherford St., Newark 07105
*(see our ad under RESINS)*

HD MicroSystems
Phone—(732) 613-2500
250 Cheesequake Rd., Parlin 08859

Scheld Assocs., Inc.
Phone—(973) 694-0637
37 Pleasantview Dr., Wayne 07470

Solar Compounds Corp.
Phone—(908) 862-2813
1201 W. Blancke St., P.O. Box 1097, Linden 07036

Technovations Technology Reviews, Inc.
Phone—(973) 537-9511
14 Red Barn Ln., Randolph 07869

## POLYSTYRENE — Expanded

International Cushioning Co.
Phone—(732) 683-9600
240 Boundary Rd., Marlboro 07746

## POLYURETHANE

**Innovative Resin Systems, Inc.**
**Emails: spatel@rez-cure.com & manny@rez-cure.com**
**Structural adhesives, coatings, pottings & encapsulating compounds**
**Phone—(973) 465-6887**
**Fax—(973) 465-0592**
**Web—www.rez-cure.com**
**257 Wilson Ave., Newark 07105**
*(see our ad under ADHESIVES)*

Polyurethane Specialties Co.
Phone—(201) 438-2325
624 Schuyler Ave., Lyndhurst 07071

## POLYURETHANE MATERIALS

Chemtura Corp.
Phone—(732) 826-6600
1000 Convery Blvd., Perth Amboy 08861

## POLYURETHANE MIXING EQUIPMENT

**Trico Poly Systems, LLC**
**Polyurethane & epoxy processing machinery, including slinger degassers**
**Phone—(973) 376-7770**
**Fax—(973) 376-7779**
**Web—www.tricopoly.com**
**Email—tricopoly@verizon.net**
**60 Brown Ave., Springfield 07081**

## POLYURETHANE PRODUCTS

Bumper Specialties, Inc.
Phone—(856) 251-9993
1607 Imperial Way, West Deptford 08066

## POPCORN

Golden Fluff, Inc.
Phone—(732) 367-5448
118 Monmouth Ave., Lakewood 08701

## PORCELAIN PRODUCTS

Boehm Porcelain, LLC
Phone—(609) 656-2200
25 Princess Diana Dr., Trenton 08638

Cybis Porcelains Studio & Gallery
Phone—(609) 392-6074
200 Elizabeth Ave., Ste. 200, Trenton 08610

Mottahedeh & Co., Inc.
Phone—(609) 409-1490
5 Corporate Dr., Cranbury 08512

*find additional suppliers at* IndustryNet.com

## PORK PROCESSING

Case Pork Roll Co., Inc.
Phone—(609) 396-8171
644 Washington St., Trenton 08611

## POTPOURRI

Jodhpuri, Inc.
Phone—(973) 299-7009
260-A Walsh Dr., Parsippany 07054

## POTTERY

Hopewell Pottery
Phone—(609) 466-9048
18 Burton Ave., Hopewell 08525
Our Name Is Mud
Phone—(856) 375-2098
15 Potter St., Ste. 1, Haddonfield 08033

## POULTRY HOUSING EQUIPMENT

Chick Master International, Inc. (H Q)
Phone—(201) 871-8810
25 Rockwood Pl., Ste. 335, Englewood 07631

## POULTRY PROCESSING

B & B Poultry Co., Inc.
Phone—(856) 692-8893
Almond Rd., P.O. Box 307, Norma 08347
Golden Platter Foods, Inc.
Phone—(973) 242-0290
37 Tompkins Point Rd., Newark 07114
Hinck's Turkey Farm, Inc.
Phone—(732) 681-0508
3930 Belmar Blvd., Neptune 07753
Mitchell, Inc., David
Phone—(856) 429-2610
210 Park Dr., Voorhees 08043
New York Poultry Co., Inc.
Phone—(908) 523-1600
3351 Tremley Point Rd., Linden 07036
San Miguel Live Poultry, LLC
Phone—(973) 482-1007
499 Orange St., Newark 07107

## POWDER BLENDING

General Machine Co. Of New Jersey
Phone—(732) 752-7900
301 Smalley Ave., Middlesex 08846

## POWDER COATING

ABCO Die Casters, Inc.
Email: jvitollo@abcodiecasters.com
Founded in 1971, serving numerous industries
throughout North America by supplying quality zinc
die castings & powder coated components
Phone—(973) 624-7030
Fax—(973) 624-7425
Web—www.abcodiecasters.com
39 Tompkins Point Rd., Newark 07114
Acme Mfg. & Coating Co.
Phone—(732) 541-2800
900 Port Reading Ave., P.O. Box 70, Port Reading
07064
All American Powder Coating
Phone—(732) 349-7001
Fax—(732) 349-7079
Email—aapowdercoating@gmail.com
2002 Route 9, Toms River 08755
Alpha Processing Co. Inc.
Phone—(973) 777-1737
210 Delawanna Ave., P.O. Box 936, Clifton 07014
Boyko's Metal Finishing Co.
Phone—(973) 623-4254
100 Poinier St., Newark 07114

**Is your company properly represented in the IndustrySection?**

If not, call... 847-864-7590

---

Bridgeview Industrial Finishers, Inc.
Serving Camden, Burlington, Gloucester Counties NJ
& Philadelphia Areas
Phone—(856) 768-3624
Fax—(856) 768-2218
Web—www.bvfinishers.com
Email—sales@bvfinishers.com
241 Terrace Blvd., Voorhees 08043

## BRIDGEVIEW

Industrial Finishers, Inc.

### 50 Years of Steady Growth
### One Stop Shopping

Powder Coating
Painting   Bakes   Epoxies
Military Spec
Precision Silkscreening

# 856-768-3624
# Fax: 856-768-2218

# www.bvfinishers.com

Extreme Painting & Powder Coating, LLC
Phone—(856) 541-8733
944 Reeves Ave., Camden 08105
J & M Enterprises
Phone—(856) 447-5090
32 North Ave., Cedarville 08311
Newark Industrial Spraying, Inc.
Phone—(973) 344-6855
12 Amsterdam St., Newark 07105
Paramount Metal Finishing Co.
Plating-Painting-Screen Printing-Assembly-Powder
Coating-Certified ISO 9001:2008
Phone—(908) 862-0772
Fax—(908) 862-9477
Web—www.pmf1.com
Email—bnegrin@pmfnj.com
1515 W. Elizabeth Ave., Linden 07036
Peerless Coatings, LLC
Providing Powder Coating, Sandblasting, Assembling
& Packaging Services, Teflon® finishes along with
Traditional Wet Paint finishes, and all types of
Metalizing.
Phone—(973) 427-8771
Fax—(973) 427-8779
Web—www.peerlesscoatings.com
Email—peerless1@verizon.net
220-A Goffle Rd., Hawthorne 07506
Pioneer Metal Finishing, Inc.
Phone—(856) 694-0400
2034 Coles Mill Rd., P.O. Box 387, Franklinville
08322
Productive Industrial Finishing
Phone—(856) 427-9646
103 American Way, Voorhees 08043
SAR Industrial Finishing, Inc.
Phone—(609) 567-2772
Fax—(609) 567-2494
Email—jsmauro@comcast.net
104 N. Route 73, Berlin 08009
SDL Studio, LLC
Phone—(732) 473-0800
1591 Route 37 W., Ste. E-4, Toms River 08755

*Search from among 430,000 U.S. manufacturers & suppliers at*
**IndustryNet.com**

---

Spray Powders, Inc.
Phone—(732) 493-1311
Fax—(732) 493-0140
Email—somabhai@aol.com
P.O. Box 76, Oakhurst 07755

# Spray Powders, Inc.
*Powder Coatings*
732-493-1311   FAX: 732-493-0140
somabhai@aol.com
PO Box 76  Oakhurst, NJ 07755

## POWDER COATING — Metal

All American Powder Coating
Phone—(732) 349-7001
Fax—(732) 349-7079
Email—aapowdercoating@gmail.com
2002 Route 9, Toms River 08755
Durex, Inc.
Email: custserv@durexinc.com
ISO 9001 Registered Contract Metal Fabrication
Facility
Phone—(908) 688-0800
Fax—(908) 688-0718
Web—www.durexinc.com
5 Stahuber Ave., Union 07083
*(see our ad under METAL FABRICATING)*
Paramount Metal Finishing Co.
Plating-Painting-Screen Printing-Assembly-Powder
Coating-Certified ISO 9001:2008
Phone—(908) 862-0772
Fax—(908) 862-9477
Web—www.pmf1.com
Email—bnegrin@pmfnj.com
1515 W. Elizabeth Ave., Linden 07036
Powtek Powder Coating, Inc.
Phone—(609) 394-6700
233 Dickinson St., Trenton 08638

## POWDER COATINGS

Innovative Powder Coatings, LLC
Phone—(856) 661-0086
9105 Burrough-Dover Ln., Pennsauken 08110
Protech Powder Coating, Inc.
Phone—(973) 257-0505
21 Audrey Pl., Fairfield 07004
Spray Powders, Inc.
Phone—(732) 493-1311
Fax—(732) 493-0140
Email—somabhai@aol.com
P.O. Box 76, Oakhurst 07755

# Spray Powders, Inc.
*Powder Coatings*
732-493-1311   FAX: 732-493-0140
somabhai@aol.com
PO Box 76  Oakhurst, NJ 07755

## POWDERED METAL PRODUCTS

Atlantic Equipment Engineers, Inc.
High purity metals, metal powders, compounds &
fabricated forms. ISO Certified
Phone—(201) 828-9400
Fax—(201) 387-0291
Web—www.micronmetals.com
Email—info@micronmetals.com
24 Industrial Ave., P.O. Box 181, Upper Saddle
River 07458

*Search from among 430,000 U.S. manufacturers & suppliers:*
**IndustryNet.com**

## POWER CORDS

**Americor Electronics, Ltd.**
   Phone—(847) 956-6200 / (800) 830-5337
   Fax—(847) 956-0300
   Web—www.americor-usa.com
   Email—info@americor-usa.com
   675 S. Lively Blvd., Elk Grove Village, IL 60007
   *(see our ads under CABLE ASSEMBLIES & CORD SETS)*

## POWER EQUIPMENT

ASCO Power Technologies, Inc.
   Phone—(856) 810-9600
   5000 Sagemore Dr., Ste. 200, Marlton 08053
SL Industries, Inc. (H Q)
   Phone—(856) 727-1500
   520 Fellowship Rd., Ste. A-114, Mount Laurel
   08054

## POWER EQUIPMENT — Outdoor

Macro Equipment Co.
   Phone—(856) 235-4235
   205 Hartford Rd., Route 38, Mount Laurel 08054

## POWER GENERATORS

Cobra Power Systems, Inc.
   Phone—(908) 486-1800
   8 America Way, Spotswood 08884
Power Pool Plus, Inc.
   Phone—(908) 454-1124
   7 Edge Rd., Alpha 08865

## POWER PLANT EQUIPMENT

JNT Technical Services, Inc.
   Phone—(201) 641-2130
   85 Industrial Ave., Little Ferry 07643

## POWER SUPPLIES

**Americor Electronics, Ltd.**
   Phone—(847) 956-6200 / (800) 830-5337
   Fax—(847) 956-0300
   Web—www.americor-usa.com
   Email—info@americor-usa.com
   675 S. Lively Blvd., Elk Grove Village, IL 60007
   *(see our ads under CABLE ASSEMBLIES & CORD SETS)*
Antron Technologies, Inc.
   Phone—(732) 205-0415
   40 Brunswick Ave., Ste. 104, Edison 08817
Globtek, Inc.
   Phone—(201) 784-1000
   186 Veterans Dr., Northvale 07647
Jerome Industries Corp.
   Phone—(908) 353-5700
   730 Division St., Elizabeth 07201
MEGA Electronics, Inc.
   Phone—(732) 249-2656
   4-B Jules Ln., New Brunswick 08901
Polytron Devices, Inc.
   Phone—(973) 345-5885
   295-303 River St., Paterson 07524
Seren I.P.S., Inc.
   Phone—(856) 205-1131
   1670 Gallagher Dr., Vineland 08360
TDI Power
   Phone—(908) 850-5088
   36 Newburgh Rd., Hackettstown 07840
TDK-Lambda, Inc.
   Phone—(732) 922-9300
   405 Essex Rd., Neptune 07753
Technology Dynamics, Inc.
   Phone—(201) 385-0500
   100 School St., Bergenfield 07621

## POWER SUPPLIES — DC

Magna-Power Electronics
   Phone—(908) 237-2200
   39 Royal Rd., Flemington 08822
Mid-Eastern Industries Div, Technology Dynamics,
   Inc
   Phone—(201) 385-0500
   100 School St., Bergenfield 07621

**ASCO®  ASCO Power Technologies, L.P.**

*Automatic transfer switches, back up power systems*

www.emersonnetworkpower.com/asco

**(800) 800-2726 / FAX: (973) 718-4333**

50 Hanover Rd.  Florham Park, NJ 07932

## POWER SUPPLIES — High Voltage

Glassman High Voltage, Inc.
   Phone—(908) 638-3800
   124 W. Main St., P.O. Box 317, High Bridge 08829

## POWER SYSTEMS

**ASCO Power Technologies, L.P. (H Q)**
   Phone—(800) 800-2726
   Fax—(973) 718-4333
   Web—www.emersonnetworkpower.com/asco
   Email—customercare@asco.com
   50 Hanover Rd., Florham Park 07932
   *(see our ad on this page)*
Transmission Technology Corp.
   Phone—(973) 305-3600
   1 High Mountain Trl., Lincoln Park 07035

## POWER SYSTEMS — Back Up

**ASCO Power Technologies, L.P. (H Q)**
   Phone—(800) 800-2726
   Fax—(973) 718-4333
   Web—www.emersonnetworkpower.com/asco
   Email—customercare@asco.com
   50 Hanover Rd., Florham Park 07932
   *(see our ad on this page)*

## POWER SYSTEMS — Stand-By

**ASCO Power Technologies, L.P. (H Q)**
   Phone—(800) 800-2726
   Fax—(973) 718-4333
   Web—www.emersonnetworkpower.com/asco
   Email—customercare@asco.com
   50 Hanover Rd., Florham Park 07932
   *(see our ad on this page)*
Como Electric, Inc.
   Phone—(732) 449-7625
   Fax—(732) 449-6896
   Email—comoelect@aol.com
   909 Wall Rd., Spring Lake 07762
   *(see our ad under GENERATORS—Electric)*

## POWER SYSTEMS — Temporary

Como Electric, Inc.
   Phone—(732) 449-7625
   Fax—(732) 449-6896
   Email—comoelect@aol.com
   909 Wall Rd., Spring Lake 07762
   *(see our ad under GENERATORS—Electric)*

*Do nationwide searches for products & services at:*
**IndustryNet.com**

## POWER TRANSMISSION BELTING

**BRECOflex Co., L.L.C.**
   Phone—(732) 460-9500 / (888) 463-1400
   Fax—(732) 542-6725
   Web—www.brecoflex.com
   Email—info@brecoflex.com
   222 Industrial Way W., Eatontown 07724
   *(see our ads under BELTING & PULLEYS)*
VIS USA, LLC
   Phone—(908) 575-0606
   210 Meister Ave., Branchburg 08876
**Volta Belting Technology**
   Phone—(973) 276-7905
   Fax—(973) 276-7908
   Web—www.voltabelting.com
   Email—sales@voltabelting.com
   11 Chapin Rd., Pine Brook 07058

## POWER TRANSMISSION COMPONENTS

BCC (U.S.A.) Inc.
   Phone—(732) 572-5450
   143 Ethel Rd. W., Piscataway 08854

## POWER TRANSMISSION EQUIPMENT

Cangro Transmission Co. Of New Jersey
   Phone—(973) 772-7662
   295 Crooks Ave., Clifton 07011
PBM Supply Co., Inc.
   Phone—(973) 839-0050
   Fax—(973) 839-4886
   Email—pbmsupply@verizon.net
   88 Cannonball Rd., P.O. Box 351, Pompton
   Lakes 07442
Total Machine Solutions, Inc.
   Phone—(973) 244-0017
   16 Spielman Rd., Fairfield 07004

## PRECAST ERECTORS

**Cranez, Inc.**
   For more than 20 yrs., serving the Tri-State area.
   Offering free no-obligation est.; providing svc. 24 hrs.,
   7 days a week & no-cost site checks. Operators are
   CCO/Natnl. Commission certified, have TWIC
   credentials & O.S.H.A 30-hrs trained
   Phone—(856) 262-0288 / (877) 262-0288
   Fax—(856) 262-2654
   Web—www.cranezincnj.com
   Email—cranez06@aol.com
   2610 S. Black Horse Pike, Williamstown 08094

*Do nationwide searches for products & services at:*
**IndustryNet.com**

*INDUSTRY*

## PRECIOUS METALS PROCESSING

**Heraeus Precious Metals North America, LLC**
Refining, trading, jewelry sweeps, karat gold,
polishing sweeps & platinum scrap
Phone—(973) 817-7878
Fax—(973) 578-2786
Web—www.heraeus.com
Email—refiningnj@heraeus.com
65 Euclid Ave., Newark 07105

**Reldan Metals Co., Div. of Abington Reldan Metals, LLC**
Phone—(800) 764-9222
Fax—(732) 238-8595
Web—www.armetals.com
Email—sales@armetals.com
550 Old Bordentown Rd., Fairless Hills, PA 19030
*(see our ad under PRECIOUS METALS REFINING)*

## PRECIOUS METALS REFINING

**Electrum, Inc.**
Environmentally Safe Solder & Precious Metal
Recycling
Phone—(732) 396-1616 / (800) 622-1192
Fax—(732) 396-9390
Web—www.electruminc.com
Email—mdouglas@electruminc.com
827 Martin St., Rahway 07065
*(also see our ad under RECYCLING — Metal)*

**Electrum, Inc.**
*Environmentally safe solder
& precious metal recycling*
www.electruminc.com
(732) 396-1616
827 Martin St. Rahway, NJ 07065

**Heraeus Precious Metals North America, LLC**
Refining, trading, jewelry sweeps, karat gold,
polishing sweeps & platinum scrap
Phone—(973) 817-7878
Fax—(973) 578-2786
Web—www.heraeus.com
Email—refiningnj@heraeus.com
65 Euclid Ave., Newark 07105

**Metallix Refining, Inc.**
Phone—(732) 936-0050
59 Avenue At The Common, Ste. 201,
Shrewsbury 07702

**Reldan Metals Co., Div. of Abington Reldan Metals, LLC**
Phone—(800) 764-9222
Fax—(732) 238-8595
Web—www.armetals.com
Email—sales@armetals.com
550 Old Bordentown Rd., Fairless Hills, PA 19030

**Reldan Metals Co.**
Div. of Abington Reldan Metals, LLC
*Precious Metal Refining*
www.armetals.com
sales@armetals.com
800-764-9222 • Fax: 732-238-8595
550 Old Bordentown Rd. • Fairless Hills, PA 19030

## PRECISION MACHINED COMPONENTS

**Central Metal Fabricators, Inc.**
Phone—(732) 938-6900
Fax—(732) 938-6902
Web—www.centralmetalfab.com
Email—info@centralmetalfab.com
300 Central Ave., Farmingdale 07727

**CNC Supermatic LLC**
Phone—(973) 627-4433
27 Old Beach Glen Rd., Rockaway 07866

---

**Crown Precision Corp.**
Phone—(973) 470-0097
61 Willet St., Ste. 13, Passaic 07055

**Marlton Pike Precision, LLC**
Phone—(856) 665-1900
728 Beechwood Ave., Cherry Hill 08002

**N. B. & Sons, LLC**
Phone—(856) 692-6191
402 E. Wheat Rd., Vineland 08360

**Triad Tool Co.**
Phone—(908) 534-1784
9 Commerce St., Branchburg 08876

**Win-Tech Precision Products, Inc.**
Phone—(973) 887-8727
5 Littell Rd., East Hanover 07936

## PRESSES — Hydraulic

**Grimco Presses Co.**
Phone—(973) 345-0660
65 1st Ave., Paterson 07514

## PRESSES — Stamping

**Bruderer Machinery, Inc.**
Phone—(201) 941-2121
1200 Hendricks Cswy., Ridgefield 07657

## PRESSURE SENSITIVE PRODUCTS

**American Biltrite, Inc.**
Phone—(856) 778-0700
105 Whittendale Dr., Moorestown 08057

## PRESSURE SENSORS

**Concept Group, Inc.**
Glass to metal seals (hermetic packages) & Vacuum
insulated components
Phone—(856) 767-5506
Fax—(856) 768-3981
Web—www.conceptgroupinc.com
Email—applications@conceptgroupinc.com
380 Cooper Rd., West Berlin 08091
*(see our ad under MACHINE PARTS — Precision)*

## PRESSURE VESSEL REPAIR

**Cotterman, Inc.**
Code Vessel Repair
Phone—(856) 464-6820 / (856) 577-0245
Fax—(856) 464-6930
Web—www.cottermaninc.com
Email—welders@cottermancorp.com
100 Hayes Ave., P.O. Box 278, Wenonah 08090
*(see our ad under PIPE FITTERS)*

## PRESSURE VESSELS

**Dusenbery Engineering Co.**
Phone—(973) 539-2200
309 E. Hanover Ave., P.O. Box 1001, Morristown 07962

**Oliver, Inc., G. J.**
Phone—(908) 454-9743
50 Industrial Rd., Phillipsburg 08865

**Tolan Machinery Co., Inc./Tolan Polishing Corp.**
Also stainless steel polishing & alloy fabrication
Phone—(973) 983-7212
Fax—(973) 983-7217
164 Franklin Ave., P.O. Box 695, Rockaway 07866

## PRESSURE WASHERS

**Pressure King, Inc.**
Phone—(201) 768-1911
231 Herbert Ave., Ste. 1, Closter 07624

## PRETZELS

**A & A Soft Pretzel Co.**
Phone—(856) 338-0208
1100 N. 32nd St., Camden 08105

**Federal Pretzel Baking Co.**
Phone—(215) 467-0505
300 Eagle Ct., P.O. Box 257, Bridgeport 08014

---

**J & J Snack Foods Corp.**
Phone—(856) 665-9534
6000 Central Hwy., Pennsauken 08109

**South Jersey Soft Pretzel, Inc.**
Phone—(856) 435-5055
Fax—(856) 627-2810
Web—www.southjerseypretzel.com
Email—info@southjerseypretzel.com
912 N. White Horse Pike, Ste. A, Stratford 08084

## PRIMERS

**Advanced Protective Products, Inc.**
Phone—(718) 359-1315
17-12 River Rd., Fair Lawn 07410

## PRINTED CIRCUIT BOARD ASSEMBLIES

**Circuit Tech Assembly, LLC**
Phone—(856) 231-0777
341 New Albany Rd., Ste. 130, Moorestown 08057

**GAB Electronic Services, LLC**
Phone—(856) 786-0108
1703 Industrial Hwy., Unit 8, Cinnaminson 08077

**JRE Incorporated**
Phone—(973) 808-0055
22 Fairfield Pl., West Caldwell 07006

**Shore P C**
Phone—(732) 380-0590
3 Meridian Rd., Eatontown 07724

**Sure Design**
Phone—(732) 919-3066
5027 Industrial Rd., Unit 3, Farmingdale 07727

## PRINTED CIRCUIT BOARD DESIGN

**PNC, Inc.**
Email: sam@pnconline.com
PCB Design, Rigid, Flex & Rigi-Flex PCBs, PCBA &
SMT Stencils
Phone—(973) 284-1600
Fax—(973) 284-1925
Web—www.pnconline.com
115 E. Centre St., Nutley 07110

## PRINTED CIRCUIT BOARD MANUFACTURING EQUIPMENT

**Argus International**
Phone—(609) 466-1677
424 Route 31 N., P.O. Box 559, Ringoes 08551

**Fancort Industries, Inc.**
Phone—(973) 575-0610
31 Fairfield Pl., West Caldwell 07006

## PRINTED CIRCUIT BOARDS

**Americor Electronics, Ltd.**
Phone—(847) 956-6200 / (800) 830-5337
Fax—(847) 956-0300
Web—www.americor-usa.com
Email—info@americor-usa.com
675 S. Lively Blvd., Elk Grove Village, IL 60007
*(see our ads under CABLE ASSEMBLIES & CORD SETS)*

**Anta Electric, Inc.**
Phone—(973) 366-2222
32 Richboynton Rd., Dover 07801

**Applicad, Inc.**
Phone—(732) 751-2555
5029 Industrial Rd., Farmingdale 07727

**AudioCodes, Inc.**
Phone—(732) 469-0880
27 Worlds Fair Dr., 1st Fl., Somerset 08873

**Circuit Reproduction Co., Inc.**
Phone—(201) 712-9292
219 Hergesell Ave., Maywood 07607

**Circuits Sales**
Phone—(732) 255-1325
104 Alissa Dr., Toms River 08753

**Cygnus, LLC**
Phone—(973) 523-0668
510 E. 41st St., Paterson 07504

**Delta Circuits, Inc.**
Phone—(973) 575-3000
26 Spielman Rd., Fairfield 07004

## PRINTED CIRCUIT BOARDS — *(cont.)*

**Doralex, Inc.**
Phone—(856) 764-0694
403 Saint Mihiel Dr., Riverside 08075

**Flextron Systems**
Phone—(856) 742-0550
85 Nicholson Rd., Gloucester City 08030

**Galaxy Circuits, Inc.**
Phone—(908) 822-1400
100 Somogyi Ct., South Plainfield 07080

**Micro Logic, Inc.**
Phone—(201) 962-7512
31 Industrial Ave., Ste. 6, Mahwah 07430

**Omega Circuits & Engineering Corp.**
Phone—(732) 246-1661
8 Terminal Rd., New Brunswick 08901

**PNC, Inc.**
Email: sam@pnconline.com
PCB Design, Rigid, Flex & Rigi-Flex PCBs, PCBA &
SMT Stencils
**Phone—(973) 284-1600**
**Fax—(973) 284-1925**
**Web—www.pnconline.com**
**115 E. Centre St., Nutley 07110**

**Precision Products Co.**
Phone—(201) 712-5757
219 Hergesell Ave., Maywood 07607

**R & D Circuits**
Phone—(732) 549-4554
3601 S. Clinton Ave., South Plainfield 07080

**Reliance Electronics, Inc.**
Phone—(973) 237-0400
20 W. End Rd., Totowa 07512

**SWEMCO**
Phone—(856) 222-9900
1215 N. Church St., Moorestown 08057

**Technical Aids, Inc.**
Phone—(973) 674-1082
219 S. 18th St., East Orange 07018

**Technobox, Inc.**
Phone—(856) 809-2306
154 Cooper Rd., Ste. 901, West Berlin 08091

## PRINTER CARTRIDGES

**Cartridge World Oakhurst**
Phone—(732) 531-4232
1815 State Route 35, Oakhurst 07755

## PRINTER SUPPLIES

**Cartridge World**
Phone—(201) 891-0990
830 Franklin Ave., Franklin Lakes 07417

**Printers' Service, Inc.**
Phone—(973) 589-7800
26 Blanchard St., Newark 07105

## PRINTERS — Computer

**Craden Peripherals Corp.**
Phone—(856) 488-0700
7860 Airport Hwy., Pennsauken 08109

**Depot America, Inc.**
Phone—(732) 919-0209
1495 Highway 34, Farmingdale 07727

**Oki Data Americas, Inc.**
Phone—(856) 235-2600
2000 Bishops Gate Blvd., Mount Laurel 08054

## PRINTERS — Digital

**Princeton Printer**
Phone—(609) 924-4630
150 Nassau St., Princeton 08542

## PRINTING

**1 2 3 Quick Print, Inc.**
Phone—(732) 442-1771
297 New Brunswick Ave., Perth Amboy 08861

**A D K Graphics, Inc.**
Phone—(609) 208-1080
325 Corporate Blvd., Robbinsville 08691

**A G F Printing, Inc.**
Phone—(973) 253-8550
92 Bogart Ave., Garfield 07026

**A J Images, Inc.**
Phone—(908) 241-6900
259 E. 1st Ave., Roselle 07203

**A-1 Business Service**
Phone—(732) 910-6995
P.O. Box 83, Rahway 07065

**A-Aaabacus Printing & Promotional Specialties Of Metuchen**
Phone—(732) 767-9204
243 Amboy Ave., Metuchen 08840

**ABC Printing**
Phone—(973) 664-1160
20 Wall St., Ste. C-5, Rockaway 07866

**ABCO Printing Co.**
Phone—(609) 259-4900
92 N. Main St., Windsor 08561

**Access Printing, Inc.**
Phone—(856) 829-1673
510 N. Belleview Ave., Riverton 08077

**Ace Lithographers**
Phone—(908) 665-1700
22 Russo Pl., Berkeley Heights 07922

**Ace Twill**
Phone—(908) 665-1700
22 Russo Pl., Berkeley Heights 07922

**Action Graphics, Inc.**
Phone—(973) 633-6500
600 Ryerson Rd., Ste. G, Lincoln Park 07035

**Action Office Supplies, Inc.**
Phone—(732) 534-3000
687 Prospect St., Ste. 480, Lakewood 08701

**Adams Printing & Graphics**
Phone—(856) 455-7177
886 N. Pearl St., Bridgeton 08302

**Advertiser, The**
Phone—(856) 694-0444
235 Blackwood Ave., P.O. Box 54, Franklinville 08322

**AELitho Group, Inc.**
Phone—(609) 239-0700
450 Broad St., P.O. Box 9000, Beverly 08010

**Affordable Offset Printing, Inc.**
Phone—(856) 661-0722
809 Hylton Rd., Ste. 11, Pennsauken 08110

**Al Quick Quality Printers, Inc.**
Phone—(201) 659-4003
77 Tuers Ave., Jersey City 07306

**Alete Printing, LLC**
Phone—(856) 468-3536
722 Dartmouth Ct., P.O. Box 371, Wenonah 08090

**Alex Real, LLC**
Phone—(732) 730-8770
501 Prospect St., Ste. 107, Lakewood 08701

**Alexander, Inc., Sandy**
Phone—(973) 470-8100
200 Entin Rd., Clifton 07014

**All Points Printing & Graphics**
Phone—(732) 892-6670
831 Arnold Ave., Point Pleasant 08742

**All The Best Invitations**
Phone—(973) 992-4033
123 W. Mount Pleasant Ave., Livingston 07039

**Allegra Princeton**
Phone—(609) 771-4000
12 Stults Rd., Ste. 100, Dayton 08810

**Allegra Print & Imaging, Inc.**
Phone—(609) 771-4000
12 Stults Rd., Dayton 08810

**Allen Group SMC**
Phone—(908) 231-1100
60 Readington Rd., Branchburg 08876

**Allied Envelope Co., Inc.**
Phone—(201) 440-2000
33 Commerce Rd., Carlstadt 07072

**Allied Printing & Graphics**
Phone—(973) 227-0520
4 Madison Rd., Fairfield 07004

**Allure Visuals & Printing**
Phone—(201) 288-1111
9 1st St., Lodi 07644

**AlphaGraphics**
Phone—(908) 233-5553
1111 U.S. Highway 22 E., Mountainside 07092

**AlphaGraphics**
Phone—(908) 277-3000
558 Central Ave., New Providence 07974

**AlphaGraphics 321**
Phone—(732) 985-6677
90 Saw Mill Pond Rd., Heller Industrial Pk., Edison 08817

**AlphaGraphics Printshops**
Phone—(732) 758-0095
68 White St., Red Bank 07701

**AlphaGraphics, Inc.**
Phone—(908) 281-9476
173 Route 206 N., Hillsborough 08844

**Alphagraphics, Inc.**
Phone—(973) 984-0066
60 Speedwell Ave., Morristown 07960

**AMREP Corporation (H Q)**
Phone—(609) 716-8200
300 Alexander Pk., Ste. 204, Princeton 08540

**Anna Soiree**
Phone—(732) 686-9570
2005 State Route 35, Ste. 19, Oakhurst 07755

**Anuco, Inc.**
Phone—(973) 887-9465
911 Charles Dr., P.O. Box 5016, Toms River 08753

**Apple Printing Co., Inc.**
Phone—(609) 561-4411
5 Weymouth Rd., P.O. Box 574, Hammonton 08037

**Archive Print, Inc.**
Phone—(732) 528-5300
3203 Atlantic Ave., Allenwood 08720

**ARG Printing, LLC**
Phone—(856) 665-5644
1601 Sherman Ave., Pennsauken 08110

**Arista Custom Tapes, Inc.**
Phone—(201) 997-7610
20 Argyle Pl., North Arlington 07031

**Ariston Multimedia, LLC**
Phone—(973) 553-2727
94 Valley Rd., Clifton 07013

**Arms Graphics**
Phone—(201) 767-6504
169 Paris Ave., Northvale 07647

**Art Graphic Impressions**
Phone—(973) 696-2800
1044 State Route 23, Ste. 101, Wayne 07470

**Art Press Printing, Inc.**
Phone—(856) 547-8953
124 Clements Bridge Rd., Barrington 08007

**Artisan Digital, Inc.**
Phone—(973) 379-2788
21 Fadem Rd., Unit 1, Springfield 07081

**ASAP Coastal Printing and Signs**
Phone—(609) 597-7421
775 N. Main St., Manahawkin 08050

**Associated Mailing & Printing Services, LLC**
Phone—(908) 541-9700
50 Tannery Rd., Ste. 2, Branchburg 08876

**Athens Printing Co., Inc.**
Phone—(201) 342-1771
95 Myer St., Hackensack 07601

**Atlantic Printing Co.**
Phone—(732) 920-2300
262 Circle Dr., Brick 08723

**Avenue Printing Co.**
Phone—(201) 652-2035
143 Franklin Tpke., Waldwick 07463

**Ayers Printing**
Phone—(908) 687-2891
1413 Chestnut Ave., Hillside 07205

**B & L Printing Co., Inc.**
Phone—(908) 707-1311
46 Old Complain Rd., Hillsborough 08844

**Bailey's Printing, Inc.**
Phone—(732) 462-8010
191 Throckmorton St., Freehold 07728

**Bannon Group**
Phone—(201) 451-6500
629 Grove St., Jersey City 07310

**Banquet Services International**
Phone—(732) 270-1188
2214 Route 37 E., Toms River 08753

**Barrington Press Inc**
Phone—(201) 843-6556
37 Spring Valley Ave., Paramus 07652

**Barton & Cooney, LLC**
Phone—(609) 747-9300
300 Richards Run, Burlington 08016

**BBC Printing**
Phone—(973) 948-7998
4 Main St., P.O. Box 276, Branchville 07826

## PRINTING — (cont.)

Bellia Print & Copy Center
Phone—(856) 582-4004
190 William L. Dalton Dr., Glassboro 08028

Bernardsville Print Center
Phone—(908) 766-4073
21 Mine Brook Rd., Bernardsville 07924

Berry Business Procedure Co.
Phone—(908) 272-6464
6 Park St., P.O. Box 845, Cranford 07016

Bill's Printing Service, Inc.
Phone—(609) 888-1841
2829 S. Broad St., Trenton 08610

Bistis Press
Phone—(973) 373-8033
1310 Clinton Ave., Irvington 07111

Blue Dog Graphics
Phone—(201) 343-3343
222 River St., Hackensack 07601

Blue Parachute
Phone—(732) 767-1320
263 Amboy Ave., Ste. 1, Metuchen 08840

blue
parachute

Commercial and Large Format Printing,
Signs & Displays, Graphic Design, Promo Items

www.bluechute.com • (732) 767-1320
263 Amboy Ave. Ste. 1 • Metuchen, NJ 08840

Boro Printing, Inc.
Phone—(732) 229-1899
813 Broadway, West Long Branch 07764

Brooke Business Forms & Supplies, Inc.
Phone—(732) 617-7550
50 U.S. Highway 9, Ste. 303, Morganville 07751

Budget Print Center
Phone—(973) 743-0073
332 Broad St., Bloomfield 07003

Budget Print Center
Phone—(856) 438-6204
177 S. Centre St., Ste. 200-K, Merchantville 08109

Budget Printing Center
Phone—(856) 596-2980
300 E.Greentree Rd., Unit 14, Marlton 08053

Budget Printing, LLC
Phone—(732) 574-1330
70 Westfield Ave., Clark 07066

Burlington Press
Phone—(609) 387-0030
328 High St., Burlington 08016

Burns, Inc., Joseph
Phone—(732) 356-7990
241 W. Union Ave., Bound Brook 08805

Business Graphics
Phone—(973) 838-9553
22 Park Pl., P.O. Box 832, Butler 07405

C & A Press, Inc.
Phone—(732) 238-1150
636 State Route 18, East Brunswick 08816

C & K Printing Co., Inc.
Phone—(973) 473-0739
203 Paterson Ave., Ste. 1, Wallington 07057

C & S Hot Stamping Co.
Phone—(201) 840-4004
20 Edgewater Pl., Edgewater 07020

C & W Systems
Phone—(201) 791-7892
17-04 Split Rock Rd., P.O. Box 201, Fair Lawn 07410

C B Printing & Graphics, Inc.
Phone—(201) 445-6500
795 Susquehanna Ave., Franklin Lakes 07417

C Graphics Studio
Phone—(201) 866-0592
410 32nd St., Union City 07087

Calandra Printing
Phone—(973) 228-1649
491 Bloomfield Ave., Caldwell 07006

Cameo Novelty & Pen
Phone—(973) 923-1600
400 Hillside Ave., Hillside 07205

Capital Offset, Inc.
Phone—(973) 279-3023
257 10th Ave., Paterson 07524

Capital Printing Corp.
Phone—(732) 560-1515
420 South Ave., Middlesex 08846

Capitol Copy Service
Phone—(609) 989-8776
116 W. State St., Trenton 08608

Castle Printing, Inc.
Phone—(973) 584-0990
1501 U.S. Highway 46, Ledgewood 07852

Challenge Printing Co., The
Phone—(973) 471-4700
2 Bridewell Pl., Clifton 07014

Cheshire Studio, Inc.
Phone—(973) 240-7360
261 Main St., 2nd Fl., Ledgewood 07852

City Print Shop, Inc.
Phone—(201) 792-6699
157 Sip Ave., Jersey City 07306

Clark Printing Co.
Phone—(201) 845-4888
441 Market St., Saddle Brook 07663

Clayton Press, Inc.
Phone—(732) 774-2624
P.O. Box 676, Asbury Park 07712

Clondalkin Pharma & Healthcare
Phone—(856) 439-1700
1224 N. Church St., Moorestown 08057

Clover Printing Corp.
Phone—(201) 641-7800
77 Park St., Ridgefield Park 07660

CMYK Printing, Inc.
Phone—(201) 458-1300
180 Coolidge Ave., Englewood 07631

Color Optics By Arcade, Inc.
Phone—(973) 664-3100
40 Green Pond Rd., Rockaway 07866

Color Screen Pros
Phone—(973) 268-5080
100 Verona Ave., Newark 07104

ColorSource, Inc.
Phone—(856) 488-8100
7025 Central Hwy., Pennsauken 08109

Colour Graphics
Phone—(856) 939-5599
521 Irish Hill Rd., Runnemede 08078

Columbia Press, Inc.
Phone—(973) 575-6535
12 Industrial Rd., P.O. Box 10723, Fairfield 07004

Command Web Family Of Companies
Phone—(201) 863-8100
100 Castle Rd., Secaucus 07094

Commercial Business Forms
Phone—(973) 682-9000
240 Cedar Knolls Rd., Ste. 203, Cedar Knolls 07927

Commercial Reprographics, Inc.
Phone—(908) 755-7070
111 Roosevelt Ave., Plainfield 07060

Com-Pak, Inc.
Phone—(856) 802-1900
365 New Albany Rd., Moorestown 08057

Comply, Inc.
Phone—(908) 862-6600
330 Dalziel Rd., Linden 07036

Composition Printing
Phone—(201) 798-0531
P.O. Box 55, Jersey City 07303

Comptime Print & Copy Center
Phone—(201) 760-2400
385 N. Franklin Tpke., Ste. 6, Ramsey 07446

Computoprint Corp.
Phone—(973) 574-8800
1360 Clifton Ave., Ste. 402, Clifton 07012

Concept Printing, Inc.
Phone—(201) 387-6000
160 Woodbine St., Ste. 2, Bergenfield 07621

Connection Printing, Inc.
Phone—(973) 423-2004
86 5th Ave., Hawthorne 07506

Contemporary Graphic Solutions, Inc.
Phone—(856) 663-7277
7001 N. Park Dr., Pennsauken 08109

Copy-Rite Printing
Phone—(609) 597-9182
378 N. Main St., Manahawkin 08050

Corbi Printing Co., Inc.
Phone—(856) 547-2555
106 W. Atlantic Ave., Audubon 08106

Cordes Printing, Inc.
Phone—(201) 652-7272
460 Braen Ave., Wyckoff 07481

Cornerstone Print & Imaging, LLC
Phone—(908) 782-7966
179 State Highway 31, Flemington 08822

Corporate Communications Group, The
Phone—(973) 808-0009
14 Henderson Dr., West Caldwell 07006

Corporate Graphic Solutions, Inc.
Phone—(201) 556-0700
11 W. Passaic St., Rochelle Park 07662

Corporate Graphics & Envelope Mfg., Inc.
Phone—(201) 880-4006
29 Brook Ave., Maywood 07607

Cox Printers
Phone—(908) 928-1010
1634 E. Elizabeth Ave., Linden 07036

Craftmaster Printing, Inc.
Phone—(732) 775-0011
2024 Corlies Ave., Neptune 07753

Craftmaster Printing, Inc.
Phone—(609) 758-5990
3 Main St., New Egypt 08533

Creative Design Plus
Phone—(732) 287-3336
1634 E. Elizabeth Ave., Linden 07036

Creative Print Group, Inc., The
Phone—(856) 486-1700
7905 Browning Rd., Ste. 112, Merchantville 08109

Creative Printing Resources, LLC
Phone—(732) 842-0240
17 Kimberly Ct., Apt. 121, Red Bank 07701

CRT International, Inc.
Phone—(973) 887-7737
260 Wagner St., Middlesex 08846

CRW Graphics, Inc.
Phone—(856) 662-9111
9100 Pennsauken Hwy., Pennsauken 08110

D & M Printing, Inc.
Phone—(973) 731-1300
46 Watson Ave., West Orange 07052

Dalfen Unlimited
Phone—(973) 344-4006
27 1/2 Lentz Ave., Newark 07105

Dash Printing, Inc.
Phone—(201) 338-2561
52 Woodbine St., Ste. 3, Bergenfield 07621

Delgen Press, Inc.
Phone—(973) 472-2266
250 Delawanna Ave., Clifton 07014

Delta Printing Co.
Phone—(201) 935-0036
1000 Wall Street W., Lyndhurst 07071

DeVece & Shaffer, Inc.
Phone—(856) 829-7282
400 Legion Ave., P.O. Box 201, Palmyra 08065

Digital Color Concepts, Inc.
Phone—(908) 264-0504
256 Sheffield St., Mountainside 07092

Digital Print Solutions, LLC
Phone—(973) 263-1890
5 Eastmans Rd., Parsippany 07054

Direct Development, LLC
Phone—(732) 739-8890
1338 State Route 36, Hazlet 07730

Direct Printing Impressions
Phone—(973) 227-6111
33 Fairfield Pl., West Caldwell 07006

Discount Office Supply
Phone—(201) 342-3030
146 Hudson St., Hackensack 07601

Diversified Impressions, Inc.
Phone—(973) 399-9041
119 Coit St., Irvington 07111

Diversiprint, Inc.
Phone—(908) 685-2225
1124 U.S. Highway 202, Ste. B-16, Raritan 08869

Divine Printing, Inc.
Phone—(732) 632-8800
131 Liberty St., Metuchen 08840

DL Printing Co., Inc.
Phone—(732) 750-1917
283 Prospect Ave., Avenel 07001

Dohrman Printing Co., Inc.
Phone—(201) 933-0346
445 Industrial Rd., Carlstadt 07072

Dolce Bros. Printing
Phone—(201) 843-0400
29 Brook Ave., Maywood 07607

Drapkin Printing Co.
Phone—(732) 381-2228
1850 Elizabeth Ave., Ste. 1, Rahway 07065

## PRINTING — (cont.)

**Drew & Rogers, Inc.**
Commercial & business form printing
**Phone—(973) 575-6210 / (800) 610-6210**
**Fax—(973) 575-7180**
**Web—www.drewandrogers.com**
**30 Plymouth St., Fairfield 07004**

DSA Graphics, LLC
Phone—(973) 625-7760
431 E. Main St., Ste. 3, Denville 07834

Duffy Printing Co.
Phone—(856) 768-1046
2389 Atco Ave., Atco 08004

Eagle Enterprises, Inc.
Phone—(856) 427-0787
11 W. Ormond Ave., Cherry Hill 08002

EarthColor
Phone—(973) 884-1300
345 Walsh Dr., Parsippany 07054

Elite Graphics, Inc.
Phone—(973) 882-9769
333 Littleton Rd., Ste. 200, Parsippany 07054

Elite Printing Service
Phone—(973) 729-0366
30 Heritage Dr., Sparta 07871

Elmwood Press, Inc.
Phone—(201) 794-6273
85 Main Ave., Elmwood Park 07407

Enterprise Press, Inc.
Phone—(201) 894-0444
1 W. Forest Ave., Englewood 07631

Entite Press, Inc.
Phone—(609) 714-9213
139 Stokes Rd., Medford Lakes 08055

Envelopes & Printed Products, Inc.
Phone—(973) 942-1232
135 Fairview Ave., Prospect Park 07508

Enviroprint USA
Phone—(732) 356-5959
11 Maiden Ln., Bound Brook 08805

Epoch Press, Inc.
Phone—(973) 357-0080
75 Wood St., Ste. B, Paterson 07524

Excel Color Graphics, Inc.
Phone—(856) 848-3345
207 W. Jersey Ave., Woodbury Heights 08097

Excellent Printing & Graphics
Phone—(973) 773-6661
333 Hazel St., Clifton 07011

Express Graphics
Phone—(973) 696-3165
17 Dupont Ter., Wayne 07470

Express It, Inc.
Phone—(856) 854-1888
61 Haddon Ave., Haddon Township 08108

Express Tag & Label Co.
Phone—(718) 965-1400
52 N. Main St., Marlboro 07746

Extreme Digital Graphics
Phone—(973) 227-5599
7 Kingsbridge Rd., Ste. 1, Fairfield 07004

F I P Graphics, Inc.
Phone—(201) 362-3194
P.O. Box 952, Maywood 07607

F S T Printing, Inc.
Phone—(732) 560-3749
1324 Bound Brook Rd., Middlesex 08846

Fairfield Litho II Corp.
Phone—(973) 575-7550
123 Lehigh Dr., Fairfield 07004

Falcon Printing Co.
Phone—(908) 232-1991
613 Central Ave., Westfield 07090

Fast Copy Printing Center
Phone—(732) 739-4646
81 Broad St., Keyport 07735

FedEx Office & Print Center
Phone—(732) 636-3580
1 Quality Way, Iselin 08830

FedEx Office & Print Center
Phone—(201) 599-0031
315 N. Route 17, Paramus 07652

FedEx Office & Print Center
Phone—(201) 818-1623
559 N. Franklin Tpke., Ramsey 07446

FedEx Office & Print Center
Phone—(908) 575-1221
399 Highway 28, Raritan 08869

FedEx Office Commercial Press
Phone—(908) 245-4400
450 W. 1st Ave., P.O. Box 379, Roselle 07203

Ferrante Press, Inc.
Phone—(973) 239-4344
516 Bloomfield Ave., Verona 07044

Ferrett Printing, Inc.
Phone—(856) 686-4896
468 Warwick Rd., Woodbury 08096

First Impression Printing, Inc.
Phone—(732) 529-5450
178-D 10th St., Piscataway 08854

**FLM Graphics Corp.**
Offset and digital printing, large format imaging &
AEC reprographics
**Phone—(973) 575-9450**
**Fax—(973) 575-6424**
**Web—www.flmgraphics.com**
**Email—info@flmgraphics.com**
**123 Lehigh Dr., Fairfield 07004**

Forms Management Services, Inc.
Phone—(201) 336-3200
162 Lodi St., Hackensack 07601

Forms Plus More, LLC
Phone—(856) 753-8886
6 Harwood Dr., Voorhees 08043

Formslink Systems, Inc.
Phone—(973) 808-8820
14 Hilldale Rd., P. O. Box 101, Pine Brook 07058

Four Star Reproduction, Inc.
Phone—(862) 268-8200
52 Paterson Ave., Ste. 2, Newton 07860

Garrison Printing Co.
Phone—(856) 488-1900
7155 Airport Hwy., Pennsauken 08109

Gateway Press
Phone—(732) 291-1757
984 State Route 36, Atlantic Highlands 07716

Gator Communication Group
Phone—(973) 233-6700
175 Route 46 W., Fairfield 07004

Gerardi Press, Inc.
Phone—(973) 627-2600
3 Luger Rd., Ste. 3, P.O. Box 545, Denville 07834

Giordano, Inc., Philip A.
Phone—(973) 546-9267
59 Garfield Ave., Garfield 07026

Glassboro Printing, Inc.
Phone—(856) 881-2600
30 N. Academy St., Glassboro 08028

Global Graphics, Inc.
Phone—(732) 287-9390
1945 State Route 27, Ste. 5, Edison 08817

Global Print Media
Phone—(732) 886-0505
421 W. County Line Rd., Lakewood 08701

Glorin Printing, Inc.
Phone—(973) 481-3233
258 Clifton Ave., Newark 07104

GM Printing
Phone—(201) 385-2525
106 Pleasant Ave., Bergenfield 07621

GMS Litho, Inc.
Phone—(973) 575-9400
16 Passaic Ave., Fairfield 07004

Goffco Industries, Inc.
Phone—(973) 492-0150
10 Park Pl., Bldg. 6-6, Butler 07405

Good Impressions Printing, Inc.
Phone—(856) 461-3232
28 Scott St., P.O. Box 409, Riverside 08075

Grandview Printing Co., Inc.
Phone—(973) 890-0006
33 W. End Rd., Totowa 07512

Graphic Center, The
Phone—(973) 366-6676
P.O. Box 595, Mount Freedom 07970

Graphic Concepts/Reproduction, Inc.
Phone—(973) 706-6400
111 Butternut Dr., Wayne 07470

Graphic Image
Phone—(856) 262-8900
1401 N. Black Horse Pike, Ste. A, Williamstown 08094

Graphic Image, Inc.
Phone—(856) 852-7007
445 Route 46, Hackettstown 07840

Graphic Impressions Printing Co.
Phone—(856) 728-2266
4391 Route 42, Turnersville 08012

Graphic Marketing Group
Phone—(973) 276-7901
7 Kingsbridge Rd., Ste. 2, Fairfield 07004

Graphic Printing Co., Inc.
Phone—(732) 627-9000
283 Lincoln Blvd., Middlesex 08846

Graphic Techniques, LLC
Phone—(856) 697-2480
10 S. West Blvd., P.O. Box 4, Newfield 08344

Graphicolor Corp.
Phone—(856) 691-2507
3490 N. Mill Rd., Vineland 08360

Graphics Depot, Inc.
Phone—(973) 927-8200
11 Middlebury Blvd., Ste. 4, Randolph 07869

Graphiry Printing
Phone—(908) 353-2223
308 Morris Ave., Elizabeth 07208

Graphix One, LLC
Phone—(732) 560-4700
725 Lincoln Blvd., Middlesex 08846

Greentree Printing
Phone—(856) 596-2330
9004 Lincoln Dr. W., Ste. G, Marlton 08053

Gregory Press, Inc.
Phone—(908) 686-0030
7 Mark Rd., Ste. A, Kenilworth 07033

Harwill Corp.
Phone—(609) 895-1955
3175 Princeton Pike, Lawrenceville 08648

Hatteras, Inc.
Phone—(732) 223-9888
56 Park Rd., Tinton Falls 07724

Hawk Graphics, Inc.
Phone—(973) 895-5569
1248 Sussex Tpke., Ste. C-9, Randolph 07869

Hayes Mindish, Inc.
Phone—(609) 641-9880
1401 N. Main St., Pleasantville 08232

Heritage, Inc.
Phone—(201) 447-2600
4 Wilsey Sq., Ste. 9, Ridgewood 07450

Hermitage Press, Inc.
Phone—(609) 882-3600
1595 5th St., Ewing 08638

Hi Land Printers
Phone—(609) 646-6319
121 S. Main St., Pleasantville 08232

Hibbert Group
Phone—(609) 394-7500
400 Pennington Ave., Trenton 08638

HighRoad Press
Phone—(201) 708-6900
220 Anderson Ave., Moonachie 07074

Hippographics, Inc. (H Q)
Phone—(856) 662-9111
9100 Pennsauken Hwy., Pennsauken 08110

Honour Of Your Presence
Phone—(973) 927-6262
19 State Route 10 E., Ste. 14, Succasunna 07876

Howard, Inc., James
Phone—(973) 928-1560
1500 Main Ave., Ste. 3, Clifton 07011

Howe's Standard Publishing Co., Inc.
Phone—(856) 691-2000
1980 S. West Blvd., Vineland 08360

Hub Print & Copy Center, The
Phone—(201) 585-7887
2037 Lemoine Ave., Fort Lee 07024

Hubler & Assocs.
Phone—(856) 906-5341
146 E. Holly Ave., Oaklyn 08107

Iken Media, LLC
Phone—(201) 372-0800
70 Triangle Blvd., Carlstadt 07072

Image Makers Printing, Copy & Sign Center
Phone—(973) 633-1771
1581 State Route 23, Wayne 07470

Impressions Unlimited Printing Co., LLC
Phone—(856) 256-0200
638 Delsea Dr., P.O. Box 386, Sewell 08080

Impressive Printing, Inc.
Phone—(201) 933-1650
313 10th St., Carlstadt 07072

Infinity Design & Printing
Phone—(908) 206-8844
1358 Burnet Ave., Union 07083

**Inserts East, Inc.**
Email: reception@insertseast.com
**Phone—(856) 663-8181**
**Fax—(856) 663-3288**
**Web—www.insertseast.com**
**7045 Central Hwy., Pennsauken 08109**

INDUSTRY

## PRINTING — *(cont.)*

**Instant Printing, Inc.**
Phone—(973) 366-6855
241 E. Blackwell St., Dover 07801

**J & R Printing, Inc.**
Phone—(609) 465-3530
301 S. Main St., Cape May Court House 08210

**J C Printing & Advertising, Inc.**
Phone—(973) 881-8612
168 8th Ave., Paterson 07514

**J K Printing**
Phone—(201) 833-8181
310 Edgewood Ave., Teaneck 07666

**Jamm Litho, Inc.**
Phone—(732) 870-1999
185 Broadway, Long Branch 07740

**Jamm Printing**
Phone—(732) 502-0110
108 W. Sylvania Ave., Neptune 07753

**JDS Graphics, Inc.**
Phone—(973) 330-3300
220 Entin Rd., Clifton 07014

**Jefferson Printing Service**
Phone—(973) 491-0019
184 Jefferson St., Newark 07105

**JEM Print Co.**
Phone—(856) 451-3885
36 Atlantic St., Bridgeton 08302

**Jersey Printing Assocs., Inc.**
Phone—(732) 872-9654
153 1st Ave., P.O. Box 355, Atlantic Highlands 07716

**JMC Design & Graphics, Inc.**
Phone—(973) 276-9033
144 Fairfield Rd., Fairfield 07004

**Johnson Copy Center, Inc., Robert**
Phone—(201) 833-8997
1438 Queen Anne Rd., Teaneck 07666

**Johnston Letter Co., Inc.**
Phone—(908) 928-1217
1634 E. Elizabeth Ave., Linden 07036

**K R B Printing For Business**
Phone—(856) 751-5200
1165 Marlkress Rd., Ste. G, Cherry Hill 08003

**Kay Printing Co.**
Phone—(973) 330-3000
220 Entin Rd., Clifton 07014

**Kemm Graphics**
Phone—(732) 718-3449
94 Providence Blvd., Kendall Park 08824

**Kintech Printing & Direct Mail**
Phone—(732) 280-6245
2400 Belmar Blvd., Ste. E-6, P.O. Box 12, Belmar 07719

**Kirkwood New York**
Phone—(201) 440-0800
1 Teaneck Rd., Ridgefield Park 07660

**KMS Printing & Graphics, Inc.**
Phone—(856) 205-0200
401 N. Brookfield St., Vineland 08361

**Knockout Graphics, Inc.**
Phone—(732) 774-3331
522 Cookman Ave., Asbury Park 07712

**Koday Press, Inc.**
Phone—(201) 387-0001
69 Armour Pl., Dumont 07628

**Kraftape Printers, Inc.**
Phone—(973) 824-3005
124 Orchard St., Newark 07102

**L & B Printing**
Phone—(908) 232-7770
2590 U.S. Highway 22, Scotch Plains 07076

**Langendorff Corp.**
Phone—(201) 659-6300
633 Grove St., Jersey City 07310

**LAS Printing**
Phone—(201) 991-5362
1 Trenton Ave., Clifton 07011

**Latta Graphics, Inc.**
Phone—(201) 440-4040
180 Cool Edge Ave., Englewood 07631

**LCI Graphics, Inc.**
Phone—(973) 893-2913
2400 Main Street Ext., Ste. 8, Sayreville 08872

**Leon Printing**
Phone—(201) 867-3206
1421 New York Ave., Union City 07087

**Liberty Envelope, Inc.**
Phone—(973) 546-5600
45 E. 5th St., Paterson 07524

**Liberty Printing, Inc.**
Phone—(609) 396-5995
1111 Chestnut Ave., Trenton 08611

**Lithotone Co.**
Phone—(201) 343-3883
255 Queen Ann Rd., Bogota 07603

**Litvany Printing, LLC, Steve**
Phone—(973) 244-0144
1275 Bloomfield Ave., Ste. 13-R, Fairfield 07004

**Local Talk Printing Club**
Phone—(973) 678-2582
26 Main St., Orange 07050

**Lombardo Graphic Consultants, Inc.**
Phone—(609) 693-1727
429 Lacey Rd., Ste. 8, Forked River 08731

**Lont & OverKamp**
Phone—(973) 942-2243
175 U.S. Highway 46, Fairfield 07004

**Lornan Litho, Inc.**
Phone—(609) 818-1198
130 Route 31 N., Ste. E, Pennington 08534

**LRP & P Graphics**
Phone—(856) 424-0158
1165 Marlkress Rd., Cherry Hill 08003

**Mackey's Print Xpress**
Phone—(732) 775-1730
1107 7th Ave., Neptune 07753

**Mail Time, Inc.**
Phone—(908) 859-5500
224 Stockton St., Phillipsburg 08865

**Main Street Graphics, Inc.**
Phone—(856) 755-3523
30 W. Main St., Maple Shade 08052

**Manzi Printers, Inc.**
Phone—(732) 542-1927
Fax—(732) 542-1977
Email—manziprinting@aol.com
132 Lewis St., Ste. B-2, Eatontown 07724

**Marange Printing, Inc.**
Phone—(973) 751-3600
195 Cortlandt St., Belleville 07109

**Market Street Printing, Inc.**
Phone—(856) 964-5995
122 N. 6th St., Camden 08102

**Marmus, Inc.**
Phone—(732) 264-3681
51 E. Front St., Keyport 07735

**Martin Printing Service, Inc.**
Phone—(201) 440-0410
63 Liberty St., Little Ferry 07643

**Master Printing, Inc.**
Phone—(201) 842-9100
445 Industrial Rd., Carlstadt 07072

**McGinnis Printing**
Phone—(732) 758-0060
20 Monmouth St., Red Bank 07701

**McKella 280**
Phone—(856) 813-1153
7025 Central Hwy., Pennsauken 08109

**Merlin Graphics, Inc.**
Phone—(201) 795-3330
194 Christie Ave., Clifton 07011

**Mid Atlantic Graphix, Inc.**
Phone—(609) 569-9990
2558 Tilton Rd., Egg Harbor Township 08234

**Minisink Press, Inc.**
Phone—(973) 383-1350
2 Water St., P.O. Box 278, Newton 07860

**Mint Printing & Design**
Phone—(973) 546-2060
475 Westminster Pl., Lodi 07644

**Minuteman Press**
Phone—(856) 817-8400
2060 Springdale Rd., Ste. 700, Cherry Hill 08003

**Minuteman Press**
Phone—(609) 883-0799
35 Scotch Rd., Ewing 08628

**Minuteman Press**
Phone—(201) 791-0550
23-51 Fair Lawn Ave., Fair Lawn 07410

**Minuteman Press**
Phone—(973) 539-0610
120 Speedwell Ave., Morristown 07960

**Minuteman Press Corp.**
Phone—(973) 624-6907
55 Commerce St., Newark 07102

**Minuteman Press International, Inc.**
Phone—(201) 866-0186
1247 Patterson Plank Rd., Secaucus 07094

**Minuteman Press Of Dover**
Phone—(973) 625-5800
25 Pine St., Ste. 10, Rockaway 07866

**Minuteman Press, Inc./Windsor Graphics**
Phone—(609) 586-3838
2100 Nottingham Way, Hamilton 08619

**MJM Impressions LLC**
Phone—(973) 423-4999
20-10 Maple Ave., Bldg. 35-E, P.O. Box 2, Fair Lawn 07410

**Mon Far Press Printing**
Phone—(212) 431-6245
13 Franklin Pl., Rutherford 07070

**Moonlight Imaging, Inc.**
Phone—(973) 300-1001
5 Plains Rd., Augusta 07822

**Morgan Printing Service, Inc.**
Phone—(732) 721-2959
333 S. Pine Ave., South Amboy 08879

**Morris County Duplicating Corp.**
Document Imaging
Phone—(973) 993-8484
Fax—(973) 605-8828
Web—www.mcdsolutions.com
Email—copies@mcdsolutions.com
1 Lafayette Ave., Morristown 07960

**Morris Forms Corp.**
Phone—(973) 829-1200
5 Saddle Rd., Cedar Knolls 07927

**Morris Graphics, Inc.**
Phone—(856) 845-4980
660 N. Broad St., Woodbury 08096

**Mountain Printing Co., Inc.**
Phone—(856) 767-7600
27 N. Atlantic Ave., P.O. Box 608, Berlin 08009

**Mr. Printer**
Phone—(732) 738-3977
466 New Brunswick Ave., Fords 08863

**MSP Digital Marketing**
Phone—(973) 298-8800
200 Forge Way, Rockaway 07866

**Narciso Printing, Inc.**
Phone—(973) 578-2088
120-22 Malvern St., Newark 07105

**Nassau Communications, Inc.**
Phone—(908) 625-8512
115 N. Gold Dr., Robbinsville 08691

**National Color Graphics**
Phone—(856) 435-6800
1755 Williamstown Rd., Erial 08081

**Nelson Press**
Commercial printing
Phone—(732) 747-0330
Fax—(732) 530-8567
Web—www.nelsonpress.net
111 E. River Rd., Rumson 07760

**NEMA Associates, Inc.**
Phone—(973) 274-0052
57 Bruen St., Newark 07105

**New Jersey Reprographics, Inc.**
Phone—(908) 789-1616
110 Center St., Garwood 07027

**New Line Printing & Technology, Inc.**
Phone—(973) 232-5003
1011 Route 22 E., Mountainside 07092

**New Print Shop, Inc.**
Phone—(609) 392-0782
558 Central Ave., New Providence 07974

**Newark Trade Typographers, Inc.**
Phone—(973) 674-3727
177 Oakwood Ave., Orange 07050

**Nextwave Web, LLC**
Phone—(973) 742-4339
229 Marshall St., Paterson 07503

**North Hudson Press**
Phone—(201) 941-2520
429 Hancock Pl., Fairview 07022

**Novatech Graphics**
Phone—(732) 469-1887
54 Birch Ave., Ste. A, Little Silver 07739

**Oceanic Graphic Printing USA**
Phone—(201) 883-1816
105 Main St., 3rd Fl., Hackensack 07601

**Ocsidot, Inc.**
Phone—(908) 789-3300
116 South Ave., Garwood 07027

**Office Depot Business Solution Div. Of New Jersey**
Phone—(973) 594-3000
4 Brighton Rd., Clifton 07012

**Old Hights Print Shop, Inc.**
Phone—(609) 443-4700
133 S. Main St., Hightstown 08520

## PRINTING — (cont.)

Oliveri Printing Corporation, Carl
Phone—(201) 438-0888
316 Main St., Ste. 1, East Rutherford 07073

On Target Printing & Graphics, LLC
Phone—(973) 287-6222
202 Fairfield Rd., Fairfield 07004

One Source Communications, Inc.
Phone—(973) 463-0250
9 Whippany Rd., Bldg. C-4, Whippany 07981

One Stop Printing, LLC
Phone—(201) 991-3320
135 Kearny Ave., Ste. B, Kearny 07032

One Two Three, Inc.
Phone—(856) 251-1238
537 Mantua Ave., Ste. B, P.O. Box 123, Woodbury 08096

Oscar Printing Services
Phone—(201) 659-1588
549 Newark Ave., Jersey City 07306

O'Shea's Printing Services Co., Inc.
Phone—(201) 343-8668
483 Main St., Hackensack 07601

Otis Graphics, Inc.
Phone—(201) 438-7120
290 Grant Ave., Lyndhurst 07071

Paci Press, Inc.
Phone—(973) 478-6550
25 First St., Rear Bldg., Lodi 07644

Pages Printing & Graphics
Phone—(201) 261-3883
300 N. Route 17, Paramus 07652

Painton Studios, Inc.
Phone—(732) 302-0200
299 U.S. Highway 22, Ste. 21, Green Brook 08812

Pamco Printers & Stationers
Phone—(609) 309-5025
P.O. Box 567, Hopewell 08525

Paragon Printing Shop
Phone—(856) 825-2497
600 Columbia Ave., Millville 08332

Paravista, Inc., Imaging & Printing
Phone—(732) 752-1222
1055 Centennial Ave., Piscataway 08854

Park Printing Services, Inc.
Phone—(856) 675-1600
7300 N. Crescent Blvd., Unit 21, Pennsauken 08110

Parkway Printing, Inc.
Phone—(732) 308-0300
52 N. Main St., Ste. C-11, Marlboro 07746

Pat Publications
Phone—(856) 424-0158
1165 Marlkress Rd., Ste. M, P.O. Box 1536, Cherry Hill 08003

Patel Printing Plus Corp.
Phone—(908) 964-6422
1036 Commerce Ave., Union 07083

Peacock Printing Products, Inc.
Phone—(201) 385-5585
48 Woodbine St., Bergenfield 07621

Pedeco Printing, Inc.
Phone—(732) 363-0510
12 Summers Dr., Jackson 08527

Penn Jersey Press
Phone—(856) 627-2200
P.O. Box 1103, Voorhees 08043

Perfect Printing, Inc.
Phone—(856) 787-1877
1533 Glen Ave., Moorestown 08057

Permalith Plastics, LLC
Phone—(856) 488-8000
6901 N. Crescent Blvd., Pennsauken 08110

Peter J. Morley LLC
Phone—(732) 264-0010
21 Village Ct., Hazlet 07730

Pharma Press, Inc.
Phone—(908) 241-4110
490 W. 1st Ave., Roselle 07203

Phoenix Business Forms, Inc.
Phone—(856) 691-2266
2231 N. East Blvd., Vineland 08360

Pine Hill Printing, Inc.
Phone—(856) 346-2915
200 Erial Rd., Pine Hill 08021

Poggi Press, The
Phone—(201) 659-0837
1501 Adams St., P.O. Box M-668, Hoboken 07030

Postcardsrus, Inc
Phone—(201) 944-7070
440 West St., Ste. 2-S, Fort Lee 07024

Premier Press, Inc.
Phone—(856) 665-0722
7120 Airport Hwy., Pennsauken 08109

Premier Printing Solutions
Phone—(732) 525-0740
508 Raritan St., Sayreville 08872

Premium Color Graphics, Inc.
Phone—(973) 472-7007
651 Garden St., Carlstadt 07072

Press Room, Inc., The
Phone—(609) 689-3817
100 Youngs Rd., Ste. 2, Mercerville 08619

Pressworks
Phone—(856) 427-9001
1879 Old Cuthbert Rd., Unit 28, Cherry Hill 08034

Print Art, Inc.
Phone—(609) 645-1940
6726 Delilah Rd., Egg Harbor Township 08234

Print Communications
Phone—(856) 488-0345
7040 Colonial Hwy., Pennsauken 08109

Print House, Inc., The
Phone—(732) 364-4254
6535 U.S. Highway 9, Howell 07731

Print Media
Phone—(973) 467-0007
232 Morris Ave., Springfield 07081

Print Shoppe
Phone—(732) 583-4343
1077-M Highway 34, Matawan 07747

Print Shoppe, Inc.
Phone—(908) 782-9213
15 Minneakoning Rd., Ste. 305, Flemington 08822

Print Sign & Design
Phone—(856) 451-8766
1791 S. Burlington Rd., Bridgeton 08302

Printech
Phone—(908) 782-9986
35 Main St., Flemington 08822

Printers Of Salem County, LLC
Phone—(856) 935-5032
38 Market St., Salem 08079

Printer's Place, Inc., The
Phone—(973) 744-8889
8 S. Fullerton Ave., Montclair 07042

Printflex
Phone—(973) 256-5900
1250 U.S. Highway 46, Little Falls 07424

Printing Craftsman, Inc.
Phone—(201) 943-0276
130 Bergen Blvd., Fairview 07022

Printing Images
Phone—(973) 839-9500
546 Ringwood Ave., Wanaque 07465

Printing Industries, LLC
Phone—(973) 334-9775
1543 U.S. Highway 46 E., Parsippany 07054

Printing Plus Of South Jersey
Phone—(856) 767-3232
406 N. Route 73, West Berlin 08091

Printing Shop Copy Center, The
Phone—(732) 826-3575
338 State St., Perth Amboy 08861

Printing Techniques, Inc.
Phone—(973) 667-2606
48 Franklin Ave., Nutley 07110

Printing To Go
Phone—(732) 462-0333
578 Park Ave., Freehold 07728

Printology
Phone—(201) 345-4632
615 Franklin Tpke., Ste. 3, Ridgewood 07450

Print-Tech Products, Inc.
Phone—(908) 231-8700
603 1st Ave., Ste. 1-C, Raritan 08869

Printworx
Phone—(609) 586-3006
2103 Whitehorse Mercerville Rd., Hamilton 08619

Prism Color Corp.
Phone—(856) 234-7515
31 Twosome Dr., Ste. 1, Moorestown 08057

Prism Digital Communications, LLC
Phone—(908) 789-7747
1011 U.S. Highway 22, Ste. 1, Mountainside 07092

Pro Printing, Inc.
Phone—(201) 346-0305
472 Broad Ave., Palisades Park 07650

Proforma Unlimited Marketing Expressions
Phone—(609) 882-0112
36 Keswick Ave., Ewing 08638

Progressive Printing Corp.
Phone—(973) 736-5800
24 Park Ave., West Orange 07052

Pyramid Imprints
Phone—(201) 384-0336
28 N. Washington Ave., Bergenfield 07621

QP2000, LLC
Phone—(732) 531-8860
827 W. Park Ave., Ocean 07712

Quality Concepts, Inc.
Phone—(856) 235-0909
730 Marne Hwy., Moorestown 08057

Quality Printing
Phone—(856) 691-7577
1181 E. Landis Ave., Ste. 3, Vineland 08360

Quality Repro Centers, Inc.
Phone—(201) 794-3905
296 Route 46 E., P.O. Box 111, Elmwood Park 07407

Quickly Printing, Inc.
Phone—(908) 687-6000
1965 Morris Ave., Union 07083

Quikie Print & Copy Shops
Phone—(732) 933-1010
703 Broad St., Shrewsbury 07702

R & R Printing & Copy Center
Phone—(732) 249-9450
1075 Easton Ave., Somerset 08873

R.J. Printing, Inc.
Phone—(973) 226-9509
5 Dodd Rd., West Caldwell 07006

Raritan Valley Printing Co.
Phone—(908) 725-4140
7 Sheephill Cir., Branchburg 08876

Ray's Reproductions, Inc.
Phone—(201) 666-5650
39 Bland St., Emerson 07630

Regen & Co., Inc.
Phone—(973) 423-4236
20-21 Wagaraw Rd., Bldg. 32, Fair Lawn 07410

Register Lithographers, Ltd.
Phone—(973) 916-2804
1155 Bloomfield Ave., Clifton 07012

Reliance Graphics, Inc.
Phone—(973) 239-5411
80 Pompton Ave., Ste. 1, Verona 07044

Repromatic Printing Co., Inc.
Phone—(973) 239-7610
216 Little Falls Rd., Unit 3, Cedar Grove 07009

Review Printing, Inc.
Phone—(856) 589-7200
53-55 E. Holly Ave., Pitman 08071

Ridgewood Press, Inc.
Phone—(201) 670-9797
609 Franklin Tpke., Ridgewood 07450

Riegel Communication Group
Phone—(609) 771-0555
One Graphics Dr., P.O. Box 7430, Ewing 08628

Riverside Acquisition Group, LLC (H Q)
Phone—(856) 802-1900
365 New Albany Rd., Moorestown 08057

Riverside Graphics, Inc.
Phone—(973) 844-1011
40 Little St., Belleville 07109

Rocco Press, Inc.
Phone—(973) 790-4000
171 Walnut St., Paterson 07522

Roned Printing
Phone—(973) 386-1848
6 DeForest Ave., Ste. 2, East Hanover 07936

Roy Press Printers
Phone—(732) 922-9460
57 Bridgewaters Dr., Apt. 17, Oceanport 07757

Royer Graphics, Inc.
Phone—(856) 344-7935
101 Lincoln Dr., Laurel Springs 08021

Royer Group, Inc.
Phone—(856) 665-6400
7120 Airport Hwy., Pennsauken 08109

S & M Press, Inc.
Phone—(973) 778-4405
169 Semel Ave., Ste. 2, Garfield 07026

S J Print Solutions
Phone—(732) 363-7711
257 Ford Rd., Howell 07731

Sanakirk, Inc.
Phone—(856) 429-0715
1400 Berlin Rd., Ste. 123, Cherry Hill 08003

© Copyright 2015 Manufacturers' News, Inc.

## PRINTING — (cont.)

**Sandoval Graphics & Printing**
Phone—(856) 435-7320
9 Minnetonka Rd., Somerdale 08083

**Sapphire Envelope & Graphics Co., Inc.**
Phone—(856) 782-2227
214 W. Davis Rd., Magnolia 08049

**Scheller Printing Co., Lewis**
Phone—(732) 843-5050
2275 Old Georges Rd., New Brunswick 08902

**Scott Graphics Printing, Inc.**
Phone—(201) 262-0473
690-D River Rd., New Milford 07646

**Second Impressions, LLC**
Phone—(732) 752-7171
149 Stelton Rd., Piscataway 08854

**Seibel Group, Inc., The**
Phone—(609) 799-3279
741 Alexander Rd., Princeton 08540

**Select Services**
Phone—(973) 467-8860
500 Morris Ave., Ste. 116, Springfield 07081

**Selover Co., LLC, R. N.**
Phone—(856) 293-9009
17 Wolf Rd., Millville 08332

**Serafino Printing Co., Inc.**
Phone—(973) 857-3450
516 Bloomfield Ave., Verona 07044

**Service Apex**
Phone—(732) 560-2222
564-A Union Ave., Bridgewater 08807

**Sheridan Communication, Inc.**
Phone—(908) 454-0700
1425 3rd Ave., Alpha 08865

**Shore Point Communications**
Phone—(732) 961-7936
160 Lehigh Ave., Ste. B, Lakewood 08701

**Showcase Graphics, LLC**
Phone—(856) 722-5400
33 E. Main St., Ste. 4, Moorestown 08057

**Showcase Printing Of Iselin**
Phone—(732) 283-0438
181 E. James Pl., Iselin 08830

**Signmasters, Inc.**
Phone—(973) 614-8300
217 Brook Ave., 2nd Fl., Front, Passaic 07055

**Sir Speedy Printing**
Phone—(609) 586-8222
3100 Quakerbridge Rd., Mercerville 08619

**Sir Speedy Printing**
Phone—(609) 267-1232
897 Rancocas Rd., Mount Holly 08060

**Sir Speedy Printing**
Phone—(856) 691-0741
22 W. Landis Ave., Ste. Q, Vineland 08360

**Sir Speedy Printing**
Phone—(201) 444-0234
405 Goffle Rd., Wyckoff 07481

**Sir Speedy Printing And Marketing Services**
Phone—(856) 488-1480
5505 Route 130 N., Pennsauken 08110

**Sir Speedy Printing and Marketing Services**
Phone—(732) 981-9011
1032 Stelton Rd., Piscataway 08854

**Sir Speedy Printing Center**
Phone—(201) 896-2727
122 Ridge Rd., Lyndhurst 07071

**Sir Speedy Printing Center**
Phone—(856) 866-0588
300 S. Lenola Rd., Ste. 22, Maple Shade 08052

**Sir Speedy Printing Centers**
Phone—(856) 251-0220
39 S. Broad St., Woodbury 08096

**Sky Printing Co.**
Phone—(201) 433-3133
338 Montgomery St., Jersey City 07302

**Skylands Press**
Phone—(973) 383-5006
57 Trinity St., P.O. Box 809, Newton 07860

**Skyline Graphics Design**
Phone—(973) 839-3329
11 Skyline Lake Dr., Ringwood 07456

**Small Business Service Center**
Phone—(856) 234-8059
122 E. Kings Hwy., Ste. 504, Maple Shade 08052

**Smith, Inc., Roy D.**
Phone—(201) 384-4163
20 Foster St., P.O. Box 537, Bergenfield 07621

**SourceCodes & Displays, Inc.**
Phone—(973) 942-1965
135 Fairview Ave., Prospect Park 07508

**Speedpro Imaging**
Phone—(973) 542-8384
52 E. Centre St., Ste. 3-B, Nutley 07110

**Sports Information Media, Inc.**
Phone—(973) 564-5014
343 Millburn Ave., Ste. 208, Millburn 07041

**Square One, Inc.**
Phone—(856) 234-6999
111 Gaither Dr., Ste. 104, Mount Laurel 08054

**Staples Contract Digital Copy Services**
Phone—(732) 346-1377
258 Fernwood Ave., Edison 08837

**Stauts Printing & Graphics**
Phone—(609) 654-5382
12 Maine Trl., Medford 08055

**Stevenson & Smith, Inc.**
Phone—(908) 862-4211
450 W. 1st Ave., Roselle 07203

**Stobbs Printing Co., Inc.**
Phone—(973) 748-4441
18 Washington St., P.O. Box 91, Bloomfield 07003

**Stone Mountain Printing**
Phone—(732) 634-4444
74 Main St., Ste. 1, Woodbridge 07095

**Sunset Printing And Engraving**
Phone—(973) 537-9600
10 Kice Ave., Wharton 07885

**Swift Co., Inc., John S.**
Phone—(201) 678-3232
375 North St., Unit N, Teterboro 07608

**Swift Print Solutions, LLC**
Phone—(908) 475-1374
405 Front St., Belvidere 07823

**Symphony Printing**
Phone—(973) 751-5100
19-21 Brook St., Belleville 07109

**Tabloid Graphic Services, Inc.**
Phone—(856) 486-0410
7101 Westfield Ave., Pennsauken 08110

**Tangent Graphics**
Phone—(201) 488-2840
151 Hobart St., Hackensack 07601

**Tanter, Inc.**
Phone—(732) 382-3555
151 Westfield Ave., Clark 07066

**Target Printing & Graphics**
Phone—(201) 883-0200
9 E. Passaic St., Hackensack 07601

**Thermo-Graphics, Inc.**
Phone—(732) 669-0252
915 E. Hazelwood Ave., Rahway 07065

**Thewal, Inc.**
Phone—(973) 635-1880
12 Center St., Chatham 07928

**TPG Graphics**
Phone—(856) 314-0117
9130 Pennsauken Hwy., Ste. C, Pennsauken 08110

**Trade Thermographers, Inc.**
Phone—(201) 489-2060
65 Worth St., South Hackensack 07606

**Treasury Printing Services**
Phone—(609) 292-5133
101 Carroll St., P.O. Box 30, Trenton 08625

**Trentypo, Inc.**
Phone—(609) 883-2198
304 Stokes Ave., Trenton 08638

**Tretina Printing, Inc.**
Phone—(732) 264-2324
1301 State Route 36, Concord Ctr., Hazlet 07730

**Trico Web, LLC**
Phone—(201) 438-3860
75 Broad St., Carlstadt 07072

**Tri-Plex Business Products, Inc / Graphic Solutions**
Phone—(973) 627-5388
400 Morris Ave., Ste. 220, Denville 07834

**Trukmann's Inc.**
Phone—(973) 538-7718
4 Wing Dr., Cedar Knolls 07927

**Type-O-Graphics, LLC**
Phone—(973) 253-3333
222 Outwater Ln., Ste. 1, Garfield 07026

**Unigraphic Guild, Inc.**
Phone—(973) 219-2348
10 Route 206, Stanhope 07874

**Unimac Graphics, LLC**
Phone—(201) 372-1000
350 Michele Pl., Carlstadt 07072

**United Envelope & Printing Co., Inc.**
Phone—(201) 699-5800
65 Railroad Ave., Ridgefield 07657

**United Forms Finishing**
Phone—(908) 687-0494
1413 Chestnut Ave., 1st Fl., Hillside 07205

**Unity Graphics & Engraving/Unity Steel Rule Die**
Phone—(201) 569-6400
210 S. Van Brunt St., P.O. Box 88, Englewood 07631

**Upper Case Printing, LLC**
Phone—(856) 875-5000
752 Porchtown, Franklinville 08322

**Urner Barry Publications**
Phone—(732) 240-5330
182 Queens Blvd., Bayville 08721

**Ventnor Print Shop Co.**
Phone—(609) 822-2974
128 N. Wyoming Ave., P.O. Box 2174, Ventnor City 08406

**Vernon Display Graphics**
Phone—(201) 935-7117
145 Commerce Rd., Carlstadt 07072

**Victor's Printing**
Phone—(856) 424-4600
3 Perina Blvd., Cherry Hill 08003

**Viskal Printing, LLC**
Phone—(973) 812-6600
40 Commerce Way, Unit E, Totowa 07512

**Waldwick Printing Co.**
Phone—(201) 652-5848
1 Harrison Ave., Waldwick 07463

**Wall Street Group, Inc.**
Phone—(201) 333-4784
1 Edward Hart Dr., Jersey City 07305

**Washington Stamp Exchange, Inc.**
Phone—(973) 966-0001
2 Vreeland Rd., Florham Park 07932

**Weaver Assocs. Printing Service, Inc.**
Phone—(908) 272-6224
945 Lincoln Ave. E., Cranford 07016

**Welter & Kreutz Printing Co.**
Phone—(201) 489-9098
51 Worth St., P.O. Box 1834, South Hackensack 07606

**Wheal-Grace Corp.**
Phone—(973) 450-8100
300 Ralph St., P.O. Box 67, Belleville 07109

**White Eagle Printing Co.**
Phone—(609) 586-2032
2550 Kuser Rd., Hamilton 08691

**Wholesale Print House**
Phone—(201) 333-7746
1757 John F. Kennedy Blvd., Jersey City 07305

**Wilcox Press**
Phone—(973) 827-7474
6 Main St., Hamburg 07419

**Williams Berell, Inc.**
Phone—(908) 486-4952
612 E. Elizabeth Ave., P.O. Box 1341, Linden 07036

**Wizard Printing Corp.**
Phone—(973) 835-8048
29 Evans Pl., Ste. 82, Pompton Plains 07444

**Woodbridge Printing Center**
Phone—(732) 855-1996
1201 U.S. Highway 9 S., Woodbridge 07095

**Word Center Printing**
Phone—(609) 586-5825
1905 Highway 33, Ste. 10, Hamilton Square 08690

**Write Impression, The**
Phone—(732) 706-3700
549 Highway 35, Red Bank 07701

**Yukon Graphics, Inc.**
Phone—(973) 575-5700
239 New Rd., Ste. B-110, Parsippany 07054

**Zenith Printing**
Phone—(856) 662-6275
7440 Baxter Ave., Merchantville 08109

---

## PRINTING — Book

**Catholic Book Publishing Corp.**
Phone—(973) 890-2400
77 W. End Rd., Totowa 07512

**Dawn Bible Students Assn.**
Phone—(201) 438-6421
199 Railroad Ave., East Rutherford 07073

**Lightning Press, Inc.**
Phone—(973) 890-4422
140 Furler St., Totowa 07512

## PRINTING — Book — *(cont.)*

Mountain Lion, Inc.
Phone—(609) 730-1665
9 Voorhees Ct., P.O. Box 799, Pennington 08534

**Pantone LLC**
**Phone—(201) 935-5500 / (888) 726-8663**
**Fax—(201) 896-0242**
**Web—www.pantone.com**
**590 Commerce Blvd., Carlstadt 07072**

R. R. Donnelley & Sons Co.
Phone—(201) 271-1000
215 County Ave., Secaucus 07094

## PRINTING — Business Card

Crown Assocs. U. S. A., Inc.
Phone—(973) 785-3477
19 Winged Foot Dr., Livingston 07039

Maclearie
Phone—(732) 974-8878
917 18th Ave., Wall 07719

Magic Printing Corp.
Phone—(732) 726-0620
386 Avenel St., Avenel 07001

## PRINTING — Carton

Metro Packaging & Imaging, Inc.
Phone—(973) 709-9100
5 Haul Rd., Wayne 07470

## PRINTING — Digital

Allegra Marketing Print Mail
Phone—(732) 404-0665
665 State Route 27, Iselin 08830

AlphaGraphics of Mahwah
Phone—(201) 327-2200
1 Lethbridge Plz., Route 17 N., Mahwah 07430

Copiers Plus
Phone—(609) 398-7676
935 West Ave., Ocean City 08226

Copyshop Office Supply & Repro Center
Phone—(732) 721-5700
921 U.S. Highway 9, South Amboy 08879

Digital Arts Imaging, LLC
Phone—(908) 237-4646
105 State Route 31, Ste. 10, Flemington 08822

Digital Productions, Inc.
Phone—(856) 224-1111
410 Southgate Ct., Mickleton 08056

Discount Digital Print, LLC
Phone—(201) 659-9600
629 Grove St., 16th Fl., Jersey City 07310

DPI Copies Printing & Graphics, Inc.
Phone—(856) 874-1355
2070 Route 70 E., Cherry Hill 08003

EarthDigital
Phone—(551) 497-5400
77 Moonachie Ave., Moonachie 07074

eDigital Graphics
Phone—(732) 968-1234
326 U.S. Highway 22, Ste. 12-A, Dunellen 08812

G & H Soho, Inc.
Phone—(201) 216-9400
413 Market St., Elmwood Park 07407

Global Soft Digital Solutions, Inc.
Phone—(201) 684-0900
500 Corporate Dr., Mahwah 07430

Happle Printing Partnership, Inc.
Phone—(609) 476-2929
81 Cape May Ave., P.O. Box 36, Dorothy 08317

JA Visual Group
Phone—(212) 463-0545
150 Commerce Rd., Unit 3, Carlstadt 07072

**Lizard Label, Inc.**
**Full scale, multi-press flexographic & digital print shop**
**Phone—(973) 808-0098 / (877) 807-0098**
**Fax—(973) 882-8829**
**Web—www.lizardlabel.com**
**Email—sales@lizardlabel.com**
**10-E Commerce Rd., Fairfield 07004**

Mount Freedom Printing, LLC
Phone—(973) 933-2700
1248 Sussex Tpke., Randolph 07869

Nu-Graphics Ii, Inc.
Phone—(973) 299-0066
84 Stonybrook Rd., P.O. Box 65, Towaco 07082

Print Group, Inc., The
Phone—(201) 487-4400
24 E. Wesley St., South Hackensack 07606

Print Tech Ltd.
Phone—(908) 232-2287
49 Fadem Rd., Springfield 07081

**Quality Repro Centers, Inc.**
**Phone—(201) 794-3905**
**Fax—(201) 794-3909**
**Web—www.qrepro.com**
**Email—qrepro@optonline.net**
**296 Route 46 E., P.O. Box 111, Elmwood Park 07407**

**Quality Repro Centers, Inc.**
*Commercial & Digital Color Printing*
**(201) 794-3905 Fax: (201) 794-3909**
**www.qrepro.com**
296 Route 46 E., P.O. Box 111
Elmwood Park, NJ 07407

Redi-Mail Direct Marketing
Phone—(973) 808-4500
107 Little Falls Rd., Fairfield 07004

Service Apex
Phone—(732) 424-1616
299 U.S. Highway 22, Green Brook 08812

Sir Speedy Westfield
Phone—(908) 232-1001
516 North Ave. E., Westfield 07090

Tri-Lon Color Graphics, Inc.
Phone—(201) 708-6900
220 Anderson Ave., Moonachie 07074

## PRINTING — Digital Offset

Agfa Corp. (H Q)
Phone—(201) 440-0111
611 River Dr., Elmwood Park 07407

Keystone Printing, Inc.
Phone—(201) 387-7252
21-C E. Madison Ave., Dumont 07628

Monte Printing & Graphics
Phone—(908) 241-6600
225 E. Clay Ave., P.O. Box 293, Roselle Park 07204

Starnet Business Solutions, Inc.
Phone—(201) 760-2600
46 Industrial Ave., Mahwah 07430

## PRINTING — Direct Mail

American Advertising
Phone—(973) 398-6200
131 Landing Rd., Landing 07850

FrontEnd Graphics
Phone—(856) 547-1600
1951 Old Cuthbert Rd., Ste. 414, Cherry Hill 08034

Quad/Graphics, Inc.
Phone—(609) 495-1200
28 Engelhard Dr., Monroe Township 08831

R. R. Donnelley & Sons Co.
Phone—(973) 882-7000
5 Henderson Dr., West Caldwell 07006

## PRINTING — Financial

American Banknote Corp. (H Q)
Phone—(201) 592-3400
2200 Fletcher Ave., Ste. 501, Fort Lee 07024

Commerce Financial Printers
Phone—(908) 241-9880
305 Cox St., Roselle 07203

Deluxe Mfg. Operations, Inc.
Phone—(973) 334-8000
105 U.S. Highway 46, Mountain Lakes 07046

McElwee & Quinn, LLC
Phone—(856) 229-7015
2070 E. Route 70, Ste. 4, Cherry Hill 08003

Merrill Corp.
Phone—(908) 688-5757
649 Rahway Ave., Union 07083

Metro Web Corp.
Phone—(201) 553-0700
5901 Tonnelle Ave., North Bergen 07047

SpectraMedia
Phone—(908) 928-1220
1634 E. Elizabeth Ave., Linden 07036

## PRINTING — Fine Art

Art Publishing Group, The
Phone—(201) 842-8500
480 Main Ave., Unit 4, Wallington 07057

Graphix Integrated, Inc.
Phone—(732) 872-8282
971 Leonardville Rd., Atlantic Highlands 07716

Wet Stone Graphics
Phone—(201) 307-1531
645 Greenway Pl., River Vale 07675

## PRINTING — Flexographic

AJ Printing Solutions, LLC
Phone—(908) 202-0974
781 Hyslip Ave., Westfield 07090

Amerifilm Converters
Phone—(973) 690-5900
85 Lincoln Hwy., Kearny 07032

J F I Printing, Inc.
Phone—(973) 759-3444
357 Cortlandt St., Belleville 07109

Print Wrap Corp.
Phone—(973) 239-1144
95 Sand Park Rd., Cedar Grove 07009

## PRINTING — Instant

ACB Reproduction
Phone—(856) 751-0360
2060 Springdale Rd., Cherry Hill 08003

Affordable Copies Center
Phone—(973) 802-1007
55 Halsey St., Newark 07102

Anisha Enterprises, Inc.
Phone—(908) 964-3380
2165 Morris Ave., Union 07083

Atlantic Printing & Graphics, LLC
Phone—(732) 493-4222
1301 W. Park Ave., Ocean 07712

B & W Printing Co., Inc.
Phone—(908) 241-3060
730 Fairfield Ave., Kenilworth 07033

BP Graphics & Printing
Phone—(732) 905-9830
315 4th St., Lakewood 08701

Copy Shop, The
Phone—(732) 286-2200
20 E. Water St., Toms River 08753

Cottrell Graphics, LLC
Phone—(732) 349-7430
1525 Prospect St., Unit 314, Lakewood 08701

Dave's Swift Print
Phone—(856) 853-8528
P.O. Box 313, Westville 08093

FedEx Office & Print Center
Phone—(856) 427-0099
1160 Marlton Pike E., Cherry Hill 08034

FedEx Office & Print Center
Phone—(732) 249-9222
212 State Route 18, East Brunswick 08816

FedEx Office & Print Center
Phone—(609) 569-8100
450 Tilton Rd., Northfield 08225

FedEx Office & Print Center
Phone—(609) 799-2863
Highway 1 & 731 Nassau, Princeton 08540

FedEx Office & Print Center
Phone—(973) 376-3966
55 U.S. Highway 22 E., Springfield 07081

Formax Printers
Phone—(732) 229-5063
200 Wall St., West Long Branch 07764

Graphic Action, Inc.
Phone—(908) 213-0055
296 S. Main St., Phillipsburg 08865

Instant Printing
Phone—(973) 675-6266
355 Main St., Orange 07050

Lavallette Printing
Phone—(732) 793-8303
301 Grand Central, Lavallette 08735

Minuteman Press
Phone—(856) 753-0055
35 W. White Horse Pike, Berlin 08009

© Copyright 2015 Manufacturers' News, Inc.

## PRINTING — Instant — (cont.)

Minuteman Press
 Phone—(732) 536-8788
 349 U.S. Highway 9, Ste. 7, Englishtown 07726
Minuteman Press
 Phone—(201) 444-0236
 19 Sheridan Ave., Ho-Ho-Kus 07423
Minuteman Press of Livingston, LLC
 Phone—(973) 992-3136
 47 E. Northfield Rd., Livingston 07039
Minuteman Press Of North Arlington
 Phone—(201) 991-1030
 75 Ridge Rd., North Arlington 07031
More Copy Printing Service
 Phone—(201) 327-1106
 358 State Route 17, Saddle River 07458
National Reprographics, Inc.
 Phone—(609) 896-4100
 3175 Princeton Pike, Lawrenceville 08648
Office Prints, The
 Phone—(201) 222-5555
 30 Journal Sq., Jersey City 07306
Omega Graphics
 Phone—(732) 530-4441
 661 Broad St., Ste. 3, Shrewsbury 07702
P I P Printing Of Livingston
 Phone—(973) 533-9330
 465 W. Mount Pleasant Ave., Livingston 07039
Pequod Communications, Inc.
 Phone—(609) 951-0300
 743 Alexander Rd., Ste. 15, Princeton 08540
Professional Printing Services
 Phone—(856) 429-8644
 116 N. Haddon Ave., Haddonfield 08033
Quikie Print & Copy Shop
 Phone—(732) 531-8860
 827 W. Park, Ocean 07712
Razor Printing
 Phone—(732) 238-7520
 78 Summerhill Rd., East Brunswick 08816
Studio 042
 Phone—(973) 509-7591
 423 Bloomfield Ave., Montclair 07042
Universal Prints, Inc.
 Phone—(201) 656-7878
 625 Newark Ave., Jersey City 07306

## PRINTING — Label

Alcop Adhesive Label Co.
 Phone—(609) 871-4400
 826 Perkins Ln., P.O. Box 398, Beverly 08010
Chesapeake Pharmaceutical & Healthcare
 Packaging
 Phone—(973) 808-8000
 6 Commerce Rd., Fairfield 07004
Control Group, The
 Phone—(201) 768-1900
 500 Walnut St., Norwood 07648
Custom Labels, Inc.
 Phone—(973) 473-1934
 61 Willet St., Bldg. J, Passaic 07055
Federal Label Systems, Inc.
 Phone—(718) 899-6000
 385 Hillside Ave., Hillside 07205
Industrial Labeling Systems, Inc.
 Phone—(973) 882-9688
 50 Kulick Rd., Fairfield 07004
Label Tek, Inc.
 Phone—(201) 390-3856
 357 Cortlandt St., Ste. 4, Belleville 07109
Mercury Printing, Inc.
 Phone—(732) 247-6828
 14 Veronica Ave., Somerset 08873
My Private Label, LLC
 Phone—(908) 441-2375
 112 East Ave., Ste. 5, Hackettstown 07840
NJ Label
 Phone—(201) 833-9200
 30 Wesley St., Unit 7, South Hackensack 07606
Promotional Graphics Etc., Inc.
 Phone—(973) 423-3900
 85 Wagaraw Rd., Hawthorne 07506
Rapid Tag & Label, Inc.
 Phone—(201) 337-5551
 5 Fir Ct., Ste. 4, Oakland 07436
Roll Flex Label Co., LLC
 Phone—(201) 489-3330
 199 Lee Pl., Hackensack 07601

Shreeji Printing Corp.
 Phone—(201) 842-9500
 55 Veterans Blvd., Carlstadt 07072
Sure Mark Labels, Inc.
 Phone—(973) 768-4859
 4 Flynn Ter., P.O. Box 501, West Orange 07052
Taunton Graphics, Inc.
 Phone—(856) 719-8084
 1049 Industrial Dr., West Berlin 08091
Trek, Inc.
 Phone—(732) 269-6300
 43 Cranmer Rd., P.O. Box 275, Bayville 08721

## PRINTING — Large Format Digital

Applied Image, Inc.
 Phone—(732) 410-2444
 800 Business Park Dr., Freehold 07728
Canvas 4 Life, Inc.
 Phone—(973) 276-3200
 30 Chapin Rd., P.O. Box 216, Pine Brook 07058
Coloredge
 Phone—(201) 716-5200
 190 Jony Dr., Carlstadt 07072
Edison Lithographing Corp.
 Phone—(201) 902-9191
 3725 Tonnelle Ave., North Bergen 07047
Mega Media Concepts Ltd.
 Phone—(973) 919-5661
 286 Houses Corner Rd., Sparta 07871
Riverside Prints LLC
 Phone—(732) 671-8222
 11 Lawrence Cir., Middletown 07748
Speed Pro Imaging Of Piscataway
 Phone—(732) 662-9860
 56 Ethel Rd. W., Ste. 14, Piscataway 08854
Triangle Repro Center
 Phone—(609) 448-8161
 222 Dutch Neck Rd., East Windsor 08520

## PRINTING — Large Format Offset

Mediagraphics, Inc.
 Phone—(973) 777-2202
 25 Somerset Pl., Clifton 07012

## PRINTING — Laser

FedEx Office & Print Center
 Phone—(856) 273-5959
 1211 Route 73, Mount Laurel 08054

## PRINTING — Letterpress

United States Business Card Co.
 Phone—(201) 863-8776
 540 39th St., Ste. 33, Union City 07087

## PRINTING — Lithographic

A To Z Printing & Promotions
 Phone—(973) 916-9995
 1455 Main Ave., Clifton 07011
Bassano Printers & Lithographers
 Phone—(973) 423-1400
 67 Royal Ave., Hawthorne 07506
BWAY Corporation
 Phone—(732) 997-4050
 6 Litho Rd., Trenton 08638
Content Critical LLC
 Phone—(201) 528-2777
 800 Central Blvd., Carlstadt 07072
MacFerren's Printing & Co.
 Phone—(856) 435-7066
 3 Democrat Rd., Gibbsboro 08026
Manifold Printers, Inc.
 Phone—(973) 345-5900
 189 Berdan Ave., Ste. 456, Wayne 07470
Novel Lithographers, Inc.
 Phone—(201) 372-3900
 1 Kero Rd., Carlstadt 07072
O'Sullivan Communications
 Phone—(973) 227-5112
 1 Fairfield Crescent, West Caldwell 07006
Regal Printers, Inc.
 Phone—(609) 693-3533
 707-3 Old Shore Rd., Forked River 08731

Renew Graphics
 Phone—(201) 802-1900
 16 W. Park Ave., Park Ridge 07656
Restaurant Graphics, Inc.
 Phone—(973) 763-4036
 67 Newark Way, Maplewood 07040

## PRINTING — Newspaper

Asbury Park Press, Inc. (H Q)
 Phone—(732) 922-6000
 3600 Highway 66, P.O. Box 1550, Neptune 07754
Catamaran Media Co., LLC
 Phone—(609) 266-1860
 3120 Fire Rd., Egg Harbor Township 08234
JB Offset Printing Corp.
 Phone—(201) 664-4400
 475 Walnut St., Norwood 07648
Kirms Printing Co., Inc.
 Phone—(732) 774-8000
 1520 Washington Ave., P.O. Box 1067, Neptune
 07753
Latinos Unidos De Nueva Jersey, LLC
 Phone—(732) 534-5959
 190 Hickory Rd., Jackson 08527
Reminder Newspaper
 Phone—(856) 825-8811
 2 W. Vine St., P.O. Box 1600, Millville 08332
South Jersey Times
 Phone—(856) 845-3300
 309 S. Broad St., P.O. Box 639, Woodbury 08096

## PRINTING — Newsprint

Webco Graphics/W.G.I. Corp.
 Phone—(732) 370-2900
 1875 Swarthmore Ave., Lakewood 08701

## PRINTING — Offset

A A Graphics, Inc.
 Phone—(201) 398-0710
 431 N. Midland Ave., Unit C, Saddle Brook 07663
A M Graphics Co., Inc.
 Phone—(201) 767-5320
 68 Schraalenburgh Rd., Harrington Park 07640
Advertisers Services Group, Inc.
 Phone—(201) 440-5577
 65 Railroad Ave., Ridgefield Park 07660
Alexy, Inc.
 Phone—(973) 467-0030
 401 Morris Ave., Springfield 07081
All American Print & Copy Center
 Phone—(732) 758-6200
 518 Highway 35, Red Bank 07701
Allegra Marketing Print & Mail
 Phone—(609) 390-1400
 533 S. Shore Rd., Marmora 08223
ALL-STATE LEGAL
 Phone—(908) 272-0800
 1 Commerce Dr., Cranford 07016
Allstate Printing Packaging, Inc.
 Phone—(973) 473-0700
 791 Paulison Ave., Ste. 3, Clifton 07011
Alma Offset Co., Inc.
 Phone—(609) 587-5480
 225 Bakers Basin Rd., P.O. Box 6487,
 Lawrenceville 08648
Alpha Graphics
 Phone—(201) 447-4800
 95 Greenwood Ave., Midland Park 07432
AlphaGraphics
 Phone—(856) 761-8000
 5 N. Olney Ave., Ste. 200, Cherry Hill 08003
AlphaGraphics
 Phone—(732) 247-0809
 401 Jersey Ave., Ste. F, New Brunswick 08901
American Graphic Systems, Inc.
 Phone—(201) 796-0666
 39-26 Broadway, Fair Lawn 07410
American Plus Printers, Inc.
 Phone—(732) 528-2170
 2604 Atlantic Ave., Wall 07719
Anthony Quality Printing, Mark
 Phone—(973) 815-1113
 187 Garibaldi Ave., Lodi 07644
Apex Printing Services, Inc.
 Phone—(908) 281-9221
 6 Ilene Ct., Bldg. 6, Unit 16, Hillsborough 08844

© Copyright 2015 Manufacturers' News, Inc.

## PRINTING — Offset — (cont.)

Apollo Quik Print Co., Inc.
Phone—(201) 488-1101
49 Orchard St., Hackensack 07601

Armor Guard Business Center
Phone—(973) 676-6900
139 Main St., Orange 07050

Automatic Data Processing, Inc. (H Q)
Phone—(973) 974-5000
1 ADP Blvd., Roseland 07068

B & B Press, Inc.
Phone—(908) 840-4323
24 Cokesbury Rd., Ste. 11, Lebanon 08833

Bartlett Printing & Graphics, Inc.
Phone—(609) 386-1525
4495 Route 130 S., Burlington 08016

BCT-NY/NJ
Phone—(201) 236-0088
11 Industrial Ave., Upper Saddle River 07458

Beacon Offset Co., Inc.
Phone—(201) 488-4241
204 Russell Pl., Hackensack 07601

Belle Mead Printing, LLC
Phone—(908) 595-9500
42 Old Camplain Rd., Hillsborough 08844

Bergen Instant Printing, Inc.
Phone—(201) 945-7303
328 Broad Ave., Ridgefield 07657

Bon Venture, Inc.
Phone—(973) 584-5699
34 Ironia Rd., P.O. Box 850, Flanders 07836

Budget Print
Phone—(201) 692-1412
426 Cedar Ln., Teaneck 07666

Budget Print Center
Phone—(609) 348-4589
2510 Atlantic Ave., Atlantic City 08401

Budget Print Center
Phone—(973) 744-5520
590 Valley Rd., Montclair 07043

Business Card Express
Phone—(856) 596-3150
8 E. Stow Rd., Ste. 140, P.O. Box 728, Marlton 08053

C & D Printing Co.
Phone—(732) 892-8044
118 Broadway, Point Pleasant Beach 08742

C & R Printing, Inc.
Phone—(201) 933-8000
400 Gotham Pkwy., Carlstadt 07072

Cape Printing Express, Inc.
Phone—(609) 884-8080
821 Shunpike Rd., Cape May 08204

Central Printing & Typesetting
Phone—(732) 929-0011
1501 Route 37 E., Toms River 08753

Centurion Printing
Phone—(908) 241-9839
761 Lexington Ave., Kenilworth 07033

Colonial Printers
Phone—(609) 921-1350
266 Witherspoon St., Princeton 08542

Colony, LLC
Phone—(973) 375-4315
852 S. Orange Ave., P.O. Box 6444, Newark 07106

Colornet, LLC
Phone—(856) 662-0652
809 Hylton Rd., Ste. 11, Pennsauken 08110

Computer Share, Inc.
Phone—(201) 680-5307
480 Washington Blvd., Jersey City 07310

Consortium Companies
Phone—(732) 512-1777
400 Raritan Center Pkwy., Edison 08837

Counter-Fit Quick Printing, Inc.
Phone—(201) 420-7926
145 Newark Ave., Belleville 07109

Craftsmen Printers, The
Phone—(973) 773-8950
855 Bloomfield Ave., Clifton 07012

Creative Color Lithographers, Inc.
Phone—(908) 789-2295
611 South Ave., Garwood 07027

D & I Printing Co., Inc.
Phone—(201) 871-3620
23 Chestnut St., Englewood 07631

D & M Printers
Phone—(908) 534-4101
43 School Rd., Whitehouse Station 08889

Deans Graphics
Phone—(609) 261-8817
16 Mill St., P.O. Box 809, Mount Holly 08060

Design 446
Phone—(732) 223-0100
2411 Atlantic Ave., Ste. 4, Manasquan 08736

DG3 North America, Inc.
Phone—(201) 946-0156
180 Pulaski St., Bayonne 07002

DG3 North America, Inc.
Phone—(201) 793-5000
100 Burma Rd., Jersey City 07305

Dogstar Digital, LLC
Phone—(732) 768-3699
429 Redmond Ave., Oakhurst 07755

Downtown Printing Center, Inc.
Phone—(732) 246-7990
46 Paterson St., New Brunswick 08901

Duca Printing Co., Inc.
Phone—(856) 767-2242
247 Haddon Ave., West Berlin 08091

Dynamic Printing & Graphics, Inc.
Phone—(973) 473-7177
250 Delawanna Ave., Clifton 07014

EarthColor, Inc.
Phone—(973) 884-1300
249 Pomeroy Rd., P.O. Box 169, Parsippany 07054

Emerson Speed Printing
Phone—(201) 265-7977
379 Kinderkamack Rd., Oradell 07649

Express Press
Phone—(973) 751-1287
145 North Ave., Belleville 07109

Express Printing, Inc.
Phone—(908) 925-6300
209 W. Saint Georges Ave., Linden 07036

Farmingdale Printing
Phone—(732) 938-2727
70 Main St., Farmingdale 07727

Fast Print, LLC
Phone—(201) 944-2350
514 Main St., Fort Lee 07024

Fidelis Group, Inc.
Phone—(201) 641-4701
223 Gates Rd., Unit A, Little Ferry 07643

Fort Nassau Graphics
Phone—(856) 853-2800
1757 Imperial Way, West Deptford 08066

Full House Printing, Inc.
Phone—(201) 798-7073
60 Newark St., Hoboken 07030

Gangi Graphics
Phone—(732) 840-8680
1669 Highway 88 W., Brick 08724

Gavin Printing, Inc.
Phone—(212) 721-9009
1057 Glen Rd., Fort Lee 07024

GMPC Printing
Phone—(973) 894-1500
1 Trenton Ave., Clifton 07011

Good Impressions, Inc.
Phone—(908) 689-3071
325 W. Washington Ave., Washington 07882

Gracis, Inc.
Phone—(201) 296-0700
25 Graphic Pl., Moonachie 07074

Graphic Imagery, Inc.
Phone—(908) 755-2882
122 Mount Bethel Rd., Ste. 2, Warren 07059

Graphics Plus Corp.
Phone—(973) 835-3744
210 W. Parkway, Ste. 7, Pompton Plains 07444

Great Northern Commercial Service, Inc.
Phone—(908) 475-8855
401 Greenwich St., Belvidere 07823

H & S Graphics
Phone—(973) 779-5880
196 Garibaldi Ave., Ste. 3, Lodi 07644

Holzer & Assocs., LLC, Philip
Phone—(212) 691-9500
350 Michelle Pl., Carlstadt 07072

Hummel Distributing Corp.
Phone—(908) 688-5300
850 Springfield Rd., P.O. Box 3199, Union 07083

Impact Printing
Phone—(732) 636-8893
762 Green St., Iselin 08830

Ink Well Printers Inc.
Phone—(908) 272-8090
38 S. 21st St., Kenilworth 07033

Inkwell Corp.
Phone—(609) 884-0350
1414 Elmira St., Cape May 08204

Instant Image Printing
Phone—(201) 945-0020
649 Bergen Blvd., Ridgefield 07657

J & J Printing Co.
Phone—(201) 858-8895
1023 Broadway, Bayonne 07002

J M J Printing & Graphics, Inc.
Phone—(973) 838-3400
1403 State Route 23, Ste. 8, Butler 07405

Jamesburg Press Madison Printing, Inc.
Phone—(732) 521-0262
9 E. Railroad Ave., Jamesburg 08831

Jon-Da Printing Co.
Phone—(201) 653-6200
234 16th St., 8th Fl., Jersey City 07310

Kern Printers & Stationers
Phone—(201) 226-0270
86 Lackawanna Ave., Unit 105, Woodland Park 07424

Keskes Printing Co.
Phone—(856) 767-4733
5 W. Taunton Ave., Berlin 08009

Kiva Printing & Graphics
Phone—(877) 777-5482
50 Cutler Ave., Westville 08093

L P B Graphics, Inc.
Phone—(732) 283-4333
512-514 Route 27, Iselin 08830

Lamb Printing, Inc.
Phone—(908) 852-5354
700 Grand Ave., Hackettstown 07840

Laser Dim Graphics & Printing
Phone—(732) 821-9000
2 Parkwood Ln., Colts Neck 07722

Laureate Press, Inc.
Phone—(609) 965-0447
1336 W. Central Ave., P.O. Box 343, Egg Harbor City 08215

**LCI Graphics, Inc.**
Commercial offset, on-demand, digital color
**Phone—(973) 893-2913**
**Fax—(888) 852-9639**
**Web—www.lcigraphics.com**
**Email—info@lcigraphics.com**
**2400 Main Street Ext., Ste. 8, Sayreville 08872**

Leader Printers
Phone—(609) 729-0161
5914 New Jersey Ave., Wildwood Crest 08260

Linder & Co., Inc.
Phone—(201) 386-8788
1183 W. Side Ave., Jersey City 07306

MacLearie Printing, LLC
Phone—(732) 681-2772
917 18th Ave., Belmar 07719

Major Printing Co., Inc.
Phone—(908) 686-7296
934 Savitt Pl., P.O. Box 1356, Union 07083

Mariano Press Co.
Phone—(732) 247-6828
14 Veronica Ave., Somerset 08873

Mark Lithography, Inc.
Phone—(973) 538-5557
220 Entin Rd., Clifton 07014

Master Printing Co.
Phone—(908) 351-1568
P.O. Box 9609, Elizabeth 07202

Master Printing, Inc.
Phone—(856) 299-8318
30 Pedricktown Woodstown Rd., P.O. Box 1, Pedricktown 08067

Mastergraphx, Inc.
Phone—(732) 329-0088
45 Stouts Ln., Ste. 14, P.O. Box 567, Monmouth Junction 08852

Menco Business Products
Phone—(908) 281-0911
178 Route 206 S., Hillsborough 08844

Merchant Street Printer, LLC
Phone—(856) 547-1991
107 E. Atlantic Ave., Audubon 08106

Minuteman Press
Phone—(973) 894-1500
1 Trenton Ave., Clifton 07011

Minuteman Press
Phone—(609) 261-1024
1299 Route 38, Ste. 2, Hainesport 08036

Minuteman Press
Phone—(732) 449-1760
1818 Highway 35, Wall 07719

INDUSTRY

## PRINTING — Offset — (cont.)

**Minuteman Press, Inc.**
Phone—(201) 288-7787
216 Boulevard, Hasbrouck Heights 07604

**Mount Freedom Printing**
Phone—(908) 362-9299
P.O. Box 285, Mount Freedom 07970

**Mr. B Offset Printing, Inc.**
Phone—(732) 396-3990
1850 Elizabeth Ave., Ste. B, Rahway 07065

**My Way Prints, Inc.**
Phone—(973) 492-1212
1376 Route 23, Butler 07405

**Na-Vet Printing Co.**
Phone—(908) 353-4441
506 Elizabeth Ave., Elizabeth 07206

**Neo Printing Co., Inc.**
Phone—(201) 489-5050
24 E. Wesley St., South Hackensack 07606

**New Standard Printing Corp.**
Phone—(973) 366-0006
118 Lincoln Ave., Dover 07801

**Nexgen Press Corp.**
Phone—(609) 528-0370
859 Bridgeboro St., Riverside 08075

**Nitka Graphics, Inc.**
Phone—(201) 797-3000
355 E. 54th St., Elmwood Park 07407

**One Source Solutions**
Phone—(973) 242-4040
220 Encin Rd., Clifton 07014

**P B A Printing**
Phone—(973) 817-9712
170 Malvern St., Newark 07105

**P I P Printing**
Phone—(732) 255-1980
2960 Yorktowne Blvd., Brick 08723

**Paper Mart, Inc.**
Phone—(973) 884-2505
151 Ridgedale Ave., East Hanover 07936

**Papson Printing Corp.**
Phone—(201) 342-2860
115 Hudson St., Hackensack 07601

**Park Avenue Printing, LLC**
Phone—(609) 989-8022
2001 S. Broad St., Trenton 08610

**Parsells Printing, Inc.**
Phone—(973) 473-2700
280 Main Ave., Passaic 07055

**Paul-Mark Printing**
Phone—(732) 462-9110
37 Stokes St., Freehold 07728

**PDEC, Inc.**
Phone—(732) 223-5995
2101 Atlantic Ave., Manasquan 08736

**Pennington Printers, Inc.**
Phone—(609) 737-0650
21 Burd St., Pennington 08534

**Perma Graphics, Inc.**
Phone—(201) 814-1200
25 Graphic Pl., Moonachie 07074

**Pinnacle Press, Inc.**
Phone—(201) 652-0500
41 Prospect St., Midland Park 07432

**Pirolli Printing Co., Inc.**
Phone—(856) 933-1285
860 W. Browning Rd., Bellmawr 08031

**Precise Printing**
Phone—(732) 271-8626
748 Lincoln Blvd., Middlesex 08846

**Precision Printing Group, LLC**
Phone—(856) 753-7903
117 Jackson Rd., Berlin 08009

**Premier Graphics, Inc.**
Phone—(732) 872-9933
500 Central Ave., Atlantic Highlands 07716

**Presto Print & Copy**
Phone—(973) 777-8377
79 S. Main St., Ste. 3, Lodi 07644

**Primary Colors Graphics**
Phone—(201) 526-9300
629 Grove St., 7th Fl., Jersey City 07310

**Princetonian Graphics, Inc.**
Phone—(732) 329-8282
45 Stouts Ln., Ste. 4, Monmouth Junction 08852

**Print Solutions**
Phone—(201) 567-9622
320 S. Dean St., Englewood 07631

**Printers Place North, LLC**
Phone—(973) 838-3741
2 Kiel Ave., Ste. 154, Kinnelon 07405

**Printing Center, Inc., The**
Phone—(973) 383-6362
1 White Lake Rd., Sparta 07871

**Printing Delite, Inc.**
Phone—(973) 676-3033
279 Sanford St., East Orange 07018

**Printmasters**
Phone—(973) 427-6598
1108 Goffle Rd., Hawthorne 07506

**Pronto Print**
Phone—(856) 232-7200
1329 Hurffville Rd., Deptford 08096

**Purcell Printing Co., Robert**
Phone—(201) 941-0375
244 Kamena St., Fairview 07022

**R & R Printing Co.**
Phone—(732) 727-6036
107 S. Stevens Ave., P.O. Box 3204, South Amboy 08879

**R J Graphics, Inc.**
Phone—(856) 848-1986
206 Crown Point Rd., P.O. Box 293, West Deptford 08086

**Ramsey Print Corp.**
Phone—(201) 460-1008
1000 Wall St. W., Ste. 2, Lyndhurst 07071

**Rapid Print & Copy Service**
Phone—(732) 238-9056
78 Summerhill Rd., East Brunswick 08816

**Roan Printing, Inc.**
Phone—(908) 526-5990
4 E. Main St., Somerville 08876

**Rogers Printing Center**
Phone—(609) 883-3238
11 Lexington Ave., Trenton 08618

**Royal Printing Service**
Phone—(201) 863-3131
441 51st St., West New York 07093

**Safeguard**
Phone—(973) 887-9500
1253 Springfield Ave., Ste. 258, New Providence 07974

**Schuyler Printing Co., Inc.**
Phone—(201) 997-8083
71 Kearny Ave., Kearny 07032

**Sir Speedy**
Phone—(609) 267-1232
897 Rancocas Rd., Westampton 08060

**Sir Speedy Printing Center**
Phone—(732) 225-2272
28 Campus Dr., Edison 08837

**Sir Speedy Printing Of East Hanover**
Phone—(973) 884-0005
50 Route 10 W., East Hanover 07936

**Spruce Run Printing**
Phone—(908) 638-6464
2005 Route 31, Clinton 08809

**Squiggly Productions, LLC**
Phone—(973) 838-7475
164 Main St., Butler 07405

**Standard Printing & Mail Service**
Phone—(973) 790-3333
30-A Plymouth St., P.O. Box 11021, Fairfield 07004

**Stuyvesant Press, Inc.**
Phone—(973) 399-3880
119 Coit St., Irvington 07111

**T C Graphics, Inc.**
Phone—(908) 276-7710
109 South Ave. W., Cranford 07016

**Tech Repro, Inc.**
Phone—(201) 489-1333
65 Zabriskie St., Hackensack 07601

**Terminal Printing Co.**
Phone—(201) 659-5924
94 River St., P.O. Box 30, Hoboken 07030

**Thomsen Litho, Inc.**
Phone—(201) 489-1133
217 Railroad Ave., Ridgefield Park 07660

**Tomad, Inc.**
Phone—(609) 965-0808
129 Cincinnati Ave., Egg Harbor City 08215

**Trenton Printing, LLC**
Phone—(609) 695-6485
1150 Southard St., Ste. 2, Trenton 08638

**Tri-City Print & Copy Center**
Phone—(973) 706-5854
155 Union Blvd., Totowa 07512

**Trinity Press, LLC**
Phone—(973) 881-0690
655 Market St., Paterson 07513

**Tropp Printing Corp.**
Phone—(212) 233-4519
8 Woodhollow Dr., Holmdel 07733

**Trout Printing LLC**
Phone—(856) 327-8366
33 Reeves St., Millville 08332

**Universal Graphics Co.**
Phone—(973) 748-4009
497 Bloomfield Ave., Bloomfield 07003

**Verna Printing Co., Inc.**
Phone—(973) 751-6462
85 Washington Ave., Belleville 07109

**Veterano Ward Commercial Printing**
Phone—(856) 429-5460
301 Bradshaw Ave., Haddonfield 08033

**Watson Graphics, Inc.**
Phone—(201) 955-0283
578 Kearny Ave., Kearny 07032

**Wiley's Lake Press, Inc.**
Phone—(973) 728-9231
1902 Greenwood Lake Tpke., Hewitt 07421

**Work Of Art Corp.**
Phone—(856) 488-1188
801 Olive Ave., Cherry Hill 08002

## PRINTING — Packaging

**Flexo Craft Prints, Inc.**
Phone—(973) 482-7200
1000 1st St., Harrison 07029

## PRINTING — Plastic

**Accurate Plastic Printers, LLC**
Phone—(973) 591-0180
30 Colfax Ave., Clifton 07013

**Kayline Processing, Inc.**
Phone—(609) 695-1440
31 Coates St., Trenton 08611

## PRINTING — Prepress

**A M Graphy**
Phone—(201) 488-0360
95 Myer St., Hackensack 07601

**Accucolor, LLC**
Phone—(732) 741-4594
771 Shrewsbury Ave., Ste. B, Shrewsbury 07702

**Afton Publishing, LLC**
Phone—(973) 579-2442
P.O. Box 1399, Andover 07821

**Alliance Design, Inc.**
Phone—(973) 904-1900
434 Union Blvd., Totowa 07512

**Bind-Rite Robbinsville**
Phone—(609) 208-1917
1 Applegate Dr., Robbinsville 08691

**Cohen Printing & Invitation**
Phone—(201) 287-0343
500 Cedar Ln., Teaneck 07666

**Contemporary, Inc.**
Phone—(201) 569-3900
161 Coolidge Ave., Englewood 07631

**Denni's Studio**
Phone—(973) 220-4898
169 Semel Ave., Garfield 07026

**Graphictone**
Phone—(201) 568-2008
360 Sylvan Ave., Ste. 4, Englewood Cliffs 07632

**Imtech Graphics, Inc.**
Phone—(201) 933-8002
545 Dell Rd., Carlstadt 07072

**Millennium Graphics, Inc.**
Phone—(732) 431-0440
35 Vanderburg Rd., Marlboro 07746

**New Jersey Business Magazine**
Phone—(973) 882-5004
310 Passaic Ave., Ste. 201, Fairfield 07004

**Rush Graphics, Inc.**
Phone—(973) 427-9393
1122 Goffle Rd., Hawthorne 07506

**S S Art & Engraving Corp.**
Phone—(908) 686-5536
1023 Commerce Ave., Union 07083

**Shorewood Digital Design & Development Center**
Phone—(201) 372-3900
1 Kero Rd., Carlstadt 07072

INDUSTRY

## PRINTING — Prepress — *(cont.)*

South Plainfield Observer
Phone—(908) 668-0010
1110 Hamilton Blvd., Ste. 1-B, South Plainfield
07080
UB Communications
Phone—(973) 331-9391
10 Lodge Ln., Parsippany 07054

## PRINTING — Promotional

All-Ways Advertising Co.
Phone—(973) 338-0700
1442 Broad St., Bloomfield 07003
**Luminer Converting Group, Inc.**
**Email: info@luminer.com**
**A leading international pressure sensitive label
printer & converter**
**Phone—(732) 886-6557**
**Fax—(732) 886-6692**
**Web—www.luminer.com**
**1925 Swarthmore Ave., Ste. 5, Lakewood
08701**
Pride Products Distributors, LLC
Phone—(973) 564-6300
673 Morris Ave., Ste. 2, Springfield 07081

## PRINTING — Rotogravure

Constant Services, Inc.
Phone—(973) 227-2990
17 Commerce Rd., Fairfield 07004

## PRINTING — Sheet Fed

Pictorial Offset Corporation
Phone—(201) 935-7100
111 Amor Ave., Carlstadt 07072

## PRINTING — Specialty

Rem Services
Phone—(609) 494-7760
310 W. 6th St., Ship Bottom 08008

## PRINTING — Thermal Transfer

**AGF Burner, Inc.**
**Phone—(732) 730-8090**
**Fax—(732) 730-8060**
**Web—www.agfburner.com**
**Email—sales@agfburner.com**
**1955 Swarthmore Ave., Unit 2, Lakewood
08701**

*(see our ad under GAS BURNERS)*

## PRINTING — Web Offset

**Inserts East, Inc.**
**Email: reception@insertseast.com**
**Phone—(856) 663-8181**
**Fax—(856) 663-3288**
**Web—www.insertseast.com**
**7045 Central Hwy., Pennsauken 08109**
RFM Printing, Inc.
Phone—(732) 938-4400
1715 Highway 34, P.O. Box 1430, Wall 07719

## PRINTING BLANKETS

Fujikura Graphics
Phone—(201) 420-5040
700 Penhorn Ave., Unit 2, Secaucus 07094

## PRINTING EQUIPMENT AND SUPPLIES

Allison Systems Corp.
Phone—(856) 461-9111
220 Adams St., Riverside 08075
Beta Screen Corp.
Phone—(201) 939-2400
707 Commercial Ave., Carlstadt 07072
Coda, Inc.
Phone—(201) 825-7400
30 Industrial Ave., Mahwah 07430

Gulton, Inc.
Phone—(908) 791-4622
116 Corporate Blvd., Ste. A, South Plainfield
07080
MRI International
Phone—(973) 383-3645
44-50 Clinton St., Newton 07860
Polytype America Corp.
Phone—(201) 995-1000
10 Industrial Ave., Mahwah 07430
Van Dam Machine Corp.
Phone—(973) 257-7050
81-B Walsh Dr., Parsippany 07054

## PRINTING EQUIPMENT AND SUPPLIES — Wholesale

Colex Imaging, Inc.
Phone—(201) 265-5670
55-57 Bushes Ln., Elmwood Park 07407
Interchange Equipment, Inc.
Phone—(973) 473-5005
90 Dayton Ave., Ste. 200, Passaic 07055
Printers Parts Store
Phone—(201) 935-9595
82 Herman St., East Rutherford 07073
Quality Discount Press Parts & Equipment, Inc.
Phone—(609) 646-2212
6088 Reega Ave., Egg Harbor Township 08234
RPL Supplies, Inc.
Phone—(973) 767-0880
141 Lanza Ave., Bldg. 3-A, Garfield 07026

## PRINTING EQUIPMENT REBUILDERS

PanPac, LLC
Phone—(856) 376-3576
212 N. Virginia Ave., Carneys Point 08069

## PRINTING MACHINERY

**Ackley Machine Corp.**
**Email: pgulotta@ackleymachine.com**
**Phone—(856) 234-3626**
**Fax—(856) 234-8657**
**Web—www.ackleymachine.com**
**1273 N. Church St., Ste. 106, Moorestown
08057**
**AGF Burner, Inc.**
**Phone—(732) 730-8090**
**Fax—(732) 730-8060**
**Web—www.agfburner.com**
**Email—sales@agfburner.com**
**1955 Swarthmore Ave., Unit 2, Lakewood
08701**

*(see our ad under GAS BURNERS)*

Diversified Graphic Machinery
Phone—(732) 933-4865
230 Highway 35, Red Bank 07701
MBO America
Phone—(609) 267-2900
4 E. Stow Rd., Ste. 12, Marlton 08053
Mosstype Corp.
Phone—(201) 444-8000
150 Franklin Tpke., Waldwick 07463

## PRINTING PLATE EQUIPMENT

Heights USA, Inc.
Phone—(609) 530-1300
1445 Lower Ferry Rd., Ewing 08618

## PRINTING PLATES

DAA International LLC
Phone—(973) 575-7444
24 Commerce Rd., Ste. L, Fairfield 07004
Flexi Printing Plate Co., Inc.
Phone—(201) 939-3600
50 Commercial Ave., Moonachie 07074
Greenwich Graphics, LLC
Phone—(212) 727-1116
234 16th St., 8th Fl., Jersey City 07310
Mark/Trece, Inc.
Phone—(973) 884-1005
160 Algonquin Pkwy., Whippany 07981

Packaging Graphics, Inc.
Phone—(856) 767-9000
435 Commerce Ln., P.O. Box 160, West Berlin
08091
Plate Craft, Inc.
Phone—(973) 736-4404
172-174 Main St., West Orange 07052
Standard Embossing Plate
Phone—(973) 344-6670
129 Pulaski St., Newark 07105
**Unity Graphics & Engraving/Unity Steel Rule
Die**
**Rubber Printing, Plate Engraving & Steel Rule Dies**
**Phone—(201) 569-6400**
**Fax—(201) 569-2956**
**Web—www.gounity.com**
**Email—unitypres@gounity.com**
**210 S. Van Brunt St., P.O. Box 88, Englewood
07631**
West Essex Graphics, Inc.
Phone—(973) 227-2400
305 Fairfield Ave., Fairfield 07004

## PRINTING PLATES — Photopolymer

Marko Engraving & Art Corp.
Phone—(201) 945-6555
439 Fairview Ave., Fairview 07022

## PRINTING PRESS ACCESSORIES

Benton Graphics, Inc.
Phone—(609) 587-4000
3 Industrial Dr., Trenton 08619
Graphic Equipment Corp.
Phone—(732) 494-5350
55 Wester Ave., Metuchen 08840
Innolutions, Inc.
Phone—(609) 490-9799
92 N. Main St., P.O. Box 384, Windsor 08561
Midlan Corp.
Phone—(201) 445-4405
3 Bohnert Pl., Waldwick 07463

## PRINTING PRESSES

Chesnut Engineering, Inc., W. R.
Phone—(973) 227-6995
14 Spielman Rd., Fairfield 07004

## PRINTING SUPPLIES

Faust Thermographic, Inc.
Phone—(908) 474-0555
325 Cantor Ave., P.O. Box 1277, Linden 07036

## PROCESS CONTROL INSTRUMENTS

**Fizzarotti Instrumentation Service**
**Process Control Instrumentation & Calibration
Control**
**Phone—(732) 833-4505**
**Fax—(732) 833-4507**
**Web—www.fizzinstrumentation.com**
**Email—mail@fizzinstrumentation.com**
**436 W. Commodore Blvd., Ste. 4, Jackson
08527**

**Fizzarotti Instrumentation Service**
Quality calibration services
www.fizzinstrumentation.com
**(732) 833-4505**
436 W. Commodore Blvd. Ste. 4
Jackson, NJ 08527

Papailias Co., Inc., J. G.
Phone—(201) 767-4027
245 Pegasus Ave., Northvale 07647

*find additional suppliers at*
**IndustryNet.com**

## PROCESS CONTROL INSTRUMENTS — *(cont.)*

**Pro-Tech Solutions South, LLC.**
Phone—(610) 539-6219
Fax—(610) 862-9666
Web—www.pro-techsouth.com
390 Rittenhouse Blvd., Norristown, PA 19403

**PRO-TECH** *Solutions South, LLC.*

Process Control
Instruments

**Tel: 610-539-6219**
**Fax: 610-862-9666**

**www.pro-techsouth.com**

390 Rittenhouse Blvd.
Norristown, PA 19403

**Status Instruments, Inc.**
Transmitters, Signal Conditioners & Digital Indicators
Phone—(800) 700-3272
Fax—(800) 700-5468
Web—www.statinst.com
Email—sales@statinst.com
456 Park Ave., P.O. Box 548, Scotch Plains 07076

## PROCESS EQUIPMENT AND SYSTEMS

Chem Flowtronics, Inc.
Phone—(973) 785-0001
195 Paterson Ave., Little Falls 07424
Koch Modular Process Systems, LLC
Phone—(201) 368-2929
45 Eisenhower Dr., Ste. 350, Paramus 07652
**Komline-Sanderson Engineering**
Phone—(908) 234-1000 / (800) 225-5457
Fax—(908) 234-9487
Web—www.komline.com
Email—info@komline.com
12 Holland Ave., Peapack 07977
Veeco Instruments, Inc.
Phone—(732) 560-5300
145 Belmont Dr., Somerset 08873
Wyssmont Co., Inc.
Phone—(201) 947-4600
1470 Bergen Blvd., Fort Lee 07024

## PROCESSING EQUIPMENT

Acrison, Inc.
Phone—(201) 440-8300
20 Empire Blvd., Moonachie 07074
Advanced Process Technology, Inc.
Phone—(732) 356-4438
200 Egel Ave., Middlesex 08846
Buhler Inc
Phone—(201) 847-0600
40 Whitney Rd., Mahwah 07430
Equipment Xchange, LLC
Phone—(609) 561-0500
309 Columbia Rd., Hammonton 08037
Hosokawa Micron Powder Systems
Phone—(908) 273-6360
10 Chatham Rd., Summit 07901
Reliable Rubber & Plastic Machinery Co.
Phone—(201) 865-1073
2008 Union Tpke., North Bergen 07047
Roben Mfg. Co., Inc.
Phone—(732) 364-6000
760 Vassar Ave., Lakewood 08701

## PRODUCE

ACB Produce, Inc.
Phone—(973) 522-1141
Fax—(973) 522-1160
Email—acbproduce@aol.com
135-137 Pacific St., Newark 07105
Custom Pak, Inc.
Phone—(856) 384-4980
800 Grove Rd., Thorofare 08086
F & S Produce Co., Inc.
Phone—(856) 453-0316
913 Bridgeton Ave., P.O. Box 489, Rosenhayn 08352
New York Produce, Inc.
Phone—(201) 223-0909
125 Seaview Dr., Secaucus 07094
Riviera Produce Corp.
Phone—(201) 227-7105
205 Jackson St., P.O. Box 6065, Englewood 07631

## PRODUCT DESIGN

### (also see 'Designers-Industrial')

**North American Sterilization & Packaging Company, Inc.**
Email: rogerm@naspco.com
Phone—(973) 209-4388 / (800) 392-6310
Fax—(973) 209-6374
Web—www.naspco.com
19 Park Dr., Franklin 07416
*(see our ad under CONTRACT MANUFACTURING—Medical)*
**Shore Plastic Technologies, Inc.**
Specializing in comprehensive consulting engineering services for product development & testing, including 3D modeling, 2D drafting, FEA, moldflow & motion analysis
Phone—(856) 327-5114
Fax—(856) 825-9296
Web—www.shoreplastictech.com
Email—info@shoreplastictech.com
215 Buck St., Millville 08332
Sigma Design Company
Phone—(732) 629-7555
200 Pond Ave., Middlesex 08846

## PRODUCT DEVELOPMENT

**Shore Plastic Technologies, Inc.**
Specializing in comprehensive consulting engineering services for product development & testing, including 3D modeling, 2D drafting, FEA, moldflow & motion analysis
Phone—(856) 327-5114
Fax—(856) 825-9296
Web—www.shoreplastictech.com
Email—info@shoreplastictech.com
215 Buck St., Millville 08332
**Sigma Design Company**
Also engineered design build fabrication
Phone—(732) 629-7555
Fax—(732) 629-7556
Web—www.sigmadesign.net
Email—info@sigmadesign.net
200 Pond Ave., Middlesex 08846
*(see our ad under MACHINE DESIGN)*

## PROJECTION SYSTEMS

Night Canyon, Inc., The
Phone—(908) 454-6344
1475 Park Ave., Alpha 08865

## PROJECTORS

VCOM International Multi-Media Corp.
Phone—(201) 229-4270
80 Little Falls Rd., Fairfield 07004

## PROJECTORS — Digital

**Triflow Corp.**
Phone—(856) 768-7159
Fax—(856) 768-2013
Web—www.triflowcorp.com
Email—sales@triflowcorp.com
150 Cooper Rd., Ste. A-1, West Berlin 08091

## PROMOTIONAL PRODUCTS

Active Imprints
Phone—(732) 329-2613
4266 U.S. Highway 1, Monmouth Junction 08852
ADV Promos & More, LLC
Phone—(609) 587-7500
12 Baltusrol St., Hamilton Square 08690
Aura Badge Co.
Phone—(856) 881-9026
264 Clayton Ave., Monroeville 08343
Csonka Cigar Requisites, Inc. (H Q)
Phone—(609) 514-2766
407 Blue Spring Rd., Princeton 08540
D and S Designs
Phone—(856) 451-0954
P.O. Box 1707, Bridgeton 08302
Distinctive Promotions, Inc.
Phone—(973) 584-6800
268 U.S. Highway 206, Ste. 404, Flanders 07836
Madison Line, The
Phone—(973) 379-1108
40 Commerce St., Springfield 07081
Newton Printing & Embroidery
Phone—(973) 827-2006
75 Main St., Franklin 07416
O. Co Imprints, LLC
Phone—(732) 530-3202
58 W. Bergen Pl., P.O. Box 8249, Red Bank 07701
Punch Products U. S. A., Inc.
Phone—(732) 574-1900
2131 Felver Ct., Rahway 07065
**Smith Enterprises**
Phone—(215) 416-9881
Fax—(856) 608-9588
Web—www.smithentpromos.com
Email—dstees@comcast.net
100 Hillside Ln., P.O. Box 1433, Mount Laurel 08054
Tauber Co., LLC, G. G.
Phone—(301) 881-3567
289 State Route 33, Ste. 12, Manalapan 07726

## PROSTHETICS

Achilles Prosthetics & Orthotics, LLC
Phone—(201) 785-9944
503 N. Franklin Tpke., Ste. 12, Ramsey 07446
Allied Orthotics & Prosthetics
Phone—(856) 273-6400
813 E. Gate Dr., Ste. A, Mount Laurel 08054
Atlantic Prosthetic & Orthotic Services, Inc.
Phone—(609) 927-6330
199 New Rd., Ste. 56, Linwood 08221
Cocco Enterprises, Inc.
Phone—(609) 393-5939
333 Chambers St., Trenton 08609
Greiner & Sons, Inc., L. J.
Phone—(973) 977-9441
63-69 Dan Forth Ave., Paterson 07501
Hanger Clinic
Phone—(609) 653-8323
210 New Rd., Ste. 7, Linwood 08221
Hanger Prosthetics & Orthotics, Inc.
Phone—(732) 919-7774
5100 Belmore Blvd., Farmingdale 07727
Integra LifeSciences Corp.
Phone—(609) 275-2700
105 Morgan Ln., Plainsboro 08536
Integra LifeSciences Corp.
Phone—(609) 275-0500
311 Enterprise Dr., Plainsboro 08536
J. C. Orthopedic, Inc.
Phone—(732) 458-7900
1680 Highway 88, Brick 08724
Jefferson Prosthetics & Orthotics
Phone—(973) 762-0780
120 Prospect St., South Orange 07079
LeGrand Assocs.
Phone—(800) 273-8565
214 W. Main St., Ste. 102, Moorestown 08057
Modern Limb & Brace Co.
Phone—(609) 757-2702
916 Somerset St., Watchung 07069

*Search from among 430,000 U.S. manufacturers & suppliers:*
**IndustryNet.com**

INDUSTRY

## PROSTHETICS — (cont.)

**Pro-Fit Prosthetic & Orthotic, LLC**
Comprehensive Prosthetic & Orthotic Patient Care
Phone—(856) 809-9954 / (800) 996-7380
Web—www.profitlab.net
Email—pro.fit@comcast.net
76 W. Jimmie Leeds Rd., Ste. 103, Galloway 08205

**Pro-Fit Prosthetic & Orthotic, LLC**
Comprehensive Prosthetic & Orthotic Patient Care
Phone—(856) 809-9954 / (800) 996-7380
Web—www.profitlab.net
Email—pro.fit@comcast.net
10 Huron Ave., Ste. 1L, Jersey City 07306

**Pro-Fit Prosthetic & Orthotic, LLC**
Comprehensive Prosthetic & Orthotic Patient Care
Phone—(856) 809-9954 / (800) 996-7380
Web—www.profitlab.net
Email—pro.fit@comcast.net
409 Coventry Dr., Phillipsburg 08865

**Pro-Fit Prosthetic & Orthotic, LLC**
Comprehensive Prosthetic & Orthotic Patient Care
Phone—(856) 809-9910 / (800) 996-7380
Fax—(856) 809-9945
Web—www.profitlab.net
Email—pro.fit@comcast.net
215 Edgewood Ave., West Berlin 08091

Comprehensive Prosthetics & Orthotic Patient Care
Pro Fit Prosthetics & Orthotics
856-809-9910
800-996-7380
Fax: 856-809-9945
www.profitlab.net
215 Edgewood Ave. West Berlin, NJ 08091

Prosthetic Orthotic Solutions International
Phone—(856) 810-7900
100 Brick Rd., Ste. 315, Marlton 08053
Rinko Orthopedic Appliances, Inc.
Phone—(201) 796-3121
2509 Broadway, Fair Lawn 07410
Total Control Orthotic Lab
Phone—(609) 499-2200
14 W. Front St., Florence 08518

## PROTEIN

**Ambix Laboratories**
Custom & P/L Liquid Protein Products
Phone—(973) 890-9002
Fax—(973) 890-9778
Web—www.ambixlabs.com
Email—ambixlab@aol.com
55 W. End Rd., Totowa 07512
*(see our ad on this page)*
MicroSurfaces, Inc.
Phone—(201) 408-5596
1 W. Forest Ave., Englewood 07631

## PROTOTYPES

Advanced Molding Concepts
Phone—(732) 390-8366
329 Wilson Ave., Aberdeen 07747
Best Cast
Phone—(201) 225-1750
822 Kinderkamack Rd., River Edge 07661
Biztech, Inc.
Phone—(973) 361-7666
3155 Route 10, Ste. 202, Denville 07834
Brown Tool & Machine Co., Inc.
Phone—(609) 397-1751
Rosemont Raven Rock Rd., P.O. Box 142, Rosemont 08556
Consolidated Prototypes, Inc.
Phone—(908) 464-6261
5 Oechsner Ct., Berkeley Heights 07922
**Defined Pro Machining, LLC**
CNC machining: prototypes, production, reverse engineering & design
Phone—(973) 941-2430
Fax—(973) 891-1039
Web—www.definedpro.com
Email—hf@definedpro.com
105 W. Dewey Ave., Ste. 205, Wharton 07885

## AMBIX LABORATORIES
NSF cGMP Certified
47 Years Specializing in:
— Liquid Protein & Nutritional Supplements
— Personal Care Products
973-890-9002 • Fax: 973-890-9778
www.ambixlabs.com • ambixlab@aol.com
55 W. End Rd. • Totowa, NJ 07512

Elena Consultants
Phone—(908) 654-8309
1175 Globe Ave., P.O. Box 1339, Mountainside 07092
Harry Shaw Model Maker Inc.
Phone—(609) 268-0647
401 Stokes Rd., Shamong 08088
I D J, Inc.
Phone—(973) 334-1517
121 Mechanic St., Boonton 07005
Ponte Model Makers, Tom
Phone—(973) 627-5906
25 Pine St., Ste. 2, Rockaway 07866
Product Development Assocs., LLC
Phone—(973) 267-0033
12 Say Dr., East Hanover 07936
Qualecon Machine
Phone—(973) 875-4144
235 Stateline Rd., Sussex 07461
Rock-Tenn Co.
Phone—(973) 594-6000
15 Garner Rd., Fairfield 07004

## PUBLIC RELATIONS

**JCPR Inc.**
Phone—(973) 850-7300
Fax—(973) 850-7399
Web—www.jcprinc.com
Email—contact@jcprinc.com
1 Gatehall Dr., Ste. 107, Parsippany 07054

## PUBLISHERS

**(also see 'Newspaper Publishers')**
A.M. Best Co.
Phone—(908) 439-2200
1 Ambest Rd., Oldwick 08858
Advocate Publishing Corp.
Phone—(973) 497-4200
171 Clifton Ave., P.O. Box 9500, Newark 07104
Aesthetic Press, Inc.
Phone—(908) 369-3777
P.O. Box 5306, North Branch 08876
American Foreclosures, Inc.
Phone—(201) 501-0200
P.O. Box 601, Oradell 07649
Anderson Publishing Ltd.
Phone—(908) 301-1995
180 Glenside Ave., Scotch Plains 07076
Beverage Media Group, Inc.
Phone—(908) 964-5060
2444 Morris Ave., Ste. 318, Union 07083
BlueSpire Strategic Marketing
Phone—(201) 740-6100
110 Summit Ave., Ste. B, Montvale 07645
Galaxy Of Graphics Ltd.
Phone—(201) 806-2100
30 Murray Hill Pkwy., Ste. 300, East Rutherford 07073
Health Resources Publishing LLC
Phone—(732) 292-1100
P.O. Box 456, Allenwood 08720
HSH Assocs.
Phone—(973) 617-8700
51 Route 23 S., Riverdale 07457
Information Today, Inc.
Phone—(609) 654-6266
143 Old Marlton Pike, Medford 08055

iVillage, Inc.
Phone—(212) 664-4444
900 Sylvan Ave., Englewood Cliffs 07632
Jersey Job Guide, Inc.
Phone—(732) 263-9675
422 Morris Ave., Ste. 5, Long Branch 07740
NJBIZ
Phone—(732) 246-7677
220 Davidson Ave., Ste. 302, Somerset 08873
Novak Co., Tony
Phone—(856) 649-4171
185 Bayview Rd., P.O. Box 333, Newport 08345
Pageworks, LLC
Phone—(908) 665-0607
P.O. Box 892, Murray Hill 07974
PaperClip Communications, Inc.
Phone—(973) 256-1333
125 Paterson Ave., Little Falls 07424
Program Dynamics, Inc.
Phone—(908) 782-9398
43 Pennsylvania Ave., P.O. Box 929, Flemington 08822
Rete Biomedical Communications Corp.
Phone—(201) 891-8205
191 Godwin Ave., Ste. 1, Wyckoff 07481
Salty Dog, The
Phone—(732) 714-8400
254 Brick Blvd., Ste. 1, Brick 08723
Sample Media, Inc.
Phone—(609) 399-1220
801 Asbury St., 3rd Fl., Ocean City 08226
Sandpaper Newspaper
Phone—(609) 494-5900
1816 Long Beach Blvd., Surf City 08008
Seawave Corp.
Phone—(609) 886-8600
1508 Route 47, Rio Grande 08242
Seidman Productions, Inc.
Phone—(856) 627-1356
254 E. Gibbsboro Rd., Ste. C, Lindenwold 08021
Shipserv
Phone—(215) 862-3353
1090 King Georges Post Rd., Edison 08837
Shoppe Cape May County Shoppers Guide
Phone—(609) 886-4112
2503 Bayshore Rd., Villas 08251
Showcase Publications, Inc.
Phone—(732) 349-7775
90 Irons St., Toms River 08753
SMR Research Corp.
Phone—(908) 852-7677
300 Valentine St., Hackettstown 07840
Transaction Publishers, Inc.
Phone—(732) 445-2280
10 Corporate Pl. S., Ste. 102, Piscataway 08854

## PUBLISHERS' REPRESENTATIVES

**M.J. Mrvica Associates, Inc.**
Phone—(856) 768-9360
Fax—(856) 753-5270
Web—www.mrvica.com
Email—mjmrvica@mrvica.com
2 W. Taunton Ave., Berlin 08009

## PUBLISHING — Book

Africa World Press, Inc.
Phone—(609) 695-3200
541 W. Ingham Ave., Ste. B, Trenton 08638

## PUBLISHING — Book — (cont.)

**Alexander Publishing, Inc.**
Phone—(201) 569-5373
8 Depot Sq., Englewood 07631

**Amphibian Press, LLC**
Phone—(856) 547-3022
309 Hutchinson Ave., Haddonfield 08033

**Barricade Books, Inc.**
Phone—(201) 944-7600
2037 Lemoine Ave., Fort Lee 07024

**Bongo Vista Publishing, LLC**
Phone—(201) 343-0252
32 Catalpa Ave., Hackensack 07601

**Books Are Back, Inc.**
Phone—(201) 447-0374
296 Woodside Ave., Ridgewood 07450

**Bromley Smith Publishers**
Phone—(732) 449-9288
1014 Wall Rd., Ste. G-3, P.O. Box 312, Spring
Lake 07762

**Career Press, Inc.**
Phone—(201) 848-0310
220 W. Parkway, Unit 12, Pompton Plains 07444

**Counsel Press, LLC**
Phone—(732) 750-9229
517 U.S. Highway 1 S., Ste. 1160, Iselin 08830

**Courier Corp.**
Phone—(201) 934-7100
1 International Blvd., Ste. 400, Mahwah 07495

**Crossfire Publications**
Phone—(973) 403-1633
551 Bloomfield Ave., Apt. C-14, West Caldwell
07006

**Enslow Publishing Group**
Phone—(908) 771-9400
40 Industrial Rd., Berkeley Heights 07922

**Frogworks.com, LLC**
Phone—(908) 832-6704
48 Sutton Rd., Lebanon 08833

**Galves Auto Price List, Inc.**
Phone—(201) 393-0051
430 Industrial Ave., Ste. 3, Teterboro 07608

**Gorgias Press**
Phone—(732) 885-8900
954 River Rd., P.O. Box 6939, Piscataway 08854

**Handyguide, Inc.**
Phone—(201) 262-9478
721 Village Rd., P.O. Box 205, Oradell 07649

**Heritage Publishing, LLC**
Phone—(732) 747-7770
620 High Bridge Rd., Colts Neck 07722

**Imagination Arts Publications**
Phone—(201) 529-5105
57 Thunderhead Pl., P.O. Box 103, Mahwah
07430

**Jersey Shore Publications**
Phone—(732) 892-1276
P.O. Box 176, Bay Head 08742

**Just Us Books, Inc.**
Phone—(973) 672-7701
P.O. Box 5306, East Orange 07019

**Kaystar Publishing**
Phone—(201) 825-2736
5 Harvey Ln., Saddle River 07458

**Kids At Our House**
Phone—(732) 548-1779
47 Stoneham Pl., Metuchen 08840

**Kovco Publishing, Inc.**
Phone—(201) 843-9099
230 W. Passaic St., Maywood 07607

**Kramer Shy & Assocs.**
Phone—(609) 646-2063
21 W. Delilah Rd., Pleasantville 08232

**Learning Links, Inc.**
Phone—(516) 437-9071
P.O. Box 326, Cranbury 08512

**Lief Group, Inc., Philip**
Phone—(609) 430-1000
371 Sayre Dr., Princeton 08540

**Machon Beer Hatorah, Inc.**
Phone—(732) 364-9638
41 E. 8th St., Lakewood 08701

**Manning Publication Co.**
Phone—(856) 375-2597
1233 Heartwood Dr., Cherry Hill 08003

**Mathematics League, Inc.**
Phone—(201) 568-6328
17 Lancaster Rd., P.O. Box 17, Tenafly 07670

**Metro Publishing Group, Inc.**
Phone—(201) 385-2000
626 McCarthy Dr., New Milford 07646

**Nersesian Publishing, Roy**
Phone—(973) 762-8604
10 Maryland Rd., Maplewood 07040

**New Horizon Press, Inc.**
Phone—(908) 604-6311
34 Church St., Liberty Corner 07938

**P & R Publishing Co.**
Phone—(908) 454-0505
1102 Marble Hill Rd., P.O. Box 817, Phillipsburg
08865

**Paulist Press**
Phone—(201) 825-7300
997 MacArthur Blvd., Mahwah 07430

**Pearson Technology**
Phone—(201) 767-5000
200 Old Tappan Rd., Old Tappan 07675

**Pegasus Group Publishing**
Phone—(973) 884-9100
188 Route 10 W., Ste. 307, East Hanover 07936

**Princeton Book Co.**
Phone—(609) 426-0602
614 U.S. Highway 130, Ste. 1-C, Hightstown
08520

**Princeton University Press**
Phone—(609) 258-4900
41 William St., Princeton 08540

**Red Letter Press, Inc.**
Phone—(201) 818-8951
16 Deerhorn Trl., Saddle River 07458

**Ross & Perry, Inc.**
Phone—(856) 429-5752
203 Chews Landing Rd., Haddonfield 08033

**Rutgers University Press**
Phone—(848) 445-7781
106 Somerset St., 3rd Fl., New Brunswick 08901

**Slack, Inc.**
Phone—(856) 848-1000
6900 Grove Rd., Thorofare 08086

**SQP, Inc.**
Phone—(609) 298-5111
3206 Route 206, P.O. Box 248, Columbus 08022

**Tage Publishing Service, Inc.**
Phone—(201) 445-3050
5 Brownstone Way, Ho-Ho-Kus 07423

**Townsend Press, Inc.**
Phone—(856) 753-0554
439 Kelley Dr., West Berlin 08091

**Trilogy Publications, LLC**
Phone—(201) 816-1211
560 Sylvan Ave., Ste. 1240, Englewood Cliffs
07632

**Wahida Clark Publishing, LLC**
Phone—(973) 678-9982
60 Evergreen Pl., Ste. 904, East Orange 07018

**Weidner Publishing Group**
Phone—(856) 486-1755
114 Woodbine Ave., Merchantville 08109

**Whitehurst & Clark, Inc.**
Phone—(908) 782-2323
1200 County Road 523, Flemington 08822

**World Scientific Publishing Co., Inc.**
Phone—(201) 487-9655
27 Warren St., Ste. 401-402, Hackensack 07601

## PUBLISHING — Directory

**Corfacts, Inc.**
Phone—(973) 998-6935
P.O. Box 10, Morris Plains 07950

**LexisNexis Martindale-Hubell**
Phone—(908) 464-6800
121 Chanlon Rd., New Providence 07974

**Manufacturers' News, Inc.**
**Phone—(847) 864-7000**
**Fax—(847) 332-1100**
**Web—www.manufacturersnews.com**
**Email—sales@manufacturersnews.com**
**1633 Central St., Evanston, IL 60201**

**New Jersey Manufacturers Register**
**Phone—(847) 864-7000**
**Fax—(847) 332-1100**
**Web—www.manufacturersnews.com**
**Email—info@manufacturersnews.com**
**1633 Central St., Evanston, IL 60201**

**R. R. Bowker**
Phone—(908) 795-3500
630 Central Ave., New Providence 07974

## PUBLISHING — Educational

**Behrman House, Inc.**
Phone—(973) 379-7200
11 Edison Pl., Springfield 07081

**Creative Competitions, Inc.**
Phone—(856) 256-2797
406 Ganttown Rd., Sewell 08080

**Jigsaw Publishing, LLC**
Phone—(973) 838-4838
8 Hemlock Ct., Butler 07405

**Kumon Publishing North America, Inc.**
Phone—(201) 836-2105
300 W. Frank Burr Blvd., Ste. 6, Teaneck 07666

**Network, The**
Phone—(973) 778-7222
105-B Van Houten Ave., P.O. Box 5338, Passaic
07055

**Pearson Education, Inc.**
Phone—(201) 236-7000
1 Lake St., Upper Saddle River 07458

**Peoples Education, Inc.**
Phone—(201) 712-0090
299 Market St., P.O. Box 513, Saddle Brook
07663

**Research & Education Assn.**
Phone—(732) 819-8880
61 Ethel Rd. W., Piscataway 08854

**SAI Global Ltd.**
Phone—(201) 986-1131
210 State Route 4 E., Paramus 07652

**Tighe Publishing Services, Inc.**
Phone—(973) 379-7770
788 Morris Tpke., Ste. 100, Short Hills 07078

**University Publications**
Phone—(732) 495-9000
562 Morley Ct., Belford 07718

**Wiener Publishers, Inc., Markus**
Phone—(609) 921-1141
231 Nassau St., Princeton 08542

## PUBLISHING — Law

**Gann Law Books, Inc.**
Phone—(973) 268-1200
1 Washington Pk., Ste. 1300, Newark 07102

## PUBLISHING — Magazine

**Advanstar Communications, Inc.**
Phone—(732) 346-3000
485 U.S. Highway 1 S., Ste. 200, Iselin 08830

**Advantage Business Media**
Phone—(973) 920-7000
100 Enterprise Dr., Ste. 600, P.O. Box 912,
Rockaway 07866

**African Telecom, Inc.**
Phone—(973) 675-9919
463 N. Arlington Ave., Ste. 17, East Orange 07017

**Airbrush Action, Inc.**
Phone—(732) 223-7878
3209 Atlantic Ave., P.O. Box 438, Allenwood
08720

**All American Crafts Publishing, Inc.**
Phone—(973) 347-6900
7 Waterloo Rd., Stanhope 07874

**Art Culinaire Magazine**
Phone—(973) 993-5500
40 Mills St., Morristown 07963

**Aviation International News**
Phone—(201) 444-5075
214 Franklin Ave., Midland Park 07432

**Bauer Publishing Co.**
Phone—(201) 569-6699
270 Sylvan Ave., Ste. 210, Englewood Cliffs
07632

**Bergen County Magazine, The**
Phone—(201) 265-2286
297 Kinderkamack Rd., Ste. 135, Oradell 07649

**Borton Enterprises**
Phone—(856) 453-9221
178 Woodruff Rd., Bridgeton 08302

**Business Today**
College student magazine publishing
**Phone—(609) 258-1111**
**Fax—(609) 258-1222**
**Web—www.businesstoday.org**
**48 University Pl., Princeton 08540**

**Business Travel Executive Magazine**
Phone—(908) 979-1974
262 Rockport Rd., Port Murray 07865

## PUBLISHING — Magazine — (cont.)

Cape Publishing, Inc.
Phone—(609) 898-4500
513 Washington St., Cape May 08204

Carstens Publications, Inc.
Phone—(973) 383-3355
108 Phil Hardin Rd., Newton 07860

Charter Financial Publishing Network, Inc.
Phone—(732) 450-8866
499 Broad St., Shrewsbury 07702

Clifton Merchant Magazine
Phone—(973) 253-4400
1288 Main Ave., Clifton 07011

Columbia Marketing Corp.
Phone—(973) 275-1700
221 Rutgers St., Maplewood 07040

Commerce Enterprises, Inc.
Phone—(201) 368-2100
61 S. Paramus Rd., Ste. 135, Paramus 07652

Contemporary Bride Magazine
Phone—(908) 756-0123
153 Geary Dr., South Plainfield 07080

CPMAG, LLC
Phone—(201) 868-8585
6903 Jackson St., Guttenberg 07093

Data Centrum Communications, Inc.
Phone—(201) 391-1911
135 Chestnut Ridge Rd., 2nd Fl., Montvale 07645

Dentistry Today, Inc.
Phone—(973) 882-4700
100 Passaic Ave., Ste. 220, Fairfield 07004

DiversityInc Media LLC
Phone—(973) 494-0500
342 Nassau St., Princeton 08540

Drug Delivery Technology, LLC
Phone—(973) 299-1200
219 Changebridge Rd., Montville 07045

Edgell Communications, Inc.
Phone—(973) 607-1300
4 Middlebury Blvd., Ste. 1, Randolph 07869

Friday Morning Quarterback
Phone—(856) 424-9114
1930 Marlton Pike E., Ste. F-36, Cherry Hill 08003

Frontline Medical Communications, Inc.
Phone—(973) 206-3434
7 Century Dr., Ste. 302, Parsippany 07054

GNC Venture Group, Inc.
Phone—(856) 690-1999
1639 Percy Ln., Vineland 08361

Greater Media Newspapers
Phone—(732) 358-5200
198 Route 9 N., P.O. Box 950, Manalapan 07726

Group C Media, Inc.
Phone—(732) 842-7433
44 Apple St., Ste. 3, Tinton Falls 07724

Hague Academic Press Ltd.
Phone—(201) 750-9091
75 Lohs Pl., Harrington Park 07640

Hi Class Living Magazine
Phone—(201) 363-0200
120 Sylvan Ave., Ste. 209, Englewood Cliffs 07632

Hobby Publications, Inc.
Phone—(732) 536-5160
83 South St., Unit 307, Freehold 07728

Homes & Estates Magazines
Phone—(973) 605-1877
173 Morris St., Morristown 07960

Industry Publications, Inc.
Phone—(973) 331-9545
3621 Hill Rd., Parsippany 07054

Intellisphere, LLC
Phone—(609) 716-7777
666 Plainsboro Rd., Ste. 300, Plainsboro 08536

International Data Group
Phone—(201) 634-2300
650 From Rd., Ste. 558, Paramus 07652

Jewish Voice
Phone—(201) 569-2845
73 Dana Pl., P.O. Box 8097, Englewood 07631

JOC Group, Inc.
Phone—(973) 776-8660
2 Penn Plz. E., 12th Fl., Newark 07105

Jury Verdict Review Publications
Phone—(973) 376-9002
45 Springfield Ave., Springfield 07081

Leonard Publications, Inc.
Phone—(973) 895-6000
10 W. Hanover Ave., P.O. Box 553, Mount Freedom 07970

Limo Digest
Phone—(609) 953-4900
3 Reeves Station Rd., Medford 08055

Magazine Of Fantasy & Science Fiction, The
Phone—(201) 876-2551
105 Leonard St., Jersey City 07307

McGraw-Hill Construction
Phone—(800) 393-6343
148 Princeton Hightstown Rd., Hightstown 08520

Metal Powder Industries Federation
Phone—(609) 452-7700
105 College Rd. E., Princeton 08540

Middlesex Publications, Inc.
Phone—(732) 435-0005
850 Carolier Ln., North Brunswick 08902

Modern Drummer Publications, Inc.
Phone—(973) 239-4140
271 Route 46 W., Ste. 212, Fairfield 07004

Music Trades Magazine Corp.
Phone—(201) 871-1965
80 West St., P.O. Box 432, Englewood 07631

N J Sport Action
Phone—(973) 783-9236
5 Riverview Dr. W., Upper Montclair 07043

N.V. Business Publishers Corp. (H Q)
Phone—(732) 502-0500
43 Main St., P.O. Box 188, Avon by the Sea 07717

New Jersey Business & Industry Assn. (H Q)
Phone—(609) 393-7707
10 W. Lafayette St., Trenton 08608

New Jersey Countryside Magazine
Phone—(908) 221-1171
134 S. Finley Ave., Basking Ridge 07920

New Jersey Media Group
Phone—(973) 434-8888
11 Melanie Ln., Unit 22-A, East Hanover 07936

New Jersey Monthly Magazine, Inc.
Phone—(973) 539-8230
55 S. Park Pl., P.O. Box 920, Morristown 07963

North Star Travel Media, LLC (H Q)
Phone—(201) 902-2000
100 Lighting Way, 2nd Fl., Secaucus 07094

Octagon Communications Corp.
Phone—(201) 569-5870
385 Sylvan Ave., Ste. 16, Englewood Cliffs 07632

Ophthalmology Times
Phone—(732) 346-3060
485F U.S. Highway 1 S., Ste. 1, Iselin 08830

PI Magazine
Phone—(732) 308-3800
4400 U.S. Highway 9, Ste. 1000, Freehold 07728

Positive Publications, LLC
Phone—(973) 218-0310
65 Madison Ave., Ste. 510, Morristown 07960

Private Journey Magazine, The
Phone—(973) 244-0301
1120 Bloomfield Ave., Ste. 107, West Caldwell 07006

Renard Communications, Inc.
Phone—(973) 912-8550
197 Mountain Ave., Springfield 07081

Ridgewood Medical Media, LLC
Phone—(201) 670-1356
P.O. Box 802, Ridgewood 07450

Rodman Publishing Corp.
Phone—(201) 825-2552
70 Hilltop Rd., 3rd Fl., Ramsey 07446

School Publications Co., Inc.
Phone—(732) 988-1100
1520 Washington Ave., P.O. Box 1067, Neptune 07753

Steppin Out Magazine
Phone—(201) 703-0911
21-07 Maple Ave., Fair Lawn 07410

Sun By The Sea
Phone—(609) 522-2721
224 W. 23rd Ave., P.O. Box 2101, Wildwood 08260

Thomas Greco Publishing Inc.
Phone—(973) 667-6922
244 Chestnut St., Ste. 202, Nutley 07110

TimeSharing Today, Inc.
Phone—(201) 871-4304
140 County Rd., Ste. 114, Tenafly 07670

Travalliance Media, LLC
Phone—(856) 505-1400
593 Rancocas Rd., Westampton 08060

U.S.A. Distributors, Inc.
Phone—(201) 348-1959
3711 Hudson Ave., Union City 07087

Vicinity Media Group
Phone—(973) 276-1688
165 Passaic Ave., Ste. 107, Fairfield 07004

Visual Impact Advertising, Inc.
Phone—(973) 763-4900
9 Highland Pl., Maplewood 07040

Vitamin Retailer
Phone—(732) 432-9600
431 Cranbury Rd., Ste. C, East Brunswick 08816

Wainer Finest Communications, Inc.
Phone—(908) 769-1160
4041-G Hadley Rd., Ste. 101, South Plainfield 07080

Wainscot Media
Phone—(201) 571-2244
110 Summit Ave., Montvale 07645

Walden-Mott Corp.
Phone—(201) 818-8630
225 N. Franklin Tpke., Ramsey 07446

Williams Publications, Inc., E. W.
Phone—(201) 592-7007
2125 Center Ave., Ste. 305, Fort Lee 07024

World Apostolate of Fatima USA
Phone—(908) 689-1701
674 Mountain View Rd., P.O. Box 976, Washington 07882

## PUBLISHING — Medical

Jannetti, Inc., Anthony J.
Phone—(856) 256-2300
200 E. Holly Ave., Sewell 08080

## PUBLISHING — Music

Lombardo Music Publications
Phone—(609) 586-9245
37 Pintinalli Dr., Trenton 08619

Macie Publishing Co.
Phone—(973) 983-8700
10 Astro Pl., Ste. 100, Rockaway 07866

Marcia's Melodies
Phone—(732) 988-3191
61 Pilgrim Pathway, Unit 3, Ocean Grove 07756

## PUBLISHING — Newsletter

Alexander Communications Group, Inc.
Phone—(973) 265-2300
712 Main St., Ste. 187-B, Boonton 07005

Black Car News
Phone—(856) 751-0656
714 Crestbrook Ave., Cherry Hill 08003

Black Car News
Phone—(856) 262-2368
420 Inverness Rd., Williamstown 08094

Buyers Laboratory LLC
Phone—(201) 488-0404
20 Railroad Ave., Hackensack 07601

Harrison Scott Publications, Inc.
Phone—(201) 659-1700
5 Marine View Plz., Ste. 400, Hoboken 07030

Healthcare Marketers Exchange
Phone—(973) 744-9505
104 Park Ave., Verona 07044

McMillan Analysis Corp.
Phone—(973) 328-1674
39 Meadowbrook Rd., Randolph 07869

Media Vista, Inc.
Phone—(732) 747-8060
60 Broad St., Ste. 100, Red Bank 07701

Physician's Weekly
Phone—(908) 766-0402
180 Mount Airy Rd., Ste. 102, Basking Ridge 07920

Powers & Co., M. J.
Phone—(973) 898-1200
65 Madison Ave., Ste. 220, Morristown 07960

WayneToday
Phone—(973) 569-7393
1 Garret Mountain Plz., P.O. Box 471, Woodland Park 07424

Workers' Disability Income System, Inc.
Phone—(732) 274-0600
56 Primrose Cir., Princeton 08540

WPI Communication, Inc.
Phone—(973) 467-8700
55 Morris Ave., Ste. 312, Springfield 07081

**MFR.    Repairs**

Phone: (201)798-3277
Fax: (201)798-8781

www.allied-pump.com
alliedpumps@gmail.com

**ALLIED PUMP CORP.**

1109 Grand Ave., Bldg. #5 • North Bergen, NJ 07047

Sump, Sewage, Boiler Feed,
Condensate, Booster Systems

## PUBLISHING — Online

Dun & Bradstreet Corp., The
Phone—(973) 921-5500
103 John F. Kennedy Pkwy., Short Hills 07078

## PUBLISHING — Periodical

American Institute Of Food Distribution, Inc.
Phone—(201) 791-5570
10 Mountain View Rd., Ste. S-125, Upper Saddle River 07458

American Lawyer's Media, Inc.
Phone—(973) 642-0075
238 Mulberry St., 2nd Fl., Newark 07102

BNP Media, Inc.
Phone—(201) 291-9001
210 E. State Route 4, Ste. 203, Paramus 07652

Children's Technology Review
Phone—(908) 284-0404
120 Main St., Flemington 08822

Civic Research Institute, Inc.
Phone—(609) 683-4450
4478 Route 27, P.O. Box 585, Kingston 08528

Frontline Medical Communications, Inc.
Phone—(973) 290-8200
7 Century Dr., Parsippany 07054

Jostens, Inc.
Phone—(973) 584-5843
86 Roseville Rd., Andover 07821

Journal America
Phone—(973) 728-8355
1950 Greenwood Lake Tpke., P.O. Box 459, Hewitt 07421

Lawyers Diary and Manual
Phone—(973) 642-1440
890 Mountain Ave., New Providence 07974

New Jersey Journal Of Pharmacy
Phone—(609) 275-4246
760 Alexander Rd., Princeton 08540

RDL Marketing Group, LLC
Phone—(732) 446-0817
352-A Sweetmann Ln., P.O. Box 385, Perrineville 08535

Sino Monthly New Jersey, Inc.
Phone—(732) 650-0688
18 Sheppard Pl., Edison 08817

SJ Magazine
Phone—(856) 722-9300
1223 N. Church St., Moorestown 08057

Society Of Naval Architects & Marine Engineers
Phone—(201) 798-4800
601 Pavonia Ave., Ste. 400, Jersey City 07306

Tatra Eagle, Inc.
Phone—(201) 288-3815
31 Madison Ave., Hasbrouck Heights 07604

Wiley & Sons, Inc., John
Phone—(201) 748-6000
111 River St., Hoboken 07030

*Search from among*
**430,000 U.S. manufacturers & suppliers at**
**IndustryNet.com**

## PULLEYS

BRECOflex Co., L.L.C.
Phone—(732) 460-9500 / (888) 463-1400
Fax—(732) 542-6725
Web—www.brecoflex.com
Email—info@brecoflex.com
222 Industrial Way W., Eatontown 07724

**BRECOflex CO., L.L.C.**
High Precision Drive Components

**Timing Belts & Pulleys**
Endless Woven Flat Belts

Superior Performance

Outstanding Eng. Support

Quick Delivery

Single Source Supplier

Polyurethane Timing Belts•
Arc Power • ATN • ATS -15 •
Profiled Belts • Covered Belts • Stock Pulleys•
Pulleys Made to Order• Idlers•Clamps•Tensioners•
Field Welders•Connecting Kits•Tension Meters

222 Industrial Way West    (732)-460-9500
Eatontown, N.J. 07724    info@brecoflex.com

## PULLEYS — Conveyor

BRECOflex Co., L.L.C.
Phone—(732) 460-9500 / (888) 463-1400
Fax—(732) 542-6725
Web—www.brecoflex.com
Email—info@brecoflex.com
222 Industrial Way W., Eatontown 07724
*(see our ads under BELTING & PULLEYS)*

## PULVERIZERS

Jet Pulverizer Co., Inc.
Phone—(856) 235-5554
1255 N. Church St., Moorestown 08057

## PUMP CONTROLS

Allied Pump Corporation
Phone—(201) 798-3277
Fax—(201) 798-8781
Web—www.allied-pump.com
Email—alliedpumps@gmail.com
1109 Grand Ave., Bldg. 5, North Bergen 07047
*(see our ad on this page)*

## PUMP PARTS

Chase Machine Co., Inc.
Phone—(201) 438-2218
127 Park Ave., P.O. Box 148, Lyndhurst 07071

Cincinnati Thermal Spray East
Phone—(973) 379-0003
80 Fadem Rd., Springfield 07081

Conhagen, Inc., Alfred (H Q)
Phone—(732) 287-4565
2035 Lincoln Hwy., Edison Sq. W., Ste. 3003, Edison 08817

J R Engineering & Machine Corp.
Phone—(908) 810-6300
663 Ramsey Ave., Hillside 07205

Sims Pump Valve Co., Inc.
Phone—(201) 792-0600
1314 Park Ave., P.O. Box 3338, Hoboken 07030

## PUMPING SYSTEMS

Arcadia Equipment, Inc.
Phone—(201) 342-3308
140 Lawrence St., Hackensack 07601

## PUMPS

**AB Industrial Equipment Co.**
An experienced pump representative & distributor serving the mid-Atlantic. We supply, repair & restore pumps, mechanical seals, motors, strainers & valves. ANSI pumps are available with a 7-year warranty
Phone—(610) 269-5791 / (800) 887-7867
Fax—(610) 269-7705
Web—www.abpump.com
Email—quote@abpump.com
P.O. Box 2321, West Chester, PA 19380

**AB Industrial Equipment Co.**

| ANSI B73.1 | Machine Tool |
| Close Coupled | Coolant |
| End Suction | Vertical |
| Multi-Stage | Non Metallic |
| Self Primer | Slurry |
| Submersible | Mag Drive |

www.abpump.com
quote@abpump.com

T: (610) 269-5791
F: (610) 269-7705

All Mechanical Services, Inc.
Phone—(732) 442-8292
430 High St., P.O. Box 110, Perth Amboy 08862

**Allied Pump Corporation**
Phone—(201) 798-3277
Fax—(201) 798-8781
Web—www.allied-pump.com
Email—alliedpumps@gmail.com
1109 Grand Ave., Bldg. 5, North Bergen 07047
*(see our ad on this page)*

**Autumn Associates, Inc.**
Phone—(732) 787-8900
Fax—(732) 495-6267
Web—www.autumnassociatesinc.com
Email—ed8901@comcast.net
761 Palmer Ave., Ste. 3A, Holmdel 07733
*(see our ad on next page)*

**Barish Pump Co., Inc.**
Phone—(631) 752-7770
Fax—(631) 454-7867
Web—www.barishpump.com
Email—sales@barishpump.com
61 Allen Blvd., Farmingdale, NY 11735

Carter Pump
Phone—(201) 568-9798
326 S. Dean St., Englewood 07631

*Do nationwide searches for products & services at:*
**IndustryNet.com**

INDUSTRY

## PUMPS — *(cont.)*

**Chalmers & Kubeck, Inc.**
Phone—(610) 494-4300
Fax—(610) 485-1484
Web—www.candk.com
Email—jmoore@candk.com
150 Commerce Dr., P.O. Box 2447, Aston, PA
19014
*(see our ad under MACHINE WORK & MACHINING)*

Excelsior Medical Corp.
Phone—(732) 776-7525
1933 Heck Ave., Neptune 07753

Flowserve Corp.
Phone—(973) 227-4565
142 Clinton Rd., Fairfield 07004

**Hayes Pump, Inc.**
Pumps, filters, seals, control systems
Phone—(973) 808-0606 / (800) 343-5020
Fax—(973) 808-7311
Web—www.hayespump.com
Email—Customerservice@hayespump.com
295 Fairfield Ave., Fairfield 07004

**Hayes Pump, Inc.**
*Quality Pumps*
**800-343-5020**
Flow solutions since 1898
**973-808-0606 • FAX: 973-808-7311**
295 Fairfield Ave. Fairfield, NJ 07004
www.hayespump.com Customerservice@hayespump.com

Heerema Co.
Phone—(973) 423-0505
200 6th Ave., Hawthorne 07506

Mid Atlantic Pump & Equipment Co.
Phone—(856) 768-3880
228 N. Route 73, Berlin 08009

## PUMPS — Centrifugal

**AB Industrial Equipment Co.**
An experienced pump representative & distributor
serving the mid-Atlantic. We supply, repair & restore
pumps, mechanical seals, motors, strainers & valves.
ANSI pumps are available with a 7-year warranty
Phone—(610) 269-5791 / (800) 887-7867
Fax—(610) 269-7705
Web—www.abpump.com
Email—quote@abpump.com
P.O. Box 2321, West Chester, PA 19380
*(see our ad under PUMPS)*

**Allied Pump Corporation**
Phone—(201) 798-3277
Fax—(201) 798-8781
Web—www.allied-pump.com
Email—alliedpumps@gmail.com
1109 Grand Ave., Bldg. 5, North Bergen 07047
*(see our ad under PUMPS)*

**Barish Pump Co., Inc.**
Phone—(631) 752-7770
Fax—(631) 454-7867
Web—www.barishpump.com
Email—sales@barishpump.com
61 Allen Blvd., Farmingdale, NY 11735

**Hayes Pump, Inc.**
Pumps, filters, seals, control systems
Phone—(973) 808-0606 / (800) 343-5020
Fax—(973) 808-7311
Web—www.hayespump.com
Email—Customerservice@hayespump.com
295 Fairfield Ave., Fairfield 07004
*(see our ad under PUMPS)*

Liquiflo Equipment Co., Inc.
Phone—(908) 518-0777
443 North Ave., Ste. 2, Garwood 07027

Sulzer Pumps (U.S.), Inc.
Phone—(856) 467-2400
621 Haron Dr., P.O. Box 487, Bridgeport 08014

Wire Equipment Mfg. Co., Inc.
Phone—(609) 499-4411
319 Birch Hollow Dr., Bordentown 08505

*find additional suppliers at*
**IndustryNet.com**

---

**Autumn Associates, Inc.**
Sump, Sewage & Heating Pumps
**732-787-8900 • FAX: 732-495-6267**
761 Palmer Ave., Ste. 3A Holmdel, NJ 07733
**www.autumnassociatesinc.com**
**Email: ed8901@comcast.net**

## PUMPS — Chemical

**AB Industrial Equipment Co.**
An experienced pump representative & distributor
serving the mid-Atlantic. We supply, repair & restore
pumps, mechanical seals, motors, strainers & valves.
ANSI pumps are available with a 7-year warranty
Phone—(610) 269-5791 / (800) 887-7867
Fax—(610) 269-7705
Web—www.abpump.com
Email—quote@abpump.com
P.O. Box 2321, West Chester, PA 19380
*(see our ad under PUMPS)*

## PUMPS — Condensate Return

**Allied Pump Corporation**
Phone—(201) 798-3277
Fax—(201) 798-8781
Web—www.allied-pump.com
Email—alliedpumps@gmail.com
1109 Grand Ave., Bldg. 5, North Bergen 07047
*(see our ad under PUMPS)*

## PUMPS — Coolant

**AB Industrial Equipment Co.**
An experienced pump representative & distributor
serving the mid-Atlantic. We supply, repair & restore
pumps, mechanical seals, motors, strainers & valves.
ANSI pumps are available with a 7-year warranty
Phone—(610) 269-5791 / (800) 887-7867
Fax—(610) 269-7705
Web—www.abpump.com
Email—quote@abpump.com
P.O. Box 2321, West Chester, PA 19380
*(see our ad under PUMPS)*

## PUMPS — Cooling Tower

**AB Industrial Equipment Co.**
An experienced pump representative & distributor
serving the mid-Atlantic. We supply, repair & restore
pumps, mechanical seals, motors, strainers & valves.
ANSI pumps are available with a 7-year warranty
Phone—(610) 269-5791 / (800) 887-7867
Fax—(610) 269-7705
Web—www.abpump.com
Email—quote@abpump.com
P.O. Box 2321, West Chester, PA 19380
*(see our ad under PUMPS)*

## PUMPS — Corrosion Resistant

**AB Industrial Equipment Co.**
An experienced pump representative & distributor
serving the mid-Atlantic. We supply, repair & restore
pumps, mechanical seals, motors, strainers & valves.
ANSI pumps are available with a 7-year warranty
Phone—(610) 269-5791 / (800) 887-7867
Fax—(610) 269-7705
Web—www.abpump.com
Email—quote@abpump.com
P.O. Box 2321, West Chester, PA 19380
*(see our ad under PUMPS)*

## PUMPS — End Suction

**AB Industrial Equipment Co.**
An experienced pump representative & distributor
serving the mid-Atlantic. We supply, repair & restore
pumps, mechanical seals, motors, strainers & valves.
ANSI pumps are available with a 7-year warranty
Phone—(610) 269-5791 / (800) 887-7867
Fax—(610) 269-7705
Web—www.abpump.com
Email—quote@abpump.com
P.O. Box 2321, West Chester, PA 19380
*(see our ad under PUMPS)*

**Allied Pump Corporation**
Phone—(201) 798-3277
Fax—(201) 798-8781
Web—www.allied-pump.com
Email—alliedpumps@gmail.com
1109 Grand Ave., Bldg. 5, North Bergen 07047
*(see our ad under PUMPS)*

## PUMPS — Fire

**Rotating Equipment Specialist Inc.**
Testing/Troubleshooting/Repairing Fire Pumps
Phone—(908) 876-5460
Fax—(908) 876-9453
Email—respumps@comcast.net
4 Valley View Rd., Long Valley 07853

## PUMPS — Fuel Oil

**AB Industrial Equipment Co.**
An experienced pump representative & distributor
serving the mid-Atlantic. We supply, repair & restore
pumps, mechanical seals, motors, strainers & valves.
ANSI pumps are available with a 7-year warranty
Phone—(610) 269-5791 / (800) 887-7867
Fax—(610) 269-7705
Web—www.abpump.com
Email—quote@abpump.com
P.O. Box 2321, West Chester, PA 19380
*(see our ad under PUMPS)*

*Need a mailing list
of manufacturers
for a telemarketing
or mail campaign?*

*Call **mni** at 847-864-7000
for company profiles on CD*

 **Manufacturers' News, Inc.**
*Identify & contact U.S. manufacturers*

## PUMPS — Gasoline Dispensing

**Multiforce Systems Corp.**
Automated fuel management integrated systems for the transportation industry
Phone—(609) 683-4242
Fax—(609) 683-4835
Web—www.fuelforce.com
Email—sales@fuelforce.com
101 Wall St., Princeton 08540

**FUELFORCE®**
Fuel Management Systems

**Multiforce Systems Corp.**

*Automated Fuel Management Systems that Authorize & Control Dispensing of Fuel*

**www.fuelforce.com**

**(609) 683-4242**

Fax: (609) 683-4835

**101 Wall St., Princeton, NJ 08540**

## PUMPS — High Pressure

**Allied Pump Corporation**
Phone—(201) 798-3277
Fax—(201) 798-8781
Web—www.allied-pump.com
Email—alliedpumps@gmail.com
1109 Grand Ave., Bldg. 5, North Bergen 07047
*(see our ad under PUMPS)*

EDI Distributors, Inc.
Phone—(856) 429-2580
20 Lakeside Ave., P.O. Box 501, Cherry Hill 08003

## PUMPS — Industrial

**AB Industrial Equipment Co.**
An experienced pump representative & distributor serving the mid-Atlantic. We supply, repair & restore pumps, mechanical seals, motors, strainers & valves. ANSI pumps are available with a 7-year warranty
Phone—(610) 269-5791 / (800) 887-7867
Fax—(610) 269-7705
Web—www.abpump.com
Email—quote@abpump.com
P.O. Box 2321, West Chester, PA 19380
*(see our ad under PUMPS)*

Camac Industries
Phone—(973) 300-5575
18 Gail Ct., Sparta 07871
Eagle Flo Pumps, Inc.
Phone—(201) 438-8595
306 Orient Way, Rutherford 07070
Godwin, a Xylem brand
Phone—(856) 467-3636
84 Floodgate Rd., Bridgeport 08014
**Hayes Pump, Inc.**
Pumps, filters, seals, control systems
Phone—(973) 808-0606 / (800) 343-5020
Fax—(973) 808-7311
Web—www.hayespump.com
Email—Customerservice@hayespump.com
295 Fairfield Ave., Fairfield 07004

**Hayes Pump, Inc.**
*Quality Pumps*
**800-343-5020**

973-808-0606 • FAX: 973-808-7311
295 Fairfield Ave. Fairfield, NJ 07004
www.hayespump.com Customerservice@hayespump.com

KNF Neuberger, Inc.
Phone—(609) 890-8600
2 Black Forest Rd., Trenton 08691
Leistritz Corp.
Phone—(201) 934-8262
165 Chestnut St., Allendale 07401
Park Pumps & Controls, Inc.
Phone—(609) 871-0944
950 Mount Holly Rd., Ste. B, Edgewater Park 08010
Tri-State Pump, Inc.
Phone—(732) 223-3222
5044 Industrial Rd., Ste. C, Farmingdale 07727
Warwick Mfg. & Equipment Co., LLC
Buy & sell used: Chemical, food, cosmetic, packaging & pharmaceutical equipment
Phone—(732) 729-0400 / (732) 241-9263
Fax—(732) 729-1235
Web—www.warwickequipment.com
Email—sales@warwickequipment.com
1112 12th St., North Brunswick 08902
*(see our ad Outside Back Cover)*

## PUMPS — Metering

**AB Industrial Equipment Co.**
An experienced pump representative & distributor serving the mid-Atlantic. We supply, repair & restore pumps, mechanical seals, motors, strainers & valves. ANSI pumps are available with a 7-year warranty
Phone—(610) 269-5791 / (800) 887-7867
Fax—(610) 269-7705
Web—www.abpump.com
Email—quote@abpump.com
P.O. Box 2321, West Chester, PA 19380
*(see our ad under PUMPS)*

## PUMPS — Oil

**AB Industrial Equipment Co.**
An experienced pump representative & distributor serving the mid-Atlantic. We supply, repair & restore pumps, mechanical seals, motors, strainers & valves. ANSI pumps are available with a 7-year warranty
Phone—(610) 269-5791 / (800) 887-7867
Fax—(610) 269-7705
Web—www.abpump.com
Email—quote@abpump.com
P.O. Box 2321, West Chester, PA 19380
*(see our ad under PUMPS)*

## PUMPS — Petroleum

**AB Industrial Equipment Co.**
An experienced pump representative & distributor serving the mid-Atlantic. We supply, repair & restore pumps, mechanical seals, motors, strainers & valves. ANSI pumps are available with a 7-year warranty
Phone—(610) 269-5791 / (800) 887-7867
Fax—(610) 269-7705
Web—www.abpump.com
Email—quote@abpump.com
P.O. Box 2321, West Chester, PA 19380
*(see our ad under PUMPS)*

## PUMPS — Rotary

**AB Industrial Equipment Co.**
An experienced pump representative & distributor serving the mid-Atlantic. We supply, repair & restore pumps, mechanical seals, motors, strainers & valves. ANSI pumps are available with a 7-year warranty
Phone—(610) 269-5791 / (800) 887-7867
Fax—(610) 269-7705
Web—www.abpump.com
Email—quote@abpump.com
P.O. Box 2321, West Chester, PA 19380
*(see our ad under PUMPS)*

## PUMPS — Sewage

**AB Industrial Equipment Co.**
An experienced pump representative & distributor serving the mid-Atlantic. We supply, repair & restore pumps, mechanical seals, motors, strainers & valves. ANSI pumps are available with a 7-year warranty
Phone—(610) 269-5791 / (800) 887-7867
Fax—(610) 269-7705
Web—www.abpump.com
Email—quote@abpump.com
P.O. Box 2321, West Chester, PA 19380
*(see our ad under PUMPS)*

**Allied Pump Corporation**
Phone—(201) 798-3277
Fax—(201) 798-8781
Web—www.allied-pump.com
Email—alliedpumps@gmail.com
1109 Grand Ave., Bldg. 5, North Bergen 07047
*(see our ad under PUMPS)*

Deltronics Corp.
Phone—(856) 825-8200
224 Bogden Blvd., P.O. Box 446, Millville 08332

## PUMPS — Sump

**AB Industrial Equipment Co.**
An experienced pump representative & distributor serving the mid-Atlantic. We supply, repair & restore pumps, mechanical seals, motors, strainers & valves. ANSI pumps are available with a 7-year warranty
Phone—(610) 269-5791 / (800) 887-7867
Fax—(610) 269-7705
Web—www.abpump.com
Email—quote@abpump.com
P.O. Box 2321, West Chester, PA 19380
*(see our ad under PUMPS)*

**Allied Pump Corporation**
Phone—(201) 798-3277
Fax—(201) 798-8781
Web—www.allied-pump.com
Email—alliedpumps@gmail.com
1109 Grand Ave., Bldg. 5, North Bergen 07047
*(see our ad under PUMPS)*

**Autumn Associates, Inc.**
Phone—(732) 787-8900
Fax—(732) 495-6267
Web—www.autumnassociatesinc.com
Email—ed8901@comcast.net
761 Palmer Ave., Ste. 3A, Holmdel 07733
*(see our ad under PUMPS)*

## PUMPS — Turbine

**AB Industrial Equipment Co.**
An experienced pump representative & distributor serving the mid-Atlantic. We supply, repair & restore pumps, mechanical seals, motors, strainers & valves. ANSI pumps are available with a 7-year warranty
Phone—(610) 269-5791 / (800) 887-7867
Fax—(610) 269-7705
Web—www.abpump.com
Email—quote@abpump.com
P.O. Box 2321, West Chester, PA 19380
*(see our ad under PUMPS)*

SC Engineering Co., Inc.
Phone—(908) 874-5955
115 Stryker Ln., Bldg. 4, Hillsborough 08844

## PUMPS — Vacuum

**Allied Pump Corporation**
Phone—(201) 798-3277
Fax—(201) 798-8781
Web—www.allied-pump.com
Email—alliedpumps@gmail.com
1109 Grand Ave., Bldg. 5, North Bergen 07047
*(see our ad under PUMPS)*

EMSE Corp.
Phone—(973) 227-9221
10 Plog Rd., Unit 1, Fairfield 07004
Evey Engineering Co., LLC
Phone—(856) 692-6705
158 Weymouth Rd., Vineland 08360
Neptune Products, Inc.
Phone—(973) 366-8200
353 E. Blackwell St., P.O. Drawer 829, Dover 07801
Trillium, Inc.
Phone—(973) 827-1661
3627 Route 23 S., Hamburg 07419

**EZSelect®.com**
**REAL-TIME** Access to Industrial Leads!

© Copyright 2015 Manufacturers' News, Inc.

## PUMPS — Water

**AB Industrial Equipment Co.**
An experienced pump representative & distributor serving the mid-Atlantic. We supply, repair & restore pumps, mechanical seals, motors, strainers & valves. ANSI pumps are available with a 7-year warranty
Phone—(610) 269-5791 / (800) 887-7867
Fax—(610) 269-7705
Web—www.abpump.com
Email—quote@abpump.com
P.O. Box 2321, West Chester, PA 19380
*(see our ad under PUMPS)*

Allied Pump Corporation
Phone—(201) 798-3277
1109 Grand Ave., Bldg. 5, North Bergen 07047

**Autumn Associates, Inc.**
Phone—(732) 787-8900
Fax—(732) 495-6267
Web—www.autumnassociatesinc.com
Email—ed8901@comcast.net
761 Palmer Ave., Ste. 3A, Holmdel 07733
*(see our ad under PUMPS)*

GMB North America, Inc.
Phone—(609) 655-2422
100 Herrod Blvd., Dayton 08810

Layne Christensen Co.
Phone—(609) 877-2700
719 Mount Holly Rd., Beverly 08010

Pul-A Pump Corp.
Phone—(973) 697-2008
29 Paradise Trl., P.O. Box 155, Stockholm 07460

Vanton Pump & Equipment Corp.
Phone—(908) 688-4216
201 Sweetland Ave., Hillside 07205

## PUMPS — Well

**Allied Pump Corporation**
Phone—(201) 798-3277
Fax—(201) 798-8781
Web—www.allied-pump.com
Email—alliedpumps@gmail.com
1109 Grand Ave., Bldg. 5, North Bergen 07047
*(see our ad under PUMPS)*

Reid Plumbing Products, LLC
Phone—(609) 466-1785
371 Route 31 N., Hopewell 08525

## PUNCHES

Atlas Recording Machines Corp.
Phone—(732) 295-3663
2140 Bridge Ave., Point Pleasant 08742

Hudson Mfg. Co.
Phone—(908) 241-3880
640 W. 1st Ave., Roselle 07203

Ultra Punch & Die Corp.
Phone—(973) 335-3200
8 N. Main St., P.O. Box 353, Boonton 07005

## PUNCHES — Metalworking

C & K Punch & Screw Machine Products
Phone—(201) 343-6750
160 Hobart St., Hackensack 07601

## PUNCHES — Ticket

Bonney-Vehslage Tool Co.
Phone—(973) 589-6975
3 Dundar Rd., Springfield 07081

## QUARRIES

Baer Aggregates, Inc.
Phone—(908) 454-4412
454 River Rd., Phillipsburg 08865

Braen Stone
Phone—(973) 383-7100
217 Limecrest Rd., Lafayette 07848

Dun-Rite Sand & Gravel Co., Inc.
Phone—(856) 825-9900
3765 Mays Landing Rd., Vineland 08361

Dun-Rite Sand & Gravel Co., Inc. (H Q)
Phone—(856) 692-2520
573 E. Grant Ave., Vineland 08360

S & Y Natural Stone, LLC
Phone—(862) 200-5156
1000 Main Ave., Clifton 07011

Tilcon, Inc., Oxford Quarry
Phone—(908) 453-4141
193 Mount Pisgah Ave., P.O. Box 120, Oxford 07863

## QUARTZ SEMICONDUCTOR COMPONENTS

United Silica Products, Inc.
Phone—(973) 209-8854
3 Park Dr., Franklin 07416

## RACE CARS & COMPONENTS

Gambardella Racing & Performance, Inc.
Phone—(856) 728-1869
1999 S. Black Horse Pike, Williamstown 08094

Jesel, Inc.
Phone—(732) 901-1800
1985 Cedar Bridge Ave., Ste. 2, Lakewood 08701

Stef's Performance Products
Phone—(732) 367-8700
693 Cross St., Lakewood 08701

T E O Fabrications, Inc.
Phone—(973) 764-5500
95 Maple Grange Rd., P.O. Box 232, Vernon 07462

## RACING SILKS

Daly's Custom Racing Apparel
Phone—(856) 768-6411
P.O. Box 355, Berlin 08009

Sipp Silk
Phone—(856) 234-6224
216 Hedgeman Rd., Moorestown 08057

## RACKS

Middle Atlantic Products, Inc.
Phone—(973) 839-1011
300 Fairfield Rd., Fairfield 07004

Titan Rack & Shelving, LLC
Phone—(732) 249-0887
101 Muirhead Ave., Trenton 08695

## RACKS — Food & Beverage

**Magna Industries, Inc.**
Phone—(732) 905-0957
Fax—(732) 367-2989
Web—www.magnaindustries.com
Email—sales@magnaindustries.com
1825 Swarthmore Ave., Ste. 1, Lakewood 08701

## RACKS — Transportation

Amer-Rac, LLC
Phone—(856) 488-6210
8128 River Rd., Pennsauken 08110

## RADAR EQUIPMENT

Electromagnetic Technologies
Phone—(973) 394-1719
50 Intervale Rd., Unit 15, Boonton 07005

## RADIATORS

Auto Cool Radiator Service
Phone—(201) 343-3099
10 Terhune Pl., Hackensack 07601

Custom Auto Radiator, Inc.
Phone—(609) 242-9700
441 S. Main St., Route 9, Forked River 08731

J & J Radiator Shop
Phone—(856) 461-3533
71 St. Mihiel Dr., Delran 08075

Midland Radiator Service Co.
Industrial radiators
Phone—(973) 340-0533 / (800) 605-8001
Fax—(973) 340-5941
Web—www.midlandradiator.com
Email—midlandrad@aol.com
420 Midland Ave., Garfield 07026

**MIDLAND RADIATOR SERVICE CO.**
AUTOMOTIVE & INDUSTRIAL RADIATORS
NEW TRUCK RADIATORS/CHARGE AIR COOLERS
RADIATORS CLEANED, REPAIRED, RECORED
DPF FILTER - MAINTENANCE & REPAIR
www.midlandradiator.com
420 Midland Ave., Garfield, NJ 07026
1-800-605-8001

Radaire Distributors, Inc.
Phone—(732) 282-1144
1318 Segart Ave., Sea Girt 08750

## RADIATORS — Automotive

Midland Radiator Service Co.
Phone—(973) 340-0533
420 Midland Ave., Garfield 07026

## RADIO COMMUNICATIONS EQUIPMENT

RC Repair
Phone—(201) 445-0361
526 Doremus Ave., Glen Rock 07452

## RADIO FREQUENCY EQUIPMENT

R F VII, Inc.
Phone—(856) 875-2121
1041 Glassboro Rd., Bldg. 6, Williamstown 08094

RF Products, Inc.
Phone—(856) 365-5500
1500 Davis St., Camden 08103

## RADIO FREQUENCY GENERATORS

**TRUMPF Photonics, Inc.**
Phone—(609) 925-8200
Fax—(609) 409-7021
Web—www.us.trumpf.com
Email—info@us.trumpf.com
2601 US Route 130 S., Cranbury 08512
*(see our ad under LASERS)*

## RADIOS

Model Electronics, Inc.
Phone—(201) 961-6200
615 E. Crescent Ave., Ramsey 07446

## RADON TESTING & MITIGATION

A & M Engineering Services Inc.
Phone—(856) 424-8151
Web—www.amengineeringservices.com
P.O. Box 4440, Cherry Hill 08034

A Lewis Home Inspection
Phone—(609) 818-0308
Web—www.lhinspection.com
20 E. Welling Ave., Pennington 08534

## RAILCAR MOVERS

**Taylor Northeast**
Providing of a broad range of services for Material Handling & Industrial Cleaning Equipment in the eastern-PA area since 1985. Services range from new & used lift truck sales, leasing & rentals to service, parts & remanufacturing
Phone—(610) 286-8080 / (800) 762-2500
Fax—(610) 286-8099
Web—www.taylornortheast.com
Email—kkoch@taylornortheast.com
931 Hemlock Rd., Morgantown, PA 19543

*Search from among 430,000 U.S. manufacturers & suppliers:*
**IndustryNet.com**

# RAILINGS

**American Discount Fence Co.**
**Residential & Commercial Fence Railings**
**Phone—(856) 939-3022**
**Fax—(856) 939-8388**
**Web—www.americandiscountfence.com**
**Email—adfc@verizon.net**
**777 W. Clements Bridge Rd., Runnemede 08078**

Cacciola Iron Works
Phone—(973) 595-0854
65 N. 9th St., Paterson 07522

Carfaro Railings Company, Frank
Phone—(908) 879-7312
70 Hacklebarney Rd., Long Valley 07853

Craftsmen Railing, Inc.
Phone—(732) 264-1080
3 Cass St., Keyport 07735

F M B, Inc.
Phone—(973) 485-5544
70 Supor Blvd., Harrison 07029

Hackensack Steel Corp.
Phone—(201) 935-0090
645 Industrial Rd., Carlstadt 07072

I-Ron-X Industries
Phone—(856) 697-3518
134 Wheat Rd., Buena 08310

**Legacy Stairs & Millwork, Inc.**
**Phone—(732) 905-7705**
**Fax—(732) 905-7750**
**Web—www.legacystairs.com**
**Email—sales@legacystairs.com**
**1000 Airport Rd., Ste. 104, Lakewood 08701**
*(see our ad under STAIRS)*

Macy Custom Iron Railings Co., J.
Phone—(201) 262-4302
116 River Rd., New Milford 07646

Rego Iron Co.
Phone—(856) 423-6779
176 Cohawkin Rd., Clarksboro 08020

Suburban Steel Craft
Phone—(973) 772-3430
22 W. 1st St., Clifton 07011

## RAILINGS — Aluminum

**Ciccone Custom Railing & Manufacturing, Inc.**
**Phone—(732) 349-7071**
**Fax—(732) 349-7079**
**Web—www.cicconerailing.com**
**Email—customrailing@gmail.com**
**2002 Route 9, Toms River 08755**

F & C Professional Aluminum Railings
Phone—(908) 753-8886
1149 W. Front St., Plainfield 07063

Railco Metalcraft, Inc.
Phone—(973) 838-2822
22 Park Pl., Butler 07405

## RAILINGS — Decorative

**Ciccone Custom Railing & Manufacturing, Inc.**
**Phone—(732) 349-7071**
**Fax—(732) 349-7079**
**Web—www.cicconerailing.com**
**Email—customrailing@gmail.com**
**2002 Route 9, Toms River 08755**

## RAILINGS — Iron & Steel

Artistic Railings, Inc.
Phone—(973) 772-8540
500 River Dr., Garfield 07026

**Ciccone Custom Railing & Manufacturing, Inc.**
**Phone—(732) 349-7071**
**Fax—(732) 349-7079**
**Web—www.cicconerailing.com**
**Email—customrailing@gmail.com**
**2002 Route 9, Toms River 08755**

Newark Steel Fabricators, Inc.
Phone—(973) 344-2904
104 Albert Ave., Newark 07105

**Portuguese Structural Steel, Inc.**
**Phone—(973) 344-1342**
**Fax—(973) 344-1730**
**Web—www.portuguesesteel.com**
**Email—paula@portuguesesteel.com**
**255 South St., Newark 07114**
*(see our ad under STRUCTURAL STEEL FABRICATION)*

Summit Group II
Phone—(201) 460-8888
333 16th St., Carlstadt 07072

## RAILINGS — Vinyl

Railing Dynamics, Inc.
Phone—(856) 327-1698
1201 N. 10th St., Millville 08332

Railing Dynamics, Inc. (H Q)
Phone—(609) 601-1300
135 Steelmanville Rd., Egg Harbor Township 08234

# RAILROAD CARS & LOCOMOTIVES

Multipower International, Inc.
Phone—(973) 727-0327
7 Woodshire Ter., P.O. Box 197, Towaco 07082

# RAILROAD EQUIPMENT

Rails Co.
Phone—(973) 763-4320
101 Newark Way, Maplewood 07040

# RAILROAD RAILS

Pandrol USA L. P.
Phone—(856) 467-3227
501 Sharptown Rd., P.O. Box 367, Bridgeport 08014

# RAILROAD SUPPLIES

**Orgo-Thermit, Inc.**
**Email—georgeanne.tutunjian@orgothermit.com**
**Mfgr. & supplier of Aluminothermic welding prods & equipment for tee-rail, crane rail & grooved rail, as well as providing comprehensive training programs for the process of joining steel rails**
**Phone—(732) 657-5781**
**Fax—(732) 657-5899**
**Web—www.orgothermit.com**
**3500 Colonial Dr. N., Manchester 08759**

# RAILS

Atlantic Track & Turnout Co.
Phone—(973) 748-5885
270 Broad St., P.O. Box 1589, Bloomfield 07003

# RANGE HOODS

J & M Air, Inc.
Phone—(908) 707-4040
189 S. Bridge St., Somerville 08876

Rangecraft Mfg. Co., Inc.
Phone—(201) 791-0440
4-40 Banta Pl., Fair Lawn 07410

# RAPID PROTOTYPES

**Day Tool & Mfg., Inc.**
**ISO 9001:2008, AS9100 Rev. C**
**Phone—(908) 439-3800**
**Fax—(908) 439-3955**
**Web—www.daytool.com**
**Email—juddcallahan@daytool.com**
**6 Carman Ln., P.O. Box 466, Whitehouse 08888**

# RAZORS & RAZOR BLADES

Industrial Razor Blade Co., Inc.
Phone—(973) 673-4286
575 Nassau St., Orange 07050

IndustryNet®.com
Find Suppliers
Nationally FREE!

# REACTORS

**Power Magnetics, Inc.**
A global provider of a wide range of custom transformers, inductors & reactors for the most demanding applications in a wide variety of industries
**Phone—(609) 695-1170 / (800) 747-0845**
**Fax—(609) 695-5907**
**Web—www.powermagneticsinc.com**
**Email—sales@powermagneticsinc.com**
**377 Reservoir St., Trenton 08618**

# REBAR

**Commercial Metals Co.**
**CMC-East Mills**
**Phone—(800) 621-0262**
**Fax—(205) 591-4554**
**Web—www.cmc.com**
**Email—salesse@cmc.com**
**101 S. 50th St., Birmingham, AL 35212**

Men Of Steel Enterprises, LLC
Phone—(877) 732-2728
4319 Route 130, Beverly 08010

NJS Sales Corp.
Phone—(856) 619-1119
2840 Mount Ephraim Ave., Camden 08104

SAS Stressteel, Inc.
Phone—(973) 244-0507
100 New Dutch Ln., Fairfield 07004

Thompson Materials Corp.
Phone—(973) 386-1400
15 Leslie Ct., Whippany 07981

# RECORD MANAGEMENT

**DocuVault Delaware Valley LLC**
**Phone—(856) 853-5160**
**Fax—(856) 853-5164**
**Web—www.docuvaultdv.com**
**Email—customerservice@docuvaultdv.com**
**1240 Forest Pkwy., Ste. 100, West Deptford 08066**

# RECORDERS — Video

LiveU, Inc.
Phone—(201) 742-5229
2 University Plz., Ste. 505, Hackensack 07601

# RECORDING STUDIO EQUIPMENT

Pendulum Audio Systems, Inc.
Phone—(908) 665-9333
P.O. Box 339, Gillette 07933

# RECREATIONAL VEHICLES

Bornmann's RV
Phone—(856) 881-7979
131 Delsea Dr. S., Glassboro 08028

# RECTIFIERS

Kinetics Industries, Inc.
Phone—(609) 883-9700
140 Stokes Ave., Ewing 08638

# RECYCLED PAPER

All American Recycling Corp.
Phone—(201) 656-3363
2 Hope St., Jersey City 07307

Atlantic Coast Fibers, LLC
Phone—(973) 614-9600
101 7th St., Passaic 07055

Empire Recycling, Inc.
Phone—(732) 393-0200
3 New York Ave., P.O. Box 17398, Jersey City 07307

Newark Group, Inc., The
Phone—(973) 465-3900
60 Lockwood St., Newark 07105

© Copyright 2015 Manufacturers' News, Inc.

A183

INDUSTRY

## RECYCLED PAPER — (cont.)

**Reliable Paper Recycling**
Working for Resource Conservation & Recycling for
over 27 years, a family owned company. Operating a
fleet of 75+ trucks & trailers
Phone—(201) 333-5244
Fax—(201) 333-6712
Web—www.reliablepaperrecycling.com
1 Caven Point Ave., Jersey City 07305

## RECYCLING

Bayshore Recycling Corp.
Phone—(732) 738-6000
75 Crows Mill Rd., P.O. Box 290, Keasbey 08832

Cape Mining & Recycling, LLC
Phone—(609) 465-3277
560 Goshen Rd., P.O. Box 246, Cape May Court
House 08210

**Donjon Recycling**
Phone—(973) 366-2716
Web—www.donjonrecycling.com
160 Richards Ave., Dover 07801

River Front Recycling & Aggregates, LLC
Phone—(856) 966-1100
1301 N. 26th St., Camden 08105

Rotondi & Sons, Inc., S. (H Q)
Phone—(973) 635-7799
3 Watchung Ave., Chatham 07928

Safety-Kleen Systems, Inc.
Phone—(908) 862-2000
1200 Sylvan St., Linden 07036

**Veolia ES Technical Solutions, LLC**
Recycling Industrial Solvents
Phone—(732) 469-5100
Fax—(732) 469-1957
Web—www.veoliaes.com
Email—ray.clark@veolia.com
125 Factory Ln., Middlesex 08846
*(see our ad under SOLVENT RECYCLING)*

Waste Management, Inc.
Phone—(609) 587-1500
107 Silvia St., Ewing 08628

## RECYCLING — Computers & Electronics

Advanced Recovery, Inc.
Phone—(973) 485-9100
50 Grafton Ave., Newark 07104

## RECYCLING — Metal

A & R Recycling Co.
Phone—(856) 829-1712
1004 Union Landing Rd., P.O. Box 2440,
Cinnaminson 08077

Colantuono & Klurman Assocs., Inc.
Phone—(973) 589-5445
225 Clifford St., P.O. Box 5150, Newark 07105

**Electrum, Inc.**
Environmentally Safe Solder & Precious Metal
Recycling
Phone—(732) 396-1616 / (800) 622-1192
Fax—(732) 396-9390
Web—www.electruminc.com
Email—mdouglas@electruminc.com
827 Martin St., Rahway 07065
*(also see our ad under PRECIOUS METALS REFINING)*

## Electrum, Inc.
*Environmentally safe solder*
*& precious metal recycling*
**www.electruminc.com**
**(732) 396-1616**
827 Martin St. Rahway, NJ 07065

**Jefferson Metals & Alloys**
Phone—(908) 296-9161
Fax—(610) 253-6865
Web—www.jeffersonmetalsandalloys.com
Email—jeffersonmetalsandalloys@
yahoo.com
827 N. Meadow St., Allentown, PA 18102

**Find suppliers nationally
using the FREE
IndustryNet mobile app.**
**Scan to begin!**
**INDUSTRYNET.COM**
THE INDUSTRIAL SEARCH ENGINE

Metal Management Northeast, Inc.
Phone—(201) 577-3200
1 Linden Ave. E., Jersey City 07305

**River Road Recycling Inc.**
Metals Recycling Center
Phone—(856) 661-0770 / (856) 661-8181
Fax—(856) 661-8384
Web—www.riverroadrecycling.com
Email—chris@philametals.com
450 37th St., P.O. Box 302, Pennsauken 08110

## River Road Recycling Inc.
*Quality Recycling Centers*
**www.riverroadrecycling.com**
**chris@philametals.com**
**856-661-0770**
**Fax: 856-661-8384**
450 37th St., PO Box 302
Pennsauken, NJ 08110

Sims Metal Management
Phone—(973) 824-8900
8-18 Noble St., Newark 07114

**United Scrap Iron & Metal Co.**
Industrial, Commercial Scrap Iron & Metal
Phone—(973) 279-1683
Fax—(973) 279-1684
Web—www.unitedscrapironandmetal.com
Email—info@unitedscrapironandmetal.com
124 Wood St., Paterson 07524
*(see our ad under SCRAP IRON & METAL RECYCLING)*

## RECYCLING EQUIPMENT

RecycleTech Corp.
Phone—(201) 475-5000
418 Falmouth Ave., Elmwood Park 07407

## REELS

Reel Parts Co.
Phone—(973) 731-9559
10 Park Ave., West Orange 07052

**IndustryNet.com**
**Find Suppliers
Nationally FREE!**

## REFLECTORS

Foremost Mfg. Co., Inc.
Phone—(908) 687-4646
941 Ball Ave., Union 07083

## REFRACTOMETERS

Rudolph Research Analytical
Phone—(973) 584-1558
55 Newburgh Rd., Hackettstown 07840

## REFRACTORIES

*(also see Clay Products)*

Kraemer Gunite, Inc.
Phone—(856) 227-8097
137 Blackwood Barnsboro Rd., Sewell 08080

## REFRACTORIES — Ceramic Fiber

Nth Degree Products, LLC
Phone—(609) 518-9447
404 Laurel Ridge Rd., Hainesport 08036

## REFRACTORY MATERIALS

CermSource, Inc
Phone—(732) 257-5002
25 Kimberly Rd., Unit A, P.O. Box 6026, East
Brunswick 08816

McNeil, Inc.
Phone—(609) 890-7007
15 Marlen Dr., Robbinsville 08691

## REFRIGERATION EQUIPMENT

Bush Refrigeration
Phone—(856) 963-1800
1700 Admiral Wilson Blvd., Pennsauken 08109

Hussmann Corp.
Phone—(856) 793-7050
3001 Irwin Rd., Ste. D, Mount Laurel 08054

International Process Plants
Phone—(609) 586-8004
17-A Marlen Dr., Hamilton 08691

## REFRIGERATION EQUIPMENT — Commercial

Coldstat Refrigeration
Phone—(201) 599-1200
60 Eisenhower Dr., Paramus 07652

Kohlder Mfg., Inc.
Phone—(856) 342-8398
1001 Line St., Camden 08103

## REFRIGERATION PARTS

Sealed Unit Parts Co., Inc.
Phone—(732) 223-6644
2230 Landmark Pl., P.O. Box 21, Allenwood
08720

*Do nationwide searches for
products & services at:*
**IndustryNet.com**

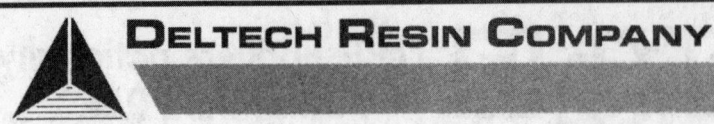

## DELTECH RESIN COMPANY

Polyurethane Dispersions, Acrylic & Styrene — Acrylic Latexes,
Alkyd & VT — Alkyd Resins, Oil Modified Urethane Resins

# 973-589-0880 FAX: 973-589-7231
49 Rutherford St., Newark, NJ 07105

**www.deltechcorp.com • danderson@deltechresins.com**

## REFRIGERATORS

Gem Refrigerator Co., Inc.
  Phone—(609) 625-2500
  176 Blvd. Route 50, Mays Landing 08330

Migali Industries, Inc.
  Phone—(856) 963-3600
  516 Lansdowne Ave., Camden 08104

**Reno's Appliance**
  **Addtl. Web: www.buyrenos.com**
  **Toll Free Ph: (866)88-RENOS**
  **Phone—(973) 247-1860 / (866) 887-3667**
  **Fax—(973) 247-1865**
  **Web—www.renosappliance.com**
  **Email—sales@renosappliance.net**
  **235 McLean Blvd., Route 20 N., Paterson**
  **07504**
    *(see our ad under APPLIANCES — Household)*

Victory Refrigeration
  Phone—(856) 428-4200
  110 Woodcrest Rd., Cherry Hill 08003

## REFUSE HANDLING EQUIPMENT

**Kucharski's Salvage**
  **Cell Ph: (862)258-0899**
  **Phone—(908) 852-3175**
  **60 Ryan Rd., Hackettstown 07840**

## RELAYS

**Americor Electronics, Ltd.**
  **Phone—(847) 956-6200 / (800) 830-5337**
  **Fax—(847) 956-0300**
  **Web—www.americor-usa.com**
  **Email—info@americor-usa.com**
  **675 S. Lively Blvd., Elk Grove Village, IL 60007**
    *(see our ads under CABLE ASSEMBLIES & CORD SETS)*

## RELIGIOUS PRODUCTS

**Biblemesh.Com**
  **Christian Foundation**
  **Phone—(973) 455-1134**
  **Web—www.kairosjournal.org**
  **P.O. Box 435, New Vernon 07976**

Devon Trading Corp.
  Phone—(973) 812-9190
  5 Fairfield Rd., Caldwell 07006

Mundo Esoterico dist inc
  Phone—(201) 766-4084
  6207 Madison St., West New York 07093

## REPLACEMENT PARTS

DSO Fluid Handling Co., Inc.
  Phone—(732) 225-9100
  300 McGaw Dr., Ste. 2, Edison 08837

Graco Manufacturing
  Phone—(856) 228-1800
  500 University Ct., Blackwood 08012

Unique Systems, Inc.
  Phone—(973) 455-0440
  4 Saddle Rd., Cedar Knolls 07927

## REPROGRAPHIC SERVICES

**Quality Repro Centers, Inc.**
  **Phone—(201) 794-3905**
  **Fax—(201) 794-3909**
  **Web—www.qrepro.com**
  **Email—qrepro@optonline.net**
  **296 Route 46 E., P.O. Box 111, Elmwood Park**
  **07407**
    *(see our ad under PRINTING — Digital)*

## RESCUE EQUIPMENT

Butco, Inc.
  Phone—(800) 872-8055
  2009 Route 130 N., Burlington 08016

## RESEARCH & DEVELOPMENT

Sarnoff Corp.
  Phone—(609) 734-2000
  201 Washington Rd., Princeton 08540

## RESEARCH SERVICES

**Survey Operation Center**
  **Phone—(609) 799-3535**
  **Fax—(609) 799-0005**
  **Web—www.mathematica-mpr.com**
  **707 Alexander Rd., Bldg. 3, Ste. 304,**
  **Princeton 08540**

## RESINS

Commercial Products Co. U. S. A.
  Phone—(973) 427-6887
  117 Ethel Ave., P.O. Box 504, Hawthorne 07507

**Deltech Resin Co.**
  **Phone—(973) 589-0880 / (973) 589-3331**
  **(800) 785-4415**
  **Fax—(973) 589-7231**
  **Web—www.deltechcorp.com**
  **Email—danderson@deltechresins.com**
  **49 Rutherford St., Newark 07105**
    *(see our ad on this page)*

Epicor, Inc.
  Phone—(908) 925-0800
  1414 E. Linden Ave., P.O. Box 1608, Linden
  07036

Polymer Dynamix, LLC
  Phone—(908) 668-0300
  238 Saint Nicholas Ave., South Plainfield 07080

Synray Corp.
  Phone—(908) 245-2600
  209 N. Michigan Ave., Kenilworth 07033

## RESINS — Epoxy

Cambridge Industries Of America Co., Inc.
  Phone—(973) 465-0077
  7-33 Amsterdam St., Newark 07105

Cardolite Corp.
  Phone—(973) 344-5015
  500 Doremus Ave., Newark 07105

## RESINS — Polyamide

Industrial Summit Technology Corp.
  Phone—(732) 238-2211
  250 Cheesequake Rd., Parlin 08859

## RESINS — Polystyrene

**Deltech Resin Co.**
  **Phone—(973) 589-0880 / (973) 589-3331**
  **(800) 785-4415**
  **Fax—(973) 589-7231**
  **Web—www.deltechcorp.com**
  **Email—danderson@deltechresins.com**
  **49 Rutherford St., Newark 07105**
    *(see our ad on this page)*

## RESINS — Urethane

**Deltech Resin Co.**
  **Phone—(973) 589-0880 / (973) 589-3331**
  **(800) 785-4415**
  **Fax—(973) 589-7231**
  **Web—www.deltechcorp.com**
  **Email—danderson@deltechresins.com**
  **49 Rutherford St., Newark 07105**
    *(see our ad on this page)*

## RESPIRATORY THERAPY EQUIPMENT

Philips Respironics
  Phone—(732) 563-3400
  200 Franklin Square Dr., Somerset 08873

## RESTAURANT EQUIPMENT & SUPPLIES

Chef's Corner
  Phone—(973) 691-1500
  178 U.S. Highway 206, Ste. B, Flanders 07836

D.W.L International Trading Co.
  Phone—(973) 916-9958
  65 Industrial Rd., Lodi 07644

**East Coast Kitchen Installations, Inc.**
  **Installation of commercial food service equipment**
  **Phone—(732) 901-8609**
  **Email—gerrylyle@optonline.net**
  **2 Robert Ave., Howell 07731**

R-S Restaurant Equipment Mfg. Corp.
  Phone—(973) 375-3388
  40 Camptown Rd., Maplewood 07040

Savco Restaurant Equipment, Inc.
  Phone—(973) 523-4464
  600 Main St., Paterson 07503

## RETAINING RINGS

Rotor Clip Company, Inc.
  Phone—(732) 469-7333
  187 Davidson Ave., Somerset 08873

## RIBBONS AND BOWS

Carson & Gebel Ribbon Co., Inc.
  Phone—(973) 627-4200
  17 Green Pond Rd., Rockaway 07866

Cottage Lace & Ribbon Co.
  Phone—(732) 776-9353
  21 TFH Plaza Union & 3rd Ave., Neptune 07753

JRM Industries, Inc.
  Phone—(973) 779-9340
  1 Mattimore St., Passaic 07055

Klein Ribbon Designs, Jeffrey
  Phone—(973) 684-4671
  176 E. 7th St., Paterson 07524

Reliant Ribbon & Trims
  Phone—(973) 881-0404
  838 21st Ave., Paterson 07513

## RIFLES

Henry Repeating Arms Company
  Phone—(201) 858-4400
  59 E. 1st St., Bayonne 07002

*find additional suppliers at*
**IndustryNet.com**

*Search from among 430,000
U.S. manufacturers & suppliers:*
**IndustryNet.com**

INDUSTRY

## RIGGING

**Bruce R. Koerner Cranes & Equipment, Inc.**
Phone—(973) 989-7990
Fax—(973) 989-1991
Web—www.koernercranes.com
Email—sales@koernercranes.com
400 Franklin Ave., Rockaway 07866
*(see our ad under CRANE RENTAL)*

## RING ASSEMBLIES — Slip

Electro-Miniatures Corp.
Phone—(201) 460-0510
68 W. Commercial Ave., Moonachie 07074

## RINGS — Iron & Steel

**Arntzen Corp.**
Mfr. Of Rolled & Welded Steel Cylinders-Cones-Pipe-Shapes-Fittings
Phone—(815) 334-0788 / (800) 957-7655
Fax—(815) 334-0778
Web—www.ArntzenRolling.com
Email—Sales@ArntzenCorp.com
14600 Washington St., Woodstock, IL 60098

**Imperial Weld Ring Corp.**
Phone—(908) 354-0011
Fax—(908) 354-9014
Web—www.imperialweldringcorp.com
Email—imperialweldring@erols.com
80-88 Front St., P.O. Box 6646, Elizabeth 07206

## RIVETS — Semi-Tubular

New Jersey Rivet Co., LLC
Phone—(856) 963-2237
1785 Haddon Ave., Camden 08103

## ROBES — Judicial, Choir, Graduation

Harbro Church Arts, Inc.
Phone—(201) 768-5500
231 Herbert Ave., P.O. Box 776, Closter 07624

Malhame Vestment
Phone—(973) 948-8401
239 Route 206, Branchville 07826

## ROBOTIC EQUIPMENT & SYSTEMS

Hudson Robotics, Inc.
Phone—(973) 376-7400
10 Stern Ave., Springfield 07081

## ROBOTS

Robodyssey Systems, LLC
Phone—(609) 585-8535
20 Quimby Ave., Trenton 08610

ST Robotics
Phone—(609) 584-7522
103 Carnagie Ctr., Ste. 300, Princeton 08540

## RODS

Amrod Corp.
Phone—(973) 344-2978
305-A Craneway St., Newark 07114

## ROLL FORMED PARTS

Roll Tech Industries
Phone—(609) 730-9500
55 Route 31 S., Ste. A, Pennington 08534

**IndustryNet.com**
**Find Suppliers Nationally FREE!**

## ROLLERS

**Continental Roller Co., Inc.**
Email: vincent@continentalroller.com
Phone—(201) 997-7999
Fax—(201) 998-5650
Web—www.continentalroller.com
75 Arlington Ave., Kearny 07032

**Hilman Rollers**
Phone—(732) 462-6277 / (888) 276-5548
Fax—(732) 462-6355
Web—www.hilmanrollers.com
Email—sales@hilmanrollers.com
12 Timber Ln., P.O. Box 45, Marlboro 07746
*(see our ad under JACKS—Hydraulic)*

Kay Machine Co.
Phone—(973) 839-4404
130 Cannonball Rd., Pompton Lakes 07442

## ROLLERS — Printing

Bottcher America Corp.
Phone—(973) 664-1241
88 Ford Rd., Ste. 8, Denville 07834

**Continental Roller Co., Inc.**
Email: vincent@continentalroller.com
Phone—(201) 997-7999
Fax—(201) 998-5650
Web—www.continentalroller.com
75 Arlington Ave., Kearny 07032

Pamarco Technologies, Inc.
Phone—(908) 241-1200
235 E. 11th Ave., Roselle 07203

## ROLLS

National Metal Finishings Corp., Inc.
Phone—(732) 752-7770
897 South Ave., P.O. Box 486, Middlesex 08846

## ROOF COATINGS

**Hackensack Roofing Co. Inc.**
Commercial, Industrial, Residential
Phone—(201) 487-5050
Fax—(201) 487-1180
Web—www.hackensackroofing.com
Email—info@hackensackroofing.com
83 First St., Hackensack 07601
*(see our ad under ROOFING CONTRACTORS)*

Karnak Corp.
Phone—(732) 388-0300
330 Central Ave., Clark 07066

Palmer Asphalt Co., Inc.
Phone—(201) 339-0855
196 W. 5th St., P.O. Box 58, Bayonne 07002

## ROOF PANELS — Metal

Interstate Panel, LLC
Phone—(609) 586-4411
67 Benson Ave., Hamilton 08610

## ROOF TRUSSES

ProBuild Co., LLC
Phone—(856) 767-3153
210 Williamstown Rd., Berlin 08009

# Merchant & Evans, Inc.
## Roofing Metal
Email: rjaconelli@ziprib.com

**800-257-6215**
**609-387-3033**
FAX: 609-387-4838

**www.ziprib.com**

308 Connecticut Dr.
Burlington, NJ 08016

**UFP Berlin, LLC**
Email: dgoldman@ufpi.com
Phone—(856) 767-0043
Fax—(856) 767-1526
Web—www.ufpi.com
159 Jackson Rd., Berlin 08009
*(see our ad under FLOOR TRUSSES)*

## ROOFING

ABC Supply Co., Inc., Bradco Div.
Phone—(732) 905-9355
691 New Hampshire Ave., Lakewood 08701

## ROOFING — Industrial

**GAF**
Phone—(973) 628-3000 / (800) 766-3411
Web—www.gaf.com
1361 Alps Rd., Wayne 07470
*(see our ad under ROOFING MATERIALS)*

**Hackensack Roofing Co. Inc.**
Commercial, Industrial, Residential
Phone—(201) 487-5050
Fax—(201) 487-1180
Web—www.hackensackroofing.com
Email—info@hackensackroofing.com
83 First St., Hackensack 07601
*(see our ad under ROOFING CONTRACTORS)*

## ROOFING — Metal

Englert, Inc.
Phone—(732) 826-8614
1200 Amboy Ave., Perth Amboy 08861

**Hackensack Roofing Co. Inc.**
Commercial, Industrial, Residential
Phone—(201) 487-5050
Fax—(201) 487-1180
Web—www.hackensackroofing.com
Email—info@hackensackroofing.com
83 First St., Hackensack 07601
*(see our ad under ROOFING CONTRACTORS)*

**Merchant & Evans, Inc.**
Phone—(609) 387-3033 / (800) 257-6215
Fax—(609) 387-4838
Web—www.ziprib.com
Email—rjaconelli@ziprib.com
308 Connecticut Dr., Burlington 08016
*(see our ad on this page)*

## ROOFING — Standing Seam

**Merchant & Evans, Inc.**
Phone—(609) 387-3033 / (800) 257-6215
Fax—(609) 387-4838
Web—www.ziprib.com
Email—rjaconelli@ziprib.com
308 Connecticut Dr., Burlington 08016
*(see our ad on this page)*

## ROOFING — Wholesale

ABC Supply Co., Inc., Bradco Div.
Phone—(973) 777-3663
45 Samworth Rd., Clifton 07012

Allied Building Products Corp.
Phone—(609) 386-5500
11 Cadillac Rd., Box 1838, Burlington 08016

© Copyright 2015 Manufacturers' News, Inc.

## ROOFING CONTRACTORS

**All Professional Remodeling Group, LLC**
Toll Free Ph: (888)919-ROOF; Second Generation
Roofing Contractor
Phone—(973) 857-9449 / (888) 919-7663
Fax—(973) 857-0991
Web—
www.allprofessionalremodelinggroup.com
Email—aprgllc@aol.com
P.O. Box 215, Cedar Grove 07009

**All Professional Remodeling Group, LLC**
*Roofing contractors*
**973-857-9449 • Fax: 973-857-0991**
www.allprofessionalremodelinggroup.com
email: aprgllc@aol.com
P.O. Box 215  Cedar Grove, NJ 07009

**Hackensack Roofing Co. Inc.**
Commercial, Industrial, Residential
Phone—(201) 487-5050
Fax—(201) 487-1180
Web—www.hackensackroofing.com
Email—info@hackensackroofing.com
83 First St., Hackensack 07601

**Hackensack Roofing Co. Inc.**
*Commercial, Industrial, Residential*
**(201) 487-5050**
**www.hackensackroofing.com**
info@hackensackroofing.com
83 First St. • Hackensack, NJ 07601

**J.T. Penyak Roofing Co., Inc.**
Phone—(908) 753-4222
Fax—(908) 753-4763
Web—www.penyakroofing.com
Email—joe@penyakroofing.com
3571 Kennedy Rd., South Plainfield 07080

**J.T. Penyak Roofing Co., Inc.**
*Quality roofing contractors*
**908-753-4222**
**www.penyakroofing.com**
3571 Kennedy Rd.
South Plainfield, NJ 07080

**Kovach Roofing**
We offer a wide variety of Residential & Commercial
services ranging from minor repairs through building
complete custom roofs & beyond
Phone—(973) 835-5330
Fax—(973) 831-9577
Web—www.kovachroofing.com
Email—kovachroofing@aol.com
225 Boulevard, Pompton Plains 07444

**KOVACH ROOFING**
*Residential & commercial roofing contractors*
**973-835-5330**
www.kovachroofing.com
225 Boulevard  Pompton Plains, NJ 07444

**Patriot Roofing, Inc.**
Phone—(609) 723-6688
Web—www.patriotroof.com
2083 Jacksonville Jobstown Rd., Jobstown
08041
**S & S Roofing Inc.**
Phone—(732) 602-0099
Fax—(732) 602-9123
2 Self Blvd., Carteret 07008

## ROOFING EQUIPMENT

Modi Systems, Inc.
Phone—(201) 525-0775
88 S. State St., Hackensack 07601

## ROOFING MATERIALS

Barrett Co.
Phone—(908) 647-0100
33 Stonehouse Rd., P.O. Box 421, Millington
07946
Cheney Flashing Co., LLC
Phone—(609) 394-8175
623 Prospect St., Trenton 08618
**GAF**
Phone—(973) 628-3000 / (800) 766-3411
Web—www.gaf.com
Email—commercialsales@gaf.com
1361 Alps Rd., Wayne 07470

**GAF**

*Corporate headquarters & commercial roofing materials*

**(800) 766-3411**
**(973) 628-3000**
**www.gaf.com**

1361 Alps Rd. • Wayne, NJ 07470

Kelly, Inc., Myles F.
Phone—(973) 481-0600
43-57 Harrison Ave., Harrison 07029
Kelly, Inc., Myles F.
Phone—(908) 245-7296
210 W. Westfield Ave., Roselle Park 07204
United Asphalt Co., Inc.
Phone—(856) 753-9811
237 N. Grove St., Berlin 08009

## ROOFING SYSTEMS — Commercial

**Kovach Roofing**
We offer a wide variety of Residential & Commercial
services ranging from minor repairs through building
complete custom roofs & beyond
Phone—(973) 835-5330
Fax—(973) 831-9577
Web—www.kovachroofing.com
Email—kovachroofing@aol.com
225 Boulevard, Pompton Plains 07444
*(see our ad under ROOFING CONTRACTORS)*
**Merchant & Evans, Inc.**
Phone—(609) 387-3033 / (800) 257-6215
Fax—(609) 387-4838
Web—www.ziprib.com
Email—rjaconelli@ziprib.com
308 Connecticut Dr., Burlington 08016
*(see our ad under ROOFING—Metal)*

## ROPE

Frank Winne & Son, Inc.
Phone—(931) 212-3720
521 Fellowship Rd., Ste. 115, Mount Laurel 08054
Kenyon & Sons, Inc., William
Phone—(732) 985-8980
90 Ethel Rd. W., Piscataway 08854

*Do nationwide searches for products & services at:*
**IndustryNet.com**

## ROPE — Synthetic

Egg Harbor Rope Products, Inc.
Phone—(609) 965-2435
5105 White Horse Pike, P.O. Box 294, Egg Harbor
City 08215

## ROUTERS — CNC

Komo Machine, Inc.
Phone—(732) 719-6222
1 Komo Dr., Lakewood 08701

## RUBBER

Dicar, Inc.
Phone—(973) 575-4220
5 Bader Rd., Pine Brook 07058

## RUBBER — Custom Molded

AME Corporation
Phone—(800) 951-0071
33 Jacksonville Rd., Ste. 2, Towaco 07082
**Captain O-Ring LLC**
Phone—(215) 839-6565
Web—www.captainoring.com
Email—sales@captainoring.com
Eastern Molding Co., Inc.
Phone—(973) 759-0220
597 Main St., Belleville 07109
TEK Molding, LLC
Phone—(973) 702-0450
1440 County Route 565, Sussex 07461

## RUBBER COMPOUNDS

**Brenntag Specialties, Inc.**
Phone—(908) 561-6100 / (800) 732-0562
Fax—(800) 543-1484
Web—www.brenntagspecialties.com
Email—specialties@brenntag.com
1000 Coolidge St., South Plainfield 07080
*(see our ad under CHEMICAL DISTRIBUTORS)*

## RUBBER EXTRUSIONS

Accu-Seal Rubber, Inc.
Phone—(732) 246-4333
18-F Home News Row, New Brunswick 08901
Herring Co., Inc., D. C.
Phone—(732) 695-2272
1750 Brielle Ave., Ste. B-2, Ocean 07712

## RUBBER FABRICATORS

Bergen Mfg. & Supply Co., Inc.
Phone—(201) 854-3461
2025 85th St., North Bergen 07047
Caserta, Inc., Thomas A.
Phone—(609) 586-2807
11 S. Gold Dr., Ste. E, Robbinsville 08691
Hutchinson Industries, Inc.
Phone—(609) 394-1010
460 Southard St., Trenton 08638

## RUBBER GOODS — Mechanical

Home Rubber Co.
Phone—(609) 394-1176
31 Wolverton Ave., Trenton 08611
Mid-State Enterprises, Inc.
Phone—(973) 427-6040
155 Van Winkle Rd., Hawthorne 07506
Minor Rubber Co., Inc.
Phone—(973) 338-6800
49 Ackerman St., Bloomfield 07003

## RUBBER PARTS — Molded

JW Industries, Inc.
Phone—(856) 235-9285
21 Elbo Ln., Mount Laurel 08054
Pure Rubber Products Co., Inc.
Phone—(973) 784-3690
300 Roundhill Dr., Ste. 5, Rockaway 07866

INDUSTRY

## RUBBER PARTS — Molded —
### (cont.)

Southland Mfg. Co.
Phone—(908) 459-5858
316 Great Meadows Rd., P.O. Box 350, Hope 07844

## RUBBER PROCESSING MACHINERY

**Warwick Mfg. & Equipment Co., LLC**
Buy & sell used: Chemical, food, cosmetic, packaging & pharmaceutical equipment
Phone—(732) 729-0400 / (732) 241-9263
Fax—(732) 729-1235
Web—www.warwickequipment.com
Email—sales@warwickequipment.com
1112 12th St., North Brunswick 08902
*(see our ad Outside Back Cover)*

## RUBBER PRODUCTS

Aarubco Rubber Co.
Phone—(973) 772-8177
259 2nd St., P.O. Box 8028, Saddle Brook 07663
Lewis-Goetz & Co., Inc.
Phone—(856) 579-1421
1571 Grandview Ave., Paulsboro 08066
Manville Rubber Products, Inc.
Phone—(908) 526-9111
1009 Kennedy Blvd., Manville 08835
Passaic Rubber Co., Inc.
Phone—(973) 696-9500
45 Demarest Dr., Wayne 07470
RubbeRecycle, LLC
Phone—(732) 363-0600
1985 Rutgers Blvd., Lakewood 08701

## RUBBER PRODUCTS — Industrial

Cherokee Rubber Co.
Phone—(973) 584-3733
5 Laurel Dr., Unit 13, Flanders 07836
General Rubber Corp.
Phone—(201) 935-1900
850 Washington Ave., Front, Carlstadt 07072
Metropolitan Rubber Co.
Phone—(201) 489-0909
135 Lawrence St., Hackensack 07601
RS Rubber Corp.
Phone—(973) 777-2200
55 Paterson Ave., P.O. Box 3400, Wallington 07057

## RUBBER PRODUCTS — Molded

Alpine Elastomer Products, LLC
Phone—(973) 299-0123
308 Division St., Boonton 07005
Ames Rubber Corp.
Phone—(973) 827-9101
19 Ames Blvd., Hamburg 07419
Hawthorne Rubber Mfg. Corp.
Phone—(973) 427-3337
35 4th Ave., P.O. Box 171, Hawthorne 07507
Itran Precision Rubber
Phone—(908) 754-8100
375 Metuchen Rd., P.O. Box 98, South Plainfield 07080
Pierce Roberts Rubber Co., Inc.
Phone—(609) 394-5245
1450 Heath Ave., P.O. Box 5007, Trenton 08638
Rubber & Silicone Products Co., Inc.
Phone—(973) 227-2300
17 Montesano Rd., Fairfield 07004

## RUBBER STAMPS

A A A Stamp & Seal Mfg. Co.
Phone—(201) 796-1500
361 N. Midland Ave., Saddle Brook 07663
A To Z Rubber Stamps
Phone—(201) 265-9595
617 Oradell Ave., Oradell 07649
Acme Rubber Stamp Works
Phone—(973) 761-7146
6 Burnett Ave., Maplewood 07040

American Marking Systems, Inc.
Phone—(973) 478-5600
1015 Paulison Ave., Clifton 07011
Anchor Rubber Stamp & Printing, Inc.
Phone—(732) 583-6578
339 Herbertsville Rd., Brick 08724
Classic Marking Products, Inc.
Phone—(973) 383-2223
10 Millpond Dr., Unit 9, Lafayette 07848
Franklin Stamp & Sign Co.
Phone—(732) 846-9235
543 Somerset St., Ste. 1, Somerset 08873
G & R Graphics, Inc.
Phone—(973) 313-2200
303 Irvington Ave., South Orange 07079
Newark Stamp & Die Works, Inc.
Phone—(973) 485-7111
35 Verona Ave., Newark 07104
Oraton Rubber Stamp Co., Inc.
Phone—(908) 496-4161
407 Route 94, Columbia 07832
Paterson Stamp Works
Phone—(973) 478-5600
1015 Paulison Ave., Clifton 07011
R. B.'s Rubber Stamp, Inc.
Phone—(201) 547-9955
551 W. Side Ave., Jersey City 07304
**Regal Stamp & Sign Co., Inc.**
Making Our Mark Since 1970. Rubber Stamps, Embossing, Seals & Signage
Phone—(201) 939-0400
Fax—(201) 939-5203
Web—www.regalstampnj.com
Email—regalstamp@verizon.net
240 Park Ave., P.O. Box 342, East Rutherford 07073
*(see our ad under RUBBER STAMPS)*

**REGAL STAMP & Sign Co., Inc.**
Printing • Indoor/Outdoor Signs • Name Badges • Corporate and Notary Seals • Marking Devices
**(201) 939-0400**
**Fax: (201) 939-5203**
**www.regalstampnj.com**
240 Park Ave., P.O. Box 342
East Rutherford, NJ 07073

Rubber Stamp Man, LLC
Phone—(732) 557-0275
1236 Route 166, Ste. 140, Toms River 08753
Shachihata, Inc., U. S. A.
Phone—(732) 370-4770
525 Oberlin Ave. S., Lakewood 08701

## RUGS

Loominaries Handweaving
Phone—(908) 832-6652
23 Big Spring Rd., Califon 07830
Michaelian & Kohlberg (H Q)
Phone—(908) 522-1004
100 Hoffman Pl., Hillside 07205

## RUST PREVENTIVES

**Hangsterfer's Laboratories, Inc.**
Phone—(856) 468-0216
Fax—(856) 468-0200
Web—www.hangsterfers.com
Email—sales@hangsterfers.com
175 Ogden Rd., Mantua 08051
*(see our ad under LUBRICANTS—Metalworking)*

## SAFES

Megasafe
Phone—(973) 691-0382
8 Sunrise Ave., Budd Lake 07828

## SAFES — Wholesale

Dornisch Enterprises, Inc.
Phone—(856) 863-1225
112 Cromwell Ct., Woodbury 08096
**SW Lock & Door Check Co.**
Phone—(201) 863-2234
Fax—(201) 863-1511
Email—swlock3701@yahoo.com
3701 Kennedy Blvd., Union City 07087

## SAFETY CONSULTANTS

**Certified Health & Safety Services, LLC**
Safe Today-Here Tomorrow
Phone—(856) 829-4463 / (800) 423-0137
Fax—(856) 786-3101
Web—www.certified-health-and-safety.com
Email—chss1@comcast.net
1902 Taylors Ln., Ste. A, Cinnaminson 08077
*(see our ad under ENVIRONMENTAL CONSULTANTS)*

## SAFETY CONSULTANTS — Regulatory Compliance

**Certified Health & Safety Services, LLC**
Safe Today-Here Tomorrow
Phone—(856) 829-4463 / (800) 423-0137
Fax—(856) 786-3101
Web—www.certified-health-and-safety.com
Email—chss1@comcast.net
1902 Taylors Ln., Ste. A, Cinnaminson 08077
*(see our ad under ENVIRONMENTAL CONSULTANTS)*
Safegate Safety Solutions
Phone—(973) 377-7000
Fax—(973) 377-4614
Web—www.safegateassociates.com
Email—ebeaulieu@safegatesolutions.com
30A Vreeland Rd., Florham Park 07932

**Safegate Safety Solutions**
Professional Safety Consultants
www.safegateassociates.com
**(973) 377-7000**
**Fax: (973) 377-4614**
30A Vreeland Rd. • Florham Park, NJ 07932

## SAFETY EQUIPMENT

**FallProof Systems LLC**
Specialists in Engineered Fall Protection Systems
Phone—(609) 325-5555
Fax—(609) 584-8882
Web—www.fallproof.com
Email—solutions@fallproof.com
61 2nd Ave., Trenton 08619
Gemtor, Inc.
Phone—(732) 583-6200
1 Johnson Ave., Matawan 07747

## SAFETY PRODUCTS

Bright Ideas USA, LLC
Phone—(732) 886-8865
890 Morris Ave., Lakewood 08701
Forty-Nine Corp.
Phone—(973) 754-0313
34 Waite St., Paterson 07524
Safe-Strap Co.
Phone—(973) 442-4623
105 W. Dewey Ave., Bldg. D, Ste. 410, Wharton 07885

*find additional suppliers at* **IndustryNet.com**

## SAFETY PRODUCTS — (cont.)

**Specified Technologies Inc.**
Firestopping Products
Phone—(908) 526-8000 / (800) 992-1180
Fax—(908) 526-9623
Web—www.stifirestop.com
Email—sales@stifirestop.com
210 Evans Way, Somerville 08876
*(see our ad under FIRE PROTECTION SYSTEMS)*

## SAFETY SYSTEMS

**FallProof Systems LLC**
Specialists in Engineered Fall Protection Systems
Phone—(609) 325-5555
Fax—(609) 584-8882
Web—www.fallproof.com
Email—solutions@fallproof.com
61 2nd Ave., Trenton 08619

## SAFETY TRAINING

**Safegate Safety Solutions**
Phone—(973) 377-7000
Fax—(973) 377-4614
Web—www.safegateassociates.com
Email—ebeaulieu@safegatesolutions.com
30A Vreeland Rd., Florham Park 07932
*(see our ad under SAFETY CONSULTANTS — Regulatory Compliance)*

## SAFETY VESTS

Bestwork Industries For The Blind, Inc.
Phone—(856) 939-5220
1940 Almay Ave., Ste. 200, Cherry Hill 08003

## SAILS

Beaton Sails, Inc.
Phone—(732) 920-6638
72 Beaton Rd., Brick 08723
Eggers Sails, Inc., John
Phone—(732) 721-4667
7076 Route 35, South Amboy 08879
Linthicum Sailmakers, Inc.
Phone—(856) 783-4288
607 Grace St., Somerdale 08083
Moorhouse Sailmakers, Inc.
Phone—(609) 654-7819
52 Stacy Haines Rd., Lumberton 08048
North Sails New Jersey
Phone—(732) 528-8899
2422 Highway 34, Manasquan 08736
Sailworks At 43
Phone—(856) 764-0888
43 Norman Ave., Delran 08075

## SALAD DRESSINGS

Walden Farms, Inc.
Phone—(908) 925-9494
1209 W. Saint Georges Ave., Linden 07036

## SALADS

Green's Fresh Fruit Salad, Inc.
Phone—(609) 641-5455
125 Shadeland Ave., P.O. Box 244, Pleasantville 08232
**Ready Pac Produce, Inc.**
Phone—(609) 499-1900
Fax—(609) 499-1406
Web—www.readypac.com
Email—info@readypac.com
700 Railroad Ave., P.O. Box 6, Florence 08518
Sheri's Cookery, Inc.
Phone—(973) 589-2060
33 Delancy St., Newark 07105
Zina's Salads, Inc.
Phone—(973) 428-0660
11 Great Meadow Ln., East Hanover 07936

## SALT & SALT PRODUCTS

Morton Salt, Inc.
Phone—(732) 826-3595
920 High St., Perth Amboy 08861

## SAMPLE BOOKS & CARDS

Flortek Corp.
Phone—(201) 436-7700
39 W. 55th St., Bayonne 07002
New York Sample Card Co., Inc.
Phone—(201) 526-9040
812 Jersey Ave., 3rd Fl., Jersey City 07310

## SAND — Silica

U.S. Silica Co.
Phone—(856) 785-0720
9035 Noble St., P.O. Box 254, Mauricetown 08329

## SAND AND GRAVEL

**ATAK Trucking, Inc.**
Phone—(917) 912-2900
Fax—(718) 227-9833
Web—www.ataktrucking.com
Email—tommyatak@yahoo.com
1341 Route 34, Matawan 07747
Buck Mining & Materials, Inc.
Phone—(732) 446-9336
P.O. Box 1386, Hightstown 08520
Eastern Concrete Materials, Inc.
Phone—(609) 698-2800
201 Route 539, Barnegat 08005
Hanson Aggregate BMC
Phone—(856) 447-4294
1101 Railroad Ave., Newport 08345
Hanson Aggregates Better Materials Corp.
Phone—(856) 447-4294
1401 Route 610, Woodbine 08270
Hanson Aggregates North America
Phone—(856) 697-1616
311 Unexpected Rd., Buena 08310
Hanson Aggregates, BMC Div.
Phone—(856) 767-3100
368 New Brooklyn Rd., P.O. Box 37, Berlin 08009
Harmony Sand & Gravel, Inc.
Phone—(908) 475-4690
3189 Belvidere Rd., Phillipsburg 08865
**Ole Hansen & Son, Inc. (H Q)**
Phone—(609) 965-3700
523 S. Leipzig Ave., P.O. Box 1020, Cologne 08213
Ole Hansen & Sons, Inc.
Phone—(609) 652-5666
100 Old Port Republic Rd., Absecon 08205
Ricci Brothers Sand Company, Inc.
Phone—(856) 785-0166
2099 Dragston Rd., P.O. Box 664, Port Norris 08349
Rosano Trucking, Inc.
Phone—(732) 542-5009
26 Maple Ave., Oceanport 07757
Saxton Falls Sand & Gravel, Inc.
Phone—(908) 852-0120
Waterloo Valley Rd., P.O. Box 576, Stanhope 07874
Tuckahoe Sand & Gravel, Inc.
Phone—(609) 861-2082
Route 610 & Sharp Rd., Tuckahoe 08250
Van Orden Sand & Gravel
Phone—(973) 839-0207
589 W. Brook Rd., Ringwood 07456
Whibco Of New Jersey
Phone—(856) 825-5200
377 Port Cumberland Rd., P.O. Box 456, Port Elizabeth 08348
WHIBCO, Inc. (H Q)
Phone—(856) 455-9200
87 E. Commerce St., Bridgeton 08302

## SANDBLASTING

**All American Powder Coating**
Phone—(732) 349-7001
Fax—(732) 349-7079
Email—aapowdercoating@gmail.com
2002 Route 9, Toms River 08755
**Armor Air Sandblasting**
Phone—(201) 947-3537
Fax—(201) 947-3537
Email—armorair@aol.com
12 Industrial Ave., Fairview 07022

**Peerless Coatings, LLC**
Providing Powder Coating, Sandblasting, Assembling & Packaging Services, Teflon® finishes along with Traditional Wet Paint finishes, and all types of Metalizing.
Phone—(973) 427-8771
Fax—(973) 427-8779
Web—www.peerlesscoatings.com
Email—peerless1@verizon.net
220-A Goffle Rd., Hawthorne 07506
Quick Strip
Phone—(732) 969-3268
1 Randolph St., Carteret 07008
Tulenko Enterprises, LLC
Phone—(973) 453-6699
176 Franklin Ave., Rockaway 07866

## SANDWICHES — Prepackaged

Lorenzo Food Group, Inc.
Phone—(201) 868-9088
196 Coolidge Ave., Englewood 07631

## SANITARY PRODUCTS

Keystone Adjustable Cap Co.
Phone—(856) 663-5740
1591 Hylton Rd., Ste. B, Pennsauken 08110

## SAUCES

Chelten House Products, Inc.
Phone—(856) 467-1600
607 Heron Dr., P.O. Box 434, Bridgeport 08014
FunniBonz, LLC
Phone—(877) 300-2669
3 Lake View Ct., Princeton Junction 08550
Great Garlic Foods, Inc.
Phone—(732) 775-3311
709 5th Ave., Bradley Beach 07720
Silver Palate Kitchens, Inc.
Phone—(201) 568-0110
211 Knickerbocker Rd., P.O. Box 512, Cresskill 07626
Violet Packing
Phone—(856) 629-7428
123 Railroad Ave., Williamstown 08094

## SAUSAGE CASINGS

Globe Packaging Co., Inc.
Phone—(201) 939-3335
368 Paterson Plank Rd., Carlstadt 07072
**Nitta Casings Inc.**
Phone—(908) 218-4400 / (800) 526-3970
Fax—(908) 725-2835
Web—www.nittacasings.com
Email—customerservice@nittacasings.com
141 Southside Ave., Bridgewater 08807

## SAUSAGE LINKING EQUIPMENT

**Nitta Casings Inc.**
Phone—(908) 218-4400 / (800) 526-3970
Fax—(908) 725-2835
Web—www.nittacasings.com
Email—customerservice@nittacasings.com
141 Southside Ave., Bridgewater 08807

## SAUSAGES

Appetito Provisions Co., Inc.
Phone—(201) 864-3410
609 10th St., P.O. Box 8098, Union City 07087
Cifelli & Sons, Inc.
Phone—(732) 238-0090
38 Obert St., P.O. Box 538, South River 08882
Corte Provisions
Phone—(973) 712-0970
574 Ferry St., Newark 07105
**Fratelli Beretta U.S.A., Inc.**
Phone—(201) 343-5161
Fax—(201) 343-5102
Web—www.fratelliberettausa.com
Email—info@fratelliberettausa.com
210 Green St., South Hackensack 07606
JMA Sausage And Meat Company, Inc.
Phone—(201) 636-2022
205 Stuyvesant Ave., Ste. 211, Lyndhurst 07071

## SAUSAGES — (cont.)

Licini Bros. Provisions, Inc.
Phone—(201) 865-1130
907 West St., Union City 07087

**Lipari's Sausage, Inc.**
**Phone—(973) 304-0137**
**Fax—(973) 304-0728**
**Web—www.liparisausage.com**
**Email—lipsaus@aol.com**
**220 6th Ave., Hawthorne 07506**
*(see our ad under MEAT PRODUCTS—Sausage)*

Lopes Co.
Phone—(973) 344-3063
304 Walnut St., Newark 07105

Los Galleguitos
Phone—(201) 865-7232
147 48th St., Union City 07087

Martin's Specialty Sausage Co.
Phone—(856) 423-4000
150 Harmony Rd., Mickleton 08056

Perrulli's Custom Meats
Phone—(732) 244-0470
1889 Route 9, Ste. 45, Toms River 08755

**Premio Foods, Inc.**
**Phone—(973) 427-1106**
**Fax—(973) 427-5251**
**Web—www.premiofoods.com**
**Email—info@premiofoods.com**
**50 Utter Ave., Hawthorne 07506**

Seabra Group (H Q)
Phone—(973) 491-0399
574 Ferry St., Newark 07105

## SAW BLADES

Forrest Mfg. Co., Inc.
Phone—(973) 473-5236
457 River Rd., Clifton 07014

Tooling Etc., LLC
Phone—(732) 752-8080
250 Hallock Ave., Ste. C, Middlesex 08846

## SAW CUTTING

**Certified Steel Company (H Q)**
**Phone—(609) 396-7600 / (800) 466-7660**
**Fax—(609) 392-6372**
**Web—www.certifiedsteel.com**
**Email—info@certifiedsteel.com**
**1333 Brunswick Ave., Ste. 200, Lawrenceville 08648**
*(see our ad under STEEL DISTRIBUTORS & WAREHOUSES)*

## SAWDUST

Sawdust Depot
Phone—(201) 703-8400
1 Boumar Pl., Elmwood Park 07407

## SAWMILLS

Boro Sawmill & Timber Co., Inc.
Phone—(973) 832-4607
139 Ryerson Ave., Wayne 07470

**Riephoff Sawmill, Inc.**
**Phone—(609) 259-7265**
**Fax—(609) 259-7267**
**Web—www.riephoffsawmill.com**
**Email—john@riephoffsawmill.com**
**763 Route 524, Allentown 08501**
*(see our ad under LUMBER)*

## SAWS

**Ferrous Saw Works**
**Phone—(973) 513-3936**
**345 Lakeview Ave., Clifton 07011**

## SCAFFOLDS & SCAFFOLDING

Safway Atlantic, LLC
Phone—(201) 636-5500
700 Commercial Ave., Carlstadt 07072

Search from among 430,000 U.S. manufacturers & suppliers: IndustryNet.com

## SCALES

Sterling Home Products, Inc.
Phone—(609) 585-8941
127 U.S. Highway 206, Ste. 22, Hamilton 08610

## SCALES — Electronic

HealthTools, LLC (H Q)
Phone—(201) 465-4381
681 Lawlins Rd., Unit 70, Wyckoff 07481

## SCALES — Industrial

Belleville Scale & Balance, LLC
Phone—(973) 759-4487
50 S. Center St., Orange 07050

**Warwick Mfg. & Equipment Co., LLC**
**Buy & sell used: Chemical, food, cosmetic, packaging & pharmaceutical equipment**
**Phone—(732) 729-0400 / (732) 241-9263**
**Fax—(732) 729-1235**
**Web—www.warwickequipment.com**
**Email—sales@warwickequipment.com**
**1112 12th St., North Brunswick 08902**
*(see our ad Outside Back Cover)*

## SCENERY

Acadia Scenic, Inc.
Phone—(201) 653-8889
130 Bay St., Jersey City 07302

## SCHOOLS — Technical & Vocational

**Salem County Vocational Technical Schools**
**Phone—(856) 769-0101**
**Fax—(856) 769-3602**
**Web—www.scvts.org**
**Email—info@scvts.org**
**880 Route 45, P.O. Box 350, Woodstown 08098**

## SCIENTIFIC EQUIPMENT

Princeton Instruments
Phone—(609) 587-9797
3660 Quakerbridge Rd., Trenton 08619

Quark Enterprises, Inc.
Phone—(856) 455-0376
320 Morton Ave., Rosenhayn 08352

## SCIENTIFIC INSTRUMENTS

Aviv Biomedical, Inc.
Phone—(732) 370-1300
750 Vassar Ave., Lakewood 08701

Blake Industries, Inc.
Phone—(908) 233-7240
660 Jerusalem Rd., Scotch Plains 07076

Evex Global
Phone—(408) 907-2994
857 State Rd., Princeton 08540

Linseis, Inc.
Phone—(609) 223-2070
109 N. Gold Dr., Robbinsville 08691

Scientific Instrument Services, Inc.
Phone—(908) 788-5550
1027 Old York Rd., Ringoes 08551

Techne, Inc.
Phone—(609) 589-2560
3 Terri Ln., Ste. 10, Burlington 08016

Uehling Instrument Co.
Phone—(973) 742-8710
473 Getty Ave., Paterson 07503

## SCISSORS

Icicle, Inc.
Phone—(732) 521-4223
341 School House Rd., Monroe Township 08831

## SCOREBOARDS

K & J Accessories, Inc.
Phone—(973) 777-6741
25 Ridgewood Rd., Clifton 07012

## SCRAP AND RECYCLED MATERIALS — Wholesale

Abington Reldan Metals, LLC
Phone—(732) 238-8550
396-402 Whitehead Ave., South River 08882

Advanced Metal Processing NJ, LLC
Phone—(856) 327-0048
326 S. Wade Blvd., Millville 08332

American Auto Salvage & Recycling, Inc.
Phone—(609) 965-2900
3113 Route 50, Mays Landing 08330

American Iron & Metal International, LLC
Phone—(856) 825-2950
301 S. 12th St., P.O. Box 965, Millville 08332

Armor Metals & Recycling
Phone—(856) 665-5715
8300 National Hwy., Ste. 2, Pennsauken 08110

Cali Carting, Inc.
Phone—(201) 991-5400
450 Bergen Ave., P.O. Box 440, Kearny 07032

Camden Iron & Metal, Inc.
Phone—(856) 365-7500
143 Harding Ave., Bellmawr 08031

Casings Of NJ, Inc.
Phone—(908) 851-7766
711 Ramsey Ave., Hillside 07205

Chinook Sciences, LLC (H Q)
Phone—(908) 272-5091
20 Commerce Dr., Ste. 350, Cranford 07016

Container Recyclers-Camden, Inc.
Phone—(856) 963-5200
267 Jefferson St., Camden 08104

Cooper Alloy Corp.
Phone—(908) 688-4216
201 Sweetland Ave., Hillside 07205

**Excel Plastics Recycling, Inc.**
**Quality Plastics. Email: ed@excelrecycling.com**
**Phone—(201) 991-2500**
**Fax—(201) 991-2526**
**Web—www.excelrecycling.net**
**Email—brian@excelrecycling.net**
**996 Belleville Tpke., Kearny 07032**

Faith Group Co. (H Q)
Phone—(732) 431-1326
195 Route 9, Ste. 205, Manalapan 07726

FCR Camden, Inc.
Phone—(856) 342-7503
2201 Mt. Ephraim Ave., Bldg. 10-A, Camden 08104

Federal Metals & Alloys
Phone—(908) 756-0900
4216 S. Clinton Ave., South Plainfield 07080

Fortune Plastic & Metal, Inc.
Phone—(201) 333-3339
20 Carbon Pl., Jersey City 07035

Freedom Metals, LLC
Phone—(973) 242-2119
960 Frelinghuysen Ave., Newark 07114

H & C Metals, Inc.
Phone—(973) 589-7778
91 Malvern St., P.O. Box 5150, Newark 07105

IESI Recycling Corp. (H Q)
Phone—(201) 443-3000
1099 Wall St. W., Ste. 250, Lyndhurst 07071

J & J Metals Trading, LLC
Phone—(732) 617-0500
26 Edie Dr., Marlboro 07746

JFD Associates, Inc.
Phone—(732) 751-9041
15 Railroad Ave., Farmingdale 07727

K & J Scrap Metal, Inc.
Phone—(201) 348-3368
609 25th St., Union City 07087

K-C International, LLC
Phone—(732) 202-9500
1608 Route 88, Ste. 301, Brick 08724

Lion Metals, Inc.
Phone—(201) 585-9191
2460 Lemoine Ave., Ste. 400-B, Fort Lee 07024

M & A Recycling
Phone—(908) 218-9191
65 Old Camplain Rd., Hillsborough 08844

Materials Reclaim Industries
Phone—(732) 979-3479
409 Joyce Kilmer Ave., Ste. 3, New Brunswick 08901

Mercer Group International, Inc.
Phone—(609) 393-4834
1519 Calhoun St., P.O. Box 5626, Trenton 08638

INDUSTRY

## SCRAP AND RECYCLED MATERIALS — Wholesale —
### (cont.)

Mid County Paper Stock, Inc.
Phone—(973) 786-7499
235 Brighton Rd., P.O. Box 624, Andover 07821

Park Stein, Inc.
Phone—(973) 340-3535
613 Route 46 E., P.O. Box 2399, Clifton 07013

Puggi Class B Recycling, A. J.
Phone—(609) 926-6991
6150 Mill Rd., Egg Harbor Township 08234

Ragonese & Sons, Inc., Patsy
Phone—(973) 344-7411
331 Adams St., Newark 07105

River Road Recycling Inc.
Phone—(856) 661-0770
450 37th St., P.O. Box 302, Pennsauken 08110

Rover & Son Iron & Steel Co., F.
Phone—(973) 484-7668
516 Central Ave., Harrison 07029

Safety-Kleen Systems, Inc.
Phone—(609) 859-2049
123 Red Lion Rd., Vincentown 08088

Schroth, Inc., Emil A.
Phone—(732) 938-5015
Yellowbrook Rd. & Copper Ave., Howell 07731

Sims Metal Management
Phone—(609) 396-0880
1511 Calhoun St., Trenton 08638

Specialty Disposal Services, Inc.
Phone—(973) 402-9246
115 Route 46, Bldg. E-37-38, Mountain Lakes 07046

Supreme Asset Management & Recovery, Inc.
Phone—(732) 370-4100
1950 Rutgers University Blvd., Lakewood 08701

Taylor Auto Parts
Phone—(973) 465-4345
222 Pacific St., Newark 07114

Trinity Recycling Of New Jersey
Phone—(973) 366-9199
116 Iron Mountain Rd., Mine Hill 07803

Unichem Industries, Inc.
Phone—(732) 463-8442
1 Bayberry Close, Piscataway 08854

**United Scrap Iron & Metal Co.**
Industrial, Commercial Scrap Iron & Metal
Phone—(973) 279-1683
Fax—(973) 279-1684
Web—www.unitedscrapironandmetal.com
Email—info@unitedscrapironandmetal.com
124 Wood St., Paterson 07524
*(see our ad under SCRAP IRON & METAL RECYCLING)*

Veolia Environmental Services
Phone—(973) 742-6789
27-33 Iowa Ave., Paterson 07503

Vinch Recycling, Inc.
Phone—(609) 393-0200
1607 N. Olden Ave., P.O. Box 55300, Trenton 08638

Vish Corp.
Phone—(201) 529-2900
200 State Route 17, Ste. 200-A, Mahwah 07430

Wade Environmental Industries
Phone—(856) 767-2760
382 Jackson Rd., Atco 08004

Win Laboratories, Ltd.
Phone—(732) 355-1355
182 Ridge Rd., Ste. D, Dayton 08810

## SCRAP IRON & METAL RECYCLING

A & A Iron & Metal Co., LLC
Phone—(201) 865-1370
2006 40th St., North Bergen 07047

### Need an IndustrySection for another state?
### Call us... 847-864-7590

---

Perone's Auto Service & Salvage
We Buy All Metals & Iron. 10-40 Yard Container Service For Demolition & Clean Ups
Phone—(732) 563-1630
Fax—(732) 563-1774
Web—www.peronesauto.com
Email—peronesauto@yahoo.com
371 US Highway 22, Green Brook 08812

**Since 1931**
*Perone's Auto Service & Salvage*
We Buy All Metals & Iron
10-40 Yard Container Service For Demolition & Clean Ups
**732.563.1630**
**FAX: 732.563.1774**
www.peronesauto.com
peronesauto@yahoo.com
371 U.S. Highway 22
Green Brook, NJ 08812

River Road Recycling Inc.
Metals Recycling Center
Phone—(856) 661-0770 / (856) 661-8181
Fax—(856) 661-8384
Web—www.riverroadrecycling.com
Email—chris@philametals.com
450 37th St., P.O. Box 302, Pennsauken 08110
*(see our ad under RECYCLING—Metal)*

Rover & Son Iron & Steel Co., F.
(FRSCO Corp.)
Phone—(973) 484-7668
Fax—(973) 484-9496
516 Central Ave., Harrison 07029

**F. Rover & Son Iron & Steel Co.**
(FRSCO Corp.)
Iron & Metal Scrap
973-484-7668 • Fax: 973-484-9496
516 Central Ave. Harrison, NJ 07029

**No Registration.**
**No Password.**
**No Hassle!**
*Source quickly & easily at*
**IndustryNet.com**

---

United Scrap Iron & Metal Co.
Industrial, Commercial Scrap Iron & Metal
Phone—(973) 279-1683
Fax—(973) 279-1684
Web—www.unitedscrapironandmetal.com
Email—info@unitedscrapironandmetal.com
124 Wood St., Paterson 07524

**United Scrap Iron & Metal Co.**
*Wholesaler of Recycled Scrap Iron & Metal*
www.unitedscrapironandmetal.com
**973-279-1683**
**Fax: 973-279-1684**
124 Wood St. Paterson, NJ 07524

## SCRAP METAL PROCESSING

Fortune Riverside Auto Parts, Inc.
Phone—(732) 381-3355
900 Leesville Ave., P.O. Box 1589, Rahway 07065

Matteo & Sons, Inc., James
Phone—(856) 845-0398
1692 Crown Point Rd., Thorofare 08086

River Road Recycling Inc.
Metals Recycling Center
Phone—(856) 661-0770 / (856) 661-8181
Fax—(856) 661-8384
Web—www.riverroadrecycling.com
Email—chris@philametals.com
450 37th St., P.O. Box 302, Pennsauken 08110
*(see our ad under RECYCLING—Metal)*

United Scrap Iron & Metal Co.
Industrial, Commercial Scrap Iron & Metal
Phone—(973) 279-1683
Fax—(973) 279-1684
Web—www.unitedscrapironandmetal.com
Email—info@unitedscrapironandmetal.com
124 Wood St., Paterson 07524
*(see our ad under SCRAP IRON & METAL RECYCLING)*

## SCREEN PRINTING

A & S Screen Printing, LP
Phone—(609) 267-4830
2305-B Garry Rd., Riverton 08077

A.B. Tees Screen Printing, LLC
Phone—(201) 239-0022
7 Sherman Ave., 3rd Fl., Jersey City 07307

A.C. Printed Sportswear, Inc.
Phone—(609) 344-5057
1319 Memorial Ave., Atlantic City 08401

A-1 Advanced Marking Technologies, LLC
Phone—(973) 627-0155
1420 Route 53, P.O. Box 485, Mount Tabor 07878

A2Z Emblems, LLC
Phone—(609) 239-9800
125 W. Route 130 N., Ste. C, Burlington 08016

Ace Screen Printing, LLC
Phone—(856) 881-1188
24 High St. W., Glassboro 08028

Action Screen Printing
Phone—(973) 209-2491
151 Main St., Franklin 07416

Adpro Imprints, Inc.
Phone—(732) 493-8555
3411 Rose Ave., Ocean 07712

AKA, Inc.
Phone—(908) 753-8112
1324 New Market Ave., South Plainfield 07080

## SCREEN PRINTING — (cont.)

All Nu Trophy & Screen Printing
Phone—(201) 807-0808
243 Teaneck Rd., Ridgefield Park 07660

All Sports Stadium, LLC
Phone—(908) 689-0411
297 Route 31 S., Washington 07882

Alpha T's, Inc.
Phone—(973) 956-7243
380 Totowa Rd., 2nd Fl., Totowa 07512

American Images, LLC
Phone—(856) 424-3944
1910 Fairfax Ave., Cherry Hill 08003

American Screen Printing
Phone—(973) 471-0206
272 Kent Ave., Wayne 07470

American Youth Enterprises, Inc.
Phone—(609) 909-1900
120 Marlin Ln., P.O. Box 653, Mays Landing 08330

Apollo East, Inc.
Phone—(856) 486-1882
7895 Airport Hwy., Pennsauken 08110

Apparel Group America, Inc.
Phone—(973) 942-6800
250 Belmont Ave., Haledon 07508

AQL Decorating Co., Inc.
Phone—(201) 941-1610
215 Bergen Blvd., Fairview 07022

Art Graphics
Phone—(856) 881-5029
54 Delsea Dr. N., Glassboro 08028

Artist Above The Rest
Phone—(609) 586-7247
4490 Nottingham Way, Trenton 08690

Atlantic Screenprinting
Phone—(201) 383-0995
339 Fairview Ave., Westwood 07675

Ayr Graphics & Printing, Inc.
Phone—(908) 241-8118
320 Chestnut St., Roselle Park 07204

Aztec Graphics, Inc.
Phone—(609) 587-1000
420 Whitehead Rd., Trenton 08619

Bad Dog T's
Phone—(201) 599-2030
498 Kinderkamack Rd., River Edge 07661

Balcis Screen Printing
Phone—(973) 835-9948
219 Wanaque Ave., Pompton Lakes 07442

Bankers Pen, Inc.
Phone—(800) 499-7367
141 Lanza Ave., Bldg. 12, Garfield 07026

Bergen Screen Printing, Inc.
Phone—(973) 595-1222
255 W. Broadway, Paterson 07522

Blue Streak Screen Printing Co.
Phone—(732) 656-0400
33 E. Railroad Ave., Monroe Township 08831

Branded Screen Printing, LLC
Phone—(908) 879-7411
45 Warren St., P.O. Box 687, Chester 07930

Brown & Co., Inc., Bill
Phone—(609) 396-9191
275 Whitehead Rd., Hamilton 08619

Camden Printworks
Phone—(856) 365-1424
1621 S. Broadway, Camden 08104

Campus Classics
Phone—(856) 234-7474
3206 Route 38, P.O. Box 757, Mount Laurel 08054

Campus Coordinates
Phone—(732) 866-6060
1711 Ginesi Dr., Ste. 1, Freehold 07728

Clarici Digital
Phone—(609) 587-7204
88 Youngs Rd., Mercerville 08619

Class Act Embroidery
Phone—(973) 394-0045
86 N. Beverwyck Rd., Ste. A, Lake Hiawatha 07034

Color Flo Graphics Corp.
Phone—(201) 525-0105
10 Dell Glen Ave., Ste. 1, Lodi 07644

Comp24, LLC
Phone—(201) 716-5200
190 Jony Dr., Carlstadt 07072

Cosmic Custom Screen Printing, LLC
Phone—(856) 629-8337
1629 N. Black Horse Pike, Williamstown 08094

Creative Embroidery Corp.
Phone—(973) 497-5700
305 3rd Ave. W., Ste. 3, Newark 07107

Creative Screen Design
Phone—(609) 424-3334
531 Route 68, P.O. Box 369, Columbus 08022

C-Sports
Phone—(856) 875-5680
2045 S. Black Horse Pike, Williamstown 08094

Custom Graphics, Inc.
Phone—(856) 691-7858
71 W. Landis Ave., Vineland 08360

Dead End Screen Prints, Inc.
Phone—(908) 754-4552
266 Lewis St., North Plainfield 07060

Deblyn Screen Printers
Phone—(908) 756-8459
717 Mountain Blvd., Watchung 07069

Decoration Design Solutions
Phone—(856) 589-1250
1299 W. Forest Grove Rd., Vineland 08360

DeMario Design & Screen Printing
Phone—(609) 645-7319
619 Church St., Pleasantville 08232

Dependabilities Screen Printing
Phone—(732) 886-0800
632 Hulses Corner Rd., Howell 07731

Designer T's
Phone—(856) 751-4545
1165 Marlkress Rd., Ste. F, Cherry Hill 08003

Design-N-Stitch, Inc.
Phone—(201) 488-1314
194 Atlantic St., Hackensack 07601

Designs By James
Phone—(856) 692-1316
892 N. Delsea Dr., Vineland 08360

Dezine Line, Inc.
Phone—(973) 989-1009
1104 Route 46 E., Ledgewood 07852

Dolly Screen Printing, Inc.
Phone—(732) 294-8979
1-19 Elm St., Freehold 07728

Dot Graphix, Inc.
Phone—(609) 660-0087
79 S. Main St., Ste. 13, Barnegat 08005

Dr. T-Shirt
Phone—(732) 223-3866
221 Parker Ave., Manasquan 08736

Eagle Embroidery & Graphix
Phone—(609) 561-1457
587 White Horse Pike, Hammonton 08037

Easy Prints, Inc.
Phone—(848) 229-2410
172 Main St., Metuchen 08840

Elmwood Industries
Phone—(201) 703-1220
8 Paul Kohner Pl., Elmwood Park 07407

EVR Screen Printing
Phone—(856) 794-8118
217 W. Peach St., Ste. 2, Vineland 08360

Excel Silk Screening
Phone—(609) 499-4990
2320 Old York Rd., Bordentown 08505

Expert Tees
Phone—(609) 828-0515
1585 Highway 73, Pennsauken 08110

Extreme Concepts, LLC
Phone—(732) 381-5100
75 E. Cherry St., Ste. 9-B, Rahway 07065

Falls Screen Printing, Inc.
Phone—(973) 812-0555
25 Amity St., Little Falls 07424

Family Screen Printing, Inc.
Phone—(856) 933-2780
104 W. Browning Rd., Bellmawr 08031

Finas Finishing, Inc.
Phone—(609) 267-4836
50 Stacy Haines Rd., Lumberton 08048

First Impressions Screen Printing
Phone—(732) 777-7872
1703 State Route 27, Edison 08817

Flying Fish Studio
Phone—(609) 884-2760
130 Park Blvd., Cape May 08204

Flying T-Shirts
Phone—(609) 463-0397
217 1st Ave., Cape May Court House 08210

G & M Printwear
Phone—(856) 742-5551
549 S. Broadway St., Gloucester City 08030

Gariel Screen Printing
Phone—(856) 848-3240
729 Mantua Pike, Woodbury 08096

Gem Sports
Phone—(201) 791-1776
36-10 Broadway, Fair Lawn 07410

Gilby's Screen Print
Phone—(973) 835-5729
615 Ringwood Ave., Pompton Lakes 07442

Harmony Printing
Phone—(732) 987-9040
504 Aldrich Rd., Ste. 22, Howell 07731

HC Graphics Screen Printing, Inc.
Phone—(973) 247-0544
238 Lindbergh Pl., Ste. 3, Paterson 07503

Hollie Studios
Phone—(908) 852-7263
200-C Valentine, P.O. Box 530, Hackettstown 07840

House Printing, LLC
Phone—(201) 772-5988
311 Kearny Ave., Kearny 07032

Ideal-Jacobs Corp.
Phone—(973) 275-5100
515 Valley St., Maplewood 07040

Image Screen Printing, Inc.
Phone—(732) 560-1817
532 Lincoln Blvd., Middlesex 08846

Imagepoint Screen Printing
Phone—(908) 684-1768
69 Water St., Newton 07860

Imprint Specialties, Inc.
Phone—(856) 456-2999
601 New Broadway, Brooklawn 08030

Imprintz Custom Printed Graphics, Inc.
Phone—(609) 386-5673
Garfield & Decatur Sts., P.O. Box 315, Beverly 08010

Infinite Print
Phone—(862) 668-3094
225 New York Ave., Jersey City 07307

Infinite Visions, LLC
Phone—(201) 866-6946
40 Enterprise Ave. N., Secaucus 07094

Initial Impact
Phone—(732) 449-4922
516 Warren Ave., Spring Lake 07762

InnerWorkings, Inc.
Phone—(732) 651-8822
7 Joanna Ct., Ste. H, East Brunswick 08816

J. R.'s Screen Printing
Phone—(973) 728-7802
1930 Greenwood Lake Tpke., P.O. Box 561, Hewitt 07421

JABS Personal Stitch, Inc.
Phone—(732) 396-9699
1120 Raritan Rd., Clark 07066

Jetty Life, LLC
Phone—(609) 296-2411
1435 Route 539, Unit A-6, Tuckerton 08087

Jill's Thrill, Inc.
Phone—(609) 395-9900
18 Hardley Dr., Cranbury 08512

Keltex Imprinted Apparel, Inc.
Phone—(609) 624-3252
428-A Woodbine Oceanview Rd., Ocean View 08230

KMBA Fashions, Inc.
Phone—(973) 789-1652
272 Elmwood Ave., Bldg. 3, East Orange 07018

Lettermen, Inc., The
Phone—(732) 608-0669
1565 Route 37 W., Toms River 08755

M&R Designs & Promotions
Phone—(908) 928-9400
21 Stone Oak Ln., Oak Ridge 07438

Mark Sports
Phone—(201) 437-9900
9 E. 31st St., Bayonne 07002

Maxtex, Inc.
Phone—(856) 767-7960
159 N. Cooper Rd., West Berlin 08091

Mayos Sportswear, Inc.
Phone—(201) 652-8570
1 Hollywood Ave., Bldg. 2-D, Ho-Ho-Kus 07423

Metro Printing & Promotions, LLC
Phone—(973) 316-1600
311 Mechanic St., Boonton 07005

Midland Screen Printing, Inc.
Phone—(201) 703-0066
280 N. Midland Ave., Bldg. H, Saddle Brook 07663

## SCREEN PRINTING — *(cont.)*

**MJ Corporate Sales, Inc.**
Phone—(856) 778-0055
109 W. Park Dr., Unit B, Mount Laurel 08054

**MJG Screen Printing & Embroidery**
Phone—(973) 575-8877
24 Commerce Rd., Ste. K, Fairfield 07004

**Modern Graphics**
Phone—(856) 728-6300
547 Cross Keys Rd., Ste. B, Sicklerville 08081

**Monogram Center**
Phone—(732) 442-1800
437 Amboy Ave., Perth Amboy 08861

**Murray's Uniforms, Inc.**
Phone—(732) 774-2671
312 Main St., Bradley Beach 07720

**New Jersey Logowear**
Phone—(609) 597-9400
100 McKinley Ave., Ste. 6, Manahawkin 08050

**Newton Trophy & Sport Center**
Phone—(973) 948-0613
1-3 Milk St., Bldg. 3, Branchville 07826

**Norgus Silk Screen Co.**
Phone—(973) 365-0600
58 Sylvan Ave., Clifton 07011

**Oasis Studios, LLC**
Phone—(908) 735-5089
244 Quakertown Rd., P.O. Box 306, Quakertown 08868

**Odd-It-Tees**
Phone—(609) 693-8337
405 S. Main St., Forked River 08731

**P. J. Screening & Embroidery**
Phone—(732) 382-5183
689 Jaques Ave., Rahway 07065

**Photo Art Stencil & Sign Corp.**
Phone—(732) 681-7300
701 17th Ave., P.O. Box 127, Lake Como 07719

**Pochet Of America, Inc.**
Phone—(973) 942-4923
415 Hamburg Tpke., Ste. 2, Wayne 07470

**Pro Image Promotions, Inc.**
Phone—(973) 252-8000
489 U.S. Highway 46, Kenvil 07847

**Professional Images, LLC**
Phone—(201) 569-4251
17 E. Linden Ave., Englewood 07631

**Promo Advertising**
Phone—(908) 810-8888
1174 Chestnut St., Union 07083

**Promo Graphics, Inc.**
Phone—(732) 629-7300
24 Howard St., Piscataway 08854

**Promotions & Unicorns Too, Inc.**
Phone—(732) 308-3444
71 W.Main St., Ste. 102, Freehold 07728

**Pro-Screen Printing, Inc.**
Phone—(201) 246-7600
590 Belleville Tpke., Bldg. 24, Kearny 07032

**R & D Promotions, Ltd.**
Phone—(732) 828-7408
164 Van Liew Ave., Milltown 08850

**Red Diamond Co., Inc.**
Phone—(973) 759-2700
368 Cortlandt St., Belleville 07109

**Reunion Gifts**
Phone—(877) 873-8646
20 Lowell Ave., Summit 07901

**RKM Enterprises, Inc.**
Phone—(609) 448-7539
177 Mercer St., Hightstown 08520

**Rocky's T's**
Phone—(856) 678-2535
61 N. Hook Rd., Pennsville 08070

**Rutler Screen Printing, Inc.**
Phone—(908) 859-3327
169 Belview Rd., Phillipsburg 08865

**S & P Tees**
Phone—(201) 996-1411
14 Frederick St., Hackensack 07601

**S & W Custom Screen Printing**
Phone—(908) 852-4808
147 Main St., Hackettstown 07840

**Screen Creations Plus**
Phone—(973) 579-5015
8 Hillside Ave., Newton 07860

**Screen Play, Inc.**
Phone—(973) 227-9014
1275 Bloomfield Ave., Ste. 5, Fairfield 07004

**Screen Reproductions Co., Inc.**
Phone—(201) 935-0830
850 Washington Ave., Carlstadt 07072

**Screening Base**
Phone—(973) 389-7950
245 W. Broadway, Paterson 07522

**Shelter Cove Embroidery Co.**
Phone—(732) 506-7700
1333 Bay Ave., Toms River 08753

**Sideline Sports**
Phone—(908) 322-9334
2566 Plainfield Ave., Scotch Plains 07076

**Smith Enterprises**
Phone—(215) 416-9881
8-A Deptford Rd., Glassboro 08028

**Smith Enterprises**
Phone—(215) 416-9881
Fax—(856) 608-9588
Web—www.smithentpromos.com
Email—dstees@comcast.net
100 Hillside Ln., P.O. Box 1433, Mount Laurel 08054

**Smitteez Sportswear**
Phone—(732) 787-5500
224 Main St., P.O. Box 274, Keansburg 07734

**Sonscreen Graphics, Inc.**
Phone—(908) 429-1657
77 Tillman St., Raritan 08869

**South Jersey Custom Screen Printing**
Phone—(856) 482-1500
481 W. Route 38, Maple Shade 08052

**South Jersey Graphics**
Phone—(856) 546-0464
203 W. Merchant St., Audubon 08106

**Special T's**
Phone—(908) 806-8337
12 Kings Ct., Flemington 08822

**Special-T-Graphics Of New Jersey, LLC**
Phone—(732) 899-7240
3105 Bridge Ave., Point Pleasant 08742

**Spoo, Inc.**
Phone—(201) 420-0075
225 NY Ave., Ste. 1, Jersey City 07307

**Sports Time**
Phone—(201) 768-1101
40 Oak St., Norwood 07648

**Stelair Design Corp.**
Phone—(732) 571-3391
570 Broadway, Long Branch 07740

**Steve's Screen Printing**
On site printing available
Phone—(732) 469-7670
Web—www.stevesscreenprinting.com
Email—ssp469@yahoo.com
660 Mitchell Ln., Martinsville 08836

**Stone Graphics Co., Inc.**
Phone—(732) 919-1111
5020 Industrial Rd., Farmingdale 07727

**Sun Embroidery Screen Printing Co.**
Phone—(609) 624-1231
12 Route 50, P.O. Box 349, Ocean View 08230

**Sun Tee, LLC**
Phone—(973) 812-0349
25 Amity St., Ste. 1, Little Falls 07424

**T D T Screen Design & Printing, Inc.**
Phone—(732) 777-1377
79 Whitehead Ave., South River 08882

**Tee Shirt Guy**
Phone—(973) 247-3442
507 E. 41st St., Paterson 07504

**Tees To Please Screen Printing**
Phone—(908) 788-5508
15 Minneakoing Dr., P.O. Box 542, Flemington 08822

**Too Many Stars**
Phone—(908) 445-8852
134 E. Westfield Ave., Roselle Park 07204

**Totally T Shirts & More**
Phone—(609) 894-0011
201 W. Hampton St., Pemberton 08068

**T-Rific Tees, LLC**
Phone—(908) 272-5140
100 N. 12th St., Ste. 2, Kenilworth 07033

**U. S. S. Corp.**
Phone—(973) 242-1110
780 Frelinghuysen Ave., Newark 07114

**Unique Screen Printing Corp., Inc.**
Phone—(908) 925-3773
1016 McKinley St., Linden 07036

**UniServ Advertising, Inc.**
Phone—(732) 774-1010
37 State Route 35 N., Neptune 07753

**Universal Silkscreen, Inc.**
Phone—(973) 221-0060
17 Memorial Dr., Paterson 07505

**University Fashions**
Phone—(856) 228-1615
1888 Winslow Rd., Bldg. B, Williamstown 08094

**Vacord Screen Printing**
Phone—(888) 787-4587
1621 S. Broadway, Camden 08104

**Valaro's Screen Printing**
Phone—(609) 597-7075
50 Mayetta Landing Rd., West Creek 08092

**Wagner Foto Screen Process**
Phone—(908) 624-0800
4 Mark Rd., Kenilworth 07033

**What A Tee 2, Inc.**
Phone—(201) 457-0060
82 Sussex St., Hackensack 07601

**Work 'N' Wear Store**
Phone—(973) 267-2373
73 Market St., Morristown 07960

**Works, The**
Phone—(908) 766-7744
17 Claremont Rd., Bernardsville 07924

**Yesterwear Productions, Inc.**
Phone—(609) 567-2544
705 Smithville Rd., Lumberton 08048

**Yippee Printing & Marketing**
Phone—(201) 313-1900
115 River Rd., Bldg. 10, Edgewater 07020

**Your Tops, Inc.**
Phone—(908) 272-0011
101 S. 21st St., Kenilworth 07033

**Zone Two, Inc.**
Phone—(732) 237-0767
245 Hickory Ln., Bayville 08721

---

## SCREEN PRINTING EQUIPMENT & SUPPLIES

**Andrus Screen Printing, LLC**
Phone—(908) 322-4299
1915 Church Ave., Scotch Plains 07076

**Hary Mfg., Inc.**
Phone—(908) 722-7100
24 Cokesbury Rd., Lebanon 08833

**Jessup, Inc., Charles**
Phone—(732) 324-0430
177 Smith St., Keasbey 08832

**Jessup, Inc., Charles M.**
Phone—(732) 324-0430
177 Smith St., Keasbey 08832

**Total Ink Solutions**
Plastisol, Supplies, Screens, Mesh, Press Wash & Color Match
Phone—(201) 487-9600 / (877) 937-6400
Fax—(201) 487-9620
Web—www.totalinksolutions.com
Email—marc@totalinksolutions.com
200 S. Newman St., Unit 4, Hackensack 07601
*(see our ad under INKS—Screen Print)*

---

## SCREENS — Aluminum

**Screens, Inc.**
Phone—(973) 633-8558
130 Ryerson Ave., Ste. 219, Wayne 07470

---

## SCREENS — Door & Window

**Screens & Fabricated Metals Corp.**
Phone—(973) 785-1414
1265 McBride Ave., P.O. Box 647, Woodland park 07424

---

## SCREW MACHINE PRODUCTS

**Accurate Screw Machine Corp.**
Phone—(973) 244-9200
10 Audrey Pl., P.O. Box 1065, Fairfield 07004

**Alben Metal Products**
Phone—(973) 279-8891
11 Iowa Ave., Paterson 07503

**Amark Industries, Inc.**
Phone—(973) 992-8900
18 Passaic Ave., Fairfield 07004

© Copyright 2015 Manufacturers' News, Inc. A193

## SCREW MACHINE PRODUCTS —
### (cont.)

BMB Fasteners, Inc.
Phone—(973) 256-4010
86 Lackawanna Ave., Ste. 208, Woodland Park
07424

**Congruent Machining Co., Inc.**
**Email: congruentmachine@yahoo.com**
**Phone—(973) 764-6767**
**Fax—(973) 875-8327**
**Web—www.congruentmachine.com**
**107 Maple Grange Rd., P.O. Box 888, Vernon**
**07462**

D & F Screw Machine Products, Inc.
Phone—(973) 887-1702
42 West St., East Hanover 07936

Deerfield Machine & Tool Co.
Phone—(973) 625-0505
23 Old Beach Glen Rd., Rockaway 07866

**E & J Machine And Tool, LLC**
**Phone—(973) 810-2312 / (973) 810-2313**
**Fax—(973) 601-7953**
**Web—www.ejmachine.com**
**Email—sales@ejmachine.com**
**12 Orben Dr., Unit 1, Landing 07850**
*(see our ad under JOB SHOPS)*

ESCO Precision, Inc.
Phone—(908) 722-0800
71 Old Camplain Rd., Hillsborough 08844

Ferrum Industries, Inc.
Phone—(201) 935-1220
735 Commercial Ave., Carlstadt 07072

Hi-Grade Products Mfg. Co.
Phone—(908) 245-4133
752 Jefferson Ave., P.O. Box 273, Kenilworth
07033

Howie Mfg. Co., Inc.
Phone—(856) 963-3560
1227 Mechanic St., Camden 08104

J & S Precision Co.
Phone—(609) 654-0900
16 Medford Evesboro Rd., Medford 08055

Johnson & Sons, Inc., S.
Phone—(908) 475-2155
1 Hardwick St., P.O. Box 66, Belvidere 07823

Johnson Engineering, Welton V.
Phone—(908) 241-3100
22 N. 26th St., Kenilworth 07033

Kearny Screw Machine Co.
Phone—(201) 998-4363
554 Elm St., Kearny 07032

Krug Industries Inc.
Phone—(973) 467-1040
65 Brown Ave., Springfield 07081

Maple Machine Co., Inc.
Phone—(609) 702-0975
Mount Holly Industrial Commons, Unit 9, Mount
Holly 08060

Salem Mfg. Co.
Phone—(973) 751-6331
115 Roosevelt Ave., Belleville 07109

Schmidt Mfg. Co., F. P.
Phone—(201) 343-4241
143 Leuning St., South Hackensack 07606

**Star-Glo Industries, LLC**
**Swiss machining & rubber molding for the welding,**
**electronics, packaging & military industries**
**Phone—(201) 939-6162**
**Fax—(201) 939-4054**
**Web—www.starglo.com**
**Email—gthomas@starglo.com**
**2 Carlton Ave., East Rutherford 07073**

**Star-Glo Industries, LLC**
*Swiss machining*
*& rubber-to-metal bonding*
**www.starglo.com • 201-939-6162**
2 Carlton Ave. East Rutherford, NJ 07073

Sumatic Co., Inc.
**Phone—(973) 772-1288**
**Fax—(973) 772-1927**
**Email—sumaticco@optonline.net**
**102 Dewitt St., P.O. Box 435, Garfield 07026**

---

Townsend Machine, Inc.
Phone—(609) 298-0400
246 Sykesville Rd., Chesterfield 08515

Valcar Precision Products, Inc.
Phone—(973) 838-7600
22 Park Pl., Butler 07405

Well Tech, Inc.
Phone—(908) 475-4539
1 Hardwick St., P.O. Box 66, Belvidere 07823

## SCREW MACHINE PRODUCTS —
### High Precision

Screw Machine Specialties
Phone—(732) 972-5400
50 U.S. Highway 9, Ste. 305, Morganville 07751

## SCREW MACHINE PRODUCTS —
### Swiss

Eastern Machining Corp.
Phone—(856) 694-3303
1197 Fries Mill Rd., Franklinville 08322

**H & H Swiss Screw Machine Products Co., Inc.**
**Email: bhardman@hhswiss.com**
**Phone—(908) 688-6390**
**Fax—(908) 688-3503**
**Web—www.hhswiss.com**
**Email—bhardman@hhswiss.com**
**1478 Chestnut Ave., Hillside 07205**

High Point Precision Products
Phone—(973) 875-6229
1 1st St., Sussex 07461

**Orion Precision Industries, Inc.**
**Phone—(732) 247-9704**
**Fax—(732) 828-8878**
**Web—www.orionprecision.com**
**Email—sales@orionprecision.com**
**8 Veronica Ave., Somerset 08873**

Quality Swiss Screw Machine Co., Inc.
Phone—(908) 654-1881
849 4th Ave., Elizabeth 07202

Quality Swiss Screw Machine Co., Inc.
Phone—(908) 654-1881
960 Mountain Ave., Mountainside 07092

Single Point Precision
Phone—(973) 625-7221
429 Rockaway Valley Rd., Ste. 2300, Boonton
07005

**Sumatic Co., Inc.**
**Phone—(973) 772-1288**
**Fax—(973) 772-1927**
**Email—sumaticco@optonline.net**
**102 Dewitt St., P.O. Box 435, Garfield 07026**

## SCREW MACHINING

**AGF Burner, Inc.**
**Phone—(732) 730-8090**
**Fax—(732) 730-8060**
**Web—www.agfburner.com**
**Email—sales@agfburner.com**
**1955 Swarthmore Ave., Unit 2, Lakewood**
**08701**
*(see our ad under GAS BURNERS)*

## SCREW MACHINING — CNC

Stanton Precision Products, LLC
Phone—(973) 838-6951
10 Park Pl., Bldg. 4, Butler 07405

## SCREWS
### (also see 'Fasteners')

ND Industries, Inc.
Phone—(201) 651-1500
128 Bauer Dr., Ste. 2, Oakland 07436

*Is your company properly*
*represented in the*
**IndustrySection?**

If not, call... 847-864-7590

---

Star Stainless Screw Co., Inc. (H Q)
Phone—(973) 256-2300
Fax—(973) 256-2423
30 W. End Rd., Totowa 07512

**Star Stainless Screw Co., Inc. (H Q)**
Screws
**(973) 256-2300**
**Fax: (973) 256-2423**
30 W. End Rd. Totowa, NJ 07512

## SCREWS — Socket Head, Cap

**EZ Sockets, Inc.**
**Standard & special alloy & stainless steel socket**
**screw products**
**Phone—(973) 376-5605 / (800) 631-7833**
**Fax—(973) 376-7130**
**Web—www.ezsockets.com**
**Email—ezsockets@juno.com**
**5 Cornell Pkwy., Springfield 07081**

## SCREWS, NUTS & BOLTS

Fastbolt Corp.
Phone—(201) 440-9100
200 Louis St., South Hackensack 07606

Ford Fasteners, Inc.
Phone—(201) 487-3151
110 S. Newman St., Hackensack 07601

Industrial Rivet & Fastener Co.
Phone—(201) 750-1040
200 Paris Ave., Northvale 07647

**Shallcross Bolt & Specialties Co.**
**The complete source for all your fastener needs**
**Phone—(908) 925-4700**
**Fax—(908) 925-8451**
**Web—www.shallcrossbolt.com**
**Email—info@shallcrossbolt.com**
**1 McCandless St., Linden 07036**
*(see our ad under BOLTS)*

## SCULPTURES

Sculpturesque, Inc.
Phone—(201) 573-9150
7 Etheridge Pl., Park Ridge 07656

## SEAFOOD — Wholesale

Azuma Foods International, Inc.
Phone—(201) 372-1112
20 Murray Hill Pkwy., Ste. 130, East Rutherford
07073

Bay Treasure Seafood, LLC
Phone—(732) 240-3474
2002 Lakewood Rd., Unit 4, Toms River 08755

Fishermans Dock Co-Op
Phone—(732) 899-1872
57 Channel Dr., P.O. Box 1314, Point Pleasant
Beach 08742

Mary Ellen Maryland Crabmeat Co., Inc.
Phone—(609) 645-0161
2613 Fire Rd., Egg Harbor Township 08234

**Off The Hook Seafood, LLC**
**Phone—(201) 444-8895**
**Fax—(201) 444-8896**
**Web—www.othseafood.com**
**Email—john@othseafood.com**
**126-A Greenwood Ave., Midland Park 07432**

**Point Lobster Co.**
**Phone—(732) 892-1718**
**Fax—(732) 892-3928**
**1 Saint Louis Ave., Point Pleasant Beach**
**08742**

True World Foods, LLC
Phone—(908) 351-1400
32-34 Papetti Plz., Elizabeth 07206

Viking Village, Inc.
Phone—(609) 494-0113
19th St. & Bayview Ave., P.O. Box 458, Barnegat
Light 08006

## SEAFOOD PROCESSING

**Atlantic Capes Fisheries, Inc.**
Phone—(609) 884-3000
Fax—(609) 884-3261
Web—www.atlanticcapes.com
Email—info@atlanticcapes.com
985 Ocean Dr., Cape May 08204

Bivalve Packing Co., Inc.
Phone—(856) 785-0270
6957 Miller Ave., P.O. Box 336, Port Norris 08349

Certified Clam Corp.
Phone—(732) 872-6650
190 Bay Ave., P.O. Box 383, Highlands 07732

Cuisine Innovations, LLC
Phone—(732) 730-9310
1920 Swarthmore Ave., Ste. 1, Lakewood 08701

Lagniappe Foods, Inc.
Phone—(973) 674-0498
546 Mitchell St., Orange 07050

**Lamonica Fine Foods**
Phone—(856) 825-8111
Fax—(856) 825-9354
Web—www.lamonicafinefoods.com
48 Gorton Rd., P.O. Box 309, Millville 08332

LM Foods, LLC
Phone—(732) 855-9500
100 Raskulinecz Rd., Carteret 07008

**Lund's Fisheries Co.**
Phone—(609) 884-7600
Fax—(609) 884-0664
Web—www.lundsfish.com
Email—info@lundsfish.com
997 Ocean Dr., P.O. Box 830, Cape May 08204

Moveable Feast, Inc.
Phone—(201) 939-4500
99 Grand St., Ste. 8, Moonachie 07074

**Off The Hook Seafood, LLC**
Phone—(201) 444-8895
Fax—(201) 444-8896
Web—www.othseafood.com
Email—john@othseafood.com
126-A Greenwood Ave., Midland Park 07432

Ruggiero Seafood, Inc.
Phone—(973) 589-0524
474 Wilson Ave., P.O. Box 5369, Newark 07105

**Snow's**
A Plant of Bumblebee Foods, Specializing in Clams Processing
Phone—(609) 884-0440 / (800) 459-0396
Fax—(609) 898-2409
Web—www.bumblebee.com
Email—larry.rossello@bumblebee.com
994 Ocean Dr., Cape May 08204

# Snow's
A Plant of Bumblebee Foods,
Speciazlizing in Clams Processing
**800-459-0396**
**609-884-0440**
FAX: 609-898-2409
994 Ocean Drive
Cape May, NJ 08204
www.bumblebee.com
larry.rossello@bumblebee.com

Sweet Water Seafood Corp.
Phone—(201) 939-6622
369 Washington Ave., Carlstadt 07072

## SEALANTS

Kenseal Construction Products Corp.
Phone—(973) 287-5858
799 Edwards Rd., Parsippany 07054

**Master Bond, Inc.**
Manufacturer of custom formulated adhesives for advanced applications
Phone—(201) 343-8983
Fax—(201) 343-2132
Web—www.masterbond.com
Email—main@masterbond.com
154 Hobart St., Hackensack 07601
*(see our ad under ADHESIVES)*

PRC-DeSoto International, Inc.
Phone—(856) 234-1600
823 E. Gate Dr., Unit 4, Mount Laurel 08054

**Specified Technologies Inc.**
Firestopping Products
Phone—(908) 526-8000 / (800) 992-1180
Fax—(908) 526-9623
Web—www.stifirestop.com
Email—sales@stifirestop.com
210 Evans Way, Somerville 08876
*(see our ad under FIRE PROTECTION SYSTEMS)*

**X-Pando Products, Inc.**
Phone—(609) 394-0150
Fax—(609) 989-4847
Web—www.xpando.com
Email—sales@xpando.com
500 Southard St., Trenton 08638

## SEALANTS — Acoustical

**Specified Technologies Inc.**
Firestopping Products
Phone—(908) 526-8000 / (800) 992-1180
Fax—(908) 526-9623
Web—www.stifirestop.com
Email—sales@stifirestop.com
210 Evans Way, Somerville 08876
*(see our ad under FIRE PROTECTION SYSTEMS)*

## SEALANTS — Silicone

Flexcraft Industries, Inc.
Phone—(973) 589-3403
390 Adams St., P.O. Box 2098, Newark 07114

## SEALING EQUIPMENT

**Prodo-Pak Corp.**
The Real Leader in Pouch & Tube Filling & Sealing Machinery, ideal for all liquids, creams, pastes & semi-viscous products
Phone—(973) 772-4500
Fax—(973) 772-0471
Web—www.prodo-pak.com
Email—sales@prodo-pak.com
77 Commerce St., P.O. Box 363, Garfield 07026

## SEALING EQUIPMENT — Carton

**Warwick Mfg. & Equipment Co., LLC**
Buy & sell used: Chemical, food, cosmetic, packaging & pharmaceutical equipment
Phone—(732) 729-0400 / (732) 241-9263
Fax—(732) 729-1235
Web—www.warwickequipment.com
Email—sales@warwickequipment.com
1112 12th St., North Brunswick 08902
*(see our ad Outside Back Cover)*

## SEALS

Allied Metrics Seals & Fasteners, Inc.
Phone—(973) 383-2487
2 Wilson Dr., Ste. 4, Sparta 07871

Colonial Seal Co.
Phone—(856) 432-0012
1114 Crown Point Rd., Westville 08093

Concept Group, Inc.
Glass to metal seals (hermetic packages) & Vacuum insulated components
Phone—(856) 767-5506
Fax—(856) 768-3981
Web—www.conceptgroupinc.com
Email—applications@conceptgroupinc.com
380 Cooper Rd., West Berlin 08091
*(see our ad under MACHINE PARTS — Precision)*

Electro Ceramic Industries
Phone—(201) 342-2630
75 Kennedy St., Hackensack 07601

**Hayes Pump, Inc.**
Pumps, filters, seals, control systems
Phone—(973) 808-0606 / (800) 343-5020
Fax—(973) 808-7311
Web—www.hayespump.com
Email—Customerservice@hayespump.com
295 Fairfield Ave., Fairfield 07004

 **Hayes Pump, Inc.**
*Quality Pumps*
**800-343-5020**
Flow solutions since 1898
973-808-0606 • FAX: 973-808-7311
295 Fairfield Ave. Fairfield, NJ 07004
www.hayespump.com Customerservice@hayespump.com

Hydraulic Packing & Seal Products
Phone—(856) 224-1120
1224 Forest Pkwy., P.O. Box 160, Paulsboro 08066

Mitronics Products, Inc.
Phone—(908) 647-5006
239 Morristown Rd., P.O. Box 196, Gillette 07933

S.S.P. Manufacturing, Inc.
Phone—(908) 852-3125
83 Spring Ln., Hackettstown 07840

Sterling Seal & Supply, Inc.
Phone—(732) 918-8004
1105 Green Grove Rd., Neptune 07753

U.S. Seal Mfg.
Phone—(732) 667-1100
400 Apgar Dr., Ste. A, Somerset 08873

## SEALS — Hermetic

Ametek Glasseal, Inc.
Phone—(732) 370-9100
485 Oberlin Ave. S., Lakewood 08701

Aspe, Inc.
Phone—(973) 808-1155
2 Daniel Rd. E., Fairfield 07004

**CinchSeal**
Established in 1994, CinchSeal® is a major manufacturer of rotary shaft seals for screw conveyors, ribbon blenders & all types of bulk handling equipment
Phone—(856) 662-5162
Fax—(856) 662-5264
Web—www.cinchseal.com
Email—jamato@cinchseal.com
731 Hylton Rd., Pennsauken 08110

Concept Group, Inc.
Glass to metal seals (hermetic packages) & Vacuum insulated components
Phone—(856) 767-5506
Fax—(856) 768-3981
Web—www.conceptgroupinc.com
Email—applications@conceptgroupinc.com
380 Cooper Rd., West Berlin 08091
*(see our ad under MACHINE PARTS — Precision)*

FRC Electrical Industries
Phone—(908) 464-3200
705 Central Ave., New Providence 07974

Harrison Seal Corp.
Phone—(908) 722-3322
1201 Kennedy Blvd., Manville 08835

## SEALS — Mechanical

Flowserve Corp.
Phone—(856) 241-7800
401 Heron Dr., P.O. Box 563, Bridgeport 08014

Frontline Industries, Inc.
Phone—(973) 373-7211
990 Chancellor Ave., Irvington 07111

**John Crane, Inc.**
Phone—(856) 241-3507
Fax—(856) 241-3531
Web—www.johncrane.com
Email—broot@johncrane.com
301 Berkeley Dr., Swedesboro 08085

*Do nationwide searches for products & services at:*
**IndustryNet.com**

## SEALS — Rotary

**CinchSeal**
Established in 1994, CinchSeal® is a major manufacturer of rotary shaft seals for screw conveyors, ribbon blenders & all types of bulk handling equipment
Phone—(856) 662-5162
Fax—(856) 662-5264
Web—www.cinchseal.com
Email—jamato@cinchseal.com
731 Hylton Rd., Pennsauken 08110

## SEALS — Rubber

APM Hexseal Corp.
Phone—(201) 569-5700
44 Honeck St., Englewood 07631
Quality Seals, Inc.
Phone—(908) 206-0410
2444 Morris Ave., Ste. 201, Union 07083
Seals Eastern, Inc.
Phone—(732) 747-9200
134 Pearl St., P.O. Box 520, Red Bank 07701

## SEALS — Shaft

**CinchSeal**
Established in 1994, CinchSeal® is a major manufacturer of rotary shaft seals for screw conveyors, ribbon blenders & all types of bulk handling equipment
Phone—(856) 662-5162
Fax—(856) 662-5264
Web—www.cinchseal.com
Email—jamato@cinchseal.com
731 Hylton Rd., Pennsauken 08110
TitanSeal, Inc.
Phone—(856) 582-7725
876 N. Lenola Rd., Ste. 3-E, Moorestown 08057

## SEASONINGS

Continental Seasoning, Inc.
Phone—(201) 837-6111
1700 Palisade Ave., P.O. Box 629, Teaneck 07666
**Kalustyan Corp.**
Spices, herbs & seasonings
Phone—(908) 688-6111
Fax—(908) 688-4415
Web—www.kalustyan.com
Email—kerri@kalustyan.com
855 Rahway Ave., Union 07083
Kerry Ingredients
Phone—(908) 782-4919
26 Minneakoning Rd., Flemington 08822
Nu Products Seasonings Co.
Phone—(201) 440-0065
74 Louis Ct., South Hackensack 07606
Sterling Food Flavorings, LLC
Phone—(732) 438-1620
182 Ridge Rd., Ste. G, Dayton 08810

## SEAT BELTS

Ortho Safe Systems International, Inc. (H Q)
Phone—(609) 587-3859
P.O. Box 9435, Trenton 08650

## SEATING

Infanti Brand Chair & Stools
Phone—(718) 447-5632
1153 W. Elizabeth Ave., Linden 07036
Majestic Industries, Inc.
Phone—(973) 473-3434
225 Passaic St., Passaic 07055

## SEATING — Automotive

E.W.E. Auto Seat Cover Co.
Phone—(201) 869-6470
8431 Kennedy Blvd., North Bergen 07047
Kisthardt Auto Products, LLC
Phone—(609) 434-0700
354 4th St., Ewing 08638
Tri-State Leather, Inc.
Phone—(908) 275-3310
504 4th Ave., Elizabeth 07202

## SEATING — Industrial

National Public Seating Corp.
Phone—(973) 594-1100
149 Entin Rd., Clifton 07014

## SEATING — Sports & Stadium

Archer Plastics, Inc.
Phone—(856) 692-0242
1510 Jesse Bridge Rd., Elmer 08318

## SEATING — Transportation

Union County Seating & Supply Co., Inc.
Phone—(908) 241-4949
121 N. Michigan Ave., Ste. E, Kenilworth 07033

## SECURITY GUARD SERVICES

**Building Security Services Inc.**
Phone—(973) 414-1111 / (800) 762-0029
Fax—(973) 414-0244
Web—www.buildingsecurity.com
Email—jferdinando@buildingsecurity.com
20 Valley St., Ste. 340, South Orange 07079
**Gateway Group One**
Phone—(973) 465-8006
604 Market St., Newark 07105

## SECURITY PRODUCTS

Ademco Distribution, Inc.
Phone—(856) 985-9050
1000 Lincoln Dr. E., Unit 4, Marlton 08053
Ketec, Inc.
Phone—(856) 778-4343
1256 N. Church St., Ste. A, Moorestown 08057
Mega Fortris Americas, Inc.
Phone—(732) 230-3015
3 Chris Ct., P.O. Box 934, Dayton 08810

## SECURITY SYSTEMS

Auto Clear, LLC
Phone—(973) 276-6161
2 Gardner Rd., Fairfield 07004
Avida, Inc.
Phone—(201) 802-0749
174-B Kinderkamack Rd., P.O. Box 2, Park Ridge 07656
Checkpoint Systems, Inc. (H Q)
Phone—(856) 848-1800
101 Wolf Dr., P.O. Box 188, Thorofare 08086
DAQ Electronics, LLC
Phone—(732) 981-0050
262 Old New Brunswick Rd., Ste. B, Piscataway 08854
**Diamond Electronics**
Phone—(609) 371-9500
Web—www.diamondelectronicsnj.com
299 Ward St., Ste. A, Hightstown 08520
ECSI International, Inc.
Phone—(973) 574-8555
790 Bloomfield Ave., Bldg. C-1, Clifton 07012
**G I Life Safety Systems**
Phone—(732) 642-7626
Fax—(609) 838-1902
Web—www.gilifesafetysystems.com
Email—mail@gilifesafetysystems.com
119 Paxson Ave., Trenton 08690
**Masi Electronics, Don**
Phone—(973) 618-6288
Email—dmedon@verizon.net
25 Walden Pl., West Caldwell 07006
National Protective Systems
Phone—(732) 922-3609
1 Meridian Rd., Eatontown 07724
Vanderbilt Industries
Phone—(973) 316-3900
2 Cranberry Rd., Parsippany 07054

*find additional suppliers at* **IndustryNet.com**

## SEEDS — Agricultural

**Greenway Seed Co.**
Phone—(201) 791-1122
Fax—(201) 791-6879
Email—greenwayseed@verizon.net
4-21 Banta Place, Fair Lawn 07410

## SEEDS — Bird

R World Enterprises
Phone—(201) 795-2428
197 Congress St., Jersey City 07307

## SEMICONDUCTOR EQUIPMENT & SUPPLIES

GCE Market, Inc.
Phone—(856) 401-8900
1001 Lower Landing Rd., Ste. 307, Blackwood 08012
Nanonex Corp.
Phone—(732) 355-1600
1 Deerpark Dr., Ste. O, Monmouth Junction 08852
Riber, Inc.
Phone—(732) 603-0680
15 Liberty St., Metuchen 08840
Rudolph Technologies, Inc.
Phone—(973) 691-1300
1 Rudolph Rd., P.O. Box 1000, Flanders 07836
Structured Materials Industries, Inc.
Phone—(732) 302-9274
201 Circle Dr. N., Unit 102-103, Piscataway 08854
Violin Memory, Inc.
Phone—(650) 396-1492
33 Wood Ave. S., 3rd Fl., Iselin 08830

## SEMICONDUCTORS

America Semiconductor, LLC
Phone—(908) 810-7364
2810 Morris Ave., Ste. 204, Union 07083
American Microsemiconductor, Inc.
Phone—(973) 377-9566
133 Kings Rd., P.O. Box 104, Madison 07940
Digitron Electronic Corp.
Phone—(908) 245-7200
144 Market St., Kenilworth 07033
Discovery Semiconductors, Inc.
Phone—(609) 434-1311
119 Silvia St., Ewing 08628
II-VI Advanced Materials
Phone—(973) 227-1551
20 Chapin Rd., Ste. 1007, P.O. Box 840, Pine Brook 07058
Ikanos Communications, Inc.
Phone—(732) 345-7500
100 Schultz Dr., Red Bank 07701
Intersil Corp.
Phone—(908) 685-6000
440 U.S. Highway 22 E., Ste. 100, Bridgewater 08807
IQE RF, LLC
Phone—(732) 271-5990
265 Davidson Ave., Ste. 141, Somerset 08873
**New Jersey Semiconductor Products, Inc.**
We are your source for all your semiconductor needs & requirements
Phone—(973) 376-2922 / (212) 227-6005
Fax—(973) 376-8960
Web—www.njsemi.com
Email—sales@njsemi.com
20 Stern Ave., Springfield 07081
NTE Electronics, Inc.
Phone—(973) 748-5089
44 Farrand St., Bloomfield 07003
**Solid State, Inc.**
Email: andrewl@solidstateinc.com
Your total solution source for electronic components
Phone—(973) 429-8700 / (800) 631-2075
Fax—(973) 429-1499
Web—www.solidstateinc.com
46 Farrand St., Bloomfield 07003
(see our ad under ELECTRONIC COMPONENTS)
Space Power Electronics, Inc.
Phone—(908) 689-6547
493 Westhill Rd., Glen Gardner 08826

## SENSORS

Advanced Cerametrics, Inc.
Phone—(609) 397-2900
245 N. Main St., P.O. Box 128, Lambertville 08530
Advanced Orientation Systems, Inc.
Phone—(908) 474-9595
2525 E. Brunswick Ave., Ste. 205, Linden 07036
**H. G. Schaevitz LLC**
**Phone—(856) 727-0250**
**102 Commerce Dr., Ste. 8, Moorestown 08057**
Heraeus Sensor Technology USA
Phone—(732) 940-4400
1901 U.S. Highway 130, North Brunswick 08902
Macro Sensors
Phone—(856) 662-8000
7300 Route 130 N., Bldg. 22, Pennsauken 08110
Mayfair Technology, LLC
Phone—(609) 802-1262
66 Witherspoon St., Princeton 08542
UTC Aerospace Systems-ISR Systems (Sensors Unlimited, Inc.)
Phone—(609) 520-0610
330 Carter Rd., Ste. 100, Princeton 08540

## SENSORS — Proximity

Fargo Controls, Inc.
Phone—(732) 389-3376
P.O. Box 539, Eatontown 07724

## SEPARATORS

Enviro-Clear Co., Inc.
Phone—(908) 638-5507
152 Cregar Rd., High Bridge 08829
New Jersey Meter Co.
Phone—(973) 345-6200
1 Hazel St., Woodland Park 07424

## SEPARATORS — Oil/Water

Admiral Filter Co.
Phone—(973) 948-3252
18 Green Pond Rd., Unit 3, Rockaway 07866
Mercer International, Inc.
Phone—(973) 543-9000
39 W. Main St., P.O. Box 540, Mendham 07945

## SERVICE STATION EQUIPMENT

**Indian Mills Pump & Tank Co.**
**Phone—(609) 268-0405**
**Fax—(609) 268-0929**
**Web—www.impumptank.com**
**Email—service@impumptank.com**
**907 Route 206, Shamong 08088**
**Michael Marra, Inc.**
**Petroleum Contractors**
**Phone—(732) 566-0444**
**Fax—(732) 566-9698**
**Web—www.marraconstruction.com**
**Email—mmi@marraconstruction.com**
**30-32 Industrial Dr., Keyport 07735**
*(see our ad under CONTRACTORS — Gas Stations)*

## SEWING CONTRACTORS

A & R Sewing Co., Inc.
Phone—(201) 332-0622
451 Communipaw Ave., Jersey City 07304
Creations By Mariola
Phone—(973) 808-9109
18 Riveredge Dr., Fairfield 07004
Spar-Tex Co., Inc.
Phone—(732) 367-4400
200 Lehigh Ave., Lakewood 08701

*Do nationwide searches for products & services at:*

**IndustryNet.com**

## SEWING MACHINE ATTACHMENTS

**Camatron Sewing Machine, Inc.**
**Industrial sewing machines for apparel & non-apparel markets**
**Phone—(201) 941-5116**
**Fax—(201) 941-4566**
**Web—www.camatron.com**
**Email—robertross@camatron.com**
**42 Bergenwood Rd., Ste. A, Fairview 07022**
Clinton Industries, Inc.
Phone—(201) 440-0400
207 Redneck Ave., Little Ferry 07643
Jesse J. Heap & Sons, Inc.
Phone—(973) 372-1559
576 S. 21st St., Irvington 07111
Sewmatic Attachments
Phone—(973) 290-9174
39 E. Hanover Ave., Morris Plains 07950

## SEWING MACHINES

**Camatron Sewing Machine, Inc.**
**Industrial sewing machines for apparel & non-apparel markets**
**Phone—(201) 941-5116**
**Fax—(201) 941-4566**
**Web—www.camatron.com**
**Email—robertross@camatron.com**
**42 Bergenwood Rd., Ste. A, Fairview 07022**
Imperial Sewing Machine Co., Inc.
Phone—(973) 374-3405
584 S. 21st St., Irvington 07111
New York Sewing Machine, Inc.
Phone—(201) 809-2009
8555 Tonnelle Ave., Unit 301, North Bergen 07047
Stony Brook Sew & Vacuums, Inc.
Phone—(609) 372-4018
191 U.S. Highway 130, Bordentown 08505

## SEWING MACHINES — Industrial

Beisler America, LLC
Phone—(908) 925-4040
1841 E. Elizabeth Ave., P.O. Box 1683, Linden 07036
Camatron Sewing Machine, Inc.
Phone—(201) 941-5116
42 Bergenwood Rd., Ste. A, Fairview 07022
Chandler Machine Co., Inc.
Phone—(212) 741-2474
400 Veterans Blvd., Carlstadt 07072
Consolidated Sewing Machine Corp.
Phone—(212) 741-7788
400 Veterans Blvd., Carlstadt 07072
Kansai Special American Machine Corp.
Phone—(973) 470-8321
1 Madison St., Ste. F-11, East Rutherford 07073
Newark Caplan Sewing Machine, Inc.
Phone—(973) 481-4400
858 Summer Ave., Newark 07104

## SEWING NOTIONS

Allary Corp. (H Q)
Phone—(908) 851-0077
2204 Morris Ave., Ste. 209, Union 07083

## SHAFTS

Daven Industries, Inc.
Phone—(973) 808-8848
55 Dwight Pl., Fairfield 07004
J R C Web Accessories, Inc.
Phone—(973) 625-3888
46 Passaic Ave., Fairfield 07004

## SHAFTS — Flexible

S.S. White Technologies, Inc.
Phone—(732) 474-1700
151 Old New Brunswick Rd., Piscataway 08854

*Search from among 430,000 U.S. manufacturers & suppliers:*

**IndustryNet.com**

## SHEDS — Storage

Laracca Mfg., Inc.
Phone—(973) 571-1452
395 Little Falls Rd., Cedar Grove 07009

## SHEET METAL ASSEMBLY

Jet Precision Metal, Inc.
Phone—(973) 423-4350
7 Schoon Ave., Hawthorne 07506

## SHEET METAL FABRICATION

A. B. Scantlebury Co.
Phone—(973) 770-3000
112 Kings Hwy., Landing 07850
Accurate Metal Fabrication, LLC
Phone—(201) 438-3733
28 John St., East Rutherford 07073
**ADM Custom Metal Fabrication, Inc.**
**Phone—(973) 284-0088**
**Web—www.admmetal.com**
**Email—info@admmetal.com**
**263 Hillside Ave., Ste. 2, Nutley 07110**

**ADM CUSTOM METAL FABRICATION, INC.**

**LATEST CNC TECHNOLOGY**
**LASER CUTTING**
**LIGHTS OUT FABRICATION**
**ROBOTIC WELDING**

GUARDS • PANELS • CONSOLES
CABINETS • TRANSITIONS • HOPPERS
FRAMEWORK • MACHINE BASES

**973-284-0088**

www.ADMmetal.com
info@admmetal.com

Air Group, LLC
Phone—(973) 887-5099
1 Prince Rd., Whippany 07981
Airside, Inc.
Phone—(973) 786-6967
246 Brighton Rd., Andover 07821
**Airtec, Inc.**
**Sheet metal fabrication, machining & laser cutting**
**Phone—(732) 382-3700**
**Fax—(732) 388-0084**
**Email—airtecunique@aol.com**
**17 W. Scott Ave., P.O. Box 1181, Rahway 07065**

**Airtec, Inc.**

*Sheet metal fabrication, machining & laser cutting*
(732) 382-3700 • Fax: (732) 388-0084
Email: airtecunique@aol.com
**17 W. Scott Avenue**
**Rahway, NJ 07065**

Alco Sheet Metal Fabricators, Inc.
Phone—(973) 772-7070
51 Chester St., Clifton 07011
Alpine Metal Products
Phone—(908) 753-4543
7 Progress St., Edison 08820
Altona Blower & Sheet Metal Work, Inc.
Phone—(201) 641-3520
23 N. Washington Ave., Little Ferry 07643
American Precision Sheet Metal Corp.
Phone—(732) 356-4306
84 Baekeland Ave., Middlesex 08846
Amerifab Corp., Inc.
Phone—(973) 777-2120
196 Garibaldi Ave., Lodi 07644

## SHEET METAL FABRICATION —
*(cont.)*

**B & S Sheet Metal Co., Inc.**
Phone—(973) 427-3739
60 5th Ave., Hawthorne 07506

**Babbitt Mfg. Co., Inc.**
Phone—(856) 692-3245
719 E. Park Ave., Vineland 08360

**Babinec Sheet Metal Works, Inc., Joseph**
Phone—(732) 388-6600
774 Martin St., Rahway 07065

**Bills, Inc., James W.**
Phone—(732) 212-1009
167 Newman Springs Rd., Ste. E, Shrewsbury 07702

**Bonland Industries, Inc.**
Phone—(732) 886-7127
890 Towbin Ave., Lakewood 08701

**Bonland Industries, Inc.**
Phone—(973) 694-3211
50 Newark Pompton Tpke., Wayne 07470

**Breure Sheet Metal Co., Inc.**
Phone—(973) 772-6423
46 Walman Ave., Clifton 07011

**Broadhurst Sheet Metal Works**
Phone—(973) 427-3972
230 Warburton Ave., Hawthorne 07506

**Brook Metal Products, Inc.**
Phone—(908) 355-1601
6 Evans Terminal, Hillside 07205

**C D S Sheet Metal, Inc.**
Phone—(856) 794-5080
1200 S. West Blvd., Ste. E, Vineland 08360

**C P S Metals, Inc.**
Phone—(856) 779-0846
450 S. Fellowship Rd., Maple Shade 08052

**Cambridge Sheet Metal, Inc.**
Phone—(973) 386-0788
14 Troy Hills Rd., Ste. 6, Whippany 07981

**Center Contracting Corp.**
Phone—(973) 523-6400
72 Putnam St., Paterson 07524

**Central Sheet Metal Fabricators, Inc.**
Phone—(732) 968-6100
897 South Ave., Ste. A, Middlesex 08846

**Chambers Sheet Metal, Bill**
Phone—(856) 848-4774
371 N. Glassboro Rd., P.O. Box 172, Woodbury Heights 08097

**Clifton Metal Products Co., Inc.**
Phone—(973) 777-6100
41 Clifton Blvd., Clifton 07011

**Coronation Sheet Metal Co., Inc.**
Phone—(908) 686-0930
2198 Stanley Ter., Union 07083

**Creative Metal Work, Inc.**
Phone—(973) 823-0408
4 Park Dr., P.O. Box 509, Franklin 07416

**Custom Cooling Services, LLC**
Phone—(609) 397-4448
99 Kingwood Stockton Rd., P.O. Box 457, Stockton 08559

**Custom Fabricators, Inc.**
Phone—(908) 862-4244
400 Commerce Rd., Linden 07036

**D'Amico Sheet Metal Works, Al**
Phone—(201) 339-1355
881 Broadway, Bayonne 07002

**Dec's Metal Fabrication, LLC**
Phone—(908) 281-0283
198 U.S. Highway Route 206, Bldg. 4, Ste. E, Hillsborough 08844

**Demand, LLC**
Phone—(908) 526-2020
36 S. Adamsville Rd., Bridgewater 08807

**Dericks Sheet Metal Works Co., Inc.**
Phone—(973) 256-1818
631 Union Blvd., Totowa 07512

**Diversatech, Inc.**
Phone—(609) 730-9668
1584 Reed Rd., Pennington 08534

**Ductworks, Inc.**
Phone—(908) 754-8190
434 W. Front St., Plainfield 07060

*Do nationwide searches for products & services at:*
**IndustryNet.com**

**Durex, Inc.**
Email: custserv@durexinc.com
ISO 9001 Registered Contract Metal Fabrication Facility
**Phone—(908) 688-0800**
**Fax—(908) 688-0718**
**Web—www.durexinc.com**
**5 Stahuber Ave., Union 07083**
*(see our ad under METAL FABRICATING)*

**Dutra Sheet Metal Co.**
Phone—(856) 692-8058
1940 S. West Blvd., Ste. E, Vineland 08360

**Eastern Sheet Metal & Plate Works, Inc.**
Phone—(908) 241-6766
169 E. Highland Pkwy., Roselle 07203

**ELMCO TWO, Inc.**
Phone—(856) 365-2244
1045 Cambridge St., Camden 08105

**Falcon Industries, Inc.**
Phone—(732) 563-9889
371 Campus Dr., Somerset 08873

**Franklen Sheet Metal Co., Inc.**
Phone—(732) 988-0808
122 S. Main St., Ocean Grove 07756

**Freehold Mfg. Assembly, Inc.**
Phone—(732) 224-9066
86 Birch Ave., P.O. Box 269, Little Silver 07739

**G & H Sheet Metal Works, Inc.**
**Phone—(973) 923-1100**
**Fax—(973) 923-8501**
**Web—www.ghsmw.com**
**Email—info@ghsmw.com**
**1423 Chestnut Ave., Hillside 07205**

**Gerard Sheet Metal Fabricators, Inc.**
Phone—(732) 257-4777
385 Lexington Ave., East Brunswick 08816

**Gild, Inc.**
Phone—(201) 398-0030
18-02 River Rd., Ste. 5, Fair Lawn 07410

**GP Precision, Inc.**
Phone—(908) 850-1940
434 Sand Shore Rd., Hackettstown 07840

**H & H Sheet Metal & Machining**
Phone—(973) 383-6880
30 White Lake Rd., Sparta 07871

**Hackettstown Sheet Metal, Inc.**
Phone—(908) 852-3752
1 Stiger St., Hackettstown 07840

**Haenssler Sheet Metal Works, Inc.**
Phone—(973) 373-6360
592 Hawthorne Ave., Newark 07112

**Halo Sheet Metal, Inc.**
Phone—(732) 901-0080
140 Lehigh Ave., Lakewood 08701

**Hutchton & Simon, Inc.**
Phone—(201) 487-1033
140 Atlantic St., Hackensack 07601

**Independent Sheet Metal Co., Inc.**
Phone—(973) 423-1150
233 Central Ave., Hawthorne 07506

**International Sheet Metal & Plate Mfg., Inc.**
Phone—(908) 722-6614
112 Veterans Memorial Dr. E., P.O. Box 5, Somerville 08876

**International Swimming Pools, Inc.**
Phone—(732) 565-9229
14-C Van Dyke Ave., New Brunswick 08901

**J & E Metal Fabricators, Inc.**
Precision Metal Fabrication Services
**Phone—(732) 548-9650**
**Fax—(732) 548-9589**
**Web—www.metalfab.com**
**Email—je@metalfab.com**
**1 Coan Pl., Metuchen 08840**

**Jason Metal Products Corp.**
Phone—(732) 396-1132
1072 Randolph Ave., Rahway 07065

**Jenkins Plumbing & Heating**
Phone—(609) 641-6262
103 S. Franklin, P.O. Box 509, Pleasantville 08232

**Jersey Sheet Metal & Machine, Inc.**
Phone—(973) 366-0101
90 E. Dickerson St., Dover 07801

**Jewel Precision Sheet Metal Machining, Inc.**
Phone—(973) 857-5545
200 Commerce Rd., Cedar Grove 07009

**K L M Mechanical Contractors, Inc.**
Phone—(201) 385-6965
109 W. Shore Ave., Dumont 07628

**Kalis Metal Components Corp.**
Phone—(908) 789-0500
231 North Ave., P.O. Box 294, Garwood 07027

**Kearny Sheet Metal Works, Inc.**
**Phone—(201) 991-4745**
**579 Davis Ave., Kearny 07032**

**Kiker Sheet Metal Corp.**
Phone—(609) 641-4890
6 S. New Rd., P.O. Box 1487, Pleasantville 08232

**Laursen Sheet Metal**
Phone—(732) 349-2821
69 Flint Rd., Toms River 08757

**Leary Heating & Air Conditioning, Inc., Bill**
Phone—(732) 494-9200
6 Green St., Metuchen 08840

**Leibrock Metal Products, Inc.**
Phone—(732) 695-0326
1800 Brielle Ave., Asbury Park 07712

**Lentine Sheet Metal, Inc.**
Phone—(908) 486-8974
1210 E. Elizabeth Ave., Linden 07036

**Link Burns Mfg. Co., Inc.**
Phone—(856) 429-6844
253 American Way, Voorhees 08043

**M C Custom Sheet Metal Fabrication, Inc.**
Phone—(856) 767-9509
215-E Old Egg Harbor Rd., Ste. E, West Berlin 08091

**Max Gurtman & Sons, Inc.**
Phone—(973) 478-7000
622 Lexington Ave., Clifton 07011

**Metal Dynamix, LLC**
Phone—(856) 235-4559
709 Fellowship Rd., Mount Laurel 08054

**Mid States Spiral, Inc.**
Phone—(215) 744-2846
1425 Grandview Ave., West Deptford 08066

**Millar Sheet Metal**
Phone—(201) 997-1990
39 Rizzolo Rd., Kearny 07032

**Neumann Sheet Metal, Inc.**
Phone—(908) 756-0415
759 North Ave., Plainfield 07062

**New Age Metal Fabricating Co.**
Phone—(973) 227-9107
26 Daniel Rd., Fairfield 07004

**Nordic Metal, LLC**
Phone—(908) 245-8900
500 S. 31st St., Kenilworth 07033

**Northeast Sheet Metal, LLC**
Phone—(973) 853-0500
870 Warwick Tpke., Hewitt 07421

**Omega Metal Works, Inc.**
Phone—(609) 298-9100
41 Stelle Rd., Chesterfield 08515

**P T L Sheet Metal, Inc.**
Phone—(201) 501-8700
70 Davies Ave., Dumont 07628

**Pabst Enterprises Equipment Co., Inc.**
Phone—(908) 353-2880
676 Pennsylvania Ave., Elizabeth 07201

**Par Sheet Metal, Inc.**
Phone—(908) 241-2477
220 W. 1st Ave., Ste. 2, Roselle 07203

**Park Roofing & Sheet Metal Co., Inc.**
Phone—(732) 257-4570
427 Whitehead Ave., Ste. 1, South River 08882

**Parr Leadburning Co., J. W.**
Phone—(973) 256-8093
87 Parkway, Little Falls 07424

**Par-Troy Sheet Metal & Conditioning, LLC**
Phone—(973) 227-1150
122 Clinton Rd., Fairfield 07004

**Passaic County Welders, Inc.**
Two northern New Jersey plants, with 45,000 sq. ft. of manufacturing area, producing a wide range of custom products, including plate, structural, sheet & bar products in carbon steel, stainless steel & aluminum
**Phone—(973) 696-1200**
**Fax—(973) 696-1411**
**Web—www.pcwfab.com**
**Email—robert@pcwfab.com**
**100 Parish Dr., Wayne 07470**
*(see our ad under STEEL FABRICATING)*

**Paterson Sheet Metal Works, Inc.**
Phone—(973) 345-4182
320 Wabash Ave., Paterson 07503

**Pemberton Fabricators, Inc.**
Phone—(609) 267-0922
30 Indel Ave., P.O. Box 227, Rancocas 08073

**Precision Metalcrafters, Inc.**
Phone—(856) 629-1020
17 Filbert St., Williamstown 08094

**INDUSTRY**

# Handi-Hut, Inc.

**Smoking Shelters, Bus Stop Passenger Shelters, Entry Canopies & Bicycle Shelters & Racks**

## www.handi-hut.com

## 973-614-1800 • Fax: 973-614-8011

### 3 Grunwald Street  Clifton, NJ 07013

## SHEET METAL FABRICATION —
*(cont.)*

R & L Sheet Metal Co.
Phone—(973) 575-8448
3 Kulick Rd., Fairfield 07004

Ranco Precision Sheet Metal, Inc.
Phone—(973) 472-8808
40 Colorado St., P.O. Box 1101, Clifton 07014

Ricklyn Co., Inc.
Phone—(908) 689-6770
460 Route 57, Port Murray 07865

Sander Mechanical Service, Inc.
Phone—(732) 560-0600
55 Columbia Rd., Ste. 1, Branchburg 08876

Service Metal Fabricating, Inc.
Phone—(973) 625-8882
10 Stickle Ave., Rockaway 07866

Shamong Mfg. Co., Inc.
Phone—(609) 654-2549
33 Bunker Hill Rd., Shamong 08088

Sheet Metal Products, Inc.
Phone—(973) 482-0450
794 N. 6th St., Newark 07107

Sperro Metal Products, LLC
Phone—(973) 335-2000
2 Skyline Dr., P.O. Box 397, Montville 07045

SSM Industries, Inc.
Phone—(856) 345-2525
1425 Grandview Ave., West Deptford 08066

Stan Catering Trucks, Inc.
Phone—(973) 253-0556
15 Circle Ave., Clifton 07011

Star Metal Products, Inc.
Phone—(908) 474-9860
1125 W. Elizabeth Ave., Linden 07036

Steck, Inc., Paul C.
Phone—(973) 376-1830
25 Brown Ave., Springfield 07081

Technimetal
Phone—(973) 428-2881
7 Melanie Ln., Ste. 3, East Hanover 07936

Toms River Sheet Metal Co.
Phone—(732) 244-2880
400 Corporate Cir., Toms River 08755

**TORNQVIST**
**Phone—(973) 686-5999**
**29 Hanes Dr., Wayne 07470**

Total Maintenance & Service, Inc.
Phone—(973) 283-0048
121 Hamburg Tpke., Bloomingdale 07403

Trenton Sheet Metal
Phone—(609) 695-6328
30 Adam Ave., Trenton 08618

United Support Solutions, Inc.
Phone—(973) 857-2298
134 Sand Park Rd., Cedar Grove 07009

Vee Dennis Mfg. Co.
Phone—(856) 428-7676
620 Park Rd., Cherry Hill 08034

VFI Fabricators, Inc.
Phone—(856) 629-8786
300 Thomas Ave., Bldg. 1, Ste. 101, Williamstown 08094

Westfield Sheet Metal Works, Inc.
Phone—(908) 276-5500
261 Monroe Ave., P.O. Box 128, Kenilworth 07033

Wilbur Sheet Metal, Inc.
Phone—(609) 393-5952
27 Ward Ave., P.O. Box 3681, Trenton 08609

## SHEET METAL FABRICATION — Precision

ADM Custom Metal Fabrication, Inc.
Phone—(973) 284-0088
Web—www.admmetal.com
Email—info@admmetal.com
263 Hillside Ave., Ste. 2, Nutley 07110

### ADM CUSTOM METAL FABRICATION, INC.

**LATEST CNC TECHNOLOGY**
**LASER CUTTING**
**LIGHTS OUT FABRICATION**
**ROBOTIC WELDING**

GUARDS • PANELS • CONSOLES
CABINETS • TRANSITIONS • HOPPERS
FRAMEWORK • MACHINE BASES

## 973-284-0088
www.ADMmetal.com
info@admmetal.com

Atlantic Air Enterprises
Phone—(732) 381-4000 / (800) 899-4279 / (732) 381-4016
Fax—(732) 499-0122
Web—www.atlanticairent.com
Email—contactus@atlanticairent.com
856 Elston St., Rahway 07065

Bayshore Metal Products, Inc.
Phone—(732) 739-9260
120 Francis St., Ste. 6, Keyport 07735

D & N Machine Mfg., Inc.
Phone—(856) 456-1366
334 Nicholson Rd., P.O. Box 67, Gloucester City 08030

Durex, Inc.
Email: custserv@durexinc.com
ISO 9001 Registered Contract Metal Fabrication Facility
Phone—(908) 688-0800
Fax—(908) 688-0718
Web—www.durexinc.com
5 Stahuber Ave., Union 07083
*(see our ad under METAL FABRICATING)*

Edker Industries, Inc.
Phone—(856) 786-1971
1401 Union Landing Rd., Cinnaminson 08077

EVS Metal
Phone—(973) 839-4432
Fax—(973) 839-4440
Web—www.evsmetal.com
Email—sales@evsmetal.com
1 Kenner Ct., Riverdale 07457

General Aviation & Electronics Mfg. Co., Inc.
Phone—(201) 487-1700
30 Jersey Pl., Hackensack 07601

GP Precision, Inc.
ISO 9001:2000 Certified
Phone—(908) 850-1940
Fax—(908) 850-5926
Web—www.gpsheetmetal.com
Email—sales@gpsheetmetal.com
434 Sand Shore Rd., Hackettstown 07840

J & E Metal Fabricators, Inc.
Precision Metal Fabrication Services
Phone—(732) 548-9650
Fax—(732) 548-9589
Web—www.metalfab.com
Email—je@metalfab.com
1 Coan Pl., Metuchen 08840

Kinetron, Inc.
Phone—(732) 918-7777
1416 S. Roller Rd., Ocean 07712

Magic Metal Works, Inc.
Phone—(201) 384-8457
40 W. Englewood Ave., Bergenfield 07621

Medin Corp.
Phone—(973) 779-2400
11 Jackson Rd., Totowa 07512

Nordt Precision Metal Mfg., Inc.
Phone—(856) 931-7444
Fax—(856) 931-2366
Email—metalfab@northprecision.com
640 Creek Rd., Bellmawr 08031

Schrader & Co., Inc.
Phone—(973) 579-2700
188 Halsey Rd., Newton 07860

Sonrise Metal, Inc.
Phone—(973) 423-4717
138 3rd Ave., Paterson 07514

Tam Metal Products, Inc.
Phone—(201) 848-7800
55 Whitney Rd., Mahwah 07430

WECOM, Inc.
Phone—(856) 863-8400
20 Warrick Ave., Glassboro 08028

## SHEET METAL MACHINERY

R.P. Machine, LLC
Phone—(973) 383-8994
906 Stillwater Rd., P.O. Box 144, Stillwater 07875

## SHEET METAL PRODUCTS

Jen-Cyn Enterprises, Inc.
Phone—(856) 541-7400
407 Atlantic Ave., Camden 08104

## SHEET MUSIC

Subito Music Corporation
Phone—(973) 857-3440
60 Depot St., Verona 07044

## SHEETS — Bed
**(also see 'Bedding')**

Golden Sheets Mfg.
Phone—(973) 925-2242
239 6th Ave., Paterson 07524

## SHELTERS

Handi-Hut, Inc.
Smoking shelters, bus stop passenger shelters, entry canopies & bicycle shelters & racks
Phone—(973) 614-1800 / (800) 603-6635
Fax—(973) 614-8011
Web—www.handi-hut.com
Email—staff@handi-hut.com
3 Grunwald St., Clifton 07013
*(also see our ad under CANOPIES — Metal)*
*(see our ad on this page)*

## SHELVING

NMN Closet, Inc.
Phone—(201) 964-9600
40 Veterans Blvd., Carlstadt 07072

SpaceNow! Corporation
Phone—(973) 504-8585
234 Emmet St., Newark 07114

## SHELVING — Steel

Handy Store Fixtures, Inc.
Phone—(973) 242-1600
337 Sherman Ave., Newark 07114

## SHELVING — Wire

K C S Metal Products, Inc.
Phone—(973) 578-2688
415 Ferry St., Newark 07105

## SHIELDING — Electromagnetic

Parker Chomerics
Phone—(908) 272-5500
135 Bryant Ave., Cranford 07016

## SHIELDING — EMI/RFI

**Bridgeview Industrial Finishers, Inc.**
**Serving Camden, Burlington, Gloucester Counties NJ**
**& Philadelphia Areas**
**Phone—(856) 768-3624**
**Fax—(856) 768-2218**
**Web—www.bvfinishers.com**
**241 Terrace Blvd., Voorhees 08043**
*(see our ad under POWDER COATING)*

Global Partners In Shielding, Inc.
Phone—(973) 574-9077
90 Dayton Ave., Ste. 13, Passaic 07055

G-O-Metric, Inc.
Phone—(856) 461-8080
215 Ash St., Delanco 08075

**Ja-Bar Silicone Corp.**
**Since 1965, mfg. specialty Silicone Elastomer Seals**
**to Mil, Federal, AMS, SAF or customer specifications.**
**Quality control system approved for Mil-I-45208.**
**Serving the Automotive, Aerospace, Commercial &**
**Medical Industries. ISO 9001:2008**
**Phone—(973) 786-5000**
**Fax—(973) 786-5546**
**Web—www.ja-bar.com**
**Email—info@ja-bar.com**
**252 Brighton Rd., P.O. Box 1249, Andover**
**07821**
*(see our ad under GASKET MATERIALS)*

Omega Shielding Products, Inc.
Phone—(973) 366-0080
9 Emery Ave., Randolph 07869

**Specialty Rubber, Inc.**
**A Veteran Owned Company**
**Phone—(609) 704-2555 / (800) 249-5848**
**Fax—(609) 704-8020**
**Web—www.specialtyrubber.com**
**Email—specrub@yahoo.com**
**4500 White Horse Pike, P.O. Box 483, Elwood**
**08217**
*(also see our ads under DIE CUTTING & GASKETS — Rubber)*

**Speciality Rubber, Inc.**
*A Veteran Owned Company*
**(800) 249-5848**
**(609) 704-2555 • Fax (609) 704-8020**
**www.specialtyrubber.com**
**specrub@yahoo.com**
4500 White Horse Pike, P.O. Box 483 • Elwood, NJ 08217

## SHIMS

Artus Corp.
Phone—(201) 568-1000
201 S. Dean St., P.O. Box 511, Englewood 07631

**Wm. H. Brewster Jr., Inc.**
**Email: sales@brewster-washers.com**
**Manufacturing Precision Parts Since 1919; Made in**
**U.S.A.**
**Phone—(973) 227-1050**
**Fax—(973) 227-2363**
**Web—www.brewster-washers.com**
**16 Kulick Rd., Fairfield 07004**
*(see our ad Outside Front Cover)*

*find additional suppliers at*
**IndustryNet.com**

## SHIP CONVERSION & REPAIR

Union Dry Dock & Repair Co., Inc.
Phone—(201) 792-9090
901 Sinatra Dr., P.O. Box M-1539, Hoboken
07030

## SHIPBUILDING

Bayonne Dry-Dock & Repair, Inc.
Phone—(201) 823-9295
Military Ocean Terminal Dock Yard, P.O. Box 240,
Bayonne 07002

Dorchester Shipyard, Inc.
Phone—(856) 785-8040
13 Front St., P.O. Box 600, Dorchester 08316

Master Shipwrights, Inc.
Phone—(732) 872-7500
25 W. Highland Ave., P.O. Box 273, Atlantic
Highlands 07716

## SHIPPING CONTAINERS

Sea Box, Inc.
Phone—(856) 303-1101
700 Union Landing Rd., 1 Sea Box Dr.,
Cinnaminson 08077

## SHIPPING CONTAINERS — Wooden

**Jan Packaging, Inc.**
**100 Harrison St., Dover 07801**
**Email: kcaristia@janpackaging.com**
**Toll Free Ph: (888)4-JANPAK**
**Phone—(973) 361-7200**
**Fax—(973) 361-3306**
**Web—www.janpackaging.com**
**P.O. Box 448, Dover 07802**
*(see our ad under PACKAGING—Industrial)*

## SHIPPING ROOM SUPPLIES

Nifty Products
Phone—(732) 591-1140
4 Jocama Blvd., Old Bridge 08857

## SHIRTS — Custom

Gambert Shirts, LLC, L.
Phone—(973) 344-3440
61 Freeman St., 5th Fl., Newark 07105

Skip Gambert & Assocs., Inc.
Phone—(973) 344-3373
436 Ferry St., Ste. 2, Newark 07105

## SHIRTS — Men's

Individualized Shirts, Inc.
Phone—(732) 826-8400
581 Cortland St., Perth Amboy 08861

## SHIRTS — Women's

Krazy Kat Sportswear, LLC
Phone—(201) 438-3399
100 Triangle Blvd., Carlstadt 07072

## SHOE MFG. EQUIPMENT & SUPPLIES

Stanbee Co., Inc.
Phone—(201) 933-9666
70 Broad St., P.O. Box 436, Carlstadt 07072

## SHOES

AeroGroup International, Inc. (H Q)
Phone—(732) 985-6900
201 Meadow Rd., Edison 08817

**Carlascio Orthopedics**
**Phone—(973) 340-6500**
**Web—www.carlascioorthopedics.com**
**1094 Main Ave., Apt. 1, Clifton 07011**

**Carlascio Orthopedics**
**Phone—(201) 333-8716**
**Fax—(201) 200-9391**
**Web—www.carlascioorthopedics.com**
**283 Grove St., Jersey City 07302**

Carrini, Inc. (H Q)
Phone—(732) 650-1775
140 Smith St., 5th Fl., Keasbey 08832

Tingley Rubber Corp.
Phone—(908) 757-7474
1551 S. Washington Ave., Ste. 403, Piscataway
08854

## SHOES — Wholesale

Josmo Shoes, Inc.
Phone—(201) 617-1477
601 59th St., West New York 07093

## SHOOTING RANGE EQUIPMENT

Newbold, Inc.
Phone—(732) 469-5654
200 Egel Ave., Middlesex 08846

Rockwood Corp. / Speedwell Targets
Phone—(908) 355-8600
410 Clermont Ter., Ste. D, Union 07083

## SHOWCASES

Kubik Maltbie, Inc.
Phone—(856) 234-0052
7000 Commerce Pkwy., Ste. C, Mount Laurel
08054

## SHOWER PRODUCTS

Jaclo Industries
Phone—(908) 653-4433
129 Dermody St., Cranford 07016

## SHREDDERS — Industrial

**Franklin Miller, Inc.**
**Phone—(973) 535-9200**
**Fax—(973) 535-6269**
**Web—www.franklinmiller.com**
**Email—info@franklinmiller.com**
**60 Okner Pkwy., P.O. Box 070663, Livingston**
**07039**

*(see our ad under CRUSHERS)*

## SHREDDING SERVICES

**DocuVault Delaware Valley LLC**
**Phone—(856) 853-5160**
**Fax—(856) 853-5164**
**Web—www.docuvaultdv.com**
**Email—customerservice@docuvaultdv.com**
**1240 Forest Pkwy., Ste. 100, West Deptford**
**08066**

## SHRINK WRAP MATERIALS

**Hillside Plastics Corp.**
**Phone—(800) 837-7731**
**Fax—(973) 923-2056**
**Web—www.hillsideplasticscorp.com**
**Email—maria@hillsideplastics.net**
**125 Long Ave., P.O. Box 609, Hillside 07205**

## SHRINK WRAPPING MACHINES

National Shrinkwrap
Phone—(732) 942-4554
6220 U.S. Highway 9, Howell 07731

*Search from among*
*430,000 U.S. manufacturers*
*& suppliers at*
**IndustryNet.com**

INDUSTRY

## SIDING CONTRACTORS

**All Professional Remodeling Group, LLC**
Toll Free Ph: (888)919-ROOF; Second Generation Roofing Contractor
**Phone—(973) 857-9449 / (888) 919-7663**
**Fax—(973) 857-0991**
**Web—**
**www.allprofessionalremodelinggroup.com**
**Email—aprgllc@aol.com**
**P.O. Box 215, Cedar Grove 07009**
*(see our ad under ROOFING CONTRACTORS)*

## SIFTING & SCREENING EQUIPMENT

Kason Corp.
Phone—(973) 467-8140
67-71 E. Willow St., Millburn 07041

## SIGN INSTALLATION

**Cranez, Inc.**
For more than 20 yrs., serving the Tri-State area. Offering free no-obligation est.; providing svc. 24 hrs., 7 days a week & no-cost site checks. Operators are CCO/Natnl. Commission certified, have TWIC credentials & O.S.H.A 30-hrs trained
**Phone—(856) 262-0288 / (877) 262-0288**
**Fax—(856) 262-2654**
**Web—www.cranezincnj.com**
**Email—cranez06@aol.com**
**2610 S. Black Horse Pike, Williamstown 08094**

## SIGN LETTERS

American Plastic Co.
Phone—(732) 388-1601
2137 Highway 1, Rahway 07065
Budget Signs
Phone—(973) 340-2086
8 Caroline Ave., Clifton 07011

## SIGN MAKING MACHINERY

**Ultraflex Systems, Inc. (H Q)**
**Phone—(973) 627-8608**
**Fax—(973) 627-8506**
**Web—www.ultraflexx.com**
**Email—info@ultraflexx.com**
**1578 Sussex Tpke., Ste. 400, Randolph 07869**

## SIGN SUPPLIES

Tube Light Co., Inc. (H Q)
Phone—(201) 641-6660
300 Park St., Moonachie 07074
**Ultraflex Systems, Inc. (H Q)**
**Phone—(973) 627-8608**
**Web—www.ultraflexx.com**
**Email—info@ultraflexx.com**
**1578 Sussex Tpke., Ste. 400, Randolph 07869**

## SIGN SYSTEMS

Lehigh Utility Assocs., Inc.
Phone—(908) 561-5252
1300 New Market Ave., P.O. Box 398, South Plainfield 07080

## SIGNAGE

A & F Sign Company LLC
Phone—(973) 278-3707
28 E. Railway Ave., Paterson 07503
**Infinite Manufacturing Group, Inc.**
Email: a.moses@infinitegroupusa.com
**Phone—(973) 649-9950**
**Web—www.infinitegroupusa.com**
**171 Coit St., Irvington 07111**
NW Sign Industries, Inc.
Phone—(856) 802-1677
360 Crider Ave., Moorestown 08057

## SIGNS

1 Stop Wraps, LLC
Phone—(732) 363-7800
1525 Prospect St., Ste. 602, Lakewood 08701

A B Stamp
Phone—(973) 383-1683
10 Mill Pine Dr., Lafayette 07848
A C Display Studios, Inc.
Phone—(609) 345-0814
2715 Arctic Ave., Atlantic City 08401
A-Affordable Sign.Com
Phone—(732) 287-0446
1053 Madison Hill Rd., Rahway 07065
ABC SignSystems, Inc.
Phone—(856) 665-0950
7970 National Hwy., P.O. Box 622, Pennsauken 08110
Abco Signs
Phone—(856) 663-6001
7300 N. Crescent Blvd., Ste. 11, Pennsauken 08110
ABS Sign Co., Inc.
Phone—(609) 522-6833
3008 Park Blvd., Wildwood 08260
Ace Sign Co., Inc.
Phone—(732) 826-3858
419 Summit Ave., Perth Amboy 08861
ACL Equipment Corp.
Phone—(973) 740-9800
257 E. Northfield Rd., P.O. Box 620, Livingston 07039
Action Sign Co., Inc.
Phone—(856) 478-0404
217 Ewan Rd., Mullica Hill 08062
Adco Signs Of New Jersey, Inc.
Phone—(908) 965-2112
57 Westfield Ave., Elizabeth 07208
Advantage Signs, Flags & Banners/ Country Crossings
Phone—(973) 579-3880
130 Newton Sparta Rd., Newton 07860
Ad-Venture Graphics, Inc.
Phone—(973) 927-0951
46 Main St., Succasunna 07876
Agin Signs & Design
Phone—(732) 297-9007
Route 1 S., Monmouth Junction 08852
All Signs Direct, LLC
Phone—(973) 736-7446
38 Washington St., West Orange 07052
Allen Signs
Phone—(609) 645-9268
600 Martin Luther King Ave., Pleasantville 08232
Alliance Sign Co., Inc.
Phone—(973) 458-0900
37 Grove St., Passaic 07055
Alpha 1 Studio, Inc.
Phone—(609) 859-2200
3 Linda Ln., Ste. A, Southampton 08088
American Display
Phone—(908) 534-2700
291 Route 22 E, Bldg. 8, P.O. Box 244, Whitehouse 08888
American Woodcarving, LLC
Phone—(973) 835-8510
1123 State Route 23, Ste. 6, Wayne 07470
Apollo Sign Co., Inc.
Phone—(973) 772-7446
835 Midland Ave., Garfield 07026
Art D'Mensions, Inc.
Phone—(908) 322-8488
1998 Scotch Plains Route 22, Scotch Plains 07076
Artcraft Sign Studio, Inc.
Phone—(856) 783-8008
738 W. Branch Ave., Pine Hill 08021
Astro Sign Co.
Phone—(856) 881-4300
230 E. High St., Route 322, Glassboro 08028
Auto Graphix
Phone—(973) 492-1300
56 Edsel Dr., Sussex 07461
B & J Sign Service
Phone—(856) 455-3636
971 Landis Ave., Pittsgrove 08318
Banner Design
Phone—(908) 687-5335
600 N. Union Ave., P.O. Box 5343, Hillside 07205
Bell Signs
Phone—(732) 738-0010
3125 Woodbridge Ave., Ste. 5-C, Edison 08837
Bergen Sign Co., Inc.
Phone—(973) 742-7755
161 E. Railway Ave., Paterson 07503

Bilcar Signs
Phone—(908) 687-3777
2131 Morris Ave., Union 07083
Bob's Signs Co.
Phone—(732) 521-4554
1918 Englishtown Rd., P.O. Box 15, Old Bridge 08857
Bono Signs & Designs, LLC
Phone—(973) 875-5488
1 Beamer Rd., Sussex 07461
Bright Signs, LLC
Phone—(732) 679-7440
2626 County Road 516, Old Bridge 08857
Brunswick Sign & Exhibit Corp.
Phone—(732) 246-2500
1510 Jersey Ave., North Brunswick 08902
Brussian Strokes Sign Co.
Phone—(973) 515-5151
15-A Melanie Ln., Ste. 3-A, East Hanover 07936
Bry-Pat Advertising Specialty & Signs
Phone—(732) 591-0999
Tennent Rd., Route 79, P.O. Box 369, Morganville 07751
C & C Signs & Banners
Phone—(609) 693-4667
812 Forepeak Dr., Forked River 08731
C L N Designs, LLC
Phone—(201) 939-2120
P.O. Box 1822, South Hackensack 07606
CAD SIGNS
Phone—(201) 267-0457
169 Lodi St., Hackensack 07601
Carl Sign, LLC
Phone—(973) 340-0210
1200 Madison Ave., Paterson 07503
Casabona Signs, LLC
Phone—(201) 325-8711
37 Grove St., Passaic 07055
Choice Signs
Phone—(732) 493-1644
3407 Rose Ave., Ste. 3, Ocean 07712
Classic Signs
Phone—(908) 668-8248
3651 S. Clinton, South Plainfield 07080
Colorcraft Sign Co.
Phone—(609) 386-1115
400 Magnolia St., Beverly 08010
Colorcraft, Inc.
Phone—(732) 892-6639
1506 Beaver Dam Rd., Point Pleasant Boro 08742
Commerce Sign Solutions, LLC
Phone—(732) 238-7000
540 Cranbury Rd., Ste. 334, East Brunswick 08816
Compass Signs, LLC
Phone—(732) 294-7977
1 Market Yard, Freehold 07728
Cueva's Signs
Phone—(908) 820-5744
853 Bayway Cir., Elizabeth 07201
Custom Lettering
Phone—(908) 454-4140
3031 Belvidere Rd., Phillipsburg 08865
D P J Signs
Phone—(732) 499-8600
245 E. Inman Ave., Rahway 07065
Danor Signs, LLC
Phone—(973) 471-2897
47 Central Ave., Passaic 07055
Davis Sign Systems
Phone—(973) 394-9909
65 Harrison St., Boonton 07005
DCI Signs & Awnings, Inc.
Phone—(973) 350-0400
110 Riverside Ave., Newark 07104
Del Sol Signs
Phone—(973) 589-8655
119 New Jersey Railroad Ave., Newark 07105
D'Elia Sign Co.
Phone—(201) 342-7231
32 W. Fort Lee Rd., Bogota 07603
Design A Sign, Inc.
Phone—(908) 656-0822
745 Lehigh Ave., Ste. 3, Union 07083
DMR Sign Systems
Phone—(973) 361-1829
215 State Route 10, Ste. 1-A, Randolph 07869
Eastern Sign Co.
Phone—(609) 927-0885
3011 Ocean Heights Ave., Ste. B, Egg Harbor Township 08234

© Copyright 2015 Manufacturers' News, Inc.

## SIGNS — *(cont.)*

East-West Service Co., Inc.
Phone—(609) 631-9000
2 Marlen Dr., Hamilton 08691

Empro Products Co., Inc.
Phone—(973) 279-1010
47 Montgomery St., Belleville 07109

FASTSIGNS®
Phone—(732) 985-1166
485 Route 1 S., Crossroads Plz., Edison 08817

FASTSIGNS®
Phone—(856) 985-8730
906 Greentree Sq., Route 73 N., Marlton 08053

FASTSIGNS®
Phone—(201) 587-8444
407 Sette Dr., Paramus 07652

FASTSIGNS®
Phone—(908) 231-0306
105 Sherman Ave., Raritan 08869

FASTSIGNS®
Phone—(201) 902-8640
255 State Route 3, Secaucus 07094

FASTSIGNS®
Phone—(908) 810-1400
2290 Route 22 E., Union 07083

Forrest Signs
Phone—(201) 670-7760
281 Greenwood Ave., Midland Park 07432

G & G Signs, Inc.
Phone—(201) 939-4099
323 2nd Ave., Lyndhurst 07071

Gail's Lettering & Design
Phone—(908) 735-4628
24 Beaver Ave., Annandale 08801

Garden State Highway Products, Inc.
Phone—(856) 692-7572
1740 E. Oak Rd., Vineland 08361

Garden State Sign Co.
Phone—(732) 363-7645
4880 U.S. Highway 9, Howell 07731

General Sign Co., Inc.
Phone—(856) 753-3535
105 Chestnut Ave., West Berlin 08091

Girtain Sign Co.
Phone—(732) 349-8499
1765 Route 9, Toms River 08755

Graphic Solutions & Signs, LLC
Phone—(201) 343-7446
82 Burlews Ct., Hackensack 07601

Gregory Signs, LLC
Phone—(973) 761-0165
1453 Springfield Ave., P.O. Box 671, Maplewood 07040

GTM Signs, Inc.
Phone—(856) 227-2333
1298 Hurffville Rd., Deptford 08096

Hank's Signs
Phone—(201) 652-5979
793 Jersey Pl., Paramus 07652

HE Designs & Awnings
Phone—(973) 751-0030
75 Rutgers St., Belleville 07109

Holding Sign Design, E. R.
Phone—(856) 227-1597
2 N. Black Horse Pike, Blackwood 08012

Hoyt Signs
Phone—(908) 859-3768
2825 Belvidere Rd., Phillipsburg 08865

Hub Sign Crane Corp.
Phone—(732) 252-9090
67 Wood Ave., Englishtown 07726

Hurricane Signs
Phone—(973) 838-3373
103 Main St., Bloomingdale 07403

Image Signs and More, LLC
Phone—(856) 665-1890
2906 N. Centre St., Pennsauken 08109

INKit Design N' Print LLC
Phone—(732) 363-8098
644 Cross St., Unit 2, Lakewood 08701

J T Graphics
Phone—(856) 931-3548
34 Mt. Ephraim Ave., Mount Ephraim 08059

JB Signs
Phone—(732) 613-3700
23 Dorchester Dr., P.O. Box 454, East Brunswick 08816

JD Graphics, Inc.
Phone—(732) 972-7790
6 Richardson Ct., Marlboro 07746

Jencks Signs Corp.
Phone—(908) 542-1400
50 Division Ave., Ste. 14, Millington 07946

Jim's Signs
Phone—(732) 381-8700
1400 Rahway Ave., Ste. 3, Avenel 07001

Kevin's Sign Co.
Phone—(609) 871-2385
1212 Bridgeboro Rd., Edgewater Park 08010

KNA Graphics, Inc.
Phone—(908) 272-4232
303 N. 14th St., Kenilworth 07033

Kraftwork Custom Design
Phone—(609) 848-0578
1837 S. Broad St., Hamilton 08610

L & M Architectural Graphics, Inc.
Phone—(973) 575-7665
20 Montesano Rd., Fairfield 07004

L J Engraving & Signs
Phone—(908) 925-3510
409 N. Wood Ave., P.O. Box 1039, Linden 07036

Lincoln Signs & Awnings, Inc.
Phone—(732) 442-3151
895 Estate St., Perth Amboy 08861

Lines & Letters DESIGNS
Phone—(732) 563-0909
1386 Mount Vernon Rd., Bridgewater 08807

Lobello Arts Corp.
Phone—(973) 887-6700
50 Route 10 W., East Hanover 07936

LouMarc Signs
Phone—(908) 575-4000
178 Route 206, Hillsborough 08844

Mag Signs, Inc.
Phone—(609) 747-9600
1208-F Columbus Rd., Burlington 08016

Majestic Signs
Phone—(201) 837-8104
951 Teaneck Rd., Teaneck 07666

Manhattan Signs, Inc.
Phone—(973) 278-3603
130 Beckwith Ave., Paterson 07503

Mantua Sign & Lighting
Phone—(856) 415-0022
550 Bridgeton Pike, Ste. 5, Mantua 08051

Mark-O-Lite Sign Co.
Phone—(732) 462-8530
1420 U.S. Highway 9, Howell 07731

Mashal Signs Co., Inc.
Phone—(201) 348-8500
568 55th St., West New York 07093

MC Signs
Phone—(609) 399-7446
231 West Ave., Ocean City 08226

McLain Studios, Inc.
Phone—(732) 775-0271
1203 Main St., Asbury Park 07712

Meadowlands Signs
Phone—(201) 426-0420
58 State Route 17, Hasbrouck Heights 07604

Metro Signs
Phone—(856) 428-9050
410 Downs Dr., P.O. Box 865, Cherry Hill 08003

Michael's Commercial Signs
Phone—(201) 868-7166
629 62nd St., Ste. 31, West New York 07093

Morris Sign Co.
Phone—(973) 386-1755
30 Troy Rd., Whippany 07981

Mr. J's Xcaliber Corp.
Phone—(973) 278-1611
39 Dundee Ave., Paterson 07503

Mr. Quick Sign
Phone—(201) 670-1690
30 Dairy St., Midland Park 07432

Mr. Sign, Inc.
Phone—(732) 560-0606
319 Bound Brook Rd., Middlesex 08846

Nemec Sign Co.
Phone—(908) 782-3175
114 Route 31, Flemington 08822

Nickel Artistic Services, LLC
Phone—(973) 627-0390
39 U.S. Highway 46, Rockaway 07866

Norman Dee Associates
Phone—(609) 348-5777
31 N. Sovereign Ave., Atlantic City 08401

Nunn & Son Custom Lettering
Phone—(732) 899-9682
10 Harding Dr., Brick 08724

Omega Specialty Products, LLC
Phone—(609) 383-8835
2511 Fire Rd., Ste. B-6, Egg Harbor Township 08234

On-Line Sign
Phone—(609) 443-1704
2 Sheffield Rd., East Windsor 08520

Parrish Sign Co., Inc.
Phone—(856) 696-4040
2242 S. Delsea Dr., Vineland 08360

Penn Jersey Weekend Directionals
Phone—(856) 858-8888
208 W. Clinton Ave., Oaklyn 08107

Philadelphia Sign Co.
Phone—(856) 829-1460
707 W. Spring Garden St., Palmyra 08065

Phil's Sign Shop
Phone—(732) 726-1555
55 Cutters Dock Rd., Woodbridge 07095

Precision Sign Works, LLC
Phone—(609) 702-9700
82 Richter Rd., Tabernacle 08088

Printing & Signs Express, Inc.
Phone—(201) 368-1255
634 Wyckoff Ave., Mahwah 07430

Pro Signs
Phone—(908) 454-4888
296 S. Main St., Phillipsburg 08865

Project Sign
Phone—(973) 763-1959
282 Irvington Rd., South Orange 07079

Regn Sign Studio, Inc.
Phone—(732) 988-3595
42 Main St., Bradley Beach 07720

Rex Sign Co.
Phone—(732) 774-1377
60 Steiner Ave., Neptune City 07753

Riedel Sign Co., Inc.
Phone—(201) 641-9121
15 Warren St., Little Ferry 07643

Rose Signs
Phone—(973) 948-0501
13 Route 206 S., Branchville 07826

Royce Signworks, Inc.
Phone—(201) 945-5536
226 DeSoto Pl., Cliffside Park 07010

Rudy Di Signs & Displays
Phone—(201) 568-6160
169 N. Dean St., Englewood 07631

Rutherford Signright Co.
Phone—(201) 935-1511
769 Morton St., East Rutherford 07073

Shore Sign & Banner
Phone—(732) 270-6020
1214 Route 37 E., Toms River 08753

Sign Boy, LLC
Phone—(856) 384-2937
370 N. Glassboro Rd., Woodbury Heights 08097

Sign Concepts
Phone—(732) 341-7624
33 Broad St., Toms River 08753

Sign Crew
Phone—(856) 665-3676
1426 Union Ave., Pennsauken 08110

Sign Effectz
Phone—(732) 388-7446
800 New Brunswick Ave., Ste. 7, Rahway 07065

Sign Maker
Phone—(732) 739-4800
1005 Union Ave., Union Beach 07735

Sign On, Inc.
Phone—(201) 384-7714
149 Washington Ave., Apt. A, Dumont 07628

Sign Tech
Phone—(908) 232-2287
361 South Ave. E., Westfield 07090

Sign Up Signs, LLC
Phone—(732) 240-6025
649 Atlantic City Blvd., Unit 2, Beachwood 08722

Signarama
Phone—(609) 878-3375
655 S. White Horse Pike, Hammonton 08037

Signarama
Phone—(732) 536-7575
349 U.S. Highway 9, Ste. 6, Manalapan 07726

Sign-A-Rama
Phone—(856) 764-9777
4000 Route 130, Ste. 25, Delran 08075

Sign-A-Rama
Phone—(609) 702-1444
1459 Highway 38, P.O. Box 360, Hainesport 08036

© Copyright 2015 Manufacturers' News, Inc.

## SIGNS — *(cont.)*

Sign-A-Rama
Phone—(973) 605-8313
166 Ridgedale Ave., Morristown 07962

Sign-A-Rama
Phone—(908) 561-4167
1030 U.S. Highway 22, North Plainfield 07060

**Sign-A-Rama**
Email: sarpisc@optonline.net
'Where The World Goes for Signs'. Specializing in electronic signs, vinyl banners, channel letter signs, digital vehicle graphics, vehicle wraps, vinyl lettering, vinyl decals, yard signs, menu boards & more
**Phone—(732) 819-8844**
**Fax—(732) 819-8242**
**Web—www.yoursignco.com**
**1633 Stelton Rd., Piscataway 08854**

Sign-A-Rama
Phone—(856) 627-5352
34 S. White Horse Pike, Somerdale 08083

Sign-A-Rama, Inc.
Phone—(201) 489-6969
379 Main St., Hackensack 07601

SignArt Graphix
Phone—(973) 770-4500
177 Stanhope Sparta Rd., Andover 07821

Signature Sign
Phone—(609) 351-2231
31 Milaystown Rd., Cream Ridge 08514

SignPros
Phone—(856) 939-1099
1215 Black Horse Pike, Glendora 08029

Signright, Inc.
Phone—(973) 731-8882
76 Ashland Ave., West Orange 07052

Signs & Graphix
Phone—(973) 226-8392
433 Bloomfield Ave., Caldwell 07006

Signs By Blohm, Inc.
Phone—(201) 262-3172
230 River Rd., New Milford 07646

Signs By Lynn
Phone—(201) 998-4273
329 Kearny Ave., Ste. A, Kearny 07032

Signs By Raymond
Phone—(732) 840-7793
626 Route 88, Point Pleasant 08742

Signs By Tomorrow
Phone—(732) 424-9785
326 U.S. Highway 22, Ste. 8-B, Green Brook 08812

Signs By Tomorrow
Phone—(973) 423-4600
1108 Goffle Rd., Ste. 1, Hawthorne 07506

Signs By Tomorrow
Phone—(732) 602-7878
825 Highway 1 S., Ste. 6, Iselin 08830

Signs For Today
Phone—(973) 983-2530
173 Upper Hibernia Rd., Rockaway 07866

Signs Of 2000
Phone—(973) 253-1333
421 Broad St., Clifton 07011

Signs Of Security, Inc.
Phone—(973) 340-8404
64 Outwater Ln., 2nd Fl., P.O. Box 468, Garfield 07026

Signs Of Sense
Phone—(973) 361-0037
79 Bassett Hwy., Dover 07801

Signs Of The Times By Beutel & Sons
Phone—(201) 391-8444
81 Park Ave., Park Ridge 07656

Signs Sealed & Delivered, Inc.
Phone—(732) 775-7227
121 Main St., Bradley Beach 07720

Signs Unlimited, Inc.
Phone—(856) 848-4942
601 Hessian Ave., National Park 08063

Sonntag Graphics, Eric
Phone—(732) 828-5200
93 John E. Busch Ave., Somerset 08873

SSI Creative Group
Phone—(856) 663-2292
20 E. Clementon Rd., Ste. 203-N, Gibbsboro 08026

Sun Neon Sign & Electric Co.
Phone—(856) 663-7667
6701-B Rudderow Ave., Pennsauken 08109

Suzie Mac Specialties, Inc.
Phone—(732) 238-3500
12-B Connery Ct., East Brunswick 08816

Szabo Signs
Phone—(609) 387-7213
1108 Neck Rd., Burlington 08016

Tally Display Corp.
Phone—(973) 777-7760
19 Gardner Rd., Ste. A, Fairfield 07004

TLC Sign & Banner, Inc.
Phone—(732) 244-4225
188 Walnut St., Toms River 08753

Tooker Sign Service
Phone—(609) 296-1000
1439 Route 539, P.O. Box 1129, Tuckerton 08087

Tradewin Sign, LLC
Phone—(609) 488-5961
699 Challenger Way, Unit D-7, Forked River 08731

Traffic Safety & Equipment Co.
Phone—(201) 327-6050
457 State Route 17, Mahwah 07430

Urban Sign & Crane, Inc.
Phone—(856) 691-8388
527 E. Chestnut Ave., P.O. Box 640, Vineland 08360

US Sign & Lighting Service, LLC
Phone—(973) 305-8900
105 Dorsa Ave., Wayne 07470

Vigg Designs, LLC
Phone—(732) 683-9400
584 Park Ave., Freehold 07728

Visual Graphic Systems, Inc.
Phone—(201) 528-2700
330 Washington Ave., Carlstadt 07072

Vital Signs
Phone—(201) 723-8488
50 Bedford Rd., Mahwah 07430

Vitale Signs
Phone—(732) 388-8401
2204 Elizabeth Ave., Rahway 07065

Walter's Signs
Phone—(856) 210-6324
159 W. White Horse Pike, Berlin 08009

Zienowicz Signs
Phone—(609) 393-4068
202 E. Canal St., Trenton 08609

## SIGNS — Architectural

C N R Products Co.
Phone—(201) 384-7003
74 Portland Ave., Bergenfield 07621

Designer Sign Systems, LLC
Phone—(201) 939-5577
352 Washington Ave., Carlstadt 07072

Eastern Sign Tech, LLC
Phone—(609) 261-2805
112 Connecticut Dr., P.O. Box 564, Burlington 08016

Signal Sign Co.
Phone—(973) 535-9277
105 Dorsa Ave., Livingston 07039

Sign-A-Rama
Phone—(973) 227-6363
400 Fairfield Rd., Ste. 5, Fairfield 07004

Signs & Custom Metal, Inc.
Phone—(201) 200-0110
62 Monitor St., Jersey City 07304

Sweet Sign Systems, Inc.
Phone—(732) 521-9300
9 Davison Ave., Ste. 4, Jamesburg 08831

## SIGNS — Digital

**Tally Display Corp.**
Toll Free Ph: (800)75-TALLY; Manufacturing LED signs & systems for large companies. Specializing in custom & one-of-a-kind projects. Offering extensive experience in broadcasting, video, advertising, signage & software creation
**Phone—(973) 777-7760 / (800) 758-2559**
**Fax—(973) 777-6220**
**Web—www.tallydisplay.com**
**Email—info@tallydisplay.com**
**19 Gardner Rd., Ste. A, Fairfield 07004**

## SIGNS — Display

Gotham Group, The
Phone—(609) 645-2211
202 W. Parkway Dr., Ste. 2, Egg Harbor Township 08234

Sonoco CorrFlex, LLC
Phone—(201) 612-4008
Heritage Plaza II, 1st Fl., 65 Harristow, Glen Rock 07452

## SIGNS — Electric

(MASAco) Michael Anthony Sign & Awning, Inc.
Phone—(732) 453-6120
21 Randolph Ave., Avenel 07001

Berlin Neon Sign, Inc.
Phone—(856) 767-0525
326 Old White Horse Pike, Waterford Works 08089

Butler Sign Company
Phone—(973) 633-5757
582 Fairfield Rd., Wayne 07470

Future Signs
Phone—(609) 695-6263
19 Bowhill Ave., Trenton 08610

Sign-A-Rama Ledgewood
Phone—(973) 584-9301
244 Main St., Ledgewood 07852

Suburban Sign Mfg., LLC
Phone—(908) 862-7222
210 Marion Ave., Linden 07036

## SIGNS — Electronic

**Sign-A-Rama**
Email: sarpisc@optonline.net
'Where The World Goes for Signs'. Specializing in electronic signs, vinyl banners, channel letter signs, digital vehicle graphics, vehicle wraps, vinyl lettering, vinyl decals, yard signs, menu boards & more
**Phone—(732) 819-8844**
**Fax—(732) 819-8242**
**Web—www.yoursignco.com**
**1633 Stelton Rd., Piscataway 08854**

**Tally Display Corp.**
Toll Free Ph: (800)75-TALLY; Manufacturing LED signs & systems for large companies. Specializing in custom & one-of-a-kind projects. Offering extensive experience in broadcasting, video, advertising, signage & software creation
**Phone—(973) 777-7760 / (800) 758-2559**
**Fax—(973) 777-6220**
**Web—www.tallydisplay.com**
**Email—info@tallydisplay.com**
**19 Gardner Rd., Ste. A, Fairfield 07004**

## SIGNS — Electronic Moving Message

**Tally Display Corp.**
Toll Free Ph: (800)75-TALLY; Manufacturing LED signs & systems for large companies. Specializing in custom & one-of-a-kind projects. Offering extensive experience in broadcasting, video, advertising, signage & software creation
**Phone—(973) 777-7760 / (800) 758-2559**
**Fax—(973) 777-6220**
**Web—www.tallydisplay.com**
**Email—info@tallydisplay.com**
**19 Gardner Rd., Ste. A, Fairfield 07004**

## SIGNS — Engraved

Matthews Engravers, Edward R.
Phone—(201) 342-4644
61 S. State St., Hackensack 07601

**Regal Stamp & Sign Co., Inc.**
Making Our Mark Since 1970. Rubber Stamps, Embossing, Seals & Signage
**Phone—(201) 939-0400**
**Fax—(201) 939-5203**
**Web—www.regalstampnj.com**
**Email—regalstamp@verizon.net**
**240 Park Ave., P.O. Box 342, East Rutherford 07073**

*(see our ad under RUBBER STAMPS)*

Trybun Engraving, LLC
Phone—(609) 242-3105
706 Old Shore Rd., Ste. 3, Forked River 08731

## SIGNS — Illuminated

Horizon Sign Co.
Phone—(609) 586-0041
340 Patterson Ave., Ste. C, Hamilton 08610

INDUSTRY

## SIGNS — LED

Aesys, Inc.
Phone—(201) 871-3223
27 Bland St., Emerson 07630

**Tally Display Corp.**
Toll Free Ph: (800)75-TALLY; Manufacturing LED signs & systems for large companies. Specializing in custom & one-of-a-kind projects. Offering extensive experience in broadcasting, video, advertising, signage & software creation
**Phone—(973) 777-7760 / (800) 758-2559**
**Fax—(973) 777-6220**
**Web—www.tallydisplay.com**
**Email—info@tallydisplay.com**
**19 Gardner Rd., Ste. A, Fairfield 07004**

## SIGNS — Metal

East Trading West Investments LLC
Phone—(973) 678-0800
200 S. Jefferson St., Orange 07050

## SIGNS — Neon

419 Neon, LLC
Phone—(732) 324-2445
364 Glenwood Ave., East Orange 07017
Ace Neon Factory, LLC
Phone—(908) 486-6366
2101 Grier Ave., Linden 07036
**Eastern Sign Tech, LLC**
Fax: (609) 518-3575
**Phone—(609) 261-2805**
**Fax—(609) 386-9905**
**Web—www.easternsigntech.com**
**Email—info@easternsigntech.com**
**112 Connecticut Dr., P.O. Box 564, Burlington 08016**

---

**Eastern Sign Tech, LLC**
*Neon, vinyl & architectural signs*
**www.easternsigntech.com**
**(609) 261-2805**
**Fax: (609) 518-3575**
112 Connecticut Dr. Burlington, NJ 08016

---

Neverending Neon
Phone—(973) 772-4840
91 Dell Glen Ave., Lodi 07644
Spectrum Neon, Inc.
Phone—(856) 317-9223
9130-B Pennsauken Hwy., Pennsauken 08110
Stand-Out Signs, Inc.
Phone—(732) 442-9399
49 W. Pond Rd., Perth Amboy 08861

## SIGNS — Nonelectric

Curtis Sign Design
Phone—(732) 928-9494
640 Herman Rd., Ste. 1, Jackson 08527
Signdesign, LLC
Phone—(732) 929-3700
206 Lake Ave., P.O. Box 892, Island Heights 08732

## SIGNS — Outdoor

Bantle's Banners & Signs
Phone—(856) 546-1112
213 Clements Bridge Rd., Barrington 08007
CBS Outdoor
Phone—(973) 575-6900
185 Highway 46, Fairfield 07004
CBS Outdoor
Phone—(732) 901-1100
1245 Towbin Ave., Lakewood 08701

## SIGNS — Plastic

Action Signs & Awards
Phone—(856) 825-2454
305 N. 11th St., Millville 08332
Allied Environmental Signage
Phone—(732) 578-1818
556 Industrial Way W., Eatontown 07724

Aquarian What's Your Sign, LLC
Phone—(732) 206-0726
37 Newtons Corner Rd., Howell 07731
Arizona Signs & Truck Lettering
Phone—(856) 482-2288
3121 Route 73 S., Maple Shade 08052
Broadway Signs, Inc.
Phone—(732) 892-6334
1029 Ocean Rd., Point Pleasant 08742
Delcrest Sign Co., Inc.
Phone—(856) 768-5552
1202 Haddonfield-Berlin Rd., Ste. 1, Voorhees 08043
Dover Signs Mfg. & Graphics, Inc.
Phone—(973) 366-2229
1471 Sussex Tpke., Randolph 07869
Fantastic Signs Co.
Phone—(732) 747-7763
351 Shrewsbury Ave., Red Bank 07701
Insign, Inc.
Phone—(856) 424-1161
1937 Olney Ave., Cherry Hill 08003
Lane Signs
Phone—(732) 349-1904
34 Central Ave., Toms River 08753
Next Day Signs & Banners, Inc.
Phone—(201) 986-1960
300 Route 17, Paramus 07652
Rozano Signs
Phone—(908) 788-5042
1005 County Road 523, Flemington 08822
Sign-A-Rama
Phone—(908) 203-8005
32 S. Main St., Manville 08835
Signs & Lines Printing
Phone—(856) 784-0400
242 Gibbsboro Rd., Lindenwold 08021
Skyline Graphic Management
Phone—(201) 798-1919
601 Adams St., P.O. Box 6147, Hoboken 07030

## SIGNS — Safety

Almetek Industries, Inc.
Phone—(908) 850-9700
2 Joy Dr., Hackettstown 07840

## SIGNS — Sandblasted

Pendergast Signs
Phone—(908) 735-9295
566 Charlestown Rd., Hampton 08827

## SIGNS — Traffic

Atlas Flasher & Supply Co., Inc.
Phone—(856) 423-3333
430 Swedesboro Ave., P.O. Box 488, Mickleton 08056
Griffin Sign Co., Inc.
Phone—(856) 786-8517
464 N. Randolph Ave., Cinnaminson 08077

## SIGNS — Wooden

Storkdelivery.Com
Phone—(201) 933-7721
232 Webster Ave., Lyndhurst 07071

## SILICATES — Sodium

P Q Corp.
Phone—(732) 750-9040
2 Paddock St., Avenel 07001

## SILICONE MEDICAL DEVICES

Engineered Silicone Products, LLC
Phone—(973) 300-5120
75 Mill St., Ste. 2, Newton 07860

## SILICONE RUBBER

Medford Silicones, Inc.
Phone—(609) 953-1092
P.O. Box 2072, Medford 08055

## SILK FABRICS

Avon Fabrics, Inc.
Phone—(732) 764-9700
484 Lincoln Blvd., Middlesex 08846
Stylex Imports & Export Co., Inc.
Phone—(201) 964-1900
425 Paterson Ave., East Rutherford 07073

## SILK SCREENING

**Total Ink Solutions**
Plastisol, Supplies, Screens, Mesh, Press Wash & Color Match
**Phone—(201) 487-9600 / (877) 937-6400**
**Fax—(201) 487-9620**
**Web—www.totalinksolutions.com**
**Email—marc@totalinksolutions.com**
**200 S. Newman St., Unit 4, Hackensack 07601**
*(see our ad under INKS—Screen Print)*

## SILK SCREENS

Screen Tech Of New Jersey, Inc.
Phone—(908) 862-8000
1800 W. Blancke St., Linden 07036

## SILVERWARE

Cambridge Silversmiths Ltd. (H Q)
Phone—(973) 227-4400
30 Hook Mountain Rd., P.O. Box 625, Pine Brook 07058
Vitali, Inc., Ubaldo
Phone—(973) 763-9310
188-190 Hilton Ave., Maplewood 07040

## SIMULATORS

Pacific Coast Systems, LLC
Phone—(908) 735-9955
4 Fox Hill Ln., Asbury 08802

## SINKS — Plastic

**Emco Industrial Plastics, Inc.**
Supplier of Plastic Sheet, Rod, Tube, Films & Prototyping
**Phone—(973) 559-5610**
**Fax—(973) 239-1595**
**Web—www.emcoplastics.com**
**Email—mailbox@emcoplastics.com**
**99 Commerce Rd., P.O. Box 2503, Cedar Grove 07009**
*(see our ad Outside Front Cover)*

## SINKS — Stainless Steel

HOUZER, Inc.
Phone—(609) 584-1900
2605 Kuser Rd., Hamilton 08691

## SITE FURNISHINGS

Environmental Site Furnishings
Phone—(281) 975-1776
700 Goldman Dr., Cream Ridge 08514

## SIZE REDUCTION EQUIPMENT

**Franklin Miller, Inc.**
**Phone—(973) 535-9200**
**Fax—(973) 535-6269**
**Web—www.franklinmiller.com**
**Email—info@franklinmiller.com**
**60 Okner Pkwy., P.O. Box 070663, Livingston 07039**
*(see our ad under CRUSHERS)*
Imperial Metal Products, Inc.
Phone—(732) 469-8181
8 W. Chimney Rock Rd., Bound Brook 08805

## SKIDS

Electronic Power Designs, Inc.
Phone—(973) 838-7055
132 Union Ave., Bloomingdale 07403

## SKIDS — *(cont.)*

**Laurel Run Pallet, LLC**
Custom built pallets and skids of any size and shape
Phone—(717) 436-5428
Fax—(717) 436-5575
Email—laurelrunpallet@hotmail.com
975 Billyville Rd., Mifflintown, PA 17059

**Laurel Run Pallet, LLC**

*Custom Built Block Pallets and Skids*

laurelrunpallet@hotmail.com

**717-436-5428 • Fax: 717-436-5575**

975 Billyville Rd.  Mifflintown, PA 17059

## SKIN CARE PRODUCTS

**Ambix Laboratories**
Custom & Private Label Skin Care Products
Phone—(973) 890-9002
Fax—(973) 890-9778
Web—www.ambixlabs.com
Email—ambixlab@aol.com
55 W. End Rd., Totowa 07512
*(see our ad under PROTEIN)*

Ameriderm Laboratories Ltd.
Phone—(973) 279-5100
126 Pennsylvania Ave., Paterson 07503

Biogenesis, Inc.
Phone—(201) 678-1992
296 Washington Ave., Hackensack 07601

Chemaid Laboratories, Inc.
Phone—(201) 843-3300
100 Mayhill St., Saddle Brook 07663

Dermarite Industries, LLC
Phone—(973) 569-9000
7777 W. Side Ave., P.O. Box 7209, North Bergen 07047

**E. T. Browne Drug Company, Inc.**
Toll Free (877)PALMERS
Phone—(201) 894-9020 / (877) 725-6377
Fax—(201) 894-5152
Web—www.palmers.com
440 Sylvan Ave., P.O. Box 1613, Englewood Cliffs 07632

Englewood Lab, LLC
Phone—(201) 567-2267
88 W. Sheffield Ave., Englewood 07631

Health & Natural Beauty USA
Phone—(848) 202-9089
140-W Ethel Rd. W., Piscataway 08854

**Imperial DAX Co., Inc.**
Phone—(973) 227-6105
Fax—(973) 808-8533
Web—www.daxhaircare.com
Email—lzawisha@imperialdax.com
120 New Dutch Ln., Fairfield 07004

Neostrata Company, Inc. (H Q)
Phone—(609) 520-0715
307 College Rd. E., Princeton 08540

New World International Corp.
Phone—(973) 881-8100
59 Dover St., Paterson 07501

PhytoCeuticals, Inc.
Phone—(201) 791-2255
37 Midland Ave., Elmwood Park 07407

Revicci, Inc.
Phone—(973) 994-1421
25 Sycamore Ter., Livingston 07039

Reviva Labs, Inc.
Phone—(856) 428-3885
705 Hopkins Rd., Haddonfield 08033

Syence Skincare Laboratories Inc.
Phone—(908) 791-0044
99 W. Mill Rd., Long Valley 07853

Unimed International, Inc.
Phone—(800) 754-6211
105 Newfield Ave., Ste. F, Edison 08837

Y, Inc.
Phone—(201) 773-8425
20-21 Wagaraw Rd., Bldg. 32, Fair Lawn 07410

*Search from among 430,000
U.S. manufacturers & suppliers:*
**IndustryNet.com**

## SKYLIGHTS

**All Professional Remodeling Group, LLC**
Toll Free Ph: (888)919-ROOF; Second Generation Roofing Contractor
Phone—(973) 857-9449 / (888) 919-7663
Fax—(973) 857-0991
Web—www.allprofessionalremodelinggroup.com
Email—aprgllc@aol.com
P.O. Box 215, Cedar Grove 07009
*(see our ad under ROOFING CONTRACTORS)*

Erick Industries, Inc.
Phone—(856) 966-2045
837 S. 9th St., Camden 08103

Fiore Skylights, Inc.
Phone—(856) 346-0118
210 E. Evergreen Ave., P.O. Box 160, Somerdale 08083

**Kovach Roofing**
Phone—(973) 835-5330
Fax—(973) 831-9577
Web—www.kovachroofing.com
Email—kovachroofing@aol.com
225 Boulevard, Pompton Plains 07444
*(see our ad under ROOFING CONTRACTORS)*

## SLINGS

Doran Sling & Assembly Corp.
Phone—(908) 351-7800
1285 Central Ave., Hillside 07205

## SLINGS — Lifting

Steelstran Industries, Inc.
Phone—(732) 574-0700
35 Mileed Way, P.O. Box 30, Avenel 07001

## SLINGS — Wire Rope

**Brown & Perkins, Inc.**
Phone—(609) 655-1150
Fax—(609) 655-1173
Web—www.brownandperkins.com
Email—sales@brownandperkins.com
1193 Route 535, P.O. Box 412, Cranbury 08512

## SLIPPERS

Gordon Mills Mfg., Inc. (H Q)
Phone—(973) 359-1080
68 Sherwood Dr., Morristown 07960

Raybold Mfg., Inc., Disposable Products Div.
Phone—(856) 327-7733
102 S. 8th St., Millville 08332

S. Goldberg & Co., Inc.
Phone—(201) 342-1200
3 University Plz., Ste. 400, Hackensack 07601

## SLITTING

**E & H Laminating & Slitting Co.**
Phone—(973) 345-1725
Fax—(973) 345-3224
Web—www.ehlam.com
Email—info@ehlam.com
138 Grand St., Paterson 07501
*(see our ad under ADHESIVES)*

## SLITTING MACHINES

Lever Mfg. Corp.
Phone—(201) 684-4400
420 State Route 17, Mahwah 07430

## SLUDGE DEWATERING EQUIPMENT

**Komline-Sanderson Engineering**
Phone—(908) 234-1000 / (800) 225-5457
Fax—(908) 234-9487
Web—www.komline.com
Email—info@komline.com
12 Holland Ave., Peapack 07977

## SNACK FOODS

Hain Celestial Group, Inc., The
Phone—(201) 935-4500
50 Knickerbocker Rd., Moonachie 07074

Leng-D'Or USA, Inc.
Phone—(732) 254-4300
50 W. Ferris St., East Brunswick 08816

Nutra Nuts, Inc. (H Q)
Phone—(201) 768-0218
180 Old Tappan Rd., Old Tappan 07675

Savoy Extraordinary Snack, LLC
Phone—(908) 252-9800
35 N. Middaugh St., Somerville 08876

Woodstock Farms Mfg.
Phone—(732) 650-9905
96 Executive Ave., Edison 08817

Yume Enterprises, LLC
Phone—(609) 588-8903
1800 E. State St., Ste. 158, Trenton 08609

## SNOW REMOVAL EQUIPMENT

Smith Brothers Services, LLC
Phone—(973) 209-7569
3212 State Route 94, Ste. 9, Franklin 07416

## SNOW REMOVAL SERVICES

**Arctic Management, LLC**
Phone—(732) 495-9300
Fax—(732) 671-5240
Web—www.arcticmanagement.com
165 Railroad Ave., Belford 07718

**John Mirza Landscaping Inc.**
Landscaping, Irrigation, Hydroseeding (Covering all your horticultural needs)
Phone—(201) 476-9677
Fax—(201) 265-1745
Web—www.mirzalandscaping.com
Email—mirzalandscaping@aol.com
49 Spring Valley Rd., Ste. B, Montvale 07645

## SOAP AND SOAP PRODUCTS

Atlantic Beach Soap Co.
Phone—(908) 272-7595
231 North Ave. W., Ste. 2, Westfield 07090

Avianne Health Care Systems
Phone—(201) 288-4100
115 1st St., Lodi 07644

Colgate-Palmolive Co.
Phone—(973) 630-1500
191 E. Hanover Ave., Morristown 07960

Inopak Ltd.
Phone—(973) 962-1121
24 Executive Pkwy., Ringwood 07456

Jobe Industries, Inc. (H Q)
Phone—(908) 862-0400
1600 W. Elizabeth Ave., P.O. Box 1367, Linden 07036

## SOFTWARE — Wholesale

Interactive Computer Center, Inc.
Phone—(732) 477-5800
482 Brick Blvd., Brick 08723

**JEMS Software & Consulting, Inc.**
Phone—(609) 585-8530
Fax—(609) 585-5539
Web—www.jemssoco.com
Email—jem@jemssoco.com
P.O. Box 10070, Trenton 08650

Nandvarik Systems
Phone—(732) 306-9999
190 Lewis St., Rahway 07065

**SHI International Corp.**
Phone—(732) 477-6479 / (888) 764-8888
Fax—(732) 868-5844
Web—www.shi.com
Email—michael_haluska@shi.com
290 Davidson Ave., Somerset 08873

## SOFTWARE DEVELOPMENT

A3 Technology, Inc.
Phone—(609) 652-7933
311 S. New York Rd., Redding Office Pk., Ste. 36, Absecon 08205

## SOFTWARE DEVELOPMENT —
### (cont.)

Abacus Systems, Inc.
Phone—(973) 875-9900
10 County Road 639, Sussex 07461

Acsis, Inc.
Phone—(856) 673-3000
9 E. Stow Rd., Ste. D, Marlton 08053

Advanced Technology Corp.
Phone—(201) 934-7127
79 N. Franklin Tpke., Ste. 103, Ramsey 07446

Aergo Solutions, Inc.
Phone—(732) 321-1500
33 Wood Ave. S., 5th Fl., Iselin 08830

Alanda Software
Phone—(201) 386-2007
391 George St., New Brunswick 08901

ALK Technologies, Inc.
Phone—(609) 683-0220
457 N. Harrison St., Princeton 08540

Altech Star, Inc.
Phone—(609) 520-9000
4365 U.S. Highway 1, Ste. 205, Princeton 08540

Altibase, Inc.
Phone—(888) 837-7333
1 Bridge Plz. N., Fort Lee 07024

Amerinex Applied Imaging, Inc.
Phone—(609) 944-8855
P.O. Box 6473, Monroe Township 08831

AS Software, Inc.
Phone—(201) 541-1900
560 Sylvan Ave., Ste. 2052, Englewood Cliffs 07632

Aumtech, Inc.
Phone—(732) 254-1875
710 Old Bridge Tpke., East Brunswick 08816

AuthentiDate Holding Corp.
Phone—(908) 787-1700
300 Connell Dr., 5th Fl., Berkeley Heights 07922

Axletree Solutions, Inc.
Phone—(732) 296-0001
2 King Arthur Ct., Lakeside W., Ste. A-1, North Brunswick 08902

AXS-ONE, Inc.
Phone—(201) 935-3400
301 Route 17, Ste. 11, Rutherford 07070

Aztec Software Assoc., Inc.
Phone—(973) 258-0011
51 Commerce St., 2nd Fl., Springfield 07081

BIO-key International, Inc. (H Q)
Phone—(732) 359-1100
3349 Highway 138, Bldg. A, Ste.E, Wall 07719

BlackStratus
Phone—(732) 393-6000
1551 S. Washington Ave., Ste. 401, Piscataway 08854

Blue Planet Solutions, Inc.
Phone—(973) 597-4555
116 Millburn Ave., Ste.108, Millburn 07041

Boston Technologies, Inc.
Phone—(856) 692-4958
610 E. Landis Ave., Vineland 08360

Burgiss Group, LLC, The
Phone—(201) 427-9600
111 River St., Ste. 10, Hoboken 07030

Business Power, Inc.
Phone—(856) 783-7390
39 Hunt Ave., Ste. C, Stratford 08084

CADCAM-E.Com, Inc.
Phone—(201) 503-1881
2115 Linwood Ave., Ste. 313, Fort Lee 07024

CAMO Software
Phone—(732) 726-9200
1 Woodbridge Ctr., Ste. 319, Woodbridge 07095

CAST, Inc. (H Q)
Phone—(201) 391-8300
11 Stonewall Ct., Woodcliff Lake 07677

Chemspeed, Inc.
Phone—(732) 329-1225
113 N. Center Dr., North Brunswick 08902

Chenoa Information Service, Inc.
Phone—(732) 549-6800
10 Parsonage Rd., Ste. 312, Edison 08837

coAction
Phone—(888) 682-3050
50 Kildee Rd., Belle Mead 08502

Cognizant Technology Solutions
Phone—(201) 801-0233
500 Frank W. Burr Blvd., Teaneck 07666

CommVault Systems, Inc.
Phone—(732) 870-4000
2 Crescent Pl., P.O. Box 900, Oceanport 07757

Compliance Educational Systems, Inc.
Phone—(856) 793-0137
P.O. Box 669, Marlton 08053

Computer Square, Inc.
Phone—(732) 346-0200
330 Mac Ln., Keasbey 08832

Data Communique, Inc.
Phone—(201) 508-6000
65 Challenger Rd., 4th Fl., Ridgefield Park 07660

**DealerApp Vantage**
**Phone—(732) 317-0089**
**Web—www.dealerappvantage.com**
**Email—info@dealerappvantage.com**
**136 11th St., Ste. 2, Piscataway 08854**

Delphus, Inc.
Phone—(973) 267-9269
152 Speedwell Ave., Morristown 07960

Desktop Alert, Inc.
Phone—(973) 727-0066
346 Main St., Chatham 07928

Dillistone Systems, Inc.
Phone—(201) 653-0013
50 Harrison St., Ste. 201-A, Hoboken 07030

Direct Computer Resources, Inc.
Phone—(201) 848-0018
120 Birch Rd., Franklin Lakes 07417

Drawbase Software
Phone—(973) 927-6814
1099 Wall St. W., Ste. 269, Lyndhurst 07071

DVTel, Inc.
Phone—(201) 368-9700
65 Challenger Rd., Ste. 2, Ridgefield Park 07660

ec2 Software Solutions
Phone—(732) 356-0070
400 Apgar Dr., Ste. I, Somerset 08873

Edmunds & Assocs.
Phone—(609) 645-7333
301-A Tilton Rd., Northfield 08225

Elevate HR, Inc.
Phone—(973) 917-3230
1055 Parsippany Blvd., Ste. 511, Parsippany 07054

Ellkay, LLC
Phone—(201) 791-0606
259 Seddle Ln., 3rd Fl., Teaneck 07666

Ericsson, Inc.
Phone—(732) 699-2000
1 Ericsson Dr., Piscataway 08854

EXP, Inc.
Phone—(732) 626-3700
285 Davidson Ave., Somerset 08873

eZCom Software, Inc.
Phone—(201) 883-1900
25 Rockwood Pl., Ste. 420, Englewood 07631

FemtoTek, Inc.
Phone—(609) 406-9680
865 Lower Ferry Rd., Ste. B-9, Ewing 08628

Folded Structures Co., LLC
Phone—(908) 237-1955
1142-A Old York Rd., Ringoes 08551

GL Consulting, Inc.
Phone—(201) 451-9121
1000 Plaza Three, Jersey City 07311

Glowpoint, Inc.
Phone—(973) 855-3411
430 Mountain Ave., Ste. 301, Murray Hill 07974

GrayHair Software, Inc.
Phone—(856) 727-9372
124 Gaither Dr., Ste. 160, Mount Laurel 08054

Grumium Labs
Phone—(732) 562-0001
4400 U.S. 9, Ste. 1000, Freehold 07728

GTBM
Phone—(201) 935-5090
351 Paterson Ave., East Rutherford 07073

Halberd Match Corp.
Phone—(609) 882-7000
1230 Parkway Ave., Ste. 306, Trenton 08628

Health Care Software, Inc.
Phone—(732) 938-5600
1350 Campus Pkwy., Neptune 07753

HealthTronics, Inc.
Phone—(973) 994-3220
354 Eisenhower Pkwy., Ste. 2150, Livingston 07039

High Speed Video
Phone—(201) 327-6801
19 Spear Rd., Ste. 104, Ramsey 07446

HumanConcepts
Phone—(908) 231-0204
1031 Route 22, Ste. 303, Bridgewater 08807

**INFINITT North America, Inc.**
**Medical imaging visualization & management software development**
**Phone—(908) 387-6960**
**Fax—(908) 387-6965**
**Web—www.infinittna.com**
**Email—sales@infinittna.com**
**755 Memorial Pkwy., Ste. 304, Phillipsburg 08865**

INFOLynx, Inc.
Phone—(201) 569-9085
500 Frank W. Burr Blvd., Ste. 14, Teaneck 07666

Informatica Corp.
Phone—(856) 642-4080
309 Fellowship Rd., Mount Laurel 08054

Infragistics, Inc.
Phone—(609) 448-2000
2 Commerce Dr., Cranbury 08512

Innovative Software Solutions, Inc. (H Q)
Phone—(856) 910-9190
3000 S. Lenola Rd., Maple Shade 08052

Insurance Services Office, Inc.
Phone—(201) 469-2000
545 Washington Blvd., Jersey City 07310

Integrated Business Systems, Inc.
Phone—(973) 575-4950
999 Riverview Dr., Ste. 280, Totowa 07512

Integrated Media Management, LLC
Phone—(908) 862-6600
330 Dalziel Rd., Linden 07036

Intellect Technologies, Inc.
Phone—(609) 454-3170
4301 U.S. Highway 1, Ste. 120, Monmouth Junction 08852

Intelligent Security Systems
Phone—(732) 855-1111
1480 U.S. Highway 9 N., Ste. 202, Woodbridge 07095

Ipacesetters
Phone—(201) 391-1500
135 Chestnut Ridge Rd., Ste. 2, Montvale 07645

iSpeech
Phone—(917) 338-7723
211 Warren St., Newark 07103

Jersey Cow Software Co., Inc.
Phone—(732) 422-0101
3031 State Route 27, Ste. A, Franklin Park 08823

Judy Lynn Software, Inc.
Phone—(732) 390-8845
278 Dunhams Corner Rd., P.O. Box 373, East Brunswick 08816

Knorr Assocs., Inc.
Phone—(973) 492-8500
10 Park Pl., P.O. Box 400, Butler 07405

L. S. Software Systems, Inc.
Phone—(732) 367-7164
419 12th St., Lakewood 08701

LabVantage Solutions, Inc.
Phone—(908) 707-4100
265 Davidson Ave., Somerset 08873

Lagniappe Health Acquisition Co.
Phone—(973) 256-7633
34 Maple Ave., Ste. 102, P.O. Box 727, Pine Brook 07058

Life Systems, Inc.
Phone—(973) 625-3716
75 E. Main St., Rockaway 07866

LOG-NET, Inc.
Phone—(732) 758-6800
230 Half Mile Rd., 3rd Fl., Red Bank 07701

Lumeta Corporation
Phone—(732) 357-3500
300 Atrium Dr., Ste. 302, Somerset 08873

Macrosoft, Inc.
Phone—(973) 889-0500
2 Sylvan Way, Parsippany 07054

Magestic Systems, Inc.
Phone—(201) 263-0090
205 Fairview Ave., Westwood 07675

Magnum Technologies, Inc.
Phone—(908) 546-7950
95 Mount Bethel Rd., Warren 07059

Marketing Advertising Promotions, Inc.
Phone—(973) 575-5656
4 Edison Pl., Fairfield 07004

Markov Processes International, LLC
Phone—(908) 608-1558
25 Deforest Ave., Ste. 102, Summit 07901

© Copyright 2015 Manufacturers' News, Inc.

## SOFTWARE DEVELOPMENT —
*(cont.)*

Med A-Z.Net, LLC
Phone—(609) 716-6991
37 Station Dr., Ste. 1-E, Princeton Junction 08550

MentisSoft, Inc.
Phone—(732) 568-4715
347 Plainfield Ave., Ste. 104, Edison 08817

MICROS Retail Systems, Inc.
Phone—(201) 866-1000
1500 Harbor Blvd., Ste. 2, Weehawken 07086

Moofwd, Inc.
Phone—(855) 266-6393
103 Carnegie Ctr., Ste. 209, Princeton 08540

Ness Technologies, Inc.
Phone—(201) 488-7222
300 Frank W. Burr Blvd., Teaneck 07666

Netcom Systems, Inc.
Phone—(732) 393-6100
200 Metroplex Dr., Edison 08817

NetWrix Corp.
Phone—(201) 490-8840
12 N. State Route 17, Ste. 104, Paramus 07652

Niksun, Inc.
Phone—(609) 936-9999
100 Nassau Park Blvd., 3rd Fl., Princeton 08540

Nxlevel Solutions
Phone—(609) 466-2828
57 Hamilton Ave., Ste. 303, Hopewell 08525

Objectif Lune, LLC
Phone—(973) 780-0100
300 Broadacres Dr., 4th Fl., Bloomfield 07003

Oli Systems, Inc.
Phone—(973) 539-4996
240 Cedar Knolls Rd., Ste. 301, Cedar Knolls 07927

OmniComm Systems, Inc.
Phone—(732) 960-2820
1100 Cornwall Rd., Ste. 111, Monmouth Junction 08852

One Source Solutions
Phone—(732) 536-0702
3 industrial Ct., Ste. 3, Freehold 07728

Oracle Corp.
Phone—(856) 359-2999
330 Fellowship Rd., Ste. 100, Mount Laurel 08054

Palayekar Cos., Inc.
Phone—(609) 426-0564
101 Interchange Plz., Ste. 105, Cranbury 08512

**Pantone LLC**
**Phone—(201) 935-5500 / (888) 726-8663**
**Fax—(201) 896-0242**
**Web—www.pantone.com**
**590 Commerce Blvd., Carlstadt 07072**

Pegasystems, Inc.
Phone—(201) 239-2300
111 Town Square Pl., Jersey City 07310

Princeton Payment Solutions
Phone—(609) 919-0700
501 Forrestal Rd., Ste. 324, Princeton 08540

Purchasingnet, Inc.
Phone—(732) 212-1500
125 Half Mile Rd., Red Bank 07701

QAD, Inc.
Phone—(856) 273-1717
10000 Midlantic Dr., Ste. 100 W., Mount Laurel 08054

QED Financial Systems, Inc.
Phone—(856) 797-1200
10000 Sagemore Dr., Ste. 10201, Marlton 08053

Quality Attributes Software
Phone—(732) 504-2200
1 Pelican Dr., Ste. 6, Bayville 08721

Quality Software Systems, Inc.
Phone—(732) 805-0400
80 Cottontail Ln., Ste. 105, Somerset 08873

Quest Diagnostics (H Q)
Phone—(973) 520-2700
3 Giralda Farms, Madison 07940

Ramco Systems Corp.
Phone—(609) 620-4871
3150 U.S. Highway 1, Ste. 130, Lawrence Township 08648

Raritan Computer, Inc.
Phone—(732) 764-8886
400 Cottontail Ln., Somerset 08873

RE Systems Group, Inc.
Phone—(201) 883-1572
1060 Main St., Ste. 200, River Edge 07661

Red Oak Software, Inc.
Phone—(973) 316-6064
115 U.S. Highway 46, Ste. F-1000, Mountain Lakes 07046

Relational Architects
Phone—(201) 420-0400
33 Newark St., Ste. 3-A, Hoboken 07030

Revelation Technologies, Inc.
Phone—(201) 594-1422
99 Kinderkamack Rd., Ste. 109, Westwood 07675

RightAnswers, Inc.
Phone—(732) 396-9010
333 Thornall St., Ste. 703, Edison 08837

Robertson Piper Software Group, Inc. (H Q)
Phone—(973) 435-3640
1500 Cardinal Dr., Chatham 07928

R-Squared Services & Solutions, Inc.
Phone—(866) 522-8558
12 Dean Ct., Princeton Junction 08550

SaaShr
Phone—(908) 722-9952
3040 U.S. Highway 22, Ste. 200, Somerville 08876

SAI Global, Inc.
Phone—(609) 955-5100
101 Morgan Ln., Ste. 301, Plainsboro 08536

Sawhney Systems, Inc.
Phone—(609) 987-5000
777 Alexander Rd., Ste. 204, Princeton 08540

Simtronics Corp.
Phone—(732) 747-0322
50 Birch Ave., Ste. 100, P.O. Box 38, Little Silver 07739

SiMX Corp.
Phone—(609) 750-9345
196 Princeton-Hightstown Rd., Bldg. 2-A, Princeton Junction 08550

Skila, A Sela2 Co.
Phone—(973) 889-1300
201 Littleton Rd., 2nd Fl., Morris Plains 07950

Slingo, Inc.
Phone—(201) 489-6727
411 Hackensack Ave., 8th Fl., Hackensack 07601

Sovereign Technology Corporation
Phone—(732) 298-8104
2200 River Rd., Unit A, Point Pleasant Boro 08742

Spacemaster, Inc.
Phone—(973) 429-1155
855 Bloomfield Ave., Glen Ridge 07028

Spirent Communications, Inc.
Phone—(908) 953-6000
211 Mount Airy Rd., Basking Ridge 07920

SQN Banking Systems, Inc.
Phone—(609) 261-5500
65 Indel Ave., P.O. Box 423, Rancocas 08073

Sterling Medical Devices
Phone—(201) 227-7569
17 Legion Pl., Rochelle Park 07662

Sterling System LLC
Phone—(732) 452-1881
22 Meridian Rd., Unit 10, Edison 08820

StrikeForce Technologies, Inc.
Phone—(732) 661-9641
1090 King Georges Post Rd., Ste. 603, Edison 08837

Syncsort, Inc.
Phone—(201) 930-9700
50 Tice Blvd., Ste. 250, Woodcliff Lake 07677

Timecruiser Computing Corp.
Phone—(973) 244-7856
9 Law Dr., Ste. 2, Fairfield 07004

Universal Business Systems, Inc.
Phone—(908) 725-8899
185 Industrial Pkwy., Ste. J, Somerville 08876

uReach Technologies, Inc.
Phone—(732) 335-5400
2137 State Highway 35, 1st Fl., Holmdel 07733

Ventraq, Inc.
Phone—(856) 866-1000
817 E. Gate Dr., Ste. 101, Mount Laurel 08054

Viamente, Inc.
Phone—(732) 686-7843
3600 State Route 66, Ste. 400, Neptune 07753

Visual Retail Plus, Inc.
Phone—(201) 678-9888
540 Hudson St., 4th Fl., Hackensack 07601

Vitech Systems Group, Inc.
Phone—(646) 344-5282
111 Wood Ave. S., Iselin 08830

vSplash Techlabs, Inc. (H Q)
Phone—(201) 355-0066
1050 Wall St. W., Ste. 630, Lyndhurst 07071

WellCare Today, LLC
Phone—(866) 656-1188
89 Headquarters Plz., Ste. 1461, Morristown 07960

World Software Corp.
Phone—(201) 444-3228
266 Harristown Rd., Ste. 201, Glen Rock 07452

Xybion Medical Systems
Phone—(973) 538-5111
201 Littleton Rd., Morris Plains 07950

## SOLAR ELECTRIC PANELS

Advanced Solar Products, Inc. (H Q)
Phone—(908) 751-5818
270 S. Main St., Ste. 203, Flemington 08822

Natcore Technology, Inc. (H Q)
Phone—(732) 576-8800
87 Maple Ave., Red Bank 07701

Petra System
Phone—(908) 462-5200
1 Cragwood Rd., Ste. 303, South Plainfield 07080

Sonali Energees USA, LLC (H Q)
Phone—(201) 297-1177
409 Grand Ave., Ste. 3, Englewood 07631

## SOLAR ENERGY EQUIPMENT

**Advanced Solar Products, Inc.**
**Phone—(908) 751-5818**
**Fax—(908) 751-5819**
**Web—www.advancedsolarproducts.com**
**Email—sales@advancedsolarproducts.com**
**270 S. Main St., Ste. 203, Flemington 08822**

Mobile Power International, LLC
Phone—(856) 784-3195
1010 Old Egg Harbor Rd., Voorhees 08043

## SOLAR ENERGY PRODUCTS

**Advanced Solar Products, Inc.**
**Phone—(908) 751-5818**
**Fax—(908) 751-5819**
**Web—www.advancedsolarproducts.com**
**Email—sales@advancedsolarproducts.com**
**270 S. Main St., Ste. 203, Flemington 08822**

Wattlots, LLC
Phone—(908) 626-1555
1932 Long Hill Rd., Millington 07946

## SOLAR THERMAL EQUIPMENT

Aquatherm Industries, Inc.
Phone—(732) 905-9002
1940 Rutgers University Blvd., Lakewood 08701

## SOLDERING FIXTURES

MB Mfg., Inc.
Phone—(908) 362-5588
1 Gwinup Rd., Blairstown 07825

## SOLDERING FLUXES

Canfield Technologies/Bow Electronic Solder
Phone—(732) 316-2100
1 S. Crossman Rd., Sayreville 08872

OKAI Corp.
Phone—(908) 687-4443
687 Lehigh Ave., Ste. 3, Union 07083

## SOLDERING IRONS

Hexacon Electric Co.
Phone—(908) 245-6200
161 W. Clay Ave., Roselle Park 07204

## SOLDERS

Coining, Inc.
Phone—(201) 791-4020
15 Mercedes Dr., Montvale 07645

## SOLDERS — (cont.)

**Scientific Alloys Corp.**
Spheres, Solders, Metal Powder Balls, Precious Metals
Phone—(973) 478-8323
Fax—(973) 478-6780
Web—www.bgaspheres.com
Email—bgaspheres@aol.com
5 Troast Ct., Clifton 07011
*(see our ad Outside Front Cover)*

## SOLENOIDS

**Americor Electronics, Ltd.**
Phone—(847) 956-6200 / (800) 830-5337
Fax—(847) 956-0300
Web—www.americor-usa.com
Email—info@americor-usa.com
675 S. Lively Blvd., Elk Grove Village, IL 60007
*(see our ads under CABLE ASSEMBLIES & CORD SETS)*
**Electromotive, Inc.**
Phone—(973) 564-8809
55 Brown Ave., Springfield 07081
**NResearch, Inc.**
Manufacturer of Chemically Inert Valves
Phone—(973) 808-8811
Fax—(973) 808-0086
Web—www.nresearch.com
Email—sales@nresearch.com
267 Fairfield Ave., West Caldwell 07006
*(see our ad under VALVES—Solenoid)*

## SOLVENT RECOVERY SYSTEMS

**Veolia ES Technical Solutions, LLC**
Recycling Industrial Solvents
Phone—(732) 469-5100
Fax—(732) 469-1957
Web—www.veoliaes.com
Email—ray.clark@veolia.com
125 Factory Ln., Middlesex 08846
*(see our ad under SOLVENT RECYCLING)*

## SOLVENT RECYCLING

**Veolia ES Technical Solutions, LLC**
Recycling Industrial Solvents
Phone—(732) 469-5100
Fax—(732) 469-1957
Web—www.veoliaes.com
Email—ray.clark@veolia.com
125 Factory Ln., Middlesex 08846

---

**Veolia ES Technical Solutions, LLC**

*Solvent recycling*

**(732) 469-5100**
**Fax: (732) 469-1957**

*www.veoliaes.com*

125 Factory Ln., Middlesex, NJ 08846

---

## SOLVENTS

**Phoenix Resins, Inc.**
Phone—(856) 303-9245
602 Union Landing Rd., Cinnaminson 08077

## SOUND CONTROL SYSTEMS

**Sound Management Group**
Phone—(908) 874-7826
5 Ilene Ct., Bldg. 7, Unit 3, P.O. Box 6060, Hillsborough 08844

## SOUND SYSTEMS

**Oklahoma Sound Corp.**
Phone—(973) 594-9000
149 Entin Rd., Clifton 07014
**Sound Environments, LLC**
Phone—(732) 840-6600
1133 Industrial Pkwy., Ste. E, Brick 08724
**Systems Design Technology**
Phone—(732) 571-4547
P.O. Box 547, West Long Branch 07764

## SOUP BASES

**Eatem Foods Company**
Phone—(856) 692-1663
1829 Gallagher Dr., Vineland 08360

## SOUPS

**Aunt Kitty's Foods, Inc.**
Phone—(856) 691-2100
270 N. Mill Rd., Vineland 08360
**Campbell Soup Co. (H Q)**
Phone—(856) 342-4800
1 Campbell Pl., Camden 08103
**Tabatchnick Fine Foods, Inc.**
Phone—(732) 247-6668
1230 Hamilton St., P.O. Box 356, Somerset 08873
**Ugo Di Lullo & Sons**
Phone—(856) 456-3700
1004 Edgewater Ave., P.O. Box 126, Westville 08093

## SOYBEAN PRODUCTS

**National Lecithin, Inc. (H Q)**
Phone—(973) 940-8920
93 Spring St., Ste. 303, Newton 07860
**WhiteWave Foods Co.**
Phone—(856) 459-3890
70 Rosenhayn Ave., Bridgeton 08302

## SPECTROMETERS

**Spectro Analytical Instruments, Inc.**
Phone—(201) 642-3000
91 McKee Dr., Mahwah 07430

## SPECTROPHOTOMETERS

**Datacolor**
Phone—(609) 924-2189
5 Princess Rd., Lawrenceville 08648

## SPHERES — BGA & PGA

**Scientific Alloys Corp.**
Spheres, Solders, Metal Powder Balls, Precious Metals
Phone—(973) 478-8323
Fax—(973) 478-6780
Web—www.bgaspheres.com
Email—bgaspheres@aol.com
5 Troast Ct., Clifton 07011
*(also see our ad Outside Front Cover)*

---

**SCIENTIFIC ALLOYS CORP.**

*Spheres • Solders • Metal Powder Balls • Precious Metals*

**WWW.BGASPHERES.COM**
**973-478-8323 • Fax: 973-478-6780**
5 Troast Ct. Clifton, NJ 07011

---

## SPICES

**Bunge North America, Inc.**
Phone—(201) 467-0200
125 Sanford Ave., Kearny 07032
**ConAgra Food Ingredients**
Phone—(609) 409-6200
6 Santa Fe Way, Cranbury 08512
**Gel Spice Co., Inc.**
Phone—(201) 339-0700
48 Hook Rd., P.O. Box 285, Bayonne 07002
**Kalustyan Corp.**
Spices, herbs & seasonings
Phone—(908) 688-6111
Fax—(908) 688-4415
Web—www.kalustyan.com
Email—kerri@kalustyan.com
855 Rahway Ave., Union 07083
**Mincing Overseas Spice Co.**
Phone—(732) 355-9944
10 Tower Rd., Bldg. KN, Dayton 08810

**Schiff Food Products Co., Inc.**
Phone—(973) 237-1990
994 Riverview Dr., Totowa 07512
**Spice Co.**
Phone—(732) 499-9070
6-C Terminal Way, Avenel 07001

## SPLICERS

**Associated Pile & Fitting**
Phone—(973) 773-8400
8 Wood Hollow Rd., Plz. 1, P.O. Box 5933, Parsippany 07054
**Vytran, LLC**
Phone—(732) 972-2880
1400 Campus Dr., Morganville 07751

## SPONGES

**Supply Plus, Inc.**
Phone—(973) 782-5930
155 Sherman Ave., Paterson 07502

## SPORTING GOODS

**Akadema, Inc.**
Phone—(973) 304-1470
140 5th Ave., Hawthorne 07506
**Aurorae (H Q)**
Phone—(551) 579-4003
46 N. Central Ave., Ramsey 07446
**Century Sports**
Phone—(732) 905-4422
1715 Oak St., Ste. 1, Lakewood 08701
**Enor Corp.**
Phone—(201) 750-1680
245 Livingston St., Northvale 07647
**Sportstar**
Phone—(732) 254-9214
19 Thomas St., South River 08882
**Suspended Aquatic Mentor**
Phone—(973) 376-3335
628 South Ave., Garwood 07027
**Venus Knitting Mills, Inc.**
Phone—(908) 464-2400
140 Spring St., Bldg. 1, New Providence 07974

## SPORTS & ATHLETIC EQUIPMENT

**Blue Gauntlet Fencing Gear, Inc.**
Phone—(201) 797-3332
280 N. Midland Ave., Bldg. W, Saddle Brook 07663
**Farrier Sporting Goods, Inc.**
Phone—(201) 891-9520
Godwin & Crescent Aves., Wyckoff 07481
**XO Athletic Co.**
Phone—(908) 964-1242
911 Springfield Rd., Union 07083

## SPORTSWEAR

**Capco Sportswear Inc. (H Q)**
Phone—(201) 939-9228
100 W. Commercial Ave., Moonachie 07074
**Central Mills, Inc.**
Phone—(732) 329-2009
473 Ridge Rd., Dayton 08810
**Mizrak**
Phone—(973) 622-0328
288 Livingston Ave., 1st Fl., Lyndhurst 07071

## SPORTSWEAR — Children's

**Sew In Style, Inc.**
Phone—(201) 868-8568
220 61st St., West New York 07093

## SPORTSWEAR — Women's

**RMI Hoobing**
Phone—(609) 387-1999
460 Veterans Dr., Burlington 08016
**Sno Skins, Inc. (H Q)**
Phone—(973) 884-8801
11 Melanie Ln., Ste. 3, East Hanover 07936

## Foremost Fire Protection, LLC

Fire Sprinkler Contractor

# 908-753-8244
### Fax: 908-753-8850

P.O. Box 434 • South Plainfield, NJ 07080

### Email: foremostfire@msn.com

## SPRAY DRYING SERVICES

American Custom Drying Co.
  Phone—(609) 387-3933
  109 Elbow Ln., Burlington 08016

## SPRAY PAINTING

**Bridgeview Industrial Finishers, Inc.**
  Serving Camden, Burlington, Gloucester Counties NJ
  & Philadelphia Areas
  Phone—(856) 768-3624
  Fax—(856) 768-2218
  Web—www.bvfinishers.com
  241 Terrace Blvd., Voorhees 08043
    *(see our ad under POWDER COATING)*
**SAR Industrial Finishing, Inc.**
  Phone—(609) 567-2772
  Fax—(609) 567-2494
  Email—jsmauro@comcast.net
  104 N. Route 73, Berlin 08009

## SPRAYING EQUIPMENT

**Peterson & Sons Tree Service, Inc.**
  Phone—(973) 347-0453
  Fax—(973) 347-0980
  P.O. Box 11, Stanhope 07874

## SPRINGS

Alfred & William, Inc.
  Phone—(908) 686-3000
  P.O. Box 364, Union 07083
Atlantic Spring Co.
  137 Highway 202 S., Ringoes 08551
  Phone—(908) 788-5800
  P.O. Box 650, Flemington 08822

---

### Atlantic Spring Co.
*Custom Metal Springs*
www.mw-ind.com / (980) 788-5800
137 Highway 202 S.
Ringoes, NJ 08551

---

Eureka Spring Co.
  999 Rahway Ave., Union 07083
  Springs for machinery & equipment
  Phone—(973) 589-4960
  Fax—(973) 589-0103
  Email—contactus@eurekaspringco.com
  P.O. Box 5067, Newark 07105
Murphy & Read Spring Mfg. Co.
  Phone—(856) 829-6887
  617 W. 6th St., P.O. Box 211, Palmyra 08065

## SPRINGS — Automotive

Jenson & Mitchell, Inc.
  Phone—(201) 332-4140
  880 Communipaw Ave., Jersey City 07304
R & H Spring & Truck Repair, Inc.
  Phone—(732) 681-9000
  4806 W. Hurley Pond Rd., Belmar 07719

## SPRINKLERS — Fire

**Fire Tech Automatic Sprinkler**
  Registered Woman-Owned Business
  Phone—(856) 228-7189
  Fax—(856) 228-7351
  Email—firetechsprinkler@comcast.net
  121 Blackwood Barnsboro Rd., Sewell 08080
**Foremost Fire Protection, LLC**
  Phone—(908) 753-8244
  Fax—(908) 753-8850
  Email—foremostfire@msn.com
  P.O. Box 434, South Plainfield 07080
    *(see our ad on this page)*
**Northeast Fire Protection**
  Phone—(908) 362-5400
  Email—estimating@northeastfire.us
  155 State Route 94, Ste. 5, Blairstown 07825

## STAGE EQUIPMENT & SUPPLIES

BML Blackbird Theatrical Services, Inc.
  Phone—(201) 617-8900
  1 Aquarium Dr., Secaucus 07094

## STAINLESS STEEL

Falcon Stainless & Alloys Corp.
  Phone—(201) 670-8300
  39 Hewson Ave., Ste. A, Waldwick 07463
**Rancocas Metals Corp.**
  A full service metals center, stocking a vast inventory
  of almost every non-ferrous metal in a wide array of
  sizes & shapes
  Phone—(609) 267-4120 / (800) 762-6382
  Fax—(609) 267-5690
  Web—www.rancocasmetals.com
  Email—sales@rancocasmetals.com
  35 Indel Ave., P.O. Box 223, Rancocas 08073
    *(see our ad under METAL SERVICE CENTERS)*

## STAINLESS STEEL BAR

**East Coast Stainless, Inc.**
  Stainless C-276, Alloy 20, 321, 347, 400, 410, 600, 625,
  800, 825 & Chrome-Moly
  Phone—(302) 366-0675
  Fax—(302) 366-0691
  Web—www.eastcoaststainless.com
  Email—sales@eastcoaststainless.com
  30 Albe Dr., Ste. E, Newark, DE 19702
    *(see our ad under PIPE—Stainless Steel)*
G M Stainless, Inc.
  Phone—(908) 575-1834
  41 Imclone Dr., Branchburg 08876

## STAINLESS STEEL DISTRIBUTORS

Midlantic Metals
  Phone—(856) 963-2822
  2201 Mount Ephraim Ave., Ste. 90, Camden
  08104
RM Metals
  Phone—(908) 222-1500
  50 Cragwood Rd., South Plainfield 07080
Summit Stainless Steel, LLC
  Phone—(732) 297-9505
  2001 Elizabeth St., North Brunswick 08902

## STAINLESS STEEL FABRICATORS

A R J Custom Fabrication, Inc.
  Phone—(609) 695-6227
  151 Taylor St., Trenton 08638
**Arntzen Corp.**
  Mfr. Of Rolled & Welded Steel Cylinders-Cones-Pipe-
  Shapes-Fittings
  Phone—(815) 334-0788 / (800) 957-7655
  Fax—(815) 334-0778
  Web—www.ArntzenRolling.com
  Email—Sales@ArntzenCorp.com
  14600 Washington St., Woodstock, IL 60098
Marlo Mfg. Co., Inc.
  Phone—(973) 423-0226
  301 Division St., Boonton 07005
**Passaic County Welders, Inc.**
  Two northern New Jersey plants, with 45,000 sq. ft. of
  manufacturing area, producing a wide range of
  custom products, including plate, structural, sheet &
  bar products in carbon steel, stainless steel &
  aluminum
  Phone—(973) 696-1200
  Fax—(973) 696-1411
  Web—www.pcwfab.com
  Email—robert@pcwfab.com
  100 Parish Dr., Wayne 07470
    *(see our ad under STEEL FABRICATING)*
STE Fabrication, Inc.
  Phone—(732) 274-0024
  28 Haypress Rd., Ste. 106, Cranbury 08512
**Versatile Welding Group, LLC**
  Steel & Aluminum
  Phone—(908) 298-8900 / (877) 939-5348
  Fax—(908) 298-9550
  Web—www.versatile-us.com
  Email—jimd@versatile-us.com
  340 Cox St., Roselle 07203
    *(see our ad under STEEL FABRICATING)*

## STAINLESS STEEL PARTS

Robert-James Sales, Inc.
  Phone—(609) 860-0900
  9 Corporate Dr., P.O. Box B, Cranbury 08512

## STAINS

Dudley Chemical Corp.
  Phone—(732) 886-3100
  125 Kenyon Dr., Ste. 1, Lakewood 08701
Target Coatings, Inc.
  Phone—(800) 752-9922
  17-12 River Rd., Fair Lawn 07410

## STAIRS

DMD Stairs & Rails, LLC
  Phone—(732) 901-0102
  370 Whitesville Rd., Ste. 8, Jackson 08527
**Legacy Stairs & Millwork, Inc.**
  Phone—(732) 905-7705
  Fax—(732) 905-7750
  Web—www.legacystairs.com
  Email—sales@legacystairs.com
  1000 Airport Rd., Ste. 104, Lakewood 08701

*continuing the tradition of exceeding expectations of personal service*

**LEGACY STAIRS & MILLWORK, INC**

expert layout, specification & cad design • conventional, curved &
custom staircases • standard & specialty railing and stair installations
**Phone 732-905-7705 • Fax 732-905-7750**
www.legacystairs.com • sales@legacystairs.com
1000 Airport Rd. • Ste 104 Lakewood, NJ 08701

## STAIRS — Iron & Steel

Baldi Iron Works, Inc.
  Phone—(973) 751-4338
  158 Belmont Ave., Belleville 07109

---

*Do nationwide searches for
products & services at:*
**IndustryNet.com**

INDUSTRY

## STAIRS — Iron & Steel — *(cont.)*

**Legacy Stairs & Millwork, Inc.**
Phone—(732) 905-7705
Fax—(732) 905-7750
Web—www.legacystairs.com
Email—sales@legacystairs.com
1000 Airport Rd., Ste. 104, Lakewood 08701
*(see our ad under STAIRS)*

Papp Iron Works, Inc.
Phone—(908) 731-1000
950 S. 2nd St., P.O. Box 3149, Plainfield 07063

Portuguese Structural Steel, Inc.
Phone—(973) 344-1342
Fax—(973) 344-1730
Web—www.portuguesesteel.com
Email—paula@portuguesesteel.com
255 South St., Newark 07114
*(see our ad under STRUCTURAL STEEL FABRICATION)*

## STAIRS — Spiral

**Ciccone Custom Railing & Manufacturing, Inc.**
Custom Metal Spiral Stairs
Phone—(732) 349-7071
Fax—(732) 349-7079
Web—www.cicconerailing.com
Email—customrailing@gmail.com
2002 Route 9, Toms River 08755

Legacy Stairs & Millwork, Inc.
Phone—(732) 905-7705
Fax—(732) 905-7750
Web—www.legacystairs.com
Email—sales@legacystairs.com
1000 Airport Rd., Ste. 104, Lakewood 08701
*(see our ad under STAIRS)*

## STAIRS — Wooden

Alvaro Stairs, LLC
Phone—(201) 864-6754
4201 Tonnelle Ave., Ste. 12, North Bergen 07047

American Stair & Rail Artisans, LLC
Phone—(732) 363-3734
687 Prospect St., Ste. 420, Lakewood 08701

B & C Custom Wood Handrail Corp.
Phone—(732) 530-6640
131 Dr. James Parker Blvd., P.O. Box 2008, Red Bank 07701

Distinctive Woodworking
Phone—(609) 877-8122
703 Van Rossum Ave., Unit 1, Beverly 08010

G & G Stairs
Phone—(732) 905-3083
2559 U.S. Highway 9, Howell 07731

Glen Rock Stair Corp.
Phone—(201) 337-9595
551 Commerce St., Franklin Lakes 07417

Greenbrook Stairs, Inc.
Phone—(908) 221-9145
14 Dayton St., Bernardsville 07924

Iacovelli Stairs, Inc.
Phone—(609) 693-3476
707 Challenger Way, Forked River 08731

Kaufman Stairs, Inc.
Phone—(732) 388-9870
150 E. Inman Ave., Rahway 07065

**Legacy Stairs & Millwork, Inc.**
Phone—(732) 905-7705
Fax—(732) 905-7750
Web—www.legacystairs.com
Email—sales@legacystairs.com
1000 Airport Rd., Ste. 104, Lakewood 08701
*(see our ad under STAIRS)*

Maranatha Ceramic Tile & Marble, Inc.
Phone—(609) 758-1168
253 Cookstown New Egypt Rd., Wrightstown 08562

R & R Stairs, Inc.
Phone—(732) 752-9400
131 Wood Ave., Middlesex 08846

Specialty Stair & Rail, LLC
Phone—(732) 359-8174
1717 State Route 34 Cliff St., Bldg. 8, P.O. Box 642, Farmingdale 07727

Wood Products, Inc.
Phone—(609) 859-0303
34 Allentown Rd., Southampton 08088

## STAMPINGS

Semiconductor Mfg.
Metal Stampings of BGA & PGA Spheres & Wire Balls
Phone—(973) 478-2880
Fax—(973) 478-6780
Web—www.bgaspheres.com
Email—bgaspheres@aol.com
5 Troast Ct., Clifton 07011

## STAMPINGS — Brass

Stamping.com, Inc.
Phone—(732) 493-4697
Fax—(732) 493-3493
Web—www.stampinginc.com
Email—stamping@juno.com
3600 Sunset Ave., Asbury Park 07712
*(see our ad under METAL STAMPINGS)*

## STAMPINGS — Fourslide

R L R Foil Stamping, LLC
Phone—(973) 778-9464
245 4th St., Passaic 07055

## STAMPINGS — Multislide

Stamping.com, Inc.
Phone—(732) 493-4697
Fax—(732) 493-3493
Web—www.stampinginc.com
Email—stamping@juno.com
3600 Sunset Ave., Asbury Park 07712
*(see our ad under METAL STAMPINGS)*

## STAMPINGS — Precision

Stamping.com, Inc.
Phone—(732) 493-4697
Fax—(732) 493-3493
Web—www.stampinginc.com
Email—stamping@juno.com
3600 Sunset Ave., Asbury Park 07712
*(see our ad under METAL STAMPINGS)*

## STAPLES AND STAPLING DEVICES

Arrow Fastener Co., LLC
Phone—(201) 843-6900
271 Mayhill St., Saddle Brook 07663

## STARCHES

Ingredion Incorporated (H Q)
Phone—(908) 685-5555
10 Finderne Ave., Ste. C, Bridgewater 08807

## STARTERS — Automotive

Middlesex Armature Service
Phone—(732) 634-3779
1155 Saint Georges Ave., Colonia 07067

Quality Rebuilders
Phone—(732) 222-9100
617 Broadway, Long Branch 07740

## STATIONERY

Engraved Images
Phone—(908) 234-0323
Route 202 & Demun Pl., P.O. Box 966, Far Hills 07931

## STEAM GENERATORS

**Electro-Steam Generator Corp.**
Email: bweigle@electrosteam.com
Phone—(609) 288-9071
Fax—(609) 288-9078
Web—www.electrosteam.com
50 Indel Ave., P.O. Box 438, Rancocas 08073

Steamist, Inc.
Phone—(201) 933-5800
25 E. Union Ave., East Rutherford 07073

## STEAM TRAPS

Selick & Bird Thermidaire
Phone—(732) 449-0017
2180 Village Rd., P.O. Box 108, Sea Girt 08750

## STEEL

Commercial Metals Co.
CMC-East Mills
Phone—(800) 621-0262
Fax—(205) 591-4554
Web—www.cmc.com
Email—salesse@cmc.com
101 S. 50th St., Birmingham, AL 35212

Erasteel, Inc.
Phone—(973) 335-8400
95 Fulton St., Boonton 07005

Metal Stock
Phone—(609) 394-1129
471 Southard St., Trenton 08638

## STEEL — Galvanized

Nicholas Galvanizing Co.
Phone—(201) 795-1010
120 Duffield Ave., Jersey City 07306

## STEEL — Hot Rolled

Commercial Metals Co.
CMC-East Mills
Phone—(800) 621-0262
Fax—(205) 591-4554
Web—www.cmc.com
Email—salesse@cmc.com
101 S. 50th St., Birmingham, AL 35212

Newark Steel & Ornamental Supply
Phone—(973) 424-9790
41-43 Frelinghuysen Ave., Newark 07114

## STEEL — Reinforcing

**Bayshore Rebar Inc.**
Reinforcing steel erection post tension specialist
Phone—(609) 484-8900
Fax—(609) 484-8969
Web—www.bayshorerebar.com
Email—info@bayshorerebar.com
1509 S. New Rd., Pleasantville 08232
*(see our ad under CONCRETE REINFORCING STEEL)*

Commercial Metals Co.
CMC-East Mills
Phone—(800) 621-0262
Fax—(205) 591-4554
Web—www.cmc.com
Email—salesse@cmc.com
101 S. 50th St., Birmingham, AL 35212

Meadow Burke Products
Phone—(201) 242-8989
269 Commercial Ave., Palisades Park 07650

## STEEL BARS

Commercial Metals Co.
CMC-East Mills
Phone—(800) 621-0262
Fax—(205) 591-4554
Web—www.cmc.com
Email—salesse@cmc.com
101 S. 50th St., Birmingham, AL 35212

Gerdau US, Inc., Sayreville
Phone—(732) 721-6600
N. Crossman Rd., P.O. Box 249, Sayreville 08872

## STEEL CUTTING

Jason Steel Co., Inc.
Phone—(856) 663-5010
1701 Hylton Rd., Pennsauken 08110

Mokes Steel, Inc.
Phone—(908) 241-5344
280 Cox St., Roselle 07203

*find additional suppliers at*
**IndustryNet.com**

# CERTIFIED STEEL COMPANY

*Steel Distributors & Warehouses*

## 800.466.7660 • Fax: 609.392.6372

### www.certifiedsteel.com

1333 Brunswick Ave., Ste. 200 Lawrenceville, NJ 08648

## STEEL DISTRIBUTORS & WAREHOUSES

AZCO Steel Co.
Phone—(908) 754-8700
1641 New Market Ave., South Plainfield 07080

**Certified Steel Company (H Q)**
**Phone—(609) 396-7600 / (800) 466-7660**
**Fax—(609) 392-6372**
**Web—www.certifiedsteel.com**
**Email—info@certifiedsteel.com**
**1333 Brunswick Ave., Ste. 200, Lawrenceville 08648**
*(see our ad on this page)*

**De Jong Iron Works, Inc.**
**And supply**
**Phone—(973) 684-1633**
**Fax—(973) 684-2309**
**Web—www.dejongiron.com**
**Email—john@dejongiron.com**
**P.O. Box 532, Hawthorne 07507**

KOPO International, Inc.
Phone—(732) 203-1505
100 Village Ct., Ste. 202, Hazlet 07730

**Metals USA, Plates & Shapes Group**
**Phone—(973) 242-1000 / (800) 524-1203**
**Fax—(973) 242-2246**
**Web—www.metalsusa.com**
**182 Frelinghuysen Ave., Newark 07114**

**Samson Metal Service**
2604 Route 130 N., Cranbury 08512
Distributor of Steel, Aluminum & Other Metals
**Phone—(609) 655-0777**
**Fax—(609) 655-3705**
**Web—www.sam-metals.com**
**Email—info@sam-metals.com**
**P.O. Box 421, Dayton 08810**

## Samson Metal Service

*Distributor of Steel, Aluminum & Other Metals*

### 609-655-0777
### Fax: 609-655-3705

### www.sam-metals.com
### info@sam-metals.com

2604 Route 130 N.
Cranbury, NJ 08512

Stulz Sickles Steel Co.
Phone—(800) 351-1776
929 Julia St., Elizabeth 07201

## STEEL FABRICATING
### (also see 'Stainless Steel Fabricators')

Ajay Metal Fabricators, Inc.
Phone—(908) 523-0558
355 Dalziel Rd., Linden 07036

Alessandra Miscellaneous Metalworks, Inc.
Phone—(973) 786-6805
75-B Mill St., Newton 07860

Allweld Iron
Phone—(201) 434-8750
160 Culber Ave., Jersey City 07305

Archer Day
Phone—(732) 417-0333
18 Mileed Way, Avenel 07001

**Arntzen Corp.**
**Mfr. Of Rolled & Welded Steel Cylinders-Cones-Pipe-Shapes-Fittings**
**Phone—(815) 334-0788 / (800) 957-7655**
**Fax—(815) 334-0778**
**Web—www.ArntzenRolling.com**
**Email—Sales@ArntzenCorp.com**
**14600 Washington St., Woodstock, IL 60098**

B & L Industrial Services, Inc.
Phone—(609) 386-9500
700 Park Ave., Unit 7, Hainesport 08036

Burgess Steel Erectors Of New Jersey, LLC
Phone—(201) 871-3500
200 W. Forest Ave., P.O. Box 5629, Englewood 07631

Century Fabricating Co., Inc.
Phone—(732) 495-3200
84 Railroad Ave., Belford 07718

Cornell & Co., Inc.
Phone—(856) 742-1900
224 Cornell Ln., Westville 08093

Custom Steel Contractors, Inc.
Phone—(973) 344-4449
17 Eastern Rd., Kearny 07032

D E B Maintenance, Inc.
Phone—(856) 786-0440
1000 Union Landing Rd., P.O. Box 13, Riverton 08077

Doran, LLC
Phone—(908) 289-9200
599 Green Ln., Union 07083

Fitzgerald Custom Fabrication, Inc.
Phone—(609) 652-8899
733 W. Bay Ave., Barnegat 08005

G & M Welding & Fabricating, Inc.
Phone—(856) 931-0443
31 W. Browning Rd., Bellmawr 08031

Garafano & Sons, Peter
Phone—(973) 278-0350
500 Marshall St., Paterson 07503

Grammer, Dempsey & Hudson Co.
Phone—(973) 589-8000
212 Rome St., Newark 07105

Grimmer & Sons, Inc., C. W.
Phone—(732) 741-2189
75 Gilbert St. W., Tinton Falls 07701

Harris Structural Steel Co., Inc.
Phone—(732) 752-6070
1640 New Market Ave., South Plainfield 07080

Hilman Rollers
Phone—(732) 462-6277 / (888) 276-5548
Fax—(732) 462-6355
Web—www.hilmanrollers.com
Email—sales@hilmanrollers.com
12 Timber Ln., P.O. Box 45, Marlboro 07746
*(see our ad under JACKS—Hydraulic)*

Holtec International (H Q)
Phone—(856) 797-0900
555 Lincoln Dr. W., Ste. 1, Marlton 08053

Integrity Iron Works Inc.
Phone—(732) 254-2200
33 Brookside Ave., P.O. Box 129, Sayreville 08872

Jersey Shore Steel, Inc.
Phone—(732) 833-8855
636 Herman Rd., Jackson 08527

Kurth & Son, Inc., Edward
Phone—(856) 227-8811
220 Blackwood Barnsboro Rd., Sewell 08080

L & L Welding Contractors, Inc.
Phone—(609) 395-1600
3 Wheeling Rd., Dayton 08810

Liberty Mechanical Contractors, Inc.
Phone—(973) 344-6131
330 Raymond Blvd., Newark 07105

MacElroy Co., Inc., J. C.
Phone—(732) 572-7100
91 Ethel Rd. W., Piscataway 08854

Maltese Iron Works, Inc., John
Phone—(732) 249-4350
1453 Jersey Ave., P.O. Box 7161, North Brunswick 08902

McNICHOLS Co.
Phone—(732) 509-3092
2 Home News Row, New Brunswick 08901

**Miletta Brothers, Inc.**
**Phone—(856) 447-4652**
**Fax—(856) 447-4699**
**Web—www.milettabrothers.net**
**Email—milettabrothersinc@verizon.net**
**194 Main St., Cedarville 08311**

Modelsmith International, Inc.
Phone—(201) 714-9519
66 Willow Ave., 2nd Fl., Hoboken 07030

Oceanic Metals LLC
Phone—(201) 662-1192
8555 Tonnelle Ave., Ste. 404, North Bergen 07047

Park Steel & Iron Co. (H Q)
Phone—(732) 775-7500
9 Evergreen Ave., Neptune City 07753

**Passaic County Welders, Inc.**
**Two northern New Jersey plants, with 45,000 sq. ft. of manufacturing area, producing a wide range of custom products, including plate, structural, sheet & bar products in carbon steel, stainless steel & aluminum**
**Phone—(973) 696-1200**
**Fax—(973) 696-1411**
**Web—www.pcwfab.com**
**Email—robert@pcwfab.com**
**100 Parish Dr., Wayne 07470**
*(see our ad on next page)*

Rahway Steel, Inc.
Phone—(732) 388-5300
625 Leesville Ave., P.O. Box 276, Rahway 07065

RCC Fabricators, Inc.
Phone—(609) 859-9350
2035 Highway 206, Vincentown 08088

Richards Industries Co.
Phone—(973) 575-7480
4 Fairfield Crescent, West Caldwell 07006

Russo & Sons, Inc., Thomas
Phone—(201) 332-4159
854 Communipaw Ave., Jersey City 07304

Shrop's Shop
Phone—(609) 465-1640
1254 S. Route 9, Cape May Court House 08210

Springfield Heating & Air Conditioning Co., Inc.
Phone—(908) 233-8400
217 Sheffield St., Mountainside 07092

Tamburri Assocs.
Phone—(856) 829-4000
1401 Industrial Hwy., Cinnaminson 08077

Tri-Steel Fabricators, Inc.
Phone—(609) 392-8660
501 Prospect St., Trenton 08618

Unlimited Steel Fabricators, Inc.
Phone—(732) 356-7534
840 Lincoln Blvd., Middlesex 08846

## STEEL FABRICATING — (cont.)

**Van Grouw Welding & Fabricating**
Also On Site Welding & Misc Steel Work
Phone—(201) 891-4199
Fax—(201) 847-0132
Email—vangrouw001@optonline.net
430 W. Main St., Wyckoff 07481

**Versatile Welding Group, LLC**
Steel & Aluminum
Phone—(908) 298-8900 / (877) 939-5348
Fax—(908) 298-9550
Web—www.versatile-us.com
Email—jimd@versatile-us.com
340 Cox St., Roselle 07203
*(see our ad on this page)*

Victory Iron Works, Inc.
Phone—(973) 427-4498
780 Mountain Ave., Wyckoff 07481

## STEEL FRAMING

Super Stud Building Products, Inc.
Phone—(732) 662-6200
2960 Woodbridge Ave., Edison 08837

## STEEL PROCESSING

Amerinox Processing, Inc.
Phone—(856) 963-2200
2201 Mount Ephraim Ave., Bldg. 90, Camden 08104
Camden Yards Steel Co., LLC
Phone—(856) 342-7100
2500 Broadway, Drawer 14, Camden 08104
Colonial Processing, Inc.
Phone—(856) 966-3313
1930 S. 6th St., Camden 08104
Jersey Cooperage Co.
Phone—(732) 254-1765
20 River Rd., Sayreville 08872
**Rover & Son Iron & Steel Co., F.**
(FRSCO Corp.)
Phone—(973) 484-7668
Fax—(973) 484-9496
516 Central Ave., Harrison 07029
*(see our ad under SCRAP IRON & METAL RECYCLING)*
Skyline Steel, LLC (H Q)
Phone—(973) 428-6100
8 Woodhollow Rd., Ste. 102, Parsippany 07054

## STEEL PRODUCTS

Duferco Steel, Inc. (H Q)
Phone—(732) 566-3130
100 Matawan Rd., Ste. 400, Matawan 07747
International Wire Co.
Phone—(732) 968-8122
27-E Kearney St., Bridgewater 08807

## STEEL ROLLING

**Arntzen Corp.**
Mfr. Of Rolled & Welded Steel Cylinders-Cones-Pipe-Shapes-Fittings
Phone—(815) 334-0788 / (800) 957-7655
Fax—(815) 334-0778
Web—www.ArntzenRolling.com
Email—Sales@ArntzenCorp.com
14600 Washington St., Woodstock, IL 60098

## STEEL SERVICE CENTERS

Allied Steel Distribution & Service Center
Phone—(973) 824-7347
118-144 Harper St., Newark 07114
Certified Steel Co.
Phone—(609) 890-7000
199 Whitehead Rd., Hamilton 08619
**Certified Steel Company (H Q)**
Phone—(609) 396-7600 / (800) 466-7660
Fax—(609) 392-6372
Web—www.certifiedsteel.com
Email—info@certifiedsteel.com
1333 Brunswick Ave., Ste. 200, Lawrenceville 08648
*(see our ad under STEEL DISTRIBUTORS & WAREHOUSES)*
Eddie Kane Steel Products, Inc.
Phone—(609) 392-1161
450 Southard St., Trenton 08638

Eddie Kane Steel Products, Inc. (H Q)
Phone—(732) 974-3339
P.O. Box 133, Spring Lake 07762
Gerber Metal Supply Co.
Phone—(908) 823-9150
2 Boundary Rd., Somerville 08876
Independent Metal Sales, Inc.
Phone—(609) 261-8090
Park & Delaware Aves., Hainesport Industrial Pk.,
P.O. Box 17, Hainesport 08036
Metals USA, Plates & Shapes Group
Phone—(973) 242-1000
182 Frelinghuysen Ave., Newark 07114
O'Neal Flat Rolled Metals
Phone—(609) 395-7007
1 Fitzgerald Ave., Monroe Township 08831
**Samson Metal Service**
2604 Route 130 N., Cranbury 08512
Distributor of Steel, Aluminum & Other Metals
Phone—(609) 655-0777
Fax—(609) 655-3705
Web—www.sam-metals.com
Email—info@sam-metals.com
P.O. Box 421, Dayton 08810
*(see our ad under STEEL DISTRIBUTORS & WAREHOUSES)*
UER Metals, Inc.
Phone—(908) 561-5800
235 Saint Nicholas Ave., P.O. Box 407, South Plainfield 07080
Unimet Metal Supply Co., Inc.
Phone—(973) 673-5700
150 Lackawanna Ave., Parsippany 07054

## STEEL SHEET

Benedict-Miller, LLC
Phone—(908) 497-1477
123 N. 8th St., Kenilworth 07033

## STEEL SLITTING

D M Steel
Phone—(973) 732-4763
279 Sherman Ave., Newark 07114

## STENCILS

Metal Etching Technology Assocs., Inc.
Phone—(609) 261-2670
140 Mount Holly Bypass, Unit 10, Lumberton 08048
**PNC, Inc.**
Email: sam@pnconline.com
PCB Design, Rigid, Flex & Rigi-Flex PCBs, PCBA & SMT Stencils
Phone—(973) 284-1600
Fax—(973) 284-1925
Web—www.pnconline.com
115 E. Centre St., Nutley 07110

## STERILIZATION MONITORING PRODUCTS

3M Co.
Phone—(908) 788-4000
500 U.S. Highway 202 N., Flemington 08822

## STERILIZATION SERVICES

**Bioactive Resources, LLC**
Phone—(908) 561-3114
Fax—(908) 561-3115
Web—www.bioactiveresources.com
Email—info@bioactiveresources.com
138 Sylvania Pl., South Plainfield 07080
**North American Sterilization & Packaging Company, Inc.**
Email: rogerm@naspco.com
Phone—(973) 209-4388 / (800) 392-6310
Fax—(973) 209-6374
Web—www.naspco.com
19 Park Dr., Franklin 07416
*(see our ad under CONTRACT MANUFACTURING—Medical)*

## STONE

H & S Stone, Inc.
Phone—(732) 364-2265
705 Cross St., Lakewood 08701

**Passaic County Welders, Inc.**

*Heavy Steel Fabrication, Shearing and Forming x 24' long*

**973-696-1200 • Fax: 973-696-1411**
www.pcwfab.com • robert@pcwfab.com

100 Parish Dr. • Wayne, NJ 07470

**Versatile Welding Group, LLC**

*Steel, Stainless & Aluminum*

**877-939-5348 • 908-298-8900**

FAX: 908-298-9550

Email: jimd@versatile-us.com

Web: www.versatile-us.com

340 Cox Street   Roselle, NJ 07203

INDUSTRY

# Engo Co.
## *Store Fixtures*

### 908-754-6600 • FAX: 908-754-6605

128 Case Dr., South Plainfield, NJ 07080

www.engoshelving.com • Email: terryf.engoco@comcast.net

## STONE — *(cont.)*

National Tile & Mosaic
  Phone—(201) 807-9800
  175 Moonachie Rd., Moonachie 07074
Shelby Caststone
  Phone—(856) 456-0668
  600 Jersey Ave., Gloucester City 08030
Thin Stone Systems, LLC
  Phone—(973) 882-7377
  23 Commerce Rd., Ste. O, Fairfield 07004
Wicki Wholesale Stone, Inc.
  Phone—(908) 637-6004
  17 Cemetery Rd., P.O. Box 104, Great Meadows 07838

## STONE — Cast

Art Stone Products
  Phone—(856) 697-5895
  113 Church St., P.O. Box 10, Newfield 08344
Van Dyk Trim Stone, LLC
  Phone—(973) 831-1802
  85 4th Ave., Haskell 07420

## STONE — Crushed

Eastern Concrete Materials, Inc.
  Phone—(908) 537-2135
  1 Railroad Ave., Glen Gardner 08826
Eastern Concrete Materials, Inc.
  Phone—(973) 827-7625
  3620 Route 23 N., Hamburg 07419
Stavola Construction Materials, Inc.
  Phone—(732) 356-7100
  810 Thompson Ave., Bound Brook 08805
Stavola Construction Materials, Inc.
  Phone—(908) 439-2800
  30 Rockaway Rd., Lebanon 08833
Tilcon Riverdale Quarry
  Phone—(973) 835-0028
  125 Hamburg Tpke., Riverdale 07457
Trap Rock Industries, Inc., Pennington Quarry
  Phone—(609) 737-3200
  120 Route 31 S., Pennington 08534

## STONE — Fabricated

Elite Stone Importers, LLC
  Phone—(732) 542-7900
  45 Park Rd., Tinton Falls 07724
Extech Building Materials
  Phone—(201) 768-2133
  100 Bogert St., Closter 07624
Granite Surfaces, LLC
  Phone—(732) 627-9200
  368 Lincoln Blvd., Middlesex 08846
Marble Systems, Inc.
  Phone—(201) 507-0111
  610 Washington Ave., Carlstadt 07072
Philadephia Soapstone Co.
  Phone—(856) 232-7627
  1001 Lower Landing Rd., Ste. 103, Blackwood 08012
Stone Galaxy
  Phone—(856) 219-3450
  4120 Blackhorse Pike, Turnersville 08012
Stone Plus Design, LLC
  Phone—(201) 438-2725
  21 Route 17 S., East Rutherford 07073

StoneShop
  Phone—(856) 795-8900
  670 Deer Rd., Ste. 202, Cherry Hill 08034
Tiles Unlimited
  Phone—(732) 566-3886
  1016 State Route 34, Ste. 9, Matawan 07747
Tri State Stone, Inc.
  Phone—(973) 344-7220
  111 Rome St., Ste. 2, Newark 07105

## STONE — Landscaping

Brida Stone, Inc.
  Phone—(856) 881-1700
  555 Mullica Hill Rd., Glassboro 08028

## STONE — Natural

**B & B Granite Block Sales, LLC**
  **Phone—(973) 465-0677**
  **Web—www.bbgraniteblock.com**
  **175 Marsh St., Newark 07114**
M & N Boychuk Stone Co., Inc.
  Phone—(973) 376-1333
  360 U.S. Highway 22, P.O. Box 133, Springfield 07081
M S International, Inc.
  Phone—(732) 650-1815
  36 Brunswick Ave., Edison 08817

## STORAGE — Household & Commercial

**Columbus Self Storage**
  **Phone—(609) 265-3800**
  **Web—www.columbusselfstorage.net**
  **2915 Route 206, Columbus 08022**
**DocuVault Delaware Valley LLC**
  **Phone—(856) 853-5160**
  **Fax—(856) 853-5164**
  **Web—www.docuvaultdv.com**
  **Email—customerservice@docuvaultdv.com**
  **1240 Forest Pkwy., Ste. 100, West Deptford 08066**

## STORAGE PRODUCTS

Archive Designs, Inc.
  Phone—(973) 242-6400
  238 Emmet St., Newark 07114

## STORAGE SYSTEMS

American Van Equipment, Inc.
  Phone—(800) 526-4743
  149 Lehigh Ave., Lakewood 08701

## STORE FIXTURES

Alternative Air & Store Fixtures
  Phone—(609) 261-5870
  3-C Mary Way, Hainesport 08036
ALU, Inc.
  Phone—(201) 617-2000
  240 Anderson Ave., Moonachie 07074
Architectural Acrylics
  Phone—(856) 751-2411
  5 Rockhill Rd., Ste. 3, Cherry Hill 08003

Bell Arte Woodworking, Inc.
  Phone—(908) 355-1199
  10 W. Mravlag Pl., Elizabeth 07201
Diversified Fixture, Inc.
  Phone—(732) 886-0600
  1930 Swarthmore Ave., Lakewood 08701
**Engo Co.**
  **Email: terryf.engoco@comcast.net**
  **Phone—(908) 754-6600**
  **Fax—(908) 754-6605**
  **Web—www.engoshelving.com**
  **Email—engo5@comcast.net**
  **128 Case Dr., South Plainfield 07080**
      *(see our ad on this page)*
Fi Companies
  Phone—(732) 727-8100
  3150 Bordentown Ave., Old Bridge 08857
Interstate Showcase & Store Fixture Co.
  Phone—(201) 467-4522
  P.O. Box 941, Teaneck 07666
Laurel Mfrs., Inc.
  Phone—(856) 461-6600
  620 Cooper St., P.O. Box 5306, Delanco 08075
Modern Showcase, Inc.
  Phone—(201) 935-2929
  610 Commercial Ave., Carlstadt 07072
**Paramount Fixture Corp.**
  **A full service mfg. source for wood, laminate & steel fixtures for your retail, commercial & residential environments**
  **Phone—(973) 485-1585 / (973) 485-8261**
  **Fax—(973) 485-3366**
  **Web—www.paramountfixturecorp.com**
  **Email—fixtureman175@aol.com**
  **175 Mount Pleasant Ave., Newark 07104**
Sawitz Store Fixture, Inc.
  Phone—(201) 842-9444
  130 Grand St., Carlstadt 07072
Shelving Depot, Inc.
  Phone—(908) 474-8000
  419 W. Elizabeth Ave., Linden 07036
Vermont Store Fixture Corporation
  Phone—(201) 652-3401
  265 Greenwood Ave., Midland Park 07432
Vira Mfg., Inc.
  Phone—(732) 442-8472
  1 Buckingham Ave., Perth Amboy 08861

## STOREFRONTS — Aluminum

Brick Glass Co.
  Phone—(732) 899-8811
  214 Midstreams Pl., Brick 08724

## STOVES AND RANGES

**Reno's Appliance**
  **Addtl. Web: www.buyrenos.com**
  **Toll Free Ph: (866)88-RENOS**
  **Phone—(973) 247-1860 / (866) 887-3667**
  **Fax—(973) 247-1865**
  **Web—www.renosappliance.com**
  **Email—sales@renosappliance.net**
  **235 McLean Blvd., Route 20 N., Paterson 07504**
      *(see our ad under APPLIANCES – Household)*

## STRAINERS

**Kraissl Co., Inc.**
  **Industry leader in the design & manufacture of superior quality strainers, filters, transfer valves & oil transfer pumps since 1926**
  **Phone—(201) 342-0008**
  **Fax—(201) 342-0025**
  **Web—www.strainers.com**
  **Email—kraissl2@aol.com**
  **299 Williams Ave., Hackensack 07601**

## STRAINERS — Industrial

Fluid Filtration Corp.
  Phone—(973) 253-7070
  102 Van Winkle Ave., Garfield 07026

*Search from among 430,000 U.S. manufacturers & suppliers:*
**IndustryNet.com**

INDUSTRY

## STRAINERS — Industrial — (cont.)

**Kraissl Co., Inc.**
Industry leader in the design & manufacture of superior quality strainers, filters, transfer valves & oil transfer pumps since 1926
Phone—(201) 342-0008
Fax—(201) 342-0025
Web—www.strainers.com
Email—kraissl2@aol.com
299 Williams Ave., Hackensack 07601

## STRAINERS — Oil & Gas

**Kraissl Co., Inc.**
Industry leader in the design & manufacture of superior quality strainers, filters, transfer valves & oil transfer pumps since 1926
Phone—(201) 342-0008
Fax—(201) 342-0025
Web—www.strainers.com
Email—kraissl2@aol.com
299 Williams Ave., Hackensack 07601

## STRAINERS — Pipeline

Glentech, Inc.
Phone—(908) 685-2205
46 4th St., Somerville 08876

**Kraissl Co., Inc.**
Industry leader in the design & manufacture of superior quality strainers, filters, transfer valves & oil transfer pumps since 1926
Phone—(201) 342-0008
Fax—(201) 342-0025
Web—www.strainers.com
Email—kraissl2@aol.com
299 Williams Ave., Hackensack 07601

## STRAPPING — Steel

**Modern International Corp.**
Phone—(732) 696-9100
Fax—(732) 696-9111
Web—www.moderninternational.net
Email—dstern@moderninternational.net
145 Cliffwood Ave., Cliffwood 07721

## STREET SWEEPING EQUIPMENT

**Keystone Plastics, Inc.**
Fax: (908) 561-3404
Web: Web: www.keystonesweeperbrushes.com
Phone—(908) 561-1300 / (800) 635-5238
Email—jackaroe1954@yahoo.com
3451 S. Clinton Ave., South Plainfield 07080

## STROBE LIGHTS

Unilux, Inc.
Phone—(201) 712-1266
59 5th St., Saddle Brook 07663

## STRUCTURAL STEEL ERECTION

**Cranez, Inc.**
For more than 20 yrs., serving the Tri-State area. Offering free no-obligation est.; providing svc. 24 hrs., 7 days a week & no-cost site checks. Operators are CCO/Natnl. Commission certified, have TWIC credentials & O.S.H.A 30-hrs trained
Phone—(856) 262-0288 / (877) 262-0288
Fax—(856) 262-2654
Web—www.cranezincnj.com
Email—cranez06@aol.com
2610 S. Black Horse Pike, Williamstown 08094

## STRUCTURAL STEEL FABRICATION

Abba Metal Works, Inc.
Phone—(973) 684-0808
337 River St., Paterson 07524
Alloy Welding Co., Inc.
Phone—(908) 218-1551
6-A Culnen Dr., Somerville 08876
ARD Steel Works Co.
Phone—(732) 926-9800
2 Lakeview Ave., Ste. 201, Piscataway 08854

Arete Development, Inc.
Phone—(973) 244-0037
20 Industrial Rd., Fairfield 07004
Arnold Steel Co., Inc.
Phone—(732) 363-1079
79 Randolph Rd., Howell 07731
Associated Anvil Iron Works
Phone—(908) 647-0290
38 Patterson Ave., Warren 07059
B. L. White Welding & Steel Co., Inc.
Phone—(973) 684-4111
527 E. 33rd St., Paterson 07504
Borrelli Steel Fabricators, LLC
Phone—(856) 690-8850
2800 Industrial Way, Vineland 08360
Capitol Steel Products, Inc.
Phone—(609) 538-9313
82 Stokes Ave., P.O. Box 5063, Trenton 08638
Central Metals, Inc.
Phone—(856) 963-5844
1054 S. 2nd St., Camden 08103
DDM Steel Construction
Phone—(856) 794-9400
3659 N. Delsea Dr., Vineland 08360
**De Jong Iron Works, Inc.**
And supply
Phone—(973) 684-1633
Fax—(973) 684-2309
Web—www.dejongiron.com
Email—john@dejongiron.com
P.O. Box 532, Hawthorne 07507
Eagle Steel & Iron, LLC
Phone—(908) 587-1025
7 Garfield St., Linden 07036
H & R Welding, LLC
Phone—(732) 920-4881
307 Drum Point Rd., Brick 08723
Industrial Metal, Inc.
Phone—(908) 362-0084
32 Lambert Rd., Blairstown 07825
Industrial Services Enterprises
Phone—(973) 366-3939
192 Franklin Rd., Dover 07801
J. B. Welding
Phone—(609) 894-9842
2 Reynolds St., Pemberton 08068
JHDS, LLC
Phone—(973) 782-4086
107 Beaverbrook Rd., Ste. 3, Lincoln Park 07035
M & J Contracting, Inc.
Phone—(732) 446-1112
85 Tracey Station, Manalapan 07726
Mainsource Metalfab, LLC
Phone—(973) 353-0988
59 Poinier St., Unit 61, Newark 07114

**Portuguese Structural Steel, Inc.**
Structural Steel Fabrication
973-344-1342 • FAX: 973-344-1730
255 South St. Newark, NJ 07114
www.portuguesesteel.com
paula@portuguesesteel.com

**Send an RFQ** (request for quote) to multiple suppliers at
**IndustryNet.com**

Mastercraft Iron, Inc.
1111 10th Ave., Neptune 07753
Phone—(732) 988-3113
Fax—(732) 988-3321
Email—pstagaard@mciron.com
P.O. Box 748, Neptune 07754

**Mastercraft Iron, Inc.**
*Structural steel fabrication*
**(732) 988-3113**
1111 10th Ave. Neptune, NJ 07753

Mitchell Welding & Iron Works, Inc.
Phone—(609) 465-7510
7 Enterprise Dr., Cape May Court House 08210
Morsemere Ironworks, Inc.
Phone—(201) 941-1133
1085 Linden Ave., Ridgefield 07657
MRP, LLC
Phone—(732) 968-6061
1640 New Market Ave., South Plainfield 07080
NCS Enterprises, Inc.
Phone—(856) 825-3275
300 M St., Millville 08332
Palmonari, Inc., J. V.
Phone—(609) 476-2642
1234 Tuckahoe Rd., P.O. Box 68, Milmay 08340
Park Steel & Iron Co.
Phone—(732) 349-2400
82 Iron St., Toms River 08753
Pearce Welding Co., LLC
Phone—(201) 488-0434
155 S. River St., Hackensack 07601
Perlen Steel Corp.
Phone—(973) 485-5522
265 Passaic St., Newark 07104
Piermount Ironworks, Inc.
Phone—(973) 837-1750
129 Old Turnpike Rd., Wayne 07470
**Portuguese Structural Steel, Inc.**
Phone—(973) 344-1342
Fax—(973) 344-1730
Web—www.portuguesesteel.com
Email—paula@portuguesesteel.com
255 South St., Newark 07114
*(see our ad on this page)*
Railroad Construction Company, Inc. (H Q)
Phone—(973) 684-0362
75-77 Grove St., Paterson 07503
Schmidt Steel, J. G.
Phone—(973) 473-4822
211 Central Ave., Passaic 07055
Skyline Steel Fabricators
Phone—(973) 882-0234
15 Just Rd., Fairfield 07004
South River Iron Works, LLC
Phone—(732) 257-1347
132 William St., South River 08882
Southern New Jersey Steel, Inc
Phone—(856) 696-1612
2591 N. East Blvd., Vineland 08360
Summit Steel Corp.
Phone—(908) 688-8817
1435 Morris Ave., Union 07083

## STRUCTURAL STEEL FABRICATION — (cont.)

Triple B Fabricating, Inc.
Phone—(973) 773-2266
61 Willett St., Ste. 12, Passaic 07055

Truckform, Inc.
Phone—(908) 526-5443
50 James St., Somerville 08876

Weir Welding Co., Inc.
Phone—(201) 939-2284
316 12th St., P.O. Box 311, Carlstadt 07072

Weld-Done Welding, Inc.
Phone—(856) 582-7080
20 Woodland Ave., Hurffville 08080

## STRUTS

Haydon Corp.
Phone—(973) 904-0800
415 Hamberg Tpke., Bldg. D, Wayne 07470

## STUCCO

California Stucco Products Corp.
Phone—(201) 457-1900
85 Zabriskie St., Hackensack 07601

Mediterranean Stucco Corp.
Phone—(973) 491-0160
111 Main St., Newark 07105

## STUDS — Steel

OEG Building Materials
Phone—(732) 667-3636
395 State Route 34, Matawan 07747

## SULFUR

**Evans Chemetics LP (H Q)**
**Phone—(201) 992-3100**
**Fax—(201) 992-3101**
**Web—www.evans-chemetics.com**
**Email—info@evans-chemetics.com**
**500 Frank W. Burr Blvd., 4th Fl., Glenpointe**
**Center West, Teaneck 07666**

**EVANS CHEMETICS LP**
*Organic Sulfur Chemistry*
**(201) 992-3100 / Fax: (201) 992-3101**
500 Frank W. Burr Blvd., 4th Floor
Glenpointe Center West • Teaneck, NJ 07666
**www.evans-chemetics.com**

## SULFURIC ACID

**Universal Chemicals Inc.**
**Phone—(973) 589-1525**
**Fax—(973) 589-8013**
**Web—www.universalchem.com**
**Email—info@universalchem.com**
**100 N. Hackensack Ave., Kearny 07032**

## SUNGLASSES

Safilo USA, Inc. (H Q)
Phone—(973) 952-2800
801 Jefferson Rd., Parsippany 07054

## SUPPLY CHAIN MANAGEMENT

**Vigna, Inc.**
**Computer Software: Warehouse & Transportation**
**Industry**
**Phone—(908) 874-4867 / (877) 464-9990**
**Web—www.vignainc.com**
**Email—sriniv@vignainc.com**
**105 Raider Blvd., Ste. 207, Hillsborough 08844**

*Do nationwide searches for products & services at:*
**IndustryNet.com**

## SURFBOARDS & ACCESSORIES

Heritage Surf & Sport, Inc.
Phone—(609) 263-3033
3700 Landis Ave., Sea Isle City 08243

## SURGE PROTECTORS

Zero Surge, Inc.
Phone—(908) 996-7700
889 State Route 12, Ste. 2, Frenchtown 08825

## SURGICAL APPLIANCES

Alto Development Corp.
Phone—(732) 938-2266
5206 Asbury Rd., P.O. Box 758, Farmingdale 07727

Ethicon, Inc.
Phone—(908) 218-0707
737 U.S. Highway 22 W., P.O. Box 151, Somerville 08876

Pacon Mfg., Corp.
Phone—(732) 764-9070
400 Pierce St., Somerset 08873

## SURGICAL EQUIPMENT

Engineered Medical Solutions Co., LLC
Phone—(908) 329-9123
85 Industrial Rd., Bldg. B, Phillipsburg 08865

## SURGICAL IMPLANTS

Angel Medical Systems, Inc.
Phone—(732) 542-5551
1163 Shrewsbury Ave., Ste. E, Shrewsbury 07702

Maquet Cardiovascular, LLC
Phone—(973) 709-7000
45 Barbour Pond Dr., Wayne 07470

Medtronic, Inc.
Phone—(516) 222-2848
300 Interpace Pkwy., Parsippany 07054

## SURGICAL INSTRUMENTS

**Automated Medical Products Co.**
**440 Cliff Rd., Sewaren 07077**
**Phone—(732) 602-7717**
**P.O. Box 2508, Edison 08818**

Buxton Biomedical, Inc. (H Q)
Phone—(973) 560-4848
15-A Melanie Ln., Unit 7, East Hanover 07936

Eastmed Enterprises, Inc.
Phone—(856) 797-0131
11 Brandywine Dr., Marlton 08053

Johnson & Johnson (H Q)
Phone—(732) 524-0400
1 Johnson & Johnson Plz., New Brunswick 08933

Maxter Corp. (H Q)
Phone—(609) 877-9700
51 Edgemont Ln., Willingboro 08046

P A K Mfg., Inc.
Phone—(973) 372-1090
704 S. 21st St., Irvington 07111

Robbins Instruments, Inc.
Phone—(973) 635-8972
2 N. Passaic Ave., P.O. Box 441, Chatham 07928

## SURVEILLANCE SYSTEMS

Infinova
Phone—(732) 355-9100
51 Stouts Ln., Monmouth Junction 08852

LTS / LT Security Inc. (H Q)
Phone—(856) 780-9888
109 W. Park Dr., Ste. C, Mount Laurel 08054

Tri-ed/Northern Video Distribution
Phone—(609) 860-0708
7 Corporate Dr., Ste. 2, Cranbury 08512

Virtual Management Services Corp.
Phone—(732) 281-1350
242 Atlantic City Blvd., Ste. 12, Bayville 08721

*find additional suppliers at*
**IndustryNet.com**

## SURVEYING EQUIPMENT & SUPPLIES

Mingolo Precision Products, Inc.
Phone—(201) 488-6300
174 S. Main St., Ste. 1, Hackensack 07601

## SWEATERS

Military Equipment Corp. Of America (H Q)
Phone—(908) 769-1000
P.O. Box 181, Mantoloking 08738

Royal Knitwear, Inc.
Phone—(201) 391-8368
115 Perry St., Park Ridge 07656

## SWEEPERS — Street

**Keystone Plastics, Inc.**
**Fax: (908) 561-3404**
**Web: Web: www.keystonesweeperbrushes.com**
**Phone—(908) 561-1300 / (800) 635-5238**
**Email—jackaroe1954@yahoo.com**
**3451 S. Clinton Ave., South Plainfield 07080**

## SWEEPING COMPOUNDS

Capital Soap Products, LLC
Phone—(973) 333-6100
33 Branch St., P.O. Box 357, Paterson 07544

## SWIMMING POOL CHEMICALS

Jersey Chemicals, Inc.
Phone—(973) 523-3736
775 River St., P.O. Box 542, Paterson 07524

Qualco, Inc.
Phone—(973) 473-1222
225 Passaic St., Passaic 07055

Rockwood Holdings, Inc. (H Q)
Phone—(609) 514-0300
100 Overlook Ctr., 1st Fl., Princeton 08540

## SWIMMING POOL CONTRACTORS

**Town & Country Pool Services, Inc.**
**Phone—(973) 993-1621**
**Fax—(973) 993-1456**
**Email—townandcountrypoolservice@**
**yahoo.com**
**40 Millbrook Rd., New Vernon 07976**

## SWIMMING POOL EQUIPMENT

Aqua Products, Inc.
Phone—(973) 857-2700
25 Rutgers Ave., Cedar Grove 07009

Cover Co., Inc., The
Phone—(908) 707-1122
19 Readington Rd., Somerville 08876

Hayward Industries, Inc.
Phone—(908) 351-5400
620 Division St., Elizabeth 07201

Jet Line Products, Inc.
Phone—(973) 690-2999
55 Jacobus Ave., Kearny 07032

SmartPool, Inc.
Phone—(732) 730-9880
687 Prospect St., Ste. 460, Lakewood 08701

Superior Pool Products, LLC
Phone—(856) 232-7774
200 Freeway Dr., Ste. 2, Blackwood 08012

## SWIMMING POOL SUPPLIES

Jersey Cover Corp.
Phone—(732) 286-6300
1746 Lakewood Rd., Toms River 08755

Merlin Industries, Inc.
Phone—(609) 807-1000
2904 E. State Street Ext., Hamilton 08619

SCP Distributors, LLC
Phone—(732) 730-1451
1985 Rutgers University Blvd., Ste. A, Lakewood 08701

## SWIMMING POOLS

Dolphin Industries Ltd.
Phone—(609) 965-5188
2141 River Rd., P.O. Box 344, Egg Harbor City 08215
Sau-Sea Swimming Pool Paints And Repair Products
Phone—(609) 859-8500
1855 Route 206, Southampton 08088
Swim 'N Play, Inc.
Phone—(732) 574-1500
313 Regina Ave., Rahway 07065

## SWINGSETS

**Mr. Fence**
**Specializing in fences and patio furniture, gazebos, wishing wells, swing-sets, arbors, lighthouses and many custom yard accessories**
**Phone—(732) 303-1614**
**Fax—(732) 303-0358**
**Web—www.cmrfence.com**
**Email—cmrfence@aol.com**
**3468 U.S. Highway 9, Ste. 2, Freehold 07728**

## SWISS CNC TURNING

**Comtron, Inc.**
**Swiss CNC turning, CNC turning, milling, brazing & turnkey assy. Mfg.**
**Phone—(732) 446-7571**
**Fax—(732) 446-5768**
**Web—www.comtroninc.com**
**Email—dlacross@comtroninc.com**
**391 State Route 33 E., Englishtown 07726**

## SWITCHES

Applied Resource Corp.
Phone—(973) 328-3882
105 W. Dewey Ave., Ste. 311, Wharton 07885
Comus International, Inc.
Phone—(973) 777-6900
454 Allwood Rd., Clifton 07012

## SWITCHES — Electric

Kraus & Naimer, Inc.
Phone—(732) 560-1240
760 New Brunswick Rd., Somerset 08873
Multi Tech Industries Corp.
Phone—(732) 431-0550
64 S. Main St., P.O. Box 159, Marlboro 07746

## SWITCHES — Membrane

**PNC, Inc.**
**Email: sam@pnconline.com**
**PCB Design, Rigid, Flex & Rigi-Flex PCBs, PCBA & SMT Stencils**
**Phone—(973) 284-1600**
**Fax—(973) 284-1925**
**Web—www.pnconline.com**
**115 E. Centre St., Nutley 07110**
Sensigraphics, Inc.
Phone—(856) 853-9100
105 W. Park Dr., Mount Laurel 08054

## SWITCHES — Motor

Control Products
Phone—(973) 887-9400
280 Ridgedale Ave., East Hanover 07936

## SWITCHES — Pressure

Pressure Controls, Inc.
Phone—(973) 751-5002
406 Courtlandt St., Belleville 07109
Sigma-Netics, Inc.
Phone—(973) 616-6900
2 N. Corporate Dr., Riverdale 07457

## SWITCHGEAR

Norsal Distribution Assocs.
Phone—(908) 638-8900
150 Cregar Rd., High Bridge 08829

## SYSTEMS INTEGRATORS

AccessIT Group, Inc.
Phone—(973) 316-6016
115 Route 46 W., Bldg. E, Ste. 35, Mountain Lakes 07046
Activu
Phone—(973) 366-5550
301 Round Hill Dr., Rockaway 07866
Admiral Integration, Inc.
Phone—(856) 429-6700
1001 Marlton Pike W., Cherry Hill 08002
AgileAccess™, LLC
Phone—(908) 788-7740
23 Londonderry Dr., Flemington 08822
Albridge Solutions, Inc.
Phone—(609) 620-5800
1009 Lenox Dr., Bldg. 4, Ste. 204, Lawrenceville 08648
All Covered
Phone—(856) 795-7330
100 Dobbs Ln., Ste. 208, Cherry Hill 08034
All Star Identification
Phone—(973) 625-4100
400 Morris Ave., Ste. 241, Denville 07834
Amdocs, Inc.
Phone—(201) 631-3200
34 Exchange Pl., Jersey City 07311
Automated Control Concepts, Inc.
Phone—(732) 922-6611
3535 State Route 66, Ste. 14, Neptune 07753
Aventa Systems, LLC
Phone—(973) 246-4853
40 Arnot St., Unit 7, Lodi 07644
Avid Communications, Inc.
Phone—(973) 625-7350
27 Bluebird Ct., P.O. Box 2481, Flemington 08822
Azzurro Group, LLC
Phone—(201) 767-0850
100 Stonehurst Ct., Northvale 07647
Bauman's Computer Solutions
Phone—(609) 920-0121
192 Route 130, Bordentown 08505
Bluenog Corp.
Phone—(732) 584-2340
285 Davidson Ave., Ste. 306, Somerset 08873
Breaker Group, Inc., The
Phone—(609) 267-1330
32-34 Mill St., Mount Holly 08060
CCSI Group, The
Phone—(908) 686-6464
1351 Morris Ave., P.O. Box 3554, Union 07083
Comport Consulting Corp.
Phone—(201) 236-0505
78 Orchard St., Ramsey 07446
Compunite Computers, Inc.
Phone—(973) 227-6008
39 U.S. Highway 46, Ste. 803, P.O. Box 3, Pine Brook 07058
Computer Ease, LLC
Phone—(973) 812-6626
153 Newark Pompton Tpke., Ste. A, Little Falls 07424
Computrs, Inc.
Phone—(973) 248-9500
294 Wanaque Ave., Pompton Lakes 07442
ComTec Systems, Inc.
Phone—(856) 691-5111
2658 N. West Blvd., Vineland 08360
**Comtel Global Services, LLC**
**Email: sales@cgstogo.com**
**Phone—(732) 225-3055**
**Fax—(732) 225-3074**
**Web—www.cgstogo.com**
**105 Newfield Ave., Ste. K, Edison 08837**
CoreMatrix Systems
Phone—(732) 332-1931
125 Half Mile Rd., Ste. 200, Red Bank 07701
Corente, Inc.
Phone—(732) 254-0210
758 Route 18, Ste. 110, East Brunswick 08816
CPI USA Inc.
Phone—(732) 494-0007
6 Doreen Ct., Edison 08820
DBM Of America, Inc.
Phone—(908) 534-1665
295 U.S. Highway 22 E., Ste. 104, Whitehouse Station 08889

Deloitte
Phone—(212) 937-8200
3 2nd St., Harborside Plaza 10, Ste. 300, Jersey City 07311
Dematic Corp.
Phone—(908) 991-9900
150 Allen Rd., Ste. 102, Basking Ridge 07920
DialConnection, LLC
Phone—(856) 753-6620
1040 Route 73 S., Berlin 08009
Digital Surroundings, LLC
Phone—(609) 912-1800
11 Princess Rd., Ste. E, Lawrence Township 08648
Dorado Systems, LLC
Phone—(856) 354-0048
8 Kings Hwy. E., Haddonfield 08033
DynTek Services, Inc.
Phone—(856) 834-1100
1120 Route 73, Ste. 100, Mount Laurel 08054
E*Pro, Inc.
Phone—(732) 283-0499
1000 U.S. Highway 9 N., Ste. 303, Woodbridge 07095
Edgesys, Inc.
Phone—(201) 727-1663
411 State Route 17, Ste. 310, Hasbrouck Heights 07604
**eMazzanti Technologies**
**Computer network systems integration**
**Phone—(201) 360-4400**
**Fax—(201) 360-4500**
**Web—www.emazzanti.net**
**Email—info@emazzanti.net**
**701 Grand St., Hoboken 07030**
Emtec, Inc.
Phone—(973) 376-4242
11 Diamond Rd., Springfield 07081
Energy Options, LLC
Phone—(732) 512-9100
256 Campus Dr., Edison 08837
EPS Corporation
Phone—(732) 747-8277
78 Apple St., Tinton Falls 07724
eSystems, Inc.
Phone—(609) 945-7437
4390 U.S. Highway 1, Ste. 301, Princeton 08540
**GMB (USA), Inc.**
**Phone—(201) 768-3577**
**Fax—(201) 221-8338**
**Web—www.gmb-usa.com**
**Email—usa@gmb-usa.com**
**190 Veterans Dr., Ste. B, Northvale 07647**
Hawk Technologies, Inc.
Phone—(732) 577-8581
3710 U.S. Highway 9 S., P.O. Box 6685, Freehold 07728
HyperTech, Inc.
Phone—(732) 635-1755
279 Central Ave., Ste. B, Metuchen 08840
**ID-Tech Solutions, Inc.**
**Phone—(718) 408-9199**
**Fax—(718) 504-4042**
**Web—www.idtechsolutions.com**
**Email—sales@idtechsolutions.com**
**505 E. County Line Rd., Lakewood 08701**
Innovative Network Solutions
Phone—(973) 299-8800
29 Cove Rd., Hopatcong 07843
INS Technologies
Phone—(973) 808-6400
P.O. Box 615, Nutley 07110
**Integrated Business Systems, Inc.**
**Phone—(973) 575-4950**
**Fax—(973) 575-4953**
**Web—www.ibsre.com**
**Email—sales@ibsre.com**
**999 Riverview Dr., Ste. 280, Totowa 07512**
Integrated Micro Systems, Inc.
Phone—(973) 904-9700
74 Lee Ave., Haledon 07508
Intuitive Technology Partners
Phone—(201) 993-7799
102 Serpentine Dr., Morganville 07751
IPKeys Technologies
Phone—(732) 389-4702
1 Industrial Way W., Ste. E-1, Eatontown 07724
IT America, Inc.
Phone—(732) 985-5100
100 Metroplex Dr., Ste. 207, Edison 08817

## SYSTEMS INTEGRATORS — *(cont.)*

IT Management
Phone—(973) 389-1200
195 Browertown Rd., Ste. 2, Little Falls 07424

Kaizen Technologies, Inc.
Phone—(732) 452-9555
1 State Route 27, Ste. 10, Edison 08820

Kavayah Solutions, Inc.
Phone—(609) 919-9797
5 Independence Way, Ste. 360, Princeton 08540

Living Intelligent, Inc.
Phone—(201) 784-0500
70 Oak St., Ste. 103, Norwood 07648

Lucid Technologies, LLC
Phone—(609) 277-4138
231 Clarksville Rd., Princeton Junction 08550

Lucille Maud Corp.
Phone—(609) 393-7555
513 N. Olden Ave., Trenton 08638

Maestro Technolgies, Inc.
Phone—(908) 458-8600
510 Thornall St., Ste. 375, Edison 08837

Masstar
Phone—(732) 542-8004
18 Heritage Rd., Eatontown 07724

Mazzanti, Inc.
Phone—(201) 360-4400
701 Grand St., Hoboken 07030

Navitend
Phone—(973) 448-0070
23 U.S. Highway 206, Stanhope 07874

NetQ Multimedia
Phone—(732) 833-9300
919 State Route 33, Ste. 52, Freehold 07728

Networking Technologies & Integration
Phone—(908) 276-1200
50 Boright Ave., Kenilworth 07033

New Jersey Business Systems, Inc.
Phone—(609) 587-5500
7-C Marlen Dr., Trenton 08691

NIC Group, The
Phone—(908) 253-8106
1130 U.S. Highway 202, Ste. E-6, Raritan 08869

Olmec Systems, Inc.
Phone—(973) 586-6590
255 W. Main St., Denville 07834

P & M Computers, Inc.
Phone—(201) 943-0353
97 Oakdene Ave., P.O. Box 270, Cliffside Park 07010

PeggNet Computers, LLC
Phone—(973) 543-1222
4 E. Main St., Ste. 3, Mendham 07945

Praxis Data Systems, Inc.
Phone—(856) 679-2256
4 Foster Ave., Ste. B & C, Gibbsboro 08026

Promedia Technology Services, Inc.
Phone—(973) 253-7600
535 U.S. Highway 46, Little Falls 07424

R A C Systems Corp.
Phone—(973) 292-3200
1-B Glimpsewood Ln., Morristown 07960

Radiant Systems, Inc.
Phone—(908) 668-1080
107 Corporate Blvd., Ste. B, South Plainfield 07080

Reliance Global Services, Inc.
Phone—(908) 769-1271
50 Cragwood Rd., Ste. 100, South Plainfield 07080

Ripen Interactive, LLC
Phone—(609) 520-8820
117 Rockingham Row, Princeton 08540

RSA Associates
Phone—(908) 806-4681
812 County Road 579, Flemington 08822

Secure Technology Integration Group, Ltd.
Phone—(201) 825-1255
15 Schneider Rd., Allendale 07401

Shaman Systems, Inc.
Phone—(908) 429-0542
402 Main St., Ste. 100-330, Metuchen 08840

Sirius Technology LLC
Phone—(201) 493-1414
1 Hollywood Ave., Ste. 19-A, Ho-Ho-Kus 07423

Sita Corp.
Phone—(732) 906-7806
347 Elizabeth Ave., Ste. 200, Somerset 08873

StarTrak Information Technologies, LLC
Phone—(703) 433-6300
395 W. Passaic St., Ste. 325, Rochelle Park 07662

Strategic Products & Services, LLC
Phone—(888) 777-7280
300 Littleton Rd., 2nd Fl., Parsippany 07054

Sunhillo Corp.
Phone—(856) 767-7676
444 Kelly Dr., West Berlin 08091

Targeted Technologies, LLC
Phone—(732) 255-9005
1735 Hooper Ave., Ste. 2, Toms River 08753

Tech Support, Inc.
Phone—(973) 627-8870
23 Pawnee Ave., Rockaway 07866

Technovision, Inc.
Phone—(732) 381-0200
1119 Raritan Rd., Ste. 2, Clark 07066

Thetica Systems, Inc.
Phone—(201) 399-7800
145 13th St., Cresskill 07626

Trident Computer Resources, Inc.
Phone—(732) 544-9333
151 Industrial Way E., Ste. A-3, Eatontown 07724

Tymac Controls Corp.
Phone—(973) 293-3339
432 U.S. Highway 206, Ste. C, Montague 07827

United ERP, LLC
Phone—(201) 567-6315
2460 Lemoine Ave., Ste. 503, Fort Lee 07024

US Logic, LLC
Phone—(609) 530-0005
2885 E. State Street Ext., Hamilton 08619

Veraciti, Inc.
Phone—(973) 887-8660
1044 Route 23, Ste. 102, Wayne 07470

Western Scientific Computers, Inc.
Phone—(973) 263-9311
28 W. Shore Rd., Mountain Lakes 07046

XTreme Technologies Group, LLC
Phone—(856) 273-7800
135 Gaither Dr., Ste. F, Mount Laurel 08054

## TABLECLOTHS

A-1 Tablecloth Co.
Phone—(201) 727-8987
450 Huyler St., Ste. 102, South Hackensack 07606

Ballard Collection, Inc.
Phone—(908) 604-0082
221 Stirling Rd., Ste. E & F, Warren 07059

Something Different Linen, Inc.
Phone—(973) 772-8019
167 Fornelius Ave., Clifton 07013

Tablecloth Co., Inc.
Phone—(973) 942-1555
514 Totowa Ave., Paterson 07522

Town & Country Linen Corp.
Phone—(732) 364-2000
475 Oberlin Ave. S., Lakewood 08701

## TABLES

DeSaussure Equipment Co., Inc.
Phone—(201) 845-4242
23 W. Howcroft Rd., Maywood 07607

## TABLEWARE — Glass

Durand Glass Mfg. Co.
Phone—(856) 327-4800
901 S. Wade Blvd., Millville 08332

## TABLEWARE — Plastic

Pyramid Poly Bags, Inc.
Phone—(718) 499-1212
600 Markley St., Port Reading 07064

## TACHOMETERS

Seaboard Instrument Co., Inc.
Phone—(609) 641-5300
4 N. 1st St., Pleasantville 08232

## TAGS AND LABELS

Arch Crown, Inc.
Phone—(973) 731-6300
460 Hillside Ave., Ste. 1, Hillside 07205

Ascot Tag & Label Co., Inc.
Phone—(973) 482-0900
577 3rd St., Newark 07107

Magnetic Ticket & Label Corp.
Phone—(973) 759-6500
151 Cortlandt St., Belleville 07109

Metro Tag & Label, Inc.
Phone—(201) 845-4747
25 E. Spring Valley Ave., Ste. 200, Maywood 07607

The Star Group
Phone—(973) 778-8600
80-A Industrial Rd., Lodi 07644

## TALLOW

**Darling Ingredients, Inc.**
Email: bfrish@darlingii.com
**Phone—(973) 465-1900 / (800) 842-5927**
**Fax—(973) 465-9247**
**Web—www.darlingii.com**
**825 Wilson Ave., Newark 07105**

## TANK CLEANING

**Atlas Disposal Options, Inc.**
Offering environmental contrs. & indl. clients a single source for all their disposal needs of almost any waste stream, utilizing our own trucks, personnel & equipment to transport & dispose of any Petroleum, Sanitary or Hazardous waste
**Phone—(973) 361-5100 / (800) 821-9741**
**Fax—(973) 361-0909**
**Web—www.wastewanted.com**
**311 E. Blackwell St., P.O. Box 546, Dover 07802**
*(see our ad under WASTE MANAGEMENT SERVICES)*

## TANK LININGS

Rema Tip Top/North America, Inc. (H Q)
Phone—(201) 768-8100
119 Rockland Ave., Northvale 07647

## TANK REMOVAL

**GWS Contractors, Inc.**
Since 1977, specializing in Environmental Remediation, Tank Removals, Emergency Response Services & Vapor Intrusion Mitigation. Providing a 24 hour, 7 day a week customer response network
**Phone—(732) 297-4847**
**Fax—(732) 297-4389**
**Web—www.gwscontractors.com**
**Email—contact@gwscontractors.com**
**105 Fresh Ponds Rd., Jamesburg 08831**

**T. Slack Environmental Services, Inc.**
Tank Solutions-Oil Tank Experts
**Phone—(908) 964-2717**
**Fax—(908) 964-4244**
**Web—www.oiltanksolutions.com**
**Email—info@oiltanksolutions.com**
**180 Market St., Kenilworth 07033**
*(also see our ad under ENVIRONMENTAL SERVICES)*

**Tank Solutions** — Oil Tank Experts
908.964.2717 Fax: 908.964.4244
**T. Slack Environmental Services, Inc.**
Tank Solutions — Oil Tank Experts
180 Market St. • Kenilworth, NJ 07033
www.oiltanksolutions.com

EZSelect®.com
REAL-TIME Access to Industrial Leads!

INDUSTRY

## TANKS

**Warwick Mfg. & Equipment Co., LLC**
Buy & sell used: Chemical, food, cosmetic, packaging
& pharmaceutical equipment
Phone—**(732) 729-0400 / (732) 241-9263**
Fax—**(732) 729-1235**
Web—**www.warwickequipment.com**
Email—**sales@warwickequipment.com**
**1112 12th St., North Brunswick 08902**
*(see our ad Outside Back Cover)*

## TANKS — Fuel

Aero Tec Laboratories, Inc.
Phone—(201) 825-1400
45 Spear Rd., Ramsey 07446
**Nutley Heating & Cooling Supply, Inc.**
Phone—**(973) 667-6880**
Fax—**(973) 667-4602**
Web—**www.nutleysupply.com**
Email—**ralpholiver@nutleysupply.com**
**156 Chestnut St., Nutley 07110**
*(see our ad under BOILERS)*

## TANKS — Liquid

BakerCorp.
Phone—(856) 467-2677
50 Gilchris Dr., Swedesboro 08085

## TANKS — Plastic

**Emco Industrial Plastics, Inc.**
Supplier of Plastic Sheet, Rod, Tube, Films &
Prototyping
Phone—**(973) 559-5610**
Fax—**(973) 239-1595**
Web—**www.emcoplastics.com**
Email—**mailbox@emcoplastics.com**
**99 Commerce Rd., P.O. Box 2503, Cedar
Grove 07009**
*(see our ad Outside Front Cover)*

## TANKS — Propane

Tarantin Industries
Phone—(732) 780-9340
86 Vanderveer Rd., Freehold 07728

## TANKS — Septic

Granville Concrete Products
Phone—(973) 584-6653
1076 Route 10, Randolph 07869

## TANKS — Truck

Vacuum Sales, Inc.
Phone—(856) 627-7790
51 Stone Rd., Lindenwold 08021

## TANNING BEDS & EQUIPMENT

PC Tan, Inc.
Phone—(201) 943-6100
1040 Wilt Ave., Ridgefield 07657

## TAPES

Dura Tape International
Phone—(908) 687-8273
2816 Morris Ave., Ste. 21, Union 07083

## TAPES — Adhesive

Decker Tape Products, Inc.
Phone—(973) 227-5350
2 Stewart Pl., Fairfield 07004
Pro-Tapes & Specialties
Phone—(732) 346-0900
621 Route 1 S., North Brunswick 08902
Universal Tape Co. (H Q)
Phone—(609) 653-3191
110 W. New Jersey Ave., Somers Point 08244

## TAPES — Binding

Snapco Mfg. Corp.
Phone—(973) 282-0300
140 Central Ave., Hillside 07205

## TAPES — Packaging

**All Size Poly Bags**
Leaders in supplying plastic bags, packaging,
shipping & warehouse supplies nationwide
Phone—**(800) 635-9959 / (732) 828-3400**
Fax—**(732) 828-7703**
Web—**www.allsizepolybags.com**
Email—**info@rksplastics.com**
**P.O. Box 836, New Brunswick 08903**
*(see our ad under BAGS—Plastic)*
Holland Manufacturing Company, Inc.
Phone—(973) 584-8141
15 Main St., P.O. Box 404, Succasunna 07876

## TAPES — Pressure Sensitive

Main Tape Co., Inc.
Phone—(609) 395-1704
1 Capital Dr., Ste. 101, Cranbury 08512
Nitto Denko America Automotive, Inc.
Phone—(732) 901-7905
1990 Rutgers Blvd., Lakewood 08701
R Tape Corporation
Phone—(908) 753-5570
6 Ingersoll Rd., South Plainfield 07080

## TAPPING MACHINERY

Cutter, Drill & Machine, Inc.
Phone—(732) 206-1112
175 Ramtown Greenville Rd., Unit 701, Howell
07731

## TAPS — Die

**Automated Tapping Systems, Inc.**
Phone—**(732) 899-2282**
Fax—**(732) 899-0277**
Web—**www.automatedtappingsystems.com**
Email—**sales@**
**automatedtappingsystems.com**
**P.O. Box 1033, Brick 08723**

**Automated Tapping Systems**
*In-Die Tapping Solutions*
**In-Die Tapping Units**
**732-899-2282 • FAX: 732-899-0277**
P.O. Box 1033  Brick, NJ 08723
**www.automatedtappingsystems.com**

## TARPAULINS

Croton Products
Phone—(732) 560-9223
514 Wellington St., Middlesex 08846
Deroche Canvas, Inc.
Phone—(908) 475-2266
283 County Road 519, Belvidere 07823
Strong Man Building Products Corp.
Phone—(973) 831-1555
240 W. Parkway, Pompton Plains 07444

## TAX CONSULTING

**Maggioncalda, Austin B.**
Phone—**(856) 696-2200**
Fax—**(856) 794-9798**
Web—**www.abmpa.com**
Email—**abmpa@comcast.net**
**5546 Chestnut Ave., P.O. Box 606, Buena
08310**

*Search from among 430,000
U.S. manufacturers & suppliers:*
**IndustryNet.com**

## TEA

Carrington Tea, LLC
Phone—(201) 261-5517
7 Reuten Dr., P.O. Box 102, Closter 07624
Eastern Tea Corp.
Phone—(609) 860-1100
1 Engelhard Dr., Monroe Township 08831
Harris Tea Co.
Phone—(856) 793-0290
344 New Albany Rd., Moorestown 08057
Reeves Enterprises, Inc.
Phone—(908) 665-9511
571 Central Ave., New Providence 07974

## TEA — Wholesale

Samuel Elliott, Inc.
Phone—(856) 773-6000
1818 Bannard St., Riverton 08077

## TEFLON® PRODUCTS

**(Teflon® is a registered trademark of DuPont)**
Plastics For Chemicals, Inc.
Phone—(609) 242-9100
710 Old Shore Rd., Forked River 08731

## TELECOMMUNICATIONS CABLING

**Como Electric, Inc.**
Phone—**(732) 449-7625**
Fax—**(732) 449-6896**
Email—**comoelect@aol.com**
**909 Wall Rd., Spring Lake 07762**
*(see our ad under GENERATORS—Electric)*

## TELECOMMUNICATIONS CONSULTANTS

**Global Communication Networks Systems Inc.**
Phone—**(973) 300-9345**
Fax—**(973) 300-9348**
Web—**www.gcns1.com**
Email—**jruby@gcns1.com**
**7 Cove Hollow Ct., Newton 07860**

**Global Communication
Networks Systems Inc.**
*Quality telecommunications consultants*
**www.gcns1.com**
**(973) 300-9345 • Fax: (973) 300-9348**
7 Cove Hollow Ct.  Newton, NJ 07860

## TELECOMMUNICATIONS EQUIPMENT

Acuative (H Q)
Phone—(973) 227-8040
30 Two Bridges Rd., Ste. 240, Fairfield 07004
Alcatel-Lucent (H Q)
Phone—(908) 582-8500
600 Mountain Ave., Murray Hill 07974
Alphion Corp.
Phone—(609) 936-9001
196 Princeton Hightstown Rd., Bldg. 1-A, 2nd Fl.,
Princeton Junction 08550
Bogen Communications, Inc.
Phone—(201) 934-8500
50 Spring St., Ste. 1, Ramsey 07446
Dialogic, Inc. (H Q)
Phone—(800) 755-4444
4 Gatehall Dr., Parsippany 07054
I T I Electronics, Inc.
Phone—(973) 890-7888
32 Stonewall Dr., Livingston 07039
InPhot, Inc.
Phone—(609) 750-0992
3490 W. Route 1, Princeton 08540
Meca Electronics, Inc.
Phone—(973) 625-0661
459 E. Main St., Denville 07834

## TELECOMMUNICATIONS EQUIPMENT — (cont.)

Netquest Corp.
Phone—(856) 866-0505
523 Fellowship Rd., Ste. 205, Mount Laurel 08054

Science Dynamics Corp.
Phone—(856) 910-1166
7150 N. Park Dr., Ste. 500, Pennsauken 08109

Spirent Communications PLC
Phone—(732) 544-8700
541 Industrial Way W., Eatontown 07724

Star Dynamic Corp.
Phone—(973) 340-3883
100 Outwater Ln., Garfield 07026

## TELECOMMUNICATIONS SERVICES

**ORBCOMM, Inc. (H Q)**
**Satellite modems & wireless remote monitoring & control systems integration for refrigerated & temperature-controlled transportation**
**Phone—(703) 433-6300 / (800) 672-2666**
**Fax—(703) 433-6400**
**Web—www.orbcomm.com**
**395 W. Passaic St., Ste. 325, Rochelle Park 07662**

Parwan Electronics Corp.
Phone—(732) 290-1900
1230 State Route 34, Aberdeen 07747

## TELEPHONE ENCLOSURES

Redyref Co.
Phone—(718) 784-3690
100 Kenner Ct., Riverdale 07457

## TELEPHONE EQUIPMENT & SYSTEMS

IPC Systems, Inc. (H Q)
Phone—(201) 253-2000
Harborside Financial Ctr., 3 2nd St., Plz. 10, 15th Fl., Jersey City 07311

Teleco Business Telephone Systems
Phone—(732) 777-7990
1883 State Route 27, Edison 08817

**US Tel Inc.**
**Service & Repair**
**Phone—(973) 473-4411 / (800) 294-0020**
**Fax—(973) 473-8870**
**Web—www.us-tel.com**
**Email—jank@us-tel.com**
**203 Patterson Ave., Ste. 3, Wallington 07057**

## TELEPHONE SYSTEMS INSTALLATION

**US Tel Inc.**
**Service & Repair**
**Phone—(973) 473-4411 / (800) 294-0020**
**Fax—(973) 473-8870**
**Web—www.us-tel.com**
**Email—jank@us-tel.com**
**203 Patterson Ave., Ste. 3, Wallington 07057**

## TELEPHONES

NICE Systems, Inc. (H Q)
Phone—(201) 964-2600
461 From Rd., Paramus 07652

## TELEPHONES — Cellular

Mizco International, Inc. (H Q)
Phone—(732) 912-2000
80 Essex Ave. E., Avenel 07001

## TELEVISION BROADCAST EQUIPMENT

Frezzolini Electronics, Inc.
Phone—(973) 427-1160
7 Valley St., Hawthorne 07506

## TELEVISION EQUIPMENT — Closed Circuit

Nuvico, Inc.
Phone—(201) 541-1605
53 Smith St., Englewood 07631

## TELEVISION STUDIO EQUIPMENT

Telescript, International LLC
Phone—(201) 767-6733
55 Walnut St., Ste. 101-A, Norwood 07648

## TEMPERATURE MEASUREMENT EQUIPMENT

**Pro-Tech Solutions South, LLC.**
**Phone—(610) 539-6219**
**Fax—(610) 862-9666**
**Web—www.pro-techsouth.com**
**390 Rittenhouse Blvd., Norristown, PA 19403**
*(see our ad under PROCESS CONTROL INSTRUMENTS)*

TIP Industries, Inc.
Phone—(609) 239-1900
340 W. Broad St., Burlington 08016

## TEMPERATURE MONITORS

Temptime Corp.
Phone—(973) 984-6000
116 The American Rd., Morris Plains 07950

## TEMPERATURE SENSORS

Sensor Scientific, Inc.
Phone—(973) 227-7790
6 Kingsbridge Rd., Fairfield 07004

Temperature Humidity Instruments LLC
Phone—(908) 354-8236
235 Main St., Ste. 281, Madison 07940

## TENNIS COURT CONSTRUCTION

**DiMilia Inc.**
**Also Surfacing**
**Phone—(973) 746-1230 / (888) 567-5464**
**Fax—(973) 746-0881**
**Web—www.kingofthecourts.com**
**Email—dimiliainc@aol.com**
**P.O. Box 3366, Montclair 07043**

**DiMilia Inc.**
*Quality Tennis Court Construction*
**(973) 746-1230**
**www.kingofthecourts.com**
P.O. Box 3366 • Montclair, NJ 07043

## TENSIONERS — Belt

**BRECOflex Co., L.L.C.**
**Phone—(732) 460-9500 / (888) 463-1400**
**Fax—(732) 542-6725**
**Web—www.brecoflex.com**
**Email—info@brecoflex.com**
**222 Industrial Way W., Eatontown 07724**
*(see our ads under BELTING & PULLEYS)*

## TERMINAL BLOCKS

**Americor Electronics, Ltd.**
**Phone—(847) 956-6200 / (800) 830-5337**
**Fax—(847) 956-0300**
**Web—www.americor-usa.com**
**Email—info@americor-usa.com**
**675 S. Lively Blvd., Elk Grove Village, IL 60007**
*(see our ads under CABLE ASSEMBLIES & CORD SETS)*

*Do nationwide searches for products & services at:*
**IndustryNet.com**

## TERMINALS

Nustar Energy L. P.
Phone—(856) 224-8903
7 N. Delaware St., Paulsboro 08066

## TEST PUBLISHERS

Educational Testing Service
Phone—(609) 921-9000
660 Rosedale Rd., Princeton 08541

## TESTING EQUIPMENT

ABC Digital Electronics, Inc.
Phone—(201) 666-6888
44 Country Squire Rd., Old Tappan 07675

Alltest Instruments
Phone—(732) 919-3339
500 Central Ave., Farmingdale 07727

Alpha Automation, Inc.
Phone—(609) 882-0366
127 Walters Ave., Trenton 08638

Brabender® Instruments, C. W.
Phone—(201) 343-8425
50 E. Wesley St., P.O. Box 2127, South Hackensack 07606

Delmhorst Instrument Co.
Phone—(973) 334-2557
51 Indian Ln. E., Towaco 07082

Dranetz Technologies
Phone—(732) 287-3680
1000 New Durham Rd., Edison 08818

**Gaston Sales & Service**
**Phone—(609) 462-0201**
**Fax—(609) 588-5428**
**Email—lengaston@aol.com**
**P.O. Box 3121, Trenton 08619**

GE Healthcare LifeSciences
Phone—(732) 457-8000
800 Centennial Ave., P.O. Box 1327, Piscataway 08855

Gerin Corp.
Phone—(732) 774-3256
1109 7th Ave., Neptune 07753

Instru-Met Corp.
Phone—(908) 851-0700
931 Lehigh Ave., Union 07083

Kershaw Instrumentation, LLC
Phone—(856) 467-5482
517 Auburn Ave., P.O. Box 163, Swedesboro 08085

Lawler Mfg. Corp.
Phone—(732) 777-2040
7 Kilmer Ct., Edison 08817

Logan Instruments Corp.
Phone—(732) 302-9888
19 Schoolhouse Rd., Ste. C, Somerset 08873

PRIMME Co., Inc.
Phone—(908) 231-9490
42 Columbia Rd., Branchburg 08876

Refinery Systems, A Div. Of Core Lab
Phone—(609) 896-2673
11 Princess Rd., Lawrenceville 08648

Siemens Healthcare Diagnostics, Inc.
Phone—(973) 927-2828
62 Flanders Bartley Rd., Flanders 07836

Terriss Consolidated Industries
Phone—(732) 988-0909
807 Summerfield Ave., P.O. Box 110, Asbury Park 07712

Thomas Scientific, Inc. (H Q)
Phone—(856) 467-2000
1654 High Hill Rd., Interstate 295, P.O. Box 99, Swedesboro 08085

Thwing-Albert Instrument Company
Phone—(856) 767-1000
14 W. Collings Ave., West Berlin 08091

## TESTING EQUIPMENT — Automatic

Intertek Laboratories, Inc.
Phone—(908) 903-1800
340 Union St., Stirling 07980

*find additional suppliers at*
**IndustryNet.com**

INDUSTRY

## TESTING EQUIPMENT — Non-Destructive

InterTest, Inc.
Phone—(908) 496-8008
303 State Route 94, Columbia 07832
MISTRAS Group, Inc.
Phone—(609) 716-4100
195 Clarksville Rd., Princeton Junction 08550
Sensor Products, Inc.
Phone—(973) 884-1755
300 Madison Ave., Ste. 100, Madison 07940

## TESTING EQUIPMENT — Telecommunications

Berkeley Varitronics Systems, Inc.
Email: sales@bvsystems.com
Phone—(732) 548-3737
Fax—(732) 548-3404
Web—www.bvsystems.com
255 Liberty St., Metuchen 08840
D B M Corp., Inc.
Phone—(201) 677-0008
32-A Spruce St., Oakland 07436
Matrix Test Equipment, Inc.
Phone—(732) 469-9510
200 Wood Ave., Middlesex 08846
OnPATH Technologies
Phone—(609) 518-4100
100 Mount Holly Bypass, Lumberton 08048
Packetstorm Communications, Inc.
Phone—(732) 544-2434
20 Meridian Rd., Eatontown 07724
Telecom Assistance Group, Inc.
Phone—(856) 753-8585
150 Cooper Rd., Ste. F-15, West Berlin 08091

## TESTING EQUIPMENT — Tensile Strength

Gaston Sales & Service
Phone—(609) 462-0201
Fax—(609) 588-5428
Email—lengaston@aol.com
P.O. Box 3121, Trenton 08619

## TESTING LABORATORIES

Product Investigations, Inc.
Phone—(610) 825-5855 / (888) 744-2020
Fax—(610) 825-7288
Web—www.productinvestigations.com
Email—sdshelanski@
productinvestigations.com
151 E. 10th Ave., Ste. B, Conshohocken, PA
19428

## TESTING SERVICES

Loricon Testing Service, Inc.
Analytical Testing-Microbiology
Phone—(732) 787-4131
Fax—(732) 264-4585
Web—www.loricontesting.com
Email—loricon55@optonline.net
55 State Route 36, Keyport 07735

**LORICON**
Testing Service, Inc.

*Meeting All Your*
*Microbiological & Analytical*
*Testing Requirements*

**Loricon Testing Service, Inc.**
**Loricon Analytical Testing Laboratory, LLC**
**(732) 787-4131** loricon55@optonline.net
*55 State Route 36* Keyport, NJ 07735

## TEXTILE CONVERTING

Associated Fabrics Corp.
Phone—(800) 232-4077
15-01 Pollitt Dr., Ste. 7, Fair Lawn 07410
Brand & Oppenheimer Co., Inc.
Phone—(732) 224-7400
188 E. Bergen Pl., Ste. 201, Red Bank 07701

## TEXTILE CUTTING

Allied Bias Products Corp.
Phone—(201) 432-6050
430 Communipaw Ave., Ste. 3, Jersey City 07304
American Fur Felt, LLC
Phone—(973) 344-3026
53 Rome St., Newark 07105
Exacta Industries, Inc.
Phone—(973) 259-0104
20 John F. Kennedy Dr. N., Bloomfield 07003
I & F Scallop Thread Co., Inc.
Phone—(201) 868-6550
6002 Adams St., West New York 07093

## TEXTILE DYEING & FINISHING

American Fabric Processors
Phone—(973) 278-0272
555 E. 31st St., Paterson 07513
E & W Textile Processors, Inc.
Phone—(973) 942-8718
293 Morrissee Ave., Haledon 07508
East Coast Embossing
Phone—(973) 777-9830
35 8th St., P.O. Box 1076, Passaic 07055
International Veiling Corp.
Phone—(973) 772-3100
244 Hazel St., 2nd Fl., Clifton 07011
Martin Corp.
Phone—(856) 451-0900
171 N. Pearl St., Bridgeton 08302
Microseal Industries, Inc.
Phone—(973) 523-0704
610 E. 36th St., P.O. Box 3054, Paterson 07509
Paul Dyeing Co.
Phone—(973) 484-1121
626 Orange St., Newark 07107
Rebtex, Inc.
Phone—(908) 722-3549
40 Industrial Pkwy., Somerville 08876
Safer Holding Corp.
Phone—(973) 482-6400
1875 McCarter Hwy., Newark 07104
Sunbrite Dye Co.
Phone—(973) 777-9830
35 8th St., P.O. Box 1076, Passaic 07055
Textile Creations, Inc. (H Q)
Phone—(609) 631-4433
8-B S. Gold Dr., Hamilton 08691

## TEXTILE EMBROIDERING

Abilitees Unlimited, Inc.
Phone—(732) 494-1513
23 Adams St., Metuchen 08840
Athletes Image, Inc.
Phone—(732) 974-1600
1865 State Route 35, Wall 07719
East Coast Custom
Phone—(732) 390-8238
242 Main St., Sayreville 08872
Semel's Embroidery & Screen Printing, Inc.
Phone—(973) 473-3959
1078 U.S. Highway 46, Clifton 07013
Sports Paradise
Phone—(609) 877-1826
4230 Route 130, Willingboro 08046
Zeek's Tees
Phone—(732) 291-2700
515 Highway 36, Belford 07718

## TEXTILE FABRICS

DAF Products, Inc.
Phone—(201) 251-1222
420 Braen Ave., Wyckoff 07481
Eastern Silk Mills, Inc.
Phone—(908) 355-6700
212 Catherine St., Elizabeth 07201
Fablok Mills, Inc.
Phone—(908) 464-1950
140 Spring St., Murray Hill 07974
Jason Mills, LLC
Phone—(732) 651-7200
440 S. Main St., Milltown 08850

Search from among 430,000
U.S. manufacturers & suppliers:
**IndustryNet.com**

Ste-Lar Textiles, Inc.
Quality textiles at wholesale prices
Phone—(856) 429-2245
Fax—(856) 429-2251
Email—steve@ste-lar.com
1301 Marlton Pike W., Cherry Hill 08002
*(see our ad under TEXTILE MILL SUPPLIES)*
Triumph Knitting, Inc.
Phone—(201) 646-0022
18-20 Di Carolis Ct., Hackensack 07601

## TEXTILE FINISHING

Diversitex, Inc. (H Q)
Phone—(973) 808-4566
376 Hollywood Ave., Ste. 203, Fairfield 07004

## TEXTILE MACHINERY

2 For 1 Machinery Group, The
Phone—(856) 321-0474
30 N. Pine Ave., Maple Shade 08052
C & S Machine, Inc.
Phone—(973) 882-1097
22 Commerce Rd., Ste. Q, Fairfield 07004
M & P Machinery
Phone—(973) 253-1004
1500 Main Ave., Ste. 31, Clifton 07011

## TEXTILE MACHINERY PARTS

A B C Machinery Corp.
Phone—(609) 971-0990
712-1 Old Shore Rd., P.O. Box 1212, Forked River
08731
Baxter Corp., The
Phone—(201) 337-1212
511 Commerce St., P.O. Box 645, Franklin Lakes
07417

## TEXTILE MILL SUPPLIES

Ste-Lar Textiles, Inc.
Quality textiles at wholesale prices
Phone—(856) 429-2245
Fax—(856) 429-2251
Web—www.ste-lartextiles.com
Email—steve@ste-lar.com
1301 Marlton Pike W., Cherry Hill 08002

**Ste-Lar Textiles, Inc.**
Distributor of textile fabrics & machinery
**856-429-2245**
**FAX: 856-429-2251**
1301 Marlton Pike W. Cherry Hill, NJ 08002

## TEXTILE PRINTING

Donray Printing
Phone—(973) 515-8100
2 Eastmans Rd., Parsippany 07054
Dye Into Print, Inc.
Phone—(973) 772-8019
167 Fornelius Ave., Clifton 07013
Stefan Enterprises, Inc.
Phone—(973) 253-6005
141 Lanza Ave., Bldg. 16-E, Garfield 07026
Tex Print USA, LLC
Phone—(201) 773-6531
20-21 Wagaraw Rd., Bldg. 37, Fair Lawn 07410
Walted Designs, Inc.
Phone—(973) 881-1944
70 Spruce St., Ste. 8, Paterson 07501

## TEXTILE PRODUCTS

A. Smith & Son, Inc.
Phone—(609) 747-0800
300 W. Broad St., Ste. A, Burlington 08016
Hedaya Home Fashions, Inc.
Phone—(908) 352-0808
1111 Jefferson Ave., Elizabeth 07201

© Copyright 2015 Manufacturers' News, Inc.

## TEXTILE TRIMMINGS & BINDINGS

All Lace Processing Corp.
Phone—(201) 867-8795
1109 Grand Ave., Unit 4, North Bergen 07047

Ardwyn Binding Products Co.
Phone—(973) 751-4002
681 Main St., Bldg. 7, Belleville 07109

Hessburg, Inc., Michale A.
Phone—(973) 777-8700
180 Autumn St., Passaic 07055

Margola Corp.
Phone—(201) 816-9500
232 S. Van Brunt St., Englewood 07631

**Offray Specialty Narrow Fabrics, Inc. (H Q)**
**Fax: (908) 879-3630**
**Phone—(908) 879-3636**
**Web—www.osnf.com**
**Email—sales@osnf.com**
**4 Essex Ave., Ste. 403, Bernardsville 07924**

Paris Lace
Phone—(973) 478-9035
1500 Main Ave., Clifton 07011

## TEXTILE WEAVERS

Jacquard Fabrics Co., Inc.
Phone—(732) 905-4545
1965 Swarthmore Ave., Lakewood 08701

Wearbest Sil-Tex Mills, Ltd.
Phone—(973) 340-8844
325 Midland Ave., P.O. Box 589, Garfield 07026

## TEXTILES

Dazian Fabrics, LLC
Phone—(201) 549-1000
18 Central Blvd., South Hackensack 07606

De Leo Textiles (H Q)
Phone—(973) 439-6801
53 Dwight Pl., Fairfield 07004

**Grant Industries, Inc.**
**Phone—(201) 791-6700**
**Fax—(201) 791-0038**
**Web—www.grantinc.com**
**Email—info@grantinc.com**
**125 Main Ave., Elmwood Park 07407**
*(see our ad under COSMETICS)*

Harbor Linen, LLC (H Q)
Phone—(856) 435-2000
2 Foster Ave., Gibbsboro 08026

**Ste-Lar Textiles, Inc.**
**Quality textiles at wholesale prices**
**Phone—(856) 429-2245**
**Fax—(856) 429-2251**
**Email—steve@ste-lar.com**
**1301 Marlton Pike W., Cherry Hill 08002**
*(see our ad under TEXTILE MILL SUPPLIES)*

## TEXTILES — Heat Resistant

Alpha Assocs., Inc.
Phone—(732) 730-1800
145 Lehigh Ave., Lakewood 08701

## TEXTILES — Industrial

Stanek Netting, Inc.
Phone—(973) 680-1616
111 Orange St., Bloomfield 07003

## TEXTILES — Nonwoven

Precision Custom Coatings, LLC
Phone—(973) 890-3873
200 Maltese Dr., Totowa 07512

## THEATRICAL EQUIPMENT & SUPPLIES

Bernhard-Link Theatrical, LLC
Phone—(201) 943-4190
815 Fairview Ave., Ste. 11, Fairview 07022

Rose Brand, Inc.
Phone—(201) 809-1730
4 Emerson Ln., Secaucus 07094

## THERMAL MANAGEMENT PRODUCTS

Amerasia International Technology, Inc.
Phone—(609) 799-9388
70 Washington Rd., Princeton Junction 08550

Robert McKeown Co., Inc.
Phone—(908) 218-9000
111 Chambers Brook Rd., Branchburg 08876

## THERMAL OXIDIZERS

Cire Technologies, Inc.
Phone—(973) 402-8301
251 Boulevard, Mountain Lakes 07046

## THERMOFORMED PLASTIC PARTS

Productive Plastics, Inc.
Phone—(856) 778-4300
103 W. Park Dr., Mount Laurel 08054

Pro-Form Packaging, Inc.
Phone—(732) 968-8123
777 North Avenue Ext., P.O. Box 4231, Dunellen 08812

## THERMOFORMING

Nelson, Inc., Louis A.
Phone—(973) 743-7404
224 Glenwood Ave., Bloomfield 07003

**SPT Packaging LLC**
**Phone—(973) 246-5635**
**Fax—(973) 246-5636**
**Web—www.sptpkg.com**
**Email—jdefelice@sptpkg.com**
**489 Clifton Ave., Clifton 07011**

UFP Technologies, Inc.
Phone—(800) 372-3172
1 Johnson Dr., Raritan 08869

## THERMOMETERS

Medical Indicators, Inc.
Phone—(609) 737-1600
16 Thomas J. Rhodes Industrial Dr., Hamilton 08619

Pyrometer Instrument Co., Inc.
Phone—(609) 443-5522
92 N. Main St., Bldg. 18-D, P.O. Box 479, Windsor 08561

## THERMOPLASTICS

**J-Mac Plastics, Inc.**
**Phone—(908) 709-1111**
**Fax—(908) 709-8908**
**Email—service@jmacplastics.com**
**40 Lafayette Pl., Kenilworth 07033**

**Wiggins Plastics, Inc.**
**Est. 1948-ISO Certified; Custom Injection/**
**Thermoplastics/Thermosets/Compression/Transfer**
**Molding**
**Phone—(973) 667-7200**
**Fax—(973) 667-3227**
**Web—www.wigginsplastics.com**
**Email—info@wigginsplastics.com**
**180 Kingsland Rd., P.O. Box 1077, Clifton 07014**
*(see our ad under PLASTIC INJECTION MOLDING)*

## THERMOSTATS — Appliance

Lux Products Corp. (H Q)
Phone—(856) 234-7905
6000 Commerce Pkwy., Ste. I, Mount Laurel 08054

## THREAD

Advance Fiber Technologies
Phone—(201) 488-2700
344 Lodi St., Hackensack 07601

Dollfus Mieg Co., Inc.
Phone—(973) 589-0606
10 Basin Dr., Ste. 130, Kearny 07032

## THREAD GRINDING

Mechanitron Corp.
Phone—(908) 620-1001
310 W. 1st Ave., Roselle 07203

## TILE

**American Stone, Inc.**
**Phone—(973) 318-7707**
**Fax—(973) 318-7667**
**Email—amerstone@aol.com**
**215 Route 22 W., Hillside 07205**

Garden State Tile Distributors, Inc.
Phone—(908) 241-4900
472 E. Westfield Ave., Roselle Park 07204

Ideal Tile Importing Co., Inc.
Phone—(732) 308-1008
2232 Route 9 S., Howell 07731

## TILE — Ceramic

**Capo Tile Co.**
**Phone—(201) 944-5119**
**492 Main St., Fort Lee 07024**

Classic Ceramic Tile, Inc.
Phone—(732) 390-7700
272 State Route 18, Ste. 3, East Brunswick 08816

DAL-Tile Corporation
Phone—(201) 729-0203
1250 Valley Brook Ave., Lyndhurst 07071

DAL-Tile Sales Service Center 186
Phone—(856) 489-3335
2030 Springdale Rd., Ste. 100, Cherry Hill 08003

**Johann Tile**
**Phone—(609) 978-0489**
**Web—www.johanntile.com**
**Email—johanntile@yahoo.com**
**P.O. Box 1165, Manahawkin 08050**

Klinges, Inc., Charles A.
Phone—(609) 641-7755
790 S. Mill Rd., Absecon 08201

**T & M Tile Contractors**
**Phone—(732) 863-1200**
**Fax—(732) 863-1205**
**Email—smattioli@tmtilecontractors.com**
**55 E. Parsonage Way, Manalapan 07726**

Vanea USA, Inc.
Phone—(201) 796-0722
410 Market St., Elmwood Park 07407

## TILE — Floor

Garden State Tile Distributors, Inc.
Phone—(732) 329-0860
1290 Route 130, Dayton 08810

Garden State Tile Distributors, Inc.
Phone—(973) 366-5035
267 Route 46 W., Dover 07801

Garden State Tile Distributors, Inc.
Phone—(856) 753-0300
790 S. Route 73, West Berlin 08091

Garden State Tile Distributors, Inc. (H Q)
Phone—(732) 938-6675
5001 Industrial Rd., Farmingdale 07727

## TIME & ATTENDANCE SYSTEMS

AMERICAN Time Recorder
Phone—(856) 691-7976
2661 Brunetta Dr., Vineland 08360

Atlantic Time Systems
Phone—(856) 692-9594
112 N. 8th St., Vineland 08360

Time Systems International, Inc.
Phone—(973) 472-2202
142 S. Van Brunt St., Englewood 07631

## TIME CLOCKS

Amano USA Holdings, Inc.
Phone—(973) 403-1900
140 Harrison Ave., Roseland 07068

## TIME CONTROLS

Amperite Co.
Phone—(201) 864-9503
4201 Tonnelle Ave., Ste. 6, North Bergen 07047

INDUSTRY

## TIME RECORDERS

Widmer Time Recorder Co., Inc.
  Phone—(201) 489-3810
  228 Park St., Hackensack 07601

## TIMERS

American Teletimer Corp.
  Phone—(908) 654-4200
  1167 Globe Ave., Mountainside 07092
Precision Multiple Controls, Inc.
  Phone—(201) 444-0600
  33 Greenwood Ave., Midland Park 07432

## TIRE DISTRIBUTORS

Reliable Tire Distributors, Inc.
  Phone—(856) 232-0700
  805 N. Black Horse Pike, P.O. Box 39, Blackwood 08012

## TIRE REPAIR MATERIALS

Coilhose Pneumatics
  Phone—(732) 432-7177
  19 Kimberly Rd., East Brunswick 08816

## TIRE RETREADING

Custom Bandag, Inc.
  Phone—(908) 862-2400
  401 E. Linden Ave., Linden 07036

## TIRES — Wholesale

Mercury Tire Co., Inc.
  Phone—(973) 785-0080
  1 Fairfield Rd., Caldwell 07006

## TITANIUM PRODUCTS

Titanium Fabrication Corp.
  Phone—(973) 227-5300
  110 Lehigh Dr., Fairfield 07004

## TOBACCO AND TOBACCO PRODUCTS

M & M Wholesale
  Phone—(201) 368-0770
  66 Market St., Saddle Brook 07663
**Sherman, Inc. (H Q), Nat**
  **Cigars, cigarettes & pipe tobacco**
  **Phone—(201) 735-9000 / (800) 221-1690**
  **Fax—(201) 735-9099**
  **Web—www.natsherman.com**
  **Email—info@natsherman.com**
  **2200 Fletcher Ave., Fort Lee 07024**

## TOFU

House Foods America Corp.
  Phone—(732) 537-9500
  801 Randolph Rd., Somerset 08873

## TOILETRIES

A. P. Deauville, LLC
  Phone—(732) 545-0200
  594 Jersey Ave., New Brunswick 08901
Alzo International, Inc.
  Phone—(732) 254-1901
  650 Jernee Mill Rd., Sayreville 08872
Essential Amenities, Inc.
  Phone—(973) 882-8441
  208 Passaic Ave., Ste. 1, Fairfield 07004
Fortitude Health
  Phone—(973) 396-8480
  101 U.S. Highway 46, Pine Brook 07058
Johnson & Johnson Consumer Companies, Inc. (H Q)
  Phone—(908) 874-1000
  199 Grandview Rd., Skillman 08558
Unipack, Inc.
  Phone—(973) 450-9880
  681 Main St., Bldg. 27, Belleville 07109

## TONER CARTRIDGES — Laser

Automatic Transfer, Inc.
  Phone—(908) 213-2830
  2 Industrial Rd., Phillipsburg 08865
Turbon Group
  Phone—(856) 665-6650
  4350 Haddonfield Rd., Ste. 300, Pennsauken 08109

## TONER CARTRIDGES — Remanufactured

Cartridge Renewal Systems
  Phone—(732) 845-9497
  13 Glendale Dr., Englishtown 07726
Cartridge World Of Wayne, LLC
  Phone—(973) 696-2880
  1055 Hamburg Tpke., Wayne 07470
Hammer Too, LLC
  Phone—(908) 688-5601
  2576-B U.S. Highway 22 E., Union 07083
Laser Save
  Phone—(732) 431-3339
  843 State Route 33, Ste. 11, Freehold 07728

## TOOL SHARPENING

Paragon Steel & Tool Co., Inc.
  Phone—(201) 997-1676
  339 Bergen Ave., Kearny 07032
Povinelli & Sons, Inc., M.
  Phone—(201) 943-0039
  318 9th St., Fairview 07022
Tri State Perfection Knife Grinding
  Phone—(609) 890-4989
  3 S. Gold Dr., Robbinsville 08691

## TOOLING

Hone-A-Matic Tool & Cutter Co.
  Phone—(732) 382-6000
  187 Wescott Dr., Rahway 07065
Hydratight Operations
  Phone—(732) 271-4100
  12 Worlds Fair Dr., Ste. A, Somerset 08873
Nymar Mfg. Co., Inc.
  Phone—(973) 366-7265
  215 State Route 10 E., Randolph 07869
Sine-Tru Tool Co., Inc.
  Phone—(732) 591-1100
  238 Boundry Rd., Marlboro 07746
United National Machine Tool, Inc.
  Phone—(609) 265-2269
  2404 Sylon Blvd., P.O. Box 608, Hainesport 08036

## TOOLING — Precision

Day Tool & Mfg., Inc.
  Phone—(908) 439-3800
  6 Carman Ln., P.O. Box 466, Whitehouse 08888
R L Tool & Die Co.
  Phone—(908) 245-7710
  739 Fairfield Ave., Kenilworth 07033

Steer traffic to your web site and leads to your inbox...

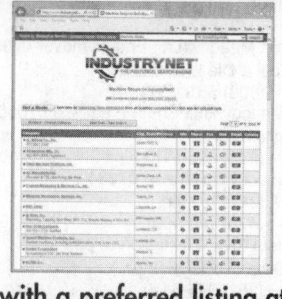

with a preferred listing at
**IndustryNet.com**

## TOOLS — Carbide

**Aloris Tool Technology Co., Inc.**
  **397-407 Getty Ave., Clifton 07011**
  **Quick change tooling**
  **Phone—(973) 772-1201 / (877) 772-1733**
  **Fax—(973) 772-8606**
  **Web—www.aloris.com**
  **Email—aloris@aloris.com**
  **P.O. Box 1529, Clifton 07015**

## Aloris Tool Technology Co., Inc.

*Quick-change tooling*

Toll Free: 877-772-1733

Fax: 973-772-8606

www.aloris.com

aloris@aloris.com

397-407 Getty Ave.
Clifton, NJ 07011

## TOOLS — Cutting

A & J Tool Specialties, Inc.
  Phone—(908) 277-0550
  235 Morris Ave., Summit 07901
**Aloris Tool Technology Co., Inc.**
  **397-407 Getty Ave., Clifton 07011**
  **Quick change tooling**
  **Phone—(973) 772-1201 / (877) 772-1733**
  **Fax—(973) 772-8606**
  **Web—www.aloris.com**
  **Email—aloris@aloris.com**
  **P.O. Box 1529, Clifton 07015**
    *(see our ad under TOOLS – Carbide)*
Armstrong & Sons, Inc.
  Phone—(732) 223-1555
  2335 Highway 34, Manasquan 08736
B & B Supply Corp.
  Phone—(201) 313-9021
  40 Arnot St., Unit 14, Lodi 07644
B & S Tool & Cutter Service, Inc.
  Phone—(201) 488-3545
  99 John St., Hackensack 07601
Du-Mor Blade Co., Inc.
  Phone—(856) 829-9384
  1002 Union Landing Rd., Cinnaminson 08077
Fecken-Kirfel America, Inc.
  Phone—(201) 891-5530
  6 Leighton Pl., Ste. 1, Mahwah 07430
Hobby Blade Specialty, Inc.
  Phone—(908) 317-9306
  725 Jerusalem Rd., Scotch Plains 07076
Machine Shop Discount Supply
  Phone—(201) 518-8472
  P.O. Box 16, Little Ferry 07643
National Steel Rule Co., Inc.
  Phone—(908) 862-3366
  750 Commerce Rd., Linden 07036
POWER HAWK Technologies, Inc.
  Phone—(973) 627-4646
  300 Forge Way, Ste. 2, Rockaway 07866
Ridge Carbide Tool Co.
  Phone—(201) 438-8777
  595 New York Ave., P.O. Box 497, Lyndhurst 07071
Tool-Krib Supply Co. (H Q)
  Phone—(973) 808-4550
  787 Passaic Ave., P.O. Box 6064, West Caldwell 07006
Vozeh Equipment Corp.
  Phone—(201) 337-4212
  509 Commerce St., Franklin Lakes 07417

## TOOLS — Diamond

Accurate Diamond Tool Corp.
Phone—(201) 265-8868
1 Palisade Ave., Emerson 07630
Dessau Co., Inc., Maurice
Phone—(201) 791-2005
15-01 Pollitt Dr., Fair Lawn 07410

## TOOLS — Hand

C T A Mfg. Corp.
Phone—(201) 896-1000
263 Veterans Blvd., Carlstadt 07072
Cementex Products, Inc.
Phone—(609) 387-1040
650 Jacksonville Rd., P.O. Box 1533, Burlington 08016
Norwolf Tool Works, Inc.
Phone—(201) 666-6655
6 Sullivan St., Westwood 07675
Osborne Co., Inc., C. S.
Phone—(973) 483-3232
125 Jersey St., Harrison 07029
Penn Tool Co.
Phone—(973) 761-4343
1776 Springfield Ave., Maplewood 07040
Proedge
Phone—(973) 742-3900
167 Genessee Ave., Paterson 07503
Tolin Design, Inc.
Phone—(201) 261-4455
16 Bland St., Emerson 07630
W.W. Manufacturing Co., Inc.
Phone—(856) 451-5700
60 Rosenhayn Ave., Bridgeton 08302

## TOOLS — Hydraulic

UNEX Corp.
Phone—(201) 512-9500
333 Route 17 N., Mahwah 07430

## TOOLS — Plumbing

Cobra Products, Inc.
Phone—(856) 241-7700
1 Warner Ct., Swedesboro 08085

## TOOLS — Pneumatic

Astro Tool Corp.
Phone—(973) 661-1299
90 Washington Ave., Nutley 07110

## TOOLS — Power

Alpha Professional Tools (H Q)
Phone—(800) 648-7229
103 Bauer Dr., Oakland 07436
Bergen County Motor & Tool Co.
Phone—(201) 796-3006
17-16 River Rd., Fair Lawn 07410
Croft Tool, Inc.
Phone—(732) 899-4885
2144 Bridge Ave., Point Pleasant Boro 08742

## TOOLS — Precision

**Graybill's Tool & Die, Inc.**
Email: geoff@graybills.com
**Phone—(717) 665-5546**
**Fax—(717) 665-3107**
**Web—www.graybills.com**
**147 W. High St., Manheim, PA 17545**
*(see our ads under MACHINE BUILDERS—Custom & MACHINING — Precision)*
Grobet File Co. Of America, LLC.
Phone—(201) 939-6700
750 Washington Ave., Carlstadt 07072
Pfingst & Co., Inc.
Phone—(908) 561-6400
105 Snyder Rd., P.O. Box 377, South Plainfield 07080

*Do nationwide searches for products & services at:*
**IndustryNet.com**

## TOOLS — Solid Carbide

Heller Co., E. P.
Phone—(973) 377-2878
21-25 Samson Ave., P.O. Box 26, Madison 07940

## TOOLS — Special

Predator Tools (H Q)
Phone—(856) 455-3790
35 S. Woodruff Rd., Bridgeton 08302

## TOOLS — Torque

Titan Technologies International, Inc.
Phone—(973) 928-5222
222 Getty Ave., Clifton 07011

## TOOLS — Wholesale

Scientific Models, Inc.
Phone—(908) 464-7070
340 Snyder Ave., Berkeley Heights 07922

## TOOLS AND DIES

A & F Tool
Phone—(973) 262-1792
930 Magnolia Ave., Elizabeth 07201
AB Precision Co.
Phone—(908) 925-1356
1506 E. Elizabeth Ave., Linden 07036
Accurate Machine & Tool Co.
Phone—(908) 245-5545
135 W. Clay Ave., P.O. Box 187, Roselle Park 07204
Aljay Tool & Die Corp.
Phone—(908) 722-2403
1213 Kennedy Blvd., Manville 08835
Altech Machine & Tool, Inc.
Phone—(201) 652-4409
230 Bank St., Ste. 1, Midland Park 07432
Amex Tool Co., Inc.
Phone—(908) 735-5176
4 Fox Hill Ln., Asbury 08802
Artmark Mold & Tool Corp.
Phone—(201) 935-3377
742 Paterson Ave., East Rutherford 07073
Bilt-Rite Tool & Die Co., Inc.
Phone—(973) 227-2882
29 Montesano Rd., Fairfield 07004
Bodine Tool & Machine Co., Inc.
Phone—(856) 234-7800
1273 N. Church St., Ste. 103, Moorestown 08057
Bowman Tool
Phone—(732) 786-0770
147 Pinebrook Rd., Englishtown 07726
Boyle Tool & Die Co., Inc.
Phone—(856) 853-1818
135 Crown Point Rd., Thorofare 08086
D C Metric Tool, Inc.
Phone—(973) 838-7590
11 Mathews Ave., Riverdale 07457
**Day Tool & Mfg., Inc.**
ISO 9001:2008, AS9100 Rev. C
**Phone—(908) 439-3800**
**Fax—(908) 439-3955**
**Web—www.daytool.com**
**Email—juddcallahan@daytool.com**
**6 Carman Ln., P.O. Box 466, Whitehouse 08888**
Ebco Tool Co.
Phone—(973) 887-5255
8-B Great Meadow Ln., East Hanover 07936
Exactal Tool & Die Ltd., Inc.
Phone—(908) 561-1177
3586 Kennedy Rd., South Plainfield 07080
F G H Systems, Inc.
Phone—(973) 625-8114
10 Prospect Pl., Denville 07834
G L Tool & Mfg. Co., Inc.
Phone—(973) 740-0001
26 Okner Pkwy., Livingston 07039
Garden State Precision, Inc.
Phone—(201) 945-6410
510 Church St., Ridgefield 07657

Hofmann Tool & Die Corp.
Phone—(201) 327-0226
356 Route 17 N., Upper Saddle River 07458
Isometric Micro Finishing Coating
Phone—(732) 906-8070
122 James St., Edison 08820
J & J Marine
Phone—(856) 228-4744
1596 Hurffville Rd., Sewell 08096
J S Tool, LLC
Phone—(732) 815-1382
187 Wescott Dr., Ste. D, Rahway 07065
**L & Z Tool & Engineering, Inc.**
Email: fcooper@lztool.com
**Phone—(908) 322-2220**
**Fax—(908) 322-3758**
**Web—www.lztool.com**
**1691 U.S. Highway 22, Watchung 07069**
Liberty Machine Tool & Die, Inc.
Phone—(908) 925-0300
903 E. Elizabeth Ave., Linden 07036
M & G Tool & Die Co.
Phone—(201) 997-0506
936 Harrison Ave., Kearny 07032
**Monroe Tool & Die, Inc.**
**Phone—(856) 629-5164**
**Fax—(856) 875-8868**
**Email—monroetooldie@yahoo.com**
**197 Sharp Rd., Williamstown 08094**
**Montrose Molders Corp.**
Precision tooling & plastic injection molding
**Phone—(908) 754-3030**
**Fax—(732) 529-4236**
**Web—www.montrosemolders.com**
**Email—bwilson@montrosemolders.com**
**25 Howard St., Piscataway 08854**
*(see our ad under PLASTIC INJECTION MOLDING)*
MS Tool Co., Inc.
Phone—(908) 245-7989
500 S. 31st St., Kenilworth 07033
Omega Tool Die
Phone—(856) 232-1015
8 International Ave., Sewell 08080
Oxbow Tool & Die Corp.
Phone—(973) 697-6647
44 Fremont Ter., Oak Ridge 07438
P M Z Tool, Inc.
Phone—(908) 647-2125
321 Warren Ave., Stirling 07980
Pahco Machine, Inc.
Phone—(609) 587-1188
572 Whitehead Rd., Ste. 101, Trenton 08619
Precision Saw & Tool Corp.
Phone—(973) 773-7302
56 Colfax Ave., Clifton 07013
Rex Tool & Mfg. Co.
Phone—(908) 925-2727
544 E. Elizabeth Ave., P.O. Box 1423, Linden 07036
Ricci Tool & Die Co.
Phone—(732) 222-2777
122 Myrtle Ave., Long Branch 07740
Roselle Tool & Die Co.
Phone—(908) 245-3133
135 W. Clay Ave., P.O. Box 103, Roselle Park 07204
Schneider & Marquard, Inc.
Phone—(973) 383-2200
112 Phil Hardin Rd., P.O. Box 39, Newton 07860
Summit Tool Co., Inc.
Phone—(201) 867-8600
719 23rd St., Union City 07087
Ultimate Tool & Mfg. Co.
Phone—(908) 241-4575
360-A Carnegie Ave., Kenilworth 07033
United Die Co., Inc.
Phone—(201) 997-0250
199 Devon Ter., Kearny 07032
Universal Tools & Mfg. Co.
Phone—(973) 379-4193
115 Victory Rd., Springfield 07081
Vantage Tool & Mfg.
Phone—(908) 647-1010
223 Stirling Rd., Warren 07059
Verden Tool & Mfg., LLC
Phone—(973) 366-7510
121 E. Blackwell St., Dover 07801
Zimmer Machinery Systems
Phone—(908) 234-2560
19 Springcroft Rd., Far Hills 07931

INDUSTRY

## TORTILLAS

Puebla Foods, Inc.
    Phone—(973) 473-4494
    118 1st St., Passaic 07055

## TOTES

**MAUSER USA LLC**
    MAUSER is a global leader in industrial packaging-
    drums & IBCs
    **Phone—(732) 353-7000 / (732) 353-7100**
    **Fax—(732) 651-9777**
    **Web—www.mausergroup.com**
    **Email—info.us@mausergroup.com**
    **35 Cotters Ln., Ste. C, East Brunswick 08816**
**Patrick J. Kelly Drums, Inc.**
    New & reconditioned industrial steel, plastic & fiber
    drums, IBCs & totes
    **Phone—(856) 963-1795 / (800) 963-1795**
    **Fax—(856) 963-1788**
    **Web—www.kellydrums.com**
    **Email—sales@kellydrums.com**
    **1810 River Ave., Camden 08105**
        *(see our ad under DRUMS)*

## TOWELS

Avanti Linens, Inc.
    Phone—(201) 641-7766
    234 Moonachie Rd., Moonachie 07074
Franco Mfg. Co., Inc. (H Q)
    Phone—(732) 494-0500
    555 Prospect St., Metuchen 08840

## TOWING EQUIPMENT

**Elizabeth Truck Center**
    Fax: (908) 352-1959
    Sales, Service, Collision & Parts
    **Phone—(908) 355-8800 / (908) 355-9200**
    **Web—www.elizabethtruckcenter.com**
    **Email—spesceJr@elizabethtruckcenter.com**
    **878 North Ave., Elizabeth 07201**
**Equipment Sales & Service**
    **Phone—(973) 743-7516**
    **Fax—(973) 743-3195**
    **Web—www.esstrucksales.com**
    **Email—danjr@esstrucksales.com**
    **152 Floyd Ave., Bloomfield 07003**

## TOYS

Kids Of America Corp.
    Phone—(973) 808-8242
    103 Route 46 W., Fairfield 07004
Model Rectifier Corp.
    Phone—(732) 225-2100
    80 Newfield Ave., P.O. Box 6312, Edison 08837
Moose Mountain Marketing, Inc. (H Q)
    Phone—(973) 884-8900
    8 Wood Hollow Rd., Ste. 302, Parsippany 07054
New Adventures, LLC (H Q)
    Phone—(973) 884-8887
    6 Deforest Ave., Ste. 7, East Hanover 07936
Panline USA, Inc.
    Phone—(201) 750-8010
    251 Union St., Northvale 07647
Peek-A-Boo Toys
    Phone—(856) 317-9100
    9040 Pensauken Hwy., Pennsauken 08110
Prime Time Toys, LLC
    Phone—(973) 839-5711
    P.O. Box 256, Pompton Lakes 07442
Reeves International, Inc.
    Phone—(973) 694-5006
    14 Industrial Rd., Pequannock 07440
Smart Gear, LLC
    Phone—(732) 663-0000
    82 Norwood Ave., Ste. 2, Deal 07723
Tiffanees Toys, Inc.
    Phone—(732) 828-6333
    601 Nassau St., Ste. 593, North Brunswick 08902
Tucker International, LLC
    Phone—(856) 216-1333
    200 W. Somerdale Rd., Ste. B, Voorhees 08043
Wish Factory, Inc., The
    Phone—(973) 744-3131
    21 Church St., Ste. 2, Montclair 07042

## TOYS — Wholesale

Carrera Of America, Inc.
    Phone—(609) 409-8510
    2 Corporate Dr., Ste. D, Cranbury 08512
Daron Worldwide Trading, Inc.
    Phone—(973) 882-0035
    24 Stewart Pl., Ste. 4, Fairfield 07004
**International Playthings LLC**
    **Phone—(973) 316-2500**
    **Fax—(973) 316-5883**
    **Web—www.intplay.com**
    **Email—info@intplay.com**
    **75D Lackawanna Ave., Parsippany 07054**

Wholesaler of Children's Toys & Games
**International Playthings LLC**
*Toys... that make a difference!*
**www.intplay.com**
**(973) 316-2500**
75D Lackawanna Ave. • Parsippany, NJ 07054

Y & W International, Inc.
    Phone—(732) 390-7722
    16 Edgeboro Rd., Unit 5, East Brunswick 08816

## TRACTORS

**Rodio Tractor Sales, Inc.**
    Dealers
    **Phone—(609) 561-0141**
    **Fax—(609) 561-4344**
    **Web—www.rodiotractor.com**
    **Email—sales@rodiotractor.com**
    **717 White Horse Pike, Hammonton 08037**

## TRAILERS

**Utility Trailer Sales Of New Jersey**
    Toll Free Ph (866)-95-PARTS; Distributor of new &
    used trailers & aftermarket parts
    **Phone—(732) 745-1222 / (866) 957-2787**
    **Fax—(732) 745-2699**
    **Web—www.utilityofnj.com**
    **Email—utility4@utilityofnj.com**
    **589 Nassau St., North Brunswick 08902**

## TRAILERS — Boat

Sealion Metal Fabricators, Inc.
    Phone—(856) 933-3914
    776 Creek Rd., Bellmawr 08031

## TRAILERS — Custom

Vending Truck, Inc.
    Phone—(732) 969-5400
    5 Litchfield Rd., East Brunswick 08816

## TRAILERS — Equipment

Green Trailers, Inc., Stephan L.
    Phone—(732) 938-5663
    74 Squankum Yellowbrook Rd., Farmingdale
    07727

## TRAILERS — Flatbed

A B Jersey Trailer Corp.
    Phone—(856) 784-7766
    100 Kresson Gibbsboro Rd., Voorhees 08043

## TRAILERS — Truck & Semi

Shafer Bros. Trailers
    Phone—(856) 358-3483
    38 Martin Ave., Pittsgrove 08318
Vanco U. S. A., LLC
    Phone—(609) 499-4141
    1170 Florence Rd., Bordentown 08505

*find additional suppliers at*
**IndustryNet.com**

## TRAILERS — Utility

D & D Trailers, Inc.
    Phone—(609) 771-0001
    100 Lexington Ave., Trenton 08618

## TRAINING AIDS

Design Assistance Corp.
    Phone—(856) 241-9500
    3 Killdeer Ct., Ste. 301, P.O. Box 215,
    Swedesboro 08085
Kidde Fire Trainers, LLC
    Phone—(201) 300-8100
    17 Philips Pkwy., Montvale 07645

## TRAINING CONSULTANTS

BlessingWhite, Inc.
    Phone—(908) 904-1000
    23 Orchard Rd., Skillman 08558

## TRANSCRIPTION SERVICES

**Brittany Transcription, LLC**
    **Phone—(973) 285-9690**
    **Fax—(973) 285-9569**
    **Web—www.brittanytranscription.com**
    **Email—info@brittanytranscription.com**
    **60 Washington St., Ste. 105, Morristown 07960**

## TRANSDUCERS

**Kulite Semiconductor Products, Inc.**
    **Phone—(201) 461-0900**
    **Fax—(201) 461-0990**
    **Web—www.kulite.com**
    **Email—info-kulite@kulite.com**
    **1 Willow Tree Rd., Leonia 07605**

## TRANSDUCERS — Pressure

American Sensor Technologies, Inc.
    Phone—(973) 448-1901
    450 Clark Dr., Ste. 4, Budd Lake 07828

## TRANSFER SWITCHES

**ASCO Power Technologies, L.P. (H Q)**
    **Phone—(800) 800-2726**
    **Fax—(973) 718-4333**
    **Web—www.emersonnetworkpower.com/asco**
    **Email—customercare@asco.com**
    **50 Hanover Rd., Florham Park 07932**
        *(see our ad under POWER SYSTEMS—Back Up)*

## TRANSFORMERS

**Americor Electronics, Ltd.**
    **Phone—(847) 956-6200 / (800) 830-5337**
    **Fax—(847) 956-0300**
    **Web—www.americor-usa.com**
    **Email—info@americor-usa.com**
    **675 S. Lively Blvd., Elk Grove Village, IL 60007**
        *(see our ads under CABLE ASSEMBLIES & CORD SETS)*
Electromech, Inc.
    Phone—(201) 934-3456
    624 Swan St., Ramsey 07446
Electronic Transformer Corp.
    Phone—(973) 942-2222
    460 Totowa Ave., Paterson 07522
Hitran Corp.
    Phone—(908) 782-5525
    362 Highway 31, Flemington 08822
Magnetic & Transformer Technologies Corp.
    Phone—(609) 371-1258
    653 Sayre Ave., Perth Amboy 08861
Magnetic & Transformer Technologies Corp. (H Q)
    Phone—(609) 371-1258
    7 Tanager Ln., Robbinsville 08691
NWL, Inc.
    Phone—(609) 298-7300
    312 Rising Sun Rd., Bordentown 08505
Power Magne-Tech Corp.
    Phone—(732) 826-4700
    653 Sayre Ave., Perth Amboy 08861

# Lacy's Express, Inc.

## Quality Importers & Exporters

## 856-299-2569 • 800-522-9397

### FAX: 856-299-8532

PO Box 130 Pedricktown, NJ 08067

### www.lacysexpress.com

## TRANSFORMERS — (cont.)

**Power Magnetics, Inc.**
A global provider of a wide range of custom transformers, inductors & reactors for the most demanding applications in a wide variety of industries
Phone—(609) 695-1170 / (800) 747-0845
Fax—(609) 695-5907
Web—www.powermagneticsinc.com
Email—sales@powermagneticsinc.com
377 Reservoir St., Trenton 08618

**Thordarson Meissner, Inc.**
Email: xformersnolan@aol.com
Quality transformers since 1895
Phone—(702) 566-0800
Fax—(702) 566-2080
Web—www.thordarsonmagnetics.com
537 E. Brooks Ave., Ste. 409, North Las Vegas, NV 89030

**Ventronics, Inc.**
Phone—(908) 272-9262
346 Monroe Ave., P.O. Box 142, Kenilworth 07033

## TRANSFORMERS — Current

**J A M B Industries**
Phone—(973) 263-9295
336 Rockaway Valley Rd., Boonton 07005

## TRANSFORMERS — Electrical

**A C Transformer Corp.**
Phone—(973) 589-8574
89 Madison St., Newark 07105

**AFP Transformers Corp.**
Phone—(732) 248-0305
206 Talmadge Rd., Edison 08817

**G & S Motor Equipment Co.**
Phone—(201) 998-9244
1800 Harrison Ave., P.O. Box 493, Kearny 07032

**Galaxy Transformer & Magnetics, LLC**
Phone—(856) 753-4546
386 Cooper Rd., West Berlin 08091

**Glen Magnetics, Inc.**
Phone—(908) 454-3717
1165 3rd Ave., Alpha 08865

**Pioneer Power Solutions, Inc. (H Q)**
Phone—(212) 867-0700
400 Kelby St., 9th Fl., Fort Lee 07024

## TRANSFORMERS — Power

**H I D Systems, Inc.**
Phone—(973) 383-8535
27 Brookfield Dr., Sparta 07871

## TRANSISTORS

**New Jersey Semiconductor Products, Inc.**
We are your source for all your semiconductor needs & requirements
Phone—(973) 376-2922 / (212) 227-6005
Fax—(973) 376-8960
Web—www.njsemi.com
Email—sales@njsemi.com
20 Stern Ave., Springfield 07081

**PowerTech**
Phone—(201) 791-5050
0-02 Fair Lawn Ave., Fair Lawn 07410

## TRANSLATORS & INTERPRETERS

**Legal Interpreters LLC**
Phone—(201) 531-5930
Web—www.legal-interpreters.com
Email—info@legal-interpreters.com
16 Jordan Ave., Wallington 07057

## TRANSMISSION EQUIPMENT

**TransAxle Corp.**
Phone—(201) 440-1911
540 Huyler St., South Hackensack 07606

## TRANSMISSION REBUILDING

**Truck Parts Specialists**
Phone—(201) 288-9333
150 Central Ave., Teterboro 07608

## TRANSMISSIONS — Automatic

**TRC**
Phone—(856) 910-7979
1700 Sherman Ave., Pennsauken 08110

## TRANSMISSIONS — Heavy Duty Truck

**Johnson & Towers, Inc.**
Detroit Diesel, Allison, MTU; Marine & Generator Services
Phone—(609) 272-1415
Fax—(609) 272-1868
Web—www.johnsontowers.com
Email—pprior@johnsontowers.com
2701 Fire Rd., Egg Harbor Township 08234

## TRANSPORTATION BROKERS

**SGF Freight Service**
Phone—(908) 351-9000
Fax—(908) 351-9099
Web—www.sgffreight.com
Email—info@sgffreight.com
142 6th St., Elizabeth 07206

## TRANSPORTATION SERVICES

**Bett A Way Traffic Systems, Inc.**
Transportation Arrangement
Phone—(908) 222-2500
Fax—(908) 222-2540
Web—www.bettaway.com
Email—iola.shapiro@bettaway.com
110 Sylvania Pl., South Plainfield 07080

**Lacy's Express, Inc.**
Phone—(856) 299-2569 / (800) 522-9397
Fax—(856) 299-8532
Web—www.lacysexpress.com
Email—bferrell@lacysexpress.com
P.O. Box 130, Pedricktown 08067
*(see our ad on this page)*

*Search from among 430,000 U.S. manufacturers & suppliers:*
**IndustryNet.com**

## TRANSPORTATION SERVICES — Hazardous Waste

**PSC Environmental Services, LLC**
Phone—(215) 822-2676 / (800) 365-9295
Fax—(215) 997-8219
Web—www.pscnow.com
Email—info@pscnow.com
2337 N. Penn Rd., Hatfield, PA 19440
*(see our ad under ENVIRONMENTAL SERVICES)*

## TRASH LINERS

**Glopak Corp.**
Phone—(908) 753-8735
132 Case Dr., South Plainfield 07080

## TRAYS — Medical

**Case Medical, Inc.**
Phone—(201) 313-1999
19 Empire Blvd., South Hackensack 07606

## TRAYS — Plastic

**Sabert Corp.**
Phone—(732) 721-5544
2288 Main Street Ext., Sayreville 08872

## TREES — Artificial

**Tropical Expressions, Inc.**
Phone—(732) 899-1733
2127 Bridge Ave., Point Pleasant 08742

## TROPHIES

**All Star Awards & Trophies, Inc.**
Phone—(856) 858-6600
866 Haddon Ave., Collingswood 08108

**Atomic Trophies, Inc.**
Phone—(732) 424-7930
201 Shevchenko Ave., South Plainfield 07080

**Awards Trophy Co.**
Phone—(908) 687-5775
611 U.S. Highway 22, Hillside 07205

**Bob's Trophy**
Phone—(201) 391-3790
6 Hamilton St., Montvale 07645

**Bridgeton Trophy & Engraving**
Phone—(856) 451-9007
641 Landis Ave., Bridgeton 08302

**Caporaso Sales Corp.**
Phone—(973) 824-7286
Fax—(973) 824-3837
Email—capsalesco2@aol.com
144 Emmet St., Newark 07114

# Caporaso Sales Corp.

*Trophies*

## 973-824-7286

## FAX: 973-824-3837

capsalesco2@aol.com

144 Emmet St.
Newark, NJ 07114

**Crown Trophy, Inc.**
Phone—(732) 462-3344
3443 Highway 9, Freehold 07728

**Freeman Products, Inc. (H Q)**
Phone—(201) 475-8888
71 Walsh Dr., Parsippany 07054

INDUSTRY

## TROPHIES — (cont.)

**Ill-Eagle Enterprises Ltd.**
Phone—(973) 237-1111
385 Main St., Little Falls 07424
**Little Falls Trophy Co.**
Phone—(973) 256-5222
555 Route 46 E., P.O. Box 1050, Little Falls 07424
**R & R Specialties**
Phone—(609) 886-6651
126 Holly Dr., Rio Grande 08242
**Town Line Trophies**
Phone—(856) 461-0540
2 Amberfield Dr., Delran 08075
**Trophy King Of Ramsey**
Phone—(201) 760-6488
503 N. Franklin Tpke., Unit 13, Ramsey 07446
**Trophy King, Inc., The**
Phone—(201) 836-1482
309 Queen Anne Rd., Teaneck 07666

## TRUCK BODIES

**Automotive Rentals, Inc.**
Phone—(856) 778-1500
4001 Leadenhall Rd., P.O. Box 5039, Mount Laurel 08054
**Barrier Enterprises, Inc.**
Phone—(973) 770-3983
175 Stanhope Sparta Rd., Andover 07821
**Cliffside Body Corp.**
Phone—(201) 945-3970
130 Broad Ave., P.O. Box 206, Fairview 07022
**Demountable Concepts, Inc.**
Phone—(856) 863-0900
200 Acorn Rd., Glassboro 08028
**Fleet Equipment Corp. (H Q)**
Phone—(201) 337-7332
567 Commerce St., Franklin Lakes 07417
**Heller Truck Body Corp.**
Phone—(973) 923-9200
138 U.S. Highway 22, Hillside 07205
**Highway Body Works, Inc.**
Phone—(201) 869-0900
8600 Tonnelle Ave., North Bergen 07047
**Holman Enterprises, Inc. (H Q)**
Phone—(856) 663-5200
244 E. Kings Hwy., Maple Shade 08052
**Norcia Corp.**
Phone—(732) 297-1101
451 Black Horse Ln., North Brunswick 08902
**Omaha Standard**
Phone—(609) 588-5400
572 Whitehead Rd., Trenton 08619
**Transstar Truck Body Welding Co., Inc.**
Phone—(908) 832-2688
514 Route 513, P.O. Box 226, Califon 07830
**Wiegers, Inc.**
Phone—(973) 778-8607
181 Fornelius Ave., Clifton 07013

## TRUCK CAPS

**Suburban Caps, Inc.**
Phone—(732) 251-4383
899 State Route 18, Old Bridge 08857

## TRUCK EQUIPMENT

**Bristol-Donald Co., Inc.**
Phone—(973) 589-2640
50 Roanoke Ave., Newark 07105
**Jack Doheny Companies, Inc.**
Phone—(973) 659-0061
15 Taylor Rd., Ste. 1, Wharton 07885

## TRUCK PARTS

**American Hose & Hydraulics, Inc.**
Phone—(973) 684-3225
700 21st Ave., Paterson 07513
**Elizabeth Truck Center**
Fax: (908) 352-1959
Sales, Service, Collision & Parts
Phone—(908) 355-8800 / (908) 355-9200
Web—www.elizabethtruckcenter.com
Email—spesceJr@elizabethtruckcenter.com
878 North Ave., Elizabeth 07201
**Ransome International**
Phone—(856) 241-8890
2320 High Hill Rd., Logan Township 08085

**TransAxle, LLC**
Phone—(856) 665-4445
2501 Route 73 S., P.O. Box 2306, Cinnaminson 08077
**Vehicle Safety Mfg., LLC**
Phone—(973) 643-3000
408 Central Ave., Newark 07107

## TRUCK REFRIGERATION EQUIPMENT

**Runnemede Truck Refrigeration**
Phone—(856) 423-4400
320 Borelli Blvd., Paulsboro 08066

## TRUCK REPAIR SERVICES

**Elizabeth Truck Center**
Fax: (908) 352-1959
Sales, Service, Collision & Parts
Phone—(908) 355-8800 / (908) 355-9200
Web—www.elizabethtruckcenter.com
Email—spesceJr@elizabethtruckcenter.com
878 North Ave., Elizabeth 07201

## TRUCK SALES & SERVICE

**Elizabeth Truck Center**
Fax: (908) 352-1959
Sales, Service, Collision & Parts
Phone—(908) 355-8800 / (908) 355-9200
Web—www.elizabethtruckcenter.com
Email—spesceJr@elizabethtruckcenter.com
878 North Ave., Elizabeth 07201

## TRUCKING

**A B Trucking Inc.**
Phone—(609) 685-4631
Fax—(609) 859-7399
P.O. Box 2051, Vincentown 08088

**(609) 685-4631 • (609) 859-7399**
P.O. Box 2051 • Vincentown, NJ 08088

**Costa Trucking LLC**
Phone—(973) 230-9314
Fax—(973) 230-0552
18 Upper Warren Way, Warren 07059
**Cranez, Inc.**
For more than 20 yrs., serving the Tri-State area. Offering free no-obligation est.; providing svc. 24 hrs., 7 days a week & no-cost site checks. Operators are CCO/Natnl. Commission certified, have TWIC credentials & O.S.H.A 30-hrs trained
Phone—(856) 262-0288 / (877) 262-0288
Fax—(856) 262-2654
Web—www.cranezincnj.com
Email—cranez06@aol.com
2610 S. Black Horse Pike, Williamstown 08094
**Glendale Warehouse Corp.**
Phone—(732) 516-1555
Fax—(732) 516-9898
Web—www.glendalewarehouse.com
Email—glendale@glendalewh.com
742 Old Post Rd., Edison 08817
*(see our ad under WAREHOUSES)*
**Jan Packaging, Inc.**
100 Harrison St., Dover 07801
Email: kcaristia@janpackaging.com
Toll Free Ph: (888)4-JANPAK
Phone—(973) 361-7200
Fax—(973) 361-3306
Web—www.janpackaging.com
P.O. Box 448, Dover 07802
*(see our ad under PACKAGING—Industrial)*
**MJD Trucking Inc.**
Phone—(856) 205-9490
Fax—(856) 205-9491
Email—dolores@mjdtrucking.net
2055 DeMarco Dr., Vineland 08360

**R & C Transport Inc.**
Phone—(201) 704-2345
Fax—(973) 537-8857
Email—llee7565@aol.com
38 E. Sterling St., Wharton 07885

## TRUCKING — Heavy Haul

**Arlington Scrap Metal Corp.**
Also scrap metal
Phone—(973) 296-2718
Fax—(973) 628-1020
Web—www.arlingtonscrapmetal.com
Email—arlingtonscrap@comcast.net
90 Newark Pompton Tpke., Ste. 5, Wayne 07470
**Bett A Way Traffic Systems, Inc.**
Transportation Arrangement
Phone—(908) 222-2500
Fax—(908) 222-2540
Web—www.bettaway.com
Email—iola.shapiro@bettaway.com
110 Sylvania Pl., South Plainfield 07080
**Industrial Contracting & Rigging**
Phone—(201) 529-5111
Fax—(201) 529-3754
Web—www.icrnj.com
Email—info@icrnj.com
41 Ramapo Valley Rd., Mahwah 07430
**JSD Refrigerated Trucking**
Phone—(856) 825-1901 / (800) 899-1901
Fax—(856) 825-6787
830 Carmel Rd., Millville 08332
*(see our ad under TRUCKING — Refrigerated)*

## TRUCKING — Refrigerated

**JSD Refrigerated Trucking**
Phone—(856) 825-1901 / (800) 899-1901
Fax—(856) 825-6787
830 Carmel Rd., Millville 08332

**JSD Refrigerated Trucking**
*Quality trucking*
**(856) 825-1901**
830 Carmel Rd. Millville, NJ 08332

## TRUCKS

**Mid-Atlantic Truck Center, Inc.**
Phone—(908) 862-8181
525 W. Linden Ave., Linden 07036

## TRUCKS — Heavy Duty

**Perone's Auto Service & Salvage**
We Buy All Metals & Iron. 10-40 Yard Container Service For Demolition & Clean Ups
Phone—(732) 563-1630
Fax—(732) 563-1774
Web—www.peronesauto.com
Email—peronesauto@yahoo.com
371 US Highway 22, Green Brook 08812
*(see our ad under SCRAP IRON & METAL RECYCLING)*

## TRUCKS — Industrial

**Action Lift Trucks, Inc.**
Phone—(973) 589-2320
Fax—(973) 824-4768
Web—www.actionlifttrucks.com
Email—actionlift@optonline.net
35 Avenue C, Newark 07114
**Raymond Of NJ, LLC**
Phone—(908) 624-9570 / (800) 800-2024
Fax—(908) 624-9553
Web—www.raymond-nj.com
Email—info@raymond-nj.com
1000 Brighton St., Union 07083
*(see our ad under MATERIAL HANDLING EQUIPMENT)*

© Copyright 2015 Manufacturers' News, Inc.

## TRUCKS — Rebuilt

**Elizabeth Truck Center**
Fax: (908) 352-1959
Sales, Service, Collision & Parts
Phone—(908) 355-8800 / (908) 355-9200
Web—www.elizabethtruckcenter.com
Email—spesceJr@elizabethtruckcenter.com
878 North Ave., Elizabeth 07201

## TUBE BENDING & FABRICATING

Kreisler Mfg. Corp.
Phone—(201) 791-0700
180 Van Riper Ave., Elmwood Park 07407
**MP Tube Works, Inc.**
Phone—(908) 317-2500
Fax—(908) 317-2969
Web—www.mptubeworksinc.com
Email—mptube@aol.com
237 Sheffield St., Mountainside 07092
New World Stainless, LLC
Phone—(732) 412-7170
100 Randolph Rd., Ste. 5, Somerset 08873
Samstubend, Inc.
Phone—(973) 278-2555
31 Maryland Ave., Paterson 07503

## TUBE FILLING

**Prodo-Pak Corp.**
The Real Leader in Pouch & Tube Filling & Sealing
Machinery, ideal for all liquids, creams, pastes &
semi-viscous products
Phone—(973) 772-4500
Fax—(973) 772-0471
Web—www.prodo-pak.com
Email—sales@prodo-pak.com
77 Commerce St., P.O. Box 363, Garfield 07026

## TUBING

Resdel Corp.
Phone—(609) 886-1111
Cape May County Industrial Pk., Rio Grande
08242

## TUBING — Brass

Industrial Tube Corp.
Phone—(908) 369-3737
297 Valley Rd., Hillsborough 08844
Trojan Tube Co.
Phone—(732) 938-5687
Yellowbrook Rd., P.O. Box 496, Farmingdale
07727

## TUBING — Glass, Precision Bore

**Precision Electronic Glass, Inc.**
Glass Custom Components
Phone—(856) 691-2234 / (800) 982-4734
Fax—(856) 691-3090
Web—www.pegglass.com
Email—info@pegglass.com
1013 Hendee Rd., Vineland 08360

## TUBING — Metal

G & J Steel & Tubing, Inc.
Phone—(908) 526-4445
406 Roycefield Rd., Hillsborough 08844
Microtube Fabricators, Inc.
Phone—(732) 469-7420
250 Lackland Dr., Middlesex 08846

## TUBING — Plastic

All State Plastics, Inc.
Phone—(732) 721-4024
237 Raritan St., South Amboy 08879
Cobon Plastics Corp.
Phone—(973) 334-6330
90 South St., Dock 5, Newark 07114
Hishi Plastics U. S. A., Inc.
Phone—(973) 633-1230
600-F Ryerson Rd., Lincoln Park 07035
Saint-Gobain Performance Plastics
Phone—(856) 423-6630
210 Harmony Rd., Mickleton 08056

Thermoplastic Biologic, LLC
Phone—(973) 383-2834
26 Brookfield Dr., Ste. C, Sparta 07871
Thermoplastic Processes
Phone—(888) 554-6400
1268 Valley Rd., P.O. Box 124, Stirling 07980
VisiPak, a Sinclair & Rush Company
Phone—(800) 949-1141
640 Dell Rd., Ste. 1, P.O. Box 0188, Carlstadt
07072
Zeus Industrial Products, Inc.
Phone—(908) 526-6500
134 Chubb Way, Branchburg 08876

## TUBING — Rubber

Armstrong Industrial Hose Products, LLC
Phone—(609) 989-5161
1400 E. State St., Hamilton 08609
Prestige Rubber Mfg.
Phone—(973) 227-2505
11 Spielman Rd., Fairfield 07004

## TUBING — Stainless Steel

Century Tube Corp.
Phone—(908) 534-2001
22 Tannery Rd., Somerville 08876
Draka Specialty Tubing
Phone—(732) 469-5902
111 Chimney Rock Rd., Bridgewater 08807
**East Coast Stainless, Inc.**
Stainless C-276, Alloy 20, 321, 347, 400, 410, 600, 625,
800, 825 & Chrome-Moly
Phone—(302) 366-0675
Fax—(302) 366-0691
Web—www.eastcoaststainless.com
Email—sales@eastcoaststainless.com
30 Albe Dr., Ste. E, Newark, DE 19702
*(see our ad under PIPE — Stainless Steel)*
M & M International
Phone—(908) 412-8300
3619 Kennedy Rd., Ste. A, South Plainfield 07080
Putnum Stainless Tubes, Inc.
Phone—(908) 232-9200
1163 Route 22 E., Mountainside 07092
RathGibson, LLC
Phone—(908) 218-1400
100 Aspen Hill Rd., North Branch 08876

## TUBING — Steel, Welded

**Arntzen Corp.**
Mfr. of Large Diameter Steel Pipe 24 inches OD to 192
inches OD
Phone—(815) 964-9413 / (800) 821-3475
Fax—(815) 964-0045
Web—www.ArntzenPipe.com
Email—PipeSales@ArntzenCorp.com
P.O. Box 898, Rockford, IL 61105

## TUBULAR PRODUCTS

Acme/Lingo Flagpoles
Phone—(609) 801-1897
1865 Route 206, Southampton 08088

## TURBINE EQUIPMENT

MAN Diesel & Turbo
Phone—(732) 582-8200
2 Amboy Ave., Bldg. 2, Woodbridge 07095

## TURBINES

**Chalmers & Kubeck, Inc.**
Phone—(610) 494-4300
Fax—(610) 485-1484
Web—www.candk.com
Email—jmoore@candk.com
150 Commerce Dr., P.O. Box 2447, Aston, PA
19014
*(see our ad under MACHINE WORK & MACHINING)*
PSEG Power
Phone—(732) 750-2062
749 Cliff Rd., Sewaren 07077

## TURBINES — Gas

Siemens Energy, Inc.
Phone—(609) 890-5000
840 Nottingham Way, Trenton 08638

## TURBINES — Hydroelectric

E-Harvest Systems (H Q)
Phone—(908) 832-0400
424 Little Brook Rd., Glen Gardner 08826

## TURBOCHARGERS

ABB Inc., Business Unit Turbocharger
Phone—(732) 932-6000
1460 Livingston Ave., P.O. Box 6005, North
Brunswick 08902

## TURNING — CNC

3D Medical Mfg., Inc.
Phone—(856) 486-9600
7145 Colonial Ln., Pennsauken 08109
**E & J Machine And Tool, LLC**
Phone—(973) 810-2312 / (973) 810-2313
Fax—(973) 601-7953
Web—www.ejmachine.com
Email—sales@ejmachine.com
12 Orben Dr., Unit 1, Landing 07850
*(see our ad under JOB SHOPS)*
**FIMS Mfg. Corp.**
Phone—(201) 845-7088
Fax—(201) 845-8287
Web—www.fimsmfg.com
Email—fimsmfg@optonline.net
8 Allerman Rd., Oakland 07436

## TURNTABLES — Audio

VPI Industries, Inc.
Phone—(732) 583-6895
77 Cliffwood Ave., Ste. 3-B, Cliffwood 07721

## TYPESETTING

Cantone Press, Inc.
Phone—(201) 569-2288
161 Coolidge Ave., Englewood 07631
J K Design, Inc.
Phone—(908) 428-4700
465 Amwell Rd., Hillsborough 08844
Main Street Communications
Phone—(908) 735-7570
15 W. Main St., Clinton 08809
Type-N-Graphic
Phone—(973) 838-6544
170 Kinnelon Rd., Ste. 12, Kinnelon 07405
Typeworks
Phone—(201) 653-8380
228 Jefferson St., Apt. 4, Hoboken 07030

## TYPESETTING — Multi-Lingual

Newtype, Inc.
Phone—(973) 361-6000
447 State Route 10, Ste. 14, Randolph 07869

## TYPEWRITERS

Elmendorf Office Supply , Inc.
Phone—(732) 295-8700
3201 Bridge Ave., Ste. 1, Point Pleasant Beach
08742

## ULTRASONIC CLEANING EQUIPMENT

Crest Ultrasonics Corp.
Phone—(609) 883-4000
10 Grumman Ave., P.O. Box 7266, Trenton 08628
Environmental Services Group/Green Power
Phone—(201) 569-2020
151 Sparta Stanhope Rd., Hopatcong 07843

## ULTRASONIC CLEANING EQUIPMENT — (cont.)

**L & R Mfg. Co., Inc.**
**Phone—(201) 991-5330**
**Fax—(201) 991-5870**
**Web—www.lrultrasonics.com**
**Email—info@lrultrasonics.com**
**577 Elm St., P.O. Box 607, Kearny 07032**
Zenith Ultrasonics
Phone—(201) 767-1332
85 Oak St., P.O. Box 412, Norwood 07648

## ULTRASONIC EQUIPMENT & SUPPLIES

Designmecha, Inc.
Phone—(973) 493-8146
73 Race St., Nutley 07110
NEXT Medical Products
Phone—(800) 458-4254
45 Columbia Rd., Branchburg 08876
Parker Laboratories, Inc.
Phone—(973) 276-9500
286 Eldridge Rd., Fairfield 07004
T A C Technical Instrument Corp.
Phone—(609) 882-2894
21 W. Piper Ave., Trenton-Mercer Airport, West Trenton 08628

## UMBRELLAS

Frankford Umbrellas
Phone—(856) 222-4134
824 E. Gate Dr., Mount Laurel 08054
Galleria Enterprises, Inc.
Phone—(646) 416-6683
300-3 State Route 17 S., Ste. E, Lodi 07644
Peerless Umbrella Co., Inc.
Phone—(973) 578-4900
427 Ferry St., Newark 07105
Rainmen U. S. A., Inc.
Phone—(201) 784-3244
10 Maple St., Norwood 07648
S. Frankford & Sons, Inc.
Phone—(856) 222-4134
110 Gaither Dr., Mount Laurel 08054

## UNIFORMS

A-1 Uniforms, Inc.
Phone—(856) 963-7680
721 Broadway, Camden 08103
Alpine Trading Co., Inc.
Phone—(201) 871-6111
400 Overpeck Pl., Englewood 07631
Ambassador Uniform Group, Inc.
Phone—(732) 792-1111
289 Highway 33 E., Manalapan 07726
Asia Trading
Phone—(973) 577-1300
390 Nye Ave., Irvington 07111
Crown Clothing Co., Inc.
Phone—(856) 691-0343
609 Paul St., Vineland 08360
DeRossi & Son Co.
Phone—(856) 691-0061
411 S. 6th St., Vineland 08360
G & K Services, Inc.
Phone—(973) 751-0464
137 Ralph St., Belleville 07109
Happy Chef Uniforms, Inc.
Phone—(973) 492-2525
22 Park Pl., Butler 07405
Hope Uniform Co., Inc.
Phone—(908) 496-4899
4 Columbia St., P.O. Box 224, Columbia 07832
Oakwood Uniform & Equipment Co.
Phone—(856) 779-7680
400 E. Main St., Maple Shade 08052
Red The Uniform Tailor, Inc.
Phone—(848) 299-0100
475 Oberlin Ave. S., Lakewood 08701
Some's World-Wide Uniforms
Phone—(201) 843-1199
314 Main St., Hackensack 07601
Strong Wear, LLC
Phone—(201) 837-7830
191 The Plaza Ave., Teaneck 07666

Team U. S. A.
Phone—(973) 596-2800
200 Badger Ave., Newark 07108
Universal Uniform
Phone—(973) 622-5700
1015 Broad St., P.O. Box 637, Newark 07102

## UNIFORMS — Medical

Doc's Duds, LLC
Phone—(732) 219-0060
92 Half Mile Rd., Red Bank 07701
NurseJoe.Com
Phone—(848) 250-9900
11 Plainfield Ave., Metuchen 08840

## UNIVERSAL JOINTS

S G Mfg. Corp.
Phone—(732) 494-6520
15 Oliver St., Metuchen 08840

## UPHOLSTERY

Bergen Auto Upholstery
Phone—(201) 457-9100
375 North St., Ste. U, Teterboro 07608

## UPHOLSTERY FABRICS

Absecon Mills, Inc.
Phone—(609) 965-5373
901 W. Aloe St., P.O. Box 672, Cologne 08213

## UPHOLSTERY SUPPLIES

**Stanley Foam Rubber Corp.**
**Phone—(973) 778-1660**
**Fax—(973) 778-9014**
**Web—www.stanleyfoam.com**
**Email—stanleyfoam@yahoo.com**
**14 Orchard St., Wallington 07057**

## URETHANE PRODUCTS

Banks Bros. Corp.
Phone—(973) 680-4488
24 Federal Plz., Bloomfield 07003

## UTILITY CONTRACTORS

**Calibration Technologies Inc.**
**Phone—(973) 267-7080**
**Fax—(973) 267-7081**
**Web—www.calibrationtech.com**
**Email—info@calibrationtech.com**
**736 Speedwell Ave., Ste. 1, Morris Plains 07950**

## VACUUM BRAZING

**Concept Group, Inc.**
**Glass to metal seals (hermetic packages) & Vacuum insulated components**
**Phone—(856) 767-5506**
**Fax—(856) 768-3981**
**Web—www.conceptgroupinc.com**
**Email—applications@conceptgroupinc.com**
**380 Cooper Rd., West Berlin 08091**
*(see our ad under MACHINE PARTS — Precision)*

## VACUUM CLEANER ATTACHMENTS & PARTS

**Advantage Vacuum Parts & Supplies**
**Distributor of commercial vacuum cleaners & parts, including belts & bags**
**Phone—(908) 228-5629 / (877) 777-6383**
**Fax—(908) 228-5991**
**Web—www.advacnj.com**
**Email—alan@advantagevacuum.com**
**110 South Ave., Ste. A, Garwood 07027**

## VACUUM CLEANERS

Advantage Vacuum LLC
Phone—(908) 228-5629
110 South Ave., Ste. A, Garwood 07027
**Advantage Vacuum Parts & Supplies**
**Distributor of commercial vacuum cleaners & parts, including belts & bags**
**Phone—(908) 228-5629 / (877) 777-6383**
**Fax—(908) 228-5991**
**Web—www.advacnj.com**
**Email—alan@advantagevacuum.com**
**110 South Ave., Ste. A, Garwood 07027**
Budd Built In Vacuum Cleaners
Phone—(201) 891-3010
445 W. Main St., Wyckoff 07481
Metropolitan Vacuum Cleaner Co., Inc.
Phone—(201) 405-2225
5 Raritan Rd., Oakland 07436

## VACUUM CLEANERS — Industrial

Elgee Mfg. Co.
Phone—(908) 647-4100
225 Stirling Rd., Warren 07059
Hafco Foundry, Inc.
Phone—(201) 447-0433
301 Greenwood Ave., Front, Midland Park 07432
Vac-U-Max
Phone—(973) 759-4600
69 William St., Belleville 07109

## VACUUM EQUIPMENT

DigiVac Co.
Phone—(732) 765-0900
105-B Church St., Matawan 07747

## VACUUM FILTERS

**Komline-Sanderson Engineering**
**Phone—(908) 234-1000 / (800) 225-5457**
**Fax—(908) 234-9487**
**Web—www.komline.com**
**Email—info@komline.com**
**12 Holland Ave., Peapack 07977**

## VACUUM SYSTEMS

Croll-Reynolds
Phone—(201) 288-9282
90 Hollister Rd., Teterboro 07608
Croll-Reynolds (H Q)
Phone—(908) 232-4200
6 Campus Dr., Parsippany 07054
Denton Vacuum, LLC
Phone—(856) 439-9100
1259 N. Church St., Bldg. 3, Moorestown 08057

## VALVE POSITION INDICATORS

Moniteur Devices, Inc.
Phone—(973) 857-1600
36 Commerce Rd., Cedar Grove 07009

## VALVES

Ceresist, Inc.
Phone—(973) 345-3231
176 E. 7th St., Paterson 07524
**Chalmers & Kubeck, Inc.**
**Phone—(610) 494-4300**
**Fax—(610) 485-1484**
**Web—www.candk.com**
**Email—jmoore@candk.com**
**150 Commerce Dr., P.O. Box 2447, Aston, PA 19014**
*(see our ad under MACHINE WORK & MACHINING)*
Chalmers & Kubeck, Inc.
Phone—(732) 993-1251
8 Jules Ln., New Brunswick 08901
Clark Cooper Div.
Phone—(856) 829-4580
941 Hamilton Ave., Roebling 08554

*Do nationwide searches for products & services at:*
**IndustryNet.com**

*find additional suppliers at*
**IndustryNet.com**

## VALVES — *(cont.)*

**East Coast Stainless, Inc.**
Stainless C-276, Alloy 20, 321, 347, 400, 410, 600, 625, 800, 825 & Chrome-Moly
Phone—(302) 366-0675
Fax—(302) 366-0691
Web—www.eastcoaststainless.com
Email—sales@eastcoaststainless.com
30 Albe Dr., Ste. E, Newark, DE 19702
*(see our ad under PIPE—Stainless Steel)*

**FCX Performance, Inc.**
Phone—(973) 575-8350
333 Route 46 W., Ste. 130, Fairfield 07004

**Fox Valve Development Corp.**
Phone—(973) 328-1011
85 Franklin Rd., Hamilton Business Pk., Dover 07801

**Goyen Valve Corp.**
Phone—(732) 364-7800
1195 Airport Rd., Lakewood 08701

**HD Supply Water Works, Inc.**
Phone—(856) 753-5566
228 Williamstown Rd., Berlin 08009

**Magnatrol Valve Corp.**
67 5th Ave., Hawthorne 07506
Bronze & Stainless Steel 2-Way Solenoid Valves.
Quick Delivery
Phone—(973) 427-4341 / (800) 711-0017
Fax—(973) 427-7611
Web—www.magnatrol.com
Email—info@magnatrol.com
P.O. Box 17, Hawthorne 07507
*(see our ad under VALVES—Solenoid)*

**Taylor Forge Stainless, Inc.**
Phone—(908) 722-1313
22 Readington Rd., P.O. Box 610, Somerville 08876

**Universal Valve Co., Inc.**
Phone—(908) 351-0606
478 Schiller St., Elizabeth 07206

## VALVES — Air

**Magnatrol Valve Corp.**
67 5th Ave., Hawthorne 07506
Bronze & Stainless Steel 2-Way Solenoid Valves.
Quick Delivery
Phone—(973) 427-4341 / (800) 711-0017
Fax—(973) 427-7611
Web—www.magnatrol.com
Email—info@magnatrol.com
P.O. Box 17, Hawthorne 07507
*(see our ad under VALVES—Solenoid)*

## VALVES — Biotech

**NResearch, Inc.**
Manufacturer of Chemically Inert Valves
Phone—(973) 808-8811
Fax—(973) 808-0086
Web—www.nresearch.com
Email—sales@nresearch.com
267 Fairfield Ave., West Caldwell 07006
*(see our ad under VALVES—Solenoid)*

## VALVES — Boiler Blow-Off

**Everlasting Valve Co.**
Phone—(908) 769-0700
108 Somogyi Ct., South Plainfield 07080

## VALVES — Compressed Natural Gas (CNG)

**Magnatrol Valve Corp.**
67 5th Ave., Hawthorne 07506
Bronze & Stainless Steel 2-Way Solenoid Valves.
Quick Delivery
Phone—(973) 427-4341 / (800) 711-0017
Fax—(973) 427-7611
Web—www.magnatrol.com
Email—info@magnatrol.com
P.O. Box 17, Hawthorne 07507
*(see our ad under VALVES—Solenoid)*

## VALVES — Control

**Emerson Instrument & Valve Services**
Phone—(609) 386-5000
120 Kissel Rd., Burlington 08016

**Magnatrol Valve Corp.**
67 5th Ave., Hawthorne 07506
Bronze & Stainless Steel 2-Way Solenoid Valves.
Quick Delivery
Phone—(973) 427-4341 / (800) 711-0017
Fax—(973) 427-7611
Web—www.magnatrol.com
Email—info@magnatrol.com
P.O. Box 17, Hawthorne 07507
*(see our ad under VALVES—Solenoid)*

**Onyx Valve Co.**
Phone—(856) 829-2888
835 Industrial Hwy., Ste. 4, Cinnaminson 08077

**Premac, Inc.**
Phone—(732) 381-7550
P.O. Box 9, Rahway 07065

## VALVES — Cryogenic

**Magnatrol Valve Corp.**
67 5th Ave., Hawthorne 07506
Bronze & Stainless Steel 2-Way Solenoid Valves.
Quick Delivery
Phone—(973) 427-4341 / (800) 711-0017
Fax—(973) 427-7611
Web—www.magnatrol.com
Email—info@magnatrol.com
P.O. Box 17, Hawthorne 07507
*(see our ad under VALVES—Solenoid)*

## VALVES — Flow Control

**Plast-O-Matic Valves, Inc.**
Phone—(973) 256-3000
1384 Pompton Ave., Ste. 1, Cedar Grove 07009

## VALVES — Gas

**GasFlo Products, Inc.**
Phone—(973) 276-9011
19 Industrial Rd., Fairfield 07004

**Magnatrol Valve Corp.**
67 5th Ave., Hawthorne 07506
Bronze & Stainless Steel 2-Way Solenoid Valves.
Quick Delivery
Phone—(973) 427-4341 / (800) 711-0017
Fax—(973) 427-7611
Web—www.magnatrol.com
Email—info@magnatrol.com
P.O. Box 17, Hawthorne 07507
*(see our ad under VALVES—Solenoid)*

## VALVES — High Pressure

**Flodyne Controls, Inc.**
Phone—(908) 464-6200
48 Commerce Dr., Murray Hill 07974

**Magnatrol Valve Corp.**
67 5th Ave., Hawthorne 07506
Bronze & Stainless Steel 2-Way Solenoid Valves.
Quick Delivery
Phone—(973) 427-4341 / (800) 711-0017
Fax—(973) 427-7611
Web—www.magnatrol.com
Email—info@magnatrol.com
P.O. Box 17, Hawthorne 07507
*(see our ad under VALVES—Solenoid)*

**Straval Co.**
Phone—(973) 340-9955
21 Columbus Ave., Garfield 07026

## VALVES — Hydrogen

**Magnatrol Valve Corp.**
67 5th Ave., Hawthorne 07506
Bronze & Stainless Steel 2-Way Solenoid Valves.
Quick Delivery
Phone—(973) 427-4341 / (800) 711-0017
Fax—(973) 427-7611
Web—www.magnatrol.com
Email—info@magnatrol.com
P.O. Box 17, Hawthorne 07507
*(see our ad under VALVES—Solenoid)*

## VALVES — Industrial

**ASCO Valve, Inc.**
Phone—(973) 966-2000
50 Hanover Rd., Florham Park 07932

**ASCO Valve, Inc.**
Phone—(973) 966-2000
50-60 Hanover Rd., Florham Park 07932

**Barworth Micro Valve, Inc.**
Phone—(973) 376-4883
673 Morris Tpke., Springfield 07081

**Fluidyne Corp.**
Phone—(856) 663-1818
9100 Collins Ave., Pennsauken 08110

## VALVES — Needle

**Britten & Travel Lite Golf, E. F.**
Phone—(908) 276-4800
22 South Ave. W., P.O. Box 246, Cranford 07016

## VALVES — Oil

**Magnatrol Valve Corp.**
67 5th Ave., Hawthorne 07506
Bronze & Stainless Steel 2-Way Solenoid Valves.
Quick Delivery
Phone—(973) 427-4341 / (800) 711-0017
Fax—(973) 427-7611
Web—www.magnatrol.com
Email—info@magnatrol.com
P.O. Box 17, Hawthorne 07507
*(see our ad under VALVES—Solenoid)*

## VALVES — Pneumatic

**ASCO Valve, Inc.**
Phone—(856) 985-8700
13000 Lincoln Dr. W., Ste. 106, Marlton 08053

**Versa Products Co., Inc.**
Phone—(201) 843-2400
22 Spring Valley Rd., Paramus 07652

## VALVES — Pressure Regulating

**Generant Co., Inc.**
Phone—(973) 838-6500
1865 Route 23 S., P.O. Box 768, Butler 07405

## VALVES — Rebuilt

**G & S Valves Fittings Co., Inc.**
Phone—(201) 868-8026
6910 Adams St., Guttenberg 07093

**S & S Valve Service, Inc.**
Phone—(732) 548-2040
105 Liberty St., Metuchen 08840

## VALVES — Rotary

**Magnatrol Valve Corp.**
67 5th Ave., Hawthorne 07506
Bronze & Stainless Steel 2-Way Solenoid Valves.
Quick Delivery
Phone—(973) 427-4341 / (800) 711-0017
Fax—(973) 427-7611
Web—www.magnatrol.com
Email—info@magnatrol.com
P.O. Box 17, Hawthorne 07507
*(see our ad under VALVES—Solenoid)*

## VALVES — Safety

**Micromat Co.**
Phone—(201) 529-3738
185 State Route 17, Mahwah 07430

## VALVES — Solenoid

**Bio-Chem Fluidics, Inc.**
Phone—(973) 263-3001
85 Fulton St., Ste. 12, Boonton 07005

**Magnatrol Valve Corp.**
67 5th Ave., Hawthorne 07506
Bronze & Stainless Steel 2-Way Solenoid Valves.
Quick Delivery
Phone—(973) 427-4341 / (800) 711-0017
Fax—(973) 427-7611
Web—www.magnatrol.com
Email—info@magnatrol.com
P.O. Box 17, Hawthorne 07507
*(see our ad on next page)*

INDUSTRY

## VALVES — Solenoid — (cont.)

**NResearch, Inc.**
Manufacturer of Chemically Inert Valves
Phone—(973) 808-8811
Fax—(973) 808-0086
Web—www.nresearch.com
Email—sales@nresearch.com
267 Fairfield Ave., West Caldwell 07006
*(see our ad on this page)*

Parker Hannifin Corp.
Phone—(973) 575-4844
45 Route 46 E., Unit 602, P.O. Box 778, Pine Brook 07058

Valcor Engineering Corp.
Phone—(973) 467-8400
2 Lawrence Rd., Springfield 07081

## VALVES — Specialty

B-Tech Valve, LLC
Phone—(609) 321-2205
200 Cinnaminson Ave., Palmyra 08065

## VALVES — Stainless Steel

**Magnatrol Valve Corp.**
67 5th Ave., Hawthorne 07506
Bronze & Stainless Steel 2-Way Solenoid Valves.
Quick Delivery
Phone—(973) 427-4341 / (800) 711-0017
Fax—(973) 427-7611
Web—www.magnatrol.com
Email—info@magnatrol.com
P.O. Box 17, Hawthorne 07507
*(see our ad on this page)*

## VALVES — Thermostatic

Holby Valve, Inc.
Phone—(973) 465-7400
24 Ferdon St., Newark 07105

## VAN CONVERSIONS — Handicapped Accessible

Drive-Master Co., Inc.
Phone—(973) 808-9709
37 Daniel Rd. West, Fairfield 07004

Funs Truck'N & Mobility
Phone—(973) 546-1900
255 Route 46 W., Saddle Brook 07663

## VAULTS

CITYSAFE, Inc.
Phone—(732) 751-0100
312 Squankum Yellowbrook Rd., Farmingdale 07727

## VEGETABLE PROCESSING

Colace Co., LLC, Thomas
Phone—(856) 384-4980
800 Grove Rd., Thorofare 08086

Comarco Products
Phone—(856) 342-7557
501 Jackson St., Camden 08104

## VEGETABLES — Frozen

Grasso Foods, Inc.
Phone—(856) 467-2222
2111 Kings Hwy., P.O. Box 127, Woolwich Township 08085

Seabrook Bros. & Sons, Inc.
Phone—(856) 455-8080
85 Finley Rd., P.O. Box 5103, Seabrook 08302

## VEHICLES

First Priority Emergency Vehicles, Inc.
Phone—(732) 657-1104
2444 Ridgeway Blvd., Bldg. 500, Manchester 08759

SLP Specialty Vehicles, Inc.
Phone—(732) 240-3696
1501 Industrial Way N., Toms River 08755

**Bronze and Stainless Steel**
## SOLENOID VALVES
3/8" to 3" 2-way

# www.magnatrol.com
## 800-711-0017 • 973-427-4341
### Fax 973-427-7611
### 67 Fifth Avenue  Hawthorne, NJ 07506

---

# NResearch, Inc.
Manufacturer of Chemically Inert Miniature Solenoid Valves
# 973-808-8811
# FAX: 973-808-0086
www.nresearch.com   sales@nresearch.com
## 267 Fairfield Avenue
## West Caldwell, NJ 07006

## VEHICLES — Handicapped Accessible

Drive-Master Co., Inc.
Wheelchair Accessible, Rental
Phone—(973) 808-9709
Fax—(973) 808-9713
Web—www.DriveMasterMobility.com
Email—info@DriveMasterMobility.com
37 Daniel Rd. West, Fairfield 07004

# Drive-Master Co., Inc.
Vehicles for the Physically Challenged
## 973-808-9709
### Fax: 973-808-9713
www.DriveMasterMobility.com
info@DriveMasterMobility.com
37 Daniel Rd. West
Fairfield, NJ 07004

## VEHICLES — Specialty Commercial

Great American Trolley Co. (H Q)
Addtl. Web: www.trolley.com
Email: rsa@trolley.com
Phone—(609) 884-0450 / (609) 884-4076
Web—www.gatrolley.com
821 Shunpike Rd., Cape May 08204

Sirchie Finger Print Labs, Inc., Vehicle Div.
Phone—(609) 654-0777
612 Gravelly Hollow Rd., P.O. Box 789, Medford 08055

## VENDING MACHINES

Betti Industries, Inc., H.
Phone—(201) 438-1300
303 Patterson Plank Rd., Carlstadt 07072

## VENETIAN BLINDS

Hudson & Bergen Co.
Phone—(201) 991-4900
350 Belleville Tpk., Kearny 07032

Spotless Shade, LLC
Phone—(732) 548-1711
1217 U.S. Highway 1, Edison 08837

## VENTILATION SYSTEMS

Building Performance Equipment, Inc.
Phone—(201) 722-1414
80 Broadway, Ste. 101, Hillsdale 07642

*Search from among 430,000 U.S. manufacturers & suppliers:*
**IndustryNet.com**

*Do nationwide searches for products & services at:*
**IndustryNet.com**

## VENTILATION SYSTEMS — (cont.)

**Reno's Appliance**
 Addtl. Web: www.buyrenos.com
 Toll Free Ph: (866)88-RENOS
 **Phone—(973) 247-1860 / (866) 887-3667**
 **Fax—(973) 247-1865**
 **Web—www.renosappliance.com**
 **Email—sales@renosappliance.net**
 **235 McLean Blvd., Route 20 N., Paterson 07504**
 *(see our ad under APPLIANCES — Household)*

## VETERINARY BIOLOGICAL PRODUCTS

DMS Laboratories, Inc.
 Phone—(908) 782-3353
 2 Darts Mill Rd., Flemington 08822

## VETERINARY EQUIPMENT & SUPPLIES

Biometallics, Inc.
 Phone—(609) 275-0133
 37 Station Dr., Princeton Junction 08550
Technidyne Corp.
 Phone—(732) 363-1055
 2190 Route 9, Ste. 9, Toms River 08755

## VETERINARY ORTHOPEDIC PRODUCTS

BioMedtrix, LLC
 Phone—(973) 331-7800
 50 Intervale Rd., Ste. 5, Boonton 07005

## VIALS — Glass

Gerresheimer Glass, Inc.
 Phone—(856) 507-5600
 91 W. Forest Grove Rd., Vineland 08360
Le Papillon
 Phone—(732) 843-6116
 120 Albany St., Ste. 300, New Brunswick 08901
**Phoenix Glass, LLC**
 **Phone—(856) 692-0100**
 **Fax—(856) 696-5155**
 **Web—www.pxglass.com**
 **Email—rohrmanf@pxglass.com**
 **615 Alvine Rd., Pittsgrove 08318**
 *(see our ad under GLASS — Decorative)*
QIS, Inc.
 Phone—(856) 455-3736
 778 Vineland Ave., P.O. Box 517, Rosenhayn 08352

## VIBRATION ANALYSIS SERVICES

**Vibration Associates**
 **Phone—(732) 671-7182**
 **Fax—(732) 671-7183**
 **Email—office@vibrationassociates.com**
 **19 Shephard Dr., P.O. Box 4123, Middletown 07748**

## VIBRATION CONTROL PRODUCTS

Ace Mounting Co., Inc.
 Phone—(732) 721-6200
 11 Cross Ave., South Amboy 08879
B Green Innovations, Inc.
 Phone—(732) 696-9333
 750 State Route 34, Ste. 8, Matawan 07747

## VIBRATION ISOLATORS

Vibration Isolation Co.
 Phone—(973) 345-8282
 225 Grand St., Paterson 07501
VMC Group, The
 Phone—(973) 838-1780
 113 Main St., P.O. Box 270, Bloomingdale 07403

## VIDEO SYSTEMS

L-3 Communications Mobile-Vision, Inc.
 Phone—(973) 263-1090
 90 Fanny Rd., Boonton 07005

## VIDEOCONFERENCING EQUIPMENT

Yorktel
 Managed Services, Cloud, Mobility, Interoperability
 **Phone—(732) 413-6000 / (866) 836-8463**
 **Fax—(732) 413-6060**
 **Web—www.yorktel.com**
 **Email—sosowski@yorktel.com**
 **81 Corbett Way, Eatontown 07724**

## VINYL PRODUCTS

AVCON
 Phone—(732) 286-9496
 1915 Swarthmore Ave., Ste. 3, Lakewood 08701
Better Sleep Co., Inc.
 Phone—(908) 393-0120
 100 Readington Rd., Ste. 2, Branchburg 08876
Suburban Building Products
 Phone—(732) 901-8900
 1178 Lakewood Farmingdale Rd., Howell 07731
Ultraflex Systems, Inc. (H Q)
 Phone—(973) 627-8608
 1578 Sussex Tpke., Ste. 400, Randolph 07869

## VISION SYSTEMS

Mnemonics, Inc.
 Phone—(856) 234-0970
 P.O. Box 877, Mount Laurel 08054

## VITAMINS

**Ambix Laboratories**
 Custom & P/L Liquid Vitamins, Minerals & Nutrients
 **Phone—(973) 890-9002**
 **Fax—(973) 890-9778**
 **Web—www.ambixlabs.com**
 **Email—ambixlab@aol.com**
 **55 W. End Rd., Totowa 07512**
 *(see our ad under PROTEIN)*
Archon Vitamin Corp.
 Phone—(973) 371-1700
 3775 Park Ave., Ste. 1, Edison 08820
DSM Nutritional Products, Inc.
 Phone—(908) 475-5300
 206 Macks Island Dr., Belvidere 07823
DSM Pharmaceutical Products, Inc. (H Q)
 Phone—(973) 257-1063
 45 Waterview Blvd., Parsippany 07054
Eagle Nutritionals
 Phone—(201) 964-1441
 485 Washington Ave., Carlstadt 07072
HerbaKraft, Inc.
 Phone—(732) 463-1000
 121 Ethel Rd. W., Ste. 6, Piscataway 08854
IVC Industries, Inc.
 Phone—(732) 308-3000
 500 Halls Mill Rd., Freehold 07728
Pharmachem Laboratories, Inc.
 Phone—(201) 246-1000
 265 Harrison Ave., Kearny 07032
Pharmachem Laboratories, Inc.
 Phone—(201) 343-3611
 130 Wesley St., South Hackensack 07606
Quality Formulation Laboratories, Inc.
 Phone—(973) 977-8800
 110 Pennsylvania Ave., Paterson 07503
Rasi Laboratories, Inc.
 Phone—(732) 873-8500
 20 Roosevelt Ave., Somerset 08873
Universal Laboratories, Inc.
 Phone—(732) 545-3130
 3 Terminal Rd., New Brunswick 08901
Vita-Pure, Inc.
 Phone—(908) 245-1212
 410 W. 1st Ave., Roselle 07203
Windmill Health Products, LLC
 Phone—(973) 575-6591
 6 Henderson Dr., Caldwell 07006

## VITAMINS — Private Label

Soma Labs, Inc.
 Phone—(732) 271-3444
 252 Wagner St., Middlesex 08846

## VOCATIONAL TRAINING CENTERS

Salem County Vocational Technical Schools
 Phone—(856) 769-0101
 Fax—(856) 769-3602
 Web—www.scvts.org
 Email—info@scvts.org
 880 Route 45, P.O. Box 350, Woodstown 08098

## VOICE COMMUNICATIONS SYSTEMS

Telegenix, Inc.
 Phone—(609) 265-3910
 71 Indel Ave., P.O. Box 577, Rancocas 08073
Voicecom Plus, Inc.
 Phone—(201) 760-2260
 63 Ramapo Valley Rd., Ste. 201-A, Mahwah 07430

## VOICE RECORDERS — Digital

Verint Systems, Inc.
 Phone—(201) 559-3788
 9 Polito Ave., 9th Fl., Lyndhurst 07071

## VOICE RESPONSE SYSTEMS

Voxware, Inc.
 Phone—(609) 514-4100
 300 American Metro Blvd., Ste. 155, Hamilton 08619

## VOLTAGE REGULATORS

J. Jeb Products, LLC
 Phone—(856) 845-4455
 10 Cutler Ave., P.O. Box 40, Westville 08093

## VOTING EQUIPMENT

Avante International Technology, Inc.
 Phone—(609) 799-8896
 70 Washington Rd., Princeton 08540

## WAFFLES

Kellogg Co.
 Phone—(609) 567-2300
 322 S. Egg Harbor Rd., Hammonton 08037

## WALL COVERINGS

Fabulous Interiors
 Phone—(973) 736-1200
 470 Prospect Ave., Ste. 105, West Orange 07052
Fidelity Industries, Inc.
 Phone—(973) 696-9120
 559 R.R. 23 S., Wayne 07470
J. Josephson, Inc.
 Phone—(201) 440-7000
 35 Horizon Blvd., South Hackensack 07606
Omni W.C., Inc.
 Phone—(732) 248-0999
 166 National Rd., Edison 08817
Sellers & Josephson, LLC
 Phone—(201) 567-1353
 559 Route 23, Wayne 07470

## WALL COVERINGS — Vinyl

Newco, Inc.
 Phone—(973) 383-7777
 1 Hicks Ave., Newton 07860
Roysons Corp.
 Phone—(973) 625-5570
 40 Vanderhoof Ave., Rockaway 07866

INDUSTRY

## WALL PANELS

Architectural Metal Designs, Inc.
  Phone—(856) 765-3000
  1505 Pineland Ave., Millville 08332
BAMCO, Inc.
  Phone—(732) 302-0889
  30 Baekeland Ave., Middlesex 08846

## WALL SYSTEMS

Allied Specialty Group, Inc.
  Phone—(201) 223-4600
  3114 Tonnelle Ave., North Bergen 07047
Contemporary Wall Systems, Inc.
  Phone—(973) 884-0474
  50 Williams Pkwy., Ste. F, P.O. Box 356, East
  Hanover 07936

## WALLETS

Westport Corp.
  Phone—(973) 575-0110
  331 Changebridge Rd., P.O. Box 2002, Pine
  Brook 07058

## WALLPAPER

Chambord Prints, Inc.
  Phone—(201) 795-2007
  38 Jackson St., Hoboken 07030
Rigo Industries, Inc.
  Phone—(973) 881-1780
  50 California Ave., Paterson 07503

## WAREHOUSE & DISTRIBUTION SERVICES

Argent Associates Inc.
  Phone—(732) 512-9009
  Fax—(732) 512-9549
  Web—www.argentassociates.com
  Email—sales@argentassociates.com
  140 Fieldcrest Ave., Edison 08837

## WAREHOUSE MANAGEMENT SOFTWARE

Vigna, Inc.
  Computer Software: Warehouse & Transportation
  Industry
  Phone—(908) 874-4867 / (877) 464-9990
  Web—www.vignainc.com
  Email—sriniv@vignainc.com
  105 Raider Blvd., Ste. 207, Hillsborough 08844

## We've Made Sales Leads Faster & Easier!

# mnileads.com

- Search mni's complete in-depth database of 430,000 industrial companies
- Unlimited free searches and instant counts & quotes; pay only for what you download
- Import leads directly into database, spreadsheet, mail merge or contact management software

## WAREHOUSES

Glendale Warehouse Corp.
  Phone—(732) 516-1555
  Fax—(732) 516-9898
  Web—www.glendalewarehouse.com
  Email—glendale@glendalewh.com
  742 Old Post Rd., Edison 08817

## Glendale Warehouse Corp.

### Quality Food Grade Warehouse

# 732-516-1555
## FAX: 732-516-9898

742 Old Post Rd.
Edison, NJ 08817

Email: glendale@glendalewh.com
www.glendalewarehouse.com

## WAREHOUSES — Cold Storage

Glendale Warehouse Corp.
  Phone—(732) 516-1555
  Fax—(732) 516-9898
  Web—www.glendalewarehouse.com
  Email—glendale@glendalewh.com
  742 Old Post Rd., Edison 08817
  *(see our ad under WAREHOUSES)*

## WAREHOUSES — Fulfillment

Argent Associates Inc.
  Phone—(732) 512-9009
  Fax—(732) 512-9549
  Web—www.argentassociates.com
  Email—sales@argentassociates.com
  140 Fieldcrest Ave., Edison 08837
Courier Systems, Inc.
  Phone—(201) 432-0550
  Fax—(201) 432-9686
  Web—www.csweb.biz
  Email—rick.murad@csweb.biz
  180 Pulaski St., Bayonne 07002
Glendale Warehouse Corp.
  Phone—(732) 516-1555
  Fax—(732) 516-9898
  Web—www.glendalewarehouse.com
  Email—glendale@glendalewh.com
  742 Old Post Rd., Edison 08817
  *(see our ad under WAREHOUSES)*

## WAREHOUSING — Transload

Glendale Warehouse Corp.
  Phone—(732) 516-1555
  Fax—(732) 516-9898
  Web—www.glendalewarehouse.com
  Email—glendale@glendalewh.com
  742 Old Post Rd., Edison 08817
  *(see our ad under WAREHOUSES)*

## WASHERS

HK Metal Craft Mfg. Corp.
  Phone—(973) 471-7770
  35 Industrial Rd., Lodi 07644

*find additional suppliers at* **IndustryNet.com**

Shallcross Bolt & Specialties Co.
  The complete source for all your fastener needs
  Phone—(908) 925-4700
  Fax—(908) 925-8451
  Web—www.shallcrossbolt.com
  Email—info@shallcrossbolt.com
  1 McCandless St., Linden 07036
  *(see our ad under BOLTS)*
Wm. H. Brewster Jr., Inc.
  Email: sales@brewster-washers.com
  Manufacturing Precision Parts Since 1919; Made in
  U.S.A.
  Phone—(973) 227-1050
  Fax—(973) 227-2363
  Web—www.brewster-washers.com
  16 Kulick Rd., Fairfield 07004
  *(see our ad Outside Front Cover)*

## WASHERS — Metallic

Wm. H. Brewster Jr., Inc.
  Email: sales@brewster-washers.com
  Manufacturing Precision Parts Since 1919; Made in
  U.S.A.
  Phone—(973) 227-1050
  Fax—(973) 227-2363
  Web—www.brewster-washers.com
  16 Kulick Rd., Fairfield 07004
  *(see our ad Outside Front Cover)*

## WASHING MACHINES — Industrial

Clayton Assocs., Inc.
  Phone—(732) 363-2100
  1650 Oak St., Lakewood 08701

## WASHING MACHINES AND DRYERS

Fairfield Laundry Machinery
  Phone—(973) 575-4330
  5 Montesano Rd., Fairfield 07004

## WASTE DISPOSAL — Hazardous

Cycle Chem, Inc.
  Phone—(908) 355-5800
  201 S. 1st St., Elizabeth 07206
Veolia ES Technical Solutions, LLC
  Recycling Industrial Solvents
  Phone—(732) 469-5100
  Fax—(732) 469-1957
  Web—www.veoliaes.com
  Email—ray.clark@veolia.com
  125 Factory Ln., Middlesex 08846
  *(see our ad under SOLVENT RECYCLING)*

## WASTE DISPOSAL EQUIPMENT

Salomon Bros. Equipment Co., Inc.
  Phone—(908) 931-9311
  P.O. Box 43, Cranford 07016

## WASTE GRINDERS

Franklin Miller, Inc.
  Phone—(973) 535-9200
  Fax—(973) 535-6269
  Web—www.franklinmiller.com
  Email—info@franklinmiller.com
  60 Okner Pkwy., P.O. Box 070663, Livingston
  07039
  *(see our ad under CRUSHERS)*

## WASTE HANDLING EQUIPMENT

Wastequip
  Phone—(856) 784-5500
  1031 Hickstown Rd., Sicklerville 08081

*Search from among 430,000 U.S. manufacturers & suppliers:* **IndustryNet.com**

## WASTE MANAGEMENT SERVICES

**Atlas Disposal Options, Inc.**
Offering environmental contrs. & indl. clients a single source for all their disposal needs of almost any waste stream, utilizing our own trucks, personnel & equipment to transport & dispose of any Petroleum, Sanitary or Hazardous waste
**Phone—(973) 361-5100 / (800) 821-9741**
**Fax—(973) 361-0909**
**Web—www.wastewanted.com**
**311 E. Blackwell St., P.O. Box 546, Dover 07802**

**Hazardous and Industrial Waste Disposal**

**(973) 361-5100**

**Fax: (973) 361-0909**

**www.wastewanted.com**

**311 E. Blackwell St., P.O. Box 546 Dover, NJ 07802**

## WASTE REDUCTION SERVICES

**PSC Environmental Services, LLC**
Phone—(215) 822-2676 / (800) 365-9295
Fax—(215) 997-8219
Web—www.pscnow.com
Email—info@pscnow.com
2337 N. Penn Rd., Hatfield, PA 19440
*(see our ad under ENVIRONMENTAL SERVICES)*

## WASTEWATER PRODUCTS

Simple Solutions Distribution, LLC (H Q)
Phone—(973) 846-7817
6 Jacobs Rd., West Milford 07480

## WASTEWATER TREATMENT EQUIPMENT

American Water Works Co., Inc. (H Q)
Phone—(856) 346-8200
1025 Laurel Oak Rd., Voorhees 08043
Dynatec Systems, Inc.
Phone—(609) 387-0330
360 Connecticut Dr., Burlington 08016
Evoqua Water Technologies
Phone—(908) 353-7230
624 Evans St., Elizabeth 07201
JDV Equipment Corp.
Phone—(973) 366-6556
1 Princeton Ave., Dover 07801
**Komline-Sanderson Engineering**
**Phone—(908) 234-1000 / (800) 225-5457**
**Fax—(908) 234-9487**
**Web—www.komline.com**
**Email—info@komline.com**
**12 Holland Ave., Peapack 07977**
Turnkey Solutions, Inc.
Phone—(201) 848-7676
45 Whitney Rd., Mahwah 07430
Veolia Water Solutions & Technologies North America, Inc.
Phone—(856) 438-1776
6981 N. Park Dr., Ste. 600, Pennsauken 08109

*Do nationwide searches for products & services at:* **IndustryNet.com**

## WATCH PARTS

Acon Watch Crown Co.
Phone—(973) 546-8585
260 Division Ave., P.O. Box 800, Garfield 07026

## WATCHES

Movado Group, Inc.
Phone—(201) 267-8000
650 From Rd., 3rd Fl., Paramus 07652
**SEIKO Corp. Of America (H Q)**
Phone—(201) 529-5730
1111 MacArthur Blvd., Mahwah 07430
**Universal Watch & Clock Jewelry Repair**
Phone—(609) 577-9435
2128 Spruce St., Ewing 08638

## WATER — Bottled

Nestle Waters North America, Inc.
Phone—(201) 451-4000
111 Thomas McGovern Dr., Jersey City 07305
Str8up Beverages, LLC
Phone—(908) 451-1393
16 Mount Bethel Rd., Ste. 260, Warren 07059
Water Shoppe, Inc., The
Phone—(856) 964-4500
112 N. 3rd St., 2nd Fl., Camden 08102

## WATER — De-Ionized

**W.D. Service Company, Inc.**
780 Creek Rd., Bellmawr 08031
**Phone—(856) 931-6100 / (800) 366-9326**
**Fax—(856) 931-4505**
**Web—www.wdserviceco.com**
**Email—sales@wdserviceco.com**
**P.O. Box 147, Bellmawr 08099**

## WATER COOLERS

Arcticcoolers, Inc.
Phone—(856) 231-0262
135 Gaither Dr., Ste. A, Mount Laurel 08054

## WATER DAMAGE RESTORATION

**Servpro Of Northwest Bergen**
Fire & Water Damage
**Phone—(201) 236-2400 / (800) 497-7179**
**Fax—(201) 670-1011**
**Web—www.servpronorthwestbergen.com**
**Email—servpro8204@aol.com**
**151 Crescent Ave., Waldwick 07463**

## WATER FILTRATION EQUIPMENT

**General Carbon Corporation**
Activated Carbon Equipment & Services for Liquid & Vapor Applications
**Phone—(973) 523-2223**
**Fax—(973) 523-1494**
**Web—www.generalcarbon.com**
**Email—sales@generalcarbon.com**
**33 Paterson St., Paterson 07501**
*(see our ad under CARBON—Activated)*
**Leem/LSS Filtration**
The one stop source for your filtration needs
**Phone—(201) 236-4833**
**Fax—(201) 236-2004**
**Web—www.leemfiltration.com**
**Email—info@leemfiltration.com**
**25 Arrow Rd., Ramsey 07446**
Liquid Solids Separation Corp.
Phone—(201) 236-4833
25 Arrow Rd., Ramsey 07446
**Orival Water Filters**
Automatic self-cleaning line pressure powered water filters
**Phone—(201) 568-3311**
**Fax—(201) 568-1916**
**Web—www.orival.com**
**Email—filters@orival.com**
**213 S. Van Brunt St., Englewood 07631**

*find additional suppliers at* **IndustryNet.com**

## WATER FILTRATION PRODUCTS

**General Carbon Corporation**
Activated Carbon Equipment & Services for Liquid & Vapor Applications
**Phone—(973) 523-2223**
**Fax—(973) 523-1494**
**Web—www.generalcarbon.com**
**Email—sales@generalcarbon.com**
**33 Paterson St., Paterson 07501**
*(see our ad under CARBON—Activated)*
**Orival Water Filters**
Automatic self-cleaning line pressure powered water filters
**Phone—(201) 568-3311**
**Fax—(201) 568-1916**
**Web—www.orival.com**
**Email—filters@orival.com**
**213 S. Van Brunt St., Englewood 07631**
**Resintech, Inc.**
Email: info@resintech.com
**Phone—(856) 768-9600**
**Fax—(856) 768-9601**
**Web—www.resintech.com**
**Email—ixresin@resintech.com**
**160 Cooper Rd., West Berlin 08091**
*(also see our ad under WATER TREATMENT COMPOUNDS)*

**Resintech, Inc.**
*Water Purification Chemicals*
**www.resintech.com**
info@resintech.com
**(856) 768-9600 • FAX: (856) 768-9601**
160 Cooper Rd. • West Berlin, NJ 08091

## WATER PURIFICATION EQUIPMENT & SYSTEMS

Fin-Tek Ozone
Phone—(973) 628-2988
6 Leo Pl., Wayne 07470
Membranes International, Inc.
Phone—(973) 998-5530
219 Margaret King Ave., P.O. Box 219, Ringwood 07456
**Ozonia North America, LLC**
For more than 35 years of experience in developing, designing, mfg. & installing treatment systems
**Phone—(201) 676-2525**
**Fax—(201) 346-5460**
**Web—www.ozonia.com**
**Email—sales@ozonia.com**
**600 Willow Tree Rd., Leonia 07605**
Pure H2O Technologies, Inc.
Phone—(973) 622-0440
211 Warren St., Ste. 318, Newark 07103
WaterDoctor, Inc.
Phone—(732) 972-4510
1030-C Campus Dr., Morganville 07751

## WATER SOFTENERS

Stain-Less Water Filters, LLC
Phone—(609) 296-2564
51 Munion Field Rd., P.O. Box 219, New Gretna 08224

## WATER SYSTEMS

**Graver Water Systems, LLC**
**Phone—(908) 516-1400**
**Fax—(908) 516-1401**
**Web—www.graver.com**
**Email—sales@graver.com**
**675 Central Ave., Ste. 3, New Providence 07974**
*(see our ad under WATER TREATMENT EQUIPMENT)*

## WATER TREATMENT CHEMICALS

Butler Engineering Assocs., Inc.
Phone—(908) 688-3300
764 Ramsey Ave., Hillside 07205

INDUSTRY

## WATER TREATMENT CHEMICALS
### — (cont.)

**Cogesco Water Technologies Corp.**
Phone—(973) 249-9711
Fax—(973) 249-6911
Web—www.cogescointl.com
Email—greche@cogescointl.com
891 Bloomfield Ave., Clifton 07012

Garratt-Callahan Co.
Phone—(732) 287-2200
306 Talmadge Rd., Edison 08817

Gulbrandsen Technologies, Inc.
Phone—(908) 238-2030
1 Riverside Way, Phillipsburg 08865

Gulbrandsen Technologies, Inc. (H Q)
Phone—(908) 735-5458
2 Main St., P.O. Box 5523, Clinton 08809

Hibrett Puratex
Phone—(856) 662-1717
7001 Westfield Ave., Pennsauken 08110

**Houghton Chemical Corp.**
Phone—(800) 777-2466
Fax—(617) 254-2713
Web—www.houghton.com
Email—bhoughton@houghton.com
30 Amor Ave., Carlstadt 07072

**Seidler Chemical & Supply Co.**
Chemicals & Chemical Re-Packaging & Distribution
Phone—(973) 465-1122
Fax—(973) 465-4469
Web—www.seidlerchem.com
Email—sales@seidlerchem.com
537 Raymond Blvd., Newark 07105

**Universal Chemicals Inc.**
Phone—(973) 589-1525
Fax—(973) 589-8013
Web—www.universalchem.com
Email—info@universalchem.com
100 N. Hackensack Ave., Kearny 07032

## WATER TREATMENT COMPOUNDS

**Resintech, Inc.**
Email: info@resintech.com
Phone—(856) 768-9600
Fax—(856) 768-9601
Web—www.resintech.com
Email—ixresin@resintech.com
160 Cooper Rd., West Berlin 08091
*(also see our ad under WATER FILTRATION PRODUCTS)*

## Resintech, Inc.
*Water Purification Chemicals*
**www.resintech.com**
info@resintech.com
(856) 768-9600 • FAX: (856) 768-9601
160 Cooper Rd. • West Berlin, NJ 08091

**Seidler Chemical & Supply Co.**
Chemicals & Chemical Re-Packaging & Distribution
Phone—(973) 465-1122
Fax—(973) 465-4469
Web—www.seidlerchem.com
Email—sales@seidlerchem.com
537 Raymond Blvd., Newark 07105

## WATER TREATMENT EQUIPMENT

ECOTEC, Inc.
Phone—(856) 205-9283
1944 E. Elmer Rd., Vineland 08361

Graver Water Systems, LLC
Phone—(908) 516-1400
Fax—(908) 516-1401
Web—www.graver.com
Email—sales@graver.com
675 Central Ave., Ste. 3, New Providence 07974
*(see our ad on this page)*

Hungerford & Terry, Inc.
Phone—(856) 881-3200
226 N. Atlantic Ave., P.O. Box 650, Clayton 08312

# Graver Water Systems, LLC
*Water Treatment Equipment*
**908-516-1400 • Fax: 908-516-1401**
**www.graver.com  sales@graver.com**
675 Central Ave., Ste. 3 New Providence, NJ 07974

Instrumentation Technology Systems, Inc.
Phone—(732) 388-0866
205 E. Inman Ave., Rahway 07065

Siemens Industry, Inc., Water Technologies
Phone—(908) 851-2277
2 Milltown Ct., Union 07083

Siemens Industry, Inc., Water Technologies
Phone—(856) 507-9000
1901 W. Garden Rd., Vineland 08360

Trident Ionic, Inc.
Phone—(908) 647-4329
19 Olsen Dr., Warren 07059

**Warwick Mfg. & Equipment Co., LLC**
Buy & sell used: Chemical, food, cosmetic, packaging & pharmaceutical equipment
Phone—(732) 729-0400 / (732) 241-9263
Fax—(732) 729-1235
Web—www.warwickequipment.com
Email—sales@warwickequipment.com
1112 12th St., North Brunswick 08902
*(see our ad Outside Back Cover)*

Water Resources New Jersey, LLC
Phone—(609) 268-7965
1609 Route 206, P.O. Box 2172, Tabernacle 08088

## WATER TREATMENT PRODUCTS

C S L Water Quality, Inc.
Phone—(908) 647-1400
156 Mount Bethel Rd., P.O. Box 4246, Warren 07059

**Graver Water Systems, LLC**
Phone—(908) 516-1400
Fax—(908) 516-1401
Web—www.graver.com
Email—sales@graver.com
675 Central Ave., Ste. 3, New Providence 07974
*(see our ad on this page)*

Siemens Industry, Inc., Water Technologies
Phone—(201) 531-9338
20 Murray Hill Pkwy., Ste. 140, East Rutherford 07073

## WATER TREATMENT SERVICES

**Tower Water Management**
Phone—(732) 249-0990
Web—www.towerwater.com
5 Shirley Ave., Ste. A, Somerset 08873

## WATER WELLS

**Pul-A Pump Corp.**
See us on YouTube, search Pulapump; Pump Pullers/ Pump Hoists
Phone—(973) 697-2008
Fax—(973) 697-5989
Web—www.pulapump.com
29 Paradise Trl., P.O. Box 155, Stockholm 07460

## WATERJET CUTTING SERVICES

Advanced Cutting Services, LLC
Phone—(908) 241-5332
169 E. Highland Pkwy., Roselle 07203

**CADPRO, Inc.**
Phone—(856) 435-0050
Fax—(856) 435-0600
Web—www.cadproinc.com
Email—elaine@cadproinc.com
114 W. Atlantic Ave., Clementon 08021

LMK Waterjet
Phone—(908) 241-8113
835 Fairfield Ave., Kenilworth 07033

**M & B Waterjet Creations Inc.**
Phone—(201) 403-5710
Web—www.mbwaterjet.com
Email—salesnj@mbwaterjet.com
650 Huyler St., Ste. 1, South Hackensack 07606

## WATERPROOFING CONTRACTORS

**Divine Energy Solutions**
Basement, sump pump, crawl space & foundation specialists
Phone—(800) 436-6535
Web—www.nwjerseyenergy.com
414 E. Blackwell St., Dover 07801

**New Jersey Basement Waterproofing**
Phone—(732) 721-4900
Web—www.njdrybasement.com
Email—smendola@pdes-usa.net
10 S. River Rd., Cranbury 08512

**Pro Tec Contracting Corp.**
Phone—(973) 428-8868
Fax—(973) 428-8829
Web—www.proteconline.com
Email—jmurphy@proteconline.com
50 Williams Pkwy., Ste. N, East Hanover 07936

**Quality 1st Basement Systems**
Basement, sump pump, crawl space & foundation specialists
Phone—(888) 680-3830
Web—www.quality1stbasementsystems.com
1160 State St., Perth Amboy 08861

## WATERPROOFING MATERIALS & COMPOUNDS

**GAF**
Phone—(973) 628-3000 / (800) 766-3411
Web—www.gaf.com
1361 Alps Rd., Wayne 07470
*(see our ad under ROOFING MATERIALS)*

## WATERWORKS EQUIPMENT & SUPPLIES

Brent Material Co.
Phone—(973) 325-3030
325 Columbia Tpke., Ste. 308, Florham Park 07932

Midlantic Supply, LLC
Phone—(856) 813-5014
8000 Midlantic Dr., Ste. 200-N., P.O. Box 506, Mount Laurel 08054

*Search from among 430,000 U.S. manufacturers & suppliers:*
**IndustryNet.com**

© Copyright 2015 Manufacturers' News, Inc.

## WAX ADDITIVES

**Munzing**
1455 Broad St., Bloomfield 07003
Formulators of Specialty Additive Defoamers for over 180 years
Phone—(973) 279-1306 / (800) 524-0055
Fax—(973) 338-0420
Web—www.munzing.com
Email—info@munzing.us
975 Ultra Dr., Clover, SC 29710

## WAX PRODUCTS

Du-Matt Corp.
Phone—(201) 861-4271
111 71st St., Guttenberg 07093

**Ross Co., Inc., Frank B.**
Waxes & Natural Butters
Phone—(732) 669-0810
Fax—(732) 669-0814
Web—www.frankbross.com
Email—techinfo@rosswaxes.com
970 New Brunswick Ave., Ste. H, Rahway 07065

*(see our ad under WAXES)*

## WAXES

(also see 'Polishes')

**Ross Co., Inc., Frank B.**
Waxes & Natural Butters
Phone—(732) 669-0810
Fax—(732) 669-0814
Web—www.frankbross.com
Email—techinfo@rosswaxes.com
970 New Brunswick Ave., Ste. H, Rahway 07065

# Frank B.
# Ross Co., Inc.

*Waxes & Natural Butters*

**(732) 669-0810**
**Fax: (732) 669-0814**

**www.frankbross.com**
email: techinfo@rosswaxes.com

970 New Brunswick Ave., Ste. H
Rahway, NJ 07065

## WEAPON SYSTEMS

EXELIS, Inc.
Phone—(973) 284-0123
77 River Rd., Clifton 07014

## WEATHERSTRIPPING

Portaseal, LLC
Phone—(973) 539-0100
1 John St., P.O. Box 1203, Morristown 07962
Thermwell Products Co., Inc.
Phone—(201) 684-4400
420 State Route 17, Mahwah 07430

## WEBBING

AISCO
Phone—(732) 574-3233
35 Mileed Way, P.O. Box 30, Avenel 07001
N.Y. Textile Mills, Inc.
Phone—(973) 777-9871
90 Dayton Ave., Bldg. 5-A, Passaic 07055

## WEIGHING SYSTEMS

**PTC Electronics, Inc.**
Phone—(201) 847-0500
Fax—(201) 847-1394
Web—www.ptcelectronics.com
Email—sales@ptcelectronics.com
P.O. Box 72, Wyckoff 07481

## WELDING

**ADM Custom Metal Fabrication, Inc.**
Phone—(973) 284-0088
Web—www.admmetal.com
Email—info@admmetal.com
263 Hillside Ave., Ste. 2, Nutley 07110
Atlas Welders & Fabricators Corp.
Phone—(908) 561-1144
2505 S. Clinton Ave., South Plainfield 07080
**Cotterman, Inc.**
Industrial Welding Job Shop, Also ASME Code welding
Phone—(856) 464-6820 / (856) 577-0245
Fax—(856) 464-6930
Web—www.cottermaninc.com
Email—welders@cottermancorp.com
100 Hayes Ave., P.O. Box 278, Wenonah 08090
*(see our ad under PIPE FITTERS)*
Exxcel Welding Corp.
Phone—(908) 735-0000
14 Brookhill Rd., Pittstown 08867
Ironbound Welding, Inc.
Phone—(973) 589-3128
156 Walnut St., Newark 07105
Maza & Maza Welding
Phone—(973) 481-4441
28 Mulock Pl., Harrison 07029
Mola Iron Works
Phone—(201) 963-3485
61 Patterson Ave., Hoboken 07030
Newark Welding Co.
Phone—(973) 642-6479
47 Morris Ave., Newark 07103
Parsell's Welding, Inc.
Phone—(609) 466-1930
354 Route 580, Blawenburg 08504
Plainfield Welders
Phone—(908) 755-6263
1130 North Ave., Plainfield 07062
State Welding
Phone—(609) 882-3288
5 Industry Ct., Ewing 08638
**Versatile Welding Group, LLC**
Steel & Aluminum
Phone—(908) 298-8900 / (877) 939-5348
Fax—(908) 298-9550
Web—www.versatile-us.com
Email—jimd@versatile-us.com
340 Cox St., Roselle 07203
*(see our ad under STEEL FABRICATING)*
VRP Lu-Max Mfg. Co., Inc.
Phone—(973) 379-5877
44 Brown Ave., Springfield 07081
Xevee Corp.
Phone—(908) 964-0444
27 Montgomery St., P. O. Box 5277, Hillside 07205

## WELDING — Plastic

**Emco Industrial Plastics, Inc.**
Supplier of Plastic Sheet, Rod, Tube, Films & Prototyping
Phone—(973) 559-5610
Fax—(973) 239-1595
Web—www.emcoplastics.com
Email—mailbox@emcoplastics.com
99 Commerce Rd., P.O. Box 2503, Cedar Grove 07009
*(see our ad Outside Front Cover)*

## WELDING — Stud

Pyroptics, Inc.
Phone—(609) 386-6930
2015 Columbus Rd., Burlington 08016

*Do nationwide searches for products & services at:*
**IndustryNet.com**

## WELDING ACCESSORIES & SUPPLIES

Airgas East, Inc.
Phone—(732) 752-4500
490 Stelton Rd., Piscataway 08854
**BRECOflex Co., L.L.C.**
Phone—(732) 460-9500 / (888) 463-1400
Fax—(732) 542-6725
Web—www.brecoflex.com
Email—info@brecoflex.com
222 Industrial Way W., Eatontown 07724
*(see our ads under BELTING & PULLEYS)*
Cerbaco Ltd.
Phone—(908) 996-1333
809 Harrison St., Frenchtown 08825
Ferrite Welding Products, Inc.
Phone—(973) 377-6636
31 S. Passaic Ave., Chatham 07928
**SOS Gases, Inc.**
Industrial & Laboratory Gas; Welding Eqpt., Rental & Repair Service
Phone—(201) 998-7800 / (800) 626-7998
Fax—(201) 998-5243
Web—www.sosgasesinc.com
Email—sosgasesinc@msn.com
1100 Harrison Ave., Kearny 07032
*(see our ad under WELDING EQUIPMENT & SUPPLIES)*

## WELDING AND CUTTING EQUIPMENT

**SOS Gases, Inc.**
Industrial & Laboratory Gas; Welding Eqpt., Rental & Repair Service
Phone—(201) 998-7800 / (800) 626-7998
Fax—(201) 998-5243
Web—www.sosgasesinc.com
Email—sosgasesinc@msn.com
1100 Harrison Ave., Kearny 07032
*(see our ad under WELDING EQUIPMENT & SUPPLIES)*

## WELDING AND FABRICATING

Advanced Welding Service, Inc.
Phone—(856) 875-2500
300 Thomas Ave., Ste. 701-1, Williamstown 08094
Airmet, Inc.
Phone—(973) 481-5550
671 N. 3rd St., Newark 07107
American Metal Fab & Welding
Phone—(201) 295-8888
706 7th St., Union City 07087
Atlantic Coastal Welding, Inc.
Phone—(732) 269-1088
16 Butler Blvd., Bayville 08721
**CADPRO, Inc.**
Phone—(856) 435-0050
Fax—(856) 435-0600
Web—www.cadproinc.com
Email—elaine@cadproinc.com
114 W. Atlantic Ave., Clementon 08021
**DIHCO, Inc.**
Phone—(201) 327-0518
Fax—(201) 327-8759
Email—DIHCO-INC@hotmail.com
612 E. Crescent Ave., Upper Saddle River 07458
*(see our ad under FABRICATORS)*
DiLauri Steel Fabricators
Phone—(973) 884-2414
5 Merrys Ln., East Hanover 07936
Double O Mfg.
Phone—(732) 752-9423
100 S. Washington Ave., Dunellen 08812
**Durex, Inc.**
Email: custserv@durexinc.com
ISO 9001 Registered Contract Metal Fabrication Facility
Phone—(908) 688-0800
Fax—(908) 688-0718
Web—www.durexinc.com
5 Stahuber Ave., Union 07083
*(see our ad under METAL FABRICATING)*
Fabrite Metal
Phone—(973) 714-1813
10 Stony Brook Rd., Rockaway 07866
IK Construction, Inc.
Phone—(908) 925-5200
1118 E. Baltimore Ave., Linden 07036

# SOS GASES INC.

- Industrial & Laboratory Gas
- Welding Equipment
- Rental & Repair Service

## (201) 998-7800
## fax (201) 998-5243
1100 Harrison Ave. • Kearny, NJ 07032

www.sosgasesinc.com

## (800) 626-7998

INDUSTRY

## WELDING AND FABRICATING —
*(cont.)*

**Interstate Welding & Mfg. Co., Inc.**
Phone—(609) 699-6950
1510 Village Ct., Edgewater Park 08010

**Keller Welding Co., LLC**
Phone—(973) 948-0046
22 Wantage Ave., Branchville 07826

**Manhattan Welding**
Boilers, burners, mech. contracting, steel fabrication, cert. welding, 24 hours
Phone—(908) 687-4494
Fax—(908) 688-6684
Web—www.manhattanwelding.com
Email—info@manhattanwelding.com
1434 Chestnut Ave., Hillside 07205
*(see our ad under BOILER REPAIRING)*

**Passaic County Welders, Inc.**
Phone—(973) 696-1200
100 Parish Dr., Wayne 07470

**Quality Sheet Metal & Welding**
Phone—(732) 752-6300
23 Clawson St., Piscataway 08854

**Versatile Welding Group, LLC**
Phone—(908) 298-8900
340 Cox St., Roselle 07203

**Wel-Fab, Inc.**
Phone—(609) 261-1393
124 Burrs Rd., Mount Holly 08060

## WELDING EQUIPMENT & SUPPLIES

**Airgas East, Inc.**
Phone—(856) 931-0900
121 Stanley Ave., Bellmawr 08031

**Airgas East, Inc.**
Phone—(973) 742-2211
2 Beckwith Ave., Paterson 07503

**Airgas East, Inc.**
Phone—(856) 692-7734
1750 Gallagher Dr., Vineland 08360

**Atlas Welding Supply Co., Inc.**
Phone—(732) 363-1148
808 Brook Rd., Lakewood 08701

**Awisco Corp.**
Phone—(973) 736-0200
24 Lakeside Ave., West Orange 07052

**Awisco West Milford, LLC**
Phone—(973) 728-9008
26 Industrial Rd., West Milford 07480

**C N I Ceramics Nozzles, Inc.**
Phone—(973) 276-1535
23 Commerce Rd., Ste. L, Fairfield 07004

**DCC Corporation**
Phone—(856) 662-7272
7250 Westfield Ave., Ste. B, Pennsauken 08110

**GTS-Welco**
Phone—(973) 589-7895
425 Avenue P, Newark 07105

**Harrison Equipment Corp.**
Phone—(973) 485-1448
500 Essex St., Harrison 07029

## LORS® machinery

1090 Lousons Road, Union, NJ 07083
p 908.964.9100 | f 908.964-4492
sales@LORS.com | www.LORS.com

## RESISTANCE WELDING EQUIPMENT AND ROBOTIC INTEGRATION

Service/Parts • Emergency 24/7 Service Available
Se Habla Español • Custom Solutions

Kawasaki

A Resistance Welding Solutions, Inc. Company　RWS

**Houser Welding Supply Co., Inc.**
Phone—(908) 526-7777
12-14 E. Main St., Somerville 08876

**Industrial Welding Supply, Inc.**
Supplying a complete line of welding machines & supplies, compressed gases, cryogenics, tools & safety equipment, as well as an array of rental welders, including electric & both gas & diesel driven
Phone—(732) 367-7100
Fax—(732) 367-6953
Web—www.weldingsupplynj.com
Email—indweldsup@aol.com
999 Airport Rd., Ste. 1, Lakewood 08701

**Industrial Welding Supply, Inc.**
Supplying a complete line of welding machines & supplies, compressed gases, cryogenics, tools & safety equipment, as well as an array of rental welders, including electric & both gas & diesel driven
Phone—(732) 721-1150
Fax—(732) 721-8076
Web—www.weldingsupplynj.com
Email—indweldsup@aol.com
4 Val St., Sayreville 08872

**International Welding Technologies, Inc.**
Phone—(856) 435-8004
2650 Egg Harbor Rd., Lindenwold 08021

**Liberty Welding Supply, Inc.**
Phone—(973) 923-2900
187 W. Fort Lee Rd., Bogota 07603

**New Age Fastening Systems, Inc.**
Phone—(856) 218-8301
11 Enterprise Ct., Sewell 08080

**Orgo-Thermit, Inc.**
Email: georgeanne.tutunjian@orgothermit.com
Mfgr. & supplier of Aluminothermic welding prods & equipment for tee-rail, crane rail & grooved rail, as well as providing comprehensive training programs for the process of joining steel rails
Phone—(732) 657-5781
Fax—(732) 657-5899
Web—www.orgothermit.com
3500 Colonial Dr. N., Manchester 08759

**Praxair**
Phone—(908) 862-7200
515 E. Edgar Rd., Linden 07036

**Resistance Welding Solutions, Inc.**
DBA: LORS Machinery
Phone—(908) 964-9100 / (800) 223-0909
Fax—(908) 964-4492
Web—www.lors.com
Email—sales@lors.com
1090 Lousons Rd., Union 07083
*(see our ad on this page)*

**SOS Gases, Inc.**
Industrial & Laboratory Gas; Welding Eqpt., Rental & Repair Service
Phone—(201) 998-7800 / (800) 626-7998
Fax—(201) 998-5243
Web—www.sosgasesinc.com
Email—sosgasesinc@msn.com
1100 Harrison Ave., Kearny 07032
*(see our ad on this page)*

**South Jersey Welding Supply Co.**
Phone—(856) 778-4440
496 Route 38 E., Maple Shade 08052

**South Jersey Welding Supply Co.**
Phone—(856) 691-9659
94 W. Forest Grove Rd., Vineland 08360

**Warwick Mfg. & Equipment Co., LLC**
Buy & sell used: Chemical, food, cosmetic, packaging & pharmaceutical equipment
Phone—(732) 729-0400 / (732) 241-9263
Fax—(732) 729-1235
Web—www.warwickequipment.com
Email—sales@warwickequipment.com
1112 12th St., North Brunswick 08902
*(see our ad Outside Back Cover)*

*find additional suppliers at*
**IndustryNet.com**

**RESISTANCE WELDING EQUIPMENT AND ROBOTIC INTEGRATION**

1090 Lousons Road, Union, NJ 07083
p 908.964.9100 | f 908.964-4492
sales@LORS.com | www.LORS.com

Service/Parts • Emergency 24/7 Service Available
Se Habla Español • Custom Solutions

A Resistance Welding Solutions, Inc. Company

Kawasaki

## WELDING MACHINERY

**Industrial Welding Supply, Inc.**
Supplying a complete line of welding machines & supplies, compressed gases, cryogenics, tools & safety equipment, as well as an array of rental welders, including electric & both gas & diesel driven
Phone—(732) 367-7100
Fax—(732) 367-6953
Web—www.weldingsupplynj.com
Email—indweldsup@aol.com
999 Airport Rd., Ste. 1, Lakewood 08701

**Industrial Welding Supply, Inc.**
Supplying a complete line of welding machines & supplies, compressed gases, cryogenics, tools & safety equipment, as well as an array of rental welders, including electric & both gas & diesel driven
Phone—(732) 721-1150
Fax—(732) 721-8076
Web—www.weldingsupplynj.com
Email—indweldsup@aol.com
4 Val St., Sayreville 08872

**Wikstrom Machines, Inc.**
Phone—(732) 826-4800
412 Summit Ave., Perth Amboy 08861

## WELDING ROBOTS

**Resistance Welding Solutions, Inc.**
DBA: LORS Machinery
Phone—(908) 964-9100 / (800) 223-0909
Fax—(908) 964-4492
Web—www.lors.com
Email—sales@lors.com
1090 Lousons Rd., Union 07083
*(see our ad on this page)*

## WELDING SAFETY PRODUCTS

**Resistance Welding Solutions, Inc.**
DBA: LORS Machinery
Phone—(908) 964-9100 / (800) 223-0909
Fax—(908) 964-4492
Web—www.lors.com
Email—sales@lors.com
1090 Lousons Rd., Union 07083
*(see our ads under WELDING ROBOTS & WELDING EQUIPMENT & SUPPLIES)*

## WELDING WIRE

**SOS Gases, Inc.**
Industrial & Laboratory Gas; Welding Eqpt., Rental & Repair Service
Phone—(201) 998-7800 / (800) 626-7998
Fax—(201) 998-5243
Web—www.sosgasesinc.com
Email—sosgasesinc@msn.com
1100 Harrison Ave., Kearny 07032
*(see our ad under WELDING EQUIPMENT & SUPPLIES)*

## WET SUITS

**Henderson Aquatic, Inc.**
Phone—(856) 825-4771
1 White Hall, Millville 08332

## WHEELCHAIR ACCESSORIES

**Active Controls, LLC**
Phone—(856) 669-0940
597 Mantua Blvd., Sewell 08080

## WHEELCHAIRS

**Drive-Master Co., Inc.**
Wheelchair Accessible, Rental
Phone—(973) 808-9709
Fax—(973) 808-9713
Web—www.DriveMasterMobility.com
Email—info@DriveMasterMobility.com
37 Daniel Rd. West, Fairfield 07004
*(see our ad under VEHICLES – Handicapped Accessible)*

## WHEELS — Diamond

**Sample Marshall Laboratories, Inc.**
Email: jpulzone@samplemarshall.com
Grinding
Phone—(201) 933-0570
Fax—(201) 933-9157
Web—www.samplemarshall.com
63 Park Ave., Lyndhurst 07071

## WIGS, TOUPEES & HAIRPIECES

**De Meo Brothers., Inc.**
Phone—(973) 778-8100
2 Brigton Ave., Passaic 07055

**Look Of Love International (H Q)**
Phone—(908) 687-9502
1795-B Route 27 S., Edison 08817

## WINCHES

**Northeast Industrial, LLC**
Phone—(609) 884-3510
661 Route 9, Cape May 08204

## WINDOW & DOOR PRODUCTS

**Bonded Insulation Products**
Phone—(973) 256-2120
657 Union Blvd., Totowa 07512

**Somfy Systems, Inc.**
Motors & control systems for retractable awnings & rolling shutters
Phone—(609) 395-1300 / (800) 647-6639
Fax—(609) 395-1750
Web—www.somfysystems.com
Email—marketing_us@somfy.com
121 Herrod Blvd., Dayton 08810

**Versatile Distributors, Inc.**
Phone—(973) 779-1400
80 Industrial Rd., Lodi 07644

*Search from among 430,000 U.S. manufacturers & suppliers:*
**IndustryNet.com**

## WINDOW CLEANING SERVICES

**All County Window Cleaning**
Phone—(973) 827-8311
Fax—(973) 827-8312
Web—www.allcountywindowcleaning.com
Email—peter@allcountywindowcleaning.com
47 State Route 94, Vernon 07462

**All County Window Cleaning**
*Quality window cleaning services*
www.allcountywindowcleaning.com
**973-827-8311**
47 State Route 94   Vernon, NJ 07462

## WINDOW SHADES

**Friedland & Bros., Inc., Ralph**
Phone—(732) 290-9800
17 Industrial Dr., Keyport 07735

**Power Shade Co., Inc.**
Phone—(201) 767-3727
112 Paris Ave., Northvale 07647

## WINDOW TREATMENTS & COVERINGS

**Art's Windows, Inc.**
Phone—(732) 367-1770
199 Ocean Ave., Lakewood 08701

**Atlantic City Shade Shop, Inc.**
Phone—(609) 641-8700
500 Tilton Rd., P.O. Box 217, Northfield 08225

**Bai Lar Interior Services, Inc.**
Phone—(732) 738-0350
554 New Brunswick Ave., Fords 08863

**C & M Shade Corp.**
Phone—(201) 807-1200
53 Dwight Pl., Fairfield 07004

**Custom Window Treatments By Wayne Lubin**
Phone—(732) 462-4961
1029 U.S. Highway 9, Howell 07731

**Drapery & More, Inc.**
Phone—(201) 271-9661
2321 Kennedy Blvd., Ste. 2401-B-1, North Bergen 07047

**FNS Custom Window Treatment**
Phone—(856) 696-4070
2954 N. West Blvd., Vineland 08360

**Griffith Shade Co.**
Phone—(973) 667-1474
308 Washington Ave., Ste. 1, Nutley 07110

**Interior Art & Design, Inc.**
Phone—(201) 488-8855
59 Oak St., Hackensack 07601

**Precision Blinds Products, Inc.**
Phone—(908) 245-7766
637 Boulevard, Kenilworth 07033

**Stessl & Neugebauer, Inc.**
Phone—(908) 277-3340
9 Industrial Pl., Summit 07901

**Stich N' Sew Centre**
Phone—(732) 363-2220
123 E County Line Rd., Lakewood 08701

**Tina's Window Decorating**
Phone—(908) 668-0066
968 Somerset St., Watchung 07069

**Window Creations By Emmy Ltd.**
Phone—(718) 965-3844
103 Summerset St., Garfield 07026

## WINDOWS

**All Professional Remodeling Group, LLC**
Toll Free Ph: (888)919-ROOF; Second Generation Roofing Contractor
Phone—(973) 857-9449 / (888) 919-7663
Fax—(973) 857-0991
Web—www.allprofessionalremodelinggroup.com
Email—aprgllc@aol.com
P.O. Box 215, Cedar Grove 07009
*(see our ad under ROOFING CONTRACTORS)*

## WINDOWS — (cont.)

All Seasons Door & Window, Inc.
Phone—(732) 238-7100
28 Edgeboro Rd., East Brunswick 08816

Architectural Window Mfg.
Phone—(201) 939-2200
359 Veterans Blvd., Rutherford 07070

**Beck Contracting**
**Commercial & Residential**
**Phone—(732) 840-1080**
**Fax—(732) 840-9492**
**Web—www.beckcontracting.com**
**Email—beckcontracting@aol.com**
**431 20th Ave., Brick 08724**

General Metal & Glass Co.
Phone—(856) 365-6323
613 Kaighn Ave., Camden 08101

Jantek Industries, LLC
Phone—(609) 654-1030
230 Route 70, Medford 08055

Joffe Lumber & Supply, Inc.
Phone—(856) 825-9550
18 Burns Ave., Vineland 08360

Kendall Mfg. Co., Inc.
Phone—(856) 227-2132
1366 Chews Landing Rd., Clementon 08021

**Lawrenceville Home Improvement Center, Inc.**
**Phone—(609) 882-6709**
**Fax—(609) 538-0507**
**Web—www.lawrencevillehomeimp.com**
**Email—russo@lawrencevillehomeimp.com**
**126 Eldridge Ave., Lawrenceville 08648**

**Lawrenceville Home Improvement Center, Inc.**
*Quality Windows*
609-882-6709 • Fax: 609-538-0507
www.lawrencevillehomeimp.com
russo@lawrencevillehomeimp.com
126 Eldridge Ave., Lawrenceville, NJ 08648

Morak, Inc.
Phone—(973) 527-7470
3 Janice Dr., Hackettstown 07840

Pella Windows & Doors
Phone—(973) 575-0200
4 Dedrick Pl., West Caldwell 07006

Phillips Safety Products, Inc.
Phone—(732) 356-1493
123 Lincoln Blvd., Middlesex 08846

## WINDOWS — Aluminum

Freedom Glass & Metal, Inc.
Phone—(856) 627-3946
4 White Horse Pike, P.O. Box 868, Clementon 08021

New Century Building Systems, Inc.
Phone—(856) 863-8036
70 Sewell St., P.O. Box 775, Glassboro 08028

Northern Architectural Systems
Phone—(201) 943-6400
111 Central Ave., Teterboro 07608

Royal Aluminum Co., Inc.
Phone—(973) 589-8880
620 Market St., Newark 07105

Skyline Windows, LLC
Phone—(201) 531-9600
210 Park Pl. E., Wood Ridge 07075

Thomas Mfg., Inc.
Phone—(908) 810-0030
630 Ramsey Ave., Hillside 07205

Tri-State Building Materials Co.
Phone—(973) 472-2377
65 Lodi St., Passaic 07055

Window Supply Corp.
Phone—(201) 392-1213
5410 Kennedy Blvd., West New York 07093

## WINDOWS — Replacement

Champion Window Of Pennsauken
Phone—(856) 662-3400
8400 Remington Ave., Ste. B, Pennsauken 08110

## WINDOWS — Vinyl

ABC Supply
Phone—(856) 455-4888
41 N. Pearl St., Bridgeton 08302

Belleville Corp.
Phone—(201) 991-6222
328 Belleville Tpke., Kearny 07032

Dor-Win Mfg. Co.
Phone—(201) 796-4300
109 Midland Ave., Elmwood Park 07407

Ideal Window Mfg., Inc.
Phone—(201) 437-4300
100 W. 7th St., Bayonne 07002

Jersey Windows & Building Supplies
Phone—(973) 482-3614
831 Broadway, Newark 07104

Silver Line Building Products, LLC
Phone—(732) 435-1000
1 Silver Line Dr., P.O. Box 6029, North Brunswick 08902

Starlight Windows Mfg., Inc.
Phone—(973) 278-9366
50 E. 25th St., Paterson 07514

Sterling Window Co.
Phone—(973) 742-1900
224 21st Ave., Paterson 07501

Survivor II, Inc.
Phone—(908) 353-1155
919 Fairmount Ave., Elizabeth 07201

Taylor Windows, Inc.
Phone—(973) 672-3000
61 Central Ave., East Orange 07018

Thermal-Chek, Inc.
Phone—(856) 742-1200
912 Broadway, Westville 08093

United Window & Door Mfg.
Phone—(973) 912-0600
24-36 Fadem Rd., Springfield 07081

Universal Windows, LLC
Phone—(856) 719-0020
407 Bloomfield Dr., West Berlin 08091

Window Shapes, Inc.
Phone—(848) 229-2431
225 Liberty St., Metuchen 08840

## WINDOWS — Vinyl Replacement

Alliance Vinyl Window Co., Inc.
Phone—(856) 456-4954
301 Crescent Blvd., Mount Ephraim 08059

Royal Prime Window Specialist, Inc.
Phone—(908) 354-7600
742 Fairfield Ave., Kenilworth 07033

## WINDOWS — Wooden

Artistic Doors & Windows
Phone—(732) 726-9400
10 S. Inman Ave., Avenel 07001

**Behnke's Building Supply**
**Phone—(201) 384-1450**
**Fax—(201) 384-8304**
**Email—kevinb@paramusbuildingsupply.com**
**42 Portland Ave., Bergenfield 07621**

**Behnke's Paramus Building Supply Co.**
**Bonneville, Andersen & Kolbe & Kolbe Windows**
**Phone—(201) 262-1818 / (800) 354-1818**
**Fax—(201) 262-9250**
**Web—www.paramusbuildingsupply.com**
**Email—kevinb@paramusbuildingsupply.com**
**P.O. Box 587, Paramus 07653**
*(see our ad under BUILDING MATERIALS)*

## WINDSHIELD WIPERS & WIPER BLADES

Clear Plus Windshield Wipers
Phone—(973) 546-8800
100 Outwater Ln., Garfield 07026

## WINE RACKS & CELLARS

Wine Products, Inc.
Phone—(732) 528-5222
2416 Highway 35, Ste. B, Manasquan 08736

## WINERY EQUIPMENT & SUPPLIES

**Corrado's Family Affair**
**There is a difference**
**Phone—(973) 340-0628**
**Fax—(973) 340-2052**
**Web—www.corradosmarket.com**
**Email—gerrycorradojr@corradosmarket.com**
**1578 Main Ave., Clifton 07011**

## WINES

Aidil Wines & Liquors
Phone—(973) 712-0950
574 Ferry St., Newark 07105

Alba Vineyard
Phone—(908) 995-7800
269 Route 627, Milford 08848

Allied Beverage Group, LLC
Phone—(856) 234-4111
901 Plesant Valley Ave., P.O. Box 5090, Mount Laurel 08054

Amalthea Cellars Farm Winery
Phone—(856) 768-8585
209 Vineyard Rd., Atco 08004

American Estates Wines, Inc.
Phone—(908) 273-5060
19 Hillside Ave., Summit 07901

Balic Winery, Inc.
Phone—(609) 625-2166
6623 Harding Hwy., Mays Landing 08330

Bellview Winery
Phone—(856) 697-7172
150 Atlantic St., Landisville 08326

Bloomfield Wines, Inc.
Phone—(973) 743-2020
339 Broad St., Bloomfield 07003

CAVA Winery & Vineyard, Inc.
Phone—(973) 823-9463
3619 State Route 94, Hamburg 07419

Cream Ridge Winery
Phone—(609) 259-9797
145 Route 539 S., P.O. Box 98, Cream Ridge 08514

Crown Jewel Importers & Marketing Corp.
Phone—(201) 461-3900
140 Sylvan Ave., Ste. 109, Englewood Cliffs 07632

Federal Wine & Liquor Co.
Phone—(856) 234-3200
1 Central Ave., Mount Laurel 08054

Four Sisters Winery
Phone—(908) 475-3671
783 County Road 519, Belvidere 07823

Grape Escape, The
Phone—(609) 409-9463
12 Stults Rd., Ste. 101, Dayton 08810

Hawk Haven Vineyard & Winery, LLC
Phone—(609) 846-7347
600 S. Railroad Ave., Rio Grande 08242

Heritage Vineyards of Richwood, LLC
Phone—(856) 589-4474
480 Mullica Hill Rd., Mullica Hill 08062

Hopewell Valley Vineyards
Phone—(609) 737-4465
46 Yard Rd., Pennington 08534

Monroeville Vineyard & Winery, LLC
Phone—(856) 521-0523
314 Richwood Rd., Monroeville 08343

Natali Vineyards, LLC
Phone—(609) 465-0075
221 N. Delsea Dr., Cape May Court House 08210

Opici Winery, Inc.
Phone—(201) 689-1200
25 DeBoer Dr., Glen Rock 07452

Plagido's Winery
Phone—(609) 567-4633
570 N. 1st Rd., Hammonton 08037

Renault Winery
Phone—(609) 965-2111
72 N. Bremen Ave., Egg Harbor City 08215

Rex Wine Vinegar Co.
Phone—(973) 589-6911
828-830 Raymond Blvd., Newark 07105

Royal Wine Corp.
Phone—(718) 534-0200
63 Lefante Way, Bayonne 07002

Sharrott Winery, LLC
Phone—(609) 567-9463
370 S. Egg Harbor Rd., Blue Anchor 08037

## WINES — (cont.)

**Shore Point Distributing Co.**
100 Shore Point Dr., Freehold 07728
Addtl. Web: www.njcoors.com
**Phone—(732) 308-3334**
**Fax—(732) 308-1610**
**Web—www.shorepoint.com**
**P.O. Box 275, Adelphia 07710**
*(see our ads under BEER & ALE & DISTILLED SPIRITS)*

Tomasello Winery, Inc.
Phone—(609) 561-0567
225 White Horse Pike, Hammonton 08037

Unionville, LLC
Phone—(908) 788-0400
9 Rocktown Rd., Ringoes 08551

W J R B, Inc.
Phone—(609) 884-1169
711 Town Bank Rd., Cape May 08204

**Wagonhouse Winery, LLC**
Sweet & dry red & white wines
**Phone—(609) 780-8019**
**Fax—(856) 294-9814**
**Web—www.wagonhousewinery.com**
**1401 State Highway 45, Swedesboro 08085**

Westfall Winery, LLC
Phone—(973) 293-3428
141 Clove Rd., Montague 07827

Winebow, Inc.
Phone—(201) 445-0620
75 Chestnut Ridge Rd., Ste. 1, Montvale 07645

## WIPING CLOTHS

American Hygiene Industries, LLC
Phone—(973) 928-6533
60 Page Rd., Clifton 07012

American Waste & Textile, LLC
Phone—(973) 589-6252
73 Vesey St., Newark 07105

Caltex Industries, Inc.
Phone—(973) 273-1707
1301 W. Elizabeth Ave., Ste. E-1, Linden 07036

ITW Professional Brands
Phone—(732) 363-9281
1295 Towbin Ave., Lakewood 08701

South Jersey Wiping Cloth
Phone—(856) 696-0129
314 Rosewood Ave., Vineland 08360

## WIRE

Modern International Corp.
Phone—(732) 696-9100
145 Cliffwood Ave., Cliffwood 07721

National Electric Wire Co.
Phone—(609) 758-3600
100 Goldman Dr., Cream Ridge 08514

UTZ, LLC
Phone—(973) 339-1100
4 Peckman Rd., Little Falls 07424

**Wheeler Industrial Corp.**
**Phone—(973) 926-0551**
**Fax—(973) 926-0984**
**Web—www.wheelermetal4u.com**
**Email—pd.coates@wheelermetal4u.com**
**485 Lyons Ave., Irvington 07111**

## WIRE — Alloy

**Wheeler Industrial Corp.**
**Phone—(973) 926-0551**
**Fax—(973) 926-0984**
**Web—www.wheelermetal4u.com**
**Email—pd.coates@wheelermetal4u.com**
**485 Lyons Ave., Irvington 07111**

## WIRE — Copper

Fisk Alloy Wire, Inc.
Phone—(973) 427-7550
10 Thomas Rd., P.O. Box 26, Hawthorne 07507

Little Falls Alloys, Inc.
Phone—(973) 278-1666
189 Caldwell Ave., Paterson 07501

Molecu-Wire Corp.
Phone—(732) 296-9473
56 Old Camplain Rd., Hillsborough 08844

**Wheeler Industrial Corp.**
**Phone—(973) 926-0551**
**Fax—(973) 926-0984**
**Web—www.wheelermetal4u.com**
**Email—pd.coates@wheelermetal4u.com**
**485 Lyons Ave., Irvington 07111**

## WIRE — EDM

**Advantage EDM**
**Phone—(973) 786-0177**
**Fax—(973) 786-0277**
**Web—www.advantageedm.com**
**Email—info@advantageedm.com**
**38 Main St., Route 206, Andover 07821**

## WIRE — Electronic

**Paige Electric Co. L. P.**
Email: hjcoffey@paigeelectric.com
**Phone—(908) 687-7810 / (800) 327-2443**
**Fax—(908) 687-8860**
**Web—www.paigecable.com**
**1160 Springfield Rd., P.O. Box 368, Union 07083**

## WIRE — Insulated

Micro-Tek Corp.
Phone—(856) 829-3855
P.O. Box 2134, Cinnaminson 08077

## WIRE — Semiconductor

Oxford Instruments Superconducting Technology, Inc.
Phone—(732) 541-1300
600 Milik St., Carteret 07008

## WIRE — Specialty

Surepure Chemetals, Inc.
Phone—(973) 377-4081
5 Nottingham Dr., Florham Park 07932

## WIRE — Stainless Steel

**Flanner & Associates**
Since 1987, specializing in representing manufacturers of fourslide parts, wire, metal, plastic, and rubber for the Aerospace, Automotive, Electronics, and Medical industries
**Phone—(609) 588-0790 / (609) 647-7821**
**Email—gflanner@optonline.net**
**104 Caitlin Ln., Hamilton 08691**

## WIRE — Steel

Evergard Steel Corp.
Phone—(908) 925-6800
1825 Pennsylvania Ave., Linden 07036

**Modern International Corp.**
**Phone—(732) 696-9100**
**Fax—(732) 696-9111**
**Web—www.moderninternational.net**
**Email—dstern@moderninternational.net**
**145 Cliffwood Ave., Cliffwood 07721**

Plasti-Clad Metal Products
Phone—(732) 449-2665
2601 Ridgewood Rd., Wall 07719

## WIRE AND CABLE

Alan Baird Industries, Inc.
Phone—(201) 652-6335
1 Hollywood Ave., Ste. 9, Ho-Ho-Kus 07423

Alpha Wire Co.
Phone—(908) 925-8000
711 Lidgerwood Ave., P.O. Box 711, Elizabeth 07207

Brim Electronics, Inc.
Phone—(201) 796-2886
120 Home Pl., Lodi 07644

**Wheeler Industrial Corp.**
**Phone—(973) 926-0551**
**Fax—(973) 926-0984**
**Web—www.wheelermetal4u.com**
**Email—pd.coates@wheelermetal4u.com**
**485 Lyons Ave., Irvington 07111**

**Carl Stahl Sava Industries, Inc.**
Mechanical Assemblies, Cable Assemblies, Idler Pulleys, Push & Pull Controls; ISO Certified
**Phone—(973) 835-0882**
**Fax—(973) 835-0877**
**Web—www.savacable.com**
**Email—sales@savacable.com**
**4 N. Corporate Dr., P.O. Box 30, Riverdale 07457**
*(see our ad under CABLE ASSEMBLIES)*

Daburn Electronics & Cable, Inc.
Phone—(973) 328-3200
44 Richboynton Rd., Dover 07801

Global Wire & Cable, Inc.
Phone—(973) 471-1000
61 Willet St., Bldg. S, Passaic 07055

ICC Cable Corp.
Phone—(201) 482-5750
2125 Center Ave., Ste. 401, Fort Lee 07024

**Jersey Strand & Cable, Inc.**
Small & Miniature Strand, Cable, Wire Rope & Braid, Ferrous & Nonferrous Metals, Stock & Custom
**Phone—(908) 213-9350 / (800) 528-3900**
**Fax—(908) 213-2203**
**Web—www.jerseystrandandcable.com**
**259 Center St., Phillipsburg 08865**

**Lapp USA**
Cables, accessories & connectors. Everything from one source
**Phone—(973) 660-9700 / (800) 774-3539**
**Fax—(973) 660-9330**
**Web—www.lappusa.com**
**Email—sales@lappusa.com**
**29 Hanover Rd., Florham Park 07932**
*(see our ad under CONNECTORS—Electric Wire & Cable)*

Liberty Electronics, Inc.
Phone—(973) 625-7963
465 E. Main St., Denville 07834

**Okonite Co., Inc., The (H Q)**
Email: seltsam@okonite.com
Setting The Standard Since 1868
**Phone—(201) 825-0300**
**Fax—(201) 825-9026**
**Web—www.okonite.com**
**Email—info@okonite.com**
**102 Hilltop Rd., P.O. Box 340, Ramsey 07446**

**THE OKONITE COMPANY**
*Wire & Cable*
**(201) 825-0300 Fax: (201) 825-9026**
**www.okonite.com**
PO Box 340 • Ramsey, NJ 07446

Okonite Co., The
Phone—(201) 825-0300
102 Hilltop Rd., Paterson 07513

**Paige Electric Co. L. P.**
Email: hjcoffey@paigeelectric.com
**Phone—(908) 687-7810 / (800) 327-2443**
**Fax—(908) 687-8860**
**Web—www.paigecable.com**
**1160 Springfield Rd., P.O. Box 368, Union 07083**

**Seminole Wire & Cable Co.**
Email: sales@seminolewire.com
**Phone—(856) 324-2929**
**Fax—(856) 438-6875**
**Web—www.seminolewire.com**
**7861 Airport Hwy., Pennsauken 08109**

TE Wire & Cable, LLC
Phone—(201) 845-9400
107 5th St., Saddle Brook 07663

U. S. Wire & Cable, Inc.
Phone—(973) 824-5529
33 Queen St., Newark 07114

V-Com
Phone—(201) 229-9800
80 Little Falls Rd., Fairfield 07004

Weber & Scher Mfg. Co., Inc.
Phone—(908) 236-8484
1231 US Highway 22 E., P.O. Box 366, Lebanon 08833

*Do nationwide searches for products & services at:*
**IndustryNet.com**

*find additional suppliers at*
**IndustryNet.com**

INDUSTRY

## WIRE AND CABLE — Electrical

Colonial Wire & Cable Of NJ, Inc.
Phone—(732) 287-1557
85 National Rd., Edison 08817

## WIRE AND CABLE HANDLING EQUIPMENT

Ulysses Machine Co.
Phone—(856) 979-3674
41 Lancelot Ln., Mount Laurel 08054

## WIRE ASSEMBLIES

**Paige Electric Co. L. P.**
Email: hjcoffey@paigeelectric.com
**Phone—(908) 687-7810 / (800) 327-2443**
**Fax—(908) 687-8860**
**Web—www.paigecable.com**
**1160 Springfield Rd., P.O. Box 368, Union 07083**

## WIRE CLOTH

Belleville Wire Cloth Co., Inc.
Phone—(973) 239-0074
18 Rutgers Ave., Cedar Grove 07009
Compass Wire Cloth, Inc.
Phone—(856) 853-7616
1942 N. Mill Rd., Vineland 08360
New Jersey Wire Cloth Co., Inc.
Phone—(973) 340-0101
55 Park Slope, Clifton 07011
**Newark Wire Cloth Co., Inc.**
**Phone—(973) 778-4478 / (800) 221-0392**
**Fax—(973) 778-4481**
**Web—www.newarkwire.com**
**Email—info@newarkwire.com**
**160 Fornelius Ave., Clifton 07013**
**Unique Wire Weaving Co., Inc.**
**Phone—(908) 688-4600**
**Fax—(908) 688-4601**
**Web—www.uniquewire.com**
**Email—cheryl@uniquewire.com**
**762 Ramsey Ave., Hillside 07205**
Wire Cloth Mfrs., Inc.
Phone—(973) 328-1000
110 Iron Mountain Rd., Mine Hill 07803

## WIRE FORMS

Allentown, Inc.
Phone—(609) 259-7951
165 Route 526, Allentown 08501
Components Corp.
Phone—(973) 627-0290
6 Kinsey Pl., Denville 07834
Form Cut Industries, Inc.
Phone—(973) 483-5154
197 Mount Pleasant Ave., Newark 07104
**General Wire & Stamping Co., Inc.**
**Precision Wire Forms & Stampings For Industry**
**Phone—(973) 366-8080 / (800) 562-0237**
**Fax—(973) 366-3982**
**Web—www.generalwire.com**
**Email—sales@generalwire.com**
**1 Emery Ave., Unit 3, Randolph 07869**
Phillips Enterprises, Inc.
Phone—(732) 493-3191
3600 Sunset Ave., P.O. Box 2286, Asbury Park 07712
**Stamping.com, Inc.**
**Phone—(732) 493-4697**
**Fax—(732) 493-3493**
**Web—www.stampinginc.com**
**Email—stamping@juno.com**
**3600 Sunset Ave., Asbury Park 07712**
*(see our ad under METAL STAMPINGS)*
Wire Forming Corp. Of New Jersey
Phone—(973) 824-5558
109 Meeker Ave., Ste. 135, Newark 07114

## WIRE HARNESS & CABLE ASSEMBLIES

Molecu-Wire Corp.
Phone—(908) 429-0300
1215 Kennedy Blvd., Manville 08835

## Bergen Cable Technology, LLC
Wire Rope Cable Assemblies
& Lockwire Replacement Safety Cable

## 973-276-9596 • 800-237-4369
## FAX: 973-276-9566

343 Kaplan Dr. Fairfield, NJ 07004
www.bergencable.com • sales@bergencable.com

Paige Electric Co. L. P.
Email: hjcoffey@paigeelectric.com
**Phone—(908) 687-7810 / (800) 327-2443**
**Fax—(908) 687-8860**
**Web—www.paigecable.com**
**1160 Springfield Rd., P.O. Box 368, Union 07083**
Syscom Tech
Phone—(856) 642-7661
1537 Glen Ave., Moorestown 08057
Thosani, Inc.
Phone—(856) 753-9000
150 Cooper Rd., Ste. E-12, West Berlin 08091

## WIRE HARNESSES

American Autowire
Phone—(856) 933-0801
150 Heller Pl., Bellmawr 08031
**Americor Electronics, Ltd.**
**Phone—(847) 956-6200 / (800) 830-5337**
**Fax—(847) 956-0300**
**Web—www.americor-usa.com**
**Email—info@americor-usa.com**
**675 S. Lively Blvd., Elk Grove Village, IL 60007**
*(see our ads under CABLE ASSEMBLIES & CORD SETS)*
VIP Industries, Inc.
Phone—(973) 472-7500
90 Brighton Rd., Clifton 07012

## WIRE MESH

**Unique Wire Weaving Co., Inc.**
**Phone—(908) 688-4600**
**Fax—(908) 688-4601**
**Web—www.uniquewire.com**
**Email—cheryl@uniquewire.com**
**762 Ramsey Ave., Hillside 07205**

## WIRE MESH PRODUCTS

Newark Wire Works, Inc.
Phone—(732) 661-2001
1059 King Georges Post Rd., Ste. 103, Edison 08837
ScreenTek Mfg. Co., Inc.
Phone—(973) 328-2121
220 Franklin Rd., Ste. B, Randolph 07869
**Unique Wire Weaving Co., Inc.**
**Phone—(908) 688-4600**
**Fax—(908) 688-4601**
**Web—www.uniquewire.com**
**Email—cheryl@uniquewire.com**
**762 Ramsey Ave., Hillside 07205**

## WIRE PROCESSING MACHINERY

New Jersey Wire Stitching Machine Co.
Phone—(856) 428-7400
1841 Old Cuthbert Rd., Cherry Hill 08034
Niehoff Endex North America, Inc.
Phone—(856) 467-4884
1 Mallard Ct., Swedesboro 08085

## WIRE PRODUCTS

Wytech Industries, Inc.
Phone—(732) 396-3900
960 E. Hazelwood Ave., Rahway 07065

## WIRE ROPE

**Bergen Cable Technology, LLC**
**Cable Assemblies, Wire Rope & Lockwire Replacement Safety Cable**
**Phone—(973) 276-9596 / (800) 237-4369**
**Fax—(973) 276-9566**
**Web—www.bergencable.com**
**Email—sales@bergencable.com**
**343 Kaplan Dr., Fairfield 07004**
*(see our ad on this page)*
**Brown & Perkins, Inc.**
**Phone—(609) 655-1150**
**Fax—(609) 655-1173**
**Web—www.brownandperkins.com**
**Email—sales@brownandperkins.com**
**1193 Route 535, P.O. Box 412, Cranbury 08512**
**Carl Stahl Sava Industries, Inc.**
**Mechanical Assemblies, Cable Assemblies, Idler Pulleys, Push & Pull Controls; ISO Certified**
**Phone—(973) 835-0882**
**Fax—(973) 835-0877**
**Web—www.savacable.com**
**Email—sales@savacable.com**
**4 N. Corporate Dr., P.O. Box 30, Riverdale 07457**
*(see our ad under CABLE ASSEMBLIES)*
**Jersey Strand & Cable, Inc.**
**Small & Miniature Strand, Cable, Wire Rope & Braid, Ferrous & Nonferrous Metals, Stock & Custom**
**Phone—(908) 213-9350 / (800) 528-3900**
**Fax—(908) 213-2203**
**Web—www.jerseystrandandcable.com**
**259 Center St., Phillipsburg 08865**
Motion Control Technologies, Inc.
Phone—(973) 361-2226
158 W. Clinton St., Ste. FF, Dover 07801
Sea Gear Marine Supply, Inc.
Phone—(609) 884-2711
1144 Route 109, Cape May 08204

## WIRE ROPE — Stainless Steel

**Carl Stahl Sava Industries, Inc.**
**Mechanical Assemblies, Cable Assemblies, Idler Pulleys, Push & Pull Controls; ISO Certified**
**Phone—(973) 835-0882**
**Fax—(973) 835-0877**
**Web—www.savacable.com**
**Email—sales@savacable.com**
**4 N. Corporate Dr., P.O. Box 30, Riverdale 07457**
*(see our ad under CABLE ASSEMBLIES)*
**Jersey Strand & Cable, Inc.**
**Small & Miniature Strand, Cable, Wire Rope & Braid, Ferrous & Nonferrous Metals, Stock & Custom**
**Phone—(908) 213-9350 / (800) 528-3900**
**Fax—(908) 213-2203**
**Web—www.jerseystrandandcable.com**
**259 Center St., Phillipsburg 08865**

## WIRE ROPE FITTINGS

**Carl Stahl Sava Industries, Inc.**
Mechanical Assemblies, Cable Assemblies, Idler Pulleys, Push & Pull Controls; ISO Certified
Phone—(973) 835-0882
Fax—(973) 835-0877
Web—www.savacable.com
Email—sales@savacable.com
4 N. Corporate Dr., P.O. Box 30, Riverdale 07457
*(see our ad under CABLE ASSEMBLIES)*

## WIRE STRAND

**Jersey Strand & Cable, Inc.**
Small & Miniature Strand, Cable, Wire Rope & Braid, Ferrous & Nonferrous Metals, Stock & Custom
Phone—(908) 213-9350 / (800) 528-3900
Fax—(908) 213-2203
Web—www.jerseystrandandcable.com
259 Center St., Phillipsburg 08865

## WIRELESS COMMUNICATION SYSTEMS

**BTECH, Inc.**
Email: sales@btechinc.com
Stationary Battery Monitors & Systems
Phone—(973) 983-1120
Fax—(973) 983-1125
Web—www.btechinc.com
Email—sales@email.btechinc.com
10 Astro Pl., Rockaway 07866

**BTECH®**
*Stationary Battery Monitors*
www.btechinc.com
(973) 983-1120 / Fax: (973) 983-1125
10 Astro Pl. • Rockaway, NJ 07866

INSTOCK Wireless Components, Inc.
Phone—(973) 335-6550
50 Intervale Rd., Ste. 15, Boonton 07005
International Tower Supply
Phone—(856) 317-0005
851 Bethel Ave., Pennsauken 08110

## WIRING DEVICES

Wire & Cable Fabricating Devices
Phone—(973) 290-9069
39 E. Hanover Ave., Ste. 1, Morris Plains 07950

## WOOD CARVING

Gianetto Wood Carvings, Vincent
Phone—(609) 877-6233
617 Delanco Rd., Beverly 08010

## WOOD FINISHES

Hood Finishing Products, Inc.
Phone—(732) 805-0088
9 Factory Ln., Middlesex 08846
Sherwin-Williams Co., The, Woodcare Products Div. (H Q)
Phone—(201) 818-7500
10 Mountainview Rd., Upper Saddle River 07458

## WOOD FINISHING SERVICES

Essex Coatings, LLC
Phone—(732) 855-9400
135 Essex Ave. E., Avenel 07001

## WOOD PRESERVING

Cox Industries
Phone—(609) 267-4700
1517 Route 38 W., P.O. Box 507, Hainesport 08036

## WOOD PRODUCTS

Mystic Timber, LLC
Phone—(908) 223-7878
95 Youmans Ave., Washington 07882
PJ Murphy Forest Products Corp. (H Q)
Phone—(973) 316-0800
150 River Rd., Bldg. L, Ste. 1, P.O. Box 300, Montville 07045
RSL, Inc.
Phone—(609) 645-9770
3049 Fernwood Ave., Egg Harbor Township 08234
Woodline Works Corp.
Phone—(732) 828-9100
625 Jersey Ave., New Brunswick 08901

## WOOD PRODUCTS — Engineered

UFP Berlin, LLC
Email: dgoldman@ufpi.com
Phone—(856) 767-0043
Fax—(856) 767-1526
Web—www.ufpi.com
159 Jackson Rd., Berlin 08009
*(see our ad under FLOOR TRUSSES)*

## WOOD PRODUCTS — Laminated

Craft Line Cabinet Corp.
Phone—(973) 777-8808
10 Walnut St., Clifton 07013

## WOOD TRUSSES

Concord Truss Co.
Phone—(856) 845-3848
692 S. Evergreen Ave., Woodbury Heights 08097
Timplex Corp.
Phone—(973) 875-5500
1370 State Route 23, Wantage 07461

## WOODWORK — Architectural

Alliance Woodwork Corp.
Phone—(732) 671-6884
19 Ogden Ct., P.O. Box 684, Middletown 07748
Artcraft Cabinets Woodworking
Phone—(201) 943-6090
165 Broad Ave., Fairview 07022
Atlas Woodworking, Inc.
Phone—(201) 784-1949
15 Naugle St., Closter 07624
Central Millwork Of New Jersey
Phone—(609) 448-7700
92 N. Main St., Bldg. 11, P.O. Box 447, Windsor 08561
Designers Kitchens, Inc.
Phone—(732) 370-5500
250 Faraday Ave., Jackson 08527
Jorgensen-Carr Ltd.
Phone—(201) 792-2278
50 Dey St., 4th Fl., Jersey City 07306
**Mountain Millwork, Inc.**
Phone—(732) 606-1701
Fax—(732) 606-1707
Web—www.mountainmillworkinc.com
Email—cvirgil@mountainmillworkinc.com
1014 Route 9, Bayville 08721

**(732) 606-1701**
Fax: (732) 606-1707
MOUNTAIN MILLWORK, INC.
1014 Route 9
Bayville, NJ 08721
www.mountainmillworkinc.com

IndustryNet®.com
Find Suppliers Nationally FREE!

**Paramount Fixture Corp.**
A full service mfg. source for wood, laminate & steel fixtures for your retail, commercial & residential environments
Phone—(973) 485-1585 / (973) 485-8261
Fax—(973) 485-3366
Web—www.paramountfixturecorp.com
Email—fixtureman175@aol.com
175 Mount Pleasant Ave., Newark 07104
**Prestige Millwork, LLC**
Phone—(908) 526-5100
Fax—(908) 526-5109
Web—www.prestigemillworkllc.com
Email—mindyz@prestigemillworkllc.com
152 U.S. Highway 206, Bldg. 17-A, Hillsborough 08844
Somerset Wood Products Co.
Phone—(908) 526-0030
10 Johnson Dr., Raritan 08869

## WOODWORKING

Citkowski Co.
Phone—(973) 390-5477
90 Dayton Ave., Passaic 07055
GT Millwork, LLC
Phone—(609) 291-9222
2180 Hedding Rd., Columbus 08022
Lardieri's Custom Woodworking, Inc.
Phone—(732) 905-6334
1830 Swarthmore Ave., Ste. 6, Lakewood 08701
Leiz Custom Woodwork, David
Phone—(908) 486-1533
2301 E. Edgar Rd., Bldg. 5-A, Linden 07036
Tea & Elle Woodworks, LLC
Phone—(732) 938-9660
5004 Industrial Rd., Farmingdale 07727
Wood Shed, Inc., The
Phone—(201) 866-7949
4500 Park Ave., Weehawken 07086
**Woodchucker, Inc., The**
Phone—(856) 575-0200
Fax—(856) 575-0222
Web—www.the-woodchucker.com
Email—omri@the-woodchucker.com
42 Bridgeton-Fairton Rd., P.O. Box 380, Fairton 08320
Woodwork & More, LLC
Phone—(856) 986-3140
24 W. Gorman Ave., Collingswood 08108

## WOODWORKING MACHINERY

Bass, Inc., Rudolf
Phone—(201) 433-3800
45 Halladay St., Jersey City 07304
Colwood Electronics, Inc.
Phone—(732) 938-5556
44 Main St., Farmingdale 07727
Ramelson Co., Inc., U. J.
Phone—(973) 589-5422
165 Thomas St., Newark 07114

## WOODWORKING TOOLS

**Charles G.G. Schmidt & Co., Inc.**
In Business Since 1926
Phone—(201) 391-5300 / (800) 724-6438
Fax—(201) 391-3565
Web—www.cggschmidt.com
Email—sales@cggschmidt.com
301 W. Grand Ave., Montvale 07645

## WRITING INSTRUMENTS

Private Label Products, Inc.
Phone—(201) 791-1177
20-21 Wagaraw Rd., Bldg. 34, Fair Lawn 07410
Rosa Pen Corp.
Phone—(201) 939-1112
155 Park Ave., Ste. 101, Lyndhurst 07071

## WROUGHT IRON PRODUCTS

Newman's Ornamental Ironworks, Inc.
Phone—(732) 223-9042
207 Union Ave., Brielle 08730

## X-RAY EQUIPMENT & SUPPLIES

A Walsh Imaging, Inc.
Phone—(973) 616-7100
55 Cannonball Rd., Pompton Lakes 07442
Kodex Inc.
Phone—(973) 235-0606
160 Park Ave., Ste. 1, Nutley 07110
Med-X-Ray Co., Inc.
Phone—(973) 673-8822
356 Glenwood Ave., East Orange 07017
Swissray International, Inc. (H Q)
Phone—(908) 353-0971
31 Gordon Rd., Piscataway 08854

## YACHTS

Cherubini Yachts, LLC
Phone—(856) 764-5319
51 Norman Ave., Riverside 08075
Egg Harbor Yachts
Phone—(609) 965-2300
801 Philadelphia Ave., Egg Harbor City 08215
Jersey Cape Yachts
Phone—(609) 965-8650
2143 River Rd., Egg Harbor City 08215
TF Yachts, LLC
Phone—(609) 965-2300
801 Philadelphia Ave., P.O. Box 702, Egg Harbor
City 08215
Viking Yacht Co.
Phone—(609) 296-6000
5738 U.S. Highway 9 N., P.O. Box 308, New
Gretna 08224

## YARNS

Ashfar Enterprises, Inc. (H Q)
Phone—(848) 202-1581
200 Metro Plex Dr., Ste. 275, Edison 08817
Brawer Bros., Inc. (H Q)
Phone—(973) 238-1800
375 Diamond Bridge Ave., P.O. Box 640,
Hawthorne 07506
Dillon Yarn Corp. (H Q)
Phone—(973) 684-1600
53 E. 34th St., Paterson 07514
Middleburg Yarn Processing Co., Inc. (H Q)
Phone—(973) 238-1800
375 Diamond Bridge Ave., P.O. Box 640,
Hawthorne 07507
Multi-Tex Products Corp.
Phone—(201) 991-7262
54 2nd Ave., Kearny 07032
Orchard Yarn & Thread Co., Inc.
Phone—(201) 804-3999
135 Kero Rd., Carlstadt 07072

# Reach Industrial Buyers Over the Internet!

## mni's Industrial Search Engine

Allows decision makers to shop for products & industrial services among the 430,000 companies in MNI's database of U.S. manufacturers & suppliers. This is the guide to *"who makes it,"* *"who does it,"* and *"who supplies it!"*

## Absolutely free to users!
## No registration, hassle or obligation!

# IndustryNet.com

INDUSTRY

# U.S. Industrial Expansion & Relocation Guide

## A state by state guide of facts, figures, business incentives and organizations to aid in company site selection and planning for expansion or relocation.

| STATE | POPULATION | LABOR FORCE | Unemp* (%) | MFRS. COs. | MFG. JOBS | LEADING MANUFACTURING INDUSTRIES (by percent employment) | COUNTY W/ MOST MFG. JOBS | RIGHT TO WORK | CORP. TAX RATE (%) | STATE SALES TAX (%) | UNEMPL. INS. TAX (%) |
|---|---|---|---|---|---|---|---|---|---|---|---|
| **AK** | 698,473 | 366,000 | 6.6 | 745 | 21,717 | Food & Kindred Products; Petroleum & Coal Products; Printing & Publishing | Anchorage | No | 1.0-9.4 | None | 1.0-5.4 |
| | No Personal Income Tax • Made in Alaska Program • AIDEA Loan Participation Program • Southeast Alaska Revolving Loan Fund • Micro-loan program for women entrepreneurs • Rural Development Initiative Fund • Rural Small Business Development Loans ||||||||||||
| **AL** | 4,708,708 | 2,109,100 | 6.0 | 5,206 | 287,742 | Transportation Equipment; Food and Kindred Products.; Fabricated Metal Products | Jefferson | Yes | 6.5 | 1.5-4.0 | 2.15-8.3 |
| | Income Tax Capital Credit • Enterprise Zone Tax Credit/Exemption • Alabama Industrial Dev. Training (AI) • Alabama Technology Network (ATN) • Industrial Development Grant Program (Site Preparation) • Industrial Access Road & Bridge • One-Stop Environmental Permitting • Industrial Revenue Bonds (IRBs) • Economic Dev. Revolving Loan Funds • TVA Economic Dev. Loan Fund • Community Dev. Block Grant/Loan Program • Appalachian Regional Commission & Delta Regional Authority Grants ||||||||||||
| **AR** | 2,889,450 | 1,315,600 | 5.8 | 3,175 | 186,611 | Food & Kindred Products; Industrial Machinery & Equipment; Fabricated Metal Products | Pulaski | Yes | 1.0-6.5 | 6.0 | 1.2-11.1 |
| | Biotechnology Development Credit • Advantage Arkansas Job Creation Credit • "Tax Back" Sales Tax Refund for expanding eligible businesses and "Tax Back" Sales Tax Refund for targeted businesses • R&D with Universities Tax Credit • Manufacturers' Investment Tax Credit • Emerging Technology Dev. Tax Credit • Existing Workforce Training Act Tax Credit • Enterprise Zone Program • Youth Apprenticeship Training Program • Arkansas Community and Economic Development Program (ACEDP) ||||||||||||
| **AZ** | 6,595,778 | 3,078,800 | 6.8 | 5,199 | 205,930 | Transportation Equipment; Industrial Machinery & Equipment; Fabricated Metal Products | Maricopa | Yes | 6.968 | 6.6 | .02-5.86 |
| | Commercial/Industrial Solar Tax Credit • Renewable Energy Tax Credit • Quality Jobs Tax Credit Program • Research & Dev. Tax Credit Program • Pollution Control Tax Credit • Solar Liquid Fuel Tax Credit • AZ Competes Fund • Arizona Job Training Program • Military Reuse Zone Program (MRZ) (Applicable to aerospace/aviation manufacturers) • Private Activity Bonds Program (PAB) • Qualified Energy Conservation Bonds (QECBs) • Additional Depreciation ||||||||||||
| **CA** | 37,691,912 | 18,822,200 | 7.2 | 25,435 | 1,463,603 | Electronic & Other Elec. Equipment; Industrial Machinery & Equipment; Food & Kindred Products | Los Angeles | No | 8.84 | 7.25 | 1.5-6.2 |
| | Research and Development Tax Credit • Net Operating Loss Carryover • Work Opportunity Tax Credit • Sales & Use Tax Exemptions for Clean Tech Manufacturing • No Finished Goods, Raw Materials or Inventory Tax • Recycling Market Development Zone Revolving Loan Program (RMDZ) • Innovation Hub (iHub) Initiative • California Bus. Investment Services (CalBIS) • Enterprise Zones (EZ) • Foreign Trade Zones • Manufacturing Enhancement Areas (MEAs) • Industrial Development Bonds ||||||||||||
| **CO** | 5,025,748 | 2,806,500 | 4.1 | 5,684 | 177,685 | Food & Kindred Products; Electronic & Other Elec. Eqpt.; Industrial Machinery & Equipment | Denver | No | 4.63 | 2.9 | 1.0-5.4 |
| | Investment Tax Credit (for businesses located in an Enterprise Zone {EZ}) • New Business Facility Tax Credit (EZ) • New Business Facility Tax Credit for Agricultural Processing (EZ) • R&D Tax Credit (EZ) • Rehabilitation of Vacant Commercial Buildings Tax Credit (EZ) • State Sales & Use Tax Exemption for Mfg. and Mining Equipment (EZ) • Refund of sales tax on purchases of equipment, machinery, machine tools, or supplies for use in an EZ • Enterprise Zones • Manufacturing Revenue Bond Program ||||||||||||
| **CT** | 3,518,288 | 1,898,800 | 6.5 | 5,118 | 201,800 | Transportation Equipment; Industrial Machinery & Equipment; Fabricated Metal Products | Hartford | No | 7.5 | 6.35 | 1.9-6.8 |
| | Urban and Industrial Site Reinvestment Tax Credit • New Jobs Creation Tax Credit • Qualified Small Business Job Creation Tax Credit • 25% Manufacturing Facility Tax Credit • Apprenticeship Training Tax Credit in manufacturing • Machinery and Equipment Expenditure Tax Credit • R&D Expenditures Tax Credit • Enterprise Zones/Tax Credit: 50% manufacturing facility tax credit for those located in an Enterprise Zone • Economic and Manufacturing Assistance Act (MAA) loans ||||||||||||
| **DE** | 885,122 | 454,100 | 6.0 | 677 | 37,450 | Chemicals & Allied Products; Food & Kindred Products; Instruments & Related Products | New Castle | No | 8.7 | None | 0.3-8.2 |
| | New Business Facility Tax Credits • Tax-Exempt Bond Financing • SBIR Bridge Grants • Renewable Energy Facilities Revolving Loan Fund • Green Energy Solutions Cash Incentive • Delaware Access Program Financing • Clean Energy Partnership Grants • Brownfield Assistance Program Grants • Delaware Strategic Fund (grant/loan programs for job creation, relocation and expansion) • Delaware Mfg. Extension Partnership • Employee Training Grants • Small Business LIFT Program ||||||||||||
| **FL** | 18,537,969 | 9,660,800 | 5.8 | 14,374 | 457,846 | Electronic & Other Elec. Equipment; Fabricated Metal Products; Food & Kindred Products | Miami-Dade | Yes | 5.5 | 6.0 | 1.03-5.4 |
| | Enterprise Zone Tax Credits • No State Personal Income Tax • Qualified Target Industry Tax Refund (QTI) • Qualified Defense and Space Contractor Tax Refund (QDSC) • Capital Investment Tax Credit (CITC) • Jobs for the Unemployed Tax Credit Program (JUTC) • Quick Response Training Program (QRT) • Incumbent Worker Training Program (IWT) • Economic Development Transportation Fund • Rural Community Development Revolving Loan Fund; Rural Infrastructure Fund ||||||||||||
| **GA** | 9,892,111 | 4,755,600 | 7.2 | 9,293 | 460,931 | Food & Kindred Products; Transportation Equipment; Industrial Machinery & Equipment | Fulton | Yes | 6.0 | 4.0 | .03-7.29 |
| | Employment Incentive Prog. (EIP) • Job Tax Credit • Less Developed Census Tracts (LDCT) Tax Incentive • Opportunity Zone (OZ) Tax Credit • Port Tax Credit Bonuses • Quality Jobs Tax Credit • R&D Tax Credit • Mega Project Tax Credit • Work Opportunity Tax Credit Prog. (WOTC) • Foreign Trade Zones (FTZ) • Retraining Tax Credit • Quick Start Employee Training • Investment Tax Credit • Appalachian Regional Commission Economic Development Loan Program • Indl. Revenue Bonds & Bond Allocation Prog. ||||||||||||
| **HI** | 1,295,178 | 669,800 | 4.0 | 1,099 | 21,185 | Food & Kindred Products; Printing & Publishing; Apparel & Other Textile Products | Honolulu | No | 4.4-6.4 | 0.5-4.0 | 1.2-5.4 |
| | No state tax on inventories, furniture, equipment or machinery • Credit against taxes paid on the purchase of capital goods, machinery, and equipment • No state tax on exported goods or services • Hi Tech Hawaii Tax Incentives Program • Hawaii Enterprise Zones Program • Hawaii Foreign Trade Zones Program • Hawaii Strategic Development Program (HSDP) Venture Capital Funds • Small Business Innovation Grants • Office of Hawaiian Affairs (OHA) Business Loan Program • Agricultural Loan Programs ||||||||||||
| **IA** | 3,007,856 | 1,713,700 | 4.3 | 5,180 | 263,450 | Food & Kindred Products; Industrial Machinery & Equipment; Fabricated Metal Products | Polk | Yes | 6.0-12.0 | 6.0 | 0.0-9.0 |
| | Grow Iowa Values Financial Assistance Program • Demonstration Fund (commercialization incentive) • Public Facilities Set-Aside Program (PFSA) • Export Trade Assistance Program (ETAP) • Enterprise Zones • New Jobs Tax Credit • High Quality Jobs Program • Brownfield/Grayfield Tax Credit Program • Targeted Jobs Withholding Tax Credit Pilot Program • Revolving Loan Funds • Local Property Tax Abatement & Exemption Program for Industrial Properties • Tax Increment Financing ||||||||||||

**\*Unemployment percentage    All stats as of 1/15**

| STATE | POPULATION | LABOR FORCE | Unemp* (%) | MFRS. COs. | MFG. JOBS | LEADING MANUFACTURING INDUSTRIES (by percent employment) | COUNTY W/ MOST MFG. JOBS | RIGHT TO WORK | CORP. TAX RATE (%) | STATE SALES TAX (%) | UNEMPL. INS. TAX (%) |
|---|---|---|---|---|---|---|---|---|---|---|---|
| ID | 1,545,801 | 772,900 | 3.9 | 2,068 | 76,638 | Food & Kindred Products; Industrial Machinery & Equipment; Lumber and Wood Products | Ada | Yes | 7.6 | 6.0 | .96-6.8 |
| ID | Partial to full property tax exemption for businesses that invest in new mfg. facilities, and/or invest a minimum of $1 billion in capital improvements, and/or employ at least 1,500 people within an Idaho county. • Hire One Refundable Tax Credit • 3% Investment Tax Credit • Net Operating Loss Deduction • 25% rebate on sales tax paid on materials to construct new facilities • Up to $100,000 per site for qualifying energy-saving improvements • Economic Development Admin. Grants | | | | | | | | | | |
| IL | 12,910,409 | 6,547,000 | 6.4 | 17,341 | 776,803 | Industrial Machinery & Equipment; Food & Kindred Products; Fabricated Metal Products | Cook | No | 9.5 | 6.5 | .70-8.4 |
| IL | Economic Development for a Growing Economy Tax Credit Program (EDGE) • Tax Increment Financing (TIF) Districts • River Edge Redevelopment Zones • 0.5% corporate tax credit for investment in mining, manufacturing or retailing, plus an additional 0.5% if employment increases over 1%. • Manufacturer's Purchase Credit (MPC) (Sales Tax Credit) • Illinois Dept. of Agriculture AgriFIRST Grant Program • Department of Commerce and Economic Opportunity (DCEO) Commerce Dev. Fund | | | | | | | | | | |
| IN | 6,423,113 | 3,258,300 | 5.7 | 9,454 | 578,321 | Transportation Equipment; Industrial Machinery & Equipment; Fabricated Metal Products | Marion | Yes | 8.5 | 7.0 | 0.5-7.4 |
| IN | No gross receipts tax; no inventory tax • Hoosier Business Investment (HBI) Tax Credit • Industrial Recovery Tax Credit • Headquarters Relocation Tax Credit • Venture Capital Investment (VCI) Tax Credit • R & D Tax Credit • Patent Income Exemption • Economic Development for a Growing Economy (EDGE) Tax Credit program • Skills Enhancement Fund (SEF) • Industrial Development Grant Fund • Indiana 21st Century Research and Technology Fund | | | | | | | | | | |
| KS | 2,885,905 | 1,495,700 | 4.3 | 3,993 | 202,351 | Transportation Equipment; Food & Kindred Products; Industrial Machinery & Equipment | Sedgwick | Yes | 4.0 | 6.15 | .11-5.4 |
| KS | Community Development Block Grant (CDBG) Economic Dev. Funds • Income Tax Exemption for LLCs, SubChapter S Corps, LLPs, Partnerships and Sole Proprietorships • Certified Development Companies • Energy Incentives • High Performance Incentive Program (HPIP) • Promoting Employment Across Kansas (PEAK) Program • Kansas Industrial Training (KIT) • Property Tax Abatement Assistance • Private Activity Bonds • Machinery & Equip. Expense Deduction • STAR Bonds • Rural Opportunity Zones | | | | | | | | | | |
| KY | 4,339,367 | 1,993,600 | 6.0 | 4,802 | 272,422 | Transportation Equipment; Food & Kindred Products; Industrial Machinery & Equipment | Jefferson | No | 4.0-6.0 | 6.0 | 1.0-10.0 |
| KY | Kentucky Business Investment (KBI) Program • Kentucky Enterprise Initiative Act (KEIA) • Direct Loan Program (KEDFA) • Industrial Revenue Bonds (IRBs) • Community Development Block Grants (CDBG) Loans • Kentucky Reinvestment Act (KRA) • Kentucky Industrial Revitalization Act (KIR) • High Tech Investment Construction Pools (Forgivable loan program) • SBIR-STTR Matching Fund Program | | | | | | | | | | |
| LA | 4,492,076 | 2,179,800 | 6.5 | 4,516 | 172,786 | Chemicals & Allied Products; Industrial Machinery & Equipment; Fabricated Metal Products | Lafayette | Yes | 4.0-8.0 | 4.0 | .11-6.2 |
| LA | Industrial Tax Exemption • Modernization Tax Credit • R & D Tax Credit • Restoration Tax Abatement • Economic Development Award Program • Enterprise Zones • Louisiana Fast Start (workforce development) | | | | | | | | | | |
| MA | 6,593,587 | 3,563,600 | 5.8 | 7,864 | 350,541 | Electronic & Other Elec. Eqpt.; Industrial Machinery & Eqpt.; Instruments & Related Prods. | Middlesex | No | 8.0 | 6.25 | 1.26-12.27 |
| MA | Mass Development Equipment Loans • Brownfields Redevelopment Fund • Emerging Technology Fund • Mass Development Exporter Financing • Southeast Regional Loan Fund (SRLF) • Brownfields Tax Credit Program • New Markets Tax Credit Program • Tax Exempt Bonds • Green Loan Program • Pre-development Loans • Small Business Purchasing Program (SBPP) • Tax Increment Financing (TIF) • Research & Development Tax Credit • Investment Tax Credit (ITC) | | | | | | | | | | |
| MD | 5,699,478 | 3,096,000 | 5.6 | 4,108 | 152,560 | Printing & Publishing; Electronic & Other Elec. Eqpt.; Industrial Machinery & Equipment | Independent | No | 8.25 | 6.0 | 2.2-13.5 |
| MD | R&D Tax Credit • One Maryland Tax Credit • Enterprise Zone Tax Credit • Job Creation Tax Credit • Biotechnology Investment Tax Credit • Cellulosic Ethanol Technology Tax Credit; Job Creation and Recovery Tax Credit • Maryland Industrial Development Financing Authority (MIDFA) • Maryland Venture Fund • Maryland Economic Development Assistant Authority and Fund (MEDAAF) • Maryland Small Business Development Financing Authority (MSBDFA) • Manufacturing Assistance Program | | | | | | | | | | |
| ME | 1,318,301 | 702,400 | 5.7 | 2,056 | 61,435 | Transportation Equipment; Food & Kindred Products; Paper & Allied Products | Cumberland | No | 3.5-8.93 | 5.0 | .86-7.95 |
| ME | Business Equipment Tax Reimbursement • Tax Increment Financing (TIF) • Employment Tax Increment Financing • Pine Tree Development Zones • Technology Tax Credits • Community Development Block Grant Program (CDBG) • Maine Technology Institute (MIT) Funding • Small Enterprise Growth Fund • State Small Business Credit Initiatives • Economic Recovery Loan Program • Regional Econ. Dev. Revolving Loan Fund • Maine Seed Capital Tax Credit Program • Major Business Expansion Bond Program | | | | | | | | | | |
| MI | 9,969,727 | 4,735,200 | 6.7 | 13,826 | 668,461 | Transportation Equipment; Industrial Machinery & Equipment; Fabricated Metal Products | Oakland | Yes | 4.35-6.0 | 6.0 | .06-10.3 |
| MI | Small Business Investment Tax Credit • Pure Michigan Business Connect • New Talent Portal • Michigan Business Development Program • Michigan Community Revitalization Program • Capital Access Program (CAP) • Michigan Pre-Seed Capital Fund • Private Activity Bonds • EB-5 Investment & Visa Program • Michigan Emerging Technologies Fund • Small Business Capital Access Program (SBCAP) • Michigan Business Growth Fund | | | | | | | | | | |
| MN | 5,266,214 | 2,990,200 | 7.3 | 9,090 | 456,373 | Industrial Machinery & Equipment; Food & Kindred Products; Printing & Publishing | Hennepin | No | 9.8 | 6.875 | 0.5-9.4 |
| MN | Work Opportunity Tax Credit • Job Opportunity Building Zones (JOBZ) Tax-Free Development Program • State Small Business Credit Initiative • Minnesota Investment Fund • Urban Initiative Loan Program • Border Cities Enterprise Zone Program • SEED Capital Investment Credit Program • Research & Development Tax Credit • Tax Increment Financing (TIF) • Small Business Development Loan Program • Foreign Trade Zones • Angel Tax Credit • RAIN Source Capital (for "Green" investments) | | | | | | | | | | |
| MO | 5,987,580 | 3,062,500 | 5.6 | 7,482 | 349,029 | Food & Kindred Products; Transportation Equipment; Industrial Machinery & Equipment | St. Louis City | No | 6.25 | 7.0 | 0-7.8 |
| MO | Enhanced Enterprise Zone Tax Credit • BUILD (Business Use Incentives for Large-Scale Development) • Enterprise Zones • Rebuilding Communities Tax Credit Program • Missouri Quality Jobs Program • Chapter 353 Property Tax Abatement • Action Fund Loans • Industrial Infrastructure Grants • Missouri Life Sciences Research Trust Fund • Chapter 100 Bonds (Property tax abatement and sales tax exemption on construction materials) • Missouri Community College New Jobs Training Program | | | | | | | | | | |
| MS | 2,951,996 | 1,246,500 | 7.3 | 2,793 | 177,255 | Transportation Equipment; Food & Kindred Products; Industrial Machinery & Equipment | Jackson | Yes | 3.0-5.0 | 7.0 | 0.2-5.4 |
| MS | Industrial Property Tax Exemption Program • Jobs Tax Credit • Manufacturing Investment Tax Credits • Mississippi Aerospace Initiative Incentives Program • Mississippi Clean Energy Initiatives Program • National or Regional Headquarters Sales Tax Credit • Property Tax Exemptions for Industrial Revenue Bond Financing & In-State Inventory • Research & Development Skills Tax Credit • Rural Economic Development Program • Sales & Use Tax Exemptions for Bond Financing and Construction/Expansion | | | | | | | | | | |
| MT | 974,989 | 519,900 | 4.3 | 1,665 | 25,112 | Lumber & Wood Products; Printing & Publishing; Food & Kindred Products | Yellowstone | No | 9.5 | 0 | 0.82-6.12 |
| MT | Montana Board of Investments Business Finance Programs • Community Development Block Grant Economic Development Program • Workforce Training Grant Program • Microbusiness Development Centers • Montana Small Business Credit Initiative (MT SSBCI) • One Stop Business Licensing | | | | | | | | | | |

**\*Unemployment percentage    All stats as of 1/15**

| STATE | POPULATION | LABOR FORCE | Unemp* (%) | MFRS. COs. | MFG. JOBS | LEADING MANUFACTURING INDUSTRIES (by percent employment) | COUNTY W/ MOST MFG. JOBS | RIGHT TO WORK | CORP. TAX RATE (%) | STATE SALES TAX (%) | UNEMPL. INS. TAX (%) |
|---|---|---|---|---|---|---|---|---|---|---|---|
| NC | 9,380,884 | 4,633,500 | 5.8 | 9,902 | 556,047 | Industrial Machinery & Equipment; Food & Kindred Products; Textile Mill Products | Mecklenburg | Yes | 6.9 | 6.75-7.0 | 0-6.84 |
| NC | Article 3J Tax Credits • N.C. Ports Tax Credits • Renewable Energy Tax Credit • Technology Development Tax Credit • Job Development Investment Grant • One North Carolina Fund • SBIR/STTR Small Business Technology Funding • Site and Infrastructure Grant Fund • Job Maintenance and Capital Development Fund • Foreign Trade Zones • Industrial Revenue Bonds • Community Development Block Grants • Road and Rail Access • North Carolina Biotechnology Center | | | | | | | | | | |
| ND | 646,844 | 417,800 | 2.7 | 1,044 | 33,866 | Industrial Machinery & Equipment; Food & Kindred Products; Fabricated Metal Products | Cass | Yes | 1.68-5.15 | 5.0 | 0.2-10.0 |
| ND | Agricultural Commodity Processing Facility Investment Tax Credit • Agricultural Products Utilization Commission (APUC) Grants • Beginning Entrepreneur Loan Guarantee Program • Biofuels Partnership in Assisting Community Expansion (PACE) Loan Programs • Biomass, Geothermal, Solar, or Wind Energy Credit • Biodiesel Tax Credits • Business and Industry Guaranteed Loan Program • Business Development Loan Program • Community Development Loan Fund (CDLF) | | | | | | | | | | |
| NE | 1,796,619 | 1,021,900 | 3.1 | 2,612 | 119,449 | Food & Kindred Products; Industrial Machinery & Equipment; Fabricated Metal Products | Douglas | Yes | 5.58-7.81 | 5.5 | 0-8.66 |
| NE | Nebraska Advantage Act (tax credits) • Tax increment financing for blighted land • A $10 million and 100-employee investment qualifies co's for personal property tax exemptions for 15 years for turbine-powered aircraft, personal computer systems, agricultural products and processing machinery. • Job Creation Tax Credit • Industrial Dev. Revenue Bonds (IDBs) • Nebraska Investment Finance Authorities • Economic Development Loan Program • Nebraska Dev. Finance Service | | | | | | | | | | |
| NH | 1,324,575 | 742,200 | 4.1 | 2,414 | 77,670 | Industrial Machinery & Equipment; Electronic & Other Elec. Eqpt.; Instruments & Related Prods. | Hillsborough | No | 8.5 | None | 0.9-7.0 |
| NH | No Inventory Taxes or Capital Gains Taxes • Economic Revitalization Zone Tax Credits • Community Development Block Grants • Coos County Job Creation Tax Credit • Job Training Fund • Energy Efficiency Loans • Research and Development Tax Credit • Industrial Revenue Bonds • Procurement Technical Assistance Program (PTAP) (Federal contract procurement assistance) • New Hampshire International Trade Resource Center (ITRC) Assistance | | | | | | | | | | |
| NJ | 8,707,739 | 4,542,700 | 6.4 | 8,990 | 390,670 | Chemicals & Allied Products; Printing & Publishing; Food & Kindred Products | Bergen | No | 9.0 | 7.0 | .4825-6.2825 |
| NJ | Bond Financing • Business Employment Incentive Prog. (BEIP) • Business Retention and Relocation Assistance Grant (BRRAG) • BRRAG Tax Credit Certificate Transfer Program • Edison Innovation Clean Energy Mfg. Fund (CEMF) • Energy Sales Tax Exemption for Certain Counties • Foreign Trade Zones • Main Street Business Assistance Program • Manufacturing Equipment and Employment Investment Tax Credit Program • New Jersey Business Growth Fund | | | | | | | | | | |
| NM | 2,009,671 | 925,500 | 6.4 | 1,757 | 47,067 | Electronic & Other Elec. Eqpt.; Food & Kindred Products; Industrial Machinery & Equipment | Bernalillo | No | 4.8-7.6 | 5.125 | 0.05-5.4 |
| NM | High Wage Jobs Tax Credit • Manufacturers' Investment Tax Credit • New Markets Tax Credit • Rural Jobs Tax Credit • Technology Jobs Tax Credit • Aircraft Manufacturing Tax Deduction • Research & Development Tax Deduction • Agricultural Business Tax Deductions and Exemptions • Advanced Energy Tax Credits • Alternative Energy Product Manufacturers Tax Credit • Renewable Energy Production Tax Credit • Solar Energy Systems Gross Receipts Tax Exemption • R&D Small Business Tax Credit | | | | | | | | | | |
| NV | 2,643,085 | 1,369,400 | 6.9 | 1,718 | 47,488 | Miscellaneous Manufacturing Industries; Printing & Publishing; Fabricated Metal Products | Clark | Yes | None | 6.85 | 0.25-5.4 |
| NV | No Inventory, Unitary Taxes, Personal Income Taxes. • Foreign Trade Zones • Less-restrictive environmental laws • Green Building Property Tax Abatements • Industrial Revenue Bonds (IDBs) • Modified Business (Payroll) Tax Abatement • Nevada Hub Zone Development • Property Tax Abatement to qualified recycling businesses • Renewable Energy Storage Sales and Property Tax Abatement • Train Employees Now (TEN) Program (customized job training) | | | | | | | | | | |
| NY | 19,541,453 | 9,526,100 | 5.9 | 15,928 | 693,061 | Printing & Publishing; Industrial Machinery & Equipment; Electronic & Other Elec. Equipment | New York | No | 6.5-7.1 | 4.0 | 1.5-9.9 |
| NY | Regional Council Capital Fund • Economic Development Purposes Grants • Environmental Investment Program • State Small Business Credit Initiative • Economic Development Fund • Industrial Effectiveness Program (IEP) • Entrepreneurial Assistance Program (EAP) • Commercial District Revolving Loan Trust Funds • Global Market Export Services (GMES) • Job Development Authority (JDA) Direct Loan Program • Manufacturing Assistance Program (MAP) • Regional Revolving Loan Trust Fund (RRLTF) | | | | | | | | | | |
| OH | 11,542,645 | 5,740,800 | 5.0 | 16,704 | 861,756 | Industrial Machinery & Equipment; Fabricated Metal Products; Transportation Equipment | Cuyahoga | No | 0.26 | 5.5 | 0.7-12.0 |
| OH | Community Reinvestment Areas • Enterprise Zones • Job Creation Tax Credit • Job Retention Tax Credit • R&D Investment Tax Credit • Site Selection Assistance • Roadwork Development (629) Account • Community Development Block Grants • 166 Direct Loan • Innovation Ohio Loan Fund • Ohio Enterprise Bond Fund • R&D Investment Loan Fund • Rapid Outreach Grant • Volume Cap (for Private Activity Bonds) • Ohio Advanced Energy Fund • Ohio Energy Gateway Fund • Workforce Guarantee Program | | | | | | | | | | |
| OK | 3,687,050 | 1,796,300 | 4.4 | 4,512 | 168,628 | Industrial Machinery & Equipment; Fabricated Metal Products; Food & Kindred Products | Tulsa | Yes | 6.0 | 4.5 | 0.3-9.2 |
| OK | Oklahoma Quality Jobs Program • Small Employer Quality Jobs Program • 21st Century Quality Jobs Program • The Investment/New Jobs Tax Credit • Aerospace Industry Engineer Work Force Tax Credit • Venture Capital Tax Credit • Work Opportunity Tax Credit Program (WOTC) • Federal Empowerment Zone Incentives • Industrial Access Roads • Foreign Trade Zones • Industrial Revenue Bonds • General Obligation Limited Tax Bonds (GOLTBs) • Tax Increment Financing | | | | | | | | | | |
| OR | 3,825,567 | 1,962,300 | 7.0 | 5,543 | 221,317 | Electronic & Other Elec. Equipment; Food & Kindred Products; Lumber & Wood Products | Multnomah | No | 0.1-7.9 | None | 2.2-5.4 |
| OR | No Inventory Tax; No Receipts/ Revenue Tax; No Worldwide Unitary Tax; No State Capital Tax on Asset Value and No Direct levies on intangible properties. • Enterprise Zones • Oregon Investment Advantage Income Tax Exemption Program • Strategic Investment Program (property tax exemption program) • Research Tax Credits • Customized Workforce Training • Industrial Site Certification/Decision-Ready Sites • Construction-in-Process (property tax exemption program) • Bus. Energy Tax Credit | | | | | | | | | | |
| PA | 12,604,767 | 6,367,600 | 5.1 | 16,104 | 762,997 | Industrial Machinery & Equipment; Food & Kindred Products; Fabricated Metal Products | Allegheny | No | 9.99 | 6.0 | 2.677-13.9976 |
| PA | Industrial Resource Centers • Enterprise Zones • First Industries Fund • Machinery and Equipment Loan Fund (MELF) • Community Economic Development Loans • New Pennsylvania Venture Capital Investment Program • Research & Development Tax Credit • Technology Commercialization Initiative • Technology Development Grant Program • Job Creation Tax Credit (JCTC) • Keystone Innovation Zone (KIZ) • Research & Development Tax Credit • Infrastructure and Facilities Improvement Program | | | | | | | | | | |
| RI | 1,053,209 | 553,400 | 7.1 | 1,670 | 57,904 | Miscellaneous Manufacturing Industries; Industrial Machinery & Equipment; Fabricated Metal Prods. | Providence | No | 9.0 | 7.0 | 1.69-9.79 |
| RI | High Performance Manufacturing Investment Tax Credit • Apportionment Exclusion for Medical and Pharmaceutical Manufacturers • Manufacturing Investment Tax Credit • Business Income Apportionment for Manufacturers • Accelerated Amortization for Defense Industry Manufacturers • Innovation Tax Credit • Foreign Trade Zones • Jobs Development Act Corporate Income Tax Reduction for Job Creation • Gross Premiums Tax Credits in Enterprise Zones • Job Creation Guarantee Program | | | | | | | | | | |

**\*Unemployment percentage    All stats as of 1/15**

| STATE | POPULATION | LABOR FORCE | Unemp* (%) | MFRS. COs. | MFG. JOBS | LEADING MANUFACTURING INDUSTRIES (by percent employment) | COUNTY W/ MOST MFG. JOBS | RIGHT TO WORK | CORP. TAX RATE (%) | STATE SALES TAX (%) | UNEMPL. INS. TAX (%) |
|---|---|---|---|---|---|---|---|---|---|---|---|
| SC | 4,561,242 | 2,197,800 | 6.7 | 4,661 | 265,567 | Industrial Machinery & Equipment; Transportation Equipment; Rubber & Misc. Plastic Products | Greenville | Yes | 5.0 | 6.0 | 0-10.67 |
| SC | No local income tax; No inventory tax; No wholesale tax; No unitary tax on worldwide profits • Job Tax Credit (JTC) • Investment Tax Credit • Corporate Headquarters Credit • Research & Development Tax Credit • Job Development Credit (JDC) • Economic Development Set-Aside Program • Enterprise Zone Retraining Credit Program • Business Dev. Corporation (BDC) loans • SC Capital Access Program (SC CAP) • InvestSC Fund • Rural Infrastructure Fund | | | | | | | | | | |
| SD | 812,383 | 452,700 | 3.3 | 1,306 | 49,615 | Food & Kindred Products; Industrial Machinery & Equipment; Misc. Manufacturing Industries | Minnehaha | Yes | None | 4.0 | 0-9.5 |
| SD | Tax refunds (sales, use & contractors' excise taxes) for new and expanding businesses • Property tax abatement program (forgives up to 100% of property taxes on a new structure or addition to an existing one) • Zero personal income tax; Zero personal property tax; Zero business inventory tax • REDI (Revolving Economic Development and Initiative) Fund • Economic Development Finance Authority (EDFA) Pooled Bond Program • Workforce Development Training Grant • APEX Loan Program | | | | | | | | | | |
| TN | 6,296,254 | 2,998,900 | 6.8 | 6,649 | 382,430 | Transportation Equipment; Industrial Machinery & Equipment; Fabricated Metal Products | Shelby | Yes | 0.25-6.5 | 7.0 | 1.1-10.6 |
| TN | Jobs Tax Credit and Jobs Tax Super Credit • Headquarters Tax Credit • Tiered Rural Opportunity Initiative Jobs Tax Credit • Integrated Supplier and Integrated Customer Tax Credit • Industrial Machinery Tax Credit • Sales and Use Tax Credit for Qualified Facility to Support an Emerging Industry • Rural Opportunity Initiative Enhanced Jobs Credit • Headquarters Relocation Expense Credit • Fast Track Job Training Assist. Program • Energy Efficient Loan Program • Green Island Corridor Grant | | | | | | | | | | |
| TX | 24,782,302 | 13,059,500 | 4.9 | 20,226 | 1,077,801 | Industrial Machinery & Equipment; Fabricated Metal Products; Food & Kindred Products | Harris | Yes | None | 6.25 | 0.78-8.25 |
| TX | No individual income tax • Texas Enterprise Fund • Emerging Technology Fund • Skills Development Fund • Self-Sufficiency Fund • Texas Capital Infrastructure Fund • Defense Economic Adjustment Assistance Grant Program (DEAGG) • Texas Leverage Fund (TLF) • Enterprise Zones • Tax Increment Financing • Economic Development Refund • Freeport and Goods in Transit Exemptions • Pollution Control Equipment Incentive • Renewable Energy Incentives • Chapter 380/381 Economic Development Agreements • Tax-Exempt Industrial Revenue Bonds • Texas Products/Business Funds • Texas Industry Dev. Program • Permit Assistance | | | | | | | | | | |
| UT | 2,784,572 | 1,436,800 | 3.6 | 3,426 | 156,053 | Food & Kindred Products; Electronic & Other Elec. Eqpt.; Chemicals & Allied Products | Salt Lake | Yes | 5.0 | 5.9-8.05 | 0.4-10.4 |
| UT | Economic Development Tax Increment Financing (EDTIF) Credit (For companies expanding or relocating to Utah) • Enterprise Zones • Industrial Assistance Funds • Capital Gains Tax Credit • Investment Tax Credit • New State Revenues Tax Credit • Renewable Energy Development Incentive • Rural Fast Track (RFT) Grant • Industrial Revenue Bonds (IRBs) and Industrial Development Bonds (IDBs) • Qualified Energy Conservation Bonds • REDI (Renewable Energy Development Incentive) • Tax Increment Financing | | | | | | | | | | |
| VA | 7,882,590 | 4,256,300 | 5.0 | 5,846 | 305,801 | Transportation Equipment; Food & Kindred Products; Printing & Publishing | Independent Cities | Yes | 6.0 | 5.0 | 0.58-6.68 |
| VA | Major Business Facility Job Tax Credit • Worker Retraining Tax Credit • Recycling Equipment Tax Credit • Green Job Creation Tax Credit • Refundable R&D Expenses Tax Credit; Port Volume Increase Tax Credit; Int'l Trade Facility Tax Credit; Barge & Rail Use Tax Credit • Enterprise Zone Job Creation Grants • Enterprise Zone Real Property Investment Grant • Governor's Opportunity Fund (GOF) • Virginia Investment Partnership Grant (VIP) • Major Eligible Employer Grant • VA Econ. Dev. Incentive Grant (VEDIG) | | | | | | | | | | |
| VT | 621,760 | 351,800 | 4.3 | 1,308 | 41,070 | Electronic & Other Elec. Equipment; Food & Kindred Products; Indl. Machinery & Equipment | Chittenden | No | 6.0-8.5 | 6.0 | 1.3-8.4 |
| VT | Micro Business Development Program (MBDP) • Vermont Global Trade Partnership (VGTP) • Machinery & Equipment Tax Credit • Vermont Seed Capital Fund • Vermont Employment Growth Incentive (VEGI) Program • Economic Advancement Tax Incentive Program • Research & Development Tax Credit • Procurement Assistance | | | | | | | | | | |
| WA | 6,664,195 | 3,502,500 | 6.2 | 6,652 | 280,946 | Transportation Equipment; Food & Kindred Products; Industrial Machinery & Equipment | King | No | None-.00484 | 6.5 | 0.52-6.03 |
| WA | Brownfields Revolving Loan Fund (BRLF) • Rural Washington Loan Fund (RWLF) • Forest Products Revolving Loan Fund • Coastal Revolving Loan Fund/Technical Assistance • Community Development Block Grants (CDBG) Float Loans • Industrial Revenue Bonds • Rural County/ Community Empowerment Zones (CEZ) Incentives including B&O Credits for New Employees in Mfg. and R&D • High Unemployment County Sales & Use Tax Deferral/Waiver for Mfg. Facilities • NEW: Innovation Partnership Zones (IPZs) | | | | | | | | | | |
| WI | 5,654,774 | 3,112,300 | 5.2 | 10,807 | 564,556 | Industrial Machinery & Equipment; Fabricated Metal Products; Food & Kindred Products | Milwaukee | No | 9.5 | 5.0 | .27-9.8 |
| WI | Business Employees' Program (BEST) • Community Development Block Grant for Economic Development Revolving Loan Fund (CDBG-ED/RLF) • Customized Labor Training Fund • Dairy 2020 Initiative • Early Planning Grant Program (EPG) • Enterprise Development Zone Program Focus in Energy • Tax Incremental Financing (TIF) • Industrial Revenue Bonds (IRBs) • Major Economic Dev. Program • Rural Economic Development Program • Technology Development Fund | | | | | | | | | | |
| WV | 1,819,777 | 792,100 | 6.3 | 1,590 | 63,912 | Industrial Machinery & Equipment; Chemicals & Allied Products; Fabricated Metal Products | Kanawha | No | 6.5 -8.5 | 6.0 | 1.5-8.5 |
| WV | West Virginia Jobs Investment Trust (WVJIT) Venture Capital Fund • Export Promotion Program • Procurement Assistance • State Microloan Program • Linked Deposit Program • Research and Commercialization Assistance Grant Program • Governor's Guaranteed Workforce Program • Strategic Research and Development Tax Credit • High Growth Business Investment Tax Credit • Chemical Alliance Zone (CAZ) • Polymer Alliance Zone (PAZ) | | | | | | | | | | |
| WY | 544,270 | 311,300 | 4.5 | 779 | 14,988 | Industrial Machinery & Equipment; Chemicals & Allied Products; Stone, Clay and Glass Products | Campbell | Yes | None | 4.0 | 0.67-10.0 |
| WY | Business Ready Community Grant & Loan Program • Industrial Development Revenue Bonds • Wyoming Partnership Challenge Loan Programs • Workforce Training Grants • Community Development Block Grant (CDBG) Community Program • Training Programs | | | | | | | | | | |

*Unemployment percentage     All stats as of 1/15

# To see a complete set of facts for each state, visit:
## www.industrialexpansionguide.com

# U.S. Industrial Expansion & Relocation Guide

## CALIFORNIA

**Greater Antelope Valley Economic Alliance (GAVEA)**
Phone—(661) 945-2741
Web—www.aveconomy.org
Email—info@aveconomy.org
1028 W. Avenue L12, Ste. 101, Lancaster, CA 93534
*Labor, Lifestyle & Los Angeles all within Your Reach*

## COLORADO

**Rocky Ford Chamber Of Commerce**
Phone—(719) 254-7483
105 N. Main St., Rocky Ford, CO 81067
*Rocky Ford is a quiet agri. comm., resting on the Hwy 50 corridor in S.E. Colorado. Offers a peaceful respite to modern day life. A historical comm. with a warm blend of a times-gone-by atmosphere & modern conveniences with down home friendly people & a great climate too! The comm offers a rich array of activities: gardening, music, theater & civic organizations, bird watching, boating, fishing, hiking, hunting, rodeos & sports. Rocky Ford is proud of its agricultural roots.*

## DELAWARE

**Greater Newark Economic Development Partnership**
Phone—(302) 294-2067
Web—www.greaternewarkde.com
Email—smithm@greaternewarkde.com
12 Penns Way, New Castle, DE 19720
*The Greater Newark, Delaware area is a strategic mid-Atlantic hub for business launch, growth and success. For innovative companies, it all adds up: easy access to major cities, highly educated workforce, a world-class research university and a vibrant culture and quality of life.*

## FLORIDA

**Business Development Board Of Martin County**
Phone—(772) 221-1380
Web—www.yesmartinfl.com
Email—tim@bdbmc.org
1002 S.E. Monterey Commons Blvd., Ste. 203, Stuart, FL 34996
*The official Economic Development Organization for Martin County, FL. Our mission is to promote economic growth by retaining and existing targeted businesses and attracting desirable new business while preserving the quality of life.*

**(772) 221-1380**
www.yesmartinfl.com
Email: tim@bdbmc.org
*Martin County Florida*
1002 S.E. Monterey Commons Blvd., Ste. 203
Stuart, FL 34996

## ILLINOIS

**Quad Cities First**
Phone—(563) 327-0160
Web—www.quadcitiesfirst.com
Email—smoore@quadcitieschamber.com
1601 River Dr., Ste. 310, Moline, IL 61265
*Quad Cities First is the lead Bi-State economic development organization for Eastern IA & Western Illinois. Our centralized region, the only place in North America where the Mississippi River & Interstate 80 intersect, offers multimodal transportation affording easy, cost-effective access to domestic & international markets.*

## INDIANA

**Jay County Development Corp.**
Phone—(260) 726-9311
Fax—(260) 726-4477
Web—www.jaycountydevelopment.org
Email—bbradley@jaycodev.org
118 S. Meridian St., Ste. B, Portland, IN 47371
*JCDC is the lead economic development organization and seeks to enhance the economic vitality of the Jay County Community.*

**Terre Haute Economic Development Corp.**
Phone—(812) 234-2524
Web—www.terrehauteedc.com
Email—info@terrehauteedc.com
630 Wabash Ave., Ste. 101, Terre Haute, IN 47807
*The Terre Haute Economic Development Corporation is a gateway to connect & assist business development, growth & diversification. The THEDC is a public-private not-for-profit economic development organization.*

**Terre Haute Economic Development Corp.**
*Business Development • Economic Development • Plant Relocation Services*
**www.terrehauteedc.com**
(812) 234-2524 • info@terrehauteedc.com
630 Wabash Ave. Ste. 101 Terre Haute, IN 47807

## IOWA

**Marshalltown Economic Development Impact Committee**
Phone—(641) 753-6645
Web—www.marshalltownworks.com
Email—deimerly@marshalltown.org
P.O. Box 1000, Marshalltown, IA 50158
*Marshall Economic Development Impact Committee (MEDIC) is a public/private full service economic development firm in Central Iowa representing Marshall County, Iowa (Population 45,000). We specialize in assisting companies interested in locating, expanding or starting in Central Iowa with a focus on advanced manufacturing, biosciences & distribution.*

## Quad Cities First
Phone—(563) 327-0160
Web—www.quadcitiesfirst.com
Email—smoore@quadcitieschamber.com
331 W. 3rd St., Davenport, IA 52801
*Quad Cities First is the lead Bi-State economic development organization for Eastern IA & Western Illinois. Our centralized region, the only place in North America where the Mississippi River & Interstate 80 intersect, offers multimodal transportation affording easy, cost-effective access to domestic & international markets.*

## MINNESOTA

**Aitkin Area Chamber Of Commerce**
Phone—(218) 927-2316
Web—www.aitkin.com
Email—upnorth@aitkin.com
P.O. Box 127, Aitkin, MN 56431
*Located at the junction of Highways 210 & 169 in central Minnesota, the Aitkin Area has a vibrant local economy with endless recreational opportunities. This makes it the perfect place to telecommute, expand or start a new business. The Aitkin Area Chamber of Commerce works closely with Aitkin County Growth to assist new & expanding businesses throughout the community.*

## NEBRASKA

**McCook Economic Development Corporation**
Phone—(308) 345-1200
(800) 658-4213
Fax—(308) 345-2152
Web—www.mccookne.org
Email—medc@mccookne.org
402 Norris Ave., Ste. 301, McCook, NE 69001
*Now known as the McCook Economic Development Corporation (MEDC), the mission of the organization has not changed-to facilitate the formation, retention, attraction, and expansion of businesses in McCook and the surrounding area.*

**Sidney Cheyenne County Economic Development**
Phone—(308) 254-4444
(308) 254-8455
Fax—(308) 254-3164
Web—www.cityofsidney.org
Email—communitydev@cityofsidney.org
1115 13th Ave., P.O. Box 79, Sidney, NE 69162
*The City of Sidney, Cheyenne County & the Cheyenne County Chamber of Commerce have provided a consolidated economic development partnership from 1991-2011 that has resulted in solid growth & momentum heading into the future. Despite economic challenges on a regional & national basis the past several months, Sidney continues to have one of the stronger economies in Nebraska. Call Community Development: 308-254-8455 or City Manager: 308-254-4444*

*Find maps and aerial views of these agencies at:*
IndustrialExpansionGuide.com

*Find up-to-the-minute facts and figures at:*
IndustrialExpansionGuide.com

**STAND OUT** from other organizations with a display ad!
Call us... 847-864-7590

© Copyright 2015 Manufacturers' News, Inc.

## Belmont County Department of Development
### Community Improvement Corporation

## DOD • CIC

## www.belmontdod.com

Email: suedouglass.belmontcounty@comcast.net

## 740-695-9678 • Fax: 740-695-1536

### 117 E. Main St. • Saint Clairsville, OH 43950

## NEW HAMPSHIRE

**City Of Dover, Business & Industrial Development Authority**
Phone—(603) 516-6043
Web—www.dover.nh.gov
Email—d.barufaldi@dover.nh.gov
288 Central Ave., Dover, NH 03820
*Business retention and outreach to enhance community wealth and job creation. Awarded one of the top 100 places to live in the U.S., by CNN Money Magazine*

## NEW MEXICO

**Carlsbad Department Of Development**
Phone—(575) 887-6562
Web—www.developcarlsbad.org
Email—departments@developcarlsbad.org
P.O. Box 1090, Carlsbad, NM 88221
*A private non-profit organization that is dedicated to the growth of Eddy County and Carlsbad's manufacturing, mining, energy production and nuclear industries. Offer local incentives and vital networking with leaders from local and state government and business organizations.*

## Carlsbad Department of Development

### (575) 887-6562

### www.developcarlsbad.org

P.O. Box 1090
Carlsbad, NM 88221

## Click through to the sites of these agencies at

### IndustrialExpansionGuide.com

**Chamber of Commerce of Truth Or Consequences & Sierra County**
Phone—(575) 894-3536
Web—www.torcchamber.org
Email—info@torcchamber.org
207 S. Foch St., Truth or Consequences, NM 87901
*Sierra County, with its rich diversity, is home to Spaceport America, proud hosts to Virgin Galactic, Space X & other hi-tech aerospace entities. Beautiful mountains, pristine desert, breathtaking Elephant Butte Lake, hot mineral springs, alternative health professionals, thriving art community, support an environment for the entrepreneurial spirit. Low cost of living & state incentives enhance business opportunities here. For information visit http:/torcchamber.org*

## NEW YORK

**Herkimer County Industrial Development Agency**
Phone—(315) 866-3000
Web—www.herkimercountyida.com
Email—mfeane@herkimercounty.org
420 E. German St., P.O. Box 390, Herkimer, NY 13350
*The mission of the Agency is to help create or retain job opportunities in Herkimer County by both assisting existing area industries and marketing the area to prospective new industries.*

## NORTH CAROLINA

**Greensboro Partnership Economic Development**
Phone—(336) 387-8312
Web—www.greensboropartnership.com
342 N. Elm St., Greensboro, NC 27401
*Greensboro Partnership Economic Development (GPED) is dedicated to seeking out specific kinds of companies that would find a relationship with Greensboro to be mutually beneficial. We identify these companies and assist with educating them on the opportunities and benefits that Greensboro holds for their businesses as well as their employees. Opportunity Thrives Here.*

## Greensboro Partnership
### Economic Development
*"Opportunity Thrives Here"*
**342 N. Elm St. Greensboro, NC**
**336.387.8312**
www.greensboropartnership.com

**NCEast Alliance**
Phone—(252) 522-2400
Web—www.nceast.org
Email—howard@nceast.org
3802 Highway 58 N., Ste. A, Kinston, NC 28504
*Premier site/building location assistance agency for eastern North Carolina-area east of Research Triangle with easy access to three (3) east coast ports & multiple commercial airports collaborating with business and education leaders to create a better workforce-STEM driven.*

## OHIO

**Community Improvement Corp., Belmont County Dept. Of Development**
Phone—(740) 695-9678
Fax—(740) 695-1536
Web—www.belmontdod.com
Email—suedouglass.belmontcounty@comcast.net
117 E. Main St., St. Clairsville, OH 43950
*Belmont County is the center of Eastern Ohio, sharing development in the Ohio River Valley with Pennsylvania and West Virginia. Situated in the Buckeye State's Appalachian foothills, it is a key region of Ohio's economic development. The Community Improvement Corporation (CIC) is located in the Belmont County seat of St. Clairsville, and is your prime point of contact for regional economic development.*

## OKLAHOMA

**Greater Oklahoma City Chamber**
Phone—(405) 297-8945
Fax—(405) 297-8908
Web—www.greateroklahomacity.com
Email—econdev@okcchamber.com
123 Park Ave., Oklahoma City, OK 73102
*The Partnership offers a multitalented team of economic development specialists who can work with you on your project. These specialists, from economic development organizations; city, county or state governments; utilities; or education entities & services work together under one cohesive team to meet your specifications-delivering rapid response times & optimizing your new Greater Oklahoma City location.*

**Ponca City Development Authority**
Phone—(580) 765-7070
Web—www.goponca.com
Email—dmyers@goponca.com
102 S. 5th St., Ponca City, OK 74601
*The mission of the Ponca City Development Authority (PCDA) is to facilitate job growth in wealth producing industries in Ponca City, Oklahoma*

**Ponca City Development Authority**
The mission of the Ponca City Development Authority (PCDA) is to facilitate job growth in wealth producing industries in Ponca City, Oklahoma
www.goponca.com / (580) 765-7070
Email: dmyers@goponca.com
102 S. 5th Street • Ponca City, OK 74601

**EXPANSION**

*Is your organization properly represented? If not, call:*
**847-864-7590**

© Copyright 2015 Manufacturers' News, Inc.

## OREGON

**Albany-Millersburg Economic Development Corp.**
Phone—(541) 926-1519
Web—www.albany-millersburg.com
Email—pasconj@peak.org
P.O. Box 548, Albany, OR 97321
*AMEDC is a private non-profit organization which serves the cities of Albany and Millersburg and Linn County. Our goal is improving local area prosperity by helping businesses expand, create jobs and prosper.*

---

## SOUTH DAKOTA

**Yankton Area Progressive Growth, Inc.**
Phone—(605) 665-9011
(800) 926-5866
Web—www.yanktonedc.com
Email—ecodev@yanktonsd.com
803 E. 4th St., Yankton, SD 57078
*YAPG works with economic development partners in the community to retain, expand & attract primary jobs, businesses & investments.*

---

## TEXAS

**Athens Economic Development Corp.**
Phone—(903) 675-4617
Fax—(903) 675-4830
Web—www.athenstexasedc.com
Email—bj@athenstexasedc.com
201 W. Corsicana St., Ste. 3, Athens, TX 75751
*The AEDC was formed in 1989 by the voters of Athens, which permits the Corporation to receive funds from a half-cent sales tax collected for economic development. Funds received by AEDC are used to promote the economic growth & vitality of Athens and provide the Corporation certain flexibility within State guidelines to assist companies with manufacturing, R&D, Transportation, Recycling, Distribution, Job Training, Headquarter facilities & city parks.*

**Greater San Marcos Partnership**
Phone—(512) 393-3400
Web—www.greatersanmarcostx.com
Email—info@greatersanmarcostx.com
1340 Wonder World Dr., Ste. 108, San Marcos, TX 78666
*Fast growing Hays & Caldwell County region. Ideally located along IH-35 half way between Austin & San Antonio. Municipal airport. Texas State University. STAR Park technology incubator. Near two international airports. Many local & state incentives available. Hot job market. Sizable & well-trained workforce. Low cost of living. Abundant developable land. Outstanding quality of life. Welcome to greater San Marcos!*

**Pasadena Chamber of Commerce**
Phone—(281) 487-7871
Web—www.pasadenachamber.org
Email—sherry@pasadenachamber.org
4334 Fairmont Pkwy., Pasadena, TX 77504
*To promote economic development & community growth to ensure the prosperity of Pasadena's businesses & citizens.*

## WISCONSIN

**Progress Lakeshore**
Phone—(920) 482-0540
Fax—(920) 682-6816
Web—www.progresslakeshore.org
Email—connie@progresslakeshore.org
202 N. 8th St., Ste. 101, Manitowoc, WI 54220
*Proactive in connecting businesses to resources, suppliers, markets and capital in Manitowoc County.*

### Progress Lakeshore

920-482-0540 • Fax: 920-682-6816

**www.progresslakeshore.org**

connie@progresslakeshore.org

202 N. 8th St., Ste. 101
Manitowoc, WI 54220

**Wisconsin Economic Development Corporation**
Phone—(608) 210-6700
Web—www.inwisconsin.com
Email—dobusiness@inwisconsin.com
201 W. Washington Ave., Madison, WI 53703
*The WEDC leads economic development efforts for the state & nurtures business growth & job creation by advancing Wisconsin's business climate. WEDC collaborates with a highly-responsive network of partners to provide the information, tools & resources businesses need to start, expand or relocate their operations In Wisconsin. To learn more about how your business can succeed in Wisconsin, visit www.inwisconsin.com, call 855-INWIBIZ or email dobusiness@ inwisconsin.com*

**America's Premiere Industrial Relocation Site!**

**U.S. Industrial Expansion & Relocation Guide**

Find facts & figures about the manufacturing climate in all 50 states. Hundreds of municipalities supply additional information & contacts.

**Absolutely free to users!**
**No registration, hassle or obligation!**

*IndustrialExpansionGuide.com*

*Want to be listed in the next edition?*
*Get listed at:*

**IndustrialExpansionGuide.com**

# ALPHABETICAL SECTION

This section is the alphabetical index for the state's manufacturers, processors, wholesalers and distributors. Included is the full address identifying the city where the company profile is presented in the geographical section of this publication. Telephone numbers are provided for quick reference. Entries are also made for alternate names of companies including divisional references indicating corporate ownership. Companies not previously listed are marked with a ★. A † indicates a wholesaler / distributor company.

(MASAco) Michael Anthony Sign & Awning, Inc., 21 Randolph Ave., Avenel, 07001 ... (732) 453-6120
1 Stop Wraps, LLC, 1525 Prospect St., Ste. 602, Lakewood, 08701 ... (732) 363-7800
1 2 3 Quick Print, Inc., 297 New Brunswick Ave., Perth Amboy, 08861 ... (732) 442-1771
10-31, Inc., 2 W. Crisman Rd., Columbia, 07832 ... (908) 496-4946
1800printme.com see. ... Graphic Imagery, Inc., Warren
21st Century Finishing, Inc., 280 N. Midland Ave., Ste. 414, Saddle Brook, 07663 ... (201) 797-0212
21st Century Optical, 5 Powder Horn Dr., Warren, 07059 ... (973) 379-2020
24 Horas-Portuguese Daily Newspaper, 68 Madison St., Newark, 07105 ... (973) 817-7400
3D Medical Manufacturing, Inc. see. ... 3D Medical Mfg., Inc., Pennsauken
3D Medical Mfg., Inc., 7145 Colonial Ln., Pennsauken, 08109 ... (856) 486-9600
3lab, Inc. (H Q), 100 W. Sheffield Ave., Englewood, 07631 ... (201) 567-9100
3M Co., 500 U.S. Highway 202 N., Flemington, 08822 ... (908) 788-4000
3M Co., 140 Algonquin Pkwy., Whippany, 07981 ... (973) 884-2500
4 & 20 see. ... BML Blackbird Theatrical Services, Inc., Secaucus
419 Neon, LLC, 364 Glenwood Ave., East Orange, 07017 ... (732) 324-2445
47 Industries, LLC, 59 2nd Ave., Raritan, 08869 ... (908) 526-8865
8 To 20 Partners, LLC, 5 Paddock St., Avenel, 07001 ... (732) 855-1400
814 Americas, 814 2nd Ave., Elizabeth, 07202 ... (908) 354-2674
911 Specialties see. ... J & G Enterprises, Inc., Nutley
★925ny, 200 Middlesex Tpke., Ste. 202, Iselin, 08830 ... (732) 404-4400
9-5 Silver House * Sumangal Jewelers see. ... Star Creation, Inc. (H Q), Piscataway
A & A Co., Inc., 2700 S. Clinton Ave., South Plainfield, 07080 ... (908) 561-2378
A & A Concrete Products, Inc., 2 S. Corporate Dr., P.O. Box 108, Riverdale, 07457 ... (973) 835-2239
†A & A Iron & Metal Co., LLC, 2006 40th St., North Bergen, 07047 ... (201) 865-1370
A & A Ironworks, Inc., 955 Burnt Meadow Rd., Hewitt, 07421 ... (973) 728-4300
A & A Soft Pretzel Co., 1100 N. 32nd St., Camden, 08105 ... (856) 338-0208
A & C Catalysts, Inc., 1600 W. Blancke St., Linden, 07036 ... (908) 474-9393
A & D Industrial & Marine Repair, 900 Port Reading Ave., Ste. B-2, Port Reading, 07064 ... (732) 541-1481
A & F Electroplating, Inc., 106 Ashland Ave., West Orange, 07052 ... (973) 736-4344
A & F Sign Company LLC, 28 E. Railway Ave., Paterson, 07503 ... (973) 278-3707
A & F Tool, 930 Magnolia Ave., Elizabeth, 07201 ... (973) 262-1792
A & J Canvas Co., Inc., Maple Spruce St., P.O. Box 30, Rosenhayn, 08352 ... (856) 451-5606
A & J Tool Specialties, Inc., 235 Morris Ave., Summit, 07901 ... (908) 277-0550
A & L Plastics Co., Inc., 2 Municipal Rd., P.O. Box 160, Newton, 07860 ... (973) 383-2221
A & R Recycling Co., 1004 Union Landing Rd., P.O. Box 2440, Cinnaminson, 08077 ... (856) 829-1712
A & R Sewing Co., Inc., 451 Communipaw Ave., Jersey City, 07304 ... (201) 332-0622
A & S Packaging & Display Corp., 120 Kero Rd., Carlstadt, 07072 ... (201) 531-1900
★A & S Screen Printing, LP, 2305-B Garry Rd., Riverton, 08077 ... (609) 267-4830
A A A Pharmaceutical, Inc., 157-160 W. Jefferson St., Paulsboro, 08066 ... (609) 288-6060
A A A Stamp & Seal Mfg. Co., 361 N. Midland Ave., Saddle Brook, 07663 ... (201) 796-1500
A A Graphics, Inc., 431 N. Midland Ave., Unit C, Saddle Brook, 07663 ... (201) 398-0710
A A K see. ... Aarhus United USA, Inc., Newark
A A Patchworks, Inc. (H Q), 311 Mechanic St., Boonton, 07005 ... (973) 810-2121
A B C Crating & Rigging Co., 1-21 Erie St., Paterson, 07524 ... (973) 684-0046
A B C Machinery Corp., 712-1 Old Shore Rd., P.O. Box 1212, Forked River, 08731 ... (609) 971-0990
A B Jersey Trailer Corp., 100 Kresson Gibbsboro Rd., Voorhees, 08043 ... (856) 784-7766
A. B. Scantlebury Co., 112 Kings Hwy., Landing, 07850 ... (973) 770-3000
A B Stamp, 10 Mill Pine Dr., Lafayette, 07848 ... (973) 383-1683
A C Display Studios, Inc., 2715 Arctic Ave., Atlantic City, 08401 ... (609) 345-0814
A C Transformer Corp., 89 Madison St., Newark, 07105 ... (973) 589-8574
A D K Graphics, Inc., 325 Corporate Blvd., Robbinsville, 08691 ... (609) 208-1080
†A D S Sale Co., Inc., 1010 Campus Dr., Morganville, 07751 ... (732) 591-0500
A G F Printing, Inc., 92 Bogart Ave., Garfield, 07026 ... (973) 253-8550
A G Machine & Tool Co., 147 E. 1st Ave., Roselle, 07203 ... (908) 241-3205
A. Gimenez Trading, LLC, 5 Wegmann Way, Oak Ridge, 07438 ... (973) 697-2240
†A. H. Harris & Sons, Inc., 160 Fairfield Rd., Fairfield, 07004 ... (973) 227-1600
A. Hantman Inc, 309 Michaels Ct., Woodbridge, 07095 ... (212) 239-1358
A J Images, Inc., 259 E. 1st Ave., Roselle, 07203 ... (908) 241-6900
A J P Scientific, Inc. see. ... E N G Scientific, Inc., Clifton
A. K. Stamping Co., Inc., 1159 Highway 22 E., Mountainside, 07092 ... (908) 232-7300
A. L. Don, 1 Dock St., Matawan, 07747 ... (732) 574-1441
A. L. Wilson Chemical Co., 1050 Harrison Ave., P.O. Box 207, Kearny, 07032 ... (201) 997-3300
A M A Centerless Grinding, Inc., 88-C Cannonball Rd., P.O. Box 14, Pompton Lakes, 07442 ... (973) 835-2919
A M Graphics Co., Inc., 68 Schraalenburgh Rd., Harrington Park, 07640 ... (201) 767-5320
★A M Graphy, 95 Myer St., Hackensack, 07601 ... (201) 488-0360
A M K Glass, Inc., 2880 Industrial Way, Vineland, 08360 ... (856) 692-1488
A Mat Control Technologies, LLC, 70 Mount Bethel Rd., Warren, 07059 ... (908) 756-1699
A N S Plastics Corp., 625 Jersey Ave., Ste. 11, New Brunswick, 08901 ... (732) 247-2776
A. P. Deauville, LLC, 594 Jersey Ave., New Brunswick, 08901 ... (732) 545-0200
A P S Supply Co., 711 Cooper St., Beverly, 08010 ... (609) 877-7900
A+ Products * A+ Group * A+ see. ... A+ Products, Inc., Marlboro
A Quick Cut see. ... Quick Cut Stamping & Embossing, Inc., Maple Shade
A R J Custom Fabrication, Inc., 151 Taylor St., Trenton, 08638 ... (609) 695-6227
A R M National Foods, Inc., 1546 Lamberton Rd., Trenton, 08611 ... (609) 394-0431
A. Smith & Son, Inc., 300 W. Broad St., Ste. A, Burlington, 08016 ... (609) 747-0800
A T Information Products, Inc., 575 Corporate Dr., Mahwah, 07430 ... (201) 529-0202
A Taste Of Olive, LLC, 106 Kings Hwy. E., Ste. A, Haddonfield, 08033 ... (856) 795-0043
A To Z Printing & Promotions, 1455 Main Ave., Clifton, 07011 ... (973) 916-9995
A To Z Rubber Stamps, 617 Oradell Ave., Oradell, 07649 ... (201) 265-9595
A. V. Bluebook, 80 Little Falls Rd., Fairfield, 07004 ... (800) 631-0868
A W Eurostile, 736 Route 35, Ocean, 07712 ... (732) 493-1883
A Walsh Imaging, Inc., 55 Cannonball Rd., Pompton Lakes, 07442 ... (973) 616-7100
A-1 Written in Stone Monuments * American Bronze & Stone see. ... American Monument Co., Closter
AAA Umbrella Co. * Satchels see. ... Rainmen U. S. A., Inc., Norwood
A-Aaabacus Printing & Promotional Specialties Of Metuchen, 243 Amboy Ave., Metuchen, 08840 ... (732) 767-9204
Aabhushan Exports Private Ltd., 155 Wood Ave., Edison, 08820 ... (732) 516-0800
Aabhushan Family Jewelers see. ... Aabhushan Exports Private Ltd., Edison
†A-Able Fence Builders, 28 Lakeside Ave., West Orange, 07052 ... (973) 325-1900
AAEON Electronics, Inc. (H Q), 11 Crown Plz., Ste. 208, Hazlet, 07730 ... (732) 203-9300
A-Affordable Sign.Com, 1053 Madison Hill Rd., Rahway, 07065 ... (732) 287-0446
Aarhus United USA, Inc., 131 Marsh St., Newark, 07114 ... (973) 344-1300
†Aaron & Co., 30 Turner Pl., Piscataway, 08854 ... (732) 752-8200
Aarubco Rubber Co., 259 2nd St., P.O. Box 8028, Saddle Brook, 07663 ... (973) 772-8177
Aavolyn Corp., 207 Bogden Blvd., P.O. Box 1097, Millville, 08332 ... (856) 327-8040
AB Precision Co., 1506 E. Elizabeth Ave., Linden, 07036 ... (908) 925-1356
A.B. Tees Screen Printing, LLC, 7 Sherman Ave., 3rd Fl., Jersey City, 07307 ... (201) 239-0022
ABAA, Inc. (H Q), P.O. Box 26, Bernardsville, 07924 ... (908) 766-4900
Abacus Systems, Inc., 10 County Road 639, Sussex, 07461 ... (973) 875-9900
Abaline Supply see. ... Pyramid Poly Bags, Inc., Port Reading
Abate Fence, Inc., 3619 Route 23, Hamburg, 07419 ... (973) 827-4167
ABB Inc. see. ... ABB Inc., Business Unit Turbocharger, North Brunswick
ABB Inc., Business Unit Turbocharger, 1460 Livingston Ave., P.O. Box 6005, North Brunswick, 08902 ... (732) 932-6000
★Abba Metal Works, Inc., 337 River St., Paterson, 07524 ... (973) 684-0808
Abba Products Corp., 1301 Central Ave., Hillside, 07205 ... (908) 353-0669
†Abbey Metal Corp., 59 Grand St., Moonachie, 07074 ... (201) 438-0330
Abbey/Watchung, LLC, 16 N. 26th St., Kenilworth, 07033 ... (908) 241-7717
Abbott Industries, 1-11 Morris St., Paterson, 07501 ... (973) 345-1116
Abbott Laboratories see. ... Abbott Point Of Care, Princeton
Abbott Point Of Care, 400 College Rd. E., Princeton, 08540 ... (609) 454-9000
Abby Bindery, LLC, 121 Christie St., Newark, 07105 ... (973) 690-5509
ABC Digital Electronics, Inc., 44 Country Squire Rd., Old Tappan, 07675 ... (201) 666-6888
ABC Printing, 20 Wall St., Ste. C-5, Rockaway, 07866 ... (973) 664-1160
ABC SignSystems, Inc., 7970 National Hwy., P.O. Box 622, Pennsauken, 08110 ... (856) 665-0950
†ABC Supply, 41 N. Pearl St., Bridgeton, 08302 ... (856) 455-4888
†ABC Supply Co., Inc., 5004 Route 130, Riverside, 08075 ... (856) 461-5252
ABC Supply Co., Inc. see. ... ABC Supply Co., Inc., Bradco Div., Clifton
ABC Supply Co., Inc. see. ... ABC Supply Co., Inc., Bradco Div., Lakewood
ABC Supply Co., Inc. see. ... ABC Supply Co., Inc., Bradco Div., Pleasantville
ABC Supply Co., Inc. see. ... ABC Supply Co., Inc., Bradco Div., Trenton
†ABC Supply Co., Inc., Bradco Div., 45 Samworth Rd., Clifton, 07012 ... (973) 777-3663
†ABC Supply Co., Inc., Bradco Div., 691 New Hampshire Ave., Lakewood, 08701 ... (732) 905-9355
†ABC Supply Co., Inc., Bradco Div., 725 W. Delilah Rd., Pleasantville, 08232 ... (609) 484-9100
†ABC Supply Co., Inc., Bradco Div., 301 Brunswick Ave., Trenton, 08618 ... (609) 393-7000
ABCO Die Casters, Inc., 39 Tompkins Point Rd., Newark, 07114 ... (973) 624-7030
ABCO Metal, LLC, 138 3rd Ave., Paterson, 07514 ... (973) 772-8160
ABCO Printing Co., 92 N. Main St., Windsor, 08561 ... (609) 259-4900
†ABCO Refrigeration Supply Corp., 395 N. 14th St., Kenilworth, 07033 ... (908) 931-0700
Abco Signs, 7300 N. Crescent Blvd., Ste. 11, Pennsauken, 08110 ... (856) 663-6001
†ABCO Systems, Inc., 15 Willet St., Ste. 4, Bloomfield, 07003 ... (201) 507-0999
Abeles & Heymann Kosher Products, 739 Ramsey Ave., Hillside, 07205 ... (908) 206-8886
Abilitees Unlimited, Inc., 23 Adams St., Metuchen, 08840 ... (732) 494-1513
Abilities Of Northwest Jersey, Inc., 264 Route 31 N., P.O. Box 251, Washington, 07882 ... (908) 689-1118
†Abington Reldan Metals, LLC, 396-402 Whitehead Ave., South River, 08882 ... (732) 238-8550
Able Gear & Machine Co., 91 Stickle Ave., Rockaway, 07866 ... (973) 983-8055
Abnote see. ... American Banknote Corp. (H Q), Fort Lee
About Our Town, Inc., 2 Lakeview Ave., Ste. 312, Piscataway, 08854 ... (732) 968-1615
ABOX Automation Corp., 2 Frassetto Way, Unit 2, Lincoln Park, 07035 ... (973) 659-9611
ABP Induction, LLC, 1460 Livingston Ave., North Brunswick, 08902 ... (732) 932-6400
Abraham's Natural Foods, 9 Long Branch Ave., P.O. Box 89, Long Branch, 07740 ... (732) 229-5799
†ABRAZIL, LLC, 1 Jacques Ave., Kendall Park, 08824 ... (732) 658-5191
Abruzzi Stone & Flooring, LLC, 1641 Marlton Pike E., Cherry Hill, 08034 ... (856) 616-0800
†ABS Brake Systems Ltd., 445 Godwin Ave., Midland Park, 07432 ... (201) 689-6893
ABS Sign Co., Inc., 3008 Park Blvd., Wildwood, 08260 ... (609) 522-6833
ABSCO, Inc., 101 Eisenhower Pkwy., Ste. 402, Roseland, 07068 ... (973) 635-9040
Absecon Industries see. ... Absecon Mills, Inc., Cologne
Absecon Mills, Inc., 901 W. Aloe St., P.O. Box 672, Cologne, 08213 ... (609) 965-5373
Absolute Packaging & Supply, Inc., 456 E. 22nd St., Paterson, 07514 ... (973) 278-0202
†AC Compacting, LLC, 1577 Livingston Ave., P.O. Box 7266, North Brunswick, 08902 ... (732) 249-6900
A.C. Printed Sportswear, Inc., 1319 Memorial Ave., Atlantic City, 08401 ... (609) 344-5057
Academia Furniture Industries, 4 Passaic St., Wood Ridge, 07075 ... (973) 472-0100
★Academy Fence Co., Inc., 119 N. Day St., Orange, 07050 ... (973) 674-0600
Acadia Scenic, Inc., 130 Bay St., Jersey City, 07302 ... (201) 653-8889
†ACB Produce, Inc., 135-137 Pacific St., Newark, 07105 ... (973) 522-1141
ACB Reproduction, 2060 Springdale Rd., Cherry Hill, 08003 ... (856) 751-0360
Accelerated CNC, LLC, 2500 S. Clinton Ave., Ste. A, South Plainfield, 07080 ... (908) 561-8875
Accent Apparel LLC, 405 Atlantic City Blvd., Beachwood, 08722 ... (732) 341-7576
Accent Fence, Inc., 1450 Bremen Ave., P.O. Box 656, Egg Harbor City, 08215 ... (609) 965-6400
Accent Kitchen & Bath Center & Countertops, 510 Englishtown Rd., Monroe, 08831 ... (732) 786-1001
Access Control Group, LLC, 2555 U.S. Highway 130 S., Ste. 2, Cranbury, 08512 ... (908) 789-8700
Access Printing, Inc., 510 N. Belleview Ave., Riverton, 08077 ... (856) 829-1673
AccessIT Group, Inc., 115 Route 46 W., Bldg. E, Ste. 35, Mountain Lakes, 07046 ... (973) 316-6016
Accessory Workshop (H Q), 16 Arcadian Ave., Ste. C-7, Paramus, 07652 ... (888) 691-3047
†Accredited Lock Supply, 1161 Paterson Plank Rd., Secaucus, 07094 ... (201) 865-5015
Accucolor, LLC, 771 Shrewsbury Ave., Ste. B, Shrewsbury, 07702 ... (732) 741-4594
Accucolor, LLC see. ... Jamm Litho, Inc., Long Branch
Accucolor, LLC see. ... Jamm Printing, Neptune
Accurate Box Co., Inc., 86 5th Ave., Paterson, 07524 ... (973) 345-2000
Accurate Bronze Bearing Co., 64 Illinois Ave., Paterson, 07503 ... (973) 345-2304

C2 © Copyright 2015 Manufacturers' News, Inc. ALPHABETICAL SECTION

Accurate Bushing Co., Inc./Smith Bearing Div.,
443 North Ave., 1st Fl., Garwood, 07027 ... (908) 789-1121
Accurate Diamond Tool Corp., 1 Palisade Ave., Emerson, 07630 ... (201) 265-8868
Accurate Door & Hardware, Inc., 10 W. End Rd., Totowa, 07512 ... (973) 812-2266
Accurate Flannel Bag Co. see. ... Accurate Flannel Bag Co., Inc., Paterson
Accurate Flannel Bag Co., Inc., 468 Totowa Ave., Ste. 3, Paterson, 07522 ... (973) 720-1800
Accurate Forming, 24 Ames Blvd., Hamburg, 07419 ... (973) 827-7155
Accurate Machine & Tool Co.,
135 W. Clay Ave., P.O. Box 187, Roselle Park, 07204 ... (908) 245-5545
Accurate Machine, LLC., 27 Arneytown Chesterfield Rd., Allentown, 08501 ... (609) 758-1381
Accurate Metal Fabrication, LLC, 28 John St., East Rutherford, 07073 ... (201) 438-3733
Accurate Mold, Inc., 900 Chestnut Ave., Somerdale, 08083 ... (856) 784-8484
Accurate Plastic Printers, LLC, 30 Colfax Ave., Clifton, 07013 ... (973) 591-0180
† Accurate Precision Fasteners Corp., 20 Honeck St., Englewood, 07631 ... (201) 567-9700
Accurate Screw Machine Corp., 10 Audrey Pl., P.O. Box 1065, Fairfield, 07004 ... (973) 244-9200
Accuratus Corporation, 35 Howard St., Phillipsburg, 08865 ... (908) 213-7070
Accu-Seal Rubber, Inc., 18-F Home News Row, New Brunswick, 08901 ... (732) 246-4333
Accuview, Inc., 40-C Cotters Ln., Ste. F, East Brunswick, 08816 ... (201) 440-2225
ACD Custom Granite, Inc., 1304 Roller Rd., Ocean, 07712 ... (732) 695-2400
† Ace Auto Salvage, 34 Stover Ave., Kearny, 07032 ... (201) 997-6178
Ace Crete Products, Inc., 250 Hickory Ln., Bayville, 08721 ... (732) 269-1400
Ace Electronics, Inc., 235 Liberty St., Metuchen, 08840 ... (732) 603-9800
Ace Glass, Inc., 1430 N. West Blvd., Vineland, 08360 ... (856) 692-3333
† Ace Janitorial Supply, Inc., 164 Franklin Tpke., Ste. 2, Mahwah, 07430 ... (201) 529-1750
Ace Lithographers, 22 Russo Pl., Berkeley Heights, 07922 ... (908) 665-1700
Ace Metal Kraft Co., Inc., 815 McBride Ave., Woodland Park, 07424 ... (973) 278-6605
Ace Mounting Co., Inc., 11 Cross Ave., South Amboy, 08879 ... (732) 721-6200
Ace Neon Factory, LLC, 2101 Grier Ave., Linden, 07036 ... (908) 486-6366
Ace Pallet Corp., 215 E. Broad St., P.O. Box 228, Paulsboro, 08066 ... (856) 423-7277
ACE Pens see. ... Rosa Pen Corp., Lyndhurst
Ace Powder Coating see. ... All Metal Polishing & Plating, Inc., Newark
Ace Reprographic Service, Inc., 74 E. 30th St., Paterson, 07514 ... (973) 684-5945
★ Ace Screen Printing, LLC, 24 High St. W., Glassboro, 08028 ... (856) 881-1188
Ace Sign Co., Inc., 419 Summit Ave., Perth Amboy, 08861 ... (732) 826-3858
Ace Steel Rule Die Co., 251 Atsion Rd., Medford, 08055 ... (609) 654-4161
Ace Tool & Mfg. Co., Inc., 532 Mulberry St., Ste. 1, Newark, 07114 ... (973) 824-0222
Ace Twill see. ... Ace Lithographers, Berkeley Heights
Ace Twill, 22 Russo Pl., Berkeley Heights, 07922 ... (908) 665-1700
ACF Organics, LLC see. ... Amish Dairy Products, LLC, Totowa
Achbjc, LLC see. ... Hansen's Cabinet Shop, Inc., Madison
Achilles Prosthetics & Orthotics, LLC,
503 N. Franklin Tpke., Ste. 12, Ramsey, 07446 ... (201) 785-9944
ACI see. ... Applicad, Inc., Farmingdale
ACI see. ... Automation & Control, Inc., Moorestown
ACI Msd see. ... Avid Communications, Inc., Flemington
★ Acino Products, LLC, 9-B S. Gold Dr., Trenton, 08691 ... (609) 695-4300
Ackerson Drapery & Decorating Services, Inc.,
500 James St., Ste. 14, Lakewood, 08701 ... (732) 905-4433
Ackley Machine Corp., 1273 N. Church St., Ste. 106, Moorestown, 08057 ... (856) 234-3626
Ackley's Sawmill, 98 W. Deerfield Rd., Bridgeton, 08302 ... (856) 451-3704
ACL Equipment Corp., 257 E. Northfield Rd., P.O. Box 620, Livingston, 07039 ... (973) 740-9800
Acme Automotive see. ... Coilhose Pneumatics, East Brunswick
Acme Door Service see. ... Acme Rolling Steel Door Corp., Ridgefield
Acme Engraving Co., Inc., 19-37 Delaware Ave., P.O. Box 1657, Passaic, 07055 ... (973) 778-0885
Acme Gear Co., Inc., 130 W. Forest Ave., P.O. Box 779, Englewood, 07631 ... (201) 568-2245
† Acme International Enterprises, Inc., 400 Lyster Ave., Saddle Brook, 07663 ... (973) 416-0400
Acme Mfg. & Coating Co.,
900 Port Reading Ave., P.O. Box 70, Port Reading, 07064 ... (732) 541-2800
Acme Model Engineering Co., 115 Victory Rd., Springfield, 07081 ... (973) 379-4193
Acme Plastics, Inc., 222 Browertown Rd., P.O. Box 806, Woodland Park, 07424 ... (973) 256-6666
Acme Rolling Steel Door Corp.,
1099 Linden Ave., P.O. Box 33, Ridgefield, 07657 ... (201) 943-7070
Acme Rubber Stamp Works, 6 Burnett Ave., Maplewood, 07040 ... (973) 761-7146
Acme/Lingo Flagpoles, 1865 Route 206, Southampton, 08088 ... (609) 801-1897
Acon Watch Crown Co., 260 Division Ave., P.O. Box 800, Garfield, 07026 ... (973) 546-8585
Acrilex, Inc., 230 Culver Ave., Jersey City, 07305 ... (201) 333-1500
Acrison, Inc., 20 Empire Blvd., Moonachie, 07074 ... (201) 440-8300
Acro Display, 2250-A Sherman Ave., Pennsauken, 08110 ... (856) 488-9710
†★ Across International, LLC, 111 Dorsa Ave., Livingston, 07039 ... (888) 988-0899
ACS Canvas & Awnings, 83 Union St., Medford, 08055 ... (609) 953-9700
ACS Waterjet see. ... Advanced Cutting Services, LLC, Roselle
Acsis, Inc., 9 E. Stow Rd., Ste. D, Marlton, 08053 ... (856) 673-3000
† A.C.T. Lighting, Inc., 122 John St., Hackensack, 07601 ... (201) 996-0884
Actavis Elizabeth, LLC, 200 Elmora Ave., Elizabeth, 07202 ... (908) 527-9100
Actavis, Inc. see. ... Actavis Elizabeth, LLC, Elizabeth
Actavis, Inc.,
Morris Corporate Ctr. 3, 400 Interpace Pkwy., Parsippany, 07054 ... (862) 261-7000
Actavis, Inc. see. ... Warner Chilcott, Rockaway
ACTEGA Kelstar, Inc., 950 S. Chester Ave., Ste. B-2, Delran, 08075 ... (856) 829-6300
Acteon, Inc., 124 Gaither Dr., Ste. 140, Mount Laurel, 08054 ... (856) 222-9988
ACTEON North America see. ... Acteon, Inc., Mount Laurel
Action Graphics, Inc., 600 Ryerson Rd., Ste. G, Lincoln Park, 07035 ... (973) 633-6500
† Action Lift Trucks, Inc., 35 Avenue C, Newark, 07114 ... (973) 589-2320
Action Office Supplies, Inc., 687 Prospect St., Ste. 480, Lakewood, 08701 ... (732) 534-3000
Action Packaging Automation, Inc.,
15 Oscar Dr., P.O. Box 190, Roosevelt, 08555 ... (609) 448-9210
Action Screen Printing, 151 Main St., Franklin, 07416 ... (973) 209-2491
Action Sign Co., Inc., 217 Ewan Rd., Mullica Hill, 08062 ... (856) 478-0404
Action Signs & Awards, 305 N. 11th St., Millville, 08332 ... (856) 825-2454
Action Supply, Inc., 1413 Stagecoach Rd., Ocean View, 08230 ... (609) 390-0663
Action Supply, Inc. see. ... Kennedy Concrete, Vineland
Actioneering Mfg. Engineers,
30 Plane St., Bldg. 12, P.O. Box 333, Boonton, 07005 ... (973) 299-1999
ACTIV International see. ... Summit Hill Flavors, Middlesex
Active Controls, LLC, 597 Mantua Blvd., Sewell, 08080 ... (856) 669-0940
Active Imprints, 4266 U.S. Highway 1, Monmouth Junction, 08852 ... (732) 329-2613
Activu, 301 Round Hill Dr., Rockaway, 07866 ... (973) 366-5550
Activu Corp. see. ... Activu, Rockaway
Actuant Corp. see. ... Hydratight Operations, Somerset
Acuative (H Q), 30 Two Bridges Rd., Ste. 240, Fairfield, 07004 ... (973) 227-8040
Acu-Data Business Products, Inc., 1572 State Route 23, Ste. D, Butler, 07405 ... (973) 838-5678
Acuity Brands Lighting, Inc. see. ... Mark Architectural Lighting, Edison

Acupac Packaging, Inc., 55 Ramapo Valley Rd., Mahwah, 07430 ... (201) 529-3434
ACuPowder International, LLC, 901 Lehigh Ave., Union, 07083 ... (908) 851-4500
Ad Plus, 111 Cambridge Ave., Linwood, 08221 ... (609) 653-7007
Adam, Gates & Co., LLC, 249 Homestead Rd., Hillsborough, 08844 ... (908) 829-3386
Adam Metal Products, 7 Orben Dr., P.O. Box 450, Ledgewood, 07852 ... (973) 770-1100
Adams Printing & Graphics, 886 N. Pearl St., Bridgeton, 08302 ... (856) 455-7177
Adapter Technologies, Inc., 154 Cooper Rd., Unit 1303, West Berlin, 08091 ... (856) 767-3930
Adco Signs Of New Jersey, Inc., 57 Westfield Ave., Elizabeth, 07208 ... (908) 965-2112
Adcomm, Inc., 89 Leuning St., 1st Fl., South Hackensack, 07606 ... (201) 342-6349
† Addressing Machine Supply, 1290 Central Ave., Hillside, 07205 ... (908) 289-7900
† Ademco Distribution, Inc., 1000 Lincoln Dr. E., Unit 4, Marlton, 08053 ... (856) 985-9050
Adhesive Films, Inc., 4 Barnet Rd., P.O. Box 651, Pine Brook, 07058 ... (973) 882-4944
ADI see. ... Ademco Distribution, Inc., Marlton
ADI Logistics see. ... Apparel Distribution, Inc., Edison
Adler, Inc., Kurt S. see. ... Blackwell Assocs., Inc., East Brunswick
ADM Corp., 100 Lincoln Blvd., Middlesex, 08846 ... (732) 469-0900
ADM Custom Metal Fabrication, Inc., 263 Hillside Ave., Ste. 2, Nutley, 07110 ... (973) 284-0088
ADM Tronics Unlimited, Inc., 224 Pegasus Ave., Northvale, 07647 ... (201) 767-6040
Admiral Filter Co., 18 Green Pond Rd., Unit 3, Rockaway, 07866 ... (973) 948-3252
Admiral Integration, Inc., 1001 Marlton Pike W., Cherry Hill, 08002 ... (856) 429-6700
Adpro Imprints, Inc., 3411 Rose Ave., Ocean, 07712 ... (732) 493-8555
Adron, Inc., 94 Fanny Rd., P.O. Box 270, Boonton, 07005 ... (973) 334-1600
ADS see. ... Air Distribution Systems, Inc., Cherry Hill
ADV Promos & More, LLC, 12 Baltusrol St., Hamilton Square, 08690 ... (609) 587-7500
Advance Fiber Technologies, 344 Lodi St., Hackensack, 07601 ... (201) 488-2700
Advance Machine, Inc., 531 Pennsylvania Ave., Linden, 07036 ... (908) 486-7244
Advance Tool & Die, Inc., 1401 Bremen Ave., Egg Harbor City, 08215 ... (856) 854-6329
Advanced Abrasives Corp., 7980 National Hwy., Pennsauken, 08110 ... (856) 665-9300
Advanced Biotech, Inc., 10 Taft Rd., Totowa, 07512 ... (973) 339-6242
† Advanced Business Machines Co., 230 Randolph Rd., Freehold, 07728 ... (732) 431-1464
Advanced Cabinets, 654 4th St., Newark, 07107 ... (973) 481-3441
Advanced Cerametrics, Inc.,
245 N. Main St., P.O. Box 128, Lambertville, 08530 ... (609) 397-2900
Advanced Cutting Services, LLC, 169 E. Highland Pkwy., Roselle, 07203 ... (908) 241-5332
Advanced Drainage Systems, Inc., 300 Progress Ct., Logan Township, 08085 ... (856) 467-4779
Advanced Fastener Industries, 130 Main St., Butler, 07405 ... (973) 283-1013
Advanced Filtration see. ... Advanced Filtration Co., Howell
† Advanced Filtration Co., 25-A Arnold Blvd., P.O. Box 324, Howell, 07731 ... (732) 901-6676
Advanced Food Systems, Inc., 21 Roosevelt Ave., Somerset, 08873 ... (732) 873-6776
Advanced Imaging Assocs., Inc., 190 Munsonhurst Rd., Ste. 6, Franklin, 07416 ... (973) 823-8999
Advanced Industrial Controls Corp.,
10 County Line Rd., Ste. 30, Somerville, 08876 ... (908) 725-7575
Advanced Industrial Technology, 640 Cambridge Rd., Paramus, 07652 ... (201) 265-1414
Advanced Marine Technology, 12 Crown Plz., Unit 204, Hazlet, 07730 ... (732) 888-8248
† Advanced Metal Processing NJ, LLC, 326 S. Wade Blvd., Millville, 08332 ... (856) 327-0048
Advanced Mfg. & Development, Inc. see. ... Metal FX Films, LLC, Bridgewater
Advanced Molding Concepts, 329 Wilson Ave., Aberdeen, 07747 ... (732) 390-8366
Advanced Orientation Systems, Inc.,
2525 E. Brunswick Ave., Ste. 205, Linden, 07036 ... (908) 474-9595
Advanced Precision, Inc., 15 Wilson Dr., Sparta, 07871 ... (973) 383-2296
Advanced Process Technology, Inc., 200 Egel Ave., Middlesex, 08846 ... (732) 356-4438
Advanced Protective Products, Inc., 17-12 River Rd., Fair Lawn, 07410 ... (718) 359-1315
† Advanced Recovery, Inc., 50 Grafton Ave., Newark, 07104 ... (973) 485-9100
Advanced Safety Products, Inc., 37 S. Valley Ave., Vineland, 08360 ... (856) 691-1700
Advanced Solar Products, Inc. see. ... SOLSTICE Mfg. Co., Flemington
Advanced Solar Products, Inc. (H Q),
270 S. Main St., Ste. 203, Flemington, 08822 ... (908) 751-5818
Advanced Specialty Gas Equipment, 241 Lackland Dr., Middlesex, 08846 ... (732) 271-9300
Advanced Technology Corp., 79 N. Franklin Tpke., Ste. 103, Ramsey, 07446 ... (201) 934-7127
Advanced Technology Group, Inc., 101 Round Hill Dr., Rockaway, 07866 ... (973) 627-6955
Advanced Welding Service, Inc.,
300 Thomas Ave., Ste. 701-1, Williamstown, 08094 ... (856) 875-2500
★ Advanstar Communications, Inc.,
485 U.S. Highway 1 S., Ste. 200, Iselin, 08830 ... (732) 346-3000
Advantage Business Media,
100 Enterprise Dr., Ste. 600, P.O. Box 912, Rockaway, 07866 ... (973) 920-7000
Advantage EDM, 38 Main St., Route 206, Andover, 07821 ... (973) 786-0177
Advantage Flags see. ... Advantage Signs, Flags & Banners/ Country Crossings, Newton
Advantage Packaging Technologies, LLC, P.O. Box 301, Carlstadt, 07072 ... (201) 832-1858
Advantage Signs, Flags & Banners/ Country Crossings,
130 Newton Sparta Rd., Newton, 07860 ... (973) 579-3880
† Advantage Vacuum LLC, 110 South Ave., Ste. A, Garwood, 07027 ... (908) 228-5629
Ad-Venture Graphics, Inc., 46 Main St., Succasunna, 07876 ... (973) 927-0951
Advertiser, The, 235 Blackwood Ave., P.O. Box 54, Franklinville, 08322 ... (856) 694-0444
Advertisers Services Group, Inc., 65 Railroad Ave., Ridgefield Park, 07660 ... (201) 440-5577
Advocate Publishing Corp., 171 Clifton Ave., P.O. Box 9500, Newark, 07104 ... (973) 497-4200
AELitho Group, Inc., 450 Broad St., P.O. Box 9000, Beverly, 08010 ... (609) 239-0700
Aeon Industries, Inc., 76 Veronica Ave., Somerset, 08873 ... (732) 246-3224
AEP Industries Inc. (H Q), 95 Chestnut Ridge Rd., Montvale, 07645 ... (201) 641-6600
Aergo Solutions, Inc., 33 Wood Ave. S., 5th Fl., Iselin, 08830 ... (732) 321-1500
Aerie Pharmaceuticals, Inc., 135 U.S. Highway 206, Ste. 15, Bedminster, 07921 ... (908) 470-4320
Aero Mfg Co., 310 Allwood Rd., P.O. Box 1250, Clifton, 07012 ... (973) 473-5300
Aero Products Co., 19-21 N. 8th St., Belleville, 07109 ... (973) 759-0959
Aero Tec Laboratories, Inc., 45 Spear Rd., Ramsey, 07446 ... (201) 825-1400
Aeroacoustic Corp., The, 169 E. Highland Pkwy., Roselle, 07203 ... (908) 241-8600
★ Aerocoat Source, LLC, 11 Morris Ave., Maple Shade, 08052 ... (856) 428-8145
Aeroflex Control Components, Inc., 40 Industrial Way E., Eatontown, 07724 ... (732) 460-0212
Aeroflex, Inc. see. ... Aeroflex Control Components, Inc., Eatontown
AeroGroup International, Inc. (H Q), 201 Meadow Rd., Edison, 08817 ... (732) 985-6900
Aerojet Rocketdyne, Inc. see ... Arde, Inc., Carlstadt
Aeronautical Instrument & Radio, Inc., 234 Garibaldi Ave., Lodi, 07644 ... (973) 473-0034
Aeropanel Corp., 661 Myrtle Ave., Boonton, 07005 ... (973) 335-9636
Aeropres Corp., 318 Valley Rd., Hillsborough, 08844 ... (908) 722-2571
Aerosource, Inc., 390 Campus Dr., Somerset, 08873 ... (732) 469-9300
Aerospace Manufacturing Corporation,
80 Van Winkle Ave., P.O. Box 3398, Wallington, 07057 ... (973) 472-2300
Aerospace Nylok, 11 Thomas Rd. S., Hawthorne, 07506 ... (973) 427-8555
Aerospace Precision Mfg. Co., Inc., 6 Hinchman Ave., Denville, 07834 ... (973) 625-2100
Aer-X-Dust Corp., P.O. Box 93, Tennent, 07763 ... (732) 946-9462
Aesthetic Press, Inc., P.O. Box 5306, North Branch, 08876 ... (908) 369-3777
Aesys, Inc., 27 Bland St., Emerson, 07630 ... (201) 871-3223
Aetrex Worldwide, Inc., 414 Alfred Ave., Teaneck, 07666 ... (201) 833-2700

© Copyright 2015 Manufacturers' News, Inc.


Affordable Copies Center, 55 Halsey St., Newark, 07102 ... (973) 802-1007
Affordable Offset Printing, Inc., 809 Hylton Rd., Ste. 11, Pennsauken, 08110 ... (856) 661-0722
Afina Corp., 40 Warren St., Paterson, 07524 ... (973) 684-7650
Aflex Extrusion Technologies, Inc.,
1600 Livingston Ave., North Brunswick, 08902 ... (732) 752-0048
AFP Transformers Corp., 206 Talmadge Rd., Edison, 08817 ... (732) 248-0305
Africa World Press, Inc., 541 W. Ingham Ave., Ste. B, Trenton, 08638 ... (609) 695-3200
African Telecom, Inc., 463 N. Arlington Ave., Ste. 17, East Orange, 07017 ... (973) 675-9919
Afton Publishing, LLC, P.O. Box 1399, Andover, 07821 ... (973) 579-2442
AG Peters & Son, Inc., 1025 N. Black Horse Pike, Runnemede, 08078 ... (856) 931-7476
Agate Lacquer Tri-Nat, LLC, 824 South Ave., Middlesex, 08846 ... (732) 968-1080
AGC Acquisition, LLC, 3740 N. West Blvd., Vineland, 08360 ... (856) 692-4435
AGF Burner, Inc., 1955 Swarthmore Ave., Unit 2, Lakewood, 08701 ... (732) 730-8090
† Agfa Corp., 400 Heller Park Ct., Dayton, 08810 ... (973) 812-0400
Agfa Corp. (H Q), 611 River Dr., Elmwood Park, 07407 ... (201) 440-0111
Agfa Graphics see. ... Agfa Corp. (H Q), Elmwood Park
AgileAccess™, LLC, 23 Londonderry Dr., Flemington, 08822 ... (908) 788-7740
Agilex Flavors & Fragrances, Inc., 140 Centennial Ave., Piscataway, 08854 ... (732) 393-7300
Agin Signs & Design, Route 1 S., Monmouth Junction, 08852 ... (732) 297-9007
Agincourt Fine Wood, 212 E. Mountain Rd., Hillsborough, 08844 ... (908) 874-4737
Agresti Construction Co., Inc., 356 Glenwood Ave., East Orange, 07017 ... (201) 825-8500
A.H. Harris & Sons, Inc. see. ... A. H. Harris & Sons, Inc., Fairfield
AHB Foods International, 823 E. Gate Dr., Unit 3, Mount Laurel, 08054 ... (856) 642-9955
Ahern's Printing & Graphics, 231 Parker Ave., Manasquan, 08736 ... (732) 223-1476
Ahle Co., Inc., J. M., 190 William St., Ste. 2-D, South River, 08882 ... (732) 238-1700
AI Technology, Inc. see. ... Amerasia International Technology, Inc., Princeton Junction
† Aidil Wines & Liquors, 574 Ferry St., Newark, 07105 ... (973) 712-0950
† Air & Gas Technologies, Inc., 42 Industrial Dr., Keyport, 07735 ... (732) 566-7227
Air & Specialties Sheet Metal, 276 Sheffield St., Mountainside, 07092 ... (908) 233-8306
Air Center, Inc., 270 Monroe Ave., Kenilworth, 07033 ... (908) 276-1992
Air Clean Co., Inc., 1135 Chestnut St., Elizabeth, 07201 ... (908) 355-1515
Air Cruisers, LLC, 1747 State Route 34, Wall Township, 07727 ... (732) 681-3527
Air Distribution Systems, Inc., 1000 Astoria Blvd., Cherry Hill, 08003 ... (856) 874-1100
Air Group, LLC, 1 Prince Rd., Whippany, 07981 ... (973) 887-5099
Air Liquide America L.P., A-Line Rd., P.O. Box 155, Gibbstown, 08027 ... (856) 423-5220
Air Liquide America L.P. see. ... Voltaix, LLC (H Q), Branchburg
Air Liquide America Specialty Gases, LLC see. ... Advanced Specialty Gas Equipment, Middlesex
Air Liquide America Specialty Gases, LLC,
2330 Hamilton Blvd., South Plainfield, 07080 ... (908) 754-7700
† Air Products & Chemicals, Inc., 405 State Route 33, Englishtown, 07726 ... (732) 446-5676
† Air Purifiers, Inc., 1 Pine St., Rockaway, 07866 ... (973) 586-3988
Air World, Inc., 126 Christie Ave., Mahwah, 07430 ... (201) 831-0700
Airborne Systems North America Of New Jersey, Inc.,
5800 Magnolia Ave., Pennsauken, 08109 ... (856) 663-1275
Airbrush Action, Inc., 3209 Atlantic Ave., P.O. Box 438, Allenwood, 08720 ... (732) 223-7878
Aires Jewelry Co., 3 Harrison Ave., Morris Plains, 07950 ... (973) 292-0950
† Airgas East, Inc., 121 Stanley Ave., Bellmawr, 08031 ... (856) 931-0900
Airgas East, Inc., 270 Benigno Blvd., Bellmawr, 08031 ... (856) 933-0544
Airgas East, Inc., 1-D Frassetto Way, Lincoln Park, 07035 ... (973) 633-9666
† Airgas East, Inc., 2 Beckwith Ave., Paterson, 07503 ... (973) 742-2211
† Airgas East, Inc., 490 Stelton Rd., Piscataway, 08854 ... (732) 752-4500
† Airgas East, Inc., 1750 Gallagher Dr., Vineland, 08360 ... (856) 692-7734
Airgas, Inc. see. ... Airgas Retail Solutions, Manalapan
Airgas, Inc. see. ... Airgas Specialty Gases, Riverton
† Airgas, Inc., 5 Iron Horse Rd., Oakland, 07436 ... (201) 337-5891
† Airgas Retail Solutions, 270 U.S. Highway 9, Manalapan, 07726 ... (732) 431-0288
Airgas Specialty Gases, 600 Union Landing Rd., Riverton, 08077 ... (856) 829-7878
† Airmatic Compressor Systems, Inc., 700 Washington Ave., Carlstadt, 07072 ... (201) 342-1300
Airmed Advisory see. ... AIRMED Biotech, LLC, Lambertville
AIRMED Biotech, LLC, 510 Titus Rd., Lambertville, 08530 ... (215) 378-9114
Airmet, Inc., 671 N. 3rd St., Newark, 07107 ... (973) 481-5550
Airoyal Division of Delta Sales see. ... Delta Sales Co., Inc., Butler
Airscan, Inc., 291 Route 22 E., Ste. 12, Lebanon, 08833 ... (908) 823-9425
Airside, Inc., 246 Brighton Rd., Andover, 07821 ... (973) 786-6967
Airtec, Inc., 17 W. Scott Ave., P.O. Box 1181, Rahway, 07065 ... (732) 382-3700
AISCO, 35 Mileed Way, P.O. Box 30, Avenel, 07001 ... (732) 574-3233
AJ Printing Solutions, LLC, 781 Hyslip Ave., Westfield, 07090 ... (908) 202-0974
AJ Tanner Ltd., 93 Harrison St., 2nd Fl., Paterson, 07501 ... (973) 523-5204
Ajay Metal Fabricators, Inc., 355 Dalziel Rd., Linden, 07036 ... (908) 523-0558
Ajinomoto North America, Inc. (H Q), 400 Kelby St., Ste. 18, Fort Lee, 07024 ... (201) 292-3200
A.K. De Rama Industrial Control Systems, Inc.,
253 Sheffield St., Mountainside, 07092 ... (908) 789-1600
AKA, Inc., 1324 New Market Ave., South Plainfield, 07080 ... (908) 753-8112
Akadema, Inc., 140 5th Ave., Hawthorne, 07506 ... (973) 304-1470
Akcros Chemicals, Inc., 500 Jersey Ave., New Brunswick, 08901 ... (732) 247-2202
Akers Biosciences, Inc., 201 Grove Rd., Thorofare, 08086 ... (856) 848-8698
Akorn, Inc., 72 Veronica Ave., Somerset, 08873 ... (732) 846-8066
★ AkPharma, Inc., 6840 Old Egg Harbor Rd., Egg Harbor Township, 08234 ... (609) 645-5100
Akrimax Pharmaceuticals, LLC (H Q),
11 Commerce Dr., 1st Fl., Ste. 100, Cranford, 07016 ... (908) 372-0506
Al & John, Inc., 444 Marshall St., Paterson, 07503 ... (973) 742-4990
Al Quick Quality Printers, Inc., 77 Tuers Ave., Jersey City, 07306 ... (201) 659-4003
† Alabaster Supply, Inc., 2317 South St., Toms River, 08753 ... (732) 330-9242
Aladdin Finishing see. ... Perfect Finishing, Inc., Clifton
Aladen Athletic Wear, LLC, 53 Cannonball Rd., Pompton Lakes, 07442 ... (973) 838-2425
Alan Baird Industries, Inc., 1 Hollywood Ave., Ste. 9, Ho-Ho-Kus, 07423 ... (201) 652-6335
Alan Chemical Corp., Inc., 843 Rahway Ave., Ste. 400, Woodbridge, 07095 ... (732) 855-6828
Alan Schatzberg & Assoc., Inc., 45 Ruta Ct., South Hackensack, 07606 ... (201) 440-8855
Alanda Software, 391 George St., New Brunswick, 08901 ... (201) 386-2007
Alba Vineyard, 269 Route 627, Milford, 08848 ... (908) 995-7800
Alben Metal Products, 11 Iowa Ave., Paterson, 07503 ... (973) 279-8891
Alberona Iron Work, Inc., 452 Scotland Rd., Orange, 07050 ... (973) 674-3375
Albert Paper Products Co., 464 Coit St., Irvington, 07111 ... (973) 373-0330
† Albert's Organics, Inc., 200 Eagle Ct., P.O. Box 624, Bridgeport, 08014 ... (856) 241-9090
Albion Engineering Co., 1250 N. Church St., Moorestown, 08057 ... (856) 235-6688
Alboum Hat Co., Inc., W., 1439 Springfield Ave., Irvington, 07111 ... (973) 371-9100
Albridge Solutions, Inc.,
1009 Lenox Dr., Bldg. 4, Ste. 204, Lawrenceville, 08648 ... (609) 620-5800
Alcaro & Alcaro Plating Co., Inc.,
112 Pine St., P.O. Box 1215, Montclair, 07042 ... (973) 746-1200
Alcatel-Lucent (H Q), 600 Mountain Ave., Murray Hill, 07974 ... (908) 582-8500
Alco Sheet Metal Fabricators, Inc., 51 Chester St., Clifton, 07011 ... (973) 772-7070
Alcoa, 9 Roy St., Dover, 07801 ... (973) 361-2310
Alcoa, Inc. see. ... Alcoa, Dover
Alcop Adhesive Label Co., 826 Perkins Ln., P.O. Box 398, Beverly, 08010 ... (609) 871-4400
Alden Leeds see. ... Mid-Continent Packaging Co., Inc. (H Q), Kearny
Alenco Fence & Pavers see. ... Alenco Fence & Supply Corp., Medford
Alenco Fence & Supply Corp., 167 Route 70, Bldg. B, Medford, 08055 ... (609) 654-6060
Aleris International, Inc. see. ... Aleris Mfg., Clayton
Aleris Mfg., 838 N. Delsea Dr., Clayton, 08312 ... (856) 881-3600
Alessandra Miscellaneous Metalworks, Inc., 75-B Mill St., Newton, 07860 ... (973) 786-6805
Alete Printing, LLC, 722 Dartmouth Ct., P.O. Box 371, Wenonah, 08090 ... (856) 468-3536
Alex Machine Shop, Inc., 267 Livingston St., P.O. Box 268, Northvale, 07647 ... (201) 768-9110
★ Alex Real, LLC, 501 Prospect St., Ste. 107, Lakewood, 08701 ... (732) 730-8770
Alex Toys see. ... Panline USA, Inc., Northvale
Alexander Communications Group, Inc.,
712 Main St., Ste. 187-B, Boonton, 07005 ... (973) 265-2300
Alexander, Inc., Sandy, 200 Entin Rd., Clifton, 07014 ... (973) 470-8100
★ Alexander Publishing, Inc., 8 Depot Sq., Englewood, 07631 ... (201) 569-5373
Alex's Custom Kitchens, LLC, 824 Paterson Ave., East Rutherford, 07073 ... (201) 933-9359
Alexy, Inc., 401 Morris Ave., Springfield, 07081 ... (973) 467-0030
Alfa Laval, Inc. see. ... DSO Fluid Handling Co., Inc., Edison
Alfa Machine Co., Inc., 2154 Highway 130 N., Monmouth Junction, 08852 ... (732) 821-0044
Alfa Production Systems, 522 Boulevard, Westfield, 07090 ... (908) 654-0255
Alfa Wassermann, Inc., 4 Henderson Dr., West Caldwell, 07006 ... (973) 882-8630
Alfred & William, Inc., P.O. Box 364, Union, 07083 ... (908) 686-3000
Alfred's Sport Shop, 32 Main St., Madison, 07940 ... (973) 377-0051
Algar-The Display Connection Inc., 131 W. Commercial Ave., Moonachie, 07074 ... (201) 438-1000
Algene Marking see. ... Dalemark Industries, Inc., Lakewood
Alice Corp., 815 Fairview Ave., Unit 9-A, Fairview, 07022 ... (201) 943-5877
Alison Control, Inc., 35 Daniel Rd. W., Fairfield, 07004 ... (973) 575-7100
Aljay Tool & Die Corp., 1213 Kennedy Blvd., Manville, 08835 ... (908) 722-2403
ALK Technologies, Inc., 457 N. Harrison St., Princeton, 08540 ... (609) 683-0220
Alkaline Corp., 20 Meridian Rd., Eatontown, 07724 ... (732) 531-7830
All Action Architectural Metal & Glass,
146 Sylvania Pl., Ste. G, South Plainfield, 07080 ... (732) 738-6655
All American Crafts Publishing, Inc., 7 Waterloo Rd., Stanhope, 07874 ... (973) 347-6900
All American Graphic Arts, 763 Ramsey Ave., Hillside, 07205 ... (908) 686-1479
All American Metal Fabricators, 34 Harold St., Tenafly, 07670 ... (201) 567-2898
All American Poly Corp., 40 Turner Pl., Piscataway, 08854 ... (732) 752-3200
All American Powder Coating, 2002 Route 9, Toms River, 08755 ... (732) 349-7001
All American Print & Copy Center, 518 Highway 35, Red Bank, 07701 ... (732) 758-6200
All American Recycling Corp., 2 Hope St., Jersey City, 07307 ... (201) 656-3363
All Bright Metal Finishing, LLC, 760 Ramsey Ave., Hillside, 07205 ... (908) 206-9411
All Cards Man see. ... United States Business Card Co., Union City
All Covered, 100 Dobbs Ln., Ste. 208, Cherry Hill, 08034 ... (856) 795-7330
All Granite & Marble Corp.,
1 Mount Vernon St., Ste. A, Ridgefield Park, 07660 ... (201) 440-6779
† All Hands Fire Equipment, LLC, 7 3rd Ave., Neptune City, 07753 ... (732) 502-8060
All Lace Processing Corp., 1109 Grand Ave., Unit 4, North Bergen, 07047 ... (201) 867-8795
All Mail Service Center * SBSC see. ... Small Business Service Center, Maple Shade
All Mechanical Services, Inc., 430 High St., P.O. Box 110, Perth Amboy, 08862 ... (732) 442-8292
All Metal Polishing & Plating, Inc., 23 George St., Newark, 07105 ... (973) 589-8070
All Metals & Forge Group, LLC, 75 Lane Rd., Fairfield, 07004 ... (973) 276-5000
All Nu Trophy & Screen Printing, 243 Teaneck Rd., Ridgefield Park, 07660 ... (201) 807-0808
All Points Printing & Graphics, 831 Arnold Ave., Point Pleasant, 08742 ... (732) 892-6670
All Poly see. ... All Poly Mfg., LLC, Manalapan
All Poly Mfg., LLC, 200 Craig Rd., Ste. 201, Manalapan, 07726 ... (732) 431-6630
All Quality Fence, 1266 Route 46, P.O. Box 85, Ledgewood, 07852 ... (973) 927-0722
All Seasons Door & Window, Inc., 28 Edgeboro Rd., East Brunswick, 08816 ... (732) 238-7100
All Seasons Ice Cream Corp., 15 E.12th St., Paterson, 07524 ... (201) 878-6790
All Signs Direct, LLC, 38 Washington St., West Orange, 07052 ... (973) 736-7446
All Sports Stadium, LLC, 297 Route 31 S., Washington, 07882 ... (908) 689-0411
All Star Awards & Trophies, Inc., 866 Haddon Ave., Collingswood, 08108 ... (856) 858-6600
★ All Star Identification, 400 Morris Ave., Ste. 241, Denville, 07834 ... (973) 625-4100
All State Medal Co., Inc., 16 Adams Pl., Lodi, 07644 ... (973) 458-1458
All State Plastics, Inc., 237 Raritan St., South Amboy, 08879 ... (732) 721-4024
All The Best Invitations, 123 W. Mount Pleasant Ave., Livingston, 07039 ... (973) 992-4033
All Tool Company, Inc., 899 Rahway Ave., Union, 07083 ... (908) 687-3636
Allary Corp. (H Q), 2204 Morris Ave., Ste. 209, Union, 07083 ... (908) 851-0077
Allegra Princeton, 12 Stults Rd., Ste. 100, Dayton, 08810 ... (609) 771-4000
Allegra * Ellco Enterprises, LTD see. ... Allegra Print & Imaging, Inc., Dayton
Allegra Marketing Print & Mail, 533 S. Shore Rd., Marmora, 08223 ... (609) 390-1400
Allegra Marketing Print Mail, 665 State Route 27, Iselin, 08830 ... (732) 404-0665
Allegra Print & Imaging, Inc., 12 Stults Rd., Dayton, 08810 ... (609) 771-4000
Allen Cabinets & Millwork, Inc., 60 Newark Pompton Tpk., Pequannock, 07440 ... (973) 694-0665
Allen Flavors, Inc., 23 Progress St., Edison, 08820 ... (908) 561-5995
Allen Group SMC, 60 Readington Rd., Branchburg, 08876 ... (908) 231-1100
Allen Linen Supply, 407 20th Ave., Paterson, 07513 ... (973) 742-6131
Allen Signs, 600 Martin Luther King Ave., Pleasantville, 08232 ... (609) 645-9268
Allen Steel Co., 202 High St., Leesburg, 08327 ... (856) 785-1171
Allentown, Inc., 165 Route 526, Allentown, 08501 ... (609) 259-7951
Allgrind Plastics, Inc., 6 Vliet Farm Rd., Asbury, 08802 ... (908) 479-4400
Alliance Design, Inc., 434 Union Blvd., Totowa, 07512 ... (973) 904-1900
Alliance Sensor Group see. ... H. G. Schaevitz LLC, Moorestown
Alliance Sign Co., Inc., 37 Grove St., Passaic, 07055 ... (973) 458-0900
Alliance Technologies Group, Inc., 3 Luger Rd., Ste. 4, Denville, 07834 ... (973) 664-1151
Alliance Vinyl Window Co., Inc. see. ... ABC Supply, Bridgeton
Alliance Vinyl Window Co., Inc., 301 Crescent Blvd., Mount Ephraim, 08059 ... (856) 456-4954
Alliance Woodwork Corp., 19 Ogden Ct., P.O. Box 684, Middletown, 07748 ... (732) 671-6884
† Allied Beverage Group, LLC,
600 Washington Ave., P.O. Box 838, Carlstadt, 07072 ... (201) 842-6200
† Allied Beverage Group, LLC,
901 Plesant Valley Ave., P.O. Box 5090, Mount Laurel, 08054 ... (856) 234-4111
Allied Bias Products Corp., 430 Communipaw Ave., Ste. 3, Jersey City, 07304 ... (201) 432-6050
† Allied Building Products Corp., 11 Cadillac Rd., Box 1838, Burlington, 08016 ... (609) 386-5500
† Allied Building Products Corp., 15 E. Union Ave., East Rutherford, 07073 ... (201) 507-8400
† Allied Building Products Corp., 850 Flora St., Elizabeth, 07201 ... (908) 820-9790
† Allied Building Products Corp., 406 State Route 23 N., Franklin, 07416 ... (973) 827-4113
† Allied Building Products Corp., 27-33 Franklin Tpke., Mahwah, 07430 ... (201) 529-3300
† Allied Building Products Corp., 27 Kentucky Ave., Paterson, 07503 ... (973) 357-1600
† Allied Building Products Corp., 320 W. Water St., Toms River, 08753 ... (732) 341-4767
† Allied Building Products Corp., 595 Union Blvd., Totowa, 07512 ... (973) 790-5500
† Allied Building Products Corp., 2065 State Route 34, Wall Township, 07719 ... (732) 449-3355

ALPHABETICAL

★ **Indicates new listing this edition.**
† **Indicates wholesaler/distributor.**

Allied Building Products Corp. see. ... Arzee Supply, Lakewood
Allied Building Products Corp. see. ... Arzee Supply Corp. Of New Jersey, Cedar Knolls
Allied Building Products Corp. see. ... Arzee Supply Corp. Of New Jersey, Elizabeth
Allied Concrete Co., Inc., 205 Franklin Ave., Rockaway, 07866 ... (973) 627-6150
† Allied Electronics, Inc., 197 State Hwy. N-18, East Brunswick, 08816 ... (732) 846-4271
Allied Envelope Co., Inc., 33 Commerce Rd., Carlstadt, 07072 ... (201) 440-2000
Allied Environmental Signage, 556 Industrial Way W., Eatontown, 07724 ... (732) 578-1818
Allied Felt Corp. see. ... Central Shippee, Inc., Bloomingdale
Allied Group, Inc., 5 Coldhill Rd., Bldg. 19, P.O. Box 209, Mendham, 07945 ... (973) 543-5404
Allied Metrics Seals & Fasteners, Inc., 2 Wilson Dr., Ste. 4, Sparta, 07871 ... (973) 383-2487
Allied Old English, Inc., 100 Markley St., Port Reading, 07064 ... (732) 636-2060
Allied Op, 810 Hooper Ave., Toms River, 08753 ... (732) 341-9191
Allied Orthotics & Prosthetics, 813 E. Gate Dr., Ste. A, Mount Laurel, 08054 ... (856) 273-6400
Allied Paper Packaging see. ... Levine Packaging Supply Corp., Fairfield
Allied Printing & Graphics, 4 Madison Rd., Fairfield, 07004 ... (973) 227-0520
Allied Printing Resources see. ... Allied Envelope Co., Inc., Carlstadt
Allied Pump Corporation, 1109 Grand Ave., Bldg. 5, North Bergen, 07047 ... (201) 798-3277
Allied Specialty Foods, Inc., 313 Hickory Pl., Vineland, 08360 ... (856) 507-1100
Allied Specialty Group, Inc., 3114 Tonnelle Ave., North Bergen, 07047 ... (201) 223-4600
† Allied Steel Distribution & Service Center, 118-144 Harper St., Newark, 07114 ... (973) 824-7347
AlliedOP, 1527 Route 27, Somerset, 08873 ... (732) 545-2885
AlliedOP, Inc. see. ... AlliedOP, Somerset
AlliedOP, Inc., 1 Emery Ave., Ste. 1, Randolph, 07869 ... (973) 328-3340
AlliedOP, Inc., 579 Goffle Rd., Wyckoff, 07481 ... (201) 444-7750
Allison Systems Corp., 220 Adams St., Riverside, 08075 ... (856) 461-9111
† Allister Business Systems, Inc., 205 E. 1st Ave., Roselle, 07203 ... (732) 972-8400
Alloy Cast Products, Inc., 700 Swenson Dr., Kenilworth, 07033 ... (908) 245-2255
Alloy Piping Products see. ... CB&I, New Brunswick
Alloy Welding Co., Inc., 6-A Culnen Dr., Somerville, 08876 ... (908) 218-1551
All-Star Pro & Sport Store, 642 State Route 35 N., Neptune, 07753 ... (732) 774-3444
All-Star Pro Trophy, 1012 Cox Cro Rd., Ste. 10, Toms River, 08755 ... (732) 364-1188
Allstate Can Corp., 1 Woodhollow Rd., Parsippany, 07054 ... (973) 560-9030
All-State Fence, Inc., 1389 Highway 9 N., Howell, 07731 ... (732) 431-4944
All-State Fence, Inc., 1389 Route 9 N., Howell, 07731 ... (732) 431-4944
ALL-STATE LEGAL, 1 Commerce Dr., Cranford, 07016 ... (908) 272-0800
Allstate Paper Box Co., Inc., 223 Raymond Blvd., Newark, 07105 ... (973) 589-2600
Allstate Printing Packaging, Inc., 791 Paulison Ave., Ste. 3, Clifton, 07011 ... (973) 473-0700
† Alltest Instruments, 500 Central Ave., Farmingdale, 07727 ... (732) 919-3339
Alltite Gasket Co. Inc., 323 William St., South River, 08882 ... (732) 254-2154
Allure Visuals & Printing, 9 1st St., Lodi, 07644 ... (201) 288-1111
All-Ways Advertising Co., 1442 Broad St., Bloomfield, 07003 ... (973) 338-0700
Allweld Iron, 160 Culber Ave., Jersey City, 07305 ... (201) 434-8750
Alma Offset Co., Inc.,
225 Bakers Basin Rd., P.O. Box 6487, Lawrenceville, 08648 ... (609) 587-5480
Almark Tool & Mfg. Co., Inc., 27 South Ave., P.O. Box 189, Garwood, 07027 ... (908) 789-2440
Almetek Industries, Inc., 2 Joy Dr., Hackettstown, 07840 ... (908) 850-9700
Aloris Tool Technology Co., Inc., 397-407 Getty Ave., Clifton, 07011 ... (973) 772-1201
Alpak Display Group, 575 N. Midland Ave., Saddle Brook, 07663 ... (201) 797-1411
Alpex Wheel Co., 29 Atwood Ave., P.O. Box 357, Tenafly, 07670 ... (201) 871-1700
Alpha Assocs., Inc., 145 Lehigh Ave., Lakewood, 08701 ... (732) 730-1800
Alpha Automation, Inc., 127 Walters Ave., Trenton, 08638 ... (609) 882-0366
Alpha Graphics, 95 Greenwood Ave., Midland Park, 07432 ... (201) 447-4800
Alpha Industries Corp. see. ... Beta Plastics Corp., Carlstadt
Alpha Industries Corp. see. ... Omega Plastics Corp., Lyndhurst
Alpha Industries Corp. see. ... Sigma Plastics Group (H Q), Lyndhurst
Alpha Industries Corp. see. ... Southeastern Plastics Corp., New Brunswick
Alpha Industries Corp. (H Q), P.O. Box 808, Lyndhurst, 07071 ... (201) 933-6000
Alpha Lehigh Tool & Machine Co., Inc., 41 Industrial Rd., Alpha, 08865 ... (908) 454-6481
Alpha 1 Studio, Inc., 3 Linda Ln., Ste. A, Southampton, 08088 ... (609) 859-2200
Alpha Precision Mold, 8 Roselle St., Linden, 07036 ... (908) 587-9090
Alpha Processing Co. Inc., 210 Delawanna Ave., P.O. Box 936, Clifton, 07014 ... (973) 777-1737
Alpha Professional Tools (H Q), 103 Bauer Dr., Oakland, 07436 ... (800) 648-7229
Alpha T's, Inc., 380 Totowa Rd., 2nd Fl., Totowa, 07512 ... (973) 956-7243
Alpha Wire Co., 711 Lidgerwood Ave., P.O. Box 711, Elizabeth, 07207 ... (908) 925-8000
AlphaGraphics, 5 N. Olney Ave., Ste. 200, Cherry Hill, 08003 ... (856) 761-8000
AlphaGraphics, 12 Stults Rd., Ste. 100, Dayton, 08810 ... (609) 860-9444
AlphaGraphics, 1111 U.S. Highway 22 E., Mountainside, 07092 ... (908) 233-5553
AlphaGraphics, 401 Jersey Ave., Ste. F, New Brunswick, 08901 ... (732) 247-0809
AlphaGraphics, 558 Central Ave., New Providence, 07974 ... (908) 277-3000
AlphaGraphics see. ... Viskal Printing, LLC, Totowa
Alphagraphics 319 see. ... Digital Print Solutions, LLC, Parsippany
AlphaGraphics, Inc., 173 Route 206 N., Hillsborough, 08844 ... (908) 281-9476
Alphagraphics, Inc., 60 Speedwell Ave., Morristown, 07960 ... (973) 984-0066
AlphaGraphics of Mahwah, 1 Lethbridge Plz., Route 17 N., Mahwah, 07430 ... (201) 327-2200
Alphagraphics Of Morristown see. ... Alphagraphics, Inc., Morristown
AlphaGraphics Printshops, 68 White St., Red Bank, 07701 ... (732) 758-0095
AlphaGraphics Printshops Of The Future see. ... AlphaGraphics Printshops, Red Bank
AlphaGraphics 321, 90 Saw Mill Pond Rd., Heller Industrial Pk., Edison, 08817 ... (732) 985-6677
Alphatec Computer Communications, 41 Merchant St., Newark, 07105 ... (973) 344-8736
Alphion Corp.,
196 Princeton Hightstown Rd., Bldg. 1-A, 2nd Fl., Princeton Junction, 08550 ... (609) 936-9001
Alpine Corp., 42 Bergenline Ave., Westwood, 07675 ... (201) 666-0959
Alpine Elastomer Products, LLC, 308 Division St., Boonton, 07005 ... (973) 299-0123
Alpine Group, Inc., The (H Q),
1 Meadowlands Plz., Ste. 801, East Rutherford, 07073 ... (201) 549-4400
Alpine Machine & Tool Corp. see. ... Alpine Corp., Westwood
Alpine Metal Products, 7 Progress St., Edison, 08820 ... (908) 753-4543
Alpine Trading Co., Inc., 400 Overpeck Pl., Englewood, 07631 ... (201) 871-6111
Alpro, Inc., 50 Romanelli Ave., South Hackensack, 07606 ... (201) 342-4498
ALPS Technologies, Inc., 500 Memorial Dr., Ste. 1, Somerset, 08873 ... (732) 764-0777
Al's Home Made Candies, 1133 Fairmount Ave., Vineland, 08360 ... (856) 691-4536
ALT Global, LLC, 3 Edison Pl., Ste. 2, Fairfield, 07004 ... (973) 287-6158
Alta Technologies, Inc., 1545 Reed Rd., P.O. Box 100, Pennington, 08534 ... (609) 538-9500
Altaflo, 23 Wilson Dr., Sparta, 07871 ... (973) 300-3344
Altech Abrasives Services, 130 Ryerson Ave., Ste. 103, Wayne, 07470 ... (973) 305-1922
Altech Machine & Tool, Inc., 230 Bank St., Ste. 1, Midland Park, 07432 ... (201) 652-4409
Altech Star, Inc., 4365 U.S. Highway 1, Ste. 205, Princeton, 08540 ... (609) 520-9000
Alternative Air & Store Fixtures, 3-C Mary Way, Hainesport, 08036 ... (609) 261-5870
alternative air llc see. ... Alternative Air & Store Fixtures, Hainesport
★ Altibase, Inc., 1 Bridge Plz. N., Fort Lee, 07024 ... (888) 837-7333
Altina's Custom Interiors,
Princeton Shopping Ctr., 301 N. Harrison, Princeton, 08540 ... (609) 924-3367
Altior, 444 Route 35 S., Bldg. B, Eatontown, 07724 ... (732) 440-1280
Alto Development Corp., 5206 Asbury Rd., P.O. Box 758, Farmingdale, 07727 ... (732) 938-2266
Altona Blower & Sheet Metal Work, Inc.,
23 N. Washington Ave., Little Ferry, 07643 ... (201) 641-3520
Altra Industrial Motion, Inc. see. ... Bauer Gear Motor, LLC, Somerset
ALU, Inc., 240 Anderson Ave., Moonachie, 07074 ... (201) 617-2000
Aluminum Shapes, LLC, 9000 River Rd., Delair, 08110 ... (800) 242-7512
★ Alvaro Stairs, LLC, 4201 Tonnelle Ave., Ste. 12, North Bergen, 07047 ... (201) 864-6754
Alva-Tech, Inc., 1208 Columbus Rd., Ste. G, Burlington, 08016 ... (609) 747-1133
Alway, Inc. (H Q), 440 U.S. Highway 202, Flemington, 08822 ... (908) 788-7220
Alzo International, Inc., 650 Jernee Mill Rd., Sayreville, 08872 ... (732) 254-1901
A.M. Best Co., 1 Ambest Rd., Oldwick, 08858 ... (908) 439-2200
A&M Industrial, Inc., 325 Commerce Rd., Linden, 07036 ... (908) 862-1800
A&M Industrial, Inc., 37 W. Cherry St., P.O. Box 1044, Rahway, 07065 ... (732) 574-1111
Am Jet Enterprises, 11 1/2 Elm St., Rockaway, 07866 ... (973) 627-5690
Amalthea Cellars Farm Winery, 209 Vineyard Rd., Atco, 08004 ... (856) 768-8585
Amano McGann, 140 Harrison Ave., Roseland, 07068 ... (973) 618-4050
Amano USA Holdings, Inc. see. ... Amano McGann, Roseland
Amano USA Holdings, Inc., 140 Harrison Ave., Roseland, 07068 ... (973) 403-1900
Amark Industries, Inc., 18 Passaic Ave., Fairfield, 07004 ... (973) 992-8900
† Amarr Garage Doors, 12 Coddington Rd., Whitehouse Station, 08889 ... (908) 534-4112
AMB Enterprises, LLC, 25 Lake St., Paterson, 07501 ... (973) 225-1070
Ambassador Uniform Group, Inc., 289 Highway 33 E., Manalapan, 07726 ... (732) 792-1111
Ambix Laboratories, 55 W. End Rd., Totowa, 07512 ... (973) 890-9002
★ Amboy Group, 1 Amboy Ave., Woodbridge, 07095 ... (732) 510-5600
Ambro Mfg. see. ... Special T's, Flemington
AMC Family, LLC see. ... J. Emanuel Chocolatier, Chester
Amcor Flexibles, Inc., 220 Shreve St., Mount Holly, 08060 ... (609) 267-5900
Amcor Rigid Plastics, 625 Sharp St., Millville, 08332 ... (856) 327-1540
AMD Fine Linens, LLC, 18 W. Forest Ave., Englewood, 07631 ... (201) 568-5255
AMD Oil Sales, LLC see. ... AMD Special Oil, LLC, Ramsey
† AMD Special Oil, LLC, 90 N. Franklin Tpke., Ramsey, 07446 ... (201) 327-0642
★ Amdocs, Inc., 34 Exchange Pl., Jersey City, 07311 ... (201) 631-3200
AME Corporation, 33 Jacksonville Rd., Ste. 2, Towaco, 07082 ... (800) 951-0071
★ Amechi Fence, 5950 Route 42, Turnersville, 08012 ... (856) 227-6691
Ameral International, Inc., 7 Railroad Ln., Brooklawn, 08030 ... (856) 456-9000
Amerasia International Technology, Inc.,
70 Washington Rd., Princeton Junction, 08550 ... (609) 799-9388
† Amerex Corp., 128 Bauer Dr., Ste. 4, Oakland, 07436 ... (201) 337-1616
America OGGI, 475 Walnut St., Norwood, 07648 ... (201) 358-6697
★ America Semiconductor, LLC, 2810 Morris Ave., Ste. 204, Union, 07083 ... (908) 810-7364
American Adhesives & Coatings, Inc., 470 Mulberry St., Newark, 07114 ... (973) 623-7070
American Advertising, 131 Landing Rd., Landing, 07850 ... (973) 398-6200
American Aluminum Casting Co., 324 Coit St., Irvington, 07111 ... (973) 372-3200
American Aluminum Co. (AMALCO), 230 Sheffield St., Mountainside, 07092 ... (908) 233-3500
American Asphalt Co., Inc., 116 Main St., West Collingswood Heights, 08059 ... (856) 456-2899
American Asphalt Co., Inc. see. ... American Asphalt Company, Inc., Burlington
American Asphalt Company, Inc., 1701 River Rd., Burlington, 08016 ... (856) 456-2899
† American Auto Salvage & Recycling, Inc., 3113 Route 50, Mays Landing, 08330 ... (609) 965-2900
American Autowire, 150 Heller Pl., Bellmawr, 08031 ... (856) 933-0801
American Banknote Corp. (H Q), 2200 Fletcher Ave., Ste. 501, Fort Lee, 07024 ... (201) 592-3400
American Beryllia, Inc., 16 1st Ave., Haskell, 07420 ... (973) 248-8080
American Biltrite, Inc., 105 Whittendale Dr., Moorestown, 08057 ... (856) 778-0700
American Bionostica, Inc., 510 Heron Dr., Ste. 203, Swedesboro, 08085 ... (856) 467-7070
American Braiding & Mfg., Inc., 247 Old Tavern Rd., Howell, 07731 ... (732) 938-6333
American Brass & Crystal, Inc., 835 Lehigh Ave., Union, 07083 ... (908) 688-8611
American By-Products Recyclers, LLC, 301 Roycefield Rd., Hillsborough, 08844 ... (973) 267-0109
American Casein Co., Inc., 109 Elbow Ln., Burlington, 08016 ... (609) 387-3130
American Chemical & Adhesive LLC, 410 Division St., Elizabeth, 07201 ... (908) 353-2260
American Coding & Marking Ink Co., 1220 North Ave., Plainfield, 07062 ... (908) 756-0373
American Comb Corp., 22 Kentucky Ave., Paterson, 07503 ... (973) 523-6551
American Compressed Gases see. ... Dry Ice Corp. (H Q), Old Tappan
American Crankshaft Grinding Co., Inc.,
851-861 Fairmount Ave., Elizabeth, 07201 ... (908) 352-5558
American Custom Drying Co., 109 Elbow Ln., Burlington, 08016 ... (609) 387-3933
American Custom Fabricators, Inc., 215-A Hickory Ln., Bayville, 08721 ... (732) 237-0037
American Custom Hydraulics, Inc., 33 Roosevelt Ave., Belleville, 07109 ... (973) 751-1440
American Display, 291 Route 22 E, Bldg. 8, P.O. Box 244, Whitehouse, 08888 ... (908) 534-2700
† American Distributors, Inc., 2 Emery Ave., Ste. 1, Randolph, 07869 ... (973) 328-1181
American Electroplating Co., 342 Lincoln Ave., Hawthorne, 07506 ... (973) 427-2300
American Envelope & Printing Co., 212 Columbus Ave., Roselle, 07203 ... (908) 241-9900
† American Estates Wines, Inc., 19 Hillside Ave., Summit, 07901 ... (908) 273-5060
American Fabric Processors, 555 E. 31st St., Paterson, 07513 ... (973) 278-0272
† American Fence Co., 326 U.S. Highway 46, Saddle Brook, 07663 ... (973) 546-4373
American Fibertek, Inc., 120 Belmont Dr., Somerset, 08873 ... (732) 302-0660
† American Filter & Tank Co., Inc.,
231 Greenwood Ave., Ste. 2, Midland Park, 07432 ... (201) 857-5056
American Fittings Corp., 17-10 Willow St., Fair Lawn, 07410 ... (201) 664-0027
American Flux & Metals Corp.,
352 E. Fleming Pike, P.O. Box 74, Winslow, 08095 ... (609) 561-7500
American Foreclosures, Inc., P.O. Box 601, Oradell, 07649 ... (201) 501-0200
American Fur Felt, LLC, 53 Rome St., Newark, 07105 ... (973) 344-3026
American Galvanizing Co., Inc., 1919 R.R. 54, Folsom, 08094 ... (609) 567-2090
American Gas & Chemical Co., 220 Pegasus Ave., Northvale, 07647 ... (201) 767-7300
American Glass Crafters, Inc., 193 Veterans Blvd., Carlstadt, 07072 ... (201) 525-1116
American Graphic Arts, Inc. see. ... On Demand Machinery, LLC, Elizabeth
American Graphic Systems, Inc., 39-26 Broadway, Fair Lawn, 07410 ... (201) 796-0666
American Halal Slaughter House, 270 Raymond Blvd., Newark, 07105 ... (973) 817-8444
† American Hanger & Fixture Corp., 687 Lehigh Ave., Union, 07083 ... (908) 687-1776
★ American Home Mfg., LLC, 4 Corporate Pl., Piscataway, 08854 ... (732) 465-1530
American Hose & Hydraulics, Inc., 700 21st Ave., Paterson, 07513 ... (973) 684-3225
American Hygiene Industries, LLC, 60 Page Rd., Clifton, 07012 ... (973) 928-6533
American Image, 45 W. Broad St., Bergenfield, 07621 ... (201) 384-9200
American Images, LLC, 1910 Fairfax Ave., Cherry Hill, 08003 ... (856) 424-3944
American Infinity Compounding Corp.,
2079 Center Square Rd., Logan Township, 08085 ... (856) 467-3030
American Ink Jet Systems, Inc., 34 Chestnut St., Emerson, 07630 ... (201) 263-9177
American Instants, Inc.,
117 Bartley Flanders Rd., P.O. Box 817, Flanders, 07836 ... (973) 584-8811

American Institute Of Food Distribution, Inc.,
10 Mountain View Rd., Ste. S-125, Upper Saddle River, 07458 (201) 791-5570
American Institute Of Pharmaceutical Technologies * AIPT see. Plenum Scientific Research, Inc., Hackensack
† American Iron & Metal International, LLC,
301 S. 12th St., P.O. Box 965, Millville, 08332 (856) 825-2950
American Jewel Window Systems * Grove Home Products see. Versatile Distributors, Inc., Lodi
American Lawyer's Media, Inc., 238 Mulberry St., 2nd Fl., Newark, 07102 (973) 642-0075
American Lighting see. North American Illumination Co., Garfield
American Machine Specialties, Inc., 51 Bergenline Ave., Westwood, 07675 (201) 664-2100
American Machine Tool Repair, 12 Middlebury Blvd., Randolph, 07869 (973) 927-0820
† American Machinery Liquidators, Inc., P.O. Box 6995, East Brunswick, 08816 (732) 390-0006
★ American Machining Co., LLC, 110 Harmon Dr., Blackwood, 08012 (856) 245-7801
American Marking Systems, Inc., 1015 Paulison Ave., Clifton, 07011 (973) 478-5600
American Marking Systems, Inc. see. Paterson Stamp Works, Clifton
American Metal Fab & Welding, 706 7th St., Union City, 07087 (201) 295-8888
American Mica Corp., 1015 Pennsylvania Ave., Linden, 07036 (908) 587-5237
American Microsemiconductor, Inc.,
133 Kings Rd., P.O. Box 104, Madison, 07940 (973) 377-9566
American Modular Power Solution, 429 Rockaway Rd., Bldg. 10, Boonton, 07005 (973) 588-4026
American Monument Co., 50 Herbert Ave., Closter, 07624 (201) 750-1000
American Monument Co. (H Q), 479 N. Dean St., Englewood, 07631 (201) 569-4455
American Panel Tec, 1640 New Market Ave., Bldg. 1-A, South Plainfield, 07080 (732) 968-0555
† American Paper & Supply Co., LLC,
10 Industrial Rd., P.O. Box 346, Carlstadt, 07072 (201) 939-4200
American Paper Products see. American Tube & Paper, Totowa
American Plastic Co., 2137 Highway 1, Rahway, 07065 (732) 388-1601
American Plus Printers, Inc., 2604 Atlantic Ave., Wall, 07719 (732) 528-2170
American Power Cord Corp., 217 Brook Ave., 3rd Fl., Passaic, 07055 (973) 574-8301
American Precision Sheet Metal Corp., 84 Baekeland Ave., Middlesex, 08846 (732) 356-4306
American Printing see. Laser Dim Graphics & Printing, Colts Neck
American Products Co., Inc., 610 Rahway Ave., Union, 07083 (908) 687-4100
American Radar Components, Inc., 39 Front St., Denville, 07834 (973) 627-5530
American Railing Design, 191 Vineyard Rd., Edison, 08817 (732) 287-1122
American Screen Printing, 272 Kent Ave., Wayne, 07470 (973) 471-0206
American Seamless Gutter & Leader Corp., 286 Hamburg Tpke., Riverdale, 07457 (973) 838-4505
American Sensor Technologies, Inc., 450 Clark Dr., Ste. 4, Budd Lake, 07828 (973) 448-1901
American Sensor Technologies, Inc. see. Macro Sensors, Pennsauken
American Showcase & Foodservice Equipment, Inc.,
19 Commerce Rd., Unit H, Fairfield, 07004 (973) 227-1277
American Spraytech, LLC, 205 Meister Ave., Branchburg, 08876 (908) 725-6060
American Stair & Rail Artisans, LLC,
687 Prospect St., Ste. 420, Lakewood, 08701 (732) 363-3734
American Standard Brands see. AS America, Inc. (H Q), Piscataway
American Stone, Inc., 215 Route 22 W., Hillside, 07205 (973) 318-7707
American Teletimer Corp., 1167 Globe Ave., Mountainside, 07092 (908) 654-4200
† AMERICAN Time Recorder, 2661 Brunetta Dr., Vineland, 08360 (856) 691-7976
American Time Recorder, Inc. see. Time Systems International, Inc., Englewood
American Traffic & Street Sign see. East Trading West Investments LLC, Orange
American Tube & Paper, 80 Furler St., Totowa, 07512 (973) 256-3600
American Van Equipment, Inc., 149 Lehigh Ave., Lakewood, 08701 (800) 526-4743
American Waste & Textile, LLC, 73 Vesey St., Newark, 07105 (973) 589-6252
American Water Works Co., Inc. (H Q), 1025 Laurel Oak Rd., Voorhees, 08043 (856) 346-8200
American Woodcarving, LLC, 1123 State Route 23, Ste. 6, Wayne, 07470 (973) 835-8510
American Youth Enterprises, Inc.,
120 Marlin Ln., P.O. Box 653, Mays Landing, 08330 (609) 909-1900
Americas Bakery, 32-50 Buffington St., P.O. Box 5099, Irvington, 07111 (973) 372-0700
Ameriderm Laboratories Ltd., 126 Pennsylvania Ave., Paterson, 07503 (973) 279-5100
Ameridia, 20 Worlds Fair Dr., Ste. F, Somerset, 08873 (732) 805-4001
Amerifab Corp., Inc., 196 Garibaldi Ave., Lodi, 07644 (973) 777-2120
Amerifast Corp., 104 Sylvania Pl., South Plainfield, 07080 (908) 754-8989
Amerifilm Converters, 85 Lincoln Hwy., Kearny, 07032 (973) 690-5900
Amerigen Pharmaceuticals, Inc. (H Q),
9 Polito Ave., Ste. 900, Lyndhurst, 07071 (732) 993-9827
Amerinex Applied Imaging, Inc., P.O. Box 6473, Monroe Township, 08831 (609) 944-8855
Amerinox Processing, Inc., 2201 Mount Ephraim Ave., Bldg. 90, Camden, 08104 (856) 963-2200
Ameritech Precision Machining Co., 425 N. Grove St., Unit 3-A, Berlin, 08009 (856) 767-1660
Ameri-Tex, Inc., 461 Frelinghuysen Ave., Newark, 07114 (973) 286-0102
Amerlux Global Lighting Solutions see. Amerlux, LLC, Oakland
Amerlux, LLC, 178 Bauer Dr., Oakland, 07436 (973) 882-5010
Amer-Rac, LLC, 8128 River Rd., Pennsauken, 08110 (856) 488-6210
AmerTac, Inc.,
1 Route 17 S., Saddle River Executive Center, Saddle River, 07458 (201) 825-0388
Ames Advanced Material, 3900 S. Clinton Ave., South Plainfield, 07080 (908) 561-1100
Ames Rubber Corp., 19 Ames Blvd., Hamburg, 07419 (973) 827-9101
Ametek Glasseal, Inc., 485 Oberlin Ave. S., Lakewood, 08701 (732) 370-9100
AMETEK, Inc. see. Ametek Glasseal, Inc., Lakewood
AMETEK, Inc. see. Coining, Inc., Montvale
AMETEK, Inc. see. Spectro Analytical Instruments, Inc., Mahwah
AMETEK, Inc. see. Vision Research, Inc., Wayne
Amex Tool Co., Inc., 4 Fox Hill Ln., Asbury, 08802 (908) 735-5176
Amfine Chemical Corp.,
10 Mountainview Rd., Ste. N-215, Upper Saddle River, 07458 (201) 818-0159
AMG Intl. see. Freeman Products, Inc. (H Q), Parsippany
Amherst Scientific, LLC, 112 Kings Hwy., Landing, 07850 (973) 770-7772
Amish Dairy Products, LLC, 41 Vreeland Ave., Ste. 101, Totowa, 07512 (973) 256-7676
AMKO Displays, LLC (H Q), 4 Barrett Ave., Moonachie, 07074 (201) 460-7199
AM-MAC, Inc., 311 Route 46 W., Fairfield, 07004 (973) 575-7567
Ammark Corp., 230 W. Parkway, Ste. 12, Pompton Plains, 07444 (973) 616-2555
Amneal Pharmaceuticals, LLC, 400 Crossing Blvd., 3rd Fl., Bridgewater, 08807 (908) 947-3120
★ Amneal Pharmaceuticals, LLC, 47 Colonial Dr., Piscataway, 08854 (732) 645-3030
★ Amory A & E Campian Dental Art, Inc., 803 Main St., Ste. 2, Toms River, 08753 (732) 240-0323
AMP Custom Rubber, Inc., 3 Cass St., Ste. 8, Keyport, 07735 (732) 888-2714
Ampal, Inc. see. United States Metal Powders, Inc., Flemington
Ampcor Technology, Inc. see. Scimedx Corp., Dover
Amperite Co., 4201 Tonnelle Ave., Ste. 6, North Bergen, 07047 (201) 864-9503
★ Amphibian Press, LLC, 309 Hutchinson Ave., Haddonfield, 08033 (856) 547-3022
AMREP Corporation (H Q), 300 Alexander Pk., Ste. 204, Princeton, 08540 (609) 716-8200
Amrod Corp., 305-A Craneway St., Newark, 07114 (973) 344-2978
AMS Products, LLC see. Object Design, Inc., Wharton
† Amsan Eagle Maintenance Supply, 80 Twin Bridge Dr., Pennsauken, 08110 (856) 317-9500
AmSan Florida see. Amsan Eagle Maintenance Supply, Pennsauken
Amscot Structural Products Corp., 241 E. Blackwell St., Dover, 07801 (973) 989-8800
AMT see. Applied Microphone Technology, Sparta
Ana Design Corp., 1 Ott St., Trenton, 08638 (609) 394-0300
Anadigics, Inc., 141 Mount Bethel Rd., Warren, 07059 (908) 668-5000
Analytical Measurements, 22 Mountain View Dr., Chester, 07930 (908) 955-7170
Analytical Sales & Services, Inc.,
237 W. Parkway, Ste. 1, Pompton Plains, 07444 (973) 616-0700
Analytical Sales and Products see. Analytical Sales & Services, Inc., Pompton Plains
Anatech Electronics, Inc.,
70 Outwater Ln., Ste. 3, P.O. Box 2217, Garfield, 07026 (973) 772-4242
Anchor Concrete Products, Inc. (H Q),
331 Newman Springs Rd., Bldg. 2, 3rd Fl., Ste. 236, Red Bank, 07701 (732) 292-2500
Anchor Glass Container Corp. see. Ardagh Group, Salem
★ Anchor Optical Co., 101 E. Gloucester Pike, Barrington, 08007 (856) 573-6865
Anchor Rubber Stamp & Printing, Inc., 339 Herbertsville Rd., Brick, 08724 (732) 583-6578
Andantex U.S.A., Inc., 1705 Valley Rd., Ocean, 07712 (732) 493-2812
Andarn Electro Service, Inc., 72 Michigan Ave., Paterson, 07503 (973) 523-6334
Andek Corporation, 850 Glen Ave., P.O. Box 392, Moorestown, 08057 (856) 786-6900
Anderol, Inc., 215 Merry Ln., East Hanover, 07936 (973) 887-7410
Andersen Corp. see. Silver Line Building Products, LLC, North Brunswick
Anderson International Foods, Inc., 95 Burma Rd., Jersey City, 07305 (516) 747-2210
Anderson Machine Co., 109 Stryker Ln., Unit 10, Hillsborough, 08844 (908) 281-7153
Anderson Monograms, 245 Fox Landing Rd., P.O. Box 163, Port Republic, 08241 (609) 652-5552
Anderson Publishing Ltd., 180 Glenside Ave., Scotch Plains, 07076 (908) 301-1995
Andler Packaging Group see. Andler South Corp., Egg Harbor Township
† Andler South Corp., 102 E. Parkway Dr., Egg Harbor Township, 08234 (609) 485-2000
Andon Brush Co., Inc., 1 Merrit Ave., Little Falls, 07424 (973) 256-6611
Andrea Aromatics, Inc., 150 Enterprise Ave., Trenton, 08638 (609) 695-7710
Andrea Foods see. Savignano Foods Corp., Orange
Andrews Glass Co. see. AGC Acquisition, LLC, Vineland
Andrex, Inc., 101 Bilby Rd., Ste. E, Hackettstown, 07840 (908) 852-4377
Andrex Systems see. Flexco Microwave, Inc., Port Murray
Andrus Screen Printing, LLC, 1915 Church Ave., Scotch Plains, 07076 (908) 322-4299
Anello Fence, LLC, 50 State Route 23, Pequannock, 07440 (973) 839-4100
Angel Medical Systems, Inc., 1163 Shrewsbury Ave., Ste. E, Shrewsbury, 07702 (732) 542-5551
Angelo's Ice Co., Inc., 100 Sylvania Pl., South Plainfield, 07080 (908) 754-4091
Anheuser-Busch Cos., Inc., 200 U.S. Highway 1 & 9, Newark, 07114 (973) 645-7700
Anheuser-Busch InBev Worldwide, Inc. see. Anheuser-Busch Cos., Inc., Newark
Anhydrides & Chemicals, Inc., 7-33 Amsterdam St., Newark, 07105 (973) 465-0077
Anisha Enterprises, Inc., 2165 Morris Ave., Union, 07083 (908) 964-3380
Ann Carol Designs, Inc., 333 Mountain Ave., Bound Brook, 08805 (732) 469-7552
Anna Soiree, 2005 State Route 35, Ste. 19, Oakhurst, 07755 (732) 686-9570
† Annin Flagmakers, 105 Eisenhower Pkwy., Ste. 203, Roseland, 07068 (973) 228-9400
Ansell Healthcare Products, LLC (H Q),
111 Wood Ave. S., Ste. 210, Iselin, 08830 (732) 345-5400
Anta Electric, Inc., 32 Richboynton Rd., Dover, 07801 (973) 366-2222
Antares Pharma, Inc., 100 Princeton S. Corporate Ctr., Ste. 300, Ewing, 08628 (609) 359-3020
Antenna Software, Inc. see. Pegasystems, Inc., Jersey City
Anthony & Sons Italian Bakery, 20 Luger Rd., Denville, 07834 (973) 625-2323
Anthony Quality Printing, Mark, 187 Garibaldi Ave., Lodi, 07644 (973) 815-1113
Anti-Hydro International, Inc., 45 River Rd., Ste. 200, Flemington, 08822 (908) 284-9000
Antique Bakery & Pizzeria, Inc., 122 Willow Ave., Hoboken, 07030 (201) 714-9323
Antistatic Industries, A Div. of ADM Tronics, Inc.,
224 Pegasus Ave., Northvale, 07647 (201) 767-6040
Antonio Mozzarella Factory, Inc., 631 Frelinghuysen Ave., Newark, 07114 (973) 353-9411
Antonio's Pasta, 545 U.S. Highway 9 N., Woodbridge, 07095 (732) 442-1640
Antonovich Furs, Inc., 125 Route 46 W., Totowa, 07512 (973) 785-0077
Antron Technologies, Inc., 40 Brunswick Ave., Ste. 104, Edison, 08817 (732) 205-0415
Antronix, Inc. (H Q), 440 Forsgate Dr., Cranbury, 08512 (609) 395-1390
Anuco, Inc., 911 Charles Dr., P.O. Box 5016, Toms River, 08753 (973) 887-9465
A-1 Advanced Marking Technologies, LLC,
1420 Route 53, P.O. Box 485, Mount Tabor, 07878 (973) 627-0155
A-1 Business Service, P.O. Box 83, Rahway, 07065 (732) 910-6995
A-1 J D K Specialties, 1 Millstream Rd., Cream Ridge, 08514 (732) 928-9495
A-1 Plastics, 136 Tichenor St., Newark, 07105 (973) 344-4441
A-1 Tablecloth Co., 450 Huyler St., Ste. 102, South Hackensack, 07606 (201) 727-8987
A-1 Uniforms, Inc., 721 Broadway, Camden, 08103 (856) 963-7680
AOS Thermal Compounds, LLC, 22 Meridian Rd., Ste. 6, Eatontown, 07724 (732) 389-5514
AP Diagnostic Laboratories, Inc., 1692 Oak Tree Rd., Ste. 17, Edison, 08820 (732) 906-7800
APB-DynaSonics, Inc., 20 W. End Rd., Totowa, 07512 (973) 785-1101
APCO see. Custom Cut Metal Products, Inc., Fairfield
Apco Extruders, Inc., 180 National Rd., Edison, 08817 (732) 287-5555
Apex Gear & Machine Co., 938 Lake St., Newark, 07104 (973) 482-5542
Apex Marble & Granite, Inc., 998 Pompton Ave., Cedar Grove, 07009 (973) 857-3655
Apex Printing Services, Inc.,
6 Ilene Ct., Bldg. 6, Unit 16, Hillsborough, 08844 (908) 281-9221
Apex Ridge see. Ridge Carbide Tool Co., Lyndhurst
Aphena Pharma Solutions-NJ, Inc., 125 Algonquin Pkwy., Whippany, 07981 (973) 887-4440
Aphrodite Marble & Granite Co., Inc., 700 Old Shore Rd., Forked River, 08731 (609) 693-4450
API Foils, Inc., 329 New Brunswick Ave., Rahway, 07065 (732) 382-6800
API Technologies Corp., 120 Corporate Blvd., South Plainfield, 07080 (908) 546-3900
Apicore US, LLC, 49 Napoleon Ct., Somerset, 08873 (732) 748-8882
A+ Products, Inc., 8 Timber Ln., Marlboro Industrial Pk., Marlboro, 07746 (732) 866-9111
APM Hexseal Corp., 44 Honeck St., Englewood, 07631 (201) 569-5700
Apogee Sound International, LLC, 50 Spring St., Ramsey, 07446 (201) 995-2001
Apollo East, Inc., 7895 Airport Hwy., Pennsauken, 08110 (856) 486-1882
Apollo Flags LLC, 594 Union Blvd., Totowa, 07512 (973) 256-8362
Apollo Quik Print Co., Inc., 49 Orchard St., Hackensack, 07601 (201) 488-1101
Apollo Sign Co., Inc., 835 Midland Ave., Garfield, 07026 (973) 772-7446
Apostolico Machine, 144 Linwood Ave., Paterson, 07502 (973) 790-3351
Apparel Distribution, Inc., 45 Saw Mill Pond Rd., Edison, 08817 (732) 287-1110
Apparel Group America, Inc., 250 Belmont Ave., Haledon, 07508 (973) 942-6800
Apparel Zone, Inc., 165 Amboy Rd., Ste. 505, Morganville, 07751 (732) 441-7780
Appetito Provisions Co., Inc., 609 10th St., P.O. Box 8098, Union City, 07087 (201) 864-3410
Apple Exhibits, 730 Grand Ave., Unit 1-A, Ridgefield, 07657 (201) 943-2775
† Apple Food Sales Co., Inc., 117 Fort Lee Rd., Ste. B-7, Leonia, 07605 (201) 592-0277
Apple Printing Co., Inc., 5 Weymouth Rd., P.O. Box 574, Hammonton, 08037 (609) 561-4411
Applegate Farm Homemade Ice Cream, Inc., 616 Grove St., Montclair, 07043 (973) 744-5900
Applegate Farms (H Q), 750 Route 202 S., Ste. 300, Bridgewater, 08807 (866) 587-5858
Applicad, Inc., 5029 Industrial Rd., Farmingdale, 07727 (732) 751-2555
Applied Engineering, Corp., 232 Palisade Ave., Garfield, 07026 (973) 772-6022
Applied Image, Inc., 800 Business Park Dr., Freehold, 07728 (732) 410-2444
† Applied Industrial Technologies, Inc., 24-C Worlds Fair Dr., Somerset, 08873 (732) 356-0522

ALPHABETICAL

Applied Microphone Technology, 104 Hillside Rd., Sparta, 07871 ... (973) 729-9333
Applied Optronics, 111 Corporate Blvd., Bldg. J, South Plainfield, 07080 ... (908) 753-6300
Applied Resource Corp., 105 W. Dewey Ave., Ste. 311, Wharton, 07885 ... (973) 328-3882
Applied Surface Technologies, 15 Hawthorne Dr., New Providence, 07974 ... (908) 464-6675
† Apria Healthcare, Inc., 1 Frassetto Way, Ste. F, Lincoln Park, 07035 ... (973) 305-0099
† Apria Healthcare, Inc., 118 Burrs Rd., Ste. C, Mount Holly, 08060 ... (609) 265-2190
APW Company, 5 Astro Pl., Ste. B, Rockaway, 07866 ... (973) 627-0643
AQL Decorating Co., Inc., 215 Bergen Blvd., Fairview, 07022 ... (201) 941-1610
Aqua Clear Tackle, P.O. Box 8454, Turnersville, 08012 ... (609) 861-1088
Aqua Products, Inc., 25 Rutgers Ave., Cedar Grove, 07009 ... (973) 857-2700
Aqua Products, Inc., 2703 River Rd., P.O. Box 231, Cinnaminson, 08077 ... (856) 829-8444
Aqua Systems, Inc. see. ... Edwards Coils Corp., Pompton Plains
Aquarian Weekly, The see ... Arts Weekly, Inc., Little Falls
Aquarian What's Your Sign, LLC, 37 Newtons Corner Rd., Howell, 07731 ... (732) 206-0726
Aquatherm Industries, Inc., 1940 Rutgers University Blvd., Lakewood, 08701 ... (732) 905-9002
Aquatrols Corp. Of America, 1273 Imperial Way, Paulsboro, 08066 ... (856) 537-6003
Arab Voice Newspaper, 85-99 Hazel St., Paterson, 07503 ... (973) 523-7815
Aram, Inc., Michael, 2102 83rd St., North Bergen, 07047 ... (201) 758-2551
† ARAMSCO, 1480 Grandview Ave., P.O. Box 29, Thorofare, 08086 ... (856) 686-7700
Arawak Paving Company, 7503 Weymouth Rd., Hammonton, 08037 ... (609) 561-4100
ARC Document Solutions, 844 Fairfield Ave., Kenilworth, 07033 ... (973) 372-5200
ARC Document Solutions, Inc. see. ... ARC Document Solutions, Kenilworth
ARC Plasmet Corp., 4131 Bergen Tpke., North Bergen, 07047 ... (201) 867-8533
Arc Reprographics, Inc., 1110 New Rd., Absecon, 08201 ... (609) 646-9324
Arcade Marketing, Inc. see. ... Color Optics By Arcade, Inc., Rockaway
Arcade Tile & Marble Co., 416 Central Ave., East Orange, 07018 ... (973) 678-4600
Arcadia Equipment, Inc., 140 Lawrence St., Hackensack, 07601 ... (201) 342-3308
Arcadian Clock Co., 189 North Ave. E., Cranford, 07016 ... (908) 276-0276
Arch Crown, Inc., 460 Hillside Ave., Ste. 1, Hillside, 07205 ... (973) 731-6300
Arch Custom Mfg Inc, 1215 S. 6th St., Camden, 08104 ... (856) 966-3835
Archcon Technology, 5000 Hadley Rd., South Plainfield, 07080 ... (908) 757-8817
Archer Day, 18 Mileed Way, Avenel, 07001 ... (732) 417-0333
† Archer Plastics, Inc., 1510 Jesse Bridge Rd., Elmer, 08318 ... (856) 692-0242
Archie's Boat Tops, LLC, 1800 Route 35, South Amboy, 08879 ... (732) 721-7566
Architectural Acrylics, 5 Rockhill Rd., Ste. 3, Cherry Hill, 08003 ... (856) 751-2411
★ Architectural Cabinetry, 51 Willow St., Washington, 07882 ... (908) 689-1600
Architectural Metal Designs, Inc., 1505 Pineland Ave., Millville, 08332 ... (856) 765-3000
Architectural Window Mfg., 359 Veterans Blvd., Rutherford, 07070 ... (201) 939-2200
Architectural Woodworking Assocs., LLC, 4 7th St., Frenchtown, 08825 ... (908) 996-7866
Archive Designs, Inc., 238 Emmet St., Newark, 07114 ... (973) 242-6400
Archive Print, Inc., 3203 Atlantic Ave., Allenwood, 08720 ... (732) 528-5300
Archon Vitamin Corp., 3775 Park Ave., Ste. 1, Edison, 08820 ... (973) 371-1700
Archtech Electronics Corp., 117 Docks Corner Rd., Ste. A, Dayton, 08810 ... (732) 355-1288
† ARCO, INC., 300 State Route 17, Unit K, Mahwah, 07430 ... (201) 828-9808
† Arctic Glacier, Inc., 2 Johnson Dr., Raritan, 08869 ... (908) 231-0100
Arctic Glacier U. S .A., Inc. see. ... Arctic Glacier, Inc., Raritan
Arctic Ice see. ... Artic Ice Mfg. & Dry Ice Co., Garfield
Arctic Ice Cream, 22 Arctic Pkwy., Ewing, 08638 ... (609) 393-4264
Arcticcoolers, Inc., 135 Gaither Dr., Ste. A, Mount Laurel, 08054 ... (856) 231-0262
Arcy Mfg. Co., Inc., 575 Industrial Rd., Carlstadt, 07072 ... (201) 635-1910
ARD Steel Works Co., 2 Lakeview Ave., Ste. 201, Piscataway, 08854 ... (732) 926-9800
Ardagh Group, 443 S. East Ave., P.O. Box 400, Bridgeton, 08302 ... (856) 455-2000
Ardagh Group, 83 Griffith St., Salem, 08079 ... (856) 935-4000
ARDE Barinco, Inc., 875 Washington Ave., Carlstadt, 07072 ... (201) 768-6070
Arde, Inc. see. ... ARDE Barinco, Inc., Carlstadt
Arde, Inc., 875 Washington Ave., Carlstadt, 07072 ... (201) 784-9880
† Arden Sales, 128 14th St., Lakewood, 08701 ... (732) 730-1418
Ardmore, Inc., 29 Riverside Ave., Bldg. 14, Newark, 07104 ... (973) 481-2406
† Ardom Bearing Group, 1000 Bennett Blvd., Ste. 7, Lakewood, 08701 ... (732) 370-2310
† Ardom Bearing Group, 3377 S. Clinton Ave., Unit 15, South Plainfield, 07080 ... (908) 755-3000
Ardwyn Binding Products Co., 681 Main St., Bldg. 7, Belleville, 07109 ... (973) 751-4002
Area Auto Racing News, Inc., 2829 S. Broad St., Trenton, 08610 ... (609) 888-3618
Arecia's Creations, 3704 Park Ave., Weehawken, 07086 ... (201) 864-7388
Arete Development, Inc., 20 Industrial Rd., Fairfield, 07004 ... (973) 244-0037
† Arett Sales Corp., 9285 Commerce Hwy., Pennsauken, 08110 ... (856) 751-1224
★ ARG Printing, LLC, 1601 Sherman Ave., Pennsauken, 08110 ... (856) 665-5644
Argo Corp., Richard Stockton College, Ste. 202, Pomona, 08240 ... (609) 652-4560
Argus International, 424 Route 31 N., P.O. Box 559, Ringoes, 08551 ... (609) 466-1677
Arias Machine Tool & Die Co., 645 Atlantic Ave., Perth Amboy, 08861 ... (732) 442-2398
Aries Precision Tool, Inc., 300 State Route 17, Ste. H, Mahwah, 07430 ... (201) 252-8550
Arista Custom Tapes, Inc., 20 Argyle Pl., North Arlington, 07031 ... (201) 997-7610
Arista Trophies & Awards, 25 Portland Ave., Bergenfield, 07621 ... (201) 387-2165
Aristocrat Embroidery Corp., 7014 Jackson St., Guttenberg, 07093 ... (201) 869-9126
★ Ariston Multimedia, LLC, 94 Valley Rd., Clifton, 07013 ... (973) 553-2727
† Ariva Distribution, Inc., 1705 Suckle Hwy., Pennsauken, 08110 ... (856) 488-0800
Arizona Beverages USA, LLC see. ... Maplewood Beverage Packers, LLC, Maplewood
Arizona Signs & Glass Tints Specialists see. ... Arizona Signs & Truck Lettering, Maple Shade
Arizona Signs & Truck Lettering, 3121 Route 73 S., Maple Shade, 08052 ... (856) 482-2288
Arlington Machine & Tool Co., 90 New Dutch Ln., Fairfield, 07004 ... (973) 276-1377
★ Armac Assocs., 71 Passaic Ave., Florham Park, 07932 ... (888) 422-3044
ARMCO Compressor Products Corp., 2042 46th St., North Bergen, 07047 ... (201) 866-6766
Armel Electronics, Inc., 1601 75th St., North Bergen, 07047 ... (201) 869-4300
Armfield, Inc., 9 Trenton Lakewood Rd., Ste. 2, Millstone Township, 08510 ... (609) 208-2800
Armor Guard Business Center, 139 Main St., Orange, 07050 ... (973) 676-6900
† Armor Metals & Recycling, 8300 National Hwy., Ste. 2, Pennsauken, 08110 ... (856) 665-5715
Armorpoxy, Inc., 805 Lehigh Ave., Union, 07083 ... (908) 810-9613
Armour Products, 176-180 5th Ave., Hawthorne, 07506 ... (973) 427-8787
Arm-R-Lite Door Mfg. Co., Inc., 2700 Hamilton Blvd., South Plainfield, 07080 ... (908) 754-2600
Arms Graphics, 169 Paris Ave., Northvale, 07647 ... (201) 767-6504
Armstrong & Sons, Inc., 2335 Highway 34, Manasquan, 08736 ... (732) 223-1555
Armstrong Industrial Hose Products, LLC, 1400 E. State St., Hamilton, 08609 ... (609) 989-5161
Arnold Desks, Inc., 1409 Chestnut Ave., P.O. Box 842, Hillside, 07205 ... (908) 686-5656
Arnold Furniture Mfrs., Inc. see. ... Arnold Desks, Inc., Hillside
Arnold Furniture Mfrs., Inc., 400 Coit St., Irvington, 07111 ... (973) 399-0505
Arnold Furniture Mfrs., Inc. see. ... Arnold Kolax Furniture, Inc., Irvington
Arnold Kolax Furniture, Inc., 146 Coit St., Irvington, 07111 ... (973) 375-3344
Arnold Reception Desks, Inc., 120 Coit St., Irvington, 07111 ... (973) 375-8101
Arnold Steel Co., Inc., 79 Randolph Rd., Howell, 07731 ... (732) 363-1079
Arol Chemical Products Co., 649 Ferry St., Newark, 07105 ... (973) 344-1510
★ Aromatic Innovations, 600 Hartle St., Sayreville, 08872 ... (732) 967-6346
Aromor Flavors & Fragrances, Inc.,
560 Sylvan Ave., Ste. 60, Englewood Cliffs, 07632 ... (201) 503-1662

Array Mfg. Tech Corp., 100 Arlington Ave., Kearny, 07032 ... (201) 997-1333
Arro-Mark Co., LLC, 158 W. Forest Ave., Englewood, 07631 ... (201) 567-4112
Arrow Engineering Co., 260 Pennsylvania Ave., Hillside, 07205 ... (908) 353-5233
Arrow Fastener Co., LLC, 271 Mayhill St., Saddle Brook, 07663 ... (201) 843-6900
Arrow Machine Co., 117 Norfolk St., Newark, 07103 ... (973) 642-2430
Arrow Shed, LLC, 1 3rd Ave., Haskell, 07420 ... (973) 835-3200
Arrow Steel, Inc., 629 E. 19th St., Paterson, 07514 ... (973) 523-1122
ARS East see. ... Asset Recovery Specialists, Inc., Swedesboro
Art Culinaire Magazine, 40 Mills St., Morristown, 07963 ... (973) 993-5500
Art D'Mensions, Inc., 1998 Scotch Plains Route 22, Scotch Plains, 07076 ... (908) 322-8488
Art Graphic Impressions, 1044 State Route 23, Ste. 101, Wayne, 07470 ... (973) 696-2800
Art Graphics, 54 Delsea Dr. N., Glassboro, 08028 ... (856) 881-5029
Art Guild, Inc., 300 Wolf Dr., West Deptford, 08086 ... (856) 853-7500
Art Guild, Inc. see. ... SYMA Systems, Inc., West Deptford
Art Material Service Co., Inc., 625 Joyce Kilmer Ave., New Brunswick, 08901 ... (732) 545-8888
Art Metalcraft Plating Co., Inc., 529 S. 2nd St., Camden, 08103 ... (856) 365-0001
Art Mold & Tool Corp. see. ... Artmark Mold & Tool Corp., East Rutherford
Art Press Printing, Inc., 124 Clements Bridge Rd., Barrington, 08007 ... (856) 547-8953
Art Publishing Group, The, 480 Main Ave., Unit 4, Wallington, 07057 ... (201) 842-8500
Art Stone Products, 113 Church St., P.O. Box 10, Newfield, 08344 ... (856) 697-5895
Artcraft Cabinets Woodworking, 165 Broad Ave., Fairview, 07022 ... (201) 943-6090
Artcraft Sign Studio, Inc., 738 W. Branch Ave., Pine Hill, 08021 ... (856) 783-8008
Artegraft, Inc., 220 N. Center Dr., North Brunswick, 08902 ... (732) 422-8333
Artex Knitting Mills, Inc., 300 Harvard Ave., P.O. Box 183, Westville, 08093 ... (856) 456-2800
Arthur Schuman, Inc., 40 New Dutch Ln., Fairfield, 07004 ... (973) 227-0030
Artic Ice Mfg. & Dry Ice Co., 158 Semel Ave., Garfield, 07026 ... (201) 370-3141
Artique Glass Studio, 483 S. Broad St., Glen Rock, 07452 ... (201) 444-3500
† Artique, Inc., P.O. Box 44, Midland Park, 07432 ... (201) 444-8989
Artisan Awning Co., 17 Jefferson St., P.O. Box 387, Newton, 07860 ... (973) 383-5608
Artisan Controls Corp., 111 Canfield Ave., Ste. B-15-18, Randolph, 07869 ... (973) 598-9400
★ Artisan Digital, Inc., 21 Fadem Rd., Unit 1, Springfield, 07081 ... (973) 379-2788
Artisan Kitchen Studio, LLC, 26 Cokesbury Rd., P.O. Box 151, Lebanon, 08833 ... (908) 236-7233
Artist Above The Rest, 4490 Nottingham Way, Trenton, 08690 ... (609) 586-7247
Artistic Doors & Windows, 10 S. Inman Ave., Avenel, 07001 ... (732) 726-9400
Artistic Fence, 757 River Dr., Passaic, 07055 ... (973) 779-4540
Artistic Marble & Granite Surfaces, Inc., 269 Goffle Rd., Hawthorne, 07506 ... (973) 304-2001
Artistic Metal Works Corp., 199 7th Ave., Hawthorne, 07506 ... (973) 304-0600
Artistic Products, LLC, 1905 Elizabeth Ave., Rahway, 07065 ... (732) 382-4141
Artistic Railings, Inc., 500 River Dr., Garfield, 07026 ... (973) 772-8540
Artmark Mold & Tool Corp., 742 Paterson Ave., East Rutherford, 07073 ... (201) 935-3377
ArtMolds see. ... EnvironMolds, LLC, Summit
Art's Embroidery, LLC, 175 Monmouth Rd., West Long Branch, 07764 ... (732) 870-1155
Arts Weekly, Inc., 52 Sindle Ave., P.O. Box 1140, Little Falls, 07424 ... (973) 812-6766
Art's Windows, Inc., 199 Ocean Ave., Lakewood, 08701 ... (732) 367-1770
Artus Corp., 201 S. Dean St., P.O. Box 511, Englewood, 07631 ... (201) 568-1000
Aryzta La Brea Bakery, Inc. see. ... Aryzta/La Brea Bakery, Swedesboro
Aryzta/La Brea Bakery, 11 Technology Dr., Swedesboro, 08085 ... (856) 417-8100
† Arzee Supply, 1905 Swarthmore Ave., Lakewood, 08701 ... (201) 935-0800
† Arzee Supply Corp. Of New Jersey, 15 E. Frederick Pl., Cedar Knolls, 07927 ... (973) 267-1576
† Arzee Supply Corp. Of New Jersey, 450 York St., Elizabeth, 07201 ... (908) 820-3700
AS America, Inc. (H Q), 1 Centennial Ave., P.O. Box 6820, Piscataway, 08855 ... (732) 980-3000
AS Software, Inc., 560 Sylvan Ave., Ste. 2052, Englewood Cliffs, 07632 ... (201) 541-1900
ASAP Coastal Printing and Signs, 775 N. Main St., Manahawkin, 08050 ... (609) 597-7421
ASAP Nameplate & Label Co. see. ... Technical Name Plate Corp., Passaic
Asbury Carbons see. ... Asbury Graphite Mills, Inc. (H Q), Asbury
Asbury Graphite Mills, Inc. (H Q),
405 Old Main St., P.O. Box 144, Asbury, 08802 ... (908) 537-2155
Asbury Park Press, 3600 Highway 66, Neptune, 07753 ... (732) 922-6000
Asbury Park Press, Inc. see. ... Asbury Park Press, Neptune
Asbury Park Press, Inc. (H Q), 3600 Highway 66, P.O. Box 1550, Neptune, 07754 ... (732) 922-6000
Ascalon Studios, Inc., 430 Cooper Rd., West Berlin, 08091 ... (856) 768-3779
Ascent Aromatics, Inc., 120 Case Dr., South Plainfield, 07080 ... (908) 755-0120
Ascentta, Inc., 370 Campus Drive, Ste. 105, Somerset, 08873 ... (732) 868-1766
ASCO Power Technologies, Inc., 5000 Sagemore Dr., Ste. 200, Marlton, 08053 ... (856) 810-9600
ASCO Power Technologies, L.P. see. ... ASCO Power Technologies, Inc., Marlton
ASCO Power Technologies, L.P. (H Q), 50 Hanover Rd., Florham Park, 07932 ... (800) 800-2726
★ ASCO Valve, Inc., 50 Hanover Rd., Florham Park, 07932 ... (973) 966-2000
ASCO Valve, Inc., 50-60 Hanover Rd., Florham Park, 07932 ... (973) 966-2000
ASCO Valve, Inc., 13000 Lincoln Dr. W., Ste. 106, Marlton, 08053 ... (856) 985-8700
Ascot Tag & Label Co., Inc., 577 3rd St., Newark, 07107 ... (973) 482-0900
Ashfar Enterprises, Inc. (H Q), 200 Metro Plex Dr., Ste. 275, Edison, 08817 ... (848) 202-1581
Ashland Aqualon, Inc., 50 S. Minnisink Ave., Parlin, 08859 ... (732) 254-1234
Ashland, Inc. see. ... Ashland Aqualon, Inc., Parlin
Ashland, Inc., 116 Summit Ave., Chatham, 07928 ... (973) 635-1551
Ashland, Inc. see. ... Ashland, Inc., International Specialty Products (H Q), Roseland
Ashland, Inc., International Specialty Products (H Q),
56 Livingston Ave., Ste. 400, Roseland, 07068 ... (973) 533-5400
Ashton Food Machinery Co., Inc., P.O. Box 60, Montville, 07045 ... (973) 521-7603
ASI Plastic, Inc., 120 Getty Ave., Paterson, 07503 ... (973) 345-7510
Asia Trading, 390 Nye Ave., Irvington, 07111 ... (973) 577-1300
★ Asiamerica Ingredients, Inc., 245 Old Hook Rd., Ste. 3, Westwood, 07675 ... (201) 497-5993
Asian Clinical Trials see. ... Suven Life Sciences Ltd., Monmouth Junction
★ ASO Safety Solutions, Inc., 300 Round Hill Dr., Ste. 6, Rockaway, 07866 ... (973) 586-9600
Aspe, Inc., 2 Daniel Rd. E., Fairfield, 07004 ... (973) 808-1155
Aspen Mfg. Co., Inc., 703 Van Rossum Ave., Unit 5, Beverly, 08010 ... (609) 871-6400
Asphalt Paving Systems, 500 N. Egg Harbor Rd., P.O. Box 530, Hammonton, 08037 ... (609) 561-4161
Aspire Pharmaceuticals, Inc., 41 Veronica Ave., Somerset, 08873 ... (732) 447-1444
ASSA, Inc. see. ... Mul-T-Lock USA, Inc., Hackensack
Assemblies Unlimited, Inc., 530 N. Michigan Ave., Kenilworth, 07033 ... (877) 273-6259
Assem-Pak, Inc., 1649 Castpa Pl., Vineland, 08360 ... (856) 692-3355
† Asset Recovery Specialists, Inc., 3 Killdeer Ct., Ste. 303, Swedesboro, 08085 ... (856) 467-9822
Associated Anvil Iron Works, 38 Patterson Ave., Warren, 07059 ... (908) 647-0290
Associated Fabrics Corp., 15-01 Pollitt Dr., Ste. 7, Fair Lawn, 07410 ... (800) 232-4077
Associated Mailing & Printing Services, LLC,
50 Tannery Rd., Ste. 2, Branchburg, 08876 ... (908) 541-9700
Associated Pile & Fitting,
8 Wood Hollow Rd., Plz. 1, P.O. Box 5933, Parsippany, 07054 ... (973) 773-8400
† Associated Plastics, Inc., 179 E. Inman Ave., Rahway, 07065 ... (732) 574-2800
† AST Bearings, LLC, 115 Main Rd., Montville, 07045 ... (973) 335-2230
Astor Chocolate Corp., 651 New Hampshire Ave., Lakewood, 08701 ... (732) 901-1001
Astro Outdoor Advertising, Inc. * Astro Outdoor * Astro Signs see. ... Astro Sign Co., Glassboro
Astro Sign Co., 230 E. High St., Route 322, Glassboro, 08028 ... (856) 881-4300

© Copyright 2015 Manufacturers' News, Inc.


Astro Tool & Machine Co., Inc., 810 Martin St., Rahway, 07065 ... (732) 382-2450
Astro Tool Corp., 90 Washington Ave., Nutley, 07110 ... (973) 661-1299
Astrodyne Corp. see ... Jerome Industries Corp., Elizabeth
Astrolab, Inc., 4 Powderhorn Dr., Warren, 07059 ... (732) 560-3800
Astronautics Corp. Of America see ... Kearfott Corporation, Guidance & Navigation Div., Little Falls
† ATAK Trucking, Inc., 1341 Route 34, Matawan, 07747 ... (917) 912-2900
† Atalanta Corporation, 1 Atalanta Plz., Elizabeth, 07206 ... (908) 351-8000
ATCO Pallet Co., 1000 Creek Rd., P.O. Box 5115, Delanco, 08075 ... (856) 461-8141
Atco Products see ... Universal Tools & Mfg. Co., Springfield
ATCO Rubber Products, Inc., 1480 N. West Blvd., Vineland, 08360 ... (856) 794-3393
ATG, Inc. see ... Advanced Technology Group, Inc., Rockaway
† Athenia Mason Supply, Inc., 72 Mina Ave., Clifton, 07011 ... (973) 253-0570
★ Athens Printing Co., Inc., 95 Myer St., Hackensack, 07601 ... (201) 342-1771
Athletes Image, Inc., 1865 State Route 35, Wall, 07719 ... (732) 974-1600
Athletic Imprinters, Inc., 775 Ashbourne Ave., Lindenwold, 08021 ... (856) 346-4545
A3 Technology, Inc.,
311 S. New York Rd., Redding Office Pk., Ste. 36, Absecon, 08205 ... (609) 652-7933
ATI Audio, 154 Cooper Road S-902, West Berlin, 08091 ... (856) 719-9900
Atlanta Drive Systems, Inc.,
1775 State Route 34, Ste. D-10, Farmingdale, 07727 ... (732) 282-0480
Atlantic Air Enterprises, 856 Elston St., Rahway, 07065 ... (732) 381-4000
★ Atlantic Beach Soap Co., 231 North Ave. W., Ste. 2, Westfield, 07090 ... (908) 272-7595
† Atlantic Capes Fisheries, Inc., 985 Ocean Dr., Cape May, 08204 ... (609) 884-3000
Atlantic Casting & Engineering, 810 Bloomfield Ave., Clifton, 07012 ... (973) 779-2450
Atlantic City Shade Shop, Inc.,
500 Tilton Rd., P.O. Box 217, Northfield, 08225 ... (609) 641-8700
Atlantic City Weekly, L. P.,
Bayport 1, 8025 Black Horse Pike, Ste. 3, Pleasantville, 08232 ... (609) 646-4848
† Atlantic Coast Container Brokerage & Sales, Inc.,
906 Oak Tree Rd., Ste. P, South Plainfield, 07080 ... (908) 755-2898
Atlantic Coast Crushers, Inc., 128 Market St., Kenilworth, 07033 ... (908) 259-9292
† Atlantic Coast Fibers, LLC, 101 7th St., Passaic, 07055 ... (973) 614-9600
Atlantic Coastal Welding, Inc., 16 Butler Blvd., Bayville, 08721 ... (732) 269-1088
Atlantic Detroit Diesel-Allison see ... Stewart & Stevenson Power Products, LLC- ADDA Div., Lodi
Atlantic Detroit Diesel-Allison, LLC,
169 Old New Brunswick Rd., Piscataway, 08854 ... (732) 752-7100
Atlantic Detroit Diesel-Allison, LLC see ... Stewart & Stevenson Power Products, LLC, ADDA Div., Lodi
Atlantic Envelope Co., 16 Passaic Ave., Unit 7, Fairfield, 07004 ... (973) 882-0436
Atlantic Equipment Engineers, Inc.,
24 Industrial Ave., P.O. Box 181, Upper Saddle River, 07458 ... (201) 828-9400
Atlantic International Technologies, Inc.,
114 Beach St., Bldg. 3, Rockaway, 07866 ... (973) 625-0053
Atlantic Kenmark Electric, Inc., 11 Ewing Ave., North Arlington, 07031 ... (201) 991-2117
Atlantic Precision Technology, LLC, 432 Quarry Ln., North Brunswick, 08902 ... (732) 648-7786
Atlantic Printing & Graphics, LLC, 1301 W. Park Ave., Ocean, 07712 ... (732) 493-4222
Atlantic Printing Co., 262 Circle Dr., Brick, 08723 ... (732) 920-2300
Atlantic Prosthetic & Orthotic Services, Inc.,
199 New Rd., Ste. 56, Linwood, 08221 ... (609) 927-6330
Atlantic Protective Pouches, 1545 Route 37 W., Unit 6, Toms River, 08755 ... (732) 240-3871
Atlantic Rubber Enterprises, 35 Union Valley Rd., Newfoundland, 07435 ... (973) 697-5900
Atlantic Screenprinting, 339 Fairview Ave., Westwood, 07675 ... (201) 383-0995
Atlantic Spring Co., 137 Highway 202 S., Ringoes, 08551 ... (908) 788-5800
Atlantic States Cast Iron Pipe Co., 183 Sitgreaves St., Phillipsburg, 08865 ... (908) 454-1161
Atlantic Stone II, LLC, 98 Somerset St., Garfield, 07026 ... (973) 928-1458
† Atlantic Time Systems, 112 N. 8th St., Vineland, 08360 ... (856) 692-9594
Atlantic Towers & St. Croix Marine Products see. Tower Systems, Inc.- Atlantic Towers & St. Croix Marine Products, Bayville
† Atlantic Track & Turnout Co., 270 Broad St., P.O. Box 1589, Bloomfield, 07003 ... (973) 748-5885
† Atlantic Window & Door, Inc., 1608 Dubac Rd., Wall Township, 07719 ... (732) 793-2452
Atlantic Zeiser, Inc., 15 Patton Dr., West Caldwell, 07006 ... (973) 228-0800
Atlantis Aromatics, Inc., 5047 Industrial Rd., Ste. 4, Farmingdale, 07727 ... (732) 919-1112
Atlas Auto Trim, Inc., 81 Highway 1, Edison, 08817 ... (732) 985-6800
† Atlas Bronze, 445 Bunting Ave., Trenton, 08611 ... (609) 599-1402
Atlas Consolidated Machine Corp., 53 Bleeker St., Paterson, 07524 ... (973) 684-5803
Atlas Copco North America, LLC (H Q),
7 Campus Dr., Ste. 200, Parsippany, 07054 ... (973) 397-3400
Atlas Desk & Office Equipment Corp.,
185-193 Central Ave., 2nd Fl., Newark, 07103 ... (973) 242-8989
Atlas Fashions, 148 Tices Ln., East Brunswick, 08816 ... (732) 254-6090
Atlas Flasher & Supply Co., Inc.,
430 Swedesboro Ave., P.O. Box 488, Mickleton, 08056 ... (856) 423-3333
Atlas Industrial Mfg. Co., 81 Somerset Pl., Clifton, 07012 ... (973) 779-3970
Atlas Marble & Granite, 44 Fadem Rd., Springfield, 07081 ... (973) 491-5454
Atlas Recording Machines Corp., 2140 Bridge Ave., Point Pleasant, 08742 ... (732) 295-3663
Atlas Refinery, Inc., 142 Lockwood St., Newark, 07105 ... (973) 589-2002
Atlas Rigging Supply Corp. * Atlantic Cordage Corp. see ... Steelstran Industries, Inc., Avenel
Atlas Welders & Fabricators Corp.,
2505 S. Clinton Ave., South Plainfield, 07080 ... (908) 561-1144
† Atlas Welding Supply Co., Inc., 808 Brook Rd., Lakewood, 08701 ... (732) 363-1148
Atlas Woodwork, 212 Wright St., Newark, 07114 ... (973) 621-9595
Atlas Woodworking, Inc., 15 Naugle St., Closter, 07624 ... (201) 784-1949
Atmos Tech Industries, 1108 Pollack Ave., Ocean, 07712 ... (732) 493-8400
Atomic Trophies, Inc., 201 Shevchenko Ave., South Plainfield, 07080 ... (732) 424-7930
Atomizing Systems Inc., 1 Hollywood Ave., Ste. 1, Ho-Ho-Kus, 07423 ... (201) 447-1222
Attitudes In Dressing, Inc., 107 Trumbull St., Bldg. B-8, Elizabeth, 07206 ... (908) 354-7218
A2Z Emblems, LLC, 125 W. Route 130 N., Ste. C, Burlington, 08016 ... (609) 239-9800
Audio Dynamix, Inc., 170 Coolidge Ave., Englewood, 07631 ... (201) 567-5488
AudioCodes, Inc., 27 Worlds Fair Dr., 1st Fl., Somerset, 08873 ... (732) 469-0880
Aumtech, Inc., 710 Old Bridge Tpke., East Brunswick, 08816 ... (732) 254-1875
Aunt Gussie's Cookies & Crackers see ... Direct Sales & Services, Garfield
Aunt Kitty's Foods, Inc., 270 N. Mill Rd., Vineland, 08360 ... (856) 691-2100
Aura Badge Co., 264 Clayton Ave., Monroeville, 08343 ... (856) 881-9026
Aurora Multimedia Corp., 205 Commercial Ct., Morganville, 07751 ... (732) 591-5800
Aurorae (H Q), 46 N. Central Ave., Ramsey, 07446 ... (551) 579-4003
Au'some Inc. (H Q),
2031 Highway 130, Ste. E., Bldg. A, Monmouth Junction, 08852 ... (732) 951-8818
Au'some LLC see ... Au'some Inc. (H Q), Monmouth Junction
AuthentiDate Holding Corp., 300 Connell Dr., 5th Fl., Berkeley Heights, 07922 ... (908) 787-1700
Auto Chic see ... MPT Industries, Dover
Auto Clear, LLC, 2 Gardner Rd., Fairfield, 07004 ... (973) 276-6161
Auto Cool Radiator Service, 10 Terhune Pl., Hackensack, 07601 ... (201) 343-3099
Auto Graphix, 56 Edsel Dr., Sussex, 07461 ... (973) 492-1300
† Auto King Parts & Supplies, 67 E. Railroad Ave., Jamesburg, 08831 ... (732) 521-0474
Auto Sun Roof, Inc. (H Q),
1305 Industrial Hwy., P.O. Box 2321, Cinnaminson, 08077 ... (856) 786-0600
Autobar Systems Corp., 1 Meridian Rd., Eatontown, 07724 ... (732) 922-3355
AutoDrill, LLC, 50 Division Ave., Ste. 18, Millington, 07946 ... (908) 542-0244
Automated Business Products, Inc. (H Q),
50 Clinton Pl., Mail Slot 1, Hackensack, 07601 ... (201) 489-1440
Automated Control Concepts, Inc.,
3535 State Route 66, Ste. 14, Neptune, 07753 ... (732) 922-6611
Automated Flexible Conveyors, Inc., 55 Walman Ave., 2nd Fl., Clifton, 07011 ... (973) 340-1695
Automated Medical Products Co., 440 Cliff Rd., Sewaren, 07077 ... (732) 602-7717
Automated Tapping Systems, Inc., 22 Davos Rd., Brick, 08724 ... (732) 899-2282
Automatic Data Processing, Inc. (H Q), 1 ADP Blvd., Roseland, 07068 ... (973) 974-5000
Automatic Machine Products, 56 Paterson Ave., Newton, 07860 ... (973) 383-9929
Automatic Plating, Inc., 3410 Jessup Rd., P.O. Box 54, West Deptford, 08086 ... (856) 845-7323
Automatic Rolls Of New Jersey, Inc., 1 Gourmet Ln., Edison, 08837 ... (732) 549-2243
★ Automatic Transfer, Inc., 2 Industrial Rd., Phillipsburg, 08865 ... (908) 213-2830
Automation & Control, Inc., 1491 Lancer Dr., Moorestown, 08057 ... (856) 234-2300
Automation Dynamics see ... ABC Digital Electronics, Inc., Old Tappan
† Automation Sales Co., 226 Beacon Hill Rd., Califon, 07830 ... (908) 832-7040
Automotive Rentals, Inc.,
4001 Leadenhall Rd., P.O. Box 5039, Mount Laurel, 08054 ... (856) 778-1500
† Autopart International, Inc., 260 Hudson St., Hackensack, 07601 ... (201) 488-4187
† Autopart International, Inc., 1773 Pine Ave., Unit A, Vineland, 08360 ... (856) 405-0346
★ Avante International Technology, Inc., 70 Washington Rd., Princeton, 08540 ... (609) 799-8896
Avanti, 2650 U.S. Highway 130., Ste. I, Cranbury, 08512 ... (609) 655-5333
Avanti Linens, Inc., 234 Moonachie Rd., Moonachie, 07074 ... (201) 641-7766
Avaya, Inc. (H Q), 211 Mount Airy Rd., Basking Ridge, 07920 ... (908) 953-6000
AVCON, 1915 Swarthmore Ave., Ste. 3, Lakewood, 08701 ... (732) 286-9496
Avenel Pallet Co., Inc., Foot Of S. 2nd St., P.O. Box 276, Dunellen, 08812 ... (732) 752-0500
Aventa Systems, LLC, 40 Arnot St., Unit 7, Lodi, 07644 ... (973) 246-4853
Avenue Printing Co., 143 Franklin Tpke., Waldwick, 07463 ... (201) 652-2035
† Avery Filter Co., Inc., 99 Kinderkamack Rd., Ste. 209, Westwood, 07675 ... (201) 666-9664
Avianne Health Care Systems, 115 1st St., Lodi, 07644 ... (201) 288-4100
Aviation International News, 214 Franklin Ave., Midland Park, 07432 ... (201) 444-5075
Avid Communications, Inc., 27 Bluebird Ct., P.O. Box 2481, Flemington, 08822 ... (973) 625-7350
Avida, Inc., 174-B Kinderkamack Rd., P.O. Box 2, Park Ridge, 07656 ... (201) 802-0749
Avionic Instruments, LLC, 1414 Randolph Ave., P.O. Box 498, Avenel, 07001 ... (732) 388-3500
Avionix Corp., 35 Ruta Ct., South Hackensack, 07606 ... (201) 343-1550
Aviv Biomedical, Inc., 750 Vassar Ave., Lakewood, 08701 ... (732) 370-1300
Avon Fabrics, Inc., 484 Lincoln Blvd., Middlesex, 08846 ... (732) 764-9700
AW Machinery, LLC, 7 Just Rd., Fairfield, 07004 ... (973) 882-3223
Award Makers see ... Little Falls Trophy Co., Little Falls
Awards Trophy Co., 611 U.S. Highway 22, Hillside, 07205 ... (908) 687-5775
† Awisco Corp., 24 Lakeside Ave., West Orange, 07052 ... (973) 736-0200
AWISCO New York Corp. see ... Awisco Corp., West Orange
AWISCO New York Corp. see ... Awisco West Milford, LLC, West Milford
† Awisco West Milford, LLC, 26 Industrial Rd., West Milford, 07480 ... (973) 728-9008
Awning Concepts & Design, Inc., 916 Route 33, Freehold, 07728 ... (732) 462-1131
Awning Shoppe, The, 190 Highway 36, Keansburg, 07734 ... (732) 787-4246
Awnings Galore see ... Clark Home Supply, Clark
Axiam Printing see ... Anisha Enterprises, Inc., Union
† Axis, Inc., 210 Meister Ave., Somerville, 08876 ... (908) 429-0090
Axis Industrial Automation see ... Axis, Inc., Somerville
Axletree Solutions, Inc.,
2 King Arthur Ct., Lakeside W., Ste. A-1, North Brunswick, 08902 ... (732) 296-0001
AXS-ONE, Inc., 301 Route 17, Ste. 11, Rutherford, 07070 ... (201) 935-3400
Aydin Jewelry, Inc., 885 Route 17 S., Ramsey, 07446 ... (201) 818-1002
Ayers Printing, 1413 Chestnut Ave., Hillside, 07205 ... (908) 687-2891
Ayesha Studio & Gallery, 21 N. Dean St., Englewood, 07631 ... (201) 503-0073
Ayr Graphics & Printing, Inc., 320 Chestnut St., Roselle Park, 07204 ... (908) 241-8118
AZCO Corp., 26 Just Rd., Fairfield, 07004 ... (973) 439-1428
† AZCO Steel Co., 1641 New Market Ave., South Plainfield, 07080 ... (908) 754-8700
★ Azden Corp., 200 Valley Rd., Ste. 101, Mount Arlington, 07856 ... (973) 810-3070
Aztec Graphics, Inc., 420 Whitehead Rd., Trenton, 08619 ... (609) 587-1000
Aztec Software Assoc., Inc., 51 Commerce St., 2nd Fl., Springfield, 07081 ... (973) 258-0011
Aztech Mfg., LLC, 147 W. Hampton St., Pemberton, 08068 ... (609) 726-1212
† Azuma Foods International, Inc.,
20 Murray Hill Pkwy., Ste. 130, East Rutherford, 07073 ... (201) 372-1112
Azuma Foods International, Inc. U.S.A. see ... Azuma Foods International, Inc., East Rutherford
Azzota Corp., 178 Franklin Rd., Randolph, 07869 ... (877) 649-2746
Azzurro Group, LLC, 100 Stonehurst Ct., Northvale, 07647 ... (201) 767-0850
B & A Flex, Inc., 34 Charlotte Dr., Bridgewater, 08807 ... (908) 722-2808
B & B Electroplating Co., 559 Pennsylvania Ave., Linden, 07036 ... (908) 925-5044
B & B Iron Works, 300 Colt St., Irvington, 07111 ... (973) 375-9000
B & B Millwork, 333 Monroe Ave., Kenilworth, 07033 ... (973) 249-0300
B & B Poultry Co., Inc., Almond Rd., P.O. Box 307, Norma, 08347 ... (856) 692-8893
B & B Press, Inc., 24 Cokesbury Rd., Ste. 11, Lebanon, 08833 ... (908) 840-4323
† B & B Supply Corp., 40 Arnot St., Unit 14, Lodi, 07644 ... (201) 313-9021
B & B Ultra-Sonic, Inc., 10 E. Main St., High Bridge, 08829 ... (908) 638-5775
B & C Custom Wood Handrail Corp.,
131 Dr. James Parker Blvd., P.O. Box 2008, Red Bank, 07701 ... (732) 530-6640
B & C Machine Co., Inc., 22 Lasinski Rd., Franklin, 07416 ... (973) 823-1120
B & G Foods, Inc. see ... Violet Packing, Williamstown
B & G Foods, Inc. (H Q), 4 Gatehall Dr., Ste. 110, Parsippany, 07054 ... (973) 401-6500
B & G International, Inc., 1085 Morris Ave., Union, 07083 ... (973) 824-0334
B & G Plastics see ... B & G International, Inc., Union
B & J Sign Service, 971 Landis Ave., Pittsgrove, 08318 ... (856) 455-3636
B & L Industrial Services, Inc., 700 Park Ave., Unit 7, Hainesport, 08036 ... (609) 386-9500
B & L Precision Grinding Corp., 7-B Ivy St., Pompton Lakes, 07442 ... (973) 839-4141
B & L Printing Co., Inc., 46 Old Camplain Rd., Hillsborough, 08844 ... (908) 707-1311
B & M Finishers, Inc., 201 S. 31st St., Kenilworth, 07033 ... (908) 241-5640
B & M Grinding Co., 50 Brown Ave., Springfield, 07081 ... (973) 564-7648
B & M Machine Co., Inc., 67-69 Greylock Ave., Belleville, 07109 ... (973) 751-0789
B & R Industries, Inc., 196 12th St., Piscataway, 08854 ... (732) 752-3022
B & S Sheet Metal Co., Inc., 60 5th Ave., Hawthorne, 07506 ... (973) 427-3739
B & S Tool & Cutter Service, Inc., 99 John St., Hackensack, 07601 ... (201) 488-3545
B & W Plastics, Inc., 20 Wilson Dr., Sparta, 07871 ... (973) 383-0020
B & W Printing Co., Inc., 730 Fairfield Ave., Kenilworth, 07033 ... (908) 241-3060
B. Braun Medical, Inc. see ... Central Admixture Pharmacy Services, Englewood
B E R Plastic Corp., 5 Curtis St., P.O. Box 2, Riverdale, 07457 ... (973) 839-2100
B Green Innovations, Inc., 750 State Route 34, Ste. 8, Matawan, 07747 ... (732) 696-9333
B. L. White Welding & Steel Co., Inc., 527 E. 33rd St., Paterson, 07504 ... (973) 684-4111



★ **Indicates new listing this edition.** † **Indicates wholesaler/distributor.**

B P Machine Co., Inc., 10 American Way, Spotswood, 08884 ... (732) 251-0449
B T Industries see. ... Bal Togs Industries, North Bergen
Babbitt Mfg. Co., Inc., 719 E. Park Ave., Vineland, 08360 ... (856) 692-3245
Babinec Sheet Metal Works, Inc., Joseph, 774 Martin St., Rahway, 07065 ... (732) 388-6600
Babysmart, LLC see. ... ABAA, Inc. (H Q), Bernardsville
Bach International see. ... Stylex Imports & Export Co., Inc., East Rutherford
Bach Tool Precision, Inc., 51 Executive Pkwy., Ringwood, 07456 ... (973) 962-6224
† Bacon & Graham, Inc., 34 E. 25th St., Paterson, 07514 ... (973) 684-1488
Bad Dog T's, 498 Kinderkamack Rd., River Edge, 07661 ... (201) 599-2030
Badge Company Of New Jersey, 223 Hamden Rd., P.O. Box 100, Annandale, 08801 ... (908) 735-7700
★ Baer Aggregates, Inc., 454 River Rd., Phillipsburg, 08865 ... (908) 454-4412
Baeta Corp., 1 Bridge Plz., Ste. 275, Fort Lee, 07024 ... (201) 471-0988
†★ Bag Factory, Inc., The, 726 N. Stiles St., Linden, 07036 ... (908) 925-7122
Bai Lar Interior Services, Inc., 554 New Brunswick Ave., Fords, 08863 ... (732) 738-0350
Baik Kwang Corp., 601 Commercial Ave., P.O. Box 7072, Carlstadt, 07072 ... (201) 507-9985
† Bailey Packaging Co., Inc., 217 Prospect Ave., Ste. 8-3B, Cranford, 07016 ... (908) 759-0991
Bailey's Printing, Inc., 191 Throckmorton St., Freehold, 07728 ... (732) 462-8010
Baird Industries see. ... Alan Baird Industries, Inc., Ho-Ho-Kus
† BakeMark USA, LLC, 1815 Route 130 N., Burlington, 08016 ... (609) 747-9000
BakerCorp., 50 Gilchris Dr., Swedesboro, 08085 ... (856) 467-2677
Bakers Bounty, 7 Maple Ave., Linden, 07036 ... (908) 587-1602
Baker's Perfection, Inc., 198 Green Pond Rd., Rockaway, 07866 ... (973) 983-0700
Bakers Puff Pastry, 1 Industrial Plz., Paterson, 07503 ... (973) 977-2255
Baker-Titan Adhesives, 25 Lake St., Paterson, 07501 ... (973) 225-1070
Bakery, The, 99 N. Washington Ave., Bergenfield, 07621 ... (201) 384-1456
Bal Togs Industries, 6605-09 Smith Ave., North Bergen, 07047 ... (201) 866-0201
★ Balcis Screen Printing, 219 Wanaque Ave., Pompton Lakes, 07442 ... (973) 835-9948
Baldi Iron Works,Inc., 158 Belmont Ave., Belleville, 07109 ... (973) 751-4338
Balic Winery, Inc., 6623 Harding Hwy., Mays Landing, 08330 ... (609) 625-2166
Ballantine Laboratories, Inc., 312 Old Allerton Rd., Annandale, 08801 ... (908) 713-7742
Ballard Collection, Inc., 221 Stirling Rd., Ste. E & F, Warren, 07059 ... (908) 604-0082
Ballet Makers, Inc. (H Q), 1 Campus Rd., Totowa, 07512 ... (973) 595-9000
Balsco Corrugated Box & Display, LLC, 160 Union Ave., East Rutherford, 07073 ... (973) 546-0500
Balthazar Bakery, 214 S. Dean St., Englewood, 07631 ... (201) 503-9717
BAMCO, Inc., 30 Baekeland Ave., Middlesex, 08846 ... (732) 302-0889
Bananafish, 250 Passaic St., Newark, 07104 ... (212) 686-4666
Banda Oriental, Inc., 777 W. Grand Ave., Rahway, 07065 ... (732) 388-8383
Bankers Pen Co., Inc., 141 Lanza Rd., Garfield, 07026 ... (718) 768-7107
★ Bankers Pen, Inc., 141 Lanza Ave., Bldg. 12, Garfield, 07026 ... (800) 499-7367
Banks Bros. Corp., 24 Federal Plz., Bloomfield, 07003 ... (973) 680-4488
Banner Chemical Corp., 111 Hill St., Orange, 07050 ... (973) 676-2900
Banner Design, 600 N. Union Ave., P.O. Box 5343, Hillside, 07205 ... (908) 687-5335
Bannister Co., Inc., 126 N. Main St., Milltown, 08850 ... (732) 828-1353
Bannon Group, 629 Grove St., Jersey City, 07310 ... (201) 451-6500
Banquet Services International, 2214 Route 37 E., Toms River, 08753 ... (732) 270-1188
Bantle's Banners & Signs, 213 Clements Bridge Rd., Barrington, 08007 ... (856) 546-1112
†★ Baosteel America, Inc., 85 Chestnut Ridge Rd., Ste. 210, Montvale, 07645 ... (201) 307-3355
Barantec, Inc., 777 Passaic Ave., Ste. 345, Clifton, 07012 ... (973) 779-8774
† Barclay Brand Ferdon,
2401 S. Clinton Ave., P.O. Box 341, South Plainfield, 07080 ... (908) 561-2100
BarCodeAmerica.com, 144 Shunpike Rd., P.O. Box 506, Madison, 07940 ... (973) 377-8182
Barcus Co., Inc., Edgar C.,
Route 45 & Park Ave., P.O. Box 128, Westville, 08093 ... (856) 456-0204
Barlics Mfg. see. ... Inman Mold & Mfg. Co., Rahway
Bar-Lo Carbon Products, Inc.,
31 W. Daniel Rd., P.O. Box 10031, Fairfield, 07004 ... (973) 227-2717
Barlow Tyrie, Inc., 1263 Glen Ave., Ste. 230, Moorestown, 08057 ... (856) 273-7878
Barnett Machine Tool Corp., 401 Supor Blvd., P.O. Box 189, Harrison, 07029 ... (973) 482-6222
Barrasso & Blasi, Inc., 1581 Springfield Ave., Maplewood, 07040 ... (973) 761-0595
Barre Monuments, 114 Atlantic City Blvd., Beachwood, 08722 ... (732) 240-2888
Barrett Co., 33 Stonehouse Rd., P.O. Box 421, Millington, 07946 ... (908) 647-0100
Barrett Paving Materials, Inc. (H Q),
3 Becker Farm Rd., Ste. 307, Roseland, 07068 ... (973) 533-1001
Barricade Books, Inc., 2037 Lemoine Ave., Fort Lee, 07024 ... (201) 944-7600
Barrier Enterprises, Inc., 175 Stanhope Sparta Rd., Andover, 07821 ... (973) 770-3983
Barrington Press Inc, 37 Spring Valley Ave., Paramus, 07652 ... (201) 843-6556
Barry Callebaut USA, LLC, 1500 Suckle Hwy., Pennsauken, 08110 ... (856) 663-2260
Bartlett Printing & Graphics, Inc., 4495 Route 130 S., Burlington, 08016 ... (609) 386-1525
Bartley Crucible Refractories,
15 Muirhead Ave., P.O. Box 5464, Trenton, 08638 ... (609) 393-0066
Bartlo Packaging, Inc., 61 Willet St., Bldg. Z, Passaic, 07055 ... (973) 778-6900
Barton & Cooney, LLC, 300 Richards Run, Burlington, 08016 ... (609) 747-9300
Barworth Micro Valve, Inc., 673 Morris Tpke., Springfield, 07081 ... (973) 376-4883
BASF Corp., 2 Pleasant View Ave., Washington, 07882 ... (908) 689-7540
BASF Corporation see. ... BASF Corp., Washington
BASF Corporation see. ... BASF Corporation, Catalysts Div., Iselin
BASF Corporation see. ... BASF Fuel Cell, Inc., Somerset
BASF Corporation (H Q), 100 Park Ave., Florham Park, 07932 ... (973) 245-6000
BASF Corporation, Catalysts Div.,
25 Middlesex-Essex Tpke., P.O. Box 770, Iselin, 08830 ... (732) 205-5000
BASF Fuel Cell, Inc., 39 Veronica Ave., Somerset, 08873 ... (732) 545-5100
★ Basha USA, LLC, 390 Broadway, Bayonne, 07002 ... (201) 339-9770
Basic Tool & Die Corp., 752 Ramsey Ave., Hillside, 07205 ... (908) 688-9155
Basil T's Brew Pub & Italian Grill, 183 Riverside Ave., Red Bank, 07701 ... (732) 842-5990
† Bass, Inc., Rudolf, 45 Halladay St., Jersey City, 07304 ... (201) 433-3800
Bassano Printers & Lithographers, 67 Royal Ave., Hawthorne, 07506 ... (973) 423-1400
Bassil Bookbinding & Finishing, Inc., 2 Alsan Way, Little Ferry, 07643 ... (201) 440-4925
★ Ba-Tampte Pickle Products, Inc., 2660 Main Rd., Franklinville, 08322 ... (856) 697-9815
† Bath Connection, The, 183 Millburn Ave., Millburn, 07041 ... (973) 467-7888
Bath Connection, The see. ... Bayonne Plumbing Supply, Inc., Bayonne
Bath Connection, The see. ... New Jersey Plumbing, Heating & Industrial Supply, LLC, Maplewood
Battaglia Contracting, Louis see. ... Capitol City Aluminum Products, Hamilton
Batten The Hatches, 70 State Route 181, Lake Hopatcong, 07849 ... (973) 663-1910
Bauer Gear Motor, LLC, 31 Schoolhouse Rd., Somerset, 08873 ... (732) 469-8770
Bauer, Inc., Susan R., 427 Margaret King Ave., Ringwood, 07456 ... (973) 657-1590
Bauer Precision, Inc., 174 Kinderkamack Rd., Ste. D, Park Ridge, 07656 ... (201) 307-0369
Bauer Publishing Co., 270 Sylvan Ave., Ste. 210, Englewood Cliffs, 07632 ... (201) 569-6699
Baum Draperies, 666 Passaic Ave., Nutley, 07110 ... (973) 661-1841
Bauman's Computer Solutions, 192 Route 130, Bordentown, 08505 ... (609) 920-0121
Baumar Industries, Inc., 29 E. Centre St., Nutley, 07110 ... (973) 667-5490
Baxter Co., Inc., E. L., 70 S. 7th Ave., P.O. Box 277, Long Branch, 07740 ... (732) 229-8219
Baxter Corp., The, 511 Commerce St., P.O. Box 645, Franklin Lakes, 07417 ... (201) 337-1212
Baxter Rubber Co., 10 Spielman Rd., Fairfield, 07004 ... (973) 227-1956
Bay Shore Canvas, 310 Firehouse Rd., Brick, 08723 ... (732) 477-8520
Bay State Milling Co., 404 Getty Ave., Clifton, 07011 ... (973) 772-1000
† Bay Treasure Seafood, LLC, 2002 Lakewood Rd., Unit 4, Toms River, 08755 ... (732) 240-3474
Bayard's Chocolate Co., Inc., 2325 Marlton Pike West, Cherry Hill, 08002 ... (856) 663-2565
Bayer Healthcare see. ... Bayer Healthcare, Consumer Care Div., Whippany
Bayer Healthcare, Consumer Care Div.,
100 Bayer Blvd., P.O. Box 915, Whippany, 07962 ... (862) 404-3000
Bayer HealthCare Pharmaceuticals (H Q), 100 Bayer Blvd., Whippany, 07981 ... (862) 404-3000
Bayer MaterialScience, LLC see. ... Bayer HealthCare Pharmaceuticals (H Q), Whippany
Bayonne Community News, 170 Broadway, Bayonne, 07002 ... (201) 437-2460
Bayonne Dry-Dock & Repair, Inc.,
Military Ocean Terminal Dock Yard, P.O. Box 240, Bayonne, 07002 ... (201) 823-9295
Bayonne Plumbing Supply, Inc. see. ... Bath Connection, The, Millburn
† Bayonne Plumbing Supply, Inc., 250 Avenue E, Bayonne, 07002 ... (201) 339-8000
Bayonne Plumbing Supply, Inc. see. New Jersey Plumbing, Heating & Industrial Supply, LLC, Maplewood
Bayshore Metal Products, Inc., 120 Francis St., Ste. 6, Keyport, 07735 ... (732) 739-9260
† Bayshore Recycling Corp., 75 Crows Mill Rd., P.O. Box 290, Keasbey, 08832 ... (732) 738-6000
Bayway Lumber, 43 Porete Ave., North Arlington, 07031 ... (201) 991-4200
BBC Printing, 4 Main St., P.O. Box 276, Branchville, 07826 ... (973) 948-7998
BBK Machining, Inc., 429 Garrison Rd., Elmer, 08318 ... (856) 358-8864
BCC (U.S.A.) Inc., 143 Ethel Rd. W., Piscataway, 08854 ... (732) 572-5450
BCG Marble & Granite Co., 370 Whitesville Rd., Jackson, 08527 ... (732) 367-3788
BCG Marble & Granite Fabricators Co., Inc. see. ... BCG Marble & Granite Co., Jackson
BCG Marble & Granite Fabricators Co., Inc., 167 Sussex St., Hackensack, 07601 ... (201) 343-8487
BCS Machine & Mfg. Corp., 3575 Kennedy Rd., South Plainfield, 07080 ... (908) 561-1656
BCT-NY/NJ, 11 Industrial Ave., Upper Saddle River, 07458 ... (201) 236-0088
B.D. Briggs, 31 Richboynton Rd., Dover, 07801 ... (973) 989-1950
B&D Donor Recognition Products see. ... B&D Marketing, Inc., Cherry Hill
B&D Marketing, Inc., 1879 Old Cuthbert Rd., Ste. 21, Cherry Hill, 08034 ... (856) 354-2004
★ BE & K Plastics, 340 E. Broad St., Burlington, 08016 ... (609) 386-3200
B/E Aerospace, Inc. see. ... B/E Consumables Management, Paramus
† B/E Consumables Management, 650 From Rd., Paramus, 07652 ... (201) 265-8770
Beachwood Canvas Works, LLC,
39 Lake Ave., P.O. Box 137, Island Heights, 08732 ... (732) 929-3168
Beacon Converters, Inc., 280 Midland Ave., P.O. Box 8208, Saddle Brook, 07663 ... (201) 797-2600
Beacon Offset Co., Inc., 204 Russell Pl., Hackensack, 07601 ... (201) 488-4241
Beacon Publishing Co., Inc., 775 Valley Rd., Clifton, 07013 ... (973) 279-8845
Beacut Abrasives Corp., 788 Paterson Ave., East Rutherford, 07073 ... (973) 249-1420
Bear Hands Ltd., 38 Main St., Little Ferry, 07643 ... (201) 807-9898
† Bearing Depot & Supply, Inc., 819 Lincoln Blvd., Ste. 1, Middlesex, 08846 ... (732) 563-2225
Beaton Sails, Inc., 72 Beaton Rd., Brick, 08723 ... (732) 920-6638
Beatrice Home Fashions, Inc.,
151 Helen St., P.O. Box 86, South Plainfield, 07080 ... (908) 561-7370
Beau Label LLC, 385 Hillside Ave., Hillside, 07205 ... (973) 318-7800
Beauticraft Slipcover Co., 9 Wynnewood Dr., Voorhees, 08043 ... (215) 625-7979
★ Beauty-Fill, LLC, 170 Circle Dr. N., Piscataway, 08854 ... (732) 802-8200
Beaver Run Farms, 300 Beaver Run Rd., Lafayette, 07848 ... (973) 875-5555
Bebe Chic, 530 Church St., Ridgefield, 07657 ... (201) 941-5414
Becker Plating, Inc., 121 Highway 35 N., Neptune, 07753 ... (732) 775-8945
Becton, Dickinson & Co. (H Q), 1 Becton Dr., Franklin Lakes, 07417 ... (201) 847-6800
BeCu Manufacturing Co., Inc., 2347 Beryllium Rd., Scotch Plains, 07076 ... (908) 233-3343
Bedding Industries Of America, 1375 Jersey Ave., North Brunswick, 08902 ... (732) 628-0800
Bedrock Granite, Inc., 803 Shrewsbury Ave., Shrewsbury, 07702 ... (732) 741-0010
Beech Woodworks, Inc., 9 Kentucky Ave., Paterson, 07503 ... (973) 225-0111
Beef International, Inc., 7010 Central Hwy., Pennsauken, 08109 ... (856) 663-6763
Behringer Corp., 17 Ridge Rd., Branchville, 07826 ... (973) 948-0226
Behrman House, Inc., 11 Edison Pl., Springfield, 07081 ... (973) 379-7200
Beilis Development, LLC (H Q),
20-21 Wagaraw Rd., Bldg. 31-B, Fair Lawn, 07410 ... (973) 559-5670
† Beisler America, LLC, 1841 E. Elizabeth Ave., P.O. Box 1683, Linden, 07036 ... (908) 925-4040
Beisler Weidmann Co., Inc., 233 Cortlandt St., Belleville, 07109 ... (973) 759-5020
Bel Fuse, Inc. (H Q), 206 Van Vorst St., Jersey City, 07302 ... (201) 432-0463
Bel Ray Co., LLC, 1201 Bowman Ave., Wall, 07719 ... (732) 938-2421
† Belair Instrument Co., Inc.,
36 Commerce St., P.O. Box 619, Springfield, 07081 ... (973) 912-8900
Bel-Art Products, Inc., 661 State Route 23, Wayne, 07470 ... (973) 694-0500
Belco Technologies Corp., 9 Entin Rd., Parsippany, 07054 ... (973) 884-4700
Belden Inc. see. ... Alpha Wire Co., Elizabeth
Belfer Group, 10 Ruckle Ave., Farmingdale, 07727 ... (732) 493-2666
Bell Arte Woodworking, Inc., 10 W. Mravlag Pl., Elizabeth, 07201 ... (908) 355-1199
Bell Container Corp., 615 Ferry St., P.O. Box 5728, Newark, 07105 ... (973) 344-4400
Bell Signs, 3125 Woodbridge Ave., Ste. 5-C, Edison, 08837 ... (732) 738-0010
Bella Palermo Pastry Shop, Inc., 619 Elizabeth Ave., Elizabeth, 07206 ... (908) 354-8610
Bellco Glass, Inc., 340 Edrudo Rd., Vineland, 08360 ... (856) 691-1075
Belle Mead Printing, LLC, 42 Old Camplain Rd., Hillsborough, 08844 ... (908) 595-9500
Belleville Corp., 328 Belleville Tpke., Kearny, 07032 ... (201) 991-6222
† Belleville Scale & Balance, LLC, 50 S. Center St., Orange, 07050 ... (973) 759-4487
Belleville Wire Cloth Co., Inc., 18 Rutgers Ave., Cedar Grove, 07009 ... (973) 239-0074
Bellia Business Products & Services, Inc., 1047 N. Broad St., Woodbury, 08096 ... (856) 845-2234
Bellia Enterprises see. ... Bellia Business Products & Services, Inc., Woodbury
Bellia Print & Copy Center, 190 William L. Dalton Dr., Glassboro, 08028 ... (856) 582-4004
Bell-Mark Sales Co., Inc.,
331 Changebridge Rd., P.O. Box 2007, Pine Brook, 07058 ... (973) 882-0202
Bellview Winery, 150 Atlantic St., Landisville, 08326 ... (856) 697-7172
Belmont Wholesale Fence Mfg., 112-114 Monroe St., Garfield, 07026 ... (973) 472-5121
Bel-Tech Stamping, Inc., 26 Industrial Rd., Ste. A, West Milford, 07480 ... (973) 728-8229
Belting Industries Co., Inc.,
20 Boright Ave., P.O. Box 310, Kenilworth, 07033 ... (908) 272-8591
Beltor Mfg. Corp., 50 Union Ave., Ste. 12, Berlin, 08009 ... (856) 768-5570
Benanti, Inc., D. F., 420 Quarry Ln., North Brunswick, 08902 ... (732) 422-3102
† Benchmark, Cane Farm, Bldg. 7, P.O. Box 214, Rosemont, 08556 ... (609) 397-1131
Benchmark Scientific, Inc., 116 Corporate Blvd., South Plainfield, 07080 ... (908) 222-1712
† Bendheim, 61 Willett St., Bldg. PP, Passaic, 07055 ... (973) 471-1733
Bendix Architectural Products, Inc., 90 Dayton Ave., Ste. 34, Passaic, 07055 ... (973) 473-4780
† Benedict-Miller, LLC, 123 N. 8th St., Kenilworth, 07033 ... (908) 497-1477
Benjamin Moore & Co., 134 Lister Ave., Newark, 07105 ... (973) 344-1200
Benjamin Moore & Co. (H Q), 101 Paragon Dr., Montvale, 07645 ... (201) 573-9600
Bennett Cabinets, Inc., 1251 Highway 1, Edison, 08837 ... (732) 548-1616
Bennett Heat Treating & Brazing Co., Inc., 690 Ferry St., Newark, 07105 ... (973) 589-0590
Bennett Plastics, Inc., 22 Kentucky Ave., Paterson, 07503 ... (973) 684-1501
Bentley Laboratories, LLC, 111 Fieldcrest Ave., Edison, 08837 ... (732) 512-0200

Bentley Mfg., Inc., 41 Ethel Rd., Piscataway, 08854 .......... (732) 572-5933
Benton Graphics, Inc., 3 Industrial Dr., Trenton, 08619 .......... (609) 587-4000
Berg Furniture U. S. A., Inc., 120 E. Gloucester Pike, Barrington, 08007 .......... (856) 310-0511
Bergen Auto Upholstery, 375 North St., Ste. U, Teterboro, 07608 .......... (201) 457-9100
Bergen Barrel & Drum Co., 43 O'Brien St., Ste. 45, Kearny, 07032 .......... (201) 998-3500
Bergen Cable Technology, LLC, 343 Kaplan Dr., Fairfield, 07004 .......... (973) 276-9596
Bergen County Magazine, The, 297 Kinderkamack Rd., Ste. 135, Oradell, 07649 .......... (201) 265-2286
† Bergen County Motor & Tool Co., 17-16 River Rd., Fair Lawn, 07410 .......... (201) 796-3006
Bergen Fence, Inc., 279 Bergen Tpke., Ridgefield Park, 07660 .......... (201) 641-2111
† Bergen Industrial Supply A division of F.W. Webb,
30 Stefanic Ave., Elmwood Park, 07407 .......... (201) 796-2600
Bergen Instant Printing, Inc., 328 Broad Ave., Ridgefield, 07657 .......... (201) 945-7303
Bergen International, LLC,
411 Route 17 S., Ste. 100, Hasbrouck Heights, 07604 .......... (201) 299-4499
Bergen Marzipan & Chocolate, 205 S. Washington Ave., Bergenfield, 07621 .......... (201) 385-8343
Bergen Metal Products, Inc., 120 Brighton Rd., Ste. 5, Clifton, 07012 .......... (973) 249-1500
Bergen Mfg. & Supply Co., Inc., 2025 85th St., North Bergen, 07047 .......... (201) 854-3461
Bergen Screen Printing, Inc., 255 W. Broadway, Paterson, 07522 .......... (973) 595-1222
Bergen Sign Co., Inc., 161 E. Railway Ave., Paterson, 07503 .......... (973) 742-7755
★ Bergen Wholesale Meats Corp., 154 Hackensack Ave., Hackensack, 07601 .......... (201) 342-2138
Berges Trenton Awning Co., Inc., 12 W. Washington Ave., Pleasantville, 08232 .......... (609) 641-7861
† Berje Inc., 700 Blair Rd., Carteret, 07008 .......... (973) 748-8980
Berkeley Contract Packaging, LLC, 530 N. Michigan Ave., Kenilworth, 07033 .......... (908) 810-4000
Berkeley Varitronics Systems, Inc., 255 Liberty St., Metuchen, 08840 .......... (732) 548-3737
Berkowitz, Inc., L.P., J. E.,
1 Gateway Blvd., P.O. Box 427, Pedricktown, 08067 .......... (856) 456-7800
Berkshire Hathaway, Inc. see. .......... Benjamin Moore & Co. (H Q), Montvale
Berkshire Hathaway, Inc. see. .......... Graver Water Systems, LLC, New Providence
Berkshire Machine, Inc., 390 Route 15 S., Wharton, 07885 .......... (973) 366-7710
Berlin Neon Sign, Inc., 326 Old White Horse Pike, Waterford Works, 08089 .......... (856) 767-0525
† Berlin Packaging, LLC, 2050 Center Ave., Ste. 400, Fort Lee, 07024 .......... (201) 947-7744
† Berliss Bearing Co.,
644 W. Mount Pleasant Ave., P.O. Box 45, Livingston, 07039 .......... (973) 992-4242
Bernafon, LLC, 2501 Cottontail Ln., Somerset, 08873 .......... (732) 560-9996
Bernard, Inc., Dennis, 142 Ely Harmony Rd., Freehold, 07728 .......... (800) 541-5456
Bernardsville Print Center, 21 Mine Brook Rd., Bernardsville, 07924 .......... (908) 766-4073
Bernhard-Link Theatrical, LLC, 815 Fairview Ave., Ste. 11, Fairview, 07022 .......... (201) 943-4190
Berry & Sons, Inc., Miller, Robbinstown Rd., P.O. Box 174, Port Norris, 08349 .......... (856) 785-1420
Berry Business Procedure Co., 6 Park St., P.O. Box 845, Cranford, 07016 .......... (908) 272-6464
Berry Plastics, 34 Engelhard Dr., Monroe Township, 08831 .......... (609) 655-4600
Berry Plastics Corp. see. .......... Berry Plastics, Monroe Township
Berry Plastics Corp. see. .......... Berry Plastics, Inc., Phillipsburg
Berry Plastics, Inc., 190 Strykers Rd., Phillipsburg, 08865 .......... (908) 454-0900
Bertot Industries, Inc., 23 Malcolm St., Ste. 1, Morristown, 07960 .......... (973) 267-0006
Best Billiards, 393 Pittstown Rd., Pittstown, 08867 .......... (908) 730-0933
Best Cast, 822 Kinderkamack Rd., River Edge, 07661 .......... (201) 225-1750
Best Drapery & Blind Mfg. Co., 1 Kresson Rd., Cherry Hill, 08034 .......... (856) 429-2242
Best Drapery & Design, Inc. see .......... Best Drapery & Blind Mfg. Co., Cherry Hill
Best Provision Co., Inc., 144 Avon Ave., Newark, 07108 .......... (973) 242-5000
Bestwork Industries For The Blind, Inc.,
1940 Almay Ave., Ste. 200, Cherry Hill, 08003 .......... (856) 939-5220
Beta Craft, Inc., 2682 Route 130, P.O. Box 536, Cranbury, 08512 .......... (609) 655-1940
Beta Industries see. .......... Beta Screen Corp., Carlstadt
Beta Iron Works, Inc., 31 Pasadena Ave., Lodi, 07644 .......... (973) 815-2730
Beta Plastics Corp., 120 Amor Ave., Carlstadt, 07072 .......... (201) 933-1400
Beta Screen Corp., 707 Commercial Ave., Carlstadt, 07072 .......... (201) 939-2400
Betar, Inc., 100 Randolph Rd., Ste. 4, Somerset, 08873 .......... (908) 359-4200
Bethel Bindery, Inc., 1500 Route 539, Tuckerton, 08087 .......... (609) 296-5043
Bethel Industries, Inc., 3423 John F. Kennedy Blvd., Jersey City, 07307 .......... (201) 656-8222
Betson Enterprises see. .......... Betti Industries, Inc., H., Carlstadt
Better Home Plastics Corp., 439 Commercial Ave., Palisades Park, 07650 .......... (201) 592-0370
Better Plastics, Inc., 1 Mallory Ave., Jersey City, 07305 .......... (201) 332-6777
Better Sleep Co., Inc., 100 Readington Rd., Ste. 2, Branchburg, 08876 .......... (908) 393-0120
Betti Industries, Inc., H., 303 Patterson Plank Rd., Carlstadt, 07072 .......... (201) 438-1300
BEUMER Corporation, 800 Apgar Dr., Somerset, 08873 .......... (732) 893-2800
Beveled Edge, 51 Mount Bethel Rd., Warren, 07059 .......... (908) 754-6772
Beverage Distribution Center, Inc., 8275 Route 130, Pennsauken, 08110 .......... (856) 665-6200
Beverage Distribution Center, Inc. see .......... Pepsi-Cola & National Brand Beverages Ltd., Pennsauken
Beverage Media Group, Inc., 2444 Morris Ave., Ste. 318, Union, 07083 .......... (908) 964-5060
Bey Electronics Corp., 39 Kentucky Ave., Paterson, 07503 .......... (973) 225-9494
BFI see. .......... Business Furniture, Inc., Elizabeth
bfi see. .......... Business Furniture, Inc., Parsippany
★ BGS, Inc., 910 E. County Line Rd., Ste. 101, Lakewood, 08701 .......... (732) 442-5000
Bhamra Chain Mfg. Co., 1020 Springfield Rd., Union City, 07087 .......... (908) 686-4555
Biazzo Dairy Products, Inc., 1145 Edgewater Ave., Ridgefield, 07657 .......... (201) 941-6800
Bielen Graphic Arts, R. J., 6 Jules Ln., New Brunswick, 08901 .......... (732) 545-3501
Bierig Bros., Inc., 3539 Reilly Ct., Vineland, 08360 .......... (856) 691-9765
Bierman Everett Foundry Co., 133 S. 20th St., Irvington, 07111 .......... (973) 373-8800
BIF New York, Inc., 465 Barell Ave., Carlstadt, 07072 .......... (201) 933-7777
Big 3 Precision Products see. .......... Big 3 Precision Mold Services, Millville
Big Apple Jewelry Mfg., 62 Railroad Ave., East Rutherford, 07073 .......... (201) 531-1600
BIG Client, LLC, 1 Industrial Way W., Bldg. E, Eatontown, 07724 .......... (732) 918-8221
Big Eye Lamp, Inc., 870 Route 530, Ste. 2, Whiting, 08759 .......... (732) 557-9400
Big 3 Precision Mold Services, 30 Gorton Rd., Millville, 08332 .......... (856) 293-1400
Bigelow Components Corp., 74 Diamond Rd., Springfield, 07081 .......... (973) 467-1200
Bihler Of America, Inc., 85 Industrial Dr., Phillipsburg, 08865 .......... (908) 213-9001
Bihler Of America, Inc. see. .......... Ultimate Training Munitions, North Branch
Bilcar Signs, 2131 Morris Ave., Union, 07083 .......... (908) 687-3777
Bilco Wire Rope see. .......... Doran Sling & Assembly Corp., Hillside
Bildisco Door Mfg., Inc., 21 Central Ave., West Orange, 07052 .......... (973) 673-2400
Bilfinger Water Technologies, 708 Challenger Way, Forked River, 08731 .......... (609) 693-9434
Bill Martin Machine, LLC, 56 Paterson Ave., Ste. 112, Newton, 07860 .......... (973) 300-5052
† Billows Electric Supply Co., Inc., 301 N. New Rd., Pleasantville, 08232 .......... (609) 345-6154
† Billows Electric Supply Co., Inc., 1719 Nottingham Way, Trenton, 08619 .......... (609) 890-2822
† Billows Electric Supply Co., Inc., 3901 New Jersey Ave., Wildwood, 08260 .......... (609) 522-7736
Bill's Canvas Shop see. .......... G & J Solutions, Inc., Woodbine
Bills, Inc., James W., 167 Newman Springs Rd., Ste. E, Shrewsbury, 07702 .......... (732) 212-1009
Bill's Printing Service, Inc., 2829 S. Broad St., Trenton, 08610 .......... (609) 888-1841
Bilt-Rite Tool & Die Co., Inc., 29 Montesano Rd., Fairfield, 07004 .......... (973) 227-2882
Bimini Bay Outfitters, Ltd. see. .......... Folsom Corp. (H Q), Mahwah
† Binder Machinery Co., Inc., 201 N. Route 73, Winslow, 08095 .......... (856) 767-5900
Bindgraphics Co., Inc., 490 W. 1st Ave., Roselle, 07203 .......... (908) 245-1110
Bindi North America, Inc., 507 Main St., Belleville, 07109 .......... (973) 751-1754
Bindi North America, Inc. (H Q), 630 Belleville Tpke., Kearny, 07032 .......... (973) 812-8118
Bind-Rite Robbinsville, 1 Applegate Dr., Robbinsville, 08691 .......... (609) 208-1917
Bind-Rite Services, Inc., 16 Horizon Blvd., South Hackensack, 07606 .......... (201) 440-5585
Bio Compression Systems, Inc., 120 W. Commercial Ave., Moonachie, 07074 .......... (201) 939-0716
Bioactive Resources, LLC, 138 Sylvania Pl., South Plainfield, 07080 .......... (908) 561-3114
BioAir Solutions, LLC, 110 Kresson-Gibbsboro Rd., Ste. 303, Voorhees, 08043 .......... (856) 258-6969
Bio-Chem Fluidics, Inc., 85 Fulton St., Ste. 12, Boonton, 07005 .......... (973) 263-3001
Bioclimatic Air Systems, 600 Delran Pkwy., Ste. D, Delran, 08075 .......... (856) 764-4300
Biofusion, Inc., 310 Godwin Ave., Ridgewood, 07450 .......... (201) 447-6241
Biogenesis, Inc., 296 Washington Ave., Hackensack, 07601 .......... (201) 678-1992
BIO-key International, Inc. (H Q),
3349 Highway 138, Bldg. A, Ste.E, Wall, 07719 .......... (732) 359-1100
★ Biological Controls, Inc., 749 Hope Rd., Eatontown, 07724 .......... (732) 542-5822
Biological Controls, Inc., 749 Hope Rd., Ste. A, Tinton Falls, 07724 .......... (732) 389-8922
† Bio-Medical Products Corp., 10 Halstead Rd., Mendham, 07945 .......... (973) 543-7434
BioMediCon, 30 E. Central Ave., Moorestown, 08057 .......... (856) 778-1880
BioMedtrix, LLC, 50 Intervale Rd., Ste. 5, Boonton, 07005 .......... (973) 331-7800
Biomet, Inc., 20-01 Pollitt Dr., Fair Lawn, 07410 .......... (201) 797-7300
Biomet, Inc. see. .......... EBI, Parsippany
Biomet Spine & Bone Healing Technologies see. .......... EBI, Parsippany
Biometallics, Inc., 37 Station Dr., Princeton Junction, 08550 .......... (609) 275-0133
Bionomic Industries, Inc., 777 Corporate Dr., Mahwah, 07430 .......... (201) 529-1094
† Bio-Ox International, Inc., 140 Ethel Rd. W., Ste. U, Piscataway, 08854 .......... (732) 650-9779
Biosearch Medical Products, Inc., 35 Industrial Pkwy., Branchburg, 08876 .......... (908) 722-5000
BioTillion, LLC, 30 Vreeland Dr., Ste. 7, Skillman, 08558 .......... (609) 454-3523
Bipore, Inc., 31 Industrial Pkwy., Northvale, 07647 .......... (201) 767-1993
Bird Toy Man, 197 S. Hillside Ave., Succasunna, 07876 .......... (973) 584-0756
Birnn Chocolates, Inc., 314 Cleveland Ave., Highland Park, 08904 .......... (732) 545-4400
Bisaga, Inc., 212 Ashland Ave., Somerdale, 08083 .......... (856) 784-7966
Bistis Press, 1310 Clinton Ave., Irvington, 07111 .......... (973) 373-8033
Bivalve Packing Co., Inc., 6957 Miller Ave., P.O. Box 336, Port Norris, 08349 .......... (856) 785-0270
Biwal Mfg. Co., Inc., 48 Industrial St. W., Clifton, 07012 .......... (973) 778-0105
Biztech, Inc., 3155 Route 10, Ste. 202, Denville, 07834 .......... (973) 361-7666
BJG, Inc. see. .......... Graphic Marketing Group, Fairfield
† BK Classic Auto Glass, LLC, 441 Cortlandt St., Belleville, 07109 .......... (973) 759-1485
Blacher Canvas Products, Inc., 604 Bound Brook Rd., Dunellen, 08812 .......... (732) 968-3666
Black Car News, 714 Crestbrook Ave., Cherry Hill, 08003 .......... (856) 751-0656
Black Car News, 420 Inverness Rd., Williamstown, 08094 .......... (856) 262-2368
Black Millwork & Center Lumber Co., 220 W. Crescent Ave., Allendale, 07401 .......... (201) 934-0100
Black Prince Distillery, Inc., 691 Clifton Ave., Clifton, 07011 .......... (973) 365-2050
Black Universities Supply Shop, The, 410 Leland Ave., Plainfield, 07062 .......... (908) 754-8088
† BlackHawk Industrial, Atlantic Tool Systems Div.,
170 5th Ave., Hawthorne, 07506 .......... (973) 238-0009
† Blackman Plumbing Supply Co., Inc., 270 Route 17 S., Mahwah, 07430 .......... (201) 529-5500
Blackstone Group L. P., The see. .......... Catalent Pharma Solutions, Inc. (H Q), Somerset
Blackstone Group L. P., The see. .......... Pinnacle Foods Group, LLC (H Q), Cherry Hill
BlackStratus, 1551 S. Washington Ave., Ste. 401, Piscataway, 08854 .......... (732) 393-6000
† Blackwell Assocs., Inc., 15 Kimberly Rd., East Brunswick, 08816 .......... (732) 238-8000
† Blake Industries, Inc., 660 Jerusalem Rd., Scotch Plains, 07076 .......... (908) 233-7240
Blanc Display Group, The, 88 King St., Ste. 1, Dover, 07801 .......... (973) 537-0090
Blanc Industries, Inc., 88 King St., Dover, 07801 .......... (973) 678-1200
Blanchette Tool & Gage Mfg.,
845 Bloomfield Ave., P.O. Box 1270, Clifton, 07012 .......... (973) 471-2100
Blanco Assocs., Inc., J., 280 9th Ave., Unit 1, Hawthorne, 07506 .......... (973) 427-0619
BLAST-MASTER Sandblasting & Painting see. .......... Tulenko Enterprises, LLC, Rockaway
Blaustein, Inc., M., 516 Millburn Ave., Short Hills, 07078 .......... (973) 379-1080
Blauth Millwork, 57 Pleasant Valley Rd., Titusville, 08560 .......... (609) 737-9502
Blend-Rite Industries, Inc., 585 Forest St., Unit 4, Orange, 07050 .......... (973) 395-3889
BlessingWhite, Inc., 23 Orchard Rd., Skillman, 08558 .......... (908) 904-1000
Blickman, Inc., 500 U.S. Highway 46, Clifton, 07011 .......... (973) 330-0557
Blinds To Go, Inc., 1800 Cedar Bridge Ave., Lakewood, 08701 .......... (732) 901-2001
Blinds To Go, Inc., 101 E. State Route 4, Paramus, 07652 .......... (732) 321-5000
Bliss Electrical Supply Co., 207 South St., Elizabeth, 07202 .......... (908) 289-9719
Blitz Safe Of America, Inc., 33 Honeck St., Englewood, 07631 .......... (201) 569-5000
Blonder Tongue Laboratories, Inc.,
1 Jake Brown Rd., P.O. Box 1000, Old Bridge, 08857 .......... (732) 679-4000
Bloomex International, Inc., 295 Molnar Dr., Elmwood Park, 07407 .......... (201) 703-9799
Bloomfield Drapery Co., Inc., 948 Paterson Ave., East Rutherford, 07073 .......... (973) 777-3566
Bloomfield Wines, Inc., 339 Broad St., Bloomfield, 07003 .......... (973) 743-2020
Blue Anchor Fence, LLC, 314 Arrowood Ave., Hammonton, 08037 .......... (609) 561-1874
Blue Army of Our Lady of Fatima see. .......... World Apostolate of Fatima USA, Washington
Blue Blade Steel, 123 N. 8th St., P.O. Box 40, Kenilworth, 07033 .......... (908) 272-2620
Blue Chip Industries, Inc., 50 Old Camplain Rd., Hillsborough, 08844 .......... (908) 704-1466
Blue Chip Technology, 267 Richwood Rd., P.O. Box 287, Richwood, 08074 .......... (856) 881-3133
Blue Dog Graphics, 222 River St., Hackensack, 07601 .......... (201) 343-3343
Blue Gauntlet Fencing Gear, Inc.,
280 N. Midland Ave., Bldg. W, Saddle Brook, 07663 .......... (201) 797-3332
Blue Parachute, 263 Amboy Ave., Ste. 1, Metuchen, 08840 .......... (732) 767-1320
Blue Planet Solutions, Inc., 116 Millburn Ave., Ste.108, Millburn, 07041 .......... (973) 597-4555
Blue Plaza, Inc. see. .......... Plaza 70 Bagels, Marlton
Blue Sage Software, 35 Lord William Penn Dr., Morristown, 07960 .......... (973) 366-1900
Blue Star Glass, Inc., 2300 U.S. Highway 1, Bldg. 31, North Brunswick, 08902 .......... (732) 422-1272
Blue Streak Screen Printing Co., 33 E. Railroad Ave., Monroe Township, 08831 .......... (732) 656-0400
Blue Streak Uniforms, LLC see. .......... Blue Streak Screen Printing Co., Monroe Township
Blueknight Energy Partners L. P.,
King & Jersey St., P.O. Box 31, Gloucester City, 08030 .......... (856) 456-6673
Bluenog Corp., 285 Davidson Ave., Ste. 306, Somerset, 08873 .......... (732) 584-2340
BlueSpire Strategic Marketing, 110 Summit Ave., Ste. B, Montvale, 07645 .......... (201) 740-6100
Bluestar Silicones U.S.A. Corp. (H Q),
2 Tower Center Blvd., Ste. 1601, East Brunswick, 08816 .......... (732) 227-2060
Bluewater Welding & Fabrication, LLC,
1089 Route 47, P.O. Box 206, Dennisville, 08214 .......... (609) 522-7352
BMB Fasteners, Inc., 86 Lackawanna Ave., Ste. 208, Woodland Park, 07424 .......... (973) 256-4010
BML Blackbird Theatrical Services, Inc., 1 Aquarium Dr., Secaucus, 07094 .......... (201) 617-8900
BMW Of North America, LLC (H Q),
300 Chestnut Ridge Rd., Woodcliff Lake, 07677 .......... (201) 307-4000
BNP Media, Inc., 210 E. State Route 4, Ste. 203, Paramus, 07652 .......... (201) 291-9001
Boards & Beams Co., LLC, 1275 Bloomfield Ave., Ste. 92, Fairfield, 07004 .......... (973) 299-6100
Bob's Signs Co., 1918 Englishtown Rd., P.O. Box 15, Old Bridge, 08857 .......... (732) 521-4554
Bob's Trophy, 6 Hamilton St., Montvale, 07645 .......... (201) 391-3790
BOBST North America, Inc., 146 Harrison Ave., Roseland, 07068 .......... (973) 226-8000

Boccella Precast, LLC, 324 New Brooklyn Rd., Berlin, 08009 .... (856) 767-3861
Bodine Tool & Machine Co., Inc.,
1273 N. Church St., Ste. 103, Moorestown, 08057 .... (856) 234-7800
Bodipure see. .... Y, Inc., Fair Lawn
Bodycote, 304 Cox St., Roselle, 07203 .... (908) 245-0717
Bodycote Thermal Processing, Inc. see. .... Bodycote, Roselle
Boehm Porcelain, LLC, 25 Princess Diana Dr., Trenton, 08638 .... (609) 656-2200
Bogen Communications, Inc., 50 Spring St., Ste. 1, Ramsey, 07446 .... (201) 934-8500
Bogue Systems, Inc., 100 Pennsylvania Ave., Paterson, 07503 .... (973) 523-2200
Boiardi Products Corp., 453 Main St., Ste. 4, Little Falls, 07424 .... (973) 256-1100
Bolt Welding & Iron Works, 78 Wall St., Trenton, 08609 .... (609) 393-3993
Bolttech Mannings, Inc., 321 Richard Mine Rd., Ste. 300, Wharton, 07885 .... (973) 537-1576
Bomar Crystal Co., 201 Blackford Ave., P.O. Box 10, Middlesex, 08846 .... (732) 356-7787
Bon Chef, Inc., 205 State Route 94, Lafayette, 07848 .... (973) 383-8848
Bon Venture, Inc., 34 Ironia Rd., P.O. Box 850, Flanders, 07836 .... (973) 584-5699
Bon Venture Services, LLC see. .... Bon Venture, Inc., Flanders
Bond Parade Floats Displays, Inc., 111 Clifton Blvd., Clifton, 07011 .... (973) 778-3333
Bonded Insulation Products, 657 Union Blvd., Totowa, 07512 .... (973) 256-2120
† Boneham Metal Products, Inc., 327 N. 14th St., Kenilworth, 07033 .... (908) 272-1200
Bongiovanni Custom Cabinet & Furniture, LLC, Mario,
7 E. Pleasant Ave., Pleasantville, 08232 .... (609) 646-8488
★ Bongo Vista Publishing, LLC, 32 Catalpa Ave., Hackensack, 07601 .... (201) 343-0252
Bon-Jour Group, LLC, 1100 Blanch Ave., Norwood, 07648 .... (201) 646-1070
Bonland Industries, Inc., 890 Towbin Ave., Lakewood, 08701 .... (732) 886-7127
Bonland Industries, Inc., 50 Newark Pompton Tpke., Wayne, 07470 .... (973) 694-3211
Bonney-Vehslage Tool Co., 3 Dundar Rd., Springfield, 07081 .... (973) 589-6975
Bono Signs & Designs, LLC, 1 Beamer Rd., Sussex, 07461 .... (973) 875-5488
bookdisplays.com see. .... City Diecutting, Inc., Morristown
Books Are Back, Inc., 296 Woodside Ave., Ridgewood, 07450 .... (201) 447-0374
Boomerang Systems, Inc., 30-A Vreeland Rd., Ste. 150, Florham Park, 07932 .... (973) 538-1194
Boomerang Used Office Furniture, 9155 River Rd., Pennsauken, 08110 .... (856) 582-0100
Boost Co., The see. .... Drink Atoast Co., Inc., Riverside
Borden Dairy Co. see. .... Farmland Dairies, Wallington
Borealis Compounds, Inc., 176 Thomas Rd., Port Murray, 07865 .... (908) 850-6200
Bornmann's RV, 131 Delsea Dr. S., Glassboro, 08028 .... (856) 881-7979
Boro Printing, Inc., 813 Broadway, West Long Branch, 07764 .... (732) 229-1899
Boro Sawmill & Timber Co., Inc., 139 Ryerson Ave., Wayne, 07470 .... (973) 832-4607
† Boro Supply Co., Inc., 2-21 Banta Pl., P.O. Box 1034, Fair Lawn, 07410 .... (201) 794-3111
Borrelli Construction see. .... Borrelli Steel Fabricators, LLC, Vineland
Borrelli Steel Fabricators, LLC, 2800 Industrial Way, Vineland, 08360 .... (856) 690-8850
Borst Cabinet Co., 15 Schierloh Ct., Ramsey, 07446 .... (201) 825-4220
Borton Enterprises, 178 Woodruff Rd., Bridgeton, 08302 .... (856) 453-9221
Bossen Architectural Millwork, Inc., 1818 Bannard St., Cinnaminson, 08077 .... (856) 786-1100
Bostik, Inc., 2000 Nolte Dr., West Deptford, 08066 .... (856) 848-8669
Boston Technologies, Inc., 610 E. Landis Ave., Vineland, 08360 .... (856) 692-4958
Bothers Woodworking, Inc., A. R.,
236 Dukes Pkwy., P.O. Box 127, Somerville, 08876 .... (908) 725-2891
† Bottcher America Corp., 88 Ford Rd., Ste. 8, Denville, 07834 .... (973) 664-1241
Bottcher America Corporation see. .... Bottcher America Corp., Denville
Bottcher Systems see. .... Bottcher America Corp., Denville
★ Bound To Last, 144 E. 9th St., Lakewood, 08701 .... (732) 942-0423
Boundary Fence & Railing see. .... Belmont Wholesale Fence Mfg., Garfield
Bowman Tool, 147 Pinebrook Rd., Englishtown, 07726 .... (732) 786-0770
Boy On A Dolphin Corp., 308 State Route 36, Port Monmouth, 07758 .... (732) 495-2200
Boyko's Metal Finishing Co., 100 Poinier St., Newark, 07114 .... (973) 623-4254
Boyle Tool & Die Co., Inc., 135 Crown Point Rd., Thorofare, 08086 .... (856) 853-1818
Bozzone Custom Woodwork, Inc., 77 N. Beverwyck Rd., Lake Hiawatha, 07034 .... (973) 334-5598
BP America, Inc. see. .... BP Lubricants USA, Inc., Wayne
BP Graphics & Printing, 315 4th St., Lakewood, 08701 .... (732) 905-9830
† BP Lubricants USA, Inc., 1500 Valley Rd., Wayne, 07470 .... (973) 633-2200
BR Welding & Industrial Services, Inc., 3 Brook Rd., Howell, 07731 .... (732) 363-8253
Brabender® Instruments, C. W.,
50 E. Wesley St., P.O. Box 2127, South Hackensack, 07606 .... (201) 343-8425
Braccio see. .... Big Apple Jewelry Mfg., East Rutherford
Bracco Diagnostics, Inc.,
259 Prospect Plains Rd., Bldg. H, Monroe Township, 08831 .... (609) 514-2200
Braco Mfg. Co. & Magic Safety Products, Inc.,
4301-B New Brunswick Ave., Ste. 2, South Plainfield, 07080 .... (732) 968-0008
Bradbury Burial Vault Co., Inc., 761 Lower Landing Rd., Blackwood, 08012 .... (856) 227-2555
Braddock Heat Treating Co., Inc., 123 Chimney Rock Rd., Bridgewater, 08807 .... (732) 356-2906
Braddock Metallurgical, Inc. see. .... Braddock Heat Treating Co., Inc., Bridgewater
Brady Worldwide, Inc. see. .... SPC Sorbent Products Co., Inc., Somerset
Braen Stone, 217 Limecrest Rd., Lafayette, 07848 .... (973) 383-7100
Braen Stone Industries see. .... Van Orden Sand & Gravel, Ringwood
Bralen, LLC, 236 U.S. Highway 206 N., Branchville, 07826 .... (973) 948-6575
Brand & Oppenheimer Co., Inc., 188 E. Bergen Pl., Ste. 201, Red Bank, 07701 .... (732) 224-7400
Brand Aromatics, Inc., 1600 Oak St., P.O. Box 3033, Lakewood, 08701 .... (732) 363-8080
Brand Muscle see. .... Graphic Express Menu Co., Inc., Clifton
Branded Screen Printing, LLC, 45 Warren St., P.O. Box 687, Chester, 07930 .... (908) 879-7411
Brandywine Scale LLC Newark Delaware see. .... Belleville Scale & Balance, LLC, Orange
Brass Shop, Inc., 611 Central Ave., Westfield, 07090 .... (908) 232-2161
Bravo Packing, 59 N. Gothwood Ave., Carneys Point, 08069 .... (856) 299-1044
Brawer Bros., Inc. (H Q),
375 Diamond Bridge Ave., P.O. Box 640, Hawthorne, 07506 .... (973) 238-1800
Brazilian Voice, 412 Chestnut St., P.O. Box 5686, Newark, 07105 .... (973) 491-6200
Bread & Bagels, 1600 Church Rd., Cherry Hill, 08002 .... (856) 667-2333
Breaker Group, Inc., The, 32-34 Mill St., Mount Holly, 08060 .... (609) 267-1330
BRECOflex Co., L.L.C., 222 Industrial Way W., Eatontown, 07724 .... (732) 460-9500
Breen Color Concentrates, Inc., 11 Kari Dr., Lambertville, 08530 .... (609) 397-8200
Breeze-Eastern Corp., 35 Melanie Ln., Whippany, 07981 .... (973) 602-1001
Brenner Metal Products Corp., 16 Main Ave., P.O. Box 16, Wallington, 07057 .... (973) 778-2466
Brenntag North America, Inc. see. .... Brenntag Specialties, Inc., South Plainfield
† Brenntag Specialties, Inc., 1000 Coolidge St., South Plainfield, 07080 .... (908) 561-6100
† Brent Material Co., 325 Columbia Tpke., Ste. 308, Florham Park, 07932 .... (973) 325-3030
Brentrick, Inc., 527 E. 39th St., Paterson, 07504 .... (973) 357-3579
Breure Heating & Air Conditioning see. .... Breure Sheet Metal Co., Inc., Clifton
Breure Sheet Metal Co., Inc., 46 Walman Ave., Clifton, 07011 .... (973) 772-6423
Brewer Assocs., 400 Apgar Dr., Unit G, Somerset, 08873 .... (732) 564-9070
Brewster Vaults & Monuments, Inc., 1017 Steeprun Rd., Millville, 08332 .... (856) 785-1412
Brewster Washers see. .... Wm. H. Brewster Jr., Inc., Fairfield
Brick Glass Co., 214 Midstreams Pl., Brick, 08724 .... (732) 899-8811
† Brick Wholesale Flower Market, 570 Mantoloking Rd., Brick, 08723 .... (732) 477-6765
Brick-Wall Corp., 25 1st Ave., Ste. 200, Atlantic Highlands, 07716 .... (732) 787-0226
Brick-Wall Corp., 2215 Lacey Rd., Forked River, 08731 .... (609) 693-6223
† Brida Stone, Inc., 555 Mullica Hill Rd., Glassboro, 08028 .... (856) 881-1700
Bridge Machine see. .... Bridge Rotary Machine Co., LLC, Palmyra
Bridge Rotary Machine Co., LLC, 614 Kennedy St., P.O. Box 45, Palmyra, 08065 .... (856) 829-3110
Bridgestate Foundry Corp., 175 Jackson Rd., Berlin, 08009 .... (856) 767-0400
Bridgeton Trophy & Engraving, 641 Landis Ave., Bridgeton, 08302 .... (856) 451-9007
Bridgeview Industrial Finishers, Inc., 241 Terrace Blvd., Voorhees, 08043 .... (856) 768-3624
Bridor, Inc. see. .... Bridor USA, Vineland
Bridor USA, 2260 Industrial Way, Vineland, 08360 .... (856) 691-8000
† Bridy Sales & Leasing Co., Inc., 115 Madison Ave., Paterson, 07524 .... (973) 345-4311
Briggs Healthcare see. .... Omnimed, Inc., Moorestown
Bright Ideas USA, LLC, 890 Morris Ave., Lakewood, 08701 .... (732) 886-8865
Bright Lights USA, Inc., 145 Shreve Ave., Barrington, 08007 .... (856) 546-5656
Bright Machinery Mfg. Group, Inc.,
239 Lindbergh Pl., Bldg. 2-A, Paterson, 07503 .... (973) 345-7405
★ Bright Side Newspaper, 1560 Route 83, Cape May Court House, 08210 .... (609) 861-2034
Bright Signs, LLC, 2626 County Road 516, Old Bridge, 08857 .... (732) 679-7440
Brim Electronics, Inc., 120 Home Pl., Lodi, 07644 .... (201) 796-2886
Brimar Industries, Inc.,
64 Outwater Ln., 3rd Fl., P.O. Box 467, Garfield, 07026 .... (973) 340-7889
Bringhurst Bros., Inc., 38 W. Taunton Rd., Berlin, 08009 .... (856) 767-0110
Brisar Industries, Inc., 150 E. 7th St., Paterson, 07524 .... (973) 278-2500
Bristol-Donald Co., Inc., 50 Roanoke Ave., Newark, 07105 .... (973) 589-2640
Bristol-Myers Squibb Company, 777 Scudders Mill Rd., Plainsboro, 08536 .... (609) 897-2000
Britten & Travel Lite Golf, E. F.,
22 South Ave. W., P.O. Box 246, Cranford, 07016 .... (908) 276-4800
Britton Cabinets, 199 Westwood Ave., Long Branch, 07740 .... (732) 222-2232
Britton Industries, Inc.,
227 Bakers Basin Rd., P.O. Box 6499, Lawrenceville, 08648 .... (609) 588-8225
Broad Street Media, 53 Haddonfield Rd., Ste. 306, Cherry Hill, 08002 .... (856) 779-3800
Broad Street Media, LLC see. .... Broad Street Media, Cherry Hill
Broad Street Media, LLC see. .... New Jersey Media Group, East Hanover
Broadhurst Sheet Metal Works, 230 Warburton Ave., Hawthorne, 07506 .... (973) 427-3972
Broadview Technologies see. .... Cambridge Industries Of America Co., Inc., Newark
Broadview Technologies, Inc. see. .... Anhydrides & Chemicals, Inc., Newark
Broadway Industries, 1 S. Middlesex Ave., Monroe, 08831 .... (609) 662-3970
Broadway Signs, Inc., 1029 Ocean Rd., Point Pleasant, 08742 .... (732) 892-6334
Brodie System, Inc., 1539 W. Elizabeth Ave., Linden, 07036 .... (908) 862-8620
Bromilow's Chocolates, Inc., 350 Rifle Camp Rd., Woodland Park, 07424 .... (973) 684-1496
Bromley Smith Publishers,
1014 Wall Rd., Ste. G-3, P.O. Box 312, Spring Lake, 07762 .... (732) 449-9288
Brook Metal Products, Inc., 6 Evans Terminal, Hillside, 07205 .... (908) 355-1601
★ Brooke Business Forms & Supplies, Inc.,
50 U.S. Highway 9, Ste. 303, Morganville, 07751 .... (732) 617-7550
Brother International Corporation, 200 Crossing Blvd., Bridgewater, 08807 .... (908) 704-1700
Brother's Quality Bakery, 365 Kearny Ave., Kearny, 07032 .... (201) 991-4364
Brothers Quality Bakery Of Allwood, 70 Market St., Clifton, 07012 .... (973) 473-1467
Brothers Quality Halal Meat see. .... New Jersey Halal Meat Packing, Paterson
★ Browbands With Bling & Other Things, 985 Farmingdale Rd., Jackson, 08527 .... (732) 740-8300
Brown & Co., C. W., 161 Kings Hwy., Mount Royal, 08061 .... (856) 423-3700
★ Brown & Co., Inc., Bill, 275 Whitehead Rd., Hamilton, 08619 .... (609) 396-9191
Brown & Perkins, Inc., 1193 Route 535, P.O. Box 412, Cranbury, 08512 .... (609) 655-1150
Brown Tool & Machine Co., Inc.,
Rosemont Raven Rock Rd., P.O. Box 142, Rosemont, 08556 .... (609) 397-1751
Brown's Awning Co., 628 West Ave., Ocean City, 08226 .... (609) 398-6262
Brown's Engraving, LLC, 12 Fort Dix Rd., Pemberton, 08068 .... (609) 894-4443
Bruderer Machinery, Inc., 1200 Hendricks Cswy., Ridgefield, 07657 .... (201) 941-2121
Brujan, Inc. see. .... Craftsmen Printers, The, Clifton
Brummer's Handmade Chocolates, 125 E. Broad St., Westfield, 07090 .... (908) 232-1904
★ Bruno The King Of Ravioli Co., 174 Union St., Hackensack, 07601 .... (201) 646-0505
Brunswick Sign & Exhibit Corp., 1510 Jersey Ave., North Brunswick, 08902 .... (732) 246-2500
Brussian Strokes Sign Co., 15-A Melanie Ln., Ste. 3-A, East Hanover, 07936 .... (973) 515-5151
Bry-Pat Advertising Specialty & Signs,
Tennent Rd., Route 79, P.O. Box 369, Morganville, 07751 .... (732) 591-0999
† BSTC Group, Inc., 135 Kinnelon Rd., Rm. 201, Kinnelon, 07405 .... (973) 492-5220
BT Specialty see. .... Bob's Trophy, Montvale
BTECH, Inc., 10 Astro Pl., Rockaway, 07866 .... (973) 983-1120
B-Tech Valve, LLC, 200 Cinnaminson Ave., Palmyra, 08065 .... (609) 321-2205
B-Tron Corp., 154 Cooper Rd., Ste. 1203, West Berlin, 08091 .... (856) 719-8485
Bucci Management Co., Inc., 603 N. 1st Rd., Hammonton, 08037 .... (609) 561-1888
Buchmann Control Panels Mfg., Inc., 5-18 Banta Pl., Fair Lawn, 07410 .... (201) 791-3161
Buck Mining & Materials, Inc., P.O. Box 1386, Hightstown, 08520 .... (732) 446-9336
† Buckhead Beef Co., 220 Raritan Ctr., P.O. Box 6988, Edison, 08837 .... (732) 661-4900
Budd Built In Vacuum Cleaners, 445 W. Main St., Wyckoff, 07481 .... (201) 891-3010
Budget Pallet, Inc., 3225 Dell Ave., North Bergen, 07047 .... (201) 330-2800
Budget Print, 426 Cedar Ln., Teaneck, 07666 .... (201) 692-1412
Budget Print Center, 2510 Atlantic Ave., Atlantic City, 08401 .... (609) 348-4589
Budget Print Center, 332 Broad St., Bloomfield, 07003 .... (973) 743-0073
Budget Print Center, 177 S. Centre St., Ste. 200-K, Merchantville, 08109 .... (856) 438-6204
Budget Print Center, 590 Valley Rd., Montclair, 07043 .... (973) 744-5520
Budget Printing Center, 300 E.Greentree Rd., Unit 14, Marlton, 08053 .... (856) 596-2980
Budget Printing, LLC, 70 Westfield Ave., Clark, 07066 .... (732) 574-1330
Budget Signs, 8 Caroline Ave., Clifton, 07011 .... (973) 340-2086
Buhl Electric, Inc., 80 Little Falls Rd., Fairfield, 07004 .... (201) 296-0600
Buhler Inc. see. .... Buhler Inc, Mahwah
Buhler Inc, 40 Whitney Rd., Mahwah, 07430 .... (201) 847-0600
Builders Architectural Millwork, 159 Newman Springs Rd. E., Shrewsbury, 07702 .... (732) 450-0056
Building Performance Equipment, Inc., 80 Broadway, Ste. 101, Hillsdale, 07642 .... (201) 722-1414
Building Specialties see. .... L & W Supply Corp., Toms River
Bumble Bee Foods, LLC see. .... Snow's, Cape May
Bumper Specialties, Inc., 1607 Imperial Way, West Deptford, 08066 .... (856) 251-9993
Bunge North America, Inc., 125 Sanford Ave., Kearny, 07032 .... (201) 467-0200
† Bunzl New Jersey, Inc., 27 Distribution Way, Monmouth Junction, 08852 .... (732) 821-7000
Bunzl USA, Inc. see. .... Bunzl New Jersey, Inc., Monmouth Junction
Buona Vita, Inc., 1 S. Industrial Blvd., Bridgeton, 08302 .... (856) 453-7972
Burger & Son, Inc., Edwin R., 732 Main St., P.O. Box 184, Sewell, 08080 .... (856) 468-2300
Burger Maker, Inc., 666 16th St., Carlstadt, 07072 .... (201) 939-4747
Burgess Steel Erectors Of New Jersey, LLC,
200 W. Forest Ave., P.O. Box 5629, Englewood, 07631 .... (201) 871-3500
Burgiss Group, LLC, The, 111 River St., Ste. 10, Hoboken, 07030 .... (201) 427-9600
Burling Instruments, Inc., 16 River Rd., P.O. Box 298, Chatham, 07928 .... (973) 635-9481

† Burlington County Overhead Door Co., Inc.,
444 Logan Ave., P.O. Box 127, Burlington, 08016 (609) 387-9092
Burlington County Times, Inc., 4284 Route 130, Willingboro, 08046 (609) 871-8000
Burlington Press, 328 High St., Burlington, 08016 (609) 387-0030
Burns Bros. & McCabe, Inc., 787 Tonnele Ave., Jersey City, 07307 (201) 795-0800
Burns, Inc., Joseph, 241 W. Union Ave., Bound Brook, 08805 (732) 356-7990
★ Burpee Material Technology, LLC, 15 Christopher Way, Eatontown, 07724 (732) 544-8900
B.U.S. Shop, The see. Black Universities Supply Shop, The, Plainfield
Bush Refrigeration, 1700 Admiral Wilson Blvd., Pennsauken, 08109 (856) 963-1800
Bush Tank Fabricators, Inc., 222 Thomas St., Newark, 07114 (973) 596-1121
Bushwick Metals see. AZCO Steel Co., South Plainfield
Bushwick Metals, LLC see. AZCO Steel Co., South Plainfield
Business Card Express, 8 E. Stow Rd., Ste. 140, P.O. Box 728, Marlton, 08053 (856) 596-3150
Business Cards Tomorrow see. Tomad, Inc., Egg Harbor City
† Business Furniture, Inc., 133 Rahway Ave., Elizabeth, 07202 (908) 355-3400
† Business Furniture, Inc., 10 Lanidex Plz. W., Ste. 202, Parsippany, 07054 (973) 503-0730
Business Graphics, 22 Park Pl., P.O. Box 832, Butler, 07405 (973) 838-9553
Business Power, Inc., 39 Hunt Ave., Ste. C, Stratford, 08084 (856) 783-7390
Business Today, 48 University Pl., Princeton, 08540 (609) 258-1111
Business Travel Executive Magazine, 262 Rockport Rd., Port Murray, 07865 (908) 979-1974
Butco, Inc., 2009 Route 130 N., Burlington, 08016 (800) 872-8055
Butensky Services Co., 3380 Route 22, P.O. Box 5020, Somerville, 08876 (908) 707-0912
Butler Engineering Assocs., Inc., 764 Ramsey Ave., Hillside, 07205 (908) 688-3300
Butler Printing & Laminating, 250 Hamburg Tpke., P.O. Box 836, Butler, 07405 (973) 838-8550
Butler Sign Company, 582 Fairfield Rd., Wayne, 07470 (973) 633-5757
Buxton Biomedical, Inc. (H Q), 15-A Melanie Ln., Unit 7, East Hanover, 07936 (973) 560-4848
Buyers Laboratory LLC, 20 Railroad Ave., Hackensack, 07601 (201) 488-0404
Buzz-Bee Cabinetry Co., 589 N. East Ave., Vineland, 08360 (856) 691-5474
BWAY Corp., 1202 Airport Rd., North Brunswick, 08902 (732) 247-6700
BWAY Corporation see. BWAY Corp., North Brunswick
BWAY Corporation, 6 Litho Rd., Trenton, 08638 (732) 997-4050
BWAY Corporation see. North America Packaging Corp. (NAMPAC), Dayton
Bylada Foods, LLC, 140 W. Commercial Ave., Moonachie, 07074 (201) 933-7474
Byram Laboratories, Inc., 1 Columbia Rd., Branchburg, 08876 (908) 252-0852
C & A Press, Inc., 636 State Route 18, East Brunswick, 08816 (732) 238-1150
C & C Jetronic, Inc., 126 Evergreen Rd., New Egypt, 08533 (609) 758-3553
C & C Metal Products Corp., 456 Nordhoff Pl., P.O. Box 7300, Englewood, 07631 (201) 569-7300
C & C Metal Products Corp. see. Metal City Findings Co., Englewood
★ C & C Signs & Banners, 812 Forepeak Dr., Forked River, 08731 (609) 693-4667
C & C Tool & Machine Co., LLC,
38 W. Scott St., P.O. Box 407, Riverside, 08075 (856) 461-6090
C & C Tool Co., LLC, 216 U.S. Highway 206, Ste. 2, Hillsborough, 08844 (908) 431-0330
C & D Cases, Inc., 407 River Rd., Unit 9, Clifton, 07014 (973) 473-4800
C & D Printing Co., 118 Broadway, Point Pleasant Beach, 08742 (732) 892-8044
C & D Sales see. Custom Embroidery, Pleasantville
C & E Canners, Inc., 1249 Mays Landing Rd., P.O. Box 229, Hammonton, 08037 (609) 561-1078
C & F Burner Co., 39 River Rd., P.O. Box 7189, North Arlington, 07031 (201) 998-8083
C & G Screws Unlimited, 2150 Route 88, Brick, 08724 (732) 892-8400
C & K Plastics, Inc., 159 Liberty St., Metuchen, 08840 (732) 549-0011
C & K Printing Co., Inc., 203 Paterson Ave., Ste. 1, Wallington, 07057 (973) 473-0739
C & K Punch & Screw Machine Products, 160 Hobart St., Hackensack, 07601 (201) 343-6750
C & L Machining Co., 110 S. New Broadway, P.O. Box 167, Brooklawn, 08030 (856) 456-1932
C & M Shade Corp., 53 Dwight Pl., Fairfield, 07004 (201) 807-1200
C & P Embroidery, LLC, 6602 Smith Ave., North Bergen, 07047 (201) 854-0388
C & R Printing, Inc., 400 Gotham Pkwy., Carlstadt, 07072 (201) 933-8000
C & S Hot Stamping Co., 20 Edgewater Pl., Edgewater, 07020 (201) 840-4004
C & S Machine, Inc., 22 Commerce Rd., Ste. Q, Fairfield, 07004 (973) 882-1097
C & S Machinery Rebuilding Corp., 636 E. 19th St., Paterson, 07514 (973) 742-7302
C & S Precision Products, LLC, 22 Park Pl., Butler, 07405 (973) 838-3644
C & S Scientific Corp., P.O. Box 1056, Hightstown, 08520 (609) 448-7037
C & S Tool Co., Inc., 304 Ridgedale Ave., East Hanover, 07936 (973) 887-6865
C & W Systems, 17-04 Split Rock Rd., P.O. Box 201, Fair Lawn, 07410 (201) 791-7892
C B Food, Inc., 1 Madison St., Bldg. B, East Rutherford, 07073 (973) 773-9224
★ C B Printing & Graphics, Inc., 795 Susquehanna Ave., Franklin Lakes, 07417 (201) 445-6500
C C & D Capital Contracting & Design, Inc., 640 North Ave., Plainfield, 07060 (908) 561-8411
C C S Stone, 9-11 Caesar Pl., Moonachie, 07074 (201) 933-1515
C D M Dust Control Of New Jersey, 15-17 S. 7th Ave., Long Branch, 07740 (732) 222-3694
C D S Sheet Metal, Inc., 1200 S. West Blvd., Ste. E, Vineland, 08360 (856) 794-5080
★ C Graphics Studio, 410 32nd St., Union City, 07087 (201) 866-0592
C. I. Filing Systems see. Custom Index, Inc., Totowa
C. J.'s Tool Mfg., Inc., 620 Route 168, Turnersville, 08012 (856) 227-7342
C L N Designs, LLC, P.O. Box 1822, South Hackensack, 07606 (201) 939-2120
C M S * Public Service Electric & Gas Co. see. PSEG Power, Sewaren
C N I Ceramics Nozzles, Inc., 23 Commerce Rd., Ste. L, Fairfield, 07004 (973) 276-1535
C N R Products Co., 74 Portland Ave., Bergenfield, 07621 (201) 384-7003
C P S Metals, Inc., 450 S. Fellowship Rd., Maple Shade, 08052 (856) 779-0846
C. R. Laurence Co., Inc., 1511 Lancer Dr., Moorestown, 08057 (856) 727-1022
C S L Water Quality, Inc., 156 Mount Bethel Rd., P.O. Box 4246, Warren, 07059 (908) 647-1400
C S L Water Treatment see. C S L Water Quality, Inc., Warren
C T A Mfg. Corp., 263 Veterans Blvd., Carlstadt, 07072 (201) 896-1000
C Technologies, Inc., 757 U.S. Highway 202/206, Bridgewater, 08807 (908) 707-1009
C W C Industries, Inc., 185 Foundry St., Newark, 07105 (973) 344-1434
Cabinet Works Corp., 511 W. Kings Hwy., Mount Ephraim, 08059 (856) 931-7289
Cabinet-Tronics, Inc., 100 Birmingham Rd., P.O. Box 198, Birmingham, 08011 (609) 267-2625
† CAC International, 30 Camptown Rd., Maplewood, 07040 (973) 371-4300
Cacciola Iron Works, 65 N. 9th St., Paterson, 07522 (973) 595-0854
Cacia's Bakery, 1010 S. Black Horse Pike, Blackwood, 08012 (856) 228-5986
CAD SIGNS, 169 Lodi St., Hackensack, 07601 (201) 267-0457
CADCAM-E.Com, Inc., 2115 Linwood Ave., Ste. 313, Fort Lee, 07024 (201) 503-1881
Caddy Corp., 509 Sharptown Rd., P.O. Box 345, Bridgeport, 08014 (856) 467-4222
Cadie Products Corp., 151 E. 11th St., Paterson, 07524 (973) 278-8300
CADPRO, Inc., 114 W. Atlantic Ave., Clementon, 08021 (856) 435-0050
Caesar's Pasta, 1001 Lower Landing Rd., Ste. 311, Blackwood, 08012 (856) 227-2585
Caffe Borbone USA, 19 Commerce Rd., Ste. G, Fairfield, 07004 (973) 227-7799
Cain Machine, Inc., 1501 Oakland Ave., Millville, 08332 (856) 825-7225
Cake Specialty, Inc., 255 Goffle Rd., Hawthorne, 07506 (973) 238-0500
Calandra Printing, 491 Bloomfield Ave., Caldwell, 07006 (973) 228-1649
Calandra's Italian & French Bakery, 204 1st Ave. W., Newark, 07107 (973) 484-5598
Calbar, LLC, 307 Bergen Ave., Kearny, 07032 (201) 246-1555
† Cal-Chlor Corp., 141 Baekeland Ave., Piscataway, 08854 (732) 271-3500
Caldwell Consumer Health, LLC (H Q), 8 Elmer St., Ste. 1, Madison, 07940 (973) 360-1090
Caled Industries, Inc., 26 Hanes Dr., Wayne, 07470 (973) 696-7575
† Cali Carting, Inc., 450 Bergen Ave., P.O. Box 440, Kearny, 07032 (201) 991-5400
California Closet Co., 2666 U.S. Highway 130, Cranbury, 08512 (609) 655-1899
California Closets, 4 Gardner Rd., Ste. 5, Fairfield, 07004 (973) 882-3800
California Stucco Products Corp., 85 Zabriskie St., Hackensack, 07601 (201) 457-1900
Calima Jewels, 215 Glen Ridge Ave., Montclair, 07042 (973) 746-2976
Calkins Media, Inc. see. Burlington County Times, Inc., Willingboro
★ Callahan Jewelers, Inc., 86 Vervalen St., Closter, 07624 (201) 768-6136
Callen Photo Mount Corp., 185 6th Ave., Ste. 1, Paterson, 07524 (973) 925-2390
CALMAC, 3-00 Banta Pl., Fair Lawn, 07410 (201) 797-1511
Caloric Color Co., Inc.,
176 Saddle River Rd., Bldg. A, South Hackensack, 07606 (973) 471-4748
Caltex Industries, Inc., 1301 W. Elizabeth Ave., Ste. E-1, Linden, 07036 (973) 273-1707
Calvaruso Clothing, G. & F., 345 Palisade Ave., Cliffside Park, 07010 (201) 945-7118
Camac Industries, 18 Gail Ct., Sparta, 07871 (973) 300-5575
Camatron Sewing Machine, Inc., 42 Bergenwood Rd., Ste. A, Fairview, 07022 (201) 941-5116
Cambio Newspaper, 604 56th St., West New York, 07093 (201) 902-0811
Cambrex Corp., 1 Meadowlands Plz., Ste. 1510, East Rutherford, 07073 (201) 804-3000
Cambridge Industries Of America Co., Inc., 7-33 Amsterdam St., Newark, 07105 (973) 465-0077
Cambridge Pavers, Inc., Jerome Ave., P.O. Box 157, Lyndhurst, 07071 (201) 933-5000
Cambridge Sheet Metal, Inc., 14 Troy Hills Rd., Ste. 6, Whippany, 07981 (973) 386-0788
Cambridge Silversmiths Ltd. (H Q),
30 Hook Mountain Rd., P.O. Box 625, Pine Brook, 07058 (973) 227-4400
Camden Glass, Inc., 111 Marlton Ave., Camden, 08105 (856) 365-0142
† Camden Iron & Metal, Inc., 143 Harding Ave., Bellmawr, 08031 (856) 365-7500
Camden Printworks, 1621 S. Broadway, Camden, 08104 (856) 365-1424
Camden Yards Steel Co., LLC, 2500 Broadway, Drawer 14, Camden, 08104 (856) 342-7100
C.A.M.E. Machine & Metal Works, Inc., 181 Pacific Ave., Jersey City, 07304 (201) 309-0005
Cameco, Inc., 100 Pine St., Verona, 07044 (973) 239-2700
Cameo Novelty & Pen, 400 Hillside Ave., Hillside, 07205 (973) 923-1600
† Camerican International, 45 Eisenhower Dr., Ste. 310, Paramus, 07652 (201) 587-0101
Camfil USA, Inc., 1 N. Corporate Dr., Riverdale, 07457 (973) 616-7300
Camin Cargo Control, Inc. (H Q), 230 Marion Ave., Linden, 07036 (908) 523-0616
CAMO Software, 1 Woodbridge Ctr., Ste. 319, Woodbridge, 07095 (732) 726-9200
CAMPAK, Inc., 119 Naylon Ave., Livingston, 07039 (973) 597-1414
Campbell Converting Corp., 703 Van Rossum Ave., Unit 2, Beverly, 08010 (609) 835-2720
Campbell Foundry Co., 800 Bergen St., Harrison, 07029 (973) 483-5480
Campbell Foundry Co. see. Campbell Foundry, Materials Div., Jackson
† Campbell Foundry, Materials Div., 630 S. Hope Chapel Rd., Jackson, 08527 (732) 408-1111
Campbell Soup Co. see. Campbell Soup Supply Co., South Plainfield
Campbell Soup Co. see. Ecce Panis, East Brunswick
Campbell Soup Co. (H Q), 1 Campbell Pl., Camden, 08103 (856) 342-4800
Campbell Soup Supply Co., 3500 S. Clinton Ave., South Plainfield, 07080 (908) 561-1660
Campus Classics, 3206 Route 38, P.O. Box 757, Mount Laurel, 08054 (856) 234-7474
Campus Coordinates, 1711 Ginesi Dr., Ste. 1, Freehold, 07728 (732) 866-6060
Camtec Industries, Inc., 28 Saddle Ridge Rd., Colts Neck, 07722 (732) 332-9800
Canam Steel Corp., 14 Harmich Rd., South Plainfield, 07080 (908) 561-3484
Canare Corp. Of America, 45 Commerce Way, Unit C, Totowa, 07512 (973) 837-0070
Canary Closets & Cabinetry, 697 Rahway Ave., Union, 07083 (908) 851-2894
Candela Corp. see. Applied Optronics, South Plainfield
Candle Artisans, Inc.,
253 E. Washington Ave., P.O. Box 190, Washington, 07882 (908) 689-2000
Canfield Technologies/Bow Electronic Solder,
1 S. Crossman Rd., Sayreville, 08872 (732) 316-2100
Cangro Industries, Inc. see. Cangro Transmission Co. Of New Jersey, Clifton
† Cangro Transmission Co. Of New Jersey, 295 Crooks Ave., Clifton, 07011 (973) 772-7662
Cantel Medical Corp. (H Q), 150 Clove Rd., 9th Fl., Little Falls, 07424 (973) 890-7220
Cantone Press, Inc., 161 Coolidge Ave., Englewood, 07631 (201) 569-2288
† Canuso, Inc., Louis P., 401 Crown Point Rd., P.O. Box 501, Thorofare, 08086 (856) 845-2700
Canvas 4 Life, Inc., 30 Chapin Rd., P.O. Box 216, Pine Brook, 07058 (973) 276-3200
Canvas Lady, The, 19 Killdeer Hill Rd., Woodbine, 08270 (609) 628-3257
Canvas Shop Of Avon, Inc., 504 Main St., Avon by the Sea, 07717 (732) 988-5775
† Caola & Co., 2 Crossroads Dr., P.O. Box 8772, Hamilton, 08691 (609) 890-7331
† CAP Barbell, Inc., 625 Rahway Ave., Union, 07083 (908) 624-1133
Capco Enterprises, Inc., 34 DeForest Ave., Ste. 3, East Hanover, 07936 (973) 884-0044
Capco Sportswear Inc. (H Q), 100 W. Commercial Ave., Moonachie, 07074 (201) 939-9228
Cape May Brewing Co., 1288 Hornet Rd., Rio Grande, 08242 (609) 849-9933
Cape May Star & Wave, 600 Park Blvd., Ste. 28, West Cape May, 08204 (609) 884-3466
Cape May Winery see. W J R B, Inc., Cape May
★ Cape Mining & Recycling, LLC,
560 Goshen Rd., P.O. Box 246, Cape May Court House, 08210 (609) 465-3277
Cape Printing Express, Inc., 821 Shunpike Rd., Cape May, 08204 (609) 884-8080
★ Cape Publishing, Inc., 513 Washington St., Cape May, 08204 (609) 898-4500
† Capespan North America, 701 N. Broadway., Ste. 102, Gloucester City, 08030 (856) 742-0242
Capintec, Inc., 6 Arrow Rd., Ste. 101, Ramsey, 07446 (201) 825-9500
Capital Foam Products, Inc.,
75 E. Union Ave., P.O. Box 7564, East Rutherford, 07073 (201) 933-5277
Capital Foods, Inc., 1701 E. Elizabeth Ave., Linden, 07036 (908) 587-9050
Capital Gasket & Rubber Corp., 325 E. Clements Bridge Rd., Runnemede, 08078 (856) 939-3670
Capital Hardware Supply see. Elgen Mfg. Co., Closter
Capital Label & Affixing Co., 1100 Taylors Ln., Unit 5, Cinnaminson, 08077 (856) 786-1700
Capital Offset, Inc., 257 10th Ave., Paterson, 07524 (973) 279-3023
Capital Printing Corp., 420 South Ave., Middlesex, 08846 (732) 560-1515
Capital Soap Products, LLC, 33 Branch St., P.O. Box 357, Paterson, 07544 (973) 333-6100
† Capital Steel Service, LLC, 82 Stokes Ave., Trenton, 08638 (609) 882-6983
Capitol Box Corp., 1300 6th St., North Bergen, 07047 (201) 867-6018
Capitol City Aluminum Products, 407 Rutgers Ave., Hamilton, 08619 (609) 587-3653
Capitol Copy Service, 116 W. State St., Trenton, 08608 (609) 989-8776
Capitol Fire Protection Co., Inc., 56 N. Logan Ave., Trenton, 08609 (609) 393-3936
Capitol Pavers & Retaining Wall, Inc.,
90 Main St., P.O. Box 3249, South Amboy, 08879 (732) 727-5460
Capitol Steel Products, Inc., 82 Stokes Ave., P.O. Box 5063, Trenton, 08638 (609) 538-9313
Caporaso Sales Corp., 144 Emmet St., Newark, 07114 (973) 824-7286
★ Capra Custom Cabinetry & Millwork, LLC,
259 E. Washington Ave., Washington, 07882 (908) 797-9848
CAPS see. Central Admixture Pharmacy Services, Englewood
Capsugel (H Q), 412 Mount Kemble Ave., Ste. 200-C, Morristown, 07960 (862) 242-1700
Captive Fastener Corp., 19 Thornton Rd., Oakland, 07436 (201) 337-6800
Capus Automation Services, Inc., 856 Highway 206, Hillsborough, 08844 (908) 281-0227
Caputo International, Inc., 112 Northfield Ave., Edison, 08837 (732) 225-5777
Cardinal Color, Inc., 50-56 1st Ave., Paterson, 07514 (973) 684-1919
Cardinal Components, Inc.,
145 U.S. Highway 46 W., Wayne Interchange I, Wayne, 07470 (973) 785-1333

ALPHABETICAL

★ Cardinal International, Inc.,
43 Route 46 E., Ste. 709, P.O. Box 897, Pine Brook, 07058 ... (973) 628-0900
Cardolite Corp., 500 Doremus Ave., Newark, 07105 ... (973) 344-5015
Care Plus NJ, Inc., 185 6th Ave., Paterson, 07524 ... (973) 553-1954
Carecam International, Inc., 10 Plog Rd., Fairfield, 07004 ... (973) 227-0720
Career Press, Inc., 220 W. Parkway, Unit 12, Pompton Plains, 07444 ... (201) 848-0310
CareFusion Corp. see. ... Vital Signs, A CareFusion Co., Totowa
† Caremark Rx, Inc., 180 Passaic Ave., Ste. 5, Fairfield, 07004 ... (973) 461-1550
Carfaro, Inc., 2075 E. State Street Ext., Trenton, 08619 ... (609) 890-6600
Carfaro Railings Company, Frank, 70 Hacklebarney Rd., Long Valley, 07853 ... (908) 879-7312
Cargille Laboratories, 55 Commerce Rd., Cedar Grove, 07009 ... (973) 239-6633
Cargille TAB-PRO Corp., 4 E. Frederick Pl., Cedar Knolls, 07927 ... (973) 267-8888
Carl Sign, LLC, 1200 Madison Ave., Paterson, 07503 ... (973) 340-0210
Carl Stahl Sava Industries, Inc.,
4 N. Corporate Dr., P.O. Box 30, Riverdale, 07457 ... (973) 835-0882
Carl Stahl Sava Industries, Inc. see. ... Jordan Mfg., LLC, Lafayette
Carlascio Inc. Orthotics, Prosthetic, Custom Shoes,
283 Grove St., Jersey City, 07302 ... (201) 333-8716
Carlascio Orthopedics see. ... Carlascio Inc. Orthotics, Prosthetic, Custom Shoes, Jersey City
Carlee Corp., 28 Piermont Rd., Rockleigh, 07647 ... (201) 768-6800
Carlen Machine Co., 1275 Bloomfield Ave., Bldg. 10, Door 89, Fairfield, 07004 ... (973) 808-1441
Carlisle Machine Works, Inc.,
412 S. Wade Blvd., Bldg. 5, P.O. Box 746, Millville, 08332 ... (856) 825-0627
Carlyle Group, The see. ... Ortho-Clinical Diagnostics, Inc. (H Q), Raritan
Carmel Furniture, Inc., 404 N. Midland Ave., Saddle Brook, 07663 ... (201) 796-0099
Carnegie Deli, Inc., 605 Washington Ave., Carlstadt, 07072 ... (201) 507-5557
★ Carol's Creations, LLC, 112 Kipling Rd., Cherry Hill, 08003 ... (856) 428-0621
† Carpathian Industries, LLC, 51 Newark St., Ste. 508, Hoboken, 07030 ... (201) 798-8883
Carpenter & Paterson, Inc., 3900 River Rd., P.O. Box 556, Pennsauken, 08110 ... (856) 488-1988
Carpenter & Paterson, Inc., 369 Jefferson St., Saddle Brook, 07663 ... (973) 772-1800
Carpenter Emergency Lighting, Inc., 2 Marlen Dr., Hamilton, 08691 ... (609) 689-3090
† Carrera Of America, Inc., 2 Corporate Dr., Ste. D, Cranbury, 08512 ... (609) 409-8510
Carrier Pigeon Illustrated Fiction & Fine Art * Carrier Pigeon Magazine see. CPMAG, LLC, Guttenberg
Carrington Co., LLC see. ... Carrington Tea, LLC, Closter
Carrington Co., LLC (H Q), 7 Reuten Dr., Closter, 07624 ... (800) 505-9546
Carrington Tea, LLC, 7 Reuten Dr., P.O. Box 102, Closter, 07624 ... (201) 261-5517
Carrini, Inc. (H Q), 140 Smith St., 5th Fl., Keasbey, 08832 ... (732) 650-1775
Carry Cases Plus, Inc. see. ... Century Service Affiliates, Inc., Paterson
Carson & Gebel Ribbon Co., Inc., 17 Green Pond Rd., Rockaway, 07866 ... (973) 627-4200
Carstens Publications, Inc., 108 Phil Hardin Rd., Newton, 07860 ... (973) 383-3355
Cartco, Inc., 621 Grape St., Hammonton, 08037 ... (978) 692-7070
Carter Co., The William, 17 The Promenade, Edgewater, 07020 ... (201) 313-1783
Carter Mfg. Co., Inc., 55 Anderson Ave., Moonachie, 07074 ... (201) 935-0770
Carter Pump, 326 S. Dean St., Englewood, 07631 ... (201) 568-9798
Carter Solution, Inc., The Jane, 45 S. 17th St., East Orange, 07018 ... (973) 677-1008
Carteret Coding, Inc., 1431 Raritan Rd., Clark, 07066 ... (732) 574-0900
Carteret Die Casting Corp., 74 Veronica Ave., P.O. Box 5610, Somerset, 08875 ... (732) 246-0070
Cartridge Actuated Devices, Inc., 40 Old Indian Spring Rd., Andover, 07821 ... (973) 347-2281
Cartridge Actuated Devices, Inc. (H Q), 51 Dwight Pl., Fairfield, 07004 ... (973) 575-1312
Cartridge Renewal Systems, 13 Glendale Dr., Englishtown, 07726 ... (732) 845-9497
† Cartridge World, 830 Franklin Ave., Franklin Lakes, 07417 ... (201) 891-0990
Cartridge World - Franklin Lakes see. ... Cartridge World, Franklin Lakes
Cartridge World In Morris Plains see. ... Petitts Ink Corp., Morris Plains
Cartridge World New Providence, LLC,
1310 Springfield Ave., New Providence, 07974 ... (908) 771-9696
Cartridge World Oakhurst, 1815 State Route 35, Oakhurst, 07755 ... (732) 531-4232
Cartridge World Of Union see. ... Hammer Too, LLC, Union
Cartridge World Of Wayne, LLC, 1055 Hamburg Tpke., Wayne, 07470 ... (973) 696-2880
Cary Compounds, LLC, 5 Nicholas Ct., Dayton, 08810 ... (732) 274-2626
Casa Di Trevi, 534 W. Westfield Ave., Roselle Park, 07204 ... (908) 259-9000
Casabona Signs, LLC, 37 Grove St., Passaic, 07055 ... (201) 325-8711
Case Medical, Inc., 19 Empire Blvd., South Hackensack, 07606 ... (201) 313-1999
Case Pork Roll Co., Inc., 644 Washington St., Trenton, 08611 ... (609) 396-8171
Case-It, 1050 Valley Brook Ave., Lyndhurst, 07071 ... (201) 804-5556
Caserta, Inc., Thomas A., 11 S. Gold Dr., Ste. E, Robbinsville, 08691 ... (609) 586-2807
Cases By Source see. ... Source Packaging, Inc., Mahwah
Cases By Source, Inc., 215 Island Rd., Mahwah, 07430 ... (201) 831-0005
Casework Design, 10 County Line Rd., Ste 26, Branchburg, 08876 ... (908) 722-7401
Casey's Executive Interiors,
152 Route 22 W., P.O. Box 7070, Green Brook, 08812 ... (732) 968-3236
Casings, Inc. see. ... Casings Of NJ, Inc., Hillside
† Casings Of NJ, Inc., 711 Ramsey Ave., Hillside, 07205 ... (908) 851-7766
Casio America, Inc. (H Q), 570 Mount Pleasant Ave., Dover, 07801 ... (973) 361-5400
Cast Classics, Inc., 65 Railroad Ave., Ridgefield, 07657 ... (201) 896-1515
CAST, Inc. (H Q), 11 Stonewall Ct., Woodcliff Lake, 07677 ... (201) 391-8300
★ Cast Lighting, LLC, 1120-A Goffle Rd., Hawthorne, 07506 ... (973) 423-2303
Cast Technology, Inc., 161 West St., South Plainfield, 07080 ... (908) 753-5155
Castellane Mfg. Co., 1405 Cantillion Blvd., P.O. Box 921, Mays Landing, 08330 ... (609) 625-3427
Castle Industries, Inc., 120 Sylvan Ave., Ste. 107, Englewood Cliffs, 07632 ... (201) 585-8400
Castle Printing, Inc., 1501 U.S. Highway 46, Ledgewood, 07852 ... (973) 584-0990
Castle Woodcraft Assocs., 161 Route 9, P.O. Box 426, Pine Beach, 08741 ... (732) 349-1519
Castner's Sawmill, 935 Fairview Lake Rd., P.O. Box 13, Stillwater, 07875 ... (973) 383-5661
Castor Jewelry, 13 N. Union St., Lambertville, 08530 ... (609) 397-0809
Casual Studio see. ... CS Apparel, Inc. (H Q), Edison
Catalent Pharma Solutions, Inc. (H Q), 14 Schoolhouse Rd., Somerset, 08873 ... (732) 537-6200
Catamaran Media Co., LLC, 3120 Fire Rd., Egg Harbor Township, 08234 ... (609) 383-8994
Catamaran Media Co., LLC, 3120 Fire Rd., Egg Harbor Township, 08234 ... (609) 266-1860
Catamaran Media Co., LLC, 507 S. Shore Rd., Marmora, 08223 ... (609) 624-8900
Catbridge Machinery, LLC, 222 New Rd., Ste. 1, Parsippany, 07054 ... (973) 808-0029
Catelli Bros. Veal & Lamb, Inc., 50 Ferry Ave., Collingswood, 08103 ... (856) 869-9293
Catelli Bros. Veal & Lamb, Inc., 776 Broad St., Shrewsbury, 07702 ... (732) 741-3687
Catering By The Maddalenas, Inc., 415 Route 31 N., Ringoes, 08551 ... (609) 466-7510
Catheter Robotics, Inc., 500 International Dr., Ste. 255, Budd Lake, 07828 ... (973) 691-2000
Catholic Book Publishing Corp., 77 W. End Rd., Totowa, 07512 ... (973) 890-2400
Catholic Star Herald, 15 N. 7th St., Camden, 08102 ... (856) 583-6142
CAVA Winery & Vineyard, Inc., 3619 State Route 94, Hamburg, 07419 ... (973) 823-9463
† Cavagna North America, Inc., 50 Napoleon Ct., Somerset, 08873 ... (732) 469-2100
Cavalier Chemical Co., 26 Papetti Plz., Elizabeth, 07206 ... (908) 558-0110
Cavalla, Inc., 111 Union St., Hackensack, 07601 ... (201) 343-3338
CB&I, 502-B Jersey Ave., New Brunswick, 08901 ... (732) 435-0777
CB&I, INC. see. ... Lummus Technology, Bloomfield
CBS Outdoor, 185 Highway 46, Fairfield, 07004 ... (973) 575-6900
CBS Outdoor, 1245 Towbin Ave., Lakewood, 08701 ... (732) 901-1100
CBS Outdoor Americas, Inc. see. ... CBS Outdoor, Fairfield
CBS Outdoor Americas, Inc. see. ... CBS Outdoor, Lakewood
CBT Supply, Inc. (H Q), 83 Jacobs Rd., Rockaway, 07866 ... (973) 586-2783
CCA Industries, Inc. (H Q), 200 Murray Hill Pkwy., East Rutherford, 07073 ... (201) 935-3232
Ccard, Inc., 17 Belleterre Dr., Manalapan, 07726 ... (732) 303-8264
CCE see. ... CADCAM-E.Com, Inc., Fort Lee
CCG Marketing Solutions see. ... Corporate Communications Group, The, West Caldwell
CCL Industries Corp. see. ... CCL Label, Inc., Hightstown
CCL Industries Corp. see. ... CCL Label, Inc., Robbinsville
CCL Label, Inc., 120 Stockton St., Hightstown, 08520 ... (609) 443-3700
CCL Label, Inc., 104 N. Gold Dr., Robbinsville, 08691 ... (609) 586-1332
CCL Label TubeDec, 92 Ark Rd., Lumberton, 08048 ... (609) 953-5050
CCSI Group, The, 1351 Morris Ave., P.O. Box 3554, Union, 07083 ... (908) 686-6464
CDI Group, Inc., 1135 W. Elizabeth Ave., Linden, 07036 ... (908) 862-1493
CDK Industry, LLC, 900 Haddonfield Rd., Cherry Hill, 08002 ... (856) 488-5456
CDS Corp., 27 Wilson Dr., Unit C, Sparta, 07871 ... (973) 300-0090
CDS Packaging, LLC, 237 Vaile Rd., Parsippany, 07054 ... (973) 219-1496
Ce De Candy, Inc., 1091 Lousons Rd., Union, 07083 ... (908) 964-0660
CEA Instrument, Inc., 160 Tillman St., Westwood, 07675 ... (201) 967-5660
Celco, Inc., 14 Industrial Ave., 3rd Fl., Mahwah, 07430 ... (201) 327-1123
Celebrity International, Inc. (H Q), 51 Saw Mill Pond Rd., Edison, 08817 ... (732) 476-2999
Celgene Corp., 86 Morris Ave., Summit, 07901 ... (908) 673-9000
★ Celldex Therapeutics, Inc., 53 Frontage Rd., Ste. 200, Hampton, 08827 ... (908) 200-7500
Cellebrite USA Corp., 7 Campus Dr., Ste. 210, Parsippany, 07054 ... (201) 848-8552
Cellunet Mfg. Co., Inc., 460 Veterans Dr., Burlington, 08016 ... (609) 386-3361
Cementex Products, Inc.,
650 Jacksonville Rd., P.O. Box 1533, Burlington, 08016 ... (609) 387-1040
Cenmed Enterprises, 121 Jersey Ave., New Brunswick, 08901 ... (732) 447-1100
Cenogenics Corp., 100 Route 520, P.O. Box 308, Morganville, 07751 ... (732) 536-6457
Cenogenics Corp. see. ... Laboratory Diagnostics Co., Inc., Morganville
Center Contracting Corp., 72 Putnam St., Paterson, 07524 ... (973) 523-6400
Center For Educational Advancement, 11 Minneakoning Rd., Flemington, 08822 ... (908) 782-1480
Center Metal Fabricators, Inc.,
1026 Black Horse Pike, P.O. Box 29, Hammonton, 08037 ... (609) 567-1808
Center Vocational Rehabilitation, 15 Meridian Rd., Ste. 1, Eatontown, 07724 ... (732) 544-1800
Centiv Services, LLC see. ... Graphic Express Menu Co., Inc., Clifton
Cento Fine Foods, 100 Cento Blvd., West Deptford, 08086 ... (856) 853-5445
Central Admixture Pharmacy Services, 160 W. Forest Ave., Englewood, 07631 ... (201) 541-0080
Central Art & Engineering, Inc.,
500 Goldman Dr., P.O. Box 289, Cream Ridge, 08514 ... (609) 758-5922
Central Components Mfg., LLC (H Q), 440 Lincoln Blvd., Middlesex, 08846 ... (732) 469-5720
† Central Connectors, Inc., 4 Bridge Plaza Dr., Ste. 1, Manalapan, 07726 ... (732) 972-3456
† Central Forklift, Inc., 415 Bell St., Piscataway, 08854 ... (732) 805-9494
Central Garden & Pet Co. see. ... Central Pet, Mahwah
Central Garden & Pet Co. see. ... Nylabone Products, Neptune City
Central Ink Corp., 2085 Center Square Rd., Unit A, Swedesboro, 08085 ... (856) 467-5562
Central Metal Fabricators, Inc., 300 Central Ave., Farmingdale, 07727 ... (732) 938-6900
Central Metals, Inc., 1054 S. 2nd St., Camden, 08103 ... (856) 963-5844
Central Mills, Inc., 473 Ridge Rd., Dayton, 08810 ... (732) 329-2009
Central Millwork Of New Jersey,
92 N. Main St., Bldg. 11, P.O. Box 447, Windsor, 08561 ... (609) 448-7700
† Central Pet, 301 Island Rd., Mahwah, 07430 ... (201) 529-5050
Central Plastics Co., 333 New Rd., Parsippany, 07054 ... (973) 808-0990
Central Poly Corp., 2400 Bedle Pl., Linden, 07036 ... (908) 862-7570
Central Printing & Typesetting, 1501 Route 37 E., Toms River, 08753 ... (732) 929-0011
Central Record Corp., The,
32 S. Main St., Ste. A, P.O. Box 1027, Medford, 08055 ... (609) 654-9221
Central Record Publications * South Jersey News * Central Record see. Journal Register Co., The, Medford
Central Safety Equipment, Inc.,
300 W. Broad St., P.O. Box 250, Burlington, 08016 ... (609) 386-6448
Central Sheet Metal Fabricators, Inc.,
897 South Ave., Ste. A, Middlesex, 08846 ... (732) 968-6100
Central Shippee, Inc., 46 Star Lake Rd., Bloomingdale, 07403 ... (973) 838-1616
Centrome, Inc. see. ... Advanced Biotech, Inc., Totowa
Centryco, Inc. see. ... Central Safety Equipment, Inc., Burlington
Centurion Printing, 761 Lexington Ave., Kenilworth, 07033 ... (908) 241-9839
Century Bathworks, Inc., 250 Lackawanna Ave., Woodland Park, 07424 ... (973) 785-4290
Century Conveyor Service, Inc., 4301 S. Clinton Ave., South Plainfield, 07080 ... (908) 205-0625
Century Engineering Co., Inc., 4 Orono St., Clifton, 07013 ... (973) 779-3900
Century Fabricating Co., Inc., 84 Railroad Ave., Belford, 07718 ... (732) 495-3200
Century Packaging, Inc., 42 Edgeboro Rd., East Brunswick, 08816 ... (732) 249-6600
Century Service Affiliates, Inc., 22 Mercer St., Ste. 1, Paterson, 07524 ... (973) 742-8118
Century Sports, 1715 Oak St., Ste. 1, Lakewood, 08701 ... (732) 905-4422
Century Tube Corp., 22 Tannery Rd., Somerville, 08876 ... (908) 534-2001
Cenveo, Inc., 25 Linden Ave. E., Jersey City, 07305 ... (201) 434-2100
Ceralli Competition Engines, Inc., 395 E. 18th St., Paterson, 07524 ... (973) 742-4972
★ Ceramcor, LLC, 1026 Samantha Way, Toms River, 08753 ... (732) 929-2833
Ceramic Magnetics, Inc., 16 Law Dr., Fairfield, 07004 ... (973) 227-4222
Ceramic Products, Inc., 221 Park St., Hackensack, 07601 ... (201) 342-8200
Cerbaco Ltd., 809 Harrison St., Frenchtown, 08825 ... (908) 996-1333
CERCO see. ... Cryogenic Equipment & Repair Co., Inc. (Cerco), Parlin
Ceresist, Inc., 176 E. 7th St., Paterson, 07524 ... (973) 345-3231
† CermSource, Inc,
25 Kimberly Rd., Unit A, P.O. Box 6026, East Brunswick, 08816 ... (732) 257-5002
Ceronics, Inc., 5 Dock St., P.O. Box 75, Matawan, 07747 ... (732) 566-5600
Certech, Inc., 1 Park Pl. W., Wood Ridge, 07075 ... (201) 939-7400
Certified Bakery, Inc., 20 Universal Pl., Carlstadt, 07072 ... (201) 635-9245
Certified Clam Corp., 190 Bay Ave., P.O. Box 383, Highlands, 07732 ... (732) 872-6650
Certified Labeling Solutions, 51 Old Camplain Rd., Hillsborough, 08844 ... (908) 704-9997
Certified Processing Corp., 184 Route 22 E., Hillside, 07205 ... (973) 923-5200
† Certified Products Co., 269 Kearney Ave., Jersey City, 07305 ... (201) 433-0013
† Certified Steel Co., 199 Whitehead Rd., Hamilton, 08619 ... (609) 890-7000
Certified Steel Company see. ... Certified Steel Co., Hamilton
† Certified Steel Company (H Q),
1333 Brunswick Ave., Ste. 200, Lawrenceville, 08648 ... (609) 396-7600
Cervinis Auto Designs see. ... Cervinis, Inc., Vineland
Cervinis, Inc., 3656 N. Mill Rd., Vineland, 08360 ... (856) 691-1744
CES see. ... Compliance Educational Systems, Inc., Marlton
CET Films, Inc., 1650 Corporate Rd. W., Lakewood, 08701 ... (732) 367-5511
Cetek, Inc. see. ... Hybrid-Tek, Inc., Clarksburg
Cetylite, Inc., 9051 River Rd., Pennsauken, 08110 ... (856) 665-6111

© Copyright 2015 Manufacturers' News, Inc.


CG Automation Solutions USA, 60 Fadem Rd., Springfield, 07081 .... (973) 379-7400
CGS see. .... Comtel Global Services, LLC, Edison
CH Technologies, Inc., 263 Center Ave., Ste. 2, Westwood, 07675 .... (201) 666-2335
Challenge Printing Co., The, 2 Bridewell Pl., Clifton, 07014 .... (973) 471-4700
† Chalmers & Kubeck, Inc., 8 Jules Ln., New Brunswick, 08901 .... (732) 993-1251
Chamberlain's VACU-Blast Sales,
1200 Bannard St., P.O. Box 225, Cinnaminson, 08077 .... (856) 829-6444
Chamberlin & Barclay, Inc.,
2 Hightstown Cranbury Station Rd., Cranbury, 08512 .... (609) 655-0700
Chambers Sheet Metal, Bill,
371 N. Glassboro Rd., P.O. Box 172, Woodbury Heights, 08097 .... (856) 848-4774
Chambord Prints, Inc., 38 Jackson St., Hoboken, 07030 .... (201) 795-2007
Chamonix see. .... Unimed International, Inc., Edison
Champion Fasteners, Inc., 707 Smithville Rd., Lumberton, 08048 .... (609) 267-5222
Champion Ink Co., Inc., 2045 88th St., North Bergen, 07047 .... (201) 868-4100
Champion Marble & Granite, Inc., 4 Kinney Rd., Manalapan, 07726 .... (732) 409-3200
Champion Plastics Corp., 220 Clifton Blvd., Clifton, 07011 .... (973) 777-9400
Champion Window Manufacturing & Supply Co., LLC see. Champion Window Of Pennsauken, Pennsauken
Champion Window Of Pennsauken, 8400 Remington Ave., Ste. B, Pennsauken, 08110 .... (856) 662-3400
Chandler see. .... Imperial Sewing Machine Co., Inc., Irvington
Chandler Machine Co., Inc., 400 Veterans Blvd., Carlstadt, 07072 .... (212) 741-2474
Chanel, Inc., 876 Centennial Ave., Piscataway, 08854 .... (732) 885-5500
Charles G.G. Schmidt & Co., Inc., 301 W. Grand Ave., Montvale, 07645 .... (201) 391-5300
Charles Machine Shop Service, Rob, 24 Rake Rd., Flemington, 08822 .... (908) 806-8512
Charmant Group, Inc., 400 American Rd., Morris Plains, 07950 .... (973) 538-1511
Charmer Sunbelt Group, The see. .... R & R Marketing, LLC, West Caldwell
★ Charter Financial Publishing Network, Inc., 499 Broad St., Shrewsbury, 07702 .... (732) 450-8866
Charter Machinery Corp. see. .... Graphic Equipment Corp., Metuchen
Chase Machine Co., Inc., 127 Park Ave., P.O. Box 148, Lyndhurst, 07071 .... (201) 438-2218
Chasen & Sons, Inc., M., 117 S. 20th St., Irvington, 07111 .... (973) 374-8956
Chasen & Sons, Inc., M., 123 S. 20th St., Irvington, 07111 .... (973) 589-8700
Chatham Brass, LLC, 1253 New Market Ave., Unit D, South Plainfield, 07080 .... (908) 668-0500
Chatham Container Display Corp., 6 Northridge Way, Warren, 07059 .... (800) 266-4848
Chatham Print & Design see. .... Thewal, Inc., Chatham
Chavant, Inc., 5043 Industrial Rd., Farmingdale, 07727 .... (732) 751-0003
Chavez Jewelry, Marie, 642 Bloomfield Ave., Verona, 07044 .... (973) 337-8551
Check-It Electronics see. .... Temperature Humidity Instruments LLC, Madison
Check-Mate Products see. .... G R Office Products, Inc., Paterson
★ Checkpoint Systems, Inc. (H Q), 101 Wolf Dr., P.O. Box 188, Thorofare, 08086 .... (856) 848-1800
† Chef's Corner, 178 U.S. Highway 206, Ste. B, Flanders, 07836 .... (973) 691-1500
Chelten House Products, Inc., 607 Heron Dr., P.O. Box 434, Bridgeport, 08014 .... (856) 467-1600
Chem Fleur see. .... Firmenich, Inc., Newark
Chem Flowtronics, Inc., 195 Paterson Ave., Little Falls, 07424 .... (973) 785-0001
Chemaid Laboratories, Inc., 100 Mayhill St., Saddle Brook, 07663 .... (201) 843-3300
Chemetall, 675 Central Ave., New Providence, 07974 .... (908) 464-6900
Chemglass, Inc., 3800 N. Mill Rd., Vineland, 08360 .... (856) 696-0014
Chemique, Inc., 315 N. Washington Ave., Moorestown, 08057 .... (856) 235-4161
Chem-Is-Try, Inc., 160-1 Liberty St., Metuchen, 08840 .... (732) 372-7311
Chemlime N. J., Inc. (H Q), 2350 South Ave., Scotch Plains, 07076 .... (908) 389-1006
Chemo Dynamics, Inc., 3 Crossman Rd. S., Sayreville, 08872 .... (732) 721-4700
Chemquip Corp., 258-262 Atlantic St., Paterson, 07503 .... (973) 684-3009
Chemsearch * Mohawk Laboratories see. .... NCH Corp., Monmouth Junction
Chemspa Industries, Inc., 22 Deforest Ave., East Hanover, 07936 .... (973) 386-1158
★ Chemspeed, Inc., 113 N. Center Dr., North Brunswick, 08902 .... (732) 329-1225
Chemtrade, 330 Doremus Ave., Newark, 07105 .... (973) 589-5300
Chemtrade Chemical, LLC see. .... Chemtrade, Newark
Chemtrade Chemical, LLC, 90 E. Halsey Rd., 3rd Fl., Parsippany, 07054 .... (973) 515-0900
Chemtrade Chemical, LLC see. .... General Chemical Corp., Berkeley Heights
Chemtrade Logistics, Inc. see. .... Chemtrade Chemical, LLC, Parsippany
Chemtura Corp. see. .... Anderol, Inc., East Hanover
Chemtura Corp., 1000 Convery Blvd., Perth Amboy, 08861 .... (732) 826-6600
Chemtura Corp. see. .... Chemtura Corp., Hatco Div., Fords
Chemtura Corp., Hatco Div., 1020 King George Post Rd., Fords, 08863 .... (732) 738-1000
Cheney Flashing Co., LLC, 623 Prospect St., Trenton, 08618 .... (609) 394-8175
Chenoa Information Service, Inc., 10 Parsonage Rd., Ste. 312, Edison, 08837 .... (732) 549-6800
Cherokee Rubber Co., 5 Laurel Dr., Unit 13, Flanders, 07836 .... (973) 584-3733
Cherry Hill Precision see. .... J.B.A.T., Inc., Cherry Hill
Cherubini Yachts, LLC, 51 Norman Ave., Riverside, 08075 .... (856) 764-5319
Chesapeake Pharmaceutical & Healthcare Packaging,
6 Commerce Rd., Fairfield, 07004 .... (973) 808-8000
Chesapeake Pharmaceutical Packaging Company, LLC see. Chesapeake Pharmaceutical & Healthcare Packaging, Fairfield
Cheshire Studio, Inc., 261 Main St., 2nd Fl., Ledgewood, 07852 .... (973) 240-7360
Chesnut Engineering, Inc., W. R., 14 Spielman Rd., Fairfield, 07004 .... (973) 227-6995
Chick Master International, Inc. (H Q),
25 Rockwood Pl., Ste. 335, Englewood, 07631 .... (201) 871-8810
Chief Neckerchief see. .... Wostbrock Embroidery, Inc., Midland Park
† Childcare Supply Co. Inc., 77 Pension Rd., Ste. 13, Englishtown, 07726 .... (732) 786-9888
Children's Apparel Network Ltd., 77 S. 1st St., Elizabeth, 07206 .... (908) 351-4477
Children's Technology Review, 120 Main St., Flemington, 08822 .... (908) 284-0404
Chilton Laboratories, 299-B Fairfield Ave., Fairfield, 07004 .... (973) 575-1990
Chinese Newsweek Corp., 32 Bridge St., Metuchen, 08840 .... (732) 744-1000
Chinook Sciences, LLC see. .... Advanced Metal Processing NJ, LLC, Millville
† Chinook Sciences, LLC (H Q), 20 Commerce Dr., Ste. 350, Cranford, 07016 .... (908) 272-5091
Chipp II, 7 Spring Hill Cir., Wayne, 07470 .... (212) 687-0850
Chiral Photonics, Inc.,
26 Chapin Rd., Unit 1104, P.O. Box 694, Pine Brook, 07058 .... (973) 732-0030
Chiromatic, Inc., 1375 Jersey Ave., North Brunswick, 08902 .... (800) 526-5116
† Chiswick Electric Co., Inc., 40 Brown Ave., Springfield, 07081 .... (973) 824-9600
Chocolate Belles, 249 Chamber Bridge Rd., Brick, 08723 .... (732) 920-2266
Choice Cabinetry, LLC, 61 5th St., Somerville, 08876 .... (908) 707-8801
Choice Signs, 3407 Rose Ave., Ste. 3, Ocean, 07712 .... (732) 493-1644
Chris Industries, Inc., 98 Industrial Ct., Freehold, 07728 .... (732) 431-1800
Chriselles Dolls, 216 Hillbrook Dr., River Edge, 07661 .... (201) 488-1905
Chris's Cookies see. .... Food & Beverage, Inc., Teterboro
Christine Valmy Inc., 285 Changebridge Rd., Ste. 1, Pine Brook, 07058 .... (973) 575-1050
Chromatic Control, LLC (H Q), 63 Fox Trail Rd., P.O. Box 374, Sparta, 07871 .... (973) 944-3996
Chromis Fiberoptics, Inc., 6 Powderhorn Dr., Warren, 07059 .... (732) 764-0900
Church & Co., 2121 Whitesville Rd., Toms River, 08755 .... (732) 363-4949
Church & Dwight Co., Inc., 326 Half Acre Rd., Cranbury, 08512 .... (609) 655-6000
Church & Dwight Co., Inc., 800 Airport Rd., Lakewood, 08701 .... (732) 730-3100
Church & Dwight Co., Inc. (H Q), 500 Charles Ewing Blvd., Ewing, 08628 .... (609) 683-5900
Church Vestment Mfg. Co., Inc., 41-43 Paterson Ave., Paterson, 07522 .... (973) 942-2833

Ciccone Custom Railing & Manufacturing, Inc., 2002 Route 9, Toms River, 08755 .... (732) 349-7071
Cifelli & Sons, Inc., 38 Obert St., P.O. Box 538, South River, 08882 .... (732) 238-0090
Cifelli & Sons Italian Sausage see. .... Cifelli & Sons, Inc., South River
CinchSeal, 731 Hylton Rd., Pennsauken, 08110 .... (856) 662-5162
Cincinnati Thermal Spray East, 80 Fadem Rd., Springfield, 07081 .... (973) 379-0003
Cincinnati Thermal Spray, Inc. see. .... Cincinnati Thermal Spray East, Springfield
Cinco Star, LLC, 2 Karnell Ct., Edison, 08820 .... (732) 744-1617
Cinderella Cheesecake Co., Inc.,
208 N. Fairview St., P.O. Box 36, Riverside, 08075 .... (856) 461-6302
Cindy Merckx Publications, LLC, 330 Oak Ave., Malaga, 08328 .... (856) 694-1600
Cintas Corp. see. .... Cintas Fire Protection, Ledgewood
† Cintas Fire Protection, 1705 U.S. Route 46 W., Ledgewood, 07852 .... (973) 347-3901
Circonix Technologies, LLC, 29 Executive Pkwy., Ringwood, 07456 .... (973) 962-6160
Circuit Reproduction Co., Inc., 219 Hergesell Ave., Maywood, 07607 .... (201) 712-9292
Circuit Tech Assembly, LLC, 341 New Albany Rd., Ste. 130, Moorestown, 08057 .... (856) 231-0777
Circuits Sales, 104 Alissa Dr., Toms River, 08753 .... (732) 255-1325
CircuLite, Inc., 250 Pehle Ave., Ste. 403, Saddle Brook, 07663 .... (201) 543-2430
Cire Technologies, Inc., 251 Boulevard, Mountain Lakes, 07046 .... (973) 402-8301
Citkowski Co., 90 Dayton Ave., Passaic, 07055 .... (973) 390-5477
Citromax USA, 444 Washington Ave., Carlstadt, 07072 .... (201) 933-8405
City Diecutting, Inc., 1 Cory Rd., Ste. C, Morristown, 07960 .... (973) 270-0370
City Glass Co., 282 Broadway, P.O. Box 178, Bayonne, 07002 .... (201) 436-8400
City Hunter see. .... Baik Kwang Corp., Carlstadt
City Print Shop, Inc., 157 Sip Ave., Jersey City, 07306 .... (201) 792-6699
City Theatrical, Inc., 475 Barell Ave., Carlstadt, 07072 .... (201) 549-1160
City/Newark Glass Co. see. .... City Glass Co., Bayonne
CITYSAFE, Inc., 312 Squankum Yellowbrook Rd., Farmingdale, 07727 .... (732) 751-0100
Civic Research Institute, Inc., 4478 Route 27, P.O. Box 585, Kingston, 08528 .... (609) 683-4450
Civil Service Leader, 313 Broad Ave., Ste. 203, Ridgefield, 07657 .... (201) 941-6397
CK Manufacturing, Inc., 8 Gardner Rd., Fairfield, 07004 .... (973) 808-3500
Clantech, Inc., 198 Highway 206 S., Hillsborough, 08844 .... (908) 281-7667
Clarici Digital, 88 Youngs Rd., Mercerville, 08619 .... (609) 587-7204
Clark Cooper Div., 941 Hamilton Ave., Roebling, 08554 .... (856) 829-4580
Clark Home Supply, 205 Westfield Ave., Clark, 07066 .... (732) 388-5447
Clark Printing Co., 441 Market St., Saddle Brook, 07663 .... (201) 845-4888
Clark's Hallmark Shop, 275 State Route 10 E., Ste. 31, Succasunna, 07876 .... (973) 584-5119
Clarkson & Ford Co., 30 Industrial St. W., Clifton, 07012 .... (973) 777-0300
Class Act Embroidery, 86 N. Beverwyck Rd., Ste. A, Lake Hiawatha, 07034 .... (973) 394-0045
Class Tool Co., 2500 S. Clinton Ave., P.O. Box 286, South Plainfield, 07080 .... (908) 561-6633
Classic Cake Co., The, 480 Evesham Rd., Cherry Hill, 08003 .... (856) 751-5448
† Classic Ceramic Tile, Inc., 272 State Route 18, Ste. 3, East Brunswick, 08816 .... (732) 390-7700
Classic Coves, P.O. Box 266, Garwood, 07027 .... (908) 344-1776
Classic Marble & Tile, 11 Main St., Little Ferry, 07643 .... (201) 440-8848
Classic Marking Products, Inc., 10 Millpond Dr., Unit 9, Lafayette, 07848 .... (973) 383-2223
Classic Printers & Converters, 140 Ethel Rd. W., Ste. K, Piscataway, 08854 .... (732) 985-1100
Classic Signs, 3651 S. Clinton, South Plainfield, 07080 .... (908) 668-8248
† Classic Tile, Inc., 325 Pine St., P.O. Box 1066, Elizabeth, 07207 .... (908) 289-8400
Claude Bamberger Molding Compounds Corp.,
111 Paterson Plank Rd., P.O. Box 67, Carlstadt, 07072 .... (201) 933-6262
Clausen Co., The, 1055 King George Post Rd., Edison, 08817 .... (732) 738-1165
Clawson Machine, Div. Of Technology General Corp.,
12 Cork Hill Rd., Franklin, 07416 .... (973) 827-8209
Clayton & Sons, LLC, Ralph, 58 Goldman Dr., Cookstown, 08511 .... (609) 758-6900
Clayton & Sons, Ralph, 103 Chestnut Ave., Egg Harbor Township, 08234 .... (609) 383-1818
Clayton & Sons, Ralph, 125 Cox Crossing Rd., West Creek, 08092 .... (609) 597-2233
Clayton & Sons, Ralph (H Q), 1355 Campus Pkwy., Neptune, 07753 .... (732) 751-7600
Clayton Assocs., Inc., 1650 Oak St., Lakewood, 08701 .... (732) 363-2100
Clayton Block Co., Inc. see. .... Clayton & Sons, LLC, Ralph, Cookstown
Clayton Block Co., Inc. see. .... Clayton Block Co., Inc, North Arlington
Clayton Block Co., Inc, 2 Porete Ave., North Arlington, 07031 .... (201) 955-6292
Clayton Block Co., Inc., 1601 18th Ave., Belmar, 07719 .... (732) 681-1414
Clayton Block Co., Inc., 1025 Route 1 S., Edison, 08837 .... (732) 549-1234
Clayton Block Co., Inc., 225 Throckmorton St., Freehold, 07728 .... (732) 462-1860
Clayton Block Co., Inc., 1355 Campus Pkwy., Neptune, 07753 .... (732) 751-7600
Clayton Block Co., Inc., 194 Chestnut St., Toms River, 08753 .... (732) 349-3700
Clayton Block Co., Inc., Route 9, Waretown, 08758 .... (609) 693-3000
Clayton Block Co., Inc. see. .... Ralph Clayton & Sons, Trenton
Clayton Concrete see. .... Clayton & Sons, LLC, Ralph, Cookstown
Clayton Press, Inc., P.O. Box 676, Asbury Park, 07712 .... (732) 774-2624
CleanZones, LLC, 640 Herman Rd., Ste. 2, Jackson, 08527 .... (732) 534-5590
Clear Plus Windshield Wipers, 100 Outwater Ln., Garfield, 07026 .... (973) 546-8800
ClearDrain, 219 Saint Mihiel Dr., Riverside, 08075 .... (856) 461-0091
Clement Pappas & Company, Inc., 1045 Parsonage Rd., Seabrook, 08302 .... (856) 455-1001
Clement Pappas & Company, Inc. (H Q),
1 Collins Dr., Ste. 200, Carneys Point, 08069 .... (856) 455-1000
Clements Industries, Inc., 50 Ruta Ct., South Hackensack, 07606 .... (201) 440-5500
Clem's Ornamental Iron Works, Inc., 110 11th St., Piscataway, 08854 .... (732) 968-7200
Cleve Shirtmakers, Inc. (H Q), P.O. Box 678, Saddle River, 07458 .... (201) 825-6122
Cliffside Body Corp., 130 Broad Ave., P.O. Box 206, Fairview, 07022 .... (201) 945-3970
Clifton Fluid Power Machinery, 295 Allwood Rd., Clifton, 07012 .... (973) 778-3923
★ Clifton Merchant Magazine, 1288 Main Ave., Clifton, 07011 .... (973) 253-4400
Clifton Metal Products Co., Inc., 41 Clifton Blvd., Clifton, 07011 .... (973) 777-6100
Clifton Mirror & Glass Co., Inc., 188 Getty Ave., Clifton, 07011 .... (973) 772-7770
Climax Brewing Co., Inc., 112 Valley Rd., Roselle Park, 07204 .... (908) 620-9585
Clinical Image Retrieval, Inc.,
376 Lafayette Rd., Ste. 202, P.O. Box 899, Sparta, 07871 .... (973) 862-6151
Clinton Envelope, 9130 Pennsauken Hwy., Ste. C, Pennsauken, 08110 .... (856) 314-3636
Clinton Industries, Inc., 207 Redneck Ave., Little Ferry, 07643 .... (201) 440-0400
Clip Strip Corp., 343 S. River St., Hackensack, 07601 .... (201) 342-9155
Clofine Dairy & Food Products, Inc.,
1407 New Rd., P.O. Box 335, Linwood, 08221 .... (609) 653-1000
Clondalkin Pharma & Healthcare, 1224 N. Church St., Moorestown, 08057 .... (856) 439-1700
ClorDiSys Solutions, Inc.,
291 Route 22 E., Salem Industrial Park 5, Lebanon, 08833 .... (908) 236-4100
Closet Butler, 3 Spielman Rd., Fairfield, 07004 .... (973) 729-9222
Closets By Design see. .... NMN Closet, Inc., Carlstadt
Closettech, 203 Woodward Rd., Englishtown, 07726 .... (732) 792-0088
Clothes Horse, Inc., 2200 Wallace Blvd., Ste. A, Cinnaminson, 08077 .... (856) 829-8460
Clover Co., Inc., F. G., 40 Stickle Ave., Rockaway, 07866 .... (973) 625-1811
Clover Printing Corp., 77 Park St., Ridgefield Park, 07660 .... (201) 641-7800
Clover Stamping Co., Inc., 60 Spruce St., Paterson, 07501 .... (973) 278-4888
Clyde's Ices & Ice Cream, Inc., 48 Gaston Ave., Garfield, 07026 .... (973) 546-2760

© Copyright 2015 Manufacturers' News, Inc.


CM Furnace, Inc., 103 Dewey St., Bloomfield, 07003 ... (973) 338-6500
CMD Media, P.O. Box 1061, Rahway, 07065 ... (732) 574-1200
CMF Limited, Inc., 599 Ingham Ave., P.O. Box 5989, Trenton, 08638 ... (609) 695-3600
CMG see ... Custom Molders Group, Somerville
CMIC CMO USA Corp., 3 Cedarbrook Dr., Ste. 3, Cranbury, 08512 ... (609) 395-9700
CMI-Promex, Inc., 7 Benjamin Green Rd., Pedricktown, 08067 ... (856) 351-1000
CMYK Printing, Inc., 180 Coolidge Ave., Englewood, 07631 ... (201) 458-1300
CNC Associates, 101 Kentile Rd., South Plainfield, 07080 ... (718) 416-3853
CNC Supermatic LLC, 27 Old Beach Glen Rd., Rockaway, 07866 ... (973) 627-4433
CNS Confectionery Products, LLC, 33 Hook Rd., Bayonne, 07002 ... (201) 823-1400
CNS Machinery see ... Pegasus Home Fashions, Inc., Elizabeth
coAction, 50 Kildee Rd., Belle Mead, 08502 ... (888) 682-3050
Coast Rubber & Gasket, Inc., 1208 Columbus Rd., Ste. G, Burlington, 08016 ... (609) 747-0110
Coast Star, The * Star News Group, The see ... Ocean Star, The, Point Pleasant Beach
Coast To Coast Leather & Vinyl, Inc., 1 Crossman Rd. S., Sayreville, 08872 ... (732) 525-8877
Coastal Amusements, Inc., 1950 Swarthmore Ave., Lakewood, 08701 ... (732) 905-6662
Coastal Imports, Inc., 31 Mulberry Ct., Unit B, Brielle, 08730 ... (732) 223-4356
Coastal Packaging, 48 Sellers St., Kearny, 07032 ... (201) 955-4414
Coaster, The, 1011 Main St., Asbury Park, 07712 ... (732) 775-3010
Coates International Ltd., 2100 Highway 34 & Ridgewood Rd., Wall, 07719 ... (732) 449-7717
Coates Precision Engineering Ltd.,
2100 Highway 34 & Ridgewood Rd., Wall, 07719 ... (732) 449-7717
† Cobalt Medical Supply, Inc., 4 Haul Rd., Wayne, 07470 ... (973) 305-0730
Cobb's Mill, LLC, 146 Cobbs Mill Rd., Bridgeton, 08302 ... (856) 451-0671
Cobon Plastics Corp., 90 South St., Dock 5, Newark, 07114 ... (973) 334-6330
Cobra Power Systems, Inc., 8 America Way, Spotswood, 08884 ... (908) 486-1800
Cobra Products, Inc., 1 Warner Ct., Swedesboro, 08085 ... (856) 241-7700
Cobyco, Inc., 65 Wilson Ave., Manalapan, 07726 ... (732) 446-4448
Cocco Enterprises, Inc., 333 Chambers St., Trenton, 08609 ... (609) 393-5939
Cockpit USA, Inc., 725 New Point Rd., Elizabeth, 07201 ... (908) 558-9704
Cocoa Processing Corp., 650 Ramsey Ave., Hillside, 07205 ... (201) 792-5866
Cococare Products, Inc., 85 Franklin Rd., Dover, 07801 ... (973) 989-8880
Coda, Inc., 30 Industrial Ave., Mahwah, 07430 ... (201) 825-7400
Codenoll Access * Codenoll see ... Database Access Systems, Inc., Mountain Lakes
Codfish Park Design, LLC, 39 Commerce St., Chatham, 07928 ... (646) 298-4050
Coffee Assocs., Inc., 178 Old River Rd., P.O. Box 240, Edgewater, 07020 ... (201) 945-1060
Coffee Co., LLC, The, 928 Boardwalk, Ocean City, 08226 ... (609) 399-5533
Cogesco Water Technologies Corp., 891 Bloomfield Ave., Clifton, 07012 ... (973) 249-9711
Cognati Cheese Co., Inc., 205 Moonachie Rd., 2nd Fl., Moonachie, 07074 ... (201) 807-9100
Cognizant Technology Solutions, 500 Frank W. Burr Blvd., Teaneck, 07666 ... (201) 801-0233
Cohen Printing & Invitation, 500 Cedar Ln., Teaneck, 07666 ... (201) 287-0343
Coherent Advanced Crystal Group, 31 Farinella Dr., East Hanover, 07936 ... (973) 240-6800
Coherent, Inc. see ... Coherent Advanced Crystal Group, East Hanover
Coilhose Pneumatics, 19 Kimberly Rd., East Brunswick, 08816 ... (732) 432-7177
Coining, Inc., 15 Mercedes Dr., Montvale, 07645 ... (201) 791-4020
Coining Mfg., LLC, 35 Monhegen, Clifton, 07013 ... (973) 253-0500
Col De Mar see ... Pt Of Vu, LLC, Hackettstown
Colace Co., LLC, Thomas, 800 Grove Rd., Thorofare, 08086 ... (856) 384-4980
Colantuono & Klurman Assocs., Inc.,
225 Clifford St., P.O. Box 5150, Newark, 07105 ... (973) 589-5445
Colas, Inc. (H Q), 163 Madison Ave., Ste. 500, Morristown, 07960 ... (973) 290-9082
Colby Farms see ... Interstate Sales New of Jersey, LLC, Voorhees
Cold Headed Fasteners, Inc., 401 Creek Rd., P.O. Box 5488, Delanco, 08075 ... (856) 461-3244
† Coldstat Refrigeration, 60 Eisenhower Dr., Paramus, 07652 ... (201) 599-1200
Cole Bros. Marble & Granite, 892 Parvins Mill Rd., Pittsgrove, 08318 ... (856) 455-7989
Colemax Group, LLC / Prima Cases, P.O. Box 103, Glen Rock, 07452 ... (201) 489-1080
Colex Imaging, Inc., 55-57 Bushes Ln., Elmwood Park, 07407 ... (201) 265-5670
Colfax Cabinet Co., Inc., 86 Ackerman Ave., Clifton, 07011 ... (973) 546-5422
Colgate-Palmolive Co., 400 Elbow Ln., Burlington, 08016 ... (609) 239-2000
Colgate-Palmolive Co., 191 E. Hanover Ave., Morristown, 07960 ... (973) 630-1500
Colie Sailmakers, Inc., 1649 Bay Ave., Point Pleasant Beach, 08742 ... (732) 892-4344
Collagen Matrix, Inc., 509 Commerce St., Franklin, 07417 ... (201) 405-1477
Collagen Matrix, Inc., 15 Thornton Rd., Oakland, 07436 ... (201) 405-1477
Collinear Machine & Design, 7 Wilson Dr., Sparta, 07871 ... (973) 300-1681
Collingswood Architectural Millwork, Inc.,
715 Taylor Ave., Collingswood, 08107 ... (856) 854-0440
Collo Ornamental Iron, Inc.,
1723 Somers Point Rd., Egg Harbor Township, 08234 ... (609) 926-8799
Colombino Headwear, Inc., 61 Willet St., Passaic, 07055 ... (973) 473-4733
Colonial Chemical, 78 Carranza Rd., Tabernacle, 08088 ... (609) 268-1200
† Colonial Commercial Corp., 275 Wagaraw Rd., Hawthorne, 07506 ... (973) 427-8224
Colonial Concrete Co., 1196 McCarter Hwy., Newark, 07104 ... (973) 482-1920
Colonial Concrete Co., 9301 Railroad Ave., North Bergen, 07047 ... (201) 435-9200
† Colonial Electric Supply Co., The,
1143 S. Route 9, Cape May Court House, 08210 ... (609) 465-7144
† Colonial Electric Supply Co., The, 469 S. White Horse Pike, Hammonton, 08037 ... (609) 704-9950
† Colonial Electric Supply Co., The, 701 W. Delilah Rd., Pleasantville, 08232 ... (609) 645-8110
† Colonial Electric Supply Co., The, 64 W. Landis Ave., Vineland, 08360 ... (856) 462-6300
Colonial Printers, 266 Witherspoon St., Princeton, 08542 ... (609) 921-1350
Colonial Processing, Inc., 1930 S. 6th St., Camden, 08104 ... (856) 966-3313
Colonial Seal Co., 1114 Crown Point Rd., Westville, 08093 ... (856) 432-0012
Colonial Wire & Cable Of NJ, Inc., 85 National Rd., Edison, 08817 ... (732) 287-1557
Colonna Brothers, Inc., 4102 Bergen Tpke., P.O. Box 808, North Bergen, 07047 ... (201) 864-1115
Colony, LLC, 852 S. Orange Ave., P.O. Box 6444, Newark, 07106 ... (973) 375-4315
Color Flo Graphics Corp., 10 Dell Glen Ave., Ste. 1, Lodi, 07644 ... (201) 525-0105
Color Optics By Arcade, Inc., 40 Green Pond Rd., Rockaway, 07866 ... (973) 664-3100
Color Screen Pros, 100 Verona Ave., Newark, 07104 ... (973) 268-5080
Color Techniques, Inc., 260 Ryan St., South Plainfield, 07080 ... (908) 412-9292
Colora Henna, 217 Washington Ave., Carlstadt, 07072 ... (201) 939-0969
Colorchem, Inc., 1010 Greenwood Lake, Ringwood, 07456 ... (973) 728-7731
Colorco, Inc., 1261 W. Elizabeth Ave., Linden, 07036 ... (908) 862-3010
Colorcraft, Inc., 1506 Beaver Dam Rd., Point Pleasant Boro, 08742 ... (732) 892-6639
Colorcraft Sign Co., 400 Magnolia St., Beverly, 08010 ... (609) 386-1115
Coloredge, 190 Jony Dr., Carlstadt, 07072 ... (201) 716-5200
Coloredge Visual see ... Coloredge, Carlstadt
Colorflo, Inc., 1261 W. Elizabeth Ave., Linden, 07036 ... (908) 862-3010
Colorful Story Books, Inc., 2 Hollywood Ct., South Plainfield, 07080 ... (908) 561-3333
Colorite, A Tekni-Plex Co., 101 Railroad Ave., Ridgefield, 07657 ... (201) 941-2900
Colornet, LLC, 809 Hylton Rd., Ste. 11, Pennsauken, 08110 ... (856) 662-0652
Coloron Plastics Corp., 169 Meister Ave., Front, Somerville, 08876 ... (908) 685-1210
ColorSource, Inc., 7025 Central Hwy., Pennsauken, 08109 ... (856) 488-8100
Colortec Printing & Mailing LLC, 424 Kelley Dr., Ste. A, West Berlin, 08091 ... (856) 767-0108
Colossus Granite & Marble, Inc., 416 Crescent Blvd., Brooklawn, 08030 ... (856) 742-0090
★ Colour Graphics, 521 Irish Hill Rd., Runnemede, 08078 ... (856) 939-5599
Colter & Peterson, Inc., 414 E. 16th St., Paterson, 07514 ... (973) 684-0901
Coltwell Industries, Inc., 55 Winans Ave., Cranford, 07016 ... (908) 276-7600
Columbia Filters, Inc., 255 Highland Cross, Rutherford, 07070 ... (201) 438-3883
Columbia Machine, 1 N. Riverview Ave., Columbia, 07832 ... (908) 475-4057
Columbia Marketing Corp., 221 Rutgers St., Maplewood, 07040 ... (973) 275-1700
Columbia Nut & Bolt, LLC, 50 Graphic Pl., Moonachie, 07074 ... (201) 641-7600
Columbia Paint Lab, Inc., 452 Communipaw Ave., Jersey City, 07304 ... (201) 435-4884
Columbia Press, Inc., 12 Industrial Rd., P.O. Box 10723, Fairfield, 07004 ... (973) 575-6535
Columbian Iron Works, Inc., 332 Vreeland Ave., Paterson, 07513 ... (973) 684-2303
Columbus Bakery, Inc., 197 Bloomfield Ave., Bloomfield, 07003 ... (973) 429-1697
Colwood Electronics, Inc., 44 Main St., Farmingdale, 07727 ... (732) 938-5556
† Comairco Equipment, Inc., 17 Progress St., Edison, 08820 ... (732) 331-1100
Comairco Equipment Ltd. see ... Comairco Equipment, Inc., Edison
Comar, LLC, 1 Comar Pl., Buena, 08310 ... (856) 692-6100
Comarco Products, 501 Jackson St., Camden, 08104 ... (856) 342-7557
† Combined Supply Co., LLC, 640 S. Broad St., P.O. Box 9192, Elizabeth, 07202 ... (908) 353-8888
Comet Tool Co., Inc., 651 Lambs Rd., Pitman, 08071 ... (856) 256-1070
Comfort Concepts, Inc., 501 Broad Ave., Ste. 7, Ridgefield, 07657 ... (201) 941-6700
Comfort Mechanical Corp., 420 Division St., P.O. Box 4135, Long Branch, 07740 ... (732) 870-2292
Comfort Revolution (H Q), 187 Route 36, Ste. 205, West Long Branch, 07764 ... (732) 272-9111
Command Nutritionals, LLC, 10 Washington Ave., Ste. 1, Fairfield, 07004 ... (973) 227-8210
Command Web Family Of Companies see ... Bind-Rite Robbinsville, Robbinsville
Command Web Family Of Companies, 100 Castle Rd., Secaucus, 07094 ... (201) 863-8100
★ Commerce Enterprises, Inc., 61 S. Paramus Rd., Ste. 135, Paramus, 07652 ... (201) 368-2100
Commerce Financial Printers, 305 Cox St., Roselle, 07203 ... (908) 241-9880
Commerce Sign Solutions, LLC,
540 Cranbury Rd., Ste. 334, East Brunswick, 08816 ... (732) 238-7000
Commercial Business Forms,
240 Cedar Knolls Rd., Ste. 203, Cedar Knolls, 07927 ... (973) 682-9000
Commercial Graphics see ... Budget Printing, LLC, Clark
† Commercial Hardware, Inc., 5 Perina Blvd., Cherry Hill, 08003 ... (856) 810-0600
Commercial Hardware, Inc. see ... Tri State Hardware, Inc., Cherry Hill
Commercial Products Co. U. S. A.,
117 Ethel Ave., P.O. Box 504, Hawthorne, 07507 ... (973) 427-6887
Commercial Reprographics, Inc., 111 Roosevelt Ave., Plainfield, 07060 ... (908) 755-7070
Commercial Water Sports, Inc., 28 Clermont Dr., Cape May Court House, 08210 ... (609) 624-3404
Communication Devices, Inc., 85 Fulton St., Unit 2, Boonton, 07005 ... (973) 334-1980
† Communications Supply Corp., 104 Sunfield Ave., Edison, 08837 ... (732) 346-1550
Community News Service, LLC, 15 Princess Rd., Ste. K, Lawrenceville, 08648 ... (609) 396-1511
Community Newspapers & Magazines Of North Jersey Media Group,
1 Garret Mountain Plz., P.O. Box 471, Woodland Park, 07424 ... (973) 569-7000
CommVault Systems, Inc., 2 Crescrent Pl., P.O. Box 900, Oceanport, 07757 ... (732) 870-4000
Compact Fluorescent Systems, 3 Adams St., Belvidere, 07823 ... (973) 729-5262
Com-Pak, Inc., 365 New Albany Rd., Moorestown, 08057 ... (856) 802-1900
Com-Pak Services see ... Com-Pak, Inc., Moorestown
Compass Display & Promotion Co., Inc., 1659 Calhoun St., Trenton, 08638 ... (609) 695-5300
Compass Signs, LLC, 1 Market Yard, Freehold, 07728 ... (732) 294-7977
Compass Wire Cloth, Inc., 1942 N. Mill Rd., Vineland, 08360 ... (856) 853-7616
Compex Corp., 439 Commerce Ln., Ste. 1, West Berlin, 08091 ... (856) 335-2277
Complete Hydraulic Works, Inc., 140 Greenwood Ave., Midland Park, 07432 ... (201) 444-7877
Complete Plastic Distributors, Inc., 778 Carver Ave., Westwood, 07675 ... (201) 666-8600
Compliance Educational Systems, Inc., P.O. Box 669, Marlton, 08053 ... (856) 793-0137
Comply, Inc., 330 Dalziel Rd., Linden, 07036 ... (908) 862-6600
Component Hardware Group, Inc.,
1890 Swarthmore Ave., P.O. Box 2020, Lakewood, 08701 ... (732) 363-4700
Components & Controls, Inc.,
495 Washington Ave., P.O. Box 437, Carlstadt, 07072 ... (201) 438-9190
Components Corp., 6 Kinsey Pl., Denville, 07834 ... (973) 627-0290
Comport Consulting Corp., 78 Orchard St., Ramsey, 07446 ... (201) 236-0505
CompoSecure, LLC, 500 Memorial Dr., Somerset, 08873 ... (908) 518-0500
Composition Printing, P.O. Box 55, Jersey City, 07303 ... (201) 798-0531
Compounders, Inc., 15 Marl Rd., P.O. Box 413, Farmingdale, 07727 ... (732) 938-5007
Compounding Engineering Solutions, Inc., 473 Highway 46 W., Clifton, 07011 ... (973) 340-4000
Comp-Solutions & Services, 621 N. Delsea Dr., Clayton, 08312 ... (856) 863-1137
Comptime Print & Copy Center, 385 N. Franklin Tpke., Ste. 6, Ramsey, 07446 ... (201) 760-2400
★ Comp24, LLC, 190 Jony Dr., Carlstadt, 07072 ... (201) 716-5200
Compunite Computers, Inc.,
39 U.S. Highway 46, Ste. 803, P.O. Box 3, Pine Brook, 07058 ... (973) 227-6008
Computa Base Machining, Inc., 411 N. Grove St., P.O. Box 340, Berlin, 08009 ... (856) 767-9517
Computer Crafts, Inc., 57 Thomas Rd., Hawthorne, 07506 ... (973) 423-3500
Computer Ease, LLC, 153 Newark Pompton Tpke., Ste. A, Little Falls, 07424 ... (973) 812-6626
Computer Share, Inc., 480 Washington Blvd., Jersey City, 07310 ... (201) 680-5307
★ Computer Square, Inc., 330 Mac Ln., Keasbey, 08832 ... (732) 346-0200
† Computer Wholesalers, Inc., 715 Willow Grove St., Ste. 5, Hackettstown, 07840 ... (908) 684-0802
Computerist, Inc., 15 Smull Ave., Ste. A, Caldwell, 07006 ... (973) 226-0100
Computoprint Corp., 1360 Clifton Ave., Ste. 402, Clifton, 07012 ... (973) 574-8800
Computrs, Inc., 294 Wanaque Ave., Pompton Lakes, 07442 ... (973) 248-9500
Computype see ... Giordano, Inc., Philip A., Garfield
ComTec Systems, Inc., 2658 N. West Blvd., Vineland, 08360 ... (856) 691-5111
Comtel Global Services, LLC, 105 Newfield Ave., Ste. K, Edison, 08837 ... (732) 225-3055
Comtrex Systems Corp., 1247 N. Church St., Ste. 7, Moorestown, 08057 ... (856) 778-0090
Comtron, Inc., 391 State Route 33 E., Englishtown, 07726 ... (732) 446-7571
Comus International, Inc., 454 Allwood Rd., Clifton, 07012 ... (973) 777-6900
ConAgra Food Ingredients, 6 Santa Fe Way, Cranbury, 08512 ... (609) 409-6200
ConAgra Foods, Inc. see ... ConAgra Food Ingredients, Cranbury
Concept Group, Inc., 380 Cooper Rd., West Berlin, 08091 ... (856) 767-5506
Concept Printing and Promotions see ... Concept Printing, Inc., Bergenfield
Concept Printing, Inc., 160 Woodbine St., Ste. 2, Bergenfield, 07621 ... (201) 387-6000
Concord Paper Mfg., Inc., 375 Sylvan Ave., Ste. 23, Englewood Cliffs, 07632 ... (201) 567-2529
Concord Products Co., Inc., 251 Benigno Blvd., Bellmawr, 08031 ... (856) 933-3000
Concord Truss Co., 692 S. Evergreen Ave., Woodbury Heights, 08097 ... (856) 845-3848
Concrete On Demand, Inc., 45 Edison Ave., Ste. 1, Oakland, 07436 ... (201) 337-0005
Confection Collection, 6754 Route 9, Howell, 07731 ... (732) 905-3039
Congoleum Corp., 3500 Quakerbridge Rd., P.O. Box 3127, Mercerville, 08619 ... (609) 584-3000
Congoleum Corp. see ... Congoleum Corp., Plt. 2, Mercerville
Congoleum Corp., Plt. 2,
3500 Quakerbridge Rd., P.O. Box 3127, Mercerville, 08619 ... (609) 584-3000
Congruent Machining Co., Inc.,
107 Maple Grange Rd., P.O. Box 888, Vernon, 07462 ... (973) 764-6767

Conhagen, Inc., Alfred (H Q),
2035 Lincoln Hwy., Edison Sq. W., Ste. 3003, Edison, 08817 ........ (732) 287-4565
Connection Printing, Inc., 86 5th Ave., Hawthorne, 07506........ (973) 423-2004
Connector Products, Inc., 1300 John Tipton Blvd., Pennsauken, 08110........ (856) 829-9190
Connector Technology, Inc.,
5 Walter E. Foran Blvd., Ste. 4005, Flemington, 08822........ (732) 745-2880
Connell Industries, Inc., 13 Fairfield Ave., West Caldwell, 07006........ (877) 926-6635
Conolog Corp., 5 Columbia Rd., Somerville, 08876........ (908) 722-8081
Conrad's Confectionery, Inc., 107 Westwood Ave., Westwood, 07675........ (201) 664-2895
Consarc see........ PV/T, Inc., Rancocas
Consarc Corp., 100 Indel Ave., P.O. Box 156, Rancocas, 08073........ (609) 267-8000
† Consolidated Bearings Company, 10 Wing Dr., Cedar Knolls, 07927........ (973) 539-8300
Consolidated Chemex Corp., 235 Jersey Ave., New Brunswick, 08901........ (732) 828-7676
Consolidated Container Co., 28-36 Slater Dr., Elizabeth, 07206........ (908) 351-7919
Consolidated Container Co., LLC, 4 Pleasant Hill Rd., Monroe Township, 08831........ (609) 655-0855
Consolidated Container Company see........ Consolidated Container Co., Elizabeth
Consolidated Container Company see........ Consolidated Container Co., LLC, Monroe Township
Consolidated Instrument, Avionics & Radio Sales & Service,
510 Industrial Ave., Teterboro, 07608........ (201) 288-1189
Consolidated Instrument Co. see.Consolidated Instrument, Avionics & Radio Sales & Service, Teterboro
Consolidated Material Converters, Inc., 74 Squankum Rd., Tinton Falls, 07724........ (732) 389-5973
Consolidated Packaging Group,
30 Bergen Tpke., P.O. Box 261, Ridgefield Park, 07660........ (201) 440-4240
Consolidated Prototypes, Inc., 5 Oechsner Ct., Berkeley Heights, 07922........ (908) 464-6261
Consolidated Sewing Machine Corp., 400 Veterans Blvd., Carlstadt, 07072........ (212) 741-7788
Consolidated Steel & Aluminum Fence,
316 N. 12th St., P.O. Box 643, Kenilworth, 07033........ (908) 272-6262
Consortium Companies, 400 Raritan Center Pkwy., Edison, 08837........ (732) 512-1777
Constant Services, Inc., 17 Commerce Rd., Fairfield, 07004........ (973) 227-2990
Construction Specialties, Inc., 3 Werner Way, Lebanon, 08833........ (908) 236-0800
Constructor - Magazine of the Associated General Contractors of America see.McGraw-Hill Construction, Hightstown
Conta-Clip, Inc., 400 Apgar Dr., Ste. D, P.O. Box 6510, Somerset, 08873........ (732) 564-0705
Container Graphics Corp.,
3535 Highway 66, Parkway 100, Bldg. 2, Neptune, 07753........ (732) 922-1180
Container Mfg., Inc., 50 Baekeland Ave., P.O. Box 428, Middlesex, 08846........ (732) 563-0100
† Container Recyclers-Camden, Inc., 267 Jefferson St., Camden, 08104........ (856) 963-5200
★ Contemporary Bride Magazine, 153 Geary Dr., South Plainfield, 07080........ (908) 756-0123
Contemporary Graphic Solutions, Inc., 7001 N. Park Dr., Pennsauken, 08109........ (856) 663-7277
Contemporary, Inc., 161 Coolidge Ave., Englewood, 07631........ (201) 569-3900
Contemporary Wall Systems, Inc.,
50 Williams Pkwy., Ste. F, P.O. Box 356, East Hanover, 07936........ (973) 884-0474
Content Critical LLC, 800 Central Blvd., Carlstadt, 07072........ (201) 528-2777
Conte's Pasta Co., Inc., 310 Wheat Rd., Vineland, 08360........ (856) 697-3400
Conti Group, The (H Q), 2045 State Route 27, Edison, 08817........ (732) 520-5000
Continental Aromatics, 1 Thomas Rd. S., Hawthorne, 07506........ (973) 238-9300
Continental Cap Co., 64 Passaic St., Wood Ridge, 07075........ (973) 778-2628
Continental Cast Stone East, 400 Cooper Rd., West Berlin, 08091........ (856) 753-4000
Continental Cast Stone Mfg., Inc. see........ Continental Cast Stone East, West Berlin
Continental Cookies, Inc., 185 S. Newman St., Hackensack, 07601........ (201) 498-1966
Continental Roller Co., Inc., 75 Arlington Ave., Kearny, 07032........ (201) 997-7999
Continental Seasoning, Inc., 1700 Palisade Ave., P.O. Box 629, Teaneck, 07666........ (201) 837-6111
† Continental-Aero (H Q), 530 Bergen St., P.O. Box 354, Harrison, 07029........ (973) 481-3000
Contract Coatings, Inc., 161 Beech St., Hackensack, 07601........ (201) 343-3131
Contract Filling, Inc., 10 Cliffside Dr., Cedar Grove, 07009........ (973) 239-6608
Control & Power Systems, Inc., 17 Spielman Rd., Fairfield, 07004........ (973) 575-3300
Control Group, The, 500 Walnut St., Norwood, 07648........ (201) 768-1900
Control Instruments Corp., 25 Law Dr., Fairfield, 07004........ (973) 575-9114
Control Products, 280 Ridgedale Ave., East Hanover, 07936........ (973) 887-9400
ConvaTec, Inc.,
CenterPoint II, Ste. 205, 1140 Route 22 E., Bridgewater, 08807........ (732) 412-5500
Convertech, Inc., 353 Richard Mine Rd., Wharton, 07885........ (973) 328-1850
† Conveyor Systems & Components, 21 Norman Ave., P.O. Box 343, Delran, 08075........ (856) 461-8084
Conveyors By North American, 156 Huron Ave., Clifton, 07013........ (973) 777-6600
† Cooper Alloy Corp., 201 Sweetland Ave., Hillside, 07205........ (908) 688-4216
Cooper Chemical Co., 20 Parker Rd., Long Valley, 07853........ (908) 876-3231
† Cooper Electric Supply Co., 17 Route 206 S., Unit 3, Augusta, 07822........ (973) 940-8905
† Cooper Electric Supply Co., 72 N. Washington Ave., Bergenfield, 07621........ (201) 385-7777
† Cooper Electric Supply Co., 933 Cedarbridge Ave., Brick, 08723........ (732) 920-3130
† Cooper Electric Supply Co., 2727 Fire Rd., Egg Harbor Township, 08234........ (609) 833-2115
† Cooper Electric Supply Co., 217 Broad Ave., Fairview, 07022........ (201) 945-5900
† Cooper Electric Supply Co., 19 Royal Rd., Flemington, 08822........ (908) 782-3200
† Cooper Electric Supply Co., 3477 U.S. Highway 9, Freehold, 07728........ (732) 462-2424
† Cooper Electric Supply Co., 1521 John F. Kennedy Blvd., Jersey City, 07305........ (201) 434-8575
† Cooper Electric Supply Co., 1805 Lower Rd., Linden, 07036........ (732) 340-0346
† Cooper Electric Supply Co., 317 E. Bay Ave., Manahawkin, 08050........ (609) 978-4666
† Cooper Electric Supply Co., 666 State Route 35, Middletown, 07748........ (732) 671-5000
† Cooper Electric Supply Co., 1 Matrix Dr., Monroe, 08831........ (732) 747-2233
† Cooper Electric Supply Co., 225 Stockton St., Phillipsburg, 08865........ (908) 454-8500
† Cooper Electric Supply Co., 412 W. 2nd St., Plainfield, 07060........ (908) 756-4090
† Cooper Electric Supply Co., 1251 Metropolitan Ave., West Deptford, 08066........ (856) 853-9922
Cooper Electric Supply Co. see........ Cooper Electric Supply Corp., Fairfield
† Cooper Electric Supply Corp., 444 Route 46 E., Fairfield, 07004........ (973) 278-8400
Cooper Industries, Inc. see........ Cooper Notification, Long Branch
Cooper Notification, 273 Branchport Ave., Long Branch, 07740........ (732) 222-6880
Cooper Panels, LLC, John, 250 Maywood Ave., Ste. C, Maywood, 07607........ (201) 487-4018
Cooper Wilbert Burial Vault Co., Inc.,
621 E. Atlantic Ave., Barrington, 08007........ (856) 547-8405
CooperSurgical, Inc. see........ Origio, Inc., Mount Laurel
Coordinated Metals Co., Inc., 626 16th St., Carlstadt, 07072........ (201) 460-7280
Coperion Corp., 663 E. Crescent Ave., Ramsey, 07446........ (201) 327-6300
Coperion K-Tron Pitman, Inc., 590 Woodbury Glassboro Rd., Sewell, 08080........ (856) 589-0500
Coperion K-Tron Pitman, Inc. see........ K-Tron Electronics, Sewell
Copiers Plus, 935 West Ave., Ocean City, 08226........ (609) 398-7676
Co-Planar, Inc., 88 Ford Rd, P.O. Box 1115, Denville, 07834........ (973) 625-3500
Copy Shop, The, 20 E. Water St., Toms River, 08753........ (732) 286-2200
Copy-Rite Printing, 378 N. Main St., Manahawkin, 08050........ (609) 597-9182
Copyshop Office Supply & Repro Center, 921 U.S. Highway 9, South Amboy, 08879........ (732) 721-5700
Corban Energy Group, 418 Falmouth Ave., Elmwood Park, 07407........ (201) 509-8555
Corbco, Inc., 40 Canterbury Dr., Forked River, 08731........ (609) 239-3279
Corbett Industries, Inc.,
39 Hewson Ave., Ste. B, P.O. Box 212, Waldwick, 07463........ (201) 445-6311
Corbi Printing Co., Inc., 106 W. Atlantic Ave., Audubon, 08106........ (856) 547-2555

Corbion see........ Corbion Caravan, Totowa
Corbion Caravan, 100 Adams Dr., Totowa, 07512........ (973) 256-8886
Corbo Jewelers, Inc., 1055 Bloomfield Ave., Clifton, 07012........ (973) 777-1635
Cordes Printing, Inc., 460 Braen Ave., Wyckoff, 07481........ (201) 652-7272
Core Laboratories, Inc. see........ Refinery Systems, A Div. Of Core Lab, Lawrenceville
Core Tech Solutions, Inc., 50 Lake Dr. E. Windsor, Hightstown, 08520........ (609) 443-1400
CoreMatrix Systems, 125 Half Mile Rd., Ste. 200, Red Bank, 07701........ (732) 332-1931
Corente, Inc., 758 Route 18, Ste. 110, East Brunswick, 08816........ (732) 254-0210
CorePharma, LLC, 215 Wood Ave., Middlesex, 08846........ (732) 868-1090
Corfacts, Inc., P.O. Box 10, Morris Plains, 07950........ (973) 998-6935
Coriant America, Inc. see........ Sycamore Networks, Inc., Mount Laurel
Corim Industries, 1112 Industrial Pkwy., Brick, 08724........ (732) 840-1670
† Corman Bag Co., 7 Evergreen Pl., Sparta, 07871........ (973) 729-2816
Cornell & Co., Inc., 224 Cornell Ln., Westville, 08093........ (856) 742-1900
Cornell Machine Co., The, 45 Brown Ave., Springfield, 07081........ (973) 379-6860
Cornerstone Pharmaceuticals, Inc., 1 Duncan Dr., Cranbury, 08512........ (609) 409-7050
Cornerstone Print & Imaging, LLC, 179 State Highway 31, Flemington, 08822........ (908) 782-7966
Corning, Inc. see........ Labnet International, Inc., Edison
Coronation Sheet Metal Co., Inc., 2198 Stanley Ter., Union, 07083........ (908) 686-0930
Coronet, Inc., 77 Wood St., Paterson, 07524........ (973) 345-7660
Corporate Communications Group, The, 14 Henderson Dr., West Caldwell, 07006........ (973) 808-0009
Corporate Graphic Solutions, Inc., 11 W. Passaic St., Rochelle Park, 07662........ (201) 556-0700
Corporate Graphics & Envelope Mfg., Inc., 29 Brook Ave., Maywood, 07607........ (201) 880-4006
Corporate Woodworking, Inc.,
368 Passaic Ave., P.O. Box 10362, Fairfield, 07004........ (973) 227-2211
Corrective Hydraulics, 731 Birch St., P.O. Box 850, Boonton, 07005........ (973) 334-3792
CorrView International, LLC, P.O. Box 8513, Landing, 07850........ (973) 770-7764
Corte Provisions, 574 Ferry St., Newark, 07105........ (973) 712-0970
Cosmetic Coatings, Inc., 219 Broad St., P.O. Box 95, Carlstadt, 07072........ (201) 438-7150
† Cosmetic Essence, Inc., 1248 S. River Rd., Cranbury, 08512........ (609) 395-1271
Cosmetic Essence, Inc., 50 Clearview Rd., Edison, 08837........ (732) 225-2031
Cosmetic Essence, Inc., 1135 Pleasantview Ter. W., Ridgefield, 07657........ (201) 941-9800
Cosmetic Essence, Inc. (H Q), 2182 Route 35 S., Holmdel, 07733........ (732) 888-7788
Cosmetics & Perfume Filling & Packaging, Inc.,
30 Engelhard Dr., Monroe, 08831........ (973) 680-8900
Cosmic Custom Screen Printing, LLC,
1629 N. Black Horse Pike, Williamstown, 08094........ (856) 629-8337
Cospack America Corp., 3856 Park Ave., Edison, 08820........ (732) 548-5858
Costa Marine Canvas & Enclosures, LLC,
1324 Moss Mill Rd., Egg Harbor City, 08215........ (609) 965-1538
Costas Architectural Woodworking, 248 Montgomery St., Bloomfield, 07003........ (973) 429-7004
Costume Gallery, 4451 Route 130 S., Burlington, 08016........ (609) 386-6601
COTE-L Industries, Inc., 1542 Jefferson St., Teaneck, 07666........ (201) 836-0733
Cottage Lace & Ribbon Co., 21 TFH Plaza Union & 3rd Ave., Neptune, 07753........ (732) 776-9353
Cotterman, Inc., 100 Hayes Ave., P.O. Box 278, Wenonah, 08090........ (856) 464-6820
Cottrell Graphics, LLC, 1525 Prospect St., Unit 314, Lakewood, 08701........ (732) 349-7430
★ Counsel Press, LLC, 517 U.S. Highway 1 S., Ste. 1160, Iselin, 08830........ (732) 750-9229
Counterfit, 1 Ironside Ct., Willingboro, 08046........ (609) 871-8888
Counter-Fit Quick Printing, Inc., 145 Newark Ave., Belleville, 07109........ (201) 420-7926
Countertops Plus, Inc., 61 Willet St., Bldg. T, Passaic, 07055........ (973) 365-2232
County Concrete Corp., 50 Railroad Ave., P.O. Box F, Kenvil, 07847........ (973) 584-7122
County Concrete Corp., 145 Ridgedale Ave., Morristown, 07960........ (973) 538-3113
County Glass & Metal Installers, Inc., 80 Dewitt Pl., Hackensack, 07601........ (201) 343-7417
County Graphics Forms Management Co., 2 Stercho Rd., Linden, 07036........ (908) 474-9797
County Seat, LLC, 77 Hudson St., Hackensack, 07601........ (201) 488-5795
Courier Corp., 1 International Blvd., Ste. 400, Mahwah, 07495........ (201) 934-7100
Courier Corp. see........ Research & Education Assn., Piscataway
Courier News, 92 E. Main St., Ste. 202, Somerville, 08876........ (908) 722-8800
Courier-Post Newspaper, 301 Cuthbert Rd., Cherry Hill, 08002........ (856) 663-6000
Couristan, Inc., 2 Executive Dr., Ste. 400, Fort Lee, 07024........ (201) 585-8500
Couse & Bolten Co., 90 South St., Dock 5, Newark, 07114........ (973) 344-6330
Covance, Inc. (H Q), 210 Carnegie Ctr., Princeton, 08540........ (609) 452-8550
Cover Co., Inc., The, 19 Readington Rd., Somerville, 08876........ (908) 707-1122
Cover-All Technologies, Inc.,
412 Mount Kemble Ave., Ste. 110-C, Morristown, 07960........ (973) 461-5200
Cox Industries, 1517 Route 38 W., P.O. Box 507, Hainesport, 08036........ (609) 267-4700
Cox Industries, Inc. see........ Cox Industries, Hainesport
Cox Merchandising, LLC, Fred, 34 Radburn Rd., Glen Rock, 07452........ (201) 310-0740
Cox Printers, 1634 E. Elizabeth Ave., Linden, 07036........ (908) 928-1010
Coyote Pallet Co., 13 Oradell Rd., Hewitt, 07421........ (973) 853-7266
Cozzoli Machine Co., 50 Schoolhouse Rd., Somerset, 08873........ (732) 564-0400
Cozzolino Furniture Design, Inc., 20 Standish Ave., West Orange, 07052........ (973) 731-9292
CPI Packaging, Inc., 50 Jiffy Rd., Somerset, 08873........ (732) 431-3500
CPI USA Inc., 6 Doreen Ct., Edison, 08820........ (732) 494-0007
★ CPMAG, LLC, 6903 Jackson St., Guttenberg, 07093........ (201) 868-8585
† CPR Container, 94 Ford Rd., Ste. 5, Denville, 07834........ (973) 625-0664
C.R. Bard, Inc. see........ Davol, Inc., Delran
C.R. Bard, Inc. (H Q), 730 Central Ave., New Providence, 07974........ (908) 277-8000
Craden Peripherals Corp., 7860 Airport Hwy., Pennsauken, 08109........ (856) 488-0700
Craft Line Cabinet Corp., 10 Walnut St., Clifton, 07013........ (973) 777-8808
Craftmaster Printing, Inc., 2024 Corlies Ave., Neptune, 07753........ (732) 775-0011
Craftmaster Printing, Inc., 3 Main St., New Egypt, 08533........ (609) 758-5990
Craftsmen Printers, The, 855 Bloomfield Ave., Clifton, 07012........ (973) 773-8950
Craftsmen Railing, Inc., 3 Cass St., Keyport, 07735........ (732) 264-1080
Craig Fabric see........ Aristocrat Embroidery Corp., Guttenberg
Cramer Plating, Inc., 4 Hoyt Ln., Belvidere, 07823........ (908) 453-2887
Crane Co. see........ Merrimac Industries, Inc., West Caldwell
Cra-Z-Art, 1578 Sussex Tpke., Bldg. 5, Randolph, 07869........ (973) 543-2037
CRC see........ Circuit Reproduction Co., Inc., Maywood
Cream Ridge Winery, 145 Route 539 S., P.O. Box 98, Cream Ridge, 08514........ (609) 259-9797
Creamer Glass, LLC, 411 N. 10th St., Millville, 08332........ (856) 327-2023
Creating Your Design, LLC, 45 Wood St., Paterson, 07524........ (973) 357-1080
Creation Flavors International LLC,
1 Richmond St., Ste. 3038, New Brunswick, 08901........ (732) 763-8622
Creations By Jeffrey, Inc., 1522 Route 37 E., Toms River, 08753........ (732) 506-0051
Creations By Mariola, 18 Riveredge Dr., Fairfield, 07004........ (973) 808-9109
Creations By Stefano, Inc., 1261 Paterson Plank Rd., Secaucus, 07094........ (201) 863-5806
Creations In Glass, 344 Main St., Hackensack, 07601........ (201) 488-0229
Creative Cabinet Designs, Inc., 301 Main St., Boonton, 07005........ (973) 402-5886
Creative Color Lithographers, Inc., 611 South Ave., Garwood, 07027........ (908) 789-2295
Creative Competitions, Inc., 406 Ganttown Rd., Sewell, 08080........ (856) 256-2797
Creative Concepts Corp., 70 Oak St., Ste. 202, Norwood, 07648........ (201) 750-1234



★ Indicates new listing this edition. † Indicates wholesaler/distributor.

Creative Costume Co., 61 Wilk Rd., Edison, 08837 ... (212) 564-5552
Creative Design Plus, 1634 E. Elizabeth Ave., Linden, 07036 ... (732) 287-3336
† Creative Displays & Designs, Inc., 349 Essex Rd., Neptune, 07753 ... (732) 918-8010
★ Creative Embroidery Corp., 305 3rd Ave. W., Ste. 3, Newark, 07107 ... (973) 497-5700
★ Creative Furniture, Inc. (H Q), 240 Mill Rd., Edison, 08817 ... (732) 248-0255
Creative Industrial Kitchens, 8 Leo Pl., Wayne, 07470 ... (973) 633-0420
Creative Industries, 1409 Astor St., P.O. Box 313, South Plainfield, 07080 ... (908) 561-5600
Creative Innovations, Inc., 20-21 Wagaraw Rd., Ste. 31-B, Fair Lawn, 07410 ... (973) 636-9060
Creative Machining Systems, Inc., 124 Youngs Rd., Mercerville, 08619 ... (609) 586-3932
Creative Metal Work, Inc., 4 Park Dr., P.O. Box 509, Franklin, 07416 ... (973) 823-0408
Creative Patterns & Mfg., Inc., 54 Freeman St., P.O. Box 5549, Newark, 07105 ... (973) 589-1391
Creative Print Group, Inc., The,
7905 Browning Rd., Ste. 112, Merchantville, 08109 ... (856) 486-1700
★ Creative Printing Resources, LLC, 17 Kimberly Ct., Apt. 121, Red Bank, 07701 ... (732) 842-0240
Creative Screen Design, 531 Route 68, P.O. Box 369, Columbus, 08022 ... (609) 424-3334
Creative Surveying see ... Durex, Inc., Union
Creative Wood Products, Inc., 370 Whiteville Rd., Jackson, 08527 ... (732) 370-0051
Creoh U. S. A., 910 E. County Line Rd., Ste. 202-A, Lakewood, 08701 ... (718) 821-0570
Crest Ultrasonics Corp., 10 Grumman Ave., P.O. Box 7266, Trenton, 08628 ... (609) 883-4000
Crestron Electronics, Inc., 15 Volvo Dr., Rockleigh, 07647 ... (201) 767-3400
Creter, Inc., Philip, 20 Monroe St., Union, 07083 ... (908) 686-2910
Creter Vault Corp., 417 Highway 202, Flemington, 08822 ... (908) 782-7771
Cricket Hill Brewing Co., Inc., 24 Kulick Rd., Fairfield, 07004 ... (973) 276-9415
Critchley's Candies, 812 Kinderkamack Rd., River Edge, 07661 ... (201) 967-1800
Criterion Chocolates, Inc., 125 Lewis St., Eatontown, 07724 ... (732) 542-7847
Criterion Publishing Co., 87 Forrest St., P.O. Box 4278, Metuchen, 08840 ... (732) 548-8300
Croda, Inc. (H Q), 300 Columbus Cir., Ste. A, Edison, 08837 ... (732) 417-0800
Croft Tool, Inc., 2144 Bridge Ave., Point Pleasant Boro, 08742 ... (732) 899-4885
Croll-Reynolds, 90 Hollister Rd., Teterboro, 07608 ... (201) 288-9282
Croll-Reynolds (H Q), 6 Campus Dr., Parsippany, 07054 ... (908) 232-4200
Cronite Co., Inc., 120 E. Halsey Rd., P.O. Box 6330, Parsippany, 07054 ... (973) 887-7900
Crop Production Services, Inc., 127 Perryville Rd., Pittstown, 08867 ... (908) 735-5545
Cross Country Box Co., Inc., 2-8 Central Ave., East Orange, 07018 ... (973) 673-8349
Cross Medical Specialties, Inc., 450 Andbro Dr., Unit 7, Pitman, 08071 ... (856) 589-3288
Crossfield Products Corp., 140 Valley Rd., Roselle Park, 07204 ... (908) 245-2800
Crossfield Products Corp see ... Crossfield Products Corp., Roselle Park
★ Crossfire Publications, 551 Bloomfield Ave., Apt. C-14, West Caldwell, 07006 ... (973) 403-1633
Croton Products, 514 Wellington St., Middlesex, 08846 ... (732) 560-9223
Crown Assocs. U. S. A., Inc., 19 Winged Foot Dr., Livingston, 07039 ... (973) 785-3477
Crown Clothing Co., Inc., 609 Paul St., Vineland, 08360 ... (856) 691-0343
Crown Custom Cleaners, 27 E. Kings Hwy., Audubon, 08106 ... (856) 310-0710
Crown Engineering Corp., 550 Squankum Yellowbrook Rd., Howell, 07731 ... (732) 938-3600
Crown Equipment Corp. see ... Crown Lift Trucks, Oakland
Crown Equipment Corp. see ... Crown Lift Trucks, Inc., Elmwood Park
†★ Crown Jewel Importers & Marketing Corp.,
140 Sylvan Ave., Ste. 109, Englewood Cliffs, 07632 ... (201) 461-3900
Crown Lift Trucks, 104 Bauer Dr., Oakland, 07436 ... (201) 337-1211
Crown Lift Trucks, Inc., 680 River Dr., Elmwood Park, 07407 ... (845) 753-5868
Crown Marketing Solution see ... Allstate Printing Packaging, Inc., Clifton
Crown Precision Corp., 61 Willet St., Ste. 13, Passaic, 07055 ... (973) 470-0097
Crown Products, Inc., 1302 Roller Rd., Ocean, 07712 ... (732) 493-0022
Crown Roll Leaf, Inc., 91 Illinois Ave., Paterson, 07503 ... (973) 742-4000
Crown Royale Ltd., 99 Broad St., P.O. Box 5238, Phillipsburg, 08865 ... (908) 859-1999
Crown Trophy Co., Inc., 86 North Ave., Garwood, 07027 ... (908) 789-0460
Crown Trophy, Inc., 3443 Highway 9, Freehold, 07728 ... (732) 462-3344
Crown Trophy-River Edge, NJ, 488 Kinderkamack Rd., River Edge, 07661 ... (201) 261-3933
CRP Industries, Inc., 35 Commerce Dr., Cranbury, 08512 ... (609) 578-4100
CRS Ink International see ... Total Ink Solutions, Hackensack
CRT International, Inc., 260 Wagner St., Middlesex, 08846 ... (973) 887-7737
CRW Graphics, Inc., 9100 Pennsauken Hwy., Pennsauken, 08110 ... (856) 662-9111
Cryofab, Inc., 540 N. Michigan Ave., P.O. Box 485, Kenilworth, 07033 ... (908) 686-3636
Cryogenic Equipment & Repair Co., Inc. (Cerco),
3143 Bordentown Ave., Bldg. 4, Parlin, 08859 ... (732) 727-1555
CryoVation, LLC, 9-B Mary Way, Hainesport, 08036 ... (609) 914-4792
Crystal Beverage Corp., 174 Sanford Ave., P.O. Box 393, Kearny, 07032 ... (201) 991-2342
Crystal World, Inc., 89 Leuning St., Ste. A-2, South Hackensack, 07606 ... (201) 488-0909
†★ Crystalware, 601 Prospect St., Lakewood, 08701 ... (732) 367-4444
Crystex Composites, LLC, 125 Clifton Blvd., Clifton, 07011 ... (973) 779-8866
CS Apparel, Inc. (H Q), 3910 Park Ave., Ste. 2, Edison, 08820 ... (732) 906-9666
CSC see ... Clip Strip Corp., Hackensack
CSI see ... Constant Services, Inc., Fairfield
★ CSI Fabricators, 15 Lexington St., Newark, 07105 ... (973) 344-0955
CSM Worldwide, Inc., 1100 Globe Ave., Mountainside, 07092 ... (908) 233-2882
Csonka Cigar Requisites, Inc. (H Q), 407 Blue Spring Rd., Princeton, 08540 ... (609) 514-2766
Csonka Worldwide see ... Csonka Cigar Requisites, Inc. (H Q), Princeton
C-Sports, 2045 S. Black Horse Pike, Williamstown, 08094 ... (856) 875-5680
CST Pavers a division of Pavestone,
23 Ridge Rd., P.O. Box 2736, Branchville, 07826 ... (973) 948-7193
CST Products, LLC, 345 Route 130, P.O. Box 402, Pedricktown, 08067 ... (856) 299-5339
CTC International, Inc., 11 York Ave., West Caldwell, 07006 ... (973) 228-2300
CTI see ... Connector Technology, Inc., Flemington
CTI Motor Drives, Inc., 105 Jackson St., South River, 08882 ... (732) 613-8390
Cueva's Signs, 853 Bayway Cir., Elizabeth, 07201 ... (908) 820-5744
Cuisine Innovations, LLC, 1920 Swarthmore Ave., Ste. 1, Lakewood, 08701 ... (732) 730-9310
Cultech, Inc., 3500 Hatley Rd., South Plainfield, 07080 ... (732) 225-2722
Cumberland & Salem Guide, 874 N. Pearl St., P.O. Box 735, Bridgeton, 08302 ... (856) 451-1177
Cumberland Dairy, Inc., 80 Edward Ave., Bridgeton, 08302 ... (856) 451-1300
† Cumberland Dairy, Inc., 899 Landis Ave., P.O. Box 308, Rosenhayn, 08352 ... (856) 451-1300
Cumberland Engraving Service, 127 W. Broad St., Bridgeton, 08302 ... (856) 451-5052
Cumberland Marble & Monument, Inc., 2858 S. West Blvd., Vineland, 08360 ... (856) 691-3334
Cumberland Vacuum Products, 720 S. West Blvd., Vineland, 08360 ... (856) 691-9155
Cumberland Valve, Inc., 746 Shiloh Pike, Bridgeton, 08302 ... (856) 451-1324
Cuny & Guerber, Inc., 2100 Kerrigan Ave., P.O. Box 1192, Union City, 07087 ... (201) 617-5800
Curbell, Inc., Plastics Div., 844 N. Lenola Rd., Ste. 6, Moorestown, 08057 ... (856) 778-1100
Curbell Plastics, Inc. see ... Curbell, Inc., Plastics Div., Moorestown
Curran Pfeiff Corp., Liddle Ave., Edison, 08837 ... (732) 225-0555
Curtis Sign Design, 640 Herman Rd., Ste. 1, Jackson, 08527 ... (732) 928-9494
Curtiss-Wright Corp. see ... Curtiss-Wright Surface Technologies, Paramus
Curtiss-Wright Corp. (H Q), 10 Waterview Blvd., 2nd Fl., Parsippany, 07054 ... (973) 541-3700
Curtiss-Wright Surface Technologies,
80 Highway 4 E., Ste. 310, Paramus, 07652 ... (201) 843-7800
Curvon Corp., 34 Apple St., Tinton Falls, 07724 ... (732) 747-3832

Custom & Wasmund Bindery, 9 Sheridan Ave., Clifton, 07011 ... (973) 815-1400
Custom Alloy Corp., 3 Washington Ave., Ste. 6, High Bridge, 08829 ... (800) 453-1724
Custom Auto Radiator, Inc., 441 S. Main St., Route 9, Forked River, 08731 ... (609) 242-9700
Custom Bandag, Inc., 401 E. Linden Ave., Linden, 07036 ... (908) 862-2400
Custom Bedding of America, Inc. see ... Orange Mattress, Clark
Custom Brush Co. Inc., 1933 Owl Ct., Cherry Hill, 08003 ... (856) 354-1673
Custom Building Products, Inc., 2115 High Hill Rd., Logan Township, 08085 ... (856) 467-9226
Custom Cabinets By Jim Bucko, Inc., 135 W. Burk Ave., Wildwood, 08260 ... (609) 889-7666
Custom Cable Crafters, Inc., 1830 Gallagher Dr., Ste. 103, Vineland, 08360 ... (856) 696-3151
Custom Concentrates see ... C B Food, Inc., East Rutherford
Custom Converters, Inc., 115 Naylon Ave., Livingston, 07039 ... (973) 994-9000
★ Custom Cooling Services, LLC,
99 Kingwood Stockton Rd., P.O. Box 457, Stockton, 08559 ... (609) 397-4448
Custom Counters By Precision, 11-17 Linden St., Passaic, 07055 ... (973) 773-0111
Custom Craft Plastics,
100 King Arthurs Ct., P.O. Box 6029, North Brunswick, 08902 ... (732) 843-3000
Custom Creations By M. D., 52 Ishmael Rd., Tuckerton, 08087 ... (609) 294-1321
Custom Cut Metal Products, Inc., 7 Daniel Rd. E., Fairfield, 07004 ... (973) 808-6803
Custom Decorators Workroom, 415 E. Main St., Denville, 07834 ... (973) 625-0516
Custom Designers, LLC, 80 Greenwood Ave., Ste. 14, Midland Park, 07432 ... (201) 652-5219
Custom Docks, Inc., 234 Route 206, Branchville, 07826 ... (973) 948-3732
Custom Embroidery, 73 E. New Jersey Ave., P.O. Box 1489, Pleasantville, 08232 ... (609) 383-9292
Custom Engraving, 29 Highland Rd., Colonia, 07067 ... (732) 574-1901
Custom Essence, Inc., 53 Veronica Ave., Somerset, 08873 ... (732) 249-6405
Custom Extrusion Technologies see ... CET Films, Inc., Lakewood
Custom Fab Pipe Supply Corp., 1-A Mount Vernon St., Ridgefield Park, 07660 ... (201) 343-3739
Custom Fabricators, Inc., 400 Commerce Rd., Linden, 07036 ... (908) 862-4244
Custom Gasket Mfg., 640 E. Palisade Ave., Englewood Cliffs, 07632 ... (201) 331-6363
Custom Graphics, Inc., 71 W. Landis Ave., Vineland, 08360 ... (856) 691-7858
Custom Heliarc Welding & Machine, Inc.,
49 Decatur St., P.O. Box 232, Columbia, 07832 ... (908) 496-8190
Custom Index, Inc., 8 Vreeland Ave., Totowa, 07512 ... (973) 890-2414
Custom Interiors, Inc., 47 W. Grand Ave., Montvale, 07645 ... (201) 573-9702
Custom Labels, Inc., 61 Willet St., Bldg. J, Passaic, 07055 ... (973) 473-1934
Custom Lettering, 3031 Belvidere Rd., Phillipsburg, 08865 ... (908) 454-4140
Custom Liners, Inc., 1555 Ruth Rd., Ste. 7, North Brunswick, 08902 ... (201) 569-1889
Custom Molders Group, 160 Meister Ave., Ste. 1, Somerville, 08876 ... (908) 218-7997
† Custom Pak, Inc., 800 Grove Rd., Thorofare, 08086 ... (856) 384-4980
Custom Products Mfg., Inc.,
430 Sand Shore Rd., Ste. 4 & 5, Hackettstown, 07840 ... (908) 852-2078
Custom Sales & Service, Inc., 275 S. 2nd Rd., P.O. Box 635, Hammonton, 08037 ... (609) 561-6900
Custom Spine, Inc. (H Q), 9 Campus Dr., Parsippany, 07054 ... (973) 808-0019
Custom Steel Contractors, Inc., 17 Eastern Rd., Kearny, 07032 ... (973) 344-4449
Custom Window Treatments By Wayne Lubin, 1029 U.S. Highway 9, Howell, 07731 ... (732) 462-4961
Custom Wood Creations, Inc., 51 Willow St., Washington, 07882 ... (908) 835-8999
Custom Wood Furniture, Inc., 37 E. Clinton St., P.O. Box 3034, Newton, 07860 ... (973) 579-4880
Custom Wood, LLC, 400 Goldman Dr., Cream Ridge, 08514 ... (609) 758-8288
Custom Woodcraft Co., 81 Park Pl., Passaic, 07055 ... (973) 472-0824
Custom Woodwork see ... F T Millwork, Red Bank
Custom Woodworking, 813 Jerusalem Rd., Scotch Plains, 07076 ... (908) 232-9525
CustomShots, 189 Silver Lake Dr., West Creek, 08092 ... (609) 296-1811
Cusumano Perma-Rail Co., 213 W. Westfield Ave., Roselle Park, 07204 ... (908) 245-9281
Cut Mark, Inc., 801 S. Church St., Ste. 6, Mount Laurel, 08054 ... (856) 234-3428
Cutler Bros. Box & Lumber Co.,
711 W. Prospect Ave., P.O. Box 217, Fairview, 07022 ... (201) 943-2535
† Cutter, Drill & Machine, Inc.,
175 Ramtown Greenville Rd., Unit 701, Howell, 07731 ... (732) 206-1112
Cutting Board Co., 291 Highway 22, Lebanon, 08833 ... (908) 725-0187
Cutting Edge Casting, Inc., 1233 W. Saint Georges Ave., Linden, 07036 ... (908) 925-7500
Cutting Edge Grower Supply LLC, 5033 Industrial Rd., Farmingdale, 07727 ... (732) 905-9220
Cutting Techniques, Inc., 651 Industrial Rd., Carlstadt, 07072 ... (201) 438-2222
CVC Thermoset Specialties, Inc., 844 N. Lenola Rd., Ste. 1, Moorestown, 08057 ... (856) 533-3000
CVE, Inc., 5 N. Corporate Dr., Riverdale, 07457 ... (201) 770-0005
CVS/Caremark Corp. see ... Caremark Rx, Inc., Fairfield
CWI see ... Computer Wholesalers, Inc., Hackettstown
CWI Architectural Millwork, LLC, 8 Deptford Rd., Dept. D, Glassboro, 08028 ... (856) 307-7900
CWS see ... Commercial Water Sports, Inc., Cape May Court House
Cyalume Specialty Products, 100 W. Main St., P.O. Box 669, Bound Brook, 08805 ... (732) 469-7760
Cybis Porcelains Studio & Gallery,
200 Elizabeth Ave., Ste. 200, Trenton, 08610 ... (609) 392-6074
Cycle Chem, Inc., 201 S. 1st St., Elizabeth, 07206 ... (908) 355-5800
Cygnus, LLC, 510 E. 41st St., Paterson, 07504 ... (973) 523-0668
Cylinder Central see ... Airgas Retail Solutions, Manalapan
Cytec Industries, Inc. (H Q), 5 Garret Mountain Plz., Woodland Park, 07424 ... (973) 357-3100
CytoTherm, 110 Sewell Ave., Trenton, 08610 ... (609) 396-1456
Czar, Inc., 51 Montgomery St., Belleville, 07109 ... (973) 278-4002
D & C Bagel Boys, Inc., 1055-C Highway 34, Matawan, 07747 ... (732) 566-4523
D & D Millwork Co., Inc., 10-12 N. 7th St., Belleville, 07109 ... (973) 759-6336
D & D Technology, Inc., 254 Elmwood Ave., P.O. Box 3636, Union, 07083 ... (908) 688-5154
D & D Trailers, Inc., 100 Lexington Ave., Trenton, 08618 ... (609) 771-0001
D & F Performance, 417 N. Grove St., Berlin, 08009 ... (856) 767-4095
D & F Screw Machine Products, Inc., 42 West St., East Hanover, 07936 ... (973) 887-1702
D & G Precision, 709 Louis Ave., Linden, 07036 ... (908) 925-1578
D & H Cutoff Co., Inc., 412-I Trimmer Rd., Bldg. 11, Califon, 07830 ... (908) 454-4961
★ D & H Pallets, LLC, 45 Verona Ave., Newark, 07104 ... (973) 481-2981
D & I Printing Co., Inc., 23 Chestnut St., Englewood, 07631 ... (201) 871-3620
D & M Printers, 43 School Rd., Whitehouse Station, 08889 ... (908) 534-4101
D & M Printing, Inc., 46 Watson Ave., West Orange, 07052 ... (973) 731-1300
D & M Sheet Metal Co., Inc., 430 Central Ave., East Rutherford, 07073 ... (201) 939-6300
D & N Machine Mfg., Inc.,
334 Nicholson Rd., P.O. Box 67, Gloucester City, 08030 ... (856) 456-1366
D & S Castings, Inc., 300 Whitehead Rd., Trenton, 08619 ... (609) 689-0100
D & W Diesel, 423 County Rd., Cliffwood, 07721 ... (732) 566-4970
D A S Installations, Inc., 176 Saddle River Rd., Bldg. D, Garfield, 07026 ... (973) 473-6858
D and S Designs, P.O. Box 1707, Bridgeton, 08302 ... (856) 451-0954
D B M Corp., Inc., 32-A Spruce St., Oakland, 07436 ... (201) 677-0008
D C Fabricators, Inc., 801 W. Front St., Florence, 08518 ... (609) 499-3000
D C Metric Tool, Inc., 11 Mathews Ave., Riverdale, 07457 ... (973) 838-7590
D C Plastic Products, 12 E. 2nd St., P.O. Box 353, Bayonne, 07002 ... (201) 339-0111
D E B Maintenance, Inc., 1000 Union Landing Rd., P.O. Box 13, Riverton, 08077 ... (856) 786-0440
D Electric Motors, Inc., 94 W. Sherman Ave., Vineland, 08360 ... (856) 696-5959
D. F. Enterprise, LLC, 3254 S. Black Horse Pike, Williamstown, 08094 ... (856) 875-1777

© Copyright 2015 Manufacturers' News, Inc.


D M Steel, 279 Sherman Ave., Newark, 07114 ........ (973) 732-4763
D P J Signs, 245 E. Inman Ave., Rahway, 07065 ........ (732) 499-8600
D R Handmade Strings, Inc., 7 Palisade Ave., Emerson, 07630 ........ (201) 599-0100
D R Music see. ........ D R Handmade Strings, Inc., Emerson
D R Technology, Inc., 73 South St., Freehold, 07728 ........ (732) 780-4664
D S F, Inc., 401 U.S. Highway 202, Raritan, 08869 ........ (908) 218-5153
Da Vinci Displays, LLC, 123 Taft Dr., Brick, 08724 ........ (732) 730-3001
DAA International LLC, 24 Commerce Rd., Ste. L, Fairfield, 07004 ........ (973) 575-7444
Daburn Electronics & Cable, Inc., 44 Richboynton Rd., Dover, 07801 ........ (973) 328-3200
† Dade Paper Co., 120 Tices Ln., East Brunswick, 08816 ........ (732) 254-3100
DAF Products, Inc., 420 Braen Ave., Wyckoff, 07481 ........ (201) 251-1222
Da-Green Electronics, Inc., 37 Main St., P.O. Box 486, South River, 08882 ........ (732) 254-2735
Daiichi Sankyo, Inc. (H Q), 2 Hilton Ct., Parsippany, 07054 ........ (973) 944-2600
Daily Journal, The, 891 E. Oak Rd., Vineland, 08360 ........ (856) 691-5000
Daily News L. P. see. ........ New York Daily News, Jersey City
Daily Princetonian Publishing Co., Inc., 48 University Pl., Princeton, 08544 ........ (609) 375-8553
Dairy Delight, LLC, 1 Industrial Dr., Rutherford, 07070 ........ (201) 939-7878
Dairyland Ice Cream, 487 Chancellor Ave., Irvington, 07111 ........ (973) 923-7625
Daisy's Bakery see. ........ Pride Gourmet Bakers, Inc., Clifton
Dalemark Industries, Inc., 575 Prospect St., Ste. 211, Lakewood, 08701 ........ (732) 367-3100
Daler-Rowney U. S. A., Ltd., 7 Corporate Dr., Cranbury, 08512 ........ (609) 655-5252
Dalfen Unlimited, 27 1/2 Lentz Ave., Newark, 07105 ........ (973) 344-4006
Dallas Group Of America, Inc., The (H Q),
374 Route 22, P.O. Box 489, Whitehouse, 08888 ........ (908) 534-7800
† DAL-Tile Corporation, 1250 Valley Brook Ave., Lyndhurst, 07071 ........ (201) 729-0203
Dal-Tile Corporation see. ........ DAL-Tile Sales Service Center 186, Cherry Hill
† DAL-Tile Sales Service Center 186,
2030 Springdale Rd., Ste. 100, Cherry Hill, 08003 ........ (856) 489-3335
Daly's Custom Racing Apparel, P.O. Box 355, Berlin, 08009 ........ (856) 768-6411
Damask's Candies, Inc., 2255 Highway 322, Woolwich Township, 08085 ........ (856) 467-1661
D'Amico Sheet Metal Works, Al, 881 Broadway, Bayonne, 07002 ........ (201) 339-1355
Dana Classic Fragrances, Inc. (H Q), 400 Lyster Ave., Saddle Brook, 07663 ........ (201) 881-8550
Dana Poly Inc., 1301 W. Elizabeth Ave., Linden, 07036 ........ (908) 474-0600
Danan Design Corp., 599 Franklin Ave., Franklin Lakes, 07417 ........ (201) 891-5342
Danfoss Hago, Inc., 1120 Globe Ave., Mountainside, 07092 ........ (908) 232-8687
Danfoss, Inc. see ........ Danfoss Hago, Inc., Mountainside
D'Angelo Metal Products Co., Inc., 360 Dalziel Rd., Linden, 07036 ........ (908) 862-8220
† Dani Leather USA, Inc., 37 Ironia Rd., Ste. 2, Flanders, 07836 ........ (973) 598-0890
Danielle Die Cut Products, Inc., 238 Lindbergh Pl., Paterson, 07503 ........ (973) 278-3000
Daniel's Custom Draperies, Inc., 620 W. Clements Bridge Rd., Runnemede, 08078 ........ (856) 939-2212
Danor Signs, LLC, 47 Central Ave., Passaic, 07055 ........ (973) 471-2897
Dan's Heating & Air Conditioning, Inc., 1007 Eastpark Blvd., Cranbury, 08512 ........ (732) 297-9162
Danson Sheet Metal, Inc. see. ........ Hutchton & Simon, Inc., Hackensack
Dantco Mixers Corp., 9 Oak St., Paterson, 07501 ........ (973) 278-8776
DAQ Electronics, LLC, 262 Old New Brunswick Rd., Ste. B, Piscataway, 08854 ........ (732) 981-0050
Darkstar Woodworking, 123 Woodland Ave., Westwood, 07675 ........ (201) 248-1575
Darling Ingredients, Inc., 825 Wilson Ave., Newark, 07105 ........ (973) 465-1900
† Daron Worldwide Trading, Inc., 24 Stewart Pl., Ste. 4, Fairfield, 07004 ........ (973) 882-0035
Dash Industries, Inc., 639 5th St., Lakewood, 08701 ........ (732) 364-5850
Dash Printing, Inc., 52 Woodbine St., Ste. 3, Bergenfield, 07621 ........ (201) 338-2561
Dason Stainless Products Co., 1773 Elizabeth Ave., Rahway, 07065 ........ (732) 382-7272
Dassault Falcon Jet Corp. (H Q),
Teterboro Airport, 200 Riser Rd., Little Ferry, 07643 ........ (201) 440-6700
Data Access Datapatch, Inc., 40 Eisenhower Dr., Ste. 101, Paramus, 07652 ........ (201) 843-5468
Data Center Depot * Gaw Technology see. ........ GAW Associates, Inc., Cherry Hill
★ Data Centrum Communications, Inc.,
135 Chestnut Ridge Rd., 2nd Fl., Montvale, 07645 ........ (201) 391-1911
Data Communique, Inc., 65 Challenger Rd., 4th Fl., Ridgefield Park, 07660 ........ (201) 508-6000
Data Delay Devices, Inc., 3 Mount Prospect Ave., Clifton, 07013 ........ (973) 773-2299
Data Technologies, Inc., 224 N. Pegasus Ave., Ste. A, Northvale, 07647 ........ (201) 784-3225
Database Access Systems, Inc.,
60 Midvale Rd., Ste. 206, P.O. Box 126, Mountain Lakes, 07046 ........ (973) 335-0800
Datacolor, 5 Princess Rd., Lawrenceville, 08648 ........ (609) 924-2189
Datamatics Management Services, Inc., 330 New Brunswick Ave., Fords, 08863 ........ (732) 738-9600
Dataprobe, Inc., 1-B Pearl Ct., Allendale, 07401 ........ (201) 934-9944
Dataram Corp., 777 Alexander Rd., Princeton, 08540 ........ (609) 799-0071
★ Datascan Graphics, Inc., 55 Madison Ave., Ste. 400, Morristown, 07960 ........ (973) 543-4800
Datatest, Inc., 300 Valley Rd., Hillsborough, 08844 ........ (908) 369-1590
Datwyler, Inc., 9012 Pennsauken Hwy., Pennsauken, 08110 ........ (856) 663-2202
Dauphin North America, 100 Fulton St., Boonton, 07005 ........ (973) 263-1100
davAgen Pharmaceuticals, LLC,
68 Veronica Ave., Ste. 1, 2 & 10, Somerset, 08873 ........ (732) 249-6363
Daven Industries, Inc., 55 Dwight Pl., Fairfield, 07004 ........ (973) 808-8848
Dave's Architectural Iron, LLC, 121 McBride Ave., Ste. C, Paterson, 07501 ........ (973) 523-6323
Dave's Swift Print, P.O. Box 313, Westville, 08093 ........ (856) 853-8528
David Aubrey, Inc, 186 Griffith St., Jersey City, 07307 ........ (201) 653-2200
David Bradley Chocolatier see. ........ Sophisticated Chocolates Mfg., Inc., Windsor
David's Cookies see. ........ Fairfield Gourmet Food Corp., Cedar Grove
Davion, Inc., 29-75 Riverside Ave., Bldg. 10, Newark, 07104 ........ (973) 485-0793
Davis Paper Dimensions, Inc., 400 Benigno Blvd., Bellmawr, 08031 ........ (856) 931-6040
Davis Sign Systems, 65 Harrison St., Boonton, 07005 ........ (973) 394-9909
Davis-Standard see. ........ Circonix Technologies, LLC, Ringwood
Davis-Standard, LLC see. ........ Circonix Technologies, LLC, Ringwood
Davis-Standard, LLC, 220 Davidson Ave., Ste. 401, Somerset, 08873 ........ (908) 722-6000
Davlyn Industries, Inc., 7 Fitzgerald Ave., Monroe Township, 08831 ........ (609) 860-5100
Davol, Inc., 1822 Underwood Blvd., Delran, 08075 ........ (856) 764-8158
Davol-Delran, Inc. see. ........ Davol, Inc., Delran
Dawn Bible Students Assn., 199 Railroad Ave., East Rutherford, 07073 ........ (201) 438-6421
Dax Hair Care Products see ........ Imperial DAX Co., Inc., Fairfield
DAX Systems, Inc., 343 New Rd., Ste. 4, Parsippany, 07054 ........ (973) 227-8111
Day Tool & Mfg., Inc., 6 Carman Ln., P.O. Box 466, Whitehouse, 08888 ........ (908) 439-3800
Daybrook Holdings, Inc. (H Q), 161 Madison Ave., 2nd Fl., Morristown, 07960 ........ (973) 538-6766
Daysol Industries, 40 Boright Ave., Kenilworth, 07033 ........ (908) 272-5900
Dayton Grey Corp., 1008 1st Ave., Asbury Park, 07712 ........ (732) 869-0060
Dazian Fabrics, LLC, 18 Central Blvd., South Hackensack, 07606 ........ (201) 549-1000
DBM Of America, Inc.,
295 U.S. Highway 22 E., Ste. 104, Whitehouse Station, 08889 ........ (908) 534-1665
DCA, Inc. see. ........ Drapery Corp. Of America, Inc., Paterson
DCC Corporation, 7250 Westfield Ave., Ste. B, Pennsauken, 08110 ........ (856) 662-7272
† DCI Cheese Co., 861 Washington Ave., Carlstadt, 07072 ........ (201) 807-0999
DCI Metro, Inc., 1 Maple St., Unit 1, East Rutherford, 07073 ........ (201) 340-4329
DCI Signs & Awnings, Inc., 110 Riverside Ave., Newark, 07104 ........ (973) 350-0400
DCM Industries LLC, 50 S. Center St., Unit 8, Orange, 07050 ........ (973) 675-3200
DDM Steel Construction, 3659 N. Delsea Dr., Vineland, 08360 ........ (856) 794-9400
DDPS, Inc. see. ........ De Dietrich U. S. A., Inc. (H Q), Mountainside
DDS, Inc., 100 Commerce Way, Ste. 5, Hackensack, 07601 ........ (888) 495-7440
De Dietrich U. S. A., Inc. (H Q), 244 Sheffield St., Mountainside, 07092 ........ (908) 317-2585
De Jong Iron Works, Inc., 223-231 Godwin Ave., Paterson, 07501 ........ (973) 684-1633
De Leo Textiles (H Q), 53 Dwight Pl., Fairfield, 07004 ........ (973) 439-6801
De Meo Brothers., Inc., 2 Brigton Ave., Passaic, 07055 ........ (973) 778-8100
† De Pasquale Salon Systems, Inc., 21-21 Broadway, Fair Lawn, 07410 ........ (201) 797-9101
De Risi Iron Works Co., 910 Asbury Ave., Asbury Park, 07712 ........ (732) 774-6570
Dead End Screen Prints, Inc., 266 Lewis St., North Plainfield, 07060 ........ (908) 754-4552
Dealaman Enterprises, Inc., 214 Mountain View Rd., Warren, 07059 ........ (908) 755-1780
Dean Technology, Inc.,
5027 Industrial Rd., Unit 4, P.O. Box 848, Farmingdale, 07727 ........ (732) 938-4499
Deans Graphics, 16 Mill St., P.O. Box 809, Mount Holly, 08060 ........ (609) 261-8817
Dearbrook Fabrics, Inc., 430 Walker St., P.O. Box 338, Fairview, 07022 ........ (201) 945-4141
D.E.B. Mfg., Inc., 850 Towbin Ave., Lakewood, 08701 ........ (732) 364-7007
Deb-El Food Products, LLC, 2 Papetti Plz., P.O. Box 876, Elizabeth, 07206 ........ (908) 351-0330
Deblyn Screen Printers, 717 Mountain Blvd., Watchung, 07069 ........ (908) 756-8459
Deborah Sales, LLC, 109 Meeker Ave., Newark, 07114 ........ (973) 344-8466
Decker Tape Products, Inc., 2 Stewart Pl., Fairfield, 07004 ........ (973) 227-5350
Decor, Inc., 60 Cedar Ln., Englewood, 07631 ........ (201) 569-1900
Decoration Design Solutions, 1299 W. Forest Grove Rd., Vineland, 08360 ........ (856) 589-1250
Decorative Iron Works, 7383 Belmont Ave., Paterson, 07522 ........ (973) 595-8517
Dec's Metal Fabrication, LLC,
198 U.S. Highway Route 206, Bldg. 4, Ste. E, Hillsborough, 08844 ........ (908) 281-0283
Dee & L, LLC, 67 Lefante Way, P.O. Box 3431, Bayonne, 07002 ........ (201) 858-0131
Deep Foods, Inc., 1090 Springfield Rd., Union, 07083 ........ (908) 810-7500
Deerfield Machine & Tool Co., 23 Old Beach Glen Rd., Rockaway, 07866 ........ (973) 625-0505
Deerfield Machine Parts see. ........ Hamelin Products, Inc., Deerfield Street
Defined Pro Machining, LLC, 105 W. Dewey Ave., Ste. 205, Wharton, 07885 ........ (973) 941-2430
Degree Day Systems, Inc.,
33 Village Park Rd., P.O. Box 510, Cedar Grove, 07009 ........ (973) 239-7900
Deitz & Sons, Inc., M., 490 Hillside Ave., Hillside, 07205 ........ (908) 686-8800
Deitz Co., Inc., 1750 Highway 34, P.O. Box 1108, Wall, 07719 ........ (732) 681-0200
DeJohn Machine Co., 2 Elm St., Garfield, 07026 ........ (973) 478-1144
DEK-TRON International Corp., 244 E. 3rd St., Plainfield, 07060 ........ (908) 226-1777
Del Buono Baking Co., 319 Black Horse Pike, Haddon Heights, 08035 ........ (856) 546-9585
Del Sol Signs, 119 New Jersey Railroad Ave., Newark, 07105 ........ (973) 589-8655
Delaire U. S. A., Inc., 1913 Atlantic Ave., Ste. R-1, Manasquan, 08736 ........ (732) 528-4520
Delaware Food Market, 6506 Ventnor Ave., Ventnor City, 08406 ........ (609) 822-0222
Delaware Valley Bindery, Inc., 18 Graphics Dr., Trenton, 08628 ........ (609) 771-1550
Delaware Valley Box & Lumber Co., 14 Austin Ave., Glendora, 08029 ........ (856) 939-1900
Delaware Valley Box & Lumber Co., 2651 E. State St. Ext., Trenton, 08619 ........ (609) 890-2900
Delaware Valley Floral Group see. ........ Delaware Valley Wholesale Florist, Inc., Sewell
† Delaware Valley Wholesale Florist, Inc., 520 Mantua Blvd., Sewell, 08080 ........ (856) 468-7000
Delcrest Sign Co., Inc., 1202 Haddonfield-Berlin Rd., Ste. 1, Voorhees, 08043 ........ (856) 768-5552
Deleet Merchandising see. ........ Printers' Service, Inc., Newark
Deleon Printing & Supply, Inc., 311 Palisade Ave., Jersey City, 07307 ........ (201) 798-8440
Delform, LLC, 225 Highland Cross, Ste. 6, Rutherford, 07070 ........ (201) 438-3915
Delgen Press, Inc., 250 Delawanna Ave., Clifton, 07014 ........ (973) 472-2266
D'Elia Sign Co., 32 W. Fort Lee Rd., Bogota, 07603 ........ (201) 342-7231
Delicious Fresh Pierogi, Inc., 594 Chestnut St., Roselle Park, 07204 ........ (908) 245-0550
Delisa Pallet Corp., 91-97 Blanchard St., Newark, 07105 ........ (973) 344-8600
Delmhorst Instrument Co., 51 Indian Ln. E., Towaco, 07082 ........ (973) 334-2557
Delmont Sawmill, 4416 Route 47, Delmont, 08314 ........ (856) 785-1018
Deloitte, 3 2nd St., Harborside Plaza 10, Ste. 300, Jersey City, 07311 ........ (212) 937-8200
Delphi Engineering & Contracting, Inc.,
131 Blackwood Barnsboro Rd., Sewell, 08080 ........ (856) 228-5700
Delphus, Inc., 152 Speedwell Ave., Morristown, 07960 ........ (973) 267-9269
Delta Circuits, Inc., 26 Spielman Rd., Fairfield, 07004 ........ (973) 575-3000
Delta Cooling Towers, Inc., 185 U.S. Highway 206, Roxbury Township, 07836 ........ (973) 586-2201
Delta Corrugated Paper Products, 199 W. Ruby Ave., Palisades Park, 07650 ........ (201) 941-1910
Delta Fence Co., 541 Spring St., Elizabeth, 07201 ........ (908) 355-9066
Delta Galil USA, Inc., 1 Harmon Plz., 5th Fl., Secaucus, 07094 ........ (201) 902-0055
Delta Machine Works, Inc., 257 Division Ave., Carlstadt, 07072 ........ (201) 935-7474
Delta Paper Corp., 8295 National Hwy., Pennsauken, 08110 ........ (856) 532-0333
Delta Printing Co., 1000 Wall Street W., Lyndhurst, 07071 ........ (201) 935-0036
Delta Sales Co., Inc., 1355 State Route 23, Butler, 07405 ........ (973) 838-0371
† Delta Tool & Polishing Supplies Co., Inc.,
45 North Ave., P.O. Box 169, Garwood, 07027 ........ (908) 518-7600
Deltech Corp. see. ........ Deltech Resin Co., Newark
Deltech Resin Co., 49 Rutherford St., Newark, 07105 ........ (973) 589-0880
Deltronic Crystal Industries, 60 Harding Ave., Dover, 07801 ........ (973) 328-7000
Deltronics Corp., 224 Bogden Blvd., P.O. Box 446, Millville, 08332 ........ (856) 825-8200
Deluxe Corp. see. ........ Deluxe Mfg. Operations, Inc., Mountain Lakes
Deluxe Italian Bakery, Inc., 680 E. Clements Bridge Rd., Runnemede, 08078 ........ (856) 939-5000
Deluxe Mfg. Operations, Inc., 105 U.S. Highway 46, Mountain Lakes, 07046 ........ (973) 334-8000
Deluxe Packaging Co., 1079 Thomas Busch Memorial Hwy., Pennsauken, 08110 ........ (856) 486-0006
Delva Tool & Machine Corp.,
1603 Industrial Hwy., P.O. Box 2249, Cinnaminson, 08077 ........ (856) 786-8700
Demand, LLC, 36 S. Adamsville Rd., Bridgewater, 08807 ........ (908) 526-2020
DeMario Design & Screen Printing, 619 Church St., Pleasantville, 08232 ........ (609) 645-7319
Dematic Corp., 150 Allen Rd., Ste. 102, Basking Ridge, 07920 ........ (908) 991-9900
Demountable Concepts, Inc., 200 Acorn Rd., Glassboro, 08028 ........ (856) 863-0900
Denali Co., LLC, The (H Q), 43 W. Front St., Ste. 11, Red Bank, 07701 ........ (732) 219-7771
Denni's Studio, 169 Semel Ave., Garfield, 07026 ........ (973) 220-4898
Dental Models & Designs, Inc., 20 Passaic St., Ste. 3, Garfield, 07026 ........ (973) 472-8009
★ Dentistry Today, Inc., 100 Passaic Ave., Ste. 220, Fairfield, 07004 ........ (973) 882-4700
Denton Vacuum, LLC, 1259 N. Church St., Bldg. 3, Moorestown, 08057 ........ (856) 439-9100
Dependabilities Screen Printing, 632 Hulses Corner Rd., Howell, 07731 ........ (732) 886-0800
Dependable Machining & Stone Co., 53 Weaverville Rd., Freehold, 07728 ........ (732) 462-0262
Depot America, Inc., 1495 Highway 34, Farmingdale, 07727 ........ (732) 919-0209
Deptford Plating, Route 41 & Dein Ave., P.O. Box 5056, Deptford, 08096 ........ (856) 227-1144
Dericks Sheet Metal Works Co., Inc., 631 Union Blvd., Totowa, 07512 ........ (973) 256-1818
Derma Sciences, Inc. (H Q), 214 Carnegie Ctr., Ste. 300, Princeton, 08540 ........ (609) 514-4744
Dermarite Industries, LLC,
7777 W. Side Ave., P.O. Box 7209, North Bergen, 07047 ........ (973) 569-9000
Derma-Safe Co., LLC, 32 Juniper Rd., Wayne, 07470 ........ (973) 839-6383
Deroche Canvas, Inc., 283 County Road 519, Belvidere, 07823 ........ (908) 475-2266
DeRossi & Son Co., 411 S. 6th St., Vineland, 08360 ........ (856) 691-0061
DeSaussure Equipment Co., Inc., 23 W. Howcroft Rd., Maywood, 07607 ........ (201) 845-4242

ALPHABETICAL

Design A Sign, Inc., 745 Lehigh Ave., Ste. 3, Union, 07083 ... (908) 656-0822
Design Accents, LLC, 1330 Hamburg Tpke., Wayne, 07470 ... (201) 660-2446
Design Assistance Corp.,
3 Killdeer Ct., Ste. 301, P.O. Box 215, Swedesboro, 08085 ... (856) 241-9500
Design Display Group, Inc., 105 Amor Ave., Carlstadt, 07072 ... (201) 438-6000
Design 446, 2411 Atlantic Ave., Ste. 4, Manasquan, 08736 ... (732) 223-0100
Design Line, Inc., 283 Cox St., Roselle, 07203 ... (908) 241-1911
Design Of Tomorrow, Inc., 24 Sherwood Ln., Fairfield, 07004 ... (973) 227-5676
Design Plan Lighting, Inc., 79 Trenton Ave., Frenchtown, 08825 ... (908) 996-7710
Design Production, Inc., 9 Industrial Pk., Waldwick, 07463 ... (201) 447-5656
Designer Sign Systems, LLC, 352 Washington Ave., Carlstadt, 07072 ... (201) 939-5577
† Designer Source, Inc., 2139 State Route 35, Holmdel, 07733 ... (732) 264-7775
Designer T's, 1165 Marlkress Rd., Ste. F, Cherry Hill, 08003 ... (856) 751-4545
Designers Kitchens, Inc., 250 Faraday Ave., Jackson, 08527 ... (732) 370-5500
Designmecha, Inc., 73 Race St., Nutley, 07110 ... (973) 493-8146
Design-N-Stitch, Inc., 194 Atlantic St., Hackensack, 07601 ... (201) 488-1314
Designs By James, 892 N. Delsea Dr., Vineland, 08360 ... (856) 692-1316
Designs In Wood, 209 Williams Ave., Barrington, 08007 ... (856) 546-8338
Desiron, 820 Colfax Ave., Kenilworth, 07033 ... (908) 241-7776
Desktop Alert, Inc., 346 Main St., Chatham, 07928 ... (973) 727-0066
Dessau Co., Inc., Maurice, 15-01 Pollitt Dr., Fair Lawn, 07410 ... (201) 791-2005
Dessau International see. ... Dessau Co., Inc., Maurice, Fair Lawn
Detail Model & Machine, 61 Woodstown Rd., Mullica Hill, 08062 ... (856) 223-0184
† Devco Corp., 131 Morristown Rd., Bldg. B, Basking Ridge, 07920 ... (908) 630-0005
DeVece & Shaffer, Inc., 400 Legion Ave., P.O. Box 201, Palmyra, 08065 ... (856) 829-7282
† Devon Trading Corp., 5 Fairfield Rd., Caldwell, 07006 ... (973) 812-9190
DeWalt Mfg. Co., Inc., 88 W. Cohawkin Rd., Clarksboro, 08020 ... (856) 423-1207
Dewey Electronics Corp., 27 Muller Rd., Oakland, 07436 ... (201) 337-4700
Dewy Meadow Foods, Inc., 1018 Rector Rd., Bridgewater, 08807 ... (908) 218-5655
Deza Machine & Tool Co., 938 E. 19th St., Paterson, 07501 ... (973) 278-6654
Dezine Line, Inc., 1104 Route 46 E., Ledgewood, 07852 ... (973) 989-1009
DGB Bearing & Technology,
700 Mid Atlantic Pkwy., P.O. Box 189, Thorofare, 08086 ... (856) 848-3200
DG3 North America, Inc., 180 Pulaski St., Bayonne, 07002 ... (201) 946-0156
DG3 North America, Inc., 100 Burma Rd., Jersey City, 07305 ... (201) 793-5000
Di Ferraro, Inc., 28 Burgess Pl., Wayne, 07470 ... (973) 694-7200
Diabetic & Athletic Foot Center, LLC, Cedarwood Plz.,
226 Route 37, Toms River, 08753 ... (732) 281-3134
Diagnostic Services, Inc., 220 Mountain Ave., Middlesex, 08846 ... (732) 271-9199
Diagnostic Specialties, 4 Leonard St., Metuchen, 08840 ... (732) 549-4011
† Diagnostix Plus, Inc., 197 Cedar Ln., Ste. 1, Teaneck, 07666 ... (201) 530-5505
DialConnection, LLC, 1040 Route 73 S., Berlin, 08009 ... (856) 753-6620
Dialight Corporation (H Q), 1501 State Highway 34 S., Farmingdale, 07727 ... (732) 919-3119
Dialogic Corp., 1515 State Route 10 E., Parsippany, 07054 ... (973) 967-6000
Dialogic, Inc. see. ... Dialogic Corp., Parsippany
★ Dialogic, Inc. (H Q), 4 Gatehall Dr., Parsippany, 07054 ... (800) 755-4444
Diamond Brite Metal Processing, 333 Cedar Ave., Ste. 1, Middlesex, 08846 ... (732) 564-1164
Diamond Case Co., 45 Fairfield Pl., West Caldwell, 07006 ... (973) 227-8707
Diamond Chemical Company, Inc.,
Union Ave. & DuBois St., P.O. Box 7428, East Rutherford, 07073 ... (201) 935-4300
Diamond Die Cutters & Embossers, 629 Grove St., 6th Fl., Jersey City, 07310 ... (201) 876-8540
† Diamond Enterprise Group, 321 Snyder Ave., Berkeley Heights, 07922 ... (908) 771-6777
Diamond Hard Chromium Co., Inc., 463 NJ Railroad Ave., Newark, 07114 ... (973) 824-9412
Diamond Lamination see. ... Diamond Enterprise Group, Berkeley Heights
Diamond Machine Co., Inc., 30 N. Valley Rd., P.O. Box 420, Roosevelt, 08555 ... (609) 490-8940
Dicar, Inc., 10 Bloomfield Ave., P.O. Box 643, Pine Brook, 07058 ... (973) 575-1174
Dicar, Inc., 5 Bader Rd., Pine Brook, 07058 ... (973) 575-4220
Die Tech, LLC, 58 McKinley St., Hackensack, 07601 ... (201) 343-8324
Die-Tech, Inc., 677 Amwell Rd., Hillsborough, 08844 ... (908) 369-6756
DigiPol Technologies see. ... Rudolph Instruments, Inc., Denville
Digital Arts Imaging, LLC, 105 State Route 31, Ste. 10, Flemington, 08822 ... (908) 237-4646
Digital Color Concepts, Inc., 256 Sheffield St., Mountainside, 07092 ... (908) 264-0504
Digital Design, Inc., 67 Sand Park Rd., Cedar Grove, 07009 ... (973) 857-0901
Digital First Media see. ... Central Record Corp., The, Medford
Digital First Media see. ... Journal Register Co., The, Medford
Digital First Media see. ... Trentonian, The, Trenton
Digital Print Solutions, LLC, 5 Eastmans Rd., Parsippany, 07054 ... (973) 263-1890
Digital Productions, Inc., 410 Southgate Ct., Mickleton, 08056 ... (856) 224-1111
Digital Surroundings, LLC, 11 Princess Rd., Ste. E, Lawrence Township, 08648 ... (609) 912-1800
Digitize, Inc., 158 Edison Rd., Lake Hopatcong, 07849 ... (973) 663-1011
Digitize International see. ... Digitize, Inc., Lake Hopatcong
Digitron Electronic Corp., 144 Market St., Kenilworth, 07033 ... (908) 245-7200
DigiVac Co., 105-B Church St., Matawan, 07747 ... (732) 765-0900
DIHCO, Inc., 612 E. Crescent Ave., Upper Saddle River, 07458 ... (201) 327-0518
Dikeman Laminating Corp., 181 Sargeant Ave., Clifton, 07013 ... (973) 473-5696
DiLauri Steel Fabricators, 5 Merrys Ln., East Hanover, 07936 ... (973) 884-2414
★ Dillistone Systems, Inc., 50 Harrison St., Ste. 201-A, Hoboken, 07030 ... (201) 653-0013
Dillon Yarn Corp. (H Q), 53 E. 34th St., Paterson, 07514 ... (973) 684-1600
Dimensional Communications Inc., 1595 MacArthur Blvd., Mahwah, 07430 ... (201) 767-1500
Dimensional Merchandising, Inc., 86 N. Main St., Wharton, 07885 ... (973) 328-1600
DiMilo Industries, 90 Dayton Ave., Ste. 38, Passaic, 07055 ... (973) 955-0460
DiNaso Building Supplies, 133 Ocean Ave., Lakewood, 08701 ... (732) 886-6666
DiNaso Staten Island, LLC see. ... DiNaso Building Supplies, Lakewood
Diocese Of Camden see. ... Catholic Star Herald, Camden
Diocese Of Paterson see. ... Beacon Publishing Co., Inc., Clifton
Diopsys, Inc., 16 Chapin Rd., Ste. 912, P.O. Box 672, Pine Brook, 07058 ... (973) 244-0622
DiPasquale Fence Co., 196 Route 9 N., Englishtown, 07726 ... (732) 536-0660
DiPietro Foods, Inc., 1701 Springfield Ave., Maplewood, 07040 ... (973) 762-4077
Direct Cabinet Sales, 265 Central Ave., Clark, 07066 ... (732) 382-8080
Direct Computer Resources, Inc., 120 Birch Rd., Franklin Lakes, 07417 ... (201) 848-0018
★ Direct Development, LLC, 1338 State Route 36, Hazlet, 07730 ... (732) 739-8890
Direct Market Desgins see. ... Liberty Envelope, Inc., Paterson
Direct Printing Impressions, 33 Fairfield Pl., West Caldwell, 07006 ... (973) 227-6111
Direct Sales & Services, 141 Lanza Ave., Bldg. 8, Garfield, 07026 ... (973) 340-4480
Dirory Industries, Inc., 39 Progress St., Edison, 08820 ... (908) 757-6650
Disc Disease Solutions, Inc. see. ... DDS, Inc., Hackensack
Disc Makers, 7905 N. Route 130, Pennsauken, 08110 ... (856) 663-9030
Disco Aluminum, 518 South Ave., Plainfield, 07060 ... (908) 754-2699
★ Discount Digital Print, LLC, 629 Grove St., 16th Fl., Jersey City, 07310 ... (201) 659-9600
Discount Office Supply, 146 Hudson St., Hackensack, 07601 ... (201) 342-3030
Discovery Semiconductors, Inc., 119 Silvia St., Ewing, 08628 ... (609) 434-1311
Dispersion Technology, Inc., 1885 Swarthmore Ave., Lakewood, 08701 ... (732) 364-4488
Display Pro Mfg. see. ... Daysol Industries, Kenilworth
Display Sales, Inc., P.O. Box 115, Spotswood, 08884 ... (732) 251-8981
Distek, Inc., 121 N. Center Dr., North Brunswick, 08902 ... (732) 422-7585
† Distinctive Promotions, Inc., 268 U.S. Highway 206, Ste. 404, Flanders, 07836 ... (973) 584-6800
Distinctive Wood Work, Inc., 70 Stacy Haines Rd., Ste. D, Lumberton, 08048 ... (609) 714-8505
Distinctive Woodworking, 703 Van Rossum Ave., Unit 1, Beverly, 08010 ... (609) 877-8122
Distributor Label Products, Inc. see. ... Certified Labeling Solutions, Hillsborough
DiTech Group see. ... Zin-Tech, Pennsauken
Div. of Mendelsohn's Kosher Pizza see. ... Ko-Fro Foods, Inc., Avenel
Dively Models, Inc., Bob, 540 Hudson St., Hackensack, 07601 ... (201) 310-2340
Diversatech, Inc., 1584 Reed Rd., Pennington, 08534 ... (609) 730-9668
Diversified Display Products, LLC,
777 Ramsey Ave., P.O. Box 913, Hillside, 07205 ... (908) 686-2200
Diversified Fixture, Inc., 1930 Swarthmore Ave., Lakewood, 08701 ... (732) 886-0600
Diversified Foam Products, Inc. see. ... Diversified Industries, Inc., Swedesboro
Diversified Graphic Machinery, 230 Highway 35, Red Bank, 07701 ... (732) 933-4865
Diversified Heat Transfer, Inc., 439 Main Rd., Route 202, Towaco, 07082 ... (718) 386-6666
Diversified Impressions, Inc., 119 Coit St., Irvington, 07111 ... (973) 399-9041
Diversified Industries, Inc., 121 High Hill Rd., Swedesboro, 08085 ... (856) 662-1981
Diversified Machine, LLC, 15 American Way, Ste. 12, Spotswood, 08884 ... (732) 251-6600
Diversified Medical Group see. ... Westcon Orthopedics, Inc., Neshanic Station
Diversified Millwork, Inc., 420 N. 2nd Rd., Unit C, Hammonton, 08037 ... (609) 270-7385
Diversified Precision Tooling, 143 Baker St., Dover, 07801 ... (973) 361-8545
Diversiprint, Inc., 1124 U.S. Highway 202, Ste. B-16, Raritan, 08869 ... (908) 685-2225
Diversitech, Inc., 18 Hamburg Tpke., Riverdale, 07457 ... (973) 835-2900
Diversitex, Inc. (H Q), 376 Hollywood Ave., Ste. 203, Fairfield, 07004 ... (973) 808-4566
Diversity Careers * Renard Communications see. ... Renard Commmunications, Inc., Springfield
DiversityInc Media LLC, 342 Nassau St., Princeton, 08540 ... (973) 494-0500
Divine Printing, Inc., 131 Liberty St., Metuchen, 08840 ... (732) 632-8800
Dixo Co., Inc., 158 Central Ave., P.O. Box 7038, Rochelle Park, 07662 ... (201) 845-6000
DL Printing Co., Inc., 283 Prospect Ave., Avenel, 07001 ... (732) 750-1917
D'Lite Products, Inc., 540 Ravine Ct., Wyckoff, 07481 ... (201) 444-0822
D&M Holdings US, Inc. (H Q), 100 Corporate Dr., Mahwah, 07430 ... (201) 762-6500
DMC, Inc., Charles Craft Fabrics see. ... Dollfus Mieg Co., Inc., Kearny
DMD Stairs & Rails, LLC, 370 Whitesville Rd., Ste. 8, Jackson, 08527 ... (732) 901-0102
DME Security & Electronics see. ... Masi Electronics, Don, West Caldwell
DMG America, LLC, 242 S. Dean St., Englewood, 07631 ... (201) 894-5505
DMI Personal Care see. ... Dimensional Merchandising, Inc., Wharton
DMR Sign Systems, 215 State Route 10, Ste. 1-A, Randolph, 07869 ... (973) 361-1829
DMS Laboratories, Inc., 2 Darts Mill Rd., Flemington, 08822 ... (908) 782-3353
★ DNE Nutraceuticals, Inc., 700 Central Ave., Farmingdale, 07719 ... (732) 806-9538
Doc's Duds, LLC, 92 Half Mile Rd., Red Bank, 07701 ... (732) 219-0060
† Dodson Global, Inc., 27 Cotters Ln., East Brunswick, 08816 ... (732) 238-7001
Dodson Vault Co., E., P.O. Box 966, Williamstown, 08094 ... (856) 728-7660
Doggett Corp., The, 30 Cherry St., Lebanon, 08833 ... (908) 236-6335
Dogstar Digital, LLC, 429 Redmond Ave., Oakhurst, 07755 ... (732) 768-3699
Dohrman Printing Co., Inc., 445 Industrial Rd., Carlstadt, 07072 ... (201) 933-0346
Dolan Creation, Inc., 255 Squankum Rd., P.O. Box 693, Farmingdale, 07727 ... (732) 938-6656
Dolce Bros. Printing, 29 Brook Ave., Maywood, 07607 ... (201) 843-0400
Dolce Vita Intimates, LLC (H Q), 1000 1st St., Harrison, 07029 ... (973) 482-8400
Dollfus Mieg Co., Inc., 10 Basin Dr., Ste. 130, Kearny, 07032 ... (973) 589-0606
Dolly Screen Printing, Inc., 1-19 Elm St., Freehold, 07728 ... (732) 294-8979
Dolph Co., John C., 320 New Rd., Monmouth Junction, 08852 ... (732) 329-2333
Dolphin Industries Ltd., 2141 River Rd., P.O. Box 344, Egg Harbor City, 08215 ... (609) 965-5188
★ Domico Upholstery Co., 1337 Delsea Dr., Woodbury, 08096 ... (856) 853-8181
Donaldson Co., Inc., R. J., 1287 Glassboro Rd., Williamstown, 08094 ... (856) 629-2737
† Donio, Inc., Frank, 692 N. Egg Harbor Rd., P.O. Box 529, Hammonton, 08037 ... (609) 561-2466
Donnelly Industries, Inc., 557 Route 23 S., Wayne, 07470 ... (973) 672-1800
Donray Printing, 2 Eastmans Rd., Parsippany, 07054 ... (973) 515-8100
Don's Drapery Mfg. Co., 145 Heckel St., Belleville, 07109 ... (973) 751-1544
Donsky Designs, 3851 Boardwalk, Apt. 2405, Atlantic City, 08401 ... (609) 345-4445
DontGetHit.com see. ... Bright Ideas USA, LLC, Lakewood
† Door Jockey, Inc., 915 18th Ave., Wall, 07719 ... (732) 942-6099
Dorado Systems, LLC, 8 Kings Hwy. E., Haddonfield, 08033 ... (856) 354-0048
Doralex, Inc., 403 Saint Mihiel Dr., Riverside, 08075 ... (856) 764-0694
Doran, LLC, 599 Green Ln., Union, 07083 ... (908) 289-9200
Doran Sling & Assembly Corp., 1285 Central Ave., Hillside, 07205 ... (908) 351-7800
D'Orazio Foods, Inc., 960 Creek Rd., Bellmawr, 08031 ... (856) 931-1900
Dorchester Shipyard, Inc., 13 Front St., P.O. Box 600, Dorchester, 08316 ... (856) 785-8040
Dornan, Inc., 333 Cedarcroft Dr., Brick, 08724 ... (732) 295-4491
† Dornisch Enterprises, Inc., 112 Cromwell Ct., Woodbury, 08096 ... (856) 863-1225
Dor-Win Mfg. Co., 109 Midland Ave., Elmwood Park, 07407 ... (201) 796-4300
Dosch King Emulsions, Inc., 16 Troy Hills Rd., Whippany, 07981 ... (973) 887-0145
★ Dot Graphix, Inc., 79 S. Main St., Ste. 13, Barnegat, 08005 ... (609) 660-0087
Double O Mfg., 100 S. Washington Ave., Dunellen, 08812 ... (732) 752-9423
Douglas Electrical Components, Inc., 5 Middlebury Blvd., Randolph, 07869 ... (973) 627-8230
Dover Signs Mfg. & Graphics, Inc., 1471 Sussex Tpke., Randolph, 07869 ... (973) 366-2229
Dover Vinyl Products, 1746 Route 9, Toms River, 08755 ... (732) 244-1444
Dow Chemical Co., The, 1500 John Tipton Blvd., Pennsauken, 08110 ... (856) 910-4900
Dow Chemical Co., The see. ... Lightscape Materials, Inc., Princeton
Dow Jones & Co., Inc., 4300 N. Route 1, Monmouth Junction, 08852 ... (609) 520-4000
Downtown Interiors, LLC, 629 Grove St., 8th Fl., Jersey City, 07310 ... (201) 798-4728
Downtown Printing Center, Inc., 46 Paterson St., New Brunswick, 08901 ... (732) 246-7990
† Dozortsev & Sons Enterprises, 411-415 John St., Elizabeth, 07202 ... (908) 353-1234
DPI Copies Printing & Graphics, Inc., 2070 Route 70 E., Cherry Hill, 08003 ... (856) 874-1355
DPT Laboratories Ltd. see. ... DPT Lakewood, LLC, Lakewood
DPT Lakewood, LLC, 1200 Paco Way, Bldg. 19, Lakewood, 08701 ... (732) 367-9000
DR Fiberglass, 2027 Route 37 E., Toms River, 08753 ... (732) 929-8448
Dr. Harvey's Healthy Formulations Inc.,
25 W. Highland Ave., Atlantic Highlands, 07716 ... (732) 787-2400
Dr Pepper Snapple Group, Inc., 1200 Milik St., Carteret, 07008 ... (732) 969-1600
Dr Pepper Snapple Group, Inc. see. ... Yoo-Hoo Chocolate Beverage Corp., Carlstadt
Dr. Praeger's see. ... Ungar's Food Products, Inc., Elmwood Park
Dr. Reddy's Laboratories, Inc. (H Q), 107 College Rd. E., Princeton, 08540 ... (609) 375-9900
Dr. T-Shirt, 221 Parker Ave., Manasquan, 08736 ... (732) 223-3866
Draka Specialty Tubing, 111 Chimney Rock Rd., Bridgewater, 08807 ... (732) 469-5902
Drake Corp., 154 Tices Ln., East Brunswick, 08816 ... (732) 254-1530
★ Drake Mills, LLC, 18 E. 5th St., Ste. B, Paterson, 07524 ... (973) 345-0008
Dranetz Technologies, 1000 New Durham Rd., Edison, 08818 ... (732) 287-3680
Drapery & More, Inc., 2321 Kennedy Blvd., Ste. 2401-B-1, North Bergen, 07047 ... (201) 271-9661
Drapery Corp. Of America, Inc., 12-16 1st Ave., Paterson, 07524 ... (973) 925-1200
Drapkin Printing Co., 1850 Elizabeth Ave., Ste. 1, Rahway, 07065 ... (732) 381-2228

© Copyright 2015 Manufacturers' News, Inc.


Drawbase Software, 1099 Wall St. W., Ste. 269, Lyndhurst, 07071 .......... (973) 927-6814
Dream On Me Industries, Inc., 125 Helen St., South Plainfield, 07080 .......... (908) 791-0555
Drew & Rogers, Inc., 30 Plymouth St., Fairfield, 07004 .......... (973) 575-6210
Drew-Wal Machine & Tool Corp., 76 Monroe St., Little Ferry, 07643 .......... (201) 641-3887
† Dreyco, Inc., 263 Veterans Blvd., Carlstadt, 07072 .......... (201) 896-9000
★ Dreyer's Lumber & Hardware, Inc., 348 Elberon Blvd., Oakhurst, 07755 .......... (732) 531-0220
† DRG International, Inc., 841 Mountain Ave., Springfield, 07081 .......... (973) 564-7555
Drink Atoast Co., Inc., 603 Harrison St., P.O. Box 204, Riverside, 08075 .......... (856) 461-1000
† Driscoll Foods, 174 Delawanna Ave., Clifton, 07014 .......... (973) 672-9400
Driscoll Label Co., Inc., 19 West St., East Hanover, 07936 .......... (973) 585-7295
DriTac Flooring Products, LLC, 60 Webro Rd., Clifton, 07012 .......... (973) 614-9000
Drive Line Service Of New Jersey, Inc., 622 U.S. Highway 46, Clifton, 07013 .......... (973) 473-7900
Drive-Master Co., Inc., 37 Daniel Rd. West, Fairfield, 07004 .......... (973) 808-9709
Drom Fragrances International, Inc., 5 Jacksonville Rd., Towaco, 07082 .......... (973) 316-8400
Drug Delivery Technology, LLC, 219 Changebridge Rd., Montville, 07045 .......... (973) 299-1200
Drug Development & Delivery see .......... Drug Delivery Technology, LLC, Montville
Dry Ice Corp. (H Q), 189 Central Ave., Old Tappan, 07675 .......... (201) 767-3200
Drytech, Inc., 54 Wrightstown Cookstown Rd., P.O. Box 249, Cookstown, 08511 .......... (609) 758-1794
★ DSA Graphics, LLC, 431 E. Main St., Ste. 3, Denville, 07834 .......... (973) 625-7760
DSM Awnings see. .......... DSM Enterprises, Inc., Eatontown
DSM Enterprises, Inc., 132 Lewis St., Unit B-5, Eatontown, 07724 .......... (732) 380-9779
DSM Nutritional Products, Inc., 206 Macks Island Dr., Belvidere, 07823 .......... (908) 475-5300
DSM Pharmaceutical Products, Inc. see. .......... DSM Nutritional Products, Inc., Belvidere
DSM Pharmaceutical Products, Inc. (H Q),
45 Waterview Blvd., Parsippany, 07054 .......... (973) 257-1063
DSO Fluid Handling Co., Inc., 300 McGaw Dr., Ste. 2, Edison, 08837 .......... (732) 225-9100
DSPCon, 380 Foothill Rd., Ste. 101, Bridgewater, 08807 .......... (908) 722-5656
DTI see .......... Dispersion Technology, Inc., Lakewood
Dtrovision, LLC, 535 E. Crescent Ave., Ste. 1, Ramsey, 07446 .......... (201) 488-3232
DU Technologies, Inc., 300 W. Commercial Ave., Moonachie, 07074 .......... (201) 729-0070
Dubell Lumber Co., 102 S. Route 73, Cedar Brook, 08018 .......... (609) 567-2467
† Dubell Lumber Co., 731 Cuthbert Blvd., Cherry Hill, 08002 .......... (856) 665-9100
† Dubell Lumber Co., 148 Route 70 E., P.O. Box 1449, Medford, 08055 .......... (609) 654-4143
Dubin Bros. Lumber Co., Inc., 710 Newton Ave., P.O. Box 85, Oaklyn, 08107 .......... (856) 854-4675
Duca Printing Co., Inc., 247 Haddon Ave., West Berlin, 08091 .......... (856) 767-2242
Duct Mate, Inc., 190 Lexington Ave., Hackensack, 07601 .......... (201) 488-8002
Ducts Sheet Metal, LLC, 6200 Main St., South Amboy, 08879 .......... (732) 727-8781
Ductworks, Inc., 434 W. Front St., Plainfield, 07060 .......... (908) 754-8190
Dudley Chemical Corp., 125 Kenyon Dr., Ste. 1, Lakewood, 08701 .......... (732) 886-3100
Duferco Steel, Inc. (H Q), 100 Matawan Rd., Ste. 400, Matawan, 07747 .......... (732) 566-3130
Duffy, Inc., Andrew B., 322 Crown Point Rd., P.O. Box 569, Thorofare, 08086 .......... (856) 845-4900
Duffy Printing Co., 2389 Atco Ave., Atco, 08004 .......... (856) 768-1046
Duffys Delicious Candies Co., Inc., 29 N. Broadway, Gloucester City, 08030 .......... (856) 456-2955
Du-Matt Corp., 111 71st St., Guttenberg, 07093 .......... (201) 861-4271
Du-Mor Blade Co., Inc., 1002 Union Landing Rd., Cinnaminson, 08077 .......... (856) 829-9384
Dun & Bradstreet Corp., The, 103 John F. Kennedy Pkwy., Short Hills, 07078 .......... (973) 921-5500
Dunbar Mfg., LLC, 2400 Egg Harbor Rd., Lindenwold, 08021 .......... (856) 346-0666
Duncan Industrial Equipment see .......... BlackHawk Industrial, Atlantic Tool Systems Div., Hawthorne
★ Dunn Fabrication, 8470 Remington Ave., Pennsauken, 08110 .......... (856) 486-3866
† Dunphey-Smith Co., 30 Progress St., Union, 07083 .......... (908) 687-6292
Dun-Rite Sand & Gravel Co., Inc., 3765 Mays Landing Rd., Vineland, 08361 .......... (856) 825-9900
Dun-Rite Sand & Gravel Co., Inc. (H Q), 573 E. Grant Ave., Vineland, 08360 .......... (856) 692-2520
Dura Tape International, 2816 Morris Ave., Ste. 21, Union, 07083 .......... (908) 687-8273
Duraamen Engineered Products, Inc., 457 Frelinghuysen Ave., Newark, 07114 .......... (973) 230-1301
Durable Solutions see. .......... Kefa Northeast, Budd Lake
Dura-Carb, Inc., 204 Chamberlain Rd., P.O. Box 407, Oak Ridge, 07438 .......... (973) 697-6665
Durand Glass Mfg. Co., 901 S. Wade Blvd., Millville, 08332 .......... (856) 327-4800
† Durawear Glove & Safety, Inc., 30 Royal Rd., Ste. 4, Flemington, 08822 .......... (908) 284-0776
Durex, Inc., 5 Stahuber Ave., Union, 07083 .......... (908) 688-0800
Duro Bag Mfg. Co., 750 Dowd Ave., Elizabeth, 07201 .......... (908) 351-2400
Duro Plating Co., Inc., 273 Kaighns Ave., Camden, 08103 .......... (856) 963-4967
Durst Corp. see. .......... Jaclo Industries, Cranford
Dusenbery Engineering Co.,
309 E. Hanover Ave., P.O. Box 1001, Morristown, 07962 .......... (973) 539-2200
Dutch's Meats, Inc., 30 Morse Ave., Ewing, 08638 .......... (609) 882-6650
Dutra Sheet Metal Co., 1940 S. West Blvd., Ste. E, Vineland, 08360 .......... (856) 692-8058
† Duva, Inc., James, 66-B Columbia Rd., Branchburg, 08876 .......... (908) 526-1222
Dux Paints, Inc., 18 Mill St., Lodi, 07644 .......... (973) 473-2376
DV8 Enterprises, LLC, 141 W. Commercial Ave., Moonachie, 07074 .......... (201) 641-4944
DVTel, Inc., 65 Challenger Rd., Ste. 2, Ridgefield Park, 07660 .......... (201) 368-9700
D.W.L International Trading Co., 65 Industrial Rd., Lodi, 07644 .......... (973) 916-9958
Dye Into Print, Inc., 167 Fornelius Ave., Clifton, 07013 .......... (973) 772-8019
† Dynaclear Packaging / Pro Pack, Inc., 500 W. Main St., Wyckoff, 07481 .......... (201) 337-1001
Dynaflow Engineering, 106 Egel Ave., Middlesex, 08846 .......... (732) 356-9790
Dyna-Lite, Inc., 1050 Commerce Ave., Union, 07083 .......... (908) 687-8800
Dynametric Tool Co., 27 Somerset Pl., Clifton, 07012 .......... (973) 471-8009
Dynamic Blending Co., Inc., 1475 S. 6th St., Camden, 08104 .......... (856) 541-6626
Dynamic Decisions, Inc., 2709 Hamilton Blvd., South Plainfield, 07080 .......... (908) 755-5000
Dynamic Die Cutting & Finishings, 104-110 South St., Newark, 07114 .......... (973) 589-8338
Dynamic Machining, Inc., 876 N. Lenola Rd., Ste. 9-A, Moorestown, 08057 .......... (856) 273-9830
Dynamic Metals, Inc., 1713 S. 2nd St., Piscataway, 08854 .......... (908) 769-5111
Dynamic Printing & Graphics, Inc., 250 Delawanna Ave., Clifton, 07014 .......... (973) 473-7177
Dynasil Corp. Of America, 385 Cooper Rd., West Berlin, 08091 .......... (856) 767-4600
Dynasil Fused Silica see .......... Dynasil Corp. Of America, West Berlin
Dynatec Systems, Inc., 360 Connecticut Dr., Burlington, 08016 .......... (609) 387-0330
DYNA-Veyor, Inc., 10 Hudson St., Newark, 07103 .......... (973) 484-1119
Dyn-Optics see .......... Chromatic Control, LLC (H Q), Sparta
DynTek, Inc. see .......... DynTek Services, Inc., Mount Laurel
DynTek Services, Inc., 1120 Route 73, Ste. 100, Mount Laurel, 08054 .......... (856) 834-1100
Dyson, Dyson & Dunn, Inc. see. .......... Grobet File Co. Of America, LLC., Carlstadt
† E & B Distributors, Inc., 400 Route 22 E., Bridgewater, 08807 .......... (732) 469-2266
E & H Laminating & Slitting Co., 138 Grand St., Paterson, 07501 .......... (973) 345-1725
E & J Machine And Tool, LLC, 12 Orben Dr., Unit 1, Landing, 07850 .......... (973) 810-2312
E & M Bindery, Inc., 11 Peekay Dr., Clifton, 07014 .......... (973) 777-9300
E & T Plastics, 824 E. Gate Dr., Ste. E, Mount Laurel, 08054 .......... (856) 787-0900
E & T Plastics Mfg. Co., Inc. see. .......... E & T Plastics, Mount Laurel
E & W Textile Processors, Inc., 293 Morrissee Ave., Haledon, 07508 .......... (973) 942-8718
E C Tronics, Inc., 855 Industrial Hwy., Unit 5, Riverton, 08077 .......... (856) 829-7161
E F Design Ltd., 600 Harbor Blvd., Unit 1022, Weehawken, 07086 .......... (201) 319-9075
E G L Co., Inc., 100 Industrial Rd., Berkeley Heights, 07922 .......... (908) 508-1111
E Greene of NC * egnc see. .......... E. Greene Of North Carolina, Inc., West Caldwell
E. Greene Of North Carolina, Inc., P.O. Box 1017, West Caldwell, 07007 .......... (973) 838-5200

E. I. du Pont de Nemours & Co. see. .......... Belco Technologies Corp., Parsippany
E. I. du Pont de Nemours & Co. see. E. I. du Pont de Nemours & Co., Chambers Works Plt., Deepwater
E. I. du Pont de Nemours & Co., Chambers Works Plt.,
67 Canal St., Deepwater, 08023 .......... (856) 299-5000
E M Orthodontic Labs, Inc., 6 Lafayette Pl., P.O. Box 112, Waldwick, 07463 .......... (201) 652-4411
E N G Scientific, Inc., 82 Industrial St. E., Clifton, 07012 .......... (973) 472-7200
E. T. Browne Drug Company, Inc.,
440 Sylvan Ave., P.O. Box 1613, Englewood Cliffs, 07632 .......... (201) 894-9020
E T Mfg., Inc., 90 Dayton Ave., Bldg. 10-C, Ste. 89, Passaic, 07055 .......... (973) 777-6662
Eagle Button Co., Inc., 700-76 Broadway, Westwood, 07675 .......... (201) 652-4063
Eagle Embroidery & Graphix, 587 White Horse Pike, Hammonton, 08037 .......... (609) 561-1457
Eagle Engineering & Automation, Inc.,
2111 Herbertsville Rd., P.O. Box 924, Point Pleasant, 08742 .......... (732) 899-2292
Eagle Enterprises, Inc., 11 W. Ormond Ave., Cherry Hill, 08002 .......... (856) 427-0787
Eagle Eyewear, Inc. (H Q), P.O. Box 486, Whitehouse, 08888 .......... (908) 236-9300
Eagle Flo Pumps, Inc., 306 Orient Way, Rutherford, 07070 .......... (201) 438-8595
Eagle Nutritionals, 485 Washington Ave., Carlstadt, 07072 .......... (201) 964-1441
Eagle Pallet, 108 S. Wade Blvd., Millville, 08332 .......... (856) 765-9444
Eagle Steel & Iron, LLC, 7 Garfield St., Linden, 07036 .......... (908) 587-1025
Eagle System Group see. .......... ESG, LLC, Flanders
† Earle Asphalt Company, 1800 Route 34, Bldg. 2, Ste. 205, Wall, 07719 .......... (732) 308-1113
Earle Asphalt Company see .......... Walter R. Earle Corporation, Jackson
Early Childhood Resources, LLC, 2165 Center Square Rd., Logan Township, 08085 .......... (856) 638-1170
Earth Friendly Products see. .......... Earth Friendly Products, Inc., Norwood
Earth Friendly Products, Inc., 380 Chestnut St., Norwood, 07648 .......... (201) 750-7701
EarthColor, 345 Walsh Dr., Parsippany, 07054 .......... (973) 884-1300
EarthColor, Inc. see. .......... EarthColor, Parsippany
EarthColor, Inc., 249 Pomeroy Rd., P.O. Box 169, Parsippany, 07054 .......... (973) 884-1300
EarthColor, Inc. see. .......... EarthDigital, Moonachie
EarthDigital, 77 Moonachie Ave., Moonachie, 07074 .......... (551) 497-5400
Easco Shower Doors Co., 3 Industrial Dr., Vernon, 07462 .......... (973) 209-4141
† East Brunswick Supply, Inc., 413 State Route 18, East Brunswick, 08816 .......... (732) 254-1015
East Coast Counter Tops, Inc., 166 Main St., P.O. Box 645, Lakewood, 08701 .......... (732) 363-7734
East Coast Custom, 242 Main St., Sayreville, 08872 .......... (732) 390-8238
East Coast Embossing, 35 8th St., P.O. Box 1076, Passaic, 07055 .......... (973) 777-9830
East Coast Panelboard, Inc., 101 Tornillo Way, Tinton Falls, 07712 .......... (732) 739-6400
East Coast Plastics, Inc., 427 Commerce Ln., Ste. 7, West Berlin, 08091 .......... (856) 768-8700
East Coast Power Systems see. .......... East Coast Panelboard, Inc., Tinton Falls
East Coast Security Products, 53 Green Pond Rd., Ste. 1, Rockaway, 07866 .......... (973) 625-3277
★ East Coast Steel, Inc., 317 Salina Rd., Sewell, 08080 .......... (856) 582-6776
East Coast Tile Imports, Inc. see .......... Classic Ceramic Tile, Inc., East Brunswick
East Performance Exhaust, 1050 U.S. Highway 22, Bldg. B, Lebanon, 08833 .......... (908) 236-2820
East Trading West Investments LLC, 200 S. Jefferson St., Orange, 07050 .......... (973) 678-0800
Eastar Plastics, Inc., 250 Circle Dr. N., Piscataway, 08854 .......... (732) 564-1899
Easter Seal Society Of New Jersey, 133 Main St., Franklin, 07416 .......... (973) 827-9066
Easter Seals New Jersey see .......... Easter Seal Society Of New Jersey, Franklin
Easter Seals New Jersey see .......... Raritan Valley Workshop, New Brunswick
Easter Seals New Jersey (H Q), 9 Terminal Rd., New Brunswick, 08901 .......... (732) 257-6662
Eastern Automation Systems,
1151 New Jersey Route 33, P.O. Box 2394, Farmingdale, 07727 .......... (732) 938-2002
Eastern Concrete Materials, Inc., 201 Route 539, Barnegat, 08005 .......... (609) 698-2800
Eastern Concrete Materials, Inc., 1 Railroad Ave., Glen Gardner, 08826 .......... (908) 537-2135
Eastern Concrete Materials, Inc., 3620 Route 23 N., Hamburg, 07419 .......... (973) 827-7625
Eastern Concrete Materials, Inc. (H Q),
475 Market St., 3rd Fl., Elmwood Park, 07407 .......... (201) 797-7979
Eastern Emblem Mfg. Corp., 509 18th St., P.O. Box 828, Union City, 07087 .......... (201) 867-3159
★ Eastern Glass Resources, Inc., 770 Supor Blvd., Harrison, 07029 .......... (973) 483-8411
† Eastern Lift Truck Co., Inc.,
549 E. Linwood Ave., Route 73 N., P.O. Box 307, Maple Shade, 08052 .......... (856) 779-8880
Eastern Machining Corp., 1197 Fries Mill Rd., Franklinville, 08322 .......... (856) 694-3303
† Eastern Marketing Corp., 24 Eisenhower Pkwy., Roseland, 07068 .......... (973) 403-8900
Eastern Metal Recycling see. .......... Camden Iron & Metal, Inc., Bellmawr
Eastern Millwork, Inc., 18 Chapel Ave., Jersey City, 07305 .......... (201) 451-9510
Eastern Molding Co., Inc., 597 Main St., Belleville, 07109 .......... (973) 759-0220
Eastern Sheet Metal & Plate Works, Inc.,
169 E. Highland Pkwy., Roselle, 07203 .......... (908) 241-6766
Eastern Sign Co., 3011 Ocean Heights Ave., Ste. B, Egg Harbor Township, 08234 .......... (609) 927-0885
Eastern Sign Tech, LLC, 112 Connecticut Dr., P.O. Box 564, Burlington, 08016 .......... (609) 261-2805
Eastern Silk Mills, Inc., 212 Catherine St., Elizabeth, 07201 .......... (908) 355-6700
Eastern Tea Corp., 1 Engelhard Dr., Monroe Township, 08831 .......... (609) 860-1100
Eastmed Enterprises, Inc., 11 Brandywine Dr., Marlton, 08053 .......... (856) 797-0131
East-West Service Co., Inc., 2 Marlen Dr., Hamilton, 08691 .......... (609) 631-9000
Easy Abrasives, LLC (H Q), 16 Passaic Ave., Unit 8, Fairfield, 07004 .......... (973) 575-7879
Easy Graphics Inc. see. .......... Seibel Group, Inc., The, Princeton
Easy Pak Services Of New Jersey, 6 Nicholas Ct., P.O. Box 676, Dayton, 08810 .......... (732) 274-2428
★ Easy Prints, Inc., 172 Main St., Metuchen, 08840 .......... (848) 229-2410
Eatem Foods Company, 1829 Gallagher Dr., Vineland, 08360 .......... (856) 692-1663
Eaton Corp. see. .......... Eaton Filtration, LLC, Tinton Falls
Eaton Corp., Electrical Div., 96 Stemmers Ln., Westampton, 08060 .......... (609) 835-4230
Eaton Filtration, LLC, 44 Apple St., Tinton Falls, 07724 .......... (732) 767-4200
EatSmart Products see. .......... HealthTools, LLC (H Q), Wyckoff
Ebco Tool Co., 8-B Great Meadow Ln., East Hanover, 07936 .......... (973) 887-5255
EBI, 399 Jefferson Rd., Parsippany, 07054 .......... (973) 299-9300
EBI see .......... Energy Beams, Inc., Bloomingdale
† EC Hair Import, Inc., 99 Murray Hill Pkwy., Ste. B, East Rutherford, 07073 .......... (201) 933-8071
Ecce Panis, 3-B Brick Plant Rd., East Brunswick, 08816 .......... (732) 254-1770
ECCO High Frequency, 2360 Hamburg Tpke., Wayne, 07470 .......... (973) 248-3366
Echo Molding, Inc., 911 Springfield Rd., Union, 07083 .......... (908) 688-0099
EchoStream Motor Group, LLC see. .......... Odyssey Specialty Vehicles, Wharton
ECI Technology, Inc., 60 Gordon Dr., Totowa, 07512 .......... (973) 890-1114
Eclipse Mfg., LLC, 438 Lanza Ave., Garfield, 07026 .......... (973) 340-9939
Eco Printing, LLC see .......... Minuteman Press, Inc., Hasbrouck Heights
Econo-PAK, 1 Wiebel Plz., Sussex, 07461 .......... (973) 875-0990
ECOTEC, Inc., 1944 E. Elmer Rd., Vineland, 08361 .......... (856) 205-9283
ECS, LLC, 1827 U.S. Highway 9, Howell, 07731 .......... (732) 462-5530
ECSI International, Inc., 790 Bloomfield Ave., Bldg. C-1, Clifton, 07012 .......... (973) 574-8555
ec2 Software Solutions, 400 Apgar Dr., Ste. I, Somerset, 08873 .......... (732) 356-0070
Ecuadorian Rainforest, LLC, 25 Main St., Bldg. 6, Belleville, 07109 .......... (973) 759-2002
†★ Eddie Kane Steel Products, Inc., 450 Southard St., Trenton, 08638 .......... (609) 392-1161
† Eddie Kane Steel Products, Inc. (H Q), P.O. Box 133, Spring Lake, 07762 .......... (732) 974-3339
†★ Edesia Oil, LLC, 225 County Road 522, Unit B, Englishtown, 07726 .......... (732) 851-7979
Edge Orthotics, Inc., 209 Pierson Ave., Edison, 08837 .......... (732) 549-3343

ALPHABETICAL

★ **Indicates new listing this edition.** † **Indicates wholesaler/distributor.**

© Copyright 2015 Manufacturers' News, Inc.


Edgell Communications, Inc., 4 Middlebury Blvd., Ste. 1, Randolph, 07869 .... (973) 607-1300
Edgesys Consulting see. .... Edgesys, Inc., Hasbrouck Heights
Edgesys, Inc., 411 State Route 17, Ste. 310, Hasbrouck Heights, 07604 .... (201) 727-1663
Edgewater Building Supply, Inc., 704 Woodlane Rd., Beverly, 08010 .... (609) 387-0136
Edgewater Mfg. Co., Inc, 17-10 Willow St., Fair Lawn, 07410 .... (201) 664-0022
Edhard Corp., 279 Blau Rd., Hackettstown, 07840 .... (908) 850-8444
† EDI Distributors, Inc., 20 Lakeside Ave., P.O. Box 501, Cherry Hill, 08003 .... (856) 429-2580
EDI/ECI see. .... Elevator Doors, Inc./Elevator Cabs, Inc., Paterson
★ eDigital Graphics, 326 U.S. Highway 22, Ste. 12-A, Dunellen, 08812 .... (732) 968-1234
Edison Finishing see. .... Foremost Wood Products, Edison
Edison Foam Processing Corp., 157 Helen St., South Plainfield, 07080 .... (732) 225-2440
Edison Lithographing Corp., 3725 Tonnelle Ave., North Bergen, 07047 .... (201) 902-9191
Edison Machine, 25 Liberty St., Metuchen, 08840 .... (732) 494-5011
Edker Industries, Inc., 1401 Union Landing Rd., Cinnaminson, 08077 .... (856) 786-1971
Ed-Mar Industries, Inc., 11 Ray Pl., Fairfield, 07004 .... (973) 808-9205
Edmund Optics, Inc. see. .... Anchor Optical Co., Barrington
Edmund Optics, Inc., 101 E. Gloucester Pike, Barrington, 08007 .... (856) 547-3488
Edmunds & Assocs., 301-A Tilton Rd., Northfield, 08225 .... (609) 645-7333
Edston Mfg. Co., Inc., 321 Warren Ave., Stirling, 07980 .... (908) 647-0116
Educational & Laboratory Systems see. .... Design Of Tomorrow, Inc., Fairfield
Educational Information & Resource Center,
107 Gilbreth Pkwy., Mullica Hill, 08062 .... (856) 582-7000
Educational Testing Service, 660 Rosedale Rd., Princeton, 08541 .... (609) 921-9000
Edwards Coils Corp., 101 Alexander Ave., Unit 6, Pompton Plains, 07444 .... (973) 835-2815
Edwards Creative Products, Inc., 910 Beechwood Ave., Cherry Hill, 08002 .... (856) 665-3200
Edwards Hydronic Parts, LLC, 101 Alexander Ave., Pompton Plains, 07444 .... (973) 835-7754
EFCO Corp. see. .... EFCO Forms, Marlboro
EFCO Forms, 77 Vanderburg Rd., Marlboro, 07746 .... (732) 308-1010
Effective Signs see. .... Mag Signs, Inc., Burlington
EFI, Inc. see. .... Electronika For Industry, Inc., Parsippany
EFX Tex, LLC, 555 E. 31st St., Paterson, 07513 .... (973) 345-7601
Egg Harbor Rope Products, Inc.,
5105 White Horse Pike, P.O. Box 294, Egg Harbor City, 08215 .... (609) 965-2435
Egg Harbor Yachts, 801 Philadelphia Ave., Egg Harbor City, 08215 .... (609) 965-2300
Eggers Sails, Inc., John, 7076 Route 35, South Amboy, 08879 .... (732) 721-4667
E-Harvest Systems (H Q), 424 Little Brook Rd., Glen Gardner, 08826 .... (908) 832-0400
EIC Industry Group Corp. (H Q), 53 Green Pond Rd., Ste. 3, Rockaway, 07866 .... (973) 983-1988
Eigen Arts, Inc., 150 Bay St., Jersey City, 07302 .... (201) 798-7310
EIRC see. .... Educational Information & Resource Center, Mullica Hill
Eisai, Inc. (H Q), 100 Tice Blvd., Woodcliff Lake, 07677 .... (201) 692-1100
Ekato Corp., 48 Spruce St., Oakland, 07436 .... (201) 825-4684
Ekornes, Inc. (H Q), 615 Pierce St., Somerset, 08873 .... (732) 302-0097
El Especial * El Especialito * Personalidades see. .... U.S.A. Distributors, Inc., Union City
Elan Chemical Company, Inc., 268 Doremus Ave., Newark, 07105 .... (973) 344-8014
ELC America Corp., 235-B Hickory Ln., Bayville, 08721 .... (732) 269-5274
Elcam Medical, Inc., 2 University Plz., Ste. 620, Hackensack, 07601 .... (201) 457-1120
Elco Glass Industries Co., Inc., 1855 Swarthmore Ave., Lakewood, 08701 .... (732) 363-6550
Elder & Jenks Co., 148 E. 5th St., Bayonne, 07002 .... (201) 437-0770
Electric Fan Engineering Co., 8 Crown Plz., Unit 105, Hazlet, 07730 .... (732) 203-0320
† Electric Forklift Repair Corp.,
837 Somerset St., P.O. Box 1126, Somerset, 08875 .... (732) 249-7757
Electrical Motor Repair Co., 809 E. State St., Trenton, 08609 .... (609) 392-6149
Electrical Wholesalers, Inc. see. .... Fox Electric Supply Co., Inc., West Caldwell
Electrical Wholesalers, Inc. see. .... Monarch Electric Co., Inc., West Caldwell
Electro Ceramic Industries, 75 Kennedy St., Hackensack, 07601 .... (201) 342-2630
Electro Impulse Laboratory, Inc., 1805 Route 33, Neptune, 07753 .... (732) 776-5800
Electro Lift, Inc., 204 Sargeant Ave., Clifton, 07013 .... (973) 471-0204
Electro Magnetic Products, Inc., 355 Crider Ave., Moorestown, 08057 .... (856) 235-3011
★ ElectroHeat Induction, 9 Spruce St., Jersey City, 07306 .... (908) 494-0726
Electroid Co., 45 Fadem Rd., Springfield, 07081 .... (973) 467-8100
Electromagnetic Technologies, 50 Intervale Rd., Unit 15, Boonton, 07005 .... (973) 394-1719
Electromech, Inc., 624 Swan St., Ramsey, 07446 .... (201) 934-3456
Electro-Miniatures Corp., 68 W. Commercial Ave., Moonachie, 07074 .... (201) 460-0510
Electromotive, Inc., 55 Brown Ave., Springfield, 07081 .... (973) 564-8809
Electronic Concepts, Inc., 526 Industrial Way W., Eatontown, 07724 .... (732) 542-7880
Electronic Drives & Controls, Inc., 17 Eastmans Rd., Parsippany, 07054 .... (973) 428-0500
Electronic Integration Services, L.L.C. see. .... Panurgy OEM, Rockaway
Electronic Marine Systems, 800 Ferndale Pl., Rahway, 07065 .... (732) 382-4344
† Electronic Measurement Laboratories, Inc., 668 Easton Ave., Somerset, 08873 .... (732) 846-4029
Electronic Measuring Devices, Inc., 15 Mill Rd., Flanders, 07836 .... (973) 691-4755
Electronic Mfg. Co., 71 Newark Way, Maplewood, 07040 .... (973) 762-1300
Electronic Power Designs, Inc., 132 Union Ave., Bloomingdale, 07403 .... (973) 838-7055
Electronic Subassemblies, Inc., 1541 New Brooklyn Rd., Sicklerville, 08081 .... (856) 629-2492
Electronic Technology, Inc., 511 Lyons Ave., Irvington, 07111 .... (973) 371-5160
Electronic Transformer Corp., 460 Totowa Ave., Paterson, 07522 .... (973) 942-2222
Electronika For Industry, Inc., 3599 Route 46, Parsippany, 07054 .... (973) 575-4994
Electronix Express see. .... RSR Electronics, Inc., Rahway
Electro-Steam Generator Corp., 50 Indel Ave., P.O. Box 438, Rancocas, 08073 .... (609) 288-9071
† Electrum, Inc., 827 Martin St., Rahway, 07065 .... (732) 396-1616
Elegant Desserts, 275 Warren St., Lyndhurst, 07071 .... (201) 933-0770
Elemco Building Controls, 14 Ilene Ct., Bldg. 11, Unit 1, Hillsborough, 08844 .... (908) 281-2201
Elementis Chromium, Inc. (H Q), 469 Old Trenton Rd., East Windsor, 08512 .... (609) 443-2000
Elementis Specialties, Inc., 400 Claremont Ave., Jersey City, 07304 .... (201) 395-5108
Elementis Specialties, Inc. (H Q), 469 Old Trenton Rd., East Windsor, 08512 .... (609) 443-2000
Elena Consultants, 1175 Globe Ave., P.O. Box 1339, Mountainside, 07092 .... (908) 654-8309
★ Elevate HR, Inc., 1055 Parsippany Blvd., Ste. 511, Parsippany, 07054 .... (973) 917-3230
Elevator Doors, Inc./Elevator Cabs, Inc., 15 Jane St., Paterson, 07522 .... (973) 790-9100
Elevator Products Corp., 100 Dermarest Dr., Wayne, 07470 .... (973) 341-8000
Elevator Technology Corp., 337 Market St., Paterson, 07501 .... (973) 523-7760
Elgee Mfg. Co., 225 Stirling Rd., Warren, 07059 .... (908) 647-4100
Elgen Mfg. Co., 10 Railroad Ave., Closter, 07624 .... (201) 964-0008
Eli Jewels, Inc., 14 Wyckoff Ave., Ramsey, 07446 .... (201) 291-4200
Eli Lilly see. .... Eli Lilly & Co., Branchburg
Eli Lilly & Co., 33 ImClone Dr., Branchburg, 08876 .... (908) 541-8100
Eli Lilly & Co. see. .... Eli Lilly (H Q), Bridgewater
Eli Lilly (H Q), 440 Route 22 E., Bridgewater, 08807 .... (908) 541-8100
Elite Graphics, Inc., 333 Littleton Rd., Ste. 200, Parsippany, 07054 .... (973) 882-9769
★ Elite Home Products, 95 Mayhill St., Ste. 3, Saddle Brook, 07663 .... (201) 880-8292
Elite Packaging Corp., 40 Cotters Ln., Ste. E, East Brunswick, 08816 .... (732) 651-9955
Elite Pharmaceuticals, Inc., 165 Ludlow Ave., Northvale, 07647 .... (201) 750-2646
Elite Printing Service, 30 Heritage Dr., Sparta, 07871 .... (973) 729-0366
Elite Stone Importers, LLC, 45 Park Rd., Tinton Falls, 07724 .... (732) 542-7900
Elite Tool, Inc., 1640 New Market Ave., P.O. Box 853, South Plainfield, 07080 .... (732) 424-1126
† Elixens America, Inc., 1443 Pinewood St., Rahway, 07065 .... (732) 388-3555
† Elizabeth Truck Center, 878 North Ave., Elizabeth, 07201 .... (908) 355-8800
Elkay Products Co., Inc., 35 Brown Ave., P.O. Box 149, Springfield, 07081 .... (973) 376-7550
Elkem, Inc., 443 County Rd., Cliffwood, 07721 .... (732) 566-1700
Ellenby Technologies, Inc., 412 Grandview Ave., Woodbury Heights, 08097 .... (856) 848-2020
Elliott Glass Co., Inc., 192 Lackawanna Ave., Ste. 103, Woodland Park, 07424 .... (973) 256-8098
Ellis Kuhnke Controls, Inc., 132 Lewis St., Unit A-2, Eatontown, 07724 .... (732) 291-3334
Ellkay, LLC, 259 Seddle Ln., 3rd Fl., Teaneck, 07666 .... (201) 791-0606
ELMCO TWO, Inc., 1045 Cambridge St., Camden, 08105 .... (856) 365-2244
Elmendorf Office Supply , Inc.,
3201 Bridge Ave., Ste. 1, Point Pleasant Beach, 08742 .... (732) 295-8700
Elmer Times Co., Inc., 21 State St., Elmer, 08318 .... (856) 358-6171
Elmi Machine & Tool Co., Inc.,
1275 Bloomfield Ave., Bldg. 5, Unit 2-B, Fairfield, 07004 .... (973) 882-1277
Elmwood Industries, 8 Paul Kohner Pl., Elmwood Park, 07407 .... (201) 703-1220
Elmwood Press, Inc., 85 Main Ave., Elmwood Park, 07407 .... (201) 794-6273
Elnik Systems, LLC, 107 Commerce Rd., Cedar Grove, 07009 .... (973) 239-6066
Elray Mfg. Co., Inc., 17 Liberty St., Glassboro, 08028 .... (856) 881-1936
ElviPharma, LLC, 60 Ethel Rd. W., Piscataway, 08854 .... (732) 433-5591
E.M. Boehm * Boehm Galleries see. .... Boehm Porcelain, LLC, Trenton
E&M Gold Beekeepers, LLC, 113 Hope Rd., Tinton Falls, 07724 .... (732) 542-6528
E&M Wedding Favors see. .... E&M Gold Beekeepers, LLC, Tinton Falls
Emabond Solutions, LLC, 49 Walnut St., Ste. 2, Norwood, 07648 .... (201) 767-7400
Embroider This Co., 7 Duck Point Trl., Wharton, 07885 .... (973) 663-5551
Embroidery By Cozy, Inc., 695 Passaic Ave., Nutley, 07110 .... (973) 661-9781
Embroidery Concept & Design, LLC, 201 Pond Ave., Middlesex, 08846 .... (732) 926-9400
Embroidery Technologies, Inc., 737 Howe St., Point Pleasant Boro, 08742 .... (732) 295-1300
Embroidme, 215 U.S. Highway 22, Green Brook, 08812 .... (732) 752-1871
EmbroidMe see. .... New Rose, Inc., Woodbury
Emco Industrial Plastics, Inc.,
99 Commerce Rd., P.O. Box 2503, Cedar Grove, 07009 .... (973) 559-5610
Emerald Performance Materials, LLC see. .... CVC Thermoset Specialties, Inc., Moorestown
Emergency Transfer Controls, Inc., 251 Nuthatch Ct., Three Bridges, 08887 .... (908) 782-1794
Emerson Electric Co. see. .... ASCO Power Technologies, L.P. (H Q), Florham Park
Emerson Electric Co. see. .... ASCO Valve, Inc., Florham Park
Emerson Fence, Inc., 10 Lincoln Blvd., P.O. Box 306, Emerson, 07630 .... (201) 265-5150
Emerson Instrument & Valve Services, 120 Kissel Rd., Burlington, 08016 .... (609) 386-5000
Emerson Speed Printing, 379 Kinderkamack Rd., Oradell, 07649 .... (201) 265-7977
EMI Industries, LLC see. .... Marlo Mfg. Co., Inc., Boonton
EMI Yoshi, Inc., 1200 Jersey Ave., North Brunswick, 08902 .... (732) 248-5533
† Emiliani Enterprises, 600 Green Ln., Union, 07083 .... (908) 964-6340
EMMC Co., 1 Nicola Pl., Belleville, 07109 .... (973) 751-0100
Emmco Development Corp., 243 Belmont Dr., Somerset, 08873 .... (732) 469-6464
Empire Blended Products, Inc., 250 Hickory Ln., Bayville, 08721 .... (732) 269-4949
Empire Designs, Inc., 7 Main St., Englishtown, 07726 .... (732) 446-6447
Empire Industries, Inc., 40 Warren St., Paterson, 07524 .... (973) 279-2050
Empire Lumber & Millwork Co., 377 Frelinghuysen Ave., Newark, 07114 .... (973) 242-2700
† Empire Recycling, Inc., 3 New York Ave., P.O. Box 17398, Jersey City, 07307 .... (732) 393-0200
† Empire Resources, 1 Parker Plz., Fort Lee, 07024 .... (201) 944-2200
Empire Telecommunications, Inc., 15 S. Van Brunt St., Englewood, 07631 .... (201) 569-3339
Empirical Labs, Inc., 41 N. Beverwyck Rd., Lake Hiawatha, 07034 .... (973) 541-9446
Empro Products Co., Inc., 47 Montgomery St., Belleville, 07109 .... (973) 279-1010
EMS Aviation, 121 Whittendale Dr., Ste. A, Moorestown, 08057 .... (856) 234-5020
EMSE Corp., 10 Plog Rd., Unit 1, Fairfield, 07004 .... (973) 227-9221
Emtec, Inc., 11 Diamond Rd., Springfield, 07081 .... (973) 376-4242
Ena Meat Packing see. .... Senat Poultry, LLC, Paterson
Encore Poly Corp., 240 W. Passaic St., Ste. 7, Maywood, 07607 .... (201) 845-4510
Encur, Inc., 200 Division St., P.O. Box 92, Keyport, 07735 .... (732) 264-2098
Endless Games, Inc., 35 Main St., Ste. B, Matawan, 07747 .... (732) 414-2213
Endo Optiks, Inc., 39 Sycamore Ave., Little Silver, 07739 .... (732) 530-6762
Endo Pharmaceutical, Inc., 8 Clarke Dr., Cranbury, 08512 .... (609) 409-9010
Endo Pharmaceuticals, Inc. see. .... Endo Pharmaceutical, Inc., Cranbury
Endot Industries, Inc., 60 Green Pond Rd., Rockaway, 07866 .... (973) 625-8500
Endurance Net, Inc., 763-B Railroad Ave., Florence, 08518 .... (609) 499-3450
ENER-G Rudox, Inc., 765 State Route 17 N., P.O. Box 467, Carlstadt, 07072 .... (201) 438-0111
Energizer Holdings, Inc. see. .... Energizer Personal Care, Cedar Knolls
Energizer Personal Care, 240 Cedar Knolls Rd., Ste. 401, Cedar Knolls, 07927 .... (973) 753-3000
Energy Beams, Inc., 185 Hamburg Tpke., Bloomingdale, 07403 .... (973) 838-3037
Energy Kinetics, Inc., 51 Molasses Hill Rd., Lebanon, 08833 .... (908) 735-2066
Energy Options, LLC, 256 Campus Dr., Edison, 08837 .... (732) 512-9100
Energy Recycling Co., LLC, 409 Joyce Kilmer Ave., New Brunswick, 08901 .... (732) 545-6619
Enesco, LLC see. .... Our Name Is Mud, Haddonfield
† Enfasco, 1675 Hylton Rd., Pennsauken, 08110 .... (856) 662-7660
† Engine Distributors, Inc., 400 University Ct., Blackwood, 08012 .... (856) 228-7298
Engineered Arresting Systems Corporation * ZAS see. Zodiac Arresting Systems America - Logan, Swedesboro
Engineered Devices Corp., 25 Bergen Tpke., Ridgefield Park, 07660 .... (201) 641-2880
Engineered Fastener Co. see. .... Enfasco, Pennsauken
Engineered Medical Solutions Co., LLC,
85 Industrial Rd., Bldg. B, Phillipsburg, 08865 .... (908) 329-9123
Engineered Plastic Products, Inc.,
269 Mercer St., P.O. Box 196, Stirling, 07980 .... (908) 647-3500
Engineered Polymer Technologies see. .... Ronald-Mark Assocs., Inc., Hillside
Engineered Precision Casting Co., 952 Palmer Ave., Middletown, 07748 .... (732) 671-2424
Engineered Silicone Products, LLC, 75 Mill St., Ste. 2, Newton, 07860 .... (973) 300-5120
Engineering Dynamics, LLC, 429 Rockaway Valley Rd., Ste. 1300, Boonton, 07005 .... (973) 794-4500
Engineering Laboratories, Inc., 360 W. Oakland Ave., Oakland, 07436 .... (201) 337-8116
England Orthopedics, Inc., 1002 Commons Way, Toms River, 08755 .... (732) 286-4444
Englert, Inc., 1200 Amboy Ave., Perth Amboy, 08861 .... (732) 826-8614
Englewood Lab, LLC, 88 W. Sheffield Ave., Englewood, 07631 .... (201) 567-2267
Engo Co., 128 Case Dr., South Plainfield, 07080 .... (908) 754-6600
Engraved Images, Route 202 & Demun Pl., P.O. Box 966, Far Hills, 07931 .... (908) 234-0323
Engraver's Bench & Greek Unique, Inc., 1212 Raymond Blvd., Newark, 07102 .... (973) 297-1810
Engraving Services Of New Jersey, 804 Columbia Rd., Toms River, 08753 .... (732) 341-0170
Enjou Chocolate, Inc., 8 Dehart St., Morristown, 07960 .... (973) 993-9090
Enor Corp., 245 Livingston St., Northvale, 07647 .... (201) 750-1680
Enpro, Inc., 1401 U.S. Highway 22, P.O. Box 418, Lebanon, 08833 .... (908) 236-2137
EnPro Industries, Inc. see. .... DGB Bearing & Technology, Thorofare
Ensinger, Inc. see. .... Hyde Co., A. L., Grenloch
Enslow Publishing Group, 40 Industrial Rd., Berkeley Heights, 07922 .... (908) 771-9400
Enterix, Inc., 236 Fernwood Ave., Edison, 08837 .... (732) 429-1899

† Enterprise Corrugated Container, LLC,
575 N. Midland Ave., P.O. Box 857, Saddle Brook, 07663 ... (201) 797-7200
† Enterprise HVAC Supply, 701 Main St., Belleville, 07109 ... (973) 759-6900
Enterprise Press, Inc., 1 W. Forest Ave., Englewood, 07631 ... (201) 894-0444
Entite Press, Inc., 139 Stokes Rd., Medford Lakes, 08055 ... (609) 714-9213
Envelopes & Printed Products, Inc., 135 Fairview Ave., Prospect Park, 07508 ... (973) 942-1232
Envirochem, Inc., 425 Whitehead Ave., South River, 08882 ... (732) 238-6700
Enviro-Clear Co., Inc., 152 Cregar Rd., High Bridge, 08829 ... (908) 638-5507
Environmental Air Systems, 801 11th Ave., P.O. Box 508, Belmar, 07719 ... (732) 681-0856
Environmental Services Group/Green Power,
151 Sparta Stanhope Rd., Hopatcong, 07843 ... (201) 569-2020
† Environmental Site Furnishings, 700 Goldman Dr., Cream Ridge, 08514 ... (281) 975-1776
EnvironMolds, LLC, 18 Bank St., Ste. 1, Summit, 07901 ... (908) 273-5401
Enviro-Pak, Inc., 125 National Rd., Edison, 08817 ... (732) 248-1600
† Enviropore, Inc., P.O. Box 443, Lumberton, 08048 ... (609) 261-1588
Enviroprint USA, 11 Maiden Ln., Bound Brook, 08805 ... (732) 356-5959
Enzon Pharmaceuticals, Inc., 20 Kingsbridge Rd., Piscataway, 08854 ... (732) 980-4500
Eonsmoke, LLC (H Q), 1500 Main Ave., Ste. 2, Clifton, 07011 ... (800) 616-3711
Eos Energy Storage, LLC, 214 Fernwood Ave., Bldg. B, Edison, 08837 ... (732) 225-8400
EPCO see. ... Engineered Precision Casting Co., Middletown
Epic Industries, 1007 Jersey Ave., New Brunswick, 08901 ... (732) 249-6867
Epic Management, Inc. see. ... Epic Millwork, Somerset
Epic Management, Inc. (H Q), 136 11th St., Ste. 1, Piscataway, 08854 ... (732) 752-6100
Epic Millwork, 1022 Hamilton St., Ste. G, Somerset, 08873 ... (732) 296-0273
Epic Millwork * Epic Interiors see. ... Epic Management, Inc. (H Q), Piscataway
Epicor, Inc., 1414 E. Linden Ave., P.O. Box 1608, Linden, 07036 ... (908) 925-0800
Epicore Networks U.S.A., Inc., 4 Lina Ln., Eastampton, 08060 ... (609) 267-9118
Epoch Press, Inc., 75 Wood St., Ste. B, Paterson, 07524 ... (973) 357-0080
Epoch Times International, Inc. see. ... New Jersey Epoch Times, South Plainfield
Epolin, 358-364 Adams St., Newark, 07105 ... (973) 465-9495
Epoplex, 1000 E. Park Ave., P.O. Box 308, Maple Shade, 08052 ... (856) 667-8399
Eppley Building & Design, Inc., 220-B Goffle Rd., Hawthorne, 07506 ... (973) 636-9499
★ E*Pro, Inc., 1000 U.S. Highway 9 N., Ste. 303, Woodbridge, 07095 ... (732) 283-0499
EPS see. ... EPS Corporation, Tinton Falls
EPS Corporation, 78 Apple St., Tinton Falls, 07724 ... (732) 747-8277
Equipment Erectors, Inc., 110 Garden St., Somerset, 08873 ... (732) 846-1212
† Equipment Marketers, 100 Melrose Ave., Cherry Hill, 08003 ... (856) 428-3355
† Equipment Sales & Service, 152 Floyd Ave., Bloomfield, 07003 ... (973) 743-7516
† Equipment Solutions Corp., 622 State Route 10, Ste. 20, Whippany, 07981 ... (973) 887-9277
† Equipment Xchange, LLC, 309 Columbia Rd., Hammonton, 08037 ... (609) 561-0500
Equitable Service see. ... Great Falls Metalworks, Inc., Paterson
Erasteel, Inc., 95 Fulton St., Boonton, 07005 ... (973) 335-8400
Erial Concrete, Inc., 965 Hickstown Rd., Sicklerville, 08081 ... (856) 784-8884
Erick Industries, Inc., 837 S. 9th St., Camden, 08103 ... (856) 966-2045
Ericsson, Inc., 1 Ericsson Dr., Piscataway, 08854 ... (732) 699-2000
† Erika Record, LLC, 37 Atlantic Way, Clifton, 07012 ... (973) 614-8500
ERL Embroidery & Screen Printing, 8 Evergreen Dr., Lincoln Park, 07035 ... (973) 633-7428
Ermenegildo Zegna Corp. (H Q), 100 W. Forest Ave., Ste. A, Englewood, 07631 ... (201) 816-0921
Ernst Co., Inc., John C., 21 Gail Ct., Sparta, 07871 ... (973) 940-1600
Ernst Flow Industries, 116 Main St., Farmingdale, 07727 ... (732) 938-5641
ES Industries, 701 S. Route 73, West Berlin, 08091 ... (856) 753-8400
Escadaus Magnetic Corp. see. ... Escadaus Magnetics, Boonton
† Escadaus Magnetics, 2 Wood Glen Way, Boonton, 07005 ... (973) 335-8888
Esco Industrial Corp., 141 Lanza Ave., Bldg. 3-B, Garfield, 07026 ... (973) 478-5888
Esco Optics, 1 Tideland Rd., P.O. Box 308, Oak Ridge, 07438 ... (973) 697-3700
ESCO Precision, Inc., 71 Old Camplain Rd., Hillsborough, 08844 ... (908) 722-0800
ESG, LLC, 3 Gold Mine Rd., Flanders, 07836 ... (973) 691-8517
ESI Electronics see. ... Electronic Subassemblies, Inc., Sicklerville
Espoma Co., 6 Espoma Rd., Millville, 08332 ... (856) 825-0542
ESS Group see. ... Colonial Chemical, Tabernacle
† Essential Amenities, Inc., 208 Passaic Ave., Ste. 1, Fairfield, 07004 ... (973) 882-8441
Essential Dental Systems, Inc.,
89 Leuning St., Ste. 2, South Hackensack, 07606 ... (201) 487-9090
Essex Coatings, LLC, 135 Essex Ave. E., Avenel, 07001 ... (732) 855-9400
Essex Fence Co., 132 U.S. Highway 46, Rockaway, 07866 ... (973) 625-4122
Essex Rise, 4 Fairfield Crescent, West Caldwell, 07006 ... (973) 575-7483
Essilor Laboratories, 5 Powderhorn Dr., Warren, 07059 ... (732) 563-9884
Essilor Of America, Inc. see. ... Essilor Laboratories, Warren
EST see. ... Eastern Sign Tech, LLC, Burlington
Estes Co., Inc., Clifford W., 182 Fairfield Rd., Ste. 8, Fairfield, 07004 ... (973) 575-4400
† Estrin Calabrese Sales Agency, 17 S. Main St., Ste. 3, Manville, 08835 ... (908) 722-9980
eSystems, Inc., 4390 U.S. Highway 1, Ste. 301, Princeton, 08540 ... (609) 945-7437
ETC see. ... Elizabeth Truck Center, Elizabeth
Ethical Alternative Products, LLC, 525 Cedar Hill Ave., Wyckoff, 07481 ... (201) 251-7771
Ethicon, Inc., 737 U.S. Highway 22 W., P.O. Box 151, Somerville, 08876 ... (908) 218-0707
Ethylene Atlantic Corp., 136 Church St., P.O. Box 430, Swedesboro, 08085 ... (856) 467-0010
Etta Controls, Inc., 31 Belgrade Ter., West Orange, 07052 ... (973) 731-6552
Euler Industries, Inc., 464 Old Tappan Rd., Old Tappan, 07675 ... (201) 666-9523
Euphonic Audio, Inc., 18 Newtown Blvd., Robbinsville, 08691 ... (888) 894-3790
Eureka Spring Co., 999 Rahway Ave., Union, 07083 ... (973) 589-4960
Euro Mechanical, Inc., 16 Industrial Ave., Fairview, 07022 ... (201) 313-8050
★ Euroimmun US, Inc., 1100 The American Rd., Ste. 1, Morris Plains, 07950 ... (973) 656-1000
Eurotek, Inc., Carlton Street 61, Unit 2, Rumson, 07760 ... (732) 224-1300
Evans Chemetics LP (H Q),
500 Frank W. Burr Blvd., 4th Fl., Glenpointe Center West, Teaneck, 07666 ... (201) 992-3100
Evans Machine & Tool Co., 410 Summit Ave., Perth Amboy, 08861 ... (732) 442-1144
Eventide, Inc., 1 Alsan Way, Little Ferry, 07643 ... (201) 641-1200
Everbind Marco Book Co., Inc., 60 Industrial Rd., P.O. Box 695, Lodi, 07644 ... (973) 458-0485
Evergard Steel Corp., 1825 Pennsylvania Ave., Linden, 07036 ... (908) 925-6800
Evergreen Printing, 101 Haag Ave., Bellmawr, 08031 ... (856) 933-0222
Everite Machine Products Co., 6995 Airport Highway Ln., Pennsauken, 08110 ... (856) 330-6700
Everlasting Valve Co., 108 Somogyi Ct., South Plainfield, 07080 ... (908) 769-0700
Ever-Ready Media Packaging, P.O. Box 40, Haworth, 07641 ... (973) 566-9333
Evertile Flooring Co., Inc., 127 Frelinghuysen Ave., Newark, 07114 ... (973) 242-7474
Evex Analytical see. ... Evex Global, Princeton
Evex Global, 857 State Rd., Princeton, 08540 ... (408) 907-2994
Evey Engineering Co., LLC, 158 Weymouth Rd., Vineland, 08360 ... (856) 692-6705
Evonik Corporation (H Q), 299 Jefferson Rd., Parsippany, 07054 ... (973) 929-8000
★ Evoqua Water Technologies, 624 Evans St., Elizabeth, 07201 ... (908) 353-7230
Evoqua Water Technologies see. ... Siemens Industry, Inc., Water Technologies, East Rutherford
Evoqua Water Technologies see. ... Siemens Industry, Inc., Water Technologies, Union
Evoqua Water Technologies see. ... Siemens Industry, Inc., Water Technologies, Vineland

EVR Screen Printing, 217 W. Peach St., Ste. 2, Vineland, 08360 ... (856) 794-8118
EVS Metal, 1 Kenner Ct., Riverdale, 07457 ... (973) 839-4432
EWC Controls, Inc., 385 State Route 33, Manalapan, 07726 ... (732) 446-3110
E.W.E. Auto Seat Cover Co., 8431 Kennedy Blvd., North Bergen, 07047 ... (201) 869-6470
Ewing Glass Co., 1354 Parkside Ave., Trenton, 08638 ... (609) 882-1818
Exacta Industries, Inc., 20 John F. Kennedy Dr. N., Bloomfield, 07003 ... (973) 259-0104
Exacta V & H Corp., 107 Whittendale Dr., Moorestown, 08057 ... (856) 235-7379
Exactal Tool & Die Ltd., Inc., 3586 Kennedy Rd., South Plainfield, 07080 ... (908) 561-1177
Excalibur Bagel & Bakery Equipment, Inc., 4-01 Banta Pl., Fair Lawn, 07410 ... (201) 797-2788
Excel Color Graphics, Inc., 207 W. Jersey Ave., Woodbury Heights, 08097 ... (856) 848-3345
Excel Die Corp., 19 Grant St., Linden, 07036 ... (908) 587-2606
Excel Display Corp., 100 Jersey Ave., Ste. A206, New Brunswick, 08901 ... (732) 246-3728
Excel Hobby Blades Corp., 481 Getty Ave., P.O. Box 1045, Paterson, 07503 ... (973) 278-4000
† Excel Plastics Recycling, Inc., 996 Belleville Tpke., Kearny, 07032 ... (201) 991-2500
Excel Silk Screening, 2320 Old York Rd., Bordentown, 08505 ... (609) 499-4990
Excellent Bakery Equipment Co., 315 Fairfield Rd., Fairfield, 07004 ... (973) 244-1664
Excellent Printing & Graphics, 333 Hazel St., Clifton, 07011 ... (973) 773-6661
Excellium Pharmaceutical, Inc., 3 Oak Rd., Ste. G, Fairfield, 07004 ... (973) 276-9600
Excelsior Medical Corp., 1933 Heck Ave., Neptune, 07753 ... (732) 776-7525
Excelsior Metal Products, LLC, 151 State Route 33, Ste. 201, Manalapan, 07726 ... (732) 651-9914
† Executive Binding Systems, Inc., 330 Franklin Tpke., Mahwah, 07430 ... (201) 642-0011
EXELIS, Inc., 77 River Rd., Clifton, 07014 ... (973) 284-0123
Exeltis, 1 Main St., Ste. 203, Chatham, 07928 ... (973) 324-0200
Exhibit Co., Inc., The, 239 Old New Brunswick Rd., Piscataway, 08854 ... (732) 465-1070
ExhibitCraft, Inc., 22 Riverview Dr., Ste. 103, Wayne, 07470 ... (973) 686-9393
Exit Zero Publishing, 109 Sunset Blvd., Ste. D, Cape May, 08204 ... (609) 770-8479
Exitflex USA, Inc., 254 Raritan Center Pkwy., Edison, 08837 ... (732) 512-9141
Exothermic Molding, Inc., 50 Lafayette Pl., Kenilworth, 07033 ... (908) 272-2299
EXP, Inc., 285 Davidson Ave., Somerset, 08873 ... (732) 626-3700
Experimental Machine & Tool, 114 Pulaski Rd., Whitehouse Station, 08889 ... (908) 534-4725
Expert Tees, 1585 Highway 73, Pennsauken, 08110 ... (609) 828-0515
Export Consultants Corp.,
250 Lackland Dr., Ste. 6, P.O. Box 308, Middlesex, 08846 ... (732) 469-0700
Express Graphics, 17 Dupont Ter., Wayne, 07470 ... (973) 696-3165
Express It, Inc., 61 Haddon Ave., Haddon Township, 08108 ... (856) 854-1888
Express Press, 145 North Ave., Belleville, 07109 ... (973) 751-1287
Express Printing, Inc., 209 W. Saint Georges Ave., Linden, 07036 ... (908) 925-6300
Express Tag & Label Co., 52 N. Main St., Marlboro, 07746 ... (718) 965-1400
Extech Building Materials, 100 Bogert St., Closter, 07624 ... (201) 768-2133
Extech Building Materials see. ... Extech Building Materials, Inc., Farmingdale
Extech Building Materials see. ... Extech Building Materials, Inc., Newark
† Extech Building Materials, Inc., 385 Asbury Rd., Farmingdale, 07727 ... (732) 919-3340
† Extech Building Materials, Inc., 61-89 Ave. K, Newark, 07105 ... (973) 274-3340
Extra Office, Inc., 580 Leesville Ave., Rahway, 07065 ... (732) 381-9773
Extracts & Ingredients Ltd., Div. Of MORRE-TEC Industries, Inc.,
1 Gary Rd., Union, 07083 ... (908) 688-9009
Extreme Concepts, LLC, 75 E. Cherry St., Ste. 9-B, Rahway, 07065 ... (732) 381-5100
Extreme Digital Graphics, 7 Kingsbridge Rd., Ste. 1, Fairfield, 07004 ... (973) 227-5599
Extreme Painting & Powder Coating, LLC, 944 Reeves Ave., Camden, 08105 ... (856) 541-8733
Extreme Pallet, 301-317 Astor St., Newark, 07114 ... (973) 596-1400
Extreme Pallet, Inc., 315 Astor St., Newark, 07114 ... (973) 286-1717
Extremity Medical, LLC, 300 Interpace Pkwy., Ste. 410, Parsippany, 07054 ... (973) 588-8980
Extruders International, Inc., 181 W. Clay Ave., Roselle Park, 07204 ... (908) 241-7750
Exxcel Welding Corp., 14 Brookhill Rd., Pittstown, 08867 ... (908) 735-0000
Exxon Mobil Corp., 1001 Billingsport Rd., Paulsboro, 08066 ... (856) 224-5000
ExxonMobil Corp. see. ... Exxon Mobil Corp., Paulsboro
E-Z Do, Inc., 40 Executive Ave., Edison, 08817 ... (732) 287-8111
†★ E-Z Edge, Inc., 6119 Adams St., West New York, 07093 ... (201) 295-1171
EZ Sockets, Inc., 5 Cornell Pkwy., Springfield, 07081 ... (973) 376-5605
eZCom Software, Inc., 25 Rockwood Pl., Ste. 420, Englewood, 07631 ... (201) 883-1900
F & A Machine Co., Inc., 133 Lincoln Blvd., Middlesex, 08846 ... (732) 356-5777
F & C Professional Aluminum Railings, 1149 W. Front St., Plainfield, 07063 ... (908) 753-8886
F & D see. ... Friedrich & Dimmock, Inc., Millville
F & G Tool & Die, Inc., 195 Sumner Ave., Kenilworth, 07033 ... (908) 241-5880
† F & H Supply, Inc, 1315 Route 77, P.O. Box 379, Bridgeton, 08302 ... (856) 451-7080
F & L Machinery & Design, Inc., 48 Commerce St., Springfield, 07081 ... (973) 218-6216
F & M Expressions Unlimited, 211 Island Rd., Mahwah, 07430 ... (201) 512-3338
F & M Machine Co., Inc., 751 Lexington Ave., Kenilworth, 07033 ... (908) 245-8830
F & R Grinding, Inc., 138 County Road 513, Frenchtown, 08825 ... (908) 996-0440
F & R Pallets, Inc., 1929 S. 4th St., Camden, 08104 ... (856) 964-8516
F & S Produce Co., Inc., 913 Bridgeton Ave., P.O. Box 489, Rosenhayn, 08352 ... (856) 453-0316
F G H Systems, Inc., 10 Prospect Pl., Denville, 07834 ... (973) 625-8114
F I P Graphics, Inc., P.O. Box 952, Maywood, 07607 ... (201) 362-3194
F M B, Inc., 70 Supor Blvd., Harrison, 07029 ... (973) 485-5544
F N A Signs see. ... Stand-Out Signs, Inc., Perth Amboy
F P Developments, Inc., 402 S. Main St., Williamstown, 08094 ... (856) 875-7100
F S T Printing, Inc., 1324 Bound Brook Rd., Middlesex, 08846 ... (732) 560-3749
F T Millwork, 9-B Catherine St., Red Bank, 07701 ... (732) 741-1216
F X I, Foamex Innovations Div., 13 Manor Rd., East Rutherford, 07073 ... (201) 933-8540
Fab Dog, Inc., 160 Gregg St., Unit 7, Lodi, 07644 ... (973) 472-5555
Fabbian USA Corp., 161 Dwight Pl., Fairfield, 07004 ... (973) 882-3824
Faber Precision, Inc., 198 Green Pond Rd., Unit D, Rockaway, 07866 ... (973) 983-1844
Fabian Couture Group International, 205 Chubb Ave., Ste. 1, Lyndhurst, 07071 ... (201) 460-7776
Fablok Mills, Inc., 140 Spring St., Murray Hill, 07974 ... (908) 464-1950
Fabric Chemical Corp., 61 Cornelison Ave., Jersey City, 07304 ... (201) 432-0440
Fabricolor Holdings, Inc.,
24 1/2 Van Houten St., P.O. Box 1856, Paterson, 07505 ... (973) 742-5800
Fabrite Metal, 10 Stony Brook Rd., Rockaway, 07866 ... (973) 714-1813
Fabulous Interiors, 470 Prospect Ave., Ste. 105, West Orange, 07052 ... (973) 736-1200
Factory Outlet Mens Clothing see. ... Palmyra Pants Co., Inc., Pennsauken
† Fagan, Inc., Ed, 769 Susquehanna Ave., Franklin Lakes, 07417 ... (201) 891-4003
Fairfield Gourmet Food Corp., 11 Cliffside Dr., Cedar Grove, 07009 ... (973) 227-2800
Fairfield Industries, Inc., 827 N. 6th St., Newark, 07107 ... (973) 483-0100
Fairfield Laundry Machinery, 5 Montesano Rd., Fairfield, 07004 ... (973) 575-4330
Fairfield Litho II Corp., 123 Lehigh Dr., Fairfield, 07004 ... (973) 575-7550
Fairfield Pallet Co., Inc., 282 Rockville Rd., P.O. Box 361, Fairton, 08320 ... (856) 455-7999
Fairfield Stamping Co., 374 Midland Ave., P.O. Box 8322, Saddle Brook, 07663 ... (201) 791-9888
Fairway Products Co., 265 Garden Rd., P.O. Box 611, Elmer, 08318 ... (856) 358-6016
★ Fairy Tales Hair Care Corp., 90-B Dayton Ave., Passaic, 07055 ... (973) 473-8182
† Faith Group Co. (H Q), 195 Route 9, Ste. 205, Manalapan, 07726 ... (732) 431-1326
Falcon Industries, Inc., 371 Campus Dr., Somerset, 08873 ... (732) 563-9889
Falcon Printing Co., 613 Central Ave., Westfield, 07090 ... (908) 232-1991

ALPHABETICAL

Falcon Safety Products, Inc.,
25 Imclone Dr., P.O. Box 1299, Branchburg, 08876 .... (908) 707-4900
Falcon Stainless & Alloys Corp., 39 Hewson Ave., Ste. A, Waldwick, 07463 .... (201) 670-8300
† FallProof Systems LLC, 61 2nd Ave., Trenton, 08619 .... (609) 325-5555
Falls Products, Inc., 220 Franklin Rd., 1st Fl., Randolph, 07869 .... (973) 537-6464
Falls Screen Printing, Inc., 25 Amity St., Little Falls, 07424 .... (973) 812-0555
Falstrom Co., 1 Falstrom Ct., P.O. Box 118, Passaic, 07055 .... (973) 777-0013
Famcam, Inc., 3 Eastmans Rd., Parsippany, 07054 .... (973) 319-3033
Family Screen Printing, Inc., 104 W. Browning Rd., Bellmawr, 08031 .... (856) 933-2780
Fancort Industries, Inc., 31 Fairfield Pl., West Caldwell, 07006 .... (973) 575-0610
Fancy Threads, 31 Railroad Pl., Hopewell, 08525 .... (609) 466-0050
Fano Machine & Tool Co., 20 Passaic St., Garfield, 07026 .... (973) 773-9353
Fantasia Industries Corp., 20 Park Pl., Paramus, 07652 .... (201) 261-7070
Fantastic Signs Co., 351 Shrewsbury Ave., Red Bank, 07701 .... (732) 747-7763
Faraj, Inc., 422 Cliff St., Fairview, 07022 .... (201) 313-4480
Farbest-Tallman Foods Corp. (H Q), 160 Summit Ave., Ste. 200, Montvale, 07645 .... (201) 573-4900
Fargo Controls, Inc., P.O. Box 539, Eatontown, 07724 .... (732) 389-3376
Farinhas Bakery, Inc., 301 Harrison Ave., Harrison, 07029 .... (973) 482-5640
Farmer Co., Arthur E., 47 Frazier St., Trenton, 08618 .... (609) 392-8722
† Farmer Electrical Supply, 16 Littell Rd., East Hanover, 07936 .... (973) 887-0510
Farmingdale Printing, 70 Main St., Farmingdale, 07727 .... (732) 938-2727
Farmland Dairies, 520 Main Ave., P.O. Box 3340, Wallington, 07057 .... (973) 777-2500
Farrier Sporting Goods, Inc., Godwin & Crescent Aves., Wyckoff, 07481 .... (201) 891-9520
Fast Copy Printing Center, 81 Broad St., Keyport, 07735 .... (732) 739-4646
Fast Doors, LLC, 1800 Copewood St., Camden, 08103 .... (856) 966-3278
Fast Print, LLC, 514 Main St., Fort Lee, 07024 .... (201) 944-2350
Fast Signs see. .... Lobello Arts Corp., East Hanover
Fast Weld Co., 502 New Brunswick Ave., Phillipsburg, 08865 .... (908) 213-0155
† Fastbolt Corp., 200 Louis St., South Hackensack, 07606 .... (201) 440-9100
† Fastenal Co., 1115 N. New Rd., Absecon, 08201 .... (609) 813-2356
† Fastenal Co., 421 Route 73 & Cushman Ave., Unit 11, Berlin, 08009 .... (856) 768-3657
† Fastenal Co., 921 Route 130 N., Burlington, 08016 .... (609) 239-3016
† Fastenal Co., 33 Route 17 S., East Rutherford, 07073 .... (201) 804-2228
† Fastenal Co., 22 Meridian Rd., Unit 2, Eatontown, 07724 .... (732) 542-7533
† Fastenal Co., 55 Carter Dr., Edison, 08817 .... (732) 777-1029
† Fastenal Co., 68-A Clinton Rd., Fairfield, 07004 .... (973) 244-0540
† Fastenal Co., 186 Gold Mine Rd., Unit 1, Flanders, 07836 .... (973) 691-0547
† Fastenal Co., 316 Black Horse Pike, Unit C, Glendora, 08029 .... (856) 939-2500
† Fastenal Co., 1026 W. Elizabeth Ave., Unit 2, Linden, 07036 .... (908) 862-8880
† Fastenal Co., 550 Lincoln Blvd., Middlesex, 08846 .... (732) 748-0140
† Fastenal Co., 987 Jersey Ave., Ste. C, New Brunswick, 08901 .... (732) 246-0248
† Fastenal Co., 443 Madison Ave., Paterson, 07524 .... (973) 278-5509
† Fastenal Co., 1163 Route 130, Robbinsville, 08691 .... (609) 259-4290
† Fastenal Co., 500 Hartle St., Ste. D, Sayreville, 08872 .... (732) 254-1117
† Fastenal Co., 1875 N. Olden Ave., Trenton, 08638 .... (609) 530-0456
† Fastenal Co., 53 S. Jefferson Rd., Ste. K, Whippany, 07981 .... (973) 428-3300
FASTENation, Inc., 120 Brighton Rd., Ste. 2, Clifton, 07012 .... (973) 591-1277
Fastpulse Technology, Inc., 220 Midland Ave., Saddle Brook, 07663 .... (973) 478-5757
FASTSIGNS®, 485 Route 1 S., Crossroads Plz., Edison, 08817 .... (732) 985-1166
FASTSIGNS®, 906 Greentree Sq., Route 73 N., Marlton, 08053 .... (856) 985-8730
FASTSIGNS®, 407 Sette Dr., Paramus, 07652 .... (201) 587-8444
FASTSIGNS®, 105 Sherman Ave., Raritan, 08869 .... (908) 231-0306
FASTSIGNS®, 255 State Route 3, Secaucus, 07094 .... (201) 902-8640
FASTSIGNS®, 2290 Route 22 E., Union, 07083 .... (908) 810-1400
Fat Murray's Doggy Treats, 3 Deer Hill Dr., P.O. Box 32, Montville, 07045 .... (973) 299-2968
★ Father & Son Design Center, LLC, 111 Clinton Rd., Ste. 1, Fairfield, 07004 .... (973) 575-8635
Faust, Inc., Rudolph, 542 South Ave. E., Cranford, 07016 .... (908) 507-5104
Faust Thermographic, Inc., 325 Cantor Ave., P.O. Box 1277, Linden, 07036 .... (908) 474-0555
Fazzio & Sons, Inc., Frank J., 458 Elwood Ave., Pitman, 08071 .... (856) 589-3760
Fazzio Machine & Steel,
3278 Glassboro Cross Keys Rd., P.O. Box 232, Glassboro, 08028 .... (856) 881-2832
† FCR Camden, Inc., 2201 Mt. Ephraim Ave., Bldg. 10-A, Camden, 08104 .... (856) 342-7503
FCS Fluidaire Cleaning Services, Inc.,
11 Industrial Dr., New Brunswick, 08901 .... (732) 964-1700
† FCX Performance, Inc., 333 Route 46 W., Ste. 130, Fairfield, 07004 .... (973) 575-8350
FEC see. .... Fleet Equipment Corp. (H Q), Franklin Lakes
Fecken-Kirfel America, Inc., 6 Leighton Pl., Ste. 1, Mahwah, 07430 .... (201) 891-5530
Federal Bronze Casting Industries, 9 Backus St., Newark, 07105 .... (973) 589-7575
Federal Casters Corp., 785 Harrison Ave., Harrison, 07029 .... (973) 483-6700
Federal Direct (H Q), 95 Main Ave., Ste. 2, Clifton, 07014 .... (973) 667-9800
Federal Label Systems, Inc., 385 Hillside Ave., Hillside, 07205 .... (718) 899-6000
† Federal Metals & Alloys, 4216 S. Clinton Ave., South Plainfield, 07080 .... (908) 756-0900
Federal Mining & Mfg. Co., 288 E. 12th Ave., Roselle, 07203 .... (908) 241-9355
† Federal Pacific Equipment, Inc., 1133 Industrial Pkwy., Ste. A, Brick, 08724 .... (732) 840-4800
Federal Plastics Corp., 570 South Ave. E., Ste. F-1, Cranford, 07016 .... (908) 272-5800
Federal Pretzel Baking Co., 300 Eagle Ct., P.O. Box 257, Bridgeport, 08014 .... (215) 467-0505
† Federal Wine & Liquor Co., 56 Hackensack Ave., P.O. Box 519, Kearny, 07032 .... (973) 624-6444
† Federal Wine & Liquor Co., 1 Central Ave., Mount Laurel, 08054 .... (856) 234-3200
FedEx Office & Print Center, 1160 Marlton Pike E., Cherry Hill, 08034 .... (856) 427-0099
FedEx Office & Print Center, 212 State Route 18, East Brunswick, 08816 .... (732) 249-9222
FedEx Office & Print Center, 1 Quality Way, Iselin, 08830 .... (732) 636-3580
FedEx Office & Print Center, 1211 Route 73, Mount Laurel, 08054 .... (856) 273-5959
FedEx Office & Print Center, 450 Tilton Rd., Northfield, 08225 .... (609) 569-8100
FedEx Office & Print Center, 315 N. Route 17, Paramus, 07652 .... (201) 599-0031
FedEx Office & Print Center, Highway 1 & 731 Nassau, Princeton, 08540 .... (609) 799-2863
FedEx Office & Print Center, 559 N. Franklin Tpke., Ramsey, 07446 .... (201) 818-1623
FedEx Office & Print Center, 399 Highway 28, Raritan, 08869 .... (908) 575-1221
FedEx Office & Print Center, 55 U.S. Highway 22 E., Springfield, 07081 .... (973) 376-3966
FedEx Office & Print Services, Inc. see. .... FedEx Office & Print Center, Cherry Hill
FedEx Office & Print Services, Inc. see. .... FedEx Office & Print Center, East Brunswick
FedEx Office & Print Services, Inc. see. .... FedEx Office & Print Center, Iselin
FedEx Office & Print Services, Inc. see. .... FedEx Office & Print Center, Mount Laurel
FedEx Office & Print Services, Inc. see. .... FedEx Office & Print Center, Northfield
FedEx Office & Print Services, Inc. see. .... FedEx Office & Print Center, Paramus
FedEx Office & Print Services, Inc. see. .... FedEx Office & Print Center, Princeton
FedEx Office & Print Services, Inc. see. .... FedEx Office & Print Center, Ramsey
FedEx Office & Print Services, Inc. see. .... FedEx Office & Print Center, Raritan
FedEx Office & Print Services, Inc. see. .... FedEx Office & Print Center, Springfield
FedEx Office & Print Services, Inc. see. .... FedEx Office Commercial Press, Roselle
FedEx Office & Print Services, Inc. see. .... FedEx Office Commercial Press, Roselle
FedEx Office Commercial Press, 450 W. 1st Ave., P.O. Box 379, Roselle, 07203 .... (908) 245-4400
Felco Products, LLC, 18 Furler St., Totowa, 07512 .... (973) 890-7979
Feldman Assocs., Inc., F. L., 811 Memorial Dr., Asbury Park, 07712 .... (732) 776-8544
Feldman Stained Glass, 401 Halladay St., Jersey City, 07304 .... (201) 434-2887
FemtoTek, Inc., 865 Lower Ferry Rd., Ste. B-9, Ewing, 08628 .... (609) 406-9680
Fence Max, 6514 Black Horse Pike, Egg Harbor Township, 08234 .... (609) 646-2430
Fences By Taylor, Inc., 1246 Highway 33, Howell, 07731 .... (732) 349-8626
Fender Musical Instruments Corp. see. .... Latin Percussion, Inc., Garfield
Ferber Plastics see. .... E T Mfg., Inc., Passaic
Ferguson Containers, 20 Industrial Rd., Phillipsburg, 08865 .... (908) 454-9755
† Ferguson Enterprises, 835 Bloomfield Ave., Clifton, 07012 .... (973) 614-9464
Ferguson Enterprises see. .... Ferguson Fire & Fabrication, Inc., Passaic
Ferguson Enterprises, Inc. see. .... Ferguson Enterprises, Clifton
† Ferguson Enterprises, Inc., 401 Main St., Avon By The Sea, 07717 .... (732) 775-5270
† Ferguson Enterprises, Inc., 830 Route 22, Bridgewater, 08807 .... (908) 725-0666
† Ferguson Enterprises, Inc., 2531 Tilton Rd., Egg Harbor Township, 08234 .... (609) 485-2266
† Ferguson Enterprises, Inc., 369 Anderson Ave., Fairview, 07022 .... (201) 945-3080
† Ferguson Enterprises, Inc., 737 S. Main St., Forked River, 08731 .... (609) 693-0077
† Ferguson Enterprises, Inc., 1 Colony Rd., Jersey City, 07305 .... (201) 369-5120
† Ferguson Enterprises, Inc., 190 Oberlin Ave. N., Lakewood, 08701 .... (732) 905-1000
† Ferguson Enterprises, Inc., 444 Livingston St., Norwood, 07648 .... (201) 768-6080
† Ferguson Enterprises, Inc., 16 Arrow Rd., Ramsey, 07446 .... (201) 236-3111
† Ferguson Enterprises, Inc., 207 Cooper Rd., Red Bank, 07701 .... (732) 530-7200
† Ferguson Enterprises, Inc., 404 Route 31 N., Ringoes, 08551 .... (609) 466-5445
† Ferguson Enterprises, Inc., 100 U.S. Highway 46, Rockaway, 07866 .... (973) 983-1177
Ferguson Enterprises, Inc. see. .... Lyon, Conklin & Co., Inc., Pennsauken
Ferguson Enterprises, Inc. see. .... Palermo Supply, Ship Bottom
Ferguson Fire & Fabrication, Inc., 151 Randolph St., Passaic, 07055 .... (973) 614-9292
Fermag Technologies, 80 Executive Ave., Edison, 08817 .... (732) 985-7300
Ferrante Press, Inc., 516 Bloomfield Ave., Verona, 07044 .... (973) 239-4344
† Ferraro Foods, Inc., 287 S. Randolphville Rd., Piscataway, 08854 .... (732) 424-3400
† Ferrell's Oil Service, 26 E. Mill St., P.O. Box 130, Pedricktown, 08067 .... (856) 299-0500
Ferrero U.S.A., Inc., 600 Cottontail Ln., Somerset, 08873 .... (732) 764-9300
Ferrett Printing, Inc., 468 Warwick Rd., Woodbury, 08096 .... (856) 686-4896
Ferris * Stahl-Meyer Foods, Inc. see. .... PRG Packing Corp. (H Q), Fort Lee
Ferrite Welding Products, Inc., 31 S. Passaic Ave., Chatham, 07928 .... (973) 377-6636
Ferro Corp. see. .... Ames Advanced Material, South Plainfield
Ferro Corp., 54 Kellogg Ct., Edison, 08817 .... (732) 287-1930
Ferro Corp. see. .... Ferro Corp., Delaware River Plt., Bridgeport
Ferro Corp., Delaware River Plt.,
170 U.S. Route 130 S., P.O. Box 309, Bridgeport, 08014 .... (856) 467-8216
Ferro Liquid Colorants Div. see. .... Ferro Corp., Edison
Ferrous Saw Works, 345 Lakeview Ave., Clifton, 07011 .... (973) 513-3936
Ferrum Industries, Inc., 735 Commercial Ave., Carlstadt, 07072 .... (201) 935-1220
Ferry Machine Corp., 75 Industrial Ave., Little Ferry, 07643 .... (201) 641-9191
† Fessenden Hall, Inc., 1050 Sherman Ave., Pennsauken, 08110 .... (856) 665-2210
Festo Didactic Inc., 1710 Highway 34, P.O. Box 686, Farmingdale, 07727 .... (732) 938-2000
Fi Companies, 3150 Bordentown Ave., Old Bridge, 08857 .... (732) 727-8100
Fiabila, Inc., 114 Iron Mountain Rd., Mine Hill, 07803 .... (973) 659-9510
Fiber Optic Systems, Inc., P.O. Box 62, Whitehouse Station, 08889 .... (908) 534-5500
Fiberguide Industries, Inc., 1 Bay St., Stirling, 07980 .... (908) 647-6601
Fiber-Lite Mfg. Co., Inc., 1152 Greenpond Rd., Newfoundland, 07435 .... (973) 208-1300
Fiber-Span, 3434 U.S. Highway 22, Ste. 120, Branchburg, 08876 .... (908) 253-9080
★ Fibrenetics, Inc., 2 Cutters Dock Rd., Woodbridge, 07095 .... (732) 636-5670
FibroLAN, Inc., 350 W. Passaic St., Ste. 23, Rochelle Park, 07662 .... (201) 843-1626
Fidelis Group, Inc., 223 Gates Rd., Unit A, Little Ferry, 07643 .... (201) 641-4701
Fidelity Industries, Inc., 559 R.R. 23 S., Wayne, 07470 .... (973) 696-9120
Fieldbrook Foods Corp. see. .... Mister Cookie Face, LLC, Lakewood
Fields, Inc., Samuel H., 197 Union St., Hackensack, 07601 .... (201) 343-4626
Fields Labs, Sam see. .... Fields, Inc., Samuel H., Hackensack
Filipino Express Newspaper, Inc.,
2711 John F. Kennedy Blvd., Jersey City, 07306 .... (201) 434-1114
Fillo Factory, Inc., 10 Fairway Ct., Northvale, 07647 .... (201) 439-1036
Fillo Factory, The see. .... Fillo Factory, Inc., Northvale
Filter & Water Technologies see. .... Filter Technologies, Inc., Monmouth Junction
Filter Research Corp. see. .... FRC Electrical Industries, New Providence
† Filter Technologies, Inc., 45 Stouts Ln., Unit 3, Monmouth Junction, 08852 .... (732) 329-2500
Filtration Solutions, Inc., 432 Sand Shore Rd., Ste. 8, Hackettstown, 07840 .... (908) 684-4000
Filtrex, Inc., 450 Hamburg Tpke., Wayne, 07470 .... (973) 595-0400
Fimbel Architectural Door Specialties,
8 Coddington Rd., Whitehouse Station, 08889 .... (908) 534-1732
FIMS Mfg. Corp., 8 Allerman Rd., Oakland, 07436 .... (201) 845-7088
Finas Finishing, Inc., 50 Stacy Haines Rd., Lumberton, 08048 .... (609) 267-4836
Fine Organics Corp., 420 Kuller Rd., P.O. Box 2277, Clifton, 07015 .... (973) 478-1000
Fine Wrap Industry, Inc., 123 Town Square Pl., Jersey City, 07310 .... (732) 960-9602
Finesse & Lucas, 40 Chestnut St., Ste. 14, Lakewood, 08701 .... (732) 367-0839
Finesse Custom Embroidery see. .... Finesse & Lucas, Lakewood
Finest Enterprises, Inc., 2107 Herbertsville Rd., Point Pleasant, 08742 .... (732) 892-1121
Finger Mates, Inc., 707 10th Ave., Belmar, 07719 .... (732) 681-4411
† FinishMaster, Inc., 700 Garfield Ave., Jersey City, 07305 .... (201) 435-1555
† Finlandia Cheese, Inc., 2001 U.S. Highway 46, Ste. 303, Parsippany, 07054 .... (973) 316-6699
Finneran Assocs., J. G., 3600 Reilly Ct., Vineland, 08360 .... (856) 696-3605
Finneran Assocs., J. G. see. .... Scientific Laboratory Supplies, Inc., Millville
Fin-Tek Ozone, 6 Leo Pl., Wayne, 07470 .... (973) 628-2988
Fiore Skylights, Inc., 210 E. Evergreen Ave., P.O. Box 160, Somerdale, 08083 .... (856) 346-0118
Fire Hooks Unlimited, 1827 Old Mill Rd., Wall, 07719 .... (732) 280-7737
Firefreeze Worldwide, Inc., 429 Rockaway Valley Rd., Boonton, 07005 .... (973) 394-1335
Firefreeze Worldwide, Inc. (H Q), 272 Highway 46, Rockaway, 07866 .... (973) 627-0722
Firehawk Industries, LLC, 309 N. Willow St., Trenton, 08618 .... (609) 393-0007
Firmenich, Inc., 150 Firmenich Way, Newark, 07114 .... (973) 589-3443
Firmenich, Inc., 250 Plainsboro Rd., Plainsboro, 08536 .... (609) 452-1000
★ First Impression Printing, Inc., 178-D 10th St., Piscataway, 08854 .... (732) 529-5450
First Impressions Screen Printing, 1703 State Route 27, Edison, 08817 .... (732) 777-7872
First Priority Emergency Vehicles, Inc.,
2444 Ridgeway Blvd., Bldg. 500, Manchester, 08759 .... (732) 657-1104
Fischer Laser Marking, Inc., 384 Otterhole Rd., West Milford, 07480 .... (973) 616-4696
Fischl Machine & Tool Co., 79 Clinton Rd., Fairfield, 07004 .... (973) 227-0767
Fisher & Sons, Inc., Harold F., 200 Ash St., Delanco, 08075 .... (856) 461-2883
Fisher Brother Sales * Fisher Capespan see. .... Capespan North America, Gloucester City
Fisher Canvas Products, Inc., 415 Saint Mary St., Burlington, 08016 .... (609) 239-2733
Fisher Co., Inc., Robert, 280 Sheffield St., Mountainside, 07092 .... (908) 928-0002
† Fishermans Dock Co-Op,
57 Channel Dr., P.O. Box 1314, Point Pleasant Beach, 08742 .... (732) 899-1872
Fishman & Son, Inc., L. see. .... Fishman Flooring Solutions, Cherry Hill

† Fishman Flooring Solutions, 621 Chapel Ave. E., Ste. A, Cherry Hill, 08034 .... (856) 857-1141
Fisk Alloy Wire, Inc., 10 Thomas Rd., P.O. Box 26, Hawthorne, 07507 .... (973) 427-7550
Fisnar, Inc., 19-C Chapin Rd. Ste. 307, Pine Brook, 07058 .... (973) 646-5044
Fitzgerald Custom Fabrication, Inc., 733 W. Bay Ave., Barnegat, 08005 .... (609) 652-8899
Fitzpak, Inc., 110 Melrich Rd., Ste. 2, Cranbury, 08512 .... (609) 860-0095
Five Roses see. .... Nicholas Galvanizing Co., Jersey City
Five Star Building Products, Inc., 2012 86th St., North Bergen, 07047 .... (201) 869-4181
Fixturecraft Corp., 1457 Raritan Rd., Ste. 201, Clark, 07066 .... (908) 272-8145
† Flame-Cut Steel, Inc., 97 E. 2nd St., Bayonne, 07002 .... (201) 436-9300
Flamingo Bay, Inc., 10 Seneca Trl., Sparta, 07871 .... (973) 726-8882
Flaroma, Inc., 96 Fanny Rd., P.O. Box 325, Mountain Lakes, 07046 .... (973) 316-8185
Flavor & Fragrance Specialties, Inc. (H Q), 3 Industrial Ave., Mahwah, 07430 .... (201) 825-2025
Flavor Development Corp., 388 Chestnut St., Norwood, 07648 .... (201) 784-8188
Flavor Dynamics, Inc., 640 Montrose Ave., South Plainfield, 07080 .... (908) 822-8855
Flavor Solutions, Inc., 120 New England Ave., Piscataway, 08854 .... (732) 354-1931
Flavors Materials International, Inc., 10-D Englehard Ave., Avenel, 07001 .... (732) 499-9700
Flech Paper Products, Inc., 55 1st Ave., Paterson, 07514 .... (973) 357-8111
Fleck Knitwear Co., Inc., 400 Leland Ave., Plainfield, 07062 .... (908) 754-8888
Fleet Equipment Corp. (H Q), 567 Commerce St., Franklin Lakes, 07417 .... (201) 337-7332
Fleetwash, Inc. see. .... Industrial Environmental, Elizabeth
Fleetwash, Inc (H Q), 26 Law Dr., Unit E, Fairfield, 07004 .... (800) 847-3735
Flemington Aluminum & Brass, Inc., 24 Junction Rd., Flemington, 08822 .... (908) 782-6317
Flemington Bituminous Corp., 205 Pennsylvania Ave., Flemington, 08822 .... (908) 782-2722
Flemington Instrument Co., Inc., 55 Sandra Rd., P.O. Box 298, Ringoes, 08551 .... (908) 782-4229
Flemington Precast & Supply, LLC, 18 Allen St., Flemington, 08822 .... (908) 782-3246
Flex Craft Co., 814 Asbury Ave., Asbury Park, 07712 .... (732) 502-9500
Flex Moulding, Inc., 112 Wells Ave., Jersey City, 07306 .... (201) 360-3634
Flexabar Corp., 1969 Rutgers Blvd., Lakewood, 08701 .... (732) 901-6500
Flexco Microwave, Inc., 17 Karville Rd., P.O. Box 115, Port Murray, 07865 .... (908) 835-1720
Flexcon Products Corp., 200 Connell Dr., Ste. 1200, Berkeley Heights, 07922 .... (908) 871-7000
Flexcraft Industries, Inc., 390 Adams St., P.O. Box 2098, Newark, 07114 .... (973) 589-3403
Flexdel Corp., 1969 Rutgers University Blvd., Lakewood, 08701 .... (732) 901-7771
Flexi Printing Plate Co., Inc., 50 Commercial Ave., Moonachie, 07074 .... (201) 939-3600
FlexiGalvanic see. .... Flexi Printing Plate Co., Inc., Moonachie
Flexline see. .... U. S. Brass & Copper, Corp., Linden
Flexmaster Canada Ltd. see. .... Novaflex Industries, Inc., West Berlin
Flexo Craft Prints, Inc., 1000 1st St., Harrison, 07029 .... (973) 482-7200
Flexon Industries see. .... U. S. Wire & Cable, Inc., Newark
Flexon Industries Corp., 1 Flexon Plz., Newark, 07114 .... (973) 824-5530
Flextron Systems, 85 Nicholson Rd., Gloucester City, 08030 .... (856) 742-0550
Flint Group, 6 Corn Rd., Dayton, 08810 .... (732) 329-4627
FLM Graphics Corp., 123 Lehigh Dr., Fairfield, 07004 .... (973) 575-9450
Flodyne Controls, Inc., 48 Commerce Dr., Murray Hill, 07974 .... (908) 464-6200
Florence Ravioli Co., 391 Park Ave., Scotch Plains, 07076 .... (908) 322-7222
Florlift Of New Jersey, Inc., 19 Gardner Rd., Ste. M, Fairfield, 07004 .... (973) 484-1717
Flortek Corp., 39 W. 55th St., Bayonne, 07002 .... (201) 436-7700
Flow Safe, Inc., 30 Broad St., Denville, 07834 .... (973) 627-8553
★ Flowonix, 500 International Dr., Ste. 200, Budd Lake, 07828 .... (973) 426-9229
Flowserve Corp., 401 Heron Dr., P.O. Box 563, Bridgeport, 08014 .... (856) 241-7800
Flowserve Corp., 142 Clinton Rd., Fairfield, 07004 .... (973) 227-4565
Flow-Turn, Inc., 1050 Commerce Ave., Ste. 1, Union, 07083 .... (908) 687-3225
Floxite Company, Inc., 31 Industrial Ave., Ste. 2, Mahwah, 07430 .... (201) 529-2019
Fluets Corp., 260 Pennsylvania Ave., Hillside, 07205 .... (908) 353-5229
Fluid Filtration Corp., 102 Van Winkle Ave., Garfield, 07026 .... (973) 253-7070
Fluidaire Cleaning Services see. .... Procedyne Corp., New Brunswick
Fluidra USA, LLC see. .... Aqua Products, Inc., Cedar Grove
Fluidyne Corp., 9100 Collins Ave., Pennsauken, 08110 .... (856) 663-1818
Fluitec International (H Q), 333 Washington St., Ste. 201, Jersey City, 07302 .... (201) 946-4584
Fluoramics, Inc., 18 Industrial Ave., Mahwah, 07430 .... (201) 825-8110
Fluorotherm Polymers, Inc., 333 New Rd., Ste. 1, Parsippany, 07054 .... (973) 575-0760
Flying Fish Brewing Co., 900 Kennedy Blvd., Somerdale, 08083 .... (856) 504-3442
Flying Fish Studio, 130 Park Blvd., Cape May, 08204 .... (609) 884-2760
Flying T-Shirts, 217 1st Ave., Cape May Court House, 08210 .... (609) 463-0397
FMDK Technologies, Inc., 63 Ramapo Valley Rd., Lobby 4, Mahwah, 07430 .... (201) 828-9822
FMP see. .... Franklin Machine Products, Inc., Lumberton
FMS Graphics see. .... Forms Management Services, Inc., Hackensack
FNS Custom Window Treatment, 2954 N. West Blvd., Vineland, 08360 .... (856) 696-4070
Foam Pack Industries Div. Of Patis, Inc., 72 Fadem Rd., Springfield, 07081 .... (973) 376-3700
Foam Rubber Fabricators, Inc., 740 Washington Ave., Ste. 1, Belleville, 07109 .... (973) 751-1445
Folded Structures Co., LLC, 1142-A Old York Rd., Ringoes, 08551 .... (908) 237-1955
Foley Co., 40 Pier Ln. W., Fairfield, 07004 .... (973) 575-8338
Foley-Waite Assocs., Inc.,
225 Belleville Ave., P.O. Box 164, Bloomfield, 07003 .... (973) 743-0700
Folsom Corp. (H Q), 43 McKee Dr., Ste. 1, P.O. Box 6660, Mahwah, 07430 .... (201) 529-3550
Food & Beverage, Inc., 100 Hollister Rd., Unit 5, Teterboro, 07608 .... (201) 288-8881
Food Ingredient Solutions, LLC, 10 Malcolm Ave., Unit 1, Teterboro, 07608 .... (201) 440-4377
Food Institute, The see. .... American Institute Of Food Distribution, Inc., Upper Saddle River
Food Sciences Corporation, 821 E. Gate Dr., Mount Laurel, 08054 .... (856) 778-8080
Foodline Piping Products Co., 225 Edgewood Ave., West Berlin, 08091 .... (856) 767-1177
† Foods Galore, Inc., 9246 Commerce Hwy., Pennsauken, 08110 .... (856) 488-1112
Foote & Jenks Corp., 1420 Crestmont Ave., Camden, 08103 .... (856) 966-0700
Foote's Slaughter House, 28 Swedesboro Rd., Monroeville, 08343 .... (856) 358-8550
Forbo Siegling, LLC, 130 Coolidge Ave., Englewood, 07631 .... (201) 567-6100
Ford Atlantic Fastener Co., Inc.,
341 Changebridge Rd., P.O. Box 733, Pine Brook, 07058 .... (973) 882-1191
† Ford Fasteners, Inc., 110 S. Newman St., Hackensack, 07601 .... (201) 487-3151
Fordion Packaging Ltd., 185 Linden St., Hackensack, 07601 .... (201) 692-1344
Forem Packaging, Inc., 2-44 Cornelia St., P.O. Box 50090, Newark, 07105 .... (973) 589-0402
Foremost Machine Builders, Inc., 23 Spielman Rd., Fairfield, 07004 .... (973) 227-0700
Foremost Mfg. Co., Inc., 941 Ball Ave., Union, 07083 .... (908) 687-4646
Foremost Wood Products, 191 Vineyard Rd., Edison, 08817 .... (718) 447-5836
Forino Kitchen Cabinets, Inc., 33 S. Maple Ave., Park Ridge, 07656 .... (201) 573-0990
Forked River Gazette, Inc., 119 Voyager Rd., Manahawkin, 08050 .... (609) 693-7490
† Forklift Headquarter, LLC, 975 Joyce Kilmer Ave., North Brunswick, 08902 .... (732) 821-1413
Form Cut Industries, Inc., 197 Mount Pleasant Ave., Newark, 07104 .... (973) 483-5154
Form, Fit & Function, LLC, 25 McLean Blvd., Paterson, 07514 .... (973) 442-2290
Forman Industries see. .... Fi Companies, Old Bridge
Formax Printers, 200 Wall St., West Long Branch, 07764 .... (732) 229-5063
Formia Marble & Stone, Inc., 219 E. 11th Ave., Roselle, 07203 .... (908) 259-0606
Formica Bros. Bakery, 2310 Arctic Ave., Atlantic City, 08401 .... (609) 348-8934
Formosa Plastics Corp. U.S.A. (H Q), 9 Peach Tree Hill Rd., Livingston, 07039 .... (973) 992-2090
Forms Management Services, Inc., 162 Lodi St., Hackensack, 07601 .... (201) 336-3200
★ Forms Plus More, LLC, 6 Harwood Dr., Voorhees, 08043 .... (856) 753-8886
Formslink Systems, Inc., 14 Hilldale Rd., P. O. Box 101, Pine Brook, 07058 .... (973) 808-8820
Forrest Mfg. Co., Inc., 457 River Rd., Clifton, 07014 .... (973) 473-5236
Forrest Signs, 281 Greenwood Ave., Midland Park, 07432 .... (201) 670-7760
Forsberg's Boat Works, Inc., 1692 W. End Dr., Point Pleasant Boro, 08742 .... (732) 892-4246
Fort Nassau Graphics, 1757 Imperial Way, West Deptford, 08066 .... (856) 853-2800
Forte Pallet, Inc., 3 Water Works Rd., Old Bridge, 08857 .... (732) 727-3879
Forthmann Machines, Inc., 1495 MacArthur Blvd., Mahwah, 07430 .... (201) 818-1221
Fortitude Health, 101 U.S. Highway 46, Pine Brook, 07058 .... (973) 396-8480
† Fortrad Instruments, LLC, 8 Franklin Rd., Mendham, 07945 .... (973) 543-2371
Fortuna Enterprise USA, Inc., 235 Country Club Dr., Moorestown, 08057 .... (856) 778-7588
† Fortune Plastic & Metal, Inc., 20 Carbon Pl., Jersey City, 07035 .... (201) 333-3339
Fortune Plastic & Metal, Inc. see. .... Fortune Riverside Auto Parts, Inc., Rahway
Fortune Riverside Auto Parts, Inc.,
900 Leesville Ave., P.O. Box 1589, Rahway, 07065 .... (732) 381-3355
Fortune Riverside Scrap see. .... Fortune Riverside Auto Parts, Inc., Rahway
Forty-Nine Corp., 34 Waite St., Paterson, 07524 .... (973) 754-0313
Foster & Co., Inc., 15 Wing Dr., Cedar Knolls, 07927 .... (973) 267-4100
Foster Engraving and Laser Co., 174 S. Main St., Ste. B, Hackensack, 07601 .... (201) 489-5979
Foster Wheeler Corp. (H Q), 53 Frontage Rd., P.O. Box 9000, Hampton, 08827 .... (908) 730-4000
Foundation For Student Communication see. .... Business Today, Princeton
Four Sisters Winery, 783 County Road 519, Belvidere, 07823 .... (908) 475-3671
Four Star Color see. .... Four Star Reproduction, Inc., Newton
Four Star Reproduction, Inc., 52 Paterson Ave., Ste. 2, Newton, 07860 .... (862) 268-8200
† Fox Electric Supply Co., Inc., 1 Dodge Dr., West Caldwell, 07006 .... (973) 227-4151
Fox Valve Development Corp.,
85 Franklin Rd., Hamilton Business Pk., Dover, 07801 .... (973) 328-1011
Fragale's Baking Co., 68-74 Gaston Ave., Garfield, 07026 .... (973) 546-0327
Fragrance Resources, Inc., 620 Route 3 W., Clifton, 07014 .... (973) 777-2979
Fragrance Resources, Inc., 275 Clark St., P.O. Box 110, Keyport, 07735 .... (732) 264-6767
Fram Trak Industries, Inc., 205 Hallock Ave., Middlesex, 08846 .... (732) 424-8400
Frame & Print, 778 Carver Ave., Westwood, 07675 .... (201) 358-0404
Frame-A-Coin Mfg., 318 Front St., Ste. 1, Belvidere, 07823 .... (973) 822-0094
Frameware, Inc., 8 Audrey Pl., Fairfield, 07004 .... (973) 808-2022
Francis Metals Co., Inc., 687 Prospect St., Ste. 430, Lakewood, 08701 .... (732) 761-0500
† Franco Apparel Group, 231 Docks Corner Rd., Dayton, 08810 .... (732) 438-5170
Franco Mfg. Co., Inc. (H Q), 555 Prospect St., Metuchen, 08840 .... (732) 494-0500
† Frank Winne & Son, Inc., 521 Fellowship Rd., Ste. 115, Mount Laurel, 08054 .... (931) 212-3720
Frankford Umbrellas, 824 E. Gate Dr., Mount Laurel, 08054 .... (856) 222-4134
Franklen Sheet Metal Co., Inc., 122 S. Main St., Ocean Grove, 07756 .... (732) 988-0808
Franklin Electronic Publishers, Inc., 8 Terri Ln., Burlington, 08016 .... (609) 386-2500
† Franklin Farms East, Inc., 111 W. Washington Ave., Washington, 07882 .... (908) 835-0016
★ Franklin Lakes Oakland, 41 Oak St., Ridgewood, 07450 .... (201) 612-5415
† Franklin Machine Products, Inc., 101 Mount Holly By Pass, Lumberton, 08048 .... (609) 267-3700
Franklin Miller, Inc., 60 Okner Pkwy., P.O. Box 070663, Livingston, 07039 .... (973) 535-9200
Franklin Precast, 20 Park Dr., Franklin, 07416 .... (973) 827-7563
Franklin Stamp & Sign Co., 543 Somerset St., Ste. 1, Somerset, 08873 .... (732) 846-9235
Frank's Aluminum Glass & Mirrors Co., 588 Park Ave., Freehold, 07728 .... (732) 462-8141
Frank's Cabinet Shop, Inc.,
1992 Burnt Mills Rd., P.O. Box 78, Pluckemin, 07978 .... (908) 658-4396
Frank's Upholstery & Draperies, 49 S. Boulevard Ave., Maple Shade, 08052 .... (856) 779-8585
Franley Products, Inc., 89 Riverwood Dr., Ste. 4, Toms River, 08755 .... (732) 244-1496
† Franzen International, Inc., 23 Birch St., Ste. 1, Midland Park, 07432 .... (201) 405-2228
Fratelli Beretta U.S.A., Inc., 210 Green St., South Hackensack, 07606 .... (201) 343-5161
Frazier Industrial Co., 91 Fairview Ave., P.O. Box F, Long Valley, 07853 .... (908) 876-3001
FRC Electrical Industries, 705 Central Ave., New Providence, 07974 .... (908) 464-3200
Frederiks Machine & Tool, Inc.,
99 Kingwood Stockton Rd., P.O. Box 247, Rosemont, 08556 .... (609) 397-4991
Fredon Development Industries, 393 State Route 94 S., Newton, 07860 .... (973) 383-7576
Fredon Welding & Iron Works Co.,
52 State Route 15, P.O. Box 260, Lafayette, 07848 .... (973) 383-6768
Freedom Fence & Building Products, 168 Wabash Ave., Paterson, 07503 .... (973) 345-0911
Freedom Glass & Metal, Inc.,
4 White Horse Pike, P.O. Box 868, Clementon, 08021 .... (856) 627-3946
Freedom Management Services see. .... Prosthetic Orthotic Solutions International, Marlton
† Freedom Metals, LLC, 960 Frelinghuysen Ave., Newark, 07114 .... (973) 242-2119
Freehold Glass & Mirror, Inc., 38 South St., Freehold, 07728 .... (732) 462-6200
Freehold Mfg. Assembly, Inc.,
86 Birch Ave., P.O. Box 269, Little Silver, 07739 .... (732) 224-9066
Freeman Products, Inc. (H Q), 71 Walsh Dr., Parsippany, 07054 .... (201) 475-8888
Freeport-McMoran Copper & Gold, 48-94 Bayway Ave., Elizabeth, 07202 .... (908) 558-4318
Freeport-McMoran Inc. see. .... Freeport-McMoran Copper & Gold, Elizabeth
Freeze see. .... Central Mills, Inc., Dayton
French Color & Fragrance Co., 488 Grand Ave., Englewood, 07631 .... (201) 567-6883
Frezzolini Electronics, Inc., 7 Valley St., Hawthorne, 07506 .... (973) 427-1160
Friday Morning Quarterback,
1930 Marlton Pike E., Ste. F-36, Cherry Hill, 08003 .... (856) 424-9114
Friedland & Bros., Inc., Ralph, 17 Industrial Dr., Keyport, 07735 .... (732) 290-9800
Friedrich & Dimmock, Inc., 2127 Wheaton Ave., P.O. Box 230, Millville, 08332 .... (856) 825-0305
Friend Skoler & Co., Inc. see. .... Madan Plastics, Inc., Cranford
Friend Skoler & Co., Inc. (H Q),
160 Pehle Ave., Ste. 303, Saddle Brook, 07663 .... (201) 712-0075
Frieri A Machine Tool Co., Inc., 1112 Belmont Ave., South Plainfield, 07080 .... (908) 753-7555
★ Frinton Laboratories, Inc., 4204 Sylon Blvd., Hainesport, 08036 .... (856) 722-7037
Frisch Plastics Corp., 81 Windsor Dr., Pine Brook, 07058 .... (973) 685-5936
Frogworks Publishing see. .... Frogworks.com, LLC, Lebanon
Frogworks.com, LLC, 48 Sutton Rd., Lebanon, 08833 .... (908) 832-6704
FrontEnd Graphics, 1951 Old Cuthbert Rd., Ste. 414, Cherry Hill, 08034 .... (856) 547-1600
Frontline Industries, Inc., 990 Chancellor Ave., Irvington, 07111 .... (973) 373-7211
Frontline Medical Communications, Inc., 7 Century Dr., Parsippany, 07054 .... (973) 290-8200
Frontline Medical Communications, Inc.,
7 Century Dr., Ste. 302, Parsippany, 07054 .... (973) 206-3434
FRP Corp., 15 Hoskier Rd., South Orange, 07079 .... (973) 763-5496
FRSCO Corp. see. .... Rover & Son Iron & Steel Co., F., Harrison
Frutarom USA, Inc., 9500 Railroad Ave., North Bergen, 07047 .... (201) 861-9500
FSR, Inc., 244 Bergen Blvd., West Paterson, 07424 .... (973) 785-4347
FTI, Inc. (H Q), 8 Vreeland Rd., Florham Park, 07932 .... (973) 443-4200
Fuchs Audio Technology, LLC, 407 Getty Ave., 2nd Fl., Clifton, 07011 .... (973) 772-4420
Fuji Film Medical Systems U.S.A., Inc., 10 Highpoint Dr., Wayne, 07470 .... (973) 633-5600
FUJIFILM Holdings America Corp. see. .... FUJIFILM U.S.A., Inc., Edison
FUJIFILM Hunt Chemicals U.S.A., Inc. (H Q), 40 Boroline Rd., Allendale, 07401 .... (201) 995-2200
FUJIFILM U.S.A., Inc., 1100 King Georges Post Rd., Edison, 08837 .... (732) 857-3000

ALPHABETICAL

Fujikura Graphics, 700 Penhorn Ave., Unit 2, Secaucus, 07094 .......... (201) 420-5040
Fujipoly America Corp., 900 Milik St., P.O. Box 119, Carteret, 07008 .......... (732) 969-0100
Fujitec America, Inc. see. .......... Fujitec America Inc., New York Region, Clifton
Fujitec America Inc., New York Region, 215 Entin Rd., Clifton, 07014 .......... (973) 330-0100
Full House Printing, Inc., 60 Newark St., Hoboken, 07030 .......... (201) 798-7073
Fuller Co., H.B. see. .......... Fuller Construction Products, Inc., H.B., Edison
Fuller Construction Products, Inc., H.B., 59 Brunswick Ave., Edison, 08817 .......... (732) 287-8330
FunniBonz, LLC, 3 Lake View Ct., Princeton Junction, 08550 .......... (877) 300-2669
Funs Truck'N & Mobility, 255 Route 46 W., Saddle Brook, 07663 .......... (973) 546-1900
Furniture Mill, Inc., The, 1536 Lower Ferry Rd., Ewing, 08628 .......... (609) 771-0274
Fuseco Inc. see. .......... Fuseco, Inc., Woodland Park
† Fuseco, Inc., 86 Lackawanna Ave., Ste. 240, Woodland Park, 07424 .......... (973) 894-3727
Future Electronics Corp.,
959 Route 46 E., Ste. 303, Parsippany Pl, Parsippany, 07054 .......... (973) 299-0400
Future Signs, 19 Bowhill Ave., Trenton, 08610 .......... (609) 695-6263
Futuretech Systems, Inc., 515 Plainfield Ave., Ste. 101, Edison, 08817 .......... (732) 777-7355
FXI, Inc. see. .......... F X I, Foamex Innovations Div., East Rutherford
G & B Machine, Inc., 35 N. Middaugh St., Ste. 2-B, Somerville, 08876 .......... (908) 722-7940
G & C Fab Con, LLC, 5 Foster Ln., Bldg. A, Flemington, 08822 .......... (908) 782-0526
G & G Designs, Inc. see. .......... G & G Signs, Inc., Lyndhurst
G & G Signs, Inc., 323 2nd Ave., Lyndhurst, 07071 .......... (201) 939-4099
G & G Stairs, 2559 U.S. Highway 9, Howell, 07731 .......... (732) 905-3083
G & H Sheet Metal Works, Inc., 1423 Chestnut Ave., Hillside, 07205 .......... (973) 923-1100
G & H Soho, Inc., 413 Market St., Elmwood Park, 07407 .......... (201) 216-9400
G & J Solutions, Inc., 419 Madison Ave., Woodbine, 08270 .......... (609) 861-9838
G & J Steel & Tubing, Inc., 406 Roycefield Rd., Hillsborough, 08844 .......... (908) 526-4445
† G & K Services, Inc., 137 Ralph St., Belleville, 07109 .......... (973) 751-0464
G & M Custom Formica Work, 120 Francis St., Bldg. C, Keyport, 07735 .......... (732) 888-0360
G & M Printwear, 549 S. Broadway St., Gloucester City, 08030 .......... (856) 742-5551
G & M Welding & Fabricating, Inc., 31 W. Browning Rd., Bellmawr, 08031 .......... (856) 931-0443
G & R Graphics, Inc., 303 Irvington Ave., South Orange, 07079 .......... (973) 313-2200
G & S Feldman, Inc., P.O. Box 1136, Oakhurst, 07755 .......... (732) 918-8838
G & S Motor Equipment Co., 1800 Harrison Ave., P.O. Box 493, Kearny, 07032 .......... (201) 998-9244
G & S Valves Fittings Co., Inc., 6910 Adams St., Guttenberg, 07093 .......... (201) 868-8026
G & W Laboratories Inc., 111 Coolidge St., South Plainfield, 07080 .......... (908) 753-2000
G A F Machine Tool Co., Inc., 39 Maple Pl., P.O. Box 18, Keyport, 07735 .......... (732) 264-8717
G B Industries II, Inc., 341 Margaret King Ave., Ringwood, 07456 .......... (973) 728-5900
G. Cotter Enterprises, Inc., 48 Brown Ave., Springfield, 07081 .......... (973) 376-5840
G L Tool & Mfg. Co., Inc., 26 Okner Pkwy., Livingston, 07039 .......... (973) 740-0001
G M Repair, Inc., 90 Millhurst Rd., Manalapan, 07726 .......... (732) 350-0304
G M Stainless, Inc., 41 Imclone Dr., Branchburg, 08876 .......... (908) 575-1834
G R Office Products, Inc., 11 Kentucky Ave., Paterson, 07503 .......... (973) 345-2769
G T Microwave, Inc., 2 Emery Ave., Ste. 2, Randolph, 07869 .......... (973) 361-5700
GAB Electronic Services, LLC,
1703 Industrial Hwy., Unit 8, Cinnaminson, 08077 .......... (856) 786-0108
GAC Model Making, LLC, 1879 Old Cuthbert Rd., Unit 38, Cherry Hill, 08034 .......... (856) 857-9848
Gadren Machine Co., 108 Main St., P.O. Box 117, Mount Ephraim, 08059 .......... (856) 456-4329
GAF, 1361 Alps Rd., Wayne, 07470 .......... (973) 628-3000
† Gaffney-Kroese Supply Corp., 50 Randolph Rd., Somerset, 08873 .......... (732) 885-9000
Gafgen Cabinetmakers, Thomas P., 5 Truman Ct., Robbinsville, 08691 .......... (609) 448-2060
Gail's Lettering & Design, 24 Beaver Ave., Annandale, 08801 .......... (908) 735-4628
Gaiser, Inc., Robert F., 292 Main St., P.O. Box 807, Butler, 07405 .......... (973) 838-0696
Gaiser's European Style Provisions, Inc., 2019 Morris Ave., Union, 07083 .......... (908) 686-3421
Galaxy Circuits, Inc., 100 Somogyi Ct., South Plainfield, 07080 .......... (908) 822-1400
Galaxy Glass & Stone, 277 Fairfield Rd., P.O. Box 10154, Fairfield, 07004 .......... (973) 575-3440
Galaxy Of Graphics Ltd.,
30 Murray Hill Pkwy., Ste. 300, East Rutherford, 07073 .......... (201) 806-2100
Galaxy Transformer & Magnetics, LLC, 386 Cooper Rd., West Berlin, 08091 .......... (856) 753-4546
Galaxy II, Inc., 235 Jersey Ave., Unit A, New Brunswick, 08901 .......... (732) 828-2686
Galicia Metal, Inc., 573 E. 19th St., Paterson, 07514 .......... (973) 278-1058
Gallant Laboratories, Inc., 142 Stockes Rd., Vincentown, 08088 .......... (609) 268-0953
Galleria Enterprises, Inc., 300-3 State Route 17 S., Ste. E, Lodi, 07644 .......... (646) 416-6683
Gallery Monograms, 360 Sherman Ave., Teaneck, 07666 .......... (201) 569-0189
Gallus BioPharmaceuticals, LLC see. .......... Gallus BioPharmaceuticals New Jersey, LLC, Princeton
Gallus BioPharmaceuticals New Jersey, LLC,
201 College Rd. E., Princeton, 08540 .......... (609) 919-3300
Galossi Glass Design, Inc., 12 Van Pelt Dr., Whitehouse Station, 08889 .......... (908) 232-2111
Galow Co., Inc., H., 15 Maple St., Norwood, 07648 .......... (201) 768-0547
Galvanotech, 330-A Dalziel Rd., Linden, 07036 .......... (908) 241-3900
Galves Auto Price List, Inc., 430 Industrial Ave., Ste. 3, Teterboro, 07608 .......... (201) 393-0051
Gambale Precast, Inc., 1 Erial Rd., Clementon, 08021 .......... (856) 784-3399
Gambardella Racing & Performance, Inc.,
1999 S. Black Horse Pike, Williamstown, 08094 .......... (856) 728-1869
Gambert Shirts, LLC, L., 61 Freeman St., 5th Fl., Newark, 07105 .......... (973) 344-3440
Gamco Industries, Inc., 7 Walnut Ave., Clark, 07066 .......... (732) 381-0700
† GAMS Power Tools & Supplies, Inc., 133-135 Schuyler Ave., Kearny, 07032 .......... (201) 955-0222
Gangi Graphics, 1669 Highway 88 W., Brick, 08724 .......... (732) 840-8680
Gann Law Books, Inc., 1 Washington Pk., Ste. 1300, Newark, 07102 .......... (973) 268-1200
Gannett Co., Inc. see. .......... Asbury Park Press, Inc. (H Q), Neptune
Gannett Co., Inc. see. .......... Courier News, Somerville
Gannett Co., Inc. see. .......... Courier-Post Newspaper, Cherry Hill
Gannett Co., Inc. see. .......... Daily Journal, The, Vineland
Gannett Co., Inc. see. .......... Hammonton News & Atlantic County Newspaper Group, Hammonton
Gannett Co., Inc. see. .......... Home News Tribune, Somerville
Gar Products, 170 Lehigh Ave., Lakewood, 08701 .......... (732) 364-2100
Garafano & Sons, Peter, 500 Marshall St., Paterson, 07503 .......... (973) 278-0350
Garan Electronics, Inc., 223 Stirling Rd., Unit C, Warren, 07059 .......... (908) 484-7100
† Garden Oaks Garden Center, 1921 U.S. Highway 22, Bound Brook, 08805 .......... (732) 356-7333
Garden State Awards, 3516 John F. Kennedy Blvd., Jersey City, 07307 .......... (201) 795-9420
Garden State Canvas Products Co.,
1671 Beaver Dam Rd., Point Pleasant Boro, 08742 .......... (732) 892-7021
Garden State Dental Lab see. .......... Garden State Dental Prosthetics, Inc., Asbury Park
Garden State Dental Prosthetics, Inc., 805 4th Ave., Asbury Park, 07712 .......... (732) 922-6650
Garden State Diesel, 97 Foster Rd., Ste. 4, Moorestown, 08057 .......... (856) 914-9797
Garden State Embroidery, 1879 Old Cuthbert Rd., Unit 10, Cherry Hill, 08034 .......... (856) 616-9490
† Garden State Engine & Equipment Co., Inc.,
3509 U.S. Highway 22, Branchburg, 08876 .......... (908) 534-5444
Garden State Engraving, 126 Perrine Ave., Piscataway, 08854 .......... (732) 463-0060
Garden State Fireworks, Inc.,
383 Carlton Rd., P.O. Box 403, Millington, 07946 .......... (908) 647-1086
Garden State Foliage, LLC, 600 Central Ave., Farmingdale, 07727 .......... (732) 751-0075
Garden State Highway Products, Inc., 1740 E. Oak Rd., Vineland, 08361 .......... (856) 692-7572
Garden State Nutritionals, LLC, 8 Henderson Dr., West Caldwell, 07006 .......... (973) 575-9200
Garden State Orthopaedic Center, Inc., 9 Post Rd., Ste. OP-1, Oakland, 07436 .......... (201) 337-5566
Garden State Orthopaedic Center, Inc. see. .......... Garden State Orthopedic, Inc., Morristown
Garden State Orthopedic, Inc., 95 Mount Kemble Ave., Morristown, 07960 .......... (973) 538-4948
Garden State Precast, Inc., 1630 Wyckoff Rd., Wall Township, 07719 .......... (732) 938-4436
Garden State Precision, Inc., 510 Church St., Ridgefield, 07657 .......... (201) 945-6410
Garden State Recycling see. .......... Empire Recycling, Inc., Jersey City
Garden State Sign Co., 4880 U.S. Highway 9, Howell, 07731 .......... (732) 363-7645
† Garden State Tile Distributors, Inc., 1290 Route 130, Dayton, 08810 .......... (732) 329-0860
† Garden State Tile Distributors, Inc., 267 Route 46 W., Dover, 07801 .......... (973) 366-5035
† Garden State Tile Distributors, Inc.,
472 E. Westfield Ave., Roselle Park, 07204 .......... (908) 241-4900
† Garden State Tile Distributors, Inc., 790 S. Route 73, West Berlin, 08091 .......... (856) 753-0300
† Garden State Tile Distributors, Inc. (H Q),
5001 Industrial Rd., Farmingdale, 07727 .......... (732) 938-6675
Garden State Woodworking Co., 344 Hoover Ave., Bloomfield, 07003 .......... (973) 748-2661
Garelick Farms, LLC see. .......... Tuscan Dairy, Inc., Burlington
Garelick Farms, LLC see. .......... Tuscan Dairy, Inc., Burlington
Garfield Cabinets & Millwork, Inc., 22 Garfield Ave., Garfield, 07026 .......... (973) 340-0507
Garfield Industries, Inc., 62 Clinton Rd., Fairfield, 07004 .......... (973) 575-8800
† Garfield Lumber & Millwork Co., 260 Lanza Ave., Garfield, 07026 .......... (973) 478-2160
Gariel Screen Printing, 729 Mantua Pike, Woodbury, 08096 .......... (856) 848-3240
Garmar Industries, Inc.,
1625 Route 322, P.O. Box 460, Woolwich Township, 08085 .......... (856) 241-9700
Garon Products, Inc., 256 Maxim Rd., Howell, 07731 .......... (732) 828-6400
Garon Products, Inc., 2430 Route 34, Ste. B-12, Manasquan, 08736 .......... (732) 223-2500
Garratt-Callahan Co., 306 Talmadge Rd., Edison, 08817 .......... (732) 287-2200
Garrett Clocks, 35 N. Middaugh St., Unit 3-C, Somerville, 08876 .......... (908) 231-9231
Garrison Printing Co., 7155 Airport Hwy., Pennsauken, 08109 .......... (856) 488-1900
Garvey Corp., 208 S. Route 73, Hammonton, 08037 .......... (609) 561-2450
Garvey Precision Machine, Inc., 19 Ironside Ct., Willingboro, 08046 .......... (609) 835-4900
Garwood Metal Co. see. .......... Kalis Metal Components Corp., Garwood
Gary's Gem Garden, 404 Route 70 E., Cherry Hill, 08034 .......... (856) 795-5077
Gas Drying, Inc., 355 W. Dewey Ave., P.O. Box 504, Wharton, 07885 .......... (973) 361-2212
GasFlo Products, Inc., 19 Industrial Rd., Fairfield, 07004 .......... (973) 276-9011
Gasoline Advertising Products see. .......... Norgus Silk Screen Co., Clifton
Gateway Press, 984 State Route 36, Atlantic Highlands, 07716 .......... (732) 291-1757
Gator Communication Group, 175 Route 46 W., Fairfield, 07004 .......... (973) 233-6700
Gauer Metal Products, Inc., 175-179 N. Michigan Ave., Kenilworth, 07033 .......... (908) 241-4080
Gaum, Inc., 1080 Route 130, P.O. Box 485, Robbinsville, 08691 .......... (609) 586-0132
Gavan Graham Electrical Products, 751 Rahway Ave., Union, 07083 .......... (908) 729-9000
Gavin Printing, Inc., 1057 Glen Rd., Fort Lee, 07024 .......... (212) 721-9009
GAW Associates, Inc., 670 Deer Rd., Unit A, Cherry Hill, 08034 .......... (856) 608-1428
GBD Cabinet Shop, LLC see. .......... Frank's Cabinet Shop, Inc., Pluckemin
† GCE Market, Inc., 1001 Lower Landing Rd., Ste. 307, Blackwood, 08012 .......... (856) 401-8900
GE Aviation Systems, LLC see. .......... Whippany Actuation System, Whippany
GE Healthcare, 900 Durham Ave., South Plainfield, 07080 .......... (908) 757-0500
GE Healthcare see. .......... GE Healthcare LifeSciences, Piscataway
GE Healthcare LifeSciences,
800 Centennial Ave., P.O. Box 1327, Piscataway, 08855 .......... (732) 457-8000
GE Printing Inc. see. .......... Tri-City Print & Copy Center, Totowa
GEA Mechanical Equipment US, Inc., 100 Fairway Ct., Northvale, 07647 .......... (201) 767-3900
Gecko Graphics, Inc., 128 Berlin Cross Keys Rd., Williamstown, 08094 .......... (856) 740-9042
Geebee Marketing, Inc., 300 Raritan Ave., 2nd Fl., Highland Park, 08904 .......... (732) 777-6033
Geiger Tool & Mfg. Co., Inc., 50 Liberty St., Passaic, 07055 .......... (973) 777-2136
Gel Concepts, LLC, 30 Leslie Ct., Whippany, 07981 .......... (973) 884-8995
Gel Spice Co., Inc., 48 Hook Rd., P.O. Box 285, Bayonne, 07002 .......... (201) 339-0700
Gelbstein Bakery, 415 Clifton Ave., Lakewood, 08701 .......... (732) 363-3636
Gellert Global Group see. .......... Atalanta Corporation, Elizabeth
Gem Refrigerator Co., Inc., 176 Blvd. Route 50, Mays Landing, 08330 .......... (609) 625-2500
Gem Sports, 36-10 Broadway, Fair Lawn, 07410 .......... (201) 791-1776
Gemini Cut Glass Co., Inc., 4 E. Forest Ave., Englewood, 07631 .......... (201) 568-7722
Gemini DJ & Pro Audio, 107 Trumbull St., Ste. F-8, Elizabeth, 07206 .......... (732) 346-0061
Gemini Plastic Films Corp., 535 Midland Ave., P.O. Box 360, Garfield, 07026 .......... (973) 340-0700
Gemtor, Inc., 1 Johnson Ave., Matawan, 07747 .......... (732) 583-6200
Genavite, LLC, 235 Clifton Blvd., Clifton, 07011 .......... (973) 779-1532
Genband, Inc. see. .......... uReach Technologies, Inc., Holmdel
Genband, Inc. see. .......... Ventraq, Inc., Mount Laurel
General Aviation & Electronics Mfg. Co., Inc.,
30 Jersey Pl., Hackensack, 07601 .......... (201) 487-1700
General Carbon Corporation, 33 Paterson St., Paterson, 07501 .......... (973) 523-2223
General Chemical Corp., 235 Snyder Ave., Berkeley Heights, 07922 .......... (908) 464-1500
General Devices, 1000 River St., Ridgefield, 07657 .......... (201) 313-7075
General Dynamics Advanced Information Systems,
7-9 Vreeland Rd., Florham Park, 07932 .......... (973) 514-4000
General Dynamics Corp. see. .......... General Dynamics Advanced Information Systems, Florham Park
General Electronic Enterprises, Inc., 132 W. Main St., Rahway, 07065 .......... (732) 381-1144
General Film Products, 107 Trumbull St., Bldg. R-2, Elizabeth, 07206 .......... (908) 351-0454
General Filter Corp., 14 Constitution Ave., Succasunna, 07876 .......... (973) 584-9220
† General Floor, Inc., 2 Pin Oak Ln., Cherry Hill, 08003 .......... (856) 424-0111
† General Floor, Inc., 777 New Durham Rd., Edison, 08817 .......... (732) 603-6100
† General Floor, Inc., 125 Market St., Kenilworth, 07033 .......... (908) 241-4888
† General Floor, Inc., 815 Hylton Rd., Pennsauken, 08110 .......... (856) 663-4750
† General Floor Industries, 190 Benigno Blvd., Bellmawr, 08031 .......... (856) 931-0012
General Floor Industries see. .......... General Floor, Inc., Cherry Hill
General Floor Industries see. .......... General Floor, Inc., Edison
General Floor Industries see. .......... General Floor, Inc., Kenilworth
General Floor Industries see. .......... General Floor, Inc., Pennsauken
General Foundries, Inc., 1 Progress Rd., North Brunswick, 08902 .......... (732) 697-9000
General Glass International, 101 Venture Way, Secaucus, 07094 .......... (201) 553-1850
General Machine & Experimental Works, 117 Gertrude Ave., Paramus, 07652 .......... (201) 843-9035
General Machine Co. Of New Jersey, 301 Smalley Ave., Middlesex, 08846 .......... (732) 752-7900
General Machine Kraft, Inc., 216 Broad St., Phillipsburg, 08865 .......... (908) 454-5955
General Magnaplate Corp., 1331 U.S. Route 1, Linden, 07036 .......... (908) 862-6200
General Metal & Glass Co., 613 Kaighn Ave., Camden, 08101 .......... (856) 365-6323
General Mills, Inc. see. .......... General Mills Progresso, Vineland
General Mills Progresso, 500 W. Elmer Rd., Vineland, 08360 .......... (856) 691-1565
General Mills/Progresso Quality Foods see. .......... General Mills Progresso, Vineland
General Pallet, LLC, 97 River Rd., Flemington, 08822 .......... (908) 238-1000
General Pencil Co., 67 Fleet St., Jersey City, 07306 .......... (201) 653-5351
General Plastics Corp., 55 La France Ave., Bloomfield, 07003 .......... (973) 748-5500
† General Plumbing Supply, Inc., 980 New Durham Rd., Edison, 08817 .......... (732) 248-1000

© Copyright 2015 Manufacturers' News, Inc.


General Polygon Systems, Inc., 203 Peterson St., Millville, 08332 .... (856) 825-3300
General Reliance Corp., 88 Ford Rd., Ste. 20, Denville, 07834 .... (973) 361-1400
† General Reproduction Products, 23 McKee Dr., Mahwah, 07430 .... (201) 934-0027
General Rubber Corp., 850 Washington Ave., Front, Carlstadt, 07072 .... (201) 935-1900
General Sign Co., Inc., 105 Chestnut Ave., West Berlin, 08091 .... (856) 753-3535
General Stamping Co., 451 E. Main St., Denville, 07834 .... (973) 627-9500
General Tool Specialties, Inc., 284 Sunnymead Rd., Hillsborough, 08844 .... (908) 874-3040
General Wire & Stamping Co., Inc., 1 Emery Ave., Unit 3, Randolph, 07869 .... (973) 366-8080
Generant Co., Inc., 1865 Route 23 S., P.O. Box 768, Butler, 07405 .... (973) 838-6500
Generation Brands, LLC see. .... Sea Gull Lighting Products, LLC., Riverside
Genesis Biotechnology Group (H Q), 1000 Waterview Dr., Hamilton, 08691 .... (609) 786-2800
Genesis Pharmaceutical, Inc. (H Q), 8 Campus Dr., Parsippany, 07054 .... (800) 459-8663
Genevieve's, Inc., 174 Ray St., Garfield, 07026 .... (973) 772-8816
Gengaro Stone, LLC, 90 S. Main St., Ocean Grove, 07756 .... (732) 776-6000
Genie House, Inc., 139 Red Lion Rd., P.O. Box 2478, Vincentown, 08088 .... (609) 859-0600
Gentek Building Products, Inc., 11 Craigwood Rd., Avenel, 07001 .... (732) 381-0900
Genzyme Corp. see. .... Genzyme Corp., Biosurgery Div., Ridgefield
Genzyme Corp., Biosurgery Div., 1125 Pleasant View Ter., Ridgefield, 07657 .... (201) 945-9550
GEO Specialty Chemicals, Inc., 1st & Essex St., Harrison, 07029 .... (973) 484-8400
Geographia Map Co., Inc., 75 Moore St., Hackensack, 07601 .... (201) 488-4411
† George A. Mathewson Co., 9-11 Foundry St., Newark, 07105 .... (973) 344-0081
George Steel see. .... Steel's Fudge, Inc., Ocean City
George Taub Products, 277 New York Ave., Jersey City, 07307 .... (201) 798-5353
Georgetti Pasta see. .... M. A. R. Kit, Inc., Cinnaminson
Georgia Pacific, Inc., 623 Riegelsville Rd., Milford, 08848 .... (908) 995-2228
Georgia-Pacific Gypsum, LLC, 1101 S. Front St., Camden, 08103 .... (856) 966-7600
Georgia-Pacific, LLC see. .... Georgia Pacific, Inc., Milford
Georgia-Pacific, LLC see. .... Georgia-Pacific Gypsum, LLC, Camden
Gerard Sheet Metal Fabricators, Inc., 385 Lexington Ave., East Brunswick, 08816 .... (732) 257-4777
Gerardi Press, Inc., 3 Luger Rd., Ste. 3, P.O. Box 545, Denville, 07834 .... (973) 627-2600
† Gerber Metal Supply Co., 2 Boundary Rd., Somerville, 08876 .... (908) 823-9150
Gerdau Ameristeel US, Inc. see. .... Gerdau US, Inc., Sayreville, Sayreville
Gerdau US, Inc., Sayreville, N. Crossman Rd., P.O. Box 249, Sayreville, 08872 .... (732) 721-6600
Gerin Corp., 1109 7th Ave., Neptune, 07753 .... (732) 774-3256
Gero Desk see. .... Hoppe Co., Inc., R. J., Newark
Ge-Ro Desk Co., 334 N. 5th St., Newark, 07107 .... (973) 485-0505
Gerresheimer Glass, Inc., 537 Crystal Ave., Vineland, 08360 .... (856) 692-3600
Gerresheimer Glass, Inc., 91 W. Forest Grove Rd., Vineland, 08360 .... (856) 507-5600
Gerresheimer Glass, Inc. see. .... Gerresheimer, Inc., Millville
Gerresheimer, Inc., 1300 Wheaton Ave., Millville, 08332 .... (856) 506-0501
Gerson Industries, Inc., 20-21 Wagaraw Rd., Bldg. 37, P.O. Box 12, Fair Lawn, 07410 .... (973) 423-6100
Gerson Mattress see. .... Gerson Industries, Inc., Fair Lawn
† Gexpro, 522 Pedricktown Rd., Swedesboro, 08085 .... (856) 241-4700
G&F Graphic Services see. .... Inserts East, Inc., Pennsauken
GFC Coatings & Chemicals, 18 Mill St., Lodi, 07644 .... (973) 272-0257
Giambri's Candy see. .... Giambri's Quality Sweets, Clementon
Giambri's Quality Sweets, 26 Brand Ave., Clementon, 08021 .... (856) 783-1099
Gianella Baking Co., 298 21st Ave., Paterson, 07501 .... (973) 523-9258
Gianetto Wood Carvings, Vincent, 617 Delanco Rd., Beverly, 08010 .... (609) 877-6233
Gibson Designs, Inc., Kathy, 1416 Willow Ave., Hoboken, 07030 .... (201) 420-0088
Gibson, Inc., George, 801 S. Church St., Ste. 6, Mount Laurel, 08054 .... (856) 234-5502
Gifford & Co., Brian L., 514 Bogden Blvd., Millville, 08332 .... (856) 327-0011
Gilby's Screen Print, 615 Ringwood Ave., Pompton Lakes, 07442 .... (973) 835-5729
Gild & Son see. .... Belleville Corp., Kearny
Gild, Inc., 18-02 River Rd., Ste. 5, Fair Lawn, 07410 .... (201) 398-0030
† Gill Assocs. Identification Systems, LLC, 2025 Hamburg Tpke., Ste. M, Wayne, 07470 .... (973) 835-5456
Gillespie, Inc., Paul J., 2565 Brunetta Dr., Vineland, 08360 .... (856) 839-0891
Gilosa Bindery, Inc., Joseph A., 555 20th Ave., Paterson, 07504 .... (973) 279-8006
Gilt Edge Folding Boxes, Inc., P.O. Box 544, Saddle Brook, 07663 .... (201) 843-1450
GINN Co., 812 Jersey Ave., Jersey City, 07310 .... (201) 216-1660
Ginsburg Bakery, Inc., 300 N. Tennessee Ave., Atlantic City, 08401 .... (609) 345-2265
Ginsey Home Solutions see. .... Ginsey Industries, Inc., Swedesboro
Ginsey Industries, Inc., 2078 Center Square Rd., Swedesboro, 08085 .... (856) 933-1300
Gio Vali Corp., 463 Grand St., Paterson, 07505 .... (973) 279-3032
Gioia Sails Inc., 1951 Rutgers University Blvd., Lakewood, 08701 .... (732) 901-6770
Giordano, Inc., Philip A., 59 Garfield Ave., Garfield, 07026 .... (973) 546-9267
Girtain Sign Co., 1765 Route 9, Toms River, 08755 .... (732) 349-8499
Givaudan Flavors Corp., 245 Merry Ln., East Hanover, 07936 .... (973) 386-9800
Givaudan Flavors Corp. see. .... Givaudan Fragrances Corp., Mount Olive
Givaudan Fragrances Corp., 300 Waterloo Valley Rd., Mount Olive, 07828 .... (973) 448-6500
G.J. Chemical Co., Inc., 128 Doremus Ave., Newark, 07105 .... (973) 589-4176
G.J. Chemical Co., Inc., 40 Veronica Ave., Somerset, 08873 .... (973) 589-1450
GL Assocs. see. .... GL Consulting, Inc., Jersey City
GL Consulting, Inc., 1000 Plaza Three, Jersey City, 07311 .... (201) 451-9121
Glasco UV, LLC, 126 Christie Ave., Ste. 1, Mahwah, 07430 .... (201) 934-3348
Glasgow, Inc. see. .... National Paving Co., Inc., Berlin
Glass Cycle Systems, Inc., 5 Mathews Ave., Riverdale, 07457 .... (973) 838-0034
Glass Dynamics, LLC, 2662 Hance Bridge Rd., Vineland, 08361 .... (856) 205-1530
Glassblowers.Com, Inc., P.O. Box 8089, Turnersville, 08012 .... (856) 232-7898
Glassboro Printing, Inc., 30 N. Academy St., Glassboro, 08028 .... (856) 881-2600
Glassman High Voltage, Inc., 124 W. Main St., P.O. Box 317, High Bridge, 08829 .... (908) 638-3800
GlassRoots, Inc., 10 Bleeker St., Newark, 07102 .... (973) 353-9555
★ Glaston America, Inc., 600-D Commerce Pkwy., Mount Laurel, 08054 .... (856) 786-1200
Glastron, Inc., 510 N. West Blvd., Vineland, 08360 .... (856) 692-0500
Glatt Air Techniques, Inc., 20 Spear Rd., Ramsey, 07446 .... (201) 825-8700
Glebar Co., 527 Commerce St., P.O. Box 623, Franklin Lakes, 07417 .... (201) 337-1500
Gleicher Mfg. Corp., 851 Jerusalem Rd., Scotch Plains, 07076 .... (908) 233-2211
Glen Magnetics, Inc., 1165 3rd Ave., Alpha, 08865 .... (908) 454-3717
† Glen Mills Inc., 220 Delawanna Ave., Clifton, 07014 .... (973) 777-0777
Glen Rock Stair Corp., 551 Commerce St., Franklin Lakes, 07417 .... (201) 337-9595
Glenbrook Technologies, Inc., 11 Emery Ave., Randolph, 07869 .... (973) 361-8866
† Glenmark Generics Inc., USA, 750 Corporate Dr., Mahwah, 07430 .... (201) 684-8000
Glenmore Plastic Industries, Inc., 115 Newfield Ave., Edison, 08837 .... (718) 649-7800
Glenro, Inc., 39 McBride Avenue Ext., Paterson, 07501 .... (973) 279-5900
Glentech, Inc., 46 4th St., Somerville, 08876 .... (908) 685-2205
† Glenwood Office Furniture II, Inc., 561 U.S. Highway 22, Hillside, 07205 .... (908) 687-3770
Glitterex Corp., 7 Commerce Dr., Cranford, 07016 .... (908) 272-9121
Global - The Total Office (H Q), 17 W. Stow Rd., P.O. Box 562, Marlton, 08053 .... (856) 596-3390
Global Business Dimensions Inc., 220 W. Parkway, Ste. 8, Pompton Plains, 07444 .... (973) 831-5866
Global Colorants, Inc., 83 Roosevelt Ave., Belleville, 07109 .... (973) 751-2227
Global Graphics, Inc., 1945 State Route 27, Ste. 5, Edison, 08817 .... (732) 287-9390
Global Ingredients, Inc., 317 9th Ave., Paterson, 07514 .... (973) 278-6677
★ Global Metals Sales Corp., 196 Inwood Ave., Montclair, 07043 .... (212) 813-3100
Global Packaging Machinery, Inc., 36 Peel St., Paterson, 07524 .... (973) 279-2300
Global Partners In Shielding see. .... GPS Specialty Doors, Inc., Passaic
Global Partners In Shielding, Inc., 90 Dayton Ave., Ste. 13, Passaic, 07055 .... (973) 574-9077
Global Print Media, 421 W. County Line Rd., Lakewood, 08701 .... (732) 886-0505
Global Seven, Inc., 198 Green Pond Rd., P.O. Box 696, Rockaway, 07866 .... (973) 664-1900
Global Soft Digital Solutions, Inc., 500 Corporate Dr., Mahwah, 07430 .... (201) 684-0900
Global Specialty Products USA, Inc., 10 Eagle Ave., Ste. 500, Mount Holly, 08060 .... (609) 518-7577
Global Wire & Cable, Inc., 61 Willet St., Bldg. S, Passaic, 07055 .... (973) 471-1000
Globe Casing Company see. .... Globe Packaging Co., Inc., Carlstadt
Globe Die Cutting Products, 76 Liberty St., P.O. Box 4339, Metuchen, 08840 .... (732) 494-7744
Globe Industries Corp., 48 Industrial St. W., Clifton, 07012 .... (973) 992-8990
Globe Mfg. Sales, Inc. see. .... A. K. Stamping Co., Inc., Mountainside
Globe Packaging Co., Inc., 368 Paterson Plank Rd., Carlstadt, 07072 .... (201) 939-3335
Globe Photoengraving Co., LLC, 19 N. Washington Ave., Little Ferry, 07643 .... (201) 489-2300
Globe Plating, Inc., 220 Miller St., Newark, 07114 .... (973) 623-1116
Globe Scientific, Inc., 610 Winters Ave., Paramus, 07652 .... (201) 599-1400
† GlobePharma, Inc., 2-B Janine Pl., New Brunswick, 08901 .... (732) 296-9700
Globtek, Inc., 186 Veterans Dr., Northvale, 07647 .... (201) 784-1000
Glocon, Inc. (Swifter Fans), 3-1 Luger Rd., Denville, 07834 .... (973) 463-7300
Glopak Corp., 132 Case Dr., South Plainfield, 07080 .... (908) 753-8735
Glorin Printing, Inc., 258 Clifton Ave., Newark, 07104 .... (973) 481-3233
Gloucester City Box Works, LLC, 775 Charles St., Gloucester City, 08030 .... (856) 456-9032
Gloucester City News, Inc., 34 S. Broadway, P.O. Box 151, Gloucester City, 08030 .... (856) 456-1199
Gloves Unlimited see. .... Childcare Supply Co. Inc., Englishtown
Glowpoint, Inc., 430 Mountain Ave., Ste. 301, Murray Hill, 07974 .... (973) 855-3411
Gluefast Co., Inc., 3535 State Route 66, Ste. 1, Neptune, 07753 .... (732) 918-4600
Glue-Fold, Inc., Div. Of Perfect Finishing, Inc., 40 Webro Rd., Clifton, 07012 .... (973) 575-8400
GM Printing, 106 Pleasant Ave., Bergenfield, 07621 .... (201) 385-2525
GMB (USA), Inc., 190 Veterans Dr., Ste. B, Northvale, 07647 .... (201) 768-3577
GMB North America, Inc., 100 Herrod Blvd., Dayton, 08810 .... (609) 655-2422
GMI, 599 State St., Perth Amboy, 08861 .... (732) 442-4572
GMPC Printing, 1 Trenton Ave., Clifton, 07011 .... (973) 894-1500
GMPC Printing see. .... Minuteman Press, Clifton
GMS Litho, Inc., 16 Passaic Ave., Fairfield, 07004 .... (973) 575-9400
★ GNC Venture Group, Inc., 1639 Percy Ln., Vineland, 08361 .... (856) 690-1999
Gnutti Carlo, 140 Ludlow Ave., Northvale, 07647 .... (201) 768-8200
Go Foton, 28 Worlds Fair Dr., Somerset, 08873 .... (732) 469-9650
Godforce Tactical, Inc., 2614-B S. Clinton Ave., South Plainfield, 07080 .... (908) 561-2021
Godwin, a Xylem brand, 84 Floodgate Rd., Bridgeport, 08014 .... (856) 467-3636
Goffco Industries, Inc., 10 Park Pl., Bldg. 6-6, Butler, 07405 .... (973) 492-0150
Gold & Reiss Corp. see. .... Kentucky Cabinet Corp., Union
Gold Attachments Sewing Supply, Inc., 7051 Kennedy Blvd., North Bergen, 07047 .... (201) 854-0320
Golden Fluff, Inc., 118 Monmouth Ave., Lakewood, 08701 .... (732) 367-5448
Golden Oil Holding Corp. see. .... Instrument Specialties Co., Inc., Boonton
Golden Plastics, Inc., 510-A Industrial Ave., Teterboro, 07608 .... (201) 393-9833
Golden Platter Foods, Inc., 37 Tompkins Point Rd., Newark, 07114 .... (973) 242-0290
★ Golden Rule Creations, 250 Terrace Rd., Franklin Lakes, 07417 .... (201) 337-4050
Golden Rule, Inc., 7150 N. Park Dr., Ste. 620, Pennsauken, 08109 .... (856) 663-3074
Golden Sheets Mfg., 239 6th Ave., Paterson, 07524 .... (973) 925-2242
Golden West Paper Converting, 121 Helen St., South Plainfield, 07080 .... (908) 412-8889
Goldstein Setting Co Inc /TA DanMar Jewelers, 2464 Morris Ave., Union, 07083 .... (908) 964-1034
G-O-Metric, Inc., 215 Ash St., Delanco, 08075 .... (856) 461-8080
Gonzalez & Tapanes, Inc. see. .... La Fe Foods, Inc., Moonachie
Good Automatic Windlass, Inc., 357 Route 72, Barnegat, 08005 .... (609) 698-4402
Good Impressions, Inc., 325 W. Washington Ave., Washington, 07882 .... (908) 689-3071
Good Impressions Printing, Inc., 28 Scott St., P.O. Box 409, Riverside, 08075 .... (856) 461-3232
Goodman & Co., Inc., Bob, 2 Steward Ln., Englishtown, 07726 .... (732) 446-0252
Goodyear Rubber Products Corp., 1583 Livingston Ave., Ste. 4, North Brunswick, 08902 .... (732) 448-1111
★ Gordon International, Inc., 6 Paragon Way, Freehold, 07728 .... (732) 431-3361
Gordon Mills Mfg., Inc. (H Q), 68 Sherwood Dr., Morristown, 07960 .... (973) 359-1080
Gordon Terminal see. .... Gordon Terminal Service Co. Of New Jersey, Inc., Bayonne
Gordon Terminal Service Co. Of New Jersey, Inc., 2 Hook Rd., P.O. Box 143, Bayonne, 07002 .... (201) 437-8300
Gordon Terminal Service Co. Of Pennsylvania see. Gordon Terminal Service Co. Of New Jersey, Inc., Bayonne
Gordon's Marine Service, 454 S. Green St., Tuckerton, 08087 .... (609) 296-5817
Gore & Assocs., Inc., W. L., 1746 State Route 34 N., Wall Township, 07727 .... (732) 681-7070
Gorgias Press, 954 River Rd., P.O. Box 6939, Piscataway, 08854 .... (732) 885-8900
Gorgo Pallet Co., 646 S. Delsea Dr., Vineland, 08360 .... (856) 692-0303
Gorkin Glass Co., Inc., 26 Race St., North Plainfield, 07060 .... (908) 756-0544
Gorsky, Inc., E., 33 South Ave., Fanwood, 07023 .... (908) 322-8580
Gotham Group, The, 202 W. Parkway Dr., Ste. 2, Egg Harbor Township, 08234 .... (609) 645-2211
† Gotham Sales Co., 302 Main St., Millburn, 07041 .... (973) 912-8412
Gottscho Printing Systems, Inc., 335 Chambers Brook Rd., Branchburg, 08876 .... (908) 688-2400
Gough Engraving & Advertising Specialties, 1745 N. Olden Avenue Ext., Ewing, 08638 .... (609) 882-8700
Gourmet Dessert Outlet, LLC, 851 Van Houten Ave., Clifton, 07013 .... (973) 815-1111
Gourmet Foods, Inc., 25 Andrews Dr., Woodland Park, 07424 .... (973) 237-1776
Gourmet Kitchen, Inc., 1238 State Route 33, Neptune, 07753 .... (732) 775-5222
Goya Foods, Inc., 650 New County Rd., Secaucus, 07094 .... (201) 865-3470
Goya Foods, Inc. (H Q), 100 Seaview Dr., Secaucus, 07094 .... (201) 348-4900
† Goyen Valve Corp., 1195 Airport Rd., Lakewood, 08701 .... (732) 364-7800
GP Chemicals, Inc. (H Q), 7225 Bergenline Ave., North Bergen, 07047 .... (201) 869-2200
GP Precision, Inc., 434 Sand Shore Rd., Hackettstown, 07840 .... (908) 850-1940
GPR Co., Inc., 22 Daniel Rd., Fairfield, 07004 .... (973) 227-6160
GPS see. .... General Plumbing Supply, Inc., Edison
GPS Specialty Doors see. .... Global Partners In Shielding, Inc., Passaic
GPS Specialty Doors, Inc., 90 Dayton Ave., Unit 4-B, Passaic, 07055 .... (973) 778-6200
Grabber Construction Products, Inc. see. .... Grabber Northeast, Pennsauken
† Grabber Northeast, 1125 Thomas Busch Memorial Hwy., Pennsauken, 08110 .... (856) 662-2525
Gracis, Inc., 25 Graphic Pl., Moonachie, 07074 .... (201) 296-0700
Graco Manufacturing, 500 University Ct., Blackwood, 08012 .... (856) 228-1800
Graduation Outlet see. .... Trim & Tassels, LLC (H Q), Fairfield

Graham Packaging Co. L. P., 600 5th St., Belvidere, 07823 .......... (908) 475-2181
Graham Partners, Inc. see. .......... TransAxle, LLC, Cinnaminson
Grammer, Dempsey & Hudson Co., 212 Rome St., Newark, 07105 .......... (973) 589-8000
Grand Displays, Inc., 12 Empire Blvd., Moonachie, 07074 .......... (201) 994-1500
Grand Equipment Of America, 267 Livingston St., Northvale, 07647 .......... (201) 784-1101
Grandview Printing Co., Inc., 33 W. End Rd., Totowa, 07512 .......... (973) 890-0006
Granite Surfaces, LLC, 368 Lincoln Blvd., Middlesex, 08846 .......... (732) 627-9200
Grant & Sons, Inc., William, 130 Fieldcrest Ave., Edison, 08837 .......... (732) 225-9000
Grant Boat Works, 120 Lakeside Dr., Ste. E, P.O. Box 597, Forked River, 08731 .......... (609) 971-1075
Grant Industries, Inc., 125 Main Ave., Elmwood Park, 07407 .......... (201) 791-6700
† Grant Supply Co., Inc., 901 Joyce Kilmer Ave., North Brunswick, 08902 .......... (732) 545-1018
† Grant Supply Co., Inc., 755 W. Delilah Rd., Pleasantville, 08232 .......... (609) 641-1114
Granulation Technology, Inc., 12 Industrial Rd., Fairfield, 07004 .......... (973) 276-0740
Granville Concrete Products, 1076 Route 10, Randolph, 07869 .......... (973) 584-6653
Grape Escape, The, 12 Stults Rd., Ste. 101, Dayton, 08810 .......... (609) 409-9463
Graph Corr, LLC, 4 Corn Rd., Dayton, 08810 .......... (732) 355-0088
Graphic Action, Inc., 296 S. Main St., Phillipsburg, 08865 .......... (908) 213-0055
Graphic Center Digital see. .......... Graphic Center, The, Mount Freedom
Graphic Center, The, P.O. Box 595, Mount Freedom, 07970 .......... (973) 366-6676
Graphic Concepts Printing, Inc. see. .......... Enviroprint USA, Bound Brook
Graphic Concepts/Reproduction, Inc., 111 Butternut Dr., Wayne, 07470 .......... (973) 706-6400
Graphic Design Worx see. .......... Hurricane Signs, Bloomingdale
Graphic Equipment Corp., 55 Wester Ave., Metuchen, 08840 .......... (732) 494-5350
Graphic Express Menu Co., Inc., 200 Clifton Blvd., Ste. 6, Clifton, 07011 .......... (973) 685-0022
Graphic Image, 1401 N. Black Horse Pike, Ste. A, Williamstown, 08094 .......... (856) 262-8900
Graphic Image, Inc., 445 Route 46, Hackettstown, 07840 .......... (908) 852-7007
Graphic Imagery, Inc., 122 Mount Bethel Rd., Ste. 2, Warren, 07059 .......... (908) 755-2882
Graphic Impressions Printing Co., 4391 Route 42, Turnersville, 08012 .......... (856) 728-2266
Graphic Marketing Group, 7 Kingsbridge Rd., Ste. 2, Fairfield, 07004 .......... (973) 276-7901
Graphic Packaging Holding Company see. .......... Graphic Packaging International, Inc., Piscataway
Graphic Packaging International, Inc.,
4100 New Brunswick Ave., Piscataway, 08854 .......... (732) 424-2100
Graphic Presentation Systems, Inc.,
262 Old New Brunswick Rd., Ste. F, Piscataway, 08854 .......... (732) 981-1120
Graphic Printing Co., Inc., 283 Lincoln Blvd., Middlesex, 08846 .......... (732) 627-9000
★ Graphic Solutions & Signs, LLC, 82 Burlews Ct., Hackensack, 07601 .......... (201) 343-7446
Graphic Techniques, LLC, 10 S. West Blvd., P.O. Box 4, Newfield, 08344 .......... (856) 697-2480
Graphicolor Corp., 3490 N. Mill Rd., Vineland, 08360 .......... (856) 691-2507
Graphics Depot, Inc., 11 Middlebury Blvd., Ste. 4, Randolph, 07869 .......... (973) 927-8200
Graphics Plus Corp., 210 W. Parkway, Ste. 7, Pompton Plains, 07444 .......... (973) 835-3744
Graphics Plus Reproduction Center, Inc. see. .......... Graphics Plus Corp., Pompton Plains
Graphict One USA see. .......... Graphictone, Englewood Cliffs
Graphictone, 360 Sylvan Ave., Ste. 4, Englewood Cliffs, 07632 .......... (201) 568-2008
Graphiry Printing, 308 Morris Ave., Elizabeth, 07208 .......... (908) 353-2223
Graphix Integrated, Inc., 971 Leonardville Rd., Atlantic Highlands, 07716 .......... (732) 872-8282
Graphix One, LLC, 725 Lincoln Blvd., Middlesex, 08846 .......... (732) 560-4700
Grassmann-Blake, Inc., 58 E. Willow St., Millburn, 07041 .......... (973) 379-6170
Grasso Foods, Inc., 2111 Kings Hwy., P.O. Box 127, Woolwich Township, 08085 .......... (856) 467-2222
Graver Technologies, LLC, 72 Lockwood St., Newark, 07105 .......... (973) 690-5290
Graver Water Systems, LLC, 675 Central Ave., Ste. 3, New Providence, 07974 .......... (908) 516-1400
Gray Contract Assembly, 102 Columbia Ave., Pitman, 08071 .......... (856) 589-3263
Gray Overhead Door Co., 439 Third Ave., Elizabeth, 07206 .......... (908) 355-3889
Gray Star, Inc., 200 Valley Rd., Ste. 200, Mount Arlington, 07856 .......... (973) 398-3331
† Graybar Electric Co., Inc., 105 E. Crest Ave., Ste. 207, Edison, 08837 .......... (973) 404-5555
GrayHair Software, Inc., 124 Gaither Dr., Ste. 160, Mount Laurel, 08054 .......... (856) 727-9372
Great American Trolley Co. (H Q), 821 Shunpike Rd., Cape May, 08204 .......... (609) 884-0450
Great American Veal Co., Inc., 50 Avenue L, Ste. 5, Newark, 07105 .......... (973) 589-6363
Great Bags see. .......... Maple Leather Co., Stockton
Great Falls Metalworks, Inc., 301 E. 22nd St., Paterson, 07514 .......... (973) 523-6811
Great Garlic Foods, Inc., 709 5th Ave., Bradley Beach, 07720 .......... (732) 775-3311
Great Northern Commercial Service, Inc., 401 Greenwich St., Belvidere, 07823 .......... (908) 475-8855
Great Notch Industries, Inc., 140 Liberty St., Hackensack, 07601 .......... (201) 343-8110
Greater Media, Inc. see. .......... Greater Media Newspapers, Manalapan
Greater Media Newspapers, 198 Route 9 N., P.O. Box 950, Manalapan, 07726 .......... (732) 358-5200
Greater New Jersey Diamond Exchange see. .......... Ski Jewelers Co., Green Brook
Green & Son, Inc., Charles E., 625 3rd St., Newark, 07107 .......... (973) 485-3630
Green & Sons, Inc., Jonathan, 48 Squankum-Yellowbrook Rd., Howell, 07731 .......... (732) 938-7007
Green Earth Press see. .......... Stuyvesant Press, Inc., Irvington
Green Enterprises, Stephan L. see. .......... Green Trailers, Inc., Stephan L., Farmingdale
Green Power Chemical see. .......... Environmental Services Group/Green Power, Hopatcong
Green Trailers, Inc., Stephan L.,
74 Squankum Yellowbrook Rd., Farmingdale, 07727 .......... (732) 938-5663
Green Tree Packing, Inc., 65 Central Ave., P.O. Box 386, Passaic, 07055 .......... (973) 473-1305
Green Village Packing Co. see. .......... Kleemeyer & Merkel, Inc., Green Village
Greenbaum Interiors, 101 Washington St., Paterson, 07505 .......... (973) 279-3000
Greenbrook Stairs, Inc., 14 Dayton St., Bernardsville, 07924 .......... (908) 221-9145
Greene Bros. Specialty Coffee Roasters, Inc.,
313 High St., Hackettstown, 07840 .......... (908) 979-0022
Greener Corp., 4 Helmly St., Bayville, 08721 .......... (732) 341-3880
Green's Fresh Fruit Salad, Inc.,
125 Shadeland Ave., P.O. Box 244, Pleasantville, 08232 .......... (609) 641-5455
Greentree Printing, 9004 Lincoln Dr. W., Ste. G, Marlton, 08053 .......... (856) 596-2330
Greenville Colorants (H Q), 20 Linden Ave. E., Jersey City, 07305 .......... (201) 595-0200
Greenwich Graphics, LLC, 234 16th St., 8th Fl., Jersey City, 07310 .......... (212) 727-1116
★ Greetingtap, LLC, 832 Spicer Ave., South Plainfield, 07080 .......... (347) 731-4263
Gregory Packaging, Inc., 247 Rome St., P.O. Box 5188, Newark, 07105 .......... (973) 465-1113
Gregory Press, Inc., 7 Mark Rd., Ste. A, Kenilworth, 07033 .......... (908) 686-0030
Gregory Signs, LLC, 1453 Springfield Ave., P.O. Box 671, Maplewood, 07040 .......... (973) 761-0165
Greif, Inc., 200 Rike Dr., Millstone Township, 08535 .......... (609) 448-5300
Greiner & Sons, Inc., L. J., 63-69 Dan Forth Ave., Paterson, 07501 .......... (973) 977-9441
Gren Machinery Co., 70 School House Rd., Somerset, 08873 .......... (732) 356-5118
Grenite Sustainability Fushions see. .......... Trinity Mfg., LLC, Metuchen
Grewe Plastics, Inc., 123 S. 15th St., Newark, 07107 .......... (973) 485-7602
† Grey Owl Indian Craft Sales Corp., 15 Meridian Rd., Ste. 5, Eatontown, 07724 .......... (732) 389-4626
Griff Decorative Films Ltd., 700 Vassar Ave., Lakewood, 08701 .......... (732) 367-2166
Griff Paper & Film see. .......... Griff Decorative Films Ltd., Lakewood
Griffin Care, LLC, 80 Manheim Ave., Bridgeton, 08302 .......... (856) 455-6870
Griffin Sign Co., Inc., 464 N. Randolph Ave., Cinnaminson, 08077 .......... (856) 786-8517
† Griffith Electric Supply Co., Inc., 4-W Chimney Rock Rd., Bridgewater, 08807 .......... (908) 203-1601
† Griffith Electric Supply Co., Inc., 5 2nd St., Trenton, 08611 .......... (609) 695-6121
Griffith Shade Co., 308 Washington Ave., Ste. 1, Nutley, 07110 .......... (973) 667-1474
Grignard Co., 505 Capobianco Plz., Rahway, 07065 .......... (732) 340-1111

Grimco Presses Co., 65 1st Ave., Paterson, 07514 .......... (973) 345-0660
Grimmer & Sons, Inc., C. W., 75 Gilbert St. W., Tinton Falls, 07701 .......... (732) 741-2189
Grinnell Concrete Pavingstones, Inc., 482 Houses Corner Rd., Sparta, 07871 .......... (973) 383-9300
Grobet File Co. Of America, LLC., 750 Washington Ave., Carlstadt, 07072 .......... (201) 939-6700
Grobet USA see. .......... Grobet File Co. Of America, LLC., Carlstadt
Groezinger Provision, Inc., 1200 7th Ave., Neptune, 07753 .......... (732) 775-3220
Group C Media, Inc., 44 Apple St., Ste. 3, Tinton Falls, 07724 .......... (732) 842-7433
Group Thermo, Inc. (H Q), 137 S. Pemberton Ave., Oceanport, 07757 .......... (908) 757-8955
Groupe SEB USA, 2121 Eden Rd., Millville, 08332 .......... (856) 825-6300
† Grove Supply, Inc., 1818 Rowland St., Cinnaminson, 08077 .......... (856) 303-2310
† Grove Supply, Inc., 3801 Park Blvd., Wildwood, 08260 .......... (609) 522-1449
Grow Co., Inc., 55 Railroad Ave., Ridgefield, 07657 .......... (201) 941-8777
Growmark FS, LLC, 60 Lehigh Ave., P.O. Box 116, Bloomsbury, 08804 .......... (908) 479-4500
† Growmark FS, LLC, 55 Silver Lake Rd., Bridgeton, 08302 .......... (856) 455-7688
Grumium Labs, 4400 U.S. 9, Ste. 1000, Freehold, 07728 .......... (732) 562-0001
Gruppo Dani see. .......... Dani Leather USA, Inc., Flanders
G&S Graphics see. .......... Squiggly Productions, LLC, Butler
GSC Imaging, LLC, 7150 N. Park Dr., Ste. 540, Pennsauken, 08109 .......... (856) 317-9301
GSS see. .......... Graphic Solutions & Signs, LLC, Hackensack
GT Millwork, LLC, 2180 Hedding Rd., Columbus, 08022 .......... (609) 291-9222
GTBM, 351 Paterson Ave., East Rutherford, 07073 .......... (201) 935-5090
GTM Signs, Inc., 1298 Hurffville Rd., Deptford, 08096 .......... (856) 227-2333
† GTS-Welco, 425 Avenue P, Newark, 07105 .......... (973) 589-7895
GTS-Welco see. .......... Praxair, Linden
G-U Tek, Inc., 266 King George Rd., Ste. B-2, Warren, 07059 .......... (908) 626-0012
Guardian Drug Co., Inc., 2 Charles Ct., Dayton, 08810 .......... (609) 860-2600
Guardian Fence Co., Inc., 180 Wright St., P.O. Box 2009, Newark, 07114 .......... (973) 824-1850
Guardrite Steel Door Corp., 81 Springdale Ave., Newark, 07107 .......... (973) 481-4424
GuardTrax, LLC, 11 Commerce Dr., Lobby, Cranford, 07016 .......... (908) 272-0114
Guerard Co., J. D., 43 Old Washington Crossing Rd., Titusville, 08560 .......... (609) 737-8892
Guernsey Crest Ice Cream Co., 134 19th Ave., Paterson, 07513 .......... (973) 742-4620
Guest Packaging see. .......... Guest Packaging, LLC, Rahway
Guest Packaging, LLC, 414 E. Inman Ave., Rahway, 07065 .......... (732) 382-7270
Guida Setting Co., 124 E. Main St., Denville, 07834 .......... (973) 625-1225
Guide Publications see. .......... Jersey Job Guide, Inc., Long Branch
Gujarat Samachar, 3 State Route 27, Ste. 307, Edison, 08820 .......... (732) 452-1755
Gulbrandsen Technologies, Inc., 1 Riverside Way, Phillipsburg, 08865 .......... (908) 238-2030
Gulbrandsen Technologies, Inc. (H Q),
2 Main St., P.O. Box 5523, Clinton, 08809 .......... (908) 735-5458
Gulton, Inc., 116 Corporate Blvd., Ste. A, South Plainfield, 07080 .......... (908) 791-4622
GumRunners, LLC, 333 Washington St., P.O. Box 392, Jersey City, 07303 .......... (201) 678-9300
Gusmer Enterprises, Inc. (H Q), 1165 Globe Ave., Mountainside, 07092 .......... (908) 301-1811
Guttenplan's Frozen Dough Specialists, Inc.,
100 Highway 36, Middletown, 07748 .......... (732) 495-9480
GV Floors, 701 Penhorn Ave., Ste. 6, Secaucus, 07094 .......... (201) 558-7889
G-Way Microwave, 38 Leuning St., South Hackensack, 07606 .......... (201) 343-6388
H & B Petroleum Co., Inc., 1 Wynding Way, Rockaway, 07866 .......... (973) 664-0144
† H & C Metals, Inc., 91 Malvern St., P.O. Box 5150, Newark, 07105 .......... (973) 589-7778
H & H Industrial Corp., 7612 N. Crescent Blvd., Pennsauken, 08110 .......... (856) 663-4444
H & H Sheet Metal & Machining, 30 White Lake Rd., Sparta, 07871 .......... (973) 383-6880
H & H Swiss Screw Machine Products Co., Inc.,
1478 Chestnut Ave., Hillside, 07205 .......... (908) 688-6390
H & R Welding, LLC, 307 Drum Point Rd., Brick, 08723 .......... (732) 920-4881
H & S Graphics, 196 Garibaldi Ave., Ste. 3, Lodi, 07644 .......... (973) 779-5880
H & S Stone, Inc., 705 Cross St., Lakewood, 08701 .......... (732) 364-2265
H & U, Inc., 375 North St., Ste. O, Teterboro, 07608 .......... (201) 530-1100
H & W Tool Co., Inc., 22 Lee Ave., Dover, 07801 .......... (973) 366-0131
H A Z Laboratories, 39 Hartmans Corner Rd., Washington, 07882 .......... (908) 453-3300
H. Cross Co., 150 W. Commercial Ave., Moonachie, 07074 .......... (201) 964-9380
H E D International, Inc., 449 Route 31, P.O. Box 246, Ringoes, 08551 .......... (609) 466-1900
H E K Machine, Inc., 785 State St., Ste. 2, Perth Amboy, 08861 .......... (732) 442-8672
H. G. Schaevitz LLC, 102 Commerce Dr., Ste. 8, Moorestown, 08057 .......... (856) 727-0250
H I D Systems, Inc., 27 Brookfield Dr., Sparta, 07871 .......... (973) 383-8535
H M S Monaco, Inc., 629 Grove St., 5th Fl., Jersey City, 07310 .......... (201) 533-0007
H P Performance, Inc., 8 Industrial Pkwy., Ringwood, 07456 .......... (973) 962-0800
H T Stamping, 19 Gardner Rd., Ste. C, Fairfield, 07004 .......... (973) 227-4858
Haas Laser Technologies, Inc., 37 Ironia Rd., Flanders, 07836 .......... (973) 598-1150
Hackensack Steel Corp., 645 Industrial Rd., Carlstadt, 07072 .......... (201) 935-0090
Hackettstown Sheet Metal, Inc., 1 Stiger St., Hackettstown, 07840 .......... (908) 852-3752
Haddon Fence Co., Inc., 1460 Route 38, Hainesport, 08036 .......... (609) 261-1286
† Haddon House Food Products, Inc., 433 Oak Glen Rd., Howell, 07731 .......... (732) 367-7901
† Haddon House Food Products, Inc. (H Q), 250 Old Marlton Pike, Medford, 08055 .......... (609) 654-7901
† Haddonstone (USA) Ltd., 201 Heller Pl., Bellmawr, 08031 .......... (856) 931-7011
Haenssler Sheet Metal Works, Inc., 592 Hawthorne Ave., Newark, 07112 .......... (973) 373-6360
Hafco Foundry, Inc., 301 Greenwood Ave., Front, Midland Park, 07432 .......... (201) 447-0433
Hagelin Flavor Technologies, 200 Meister Ave., Branchburg, 08876 .......... (908) 707-4400
★ Hague Academic Press Ltd., 75 Lohs Pl., Harrington Park, 07640 .......... (201) 750-9091
Hahn's Woodworking Co., Inc., 181 Meister Ave., Somerville, 08876 .......... (908) 722-2742
Haier America Trading, LLC (H Q), 1800 Valley Rd., Wayne, 07470 .......... (973) 617-1800
Hain Celestial Group, Inc., The, 50 Knickerbocker Rd., Moonachie, 07074 .......... (201) 935-4500
Haines & Kibblehouse, Inc. see. .......... Warren Materials, Stewartsville
Hainesport Tool & Maintenance, 1924 Ark Rd., Hainesport, 08036 .......... (609) 261-0016
Hair Systems, Inc., 30 Park Ave., P.O. Box 449, Englishtown, 07726 .......... (732) 446-2202
Hajoca Corp. see. .......... Weinstein Supply Co., Egg Harbor Township
Hajoca Corp. see. .......... Weinstein Supply Co., Vineland
Hajoca Corp. see. .......... Weinstein Supply Corp., Camden
Halberd Match Corp., 1230 Parkway Ave., Ste. 306, Trenton, 08628 .......... (609) 882-7000
Haledon Auto Parts, 269 Haledon Ave., Haledon, 07508 .......... (973) 595-8200
Halkias Gear & Machine Works, 14 Willow St., Bloomfield, 07003 .......... (973) 748-4901
Hall Co. Abrasives, William R., 901 E. Gibbsboro Rd., Lindenwold, 08021 .......... (856) 784-6700
Hall Mfg. Corp., 297 Margaret King Ave., Ringwood, 07456 .......... (973) 962-6022
Halma Holdings, Inc. see. .......... Bio-Chem Fluidics, Inc., Boonton
Halma Holdings, Inc. see. .......... Fiberguide Industries, Inc., Stirling
Halma Holdings, Inc. see. .......... Perma Pure, LLC, Toms River
Halo Farm, Inc., 970 Spruce St., Lawrenceville, 08648 .......... (609) 695-3311
Hal-O Mfg. Co., 137 Meeker Ave., Newark, 07114 .......... (973) 824-6122
Halo Pharmaceutical, Inc., 30 N. Jefferson Rd., Whippany, 07981 .......... (973) 428-4000
Halo Sheet Metal, Inc., 140 Lehigh Ave., Lakewood, 08701 .......... (732) 901-0080
Halocarbon Products Corp. (H Q),
887 Kinderkamack Rd., 2nd Fl., River Edge, 07661 .......... (201) 262-8899
Halsted Corp., 78 Halladay St., Jersey City, 07304 .......... (201) 433-3323
Hamburg Stone Quarry see. .......... Eastern Concrete Materials, Inc., Hamburg

© Copyright 2015 Manufacturers' News, Inc.


Hamelin Products, Inc.,
1616 Highway 77, P.O. Box 153, Deerfield Street, 08313 .......... (856) 451-2935
Hamilltime Enterprises, Inc., 1761 U.S. Highway 9, Howell, 07731 .......... (732) 303-5998
Hamilton Bell Co., Inc., 30 Craig Rd., Montvale, 07645 .......... (201) 391-4100
Hamilton Buhl, 80 Little Falls Rd., Fairfield, 07004 .......... (201) 229-9800
Hamilton Embroidery, Inc., 907-909 21st St., Union City, 07087 .......... (201) 867-4084
Hamilton Transit Corporate Center, 572 Whitehead Rd., Trenton, 08619 .......... (609) 587-1188
Hammer Mfg. Co., Inc., 417 Commerce Rd., P.O. Box 1340, Linden, 07036 .......... (908) 862-1730
★ Hammer Too, LLC, 2576-B U.S. Highway 22 E., Union, 07083 .......... (908) 688-5601
Hammonton Gazette, Inc., 233 Bellevue Ave., P.O. Box 1228, Hammonton, 08037 .......... (609) 704-1939
Hammonton Mold Co., Inc., 4171 S. Black Horse Pike, Williamstown, 08094 .......... (856) 728-9112
Hammonton News & Atlantic County Newspaper Group,
115 12th St., Hammonton, 08037 .......... (609) 561-2300
Hamon Corp., 58 E. Main St., P.O. Box 1500, Somerville, 08876 .......... (908) 685-4000
Hampton Forge, Ltd., 442 State Route 35, Eatontown, 07724 .......... (732) 389-5507
Handi-Hut, Inc., 3 Grunwald St., Clifton, 07013 .......... (973) 614-1800
Handler Mfg. Co., Inc., 612 North Ave. E., Westfield, 07090 .......... (908) 233-7796
Handmade Furniture Co., 612 Main St., West Creek, 08092 .......... (609) 597-2708
Handy & Harman Ltd. see. .......... Microtube Fabricators, Inc., Middlesex
Handy Store Fixtures, Inc., 337 Sherman Ave., Newark, 07114 .......... (973) 242-1600
Handyguide, Inc., 721 Village Rd., P.O. Box 205, Oradell, 07649 .......... (201) 262-9478
Hanesbrands, Inc. see. .......... Maidenform Brands, Inc., Iselin
Hanger Clinic, 210 New Rd., Ste. 7, Linwood, 08221 .......... (609) 653-8323
Hanger, Inc. see. .......... Hanger Clinic, Linwood
Hanger, Inc. see. .......... Hanger Prosthetics & Orthotics, Voorhees
Hanger, Inc. see. .......... Hanger Prosthetics & Orthotics, Inc., Edison
Hanger, Inc. see. .......... Hanger Prosthetics & Orthotics, Inc., Farmingdale
Hanger, Inc. see. .......... Hanger Prosthetics & Orthotics, Inc., West Orange
† Hanger Prosthetics & Orthotics, 201 White Horse Rd. E., Voorhees, 08043 .......... (856) 309-0709
Hanger Prosthetics & Orthotics, Inc., 265 Fernwood Ave., Edison, 08837 .......... (732) 417-0480
Hanger Prosthetics & Orthotics, Inc., 5100 Belmore Blvd., Farmingdale, 07727 .......... (732) 919-7774
Hanger Prosthetics & Orthotics, Inc.,
59 Main St., Ste. 111, West Orange, 07052 .......... (973) 736-0628
Hangsterfer's Laboratories, Inc., 175 Ogden Rd., Mantua, 08051 .......... (856) 468-0216
Hankin Environmental Systems, Inc.,
1 Harvard Way, Ste. 6, P.O. Box 5759, Hillsborough, 08844 .......... (908) 722-9595
Hank's Signs, 793 Jersey Pl., Paramus, 07652 .......... (201) 652-5979
† Hannecke Display Systems, Inc., 91 Fulton St., Unit 4, Boonton, 07005 .......... (973) 335-0434
Hanover Direct, Inc. (H Q), 1500 Harbor Blvd., 1st Fl., Weehawken, 07086 .......... (201) 863-7300
Hanover Foods Corp. see. .......... Aunt Kitty's Foods, Inc., Vineland
Hanovia Specialty Lighting LLC, 6 Evans St., Fairfield, 07004 .......... (973) 651-5510
Hansen Awning Co., 18 Church Rd., Rio Grande, 08242 .......... (609) 886-1685
Hansen Co., Inc., Joseph C., 629 Grove St., Ste. 26, Jersey City, 07310 .......... (201) 222-1677
Hansen Machine & Tool Co., Inc., 27 Walnut Ave., Clark, 07066 .......... (732) 340-0466
Hansen's Cabinet Shop, Inc., 42 Park Ave., Madison, 07940 .......... (973) 377-2444
Hansome Energy Systems, Inc., 365 Dalziel Rd., Linden, 07036 .......... (908) 862-9044
Hanson Aggregate BMC, 1101 Railroad Ave., Newport, 08345 .......... (856) 447-4294
† Hanson Aggregates Better Materials Corp., 1401 Route 610, Woodbine, 08270 .......... (856) 447-4294
Hanson Aggregates, BMC Div., 368 New Brooklyn Rd., P.O. Box 37, Berlin, 08009 .......... (856) 767-3100
Hanson Aggregates North America, 311 Unexpected Rd., Buena, 08310 .......... (856) 697-1616
Hanssem Corp., 155 Helen St., South Plainfield, 07080 .......... (908) 754-4949
Hap Engraving Ltd., 106 Windsor Way, Berkeley Heights, 07922 .......... (201) 223-4800
★ Happle Printing Partnership, Inc.,
81 Cape May Ave., P.O. Box 36, Dorothy, 08317 .......... (609) 476-2929
Happy Chef Uniforms, Inc., 22 Park Pl., Butler, 07405 .......... (973) 492-2525
Harbor Linen, LLC see. .......... Superior Drapery Co. & Harbor Linen Co, Gibbsboro
Harbor Linen, LLC (H Q), 2 Foster Ave., Gibbsboro, 08026 .......... (856) 435-2000
Harbro Church Arts, Inc., 231 Herbert Ave., P.O. Box 776, Closter, 07624 .......... (201) 768-5500
Hard Rock Marble & Granite, Inc., 1101 Chestnut St., Roselle, 07203 .......... (908) 620-9150
Harland America, 1803 Underwood Blvd., Delran, 08075 .......... (856) 764-9622
Harley Tool & Machine, Inc., 24 McDermott Pl., Bergenfield, 07621 .......... (201) 244-8899
HarMac Rebar & Steel Corp., 301 Hartle St., Sayreville, 08872 .......... (732) 651-7822
Harmony Printing, 504 Aldrich Rd., Ste. 22, Howell, 07731 .......... (732) 987-9040
Harmony Sand & Gravel, Inc., 3189 Belvidere Rd., Phillipsburg, 08865 .......... (908) 475-4690
Harout Tool & Machine Corp., 9-11 Dyatt Pl., Hackensack, 07601 .......... (201) 646-0664
Harrington Parker see. .......... Agresti Construction Co., Inc., East Orange
Harris Freeman & Co., Inc. see. .......... Harris Tea Co., Moorestown
Harris Kenya Gem Co., Tom, 6504 Ventnor Ave., Ventnor City, 08406 .......... (609) 823-3315
Harris Miniature Golf Courses, Inc., 141 W. Burk Ave., Wildwood, 08260 .......... (609) 522-4200
Harris Structural Steel Co., Inc.,
1640 New Market Ave., South Plainfield, 07080 .......... (732) 752-6070
Harris Tea Co., 344 New Albany Rd., Moorestown, 08057 .......... (856) 793-0290
Harrison Electro Mechanical Corp., 1607 Coach St., Rahway, 07065 .......... (732) 382-6008
† Harrison Equipment Corp., 500 Essex St., Harrison, 07029 .......... (973) 485-1448
Harrison Hose & Tubing, Inc., 2705 Kuser Rd., Trenton, 08691 .......... (609) 631-8804
Harrison Machine & Tool, Inc., 21 Lexington Ave., Trenton, 08618 .......... (609) 883-0800
Harrison Scott Publications, Inc.,
5 Marine View Plz., Ste. 400, Hoboken, 07030 .......... (201) 659-1700
Harrison Seal Corp., 1201 Kennedy Blvd., Manville, 08835 .......... (908) 722-3322
Harry Shaw Model Maker Inc., 401 Stokes Rd., Shamong, 08088 .......... (609) 268-0647
Harsco Corp., 1800 Lower Rd., Linden, 07036 .......... (732) 396-1269
Harsco Infrastructure see. .......... Harsco Corp., Linden
† Hart Industries, Inc., 135 Crown Rd., Thorofare, 08086 .......... (856) 686-1455
Hartin Paint & Filler Corp., 14th & Broad Sts., Carlstadt, 07072 .......... (201) 438-3300
Har-Tru Sports, 1715 Oak St., Ste. 1, Lakewood, 08701 .......... (434) 295-6167
Har-Tru Sports Corp. see. .......... Har-Tru Sports, Lakewood
Hartz Mountain Corp., The, 400 Plaza Dr., Secaucus, 07094 .......... (201) 271-4800
Harvard Printing see. .......... Gator Communication Group, Fairfield
† Harvey Industries, Inc., Sid, 159 E. 1st Ave., Roselle, 07203 .......... (908) 245-8688
† Harvey Industries, Inc., Sid, 1684 5th St., Trenton, 08638 .......... (609) 882-1766
Harvey Westbury Corp. (H Q), 160 Littleton Rd., Ste. 308, Parsippany, 07054 .......... (201) 468-7779
Harwill Corp., 3175 Princeton Pike, Lawrenceville, 08648 .......... (609) 895-1955
Harwill Express Press see. .......... Harwill Corp., Lawrenceville
Hary Mfg., Inc., 24 Cokesbury Rd., Lebanon, 08833 .......... (908) 722-7100
Hasbrouck Heights Publication Co. see. .......... Observer, Hasbrouck Heights
Hathaway Plastics, Inc., 911 Springfield Rd., Union, 07083 .......... (908) 688-9494
Hatteras, Inc., 56 Park Rd., Tinton Falls, 07724 .......... (732) 223-9888
Hausmann Industries, Inc., 130 Union St., Northvale, 07647 .......... (201) 767-0255
Haward Corporation, 29 Porete Ave., North Arlington, 07031 .......... (201) 991-8777
Hawk Graphics, Inc., 1248 Sussex Tpke., Ste. C-9, Randolph, 07869 .......... (973) 895-5569
Hawk Haven Vineyard & Winery, LLC, 600 S. Railroad Ave., Rio Grande, 08242 .......... (609) 846-7347
Hawk Precision, Inc., 849 Hawks Bridge Rd., Salem, 08079 .......... (856) 299-2800
★ Hawk Technologies, Inc.,
3710 U.S. Highway 9 S., P.O. Box 6685, Freehold, 07728 .......... (732) 577-8581
Hawthorne Paint Co., Inc., 66 5th Ave., Hawthorne, 07506 .......... (973) 423-2335
Hawthorne Press, 463 Lafayette Ave., P.O. Box 1, Hawthorne, 07507 .......... (973) 427-3330
Hawthorne Rubber Mfg. Corp., 35 4th Ave., P.O. Box 171, Hawthorne, 07507 .......... (973) 427-3337
Haydon Corp., 415 Hamberg Tpke., Bldg. D, Wayne, 07470 .......... (973) 904-0800
Hayes Mindish, Inc., 1401 N. Main St., Pleasantville, 08232 .......... (609) 641-9880
† Hayes Pump, Inc., 295 Fairfield Ave., Fairfield, 07004 .......... (973) 808-0606
HAYNES Corp., 6 Carman Ln., P.O. Box 467, Whitehouse, 08888 .......... (908) 439-4600
Hays Sheet Metal, Inc., 7070 Kaighns Ave., Bldg. B, Pennsauken, 08109 .......... (856) 662-7722
Hayward Industries, Inc., 620 Division St., Elizabeth, 07201 .......... (908) 351-5400
† HBC Home & Hardware, 324-A Half Acre Rd., Cranbury, 08512 .......... (609) 860-9990
HBC Home & Hardware Products see. .......... HBC Home & Hardware, Cranbury
HC Graphics Screen Printing, Inc., 238 Lindbergh Pl., Ste. 3, Paterson, 07503 .......... (973) 247-0544
HD MicroSystems, 250 Cheesequake Rd., Parlin, 08859 .......... (732) 613-2500
† HD Supply Water Works, Inc., 228 Williamstown Rd., Berlin, 08009 .......... (856) 753-5566
HD Supply Waterworks, Inc. see. .......... HD Supply Water Works, Inc., Berlin
HE Designs & Awnings, 75 Rutgers St., Belleville, 07109 .......... (973) 751-0030
Head Masters, Inc., 263 Route 46 W., Saddle Brook, 07663 .......... (201) 843-6666
Heads Up Industries, 132 Van Liew Ave., Ste. 4, Milltown, 08850 .......... (732) 846-3388
Headwear Creations, Inc., 200 Wright St., Newark, 07114 .......... (973) 622-1144
★ Health & Natural Beauty USA, 140-W Ethel Rd. W., Piscataway, 08854 .......... (848) 202-9089
Health Care Software, Inc., 1350 Campus Pkwy., Neptune, 07753 .......... (732) 938-5600
Health Monitor Network see. .......... Data Centrum Communications, Inc., Montvale
Health Resources Publishing LLC, P.O. Box 456, Allenwood, 08720 .......... (732) 292-1100
Healthcare Marketers Exchange, 104 Park Ave., Verona, 07044 .......... (973) 744-9505
HealthTools, LLC (H Q), 681 Lawlins Rd., Unit 70, Wyckoff, 07481 .......... (201) 465-4381
HealthTronics, Inc., 354 Eisenhower Pkwy., Ste. 2150, Livingston, 07039 .......... (973) 994-3220
Healthy Food Brands, LLC, 122 Quentin Ave., New Brunswick, 08901 .......... (212) 444-9909
Hearthside Food Solutions, LLC see. .......... Quality Bakery Products Of New Jersey, Inc., Willingboro
Heartland Payment Systems, Inc. (H Q),
90 Nassau St., 2nd Fl., Princeton, 08542 .......... (609) 683-3831
† Heath Lumber Co., 1580 N. Olden Avenue Ext., Ewing, 08638 .......... (609) 392-1166
Heat-Timer Corp., 20 New Dutch Ln., Fairfield, 07004 .......... (973) 575-4004
Hedaya Bros. see. .......... Hedaya Home Fashions, Inc., Elizabeth
Hedaya Home Fashions, Inc., 1111 Jefferson Ave., Elizabeth, 07201 .......... (908) 352-0808
† Heerema Co., 200 6th Ave., Hawthorne, 07506 .......... (973) 423-0505
Heights USA, Inc., 1445 Lower Ferry Rd., Ewing, 08618 .......... (609) 530-1300
Heilind Electronics, Inc. see. .......... Interstate Connecting Components, Inc., Lumberton
Heinkel Filtering Systems, Inc., 520 Sharptown Rd., Swedesboro, 08085 .......... (856) 467-3399
Heisler Industries, Inc., 224 Passaic Ave., Fairfield, 07004 .......... (973) 227-6300
★ Helidex, LLC (H Q), 186 Paterson Ave., Ste. 303, East Rutherford, 07073 .......... (201) 636-2546
Heller Co., E. P., 21-25 Samson Ave., P.O. Box 26, Madison, 07940 .......... (973) 377-2878
Heller Industries, Inc., 4 Vreeland Rd., Ste. 1, Florham Park, 07932 .......... (973) 377-6800
Heller Truck Body Corp., 138 U.S. Highway 22, Hillside, 07205 .......... (973) 923-9200
Helm Dental, Inc., 111 Troast St., Hackensack, 07601 .......... (201) 342-2915
Helricks Picture Framing, Inc., 158 W. Clinton St., Ste. G, Dover, 07801 .......... (973) 361-1301
Hematechnologies, Inc., 291 U.S. Highway 22, Ste. 12, Lebanon, 08833 .......... (908) 823-9430
Hemispherx Biopharma, Inc., 783 Jersey Ave., New Brunswick, 08901 .......... (732) 249-3250
Henderson Aquatic, Inc., 1 White Hall, Millville, 08332 .......... (856) 825-4771
★ Hengstenberg GmbH, 90 Pershing Pl., Cresskill, 07626 .......... (201) 568-6596
Henrich, Inc., Harold R., 300 Syracuse Ct., Lakewood, 08701 .......... (732) 370-4455
Henriques Yachts, Inc., 198 Hilton Ave., Bayville, 08721 .......... (732) 269-1180
Henry Corp., E. P., 201 Park Ave., P.O. Box 615, Woodbury, 08096 .......... (856) 845-6200
Henry Machine Shop, Inc., 345 Market St., Kenilworth, 07033 .......... (908) 925-2218
Henry Repeating Arms Company, 59 E. 1st St., Bayonne, 07002 .......... (201) 858-4400
Henry Schein, Inc. see. .......... Sullivan Dental Products, Inc., Montville
Henschel-Steinau, Inc., 50 Commerce Dr., Allendale, 07401 .......... (201) 760-4100
Heraeus, Inc. see. .......... Heraeus Precious Metals North America, LLC, Newark
Heraeus Precious Metals North America, LLC, 65 Euclid Ave., Newark, 07105 .......... (973) 817-7878
† Heraeus Sensor Technology USA, 1901 U.S. Highway 130, North Brunswick, 08902 .......... (732) 940-4400
HerbaKraft, Inc., 121 Ethel Rd. W., Ste. 6, Piscataway, 08854 .......... (732) 463-1000
Herbalist & Alchemist, Inc., 51 S. Wandling Ave., Washington, 07882 .......... (908) 689-9020
Hercules Enterprises, LLC, 321 Valley Rd., Hillsborough, 08844 .......... (908) 369-0000
Hercules Welding & Machine Co., 616 5th St., Palmyra, 08065 .......... (856) 829-1820
Hercules World Industries see. .......... Atlantic Rubber Enterprises, Newfoundland
Heritage Bag Co. see. .......... Heritage Bag Co., Inc., Swedesboro
Heritage Bag Co., Inc., 2321 High Hill Rd., Swedesboro, 08085 .......... (856) 467-2247
Heritage, Inc., 4 Wilsey Sq., Ste. 9, Ridgewood, 07450 .......... (201) 447-2600
Heritage Pharmaceuticals, Inc. (H Q),
12 Christopher, Ste. 300, Eatontown, 07724 .......... (732) 429-1000
★ Heritage Publishing, LLC, 620 High Bridge Rd., Colts Neck, 07722 .......... (732) 747-7770
† Heritage Surf & Sport, Inc., 3700 Landis Ave., Sea Isle City, 08243 .......... (609) 263-3033
Heritage Towers, Inc., 910 Shunpike Rd., Ste. B, Cape May, 08204 .......... (609) 884-5999
Heritage Vineyards of Richwood, LLC,
480 Mullica Hill Rd., Mullica Hill, 08062 .......... (856) 589-4474
Hermitage Press, Inc., 1595 5th St., Ewing, 08638 .......... (609) 882-3600
Heroflon USA Corp., Home State Road 249, Hillsborough, 08844 .......... (908) 829-4949
Hero's Salute Awards Co., 1875 State Route 23, Wayne, 07470 .......... (973) 696-5085
Herring Co., Inc., D. C., 1750 Brielle Ave., Ste. B-2, Ocean, 07712 .......... (732) 695-2272
Hess Corp., 2800 U.S. Highway 1, North Brunswick, 08902 .......... (732) 940-3705
† Hess Corp., 123 Derousse Ave., Pennsauken, 08110 .......... (856) 663-5111
Hess Corp., 1 Hess Plz., Woodbridge, 07095 .......... (732) 750-6000
Hess Glass Products, 601 N. Orchard Rd., Vineland, 08360 .......... (856) 691-1432
Hessburg, Inc., Michale A., 180 Autumn St., Passaic, 07055 .......... (973) 777-8700
Hester Bros., Inc., 114 Beach St., Ste. 5, Rockaway, 07866 .......... (862) 432-5183
Hexacon Electric Co., 161 W. Clay Ave., Roselle Park, 07204 .......... (908) 245-6200
Heyco Products, Inc., 1800 Industrial Way N., Toms River, 08755 .......... (732) 286-4336
Hi Class Living Magazine, 120 Sylvan Ave., Ste. 209, Englewood Cliffs, 07632 .......... (201) 363-0200
Hi Land Printers, 121 S. Main St., Pleasantville, 08232 .......... (609) 646-6319
Hibbert Group, 400 Pennington Ave., Trenton, 08638 .......... (609) 394-7500
Hibrett Puratex, 7001 Westfield Ave., Pennsauken, 08110 .......... (856) 662-1717
Hickok Matthews Co., 337 Main Rd., Montville, 07045 .......... (973) 335-3400
Hickory Industries, Inc., 4900 W. Side Ave., North Bergen, 07047 .......... (201) 223-0050
HID Ultraviolet see. .......... H I D Systems, Inc., Sparta
Hiemer & Co., Edward W., 141 Wabash Ave., Clifton, 07011 .......... (973) 772-5081
† High Bridge Stone Co., Inc., 187 Marsh St., Newark, 07114 .......... (973) 344-5522
† High Grade Beverage, 891 Georges Rd., Monmouth Junction, 08852 .......... (732) 821-7600
† High Grade Beverage, 86 Canfield Ave., Randolph, 07869 .......... (973) 927-1400
High Point Brewing Co., Inc., 22 Park Pl., Butler, 07405 .......... (973) 838-7400
High Point Precision Products, 1 1st St., Sussex, 07461 .......... (973) 875-6229

ALPHABETICAL

★ **Indicates new listing this edition.** † **Indicates wholesaler/distributor.**

High Precision Machine Shop, LLC,
1275 Bloomfield Ave., Ste. 63, Fairfield, 07004 .......... (973) 227-5110
High Speed Video, 19 Spear Rd., Ste. 104, Ramsey, 07446.......... (201) 327-6801
High Standard Construction see..........Fazzio & Sons, Inc., Frank J., Pitman
High Technology Corp., 144 South St., Hackensack, 07601.......... (201) 488-0010
Highland Metal Products, Inc., 153 E. Highland Pkwy., Roselle, 07203.......... (908) 245-4848
★ HighRoad Press, 220 Anderson Ave., Moonachie, 07074.......... (201) 708-6900
Highway Body Works, Inc., 8600 Tonnelle Ave., North Bergen, 07047.......... (201) 869-0900
Hi-Grade Products Mfg. Co.,
752 Jefferson Ave., P.O. Box 273, Kenilworth, 07033.......... (908) 245-4133
Hilin Life Products, Inc., 211 Warren St., Ste. 211, Newark, 07103.......... (973) 648-0265
Hill Cross Co., Inc., 543 56th St., P.O. Box 60, West New York, 07093.......... (201) 864-3393
Hill Machine, Inc., 295 Governor St., Paterson, 07501.......... (973) 684-2808
Hillenbrand, Inc. see..........Coperion Corp., Ramsey
Hillenbrand, Inc. see..........Coperion K-Tron Pitman, Inc., Sewell
Hillman Graphic Products, P.O. Box 5233, Somerset, 08875.......... (201) 487-6900
Hillside Bottling Corp., 1 Evans Terminal, Hillside, 07205.......... (908) 353-6773
Hillside Candy Co., 35 Hillside Ave., Hillside, 07205.......... (973) 926-2300
† Hillside Paper Products, Inc., 20 Butler St., Elizabeth, 07206.......... (908) 352-3300
Hillside Plastics Corp., 125 Long Ave., P.O. Box 609, Hillside, 07205.......... (800) 837-7731
Hillside Spinning & Stamping Co., Inc., 1060 Commerce Ave., Union, 07083.......... (908) 964-3080
Hillside Wire Cloth, Inc., 109 Roosevelt Ave., Belleville, 07109.......... (973) 751-3131
Hilltop Honey, LLC, 15 Hill St., North Caldwell, 07006.......... (201) 953-0198
Hilman, Incorporated see..........Hilman Rollers, Marlboro
Hilman Rollers, 12 Timber Ln., P.O. Box 45, Marlboro, 07746.......... (732) 462-6277
Hinchman & Son, Inc., Herbert J., 26 Pike Dr., Wayne, 07470.......... (973) 942-2063
Hinck's Turkey Farm, Inc., 3930 Belmar Blvd., Neptune, 07753.......... (732) 681-0508
Hi-Per Tech Brake Products, Inc.,
100 Delsea Dr., P.O. Box 770, Glassboro, 08028.......... (856) 881-0900
Hippographics, Inc. see..........CRW Graphics, Inc., Pennsauken
Hippographics, Inc. (H Q), 9100 Pennsauken Hwy., Pennsauken, 08110.......... (856) 662-9111
† Hisco, Inc., 55 Veronica Ave., Somerset, 08873.......... (732) 745-2828
Hishi Plastics U. S. A., Inc., 600-F Ryerson Rd., Lincoln Park, 07035.......... (973) 633-1230
Hispano Publishing, LLC, 437 Linden Ave., Elizabeth, 07208.......... (908) 351-9390
Hitachi America Ltd. see..........
..........Mitsubishi Hitachi Power Systems America - Energy & Environment, Basking Ridge
Hitachi Chemical see..........HD MicroSystems, Parlin
Hitran Corp., 362 Highway 31, Flemington, 08822.......... (908) 782-5525
HK Metal Craft Mfg. Corp., 35 Industrial Rd., Lodi, 07644.......... (973) 471-7770
† HKK Chain Corp. Of America, 9 Riverside Dr., P.O. Box 604, Pine Brook, 07058.......... (973) 575-7860
HMG Sales Corp. see..........American Hanger & Fixture Corp., Union
Hobby Blade Specialty, Inc., 725 Jerusalem Rd., Scotch Plains, 07076.......... (908) 317-9306
Hobby Publications, Inc., 83 South St., Unit 307, Freehold, 07728.......... (732) 536-5160
Hoboken Hearth Products, LLC, 46 Bi-State Plz., Westwood, 07675.......... (551) 206-3350
Hockmeyer Equipment Corp., 610 Supor Blvd., Ste. 1, Harrison, 07029.......... (973) 482-0225
Hoeganaes Corp. (H Q), 1001 Taylors Ln., Cinnaminson, 08077.......... (856) 829-2220
Hofer Machine & Tool Co., Inc., 126 Linda Vista Ave., North Haledon, 07508.......... (973) 427-1195
Hoffman Equipment & Rentals see..........Hoffman Equipment, Inc., Piscataway
† Hoffman Equipment, Inc., 300 S. Randolphville Rd., Piscataway, 08854.......... (732) 752-3600
† Hoffman Equipment, Inc., 2610 S. Black Horse Pike, Williamstown, 08094.......... (856) 875-0036
Hoffman Extrusions, Inc.,
103 1/2 Mount Tabor Way, P.O. Box 397, Ocean Grove, 07756.......... (732) 774-2728
Hoffman Precision Plastics, Inc.,
548 Almonesson Rd., P.O. Box 338, Blackwood, 08012.......... (856) 228-3550
Hoffman/New Yorker, Inc. (H Q), 46 Clinton Pl., Hackensack, 07601.......... (201) 488-1800
Hofmann Tool & Die Corp., 356 Route 17 N., Upper Saddle River, 07458.......... (201) 327-0226
Ho-Ho-Kus, Inc., 189-201 Lyon St., Paterson, 07524.......... (973) 278-2274
Holby Valve, Inc., 24 Ferdon St., Newark, 07105.......... (973) 465-7400
Holcim (US), Inc. see..........Holcim U.S., Camden
Holcim U.S., 595 Morgan Blvd., Camden, 08104.......... (856) 964-2555
Holding Sign Design, E. R., 2 N. Black Horse Pike, Blackwood, 08012.......... (856) 227-1570
Holland Manufacturing Company, Inc.,
15 Main St., P.O. Box 404, Succasunna, 07876.......... (973) 584-8141
Holler Metal Fabricators, Inc., 215 Liberty St., Metuchen, 08840.......... (732) 635-9050
Hollie Studios, 200-C Valentine, P.O. Box 530, Hackettstown, 07840.......... (908) 852-7263
Holman Enterprises, Inc. see..........Automotive Rentals, Inc., Mount Laurel
Holman Enterprises, Inc. (H Q), 244 E. Kings Hwy., Maple Shade, 08052.......... (856) 663-5200
Holographic Finishing, Inc.,
501 Hendricks Cswy., P.O. Box 597, Ridgefield, 07657.......... (201) 941-4651
Holtec International (H Q), 555 Lincoln Dr. W., Ste. 1, Marlton, 08053.......... (856) 797-0900
Holzer & Assocs., LLC, Philip, 350 Michelle Pl., Carlstadt, 07072.......... (212) 691-9500
Homasote Co., 932 Lower Ferry Rd., P.O. Box 7240, Trenton, 08628.......... (609) 883-3300
† Home Essentials, Inc., 1 Terminal Way, Avenel, 07001.......... (732) 388-4008
Home News Tribune, 92 E. Main St., Somerville, 08876.......... (908) 722-8800
Home Rubber Co., 31 Wolverton Ave., Trenton, 08611.......... (609) 394-1176
Homes & Estates Magazines, 173 Morris St., Morristown, 07960.......... (973) 605-1877
Homestead Fence Contractors, LLC, 637 Main St., West Creek, 08092.......... (609) 296-1829
Homiek Sheet Metal Fabrication & HVAC Supplies, Inc.,
1352 Route 9, Lakewood, 08701.......... (732) 364-7644
Hone-A-Matic Tool & Cutter Co., 187 Wescott Dr., Rahway, 07065.......... (732) 382-6000
Honeyware, Inc., 244 Dukes St., Kearny, 07032.......... (201) 997-5900
Honeywell Aerospace see..........EMS Aviation, Moorestown
Honeywell HBS, 534 Fellowship Rd., Mount Laurel, 08054.......... (856) 437-1832
Honeywell International, Inc. see..........Honeywell HBS, Mount Laurel
Honeywell International, Inc. (H Q), 101 Columbia Rd., Morristown, 07962.......... (973) 455-2000
Honour Of Your Presence, 19 State Route 10 E., Ste. 14, Succasunna, 07876.......... (973) 927-6262
Hood Finishing Products, Inc., 9 Factory Ln., Middlesex, 08846.......... (732) 805-0088
Hookway Enterprises see..........Megasafe, Budd Lake
Hope Uniform & Security Products see..........Hope Uniform Co., Inc., Columbia
Hope Uniform Co., Inc., 4 Columbia St., P.O. Box 224, Columbia, 07832.......... (908) 496-4899
Hopewell Pottery, 18 Burton Ave., Hopewell, 08525.......... (609) 466-9048
Hopewell Valley Vineyards, 46 Yard Rd., Pennington, 08534.......... (609) 737-4465
Hoppe Co., Inc., R. J., 340 N. 5th St., Newark, 07107.......... (973) 485-5665
Hoppecke Batterys, Inc., 1960 Old Cuthbert Rd., Ste. 130, Cherry Hill, 08034.......... (856) 616-0032
Horiba Instruments, Inc. see..........HORIBA Scientific, Edison
HORIBA Scientific, 3880 Park Ave., Edison, 08820.......... (732) 494-8660
Horizon Label, LLC, 1049 Industrial Dr., West Berlin, 08091.......... (856) 767-0777
Horizon Printing see..........Tanter, Inc., Clark
Horizon Sign Co., 340 Patterson Ave., Ste. C, Hamilton, 08610.......... (609) 586-0041
Horizon Tool & Mold, Inc., 56 Paterson Ave., Newton, 07860.......... (973) 300-0393
† Hose Shop, Inc., The, 100 New England Ave., Ste. 2, Piscataway, 08854.......... (732) 562-1000
Hosokawa Micron Powder Systems, 10 Chatham Rd., Summit, 07901.......... (908) 273-6360
Hospi-Tel Mfg. Co., Inc., 545 N. Arlington Ave., East Orange, 07017.......... (973) 678-7100
Hotfoil-EHS, Inc., 2960 E. State Street Ext., Hamilton, 08619.......... (609) 588-0900
Houghton Chemical Corp., 30 Amor Ave., Carlstadt, 07072.......... (800) 777-2466
Houpert Truck Service, 115 Atlantic Ave., P.O. Box 8, Berlin, 08009.......... (856) 767-0145
House Foods America Corp., 801 Randolph Rd., Somerset, 08873.......... (732) 537-9500
House Of Gold, Inc., 1505 Suckle Hwy., Pennsauken, 08110.......... (856) 665-0020
House Of Granite & Marble, Inc.,
1920 Swarthmore Ave., Ste. 4, Lakewood, 08701.......... (732) 367-7211
★ House Printing, LLC, 311 Kearny Ave., Kearny, 07032.......... (201) 772-5988
Housechem, A Div. of Menshen Packaging U.S.A., Inc.,
25 Industrial Park, Waldwick, 07463.......... (201) 445-8808
† Houser Welding Supply Co., Inc., 12-14 E. Main St., Somerville, 08876.......... (908) 526-7777
HOUZER, Inc., 2605 Kuser Rd., Hamilton, 08691.......... (609) 584-1900
Hovione, LLC, 40 Lake Dr., East Windsor, 08520.......... (609) 918-2600
Howard A. Schaevitz Technologies Inc see..........Macro Sensors, Pennsauken
Howard, Inc., James, 1500 Main Ave., Ste. 3, Clifton, 07011.......... (973) 928-1560
Howell Precision Tool Co., 415 Cranberry Rd., Farmingdale, 07727.......... (732) 919-7300
Howe's Standard Publishing Co., Inc., 1980 S. West Blvd., Vineland, 08360.......... (856) 691-2000
Howie Mfg. Co., Inc., 1227 Mechanic St., Camden, 08104.......... (856) 963-3560
Howman Assocs., Inc., 12 Garden St., Edison, 08817.......... (732) 985-7474
Howman Controls see..........Howman Assocs., Inc., Edison
Howman Electronics, Route 22 E., Salem Industrial Pk., Whitehouse, 08888.......... (908) 534-2247
Howman Engineering see..........Howman Electronics, Whitehouse
Hoyt Corp., 520 S. Dean St., Englewood, 07631.......... (201) 894-0707
Hoyt Signs, 2825 Belvidere Rd., Phillipsburg, 08865.......... (908) 859-3768
H.P. Machine Shop, Inc., 415 Oxford St., Vineland, 08360.......... (856) 692-1192
HSH Assocs., 51 Route 23 S., Riverdale, 07457.......... (973) 617-8700
HTD Heat Trace, Inc., 8 Bartles Corner Rd., Unit 104, Flemington, 08822.......... (908) 788-5210
H2L, LLC, 4201 Tonnelle Ave., Ste. 2, North Bergen, 07047.......... (201) 864-0060
H2m Beverages, 223 Wanaque Ave., POMPTON LAKES, 07442.......... (973) 831-2010
Hub Print & Copy Center, The, 2037 Lemoine Ave., Fort Lee, 07024.......... (201) 585-7887
Hub Sign Crane Corp., 67 Wood Ave., Englishtown, 07726.......... (732) 252-9090
Hubbell Lighting, Inc. see..........Kurt Versen Inc, Westwood
Huber Corp., J.M. (H Q), 499 Thornall St., 8th Fl., Edison, 08837.......... (732) 549-8600
Hubler & Assocs., 146 E. Holly Ave., Oaklyn, 08107.......... (856) 906-5341
Hudson & Bergen Co., 350 Belleville Tpk., Kearny, 07032.......... (201) 991-4900
Hudson Awning & Sign Co., Inc., 27 Cottage St., Bayonne, 07002.......... (201) 339-7171
Hudson Bread, 5601-5711 Tonnelle Ave., North Bergen, 07047.......... (201) 422-7900
Hudson Community Enterprises, 780 Montgomery St., Jersey City, 07306.......... (201) 432-5959
Hudson Display Corp., 831 Frelinghuysen Ave., Newark, 07114.......... (973) 623-8255
† Hudson Heating Wholesaler, Inc., 1109 Grand Ave., Ste. 1, North Bergen, 07047.......... (201) 348-6700
Hudson Industries Corp., 271 U.S. Highway 46, Ste. F-207, Fairfield, 07004.......... (973) 402-0100
Hudson Mfg. Co., 640 W. 1st Ave., Roselle, 07203.......... (908) 241-3880
† Hudson News Distributors, LLC, 5903 W. Side Ave., North Bergen, 07047.......... (201) 867-3600
Hudson Reporter see..........Bayonne Community News, Bayonne
Hudson Reporter Assocs., LP,
1400 Washington St., P.O. Box 3069, Hoboken, 07030.......... (201) 798-7800
Hudson Robotics, Inc., 10 Stern Ave., Springfield, 07081.......... (973) 376-7400
Hudson Services LLC see..........Hudson Awning & Sign Co., Inc., Bayonne
Hudson United Glass & Window Corp., 476 Hudson St., Hackensack, 07601.......... (201) 440-3937
Huggins Aluminum Products, 576 N. Route 73, West Berlin, 08091.......... (856) 767-0506
Huggins Awnings & Patio Rooms see..........Huggins Aluminum Products, West Berlin
HumanConcepts, 1031 Route 22, Ste. 303, Bridgewater, 08807.......... (908) 231-0204
Humanscale Corp., 220 Circle Dr. N., Piscataway, 08854.......... (732) 537-2944
Humanscale Corporation see..........Humanscale Corp., Piscataway
Hummel Croton, Inc., 10 Harmich Rd., South Plainfield, 07080.......... (908) 754-1800
Hummel Distributing Corp., 850 Springfield Rd., P.O. Box 3199, Union, 07083.......... (908) 688-5300
Hummel Machine & Tool Co., 580 Davis Ave., Kearny, 07032.......... (201) 991-5200
Hun Machine Works, Inc., 51 Whittaker St., P.O. Box 189, Riverside, 08075.......... (856) 461-7112
Hungerford & Terry, Inc., 226 N. Atlantic Ave., P.O. Box 650, Clayton, 08312.......... (856) 881-3200
Hunter Mfg. Services, Inc., 19 Just Rd., Fairfield, 07004.......... (973) 365-5880
Hunter Products, Inc., 792 Partridge Dr., P.O. Box 6795, Bridgewater, 08807.......... (908) 526-8440
† Hunter Walton & Co., Inc., 120 Circle Dr. N., Piscataway, 08854.......... (732) 805-0808
Hunterdon Ornamental Concrete, Inc.,
440 Highway 22, Whitehouse Station, 08889.......... (908) 534-4556
Hunterdon Transformer Co., 75 Industrial Rd., Alpha, 08865.......... (908) 454-2400
Hunterdon Transformer Co. see..........Torelco, Inc., Alpha
Hurricane Signs, 103 Main St., Bloomingdale, 07403.......... (973) 838-3373
Hussmann Corp., 3001 Irwin Rd., Ste. D, Mount Laurel, 08054.......... (856) 793-7050
Hutchinson Cabinets, LLC, 244 Bark Bridge Rd., Sewell, 08080.......... (856) 468-5500
Hutchinson Co., William T., 453 Lehigh Ave., Union, 07083.......... (908) 688-0533
Hutchinson Industries, Inc., 460 Southard St., Trenton, 08638.......... (609) 394-1010
Hutchton & Simon, Inc., 140 Atlantic St., Hackensack, 07601.......... (201) 487-1033
Hybrid-Tek, Inc., 9 Trenton Lakewood Rd., Ste. 1, Clarksburg, 08510.......... (609) 259-3355
HYCHEM Corporation, 611 Main St., Ste. B-2, Belmar, 07719.......... (732) 280-8803
Hycrete, Inc., 462 Barell Ave., Carlstadt, 07072.......... (201) 386-8110
Hyde Co., A. L., 1 Main St., P.O. Box 62, Grenloch, 08032.......... (856) 227-0500
Hydratight Operations, 12 Worlds Fair Dr., Ste. A, Somerset, 08873.......... (732) 271-4100
Hydraulic Packing & Seal Products,
1224 Forest Pkwy., P.O. Box 160, Paulsboro, 08066.......... (856) 224-1120
Hydrocote see..........Hood Finishing Products, Inc., Middlesex
Hydro-Mechanical Systems, Inc.,
1030 Delsea Dr., P.O. Box 87, Westville, 08093.......... (856) 848-8888
Hydromer, Inc. see..........Biosearch Medical Products, Inc., Branchburg
Hydromer, Inc., 35 Industrial Pkwy., Branchburg, 08876.......... (908) 722-5000
Hygloss Products, Inc., 45 Hathaway St., Wallington, 07057.......... (973) 458-1700
Hygrade Business Group, Inc., 232 Entin Rd., P.O. Box 1099, Clifton, 07014.......... (973) 249-6700
HyperTech, Inc., 279 Central Ave., Ste. B, Metuchen, 08840.......... (732) 635-1755
★ HYSO, LLC, 430 Gotham Pkwy., 2nd Fl., Carlstadt, 07072.......... (201) 635-9555
Hy-Tech Metal Works, Inc., 1252 South Ave., Plainfield, 07062.......... (908) 757-6754
Hytek Industries Corp., 215 Comanche Dr., P.O. Box 56, Oceanport, 07757.......... (732) 229-5730
Hy-Test Packaging Corp., 515 E. 41st St., Paterson, 07504.......... (973) 754-7000
Hytorc see..........UNEX Corp., Mahwah
I & E Co., 150 Main St., Ogdensburg, 07439.......... (973) 579-0009
I & F Scallop Thread Co., Inc., 6002 Adams St., West New York, 07093.......... (201) 868-6550
I C Machine, Inc., 199 U.S. Highway 46, Budd Lake, 07828.......... (973) 252-7083
I D J, Inc., 121 Mechanic St., Boonton, 07005.......... (973) 334-1517
I Did It Metal Art, Inc., 53 Gables Way, Jackson, 08527.......... (732) 866-8481
I G I Laboratories, Inc., 105 Lincoln Ave., P.O. Box 687, Buena, 08310.......... (856) 697-1441
I S E Farms, Inc., 110 Goodspring Rd., P.O. Box 567, Broadway, 08808.......... (908) 454-4148
I Shor see..........Shor International Corp., Madison
I T I Electronics, Inc., 32 Stonewall Dr., Livingston, 07039.......... (973) 890-7888

I T O X, LLC, 15 Corporate Pl. S., Ste. 201, Piscataway, 08854 ... (732) 390-2815
Iacovelli Stairs, Inc., 707 Challenger Way, Forked River, 08731 ... (609) 693-3476
† IBF Corp., 44 Plauderville Ave., Garfield, 07026 ... (973) 546-0055
† IBOCO Corp., 26 Northfield Ave., Edison, 08837 ... (732) 417-0066
IBS see. ... Integrated Business Systems, Inc., Totowa
† ICC Cable Corp., 2125 Center Ave., Ste. 401, Fort Lee, 07024 ... (201) 482-5750
ICC Industries, Inc. see. ... Frutarom USA, Inc., North Bergen
ICCI see. ... Interactive Computer Center, Inc., Brick
Ice King & Cold Storage, Inc., 4045 Route 33 W., Tinton Falls, 07753 ... (732) 922-0852
Icicle, Inc., 341 School House Rd., Monroe Township, 08831 ... (732) 521-4223
ICM see. ... Industrial Consulting & Marketing, Fair Lawn
Icy Cools, Inc., 15 Oscar Dr., P.O. Box 686, Roosevelt, 08555 ... (609) 448-0172
I.D. Systems, Inc., 123 Tice Blvd., Ste. 101, Woodcliff Lake, 07677 ... (201) 996-9000
Id Technology, 48 Spruce St., Oakland, 07436 ... (888) 405-4574
Ideal Plating & Polishing Co.,
681 Main St., Bldg. 39, P.O. Box 100, Belleville, 07109 ... (973) 759-5559
† Ideal Tile Importing Co., Inc., 2232 Route 9 S., Howell, 07731 ... (732) 308-1008
Ideal Window Mfg., Inc., 100 W. 7th St., Bayonne, 07002 ... (201) 437-4300
Ideal-Jacobs Corp., 515 Valley St., Maplewood, 07040 ... (973) 275-5100
IDL TechniEdge, LLC, 30 Boright Ave., Kenilworth, 07033 ... (908) 497-9818
IDP Films, 24 Commerce Rd., Ste. P, Fairfield, 07004 ... (973) 227-1661
ID-Tech Solutions, Inc., 505 E. County Line Rd., Lakewood, 08701 ... (718) 408-9199
IESI Corp. see. ... IESI Recycling Corp. (H Q), Lyndhurst
† IESI Recycling Corp. (H Q), 1099 Wall St. W., Ste. 250, Lyndhurst, 07071 ... (201) 443-3000
IFC Products, Inc., 568 E. Elizabeth Ave., P.O. Box 2175, Linden, 07036 ... (908) 587-1221
IFC Solutions, 1601 E. Linden Ave., Linden, 07036 ... (908) 862-8810
IFCO Systems, 320 Dulty's Ln., P.O. Box 1333, Burlington, 08016 ... (609) 386-5200
IFCO Systems North America, Inc. see. ... IFCO Systems, Burlington
IFS, Inc. see. ... International Foodsource, LLC, Dover
IHI Ionbond, 200 Roundhill Dr., Rockaway, 07866 ... (973) 586-4700
IHI Ionbond, LLC see. ... IHI Ionbond, Rockaway
II-VI Advanced Materials,
20 Chapin Rd., Ste. 1007, P.O. Box 840, Pine Brook, 07058 ... (973) 227-1551
II-VI Incorporated see. ... II-VI Advanced Materials, Pine Brook
IK Construction, Inc., 1118 E. Baltimore Ave., Linden, 07036 ... (908) 925-5200
Ikanos Communications, Inc., 100 Schultz Dr., Red Bank, 07701 ... (732) 345-7500
Ikaria, Inc. (H Q), 53 Frontage Rd., P.O. Box 9001, Hampton, 08827 ... (908) 238-6600
★ Iken Media, LLC, 70 Triangle Blvd., Carlstadt, 07072 ... (201) 372-0800
† IKO International, Inc., 91 Walsh Dr., Parsippany, 07054 ... (973) 402-0254
iKreative VC see. ... Minuteman Press Of North Arlington, North Arlington
ILI Publishing see. ... SAI Global Ltd., Paramus
Ilie's Eternally Flawless, 275 E. State Route 4, Paramus, 07652 ... (201) 487-1991
★ Ilkem Marble & Granite, 2010 Springdale Rd., Ste. 200, Cherry Hill, 08003 ... (856) 433-8714
Ill-Eagle Enterprises Ltd., 385 Main St., Little Falls, 07424 ... (973) 237-1111
Illinois Tool Works, Inc. see. ... ITW Covid Security Group, Cranbury
Illinois Tool Works, Inc. see. ... ITW Professional Brands, Lakewood
Illinois Tool Works, Inc. see. ... ITW Thielex, Somerset
Illinois Tool Works, Inc. see. ... Signode Packaging Group, Newark
Illinois Tool Works, Inc. see. ... Truck Parts Specialists, Teterboro
Illuminating Experiences, LLC, 625 Jersey Ave., Unit 7, New Brunswick, 08901 ... (732) 745-5858
Illusion Engraved, 311 Fayette St., Perth Amboy, 08861 ... (732) 442-4488
I.M.A. Brass see. ... International Mercantile Agencies, Inc., New Brunswick
Image Makers Printing, Copy & Sign Center, 1581 State Route 23, Wayne, 07470 ... (973) 633-1771
Image Screen Printing, Inc., 532 Lincoln Blvd., Middlesex, 08846 ... (732) 560-1817
Image Signs and More, LLC, 2906 N. Centre St., Pennsauken, 08109 ... (856) 665-1890
Image Systems For Business, 22 Worlds Fair Dr., Ste. E, Somerset, 08873 ... (732) 302-1500
Imagepoint Screen Printing, 69 Water St., Newton, 07860 ... (908) 684-1768
Imagery Embroidery Corporation, 2907-2911 Jeannette St., Union City, 07087 ... (201) 343-9333
Imagination Arts Publications,
57 Thunderhead Pl., P.O. Box 103, Mahwah, 07430 ... (201) 529-5105
Imagine America, LLC see. ... Imagine Corp., The, Prospect Park
Imagine Corp., The, 320 N. 6th St., Prospect Park, 07508 ... (973) 942-2888
ImClone see. ... Eli Lilly & Co., Branchburg
IMCO, Inc., 858 N. Lenola Rd., Bldg. 1, Moorestown, 08057 ... (856) 499-2214
Imco Reinforced Plastics, Inc., 858 N. Lenola Rd., Moorestown, 08057 ... (856) 235-7254
IMM see. ... Integrated Media Management, LLC, Linden
Immunomedics, Inc., 300 The American Rd., Morris Plains, 07950 ... (973) 605-8200
Immunostics, Inc., 3505 Sunset Ave., Ocean, 07712 ... (732) 918-0770
★ Impact Displays Group, LLC, 310 13th St., Carlstadt, 07072 ... (212) 842-1800
Impact Instrumentation, Inc., 27 Fairfield Pl., West Caldwell, 07006 ... (973) 882-1212
Impact Printing, 762 Green St., Iselin, 08830 ... (732) 636-8893
Impact Unlimited, Inc., 250 Ridge Rd., P.O. Box 558, Dayton, 08810 ... (732) 274-2000
IMPANDEX INC. see. ... Glen Mills Inc., Clifton
Imperial Billiards Corp., 2 Sandy Ln., Hardwick, 07825 ... (908) 459-4825
Imperial DAX Co., Inc., 120 New Dutch Ln., Fairfield, 07004 ... (973) 227-6105
Imperial Design, 729 Charles St., Gloucester City, 08030 ... (856) 742-8480
Imperial Drug & Spice Corp., 5620 Kennedy Blvd. W., West New York, 07093 ... (201) 348-1551
Imperial Electro Plating, 52 Park Ave., Lyndhurst, 07071 ... (201) 438-9450
Imperial Machine & Tool Co., 8 W. Crisman Rd., Columbia, 07832 ... (908) 496-8100
Imperial Metal Products, Inc., 8 W. Chimney Rock Rd., Bound Brook, 08805 ... (732) 469-8181
Imperial Sewing Machine Co., Inc., 584 S. 21st St., Irvington, 07111 ... (973) 374-3405
Imperial Weld Ring Corp., 80-88 Front St., P.O. Box 6646, Elizabeth, 07206 ... (908) 354-0011
Imperial Welding see. ... G & M Welding & Fabricating, Inc., Bellmawr
Importers Service Corp., 65 Brunswick Ave., Edison, 08817 ... (732) 248-1946
Impressions Unlimited Printing Co., LLC,
638 Delsea Dr., P.O. Box 386, Sewell, 08080 ... (856) 256-0200
Impressive Printing, Inc., 313 10th St., Carlstadt, 07072 ... (201) 933-1650
Imprint see. ... Just Us Books, Inc., East Orange
Imprint Specialties, Inc., 601 New Broadway, Brooklawn, 08030 ... (856) 456-2999
Imprintz Custom Printed Graphics, Inc.,
Garfield & Decatur Sts., P.O. Box 315, Beverly, 08010 ... (609) 386-5673
IMS Pet Industries, 34 Passaic St., Wood Ridge, 07075 ... (973) 249-0026
Imtech Graphics, Inc., 545 Dell Rd., Carlstadt, 07072 ... (201) 933-8002
In Stitches Embroidery, Inc., 1020 Campus Dr., Morganville, 07751 ... (732) 460-2660
InBeau, Inc., 101 W. Palisade, Englewood, 07631 ... (201) 227-8875
Incentive Gourmet see. ... Nouveautes, Inc., Fairfield
Indasa U. S. A., Inc., 23 Madison Rd., Fairfield, 07004 ... (800) 916-0090
Indco, Inc., 511 Essex St., P.O. Box 109, Gloucester City, 08030 ... (856) 456-6100
Indemax, Inc., 1 Industrial Dr., Vernon, 07462 ... (973) 209-2424
Independence Cryogenic Engineering, LLC,
891 Route 9 N., P.O. Box 527, Little Egg Harbor, 08087 ... (609) 294-0012
Independence Plating Corp., 107 Alabama Ave., Paterson, 07503 ... (973) 523-1776
† Independent Imaging, 1819 Underwood Blvd., Unit 1, Delran, 08075 ... (856) 764-9729
Independent Machine Co., 2 Stewart Pl., Fairfield, 07004 ... (973) 882-0060
† Independent Metal Sales, Inc.,
Park & Delaware Aves., Hainesport Industrial Pk., P.O. Box 17, Hainesport, 08036 ... (609) 261-8090
Independent Sheet Metal Co., Inc., 233 Central Ave., Hawthorne, 07506 ... (973) 423-1150
Index Security, Inc. (H Q), 500 Parker Ave., Ste. G, Deal, 07723 ... (732) 531-9209
† Indexing Technologies, Inc., 37 Orchard St., Ramsey, 07446 ... (201) 934-6333
Individualized Shirts, Inc., 581 Cortland St., Perth Amboy, 08861 ... (732) 826-8400
Indofine Chemical Co., Inc., 121 Stryker Ln., Hillsborough, 08844 ... (908) 359-6778
Inductotherm Corp. see. ... Consarc Corp., Rancocas
Inductotherm Corp. see. ... Electro-Steam Generator Corp., Rancocas
Inductotherm Corp., 10 Indel Ave., P.O. Box 157, Rancocas, 08073 ... (609) 267-9000
Inductotherm Corp. see. ... Jomar Corp., Egg Harbor Township
Inductotherm Corp. see. ... PV/T, Inc., Rancocas
Inductotherm Corp. see. ... Rancocas Metals Corp., Rancocas
Inductotherm Corp. see. ... Telegenix, Inc., Rancocas
† InduKey North America, LLC, 329 Moore Ave., Leonia, 07605 ... (877) 588-2172
Industrial Automation Systems Engineering Co., Inc.,
161 Industrial Pkwy., Unit 6, Branchburg, 08876 ... (908) 218-1104
Industrial Brake & Clutch Exchange,
2 U.S. Highway 9, Ste. 4, Morganville, 07751 ... (732) 970-0090
Industrial Brush Co., Inc., 105 Clinton Rd., Fairfield, 07004 ... (973) 575-0455
† Industrial Combustion Associates Inc.,
20 Worlds Fair Dr., Ste. C, Somerset, 08873 ... (732) 271-0300
Industrial Consulting & Marketing,
20-21 Wagaraw Rd., Bldg. 38, Fair Lawn, 07410 ... (973) 427-2474
† Industrial Controls Distributors, LLC, 17 Christopher Way, Eatontown, 07724 ... (732) 918-9000
Industrial Drum Co., 784 New Jersey Ave., P.O. Box 586, Glassboro, 08028 ... (856) 881-2000
Industrial Electronic Devices, Inc.,
8 Bartles Corner Rd., Bldg. 101, Flemington, 08822 ... (908) 806-2255
Industrial Environmental, 176 W. Westfield Ave., Elizabeth, 07201 ... (908) 241-3830
Industrial Ferguson Foundry, 2365 Route 22 W., P.O. Box 531, Union, 07083 ... (908) 686-8888
Industrial Filters Co., Inc., 9 Industrial Rd., Fairfield, 07004 ... (973) 575-0533
Industrial Hard Chromium Co., 7 Rome St., Newark, 07105 ... (973) 344-2265
Industrial Hydraulics & Rubber, LLC, 458 Atlantic Ave., Camden, 08104 ... (856) 966-2600
† Industrial Instrumentation Services, Inc.,
1400 Rahway Ave., Ste. 4, Avenel, 07001 ... (732) 815-9090
Industrial Labeling Systems, Inc., 50 Kulick Rd., Fairfield, 07004 ... (973) 882-9688
Industrial Machine & Engineering Co., 1807 W. Elizabeth Ave., Linden, 07036 ... (908) 862-8874
Industrial Machine Corp., 44 Lehigh Ave., Paterson, 07503 ... (973) 345-1800
Industrial Metal, Inc., 32 Lambert Rd., Blairstown, 07825 ... (908) 362-0084
Industrial Products Corp., 1 Hollywood Ave., Ste. 30, Ho-Ho-Kus, 07423 ... (201) 652-5913
Industrial Razor Blade Co., Inc., 575 Nassau St., Orange, 07050 ... (973) 673-4286
Industrial Rivet & Fastener Co., 200 Paris Ave., Northvale, 07647 ... (201) 750-1040
Industrial Rubber Co., 938-940 S. Elmora Ave., Elizabeth, 07202 ... (908) 351-1550
Industrial Services Enterprises, 192 Franklin Rd., Dover, 07801 ... (973) 366-3939
Industrial Summit Technology Corp., 250 Cheesequake Rd., Parlin, 08859 ... (732) 238-2211
Industrial Tube Corp., 297 Valley Rd., Hillsborough, 08844 ... (908) 369-3737
Industrial Water Technologies, Inc., 6 Village Ct., Hazlet, 07730 ... (732) 888-1233
Industrial Welding Co., 655 Ferry St., Newark, 07105 ... (973) 589-3100
† Industrial Welding Supply, Inc., 999 Airport Rd., Ste. 1, Lakewood, 08701 ... (732) 367-7100
† Industrial Welding Supply, Inc., 4 Val St., Sayreville, 08872 ... (732) 721-1150
Industry Publications, Inc., 3621 Hill Rd., Parsippany, 07054 ... (973) 331-9545
Industry Today see. ... Positive Publications, LLC, Morristown
Inergetics, Inc., 550 Broad St., 12th Fl., Newark, 07102 ... (908) 604-2500
Infanti Brand Chair & Stools, 1153 W. Elizabeth Ave., Linden, 07036 ... (718) 447-5632
Infanti Seating see. ... Infanti Brand Chair & Stools, Linden
Infinite Manufacturing Group, Inc., 171 Coit St., Irvington, 07111 ... (973) 649-9950
Infinite Print, 225 New York Ave., Jersey City, 07307 ... (862) 668-3094
Infinite Visions, LLC, 40 Enterprise Ave. N., Secaucus, 07094 ... (201) 866-6946
INFINITT North America, Inc.,
755 Memorial Pkwy., Ste. 304, Phillipsburg, 08865 ... (908) 387-6960
Infinity Design & Printing, 1358 Burnet Ave., Union, 07083 ... (908) 206-8844
Infinova, 51 Stouts Ln., Monmouth Junction, 08852 ... (732) 355-9100
Info System, 345 Main Ave., Wallington, 07057 ... (973) 777-4448
INFOLynx, Inc., 500 Frank W. Burr Blvd., Ste. 14, Teaneck, 07666 ... (201) 569-9085
Infor Metal & Tooling Manufacturing Corporation,
16 Commerce Rd., Cedar Grove, 07009 ... (973) 571-9520
Informatica Corp., 309 Fellowship Rd., Mount Laurel, 08054 ... (856) 642-4080
Information Today, Inc., 143 Old Marlton Pike, Medford, 08055 ... (609) 654-6266
Infragistics, Inc., 2 Commerce Dr., Cranbury, 08512 ... (609) 448-2000
Ingersoll-Rand Co. Ltd. see. ... Trane, Inc. (H Q), Piscataway
Ingredion Inc. see. ... Ingredion Incorporated (H Q), Bridgewater
Ingredion Incorporated (H Q), 10 Finderne Ave., Ste. C, Bridgewater, 08807 ... (908) 685-5555
Initial Impact, 516 Warren Ave., Spring Lake, 07762 ... (732) 449-4922
Iniven, A Div. Of Conolog Corp., 5 Columbia Rd., Somerville, 08876 ... (908) 722-8081
Injection Works, Inc., 104 Gaither Dr., Mount Laurel, 08054 ... (856) 802-6444
Injectron Corp., 1000 S. 2nd St., P.O. Box 3012, Plainfield, 07063 ... (908) 753-1990
Ink Well Printers Inc., 38 S. 21st St., Kenilworth, 07033 ... (908) 272-8090
INKit Design N' Print LLC, 644 Cross St., Unit 2, Lakewood, 08701 ... (732) 363-8098
Inkwell Corp., 1414 Elmira St., Cape May, 08204 ... (609) 884-0350
Inman Mold & Mfg. Co., 815 Martin St., P.O. Box 1143, Rahway, 07065 ... (732) 381-6229
InMat Inc., 216 U.S. Highway 206, Ste. 7, Hillsborough, 08844 ... (908) 874-7788
Inner Spaces Lighting And Design, LLC, 98 Copley Ave., Teaneck, 07666 ... (201) 692-0702
InnerWorkings, Inc., 7 Joanna Ct., Ste. H, East Brunswick, 08816 ... (732) 651-8822
Innocor, Inc. (H Q), 187 State Route 36, Ste. 101, West Long Branch, 07764 ... (732) 263-0800
Innodyne Engineering, 1711 Ginesi Dr., Unit 2, Freehold, 07728 ... (646) 240-0200
Innolutions, Inc., 92 N. Main St., P.O. Box 384, Windsor, 08561 ... (609) 490-9799
InnoPharma, Inc., 10 Knightsbridge Rd., Piscataway, 08854 ... (732) 885-2939
Innophos, Inc. (H Q), 259 Prospect Plains Rd., Bldg. A, Cranbury, 08512 ... (609) 495-2495
Innovation Concepts, Inc. (H Q), 870 Warwick Tpke., Hewitt, 07421 ... (973) 853-5300
Innovative Carpets, 45 Legion Dr., Cresskill, 07626 ... (201) 894-1008
Innovative Cosmetics, Inc., 270 Clifton Blvd., Clifton, 07011 ... (973) 773-7700
Innovative Cutting Concepts, LLC, 203 Cates Rd., Egg Harbor Township, 08234 ... (609) 484-9960
† Innovative Glass & Mirror, Inc., 15 Chambersbridge Rd., Lakewood, 08701 ... (732) 961-2267
Innovative Labeling, Inc., 12 Gloria Ln., Ste. 4, Fairfield, 07004 ... (973) 227-4800
† Innovative Marking Systems, Inc., 105 Forest Rd., Fanwood, 07023 ... (908) 322-2900
Innovative Mfg., Inc., 198 U.S. Highway 206, Ste. 4, Hillsborough, 08844 ... (908) 904-1884
Innovative Network Solutions, 29 Cove Rd., Hopatcong, 07843 ... (973) 299-8800
Innovative Photonic Solutions,
4250 U.S. Highway 1, Ste. 1, Monmouth Junction, 08852 ... (732) 355-9300
Innovative Powder Coatings, LLC, 9105 Burrough-Dover Ln., Pennsauken, 08110 ... (856) 661-0086

Innovative Power Solutions, LLC, 373 South St., Eatontown, 07724 (732) 544-1075
Innovative Resin Systems, Inc., 257 Wilson Ave., Newark, 07105 (973) 465-6887
Innovative Software Solutions, Inc. (H Q),
3000 S. Lenola Rd., Maple Shade, 08052 (856) 910-9190
Inoac - Crest Foam, 100 Carol Pl., Moonachie, 07074 (201) 807-0809
Inopak Ltd., 24 Executive Pkwy., Ringwood, 07456 (973) 962-1121
In-Pak Services, Inc., 474 Getty Ave., Clifton, 07011 (973) 595-5250
In-Phase Technologies, Inc.,
401 Bordentown Hedding Rd., Bldg. 4, Ste. A, Bordentown, 08505 (609) 298-9555
InPhot, Inc., 3490 W. Route 1, Princeton, 08540 (609) 750-0992
Inrad Optics, Inc., 181 Legrand Ave., Northvale, 07647 (201) 767-1910
INS Technologies, P.O. Box 615, Nutley, 07110 (973) 808-6400
Inserts East, Inc., 7045 Central Hwy., Pennsauken, 08109 (856) 663-8181
Insign, Inc., 1937 Olney Ave., Cherry Hill, 08003 (856) 424-1161
Insmed, Inc., 10 Finderne Ave., Bridgewater, 08807 (908) 977-9900
Instant Image Printing, 649 Bergen Blvd., Ridgefield, 07657 (201) 945-0020
Instant Printing, 355 Main St., Orange, 07050 (973) 675-6266
Instant Printing, Inc., 241 E. Blackwell St., Dover, 07801 (973) 366-6855
INSTOCK Wireless Components, Inc., 50 Intervale Rd., Ste. 15, Boonton, 07005 (973) 335-6550
Instrument Specialties Co., Inc., 661 Myrtle Ave., Boonton, 07005 (973) 335-2136
Instrumentation Design & Service Co., 256 Bearfort Rd., West Milford, 07480 (973) 728-3748
Instrumentation Technology Systems, Inc., 205 E. Inman Ave., Rahway, 07065 (732) 388-0866
Instru-Met Corp., 931 Lehigh Ave., Union, 07083 (908) 851-0700
Insulite, Inc., 1890 Church Rd., Toms River, 08753 (732) 255-1700
Insurance Services Office, Inc., 545 Washington Blvd., Jersey City, 07310 (201) 469-2000
Intarome Fragrance & Flavor Corp., 370 Chestnut St., Norwood, 07648 (201) 767-8700
Intec, Inc. see. International Riding Helmets, Inc., Keyport
Intech Corp., 250 Herbert Ave., Closter, 07624 (201) 767-8066
Integra LifeSciences Corp., 105 Morgan Ln., Plainsboro, 08536 (609) 275-2700
Integra LifeSciences Corp., 311 Enterprise Dr., Plainsboro, 08536 (609) 275-0500
Integrated Business Systems, Inc., 999 Riverview Dr., Ste. 280, Totowa, 07512 (973) 575-4950
† Integrated Document Technologies, 1 Cardinal Dr., Little Falls, 07424 (973) 237-1200
Integrated Laminate Systems, 1301 Industrial Hwy., Riverton, 08077 (856) 786-6500
Integrated Media Management, LLC, 330 Dalziel Rd., Linden, 07036 (908) 862-6600
★ Integrated Micro Systems, Inc., 74 Lee Ave., Haledon, 07508 (973) 904-9700
Integrated Microwave Technologies, LLC,
200 International Dr., Mount Olive, 07828 (908) 852-3700
Integrated Packaging Systems, 3 Luger Rd., Ste. 5, Denville, 07834 (973) 664-0020
Integrity Iron Works Inc., 33 Brookside Ave., P.O. Box 129, Sayreville, 08872 (732) 254-2200
Integrity Precision Products, 7 Reuten Dr., Closter, 07624 (201) 767-0700
Intek Plastics, Inc., 150 5th Ave., Hawthorne, 07506 (973) 427-7331
Intek/Elite Plastics see. Intek Plastics, Inc., Hawthorne
Intelco Of Delaware Valley, 250 Harvard Ave., P.O. Box 9, Westville, 08093 (856) 456-6755
★ Intellect Technologies, Inc.,
4301 U.S. Highway 1, Ste. 120, Monmouth Junction, 08852 (609) 454-3170
Intelligent Security Systems,
1480 U.S. Highway 9 N., Ste. 202, Woodbridge, 07095 (732) 855-1111
Intelligrated, 265 Davidson Ave., Ste. 219, Somerset, 08873 (732) 302-2590
Intelligrated, Inc. see. Intelligrated, Somerset
Intellisphere, LLC, 666 Plainsboro Rd., Ste. 300, Plainsboro, 08536 (609) 716-7777
Intense-US, 1200 Airport Rd., Ste. A, North Brunswick, 08902 (732) 249-2228
Inteplast Group Ltd. (H Q), 9 Peach Tree Hill Rd., Livingston, 07039 (973) 994-8000
† Interactive Computer Center, Inc., 482 Brick Blvd., Brick, 08723 (732) 477-5800
INTERCAT, Inc. (H Q), 2399 Highway 34, Ste. C-1, Manasquan, 08736 (732) 223-4644
Interchange Equipment, Inc., 90 Dayton Ave., Ste. 200, Passaic, 07055 (973) 473-5005
Interfashion Cosmetics Corp., 32 Henry St., Teterboro, 07608 (201) 288-5858
Interfoam Fabricators, Inc., 155 McBride Ave., Paterson, 07501 (973) 633-8805
Intergel Vitamin Co., 191 40th St., Irvington, 07111 (973) 371-4400
★ Interior Art & Design, Inc., 59 Oak St., Hackensack, 07601 (201) 488-8855
Interline Brands, Inc. see. Interline Brands, Inc. (H Q), Mount Laurel
† Interline Brands, Inc. (H Q), 804 Eastgate Dr., Ste. 100, Mount Laurel, 08054 (856) 439-1222
Interline New Jersey see. Interline Brands, Inc. (H Q), Mount Laurel
Interlink Products International, Inc., 1315 E. Elizabeth Ave., Linden, 07036 (908) 862-8090
Intermarket Technology, Inc., 92 Newark Pompton Tpke., Wayne, 07470 (973) 872-9090
International Aromatics, Inc., 200 Anderson Ave., Moonachie, 07074 (201) 964-0900
† International Beauty Products,
26 Chapin Rd., Ste. 1108, P.O. Box 708, Pine Brook, 07058 (973) 575-6400
International Coconut Corp., 225 W. Grand St., Elizabeth, 07202 (908) 289-1555
International Compressor Co., Inc., 361 Jelliff Ave., Newark, 07108 (973) 824-7170
International Container Co.. see. Paperboard Products Co., Hackensack
International Converting Machinery, Inc., 45 Camelot Dr., West Milford, 07480 (973) 728-2600
International Cord Sets, Inc., 6 Spielman Rd., Fairfield, 07004 (973) 227-2118
International Crystal Laboratories, 11 Erie St., Ste. 2, Garfield, 07026 (973) 478-8944
International Cushioning Co., 240 Boundary Rd., Marlboro, 07746 (732) 683-9600
International Data Group, 650 From Rd., Ste. 558, Paramus, 07652 (201) 634-2300
International Delights Bakery Co., 230 Brighton Rd., Clifton, 07012 (973) 928-5582
International Emergency Vehicles see. First Priority Emergency Vehicles, Inc., Manchester
International Flavors & Fragrances, Inc., 150 Docks Corner Rd., Dayton, 08810 (732) 329-4600
International Flavors & Fragrances, Inc., 600 Highway 36, Hazlet, 07730 (732) 264-4500
International Foam Products, Inc., P.O. Box 545, Stanhope, 07874 (201) 909-0950
International Foodsource, LLC, 52 Richboynton Rd., Dover, 07801 (973) 361-7044
International Forge, LLC, 14 Doty Rd., Haskell, 07420 (973) 729-0359
International Glass Work, Inc.,
723 E. Park Ave., P.O. Box 1015, Vineland, 08360 (856) 691-5628
† International Mercantile Agencies, Inc.,
18 Home News Row, New Brunswick, 08901 (732) 246-3900
International Micro Industries, Inc.,
1951 Old Cuthbert Rd., Bldg. 404, Cherry Hill, 08034 (856) 616-0051
International Paint, LLC, 2270 Morris Ave., Union, 07083 (908) 686-1300
International Paper Co., 100 E. Gloucester Pike, Barrington, 08007 (856) 546-7000
International Paper Co., 370 Benigno Blvd., Bellmawr, 08031 (856) 931-8000
International Paper Co., 101 Ford Ave., Milltown, 08850 (732) 828-1700
International Paper Co., 140 Summerhill Rd., Spotswood, 08884 (732) 251-2000
International Paper Co., 33 Phoenix Dr., Thorofare, 08086 (856) 853-7000
International Paper Co. see. Shorewood Digital Design & Development Center, Carlstadt
† International Playthings LLC, 75D Lackawanna Ave., Parsippany, 07054 (973) 316-2500
International Process Equipment Co., 9300 Route 130 N., Pennsauken, 08110 (856) 665-4007
International Process Plants, 17-A Marlen Dr., Hamilton, 08691 (609) 586-8004
International Products Corp., 201 Connecticut Dr., Burlington, 08016 (609) 386-8770
International Riding Helmets, Inc.,
21 Industrial Dr., Old Bridge Township, Keyport, 07735 (732) 290-3000
International Roll Forms, Inc., 8 International Ave., Sewell, 08080 (856) 228-7333
International Sheet Metal & Plate Mfg., Inc.,
112 Veterans Memorial Dr. E., P.O. Box 5, Somerville, 08876 (908) 722-6614
International Swimming Pools, Inc., 14-C Van Dyke Ave., New Brunswick, 08901 (732) 565-9229
International Tool & Machine, LLC, 446 Hillside Ave., Hillside, 07205 (908) 687-5580
International Tool & Mfg., Inc., 30 Sherwood Ln., Ste. 10, Fairfield, 07004 (973) 227-6767
International Tower Supply, 851 Bethel Ave., Pennsauken, 08110 (856) 317-0005
International Veiling Corp., 244 Hazel St., 2nd Fl., Clifton, 07011 (973) 772-3100
International Vitamin Corp. see. IVC Industries, Inc., Freehold
International Welding Technologies, Inc.,
2650 Egg Harbor Rd., Lindenwold, 08021 (856) 435-8004
† International Wire Co., 27-E Kearney St., Bridgewater, 08807 (732) 968-8122
Interplast, Inc., 100 Connecticut Dr., P.O. Box 1328, Burlington, 08016 (609) 386-4990
Interplex Industries, Inc. see. Interplex NAS Inc., Beta Div., Northvale
Interplex NAS Inc., Beta Div., 232 Pegasus Ave., Northvale, 07647 (201) 367-1300
Intersil Corp., 440 U.S. Highway 22 E., Ste. 100, Bridgewater, 08807 (908) 685-6000
Interspec, 5025 Industrial Rd., Farmingdale, 07727 (732) 938-4114
Interstate Architectural & Iron, Inc., 243 Laird Ave., Cliffside Park, 07010 (201) 941-0393
† Interstate Battery System Of America, Inc.,
408 Commerce Ln., West Berlin, 08091 (856) 767-3903
† Interstate Connecting Components, Inc.,
120 Mount Holly Byp., Lumberton, 08048 (856) 722-5535
Interstate Container Brunswick, LLC, 501 Finnegan Ln., North Brunswick, 08902 (732) 821-8100
Interstate Panel, LLC, 67 Benson Ave., Hamilton, 08610 (609) 586-4411
Interstate Resources, Inc. see. Interstate Container Brunswick, LLC, North Brunswick
Interstate Sales New of Jersey, LLC,
1226 Haddonfield-Berlin Rd., Unit C-2, Voorhees, 08043 (856) 433-8692
Interstate Showcase & Store Fixture Co., P.O. Box 941, Teaneck, 07666 (201) 467-4522
Interstate Welding & Mfg. Co., Inc., 1510 Village Ct., Edgewater Park, 08010 (609) 699-6950
Intertek Laboratories, Inc., 340 Union St., Stirling, 07980 (908) 903-1800
InterTest, Inc., 303 State Route 94, Columbia, 07832 (908) 496-8008
inTEST Corp., 804 E. Gate Dr., Ste. 200, Mount Laurel, 08054 (856) 505-8800
INTEX Millwork Solutions, LLC, 20 Bogden Blvd., Millville, 08332 (856) 293-4100
★ Intuitive Technology Partners, 102 Serpentine Dr., Morganville, 07751 (201) 993-7799
InventeK Colloidal Cleaners, LLC (USA), 106 Gaither Dr., Mount Laurel, 08054 (856) 206-0058
Inventors Shop, The, 800 Industrial Hwy., Cinnaminson, 08077 (856) 303-8787
Inversand Co., 226 N. Atlantic Ave., P.O. Box 650, Clayton, 08312 (856) 881-2345
Invitations By Camille * Our Town Printing see. Jimcam Publishing, Inc., Maywood
Ipacesetters, 135 Chestnut Ridge Rd., Ste. 2, Montvale, 07645 (201) 391-1500
IPAK, Inc, 301 Grove Rd., West Deptford, 08086 (856) 486-0066
IPC Systems, Inc. (H Q),
Harborside Financial Ctr., 3 2nd St., Plz. 10, 15th Fl., Jersey City, 07311 (201) 253-2000
IPEC see. International Process Equipment Co., Pennsauken
IPKeys Technologies, 1 Industrial Way W., Ste. E-1, Eatontown, 07724 (732) 389-4702
IPS see. Eastar Plastics, Inc., Piscataway
IPS see. Integrated Packaging Systems, Denville
Ipsen Biopharmaceuticals, Inc., 106 Allen Rd., 3rd Fl., Basking Ridge, 07920 (866) 837-2422
IQE RF, LLC, 265 Davidson Ave., Ste. 141, Somerset, 08873 (732) 271-5990
Iron Bound Metal, Inc., 238 Emmet St., Newark, 07114 (973) 242-5704
Iron Mountain Plastics, Inc., 112 Greenwood Ave., Midland Park, 07432 (201) 445-0063
Ironbound Trophy Center, 289 Lafayette St., Ste. A, Newark, 07105 (973) 344-3872
Ironbound Welding, Inc., 156 Walnut St., Newark, 07105 (973) 589-3128
I-Ron-X Industries, 134 Wheat Rd., Buena, 08310 (856) 697-3518
Irving Rice & Co., 161 Docks Corner Rd., Dayton, 08810 (609) 655-6890
ISCO, 1 Commerce Dr., Bldg. 3, Barrington, 08007 (856) 672-9182
ISE America, Inc. see. I S E Farms, Inc., Broadway
I-See Optical Laboratories, Inc., 44 W. Church St., Blackwood, 08012 (856) 227-9300
Island Container Corp. see. Alpak Display Group, Saddle Brook
Island Container Corp. see. Enterprise Corrugated Container, LLC, Saddle Brook
Isolantite Mfg. Co., Inc., 337 Warren Ave., Stirling, 07980 (908) 647-3333
Isolatek International (H Q), 41 Furnace St., Stanhope, 07874 (973) 347-1200
Isometric Micro Finishing Coating, 122 James St., Edison, 08820 (732) 906-8070
ISOWAVE, 64 Harding Ave., Dover, 07801 (973) 328-7000
iSpeech, 211 Warren St., Newark, 07103 (917) 338-7723
iSpeech.org see. iSpeech, Newark
Istec Corp., 5 Park Lake Rd., Ste. 6, Sparta, 07871 (973) 383-9888
IT America, Inc., 100 Metroplex Dr., Ste. 207, Edison, 08817 (732) 985-5100
IT Management, 195 Browertown Rd., Ste. 2, Little Falls, 07424 (973) 389-1200
Italian Peoples Bakery, Inc., 307 Hudson St., Trenton, 08611 (609) 396-9869
Italian Tribune see. Italian Tribune Publishing Co., Montclair
Italian Tribune Publishing Co., 7 N. Willow St., Ste. 8-C, Montclair, 07042 (973) 860-0101
Itran Precision Rubber,
375 Metuchen Rd., P.O. Box 98, South Plainfield, 07080 (908) 754-8100
ITS see. Instrumentation Technology Systems, Inc., Rahway
It's Exciting Lighting, LLC, 1270 Glen Ave., Moorestown, 08057 (856) 727-5200
ITW Covid Security Group, 32 Commerce Dr., Ste. 1, Cranbury, 08512 (609) 395-5600
ITW Professional Brands, 1295 Towbin Ave., Lakewood, 08701 (732) 363-9281
ITW Thielex, 95 Commerce Dr., Somerset, 08873 (732) 873-5500
IVC Industries, Inc. see. Intergel Vitamin Co., Irvington
IVC Industries, Inc., 500 Halls Mill Rd., Freehold, 07728 (732) 308-3000
iVillage, Inc., 900 Sylvan Ave., Englewood Cliffs, 07632 (212) 664-4444
★ Ivo Delicious Meat Products, Inc., 206 Dayton Ave., Passaic, 07055 (973) 223-4044
Ivoclar Vivadent Mfg., Inc., 500 Memorial Dr., Somerset, 08873 (732) 563-4755
Ivyskin, LLC, 282 Grand Ave., Englewood, 07631 (201) 266-5555
IWC see. International Wire Co., Bridgewater
J & D Tool, LLC, 5 Grant St., Linden, 07036 (908) 486-5353
J & E Metal Fabricators, Inc., 1 Coan Pl., Metuchen, 08840 (732) 548-9650
J & G Enterprises, Inc., 182 High St., Nutley, 07110 (973) 667-7673
†★ J & H Berge, Inc., 4111 S. Clinton Ave., South Plainfield, 07080 (908) 561-1234
J & J Corp., Inc., 8607 River Rd., North Bergen, 07047 (201) 313-0900
J & J Custom Metal Fabricators, Inc., 85 5th Ave., Ste. 17, Paterson, 07524 (973) 977-9373
J & J Engraving, 45 Worth St., South Hackensack, 07606 (201) 342-0798
†★ J & J Industrial Supply, Inc.,
113 E. Centre St., P.O. Box 110174, Nutley, 07110 (973) 235-0100
J & J Marine, 1596 Hurffville Rd., Sewell, 08096 (856) 228-4744
J & J Materials, Inc., 49 Laurel Ave., P.O. Box 2128, Neptune City, 07753 (732) 988-3300
† J & J Metals Trading, LLC, 26 Edie Dr., Marlboro, 07746 (732) 617-0500
J & J Printing Co., 1023 Broadway, Bayonne, 07002 (201) 858-8895
J & J Radiator Shop, 71 St. Mihiel Dr., Delran, 08075 (856) 461-3533
J & J Snack Foods Corp. see. Federal Pretzel Baking Co., Bridgeport
★ J & J Snack Foods Corp., 361 Benigno Blvd., Ste. A, Bellmawr, 08031 (856) 933-3597

© Copyright 2015 Manufacturers' News, Inc.


J & J Snack Foods Corp., 6000 Central Hwy., Pennsauken, 08109 ........ (856) 665-9534
J & J Snack Foods Corp. see. ........ Uptown Bakeries/J & J Snack Foods, Bridgeport
J & K Ingredients, Inc., 160 E. 5th St., Paterson, 07524 ........ (973) 340-8700
★ J & L Boat Canvas, 190 Drum Point Rd., Brick, 08723 ........ (732) 262-1535
J & M Air, Inc., 189 S. Bridge St., Somerville, 08876 ........ (908) 707-4040
J & M Enterprises, 32 North Ave., Cedarville, 08311 ........ (856) 447-5090
J & M Mfg., Inc., 54 Main St., P.O. Box 43, High Bridge, 08829 ........ (908) 638-6727
J & M Precision Enterprises, Inc., 8103 River Rd., Pennsauken, 08110 ........ (856) 661-9595
J & R Lamb Studios, Inc., 190 Greenwood Ave., Midland Park, 07432 ........ (201) 891-8585
J & R Pallets see. ........ F & R Pallets, Inc., Camden
J & R Printing, Inc., 301 S. Main St., Cape May Court House, 08210 ........ (609) 465-3530
J & R Rebuilders, Inc., 330 Washington Ave., Laurel Springs, 08021 ........ (856) 627-1414
J & S Finishing, Inc., 443 62nd St., West New York, 07093 ........ (201) 854-0338
J & S Precision Co., 16 Medford Evesboro Rd., Medford, 08055 ........ (609) 654-0900
J A M B Industries, 336 Rockaway Valley Rd., Boonton, 07005 ........ (973) 263-9295
J A Machine & Tool Co., Inc., 84 Herbert Ave., Closter, 07624 ........ (201) 767-1308
J. B. & Sons Concrete Products Co., 358 New Brooklyn Rd., Berlin, 08009 ........ (856) 767-4140
J B Electronics see. ........ Multiforce Systems Corp., Princeton
J. B. Welding, 2 Reynolds St., Pemberton, 08068 ........ (609) 894-9842
J. C. Orthopedic, Inc., 1680 Highway 88, Brick, 08724 ........ (732) 458-7900
J C Printing & Advertising, Inc., 168 8th Ave., Paterson, 07514 ........ (973) 881-8612
J D M Woodworking & Cabinetry, 226 Huyler St., South Hackensack, 07606 ........ (201) 646-1480
J. Emanuel Chocolatier, 461-B Main St., Chester, 07930 ........ (908) 955-7591
J F I Printing, Inc., 357 Cortlandt St., Belleville, 07109 ........ (973) 759-3444
J. J. Orly, Inc., 20 Commerce Dr., Ste. 128, Cranford, 07016 ........ (908) 276-9212
J. Jeb Products, LLC, 10 Cutler Ave., P.O. Box 40, Westville, 08093 ........ (856) 845-4455
J. Josephson, Inc., 35 Horizon Blvd., South Hackensack, 07606 ........ (201) 440-7000
J K A Specialties Mfg., Inc., 157 Eayrestown Rd., Southampton, 08088 ........ (609) 859-2090
J K Design, Inc., 465 Amwell Rd., Hillsborough, 08844 ........ (908) 428-4700
J K Printing, 310 Edgewood Ave., Teaneck, 07666 ........ (201) 833-8181
J M C Tool & Mfg. Co., 845 Fairfield Ave., Kenilworth, 07033 ........ (908) 241-8950
J. M. Fry Company, Inc. see. ........ J.M. Fry Co., Inc., East Brunswick
J M J Printing & Graphics, Inc., 1403 State Route 23, Ste. 8, Butler, 07405 ........ (973) 838-3400
J M J Profile, Inc., 154 Copper Rd., Unit 1303, West Berlin, 08091 ........ (856) 767-3930
J M J Woodworking, Inc., 100 8th St., Bldg. 300, Passaic, 07055 ........ (973) 471-6449
J M L Computer Products, Inc., 9 Wheelwright Ln., Cherry Hill, 08003 ........ (856) 753-8500
J M Machine Co., LLC, 5 Central Ave., Ste. 2, P.O. Box 1863, Clifton, 07011 ........ (973) 253-2188
J M T Design, Inc., 914 Route 33, Fairfield Industrial Pk., Freehold, 07728 ........ (732) 409-6661
J N R Machine & Tool, 12 Ilene Ct., Bldg. 12, Unit 2, Hillsborough, 08844 ........ (908) 281-6603
J R C Web Accessories, Inc., 46 Passaic Ave., Fairfield, 07004 ........ (973) 625-3888
J R Engineering & Machine Corp., 663 Ramsey Ave., Hillside, 07205 ........ (908) 810-6300
J. R.'s Screen Printing,
1930 Greenwood Lake Tpke., P.O. Box 561, Hewitt, 07421 ........ (973) 728-7802
J S Designs, 321 Oakshade Rd., Shamong, 08088 ........ (609) 268-3018
J S Studios see. ........ Shedd Designs, LLC, John, Rocky Hill
J S Tool, LLC, 187 Wescott Dr., Ste. D, Rahway, 07065 ........ (732) 815-1382
J T D Sales, LLC (H Q), 71 Bloomfield Ave., Newark, 07104 ........ (973) 482-5070
J T Graphics, 34 Mt. Ephraim Ave., Mount Ephraim, 08059 ........ (856) 931-3548
J W S Computers, Inc., 20 S. Main, Lambertville, 08530 ........ (908) 730-6628
J Z D, LLC, 733 Route 18, East Brunswick, 08816 ........ (732) 257-2727
JA Visual Group, 150 Commerce Rd., Unit 3, Carlstadt, 07072 ........ (212) 463-0545
Ja-Bar Silicone Corp., 252 Brighton Rd., P.O. Box 1249, Andover, 07821 ........ (973) 786-5000
Jabat, Inc. see. ........ Jabat, Inc., K., Green Brook
Jabat, Inc., K., 342 Highway 22 W., Green Brook, 08812 ........ (732) 469-8177
Jabel see. ........ Jocely, Inc., Mountainside
JABS Personal Stitch, Inc., 1120 Raritan Rd., Clark, 07066 ........ (732) 396-9699
JACE Systems, Inc., 5 Rockhill Rd., Ste. 2, Cherry Hill, 08003 ........ (800) 800-4276
★ Jack Doheny Companies, Inc., 15 Taylor Rd., Ste. 1, Wharton, 07885 ........ (973) 659-0061
Jack Georges, Inc., 823 Main Ave., Passaic, 07055 ........ (973) 777-6999
Jackie Evans, Inc., 1823 3rd St., Passaic, 07055 ........ (973) 471-6991
Jackson Racing Engines, Inc., Henry, 787 Route 537, Cream Ridge, 08514 ........ (609) 758-7476
Jaclo Industries, 129 Dermody St., Cranford, 07016 ........ (908) 653-4433
Jaclyn, Inc., 197 W. Spring Valley Ave., Ste. 1, Maywood, 07607 ........ (201) 909-6000
Jacobus Pharmaceutical Co., Inc., 37 Cleveland Ln., Princeton, 08540 ........ (609) 921-7447
Jacobus Pharmaceutical Co., Inc., P.O. Box 5290, Princeton, 08540 ........ (609) 799-8221
Jacquard Fabrics Co., Inc., 1965 Swarthmore Ave., Lakewood, 08701 ........ (732) 905-4545
Jade Apparel, Inc., 133 Kossuth St., Newark, 07105 ........ (973) 522-1003
Jade Eastern Trading, Inc., 245 Moonachie Rd., Moonachie, 07074 ........ (201) 440-8500
Jafco Industries, LLC, 136 Lincoln Blvd., Middlesex, 08846 ........ (732) 356-1502
Jagielky's Home Made Candy, 5115 Ventnor Ave., Ventnor City, 08406 ........ (609) 823-6501
† Jaguar Land Rover North America, 555 MacArthur Blvd., Mahwah, 07430 ........ (201) 818-8500
James Alexander Corp., 845 State Route 94, Blairstown, 07825 ........ (908) 362-9266
James Candy Company, 1519 Boardwalk, Atlantic City, 08401 ........ (609) 344-1519
James Candy Company, Inc. see. ........ James Candy Company, Atlantic City
James Co., The Tom see. ........ Individualized Shirts, Inc., Perth Amboy
James D. Morrissey, Inc. see. ........ Ward Sand & Materials, Vincentown
Jamesburg Press Madison Printing, Inc., 9 E. Railroad Ave., Jamesburg, 08831 ........ (732) 521-0262
Jamis Bicycle see. ........ Joannou Cycle Co., Inc., G., Northvale
Jamm Litho, Inc., 185 Broadway, Long Branch, 07740 ........ (732) 870-1999
Jamm Printing see. ........ Accucolor, LLC, Shrewsbury
Jamm Printing see. ........ Jamm Litho, Inc., Long Branch
Jamm Printing, 108 W. Sylvania Ave., Neptune, 07753 ........ (732) 502-0110
Jamol Laboratories, Inc., 13 Ackerman Ave., P.O. Box 313, Emerson, 07630 ........ (201) 262-6363
Jan Fence Co., Inc., 4 Industrial Rd., Pompton Plains, 07444 ........ (973) 694-4055
Jan L, Inc., 26 Mill St., Ste. 26, Mount Holly, 08060 ........ (609) 261-1133
Jan Packaging, Inc., 100 Harrison St., Dover, 07801 ........ (973) 361-7200
Jan-Mar Industries, 568 Hillsdale, P.O. Box 314, Hillsdale, 07642 ........ (201) 664-3930
Jannetti, Inc., Anthony J., 200 E. Holly Ave., Sewell, 08080 ........ (856) 256-2300
Jannetti Publications see. ........ Jannetti, Inc., Anthony J., Sewell
Janssen Pharmaceuticals, Inc.,
1125 Trenton-Harbourton Rd., P.O. Box 200, Titusville, 08560 ........ (908) 218-6000
Janssen Research & Development, LLC, A Div. of Johnson & Johnson,
920 U.S. Highway 202, P.O. Box 300, Raritan, 08869 ........ (908) 704-4000
Jantek Industries, LLC, 230 Route 70, Medford, 08055 ........ (609) 654-1030
Jarahian Millwork, Inc., 870 Route 530, Ste. 4, Whiting, 08759 ........ (732) 240-5151
Jarchem Industries, Inc., 414 Wilson Ave., Newark, 07105 ........ (973) 344-0600
Jarco Industries, Inc., 1803 Union Valley Rd., West Milford, 07480 ........ (973) 728-5012
Jarco U. S. Casting Corp., 109 45th St., Union City, 07087 ........ (201) 271-0003
Jarden Corp. see. ........ Quickie Mfg. Corp. (H Q), Cinnaminson
Jarrdd.Co, 141 Shreve Ave., Barrington, 08007 ........ (856) 310-0100
Jason Furniture & Plastic Covers, Inc., 334 State St., Perth Amboy, 08861 ........ (732) 442-9700
Jason Industrial Inc., 340 Kaplan Dr., P.O. Box 10004, Fairfield, 07004 ........ (973) 227-4904
Jason Metal Products Corp., 1072 Randolph Ave., Rahway, 07065 ........ (732) 396-1132
Jason Mills, LLC, 440 S. Main St., Milltown, 08850 ........ (732) 651-7200
Jason Steel Co., Inc., 1701 Hylton Rd., Pennsauken, 08110 ........ (856) 663-5010
J.A.W. Products, Inc., 835 Industrial Hwy., Unit 125, Cinnaminson, 08077 ........ (856) 829-3210
Jay Bee Oil & Gas, Inc., 1720 U.S. Highway 22 E., Union, 07083 ........ (908) 686-1493
Jay-Bee Lamp & Shade Co., Inc., 33 Hoover Ave., Passaic, 07055 ........ (973) 473-1569
Jaygo, Inc., 7 Emery Ave., Randolph, 07869 ........ (908) 688-3600
JB Offset Printing Corp., 475 Walnut St., Norwood, 07648 ........ (201) 664-4400
JB Signs, 23 Dorchester Dr., P.O. Box 454, East Brunswick, 08816 ........ (732) 613-3700
J.B.A.T., Inc., 28 Coles Ave., Cherry Hill, 08002 ........ (856) 667-7307
★ JCW Rolling & Fabrication, 60 Liberty St., Metuchen, 08840 ........ (732) 548-7636
† J.D. Beverage Co., 10 Richards St., Newark, 07105 ........ (973) 344-8149
JD Graphics, Inc., 6 Richardson Ct., Marlboro, 07746 ........ (732) 972-7790
J.D. Machine Parts, Inc., 158 W. Weymouth Rd., Vineland, 08360 ........ (856) 691-8430
JDM Engineering, 60 Jerseyville Ave., Freehold, 07728 ........ (732) 780-0770
JDS Graphics, Inc., 220 Entin Rd., Clifton, 07014 ........ (973) 330-3300
JDS Uniphase Corp. see. ........ JDSU, Robbinsville
JDSU, 2 Applegate Dr., Robbinsville, 08691 ........ (609) 632-0800
JDV Equipment Corp., 1 Princeton Ave., Dover, 07801 ........ (973) 366-6556
Jeans Canvas * Resort Chairs * Custom Sandbox Covers see. ........ Kerry Wilkens, Inc., Belford
JED Display, LLC, 55 Arlington Ave., Kearny, 07032 ........ (201) 340-2329
Jedco Adhesives Co., Div. Of Morre-Tec Industries, Inc.,
1 Gary Rd., Union, 07083 ........ (908) 688-9009
Jefferson Lumber & Millwork Corp., 298 Espanong Rd., Lake Hopatcong, 07849 ........ (973) 663-3100
† Jefferson Medical & Imaging, Inc.,
5470 Berkshire Valley Rd., P.O. Box 254, Oak Ridge, 07438 ........ (973) 697-5077
★ Jefferson Printing Service, 184 Jefferson St., Newark, 07105 ........ (973) 491-0019
Jefferson Prosthetics & Orthotics, 120 Prospect St., South Orange, 07079 ........ (973) 762-0780
JEM Print Co., 36 Atlantic St., Bridgeton, 08302 ........ (856) 451-3885
Jem Printing see. ........ Printech, Flemington
Jema-American, Inc., 824 South Ave., Middlesex, 08846 ........ (732) 968-5333
Jencks Signs Corp., 50 Division Ave., Ste. 14, Millington, 07946 ........ (908) 542-1400
† Jen-Cyn Enterprises, Inc., 407 Atlantic Ave., Camden, 08104 ........ (856) 541-7400
Jenkins & Sons, Inc., M. W.,
444 Pompton Ave., P.O. Box 303, Cedar Grove, 07009 ........ (973) 239-5150
Jenkins, Inc., Brad, 291 Mount Kemble Ave., Morristown, 07960 ........ (973) 331-1995
Jenkins Plumbing & Heating,
103 S. Franklin, P.O. Box 509, Pleasantville, 08232 ........ (609) 641-6262
Jenson & Mitchell, Inc., 880 Communipaw Ave., Jersey City, 07304 ........ (201) 332-4140
Jerhel Plastics, Inc. (H Q), 63 New Hook Rd., Bayonne, 07002 ........ (201) 436-6662
Jerome Industries Corp., 730 Division St., Elizabeth, 07201 ........ (908) 353-5700
Jersey Artisan Distilling, 32 Pier Ln. W., Bldg. C, Fairfield, 07004 ........ (973) 521-7623
Jersey Cape Yachts, 2143 River Rd., Egg Harbor City, 08215 ........ (609) 965-8650
Jersey Chemicals, Inc., 775 River St., P.O. Box 542, Paterson, 07524 ........ (973) 523-3736
Jersey Cooperage Co., 20 River Rd., Sayreville, 08872 ........ (732) 254-1765
Jersey Cover Corp., 1746 Lakewood Rd., Toms River, 08755 ........ (732) 286-6300
Jersey Cow Software Co., Inc.,
3031 State Route 27, Ste. A, Franklin Park, 08823 ........ (732) 422-0101
† Jersey Diesel, 487 Main St., Dorchester, 08316 ........ (856) 785-8810
Jersey Door Control, Inc./ Bulldog Associates see. ........ Door Jockey, Inc., Wall
Jersey Granite & Tile, LLC, 234 Boundary Rd., Ste. 4, Marlboro, 07746 ........ (732) 683-1600
Jersey Jack Pinball, Inc., 1645 Oak St., Lakewood, 08701 ........ (732) 364-9900
Jersey Job Guide, Inc., 422 Morris Ave., Ste. 5, Long Branch, 07740 ........ (732) 263-9675
Jersey Journal, The, 1 Harmon Plz., Ste. 1010, Secaucus, 07094 ........ (201) 653-1000
Jersey Machine Tool Repairing & Rebuilding Co.,
1275 Bloomfield Ave., Bldg. 2, Unit 10, Fairfield, 07004 ........ (973) 575-1044
Jersey Metalworks, LLC, 1022 Hamilton St., Ste. A, Somerset, 08873 ........ (732) 565-1313
Jersey Microwave, LLC, 230 U.S. Highway 206, Ste. 407, Flanders, 07836 ........ (908) 684-2390
† Jersey Paper Plus, Inc., 600 Federal Blvd., Carteret, 07008 ........ (732) 750-1900
Jersey Paw Prints, P.O. Box 26, Mays Landing, 08330 ........ (609) 909-5100
Jersey Precast Corporation, 853 Nottingham Way, Trenton, 08638 ........ (609) 689-3700
Jersey Printing Assocs., Inc.,
153 1st Ave., P.O. Box 355, Atlantic Highlands, 07716 ........ (732) 872-9654
Jersey Sheet Metal & Machine, Inc., 90 E. Dickerson St., Dover, 07801 ........ (973) 366-0101
Jersey Shore Coffee Roasters, LLC, 64 Thompson Ave., Ste. B, Leonardo, 07737 ........ (732) 291-0505
Jersey Shore CPL, Inc., 301-C Commerce Dr., Freehold, 07728 ........ (732) 308-9990
Jersey Shore News Magazine see. ........ Sandpaper Newspaper, Surf City
Jersey Shore Publications, P.O. Box 176, Bay Head, 08742 ........ (732) 892-1276
Jersey Shore Steel, Inc., 636 Herman Rd., Jackson, 08527 ........ (732) 833-8855
Jersey Steel Doors, Inc., 95 N. 11th St., Newark, 07107 ........ (973) 482-4020
Jersey Strand & Cable, Inc., 259 Center St., Phillipsburg, 08865 ........ (908) 213-9350
Jersey Tank Fabricators, Inc., 1271 New Market Ave., South Plainfield, 07080 ........ (908) 561-2865
Jersey Tempered Glass, Inc.,
2035 Briggs Rd., P.O. Box 205, Mount Laurel, 08054 ........ (856) 273-8700
Jersey Windows & Building Supplies, 831 Broadway, Newark, 07104 ........ (973) 482-3614
JerseyCarts, LLC, 6 Whiskey Ln., Flemington, 08822 ........ (908) 806-6400
† Jesco, Inc., 118 Saint Nicholas Ave., South Plainfield, 07080 ........ (908) 821-1400
Jescraft, 201 W. Fort Lee Rd., Bogota, 07603 ........ (201) 488-4545
Jesel, Inc., 1985 Cedar Bridge Ave., Ste. 2, Lakewood, 08701 ........ (732) 901-1800
★ Jesper Office, LLC, 745 Route 202/206 S., Ste. 300, Somerville, 08876 ........ (908) 218-4200
Jesse J. Heap & Sons, Inc., 576 S. 21st St., Irvington, 07111 ........ (973) 372-1559
Jessup, Inc., Charles, 177 Smith St., Keasbey, 08832 ........ (732) 324-0430
† Jessup, Inc., Charles M., 177 Smith St., Keasbey, 08832 ........ (732) 324-0430
Jet Industrial Electronics Corp., 104 Ridge Rd., Oak Ridge, 07438 ........ (973) 697-2300
† Jet Line Products, Inc., 55 Jacobus Ave., Kearny, 07032 ........ (973) 690-2999
Jet Precision Metal, Inc., 7 Schoon Ave., Hawthorne, 07506 ........ (973) 423-4350
Jet Pulverizer Co., Inc., 1255 N. Church St., Moorestown, 08057 ........ (856) 235-5554
★ Jetek Enterprises, LLC, 4329 Atlantic Brigantine Blvd., Brigantine, 08203 ........ (609) 266-4700
† Jetro Cash & Carry, Inc., 1 Amity St., Jersey City, 07304 ........ (201) 434-4334
Jettron Products, Inc., 56 Route 10 W., P.O. Box 337, East Hanover, 07936 ........ (973) 887-0571
★ Jetty Life, LLC, 1435 Route 539, Unit A-6, Tuckerton, 08087 ........ (609) 296-2411
Jewel Precision Sheet Metal Machining, Inc.,
200 Commerce Rd., Cedar Grove, 07009 ........ (973) 857-5545
Jeweler's Gallery Corp., 9 W. Main St., Mendham, 07945 ........ (973) 543-6117
Jewelry Arts Mfg., Inc., 1701 Summit Ave., Union City, 07087 ........ (201) 864-5188
★ Jewelry Design Gallery, Inc., 357 U.S. Highway 9, Ste. 18, Englishtown, 07726 ........ (732) 536-1184
Jewelry Tool & Die Co., 4 Mark Rd., Ste. G, Kenilworth, 07033 ........ (908) 686-3500
Jewelry Tray & Pad Co., Inc., 1150 Edgewater Ave., Ridgefield, 07657 ........ (201) 941-4300
★ Jewish Voice, 73 Dana Pl., P.O. Box 8097, Englewood, 07631 ........ (201) 569-2845
† JFC International, Inc., 55 Wildcat Way, Linden, 07036 ........ (908) 525-4400
† JFD Associates, Inc., 15 Railroad Ave., Farmingdale, 07727 ........ (732) 751-9041
JG Machine Works, 2182 State Route 35, Holmdel, 07733 ........ (732) 203-2077

ALPHABETICAL

★ Indicates new listing this edition.
† Indicates wholesaler/distributor.

★ JHDS, LLC, 107 Beaverbrook Rd., Ste. 3, Lincoln Park, 07035 .......... (973) 782-4086
JHP Pharmaceuticals, LLC, 1 Upper Pond Rd., Bldg. D, Parsippany, 07054 .......... (973) 658-3530
Jigsaw Publishing, LLC, 8 Hemlock Ct., Butler, 07405 .......... (973) 838-4838
Jill's Thrill, Inc., 18 Hardley Dr., Cranbury, 08512 .......... (609) 395-9900
Jimcam Publishing, Inc., 19 W. Pleasant Ave., Maywood, 07607 .......... (201) 843-5700
Jimmy's Cookies, LLC, 18-01 River Rd., Fair Lawn, 07410 .......... (201) 797-8900
Jim's Signs, 1400 Rahway Ave., Ste. 3, Avenel, 07001 .......... (732) 381-8700
J.I.T. Mfg., Inc., 50 Peel St., Paterson, 07524 .......... (973) 247-7300
JJ Products, Inc., 133 Mountain Ave., West Caldwell, 07006 .......... (973) 228-3460
JM Custom Design Millwork, 101 Hobart St., Hackensack, 07601 .......... (201) 487-8990
J.M. Fry Co., Inc., 124 Tices Ln., Ste. A, East Brunswick, 08816 .......... (732) 238-1060
JM Lifestyles, LLC, 215 State Route 10, Ste. 3, Randolph, 07869 .......... (973) 668-5057
JMA * Torino Sausage Co. see .......... JMA Sausage And Meat Company, Inc., Lyndhurst
JMA Sausage And Meat Company, Inc.,
205 Stuyvesant Ave., Ste. 211, Lyndhurst, 07071 .......... (201) 636-2022
J-Mac Plastics, Inc., 40 Lafayette Pl., Kenilworth, 07033 .......... (908) 709-1111
JMC Design & Graphics, Inc., 144 Fairfield Rd., Fairfield, 07004 .......... (973) 276-9033
JMK Tool, Die & Mfg. Co., Inc., 19 W. Passaic St., Rochelle Park, 07662 .......... (201) 845-4710
JMM Signs, LLC see .......... Sign-A-Rama, Manville
JNT Technical Services, Inc., 85 Industrial Ave., Little Ferry, 07643 .......... (201) 641-2130
Jo Bella Machine Mfg., 232 Washington Ave., Carteret, 07008 .......... (732) 541-7076
† Joannou Cycle Co., Inc., G., 151 Ludlow Ave., Northvale, 07647 .......... (201) 768-9050
Jobe Industries, Inc. (H Q),
1600 W. Elizabeth Ave., P.O. Box 1367, Linden, 07036 .......... (908) 862-0400
JOC Group, Inc., 2 Penn Plz. E., 12th Fl., Newark, 07105 .......... (973) 776-8660
Jocely, Inc., 280 Sheffield St., Mountainside, 07092 .......... (800) 526-4597
JOCO Precision, Inc., 333 Dalziel Rd., Linden, 07036 .......... (908) 862-1611
Jo-De Machine Co., Inc., 43 Ethel Ave., Hawthorne, 07506 .......... (973) 427-9555
Jodhpuri Collections, LLC * Flora Garden, Inc see .......... Jodhpuri, Inc., Parsippany
Jodhpuri, Inc., 260-A Walsh Dr., Parsippany, 07054 .......... (973) 299-7009
Joey's Fine Foods, Inc., 135 Manchester Pl., Newark, 07104 .......... (973) 482-1400
Joffe Lumber & Supply, Inc., 18 Burns Ave., Vineland, 08360 .......... (856) 825-9550
Johanna Foods, Inc., 20 Johanna Farms Rd., P.O. Box 272, Flemington, 08822 .......... (908) 788-2200
Johanson Mfg. Corp., 301 Rockaway Valley Rd., Boonton, 07005 .......... (973) 334-2676
John Crane, Inc., 301 Berkeley Dr., Swedesboro, 08085 .......... (856) 241-3507
John Crane, Inc. see .......... U.S. Seal Mfg., Somerset
John Wm. Macy CheeseSticks, Inc., 80 Kipp Ave., Elmwood Park, 07407 .......... (201) 791-8036
† Johns Manville, 437 North Grove St., Berlin, 08009 .......... (856) 768-7000
Johns Manville, 1000 Liddle Ave., Edison, 08837 .......... (732) 225-9190
Johnson & Johnson see .......... Ethicon, Inc., Somerville
Johnson & Johnson see .......... Janssen Pharmaceuticals, Inc., Titusville
Johnson & Johnson see. Janssen Research & Development, LLC, A Div. of Johnson & Johnson, Raritan
Johnson & Johnson see .......... Johnson & Johnson Consumer Companies, Inc. (H Q), Skillman
Johnson & Johnson (H Q), 1 Johnson & Johnson Plz., New Brunswick, 08933 .......... (732) 524-0400
Johnson & Johnson Consumer Companies, Inc. (H Q),
199 Grandview Rd., Skillman, 08558 .......... (908) 874-1000
Johnson & Mayer, Inc., 58 Hobart St., Hackensack, 07601 .......... (201) 646-1717
Johnson & Sons, Inc., S., 1 Hardwick St., P.O. Box 66, Belvidere, 07823 .......... (908) 475-2155
† Johnson & Towers, Inc., 2701 Fire Rd., Egg Harbor Township, 08234 .......... (609) 272-1415
Johnson & Towers, Inc., 2021 Briggs Rd., P.O. Box 4000, Mount Laurel, 08054 .......... (856) 234-6990
Johnson Atelier, 60 Sculptors Way, Mercerville, 08619 .......... (609) 890-7777
Johnson Copy Center, Inc., Robert, 1438 Queen Anne Rd., Teaneck, 07666 .......... (201) 833-8997
Johnson Engineering, Welton V., 22 N. 26th St., Kenilworth, 07033 .......... (908) 241-3100
Johnson Matthey, Inc. see .......... INTERCAT, Inc. (H Q), Manasquan
Johnson Matthey, Inc. see .......... Johnson Matthey Pharmaceutical Materials, Paulsboro
Johnson Matthey, Inc., 2001 Nolte Dr., West Deptford, 08066 .......... (856) 384-7000
Johnson Matthey Pharmaceutical Materials, 2003 Nolte Dr., Paulsboro, 08066 .......... (856) 384-7001
Johnson Truck Center see .......... Johnson & Towers, Inc., Egg Harbor Township
† Johnson's Appliances & Bedding,
930 Asbury Ave., P.O. Box 95, Ocean City, 08226 .......... (609) 399-1598
† Johnson's Appliances & Bedding, 2510 New York Ave., Wildwood, 08260 .......... (609) 522-1421
Johnston Letter Co., Inc., 1634 E. Elizabeth Ave., Linden, 07036 .......... (908) 928-1217
Johnstone Supply see .......... Z & Z Holding Co Inc, Kenilworth
Johnstone Supply, Inc. see .......... Z & Z Holding Co Inc, Kenilworth
Jomar Corp., 115 E. Parkway Dr., Egg Harbor Township, 08234 .......... (609) 646-8000
Jonart Metals, LLC, 710 New Brunswick Ave., P.O. Box 333, Rahway, 07065 .......... (732) 382-0300
Jonathan Leasing Corp., 17 Water St., Lebanon, 08833 .......... (908) 226-3434
Jon-Da Printing Co., 234 16th St., 8th Fl., Jersey City, 07310 .......... (201) 653-6200
Jones & Son, Inc., William, 238 Liberty St., Camden, 08104 .......... (856) 963-1199
Jordan Mfg., LLC, 28 Randazzo Rd., P.O. Box 226, Lafayette, 07848 .......... (973) 383-8363
Jorgensen-Carr Ltd., 50 Dey St., 4th Fl., Jersey City, 07306 .......... (201) 792-2278
Jory Engravers, Inc., 23 W. Erie Ave., Rutherford, 07070 .......... (201) 939-1546
Joseph Castings, Inc., 25 Brook Ave., Maywood, 07607 .......... (201) 712-0717
Joseph Oat Corp., 2500 S. Broadway, Camden, 08104 .......... (856) 541-2900
† Josmo Shoes, Inc., 601 59th St., West New York, 07093 .......... (201) 617-1477
Jost Brothers, Inc., 295 Jost Dr., Oxford, 07863 .......... (908) 453-2266
Jostens, Inc., 86 Roseville Rd., Andover, 07821 .......... (973) 584-5843
Joti Kitchens, 413 S. Main St., Pleasantville, 08232 .......... (609) 383-1350
★ Journal America, 1950 Greenwood Lake Tpke., P.O. Box 459, Hewitt, 07421 .......... (973) 728-8355
Journal Multimedia see .......... NJBIZ, Somerset
Journal Register Co., The, 32 S. Main St., Ste. A, Medford, 08055 .......... (609) 654-5000
Joyrei Enterprises, Inc., 3143 Bordentown Ave., Parlin, 08859 .......... (732) 727-0742
JP Rotella Co., Inc., 20 E. Barbour St., Haledon, 07508 .......... (973) 942-2559
J.P. Veggies, Inc., 222 New Rd., Parsippany, 07054 .......... (973) 808-1540
JRE Incorporated, 22 Fairfield Pl., West Caldwell, 07006 .......... (973) 808-0055
JRM Industries, Inc., 1 Mattimore St., Passaic, 07055 .......... (973) 779-9340
J.R.M. Products, Inc., 701 Locust St., Keyport, 07735 .......... (732) 495-3092
JSM Co., 1052 Wayside Rd., Tinton Falls, 07712 .......... (732) 695-9577
Judy Lynn Software, Inc.,
278 Dunhams Corner Rd., P.O. Box 373, East Brunswick, 08816 .......... (732) 390-8845
Julius Machine & Tool Co., B-14 Merry Ln., East Hanover, 07936 .......... (973) 515-8540
† Jump Apparel, 350 Secaucus Rd., Secaucus, 07094 .......... (201) 558-9191
Jury Verdict Review Publications, 45 Springfield Ave., Springfield, 07081 .......... (973) 376-9002
★ JUST Nation, LLC, 359 Central Ave., Newark, 07103 .......... (973) 485-5878
Just Us Books, Inc., P.O. Box 5306, East Orange, 07019 .......... (973) 672-7701
J.V.M. Sales, Inc., 3401-A Tremley Point Rd., Linden, 07036 .......... (908) 862-4866
JW Industries, Inc., 21 Elbo Ln., Mount Laurel, 08054 .......... (856) 235-9285
K & A Industries, Inc., 51 Cragwood Rd., Ste. 204, South Plainfield, 07080 .......... (908) 226-7000
K & C Fund Raising & Embroidery, 101 S. Delsea Dr., Clayton, 08312 .......... (856) 881-6019
K & J Accessories, Inc., 25 Ridgewood Rd., Clifton, 07012 .......... (973) 777-6741
† K & J Scrap Metal, Inc., 609 25th St., Union City, 07087 .......... (201) 348-3368
K & K Automotive, Inc., 979 Main Ave., Passaic, 07055 .......... (973) 777-2235
K & R Precision Machining, 54 S. Front St., Bergenfield, 07621 .......... (201) 385-8855
K B Custom Interiors, 10-B Greenwood Ave., Woodbury, 08096 .......... (856) 845-9112
† K C S Metal Products, Inc., 415 Ferry St., Newark, 07105 .......... (973) 578-2688
K D Industries, Inc., 18 Falstrom Ct., Passaic, 07055 .......... (973) 594-4800
K G Designs, Inc., 581 Ogden Ave., Teaneck, 07666 .......... (201) 692-1852
K G M Precision Corp., 1875 Route 206, Southampton, 08088 .......... (609) 801-0210
K H Machine Works, 4322 Grand Ave., North Bergen, 07047 .......... (201) 867-2338
K L M Mechanical Contractors, Inc., 109 W. Shore Ave., Dumont, 07628 .......... (201) 385-6965
K R B Printing For Business, 1165 Marlkress Rd., Ste. G, Cherry Hill, 08003 .......... (856) 751-5200
K R Electronics, Inc., 91 Avenel St., Avenel, 07001 .......... (732) 636-1900
† K. S. I. Trading Corp., 100 Wade Ave., Ste. A, South Plainfield, 07080 .......... (908) 668-1380
K T S Machine Shop, 60 Bushes Ln., Elmwood Park, 07407 .......... (201) 791-2228
K V K U. S. A., Inc., 19-A Home News Row, New Brunswick, 08901 .......... (732) 846-2355
K W, Inc., 1536 Lower Ferry Rd., Ewing, 08618 .......... (609) 882-6363
† Kaffe Magnum Opus, 500 S. Wade Blvd., Millville, 08332 .......... (856) 327-9962
Kahle Automation, 89 Headquarters Plz., Ste. 355, Morristown, 07960 .......... (973) 993-1850
Kahle Engineering Corp. see .......... Kahle Automation, Morristown
Kaistar Research & Development, LLC, 15 Wilson Dr., Sparta, 07871 .......... (973) 362-1487
Kaizen Technologies, Inc., 1 State Route 27, Ste. 10, Edison, 08820 .......... (732) 452-9555
† KALDOR Emergency Lights, LLC, 19 Vanderburg Rd., Marlboro, 07746 .......... (732) 780-6707
Kalis Metal Components Corp., 231 North Ave., P.O. Box 294, Garwood, 07027 .......... (908) 789-0500
Ka-Lor Cubicle & Supply Co., Inc., P.O. Box 804, Fair Lawn, 07410 .......... (201) 891-8077
Kalustyan Corp., 855 Rahway Ave., Union, 07083 .......... (908) 688-6111
† Kaman Industrial Technologies Corp., 502 Bloy St., Hillside, 07205 .......... (908) 687-0004
† Kaman Industrial Technologies Corp., 195 Borelli Rd., Paulsboro, 08066 .......... (856) 227-7000
† Kaman Industrial Technologies Corp.,
195 Borrelli Blvd., Ste. B, Paulsboro, 08066 .......... (856) 284-7400
Kamdem Group * Creation Flavors see .......... Creation Flavors International LLC, New Brunswick
Kampack, Inc., 100 Frontage Rd., Newark, 07114 .......... (973) 589-7400
Kane Wood Fuel, LLC, 512 Cedar Ave., Pitman, 08071 .......... (856) 589-3292
† Kanebridge Corp., 153 Bauer Dr., Oakland, 07436 .......... (201) 337-3200
Kane-M, Inc., 1 Madison St., Ste. F-9, East Rutherford, 07073 .......... (973) 777-2797
Kansai Special American Machine Corp.,
1 Madison St., Ste. F-11, East Rutherford, 07073 .......... (973) 470-8321
Kaplan & Zubrin, Inc., 2nd & Kaighn Ave., Camden, 08103 .......... (856) 964-1083
Kaplan Industries, Inc., 10 Morris Ave., Route 73, Maple Shade, 08052 .......... (856) 779-8181
Kappus Plastics Co., Inc., 61-65 Route 31 S., P.O. Box 151, Hampton, 08827 .......... (908) 537-2288
KapStone Paper And Packaging Corp. see .......... Kampack, Inc., Newark
Karcher North America see .......... Graco Manufacturing, Blackwood
† Karl's Appliance, LLC, 65 Passaic Ave., Fairfield, 07004 .......... (973) 227-1777
Karnak Corp., 330 Central Ave., Clark, 07066 .......... (732) 388-0300
Karr Glass, Inc., Peggy, 100 Washington St., Randolph, 07869 .......... (973) 659-1200
Kashmir Crown Bakery, 710 W. Linden Ave., Linden, 07036 .......... (908) 474-1470
★ Kashmir Crown Baking, LLC, 1030 W. Linden Ave., Linden, 07036 .......... (908) 474-0970
Kason Corp., 67-71 E. Willow St., Millburn, 07041 .......... (973) 467-8140
Katena Products, Inc., 4 Stewart Ct., Denville, 07834 .......... (973) 989-1600
Kathy Jeanne, Inc., 7 Industrial Rd., Fairfield, 07004 .......... (973) 575-9898
Kaufman Iron Works, Inc., J., 217 Godwin Ave., Paterson, 07501 .......... (718) 991-5400
Kaufman Mfg. Group * Kaufman Iron Works * Bedlam Architect see .......... T. S. Gates, Inc., Paterson
Kaufman Stairs, Inc., 150 E. Inman Ave., Rahway, 07065 .......... (732) 388-9870
Kaupp & Sons, Inc., C. B., 6 Newark Way, Maplewood, 07040 .......... (973) 761-4000
Kautex Machines, Inc.,
201 Chambers Brook Rd., P.O. Box 5329, North Branch, 08876 .......... (908) 252-9350
Kavango, Inc., 544 Lincoln Blvd., Middlesex, 08846 .......... (732) 424-2430
Kavayah Solutions, Inc., 5 Independence Way, Ste. 360, Princeton, 08540 .......... (609) 919-9797
Kavon Filter Products Co., Inc.,
5022 Industrial Rd., P.O. Box 1166, Wall Township, 07719 .......... (732) 938-3135
Kay, Inc., Scott, 780 Palisade Ave., Teaneck, 07666 .......... (201) 287-0100
Kay Machine Co., 130 Cannonball Rd., Pompton Lakes, 07442 .......... (973) 839-4404
Kay Printing Co. see .......... JDS Graphics, Inc., Clifton
Kay Printing Co., 220 Entin Rd., Clifton, 07014 .......... (973) 330-3000
Kay Window Fashions, Inc., 271 2nd St., Saddle Brook, 07663 .......... (862) 591-1555
Kayden Mfg., Inc., 83-A Burlews Ct., Hackensack, 07601 .......... (201) 880-9898
Kaydon Corp. see .......... Canfield Technologies/Bow Electronic Solder, Sayreville
Kayline Processing, Inc., 31 Coates St., Trenton, 08611 .......... (609) 695-1440
KayPENTAX, 3 Paragon Dr., Montvale, 07645 .......... (973) 628-6200
★ Kaystar Publishing, 5 Harvey Ln., Saddle River, 07458 .......... (201) 825-2736
KB Acrylics, Inc., I-295 Industrial Ctr., Bldg. B, Box 47, Westville, 08093 .......... (856) 589-3110
KB Design Group, Inc. see .......... KB Acrylics, Inc., Westville
KBM Kitchen & Bath, 75 Harrison St., Little Falls, 07424 .......... (973) 890-4900
KC Caps see .......... Capco Sportswear Inc. (H Q), Moonachie
† K-C International, LLC, 1608 Route 88, Ste. 301, Brick, 08724 .......... (732) 202-9500
KCB Bakery & Food Distribution see .......... Kashmir Crown Baking, LLC, Linden
KD Envelopes & Printing, LLC, 7 Mark Rd., Kenilworth, 07033 .......... (908) 686-1798
KDF Reprographics, Inc., 10 Volvo Dr., Rockleigh, 07647 .......... (201) 784-9991
Kearfott Corporation, Guidance & Navigation Div.,
1150 McBride Ave., Little Falls, 07424 .......... (973) 785-6000
Kearny Screw Machine Co., 554 Elm St., Kearny, 07032 .......... (201) 998-4363
Kearny Sheet Metal Works, Inc., 579 Davis Ave., Kearny, 07032 .......... (201) 991-4745
Kearny Smelting & Refining, Inc., 936 Harrison Ave., Ste. 5, Kearny, 07032 .......... (201) 991-7276
Kearny Steel Container Corp., 401 South St., Newark, 07105 .......... (973) 589-2070
Keator Bilt Custom Cabinets, 805 2nd Ave., Asbury Park, 07712 .......... (732) 776-5133
†★ Keehn Power Products, 132 Johnson Ave., Hackensack, 07601 .......... (201) 489-4454
Kefa Northeast, P.O. Box 88, Budd Lake, 07828 .......... (201) 664-5487
† Keith Industries, Inc., 248 Astor St., Newark, 07114 .......... (973) 642-3332
Kelken Construction Systems see .......... Kelken-Gold, Inc., Sayreville
Kelken-Gold, Inc., 550 Hartle St., Ste. C, Sayreville, 08872 .......... (732) 416-6730
Keller Welding Co., LLC, 22 Wantage Ave., Branchville, 07826 .......... (973) 948-0046
Kelles, Inc., 20 Hoiles Dr., Kenilworth, 07033 .......... (908) 241-9300
Kellogg Co., 322 S. Egg Harbor Rd., Hammonton, 08037 .......... (609) 567-2300
Kelly Graphics, LLC see .......... Sir Speedy Printing Centers, Woodbury
† Kelly, Inc., Myles F., 43-57 Harrison Ave., Harrison, 07029 .......... (973) 481-0600
† Kelly, Inc., Myles F., 210 W. Westfield Ave., Roselle Park, 07204 .......... (908) 245-7296
Keltex Imprinted Apparel, Inc.,
428-A Woodbine Oceanview Rd., Ocean View, 08230 .......... (609) 624-3252
Kemm Graphics, 94 Providence Blvd., Kendall Park, 08824 .......... (732) 718-3449
† Kemperle, Inc., Albert, 626 E. Elizabeth Ave., Linden, 07036 .......... (908) 925-6133
Kempton Wood Products, LLC, 2800 Ridgewood Rd., Wall, 07719 .......... (732) 449-8673
Kem-Wove, Inc. see .......... International Foam Products, Inc., Stanhope
Kenco Wire & Iron Products, Inc., 425 Carr Ave., Keansburg, 07734 .......... (732) 495-3000
Kendall Mfg. Co., Inc., 1366 Chews Landing Rd., Clementon, 08021 .......... (856) 227-2132
Keneco, Inc., 123 N. 8th St., P.O. Box 121, Kenilworth, 07033 .......... (908) 241-3700

© Copyright 2015 Manufacturers' News, Inc.


Kenilworth Anodizing see. .... B & M Finishers, Inc., Kenilworth
Ken-Mar Machine & Mfg., 477 E. 30th St., Paterson, 07504 .... (973) 278-5827
Kennedy Concrete, 1969 S. East Ave., Vineland, 08360 .... (856) 692-8650
† Kennedy Cos., The, 8000 Midlantic Dr., Ste. 200-N, Mount Laurel, 08054 .... (856) 813-5000
Kennedy Opticians, 552 Boulevard, Kenilworth, 07033 .... (908) 276-2020
Kenney Steel Treating Corp., 100 Quincy Pl., Kearny, 07032 .... (201) 998-4420
Kenny Wilbert Vault Co., 40 Shades of Death Rd., Great Meadows, 07838 .... (908) 637-4736
Kenrich Petrochemicals, Inc., 140 E. 22nd St., P.O. Box 32, Bayonne, 07002 .... (201) 823-9000
† Kenseal Construction Products Corp., 799 Edwards Rd., Parsippany, 07054 .... (973) 287-5858
† Kent International Inc., 60 E. Halsey Rd., Parsippany, 07054 .... (973) 434-8181
Kentucky Cabinet Corp., 601 Lehigh Ave., Union, 07083 .... (347) 452-5797
Kenvil Weldery & Machine, Inc., 15 Kings Pkwy., Ledgewood, 07852 .... (973) 584-1729
Kenyon & Sons, Inc., William, 90 Ethel Rd. W., Piscataway, 08854 .... (732) 985-8980
Kern & Szalai Machine, LLC, 351 Crider Ave., Moorestown, 08057 .... (856) 802-1500
Kern Printers & Stationers,
86 Lackawanna Ave., Unit 105, Woodland Park, 07424 .... (201) 226-0270
Kerry, Inc. see. .... Kerry Ingredients, Flemington
Kerry, Inc. see. .... Kerry Ingredients & Flavors, Clark
Kerry Ingredients, 26 Minneakoning Rd., Flemington, 08822 .... (908) 782-4919
Kerry Ingredients & Flavors, 160 Terminal Ave., Clark, 07066 .... (732) 882-0202
Kerry Wilkens, Inc., 780 State Route 36, Belford, 07718 .... (732) 787-0070
Kershaw Instrumentation, LLC,
517 Auburn Ave., P.O. Box 163, Swedesboro, 08085 .... (856) 467-5482
Keskes Printing Co., 5 W. Taunton Ave., Berlin, 08009 .... (856) 767-4733
Kessler Ellis Products Co., Inc.,
10 Industrial Way E., Ste. 6, Eatontown, 07724 .... (732) 935-1320
† Kessler Industries, Inc., 500 Green St., Woodbridge, 07095 .... (973) 684-2130
Kessler Sales & Distribution see. .... Kessler Industries, Inc., Woodbridge
Kessler Steel Rule Die, Inc.,
1004 Industrial Dr., Ste. 10, West Berlin, 08091 .... (856) 767-0231
Ketec, Inc., 1256 N. Church St., Ste. A, Moorestown, 08057 .... (856) 778-4343
Kevin's Sign Co., 1212 Bridgeboro Rd., Edgewater Park, 08010 .... (609) 871-2385
Key International, Inc., 4 Corporate Dr., Cranbury, 08512 .... (609) 619-3685
Key Joy International * KJ USA see. .... Key Joy USA, LLC, Edison
★ Key Joy USA, LLC, 3 Kellogg Ct., Ste. 12, Edison, 08817 .... (732) 339-0450
† KeyImpact Sales & Systems, Inc., 95 Connecticut Dr., Burlington, 08016 .... (609) 265-8300
Key-Pak Machines By Luciano Packaging Technologies, Inc,
29 County Line Rd., Somerville, 08876 .... (908) 722-3222
Keystone Adjustable Cap Co., 1591 Hylton Rd., Ste. B, Pennsauken, 08110 .... (856) 663-5740
Keystone Folding Box Co., Inc., 367 Verona Ave., Newark, 07104 .... (973) 483-1054
Keystone Industries, 616 Hollywood Ave., Cherry Hill, 08002 .... (856) 663-4700
Keystone Packaging Service, Inc., 555 Warren St., Phillipsburg, 08865 .... (908) 454-8567
Keystone Plastics, Inc., 3451 S. Clinton Ave., South Plainfield, 07080 .... (908) 561-1300
Keystone Printing, Inc., 21-C E. Madison Ave., Dumont, 07628 .... (201) 387-7252
KeyValet, 15 Industrial Dr., P.O. Box 1099, Laurence Harbor, 08879 .... (732) 521-1394
Kidde Fire Trainers, LLC, 17 Philips Pkwy., Montvale, 07645 .... (201) 300-8100
Kids At Our House, 47 Stoneham Pl., Metuchen, 08840 .... (732) 548-1779
Kids Of America Corp., 103 Route 46 W., Fairfield, 07004 .... (973) 808-8242
Kiker Sheet Metal Corp., 6 S. New Rd., P.O. Box 1487, Pleasantville, 08232 .... (609) 641-4890
Kimco Products, LLC, 64 E. Midland Ave., Ste. 5, Paramus, 07652 .... (201) 265-6800
Kin Core, 70 North St., P.O. Box 485, Bloomsbury, 08804 .... (908) 479-1188
Kinedyne Corp. (H Q), 151 Industrial Pkwy., Branchburg, 08876 .... (908) 231-1800
Kinesys Automation, Inc., 5 Fir Ct., Unit 3, Oakland, 07436 .... (201) 337-5000
Kinetics Industries, Inc., 140 Stokes Ave., Ewing, 08638 .... (609) 883-9700
Kinetics Infrared, 40 Pier Ln. W., Fairfield, 07004 .... (973) 575-5332
Kinetron, Inc., 1416 S. Roller Rd., Ocean, 07712 .... (732) 918-7777
KING, C. C. see. .... NCS Enterprises, Inc., Millville
King Engine Bearings, 371 Little Falls Rd., Ste. 5, Cedar Grove, 07009 .... (973) 857-0705
Kings Candy Co., Inc., 55 Bank St., P.O. Box 264, Elmwood Park, 07407 .... (201) 791-4444
Kingwood Industrial Products, Inc.,
261 Main St., Unit 1 & 2, Hackettstown, 07840 .... (908) 852-8655
Kinnarney Rubber Co., Inc., 450 Main St., P.O. Box 37, Mantua, 08051 .... (856) 468-1320
Kinnery Metal, 11 Exchange Pl., Passaic, 07055 .... (973) 473-4664
★ Kintech Printing & Direct Mail,
2400 Belmar Blvd., Ste. E-6, P.O. Box 12, Belmar, 07719 .... (732) 280-6245
Kirker Enterprises, Inc., 55 E. 6th St., Paterson, 07524 .... (973) 754-9000
Kirker Enterprises, Inc. see. .... Tevco Enterprises, Inc., South Plainfield
Kirkwood New York, 1 Teaneck Rd., Ridgefield Park, 07660 .... (201) 440-0800
Kirms * Kirms Printing see. .... School Publications Co., Inc., Neptune
Kirms Printing Co., Inc., 1520 Washington Ave., P.O. Box 1067, Neptune, 07753 .... (732) 774-8000
Kismet Furniture, Inc., 80 George St., Paterson, 07503 .... (973) 278-3117
Kissler & Co., Inc., 770 Central Blvd., Carlstadt, 07072 .... (201) 896-9600
Kisthardt Auto Products, LLC, 354 4th St., Ewing, 08638 .... (609) 434-0700
Kitchen & BathWorks see. .... United Supply Co., Inc., Plainfield
Kitchen King, Inc., 1561 Route 9, Toms River, 08755 .... (732) 341-9660
Kitchen Kraftsman, The, 343 State Route 34, Matawan, 07747 .... (732) 583-3321
Kiva Printing & Graphics, 50 Cutler Ave., Westville, 08093 .... (877) 777-5482
Kleemeyer & Merkel, Inc., 68 Britten Rd., P.O. Box 204, Green Village, 07935 .... (973) 377-0875
Klein Recycling, 2156 Camplain Rd., Hillsborough, 08844 .... (908) 722-2288
Klein Ribbon Designs, Jeffrey, 176 E. 7th St., Paterson, 07524 .... (973) 684-4671
† Klingelhofer Corp., 165 Mill Ln., Mountainside, 07092 .... (908) 232-7200
† Klinges, Inc., Charles A., 790 S. Mill Rd., Absecon, 08201 .... (609) 641-7755
Klose Assocs., Inc., 804 Broadway, West Long Branch, 07764 .... (732) 229-8950
KMBA Fashions, Inc., 272 Elmwood Ave., Bldg. 3, East Orange, 07018 .... (973) 789-1652
★ KMS Printing & Graphics, Inc., 401 N. Brookfield St., Vineland, 08361 .... (856) 205-0200
KNA Graphics, Inc., 303 N. 14th St., Kenilworth, 07033 .... (908) 272-4232
KNF Corp. see. .... KNF Flexpak Corporation., Jersey City
KNF Flexpak Corporation., 44 Howell St., Jersey City, 07306 .... (201) 656-4012
KNF Neuberger, Inc., 2 Black Forest Rd., Trenton, 08691 .... (609) 890-8600
Knickerbocker * Alloy Stainless Products see. .... Knickerbocker Machine Shop, Inc., Totowa
Knickerbocker Bed Co., 770 Commercial Ave., Carlstadt, 07072 .... (201) 933-3100
Knickerbocker Machine Shop, Inc., 611 Union Blvd., Totowa, 07512 .... (973) 256-1616
Knick-Knack, Inc., 20 Henry St., Teterboro, 07608 .... (201) 727-9339
Knockout Graphics, Inc., 522 Cookman Ave., Asbury Park, 07712 .... (732) 774-3331
† Knopf Automotive, LLC, 93 Shrewsbury Ave., Apt. 1, Red Bank, 07701 .... (732) 212-0444
Knorr Assocs., Inc., 10 Park Pl., P.O. Box 400, Butler, 07405 .... (973) 492-8500
Koamtac, Inc., 116 Village Blvd., Ste. 305, Princeton, 08540 .... (609) 256-4700
Koba Corp., 60 Baekeland Ave., Middlesex, 08846 .... (732) 469-0110
KOBO Products, Inc., 3474 S. Clinton Ave., South Plainfield, 07080 .... (908) 757-0033
Kobolak & Son, Inc., 1818 Bannard St., Cinnaminson, 08077 .... (856) 829-6106
Kobrick Coffee Co., Inc., 693 Luis Marin Blvd., Jersey City, 07310 .... (201) 656-6313

Koch Modular Process Systems, LLC,
45 Eisenhower Dr., Ste. 350, Paramus, 07652 .... (201) 368-2929
Koday Press, Inc., 69 Armour Pl., Dumont, 07628 .... (201) 387-0001
Kodex Inc., 160 Park Ave., Ste. 1, Nutley, 07110 .... (973) 235-0606
Koellmann Gear Corp., 8 Industrial Pk., Waldwick, 07463 .... (201) 447-0200
Ko-Fro Foods, Inc., 23 Mileed Way, Avenel, 07001 .... (732) 499-8282
Kohlder Mfg., Inc., 1001 Line St., Camden, 08103 .... (856) 342-8398
Kole Design, LLC, 35 Cedar Ct., Freehold, 07728 .... (732) 252-9365
Koll Machine & Tool Co., Frank G.,
390 Warburton Pl., P.O. Box 464, Long Branch, 07740 .... (732) 870-2966
Kolmar Laboratories, Inc. see. .... Acupac Packaging, Inc., Mahwah
Komline-Sanderson Engineering, 12 Holland Ave., Peapack, 07977 .... (908) 234-1000
Komo Machine, Inc., 1 Komo Dr., Lakewood, 08701 .... (732) 719-6222
Kompac Technologies, LLC, 7 Commerce St., Ste. 1, Somerville, 08876 .... (908) 534-8411
Konica Minolta Business Solutions U. S. A., Inc. (H Q),
100 Williams Dr., Ramsey, 07446 .... (201) 825-4000
Kontos Foods, Inc., 100 6th Ave., P.O. Box 628, Paterson, 07544 .... (973) 278-2800
Kooltronic, Inc., 30 Pennington-Hopewell Rd., P.O. Box 240, Pennington, 08534 .... (609) 466-3400
Kop-Coat, Inc., 36 Pine St., Rockaway, 07866 .... (973) 625-3100
† KOPO International, Inc., 100 Village Ct., Ste. 202, Hazlet, 07730 .... (732) 203-1505
Korea Daily, Inc., 10 E. Brinkerhoff Ave., Ste. 2-B, Palisades Park, 07650 .... (201) 944-8299
Korean Bergen News, 210 Sylvan Ave., Ste. 23, Englewood Cliffs, 07632 .... (201) 894-9061
Kornspan Jewelry, Inc., 1131 W. Saint Georges Ave., Linden, 07036 .... (908) 925-1101
Koslow Scientific Co., 172 Walkers Ln., Englewood, 07631 .... (201) 541-9100
Kovco Publishing, Inc., 230 W. Passaic St., Maywood, 07607 .... (201) 843-9099
KPMC, Inc., 113 Walters Ave., Trenton, 08638 .... (609) 538-1100
Kraemer Gunite, Inc., 137 Blackwood Barnsboro Rd., Sewell, 08080 .... (856) 227-8097
Kraemer Koating, Inc., 1925 Swarthmore Ave., Lakewood, 08701 .... (732) 886-6315
Kraft Power Corp., 241 W. Parkway, Pompton Plains, 07444 .... (973) 835-9800
★ Kraftape Printers, Inc., 124 Orchard St., Newark, 07102 .... (973) 824-3005
Kraftware Corp., 270 Cox St., Roselle, 07203 .... (908) 259-8883
Kraftwork Custom Design, 1837 S. Broad St., Hamilton, 08610 .... (609) 848-0578
Kraissl Co., Inc., 299 Williams Ave., Hackensack, 07601 .... (201) 342-0008
Kramer Electronics USA, Inc./Sierra Video Systems (H Q),
6 State Route 173 W., Clinton, 08809 .... (908) 735-0018
Kramer Industries, Inc., 140 Ethel Rd. W., Ste. U, Piscataway, 08854 .... (732) 650-9599
★ Kramer Shy & Assocs., 21 W. Delilah Rd., Pleasantville, 08232 .... (609) 646-2063
Kratos-CTI, 9 Whippany Rd., Bldg. A-1, Whippany, 07981 .... (973) 884-2580
Kratos-New England see. .... Kratos-CTI, Whippany
Kratt Pitch Pipe Co., Wm, 40 Lafayette Pl., Kenilworth, 07033 .... (908) 709-8901
Kraus & Naimer, Inc., 760 New Brunswick Rd., Somerset, 08873 .... (732) 560-1240
Krause Candy, Inc., Mrs. Hanna, 89 Westview Ave., Paramus, 07652 .... (201) 843-0337
Krause's Homemade Candy Co., 50 Bergen Blvd., Fairview, 07022 .... (201) 943-4790
Krazy Kat Sportswear, LLC, 100 Triangle Blvd., Carlstadt, 07072 .... (201) 438-3399
Kreisler Mfg. Corp., 180 Van Riper Ave., Elmwood Park, 07407 .... (201) 791-0700
Kremers Urban Pharmaceuticals, Inc. (H Q),
902 Carnegie Ctr., Ste. 360, Princeton, 08540 .... (609) 936-5940
Krohn Industries, Inc., 303 Veterans Blvd., P.O. Box 98, Carlstadt, 07072 .... (201) 933-9696
Kronos, Inc. see. .... SaaShr, Somerville
Kronos Worldwide, Inc., 5 Cedarbrook Dr., Ste. 2, Cranbury, 08512 .... (609) 860-6200
Krowne Metal Corp., 100 Haul Rd., Wayne, 07470 .... (973) 305-3300
Krug Industries Inc., 65 Brown Ave., Springfield, 07081 .... (973) 467-1040
Kruysman Co., Ron, 7100 W. Buckshutem Rd., Millville, 08332 .... (856) 327-0605
† KTK Corp., 65 Midvale Rd., Edison, 08817 .... (732) 985-0447
K-Tron Electronics, 590 Woodbury Glassboro Rd., Sewell, 08080 .... (856) 232-2300
† Kube-Pak Corp., 194 Route 526, Allentown, 08501 .... (609) 259-3114
Kubik Maltbie, Inc., 7000 Commerce Pkwy., Ste. C, Mount Laurel, 08054 .... (856) 234-0052
Kuehn Bevel, Inc., 10 Furnace St., Stanhope, 07874 .... (973) 584-8282
Kuehne Co., 86 Hackensack Ave., Kearny, 07032 .... (973) 589-0700
Kuhl Corp., 39 Kuhl Rd., P.O. Box 26, Flemington, 08822 .... (908) 782-5696
Kuiken Brothers see. .... Kuiken Brothers Commercial, Garfield
† Kuiken Brothers Commercial, 485 River Dr., Garfield, 07026 .... (973) 772-0044
Kuiken Brothers Company, Inc. see. .... Kuiken Brothers Commercial, Garfield
Kuiken Brothers Company, Inc.,
6-02 Fair Lawn Ave., P.O. Box 1040, Fair Lawn, 07410 .... (201) 796-2082
† Kuiken Brothers Company, Inc., 145 Lake Ave., Midland Park, 07432 .... (201) 652-1000
† Kuiken Brothers Company, Inc., 31 State Route 10 E., Succasunna, 07876 .... (973) 584-2444
Kuiken Brothers Company, Inc., 175 Route 23, Wantage, 07461 .... (973) 875-5106
Kulite Semiconductor Products, Inc., 1 Willow Tree Rd., Leonia, 07605 .... (201) 461-0900
† Kumar & Kumar, Inc., 57 Denise Dr., Edison, 08820 .... (732) 322-0435
Kumon Publishing North America, Inc.,
300 W. Frank Burr Blvd., Ste. 6, Teaneck, 07666 .... (201) 836-2105
Kuntz Co., Inc., R. T.,
5146 W. Hurley Pond Rd., P.O. Box 476, Farmingdale, 07727 .... (732) 751-1770
Kupelian Foods, Inc., 146 Bergen Tpke., Ridgefield Park, 07660 .... (201) 440-8055
Kurt Versen Inc, 10 Charles St., Westwood, 07675 .... (201) 664-8200
Kurth & Son, Inc., Edward, 220 Blackwood Barnsboro Rd., Sewell, 08080 .... (856) 227-8811
Kushner Draperies Mfg., LLC, 5305 Route 70, Pennsauken, 08109 .... (856) 317-9696
Kwality Foods, LLC, 1734 Oak Tree Rd., Edison, 08820 .... (732) 906-1941
KWG Industries, LLC, 330 Roycefield Rd., Unit B, Hillsborough, 08844 .... (908) 218-8900
Kyocera Document Solutions America, Inc. see. .... Allister Business Systems, Inc., Roselle
Kyocera Document Solutions America, Inc. (H Q),
225 Sand Rd., Fairfield, 07004 .... (973) 808-8444
L & B Printing, 2590 U.S. Highway 22, Scotch Plains, 07076 .... (908) 232-7770
L & D's Sapore Ravioli & Cheese, Inc., 429-B Lincoln Blvd., Middlesex, 08846 .... (732) 563-9190
L & L Kiln Mfg. Co., Inc., 505 Sharptown Rd., Swedesboro, 08085 .... (856) 294-0077
L & L Redi-Mix, Inc., 1939 U.S. Highway 206, Southampton, 08088 .... (800) 696-2271
L & L Welding Contractors, Inc., 3 Wheeling Rd., Dayton, 08810 .... (609) 395-1600
L & M Architectural Graphics, Inc., 20 Montesano Rd., Fairfield, 07004 .... (973) 575-7665
L & M Art Gallery, LLC, 126 Elmora Ave., Elizabeth, 07202 .... (908) 351-2633
L & M Machine & Tool Co., Inc., 105 Lehigh Ave., Paterson, 07503 .... (973) 523-5288
L & R Mfg. Co., Inc., 577 Elm St., P.O. Box 607, Kearny, 07032 .... (201) 991-5330
† L & W Supply Corp., 126 Route 94, Blairstown, 07825 .... (908) 362-6103
† L & W Supply Corp., 1351 Route 37 W., Toms River, 08755 .... (732) 341-3737
L & Z Tool & Engineering, Inc., 1691 U.S. Highway 22, Watchung, 07069 .... (908) 322-2220
L E C Electronics, Inc., 814 Warsaw Ave., Blackwood, 08012 .... (856) 227-3953
L J Engraving & Signs, 409 N. Wood Ave., P.O. Box 1039, Linden, 07036 .... (908) 925-3510
L M Air Technology, Inc., 1467 Pinewood St., Rahway, 07065 .... (732) 381-8200
L M C Corp., 23 E. 23rd St., Paterson, 07514 .... (973) 279-3573
L M C Precision, Inc., 91 Rome St., Ste. 93, Newark, 07105 .... (973) 522-0005
L P B Graphics, Inc., 512-514 Route 27, Iselin, 08830 .... (732) 283-4333
L R P & P Graphics see. .... Pat Publications, Cherry Hill

ALPHABETICAL

★ **Indicates new listing this edition.**

† **Indicates wholesaler/distributor.**

L S P Industrial Ceramics,
34 Mount Airy Village Rd., P.O. Box 302, Lambertville, 08530 ... (609) 397-8330
L. S. Software Systems, Inc., 419 12th St., Lakewood, 08701 ... (732) 367-7164
L V Adhesive, Inc., 341 Michele Pl., Carlstadt, 07072 ... (212) 925-2600
L-3 Communications Corp. see. L-3 Communications Corp., Space & Navigation Systems, Budd Lake
L-3 Communications Corp. see. ... L-3 Communications Mobile-Vision, Inc., Boonton
L.A. Champon & Co., Inc. (H Q), 266 Broadway, Long Branch, 07740 ... (732) 923-0003
La Dominica, 635 56th St., West New York, 07093 ... (201) 348-4294
La Esperanza Baking, 148 W. Forest Ave., Englewood, 07631 ... (201) 871-1934
La Favorite Industries, Inc., 33 Shady St., Paterson, 07524 ... (973) 279-1266
† La Fe Foods, Inc., 230 Moonachie Ave., Moonachie, 07074 ... (201) 329-6260
La Forge De Style, 57 Romanelli Ave., South Hackensack, 07606 ... (201) 488-1955
La Sierra Coffee Roasters, LLC, 42 Bartley Rd., Flanders, 07836 ... (973) 927-9595
Label Graphics Mfg., 315 Fairfield Rd., Unit 1, Fairfield, 07004 ... (973) 890-5665
Label Graphics Mfg., Inc. see. ... Label Graphics Mfg., Fairfield
Label Graphics Mfg., Inc., 175 Paterson Ave., Little Falls, 07424 ... (973) 890-5665
Label Master, Inc., 89 Dell Glen Ave., Lodi, 07644 ... (973) 546-3110
★ Label Tek, Inc., 357 Cortlandt St., Ste. 4, Belleville, 07109 ... (201) 390-3856
Labern Machine Products, 3388 Highway 22 W., Branchburg, 08876 ... (908) 722-1970
† Labnet International, Inc., 31 Mayfield Ave., Edison, 08837 ... (732) 417-0700
Laboratory Diagnostics Co., Inc.,
100 Route 520, P.O. Box 160, Morganville, 07751 ... (732) 536-6300
† Lab-Tech, Inc., 103 Stonehurst Ct., Northvale, 07647 ... (201) 784-1093
LabVantage Solutions, Inc., 265 Davidson Ave., Somerset, 08873 ... (908) 707-4100
Lacas Coffee Co., 7950 National Hwy., Pennsauken, 08110 ... (856) 910-8662
★ Lacey Cash Registers & Business Machines Co.,
2180 Llewellyn Pkwy., P.O. Box 1151, Forked River, 08731 ... (609) 971-9494
LACOA, Inc., 34 Waite St., Paterson, 07524 ... (973) 754-1000
LaCour, Inc., 36 Kulick Rd., Fairfield, 07004 ... (973) 227-4755
Laeger Metal Spinning Co., Inc., 1514 E. Elizabeth Ave., Linden, 07036 ... (908) 925-5530
Lager Glass Co., Inc., 1913 Heck Ave., P.O. Box 426, Neptune, 07753 ... (732) 775-9220
Laggren's, LLC, P.O. Box 7173, Monroe Township, 08831 ... (609) 235-9883
Lagniappe Foods, Inc., 546 Mitchell St., Orange, 07050 ... (973) 674-0498
Lagniappe Health Acquisition Co.,
34 Maple Ave., Ste. 102, P.O. Box 727, Pine Brook, 07058 ... (973) 256-7633
Laird & Co., Inc., 1 Laird Rd., Eatontown, 07724 ... (732) 542-0312
Laird Plastics, Inc., 135 Fieldcrest Ave., Ste. 135-F, Edison, 08837 ... (732) 593-2777
★ Lake Hopatcong News, 37 Nolans Point Park Rd., Lake Hopatcong, 07849 ... (973) 663-2800
Lake Small Engine Repair, LLC, 283 Cedar Grove Ln., Somerset, 08873 ... (732) 873-9047
Lally-Pak, Inc., 1209 Central Ave., Hillside, 07205 ... (908) 353-3344
Lamar Diamond Jewelry Corp.,
5600 John F. Kennedy Blvd., Ste. 109, West New York, 07093 ... (201) 863-8683
Lamart Corp., 16 Richmond St., Clifton, 07011 ... (973) 772-6262
Lamatek, Inc., 1226 Forest Pkwy., West Deptford, 08066 ... (856) 599-6000
Lamb Printing, Inc., 700 Grand Ave., Hackettstown, 07840 ... (908) 852-5354
Laminate Creations, LLC, 1235 Hurffville Rd., Deptford, 08096 ... (856) 232-8323
Laminated Industries, Inc., 2000 Brunswick Ave., Linden, 07036 ... (908) 862-5995
Laminetics, Inc., 1263 River Ave., Lakewood, 08701 ... (732) 367-1116
Lamitech, Inc., 322 Half-Acre Rd., Cranbury, 08512 ... (609) 860-8037
Lamonica Fine Foods, 48 Gorton Rd., P.O. Box 309, Millville, 08332 ... (856) 825-8111
Lamson Airtubes, LLC, 10 Millpond Dr., Unit 4, Lafayette, 07848 ... (973) 300-4267
Lanco York, Inc., 864 E. 25th St., Paterson, 07513 ... (973) 278-7400
Landice, Inc., 111 Canfield Ave., Unit A-1, Randolph, 07869 ... (973) 927-9010
Landsman Custom Picture Framing, 600 S. White Horse Pike, Somerdale, 08083 ... (856) 784-2145
★ Landsman Uniforms, Inc.,
4450 Black Horse Pike, Ste. 3958, Mays Landing, 08330 ... (609) 909-1000
Landsman's, The see. ... Landsman Custom Picture Framing, Somerdale
Landzettel & Sons, Inc., 17-12 River Rd., Fair Lawn, 07410 ... (201) 796-3506
Lane Bond Traders, 27 Cedar Lake Rd., Denville, 07834 ... (973) 586-2720
Lane Signs, 34 Central Ave., Toms River, 08753 ... (732) 349-1904
Langendorff Corp., 633 Grove St., Jersey City, 07310 ... (201) 659-6300
Lanman & Kemp-Barclay & Co., Inc.,
25 Woodland Ave., P.O. Box 421, Westwood, 07675 ... (201) 666-4990
† Lantek Corporation, 29 Brookfield Dr., Sparta, 07871 ... (973) 579-8100
Lapp USA, 29 Hanover Rd., Florham Park, 07932 ... (973) 660-9700
Laracca Mfg., Inc., 395 Little Falls Rd., Cedar Grove, 07009 ... (973) 571-1452
Lardieri's Custom Woodworking, Inc.,
1830 Swarthmore Ave., Ste. 6, Lakewood, 08701 ... (732) 905-6334
LaRosa Bakery, Inc., 79 Neuman Springs Rd. E., Shrewsbury, 07702 ... (732) 842-4324
Larson-Juhl, LLC, 165 Clinton Rd., Caldwell, 07006 ... (973) 439-1801
Larue Manufacturing Corporation see. ... American Display, Whitehouse
LAS Printing, 1 Trenton Ave., Clifton, 07011 ... (201) 991-5362
Laser Dim Graphics & Printing, 2 Parkwood Ln., Colts Neck, 07722 ... (732) 821-9000
Laser Energetics, Inc., 3535 Quakerbridge Rd., Ste. 700, Mercerville, 08619 ... (609) 587-8250
Laser Save, 843 State Route 33, Ste. 11, Freehold, 07728 ... (732) 431-3339
★ Laser Xpressions, Inc., 3710 Route 9 S., 2nd Fl., Freehold, 07728 ... (732) 303-9530
Lasercam, Inc., 1039 Hoyt Ave., Ridgefield, 07657 ... (201) 941-1262
LaserMan Fabricating see. ... LazyMan Mfg., Belvidere
Lasermetrics Division see. ... Fastpulse Technology, Inc., Saddle Brook
Lassonde Industries, Inc. see ... Clement Pappas & Company, Inc. (H Q), Carneys Point
Last Chance Rebuilt Corp., 340 W. 1st Ave., Roselle, 07203 ... (908) 245-4421
Lasting Impression, Inc., 333 S. Dean St., Englewood, 07631 ... (201) 871-7388
† Latico Leather, 321 Palmer Rd., Ste. A, Denville, 07834 ... (973) 442-9622
Latin Percussion, Inc., 160 Belmont Ave., Garfield, 07026 ... (973) 330-9103
Latinos Unidos De Nueva Jersey, LLC, 190 Hickory Rd., Jackson, 08527 ... (732) 534-5959
Latta Graphics, Inc., 180 Cool Edge Ave., Englewood, 07631 ... (201) 440-4040
Lattimer USA, 3603 N. Mill Rd., Vineland, 08360 ... (856) 691-2203
Lauderdale Millwork, Inc., 77 Industrial Rd., Berkeley Heights, 07922 ... (908) 508-9550
Laura's Fudge, Inc., 357 E. Wildwood Ave., P.O. Box 871, Wildwood, 08260 ... (609) 729-1555
Laureate Press, Inc.,
1336 W. Central Ave., P.O. Box 343, Egg Harbor City, 08215 ... (609) 965-0447
Laurel Mfrs., Inc., 620 Cooper St., P.O. Box 5306, Delanco, 08075 ... (856) 461-6600
Laursen Sheet Metal, 69 Flint Rd., Toms River, 08757 ... (732) 349-2821
Lavallette Printing, 301 Grand Central, Lavallette, 08735 ... (732) 793-8303
Lavoz Spanish Newspapers, P.O. Box 899, Elizabeth, 07207 ... (908) 352-6654
Law Coffee Co. see. ... W.B. Law & Son, Inc., Newark
★ Lawall & Son, Inc., Harry J.,
3071 E. Chestnut Ave., Ste. C-9, Vineland, 08361 ... (856) 691-7764
Lawler Mfg. Corp., 7 Kilmer Ct., Edison, 08817 ... (732) 777-2040
Lawler Woodwork, LLC, 938 Lakewood Farmingdale Rd., Howell, 07731 ... (732) 942-7204
Lawrence Custom Drapery Shop, 323 4th St., Ewing, 08638 ... (609) 695-3877
Lawrence Mold and Tool Corp., 1412 Ohio Ave., Lawrenceville, 08648 ... (609) 392-5422

Lawyers Diary and Manual, 890 Mountain Ave., New Providence, 07974 ... (973) 642-1440
Layne Christensen Co., 719 Mount Holly Rd., Beverly, 08010 ... (609) 877-2700
Lazar Technologies, Inc., 39 Evergreen St., Hazlet, 07730 ... (732) 739-9622
LazyMan Mfg., 616 Hardwick St., P.O. Box 327, Belvidere, 07823 ... (908) 475-5315
LB Book Bindery, LLC, 19 Gardner Rd., Ste. I, Fairfield, 07004 ... (973) 244-0442
LBU, Inc., 217 Brook Ave., Ste. 6, Passaic, 07055 ... (973) 773-4800
LC Engineers, Inc., 1471 Pinewood St., Rahway, 07065 ... (732) 340-9190
L.C. Machine Shop, Inc., 249 S. White Horse Pike, Berlin, 08009 ... (856) 767-1111
LCI Graphics, Inc., 2400 Main Street Ext., Ste. 8, Sayreville, 08872 ... (973) 893-2913
LDA see. ... Leak Detection Associates, Inc., Vineland
Le Monde Deluxe, 232 White Horse Pike, Collingswood, 08107 ... (856) 854-5440
Le Papillon, 120 Albany St., Ste. 300, New Brunswick, 08901 ... (732) 843-6116
Lea Furs, Inc. Ltd., 45 S. Broad St., Ridgewood, 07450 ... (201) 444-5554
Leader Printers, 5914 New Jersey Ave., Wildwood Crest, 08260 ... (609) 729-0161
Leak Detection Associates, Inc., 3003 N. Mill Rd., Vineland, 08360 ... (856) 405-6636
Learning Ally, 20 Roszel Rd., Princeton, 08540 ... (609) 452-0606
★ Learning Links, Inc., P.O. Box 326, Cranbury, 08512 ... (516) 437-9071
Leary Heating & Air Conditioning, Inc., Bill, 6 Green St., Metuchen, 08840 ... (732) 494-9200
Leather Handle Mfg. Co., 44 Dickerson St., Newark, 07103 ... (973) 485-2866
Lebanon Cheese Co., Inc., 3 Railroad Ave., P.O. Box 63, Lebanon, 08833 ... (908) 236-2611
Leco Plastics, Inc., 130 Gamewell St., Hackensack, 07601 ... (201) 343-3330
Lee Electric, Inc., 309-11 51st St., P.O. Box 238, West New York, 07093 ... (201) 866-3656
Lee Linear, 727 South Ave., Piscataway, 08854 ... (732) 752-5200
Lee Sims Chocolates, 743 Bergen Ave., Jersey City, 07306 ... (201) 433-1308
LEEM/LSS Filtration see. ... Liquid Solids Separation Corp., Ramsey
Lee's Woodworking, Inc., 726 Walling Ave., Belmar, 07719 ... (732) 681-1002
Left-Handed Libra see. ... Carter Solution, Inc., The Jane, East Orange
Legacy Stairs & Millwork, Inc., 1000 Airport Rd., Ste. 104, Lakewood, 08701 ... (732) 905-7705
Legacy System see. ... US Logic, LLC, Hamilton
Legend Machine & Grinding, LLC, 36 S. Adamsville Rd., Somerville, 08876 ... (908) 685-1100
Leggett & Platt see. ... Edison Foam Processing Corp., South Plainfield
Leggett & Platt, Inc. see. ... Edison Foam Processing Corp., South Plainfield
Legislative Index Of New Jersey, 172 W. State St., Trenton, 08608 ... (609) 393-2291
LeGrand Assocs., 214 W. Main St., Ste. 102, Moorestown, 08057 ... (800) 273-8565
Legrand North America see. ... Middle Atlantic Products, Inc., Fairfield
Lehigh Cement Co., 66 Demarest Rd., Sparta, 07871 ... (973) 579-2111
Lehigh Fluid Power, Inc., 1413 Route 179, Lambertville, 08530 ... (609) 397-3487
Lehigh Hanson, Inc. see. ... Hanson Aggregate BMC, Newport
Lehigh Hanson, Inc. see. ... Hanson Aggregates Better Materials Corp., Woodbine
Lehigh Hanson, Inc. see. ... Hanson Aggregates North America, Buena
Lehigh Hanson, Inc. see. ... Hanson Aggregates, BMC Div., Berlin
Lehigh Hanson, Inc. see. ... Lehigh Cement Co., Sparta
Lehigh Precision Co., Inc., P.O. Box 214, Elizabeth, 07207 ... (908) 351-6600
Lehigh Utility Assocs., Inc.,
1300 New Market Ave., P.O. Box 398, South Plainfield, 07080 ... (908) 561-5252
Leibrock Metal Products, Inc., 1800 Brielle Ave., Asbury Park, 07712 ... (732) 695-0326
Leif J. Ostberg, Inc. (H Q), 401 Hamburg Tpke., Ste. 305, Wayne, 07470 ... (973) 956-6990
Leistritz Corp., 165 Chestnut St., Allendale, 07401 ... (201) 934-8262
Leiz Custom Woodwork, David, 2301 E. Edgar Rd., Bldg. 5-A, Linden, 07036 ... (908) 486-1533
Leland Ltd., Inc.,
2614 S. Clinton Ave., P.O. Box 466, South Plainfield, 07080 ... (908) 561-2000
Lenape Porcelain Products see. ... Lenape Products, Inc., Trenton
Lenape Products, Inc. see. ... Easco Shower Doors Co., Vernon
Lenape Products, Inc., 600 Plum St., Trenton, 08638 ... (609) 394-5376
Leneta Co., Inc., 15 Whitney Rd., Mahwah, 07430 ... (201) 847-9300
Leng-D'Or USA, Inc., 50 W. Ferris St., East Brunswick, 08816 ... (732) 254-4300
Lens Co., Inc., 700 Route 46 W., Unit 7, Clifton, 07013 ... (973) 546-0866
Lens Mode, Inc., 150 Main St., Ste. 1, Millburn, 07041 ... (973) 467-2000
Lentine Sheet Metal, Inc., 1210 E. Elizabeth Ave., Linden, 07036 ... (908) 486-8974
Lentron Corp., 24 Ironia Rd., Flanders, 07836 ... (973) 252-9668
Leon Printing, 1421 New York Ave., Union City, 07087 ... (201) 867-3206
Leonard Novelty Bakery see. ... Royal Baking Co., Moonachie
Leonard Publications, Inc.,
10 W. Hanover Ave., P.O. Box 553, Mount Freedom, 07970 ... (973) 895-6000
Leo's Famous Yum Yum, 7 Tomlinson Mill Rd., Ste. 5, Medford, 08055 ... (856) 797-8771
Lerro Products, Inc., 1321 Walnut St., Camden, 08103 ... (856) 203-3561
Lettermen, Inc., The, 1565 Route 37 W., Toms River, 08755 ... (732) 608-0669
Level Four Orthotics & Prosthetics, Inc. see. ... Cocco Enterprises, Inc., Trenton
Lever Mfg. Corp., 420 State Route 17, Mahwah, 07430 ... (201) 684-4400
Levine Industries, 86 Levine St., South Paterson Sta., Paterson, 07503 ... (973) 742-1000
Levine Packaging Supply Corp., 400 U.S. Highway 46 E., Fairfield, 07004 ... (973) 575-3383
Levy & Rappel, Inc., 339 10th St., Saddle Brook, 07663 ... (973) 478-6511
† Lewis-Goetz & Co., Inc., 1571 Grandview Ave., Paulsboro, 08066 ... (856) 579-1421
LexisNexis Martindale-Hubell, 121 Chanlon Rd., New Providence, 07974 ... (908) 464-6800
LG Electronics USA, Inc. (H Q), 1000 Sylvan Ave., Englewood Cliffs, 07632 ... (201) 816-2000
Liberty Brand Pastries & Foods, 2409 Central Ave., Union City, 07087 ... (201) 863-3350
Liberty Electronics, 465 Route 53, Denville, 07834 ... (973) 625-7966
Liberty Electronics, Inc., 465 E. Main St., Denville, 07834 ... (973) 625-7963
Liberty Envelope, Inc., 45 E. 5th St., Paterson, 07524 ... (973) 546-5600
Liberty Lamp & Shade see. ... Jay-Bee Lamp & Shade Co., Inc., Passaic
Liberty Machine Tool & Die, Inc., 903 E. Elizabeth Ave., Linden, 07036 ... (908) 925-0300
Liberty Mechanical Contractors, Inc., 330 Raymond Blvd., Newark, 07105 ... (973) 344-6131
Liberty Precision Industries see. ... Geiger Tool & Mfg. Co., Inc., Passaic
Liberty Printing, Inc., 1111 Chestnut Ave., Trenton, 08611 ... (609) 396-5995
Liberty Sport, Inc., 107 Fairfield Rd., Fairfield, 07004 ... (973) 882-0986
† Liberty Welding Supply, Inc., 187 W. Fort Lee Rd., Bogota, 07603 ... (973) 923-2900
Library Automation Technologies, 2 E. Atlantic Ave., Somerdale, 08083 ... (856) 566-4121
Licini Bros. Provisions, Inc., 907 West St., Union City, 07087 ... (201) 865-1130
LiDestri Foods, Inc., 1550 John Tipton Blvd., Pennsauken, 08110 ... (856) 662-1800
Lieberfarb, Inc., 2100 Felver Ct., Rahway, 07065 ... (973) 676-9090
Lief Group, Inc., Philip, 371 Sayre Dr., Princeton, 08540 ... (609) 430-1000
★ Life & Leisure, LLC, 234 Main St., Ste. 2, Lincoln Park, 07035 ... (973) 696-8009
★ Life A Stitch, 37 Jackson Ave., Carteret, 07008 ... (732) 969-0232
Life Of The Party, LLC, 832 Ridgewood Ave., Ste. 4, North Brunswick, 08902 ... (732) 828-0886
Life Science Laboratories, LLC, 170 Oberlin Ave. N., Ste. 26, Lakewood, 08701 ... (732) 367-1900
★ Life Science Labs Supplements, LLC, 170 Oberlin Ave., Lakewood, 08701 ... (732) 367-1749
Life Systems, Inc., 75 E. Main St., Rockaway, 07866 ... (973) 625-3716
Life Systems Software see. ... Life Systems, Inc., Rockaway
LifeCell Corp., 1 Millennium Way, Branchburg, 08876 ... (908) 947-1100
LifeGas, LLC, 174 Ridge Rd., Ste. A, Dayton, 08810 ... (866) 543-3427
Lifetime Brands, Inc. see. ... Lifetime Brands, Inc., Distribution Center, Robbinsville

† Lifetime Brands, Inc., Distribution Center, 12 Applegate Dr., Robbinsville, 08691 .......... (609) 208-1500
† Liftec, Inc., 124 Sylvania Pl., South Plainfield, 07080 .......... (908) 769-0034
Light Age, Inc., 500 Apgar Dr., Ste. 1, Somerset, 08873 .......... (732) 563-0600
Lightfield Ammunition Corp., 912 Highway 33, Freehold, 07728 .......... (732) 462-9200
Lighting Prevention Systems, Inc., 154 Cooper Rd., Unit 1201, P.O. Box 353, West Berlin, 08091 .......... (856) 767-7806
Lightning Press, Inc., 140 Furler St., Totowa, 07512 .......... (973) 890-4422
Lightning Prevention Systems, Inc., 154 Cooper Rd., Ste. 1201, West Berlin, 08091 .......... (856) 767-7209
Lightscape Materials, Inc., 201 Washington Rd., Princeton, 08540 .......... (609) 734-2227
Li'l Inspirations, LLC, P.O. Box 5754, Hillsborough, 08844 .......... (908) 369-5840
Lilo Maternity, LLC, 1526 Laguna Ln., Lakewood, 08701 .......... (732) 370-5456
Limo Digest, 3 Reeves Station Rd., Medford, 08055 .......... (609) 953-4900
Limpert Bros., Inc., 202 N. West Blvd., Vineland, 08360 .......... (856) 691-1353
Lincoln Dental Supply, Inc., 616 Hollywood Ave., Cherry Hill, 08002 .......... (856) 488-1333
Lincoln Electric Products Co., Inc., 947 Lehigh Ave., Union, 07083 .......... (908) 688-2900
Lincoln Marble Works, 785 Martin St., P.O. Box 111, Rahway, 07065 .......... (732) 381-9098
Lincoln Mold & Die Corp., 225 E. 1st Ave., Roselle, 07203 .......... (908) 241-3344
Lincoln Monument Co., Inc., 405 Orange Rd., Montclair, 07042 .......... (973) 744-1800
Lincoln Signs & Awnings, Inc., 895 Estate St., Perth Amboy, 08861 .......... (732) 442-3151
Linde Electronics & Specialty Gases, 80 Industrial Dr., Alpha, 08865 .......... (908) 454-7455
Linde Gas North America, LLC, 1 Greenwich St., Ste. 200, Stewartsville, 08886 .......... (800) 755-9277
Linde Group, The see. .......... LifeGas, LLC, Dayton
Linde, LLC see. .......... Linde North America, Inc. (H Q), New Providence
Linde North America, Inc. see. .......... Linde Gas North America, LLC, Stewartsville
Linde North America, Inc. (H Q), 575 Mountain Ave., New Providence, 07974 .......... (908) 464-8100
Linden Mold & Tool Corp., 155 Wescott Dr., P.O. Box C, Rahway, 07065 .......... (732) 381-1411
Linder & Co., Inc., 1183 W. Side Ave., Jersey City, 07306 .......... (201) 386-8788
Lindstrom & King Co., Inc., 108 McLean Blvd., Paterson, 07514 .......... (973) 279-2511
Lineaaqua, LLC, 2216 Hamilton Blvd., South Plainfield, 07080 .......... (908) 226-1199
Linear Photonics, LLC, 3 Nami Ln., Ste. 7-C, Hamilton, 08619 .......... (609) 584-5747
Linearizer Technology, Inc., 3 Nami Ln., Ste. 9-C, Hamilton, 08619 .......... (609) 584-8424
Lines & Letters DESIGNS, 1386 Mount Vernon Rd., Bridgewater, 08807 .......... (732) 563-0909
Lingraphica see. .......... Lingraphicare America, Inc., Princeton
Lingraphicare America, Inc., 103 Carnegie Ctr., Ste. 204, Princeton, 08540 .......... (609) 275-1300
Link Burns Mfg. Co., Inc., 253 American Way, Voorhees, 08043 .......... (856) 429-6844
Link Computer Graphics, Inc., 17-A Daniel Rd., Fairfield, 07004 .......... (973) 808-8990
Link News Inc., The, 176 Broadway, P.O. Box 120, Long Branch, 07740 .......... (732) 222-4300
Link Theory, 165 Polito Ave., Lyndhurst, 07071 .......... (201) 728-5700
Link Theory Holdings (US), Inc. see. .......... Link Theory, Lyndhurst
Linker Machines, 20 Pine St., Rockaway, 07866 .......... (973) 983-0001
Linseis, Inc., 109 N. Gold Dr., Robbinsville, 08691 .......... (609) 223-2070
Linthicum Sailmakers, Inc., 607 Grace St., Somerdale, 08083 .......... (856) 783-4288
Lion Brand Yarn Co. see. .......... Orchard Yarn & Thread Co., Inc., Carlstadt
† Lion Metals, Inc., 2460 Lemoine Ave., Ste. 400-B, Fort Lee, 07024 .......... (201) 585-9191
Lionelli, 345 Florida Grove Rd., Perth Amboy, 08861 .......... (732) 826-7270
Lioni Latticini, Inc., 555 Lehigh Ave., Union, 07083 .......... (908) 686-6061
Lipari's Sausage, Inc., 220 6th Ave., Hawthorne, 07506 .......... (973) 304-0137
Lipman see. .......... Colace Co., LLC, Thomas, Thorofare
Lipman see. .......... Custom Pak, Inc., Thorofare
Lipo Chemicals, Inc., 1515 W. Blancke St., Linden, 07036 .......... (973) 926-0331
Lipo Chemicals, Inc., 207 19th Ave., Paterson, 07504 .......... (973) 345-8600
Lippincott Marine, 74 Norman Ave., Delran, 08075 .......... (856) 764-8282
Liquid Glass Enterprises, Inc., 93 Railroad Ave., Bergenfield, 07621 .......... (201) 387-6755
Liquid Solids Separation Corp., 25 Arrow Rd., Ramsey, 07446 .......... (201) 236-4833
Liquiflo Equipment Co., Inc., 443 North Ave., Ste. 2, Garwood, 07027 .......... (908) 518-0777
Liquiflo, Inc., 7 Wilpert Rd., Bridgewater, 08807 .......... (732) 271-4600
Lithotone Co., 255 Queen Ann Rd., Bogota, 07603 .......... (201) 343-3883
Lithuanian Bakery, Inc., T. J., 131 Inslee Pl., Elizabeth, 07206 .......... (908) 354-0970
Little Falls Alloys, Inc., 189 Caldwell Ave., Paterson, 07501 .......... (973) 278-1666
Little Falls Trophy Co., 555 Route 46 E., P.O. Box 1050, Little Falls, 07424 .......... (973) 256-5222
Little House Candles, 20 Province Line Rd., New Egypt, 08533 .......... (609) 758-2996
Little Joe Industries, 10 Ilene Ct., Ste. 4, Hillsborough, 08844 .......... (908) 359-5213
LittleGifts, Inc. (H Q), 600 Meadowlands Pkwy., Ste. 131, Secaucus, 07094 .......... (212) 868-2559
Litvany Printing, LLC, Steve, 1275 Bloomfield Ave., Ste. 13-R, Fairfield, 07004 .......... (973) 244-0144
★ LiveU, Inc., 2 University Plz., Ste. 505, Hackensack, 07601 .......... (201) 742-5229
Living Intelligent, Inc., 70 Oak St., Ste. 103, Norwood, 07648 .......... (201) 784-0500
Livingston & W, Inc., 973-B New Durham Rd., Edison, 08817 .......... (732) 287-5790
Lizard Label, Inc., 10-E Commerce Rd., Fairfield, 07004 .......... (973) 808-0098
Lloyd's Awnings see. .......... Lloyd's Of Millville, Inc., Millville
Lloyd's Of Millville, Inc., 208 S. Wade Blvd., Millville, 08332 .......... (856) 825-0345
LM Foods, LLC, 100 Raskulinecz Rd., Carteret, 07008 .......... (732) 855-9500
LMK Waterjet, 835 Fairfield Ave., Kenilworth, 07033 .......... (908) 241-8113
LMT Mercer Group, Inc., 690 Puritan Ave., Lawrence Township, 08648 .......... (609) 989-0399
LNS Industries, Inc., P.O. Box 98, Somers Point, 08244 .......... (609) 927-6656
Lobello Arts Corp., 50 Route 10 W., East Hanover, 07936 .......... (973) 887-6700
Local Talk Printing Club, 26 Main St., Orange, 07050 .......... (973) 678-2582
Lockheed Martin, 199 Borton Landing Rd., Rm. 108-108, P.O. Box 1027, Moorestown, 08057 .......... (856) 722-4100
Lockheed Martin Corp. see. .......... Lockheed Martin, Moorestown
Lockrey Company LLC, 1280 Old York Rd., Burlington, 08016 .......... (856) 665-4794
Lockwood's Electric Motor Service, Inc., 2239 Nottingham Way, Trenton, 08619 .......... (609) 587-2333
Loeffler's Gourmet, 482 Whitehead Rd., Trenton, 08619 .......... (609) 695-5068
Log Power, Inc., 646 Route 524, P.O. Box 597, Allentown, 08501 .......... (609) 259-9709
Logan Instruments Corp., 19 Schoolhouse Rd., Ste. C, Somerset, 08873 .......... (732) 302-9888
LoGatto Bookbinding, Inc., 390 Paterson Ave., P.O. Box 7483, East Rutherford, 07073 .......... (201) 438-4344
LOG-NET, Inc., 230 Half Mile Rd., 3rd Fl., Red Bank, 07701 .......... (732) 758-6800
Logo Knits, Inc., 42-A Cindy Ln., Ocean, 07712 .......... (732) 382-6961
Logomania, Inc. see. .......... Composition Printing, Jersey City
Logotech, Inc., 18 Madison Rd., Fairfield, 07004 .......... (973) 882-9595
Lola Products see. .......... The Fifty/Fifty Group, Inc, Hackensack
Lollytogs, Ltd. see. .......... LT Apparel Group, Dayton
Lombardo Graphic Consultants, Inc., 429 Lacey Rd., Ste. 8, Forked River, 08731 .......... (609) 693-1727
★ Lombardo Music Publications, 37 Pintinalli Dr., Trenton, 08619 .......... (609) 586-9245
Long Branch Mfg. & Design * LBM Design see. ..... Poandl Brothers Woodworking, Inc., Long Branch
Long Reach High Reach, LLC, 890 E. Rte. 70, Ste. B, Marlton, 08053 .......... (856) 797-6999
Long Valley Equipment, 165 Fairview Ave., Long Valley, 07853 .......... (908) 876-1022
† Longo Electrical-Mechanical, 1 Harry Shupe Blvd., Wharton, 07885 .......... (973) 537-0400
Longo's Cabinet Shop, 101 Monroe St., Garfield, 07026 .......... (973) 472-3567
Lont & OverKamp, 175 U.S. Highway 46, Fairfield, 07004 .......... (973) 942-2243
Lonza, Inc., 90 Boroline Rd., Allendale, 07401 .......... (201) 316-9200
Lonza, Inc., 70 Tyler Pl., South Plainfield, 07080 .......... (908) 561-5200
Lonza Personal Care see. .......... Lonza, Inc., South Plainfield
Look Of Love International (H Q), 1795-B Route 27 S., Edison, 08817 .......... (908) 687-9502
Loominaries Handweaving, 23 Big Spring Rd., Califon, 07830 .......... (908) 832-6652
Lopes Co., 304 Walnut St., Newark, 07105 .......... (973) 344-3063
† Lorco Petroleum Services, 450 S. Front St., Elizabeth, 07202 .......... (908) 820-8800
Lordon, Inc., 453 Route 46, Ste. 1-A, Hackettstown, 07840 .......... (908) 813-1143
L'Oreal U S A, Inc., 222 Terminal Ave., Clark, 07066 .......... (732) 499-2838
L'Oreal U S A, Inc., 81 New England Ave., Piscataway, 08854 .......... (732) 562-5000
Lorenzo & Sons Provisions see. .......... Lorenzo Food Group, Inc., Englewood
★ Lorenzo Food Group, Inc., 196 Coolidge Ave., Englewood, 07631 .......... (201) 868-9088
Lornan Litho, Inc., 130 Route 31 N., Ste. E, Pennington, 08534 .......... (609) 818-1198
LORS Machinery see. .......... Resistance Welding Solutions, Inc., Union
LOR-TECH Plastics, LLC, 3 Eastmans Rd., Unit 3, Parsippany, 07054 .......... (973) 503-1750
Los Galleguitos, 147 48th St., Union City, 07087 .......... (201) 865-7232
Losurdo Foods, Inc., 20 Owens Rd., Hackensack, 07601 .......... (201) 343-6680
Lotito Foods, Inc., 510 E. 35th St., Paterson, 07504 .......... (973) 684-2900
Lotito Foods, Inc./Mrs. Mazzula Foods see. .......... Lotito Foods, Inc., Paterson
Lotito Foods, Inc./Mrs. Mazzula Foods, 240 Carter Dr., Edison, 08817 .......... (732) 248-0222
† Lotus Exim International, Inc., 16 Leliarts Ln., Elmwood Park, 07407 .......... (201) 475-2810
Louis Iron Works, 218 Lackawanna Ave., Newark, 07103 .......... (973) 624-2700
LouMarc Signs, 178 Route 206, Hillsborough, 08844 .......... (908) 575-4000
★ Love Farms, LLC, 204 Albion Ave., Paterson, 07502 .......... (973) 942-5683
Love Pallet Company, LLC., 460 Mundet Pl., P.O. Box 774, Hillside, 07205 .......... (908) 964-3385
Loveline Industries, Inc., 90 Dayton Ave., Ste. 33, Passaic, 07055 .......... (973) 928-3427
Loving Pets Corp., 110 Melrich Rd., Ste. 1, Cranbury, 08512 .......... (609) 655-3700
Lower County Recycle see. .......... Erial Concrete, Inc., Sicklerville
LPS Industries, Inc., 10 Caesar Pl., Moonachie, 07074 .......... (201) 438-3515
LRB Performance Machine Co., 22-B Lasinski Rd., Franklin, 07416 .......... (973) 209-7770
LRC Associates, Inc., 328 S. 2nd St., Millville, 08332 .......... (215) 244-1150
LRHR, LLC see. .......... Long Reach High Reach, LLC, Marlton
LRM Packaging, Inc., 41 James St., South Hackensack, 07606 .......... (201) 342-2530
LRP & P Graphics, 1165 Marlkress Rd., Cherry Hill, 08003 .......... (856) 424-0158
LT Apparel Group, 301 Herrod Blvd., P.O. Box 1001, Dayton, 08810 .......... (732) 438-5500
L-3 Communications Corp., 1 Federal St., Camden, 08102 .......... (856) 338-3000
L-3 Communications Corp., Space & Navigation Systems, 450 Clark Dr., Budd Lake, 07828 .......... (973) 446-4000
L-3 Communications Mobile-Vision, Inc., 90 Fanny Rd., Boonton, 07005 .......... (973) 263-1090
LTS / LT Security Inc. (H Q), 109 W. Park Dr., Ste. C, Mount Laurel, 08054 .......... (856) 780-9888
LTS Lohmann Therapy Systems Corp., 21 Henderson Dr., West Caldwell, 07006 .......... (973) 244-2026
Lubriplate Lubricants Co., 129 Lockwood St., Newark, 07105 .......... (973) 589-9150
Lubrizol Advanced Materials, Inc., 1 Industrial W., Clifton, 07012 .......... (973) 471-1300
Lubrizol Advanced Materials, Inc., 76 Porcupine Rd., Pedricktown, 08067 .......... (856) 351-2100
Lubrizol Corp. see. .......... Lubrizol Advanced Materials, Inc., Clifton
Lubrizol Corp., The see. .......... Lubrizol Advanced Materials, Inc., Clifton
† Luca Laundry Equipment, Inc., 1500 W. Blancke St., Linden, 07036 .......... (908) 862-2200
Lucas & Son, H. N., 211 Carriage Ln., Delran, 08075 .......... (856) 764-2400
Lucas America Inc. see. .......... Beisler America, LLC, Linden
Lucid Lighting, LLC, 811 Rosemont Ringoes Rd., Stockton, 08559 .......... (609) 649-0596
Lucid Technologies, LLC, 231 Clarksville Rd., Princeton Junction, 08550 .......... (609) 277-4138
Lucille Maud Corp., 513 N. Olden Ave., Trenton, 08638 .......... (609) 393-7555
Lucille's Own Made Candy Co., 156 E. Route 72, Manahawkin, 08050 .......... (609) 597-7300
Lucy's Ravioli Kitchen & Market, 830 State Rd., Princeton, 08540 .......... (609) 924-3623
★ Lum Tech Lighting, Inc., 201 Commerce Dr., Ste. 5, Moorestown, 08057 .......... (856) 234-2211
Lumenarc, Inc., 37 Fairfield Pl., West Caldwell, 07006 .......... (973) 227-8048
★ Lumeta Corporation, 300 Atrium Dr., Ste. 302, Somerset, 08873 .......... (732) 357-3500
Luminaire Lighting Corp., 5 Sutton Pl., Edison, 08817 .......... (732) 549-0056
Luminer Converting Group, Inc., 1925 Swarthmore Ave., Ste. 5, Lakewood, 08701 .......... (732) 886-6557
Lumitron Corp., Inc., 35 Russo Pl., Berkeley Heights, 07922 .......... (908) 273-8998
Lummus Technology, 1515 Broad St., Bloomfield, 07003 .......... (973) 893-3000
Lund's Fisheries Co., 997 Ocean Dr., P.O. Box 830, Cape May, 08204 .......... (609) 884-7600
LUSO Machine, Inc., 29 Avenue C, Newark, 07114 .......... (973) 242-1717
Luso-Americano Co., Inc., 88 Ferry St., Newark, 07105 .......... (973) 589-4600
Lutjens Co., Inc., G., 80 George St., Paterson, 07503 .......... (973) 278-9639
Lux Entertainment, LLC, 629 E. 19th St., Paterson, 07514 .......... (888) 282-8425
Lux Products Corp. (H Q), 6000 Commerce Pkwy., Ste. I, Mount Laurel, 08054 .......... (856) 234-7905
Luxottica Retail North America, Inc. see. .......... Pearle Vision, Inc., Toms River
LycoRed Corp., 377 Crane St., Orange, 07050 .......... (877) 592-6733
Lydia's Land, LLC, P.O. Box 852, Marlton, 08053 .......... (856) 983-7258
† Lymphedema Products, LLC, 750 State Route 34, Ste. 7, Matawan, 07747 .......... (732) 290-2888
Lynch Exhibits, 7 Campus Dr., Burlington, 08016 .......... (609) 387-1600
Lynn Mechanical Contractors, 1810 Rowland St., Riverton, 08077 .......... (856) 829-1717
† **Lyon, Conklin & Co., Inc., 1165 Thomas Busch Memorial Hwy., Pennsauken, 08110** .......... (856) 488-0191
LyondellBasell Industries, 340 Meadow Rd., Edison, 08817 .......... (732) 777-2272
LyondellBasell Industries, 300 Doremus Ave., Newark, 07105 .......... (973) 578-2200
† M & A Recycling, 65 Old Camplain Rd., Hillsborough, 08844 .......... (908) 218-9191
M & D Precision Centerless Grinding, Inc., 120 Kossuth St., Riverside, 08075 .......... (856) 764-1616
M & F Machine Works, 243-245 Custer Ave., Jersey City, 07305 .......... (201) 433-4085
M & F Worldwide Corp. see. .......... Mafco Worldwide Corp., Camden
M & G Food, Inc., 1295 Main Ave., Clifton, 07011 .......... (973) 340-0340
M & G Tool & Die Co., 936 Harrison Ave., Kearny, 07032 .......... (201) 997-0506
M & J Contracting, Inc., 85 Tracey Station, Manalapan, 07726 .......... (732) 446-1112
M & M Grinding, LLC, 132 Lewis St., Eatontown, 07724 .......... (732) 542-1157
M & M International, 3619 Kennedy Rd., Ste. A, South Plainfield, 07080 .......... (908) 412-8300
M & M Welding & Steel Fabricating, 344 Essex St., P.O. Box 168, Stirling, 07980 .......... (908) 647-6060
† M & M Wholesale, 66 Market St., Saddle Brook, 07663 .......... (201) 368-0770
† M & N Boychuk Stone Co., Inc., 360 U.S. Highway 22, P.O. Box 133, Springfield, 07081 .......... (973) 376-1333
M & P Machinery, 1500 Main Ave., Ste. 31, Clifton, 07011 .......... (973) 253-1004
M & R Diamond Quilting Co., Inc., 35 South Ave., Fanwood, 07023 .......... (908) 322-4178
M & S Machine & Tool Corp., 108 Maryland Ave., Paterson, 07503 .......... (973) 345-5847
M. A. R. Kit, Inc., 1095 Cinnaminson Ave., Cinnaminson, 08077 .......... (856) 829-5992
M B C Food Machinery Corp., 78 McKinley St., Hackensack, 07601 .......... (201) 489-7000
M C Custom Sheet Metal Fabrication, Inc., 215-E Old Egg Harbor Rd., Ste. E, West Berlin, 08091 .......... (856) 767-9509
† M C Machinery Systems, Inc., 16 Chapin Rd., P.O. Box 405, Pine Brook, 07058 .......... (973) 244-1501
M C Machinery Systems, Inc., Mitsubishi E D M/Laser Div. see. M C Machinery Systems, Inc., Pine Brook

ALPHABETICAL

© Copyright 2015 Manufacturers' News, Inc.


M H Optical Supplies, Inc., 128 Leuning St., South Hackensack, 07606 (201) 489-1110
M J H Gear & Tool Co., Inc., 15 Maple St., Norwood, 07648 (212) 246-3800
M K S, Inc., 7 N. Industrial Blvd., Bridgeton, 08302 (856) 451-5545
M M T C, Inc., 12 Roszel Rd., Ste. A-203, Princeton, 08540 (609) 520-9699
† M. O. Industries, Inc., 9 Whippany Rd., Bldg. B1-2, Whippany, 07981 (973) 386-9228
M R L Mfg. Corp., 59 Lee Ave., P.O. Box 8440, Haledon, 07508 (973) 790-1744
† M S International, Inc., 36 Brunswick Ave., Edison, 08817 (732) 650-1815
† M. S. Plastics Packaging Co., Inc., 10 Park Pl., Bldg. 2-1A-2, Butler, 07405 (973) 492-2400
M T I Precision Products, LLC, 730 Airport Rd., Lakewood, 08701 (732) 905-7440
Mabey, Inc. see. Mabey Inc., Piscataway
† Mabey Inc., 218 N. Randolphville Rd., Piscataway, 08854 (732) 752-6600
Mac Metals, Inc., 936 Harrison Ave., CN 670, Kearny, 07032 (201) 997-8001
MAC Products, Inc., 60 Pennsylvania Ave., P.O. Box 469, Kearny, 07032 (973) 344-0700
† MacAuley, Inc., James R.,
1 Industrial Dr., P.O. Box 704, Waterford Works, 08089 (856) 767-3474
MacElroy Co., Inc., J. C., 91 Ethel Rd. W., Piscataway, 08854 (732) 572-7100
MacFerren's Printing & Co., 3 Democrat Rd., Gibbsboro, 08026 (856) 435-7066
Machine Corp., E. B., 320 Richard Mine Rd., Wharton, 07885 (973) 442-7729
Machine Parts, Inc., 17 Ferdon St., Newark, 07105 (973) 491-5444
Machine Plus, Inc., 97 4th Ave., Haskell, 07420 (973) 839-8884
Machine Shop At Engine Specialties, The, 203 Carriage Ln., Delran, 08075 (856) 764-8701
† Machine Shop Discount Supply, P.O. Box 16, Little Ferry, 07643 (201) 518-8472
Machine Tech, 3125 Woodbridge Ave., Ste. 4, Edison, 08837 (732) 738-6810
Machon Beer Hatorah, Inc., 41 E. 8th St., Lakewood, 08701 (732) 364-9638
Macie Publishing Co., 10 Astro Pl., Ste. 100, Rockaway, 07866 (973) 983-8700
† Mack Boring & Parts Co., 2365 U.S. Highway 22 W., P.O. Box 3116, Union, 07083 (908) 964-0700
Mackey's Print Xpress, 1107 7th Ave., Neptune, 07753 (732) 775-1730
Maclearie, 917 18th Ave., Wall, 07719 (732) 974-8878
MacLearie Printing, LLC, 917 18th Ave., Belmar, 07719 (732) 681-2772
† Macro Equipment Co., 205 Hartford Rd., Route 38, Mount Laurel, 08054 (856) 235-4235
Macro Sensors, 7300 Route 130 N., Bldg. 22, Pennsauken, 08110 (856) 662-8000
Macrosoft, Inc., 2 Sylvan Way, Parsippany, 07054 (973) 889-0500
Mactex, LLC, 489-A Getty Ave., Clifton, 07011 (973) 340-3131
Macy Custom Iron Railings Co., J., 116 River Rd., New Milford, 07646 (201) 262-4302
Mada Medical Products, Inc., 625 Washington Ave., Carlstadt, 07072 (201) 460-0454
Madan Plastics, Inc., 108 N. Union Ave., Ste. 3, Cranford, 07016 (908) 276-8484
Maddak Inc. see. Bel-Art Products, Inc., Wayne
Maddak Inc., 661 State Route 23, Wayne, 07470 (973) 628-7600
Maddalenas Cheesecake & Catering see. Catering By The Maddalenas, Inc., Ringoes
Madison Dearborn Partners, LLC see. Ikaria, Inc. (H Q), Hampton
Madison Industries, Inc., 554 Waterworks Rd., Old Bridge, 08857 (732) 727-2225
Madison Line, The, 40 Commerce St., Springfield, 07081 (973) 379-1108
Madison Printing Service see. Jamesburg Press Madison Printing, Inc., Jamesburg
† Madsen & Howell, Inc., 500 Market St., Ste. 1, Perth Amboy, 08861 (732) 826-4000
Maestro Technolgies, Inc., 510 Thornall St., Ste. 375, Edison, 08837 (908) 458-8600
Mafco Worldwide Corp., 300 Jefferson St., Camden, 08104 (856) 964-8840
★ Mag Signs, Inc., 1208-F Columbus Rd., Burlington, 08016 (609) 747-9600
★ Magazine Of Fantasy & Science Fiction, The,
105 Leonard St., Jersey City, 07307 (201) 876-2551
Magestic Systems, Inc., 205 Fairview Ave., Westwood, 07675 (201) 263-0090
Maggio Data Forms Printing Ltd., 171 Heller Pl., Bellmawr, 08031 (856) 931-7805
Magic Metal Works, Inc., 40 W. Englewood Ave., Bergenfield, 07621 (201) 384-8457
Magic Printing Corp., 386 Avenel St., Avenel, 07001 (732) 726-0620
Maglione's Italian Ices, 111 Madison St., Iselin, 08830 (732) 283-0705
Magna Industries, Inc., 1825 Swarthmore Ave., Ste. 1, Lakewood, 08701 (732) 905-0957
Magnalube, Inc., 1331 W. Edgar Rd., P.O. Box 1250, Linden, 07036 (718) 729-1000
Magna-Power Electronics, 39 Royal Rd., Flemington, 08822 (908) 237-2200
Magnatrol Valve Corp. see. Clark Cooper Div., Roebling
Magnatrol Valve Corp., 67 5th Ave., Hawthorne, 07506 (973) 427-4341
Magnetic & Transformer Technologies Corp., 653 Sayre Ave., Perth Amboy, 08861 (609) 371-1258
Magnetic & Transformer Technologies Corp. (H Q),
7 Tanager Ln., Robbinsville, 08691 (609) 371-1258
Magnetic Metals Corp., 1900 Hayes Ave., Camden, 08105 (856) 964-7842
Magnetic Ticket & Label Corp., 151 Cortlandt St., Belleville, 07109 (973) 759-6500
Magnolia Beef Co., LLC, 1070 Magnolia Ave., Elizabeth, 07201 (908) 352-9412
Magnum see. Magnum Technologies, Inc., Warren
Magnum Technologies, Inc., 95 Mount Bethel Rd., Warren, 07059 (908) 546-7950
MagnumComputer Recycling see. Thanks For Being Green, LLC, Merchantville
Maidenform Brands, Inc., 485 U.S. Highway 1 S., Bldg. F, Iselin, 08830 (732) 621-2500
★ Mail Time, Inc., 224 Stockton St., Phillipsburg, 08865 (908) 859-5500
Main & Sons, Inc., Robert A., 555 Goffle Rd., P.O. Box 159, Wyckoff, 07481 (201) 447-3700
Main Attractions, Inc., 85 Newfield Ave., Edison, 08837 (732) 225-3500
† Main Electric Supply Co., Inc.,
24 Public Rd., P.O. Box 7323, Monroe Township, 08831 (609) 860-8500
Main Street Awards, Inc., 55 N. Main St., P.O. Box 323, Windsor, 08561 (609) 448-6324
Main Street Communications, 15 W. Main St., Clinton, 08809 (908) 735-7570
Main Street Graphics, Inc., 30 W. Main St., Maple Shade, 08052 (856) 755-3523
Main Tape Co., Inc., 1 Capital Dr., Ste. 101, Cranbury, 08512 (609) 395-1704
† Mainetti USA, Inc., 300 Mac Ln., Keasbey, 08832 (201) 215-2900
Mainland Plate Glass Co., Inc., 53 E. West Jersey Ave., Pleasantville, 08232 (609) 641-6553
★ Mainsource Metalfab, LLC, 59 Poinier St., Unit 61, Newark, 07114 (973) 353-0988
Mainstream Custom Air Handling Units, 47 Russo Pl., Berkeley Heights, 07922 (908) 931-1010
Maintape, Inc., 1 Capital Dr., Ste. 101, Bldg. 1, Cranbury, 08512 (609) 395-1704
† Majestic Fence Co., Inc., 6839 US Highway 9, Howell, 07731 (732) 363-8181
Majestic Industries, Inc., 225 Passaic St., Passaic, 07055 (973) 473-3434
Majestic Optical Coatings, 152 Willow Way, Clark, 07066 (732) 388-5604
Majestic Signs, 951 Teaneck Rd., Teaneck, 07666 (201) 837-8104
Majka & Sons Fuel Service, Joseph A., 568 Paulison Ave., Clifton, 07011 (973) 777-8484
Majka Railing, Inc., 125 McBride Ave., Paterson, 07501 (973) 247-7603
Major Printing Co., Inc., 934 Savitt Pl., P.O. Box 1356, Union, 07083 (908) 686-7296
Making Waves, Inc., 1916 Old Cuthbert Rd., Ste. B-20, Cherry Hill, 08034 (856) 795-9311
Makino, Inc. see. Single Source Technologies, Pine Brook
★ Malhame Vestment, 239 Route 206, Branchville, 07826 (973) 948-8401
Malin Corp., James S., 3 Victoria Ln., Ringwood, 07456 (973) 831-9135
† Malincho Inc, 2545 Fire Rd., Ste. 3, Egg Harbor Township, 08234 (609) 677-6090
Malletech, LLC, 1107 11th Ave., Neptune, 07753 (732) 774-0011
Malt Products Corp., 121 E. Hunter Ave., Maywood, 07607 (201) 845-9106
Malt Products Corp., 88 Market St., P.O. Box 898, Saddle Brook, 07663 (201) 845-4420
Maltbie see. Kubik Maltbie, Inc., Mount Laurel
Maltese Iron Works, Inc., John,
1453 Jersey Ave., P.O. Box 7161, North Brunswick, 08902 (732) 249-4350
Malwin Electronics Corp., 52 E. 22nd St., Paterson, 07514 (973) 881-1500
MAN Diesel & Turbo, 2 Amboy Ave., Bldg. 2, Woodbridge, 07095 (732) 582-8200
Manasquan Sight Saver Optical, 1407 W. Atlantic Ave., Manasquan, 08736 (732) 223-4242
Mancine Optical Co., 2910 Route 130, Ste. 1, Delran, 08075 (856) 764-0200
Manco Plating, Inc., 390 Park Ave., P.O. Box 7025, Newark, 07107 (973) 485-6800
Mane USA, Inc., 60 Demarest Dr., Wayne, 07470 (973) 633-5533
Manfredi Orthotic & Prosthetic Affiliates, LLC,
749 Hope Rd., Eatontown, 07724 (732) 380-0366
Mango Custom Cabinets, Inc., 216 W. Stiger St., Hackettstown, 07840 (908) 813-3077
Manhattan Chocolates Co., 186 E. 22nd St., Bayonne, 07002 (201) 339-6886
Manhattan Door Corp., 109 Kero Rd., Carlstadt, 07072 (718) 963-1111
Manhattan Drug Co., Inc., 225 Long Ave., Bldg. 15, 3rd Fl., Hillside, 07205 (973) 926-0816
Manhattan Flag & Pole see. Manhattan Signs, Inc., Paterson
Manhattan Signs, Inc., 130 Beckwith Ave., Paterson, 07503 (973) 278-3603
Manifold Printers, Inc., 189 Berdan Ave., Ste. 456, Wayne, 07470 (973) 345-5900
Manischewitz Co., The see. R.A.B. Food Group, LLC, Newark
Manischewitz Co., The (H Q), 80 Avenue K, Newark, 07105 (201) 553-1100
Manley Performance Products, Inc., 1960 Swarthmore Ave., Lakewood, 08701 (732) 905-3366
★ Manning Publication Co., 1233 Heartwood Dr., Cherry Hill, 08003 (856) 375-2597
Mannington Mills, Inc., 75 Mannington Mills Rd., P.O. Box 30, Salem, 08079 (856) 935-3000
Manolucci Designs, 220 61st St., Ste. 2-D, West New York, 07093 (201) 861-2259
★ Mantua Sign & Lighting, 550 Bridgeton Pike, Ste. 5, Mantua, 08051 (856) 415-0022
Manufacturers' Brush Corp., 69 King St., Dover, 07801 (973) 882-6966
Manutech, Inc., 29 State St., P.O.Box 758, Elmer, 08318 (856) 358-6136
Manville Rubber Products, Inc., 1009 Kennedy Blvd., Manville, 08835 (908) 526-9111
Manzi Printers, Inc., 132 Lewis St., Ste. B-2, Eatontown, 07724 (732) 542-1927
MAPEI Corp., Off White Head Ave., P.O. Box 105, South River, 08882 (732) 254-8001
MAPEI New Jersey see. MAPEI Corp., South River
Maple Leather Co., 14 Raven Rock Rd., P.O. Box 319, Stockton, 08559 (609) 397-1199
Maple Machine Co., Inc.,
Mount Holly Industrial Commons, Unit 9, Mount Holly, 08060 (609) 702-0975
Maplewood Beverage Packers, LLC, 45 Camptown Rd., Maplewood, 07040 (973) 416-4582
Maquet, 15 Law Dr., Fairfield, 07004 (973) 244-6100
Maquet Cardiovascular, LLC see. Maquet, Fairfield
Maquet Cardiovascular, LLC, 45 Barbour Pond Dr., Wayne, 07470 (973) 709-7000
Mara Polishing & Plating Corp., 105-107 W. Peddie St., Newark, 07112 (973) 242-0800
Maranatha Ceramic Tile & Marble, Inc.,
253 Cookstown New Egypt Rd., Wrightstown, 08562 (609) 758-1168
Maranatha Now Inc. see. Atlas Bronze, Trenton
Maranatha Wood Stairs see. Maranatha Ceramic Tile & Marble, Inc., Wrightstown
Marange Printing, Inc., 195 Cortlandt St., Belleville, 07109 (973) 751-3600
Mara's Gourmet Cheesecake, 281 Speedwell Ave., Morristown, 07960 (973) 682-9200
Marathon Enterprises, Inc. (H Q), 9 Smith St., Englewood, 07631 (201) 935-3330
Marble & Granite Fabricators, 950 Pennsylvania Ave., Trenton, 08638 (609) 392-2792
Marble & Stone Crafters, LLC, 50 Johnson Ave., Ste. F, Hackensack, 07601 (201) 343-2840
Marble Factory, 800 Magnolia Ave., Elizabeth, 07201 (908) 353-2264
Marble Systems, Inc., 610 Washington Ave., Carlstadt, 07072 (201) 507-0111
Marcacci Meats, Inc., 1853 Vine Rd., Vineland, 08361 (856) 691-4848
† Marchesini Packaging Machinery, 43 Fairfield Pl., West Caldwell, 07006 (973) 575-7445
★ Marcia's Melodies, 61 Pilgrim Pathway, Unit 3, Ocean Grove, 07756 (732) 988-3191
Marcone Appliance Parts Center see. Marcone Supplies, Kenilworth
Marcone Appliance Parts Center see. Marcone Supply, Hackensack
† Marcone Supplies, 870 Boulevard, Ste. 4, Kenilworth, 07033 (973) 371-8800
† Marcone Supply, 180 Main St., Hackensack, 07601 (201) 489-6444
† Marcor Development Corp., 341 Michele Pl., Carlstadt, 07072 (201) 935-2111
Mardee Co., Inc., 242 Saint Nicholas Ave., South Plainfield, 07080 (908) 753-4343
Marfori Family Eye Care, 20 Brick Plz., Brick, 08723 (732) 920-1775
Margola Corp., 232 S. Van Brunt St., Englewood, 07631 (201) 816-9500
Mariano Press see. Mercury Printing, Inc., Somerset
Mariano Press Co., 14 Veronica Ave., Somerset, 08873 (732) 247-6828
Marindus Co., Inc, P.O. Box 663, Englewood, 07631 (201) 567-8383
Marine Development & Research see. Hy-Test Packaging Corp., Paterson
Marine Development & Research Corp., 515 E. 41st St., Paterson, 07504 (973) 754-7087
Marine Electric Systems, Inc., 80 Wesley St., South Hackensack, 07606 (201) 531-8600
Marino Building Systems see. American Panel Tec, South Plainfield
Marinoware see. Ware Industries, Inc., South Plainfield
Maritime Tool see. T P S Machining, Manasquan
† MarJam Supply Co., 6 International Way, Newark, 07114 (973) 491-6030
† MarJam Supply Co., 615 W. Delilah Rd., Pleasantville, 08232 (609) 407-1234
Mark Architectural Lighting, 3 Kilmer Rd., Edison, 08817 (732) 985-2600
Mark Lithography, Inc., 220 Entin Rd., Clifton, 07014 (973) 538-5557
Mark I Industries, Inc., 910 Shunpike Rd., Cape May, 08204 (609) 884-0051
★ Mark Sports, 9 E. 31st St., Bayonne, 07002 (201) 437-9900
Markbilt Technical Fabrics Corp., 1875 McCarter Hwy., Newark, 07104 (973) 482-6400
Market Street Printing, Inc., 122 N. 6th St., Camden, 08102 (856) 964-5995
Marketeer, The see. New Jersey Media Group, East Hanover
Marketing Advertising Promotions, Inc., 4 Edison Pl., Fairfield, 07004 (973) 575-5656
Marko Engraving & Art Corp., 439 Fairview Ave., Fairview, 07022 (201) 945-6555
Mark-O-Lite Sign Co., 1420 U.S. Highway 9, Howell, 07731 (732) 462-8530
Markov Processes International, LLC,
25 Deforest Ave., Ste. 102, Summit, 07901 (908) 608-1558
Mark's Adhesive Co. * Aqua Based Technologies see. ADM Tronics Unlimited, Inc., Northvale
Mark/Trece, Inc., 160 Algonquin Pkwy., Whippany, 07981 (973) 884-1005
Marleen, Inc., 1101 N. 10th St., P.O. Box 70, Millville, 08332 (856) 327-8281
Marlo Mfg. Co., Inc., 301 Division St., Boonton, 07005 (973) 423-0226
Marlo Plastic Products, Inc., 289 State Route 33, Manalapan, 07726 (732) 792-1984
Marlow Candy & Nut Co., 65 Honeck St., Englewood, 07631 (201) 569-7606
Marlton Pike Precision, LLC, 728 Beechwood Ave., Cherry Hill, 08002 (856) 665-1900
Marlyn Sheet Metal, Inc., 606 N. Delsea Dr., Clayton, 08312 (856) 863-6900
Marmo Enterprises, Inc., 468 Elizabeth Ave., Somerset, 08873 (908) 486-4421
Marmon Group, LLC, The see. Aerospace Nylok, Hawthorne
Marmon Group, LLC, The see. TE Wire & Cable, LLC, Saddle Brook
Marmus, Inc., 51 E. Front St., Keyport, 07735 (732) 264-3681
Marotta Controls, Inc., 78 Boonton Ave., P.O. Box 427, Montville, 07045 (973) 334-7800
Marquis see. Jade Eastern Trading, Inc., Moonachie
Mars Chocolate North America, 800 High St., Hackettstown, 07840 (908) 852-1000
Mars, Incorporated see. Mars Chocolate North America, Hackettstown
Mars International, Inc., 60 Kingsbridge Rd., Piscataway, 08854 (908) 233-0044
Marsden, Inc., 6800 Westfield Ave., Pennsauken, 08110 (856) 663-2227
Marshall, Inc., G. E., 810 S. Broad St., Trenton, 08611 (609) 392-2464
Marshall Industrial Technologies, 529 S. Clinton Ave., Trenton, 08611 (609) 394-7153
Martek Industries, Inc., 600 Deer Rd., Ste. 8, Cherry Hill, 08034 (856) 427-9411
Martin Corp., 171 N. Pearl St., Bridgeton, 08302 (856) 451-0900

Martin, Inc., H. S., 1149 Southeast Blvd., Vineland, 08360 ... (856) 692-8700
Martin Printing Service, Inc., 63 Liberty St., Little Ferry, 07643 ... (201) 440-0410
Martin Sprocket & Gear, Inc., 7 Highpoint Dr., Wayne, 07470 ... (973) 633-5700
Martin Tool Co., Inc., 60 Route 15 S., Wharton, 07885 ... (973) 361-9212
Martin's Specialty Sausage Co., 150 Harmony Rd., Mickleton, 08056 ... (856) 423-4000
† Maruka U.S.A., Inc.,
45 Route 46 E., Ste. 610, P.O. Box 747, Pine Brook, 07058 ... (973) 487-3800
Marvic Corp./A.J.D. Stone, 2450 Iorio St., Union, 07083 ... (908) 686-4340
Marvin Window Sales see. ... Morak, Inc., Hackettstown
† Mary Ellen Maryland Crabmeat Co., Inc.,
2613 Fire Rd., Egg Harbor Township, 08234 ... (609) 645-0161
MASAco * MASA Architectural Canopies see.(MASAco) Michael Anthony Sign & Awning, Inc., Avenel
Masco Corp. see. ... Arrow Fastener Co., LLC, Saddle Brook
Masco Corp. see. ... Cobra Products, Inc., Swedesboro
† Masda Corp., 22 Troy Rd., P.O. Box D, Whippany, 07981 ... (973) 386-1100
Mashal Signs Co., Inc., 568 55th St., West New York, 07093 ... (201) 348-8500
Masi Electronics, Don, 25 Walden Pl., West Caldwell, 07006 ... (973) 618-6288
Massarelli's Lawn Ornaments, 500 S. Egg Harbor Rd., Hammonton, 08037 ... (609) 567-9700
Masstar, 18 Heritage Rd., Eatontown, 07724 ... (732) 542-8004
Master Bond, Inc., 154 Hobart St., Hackensack, 07601 ... (201) 343-8983
Master Business Forms Co., 195 Allwood Rd., Clifton, 07012 ... (973) 594-8743
Master Craft Steel Rule Die, 84 Bell St., Orange, 07050 ... (973) 674-7662
Master Craftsman, LLC, 417 N. Grove St., Bldg. 2, Unit D, Berlin, 08009 ... (856) 768-8088
Master Cutlery, Inc., 700 Penhorn Ave., Secaucus, 07094 ... (201) 271-7600
Master Drapery Workroom, Inc., 220 N. 14th St., Kenilworth, 07033 ... (908) 272-4404
Master Metal Polishing Corp., 57 Wood St., Paterson, 07520 ... (973) 684-0119
Master Printing Co., P.O. Box 9609, Elizabeth, 07202 ... (908) 351-1568
Master Printing, Inc., 445 Industrial Rd., Carlstadt, 07072 ... (201) 842-9100
★ Master Printing, Inc.,
30 Pedricktown Woodstown Rd., P.O. Box 1, Pedricktown, 08067 ... (856) 299-8318
Master Repro, Inc. see. ... Alpha Graphics, Midland Park
Master Shipwrights, Inc.,
25 W. Highland Ave., P.O. Box 273, Atlantic Highlands, 07716 ... (732) 872-7500
Master Tool Corp.,
342 Squankum Yellowbrook Rd., P.O. Box 7, Farmingdale, 07727 ... (732) 919-1010
Master Wire Mfg., Inc.,
1019 Black Horse Pike, Route 322, P.O. Box 328, Hammonton, 08037 ... (609) 567-1616
Mastercool, Inc., 1 Aspen Dr., Randolph, 07869 ... (973) 252-9119
Mastercraft Electroplating, 801 Magnolia Ave., Elizabeth, 07201 ... (908) 354-4404
Mastercraft Iron, Inc., 1111 10th Ave., Neptune, 07753 ... (732) 988-3113
Mastercrafts, 152 Louis St., South Hackensack, 07606 ... (201) 641-6555
Mastergraphx, Inc.,
45 Stouts Ln., Ste. 14, P.O. Box 567, Monmouth Junction, 08852 ... (732) 329-0088
Masters Interiors, Inc., 1500 Main Ave., Clifton, 07011 ... (973) 253-0784
Matawan Stained Glass, 77-A Main St., Matawan, 07747 ... (732) 583-1030
Matchless Metal Polish Co. see. ... Matchless United Co., Linden
Matchless United Co., 801 E. Linden Ave., Linden, 07036 ... (908) 862-7300
† Material Handling Supply, Inc., 1 Old Salem Rd., Brooklawn, 08030 ... (856) 541-1290
† Materials Reclaim Industries,
409 Joyce Kilmer Ave., Ste. 3, New Brunswick, 08901 ... (732) 979-3479
Math League Press see. ... Mathematics League, Inc., Tenafly
Mathematics League, Inc., 17 Lancaster Rd., P.O. Box 17, Tenafly, 07670 ... (201) 568-6328
MATHESON see. ... Matheson Tri-Gas, Inc., Basking Ridge
Matheson Tri-Gas, Inc., 150 Allen Rd., Ste. 302, Basking Ridge, 07920 ... (908) 991-9200
Matheson Tri-Gas, Inc. see. ... Valley National Gases, WV LLC, West Deptford
Matrix Controls Co., Inc., 330 Elizabeth Ave., Somerset, 08873 ... (732) 469-5551
† Matrix Distributors, Inc., 110 Tices Ln., Ste. 5-B, East Brunswick, 08816 ... (732) 698-9991
Matrix Test Equipment, Inc., 200 Wood Ave., Middlesex, 08846 ... (732) 469-9510
Matteo & Sons, Inc., James, 1692 Crown Point Rd., Thorofare, 08086 ... (856) 845-0398
Matthews Engravers, Edward R., 61 S. State St., Hackensack, 07601 ... (201) 342-4644
Matthias Paper Corp., 301 Arlington Blvd., P.O. Box 130, Swedesboro, 08085 ... (856) 467-6970
† Matting World, P.O. Box 43, Beverly, 08010 ... (609) 641-4747
MAUSER USA LLC, 35 Cotters Ln., Ste. C, East Brunswick, 08816 ... (732) 353-7000
Mauser USA LLC, 14 Convery Blvd., Woodbridge, 07095 ... (732) 634-6000
Maverick Industries, Inc., 94 Mayfield Ave., Edison, 08837 ... (732) 417-9666
Max Graphics see. ... Maxtex, Inc., West Berlin
Max Gurtman & Sons, Inc., 622 Lexington Ave., Clifton, 07011 ... (973) 478-7000
Maxflight Corp., 1 Executive Dr., Toms River, 08755 ... (732) 281-2007
★ Maximum Material Handling, LLC, 750 Edwards Rd., Parsippany, 07054 ... (973) 227-1227
Maxter Corp. (H Q), 51 Edgemont Ln., Willingboro, 08046 ... (609) 877-9700
Maxtex, Inc., 159 N. Cooper Rd., West Berlin, 08091 ... (856) 767-7960
Mayab Happy Tacos, Inc., 450 Florida Grove Rd., Perth Amboy, 08861 ... (732) 293-0400
★ Mayabeque Products Corp., 7424 Bergenline Ave., Ste. 1, North Bergen, 07047 ... (201) 869-0531
Mayer/Berkshire Corp. (H Q), 25 Edison Rd., P.O. Box 244, Wayne, 07474 ... (973) 696-6200
Mayfair Technology, LLC, 66 Witherspoon St., Princeton, 08542 ... (609) 802-1262
Mayos Sportswear, Inc., 1 Hollywood Ave., Bldg. 2-D, Ho-Ho-Kus, 07423 ... (201) 652-8570
Maywood Furniture Corp. see. ... DeSaussure Equipment Co., Inc., Maywood
Maza & Maza Welding, 28 Mulock Pl., Harrison, 07029 ... (973) 481-4441
Mazmet, 1050 Bristol Rd., Mountainside, 07092 ... (908) 654-7686
Mazzanti, Inc., 701 Grand St., Hoboken, 07030 ... (201) 360-4400
MB Mfg., Inc., 1 Gwinup Rd., Blairstown, 07825 ... (908) 362-5588
† MBO America, 4 E. Stow Rd., Ste. 12, Marlton, 08053 ... (609) 267-2900
MC Signs, 231 West Ave., Ocean City, 08226 ... (609) 399-7446
McBride Awning Co., 304 Richmond Ave., Point Pleasant Beach, 08742 ... (732) 892-6256
McCain Foods USA, Inc., 11 Gregg St., Lodi, 07644 ... (201) 368-0600
MCC/Norsal see. ... Microwave Consulting Corp., Paterson
McCormicks Bindery, Inc., 5815 Magnolia Ave., Pennsauken, 08109 ... (856) 663-8035
MCD Print & Document Solutions see. ... Morris County Duplicating Corp., Morristown
McElwee & Quinn, LLC, 2070 E. Route 70, Ste. 4, Cherry Hill, 08003 ... (856) 229-7015
McGinnis Printing, 20 Monmouth St., Red Bank, 07701 ... (732) 758-0060
★ McGraw-Hill Construction, 148 Princeton Hightstown Rd., Hightstown, 08520 ... (800) 393-6343
McGraw-Hill Financial, Inc. see. ... McGraw-Hill Construction, Hightstown
McGrory Glass, Inc., 1400 Grandview Ave., Paulsboro, 08066 ... (856) 579-3200
† McIntosh Controls Corp., 218 Little Falls Rd., Unit 1, Cedar Grove, 07009 ... (973) 433-4700
† McJunkin Red Man Corporation, 305 Center Ave., Waterford Works, 08089 ... (856) 753-7690
McKella 280, 7025 Central Hwy., Pennsauken, 08109 ... (856) 813-1153
† McKesson Corp., 400 Delran Pkwy., Delran, 08075 ... (856) 461-7800
† McKesson Medical-Surgical, 1130 Commerce Blvd., Swedesboro, 08085 ... (856) 241-1709
McKnight Drapery Services, 126 Majestic S., Lincroft, 07738 ... (732) 741-3655
McLain Studios, Inc., 1203 Main St., Asbury Park, 07712 ... (732) 775-0271
† McLane Burlington, 600 Commerce Dr., Burlington, 08016 ... (609) 239-5000
McLane Company, Inc., Foodservice Division see. ... McLane Burlington, Burlington
McLane Company, Inc., Grocery Div. see. ... McLane New Jersey, Carneys Point
† McLane New Jersey, 742 Courses Landing Rd., Carneys Point, 08069 ... (856) 351-6200
McLean Packaging Corp., 1504 Glen Ave., Moorestown, 08057 ... (856) 359-2600
† McMaster-Carr Supply Co., 200 New Canton Way, Robbinsville, 08691 ... (609) 259-8900
McMillan Analysis Corp., 39 Meadowbrook Rd., Randolph, 07869 ... (973) 328-1674
McNally Instruments, LLC, 11 Longview Rd., Rockaway, 07866 ... (973) 983-9153
McNeil, Inc., 15 Marlen Dr., Robbinsville, 08691 ... (609) 890-7007
† McNICHOLS Co., 2 Home News Row, New Brunswick, 08901 ... (732) 509-3092
MCT CABLE see. ... Motion Control Technologies, Inc., Dover
† MCT Dairies, Inc., 15 Bleeker St., Millburn, 07041 ... (973) 258-9600
McWane, Inc. see. ... Atlantic States Cast Iron Pipe Co., Phillipsburg
McWilliams Forge Co., 387 Franklin Ave., Rockaway, 07866 ... (973) 627-0200
MDI Mfg., Inc., 100 Syracuse Ct., Lakewood, 08701 ... (732) 994-5599
Meadow Burke Products, 269 Commercial Ave., Palisades Park, 07650 ... (201) 242-8989
Meadow Fox, LLC see. ... Key-Pak Machines By Luciano Packaging Technologies, Inc, Somerville
Meadowbrook Inventions, Inc.,
260 Mine Brook Rd., P.O. Box 960, Bernardsville, 07924 ... (908) 766-0606
Meadowlands Bindery, Inc., 146 W. Commercial Ave., Moonachie, 07074 ... (201) 935-6161
★ Meadowlands Signs, 58 State Route 17, Hasbrouck Heights, 07604 ... (201) 426-0420
Meadows Knitting Corp., 1875 McCarter Hwy., Newark, 07104 ... (973) 482-6400
MEC TECH, Inc., 2200 Industrial Way S., Toms River, 08755 ... (732) 505-0308
Meca Electronics, Inc., 459 E. Main St., Denville, 07834 ... (973) 625-0661
Mecca & Sons Trucking Corp. see. ... Cocoa Processing Corp., Hillside
Mecca & Sons Trucking Corp. (H Q),
580 Luis Munoz Marin Blvd., Jersey City, 07310 ... (201) 792-5866
Mecca Halal Wholesale see. ... American Halal Slaughter House, Newark
Mechanical Components Corp., 145 Yellowbrook Rd., Farmingdale, 07727 ... (732) 938-3737
Mechanical Ingenuity Corp., 61 Riordan Pl., Shrewsbury, 07702 ... (732) 842-8889
Mechanical Precision, Inc., 11 Hopewell Ave., Flemington, 08822 ... (908) 782-2511
Mechanitron Corp., 310 W. 1st Ave., Roselle, 07203 ... (908) 620-1001
Mech-Tronics, 100 Campus Dr., Mount Holly, 08060 ... (609) 267-0680
Med A-Z.Net, LLC, 37 Station Dr., Ste. 1-E, Princeton Junction, 08550 ... (609) 716-6991
Med Laurel, LLC see. ... Laurel Mfrs., Inc., Delanco
Meda Pharmaceuticals, Inc. (H Q), 265 Davidson Ave., Somerset, 08873 ... (732) 564-2200
Medallion International, Inc., 233 W. Parkway, Pompton Plains, 07444 ... (973) 616-3401
Medco Manufacturing Co. see. ... Medco West, Hackensack
Medco West, 25-21 Di Carolis Ct., Hackensack, 07601 ... (201) 457-9260
MedConnection, LLC, 65 Howard St., Phillipsburg, 08865 ... (908) 213-7012
Medford Cedar Products, Inc., 59 Old Red Lion Rd., Vincentown, 08088 ... (609) 859-1400
Medford Concrete Co., 4 Tidswell Ave., P.O. Box 273, Medford, 08055 ... (609) 654-2200
† Medford Silicones, Inc., P.O. Box 2072, Medford, 08055 ... (609) 953-1092
Medford Speed & Machine, Inc., 132 Red Lion Rd., Southampton, 08088 ... (609) 801-0808
Media Vista, Inc., 60 Broad St., Ste. 100, Red Bank, 07701 ... (732) 747-8060
Mediagraphics, Inc., 25 Somerset Pl., Clifton, 07012 ... (973) 777-2202
Medical Decision Point see. ... BlueSpire Strategic Marketing, Montvale
Medical Indicators, Inc., 16 Thomas J. Rhodes Industrial Dr., Hamilton, 08619 ... (609) 737-1600
Medical Packaging, Inc., 470 Route 31, P.O. Box 500, Ringoes, 08551 ... (609) 466-8991
Medicines Co., The, 8 Sylvan Way, Parsippany, 07054 ... (973) 290-6000
Medin Corp., 11 Jackson Rd., Totowa, 07512 ... (973) 779-2400
★ Mediterranean Stucco Corp., 111 Main St., Newark, 07105 ... (973) 491-0160
Mednet Healthcare Technologies, Inc., 275 Phillips Blvd., Ewing, 08618 ... (609) 671-1790
MedPlast Group, 225 Old Egg Harbor Rd., West Berlin, 08091 ... (856) 753-7600
MedPlast, Inc. see. ... MedPlast Group, West Berlin
Medrecon, Inc., 257 South Ave., Garwood, 07027 ... (908) 789-2050
Medtronic, Inc., 300 Interpace Pkwy., Parsippany, 07054 ... (516) 222-2848
Medtronic, Inc. see. ... TYRX, Inc., Monmouth Junction
† Med-X International, Inc., 20 Foster St., Bergenfield, 07621 ... (201) 387-8556
† Med-X-Ray Co., Inc., 356 Glenwood Ave., East Orange, 07017 ... (973) 673-8822
Meese Orbitron Dunne Co., 535 N. Midland Ave., Saddle Brook, 07663 ... (201) 796-4667
MEGA Electronics, Inc., 4-B Jules Ln., New Brunswick, 08901 ... (732) 249-2656
★ Mega Fortris Americas, Inc., 3 Chris Ct., P.O. Box 934, Dayton, 08810 ... (732) 230-3015
Mega Media Concepts Ltd., 286 Houses Corner Rd., Sparta, 07871 ... (973) 919-5661
Mega Pumps, L. P., 611 Industrial Way W., Eatontown, 07724 ... (732) 578-9100
★ Megas Yeeros, LLC, 165 Chubb Ave., Lyndhurst, 07071 ... (212) 777-6342
Megasafe, 8 Sunrise Ave., Budd Lake, 07828 ... (973) 691-0382
★ MegaStrike, Inc., 331 Fairfield Rd., Ste. B-1, Freehold, 07728 ... (732) 780-7383
Megawatt Machine Services, LLC, 417 Elizabeth Ave., Somerset, 08873 ... (732) 805-4000
MEL Chemicals, 500 Barbertown Point Breeze Rd., Flemington, 08822 ... (908) 782-5800
† Melfast, Inc., 18 Passaic Ave., Unit 4-5, Fairfield, 07004 ... (973) 227-0045
Melitta U. S. A., 1401 Berlin Rd., Cherry Hill, 08034 ... (856) 428-7202
† Mel-Pak Equipment Co., 649 U.S. Highway 206, Ste. 9-303, Hillsborough, 08844 ... (201) 825-2624
Melton Industries see. ... Melton Sales & Service, Inc., Burlington
Melton Sales & Service, Inc., 511 Elbow Ln., Burlington, 08016 ... (609) 699-4800
Membrane Structure Solutions, Inc., 340 N. Wyoming Ave., South Orange, 07079 ... (908) 520-0112
Membranes International, Inc.,
219 Margaret King Ave., P.O. Box 219, Ringwood, 07456 ... (973) 998-5530
Memorial Arts, Inc., 1172 E. Ridgewood Ave., Ridgewood, 07450 ... (201) 652-4301
Men Of Steel Enterprises, LLC, 4319 Route 130, Beverly, 08010 ... (877) 732-2728
Men of Steel Rebar Fabricators, LLC see. ... Men Of Steel Enterprises, LLC, Beverly
Menasha Packaging Company, LLC see. ... Strive Group, LLC, The, Lyndhurst
Menco Business Products, 178 Route 206 S., Hillsborough, 08844 ... (908) 281-0911
MEND Tech, Inc., 38 Irving Pl., Garfield, 07026 ... (973) 340-9212
Mendel Co. (H Q), 12-C Great Meadow Ln., East Hanover, 07936 ... (973) 599-1300
Mendoker's Quality Bakery, Inc., 34 W. Railroad Ave., Jamesburg, 08831 ... (732) 521-0056
Mennekes Electronics, Inc., 277 Fairfield Rd., Fairfield, 07004 ... (973) 882-8333
Menshen Packaging U.S.A., Inc., 21 Industrial Park, Waldwick, 07463 ... (201) 445-7436
MentisSoft, Inc., 347 Plainfield Ave., Ste. 104, Edison, 08817 ... (732) 568-4715
Menu Foods, Inc., 9130 Griffith Morgan Ln., Pennsauken, 08110 ... (856) 662-7412
Merc USA, Inc., 41 Newman St., Hackensack, 07601 ... (201) 489-3527
Mercer Coating & Lining Co., Inc.,
1410 E. Linden Ave., P.O. Box 1656, Linden, 07036 ... (908) 925-5000
Mercer Gasket & Shim, Inc., 110 Benigno Blvd., Bellmawr, 08031 ... (856) 931-5000
† Mercer Group International, Inc.,
1519 Calhoun St., P.O. Box 5626, Trenton, 08638 ... (609) 393-4834
Mercer International, Inc., 39 W. Main St., P.O. Box 540, Mendham, 07945 ... (973) 543-9000
Mercer Machine & Tool Products, 332 Darcy Ave., Trenton, 08629 ... (609) 587-1106
Mercer Occupational Training, 600 New York Ave., Trenton, 08638 ... (609) 393-2483
Mercer Rubber see. ... Mercer Gasket & Shim, Inc., Bellmawr
Merchant & Evans, Inc., 308 Connecticut Dr., Burlington, 08016 ... (609) 387-3033
Merchant Street Printer, LLC, 107 E. Atlantic Ave., Audubon, 08106 ... (856) 547-1991
Merck & Co., Inc., 2000 Galloping Hill Rd., Kenilworth, 07033 ... (908) 298-4000
Merck & Co., Inc., 126 E. Lincoln Ave., P.O. Box 2000, Rahway, 07065 ... (732) 594-4000

ALPHABETICAL

© Copyright 2015 Manufacturers' News, Inc.


Merck & Co., Inc. (H Q), 1 Merck Dr., P.O. Box 100, Whitehouse Station, 08889 (908) 423-1000
Mercury Adhesives, Inc., 140 Dayton Ave., Passaic, 07055 (973) 472-3307
Mercury Commercial Electronics, 2 Henderson Dr., Ste. B, Caldwell, 07006 (973) 244-1040
Mercury Floor Machines, Inc., 110 S. Van Brunt St., Englewood, 07631 (201) 568-4606
Mercury Lighting Products Co., 20 Audrey Pl., Fairfield, 07004 (973) 244-9444
Mercury Plastic Bag Co., Inc., 168 7th St., Passaic, 07055 (973) 778-7200
Mercury Printing, Inc., 14 Veronica Ave., Somerset, 08873 (732) 247-6828
Mercury Systems, Inc. see. Mercury Commercial Electronics, Caldwell
† Mercury Tire Co., Inc., 1 Fairfield Rd., Caldwell, 07006 (973) 785-0080
Meredith Paving Corp., 1300 Union Landing Rd., Cinnaminson, 08077 (856) 829-4343
Merial Ltd., 631 U.S. Highway 1, North Brunswick, 08902 (732) 729-5700
Meridian Surfaces, 677 Ramapo Valley Rd., Oakland, 07436 (201) 337-7888
Merit Trophies & Engraving, Inc., 184 Main St., Hackensack, 07601 (201) 487-5780
Merlin Controls see. FMDK Technologies, Inc., Mahwah
Merlin Graphics, Inc., 194 Christie Ave., Clifton, 07011 (201) 795-3330
Merlin Industries, Inc., 2904 E. State Street Ext., Hamilton, 08619 (609) 807-1000
Merlino Marble & Granite, Inc., 92 Route 50, Ocean View, 08230 (609) 624-9500
Merrill Corp., 649 Rahway Ave., Union, 07083 (908) 688-5757
Merrimac Industries, Inc., 41 Fairfield Pl., West Caldwell, 07006 (973) 575-1300
Merry Modes 2000, 61 Willet St., Ste. 2, Passaic, 07055 (973) 773-2501
Mersen USA BN Corp., 400 Myrtle Ave., Boonton, 07005 (973) 334-0700
Mershon Concrete, LLC, Route 130 S., P.O. Box 254, Bordentown, 08505 (609) 298-2150
Merton Tech, LLC, 168 Central Ave., Rochelle Park, 07662 (201) 881-0555
Mesa Laboratories, Inc., 10 Park Pl., Ste. 3, Butler, 07405 (973) 492-8400
MESCO see. Muenz Engineered Sales Co., Summit
† Metal Associates, Inc., 230 W. Parkway, Unit 3-2, Pompton Plains, 07444 (973) 835-8480
Metal City Findings Co., 456 Nordhoff Pl., P.O. Box 7300, Englewood, 07631 (201) 569-7300
Metal Components, 92 Maryland Ave., Paterson, 07503 (973) 247-1204
Metal Cutting Corp., 89 Commerce Rd., Cedar Grove, 07009 (973) 239-1101
Metal Dynamix, LLC, 709 Fellowship Rd., Mount Laurel, 08054 (856) 235-4559
Metal Etching Technology Assocs., Inc.,
140 Mount Holly Bypass, Unit 10, Lumberton, 08048 (609) 261-2670
★ Metal FX Films, LLC, 27 Kearney St., Unit B, Bridgewater, 08807 (732) 560-1297
Metal Graphics, Inc., 49 Empire St., Newark, 07114 (973) 242-0300
Metal Management Northeast, Inc., 1 Linden Ave. E., Jersey City, 07305 (201) 577-3200
Metal Masters, 630 Laurel St., Beverly, 08010 (609) 332-3176
Metal Masters, 1 Lower Oak Grove Rd., Frenchtown, 08825 (908) 996-2555
Metal Powder Industries Federation, 105 College Rd. E., Princeton, 08540 (609) 452-7700
† Metal Stock, 471 Southard St., Trenton, 08638 (609) 394-1129
Metal Textiles Corp., 970 New Durham Rd., Edison, 08818 (732) 287-0800
Metalfab, Inc., 11 Prices Switch Rd., P.O. Box 9, Vernon, 07462 (973) 764-2000
Metalico, Inc. (H Q), 186 North Ave. E., Cranford, 07016 (908) 497-9610
Metaline Products Co., Inc.,
101 N. Feltus St. & 241 Raritan St., South Amboy, 08879 (732) 721-1373
Metallix Refining, Inc., 59 Avenue At The Common, Ste. 201, Shrewsbury, 07702 (732) 936-0050
Metallo Gasket Co., Inc., 16 Bethany St., New Brunswick, 08901 (732) 545-7223
Metals USA, Inc. see. Metals USA, Plates & Shapes Group, Newark
† Metals USA, Plates & Shapes Group, 182 Frelinghuysen Ave., Newark, 07114 (973) 242-1000
Metem Corp., 700 Parsippany Rd., Parsippany, 07054 (973) 887-6635
Metfab Metals, LLC, 560 Freeman St., Orange, 07050 (973) 675-7676
Method Assocs., Inc., 120 Francis St., Ste. 2, Keyport, 07735 (732) 888-0444
Meto Lift, Inc., 556 Commerce St., Franklin Lakes, 07417 (201) 405-0311
Metricon Corp., 12 N. Main St., P.O. Box 63, Pennington, 08534 (609) 737-1052
† Metro America Sales, Inc., 137 South Ave., Fanwood, 07023 (908) 490-0001
Metro Bowl, 37-02 Broadway, Fair Lawn, 07410 (201) 791-2995
Metro Candy Apple Corp., 203 Paterson Ave., Ste. 1, Wallington, 07057 (973) 772-0837
Metro Flag Co., 353 Richard Mine Rd., Unit 100, Wharton, 07885 (973) 366-1776
† Metro Hydraulic Jack Co., 1271 McCarter Hwy., P.O. Box 9410, Newark, 07104 (973) 350-0111
† Metro Industrial Supply, Inc., 200 Charles St., Garfield, 07026 (973) 546-5660
Metro Mold Components see. Metro America Sales, Inc., Fanwood
Metro Packaging & Imaging, Inc., 5 Haul Rd., Wayne, 07470 (973) 709-9100
Metro Printing & Promotions, LLC, 311 Mechanic St., Boonton, 07005 (973) 316-1600
★ Metro Publishing Group, Inc., 626 McCarthy Dr., New Milford, 07646 (201) 385-2000
Metro Signs, 410 Downs Dr., P.O. Box 865, Cherry Hill, 08003 (856) 428-9050
Metro Tag & Label, Inc., 25 E. Spring Valley Ave., Ste. 200, Maywood, 07607 (201) 845-4747
Metro Web Corp., 5901 Tonnelle Ave., North Bergen, 07047 (201) 553-0700
Metro-Chem, Inc., 24 Pennsylvania Ave., P.O. Box 401, Kearny, 07032 (973) 589-2800
Metropole, Inc., 214 Clifton Blvd., Clifton, 07011 (973) 473-2727
Metropolitan Corporate Counsel, 1180 Wychwood Rd., Mountainside, 07092 (908) 654-4840
★ Metropolitan Mfg., Inc., 450 Murray Hill Pkwy., East Rutherford, 07073 (201) 933-8111
Metropolitan Rubber Co., 135 Lawrence St., Hackensack, 07601 (201) 489-0909
Metropolitan Vacuum Cleaner Co., Inc., 5 Raritan Rd., Oakland, 07436 (201) 405-2225
Metropolitan Window Fashions, 799 Route 17 S., Paramus, 07652 (201) 689-6030
Mettler-Toledo, LLC see. Ohaus Corp., Parsippany
Metuchen Capacitors, Inc.,
2139 Highway 35, Ste. 2, P.O. Box 399, Holmdel, 07733 (732) 888-9700
Mfrs. Aid, Inc., 425 Whitehead Ave., South River, 08882 (732) 613-6555
† MG America, Inc., 31 Kulick Rd., Fairfield, 07004 (973) 808-8185
† MHE, Inc., 47 Atlantic Ave., Long Branch, 07740 (732) 571-6112
Miami Onion Roll Co., 111 Berkshire Ave., Paterson, 07502 (973) 389-2202
Miceli Cabinet Corp., 128 Madison Ave., Englewood, 07631 (201) 933-4004
Michael Foods, Inc., 847 North Ave., Elizabeth, 07201 (908) 282-7140
Michael Foods, Inc. see. Papetti's Hygrade Egg Products, Inc., Elizabeth
† Michael Halebian & Co., Inc., 557 Washington Ave., Carlstadt, 07072 (201) 935-3535
Michaelian & Kohlberg (H Q), 100 Hoffman Pl., Hillside, 07205 (908) 522-1004
Michael's Commercial Signs, 629 62nd St., Ste. 31, West New York, 07093 (201) 868-7166
MICRO, 140 Belmont Dr., Somerset, 08873 (732) 302-0800
Micro Logic, Inc., 31 Industrial Ave., Ste. 6, Mahwah, 07430 (201) 962-7512
Micro Molding, Inc., 65 Howard St., Phillipsburg, 08865 (908) 454-1225
Micro Steel Rule Die see. Product Identification Co., Inc., Garfield
Micro-Air, Inc., 124 Route 526, Allentown, 08501 (609) 259-2636
Microcast Technologies Corp., 1611 W. Elizabeth Ave., Linden, 07036 (908) 523-9503
Microdata Instrument, Inc., 1207 Hogan Dr., South Plainfield, 07080 (908) 222-1717
Microelettrica-USA, LLC, 4 Middlebury Blvd., Ste. 12, Randolph, 07869 (973) 598-0806
Microfold, Inc., 375 North St., Unit C, Teterboro, 07608 (201) 641-5052
Microgen, Inc., 33 Clinton Rd., Ste. 102, West Caldwell, 07006 (973) 575-9025
Microlab/FXR, 25 Eastmans Rd., Parsippany, 07054 (973) 386-9696
Micromat Co., 185 State Route 17, Mahwah, 07430 (201) 529-3738
Micromedia Publications, Inc., 15 Union Ave., P.O. Box 521, Lakehurst, 08733 (732) 657-7344
Micron Fastener, Inc., 85-99 Hazel St., Paterson, 07503 (973) 278-4100
† Micron Optics, 14 Ridgedale Ave., Ste. 125, Cedar Knolls, 07927 (973) 267-5047
MICROS Retail Systems, Inc., 1500 Harbor Blvd., Ste. 2, Weehawken, 07086 (201) 866-1000
Microseal Industries, Inc., 610 E. 36th St., P.O. Box 3054, Paterson, 07509 (973) 523-0704
MicroSurfaces, Inc., 1 W. Forest Ave., Englewood, 07631 (201) 408-5596
Micro-Tek Corp., P.O. Box 2134, Cinnaminson, 08077 (856) 829-3855
Microtube Fabricators, Inc., 250 Lackland Dr., Middlesex, 08846 (732) 469-7420
Microwave Consulting Corp., 150 Railroad Ave., Paterson, 07501 (973) 523-6700
Microwave Product Digest * MPD see. Octagon Communications Corp., Englewood Cliffs
Mid Atlantic Graphix, Inc., 2558 Tilton Rd., Egg Harbor Township, 08234 (609) 569-9990
† Mid Atlantic Pump & Equipment Co., 228 N. Route 73, Berlin, 08009 (856) 768-3880
† Mid County Paper Stock, Inc., 235 Brighton Rd., P.O. Box 624, Andover, 07821 (973) 786-7499
Mid Jersey Building Supply, 2486 Ridgeway Blvd., Manchester, 08759 (732) 657-2000
Mid Jersey Pet Supply, 296 Pershing Ave., Carteret, 07008 (732) 541-2807
Mid State Bindery, 148 Sylvania Pl., South Plainfield, 07080 (908) 755-9388
Mid State Controls, Inc., 8 Crown Plz., Ste. 102, Hazlet, 07730 (732) 335-0500
Mid State Filigree Systems, Inc.,
22 Brickyard Rd., P.O. Box 435, Cranbury, 08512 (609) 448-8700
Mid States Spiral, Inc., 1425 Grandview Ave., West Deptford, 08066 (215) 744-2846
† Mid-Atlantic CNC, Inc., 260 Evans Way, Branchburg, 08876 (908) 809-1100
Mid-Atlantic Engine Supply,
Route 130 S. & Pennsauken St., P.O. Box 2270, Cinnaminson, 08077 (856) 829-7798
† Mid-Atlantic Truck Center, Inc., 525 W. Linden Ave., Linden, 07036 (908) 862-8181
Mid-Continent Packaging Co., Inc. (H Q),
55 Jacobus Ave., 1st Fl., Kearny, 07032 (973) 589-3544
Middle Atlantic Products, Inc., 300 Fairfield Rd., Fairfield, 07004 (973) 839-1011
Middleburg Yarn Processing Co., Inc. (H Q),
375 Diamond Bridge Ave., P.O. Box 640, Hawthorne, 07507 (973) 238-1800
Middlesex Armature Service, 1155 Saint Georges Ave., Colonia, 07067 (732) 634-3779
Middlesex Industrial Sales, Inc., 522 New Brunswick Ave., Fords, 08863 (732) 738-0537
Middlesex Publications, Inc., 850 Carolier Ln., North Brunswick, 08902 (732) 435-0005
Mid-Eastern Industries Div, Technology Dynamics, Inc,
100 School St., Bergenfield, 07621 (201) 385-0500
Midhattan Woodworking, 3130 Bordentown Ave., Old Bridge, 08857 (732) 727-3020
Midlan Corp., 3 Bohnert Pl., Waldwick, 07463 (201) 445-4405
Midland Radiator Service Co., 420 Midland Ave., Garfield, 07026 (973) 340-0533
Midland Screen Printing, Inc.,
280 N. Midland Ave., Bldg. H, Saddle Brook, 07663 (201) 703-0066
† Midlantic Metals, 2201 Mount Ephraim Ave., Ste. 90, Camden, 08104 (856) 963-2822
Mid-Lantic Precision, Inc., 940 Market St., Gloucester City, 08030 (856) 456-3810
† Midlantic Supply, LLC,
8000 Midlantic Dr., Ste. 200-N., P.O. Box 506, Mount Laurel, 08054 (856) 813-5014
MidOcean Partners see. Agilex Flavors & Fragrances, Inc., Piscataway
Mid-State Enterprises, Inc., 155 Van Winkle Rd., Hawthorne, 07506 (973) 427-6040
† Mid-State Lumber Corp., 200 Industrial Pkwy., Branchburg, 08876 (908) 725-4900
Midway Machine Product Corp.,
763-A Railroad Ave., P.O. Box 129, Florence, 08518 (609) 499-4377
Midwest Medical Supply Co., LLC see. Midwest Medical Supply Company, LLC, Secaucus
† Midwest Medical Supply Company, LLC, 200 Seaview Dr., Secaucus, 07094 (201) 223-4602
Miel Patisserie, LLC, 1990 Route 70 E., Ste. 14, Cherry Hill, 08003 (856) 424-6435
Miele Iron Works, Inc., 2340 Route 22 E., Union, 07083 (908) 686-0943
Migali Industries, Inc., 516 Lansdowne Ave., Camden, 08104 (856) 963-3600
Mikros Systems Corp., 707 Alexander Rd., Princeton, 08540 (609) 987-1513
Mil-Comm Products Co., Inc., 2 Carlton Ave., East Rutherford, 07073 (201) 935-8561
Milestone PharmTech USA, Inc.,
100 Jersey Ave., Bldg. D, Box D-4, New Brunswick, 08901 (732) 579-8201
Milestone Scientific, Inc. (H Q),
220 S. Orange Ave., Ste. 102, Livingston, 07039 (973) 535-2717
Miletta Brothers, Inc., 194 Main St., Cedarville, 08311 (856) 447-4652
Military Equipment Corp. Of America (H Q), P.O. Box 181, Mantoloking, 08738 (908) 769-1000
Millar Sheet Metal, 39 Rizzolo Rd., Kearny, 07032 (201) 997-1990
Millennium see. Millennium Systems International, Parsippany
Millennium Graphics, Inc., 35 Vanderburg Rd., Marlboro, 07746 (732) 431-0440
Millennium Systems International, 28 Eastmans Rd., Parsippany, 07054 (973) 402-9500
Miller & Sons, Inc., 24 Belleville Ave., Belleville, 07109 (973) 759-6445
Miller & Sons, Inc., I. V., 15 Cindy Ln., Ocean, 07712 (732) 493-4040
★ Miller Corp., Carol S., 98 Saddlewood Dr., Ste. A, Hillsdale, 07642 (201) 406-4578
Miller Fabricators, 1135 Mount Ephraim Ave., Camden, 08103 (856) 541-9499
Miller, LLC, Sally (H Q), 30 N. Main St., Milltown, 08850 (732) 729-4840
Millimeter Wave Technology, 90 Dayton Ave., Ste. 6-E, Passaic, 07055 (845) 369-7808
Millner Kitchens, Inc., 200-B Whitehead Rd., Ste. 108, Hamilton, 08619 (609) 890-7300
Millson Precision Machining, 145 11th St., Piscataway, 08854 (732) 424-1700
Milltex Home Decorator see. Milltex Mfg. Co., Brick
Milltex Mfg. Co., 1101 Industrial Pkwy., Brick, 08724 (732) 840-3021
Millwood, Inc., 7 Brick Plant Rd., Ste. C, South River, 08882 (732) 967-8818
Milspray, LLC, 845 Towbin Ave., Lakewood, 08701 (732) 886-2223
Minalex Corp., 25 Coddington Rd., P.O. Box 247, Whitehouse Station, 08889 (908) 534-4044
Mincing Overseas Spice Co., 10 Tower Rd., Bldg. KN, Dayton, 08810 (732) 355-9944
Mindray North America, 800 MacArthur Blvd., Mahwah, 07430 (201) 995-8000
† Minerais U. S., LLC, 105 Raider Blvd., Ste. 104, Hillsborough, 08844 (908) 874-7666
† Mingolo Precision Products, Inc., 174 S. Main St., Ste. 1, Hackensack, 07601 (201) 488-6300
Mini Frost Foods Corp., 1237 Belmont Ave., Haledon, 07508 (973) 427-4258
Mini Precision Devices, Inc., 615 Pennsylvania Ave., Elizabeth, 07201 (908) 351-7423
Miniature Folding, 300 9th Ave., Hawthorne, 07506 (201) 773-6477
Miniature Folding, Inc., 14 Wenzel St., Elmwood Park, 07407 (201) 773-6477
Minisink Press, Inc., 2 Water St., P.O. Box 278, Newton, 07860 (973) 383-1350
Minitec Corp., 158 W. Clinton St., Ste. V, Dover, 07801 (973) 989-1426
Minor Rubber Co., Inc., 49 Ackerman St., Bloomfield, 07003 (973) 338-6800
Mint Printing & Design, 475 Westminster Pl., Lodi, 07644 (973) 546-2060
Minuteman Press, 35 W. White Horse Pike, Berlin, 08009 (856) 753-0055
Minuteman Press, 2060 Springdale Rd., Ste. 700, Cherry Hill, 08003 (856) 817-8400
Minuteman Press, 1 Trenton Ave., Clifton, 07011 (973) 894-1500
Minuteman Press, 349 U.S. Highway 9, Ste. 7, Englishtown, 07726 (732) 536-8788
Minuteman Press, 35 Scotch Rd., Ewing, 08628 (609) 883-0799
Minuteman Press, 23-51 Fair Lawn Ave., Fair Lawn, 07410 (201) 791-0550
Minuteman Press, 1299 Route 38, Ste. 2, Hainesport, 08036 (609) 261-1024
Minuteman Press, 19 Sheridan Ave., Ho-Ho-Kus, 07423 (201) 444-0236
Minuteman Press, 120 Speedwell Ave., Morristown, 07960 (973) 539-0610
Minuteman Press, 1818 Highway 35, Wall, 07719 (732) 449-1760
Minuteman Press see. Roan Printing, Inc., Somerville
Minuteman Press Corp., 55 Commerce St., Newark, 07102 (973) 624-6907
Minuteman Press, Inc. see. Arms Graphics, Northvale
Minuteman Press, Inc., 216 Boulevard, Hasbrouck Heights, 07604 (201) 288-7787
Minuteman Press, Inc./Windsor Graphics, 2100 Nottingham Way, Hamilton, 08619 (609) 586-3838

Minuteman Press International, Inc.,
1247 Patterson Plank Rd., Secaucus, 07094 ........ (201) 866-0186
Minuteman Press Of Dover, 25 Pine St., Ste. 10, Rockaway, 07866 ........ (973) 625-5800
Minuteman Press of Livingston, LLC, 47 E. Northfield Rd., Livingston, 07039 ........ (973) 992-3136
Minuteman Press Of North Arlington, 75 Ridge Rd., North Arlington, 07031 ........ (201) 991-1030
Mira Plastics Co., Inc.,
1 Mira Ave., Fredon Twp., P. O. Box 399, Newton, 07860 ........ (973) 383-6380
Mirrotek International, LLC, 90 Dayton Ave., Bldg. 1-F, Passaic, 07055 ........ (973) 472-1400
Misco Enterprises see. ........ Missry Assocs., Inc., Dunellen
Missry Assocs., Inc., 100 S. Washington Ave., Dunellen, 08812 ........ (732) 752-7500
Mister Cookie Face, LLC, 1989 Rutgers University Blvd., Lakewood, 08701 ........ (732) 370-5533
MISTRAS Group, Inc., 195 Clarksville Rd., Princeton Junction, 08550 ........ (609) 716-4100
Mitchell, Inc., David, 210 Park Dr., Voorhees, 08043 ........ (856) 429-2610
Mitchell Products, LLC, 1205 W. Main St., Millville, 08332 ........ (856) 327-2005
Mitchell Welding & Iron Works, Inc.,
7 Enterprise Dr., Cape May Court House, 08210 ........ (609) 465-7510
Mitchell's Woodworking, LLC,
780 Jacksonville Mount Holly Rd., Westampton, 08060 ........ (609) 261-7500
Miter Box, LLC, 4-21 Banta Pl., Ste. B, Fair Lawn, 07410 ........ (201) 773-6209
Mitronics Products, Inc., 239 Morristown Rd., P.O. Box 196, Gillette, 07933 ........ (908) 647-5006
Mitronix, Inc., 239 Old Tappan Rd., Old Tappan, 07675 ........ (201) 263-0063
Mitsubishi Hitachi Power Systems America - Energy & Environment,
645 Martinsville Rd., Basking Ridge, 07920 ........ (908) 605-2800
Mitsubishi Tanabe Pharma America, Inc. (H Q),
525 Washington Blvd., Ste. 400, Jersey City, 07310 ........ (908) 607-1980
Mitsubishi World see. ........ M C Machinery Systems, Inc., Pine Brook
Mitsui & Co. U. S. A., Inc. see. ........ Mitsui Foods, Inc., Norwood
Mitsui Foods, Inc., 35 Maple St., Norwood, 07648 ........ (201) 750-0500
Mitsui International see. ........ Mitsui Foods, Inc., Norwood
† Mivila Corp., 226 Getty Ave., Paterson, 07503 ........ (973) 278-4148
Mivila Foods see. ........ Mivila Corp., Paterson
Mizco International, Inc. (H Q), 80 Essex Ave. E., Avenel, 07001 ........ (732) 912-2000
Mizrak, 288 Livingston Ave., 1st Fl., Lyndhurst, 07071 ........ (973) 622-0328
★ MJ Corporate Sales, Inc., 109 W. Park Dr., Unit B, Mount Laurel, 08054 ........ (856) 778-0055
† M&J Frank, Inc., 29 Eagle Rock Ave., East Hanover, 07936 ........ (973) 887-1040
MJG Screen Printing & Embroidery, 24 Commerce Rd., Ste. K, Fairfield, 07004 ........ (973) 575-8877
MJG Technologies, Inc., 832 Camden Ave., Blackwood, 08012 ........ (856) 228-6118
MJM Impressions LLC,
20-10 Maple Ave., Bldg. 35-E, P.O. Box 2, Fair Lawn, 07410 ........ (973) 423-4999
MMC Steel Rule Dies, 864 New Brunswick Ave., Piscataway, 08854 ........ (973) 760-3286
MMP, Inc., 3470 S. Clinton Ave., South Plainfield, 07080 ........ (908) 561-4435
MMS - A Medical Supply Company see. ........ Midwest Medical Supply Company, LLC, Secaucus
Mnemonics, Inc., P.O. Box 877, Mount Laurel, 08054 ........ (856) 234-0970
Mobile Power, Inc., 392 Watters Rd., Hackettstown, 07840 ........ (908) 852-3117
Mobile Power International, LLC, 1010 Old Egg Harbor Rd., Voorhees, 08043 ........ (856) 784-3195
Mobility Parts & Service see. ........ Active Controls, LLC, Sewell
† Model Electronics, Inc., 615 E. Crescent Ave., Ramsey, 07446 ........ (201) 961-6200
Model Rectifier Corp., 80 Newfield Ave., P.O. Box 6312, Edison, 08837 ........ (732) 225-2100
Modelsmith International, Inc., 66 Willow Ave., 2nd Fl., Hoboken, 07030 ........ (201) 714-9519
Modern Boat Works, Inc., P.O. Box 456, Oceanville, 08231 ........ (609) 241-8916
Modern Drummer see. ........ Modern Drummer Publications, Inc., Fairfield
Modern Drummer Publications, Inc.,
271 Route 46 W., Ste. 212, Fairfield, 07004 ........ (973) 239-4140
Modern Equipment Co., Inc., 19 Ann St., Bordentown, 08505 ........ (609) 298-2100
Modern Fence & Construction, LLC,
1527 Livingston Ave., North Brunswick, 08902 ........ (732) 238-5588
Modern Graphics, 547 Cross Keys Rd., Ste. B, Sicklerville, 08081 ........ (856) 728-6300
† Modern Group Ltd., 75 New St., Edison, 08837 ........ (800) 846-5840
† Modern Group Ltd., 112-128 Route 17 N., Hasbrouck Heights, 07604 ........ (201) 288-1441
Modern International Corp., 145 Cliffwood Ave., Cliffwood, 07721 ........ (732) 696-9100
Modern Limb & Brace Co., 916 Somerset St., Watchung, 07069 ........ (908) 757-2702
Modern Limb & Brace Co. see. ........ Oertel Orthopedics, Inc., Union
Modern Metric Machine, 101 Nicholson Rd., Audubon, 08106 ........ (856) 547-4044
Modern Showcase, Inc., 610 Commercial Ave., Carlstadt, 07072 ........ (201) 935-2929
† Modern Technologies Group, Inc., 3 Reeves Station Rd., Medford, 08055 ........ (609) 714-8900
Modi Systems, Inc., 88 S. State St., Hackensack, 07601 ........ (201) 525-0775
Mod-Tek Converting, LLC, 2550 Haddonfield Rd., Ste. E, Pennsauken, 08110 ........ (856) 662-6884
Modular Packaging Systems, Inc., 6 Aspen Dr., Randolph, 07869 ........ (973) 970-9393
† Moe Distributors, Inc., 55 Abbett Ave., Morristown, 07960 ........ (973) 539-8200
Mohawk Tile & Marble Distributors see. ........ Klinges, Inc., Charles A., Absecon
Mokes Steel, Inc., 280 Cox St., Roselle, 07203 ........ (908) 241-5344
Mola Iron Works, 61 Patterson Ave., Hoboken, 07030 ........ (201) 963-3485
Mold Polishing Co., Inc., 45 North Ave., P. O. Box 96, Garwood, 07027 ........ (908) 518-9191
Molded Fiberglass Products, 3 Industry Ct., Trenton, 08638 ........ (609) 538-8822
Molecular Rearrangement, Inc. see. ........ MRI International, Newton
Molecu-Wire Corp., 56 Old Camplain Rd., Hillsborough, 08844 ........ (732) 296-9473
★ Molecu-Wire Corp., 1215 Kennedy Blvd., Manville, 08835 ........ (908) 429-0300
† Momeni, Inc., 60 Broad St., Carlstadt, 07072 ........ (212) 532-9577
Momma's Home Made, LLC,
1225 Haddonfield Berlin Rd., Southgate Plz., Ste. 2, Voorhees, 08043 ........ (856) 753-3250
Mon Far Press Printing, 13 Franklin Pl., Rutherford, 07070 ........ (212) 431-6245
Mona Lisa Cosmetics, Inc., 280 N. Midland Ave., Ste. 520, Saddle Brook, 07663 ........ (201) 791-5644
Monarch Art Plastics, LLC, 3838 Church Rd., Mount Laurel, 08054 ........ (856) 235-5151
Monarch Color Corp., 7247 Browning Rd., Pennsauken, 08109 ........ (856) 662-0432
† Monarch Electric Co., Inc., 1 Dodge Dr., West Caldwell, 07006 ........ (973) 227-4151
† Monarch Electric Supply Co., 1527 Livingston Ave., North Brunswick, 08902 ........ (732) 249-1616
Monarch Mfg. Works, Inc., 7249-B Browning Rd., Merchantville, 08109 ........ (856) 241-1500
Monarch Moor Whips, 1104 Tiller Ave., Beachwood, 08722 ........ (732) 244-4584
Monarch Plastics see. ........ Monarch Art Plastics, LLC, Mount Laurel
Monarch Towel Co., Inc., 737 Cortlandt St., Perth Amboy, 08861 ........ (732) 442-0442
Mondelez International, Inc., 22-11 State Route 208, Fair Lawn, 07410 ........ (201) 794-4000
Mondi, 1100 Slocum Ave., Ridgefield, 07657 ........ (201) 585-8875
Mondi Akrosil, LLC see. ........ Tekkote Corp., Leonia
Mondo International, Inc., 464 Coit St., P.O. Box 894, Irvington, 07111 ........ (973) 256-6123
Mon-Eco Industries, Inc., 5 Joanna Ct., East Brunswick, 08816 ........ (732) 257-7942
Monick Mfg. Corp., 2619 Route 206, Mount Holly, 08060 ........ (609) 267-0777
Moniteur Devices, Inc., 36 Commerce Rd., Cedar Grove, 07009 ........ (973) 857-1600
Monitor Products, Inc., 7-A Marlen Dr., Robbinsville, 08691 ........ (609) 584-0505
Monitoring Solutions, Inc., 78 Route 173, Ste. 7, Hampton, 08827 ........ (908) 713-0172
† Monkey Joe's Big Nut Co., 205 N. White Horse Pike, Laurel Springs, 08021 ........ (856) 627-4600
Monmouth & Ocean County Awning Co., 508 Main St., Asbury Park, 07712 ........ (732) 775-4881
Monmouth BioProducts, 3 Industrial Ct., Ste. 4, Freehold, 07728 ........ (732) 863-0300
Monmouth Journal, The, 212 Maple Ave., Red Bank, 07701 ........ (732) 747-7007
Monmouth Rubber & Plastics Corp., 75 Long Branch Ave., Long Branch, 07740 ........ (732) 229-3444
Monogram Center, 437 Amboy Ave., Perth Amboy, 08861 ........ (732) 442-1800
Monogram Madness, 50 Main St., Succasunna, 07876 ........ (973) 927-5278
Monogram Shoppe, 5 S. Broad St., Woodbury, 08096 ........ (856) 845-9299
MonoSol Rx, LLC (H Q), 30 Technology Dr., Warren, 07059 ........ (908) 941-1900
Monroe Machine & Design, Inc., 566 Buckelew Ave., Monroe Township, 08831 ........ (732) 521-3434
Monroe Tool & Die, Inc., 197 Sharp Rd., Williamstown, 08094 ........ (856) 629-5164
★ Monroeville Vineyard & Winery, LLC, 314 Richwood Rd., Monroeville, 08343 ........ (856) 521-0523
Monster Coatings, Inc., 306-A Capitol St., Saddle Brook, 07663 ........ (973) 983-7662
Monte Printing & Graphics,
225 E. Clay Ave., P.O. Box 293, Roselle Park, 07204 ........ (908) 241-6600
Monteath Moulding, 3150 Bordentown Ave., Old Bridge, 08857 ........ (732) 727-4000
Montena Taranto Foods, Inc., 400 Victoria Ter., Ridgefield, 07657 ........ (201) 943-8484
Monter Lite Co., Inc., 560 Lincoln Blvd., Ste. 2, Middlesex, 08846 ........ (732) 748-1288
Montrose Molders Corp., 25 Howard St., Piscataway, 08854 ........ (908) 754-3030
Monuments Are Forever, Inc., 200 E. Edgar Rd., Ste. 1-A, Linden, 07036 ........ (908) 862-0220
Moofwd, Inc., 103 Carnegie Ctr., Ste. 209, Princeton, 08540 ........ (855) 266-6393
Moonlight Imaging, Inc., 5 Plains Rd., Augusta, 07822 ........ (973) 300-1001
Moorhouse Sailmakers, Inc., 52 Stacy Haines Rd., Lumberton, 08048 ........ (609) 654-7819
Moose Mountain Marketing, Inc. (H Q),
8 Wood Hollow Rd., Ste. 302, Parsippany, 07054 ........ (973) 884-8900
† Morak, Inc., 3 Janice Dr., Hackettstown, 07840 ........ (973) 527-7470
Moran Power Dynamics, 263 Route 537 E., Colts Neck, 07722 ........ (732) 544-8443
More Copy Printing Service, 358 State Route 17, Saddle River, 07458 ........ (201) 327-1106
Moreng Metal Products, 100 W. End Rd., Totowa, 07512 ........ (973) 256-2001
Moretrench American Corp., 100 Stickle Ave., Rockaway, 07866 ........ (973) 627-2100
Morgan Advanced Ceramics, Inc., 26 Madison Rd., Fairfield, 07004 ........ (973) 227-8877
Morgan Printing Service, Inc., 333 S. Pine Ave., South Amboy, 08879 ........ (732) 721-2959
Morgan Technical Ceramics see. ........ Morgan Advanced Ceramics, Inc., Fairfield
Morinaga America, Inc., 400 Kelby St., 14th Fl., Fort Lee, 07024 ........ (201) 947-0408
Morito see. ........ Kane-M, Inc., East Rutherford
MORO Corp. see. ........ Ahle Co., Inc., J. M., South River
MORRE-TEC Industries, Inc. see. Extracts & Ingredients Ltd., Div. Of MORRE-TEC Industries, Inc., Union
MORRE-TEC Industries, Inc. see. ........ Jedco Adhesives Co., Div. Of Morre-Tec Industries, Inc., Union
MORRE-TEC Industries, Inc., 1 Gary Rd., Union, 07083 ........ (908) 688-9009
Morris County Duplicating Corp., 1 Lafayette Ave., Morristown, 07960 ........ (973) 993-8484
Morris Forms Corp., 5 Saddle Rd., Cedar Knolls, 07927 ........ (973) 829-1200
Morris Graphics, Inc., 660 N. Broad St., Woodbury, 08096 ........ (856) 845-4980
Morris Industries, Inc., 777 Route 23, P.O. Box 278, Pompton Plains, 07444 ........ (973) 835-6600
Morris Magnetos, Inc., 103 Washington St., Morristown, 07960 ........ (973) 540-9171
Morris Sign Co., 30 Troy Rd., Whippany, 07981 ........ (973) 386-1755
Morris Tool & Machine Co., 80 Upper Hibernia Rd., Rockaway, 07866 ........ (973) 983-9209
Morsemere Ironworks, Inc., 1085 Linden Ave., Ridgefield, 07657 ........ (201) 941-1133
Morton Salt, Inc., 920 High St., Perth Amboy, 08861 ........ (732) 826-3595
Moser Co. see. ........ Moser Jewel Co., Phillipsburg
Moser Jewel Co., 518 Route 57, Phillipsburg, 08865 ........ (908) 454-1155
MossFauset Woodworking, 49 Harrison St., 13th Fl., Hoboken, 07030 ........ (201) 714-9797
Mosstype Corp., 150 Franklin Tpke., Waldwick, 07463 ........ (201) 444-8000
Motek Industries, LLC, 250 Park Ave., Teaneck, 07666 ........ (201) 836-4167
Mother's Kitchen, Inc., 499 Veterans Dr., Burlington, 08016 ........ (609) 589-3033
Motif Industries, Inc., 8 Commerce Rd., Fairfield, 07004 ........ (973) 575-1800
Motion Control Technologies, Inc., 158 W. Clinton St., Ste. FF, Dover, 07801 ........ (973) 361-2226
Motion Industries, Inc. see. ........ AST Bearings, LLC, Montville
† Motion Industries, Inc., 141 Market St., Ste. 8, Kenilworth, 07033 ........ (908) 241-1047
† Motion Industries, Inc., 12-D Jules Ln., New Brunswick, 08901 ........ (732) 828-8711
† Motion Industries, Inc., 600 Hollister Rd., Teterboro, 07608 ........ (201) 288-8111
† Motion Industries, Inc., 9A S. Gold Dr., Trenton, 08691 ........ (609) 588-0555
Motion Systems Corp., 600 Industrial Way W., Eatontown, 07724 ........ (732) 222-1800
Mottahedeh & Co., Inc., 5 Corporate Dr., Cranbury, 08512 ........ (609) 409-1490
Mount Construction Co., Inc. (H Q),
427 S. White Horse Pike, P.O. Box 619, Berlin, 08009 ........ (856) 768-8493
Mount Freedom Printing, P.O. Box 285, Mount Freedom, 07970 ........ (908) 362-9299
★ Mount Freedom Printing, LLC, 1248 Sussex Tpke., Randolph, 07869 ........ (973) 933-2700
Mount Group see. ........ Mount Construction Co., Inc. (H Q), Berlin
Mountain Lion, Inc., 9 Voorhees Ct., P.O. Box 799, Pennington, 08534 ........ (609) 730-1665
Mountain Millwork, 14 Clifton Ave. S., Lakewood, 08701 ........ (732) 901-9400
Mountain Millwork, Inc., 1014 Route 9, Bayville, 08721 ........ (732) 606-1701
Mountain Printing Co., Inc., 27 N. Atlantic Ave., P.O. Box 608, Berlin, 08009 ........ (856) 767-7600
Mountain Top Logging, LLC, P.O. Box 324, Lebanon, 08833 ........ (908) 413-2982
Movado Group, Inc., 650 From Rd., 3rd Fl., Paramus, 07652 ........ (201) 267-8000
Moveable Feast, Inc., 99 Grand St., Ste. 8, Moonachie, 07074 ........ (201) 939-4500
Mozer, Inc., Theodore E., 601 W. 4th St., P.O. Box 25, Palmyra, 08065 ........ (856) 829-1432
MP Technologies, LLC (H Q), 345 Claremont Ave., Ste. 26, Montclair, 07042 ........ (646) 366-1155
MP Tube Works, Inc., 237 Sheffield St., Mountainside, 07092 ........ (908) 317-2500
MPI see. ........ Markov Processes International, LLC, Summit
MPM Display, Inc., 74 Woolsey St., Irvington, 07111 ........ (973) 374-3477
MPT Delivery Systems, Inc., 95 Prince St., Paterson, 07501 ........ (973) 279-4132
MPT Industries, 85 Franklin Rd., Hamilton Bus. Park, Ste. 6-B, Dover, 07801 ........ (973) 989-9220
Mr. B. Fence Co., 325 Stokes Ave., Trenton, 08638 ........ (609) 882-1896
Mr. B Offset Printing, Inc., 1850 Elizabeth Ave., Ste. B, Rahway, 07065 ........ (732) 396-3990
M&R Designs & Promotions, 21 Stone Oak Ln., Oak Ridge, 07438 ........ (908) 928-9400
Mr. Drive Shaft, 5134-A Hurley Pond Rd., Farmingdale, 07727 ........ (732) 938-4118
Mr. Fence, 3468 U.S. Highway 9, Ste. 2, Freehold, 07728 ........ (732) 303-1614
★ Mr. Green Tea Ice Cream Co., 25 Church St., Unit 104, Keyport, 07735 ........ (732) 446-9800
Mr. Ice Bucket, LLC, 345 Sandford St., New Brunswick, 08901 ........ (732) 545-0420
Mr. J's Xcaliber Corp., 39 Dundee Ave., Paterson, 07503 ........ (973) 278-1611
Mr. Pasta, 159 Ridge Rd., North Arlington, 07031 ........ (201) 991-5959
Mr. Paul's Custom Cabinets, 2416 Highway 35, Manasquan, 08736 ........ (732) 528-9427
Mr. Printer, 466 New Brunswick Ave., Fords, 08863 ........ (732) 738-3977
Mr. Quick Sign, 30 Dairy St., Midland Park, 07432 ........ (201) 670-1690
Mr. Sign see. ........ JD Graphics, Inc., Marlboro
Mr. Sign, Inc., 319 Bound Brook Rd., Middlesex, 08846 ........ (732) 560-0606
MRC Global, Inc. see. ........ McJunkin Red Man Corporation, Waterford Works
MRI International, 44-50 Clinton St., Newton, 07860 ........ (973) 383-3645
MRP, LLC, 1640 New Market Ave., South Plainfield, 07080 ........ (732) 968-6061
M&S Canada Corp., 8 Arosa Hill, Lakewood, 08701 ........ (732) 901-6636
MS International, Inc. see. ........ M S International, Inc., Edison
MS Tool Co., Inc., 500 S. 31st St., Kenilworth, 07033 ........ (908) 245-7989
MSC Industrial Direct Co., Inc. see. ........ MSC Industrial Supply Co., Edison
† MSC Industrial Supply Co., 105 Newfield Ave., Ste. E, Edison, 08837 ........ (732) 512-9555

ALPHABETICAL

★ Indicates new listing this edition. † Indicates wholesaler/distributor.

© Copyright 2015 Manufacturers' News, Inc.


MSD Precision, 300 Thomas Ave., Bldg. 6, Williamstown, 08094 ... (856) 262-8142
MSI see. ... M S International, Inc., Edison
MSI see. ... MicroSurfaces, Inc., Englewood
MSP Digital Marketing, 200 Forge Way, Rockaway, 07866 ... (973) 298-8800
MTT Corp. see. ... Magnetic & Transformer Technologies Corp., Perth Amboy
MTT Corp. see. ... Magnetic & Transformer Technologies Corp. (H Q), Robbinsville
† Muenz Engineered Sales Co., 21 Chatham Rd., Summit, 07901 ... (908) 273-6755
Muffins & Stuff, 53 Jersey St., Paterson, 07501 ... (973) 881-9900
Muirhead Foods see. ... Muirhead Of Ringoes New Jersey, Inc., Ringoes
Muirhead Of Ringoes New Jersey, Inc., 43 U.S. Highway 202, Ringoes, 08551 ... (908) 782-7803
Mulberry Metal Products, Inc., 2199 Stanley Ter., Union, 07083 ... (908) 688-8850
† Mulcare Pipeline Solutions, 9 Mars Ct., Ste. C-4, Boonton, 07005 ... (973) 335-4800
Mulhern Belting, Inc., 148 Bauer Dr., P.O. Box 620, Oakland, 07436 ... (201) 337-5700
Mullin Glass Co., Inc., 268 Main St., Butler, 07405 ... (973) 838-6767
Multi Plastics Extrusions, 30 Production Way, Avenel, 07001 ... (732) 388-2300
Multi Tech Industries Corp., 64 S. Main St., P.O. Box 159, Marlboro, 07746 ... (732) 431-0550
Multiforce Systems Corp., 101 Wall St., Princeton, 08540 ... (609) 683-4242
Multimatic, 162 Veterans Dr., P.O. Box 156, Northvale, 07647 ... (201) 767-9660
Multimode Fiber Optics, Inc., 432 Sand Shore Rd., Unit 1, Hackettstown, 07840 ... (908) 684-5802
MultiPackaging Solutions, 901 Durham Ave., South Plainfield, 07080 ... (908) 757-6000
Multi-Pak Corp., 180 Atlantic St., Hackensack, 07601 ... (201) 342-7474
Multi-Pak Packaging, 19 Spielman Rd., Fairfield, 07004 ... (973) 439-1182
Multi-Plastics, Inc. see. ... Multi Plastics Extrusions, Avenel
Multi-Plastics, Inc., 210 Commodore Dr., Swedesboro, 08085 ... (856) 241-9014
† Multipower International, Inc., 7 Woodshire Ter., P.O. Box 197, Towaco, 07082 ... (973) 727-0327
Multi-Tex Products Corp., 54 2nd Ave., Kearny, 07032 ... (201) 991-7262
Mul-T-Lock USA, Inc., 100 Commerce Way, Ste. 2, Hackensack, 07601 ... (973) 778-3222
Mundi Westport Group see. ... Westport Corp., Pine Brook
† Mundo Esoterico dist inc, 6207 Madison St., West New York, 07093 ... (201) 766-4084
Munire Furniture, Inc., 91 New England Ave., Piscataway, 08854 ... (732) 339-6070
Munzing, 1455 Broad St., Bloomfield, 07003 ... (973) 279-1306
Muralo see. ... Elder & Jenks Co., Bayonne
Muralo Co., Inc see. ... Elder & Jenks Co., Bayonne
Muralo Co., Inc., 148 E. 5th St., Bayonne, 07002 ... (201) 437-0770
Muralo Co., Inc. see. ... Norton & Son, Inc., Bayonne
Muralo Co., Inc. see. ... Norton & Son, Inc., Bayonne
Murphy & Read Spring Mfg. Co., 617 W. 6th St., P.O. Box 211, Palmyra, 08065 ... (856) 829-6887
Murphy Fence Co., Inc., 507 Seashore Rd., Cape May, 08204 ... (609) 886-1635
Murray's Uniforms, Inc., 312 Main St., Bradley Beach, 07720 ... (732) 774-2671
Musco Sports Lighting, LLC, 5146 W. Hurley Pond Rd., Farmingdale, 07727 ... (732) 751-9114
Mushroom Wisdom, Inc., 1 Madison St., Bldg. F, East Rutherford, 07073 ... (973) 470-0010
Music Trades Magazine Corp., 80 West St., P.O. Box 432, Englewood, 07631 ... (201) 871-1965
† Musical Distributors Group, LLC, 9 Mars Ct., Unit C-3, Boonton, 07005 ... (973) 335-7888
MW Industries, Inc. see. ... Accurate Screw Machine Corp., Fairfield
MW Industries, Inc. see. ... Atlantic Spring Co., Ringoes
MWT Materials see. ... Millimeter Wave Technology, Passaic
★ My Private Label, LLC, 112 East Ave., Ste. 5, Hackettstown, 07840 ... (908) 441-2375
My Way Prints, Inc., 1376 Route 23, Butler, 07405 ... (973) 492-1212
MYAT, Inc., 360 Franklin Tpke., Mahwah, 07430 ... (201) 684-0100
Myers Group, LLC, The, 74 Blanchard Rd., South Orange, 07079 ... (973) 761-6414
★ MYOS Corp. (H Q), 45 Horsehill Rd., Ste. 106, Cedar Knolls, 07927 ... (973) 509-0444
Myron Corp., 205 Maywood Ave., Maywood, 07607 ... (201) 843-6464
★ Mystic Timber, LLC, 95 Youmans Ave., Washington, 07882 ... (908) 223-7878
N & J Machine Products Corp., 52 Bruen St., Newark, 07105 ... (973) 589-0031
N. B. & Sons, LLC, 402 E. Wheat Rd., Vineland, 08360 ... (856) 692-6191
N. B. C. Engraving Co., Inc., 228 Park St., Hackensack, 07601 ... (201) 387-8011
N D S Technologies, Inc., 891 E. Oak Rd., Vineland, 08360 ... (856) 691-0330
N J Sport Action, 5 Riverview Dr. W., Upper Montclair, 07043 ... (973) 783-9236
N. M. Knight Co., Inc., 1001 S. 2nd St., P.O. Box 1099, Millville, 08332 ... (856) 327-4855
Nadri Jewelry Group, 2 Executive Dr., Ste. 500, Fort Lee, 07024 ... (201) 585-0088
Nal-Pak Paper Specialties, LLC, 18 Monterey Ln., Englishtown, 07726 ... (732) 462-5196
Nandvarik Systems, 190 Lewis St., Rahway, 07065 ... (732) 306-9999
Nannette see. ... Children's Apparel Network Ltd., Elizabeth
Nanonex Corp., 1 Deerpark Dr., Ste. O, Monmouth Junction, 08852 ... (732) 355-1600
Nano's, LLC, 22 Park Pl., P.O. Box 41, Butler, 07405 ... (973) 616-1515
Nanoshade Solar see ... Natcore Technology, Inc. (H Q), Red Bank
Napco Cabinets, Inc., 6938 Westfield Ave., Pennsauken, 08110 ... (856) 665-0253
Napoleon/Lynx, 25 Empire Blvd., South Hackensack, 07606 ... (973) 278-5588
Narad Marketing Corporation, 200 Piaget Ave., Clifton, 07011 ... (973) 881-0206
Narciso Printing, Inc., 120-22 Malvern St., Newark, 07105 ... (973) 578-2088
Narva Kitchens & Closets * ICUTWOOD see. ... Narva Kitchens & Closets, Inc., Springfield
Narva Kitchens & Closets, Inc., 101 Victory Rd., Springfield, 07081 ... (718) 735-7722
Nasa Machine Tools, Inc., 1-B Frassetto Way, Lincoln Park, 07035 ... (973) 633-5200
Nasco, Inc. see. ... Par Sheet Metal, Inc., Roselle
Nash Engraving, Inc., 528 Nicholson Rd., Gloucester City, 08030 ... (856) 456-5656
Nash Industries see. ... Nash Engraving, Inc., Gloucester City
Nassau Communications, Inc., 115 N. Gold Dr., Robbinsville, 08691 ... (908) 625-8512
† Nassau Lens Co., Inc., 160 LeGrand Ave., Northvale, 07647 ... (201) 767-8033
Nasto's Ice Cream Co., Inc., 236 Jefferson St., Newark, 07105 ... (973) 589-3333
Natale Machine & Tool Co., Inc., 339 13th St., Carlstadt, 07072 ... (201) 933-5500
Natale's Summit Bakery, 185 Broad St., Summit, 07901 ... (908) 277-2074
Natali Vineyards, LLC, 221 N. Delsea Dr., Cape May Court House, 08210 ... (609) 465-0075
Natcore Technology, Inc. (H Q), 87 Maple Ave., Red Bank, 07701 ... (732) 576-8800
National Casein Co. see. ... National Casein Of New Jersey, Riverton
National Casein Of New Jersey,
401 Martha's Ln., P.O. Box 226, Riverton, 08077 ... (856) 829-1880
National Ceramic Co., Inc., 500 Southard St., Trenton, 08638 ... (609) 394-5373
National Christmas Products, 2 Commerce Dr., Cranford, 07016 ... (908) 709-4141
National Color Graphics, 1755 Williamstown Rd., Erial, 08081 ... (856) 435-6800
National Communication, Inc., 69 Washington St., West Orange, 07052 ... (973) 325-3151
National Display see. ... National Display Group, Inc., Pennsauken
National Display Group, Inc., 6850 River Rd., Pennsauken, 08110 ... (856) 661-1212
National Electric Wire Co., 100 Goldman Dr., Cream Ridge, 08514 ... (609) 758-3600
† National Electronic Alloys, Inc., 3 Fir Ct., Oakland, 07436 ... (201) 337-9400
National Environmental Service Co. see. ... National Environmental Services Co., Hackettstown
National Environmental Service Co. (H Q), 7 Hampshire Dr., Mendham, 07945 ... (973) 543-4586
National Environmental Services Co., 700 Grand Ave., Hackettstown, 07840 ... (908) 813-1195
National Equipment Co.,
342 Squankum Yellowbrook Rd., P.O. Box 674, Farmingdale, 07727 ... (732) 938-5084
National Flag & Display Co., Inc. see. ... Metro Flag Co., Wharton
National Gypsum Co., 1818 River Rd., Burlington, 08016 ... (609) 499-3300
National Lecithin, Inc. (H Q), 93 Spring St., Ste. 303, Newton, 07860 ... (973) 940-8920
National Lighting Co., Inc., 522 Cortlandt St., Belleville, 07109 ... (973) 751-1600
National Metal Finishings Corp., Inc.,
897 South Ave., P.O. Box 486, Middlesex, 08846 ... (732) 752-7770
National Mfg. Co., Inc., 12 River Rd., Chatham, 07928 ... (973) 635-8846
National Mill Industry, Inc. (H Q), 22 Jackson Dr., Cranford, 07016 ... (908) 862-8400
National Packaging Corp., 14 Campus Dr., Kearny, 07032 ... (973) 344-0100
National Paint Industries, 1999 Elizabeth St., North Brunswick, 08902 ... (732) 821-3200
National Paint Industries see. ... Talon Paint Products, Inc., North Brunswick
† National Parts Supply Co., Inc., 56 State Route 31, Flemington, 08822 ... (908) 782-3530
† National Parts Supply Co., Inc., 535 Milltown Rd., North Brunswick, 08902 ... (732) 247-5171
National Paving Co., Inc., 148 Williamstown Rd., P.O. Box 5, Berlin, 08009 ... (856) 767-1950
National Pipe Hanger Corp., 200 Campus Dr., R.R. 30, Mount Holly, 08060 ... (609) 261-5353
National Precision Tool Co., Inc., 24 Sherwood Ln., Fairfield, 07004 ... (973) 227-5005
National Protective Systems, 1 Meridian Rd., Eatontown, 07724 ... (732) 922-3609
† National Public Seating Corp., 149 Entin Rd., Clifton, 07014 ... (973) 594-1100
National Refrigerants, Inc., 661 Kenyon Ave., Bridgeton, 08302 ... (856) 455-4555
National Reprographics, Inc., 3175 Princeton Pike, Lawrenceville, 08648 ... (609) 896-4100
National Reprographics, Inc. see. ... Rethink Color, a division of NRI, Lawrenceville
National Sales Of Central NJ see. ... National Shrinkwrap, Howell
National Shrinkwrap, 6220 U.S. Highway 9, Howell, 07731 ... (732) 942-4554
National Steel Rule Co., Inc., 750 Commerce Rd., Linden, 07036 ... (908) 862-3366
† National Tile & Mosaic, 175 Moonachie Rd., Moonachie, 07074 ... (201) 807-9800
National Tree Company see. ... National Christmas Products, Cranford
Natural Dental Studios, Inc.,
216 U.S. Highway 206, Ste. 23, Hillsborough, 08844 ... (908) 281-0089
Natural Flavors, Inc., 268 Doremus Ave., Newark, 07105 ... (973) 589-1230
Natural Stone Kitchen & Bath, 2280 U.S. Highway 130, North Brunswick, 08902 ... (732) 297-5450
Nature's Choice Corp., 40 Foul Rift Rd., Belvidere, 07823 ... (908) 475-1804
Nature's Choice Corp., 482 Houses Corner Rd., Sparta, 07871 ... (201) 333-5244
Naturex Inc., 375 Huyler St., South Hackensack, 07606 ... (201) 440-5000
Nautical Canvas Designs, 506 Elizabeth Ave., Point Pleasant Beach, 08742 ... (732) 892-7677
Na-Vet Printing Co., 506 Elizabeth Ave., Elizabeth, 07206 ... (908) 353-4441
Navinta, LLC, 1499 Lower Ferry Rd., Trenton, 08618 ... (609) 883-1135
Navistar International Corp. see. ... Ransome International, Logan Township
Navitend, 23 U.S. Highway 206, Stanhope, 07874 ... (973) 448-0070
Nazdar Co., 7055 Central Hwy., Pennsauken, 08109 ... (856) 663-7878
Nazdar Source One see. ... Nazdar Co., Pennsauken
NBCUniversal Media, LLC see. ... iVillage, Inc., Englewood Cliffs
N-C Carpet Binding & Equipment Corp., 858 Summer Ave., Newark, 07104 ... (973) 481-3500
NCH Corp., 34 Stouts Ln., P.O. Box 25, Monmouth Junction, 08852 ... (732) 329-8111
NCS Enterprises, Inc., 300 M St., Millville, 08332 ... (856) 825-3275
ND Industries, Inc., 128 Bauer Dr., Ste. 2, Oakland, 07436 ... (201) 651-1500
NEAC, Inc., 526 Pacific Ave., #2202, Atlantic City, 08401 ... (908) 903-9100
Nedco Conveyor Technology Co., 967 Lehigh Ave., Union, 07083 ... (908) 964-9400
NEI Group, Inc., 44 Burlews Ct., Hackensack, 07601 ... (201) 488-5858
NEI Group, Inc. see. ... SJA Jewelry, Inc., Hackensack
Neill Supply Co., Inc., 700 Schuyler Ave., Lyndhurst, 07071 ... (201) 939-1100
Nelson Custom Case Co., 1014 State Route 173, Bloomsbury, 08804 ... (908) 479-6902
Nelson Enterprises see. ... Nelson Custom Case Co., Bloomsbury
Nelson Glass & Aluminum Co., Inc., 45 Spring St., Princeton, 08542 ... (609) 924-2880
Nelson, Inc., Louis A., 224 Glenwood Ave., Bloomfield, 07003 ... (973) 743-7404
Nelson Press, 111 E. River Rd., Rumson, 07760 ... (732) 747-0330
NEMA Associates, Inc., 57 Bruen St., Newark, 07105 ... (973) 274-0052
Nemec Sign Co., 114 Route 31, Flemington, 08822 ... (908) 782-3175
Neo Printing Co., Inc., 24 E. Wesley St., South Hackensack, 07606 ... (201) 489-5050
† Neopost, Inc., 2 Ridgedale Ave., 1st Fl., Cedar Knolls, 07927 ... (973) 647-6700
Neopost USA, Inc. see. ... Neopost, Inc., Cedar Knolls
NeoStem, Inc. see. ... Progenitor Cell Therapy, LLC, Allendale
Neostrata Company, Inc. (H Q), 307 College Rd. E., Princeton, 08540 ... (609) 520-0715
Nephros, Inc., 41 Grand Ave., Ste. 201, River Edge, 07661 ... (201) 343-5202
Neptune Auto Supply, Inc., 51 TFH Plz., Neptune City, 07753 ... (732) 774-0002
Neptune Products, Inc., 353 E. Blackwell St., P.O. Drawer 829, Dover, 07801 ... (973) 366-8200
Nersesian Publishing, Roy, 10 Maryland Rd., Maplewood, 07040 ... (973) 762-8604
NES Enterprises, Inc., 513 Washington Ave., Carlstadt, 07072 ... (201) 964-1400
NESCO see. ... National Environmental Service Co. (H Q), Mendham
Ness Technologies, Inc., 300 Frank W. Burr Blvd., Teaneck, 07666 ... (201) 488-7222
Nestle Health Science see. ... Nestle Healthcare Nutrition, Inc. (H Q), Florham Park
Nestle Healthcare Nutrition, Inc. (H Q),
12 Vreeland Rd., 2nd Fl., P.O. Box 697, Florham Park, 07932 ... (973) 593-7500
Nestle USA, Inc. see. ... Nestle' USA, Inc., Beverage Div., Freehold
Nestle' USA, Inc., Beverage Div., 61 Jerseyville Ave., Freehold, 07728 ... (732) 462-1300
Nestle Waters North America, Inc.,
111 Thomas McGovern Dr., Jersey City, 07305 ... (201) 451-4000
Nestle' Waters North America, Inc. see ... Nestle Waters North America, Inc., Jersey City
Netcom Systems, Inc., 200 Metroplex Dr., Edison, 08817 ... (732) 393-6100
★ NetQ Multimedia, 919 State Route 33, Ste. 52, Freehold, 07728 ... (732) 833-9300
Netquest Corp., 523 Fellowship Rd., Ste. 205, Mount Laurel, 08054 ... (856) 866-0505
Network Access Systems, 19 Isaac Dr., Dayton, 08810 ... (732) 355-9770
Network Marketing Associates see. ... NEMA Associates, Inc., Newark
Network, The, 105-B Van Houten Ave., P.O. Box 5338, Passaic, 07055 ... (973) 778-7222
Networking Technologies & Integration, 50 Boright Ave., Kenilworth, 07033 ... (908) 276-1200
NetWrix Corp., 12 N. State Route 17, Ste. 104, Paramus, 07652 ... (201) 490-8840
Neu Med, Inc. see. ... Neurotron Medical, West Trenton
Neumann Sheet Metal, Inc., 759 North Ave., Plainfield, 07062 ... (908) 756-0415
Neurotron Medical, 800 Silvia St., West Trenton, 08628 ... (609) 896-3444
Neuweiler, Inc., Karl H., 23 Russo Pl., Berkeley Heights, 07922 ... (908) 464-6532
Neverending Neon, 91 Dell Glen Ave., Lodi, 07644 ... (973) 772-4840
New Adventures, LLC (H Q), 6 Deforest Ave., Ste. 7, East Hanover, 07936 ... (973) 884-8887
New Age Fastening Systems, Inc., 11 Enterprise Ct., Sewell, 08080 ... (856) 218-8301
New Age Metal Fabricating Co., 26 Daniel Rd., Fairfield, 07004 ... (973) 227-9107
New Brunswick Lamp Shade Co., 7 Terminal Rd., New Brunswick, 08901 ... (732) 545-0377
New Brunswick Plating, Inc., 1010 Jersey Ave., New Brunswick, 08901 ... (732) 545-6522
† New Brunswick Saw Service, Inc., 400 Lincoln Blvd., Middlesex, 08846 ... (908) 755-2366
New Century Building Systems, Inc.,
70 Sewell St., P.O. Box 775, Glassboro, 08028 ... (856) 863-8036
★ New Century Wood Products, 131 Lincoln Blvd., Middlesex, 08846 ... (732) 271-2557
New Crushed Toast Corp., 625 Pennsylvania Ave., Linden, 07036 ... (908) 925-2920
New England Bedding Transport, 102 3rd Ave., Kearny, 07032 ... (201) 997-2337
New Era Converting Machinery, 235 Route 20, Paterson, 07504 ... (201) 670-4848
New Era Enterprises, Inc., 208 N. West Blvd., Rear, Newfield, 08344 ... (856) 794-2005
★ New Granite & Marble, LLC, 35 8th St., Ste. 6, Passaic, 07055 ... (973) 767-6216
New Horizon Lighting, Inc., 632 Cedar Swamp Rd., Jackson, 08527 ... (732) 833-8086

New Horizon Press, Inc., 34 Church St., Liberty Corner, 07938 ... (908) 604-6311
New Industrial Foam Corp., 1355 W. Front St., P.O. Box 3120, Plainfield, 07063 ... (908) 561-4010
New Jersey Beer Co., LLC, 4201 Tonnelle Ave., North Bergen, 07047 ... (201) 758-8342
New Jersey Business & Industry Assn. see. ... New Jersey Business Magazine, Fairfield
New Jersey Business & Industry Assn. (H Q), 10 W. Lafayette St., Trenton, 08608 ... (609) 393-7707
New Jersey Business Forms Mfg. Corp., 55 W. Sheffield Ave., Englewood, 07631 ... (201) 569-4500
New Jersey Business Magazine, 310 Passaic Ave., Ste. 201, Fairfield, 07004 ... (973) 882-5004
New Jersey Business Systems, Inc., 7-C Marlen Dr., Trenton, 08691 ... (609) 587-5500
New Jersey Countryside Magazine, 134 S. Finley Ave., Basking Ridge, 07920 ... (908) 221-1171
New Jersey Diamond Products Co., 108 Kentucky Ave., Paterson, 07503 ... (973) 684-0949
New Jersey Epoch Times, 50 Cragwood Rd., South Plainfield, 07080 ... (908) 548-8380
New Jersey Frame & Moulding Co., 62 Kearney St., Paterson, 07522 ... (973) 684-6001
New Jersey Galvanizing & Tinning Works, Inc., 139 Haynes Ave., 1st Fl., Newark, 07114 ... (973) 242-3200
New Jersey Granite & Marble Corp., 50 S. Center St., Unit 3, Orange, 07050 ... (973) 266-8952
New Jersey Halal Meat Packing, 841 Main St., Paterson, 07503 ... (973) 684-3648
New Jersey Hardwoods, Inc., 1340 W. Front St., Plainfield, 07063 ... (908) 754-0990
New Jersey Herald, The, 2 Spring St., P.O. Box 10, Newton, 07860 ... (973) 383-1500
New Jersey Iron, Inc., 905 Patterson Rd., Jackson, 08527 ... (732) 928-7242
New Jersey Jewish News, 901 Route 10, Whippany, 07981 ... (973) 887-3900
New Jersey Journal Of Pharmacy, 760 Alexander Rd., Princeton, 08540 ... (609) 275-4246
★ New Jersey Logowear, 100 McKinley Ave., Ste. 6, Manahawkin, 08050 ... (609) 597-9400
New Jersey Machine & Tool Co., 257 Houses Corner Rd., Lafayette, 07848 ... (973) 383-6102
New Jersey Media Group, 11 Melanie Ln., Unit 22-A, East Hanover, 07936 ... (973) 434-8888
New Jersey Meter Co., 1 Hazel St., Woodland Park, 07424 ... (973) 345-6200
New Jersey Microsystems, Inc., 211 Warren St., Ste. 31, Newark, 07103 ... (973) 297-1450
New Jersey Monthly Magazine, Inc., 55 S. Park Pl., P.O. Box 920, Morristown, 07963 ... (973) 539-8230
New Jersey Plastics see. ... Consolidated Container Co., LLC, Monroe Township
† New Jersey Plumbing, Heating & Industrial Supply, LLC, 91 Newark Way, Maplewood, 07040 ... (973) 761-4567
New Jersey Precision Technologies, Inc., 1081 Bristol Rd., Mountainside, 07092 ...
New Jersey Pulverizing Co., Inc. see. ... Ace Crete Products, Inc., Bayville
New Jersey Pulverizing Co., Inc. see. ... Empire Blended Products, Inc., Bayville
New Jersey Reprographics, Inc., 110 Center St., Garwood, 07027 ... (908) 789-1616
New Jersey Rivet Co., LLC, 1785 Haddon Ave., Camden, 08103 ... (856) 963-2237
† New Jersey Semiconductor Products, Inc., 20 Stern Ave., Springfield, 07081 ... (973) 376-2922
New Jersey Stair & Rail, Inc., 746 Lloyd Rd., Matawan, 07747 ... (732) 583-8400
New Jersey Wire Cloth Co., Inc., 55 Park Slope, Clifton, 07011 ... (973) 340-0101
New Jersey Wire Stitching Machine Co., 1841 Old Cuthbert Rd., Cherry Hill, 08034 ... (856) 428-7400
New Life Color Reproduction, Inc., 610 Broad Ave., Ridgefield, 07657 ... (201) 943-7005
New Line Printing & Technology, Inc., 1011 Route 22 E., Mountainside, 07092 ... (973) 232-5003
New Page Books see. ... Career Press, Inc., Pompton Plains
New Print Shop, Inc., 558 Central Ave., New Providence, 07974 ... (609) 392-0782
New Rose, Inc., 1500 Almonesson Rd., Ste. 8, Woodbury, 08096 ... (856) 812-0509
New Standard Printing Corp., 118 Lincoln Ave., Dover, 07801 ... (973) 366-0006
New WinCup Holdings, Inc. see. ... WinCup, Metuchen
New World International Corp., 59 Dover St., Paterson, 07501 ... (973) 881-8100
New World Stainless, LLC, 100 Randolph Rd., Ste. 5, Somerset, 08873 ... (732) 412-7170
New York Blackboard of NJ, Inc., 83 U.S. Highway 22, Hillside, 07205 ... (973) 926-1600
New York Corrugated Box Co., LLC, 239 Lindberg Pl., Ste. 1, Paterson, 07503 ... (973) 742-5000
New York Corrugated Box, LLC, 239 Lindbergh Pl., Ste. Ll, Paterson, 07503 ... (973) 742-5000
New York Daily News, 125 Theodore Conrad Dr., Jersey City, 07305 ... (201) 946-6000
New York Folding Box Co., 20 Continental Dr., Stanhope, 07874 ... (973) 347-6932
New York Poultry Co., Inc., 3351 Tremley Point Rd., Linden, 07036 ... (908) 523-1600
† New York Produce, Inc., 125 Seaview Dr., Secaucus, 07094 ... (201) 223-0909
New York Sample Card Co., Inc., 812 Jersey Ave., 3rd Fl., Jersey City, 07310 ... (201) 526-9040
New York Sewing Machine, Inc., 8555 Tonnelle Ave., Unit 301, North Bergen, 07047 ... (201) 809-2009
Newark Asphalt Corp., 30 Passaic St., Newark, 07104 ... (973) 268-3636
Newark Auto Products see. ... Newark Auto Top Co., Inc., East Orange
Newark Auto Top Co., Inc., 23 Centerway, East Orange, 07017 ... (973) 677-9935
Newark Brush Company, 1 Silver Ct., Springfield, 07081 ... (973) 376-1000
Newark Caplan Sewing Machine, Inc., 858 Summer Ave., Newark, 07104 ... (973) 481-4400
Newark Dental Pemco, 35 Stern Ave., P.O. Box 249, Springfield, 07081 ... (973) 564-9622
Newark Group, Inc., The, 60 Lockwood St., Newark, 07105 ... (973) 465-3900
Newark Group, Inc., The (H Q), 20 Jackson Dr., Cranford, 07016 ... (908) 276-4000
Newark Industrial Spraying, Inc., 12 Amsterdam St., Newark, 07105 ... (973) 344-6855
Newark Liner & Washer, Inc., 819 Broadway, Newark, 07104 ... (973) 482-5400
Newark Mold & Tool, Inc., 147 New Jersey Railroad Ave., Newark, 07105 ... (973) 578-2881
Newark Morning Ledger Co., 1 Star Ledger Plz., Newark, 07102 ... (973) 392-4141
Newark Morning Ledger Co. see. ... Star Ledger, Pine Brook
Newark Recycled Fibers see. ... Newark Group, Inc., The, Newark
Newark Stamp & Die Works, Inc., 35 Verona Ave., Newark, 07104 ... (973) 485-7111
† Newark Steel & Ornamental Supply, 41-43 Frelinghuysen Ave., Newark, 07114 ... (973) 424-9790
Newark Steel Fabricators, Inc., 104 Albert Ave., Newark, 07105 ... (973) 344-2904
Newark Trade Typographers, Inc., 177 Oakwood Ave., Orange, 07050 ... (973) 674-3727
Newark Welding Co., 47 Morris Ave., Newark, 07103 ... (973) 642-6479
Newark Wire Cloth Co., Inc., 160 Fornelius Ave., Clifton, 07013 ... (973) 778-4478
Newark Wire Works, Inc., 1059 King Georges Post Rd., Ste. 103, Edison, 08837 ... (732) 661-2001
Newbold, Inc., 200 Egel Ave., Middlesex, 08846 ... (732) 469-5654
Newco, Inc. see. ... Butler Printing & Laminating, Butler
Newco, Inc., 1 Hicks Ave., Newton, 07860 ... (973) 383-7777
Newly Weds Foods, Inc. see ... Continental Seasoning, Inc., Teaneck
Newman's Ornamental Ironworks, Inc., 207 Union Ave., Brielle, 08730 ... (732) 223-9042
News Of Cumberland County, The, 93 5th St., Salem, 08079 ... (856) 451-1000
Newton Printing & Embroidery, 75 Main St., Franklin, 07416 ... (973) 827-2006
Newton T & M Corp., 119 Fredon Springdale Rd., Newton, 07860 ... (973) 383-1232
Newton Trophy & Sport Center, 1-3 Milk St., Bldg. 3, Branchville, 07826 ... (973) 948-0613
Newtype, Inc., 447 State Route 10, Ste. 14, Randolph, 07869 ... (973) 361-6000
Nexcore Technology, Inc., 150 Hopper Ave., Waldwick, 07463 ... (201) 968-9400
★ Nexgen Press Corp., 859 Bridgeboro St., Riverside, 08075 ... (609) 528-0370
Next Day Signs & Banners, Inc., 300 Route 17, Paramus, 07652 ... (201) 986-1960
★ NEXT Medical Products, 45 Columbia Rd., Branchburg, 08876 ... (800) 458-4254
Next Step Orthopedics, Inc., 331 Main St., West Orange, 07052 ... (973) 736-2244
Nextwave Web, LLC, 229 Marshall St., Paterson, 07503 ... (973) 742-4339
Nexus Plastics, Inc., 1 Loretto Ave., Hawthorne, 07506 ... (973) 427-3311
NHCS see. ... Nutley Heating & Cooling Supply Co., Inc., Clifton

NIC Group, The, 1130 U.S. Highway 202, Ste. E-6, Raritan, 08869 ... (908) 253-8106
NICE Systems, Inc. (H Q), 461 From Rd., Paramus, 07652 ... (201) 964-2600
Nicholas Designs, R., 41 Portland Ave., Bergenfield, 07621 ... (201) 385-8713
Nicholas Galvanizing Co., 120 Duffield Ave., Jersey City, 07306 ... (201) 795-1010
Nickel Artistic Services, LLC, 39 U.S. Highway 46, Rockaway, 07866 ... (973) 627-0390
Nicolos Italian Bakery & Deli, Inc., 6 Baldwin St., Montclair, 07042 ... (973) 746-1398
Niehoff Endex North America, Inc., 1 Mallard Ct., Swedesboro, 08085 ... (856) 467-4884
Nifty Products, 4 Jocama Blvd., Old Bridge, 08857 ... (732) 591-1140
Night Canyon, Inc., The, 1475 Park Ave., Alpha, 08865 ... (908) 454-6344
† Nikko Ceramics, Inc., 815 Fairview Ave., Ste. 9, Fairview, 07022 ... (201) 840-5200
Niksun, Inc., 100 Nassau Park Blvd., 3rd Fl., Princeton, 08540 ... (609) 936-9999
Ninsa Vinyl Fence, LLC, 125 Lincoln St., Hammonton, 08037 ... (609) 561-5397
Nippon Thompson Co. Ltd. see. ... IKO International, Inc., Parsippany
† Nishimoto Trading Co. Ltd., 602 Washington Ave., Carlstadt, 07072 ... (201) 804-1600
Nistica, Inc., 745 U.S. Highway 202-206, Ste. 201, Bridgewater, 08807 ... (908) 707-9500
Nitka Graphics, Inc., 355 E. 54th St., Elmwood Park, 07407 ... (201) 797-3000
Nitta Casings Inc., 141 Southside Ave., Bridgewater, 08807 ... (908) 218-4400
Nitto Denko America Automotive, Inc., 1990 Rutgers Blvd., Lakewood, 08701 ... (732) 901-7905
Nitto Denko America, Inc. see. ... Nitto Denko America Automotive, Inc., Lakewood
NJ Beer Co. see. ... New Jersey Beer Co., LLC, North Bergen
NJ Engineering & Supply see. ... Yecies, Inc., Herman W., West Orange
NJ Label, 30 Wesley St., Unit 7, South Hackensack, 07606 ... (201) 833-9200
N.J. Plastics Machining & Fabricating, Inc., 46 Liverpool Ave., P.O. Box 646, Egg Harbor City, 08215 ... (609) 965-1550
NJBIZ, 220 Davidson Ave., Ste. 302, Somerset, 08873 ... (732) 246-7677
NJN Publishing, Inc. see. ... NJN Publishing Independent Press, Inc., New Providence
NJN Publishing, Inc. (H Q), 8 Minneakoning Rd., Flemington, 08822 ... (908) 782-4747
NJN Publishing Independent Press, Inc., 309 South St., New Providence, 07974 ... (908) 464-1025
NJS Sales Corp., 2840 Mount Ephraim Ave., Camden, 08104 ... (856) 619-1119
★ NMK Resources, 650 Grove Rd., Ste. 111, Paulsboro, 08066 ... (856) 686-4904
NMN Closet, Inc., 40 Veterans Blvd., Carlstadt, 07072 ... (201) 964-9600
Nobleworks, Inc., 500 Patterson Plank Rd., Union City, 07087 ... (201) 420-0095
Nodeco Machine Service, 5 Wayside Ln., Lebanon, 08833 ... (908) 236-7996
Nofire Technologies, Inc., 5 James St., South Hackensack, 07606 ... (201) 818-1616
Noisecom Boonton Microlab see. ... Wireless Telecom Group, Inc., Parsippany
Nomadic Display, 4-6 Just Rd., Fairfield, 07004 ... (862) 210-8120
Norcia Corp., 451 Black Horse Ln., North Brunswick, 08902 ... (732) 297-1101
Norco, Inc., 237 South Ave., P.O. Box 186, Garwood, 07027 ... (908) 789-1550
Nordic Metal, LLC, 500 S. 31st St., Kenilworth, 07033 ... (908) 245-8900
Nordt Precision Metal Mfg., Inc., 640 Creek Rd., Bellmawr, 08031 ... (856) 931-7444
Norell, Inc., 314 Arbor Ave., P.O. Box 307, Landisville, 08326 ... (856) 697-0020
Norge Building Supply see. ... Allied Building Products Corp., Totowa
Norgus Silk Screen Co., 58 Sylvan Ave., Clifton, 07011 ... (973) 365-0600
Noritake Co., Inc. (H Q), 15-22 Fair Lawn Ave., Fair Lawn, 07410 ... (201) 796-2222
Norland Products, Inc., 2540 Route 130, Ste. 100, Cranbury, 08512 ... (609) 395-1966
Norman Dee Associates, 31 N. Sovereign Ave., Atlantic City, 08401 ... (609) 348-5777
Norman's Dairy Delight see. ... Dairy Delight, LLC, Rutherford
Norman's Glass & Auto Services, Inc., 4482 Route 130 S., Burlington, 08016 ... (609) 386-7100
Normiska Corp. see. ... Schundler Co., Inc., Edison
Norpak Corp., 70 Blanchard St., Newark, 07105 ... (973) 589-4200
Norsal Distribution Assocs., 150 Cregar Rd., High Bridge, 08829 ... (908) 638-8900
† Norstat, Inc., 300 Round Hill Dr., Ste. 4, Rockaway, 07866 ... (973) 586-2500
North America Packaging Corp. (NAMPAC), 7 Wheeling Rd., Dayton, 08810 ... (732) 997-4100
North American Elevator, Inc., 609 W. Elizabeth Ave., Linden, 07036 ... (908) 523-1234
North American Illumination Co., 79 Commerce St., Garfield, 07026 ... (973) 478-4700
North American Packaging, LLC see. ... Econo-PAK, Sussex
North American Sterilization & Packaging Company, Inc., 19 Park Dr., Franklin, 07416 ... (973) 209-4388
North Bergen Marble & Granite Corp., 217 Palisade Ave., Cliffside Park, 07010 ... (201) 945-9988
North East Publishing see. ... Contemporary Bride Magazine, South Plainfield
★ North Hudson Press, 429 Hancock Pl., Fairview, 07022 ... (201) 941-2520
North Jersey Media Group see. ... Record, The, Woodland Park
North Jersey Media Group, Inc. see.. Community Newspapers & Magazines Of North Jersey Media Group, Woodland Park
North Jersey Media Group, Inc. see. ... Franklin Lakes Oakland, Ridgewood
North Jersey Media Group, Inc. see. ... North Jersey Media Group Inc., Rockaway
North Jersey Media Group Inc., 100 Commons Way, Rockaway, 07866 ... (973) 586-8000
★ North Jersey Media Group, Inc., 181 Milburn Ave., Ste. 201, Millburn, 07041 ... (973) 921-6451
North Jersey Media Group, Inc., 1 Garret Mountain Plz., P.O. Box 471, Woodland Park, 07424 ... (973) 569-7000
North Jersey Media Group, Inc. see. ... Record, The, Woodland Park
North Jersey Media Group, Inc. see. ... South Bergenite, Rutherford
North Jersey Media Group, Inc. see. ... Verona-Cedar Grove Times, Montclair
North Jersey Media Group, Inc. see. ... WayneToday, Woodland Park
North Jersey Metal Fabricators, Inc., 130 Ryerson Ave., Ste. 107, Wayne, 07470 ... (973) 305-9830
North Jersey Paper Box Corp., 132 32nd St., P.O. Box 700, Union City, 07087 ... (201) 348-4233
North Jersey Prosthetics & Orthotics, 39 Broad Ave., Palisades Park, 07650 ... (201) 943-4448
North Jersey Ravioli Co., 65 Pacific Ave., Garfield, 07026 ... (973) 772-5050
North Jersey Window Treatments, LLC, 164 South St., Hackensack, 07601 ... (201) 487-2121
North Sails New Jersey, 2422 Highway 34, Manasquan, 08736 ... (732) 528-8899
North Star Travel Media, LLC (H Q), 100 Lighting Way, 2nd Fl., Secaucus, 07094 ... (201) 902-2000
Northeast Bindery, Inc., 419 Trumbull St., Elizabeth, 07206 ... (908) 436-3737
Northeast Concrete Products, LLC, 937 Burnt Meadow Rd., P.O. Box 963, Hewitt, 07421 ... (973) 728-1667
Northeast Foods, Inc. see. ... Automatic Rolls Of New Jersey, Inc., Edison
† Northeast Industrial, LLC, 661 Route 9, Cape May, 08204 ... (609) 884-3510
Northeast Lock Corp., 48 Oak St., Clifton, 07014 ... (973) 777-7509
Northeast Medical Systems Corp., 901 Beechwood Ave., Cherry Hill, 08002 ... (856) 910-8111
Northeast Pallet Recycling, LLC, 133 Yellowbrook Rd., Farmingdale, 07727 ... (732) 751-1919
Northeast Pro-Tech, Inc., 61 Willet St., Bldg. L, Passaic, 07055 ... (973) 777-5654
Northeast Sheet Metal, LLC, 870 Warwick Tpke., Hewitt, 07421 ... (973) 853-0500
Northern Architectural Systems, 111 Central Ave., Teterboro, 07608 ... (201) 943-6400
Northwest Essex Community Healthcare Network, Inc., 83 Walnut St., Montclair, 07042 ... (973) 744-7733
Norton & Son, Inc., 148 E. 5th St., Bayonne, 07002 ... (201) 437-0770
Norwalt Design, Inc., 961 Route 10 E., Bldg. 2-A, Randolph, 07869 ... (973) 927-3200
Norwolf Tool Works, Inc., 6 Sullivan St., Westwood, 07675 ... (201) 666-6655
Norwood Printing see. ... Control Group, The, Norwood
Nosaj Disposables, Inc., 3 Security Dr., Ste. 312, P.O. Box 355, Cranbury, 08512 ... (800) 631-3809
Nosotros, News, P.O. Box 1337, Toms River, 08754 ... (732) 845-1911

★ Indicates new listing this edition. † Indicates wholesaler/distributor.

ALPHABETICAL

Nostrum Pharmaceuticals, LLC (H Q), 1370 Hamilton St., Somerset, 08873 .............. (732) 543-2440
Notie Corp., 177-A Route 526, Allentown, 08501 .............. (609) 259-3477
Nourison Industries (H Q), 5 Sampson St., Saddle Brook, 07663 .............. (201) 368-6900
Nouveau Prosthetics & Orthotics, 984 State Route 36, Hazlet, 07730 .............. (732) 739-0888
Nouveautes, Inc., 70 Clinton Rd., Fairfield, 07004 .............. (973) 882-8850
Nova Precision Products, Inc., 160 Franklin Ave., Rockaway, 07866 .............. (973) 625-1586
Nova Specialty Chemicals, LLC, 404 E. Main St., Rockaway, 07866 .............. (973) 586-2147
Nova Systems, 246 Cozy Lake Rd., Oak Ridge, 07438 .............. (973) 697-3281
Novaflex Industries, Inc., 1024 Industrial Dr., West Berlin, 08091 .............. (856) 768-2275
Novak Co., Tony, 185 Bayview Rd., P.O. Box 333, Newport, 08345 .............. (856) 649-4171
Novapac Laboratories, Inc., 545 N. Arlington Ave., East Orange, 07017 .............. (973) 414-8800
Novartis Consumer Health (H Q), 200 Kimball Dr., Parsippany, 07054 .............. (973) 503-8000
Novartis Finance Corp. see .............. Novartis Pharmaceuticals Corp. (H Q), East Hanover
Novartis Pharmaceuticals Corp. see .............. Sandoz, Inc. (H Q), Princeton
Novartis Pharmaceuticals Corp. (H Q), 1 Health Plz., East Hanover, 07936 .............. (862) 778-8300
Novatech Graphics, 54 Birch Ave., Ste. A, Little Silver, 07739 .............. (732) 469-1887
Novel Box Co. Ltd., 825 Lehigh Ave., Union, 07083 .............. (908) 686-7772
Novel Laboratories, Inc., 400 Campus Dr., Somerset, 08873 .............. (908) 603-6000
Novel Lithographers, Inc., 1 Kero Rd., Carlstadt, 07072 .............. (201) 372-3900
Novell Enterprises, Inc., 2100 Felver Ct., Rahway, 07065 .............. (732) 428-8300
Novelty Cone Co., Inc., 807 Sherman Ave., Pennsauken, 08110 .............. (856) 665-9525
Novembal U. S. A., A Tetra Pak Co., 3 Greek Ln., Edison, 08817 .............. (732) 287-4949
Novo Nordisk, Inc. (H Q), 800 Scudders Mill Rd., Plainsboro, 08536 .............. (609) 987-5800
Novum Industries, Inc. see .............. Cottage Lace & Ribbon Co., Neptune
Nowak, Inc., 17 Robert St., Ste. B-5, Wharton, 07885 .............. (973) 366-7208
NPS Pharmaceuticals, Inc. (H Q), 550 Hills Dr., Bedminster, 07921 .............. (908) 450-5300
NResearch, Inc., 267 Fairfield Ave., West Caldwell, 07006 .............. (973) 808-8811
† NRG Energy, Inc. (H Q), 211 Carnegie Ctr., Princeton, 08540 .............. (609) 524-4500
NRI see .............. National Reprographics, Inc., Lawrenceville
NRI see .............. Rethink Color, a division of NRI, Lawrenceville
NTE Electronics, Inc., 44 Farrand St., Bloomfield, 07003 .............. (973) 748-5089
Nth Degree Products, LLC, 404 Laurel Ridge Rd., Hainesport, 08036 .............. (609) 518-9447
Nu E-Z Custom Bindery, LLC, 111 Essex St., Hackensack, 07601 .............. (201) 488-4140
Nu Products Seasonings Co., 74 Louis Ct., South Hackensack, 07606 .............. (201) 440-0065
★ Nuclear Diagnostic Products, Inc., 101 Round Hill Dr., Rockaway, 07866 .............. (973) 664-9696
Nucor Corp. see .............. Skyline Steel, LLC (H Q), Parsippany
Nu-Graphics Ii, Inc., 84 Stonybrook Rd., P.O. Box 65, Towaco, 07082 .............. (973) 299-0066
Nulab Furniture Corp., 11 Federal Rd., Monroe Township, 08831 .............. (732) 792-0050
† Numax, Inc., 7251-B Browning Rd., Pennsauken, 08109 .............. (856) 910-0088
Nunn & Son Custom Lettering, 10 Harding Dr., Brick, 08724 .............. (732) 899-9682
★ NurseJoe.Com, 11 Plainfield Ave., Metuchen, 08840 .............. (848) 250-9900
† Nustar Energy L. P., 7 N. Delaware St., Paulsboro, 08066 .............. (856) 224-8903
Nu-Style Embroidery & Button Co., Inc., 5212 Polk St., West New York, 07093 .............. (201) 864-1808
Nu-Style Embroidery & Trimming, 5212 Polk St., West New York, 07093 .............. (201) 864-1808
† Nutley Heating & Cooling Supply Co.,
5016 Industrial Rd., Wall Township, 07727 .............. (732) 919-1933
Nutley Heating & Cooling Supply Co., Inc. see .... Nutley Heating & Cooling Supply Co., Wall Township
† Nutley Heating & Cooling Supply Co., Inc., 50 Page Rd., Clifton, 07012 .............. (973) 470-8844
Nutra Nuts, Inc. (H Q), 180 Old Tappan Rd., Old Tappan, 07675 .............. (201) 768-0218
Nutra-Med Packaging, Inc., 385 Franklin Ave., Ste. E, Rockaway, 07866 .............. (973) 625-2274
Nutri Pet Research, Inc./NUPRO Supplements,
227 State Route 33 E., Manalapan, 07726 .............. (732) 786-8822
Nutrition North America, 10 Saddle Rd., Cedar Knolls, 07927 .............. (973) 734-0023
Nuts On Line see .............. Nuts.Com, Cranford
Nutsco, Inc., 1115 S. 2nd St., Camden, 08103 .............. (856) 966-6400
Nuts.Com, 125 Moen St., Cranford, 07016 .............. (908) 523-0333
Nuvico, Inc., 53 Smith St., Englewood, 07631 .............. (201) 541-1605
Nu-World Corp., 300 Milik St., Carteret, 07008 .............. (732) 541-6300
N.V. Business Publishers Corp. (H Q),
43 Main St., P.O. Box 188, Avon by the Sea, 07717 .............. (732) 502-0500
NVE, Inc., 15 Whitehall Rd., Andover, 07821 .............. (973) 786-7868
NW Sign Industries, Inc., 360 Crider Ave., Moorestown, 08057 .............. (856) 802-1677
NWL, Inc., 312 Rising Sun Rd., Bordentown, 08505 .............. (609) 298-7300
Nxlevel Solutions, 57 Hamilton Ave., Ste. 303, Hopewell, 08525 .............. (609) 466-2828
NY Enterprise see .............. Mon Far Press Printing, Rutherford
N.Y. Textile Mills, Inc., 90 Dayton Ave., Bldg. 5-A, Passaic, 07055 .............. (973) 777-9871
Nylabone Products,
1 TFH Plz., 3rd & Union Ave., P.O. Box 427, Neptune City, 07753 .............. (732) 988-8400
Nymar Mfg. Co., Inc., 215 State Route 10 E., Randolph, 07869 .............. (973) 366-7265
NYP Corp., 805 E. Grand St., Elizabeth, 07201 .............. (908) 351-6550
O & C Die Cutters & Finishers, 16 Andrews Dr., West Paterson, 07424 .............. (973) 890-7778
O & S Research, Inc., 1912 Bannard St., P.O. Box 221, Cinnaminson, 08077 .............. (856) 829-2800
O. Co Imprints, LLC, 58 W. Bergen Pl., P.O. Box 8249, Red Bank, 07701 .............. (732) 530-3202
O K Tool & Die Co., 603 Bluebell Rd., Williamstown, 08094 .............. (856) 629-5757
O M P Technologies, Inc., 24-H Commerce Rd., Fairfield, 07004 .............. (973) 808-5543
O. R. Comfort, LLC, 28 Appleton Rd., Glen Ridge, 07028 .............. (973) 239-1950
Oakwood Uniform & Equipment Co., 400 E. Main St., Maple Shade, 08052 .............. (856) 779-7680
Oasis CD Mfg. see .............. Oasis Recording, Inc., Delair
Oasis Foods Co., 635 Ramsey Ave., P.O. Box 697, Hillside, 07205 .............. (908) 964-0477
Oasis Recording, Inc., 7905 N. Crescent Blvd., Delair, 08110 .............. (888) 296-2747
Oasis Studios, LLC, 244 Quakertown Rd., P.O. Box 306, Quakertown, 08868 .............. (908) 735-5089
Oavco Bearings see .............. Oavco Ltd., LLC, Princeton
★ Oavco Ltd., LLC, 103 Carnegie Ctr., Princeton, 08540 .............. (609) 454-5340
† Oberg & Lindquist Corp., 671 Broadway, Westwood, 07675 .............. (201) 664-1300
Object Design, Inc., 105 W. Dewey Ave., Bldg. C, Unit 5, Wharton, 07885 .............. (973) 442-5790
Objectif Lune, LLC, 300 Broadacres Dr., 4th Fl., Bloomfield, 07003 .............. (973) 780-0100
O'Brien Co., Inc., J., 40 Commerce St., Springfield, 07081 .............. (973) 379-8844
Observer, P.O. Box 445, Hasbrouck Heights, 07604 .............. (201) 288-0333
Occupational Center, The, 301 Cox St., Roselle, 07203 .............. (908) 241-7200
Occupational Training Center, 215 W. White Horse Pike, Berlin, 08009 .............. (856) 768-0845
Ocean City Vinyl Fence Co., Inc., 719 Haven Ave., Ocean City, 08226 .............. (609) 399-8288
Ocean Granite Marble, LLC, 140 7th Ave., Unit 9, Little Egg Harbor, 08087 .............. (609) 296-1800
Ocean Power Technologies, Inc., 1590 Reed Rd., Pennington, 08534 .............. (609) 730-0400
Ocean Rockets, Inc., 5 Mosquito Landing Rd., Tuckahoe, 08250 .............. (609) 628-4445
Ocean Spray Cranberries, Inc., 104 E. Park St., Bordentown, 08505 .............. (609) 298-0905
Ocean Star, The, 421 River Ave., Point Pleasant Beach, 08742 .............. (732) 899-7606
Ocean Yachts, Inc., 2713 Green Bank Rd., Egg Harbor City, 08215 .............. (609) 965-4616
Oceana Designs, Inc., 450 Oberlin Ave. S., Lakewood, 08701 .............. (732) 987-6944
Oceanic Electrical Mfg. Co., 248-256 3rd St., Elizabeth, 07206 .............. (908) 355-1900
Oceanic Graphic Printing USA, 105 Main St., 3rd Fl., Hackensack, 07601 .............. (201) 883-1816
Oceanic Metals LLC, 8555 Tonnelle Ave., Ste. 404, North Bergen, 07047 .............. (201) 662-1192
Ocsidot, Inc., 116 South Ave., Garwood, 07027 .............. (908) 789-3300
Octagon Communications Corp.,
385 Sylvan Ave., Ste. 16, Englewood Cliffs, 07632 .............. (201) 569-5870
Octal Corporation, 125 Galway Pl., Ste. B, Teaneck, 07666 .............. (201) 862-1010
Odd-It-Tees, 405 S. Main St., Forked River, 08731 .............. (609) 693-8337
Odyssey Specialty Vehicles, 317 Richard Mine Rd., Wharton, 07885 .............. (973) 328-2667
OEG Building Materials, 395 State Route 34, Matawan, 07747 .............. (732) 667-3636
Oertel Orthopedics, Inc., 2095 U.S. Highway 22 W., Union, 07083 .............. (908) 688-1818
Off The Hook Seafood, LLC, 126-A Greenwood Ave., Midland Park, 07432 .............. (201) 444-8895
Office Depot Business Solution Div. Of New Jersey,
4 Brighton Rd., Clifton, 07012 .............. (973) 594-3000
Office Depot, Inc. see .............. Office Depot Business Solution Div. Of New Jersey, Clifton
Office Prints, The, 30 Journal Sq., Jersey City, 07306 .............. (201) 222-5555
Officemate International Corp., 90 Newfield Ave., Edison, 08837 .............. (732) 225-7422
Offray Specialty Narrow Fabrics, Inc. (H Q),
4 Essex Ave., Ste. 403, Bernardsville, 07924 .............. (908) 879-3636
OFS Fitel, LLC see .............. OFS Fitel, LLC, Specialty Photonics Div., Somerset
OFS Fitel, LLC, Specialty Photonics Div., 25 Schoolhouse Rd., Somerset, 08873 .............. (732) 748-7400
† Ogura Industrial Corp., 100 Randolph Rd., 2nd Fl., Somerset, 08873 .............. (732) 271-7361
Ohaus Corp., 7 Campus Dr., Ste. 310, Parsippany, 07054 .............. (973) 377-9000
OHM Laboratories, Inc., 14 Terminal Rd., New Brunswick, 08901 .............. (732) 514-4380
OHM Laboratories, Inc.,
1385 Livingston Ave., P.O. Box 7397, North Brunswick, 08902 .............. (732) 418-2235
★ Oil Tank Services, 505 E. 1st Ave., Roselle, 07203 .............. (908) 241-5011
† Oilmatic Systems, LLC, 155 Smith St., P.O. Box 185, Keasbey, 08832 .............. (732) 324-9890
O.K. Tool Corp., 1233 North Ave., Plainfield, 07062 .............. (908) 561-9920
OKAI Corp., 687 Lehigh Ave., Ste. 3, Union, 07083 .............. (908) 687-4443
Oki Data Americas, Inc., 2000 Bishops Gate Blvd., Mount Laurel, 08054 .............. (856) 235-2600
Oklahoma Sound Corp., 149 Entin Rd., Clifton, 07014 .............. (973) 594-9000
Okonite Co., Inc., The see .............. Okonite Co., The, Paterson
Okonite Co., Inc., The (H Q), 102 Hilltop Rd., P.O. Box 340, Ramsey, 07446 .............. (201) 825-0300
Okonite Co., The, 102 Hilltop Rd., Paterson, 07513 .............. (201) 825-0300
Old Bridge Chemical, Inc., 554 Waterworks Rd., Old Bridge, 08857 .............. (732) 727-2225
Old Fashioned Kitchen, Inc., 1045 Towbin Ave., Lakewood, 08701 .............. (732) 364-4100
Old Hights Print Shop, Inc., 133 S. Main St., Hightstown, 08520 .............. (609) 443-4700
Old Monmouth Candies see .............. Old Monmouth Peanut Brittle Co., Freehold
Old Monmouth Peanut Brittle Co., 627 Park Ave., Freehold, 07728 .............. (732) 462-1311
Oldcastle BuildingEnvelope®, 1500 Glen Ave., Moorestown, 08057 .............. (866) 653-2278
Oldcastle, Inc. see .............. Allied Building Products Corp., East Rutherford
Oldcastle, Inc. see .............. Anchor Concrete Products, Inc. (H Q), Red Bank
Oldcastle Precast, Inc., 1920 12th St., Williamstown, 08094 .............. (609) 561-3400
Olde Granddad Industries, 1 Market St., Passaic, 07055 .............. (201) 997-1899
Ole Hansen & Son, Inc. see .............. Ole Hansen & Sons, Inc., Absecon
Ole Hansen & Son, Inc. (H Q),
523 S. Leipzig Ave., P.O. Box 1020, Cologne, 08213 .............. (609) 965-3700
Ole Hansen & Sons, Inc., 100 Old Port Republic Rd., Absecon, 08205 .............. (609) 652-5666
Oli Systems, Inc., 240 Cedar Knolls Rd., Ste. 301, Cedar Knolls, 07927 .............. (973) 539-4996
Oliner Fibre Co., Inc., 2391 Vauxhall Rd., P.O. Box 308, Union, 07083 .............. (908) 688-5800
Oliver, Inc., G. J., 50 Industrial Rd., Phillipsburg, 08865 .............. (908) 454-9743
Oliver Mfg. Supply Co.,
730 Port Reading Ave., P.O. Box 274, Port Reading, 07064 .............. (732) 634-8100
† Oliveri & Sons, Inc., A., 4401 Dell Ave., P.O. Box 88, North Bergen, 07047 .............. (201) 319-9112
Oliveri Printing Corporation, Carl,
316 Main St., Ste. 1, East Rutherford, 07073 .............. (201) 438-0888
† Olla Beauty Supply, Inc.,
10 New Maple Ave., Unit 301-A, P.O. Box 898, Pine Brook, 07058 .............. (973) 575-5260
Olmec Systems, Inc., 255 W. Main St., Denville, 07834 .............. (973) 586-6590
Olsen Machine, LLC, 2504 Route 73, Cinnaminson, 08077 .............. (856) 662-2121
Olson Motor & Control Co., Inc., 100 Old Camplain Rd., Hillsborough, 08844 .............. (908) 231-1500
Olympic Controls Corp. see .............. Amperite Co., North Bergen
Olympic EDM & Waterjet, Inc., 20 Kiel Ave., Butler, 07405 .............. (973) 492-0664
Olympic Tool Co. see .............. ELC America Corp., Bayville
OM Group, Inc. see .............. OMG Electronic Chemicals, LLC, South Plainfield
Omaha Standard, 572 Whitehead Rd., Trenton, 08619 .............. (609) 588-5400
Omaha World-Herald Co. see .............. World Media Enterprises, Inc., Pleasantville
Omavi Clothing Co. (H Q), 701-703 McCarter Hwy., Ste. 102, Newark, 07102 .............. (973) 642-2000
Omega Circuits & Engineering Corp., 8 Terminal Rd., New Brunswick, 08901 .............. (732) 246-1661
Omega Graphics, 661 Broad St., Ste. 3, Shrewsbury, 07702 .............. (732) 530-4441
Omega Heat Transfer Co., Inc., 329 New Brunswick Ave., Rahway, 07065 .............. (732) 340-0023
Omega Metal Works, Inc., 41 Stelle Rd., Chesterfield, 08515 .............. (609) 298-9100
Omega Packaging Corp., 55 Kings Rd., Totowa, 07512 .............. (973) 890-9505
Omega Plastics Corp.,
Page & Schuyler Ave., Bldg. 3, P.O. Box 808, Lyndhurst, 07071 .............. (201) 933-5353
Omega Precision Corp., 1384 Pompton Ave., Ste. 3, Cedar Grove, 07009 .............. (973) 256-3422
Omega Shielding Products, Inc., 9 Emery Ave., Randolph, 07869 .............. (973) 366-0080
Omega Specialty Products, LLC,
2511 Fire Rd., Ste. B-6, Egg Harbor Township, 08234 .............. (609) 383-8835
Omega Tool Die, 8 International Ave., Sewell, 08080 .............. (856) 232-1015
OMG Electronic Chemicals, LLC,
400 Corporate Ct., Ste. A, South Plainfield, 07080 .............. (908) 222-5800
Omni Baking Co., 2621 Freddy Ln., Vineland, 08360 .............. (856) 205-1485
Omni W.C., Inc., 166 National Rd., Edison, 08817 .............. (732) 248-0999
Omnia Industries, Inc., 5 Cliffside Dr., P.O. Box 330, Cedar Grove, 07009 .............. (973) 239-7272
OmniComm Systems, Inc., 1100 Cornwall Rd., Ste. 111, Monmouth Junction, 08852 ... (732) 960-2820
Omnimed, Inc., 800 Glen Ave., Moorestown, 08057 .............. (856) 359-2231
Omnitek, Inc., 20 Newburgh Rd., Hackettstown, 07840 .............. (908) 852-8500
On Demand Machinery, LLC, 150 Broadway, Elizabeth, 07206 .............. (908) 351-6906
On Target Printing & Graphics, LLC, 202 Fairfield Rd., Fairfield, 07004 .............. (973) 287-6222
★ On The Level Counter Top, Inc., 825 Brook Rd., Lakewood, 08701 .............. (732) 370-4186
One Equity Partners, LLC see .............. Sonneborn, LLC, Parsippany
One Source Communications, Inc., 9 Whippany Rd., Bldg. C-4, Whippany, 07981 ..... (973) 463-0250
One Source Solutions, 220 Encin Rd., Clifton, 07014 .............. (973) 242-4040
One Source Solutions, 3 industrial Ct., Ste. 3, Freehold, 07728 .............. (732) 536-0702
One Stop Packaging, LLC, 71-B Kingsland Ave., Clifton, 07014 .............. (973) 272-0170
One Stop Printing, LLC, 135 Kearny Ave., Ste. B, Kearny, 07032 .............. (201) 991-3320
One Two Three, Inc., 537 Mantua Ave., Ste. B, P.O. Box 123, Woodbury, 08096 .............. (856) 251-1238
† O'Neal Flat Rolled Metals, 1 Fitzgerald Ave., Monroe Township, 08831 .............. (609) 395-7007
O'Neal Steel, Inc. see .............. O'Neal Flat Rolled Metals, Monroe Township
O'Neil Color & Compounding Corp., 61 River Dr., Garfield, 07026 .............. (973) 777-8999
OnGuard Fence Systems, 18 Culnen Dr., Branchburg, 08876 .............. (908) 429-5522
Onkyo USA Corp. (H Q), 18 Park Way, Upper Saddle River, 07458 .............. (201) 785-2600
On-Line Sign, 2 Sheffield Rd., East Windsor, 08520 .............. (609) 443-1704
OnPATH Technologies, 100 Mount Holly Bypass, Lumberton, 08048 .............. (609) 518-4100

© Copyright 2015 Manufacturers' News, Inc.


Onwards, Inc. (H Q), 10 Connor Dr., Manalapan, 07726 .......... (732) 309-7348
Onyx Valve Co., 835 Industrial Hwy., Ste. 4, Cinnaminson, 08077 .......... (856) 829-2888
Oori Trading, Inc., 230 Union St., P.O. Box 154, Northvale, 07647 .......... (201) 367-3030
Opdyke Awning, Inc., 2036 State Route 35, Wall Township, 07719 .......... (732) 449-5940
Operations Technology, Inc., 30 Lambert Rd., P.O. Box 408, Blairstown, 07825 .......... (908) 362-6200
OPEX Corporation, 305 Commerce Dr., Moorestown, 08057 .......... (856) 727-1100
★ Ophthalmology Times, 485F U.S. Highway 1 S., Ste. 1, Iselin, 08830 .......... (732) 346-3060
† Opici Winery, Inc., 25 DeBoer Dr., Glen Rock, 07452 .......... (201) 689-1200
Oppenheim Plastics Co., Inc., 90 Broadway, Woodcliff Lake, 07677 .......... (201) 391-3811
OPS Diagnostics, LLC, 291 U.S. Highway 22 E., Bldg. 6, Lebanon, 08833 .......... (908) 253-3444
Optical Insight, LLC, 778 Highway 1, North Brunswick, 08902 .......... (732) 828-3937
Oracle Corp., 330 Fellowship Rd., Ste. 100, Mount Laurel, 08054 .......... (856) 359-2999
Orange Mattress, 77 Central Ave., Clark, 07066 .......... (973) 761-1100
Oraton Rubber Stamp Co., Inc., 407 Route 94, Columbia, 07832 .......... (908) 496-4161
ORBCOMM, Inc. see. .......... StarTrak Information Technologies, LLC, Rochelle Park
ORBCOMM, Inc. (H Q), 395 W. Passaic St., Ste. 325, Rochelle Park, 07662 .......... (703) 433-6300
Orchard Yarn & Thread Co., Inc., 135 Kero Rd., Carlstadt, 07072 .......... (201) 804-3999
Organize It All, Inc., 24 River St., Ste. 201, Bogota, 07603 .......... (201) 488-0808
Orgo-Thermit, Inc., 3500 Colonial Dr. N., Manchester, 08759 .......... (732) 657-5781
Orient Corp. Of America (H Q), 6 Commerce Dr., Ste. 301, Cranford, 07016 .......... (908) 298-0990
Oriental Aromatics, Inc., 21 Spielman Rd., Fairfield, 07004 .......... (973) 227-0400
Original Bagel & Bialy Co., 2 Fairfield Crescent, West Caldwell, 07006 .......... (973) 227-5777
Origio, Inc., 77 Elbo Ln., Mount Laurel, 08054 .......... (856) 762-2000
Orion Precision Industries, Inc., 8 Veronica Ave., Somerset, 08873 .......... (732) 247-9704
Orival Water Filters, 213 S. Van Brunt St., Englewood, 07631 .......... (201) 568-3311
Orlando Bakery, 236 Harrison Ave., Lodi, 07644 .......... (973) 772-8883
Orpak USA, 100 1st St., Ste. 200, Hackensack, 07601 .......... (201) 441-9820
Orpheus Ltd., 40 Woodland Ave., Rockaway, 07866 .......... (973) 983-1400
Ortho Remedy, Inc., The, 522 Anderson Ave., Cliffside Park, 07010 .......... (201) 943-3900
Ortho Safe Systems International, Inc. (H Q), P.O. Box 9435, Trenton, 08650 .......... (609) 587-3859
Ortho-Clinical Diagnostics, Inc. (H Q),
1001 U.S. Highway 202, P.O. Box 350, Raritan, 08869 .......... (908) 218-1300
Orthodox Baking Co., Inc., 555 Cortlandt St., Belleville, 07109 .......... (973) 844-9393
Ortho-Dynamics, Inc., 210 E. 16th St., Paterson, 07524 .......... (973) 742-4390
Orthofeet, Inc., 152-A Veterans Dr., Northvale, 07647 .......... (201) 767-6224
Orthologix, LLC, 2301 E. Evesham Rd., Ste. 303, Voorhees, 08043 .......... (856) 651-1510
Orycon Control Technology, Inc., 3407 Rose Ave., Ocean, 07712 .......... (732) 922-2400
Osborne Co., Inc., C. S., 125 Jersey St., Harrison, 07029 .......... (973) 483-3232
Osborn's Mill, 149 Yellowbrook Rd., Farmingdale, 07727 .......... (732) 751-0889
Oscar Printing Services, 549 Newark Ave., Jersey City, 07306 .......... (201) 659-1588
O'Shea's Printing Services Co., Inc., 483 Main St., Hackensack, 07601 .......... (201) 343-8668
Oshko International Corp., 115 Riverbend Dr., North Brunswick, 08902 .......... (732) 821-8222
OSI Laser Diode, Inc., 4 Olsen Ave., Edison, 08820 .......... (732) 549-9001
OSI Systems, Inc. see. .......... OSI Laser Diode, Inc., Edison
Ossur Americas, Inc., 1414 Metropolitan Ave., Paulsboro, 08066 .......... (856) 345-6000
Ostlund, Inc., Cal, 555 N. Michigan Ave., Kenilworth, 07033 .......... (908) 688-4466
O'Sullivan Communications, 1 Fairfield Crescent, West Caldwell, 07006 .......... (973) 227-5112
Other Orthodontic Co., Inc., 22 Gail Ct., Sparta, 07871 .......... (973) 383-8662
Oticon, Inc., 580 Howard Ave., Somerset, 08873 .......... (732) 560-1220
Otis Graphics, Inc., 290 Grant Ave., Lyndhurst, 07071 .......... (201) 438-7120
O&T-Suter Conservation, LLC, 96 Hillside Ave., Emerson, 07630 .......... (201) 265-0262
Our Name Is Mud, 15 Potter St., Ste. 1, Haddonfield, 08033 .......... (856) 375-2098
Our Name Is Mud.com see. .......... Our Name Is Mud, Haddonfield
Out Island Sport Yachts, Inc., 107 Edgewood Ave., West Berlin, 08091 .......... (609) 861-4000
† Outwater Plastics/Industries, Inc., 24 River Rd., P.O. Box 500, Bogota, 07603 .......... (201) 498-8750
Ovadia Corp., 101 E. Main St., 2nd Fl., Little Falls, 07424 .......... (973) 256-9200
Overhead Door Corp. see. .......... Burlington County Overhead Door Co., Inc., Burlington
† Owens & Minor, Inc., 1220 Forest Pkwy., Paulsboro, 08066 .......... (856) 423-9900
Owens Corning, 1249 Newark Tpke., Kearny, 07032 .......... (201) 998-5666
Owens Plastic Products, Inc., 393 Main St., P.O. Box 118, Cedarville, 08311 .......... (856) 447-3500
Oxberry, LLC, 180 Broad St., Carlstadt, 07072 .......... (201) 935-3000
Oxbow Tool & Die Corp., 44 Fremont Ter., Oak Ridge, 07438 .......... (973) 697-6647
Oxford Instruments America, Inc. see.Oxford Instruments Superconducting Technology, Inc., Carteret
Oxford Instruments Superconducting Technology, Inc.,
600 Milik St., Carteret, 07008 .......... (732) 541-1300
OxyVinyls, P.O. Box 411, Pedricktown, 08067 .......... (856) 299-8498
OxyVinyls L. P. see. .......... OxyVinyls, Pedricktown
Oystar USA, Inc., 523 Raritan Centre S.W., Edison, 08837 .......... (732) 343-7600
Ozer International, LLC, 145 Manchester Pl., Newark, 07104 .......... (973) 497-5656
Ozonia North America, LLC, 600 Willow Tree Rd., Leonia, 07605 .......... (201) 676-2525
† P & A Auto Parts, Inc., 396 Midland Ave., Garfield, 07026 .......... (973) 405-6068
† P & A Auto Parts, Inc., 530 River St., Hackensack, 07601 .......... (201) 843-7156
† P & A Crane & Hoist Co., 369 Reuter Ave., Elizabeth, 07202 .......... (908) 527-6990
P & E Technologies, Inc., 5140 W. Hurley Pond Rd., Farmingdale, 07727 .......... (732) 751-1515
P & J Machine Co., 261 Crosskeys Rd., P.O. Box 178, Berlin, 08009 .......... (856) 767-8441
★ P & M Computers, Inc., 97 Oakdene Ave., P.O. Box 270, Cliffside Park, 07010 .......... (201) 943-0353
P & R Fasteners, Inc., 325 Pierce St., Somerset, 08873 .......... (732) 302-3600
P & R Publishing Co., 1102 Marble Hill Rd., P.O. Box 817, Phillipsburg, 08865 .......... (908) 454-0505
P & S Blizzard Corp., 722 Madison Ave., Paterson, 07501 .......... (973) 523-1700
P A K Mfg., Inc., 704 S. 21st St., Irvington, 07111 .......... (973) 372-1090
P B A Printing, 170 Malvern St., Newark, 07105 .......... (973) 817-9712
P C R Technologies, Inc., 26 Chapin Rd., Unit 1111, Pine Brook, 07058 .......... (973) 882-0017
P D Q Electronics Components Co., Inc., 1113 Tiller Ave., Beachwood, 08722 .......... (732) 281-0025
P. F. Laboratories, Inc., 700 Union Blvd., Totowa, 07512 .......... (973) 256-3100
P I P Printing, 2960 Yorktowne Blvd., Brick, 08723 .......... (732) 255-1980
P I P Printing Of Livingston, 465 W. Mount Pleasant Ave., Livingston, 07039 .......... (973) 533-9330
P. J. Screening & Embroidery, 689 Jaques Ave., Rahway, 07065 .......... (732) 382-5183
P K M Panel Systems Corp., 43 Ferry St., P.O. Box 272, South River, 08882 .......... (732) 238-6760
★ P M C Diners, Inc., 56 Spruce St., Oakland, 07436 .......... (201) 337-6146
P M Z Tool, Inc., 321 Warren Ave., Stirling, 07980 .......... (908) 647-2125
P Q Corp., 2 Paddock St., Avenel, 07001 .......... (732) 750-9040
P T L Sheet Metal, Inc., 70 Davies Ave., Dumont, 07628 .......... (201) 501-8700
Pabst Enterprises Equipment Co., Inc.,
676 Pennsylvania Ave., Elizabeth, 07201 .......... (908) 353-2880
† PAC Tool & Supply Co., Inc.,
420 Paterson Ave., P.O. Box 7482, East Rutherford, 07073 .......... (201) 933-8550
Pace Packaging Corp., 3 Sperry Rd., Fairfield, 07004 .......... (973) 227-1040
Paci Press, Inc., 25 First St., Rear Bldg., Lodi, 07644 .......... (973) 478-6550
Pacicco & Co. Jewelers, 331 Broad Ave., Leonia, 07605 .......... (201) 947-1106
Pacific Coast Systems, LLC, 4 Fox Hill Ln., Asbury, 08802 .......... (908) 735-9955
Pacira Pharmaceuticals, Inc. (H Q), 5 Sylvan Way, Parsippany, 07054 .......... (973) 254-3560
Package Development Co., Inc., 100 Round Hill Dr., Ste. 8, Rockaway, 07866 .......... (973) 983-8500

Packaging Consultants Assocs.,
7300 N. Crescent Blvd., Unit 14, Pennsauken, 08110 .......... (856) 488-0277
Packaging Corp. Of America see.Packaging Corp. Of America, Cranbury Creative Design Center, Marlton
Packaging Corp. Of America, Cranbury Creative Design Center,
8 E. Stow Rd., Ste. 100, Marlton, 08053 .......... (856) 596-5020
Packaging Graphics, Inc., 435 Commerce Ln., P.O. Box 160, West Berlin, 08091 .......... (856) 767-9000
Packaging Machinery & Equipment Co., 181 Watson Ave., West Orange, 07052 .......... (973) 325-2418
Packaging Unlimited, Inc., 17 Chelten Way, Bldg. A, Trenton, 08638 .......... (609) 394-9400
Packet Media Group see. .......... Princeton Packet, Inc., Princeton
Packetstorm Communications, Inc., 20 Meridian Rd., Eatontown, 07724 .......... (732) 544-2434
Pacon Mfg., Corp., 400 Pierce St., Somerset, 08873 .......... (732) 764-9070
Pacor, Inc., 333 Rising Sun Rd., Bordentown, 08505 .......... (609) 324-1100
Pafa Training Center, Inc.,
1301 W. Forest Grove Rd., Bldg. 3-C, Vineland, 08360 .......... (856) 696-1414
Pages Printing & Graphics, 300 N. Route 17, Paramus, 07652 .......... (201) 261-3883
Pageworks, LLC, P.O. Box 892, Murray Hill, 07974 .......... (908) 665-0607
Paglia & Son, Inc., D., 280 Sheffield St., Mountainside, 07092 .......... (908) 654-5999
Pahco Machine, Inc., 572 Whitehead Rd., Ste. 101, Trenton, 08619 .......... (609) 587-1188
Paige Electric Co. L. P., 1160 Springfield Rd., P.O. Box 368, Union, 07083 .......... (908) 687-7810
Paige Packaging, 1 Paul Kohner Pl., Elmwood Park, 07407 .......... (973) 483-0505
Painting, Inc., 60 Luening St., South Hackensack, 07606 .......... (201) 489-6565
Painton Studios, Inc., 299 U.S. Highway 22, Ste. 21, Green Brook, 08812 .......... (732) 302-0200
Palayekar Cos., Inc., 101 Interchange Plz., Ste. 105, Cranbury, 08512 .......... (609) 426-0564
† Palermo Supply, 1819 Central Ave., Ship Bottom, 08008 .......... (609) 494-0343
Palisades Dental, LLC, 111 Cedar Ln., P.O. Box 5419, Englewood, 07631 .......... (201) 569-0050
Pallet Cos. see. .......... IFCO Systems, Burlington
† Pallet Express, Inc., 70 Caroline Ave., Clifton, 07011 .......... (973) 633-5858
Pallmann Industries, Inc., 820 Bloomfield Ave., Clifton, 07012 .......... (973) 471-1450
Palma, Inc., 14 Salter Pl., P.O. Box 2539, Bloomfield, 07003 .......... (800) 336-7256
Palmer Asphalt Co., Inc., 196 W. 5th St., P.O. Box 58, Bayonne, 07002 .......... (201) 339-0855
Palmer Electronics, Inc., 156 Belmont Ave., Garfield, 07026 .......... (973) 772-5900
Palmetto Adhesives Co. see. .......... Palmetto Adhesives Co., Inc., Bridgeton
Palmetto Adhesives Co., Inc., 1785 Burlington Rd., Bridgeton, 08302 .......... (856) 451-0405
Palmonari, Inc., J. V., 1234 Tuckahoe Rd., P.O. Box 68, Milmay, 08340 .......... (609) 476-2642
Palmyra Pants Co., Inc., 9370 Route 130 N., Pennsauken, 08110 .......... (856) 662-0398
Palnar see. .......... Palayekar Cos., Inc., Cranbury
Pamarco Global Graphics see. .......... Pamarco Technologies, Inc., Roselle
Pamarco Global Graphics, Imaging Div., 1 Roto Ave., Palmyra, 08065 .......... (856) 829-4585
Pamarco Technologies, Inc. see. .......... Pamarco Global Graphics, Imaging Div., Palmyra
Pamarco Technologies, Inc., 235 E. 11th Ave., Roselle, 07203 .......... (908) 241-1200
Pamco Printers & Stationers, P.O. Box 567, Hopewell, 08525 .......... (609) 309-5025
Pan American Coffee Co., LLC, 500 16th St., Hoboken, 07030 .......... (201) 963-2329
Pan Technology, 117 Moonachie Ave., Carlstadt, 07072 .......... (201) 438-7878
Panasonic Corp. Of North America (H Q), 2 River Front Plz., Newark, 07102 .......... (201) 348-7500
Panasonic Industrial Devices Sales Co. Of America (H Q),
2 River Front Plz., 7th Fl., Newark, 07102 .......... (908) 464-3550
Pandrol USA L. P., 501 Sharptown Rd., P.O. Box 367, Bridgeport, 08014 .......... (856) 467-3227
★ Panel Components & Systems, Inc., 149 Main St., Stanhope, 07874 .......... (973) 448-9400
Panelcraft, Inc., 105 W. Dewey Ave., Bldg. C, Unit 16, Wharton, 07885 .......... (973) 895-2700
Panera Bread Co., Inc. see. .......... Panera Bread Co., LLC, Fairfield
Panera Bread Co., LLC, 5 E. Evans St., Fairfield, 07004 .......... (973) 276-0250
Panline USA, Inc., 251 Union St., Northvale, 07647 .......... (201) 750-8010
PanPac, LLC, 212 N. Virginia Ave., Carneys Point, 08069 .......... (856) 376-3576
Pantina Cosmetics, Inc., 30 Henry St., Teterboro, 07608 .......... (201) 288-7767
Pantone LLC, 590 Commerce Blvd., Carlstadt, 07072 .......... (201) 935-5500
Panurgy OEM, 701 Ford Rd., Rockaway, 07866 .......... (973) 625-4056
† Panza & Sons, Ltd., A., 141 Fieldcrest Ave., Edison, 08837 .......... (732) 225-1314
Panzarotti Tarantini Pizza, Inc.,
2060 Springdale Rd., Ste. 300, Cherry Hill, 08003 .......... (856) 489-0026
Papailias Co., Inc., J. G., 245 Pegasus Ave., Northvale, 07647 .......... (201) 767-4027
Papco Industries, Inc., 245 Pegasus Ave., Northvale, 07647 .......... (201) 767-9051
Paper Mart, Inc., 151 Ridgedale Ave., East Hanover, 07936 .......... (973) 884-2505
Paper Tube & Core, Inc., 239 Lindbergh Pl., Paterson, 07503 .......... (973) 977-8823
Paperboard Products Co., 21 Shafer Pl., Hackensack, 07601 .......... (201) 440-1600
PaperClip Communications, Inc., 125 Paterson Ave., Little Falls, 07424 .......... (973) 256-1333
Papertec, Inc., 141 Lanza Ave., Bldg. 29, Garfield, 07026 .......... (862) 591-1100
Papetti's Hygrade Egg Products, Inc., 877 North Ave. E., Elizabeth, 07201 .......... (908) 282-7140
Papp Iron Works, Inc., 950 S. 2nd St., P.O. Box 3149, Plainfield, 07063 .......... (908) 731-1000
Papson Printing Corp., 115 Hudson St., Hackensack, 07601 .......... (201) 342-2860
Par Code Symbology, Inc., 119 Harrison Ave., P.O. Box 87, Roseland, 07068 .......... (973) 618-0550
Par Pharmaceutical Cos., Inc., 300 Tice Blvd., Woodcliff Lake, 07677 .......... (201) 802-4000
Par Pharmaceutical Cos., Inc. see. .......... Strativa Pharmaceuticals (H Q), Woodcliff Lake
Par Sheet Metal, Inc., 220 W. 1st Ave., Ste. 2, Roselle, 07203 .......... (908) 241-2477
Paradigm Packaging, LLC (H Q), 141 N. 5th St., Saddle Brook, 07663 .......... (201) 507-0900
Paragon Printing Shop, 600 Columbia Ave., Millville, 08332 .......... (856) 825-2497
Paragon Steel & Tool Co., Inc., 339 Bergen Ave., Kearny, 07032 .......... (201) 997-1676
Paramount Bakeries, Inc., 61 Davenport Ave., Newark, 07107 .......... (973) 482-6638
Paramount Cosmetics, Inc., 93 Entin Rd., Ste. 4, Clifton, 07014 .......... (973) 472-2323
Paramount Fixture Corp., 175 Mount Pleasant Ave., Newark, 07104 .......... (973) 485-1585
Paramount Metal Finishing Co., 1515 W. Elizabeth Ave., Linden, 07036 .......... (908) 862-0772
Paramount Products, Inc., 1104 Industrial Pkwy., Brick, 08724 .......... (732) 458-9200
Paravista, Inc., Imaging & Printing, 1055 Centennial Ave., Piscataway, 08854 .......... (732) 752-1222
Parenta & Sons Enterprises, Inc., 85 Fulton St., Unit 9-B, Boonton, 07005 .......... (973) 334-9266
Paris Art Label Co., Inc. see. .......... Princeton Label Co., Robbinsville
Paris Business Products, Inc., 800 Highland Dr., Westampton, 08060 .......... (609) 265-9200
Paris Lace, 1500 Main Ave., Clifton, 07011 .......... (973) 478-9035
Pariser Industries, Inc., 91 Michigan Ave., Paterson, 07503 .......... (973) 569-9090
Park Avenue Printing, LLC, 2001 S. Broad St., Trenton, 08610 .......... (609) 989-8022
Park Plus, Inc., 480 Main Ave., Ste. 1, Wallington, 07057 .......... (973) 574-8020
Park Printing Services, Inc.,
7300 N. Crescent Blvd., Unit 21, Pennsauken, 08110 .......... (856) 675-1600
† Park Pumps & Controls, Inc.,
950 Mount Holly Rd., Ste. B, Edgewater Park, 08010 .......... (609) 871-0944
Park Roofing & Sheet Metal Co., Inc.,
427 Whitehead Ave., Ste. 1, South River, 08882 .......... (732) 257-4570
Park Sales, P.O. Box 586, Point Pleasant Beach, 08742 .......... (732) 899-0684
Park Steel & Iron Co., 82 Iron St., Toms River, 08753 .......... (732) 349-2400
Park Steel & Iron Co. (H Q), 9 Evergreen Ave., Neptune City, 07753 .......... (732) 775-7500
† Park Stein, Inc., 613 Route 46 E., P.O. Box 2399, Clifton, 07013 .......... (973) 340-3535
Parkeon, Inc., 40 Twosome Dr., Ste. 7, Moorestown, 08057 .......... (856) 234-8000
Parker Chomerics, 135 Bryant Ave., Cranford, 07016 .......... (908) 272-5500

ALPHABETICAL

C44 © Copyright 2015 Manufacturers' News, Inc. ALPHABETICAL SECTION

Parker Hannifin Corp.,
45 Route 46 E., Unit 602, P.O. Box 778, Pine Brook, 07058 .... (973) 575-4844
Parker Hannifin Corporation see. .... Parker Chomerics, Cranford
Parker Hannifin Corporation see. .... Parker Hannifin Corp., Pine Brook
Parker Laboratories, Inc., 286 Eldridge Rd., Fairfield, 07004 .... (973) 276-9500
Parker3d, 1325 Terrill Rd., Scotch Plains, 07076 .... (908) 322-5552
Parkway Plastics, Inc., 561 Stelton Rd., Piscataway, 08854 .... (732) 752-3636
Parkway Printing, Inc., 52 N. Main St., Ste. C-11, Marlboro, 07746 .... (732) 308-0300
Parkway Wire Frame Co., Inc., 249 Astor St., Newark, 07114 .... (973) 242-5220
Parkway-Kew Corp., 2095 Excelsior Ave., North Brunswick, 08902 .... (732) 398-2100
Parlin Precision Products, Inc., 999 Route 9, Parlin, 08859 .... (732) 727-6111
Par-Metal, Inc., 29 Ewing Ave., North Arlington, 07031 .... (201) 955-0800
Parr Leadburning Co., J. W., 87 Parkway, Little Falls, 07424 .... (973) 256-8093
Parrish Sign Co., Inc., 2242 S. Delsea Dr., Vineland, 08360 .... (856) 696-4040
Parsells Printing, Inc., 280 Main Ave., Passaic, 07055 .... (973) 473-2700
Parsell's Welding, Inc., 354 Route 580, Blawenburg, 08504 .... (609) 466-1930
Parsons Cabinetry, Inc., 80 George St., Paterson, 07503 .... (973) 279-4954
Part-Rite, Inc., 19 Butler Ave., Bayville, 08721 .... (732) 269-5000
Par-Troy Sheet Metal & Conditioning, LLC, 122 Clinton Rd., Fairfield, 07004 .... (973) 227-1150
† Parts Cleaning Technologies, LLC,
835 Industrial Hwy., Ste. 1, Cinnaminson, 08077 .... (856) 786-8686
† Parts Distributors, LLC, 901 N. Lenola Rd., P.O. Box 832, Moorestown, 08057 .... (856) 778-1400
Parwan Electronics Corp., 1230 State Route 34, Aberdeen, 07747 .... (732) 290-1900
pasemedical.com see. .... Parenta & Sons Enterprises, Inc., Boonton
Passaic Color & Chemicals Co. see. .... Royce Assocs., L. P., Paterson
Passaic County Welders, Inc., 100 Parish Dr., Wayne, 07470 .... (973) 696-1200
Passaic Leather Coat, Inc., 51 Market St., Passaic, 07055 .... (973) 777-4026
Passaic Rubber Co., Inc., 45 Demarest Dr., Wayne, 07470 .... (973) 696-9500
Pat Publications,
1165 Marlkress Rd., Ste. M, P.O. Box 1536, Cherry Hill, 08003 .... (856) 424-0158
PatchAmp, Inc., 20 E. Kennedy St., Hackensack, 07601 .... (201) 457-1504
Patel Printing Plus Corp., 1036 Commerce Ave., Union, 07083 .... (908) 964-6422
Paterson Monuments Co., Inc., 317 Totowa Ave., Paterson, 07502 .... (973) 942-0727
Paterson Packaging, 269 Wilson St., Saddle Brook, 07663 .... (201) 398-9693
Paterson Pickle Co., 285 4th Ave., Paterson, 07514 .... (973) 523-1000
Paterson Sheet Metal Works, Inc., 320 Wabash Ave., Paterson, 07503 .... (973) 345-4182
Paterson Stamp Works, 1015 Paulison Ave., Clifton, 07011 .... (973) 478-5600
Patriarch Partners, LLC see. .... Acme International Enterprises, Inc., Saddle Brook
Patriarch Partners, LLC see. .... Dana Classic Fragrances, Inc. (H Q), Saddle Brook
Patrick J. Kelly Drums, Inc., 1810 River Ave., Camden, 08105 .... (856) 963-1795
Patriot American Solutions, LLC, 5 Astro Pl., Rockaway, 07866 .... (973) 586-2717
Patriot Marine Fabricating, 708-4 Old Shore Rd., Forked River, 08731 .... (609) 693-5542
Patriot Pickle, 20 Edison Dr., Wayne, 07470 .... (973) 709-9487
Patty-O-Matic, Inc., Route 547, P.O. Box 404, Farmingdale, 07727 .... (732) 938-2757
Patwin Plastics, Inc., 2300 E. Linden Ave., Linden, 07036 .... (908) 486-6600
Paul Dyeing Co., 626 Orange St., Newark, 07107 .... (973) 484-1121
Paulaur Corp., 105 Melrich Rd., Cranbury, 08512 .... (609) 395-8844
Paulist Press, 997 MacArthur Blvd., Mahwah, 07430 .... (201) 825-7300
Paul-Mark Printing, 37 Stokes St., Freehold, 07728 .... (732) 462-9110
Paul's Custom Awards & Trophy, Inc., 200 White Horse Pike, Barrington, 08007 .... (856) 547-7777
Paulsboro Refining Co., 800 Billingsport Rd., Paulsboro, 08066 .... (856) 224-6000
Paverart, LLC, 2512 Egg Harbor Rd., Ste. C, Lindenwold, 08021 .... (856) 783-7000
Pazera Assocs., Inc. see. .... Pazera Cabinets Door, Old Bridge
Pazera Cabinets Door, 3160 Bordentown Ave., Old Bridge, 08857 .... (732) 727-1600
PBF Energy Partners L. P. see. .... Paulsboro Refining Co., Paulsboro
PBF Energy Partners L. P. see. .... Paulsboro Refining Co., Paulsboro
PBF Energy Partners L. P. (H Q), 1 Sylvan Way, Parsippany, 07054 .... (973) 455-7500
PBL Assay Science, 131 Ethel Rd. W., Ste. 6, Piscataway, 08854 .... (732) 777-9123
PBL Biomedical Labs * PBL InterferonSource see. .... PBL Assay Science, Piscataway
† PBM Supply Co., Inc., 88 Cannonball Rd., P.O. Box 351, Pompton Lakes, 07442 .... (973) 839-0050
† PC Tan, Inc., 1040 Wilt Ave., Ridgefield, 07657 .... (201) 943-6100
PCG see. .... Premium Color Graphics, Inc., Carlstadt
PCSI see. .... Princeton Computer Support, Inc., Princeton
PDEC, Inc., 2101 Atlantic Ave., Manasquan, 08736 .... (732) 223-5995
PD-LD, Inc., 30-B Pennington-Hopewell Rd., Pennington, 08534 .... (609) 564-7900
PDQ Plastics, Inc., 7 Hook Rd., P.O. Box 1001, Bayonne, 07002 .... (201) 823-0270
Peace Medical, Inc., 50 S. Center St., Ste. 11, Orange, 07050 .... (973) 672-2120
Peach Boutique, The, 1139 E. Jersey St., Ste. 319, Elizabeth, 07201 .... (908) 351-0739
Peacock Printing Products, Inc., 48 Woodbine St., Bergenfield, 07621 .... (201) 385-5585
PeaPodz, LLC, 79 S. Central Ave., Ramsey, 07446 .... (201) 362-8883
Pearce Welding Co., LLC, 155 S. River St., Hackensack, 07601 .... (201) 488-0434
Pearle Vision, Inc., 1278 Hooper Ave., Toms River, 08753 .... (732) 505-0533
Pearson Education, Inc., 1 Lake St., Upper Saddle River, 07458 .... (201) 236-7000
Pearson Education, Inc. see. .... Pearson Technology, Old Tappan
Pearson Technology, 200 Old Tappan Rd., Old Tappan, 07675 .... (201) 767-5000
PEC see. .... Parwan Electronics Corp., Aberdeen
Pecata Enterprises, Inc., 18 Market St., Paterson, 07501 .... (973) 523-5866
Pechter's Bakery see. .... R. P. Baking Co., Harrison
Pedeco Printing, Inc., 12 Summers Dr., Jackson, 08527 .... (732) 363-0510
Pedestal Pallet Co., 777 N. Avenue Ext., P.O. Box 450, Dunellen, 08812 .... (732) 968-7488
PediatRx, Inc. (H Q), 90 Fairmount Rd. W., P.O. Box 423, Califon, 07830 .... (908) 975-0753
Pedrick Tool & Machine Co., 1518 Bannard St., P.O. Box 190, Riverton, 08077 .... (856) 829-8900
Pee Wee Molding Corp., 240 Circle Dr. N., Piscataway, 08854 .... (732) 469-0200
Peek-A-Boo Toys, 9040 Pensauken Hwy., Pennsauken, 08110 .... (856) 317-9100
Peerless Coatings, LLC, 220-A Goffle Rd., Hawthorne, 07506 .... (973) 427-8771
Peerless Concrete Products, Inc., 246 Main St., Butler, 07405 .... (973) 838-3060
Peerless Dust Killer * Harwal Sales * Paxon Manufacturing see. .... Banner Chemical Corp., Orange
Peerless Umbrella Co., Inc., 427 Ferry St., Newark, 07105 .... (973) 578-4900
PEG see. .... Precision Electronic Glass, Inc., Vineland
Pegasus Group Publishing, 188 Route 10 W., Ste. 307, East Hanover, 07936 .... (973) 884-9100
Pegasus Home Fashions, Inc.,
107 Trumbull St., Bldg. G-1, P.O. Box 9030, Elizabeth, 07206 .... (908) 965-1919
Pegasus Products, Inc., 19 Readington Rd., Somerville, 08876 .... (908) 707-1122
Pegasystems, Inc., 111 Town Square Pl., Jersey City, 07310 .... (201) 239-2300
PeggNet Computers, LLC, 4 E. Main St., Ste. 3, Mendham, 07945 .... (973) 543-1222
Pekay Industries, Inc., Southard Ave., P.O. Box 559, Farmingdale, 07727 .... (732) 938-2722
Pella Corp. see. .... Pella Windows & Doors, West Caldwell
Pella Windows & Doors, 4 Dedrick Pl., West Caldwell, 07006 .... (973) 575-0200
Pem All Fire Extinguisher Corp.,
39-A Myrtle St., P.O. Box 586, Cranford, 07016 .... (908) 276-0211
Pemberton Fabricators, Inc., 30 Indel Ave., P.O. Box 227, Rancocas, 08073 .... (609) 267-0922
Pendergast Signs, 566 Charlestown Rd., Hampton, 08827 .... (908) 735-9295
PendoTECH see. .... Mayfair Technology, LLC, Princeton
Pendulum Audio Systems, Inc., P.O. Box 339, Gillette, 07933 .... (908) 665-9333
Penetone Corp., 700 Gotham Pkwy., Ste. 2, Carlstadt, 07072 .... (201) 567-3000
Penetone Corp. (H Q), 1000 Herrontown Rd., Ste. 2, Princeton, 08540 .... (609) 921-0501
Pengad, Inc., 55 Oak St., P.O. Box 99, Bayonne, 07002 .... (201) 436-5625
Penn Color, Inc., 30 Kohner Pl., Elmwood Park, 07407 .... (201) 791-5100
Penn Jersey Building Materials, Inc., 247 Cedar Swamp Rd., Bridgeport, 08014 .... (856) 467-0400
Penn Jersey Building Materials, Inc.,
2819 Fire Rd., Egg Harbor Township, 08234 .... (609) 485-0068
Penn Jersey Paint Co., Inc., 1255 McCarter Hwy., Newark, 07104 .... (973) 482-5430
Penn Jersey Press, P.O. Box 1103, Voorhees, 08043 .... (856) 627-2200
Penn Jersey Weekend Directionals, 208 W. Clinton Ave., Oaklyn, 08107 .... (856) 858-8888
Penn Metal Finishing Co., Inc., 700 Jacksonville Rd., Burlington, 08016 .... (609) 387-3400
† Penn Supply, Inc., 618 E. State St., Trenton, 08609 .... (609) 394-1151
Penn Tool Co., 1776 Springfield Ave., Maplewood, 07040 .... (973) 761-4343
Pennington Furnace Supply, Inc., 6 Brookside Ave., Pennington, 08534 .... (609) 737-2500
Pennington Printers, Inc., 21 Burd St., Pennington, 08534 .... (609) 737-0650
† Pennock Co., 7135 Colonial Ln., Pennsauken, 08109 .... (215) 492-7900
Penny Plate, LLC (H Q), 14000 Horizon Way, Ste. 300, Mount Laurel, 08054 .... (856) 429-7583
Penny Press see. .... Merchant Street Printer, LLC, Audubon
Pennysaver see. .... Middlesex Publications, Inc., North Brunswick
Penta Glass Industries, Inc., 71 Hepworth Pl., Garfield, 07026 .... (973) 478-2110
Pentax Medical Co. see. .... PENTAX Of America, Inc., Montvale
PENTAX Of America, Inc. see. .... KayPENTAX, Montvale
PENTAX Of America, Inc., 3 Paragon Dr., Ste. 1, Montvale, 07645 .... (201) 571-2300
Pentek, Inc., 1 Park Way, 2nd Fl., Upper Saddle River, 07458 .... (201) 818-5900
Peoples Bakery, Inc. see. .... Italian Peoples Bakery, Inc., Trenton
Peoples Education, Inc., 299 Market St., P.O. Box 513, Saddle Brook, 07663 .... (201) 712-0090
Peoplevision, Inc., 311 E. 1st Ave., Bldg. A, Roselle, 07203 .... (973) 509-2056
Pepco Mfg. Co. see. .... Fiore Skylights, Inc., Somerdale
Pepco Mfg. Co., 210 E. Evergreen Ave., P.O. Box 160, Somerdale, 08083 .... (856) 783-3700
Pepsi Beverages Co. see. .... Beverage Distribution Center, Inc., Pennsauken
Pepsi Beverages Company, 2200 New Brunswick Ave., Piscataway, 08854 .... (732) 424-3000
PepsiCo, Inc. see. .... Beverage Distribution Center, Inc., Pennsauken
Pepsi-Cola & National Brand Beverages Ltd.,
8191 N. U.S. Route 130, Pennsauken, 08110 .... (856) 665-6200
Pequod Communications, Inc., 743 Alexander Rd., Ste. 15, Princeton, 08540 .... (609) 951-0300
Peragallo Pipe Organ Co., 306 Buffalo Ave., Paterson, 07503 .... (973) 684-3414
Perfect Finishing, Inc. see. .... Glue-Fold, Inc., Div. Of Perfect Finishing, Inc., Clifton
Perfect Finishing, Inc., 40 Webro Rd., Clifton, 07012 .... (973) 472-7400
Perfect Pearl Co., Inc., 100 State St., Moonachie, 07074 .... (201) 705-5200
Perfect Printing, Inc., 1533 Glen Ave., Moorestown, 08057 .... (856) 787-1877
Perfect Remedy Packaging, Inc., 224 Washington St., Perth Amboy, 08861 .... (732) 697-0055
Perfectone Mold Co., 277 New York Ave., Jersey City, 07307 .... (201) 798-5353
Per-Fil Industries, Inc., 407 Adams St., P.O. Box 9, Riverside, 08075 .... (856) 461-5700
Performance Food Group, Inc. see. .... Performance Food Group-AFI Foodservice, Elizabeth
† Performance Food Group-AFI Foodservice, 1 Ikea Dr., Elizabeth, 07207 .... (908) 629-1800
Performance Industries, Inc., 51 Tucker St., Trenton, 08618 .... (609) 392-1450
Perilstein Glass, 285 Howe Ave., P.O. Box 84, Passaic, 07055 .... (973) 777-3610
Perkins Co., Inc., P. W., 221 Commissioners Pike, Woodstown, 08098 .... (856) 769-3525
Perlen Steel Corp., 265 Passaic St., Newark, 07104 .... (973) 485-5522
Perma Graphics, Inc., 25 Graphic Pl., Moonachie, 07074 .... (201) 814-1200
Perma Pure, LLC, 8 Executive Dr., Toms River, 08755 .... (732) 244-0010
Permabond, LLC (H Q), 223 Churchill Ave., Somerset, 08873 .... (732) 868-1372
PermaDur Industries see. .... SISSCO Material Handling, Hillsborough
Permadur Industries, Inc., 186 U.S. Highway 206 S., Hillsborough, 08844 .... (908) 359-9767
Permalith Plastics, LLC, 6901 N. Crescent Blvd., Pennsauken, 08110 .... (856) 488-8000
† Perrotti Sales, 19 Woodside Ln., Flemington, 08822 .... (908) 806-8899
★ Perrulli's Custom Meats, 1889 Route 9, Ste. 45, Toms River, 08755 .... (732) 244-0470
Perry Products Corp., 25 Hainesport-Mount Laurel Rd., Hainesport, 08036 .... (609) 267-1600
Perry's, 11 N. 5th Ave., Long Branch, 07740 .... (732) 222-5040
Personalized Paraphernalia, 22 Division St., Somerville, 08876 .... (908) 526-0602
Pertech Inks Corp., 140 Grand St., Carlstadt, 07072 .... (908) 354-1700
Peter J. Morley LLC, 21 Village Ct., Hazlet, 07730 .... (732) 264-0010
Peter Lumber Co., 300 E. Washington Ave., P.O. Box 32, Pleasantville, 08232 .... (609) 641-9000
Peterson & Marsh Metals * Jersey Machine & Tool see. .... KWG Industries, LLC, Hillsborough
Peterson Bros. Mfg., 10 Baekeland Ave., Middlesex, 08846 .... (732) 271-8240
Peterson Stamping & Mfg. Co.,
75 N. Michigan Ave., P.O. Box 190, Kenilworth, 07033 .... (908) 241-0900
Peterson Steel Rule Die Corp., 35 Broad St., Carlstadt, 07072 .... (201) 935-6180
Petitts Ink Corp., 1745 State Route 10, Ste. 4, Morris Plains, 07950 .... (973) 984-2400
Petra System, 1 Cragwood Rd., Ste. 303, South Plainfield, 07080 .... (908) 462-5200
Petro Extrusion Technologies, Inc., 490 South Ave., Garwood, 07027 .... (908) 789-3338
Petro Marine see. .... A&M Industrial, Inc., Linden
Petro Packaging Co., Inc., 16 Quine St., P.O. Box 546, Cranford, 07016 .... (908) 272-4054
Petro Plastics, 450 South Ave., P.O. Box 167, Garwood, 07027 .... (908) 789-1200
Petronio Shoe Products Corp., 305 Cortlandt St., Belleville, 07109 .... (973) 751-7579
Pettit Paint see. .... Kop-Coat, Inc., Rockaway
Pfingst & Co., Inc., 105 Snyder Rd., P.O. Box 377, South Plainfield, 07080 .... (908) 561-6400
Pflaumer Bros., 1008 Whitehead Road Ext., Ewing, 08638 .... (609) 883-4610
★ Pharma Press, Inc., 490 W. 1st Ave., Roselle, 07203 .... (908) 241-4110
Pharmaceutical Innovations, 897 Frelinghuysen Ave., Newark, 07114 .... (973) 242-2901
Pharmachem Laboratories, Inc. see. .... MPT Delivery Systems, Inc., Paterson
Pharmachem Laboratories, Inc., 265 Harrison Ave., Kearny, 07032 .... (201) 246-1000
Pharmachem Laboratories, Inc., 130 Wesley St., South Hackensack, 07606 .... (201) 343-3611
Pharmacy Purchasing & Products * Medical Lab Management Magazine see. Ridgewood Medical Media, LLC, Ridgewood
Pharmakon Corp., 2200 Wallace Blvd., Unit C, P.O. Box 217, Cinnaminson, 08077 .... (856) 829-3161
Pharmaseq, Inc., 11 Deerpark Dr., Ste. 104, Monmouth Junction, 08852 .... (732) 355-0100
PharMEDium, 43 Distribution Blvd., Edison, 08817 .... (732) 287-8655
PharMEDium Services, LLC see. .... PharMEDium, Edison
Phelps Mfg., LLC, 567 Brass Castle Rd., Oxford, 07863 .... (908) 453-2288
Phibro Animal Health Corp.,
300 Frank W. Burr Blvd., Stn. 21, Glenpointe Center East, 3rd Fl., Teaneck, 07666 .... (201) 329-7300
Phibro Animal Health Corp. see. .... Phibro-Tech, Inc., Teaneck
Phibro-Tech, Inc.,
300 Frank W. Burr Blvd., Ste. 21, Glenpointe Center East, 3rd Fl., Teaneck, 07666 .... (201) 329-7300
Philadelphia Rapid Transit, 2650 Haddonfield Rd., Pennsauken, 08110 .... (856) 488-0202
Philadelphia Sign Co., 707 W. Spring Garden St., Palmyra, 08065 .... (856) 829-1460
Philadelphia Soapstone Co., 1001 Lower Landing Rd., Ste. 103, Blackwood, 08012 .... (856) 232-7627
Philcorr, LLC, 2317 Almond Rd., Vineland, 08360 .... (856) 205-0557
Philee, LLC see. .... Shore Sign & Banner, Toms River
Philips Healthcare see. .... Philips Respironics, Somerset

© Copyright 2015 Manufacturers' News, Inc.


Philips Lifeline see. ........ Philips Lighting North America, Somerset
Philips Lighting North America, 200 Franklin Square Dr., Somerset, 08873 ........ (732) 563-3000
Philips Lighting North America see. ........ Philips Luminaries NA, Union
† Philips Luminaries NA, 2345 Vauxhall Rd., P.O. Box 129, Union, 07083 ........ (908) 964-7000
Philips Respironics, 200 Franklin Square Dr., Somerset, 08873 ........ (732) 563-3400
Phillips 66 Co. see. ........ Phillips 66 Bayway Refinery, Linden
Phillips Enterprises, Inc.,
3600 Sunset Ave., P.O. Box 2286, Asbury Park, 07712 ........ (732) 493-3191
Phillips Ostroff see. ........ Beauticraft Slipcover Co., Voorhees
Phillips Precision, Inc., 7 Paul Kohner Pl., Elmwood Park, 07407 ........ (201) 797-8820
Phillips Safety Products, Inc., 123 Lincoln Blvd., Middlesex, 08846 ........ (732) 356-1493
Phillips Scientific, 31 Industrial Ave., Ste. 1, Mahwah, 07430 ........ (201) 934-8015
Phillips 66 Bayway Refinery, 1400 Park Ave., Linden, 07036 ........ (908) 523-5000
Phillipsburg Marble Co., 1 Marble Hill Rd., P.O. Box 172, Phillipsburg, 08865 ........ (908) 859-3435
Phil-Lu, Inc., 1206 Herbert Ave., Ocean, 07712 ........ (732) 531-6338
Phil-Mar Industries, 1800 Copewood St., Camden, 08103 ........ (856) 966-0931
Phil's Sign Shop, 55 Cutters Dock Rd., Woodbridge, 07095 ........ (732) 726-1555
Phoenix Business Forms, Inc., 2231 N. East Blvd., Vineland, 08360 ........ (856) 691-2266
Phoenix Chemical, Inc., 60 4th St., Somerville, 08876 ........ (908) 707-0232
Phoenix Down Corp., 85 US Highway 46, Totowa, 07512 ........ (973) 812-8100
Phoenix Friction Products, Inc., 276-278 Lincoln Blvd., Middlesex, 08846 ........ (732) 667-7937
Phoenix Glass, LLC, 615 Alvine Rd., Pittsgrove, 08318 ........ (856) 692-0100
Phoenix Industries, LLC, 105 W. Dewey Ave., P.O. Box 416, Wharton, 07885 ........ (973) 366-4199
Phoenix Machine, 4 Gold Mine Rd., Flanders, 07836 ........ (973) 691-8029
Phoenix Machine Rebuilders see. ........ Phoenix Machine, Flanders
Phoenix Mfg., Inc., 1306 Brielle Ave., Ocean, 07712 ........ (732) 380-1666
Phoenix Precision, Inc., 2963 Route 23, Newfoundland, 07435 ........ (973) 208-8877
Phoenix Resins, Inc., 602 Union Landing Rd., Cinnaminson, 08077 ........ (856) 303-9245
Phoenix Systems, LLC, 39 Morningside Ave., North Haledon, 07508 ........ (201) 857-3901
Phoenix Tool & Machine, Inc., 1044 Industrial Dr., Unit 5, West Berlin, 08091 ........ (856) 753-5565
Photo Art Stencil & Sign Corp., 701 17th Ave., P.O. Box 127, Lake Como, 07719 ........ (732) 681-7300
Photon Technology International, 3880 Park Ave., Edison, 08820 ........ (732) 494-8660
Photothrow, Inc., 280 N. Midland Ave., Bldg. J-1, Saddle Brook, 07663 ........ (855) 645-4438
PHT Aerospace, LLC, 230 West Pkwy., Ste. 2, Pompton Plains, 07444 ........ (973) 831-1230
Physician's Weekly, 180 Mount Airy Rd., Ste. 102, Basking Ridge, 07920 ........ (908) 766-0402
Physiotherapy Assocs., Inc. see. ........ Prosthetic Orthotic Solutions International, Marlton
Physitemp Instruments, Inc., 154 Huron Ave., Clifton, 07013 ........ (973) 779-5577
PhytoCeuticals, Inc., 37 Midland Ave., Elmwood Park, 07407 ........ (201) 791-2255
★ PI Magazine, 4400 U.S. Highway 9, Ste. 1000, Freehold, 07728 ........ (732) 308-3800
PI/Acton * Princeton Instruments/Acton see. ........ Princeton Instruments, Trenton
PIC Corp., 1101 W. Elizabeth Ave., P.O. Box 4258, Linden, 07036 ........ (908) 862-7977
Picasso Lighting Industries, LLC, 46 Sellers St., Kearny, 07032 ........ (201) 246-8188
Pickle King, 220 Ellison St., Paterson, 07505 ........ (973) 977-2095
Pickle-Licious, 384 Cedar Ln., Teaneck, 07666 ........ (201) 833-0100
Pictorial Offset Corporation, 111 Amor Ave., Carlstadt, 07072 ........ (201) 935-7100
Picture-It, Inc., 1703 State Route 27, Edison, 08817 ........ (732) 819-0420
Picut Manufacturing Company, Inc. see. ........ American Products Co., Inc., Union
Picut Manufacturing Company, Inc., 140 Mount Bethel Rd., Warren, 07059 ........ (908) 754-1333
Piece Of Cake Gourmet Ice Cream, Inc., 62 W. Inman Ave., Rahway, 07065 ........ (732) 382-0281
Pierce Roberts Rubber Co., Inc.,
1450 Heath Ave., P.O. Box 5007, Trenton, 08638 ........ (609) 394-5245
Piermount Ironworks, Inc., 129 Old Turnpike Rd., Wayne, 07470 ........ (973) 837-1750
Pierre Fabre Dermo Cosmetique, USA see. ........ Genesis Pharmaceutical, Inc. (H Q), Parsippany
Pierson Construction Co., Inc., R. E. see. ........ Pierson Materials Co., Inc., R. E., Bridgeport
Pierson Construction Co., Inc., R. E. see. ........ Pierson Materials Corp., R. E., Vineland
Pierson Construction Co., Inc., R. E. see. ........ Pierson Materials Inc., R. E., Bridgeport
Pierson Construction Co., Inc., R. E. see. ........ Pierson Materials, Inc., R. E., Mount Holly
Pierson Construction Co., Inc., R. E. see. ........ Pierson Materials, Inc., R. E., Williamstown
Pierson Construction Co., Inc., R. E. (H Q),
426 Swedesboro Rd., Pilesgrove, 08098 ........ (856) 769-8244
Pierson Industries, Inc., 7 Astro Pl., Rockaway, 07866 ........ (973) 627-7945
Pierson Materials Co., Inc., R. E.,
860 Oak Grove Rd., P.O. Box 704, Bridgeport, 08014 ........ (856) 467-1421
Pierson Materials Corp., R. E., 184 W. Sherman Ave., Vineland, 08360 ........ (856) 696-2901
Pierson Materials Inc., R. E.,
860 Oak Grove Rd., P.O. Box 704, Bridgeport, 08014 ........ (856) 467-4199
Pierson Materials, Inc., R. E., 1550 Route 38, Mount Holly, 08060 ........ (609) 267-2257
† Pierson Materials, Inc., R. E., 151 Industrial Dr., Williamstown, 08094 ........ (856) 740-2400
Pike & Co., Inc., E. W., 2149 Price St., Rahway, 07065 ........ (732) 396-0002
Pilot Chemical Co., 267 Homestead Ave., Avenel, 07001 ........ (732) 634-6613
Pilot Chemical Company see. ........ Pilot Chemical Co., Avenel
PIM Brands, LLC, 500 Pierce St., Somerset, 08873 ........ (732) 560-8300
Pin Point Container Corp., 669 Tanyard Rd., Deptford, 08096 ........ (856) 848-2115
† Pine Environmental Services, LLC, 92 N. Main St., Bldg. 20, Windsor, 08561 ........ (609) 371-9663
Pine Hill Machine Shop & Welding, 44 W. 3rd Ave., Pine Hill, 08021 ........ (856) 783-9842
Pine Hill Printing, Inc., 200 Erial Rd., Pine Hill, 08021 ........ (856) 346-2915
Pinnacle Cosmetics Packaging, LLC,
80 Market St., P.O. Box 733, Kenilworth, 07033 ........ (908) 241-7777
Pinnacle Foods Group, LLC (H Q), 121 Woodcrest Rd., Cherry Hill, 08003 ........ (856) 969-7100
Pinnacle Press, Inc., 41 Prospect St., Midland Park, 07432 ........ (201) 652-0500
† Pioneer Bearing Corp., 623 Eagle Rock Ave., Ste. 135, West Orange, 07052 ........ (973) 325-9095
Pioneer Industries, Inc., 171 S. Newman St., Hackensack, 07601 ........ (201) 933-1900
Pioneer Machine & Tool Co., 425 E. Broadway, P.O. Box 8, Maple Shade, 08052 ........ (856) 779-8800
Pioneer Metal Finishing, Inc.,
2034 Coles Mill Rd., P.O. Box 387, Franklinville, 08322 ........ (856) 694-0400
Pioneer Packaging, 31 Wilson Dr., Sparta, 07871 ........ (973) 300-9300
Pioneer Power Solutions, Inc. (H Q), 400 Kelby St., 9th Fl., Fort Lee, 07024 ........ (212) 867-0700
Pioneer Research Co., 97 Foster Rd., Ste. 5, Moorestown, 08057 ........ (856) 866-9191
PIP Printing see. ........ My Way Prints, Inc., Butler
Pipe Guards Bollards, LLC, 478 Schiller St., Elizabeth, 07206 ........ (908) 354-2259
† Pipeline Supply Co., 203 Egel Ave., Middlesex, 08846 ........ (732) 560-1509
Piping Solutions, Inc., 81 Chimney Rock Rd., Ste. 3, Bridgewater, 08807 ........ (732) 537-1009
Piramal Glass USA, Inc., 918 E. Malaga Rd., Williamstown, 08094 ........ (856) 728-9300
Piramal Glass-USA, Inc. (H Q),
401 Route 73 N., Bldg. 10, Ste. 202, Lake Center Executive Pk., Marlton, 08053 ........ (856) 293-6400
Pirolli Printing Co., Inc., 860 W. Browning Rd., Bellmawr, 08031 ........ (856) 933-1285
Pit Bull Tire Lock Corp., 205 W. Main St., 4th Fl., Somerville, 08876 ........ (888) 304-5625
PJ Murphy Forest Products Corp. (H Q),
150 River Rd., Bldg. L, Ste. 1, P.O. Box 300, Montville, 07045 ........ (973) 316-0800
PK Precision Machining, Inc., 7 Mathews Ave., Riverdale, 07457 ........ (973) 925-2020
PL Custom * Rescue 1 * NJEV see. ........ PL Custom Body & Equipment Co., Manasquan
PL Custom Body & Equipment Co., 2201 Atlantic Ave., Manasquan, 08736 ........ (732) 223-1411
Plagido's Winery, 570 N. 1st Rd., Hammonton, 08037 ........ (609) 567-4633
Plainfield Welders, 1130 North Ave., Plainfield, 07062 ........ (908) 755-6263
Planet Earth Biodiesel see. ........ American By-Products Recyclers, LLC, Hillsborough
PlanITROI Inc, 100-10 Ford Rd., Denville, 07834 ........ (973) 664-0700
Plant Food Co., Inc., 38 Hightstown Cranbury Station Rd., Cranbury, 08512 ........ (609) 448-0935
Plaque Art Creations Co., 401 S. 2nd St., Harrison, 07029 ........ (973) 482-2536
Plasma Powders & Systems, Inc.,
228 Boundary Rd., Ste. 2, P.O. Box 132, Marlboro, 07746 ........ (732) 431-0992
Plasmatic Systems, Inc., 1327 Aaron Rd., North Brunswick, 08902 ........ (732) 297-9107
Plastasonics, Inc., 5031 Industrial Rd., Farmingdale, 07727 ........ (732) 938-7694
Plastic Monofil Co. Ltd., 25 Howard St., Piscataway, 08854 ........ (732) 629-7701
★ Plastic Plus Group, LLC, 600 Meadowlands Pkwy., Secaucus, 07094 ........ (201) 561-0404
Plastic Plus, Inc. (H Q), 184 Willet St., Passaic, 07055 ........ (973) 614-0271
† Plastic Services, Inc., 200 Pacific Ave., Jersey City, 07304 ........ (201) 200-1200
Plasti-Clad Metal Products, 2601 Ridgewood Rd., Wall, 07719 ........ (732) 449-2665
Plastics Concepts see. ........ Central Art & Engineering, Inc., Cream Ridge
Plastics Consulting & Mfg. Co., 1431 Ferry Ave., Camden, 08104 ........ (856) 963-7700
Plastics For Chemicals, Inc., 710 Old Shore Rd., Forked River, 08731 ........ (609) 242-9100
Plastiform Packaging, Inc.,
114 Beach St., Bldg. 6, P.O.Box 186, Rockaway, 07866 ........ (973) 983-8900
Plast-O-Matic Valves, Inc., 1384 Pompton Ave., Ste. 1, Cedar Grove, 07009 ........ (973) 256-3000
† Plate Concepts, Inc., 1221 U.S. Highway 22, Ste. 3, Lebanon, 08833 ........ (908) 236-9570
Plate Craft, Inc., 172-174 Main St., West Orange, 07052 ........ (973) 736-4404
Plaza 70 Bagels, 65 Highway 70 E., Marlton, 08053 ........ (856) 983-5151
Pleating Plus Ltd., 527 40th St., Union City, 07087 ........ (201) 863-2991
Plenum Scientific Research, Inc., 210 Lee Pl., Hackensack, 07601 ........ (201) 489-2771
Plum Street Pottery see. ........ Easco Shower Doors Co., Vernon
† Plus Packaging, Inc., 10 Mount Pleasant Rd., Morristown, 07960 ........ (973) 538-2216
Plymouth Printing Co., Inc. (H Q),
450 North Ave., P.O. Box 68, Cranford, 07016 ........ (908) 276-8100
Plymovent Corporation (H Q), 115 Melrich Rd., Ste. 2, Cranbury, 08512 ........ (609) 395-3500
† Plywood & Door Mfrs. Corp. (H Q),
1435 Morris Ave., 3rd Fl., P.O. Box 1212, Union, 07083 ........ (908) 687-7890
PMC Group, Inc. (H Q), 1288 Route 73, Mount Laurel, 08054 ........ (856) 533-1866
PMC, Inc. see. ........ General Plastics Corp., Bloomfield
PMC, Inc. see. ........ Komo Machine, Inc., Lakewood
PMC Industries, 275 Hudson St., Hackensack, 07601 ........ (201) 342-3684
PMMI see. ........ Precision Metal Machining, Inc., Carlstadt
PMP Composites Corp. see. ........ Hamilton Transit Corporate Center, Trenton
PMPC see. ........ Precious Metals Processing Consultants, Inc., Palisades Park
P/N Metalworks see. ........ Patriot Marine Fabricating, Forked River
PNC, Inc., 115 E. Centre St., Nutley, 07110 ........ (973) 284-1600
PNY Technologies, Inc., 100 Jefferson Rd., Parsippany, 07054 ........ (973) 515-9700
Poandl Brothers Woodworking, Inc.,
20 N. 7th Ave., P.O. Box 4015, Long Branch, 07740 ........ (732) 229-8585
Pochet Of America, Inc., 415 Hamburg Tpke., Ste. 2, Wayne, 07470 ........ (973) 942-4923
Pochet Of America, Inc. see. ........ Qualipac America Corp., West Paterson
Poggi Press, The, 1501 Adams St., P.O. Box M-668, Hoboken, 07030 ........ (201) 659-0837
Polaris Plate Heat Exchangers, 106 Apple St., Ste. 106, Tinton Falls, 07724 ........ (732) 345-7188
★ Polinas Plastics America, Inc., 98 Scoles Ave., Clifton, 07012 ........ (973) 777-8950
Polished Metals Ltd., 487 Hillside Ave., Ste. 5, Hillside, 07205 ........ (908) 688-1188
Polmar Iron Work, Inc., 673 New Brunswick Ave., Rahway, 07065 ........ (732) 882-0900
Polo Machine, Inc., 223 Banta Ave., P.O. Box 403, Garfield, 07026 ........ (973) 340-9984
Poly Express, LLC, 318 McLean Blvd., Bldg. 5, Paterson, 07504 ........ (800) 843-7659
Poly Molding, LLC, 96 4th Ave., Haskell, 07420 ........ (973) 835-7161
Poly One Corp., 297 Ferry St., Newark, 07105 ........ (973) 522-2800
Polyair Inter Pack, Inc. see. ........ Polyair North East, Carlstadt
Polyair North East, 495 Meadow Ln., Carlstadt, 07072 ........ (201) 804-1700
Polycel Structural Foam, Inc., 68 County Line Rd., Somerville, 08876 ........ (908) 722-5254
Polycracker, Inc., 487 Division St., Boonton, 07005 ........ (973) 335-2828
Polyfil Corp., 74 Green Pond Rd., P.O. Box 130, Rockaway, 07866 ........ (973) 627-4070
Poly-Gel, LLC, 30 Leslie Ct., Whippany, 07981 ........ (973) 884-3300
Polymer Dynamix, LLC, 238 Saint Nicholas Ave., South Plainfield, 07080 ........ (908) 668-0300
Polymer Solutions International, Inc., 9 Roxbury Dr., Medford, 08055 ........ (609) 714-2899
Polymer Technologies, Inc., 10 Clifton Blvd., Clifton, 07011 ........ (973) 778-9100
Polymeric Resources Corporation, Inc., 55 Haul Rd., Wayne, 07470 ........ (973) 694-4141
PolyOne Corp. see. ........ Poly One Corp., Newark
Polytech Design, Inc., 26 W. 1st St., Clifton, 07011 ........ (973) 340-1390
Polytron Devices, Inc., 295-303 River St., Paterson, 07524 ........ (973) 345-5885
Polytype America Corp., 10 Industrial Ave., Mahwah, 07430 ........ (201) 995-1000
Polyurethane Specialties Co., 624 Schuyler Ave., Lyndhurst, 07071 ........ (201) 438-2325
Polyvel, Inc., 100 9th St., Hammonton, 08037 ........ (609) 567-0080
POLY-Version, Inc., 49 Fisk St., Jersey City, 07305 ........ (201) 451-0600
Pompton Millwork, Inc., 1458 Ringwood Ave., Haskell, 07420 ........ (973) 835-0585
Ponte Model Makers, Tom, 25 Pine St., Ste. 2, Rockaway, 07866 ........ (973) 627-5906
Pooka, Inc., 87 Halsey St., Newark, 07102 ........ (973) 954-2471
Pool Corporation see. ........ SCP Distributors, LLC, Lakewood
Pool Corporation see. ........ Superior Pool Products, LLC, Blackwood
Poor Boy Pallet, LLC, 45 Finley Rd., Bridgeton, 08302 ........ (856) 451-3771
Poplar Bindery, Inc., 300 Mill St., Moorestown, 08057 ........ (856) 727-8030
Portable Container Services, 101 Eisenhower Pkwy., Ste. 300, Roseland, 07068 ........ (973) 515-4721
Porta-Display, Inc., 790 Bloomfield Ave., Ste. B-2, Clifton, 07012 ........ (973) 574-0057
Portaseal, LLC, 1 John St., P.O. Box 1203, Morristown, 07962 ........ (973) 539-0100
Portaseal Weatherstripping see. ........ Portaseal, LLC, Morristown
† Porteous Fastener Co., Inc., 1000 Amboy Ave., Ste. 1, Perth Amboy, 08861 ........ (732) 376-8420
Portfirio Italian Food, Inc., 320 Anderson St., Trenton, 08611 ........ (609) 393-4116
Portuguese Structural Steel, Inc., 255 South St., Newark, 07114 ........ (973) 344-1342
Positive Publications, LLC, 65 Madison Ave., Ste. 510, Morristown, 07960 ........ (973) 218-0310
Post Eagle Newspaper, Inc., 800 Van Houten Ave., Clifton, 07013 ........ (973) 473-5414
Post Office Digital, Inc., 33 Hilliard Ave., Edgewater, 07020 ........ (201) 945-8119
★ Post To Post, LLC, 2545 Fire Rd., Ste. 1, Egg Harbor Township, 08234 ........ (609) 646-9300
Postalogic, LLC, 64 Outwater Ln., Ste. 1, Garfield, 07026 ........ (973) 546-1400
★ Postcardsrus, Inc, 440 West St., Ste. 2-S, Fort Lee, 07024 ........ (201) 944-7070
Potdevin Machine Co., 26 Fairfield Pl., West Caldwell, 07006 ........ (201) 288-1941
Potters Industries, Inc., 600 Industrial Rd., Carlstadt, 07072 ........ (201) 460-0666
Povinelli & Sons, Inc., M., 318 9th St., Fairview, 07022 ........ (201) 943-0039
Powell Electronics, Inc., 200 Commodore Dr., Logan Township, 08085 ........ (856) 241-8000
Power Bag & Film, LLC, 189 W. Valley Brook Rd., Califon, 07830 ........ (908) 832-6648
Power Container Corp., 33 Schoolhouse Rd., Somerset, 08873 ........ (732) 560-3655
Power Dynamics, Inc., 145 Algonquin Pkwy., Whippany, 07981 ........ (973) 560-0019
POWER HAWK Technologies, Inc., 300 Forge Way, Ste. 2, Rockaway, 07866 ........ (973) 627-4646
Power Magne-Tech Corp., 653 Sayre Ave., Perth Amboy, 08861 ........ (732) 826-4700

ALPHABETICAL

Power Magnetics, Inc., 377 Reservoir St., Trenton, 08618 ... (609) 695-1170
Power Mist Racing, LLC, 67 Stickles Pond Rd., Newton, 07860 ... (973) 383-1061
Power Pool Plus, Inc., 7 Edge Rd., Alpha, 08865 ... (908) 454-1124
Power Shade Co., Inc., 112 Paris Ave., Northvale, 07647 ... (201) 767-3727
★ Powercomm Solutions, LLC, 15 Minneakoning Rd., Ste. 311, Flemington, 08822 ... (908) 806-7025
Powers & Co., M. J., 65 Madison Ave., Ste. 220, Morristown, 07960 ... (973) 898-1200
powersolution.com see. ... Sirius Technology LLC, Ho-Ho-Kus
★ Powerspec, Inc., 1 Linsley Pl., Metuchen, 08840 ... (732) 494-9490
PowerTech, 0-02 Fair Lawn Ave., Fair Lawn, 07410 ... (201) 791-5050
Powertronic, Inc., 3092 Shafto Rd., Unit 7, Tinton Falls, 07753 ... (732) 643-1500
Powtek Powder Coating, Inc., 233 Dickinson St., Trenton, 08638 ... (609) 394-6700
PPG Aerospace see. ... PRC-DeSoto International, Inc., Mount Laurel
PPG Aerospace see. ... PRC-DeSoto International, Inc., Mount Laurel
PPI-Time Zero, Inc., 11 Madison Rd., Fairfield, 07004 ... (973) 278-6500
PPS see. ... Princeton Payment Solutions, Princeton
PQ Corporation see. ... P Q Corp., Avenel
Praxair, 515 E. Edgar Rd., Linden, 07036 ... (908) 862-7200
† Praxair, Inc., 554 Shell Rd., Penns Grove, 08069 ... (856) 299-3500
Praxair, Inc. see. ... Praxair, Inc., Rairatan Bay, Plt. 907, Keasbey
Praxair, Inc., Rairatan Bay, Plt. 907, 60 Crows Mill Rd., Keasbey, 08832 ... (732) 738-4150
★ Praxis Data Systems, Inc., 4 Foster Ave., Ste. B & C, Gibbsboro, 08026 ... (856) 679-2256
PRC Custom Resins see. ... Polymeric Resources Corporation, Inc., Wayne
PRC Laser, 350 N. Frontage Rd., Landing, 07850 ... (973) 347-0100
PRC-DeSoto International, Inc., 823 E. Gate Dr., Unit 4, Mount Laurel, 08054 ... (856) 234-1600
Precast Concrete Sales Co. see. ... Precast Mfg. Co., LLC, Phillipsburg
Precast Mfg. Co., LLC, 187 Strykers Rd., Phillipsburg, 08865 ... (908) 454-2122
Precast Systems, Inc., 57 Sharon Station Rd., Allentown, 08501 ... (609) 208-1987
Precious Cosmetics Corp., 296 Midland Ave., Saddle Brook, 07663 ... (973) 478-4633
Precious Metals Processing Consultants, Inc.,
430 Bergen Blvd., Palisades Park, 07650 ... (201) 944-8053
Precise Components & Tool Design, Inc.,
10 Clifton Blvd., Unit A-4, Clifton, 07011 ... (973) 928-2928
Precise Continental, 1 Cape May St., Harrison, 07029 ... (973) 350-0330
Precise Machine & Tool, Inc., 369 Knickerbocker Ave., Paterson, 07503 ... (201) 790-3320
Precise Printing, 748 Lincoln Blvd., Middlesex, 08846 ... (732) 271-8626
Precise Tool & Mold Co., Inc., 240 E. Lackland Dr., Middlesex, 08846 ... (732) 469-3062
Precision Automation Company, Inc. see. ... New Jersey Wire Stitching Machine Co., Cherry Hill
Precision Automation Company, Inc., 1841 Old Cuthbert Rd., Cherry Hill, 08034 ... (856) 428-7400
Precision Ball Specialties, Inc., 1451 Glassboro Rd., Williamstown, 08094 ... (856) 881-5646
Precision Blinds Products, Inc., 637 Boulevard, Kenilworth, 07033 ... (908) 245-7766
Precision Cabinets, 410 E. Freehold Rd., Freehold, 07728 ... (732) 462-3342
Precision Castparts Corp. see. ... McWilliams Forge Co., Rockaway
Precision Custom Coatings, LLC, 200 Maltese Dr., Totowa, 07512 ... (973) 890-3873
Precision Electronic Glass, Inc., 1013 Hendee Rd., Vineland, 08360 ... (856) 691-2234
Precision Engraving II, Inc.,
13 Ridgedale Ave., P.O. Box 243, East Hanover, 07936 ... (973) 887-3350
Precision Escalators, 147 N. Michigan Ave., Kenilworth, 07033 ... (908) 259-9017
† Precision Fasteners, Inc., 24 Worlds Fair Dr., Ste. D, Somerset, 08873 ... (732) 627-0032
Precision Filaments, 17 Bannard St., Ste. 30, Freehold, 07728 ... (732) 462-3755
Precision Forms, Inc., 97 Decker Rd., Butler, 07405 ... (973) 838-3800
Precision Graphics, Inc., 21 County Line Rd., Somerville, 08876 ... (908) 707-8880
Precision Machined Products, LLC, 24 Kulick Rd., Fairfield, 07004 ... (973) 227-9538
Precision Metal Machining, Inc., 800 Central Blvd., Ste. C, Carlstadt, 07072 ... (201) 843-7427
Precision Metalcrafters, Inc., 17 Filbert St., Williamstown, 08094 ... (856) 629-1020
Precision Mfg., LLC, 177 Gould Ave., Paterson, 07503 ... (973) 278-6600
Precision Mirror & Glass, Inc., 89 Route 35 N., Eatontown, 07724 ... (732) 389-8175
Precision Multiple Controls, Inc., 33 Greenwood Ave., Midland Park, 07432 ... (201) 444-0600
Precision Numerical Technology, Inc., 31 Ardsley Pl., Morganville, 07751 ... (732) 591-4884
Precision Orthotic Lab International, 1595 Imperial Way, West Deptford, 08066 ... (856) 848-6226
Precision Parts Unlimited, Inc., 24 Patriot Crossing, Rockaway, 07866 ... (973) 659-3300
Precision Press see. ... New Jersey Reprographics, Inc., Garwood
Precision Printing Group, LLC, 117 Jackson Rd., Berlin, 08009 ... (856) 753-7903
Precision Products Co., 219 Hergesell Ave., Maywood, 07607 ... (201) 712-5757
Precision Rollers, Inc., 155 Cooper Rd., West Berlin, 08091 ... (856) 768-7696
Precision Saw & Tool Corp., 56 Colfax Ave., Clifton, 07013 ... (973) 773-7302
Precision Screen Printing see. ... Precision Sign Works, LLC, Tabernacle
Precision Shape Solutions, 243 E. Blackwell St., Dover, 07801 ... (973) 989-7199
Precision Shoe Brace & Limb, LLC,
618 W. Elizabeth Ave., P.O. Box 1213, Linden, 07036 ... (908) 523-0026
Precision Shower Doors, Inc., 359 Essex Rd., Tinton Falls, 07753 ... (732) 389-8175
Precision Sign Works, LLC, 82 Richter Rd., Tabernacle, 08088 ... (609) 702-9700
Precision Specialists Machine, LLC,
1004 Industrial Dr., Ste. 5, West Berlin, 08091 ... (856) 768-5990
Precision Specialties, 120 Greylock Ave., Belleville, 07109 ... (973) 751-7588
Precision Steel Rule Die, 400 Benigno Blvd., Rear, Bellmawr, 08031 ... (856) 931-2548
Precision Technology, Inc., 50 Maple St., P.O. Box 422, Norwood, 07648 ... (201) 767-1600
Precision Tool & Engineering, Inc., 123 Florence Ave., Trenton, 08618 ... (609) 882-9223
Precision Welding, 845 Berkshire Valley Rd., Wharton, 07885 ... (973) 366-7316
Predator Tools (H Q), 35 S. Woodruff Rd., Bridgeton, 08302 ... (856) 455-3790
Pre-Fab Structures, Inc., 907 Wedgewood Way, Atco, 08004 ... (856) 768-4257
Preferred Display, Inc., 310 Brighton Rd., Clifton, 07012 ... (973) 405-5137
† Preferred Plastics & Packaging Co., Inc.,
681 Main St., Ste. 42, Belleville, 07109 ... (973) 759-1510
Preferred Plastics Corp., 6512 Park Ave., Pennsauken, 08109 ... (856) 662-6250
Premac, Inc., P.O. Box 9, Rahway, 07065 ... (732) 381-7550
Premier Compaction Systems, 264 Lackawanna Ave., Woodland Park, 07424 ... (973) 305-6646
Premier Die Casting Co., Inc., 1177 Rahway Ave., Avenel, 07001 ... (732) 634-3000
Premier Graphics, Inc., 500 Central Ave., Atlantic Highlands, 07716 ... (732) 872-9933
Premier Press, Inc., 7120 Airport Hwy., Pennsauken, 08109 ... (856) 665-0722
Premier Printing Solutions, 508 Raritan St., Sayreville, 08872 ... (732) 525-0740
Premier Specialties, Inc., 236 Blackford Ave., Middlesex, 08846 ... (732) 469-6615
Premier Vinyl see. ... Master Wire Mfg., Inc., Hammonton
Premio Foods, Inc., 50 Utter Ave., Hawthorne, 07506 ... (973) 427-1106
Premium Color Graphics, Inc., 651 Garden St., Carlstadt, 07072 ... (973) 472-7007
Premium Service Printing see. ... B & L Printing Co., Inc., Hillsborough
Prentco Co., 952 Koehl Ave., Union, 07083 ... (908) 687-9518
Presentation Solutions, Inc., 432 Clearstream Rd., Jackson, 08527 ... (732) 961-1960
President Container Group, 200 W. Commercial Ave., Moonachie, 07074 ... (201) 933-7500
President Container Group see. ... Tech-Pak, Inc., Wood Ridge
Press Of Atlantic City, The see. ... World Media Enterprises, Inc., Pleasantville
Press Room, Inc., The, 100 Youngs Rd., Ste. 2, Mercerville, 08619 ... (609) 689-3817
Presscrete Co., Inc., The, 128 Oak Tree Ave., South Plainfield, 07080 ... (908) 757-8600
Pressto Graphics, Inc., 467 Lakehurst Rd., P.O. Box 467, Toms River, 08755 ... (732) 286-9300
Pressure Controls, Inc., 406 Courtlandt St., Belleville, 07109 ... (973) 751-5002
† Pressure King, Inc., 231 Herbert Ave., Ste. 1, Closter, 07624 ... (201) 768-1911
Pressworks, 1879 Old Cuthbert Rd., Unit 28, Cherry Hill, 08034 ... (856) 427-9001
Prestige Assocs., Inc., 39 Mead St., Trenton, 08638 ... (609) 393-1509
Prestige Millwork, LLC, 152 U.S. Highway 206, Bldg. 17-A, Hillsborough, 08844 ... (908) 526-5100
Prestige Rubber Mfg., 11 Spielman Rd., Fairfield, 07004 ... (973) 227-2505
Presto Print & Copy, 79 S. Main St., Ste. 3, Lodi, 07644 ... (973) 777-8377
PRG Light, Inc., 915 Secaucus Ave., Secaucus, 07094 ... (201) 758-4000
PRG Packing Corp. (H Q), 2071 Lemoine Ave., Fort Lee, 07024 ... (201) 242-5500
Priamo Designs Ltd., 6614 Broadway, West New York, 07093 ... (201) 861-8808
Price Millwork, 305 Dennis Dr., Absecon, 08201 ... (609) 652-0123
Pride Gourmet Bakers, Inc., 450 Getty Ave., Clifton, 07011 ... (973) 340-3200
Pride Products Distributors, LLC, 673 Morris Ave., Ste. 2, Springfield, 07081 ... (973) 564-6300
Pride Products, Inc., 5 Slater Dr., Elizabeth, 07206 ... (908) 353-6800
Pride Solvents & Chemical Co., 211 Randolph Ave., Avenel, 07001 ... (732) 499-0125
Pride Tempered Glass Products, LLC, 2001 S. 6th St., Camden, 08104 ... (856) 365-1200
Primary Colors Graphics, 629 Grove St., 7th Fl., Jersey City, 07310 ... (201) 526-9300
Primary Systems, Inc., 30 State Route 18, Ste. 1, Old Bridge, 08857 ... (732) 679-2200
Prime Fur & Leather, Inc., 2931 Industrial Ave., Fairview, 07022 ... (201) 941-9600
Prime Ingredients, Inc., 280 N. Midland Ave., Bldg. U, Saddle Brook, 07663 ... (201) 791-6655
Prime Pack, LLC, 262 Old New Brunswick Rd., Ste. N, Piscataway, 08854 ... (732) 253-7734
Prime Time Toys, LLC, P.O. Box 256, Pompton Lakes, 07442 ... (973) 839-5711
Primepak Company, 133 Cedar Ln., Ste. 104, Teaneck, 07666 ... (201) 836-5060
† PrimeSource Building Products, Inc., 20 Van Dyke Ave, New Brunswick, 08901 ... (732) 296-0600
Primex Plastics Corp. see. ... O'Neil Color & Compounding Corp., Garfield
Primex Plastics Corp., 65 River Dr., Garfield, 07026 ... (973) 470-8000
PRIMME Co., Inc., 42 Columbia Rd., Branchburg, 08876 ... (908) 231-9490
Prince Donut Co., Inc., 2345 E. Linden Ave., Linden, 07036 ... (908) 925-2262
Princetel, Inc., 2560 E. State Street Ext., Hamilton, 08619 ... (609) 588-8801
Princeton BioMeditech Corp., 4242 U.S. Highway 1, Monmouth Junction, 08852 ... (732) 274-1000
Princeton Book Co., 614 U.S. Highway 130, Ste. 1-C, Hightstown, 08520 ... (609) 426-0602
Princeton Case Co., Inc., 615 Sherwood Pkwy., Mountainside, 07092 ... (908) 687-1750
Princeton Chromatography, Inc., 1206 Cranbury-S. River Rd., Cranbury, 08512 ... (609) 860-1803
† Princeton Computer Support, Inc.,
3490 U.S. Highway 1, Ste. 15-E, Princeton, 08540 ... (609) 520-0770
Princeton Instruments, 3660 Quakerbridge Rd., Trenton, 08619 ... (609) 587-9797
Princeton Label Co., 1226 U.S. Highway 130, Robbinsville, 08691 ... (609) 490-0800
Princeton Lightwave, Inc., 2555 U.S. Highway 130, Ste. 1, Cranbury, 08512 ... (609) 495-2600
Princeton Microwave Technology, 5 Nami Ln., Trenton, 08619 ... (609) 586-8140
Princeton Molding Group see. ... Aflex Extrusion Technologies, Inc., North Brunswick
Princeton Packet, Inc., 300 Witherspoon St., P.O. Box 350, Princeton, 08542 ... (609) 924-3244
Princeton Payment Solutions, 501 Forrestal Rd., Ste. 324, Princeton, 08540 ... (609) 919-0700
Princeton Power Systems, Inc.,
3175 Princeton Pike, Ste. C, Lawrenceville, 08648 ... (609) 955-5390
Princeton Printer, 150 Nassau St., Princeton, 08542 ... (609) 924-4630
Princeton Separation, Inc., 100 Commerce Dr., Freehold, 07728 ... (732) 431-3338
Princeton Tec, 5198 Route 130 N., Bordentown, 08505 ... (609) 298-9331
Princeton Tec, 110 Collings Ave., West Berlin, 08091 ... (609) 298-9331
Princeton University Press, 41 William St., Princeton, 08540 ... (609) 258-4900
Princetonian Graphics, Inc., 45 Stouts Ln., Ste. 4, Monmouth Junction, 08852 ... (732) 329-8282
Print & Peel see. ... L V Adhesive, Inc., Carlstadt
Print Art, Inc., 6726 Delilah Rd., Egg Harbor Township, 08234 ... (609) 645-1940
Print C B F see. ... Commercial Business Forms, Cedar Knolls
Print Com see. ... Print Communications, Pennsauken
Print Communications, 7040 Colonial Hwy., Pennsauken, 08109 ... (856) 488-0345
Print Group, Inc., The, 24 E. Wesley St., South Hackensack, 07606 ... (201) 487-4400
Print Group, The see. ... Neo Printing Co., Inc., South Hackensack
Print House, Inc., The, 6535 U.S. Highway 9, Howell, 07731 ... (732) 364-4254
Print It see. ... Postcardsrus, Inc, Fort Lee
Print Media, 232 Morris Ave., Springfield, 07081 ... (973) 467-0007
Print Shack see. ... R.J. Printing, Inc., West Caldwell
Print Shoppe, 1077-M Highway 34, Matawan, 07747 ... (732) 583-4343
Print Shoppe, Inc., 15 Minneakoning Rd., Ste. 305, Flemington, 08822 ... (908) 782-9213
Print Sign & Design, 1791 S. Burlington Rd., Bridgeton, 08302 ... (856) 451-8766
Print Solutions, 320 S. Dean St., Englewood, 07631 ... (201) 567-9622
Print Tech Ltd., 49 Fadem Rd., Springfield, 07081 ... (908) 232-2287
Print Tech Ltd. see. ... Sign Tech, Westfield
Print Wrap Corp., 95 Sand Park Rd., Cedar Grove, 07009 ... (973) 239-1144
Printech, 35 Main St., Flemington, 08822 ... (908) 782-9986
Printers Of Salem County, LLC, 38 Market St., Salem, 08079 ... (856) 935-5032
† Printers Parts Store, 82 Herman St., East Rutherford, 07073 ... (201) 935-9595
Printer's Place, Inc., The, 8 S. Fullerton Ave., Montclair, 07042 ... (973) 744-8889
Printers Place North, LLC, 2 Kiel Ave., Ste. 154, Kinnelon, 07405 ... (973) 838-3741
Printers' Service, Inc., 26 Blanchard St., Newark, 07105 ... (973) 589-7800
Printflex, 1250 U.S. Highway 46, Little Falls, 07424 ... (973) 256-5900
Printing & Signs Express, Inc., 634 Wyckoff Ave., Mahwah, 07430 ... (201) 368-1255
Printing Center, Inc., The, 1 White Lake Rd., Sparta, 07871 ... (973) 383-6362
Printing Craftsman, Inc., 130 Bergen Blvd., Fairview, 07022 ... (201) 943-0276
Printing Delite, Inc., 279 Sanford St., East Orange, 07018 ... (973) 676-3033
Printing Gone Postal see. ... Happle Printing Partnership, Inc., Dorothy
Printing Images, 546 Ringwood Ave., Wanaque, 07465 ... (973) 839-9500
Printing Industries, LLC, 1543 U.S. Highway 46 E., Parsippany, 07054 ... (973) 334-9775
Printing Plus Of South Jersey, 406 N. Route 73, West Berlin, 08091 ... (856) 767-3232
Printing Shop Copy Center, The, 338 State St., Perth Amboy, 08861 ... (732) 826-3575
Printing Techniques, Inc., 48 Franklin Ave., Nutley, 07110 ... (973) 667-2606
Printing To Go, 578 Park Ave., Freehold, 07728 ... (732) 462-0333
Printmasters, 1108 Goffle Rd., Hawthorne, 07506 ... (973) 427-6598
★ Printology, 615 Franklin Tpke., Ste. 3, Ridgewood, 07450 ... (201) 345-4632
Print-Tech Products, Inc., 603 1st Ave., Ste. 1-C, Raritan, 08869 ... (908) 231-8700
Printworx, 2103 Whitehorse Mercerville Rd., Hamilton, 08619 ... (609) 586-3006
Prinz Woodworking, Inc., 381 E. 22nd St., Paterson, 07514 ... (973) 977-2345
Prism Color Corp., 31 Twosome Dr., Ste. 1, Moorestown, 08057 ... (856) 234-7515
★ Prism Digital Communications, LLC,
1011 U.S. Highway 22, Ste. 1, Mountainside, 07092 ... (908) 789-7747
Prismacolor Corp., 120 E. Halsey Rd., P.O. Box 6330, Parsippany, 07054 ... (973) 887-7900
Prismatix Decal, Inc., 324 Railroad Ave., Hackensack, 07601 ... (201) 525-2800
Private Investigators Magazine see. ... PI Magazine, Freehold
★ Private Journey Magazine, The,
1120 Bloomfield Ave., Ste. 107, West Caldwell, 07006 ... (973) 244-0301
Private Label Products, Inc., 20-21 Wagaraw Rd., Bldg. 34, Fair Lawn, 07410 ... (201) 791-1177
Pro Image Promotions, Inc., 489 U.S. Highway 46, Kenvil, 07847 ... (973) 252-8000

Pro Line Mfg. Co., LLC, 186 Parish Dr., Wayne, 07470 (973) 692-9696
Pro Mach, Inc. see. Id Technology, Oakland
★ Pro Machine Co., 5 Sicomac Rd., Haledon, 07508 (973) 855-9935
Pro Plastics, Inc., 1190 Sylvan St., P.O. Box 1489, Linden, 07036 (908) 925-5555
Pro Printing, Inc., 472 Broad Ave., Palisades Park, 07650 (201) 346-0305
Pro Science see. Graphic Action, Inc., Phillipsburg
Pro Signs, 296 S. Main St., Phillipsburg, 08865 (908) 454-4888
ProBuild Co., LLC, 210 Williamstown Rd., Berlin, 08009 (856) 767-3153
ProBuild Co., LLC, 817 Eastgate Dr., Ste. 101, Mount Laurel, 08054 (856) 505-1100
ProBuild East see. ProBuild Co., LLC, Berlin
ProBuild Holdings, Inc. see. ProBuild Co., LLC, Berlin
ProBuild Holdings, Inc. see. ProBuild Co., LLC, Mount Laurel
Procedyne Corp., 11 Industrial Dr., New Brunswick, 08901 (732) 249-8347
Process Components, 301 John Wall Rd., Monroe Township, 08831 (732) 786-1500
Process Research Products, 1013 Whitehead Road Ext., Trenton, 08638 (609) 882-0400
Pro-Comm, Inc., 1105 Industrial Pkwy., Brick, 08724 (732) 206-0660
Procomp, Inc. see. Process Components, Monroe Township
Procter & Gamble Co., The see. Procter & Gamble Mfg. Co., Avenel
Procter & Gamble Mfg. Co., 100 Essex Ave. E., Avenel, 07001 (732) 602-4500
Prodo-Pak Corp., 77 Commerce St., P.O. Box 363, Garfield, 07026 (973) 772-4500
Produce News, The, 800 Kinderkamack Rd., Ste. 100, Oradell, 07649 (201) 986-7990
Product Development Assocs., LLC, 12 Say Dr., East Hanover, 07936 (973) 267-0033
Product Identification Co., Inc., 141 Lanza Ave., Bldg. 19, Garfield, 07026 (973) 955-4747
Production Resource Group, LLC see. PRG Light, Inc., Secaucus
Productive Industrial Finishing, 103 American Way, Voorhees, 08043 (856) 427-9646
Productive Plastics, Inc., 103 W. Park Dr., Mount Laurel, 08054 (856) 778-4300
Proedge, 167 Genessee Ave., Paterson, 07503 (973) 742-3900
Professional Environment Systems, 49 O'Brien Rd., Kearny, 07032 (201) 991-3000
Professional Images see. Professional Images, LLC, Englewood
Professional Images, LLC, 17 E. Linden Ave., Englewood, 07631 (201) 569-4251
Professional Printing Services, 116 N. Haddon Ave., Haddonfield, 08033 (856) 429-8644
Pro-Fit Prosthetic & Orthotic, LLC, 215 Edgewood Ave., West Berlin, 08091 (856) 809-9910
★ Proform Acoustic Surfaces LLC, 307 Julianne Ter., Secaucus, 07094 (201) 553-9614
Pro-Form Packaging, Inc.,
777 North Avenue Ext., P.O. Box 4231, Dunellen, 08812 (732) 968-8123
Proforma Ayr Graphics & Printing see. Ayr Graphics & Printing, Inc., Roselle Park
Proforma Spectrum Graphics,
373 Route 46 W., Bldg. D, Ste. 130, Fairfield, 07004 (973) 882-8666
Proforma Unlimited Marketing Expressions, 36 Keswick Ave., Ewing, 08638 (609) 882-0112
ProGasket Aerospace & Automotive, LLC, 14 Doty Rd., Haskell, 07420 (973) 831-4533
Progenitor Cell Therapy, LLC, 4 Pearl Ct., Ste. C, Allendale, 07401 (201) 883-5300
Program Dynamics, Inc., 43 Pennsylvania Ave., P.O. Box 929, Flemington, 08822 (908) 782-9398
Progress Display, Inc., 39 Progress St., Edison, 08820 (908) 757-6650
Progress Machine Shop, Inc., 41 Kentucky Ave., Paterson, 07503 (973) 278-4999
Progressive Dimensions, Inc., 44 Flint Rd., Toms River, 08757 (732) 244-0109
Progressive Machine Co., 293 Hudson St., Hackensack, 07601 (201) 342-3636
Progressive Printing Corp., 24 Park Ave., West Orange, 07052 (973) 736-5800
Progressive Tool & Mfg. Co., 708 Fairfield Ave., Kenilworth, 07033 (908) 245-7010
Progressive-Ruesch Machine Co., LLC, 21 Van Natta Dr., Ringwood, 07456 (973) 962-7700
ProImage Apparel, LLC, 280 N. Midland Ave., Bldg. H, Saddle Brook, 07663 (201) 773-9292
Project Sign, 282 Irvington Rd., South Orange, 07079 (973) 763-1959
Projects, Inc., 310 Orange St., Millville, 08332 (856) 825-7312
Prolong Pharmaceuticals, 300 Corporate Ct., Ste. B, South Plainfield, 07080 (908) 444-4660
Promedia Technology Services, Inc., 535 U.S. Highway 46, Little Falls, 07424 (973) 253-7600
Promeko, Inc., 543 59th St., West New York, 07093 (201) 861-6446
Promo Advertising, 1174 Chestnut St., Union, 07083 (908) 810-8888
Promo Graphics, Inc., 24 Howard St., Piscataway, 08854 (732) 629-7300
Pro-Motion Engines, LLC, 2 Great Meadow Ln., Apt. B, East Hanover, 07936 (973) 884-5936
Promotion In Motion Cos., Inc., The see. PIM Brands, LLC, Somerset
Promotion In Motion Cos., Inc., The (H Q), 25 Commerce Dr., Allendale, 07401 (201) 784-5800
† Pro-Motion Industries, LLC, 102 Allied Pkwy., Sicklerville, 08081 (856) 809-0040
Promotion Works, 45 Wadsworth St., Wallington, 07057 (201) 842-1107
Promotional Graphics Etc., Inc., 85 Wagaraw Rd., Hawthorne, 07506 (973) 423-3900
Promotions & Unicorns Too, Inc., 71 W.Main St., Ste. 102, Freehold, 07728 (732) 308-3444
Pronto Print, 1329 Hurffville Rd., Deptford, 08096 (856) 232-7200
Proof Productions, Inc., 599 Mantua Blvd., Sewell, 08080 (856) 442-0700
† Pro-Pac Services, Inc., 15 Van Natta Dr., Ringwood, 07456 (973) 962-8080
† Propane Power Corporation, a Div. of Suburban Propane,
915 Delancy St., Newark, 07105 (973) 589-3030
Props, Displays & Interiors, Inc., 45 Glenwood Pl., East Orange, 07017 (862) 704-6463
ProQuest, LLC see. R. R. Bowker, New Providence
Pro-Screen Printing, Inc., 590 Belleville Tpke., Bldg. 24, Kearny, 07032 (201) 246-7600
Prosthetic Orthotic Solutions International,
100 Brick Rd., Ste. 315, Marlton, 08053 (856) 810-7900
† Protameen Chemicals, Inc., 375 Minnisink Rd., Totowa, 07512 (973) 256-4374
Pro-Tapes & Specialties, 621 Route 1 S., North Brunswick, 08902 (732) 346-0900
Protech Chemicals Ltd. see. Protech Powder Coating, Inc., Fairfield
Protech Powder Coating, Inc., 21 Audrey Pl., Fairfield, 07004 (973) 257-0505
Protection One Alarm Monitoring, Inc. see. Protection One, Inc., East Hanover
Protection One, Inc., 50 Williams Pkwy., Ste. L, East Hanover, 07936 (973) 227-3421
† Proven Technology, Inc., 5 Woodshire Way, Hillsborough, 08844 (908) 359-7888
Provost Square Assocs., 6 Provost Sq., Caldwell, 07006 (973) 403-8755
Prudent Publishing Co., 400 N. Frontage Rd., Landing, 07850 (973) 347-4554
Prudent Publishing Co. (H Q), 65 Challenger Rd., Ridgefield Park, 07660 (201) 641-7900
Pryce Bros. Woodworking see. Mountain Millwork, Inc., Bayville
Prysmian Power Cables & Systems, LLC,
5 Hollywood Ct., South Plainfield, 07080 (908) 791-2828
PSEG Power, 749 Cliff Rd., Sewaren, 07077 (732) 750-2062
PSS World Medical, Inc. see. PSS/World Medical, Inc., Fairfield
† PSS/World Medical, Inc., 208 Passaic Ave., Ste. 2, Fairfield, 07004 (973) 775-8600
Pt Of Vu, LLC, 52 Edinborough Ct., Hackettstown, 07840 (908) 979-1360
† PTC Electronics, Inc., 45 Whitney Rd., Ste. B-9, Mahwah, 07430 (201) 847-0500
PTC Therapeutics, Inc., 100 Corporate Ct., South Plainfield, 07080 (908) 222-7000
PTI see. Polymer Technologies, Inc., Clifton
Puebla Foods, Inc., 118 1st St., Passaic, 07055 (973) 473-4494
† Puggi Class B Recycling, A. J., 6150 Mill Rd., Egg Harbor Township, 08234 (609) 926-6991
Puglisi Egg Farms, Inc., 75 Easy St., Howell, 07731 (732) 938-2373
Pul-A Pump Corp., 29 Paradise Trl., P.O. Box 155, Stockholm, 07460 (973) 697-2008
Pulaski Meat Products Co., 123 N. Wood Ave., Linden, 07036 (908) 925-5380
Pulcin Machine, 13 Cedar Ln., Bordentown, 08505 (609) 387-3060
Pulsar Microwave Corp., 48 Industrial St. W., Clifton, 07012 (973) 779-6262
PulseTor, LLC, 1580 Reed Rd., Ste. C-2, Pennington, 08534 (609) 303-0578

Punch Products U. S. A., Inc., 2131 Felver Ct., Rahway, 07065 (732) 574-1900
PuraCap Pharmaceutical, LLC, 1001 Durham Ave., South Plainfield, 07080 (908) 941-5456
Puratos Corp., 1941 Old Cuthbert Rd., Cherry Hill, 08034 (856) 428-4300
† Puratos Corp., 945 Sherman Ave., Pennsauken, 08110 (856) 661-3112
Purcell Printing Co., Robert, 244 Kamena St., Fairview, 07022 (201) 941-0375
Purchasingnet, Inc., 125 Half Mile Rd., Red Bank, 07701 (732) 212-1500
Purdue Pharma L. P. see. P. F. Laboratories, Inc., Totowa
Pure H2O Technologies, Inc., 211 Warren St., Ste. 318, Newark, 07103 (973) 622-0440
Pure Rubber Products Co., Inc., 300 Roundhill Dr., Ste. 5, Rockaway, 07866 (973) 784-3690
Purest Colloids, Inc., 600 Highland Dr., Ste. 602, Mount Holly, 08060 (609) 267-2112
Purple Pebble, LLC (H Q), 58 Grand Ave., Waldwick, 07463 (201) 444-7439
Purves Marine Works, 197 Main St., West Creek, 08092 (609) 296-1263
Putnum Stainless Tubes, Inc., 1163 Route 22 E., Mountainside, 07092 (908) 232-9200
PV/T, Inc., 100 Indel Ave., P.O. Box 156, Rancocas, 08073 (609) 267-3933
Pyramid Imprints, 28 N. Washington Ave., Bergenfield, 07621 (201) 384-0336
Pyramid Poly Bags, Inc., 600 Markley St., Port Reading, 07064 (718) 499-1212
Pyrometer Instrument Co., Inc.,
92 N. Main St., Bldg. 18-D, P.O. Box 479, Windsor, 08561 (609) 443-5522
Pyroptics, Inc., 2015 Columbus Rd., Burlington, 08016 (609) 386-6930
Pyrotechnic Industries, Inc., 1640 Garden Rd., Vineland, 08360 (856) 697-1023
Pyrotecnico see. Pyrotechnic Industries, Inc., Vineland
Pyrotecnico see. Pyrotechnic Industries, Inc., Vineland
Q. E. P. Co., Inc. see. Boiardi Products Corp., Little Falls
Q Glass Co., Inc., 624 Main Rd., Towaco, 07082 (973) 335-5191
QAD, Inc., 10000 Midlantic Dr., Ste. 100 W., Mount Laurel, 08054 (856) 273-1717
★ QED Financial Systems, Inc., 10000 Sagemore Dr., Ste. 10201, Marlton, 08053 (856) 797-1200
QEI Corp., 1 Airport Dr., P.O. Box 805, Williamstown, 08094 (856) 728-2020
QIS, Inc., 778 Vineland Ave., P.O. Box 517, Rosenhayn, 08352 (856) 455-3736
† QLT.com, 238 Boundary Rd., Unit 304, Marlboro, 07746 (732) 431-0740
Q-Pak, Inc., 2145 McCarter Hwy., Newark, 07104 (973) 483-4404
QPSI see. Quality Packaging Specialists International, LLC, Burlington
QP2000, LLC, 827 W. Park Ave., Ocean, 07712 (732) 531-8860
QRS Beauty Corp., 11 Commercial Ave., Fairview, 07022 (201) 313-0305
QSSI see. Quality Software Systems, Inc., Somerset
Q-T Foundations Co., Inc., 496 Kinderkamack Rd., Ste. 107, Oradell, 07649 (201) 986-7800
Quad/Graphics, Inc., 28 Engelhard Dr., Monroe Township, 08831 (609) 495-1200
Quadrangle Products, 28 Harrison Ave., Bldg. 16-D, Englishtown, 07726 (732) 792-1234
Quadriga Art, Inc., 825 Hylton Rd., Pennsauken, 08110 (856) 663-2500
Qualco, Inc., 225 Passaic St., Passaic, 07055 (973) 473-1222
Qualecon Machine, 235 Stateline Rd., Sussex, 07461 (973) 875-4144
Qualipac America Corp., 1 Garret Mountain Plz., 5th Fl., West Paterson, 07424 (973) 389-7730
Qualis Packaging, 550 Hadley Rd., South Plainfield, 07080 (908) 753-7300
Qualiturn Corp., 205 Columbus Ave., Roselle, 07203 (908) 241-4909
Quality Attributes Software, 1 Pelican Dr., Ste. 6, Bayville, 08721 (732) 504-2200
Quality Bakery Products Of New Jersey, Inc.,
24 Ironside Ct., Willingboro, 08046 (609) 871-7393
Quality Coatings, Island Dragway Rd., P.O. Box 13, Great Meadows, 07838 (908) 637-4556
Quality Concepts, Inc., 730 Marne Hwy., Moorestown, 08057 (856) 235-0909
Quality Cosmetics Mfg., 4455 S. Clinton Ave., South Plainfield, 07080 (908) 755-9588
† Quality Discount Press Parts & Equipment, Inc.,
6088 Reega Ave., Egg Harbor Township, 08234 (609) 646-2212
† Quality Electric Motor Service, Inc.,
396 State Route 18, East Brunswick, 08816 (732) 257-6655
Quality Formulation Laboratories, Inc.,
110 Pennsylvania Ave., Paterson, 07503 (973) 977-8800
Quality Industries, Inc., 204 Getty Ave., Clifton, 07011 (973) 478-4425
Quality Metal Finishing Corp., 80 George St., 1st Fl., Paterson, 07503 (973) 345-0963
Quality Packaging Specialists International, LLC,
5 Cooper St., Burlington, 08016 (609) 239-0503
Quality Paper Converters Of New Jersey, Inc.,
673 S. 21st St., Irvington, 07111 (973) 399-1200
Quality Printing, 1181 E. Landis Ave., Ste. 3, Vineland, 08360 (856) 691-7577
Quality Rebuilders, 617 Broadway, Long Branch, 07740 (732) 222-9100
Quality Rebuilders, Inc., 969 Market St., Paterson, 07513 (973) 523-8800
Quality Repro Centers, Inc.,
296 Route 46 E., P.O. Box 111, Elmwood Park, 07407 (201) 794-3905
† Quality Seals, Inc., 2444 Morris Ave., Ste. 201, Union, 07083 (908) 206-0410
Quality Sheet Metal & Welding, 23 Clawson St., Piscataway, 08854 (732) 752-6300
Quality Software Systems, Inc., 80 Cottontail Ln., Ste. 105, Somerset, 08873 (732) 805-0400
Quality Solid Surface, Inc., 333 Vreeland Ave., Paterson, 07513 (973) 357-9770
Quality Swiss Screw Machine Co., Inc., 849 4th Ave., Elizabeth, 07202 (908) 654-1881
Quality Swiss Screw Machine Co., Inc., 960 Mountain Ave., Mountainside, 07092 (908) 654-1881
Quantem Corp., 1457 Lower Ferry Rd., Trenton, 08618 (609) 883-9191
Quantum Coating, Inc., 1259 N. Church St., Bldg. 1, Moorestown, 08057 (856) 231-0706
Quantum Concepts, Inc., 24 River Rd., Ste. 12, Bogota, 07603 (201) 343-2008
Quantum Pharmaceuticals, Inc. (H Q), P.O. Box 244, Ogdensburg, 07439 (877) 873-3762
Quark Enterprises, Inc., 320 Morton Ave., Rosenhayn, 08352 (856) 455-0376
Quartz Technology, Inc., 1355 Plymouth Rd., Bridgewater, 08807 (908) 526-6362
Quest Diagnostics see. Enterix, Inc., Edison
Quest Diagnostics (H Q), 3 Giralda Farms, Madison, 07940 (973) 520-2700
Quest Industries, LLC, 480 Mundet Pl., Hillside, 07205 (908) 851-9070
Quick Cut Stamping & Embossing, Inc., 815 E. Main St., Maple Shade, 08052 (856) 321-0050
Quick Strip, 1 Randolph St., Carteret, 07008 (732) 969-3268
Quickie Mfg. Corp. (H Q), 1150 Taylors Ln., P.O. Box 156, Cinnaminson, 08077 (856) 829-7900
Quickly Printing, Inc., 1965 Morris Ave., Union, 07083 (908) 687-6000
Quikie Print & Copy Shop see. QP2000, LLC, Ocean
Quikie Print & Copy Shop, 827 W. Park, Ocean, 07712 (732) 531-8860
Quikie Print & Copy Shops see. QP2000, LLC, Ocean
Quikie Print & Copy Shops see. Quikie Print & Copy Shop, Ocean
Quikie Print & Copy Shops, 703 Broad St., Shrewsbury, 07702 (732) 933-1010
QUIKRETE Cos., Inc., The see. CST Pavers a division of Pavestone, Branchville
QUIKRETE Cos., Inc., The see. QUIKRETE Cos., Inc, The, Berlin
QUIKRETE Cos., Inc, The, 22 Union Ave., Berlin, 08009 (856) 768-6642
QUIKRETE Cos., Inc., The see. Tri-State QUIKRETE, Flanders
Quincas Corp., 112 East Ave., Unit 7-A, Hackettstown, 07840 (908) 850-3914
Quincy Newspapers, Inc. see. New Jersey Herald, The, Newton
R & D Circuits, 3601 S. Clinton Ave., South Plainfield, 07080 (732) 549-4554
★ R & D Promotions, Ltd., 164 Van Liew Ave., Milltown, 08850 (732) 828-7408
R & H Spring & Truck Repair, Inc., 4806 W. Hurley Pond Rd., Belmar, 07719 (732) 681-9000
R & J Control, Inc., 58 Harding Ave., Dover, 07801 (973) 328-6880
R & L Sheet Metal Co., 3 Kulick Rd., Fairfield, 07004 (973) 575-8448
R & M Mfg., Inc., 20 Abeel Rd., Monroe, 08831 (609) 495-8032

ALPHABETICAL

R. & M. Mold Mfg. Co., LLC,
1022 Route 173 E., P.O. Box 578, Bloomsbury, 08804 (908) 479-4444
R & R Graphics, Inc., 1724 Route 70 E., Unit B, Cherry Hill, 08003 (856) 751-7671
† R & R Marketing, LLC, 2900 E. State Street Ext., Trenton, 08619 (609) 587-6103
† R & R Marketing, LLC, 10 Patton Dr., West Caldwell, 07006 (973) 228-5100
R & R Plastics, Inc., 62-70 Myrtle Ave., Passaic, 07055 (973) 365-8083
R & R Printing & Copy Center, 1075 Easton Ave., Somerset, 08873 (732) 249-9450
R & R Printing Co., 107 S. Stevens Ave., P.O. Box 3204, South Amboy, 08879 (732) 727-6036
R & R Specialties, 126 Holly Dr., Rio Grande, 08242 (609) 886-6651
R & R Stairs, Inc., 131 Wood Ave., Middlesex, 08846 (732) 752-9400
R & T Custom Cabinets, 1311 Herbert Blvd., Williamstown, 08094 (856) 728-1979
R & T Stone see. Stone Galaxy, Turnersville
★ R A C Systems Corp., 1-B Glimpsewood Ln., Morristown, 07960 (973) 292-3200
R A M Hydraulics, 215 B. Hickory Ln., P.O. Box 416, Bayville, 08721 (732) 237-0904
R A S Process Equipment, 324 Meadowbrook Rd., Robbinsville, 08691 (609) 371-1000
R. B.'s Rubber Stamp, Inc., 551 W. Side Ave., Jersey City, 07304 (201) 547-9955
† R. E. Michel Co., Inc., 895 Towbin Ave., Lakewood, 08701 (732) 886-3592
† R. E. Michel Co., Inc., 262 Old New Brunswick Rd., Piscataway, 08854 (732) 465-9700
R F L Electronics, Inc., 353 Powerville Rd., Boonton, 07005 (973) 334-3100
R F VII, Inc., 1041 Glassboro Rd., Bldg. 6, Williamstown, 08094 (856) 875-2121
R G I, Inc., 27 Union Valley Rd., Newfoundland, 07435 (973) 697-2624
R J Graphics, Inc., 206 Crown Point Rd., P.O. Box 293, West Deptford, 08086 (856) 848-1986
R J Hoppe Store Construction see. Ge-Ro Desk Co., Newark
R K E Athletic Lettering, 1901 State Route 71, Ste. 1-C, Belmar, 07719 (732) 280-1111
★ R. K. Industries, Inc., 259 Overbrook Ave., Oakhurst, 07755 (732) 531-1123
R L E Industries, LLC, 35 Kulick Rd., Fairfield, 07004 (973) 276-1444
R L R Foil Stamping, LLC, 245 4th St., Passaic, 07055 (973) 778-9464
R L Tool & Die Co., 739 Fairfield Ave., Kenilworth, 07033 (908) 245-7710
R M F Assocs., Inc., 202 Carolyn Rd., Union, 07083 (908) 687-9355
R. P. Baking Co., 840 Jersey St., Harrison, 07029 (973) 483-3374
R. R. Bowker, 630 Central Ave., New Providence, 07974 (908) 795-3500
R. R. Donnelley & Sons Co., 215 County Ave., Secaucus, 07094 (201) 271-1000
R. R. Donnelley & Sons Co., 5 Henderson Dr., West Caldwell, 07006 (973) 882-7000
R S Microwave Co., Inc., 22 Park Pl., P.O. Box 273, Butler, 07405 (973) 492-1207
R S R Food Service Equipment Corp.,
6574 Delilah Rd., Egg Harbor Township, 08234 (609) 646-5158
R T B Fabricators, Inc., 220 Lincoln Blvd., Middlesex, 08846 (732) 469-4127
R T I, Inc., 401 Hasbrouck Blvd., Oradell, 07649 (201) 261-5852
R Tape Corporation see. CET Films, Inc., Lakewood
R Tape Corporation, 6 Ingersoll Rd., South Plainfield, 07080 (908) 753-5570
R V Tech, Inc., 801 Magnolia Ave., Bldg. 3-B, Elizabeth, 07201 (908) 469-8701
R Welding, 97 Main St., Waretown, 08758 (609) 971-6017
R World Enterprises, 197 Congress St., Jersey City, 07307 (201) 795-2428
R.A.B. Food Group, LLC, 80 Avenue K, Newark, 07105 (201) 553-1100
RAB Lighting, Inc., 170 Ludlow Ave., Northvale, 07647 (201) 784-8600
Rabell Precision, Inc., 8 Queen Anne Rd., Bogota, 07603 (201) 473-7373
Rack Design Group Inc. / BarCodeAmerica.com, 81 Clinton Rd., Fairfield, 07004 (973) 377-8182
RAD Data Communications, Inc., 900 Corporate Dr., Ste. 1, Mahwah, 07430 (201) 529-1100
Radaire Distributors, Inc., 1318 Segart Ave., Sea Girt, 08750 (732) 282-1144
Radco Enterprises, Inc., 734 Oxford St., Vineland, 08360 (856) 691-3125
Radiant Communications Corp.,
5001 Hadley Rd., P.O. Box 867, South Plainfield, 07080 (908) 757-7444
Radiant Consulting see. Radiant Systems, Inc., South Plainfield
Radiant Energy Systems, Inc., 175 N. Ethel Ave., Hawthorne, 07506 (973) 423-5220
Radiant Systems, Inc., 107 Corporate Blvd., Ste. B, South Plainfield, 07080 (908) 668-1080
Radiant Thermal Products Co., 640 W. 1st Ave., Roselle, 07203 (908) 241-7700
Radiation Systems, Inc., 455 W. Main St., Wyckoff, 07481 (201) 891-7515
Radii, Inc., 66 Willow Ave., 3rd Fl., Hoboken, 07030 (201) 420-4700
Radio Systems Design, Inc., 601 Heron Dr., Logan Township, 08085 (856) 467-8000
Raffetto's Corp., 62 W. Commercial Ave., Moonachie, 07074 (201) 372-1222
★ RaGar Co., Inc., 2106 Kings Hwy., Asbury Park, 07712 (732) 493-1416
† Ragonese & Sons, Inc., Patsy, 331 Adams St., Newark, 07105 (973) 344-7411
† R.A.H. Carpet Supplies, Inc., 80 Willow St., East Rutherford, 07073 (973) 778-4759
† Rahway Electric Supply, Inc., 1684 Essex St., Rahway, 07065 (732) 381-6060
Rahway Steel Drum Co. (H Q), 202 Elliot St., Avenel, 07001 (732) 382-0113
Rahway Steel, Inc., 625 Leesville Ave., P.O. Box 276, Rahway, 07065 (732) 388-5300
Railco Metalcraft, Inc., 22 Park Pl., Butler, 07405 (973) 838-2822
Railing Dynamics, Inc., 1201 N. 10th St., Millville, 08332 (856) 327-1698
Railing Dynamics, Inc. (H Q),
135 Steelmanville Rd., Egg Harbor Township, 08234 (609) 601-1300
Railroad Construction Company, Inc. see. RCC Fabricators, Inc., Vincentown
Railroad Construction Company, Inc. (H Q), 75-77 Grove St., Paterson, 07503 (973) 684-0362
Rails Co., 101 Newark Way, Maplewood, 07040 (973) 763-4320
Rainbow Specialty Colors, Inc., 27 Utter Ave., Ste. B, Hawthorne, 07506 (973) 304-0912
Rainmen U. S. A., Inc., 10 Maple St., Norwood, 07648 (201) 784-3244
RAK Foam Sales, Inc., 1355 W. Front St., P.O. Box 3248, Plainfield, 07063 (908) 668-1122
Rako Machine Products, Inc., 845 Monmouth Rd., Cream Ridge, 08514 (609) 758-1200
Ralph Clayton & Sons, 1144 New York Ave., Trenton, 08638 (609) 695-0767
Ram Electronic Industries Inc., 1704 Taylors Ln., Ste. 7, Cinnaminson, 08077 (856) 864-0999
Rambusch Company, 160 Cornelison Ave., Jersey City, 07304 (201) 333-2525
Rambusch Lighting see. Rambusch Company, Jersey City
Ramco Equipment Corp., 32 Montgomery St., Hillside, 07205 (908) 687-6700
Ramco Mfg. Co., Inc., 365 Carnegie Ave., Kenilworth, 07033 (908) 245-4500
Ramco Systems Corp., 3150 U.S. Highway 1, Ste. 130, Lawrence Township, 08648 (609) 620-4871
Rame-Hart, Inc., 5 Emery Ave., Ste. 1, Randolph, 07869 (973) 335-0560
Rame-Hart Instrument Co., LLC, 19 Route 10 E., Ste. 11, Succasunna, 07876 (973) 448-0305
Ramelson Co., Inc., U. J., 165 Thomas St., Newark, 07114 (973) 589-5422
Ramsay Cabinetmakers, Inc., David, 310 Mill St., Moorestown, 08057 (856) 234-7776
Ramsey Model Design, David A., P.O. Box 87, Clarksburg, 08510 (609) 259-6757
Ramsey Print Corp., 1000 Wall St. W., Ste. 2, Lyndhurst, 07071 (201) 460-1008
Ranbaxy, Inc. see. OHM Laboratories, Inc., New Brunswick
Ranbaxy, Inc. see. OHM Laboratories, Inc., North Brunswick
Ranbaxy, Inc. (H Q), 600 College Rd. E., Ste. 2100, Princeton, 08540 (609) 720-9200
Ranco Precision Sheet Metal, Inc.,
40 Colorado St., P.O. Box 1101, Clifton, 07014 (973) 472-8808
† Rancocas Metals Corp., 35 Indel Ave., P.O. Box 223, Rancocas, 08073 (609) 267-4120
Rand Diversified, 3 Ethel Rd., Ste. 301, Edison, 08817 (732) 287-2525
Randa Corp. see. Randa Luggage Co., Bloomfield
† Randa Luggage Co., 200 Broadacres Dr., 2nd Fl., Bloomfield, 07003 (973) 873-9050
Randall Mfg. Co., Inc., 200 Sylvan Ave., Newark, 07104 (973) 484-7600
RANDCASTLE Extrusion Systems, Inc.,
220 Little Falls Rd., Unit 6, Cedar Grove, 07009 (973) 239-1150

Rangecraft Mfg. Co., Inc., 4-40 Banta Pl., Fair Lawn, 07410 (201) 791-0440
Ranger Industries, Inc., 15 Park Rd., Tinton Falls, 07724 (732) 389-1101
† Ransome International, 2320 High Hill Rd., Logan Township, 08085 (856) 241-8890
RAO Contract Sales, Inc., 392 Atwood Pl., Wyckoff, 07481 (201) 652-1500
Rapid Models & Prototypes, Inc., 1311 Marlkress Rd., Cherry Hill, 08003 (856) 933-2929
Rapid Print & Copy Service, 78 Summerhill Rd., East Brunswick, 08816 (732) 238-9056
Rapid Tag & Label, Inc., 5 Fir Ct., Ste. 4, Oakland, 07436 (201) 337-5551
Raritan Computer, Inc., 400 Cottontail Ln., Somerset, 08873 (732) 764-8886
Raritan Engineering Co., Inc., 530 Orange St., Millville, 08332 (856) 825-4900
Raritan Packaging Industries, Inc., 570 Jersey Ave., New Brunswick, 08901 (732) 246-7200
Raritan Pharmaceuticals, Inc., 8 Joanna Ct., East Brunswick, 08816 (732) 432-8200
Raritan Printing Plus Flags & Banners, Inc.,
109 N. Feltus St., South Amboy, 08879 (732) 721-2121
Raritan Valley Printing Co., 7 Sheephill Cir., Branchburg, 08876 (908) 725-4140
Raritan Valley Workshop, 9 Terminal Rd., New Brunswick, 08901 (732) 828-8080
Rasi Laboratories, Inc., 20 Roosevelt Ave., Somerset, 08873 (732) 873-8500
Rasta Imposta see. Silvertop Assocs., Inc., Runnemede
RathGibson, LLC, 100 Aspen Hill Rd., North Branch, 08876 (908) 218-1400
Raue Screw Machine Product Co.,
173 Oak Ridge Rd., P.O. Box 207, Oak Ridge, 07438 (973) 697-7500
Rauhauser's Candy, 721 Asbury Ave., Ocean City, 08226 (609) 399-1465
Rawco, Inc., 452 Route 513, Califon, 07830 (908) 832-7700
Raybold Mfg., Inc., 102 S. 8th St., Millville, 08332 (856) 327-7733
Raybold Mfg., Inc., Disposable Products Div.,
102 S. 8th St., Millville, 08332 (856) 327-7733
Raymond Of NJ, LLC, 1000 Brighton St., Union, 07083 (908) 624-9570
Ray's Reproductions, Inc., 39 Bland St., Emerson, 07630 (201) 666-5650
Raz Performance Machine, 247 Harding Hwy., Vineland, 08360 (856) 697-4275
Razac Products Co., Inc., 25 Brenner St., Newark, 07108 (973) 622-3700
RAZA-Designs, Inc., 220 61st St., Ste. 2-C, West New York, 07093 (201) 430-8590
Razor Printing, 78 Summerhill Rd., East Brunswick, 08816 (732) 238-7520
RB & A, Inc., 350 Sparta Ave., Bldg. C, Sparta, 07871 (973) 726-0830
RBC Bearings, Inc., 400 Sullivan Way, West Trenton, 08628 (609) 882-5050
RC Fine Foods, Inc., 139 Stryker Ln., Hillsborough, 08844 (908) 359-5500
RC Repair, 526 Doremus Ave., Glen Rock, 07452 (201) 445-0361
RCC Fabricators, Inc., 2035 Highway 206, Vincentown, 08088 (609) 859-9350
RDL Marketing Group, LLC,
352-A Sweetmann Ln., P.O. Box 385, Perrineville, 08535 (732) 446-0817
RDO Induction LLC, 2170 State Route 57 W., Washington, 07882 (908) 835-7222
Re Community see. FCR Camden, Inc., Camden
RE Systems Group, Inc., 1060 Main St., Ste. 200, River Edge, 07661 (201) 883-1572
REA see. Research & Education Assn., Piscataway
Reade Manufacturing Co., 2590 Ridgeway Blvd., Manchester, 08759 (732) 657-6451
Readington Farms, Inc., 12 Mill Rd., P.O. Box 164, Whitehouse, 08888 (908) 534-2121
Ready Pac, 101 Arlington Blvd., Swedesboro, 08085 (856) 241-0900
Ready Pac Produce, Inc. see. Ready Pac, Swedesboro
Ready Pac Produce, Inc., 700 Railroad Ave., P.O. Box 6, Florence, 08518 (609) 499-1900
Reagent Chemical & Research, Inc., 115 U.S. Highway 202, Ringoes, 08551 (908) 284-2800
Real Kosher LLC, 146 Christie St., Newark, 07105 (973) 690-5394
Rebco, Inc., 1171 Madison Ave., Ste. 1, Paterson, 07503 (973) 684-0200
Rebtex, Inc., 40 Industrial Pkwy., Somerville, 08876 (908) 722-3549
Rebuilt Parts Co., 7929 River Rd., Pennsauken, 08110 (856) 662-3252
† Rebuth Metal Services, 2262 Stocker Ln., P.O. Box 488, Scotch Plains, 07076 (908) 889-6400
Reckitt Benckiser, Inc., 399 Interpace Pkwy., P.O. Box 225, Parsippany, 07054 (973) 404-2600
Reckitt Benckiser, Inc. see. Reckitt Benckiser, LLC, Hillsborough
Reckitt Benckiser, LLC,
799 U.S. Highway 206, P.O. Box 5817, Hillsborough, 08844 (908) 533-2000
ReConserve, Inc., 1250 Amboy Ave., Perth Amboy, 08861 (732) 826-4240
Record, The, 1 Garret Mountain Plz., P.O. Box 471, Woodland Park, 07424 (973) 569-7770
Recorder Newspaper Co., 530 E. Main St., P.O. Box 600, Chester, 07930 (908) 766-3900
Recorder Publishing Co. see. Recorder Newspaper Co., Chester
Recorder Publishing Co. (H Q),
17-19 Morristown Rd., P.O. Box 687, Bernardsville, 07924 (908) 766-3900
Rectico, Inc., 12 Gloria Ln., Unit 1, Fairfield, 07004 (973) 575-0009
RecycleTech Corp., 418 Falmouth Ave., Elmwood Park, 07407 (201) 475-5000
Red Bank Cabinet Co., 548 Shrewsbury Ave., Tinton Falls, 07701 (732) 741-8080
Red Diamond Co., Inc., 368 Cortlandt St., Belleville, 07109 (973) 759-2700
Red Feather Marketing Group, 332 Main St., Madison, 07940 (973) 966-1399
Red Letter Press, Inc., 16 Deerhorn Trl., Saddle River, 07458 (201) 818-8951
Red Oak Software, Inc.,
115 U.S. Highway 46, Ste. F-1000, Mountain Lakes, 07046 (973) 316-6064
Red Sea Press, Inc., The see. Africa World Press, Inc., Trenton
Red Square Foods, Inc., 62 Berry St., Somerset, 08873 (732) 846-0190
Red Tag Brand see. Omavi Clothing Co. (H Q), Newark
Red The Uniform Tailor, Inc., 475 Oberlin Ave. S., Lakewood, 08701 (848) 299-0100
Reddaway Mfg. Co., Inc., 32 Euclid Ave., Newark, 07105 (973) 589-1410
Redfield Corp., 336 W. Passaic St., Rochelle Park, 07662 (201) 845-3990
Redi Packaging, Inc., 265 Highway 36, Ste. 109, West Long Branch, 07764 (732) 544-1480
Redi Print see. Papson Printing Corp., Hackensack
Redi-Mail Direct Marketing, 107 Little Falls Rd., Fairfield, 07004 (973) 808-4500
Redkeys Dies, Inc., 1307 Market St., Gloucester City, 08030 (856) 456-7890
Redkoh see. Datatest, Inc., Hillsborough
Redkoh Industries, Inc., 300 Valley Rd., Hillsborough, 08844 (908) 369-1590
Redwallet Connection, LLC, 907 21st St., Union City, 07087 (201) 223-2644
Redyref Co., 100 Kenner Ct., Riverdale, 07457 (718) 784-3690
Reed & Perrine Sales, Inc., 396 Main St., P.O. Box 100, Tennent, 07763 (732) 446-6363
Reed Elsevier, Inc. see. LexisNexis Martindale-Hubell, New Providence
Reed-Lane, Inc., 359 Newark Pompton Tpke., Wayne, 07470 (973) 709-1090
Reedy International Corp., 25 E. Front St., Ste. 200, Keyport, 07735 (732) 264-1777
Reel Parts Co., 10 Park Ave., West Orange, 07052 (973) 731-9559
Rees Scientific Corp., 1007 Whitehead Road Ext., Trenton, 08638 (609) 530-1055
Reeves Enterprises, Inc., 571 Central Ave., New Providence, 07974 (908) 665-9511
Reeves International, Inc., 14 Industrial Rd., Pequannock, 07440 (973) 694-5006
Reeves International, Inc., 34 Owens Dr., Wayne, 07470 (973) 956-9555
Refinery Systems, A Div. Of Core Lab, 11 Princess Rd., Lawrenceville, 08648 (609) 896-2673
Reflective Metals, Inc., 1001 Hopewell Ave., Ocean, 07712 (732) 918-7490
Reflex Analytical Corporation, 643 Albert Pl., Ridgewood, 07450 (201) 444-8958
Regal Printers, Inc., 707-3 Old Shore Rd., Forked River, 08731 (609) 693-3533
Regal Stamp & Sign Co., Inc.,
240 Park Ave., P.O. Box 342, East Rutherford, 07073 (201) 939-0400
Regale, Inc., Kristian, 4 Forest Ave., Ste. 202, Paramus, 07652 (201) 587-9800
Regal-Pinnacle Mfg., Inc., 220 Route 70, Ste. A, Medford, 08055 (609) 714-2330

Regen & Co., Inc., 20-21 Wagaraw Rd., Bldg. 32, Fair Lawn, 07410 ... (973) 423-4236
Regency Elevator Products, 870 Mount Prospect Ave., Newark, 07104 ... (973) 481-1400
Reggiani Lighting USA, Inc., 372 Starke Rd., Carlstadt, 07072 ... (201) 372-1717
Register Lithographers, Ltd., 1155 Bloomfield Ave., Clifton, 07012 ... (973) 916-2804
Regn Sign Studio, Inc., 42 Main St., Bradley Beach, 07720 ... (732) 988-3595
Rego Iron Co., 176 Cohawkin Rd., Clarksboro, 08020 ... (856) 423-6779
Rehtek Machine Co., 135 Monroe St., Passaic, 07055 ... (973) 365-2101
Reid Book Binding, D., 543 New Durham Rd., Metuchen, 08840 ... (732) 494-9589
Reid Plumbing Products, LLC, 371 Route 31 N., Hopewell, 08525 ... (609) 466-1785
Reinco, Inc., 520 North Ave., Plainfield, 07060 ... (908) 755-0921
Reiss Mfg., Inc., 75 Mount Vernon Rd., P.O. Box 310, Englishtown, 07726 ... (732) 446-6100
Relational Architects, 33 Newark St., Ste. 3-A, Hoboken, 07030 ... (201) 420-0400
† Relay Specialties, Inc., 17 Raritan Rd., P.O. Box 7000, Oakland, 07436 ... (201) 337-1000
Reliable Electric Motor Repair, Inc., 19 California Ave., Paterson, 07503 ... (973) 278-8122
Reliable Envelope & Graphics, Inc., 85 Main Ave., Elmwood Park, 07407 ... (201) 794-7756
Reliable Rubber & Plastic Machinery Co.,
2008 Union Tpke., North Bergen, 07047 ... (201) 865-1073
† Reliable Tire Distributors, Inc.,
805 N. Black Horse Pike, P.O. Box 39, Blackwood, 08012 ... (856) 232-0700
Reliable Wood Products see. ... Nature's Choice Corp., Sparta
Reliance Electronics, Inc., 20 W. End Rd., Totowa, 07512 ... (973) 237-0400
Reliance Global Services, Inc.,
50 Cragwood Rd., Ste. 100, South Plainfield, 07080 ... (908) 769-1271
Reliance Graphics, Inc., 80 Pompton Ave., Ste. 1, Verona, 07044 ... (973) 239-5411
★ Reliance Plastic & Chemical Corp.,
38-27 Wilson St., P.O. Box 395, Fair Lawn, 07410 ... (201) 797-8014
Reliant Group, 318 McLean Blvd., Paterson, 07504 ... (973) 977-8799
Reliant Ribbon & Trims, 838 21st Ave., Paterson, 07513 ... (973) 881-0404
Rem Services, 310 W. 6th St., Ship Bottom, 08008 ... (609) 494-7760
Rema Tip Top/North America, Inc. (H Q), 119 Rockland Ave., Northvale, 07647 ... (201) 768-8100
Reminder Newspaper, 2 W. Vine St., P.O. Box 1600, Millville, 08332 ... (856) 825-8811
Remington Industries, Inc., Cordes Machine Div.,
269 Sheffield St., Mountainside, 07092 ... (908) 233-2600
Rempac Foam, LLC (H Q), 370 W. Passaic St., Rochelle Park, 07662 ... (973) 881-8880
Renaissance Marble & Granite, 107 Harmon Dr., Blackwood, 08012 ... (856) 227-3535
Renard Commmunications, Inc., 197 Mountain Ave., Springfield, 07081 ... (973) 912-8550
Renault Winery, 72 N. Bremen Ave., Egg Harbor City, 08215 ... (609) 965-2111
Renell Label Print, Inc., 15 Sunflower Ave., Paramus, 07652 ... (201) 652-6544
Renew Graphics, 16 W. Park Ave., Park Ridge, 07656 ... (201) 802-1900
Renewable BioSystems, LLC, 20 Spielman Rd., Fairfield, 07004 ... (973) 769-0600
Rennie Mfg. & Metal Finishing Co., Inc.,
12-14 Rennie Pl., P.O. Box 285, Lodi, 07644 ... (973) 773-9175
★ Rent-Rite Lift Truck Services,
73 Green Pond Rd., P.O. Box 349, Rockaway, 07866 ... (973) 586-4477
Repco, Inc., 6 Eves Dr., Marlton, 08053 ... (800) 822-9190
Repromatic Printing Co., Inc.,
216 Little Falls Rd., Unit 3, Cedar Grove, 07009 ... (973) 239-7610
Republic Mold & Tool Co., Inc., 109 Bradford Ave., Linden, 07036 ... (908) 862-3344
RER Supply see. ... Riverdale Environmental Recycling, Riverdale
Resdel Corp., Cape May County Industrial Pk., Rio Grande, 08242 ... (609) 886-1111
Research & Education Assn., 61 Ethel Rd. W., Piscataway, 08854 ... (732) 819-8880
Research & Mfg. Corp. Of America, 1130 W. Elizabeth Ave., Linden, 07036 ... (908) 862-6744
Research Diets, Inc., 20 Jules Ln., New Brunswick, 08901 ... (732) 247-2390
Resec Systems, LLC, 93 S. Railroad Ave., Ste. A, Bergenfield, 07621 ... (201) 384-6960
Resintech, Inc., 160 Cooper Rd., West Berlin, 08091 ... (856) 768-9600
Resistance Welding Solutions, Inc., 1090 Lousons Rd., Union, 07083 ... (908) 964-9100
Resolv Corporation, 410 Division St., Elizabeth, 07201 ... (973) 676-5141
Resource Systems, Inc., 7 Merry Ln., East Hanover, 07936 ... (973) 884-0650
Restaurant Depot, LLC see. ... Jetro Cash & Carry, Inc., Jersey City
† Restaurant Depot, LLC, 1050 Thomas Busch Memorial Hwy., Pennsauken, 08110 ... (856) 488-4288
Restaurant Graphics, Inc., 67 Newark Way, Maplewood, 07040 ... (973) 763-4036
Restek Corp. see. ... Glastron, Inc., Vineland
Rete Biomedical Communications Corp., 191 Godwin Ave., Ste. 1, Wyckoff, 07481 ... (201) 891-8205
Rethink Color see. ... National Reprographics, Inc., Lawrenceville
Rethink Color, a division of NRI, 3175 Princeton Pike, Lawrenceville, 08648 ... (609) 896-4100
Retrospect, The, 732 Haddon Ave., P.O. Box 296, Collingswood, 08108 ... (856) 854-1400
Reunion Gifts, 20 Lowell Ave., Summit, 07901 ... (877) 873-8646
Reuther Engineering & Machining Co., Inc., 126 S. 14th St., Newark, 07107 ... (973) 485-5800
Reuther Material Co., Inc., 5303 Tonnelle Ave., North Bergen, 07047 ... (201) 863-3550
Revelation Technologies, Inc., 99 Kinderkamack Rd., Ste. 109, Westwood, 07675 ... (201) 594-1422
Revent, Inc., 100 Ethel Rd. W., Piscataway, 08854 ... (732) 777-9433
Revicci, Inc., 25 Sycamore Ter., Livingston, 07039 ... (973) 994-1421
Review Printing, Inc., 53-55 E. Holly Ave., Pitman, 08071 ... (856) 589-7200
Review Publishing L. P. see. ... Atlantic City Weekly, L. P., Pleasantville
Reviva Labs, Inc., 705 Hopkins Rd., Haddonfield, 08033 ... (856) 428-3885
Revive Personal Products see. ... Caldwell Consumer Health, LLC (H Q), Madison
Rex Bedding & Sleep Products, 300 W. 4th St., Plainfield, 07060 ... (908) 668-0220
Rex Lumber Co., 1 Station St., P.O. Box 1776, Englishtown, 07726 ... (732) 446-4200
Rex Sign Co., 60 Steiner Ave., Neptune City, 07753 ... (732) 774-1377
Rex Tool & Mfg. Co., 544 E. Elizabeth Ave., P.O. Box 1423, Linden, 07036 ... (908) 925-2727
Rex Wine Vinegar Co., 828-830 Raymond Blvd., Newark, 07105 ... (973) 589-6911
Rexam Healthcare Packaging, Inc., 14-B Brass Castle Rd., Washington, 07882 ... (908) 689-1660
Rexam, Inc. see. ... Rexam Healthcare Packaging, Inc., Washington
Rexell Foods Corp., 120 Orchard St., Newark, 07102 ... (973) 741-0404
RF Products, Inc., 1500 Davis St., Camden, 08103 ... (856) 365-5500
RFC Container Co., 2066 S. East Ave., Vineland, 08360 ... (856) 692-0404
RFM Printing, Inc., 1715 Highway 34, P.O. Box 1430, Wall, 07719 ... (732) 938-4400
RG Group see. ... Van Air & Hydraulics, Inc., Maple Shade
Rhoads Metal Works, Inc., 1551 John Tipton Blvd., Pennsauken, 08110 ... (856) 486-1551
Rhodes & Rhodes Millwork Co., Inc.,
3011 Ocean Heights Ave., Unit A, Egg Harbor Township, 08234 ... (609) 653-3180
Riber, Inc., 15 Liberty St., Metuchen, 08840 ... (732) 603-0680
Ricci Brothers Sand Company, Inc.,
2099 Dragston Rd., P.O. Box 664, Port Norris, 08349 ... (856) 785-0166
Ricci Tool & Die Co., 122 Myrtle Ave., Long Branch, 07740 ... (732) 222-2777
Rich Art Color Co., Inc., 202 Pegasus Ave., Northvale, 07647 ... (201) 767-0009
Rich Products see. ... Mother's Kitchen, Inc., Burlington
Rich Products, 1910 Gallagher Dr., Vineland, 08360 ... (856) 696-5600
Rich Products Corp. see. ... Mother's Kitchen, Inc., Burlington
Rich Products Corp. see. ... Rich Products, Vineland
Richard Tashjian Int'l see. ... R T I, Inc., Oradell
Richards Chocolates Co., Inc., Al, 851 Broadway, Bayonne, 07002 ... (201) 436-0915
† Richards Co., 437 Boulevard, P.O. Box 199, Elmwood Park, 07407 ... (201) 797-6300
Richards Industries Co., 4 Fairfield Crescent, West Caldwell, 07006 ... (973) 575-7480
Richards Mfg., 517 Lyons Ave., Irvington, 07111 ... (973) 371-1771
Richardson Co., J. B., 1603 N. Olden Ave., Trenton, 08638 ... (609) 695-7474
Richland Glass Co., Inc., 1640 S. West Blvd., Vineland, 08360 ... (856) 691-1697
Richmond Industries, Inc., 1 Chris Ct., Dayton, 08810 ... (732) 355-1616
Rich's Kitchens, Inc., 309 Hamburg Tpke., Butler, 07405 ... (973) 838-4026
Ricklyn Co., Inc., 460 Route 57, Port Murray, 07865 ... (908) 689-6770
Rico Foods, Inc., 527 E. 18th St., Paterson, 07514 ... (973) 278-0589
†★ Rides4U, Inc., 221 Evans Way, Ste. E, Somerville, 08876 ... (908) 526-8009
Ridge Carbide Tool Co., 595 New York Ave., P.O. Box 497, Lyndhurst, 07071 ... (201) 438-8777
Ridge Doors, 335 New Rd., P.O. Box 180, Monmouth Junction, 08852 ... (732) 329-2311
Ridge Precision Products Inc., 288 U.S. Highway 46, Ste. D, Dover, 07801 ... (973) 361-3508
Ridgewood Awning Co., Inc., 445 W. Main St., Ste. 6, Wyckoff, 07481 ... (201) 847-0909
Ridgewood Medical Media, LLC, P.O. Box 802, Ridgewood, 07450 ... (201) 670-1356
Ridgewood Press, Inc., 609 Franklin Tpke., Ridgewood, 07450 ... (201) 670-9797
Ridgid Paper Tube Corp., 10 Owens Dr., Wayne, 07470 ... (973) 942-7000
Riedel Sign Co., Inc., 15 Warren St., Little Ferry, 07643 ... (201) 641-9121
Riegel Communication Group, One Graphics Dr., P.O. Box 7430, Ewing, 08628 ... (609) 771-0555
Riephoff Sawmill, Inc., 763 Route 524, Allentown, 08501 ... (609) 259-7265
Ries Co., Inc., R. E., 107 Lake Ave., Brielle, 08730 ... (732) 892-1842
RightAnswers, Inc., 333 Thornall St., Ste. 703, Edison, 08837 ... (732) 396-9010
Rigo Industries, Inc., 50 California Ave., Paterson, 07503 ... (973) 881-1780
Rimex Metals (USA) Inc, 2850 Woodbridge Ave., Edison, 08837 ... (732) 549-3800
Rimmel Rogers, Inc., 250 Passaic St., Newark, 07104 ... (201) 998-4700
Rimtec Corp., 1702 Beverly Rd., Burlington, 08016 ... (609) 387-0011
Ring Container Technologies, 50 Fadem Rd., Ste. 1, Springfield, 07081 ... (973) 258-0707
Ring Container Technologies, Inc. see. ... Ring Container Technologies, Springfield
Ringel Bros., Inc., 7 W. Shelton Ter., P.O. Box 727, Hillside, 07205 ... (908) 688-9222
Rinko Orthopedic Appliances, Inc., 2509 Broadway, Fair Lawn, 07410 ... (201) 796-3121
Rios Engraving, 1 Maple Ave., Morristown, 07960 ... (973) 539-5749
Ripen eCommerce see. ... Ripen Interactive, LLC, Princeton
Ripen Interactive, LLC, 117 Rockingham Row, Princeton, 08540 ... (609) 520-8820
Rise-N-Shine, LLC (H Q), 17 Woodport Rd., Ste. 1-E, Sparta, 07871 ... (973) 729-4141
Rite Packaging see. ... Shelving Depot, Inc., Linden
River Front Recycling & Aggregates, LLC, 1301 N. 26th St., Camden, 08105 ... (856) 966-1100
River Horse, 2 Graphics Dr., Trenton, 08628 ... (609) 883-0890
† River Road Recycling Inc., 450 37th St., P.O. Box 302, Pennsauken, 08110 ... (856) 661-0770
Riverdale Color Mfg., Inc., 1 Walnut St., Perth Amboy, 08861 ... (732) 376-9300
Riverdale Environmental Recycling, 1 Riverdale Rd., Riverdale, 07457 ... (973) 616-6654
Rivers Edge Woodworks & Design, 90 Dayton Ave., Passaic, 07055 ... (973) 337-2288
Riverside Acquisition Group, LLC see. ... Com-Pak, Inc., Moorestown
Riverside Acquisition Group, LLC (H Q), 365 New Albany Rd., Moorestown, 08057 ... (856) 802-1900
★ Riverside Graphics, Inc., 40 Little St., Belleville, 07109 ... (973) 844-1011
Riverside Image see. ... Riverside Prints LLC, Middletown
Riverside Partners, LLC see. ... Water-Jel Technologies, Carlstadt
Riverside Prints LLC, 11 Lawrence Cir., Middletown, 07748 ... (732) 671-8222
† Riviera Produce Corp., 205 Jackson St., P.O. Box 6065, Englewood, 07631 ... (201) 227-7105
† Rizzo Fine Arts Inc., Nicholas F., 32 Watchung Ave., Chatham, 07928 ... (973) 635-7278
R.J. Printing, Inc., 5 Dodd Rd., West Caldwell, 07006 ... (973) 226-9509
RJD Machine Products, Inc., 1424 Heath Ave., Ewing, 08638 ... (609) 392-1515
R-Kane Products, Inc., 8351 National Hwy., Pennsauken, 08110 ... (856) 663-0644
RKM Enterprises, Inc., 177 Mercer St., Hightstown, 08520 ... (609) 448-7539
† RM Metals, 50 Cragwood Rd., South Plainfield, 07080 ... (908) 222-1500
RMI Hoobing, 460 Veterans Dr., Burlington, 08016 ... (609) 387-1999
Roan Printing, Inc., 4 E. Main St., Somerville, 08876 ... (908) 526-5990
Robalo Enterprises, 104 New Era Dr., South Plainfield, 07080 ... (908) 753-1075
Robbins Instruments, Inc., 2 N. Passaic Ave., P.O. Box 441, Chatham, 07928 ... (973) 635-8972
RobDav Distributors, Inc., 1251 Yardville Allentown Rd., Allentown, 08501 ... (609) 259-6335
Roben Mfg. Co., Inc., 760 Vassar Ave., Lakewood, 08701 ... (732) 364-6000
Robert Lighting & Energy Industries, LLC see. ... R L E Industries, LLC, Fairfield
† Robert McKeown Co., Inc., 111 Chambers Brook Rd., Branchburg, 08876 ... (908) 218-9000
Robert Technologies, Inc., 37 Main St., South River, 08882 ... (732) 254-6389
Robert Young & Sons, Inc., 25 Grafton Ave., Newark, 07104 ... (973) 483-0451
Robertet Flavors, Inc., 10 Colonial Dr., Piscataway, 08854 ... (732) 981-8300
Robertet-Novarome Fragrances, Inc., 400 International Dr., Mount Olive, 07828 ... (973) 575-4550
† Robert-James Sales, Inc., 9 Corporate Dr., P.O. Box B, Cranbury, 08512 ... (609) 860-0900
Robertson Industries, 19 State Route 23, Montague, 07827 ... (973) 293-8666
Robertson Piper Software Group, Inc. see. ... Lagniappe Health Acquisition Co., Pine Brook
Robertson Piper Software Group, Inc. (H Q), 1500 Cardinal Dr., Chatham, 07928 ... (973) 435-3640
Robessa Enterprises, Inc., 1030 Delsea Dr., P.O. Box 72, Westville, 08093 ... (856) 251-0055
Robinson Tech International Corp., 310 Fairfield Rd., Fairfield, 07004 ... (973) 287-6458
Robodyssey Systems, LLC, 20 Quimby Ave., Trenton, 08610 ... (609) 585-8535
Robotunits, Inc., 5 Chris Ct., Ste. G, Dayton, 08810 ... (732) 438-0500
Robro Mfg., Inc., 288 10th Ave., Paterson, 07524 ... (973) 279-7237
Robyn Packaging Co., Inc., 31 Augusta Dr., Wayne, 07470 ... (973) 696-2059
Rocco Press, Inc., 171 Walnut St., Paterson, 07522 ... (973) 790-4000
Roche Holdings, Inc. see. ... Roche Nutley, Nutley
Roche Molecular Diagnostics see. ... Roche Molecular Systems, Inc., Branchburg
Roche Molecular Systems, Inc., 1080 U.S. Highway 202 S., Branchburg, 08876 ... (908) 253-7200
Roche Nutley, 340 Kingsland St., Nutley, 07110 ... (973) 235-5000
† Rocket Building Supply Co., Inc., 13 Hewson Ave., Waldwick, 07463 ... (201) 652-8884
Rockland Bakery, Inc. see. ... R. P. Baking Co., Harrison
Rockline Industries, Inc., 1 Kramer Dr., P.O. Box 189, Montville, 07045 ... (973) 257-9346
RockTenn see. ... Rock-Tenn Co., Dayton
RockTenn see. ... Rock-Tenn Co., Fairfield
RockTenn see. ... Rock-Tenn Co., Newark
Rock-Tenn Co. see. ... Graph Corr, LLC, Dayton
Rock-Tenn Co., 1 Corn Rd., P.O. Box 440, Dayton, 08810 ... (732) 274-2500
Rock-Tenn Co., 15 Garner Rd., Fairfield, 07004 ... (973) 594-6000
Rock-Tenn Co., 2013 McCarter Hwy., Newark, 07104 ... (973) 268-4938
Rockwell Automation, Inc., 165 Fieldcrest Ave., Raritan Ctr., Edison, 08837 ... (732) 225-1360
Rockwood Corp. / Speedwell Targets, 410 Clermont Ter., Ste. D, Union, 07083 ... (908) 355-8600
Rockwood Holdings, Inc. (H Q), 100 Overlook Ctr., 1st Fl., Princeton, 08540 ... (609) 514-0300
Rockwood Specialties see. ... Rockwood Holdings, Inc. (H Q), Princeton
★ Rocky's T's, 61 N. Hook Rd., Pennsville, 08070 ... (856) 678-2535
Rod Borden & Assocs., Inc. see. ... RB & A, Inc., Sparta
† Rodio Tractor Sales, Inc., 717 White Horse Pike, Hammonton, 08037 ... (609) 561-0141
Rodman Publishing Corp., 70 Hilltop Rd., 3rd Fl., Ramsey, 07446 ... (201) 825-2552
Roelyn Litho, Inc., 687 Propect St., Unit 410, Lakewood, 08701 ... (732) 942-9650
ROFIN-SINAR, Inc. see. ... PRC Laser, Landing
Rogers Containers see. ... Robessa Enterprises, Inc., Westville

ALPHABETICAL

★ Indicates new listing this edition. † Indicates wholesaler/distributor.

Rogers Printing Center, 11 Lexington Ave., Trenton, 08618 ........ (609) 883-3238
Rolferry's see. ........ Imprint Specialties, Inc., Brooklawn
Roll Flex Label Co., LLC, 199 Lee Pl., Hackensack, 07601 ........ (201) 489-3330
Roll Tech Industries, 55 Route 31 S., Ste. A, Pennington, 08534 ........ (609) 730-9500
Rolled Products see. ........ Aleris Mfg., Clayton
Rollon Corp., 101 Bilby Rd., Ste. B, Hackettstown, 07840 ........ (973) 300-5492
† Roma Food Enterprises, Inc., 1 Roma Blvd., Piscataway, 08854 ........ (732) 463-7662
† Roma Moulding, Inc., 115 Northfield Ave., Edison, 08837 ........ (732) 346-0999
† Roma Of Mid-Atlantic, 301 Heron Dr., Swedesboro, 08085 ........ (856) 467-8100
Romano & Son, Inc., 501 Baldwin Ave., Lodi, 07644 ........ (973) 472-3240
Romar Machine & Tool Co., 521 Commerce St., Franklin Lakes, 07417 ........ (201) 337-7111
Ronald-Mark Assocs., Inc., 1227 Central Ave., P.O. Box 776, Hillside, 07205 ........ (908) 558-0011
Ronald-Mark Assocs., Inc., 150 N. Summit Ave., P.O. Box 355, Pitman, 08071 ........ (856) 582-6766
† RONDO Inc. USA, 51 Joseph St., Moonachie, 07074 ........ (201) 229-9700
Roned Printing, 6 DeForest Ave., Ste. 2, East Hanover, 07936 ........ (973) 386-1848
Ronic, Inc., 173 Ray St., Garfield, 07026 ........ (973) 772-2217
Ronpak, Inc., 4301 New Brunswick Ave., South Plainfield, 07080 ........ (732) 968-8000
† Ronstan Paper & Packaging, 72 James Way, Eatontown, 07724 ........ (732) 389-1040
Roof Deck, Inc., 80 Twin Rivers Dr., P.O. Box 295, Hightstown, 08520 ........ (609) 448-6666
Roosevelt Paper Co., 1 Roosevelt Dr., Mount Laurel, 08054 ........ (856) 303-4100
Roper Industries, Inc. see. ........ Princeton Instruments, Trenton
Rosa Pen Corp., 155 Park Ave., Ste. 101, Lyndhurst, 07071 ........ (201) 939-1112
Rosa-Ly Pirogi, 256 Madison Ave., Irvington, 07111 ........ (973) 371-0650
Rosano Trucking, Inc., 26 Maple Ave., Oceanport, 07757 ........ (732) 542-5009
Rosco, Inc., 55 South Ave., P.O. Box 184, Garwood, 07027 ........ (908) 789-1020
Rose Brand, Inc., 4 Emerson Ln., Secaucus, 07094 ........ (201) 809-1730
Rose Signs, 13 Route 206 S., Branchville, 07826 ........ (973) 948-0501
Roselle Tool & Die Co., 135 W. Clay Ave., P.O. Box 103, Roselle Park, 07204 ........ (908) 245-3133
Roselli Co., L. E. see. ........ Roselli's Food Specialties, Inc., L. E., Medford
Roselli's Food Specialties, Inc., L. E., 155 Church Rd., Medford, 08055 ........ (609) 654-4816
Roseman's Boat Yard & Charter, 5 Roseman Ln., Cape May, 08204 ........ (609) 884-3370
Rosenberger Of North America, LLC see. ........ Toth Inc., Pennsauken
Roseville Tool & Mfg., 22 Okner Pkwy., Livingston, 07039 ........ (973) 992-5405
★ Ross & Perry, Inc., 203 Chews Landing Rd., Haddonfield, 08033 ........ (856) 429-5752
Ross Co., Inc., Frank B., 970 New Brunswick Ave., Ste. H, Rahway, 07065 ........ (732) 669-0810
Ross, Inc., A. W., 297 Monroe St., Passaic, 07055 ........ (973) 471-5900
Rotech Tool & Mold Co., Inc., 824 Fairfield Ave., Kenilworth, 07033 ........ (908) 241-9669
★ Roth Studio Collection, LLC, The Judith, 3 Stone House Rd., Mendham, 07945 ........ (973) 543-4455
Rotondi & Sons, Inc., S., 139 Reeder Rd., Phillipsburg, 08865 ........ (908) 475-1916
Rotondi & Sons, Inc., S. (H Q), 3 Watchung Ave., Chatham, 07928 ........ (973) 635-7799
Rotor Clip Company, Inc., 187 Davidson Ave., Somerset, 08873 ........ (732) 469-7333
Rotuba Extruders, Inc., 1401 S. Park Ave., Linden, 07036 ........ (908) 486-1000
Roval Lumber & Millwork Co., Inc.,
455 Schuyler Ave., P.O. Box 443, Kearny, 07032 ........ (201) 991-8550
† Rover & Son Iron & Steel Co., F., 516 Central Ave., Harrison, 07029 ........ (973) 484-7668
ROWA Group USA, LLC, 100 9th St., Hammonton, 08037 ........ (609) 567-8600
Rowa, Inc. see ........ ROWA Group USA, LLC, Hammonton
Roy Press Printers, 57 Bridgewaters Dr., Apt. 17, Oceanport, 07757 ........ (732) 922-9460
Royal Adhesive, Inc., 48 Burgess Pl., Wayne, 07470 ........ (973) 694-0845
Royal Adhesives & Sealants, LLC see. ........ Royal Adhesive, Inc., Wayne
Royal Aluminum Co., Inc., 620 Market St., Newark, 07105 ........ (973) 589-8880
Royal Baking Co., 8 Empire Blvd., Moonachie, 07074 ........ (201) 296-0888
Royal Cabinet Co., Inc., 152 U.S. Highway 206, Unit 14-D, Hillsborough, 08844 ........ (908) 203-8000
† Royal Deluxe Accessories, LLC, 2563 Brunswick Ave., Bldg. O, Linden, 07036 ........ (908) 523-0550
Royal Instruments Div. see. ........ Components & Controls, Inc., Carlstadt
Royal Knitwear, Inc., 115 Perry St., Park Ridge, 07656 ........ (201) 391-8368
★ Royal Lace Co., Inc., 902 E. Hazelwood Ave., Rahway, 07065 ........ (718) 495-9327
Royal Masters Grinders, Inc., 143 Bauer Dr., P.O Box 630, Oakland, 07436 ........ (201) 337-8500
Royal Prime Window Specialist, Inc., 742 Fairfield Ave., Kenilworth, 07033 ........ (908) 354-7600
Royal Printing Service, 441 51st St., West New York, 07093 ........ (201) 863-3131
Royal Seamless Corp., 1000 Airport Rd., Ste. 202, Lakewood, 08701 ........ (732) 901-9595
Royal Slide Sales Co., Inc., 42 Hepworth Pl., Garfield, 07026 ........ (973) 777-1177
Royal Sovereign International, Inc., 2 Volvo Dr., Rockleigh, 07647 ........ (201) 750-1020
Royal Wine Corp., 63 Lefante Way, Bayonne, 07002 ........ (718) 534-0200
Royal Woven Label, Inc. see. ........ R-Pac International Corp., Clifton
Royale Cosmetics Corp., 4-A Jules Ln., New Brunswick, 08901 ........ (732) 246-7275
Royce Assocs., L. P., 28-36 Paterson St., Paterson, 07501 ........ (973) 279-0400
Royce Assocs., L. P. (H Q), 35 Carlton Ave., East Rutherford, 07073 ........ (201) 438-5200
† Royce Leather, 501 Penhorn Ave., Ste. 9, Secaucus, 07094 ........ (201) 330-7720
Royce Signworks, Inc., 226 DeSoto Pl., Cliffside Park, 07010 ........ (201) 945-5536
Royer Graphics, Inc., 101 Lincoln Dr., Laurel Springs, 08021 ........ (856) 344-7935
Royer Group, Inc., 7120 Airport Hwy., Pennsauken, 08109 ........ (856) 665-6400
Royle Systems Group, LLC, 111 Bauer Dr., Ste. 2, Oakland, 07436 ........ (201) 644-0345
Roysons Corp., 40 Vanderhoof Ave., Rockaway, 07866 ........ (973) 625-5570
Rozano Signs, 1005 County Road 523, Flemington, 08822 ........ (908) 788-5042
† R.P. Machine, LLC, 906 Stillwater Rd., P.O. Box 144, Stillwater, 07875 ........ (973) 383-8994
R-Pac International Corp., 69 Kingsland Ave., Marino Plz. 1, Clifton, 07014 ........ (973) 916-1600
†★ RPL Supplies, Inc., 141 Lanza Ave., Bldg. 3-A, Garfield, 07026 ........ (973) 767-0880
RPM International, Inc. see. ........ Stonhard, A Div. Of StonCor Group, Maple Shade
RPR Graphics, Inc., 1136 U.S. Highway 22, P.O. Box 1159, Mountainside, 07092 ........ (908) 654-8080
R&R Cosmetics, LLC, 1140 Randolph Ave., Rahway, 07065 ........ (732) 340-1000
R.S. Phillips Steel, LLC, 128 Lake Pochung Rd., Sussex, 07461 ........ (973) 827-6464
R-S Restaurant Equipment Mfg. Corp., 40 Camptown Rd., Maplewood, 07040 ........ (973) 375-3388
RS Rubber Corp., 55 Paterson Ave., P.O. Box 3400, Wallington, 07057 ........ (973) 777-2200
RSA Associates, 812 County Road 579, Flemington, 08822 ........ (908) 806-4681
RSL, Inc., 3049 Fernwood Ave., Egg Harbor Township, 08234 ........ (609) 645-9770
RSL, Inc. (H Q), 3092 English Creek Ave., Egg Harbor Township, 08234 ........ (609) 484-1600
R-Squared Services & Solutions, Inc., 12 Dean Ct., Princeton Junction, 08550 ........ (866) 522-8558
† RSR Electronics, Inc., 900 Hart St., Rahway, 07065 ........ (732) 381-8777
RTS Packaging, LLC, 869 State Highway 12, Frenchtown, 08825 ........ (908) 782-0505
Rubber & Silicone Products Co., Inc., 17 Montesano Rd., Fairfield, 07004 ........ (973) 227-2300
Rubber Fab Technologies Group, 26 Brookfield Dr., Sparta, 07871 ........ (973) 579-2959
Rubber Fabrication & Molding, Inc.,
1100 Route 519, P.O. Box 412, Johnsonburg, 07846 ........ (908) 852-7725
Rubber Stamp Engraving, 386 Avenel St., Avenel, 07001 ........ (732) 726-5664
Rubber Stamp Man, LLC, 1236 Route 166, Ste. 140, Toms River, 08753 ........ (732) 557-0275
RubbeRecycle, LLC, 1985 Rutgers Blvd., Lakewood, 08701 ........ (732) 363-0600
Rudco Products, Inc., 114 E. Oak Rd., Vineland, 08360 ........ (856) 691-0800
Rudolph Instruments, Inc., 400 Morris Ave., Ste. 120, Denville, 07834 ........ (973) 983-6700
Rudolph Research Analytical, 55 Newburgh Rd., Hackettstown, 07840 ........ (973) 584-1558
Rudolph Technologies, Inc., 1 Rudolph Rd., P.O. Box 1000, Flanders, 07836 ........ (973) 691-1300
Rudy Di Signs & Displays, 169 N. Dean St., Englewood, 07631 ........ (201) 568-6160
Rudy's & Vitor's V. A. S. Co., Inc.,
521 W. Hazelwood Ave., P.O. Box 1544, Rahway, 07065 ........ (732) 388-0334
Ruedi Kuhns Wood Shop, 509 Berckman St., Plainfield, 07062 ........ (908) 755-6947
Ruffino Packaging, Inc., 63 Green St., Hackensack, 07601 ........ (201) 487-1260
† Rugby ABP Corp., 60 Joseph St., Moonachie, 07074 ........ (201) 807-9701
Rugby IPD Corp. see. ........ Rugby ABP Corp., Moonachie
Ruggieri Precision Machine, LLC, 1404 Route 179, Lambertville, 08530 ........ (609) 397-4378
Ruggiero Seafood, Inc., 474 Wilson Ave., P.O. Box 5369, Newark, 07105 ........ (973) 589-0524
Rule One, Inc., 68 E. Centre St., Nutley, 07110 ........ (973) 661-4563
Rummel Industries, Inc., 697 Rahway Ave., P.O. Box 1326, Union, 07083 ........ (908) 688-6600
† Rumsey Electric Co., 311 N. Clinton Ave., Trenton, 08638 ........ (609) 989-9400
† Runnemede Truck Refrigeration, 320 Borelli Blvd., Paulsboro, 08066 ........ (856) 423-4400
Runtak Rails, LLC, 174 Kinderkamack Rd., Ste. A, Park Ridge, 07656 ........ (201) 391-0380
Ruoff & Sons, Inc., 1030 Rose Ave., P.O. Box 320, Runnemede, 08078 ........ (856) 931-2064
Rush Graphics, Inc., 1122 Goffle Rd., Hawthorne, 07506 ........ (973) 427-9393
Rush Index Tabs, Inc., 60 Willow St., East Rutherford, 07073 ........ (201) 531-1555
Russo & Sons, Inc., Thomas, 854 Communipaw Ave., Jersey City, 07304 ........ (201) 332-4159
Rust-Oleum Corp., 480 Frelinghuysen Ave., Newark, 07114 ........ (732) 469-8100
Rust-Oleum Corp. see. ........ Rust-Oleum Corp., ZINSSER Brands, Somerset
Rust-Oleum Corp., ZINSSER Brands, 173 Belmont Dr., Somerset, 08873 ........ (732) 469-8100
Rutan Poly Industries, Inc., 39 Siding Pl., Mahwah, 07430 ........ (201) 529-1474
Rutgers University Press, 106 Somerset St., 3rd Fl., New Brunswick, 08901 ........ (848) 445-7781
Rutherford Signright Co., 769 Morton St., East Rutherford, 07073 ........ (201) 935-1511
Rutler Screen Printing, Inc., 169 Belview Rd., Phillipsburg, 08865 ........ (908) 859-3327
RW Delights, Inc., 50 Division Ave., Ste. 44, Millington, 07946 ........ (718) 683-1038
R-Way Tooling & Metal Works, 224 S. Lincoln Ave., Vineland, 08361 ........ (856) 692-2218
Ryan Custom Machine see. ........ Ryan Industrial Service, Inc., Matawan
† Ryan Herco Flow Solutions Corp.,
50 Tannery Rd., Reading Industrial Ctr., Bldg. 3, Somerville, 08876 ........ (908) 534-6111
Ryan Industrial Service, Inc., 80 Freneau Ave., Matawan, 07747 ........ (732) 566-9538
S & B Pallet Co., 1348 S. 2nd St., Plainfield, 07063 ........ (908) 756-3606
S & G Tool Aid Corp., 43 E. Alpine St., Newark, 07114 ........ (973) 824-7730
S & M Press, Inc., 169 Semel Ave., Ste. 2, Garfield, 07026 ........ (973) 778-4405
S & P Metal Finishing Corp., 185 Oakland St., Trenton, 08618 ........ (609) 393-4833
S & P Tees, 14 Frederick St., Hackensack, 07601 ........ (201) 996-1411
S & R Designs, Inc., 36 W. Route 70, Ste. 213, Marlton, 08053 ........ (856) 985-0303
† S & R Sales, Inc., 1 Sandart Plz., Jackson, 08527 ........ (732) 905-0278
S & S Custom Covers LLC, 2034 Bridge Ave., Point Pleasant, 08742 ........ (732) 903-7518
S & S Mfg., Inc., 115 Fieldcrest Ave., Edison, 08837 ........ (732) 698-2400
S & S Precision, 2205 Sherman Ave., Pennsauken, 08110 ........ (856) 662-0006
S & S Printing, 610 S. White Horse Pike, Somerdale, 08083 ........ (856) 784-2718
S & S Valve Service, Inc., 105 Liberty St., Metuchen, 08840 ........ (732) 548-2040
S & W Custom Screen Printing, 147 Main St., Hackettstown, 07840 ........ (908) 852-4808
S & W Fabricators, Inc.,
100 S. Delsea Dr., Ste. 300, P.O. Box 664, Glassboro, 08028 ........ (856) 881-8068
★ S & Y Natural Stone, LLC, 1000 Main Ave., Clifton, 07011 ........ (862) 200-5156
S C C Concrete, 1051 River Rd., P.O. Box 47, Phillipsburg, 08865 ........ (908) 859-2172
S D I Technologies, Inc., 1299 Main St., Rahway, 07065 ........ (877) 895-8324
★ S. E. R. Diecutting, 7300 N. Crescent Blvd., Unit 5, Pennsauken, 08110 ........ (856) 665-8805
S. Frankford & Sons, Inc., 110 Gaither Dr., Mount Laurel, 08054 ........ (856) 222-4134
S. G. Footwear see. ........ S. Goldberg & Co., Inc., Hackensack
S G Mfg. Corp., 15 Oliver St., Metuchen, 08840 ........ (732) 494-6520
S. Goldberg & Co., Inc., 3 University Plz., Ste. 400, Hackensack, 07601 ........ (201) 342-1200
S H P C, Inc., 187 Christie St., P.O. Box 5328, Newark, 07105 ........ (973) 589-5242
S J Print Solutions, 257 Ford Rd., Howell, 07731 ........ (732) 363-7711
S L M Mfg. Corp., 47 Langstaff Ave., Edison, 08817 ........ (732) 469-7500
S M Counter Tops, LLC, 432 Boston Ave., Egg Harbor Township, 08234 ........ (609) 926-9301
S. Parker Hardware Mfg., 1 Parker Dr., P.O. Box 9882, Englewood, 07631 ........ (201) 569-1600
S S Art & Engraving Corp., 1023 Commerce Ave., Union, 07083 ........ (908) 686-5536
S S M Industries, Inc. see. ........ Mid States Spiral, Inc., West Deptford
S S M Industries, Inc. see. ........ SSM Industries, Inc., West Deptford
S S Tool & Mfg. Co., Inc., 1 Garfield St., Linden, 07036 ........ (908) 486-5497
SaaShr, 3040 U.S. Highway 22, Ste. 200, Somerville, 08876 ........ (908) 722-9952
Saba Software, Inc. see. ........ HumanConcepts, Bridgewater
Sabert Corp., 2288 Main Street Ext., Sayreville, 08872 ........ (732) 721-5544
Sabinsa Corp., 20 Lake Dr., East Windsor, 08520 ........ (732) 777-1111
Sabre Die Cutting Co., Inc., 68 Mill St., Paterson, 07501 ........ (973) 357-9800
Sabrett Frankfurters see. ........ Marathon Enterprises, Inc. (H Q), Englewood
Saco & Birnbaum Fine Woodworking, 71 Glenwood Pl., East Orange, 07017 ........ (973) 675-8999
Safas Corp., 2 Ackerman Ave., Clifton, 07011 ........ (973) 772-5252
Safeguard, 1253 Springfield Ave., Ste. 258, New Providence, 07974 ........ (973) 887-9500
Safeguard Business Systems, Inc. see. ........ Safeguard, New Providence
Safer Holding Corp. see. ........ Markbilt Technical Fabrics Corp., Newark
Safer Holding Corp. see. ........ Meadows Knitting Corp., Newark
Safer Holding Corp., 1875 McCarter Hwy., Newark, 07104 ........ (973) 482-6400
Safe-Strap Co., 105 W. Dewey Ave., Bldg. D, Ste. 410, Wharton, 07885 ........ (973) 442-4623
Safety Glow see. ........ LittleGifts, Inc. (H Q), Secaucus
Safety-Kleen Systems, Inc., 1200 Sylvan St., Linden, 07036 ........ (908) 862-2000
† Safety-Kleen Systems, Inc., 116 Skyline Dr., South Plainfield, 07080 ........ (908) 791-9600
† Safety-Kleen Systems, Inc., 123 Red Lion Rd., Vincentown, 08088 ........ (609) 859-2049
† Safilo USA, Inc. (H Q), 801 Jefferson Rd., Parsippany, 07054 ........ (973) 952-2800
SAFRAN USA, Inc. see. ........ Aerosource, Inc., Somerset
† Safway Atlantic, LLC, 700 Commercial Ave., Carlstadt, 07072 ........ (201) 636-5500
Safway Group Holding, LLC see. ........ Safway Atlantic, LLC, Carlstadt
SAI Global, Inc. see. ........ SAI Global Ltd., Paramus
SAI Global, Inc., 101 Morgan Ln., Ste. 301, Plainsboro, 08536 ........ (609) 955-5100
SAI Global Ltd., 210 State Route 4 E., Paramus, 07652 ........ (201) 986-1131
Sailworks At 43, 43 Norman Ave., Delran, 08075 ........ (856) 764-0888
Saint-Gobain Performance Plastics, 460 Milltown Rd., Bridgewater, 08807 ........ (908) 218-8888
Saint-Gobain Performance Plastics, 210 Harmony Rd., Mickleton, 08056 ........ (856) 423-6630
Saint-Gobain Performance Plastics, 150 Dey Rd., Wayne, 07470 ........ (973) 696-4700
SAK Technologies, Inc., 134 Gaston Ave., Garfield, 07026 ........ (973) 340-8300
Sakar International, Inc. (H Q), 195 Carter Dr., Edison, 08817 ........ (732) 248-1306
Salad Chef see. ........ Green's Fresh Fruit Salad, Inc., Pleasantville
Salem Mfg. Co., 115 Roosevelt Ave., Belleville, 07109 ........ (973) 751-6331
Salem Oak Homes see. ........ Penn Jersey Weekend Directionals, Oaklyn
★ Salem Steel N.A., LLC (H Q), 80 Route 4 E., Ste. 168, Paramus, 07652 ........ (201) 843-1000
Salerno's Kitchen Cabinets, Inc., 599 N. Midland Ave., Saddle Brook, 07663 ........ (201) 794-1990
Salkin's Jewel Case, Inc.,
3585 Highway 9, South Freehold Shopping Ctr., Freehold, 07728 ........ (732) 462-3311
† Salomon Bros. Equipment Co., Inc., P.O. Box 43, Cranford, 07016 ........ (908) 931-9311

Salon Interiors, 62 Leuning St., South Hackensack, 07606 ........ (201) 488-7888
Salto Decorators, LLC, 80-82 Kinderkamack Rd., Oradell, 07649 ........ (201) 261-2518
Salty Dog, The, 254 Brick Blvd., Ste. 1, Brick, 08723 ........ (732) 714-8400
Sama Plastics Corp., 20 Sand Park Rd., Cedar Grove, 07009 ........ (973) 239-7200
Sample Marshall Laboratories, Inc., 63 Park Ave., Lyndhurst, 07071 ........ (201) 933-0570
Sample Media, Inc., 801 Asbury St., 3rd Fl., Ocean City, 08226 ........ (609) 399-1220
Sam's Custom Woodworking, 14 Dunham Ln., Mount Holly, 08060 ........ (609) 267-4962
† Samson Metal Service, 2604 Route 130 N., Cranbury, 08512 ........ (609) 655-0777
Samson Sign * American Trademark Co. see........ Superior Trademark, Inc., Waldwick
Samstubend, Inc., 31 Maryland Ave., Paterson, 07503 ........ (973) 278-2555
Samsung Electronics America, Inc., 85 Challenger Rd., Ridgefield Park, 07660 ........ (201) 229-4000
† Samuel Elliott, Inc., 1818 Bannard St., Riverton, 08077 ........ (856) 773-6000
Samuel, Inc., 60 W. Englewood, Bergenfield, 07621 ........ (201) 439-1555
Samuelson Furniture, Inc., 11-13 Maryland Ave., Paterson, 07503 ........ (973) 333-6090
San Marco Ravioli, Inc., 38 Davey St., Bloomfield, 07003 ........ (973) 748-4545
San Marel Designs, Inc., 98 U.S. Highway 46, Ste. 10, Budd Lake, 07828 ........ (973) 426-9554
★ San Miguel Live Poultry, LLC, 499 Orange St., Newark, 07107 ........ (973) 482-1007
Sanakirk, Inc., 1400 Berlin Rd., Ste. 123, Cherry Hill, 08003 ........ (856) 429-0715
★ Sander Mechanical Service, Inc., 55 Columbia Rd., Ste. 1, Branchburg, 08876 ........ (732) 560-0600
Sandik Mfg., Inc., 100 8th St., Bldg. 33-A, Passaic, 07055 ........ (973) 779-0707
SandKamp Woodworks, LLC, 430 Communipaw Ave., Jersey City, 07304 ........ (201) 200-0101
Sandoval Graphics & Printing, 9 Minnetonka Rd., Somerdale, 08083 ........ (856) 435-7320
Sandoz, Inc. (H Q), 506 Carnegie Ctr., Ste. 400, Princeton, 08540 ........ (609) 627-8500
Sandpaper Newspaper, 1816 Long Beach Blvd., Surf City, 08008 ........ (609) 494-5900
Sandpiper Embroidery, Inc., 5905 New Jersey Ave., Wildwood Crest, 08260 ........ (609) 522-4560
Sandvik Coromant see........ Sandvik, Inc. (H Q), Fair Lawn
Sandvik, Inc. see........ Sandvik Process Systems, LLC, Totowa
Sandvik, Inc. (H Q), 1702 Nevins Rd., P.O. Box 428, Fair Lawn, 07410 ........ (201) 794-5000
Sandvik Process Systems, LLC, 21 Campus Rd., Totowa, 07512 ........ (973) 790-1600
Sankar Assocs., Inc., 14 Empire Blvd., Moonachie, 07074 ........ (201) 994-1700
Sanofi U. S. (H Q), 55 Corporate Dr., Bridgewater, 08807 ........ (908) 981-5000
Santos Bakery, 123 Hudson St., Newark, 07103 ........ (973) 732-7200
† Sanzo Ltd., 35 Munsee Dr., Cranford, 07016 ........ (908) 276-6654
Sap Seal Products, 52 Woodbine St., Bergenfield, 07621 ........ (201) 385-5553
Sapphire Envelope & Graphics Co., Inc., 214 W. Davis Rd., Magnolia, 08049 ........ (856) 782-2227
Sapuco Cheese see........ DCI Cheese Co., Carlstadt
SAR Industrial Finishing, Inc., 104 N. Route 73, Berlin, 08009 ........ (609) 567-2772
Saracino Monuments, LLC, Frank, 359 Bergen Blvd., Fairview, 07022 ........ (201) 945-1266
Sarkli Repechage Ltd., 300 Castle Rd., Secaucus, 07094 ........ (201) 549-4200
Sarlo Tool & Machine Co., 62 Suburban Blvd., Delran, 08075 ........ (856) 461-3206
Sarnoff Corp., 201 Washington Rd., Princeton, 08540 ........ (609) 734-2000
SAS Stressteel, Inc., 100 New Dutch Ln., Fairfield, 07004 ........ (973) 244-0507
Sasa Demarle, Inc., 8 Corporate Dr., Cranbury, 08512 ........ (609) 395-0219
Satec, Inc. (H Q), 10 Milltown Ct., Union, 07083 ........ (908) 686-9510
Satesa Corp., 154 W. Forest Ave., Englewood, 07631 ........ (201) 871-8989
Satterfield Originals, 130 Bodman Pl., Apt. 2, Red Bank, 07701 ........ (908) 902-0290
Saturn Overhead Equipment, LLC, 100 Apgar Dr., Somerset, 08873 ........ (732) 560-7210
Saturn Tool & Die, Inc., 1064 Commerce Ave., Union, 07083 ........ (908) 964-0504
Sau-Sea Swimming Pool Paints And Repair Products,
1855 Route 206, Southampton, 08088 ........ (609) 859-8500
Sava Industries, Inc. see........ Carl Stahl Sava Industries, Inc., Riverdale
† Savco Restaurant Equipment, Inc., 600 Main St., Paterson, 07503 ........ (973) 523-4464
Savignano Foods Corp., 107 S. Jefferson St., Orange, 07050 ........ (973) 673-7537
Savita Naturals Ltd., 617 Heron Dr., Swedesboro, 08085 ........ (856) 467-4949
Savoury Systems International, Inc.,
230 Industrial Pkwy., Ste. C, P.O. Box 5487, Branchburg, 08876 ........ (908) 526-2524
★ Savoy Extraordinary Snack, LLC, 35 N. Middaugh St., Somerville, 08876 ........ (908) 252-9800
Sawdust Depot, 1 Boumar Pl., Elmwood Park, 07407 ........ (201) 703-8400
Sawhney Systems, Inc., 777 Alexander Rd., Ste. 204, Princeton, 08540 ........ (609) 987-5000
Sawitz Store Fixture, Inc., 130 Grand St., Carlstadt, 07072 ........ (201) 842-9444
Saxton Falls Sand & Gravel, Inc.,
Waterloo Valley Rd., P.O. Box 576, Stanhope, 07874 ........ (908) 852-0120
SC Engineering Co., Inc., 115 Stryker Ln., Bldg. 4, Hillsborough, 08844 ........ (908) 874-5955
† Scaasis Originals, Inc./Oceanic Trading Co., 1006 11th Ave., Neptune, 07753 ........ (732) 775-7474
Scala Pastry, 1896 U.S. Highway 130, North Brunswick, 08902 ........ (732) 398-9808
Scales Industrial Technologies, Inc. see...... Scales Industrial Technologies, Inc of NJ, Woodland Park
† Scales Industrial Technologies, Inc of NJ,
185 Lackawanna Ave., Woodland Park, 07424 ........ (973) 890-1010
Scandia Packaging Machinery Co., 15 Industrial Rd., Fairfield, 07004 ........ (973) 473-6100
Schadler & Sons, Inc., John, 242 S. Parkway, P.O. Box 1068, Clifton, 07014 ........ (973) 777-5620
Schaedler Precision Rules see........ Schaedler Quinzel, Inc. (H Q), Parsippany
Schaedler Quinzel, Inc. (H Q),
1259 U.S. Highway 46, Ste. 4, Parsippany, 07054 ........ (973) 263-4949
Schaefer, Inc., Ernest, 731 Lehigh Ave., Union, 07083 ........ (908) 964-1280
Schaff Piano Supply Co. see........ Schadler & Sons, Inc., John, Clifton
Schaffner EMC, Inc., 52 Mayfield Ave., Edison, 08837 ........ (732) 225-9533
Schairer Bros., 254 S. Bremen Ave., Egg Harbor City, 08215 ........ (609) 965-0996
Schairer Tree Removal see........ Schairer Bros., Egg Harbor City
Schall Mfg., Inc., 3501 Rose Ave., Ocean, 07712 ........ (732) 918-8800
Scheld Assocs., Inc., 37 Pleasantview Dr., Wayne, 07470 ........ (973) 694-0637
Scheller Printing Co., Lewis, 2275 Old Georges Rd., New Brunswick, 08902 ........ (732) 843-5050
Schiff Food Products Co., Inc., 994 Riverview Dr., Totowa, 07512 ........ (973) 237-1990
Schindler Elevator Corp. see........ Elevator Products Corp., Wayne
Schindler Elevator Corp., 840 N. Lenola Rd., Ste. 4, Moorestown, 08057 ........ (856) 234-2220
Schindler Elevator Corp. (H Q), 20 Whippany Rd., Morristown, 07960 ........ (973) 397-6500
Schlumberger Ltd. see........ Schlumberger-Princeton Technology Center, Princeton Junction
Schlumberger-Princeton Technology Center,
20 Wallace Rd., Princeton Junction, 08550 ........ (609) 799-1000
Schmidt Co., Inc., J. G.,
354 U.S. Highway 22, P.O. Box 880, Green Brook, 08812 ........ (732) 563-9500
Schmidt Mfg. Co., F. P., 143 Leuning St., South Hackensack, 07606 ........ (201) 343-4241
Schmidt Steel, J. G., 211 Central Ave., Passaic, 07055 ........ (973) 473-4822
Schneider & Marquard, Inc., 112 Phil Hardin Rd., P.O. Box 39, Newton, 07860 ........ (973) 383-2200
Schneider Electric, 2001 Highway 46, Ste. 402, Parsippany, 07054 ........ (973) 263-6100
Schneider Electric USA, Inc. see........ Schneider Electric, Parsippany
† Schofield Co., Inc., George, 831 E. Main St., Bridgewater, 08807 ........ (732) 356-0858
Schofield Stone & Stone Center At Bridgewater see........ Schofield Co., Inc., George, Bridgewater
School Photo Marketing see........ Millennium Graphics, Inc., Marlboro
School Publications Co., Inc.,
1520 Washington Ave., P.O. Box 1067, Neptune, 07753 ........ (732) 988-1100
Schott Bros., Inc., 735 Rahway Ave., Union, 07083 ........ (908) 527-0011
Schrader & Co., Inc., 188 Halsey Rd., Newton, 07860 ........ (973) 579-2700
Schratter Foods, Inc. see........ Cognati Cheese Co., Inc., Moonachie
† Schratter Foods, Inc. (H Q), 333 Fairfield Rd., Fairfield, 07004 ........ (973) 575-3226
Schreiber Co., Don see........ Jonathan Leasing Corp., Lebanon
Schreiber, Inc., Earle C., 1 Bethany Rd., Bldg. 1, Ste. 13, Hazlet, 07730 ........ (732) 335-1424
Schreyer Embroidery Co., Inc., 50 Industrial Ave., Fairview, 07022 ........ (201) 943-6221
Schripps European Bread, Inc., 5410 Tonnelle Ave., North Bergen, 07047 ........ (201) 867-0909
† Schroth, Inc., Emil A., Yellowbrook Rd. & Copper Ave., Howell, 07731 ........ (732) 938-5015
Schtiller & Plevy, Inc., 695 S. 12th St., Newark, 07103 ........ (973) 242-4600
Schulz Electric Company, The see........ Reliable Electric Motor Repair, Inc., Paterson
Schundler Co., Inc., 150 Whitman Ave., Edison, 08817 ........ (732) 287-2244
Schutz Container Systems, Inc.,
200 Aspen Hill Rd., P.O. Box 5950, North Branch, 08876 ........ (908) 526-6161
Schuyler Printing Co., Inc., 71 Kearny Ave., Kearny, 07032 ........ (201) 997-8083
Schwan Cosmetics U.S.A., Inc., 21 Gordon Rd., Piscataway, 08854 ........ (732) 777-6800
Schweitzer Special Machines see........ MS Tool Co., Inc., Kenilworth
Schweitzer-Mauduit International see........ Schweitzer-Mauduit International, Inc., Spotswood
Schweitzer-Mauduit International, Inc., 85 Main St., Spotswood, 08884 ........ (732) 723-6100
Sci-Bore, Inc., 364 Glenwood Ave., Bldg. 18-E, East Orange, 07017 ........ (973) 414-9001
Sciecure Pharma, Inc., 11 Deerpark Dr., Ste. 120, Monmouth Junction, 08852 ........ (732) 329-8089
Science Dynamics Corp., 7150 N. Park Dr., Ste. 500, Pennsauken, 08109 ........ (856) 910-1166
Scientific Alloys Corp., 5 Troast Ct., Clifton, 07011 ........ (973) 478-8323
Scientific Design Co., Inc., 49 Industrial Ave., Little Ferry, 07643 ........ (201) 641-0500
Scientific Industries, Inc., 660 Kinderkamack Rd., Ste. 203, Oradell, 07649 ........ (973) 473-6900
Scientific Instrument Services, Inc., 1027 Old York Rd., Ringoes, 08551 ........ (908) 788-5550
Scientific Labeling Systems, Inc., 339 6th Ave. W., Newark, 07107 ........ (973) 722-8229
† Scientific Laboratory Supplies, Inc., 1401 Wade Blvd., Millville, 08332 ........ (856) 327-4410
Scientific Machine, 700 Cedar Ave., P.O. Box 67, Middlesex, 08846 ........ (732) 356-1553
Scientific Materials Corp., 30 Vail Ter., P.O. Box 5298, Somerville, 08876 ........ (908) 218-0010
†★ Scientific Models, Inc., 340 Snyder Ave., Berkeley Heights, 07922 ........ (908) 464-7070
Scimedx Corp., 53 Richboynton Rd., Dover, 07801 ........ (973) 625-8822
Scivanta Medical Corp. (H Q), 215 Morris Ave., Spring Lake, 07762 ........ (732) 282-1055
Sconda Canvas Products see........ Main Attractions, Inc., Edison
Scories, Inc., 28 Vassar Ave., P.O. Box 4223, Newark, 07112 ........ (973) 923-1372
Scott Graphics Printing, Inc., 690-D River Rd., New Milford, 07646 ........ (201) 262-0473
† SCP Distributors, LLC, 1985 Rutgers University Blvd., Ste. A, Lakewood, 08701 ........ (732) 730-1451
Scrap Metal Recycling & Processing see........ River Road Recycling Inc., Pennsauken
Screaming Eagle Metal Products see........ Leibrock Metal Products, Inc., Asbury Park
Screen And Digital Supply see........ Jessup, Inc., Charles M., Keasbey
Screen Creations Plus, 8 Hillside Ave., Newton, 07860 ........ (973) 579-5015
Screen Play, Inc., 1275 Bloomfield Ave., Ste. 5, Fairfield, 07004 ........ (973) 227-9014
Screen Printing USA see........ Jill's Thrill, Inc., Cranbury
Screen Reproductions Co., Inc., 850 Washington Ave., Carlstadt, 07072 ........ (201) 935-0830
Screen Tech Of New Jersey, Inc., 1800 W. Blancke St., Linden, 07036 ........ (908) 862-8000
★ Screening Base, 245 W. Broadway, Paterson, 07522 ........ (973) 389-7950
Screens & Fabricated Metals Corp.,
1265 McBride Ave., P.O. Box 647, Woodland park, 07424 ........ (973) 785-1414
Screens, Inc., 130 Ryerson Ave., Ste. 219, Wayne, 07470 ........ (973) 633-8558
ScreenTek Mfg. Co., Inc., 220 Franklin Rd., Ste. B, Randolph, 07869 ........ (973) 328-2121
Screen-Trans Development Corp., 100 Grand St., Moonachie, 07074 ........ (201) 933-7800
Screw Machine Specialties, 50 U.S. Highway 9, Ste. 305, Morganville, 07751 ........ (732) 972-5400
Screws Unlimited see........ C & G Screws Unlimited, Brick
Sculpture House, Inc., 405 Skillman Rd., P.O. Box 69, Skillman, 08558 ........ (609) 466-2986
Sculpturesque, Inc., 7 Etheridge Pl., Park Ridge, 07656 ........ (201) 573-9150
SDALC see........ AlphaGraphics, Cherry Hill
SDL Coating see........ SDL Studio, LLC, Toms River
SDL Studio, LLC, 1591 Route 37 W., Ste. E-4, Toms River, 08755 ........ (732) 473-0800
SDS see........ Specialty Disposal Services, Inc., Mountain Lakes
† Sea Box, Inc., 700 Union Landing Rd., 1 Sea Box Dr., Cinnaminson, 08077 ........ (856) 303-1101
Sea Breeze Fruit Flavors, Inc., 441 Route 202, Towaco, 07082 ........ (973) 334-7777
Sea Gear Marine Supply, Inc., 1144 Route 109, Cape May, 08204 ........ (609) 884-2711
Sea Gull Lighting Products, LLC.,
301 W. Washington St., P.O. Box 329, Riverside, 08075 ........ (856) 764-0500
Sea Isle Ice Co., Inc., 230 42nd St., Sea Isle City, 08243 ........ (609) 263-8794
Seaboard Instrument Co., Inc., 4 N. 1st St., Pleasantville, 08232 ........ (609) 641-5300
Seaboard Paper & Twine, LLC, 37 E. 6th St., Paterson, 07524 ........ (973) 413-8100
Seabra Group see........ Aidil Wines & Liquors, Newark
Seabra Group see........ Corte Provisions, Newark
Seabra Group (H Q), 574 Ferry St., Newark, 07105 ........ (973) 491-0399
Seabrook Bros. & Sons, Inc., 85 Finley Rd., P.O. Box 5103, Seabrook, 08302 ........ (856) 455-8080
Seagrave Coatings Corp., 209 N. Michigan Ave., Kenilworth, 07033 ........ (201) 933-1000
Seagull Stained Glass, 1917 Kuehnle Ave., Atlantic City, 08401 ........ (609) 345-3126
Seajay Mfg. Co., 9 Memorial Dr., Ste. 1, Neptune, 07753 ........ (732) 774-0900
Seal Spout Corp., 50 Allen Rd., P.O. Box 74, Liberty Corner, 07938 ........ (908) 647-1900
Sealed Air Corp. see........ CPI Packaging, Inc., Somerset
Sealed Air Corp., 301 Mayhill St., Saddle Brook, 07663 ........ (201) 712-7000
Sealed Air Corp. (H Q), 200 Riverfront Blvd., 3rd Fl., Elmwood Park, 07407 ........ (201) 791-7600
Sealed Unit Parts Co., Inc., 2230 Landmark Pl., P.O. Box 21, Allenwood, 08720 ........ (732) 223-6644
Sealion Metal Fabricators, Inc., 776 Creek Rd., Bellmawr, 08031 ........ (856) 933-3914
Seals Eastern, Inc., 134 Pearl St., P.O. Box 520, Red Bank, 07701 ........ (732) 747-9200
Sealy, Inc. see........ Sealy Mattress Co. Of New Jersey, Paterson
Sealy Mattress Co. Of New Jersey, 697 River St., Paterson, 07524 ........ (973) 345-8800
Seashore Glass & Mirror, 2547 Fire Rd., Ste. 2-B, Egg Harbor Township, 08234 ........ (609) 407-6032
† Seashore Supply Of Wildwood, 306 Wildwood Ave., Wildwood, 08260 ........ (609) 522-1491
Seawave Corp., 1508 Route 47, Rio Grande, 08242 ........ (609) 886-8600
Secaucus Home News, 766 Irving Pl., Secaucus, 07094 ........ (201) 867-2071
Second Impressions, LLC, 149 Stelton Rd., Piscataway, 08854 ........ (732) 752-7171
Secure Technology Integration Group, Ltd., 15 Schneider Rd., Allendale, 07401 ........ (201) 825-1255
Security Fabricators, Inc., 316 N. 12th St., P.O. Box 643, Kenilworth, 07033 ........ (908) 272-9171
Sedtek, Inc., 113 Meadow St., Hackensack, 07601 ........ (201) 489-4040
Seibel Group, Inc., The, 741 Alexander Rd., Princeton, 08540 ........ (609) 799-3279
Seibert Machine & Tool, Inc., 4405 S. Clinton Ave., South Plainfield, 07080 ........ (908) 754-0774
† Seidler Chemical & Supply Co., 537 Raymond Blvd., Newark, 07105 ........ (973) 465-1122
Seidler Chemical Co. see........ Seidler Chemical & Supply Co., Newark
Seidman Productions, Inc., 254 E. Gibbsboro Rd., Ste. C, Lindenwold, 08021 ........ (856) 627-1356
SEIKO Corp. Of America see........ Seiko Optical Products Of America, Inc. (H Q), Mahwah
SEIKO Corp. Of America (H Q), 1111 MacArthur Blvd., Mahwah, 07430 ........ (201) 529-5730
Seiko Optical Products Of America, Inc. (H Q),
575 Corporate Dr., Ste. 205, Mahwah, 07430 ........ (201) 529-9099
Sekisui America Corp. (H Q), 333 Meadowlands Pkwy., 4th Fl., Secaucus, 07094 ........ (201) 423-7960
Selco Mfg. Corp., 3 Fairfield Crescent, West Caldwell, 07006 ........ (973) 244-1177
Select Enterprises, Inc., 71 Executive Ave., Edison, 08817 ........ (732) 287-8622
Select Machine Tool, Inc., 19 Thompson Ave., Mount Ephraim, 08059 ........ (856) 933-2100

Select Services, 500 Morris Ave., Ste. 116, Springfield, 07081 ... (973) 467-8860
Selective Coatings & Inks, Inc., 5008 Industrial Rd., Farmingdale, 07727 ... (732) 938-7677
Selick & Bird Thermidaire, 2180 Village Rd., P.O. Box 108, Sea Girt, 08750 ... (732) 449-0017
Sellers & Josephson, LLC, 559 Route 23, Wayne, 07470 ... (201) 567-1353
Selling Precision, Inc., 264 Marshall Hill Rd., West Milford, 07480 ... (973) 728-1214
Selover Co., LLC, R. N., 17 Wolf Rd., Millville, 08332 ... (856) 293-9009
Semel's Embroidery & Screen Printing, Inc.,
1078 U.S. Highway 46, Clifton, 07013 ... (973) 473-3959
Semiconductor Mfg., 5 Troast Ct., Clifton, 07011 ... (973) 478-2880
Seminole Wire & Cable Co., 7861 Airport Hwy., Pennsauken, 08109 ... (856) 324-2929
Senat Poultry, LLC, 28 Warren St., Paterson, 07524 ... (973) 742-4790
Senior Publishing * School Publishing see. ... Kirms Printing Co., Inc., Neptune
Sensient Cosmetic & Pharmaceutical Technologies,
107 Wade Ave., South Plainfield, 07080 ... (908) 757-4500
Sensient Technologies Corp. see. Sensient Cosmetic & Pharmaceutical Technologies, South Plainfield
Sensigraphics, Inc., 105 W. Park Dr., Mount Laurel, 08054 ... (856) 853-9100
Sensonics, Inc., 125 White Horse Pike, P.O. Box 112, Haddon Heights, 08035 ... (800) 547-8838
Sensor Products, Inc., 300 Madison Ave., Ste. 100, Madison, 07940 ... (973) 884-1755
Sensor Scientific, Inc., 6 Kingsbridge Rd., Fairfield, 07004 ... (973) 227-7790
Sentinel Gloucester County, The see. ... Cindy Merckx Publications, LLC, Malaga
Sentrex Ingredients, LLC, 350 Cantor Ave., Linden, 07036 ... (908) 862-4440
★ Sequins City, 1302 13th St., North Bergen, 07047 ... (201) 348-8111
Serafino Printing Co., Inc., 516 Bloomfield Ave., Verona, 07044 ... (973) 857-3450
Seren I.P.S., Inc., 1670 Gallagher Dr., Vineland, 08360 ... (856) 205-1131
Serrani's Bakery, 114 S. Essex Ave., Orange, 07050 ... (973) 678-1777
Serratelli Hat Co., Inc., 418-26 Central Ave., P.O. Box 7069, Newark, 07107 ... (973) 623-4133
★ Service Apex, 564-A Union Ave., Bridgewater, 08807 ... (732) 560-2222
Service Apex, 299 U.S. Highway 22, Green Brook, 08812 ... (732) 424-1616
Service Concrete Co., 173 Oak Ridge Rd., P.O. Box 235, Oak Ridge, 07438 ... (973) 697-4040
† Service Lamp Corp., 112 Route 73, Voorhees, 08043 ... (856) 768-0404
Service Machine Co., 311 Lincoln Blvd., Middlesex, 08846 ... (732) 356-9021
Service Metal Fabricating, Inc. see. ... Precision Shape Solutions, Dover
Service Metal Fabricating, Inc. see. ... Precision Shape Solutions, Dover
Service Metal Fabricating, Inc., 10 Stickle Ave., Rockaway, 07866 ... (973) 625-8882
Servolift, LLC, 35 Righter Rd., Randolph, 07869 ... (973) 442-7878
Servometer-PMG, LLC, 501 Little Falls Rd., Cedar Grove, 07009 ... (973) 785-4630
Severino Pasta Mfg. Co., 110 Haddon Ave., Westmont, 08108 ... (856) 854-7666
Severna Operations, Inc., 3 Eastmans Rd., Parsippany, 07054 ... (973) 503-1600
Sew Ann Sew Thomas Enterprises, 153 Pearl St., Paterson, 07501 ... (973) 742-2664
Sew In Style, Inc., 220 61st St., West New York, 07093 ... (201) 868-8568
Sew Many Gifts, Inc., 6 Cranston Ct., Princeton Junction, 08550 ... (609) 275-4532
SEW-Eurodrive, Inc., 2107 High Hill Rd., P.O. Box 481, Bridgeport, 08014 ... (856) 467-2277
Sewmatic Attachments, 39 E. Hanover Ave., Morris Plains, 07950 ... (973) 290-9174
SGS North America, Inc. (H Q), 201 Route 17 N., Rutherford, 07070 ... (201) 508-3000
Shachihata, Inc. see. ... Shachihata, Inc., U. S. A., Lakewood
Shachihata, Inc., U. S. A., 525 Oberlin Ave. S., Lakewood, 08701 ... (732) 370-4770
Shadow Racing & Hobby Products, Inc., 70 1st Ave., Paterson, 07514 ... (973) 684-7270
Shafer Bros. Trailers, 38 Martin Ave., Pittsgrove, 08318 ... (856) 358-3483
Shaffer Products, Inc., 20 Milltown Rd., P.O. Box 427, Union, 07083 ... (908) 206-1980
† Shallcross Bolt & Specialties Co., 1 McCandless St., Linden, 07036 ... (908) 925-4700
Shaman Systems, Inc., 402 Main St., Ste. 100-330, Metuchen, 08840 ... (908) 429-0542
Shamong Mfg. Co., Inc., 33 Bunker Hill Rd., Shamong, 08088 ... (609) 654-2549
Shamrock Technologies, Inc., 255 Pacific St., Newark, 07114 ... (973) 242-2999
Shanghai Freemen Americas, LLC (H Q),
377 Hoes Ln., Ste. 240, Piscataway, 08854 ... (732) 981-1288
★ Shanghai Optics, Inc. (H Q), 17 Brant Ave., Ste. 6, Clark, 07066 ... (732) 321-6915
Shangri La Farm, LLC, 1055 Maxim Southard Rd., Howell, 07731 ... (732) 901-8777
Shared Systems Technology, Inc., 127 Salem Ave., Thorofare, 08086 ... (856) 218-7900
Sharp Electronics Corp. (H Q), 1 Sharp Plz., Mahwah, 07430 ... (201) 529-8200
Sharrott Winery, LLC, 370 S. Egg Harbor Rd., Blue Anchor, 08037 ... (609) 567-9463
Shearman Cabinets, Inc., 195 N. Munn Ave., East Orange, 07017 ... (973) 677-0071
Shedd Designs, LLC, John, 200 Washington St., P.O. Box 276, Rocky Hill, 08553 ... (609) 924-6394
Sheet Metal Products, Inc., 794 N. 6th St., Newark, 07107 ... (973) 482-0450
Shekia Group, LLC, The, 1130 King Georges Post Rd., Edison, 08837 ... (732) 372-7668
Shelby Caststone, 600 Jersey Ave., Gloucester City, 08030 ... (856) 456-0668
Shell Packaging see. ... Flexcon Products Corp., Berkeley Heights
Shelter Cove Embroidery Co., 1333 Bay Ave., Toms River, 08753 ... (732) 506-7700
Shelton, LLC, Todd, 450 Murray Hill Pkwy., Ste. C-2, East Rutherford, 07073 ... (551) 655-4106
Shelving Depot, Inc., 419 W. Elizabeth Ave., Linden, 07036 ... (908) 474-8000
Sheridan Communication, Inc., 1425 3rd Ave., Alpha, 08865 ... (908) 454-0700
Sheridan Optical Co., Inc., 108 Clinton Ave., Pitman, 08071 ... (856) 582-0963
Sheri's Cookery, Inc., 33 Delancy St., Newark, 07105 ... (973) 589-2060
Sherman & Son, Inc., W. F., 84 Broad St., Manasquan, 08736 ... (732) 223-1505
Sherman, Inc. (H Q), Nat, 2200 Fletcher Ave., Fort Lee, 07024 ... (201) 735-9000
Sherwin-Williams Co., The, 6 Currie Ave., Wallington, 07057 ... (201) 933-3800
Sherwin-Williams Co., The see. Sherwin-Williams Co., The, Woodcare Products Div. (H Q), Upper Saddle River
Sherwin-Williams Co., The, Woodcare Products Div. (H Q),
10 Mountainview Rd., Upper Saddle River, 07458 ... (201) 818-7500
SHI see. ... SHI International Corp., Somerset
† SHI International Corp., 290 Davidson Ave., Somerset, 08873 ... (732) 477-6479
† Shingle & Gibb Company, 845 Lancer Dr., Moorestown, 08057 ... (856) 234-8500
Shionogi, Inc. (H Q), 300 Campus Dr., Florham Park, 07932 ... (973) 966-6900
Shiprite Packaging, Inc., 161 Woodbine St., Bergenfield, 07621 ... (201) 385-4747
Shipserv, 1090 King Georges Post Rd., Edison, 08837 ... (215) 862-3353
Shira Esthetics, Inc., 65 S. 21st St., Ste. 2, Kenilworth, 07033 ... (908) 497-9497
Shiseido America, Inc. see. ... Davlyn Industries, Inc., Monroe Township
Shiseido America, Inc., 366 Princeton Hightstown Rd., East Windsor, 08520 ... (609) 371-5800
Shoemaker's Automotive Machine, 176 Kings Hwy., Cape May Court House, 08210 ... (609) 624-0847
Shooting Star, Inc., 2500 Plainfield Ave., Scotch Plains, 07076 ... (908) 789-2500
Shoppe Cape May County Shoppers Guide, 2503 Bayshore Rd., Villas, 08251 ... (609) 886-4112
Shor International Corp., 77 Fairwood Rd., Madison, 07940 ... (973) 520-8777
Shore Awning Co., Inc., 556 Industrial Way W., Eatontown, 07724 ... (732) 578-1882
Shore Microsystems, Inc., 45 Memorial Pkwy., Long Branch, 07740 ... (732) 870-0800
Shore P C, 3 Meridian Rd., Eatontown, 07724 ... (732) 380-0590
Shore Point Communications, 160 Lehigh Ave., Ste. B, Lakewood, 08701 ... (732) 961-7936
† Shore Point Distributing Co., 100 Shore Point Dr., Freehold, 07728 ... (732) 308-3334
Shore Precision Mfg., Inc., 1000 Industrial Way N., Unit D, Toms River, 08755 ... (732) 914-0949
Shore Sign & Banner, 1214 Route 37 E., Toms River, 08753 ... (732) 270-6020
Shorewood Digital Design & Development Center, 1 Kero Rd., Carlstadt, 07072 ... (201) 372-3900
Short Run Stamping Co., Inc., The, 925 E. Linden Ave., Linden, 07036 ... (908) 862-1070
Shovlin Mattress Factory see. ... M & R Diamond Quilting Co., Inc., Fanwood
Showcase Graphics, LLC, 33 E. Main St., Ste. 4, Moorestown, 08057 ... (856) 722-5400
Showcase Printing Of Iselin, 181 E. James Pl., Iselin, 08830 ... (732) 283-0438
Showcase Publications, Inc., 90 Irons St., Toms River, 08753 ... (732) 349-7775
Showtech, Inc., 40 Entin Rd., Clifton, 07014 ... (973) 249-6336
Shreeji Printing Corp., 55 Veterans Blvd., Carlstadt, 07072 ... (201) 842-9500
Shriver's Salt Water Taffy & Fudge,
9th St. & Boardwalk, P.O. Box 899, Ocean City, 08226 ... (609) 399-0100
Shrop's Shop, 1254 S. Route 9, Cape May Court House, 08210 ... (609) 465-1640
Shukla Medical see. ... S.S. White Technologies, Inc., Piscataway
Shuren & Cullen, Inc. * Shuren Upholstery see. ... Lawrence Custom Drapery Shop, Ewing
Shure-Pak Corp., 1500 N. 10th St., P.O. Box 105, Millville, 08332 ... (856) 825-0808
Shurts Frames & Molding, Don, 294 Lanes Mill Rd., Howell, 07731 ... (732) 363-1323
SICA Metal Products,
1775 Hurffville Rd., Route 41, P.O. Box 5525, Deptford, 08096 ... (856) 227-6616
Sico Systems Control, Inc., 1263 Ringwood Ave., Haskell, 07420 ... (973) 831-9110
Sideline Sports, 2566 Plainfield Ave., Scotch Plains, 07076 ... (908) 322-9334
Siegfried USA, LLC, 33 Industrial Park Rd., Pennsville, 08070 ... (856) 678-3601
Siemens Corporation see. ... Siemens Hearing Instruments, Inc., Piscataway
Siemens Energy, Inc., 840 Nottingham Way, Trenton, 08638 ... (609) 890-5000
Siemens Healthcare Diagnostics, Inc.,
62 Flanders Bartley Rd., Flanders, 07836 ... (973) 927-2828
Siemens Hearing Instruments, Inc.,
10 Constitution Ave., P.O. Box 1397, Piscataway, 08855 ... (732) 562-6600
Siemens Industry, Inc., Water Technologies,
20 Murray Hill Pkwy., Ste. 140, East Rutherford, 07073 ... (201) 531-9338
Siemens Industry, Inc., Water Technologies, 2 Milltown Ct., Union, 07083 ... (908) 851-2277
Siemens Industry, Inc., Water Technologies,
1901 W. Garden Rd., Vineland, 08360 ... (856) 507-9000
Siemens Infrastructure & Cities, Building Technologies,
8 Fernwood Rd., Florham Park, 07932 ... (973) 593-2600
Sierra Packaging, Inc., 60 State Route 36, Ste. C, West Long Branch, 07764 ... (732) 571-2900
SightLogix, Inc., 745 Alexander Rd., Ste. 5 & 6, Princeton, 08540 ... (609) 951-0008
SIGMA Corp. see. ... Environmental Site Furnishings, Cream Ridge
† SIGMA Corp. (H Q), 700 Goldman Dr., P.O. Box 300, Cream Ridge, 08514 ... (609) 758-0800
Sigma Design Company, 200 Pond Ave., Middlesex, 08846 ... (732) 629-7555
Sigma Engineering & Consulting Assocs., 220 Lincoln Blvd., Middlesex, 08846 ... (732) 356-3046
Sigma Plastics Group see. ... Sigma Stretch Film, Lyndhurst
Sigma Plastics Group (H Q),
Page & Schuyler Aves., Bldg. 5, P.O. Box 808, Lyndhurst, 07071 ... (201) 933-6000
Sigma Stretch Film, Page Ave., Bldg. 5 & 8, P.O. Box 808, Lyndhurst, 07071 ... (201) 507-9100
Sigma-Netics, Inc., 2 N. Corporate Dr., Riverdale, 07457 ... (973) 616-6900
Sign Boy, LLC, 370 N. Glassboro Rd., Woodbury Heights, 08097 ... (856) 384-2937
Sign Concepts, 33 Broad St., Toms River, 08753 ... (732) 341-7624
Sign Crew, 1426 Union Ave., Pennsauken, 08110 ... (856) 665-3676
Sign Effectz, 800 New Brunswick Ave., Ste. 7, Rahway, 07065 ... (732) 388-7446
Sign Maker, 1005 Union Ave., Union Beach, 07735 ... (732) 739-4800
Sign On, Inc., 149 Washington Ave., Apt. A, Dumont, 07628 ... (201) 384-7714
Sign Tech, 361 South Ave. E., Westfield, 07090 ... (908) 232-2287
Sign Up Signs & Promotions see. ... Sign Up Signs, LLC, Beachwood
Sign Up Signs, LLC, 649 Atlantic City Blvd., Unit 2, Beachwood, 08722 ... (732) 240-6025
Signal Graphics see. ... Mid Atlantic Graphix, Inc., Egg Harbor Township
Signal Sign Co., 105 Dorsa Ave., Livingston, 07039 ... (973) 535-9277
Signalcrafters Tech, Inc., 57 Eagle Rock Ave., East Hanover, 07936 ... (973) 781-0880
Sign-A-Rama see. ... KNA Graphics, Inc., Kenilworth
Signarama, 655 S. White Horse Pike, Hammonton, 08037 ... (609) 878-3375
Signarama, 349 U.S. Highway 9, Ste. 6, Manalapan, 07726 ... (732) 536-7575
Sign-A-Rama, 4000 Route 130, Ste. 25, Delran, 08075 ... (856) 764-9777
Sign-A-Rama, 400 Fairfield Rd., Ste. 5, Fairfield, 07004 ... (973) 227-6363
Sign-A-Rama, 1459 Highway 38, P.O. Box 360, Hainesport, 08036 ... (609) 702-1444
Sign-A-Rama, 32 S. Main St., Manville, 08835 ... (908) 203-8005
Sign-A-Rama, 166 Ridgedale Ave., Morristown, 07962 ... (973) 605-8313
Sign-A-Rama, 1030 U.S. Highway 22, North Plainfield, 07060 ... (908) 561-4167
Sign-A-Rama, 1633 Stelton Rd., Piscataway, 08854 ... (732) 819-8844
Sign-A-Rama, 34 S. White Horse Pike, Somerdale, 08083 ... (856) 627-5352
Sign-A-Rama, Inc., 379 Main St., Hackensack, 07601 ... (201) 489-6969
Sign-A-Rama Ledgewood, 244 Main St., Ledgewood, 07852 ... (973) 584-9301
SignArt Graphix, 177 Stanhope Sparta Rd., Andover, 07821 ... (973) 770-4500
Signature Marketing & Mfg., 301 Wagaraw Rd., Hawthorne, 07506 ... (973) 427-3700
Signature Sign, 31 Milaystown Rd., Cream Ridge, 08514 ... (609) 351-2231
Signdesign, LLC, 206 Lake Ave., P.O. Box 892, Island Heights, 08732 ... (732) 929-3700
Signmasters, Inc., 217 Brook Ave., 2nd Fl., Front, Passaic, 07055 ... (973) 614-8300
Signode Packaging Group, 151 Fabyan Pl., Newark, 07112 ... (800) 235-4066
SignPros, 1215 Black Horse Pike, Glendora, 08029 ... (856) 939-1099
Signright, Inc., 76 Ashland Ave., West Orange, 07052 ... (973) 731-8882
Signs & Custom Metal, Inc., 62 Monitor St., Jersey City, 07304 ... (201) 200-0110
Signs & Graphix, 433 Bloomfield Ave., Caldwell, 07006 ... (973) 226-8392
Signs & Lines Printing, 242 Gibbsboro Rd., Lindenwold, 08021 ... (856) 784-0400
Signs By Blohm, Inc., 230 River Rd., New Milford, 07646 ... (201) 262-3172
Signs By Lynn, 329 Kearny Ave., Ste. A, Kearny, 07032 ... (201) 998-4273
Signs By Raymond, 626 Route 88, Point Pleasant, 08742 ... (732) 840-7793
Signs By Tomorrow, 326 U.S. Highway 22, Ste. 8-B, Green Brook, 08812 ... (732) 424-9785
Signs By Tomorrow, 1108 Goffle Rd., Ste. 1, Hawthorne, 07506 ... (973) 423-4600
Signs By Tomorrow, 825 Highway 1 S., Ste. 6, Iselin, 08830 ... (732) 602-7878
Signs For Today, 173 Upper Hibernia Rd., Rockaway, 07866 ... (973) 983-2530
Signs Of Security, Inc.,
64 Outwater Ln., 2nd Fl., P.O. Box 468, Garfield, 07026 ... (973) 340-8404
Signs Of Sense, 79 Bassett Hwy., Dover, 07801 ... (973) 361-0037
Signs Of The Times By Beutel & Sons, 81 Park Ave., Park Ridge, 07656 ... (201) 391-8444
Signs Of 2000, 421 Broad St., Clifton, 07011 ... (973) 253-1333
Signs Sealed & Delivered, Inc., 121 Main St., Bradley Beach, 07720 ... (732) 775-7227
Signs Unlimited, Inc., 601 Hessian Ave., National Park, 08063 ... (856) 848-4942
Sika Corp., 995 Towbin Ave., Lakewood, 08701 ... (973) 473-3330
Sika Corporation, 201 Polito Ave., Lyndhurst, 07071 ... (201) 933-8800
Silberstein, Inc., M., 428 Broad St., Shrewsbury, 07702 ... (732) 741-1762
Silgan Containers, LLC see. ... Silgan Containers Mfg. Corp., Edison
Silgan Containers Mfg. Corp., 135 National Rd., Edison, 08817 ... (732) 287-0300
★ Silipos, Inc., 4 Brighton Rd., Ste. 320, Clifton, 07012 ... (973) 928-5900
Silkhouse International, Inc., 28 Garden Pl., Ste. 128, Edgewater, 07020 ... (201) 945-4569
Siloa, Inc. (H Q), 2493 Lamington Rd., Ste. C, Bedminster, 07921 ... (908) 234-9040
Silver Brush Ltd., 92 N. Main St., Bldg. 18-E, P.O. Box 414, Windsor, 08561 ... (609) 443-4900
Silver Cloud Mfg. Co., 525 Orange St., Millville, 08332 ... (856) 825-8900
Silver Line Building Products, LLC see. ... Custom Craft Plastics, North Brunswick

Silver Line Building Products, LLC, 1 Silver Line Dr., P.O. Box 6029, North Brunswick, 08902 ... (732) 435-1000
Silver Palate Kitchens, Inc., 211 Knickerbocker Rd., P.O. Box 512, Cresskill, 07626 ... (201) 568-0110
Silver Stones International, LLC, 902 E. County Line Rd., Ste. 200, Lakewood, 08701 ... (732) 886-0011
Silverton Marine see. ... Egg Harbor Yachts, Egg Harbor City
Silvertop Assocs., Inc., 600 E. Clements Bridge Rd., Runnemede, 08078 ... (856) 939-9599
Silvi Concrete Products, Inc., 470 State Highway 33, Englishtown, 07726 ... (267) 907-9150
Simmons Foods, Inc. see. ... Menu Foods, Inc., Pennsauken
Simple Solutions Distribution, LLC (H Q), 6 Jacobs Rd., West Milford, 07480 ... (973) 846-7817
Simple Step, LLC, 12 W. Owassa Tpke., Newton, 07860 ... (973) 948-2938
Sims Metal Management see. ... Metal Management Northeast, Inc., Jersey City
Sims Metal Management see. ... Metal Management Northeast, Inc., Jersey City
Sims Metal Management, 8-18 Noble St., Newark, 07114 ... (973) 824-8900
† Sims Metal Management, 1511 Calhoun St., Trenton, 08638 ... (609) 396-0880
Sims Pump Valve Co., Inc., 1314 Park Ave., P.O. Box 3338, Hoboken, 07030 ... (201) 792-0600
Simtronics Corp., 50 Birch Ave., Ste. 100, P.O. Box 38, Little Silver, 07739 ... (732) 747-0322
SiMX Corp., 196 Princeton-Hightstown Rd., Bldg. 2-A, Princeton Junction, 08550 ... (609) 750-9345
Sinclair & Rush, Inc. see. ... VisiPak, a Sinclair & Rush Company, Carlstadt
Sine-Tru Tool Co., Inc., 238 Boundry Rd., Marlboro, 07746 ... (732) 591-1100
Single Point Precision, 429 Rockaway Valley Rd., Ste. 2300, Boonton, 07005 ... (973) 625-7221
† Single Source Technologies, 30 Chapin Rd., Ste. 1208, P.O. Box 655, Pine Brook, 07058 ... (973) 227-6601
Sino Monthly New Jersey, Inc., 18 Sheppard Pl., Edison, 08817 ... (732) 650-0688
Sipp Silk, 216 Hedgeman Rd., Moorestown, 08057 ... (856) 234-6224
Sir Speedy see. ... Budget Print Center, Montclair
Sir Speedy, 897 Rancocas Rd., Westampton, 08060 ... (609) 267-1232
Sir Speedy Printing, 3100 Quakerbridge Rd., Mercerville, 08619 ... (609) 586-8222
Sir Speedy Printing, 897 Rancocas Rd., Mount Holly, 08060 ... (609) 267-1232
Sir Speedy Printing, 22 W. Landis Ave., Ste. Q, Vineland, 08360 ... (856) 691-0741
Sir Speedy Printing, 405 Goffle Rd., Wyckoff, 07481 ... (201) 444-0234
Sir Speedy Printing And Marketing Services, 5505 Route 130 N., Pennsauken, 08110 ... (856) 488-1480
Sir Speedy Printing and Marketing Services, 1032 Stelton Rd., Piscataway, 08854 ... (732) 981-9011
Sir Speedy Printing Center, 28 Campus Dr., Edison, 08837 ... (732) 225-2272
Sir Speedy Printing Center, 122 Ridge Rd., Lyndhurst, 07071 ... (201) 896-2727
Sir Speedy Printing Center, 300 S. Lenola Rd., Ste. 22, Maple Shade, 08052 ... (856) 866-0588
Sir Speedy Printing Centers, 39 S. Broad St., Woodbury, 08096 ... (856) 251-0220
Sir Speedy Printing Of East Hanover, 50 Route 10 W., East Hanover, 07936 ... (973) 884-0005
Sir Speedy Westfield, 516 North Ave. E., Westfield, 07090 ... (908) 232-1001
Sirchie Acquisition Co. see. ... Sirchie Finger Print Labs, Inc., Vehicle Div., Medford
Sirchie Finger Print Labs, Inc. see. ... Sirchie Finger Print Labs, Inc., Vehicle Div., Medford
Sirchie Finger Print Labs, Inc., Vehicle Div., 612 Gravelly Hollow Rd., P.O. Box 789, Medford, 08055 ... (609) 654-0777
Sirius Technology LLC, 1 Hollywood Ave., Ste. 19-A, Ho-Ho-Kus, 07423 ... (201) 493-1414
SISCO Mfg. Co., Inc., 7930 National Hwy., Pennsauken, 08110 ... (856) 486-7550
SISSCO Material Handling, 186 Route 206 S., Hillsborough, 08844 ... (908) 359-9767
Sita Corp., 347 Elizabeth Ave., Ste. 200, Somerset, 08873 ... (732) 906-7806
SJ Magazine, 1223 N. Church St., Moorestown, 08057 ... (856) 722-9300
SJ Printer see. ... Sanakirk, Inc., Cherry Hill
SJA Jewelry, Inc., 44 Burlews Ct., Hackensack, 07601 ... (201) 837-0990
SK Custom Creations, Inc., 50 Furler St., Totowa, 07512 ... (973) 754-9261
Ski Jewelers Co., 299 Route 22, Green Brook, 08812 ... (732) 752-6446
Skila, A Sela2 Co., 201 Littleton Rd., 2nd Fl., Morris Plains, 07950 ... (973) 889-1300
Skip Gambert & Assocs., Inc., 436 Ferry St., Ste. 2, Newark, 07105 ... (973) 344-3373
Skripak Metal Fabricators, Inc., 170 Oberlin Ave. N., Unit 17, Lakewood, 08701 ... (732) 364-9662
Sky Frame & Art, Inc., 28 Evans Terminal, Hillside, 07205 ... (908) 354-5656
Sky Printing Co., 338 Montgomery St., Jersey City, 07302 ... (201) 433-3133
Skylands Press, 57 Trinity St., P.O. Box 809, Newton, 07860 ... (973) 383-5006
Skyline Graphic Management, 601 Adams St., P.O. Box 6147, Hoboken, 07030 ... (201) 798-1919
Skyline Graphics Design, 11 Skyline Lake Dr., Ringwood, 07456 ... (973) 839-3329
Skyline Steel Fabricators, 15 Just Rd., Fairfield, 07004 ... (973) 882-0234
Skyline Steel, LLC see. ... Associated Pile & Fitting, Parsippany
Skyline Steel, LLC (H Q), 8 Woodhollow Rd., Ste. 102, Parsippany, 07054 ... (973) 428-6100
Skyline Windows, LLC, 210 Park Pl. E., Wood Ridge, 07075 ... (201) 531-9600
SL Industries, Inc. see. ... R F L Electronics, Inc., Boonton
SL Industries, Inc. (H Q), 520 Fellowship Rd., Ste. A-114, Mount Laurel, 08054 ... (856) 727-1500
Slack, Inc., 6900 Grove Rd., Thorofare, 08086 ... (856) 848-1000
Sleepable Sofas Ltd., 6 Empire Blvd., Moonachie, 07074 ... (973) 546-4502
Sliker Machine Werkes, LLC, 2 Maple St., P.O. Box 53, South River, 08882 ... (732) 238-0331
Slingo, Inc., 411 Hackensack Ave., 8th Fl., Hackensack, 07601 ... (201) 489-6727
Sloan & Co., Inc., 38 Fairfield Pl., West Caldwell, 07006 ... (973) 227-3555
SLP Specialty Vehicles, Inc., 1501 Industrial Way N., Toms River, 08755 ... (732) 240-3696
SLS, Inc. see. ... Scientific Laboratory Supplies, Inc., Millville
Small Business Service Center, 122 E. Kings Hwy., Ste. 504, Maple Shade, 08052 ... (856) 234-8059
smALL Quantities New Jersey, Inc., 66 Ethel Rd., Edison, 08817 ... (732) 248-9009
Smart Gear, LLC, 82 Norwood Ave., Ste. 2, Deal, 07723 ... (732) 663-0000
SMARTdesks see. ... CBT Supply, Inc. (H Q), Rockaway
Smarties Candy Co. see. ... Ce De Candy, Inc., Union
Smartlite, LLC, 25 Madison Ave., Clifton, 07011 ... (973) 470-9400
Smartplay International, Inc., 1550 Bridgeboro Rd., Edgewater Park, 08010 ... (609) 880-1860
SmartPool, Inc., 687 Prospect St., Ste. 460, Lakewood, 08701 ... (732) 730-9880
Smith & Son, Inc., R. P., Main St., P.O. Box 209, Succasunna, 07876 ... (973) 584-4063
Smith Brothers Services, LLC, 3212 State Route 94, Ste. 9, Franklin, 07416 ... (973) 209-7569
Smith Enterprises, 8-A Deptford Rd., Glassboro, 08028 ... (215) 416-9881
Smith Filter Corp., 16 Van Dyke Ave., New Brunswick, 08901 ... (732) 745-2600
Smith, Inc., Roy D., 20 Foster St., P.O. Box 537, Bergenfield, 07621 ... (201) 384-4163
Smith Steel Rule Die, Michael, 2479 S. Main Rd., Vineland, 08360 ... (856) 692-5510
Smith Tool & Mfg., R. G., 245 South St., Newark, 07114 ... (973) 344-1395
Smith's Concrete Products, 3504 S. West Blvd., Vineland, 08360 ... (856) 696-3102
Smitteez Sportswear, 224 Main St., P.O. Box 274, Keansburg, 07734 ... (732) 787-5500
SMP * SMP, Inc. see. ... Sheet Metal Products, Inc., Newark
SMR Research Corp., 300 Valentine St., Hackettstown, 07840 ... (908) 852-7677
SNAME see. ... Society Of Naval Architects & Marine Engineers, Jersey City
Snap Action, Inc., 1260 Route 22 W., Mountainside, 07092 ... (908) 654-4380
Snapco Mfg. Corp., 140 Central Ave., Hillside, 07205 ... (973) 282-0300

Sno Skins, Inc. (H Q), 11 Melanie Ln., Ste. 3, East Hanover, 07936 ... (973) 884-8801
Snow Joe, LLC, 86 Executive Ave., Edison, 08817 ... (866) 766-9563
Snow's, 994 Ocean Dr., Cape May, 08204 ... (609) 884-0440
Snyder Machine Co., 214 Sunnymead Rd., Hillsborough, 08844 ... (908) 359-2745
Snyder's-Lance, Inc. see. ... The Snack Factory, LLC., Skillman
Society Of Naval Architects & Marine Engineers, 601 Pavonia Ave., Ste. 400, Jersey City, 07306 ... (201) 798-4800
Sofield Mfg. Co., Inc., 2 Main St., Ridgefield Park, 07660 ... (201) 943-1118
Sofradir EC, Inc., 373 U.S. Highway 46, Ste. E, Fairfield, 07004 ... (973) 882-0211
Solar Color Chemical Corp., 180 River Rd., Edgewater, 07020 ... (201) 945-5775
Solar Compounds Corp., 1201 W. Blancke St., P.O. Box 1097, Linden, 07036 ... (908) 862-2813
★ Solar Furnace Glass, 4 Camp Wasigan Rd., Blairstown, 07825 ... (908) 362-9661
Solar Products, Inc., 228 Wanaque Ave., Pompton Lakes, 07442 ... (973) 835-6581
Solbern, 8 Kulick Rd., Fairfield, 07004 ... (973) 227-3030
Solgar, Inc., 500 Willow Tree Rd., Leonia, 07605 ... (201) 944-2311
† Solid State, Inc., 46 Farrand St., Bloomfield, 07003 ... (973) 429-8700
SolidSurface Designs, Inc., 1651 Sherman Ave., Pennsauken, 08110 ... (856) 910-7720
Soligenix, Inc., 29 Emmons Dr., Ste. C-10, Princeton, 08540 ... (609) 538-8200
Solmor Mfg. Co., Inc., 164 Emmet St., Newark, 07114 ... (973) 824-7203
SOLSTICE Mfg. Co., 270 S. Main St., Ste. 102, Flemington, 08822 ... (908) 284-0096
Solvay see. ... Solvay U. S. A., Inc., Cranbury
Solvay America, Inc. see. ... Solvay U. S. A., Inc., Cranbury
Solvay Specialty Polymers USA, Inc., 10 Leonard Ln., West Deptford, 08086 ... (856) 853-8119
Solvay U. S. A., Inc., 8 Cedar Brook Dr., CN-7500, Cranbury, 08512 ... (609) 860-4000
Solv-Tec, Inc., 3860 Sylon Blvd., Hainesport, 08036 ... (609) 261-4242
Soma Labs, Inc., 252 Wagner St., Middlesex, 08846 ... (732) 271-3444
★ Somerset Glass Co., Inc., 2086 U.S. Highway 130, North Brunswick, 08902 ... (732) 297-7444
Somerset Prosthetic & Orthotics, Inc., 56 W. Union Ave., Bound Brook, 08805 ... (732) 560-2830
Somerset Wood Products Co., 10 Johnson Dr., Raritan, 08869 ... (908) 526-0030
Some's World-Wide Uniforms, 314 Main St., Hackensack, 07601 ... (201) 843-1199
Something Different Linen see. ... Dye Into Print, Inc., Clifton
Something Different Linen, Inc., 167 Fornelius Ave., Clifton, 07013 ... (973) 772-8019
Somfy Systems, Inc., 121 Herrod Blvd., Dayton, 08810 ... (609) 395-1300
Sommers Plastic Products, Inc., 31 Styertowne Rd., Clifton, 07012 ... (973) 777-7888
SOMS LLC see. ... Southern Ocean Marine Sportswear, Barnegat
Sonali Energees USA, LLC (H Q), 409 Grand Ave., Ste. 3, Englewood, 07631 ... (201) 297-1177
Sonar Products, Inc., 609-611 Industrial Rd., Carlstadt, 07072 ... (201) 729-1116
Sonepar USA see. ... Cooper Electric Supply Co., Monroe
Sonetronics, Inc., 1718 State Route 71, P.O. Box L, Belmar, 07719 ... (732) 681-5016
Sonneborn, LLC, 600 Parsippany Rd., Ste. 100, Parsippany, 07054 ... (201) 760-2940
Sonntag Graphics, Eric, 93 John E. Busch Ave., Somerset, 08873 ... (732) 828-5200
Sonntek, Inc., 125 Pleasant Ave., Upper Saddle River, 07458 ... (201) 236-9300
Sonoco see. ... Sonoco CorrFlex, LLC, Glen Rock
Sonoco see. ... Sonoco Products Co., Dayton
Sonoco CorrFlex, LLC, Heritage Plaza II, 1st Fl., 65 Harristow, Glen Rock, 07452 ... (201) 612-4008
Sonoco Products Co., 5 Stults Rd., Dayton, 08810 ... (609) 655-0300
Sonrise Metal, Inc., 138 3rd Ave., Paterson, 07514 ... (973) 423-4717
★ Sonscreen Graphics, Inc., 77 Tillman St., Raritan, 08869 ... (908) 429-1657
Sony Electronics, Inc., 1 Sony Dr., Park Ridge, 07656 ... (201) 930-1000
Sophisticated Chocolates Mfg., Inc., 92 N. Main St., Windsor, 08561 ... (609) 443-4747
Sophisticated Storage Solutions, LLC, 7-W Chimney Rock Rd., Bridgewater, 08807 ... (732) 356-4200
† SOS Gases, Inc., 1100 Harrison Ave., Kearny, 07032 ... (201) 998-7800
Sound Environments, LLC, 1133 Industrial Pkwy., Ste. E, Brick, 08724 ... (732) 840-6600
Sound Management Group, 5 Ilene Ct., Bldg. 7, Unit 3, P.O. Box 6060, Hillsborough, 08844 ... (908) 874-7826
Soundview Paper Co., 1 Market St., Elmwood Park, 07407 ... (201) 796-4000
Source Packaging, Inc., 215 Island Rd., Mahwah, 07430 ... (201) 831-0005
SourceCodes & Displays, Inc., 135 Fairview Ave., Prospect Park, 07508 ... (973) 942-1965
South Bergenite, 9 Lincoln Ave., Rutherford, 07070 ... (201) 933-1166
South Jersey Custom Screen Printing, 481 W. Route 38, Maple Shade, 08052 ... (856) 482-1500
South Jersey Farmers Exchange, Inc., 101 East Ave., Woodstown, 08098 ... (856) 769-0062
South Jersey Graphics, 203 W. Merchant St., Audubon, 08106 ... (856) 546-0464
South Jersey Ice & Cold Storage LLC, 544 E. Pear St., Vineland, 08360 ... (856) 692-3990
South Jersey Lumbermans, Inc., 6268 Holly St., Mays Landing, 08330 ... (609) 965-1411
South Jersey Media see. ... South Jersey Times, Salem
South Jersey Metal, Inc., 1651 Hurffville Rd., Route 41, P.O. Box 5148, Deptford, 08096 ... (856) 228-0642
South Jersey Precision Tool & Mold, Inc., 4375 S. Lincoln Ave., Vineland, 08361 ... (856) 327-0500
★ South Jersey Publishing Co., 1000 W. Washington Ave., Pleasantville, 08232 ... (609) 272-7000
South Jersey Soft Pretzel, Inc., 912 N. White Horse Pike, Ste. A, Stratford, 08084 ... (856) 435-5055
South Jersey Times, 93 5th St., Salem, 08079 ... (856) 935-1500
South Jersey Times, 309 S. Broad St., P.O. Box 639, Woodbury, 08096 ... (856) 845-3300
† South Jersey Welding Supply Co., 496 Route 38 E., Maple Shade, 08052 ... (856) 778-4440
† South Jersey Welding Supply Co., 94 W. Forest Grove Rd., Vineland, 08360 ... (856) 691-9659
† South Jersey Wiping Cloth, 314 Rosewood Ave., Vineland, 08360 ... (856) 696-0129
South Mill Design, LLC, 131 S. Mill Rd., Princeton Junction, 08550 ... (877) 466-0273
South Plainfield Observer, 1110 Hamilton Blvd., Ste. 1-B, South Plainfield, 07080 ... (908) 668-0010
South River Iron Works, LLC, 132 William St., South River, 08882 ... (732) 257-1347
South State, Inc., 1340 Glassboro Rd., Williamstown, 08094 ... (856) 881-6030
South State Materials, LLC, 202 Reeves Rd., P.O. Box 68, Bridgeton, 08302 ... (856) 451-5300
South State Materials, LLC see. ... South State, Inc., Williamstown
Southeastern Plastics Corp., 15 Home News Row, New Brunswick, 08901 ... (732) 846-8500
Southern New Jersey Steel, Inc, 2591 N. East Blvd., Vineland, 08360 ... (856) 696-1612
Southern Ocean Marine Sportswear, 79 S. Main St., Ste. 2, Barnegat, 08005 ... (609) 698-8868
Southland Mfg. Co., 316 Great Meadows Rd., P.O. Box 350, Hope, 07844 ... (908) 459-5858
Sovereign Technology Corporation, 2200 River Rd., Unit A, Point Pleasant Boro, 08742 ... (732) 298-8104
Sowa Corp., 223 Murray St., Newark, 07114 ... (973) 297-0008
Sox Trot, Inc., 373 Grand Ave., Palisades Park, 07650 ... (201) 944-5250
Sozio, Inc., 51 Ethel Rd. W., Piscataway, 08854 ... (732) 572-5600
SP Industries, Inc. see. ... Maddak Inc., Wayne
SP Industries, Inc. see. ... Wilmad-LabGlass, Vineland
SP Industries, Wilmad-LabGlass Div. see. ... Wilmad-LabGlass, Vineland
Space Power Electronics, Inc., 493 Westhill Rd., Glen Gardner, 08826 ... (908) 689-6547
Spacemaster, Inc., 855 Bloomfield Ave., Glen Ridge, 07028 ... (973) 429-1155
SpaceNow! Corporation, 234 Emmet St., Newark, 07114 ... (973) 504-8585
Spadix Technologies, Inc., 110 Egel Ave., Middlesex, 08846 ... (732) 356-6906



★ Indicates new listing this edition. † Indicates wholesaler/distributor.

★ Spark Holland, Inc., 816 Delsea Dr. N., Glassboro, 08028 .... (609) 799-7250
Spark Wire Products Co., Inc., 158 River Rd., Clifton, 07014 .... (973) 773-6945
Sparkle Embroidery Monograms, 550 Bridgeton Pike, Ste. 12, Mantua, 08051 .... (856) 468-0304
Sparks Belting Co., 5 Spielman Rd., Fairfield, 07004 .... (973) 227-4100
Sparks Belting Co., Inc. see. .... Sparks Belting Co., Fairfield
Sparta Ready Mix see. .... Sparta Sand & Gravel Co., Inc., Sparta
Sparta Sand & Gravel Co., Inc., 33 Demarest Rd., Sparta, 07871 .... (973) 383-4651
Spartan Air Purification, 150 Cooper Rd., Ste. E-14, West Berlin, 08091 .... (856) 768-2929
Spar-Tex Co., Inc., 200 Lehigh Ave., Lakewood, 08701 .... (732) 367-4400
Spaulding Fabricators Inc., 1136 Industrial Pkwy., Brick, 08724 .... (732) 840-4433
SPC Sorbent Products Co., Inc., 645 Howard Ave., Somerset, 08873 .... (732) 302-0080
Spec Steel Rule Dies, Inc., 92 N. Main St., Bldg. 1-B, P.O. Box 33, Windsor, 08561 .... (609) 443-9200
Special Optics Manufacture & Design, Inc., 315 Richard Mine Rd., Wharton, 07885 .... (973) 366-7289
Special T's, 12 Kings Ct., Flemington, 08822 .... (908) 806-8337
Special-T-Graphics Of New Jersey, LLC, 3105 Bridge Ave., Point Pleasant, 08742 .... (732) 899-7240
Specialty Castings, Inc., 42 Curtis Ave., Woodbury, 08096 .... (856) 845-3105
† Specialty Disposal Services, Inc., 115 Route 46, Bldg. E-37-38, Mountain Lakes, 07046 .... (973) 402-9246
Specialty Fabricators, LLC, 118 Meany Rd., Wrightstown, 08562 .... (609) 758-6995
Specialty Lighting Industries, Inc., 1306 Doris Ave., Ocean, 07712 .... (732) 517-0800
Specialty Paper Box Co., 14 Highland Dr., North Caldwell, 07006 .... (973) 396-8556
Specialty Rubber, Inc., 4500 White Horse Pike, P.O. Box 483, Elwood, 08217 .... (609) 704-2555
Specialty Stair & Rail, LLC, 1717 State Route 34 Cliff St., Bldg. 8, P.O. Box 642, Farmingdale, 07727 .... (732) 359-8174
Specified Technologies Inc., 210 Evans Way, Somerville, 08876 .... (908) 526-8000
Spectra Colors Corp., 25 Rizzolo Rd., Kearny, 07032 .... (201) 997-0606
Spectrachem, 10 Dell Glen Ave., Ste. 3-A, Lodi, 07644 .... (973) 253-3553
SpectraMedia, 1634 E. Elizabeth Ave., Linden, 07036 .... (908) 928-1220
Spectrex, Inc., 218 Little Falls Rd., Unit 12, Cedar Grove, 07009 .... (973) 239-8398
Spectro Analytical Instruments, Inc., 91 McKee Dr., Mahwah, 07430 .... (201) 642-3000
★ Spectrum Chemical Mfg. Corp., 769 Jersey Ave., New Brunswick, 08901 .... (732) 214-1300
Spectrum Foils, Inc., 68 Ivy Creek Dr., Little Egg Harbor, 08087 .... (973) 481-0808
Spectrum Neon, Inc., 9130-B Pennsauken Hwy., Pennsauken, 08110 .... (856) 317-9223
Spectrum Tool, 56 Paterson Ave., Newton, 07860 .... (973) 579-0087
Speed Pro Imaging Of Piscataway, 56 Ethel Rd. W., Ste. 14, Piscataway, 08854 .... (732) 662-9860
Speedpro Imaging, 52 E. Centre St., Ste. 3-B, Nutley, 07110 .... (973) 542-8384
Speedwell see. .... Rockwood Corp. / Speedwell Targets, Union
SPEM Corp., 403 Bell St., Piscataway, 08854 .... (732) 356-3366
Spencer Industries, Inc., 80 Holmes St., P.O. Box 128, Belleville, 07109 .... (973) 751-2200
Sperro Metal Products, LLC, 2 Skyline Dr., P.O. Box 397, Montville, 07045 .... (973) 335-2000
SPEX CertiPrep, Inc., 203 Norcross Ave., Metuchen, 08840 .... (732) 549-7144
Spex Criminalistics see. .... Spex Forensics, Metuchen
★ Spex Forensics, 203 Norcross Ave., Metuchen, 08840 .... (732) 549-7144
Spice Co., 6-C Terminal Way, Avenel, 07001 .... (732) 499-9070
Spink & Gabor, Inc., 11 Troast Ct., Clifton, 07011 .... (973) 478-4551
Spiral Binding Co., Inc., 1 Maltese Dr., Totowa, 07512 .... (973) 256-0666
Spiral James Burn see. .... Spiral Binding Co., Inc., Totowa
Spirent Communications, Inc. see. .... Spirent Communications PLC, Eatontown
Spirent Communications, Inc., 211 Mount Airy Rd., Basking Ridge, 07920 .... (908) 953-6000
Spirent Communications PLC, 541 Industrial Way W., Eatontown, 07724 .... (732) 544-8700
Spoo, Inc., 225 NY Ave., Ste. 1, Jersey City, 07307 .... (201) 420-0075
Sports Information Media, Inc., 343 Millburn Ave., Ste. 208, Millburn, 07041 .... (973) 564-5014
Sports Paradise, 4230 Route 130, Willingboro, 08046 .... (609) 877-1826
Sports Time, 40 Oak St., Norwood, 07648 .... (201) 768-1101
Sportstar, 19 Thomas St., South River, 08882 .... (732) 254-9214
Spotless Shade, LLC, 1217 U.S. Highway 1, Edison, 08837 .... (732) 548-1711
Spray Coat Finishing Co., Inc., 1125 Kaighn Ave., Camden, 08103 .... (856) 541-0950
Spray Powders, Inc., 23 Cindly Ln., Ocean, 07712 .... (732) 493-1311
Spray-Tek, Inc., 344 Cedar Ave., Middlesex, 08846 .... (732) 469-0050
Spring Time Bedding Corp., 25 Central Ave., Teterboro, 07608 .... (973) 473-5400
Springdale Farm Market, Inc., 1638 Springdale Rd., Cherry Hill, 08003 .... (856) 424-8674
Springfield Heating & Air Conditioning Co., Inc., 217 Sheffield St., Mountainside, 07092 .... (908) 233-8400
Springfield Metal Products Co., 8 Commerce St., Springfield, 07081 .... (973) 379-4600
Spruce Run Printing, 2005 Route 31, Clinton, 08809 .... (908) 638-6464
Sprung Monument Corp. see. .... Woodbridge Monument Factory, Inc., Woodbridge
SPX Corporation see. .... Weil-McLain, Mount Laurel
SQN Banking Systems, Inc., 65 Indel Ave., P.O. Box 423, Rancocas, 08073 .... (609) 261-5500
★ SQP, Inc., 3206 Route 206, P.O. Box 248, Columbus, 08022 .... (609) 298-5111
Square One, Inc., 111 Gaither Dr., Ste. 104, Mount Laurel, 08054 .... (856) 234-6999
Squiggly Productions, LLC, 164 Main St., Butler, 07405 .... (973) 838-7475
SRI International see. .... Sarnoff Corp., Princeton
SRS, Inc., 74 Liberty St., P.O. Box 4277, Metuchen, 08840 .... (732) 548-6630
SS Studios see. .... S S Art & Engraving Corp., Union
SS White Burs, Inc., 1145 Towbin Ave., Lakewood, 08701 .... (800) 535-2877
S.S. White Technologies, Inc., 151 Old New Brunswick Rd., Piscataway, 08854 .... (732) 474-1700
SSI Creative Group, 20 E. Clementon Rd., Ste. 203-N, Gibbsboro, 08026 .... (856) 663-2292
SSM Industries, Inc., 1425 Grandview Ave., West Deptford, 08066 .... (856) 345-2525
S.S.P. Manufacturing, Inc., 83 Spring Ln., Hackettstown, 07840 .... (908) 852-3125
SSSS LLC see. .... Coldstat Refrigeration, Paramus
† SST Corp., 635 Brighton Rd., Clifton, 07012 .... (973) 473-4300
St. Croix Marine Products, Inc., 235 Hickory Ln., Bayville, 08721 .... (732) 237-8800
ST Robotics, 103 Carnagie Ctr., Ste. 300, Princeton, 08540 .... (609) 584-7522
Stag Bros. Cast Stone, 720 Vassar Ave., Lakewood, 08701 .... (732) 363-6582
Stained Glass Design, Inc., 87 Dellglen Ave., Lodi, 07644 .... (973) 772-5070
Stain-Less Water Filters, LLC, 51 Munion Field Rd., P.O. Box 219, New Gretna, 08224 .... (609) 296-2564
Staloff Bros., 22 Lewis Ave., Jersey City, 07306 .... (201) 653-6479
Stamm International Corp. (H Q), 1530 Palisade Ave., P.O. Box 1929, Fort Lee, 07024 .... (201) 947-1700
Stampex Tool&Die, Inc., 75 4th Ave., Haskell, 07420 .... (973) 839-4040
Stamping.com see. .... Phillips Enterprises, Inc., Asbury Park
Stamping.com, Inc., 3600 Sunset Ave., Asbury Park, 07712 .... (732) 493-4697
Stamplus Mfg., Inc., 654 W. 1st Ave., Roselle, 07203 .... (908) 241-8844
Stan Catering Trucks, Inc., 15 Circle Ave., Clifton, 07011 .... (973) 253-0556
Stanbee Co., Inc., 70 Broad St., P.O. Box 436, Carlstadt, 07072 .... (201) 933-9666
Standard Embossing Plate, 129 Pulaski St., Newark, 07105 .... (973) 344-6670
Standard Merchandising Co. (H Q), 1125 Wright Ave., Camden, 08103 .... (856) 964-9700
Standard Pipe Products, Inc., 15 North Ave., Garwood, 07027 .... (908) 264-8284
Standard Printing & Mail Service, 30-A Plymouth St., P.O. Box 11021, Fairfield, 07004 .... (973) 790-3333
Standard Publishing see. .... Howe's Standard Publishing Co., Inc., Vineland
Standard Tech Applied Resource, 824 South Ave., Middlesex, 08846 .... (732) 968-6776
Stand-Out Signs, Inc., 49 W. Pond Rd., Perth Amboy, 08861 .... (732) 442-9399
Stanek Netting, Inc., 111 Orange St., Bloomfield, 07003 .... (973) 680-1616
Stanley Access Technologies, LLC, 17 Marlen Dr., Ste. C, Trenton, 08691 .... (609) 890-0877
† Stanley Foam Rubber Corp., 14 Orchard St., Wallington, 07057 .... (973) 778-1660
Stanson Corp., 2 N. Hackensack Ave., Kearny, 07032 .... (973) 344-8666
Stanton Precision Products, LLC, 10 Park Pl., Bldg. 4, Butler, 07405 .... (973) 838-6951
Staples Contract Digital Copy Services, 258 Fernwood Ave., Edison, 08837 .... (732) 346-1377
Staples, Inc. see. .... Staples Contract Digital Copy Services, Edison
Stapling Machine Co., LLC, 41 Pine St., Rockaway, 07866 .... (973) 627-4400
Stapling Machine Distribution see. .... Stapling Machine Co., LLC, Rockaway
Star Binding see. .... Allied Bias Products Corp., Jersey City
Star Creation, Inc. (H Q), 1506 Stelton Rd., Piscataway, 08854 .... (732) 819-7070
Star Dynamic Corp., 100 Outwater Ln., Garfield, 07026 .... (973) 340-3883
Star Embroidery Corp., 305 3rd Ave. W., Newark, 07107 .... (973) 481-4300
Star Heel Plate see. .... S H P C, Inc., Newark
Star Ledger, 26 Riverside Dr., Pine Brook, 07058 .... (973) 882-6120
Star Metal Products, Inc., 1125 W. Elizabeth Ave., Linden, 07036 .... (908) 474-9860
† Star Micronics America, Inc. (H Q), 1150 King Georges Post Rd., Edison, 08837 .... (732) 623-5500
Star News Group, 13 Broad St., Manasquan, 08736 .... (732) 223-0076
Star Ravioli Mfg. Co., Inc., 2 Anderson Ave., Moonachie, 07074 .... (201) 933-6427
Star Snacks, LLC, 105 Harbor Dr., Jersey City, 07305 .... (201) 200-9820
Star Soap & Candle, LLC, 300 Industrial Ave., Ridgefield Park, 07660 .... (201) 690-9090
Star Stainless Screw Co., Inc. (H Q), 30 W. End Rd., Totowa, 07512 .... (973) 256-2300
Starfire Lighting, Inc., 7 Donna Dr., Wood Ridge, 07075 .... (201) 438-9540
Star-Glo Industries, LLC, 2 Carlton Ave., East Rutherford, 07073 .... (201) 939-6162
Starlight Windows Mfg., Inc., 50 E. 25th St., Paterson, 07514 .... (973) 278-9366
Starnet Business Solutions, Inc., 46 Industrial Ave., Mahwah, 07430 .... (201) 760-2600
StarTrak Information Technologies, LLC, 395 W. Passaic St., Ste. 325, Rochelle Park, 07662 .... (703) 433-6300
Sta-Seal, Inc., 5205 Route 130 S., Bordentown, 08505 .... (609) 924-0300
State Container Corp., 111 W. Commercial Ave., Moonachie, 07074 .... (201) 933-5200
State Metal Industries, Inc., 941 S. 2nd St., Camden, 08103 .... (856) 964-1510
State Tool Gear Co., Inc., 211 Camden St., Newark, 07103 .... (973) 642-6181
★ State Welding, 5 Industry Ct., Ewing, 08638 .... (609) 882-3288
Stateline Fabricators, LLC, 167 Bronico Way, Phillipsburg, 08865 .... (908) 387-8800
Staten Island Publications, Inc. see. .... Newark Morning Ledger Co., Newark
Staten Island Publications, Inc. see. .... News Of Cumberland County, The, Salem
Staten Island Publications, Inc. see. .... South Jersey Times, Salem
Staten Island Publications, Inc. see. .... Times Of Trenton, Trenton
Statewide Granite & Marble, 3257 Kennedy Blvd., Jersey City, 07306 .... (201) 653-1700
† Stauff Corp., 7 William Demarest Pl., Waldwick, 07463 .... (201) 444-7800
Stauts Printing & Graphics, 12 Maine Trl., Medford, 08055 .... (609) 654-5382
Stavola Construction Materials, Inc., 810 Thompson Ave., Bound Brook, 08805 .... (732) 356-7100
Stavola Construction Materials, Inc., 30 Rockaway Rd., Lebanon, 08833 .... (908) 439-2800
Stavola Contracting Co., Inc. see. .... Stavola Construction Materials, Inc., Bound Brook
Stavola Contracting Co., Inc. see. .... Stavola Construction Materials, Inc., Lebanon
Stavola Contracting Co., Inc., 120 Old Bergen Mill Rd., Englishtown, 07726 .... (732) 542-2328
Stavola Contracting Co., Inc., 175 Drift Rd., Tinton Falls, 07724 .... (732) 542-2328
Stavola Old Bridge Materials, 85 Waterworks Rd., Old Bridge, 08857 .... (732) 721-6900
Stay Focused Marketing, 157 Veterans Dr., Northvale, 07647 .... (201) 750-5050
STE Fabrication, Inc., 28 Haypress Rd., Ste. 106, Cranbury, 08512 .... (732) 274-0024
Steamaster see. .... Steamist, Inc., East Rutherford
Steamist, Inc., 25 E. Union Ave., East Rutherford, 07073 .... (201) 933-5800
Steck, Inc., Paul C., 25 Brown Ave., Springfield, 07081 .... (973) 376-1830
Steel Fab see. .... Garafano & Sons, Peter, Paterson
Steel Technologies Corp. see. .... MacElroy Co., Inc., J. C., Piscataway
Steel's Fudge, Inc., 1928 E. Riverside Dr., Atlantic City, 08401 .... (609) 345-4051
Steel's Fudge, Inc., 1000 Boardwalk, Ocean City, 08226 .... (609) 398-2383
Steel's Fudge, Inc. (H Q), 2719 Boardwalk, Atlantic City, 08401 .... (609) 345-4051
Steelson, LLC * Bags PlUS see. .... Steelson Packaging, Rochelle Park
Steelson Packaging, 190 W. Passaic St., Rochelle Park, 07662 .... (201) 909-0011
Steelstran Industries, Inc. see. .... AISCO, Avenel
Steelstran Industries, Inc., 35 Mileed Way, P.O. Box 30, Avenel, 07001 .... (732) 574-0700
Steering Systems, Inc. see. .... C. J.'s Tool Mfg., Inc., Turnersville
Stefan Enterprises, Inc., 141 Lanza Ave., Bldg. 16-E, Garfield, 07026 .... (973) 253-6005
★ Stefano Fence Systems, Inc., 737 New Durham Rd., Edison, 08817 .... (732) 321-5050
Stef's Performance Products, 693 Cross St., Lakewood, 08701 .... (732) 367-8700
Steimling & Son, Inc.-Machinist, 7 Nickel Ave., Sayreville, 08872 .... (732) 613-1550
Steinen Mfg. Co., Wm., 29 E. Halsey Rd., Parsippany, 07054 .... (973) 887-6400
Steiner Paper Corp., 4000 Borden Town Ave., Sayreville, 08872 .... (732) 651-6009
Stelair Design Corp., 570 Broadway, Long Branch, 07740 .... (732) 571-3391
† Ste-Lar Textiles, Inc., 1301 Marlton Pike W., Cherry Hill, 08002 .... (856) 429-2245
Stelron Cam Co., 1495 MacArthur Blvd., Mahwah, 07430 .... (201) 529-5450
Stelron Components, Inc. see. .... Stelron Cam Co., Mahwah
Stelton Cabinet & Supply, 1358 Stelton Rd., Piscataway, 08854 .... (732) 985-1035
Stepan Co., 220 4th St., Fieldsboro, 08505 .... (609) 298-1222
Stepan Co., 100 W. Hunter Ave., Maywood, 07607 .... (201) 845-3030
Stephen Gould Corporation, 35 S. Jefferson Rd., Whippany, 07981 .... (973) 428-1510
Stephen Plastics, Inc., Douglas, 22-36 Green St., Paterson, 07501 .... (973) 523-3030
Steppin Out Magazine, 21-07 Maple Ave., Fair Lawn, 07410 .... (201) 703-0911
Steralon * SourceOne see. .... Medin Corp., Totowa
Sterling Food Flavorings, LLC, 182 Ridge Rd., Ste. G, Dayton, 08810 .... (732) 438-1620
Sterling Home Products, Inc., 127 U.S. Highway 206, Ste. 22, Hamilton, 08610 .... (609) 585-8941
Sterling Medical Devices, 17 Legion Pl., Rochelle Park, 07662 .... (201) 227-7569
Sterling Products, 90 Dayton Ave., Bldg. 12-C, Ste. 77, Passaic, 07055 .... (973) 471-2858
Sterling Seal & Supply, Inc., 1105 Green Grove Rd., Neptune, 07753 .... (732) 918-8004
Sterling System LLC, 22 Meridian Rd., Unit 10, Edison, 08820 .... (732) 452-1881
Sterling Window Co., 224 21st Ave., Paterson, 07501 .... (973) 742-1900
Sternvent, 5 Stahuber Ave., Union, 07083 .... (908) 688-0807
Stessl & Neugebauer, Inc., 9 Industrial Pl., Summit, 07901 .... (908) 277-3340
Stetsers J.D. Canvas Products, Inc., 644 Billings Ave., Paulsboro, 08066 .... (856) 423-4901
Stetz Machine Shop, John, 17 Highway 36, Middletown, 07748 .... (732) 495-0847
Stevens Cabinet & Millwork, 776 Frenchtown Rd., Milford, 08848 .... (908) 996-6290
† Stevens Industries, Inc., 39 Avenue C, P.O. Box 8, Bayonne, 07002 .... (201) 437-6500
Stevens Products, Inc., 128 N. Park St., East Orange, 07017 .... (973) 672-2140
Stevens-Dunbar Cos., Inc. see. .... Stevens Industries, Inc., Bayonne
Stevenson & Smith, Inc., 450 W. 1st Ave., Roselle, 07203 .... (908) 862-4211
Steve's Screen Printing, 660 Mitchell Ln., Martinsville, 08836 .... (732) 469-7670

Stewart & Stevenson, LLC see. .............. Stewart & Stevenson Power Products, LLC- ADDA Div., Lodi
Stewart & Stevenson Power Products, LLC- ADDA Div. see..Atlantic Detroit Diesel-Allison, LLC, Piscataway
† Stewart & Stevenson Power Products, LLC- ADDA Div., 180 Route 17 S., P.O. Box 950, Lodi, 07644 .......... (201) 489-5800
Stewart & Stevenson Power Products, LLC- ADDA Div. see.Stewart & Stevenson Power Products, LLC, ADDA Div., Lodi
Stewart & Stevenson Power Products, LLC, ADDA Div., 33 Gregg St., Lodi, 07644 .... (201) 291-8415
Stewart Business Forms, Inc., 28 Redstone Ridge, P.O. Box 715, Voorhees, 08043 .......... (856) 768-2011
Stewart, Inc., Robert, 120 Little St., Belleville, 07109 .......... (973) 751-5151
Stewart-Morris, Inc., 71 Kings Rd., Madison, 07940 .......... (973) 822-2777
★ Stich N' Sew Centre, 123 E County Line Rd., Lakewood, 08701 .......... (732) 363-2220
† Stickel Packaging Supply, 1991 Rutgers University Blvd., Lakewood Industrial Pk., Lakewood, 08701 .......... (732) 905-2811
Stiefel Corp., George G. (H Q), 364 N. Farview Ave., Paramus, 07652 .......... (201) 967-0868
STIGroup see. .......... Secure Technology Integration Group, Ltd., Allendale
Stiles Enterprises, Inc., 114 Beach St., P.O. Box 92, Rockaway, 07866 .......... (973) 625-9660
Stirrup Metal Products Corp., 215 Emmet St., Newark, 07114 .......... (973) 824-7086
★ Stitch-It-Up Embroidery, 151 Fisher Rd., Mahwah, 07430 .......... (201) 512-9881
Stobbs Printing Co., Inc., 18 Washington St., P.O. Box 91, Bloomfield, 07003 .......... (973) 748-4441
Stollen Machine & Tool Co., Inc., 761 Lexington Ave., Kenilworth, 07033 .......... (908) 241-0622
Stonco Lighting * Crescent Lighting * Exceline see. .......... Philips Luminaries NA, Union
★ Stone Crafters, LLC, 6084 Reega Ave., Egg Harbor Township, 08234 .......... (609) 646-0406
Stone Galaxy, 4120 Blackhorse Pike, Turnersville, 08012 .......... (856) 219-3450
Stone Graphics Co., Inc., 5020 Industrial Rd., Farmingdale, 07727 .......... (732) 919-1111
Stone, Inc., A. E., 1435 Doughty Rd., Egg Harbor Township, 08234 .......... (609) 641-2781
Stone, Inc., A. E. see. .......... Winslow Hot Mix, LLC, Hammonton
Stone Industries, Inc., 400-402 Central Ave., Haledon, 07508 .......... (973) 595-6250
Stone Industries, Inc. see. .......... Van Orden Sand & Gravel, Ringwood
Stone King, Inc., 900 Lincoln Blvd., Ste. 1, Middlesex, 08846 .......... (732) 868-8687
Stone Mountain Printing, 74 Main St., Ste. 1, Woodbridge, 07095 .......... (732) 634-4444
Stone Plus Design, LLC, 21 Route 17 S., East Rutherford, 07073 .......... (201) 438-2725
Stone Surfaces, Inc., 890 Paterson Plank Rd., East Rutherford, 07073 .......... (201) 935-8803
Stone Surfaces Of Central Jersey, Inc., 690 Jersey Ave., Unit 13, New Brunswick, 08901 .......... (732) 745-1727
Stone Systems Of NJ, 95 8th St., P.O. Box 4207, Passaic, 07055 .......... (973) 778-5525
Stone Tech Fabrication, 930 New York Ave., Trenton, 08638 .......... (609) 984-8818
★ StoneShop, 670 Deer Rd., Ste. 202, Cherry Hill, 08034 .......... (856) 795-8900
Stonhard, A Div. Of StonCor Group see. .......... Epoplex, Maple Shade
Stonhard, A Div. Of StonCor Group, 1000 E. Park Ave., P.O. Box 308, Maple Shade, 08052 .......... (856) 779-7500
Stonite Coil Corp., 476 Route 156, P.O. Box 11036, Yardville, 08620 .......... (609) 585-6600
† Stony Brook Sew & Vacuums, Inc., 191 U.S. Highway 130, Bordentown, 08505 .......... (609) 372-4018
Storage Engine, Inc., 1 Sheila Dr., Eatontown, 07724 .......... (732) 747-6995
Storkdelivery.Com, 232 Webster Ave., Lyndhurst, 07071 .......... (201) 933-7721
Stout's Metal Products, 222 Lincoln Ave., Collingswood, 08108 .......... (856) 854-7938
Strategic Products & Services, LLC, 300 Littleton Rd., 2nd Fl., Parsippany, 07054 .......... (888) 777-7280
Strativa Pharmaceuticals (H Q), 300 Tice Blvd., Woodcliff Lake, 07677 .......... (201) 802-4000
† Strauss Discount Auto, 7-C Brick Plant Rd., South River, 08882 .......... (732) 390-9000
Straval Co., 21 Columbus Ave., Garfield, 07026 .......... (973) 340-9955
StreetGlow, Inc. (H Q), 57 Oak St., Norwood, 07648 .......... (973) 709-9000
Str8up Beverages, LLC, 16 Mount Bethel Rd., Ste. 260, Warren, 07059 .......... (908) 451-1393
Streit & Son Co., Inc., Carl, 703 Atkins Ave., Neptune, 07753 .......... (732) 775-0803
StrikeForce Technologies, Inc., 1090 King Georges Post Rd., Ste. 603, Edison, 08837 .......... (732) 661-9641
Strive Group, LLC, The, 160 Chubb Ave., Ste. 101, Lyndhurst, 07071 .......... (973) 893-1300
Strong Man Building Products Corp., 240 W. Parkway, Pompton Plains, 07444 .......... (973) 831-1555
† Strong Wear, LLC, 191 The Plaza Ave., Teaneck, 07666 .......... (201) 837-7830
Strongwall Industries, Inc., 107 Chestnut St., Ridgewood, 07450 .......... (201) 445-4633
Structural Group, Inc. see. .......... Shared Systems Technology, Inc., Thorofare
† Structured Materials Industries, Inc., 201 Circle Dr. N., Unit 102-103, Piscataway, 08854 .......... (732) 302-9274
Stryker Corp., 2 Pearl Ct., Allendale, 07401 .......... (201) 760-8000
Stryker Corporation see. .......... Stryker Corp., Allendale
Stryker Corporation see. .......... Stryker Orthopaedics, Mahwah
Stryker Orthopaedics, 325 Corporate Dr., Mahwah, 07430 .......... (201) 831-5000
Stryker Spine see. .......... Stryker Corp., Allendale
Stuart Mills, Inc., 25 Stillwater Rd., Newton, 07860 .......... (973) 579-5717
Stuart Steel Protection Corp., 411 Elizabeth Ave., Somerset, 08873 .......... (732) 469-5544
★ Studio Feifish, Llc, 54 Ironia Rd., Randolph, 07869 .......... (973) 303-3287
Studio J/Architectural Glass Effects, 215 Pennsylvania Ave., Paterson, 07503 .......... (973) 569-0200
Studio L Contracting, LLC, 1401 Palisade Ave., Teaneck, 07666 .......... (201) 837-1650
Studio 042, 423 Bloomfield Ave., Montclair, 07042 .......... (973) 509-7591
Stull Technologies, Inc., 17 Veronica Ave., Somerset, 08873 .......... (732) 873-5000
† Stulz Sickles Steel Co., 929 Julia St., Elizabeth, 07201 .......... (800) 351-1776
Stuyvesant Press, Inc., 119 Coit St., Irvington, 07111 .......... (973) 399-3880
Style Rite Of America, Inc., 118 Seger Ave., Clifton, 07011 .......... (973) 478-1100
Styles Mfg. Co., Inc., A. E., 416 Richmond Ave., P.O. Box 1306, Point Pleasant Beach, 08742 .......... (732) 899-0872
Stylex, 740 Coopertown Rd., P.O. Box 5038, Delanco, 08075 .......... (856) 461-5600
† Stylex Imports & Export Co., Inc., 425 Paterson Ave., East Rutherford, 07073 .......... (201) 964-1900
Stylus Custom Apparel, Inc., 729 E. Elizabeth Ave., Linden, 07036 .......... (908) 587-0800
Subaru Of America, Inc. (H Q), 2235 Route 70 W., Subaru Plz., Cherry Hill, 08002 .......... (856) 488-8500
Subito Music Corporation, 60 Depot St., Verona, 07044 .......... (973) 857-3440
Sublimation Mall see. .......... Photothrow, Inc., Saddle Brook
† Suburban Auto Seat Co., Inc., 35 Industrial Rd., Lodi, 07644 .......... (973) 778-9227
Suburban Building Products, 1178 Lakewood Farmingdale Rd., Howell, 07731 .......... (732) 901-8900
★ Suburban Caps, Inc., 899 State Route 18, Old Bridge, 08857 .......... (732) 251-4383
Suburban Fence Co., 532 Mulberry St., Trenton, 08638 .......... (609) 452-2630
Suburban Glass & Mirror, Inc., 231 Herbert Ave., Closter, 07624 .......... (201) 768-9586
Suburban Glass & Mirror, Inc., 418 S. Broad St., Ridgewood, 07450 .......... (201) 447-0440
Suburban Monument & Vault, 203 Sherman Ave., P.O. Box 2370, Newark, 07114 .......... (973) 242-7007
Suburban Propane Partners, L.P. see.Propane Power Corporation, a Div. of Suburban Propane, Newark
† Suburban Propane Partners, L.P. (H Q), 240 Route 10 W., P.O. Box 206, Whippany, 07981 .......... (973) 887-5300
Suburban Seating see. .......... Suburban Auto Seat Co., Inc., Lodi
Suburban Sign Mfg., LLC, 210 Marion Ave., Linden, 07036 .......... (908) 862-7222
Suburban Steel Craft, 22 W. 1st St., Clifton, 07011 .......... (973) 772-3430
Suffern Plating Co., 210 Garibaldi Ave., P.O. Box 755, Lodi, 07644 .......... (973) 473-4404
Suite-K Value Added Services, LLC see. .......... Irving Rice & Co., Dayton
† Sullivan Dental Products, Inc., 45 U.S. Highway 46, Montville, 07058 .......... (973) 227-3533

Sulzer Pumps (U.S.), Inc., 621 Haron Dr., P.O. Box 487, Bridgeport, 08014 .......... (856) 467-2400
Sumatic Co., Inc., 102 Dewitt St., P.O. Box 435, Garfield, 07026 .......... (973) 772-1288
Summit Brass & Bronze Works, Inc., 112 71st St., Guttenberg, 07093 .......... (201) 861-2080
Summit Chemical Specialty Products, 45 River Rd., Ste. 300, Flemington, 08822 .......... (908) 782-9500
Summit Filter Corporation, 20 Milltown Rd., P.O. Box 427, Union, 07083 .......... (908) 687-3500
Summit Group II, 333 16th St., Carlstadt, 07072 .......... (201) 460-8888
Summit Hill Flavors, 253 Lackland Dr. W., Middlesex, 08846 .......... (732) 805-0335
† Summit Import Corp., 100 Summit Pl., Jersey City, 07305 .......... (201) 985-9800
Summit International Filtration Systems, 500 W. Main St., Ste. 10, Wyckoff, 07481 .......... (201) 847-2370
Summit Millwork & Supply, Inc., 235 Morris Ave., Summit, 07901 .......... (908) 277-0039
† Summit Stainless Steel, LLC, 2001 Elizabeth St., North Brunswick, 08902 .......... (732) 297-9505
Summit Steel Corp., 1435 Morris Ave., Union, 07083 .......... (908) 688-8817
Summit Tool Co., Inc., 719 23rd St., Union City, 07087 .......... (201) 867-8600
SumTotal Systems, Inc. see. .......... SumTotal Systems, LLC, Parsippany
SumTotal Systems, LLC, 600 Parsippany Rd., Parsippany, 07054 .......... (973) 364-0480
Sun By The Sea, 224 W. 23rd Ave., P.O. Box 2101, Wildwood, 08260 .......... (609) 522-2721
Sun Capital Partners, Inc. see. .......... AS America, Inc. (H Q), Piscataway
Sun Chemical Corp. see. .......... K V K U. S. A., Inc., New Brunswick
Sun Chemical Corp., 631 Central Ave., Carlstadt, 07072 .......... (201) 933-4500
Sun Chemical Corp., 390 Central Ave., East Rutherford, 07073 .......... (201) 438-4041
Sun Chemical Corp., 35 Waterview Blvd., Ste. 100, Parsippany, 07054 .......... (973) 404-6000
Sun Chemical Corp. see. .......... US Ink Corp. (H Q), Carlstadt
Sun Dial & Panel Corp., 2 Daniel Rd., Fairfield, 07004 .......... (973) 226-4334
Sun Embroidery Screen Printing Co., 12 Route 50, P.O. Box 349, Ocean View, 08230 .......... (609) 624-1231
Sun Neon Sign & Electric Co., 6701-B Rudderow Ave., Pennsauken, 08109 .......... (856) 663-7667
Sun Pharmaceutical Industries, Inc., 270 Prospect Plains Rd., Cranbury, 08512 .......... (609) 495-2800
Sun Plastech Inc., 1055 Parsippany Blvd., Ste. 405, Parsippany, 07054 .......... (973) 257-1999
Sun Tee, LLC, 25 Amity St., Ste. 1, Little Falls, 07424 .......... (973) 812-0349
Sunbelt Corp., 63 Atwood Pl., Wayne, 07470 .......... (803) 329-9787
Sunbrite Dye Co., 35 8th St., P.O. Box 1076, Passaic, 07055 .......... (973) 777-9830
SunFlex Packagers, Inc., 2 Commerce Dr., Cranford, 07016 .......... (908) 709-1500
Sunflower Glass Studio, 877 Sergeantsville Rd., Stockton, 08559 .......... (609) 397-1535
Sunhillo Corp., 444 Kelly Dr., West Berlin, 08091 .......... (856) 767-7676
Sunny Delight Beverages Co., 10 Corn Rd., Dayton, 08810 .......... (732) 329-2391
Sunny Slope Farms, 400 Greenwich Rd., Bridgeton, 08302 .......... (856) 451-0022
Sunrise Pharmaceutical, Inc., 665 E. Lincoln Ave., Rahway, 07065 .......... (732) 382-6085
Sunset Florist, LLC, 470 Bergen Blvd., Ridgefield, 07657 .......... (201) 941-5411
Sunset Printing And Engraving, 10 Kice Ave., Wharton, 07885 .......... (973) 537-9600
† Sunshine Bouquet Co., 3 Chris Ct., Ste. A, P.O. Box 892, Dayton, 08810 .......... (732) 274-2900
Sunshine Metal & Sign, Inc., 467 Maryland St., Orange, 07050 .......... (973) 676-4432
Supco see. .......... Sealed Unit Parts Co., Inc., Allenwood
Super Bags see. .......... Alex Real, LLC, Lakewood
Super Laundry Equipment Corp. see. .......... Luca Laundry Equipment, Inc., Linden
Super Stud Building Products, Inc., 2960 Woodbridge Ave., Edison, 08837 .......... (732) 662-6200
Superior Custom Kitchens, LLC, 126 Mount Bethel Rd., Warren, 07059 .......... (908) 753-6005
Superior Drapery Co. & Harbor Linen Co, 2 Foster Ave., Gibbsboro, 08026 .......... (856) 435-2000
Superior Graphics & Signs, Inc., 576 Casino Dr., Howell, 07731 .......... (732) 625-0101
Superior Marine Canvas Corp., 75 Belfiore Dr., Swedesboro, 08085 .......... (856) 241-1724
† Superior Office Systems, Inc., 19 Gross Ave., Edison, 08837 .......... (732) 738-0093
† Superior Pool Products, LLC, 200 Freeway Dr., Ste. 2, Blackwood, 08012 .......... (856) 232-7774
Superior Powder Coating, Inc., 600 Progress St., Elizabeth, 07201 .......... (908) 351-8707
Superior Printing Ink Co., Inc., 666 E. Linwood Ave., Maple Shade, 08052 .......... (856) 482-9066
Superior Printing Ink Co., Inc., 100 North St., Teterboro, 07608 .......... (201) 478-5600
Superior Signal Company LLC, 178 W. Greystone Rd., Old Bridge, 08857 .......... (732) 251-0800
Superior Tool & Mfg. Co., Inc., 42 Columbia Rd., Branchburg, 08876 .......... (908) 526-9011
Superior Trademark, Inc., 45 Zazzetti St., P.O. Box 35, Waldwick, 07463 .......... (201) 652-1900
Supply Plus, Inc., 155 Sherman Ave., Paterson, 07502 .......... (973) 782-5930
† Supply Source, 64 Oak Ave., Tenafly, 07670 .......... (201) 735-0232
Supply Technologies, LLC see. .......... Columbia Nut & Bolt, LLC, Moonachie
† Supplyone, Inc., 1200 Madison Ave., Paterson, 07503 .......... (718) 392-7400
SupplyOne, Inc., 1090 Thomas Busch Memorial Hwy., Pennsauken, 08110 .......... (856) 727-1010
Support Systems Specialties, Inc., 25 Ridge Rd., P.O. Box 269, South Plainfield, 07080 .......... (908) 510-4349
† Supreme Asset Management & Recovery, Inc., 1950 Rutgers University Blvd., Lakewood, 08701 .......... (732) 370-4100
† Supreme Energy, Inc., 532 Freeman St., Orange, 07050 .......... (973) 678-1800
Supreme Ink Co., Inc., 65 McWhorter St., Newark, 07105 .......... (973) 344-2922
Supreme Mfg. Co., Inc., 5 Connerty Ct., East Brunswick, 08816 .......... (732) 254-0087
Supreme Oil Co., Inc., 80 S. Dean St., Englewood, 07631 .......... (201) 567-3177
Supreme Ribbon see. .......... Walted Designs, Inc., Paterson
Supreme Silk Screen & Embroidery Co. see. .......... BCS Machine & Mfg. Corp., South Plainfield
Supreme Steel Rule Dies, Inc., 985 Madison Ave., Paterson, 07501 .......... (973) 345-9474
Sure Design, 5027 Industrial Rd., Unit 3, Farmingdale, 07727 .......... (732) 919-3066
Sure Mark Labels, Inc., 4 Flynn Ter., P.O. Box 501, West Orange, 07052 .......... (973) 768-4859
Surepure Chemetals, Inc., 5 Nottingham Dr., Florham Park, 07932 .......... (973) 377-4081
Surface Technology, Inc., 105 N. Gold Dr., Robbinsville, 08691 .......... (609) 259-0099
★ Surfside Products, Inc., 1733 Main St., P.O. Box 692, Port Norris, 08349 .......... (856) 785-2115
Survivor II, Inc., 919 Fairmount Ave., Elizabeth, 07201 .......... (908) 353-1155
★ Suspended Aquatic Mentor, 628 South Ave., Garwood, 07027 .......... (973) 376-3335
Sussex Innovations, LLC, 137 Libertyville Rd., Wantage, 07461 .......... (917) 699-9489
Sussex Meat Packing, Inc., 205 Route 23, Sussex, 07461 .......... (973) 875-5641
Sutherland Packaging, Inc., 254 Brighton Ave., P.O. Box 1429, Andover, 07821 .......... (973) 786-5141
Suven Life Sciences Ltd., 1100 Cornwall Rd., Monmouth Junction, 08852 .......... (732) 274-0037
Suzie Mac Specialties, Inc., 12-B Connery Ct., East Brunswick, 08816 .......... (732) 238-3500
Swan Brothers see. .......... Easy Prints, Inc., Metuchen
Swanson Assocs., P.O. Box 151, Wayne, 07470 .......... (973) 984-5930
Swatch Group (U.S.), Inc. (H Q), 1200 Harbor Blvd., 7th Fl., Weehawken, 07086 .......... (201) 271-1400
Sweet Potato Pie, Inc., 140 Auburn St., Paterson, 07501 .......... (973) 279-3405
Sweet Sign Systems, Inc., 9 Davison Ave., Ste. 4, Jamesburg, 08831 .......... (732) 521-9300
Sweet Success, 14 Ellison Rd., Watchung, 07069 .......... (908) 561-2997
Sweet Water Seafood Corp., 369 Washington Ave., Carlstadt, 07072 .......... (201) 939-6622
SWEMCO, 1215 N. Church St., Moorestown, 08057 .......... (856) 222-9900
Swenson Welding & Fabrication, Bill, 707 W. Duerer St., Egg Harbor City, 08215 .......... (609) 653-1177
Swepco Tube, LLC, 1 Clifton Blvd., Clifton, 07011 .......... (973) 778-3000
SWI International * Superwash see. .......... Polycracker, Inc., Boonton
SWI International, Inc., 487 Division St., Boonton, 07005 .......... (973) 334-2525
Swift Co., Inc., John S., 375 North St., Unit N, Teterboro, 07608 .......... (201) 678-3232
† Swift Electrical Supply Co., Inc., 100 Hollister Rd., Teterboro, 07608 .......... (201) 462-0900
Swift Print Solutions, LLC, 405 Front St., Belvidere, 07823 .......... (908) 475-1374

ALPHABETICAL

★ Indicates new listing this edition. † Indicates wholesaler/distributor.

Swift-Track, Inc. (H Q), 58 Schlosser Dr., Rochelle Park, 07662 .... (201) 226-9537
Swim 'N Play, Inc., 313 Regina Ave., Rahway, 07065 .... (732) 574-1500
Swintec East (H Q), 320 W. Commercial Ave., Moonachie, 07074 .... (201) 935-0115
Swisher Hygiene, Inc. see. .... Swisher Hygiene Inc., Linden
Swisher Hygiene Inc., 1805 Lower Rd., Linden, 07036 .... (800) 221-0806
Swiss Orthopedic Co., Inc., 188 Highway 206, Hillsborough, 08844 .... (908) 874-5522
★ Swissray International, Inc. (H Q), 31 Gordon Rd., Piscataway, 08854 .... (908) 353-0971
Swisstex Co., 220 61st St., 2nd Fl., West New York, 07093 .... (201) 861-8000
Switch Vision, 103 Fairfield Rd., Fairfield, 07004 .... (973) 582-2304
Switlik Parachute Co., Inc., 1325 E. State St., Trenton, 08609 .... (609) 587-3300
SWM International see. .... Schweitzer-Mauduit International, Inc., Spotswood
Sycamore Networks, Inc., 100 Century Pkwy, Ste. 120, Mount Laurel, 08054 .... (856) 359-9301
Syence Skincare Laboratories Inc., 99 W. Mill Rd., Long Valley, 07853 .... (908) 791-0044
SYMA Systems, Inc., 300 Wolf Dr., West Deptford, 08086 .... (856) 686-4190
Symbology Enterprises, Inc., 185 Industrial Pkwy., Ste. H, Somerville, 08876 .... (908) 725-1699
Symcon, Inc., 47 Cedar Ln., West Milford, 07480 .... (201) 967-7378
Symphony Printing, 19-21 Brook St., Belleville, 07109 .... (973) 751-5100
Symrise, Inc. see. .... Symrise Purescents, Lakewood
Symrise, Inc., 180 Industrial Pkwy., Branchburg, 08876 .... (908) 429-6946
Symrise, Inc., 300 North St., Teterboro, 07608 .... (201) 288-3200
Symrise Purescents, 1715 Oak St., Ste. 3, Lakewood, 08701 .... (732) 922-2520
Syncsort, Inc., 50 Tice Blvd., Ste. 250, Woodcliff Lake, 07677 .... (201) 930-9700
Synergem, 2323 Randolph Ave., Avenel, 07001 .... (732) 225-0001
Synergy Microwave Corp., 201 McLean Blvd., Paterson, 07504 .... (973) 881-8800
Synray Corp., 209 N. Michigan Ave., Kenilworth, 07033 .... (908) 245-2600
† Syntex Group, Inc., 1838 Downs Ave., Clementon, 08021 .... (856) 566-0058
Synthetic Surfaces Inc., P.O. Box 241, Scotch Plains, 07076 .... (908) 233-6803
SYSCO Corp. see. .... Buckhead Beef Co., Edison
SYSCO Corp. see. .... SYSCO Food Services Of Metro New York, LLC, Jersey City
SYSCO Corp. see. .... Sysco Guest Supply (H Q), Monmouth Junction
† SYSCO Food Services Of Metro New York, LLC,
20 Theodore Conrad Dr., Jersey City, 07305 .... (201) 433-2000
Sysco Guest Supply see. .... Guest Packaging, LLC, Rahway
Sysco Guest Supply (H Q),
4301 Highway 1, P.O. Box 902, Monmouth Junction, 08852 .... (609) 514-9696
Syscom Tech, 1537 Glen Ave., Moorestown, 08057 .... (856) 642-7661
Systech Solutions, Inc., 2540 U.S. Highway 130, Ste. 128, Cranbury, 08512 .... (609) 395-8400
Systems Design Technology, P.O. Box 547, West Long Branch, 07764 .... (732) 571-4547
Systems House, Inc., The, 1033 U.S. Highway 46, Clifton, 07013 .... (973) 777-8050
Systems Sales Corp., 1345 Campus Pkwy., Neptune, 07753 .... (732) 751-0600
Szabo Signs, 1108 Neck Rd., Burlington, 08016 .... (609) 387-7213
T & A Metal Products, Inc.,
1671 Hurffville Rd., P.O. Box 1805, Deptford, 08096 .... (856) 227-1700
† T & B Specialties, Inc., 479 Wright Debow Rd., Jackson, 08527 .... (732) 928-4500
T & E Industries, Inc., 215 Watchung Ave., Orange, 07050 .... (973) 672-5454
T & M Pallet Co., Inc., 116 Edison Rd., Stewartsville, 08886 .... (908) 454-3042
T & P Machine Shop, 600 Prospect Ave., Piscataway, 08854 .... (732) 424-9141
T & T Cabinet Works, Inc., 388 River St., Paterson, 07524 .... (973) 279-0909
† T & T Marketing, Inc., P.O. Box 120, Allamuchy, 07820 .... (973) 426-0453
T A C Technical Instrument Corp.,
21 W. Piper Ave., Trenton-Mercer Airport, West Trenton, 08628 .... (609) 882-2894
T. A. Systems, Inc. see. .... Emabond Solutions, LLC, Norwood
T C Graphics, Inc., 109 South Ave. W., Cranford, 07016 .... (908) 276-7710
T D T Screen Design & Printing, Inc., 79 Whitehead Ave., South River, 08882 .... (732) 777-1377
T E O Fabrications, Inc., 95 Maple Grange Rd., P.O. Box 232, Vernon, 07462 .... (973) 764-5500
T G Mfg., Inc., 299 Old Forks Rd., Hammonton, 08037 .... (609) 561-0022
T J Mfg., Inc., Allaire Airport, Bldg. 25, P.O. Box 2361, Farmingdale, 07727 .... (732) 938-7325
T J's Sportwide Trophy & Awards, 236 S. Salem St., Randolph, 07869 .... (973) 989-8775
T K L Specialty Piping, 175 Broad St., P.O. Box 5149, Phillipsburg, 08865 .... (908) 454-0030
T M Industries, Inc., 729 Route 625 S., Hampton, 08827 .... (908) 730-7674
T M U, Inc. see. .... Mark I Industries, Inc., Cape May
T M U, Inc., 910 Shunpike Rd., Cape May, 08204 .... (609) 884-7656
T N R Tool & Machine Co., 2 Coddington Ave., North Plainfield, 07060 .... (908) 754-4010
T P S Machining, 204 E. Main St., Manasquan, 08736 .... (732) 223-9305
T R B Electro Corp., 6 Morris St., P.O. Box 840, Paterson, 07501 .... (973) 278-9014
T. S. Gates, Inc., 202 12th Ave., Paterson, 07501 .... (973) 523-7323
Tabatchnick Fine Foods, Inc.,
1230 Hamilton St., P.O. Box 356, Somerset, 08873 .... (732) 247-6668
Tablecloth Co., Inc., 514 Totowa Ave., Paterson, 07522 .... (973) 942-1555
Tabloid Graphic Services, Inc., 7101 Westfield Ave., Pennsauken, 08110 .... (856) 486-0410
TAF Tooling, LLC, 1100 E. Linden Ave., Linden, 07036 .... (908) 474-0294
Tage Publishing Service, Inc., 5 Brownstone Way, Ho-Ho-Kus, 07423 .... (201) 445-3050
Takara Belmont U. S. A., Inc., 101 Belmont Dr., Somerset, 08873 .... (732) 469-5000
Takasago International Corp., 267 Union St., Northvale, 07647 .... (201) 767-9001
Takasago International Corp., 4 Volvo Dr., P.O. Box 932, Rockleigh, 07647 .... (201) 767-9001
Talbot Assocs., Inc., 11 Cleveland Pl., Springfield, 07081 .... (973) 376-9570
Tally Display Corp., 19 Gardner Rd., Ste. A, Fairfield, 07004 .... (973) 777-7760
Talon Paint Products, Inc., 1999 Elizabeth St., North Brunswick, 08902 .... (732) 821-3200
Tam Metal Products, Inc., 55 Whitney Rd., Mahwah, 07430 .... (201) 848-7800
Tamburri Assocs., 1401 Industrial Hwy., Cinnaminson, 08077 .... (856) 829-4000
Tamir Biotechnology, Inc. (H Q), 11 Deer Park Dr., Monmouth Junction, 08852 .... (732) 823-1003
Tandem Graphics, Inc., 207 Wanaque Ave., Pompton Lakes, 07442 .... (973) 513-9779
Tangent Graphics, 151 Hobart St., Hackensack, 07601 .... (201) 488-2840
Tanis & Sons, Inc., Joel, 17-68 River Rd., Fair Lawn, 07410 .... (201) 796-1556
Tanner Assocs., 600 Palisade Ave., Union City, 07087 .... (201) 865-4500
Tanter, Inc., 151 Westfield Ave., Clark, 07066 .... (732) 382-3555
Tap For Message see. .... Greetingtap, LLC, South Plainfield
† Tarantin Industries, 86 Vanderveer Rd., Freehold, 07728 .... (732) 780-9340
Target Coatings, Inc., 17-12 River Rd., Fair Lawn, 07410 .... (800) 752-9922
Target Printing & Graphics, 9 E. Passaic St., Hackensack, 07601 .... (201) 883-0200
Targeted Technologies, LLC, 1735 Hooper Ave., Ste. 2, Toms River, 08753 .... (732) 255-9005
Targum Publishing Co., 126 College Ave., Ste. 431, New Brunswick, 08901 .... (732) 932-7051
Task U. S. A., 3 Cass St., Keyport, 07735 .... (732) 739-0377
Taste It Presents, Inc., 200 Sumner Ave., Kenilworth, 07033 .... (908) 241-9191
TATA Chemicals North America, Inc. (H Q),
100 Enterprise Dr., 7th Fl., Rockaway, 07866 .... (973) 599-5500
Tata Global Beverages (H Q), 155 Chestnut Ridge Rd., 2nd Fl., Montvale, 07645 .... (201) 571-0300
Tatra Eagle, Inc., 31 Madison Ave., Hasbrouck Heights, 07604 .... (201) 288-3815
Tatz Industries, Inc., William, 11 Railroad Pl., Belleville, 07109 .... (973) 751-0720
Tauber Co., LLC, G. G., 289 State Route 33, Ste. 12, Manalapan, 07726 .... (301) 881-3567
Taunton Graphics, Inc., 1049 Industrial Dr., West Berlin, 08091 .... (856) 719-8084
Taurus Display Corp., 1249 Glen Ave., Moorestown, 08057 .... (856) 793-3500
† Taurus International, Inc., 275 N. Franklin Tpke., Ste. 3, Ramsey, 07446 .... (201) 825-2420
Taurus Precision, Inc., 129 Paterson Ave., Little Falls, 07424 .... (973) 785-9254
† Taylor Auto Parts, 222 Pacific St., Newark, 07114 .... (973) 465-4345
Taylor Corp. see. .... Oraton Rubber Stamp Co., Inc., Columbia
Taylor Fence Co., 1246 Route 33, Farmingdale, 07727 .... (732) 747-5498
Taylor Forge Stainless, Inc.,
22 Readington Rd., P.O. Box 610, Somerville, 08876 .... (908) 722-1313
Taylor Made Cabinets, 516 E. Bay Ave., Manahawkin, 08050 .... (609) 978-6900
Taylor Made Custom Cabinetry, Inc.,
7035 Central Hwy., Ste. 200, Pennsauken, 08109 .... (856) 786-5433
Taylor Microwave, Inc., 48 Industrial W., Clifton, 07012 .... (973) 890-7763
† Taylor Oil Co., Inc., 77 2nd St., P.O. Box 974, Somerville, 08876 .... (908) 725-7737
Taylor Windows, Inc., 61 Central Ave., East Orange, 07018 .... (973) 672-3000
TBC Partners, LLC, 743 Alexander Rd., Ste. 15, Princeton, 08540 .... (855) 937-6466
TBL Plastics see. .... Thermoplastic Biologic, LLC, Sparta
TBT Group, Inc., 191 Heller Pl., Bellmawr, 08031 .... (856) 753-4500
† TC Petroleum, 575 Prospect St., Ste. 264, Lakewood, 08701 .... (732) 367-2116
TCP Reliable, Inc., 551 Raritan Center Pkwy., Edison, 08837 .... (732) 346-9200
TCS Technologies, Inc., 430 Sand Shore Rd., Unit 1, Hackettstown, 07840 .... (908) 852-7555
TD see. .... Touch Dynamic, Inc., Irvington
TDC Instore see. .... Taurus Display Corp., Moorestown
TDI Power, 36 Newburgh Rd., Hackettstown, 07840 .... (908) 850-5088
TDK-Lambda Americas, Inc. see. .... TDK-Lambda, Inc., Neptune
TDK-Lambda, Inc., 405 Essex Rd., Neptune, 07753 .... (732) 922-9300
TE Connectivity see. .... Tyco Electronics Subsea Communications, LLC (H Q), Eatontown
TE SubCom see. .... Tyco Electronics Subsea Communications, LLC (H Q), Eatontown
TE Wire & Cable, LLC, 107 5th St., Saddle Brook, 07663 .... (201) 845-9400
Tea & Elle Woodworks, LLC, 5004 Industrial Rd., Farmingdale, 07727 .... (732) 938-9660
TeaForHealth see. .... Samuel Elliott, Inc., Riverton
Team Industrial Services, 4 Killdeer Ct., Ste. 300, Swedesboro, 08085 .... (610) 859-7800
Team U. S. A., 200 Badger Ave., Newark, 07108 .... (973) 596-2800
Tec Cast, Inc., 440 Meadow Ln., Carlstadt, 07072 .... (201) 935-3885
Tec Installations, Inc., 375 E. 22nd St., Paterson, 07514 .... (973) 684-0503
Tech 2 Go see. .... S D I Technologies, Inc., Rahway
Tech Air Service see. .... Total Maintenance & Service, Inc., Bloomingdale
Tech Art, Inc., 12 E. 5th St., Paterson, 07524 .... (201) 525-0044
Tech Products Co., Inc., 300 Greenwood Ave., Midland Park, 07432 .... (201) 444-7777
Tech Repro, Inc., 65 Zabriskie St., Hackensack, 07601 .... (201) 489-1333
Tech Support, Inc., 23 Pawnee Ave., Rockaway, 07866 .... (973) 627-8870
Tech 21 USA, Inc., 790 Bloomfield Ave., Ste. B-1, Clifton, 07012 .... (973) 777-6996
Techflex, 29 Brookfield Dr., Sparta, 07871 .... (973) 300-9242
Techline Extrusion Systems, 89 4th Ave., Haskell, 07420 .... (973) 831-0317
Technatron, Inc., 78 Route 173 W., Ste. 9, Hampton, 08827 .... (908) 238-1122
Techne, Inc., 3 Terri Ln., Ste. 10, Burlington, 08016 .... (609) 589-2560
Technical Aids, Inc., 219 S. 18th St., East Orange, 07018 .... (973) 674-1082
Technical Fabricators, Inc., 203 Wood Ave., Ste. A, Middlesex, 08846 .... (732) 469-7373
Technical Glass Products, Inc., 243 E. Blackwell St., Ste. B, Dover, 07801 .... (973) 989-5500
Technical Name Plate Corp., 92 1st St., Passaic, 07055 .... (973) 773-4256
Technical Processing, Inc., 81 Dale Ave., Paterson, 07501 .... (973) 278-4950
Technical Products Co., 264 Park Ave., Caldwell, 07006 .... (973) 228-2258
Technical Systems Group, Inc., 28 Muller Pl., Little Falls, 07424 .... (973) 785-1118
Technidyne Corp., 2190 Route 9, Ste. 9, Toms River, 08755 .... (732) 363-1055
TechniEdge see. .... IDL TechniEdge, LLC, Kenilworth
Technimetal, 7 Melanie Ln., Ste. 3, East Hanover, 07936 .... (973) 428-2881
Technimold, Inc., 715 Jerusalem Rd., Scotch Plains, 07076 .... (908) 232-8331
Technique Precision Co. see. .... Bisaga, Inc., Somerdale
Technitool, Inc., 1028 Industrial Dr., West Berlin, 08091 .... (856) 768-2707
Techno Design, Inc., 11 Erie St., Front, Garfield, 07026 .... (973) 478-0930
Technobox, Inc., 154 Cooper Rd., Ste. 901, West Berlin, 08091 .... (856) 809-2306
★ TechnoGym U. S. A. Corp., 700 U.S. Highway 46 E., Fairfield, 07004 .... (206) 623-1488
Technol Fuel Conditioners, Inc., 145 Wyckoff Rd., Ste. 300, Eatontown, 07724 .... (732) 542-0111
Technology Dynamics, Inc., 100 School St., Bergenfield, 07621 .... (201) 385-0500
Technology General Corp. see. .... Clawson Machine, Div. Of Technology General Corp., Franklin
Technology General Corp. (H Q), 12 Cork Hill Rd., Franklin, 07416 .... (973) 827-4143
Technovations Technology Reviews, Inc., 14 Red Barn Ln., Randolph, 07869 .... (973) 537-9511
Technovision, Inc., 1119 Raritan Rd., Ste. 2, Clark, 07066 .... (732) 381-0200
Tech-Optics International, 600 Deer Rd., Cherry Hill, 08034 .... (856) 795-8585
Tech-Pak, Inc., 100 Blum, P.O. Box 51, Wood Ridge, 07075 .... (201) 935-3800
Tee Pee Packaging Corp., 85 Harrison St., Dover, 07801 .... (973) 328-6500
Tee Shirt Guy, 507 E. 41st St., Paterson, 07504 .... (973) 247-3442
† Tees & Novelties, Inc., P.O. Box 2059, Garfield, 07026 .... (973) 574-7591
Tees To Please Screen Printing,
15 Minneakoing Dr., P.O. Box 542, Flemington, 08822 .... (908) 788-5508
Teesing USA, LLC, 10 Millpond Dr., Unit 7, Lafayette, 07848 .... (973) 383-0691
Teixeira's Bakery, 113-129 Kossuth St., P.O. Box 5550, Newark, 07105 .... (973) 589-8875
TEK Molding, LLC, 1440 County Route 565, Sussex, 07461 .... (973) 702-0450
Tekkote Corp. see. .... Mondi, Ridgefield
Tekkote Corp., 580 Willow Tree Rd., Leonia, 07605 .... (201) 585-8875
Tekmet, LLC, 400 Myrtle Ave., Ste. A, Boonton, 07005 .... (973) 376-1700
Teknicom Sales Co., 470 Commercial Ave., Palisades Park, 07650 .... (201) 327-4500
Teknics Industries, Inc., 170 Beaver Brook Rd., Lincoln Park, 07035 .... (973) 633-7575
Tekni-Plex, Inc. see. .... Colorite, A Tekni-Plex Co., Ridgefield
Tekni-Plex, Inc., 201 Industrial Pkwy., Somerville, 08876 .... (908) 722-4800
Tekni-Plex, Inc. see. .... Tri-Seal, Flemington
† Tekris Power Electronics, Inc., 1675 State Route 34, Farmingdale, 07727 .... (732) 938-4996
Tektite Industries, Inc., 309 N. Clinton Ave., Trenton, 08638 .... (609) 656-0600
†★ Teleco Business Telephone Systems, 1883 State Route 27, Edison, 08817 .... (732) 777-7990
Telecom Assistance Group, Inc., 150 Cooper Rd., Ste. F-15, West Berlin, 08091 .... (856) 753-8585
Teledex, Inc. (H Q), 1 Atlas St., Kenilworth, 07033 .... (908) 964-8109
Teledynamics, LLC, 45 Indian Ln. E., Ste. 1, Towaco, 07082 .... (973) 248-3360
Telegence Corp., 383 Kings Hwy. N., Ste. B-1, Cherry Hill, 08034 .... (856) 755-1717
Telegenix, Inc., 71 Indel Ave., P.O. Box 577, Rancocas, 08073 .... (609) 265-3910
Telemark CNC, LLC, 429 Rockaway Valley Rd., Bldg. 2200, Boonton, 07005 .... (973) 794-4857
Telemetrics, Inc., 6 Leighton Pl., Ste. 4, Mahwah, 07430 .... (201) 848-9818
Telescript International see. .... Telescript, International LLC, Norwood
Telescript, International LLC, 55 Walnut St., Ste. 101-A, Norwood, 07648 .... (201) 767-6733
Tel-Instrument Electronics Corp., 1 Branca Rd., East Rutherford, 07073 .... (201) 933-1600
Telmark Packaging Corp., 30 Freneau Ave., Ste. 2-B, Matawan, 07747 .... (732) 739-9100
Temperature Humidity Instruments LLC, 235 Main St., Ste. 281, Madison, 07940 .... (908) 354-8236
Temperature Processing Co., Inc., 228 River Rd., North Arlington, 07031 .... (201) 991-8000
Templar Food Products see. .... Reeves Enterprises, Inc., New Providence
★ Temptime Corp., 116 The American Rd., Morris Plains, 07950 .... (973) 984-6000

TEMPTIME Corp., 116 The American Rd., 2nd Fl., Morris Plains, 07950 .......... (973) 984-6000
Tenax Finishing Products Co., 390 Adams St., Newark, 07114 .......... (973) 589-9000
Tension Corporation see.......... Tension Envelope Corp., South Hackensack
Tension Envelope Corp., 19 Wesley St., South Hackensack, 07606 .......... (201) 487-1880
Terminal Printing Co., 94 River St., P.O. Box 30, Hoboken, 07030.......... (201) 659-5924
Terra Chips see.......... Hain Celestial Group, Inc., The, Moonachie
TerraCycle, Inc., 121 New York Ave., Trenton, 08638.......... (609) 393-4252
Terrigno's Bakery, 632 N. Pearl St., Bridgeton, 08302 .......... (856) 451-6368
Terriss Consolidated Industries,
807 Summerfield Ave., P.O. Box 110, Asbury Park, 07712.......... (732) 988-0909
Terumo Medical Corp. (H Q), 2101 Cottontail Ln., Somerset, 08873 .......... (732) 302-4900
Terzano Cabinetry, Inc., 111 Leuning St., Unit G, South Hackensack, 07606.......... (201) 373-9500
Tess-Com, Inc., 400 South Ave., Ste. 11, Middlesex, 08846.......... (732) 560-8100
★ Tessie's Soap Box, 65 South St., Jersey City, 07307.......... (201) 533-8337
Tessler & Weiss, Inc., 2389 Vauxhall Rd., P.O. Box 3414, Union, 07083 .......... (908) 686-0513
Testrite Instrument Co., 216 S. Newman St., Hackensack, 07601.......... (201) 543-0240
Testrite Visual Products see.......... Testrite Instrument Co., Hackensack
Tetley Harris Food Group see. .......... Tata Global Beverages (H Q), Montvale
Tetra Pak, Inc. see.......... Novembal U. S. A., A Tetra Pak Co., Edison
Tetra Products see. .......... FTI, Inc. (H Q), Florham Park
Teva Pharmaceuticals USA, Inc. see.......... Teva Pharmaceuticals U.S.A., Inc., Fairfield
Teva Pharmaceuticals U.S.A., Inc., 8-10 Gloria Ln., Fairfield, 07004.......... (973) 575-2775
Tevco Enterprises, Inc., 110 Pomponio Ave., South Plainfield, 07080.......... (908) 754-7306
★ Tex Print USA, LLC, 20-21 Wagaraw Rd., Bldg. 37, Fair Lawn, 07410 .......... (201) 773-6531
Texas Canvas Co., 266 Union Blvd., Totowa, 07512.......... (973) 278-3802
TEX-NET, Inc., 763-B Railroad Ave., Florence, 08518 .......... (609) 499-9111
Texpack, Inc. see.......... Lamitech, Inc., Cranbury
Textile Creations, Inc. (H Q), 8-B S. Gold Dr., Hamilton, 08691.......... (609) 631-4433
Textiles By Anthony, Inc., 61 Willett St., Bldg. 12, 2nd Fl., Passaic, 07055 .......... (973) 773-2501
TF Yachts, LLC, 801 Philadelphia Ave., P.O. Box 702, Egg Harbor City, 08215.......... (609) 965-2300
TGZ Acquisition Co. see. .......... JACE Systems, Inc., Cherry Hill
Thal Precision Industries, Inc., 19-A Walnut Ave., Clark, 07066 .......... (732) 381-6106
†★ Thanks For Being Green, LLC, 5070-B Central Hwy., Merchantville, 08109 .......... (856) 333-0991
The CLI Group, 932 Market St., Paterson, 07513.......... (973) 279-9174
The Display Connection see.......... Algar-The Display Connection Inc., Moonachie
The Fifty/Fifty Group, Inc, 343 S. River St., Hackensack, 07601 .......... (201) 343-1243
The Fireplace Place, 264 U.S. Highway 46 E., Fairfield, 07004.......... (973) 227-8540
The Ice Cream & Yogurt Professionals see. .......... Panza & Sons, Ltd., A., Edison
The Lifestyle Company, Inc., 6 Paragon Way, Ste. 112, Freehold, 07728.......... (732) 303-7849
† The Liner Co., Inc., 7 Meadows Run Dr., Colts Neck, 07722.......... (732) 761-0700
The New Town Press, 421 Stone Meeting House Rd., Woolwich Township, 08085 .......... (856) 467-3113
The Observer, 39 Seeley Ave., Kearny, 07032 .......... (201) 991-1600
The Pork Roll Store see.......... RobDav Distributors, Inc., Allentown
The Snack Factory, LLC., 11 Tamarack Cir., Skillman, 08558.......... (609) 683-5400
The Star Group, 80-A Industrial Rd., Lodi, 07644.......... (973) 778-8600
The Westfield Leader/Scotch Plains-Fanwood Times see.. Watchung Communications, Inc., Westfield
Themac, Inc., 405 Railroad Ave., P.O. Box 44, East Rutherford, 07073.......... (201) 438-2313
Therapedic International, Inc. (H Q),
103 College Rd. E., 2nd Fl., Princeton, 08540.......... (609) 720-0700
ThermaFreeze Products Corp. (H Q), 107 Maple Grange Rd., Vernon, 07462.......... (877) 777-8397
Thermal Innovations Corp., 2220 Landmark Pl., Ste. 1, Manasquan, 08736.......... (732) 223-1812
Thermal-Chek, Inc., 912 Broadway, Westville, 08093 .......... (856) 742-1200
Therma-Tech Corp., 300 Dakota St., Paterson, 07503 .......... (973) 345-0076
Thermo Cote, Inc., 198 Green Pond Rd., Ste. 5, Rockaway, 07866.......... (973) 464-3575
Thermo Fisher Scientific, 755 U.S. Highway 202, Bridgewater, 08807.......... (908) 526-1800
Thermo Fisher Scientific, Inc. see. .......... Thermo Fisher Scientific, Bridgewater
Thermo Fisher Scientific, Inc. see. .......... Thermo Fisher Scientific Inc., Fair Lawn
† Thermo Fisher Scientific Inc., 1 Reagent Ln., Fair Lawn, 07410 .......... (201) 796-7100
Thermo Plastics Technologies, Inc., 1119 Morris Ave., Union, 07083 .......... (908) 687-4833
Thermo Systems, LLC (H Q), 84 Twin Rivers Dr., East Windsor, 08520.......... (609) 371-3300
Thermo-Graphics, Inc., 915 E. Hazelwood Ave., Rahway, 07065 .......... (732) 669-0252
Thermoplastic Biologic, LLC, 26 Brookfield Dr., Ste. C, Sparta, 07871 .......... (973) 383-2834
Thermoplastic Processes, 1268 Valley Rd., P.O. Box 124, Stirling, 07980.......... (888) 554-6400
Thermoplastic Processes, Inc. see.......... Thermoplastic Processes, Stirling
Thermoseal Industries, LLC, 400 Water St., Gloucester City, 08030.......... (856) 456-3109
Thermwell Products Co., Inc., 420 State Route 17, Mahwah, 07430 .......... (201) 684-4400
★ Thetica Systems, Inc., 145 13th St., Cresskill, 07626 .......... (201) 399-7800
Thewal, Inc., 12 Center St., Chatham, 07928.......... (973) 635-1880
Theysken's see.......... Link Theory, Lyndhurst
Thin Stone Systems, LLC, 23 Commerce Rd., Ste. O, Fairfield, 07004 .......... (973) 882-7377
Thinfilms, Inc., 15 Ilene Ct., Ste. 6, Hillsborough, 08844 .......... (908) 359-7014
Thomas & Betts Corp. see. .......... Thomas & Betts Corp., Elastimold Div., Hackettstown
Thomas & Betts Corp., Elastimold Div., 1 Esna Pk., Hackettstown, 07840.......... (908) 852-1122
† Thomas & Co., Inc., P. L., 119 Headquarters Plz., Morristown, 07960.......... (973) 984-0900
Thomas & Skinner, Inc. see. .......... Ceramic Magnetics, Inc., Fairfield
Thomas Collace Co. see. .......... Custom Pak, Inc., Thorofare
Thomas Greco Publishing Inc., 244 Chestnut St., Ste. 202, Nutley, 07110.......... (973) 667-6922
Thomas Instrumentation, Inc., 118 Kings Hwy., Cape May Court House, 08210 .......... (609) 624-7777
Thomas Instrumentation, Inc. (H Q),
133 Landing Rd., Cape May Court House, 08210.......... (609) 624-2630
Thomas Mfg., Inc., 630 Ramsey Ave., Hillside, 07205.......... (908) 810-0030
Thomas Scientific, Inc. (H Q),
1654 High Hill Rd., Interstate 295, P.O. Box 99, Swedesboro, 08085.......... (856) 467-2000
Thomas Sweet Chocolates, Inc., 29 Palmer Sq. W., Princeton, 08542.......... (609) 924-7222
Thompson Materials Corp., 15 Leslie Ct., Whippany, 07981.......... (973) 386-1400
Thomsen Litho, Inc., 217 Railroad Ave., Ridgefield Park, 07660 .......... (201) 489-1133
Thomson Lamination Co., Inc., 504 E. Linwood Ave., Maple Shade, 08052.......... (856) 779-8521
★ Thomson Reuters Corp., 492 River Rd., Nutley, 07110.......... (973) 662-3070
Thomson Reuters Holdings, Inc. see. .......... Thomson Reuters Corp., Nutley
Thoramet Surgical Products, Inc., 301 Route 17-N, Ste. 800, Rutherford, 07070 .......... (973) 399-7792
Thorlabs, Inc., 56 Sparta Ave., Newton, 07860.......... (973) 300-3000
Thosani, Inc., 150 Cooper Rd., Ste. E-12, West Berlin, 08091 .......... (856) 753-9000
3D Biotek, LLC, 1 Ilene Ct., Hillsborough, 08844 .......... (732) 729-6270
ThreeTwelve LLC see.......... Murray's Uniforms, Inc., Bradley Beach
ThromboGenics, Inc., 101 Wood Ave. S., Ste. 600, Iselin, 08830.......... (732) 590-2900
Thumann, Inc., 670 Dell Rd., Carlstadt, 07072 .......... (201) 935-3636
Thwing-Albert Instrument Company, 14 W. Collings Ave., West Berlin, 08091 .......... (856) 767-1000
† ThyssenKrupp Materials NA Copper & Brass Sales Div.,
800 Arlington Blvd., Ste. C, Swedesboro, 08085.......... (610) 586-1800
ThyssenKrupp Materials NA, Inc. see.ThyssenKrupp Materials NA Copper & Brass Sales Div., Swedesboro
TICO Mfg., Inc., 1044 Industrial Dr., Unit 9, West Berlin, 08091 .......... (856) 767-8430
Tidewater Workshop see.......... Modern Boat Works, Inc., Oceanville

Tielmann, Inc., D. R., 1208 State Route 34, Ste. 1, Matawan, 07747.......... (732) 332-1860
Tiffanees Toys, Inc., 601 Nassau St., Ste. 593, North Brunswick, 08902.......... (732) 828-6333
★ Tighe Publishing Services, Inc.,
788 Morris Tpke., Ste. 100, Short Hills, 07078 .......... (973) 379-7770
Tilcon see.......... Tilcon Riverdale Quarry, Riverdale
Tilcon, Inc., Oxford Quarry,
193 Mount Pisgah Ave., P.O. Box 120, Oxford, 07863.......... (908) 453-4141
Tilcon New York Asphalt Constructions see.......... Tilcon Totowa Asphalt, Totowa
Tilcon New York Inc. see.......... Tilcon New York, Inc., Wharton
Tilcon New York, Inc., 625 Mount Hope Rd., Wharton, 07885.......... (973) 366-7741
Tilcon New York Inc. see.......... Tilcon Riverdale Quarry, Riverdale
Tilcon New York Inc. see.......... Tilcon Totowa Asphalt, Totowa
Tilcon New York Inc. see.......... Tilcon, Inc., Oxford Quarry, Oxford
Tilcon Riverdale Quarry, 125 Hamburg Tpke., Riverdale, 07457.......... (973) 835-0028
Tilcon Totowa Asphalt, 859 Riverview Dr., Totowa, 07512.......... (973) 256-8300
Tiles Unlimited, 1016 State Route 34, Ste. 9, Matawan, 07747 .......... (732) 566-3886
Tilton Rack & Basket Corp., 66 Passaic Ave., Fairfield, 07004.......... (973) 226-6010
TimBar Corp., 15-01 Pollitt Dr., Unit 9, Fair Lawn, 07410.......... (201) 568-7300
TimBar Packaging & Display see. .......... TimBar Corp., Fair Lawn
Time Systems International, Inc. see.......... AMERICAN Time Recorder, Vineland
† Time Systems International, Inc., 142 S. Van Brunt St., Englewood, 07631 .......... (973) 472-2202
Timecruiser Computing Corp., 9 Law Dr., Ste. 2, Fairfield, 07004 .......... (973) 244-7856
Times Of Trenton, 413 River View Plz., Trenton, 08611.......... (609) 989-5454
TimeSharing Today, Inc., 140 County Rd., Ste. 114, Tenafly, 07670.......... (201) 871-4304
Timplex Corp., 1370 State Route 23, Wantage, 07461 .......... (973) 875-5500
Tim's Automotive Machine Shop, 1760 Highway 37 E., Toms River, 08753 .......... (732) 573-0600
Tina's Window Decorating, 968 Somerset St., Watchung, 07069.......... (908) 668-0066
Tingley Rubber Corp., 1551 S. Washington Ave., Ste. 403, Piscataway, 08854.......... (908) 757-7474
Tingue, Brown & Co. (H Q), 535 N. Midland Ave., Saddle Brook, 07663 .......... (201) 796-4490
TIP Industries, Inc., 340 W. Broad St., Burlington, 08016 .......... (609) 239-1900
TIP TEMPerature Products see. .......... TIP Industries, Inc., Burlington
Tipico Products, Inc., 490 Oberlin Ave. S., Lakewood, 08701.......... (732) 942-8820
Titan Converting, 150 Fieldcrest Ave., Ste. A, Edison, 08837 .......... (732) 225-2080
Titan Implants, Inc., 18 Columbia Ave., Bergenfield, 07621.......... (201) 439-0027
Titan Rack & Shelving, LLC, 101 Muirhead Ave., Trenton, 08695.......... (732) 249-0887
TITAN Technologies International see. .......... Arlington Machine & Tool Co., Fairfield
★ Titan Technologies International, Inc., 222 Getty Ave., Clifton, 07011 .......... (973) 928-5222
Titanium Fabrication Corp., 110 Lehigh Dr., Fairfield, 07004.......... (973) 227-5300
† Titanium Industries, Inc., 18 Green Pond Rd., Rockaway, 07866.......... (973) 983-1185
TitanSeal, Inc., 876 N. Lenola Rd., Ste. 3-E, Moorestown, 08057.......... (856) 582-7725
TJK Machine, LLC, 870 E. Elmer Rd., Vineland, 08360.......... (856) 691-7811
TLC Sign & Banner, Inc., 188 Walnut St., Toms River, 08753.......... (732) 244-4225
T-M Vacuum Products, Inc., 630 S. Warrington Ave., Cinnaminson, 08077 .......... (856) 829-2000
T/Mac, Inc., 100 Jersey Ave., Bldg. D-6, New Brunswick, 08901.......... (732) 247-0022
TMP International, Inc., 15 Hamburg Tpke., Bloomingdale, 07403.......... (973) 838-7072
TMS see.......... Total Machine Solutions, Inc., Fairfield
TNA Litho Group, Inc. see.......... Farmingdale Printing, Farmingdale
TNG Creative see. .......... Type-N-Graphic, Kinnelon
Todd Architectural Models, 54 Mountainview Rd., P.O. Box 1002, Chatham, 07928.... (973) 507-4072
Tofutti Brands, Inc., 50 Jackson Dr., Cranford, 07016 .......... (908) 272-2400
Tolan Machinery Co., Inc./Tolan Polishing Corp.,
164 Franklin Ave., P.O. Box 695, Rockaway, 07866.......... (973) 983-7212
Tolin Design, Inc., 16 Bland St., Emerson, 07630.......... (201) 261-4455
Toll Compaction Group, LLC, 14 Memorial Dr., Neptune, 07753.......... (732) 776-8225
Tomad, Inc., 129 Cincinnati Ave., Egg Harbor City, 08215.......... (609) 965-0808
Tomasello Winery, Inc., 225 White Horse Pike, Hammonton, 08037.......... (609) 561-0567
Tomcel Machine, Inc., 86 Lackawanna Ave., West Paterson, 07424.......... (973) 256-8257
Tomer Laboratories, 350 Campus Dr., Somerset, 08873 .......... (732) 560-1885
Tomken Plating Co., Inc., 625 Pear St., P.O. Box 2323, Riverton, 08077 .......... (856) 829-0607
Tomorrow's Heirlooms Handcrafted Gemstone Jewelry,
2 Chambers St., Princeton, 08542.......... (609) 921-9440
TomPat Technologies, Inc., 28 Muller Pl., Little Falls, 07424.......... (973) 785-1118
Toms River Sheet Metal Co., 400 Corporate Cir., Toms River, 08755.......... (732) 244-2880
Tone Embroidery, Inc., 333 Bergen Blvd., Fairview, 07022 .......... (201) 943-1082
Toni Embroidery Co., 475 Broadway, Westwood, 07675 .......... (201) 664-6909
Tony Jones Apparel, Inc., 300-1 Route 17 S., Unit C, Lodi, 07644 .......... (973) 773-6200
★ Too Many Stars, 134 E. Westfield Ave., Roselle Park, 07204.......... (908) 445-8852
TOOC see.......... Other Orthodontic Co., Inc., Sparta
Tooker Sign Service, 1439 Route 539, P.O. Box 1129, Tuckerton, 08087 .......... (609) 296-1000
Tool Shop, Inc., 335 Chestnut Ave., P.O. Box 36, West Berlin, 08091.......... (856) 767-8077
Tooling Etc., LLC, 250 Hallock Ave., Ste. C, Middlesex, 08846.......... (732) 752-8080
† Tool-Krib Supply Co. (H Q),
787 Passaic Ave., P.O. Box 6064, West Caldwell, 07006 .......... (973) 808-4550
Top Knobs USA, Inc., 170 Township Line Rd., Bldg. D, Hillsborough, 08844 .......... (908) 359-6174
Top Line Co., 2131 Bethel Ave., Pennsauken, 08110.......... (856) 662-6400
Top Line Seating, Inc., 540 S. 31st St., Kenilworth, 07033.......... (908) 241-9051
Top Notch Plastics, 217 Bradwick Way, Marlboro, 07746.......... (732) 946-0049
Top Safety Products Co., 160 Meister Ave., Ste. 16, Branchburg, 08876 .......... (908) 707-8680
Top Shops, LLC, 361 W. Dewey Ave., Ste. 8, Wharton, 07885.......... (973) 442-0050
Topco, Inc., 107 Trumbull St., Elizabeth, 07206.......... (908) 352-6720
Topcon Medical Systems, Inc., 111 Bauer Dr., Oakland, 07436.......... (201) 599-5100
Topline Products Co., Inc., 155 Route 46 W., 2nd Fl., Wayne, 07470.......... (973) 785-1600
Torbal see. .......... Scientific Industries, Inc., Oradell
Torelco, Inc., 55 Industrial Dr., Alpha, 08865.......... (908) 387-0814
TORNQVIST, 29 Hanes Dr., Wayne, 07470.......... (973) 686-5999
Torpac, Inc., 333 U.S. Highway 46, Fairfield, 07004.......... (973) 244-1125
Toscana Cheese Co., Inc., 575 Windsor Dr., Secaucus, 07094 .......... (201) 617-1500
Total Control Orthotic Lab, 14 W. Front St., Florence, 08518.......... (609) 499-2200
Total Ink Solutions, 200 S. Newman St., Unit 4, Hackensack, 07601.......... (201) 487-9600
† Total Machine Solutions, Inc., 16 Spielman Rd., Fairfield, 07004.......... (973) 244-0017
Total Maintenance & Service, Inc., 121 Hamburg Tpke., Bloomingdale, 07403.......... (973) 283-0048
Total Specialties USA, Inc., 5 N. Stiles St., Linden, 07036.......... (908) 862-9300
Totally T Shirts & More, 201 W. Hampton St., Pemberton, 08068.......... (609) 894-0011
Toth Inc., 6970 Central Hwy., Pennsauken, 08109.......... (856) 662-8700
Toth Technologies * Rosenberger-Toth see. .......... Toth Inc., Pennsauken
Totowa Precision Tooling, Inc., 500 Riverview Dr., Totowa, 07512.......... (973) 256-2283
Touch Dynamic, Inc., 17 Camptown Rd., Irvington, 07111.......... (732) 382-5701
Toufayan Bakery, Inc., 175 Railroad Ave., Ridgefield, 07657 .......... (201) 941-2000
Tovli, Inc., 49 Hunter St., Newark, 07114 .......... (718) 417-6677
Tower Systems, Inc.- Atlantic Towers & St. Croix Marine Products,
235 Hickory Ln., P.O. Box D, Bayville, 08721 .......... (732) 237-8800
† Town & Country Linen Corp., 475 Oberlin Ave. S., Lakewood, 08701 .......... (732) 364-2000

ALPHABETICAL

Town & Country Plastics, Inc., P.O. Box 269, Morganville, 07751 ... (732) 780-5300
Town Line Trophies, 2 Amberfield Dr., Delran, 08075 ... (856) 461-0540
Towne Technologies, Inc., 6-10 Bell Ave., P.O. Box 460, Somerville, 08876 ... (908) 722-9500
Townsend Farms, Inc., 3501 S. East Blvd., Vineland, 08360 ... (856) 825-5240
Townsend Machine, Inc., 246 Sykesville Rd., Chesterfield, 08515 ... (609) 298-0400
Townsend Press, Inc., 439 Kelley Dr., West Berlin, 08091 ... (856) 753-0554
Toyo Ink America, 4301 New Brunswick Ave., Ste. A, South Plainfield, 07080 ... (732) 752-5660
Toyo Ink America, LLC, 30 Murray Hill Pkwy., Ste. 100, East Rutherford, 07073 ... (201) 804-0616
TPG Graphics, 9130 Pennsauken Hwy., Ste. C, Pennsauken, 08110 ... (856) 314-0117
Trace Environmental Systems, Inc., 7 Park Lake Rd., Unit 9, Sparta, 07871 ... (973) 383-3550
Tracer Tool & Machine Co., Inc., 32 Iron Horse Rd., Oakland, 07436 ... (201) 337-6184
Tracy's Stained Glass Studio, 11 New Providence Ave., Summit, 07901 ... (908) 273-8040
Trade Images, 701 S. Harding Hwy., Buena, 08310 ... (856) 697-2700
Trade Thermographers, Inc., 65 Worth St., South Hackensack, 07606 ... (201) 489-2060
Tradewin Sign, LLC, 699 Challenger Way, Unit D-7, Forked River, 08731 ... (609) 488-5961
Traffic Safety & Equipment Co., 457 State Route 17, Mahwah, 07430 ... (201) 327-6050
Trakman, LLC see ... Ka-Lor Cubicle & Supply Co., Inc., Fair Lawn
Trane Co., 2231 E. State St., Trenton, 08619 ... (609) 587-3400
Trane Commercial Systems see ... Trane Co., Trenton
Trane, Inc. (H Q), 1 Centennial Ave., P.O. Box 6820, Piscataway, 08855 ... (732) 652-7100
Trans World Marketing Corp., 360 Murray Hill Pkwy., East Rutherford, 07073 ... (201) 935-5565
Transaction Publishers, Inc.,
10 Corporate Pl. S., Ste. 102, Piscataway, 08854 ... (732) 445-2280
† TransAxle Corp., 540 Huyler St., South Hackensack, 07606 ... (201) 440-1911
TransAxle, LLC see ... TransAxle Corp., South Hackensack
TransAxle, LLC, 2501 Route 73 S., P.O. Box 2306, Cinnaminson, 08077 ... (856) 665-4445
TransAxle, LLC see ... TRC, Pennsauken
TransDigm, Inc. see ... Airborne Systems North America Of New Jersey, Inc., Pennsauken
Transistors Devices see ... TDI Power, Hackettstown
Transition Metals Technology, 314 N. West Ave., Wenonah, 08090 ... (856) 468-6747
Transmission Technology Corp., 1 High Mountain Trl., Lincoln Park, 07035 ... (973) 305-3600
Transparent Office Products, LLC, 2550 Haddonfield Rd., Pennsauken, 08110 ... (856) 488-5455
Transstar Truck Body Welding Co., Inc.,
514 Route 513, P.O. Box 226, Califon, 07830 ... (908) 832-2688
TransWeb, LLC, 1473 W. Forest Grove Rd., Vineland, 08360 ... (856) 205-1313
Trap Rock, 27 Maple Ave., Mount Holly, 08060 ... (609) 265-8500
Trap Rock Ind., LLC see ... Sta-Seal, Inc., Bordentown
Trap Rock Ind., LLC see ... Trap Rock, Mount Holly
Trap Rock Ind., LLC, 4415 Route 27, P.O. Box 419, Kingston, 08528 ... (609) 924-0300
Trap Rock Ind., LLC see ... Trap Rock Industries, Keasbey
Trap Rock Ind., LLC see ... Trap Rock Industries, Inc., Pennington Quarry, Pennington
Trap Rock Industries see ... Trap Rock Ind., LLC, Kingston
Trap Rock Industries, Foot of Crows Mill Rd., Keasbey, 08832 ... (732) 738-4222
Trap Rock Industries, Inc., Pennington Quarry,
120 Route 31 S., Pennington, 08534 ... (609) 737-3200
Trap-Zap Environmental Systems, Inc., 255 Braen Ave., Wyckoff, 07481 ... (201) 251-9970
Travalliance Media, LLC, 593 Rancocas Rd., Westampton, 08060 ... (856) 505-1400
Travel Tribe, LLC see ... Travalliance Media, LLC, Westampton
Traycon Manufacturing Company, 555 Barell Ave., Carlstadt, 07072 ... (201) 939-5555
†★ TRC, 1700 Sherman Ave., Pennsauken, 08110 ... (856) 910-7979
Treasure Hunt, 1223 S. Main St., Phillipsburg, 08865 ... (908) 454-0880
Treasury Printing Services, 101 Carroll St., P.O. Box 30, Trenton, 08625 ... (609) 292-5133
Trek Connect, 120 Mount Holly Bypass, Lumberton, 08048 ... (856) 608-0901
Trek, Inc., 43 Cranmer Rd., P.O. Box 275, Bayville, 08721 ... (732) 269-6300
Trek Label see ... Trek, Inc., Bayville
Trek II Products, Inc., 570 Jersey Ave., New Brunswick, 08901 ... (732) 214-9200
Tremont Co., Inc., I. W., 18 Utter Ave., Hawthorne, 07506 ... (973) 427-3800
Trend Machine, Inc., 793 Martin St., P.O. Box 218, Rahway, 07065 ... (732) 382-4170
Trend Printing International Label, Inc.,
1183 Edgewater Ave., Ridgefield, 07657 ... (201) 941-6611
Trent Corp., The,
1384 Yardville Hamilton Square Rd., P.O. Box 2650, Trenton, 08690 ... (609) 587-7515
Trenton Corrugated Products, Inc., 17 Cheltan Way, Trenton, 08638 ... (609) 695-0808
Trenton Halal Packing Co., 610 Roebling Ave., Trenton, 08611 ... (609) 394-0331
Trenton Joe's Embroidery, 4 Scotch Rd., Ewing, 08628 ... (609) 538-9450
Trenton Metal Decorating see ... BWAY Corporation, Trenton
Trenton Printing, LLC, 1150 Southard St., Ste. 2, Trenton, 08638 ... (609) 695-6485
Trenton Sheet Metal, 30 Adam Ave., Trenton, 08618 ... (609) 695-6328
Trenton Steak Co., 539 Chestnut Ave., Trenton, 08611 ... (609) 695-6776
Trentonian, The, 600 Perry St., Trenton, 08618 ... (609) 989-7800
Trentypo, Inc., 304 Stokes Ave., Trenton, 08638 ... (609) 883-2198
Trentypo, Inc., 312 Stokes Ave., P.O. Box 304, Trenton, 08638 ... (609) 883-5971
Tressos Atlantic City, The see ... South Jersey Publishing Co., Pleasantville
Tretina Printing, Inc., 1301 State Route 36, Concord Ctr., Hazlet, 07730 ... (732) 264-2324
Tri Phase Tool Co., 2345 Route 9, Ste. 10, Toms River, 08755 ... (732) 370-4737
† Tri State Hardware, Inc., 5 Perina Blvd., Cherry Hill, 08003 ... (856) 810-0990
Tri State Perfection Knife Grinding, 3 S. Gold Dr., Robbinsville, 08691 ... (609) 890-4989
Tri State Stone, Inc., 111 Rome St., Ste. 2, Newark, 07105 ... (973) 344-7220
† Tri Vantage, LLC, 16 Worlds Fair Dr., Somerset, 08873 ... (732) 868-8400
Triad Tool Co., 9 Commerce St., Branchburg, 08876 ... (908) 534-1784
★ Triangle Automatic, Inc., 105 W. Dewey Ave., Ste. 305, Wharton, 07885 ... (973) 625-3830
Triangle Ink Co., Inc., 53-57 Van Dyke St., Wallington, 07057 ... (201) 935-2777
Triangle Mfg., 116 Pleasant Ave., Upper Saddle River, 07458 ... (201) 825-1212
Triangle Repro Center, 222 Dutch Neck Rd., East Windsor, 08520 ... (609) 448-8161
Triangle Tube Phase III, Inc., 1 Triangle Ln., Blackwood, 08012 ... (856) 228-8881
Triarco Industries, Inc. (H Q), 2 Brighton Rd., Ste. 404, Clifton, 07012 ... (973) 942-5100
Tri-Chem, Inc., 681 Main St., Ste. 27, Belleville, 07109 ... (973) 751-9200
Tri-City Print & Copy Center, 155 Union Blvd., Totowa, 07512 ... (973) 706-5854
Trico Hose & Gasket Corp.,
700-2 Challenger Way, Lacey Business Pk., Forked River, 08731 ... (609) 693-5301
†★ Trico Lift, Inc., 418 Southgate Ct., Mickleton, 08056 ... (800) 468-7426
† Trico Lift, Inc. (H Q), 1101 Wheaton Ave., Millville, 08332 ... (856) 776-2350
Trico Poly Systems, LLC, 60 Brown Ave., Springfield, 07081 ... (973) 376-7770
★ Trico Web, LLC, 75 Broad St., Carlstadt, 07072 ... (201) 438-3860
Tri-Comp, Inc., 230 West Pkwy., Unit 14, Pompton Plains, 07444 ... (973) 835-1110
Tri-Cor Flexible Packaging, Inc., 27 Brookfield Dr., Sparta, 07871 ... (973) 940-1500
† TricorBraun, 250 Pehle Ave., Ste. 100, Saddle Brook, 07663 ... (201) 556-4800
TricorBraun, Inc. see ... TricorBraun, Saddle Brook
† Tri-County Building Supplies, Inc.,
14 Reading Ave., Cape May Court House, 08210 ... (609) 465-5021
† Tri-County Building Supplies, Inc.,
211 Stites & Railroad Aves., Cape May Court House, 08210 ... (609) 465-7839
† Tri-County Building Supplies, Inc., 1001 Doughty Rd., Pleasantville, 08232 ... (609) 646-0950
Tri-Delta Plastics, Inc., 208 Cougar Ct., Hillsborough, 08844 ... (908) 722-6021
Trident Computer Resources, Inc.,
151 Industrial Way E., Ste. A-3, Eatontown, 07724 ... (732) 544-9333
Trident Ionic, Inc., 19 Olsen Dr., Warren, 07059 ... (908) 647-4329
Tri-Ed Distribution, Inc. see ... Tri-ed/Northern Video Distribution, Cranbury
† Tri-ed/Northern Video Distribution, 7 Corporate Dr., Ste. 2, Cranbury, 08512 ... (609) 860-0708
T-Rific Tees, LLC, 100 N. 12th St., Ste. 2, Kenilworth, 07033 ... (908) 272-5140
Triform Products, Inc., 219 Lafayette St., Paterson, 07524 ... (973) 278-2042
† TRI-K Industries, Inc., 2 Stewart Ct., P.O. Box 10, Denville, 07834 ... (973) 298-8850
Trillium, Inc., 3627 Route 23 S., Hamburg, 07419 ... (973) 827-1661
Trilogy Publications, LLC,
560 Sylvan Ave., Ste. 1240, Englewood Cliffs, 07632 ... (201) 816-1211
Tri-Lon Color Graphics, Inc., 220 Anderson Ave., Moonachie, 07074 ... (201) 708-6900
Trim & Tassels, LLC (H Q), 204 Passaic Ave., Unit 3, Fairfield, 07004 ... (973) 808-1566
Trim Brush Co., Inc., 22 Littell Rd., East Hanover, 07936 ... (973) 887-2525
Trimarco Jewelers, Inc., 1847-1849 Springfield Ave., Maplewood, 07040 ... (973) 762-7380
Trimble Navigation Ltd. see ... ALK Technologies, Inc., Princeton
Trinity Mfg., LLC, 60 Leonard St., Metuchen, 08840 ... (732) 549-2866
Trinity Press, LLC, 655 Market St., Paterson, 07513 ... (973) 881-0690
† Trinity Recycling Of New Jersey, 116 Iron Mountain Rd., Mine Hill, 07803 ... (973) 366-9199
Tripician Macaroons, 640 White Horse Pike, Absecon, 08201 ... (609) 645-1546
Triple B Fabricating, Inc., 61 Willett St., Ste. 12, Passaic, 07055 ... (973) 773-2266
Triple D Enterprises, Inc., 135 Eayrestown Rd., Southampton, 08088 ... (609) 859-3000
Triple S Industries, 1108 E. Linden Ave., P.O. Box 1293, Linden, 07036 ... (908) 862-0110
Triple-T Cutting Tools, Inc., 135 Edgewood Ave., West Berlin, 08091 ... (856) 768-0800
Tri-Plex Business Products, Inc / Graphic Solutions,
400 Morris Ave., Ste. 220, Denville, 07834 ... (973) 627-5388
Tri-Plex Graphic Solutions see ... Tri-Plex Business Products, Inc / Graphic Solutions, Denville
Tris Pharma, Inc., 2033 U.S. Highway 130, Ste. D, Monmouth Junction, 08852 ... (732) 940-2800
Tri-Seal, 112 Church St., Flemington, 08822 ... (908) 782-4000
Tri-State Building Materials Co., 65 Lodi St., Passaic, 07055 ... (973) 472-2377
Tri-State Crating & Pallet Co., 85 Fulton St., Paterson, 07501 ... (973) 357-8293
Tri-State Fences & Supply, Inc., 806 Route 23, Sussex, 07461 ... (973) 875-3213
Tri-State Glass & Mirror, Inc., 11-A Jocama Blvd., Old Bridge, 08857 ... (732) 591-5545
Tri-State Leather, Inc., 504 4th Ave., Elizabeth, 07202 ... (908) 275-3310
Tri-State Pump, Inc., 5044 Industrial Rd., Ste. C, Farmingdale, 07727 ... (732) 223-3222
Tri-State QUIKRETE, 150 Gold Mine Rd., Flanders, 07836 ... (973) 347-4569
Tri-State Tape & Label Co., Inc.,
351 Railroad Ave., P.O. Box 377, Beverly, 08010 ... (800) 682-7892
Tri-Steel Fabricators, Inc., 501 Prospect St., Trenton, 08618 ... (609) 392-8660
Tri-Tech Tool & Design Co., Inc., 30 Cherry St., South Bound Brook, 08880 ... (732) 469-5433
Triton Associated Industries, Inc.,
North Brewster Rd., P.O. Box 627, Buena, 08310 ... (856) 697-3050
Triumph Knitting, Inc., 18-20 Di Carolis Ct., Hackensack, 07601 ... (201) 646-0022
Trodat USA, 48 Hellar Pk., Somerset, 08873 ... (732) 529-8500
Troemner, LLC, Henry, 201 Wolf Dr., P.O. Box 87, Thorofare, 08086 ... (856) 686-1600
Trojan Tube Co., Yellowbrook Rd., P.O. Box 496, Farmingdale, 07727 ... (732) 938-5687
Trolex Corp., 20 Bushes Ln., Elmwood Park, 07407 ... (201) 794-8004
Tronex Healthcare * Tronex Safety Solutions * Tronex Government see. Tronex International, Inc., Mount Olive
Tronex International, Inc., 300 International Dr., Mount Olive, 07828 ... (973) 335-2888
Tropar Mfg. Co., Inc., 5 Vreeland Rd., Florham Park, 07932 ... (973) 822-2400
Trophies Unlimited, 122 Fernwood Ave., Trenton, 08610 ... (609) 298-3544
Trophy King, Inc., The see ... Trophy King Of Ramsey, Ramsey
Trophy King, Inc., The, 309 Queen Anne Rd., Teaneck, 07666 ... (201) 836-1482
Trophy King Of Ramsey, 503 N. Franklin Tpke., Unit 13, Ramsey, 07446 ... (201) 760-6488
Tropical Cheese Industries, Inc., 450 Fayette St., Perth Amboy, 08861 ... (732) 442-4898
Tropical Expressions, Inc., 2127 Bridge Ave., Point Pleasant, 08742 ... (732) 899-1733
Tropp Printing Corp., 8 Woodhollow Dr., Holmdel, 07733 ... (212) 233-4519
Trout Printing LLC, 33 Reeves St., Millville, 08332 ... (856) 327-8366
Troy Chemicals, 1 Avenue L, Newark, 07105 ... (973) 589-2500
Troy Corp. see ... FTI, Inc. (H Q), Florham Park
Troy Corp. see ... Troy Chemicals, Newark
Troy Corp. see ... Troy Chemicals, Newark
Troy Corp., 8 Vreeland Rd., Florham Park, 07932 ... (973) 443-4200
Troy Hills Mfg., Inc., 2 Como Ct., P.O. Box 98, Towaco, 07082 ... (973) 263-1885
Troy-Onic, Inc., 90 Dell Ave., P.O. Box 494, Kenvil, 07847 ... (973) 584-6830
Tru Mfg., Inc., 40 Oak St., Norwood, 07648 ... (201) 768-4050
Truck Parts Specialists, 150 Central Ave., Teterboro, 07608 ... (201) 288-9333
Truckform, Inc., 50 James St., Somerville, 08876 ... (908) 526-5443
True World Foods see ... True World Group, LLC (H Q), Rockleigh
† True World Foods, LLC, 32-34 Papetti Plz., Elizabeth, 07206 ... (908) 351-1400
True World Group, LLC see ... Crystal World, Inc., South Hackensack
True World Group, LLC see ... True World Foods, LLC, Elizabeth
True World Group, LLC (H Q), 24 Link Dr., Rockleigh, 07647 ... (201) 750-0024
Tru-Form Cosmetics, Inc., 50 Springfield Ave., Springfield, 07081 ... (973) 564-9111
Trukmann's Inc., 4 Wing Dr., Cedar Knolls, 07927 ... (973) 538-7718
Trukmann's Reprographics see ... Trukmann's Inc., Cedar Knolls
Trumbull Asphalt Co. see ... Owens Corning, Kearny
TRUMPF, Inc. see ... TRUMPF Photonics, Inc., Cranbury
TRUMPF Photonics, Inc., 2601 US Route 130 S., Cranbury, 08512 ... (609) 925-8200
Trybun Engraving, LLC, 706 Old Shore Rd., Ste. 3, Forked River, 08731 ... (609) 242-3105
Tryco Tool & Mfg., Inc., 363 S. Jefferson St., Orange, 07050 ... (973) 674-6867
Trylon * Trylon Railing see ... Trylon Metal Works Inc., Lyndhurst
Trylon Metal Works Inc., 136 Park Ave., Lyndhurst, 07071 ... (201) 939-8282
Tube Craft Of America, 667 Lebanon Ave., Williamstown, 08094 ... (856) 629-5626
† Tube Light Co., Inc. (H Q), 300 Park St., Moonachie, 07074 ... (201) 641-6660
Tubelite Co., Inc. see ... Tube Light Co., Inc. (H Q), Moonachie
Tuckahoe Mfg., 327 Tuckahoe Rd., Vineland, 08360 ... (856) 696-4100
Tuckahoe Sand & Gravel, Inc., Route 610 & Sharp Rd., Tuckahoe, 08250 ... (609) 861-2082
Tucker International, LLC, 200 W. Somerdale Rd., Ste. B, Voorhees, 08043 ... (856) 216-1333
Tuers Aluminum, LLC, 2562 Lakewood-Allenwood Rd., Howell, 07731 ... (732) 458-2031
Tulenko Enterprises, LLC, 176 Franklin Ave., Rockaway, 07866 ... (973) 453-6699
† Tulnoy Lumber, Inc., 9-D Raskulinecz Rd., Carteret, 07008 ... (732) 634-4000
TUMI, Inc. (H Q), 1001 Durham Ave., South Plainfield, 07080 ... (908) 756-4400
Tun Tavern Restaurant & Brewery, 2 Convention Blvd., Atlantic City, 08401 ... (609) 347-7800
Tunnel Barrel & Drum Co., Inc., 85 Triangle Blvd., Carlstadt, 07072 ... (201) 933-1444
Tur Machine, LLC, 198 U.S. Highway 206, Ste. 5, Hillsborough, 08844 ... (908) 874-0235
Turbobraze Corp., 687 Lehigh Ave., P.O. Box 897, Union, 07083 ... (908) 687-1030
Turbon Group, 4350 Haddonfield Rd., Ste. 300, Pennsauken, 08109 ... (856) 665-6650
Turnkey Solutions, Inc., 45 Whitney Rd., Mahwah, 07430 ... (201) 848-7676
† Turtle & Hughes, Inc., 188 Foothill Rd., Bridgewater, 08807 ... (732) 560-5575

† Turtle & Hughes, Inc., 1900 Lower Rd., Linden, 07036 .... (732) 574-3600
Turul Bookbindery, Inc., 60 Route 15 S., Wharton, 07885 .... (973) 361-2810
Tuscan Dairy, Inc., 117 Cumberland Blvd., Burlington, 08016 .... (609) 499-2600
† TW Metals, Inc., 27 Engelhard Dr., Monroe Township, 08831 .... (609) 655-4120
Twin Glass Co., 6422 Black Horse Pike, Egg Harbor Township, 08234 .... (609) 645-8834
Twin Modular Services, Inc.,
1001 Lower Landing Rd., Ste. 607, Blackwood, 08012 .... (856) 227-0057
Two Brothers Iron Works, 3709 Liberty Ave., North Bergen, 07047 .... (201) 866-7970
2 For 1 Machinery Group, The, 30 N. Pine Ave., Maple Shade, 08052 .... (856) 321-0474
Two River Times, 75 W. Front St., Ste. 2, Red Bank, 07701 .... (732) 219-5788
TX Technology Corp., 100 Ford Rd., Unit 100-18, Denville, 07834 .... (973) 442-7500
Tyber Medical, LLC (H Q),
89 Headquarters Plz. N., Ste. 1464, Morristown, 07960 .... (866) 761-0933
Tyco see. .... Goyen Valve Corp., Lakewood
Tyco see. .... Westlock Controls Corp., Saddle Brook
Tyco (H Q), 9 Roszel Rd., Princeton, 08540 .... (609) 720-4200
Tyco Electronics Subsea Communications, LLC (H Q),
250 Industrial Way W., Eatontown, 07724 .... (732) 578-7000
Tyger Scientific, Inc., 324 Stokes Ave., Ewing, 08638 .... (609) 434-0144
Tymac Controls Corp., 432 U.S. Highway 206, Ste. C, Montague, 07827 .... (973) 293-3339
Type-N-Graphic, 170 Kinnelon Rd., Ste. 12, Kinnelon, 07405 .... (973) 838-6544
Type-O-Graphics, LLC, 222 Outwater Ln., Ste. 1, Garfield, 07026 .... (973) 253-3333
Typeworks, 228 Jefferson St., Apt. 4, Hoboken, 07030 .... (201) 653-8380
TYRX, Inc., 1 Deer Park Dr., Ste. G, Monmouth Junction, 08852 .... (732) 246-8676
Tyz-All Plastics, LLC, 130 Gamewell St., Hackensack, 07601 .... (201) 343-1200
U. S. A. Tolerance Rings, 85 Route 31 N., Pennington, 08534 .... (609) 745-5000
U. S. Artistic Monument Co., Inc., 262 Main Ave., Clifton, 07014 .... (973) 777-7786
U. S. Blade Mfg., 90 Myrtle St., Cranford, 07016 .... (908) 272-2898
U. S. Brass & Copper, Corp.,
641 E. Elizabeth Ave., P.O. Box 1052, Linden, 07036 .... (908) 486-3322
U. S. Cast, 321 Willow Grove Rd., Pittsgrove, 08318 .... (856) 347-2342
U. S. Concrete, Inc. see. .... Eastern Concrete Materials, Inc. (H Q), Elmwood Park
U. S. Drop Forge Corp., Highway 551, P.O. Box 131, Swedesboro, 08085 .... (856) 467-0500
U. S. S. Corp., 780 Frelinghuysen Ave., Newark, 07114 .... (973) 242-1110
U. S. Wire & Cable, Inc., 33 Queen St., Newark, 07114 .... (973) 824-5529
† UAC Packaging, LLC, 330 Roycefield Rd., Unit C, Hillsborough, 08844 .... (908) 595-6890
UB Communications, 10 Lodge Ln., Parsippany, 07054 .... (973) 331-9391
Uehling Instrument Co., 473 Getty Ave., Paterson, 07503 .... (973) 742-8710
† UER Metals, Inc.,
235 Saint Nicholas Ave., P.O. Box 407, South Plainfield, 07080 .... (908) 561-5800
UFP Berlin, LLC, 159 Jackson Rd., Berlin, 08009 .... (856) 767-0043
UFP Technologies, Inc., 1 Johnson Dr., Raritan, 08869 .... (800) 372-3172
Ugo Di Lullo & Sons, 1004 Edgewater Ave., P.O. Box 126, Westville, 08093 .... (856) 456-3700
Uhlmann Packaging Systems, 44 Indian Ln. E., Towaco, 07082 .... (973) 402-8855
Ukrainian National Affiliation, Inc.,
2200 State Route 10, P.O. Box 280, Parsippany, 07054 .... (973) 292-9800
Ukrainian Weekly see. .... Ukrainian National Affiliation, Inc., Parsippany
Ulanet Co., George, 413-415 Market St., Newark, 07105 .... (973) 589-4876
Ulma Form Works, Inc., 58 5th Ave., Hawthorne, 07506 .... (973) 636-2040
Ultimate Spinning & Turning Corp., 9 Willow St., Moonachie, 07074 .... (201) 372-9740
Ultimate Textile see. .... Pecata Enterprises, Inc., Paterson
Ultimate Tool & Mfg. Co., 360-A Carnegie Ave., Kenilworth, 07033 .... (908) 241-4575
Ultimate Trading see. .... Ultimate Trading Corp., Fairfield
Ultimate Trading Corp., 4 Just Rd., Fairfield, 07004 .... (973) 228-7700
Ultimate Training Munitions, 55 Readington Rd., North Branch, 08876 .... (908) 725-9000
Ultra Chemical, Inc., 2 Bridge Ave., Ste. 630, Red Bank, 07701 .... (732) 224-0200
Ultra Clean Technologies Corp., 1274 Highway 77, Bridgeton, 08302 .... (856) 451-2176
Ultra Punch & Die Corp., 8 N. Main St., P.O. Box 353, Boonton, 07005 .... (973) 335-3200
Ultraflex Systems, Inc. (H Q), 1578 Sussex Tpke., Ste. 400, Randolph, 07869 .... (973) 627-8608
Ultra/Standard Distributor see. .... Olla Beauty Supply, Inc., Pine Brook
Ulysses Machine Co., 41 Lancelot Ln., Mount Laurel, 08054 .... (856) 979-3674
Unette Corp., 1578 Sussex Tpke., Randolph, 07869 .... (973) 328-6800
UNEX Corp., 333 Route 17 N., Mahwah, 07430 .... (201) 512-9500
UNEX Manufacturing, Inc., 50 Progress Pl., Jackson, 08527 .... (732) 928-2800
Ungarini Iron Works, LLC, 56 N. Logan Ave., Trenton, 08609 .... (609) 392-0540
Ungar's Food Products, Inc., 9 Boumar Pl., Elmwood Park, 07407 .... (201) 703-1300
Ungerer & Co., 4 Bridgewater Ln., P.O. Box U, Lincoln Park, 07035 .... (973) 628-0600
† Unichem Industries, Inc., 1 Bayberry Close, Piscataway, 08854 .... (732) 463-8442
Unicor Federal Prison Industries, Inc.,
5835 Doughboy Loop, P.O. Box 38, Fort Dix, 08640 .... (609) 723-1100
Unicorp, Inc., 291 Cleveland St., Orange, 07050 .... (973) 674-1700
Unified Resources In Display, Inc./Display Pro Manufacturing,
40 Boright Ave., Kenilworth, 07033 .... (908) 272-1112
Unifoil Corp., 12 Daniel Rd., Ste. 101, Fairfield, 07004 .... (973) 244-9900
Unifoil Corp., 12 Vanil Rd. E., Fairfield, 07004 .... (973) 244-9900
Unigraphic Guild, Inc., 10 Route 206, Stanhope, 07874 .... (973) 219-2348
Unik International, Inc., 40 Triangle Blvd., Carlstadt, 07072 .... (201) 531-1777
Unilever North America, 700 Sylvan Ave., Englewood Cliffs, 07632 .... (201) 567-8000
Unilite Co., Inc., 151 River Rd., Nutley, 07110 .... (973) 667-1674
Unilux, Inc., 59 5th St., Saddle Brook, 07663 .... (201) 712-1266
Unimac Graphics, LLC, 350 Michele Pl., Carlstadt, 07072 .... (201) 372-1000
Unimade Metals, Inc., 115 Patterson St., Hillsdale, 07642 .... (201) 666-7747
Unimed International, Inc., 105 Newfield Ave., Ste. F, Edison, 08837 .... (800) 754-6211
† Unimet Metal Supply Co., Inc., 150 Lackawanna Ave., Parsippany, 07054 .... (973) 673-5700
Union Beverage Packers, LLC, 600 N. Union Ave., Hillside, 07205 .... (908) 206-9111
Union City Filament Corp., 1039-A Hoyt Ave., P.O. Box 777, Ridgefield, 07657 .... (201) 945-3366
Union City Mirror & Table Co., 129 34th St., Union City, 07087 .... (201) 867-1827
Union County Plate Glass Co. (H Q),
1050 Elizabeth Ave., P.O. Box 9027, Elizabeth, 07201 .... (908) 354-0380
Union County Seating & Supply Co., Inc.,
121 N. Michigan Ave., Ste. E, Kenilworth, 07033 .... (908) 241-4949
Union Dry Dock & Repair Co., Inc.,
901 Sinatra Dr., P.O. Box M-1539, Hoboken, 07030 .... (201) 792-9090
Union Hill Corp. (H Q), 34 Water St., Englishtown, 07726 .... (732) 786-9422
Union Rubber, Inc., 232 Allen St., Trenton, 08618 .... (609) 396-9328
Union Tool & Mold Co., 220 Rutgers St., Maplewood, 07040 .... (973) 763-6611
Unionville, LLC, 9 Rocktown Rd., Ringoes, 08551 .... (908) 788-0400
Unionwear/New Jersey Headwear Corp., 305 3rd Ave. W., Ste. 5, Newark, 07107 .... (973) 497-0102
Unipack, Inc., 681 Main St., Bldg. 27, Belleville, 07109 .... (973) 450-9880
Unipro Uniforms see. .... Asia Trading, Irvington
Unique Aluminum Extrusion, LLC, 333 Cedar Ave., Ste. 6, Middlesex, 08846 .... (732) 271-0006
Unique Embroidery, Inc., 1030 Pleasantview Ter., Ridgefield, 07657 .... (201) 943-9191

Unique Lighting, LLC, 555 7th St., Somers Point, 08244 .... (609) 926-8966
Unique Metal Products Co., Inc.,
17 W. Scott Ave., P.O. Box 1181, Rahway, 07065 .... (732) 388-1888
Unique Screen Printing Corp., Inc., 1016 McKinley St., Linden, 07036 .... (908) 925-3773
Unique Systems, Inc., 4 Saddle Rd., Cedar Knolls, 07927 .... (973) 455-0440
Unique Technologies Assocs., 42 Milled Way, Avenel, 07001 .... (732) 882-0777
Unique Wire Weaving Co., Inc., 762 Ramsey Ave., Hillside, 07205 .... (908) 688-4600
Uni-Select USA, Inc. see. .... Parts Distributors, LLC, Moorestown
UniServ Advertising, Inc., 37 State Route 35 N., Neptune, 07753 .... (732) 774-1010
Unit Pack Co., Inc., 7 Lewis Rd., Cedar Grove, 07009 .... (973) 239-4112
United Asphalt Co., Inc., 237 N. Grove St., Berlin, 08009 .... (856) 753-9811
United Blower Co., Inc., 22 Westbrook Dr., Morganville, 07751 .... (201) 601-5700
† United Candy & Tobacco Co., 7408 Tonnelle Ave., North Bergen, 07047 .... (201) 943-8675
United Capital Corp. see. .... AFP Transformers Corp., Edison
United Capital Corp. see. .... Metal Textiles Corp., Edison
United Die Co., Inc., 199 Devon Ter., Kearny, 07032 .... (201) 997-0250
† United Electric Supply Co., 1150 W. Garden Rd., Vineland, 08360 .... (856) 691-6668
United Energy Corp., 3526 U.S. Highway 9 S., Ste. 103, Howell, 07731 .... (732) 994-5225
★ United Envelope & Printing Co., Inc., 65 Railroad Ave., Ridgefield, 07657 .... (201) 699-5800
United Equipment & Fabricators, 175 Orange St., Newark, 07103 .... (973) 242-2737
United ERP, LLC, 2460 Lemoine Ave., Ste. 503, Fort Lee, 07024 .... (201) 567-6315
United Forms Finishing, 1413 Chestnut Ave., 1st Fl., Hillside, 07205 .... (908) 687-0494
United Hospital Supply Corp., 4422 Route 130 S., Burlington, 08016 .... (609) 387-7580
United Label Corp., 65 Chambers St., Newark, 07105 .... (973) 589-6500
★ United Motor Parts, Inc., 1130 Teaneck Rd., Teaneck, 07666 .... (201) 837-6760
United National Machine Tool, Inc.,
2404 Sylon Blvd., P.O. Box 608, Hainesport, 08036 .... (609) 265-2269
United Natural Foods, Inc. see. .... Albert's Organics, Inc., Bridgeport
United Natural Foods, Inc. see. .... Woodstock Farms Mfg., Edison
United Plastics Group, Inc., 30 Commerce Dr., Somerset, 08873 .... (732) 873-1848
United Products & Instruments, Inc. (H Q),
182 Ridge Rd., Ste. E, Dayton, 08810 .... (732) 274-1155
United Refrigeration, Inc. see. .... National Refrigerants, Inc., Bridgeton
† United Scrap Iron & Metal Co., 124 Wood St., Paterson, 07524 .... (973) 279-1683
United Silica Products, Inc., 3 Park Dr., Franklin, 07416 .... (973) 209-8854
United Sport Apparel, 20 Gloria Ln., Fairfield, 07004 .... (973) 575-7840
United States Box Corp., 1296 McCarter Hwy., Newark, 07104 .... (973) 481-2000
United States Business Card Co., 540 39th St., Ste. 33, Union City, 07087 .... (201) 863-8776
United States Metal Powders, Inc., 408 U.S. Highway 202, Flemington, 08822 .... (908) 782-5454
United States Spray Finishing Co., Inc., 70 Blanchard St., Newark, 07105 .... (973) 589-3490
United Stationers, Inc. see. .... United Stationers Supply Co., Cranbury
† United Stationers Supply Co., 100 Liberty Way, Cranbury, 08512 .... (609) 619-4000
† United Supply Co., Inc., 7 Chris Ct., Ste. A, Dayton, 08810 .... (732) 329-6301
† United Supply Co., Inc., 457 W. End Ave., Plainfield, 07060 .... (908) 757-3232
United Support Solutions, Inc., 134 Sand Park Rd., Cedar Grove, 07009 .... (973) 857-2298
United Vacuum Pumps, Inc. see. .... Trillium, Inc., Hamburg
United Window & Door Mfg., 24-36 Fadem Rd., Springfield, 07081 .... (973) 912-0600
Unity Brand Halal Products, 94 Orange St., Newark, 07102 .... (973) 624-4847
Unity Fuels, LLC, 225 Industrial Ave., Ridgefield Park, 07660 .... (201) 641-5000
Unity Graphics & Engraving/Unity Steel Rule Die,
210 S. Van Brunt St., P.O. Box 88, Englewood, 07631 .... (201) 569-6400
Unity Steel Rule Die see. .... Unity Graphics & Engraving/Unity Steel Rule Die, Englewood
Universal Business Systems, Inc.,
185 Industrial Pkwy., Ste. J, Somerville, 08876 .... (908) 725-8899
† Universal Chemicals Inc., 100 N. Hackensack Ave., Kearny, 07032 .... (973) 589-1525
Universal Electric Motor Service, Inc., 131 S. Newman St., Hackensack, 07601 .... (201) 968-1000
Universal Filters, Inc., 1207 Main St., Asbury Park, 07712 .... (732) 774-8555
Universal Forest Products, Inc. see. .... UFP Berlin, LLC, Berlin
Universal Graphics Co., 497 Bloomfield Ave., Bloomfield, 07003 .... (973) 748-4009
Universal Laboratories, Inc., 3 Terminal Rd., New Brunswick, 08901 .... (732) 545-3130
Universal Metalcraft, Inc., 24 Burgess Pl., Wayne, 07470 .... (973) 345-3284
Universal Mold & Tool, Inc., 1200 S. West Blvd., Bldg. 4, Vineland, 08360 .... (856) 563-0488
Universal Nutrition, Inc. see. .... Universal Laboratories, Inc., New Brunswick
† Universal Preserv-A-Chem, Inc., 60 Jiffy Rd., Somerset, 08873 .... (732) 568-1266
Universal Prints, Inc., 625 Newark Ave., Jersey City, 07306 .... (201) 656-7878
Universal Silkscreen, Inc., 17 Memorial Dr., Paterson, 07505 .... (973) 221-0060
Universal Supply Group see. .... Colonial Commercial Corp., Hawthorne
Universal Tape Co. (H Q), 110 W. New Jersey Ave., Somers Point, 08244 .... (609) 653-3191
Universal Tools & Mfg. Co., 115 Victory Rd., Springfield, 07081 .... (973) 379-4193
Universal Uniform, 1015 Broad St., P.O. Box 637, Newark, 07102 .... (973) 622-5700
Universal Valve Co., Inc., 478 Schiller St., Elizabeth, 07206 .... (908) 351-0606
Universal Windows, LLC, 407 Bloomfield Dr., West Berlin, 08091 .... (856) 719-0020
University Apparel, Inc., 2501 Mount Holly Rd., Ste. 262, Burlington, 08016 .... (609) 871-3601
University Fashions, 1888 Winslow Rd., Bldg. B, Williamstown, 08094 .... (856) 228-1615
University Publications, 562 Morley Ct., Belford, 07718 .... (732) 495-9000
Unlimited Steel Fabricators, Inc., 840 Lincoln Blvd., Middlesex, 08846 .... (732) 356-7534
Unlimited Stone Designs, 7 McLean Blvd., Paterson, 07514 .... (973) 523-2224
UPEI see. .... United Scrap Iron & Metal Co., Paterson
Upper Case Printing, LLC, 752 Porchtown, Franklinville, 08322 .... (856) 875-5000
Uptown Bakeries/J & J Snack Foods,
300 Eagle Ct., P.O. Box 257, Bridgeport, 08014 .... (856) 467-9552
† Urban Millwork & Supply Corp., 90 2nd Ave., Paterson, 07514 .... (973) 278-7072
Urban Sign & Crane, Inc., 527 E. Chestnut Ave., P.O. Box 640, Vineland, 08360 .... (856) 691-8388
uReach Technologies, Inc., 2137 State Highway 35, 1st Fl., Holmdel, 07733 .... (732) 335-5400
Urner Barry Publications, 182 Queens Blvd., Bayville, 08721 .... (732) 240-5330
Urvesh Granite (USA), Inc., 1777 Route 130 S., North Brunswick, 08902 .... (201) 369-3934
US Concrete Materials, LLC, 189 Berkley Pl., Dumont, 07628 .... (201) 385-6470
US Electrical Services, Inc. see. .... Monarch Electric Supply Co., North Brunswick
US Electrical Services, Inc. see. .... Rahway Electric Supply, Inc., Rahway
† US Foods, Inc., 1051 Amboy Ave., Perth Amboy, 08861 .... (732) 934-3400
US Ink see. .... Sun Chemical Corp., East Rutherford
US Ink Corp., 390 Central Ave., East Rutherford, 07073 .... (201) 438-4041
US Ink Corp. (H Q), 631 Central Ave., Carlstadt, 07072 .... (201) 935-8666
U.S. Laser Corp., 825 Windham Ct. N., Ste. 2, Wyckoff, 07481 .... (201) 848-9200
US Logic, LLC, 2885 E. State Street Ext., Hamilton, 08619 .... (609) 530-0005
US Magic Box, Inc., 221 McArthur Ave., Garfield, 07026 .... (973) 772-2070
U.S. 1 Publishing Co., 15 Princess Rd., Lawrenceville, 08648 .... (609) 452-7000
U.S. ProPack, Inc., 341 Fairfield Rd., Freehold, 07728 .... (732) 294-4500
U.S. Pulp & Paper Corp., 1930 Marlton Pike E., Ste. N-73, Cherry Hill, 08003 .... (856) 489-3500
U.S. Seal Mfg., 400 Apgar Dr., Ste. A, Somerset, 08873 .... (732) 667-1100
US Sign & Lighting Service, LLC, 105 Dorsa Ave., Wayne, 07470 .... (973) 305-8900
U.S. Silica Co., 9035 Noble St., P.O. Box 254, Mauricetown, 08329 .... (856) 785-0720

U.S. Silica Company see. .... U.S. Silica Co., Mauricetown
† U.S. Tech, Inc., P.O. Box 152, Franklin Lakes, 07417 .... (800) 783-8187
US Wire & Cable see. .... Flexon Industries Corp., Newark
USA Beading see. .... Faraj, Inc., Fairview
U.S.A. Distributors, Inc., 3711 Hudson Ave., Union City, 07087 .... (201) 348-1959
★ USA Tealight, LLC, 4 Craigwood Rd., Avenel, 07001 .... (732) 943-2408
USG Corp. see. .... USG Corp., Port Reading Plt., Port Reading
USG Corp., Port Reading Plt., 300 Markley St., Port Reading, 07064 .... (732) 636-7900
UTC Aerospace Systems, ISR & Propeller Systems see. UTC Aerospace Systems-ISR Systems (Sensors Unlimited, Inc.), Princeton
UTC Aerospace Systems-ISR Systems (Sensors Unlimited, Inc.),
330 Carter Rd., Ste. 100, Princeton, 08540 .... (609) 520-0610
UTE Microwave, Inc., 3500 Sunset Ave., Ste. D-1, Ocean, 07712 .... (732) 922-1009
Utility Development Corp., 112 Naylon Ave., Livingston, 07039 .... (973) 994-4334
Utility Industries, Inc., 500 Springdale Rd., Ste. K-1, Somerdale, 08083 .... (856) 435-6969
Utility Tool Co., 15 Orange St., Bloomfield, 07003 .... (973) 743-8010
† Utility Trailer Sales Of New Jersey, 589 Nassau St., North Brunswick, 08902 .... (732) 745-1222
UTM, Inc. see. .... Ultimate Training Munitions, North Branch
UTZ, LLC, 4 Peckman Rd., Little Falls, 07424 .... (973) 339-1100
Uvitec Printing Ink, Inc., 14 Mill St., Lodi, 07644 .... (973) 778-0737
V & L Machine Tool Co., Inc., 30 Sherwood Ln., Ste. 11, Fairfield, 07004 .... (973) 808-5858
V & R Design Co., 941 State St., Perth Amboy, 08861 .... (732) 442-9249
V & S Amboy Galvanizing, 1190 Amboy Ave., Perth Amboy, 08861 .... (732) 442-7555
V E P Manufacturing Inc., 575 S. Hope Chapel Rd., Jackson, 08527 .... (732) 657-0666
V G Controls, Inc., 11 Butternut Dr., Vernon, 07462 .... (973) 764-6500
V H Machine Tool Co., 29 Smith Ave., Fair Lawn, 07410 .... (973) 427-8666
V L V Assocs., Inc., 30-C Ridgedale Ave., East Hanover, 07936 .... (973) 428-2884
V M C Die Cutting Corp., 357 Cortlandt St., Belleville, 07109 .... (973) 450-4655
V M Glass Co., 3231 N. Mill Rd., Vineland, 08360 .... (856) 794-9333
V. Tech Instruments, Inc., 171 Burns Ave., Lodi, 07644 .... (973) 546-7635
★ Vacord Screen Printing, 1621 S. Broadway, Camden, 08104 .... (888) 787-4587
Vac's Bandage Co., 163 Pennsylvania Ave., Paterson, 07503 .... (973) 345-3355
Vac-U-Max, 69 William St., Belleville, 07109 .... (973) 759-4600
Vacuum Sales, Inc., 51 Stone Rd., Lindenwold, 08021 .... (856) 627-7790
Vahl, Inc., 34 Kennedy Blvd., East Brunswick, 08816 .... (718) 492-6655
Valaro's Screen Printing, 50 Mayetta Landing Rd., West Creek, 08092 .... (609) 597-7075
Valcar Precision Products, Inc., 22 Park Pl., Butler, 07405 .... (973) 838-7600
Valconn Electronics, Inc., 909 Rahway Ave., Union, 07083 .... (908) 687-1600
Valcor Engineering Corp., 2 Lawrence Rd., Springfield, 07081 .... (973) 467-8400
Valenta & Sons, Inc., Jerry, 40 Schoon Ave., Hawthorne, 07506 .... (973) 423-2220
Valeur Corp., Oilco U. S. A. Div.,
596 Ridge Rd., P.O. Box 226, Monmouth Junction, 08852 .... (732) 329-4666
Valhi, Inc. see. .... Kronos Worldwide, Inc., Cranbury
Valid USA, Inc., 800 Montrose Ave., South Plainfield, 07080 .... (908) 668-0999
Validus Pharmaceuticals, LLC,
119 Cherry Hill Rd., Ste. 310, Parsippany, 07054 .... (973) 265-2777
Valle Precision Machine Co., Inc., 58 Myrtle Ave., Passaic, 07055 .... (973) 773-3037
Valley Die-Cutting Co., Inc., 10 Park Ave., West Orange, 07052 .... (973) 731-8884
† Valley National Gases, WV LLC, 201 Crown Point Rd., West Deptford, 08086 .... (856) 848-7321
Valley Plastic Molding Co., Inc., P.O. Box 30, Boonton, 07005 .... (973) 334-2100
Valley Shepherd Creamery, 50 Fairmount Rd., Long Valley, 07853 .... (908) 876-3200
Valofurniture.com see. .... Dauphin North America, Boonton
Value Eyewear, Inc., 1454 Main Ave., Clifton, 07011 .... (973) 478-6500
† Van Air & Hydraulics, Inc., 612 E. Woodlawn Ave., Maple Shade, 08052 .... (856) 779-7300
Van Dam Machine Corp., 81-B Walsh Dr., Parsippany, 07054 .... (973) 257-7050
Van Dessel Sports, LLC, 15 W. Main St., Ste. 2, Mendham, 07945 .... (973) 543-2599
Van Dyk Trim Stone, LLC, 85 4th Ave., Haskell, 07420 .... (973) 831-1802
Van Grouw Welding & Fabricating, 430 W. Main St., Wyckoff, 07481 .... (201) 891-4199
Van Holten's Chocolates see. .... Van Holten's Homemade Candy, Inc., Brick
★ Van Holten's Homemade Candy, Inc., 1893 Route 88, Brick, 08724 .... (732) 840-0888
Van Hydraulics, 643 Sayre Ave., Perth Amboy, 08861 .... (732) 442-5500
Van Ness Plastic Molding Co., 400 Brighton Rd., Clifton, 07012 .... (973) 778-9500
Van Nick Pallet, Inc., 104 Snyder Rd., South Plainfield, 07080 .... (908) 753-1800
Van Orden Sand & Gravel, 589 W. Brook Rd., Ringwood, 07456 .... (973) 839-0207
Vanco Millwork, Inc., 18 Microlab Rd., Livingston, 07039 .... (973) 992-3061
Vanco U. S. A., LLC, 1170 Florence Rd., Bordentown, 08505 .... (609) 499-4141
Van-Con, Inc., 123 William St., Middlesex, 08846 .... (732) 356-8484
Vanderbilt Industries, 2 Cranberry Rd., Parsippany, 07054 .... (973) 316-3900
Vandereems Mfg. Co., Inc., 40 Schoon Ave., Hawthorne, 07506 .... (973) 427-2355
Vandermolen Corp., 119 Dorsa Ave., Livingston, 07039 .... (973) 992-8506
Vanea USA, Inc., 410 Market St., Elmwood Park, 07407 .... (201) 796-0722
Vanguard Packaging, Inc., 620 Ramsey Ave., Hillside, 07205 .... (973) 391-9200
Vanguard Research Industries,
239 Saint Nicholas Ave., South Plainfield, 07080 .... (908) 753-2770
Vannote Custom Canvas, 1904 Grand Central Ave., Lavallette, 08735 .... (732) 830-6555
Vansco, Inc., 138-B Cannonball Rd., Pompton Lakes, 07442 .... (973) 835-8423
Vantage Apparel, 100 Vantage Dr., Avenel, 07001 .... (732) 340-3000
Vantage Oleochemicals, Inc. see. .... Lipo Chemicals, Inc., Paterson
Vantage Tool & Mfg., 223 Stirling Rd., Warren, 07059 .... (908) 647-1010
Vanton Pump & Equipment Corp., 201 Sweetland Ave., Hillside, 07205 .... (908) 688-4216
Varda International Corp., 41 S. Spring St., Elizabeth, 07201 .... (908) 354-9090
VAR-LAC-OID Chemical Co., Inc.,
24 Industrial Ave., P.O. Box 181, Upper Saddle River, 07458 .... (201) 236-8800
Vaswani, Inc., 18 Bernadette Ct., Springfield, 07081 .... (973) 376-4425
VC Marketing see. .... Vandermolen Corp., Livingston
V-Com see. .... Hamilton Buhl, Fairfield
V-Com, 80 Little Falls Rd., Fairfield, 07004 .... (201) 229-9800
VCOM International Multi-Media Corp. see. .... A. V. Bluebook, Fairfield
VCOM International Multi-Media Corp. see. .... Buhl Electric, Inc., Fairfield
VCOM International Multi-Media Corp. see. .... Hamilton Buhl, Fairfield
VCOM International Multi-Media Corp. see. .... V-Com, Fairfield
VCOM International Multi-Media Corp., 80 Little Falls Rd., Fairfield, 07004 .... (201) 229-4270
V-Custom Millwork, Inc., 1480 Highway 22, P.O. Box 6842, Bridgewater, 08807 .... (732) 469-9600
VDM Metals USA, LLC, 306 Columbia Tpke., Florham Park, 07932 .... (973) 437-1664
† Veckridge Chemical Co., Inc., 60 Central Ave., Kearny, 07032 .... (973) 344-1818
Vector Precision Machining, Inc., 1558 Janvier Rd., Williamstown, 08094 .... (856) 740-5131
VectraCor, Inc., 785 Totowa Rd., Ste. 100, Totowa, 07512 .... (973) 904-0444
Vee Dennis Mfg. Co., 620 Park Rd., Cherry Hill, 08034 .... (856) 428-7676
Veeco Instruments Inc. see. .... Veeco Instruments, Inc., Somerset
Veeco Instruments, Inc., 145 Belmont Dr., Somerset, 08873 .... (732) 560-5300
VeggieLand see. .... J.P. Veggies, Inc., Parsippany
Vehicle Safety Mfg., LLC, 408 Central Ave., Newark, 07107 .... (973) 643-3000
Vending Truck, Inc., 5 Litchfield Rd., East Brunswick, 08816 .... (732) 969-5400
Vention Medical, 6 Century Rd., South Plainfield, 07080 .... (908) 561-0717
Ventnor Print Shop Co.,
128 N. Wyoming Ave., P.O. Box 2174, Ventnor City, 08406 .... (609) 822-2974
Ventraq, Inc., 817 E. Gate Dr., Ste. 101, Mount Laurel, 08054 .... (856) 866-1000
Ventronics, Inc., 346 Monroe Ave., P.O. Box 142, Kenilworth, 07033 .... (908) 272-9262
Venus Knitting Mills, Inc., 140 Spring St., Bldg. 1, New Providence, 07974 .... (908) 464-2400
† Veolia Environmental Services, 27-33 Iowa Ave., Paterson, 07503 .... (973) 742-6789
Veolia Environmental Services North America Corp. see. .... Veolia Environmental Services, Paterson
Veolia Environmental Services North America Corp. see. Veolia ES Technical Solutions, LLC, Middlesex
Veolia ES Technical Solutions, LLC, 125 Factory Ln., Middlesex, 08846 .... (732) 469-5100
Veolia Water North America see. Veolia Water Solutions & Technologies North America, Inc., Pennsauken
Veolia Water Solutions & Technologies North America, Inc.,
6981 N. Park Dr., Ste. 600, Pennsauken, 08109 .... (856) 438-1776
Veraciti, Inc., 1044 Route 23, Ste. 102, Wayne, 07470 .... (973) 887-8660
Verbex Acquisition Corp. see. .... Voxware, Inc., Hamilton
Verden Tool & Mfg., LLC, 121 E. Blackwell St., Dover, 07801 .... (973) 366-7510
Verint Systems, Inc., 9 Polito Ave., 9th Fl., Lyndhurst, 07071 .... (201) 559-3788
Verisk Analytics, Inc. see. .... Insurance Services Office, Inc., Jersey City
Veritiv Corp. see. .... xpedx, Clifton
Veritiv Corp. see. .... xpedx, Clifton
Veritiv Corp. see. .... xpedx LLC A veritiv Company, Westampton
Vermes Machine Co., Inc., 351 Crider Ave., Moorestown, 08057 .... (856) 642-9300
Vermont Store Fixture Corp. see. .... Vermont Store Fixture Corporation, Midland Park
Vermont Store Fixture Corporation, 265 Greenwood Ave., Midland Park, 07432 .... (201) 652-3401
Verna Printing Co., Inc., 85 Washington Ave., Belleville, 07109 .... (973) 751-6462
Vernon Co., The see. .... Vernon Display Graphics, Carlstadt
Vernon Display Graphics, 145 Commerce Rd., Carlstadt, 07072 .... (201) 935-7117
Vernon-Sal, Inc. see. .... Vernon Display Graphics, Carlstadt
Verona-Cedar Grove Times, 130 Valley Rd., Montclair, 07042 .... (973) 233-5048
Verrex Corp., 1130 Route 22, Mountainside, 07092 .... (908) 232-7000
Versa Products Co., Inc., 22 Spring Valley Rd., Paramus, 07652 .... (201) 843-2400
Versabar Corp., 100 Maltese Dr., Totowa, 07512 .... (973) 279-8400
Versatile Distributors, Inc., 80 Industrial Rd., Lodi, 07644 .... (973) 779-1400
Versatile Printing Applications see. .... Burns, Inc., Joseph, Bound Brook
Versatile Welding Group, LLC, 340 Cox St., Roselle, 07203 .... (908) 298-8900
Verseidag Seemee US, Inc. (H Q), 4 Aspen Dr., Randolph, 07869 .... (973) 252-1189
Vertellus Performance Materials, Inc., 40 Avenue A, Bayonne, 07002 .... (201) 858-8810
Vertellus Specialties, Inc. see. .... Vertellus Performance Materials, Inc., Bayonne
Vertical Pharmaceuticals, Inc. (H Q),
2500 Main St., Ste. 6, Sayreville, 08872 .... (732) 721-0070
Vertical Source, Inc. (H Q), 812 Broad St., Shrewsbury, 07702 .... (732) 530-5330
Vertol Machine, 15 Burns Ave., Vineland, 08360 .... (856) 327-2489
Veterano Ward Commercial Printing, 301 Bradshaw Ave., Haddonfield, 08033 .... (856) 429-5460
VFI Fabricators, Inc.,
300 Thomas Ave., Bldg. 1, Ste. 101, Williamstown, 08094 .... (856) 629-8786
★ VGS Group, Inc., 197 State Route 18, Ste. 235, East Brunswick, 08816 .... (732) 887-5912
Viamente, Inc., 3600 State Route 66, Ste. 400, Neptune, 07753 .... (732) 686-7843
Vianini Pipe, Inc., 39 County Line Rd., Whitehouse Station, 08889 .... (908) 534-4021
Vibra Screw, Inc., 755 Union Blvd., Totowa, 07512 .... (973) 256-7410
Vibration Isolation Co., 225 Grand St., Paterson, 07501 .... (973) 345-8282
† Vic Gerard Golf Cars, 281 Squankum Rd., Farmingdale, 07727 .... (732) 938-4464
Vicinity Media Group, 165 Passaic Ave., Ste. 107, Fairfield, 07004 .... (973) 276-1688
Victor Settings, Inc. see. .... Victor's Three-D, Inc., Maywood
Victorian Glass Carver, 5515 Toms Ave., Pennsauken, 08109 .... (856) 662-1391
Victor's Printing, 3 Perina Blvd., Cherry Hill, 08003 .... (856) 424-4600
Victor's Three-D, Inc., 25 Brook Ave., Maywood, 07607 .... (201) 845-4433
Victory Box Corp., 645 W. 1st Ave., Roselle, 07203 .... (908) 245-5100
Victory International U. S. A., LLC, 75 Newfield Ave., Edison, 08837 .... (732) 417-1040
Victory Iron Works, Inc., 780 Mountain Ave., Wyckoff, 07481 .... (973) 427-4498
† Victory Packaging, Inc., 8 Corn Rd., Ste. 2, Dayton, 08810 .... (732) 274-1745
Victory Refrigeration, 110 Woodcrest Rd., Cherry Hill, 08003 .... (856) 428-4200
Victory White Metal Co., Inc., 129 Victoria Pl. W., Fort Lee, 07024 .... (201) 585-0747
Vieira's Bakery, 34-48 Avenue K, Newark, 07105 .... (973) 589-7719
Vieiras Bakery, Inc., 34 Avenue K, Ste. 48, Newark, 07105 .... (973) 465-1212
Vigg Designs, LLC, 584 Park Ave., Freehold, 07728 .... (732) 683-9400
Viking Marine Products, Inc., 1160 State St., Ste. 17, Perth Amboy, 08861 .... (732) 826-4559
Viking Mold & Tool, Inc., 64 Tuckahoe Rd., Dorothy, 08317 .... (609) 476-9333
† Viking Village, Inc.,
19th St. & Bayview Ave., P.O. Box 458, Barnegat Light, 08006 .... (609) 494-0113
Viking Yacht Co., 5738 U.S. Highway 9 N., P.O. Box 308, New Gretna, 08224 .... (609) 296-6000
★ Viking Yachting Center, Inc., 5724 N. Route 9, New Gretna, 08224 .... (609) 296-2388
Vikolya Corp., 140 Ethel Rd. W., Unit J, Piscataway, 08854 .... (732) 529-5540
Villadom Times, The, 333 Godwin Ave., P.O. Box 96, Midland Park, 07432 .... (201) 652-0744
Village Opticians, 550 Route 530, Whiting, 08759 .... (732) 350-1900
Vils Pharma, Inc., 135 Glendale Ave., Edison, 08817 .... (732) 777-6023
Vincent & Co., Inc., J.,
420 Route 34, Ste. 301, P.O. Box 448, Colts Neck, 07722 .... (732) 256-4410
† Vinch Recycling, Inc., 1607 N. Olden Ave., P.O. Box 55300, Trenton, 08638 .... (609) 393-0200
Vinchem, Inc., 301 Main St., P.O. Box 639, Chatham, 07928 .... (973) 635-4841
Vineland Packaging Corp., 3602 N. Mill Rd., Vineland, 08360 .... (856) 794-3300
Vineland Syrup, Inc., 723 Southeast Blvd., Vineland, 08360 .... (856) 691-5772
Vin-Law Machine & Tool Co., Inc.,
3 Kulick Rd., P.O. Box 10950, Fairfield, 07004 .... (973) 227-5100
Vintage Vibe ltd., 114 Beach St., Bldg. 5, Ground Fl., Rockaway, 07866 .... (973) 989-2178
Vinylast, Inc., 1830 Swarthmore Ave., Lakewood, 08701 .... (732) 367-7200
Violet Packing, 123 Railroad Ave., Williamstown, 08094 .... (856) 629-7428
Violin Memory, Inc., 33 Wood Ave. S., 3rd Fl., Iselin, 08830 .... (650) 396-1492
VIP Industries, Inc., 90 Brighton Rd., Clifton, 07012 .... (973) 472-7500
VIP Optical Laboratories, Inc., 325 Dalziel Rd., Linden, 07036 .... (908) 523-1422
Vira Mfg., Inc., 1 Buckingham Ave., Perth Amboy, 08861 .... (732) 442-8472
Virginia American Industries, Inc. see. .... American Galvanizing Co., Inc., Folsom
Virtual Management Services Corp.,
242 Atlantic City Blvd., Ste. 12, Bayville, 08721 .... (732) 281-1350
VIS USA, LLC, 210 Meister Ave., Branchburg, 08876 .... (908) 575-0606
Viscot Medical, LLC, 32 West St., P.O. Box 351, East Hanover, 07936 .... (973) 887-9273
† Vish Corp., 200 State Route 17, Ste. 200-A, Mahwah, 07430 .... (201) 529-2900
Vision Lighting, Inc., 48 N. 2nd St., Paterson, 07522 .... (973) 720-1200
Vision Research, Inc., 100 Dey Rd., Wayne, 07470 .... (973) 696-4500
VisiPak, a Sinclair & Rush Company,
640 Dell Rd., Ste. 1, P.O. Box 0188, Carlstadt, 07072 .... (800) 949-1141
Viskal Printing, LLC, 40 Commerce Way, Unit E, Totowa, 07512 .... (973) 812-6600
Vistar Corp. see. .... Roma Food Enterprises, Inc., Piscataway

© Copyright 2015 Manufacturers' News, Inc.


Vistar Corp. see ... Roma Of Mid-Atlantic, Swedesboro
Visual Architectural Designs, Inc., 15 Harmich Rd., South Plainfield, 07080 ... (908) 754-3000
Visual Graphic Systems, Inc., 330 Washington Ave., Carlstadt, 07072 ... (201) 528-2700
Visual Impact Advertising, Inc., 9 Highland Pl., Maplewood, 07040 ... (973) 763-4900
Visual Packaging Corp., 91 4th Ave., Haskell, 07420 ... (973) 835-7055
Visual Retail Plus, Inc., 540 Hudson St., 4th Fl., Hackensack, 07601 ... (201) 678-9888
Vitaire Corp., 141 Lanza Ave., 4th Fl., Garfield, 07026 ... (973) 473-2244
Vital Signs, 50 Bedford Rd., Mahwah, 07430 ... (201) 723-8488
Vital Signs, A CareFusion Co., 20 Campus Rd., Totowa, 07512 ... (973) 956-5300
Vitale Signs, 2204 Elizabeth Ave., Rahway, 07065 ... (732) 388-8401
Vitali, Inc., Ubaldo, 188-190 Hilton Ave., Maplewood, 07040 ... (973) 763-9310
Vitamia & Sons, 206 Harrison Ave., Lodi, 07644 ... (973) 546-1140
Vitamin Retailer, 431 Cranbury Rd., Ste. C, East Brunswick, 08816 ... (732) 432-9600
Vitamins for Life, LLC, 1806 Bellmore St., P.O. Box 853, Oakhurst, 07755 ... (732) 663-1559
Vita-Pure, Inc., 410 W. 1st Ave., Roselle, 07203 ... (908) 245-1212
Vitaquest International, LLC, 8 Henderson Dr., West Caldwell, 07006 ... (973) 575-9200
Vitech Systems Group, Inc., 111 Wood Ave. S., Iselin, 08830 ... (646) 344-5282
VitroCom FBN NJ Mfg. see ... VitroCom, Inc., Mountain Lakes
VitroCom, Inc., 8 Morris Ave., P.O. Box 125, Mountain Lakes, 07046 ... (973) 402-1443
Viva Mexican Restaurant, 117 Broad St., Unit 1, Flemington, 08822 ... (908) 788-0744
Viz Mold & Die Ltd., 210 Industrial Pkwy., Northvale, 07647 ... (201) 784-8383
Viz Plastic Products Ltd., 210 Industrial Pkwy., Northvale, 07647 ... (201) 784-4442
VMC Group, The, 113 Main St., P.O. Box 270, Bloomingdale, 07403 ... (973) 838-1780
Vogelsang Fastener Corp, 1790 Swarthmore Ave., Lakewood, 08701 ... (732) 364-0444
★ Voicecom Plus, Inc., 63 Ramapo Valley Rd., Ste. 201-A, Mahwah, 07430 ... (201) 760-2260
Voigt & Schweitzer, LLC see ... V & S Amboy Galvanizing, Perth Amboy
Voigt Lighting, 79 Commerce St., Garfield, 07026 ... (973) 928-2252
Volta Belting Technology, 11 Chapin Rd., Pine Brook, 07058 ... (973) 276-7905
Volta Corp., 11 Industrial Dr., P.O. Box 1027, Laurence Harbor, 08879 ... (732) 583-3300
Voltaix, LLC (H Q), 3121 U.S. Highway 22, P.O. Box 5357, Branchburg, 08876 ... (908) 231-9060
Von Roll USA, Inc. see ... Dolph Co., John C., Monmouth Junction
Voorheis Industries, Inc., 369 Thornden St., South Orange, 07079 ... (973) 227-2446
Vo-Toys, Inc., 400 S. 5th St., Harrison, 07029 ... (973) 484-0088
Voxware, Inc., 300 American Metro Blvd., Ste. 155, Hamilton, 08619 ... (609) 514-4100
Vozeh Equipment Corp., 509 Commerce St., Franklin Lakes, 07417 ... (201) 337-4212
VPI Industries, Inc., 77 Cliffwood Ave., Ste. 3-B, Cliffwood, 07721 ... (732) 583-6895
VRP Lu-Max Mfg. Co., Inc., 44 Brown Ave., Springfield, 07081 ... (973) 379-5877
† V.S. Systematics, Inc., 300 S. Michigan Ave., 1st Fl., Kenilworth, 07033 ... (908) 241-5110
★ vSplash Techlabs, Inc. (H Q), 1050 Wall St. W., Ste. 630, Lyndhurst, 07071 ... (201) 355-0066
Vulcan Tool Co., Inc., 1080-C Garden State Rd., Union, 07083 ... (908) 686-0550
Vytran, LLC, 1400 Campus Dr., Morganville, 07751 ... (732) 972-2880
W & E Baum, Inc., 89 Bannard St., Freehold, 07728 ... (732) 866-1881
W & E Sales Co., Inc., 370 Elizabeth Ave., Newark, 07112 ... (973) 824-2000
W & H Systems, Inc., 120 Asia Pl., Carlstadt, 07072 ... (201) 933-7840
W B C Industries, Inc., 625 Central Ave., Westfield, 07090 ... (908) 789-1234
W J R B, Inc., 711 Town Bank Rd., Cape May, 08204 ... (609) 884-1169
W. R. Grace & Co., 2133 85th St., North Bergen, 07047 ... (201) 869-5220
† W. W. Grainger, Inc., 308 Allwood Rd., Clifton, 07012 ... (973) 777-7700
† W. W. Grainger, Inc., 55 Jackson Dr., Cranford, 07016 ... (908) 272-7156
† W. W. Grainger, Inc., 560-596 Bercik St., Ste. 1, Elizabeth, 07201 ... (908) 787-1952
† W. W. Grainger, Inc., 277 Route 46 W., Fairfield, 07004 ... (973) 227-7220
† W. W. Grainger, Inc., 819 E. Gate Dr., Mount Laurel, 08054 ... (856) 234-8550
† W. W. Grainger, Inc., 1585 N. Olden Ave., Trenton, 08638 ... (609) 394-2620
W Y Plastic Industry, Inc., 2500 Secaucus Rd., North Bergen, 07047 ... (201) 617-8000
Waage Electric, Inc., 720 Colfax Ave., P.O. Box 337, Kenilworth, 07033 ... (908) 245-9363
Wacoal America, Inc., 1 Wacoal Plz., Lyndhurst, 07071 ... (201) 933-8400
† Wade Environmental Industries, 382 Jackson Rd., Atco, 08004 ... (856) 767-2760
Wagner Carbide Saw Div. see ... Tooling Etc., LLC, Middlesex
Wagner Foto Screen Process, 4 Mark Rd., Kenilworth, 07033 ... (908) 624-0800
Wagner Industries, Inc., 51 Sparta Rd., Stanhope, 07874 ... (973) 347-0800
Wagner Provisions Co., Inc., 54 E. Broad St., P.O. Box 169, Gibbstown, 08027 ... (856) 423-1630
Wagner Rack, Inc., 2 Broad St., Clifton, 07013 ... (973) 278-6966
Wagonhouse Winery, LLC, 1401 State Highway 45, Swedesboro, 08085 ... (609) 780-8019
★ Wahida Clark Publishing, LLC, 60 Evergreen Pl., Ste. 904, East Orange, 07018 ... (973) 678-9982
Wainer Finest Communications, Inc.,
4041-G Hadley Rd., Ste. 101, South Plainfield, 07080 ... (908) 769-1160
Wainscot Media, 110 Summit Ave., Montvale, 07645 ... (201) 571-2244
Wakefern Food Corp. see ... Readington Farms, Inc., Whitehouse
† Wakefern Food Corp. (H Q), 5000 Riverside Dr., Keasbey, 08832 ... (732) 906-5932
Walden Farms, Inc., 1209 W. Saint Georges Ave., Linden, 07036 ... (908) 925-9494
Walden Lang In-Pak see ... In-Pak Services, Inc., Clifton
Walden-Mott Corp., 225 N. Franklin Tpke., Ramsey, 07446 ... (201) 818-8630
Waldwick Printing Co., 1 Harrison Ave., Waldwick, 07463 ... (201) 652-5848
Walk The Technology Solution,
9000 Commerce Pkwy., Ste. H, Mount Laurel, 08054 ... (856) 222-0643
Wall Street Group, Inc., 1 Edward Hart Dr., Jersey City, 07305 ... (201) 333-4784
Wallace Blinds see ... Atlantic City Shade Shop, Inc., Northfield
Wallace Eannace Associates, Inc., 779 Susquehanna Ave., Franklin Lakes, 07417 ... (201) 891-9550
Walpole Outdoors see ... Walpole Woodworkers, Inc., Morris Plains
Walpole Woodworkers, Inc., 540 Tabor Rd., Morris Plains, 07950 ... (973) 539-3555
Walted Designs, Inc., 70 Spruce St., Ste. 8, Paterson, 07501 ... (973) 881-1944
Walter Machine Co., Inc., The,
84-98 Cambridge Ave., P.O. Box 7700, Jersey City, 07307 ... (201) 656-5654
Walter R. Earle Corporation, 655 S. Hope Chapel Rd., Jackson, 08527 ... (732) 657-8551
Walter's Signs, 159 W. White Horse Pike, Berlin, 08009 ... (856) 210-6324
Walther Electric Corp., F., 12 Worlds Fair Dr., Ste. F, Somerset, 08873 ... (732) 537-9201
Waltron see ... Waltron, Bull & Roberts, LLC, Whitehouse
Waltron, Bull & Roberts, LLC, 50 Tannery Rd., P.O. Box 70, Whitehouse, 08888 ... (908) 534-5100
Wantage Stone, LLC, 80 State Route 23, Hamburg, 07419 ... (973) 702-7866
Ward & Sons, Inc., J. B., 1434 Route 565, Wantage, 07461 ... (973) 827-4600
Ward LaFrance, Inc., 37 W. Broad St., Paulsboro, 08066 ... (609) 922-8383
Ward Sand & Materials, 223 Sooy Place Rd., Vincentown, 08088 ... (609) 859-2860
Ware Industries, Inc., 400 Metuchen Rd., South Plainfield, 07080 ... (908) 757-9000
Warner Chilcott, 100 Enterprise Dr., Ste. 280, Rockaway, 07866 ... (973) 442-3200
Warren Lightning Rod Co., 2 Richey Ave., Collingswood, 08107 ... (856) 854-7000
Warren Materials, 703 Route 57, Stewartsville, 08886 ... (908) 859-3333
Warren Mfg. Corp., 23 Bloomfield Ave., Pine Brook, 07058 ... (973) 227-4220
Warren Pallet Co., Inc., 601 County Road 627, Bloomsbury, 08804 ... (908) 995-7172
Warwick Mfg. & Equipment Co., LLC, 1112 12th St., North Brunswick, 08902 ... (732) 729-0400
† Washington Professional Systems, Inc.,
109 Gaither Dr., Ste. 301, Mount Laurel, 08054 ... (856) 273-8688
Washington Stamp Exchange, Inc., 2 Vreeland Rd., Florham Park, 07932 ... (973) 966-0001

Waste Management, Inc., 107 Silvia St., Ewing, 08628 ... (609) 587-1500
Wastequip, 1031 Hickstown Rd., Sicklerville, 08081 ... (856) 784-5500
Wastequip, Inc. see ... Wastequip, Sicklerville
Wastequip, Inc., 460 New Brooklyn Rd., Williamstown, 08094 ... (856) 629-9222
Watchung Communications, Inc., 251 North Ave. W., Westfield, 07090 ... (908) 232-4407
★ Water Ice Factory, Inc., 15 Evergreen Rd, Chatham, 08084 ... (856) 627-6831
★ Water Mark Technologies, Inc.,
762 State Route 15 S., Ste. 2-B, Lake Hopatcong, 07849 ... (973) 663-3438
† Water Resources New Jersey, LLC,
1609 Route 206, P.O. Box 2172, Tabernacle, 08088 ... (609) 268-7965
Water Shoppe, Inc., The, 112 N. 3rd St., 2nd Fl., Camden, 08102 ... (856) 964-4500
WaterDoctor, Inc., 1030-C Campus Dr., Morganville, 07751 ... (732) 972-4510
Water-Jel Technologies, 50 Broad St., Carlstadt, 07072 ... (201) 507-8300
Waterloov * Mark of Perfection see ... R. K. Industries, Inc., Oakhurst
Watson Assocs., Inc., 800 Grove Rd., Thorofare, 08086 ... (856) 845-8800
Watson Graphics, Inc., 578 Kearny Ave., Kearny, 07032 ... (201) 955-0283
Wattlots, LLC, 1932 Long Hill Rd., Millington, 07946 ... (908) 626-1555
Waveline, Inc., 160 Passaic Ave., Fairfield, 07004 ... (973) 808-9113
Wayne County Foods, Inc., 360 Coit St., Irvington, 07111 ... (973) 399-0101
† Wayne Electrical Supply Co., 255 W. Parkway, Pompton Plains, 07444 ... (973) 839-6500
Wayne Meat Corp., 2234 Hamburg Tpke., Wayne, 07470 ... (973) 835-0211
WayneToday, 1 Garret Mountain Plz., P.O. Box 471, Woodland Park, 07424 ... (973) 569-7393
W.B. Law & Son, Inc., 280 Wilson Ave., Unit B, Newark, 07105 ... (973) 344-2270
W.D. Service Company, Inc., 780 Creek Rd., Bellmawr, 08031 ... (856) 931-6100
Wearbest Sil-Tex Mills, Ltd., 325 Midland Ave., P.O. Box 589, Garfield, 07026 ... (973) 340-8844
Weather Tek Aluminum Corp.,
123 N. Washington Ave., P.O. Box 405, Dunellen, 08812 ... (732) 752-0313
Weathercraft Mfg. Co., 13 Emerson Plz. E., Emerson, 07630 ... (201) 262-0055
Weatherford International Ltd. see ... Bilfinger Water Technologies, Forked River
Weaver Assocs. Printing Service, Inc., 945 Lincoln Ave. E., Cranford, 07016 ... (908) 272-6224
Weaver Printing & Digital Copies see ... Weaver Assocs. Printing Service, Inc., Cranford
Web Industries, Inc., 5 Mars Ct., P.O. Box 237, Montville, 07045 ... (973) 335-1200
Webco Graphics see ... Webco Graphics/W.G.I. Corp., Lakewood
Webco Graphics/W.G.I. Corp., 1875 Swarthmore Ave., Lakewood, 08701 ... (732) 370-2900
Web-Cote Industries, Inc., 141 Wheatsworth Rd., P.O. Box 120, Hamburg, 07419 ... (973) 827-2299
Weber & Doebrich, Inc., 119 61st St., West New York, 07093 ... (201) 867-1540
Weber & Scher Mfg. Co., Inc.,
1231 US Highway 22 E., P.O. Box 366, Lebanon, 08833 ... (908) 236-8484
Webtech, Inc., 108 N. Gold Dr., Robbinsville, 08691 ... (609) 259-2800
WECOM, Inc., 20 Warrick Ave., Glassboro, 08028 ... (856) 863-8400
Weidner Publishing Group, 114 Woodbine Ave., Merchantville, 08109 ... (856) 486-1755
Weil-McLain, 17000 Commerce Pkwy., Ste. B, Mount Laurel, 08054 ... (856) 866-7400
† Weinstein Supply Co., 3187 Fire Rd., Egg Harbor Township, 08234 ... (609) 677-0666
† Weinstein Supply Co., 4019 S. Main Rd., Vineland, 08360 ... (856) 825-1460
† Weinstein Supply Corp., 1687 Haddon Ave., Camden, 08103 ... (856) 964-1700
Weir Welding Co., Inc., 316 12th St., P.O. Box 311, Carlstadt, 07072 ... (201) 939-2284
Weiss & Sons, Inc., I., 815 Fairview Ave., Ste. 10, Fairview, 07022 ... (201) 402-6500
Weiss-Aug Co. Inc., 220 Merry Ln., East Hanover, 07936 ... (973) 887-7600
Welco Acetylene Corp., 321 Roanoke Ave., Newark, 07105 ... (973) 465-1043
Weldall Welding & Ironworks, 115-117 S. Day St., Orange, 07050 ... (973) 674-8868
Weld-Done Welding, Inc., 20 Woodland Ave., Hurffville, 08080 ... (856) 582-7080
Weldon Asphalt Co., 1100 Harrison Ave., Kearny, 07032 ... (201) 991-3200
Weldon Asphalt Co., 311 W. Main St., Rockaway, 07866 ... (973) 627-7500
Weldon Asphalt Co., 1 Eisenhower Pkwy., Roseland, 07068 ... (973) 228-7473
Weldon Asphalt Co., 1 New Providence Rd., Watchung, 07060 ... (908) 233-9440
Weldon Asphalt Corp., 2000 Marshes Dock Rd., Linden, 07036 ... (908) 862-0646
Weldon Machine & Boring, Inc., 134 Wood Ave., Middlesex, 08846 ... (732) 356-1887
Weldon Materials, Inc. see ... Weldon Asphalt Co., Kearny
Weldon Materials, Inc. see ... Weldon Asphalt Co., Rockaway
Weldon Materials, Inc. see ... Weldon Asphalt Co., Roseland
Weldon Materials, Inc. see ... Weldon Asphalt Co., Watchung
Weldon Materials, Inc. see ... Weldon Asphalt Corp., Linden
Weldon Materials, Inc., 181 Route 181, Lake Hopatcong, 07849 ... (973) 663-1800
Weldon Materials, Inc. (H Q), 141 Central Ave., Westfield, 07090 ... (908) 233-4444
Wel-Fab, Inc., 124 Burrs Rd., Mount Holly, 08060 ... (609) 261-1393
Well Tech, Inc., 1 Hardwick St., P.O. Box 66, Belvidere, 07823 ... (908) 475-4539
Wellbilt Industries, 2 Maple Ave., Linden, 07036 ... (908) 486-6002
WellCare Today, LLC, 89 Headquarters Plz., Ste. 1461, Morristown, 07960 ... (866) 656-1188
Welter & Kreutz Printing Co.,
51 Worth St., P.O. Box 1834, South Hackensack, 07606 ... (201) 489-9098
† WENCO Machinery Corp., 355 Margaret King Ave., Ringwood, 07456 ... (973) 657-9660
Werko Machine Co., Inc., 9200 Collins Ave., Pennsauken, 08110 ... (856) 662-0669
West Electronics, Inc., 5 Terri Ln., Ste. 15, P.O. Box 366, Burlington, 08016 ... (609) 387-4300
West Essex Graphics, Inc., 305 Fairfield Ave., Fairfield, 07004 ... (973) 227-2400
West Essex Tribune, Inc.,
495 S. Livingston Ave., P.O. Box 65, Livingston, 07039 ... (973) 992-1771
West Hudson Industries, 1687 Saint Georges Ave., Rahway, 07065 ... (732) 381-6800
West Hudson Millwork, Inc., 60 Arlington Ave., Kearny, 07032 ... (201) 991-7191
West Machine Works, Inc., 101 Liberty St., Metuchen, 08840 ... (732) 549-2183
West Pattern Works, Inc., 124 S. Main St., Cranbury, 08512 ... (609) 443-6241
West Side Precision Machine Products, Inc.,
280 Lincoln Blvd., Middlesex, 08846 ... (732) 560-9006
Westco Fruit & Nut Products Co., Inc., 93-97 Coit St., Irvington, 07111 ... (973) 373-1866
Westcon Orthopedics, Inc., 4 Craig Rd., Neshanic Station, 08853 ... (908) 806-8981
Western Scientific Computers, Inc., 28 W. Shore Rd., Mountain Lakes, 07046 ... (973) 263-9311
Westfall Winery, LLC, 141 Clove Rd., Montague, 07827 ... (973) 293-3428
Westfield Sheet Metal Works, Inc.,
261 Monroe Ave., P.O. Box 128, Kenilworth, 07033 ... (908) 276-5500
Westlock Controls Corp., 280 N. Midland Ave., Ste. 258, Saddle Brook, 07663 ... (201) 794-7650
Weston Machine, 161 11th St., Piscataway, 08854 ... (732) 752-2711
† Westport Corp., 331 Changebridge Rd., P.O. Box 2002, Pine Brook, 07058 ... (973) 575-0110
Westside Engravers, 76 N. West Ave., Bridgeton, 08302 ... (856) 455-4790
Westward Pharmaceutical Corp., 2 Esterbrook Ln., Cherry Hill, 08003 ... (856) 424-3700
West-Ward Pharmaceutical Corp., 401 Industrial Way W., Eatontown, 07724 ... (732) 542-1191
Westwood Products, Inc., 330 William St., P.O. Box 610, South River, 08882 ... (732) 651-7700
Wet Stone Graphics, 645 Greenway Pl., River Vale, 07675 ... (201) 307-1531
WGJF Mfg. Corp. see ... Hammer Mfg. Co., Inc., Linden
What A Tee 2, Inc., 82 Sussex St., Hackensack, 07601 ... (201) 457-0060
Wheal-Grace Corp., 300 Ralph St., P.O. Box 67, Belleville, 07109 ... (973) 450-8100
Wheaton Co., R. W., 215 W. Clay Ave., P.O. Box 4017, Roselle Park, 07204 ... (908) 241-4955
Wheaton Glass Warehouse, 1501 N. 10th St., Millville, 08332 ... (856) 327-5228
Wheaton Industries, Inc., 1501 N. 10th St., Millville, 08332 ... (856) 825-1100



**★ Indicates new listing this edition.**

**† Indicates wholesaler/distributor.**

 © Copyright 2015 Manufacturers' News, Inc. 

Wheelchair Gear, 126 Cindy Dr., Egg Harbor Township, 08234 ... (609) 653-6787
Wheeler Industrial Corp., 485 Lyons Ave., Irvington, 07111 ... (973) 926-0551
Whibco, Inc. see. ... Whibco Of New Jersey, Port Elizabeth
WHIBCO, Inc. (H Q), 87 E. Commerce St., Bridgeton, 08302 ... (856) 455-9200
Whibco Of New Jersey, 377 Port Cumberland Rd., P.O. Box 456, Port Elizabeth, 08348 ... (856) 825-5200
Whibco of NJ see. ... WHIBCO, Inc. (H Q), Bridgeton
Whippany Actuation System, 110 Algonquin Pkwy., Whippany, 07981 ... (973) 428-9898
Whips International see. ... CDK Industry, LLC, Cherry Hill
White Conveyors, Inc., 10 Boright Ave., Kenilworth, 07033 ... (800) 524-0273
White Eagle Monumental Co., Inc., 257 Ridge Rd., North Arlington, 07031 ... (201) 991-0094
White Eagle Printing Co., 2550 Kuser Rd., Hamilton, 08691 ... (609) 586-2032
White Lotus Home, 431 Raritan Ave., Highland Park, 08904 ... (732) 828-2111
White Marine, Inc., 500 Division St., Perth Amboy, 08861 ... (732) 826-4491
White Valley Memorials see. ... William B. Snelbaker & Son, Woodbury
White Valley Memorials (H Q), 292 W. White Horse Pike, Berlin, 08009 ... (856) 767-3030
Whitehouse Machine, LLC, 3585 U.S. Highway 22 E., Somerville, 08876 ... (908) 534-4722
Whitehurst & Clark, Inc., 1200 County Road 523, Flemington, 08822 ... (908) 782-2323
WhiteWave Foods Co., 70 Rosenhayn Ave., Bridgeton, 08302 ... (856) 459-3890
Whitlock Packaging Corp., 92 N. Main St., Wharton, 07885 ... (973) 361-9794
Whittle & Mutch, Inc., 712 Fellowship Rd., Mount Laurel, 08054 ... (856) 235-1165
★ Wholesale Print House, 1757 John F. Kennedy Blvd., Jersey City, 07305 ... (201) 333-7746
Wick It, LLC, 1 Gregory Ave., Passaic, 07055 ... (973) 249-2970
Wicki Wholesale Stone, Inc., 17 Cemetery Rd., P.O. Box 104, Great Meadows, 07838 ... (908) 637-6004
Wicks Group Of Cos., LLC, The see. ... North Star Travel Media, LLC (H Q), Secaucus
Wide Band Systems, Inc., 389 Franklin Ave., Rockaway, 07866 ... (973) 586-6500
Widmer Time Recorder Co., Inc., 228 Park St., Hackensack, 07601 ... (201) 489-3810
Wiegers, Inc., 181 Fornelius Ave., Clifton, 07013 ... (973) 778-8607
Wiener Publishers, Inc., Markus, 231 Nassau St., Princeton, 08542 ... (609) 921-1141
Wiggins Plastics, Inc., 180 Kingsland Rd., P.O. Box 1077, Clifton, 07014 ... (973) 667-7200
Wikstrom Machines, Inc., 412 Summit Ave., Perth Amboy, 08861 ... (732) 826-4800
Wilbur Sheet Metal, Inc., 27 Ward Ave., P.O. Box 3681, Trenton, 08609 ... (609) 393-5952
Wilcox Press, 6 Main St., Hamburg, 07419 ... (973) 827-7474
Wilenta Feed, Inc., 46 Henry St., Secaucus, 07094 ... (201) 863-3035
Wiley & Sons, Inc., John, 111 River St., Hoboken, 07030 ... (201) 748-6000
Wiley's Lake Press, Inc., 1902 Greenwood Lake Tpke., Hewitt, 07421 ... (973) 728-9231
Wilkstone, LLC, 128 19th Ave., Paterson, 07513 ... (973) 684-5100
Willard Bros. Lumber, 300 Basin Rd., Trenton, 08619 ... (609) 890-1990
William B. Snelbaker & Son, 43 Cooper St., Woodbury, 08096 ... (856) 845-0634
William Usdan & Sons LLC, 140 Little St., Belleville, 07109 ... (973) 844-9988
Williams Berell, Inc., 612 E. Elizabeth Ave., P.O. Box 1341, Linden, 07036 ... (908) 486-4952
Williams Publications, Inc., E. W., 2125 Center Ave., Ste. 305, Fort Lee, 07024 ... (201) 592-7007
† Williams Scotsman, Inc., 35 Ford Ln., Kearny, 07032 ... (973) 589-1234
† Willier Electric Motor Repair Co., Inc., 1 Linden Ave., P.O. Box 98, Gibbsboro, 08026 ... (856) 627-3535
Willow Graphics see. ... Tooker Sign Service, Tuckerton
Willow Iron Works, 67 Pollock Ave., Jersey City, 07305 ... (201) 659-7266
Willrich Precision Instrument, Inc., 80 Broadway, Cresskill, 07626 ... (201) 567-1411
Will's Custom Displays & Woodwork, 1202 E. Elizabeth Ave., Linden, 07036 ... (908) 925-0008
Wilmad-LabGlass, 1172 N. West Blvd., Vineland, 08360 ... (856) 691-3200
Wilpak Industries, Inc., 244 Dukes St., Kearny, 07032 ... (201) 997-7600
Wilson Reconditioning & Design Co., LLC, 117 S. Rutherford Ave., Franklin, 07416 ... (973) 823-6317
† Win Laboratories, Ltd., 182 Ridge Rd., Ste. D, Dayton, 08810 ... (732) 355-1355
Winco see. ... D.W.L International Trading Co., Lodi
WinCup, 190 Liberty St., Metuchen, 08840 ... (732) 494-1999
Windmill Health Products, LLC, 6 Henderson Dr., Caldwell, 07006 ... (973) 575-6591
★ Window Covering Concepts, 29 Bella Rd., Lumberton, 08048 ... (609) 261-1181
★ Window Creations By Emmy Ltd., 103 Summerset St., Garfield, 07026 ... (718) 965-3844
Window Shapes, Inc., 225 Liberty St., Metuchen, 08840 ... (848) 229-2431
Window Supply Corp., 5410 Kennedy Blvd., West New York, 07093 ... (201) 392-1213
★ Windowscapes, 5 Winay Ter., Long Valley, 07853 ... (908) 850-0678
Wine Products, Inc., 2416 Highway 35, Ste. B, Manasquan, 08736 ... (732) 528-5222
† Winebow, Inc., 75 Chestnut Ridge Rd., Ste. 1, Montvale, 07645 ... (201) 445-0620
Winetak see. ... TricorBraun, Saddle Brook
WingIt Innovations, LLC, 714 5th Ave., Bradley Beach, 07720 ... (732) 869-4466
Winslow Hot Mix, LLC, 784 Piney Hollow Rd., Hammonton, 08037 ... (609) 561-2100
Winsome Digital, Inc. see. ... Gotham Group, The, Egg Harbor Township
Win-Tech Precision Products, Inc., 5 Littell Rd., East Hanover, 07936 ... (973) 887-8727
Winter, Inc. & Co., F. W., Delaware Ave. & Elm St., Camden, 08102 ... (856) 963-7490
Winter Scale & Equipment, 20-A Kulick Rd., Fairfield, 07004 ... (888) 808-3611
Wire & Cable Fabricating Devices, 39 E. Hanover Ave., Ste. 1, Morris Plains, 07950 ... (973) 290-9069
Wire Cloth Mfrs., Inc., 110 Iron Mountain Rd., Mine Hill, 07803 ... (973) 328-1000
Wire Equipment Mfg. Co., Inc., 319 Birch Hollow Dr., Bordentown, 08505 ... (609) 499-4411
Wire Forming Corp. Of New Jersey, 109 Meeker Ave., Ste. 135, Newark, 07114 ... (973) 824-5558
Wire Newspaper, The see. ... Broad Street Media, Cherry Hill
Wireless Telecom Group, Inc., 25 Eastmans Rd., Parsippany, 07054 ... (973) 386-9696
Wireworks Corp., 380 Hillside Ave., Hillside, 07205 ... (908) 686-7400
Wisco Promo & Uniform, Inc., 160 Route 46 E., Saddle Brook, 07663 ... (973) 767-2022
Wise Tag & Label Co., Inc., 1077 Thomas Busch Memorial Hwy., Pennsauken, 08110 ... (856) 663-2400
Wish Factory, Inc., The, 21 Church St., Ste. 2, Montclair, 07042 ... (973) 744-3131
Witte Co., Inc., The, 507 Route 31 S., P.O. Box 47, Washington, 07882 ... (908) 689-6500
Wizard Printing Corp., 29 Evans Pl., Ste. 82, Pompton Plains, 07444 ... (973) 835-8048
WJJ & Company see. ... Papertec, Inc., Garfield
WL Interiors see. ... Wood & Laminates, Inc., Lodi
Wm. H. Brewster Jr., Inc., 16 Kulick Rd., Fairfield, 07004 ... (973) 227-1050
† WMS Gaming, Inc., 2511 Fire Rd., Ste. A-10, Egg Harbor Township, 08234 ... (609) 569-0100
WMS Industries, Inc. see. ... WMS Gaming, Inc., Egg Harbor Township
†★ W&O Supply, Inc., 7 W. Baltimore Ave., Linden, 07036 ... (908) 486-5338
Wockhardt USA, LLC (H Q), 20 Waterview Blvd., Ste. 3, Parsippany, 07054 ... (973) 257-4960
Woerner Machine & Tool Co., 700 Grand Ave., Bldg. 7, Hackettstown, 07840 ... (908) 979-0042
Wolek's Ornamental Iron Works, 1719 H St., Route 71 W., Belmar, 07719 ... (732) 681-5929
Wood & Laminates, Inc., 102 Route 46 E., Lodi, 07644 ... (973) 773-7475
Wood Artisans, Inc., 49 Oak St., Norwood, 07648 ... (201) 768-1663
Wood Products, Inc., 34 Allentown Rd., Southampton, 08088 ... (609) 859-0303
Wood Shed, Inc., The, 4500 Park Ave., Weehawken, 07086 ... (201) 866-7949
Wood Shop, 24 Water St., Englishtown, 07726 ... (732) 446-3377
Wood Works, 1111 N. Black Horse Pike, Williamstown, 08094 ... (856) 728-4520
Woodbridge Machine & Tool Co., Inc., 259 Bergen St., Woodbridge, 07095 ... (732) 634-0179
Woodbridge Monument Factory, Inc., 10 Main St., Ste. K, Woodbridge, 07095 ... (732) 634-1521
Woodbridge Printing Center, 1201 U.S. Highway 9 S., Woodbridge, 07095 ... (732) 855-1996
Woodchucker, Inc., The, 42 Bridgeton-Fairton Rd., P.O. Box 380, Fairton, 08320 ... (856) 575-0200
Woodhaven Lumber & Millwork, Inc., 200 James St., P.O. Box 870, Lakewood, 08701 ... (732) 901-0030
† Woodhaven Lumber & Millwork, Inc., 725 E. Bay Ave., Manahawkin, 08050 ... (609) 597-1118
★ Woodhut, LLC, 339 Fairfield Rd., Freehold, 07728 ... (732) 414-6440
Woodland Mfg. Co., Inc., 1936 E. State St., Hamilton, 08619 ... (609) 587-4180
Woodline Works Corp., 625 Jersey Ave., New Brunswick, 08901 ... (732) 828-9100
Wood-O-Rama, Inc., 100 67th St., Closter, 07624 ... (201) 768-1180
Woodroof Metal Shop, 73 Water St., Bridgeton, 08302 ... (856) 455-1111
Woodruff Energy, Inc., 73 Water St., P.O. Box 777, Bridgeton, 08302 ... (856) 455-1111
Woodshop, Inc., The, 58 Flint Rd., Toms River, 08757 ... (732) 349-8006
Woodstock Farms Mfg., 96 Executive Ave., Edison, 08817 ... (732) 650-9905
Woodstown Ice & Coal Co., 50 E. Grant St., P.O. Box 285, Woodstown, 08098 ... (856) 769-0069
Woodtec, Inc., 300 Stiger St., Hackettstown, 07840 ... (908) 979-0180
Woodward Jogger Aerators, Inc., 45 Carlton Ave., East Rutherford, 07073 ... (201) 933-6800
Woodwork & More, LLC, 24 W. Gorman Ave., Collingswood, 08108 ... (856) 986-3140
Woodwork 4 U, LLC, 205 Frelinghuysen Ave., Newark, 07114 ... (973) 643-3044
Word Center Printing, 1905 Highway 33, Ste. 10, Hamilton Square, 08690 ... (609) 586-5825
Work 'N' Wear Store, 73 Market St., Morristown, 07960 ... (973) 267-2373
Work Of Art Corp., 801 Olive Ave., Cherry Hill, 08002 ... (856) 488-1188
★ Workers' Disability Income System, Inc., 56 Primrose Cir., Princeton, 08540 ... (732) 274-0600
Works, The, 17 Claremont Rd., Bernardsville, 07924 ... (908) 766-7744
Workshop Stone, 281 Mount Pleasant Ave., Newark, 07104 ... (973) 230-9212
World Apostolate of Fatima USA, 674 Mountain View Rd., P.O. Box 976, Washington, 07882 ... (908) 689-1701
World Journal see. ... World Journal, Inc., Metuchen
World Journal, Inc., 41-A Bridge St., Metuchen, 08840 ... (732) 632-8890
World Media Enterprises, Inc., 1000 W. Washington Ave., Pleasantville, 08232 ... (609) 272-7000
World Neon see. ... 419 Neon, LLC, East Orange
★ World Scientific Publishing Co., Inc., 27 Warren St., Ste. 401-402, Hackensack, 07601 ... (201) 487-9655
World Software Corp., 266 Harristown Rd., Ste. 201, Glen Rock, 07452 ... (201) 444-3228
† World Wide Metric, Inc., 37 Readington Rd., P.O. Box 5267, Branchburg, 08876 ... (732) 247-2300
World Wide Packaging, LLC, 15 Vreeland Rd., Florham Park, 07932 ... (973) 805-6500
World Wide Safe Brokers see. ... Dornisch Enterprises, Inc., Woodbury
WorldPac see. ... Worldwide Parts & Accessories Corp., Dayton
WORLDPAC, Inc. see. ... Worldwide Parts & Accessories Corp., Dayton
World's Finest, Inc., 267 Hamilton Ave., Trenton, 08609 ... (609) 394-8001
† Worldwide Parts & Accessories Corp., 300 Herrod Blvd., Dayton, 08810 ... (732) 230-5000
† Worldwide Supply, LLC, 1 Park Dr., Franklin, 07416 ... (973) 823-6400
Worrall Community Newspapers, Inc., 1291 Stuyvesant Ave., P.O. Box 1596, Union, 07083 ... (908) 686-7700
Worthington Biochemical Corp., 730 Vassar Ave., Lakewood, 08701 ... (732) 942-1660
Wortmann Machine Works, Inc., E., 50 Hollister Rd., P.O. Box 1657, Teterboro, 07608 ... (201) 288-1654
Wostbrock Embroidery, Inc., 11 Paterson Ave., Midland Park, 07432 ... (201) 445-3074
Wowtrim, 178 W. Westfield Ave., Roselle Park, 07204 ... (732) 340-0766
Woyshner Service Co., Inc., 813 Edgewood Ave., Riverside, 08075 ... (856) 461-9196
WP Ducts, 219 U.S. Highway 206, P.O. Box 547, Andover, 07821 ... (973) 786-7179
WPI Communication, Inc., 55 Morris Ave., Ste. 312, Springfield, 07081 ... (973) 467-8700
Wrapade Packaging Systems, LLC, 27 Law Dr., Ste. B, Fairfield, 07004 ... (973) 773-6150
Wright & Lato see. ... Novell Enterprises, Inc., Rahway
Write Impression, The, 549 Highway 35, Red Bank, 07701 ... (732) 706-3700
† Wurth International Trading America, 91 Grant St., Ramsey, 07446 ... (201) 995-1111
W.W. Manufacturing Co., Inc., 60 Rosenhayn Ave., Bridgeton, 08302 ... (856) 451-5700
Wyanoke Group, The see. ... Slack, Inc., Thorofare
WYLD Grand Format Imaging, LLC, 1618 E. Elizabeth Ave., Linden, 07036 ... (908) 587-2995
Wyssmont Co., Inc., 1470 Bergen Blvd., Fort Lee, 07024 ... (201) 947-4600
Wytech Industries, Inc., 960 E. Hazelwood Ave., Rahway, 07065 ... (732) 396-3900
Xcaliber Corp. see. ... Mr. J's Xcaliber Corp., Paterson
Xceedium, Inc., 30 Montgomery St., Ste. 1020, Jersey City, 07302 ... (201) 536-1000
Xenopore Corp., 299 Wagaraw Rd., Hawthorne, 07506 ... (973) 423-2400
Xerimis Inc., 102 Executive Dr., Moorestown, 08057 ... (856) 727-9940
Xevee Corp., 27 Montgomery St., P. O. Box 5277, Hillside, 07205 ... (908) 964-0444
X-L Plastics, Inc., 220 Clifton Blvd., Clifton, 07011 ... (973) 777-1888
XO Athletic Co., 911 Springfield Rd., Union, 07083 ... (908) 964-1242
X-Pando Products, Inc., 500 Southard St., Trenton, 08638 ... (609) 394-0150
† xpedx, 261 River Rd., Clifton, 07014 ... (973) 405-2310
† xpedx, 261 River Rd., Clifton, 07014 ... (973) 405-2300
† xpedx LLC A veritiv Company, 1200 Highland Dr., Ste. 1-B, Westampton, 08060 ... (609) 518-9700
Xpresa Labels Corp., 681 Eagle Rock Ave., West Orange, 07052 ... (973) 669-8444
Xpresa Woven Label Designs see. ... Xpresa Labels Corp., West Orange
X-Rite, Inc. see. ... Pantone LLC, Carlstadt
XTreme Technologies Group, LLC, 135 Gaither Dr., Ste. F, Mount Laurel, 08054 ... (856) 273-7800
Xybion Medical Systems, 201 Littleton Rd., Morris Plains, 07950 ... (973) 538-5111
Xylem Dewatering * Godwin Pumps see. ... Godwin, a Xylem brand, Bridgeport
Xylem, Inc. see. ... Godwin, a Xylem brand, Bridgeport
† Y & W International, Inc., 16 Edgeboro Rd., Unit 5, East Brunswick, 08816 ... (732) 390-7722
Y, Inc., 20-21 Wagaraw Rd., Bldg. 32, Fair Lawn, 07410 ... (201) 773-8425
Yale Hook & Eye Co., Inc., 33 Race St., Hillside, 07205 ... (973) 824-1440
Yank Marine, Inc. see. ... Jersey Diesel, Dorchester
Yank Marine, Inc., Mosquito Landing Rd., P.O. Box 569, Tuckahoe, 08250 ... (609) 628-2928
Y.C. Cable East, Inc., 240 Circle Dr. N., Piscataway, 08854 ... (732) 868-0800
† Yecies, Inc., Herman W., 11 Roosevelt Ave., P.O. Box 6186, West Orange, 07052 ... (973) 736-7362
Yellow Stone Distributing Co., 50 Kulick Rd., Fairfield, 07004 ... (973) 808-8188
Yerg Accounting Supplies, 85 Washington Ave., Belleville, 07109 ... (973) 759-4041
Yesterwear Productions, Inc., 705 Smithville Rd., Lumberton, 08048 ... (609) 567-2544
Yippee Printing & Marketing, 115 River Rd., Bldg. 10, Edgewater, 07020 ... (201) 313-1900
Yonkers Plywood Mfg., 3130 Bordentown Ave., P.O. Box 152, Old Bridge, 08857 ... (732) 727-1200
Yoo-Hoo Chocolate Beverage Corp., 600 Commercial Ave., Carlstadt, 07072 ... (201) 933-0070
Young Asphalt Paving Materials, Robert, 830 Burnt Meadow Rd., Hewitt, 07421 ... (973) 728-8133
Your Tops, Inc., 101 S. 21st St., Kenilworth, 07033 ... (908) 272-0011
Yuhl Products, Inc., 15 N. 7th St., Kenilworth, 07033 ... (908) 276-5180
Yukon Graphics, Inc., 239 New Rd., Ste. B-110, Parsippany, 07054 ... (973) 575-5700
★ Yume Enterprises, LLC, 1800 E. State St., Ste. 158, Trenton, 08609 ... (609) 588-8903
Z & R Cutter Service, Inc., 50 Division Ave., Ste. 21, Millington, 07946 ... (908) 647-6757
† Z & Z Holding Co Inc, 370 Market St., P.O. Box 239, Kenilworth, 07033 ... (908) 298-1212
Z I Parts Co., 215 Cristiani St., Cranford, 07016 ... (908) 241-0109

ZaGO Mfg. Co., Inc., 21 E. Runyon St., Newark, 07114 .................................. (973) 643-6700
Zaiya, Inc., 185 Kenneth St., Hackensack, 07601 ........................................ (201) 343-3988
Zala Machine Co., Inc., 109 Stryker Ln., Ste. 11, Hillsborough, 08844 ......... (908) 431-9106
Zaller Studios, Inc., 265 Watsessing Ave., Bloomfield, 07003 ...................... (973) 743-5175
Zaralo, LLC, 1 Cape May St., Harrison, 07029 ............................................... (862) 902-5220
Zaxcom, Inc., 230 West Pkwy., Unit 9, Pompton Plains, 07444 .................... (973) 835-5000
Zeek's Tees, 515 Highway 36, Belford, 07718 ............................................. (732) 291-2700
Zenex Precision Products Corp., 69 George St., Paterson, 07503 ................. (973) 523-6910
Zenith Precision, Inc., 536 Paterson Ave., East Rutherford, 07073 .............. (201) 933-8640
★ Zenith Printing, 7440 Baxter Ave., Merchantville, 08109 ............................ (856) 662-6275
Zenith Ultrasonics, 85 Oak St., P.O. Box 412, Norwood, 07648 ................... (201) 767-1332
Zeregas Sons, Inc., A., 20-01 Broadway, P.O. Box 241, Fair Lawn, 07410 .. (201) 797-1400
Zero Surge, Inc., 889 State Route 12, Ste. 2, Frenchtown, 08825 ................ (908) 996-7700
Zero Tolerance Machine, 1650 Glassboro Rd., Williamstown, 08094 ............ (856) 881-9072
Zeta Products, Inc., 1060 Garden State Rd., Union, 07083 ........................... (908) 688-0440
Zeus Industrial Products, Inc., 134 Chubb Way, Branchburg, 08876 ............ (908) 526-6500
Zeus Scientific, Inc., 200 Evans Way, Somerville, 08876 ............................. (908) 526-3744
★ Ziegler Chemical & Mineral Corp., 600 Prospect Ave., Piscataway, 08854 .. (732) 752-4111
Ziegler Chemical & Mineral Corp.,
    600 Prospect Ave., Bldg. A, Piscataway, 08854 ...................................... (732) 752-4111
Zienowicz Signs, 202 E. Canal St., Trenton, 08609 ..................................... (609) 393-4068
Ziezer Tool Co., Inc., 960 Koehl Ave., Union, 07083 .................................... (908) 686-1332
Zimmer Holdings, Inc. see. ............................... Zimmer Trabecular Metal Technology, Parsippany
Zimmer Holdings, Inc. see. ............................................ Zimmer Tri-State, Inc., Mount Laurel
Zimmer Machinery Systems, 19 Springcroft Rd., Far Hills, 07931 ............... (908) 234-2560
Zimmer Trabecular Metal Technology, 10 Pomerov Rd., Parsippany, 07054 ... (973) 576-0032
Zimmer Tri-State, Inc., 1001 Briggs Rd., Ste. 275, Mount Laurel, 08054 ..... (856) 778-8300
Zina's Salads, Inc., 11 Great Meadow Ln., East Hanover, 07936 ................. (973) 428-0660
Zinicola Baking Co., 127 King St., Nutley, 07110 ......................................... (973) 667-1306
Zin-Tech, 1416 Union Ave., Pennsauken, 08110 .......................................... (856) 661-0900
ZK Software (H Q), 201 Circle Dr. N., Ste. 116, Piscataway, 08854 ............. (732) 412-6007
Zodiac Aerospace Evacuation Systems America see. ....................... Air Cruisers, LLC, Wall Township
Zodiac Aerospace, Inc. see. ..................... Zodiac Arresting Systems America - Logan, Swedesboro
Zodiac Arresting Systems America - Logan,
    2239 High Hill Rd., Swedesboro, 08085 .................................................. (856) 241-8620
Zone Defense, Inc., 4 Emery Ave., Randolph, 07869 ................................... (973) 328-0436
Zone Two, Inc., 245 Hickory Ln., Bayville, 08721 ........................................ (732) 237-0767
Zonefirst see. ........................................................... Trolex Corp., Elmwood Park
† Zucca, Inc., L. J., 760 S. Delsea Dr., P.O. Box 1447, Vineland, 08362 ...... (856) 692-7425
Zumtobel Lighting, Inc., 17-09 Zink Pl., Unit 7, Fair Lawn, 07410 ................ (973) 340-8900
Zvonko Stulic & Son, Inc., 21 Main St., Newark, 07105 ............................... (973) 589-3773
Zydus Pharmaceuticals USA, Inc., 73 Route 31 N., Pennington, 08534 ...... (609) 730-1900
Zymet, Inc., 7 Great Meadow Ln., East Hanover, 07936 .............................. (973) 428-5245
Zytron Control Products, Inc., 20 Lexington Ave., Trenton, 08618 ............... (609) 771-0101

ALPHABETICAL

# Industry Database Subscriptions at EZSelect.com

**EZSelect.com** is online database software offering real-time access to the freshest info! **mni** databases give you the flexibility to find new leads the way **YOU need them!** Select a database and target new customers or suppliers by industry! **For additional industries, call 800-221-2172 or visit EZSelect.com.**

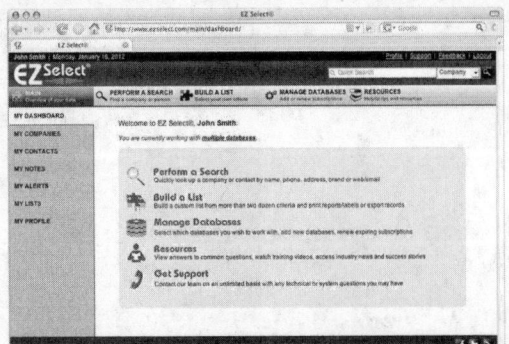

Learn how an EZSelect.com subscription to our industrial information databases can empower you today!

| SIC | Industry Description | EZSelect.com Full Subscription | EZSelect.com 20+ Emp. Subscription | EZSelect.com Basic Subscription |
|-----|---------------------|-------------------------------|-----------------------------------|-------------------------------|
| | **NATIONAL DATABASES BY INDUSTRY @ EZSelect.com subscription\*** | | | |
| 20 | **Food and Kindred Products** | $1,340 | $856 | $469 |
| 27 | **Printing and Publishing** | $2,080 | $845 | $728 |
| 28 | **Chemicals & Allied Products** | $1,048 | $676 | $367 |
| 30 | **Rubber & Misc. Plastic Products** | $1,054 | $749 | $369 |
| 34 | **Fabricated Metal Products** | $1,946 | $1,080 | $681 |
| 35 | **Industrial & Comm. Machinery & Computer Equipment** | $2,457 | $1,178 | $860 |
| 36 | **Electronic & Other Electric Equip.** | $1,079 | $734 | $378 |
| 50 | **Wholesale Trade (durable)** | $2,152 | $1,040 | $753 |
| 51 | **Wholesale Trade (non-durable)** | $956 | $614 | $335 |
| 73 | **Software Systems & Design** | $494 | $369 | $173 |

Visit **EZSelect.com** for these and other U.S. industrial databases

**mni** **Manufacturers' News, Inc.**
Directories & Databases since 1912

1633 Central St., Evanston, IL 60201 • 888-752-5200

# GEOGRAPHICAL SECTION

This section provides full profiles for the state's manufacturers, processors, wholesalers and distributors. The section is organized in alphabetical order by cities within the state. Company profiles are arranged in alphabetical order by company name. If a company did not provide an annual sales figure, some company sales figures have been estimated based upon U.S. Dept. of Commerce data of sales per employee by Standard Industrial Classifications. Beneath each city is the county where it is located, a map reference and city population from recent census data.
**NEW ENTRY** above a profile indicates a company not previously listed. A † indicates a wholesaler / distributor company.

## Aberdeen

(Monmouth—N.E.)

**ADVANCED MOLDING CONCEPTS**

329 Wilson Ave. (07747)
**Phone—(732) 390-8366**
Email—mikegamc@aol.com
Owner—Mike Guglielmo
SIC—3543; 3599; 3544; 3089; NAICS—333514; *Custom prototypes & precision machining of medical instruments, including thermoform packaging & text fixtures*
Employs—6; Estab.—1988
Sales—under $500,000
Distrib.—National
Privately owned corporation

**PARWAN ELECTRONICS CORP.**

1230 State Route 34 (07747-1152)
**Phone—(732) 290-1900**
Fax—(732) 566-8771
www.voicesaver.com
Email—info@voicesaver.com
Pres.—Suraj Tschand
Ex. V.-P.—Ajay P. Tschand
SIC—3661; 3669; *Telecom systems, including calling cards, patient reminders, autodialing, call routing & messaging & pinless, notification & smartphone app infrastructure; Brand name—VoiceSaver; CardSaver; DialSaver; Insight IVR; CallAhead; DialBlaster; USANotify*
Employs—25; Estab.—1984
6,000 sq ft site, Distrib.—Intl.
Privately owned corporation
AKA: PEC

## Absecon

(Atlantic—S.E.)

**A3 TECHNOLOGY, INC.**

311 S. New York Rd., Redding Office Pk., Ste. 36 (08205)
**Phone—(609) 652-7933**
Fax—(609) 652-9989
www.a3technologyinc.com
Email—karen@a3technologyinc.com
Pres., CEO—Karen Vargas
SIC—7372; 7373; NAICS—541512; *Computer software development & integrated systems*
Employs—90; Estab.—2001
Sales—$10Mil-$25Mil
Distrib.—Regional
Privately owned corporation

**ARC REPROGRAPHICS, INC.**

1110 New Rd. (08201)
**Phone—(609) 646-9324**
Fax—(609) 272-0583
www.arcrepro.com
Email—mail@arcrepro.com
Pres.—John Curry
GM—Kevin Curry
Prodn. Mgr.—Stuart Smith
SIC—2752; 2791; NAICS—323122; *Blueprinting & typesetting*
Employs—7; Estab.—1985
Sales—$500,000-$1Mil
5,000 sq ft site, Distrib.—Local
Privately owned corporation

**†FASTENAL CO.**

1115 N. New Rd. (08201)
**Phone—(609) 813-2356**
Fax—(609) 813-2356
www.fastenal.com
Email—njata@stores.fastenal.com
GM—Wayne Winn
Sales Mgr.—James Hunter
SIC—5072; 5084; 5085; *Wholesaler of fasteners, safety equipment, tools & abrasives*
Employs—3; Estab.—2003
Distrib.—Local
Publicly owned corporation
Parent co.—Fastenal Co., Winona, MN
　Phone—(507) 454-5374
　See Parent Co. Section for full profile.

**†KLINGES, INC., CHARLES A.**

790 S. Mill Rd. (08201)
**Phone—(609) 641-7755**
Fax—(609) 645-9271
www.mohawktile.com
Email—bobklinges@msn.com
Co-Pres.—Bob Klinges, Sr.
Co-Pres.—Michael Klinges
Br. Mgr.—John Pronzati
SIC—5032; *Distributor of ceramic, granite & marble tile*
Employs—3; Estab.—1958
Sales—under $500,000
60,000 sq ft site, Distrib.—National
Privately owned sub-S corp.
DBA: Mohawk Tile & Marble Distributors
Parent co.—Klinges, Inc., Charles A., King Of Prussia, PA
　Phone—(610) 279-2700
　See Parent Co. Section for full profile.

**OLE HANSEN & SONS, INC.**

Div. of Ole Hansen & Son, Inc.
100 Old Port Republic Rd. (08205)
**Phone—(609) 652-5666**
Fax—(609) 652-5885
www.olehansen.com
Email—dgoddard@olehansen.com
Supervisor—Chris Patterson
Weighmaster—Sherri Lentz
SIC—1442; *Sand & gravel mining*
Employs—4
Distrib.—Local
Privately owned corporation
Parent co.—Ole Hansen & Son, Inc., Cologne, NJ
　Phone—(609) 965-3700
　See Parent Co. Section for full profile.

**PRICE MILLWORK**

305 Dennis Dr. (08201)
**Phone—(609) 652-0123**
Fax—(609) 652-0768
www.pricemillwork.com
Owner—Gary Price
SIC—2431; NAICS—321900; *Millwork*
Employs—1; Estab.—1983
Sales—under $500,000
1,100 sq ft site, Distrib.—National
Sole ownership

**TRIPICIAN MACAROONS**

640 White Horse Pike (08201)
**Phone—(609) 645-1546**
National—(800) 645-4815
Fax—(609) 645-7567
www.tripicians.com
Email—info@boardwalkmacaroons.com
Ptnr.—Mark Sabino
Ptnr.—Cindy Sabino
SIC—2052; *Macaroons*
Employs—6; Estab.—1910
Sales—under $500,000
Distrib.—National
Privately owned corporation

## Allamuchy

(Warren—N.W.)

**†T & T MARKETING, INC.**

P.O. Box 120 (07820)
**Phone—(973) 426-0453**
　　(800) 608-1577
Fax—(973) 426-0457
www.ttmarketinginc.com
Email—info@ttmarketinginc.com
Pres., CEO—Tom Jordan
Dir., Admn. & Fin.—John Reills
Fin. Mgr.—Anne Dolce
Sales & Mktg. Admn.—Jessica Hoogendoorn
SIC—5162; *Distributor of PVC, TPE, TPU, FEP, TPV, polyolefin & nylon compounds for wire & cable industry; Brand name— Axiall; Firestone-Textiles; ExxonMobil Chemical; Modern Dispersions; Borealis; UNIGEL; HUNTSMAN; AGC Chemicals; UNITAPE*
Employs—23; Estab.—1988
Distrib.—Intl.
Privately owned corporation

## Allendale

(Bergen—N.E.)

**BLACK MILLWORK & CENTER LUMBER CO.**

220 W. Crescent Ave. (07401)
**Phone—(201) 934-0100**
Fax—(201) 934-1080
www.blackmillwork.com
Pres.—Michael Rottenberg
Cont.—Manny Rottenberg
Sales Rep.—Patty Straub
SIC—2431; NAICS—321900; *Millwork*
Employs—10; Estab.—1922
20,000 sq ft site, Distrib.—National
Sole ownership

**DATAPROBE, INC.**

1-B Pearl Ct. (07401)
**Phone—(201) 934-9944**
National—(800) 436-3284
Fax—(201) 934-9090
www.dataprobe.com
Email—sales@dataprobe.com
Pres.—David Weiss
CTO—Jeff Schaefer
V.-P., Sales—George Foote
V.-P., Opers.—James Kalmynios
Dir., Engrg.—Charles Palanzo
Accts. Payable Mgr.—Latresha Jackson
SIC—3625; 3679; *Electronic equipment, including remote power controls & A/B switches & remote site management services*
Employs—15; Estab.—1969
20,000 sq ft site, Distrib.—Intl.
Privately owned corporation

**FUJIFILM HUNT CHEMICALS U.S.A., INC. (H Q)**

40 Boroline Rd. (07401)
**Phone—(201) 995-2200**
National—(877) 385-4486
Fax—(201) 995-2457
www.fujihuntusa.com
Email—contacthunt@fujifilm.com
Pres.—Toshiki Taguchi
Pres. & COO, Smart Surfaces—Steven Escaravage
Sr. V.-P.—Timothy Kearney
V.-P. & GM, Fine Chemicals—Michael Murray
V.-P., Hum. Res.—Vincent Briganti
V.-P., Bus. Dev. & GM—R. Scott Clouston
Hum. Res. Mgr.—Valerie Usher
SIC—2869; 2899; *Corporate headquarters; specialty chemicals for the photographic, graphic arts & specialty chemical industries*
Employs—50
Sales—$97Mil
Distrib.—Intl.
Privately owned corporation
ISO rating—9001

**HENSCHEL-STEINAU, INC.**

50 Commerce Dr. (07401)
**Phone—(201) 760-4100**
National—(800) 526-0133
Fax—(201) 760-4158
www.hspop.com
Pres.—Gary Forman
CFO—Paul Kapoian
Ex. V.-P.—Mike Luberto
V.-P., Prod.—Matthew Carey
Dir., MIS—Adam Rass
Special Qual. Coord.—Bryan Sachs
SIC—2541; *Point-of-purchase displays*
Employs—40; Estab.—1959
Sales—over $20Mil
Distrib.—Intl.
Privately owned corporation

**LEISTRITZ CORP.**

165 Chestnut St. (07401)
**Phone—(201) 934-8262**
Fax—(201) 934-8266
www.leistritzcorp.com/pumps
Email—staff@leistritzcorp.com
Pres.—Sven Olson
Sales Mgr.—Jeffrey DeVaul
Off. Mgr.—Dolores Sydoruk
SIC—3561; NAICS—333911; *Industrial pumps*
Employs—18; Estab.—1905
12,000 sq ft site, Distrib.—Intl.
Privately owned corporation

**LONZA, INC.**

90 Boroline Rd. (07401-1629)
**Phone—(201) 316-9200**
National—(800) 777-1875
Fax—(201) 785-9973
www.lonza.com
Email—contact.allendale@lonza.com
Pres.—Jeanne Thoma

GEOGRAPHICAL

## Allendale—(cont.)

Gen. Counsel—Scott Waldman
Cont.—Andy Hoy
Pur. Mgr.—Robert Williams
Hum. Res. Mgr.—Terry Krezmer
Mktg. Comms. Mgr., Global—
   Donna Weinstock
SIC—2819; *Corporate
   headquarters & industrial
   chemicals; Brand name—
   Acrawax; Bardac; Carboshield;
   Carnipure; Dantabrom; Fiberaid;
   Geogard; Glyco; Glycolube;
   Glydant Plus; Laracare; L-
   Carnipure; L-Carnitine;
   Lonzaserve; Meta; Natrulon*
Employs—161; Estab.—1958
Sales—$300Mil-$400Mil
Distrib.—Intl.
Publicly owned corporation
ISO rating—9001:2000

### PROGENITOR CELL THERAPY, LLC

Div. of NeoStem, Inc.
4 Pearl Ct., Ste. C (07401)
**Phone—(201) 883-5300**
Fax—(201) 883-1406
www.pctcelltherapy.com
Email—bdm@pctcelltherapy.com
Pres.—Robert Preti
COO—Jeff Liter
V-P., Bus. Dev.—George
   Goldberger
SIC—2836; *Contract
   manufacturing of cell & tissue-
   based therapeutics for the
   biopharmaceutical industry*
Employs—60; Estab.—1997
30,000 sq ft site, Distrib.—National
Parent co.—NeoStem, Inc., New
   York, NY
   Phone—(212) 584-4180
   See Parent Co. Section for full profile.

### PROMOTION IN MOTION COS., INC., THE (H Q)

25 Commerce Dr. (07401)
**Phone—(201) 784-5800**
National—(800) 369-7391
Fax—(201) 784-1010
www.promotioninmotion.com
Email—mail@
   promotioninmotion.com
Pres., CEO—Michael Rosenberg
COO—Basant Dwivedi
CFO—Robert Purcell
Ex. V-P., Sales—Jeff Brown
V-P., Mktg.—Josh Shapiro
Dir., IT—Robert Lascar
SIC—2064; 2066; NAICS—
   311300; *Corporate headquarters;
   candy & fruit rolls & snacks;
   Brand name—Sun-Maid®;
   Welch's®; Fisher®; Sour Jacks®;
   Nuclear Sqworms™; Bake
   Shoppe Chocolate Chip Cookie
   Dough Miniatures™; Buddy
   Bears®; Original Gummy
   Factory®; Tuxedos®; TOGGI®;
   Juicefuls®*
Employs—40; Estab.—1980
Sales—$10Mil-$25Mil (est)
Distrib.—Intl.
Sole ownership

### SECURE TECHNOLOGY INTEGRATION GROUP, LTD.

15 Schneider Rd. (07401)
**Phone—(201) 825-1255**
Fax—(888) 881-6661
www.stig.net
Email—sales@stig.net
Pres.—Richard Shinnick
IT Mgr.—Jon Kobrick
SIC—7373; *Computer network
   system integration, including
   LANs & WANs*
Employs—19; Estab.—1999
2,000 sq ft site, Distrib.—Intl.
Privately owned corporation
AKA: STIGroup

### STRYKER CORP.

Div. of Stryker Corporation
2 Pearl Ct. (07401)
Mail addr: 59 Route 17 S.,
   Allendale (07401)
**Phone—(201) 760-8000**
National—(866) 457-7463
Fax—(201) 962-4108
www.stryker.com
Email—info@stryker.com
IT Mgr.—James Anastasio
Hum. Res. Mgr.—Nicole Maceri
SIC—2599; 3842; *Orthopaedic
   beds for spinal cord patients*
Employs—180; Estab.—2003
Sales—over $1Bil
Distrib.—Intl.
Publicly owned corporation
AKA: Stryker Spine
Parent co.—Stryker Corporation,
   Portage, MI
   Phone—(269) 385-2600
   See Parent Co. Section for full profile.

---

## Allentown

(Monmouth—N.E.)

### ACCURATE MACHINE, LLC.

27 Arneytown Chesterfield Rd.
   (08501)
**Phone—(609) 758-1381**
Fax—(609) 758-7098
Email—accuratemac10709@
   msn.com
Pres.—Tony Scharko
SIC—3599; *Machined parts, low
   to high volume, prototype &
   production runs*
Employs—5; Estab.—1997
2,500 sq ft site, Distrib.—Local
Limited Liability Company

### ALLENTOWN, INC.

165 Route 526 (08501)
**Phone—(609) 259-7951**
National—(800) 762-2243
Fax—(609) 259-0449
www.allentowninc.com
Email—vpombo@allentowninc.com
CEO—Michael Coiro, Sr.
Pres.—John Coiro
V-P., Sales & Mktg.—Vince Pombo
Dir., Sales Opers.—Lori Sue
   Mount
Dir., Mktg. & Intl. Distributors—
   Kevin Johnson
Dir., Engrg.—Paul O'Dwyer
Dir., Fin.—Andrew Faras, Jr.
Dir., Air Flow Tech.—Brian M.
   Bilecki
Hum. Res. Mgr.—Mary Taylor
SIC—3496; *Stainless steel wire
   caging equipment*
Employs—250; Estab.—1967
300,000 sq ft site, Distrib.—Intl.

### †KUBE-PAK CORP.

194 Route 526 *(08501)*
**Phone—(609) 259-3114**
Fax—(609) 259-0487
www.kubepak.com
Email—sales@kubepak.com
Pres.—William Swanekamp
V-P.—John Swanekamp
V-P.—Rob Swanekamp
Cont.—Darren Forry
SIC—5193; *Wholesaler of
   greenhouse plants, including
   grown plugs & rooted cuttings*
Employs—110; Estab.—1957
840,000 sq ft site, Distrib.—
   National
Privately owned sub-S corp.

### LOG POWER, INC.

646 Route 524, P.O. Box 597
   (08501)
**Phone—(609) 259-9709**
National—(800) 454-5647
www.logpower.com
Pres.—Robert Hooper

V-P.—Meriam Hooper
SIC—2426; *Hardwood floors,
   including long & wide plank &
   exotic wood flooring*
Employs—15; Estab.—1979
35,000 sq ft site, Distrib.—National
Privately owned corporation

### MICRO-AIR, INC.

124 Route 526 (08501)
**Phone—(609) 259-2636**
Fax—(609) 259-6601
www.microair.net
Email—anna@microair.net
Pres.—Andrew Spaziani
V-P.—Elizabeth J. Spaziani
GM—Russ Buzinski
Pur. Mgr.—Anna Vance
SIC—3585; 3564; 3822; NAICS—
   334513; *Electronic controls &
   environmental control systems
   for heating, A/C, marine & home
   applications & truck stops;
   Brand name—FX-1 Controllers;
   F-X2 Controllers*
Employs—20; Estab.—1988
10,000 sq ft site, Distrib.—Intl.
Privately owned sub-S corp.
ISO rating—9001

### NOTIE CORP.

177-A Route 526 (08501)
**Phone—(609) 259-3477**
Fax—(609) 259-1921
www.notiecorp.com
Email—mike@notiecorp.com
Plt. Mgr.—Mike Weatherholtz
SIC—2448; NAICS—321920;
   *Wooden pallets*
Employs—5; Estab.—1979
35,000 sq ft site, Distrib.—
   Regional
Privately owned corporation

### PRECAST SYSTEMS, INC.

57 Sharon Station Rd. (08501)
**Phone—(609) 208-1987**
Fax—(609) 208-1966
www.precastinc.com
Plt. Mgr.—Phil Potter
Admn. Mgr.—Barbara Post
Plt. Engr.—Rob Demayo
SIC—3272; *Precast concrete
   products*
Employs—25; Estab.—1981
Sales—$2.5Mil-$5Mil
Distrib.—Regional
Privately owned corporation

### RIEPHOFF SAWMILL, INC.

763 Route 524 *(08501)*
**Phone—(609) 259-7265**
Fax—(609) 259-7267
www.riephoffsawmill.com
Email—john@riephoffsawmill.com
Pres.—John Falconio
Bookkeeper—Linda Watson
SIC—2421; 2499; *Lumber
   processing & crane mats,
   dunnage, shoring, trailer decking
   & tree stakes*
Employs—20; Estab.—1965
Sales—$1Mil-$5Mil
11,750 sq ft site, Distrib.—Regional
Sole ownership

### ROBDAV DISTRIBUTORS, INC.

1251 Yardville Allentown Rd.
   (08501)
**Phone—(609) 259-6335**
Fax—(609) 259-0524
www.theporkrollstore.com
Pres.—Robby Goldstein
Plt. Mgr.—David Battisti
SIC—2011; NAICS—311611; *Beef
   & pork processing*
Employs—10; Estab.—1985
Sales—$500,000-$1Mil
Distrib.—National
Privately owned corporation
AKA: The Pork Roll Store

## Allenwood

(Monmouth—N.E.)

### AIRBRUSH ACTION, INC.

3209 Atlantic Ave., P.O. Box 438
   (08720)
**Phone—(732) 223-7878**
Fax—(732) 223-2855
www.airbrushaction.com
Email—info@airbrushaction.com
Pres.—Cliff Stieglitz
Circ. Mgr.—Jaclyn Cassrey
Sales Rep.—Louis Cunha
SIC—2721; *Magazine publishing*
Employs—10; Estab.—1987
Sales—$500,000-$1Mil
Distrib.—Intl.
Privately owned corporation

### ARCHIVE PRINT, INC.

3203 Atlantic Ave. (08720)
**Phone—(732) 528-5300**
www.archiveprint.com
Email—info@archiveprint.com
Pres.—David Thiel
SIC—2759; *Fine art digital giclee
   printing*
Employs—1; Estab.—2001
Sales—under $500,000
600 sq ft site, Distrib.—Local
Privately owned corporation

### HEALTH RESOURCES PUBLISHING LLC

P.O. Box 456 (08720)
**Phone—(732) 292-1100**
National—(800) 516-4343
Fax—(732) 292-1111
www.healthresourcesonline.com
Email—info@
   healthresourcesonline.com
CEO—Robert Jenkins
Publisher—Robert Jenkins, Sr.
SIC—2731; 2721; 2741;
   *Management news & reference
   information, database, book,
   guide, manual, special report &
   custom research project
   publishing for health, workplace
   wellness & managed care
   executives & professionals;
   Brand name—Health Resources
   Online; Managed Care
   Information Center; Wellness
   Management Information Center;
   Health Grants Information Center*
Employs—5; Estab.—1978
Sales—under $500,000
Distrib.—Intl.
Limited Liability Company

### SEALED UNIT PARTS CO., INC.

2230 Landmark Pl., P.O. Box 21
   (08720)
**Phone—(732) 223-6644**
National—(800) 458-2818
Fax—(732) 223-1617
www.supco.com
Email—info@supco.com
Pres., CEO—Christopher
   Mancuso
Ex. V-P.—Anthony Mancuso
V-P., Sales & Mktg.—James Adcox
IT Mgr.—Jim Yhnell
Hum. Res. Mgr.—Michael Howard
SIC—3585; *Air conditioning &
   refrigeration parts*
Employs—95; Estab.—1945
100,000 sq ft site, Distrib.—Intl.
Privately owned corporation
AKA: Supco

## Alpha

(Warren—N.W.)

### ALPHA LEHIGH TOOL & MACHINE CO., INC.

41 Industrial Rd. (08865)
**Phone—(908) 454-6481**
Fax—(908) 454-0567

## Alpha—(cont.)

www.alphalehigh.com
Email—sales@alphalehigh.com
Pres.—William S. Green
SIC—3599; *Precision machining job shop*
Employs—42; Estab.—1956
Sales—$5Mil-$10Mil (est)
Distrib.—National
Privately owned corporation

**GLEN MAGNETICS, INC.**
1165 3rd Ave. (08865)
**Phone—(908) 454-3717**
Fax—(908) 454-2702
www.glenmagnetics.com
Email—gmiinfo@ glenmagnetics.com
Pres.—John DiSarro
Ex. V.-P., Sales—W. Cabot Thomas
Dir., IT—Patrick DiSarro
Plt. Mgr.—Robert Badway
SIC—3612; NAICS—335311; *Electric transformers*
Employs—35; Estab.—1973
32,000 sq ft site, Distrib.—National
Privately owned corporation

**HUNTERDON TRANSFORMER CO.**
75 Industrial Rd. (08865-4080)
**Phone—(908) 454-2400**
Fax—(908) 454-6266
www.hunterdontransformer.com
Email—sales@ hunterdontransformer.com
Pres.—Mark Brock
V.-P., Treas.—Peter Droelle
V.-P., Sales & Mktg.—Carol Liotta
V.-P., Engrg. & Sales—Richard McCabe
Hum. Res. Mgr.—Theresa Mack
SIC—3677; NAICS—334416; *Company headquarters & transformers, inductors & reactors*
Employs—100; Estab.—1957
Sales—$10Mil-$15Mil
45,000 sq ft site, Distrib.—Local
Privately owned sub-S corp.
ISO rating—9001:2008

**LINDE ELECTRONICS & SPECIALTY GASES**
80 Industrial Dr. (08865)
**Phone—(908) 454-7455**
National—(800) 932-0624
Fax—(908) 454-7784
www.linde.com
Email—linde@linde.com
Plt. Mgr.—Steve Earl
SIC—2813; NAICS—325120; *Industrial & environmental gases*
Employs—100; Estab.—1999
Sales—$10Mil-$25Mil
40,000 sq ft site, Distrib.—Local
Privately owned corporation

**NIGHT CANYON, INC., THE**
1475 Park Ave. (08865)
**Phone—(908) 454-6344**
Fax—(908) 454-6373
Email—mikea@bigskyindustries.net
Pres.—Mark Smith
Sales & Mktg. Mgr.—Chrysa Smith
SIC—3861; 3646; NAICS— 335122; *Movie theatre projectors, speakers, consoles & lighting*
Employs—20; Estab.—1997
Sales—$5Mil-$10Mil (est)
Distrib.—Intl.
Privately owned corporation

**POWER POOL PLUS, INC.**
7 Edge Rd. (08865)
**Phone—(908) 454-1124**
Fax—(908) 454-1125
www.powerpoolplus.com
Email—info@powerpoolplus.com
V.-P., GM—Brent Kephart
Mktg. Mgr.—Ted Shelson

SIC—3621; 5084; NAICS— 335312; *Manufacturer & distributor of power generators & service for the refrigerated transportation industry; Brand name—Power Pool Plus PortaPack; Power Pool Plus Power Pack; Cummins; ESL; Marathon; Wacker*
Employs—18; Estab.—1990
Sales—$1Mil-$2.5Mil
10,000 sq ft site, Distrib.—Intl.
Sole ownership

**SHERIDAN COMMUNICATION, INC.**
1425 3rd Ave. (08865)
**Phone—(908) 454-0700**
Fax—(908) 454-2554
www.sheridanprinting.com
Email—copyrightform@ sheridanprinting.com
CEO—James Sheridan
Pres.—Wayne Pesaresi
SIC—2752; 2759; 2791; NAICS— 323122; *Offset & 4-color printing & electonic prepress*
Employs—50; Estab.—1956
Sales—$5Mil-$10Mil (est)
Distrib.—Regional
Privately owned corporation

**TORELCO, INC.**
Div. of Hunterdon Transformer Co.
55 Industrial Dr. (08865)
**Phone—(908) 387-0814**
National—(800) 867-3526
Fax—(908) 387-0817
www.torelco.com
Email—info@torelco.com
Pres.—Matt Peterson
GM—Frank Tamn
Off. Mgr.—Florence Lee
SIC—3677; NAICS—334416; *Transformers, inductors & reactors*
Employs—15; Estab.—1962
5,000 sq ft site, Distrib.—Intl.
Sole ownership
Parent co.—Hunterdon Transformer Co., Alpha, NJ
Phone—(908) 454-2400
See Parent Co. Section for full profile.

## Andover
(Sussex—N.W.)

**ADVANTAGE EDM**
38 Main St., Route 206 *(07821)*
**Phone—(973) 786-0177**
Fax—(973) 786-0277
www.advantageedm.com
Email—info@advantageedm.com
Pres.—Alex Gilsenan
SIC—3599; *Electrical discharge machining job shop*
Employs—20; Estab.—1997
Sales—$2.5Mil-$5Mil
10,000 sq ft site, Distrib.—National
Privately owned corporation

**AFTON PUBLISHING, LLC**
P.O. Box 1399 (07821)
**Phone—(973) 579-2442**
Fax—(973) 579-2842
www.aftonpublishing.com
Email—info@aftonpublishing.com
Ptnr. & Pres.—Patricia J. Cunningham
Ptnr.—John Cunningham
SIC—2791; NAICS—323122; *Electronic prepress*
Employs—2; Estab.—1973
Distrib.—Regional
Privately owned corporation

**AIRSIDE, INC.**
246 Brighton Rd. (07821)
**Phone—(973) 786-6967**
Fax—(973) 579-6949
Email—airside@airside.org
Pres.—Mario Cavellone

SIC—3444; *Sheet metal fabrication & HVAC ducts*
Employs—10; Estab.—2004
Sales—under $500,000
Distrib.—Local
Privately owned corporation

**BARRIER ENTERPRISES, INC.**
175 Stanhope Sparta Rd. (07821)
**Phone—(973) 770-3983**
Fax—(973) 770-2829
CEO—Thomas Stiffen
Foreman—Jerry Lawler
SIC—3713; NAICS—336211; *Rebuilt truck & bus bodies*
Employs—4; Estab.—1992
Sales—$500,000-$1Mil
Distrib.—Regional
Privately owned corporation

**CARTRIDGE ACTUATED DEVICES, INC.**
40 Old Indian Spring Rd. (07821)
**Phone—(973) 347-2281**
Fax—(973) 347-3956
www.cartactdev.com
Email—info@cartactdev.com
V.-P.—Ed Soohoo
Off. Mgr.—Karen Dooney
SIC—2892; NAICS—325920; *Pyrotechnic devices*
Employs—30; Estab.—1968
Sales—$1Mil-$2.5Mil
Distrib.—Intl.
Privately owned corporation
Parent co.—Cartridge Actuated Devices, Inc., Fairfield, NJ
Phone—(973) 575-1312
See Parent Co. Section for full profile.

**JA-BAR SILICONE CORP.**
252 Brighton Rd., P.O. Box 1249 *(07821)*
**Phone—(973) 786-5000**
Fax—(973) 786-5546
www.ja-bar.com
Email—info@ja-bar.com
Pres.—Gilbert Jacobs
V.-P., Div. Mgr.—Robert Lisofski
V.-P. & Div. Mgr., EMI—Mark A. Derr
Matls. & Pur. Mgr.—Cookie Stephens
Cust. Serv. Mgr.—Maria Cruz
Sales Engr.—Al Piccotti
Sales Engr.—Rich Latham
SIC—2822; 3053; 2891; NAICS— 325212; *Silicone rubber sheets, molded seals, gaskets, extrusions, EMI & RFI shielding materials, windows, o-rings & adhesives*
Employs—78; Estab.—1965
Sales—$16Mil
32,000 sq ft site, Distrib.—Intl.
Sole ownership
ISO rating—9001:2008

**JOSTENS, INC.**
86 Roseville Rd. (07821)
**Phone—(973) 584-5843**
Fax—(973) 347-5893
www.jostens.com
Email—service@jostens.com
GM—Lou Esposito
SIC—2721; *Periodical publishing*
Employs—6; Estab.—1989
Sales—under $500,000
Distrib.—Local
Privately owned corporation
Parent co.—Jostens, Inc., Minneapolis, MN
Phone—(952) 830-3300
See Parent Co. Section for full profile.

**†MID COUNTY PAPER STOCK, INC.**
235 Brighton Rd., P.O. Box 624 (07821)
**Phone—(973) 786-7499**
Email—midcountypaper@ yahoo.com
Pres.—James Koukoulas

SIC—5093; *Wholesaler of recycled paper*
Employs—10
Distrib.—Local
Privately owned corporation

**NVE, INC.**
15 Whitehall Rd. (07821)
**Phone—(973) 786-7868**
National—(800) 543-5463
Fax—(973) 786-7730
www.stacker2.com
Email—sales@nveusa.com
Pres.—Robert Occhifinto
Sales & Mktg. Mgr.—Karen Finocchio
IT Mgr.—Philip Yang
SIC—2833; NAICS—325411; *Herbal supplements*
Employs—75; Estab.—1997
Distrib.—Intl.
Privately owned corporation

**SIGNART GRAPHIX**
177 Stanhope Sparta Rd. (07821)
**Phone—(973) 770-4500**
Fax—(973) 770-4474
www.signartnj.com
Email—sales@signartnj.com
Pres.—Diane Lounsbery
Sales Exec.—Michael Castoro
SIC—3993; *Interior & exterior signs*
Employs—11; Estab.—2011
Sales—$1Mil-$2Mil
18,000 sq ft site, Distrib.— Regional
Limited Liability Company

**SUTHERLAND PACKAGING, INC.**
254 Brighton Ave., P.O. Box 1429 (07821)
**Phone—(973) 786-5141**
Fax—(973) 786-6030
www.sudsbox.com
Email—info@sudsbox.com
Pres.—Thomas W. Sutherland
V.-P., Mfg.—Bob Roberts
V.-P., Opers.—Doug DeMarco
V.-P.—Daniel Sutherland
Sales Mgr.—Eric Stanton
SIC—2653; NAICS—322211; *Corrugated boxes & displays*
Employs—65; Estab.—1964
Sales—$10Mil-$20Mil
Distrib.—National
Privately owned sub-S corp.

**WP DUCTS**
219 U.S. Highway 206, P.O. Box 547 (07821)
**Phone—(973) 786-7179**
Fax—(973) 786-7079
Pres.—William Pierce, Jr.
SIC—3444; *Ductwork*
Employs—2; Estab.—1999
Sales—under $500,000
Distrib.—Regional
Privately owned corporation

## Annandale
(Hunterdon—N.W.)

**BADGE COMPANY OF NEW JERSEY**
223 Hamden Rd., P.O. Box 100 (08801)
**Phone—(908) 735-7700**
National—(800) 469-9333
Fax—(908) 735-2355
www.njbadges.com
Email—info@njbadges.com
GM—Robert Marlow

GEOGRAPHICAL

## Annandale—(cont.)

SIC—3499; 3089; 3199; 5099;
NAICS—316999; *Manufacturer
& distributor of badges, badge
holders & public safety products;
Brand name—Smith & Warren
Co.; V.H. Blackinton Co.; Strong
Leather Co.; Perfect Fit Wallets;
Fargo ID Co.; Peerless
Handcuffs; Hook-Fast Inc.; Ga-
Rel Co.; Streamlight*
Employs—3; Estab.—1974
Sales—under $1Mil
2,000 sq ft site, Distrib.—National
Limited Liability Company

### BALLANTINE LABORATORIES, INC.

312 Old Allerton Rd. (08801)
**Phone—(908) 713-7742**
Fax—(908) 713-7742
www.ballantinelabs.com
Email—sales@ballantinelabs.com
Pres.—Russell McAdoo
V-P., Opers.—Dean McAdoo
Cont., GM, Sales & Mktg. Mgr.—
Constantin Geangu
SIC—3679; *Electronic test &
measurement equipment*
Employs—6; Estab.—1926
Sales—under $500,000
Distrib.—Intl.
Privately owned corporation

### GAIL'S LETTERING & DESIGN

24 Beaver Ave. (08801)
**Phone—(908) 735-4628**
Fax—(908) 735-4118
Email—travis@blast.net
Pres.—Gail Kugelman
SIC—3993; 2759; NAICS—
323100; *Interior & exterior signs
& truck lettering*
Employs—2; Estab.—1984
Sales—under $500,000
12,000 sq ft site, Distrib.—Local

## Asbury

(Warren—N.W.)

### ALLGRIND PLASTICS, INC.

6 Vliet Farm Rd. (08802)
Mail addr: P.O. Box 363,
Bloomsbury (08804-0363)
**Phone—(908) 479-4400**
Fax—(908) 479-4067
www.allgrind.com
Email—info@allgrind.com
Pres., Fin. & R & D Mgr.—Bill
Willoughby
SIC—3599; 3089; *Custom
grinding, granulating,
pulverizing, sifting & blending &
destructive grinding of non-
hazardous dry new & scrap
materials for the plastics,
chemicals, additives & bulk dry
materials industries*
Employs—13; Estab.—1978
Sales—$1Mil-$2Mil
43,500 sq ft site, Distrib.—Intl.
Privately owned sub-S corp.

### AMEX TOOL CO., INC.

4 Fox Hill Ln. (08802)
**Phone—(908) 735-5176**
Fax—(908) 730-6103
Pres.—Hubert Stria
V-P.—Ron Stria
SIC—3599; *Precision tool & die
job shop*
Employs—10; Estab.—1981
Sales—$500,000-$1Mil
Distrib.—National
Privately owned corporation

### ASBURY GRAPHITE MILLS, INC. (HQ)

405 Old Main St., P.O. Box 144
(08802)
**Phone—(908) 537-2155**
Fax—(908) 537-2908
www.asbury.com

Email—asbury@asbury.com
Chrm.—Marvin Riddle
CEO—Stephen Riddle
Pres.—Carol Kalmar
V-P., Sales—Lew Fish
V-P., Mfg.—Gary Ziegler
V-P., Mktg.—Nicholas Mares
Corp. Qual. Mgr.—Stephen Polgar
MIS Mgr.—Michael G. Ball
Sales & Mktg. Coord.—Dorothy J.
Cole
SIC—3295; 3624; *Corporate
headquarters; graphite*
Employs—30; Estab.—1895
Distrib.—Intl.
Privately owned corporation
ISO rating—9001:2008
AKA: Asbury Carbons

### PACIFIC COAST SYSTEMS, LLC

4 Fox Hill Ln. (08802)
**Phone—(908) 735-9955**
Fax—(908) 730-6103
www.pcs-ied.com
Pres.—James Mork
V-P.—Ron Stria
SIC—3699; *Military simulation &
training equipment*
Employs—5; Estab.—2002
Sales—$500,000-$1Mil
Distrib.—Intl.
Limited Liability Company

---

## Asbury Park

(Monmouth—N.E.)

### CLAYTON PRESS, INC.

P.O. Box 676 (07712)
**Phone—(732) 774-2624**
Fax—(732) 774-2814
Pres.—David Roszel
SIC—2759; NAICS—323100;
*Commercial printing*
Employs—3; Estab.—1900
Sales—under $500,000
Distrib.—Local
Privately owned corporation

### COASTER, THE

1011 Main St. (07712)
**Phone—(732) 775-3010**
Fax—(732) 775-8345
www.thecoaster.net
Email—editor@thecoaster.net
Ptnr. & Editor—Ellen Carroll
Ptnr.—Michael Booth
SIC—2711; *Newspaper
publishing*
Employs—13; Estab.—1983
Distrib.—Local
Privately owned partnership

### DAYTON GREY CORP.

1008 1st Ave. (07712)
**Phone—(732) 869-0060**
Fax—(732) 869-0006
www.daytongrey.com
Email—daytongrey@aol.com
Ptnr.—Hal Levenstein
Ptnr.—Dan France
SIC—3471; 3479; *Metal finishing,
powder coating, plating &
polishing*
Employs—7; Estab.—1998
Sales—$1.5Mil-$2Mil
Distrib.—National
Privately owned corporation

### DE RISI IRON WORKS CO.

910 Asbury Ave. (07712)
**Phone—(732) 774-6570**
Fax—(732) 774-6570
Pres.—Santo De Risi
SIC—3446; NAICS—332323;
*Architectural & ornamental
ironwork*
Employs—2; Estab.—1966
Sales—under $500,000 (est)
Distrib.—Local

### FELDMAN ASSOCS., INC., F. L.

811 Memorial Dr. (07712)
**Phone—(732) 776-8544**
Fax—(732) 774-1468
www.customwoodworking.info
Email—frank@
customwoodworking.info
Pres.—Frank Feldman
SIC—2434; 2511; NAICS—
337110; *Wooden cabinets &
furniture*
Employs—8; Estab.—1980
8,000 sq ft site, Distrib.—Local
Privately owned sub-S corp.

### FLEX CRAFT CO.

814 Asbury Ave. (07712)
**Phone—(732) 502-9500**
Fax—(732) 502-9503
www.flexcraft.com
Email—info@flexcraft.com
Pres.—Russell Smith
Plt. Opers. Mgr.—Wayne Powell
SIC—3089; *Plastic blow molding
& injection molding*
Employs—60; Estab.—1972
30,000 sq ft site, Distrib.—Intl.
Privately owned corporation

### GARDEN STATE DENTAL PROSTHETICS, INC.

805 4th Ave. (07712)
**Phone—(732) 922-6650**
National—(800) 421-7645
Fax—(732) 922-6659
Email—lab7645@aol.com
Pres.—Michael A. Dipersio
SIC—3842; *Full & partial
dentures, night guards &
retainers*
Employs—4; Estab.—1989
Sales—under $500,000
900 sq ft site, Distrib.—Regional
Privately owned corporation
AKA: Garden State Dental Lab

### KEATOR BILT CUSTOM CABINETS

805 2nd Ave. (07712)
**Phone—(732) 776-5133**
Fax—(732) 776-8319
Email—keatorbilt@optonline.net
Owner—Andrew Keator
Proj. Mgr.—Sebastian Sica
SIC—2521; 2511; NAICS—
337211; *Wooden & laminate
cabinets*
Employs—3; Estab.—1982
Sales—under $500,000
Distrib.—Regional
Sole ownership

### KNOCKOUT GRAPHICS, INC.

522 Cookman Ave. (07712)
**Phone—(732) 774-3331**
Fax—(732) 774-8889
www.knockout8.com
Email—info@smithmade.org
Pres.—Margaret Brunett
CFO—Kyle Lepree
Prod. Mgr.—Sue Belford
Graphic Designer—Brian Wrensen
Graphic Designer—Matt Guiea
SIC—2759; NAICS—323100;
*Commercial printing*
Employs—7; Estab.—1990
3,500 sq ft site, Distrib.—Intl.
Privately owned corporation

### LEIBROCK METAL PRODUCTS, INC.

1800 Brielle Ave. (07712)
**Phone—(732) 695-0326**
Fax—(732) 695-1197
Pres., CEO—William Vogel
V-P.—William Vogel, Jr.
SIC—3444; *Sheet metal
fabrication*
Employs—8; Estab.—1979
10,000 sq ft site, Distrib.—
Regional
Privately owned corporation
AKA: Screaming Eagle Metal
Products

### MCLAIN STUDIOS, INC.

1203 Main St. (07712)
**Phone—(732) 775-0271**
Fax—(732) 774-2250
www.mclainstudios.com
Email—jlm@mclainstudios.com
Pres.—Jim McLain
SIC—3993; *Yard, political
campaign, real estate &
commercial signs & vehcile
lettering*
Employs—2; Estab.—1945
Sales—under $500,000
10,000 sq ft site, Distrib.—
Regional
Privately owned sub-S corp.

### MONMOUTH & OCEAN COUNTY AWNING CO.

508 Main St. (07712)
**Phone—(732) 775-4881**
Fax—(732) 775-4881
Owner—Douglas Maxwell
SIC—2394; NAICS—314912;
*Canvas awnings*
Employs—6; Estab.—1942
Sales—under $500,000
Distrib.—Local
Privately owned corporation

### PHILLIPS ENTERPRISES, INC.

3600 Sunset Ave., P.O. Box 2286
(07712)
**Phone—(732) 493-3191**
Fax—(732) 493-3493
www.phillipsentinc.com
Email—info@phillipsentinc.com
Pres.—Joe Phillips
V-P.—Paul Phillips
Plt. Mgr.—Brian Phillips
SIC—3315; 3469; *Wire forming &
metal stampings*
Employs—7; Estab.—1960
Sales—$500,000-$1Mil
Distrib.—National
Privately owned corporation
AKA: Stamping.com

**NEW ENTRY**

### RAGAR CO., INC.

2106 Kings Hwy. (07712)
**Phone—(732) 493-1416**
National—(888) 999-6648
Fax—(732) 493-4476
www.ragar-company.com
Email—sales@ragar-company.com
Pres., CEO—Lisa Raimondo
SIC—2499; 3199; *Wooden &
leather jewelry boxes*
Employs—5; Estab.—1992
Sales—$1Mil-$2.5Mil
20,000 sq ft site, Distrib.—Intl.
Privately owned corporation

### STAMPING.COM, INC.

3600 Sunset Ave. (07712)
**Phone—(732) 493-4697**
Fax—(732) 493-3493
www.stampinginc.com
Email—stamping@juno.com
Owner—Charles Molnar, Jr.
SIC—3469; *Precision metal
stampings*
Employs—3; Estab.—2008
Sales—$1Mil
12,500 sq ft site, Distrib.—Intl.
Privately owned corporation

### TERRISS CONSOLIDATED INDUSTRIES

807 Summerfield Ave., P.O. Box
110 (07712)
**Phone—(732) 988-0909**
National—(800) 342-1611
Fax—(732) 502-0526
www.terriss.com
Email—terriss@terriss.com
V-P.—Edward J. Della Zanna
V-P.—Judith Bodnovich
V-P.—Marc Epstein

## Asbury Park—(cont.)

SIC—3829; 3821; 3589; NAICS—339111; *Eco-friendly scientific instruments & laboratory supplies for product quality testing for the food, beverage, chemical, pharmaceutical, water & wastewater industries*
Employs—15; Estab.—1895
Sales—$1Mil-$5Mil
25,000 sq ft site, Distrib.—Intl.
Privately owned corporation

**UNIVERSAL FILTERS, INC.**

1207 Main St. (07712)
**Phone—(732) 774-8555**
Fax—(732) 774-8594
Email—universalfilters@aol.com
Pres., Fin. & MIS Mgr.—Jerrold D. Kolton
V-P., GM & R & D—S. David Tafara
SIC—3569; *Liquid filter bags*
Employs—15
Distrib.—Intl.

---

## Atco

(Camden—S.W.)

**AMALTHEA CELLARS FARM WINERY**

209 Vineyard Rd. (08004)
**Phone—(856) 768-8585**
www.amaltheacellars.com
Email—winery@amaltheacellars.com
Owner—Louis Caracciolo
SIC—2084; NAICS—312130; *Handcrafted red & white wines*
Employs—2; Estab.—1982
Sales—under $500,000
Distrib.—Regional
Limited Liability Company

**DUFFY PRINTING CO.**

2389 Atco Ave. (08004)
**Phone—(856) 768-1046**
Fax—(856) 768-4742
Pres.—Alan Duffy
SIC—2759; NAICS—323100; *Commercial printing*
Employs—5
Sales—$500,000-$1Mil (est)
Distrib.—Intl.

**PRE-FAB STRUCTURES, INC.**

907 Wedgewood Way (08004)
**Phone—(856) 768-4257**
Fax—(856) 767-9332
www.pre-fabstructures.com
Email—info@pre-fabstructures.com
Pres.—Bill Johnson
Supervisor—Mike Johnson
SIC—3448; NAICS—332311; *Prefabricated aluminum buildings*
Employs—10; Estab.—1983
Sales—$1Mil-$5Mil
8,000 sq ft site, Distrib.—National
Sole ownership

**†WADE ENVIRONMENTAL INDUSTRIES**

382 Jackson Rd. (08004)
**Phone—(856) 767-2760**
Fax—(856) 767-0698
Email—wadeenviro@aol.com
Pres.—Andrew Wade
Off. Mgr.—Gregory Sharp
SIC—5093; *Wholesaler of recycled metal scrap*
Employs—5; Estab.—1940
Sales—under $500,000
Distrib.—Local
Privately owned corporation

## Atlantic City

(Atlantic—S.E.)

**A C DISPLAY STUDIOS, INC.**

2715 Arctic Ave. (08401)
**Phone—(609) 345-0814**
Fax—(609) 345-2715
Off. Mgr.—Jackie Boyd
SIC—3993; *Interior & exterior signs*
Employs—6; Estab.—1980
Sales—under $500,000
Distrib.—Local
Privately owned corporation

**A.C. PRINTED SPORTSWEAR, INC.**

1319 Memorial Ave. (08401)
**Phone—(609) 344-5057**
Fax—(609) 348-4640
www.acprinted.com
Email—john@acprinted.com
Pres.—Edward Dinick Antonia
GM & IT Mgr.—John Hesson
SIC—2396; *T-shirt screen printing*
Employs—2; Estab.—1970
Sales—under $500,000
Distrib.—National
Privately owned corporation

**BUDGET PRINT CENTER**

2510 Atlantic Ave. (08401)
**Phone—(609) 348-4589**
Fax—(609) 348-2778
Ptnr.—Ellen Fishlevich
Ptnr.—Ben Fishlevich
SIC—2752; 2791; NAICS—323122; *Offset printing & computerized typesetting*
Employs—2; Estab.—1977
Sales—under $500,000
Distrib.—Local
Privately owned partnership

**DONSKY DESIGNS**

3851 Boardwalk, Apt. 2405 (08401)
**Phone—(609) 345-4445**
www.daviddonsky.com
Email—david@donskydesigns.com
Owner—David Donsky
SIC—3911; *Custom jewelry, including watches, loose lab graded diamonds, loose color stones & rare gem specimens*
Employs—2; Estab.—2002
Sales—under $500,000
500 sq ft site, Distrib.—Intl.
Limited Liability Company

**FORMICA BROS. BAKERY**

2310 Arctic Ave. (08401)
**Phone—(609) 348-8934**
Fax—(609) 344-2777
www.formicabrosbakery.com
Owner—Frank Formica
Dir., Mktg.—Michelle Giampaolo
Off. Mgr.—Brenda Logpileggi
Asst. Off. Mgr.—John Penman
SIC—2051; 2052; NAICS—311812; *Breads, cookies & cakes*
Employs—35; Estab.—1919
Sales—$1Mil-$2.5Mil
Distrib.—Regional
Privately owned corporation

**GINSBURG BAKERY, INC.**

300 N. Tennessee Ave. (08401)
**Phone—(609) 345-2265**
Fax—(609) 345-2268
www.ginsburgbakery.com
Email—bageldan@ginsburgbakery.com
CEO—John V. Mulloy, Sr.
V-P., Opers.—John Mulloy, Jr.
Hum. Res. Mgr.—Sylvia Delvalle
Plt. Engr.—George Sanderlin

SIC—2051; NAICS—311812; *Fresh & frozen bread, bagels & rolls*
Employs—180; Estab.—1903
70,000 sq ft site, Distrib.—Regional
Privately owned sub-S corp.

**JAMES CANDY COMPANY**

1519 Boardwalk *(08401)*
**Phone—(609) 344-1519**
(800) 441-1404
National—(800) 938-2339
Fax—(609) 344-0246
www.jamescandy.com
Email—sales@jamescandy.com
Pres.—Frank J. Glaser
Ex. V-P., Sales & Mktg. & COO—Lisa Glaser Whitley
CFO—Rose Gedicke
SIC—2064; 2066; 2052; 2051; NAICS—311812; *Salt water taffy, cream mints, macaroons, peanut butter chews, chocolates & fudge; Brand name—James' Candy; Fralinger's Salt Water Taffy and Bayard's Chocolates*
Employs—100; Estab.—1880
Sales—$5Mil-$10Mil
Distrib.—National
Privately owned sub-S corp.
AKA: James Candy Company, Inc.

**NEAC, INC.**

526 Pacific Ave., #2202 (08401)
**Phone—(908) 903-9100**
National—(800) 632-2462
Fax—(888) 360-7606
www.neacinc.com
Email—info@neacinc.com
Pres.—Joel H. Miller
SIC—3499; 3089; 3469; 3599; NAICS—332710; *Contract manufacturing of metal & plastic parts & components, including stamping, die casting, machining, injection molding & assembly; Brand name—Rising*
Employs—5; Estab.—1988
Distrib.—Intl.
Privately owned sub-S corp.

**NORMAN DEE ASSOCIATES**

31 N. Sovereign Ave. (08401)
**Phone—(609) 348-5777**
Email—normandee312@mac.com
Owner—Norman Dee Grossman
SIC—3993; *Interior & exterior signs*
Employs—2; Estab.—1974
Sales—under $500,000
Distrib.—National
Sole ownership

**SEAGULL STAINED GLASS**

1917 Kuehnle Ave. (08401)
**Phone—(609) 345-3126**
Email—nspolitino@comcast.net
Proprietor & Ptnr.—Linda Spolitino
Ptnr.—Nicholas Spolitino
SIC—3231; NAICS—327215; *Sand carved glass*
Employs—2; Estab.—1982
Sales—under $500,000
Distrib.—National
Sole ownership

**STEEL'S FUDGE, INC.**

1928 E. Riverside Dr. (08401)
Mail addr: 2719 Boardwalk, Atlantic City (08401)
**Phone—(609) 345-4051**
Fax—(609) 541-2621
www.steelsfudge.com
Email—info@steelsfudge.com
Opers. Mgr.—Andy Stipa
SIC—2064; NAICS—311300; *Fudge candy*
Employs—40; Estab.—1919
Distrib.—Local
Privately owned corporation

Parent co.—Steel's Fudge, Inc., Atlantic City, NJ
Phone—(609) 345-4051
See Parent Co. Section for full profile.

**STEEL'S FUDGE, INC. (H Q)**

2719 Boardwalk (08401)
**Phone—(609) 345-4051**
National—(888) 783-3571
Fax—(609) 345-1870
www.steelsfudge.com
Email—info@steelsfudge.com
Pres.—George Steel
Manager—Steve Plettner
SIC—2064; NAICS—311300; *Corporate headquarters; fudge & salt water taffy*
Employs—3
Sales—$500,000-$1Mil (est)
Distrib.—National
Privately owned corporation

**TUN TAVERN RESTAURANT & BREWERY**

2 Convention Blvd. (08401)
**Phone—(609) 347-7800**
Fax—(609) 347-2536
www.tuntavern.com
Email—tunbrewmaster@tuntavern.com
Pres.—Montgomery Dahm
SIC—2082; *Beer*
Employs—30; Estab.—1997
Distrib.—Regional
Privately owned corporation

---

## Atlantic Highlands

(Monmouth—N.E.)

**BRICK-WALL CORP.**

25 1st Ave., Ste. 200 (07716)
**Phone—(732) 787-0226**
Pres.—Lawrence Hesse
CFO—Larry Mulcahy
SIC—2951; *Corporate headquarters & asphalt paving compounds*
Employs—29
Sales—$1Mil-$2.5Mil (est)
Privately owned corporation

**DR. HARVEY'S HEALTHY FORMULATIONS INC.**

25 W. Highland Ave. *(07716)*
**Phone—(732) 787-2400**
National—(866) 362-4123
Fax—(732) 787-2445
www.drharveys.com
Email—info@drharveys.com
Owner—Harvey Cohen
SIC—2047; *Health foods for companion pets*
Employs—6; Estab.—2006
Sales—$2.5Mil-$5Mil (est)
Distrib.—National
Privately owned corporation

**GATEWAY PRESS**

984 State Route 36 (07716)
**Phone—(732) 291-1757**
Fax—(732) 291-3203
www.gatewaypressllc.com
Email—info@gatewaypressllc.com
Owner—James Meyer
SIC—2759; 2752; NAICS—323100; *Commercial offset & instant printing*
Employs—3; Estab.—1979
Sales—under $500,000
Distrib.—Regional
Privately owned partnership

**GRAPHIX INTEGRATED, INC.**

971 Leonardville Rd. (07716)
**Phone—(732) 872-8282**
www.graphixgroup.com
Email—ebay_posters@yahoo.com
Prodn. Mgr.—Alex Kreymerman

GEOGRAPHICAL

## Atlantic Highlands— (cont.)

SIC—2759; 3479; NAICS—323100; *Giclee printing, shadow boxes, laser engraving, custom framing & mat cutting*
Employs—4; Estab.—2000
Sales—$1Mil-$2.5Mil
2,000 sq ft site, Distrib.—Intl.
Privately owned corporation

**JERSEY PRINTING ASSOCS., INC.**
153 1st Ave., P.O. Box 355 (07716)
**Phone—(732) 872-9654**
Fax—(732) 872-9309
www.jerseyprinting.com
Email—files2jpa@aol.com
Pres.—Greg Heh
Prod. Mgr.—Robert Bartus
Acct. Exec.—Mike Matulonis
SIC—2759; NAICS—323100; *Commercial printing*
Employs—25; Estab.—1980
12,000 sq ft site, Distrib.—Regional
Privately owned corporation

**MASTER SHIPWRIGHTS, INC.**
25 W. Highland Ave., P.O. Box 273 (07716)
**Phone—(732) 872-7500**
Pres.—Hans MiKaitis
SIC—3732; *Shipbuilding*
Employs—1; Estab.—1967
Sales—under $500,000 (est)
Distrib.—National
Privately owned corporation

**PREMIER GRAPHICS, INC.**
500 Central Ave. (07716)
**Phone—(732) 872-9933**
Fax—(732) 872-9335
www.premiergraphics.com
Email—premiergraphics@yahoo.com
Pres.—Toni Madalone
V-P.—Scott Madalone
Bookkeeper—Lynn Mantz
SIC—2752; 2791; NAICS—323122; *Offset printing & typesetting*
Employs—20; Estab.—2000
Sales—$1Mil-$2.5Mil
25,000 sq ft site, Distrib.—Regional
Privately owned corporation

## Audubon
(Camden—S.W.)

**CORBI PRINTING CO., INC.**
106 W. Atlantic Ave. (08106)
**Phone—(856) 547-2555**
National—(800) 596-2444
Fax—(856) 547-2999
Pres.—Thomas Corbi
Off. Mgr.—Marie Bush
SIC—2759; NAICS—323100; *Commercial printing*
Employs—8; Estab.—1970
Sales—under $500,000
Distrib.—Local
Privately owned corporation

**CROWN CUSTOM CLEANERS**
27 E. Kings Hwy. (08106)
**Phone—(856) 310-0710**
Fax—(856) 310-1009
www.crowncustomcleaners.com
Email—crowncustomcleaner@yahoo.com
Owner—Bruce Yun
IT Mgr. & Design Coord.—Louis Parker
SIC—2391; 2392; *Custom draperies & textile household cushions*
Employs—2
Distrib.—Intl.
Privately owned corporation

**MERCHANT STREET PRINTER, LLC**
107 E. Atlantic Ave. (08106)
**Phone—(856) 547-1991**
National—(800) 669-1991
Fax—(856) 547-4158
www.p-press.net
Email—ppress@comcast.net
Owner—Charlotte Skeggs
SIC—2752; 3993; NAICS—323100; *Offset printing & advertising specialties*
Employs—4; Estab.—1984
Sales—over $500,000
Distrib.—National
Limited Liability Company
AKA: Penny Press

**MODERN METRIC MACHINE**
101 Nicholson Rd. (08106)
**Phone—(856) 547-4044**
Fax—(856) 547-5151
Email—modernmetric@yahoo.com
Owner & Pres.—Paul Volkwine
GM—Michael Volkwine
SIC—3599; *General machining job shop*
Employs—6; Estab.—1972
Sales—$500,000-$1Mil
4,500 sq ft site, Distrib.—Regional
Privately owned corporation

**SOUTH JERSEY GRAPHICS**
203 W. Merchant St. (08106)
**Phone—(856) 546-0464**
Fax—(856) 546-0461
Email—sjgraphics@snip.net
Ptnr.—James Fleming
Ptnr.—John Gricco
Corp. Secy.—Pat Bradley
SIC—2396; *T-shirt screen printing*
Employs—5; Estab.—1980
Sales—under $500,000
Distrib.—Local
Privately owned partnership

## Augusta
(Sussex—N.W.)

**†COOPER ELECTRIC SUPPLY CO.**
17 Route 206 S., Unit 3 (07822)
**Phone—(973) 940-8905**
Fax—(973) 940-8903
www.cooper-electric.com
Email—cooperonline@cooper-electric.com
Manager—Dean Cosentino
SIC—5063; *Distributor of electrical equipment & supplies, including wire & cable*
Employs—4
Distrib.—Local
Privately owned corporation
Parent co.—Cooper Electric Supply Co., Monroe, NJ
Phone—(732) 747-2233
See Parent Co. Section for full profile.

**MOONLIGHT IMAGING, INC.**
5 Plains Rd. (07822)
**Phone—(973) 300-1001**
Fax—(973) 948-7500
www.moonlightimaging.com
Email—dan@moonlightimaging.com
V-P.—Daniel Van Demoere
SIC—2759; *Commercial printing*
Employs—8
Sales—$1Mil-$2.5Mil (est)
3,500 sq ft site, Distrib.—National
Privately owned corporation

## Avenel
(Middlesex—N.E.)

**(MASACO) MICHAEL ANTHONY SIGN & AWNING, INC.**
21 Randolph Ave. (07001)
**Phone—(732) 453-6120**
Fax—(732) 453-6126
www.masign.com
Email—sales@masign.com

Pres.—Michael Bradley
Hum. Res. Mgr.—Melissa Bradley
SIC—3993; 2394; 3444; NAICS—314912; *Electric signs, including storefront signage, in-store & LED displays, fabric awnings, architectural extruded aluminum canopies, sunshade items & louvers; Brand name—Ecoshade; Extrudeck; Imagination; Alumiframe; Vision*
Employs—35; Estab.—1988
Sales—$7.5Mil
44,000 sq ft site, Distrib.—National
Privately owned sub-S corp.
ISO rating—9001
AKAs: MASAco & MASA Architectural Canopies

**8 TO 20 PARTNERS, LLC**
5 Paddock St. (07001)
**Phone—(732) 855-1400**
        (732) 855-2569
Fax—(732) 855-7457
Pres.—Saul Tawil
CFO—Arnold Dunn
Hum. Res. Mgr.—Anthony Montolio
SIC—2369; *Children's clothing*
Employs—150
Sales—$10Mil-$25Mil (est)
Distrib.—Intl.
Limited Liability Company

**AISCO**
Div. of Steelstran Industries, Inc.
35 Mileed Way, P.O. Box 30 (07001)
**Phone—(732) 574-3233**
National—(800) 458-5722
Fax—(732) 574-9191
www.atlantic-group.com
Email—sales@aiscoslings.com
Pres.—Susan Gronbeck
SIC—2241; NAICS—313221; *Lifting & securing webbing products*
Employs—15; Estab.—1977
Distrib.—Intl.
Privately owned corporation
Parent co.—Steelstran Industries, Inc., Avenel, NJ
Phone—(732) 574-0700
See Parent Co. Section for full profile.

**ARCHER DAY**
18 Mileed Way (07001)
**Phone—(732) 417-0333**
Fax—(732) 396-4533
www.archerday.com
Email—sales@archerday.com
Pres.—William DeMott
SIC—3312; *Steel fabrication*
Employs—25; Estab.—1997
Sales—under $500,000
10,000 sq ft site, Distrib.—Regional
Privately owned corporation

**ARTISTIC DOORS & WINDOWS**
10 S. Inman Ave. (07001)
**Phone—(732) 726-9400**
National—(800) 278-3667
Fax—(732) 726-9494
www.artisticdoorsandwindows.com
Email—info@artisticdoorsandwindows.com
Pres.—Enrico Autovino
V-P., Sales—Guy Cichy
V-P.—John Autovino
Administrator—Margaret Karlsberg
SIC—2431; 2499; NAICS—321900; *Custom hardwood doors & windows & high-end fenestration products*
Employs—45; Estab.—1990
Sales—$5Mil-$10Mil
45,000 sq ft site, Distrib.—National
Privately owned corporation

**AVIONIC INSTRUMENTS, LLC**
1414 Randolph Ave., P.O. Box 498 (07001)
**Phone—(732) 388-3500**
Fax—(732) 382-4996
www.avionicinstruments.com
Email—sales@avionicinstruments.com
Opers. Mgr.—Tony Gatta
Fin. Mgr.—Leanne Nielson
Pur. Agt.—Dan Scardelli
SIC—3629; NAICS—335999; *Power conversion products, including static inverters, frequency converters, transformer rectifiers, light dimmers & power supplies for aerospace, commercial & military applications*
Employs—180; Estab.—1971
Distrib.—Intl.
Privately owned corporation

**DL PRINTING CO., INC.**
283 Prospect Ave. (07001)
**Phone—(732) 750-1917**
National—(800) 625-2679
Fax—(732) 750-1400
www.dlprinting.net
Email—dave@dlprinting.net
Pres.—Dave Lospinoso
SIC—2759; NAICS—323100; *Commercial printing*
Employs—5; Estab.—1983
Sales—$500,000-$1Mil
2,500 sq ft site, Distrib.—National
Privately owned corporation

**ESSEX COATINGS, LLC**
135 Essex Ave. E. (07001)
**Phone—(732) 855-9400**
Fax—(732) 855-9460
www.essexcoatings.com
Email—info@essexcoatings.com
Off. Mgr.—Liz Flott
SIC—2499; *Wood composite panel UV coating service*
Employs—10; Estab.—1974
Sales—$1Mil-$2.5Mil (est)
30,000 sq ft site, Distrib.—Intl.
Limited Liability Company

**FLAVORS MATERIALS INTERNATIONAL, INC.**
10-D Englehard Ave. (07001)
**Phone—(732) 499-9700**
Fax—(732) 499-7090
www.flavormaterials.com
Email—info@flavormaterials.com
Pres.—Paul Ahn
Hum. Res. Mgr.—James Gary
Proj. Coord.—Jennifer Santiago
SIC—2087; NAICS—311900; *Food flavorings*
Employs—25; Estab.—1990
25,000 sq ft site, Distrib.—Intl.
Privately owned corporation

**GENTEK BUILDING PRODUCTS, INC.**
11 Craigwood Rd. (07001)
**Phone—(732) 381-0900**
National—(800) 729-2522
Fax—(732) 827-2320
www.gentekinc.com
Email—gentekinfo@gentekinc.com
Plt. Mgr.—Bhavin Patel
Hum. Res. Mgr.—Jamie Hoffman
Hum. Res. Generalist—Barbara Vergura
SIC—3444; 3499; NAICS—331319; *Custom steel & aluminum coil metal products & siding accessories for home exterior projects*
Employs—165; Estab.—1964
300,000 sq ft site, Distrib.—Intl.
Publicly owned corporation
ISO rating—9001:2000

# Avenel—(cont.)

Parent co.—Gentek Building
Products, Inc., Cuyahoga Falls,
OH
Phone—(330) 929-1811
See Parent Co. Section for full profile.

**†HOME ESSENTIALS, INC.**
1 Terminal Way (07001)
**Phone—(732) 388-4008**
Fax—(732) 388-4403
Email—homeessentials@
americanhei.com
Off. Mgr.—Rashad Hassan
SIC—5023; *Distributor of textile
home furnishings, including
linens, towels & washcloths*
Employs—10; Estab.—2000
Sales—$10Mil-$15Mil
Distrib.—Intl.
Privately owned corporation

**†INDUSTRIAL INSTRUMENTATION
SERVICES, INC.**
1400 Rahway Ave., Ste. 4 (07001-
2226)
**Phone—(732) 815-9090**
National—(877) 215-9090
Fax—(732) 815-9092
www.iisinc.biz
Email—rmakoski@iisinc.biz
Pres.—William Ball
V-P.—Ray Makoski
Opers. Mgr.—Mark Michaud
Contract Svcs. Mgr.—Paul
Boucher
SIC—5085; *Distributor of
industrial instrumentation
components; Brand name—
Partlow; Hach; GLI; Moore
Industries; Accutech; Vaisala;
West Instruments; Pyromation;
Setra; Precision Digital*
Employs—21; Estab.—1985
Sales—$1Mil-$2.5Mil
8,000 sq ft site, Distrib.—National
Privately owned partnership

**JIM'S SIGNS**
1400 Rahway Ave., Ste. 3 (07001)
**Phone—(732) 381-8700**
www.jimsigns.com
Email—jim@jimsigns.com
Owner & Pres.—Jim Petrocy
Designer—Dave Urban
Designer—Sean Pelletier
SIC—3993; 2759; 2394; 3089;
NAICS—314912; *Plastic &
reflective safety, ADA, room &
traffic interior & exterior signs,
displays, awnings, canopies,
posters, plaques, vehicle
graphics & wraps & vinyl
lettering, screen printing, stencils
& graphic design*
Employs—10; Estab.—1991
10,000 sq ft site, Distrib.—Local
Privately owned corporation

**K R ELECTRONICS, INC.**
91 Avenel St. (07001)
**Phone—(732) 636-1900**
Fax—(732) 636-1982
www.krfilters.com
Email—sales@krfilters.com
Pres.—Charles Kiall
SIC—3679; *Electronic filters*
Employs—13; Estab.—1977
Sales—under $500,000
Distrib.—National
Privately owned corporation

**KO-FRO FOODS, INC.**
23 Mileed Way (07001)
**Phone—(732) 499-8282**
Fax—(732) 770-4394
www.mendelsohns.com
Email—info@mendelsohns.com
CEO—Calvin Mendelsohn
Pres.—J. R. Mendelsohn
Sales Mgr.—Morty Breiner

SIC—2038; NAICS—311412;
*Frozen pizza & lasagna; Brand
name—Mendelsohn's*
Employs—10; Estab.—1969
Sales—$1Mil-$2.5Mil
Distrib.—National
Privately owned corporation
AKA: Div. of Mendelsohn's Kosher
Pizza

**MAGIC PRINTING CORP.**
386 Avenel St. (07001)
**Phone—(732) 726-0620**
Fax—(732) 726-1294
www.printingbymagic.com
Email—magicptg@aol.com
Pres.—Steven Glassman
Cust. Serv. Rep.—Jodi Walsh
SIC—2752; 3953; NAICS—
339943; *Business card &
stationery printing & rubber
stamps to the trade*
Employs—20; Estab.—1980
Sales—$500,000-$1Mil
6,800 sq ft site, Distrib.—Local
Privately owned corporation

**MIZCO INTERNATIONAL, INC. (H Q)**
80 Essex Ave. E. (07001)
**Phone—(732) 912-2000**
National—(800) 266-4026
Fax—(732) 912-2001
www.mizco.com
Email—info@mizco.com
Pres., CEO—Albert Mizrahi
V-P.—Sam Mizrahi
SIC—3663; *Corporate
headquarters; cell phone wired
& wireless headsets &
accessories (mfg. done
overseas); Brand name—
Cellular Innovations; DigiPower;
iEssentials*
Employs—50
Sales—$10Mil-$25Mil (est)

**MULTI PLASTICS EXTRUSIONS**
Div. of Multi-Plastics, Inc.
30 Production Way (07001)
**Phone—(732) 388-2300**
National—(800) 732-2300
Fax—(732) 388-1133
www.multi-plastics.com
Email—extorders@multi-
plastics.com
Plt. Mgr.—Doug Griswold
SIC—3086; NAICS—326100;
*Plastic packaging film*
Employs—87
Distrib.—National
Privately owned corporation
Parent co.—Multi-Plastics, Inc.,
Lewis Center, OH
Phone—(740) 548-4894
See Parent Co. Section for full profile.

**P Q CORP.**
Div. of PQ Corporation
2 Paddock St. (07001)
**Phone—(732) 750-9040**
Fax—(732) 634-2840
www.pqcorp.com
Email—info@pqcorp.com
Plt. Mgr.—Ted Freeman
Off. Admn.—Laurene Urban
SIC—2819; *Silicate gels*
Employs—20; Estab.—1977
Sales—$10Mil-$25Mil
Distrib.—Intl.
Privately owned corporation
ISO rating—9001:2000
Parent co.—PQ Corporation,
Malvern, PA
Phone—(610) 651-4200
See Parent Co. Section for full profile.

**PILOT CHEMICAL CO.**
Div. of Pilot Chemical Company
267 Homestead Ave. (07001)
**Phone—(732) 634-6613**
Fax—(732) 634-7971
www.pilotchemical.com
Email—info@pilotchemical.com
Off. Mgr.—Kim Fletcher

Maint. Mgr.—Gill Graves
SIC—2841; 2843; NAICS—
325611; *Surfactants*
Employs—25; Estab.—1964
Distrib.—Intl.
Privately owned corporation
ISO rating—9002
Parent co.—Pilot Chemical
Company, Cincinnati, OH
Phone—(513) 326-0600
See Parent Co. Section for full profile.

**PREMIER DIE CASTING CO., INC.**
1177 Rahway Ave. (07001)
**Phone—(732) 634-3000**
Fax—(732) 634-0590
www.diecasting.com
Email—info@diecasting.com
Pres.—Leonard Cordaro
Hum. Res. Mgr.—Blanca Diaz
Engr.—Ed Zaremba
Pur. Agt.—Mary Henning
SIC—3363; 3364; NAICS—
331521; *Zinc & aluminum die
castings*
Employs—80; Estab.—1945
Sales—$10Mil-$15Mil
65,000 sq ft site, Distrib.—National
Privately owned sub-S corp.
ISO rating—9001:2000

**PRIDE SOLVENTS & CHEMICAL CO.**
211 Randolph Ave. (07001)
**Phone—(732) 499-0125**
Fax—(732) 381-3614
www.pridesol.com
Email—jstipicevic@pridesol.com
Br. Mgr.—Gary Kalundt
Plt. Mgr.—Ed Schmidt
SIC—2869; 2865; NAICS—
325411; *Industrial chemicals &
solvents, including aliphatic &
aromatic hydrocarbons, acids,
alkalies, alcohols, esters &
terpines & pharmaceutical
products, including liquids,
creams & ointments,
antioxidants, vitamins & flavor
enhancers*
Employs—50; Estab.—1990
Sales—$10Mil-$25Mil (est)
Distrib.—Regional
Sole ownership
Parent co.—Pride Solvents &
Chemical Co., Holtsville, NY
Phone—(631) 758-0200
See Parent Co. Section for full profile.

**PROCTER & GAMBLE MFG. CO.**
Div. of Procter & Gamble Co., The
100 Essex Ave. E. (07001)
**Phone—(732) 602-4500**
National—(800) 331-3774
Fax—(732) 382-5298
www.pg.com
Email—info@pg.com
Br. Mgr.—Sandy Moshier
IT Mgr.—Joe Santamassino
Fin. Mgr.—David Wagner
SIC—2844; NAICS—325600;
*Industrial perfumes for
detergents & cleaning supplies*
Employs—70; Estab.—1992
Distrib.—Intl.
Publicly owned corporation
Parent co.—Procter & Gamble Co.,
The, Cincinnati, OH
Phone—(513) 983-1100
See Parent Co. Section for full profile.

**RAHWAY STEEL DRUM CO. (H Q)**
202 Elliot St. (07001)
**Phone—(732) 382-0113**
(800) 260-3786
Fax—(732) 382-6713
www.rahwaysteeldrum.com
Email—info@rahwaysteeldrum.com
Pres.—Michael Foglia
V-P. & Dir., Opers.—William
Guttridge
Manager—Michael Guttridge

SIC—3412; NAICS—332439;
*Company headquarters; steel,
plastic fiber & IBC containers &
plastic & steel pails & drums
(mfg. subcontracted); Brand
name—Greif; Mauser; (Russell-
Stanley) Schutz; Vanguard; US
Can; Pheonix; Williamsport Steel
Container*
Employs—25; Estab.—1941
Distrib.—National
Privately owned corporation

**RUBBER STAMP ENGRAVING**
386 Avenel St. (07001)
**Phone—(908) 400-9890**
(732) 726-5664
Email—stamps2go@gmail.com
Owner & Pres.—Steven Glassman
SIC—3089; 3993; 2791; NAICS—
323122; *Plastic engraving,
interior & exterior signs, self-
inking & pre-inked stamps &
typesetting; Brand name—
Trodat; Ideal; Millennium; Cosco*
Employs—15; Estab.—1972
Sales—under $500,000
1,300 sq ft site, Distrib.—Regional
Privately owned corporation

**SPICE CO.**
6-C Terminal Way (07001)
**Phone—(732) 499-9070**
Fax—(732) 499-9139
www.spice-co.com
Email—ocecips@aol.com
Ptnr.—Andy Barna
Ptnr.—Jim Peterkin
SIC—2099; *Spices*
Employs—70; Estab.—1990
Sales—$10Mil-$25Mil (est)
Distrib.—Regional
Privately owned corporation

**STEELSTRAN INDUSTRIES, INC.**
35 Mileed Way, P.O. Box 30
(07001)
**Phone—(732) 574-0700**
Fax—(732) 574-9191
www.atlantic-group.com
Email—sales@atlantic-group.com
CEO—Peter Gronbeck
Pres.—Susan Gronbeck
COO—Arthur Jeronimo
V-P.—Thomas Burns
SIC—2399; 2499; *Corporate
headquarters & rope & wooden
marine ladders, nylon &
polyester lifting slings & wire
rope*
Employs—5; Estab.—1972
Sales—$1Mil-$2.5Mil
Distrib.—National
Privately owned corporation
AKAs: Atlas Rigging Supply Corp.
& Atlantic Cordage Corp.

**SYNERGEM**
2323 Randolph Ave. (07001)
Mail addr: P.O. Box 6292, Edison
(08818)
**Phone—(732) 225-0001**
Fax—(732) 225-7555
www.synergem.com
Chrm.—Thomas DeMaeyer
Pres.—Amy P. Silverman
Fin. & Hum. Res. Mgr.—Peggy
Downey
Proj. Coord.—Mark Ruppert
SIC—3695; NAICS—334613; *CD
& DVD duplication/replication &
webkeys*
Employs—14; Estab.—1985
20,000 sq ft site, Distrib.—National
Privately owned corporation

**UNIQUE TECHNOLOGIES ASSOCS.**
42 Milled Way (07001)
**Phone—(732) 882-0777**
Fax—(732) 882-1777
www.uniquetechnologies.com
Pres.—Eugene Kverel
V-P.—Gary Elias
Off. Mgr.—Rochelle Forbes

GEOGRAPHICAL

## Avenel—(cont.)

SIC—2992; NAICS—324191; *Graphite lubricants*
Employs—10; Estab.—1996
Sales—$500,000-$1Mil
Distrib.—Local
Privately owned corporation

NEW ENTRY
**USA TEALIGHT, LLC**
4 Craigwood Rd. (07001)
**Phone—(732) 943-2408**
www.usatealight.com
Pres.—Michael Zohar
SIC—3999; *Tealight candles*
Employs—15
Sales—$1Mil-$2.5Mil (est)
Limited Liability Company

**VANTAGE APPAREL**
100 Vantage Dr. (07001)
**Phone—(732) 340-3000**
National—(800) 221-0020
Fax—(732) 340-3165
www.vantageapparel.com
Email—ericw@vantageapparel.com
Pres.—Ira Neaman
COO—Eric Wukitsch
V-P., Cust. Experience & Prodn.—Kevin Schardt
Sales Mgr., Natl.—Pete Waldron
Prodn. Mgr.—Januz Kupa
Hum. Res. Mgr.—Lori Girtanner
Commissions, Licensing & Royalties Admn.—Marie Augustyn
SIC—2389; *Logo & identity apparel*
Employs—500; Estab.—1976
Sales—$25Mil-$100Mil
Distrib.—National
Sole ownership

## Avon by the Sea
(Monmouth—N.E.)

**CANVAS SHOP OF AVON, INC.**
504 Main St. (07717)
**Phone—(732) 988-5775**
Fax—(732) 988-1775
www.canvasshopofavon.webs.com
Email—canvasshopofavon@aol.com
Pres.—R. Glovich
SIC—2394; NAICS—314912; *Canvas boat covers & awnings*
Employs—6; Estab.—1982
Sales—under $500,000
Distrib.—Regional
Privately owned corporation

†**FERGUSON ENTERPRISES, INC.**
401 Main St. (07717)
**Phone—(732) 775-5270**
Fax—(732) 775-1884
www.ferguson.com
Email—david.golini@ferguson.com
Br. Mgr.—David Hulse
Sales Rep.—Michael Denning
SIC—5074; *Distributor of plumbing & heating supplies*
Employs—10; Estab.—1997
Distrib.—Local
Publicly owned corporation
Parent co.—Ferguson Enterprises, Inc., Newport News, VA
Phone—(757) 874-7795
See Parent Co. Section for full profile.

**N.V. BUSINESS PUBLISHERS CORP. (H Q)**
43 Main St., P.O. Box 188 (07717)
**Phone—(732) 502-0500**
Fax—(732) 502-9606
www.nvpublications.com
Email—lprazych@nvpublications.com
Vice Chrm., Pres.—Tom Vilardi
Ex. Publisher—Robyn Smith
V-P., Editor—Jim Curley

SIC—2721; *Corporate headquarters; weekly, bi-weekly, monthly & bi-monthly magazines & trade journals for the corrugated, folding carton, flexographic printing & recycling industries; Brand name—Board Converting News; Board Converting News International; Davison's Box & Carton Blue Book; CORRUGATED Today; Flexo Market News; Folding Carton industry; International Paper Board Industry; Recycling Markets*
Employs—5; Estab.—1985
Distrib.—National
Privately owned corporation

## Barnegat
(Ocean—S.E.)

NEW ENTRY
**DOT GRAPHIX, INC.**
79 S. Main St., Ste. 13 (08005)
**Phone—(609) 660-0087**
Pres.—Joe Lopes
Shop Mgr.—Mike Devaney
SIC—2396; *T-shirt screen printing*
Employs—10; Estab.—2006
Sales—$1Mil-$2.5Mil
8,000 sq ft site, Distrib.—Local
Privately owned corporation

**EASTERN CONCRETE MATERIALS, INC.**
201 Route 539 (08005)
**Phone—(609) 698-2800**
Fax—(609) 698-1902
www.eastern-concrete.com
Email—service@eastern-concrete.com
Br. Mgr.—Tracy Davies
SIC—3281; NAICS—327991; *Sand processing*
Employs—6; Estab.—1996
Sales—under $500,000
Distrib.—Regional
Publicly owned corporation
Parent co.—Eastern Concrete Materials, Inc., Elmwood Park, NJ
Phone—(201) 797-7979
See Parent Co. Section for full profile.

**FITZGERALD CUSTOM FABRICATION, INC.**
733 W. Bay Ave. (08005)
Mail addr: 6 Saint John's Ln., Port Republic (08241)
**Phone—(609) 652-8899**
Fax—(609) 652-8899
Email—fitzgerald1@comcast.net
Pres.—Edwin Fitzgerald
SIC—3312; *Steel fabrication*
Employs—2; Estab.—1978
Sales—under $500,000
Distrib.—Regional

**GOOD AUTOMATIC WINDLASS, INC.**
357 Route 72 (08005)
**Phone—(609) 698-4402**
National—(800) 780-4655
Fax—(609) 698-3698
www.goodwindlass.com
Email—support@goodwindlass.com
Sr. V-P., GM—Thomas J. Ring
Sr. V-P., Fin.—Fred W. Good
V-P., Sales—Thomas A. Ring
SIC—3462; 3599; NAICS—332111; *Anchor windlasses for 20-foot to 55-foot boats, including pivoting anchor rollers, depth color-coded anchor line/chain kits & machine shop services; Brand name—Good Automatic Windlass; Good Anchor Line Kits*
Employs—3; Estab.—1958
Sales—$300,000-$500,000
3,200 sq ft site, Distrib.—National
Privately owned corporation

**SOUTHERN OCEAN MARINE SPORTSWEAR**
79 S. Main St., Ste. 2 (08005)
**Phone—(609) 698-8868**
National—(888) 408-7667
Fax—(609) 698-5700
www.soms4u.com
Email—sherry@soms4u.com
Owner—Sherry Haferbier
SIC—2395; 2396; 5199; *Manufacturer of embroidered & screen-printed apparel & distributor of promotional products for schools, sports teams, clubs & organizations; Brand name—Gildan; Carhartt; Fruit of the Loom; Champion; Russell; Bella; Alternative Apparel; Nike; Adidas; Ashworth*
Employs—4; Estab.—1999
Sales—under $500,000
2,300 sq ft site, Distrib.—National
Limited Liability Company
AKA: SOMS LLC

## Barnegat Light
(Ocean—S.E.)

†**VIKING VILLAGE, INC.**
19th St. & Bayview Ave., P.O. Box 458 (08006)
**Phone—(609) 494-0113**
Fax—(609) 361-9536
www.vikingvillage.net
Email—kenhook@vikingvillage.net
Pres.—Louis Puskas, Jr.
Manager—Ernie Panacek
Manager—Karter E. Larson
SIC—5146; *Distributor of fresh fish & seafood*
Employs—15; Estab.—1975
Sales—$1Mil-$2.5Mil
Distrib.—Intl.
Privately owned corporation

## Barrington
(Camden—S.W.)

NEW ENTRY
**ANCHOR OPTICAL CO.**
Div. of Edmund Optics, Inc.
101 E. Gloucester Pike (08007)
**Phone—(856) 573-6865**
Fax—(856) 546-1965
www.anchoroptics.com
Email—sales@edmundoptics.com
Dir., Mktg.—Kirsten Bjork Jones
Prodn. Line Mgr.—David Henz
SIC—3827; 3499; 3674; *Commercial, experimental, specialty, fiber & educational optics, magnifiers, magnets, optical equipment & tools, lasers & microscopes*
Employs—100
Sales—$5Mil-$10Mil (est)
Privately owned corporation
Parent co.—Edmund Optics, Inc., Barrington, NJ
Phone—(856) 547-3488
See Parent Co. Section for full profile.

**ART PRESS PRINTING, INC.**
124 Clements Bridge Rd. (08007)
**Phone—(856) 547-8953**
Fax—(856) 546-8408
Email—artpress1@verizon.net
Owner & Pres.—Robert McHugh
SIC—2759; 2791; NAICS—323122; *Commercial printing & typesetting*
Employs—10; Estab.—1957
Sales—under $500,000
Distrib.—Local
Privately owned corporation

**BANTLE'S BANNERS & SIGNS**
213 Clements Bridge Rd. (08007)
**Phone—(856) 546-1112**
Fax—(856) 546-1112
Email—bantlesign@comcast.net

Owner—Janice Bantle
SIC—3993; 3953; 2759; 2396; NAICS—339943; *Street, door, window & magnetic vehicle signs, nameplates, truck lettering, rubber stamps & t-shirt & advertising specialty items screen printing*
Employs—3; Estab.—1995
Sales—under $500,000
Distrib.—Local
Sole ownership

**BERG FURNITURE U. S. A., INC.**
120 E. Gloucester Pike (08007)
**Phone—(856) 310-0511**
Fax—(856) 310-0512
www.bergfurniture.com
Email—berg-usa@bergfurniture.com
V-P.—Almog Lieber
Cont., Acctg. & Acct. Mgr.—Larry Newman
Cust. Serv. Rep.—Sarah LaRue
SIC—2511; *Juvenile furniture*
Employs—90; Estab.—1984
144,000 sq ft site, Distrib.—Intl.
Privately owned sub-S corp.

**BRIGHT LIGHTS USA, INC.**
145 Shreve Ave. (08007)
**Phone—(856) 546-5656**
Fax—(856) 546-9191
www.brightlightsusa.com
Email—info@brightlightsusa.com
Pres.—Daniel Farber
SIC—3764; 3489; NAICS—332995; *Mechanical & electromechanical defense spare parts*
Employs—84; Estab.—1990
Sales—$5Mil-$10Mil
134,000 sq ft site, Distrib.—National
Privately owned sub-S corp.

**COOPER WILBERT BURIAL VAULT CO., INC.**
621 E. Atlantic Ave. (08007)
**Phone—(856) 547-8405**
National—(888) 547-8405
Fax—(856) 547-5454
www.coopervault.com
Pres.—Paul Cooper
Opers. Mgr.—Bryan Spitak
SIC—3272; *Corporate headquarters & concrete burial vaults*
Employs—15; Estab.—1979
Sales—$1Mil-$2.5Mil
Distrib.—Local
Privately owned corporation

**DESIGNS IN WOOD**
209 Williams Ave. (08007)
**Phone—(856) 546-8338**
Fax—(856) 546-8338
Owner, Plt. & Sales Mgr.—Richard Feldstein
SIC—2511; *Hardwood furniture*
Employs—1; Estab.—1975
Sales—under $500,000
Distrib.—Regional
Sole ownership

**EDMUND OPTICS, INC.**
101 E. Gloucester Pike (08007-1380)
**Phone—(856) 547-3488**
National—(800) 363-1992
Fax—(856) 547-3292
www.edmundoptics.com
Email—sales@edmundoptics.com
Chrm., CEO—Robert Edmund
CFO—Jason Mulliner
COO—Samuel Sadoulet
V-P., Global Sales—Thomas Kessler
V-P., Opers.—Susan O'Keefe
V-P., Mktg.—Marisa Edmund
Sr. Dir., Hum. Res.—Susan Tunney
Dir., Mktg. Comms.—Kirsten Bjork-Jones

## Barrington—(cont.)

Database Dev. Mgr.—Jeff Harvey
SIC—3827; 3569; NAICS—
333314; *Corporate headquarters
& optical lens, machine vision
systems, lasers & positioning
equipment*
Employs—165; Estab.—1942
96,000 sq ft site, Distrib.—Intl.
Privately owned corporation
ISO rating—9001:2008

### INTERNATIONAL PAPER CO.

100 E. Gloucester Pike (08007)
**Phone—(856) 546-7000**
Fax—(901) 334-3932
www.internationalpaper.com
Email—rick.ludvigsen@comcbpr.ipa
Cont.—William Zorzanello
GM—Andrew Fescoe
Sales Mgr.—Mike Sanchez
Mfg. Mgr.—Keith Fischer
SIC—2653; NAICS—322211;
*Corrugated boxes*
Employs—140; Estab.—1965
300,000 sq ft site, Distrib.—
National
Publicly owned corporation
Parent co.—International Paper
Co., Memphis, TN
Phone—(901) 419-9000
See Parent Co. Section for full profile.

### ISCO

1 Commerce Dr., Bldg. 3 (08007)
**Phone—(856) 672-9182**
Fax—(856) 672-0121
Manager—Aaron Snethen
SIC—2448; *Wooden pallets*
Employs—50; Estab.—2012
Sales—under $500,000
1,200 sq ft site, Distrib.—Local
Privately owned corporation

### JARRDD.CO

141 Shreve Ave. (08007)
**Phone—(856) 310-0100**
Fax—(856) 310-0022
Pres.—David Farber
Sales Rep.—Marie Nuciforo
SIC—3452; *Manufacturer &
distributor of military spare parts,
including bolts, nuts, screws &
fasteners*
Employs—6; Estab.—1996
Sales—$500,000-$1Mil
14,000 sq ft site, Distrib.—Intl.
Privately owned corporation

### PAUL'S CUSTOM AWARDS &
TROPHY, INC.

200 White Horse Pike (08007)
**Phone—(856) 547-7777**
Fax—(856) 546-6699
www.paulsawards.com
Email—info@paulsawards.com
Pres.—Paul McGuigan
Sales Mgr.—Kevin McGuigan
SIC—3479; 3499; 3089; *Trophy
engraving & plaques*
Employs—8; Estab.—1975
Sales—under $500,000
Distrib.—Local
Privately owned corporation

## Basking Ridge

(Somerset—N.E.)

### AVAYA, INC. (H Q)

211 Mount Airy Rd. (07920)
**Phone—(908) 953-6000**
National—(866) 462-8292
www.avaya.com
Email—execoffice@avaya.com
Pres., CEO—Kevin Kennedy
Pres., Field Opers. & Sr. V-P.,
Global Sales & Mktg.—Joel
Hackney
Pres., Opers. & Sr. V-P.—Jim
Chirico
Pres., Labs—Ravi Sethi
Sr. V-P., CIO—Stephen J. Gold

Chief Administrative Officer—
Pamela Craven
Sr. V-P., Hum. Res.—Roger
Gaston
V-P., Developer Rels.—Eric
Rossman
Treas.—Matthew Booher
SIC—3669; NAICS—334220;
*Corporate headquarters;
business communication
equipment, applications &
systems*
Employs—2000
Worldwide: 20,000
Sales—$4.33Bil

### DEMATIC CORP.

150 Allen Rd., Ste. 102 (07920)
**Phone—(908) 991-9900**
National—(877) 725-7500
Fax—(908) 991-9901
www.dematic.com
Email—usinfo@dematic.com
GM—Tom Dancer
SIC—7373; NAICS—541512;
*Material handling systems
integration, including paperless
picking, automated storage &
retrieval, material flow conveyors
& high-speed sortation systems;
Brand name—Dematic;
Rapistan; PickDirector;
SortDirector; DirectorIT;
RapidPick; Dematic Multishuttle;
FlexSort; MCS*
Employs—25; Estab.—1939
Distrib.—Regional
Privately owned corporation
ISO rating—9001
Parent co.—Dematic Corp., Grand
Rapids, MI
Phone—(616) 913-7700
See Parent Co. Section for full profile.

### †DEVCO CORP.

131 Morristown Rd., Bldg. B
(07920)
**Phone—(908) 630-0005**
National—(800) 323-3826
Fax—(908) 630-0045
www.devcocorp.com
Email—info@devcocorp.com
GM—Bill Durnan
SIC—5084; *Distributor of
lubrication equipment & supplies*
Employs—7; Estab.—1980
Distrib.—National
Privately owned corporation

### IPSEN BIOPHARMACEUTICALS,
INC.

106 Allen Rd., 3rd Fl. (07920)
**Phone—(866) 837-2422**
Fax—(908) 275-6301
www.ipsen.com
Pres., N. America—Cynthia
Schwalm
Facilities Mgr.—Ronnie Volino
Hum. Res. Mgr.—Nicole Hull
SIC—2836; *Biopharmaceuticals
for endocrine & neurologic
disorders; Brand name—
Increlex®*
Employs—40; Estab.—2004
Sales—$500,000-$1Mil
Distrib.—Intl.
Privately owned corporation

### MATHESON TRI-GAS, INC.

150 Allen Rd., Ste. 302 (07920-
2977)
**Phone—(908) 991-9200**
Fax—(908) 604-1465
www.mathesongas.com
Email—info@mathesongas.com
Ex. Chrm., Board of Dirs.—Bill
Kroll
Pres., CEO—Scott Kallman
Ex. V-P., CFO—Joe Bellitto
Corp. MarComm Mgr.—Beth
Sullivan

SIC—2813; NAICS—325120;
*Company headquarters &
industrial gases; Brand name—
MATHESON*
Employs—75; Estab.—1927
Sales—$25Mil-$50Mil
Distrib.—National
Privately owned corporation
AKA: MATHESON

### MITSUBISHI HITACHI POWER
SYSTEMS AMERICA - ENERGY &
ENVIRONMENT

Div. of Hitachi America Ltd.
645 Martinsville Rd. (07920)
**Phone—(908) 605-2800**
Fax—(908) 604-6211
www.hitachipowersystems.us
Email—info@
hitachipowersystems.us
Pres., CEO—Hank E. Bartoli
Sr. V-P., Proj. Opers.—William
Buffa
Ex. V-P., Comml. Opers.—Mani
Seshamani
V-P., Sales & Mktg.—Dave J.
Brozek
SIC—3564; NAICS—333400;
*Industrial air filtration systems*
Employs—150; Estab.—2005
Sales—$6Mil-$10Mil
Distrib.—Intl.
Publicly owned corporation
Parent co.—Hitachi America Ltd.,
Tarrytown, NY
Phone—(914) 332-5800
See Parent Co. Section for full profile.

### NEW JERSEY COUNTRYSIDE
MAGAZINE

134 S. Finley Ave. (07920)
Mail addr.: P.O. Box 665, Oldwick
(08858)
**Phone—(908) 221-1171**
Fax—(908) 887-1656
www.njcountryside.com
Email—info@njcountryside.com
Owner, Publisher & Editor—Allene
Stanton Fay
Mng. Editor—Darcey Gohring
Adv. Sales & Bus. Mgr.—Joanne
K. McClain
SIC—2721; *Bimonthly regional
lifestyle magazine publishing,
including food & wine, arts &
entertainment, home & garden &
cultural events; Brand name—
New Jersey Countryside
Magazine*
Employs—3; Estab.—1990
Sales—$500,000-$1Mil
Distrib.—National
Limited Liability Company

### PHYSICIAN'S WEEKLY

180 Mount Airy Rd., Ste. 102
(07920)
**Phone—(908) 766-0402**
Fax—(908) 766-0421
www.physweekly.com
Email—clayr@pri-medpoc.com
Pres.—Clay Romweber
SIC—2741; *Medical newsletter
publishing*
Employs—10; Estab.—1984
Sales—$500,000-$1Mil
Distrib.—National
Limited Liability Company

### SPIRENT COMMUNICATIONS, INC.

211 Mount Airy Rd. (07920)
**Phone—(908) 953-6000**
www.spirent.com
CEO—Kevin Kennedy
CFO—Adi Sfadia
Cont.—Helene VanDerClock
SIC—7372; *Internet & video
conferencing software
development*
Employs—40; Estab.—1994
Distrib.—Intl.
Privately owned corporation

Parent co.—Spirent
Communications, Inc.,
Calabasas, CA
Phone—(818) 676-2300
See Parent Co. Section for full profile.

## Bay Head

(Ocean—S.E.)

### JERSEY SHORE PUBLICATIONS

P.O. Box 176 (08742)
**Phone—(732) 892-1276**
Fax—(732) 892-3365
www.jerseyshorevacation.com
Email—jsvacation@aol.com
Publisher & Editor—George
Valente
SIC—2731; 2721; *Book &
magazine publishing*
Employs—6; Estab.—1993
Sales—under $500,000 (est)
Distrib.—Regional

## Bayonne

(Hudson—N.E.)

**NEW ENTRY**
### BASHA USA, LLC

390 Broadway (07002)
**Phone—(201) 339-9770**
Fax—(201) 339-9771
Owner—M. Merget
SIC—2011; *Meat processing*
Employs—4
Sales—$1Mil-$2.5Mil (est)
Limited Liability Company

### BAYONNE COMMUNITY NEWS

170 Broadway (07002)
**Phone—(201) 437-2460**
Fax—(201) 437-7127
www.hudsonreporter.com
Pres.—Lucha Malato
SIC—2711; *Newspaper
publishing*
Employs—9; Estab.—1978
Sales—$1Mil-$2.5Mil
Distrib.—Local
Privately owned corporation
AKA: Hudson Reporter

### BAYONNE DRY-DOCK & REPAIR,
INC.

Military Ocean Terminal Dock
Yard, P.O. Box 240 (07002)
**Phone—(201) 823-9295**
Fax—(201) 823-9298
www.bayonnedrydock.com
Email—info@bayonnedrydock.com
Pres.—Mike Cranston
Hum. Res. Mgr.—Roberta St.
Bernard
Off. Mgr.—Kevin Sullivan
SIC—3731; *Rebuilt ships*
Employs—20; Estab.—1999
Sales—$5Mil-$10Mil
Distrib.—Local
Privately owned corporation

### †BAYONNE PLUMBING SUPPLY, INC.

250 Avenue E (07002)
**Phone—(201) 436-2211**
    (201) 339-8000
National—(800) 713-7473
Fax—(201) 436-2163
www.bayonneplumbingsupply.com
Email—info@
bayonneplumbingsupply.com
Ptnr.—Richard Epstein
Ptnr.—Chris Bayonne
SIC—5031; 5063; *Corporate
headquarters & wholesaler of
bathroom accessories, including
cabinets, decorative lighting,
shower faucets & towel racks*
Employs—6; Estab.—1993
Sales—under $500,000
Distrib.—Regional
Privately owned corporation
AKA: Bath Connection, The

GEOGRAPHICAL

# Bayonne—(cont.)

**CITY GLASS CO.**
282 Broadway, P.O. Box 178 (07002)
**Phone—(201) 436-8400**
Fax—(201) 436-9316
www.citynewarkglass.com
Email—cng@citynewarkglass.com
Pres.—Allan McCleod
Bookkeeper—Diane Tonne
SIC—3231; 3446; 2399; NAICS—327215; *Architectural metals, glass & custom flags & banners*
Employs—50; Estab.—1891
Distrib.—Local
Privately owned corporation
AKA: City/Newark Glass Co.

**CNS CONFECTIONERY PRODUCTS, LLC**
33 Hook Rd. (07002)
**Phone—(201) 823-1400**
Fax—(201) 823-2452
www.cnscoinc.com
Email—carol@cnscoinc.com
Pres., Opers. Mgr.—Eva Deutsch
V-P., R & D—Miriam Gross
Fin. Mgr. & Bookkeeper—Carol Ranieri
SIC—2064; NAICS—311300; *Bulk sweetened, toasted & desiccated coconut flakes, chocolate chips, sprinkles & raisins for wholesale bakeries, foodservice distributors, ice cream manufacturers & grocery & dollar store retailers; Brand name—CNS; Unipro*
Employs—12; Estab.—1995
Sales—$3Mil-$5Mil
40,000 sq ft site, Distrib.—National
Limited Liability Company

**D C PLASTIC PRODUCTS**
12 E. 2nd St., P.O. Box 353 (07002)
**Phone—(201) 339-0111**
Fax—(201) 339-2668
Pres.—David Moskovits
Off. Mgr.—Sandy Mallano
SIC—2673; NAICS—326121; *Plastic garbage bags*
Employs—15; Estab.—1984
50,000 sq ft site, Distrib.—Regional
Privately owned corporation

**D'AMICO SHEET METAL WORKS, AL**
881 Broadway (07002)
**Phone—(201) 339-1355**
Owner & Pres.—Al D'Amico
SIC—3444; *Sheet metal fabrication*
Employs—1; Estab.—1962
Sales—under $500,000
Distrib.—Local
Sole ownership

**DEE & L, LLC**
67 Lefante Way, P.O. Box 3431 (07002)
**Phone—(201) 858-0131**
   (201) 858-0138
National—(800) 421-3447
Fax—(201) 858-2530
Email—larrykahn@deeandl.com
Dir., Opers.—Larry Kahn
Off. Mgr.—Evelyn Consuegra
SIC—2035; 2086; NAICS—311999; *Mayonnaises, salad dressings & fruit drinks*
Employs—20; Estab.—2011
Sales—$500,000-$1Mil
Distrib.—Intl.
Privately owned corporation

**DG3 NORTH AMERICA, INC.**
180 Pulaski St. (07002)
**Phone—(201) 946-0156**
Fax—(201) 946-0189
www.dg3.com
Email—theodore.taylor@dg3.com

Ex. V-P.—Jonathan Vitale
Ex. V-P.—Seth Diamond
Hum. Res. Mgr.—Otto Garcia
Cust. Serv. Rep.—Theodore Taylor
SIC—2752; NAICS—323100; *Offset printing*
Employs—100; Estab.—1914
67,238 sq ft site, Distrib.—National
Privately owned corporation

**ELDER & JENKS CO.**
Div. of Muralo Co., Inc.
148 E. 5th St. (07002)
**Phone—(201) 437-0770**
National—(800) 631-3440
Fax—(201) 437-0664
www.muralo.com
Email—snorton.devine@muralocompany.com
V-P.—Mike Norton
Hum. Res. Mgr.—Stephanie Fisk
SIC—3991; NAICS—339994; *Paint brushes & rollers*
Employs—40; Estab.—1793
100,000 sq ft site, Distrib.—National
Privately owned corporation
AKA: Muralo
Parent co.—Muralo Co., Inc., Bayonne, NJ
Phone—(201) 437-0770
See Parent Co. Section for full profile.

**†FLAME-CUT STEEL, INC.**
97 E. 2nd St. (07002)
**Phone—(201) 436-9300**
Fax—(201) 436-9317
Email—flamecut1@yahoo.com
Pres.—Ramesh Nuthi
Off. Mgr.—Kirti Nuthi
SIC—5051; 3443; 3599; *Metal service center, including plate & structural products, precision & high-definition plasma cutting of metals, waterjetting, CNC bending & related precision fabrication*
Employs—12; Estab.—1940
Sales—$2.5Mil-$5Mil
21,000 sq ft site, Distrib.—National
Privately owned corporation

**FLORTEK CORP.**
39 W. 55th St. (07002)
**Phone—(201) 436-7700**
Fax—(201) 436-9132
Pres.—Warren Harris
Off. Mgr.—Esther Torado
SIC—2789; NAICS—323100; *Upholstery, textile & wall covering swatch sample books & cards*
Employs—45; Estab.—1968
Sales—$6Mil-$10Mil
Distrib.—National
Privately owned corporation

**GEL SPICE CO., INC.**
48 Hook Rd., P.O. Box 285 (07002)
**Phone—(201) 339-0700**
National—(800) 922-0230
Fax—(201) 339-0072
www.gelspice.com
Email—sales@glspice.com
Pres.—Andre Engel
CFO—Sam Baum
Sr. V-P.—Gershon Engel
V-P., Sales—Sherman Engel
SIC—2099; 2068; 2087; NAICS—311911; *Spices, seasonings, seeds, extracts & baking ingredients for the bakery, foodservice, drug, retail grocery & discount markets*
Employs—225; Estab.—1955
Sales—$100Mil
150,000 sq ft site, Distrib.—National
Privately owned corporation

**GORDON TERMINAL SERVICE CO. OF NEW JERSEY, INC.**
Div. of Gordon Terminal Service Co. Of Pennsylvania
2 Hook Rd., P.O. Box 143 (07002)
**Phone—(201) 437-8300**
Fax—(201) 437-2611
www.gtscofnj.com
Email—info@gtscofpa.com
V-P., GM—Thomas S. Gordon
Hum. Res. Mgr.—Robert Mettrick
Off. Mgr.—James Zago
SIC—2992; NAICS—324191; *Industrial lubricants compounding*
Employs—70; Estab.—1967
Distrib.—Intl.
Privately owned corporation
AKA: Gordon Terminal
Parent co.—Gordon Terminal Service Co. Of Pennsylvania, McKees Rocks, PA
Phone—(412) 331-9410
See Parent Co. Section for full profile.

**HENRY REPEATING ARMS COMPANY**
59 E. 1st St. (07002)
**Phone—(201) 858-4400**
National—(866) 200-2354
Fax—(201) 858-4435
www.henryrepeating.com
Email—anthony@henryrepeating.com
Owner & Pres.—Anthony Imperato
V-P., CFO—Lemana Saran
GM—Andy Wickstrom
SIC—3484; NAICS—332994; *Company headquarters & firearms, including rifles; Brand name—Henry®*
Employs—200; Estab.—1993
Sales—$100Mil
109,000 sq ft site, Distrib.—Intl.
Privately owned sub-S corp.

**HUDSON AWNING & SIGN CO., INC.**
27 Cottage St. (07002)
**Phone—(201) 339-7171**
National—(800) 624-1012
Fax—(201) 339-9858
www.hudsonawning.com
Email—moreinfo@hudsonawning.com
Pres.—Edward Burak
V-P.—Lynda Burak
Fin. & Hum. Res. Mgr.—Barbara J. Petersen
SIC—2394; 3993; NAICS—314912; *Lightweight fabric & membrane structures, signs, canopies, awnings & shading systems; Brand name—HUDCO Lightweight Frame Systems*
Employs—35; Estab.—1881
9,500 sq ft site, Distrib.—National
Privately owned sub-S corp.
AKA: Hudson Services LLC

**IDEAL WINDOW MFG., INC.**
100 W. 7th St. (07002)
**Phone—(201) 437-4300**
National—(800) 631-3400
Fax—(201) 437-4833
www.idealwindow.com
Email—info@idealwindow.com
CFO—Carlene Balance
V-P., Mfg.—John Parker
Dir., Hum. Res.—Chris Megalos
Creative Dir.—Beth O'Rourke
GM—John Schack
MIS Mgr.—Gamal Basharahil
SIC—3089; *Vinyl windows & doors*
Employs—130; Estab.—1924
200,000 sq ft site, Distrib.—Regional
Privately owned sub-S corp.

**J & J PRINTING CO.**
1023 Broadway (07002)
**Phone—(201) 858-8895**
Fax—(201) 858-1635

Owner—Fran Tagliareni
Graphic Designer—Jennifer Tagliareni
SIC—2752; 2791; NAICS—323122; *Offset printing & typesetting*
Employs—6; Estab.—1973
Sales—$500,000-$1Mil (est)
Distrib.—National
Sole ownership

**JERHEL PLASTICS, INC. (H Q)**
63 New Hook Rd. (07002)
**Phone—(201) 436-6662**
Fax—(201) 436-6121
www.jerhel.com
Email—info@jerhel.com
Pres.—Leonard Mecca
Cont.—Larry Kausman
SIC—3089; *Corporate headquarters; plastic injection & blow-molded packaging products for the cosmetics & pharmaceutical industries (mfg. done in China)*
Employs—10; Estab.—1989
Sales—$1Mil-$2.5Mil (est)
Distrib.—Intl.
Privately owned corporation

**KENRICH PETROCHEMICALS, INC.**
140 E. 22nd St., P.O. Box 32 (07002)
**Phone—(201) 823-9000**
National—(866) 536-7424
Fax—(201) 823-0691
www.4kenrich.com
Email—customerservice@4kenrich.com
Pres.—Salvatore J. Monte
V-P., Fin. & Opers.—Charles A. Lucania
V-P., Gen. Counsel—Michelle M. Monte
V-P., Tech.—Eric M. Monte
V-P.—Erika G. Monte
Sales Mgr.—Hartmut H. Schlaubitz
Plt. Mgr.—N. Moran
SIC—2899; *Chemical additives, including titanates, zirconates, plasticizers & dispersions; Brand name—Ken-React®; Ken-Stat®; Kenflex®; Kenplast®; Kenmix®; Ken-Color®; Drimix®; Dryspersion®; Ken-Mag®; Ken-Zinc®; Kenlastic®; Ken-Stat(r);Silacto; Ridacto; KR; LICA; L; NZ; CAPS; CAPOW*
Employs—30; Estab.—1945
Sales—$5Mil-$10Mil
75,000 sq ft site, Distrib.—Intl.
Privately owned corporation

**MANHATTAN CHOCOLATES CO.**
186 E. 22nd St. (07002)
**Phone—(201) 339-6886**
Fax—(201) 339-6760
www.manhattanchocolates.com
GM—Michael Herzod
Manager—Howard N. Carnoff
SIC—2064; NAICS—311300; *Chocolates & candies; Brand name—Shufra Chocolatier; Manhattan Chocolates*
Employs—50
Sales—$10Mil-$25Mil
Distrib.—Regional
Privately owned corporation

[NEW ENTRY]
**MARK SPORTS**
9 E. 31st St. (07002)
**Phone—(201) 437-9900**
www.marksportsnj.com
Email—marksports.landante@gmail.com
Owner—Dominick Landante

## Bayonne—(cont.)

SIC—2396; 2395; *T-shirt screen printing & embroidery*
Employs—2; Estab.—1999
Sales—under $500,000
Distrib.—Local
Privately owned corporation

### MURALO CO., INC.

148 E. 5th St. (07002)
**Phone—(201) 437-0770**
National—(800) 631-3440
Fax—(201) 437-0664
www.muralo.com
Email—info@muralocompany.com
Pres.—James F. Norton
CFO—Charles P. Lee, Jr.
Sales Mgr.—Peter Seaborg
Pur. Mgr.—Kathy Santella
Hum. Res. Mgr.—Stephanie Fisk
SIC—2851; 3991; NAICS—325510; *Corporate headquarters & paints, brushes, rollers & architectural coatings*
Employs—50; Estab.—1894
Sales—$25Mil–$50Mil
Distrib.—Intl.
Privately owned corporation

### NORTON & SON, INC.

Div. of Muralo Co., Inc.
148 E. 5th St. (07002)
**Phone—(201) 437-0770**
National—(800) 631-3440
Fax—(201) 437-0664
www.muralo.com
Email—info@muralocompany.com
V-P., Mfg.—Ed Norton III
SIC—3479; 3471; NAICS—332813; *Architecural coatings*
Employs—100; Estab.—1944
Distrib.—Regional
Privately owned corporation
AKA: Muralo Co., Inc.
Parent co.—Muralo Co., Inc., Bayonne, NJ
Phone—(201) 437-0770
See Parent Co. Section for full profile.

### PALMER ASPHALT CO., INC.

196 W. 5th St., P.O. Box 58 (07002)
**Phone—(201) 339-0855**
National—(800) 352-9898
Fax—(201) 339-8320
www.palmerasphalt.com
Email—sales@palmerasphalt.com
Pres.—Van Ripps
Dir., Opers.—Tammy Cabrera
SIC—2952; 2821; NAICS—324122; *Energy saving roof coatings, cool roof coatings, sustainable roof coatings, heat reflective roof coatings & roof restoration & maintenance coatings, including roof repair cements, colored roof coatings & waterproofing products; Brand name—BULLDOG; DUREX*
Employs—10; Estab.—1932
Sales—over $5Mil
40,000 sq ft site, Distrib.—Intl.
Privately owned sub-S corp.

### PDQ PLASTICS, INC.

7 Hook Rd., P.O. Box 1001 *(07002)*
**Phone—(201) 823-0270**
Fax—(201) 823-0345
www.pdqplastics.com
Email—hartson@pdqplastics.com
Pres.—Barry Nathans
V-P., GM—Hartson Poland
SIC—3089; *Plastic pallets*
Employs—22; Estab.—1969
Sales—$1Mil–$5Mil
Distrib.—Intl.
Privately owned corporation

### PENGAD, INC.

55 Oak St., P.O. Box 99 (07002)
**Phone—(201) 436-5625**
National—(800) 631-6989
Fax—(201) 436-9550

www.pengad.com
Email—sales@pengad.com
Pres.—Thomas S. Pierson
V-P., Sales—Pat Verga
Sales Mgr.—Judy Herring
SIC—3955; NAICS—339944; *Corporate headquarters & printed report covers, presentation folders & custom index tabs for the legal professional industry*
Employs—20; Estab.—1936
Distrib.—National
Privately owned corporation

### RICHARDS CHOCOLATES CO., INC., AL

851 Broadway (07002)
**Phone—(201) 436-0915**
Fax—(201) 443-8498
www.alrichardschocolates.net
Email—info@alrichardschocolates.net
Pres.—Fred Stancampiano
Maint. Mgr.—John Stan
SIC—2066; NAICS—311300; *Chocolate candy*
Employs—10; Estab.—1981
Sales—under $500,000
7,500 sq ft site, Distrib.—Local
Privately owned corporation

### ROYAL WINE CORP.

63 Lefante Way (07002)
**Phone—(718) 534-0200**
            (718) 384-2400
Fax—(718) 384-5329
www.royalwine.com
Email—info@royalwine.com
Pres., CEO—David Herzog
CFO—Sheldon Ginsburg
Sr. V-P.—Philip Herzog
Ex. V-P.—Nathan Herzog
V-P., Food Div.—Harold Weiss
V-P., Mktg.—Jay Buchsbaum
V-P., Metro Mktg.—Howard Wang
SIC—2084; NAICS—312130; *Corporate headquarters & wine; Brand name—Baron Herzog; Kedem; Bartenura; Teal Lake; Alfasi; Goose Bay*
Employs—150; Estab.—1948
Sales—$50Mil–$100Mil
Distrib.—Intl.
Privately owned partnership

### †STEVENS INDUSTRIES, INC.

39 Avenue C, P.O. Box 8 (07002)
**Phone—(201) 437-6500**
Fax—(201) 437-0366
www.dunbarsales.com
Email—maryann@rubensteinprop.com
Pres.—William Rubenstein
Sr. Sales Coord.—Maryann Flora
SIC—5172; 5198; 5169; *Distributor of lubricants, corrosion preventatives, coating compounds & epoxies*
Employs—15; Estab.—1965
Sales—$3,000
20,000 sq ft site, Distrib.—Intl.
Privately owned corporation
AKA: Stevens-Dunbar Cos., Inc.

### VERTELLUS PERFORMANCE MATERIALS, INC.

Div. of Vertellus Specialties, Inc.
40 Avenue A (07002)
**Phone—(201) 858-8810**
National—(800) 227-2436
Fax—(201) 437-2728
www.vertellus.com
Dir., Bus.—Tom Pensak
SIC—3479; 2891; NAICS—325520; *Coatings & adhesives*
Employs—40; Estab.—1982
Distrib.—Intl.
Privately owned corporation
ISO rating—9002
Parent co.—Vertellus Specialties, Inc., Indianapolis, IN
Phone—(317) 247-8141
See Parent Co. Section for full profile.

## Bayville

(Ocean—S.E.)

### ACE CRETE PRODUCTS, INC.

Div. of New Jersey Pulverizing Co., Inc.
250 Hickory Ln. (08721)
**Phone—(732) 269-1400**
Fax—(732) 269-1414
www.acecreteproducts.com
Email—inforequest@acecreteproducts.com
Pres.—Martin E. Tanzer
Plt. Mgr.—Robert McGowan
SIC—1442; 3272; 5032; NAICS—212321; *Manufacturer & distributor of industrial & specialty washed & dried high grade silica sands, blended bagged cement mixes, blacktop, grouts, industrial cement colors & blended specialty products*
Employs—12; Estab.—1960
Sales—$5Mil–$6Mil
300,000 sq ft site, Distrib.—Local
Privately owned sub-S corp.
Parent co.—New Jersey Pulverizing Co., Inc., Syosset, NY
Phone—(516) 921-9595
See Parent Co. Section for full profile.

### AMERICAN CUSTOM FABRICATORS, INC.

215-A Hickory Ln. (08721)
**Phone—(732) 237-0037**
National—(800) 338-8223
Fax—(732) 237-0039
www.americanrailings.com
Email—info@americanrailings.com
Pres.—Jacqueline Schinder
V-P. & Hum. Res. Mgr.—Robert Schinder, Jr.
Shop Foreman—Greg Murray
SIC—3446; 3444; NAICS—332323; *Structural aluminum, ornamental metal, stainless steel, aluminum & bronze fabrication of hand railings & truck ladder racks*
Employs—8; Estab.—1983
7,200 sq ft site, Distrib.—Regional
Privately owned corporation

### ATLANTIC COASTAL WELDING, INC.

16 Butler Blvd. (08721)
**Phone—(732) 269-1088**
            (609) 618-1602
National—(800) 434-8265
Fax—(732) 269-7992
www.speedytanks.com
Email—info@speedytanks.com
Pres.—John Gallo
Off. Mgr.—Tricia Lattanzi
SIC—3499; 3444; 3312; 3599; *Welding & metal, aluminum & steel fabrication of gas, diesel, holding, water & storage tanks, including waterjet cutting services*
Employs—6; Estab.—1978
Sales—$500,000–$1Mil
6,000 sq ft site, Distrib.—National
Privately owned corporation

### ELC AMERICA CORP.

235-B Hickory Ln. (08721)
**Phone—(732) 269-5274**
Fax—(732) 269-5276
www.olympic-tool.com
Email—ecassella@olympic-tool.com
Pres.—Edmund Cassella
Off. Mgr.—Amy Henry
SIC—3599; *Precision & general machining job shop*
Employs—8; Estab.—2004
Sales—$500,000–$1Mil
5,000 sq ft site, Distrib.—National
Sole ownership
DBA: Olympic Tool Co.

### EMPIRE BLENDED PRODUCTS, INC.

Div. of New Jersey Pulverizing Co., Inc.
250 Hickory Ln. (08721)
**Phone—(732) 269-4949**
Fax—(732) 269-0497
www.empireblended.com
Email—customerservice@empireblended.com
Pres.—Jay Gornitzky
V-P.—Randy Gornitzky
Off. Mgr.—Nancy Steward
SIC—3272; *Concrete products; Brand name—Empire Blended; Ace-Crete; Rainbow*
Employs—31; Estab.—1946
85,000 sq ft site, Distrib.—Regional
Privately owned corporation
Parent co.—New Jersey Pulverizing Co., Inc., Syosset, NY
Phone—(516) 921-9595
See Parent Co. Section for full profile.

### GREENER CORP.

4 Helmly St. (08721)
**Phone—(732) 341-3880**
National—(800) 634-9933
Fax—(732) 286-7842
www.greenercorp.com
Email—custserv@greenercorp.com
V-P.—Matthew Wojtech
SIC—3565; NAICS—333993; *Parts for packaging machinery*
Employs—24; Estab.—1977
Distrib.—Intl.
Privately owned corporation

### HENRIQUES YACHTS, INC.

198 Hilton Ave. (08721)
**Phone—(732) 269-1180**
Fax—(732) 269-1606
www.henriquesyachts.com
Email—henriquesyachts@henriquesyachts.net
CEO—Manuel Costa
Pres.—Natalie Henriques-Costa
V-P.—Maria Henriques-DeMers
SIC—3732; *Sportsfishing boats*
Employs—7; Estab.—1977
40,000 sq ft site, Distrib.—Intl.
Privately owned corporation

### MOUNTAIN MILLWORK, INC.

1014 Route 9 *(08721)*
**Phone—(732) 606-1701**
Fax—(732) 606-1707
www.mountainmillworkinc.com
Email—cvirgil@mountainmillworkinc.com
Ptnr.—Edward Pryce
Ptnr.—Raymond Pryce
Buyer—Charlie Virgil
SIC—2431; NAICS—321900; *Architectural woodwork*
Employs—7
Sales—$500,000–$1Mil
Distrib.—Local
AKA: Pryce Bros. Woodworking

### PART-RITE, INC.

19 Butler Ave. (08721)
**Phone—(732) 269-5000**
National—(800) 225-0020
Fax—(732) 269-9734
www.part-rite.com
Email—partrite@verizon.net
Manager—Mark Buglio
SIC—3714; 5013; *Rebuilt automotive torque converters & distributor of automotive transmission parts*
Employs—12; Estab.—1979
7,500 sq ft site, Distrib.—Regional
Privately owned corporation

### QUALITY ATTRIBUTES SOFTWARE

1 Pelican Dr., Ste. 6 (08721)
**Phone—(732) 504-2200**
Fax—(732) 269-5462
www.qualityattributes.com
Email—info@qualityattributes.com
Ex. V-P.—Ken Echevarria

GEOGRAPHICAL

## Bayville—(cont.)

V-P., Mktg. & PR—Marisa K. Diaz
V-P., Hum. Res.—Ashley Garrigus
V-P.—John Butterly
SIC—7372; *Facility data management software development for building energy & cost management applications; Brand name—IntelliFace™*
Employs—8; Estab.—2003
Distrib.—National
Privately owned corporation

### R A M HYDRAULICS

215 B. Hickory Ln., P.O. Box 416 (08721)
Phone—(732) 237-0904
Fax—(732) 237-0906
www.ramhydraulicsinc.com
Pres.—Michael Mattei
SIC—3593; NAICS—333995; *Hydraulic cylinders*
Employs—7; Estab.—1987
Sales—$1Mil-$2.5Mil
Distrib.—Regional
Sole ownership

### ST. CROIX MARINE PRODUCTS, INC.

235 Hickory Ln. (08721)
Phone—(732) 237-8800
Fax—(732) 237-8811
www.davit.com
Email—stcroix@davit.com
Pres.—Steve Tull
SIC—3536; NAICS—333923; *Sail & power boat removable & rotating davits*
Employs—6; Estab.—1980
Sales—$500,000-$1Mil
Distrib.—Intl.
Privately owned corporation

### TOWER SYSTEMS, INC.- ATLANTIC TOWERS & ST. CROIX MARINE PRODUCTS

235 Hickory Ln., P.O. Box D (08721)
Phone—(732) 237-8800
National—(800) 831-8889
Fax—(732) 237-8811
www.atlantictowers.com
Email—sgolden@atlantictowers.com
Pres.—Steve Tull
Dir., Sales, Marine—Shelley Golden
SIC—3446; 3444; 3429; 2531; NAICS—336612; *Fabricated aluminum boat accessories, t-tops, outriggers, towers, arches & deck covers, davits, cranes & Euro Helm seating; Brand name—Atlantic Towers; Tower In A Box; St. Croix Euro Helm*
Employs—7; Estab.—1981
Distrib.—Intl.
Privately owned corporation
AKA: Atlantic Towers & St. Croix Marine Products

### TREK, INC.

43 Cranmer Rd., P.O. Box 275 (08721)
Phone—(732) 269-6300
Fax—(732) 269-9178
www.treklabel.com
Email—sales@treklabel.com
Pres.—Jack Dynarski
Corp. Secy.—Joyce Dynarski
Sales Mgr.—John J. Dynarski, Jr.
SIC—2672; 2759; NAICS—322222; *Short-run digital printed labels, including sequential numbering, bar codes, color press printing, label dispensers, applicators, printers supplies & accessories; Brand name—Datamax; Primera; Sato; Zebra; Labelmate; Compulabel; Sony*
Employs—4; Estab.—1983
Distrib.—National
Privately owned corporation
DBA: Trek Label

### URNER BARRY PUBLICATIONS

182 Queens Blvd. (08721)
Mail addr: P.O. Box 389, Toms River (08754)
Phone—(732) 240-5330
National—(800) 932-0617
Fax—(732) 341-0891
www.urnerbarry.com
Email—printshop@urnerbarry.com
Pres., Publisher—Paul Brown, Jr.
Accts. & Sales & Mktg. Mgr.—Jay Bailey
SIC—2759; 2752; 2721; NAICS—323100; *Commercial, offset, envelope, business card & letterhead printing & market news publishing*
Employs—40; Estab.—2001
Sales—$5Mil-$10Mil (est)
Distrib.—Local
Privately owned corporation

### VIRTUAL MANAGEMENT SERVICES CORP.

242 Atlantic City Blvd., Ste. 12 (08721)
Phone—(732) 281-1350
National—(877) 323-2288
Fax—(732) 281-1365
www.vmscctv.com
Email—jason@vmscctv.com
Owner—Jason Gonzalez
SIC—3663; NAICS—334220; *Video surveillance equipment, including CCTVs*
Employs—5; Estab.—2003
Distrib.—National
Privately owned corporation

### ZONE TWO, INC.

245 Hickory Ln. (08721)
Phone—(732) 237-0767
Fax—(732) 237-0768
Email—zone.orders@comcast.net
Pres.—Rick Gettis
GM—Nancy Berthelsen
SIC—2396; *Textile screen printing*
Employs—11; Estab.—1985
Sales—$500,000-$1Mil
7,500 sq ft site, Distrib.—Local
Privately owned corporation

## Beachwood
(Ocean—S.E.)

### ACCENT APPAREL LLC

405 Atlantic City Blvd. (08722)
Phone—(732) 341-7576
Fax—(732) 341-8118
www.aaipromo.com
Email—kevin@accentapparelinc.com
Owner—Kevin McMahon
Pres.—Lisa McMahon
V-P.—Kevin J. McMahon, Sr.
SIC—2395; 2396; 2759; *Embroidery, screen printing & direct-to-garment printing of t-shirts, staff shirts, jackets, hats, uniforms, signs & banners*
Employs—3; Estab.—2004
Sales—under $500,000
2,800 sq ft site, Distrib.—National
Limited Liability Company

### BARRE MONUMENTS

114 Atlantic City Blvd. (08722)
Phone—(732) 240-2888
Fax—(732) 240-0940

Owner—Michael Maloney
SIC—3366; 3281; NAICS—331525; *Cast bronze & granite memorials*
Employs—3; Estab.—1973
Distrib.—Regional
Sole ownership

### MONARCH MOOR WHIPS

1104 Tiller Ave. (08722)
Phone—(732) 244-4584
National—(800) 793-3833
Fax—(732) 341-0282
www.monarchproducts.com
Email—brushaber@monarchproducts.com
Pres. & Fin. Mgr.—Donald Brushaber
Off. Mgr.—Debbie Baldwin
SIC—3599; *Marine machining job shop*
Employs—3; Estab.—1971
Sales—$500,000-$1Mil
4,200 sq ft site, Distrib.—Intl.
Privately owned sub-S corp.

### P D Q ELECTRONICS COMPONENTS CO., INC.

1113 Tiller Ave. (08722)
Phone—(732) 281-0025
Fax—(732) 281-0047
www.blazakmfg.com
Email—tom@blazakmfg.com
Owner, Pres. & R & D Mgr.—Thomas Blazak
Fin. & MIS Mgr.—Ellen Mondelli
SIC—3469; *Metal stampings*
Employs—9; Estab.—1955
Sales—$500,000-$1Mil
10,000 sq ft site, Distrib.—National
Privately owned corporation

### SIGN UP SIGNS, LLC

649 Atlantic City Blvd., Unit 2 (08722)
Phone—(732) 240-6025
Fax—(732) 240-6025
www.larrythesignguy.com
Ptnr. & Mng. Member—Larry Snover
Ptnr.—Steve Johnson
SIC—3993; *Interior & exterior signs, vinyl banners & tradeshow signage*
Employs—2
Limited Liability Company
AKA: Sign Up Signs & Promotions

## Bedminster
(Somerset—N.E.)

### AERIE PHARMACEUTICALS, INC.

135 U.S. Highway 206, Ste. 15 (07921)
Phone—(908) 470-4320
Fax—(908) 470-4329
www.aeriepharma.com
Email—ssingh@aeriepharma.com
CEO—Vince Anido
SIC—2834; *Pharmaceutical drug candidates for glaucoma in Phase III clinical trials*
Employs—20; Estab.—2007
Sales—$10Mil-$25Mil
Distrib.—National
Privately owned corporation

### NPS PHARMACEUTICALS, INC. (H Q)

550 Hills Dr. (07921)
Phone—(908) 450-5300
Fax—(908) 450-5351
www.npsp.com
Email—info@npsp.com
CEO—Francois Nader
Pres., Intl.—Eric Pauwels
CFO—Luke M. Beshar
Ex. V-P., Chief Med. Officer—Roger J. Garceau
Dir., Hum. Res.—Jeffrey Brodskey

SIC—2834; *Corporate headquarters; drug candidates in Phase III clinical trials (mfg. subcontracted)*
Employs—200; Estab.—1982
Sales—$100Mil-$250Mil (est)
Distrib.—Intl.
Publicly owned corporation

### SILOA, INC. (H Q)

2493 Lamington Rd., Ste. C (07921)
Phone—(908) 234-9040
Fax—(908) 234-9015
www.siloa.com
Pres.—Mark Bellard
Dir., Prod. Dev.—Joe Walsh
SIC—3089; 3499; 3085; NAICS—326160; *Corporate headquarters; plastic & metal molded cosmetic packaging supplies & blow molded bottles (mfg. done overseas)*
Employs—3; Estab.—2000
Sales—over $3Mil
Distrib.—Intl.
Privately owned corporation

## Belford
(Monmouth—N.E.)

### CENTURY FABRICATING CO., INC.

84 Railroad Ave. (07718)
Phone—(732) 495-3200
Fax—(732) 787-5838
www.centuryweldingnj.com
GM & R & D Mgr.—Daniel Nankenvis
SIC—3312; *Steel fabrication*
Employs—1; Estab.—1948
Sales—under $500,000
5,750 sq ft site, Distrib.—Regional
Privately owned corporation

### KERRY WILKENS, INC.

780 State Route 36 (07718)
Phone—(732) 787-0070
National—(866) 852-3224
Fax—(732) 787-0591
www.beachtimeproducts.com
Email—denisea@jeanscanvas.com
Pres., Store Mgr.—Kerry Wilkens
Accts. Mgr.—Denisea D. Phelps
SIC—2394; 2369; 2339; 2329; NAICS—314912; *Canvas tarpaulins, custom sandbox covers, awnings, sail bags, boat covers & enclosures, nautical gifts & beach gear*
Employs—7; Estab.—1979
Company-wide: 13
Sales—$1.4Mil
6,000 sq ft site, Distrib.—Intl.
Privately owned corporation
AKAs: Jeans Canvas & Resort Chairs & Custom Sandbox Covers

### UNIVERSITY PUBLICATIONS

562 Morley Ct. (07718)
Phone—(732) 495-9000
National—(800) 473-9177
Fax—(732) 495-9002
Email—universitypub@comcast.net
Owner—Frank Lake
Sales Rep.—Karen Stone
SIC—2741; *Daily planner & college yearbook publishing*
Employs—7; Estab.—1986
Sales—under $500,000
Distrib.—Regional
Privately owned corporation

### ZEEK'S TEES

515 Highway 36 (07718)
Phone—(732) 291-2700
Fax—(732) 291-2745
www.zeekstees.com
Email—frank@zeekstees.com
Owner—Frank Zechman
Fin. Mgr.—Dianne Zechman

## Belford—(cont.)

SIC—2395; 2396; 2759; 3993; *Textile embroidery, screen & digital printing & advertising specialties*
Employs—6; Estab.—1984
Sales—$500,000-$1Mil
1,300 sq ft site, Distrib.—National
Sole ownership

## Belle Mead

(Somerset—N.E.)

### COACTION

50 Kildee Rd. (08502)
**Phone—(888) 682-3050**
Fax—(732) 636-4884
www.coaction.com
Email—info@coaction.com
Pres.—Jagdish Talreja
SIC—7372; *Invoicing, collections & customer risk management software development*
Employs—20
Distrib.—Intl.
Limited Liability Company

## Belleville

(Essex—N.E.)

### AERO PRODUCTS CO.

19-21 N. 8th St. (07109)
**Phone—(973) 759-0959**
Fax—(973) 759-1818
Pres.—David Bucci
SIC—3599; *General machining job shop*
Employs—20; Estab.—1945
Distrib.—National
Privately owned corporation

### AMERICAN CUSTOM HYDRAULICS, INC.

33 Roosevelt Ave. (07109)
**Phone—(973) 751-1440**
Fax—(973) 759-6868
www.americancustomhydraulics.com
Email—amcusthyds@aol.com
Owner—Jean Zachar
Pres.—Ed Sinclair
SIC—3594; 3559; NAICS—333996; *Rebuilt hydraulic equipment & machines*
Employs—28; Estab.—1988
Sales—$5.7Mil
Distrib.—Intl.
Privately owned corporation

### ARDWYN BINDING PRODUCTS CO.

681 Main St., Bldg. 7 (07109)
**Phone—(973) 751-4002**
Fax—(973) 751-6672
Email—k-naeg@aol.com
Ptnr. & Sales Mgr.—Kathy Naegele
Ptnr.—Richard Gilbert
Qual. Mgr.—Adam Gilbert
SIC—2241; NAICS—313221; *Bindings, trimmings, twist cord braids & fringe*
Employs—65; Estab.—1944
50,000 sq ft site, Distrib.—Intl.
Privately owned corporation

### B & M MACHINE CO., INC.

67-69 Greylock Ave. (07109)
**Phone—(973) 751-0789**
Fax—(973) 751-1682
www.bmmachine.com
Email—info@bmmachine.com
Pres.—Richard Bing
GM—Denis Nelson
Sales Mgr.—Kevin Bing
Off. Mgr.—Liz Cifelli

SIC—3599; *Contract machine work & precision machining of metals & plastics, including production runs, short-runs & CNC milling & turning; Brand name—Brusso®; B & M Spring Pin Insertion tool*
Employs—18; Estab.—1947
10,000 sq ft site, Distrib.—Intl.
Privately owned corporation

### BALDI IRON WORKS, INC.

158 Belmont Ave. (07109)
**Phone—(973) 751-4338**
Fax—(973) 751-6977
Pres.—Rocco Baldi
Secy-Treas.—Judith Baldi
SIC—3446; NAICS—332323; *Ornamental iron stairs*
Employs—5; Estab.—1978
Sales—$500,000-$1Mil
Distrib.—Regional
Privately owned corporation

### BEISLER WEIDMANN CO., INC.

233 Cortlandt St. (07109)
**Phone—(973) 759-5020**
Fax—(973) 759-2754
www.bwpackaging.com
Email—beweco@verizon.net
Pres.—Warren Beisler
Salesman—Harry Lee
SIC—2653; NAICS—322211; *Corrugated boxes*
Employs—12; Estab.—1921
Distrib.—National
Privately owned corporation

### BINDI NORTH AMERICA, INC.

507 Main St. (07109)
**Phone—(973) 751-1754**
Fax—(973) 751-5443
www.bindiusa.com
Email—service@bindiusa.com
Pur. Mgr.—Trish Bortone
Manager—Christopher Clementius
Hum. Res. Coord.—Samara Salarios
SIC—2024; *Frozen desserts*
Employs—50; Estab.—2000
Distrib.—Intl.
Privately owned corporation
Parent co.—Bindi North America, Inc., Kearny, NJ
Phone—(973) 812-8118
See Parent Co. Section for full profile.

### †BK CLASSIC AUTO GLASS, LLC

441 Cortlandt St. (07109)
**Phone—(973) 759-1485**
National—(800) 288-6452
Fax—(973) 450-4150
Email—bkclassicag@gmail.com
Owner—Robert Kent
SIC—5013; *Distributor of classic automotive glass*
Employs—1; Estab.—2013
Distrib.—Intl.
Limited Liability Company

### COUNTER-FIT QUICK PRINTING, INC.

145 Newark Ave. (07109)
**Phone—(201) 420-7926**
Fax—(973) 751-5688
Pres.—Alan Nelson
SIC—2752; 2791; NAICS—323122; *Offset printing & typesetting*
Employs—1; Estab.—1984
Sales—under $500,000
Distrib.—Intl.
Privately owned corporation

### CZAR, INC.

51 Montgomery St. (07109)
**Phone—(973) 278-4002**
Fax—(973) 841-2832
www.czarincorporated.com
Email—aza-czarincorporated@gmail.com
Pres., Pers. Mgr.—Aza Gershkovich

SIC—2511; *Wooden furniture*
Employs—11; Estab.—1984
12,000 sq ft site, Distrib.—Local
Privately owned corporation

### D & D MILLWORK CO., INC.

10-12 N. 7th St. (07109-1116)
**Phone—(973) 759-6336**
    (973) 759-6663
National—(877) 941-5724
Fax—(973) 759-7737
www.ddmillworkcompany.com
Email—baddnd@comcast.net
Pres.—Bernard D'Avella
SIC—2431; 2541; 2542; NAICS—326130; *Wooden & plastic laminate cabinets, countertops & millwork for commercial & residential applications & trade show projects, including furniture repair & refinishing*
Employs—5; Estab.—1946
Sales—under $1Mil
3,600 sq ft site, Distrib.—Regional
Privately owned corporation

### DON'S DRAPERY MFG. CO.

145 Heckel St. (07109)
**Phone—(973) 751-1544**
National—(888) 655-3667
Fax—(973) 751-6116
www.donsdrapery.com
Email—sales@donsdrapery.com
Pres.—Joyce Dolan
V-P.—Robert Spagnardi
SIC—2391; NAICS—314121; *Draperies, blinds & window treatments*
Employs—16; Estab.—1954
Sales—$500,000-$1Mil
13,000 sq ft site, Distrib.—Local
Privately owned corporation

### EASTERN MOLDING CO., INC.

597 Main St. (07109)
**Phone—(973) 759-0220**
Fax—(973) 759-0294
www.easternmoldingcompany.com
Email—info@easternmoldingcompany.com
Pres.—Peter De Nicholas
Plt. Mgr.—Joe Wolf
SIC—3069; *Molded rubber parts*
Employs—7; Estab.—1948
Distrib.—Regional
Privately owned corporation

### ECUADORIAN RAINFOREST, LLC

25 Main St., Bldg. 6 (07109-3059)
**Phone—(973) 759-2002**
Fax—(973) 759-3002
www.intotherainforest.com
Email—info@intotherainforest.com
Pres.—Marlene Siegel
V-P.—Steve Siegel
SIC—2833; *Contract manufacturer of dietary supplements & fruit, marine, spice & vegetable powders & extracts for the nutraceutical industry*
Employs—15; Estab.—1997
Sales—$5Mil-$10Mil (est)
Distrib.—Intl.
Limited Liability Company

### EMMC CO.

1 Nicola Pl. (07109)
**Phone—(973) 751-0100**
Fax—(973) 751-0123
Email—emmc_co@msn.com
Pres.—Byshek Gasior
Machinist—Tom Gasior
SIC—3599; 2759; *General machining, fabricating & welding job shop & commercial printing*
Employs—3; Estab.—2003
Sales—under $500,000
9,000 sq ft site, Distrib.—Regional
Sole ownership

### EMPRO PRODUCTS CO., INC.

47 Montgomery St. (07109)
**Phone—(973) 279-1010**
National—(800) 752-0675
Fax—(973) 279-5088
www.emproducts.com
Email—orders@emproducts.com
Pres.—Darsh Mehta
V-P., Sales—Vinny Verma
SIC—3993; *Interior & exterior signs*
Employs—10; Estab.—1987
Sales—$500,000-$1Mil
Distrib.—National
Sole ownership

### †ENTERPRISE HVAC SUPPLY

701 Main St. *(07109)*
**Phone—(973) 759-6900**
Fax—(973) 759-6400
www.enterprisehvacsupply.org
Email—sales@enterprisehvacsupply.org
Ptnr.—Humberto Gonzalez
Ptnr.—Beatrice Gonzalez
SIC—5075; NAICS—332813; *Distributor of HVAC products, machinery, equipment, parts & accessories*
Employs—6; Estab.—1998
Sales—under $500,000
Distrib.—Local
Sole ownership

### EXPRESS PRESS

145 North Ave. (07109)
**Phone—(973) 751-1287**
Fax—(973) 751-5688
Email—rob.express@comcast.net
Owner—Robert LaRiccia
Sales Rep.—Sal Rosamilia
SIC—2752; NAICS—323100; *Offset printing*
Employs—2; Estab.—1984
Sales—under $500,000
Distrib.—Local
Sole ownership

### FOAM RUBBER FABRICATORS, INC.

740 Washington Ave., Ste. 1 (07109)
**Phone—(973) 751-1445**
Fax—(973) 751-7014
Pres.—Arthur Lerner
SIC—3086; NAICS—326100; *Urethane foam fabrication*
Employs—15; Estab.—1960
Distrib.—Regional
Privately owned sub-S corp.

### †G & K SERVICES, INC.

137 Ralph St. (07109)
**Phone—(973) 751-0464**
Fax—(973) 751-4140
www.gkservices.com
Email—gkweb@gkservices.com
Plt. Mgr.—Joseph E. Sherwood
SIC—5136; 5137; *Distributor of general purpose & government uniforms*
Employs—70
Sales—$25Mil-$50Mil
Distrib.—National
Publicly owned corporation
Parent co.—G & K Services, Inc., Minnetonka, MN
Phone—(952) 912-5500
See Parent Co. Section for full profile.

### GLOBAL COLORANTS, INC.

83 Roosevelt Ave. (07109)
**Phone—(973) 751-2227**
Fax—(973) 751-2606
Email—globalfdc@aol.com
V-P. & Plt. Mgr.—Frank Penta
SIC—2844; NAICS—325600; *Chemical cosmetic & personal care product raw materials*
Employs—2; Estab.—1996
Sales—under $500,000
Distrib.—National
Privately owned corporation

GEOGRAPHICAL

## Belleville—(cont.)

**HE DESIGNS & AWNINGS**
75 Rutgers St. (07109)
**Phone—(973) 751-0030**
Fax—(973) 751-5128
Email—signs@finishlinenj.com
Pres.—Kevin Horan
V-P.—Chris Horan
SIC—3993; *Signs, vehicle graphics & banners*
Employs—4; Estab.—2011
Sales—under $500,000
Distrib.—Regional
Privately owned corporation

**HILLSIDE WIRE CLOTH, INC.**
109 Roosevelt Ave. (07109)
Mail addr: P.O. Box 1190, Bloomfield (07003-1190)
**Phone—(973) 751-3131**
National—(800) 826-7395
Fax—(973) 470-8183
www.hillsidewirecloth.com
Email—dawn@hillsidewirecloth.com
Pres.—William Messenger
Sales Rep.—Dawn M. Busichio
SIC—3496; *Stainless steel baskets & strainers*
Employs—15; Estab.—1985
Sales—$1Mil-$5Mil
10,000 sq ft site, Distrib.—Intl.
Privately owned corporation

**IDEAL PLATING & POLISHING CO.**
681 Main St., Bldg. 39, P.O. Box 100 *(07109)*
**Phone—(973) 759-5559**
Fax—(973) 759-0277
Email—rfknigge@gmail.com
Pres.—Ronald Knigge
SIC—3471; NAICS—332813; *Electroplating*
Employs—5; Estab.—1920
Distrib.—Local
Privately owned corporation

**J F I PRINTING, INC.**
357 Cortlandt St. (07109)
**Phone—(973) 759-3444**
Fax—(973) 759-3440
Email—jfiindustries@aol.com
Pres.—Joseph Iannone
SIC—2672; NAICS—322222; *Pressure-sensitive adhesive labels flexographic printing*
Employs—4; Estab.—1999
Sales—$1Mil-$2.5Mil
Distrib.—Regional
Privately owned corporation

**NEW ENTRY**
**LABEL TEK, INC.**
357 Cortlandt St., Ste. 4 (07109)
**Phone—(201) 390-3856**
Fax—(973) 759-4550
CEO—Rusty Pace
SIC—2759; *Commercial label printing*
Employs—8; Estab.—2004
Sales—$1Mil-$2.5Mil
1,000 sq ft site, Distrib.—National
Privately owned corporation

**MAGNETIC TICKET & LABEL CORP.**
151 Cortlandt St. (07109)
**Phone—(973) 759-6500**
Fax—(973) 450-4703
www.mtlcard.com
Email—tagsales@magticket.com
Plt. Mgr.—Yahya Kashani
Cust. Serv. Mgr.—Deena Reijers
Shpg. Mgr.—Frank Yagual
SIC—2759; NAICS—323100; *Tags & labels*
Employs—27; Estab.—1988
80,000 sq ft site, Distrib.—Intl.
Privately owned corporation
Parent co.—Magnetic Ticket & Label Corp., Dallas, TX
    Phone—(214) 634-8600
    See Parent Co. Section for full profile.

**MARANGE PRINTING, INC.**
195 Cortlandt St. (07109)
**Phone—(973) 751-3600**
Fax—(973) 751-8711
www.marangeprinting.com
Email—sales@marangeprinting.com
V-P., CEO—Angelo Autiero
Pres.—Mario Autiero
Plt. Mgr.—Phillip Mihalik
Off. Mgr.—Teresa Frankowski
SIC—2759; NAICS—323100; *Commercial printing*
Employs—35; Estab.—1986
Distrib.—National
Sole ownership

**MILLER & SONS, INC.**
24 Belleville Ave. *(07109)*
**Phone—(973) 759-6445**
            (973) 759-6446
Fax—(973) 759-1625
www.millerplatingnj.com
Email—millerplating@aol.com
Ptnr. & V-P.—Edward Miller
Ptnr.—Elizabeth Miller
V-P.—George Miller
SIC—3471; 3479; NAICS—332813; *Electroplating, including anodizing, hard coating, iriditing, black oxide, electroless nickel tin, cadmium zinc, phosphating, passivation, dry film lube & chrome & zinc/nickel alloy/RoHs compliant finishes*
Employs—10; Estab.—1913
Sales—$1Mil-$5Mil
20,000 sq ft site, Distrib.—Regional
Privately owned sub-S corp.

**NATIONAL LIGHTING CO., INC.**
522 Cortlandt St. (07109)
**Phone—(973) 751-1600**
National—(800) 969-6285
Fax—(973) 751-4931
www.natltg.com
Email—wsiegel@natltg.com
Pres.—Warren Siegel
Hum. Res., IT & Off. Mgr.—Wendy Elliott
Bookkeeper—Nidia Bernal
SIC—3646; NAICS—335122; *Commercial lighting fixtures*
Employs—30; Estab.—1941
90,000 sq ft site, Distrib.—National
Privately owned sub-S corp.

**ORTHODOX BAKING CO., INC.**
555 Cortlandt St. (07109)
**Phone—(973) 844-9393**
Fax—(973) 844-0999
www.oberlanderbaking.com
Pres.—Michael Oberlander
GM—Joseph Berger
SIC—2051; 2052; NAICS—311812; *Gluten-free cakes, cookies & brownies*
Employs—10; Estab.—1950
Sales—$500,000-$1Mil
Distrib.—National
Privately owned corporation

**PETRONIO SHOE PRODUCTS CORP.**
305 Cortlandt St. (07109)
**Phone—(973) 751-7579**
Fax—(973) 759-7324
www.petronioshoeproducts.com
Email—info@petronioshoeproducts.com
Pres.—Donald Rinaldi
Plt. Mgr.—Charles Penola
SIC—2842; 2891; NAICS—325612; *Professional-grade cleaning, polishing & adhesive products for shoe repair shops*
Employs—8; Estab.—1926
Sales—$500,000-$1Mil
Distrib.—National
Privately owned corporation

**PRECISION SPECIALTIES**
120 Greylock Ave. (07109)
**Phone—(973) 751-7588**
National—(800) 500-7548
Fax—(973) 759-8608
www.prespec.com
Email—prespec@aol.com
Pres.—Richard Pfuhler
SIC—3451; 3545; NAICS—332721; *Threaded inserts for plastics, ultrasonic, heat & mold-in inserts & custom screw machine products*
Employs—5; Estab.—1986
Sales—$500,000-$1Mil
3,500 sq ft site, Distrib.—National
Privately owned sub-S corp.

**†PREFERRED PLASTICS & PACKAGING CO., INC.**
681 Main St., Ste. 42 (07109)
**Phone—(973) 759-1510**
www.prefplastics.com
Email—info@prefplastics.com
Pres.—Randolph Swickle
CFO—Gary Wool
Cont.—Ron Rizzo
Opers. Mgr.—Kenneth Notaro
SIC—5113; 5162; 5084; *Distributor of packaging materials & equipment, including stretch film & sheet, tape, markers & corrugated boxes; Brand name—AEP Industries; Intertape Polymer Group; Easiwrap*
Employs—30; Estab.—1983
Distrib.—National
Privately owned corporation

**PRESSURE CONTROLS, INC.**
406 Courtlandt St. (07109)
**Phone—(973) 751-5002**
Fax—(973) 751-9653
www.pressurecontrols.biz
Email—pci.paul@verizon.net
Plt. Mgr.—Paul Emmarco
SIC—3679; 3643; NAICS—335931; *Pressure switches, flow switches & vacuum switches*
Employs—26; Estab.—1984
Sales—$1Mil-$2.5Mil
Distrib.—Intl.
Privately owned corporation

**RED DIAMOND CO., INC.**
368 Cortlandt St. (07109)
**Phone—(973) 759-2700**
Fax—(973) 450-0069
www.njsportswear.com
Pres.—Marc Tartaglia
V-P.—Micheal Tartaglia
SIC—2396; *Textile screen printing*
Employs—5; Estab.—1947
Distrib.—Regional
Privately owned corporation

**NEW ENTRY**
**RIVERSIDE GRAPHICS, INC.**
40 Little St. (07109)
**Phone—(973) 844-1011**
Fax—(973) 844-1022
www.riversidegraphics.org
Email—paul@riversidegraphics.org
Pres.—Paul Caprio
SIC—2759; *Commercial printing & graphic design services*
Employs—10; Estab.—2003
Sales—$1Mil-$2.5Mil (est)
5,000 sq ft site, Distrib.—Intl.
Privately owned corporation

**SALEM MFG. CO.**
115 Roosevelt Ave. (07109)
**Phone—(973) 751-6331**
Fax—(973) 751-4711
Email—salemmfg@aol.com
Pres., Sales Mgr.—Jerome M. Lipiec
Admn. Mgr.—Kathy Lipiec

SIC—3451; NAICS—332721; *Screw machine products*
Employs—8; Estab.—1943
Sales—$500,000-$1Mil
6,000 sq ft site, Distrib.—Local
Privately owned corporation

**SPENCER INDUSTRIES, INC.**
80 Holmes St., P.O. Box 128 (07109)
**Phone—(973) 751-2200**
National—(800) 329-0330
Fax—(973) 751-2471
www.spencerindinc.com
Email—sales@spencerindinc.com
Pres.—Martin Lawrence
SIC—3599; 3679; 3496; NAICS—488300; *Corporate headquarters & military replacement parts, including electronic & electromechanical assemblies & tiedowns*
Employs—25; Estab.—1962
Sales—$1Mil-$5Mil
20,000 sq ft site, Distrib.—Intl.
Privately owned sub-S corp.
ISO rating—9001:2008

**STEWART, INC., ROBERT**
120 Little St. (07109)
**Phone—(973) 751-5151**
Fax—(973) 751-2383
Email—stewartinc@worldnet.att.net
Chrm.—George Goldman
Pres.—Robert Goldman
SIC—2323; *Men's & boys' neckwear*
Employs—15; Estab.—1919
Sales—$1Mil-$5Mil
Distrib.—National
Privately owned corporation

**SYMPHONY PRINTING**
19-21 Brook St. (07109)
Mail addr: P.O. Box 1512, Bloomfield (07003)
**Phone—(973) 751-5100**
Fax—(973) 751-0551
www.symphonyprinting.com
Email—solutions@symphonyprinting.com
Pres.—Leroy Johnson
SIC—2759; NAICS—323100; *Commercial printing*
Employs—6; Estab.—1997
Sales—under $500,000
Distrib.—National
Privately owned corporation

**TATZ INDUSTRIES, INC., WILLIAM**
11 Railroad Pl. (07109)
**Phone—(973) 751-0720**
Fax—(973) 751-0166
Email—wtatzind@optonline.net
Pres.—William Tatz
V-P.—Joseph Tatz
Off. Mgr.—Marilyn Bermudez
SIC—2041; 2051; NAICS—311211; *Custom blended bakery products, including co-packaging*
Employs—5; Estab.—1964
Sales—$1Mil
Distrib.—National
Privately owned corporation

**TRI-CHEM, INC.**
681 Main St., Ste. 27 (07109)
**Phone—(973) 751-9200**
Fax—(973) 450-1260
www.trichem.com
Email—trichemss@aol.com
Pres.—Jitu Patel
Plt. Mgr.—Richard Keegan
SIC—3952; *Water-based craft paints*
Employs—4; Estab.—1949
Distrib.—Intl.
Privately owned corporation

**UNIPACK, INC.**
681 Main St., Bldg. 27 (07109)
**Phone—(973) 450-9880**
Fax—(973) 450-4858

## Belleville—(cont.)

www.unipackinc.com
Email—infonj@unipackinc.com
Pres.—Dinesh Patel
GM—Jitu Patel
SIC—2844; NAICS—325600;
Toiletries
Employs—10; Estab.—1992
Sales—$500,000-$1Mil
20,000 sq ft site, Distrib.—National
Privately owned corporation

### V M C DIE CUTTING CORP.
357 Cortlandt St. (07109)
**Phone—(973) 450-4655**
Fax—(973) 450-0093
www.vmcdiecutting.net
Pres.—Vincenza Reczynski
Plt. Mgr.—Victor Reczynski
Prodn. Mgr.—Chris Reczynski
Pressman—Mike Reczynski
SIC—2675; 2789; NAICS—
323121; Die cutting, embossing,
foil stamping & gold leafing of
paper
Employs—4; Estab.—1988
Sales—$500,000-$1Mil
Distrib.—Local
Privately owned corporation

### VAC-U-MAX
69 William St. (07109)
**Phone—(973) 759-4600**
National—(800) 822-8629
Fax—(973) 759-6449
www.vac-u-max.com
Email—info@vac-u-max.com
Pres., CEO—Stevens P. Pendleton
V-P., Secy-Treas.—Charlotte W.
Pendleton
V-P., Sales & Mktg. & Asst. GM—
Doan Pendleton
V-P., Admn. & Fin.—Rose Brosius
Sales Mgr., Intl.—Ben Samuel
Prodn. Mgr.—Mike Lemanowicz
Chief Engr.—Tony Branco
Pur. Agt.—Mark McGuire
SIC—3535; 3589; NAICS—
333922; Industrial vacuum
cleaners & pneumatic conveying
equipment
Employs—50; Estab.—1955
70,000 sq ft site, Distrib.—Intl.
Privately owned sub-S corp.

### VERNA PRINTING CO., INC.
85 Washington Ave. (07109)
**Phone—(973) 751-6462**
Fax—(973) 759-4939
Email—vernaprinting@aol.com
Pres.—John Verna
Corp. Secy.—Sharon Verna
SIC—2752; NAICS—323100;
Offset printing
Employs—8; Estab.—1970
Sales—under $500,000
Distrib.—Local
Privately owned corporation

### WHEAL-GRACE CORP.
300 Ralph St., P.O. Box 67 (07109)
**Phone—(973) 450-8100**
Fax—(973) 450-5394
www.wheal-grace.com
Email—info@wheal-grace.com
Pres.—Nancy Salvini
V-P., GM—Jim Parrinello
Dir., Mktg.—Emil Salvini
IT Mgr.—Scott Nagle
SIC—2759; 2752; NAICS—
323100; Commercial, offset &
digital printing; Brand name—
Green Print environmentally
friendly printing
Employs—19; Estab.—1949
Sales—$6Mil
23,400 sq ft site, Distrib.—Intl.
Privately owned sub-S corp.

### WILLIAM USDAN & SONS LLC
140 Little St. (07109)
**Phone—(973) 844-9988**
Fax—(973) 844-9909

www.wm-usdan.com
Email—sales@wm-usdan.com
Pres.—Simon Markman
SIC—2679; 2395; 5199; NAICS—
322200; Paper & fabric
converting & distributor of paper
& yarn for home furnishings &
apparel & printed tissue for
plastic interleaving, shipping &
factory supplies; Brand name—
PLEAT-X
Employs—5; Estab.—1925
Sales—$1Mil-$2.5Mil
25,000 sq ft site, Distrib.—National
Limited Liability Company

### YERG ACCOUNTING SUPPLIES
85 Washington Ave. (07109)
**Phone—(973) 759-4041**
National—(800) 724-5308
Fax—(973) 759-5446
www.yergpads.com
Email—yergpads@comcast.net
Pres.—Kathleen Yerg Marmo
Secy., Off. Mgr.—Frank P. Marmo
SIC—2621; NAICS—322100;
Columnar accounting pads &
analysis filing covers & pads;
Brand name—Yerg Softone
Analysis Pads; Improved
Workpaper Covers
Employs—3; Estab.—1909
Sales—$400,000
7,500 sq ft site, Distrib.—National
Privately owned corporation

---

## Bellmawr
(Camden—S.W.)

### †AIRGAS EAST, INC.
121 Stanley Ave. (08031)
**Phone—(856) 931-0900**
National—(888) 718-0685
Fax—(856) 933-0129
www.airgas.com
Email—info@airgas.com
GM—Joe Sergi
SIC—5084; 5085; Distributor of
welding equipment & supplies,
including gases
Employs—2; Estab.—1980
Sales—under $500,000
Distrib.—National
Publicly owned corporation
Parent co.—Airgas East, Inc.,
Salem, NH
Phone—(603) 890-4600
See Parent Co. Section for full profile.

### AIRGAS EAST, INC.
270 Benigno Blvd. (08031)
**Phone—(856) 933-0544**
Fax—(856) 933-1606
www.airgas.com
Email—info@airgas.com
Sales & Mktg. Mgr.—Sue Krotzer
Plt. Mgr.—Rob Kimley
Dist. Mgr.—Ken Short
Supervisor—Christopher Clark
SIC—2813; NAICS—325120;
Medical gases
Employs—30; Estab.—1986
Distrib.—National
Publicly owned corporation
Parent co.—Airgas East, Inc.,
Salem, NH
Phone—(603) 890-4600
See Parent Co. Section for full profile.

### AMERICAN AUTOWIRE
150 Heller Pl. (08031)
**Phone—(856) 933-0801**
         (856) 933-0802
National—(800) 482-9473
Fax—(856) 933-0805
www.americanautowire.com
Email—info@americanautowire.com
Pres.—Michael Manning
COO—Jim Cardona
V-P.—Frank Colonna
Dir., IT—Jeff Moore
Fin. & Hum. Res. Mgr.—Keith
Smith

SIC—3679; Wiring harnesses, kits
& accessories for the street rod
industry; Brand name—Highway
Series; Factory Fit; Builder
Series; Classic Update Series;
Power Plus Series
Employs—67; Estab.—1987
Sales—over $5Mil
28,500 sq ft site, Distrib.—Intl.
Privately owned sub-S corp.

### †CAMDEN IRON & METAL, INC.
143 Harding Ave. (08031)
**Phone—(856) 365-7500**
National—(800) 727-2748
Fax—(856) 219-3876
www.emrgroup.com
Email—ukinfo@emrgroup.com
Pres., CEO—Joseph Balzano
IT Mgr.—Chris Healey
Hum. Res. Mgr.—Stephen D'ottavi
SIC—5093; Corporate
headquarters & wholesaler of
scrap iron & nonferrous metals
Employs—38; Estab.—1929
Distrib.—National
Privately owned corporation
AKA: Eastern Metal Recycling

### CONCORD PRODUCTS CO., INC.
251 Benigno Blvd. (08031)
**Phone—(856) 933-3000**
National—(800) 220-5043
Fax—(856) 933-9339
www.concordproducts.com
Email—sales@
concordproducts.com
Pres.—Larry Anthonsen
V-P., Opers.—Erik L. Anthonsen
SIC—2522; NAICS—337214;
Office furniture; Brand name—
System 2000; System 1900;
Conceil 2.0; Conceil 3.0;
Freedom; Constow; Conseat;
Latvenas; Latvenas Cube desk;
Convene; Condition; Heaton;
Lepold; Architectural Elements;
Benched; Architectural
Simplicity
Employs—55; Estab.—1968
80,000 sq ft site, Distrib.—National
Privately owned corporation

### DAVIS PAPER DIMENSIONS, INC.
400 Benigno Blvd. (08031)
**Phone—(856) 931-6040**
Fax—(856) 931-9951
Email—dpdproduction@aol.com
Pres.—Betty Davis
V-P.—Fred Davis
Corp. Secy.—Joanne Wescott
SIC—2675; NAICS—322200; Die
cutting, embossing, foil
stampings & hand assembly
work
Employs—16; Estab.—1991
Sales—$5Mil-$10Mil
Distrib.—Intl.
Privately owned corporation

### D'ORAZIO FOODS, INC.
960 Creek Rd. (08031)
Mail addr: P.O. Box 243, Bellmawr
(08099)
**Phone—(856) 931-1900**
National—(888) 328-7287
Fax—(856) 931-1907
www.dorazio.com
Email—tdorazio@dorazio.com
Pres.—Anthony D'Orazio
V-P., Sales & Mktg.—Terri
D'Orazio-Bank
V-P., Opers.—Frank D'Orazio
SIC—2098; NAICS—311823;
Frozen pasta
Employs—100; Estab.—1964
Distrib.—National
Privately owned corporation

### EVERGREEN PRINTING
101 Haag Ave. (08031)
**Phone—(856) 933-0222**
National—(800) 922-0252
Fax—(856) 933-2972

www.egpp.com
V-P., Sales & Mktg.—John
Dreisbach
Whse. Mgr.—Bob Metzger
SIC—2711; Newspaper printing &
publishing
Employs—100; Estab.—1961
Sales—$50Mil-$100Mil
Distrib.—National
Privately owned corporation

### FAMILY SCREEN PRINTING, INC.
104 W. Browning Rd. (08031)
**Phone—(856) 933-2780**
Fax—(856) 933-2782
Email—familyscreenprinting@
comcast.net
Pres.—Bob Armstrong
Off. Mgr.—Joyce Gallen
Graphic Artist—Alex Garcia
SIC—2396; 2395; Apparel screen
printing & embroidery
Employs—6; Estab.—1991
Sales—$1Mil-$2.5Mil
Distrib.—Local
Privately owned corporation

### G & M WELDING & FABRICATING, INC.
31 W. Browning Rd. (08031)
**Phone—(856) 931-0443**
Fax—(856) 931-0424
www.imperialwelding.net
Email—info@imperialwelding.net
Pres.—George Liontas
SIC—3312; 3499; Steel & metal
fabrication
Employs—5; Estab.—1988
Sales—under $500,000
2,500 sq ft site, Distrib.—Local
Privately owned corporation
AKA: Imperial Welding

### †GENERAL FLOOR INDUSTRIES
190 Benigno Blvd. (08031)
**Phone—(856) 931-0012**
Fax—(856) 931-0731
www.generalfloor.com
Email—info@generalfloor.com
Pres.—David Cometz
V-P.—Michael Cometz
Corp. Secy.—Sonia Cometz
SIC—5023; 5031; Company
headquarters & wholesaler of
carpet & laminate, hardwood &
vinyl flooring
Employs—85; Estab.—1983
Distrib.—Regional
Privately owned corporation

### †HADDONSTONE (USA) LTD.
201 Heller Pl. (08031)
**Phone—(856) 931-7011**
Fax—(856) 931-0040
www.haddonstone.com
Email—info@haddonstone.com
V-P.—Myla Policarpo
SIC—5032; Distributor of fine cast
limestone garden & landscape
ornaments, fireplaces &
architectural stonework
Employs—8; Estab.—1991
Sales—over $500,000
Distrib.—Intl.
Privately owned corporation
Parent co.—Haddonstone (USA)
Ltd., Pueblo, CO
Phone—(719) 948-4554
See Parent Co. Section for full profile.

### INTERNATIONAL PAPER CO.
370 Benigno Blvd. (08031)
**Phone—(856) 931-8000**
Fax—(856) 931-2751
www.internationalpaper.com
Email—info@ipaper.com
Mfg. Mgr.—Steven Forlano
Cust. Serv. Mgr.—Wendy Yates
Env. Mgr.—Frank Gayeski
SIC—2653; NAICS—322211;
Corrugated boxes
Employs—84; Estab.—1957
Distrib.—Local
Publicly owned corporation

GEOGRAPHICAL

## Bellmawr—(cont.)

Parent co.—International Paper Co., Memphis, TN
Phone—(901) 419-9000
See Parent Co. Section for full profile.

**NEW ENTRY**

### J & J SNACK FOODS CORP.

361 Benigno Blvd., Ste. A (08031)
Phone—**(856) 933-3597**
Fax—(856) 933-0837
www.jjsnack.com
Email—consumerrelations@ jjsnack.com
Manager—Bob Cranmer
SIC—2045; *Frozen pretzel dough*
Employs—150
Sales—$25Mil-$50Mil (est)
Distrib.—Intl.
Publicly owned corporation
Parent co.—J & J Snack Foods Corp., Pennsauken, NJ
Phone—(856) 665-9534
See Parent Co. Section for full profile.

### MAGGIO DATA FORMS PRINTING LTD.

171 Heller Pl. (08031)
Phone—**(856) 931-7805**
Fax—(856) 931-1528
www.maggio.com
Email—forms@maggio.com
GM—Adolf Fiebelkorn
SIC—2761; NAICS—323116; *Business form printing*
Employs—35; Estab.—1979
Distrib.—Intl.
Privately owned corporation
Parent co.—Maggio Data Forms Printing Ltd., Hauppauge, NY
Phone—(631) 348-0343
See Parent Co. Section for full profile.

### MERCER GASKET & SHIM, INC.

110 Benigno Blvd. (08031)
Phone—**(856) 931-5000**
National—(800) 210-5000
Fax—(856) 931-6400
www.mercergasket.com
Email—mercer@mercergasket.com
Chrm.—Gloria Taraborelli
Pres.—Pete Taraborelli
Sales Rep.—Trisha Glaser
SIC—3053; NAICS—339991; *Gaskets, including metal, semi-metallic, spiral wound, camprofile, soft & non-asbestos & shims*
Employs—25; Estab.—1919
Distrib.—National
Privately owned corporation
AKA: Mercer Rubber

### NORDT PRECISION METAL MFG., INC.

640 Creek Rd. *(08031)*
Phone—**(856) 931-7444**
Fax—(856) 931-2366
Email—metalfab@ northprecision.com
V-P.—Dolores Nordt
Sales Mgr.—Charles Grady
SIC—3444; *Precision sheet metal fabrication*
Employs—23; Estab.—1964
Sales—$3Mil
21,500 sq ft site, Distrib.—Regional
Privately owned sub-S corp.

### PIROLLI PRINTING CO., INC.

860 W. Browning Rd. (08031)
Phone—**(856) 933-1285**
Fax—(856) 931-8513
www.pirolliprinting.com
Email—contact@pirolliprinting.com
Pres.—Kathleen A. Pirolli
V-P.—Eugene Pirolli

SIC—2752; NAICS—323100; *Offset printing, including forms, brochures, pocket folders, stationery, newsletters, labels, stickers & posters*
Employs—17; Estab.—1970
Sales—$500,000-$1Mil
Distrib.—Local
Privately owned corporation

### PRECISION STEEL RULE DIE

400 Benigno Blvd., Rear (08031)
Mail addr: P.O. Box 1042, Merchantville (08109-0542)
Phone—**(856) 931-2548**
Fax—(856) 931-2578
www.precisionsteelruledies.com
Email—precisiondie@verizon.net
Owner—Michael Sheahan
Off. Mgr.—Susan Morris
SIC—3544; NAICS—333500; *Flat steel rule cutting dies for gasket, custom folding carton, leather, foam & corrugated manufacturing processes, including packaging design, heat sealing boards & fixtures & printing polyester films*
Employs—3; Estab.—1992
Sales—under $500,000
Distrib.—National
Limited Liability Company

### SEALION METAL FABRICATORS, INC.

776 Creek Rd. (08031)
Phone—**(856) 933-3914**
Fax—(856) 933-3071
www.sealiontrailers.com
Email—sales@sealiontrailers.com
Pres., MIS Mgr.—Louis D'Orazio
V-P., Fin.—Michael Natale
SIC—3799; *Boat trailers; Brand name—Sealion Trailers*
Employs—10; Estab.—1961
Sales—$1Mil-$5Mil
10,000 sq ft site, Distrib.—Regional
Privately owned sub-S corp.

### TBT GROUP, INC.

191 Heller Pl. (08031)
Mail addr: 267 5th Ave., Ste. B-103, New York (10016)
Phone—**(856) 753-4500**
Fax—(212) 685-1897
www.tbtgroup.net
Email—info@tbtgroup.net
Plt. Mgr.—Elias Medina
SIC—3679; *Customized piezoelectric materials & ceramics for technical applications*
Employs—4; Estab.—2008
Distrib.—Intl.
Privately owned corporation
Parent co.—TBT Group, Inc., New York, NY
Phone—(212) 685-1839
See Parent Co. Section for full profile.

### W.D. SERVICE COMPANY, INC.

780 Creek Rd. *(08031)*
Mail addr: P.O. Box 147, Bellmawr (08099-0147)
Phone—**(856) 931-6100**
(800) 366-9326
Fax—(856) 931-4505
www.wdserviceco.com
Email—sales@wdserviceco.com
CEO—Paul A. Cuccinello
SIC—2819; 2873; NAICS—325311; *Concentrated reagent grade ammonia solutions & deionized water in 1-gallon, 5-gallon, 15-gallon & 50-gallon totes & bulk containers*
Employs—9; Estab.—1956
Sales—over $1Mil
6,000 sq ft site, Distrib.—National
Privately owned corporation
ISO rating—9001

## Belmar

*(Monmouth—N.E.)*

### CLAYTON BLOCK CO., INC.

1601 18th Ave. (07719)
Mail addr: P.O. Box 3015, Lakewood (08701)
Phone—**(732) 681-1414**
(732) 905-3131
National—(800) 662-3044
Fax—(732) 681-5103
www.claytonco.com
Email—jdooley@claytonsonline.com
Store Mgr.—Jerry Dooley
SIC—3271; NAICS—327331; *Concrete block*
Employs—15
Distrib.—Local
Privately owned corporation
Parent co.—Clayton Block Co., Inc., Neptune, NJ
Phone—(732) 751-7600
See Parent Co. Section for full profile.

### ENVIRONMENTAL AIR SYSTEMS

801 11th Ave., P.O. Box 508 (07719)
Phone—**(732) 681-0856**
Fax—(732) 681-1653
www.environmentalairsystems.com
Email—environmental@ optonline.net
Pres.—Glenn Brand
Off. Mgr.—Lisa O'Connor
SIC—3444; *Custom HVAC ducts, including duct & pipe fabrication, automated controls & boilers*
Employs—10; Estab.—1985
10,500 sq ft site, Distrib.—Regional
Privately owned sub-S corp.

### FINGER MATES, INC.

707 10th Ave. (07719)
Phone—**(732) 681-4411**
National—(800) 635-2785
Fax—(732) 280-8351
www.formula10.com
Email—customerservice@ formula10.com
CEO—Anthony Esposito
Pres.—Lou Alfieri
Mktg. Mgr.—Brian Esposito
SIC—2844; NAICS—325600; *Fingernail treatment, skin care & hair care products; Brand name—Hurry Up Glue Dry; Nails Alive; Formula 10; Varoom; WOW I GOT HAIR; Lipstix; Celiberity Lips; Nailteins; Nail Life*
Employs—7; Estab.—1982
24,000 sq ft site, Distrib.—Intl.
Privately owned sub-S corp.

### HYCHEM CORPORATION

611 Main St., Ste. B-2 (07719)
Phone—**(732) 280-8803**
Fax—(732) 280-8871
www.hychemcorp.com
Email—info@hychemcorp.com
Pres.—Henry Yard
Opers. Mgr.—John Yard
Off. Mgr.—Margaret McNally
SIC—2899; 2869; *Surfactants, oleochemicals & esters*
Employs—20; Estab.—1997
Distrib.—National
Privately owned sub-S corp.

**NEW ENTRY**

### KINTECH PRINTING & DIRECT MAIL

2400 Belmar Blvd., Ste. E-6, P.O. Box 12 (07719)
Phone—**(732) 280-6245**
Fax—(732) 280-1893
www.kintechinc.com
Email—info@kintechinc.com
Ptnr.—Gary Porter
Ptnr.—Carol Cotta

SIC—2759; *Commercial printing & promotional item screen printing, including mousepads, coffee mugs & pens*
Employs—10; Estab.—1998
Sales—$500,000-$1Mil
Distrib.—National
Privately owned corporation

### LEE'S WOODWORKING, INC.

726 Walling Ave. (07719)
Phone—**(732) 681-1002**
Fax—(732) 681-1005
www.leeswoodworking.com
Email—bill@leeswoodworking.com
Owner—Bill Lee
SIC—2511; 2434; 2431; *Custom, residential & commercial furniture & cabinets*
Employs—2; Estab.—2004
Sales—under $500,000
Distrib.—Local
Privately owned corporation

### MACLEARIE PRINTING, LLC

917 18th Ave. (07719)
Phone—**(732) 681-2772**
Fax—(732) 681-2775
www.maclearie.com
Pres.—James MacLearie
SIC—2752; 2791; NAICS—323122; *Offset printing & typesetting*
Employs—6; Estab.—1987
Sales—under $500,000
Distrib.—Local
Limited Liability Company

### R & H SPRING & TRUCK REPAIR, INC.

4806 W. Hurley Pond Rd. (07719)
Phone—**(732) 681-9000**
Fax—(732) 681-5887
www.rnhspring.com
Email—frank@rnhspring.com
Pres.—Frank Todero, Sr.
V-P.—Elizabeth Todero
SIC—3493; 5084; NAICS—332611; *Rebuilt automotive & truck leaf springs & distributor of commercial & non-commercial snowplows*
Employs—10; Estab.—1946
Sales—$500,000-$1Mil
8,000 sq ft site, Distrib.—Regional
Privately owned corporation

### R K E ATHLETIC LETTERING

1901 State Route 71, Ste. 1-C (07719)
Phone—**(732) 280-1111**
Fax—(732) 681-4349
www.rkeathletic.com
Email—tedrke@optonline.net
Owner—Ted Maciejewski
Manager—Jonathan Jones
SIC—2395; *Textile embroidery*
Employs—6; Estab.—1976
Sales—$1Mil-$2.5Mil
Distrib.—Local
Privately owned sub-S corp.

### SONETRONICS, INC.

1718 State Route 71, P.O. Box L (07719)
Phone—**(732) 681-5016**
Fax—(732) 681-5216
www.sonetronics.com
Email—headset@sonetronics.com
Pres.—Gary Kuskin
V-P.—Debi Kuskin-Brown
Ex. Mgr.—Michael T. Kuskin
SIC—3669; 3661; NAICS—334290; *Military communications equipment, including headsets, handsets, earphones, cable assemblies & connectors, including plastic injection molding & contract labor assembly*
Employs—85; Estab.—1961
25,000 sq ft site, Distrib.—Local
Privately owned corporation
ISO rating—9001:2000

## Belmar—(cont.)

**WOLEK'S ORNAMENTAL IRON WORKS**
1719 H St., Route 71 W. (07719)
Phone—**(732) 681-5929**
Fax—(732) 681-5929
Owner—Paul Wolek
Off. Mgr.—Frank Wolek
SIC—3446; NAICS—332323;
*Ornamental ironwork*
Employs—2; Estab.—1959
Sales—under $500,000
1,800 sq ft site, Distrib.—Regional
Sole ownership

## Belvidere
(Warren—N.W.)

**COMPACT FLUORESCENT SYSTEMS**
3 Adams St. (07823)
Phone—**(973) 729-5262**
(908) 475-8991
Fax—(973) 729-1271
www.cfsinc.us
Email—cfsinc@
cfslighting.comcastbiz.net
Chrm.—Dory Broyer
Pres.—Gary Broyer
Shop Mgr.—Nick Broyer
SIC—3646; NAICS—335122;
*Industrial lighting fixtures*
Employs—3; Estab.—1992
Sales—$500,000-$1Mil
Distrib.—National
Privately owned corporation

**CRAMER PLATING, INC.**
4 Hoyt Ln. (07823)
Phone—**(908) 453-2887**
Fax—(908) 453-0023
Email—davecramer@
centurylink.net
Pres.—David Cramer
Secy. & Off. Mgr.—Ann Howell
SIC—3471; NAICS—332813;
*Metal finishing*
Employs—25; Estab.—1960
Sales—$1Mil-$2Mil
Distrib.—Local
Privately owned corporation

**DEROCHE CANVAS, INC.**
283 County Road 519 (07823)
Phone—**(908) 475-2266**
Fax—(908) 475-2760
Pres.—Dan C. Deroche
SIC—2394; NAICS—314912;
*Industrial truck tarps*
Employs—2; Estab.—2000
Sales—under $500,000 (est)
Distrib.—Regional
Privately owned corporation

**DSM NUTRITIONAL PRODUCTS, INC.**
Div. of DSM Pharmaceutical
Products, Inc.
206 Macks Island Dr. (07823)
Phone—**(908) 475-5300**
Fax—(908) 475-7426
www.dsm.com
Email—jennifer.moorcroft@
dsm.com
Site Dir.—Dave Ellis
Sr. Bus. Coord., Hum. Res.—
Donna Smith
SIC—2833; NAICS—325411;
*Vitamins & nutritional additives*
Employs—350; Estab.—1920
Distrib.—Intl.
Privately owned corporation
ISO rating—9002
Parent co.—DSM Pharmaceutical
Products, Inc., Parsippany, NJ
Phone—(973) 257-1063
See Parent Co. Section for full profile.

**FOUR SISTERS WINERY**
783 County Road 519 (07823)
Mail addr: 10 Doe Hollow Ln.,
Belvidere (07823)
Phone—**(908) 475-3671**
Fax—(908) 475-3555
www.foursisterswinery.com
Email—matty@goes.com
Pres. & Event Planner—Robert
Matarazzo
V-P.—Valerie Tishuk
SIC—2084; NAICS—312130;
*Wines*
Employs—9; Estab.—1984
Sales—under $500,000
1,800 sq ft site, Distrib.—Local
Sole ownership

**FRAME-A-COIN MFG.**
318 Front St., Ste. 1 (07823-1537)
Phone—**(973) 822-0094**
Fax—(973) 593-8380
www.frameacoin.com
Email—alewis@frameacoin.com
Pres.—Andrew Lewis
V-P.—Amy Lewis
SIC—3089; *American-made high-
grade plastic sleeves/holders for
coins & currency*
Employs—6; Estab.—1988
Sales—$500,000-$1Mil
4,000 sq ft site, Distrib.—Intl.
Limited Liability Company

**GRAHAM PACKAGING CO. L. P.**
600 5th St. (07823)
Phone—**(908) 475-2181**
Fax—(908) 475-4724
www.grahampackaging.com
Email—sales@
grahampackaging.com
Plt. Mgr.—Joe Richey
Admn. Mgr.—Cindy Barrington
Hum. Res. Mgr.—Kim Henry
Cust. Serv. Mgr.—Alex Duque
SIC—3085; NAICS—326160;
*Plastic bottles*
Employs—115; Estab.—1995
156,000 sq ft site, Distrib.—Intl.
Privately owned corporation
Parent co.—Graham Packaging
Co. L. P., York, PA
Phone—(717) 849-8500
See Parent Co. Section for full profile.

**GREAT NORTHERN COMMERCIAL SERVICE, INC.**
401 Greenwich St. (07823)
Phone—**(908) 475-8855**
(973) 697-5807
Fax—(908) 475-3299
Email—grtnth@embarqmail.com
Pres., Off. Mgr.—Anna Quinn
Treas.—Dennis Quinn
SIC—2752; NAICS—323100;
*Offset printing*
Employs—4; Estab.—1986
Sales—under $500,000
8,000 sq ft site, Distrib.—Regional
Privately owned corporation

**JOHNSON & SONS, INC., S.**
1 Hardwick St., P.O. Box 66
(07823)
Phone—**(908) 475-2155**
(908) 475-2156
Fax—(908) 475-3467
www.sjsMetalworks.com
Email—sjsco@earthlink.net
Pres.—Gus Johnson
V-P.—Erik Johnson
SIC—3451; NAICS—332721;
*Screw machine products,
including CNC milling, turning &
welding*
Employs—35; Estab.—1926
38,000 sq ft site, Distrib.—National
Privately owned corporation
Also see: Well Tech, Inc., same
loc.

**LAZYMAN MFG.**
616 Hardwick St., P.O. Box 327
(07823)
Phone—**(908) 475-5315**
Fax—(908) 475-3165
www.lazyman.com
Email—sales@lazyman.com
Pres., CFO—Brian D. Sadowski
Dir., Opers.—Brian Haun
Plt. & R & D Mgr.—Donald
Nawrocki
SIC—3433; 3444; 3471; 3479;
NAICS—333414; *Gas barbecue
grills & sheet metal fabrication,
including bending, TIG, MIG &
spot welding, grinding, polishing
& powder coating*
Employs—15; Estab.—1936
Sales—$1Mil-$5Mil
25,000 sq ft site, Distrib.—Intl.
Privately owned sub-S corp.
DBA: LaserMan Fabricating

**NATURE'S CHOICE CORP.**
40 Foul Rift Rd. (07823)
Mail addr: 1 Caven Point Ave.,
Jersey City (07305)
Phone—**(908) 475-1804**
Fax—(908) 687-3122
www.reliablewoodproducts.com
Email—sales@
natureschoicecorp.com
Site Mgr.—Brad Muffley
SIC—2875; NAICS—325314;
*Mulch compost & top soil*
Employs—10; Estab.—1991
Distrib.—Regional
Privately owned corporation
Parent co.—Nature's Choice
Corp., Sparta, NJ
Phone—(201) 333-5244
See Parent Co. Section for full profile.

**SWIFT PRINT SOLUTIONS, LLC**
405 Front St. (07823)
Phone—**(908) 475-1374**
(908) 235-8549
Fax—(908) 475-5496
www.swiftprintsolutions.com
Email—linda@
swiftprintsolutions.com
Owner—Linda Swift
SIC—2759; 2752; 2396; 3993;
NAICS—323100; *Commercial,
screen & instant printing &
graphic design of promotional
items & direct mail campaigns,
including web design*
Employs—4; Estab.—2009
Sales—under $500,000
Distrib.—National
Limited Liability Company

**WELL TECH, INC.**
1 Hardwick St., P.O. Box 66
(07823-0066)
Phone—**(908) 475-4539**
Fax—(908) 475-3467
Pres.—Gustav Johnson
GM—Karen Robison
SIC—3451; NAICS—332721;
*Screw machine products*
Employs—30; Estab.—1927
Sales—$2.5Mil-$5Mil (est)
Distrib.—National
Privately owned corporation
Also see: Johnson & Sons, Inc.,
S., same loc.

## Bergenfield
(Bergen—N.E.)

**AMERICAN IMAGE**
45 W. Broad St. (07621)
Phone—**(201) 384-9200**
National—(800) 385-9223
Fax—(201) 384-5185
www.americanimageawards.com
Email—sales@
americanimageawards.com
Pres.—John Paragian
GM—Janine Stuart
SIC—3479; 3993; 3961; NAICS—
339900; *Engraved awards,
signs, name badges,
promotional items & emblematic
jewelry*
Employs—15; Estab.—1950
7,000 sq ft site, Distrib.—Intl.
Privately owned corporation

**ARISTA TROPHIES & AWARDS**
25 Portland Ave. (07621)
Phone—**(201) 387-2165**
National—(800) 597-2165
Fax—(201) 387-0955
www.aristatrophies.com
Email—aristatrophies@aol.com
Owner—David Cassens
Shop Mgr.—Brian Hillmer
SIC—3479; 3993; *Custom & laser
engraving of signs, banners,
nameplates, legend plates, 2nd
power source generator signs,
valve tags, valve chart signs,
valve location floor plan signs &
police & fire auto shields/badges*
Employs—3; Estab.—1980
Sales—$500,000-$1Mil
4,000 sq ft site, Distrib.—Regional
Sole ownership

**BAKERY, THE**
99 N. Washington Ave. (07621)
Phone—**(201) 384-1456**
Owner—Brian Driscoll
SIC—2051; NAICS—311812;
*Bakery products, including
cakes, bread & cookies*
Employs—10; Estab.—1957
Distrib.—Regional
Sole ownership

**BERGEN MARZIPAN & CHOCOLATE**
205 S. Washington Ave. (07621)
Phone—**(201) 385-8343**
Fax—(201) 385-0042
Email—bergenmarzipan@
yahoo.com
Pres.—Eddie Serpin
Whse. Mgr.—Mike Lasa
SIC—2066; NAICS—311300;
*Chocolate & marzipan candies*
Employs—3; Estab.—1987
Distrib.—National
Privately owned sub-S corp.

**C N R PRODUCTS CO.**
74 Portland Ave. (07621)
Phone—**(201) 384-7003**
Fax—(201) 387-2624
www.cnrproducts.com
Email—postmaster@
cnrproducts.com
Owner & Sales Mgr.—Peter
Rebsch
SIC—3993; *Architectural
commercial signs*
Employs—5; Estab.—1992
Sales—under $500,000
2,500 sq ft site, Distrib.—Intl.
Sole ownership

**CONCEPT PRINTING, INC.**
160 Woodbine St., Ste. 2 (07621)
Phone—**(201) 387-6000**
Fax—(201) 387-6363
www.conceptprintinginc.com
Email—sales@
conceptprintinginc.com
Pres.—Kerry Monahan-Gaughan
V-P.—Patrick Monahan
Sales Mgr.—Nicholas O'Brien
Off. Mgr.—Kelley O'Brien Dionne
Shop Mgr.—Omar Brown
Graphic Artist—AnnMarie
Hartmann
SIC—2752; 2396; 2395; 3993;
NAICS—323100; *Offset & screen
printing, embroidery &
promotional products*
Employs—6; Estab.—1990
2,500 sq ft site, Distrib.—National
Privately owned sub-S corp.
AKA: Concept Printing and
Promotions

GEOGRAPHICAL

## Bergenfield—(cont.)

**†COOPER ELECTRIC SUPPLY CO.**
72 N. Washington Ave. (07621)
**Phone—(201) 385-7777**
Fax—(201) 385-4434
www.cooper-electric.com
Email—gabe.ferrari@cooper-electric.com
Sales Mgr., Inside—Gabe Ferrari
Br. Mgr.—Don Szabo
Dept. Mgr.—Bill Jadge
SIC—5063; *Distributor of electrical supplies, commercial lighting, generators & power systems*
Employs—20; Estab.—1962
Distrib.—Local
Privately owned corporation
Parent co.—Cooper Electric Supply Co., Monroe, NJ
Phone—(732) 747-2233
See Parent Co. Section for full profile.

**DASH PRINTING, INC.**
52 Woodbine St., Ste. 3 (07621)
**Phone—(201) 338-2561**
Fax—(212) 202-5288
www.dashprinting.com
Email—davida@dashprinting.com
Owner—David Ashendorf
Dir., Mktg.—Rachel Feiner
SIC—2759; *Commercial printing, including digital printing*
Employs—3; Estab.—2001
Sales—under $500,000
Distrib.—National
Sole ownership
Parent co.—Dash Printing, Inc., New York, NY
Phone—(212) 643-8534
See Parent Co. Section for full profile.

**GM PRINTING**
106 Pleasant Ave. (07621)
**Phone—(201) 385-2525**
www.gmprint1.com
Email—info@gmprint1.com
Pres.—Greg Madison
SIC—2752; 2759; 2791; NAICS—323119; *Instant, commercial & large-format printing, electronic prepress & graphic & package design*
Employs—7; Estab.—1984
Sales—$500,000-$1Mil
Distrib.—Regional
Sole ownership

**HARLEY TOOL & MACHINE, INC.**
24 McDermott Pl. (07621)
**Phone—(201) 244-8899**
Fax—(201) 244-0002
Email—bobharley2000@yahoo.com
Owner & Pres.—Robert Harley
Off. Mgr.—Patrick Harley
SIC—3599; *CNC & general machining job shop*
Employs—4; Estab.—1925
Sales—$300,000-$500,000
4,000 sq ft site, Distrib.—Local
Privately owned corporation

**K & R PRECISION MACHINING**
54 S. Front St. (07621)
**Phone—(201) 385-8855**
Fax—(201) 385-2640
Pres.—Rick Penser
Machinist—Tom Schreiber
SIC—3599; *Precision machining job shop*
Employs—5; Estab.—1992
2,000 sq ft site, Distrib.—Local
Privately owned corporation

**LIQUID GLASS ENTERPRISES, INC.**
93 Railroad Ave. (07621)
Mail addr: P.O. Box 1170, Teaneck (07666)
**Phone—(201) 387-6755**
National—(800) 548-5307
Fax—(201) 387-2168
www.liquidglass.com
Email—jheywang@ix.netcom.com

Pres. & Chief Scientist—John R. Heywang
Sr. V-P.—Laura Heywang
Cust. Serv. Mgr.—Ruth Howard
SIC—2842; NAICS—325612; *Liquid automotive, marine, aircraft & industrial/commercial appearance polishes & finishes*
Employs—5; Estab.—1984
5,000 sq ft site, Distrib.—Intl.
Privately owned corporation

**MAGIC METAL WORKS, INC.**
40 W. Englewood Ave. (07621)
**Phone—(201) 384-8457**
Pres.—Vic Dabaghian
Plt. Mgr.—Jacques Dabaghian
SIC—3444; *Precision sheet metal fabrication*
Employs—5; Estab.—1982
Sales—$1Mil-$2.5Mil
Distrib.—Local
Privately owned corporation

**†MED-X INTERNATIONAL, INC.**
20 Foster St. (07621)
Mail addr: P.O. Box 101, Tenafly (07670)
**Phone—(201) 387-8556**
Fax—(201) 387-8499
www.med-x.com
Email—topmed@aol.com
Pres.—Gary Malajian
Mktg. Mgr.—Marie McKenna
SIC—5047; *Distributor of medical supplies; Brand name—NicePak; PDI; Argon Medical*
Employs—3; Estab.—1982
Sales—$2.5Mil
1,000 sq ft site, Distrib.—Intl.
Privately owned corporation

**MID-EASTERN INDUSTRIES DIV, TECHNOLOGY DYNAMICS, INC**
100 School St. (07621)
**Phone—(201) 385-0500**
Fax—(201) 385-0702
www.mideastind.com
Email—dellenback@mideastind.com
V-P., GM—Daniel R. Ellenback
Comp.—Dan Cavalli
Sales & Mktg. Mgr.—Mark Jacobus
Prodn. Mgr.—Ronald Daisey
MIS Mgr.—Eli Levy
SIC—3679; 3621; NAICS—335312; *Linear power supplies & DC power systems*
Employs—110; Estab.—1959
Sales—$5Mil-$10Mil
30,000 sq ft site, Distrib.—National
Sole ownership
ISO rating—9002
Also see: Technology Dynamics, Inc., same loc.

**NICHOLAS DESIGNS, R.**
41 Portland Ave. (07621)
**Phone—(201) 385-8713**
Fax—(201) 385-7755
Owner & GM—Robert Stephan
SIC—2499; *Wooden picture frames*
Employs—1; Estab.—1986
Sales—under $500,000
Distrib.—Local
Sole ownership

**PEACOCK PRINTING PRODUCTS, INC.**
48 Woodbine St. (07621)
**Phone—(201) 385-5585**
National—(800) 221-0275
Fax—(201) 501-8566
www.peacockprinting.com
Email—info@peacockprinting.com
Pres., CEO—Craig Langslet
SIC—2759; 2752; NAICS—323100; *Commercial, instant, digital, offset & color printing*
Employs—20; Estab.—1976
10,000 sq ft site, Distrib.—National
Privately owned corporation

**PYRAMID IMPRINTS**
28 N. Washington Ave. (07621)
**Phone—(201) 384-0336**
Fax—(201) 384-0336
www.pyramidimprints.com
Email—info@pyramidimprints.com
Owner—Eleanor Garcia
SIC—2759; 2396; 2395; 3993; NAICS—323100; *Commercial screen printing, textile embroidery, heat transfering & promotional items; Brand name—Anvil; F.O.L.; Gildan; Jerzees; Yupong; Hanes; Champion; Nike; Augusta; Addidas; Outerbanks; L.A.T.*
Employs—2; Estab.—1977
Sales—under $500,000
1,700 sq ft site, Distrib.—National
Sole ownership

**RESEC SYSTEMS, LLC**
93 S. Railroad Ave., Ste. A (07621-2352)
**Phone—(201) 384-6960**
Fax—(201) 384-6990
www.resecsystems.com
Email—sales@resecsystems.com
Owner—Bob Schulkin
SIC—3559; 3829; 3569; *Automated high-speed inspection & sorting equipment for quality control applications of precision machined parts; Brand name—ShadowGage Sorters*
Employs—4; Estab.—1979
Sales—under $500,000
1,200 sq ft site, Distrib.—National
Limited Liability Company

**SAMUEL, INC.**
60 W. Englewood (07621)
**Phone—(201) 439-1555**
Fax—(201) 439-1565
Pres.—Steve Samuel
Mktg. Mgr.—Sam Samuel
SIC—3911; NAICS—339911; *Precious metal jewelry*
Employs—20; Estab.—1979
Distrib.—Intl.
Privately owned corporation

**SAP SEAL PRODUCTS**
52 Woodbine St. (07621)
**Phone—(201) 385-5553**
Fax—(201) 384-2488
www.sapseal.com
Email—sapsealcap@aol.com
Pres.—Ernie Ness
SIC—3089; *Lubricant-prefilled reusable threaded plastic caps for nuts & bolts*
Employs—5; Estab.—1980
Sales—$500,000-$1Mil
Distrib.—Regional
Privately owned corporation

**SHIPRITE PACKAGING, INC.**
161 Woodbine St. (07621)
**Phone—(201) 385-4747**
National—(800) 721-7447
Fax—(201) 385-2448
www.shipritebags.com
Email—mayer@shipritebags.com
Pres., GM—Mayer Schlisser
Off. Mgr.—Tricia Rubinetti
SIC—2673; *Plastic bags*
Employs—2; Estab.—1992
Distrib.—National
Privately owned corporation

**SMITH, INC., ROY D.**
20 Foster St., P.O. Box 537 (07621)
**Phone—(201) 384-4163**
Fax—(201) 384-1889
Email—rdsinc537@aol.com
Owner—Roy D. Smith
Pres.—Eric Zymet

SIC—2759; NAICS—323100; *Commercial printing*
Employs—5; Estab.—1981
Sales—$500,000-$1Mil
Distrib.—National
Privately owned corporation

**TECHNOLOGY DYNAMICS, INC.**
100 School St. (07621)
**Phone—(201) 385-0500**
Fax—(201) 385-0702
www.theallpower.com
Email—mark@theallpower.com
Pres.—Aron Levy
V-P., Mktg.—Mark Jacobus
Sales Mgr., Intl.—Mike Levy
Fin. Mgr.—Dan Cavalli
SIC—3679; 3621; NAICS—335312; *Switching power supplies & DC-DC converters for the commercial & military industries*
Employs—90; Estab.—1976
45,000 sq ft site, Distrib.—Intl.
Privately owned corporation
Also see: Mid-Eastern Industries Div., Technology Dynamics, Inc., same loc.

**TITAN IMPLANTS, INC.**
18 Columbia Ave. (07621)
**Phone—(201) 439-0027**
National—(866) 439-0470
Fax—(201) 439-1145
www.titanimplants.com
Email—support@titanimplants.com
Pres., Hum. Res. Mgr.—Cyril Chen
V-P.—Krystle Chen
Software Engr.—Vinod Gadhiraju
SIC—3843; NAICS—339114; *Dental implants, attachments & accessories*
Employs—21; Estab.—2000
Sales—$500,000-$1Mil
Distrib.—Intl.
Privately owned corporation

---

## Berkeley Heights
(Union—N.E.)

**ACE LITHOGRAPHERS**
22 Russo Pl. (07922)
**Phone—(908) 665-1700**
Fax—(908) 665-9717
www.acelitho.com
Email—info@acelitho.com
Pres.—John Cooper
Fin. Mgr.—Brett Cooper
SIC—2759; 2752; NAICS—323100; *Commercial, offset & digital printing*
Employs—28; Estab.—1972
Sales—$5Mil-$7Mil
15,000 sq ft site, Distrib.—National
Privately owned sub-S corp.
AKA: Ace Twill

**ACE TWILL**
22 Russo Pl. (07922)
**Phone—(908) 665-1700**
Fax—(908) 665-9717
www.twill.com
Email—info@acelitho.com
Sales Rep.—George Twill
SIC—2759; 2752; NAICS—323100; *Digital & offset printing*
Employs—30; Estab.—1947
Sales—$500,000-$1Mil
12,000 sq ft site, Distrib.—Regional
Privately owned corporation

**AUTHENTIDATE HOLDING CORP.**
300 Connell Dr., 5th Fl. (07922)
**Phone—(908) 787-1700**
www.authentidate.com
Pres., CEO—O'Connell Benjamin
Treas., CFO—William Marshall

## Berkeley Heights—(cont.)

SIC—7372; *Healthcare IT & SaaS workflow software development for hospital discharge, referral & order management & remote patient monitoring telehealth products & services*
Employs—32
Distrib.—Intl.
Publicly owned corporation

**CONSOLIDATED PROTOTYPES, INC.**
5 Oechsner Ct. (07922)
**Phone—(908) 464-6261**
Fax—(908) 464-6739
Email—consolidatedpro@verizon.com
Pres.—Jack Horner
SIC—3543; NAICS—332997; *Industrial prototypes*
Employs—1; Estab.—1965
Sales—under $500,000
Distrib.—National
Sole ownership

†**DIAMOND ENTERPRISE GROUP**
321 Snyder Ave. (07922)
**Phone—(908) 771-6777**
National—(800) 889-9884
Fax—(908) 771-6770
www.diamondenterprise.com
Email—info@diamondenterprise.com
Owner—Robert Mornan
CFO—Mark Mornan
Off. Mgr.—Rhonda Coulter
SIC—5084; 5085; *Wholesaler of laminating equipment & supplies*
Employs—9; Estab.—1993
Sales—$1.8Mil
11,100 sq ft site, Distrib.—Regional
Limited Liability Company
AKA: Diamond Lamination

**E G L CO., INC.**
100 Industrial Rd. (07922)
**Phone—(908) 508-1111**
National—(800) 345-9010
Fax—(908) 508-1122
www.egl-lighting.com
Email—sales@egl-lighting.com
Pres.—Harold Cortese
V-P., Sales—Tom Cortese
IT & Plt. Mgr.—Doug Cortese
SIC—3641; NAICS—335110; *Neon & LED sign lights & components*
Employs—100; Estab.—1927
80,000 sq ft site, Distrib.—Intl.
Privately owned corporation

**ENSLOW PUBLISHING GROUP**
40 Industrial Rd. (07922)
**Phone—(908) 771-9400**
National—(800) 398-2504
Fax—(908) 771-0925
www.enslow.com
Email—enslow@enslow.com
Pres.—Mark Enslow
SIC—2731; *Book publishing*
Employs—30; Estab.—1976
Sales—$500,000-$1Mil
Distrib.—Intl.
Privately owned corporation

**FLEXCON PRODUCTS CORP.**
200 Connell Dr., Ste. 1200 (07922)
**Phone—(908) 871-7000**
Fax—(908) 871-7171
www.flexconcontainer.com
Email—info@flexconcontainer.com
Pres., GM & Plt. Mgr.—Stephen M. Beckerman
V-P.—Ken Beckerman
Cust. Serv. Rep.—Joyce Zarro

SIC—3089; *Plastic storage containers*
Employs—50; Estab.—1996
Sales—$5Mil-$10Mil (est)
Distrib.—Intl.
Privately owned corporation
AKA: Shell Packaging

**GENERAL CHEMICAL CORP.**
Div. of Chemtrade Chemical, LLC
235 Snyder Ave. (07922)
**Phone—(908) 464-1500**
Fax—(908) 464-7726
www.generalchem.com
Email—info@genchemcorp.com
Dir., Opers.—Walter Kramer
SIC—2869; NAICS—325188; *Industrial inorganic chemicals*
Employs—20
Sales—$50Mil-$100Mil
Distrib.—Local
Publicly owned corporation
Parent co.—Chemtrade Chemical, LLC, Parsippany, NJ
Phone—(973) 515-0900
See Parent Co. Section for full profile.

**HAP ENGRAVING LTD.**
106 Windsor Way (07922)
**Phone—(201) 223-4800**
Email—shane@hapengraving.com
Manager—Shane Levin
SIC—3479; 3469; NAICS—333500; *Sculpture engraving, embossing, metal dies & hot stampings & combination & stamping plates for the folding carton & graphic arts industries*
Employs—15; Estab.—1929
8,000 sq ft site, Distrib.—Intl.
Privately owned corporation

**LAUDERDALE MILLWORK, INC.**
77 Industrial Rd. (07922)
**Phone—(908) 508-9550**
(908) 333-3351
Fax—(888) 883-6235
www.lauderdalemillwork.com
Email—jvlauderdale@gmail.com
Owner & Pres.—John Lauderdale
Off. Admn.—Kathy Hoffman
SIC—2431; NAICS—321900; *Wooden cabinets, doors, mouldings & millwork*
Employs—4; Estab.—1997
Sales—$1Mil-$2.5Mil
Distrib.—Regional
Privately owned corporation

**LUMITRON CORP., INC.**
35 Russo Pl. (07922)
**Phone—(908) 273-8998**
Fax—(908) 273-0853
www.lumitron.com
Email—sales@lumitron.com
Pres.—Harry Chassie
Sales Mgr., Inside—Amy Tefft
Off. Mgr.—Karen Chassie
Administrator—Anna Auseichyk
SIC—3648; NAICS—335129; *Aerospace lighting components, including subminiature lamps, night vision components & light emitting diodes*
Employs—19; Estab.—1975
Sales—$500,000-$1Mil
2,500 sq ft site, Distrib.—Intl.
Privately owned corporation
ISO rating—9001:2008

**MAINSTREAM CUSTOM AIR HANDLING UNITS**
47 Russo Pl. (07922)
Mail addr: P.O. Box 353, Cranford (07016)
**Phone—(908) 931-1010**
National—(800) 828-2645
Fax—(908) 508-9092
www.mainstream-corp.com
Email—info@customahu.com
Member & Hum. Res. Mgr.—Derrick Markham

SIC—3564; NAICS—333400; *Industrial air-handling units for the pharmaceutical, research laboratory & healthcare industries*
Employs—50; Estab.—1994
Sales—$500,000-$1Mil
Distrib.—National
Limited Liability Company

**NEUWEILER, INC., KARL H.**
23 Russo Pl. (07922)
**Phone—(908) 464-6532**
Fax—(908) 464-6086
Email—karlneuweilerinc@verizon.net
Pres.—Dan Neuweiler, Sr.
SIC—3599; *Machine parts*
Employs—10; Estab.—1953
Sales—$1Mil-$2.5Mil
6,500 sq ft site, Distrib.—National
Privately owned corporation

NEW ENTRY
†**SCIENTIFIC MODELS, INC.**
340 Snyder Ave. (07922)
**Phone—(908) 464-7070**
Fax—(908) 665-9383
www.micromark.com
Owner—John Frisoli
SIC—5084; 5072; *Distributor of tools & hardware, including hand & power tools*
Employs—20

## Berlin
(Camden—S.W.)

**AMERITECH PRECISION MACHINING CO.**
425 N. Grove St., Unit 3-A (08009)
**Phone—(856) 767-1660**
Fax—(856) 767-1704
Owner—Joseph Speyerer
SIC—3599; *Precision machining job shop*
Employs—2; Estab.—2008
Sales—under $500,000 (est)
Distrib.—Local
Sole ownership

**BELTOR MFG. CORP.**
50 Union Ave., Ste. 12 (08009)
**Phone—(856) 768-5570**
(856) 424-1900
Fax—(856) 768-5723
www.beltormfg.com
Email—beltormfginc@hotmail.com
Pres. & V-P.—Derek Torok
SIC—2391; 2591; NAICS—314121; *Cubicle curtains & curtain tracks*
Employs—6; Estab.—1948
Sales—over $500,000
2,100 sq ft site, Distrib.—Intl.
Privately owned corporation

**BOCCELLA PRECAST, LLC**
324 New Brooklyn Rd. (08009)
**Phone—(856) 767-3861**
Fax—(856) 753-2869
www.boccellaprecast.com
Email—info@boccellaprecast.com
Owner—Joseph Boccella
Cont.—Carol Shahin
Design Mgr.—Robert Sharp
SIC—3272; *Prestressed concrete hollow-core planks*
Employs—10; Estab.—1969
Sales—$6Mil-$10Mil
Distrib.—Regional
Limited Liability Company

**BRIDGESTATE FOUNDRY CORP.**
175 Jackson Rd. (08009)
**Phone—(856) 767-0400**
Fax—(856) 767-4320
Corp. Secy.—Diane Taylor
GM—Ed Ciel
Off. Mgr.—Kim Dwyer

SIC—3462; NAICS—332111; *Cast iron manhole frames, covers & grates*
Employs—10; Estab.—1950
Sales—under $500,000
Distrib.—National
Privately owned corporation

**BRINGHURST BROS., INC.**
38 W. Taunton Rd. (08009)
**Phone—(856) 767-0110**
Fax—(856) 767-0224
www.bringhurstmeats.com
Email—brinmeat@verizon.net
Pres.—Ralph Bringhurst, Jr.
V-P., Secy-Treas.—Jeff Bringhurst
Bookkeeper—Nancy Bringhurst
SIC—2011; 2013; NAICS—311611; *Bacon, kielbasa, bologna, scrapple, sausage & deer processing*
Employs—20; Estab.—1934
Sales—$1Mil-$2.5Mil
Distrib.—Regional
Privately owned corporation

**COMPUTA BASE MACHINING, INC.**
411 N. Grove St., P.O. Box 340 (08009)
**Phone—(856) 767-9517**
Fax—(856) 767-8541
www.computabase.com
Email—cbmrosado@aol.com
Pres.—Augustin Rosado
V-P., Qual. Control—Robert Fraser
Off. Mgr.—Kathleen Di Bruno
SIC—3499; 3559; 3449; 3444; *Fabrication & precision machining job shop*
Employs—14; Estab.—1981
Sales—$1Mil-$3Mil
20,000 sq ft site, Distrib.—National
Privately owned sub-S corp.
ISO rating—9001:2008, AS9100:2009C

**D & F PERFORMANCE**
417 N. Grove St. (08009)
**Phone—(856) 767-4095**
www.dfperformance.com
Email—support@dfperformance.com
Ptnr.—David R. Thornton, Sr.
Ptnr.—David R. Thornton, Jr.
SIC—3519; 5013; 5084; *Rebuilt performance engines & distributor of engine parts, including cylinder heads & fuel injection systems*
Employs—2; Estab.—1976
Sales—under $500,000
Distrib.—Intl.
Privately owned partnership

**DALY'S CUSTOM RACING APPAREL**
P.O. Box 355 (08009)
**Phone—(856) 768-6411**
National—(800) 227-4557
Fax—(856) 768-6410
www.dalyssilks.com
Email—dalyssilks@comcast.net
CEO—Ryan Daly
SIC—2389; *Horse racing apparel, including jockey silks*
Employs—3; Estab.—1975
Sales—under $500,000
Distrib.—Intl.
Privately owned corporation

**DIALCONNECTION, LLC**
1040 Route 73 S. (08009)
**Phone—(856) 753-6620**
National—(888) 770-7706
Fax—(856) 753-4210
www.dialconnection.com
Email—info@dialconnection.com
Pres.—Michael Vesper
Ex. V-P.—David Sargent

GEOGRAPHICAL

## Berlin—(cont.)

SIC—7373; *Computer network system integration, including LANs & WANs, custom software development, project management, long term strategic planning & other professional services*
Employs—10
Distrib.—Intl.
Limited Liability Company

**†FASTENAL CO.**
421 Route 73 & Cushman Ave., Unit 11 (08009)
**Phone—(856) 768-3657**
Fax—(856) 768-3962
www.fastenal.com
Email—njber@stores.fastenal.com
Br. Mgr.—David Gabrielski
SIC—5072; 5084; *Wholesaler of fasteners, safety equipment, tools & abrasives*
Employs—1; Estab.—2005
Distrib.—Local
Publicly owned corporation
Parent co.—Fastenal Co., Winona, MN
　Phone—(507) 454-5374
　See Parent Co. Section for full profile.

**HANSON AGGREGATES, BMC DIV.**
Div. of Lehigh Hanson, Inc.
368 New Brooklyn Rd., P.O. Box 37 (08009)
**Phone—(856) 767-3100**
Fax—(856) 767-5909
www.hanson.com
Email—enquiries@hanson.com
Plt. Mgr.—Frank Berghof
SIC—3281; NAICS—327991; *Sand & gravel processing*
Employs—18; Estab.—1897
Sales—$500,000-$1Mil
Distrib.—Intl.
Publicly owned corporation
Parent co.—Lehigh Hanson, Inc., Irving, TX
　Phone—(972) 653-5500
　See Parent Co. Section for full profile.

**†HD SUPPLY WATER WORKS, INC.**
Div. of HD Supply Waterworks, Inc.
228 Williamstown Rd. (08009)
**Phone—(856) 753-5566**
Fax—(856) 753-5455
www.waterworks.hdsupply.com
Email—info@hdsupplywaterworks.com
GM—Rusty Miller
Opers. Mgr.—Kevin Jones
SIC—5085; *Distributor of waterworks valves, hydrants & pipes*
Employs—8; Estab.—1991
Sales—$6Mil-$10Mil
10,000 sq ft site, Distrib.—Local
Publicly owned corporation
Parent co.—HD Supply Waterworks, Inc., Thomasville, GA
　Phone—(229) 226-1433
　See Parent Co. Section for full profile.

**HOUPERT TRUCK SERVICE**
115 Atlantic Ave., P.O. Box 8 (08009)
**Phone—(856) 767-0145**
Fax—(856) 767-0567
Email—houpert@horizon.com
Owner—Deborah Baccellieri
Corp. Secy.—Diane Siracuse
Plt. Mgr.—Russell Rodrigo
Parts Mgr.—Ted Bair
Serv. Advisor—Dennis O'Donnell
SIC—3519; *Rebuilt diesel engines & truck service*
Employs—11; Estab.—1950
22,000 sq ft site, Distrib.—Regional
Sole ownership

**J. B. & SONS CONCRETE PRODUCTS CO.**
358 New Brooklyn Rd. (08009)
**Phone—(856) 767-4140**
Fax—(856) 767-7228
Owner—Joseph Boccella
SIC—3272; *Precast concrete products*
Employs—15; Estab.—1975
Distrib.—Local
Privately owned corporation

**†JOHNS MANVILLE**
437 North Grove St. (08009)
**Phone—(856) 768-7000**
Fax—(856) 768-7061
www.jm.com
Email—webmaster@jm.com
Hum. Res. Mgr.—Joe Catania
Whse. Mgr.—Debbie Carter
Sales Supv.—Adam Jenny
SIC—5033; *Distributor of fiberglass*
Employs—14; Estab.—1858
650,000 sq ft site, Distrib.—National
Publicly owned corporation
Parent co.—Johns Manville, Denver, CO
　Phone—(303) 978-2000
　See Parent Co. Section for full profile.

**KESKES PRINTING CO.**
5 W. Taunton Ave. (08009)
**Phone—(856) 767-4733**
Fax—(856) 767-4037
www.keskes.com
Email—keskes.pc@verizon.net
Owner—Jean Keskes
Administrator—Kimberly Keskes
SIC—2752; 2759; NAICS—323122; *Offset, digital & letterpress printing*
Employs—5; Estab.—1972
Distrib.—Local
Sole ownership

**L.C. MACHINE SHOP, INC.**
249 S. White Horse Pike (08009)
**Phone—(856) 767-1111**
Fax—(856) 753-1854
Email—lcxmach@verizon.net
Pres.—George Kelling
Prodn. Mgr.—Jeffrey Banks
Off. Mgr.—Dawn Barcia
SIC—3599; *General machining job shop*
Employs—10; Estab.—1945
Sales—$500,000-$1Mil
9,000 sq ft site, Distrib.—Local
Privately owned corporation

**MASTER CRAFTSMAN, LLC**
417 N. Grove St., Bldg. 2, Unit D (08009)
**Phone—(856) 768-8088**
Fax—(856) 768-9088
Pres.—Patt Plungis
Mng. Dir.—Matthew Plungis
SIC—2431; NAICS—321900; *Architectual millwork*
Employs—3; Estab.—1992
Sales—over $500,000
5,000 sq ft site, Distrib.—Regional
Limited Liability Company

**†MID ATLANTIC PUMP & EQUIPMENT CO.**
228 N. Route 73 (08009)
**Phone—(856) 768-3880**
National—(877) 643-7867
Fax—(856) 768-0925
www.mapeco.com
Email—sales@mapeco.com
Pres.—Dennis Zepp
SIC—5084; 5074; *Wholesaler of industrial, commercial & municipal pumps, sewage grinder pumps, pump control systems & prepackaged water booster & solids handling pump stations; Brand name—FE Myers; Homa; Yeomans\* Grundfos; Cascade; Cornell; Flowtronix; Tsurumi; Thern*
Employs—10; Estab.—1984
Sales—$5Mil
5,000 sq ft site, Distrib.—Intl.
Privately owned corporation

**MINUTEMAN PRESS**
35 W. White Horse Pike (08009)
**Phone—(856) 753-0055**
Fax—(856) 753-1785
www.berlin.minutemanpress.com
Email—mmpberlingraphics@comcast.net
Pres., Sales Mgr.—Kevin J. Humphrey
Fin., MIS & Opers. Mgr.—Karen Humphrey
SIC—2759; 2752; NAICS—323100; *Commercial & digital instant & full-color printing & graphic design*
Employs—4; Estab.—1988
Sales—under $500,000
1,600 sq ft site, Distrib.—Regional
Privately owned sub-S corp.

**MOUNT CONSTRUCTION CO., INC. (H Q)**
427 S. White Horse Pike, P.O. Box 619 (08009)
**Phone—(856) 768-8493**
Fax—(856) 753-1453
www.mountconstruction.com
Email—info@mountconstruction.com
Pres., CEO—Dave Smith
SIC—2951; 1429; *Corporate headquarters; bituminous concrete & crushed stone*
Employs—13
Sales—$500,000-$1Mil (est)
Distrib.—Regional
AKA: Mount Group

**MOUNTAIN PRINTING CO., INC.**
27 N. Atlantic Ave., P.O. Box 608 (08009)
**Phone—(856) 767-7600**
Fax—(856) 767-2698
www.mountainprinting.com
Pres.—Rose Marie DePasquale
SIC—2759; NAICS—323100; *Computer-to-plate commercial printing*
Employs—30; Estab.—1962
57,000 sq ft site, Distrib.—Intl.
Privately owned corporation

**NATIONAL PAVING CO., INC.**
Div. of Glasgow, Inc.
148 Williamstown Rd., P.O. Box 5 (08009)
**Phone—(856) 767-1950**
Fax—(856) 767-0806
www.glasgowinc.com
GM—Bill Rambo
Sales Mgr.—Joe DiFiore
Plt. Mgr.—Joe Caromano
SIC—2951; NAICS—324121; *Asphalt paving compounds*
Employs—9; Estab.—1968
Sales—$1Mil-$5Mil
Distrib.—Local
Privately owned corporation
Parent co.—Glasgow, Inc., Glenside, PA
　Phone—(215) 884-8800
　See Parent Co. Section for full profile.

**OCCUPATIONAL TRAINING CENTER**
215 W. White Horse Pike (08009)
**Phone—(856) 768-0845**
Fax—(856) 767-1378
www.arccamden.org
Email—lmcclain@arccamden.org
Ex. Dir.—Loret McClain
Hum. Res. Mgr.—Dawn Paker
SIC—3999; 3089; *Contract assembly & packaging, including liquid filling & inspections*
Employs—35; Estab.—1956
Sales—$1Mil-$2.5Mil
Distrib.—Local
Privately owned corporation

**P & J MACHINE CO.**
261 Crosskeys Rd., P.O. Box 178 (08009)
**Phone—(856) 767-8441**
Fax—(856) 768-0205
Email—pjmachineco@aol.com
Owner—John Pepe
SIC—3599; 3544; NAICS—333500; *CNC & conventional machining & tooling of precision & general metal parts, including shafts, screws, pins, rollers & washers*
Employs—3; Estab.—1966
Sales—under $500,000
5,000 sq ft site, Distrib.—Regional
Sole ownership

**PRECISION PRINTING GROUP, LLC**
117 Jackson Rd. (08009)
**Phone—(856) 753-7903**
National—(800) 625-9525
Fax—(856) 753-0307
www.precisionprinting.pro
Email—info@precisionprinting.pro
Pres.—Lori Colucci
GM—John Riebel
Cust. Serv. Rep.—Karen Salcedo
SIC—2752; 2791; 2789; NAICS—323122; *Prepress & offset digital printing & binding & finishing*
Employs—40; Estab.—1984
55,000 sq ft site, Distrib.—National
Privately owned corporation

**PROBUILD CO., LLC**
Div. of ProBuild Holdings, Inc.
210 Williamstown Rd. (08009)
**Phone—(856) 767-3153**
Fax—(856) 768-7796
www.probuild.com
Email—info@probuild.com
Plt. Mgr.—Russ Gervasi
SIC—2439; NAICS—321200; *Wooden roof & floor trusses*
Employs—30; Estab.—1973
Distrib.—Local
Privately owned corporation
AKA: ProBuild East
Parent co.—ProBuild Holdings, Inc., Denver, CO
　Phone—(303) 262-8500
　See Parent Co. Section for full profile.

**QUIKRETE COS., INC, THE**
Div. of QUIKRETE Cos., Inc., The
22 Union Ave. (08009)
**Phone—(856) 768-6642**
National—(800) 257-5328
Fax—(856) 768-6708
www.quikrete.com
Email—info@quikrete.com
Plt. Mgr.—Mark Koltura
Cust. Serv. Rep.—Diane Firrincili
SIC—3272; *Packaged concrete, bulk mortar & grout*
Employs—50; Estab.—1997
Distrib.—Regional
Privately owned corporation
Parent co.—QUIKRETE Cos., Inc., The, Atlanta, GA
　Phone—(404) 634-9100
　See Parent Co. Section for full profile.

**SAR INDUSTRIAL FINISHING, INC.**
104 N. Route 73 (08009)
**Phone—(609) 567-2772**
Fax—(609) 567-2494
Email—jsmauro@comcast.net
Pres.—Ralph Mauro
V-P.—Patricia Mauro
Supervisor—Joe Mauro

## Berlin—(cont.)

SIC—3479; *Industrial spray painting of machinery & metal parts*
Employs—18; Estab.—1968
Sales—$1Mil-$2.5Mil
Distrib.—Regional
Privately owned corporation

**UFP BERLIN, LLC**
Div. of Universal Forest Products, Inc.
159 Jackson Rd. *(08009)*
**Phone—(856) 767-0043**
Fax—(856) 767-1526
www.ufpi.com
Email—info@ufpi.com
GM—David Goldman
Hum. Res. Mgr.—Heather Williams
SIC—2439; 2435; 2436; NAICS—321211; *Wooden roof trusses & wall panels*
Employs—60; Estab.—1951
Sales—$10Mil-$25Mil (est)
Distrib.—Intl.
Publicly owned corporation
Parent co.—Universal Forest Products, Inc., Grand Rapids, MI
Phone—(616) 364-6161
See Parent Co. Section for full profile.

**UNITED ASPHALT CO., INC.**
237 N. Grove St. (08009)
Mail addr: P.O. Box 291, Cedar Brook (08018-0291)
**Phone—(856) 753-9811**
National—(800) 843-0317
Fax—(856) 753-9809
www.unitedasphalt.com
Email—steve@unitedasphalt.com
Pres., GM—Mark Umosella
Cont.—John Laratta
Sales Mgr.—Stephen Umosella
SIC—2952; NAICS—324122; *Roofing asphalt*
Employs—20; Estab.—1960
Sales—$10Mil-$15Mil
Distrib.—Regional
Privately owned corporation

**WALTER'S SIGNS**
159 W. White Horse Pike (08009)
**Phone—(856) 210-6324**
www.walterssigns.com
Email—sales@walterssigns.com
Owner—Walter Schmitz
Installation Mgr.—Andrew Schmitz
SIC—3993; 2759; 2396; *Interior & exterior signs, commercial printing & apparel screen printing, including vinyl & neon signs, business cards, brochures, labels & custom t-shirts*
Employs—2; Estab.—2006
Sales—under $500,000
Distrib.—Regional
Privately owned corporation

**WHITE VALLEY MEMORIALS (H Q)**
292 W. White Horse Pike (08009)
**Phone—(856) 767-3030**
      (856) 767-0170
Fax—(856) 767-7976
www.monumentsofdistinction.com
Owner—Al Cohlmyer
SIC—3281; *Company headquarters; stone monuments*
Employs—1
Sales—under $500,000 (est)
Distrib.—Local
Sole ownership

## Bernardsville
(Somerset—N.E.)

**ABAA, INC. (H Q)**
P.O. Box 26 (07924)
**Phone—(908) 766-4900**
National—(800) 756-5590
www.babysmart.com

Email—diane@babysmart.com
Owner—Diane Zissu
SIC—3086; *Corporate headquarters; plastic foam baby booster seats (mfg. subcontracted); Brand name—Cooshee®*
Employs—4; Estab.—1993
Sales—$500,000-$1Mil (est)
Distrib.—Intl.
Privately owned corporation
AKA: Babysmart, LLC

**BERNARDSVILLE PRINT CENTER**
21 Mine Brook Rd. (07924)
**Phone—(908) 766-4073**
Fax—(908) 766-7633
Email—sales@bvillepc.com
Pres.—Richard C. Steinberg
SIC—2759; 2752; 2789; NAICS—323121; *Digital instant, commercial, 1-4 color offset & architectural printing of full-color posters & banners & binding, laminating & mailing services*
Employs—7; Estab.—1989
Sales—$1Mil-$5Mil
2,700 sq ft site, Distrib.—Regional
Privately owned corporation

**GREENBROOK STAIRS, INC.**
14 Dayton St. (07924)
Mail addr: P.O. Box 126, Basking Ridge (07920)
**Phone—(908) 221-9145**
Fax—(908) 766-2458
Email—gbstairs@aol.com
Pres.—Keith Fitting
SIC—2431; NAICS—321900; *Wooden stairs & railings*
Employs—8; Estab.—1979
5,000 sq ft site, Distrib.—Local
Privately owned corporation

**MEADOWBROOK INVENTIONS, INC.**
260 Mine Brook Rd., P.O. Box 960 (07924)
**Phone—(908) 766-0606**
Fax—(908) 766-6878
www.meadowbrookinventions.com
Email—info@meadowbrookinventions.com
Pres.—Harold Sutton
Opers. Mgr.—Eric Goetz
SIC—3497; 2675; 3089; NAICS—322200; *Polyester, metal & heat fusible fiber glitter, including precision cutting for industrial applications*
Employs—42
Sales—$10Mil-$25Mil (est)
Distrib.—Intl.

**OFFRAY SPECIALTY NARROW FABRICS, INC. (H Q)**
4 Essex Ave., Ste. 403 (07924-2265)
**Phone—(908) 879-3636**
Fax—(908) 953-2976
www.osnf.com
Email—sales@osnf.com
Pres., CEO—Denise A. Offray
Cont.—Erik Conrad
Hum. Res. Mgr.—Jill Lusto
SIC—2241; *Corporate headquarters; specialty high-performance textiles & narrow fabrics; Brand name—E-Z Lace; Conductiles; Sentry FR*
Employs—9; Estab.—1876
Sales—$2.5Mil-$5Mil
Distrib.—Intl.
Sole ownership

**RECORDER PUBLISHING CO. (H Q)**
17-19 Morristown Rd., P.O. Box 687 (07924)
**Phone—(908) 766-3900**
National—(800) 624-3684
Fax—(908) 766-6365
www.recordernewspapers.com
Email—charliez@recordernewspapers.com
Ptnr.—Stephen W. Parker

Ptnr.—Elizabeth K. Parker
Editor—Charlie Zavalick
Dir., Adv.—Jerry O'Donnell
SIC—2711; *Company headquarters; newspaper publishing*
Employs—50
Distrib.—Regional
Privately owned corporation

**WORKS, THE**
17 Claremont Rd. (07924)
Mail addr: 22 Upland Way, Verona (07044)
**Phone—(908) 766-7744**
www.theprintablefashion.com/theworks
Email—theworks17@verizon.net
Owner—Bob Ditrani
SIC—2396; *T-shirt screen printing*
Employs—1; Estab.—1997
Sales—under $500,000
Distrib.—Regional

## Beverly
(Burlington—S.E.)

**A P S SUPPLY CO.**
711 Cooper St. (08010)
**Phone—(609) 877-7900**
Fax—(609) 877-6187
www.apscork.com
Pres.—Stan Lewis
Estimator—Scott Mark
SIC—2655; NAICS—322214; *Fiber expansions*
Employs—17; Estab.—1980
15,000 sq ft site, Distrib.—National
Privately owned corporation

**AELITHO GROUP, INC.**
450 Broad St., P.O. Box 9000 (08010)
**Phone—(609) 239-0700**
National—(800) 235-8888
Fax—(609) 239-8493
www.aelitho.com
Email—aelitho@aol.com
Pres.—Annette Yellin
IT Mgr.—Ken Howard
SIC—2752; NAICS—323100; *Printing, including forms, business cards, letterheads & envelopes for inventory services, management & commercial applications*
Employs—80; Estab.—1962
20,000 sq ft site, Distrib.—Regional
Privately owned sub-S corp.

**ALCOP ADHESIVE LABEL CO.**
826 Perkins Ln., P.O. Box 398 (08010)
**Phone—(609) 871-4400**
National—(888) 313-3017
Fax—(609) 871-3017
www.alcoplabels.com
Email—info@alcoplabels.com
Pres.—Wilmer P. Webster III
Cust. Serv. Rep.—Wendy Cannon
SIC—2759; *Label printing*
Employs—12; Estab.—1965
Sales—$1Mil-$2.5Mil
Distrib.—Local
Privately owned corporation

**ASPEN MFG. CO., INC.**
703 Van Rossum Ave., Unit 5 (08010)
**Phone—(609) 871-6400**
National—(800) 327-1794
Fax—(609) 871-6430
www.aspensafety.com
Email—am4323@aol.com
Pres.—John DeFulgentis
Cont.—Veronica Hosack
SIC—3633; 3632; NAICS—335224; *Residential washer, dryer, refrigerator & range parts*
Employs—10; Estab.—1982
5,000 sq ft site, Distrib.—National
Privately owned corporation

**CAMPBELL CONVERTING CORP.**
703 Van Rossum Ave., Unit 2 (08010)
**Phone—(609) 835-2720**
Fax—(609) 877-2532
www.campbellconverting.com
Email—campbellccccorp@aol.com
Owner & Pres.—C. Norman Campbell
V-P.—John Campbell
SIC—2679; 2611; 2759; NAICS—322200; *Paper converting & wide-format printing*
Employs—8; Estab.—1989
Sales—$500,000-$1Mil
Distrib.—Regional
Privately owned sub-S corp.

**COLORCRAFT SIGN CO.**
400 Magnolia St. (08010)
**Phone—(609) 386-1115**
National—(800) 732-1575
Fax—(609) 386-0429
www.colorcraftsign.com
Email—colorcraft1978@comcast.net
Owner—Steve Molnar
SIC—3993; 3089; 2395; 2396; *Full-color graphics, vinyl, vehicle & bus lettering, corrugated plastic, interior, exterior, PVC & LED signs, silk screening, embroidery, laser & rotary engraving, banners, decals, badges, trophies & plaques*
Employs—8; Estab.—1978
Sales—under $500,000
2,900 sq ft site, Distrib.—National
Sole ownership

**DISTINCTIVE WOODWORKING**
703 Van Rossum Ave., Unit 1 (08010)
**Phone—(609) 877-8122**
Fax—(609) 877-9171
www.distinctivestairsolutions.com
Email—robthestairman@yahoo.com
Owner—Robert Hoffman
Manager—Nick Tantarom
SIC—2431; NAICS—321900; *Wooden & metal stairs*
Employs—10; Estab.—1986
Sales—$500,000-$1Mil
Distrib.—Regional
Sole ownership

**EDGEWATER BUILDING SUPPLY, INC.**
704 Woodlane Rd. (08010)
**Phone—(609) 387-0136**
Fax—(609) 387-3860
Pres.—Paul Witkowski
V-P.—David Witkowski
SIC—2421; 2431; NAICS—321900; *Lumber processing & custom millwork*
Employs—3; Estab.—1975
Sales—$500,000-$1Mil
Distrib.—Regional
Privately owned corporation

**GIANETTO WOOD CARVINGS, VINCENT**
617 Delanco Rd. (08010)
**Phone—(609) 877-6233**
www.ducksandsuch.com
Owner—Vincent Gianetto III
SIC—2499; *Wood carvings*
Employs—1; Estab.—1983
Sales—under $500,000
Distrib.—National
Sole ownership

**IMPRINTZ CUSTOM PRINTED GRAPHICS, INC.**
Garfield & Decatur Sts., P.O. Box 315 (08010)
**Phone—(609) 386-5673**
Fax—(609) 386-2281
www.imprintz.net
Email—imprintz@imprintz.net
Pres.—Leah Arter

GEOGRAPHICAL

## Beverly—(cont.)

SIC—2396; *Screen printing*
Employs—4; Estab.—1989
Sales—$500,000-$1Mil
Distrib.—Local
Privately owned corporation

### LAYNE CHRISTENSEN CO.

719 Mount Holly Rd. (08010)
**Phone—(609) 877-2700**
Fax—(609) 877-7433
www.layne.com
Email—rtmisek@
laynechristensen.com
Hum. Res. Mgr.—Michelle Ryan
Field Supt.—Joe Yost
SIC—3561; NAICS—333911;
*Rebuilt water pumps*
Employs—10; Estab.—1981
Sales—$1Mil-$2.5Mil (est)
Distrib.—Regional
Publicly owned corporation
Parent co.—Layne Christensen
Co., The Woodlands, TX
Phone—(281) 475-2600
See Parent Co. Section for full profile.

### †MATTING WORLD

P.O. Box 43 (08010)
**Phone—(609) 641-4747**
National—(800) 257-8557
Fax—(609) 641-7766
www.ojsupply.com
Email—ojsupply@comcast.net
Ptnr.—Marialynn Patalano
Ptnr.—Enzo Marcozzi
Off. Mgr.—Ann Gilbert
SIC—5023; 5087; *Distributor of mats & janitorial supplies*
Employs—3; Estab.—1950
Sales—$300,000
Distrib.—National
Limited Liability Company

### MEN OF STEEL ENTERPRISES, LLC

4319 Route 130 (08010)
**Phone—(877) 732-2728**
Fax—(609) 871-2200
www.menofsteelrebar.com
Email—info@
menofsteelenterprises.com
Pres.—Robert Vogelbacher
SIC—3449; *Rebar fabrication*
Employs—22; Estab.—2003
Sales—$2.5Mil-$5Mil (est)
Distrib.—Regional
Limited Liability Company
AKA: Men of Steel Rebar
Fabricators, LLC

### METAL MASTERS

630 Laurel St. (08010)
**Phone—(609) 332-3176**
Fax—(856) 428-8440
www.metalmasters.us
Email—arlissy@msn.com
Owner—Israel Gaitelband
SIC—3499; 3444; *Metal & stainless steel fabrication*
Employs—2; Estab.—1987
Sales—under $500,000
Distrib.—Regional
Privately owned corporation

### TRI-STATE TAPE & LABEL CO., INC.

351 Railroad Ave., P.O. Box 377
(08010)
**Phone—(800) 682-7892**
(609) 387-4600
Fax—(609) 387-3691
www.tristatelabel.com
Email—dwimer@tristatelabel.com
Pres.—David F. Wimer
GM—Dianne Gleason
Prodn. Mgr.—Ron Davis
Off. Mgr.—Meg Wimer

SIC—2672; 2759; 2752; NAICS—322222; *Flexible packaging, digital, offset, thermal, flexographic & silkscreen printing, custom, preprinted & pressure-sensitive labels & RFID & EAS tags, including die cutting, laminating, sheeting & slitting; Brand name—3M; Avery; Adchem; Spinnaker; Flexcon; International Tape; 3Sigma; Filmquest; Zebra Printers; Shurtape; Amcor; Jen-Coat; Iimak*
Employs—7; Estab.—1968
Sales—$1.5Mil
8,000 sq ft site, Distrib.—National
Privately owned corporation

---

## Birmingham

(Burlington—S.E.)

### CABINET-TRONICS, INC.

100 Birmingham Rd., P.O. Box 198
(08011)
**Phone—(609) 267-2625**
Fax—(609) 267-0034
www.cabinettronics.com
Email—cabinettronics@aol.com
Pres.—Michael Lockwood
GM—Lori Lockwood
Off. Mgr.—Susan Kramar
Proj. Mgr.—John Wade
SIC—2431; NAICS—321900;
*Commercial grade millwork & casework*
Employs—15; Estab.—1981
Sales—$1Mil-$2.5Mil
Distrib.—Regional
Privately owned corporation

---

## Blackwood

(Camden—S.W.)

NEW ENTRY

### AMERICAN MACHINING CO., LLC

110 Harmon Dr. (08012)
**Phone—(856) 245-7801**
Fax—(856) 245-7803
www.americanmachiningco.com
Email—bill@
americanmachiningco.com
Owner—Bill Ehsign
SIC—3599; *CNC & wire EDM machining job shop*
Employs—5
Sales—$500,000-$1Mil (est)
Limited Liability Company

### BRADBURY BURIAL VAULT CO., INC.

761 Lower Landing Rd. (08012)
**Phone—(856) 227-2555**
Fax—(856) 227-3726
Pres.—Lawrence A. Kenney
Plt. Mgr.—Peter Giannone
SIC—3272; *Concrete burial vaults*
Employs—23; Estab.—1950
Distrib.—Local
Privately owned corporation

### CACIA'S BAKERY

1010 S. Black Horse Pike (08012)
**Phone—(856) 228-5986**
www.caciabakery.com
Email—information@
caciabakery.com
Owner—Raymond Cacia
SIC—2051; NAICS—311812;
*Bread*
Employs—4; Estab.—1953
Sales—under $500,000
Distrib.—Local
Sole ownership

### CAESAR'S PASTA

1001 Lower Landing Rd., Ste. 311
(08012)
**Phone—(856) 227-2585**
National—(888) 432-2372
Fax—(856) 227-1910
www.caesarspasta.com

Email—caesarspasta@
caesarspasta.com
Pres.—Michael Lodato
V-P. & Hum. Res. Mgr.—Ronald R.
Lodato, Sr.
SIC—2098; 2038; NAICS—311823; *Frozen pasta meals, including meat, cheese & vegetable filled with sauce & without sauce ravioli, gnocchi, cavetelli, tortellini, cannelloni, eggplant, stuffed shells & lasagna & meatballs; Brand name—Sieilien Chefs Inc.*
Employs—50; Estab.—1968
Distrib.—Intl.
Privately owned sub-S corp.

### †ENGINE DISTRIBUTORS, INC.

400 University Ct. (08012)
**Phone—(856) 228-7298**
Fax—(856) 228-5531
www.edi-dist.com
Pres.—Glenn Cummings
V-P.—Glenn Cummings III
V-P.—Jamie Cummings
Cont. & IT Mgr.—Dave Kennedy
SIC—5084; *Corporate headquarters & distributor of industrial engines, marine engine parts & water cooled exhaust systems*
Employs—40; Estab.—1970
44,000 sq ft site, Distrib.—Intl.
Privately owned corporation

### †GCE MARKET, INC.

1001 Lower Landing Rd., Ste. 307
(08012)
**Phone—(856) 401-8900**
Fax—(856) 401-9871
www.gcemarket.com
Email—info@gcemarket.com
CEO & Dir., Sales—Jaydeep Patel
SIC—5065; *Corporate headquarters & wholesaler of refurbished wafer processing & automated test equipment*
Company-wide Emp.: 22 (est.)
Privately owned corporation

### GRACO MANUFACTURING

Div. of Karcher North America
500 University Ct. (08012)
**Phone—(856) 228-1800**
Fax—(856) 228-2211
www.gracomfg.com
Email—support@gracomfg.com
Hum. Res. Mgr.—Todd McGovern
Cust. Serv. Mgr.—Tracy Reed
SIC—3589; 5087; NAICS—333319; *Manufacturer & distributor of aftermarket repair & replacement parts for commercial floor care equipment*
Employs—60; Estab.—1972
Sales—$6Mil-$10Mil
50,000 sq ft site, Distrib.—National
Privately owned corporation
Parent co.—Karcher North
America, Englewood, CO
Phone—(303) 738-2400
See Parent Co. Section for full profile.

### HOFFMAN PRECISION PLASTICS, INC.

548 Almonesson Rd., P.O. Box
338 (08012)
**Phone—(856) 228-3550**
Fax—(856) 232-2012
Email—hoffmanprecision@
verizon.net
Pres.—Robert J. Hoffman, Sr.
V-P., Treas., Fin.—Rita Hoffman
Lewis
SIC—3089; 3544; NAICS—333500; *Custom plastic injection molding & tooling*
Employs—8; Estab.—1973
Sales—$1Mil-$5Mil
7,300 sq ft site, Distrib.—National
Privately owned corporation

### HOLDING SIGN DESIGN, E. R.

2 N. Black Horse Pike (08012)
**Phone—(856) 227-1570**
Fax—(856) 227-3499
Email—signanddesign@verizon.net
Owner—Roxanne Holding
Sales Mgr.—Edward Holding
SIC—3993; *Interior & exterior signs*
Employs—2; Estab.—1994
Sales—under $500,000
Distrib.—Local
Sole ownership

### I-SEE OPTICAL LABORATORIES, INC.

44 W. Church St. (08012)
**Phone—(856) 227-9300**
National—(800) 334-5367
Fax—(800) 348-4733
Pres.—Michael Palkovicz
Off. Mgr.—John Rowand
SIC—3851; NAICS—339100;
*Eyeglass lenses*
Employs—20; Estab.—1982
Sales—$2.5Mil-$5Mil (est)
Distrib.—Local
Privately owned corporation

### L E C ELECTRONICS, INC.

814 Warsaw Ave. (08012)
**Phone—(856) 227-3953**
Fax—(856) 227-8631
www.leccoolers.com
Email—info@leccoolers.com
Pres.—Elsie Lewis
SIC—3519; *Marine after-cooler systems*
Employs—5; Estab.—1980
Sales—under $500,000
3,000 sq ft site, Distrib.—Intl.
Privately owned corporation

### MJG TECHNOLOGIES, INC.

832 Camden Ave. (08012)
**Phone—(856) 228-6118**
www.electricmatch.com
Email—info@electricmatch.com
Pres.—Jeff Genzel
SIC—3699; 5051; *Manufacturer of electric matches, igniters & squibs for the pyrotechnics, blasting & related industries & distributor of wire products*
Employs—3; Estab.—2003
Sales—$1Mil-$2.5Mil
Distrib.—Intl.
Privately owned corporation

### PHILADEPHIA SOAPSTONE CO.

1001 Lower Landing Rd., Ste. 103
(08012)
**Phone—(856) 232-7627**
Fax—(856) 232-7622
www.soapstonecompany.com
Email—joemack@
phillysoapstone.com
Owner—Joseph McElhiney
SIC—3281; *Soapstone fabrication, including slabs & countertops*
Employs—5
Sales—under $500,000 (est)

### †RELIABLE TIRE DISTRIBUTORS, INC.

805 N. Black Horse Pike, P.O. Box
39 (08012)
**Phone—(856) 232-0700**
National—(800) 342-3426
Fax—(856) 228-3118
www.reliabletire.com
Email—mikeb@reliabletire.com
CEO—Mike Betz
Pres.—Richard Betz
Cont.—Michael Tofani
SIC—5014; *Corporate headquarters & distributor of tires*
Employs—60
Distrib.—Intl.
Privately owned sub-S corp.

## Blackwood—(cont.)

**RENAISSANCE MARBLE & GRANITE**
107 Harmon Dr. (08012)
**Phone—(856) 227-3535**
Fax—(856) 227-3698
www.renmarble.com
Email—mhernandez@
renmarble.com
Pres.—Mark Hernandez
Hum. Res. Mgr.—Justin Steel
SIC—3281; NAICS—327991;
Marble & granite products
Employs—40; Estab.—1989
23,000 sq ft site, Distrib.—Local
Privately owned corporation

**†SUPERIOR POOL PRODUCTS, LLC**
Div. of Pool Corporation
200 Freeway Dr., Ste. 2 (08012)
**Phone—(856) 232-7774**
Fax—(856) 232-5313
www.superiorpoolproducts.com
Email—sales@sppdistributors.com
Br. Mgr.—Russel Bacon
Hum. Res. Mgr.—Sharon Teti
SIC—5091; Distributor of
swimming pool products
Employs—12; Estab.—1967
Sales—$1Mil-$2.5Mil
40,000 sq ft site, Distrib.—
Regional
Publicly owned corporation
Parent co.—Pool Corporation,
Covington, LA
Phone—(985) 892-5521
See Parent Co. Section for full profile.

**TRIANGLE TUBE PHASE III, INC.**
1 Triangle Ln. (08012)
**Phone—(856) 228-8881**
Fax—(856) 228-3584
www.triangletube.com
Email—sales@triangletube.com
Pres., CEO—Daniel Lasserre
Acct. Mgr.—Linda Camillo
IT Mgr.—Mark Allen
Hum. Res. Mgr.—Maureen
Campbell
SIC—3498; 3433; NAICS—
332996; Stainless steel hot water
heating equipment, including
water heaters, tankless coils,
condensing boilers & HVAC
products for the residential,
commercial & industrial
industries
Employs—50; Estab.—1946
100,000 sq ft site, Distrib.—
National
Privately owned corporation

**TWIN MODULAR SERVICES, INC.**
1001 Lower Landing Rd., Ste. 607
(08012-3122)
**Phone—(856) 227-0057**
Fax—(856) 227-5540
www.guardhousesonline.com
Email—peter@twinmodular.com
Pres.—Peter Broderick
V-P.—Paul Broderick
SIC—3448; Prefabricated metal
modular guard houses, booths &
shacks
Employs—3; Estab.—1987
Sales—under $500,000
5,000 sq ft site, Distrib.—National
Privately owned corporation

## Blairstown

(Warren—N.W.)

**INDUSTRIAL METAL, INC.**
32 Lambert Rd. (07825)
Mail addr: 169 Cedar Lake Rd.,
Blairstown (07825)
**Phone—(908) 362-0084**
Fax—(908) 362-0087
www.industrialmetalinc.com
Pres.—Dan O'Hern
Prodn. Mgr.—Mike Reade

SIC—3441; 3312; NAICS—
332312; Stainless steel
equipment
Employs—8; Estab.—1991
Sales—$1Mil-$2.5Mil
Distrib.—Intl.
Privately owned corporation

**JAMES ALEXANDER CORP.**
845 State Route 94 (07825)
**Phone—(908) 362-9266**
Fax—(908) 362-5019
www.james-alexander.com
Email—info@james-alexander.com
Pres.—Francesca Fazzolari
V-P.—David Robinson
Dir., Sales—Carol Gamsby
SIC—3231; 3089; NAICS—
327215; Contract packaging,
including crushable glass &
plastic ampoule filling & sealing
for the pharmaceutical industry
Employs—100; Estab.—1976
30,000 sq ft site, Distrib.—Intl.
Privately owned corporation

**†L & W SUPPLY CORP.**
126 Route 94 (07825)
**Phone—(908) 362-6103**
Fax—(908) 362-9287
www.lwsupply.com
Email—lwwebmaster@
lwsupply.com
Br. Mgr.—Tony Amadales
SIC—5031; 5033; Distributor of
building materials, including
wallboard & acoustical ceilings
Employs—5; Estab.—1976
Distrib.—Local
Publicly owned corporation
Parent co.—L & W Supply Corp.,
Chicago, IL
Phone—(312) 436-4000
See Parent Co. Section for full profile.

**MB MFG., INC.**
1 Gwinup Rd. (07825)
**Phone—(908) 362-5588**
Fax—(908) 362-5115
www.mb-mfg.com
Email—cs@mb-mfg.com
Owner & Pres.—Mark Beesley
Prodn. Mgr.—Gil Repetto
Off. Mgr.—Christine Veene
SIC—3672; NAICS—334412;
Adjustable wave solder pallets &
selective solder fixtures for
printed circuit board assembly,
including cleaning baskets,
tooling, general machining, CNC
milling & turning & composites
Employs—7; Estab.—1986
6,000 sq ft site, Distrib.—Intl.
Privately owned corporation

**OPERATIONS TECHNOLOGY, INC.**
30 Lambert Rd., P.O. Box 408
(07825)
**Phone—(908) 362-6200**
Fax—(908) 362-5966
www.optek.net
Email—info@optek.net
Pres.—Richard B. Amon
IT Mgr.—George Sappah
Off. Mgr.—Elisse Pfeiffer
R & D Mgr.—Craig Smigel
SIC—3829; Inspection &
measurement instruments
Employs—14; Estab.—1978
Sales—$1Mil-$5Mil
15,000 sq ft site, Distrib.—Intl.
Privately owned sub-S corp.

**NEW ENTRY**
**SOLAR FURNACE GLASS**
4 Camp Wasigan Rd. (07825)
**Phone—(908) 362-9661**
Email—solarfurnace@earthlink.net
Owner—Al Hough

SIC—3231; 3229; Decorative
glass
Employs—1; Estab.—1965
Sales—under $500,000
1,500 sq ft site, Distrib.—Intl.
Sole ownership

## Blawenburg

(Somerset—N.E.)

**PARSELL'S WELDING, INC.**
354 Route 580 (08504)
Mail addr: P.O. Box 409, Hopewell
(08525)
**Phone—(609) 466-1930**
Fax—(609) 466-2560
Owner—Art Parsell
SIC—3599; Welding job shop
Employs—1; Estab.—1974
Sales—under $500,000
Distrib.—Local
Privately owned corporation

## Bloomfield

(Essex—N.E.)

**†ABCO SYSTEMS, INC.**
15 Willet St., Ste. 4 (07003)
**Phone—(201) 507-0999**
Fax—(201) 507-0534
www.abcosystems.net
Email—sethw@abcosystems.net
Pres.—Seth Weisberg
CFO—Andy Noble
V-P., Sales—Thomas Hoff
Engr.—Matt Lopreato
SIC—5084; 5085; Distributor of
industrial handling equipment
Employs—12; Estab.—1982
Distrib.—Local
Privately owned corporation

**ALL-WAYS ADVERTISING CO.**
1442 Broad St. (07003)
**Phone—(973) 338-0700**
Fax—(973) 338-1410
www.awadv.com
Email—awa@awadv.com
Pres.—Rob Lieberman
SIC—2759; NAICS—323100;
Promotional product commercial
printing & graphic design,
including drinking bottles,
clipboards, clocks, coasters &
corporate marketing gifts
Employs—30; Estab.—1998
Sales—$500,000-$1Mil
Distrib.—National
Privately owned corporation

**†ATLANTIC TRACK & TURNOUT CO.**
270 Broad St., P.O. Box 1589
(07003)
**Phone—(973) 748-5885**
National—(800) 631-1274
Fax—(973) 748-4520
www.atlantictrack.com
Email—info@atlantictrack.com
Owner—Peter Hughes
IT Mgr.—Stacy Weisel
Hum. Res. Mgr.—Barbara
Borbisgrie
SIC—5051; 5088; Company
headquarters & distributor of
new & used relay rails,
trackwork, OTM & railroad
accessories for transit systems
Employs—15; Estab.—1980
Sales—under $500,000
Distrib.—Intl.
Privately owned corporation

**BANKS BROS. CORP.**
24 Federal Plz. (07003)
**Phone—(973) 680-4488**
Fax—(973) 680-9064
www.banksbroscorp.com
Pres.—Stanley Banks
Hum. Res. Mgr.—Arnold
Kronelsod

SIC—3069; Corporate
headquarters & molded urethane
products
Employs—4; Estab.—1985
Distrib.—Regional
Privately owned corporation

**BLOOMFIELD WINES, INC.**
339 Broad St. (07003)
**Phone—(973) 743-2020**
National—(877) 946-3664
www.winemo.com
Manager—Kurt Pato
SIC—2084; Wines
Employs—4
Sales—$1Mil-$2.5Mil (est)

**BUDGET PRINT CENTER**
332 Broad St. (07003)
**Phone—(973) 743-0073**
Fax—(973) 743-2875
www.budgetprintingofbloomfield.c
om
Email—budgetprint.center@
verizon.net
Owner—Thomas D. DeStefano
SIC—2752; 2759; NAICS—
323100; Offset & digital printing
Employs—8; Estab.—1980
Sales—$500,000-$1Mil
1,325 sq ft site, Distrib.—Local
Sole ownership

**CM FURNACE, INC.**
103 Dewey St. (07003)
**Phone—(973) 338-6500**
Fax—(973) 338-1625
www.cmfurnaces.com
Email—info@cmfurnaces.com
Pres.—David Neill
V-P., Sales—James Neill
Dir., Hum. Res.—Gerri Cantanzaro
GM—Ernie Renzulli
SIC—3567; NAICS—333994;
High-temperature electric batch
& continuous laboratory &
production furnaces
Employs—46; Estab.—1946
30,000 sq ft site, Distrib.—Intl.
Privately owned corporation

**COLUMBUS BAKERY, INC.**
197 Bloomfield Ave. (07003)
**Phone—(973) 429-1697**
Fax—(973) 429-3314
Pres.—Jack Gambino
SIC—2051; NAICS—311812;
Bakery products; Brand name—
Italian Breads; French Breads;
Rolls
Employs—9; Estab.—1963
Sales—$750,000
Distrib.—Local
Privately owned sub-S corp.

**COSTAS ARCHITECTURAL
WOODWORKING**
248 Montgomery St. (07003)
**Phone—(973) 429-7004**
Fax—(973) 429-8114
Ptnr.—Oscar Costa
SIC—2434; 2431; NAICS—
337110; Custom residential &
commercial kitchen cabinets
Employs—8
Sales—under $500,000
Distrib.—Local
Limited Liability Company

**†EQUIPMENT SALES & SERVICE**
152 Floyd Ave. (07003)
**Phone—(973) 743-7516**
National—(800) 423-7516
Fax—(973) 743-3195
www.esstrucksales.com
Email—danjr@esstrucksales.com
Owner—Dan DePalma

GEOGRAPHICAL

## Bloomfield—(cont.)

SIC—5012; 5013; *Wholesaler of tow trucks & recovery equipment & truck accessories & parts, including new & used wreckers & car carriers, unmounted tow truck bodies & equipment & add-on wheel lifts & underlifts; Brand name—Chevron; Dynamic; Zacklift; Sneeker; B & B Industries*
Employs—8; Estab.—1980
Distrib.—Intl.
Privately owned corporation

**EXACTA INDUSTRIES, INC.**
20 John F. Kennedy Dr. N. (07003)
**Phone—(973) 259-0104**
Fax—(973) 259-0107
www.exactagarment.com
Email—contactus@
exactagarment.com
Pres.—Ory Giberstein
Dir., Opers. & Sales—Perry Friedman
SIC—2399; *Contract textile cutting*
Employs—50; Estab.—1987
Distrib.—Intl.
Privately owned corporation

**FOLEY-WAITE ASSOCS., INC.**
225 Belleville Ave., P.O. Box 164 (07003)
**Phone—(973) 743-0700**
Email—foleywaite@aol.com
Chrm. & V.-P.—Kathryn W. Schackner
Pres.—Kelly Konklin
Off. Mgr.—James Konklin
Proj. Mgr.—Marek Pogorcelski
SIC—2431; NAICS—321900; *Architectural millwork*
Employs—9; Estab.—1977
Sales—$1Mil-$2.5Mil
8,700 sq ft site, Distrib.—Regional
Privately owned corporation

**GARDEN STATE WOODWORKING CO.**
344 Hoover Ave. (07003)
**Phone—(973) 748-2661**
Fax—(973) 748-8826
Pres.—John Falk
SIC—2431; NAICS—321900; *Millwork*
Employs—3; Estab.—1976
Sales—under $500,000
Distrib.—Local
Privately owned corporation

**GENERAL PLASTICS CORP.**
Div. of PMC, Inc.
55 La France Ave. (07003-5681)
**Phone—(973) 748-5500**
     (973) 429-5621
Fax—(973) 748-3988
www.generalplasticscorp.com
Email—info@gpnorth.com
Pres.—Robert Scher
Sales Mgr.—Chuck Hassler
SIC—2851; 3479; NAICS—325510; *Fluoropolymer coatings & liquid & powder paint applicators; Brand name—Genton; Gental; Identasleeve; Durasleeve; Fray Check; Sergene*
Employs—13; Estab.—1951
Sales—$1Mil-$5Mil
50,000 sq ft site, Distrib.—Intl.
Privately owned corporation
Parent co.—PMC, Inc., Sun Valley, CA
Phone—(818) 896-1101
See Parent Co. Section for full profile.

**HALKIAS GEAR & MACHINE WORKS**
14 Willow St. (07003)
**Phone—(973) 748-4901**
Fax—(973) 777-5812
Pres., Pers. Mgr.—James Halkias
V.-P., Plt. Opers.—Ross Halkias

SIC—3462; NAICS—332111; *Precision gears*
Employs—4; Estab.—1972
Sales—under $500,000
5,800 sq ft site, Distrib.—Regional
Privately owned sub-S corp.

**LUMMUS TECHNOLOGY**
Div. of CB&I, INC.
1515 Broad St. (07003)
**Phone—(973) 893-3000**
Fax—(973) 893-3131
www.cbi.com
Email—info@cbi.com
Pres.—Daniel McCorthy
Dir., Hum. Res.—Kay Bell-Reiter
Mktg. Mgr.—Maria Principe
SIC—3443; 3559; *Heat transfer equipment, including technical & engineering services for the energy & petrochemical industries*
Employs—400; Estab.—1907
Sales—$1Mil-$2.5Mil
Distrib.—Intl.
Publicly owned corporation
Parent co.—CB&I, INC., The Woodlands, TX
Phone—(832) 513-1800
See Parent Co. Section for full profile.

**MINOR RUBBER CO., INC.**
49 Ackerman St. (07003)
**Phone—(973) 338-6800**
National—(800) 433-6886
Fax—(973) 893-1399
www.minorrubber.com
Email—sales@minorrubber.com
Pres.—David Humphreys
V.-P., Sales—Thomas Fitzhenry
Secy., Hum. Res. Mgr.—Sandra Humphreys
Treas., Acctg. Mgr.—Theresa Trumpore
Info. Sys. Mgr.—Joshua Gordon
Qual. Control Mgr.—Jeff Hillringhouse
SIC—3061; 3069; NAICS—326291; *Standard, custom, molded, extruded, dipped & fabricated mechanical rubber goods; Brand name—Mirco*
Employs—28; Estab.—1914
Sales—$10Mil
150,000 sq ft site, Distrib.—Intl.
Privately owned corporation

**MUNZING**
1455 Broad St. (07003)
Mail addr: 975 Ultra Dr., Clover (29710-8653)
**Phone—(973) 279-1306**
     (800) 524-0055
Fax—(973) 338-0420
www.munzing.com
Email—info@munzing.us
V.-P., Mfg. & Prod. Mgmt.—Mike Riggs
V.-P., Res.—Frank Portaro
Mng. Dir.—Michael Gaffney
Pur. Mgr.—Patricia Torre
IT Mgr.—Daniel Koziupa
Cust. Serv. Mgr.—Diane Czifra
Mktg. Coord.—Alicia Colacci
SIC—2819; 2843; 2842; NAICS—311900; *Defoamers, dispersants, rheology modifiers, emulsifiers, wetting & leveling agents, micronized & coated waxes & wax dispersions; Brand name—Agitan; Ceretan; DeeFo; Edaplan; FoamBan; FoamTrol; Luba-Print; Metolat; Tafigel; Zinplex*
Employs—39; Estab.—1952
40,000 sq ft site, Distrib.—Intl.
Privately owned corporation
ISO rating—9001

**NELSON, INC., LOUIS A.**
224 Glenwood Ave. (07003)
**Phone—(973) 743-7404**
National—(888) 743-7404
Fax—(973) 743-8480

www.lanelson.com
Email—david@lanelson.com
Pres., MIS Mgr.—David Sibilia
V.-P., R & D—Stephen Cariani
Off. Mgr.—Martha Marshall
SIC—3599; 3544; NAICS—332997; *Thermoforming, metal tooling, prototypes, models, wood patterns, tooling & aluminum*
Employs—12; Estab.—1947
Sales—$1Mil-$2.5Mil
7,000 sq ft site, Distrib.—Regional
Privately owned corporation

**NTE ELECTRONICS, INC.**
44 Farrand St. (07003)
**Phone—(973) 748-5089**
National—(800) 631-1250
Fax—(973) 748-6224
www.nteinc.com
Owner—Andrew Licari
IT Mgr.—John Gido
Hum. Res. Mgr.—Beth Garris
SIC—3674; NAICS—334413; *Semiconductor components*
Employs—72; Estab.—1979
Distrib.—Intl.
Privately owned corporation

**OBJECTIF LUNE, LLC**
300 Broadacres Dr., 4th Fl. (07003)
**Phone—(973) 780-0100**
Fax—(973) 338-8885
www.objectiflune.com
Pres.—Howard Silverstein
IT Mgr.—Giovanni Atanasio
Off. Mgr.—Rhonda Frobose
Sales Rep., Inside—Joe McDonald
SIC—7372; *Transactional document & business form printing software development*
Employs—15; Estab.—1993
Sales—under $500,000
Distrib.—Intl.
Limited Liability Company

**PALMA, INC.**
14 Salter Pl., P.O. Box 2539 (07003)
**Phone—(800) 336-7256**
Fax—(973) 429-2149
www.palmainc.com
Bookkeeper—Lori Henle
SIC—2851; NAICS—325510; *Epoxy flooring mixtures*
Employs—15; Estab.—1989
Sales—$1Mil-$2.5Mil
Distrib.—Regional
Privately owned corporation

**†RANDA LUGGAGE CO.**
Div. of Randa Corp.
200 Broadacres Dr., 2nd Fl. (07003)
**Phone—(973) 873-9050**
Fax—(973) 338-5258
www.badanco.com
Email—info@randaluggage.com
Pres.—Terry Tackett
Pricing Cost Coord.—Wendy Bones
SIC—5099; *Distributor of luggage*
Employs—50; Estab.—1996
Distrib.—Intl.
Privately owned corporation
Parent co.—Randa Corp., New York, NY
Phone—(212) 768-8800
See Parent Co. Section for full profile.

**SAN MARCO RAVIOLI, INC.**
38 Davey St. (07003)
**Phone—(973) 748-4545**
Fax—(973) 748-1918
Email—psiciliano@
sanmarcofoodsco.com
Pres.—Eugene Siciliano
V.-P.—Paul Siciliano
Hum. Res. & Off. Mgr.—Jennifer Siciliano

SIC—2038; NAICS—311823; *Frozen pasta*
Employs—14; Estab.—1983
Distrib.—National
Privately owned corporation

**†SOLID STATE, INC.**
46 Farrand St. (07003)
**Phone—(973) 429-8700**
     (800) 631-2075
Fax—(973) 429-1499
www.solidstateinc.com
Email—sales@solidstateinc.com
Pres.—Andrew Licari
Sales Mgr., Inside—Joseph Defalco
Opers. Mgr.—Edward Cecehovsky
Hum. Res. Mgr.—Barbara Perry
Pur. Agt.—Ian Wagner
SIC—5065; *Distributor of electronic components, including transistors, diodes, LEDs, rectifiers, SCRs, diacs, triacs & conductors; Brand name—Solid State; NTE; Vishay; Littelfuse; Kinbright; Isocom; APD*
Employs—60; Estab.—1968
Sales—$6Mil-$10Mil
70,000 sq ft site, Distrib.—Intl.
Privately owned corporation

**STANEK NETTING, INC.**
111 Orange St. (07003)
**Phone—(973) 680-1616**
Fax—(973) 680-8008
www.staneknetting.com
Email—staneknetting@aol.com
Pres.—Jeremy Stanek
SIC—2211; *Industrial & athletic raschel knitted mesh fabrics*
Employs—5; Estab.—1993
Sales—$1Mil-$2.5Mil
Distrib.—National
Privately owned sub-S corp.

**STOBBS PRINTING CO., INC.**
18 Washington St., P.O. Box 91 (07003)
**Phone—(973) 748-4441**
Fax—(973) 748-2395
Pres.—Gail Tunstead
V.-P.—Evelyn Padalino
SIC—2759; NAICS—323100; *Commercial printing*
Employs—5; Estab.—1947
Sales—under $500,000
5,000 sq ft site, Distrib.—Regional
Privately owned corporation

**UNIVERSAL GRAPHICS CO.**
497 Bloomfield Ave. (07003)
**Phone—(973) 748-4009**
Fax—(973) 748-9884
www.universalgraphicco.com
Email—mzwier@aol.com
Pres.—Michael Zwier
V.-P.—Joan Zwier
SIC—2759; 2752; NAICS—323100; *Commercial offset printing*
Employs—5; Estab.—1981
Sales—$500,000-$1Mil
Distrib.—National
Privately owned corporation

**UTILITY TOOL CO.**
15 Orange St. (07003)
**Phone—(973) 743-8010**
Fax—(973) 743-8123
Email—utilitytl@aol.com
Pres., Fin., MIS & R & D Mgr.—Tony Nigro
SIC—3599; *Precision machining job shop*
Employs—2; Estab.—1960
Sales—under $500,000
3,000 sq ft site, Distrib.—Local
Sole ownership

**ZALLER STUDIOS, INC.**
265 Watsessing Ave. (07003)
**Phone—(973) 743-5175**
www.zallerstudiosinc.com

## Bloomfield—(cont.)

Email—gabe@zallerstudiosinc.com
Pres.—Gabriel Pereira
SIC—2541; 2542; NAICS—
323100; *Point-of-purchase
displays & vinyl, large-format,
digital & screen printing*
Employs—6; Estab.—1974
Sales—$500,000-$1Mil
Distrib.—National
Privately owned corporation

## Bloomingdale
(Passaic—N.E.)

**CENTRAL SHIPPEE, INC.**
46 Star Lake Rd. (07403)
**Phone—(973) 838-1616**
National—(800) 631-8968
Fax—(973) 838-8273
www.centralshippee.com
Pres.—Eric Hubner
SIC—2399; 2299; *Manufacturer of
custom woven decorative
tablecloths, scarves & banners &
distributor of felt, fabrics &
fixtures for the craft & hobby,
display, exhibit & manufacturing
industries*
Employs—30; Estab.—1928
Sales—$1Mil-$5Mil
Distrib.—National
Privately owned corporation
DBA: Allied Felt Corp.

**ELECTRONIC POWER DESIGNS,
INC.**
132 Union Ave. (07403)
**Phone—(973) 838-7055**
Fax—(973) 838-7655
www.epowerdesign.com
Email—epdepd1@optimum.net
Pres.—Gregory J. Brown
Off. Mgr.—Sheila J. Brown
SIC—2448; 3625; NAICS—
321920; *Gaseous piping skids &
industrial control panels*
Employs—15; Estab.—1971
Sales—$1Mil-$2.5Mil
Distrib.—Intl.
Privately owned corporation

**ENERGY BEAMS, INC.**
185 Hamburg Tpke. (07403)
**Phone—(973) 838-3037**
Fax—(973) 492-1706
www.energybeams.com
Email—ebifab@optonline.net
Pres.—John Richard
V-P.—Tom Richard
Plt. Mgr.—Mike Richard
Bookkeeper—Ronni Aiello
SIC—3559; *CNC & precision
machining job shop*
Employs—16; Estab.—1964
3,800 sq ft site, Distrib.—Regional
Privately owned sub-S corp.
AKA: EBI

**HURRICANE SIGNS**
103 Main St. (07403)
**Phone—(973) 838-3373**
www.hurricanesigns.com
Email—info@hurricanesigns.com
Owner—Ronald Kelemen
Off. Mgr.—Lucy Kelemen
SIC—3993; NAICS—339950;
*Metal, acrylic & magnetic
business signs & graphics*
Employs—3; Estab.—1992
Sales—under $500,000 (est)
Distrib.—National
Limited Liability Company
AKA: Graphic Design Worx

**TMP INTERNATIONAL, INC.**
15 Hamburg Tpke. (07403)
**Phone—(973) 838-7072**
Fax—(973) 838-8202
www.spawn.com
V-P., Prod.—Ed Frank

SIC—3942; *Highly detailed toy
models of musicians &
characters from movies, comics,
video games & sports*
Employs—25
Sales—$1Mil-$2.5Mil (est)
Distrib.—Intl.
Privately owned corporation

**TOTAL MAINTENANCE & SERVICE,
INC.**
121 Hamburg Tpke. (07403)
**Phone—(973) 283-0048**
Fax—(973) 283-1227
www.tmanvs.com
Email—tapms@optimum.net
Pres.—Dennis Palmer, Sr.
Sales Mgr.—Keith Ehlbeck
SIC—3444; *Sheet metal
fabrication & HVAC contracting,
including heating, ventilation &
air conditioning*
Employs—7; Estab.—1971
Sales—$500,000-$1Mil
6,000 sq ft site, Distrib.—Local
Privately owned corporation
AKA: Tech Air Service

**VMC GROUP, THE**
113 Main St., P.O. Box 270 (07403)
**Phone—(973) 838-1780**
National—(800) 569-8423
Fax—(973) 492-8430
www.thevmcgroup.com
Email—jwilson@thevmcgroup.com
Chrm.—Richard Berger
CEO—John Wilson, Jr.
Pres.—John Giuliano
V-P.—Tom Steele
SIC—3829; *Company
headquarters & vibration
isolation products for the HVAC,
military, defense, aerospace,
industrial & construction
industries; Brand name—VMC;
Korfund; Aeroflex International
Isolators; Amber/Booth*
Employs—110; Estab.—1997
Sales—$35Mil
120,000 sq ft site, Distrib.—Intl.
Privately owned corporation

## Bloomsbury
(Hunterdon—N.W.)

**GROWMARK FS, LLC**
60 Lehigh Ave., P.O. Box 116
(08804)
**Phone—(908) 479-4500**
Fax—(908) 479-1411
www.growmarkfs.com
Email—bloomsbury@
growmarkfs.com
Sales Mgr.—Rick Klevze
Whse. Mgr.—Esmond Crooke
Asst. Mgr.—Bill Dicky
Bookkeeper—Phil Carlson
SIC—2875; NAICS—325314;
*Fertilizer blending*
Employs—10; Estab.—1963
Sales—$11Mil-$25Mil
Distrib.—Regional
Limited Liability Company
Parent co.—Growmark FS, LLC,
Milford, DE
Phone—(302) 422-3002
See Parent Co. Section for full profile.

**KIN CORE**
70 North St., P.O. Box 485 (08804)
**Phone—(908) 479-1188**
Fax—(908) 479-1187
Pres.—John Haday
SIC—3089; *Plastic products*
Employs—2; Estab.—1992
Sales—under $500,000
16,000 sq ft site, Distrib.—National
Privately owned corporation

**NELSON CUSTOM CASE CO.**
1014 State Route 173 (08804)
**Phone—(908) 479-6902**
Fax—(908) 479-6903

www.nelson-enterprises.com
Email—sales@nelson-
enterprises.com
Owner—William A. Nelson III
Bus. & Fin. Mgr.—Terri Nelson
Case & Rental Mgr.—Randy Werd
SIC—3412; 3089; *ATA style
custom cases, including LED,
instrument, culinary & podium
cases; Brand name—Road
Cases*
Employs—3; Estab.—1990
Sales—under $500,000
5,000 sq ft site, Distrib.—National
Sole ownership
AKA: Nelson Enterprises

**R. & M. MOLD MFG. CO., LLC**
1022 Route 173 E., P.O. Box 578
(08804)
**Phone—(908) 479-4444**
Fax—(908) 479-4915
www.rmmold.com
Email—rmmold@embarqmail.com
Owner & Pres.—John A. Roser, Jr.
SIC—3544; NAICS—333500;
*Metal injection, plastic & die-cast
molds & dies*
Employs—4; Estab.—1981
Sales—$500,000
4,000 sq ft site, Distrib.—Intl.
Limited Liability Company

**WARREN PALLET CO., INC.**
601 County Road 627 (08804)
**Phone—(908) 995-7172**
Fax—(908) 995-4146
www.warrenpallet.com
Email—warrenpalletco@ptd.net
Pres.—Donald Tigar, Sr.
Secy., GM—Donald Tigar, Jr.
Sales Mgr.—Lisa Tigar
SIC—2448; NAICS—321920;
*Custom, new & reconditioned
wooden pallets, including heat
treating*
Employs—18; Estab.—1977
Sales—$1Mil-$5Mil
Distrib.—Regional
Privately owned corporation

## Blue Anchor
(Hunterdon—N.W.)

**SHARROTT WINERY, LLC**
370 S. Egg Harbor Rd. (08037)
**Phone—(609) 567-9463**
Fax—(609) 567-9468
www.sharrottwinery.com
Email—contact@sharrottwinery.com
Pres.—Larry Sharrott
SIC—2084; NAICS—312130; *Red
& white wines*
Employs—10; Estab.—2003
Sales—$500,000-$1Mil
2,500 sq ft site, Distrib.—Local
Limited Liability Company

## Bogota
(Bergen—N.E.)

**D'ELIA SIGN CO.**
32 W. Fort Lee Rd. (07603)
**Phone—(201) 342-7231**
Fax—(201) 342-7231
www.deliasigncompany.com
Email—delia92@optimum.net
Owner—Nicholas D'Elia
SIC—3993; *Interior & exterior
signs*
Employs—2; Estab.—1957
Sales—under $500,000
5,000 sq ft site, Distrib.—Local
Privately owned corporation

**JESCRAFT**
201 W. Fort Lee Rd. (07603)
**Phone—(201) 488-4545**
National—(800) 524-1142
Fax—(201) 488-7359
www.jescraft.com
Email—inquiry@jescraft.com

Pres., CFO—Michael Brown
Cust. Serv. & Hum. Res. Mgr.—
Leslie Cappadona
SIC—3537; 3531; *Construction
job site material handling
equipment & accessories; Brand
name—Jescraft*
Employs—10; Estab.—1946
12,000 sq ft site, Distrib.—National
Privately owned corporation

**†LIBERTY WELDING SUPPLY, INC.**
187 W. Fort Lee Rd. (07603)
**Phone—(973) 923-2900**
Fax—(201) 313-9910
Email—libertyweldingsupply@
aol.com
Pres.—Robert Safranek
Off. Mgr.—Ruth Zachary
SIC—5084; 5085; *Distributor of
new & warranted used welding
equipment & supplies & safety
products, including service*
Employs—2; Estab.—1993
Distrib.—Regional
Privately owned corporation

**LITHOTONE CO.**
255 Queen Ann Rd. (07603)
**Phone—(201) 343-3883**
Fax—(201) 343-3883
Email—lithotone@earthlink.net
Pres.—James Fessel
Off. Mgr.—Mary Fessel
SIC—2759; NAICS—323100;
*Commercial printing*
Employs—4; Estab.—1980
Sales—under $500,000
Distrib.—Local
Privately owned corporation

**ORGANIZE IT ALL, INC.**
24 River St., Ste. 201 (07603)
**Phone—(201) 488-0808**
National—(800) 255-9365
Fax—(201) 488-6535
Pres.—James Lee
SIC—3089; *Corporate
headquarters & plastic
housewares, storage boxes &
hangers*
Employs—30; Estab.—1980
Distrib.—Regional
Privately owned corporation

**†OUTWATER PLASTICS/INDUSTRIES,
INC.**
24 River Rd., P.O. Box 500 (07603)
**Phone—(201) 498-8750**
National—(800) 631-8375
Fax—(800) 888-3315
www.outwatercatalogs.com
Email—info@outwaterplastics.com
Pres.—Peter Kessler
Cont.—Diane Farrell
Opers. Mgr.—Matt Lucas
IT Mgr.—Rich Fallon
Hum. Res. Mgr.—Isabel Carballo
Off. Mgr., Sales—Susan Molnar
SIC—5031; 5162; 5063; *Corporate
headquarters & distributor of
interior architectural products,
including plastic tee mouldings,
u-channels & lighting fixtures*
Employs—125; Estab.—1971
Distrib.—Intl.
Privately owned corporation

**QUANTUM CONCEPTS, INC.**
24 River Rd., Ste. 12 (07603)
**Phone—(201) 343-2008**
Fax—(201) 343-2979
www.quantumconcepts.com
Email—andrea@qcimd.com
Pres.—Paul Viola
Off. Mgr.—Miriam Carrillo
SIC—3841; *Medical instruments*
Employs—12; Estab.—1984
Sales—$1Mil-$2.5Mil
Distrib.—Local
Privately owned corporation

GEOGRAPHICAL

## Bogota—(cont.)

**RABELL PRECISION, INC.**
8 Queen Anne Rd. (07603)
**Phone—(201) 473-7373**
Pres., GM—John Rabell
SIC—3599; *Precision machining job shop*
Employs—2; Estab.—1987
Sales—under $500,000
Distrib.—Regional
Privately owned corporation

---

# Boonton

(Morris—N.W.)

**A A PATCHWORKS, INC. (H Q)**
311 Mechanic St. *(07005)*
**Phone—(973) 810-2121**
Fax—(973) 810-2122
www.aapatchworks.com
Email—artwork@
aapatchworks.com
Pres.—Frank Wagenhoffer
Off. Mgr.—Darlene Francin
SIC—2395; 2396; *Corporate headquarters; embroidered patches & emblems (mfg. done overseas)*
Employs—8; Estab.—1995
Sales—over $1Mil
3,700 sq ft site, Distrib.—Intl.
Privately owned sub-S corp.

**ACTIONEERING MFG. ENGINEERS**
30 Plane St., Bldg. 12, P.O. Box 333 (07005)
**Phone—(973) 299-1999**
Fax—(973) 335-6957
www.actioneeringmfg.com
Email—sales@actioneeringmfg.com
Owner—Nick Debald
Off. Mgr.—Trudy Hickox
SIC—3599; *Precision machining job shop*
Employs—6; Estab.—1985
5,000 sq ft site, Distrib.—Local
Sole ownership

**ADRON, INC.**
94 Fanny Rd., P.O. Box 270 (07005)
**Phone—(973) 334-1600**
Fax—(973) 316-8949
Ex. Pres.—Robert L. Anaducci
Hum. Res. Mgr.—Bill Anaducci
Pur. Agt.—Diane Rutter
SIC—2087; NAICS—311900; *Food flavorings*
Employs—30; Estab.—1930
Sales—$500,000-$1Mil
Distrib.—National
Privately owned corporation

**AEROPANEL CORP.**
661 Myrtle Ave. *(07005)*
**Phone—(973) 335-9636**
Fax—(973) 263-6304
www.aeropanel.com
Email—lfix@aeropanel.com
V-P., GM—Jack Miller
Hum. Res. Mgr.—Sue Abate
SIC—3728; *Illuminated aircraft control & information panels*
Employs—22; Estab.—1981
29,000 sq ft site, Distrib.—Intl.
Privately owned corporation
ISO rating—AS9100

**ALEXANDER COMMUNICATIONS GROUP, INC.**
712 Main St., Ste. 187-B (07005)
**Phone—(973) 265-2300**
National—(800) 232-4317
Fax—(973) 402-6056
www.alexcommgrp.com
Email—info@alexcommgrp.com
Pres.—Lawrence Alexander
Cust. Serv. Rep.—Mary Pagliaroli

SIC—2741; *Newsletter publishing & printing*
Employs—11; Estab.—2007
Sales—$500,000-$1Mil (est)
Distrib.—Intl.
Privately owned corporation

**ALPINE ELASTOMER PRODUCTS, LLC**
308 Division St. (07005)
**Phone—(973) 299-0123**
(908) 216-4359
Fax—(973) 299-0220
www.alpineelastomer.com
Email—info@alpineelastomer.com
Owner—David McCrink
CFO—Vickie Sterflinger
SIC—3069; 3089; 3053; *Custom molded rubber & plastic products, including injection molding, gasket die cutting & design & sourcing services*
Employs—4; Estab.—2003
Sales—$500,000
2,500 sq ft site, Distrib.—Intl.
Limited Liability Company

**AMERICAN MODULAR POWER SOLUTION**
429 Rockaway Rd., Bldg. 10 (07005)
Mail addr: 8 S. Rockaway Dr., Boonton (07005)
**Phone—(973) 588-4026**
Fax—(973) 588-4027
www.ampsnj.com
Email—gregl@ampsnj.com
Pres. & Sales Mgr.—Greg Lowndes
SIC—3612; NAICS—335313; *Modular electrical substations*
Employs—6
Sales—under $500,000
1,000 sq ft site, Distrib.—Intl.
Privately owned corporation

**BIO-CHEM FLUIDICS, INC.**
Div. of Halma Holdings, Inc.
85 Fulton St., Ste. 12 (07005)
**Phone—(973) 263-3001**
Fax—(973) 263-2880
www.biochemfluidics.com
Email—info@biochemfluidics.com
Pres.—Timothy O' Sullivan
Cont.—Mark Nielson
Sales Rep., Natl.—John Albrecht
SIC—3491; 3561; NAICS—332911; *Precision fluid handling components, including miniature solenoid valves & pumps for aggressive & high purity fluids*
Employs—60; Estab.—1983
2,700 sq ft site, Distrib.—Intl.
Publicly owned corporation
Parent co.—Halma Holdings, Inc., Cincinnati, OH
Phone—(513) 772-5501
See Parent Co. Section for full profile.

**BIOMEDTRIX, LLC**
50 Intervale Rd., Ste. 5 (07005)
**Phone—(973) 331-7800**
Fax—(973) 331-7809
www.biomedtrix.com
Email—info@biomedtrix.com
Member—Joseph Pych
Pres.—Christopher Sidebotham
Accts. Mgr.—David Helms
Mktg. Mgr.—Betsy Sives
SIC—3841; *Veterinary orthopedic implants*
Employs—8; Estab.—1990
Distrib.—Intl.
Limited Liability Company

**COMMUNICATION DEVICES, INC.**
85 Fulton St., Unit 2 (07005-1912)
**Phone—(973) 334-1980**
National—(800) 359-8561
Fax—(973) 334-0545
www.commdevices.com
Email—info@commdevices.com
Pres.—Tadhg Kelly

Acctg. & Hum. Res. Mgr.—Peace Chen
SIC—3663; NAICS—334220; *Data encryption & security devices*
Employs—12; Estab.—1976
Sales—$5Mil-$10Mil
Distrib.—National
Privately owned corporation

**CORRECTIVE HYDRAULICS**
731 Birch St., P.O. Box 850 (07005)
**Phone—(973) 334-3792**
Fax—(973) 334-6927
Pres.—Eugene Mini
GM—Arnie O'Grady
SIC—3589; 3594; NAICS—333319; *Hydraulics, including compactor, baler, lift & hydraulic repair service*
Employs—8; Estab.—1980
30,000 sq ft site, Distrib.—Regional
Privately owned corporation

**CREATIVE CABINET DESIGNS, INC.**
301 Main St. (07005)
**Phone—(973) 402-5886**
Fax—(973) 402-1326
Pres.—Manuel Silva
GM—John Lockburner
Designer—Gary Murphy
SIC—2434; NAICS—337110; *Wooden kitchen & bathroom cabinets*
Employs—10; Estab.—1989
Sales—$500,000-$1Mil (est)
Distrib.—Regional
Privately owned corporation

**DAUPHIN NORTH AMERICA**
100 Fulton St. (07005)
**Phone—(973) 263-1100**
National—(800) 631-1186
Fax—(973) 263-3551
www.dauphin.com
Email—cnewman@dauphin.com
CEO—Nick Bayvel
Pres.—Gary Chin
Cont., Hum. Res. Mgr.—Art Tolantino
Dir., Operation—Lothar Maron
IT Mgr.—Mike Wiggins
Pur. Agt.—Phyllis Stymacks
Cust. Serv. Rep.—Catalina Velez
SIC—2521; NAICS—337211; *Office chairs*
Employs—75; Estab.—1982
70,000 sq ft site, Distrib.—Intl.
Privately owned corporation
AKA: Valofurniture.com

**DAVIS SIGN SYSTEMS**
65 Harrison St. (07005)
**Phone—(973) 394-9909**
Fax—(973) 394-9910
www.davissignsystems.com
Pres.—Elaine Davis
SIC—3993; *Signs*
Employs—3; Estab.—2004
Sales—under $500,000
Distrib.—Regional
Privately owned corporation

**ELECTROMAGNETIC TECHNOLOGIES**
50 Intervale Rd., Unit 15 (07005)
**Phone—(973) 394-1719**
Fax—(973) 394-1710
www.etiworld.com
Email—sales@etiworld.com
CEO—John Howard
IT Mgr.—Steve Jalil
Hum. Res. Mgr.—Wenny Lin
Qual. Assur. Supv.—Geraldina Schasster

SIC—3812; 3663; NAICS—334511; *Radar & antenna microwave couplers, hybrids & components*
Employs—40; Estab.—2003
Sales—$500,000-$1Mil
Distrib.—Intl.
Privately owned corporation

**ENGINEERING DYNAMICS, LLC**
429 Rockaway Valley Rd., Ste. 1300 (07005)
**Phone—(973) 794-4500**
www.eng-dyn.com
Owner—Richard G. Spitzlei
SIC—3599; *General & CNC machining job shop*
Employs—2; Estab.—2002
Sales—$500,000-$1Mil
Distrib.—Regional
Limited Liability Company

**ERASTEEL, INC.**
95 Fulton St. (07005)
**Phone—(973) 335-8400**
National—(800) 969-6444
Fax—(973) 335-8420
www.erasteel.com
Email—infonorthamerica@eramet-erasteel.com
Mng. Dir.—Ken Bagady
Hum. Res. & Qual. Sys. Admn. Mgr.—Karen A. Hecker
SIC—3312; *Corporate headquarters & high-speed steels for cutting tools, drills, end mills, taps, saws & knives*
Employs—20; Estab.—1984
Sales—$5Mil-$10Mil (est)
Distrib.—Regional
Privately owned corporation
ISO rating—9001:2008

**†ESCADAUS MAGNETICS**
2 Wood Glen Way (07005)
**Phone—(973) 335-8888**
Fax—(973) 263-0888
Email—henry.kuo@escadaus.com
V-P.—Henry Kuo
SIC—5099; *Distributor of magnets & magnetic components; Brand name—High Performance Rare Earth Magnets*
Employs—4; Estab.—1992
Sales—$1Mil-$2.5Mil
Distrib.—National
Limited Liability Company
AKA: Escadaus Magnetic Corp.

**FIREFREEZE WORLDWIDE, INC.**
429 Rockaway Valley Rd. (07005)
**Phone—(973) 394-1335**
www.firefreeze.com
Email—info@firefreeze.com
Sales Rep., Outside—Ray Giessler
SIC—2899; *Fire suppression agents*
Employs—2; Estab.—1993
Sales—under $500,000
Distrib.—Intl.
Privately owned corporation
Parent co.—Firefreeze Worldwide, Inc., Rockaway, NJ
Phone—(973) 627-0722
See Parent Co. Section for full profile.

**†HANNECKE DISPLAY SYSTEMS, INC.**
91 Fulton St., Unit 4 (07005)
**Phone—(973) 335-0434**
National—(800) 345-8631
Fax—(973) 335-1274
www.hannecke.com
Email—info.usa@hannecke.com
Pres.—Cuno VonOlhausen
Dir., Sales & Mktg.—Michaela Fedorko
SIC—5099; *Distributor of display systems*
Employs—7; Estab.—1985
Sales—$500,000-$1Mil
Distrib.—Intl.
Privately owned corporation

## Boonton—(cont.)

**I D J, INC.**
121 Mechanic St. (07005)
**Phone—(973) 334-1517**
Fax—(973) 334-2237
Email—idjinc@optonline.net
Pres.—Julian Pop
SIC—3543; NAICS—332997;
 *Industrial prototypes*
Employs—1; Estab.—1987
Sales—under $500,000
Distrib.—Regional
Sole ownership

**INSTOCK WIRELESS COMPONENTS, INC.**
50 Intervale Rd., Ste. 15 (07005)
**Phone—(973) 335-6550**
Fax—(973) 335-6770
www.instockwireless.com
Email—sales@instockwireless.com
Pres.—Mike Davo
Chief Technical Officer—Richard Armstrong
SIC—3663; 3669; NAICS—334220; *RF microwave power dividers, combiners & splitters for wireless broadband signal transmission & distribution; Brand name—INSTOCK Wireless Components*
Employs—10; Estab.—2005
Sales—$1Mil-$2.5Mil
Distrib.—Intl.
Privately owned corporation

**INSTRUMENT SPECIALTIES CO., INC.**
Div. of Golden Oil Holding Corp.
661 Myrtle Ave. *(07005)*
**Phone—(973) 335-2136**
Fax—(973) 335-5740
www.inscousa.com
Email—info@inscousa.com
GM—Jack Miller
Off. Mgr.—Susan Abate
SIC—3829; *Aircraft engine monitoring instruments*
Employs—19; Estab.—1991
27,000 sq ft site, Distrib.—Intl.
Privately owned corporation
Parent co.—Golden Oil Holding Corp., Houston, TX
 Phone—(713) 626-1110
 See Parent Co. Section for full profile.

**J A M B INDUSTRIES**
336 Rockaway Valley Rd. (07005)
**Phone—(973) 263-9295**
www.jambindustries.com
Email—abudgin@optonline.net
Owner—Alexander Budlin
SIC—3612; NAICS—335311;
 *Current transformers*
Employs—3
Sales—under $500,000
Distrib.—Intl.
Sole ownership

**JOHANSON MFG. CORP.**
301 Rockaway Valley Rd. (07005)
**Phone—(973) 334-2676**
Fax—(973) 334-2954
www.johansonmfg.com
Email—njohanson@johansonmfg.com
Pres., CEO—Nancy Johanson
V.-P., Opers.—Robert Pisapia
Hum. Res. Mgr.—Lisa Phillips
Cust. Serv. Rep.—Kerry Sarnowski
SIC—3679; *Electronic components, including trimmer capacitors, variable inductors, resistive products & packaging services*
Employs—60; Estab.—1945
Sales—$6Mil-$10Mil
50,000 sq ft site, Distrib.—Intl.
Privately owned corporation
ISO rating—9001:2008

**L-3 COMMUNICATIONS MOBILE-VISION, INC.**
Div. of L-3 Communications Corp.
90 Fanny Rd. (07005)
**Phone—(973) 263-1090**
National—(800) 336-8475
Fax—(973) 316-9509
www.mobile-vision.com
Email—info.mvi@l-3.com
Pres.—Leo Lorenzetti
Hum. Res. Mgr.—Kris Delmauro
SIC—3861; *Police car video systems*
Employs—70; Estab.—1987
Sales—$26Mil-$50Mil
24,000 sq ft site, Distrib.—National
Publicly owned corporation
Parent co.—L-3 Communications Corp., New York, NY
 Phone—(212) 697-1111
 See Parent Co. Section for full profile.

**MARLO MFG. CO., INC.**
Div. of EMI Industries, LLC
301 Division St. (07005)
**Phone—(973) 423-0226**
National—(800) 222-0450
Fax—(973) 423-1638
www.marlomfg.com
Email—info@marlomfg.com
Ex. V.-P.—Paul Peruccio
Sales Mgr.—Frank Hailinis
Cust. Serv. Mgr.—Omar Solovic
SIC—3398; 3556; 2599; NAICS—332811; *Stainless steel restaurant equipment*
Employs—50; Estab.—1971
30,000 sq ft site, Distrib.—National
Privately owned sub-S corp.
Parent co.—EMI Industries, LLC, Tampa, FL
 Phone—(813) 626-3166
 See Parent Co. Section for full profile.

**MERSEN USA BN CORP.**
400 Myrtle Ave. (07005)
**Phone—(973) 334-0700**
National—(800) 526-0877
Fax—(973) 334-6394
www.mersen.com
Email—us.cbd@mersen.com
Pres.—Didier Muller
Cont.—Gary Pavlosky
GM—Cedric Fontes
Pur. Mgr.—Brett Rodas
IT Mgr.—Susan Fort
Qual. Control Mgr.—Sarang Shah
SIC—3624; NAICS—335991; *Corporate headquarters & carbon electrical brushes for motors & generators*
Employs—120; Estab.—1942
Sales—$10Mil-$20Mil
63,000 sq ft site, Distrib.—Intl.
Privately owned corporation
ISO rating—9001:2000

**METRO PRINTING & PROMOTIONS, LLC**
311 Mechanic St. (07005)
**Phone—(973) 316-1600**
Fax—(973) 316-1700
www.metroprintingusa.com
Email—steve@metroprintingusa.com
Owner—Steve Rotella
SIC—2396; 2759; NAICS—323100; *T-shirt screen & offset printing*
Employs—6; Estab.—1998
Sales—under $500,000
Distrib.—Local
Limited Liability Company

**†MULCARE PIPELINE SOLUTIONS**
9 Mars Ct., Ste. C-4 *(07005-9310)*
**Phone—(973) 335-4800**
Fax—(973) 402-1558
www.mulcare.com
Email—mulcaremail@mulcare.com
Pres.—Robert Engdahl
V.-P.—Stephen Goodson
Dir., Sales—Scott Vigil

Technical Dir.—Kevin Gross
Hum. Res. Mgr. & Ex. Coord.—Mary Ellen Clement
SIC—5084; 5085; *Distributor of natural gas distribution equipment & supplies; Brand name—Sensus; Cold Weather Technologies; Chevron Phillips; Performance Pipe; Nupi Electrofusion; Nordstrom Valves & Sealant; Connectra Fusion; Bascom-Turner Instruments; KMC Ball Valves; Dresser; YZ Systems; 3M*
Employs—15; Estab.—1923
Distrib.—National
Privately owned corporation

**†MUSICAL DISTRIBUTORS GROUP, LLC**
9 Mars Ct., Unit C-3 (07005)
**Phone—(973) 335-7888**
National—(866) 632-8346
Fax—(973) 335-7779
www.musicaldistributors.com
Email—info@musicaldistributors.com
Pres.—Steven Savvides
V.-P., Sales & Mktg.—Jack Thompson
SIC—5064; *Distributor of audio equipment, including amplifiers, microphones & guitar setup & stations*
Employs—12; Estab.—2003
Distrib.—National
Limited Liability Company

**PARENTA & SONS ENTERPRISES, INC.**
85 Fulton St., Unit 9-B (07005)
**Phone—(973) 334-9266**
National—(800) 332-5581
Fax—(973) 334-9368
Email—jparenta@tellurian.com
Pres.—Joseph Parenta
Secy.-Treas.—Dominick Parenta
Opers. Mgr.—Tom Cole
Off. Mgr.—Peggy Lo Flesh
SIC—3563; *Remanufactured compressed gas equipment for laboratory, medical & industrial gases, including rental equipment for hospital medical gases & vacuum systems shutdowns*
Employs—15; Estab.—1964
7,200 sq ft site, Distrib.—Regional
Privately owned sub-S corp.
AKA: pasemedical.com

**POLYCRACKER, INC.**
487 Division St. (07005)
**Phone—(973) 335-2828**
National—(800) 334-2524
Fax—(973) 402-7222
www.fisheyeterminator.com/polycracker
Email—polycracker@netscape.com
Pres.—Sherylin Doyle
MIS & Opers. Mgr.—Sharron L. Lippman
SIC—2841; NAICS—325611; *Biodegradable, environmentally safe & nontoxic car prep wash & detergent cleaning products for automotive painting applications*
Employs—3; Estab.—1985
Sales—under $500,000
Distrib.—National
Privately owned corporation
Also see: SWI International, Inc., same loc.
AKAs: SWI International & Superwash

**R F L ELECTRONICS, INC.**
Div. of SL Industries, Inc.
353 Powerville Rd. (07005)
**Phone—(973) 334-3100**
Fax—(973) 334-3863
www.rflelect.com
Email—sales@rflelect.com
Pres.—Tony King

V.-P., Opers.—Chris Cross
V.-P., New Bus. Dev.—Motty Anavi
Interim V.-P., Engrg. & Sales & Mktg.—Richard Wissenbach
V.-P., Fin.—Debbie Chen
Sr. Sales Coord.—Kathleen Walsh
SIC—3679; *Electronic communication & relaying teleprotection products*
Employs—110; Estab.—1922
Sales—$10Mil-$25Mil
Distrib.—Intl.
Publicly owned corporation
ISO rating—9001:2008
Parent co.—SL Industries, Inc., Mount Laurel, NJ
 Phone—(856) 727-1500
 See Parent Co. Section for full profile.

**SINGLE POINT PRECISION**
429 Rockaway Valley Rd., Ste. 2300 (07005)
**Phone—(973) 625-7221**
Fax—(973) 625-7331
www.singlepointprecision.com
Email—bob@singlepointprecision.com
Owner & Plt. Mgr.—Robert Pietrowicz
SIC—3441; NAICS—332312; *Swiss screw machine products*
Employs—1; Estab.—1994
Privately owned corporation

**SWI INTERNATIONAL, INC.**
487 Division St. (07005)
**Phone—(973) 334-2525**
National—(800) 334-2524
Fax—(973) 402-7222
www.superwash-cleaner.com
Email—superwashcleaner@aol.com
Pres. & Manager—Sharon Lippman
SIC—2841; NAICS—325611; *Detergents & degreasers*
Employs—5; Estab.—1980
Sales—under $500,000
Distrib.—Intl.
Sole ownership
Also see: Polycracker, Inc., same loc.

**TEKMET, LLC**
400 Myrtle Ave., Ste. A (07005)
Mail addr: 16 South Ave. W., Pmb 155, Cranford (07016)
**Phone—(973) 376-1700**
Fax—(973) 376-0193
Pres.—Richard Polese
SIC—3469; *Metal stampings*
Employs—30
17,000 sq ft site, Distrib.—National
Limited Liability Company

**TELEMARK CNC, LLC**
429 Rockaway Valley Rd., Bldg. 2200 (07005)
**Phone—(973) 794-4857**
Fax—(973) 541-9449
www.telemarkllc.com
Email—sales@telemarkllc.com
Owner—William Hovey
SIC—3599; 3089; *Precision Swiss CNC machining of stainless steel, alloys & plastics, including valves, screws, shafts, seats, collimators, connectors & housings of 0.0025mm to 0.0001 inch*
Employs—5; Estab.—2003
Sales—$500,000-$1Mil
8,000 sq ft site, Distrib.—National
Limited Liability Company
ISO rating—9001

**ULTRA PUNCH & DIE CORP.**
8 N. Main St., P.O. Box 353 (07005)
**Phone—(973) 335-3200**
National—(800) 631-9382
Fax—(973) 334-0611
www.ultrapd.com
Email—sales@ultrapd.com

GEOGRAPHICAL

## Boonton—(cont.)

GM & Fin. Mgr.—Joseph Hogh, Sr.
R & D Mgr.—Joseph Hogh, Jr.
Shop Foreman—James Hogh
SIC—3544; NAICS—333500;
  *Carbide & steel punches & die
  bushings*
Employs—12; Estab.—1975
Sales—$1Mil-$2Mil
10,000 sq ft site, Distrib.—Intl.
Privately owned sub-S corp.

### VALLEY PLASTIC MOLDING CO., INC.

P.O. Box 30 (07005)
**Phone—(973) 334-2100**
Fax—(973) 335-0620
Pres., CFO—Mike Berhman
Qual. Control Mgr.—Herman
  Wisdom
Fin. Mgr.—Mel Hacht
SIC—3089; *Custom compression
  molding & thermoset transfers*
Employs—8; Estab.—1928
Sales—$500,000-$1Mil
13,100 sq ft site, Distrib.—Intl.
Privately owned corporation

## Bordentown

(Burlington—S.E.)

### BAUMAN'S COMPUTER SOLUTIONS

192 Route 130 (08505)
**Phone—(609) 920-0121**
Fax—(609) 298-0977
Email—henry.l.bauman@gmail.com
Owner & IT Mgr.—Henry Bauman
SIC—7373; *Computer network
  systems integration, including
  LANs & computer repair &
  consulting services*
Employs—1; Estab.—2008
Sales—under $500,000
Distrib.—Regional
Sole ownership

### EXCEL SILK SCREENING

2320 Old York Rd. (08505)
**Phone—(609) 499-4990**
Fax—(609) 499-7797
www.silkscreeningbordentown.com
Pres.—Brian Noble
SIC—2396; 2395; *Apparel screen
  printing & embroidery*
Employs—1; Estab.—1999
Distrib.—National
Privately owned corporation

### IN-PHASE TECHNOLOGIES, INC.

401 Bordentown Hedding Rd.,
  Bldg. 4, Ste. A (08505)
**Phone—(609) 298-9555**
Fax—(609) 298-0098
www.in-phasetech.com
Email—sales2100@in-
  phasetech.com
Pres.—Ed MacMullen
CFO—Bobb Twiggs
V-P., Engrg.—Howard Salvesen
Mfg. Mgr.—Pete Sabatini
Administrator—Jane Jordan
SIC—3825; NAICS—334500;
  *Electronic test equipment*
Employs—30; Estab.—1991
20,000 sq ft site, Distrib.—Intl.
Privately owned corporation

### MERSHON CONCRETE, LLC

Route 130 S., P.O. Box 254
  (08505)
**Phone—(609) 298-2150**
National—(800) 755-7837
Fax—(609) 298-7969
www.mershonconcrete.com
V-P. & IT Mgr.—Patrick T. Greber
SIC—3272; 3273; NAICS—
  327320; *Precast & ready-mixed
  concrete*
Employs—40; Estab.—1954
Distrib.—Regional
Privately owned corporation

### MODERN EQUIPMENT CO., INC.

19 Ann St. (08505)
**Phone—(609) 298-2100**
National—(800) 866-3376
Fax—(609) 298-2384
www.moderngroup.com
Email—dunigant@
  moderngroup.com
Owner—David Dunigan
SIC—2541; 2542; *Wooden &
  metal commercial cabinets*
Employs—24; Estab.—1958
Sales—$1Mil-$2.5Mil (est)
Distrib.—Local
Privately owned corporation

### NWL, INC.

312 Rising Sun Rd. (08505)
**Phone—(609) 298-7300**
Fax—(609) 298-1982
www.nwl.com
Email—dinman@nwl.com
Pres., CEO—David Seitz
V-P.—Helmut Herder
IT Mgr.—Roger Zara
Hum. Res. Mgr.—Thomas Thorn
Prog. Mgr., Military—Dean Inman
Asst. Hum. Res. Mgr.—Brooke
  Brennan
SIC—3612; NAICS—335311;
  *Corporate headquarters &
  transformers*
Employs—150
Company-wide: 225
Sales—$25Mil-$50Mil
Distrib.—Intl.
Sole ownership
ISO rating—9001

### OCEAN SPRAY CRANBERRIES, INC.

104 E. Park St. (08505)
**Phone—(609) 298-0905**
Fax—(609) 298-8353
www.oceanspray.com
Email—sales@oceanspray.com
Cont.—Mike Brumfield
Plt. Mgr.—Bill Garcia
Hum. Res. Mgr.—Kristen Burnett
Hum. Res. Admn.—Kelly Collins
SIC—2033; NAICS—311421;
  *Cranberry juice*
Employs—250; Estab.—1947
500,000 sq ft site, Distrib.—
  Regional
Privately owned corporation
Parent co.—Ocean Spray
  Cranberries, Inc., Middleboro,
  MA
  Phone—(508) 946-1000
  See Parent Co. Section for full profile.

### PACOR, INC.

333 Rising Sun Rd. (08505)
**Phone—(609) 324-1100**
National—(888) 918-0800
Fax—(609) 324-1106
www.pacorinc.com
Email—oem@pacorinc.com
Pres., CEO—Ronald Latini
Ex. V-P.—William J. Wheatley
V-P.—Jack Wheatley
Dir., Sales—Louis Damelio
Dir., Hum. Res.—Jennifer Luling
Dir., Qual. & Safety—Kathleen
  Goodwill
IT Mgr.—Anna Kazmierczuk
SIC—3296; NAICS—327993;
  *Corporate headquarters &
  thermal & acoustic fiberglass
  insulation*
Employs—45; Estab.—1921
Sales—$1Mil-$5Mil
80,000 sq ft site, Distrib.—National
Privately owned corporation
ISO rating—9001

### PRINCETON TEC

5198 Route 130 N. (08505)
Mail addr: P.O. Box 8057, Trenton
  (08650)
**Phone—(609) 298-9331**
National—(800) 257-9080
Fax—(609) 298-9601

www.princetontec.com
Email—info@princetontec.com
Pres.—Arthur W. Stephens
Dir., Sales & Sales Mgr., Natl.—
  David Cozzone
Opers. & Prodn. Mgr.—Debra
  Safranko
IT Mgr.—Rich Shenowski
Hum. Res. Mgr.—Laura Papp
SIC—3648; NAICS—335129;
  *Company headquarters &
  flashlights; Brand name—
  Princeton Tec*
Employs—110; Estab.—1975
Sales—$8Mil
42,000 sq ft site, Distrib.—Intl.
Privately owned corporation

### PULCIN MACHINE

13 Cedar Ln. (08505)
**Phone—(609) 387-3060**
Fax—(609) 387-2391
Owner—Paul Mara
SIC—3599; *General machining
  job shop*
Employs—1; Estab.—1974
Sales—under $500,000 (est)
Distrib.—Local
Sole ownership

### STA-SEAL, INC.

Div. of Trap Rock Ind., LLC
5205 Route 130 S. (08505)
Mail addr: P.O. Box 419, Kingston
  (08528)
**Phone—(609) 924-0300**
Fax—(609) 924-5734
www.traprock.com
Email—gmorgan@traprock.com
Manager—Gilbert Girard
SIC—2951; NAICS—324121; *Hot
  mix asphalt*
Employs—3
Sales—under $500,000 (est)
Distrib.—Local
Privately owned corporation
Parent co.—Trap Rock Ind., LLC,
  Kingston, NJ
  Phone—(609) 924-0300
  See Parent Co. Section for full profile.

NEW ENTRY
### STONY BROOK SEW & VACUUMS, INC.

191 U.S. Highway 130 (08505)
**Phone—(609) 372-4018**
www.stonybrooksewandvac.com
Email—stonybrooksewandvac@
  comcast.net
Owner—Howard Anderson
SIC—3639; NAICS—333298;
  *Rebuilt sewing machines &
  vacuum cleaners*
Employs—10
Sales—$1Mil-$2.5Mil (est)

### VANCO U. S. A., LLC

1170 Florence Rd. (08505)
**Phone—(609) 499-4141**
Fax—(609) 499-8865
www.vancotrailers.com
Email—info@vancotrailers.com
Chrm., CFO—James Massaro
Plt. Mgr.—Al Blakeslee
SIC—3715; NAICS—336212; *Dry
  freight trailers & truck bodies*
Employs—4
113,000 sq ft site, Distrib.—
  National
Privately owned corporation

### WIRE EQUIPMENT MFG. CO., INC.

319 Birch Hollow Dr. (08505)
Mail addr: P.O. Box 135, Roebling
  (08554)
**Phone—(609) 499-4411**
Fax—(609) 499-4488
www.wempumsmfg.net
Email—wempumps@comcast.net
Pres.—Christine Stone-Quinn

SIC—3561; NAICS—333911;
  *Molten metal centrifugal pumps*
Employs—1; Estab.—1950
Sales—under $500,000
500 sq ft site, Distrib.—Intl.
Privately owned corporation

## Bound Brook

(Somerset—N.E.)

### ANN CAROL DESIGNS, INC.

333 Mountain Ave. (08805)
**Phone—(732) 469-7552**
Fax—(732) 469-7552
www.anncaroldesigns.com
Email—jschroeder@
  anncaroldesigns.com
Pres.—Janet Schroeder
SIC—3911; NAICS—339911;
  *Custom handcrafted
  contemporary sterling silver
  jewelry*
Employs—2; Estab.—1986
Sales—under $500,000
1,000 sq ft site, Distrib.—National
Privately owned sub-S corp.

### BURNS, INC., JOSEPH

241 W. Union Ave. (08805)
**Phone—(732) 356-7990**
Fax—(732) 469-6766
www.getvpa.com
Email—orders@getvpa.com
Pres., CEO—Mary McClintock
Graphic Designer—Nancy
  McClintock
Accts. Rec. Rep.—Mafalda
  McClintock
SIC—2752; NAICS—323100;
  *Variable, digital color & black &
  white printing*
Employs—10; Estab.—1988
3,500 sq ft site, Distrib.—Regional
Privately owned corporation
AKA: Versatile Printing
  Applications

### CYALUME SPECIALTY PRODUCTS

100 W. Main St., P.O. Box 669
  (08805)
**Phone—(732) 469-7760**
Fax—(732) 469-3666
www.cyalume.com
Email—info@cyalume.com
Pres.—James G. Schleck
COO—Thomas Cornelson
V-P., R & D—Vilas Chopdekar
V-P., Prod. Dev.—Hemant Desai
V-P., Qual. Sys.—Dina Kisver
Logistics Coord.—Vicki Torntore
SIC—2819; 2869; 2899; 2834;
  NAICS—325412; *Bulk active
  pharmaceutical ingredients,
  pharmaceutical polymers,
  custom chemical synthesis &
  high-performance polymers &
  monomers, including chemical
  research & development; Brand
  name—Myris-100; Glucosapure*
Employs—28; Estab.—1970
Sales—$5Mil-$7Mil
42,000 sq ft site, Distrib.—Intl.
Limited Liability Company
ISO rating—9001:2000

### ENVIROPRINT USA

11 Maiden Ln. (08805)
**Phone—(732) 356-5959**
National—(877) 830-6060
Fax—(732) 469-0889
www.enviroprintusastore.com
Email—jerry@enviroprintusa.com
Pres., Fin. & R & D Mgr.—Gerald
  F. Truppelli
V-P., Mktg.—Ryan Devesty
V-P.—Gerald S. Truppelli

## Bound Brook—(cont.)

SIC—2759; NAICS—323100; *Eco-friendly soy-based digital & commercial printing of booklets, brochures, business, folded & holiday cards, postcards, pocket folders, sell sheets & posters*
Employs—7; Estab.—1969
Sales—$1Mil-$2.5Mil
15,000 sq ft site, Distrib.—Intl.
Privately owned corporation
AKA: Graphic Concepts Printing, Inc.

### †GARDEN OAKS GARDEN CENTER

1921 U.S. Highway 22 (08805)
**Phone—(732) 356-7333**
National—(800) 590-7433
Fax—(732) 356-7202
www.gardenoaks.com
Email—gardenoaks@aol.com
Owner—Madeline Wenz
Manager—Lisa Serridge
SIC—5021; 5099; 5199; *Full-line distributor of outdoor, lawn & garden products, including storage sheds, swing sets, pond products, gazebos, fencing, fireplaces & lawn furniture*
Employs—20; Estab.—1971
Sales—$500,000-$1Mil
Distrib.—Local
Privately owned corporation

### IMPERIAL METAL PRODUCTS, INC.

8 W. Chimney Rock Rd. (08805)
**Phone—(732) 469-8181**
Fax—(732) 469-0077
www.jerseycrusher.com
Email—imperial.metal@verizon.net
Pres.—John Karmazyn
SIC—3599; 3569; 3444; *Stainless steel size reduction machinery & systems*
Employs—5; Estab.—1982
8,500 sq ft site, Distrib.—Intl.
Privately owned corporation

### SOMERSET PROSTHETIC & ORTHOTICS, INC.

56 W. Union Ave. (08805)
**Phone—(732) 560-2830**
Fax—(732) 560-2832
www.somersetpo.com
Email—info@somersetpo.com
Pres.—Glen Honcharik
V-P.—Joseph Evans
SIC—3842; *Custom & off-the-shelf orthopedic bracing, including knee, AFOs, KAFOs & spinal braces for scoliosis & fractures & custom designed artificial upper extremity limbs*
Employs—2; Estab.—1992
Sales—under $500,000
Distrib.—Local
Privately owned corporation

### STAVOLA CONSTRUCTION MATERIALS, INC.

Div. of Stavola Contracting Co., Inc.
810 Thompson Ave. (08805)
Mail addr: P.O. Box 482, Red Bank (07701)
**Phone—(732) 356-7100**
Fax—(732) 356-2175
www.stavola.com
Email—information@stavola.com
Corp. Secy.—Helen Stokes
GM—John Davies
IT Mgr.—Jim Bean
Hum. Res. Mgr.—Dominique Goode
Plt. Supt.—Juan Berrios
Pur. Agt.—Bruce Todd
SIC—3281; 2951; 1429; NAICS—327991; *Construction stone aggregates & asphalt paving materials*
Employs—50; Estab.—1948
Distrib.—Regional
Privately owned corporation

Parent co.—Stavola Contracting Co., Inc., Tinton Falls, NJ
Phone—(732) 542-2328
See Parent Co. Section for full profile.

## Bradley Beach
(Monmouth—N.E.)

### GREAT GARLIC FOODS, INC.

709 5th Ave. (07720)
**Phone—(732) 775-3311**
Fax—(732) 774-9386
Email—ggarlfoods@aol.com
Pres.—Joe Desantis, Jr.
SIC—2035; *Garlic & pesto sauce & spreads*
Employs—10; Estab.—1979
Sales—$2.6Mil-$5Mil
11,000 sq ft site, Distrib.—National
Privately owned corporation

### MURRAY'S UNIFORMS, INC.

312 Main St. (07720)
**Phone—(732) 774-2671**
Fax—(732) 774-3883
Email—abart56@aol.com
Pres.—Andrew Bartlett
V-P.—Louanne Bartlett
V-P.—Stephen Bartlett
SIC—2396; 2395; *Textile screen printing & embroidery*
Employs—3; Estab.—1971
Sales—under $500,000
Distrib.—Regional
Limited Liability Company
AKA: ThreeTwelve LLC

### REGN SIGN STUDIO, INC.

42 Main St. (07720)
**Phone—(732) 988-3595**
Fax—(732) 988-0337
www.regnsignco.com
Email—regnsignco@aol.com
Pres., CEO—Lori Regn
SIC—3993; *Interior & exterior signs*
Employs—3; Estab.—1980
Sales—under $500,000
2,000 sq ft site, Distrib.—National
Privately owned corporation

### SIGNS SEALED & DELIVERED, INC.

121 Main St. (07720)
**Phone—(732) 775-7227**
Fax—(732) 775-7229
www.signssealedanddelivered.net
Email—ssdinc@optonline.net
Co-Pres.—Peter Schulle
Off. Mgr.—Rob Alfano
SIC—3993; *Interior & exterior signs, vinyl lettering & vehicle wraps*
Employs—3; Estab.—1990
Sales—under $500,000
Distrib.—Regional
Privately owned corporation

### WINGIT INNOVATIONS, LLC

714 5th Ave. (07720)
**Phone—(732) 869-4466**
National—(877) 894-6448
Fax—(732) 869-9474
www.wingits.com
Owner & Fin. Mgr.—Sal Sisto
Cust. Serv. Rep.—Tami Morales
SIC—3429; 3842; NAICS—339993; *Fasteners, grab bars, shower rods & tub benches for the hospitality & health care industries*
Employs—2; Estab.—2005
Sales—under $500,000 (est)
Distrib.—National
Limited Liability Company

## Branchburg
(Somerset—N.E.)

### ALLEN GROUP SMC

60 Readington Rd. (08876)
**Phone—(908) 231-1100**
Fax—(908) 231-9663

www.allengroupmarketing.com
Pres.—Steven Hegna
GM—Jim Gibson
SIC—2754; 2752; 2791; NAICS—323111; *Envelope & offset printing & typesetting & direct mailing*
Employs—60; Estab.—1969
Distrib.—Intl.
Privately owned corporation

### AMERICAN SPRAYTECH, LLC

205 Meister Ave. (08876)
**Phone—(908) 725-6060**
Fax—(908) 725-1932
www.americanspraytech.com
Pres.—Allen S. Lalwani
Sales & Mktg. Mgr.—Bill Leuschen
Hum. Res. Mgr.—Sangeeta Lalwani
Cust. Serv. Mgr.—Fran Harcarik
SIC—2844; 2841; NAICS—325611; *Contract manufacturer of cosmetics, air fresheners, foam soap, conditioner, hair & foot sprays, mousse & shampoo*
Employs—19; Estab.—2003
Sales—$500,000-$1Mil
Distrib.—National
Limited Liability Company

### ASSOCIATED MAILING & PRINTING SERVICES, LLC

50 Tannery Rd., Ste. 2 (08876-6034)
**Phone—(908) 541-9700**
Fax—(908) 823-4733
www.amps-marketing.com
Email—assocmail@amps-marketing.com
Pres.—Christopher Halligan
Prodn. Mgr.—John Halligan
Data Mgr.—Laurie Morris
SIC—2759; NAICS—323100; *Commercial printing, mailing services & marketing support*
Employs—12; Estab.—2002
Sales—$1.2Mil
Distrib.—Regional
Limited Liability Company

### BETTER SLEEP CO., INC.

100 Readington Rd., Ste. 2 (08876)
**Phone—(908) 393-0120**
Fax—(908) 393-0126
www.better-bath.com
Email—info@better-sleep.com
CEO—Robert Emery
Pres.—William Emery
Plt. Mgr.—John Matthew
Bookkeeper—Tami Griesi
SIC—3089; *Vinyl bath pillows & shower caddies*
Employs—10; Estab.—1950
Distrib.—National
Privately owned corporation

### BIOSEARCH MEDICAL PRODUCTS, INC.

35 Industrial Pkwy. (08876)
**Phone—(908) 722-5000**
National—(800) 326-5976
Fax—(908) 526-3633
www.biosearch.com
Email—mcdyck@hydromer.com
Pres., CEO & V-P.—Manfred F. Dyck
V-P., Fin. & CFO—Robert Y. Lee
V-P., Qual. Assur. & Dir., Hum. Res.—John S. Konar
Asst. Dir.—Joan Newman

SIC—2821; 3841; NAICS—325211; *Biocompatible hydrophilic polymer coatings for medical product manufacturing & biofeedback monitors & probes for incontinence & constipation*
Employs—50; Estab.—1975
Sales—$11Mil-$25Mil
40,000 sq ft site, Distrib.—Intl.
Publicly owned corporation
Also see: Hydromer, Inc., same loc.
AKA: Hydromer, Inc.

### BYRAM LABORATORIES, INC.

1 Columbia Rd. (08876)
**Phone—(908) 252-0852**
National—(800) 766-1212
Fax—(908) 252-0822
www.byramlabs.com
Email—sales@byramlabs.com
Pres.—Monte J. Prince
Dir., Tech. Svcs.—Alex Thompson
Dir., Tech. Svcs.—Kenn Miles
Sales Engr.—Joe Poliseno
Administrator—Diane Gawlikowski
SIC—3825; NAICS—334500; *Automatic meter reading systems, including kwh & digital/analog panel meters & electricial test equipment; Brand name—Elster Electricity; ABB; Fluke; Megger; Jewell; Aemc; Simpson; Yokogawa; GE; Crompton; American Solenoid*
Employs—24; Estab.—1910
16,000 sq ft site, Distrib.—National
Privately owned corporation
ISO rating—9001

### CASEWORK DESIGN

10 County Line Rd., Ste 26 (08876)
**Phone—(908) 722-7401**
Fax—(908) 722-2268
Owner—Michael Rowden
SIC—2541; 2542; 2451; NAICS—321991; *Store & commercial fixtures, business cabinets, counters & reception desks*
Employs—3; Estab.—1989
Sales—under $500,000
3,000 sq ft site, Distrib.—Local
Limited Liability Company

### †DUVA, INC., JAMES

66-B Columbia Rd. (08876)
**Phone—(908) 526-1222**
Fax—(908) 526-9333
www.jamesduva.com
Email—sales@jamesduva.com
Pres.—James Duva
Whse. Mgr.—Jesse Kronr
SIC—5085; *Wholesaler of pipe, hose & fittings*
Employs—8; Estab.—1978
Sales—$6Mil
18,000 sq ft site, Distrib.—Intl.
Privately owned sub-S corp.

### ELI LILLY & CO.

Div. of Eli Lilly
33 ImClone Dr. (08876)
**Phone—(908) 541-8100**
www.imclone.com
Email—media@imclone.com
Assoc. V-P., Fin. Analysis & Plng.—Lori Macomber
Asst. V-P., Dev. & Organizational Learning—Kristin Zemanek
Dir., Portfolio & Proj. Mgmt.—Cindy Toste
SIC—2834; *Oncology pharmaceutical drug candidates in Phase I, II & III clinical trials; Brand name—ERBITUX®*
Employs—650; Estab.—2001
Limited Liability Company
AKA: ImClone
Parent co.—Eli Lilly, Bridgewater, NJ
Phone—(908) 541-8100
See Parent Co. Section for full profile.

GEOGRAPHICAL

# Branchburg—(cont.)

**FALCON SAFETY PRODUCTS, INC.**
25 Imclone Dr., P.O. Box 1299 (08876)
**Phone—(908) 707-4900**
National—(800) 332-5266
Fax—(908) 707-8855
www.falconsafety.com
Pres.—Phil Lapin
Off. Mgr.—Maria Carpio
Qual. Control & Safety Mgr.—
  Diane Issendorf
SIC—3861; 2813; NAICS—
325120; *Compressed gas computer cleaning products*
Employs—60; Estab.—1954
55,000 sq ft site, Distrib.—Intl.
Privately owned corporation

**FIBER-SPAN**
3434 U.S. Highway 22, Ste. 120 (08876-6011)
**Phone—(908) 253-9080**
Fax—(908) 253-9086
www.fiber-span.com
Email—techinfo@fiber-span.com
CEO—Hal Halpern
Pres.—Henry Wojtunik
Dir., Engrg.—Dino Giordano
Bus. & Hum. Res. Mgr.—Linda
  Torocco
SIC—3663; NAICS—334220; *RF ON FIBER(R) communication network products for in-building, in-tunnel & outdoor coverage extension systems for the commercial wireless, public safety, government & military markets*
Employs—15; Estab.—1995
Sales—$2.5Mil-$5Mil (est)
Distrib.—Intl.
Privately owned corporation

**G M STAINLESS, INC.**
41 Imclone Dr. (08876)
**Phone—(908) 575-1834**
Fax—(908) 575-1836
www.gmstainless.com
Email—info@gmstainless.com
Pres.—Walter Gauer
Sales Mgr.—Carol Gauer
SIC—3499; *Stainless steel shearing & edge conditioning & brake formed angle & channel; Brand name—Gauer Bar*
Employs—10; Estab.—1980
Sales—$2.5Mil-$5Mil
Distrib.—National
Privately owned corporation

**†GARDEN STATE ENGINE & EQUIPMENT CO., INC.**
3509 U.S. Highway 22 (08876)
**Phone—(908) 534-5444**
  (800) 479-3857
Fax—(908) 534-5623
www.gseecrane.com
Email—sales@gseecrane.com
GM—John Meyer
Acctg. Mgr.—John Devine
SIC—5084; *Distributor of truck-mounted cranes & parts; Brand name—National Crane; Elliott Cranes; Tadano Cranes; Princeton Forklifts; Manitou Forklifts; Sunfab Pumps; Cormach Cranes; IMT Cranes*
Employs—15; Estab.—1977
10,000 sq ft site, Distrib.—National
Privately owned corporation

**GOTTSCHO PRINTING SYSTEMS, INC.**
335 Chambers Brook Rd. (08876)
**Phone—(908) 688-2400**
Fax—(267) 387-3015
www.gottscho.com
Email—pkatz@gottscho.com
Aftersales Mgr.—Paulette Katz
SIC—3555; NAICS—333293; *Printing & code marking machines & supplies for the packaging industry*
Employs—5; Estab.—1904
Distrib.—Regional
Privately owned corporation

**HAGELIN FLAVOR TECHNOLOGIES**
200 Meister Ave. (08876)
**Phone—(908) 707-4400**
National—(800) 229-2112
Fax—(908) 707-4408
www.hagelin.com
Email—flavor@hagelin.com
Pres.—Craig Hagelin
V-P., Flavor Div.—Richard
  Davidson
V-P., Opers. & Hum. Res. Mgr.—
  Barry Fielding
SIC—2087; NAICS—311900; *Company headquarters & flavors for the food industry; Brand name—SucraVal™*
Employs—65; Estab.—1966
Sales—$10Mil-$15Mil
35,000 sq ft site, Distrib.—Intl.
Privately owned corporation

**HYDROMER, INC.**
35 Industrial Pkwy. (08876)
**Phone—(908) 722-5000**
National—(877) 493-7663
Fax—(908) 526-3633
www.hydromer.com
Email—sales@hydromer.com
Pres., CEO—Manfred F. Dyck
CFO—Robert Lee
Ex. V-P., Opers.—Martin C. Von
  Dyck
Hum. Res. Mgr.—John Konar
SIC—2821; NAICS—325211; *Hydrophilic polymer-based & hydrogel products for the medical device, pharmaceutical, animal health, biotechnology, plastics & cosmetic/personal care industries; Brand name—Hydromer; Aquadapt; Aquamere;Aquatrix; T-HEXX; Dermaseal; Sea-Slide*
Employs—70; Estab.—1980
36,000 sq ft site, Distrib.—Intl.
ISO rating—13485
Also see: Biosearch Medical
  Products, Inc., same loc.

**INDUSTRIAL AUTOMATION SYSTEMS ENGINEERING CO., INC.**
161 Industrial Pkwy., Unit 6 (08876)
**Phone—(908) 218-1104**
Fax—(908) 218-1337
www.iase.net
Email—info@iase.net
Pres., R & D Mgr.—Michael
  D'Egidio
V-P.—Michael Cinicolo
Cont.—Maria D'Egidio
Sales Mgr.—Alan Ekstedt
Proj. Mgr.—Michael Mercandetti
SIC—3565; NAICS—333993; *Robotic packaging machinery*
Employs—20; Estab.—1987
15,000 sq ft site, Distrib.—National
Privately owned corporation

**KINEDYNE CORP. (H Q)**
151 Industrial Pkwy. (08876)
**Phone—(908) 231-1800**
National—(800) 848-6057
Fax—(908) 231-1379
www.kinedyne.com
Email—abellerive@kinedyne.com
Pres.—James M. Klausmann
Ex. V-P.—James Klausmann II
Cont.—Robert Sawchuk
IT Mgr.—Mark Michael
SIC—2298; 2399; *Corporate headquarters; cargo control equipment & systems*
Employs—20; Estab.—1968
Sales—$50Mil
25,000 sq ft site, Distrib.—Intl.

**LABERN MACHINE PRODUCTS**
3388 Highway 22 W. (08876)
**Phone—(908) 722-1970**
Pres.—Larry Remaly
SIC—3599; *CNC machining*
Employs—17; Estab.—1945
Sales—$500,000-$1Mil
24,000 sq ft site, Distrib.—Local
Privately owned corporation

**LIFECELL CORP.**
1 Millennium Way (08876)
**Phone—(908) 947-1100**
National—(800) 367-5737
Fax—(908) 947-1200
www.lifecell.com
Email—contact@lifecell.com
V-P., Qual., Regulatory & Tissue
  Svcs.—Frances Harrison
SIC—3842; *Acellular dermal matrix for human tissue regeneration*
Employs—900; Estab.—1986
Sales—$6Mil-$10Mil
Distrib.—Regional
Privately owned corporation

**†MID-ATLANTIC CNC, INC.**
260 Evans Way (08876)
**Phone—(908) 809-1100**
National—(800) 262-9590
Fax—(908) 809-1199
www.midatlanticcnc.com
Email—gproscia@
  midatlanticcnc.com
Ptnr. & V-P.—Richard Knof
Pres.—Robert Morrison
V-P., Fin. & IT Mgr.—Gary Proscia
SIC—5084; *Corporate headquarters & wholesaler of CNC machinery & replacement parts*
Employs—25; Estab.—1988
Distrib.—Regional
Privately owned corporation

**†MID-STATE LUMBER CORP.**
200 Industrial Pkwy. (08876)
**Phone—(908) 725-4900**
Fax—(908) 725-0310
www.midstatelumber.com
Email—garyb@midstatelumber.com
Ptnr. & V-P., Sales & Mktg.—
  Kenneth Bernstein
Ptnr. & V-P., Opers.—Gary
  Bernstein
Ptnr. & V-P., Fin.—David Bernstein
SIC—5031; *Corporate headquarters & wholesaler of building products, including dimensional kiln-dried & green Douglas fir lumber, dimensional kiln-dried Hemlock fir, Douglas fir plywood, sheathing & underlayment, stairs & railings; Brand name—Trex; James Hardi Siding; Royal Moulding; Blue Star; Interfor; Selkirk; Simpson; CMPC; Roseburg Forest Pdts; Sierra Pacific; Hampton*
Employs—50; Estab.—1976
Sales—$100Mil
Distrib.—Regional
Privately owned corporation

[NEW ENTRY]
**NEXT MEDICAL PRODUCTS**
45 Columbia Rd. (08876)
**Phone—(800) 458-4254**
Fax—(800) 730-9024
www.nextmedicalproducts.com
Email—customerservice@
  nextmedicalproducts.com
Dir., Cust. Serv.—John Buday
SIC—2899; 3841; 3842; NAICS—334510; *Ultrasound scanning gels & medical devices for healthcare practitioners; Brand name—Sono 600; Sono 900; Sono 950; Sono 1100; High Z; Shear Gel; Clear Image; Clear Image Singles; UltraBioSterile; Ultragel II; Soundsafe; Sonotrace; Soundclear; Pyrogel*
Employs—6; Estab.—2012
12,750 sq ft site, Distrib.—Intl.
ISO rating—9001

**ONGUARD FENCE SYSTEMS**
18 Culnen Dr. (08876)
**Phone—(908) 429-5522**
National—(866) 321-0001
Fax—(908) 429-9933
www.onguardfencesystems.net
Email—service@
  onguardfencesystems.net
Pres.—Thomas Chen
V-P.—Jinslian Ctao
Cust. Serv. Rep.—Cheryl Smith
SIC—3446; *Ornamental aluminum fencing & gates*
Employs—30; Estab.—2006
Sales—$2.5Mil-$5Mil (est)
Distrib.—Intl.
Privately owned corporation

**PRIMME CO., INC.**
42 Columbia Rd. (08876)
**Phone—(908) 231-9490**
National—(888) 720-6995
Fax—(908) 526-5058
www.primme.com
Email—info@primme.com
Pres.—Ed Braunig
SIC—3829; *Ink & coatings testing equipment & accessories, including hand brayers, blankets & volumeters*
Employs—9; Estab.—1991
Sales—under $500,000
4,000 sq ft site, Distrib.—Intl.
Privately owned corporation
Also see: Superior Tool & Mfg. Co.,
  Inc., same loc.

**RARITAN VALLEY PRINTING CO.**
7 Sheephill Cir. (08876)
**Phone—(908) 725-4140**
Fax—(908) 725-5360
Email—rvprinting@aol.com
Ptnr. & Pres.—Arthur E. Fritz
Ptnr. & V-P.—Marie Fritz
SIC—2759; 3993; NAICS—323100; *Commercial printing, signs & banners*
Employs—3; Estab.—1973
Sales—$250,000
1,500 sq ft site, Distrib.—Local
Privately owned corporation

**†ROBERT MCKEOWN CO., INC.**
111 Chambers Brook Rd. (08876)
**Phone—(908) 218-9000**
National—(800) 631-1125
Fax—(908) 218-8949
www.robertmckeown.com
Email—sales@robertmckeown.com
Pres.—Lindsey McKeown
V-P.—Dawson McKeown, Jr.
GM—Carmen Gerrone
Sales Mgr.—John Wood
Opers. Mgr.—Jeffrey Vozzo
Qual. Control Mgr.—Mike
  Theodorakis

## Branchburg—(cont.)

SIC—5065; 5162; *Distributor of engineered specialty materials for electronic assembly, including circuit protection, thermal management & EMI/ESD suppression products for high technology applications; Brand name—Dow Corning; Chomerics; Henkel; St. Gobain; IPG; 3M; Loctite*
Employs—25; Estab.—1937
Sales—$9.8Mil-$12.5Mil
15,000 sq ft site, Distrib.—National
Privately owned sub-S corp.
ISO rating—9001:2008

**ROCHE MOLECULAR SYSTEMS, INC.**
Div. of Roche Molecular Diagnostics
1080 U.S. Highway 202 S. (08876)
**Phone—(908) 253-7200**
Fax—(908) 253-7648
www.roche-diagnostics.com
Email—mediarelations@roche.com
Sr. Hum. Res. Mgr.—Kristen Cohen
Facility Mgr.—Donald Dantoni
SIC—2835; NAICS—325412; *Diagnostic & blood screening assays for infectious diseases*
Employs—500
Sales—$100Mil-$250Mil (est)
Distrib.—Intl.
Publicly owned corporation
Parent co.—Roche Molecular Diagnostics, Pleasanton, CA
Phone—(925) 730-8000
See Parent Co. Section for full profile.

NEW ENTRY
**SANDER MECHANICAL SERVICE, INC.**
55 Columbia Rd., Ste. 1 (08876)
**Phone—(732) 560-0600**
Fax—(732) 560-5757
www.sanmec.com
Email—solutions@sanmec.com
Pres.—Robert Bittel
Off. Mgr.—Cindy Bittel
SIC—3444; *Sheet metal fabrication, including HVAC ducts*
Employs—20; Estab.—1965
Sales—$1Mil-$2.5Mil (est)
Distrib.—Regional
Limited Liability Company

**SAVOURY SYSTEMS INTERNATIONAL, INC.**
230 Industrial Pkwy., Ste. C, P.O. Box 5487 (08876)
**Phone—(908) 526-2524**
Fax—(908) 526-2632
www.savourysystems.com
Email—cs@savourysystems.com
Pres.—David Adams
Treas.—Elizabeth Adams
Technical Sales Mgr.—Kevin McDermott
Mktg. Mgr.—Jacqueline Sun
SIC—2099; *Yeast, organic yeast & seafood extracts, natural flavor bases, HVPs, non-GMO products & salt & MSG replacements; Brand name—Savorganic; SavourSalt*
Employs—18; Estab.—1997
Sales—$18Mil
44,000 sq ft site, Distrib.—Intl.
Privately owned sub-S corp.

**SUPERIOR TOOL & MFG. CO., INC.**
42 Columbia Rd. (08876)
**Phone—(908) 526-9011**
National—(800) 246-8959
Fax—(908) 526-5058
www.superiortoolonline.com
Email—suprtool@verizon.net
Pres.—Ed Braunig

SIC—3599; *Precision machining, including CNC milling, turning & wire EDM of special industrial machinery & custom built industrial machinery*
Employs—10; Estab.—1959
Sales—$500,000-$1Mil
Distrib.—National
Privately owned corporation
Also see: PRIMME Co., Inc., same loc.

**SYMRISE, INC.**
180 Industrial Pkwy. (08876)
**Phone—(908) 429-6946**
National—(800) 422-1559
www.symrise.com
Email—info@symrise.com
V-P.—Mike O'Hara
Shpg. Mgr.—Nuno Miranda
SIC—2844; 2869; *Natural & synthetic fragrances*
Employs—50
Sales—$10Mil-$25Mil (est)
Distrib.—Local
Privately owned corporation
Parent co.—Symrise, Inc., Teterboro, NJ
Phone—(201) 288-3200
See Parent Co. Section for full profile.

**TOP SAFETY PRODUCTS CO.**
160 Meister Ave., Ste. 16 (08876)
**Phone—(908) 707-8680**
National—(800) 242-6651
Fax—(908) 707-8326
www.topsafety.com
Email—contact@topsafety.com
Pres., CEO, Fin. & R & D Mgr.—Gerald P. Kutsop
GM & Sales Mgr.—Ken Kallish
Accts. Mgr.—Rich Schneider
Opers. Mgr.—Dinesh Patel
Off. Mgr.—Mary Ann Melton
Shpg. Supv.—John Wene
SIC—3842; *First aid kits*
Employs—15; Estab.—1978
Sales—$1Mil-$5Mil
10,000 sq ft site, Distrib.—Intl.
Privately owned sub-S corp.

**TRIAD TOOL CO.**
9 Commerce St. (08876)
**Phone—(908) 534-1784**
Fax—(908) 534-1802
www.triadtool.com
Email—sales@triadtool.com
Pres., CEO—Eric Wichelhaus
V-P.—Jim Wichelhaus
Hum. Res. Mgr.—Margaret Hurley
SIC—3544; 3599; NAICS—333500; *Aerospace, medical & communication equipment subassembly & precision CNC machining & wire EDM job shop*
Employs—45; Estab.—1933
Sales—$11Mil-$25Mil
30,000 sq ft site, Distrib.—National
Privately owned corporation
ISO rating—9001:2008

**VIS USA, LLC**
210 Meister Ave. (08876)
**Phone—(908) 575-0606**
www.visusa.com
Email—customerservice@visusa.com
Pres., Fin. & MIS Mgr.—Rene Morf
Off. Mgr.—Linda Morf
SIC—3496; 3423; *Power transmission & conveyor belting & belt fabrication tools*
Employs—15; Estab.—1994
20,000 sq ft site, Distrib.—Intl.
Limited Liability Company

**VOLTAIX, LLC (H Q)**
Div. of Air Liquide America L.P.
3121 U.S. Highway 22, P.O. Box 5357 (08876)
**Phone—(908) 231-9060**
National—(800) 865-8249
Fax—(908) 895-0857
www.voltaix.com

Email—info@voltaix.com
Pres., CEO—Paul Burlingame
Sr. V-P.—Michael Pikulin
Ex. V-P.—Mark Wilkinson
V-P., Admn. & Fin.—Ann Marie Hansen
Dir., Global Sales & Mktg.—Gregory T. Muhr
Acct. Mgr.—Jennifer Derogatis
Prod. Mgr.—German Shekk
Pur. Agt.—Brian Soos
SIC—2899; *Company headquarters; electronic chemicals for semiconductor deposition application*
Employs—95; Estab.—1987
Sales—$2.5Mil-$5Mil
Distrib.—Regional
Publicly owned corporation
ISO rating—9000
Parent co.—Air Liquide America L.P., Houston, TX
Phone—(713) 624-8000
See Parent Co. Section for full profile.

**†WORLD WIDE METRIC, INC.**
37 Readington Rd., P.O. Box 5267 (08876)
**Phone—(732) 247-2300**
National—(855) 225-5996
Fax—(732) 247-7258
www.worldwidemetric.com
Email—sales@worldwidemetric.com
CEO—George Contos
Pres.—Theo Contos
SIC—5085; 5051; *Corporate headquarters & distributor of metric pipe, valves & fittings for marine & industrial applications*
Employs—16; Estab.—1970
Distrib.—Intl.
Privately owned corporation

**ZEUS INDUSTRIAL PRODUCTS, INC.**
134 Chubb Way (08876)
**Phone—(908) 526-6500**
www.zeusinc.com
Email—support@zeusinc.com
IT Mgr.—Kevin Resinger
Hum. Res. Mgr.—Mike Ferraro
SIC—3082; NAICS—326121; *Fluoropolymer & specialized PTFE tubing; Brand name—Sub-Lite-Wall; PET Lay-Flat; PFA Lay-Flat; Dual Tube; HePTFE; Infinion; Centroid; Snaptube; PEEKshrink*
Employs—200; Estab.—1966
60,000 sq ft site, Distrib.—Intl.
Privately owned corporation
ISO rating—9001:2000
Parent co.—Zeus Industrial Products, Inc., Orangeburg, SC
Phone—(803) 268-9500
See Parent Co. Section for full profile.

## Branchville
(Sussex—N.W.)

**BBC PRINTING**
4 Main St., P.O. Box 276 (07826)
**Phone—(973) 948-7998**
National—(866) 948-7998
Fax—(973) 948-6605
www.bbcprint.com
Email—info@bbcprint.com
Owner—Duncan F. Caldwell
SIC—2759; 2752; *Digital, large-format & offset printing; Brand name—Birchcraft; Carlsoncraft*
Employs—4; Estab.—1998
Sales—under $500,000
Distrib.—National
Sole ownership

**BEHRINGER CORP.**
17 Ridge Rd. (07826)
**Phone—(973) 948-0226**
Fax—(973) 948-2562
www.behringersystems.com
Email—cserv@behringersystems.com

Pres., GM—Ted Hinds
Sales Mgr.—Robert Schultz
Fin. Mgr.—George Wink
SIC—3429; 3492; NAICS—332912; *Pipe & tube hangers, filtration products & high pressure shut-off & control valves for fluid power applications*
Employs—40; Estab.—1869
Sales—over $10Mil
75,000 sq ft site, Distrib.—Intl.

**BRALEN, LLC**
236 U.S. Highway 206 N. (07826)
**Phone—(973) 948-6575**
Fax—(973) 948-6261
Email—parrothead29@hotmail.com
Plt. Mgr.—E. J. Syphers
Off. Mgr.—Kathleen Allen
Manager—Daniel Allen
SIC—3599; *General machining job shop*
Employs—4; Estab.—2010
12,000 sq ft site, Distrib.—Regional
Limited Liability Company

**CST PAVERS A DIVISION OF PAVESTONE**
Div. of QUIKRETE Cos., Inc., The
23 Ridge Rd., P.O. Box 2736 (07826)
**Phone—(973) 948-7193**
Fax—(973) 948-2771
www.cstpavers.com
Email—info@cstpavers.com
Pres.—William R. Magill
SIC—3272; *Concrete pavers & retaining wall systems; Brand name—Roman Cobble; MONO-CAST One Piece Pavers; Fishscales; VERSA-LOK Retaining Wall; VERSA-LOK Veranda Wall; VERSA-LOK Handystone*
Employs—57; Estab.—2014
Distrib.—National
Privately owned corporation
Parent co.—QUIKRETE Cos., Inc., The, Atlanta, GA
Phone—(404) 634-9100
See Parent Co. Section for full profile.

**CUSTOM DOCKS, INC.**
234 Route 206 (07826)
**Phone—(973) 948-3732**
Fax—(973) 948-2729
www.customdocks.net
Email—custom_docks@yahoo.com
Pres.—Bob Petura
Off. Mgr.—Joanne Pickell
SIC—3448; NAICS—332311; *Aluminum boat docks*
Employs—7; Estab.—1956
Sales—under $500,000
Distrib.—Local
Privately owned corporation

**KELLER WELDING CO., LLC**
22 Wantage Ave. (07826)
**Phone—(973) 948-0046**
Email—kellerwelding@embarqmail.com
Owner & Pres.—Jeremy Hughen
SIC—3599; 3499; *Fabrication & welding of steel, aluminum, stainless & cast iron, including molds, tools & dies*
Employs—4; Estab.—1978
Sales—$500,000-$1Mil
Distrib.—Local
Limited Liability Company

NEW ENTRY
**MALHAME VESTMENT**
239 Route 206 (07826)
**Phone—(973) 948-8401**
National—(877) 240-7622
Fax—(973) 948-8405
www.abbeybrand.com
Email—orders@abbeybrand.com
GM—James Pecoy

GEOGRAPHICAL

## Branchville—(cont.)

SIC—2389; *Religious garments; Brand name—Abbey*
Employs—12; Estab.—1976
Sales—$500,000-$1Mil
Distrib.—National
Privately owned corporation

### NEWTON TROPHY & SPORT CENTER

1-3 Milk St., Bldg. 3 (07826)
**Phone—(973) 948-0613**
Fax—(973) 948-2846
www.newtontrophy.com
Email—trophy@newtontrophy.com
Pres.—Linda Moran
SIC—2399; 2395; 3993; *Textile screen printing, embroidery & promotional products*
Employs—5; Estab.—1964
Sales—under $500,000
Distrib.—Regional
Privately owned corporation

### ROSE SIGNS

13 Route 206 S. (07826)
**Phone—(973) 948-0501**
Fax—(973) 948-6269
Email—rosesigns@yahoo.com
Owner—Rosemarie Devries
SIC—3993; *Interior & exterior signs*
Employs—2; Estab.—1983
Sales—under $500,000
Distrib.—Local

## Brick

(Ocean—S.E.)

### ANCHOR RUBBER STAMP & PRINTING, INC.

339 Herbertsville Rd. (08724)
**Phone—(732) 583-6578**
National—(888) 583-3338
Fax—(732) 583-1111
www.anchorstamp.com
Email—sales@anchorstamp.com
Pres.—Thomas McTague
Secy-Treas.—Pat McTague
GM—Tom McTague
SIC—3953; 3993; NAICS—339943; *Rubber stamps, marking devices & embossers, including notary, corporate, architects & engineers*
Employs—3; Estab.—1935
Sales—under $500,000
1,000 sq ft site, Distrib.—Local

### ATLANTIC PRINTING CO.

262 Circle Dr. (08723)
**Phone—(732) 920-2300**
Fax—(732) 920-3050
www.atlanticprintingcompany.com
Email—joe@atlanticprintingcompany.com
Pres.—Joseph Vrabel
SIC—2759; NAICS—323100; *Commercial printing*
Employs—2; Estab.—1990
Sales—under $500,000
Distrib.—Local
Privately owned corporation

### AUTOMATED TAPPING SYSTEMS, INC.

22 Davos Rd. *(08724)*
Mail addr: P.O. Box 1033, Brick (08723)
**Phone—(732) 899-2282**
National—(888) 287-1827
Fax—(732) 899-0277
www.automatedtappingsystems.com
Email—sales@automatedtappingsystems.com
Pres.—William R. Pfister
MIS Mgr.—Craig Wood
Off. Mgr.—Rosemarie Iacullo

SIC—3544; NAICS—333500; *Indie tapping units*
Employs—10; Estab.—1976
Sales—over $1Mil
2,500 sq ft site, Distrib.—Intl.
Privately owned corporation

### BAY SHORE CANVAS

310 Firehouse Rd. (08723)
**Phone—(732) 477-8520**
Email—bayshorecanvas@verizon.net
Owner—Joe Cannella
SIC—2394; NAICS—314912; *Boating canvas*
Employs—1; Estab.—1999
Sales—under $200,000
Distrib.—Local
Sole ownership

### BEATON SAILS, INC.

72 Beaton Rd. (08723)
**Phone—(732) 920-6638**
Pres.—Mark Beaton
SIC—2394; NAICS—314912; *Canvas sails*
Employs—2; Estab.—1988
Sales—under $500,000
Distrib.—Intl.
Privately owned corporation

### BRICK GLASS CO.

214 Midstreams Pl. (08723)
**Phone—(732) 899-8811**
Fax—(732) 899-8818
www.brickglass.com
Email—orders@brickglass.com
Owner—Louis Raccuglia
Engr.—Anthony Desa
SIC—3444; 3231; 3211; NAICS—327215; *Aluminum storefronts, curtain walls, ribbon & operating windows, frameless & standard shower enclosures & custom mirrors*
Employs—6; Estab.—1972
Sales—$1Mil-$2.5Mil
Distrib.—Local
Privately owned corporation

### †BRICK WHOLESALE FLOWER MARKET

570 Mantoloking Rd. (08723)
**Phone—(732) 477-6765**
Fax—(732) 477-6630
www.yourflowermarket.com
Email—brickflowermarket@gmail.com
Pres., GM—Nancy Petrellese
SIC—5193; *Distributor of fresh-cut flowers & plants*
Employs—5; Estab.—1958
Sales—$250,000
2,500 sq ft site, Distrib.—Regional
Limited Liability Company

### C & G SCREWS UNLIMITED

2150 Route 88 (08724)
**Phone—(732) 892-8400**
National—(800) 628-5735
Fax—(732) 701-3608
Email—screws732@aol.com
Pres.—Sharon Petriello
V-P.—Joseph Petriello
SIC—3429; *Screws, nuts & bolts*
Employs—10; Estab.—1981
Sales—under $500,000
15,000 sq ft site, Distrib.—National
Privately owned corporation
AKA: Screws Unlimited

### CHOCOLATE BELLES

249 Chamber Bridge Rd. (08723)
**Phone—(732) 920-2266**
www.thechocolatebelles.com
Email—server@thechocolatebelles.com
Owner—Ann Shortt
SIC—2064; NAICS—311300; *Chocolate bunnies candy*
Employs—2
Distrib.—Local
Privately owned corporation

### †COOPER ELECTRIC SUPPLY CO.

933 Cedarbridge Ave. (08723)
**Phone—(732) 920-3130**
Fax—(732) 920-2235
www.cooper-electric.com
Email—greg.wilson@cooper-electric.com
Br. Mgr.—Gary Wilson
Sales Rep.—Paul Monia
SIC—5063; *Distributor of electrical equipment & supplies, including wire, cable & switches*
Employs—15; Estab.—1988
Distrib.—Regional
Privately owned corporation
Parent co.—Cooper Electric Supply Co., Monroe, NJ
Phone—(732) 747-2233
See Parent Co. Section for full profile.

### CORIM INDUSTRIES

1112 Industrial Pkwy. (08724)
**Phone—(732) 840-1670**
    (800) 942-4201
Fax—(732) 840-1608
www.corimindustries.com
Email—natan@corimindustries.com
Pres.—Sam Teren
Sales Mgr., Natl.—Natan Teren
SIC—2095; NAICS—311920; *Coffee roasting & packing*
Employs—20; Estab.—1990
Sales—$1Mil-$5Mil
Distrib.—Local
Privately owned corporation

### DA VINCI DISPLAYS, LLC

123 Taft Dr. (08724)
**Phone—(732) 730-3001**
National—(877) 730-3001
Fax—(732) 730-3006
www.davincidisplays.com
Email—donald@davincidisplays.com
CEO—Donna Tietjen
Pres.—Donald Tietjen
SIC—2542; *Plastic displays & fixtures for retail stores*
Employs—2; Estab.—2006
Sales—$300,000-$500,000
3,000 sq ft site, Distrib.—National
Limited Liability Company

### DORNAN, INC.

333 Cedarcroft Dr. (08724)
**Phone—(732) 295-4491**
www.dornaninc.com
Email—rdornan@comcast.net
Pres.—Rita Dornan
SIC—3366; 3369; 2511; *Brass & pewter miniature castings & jewelry & hand-carved wooden sculptural household furniture*
Employs—2; Estab.—1976
Sales—under $500,000 (est)

### †FEDERAL PACIFIC EQUIPMENT, INC.

1133 Industrial Pkwy., Ste. A (08724-2582)
**Phone—(732) 840-4800**
Fax—(732) 840-4833
www.fpeparts.com
Email—jcifrodella@fpeparts.com
Pres., Hum. Res. Mgr.—John Cifrodella
SIC—5063; *Wholesaler of electric circuit breakers & circuit breaker components; Brand name—Federal Pacific Equipment; Westinghouse; Sylvania; Challenger*
Employs—3; Estab.—1995
Distrib.—National
Privately owned corporation

### GANGI GRAPHICS

1669 Highway 88 W. (08724)
**Phone—(732) 840-8680**
Fax—(732) 840-7664
www.gangigraphics.com
Email—info@gangigraphics.com
Ptnr.—John Gangi
Ptnr.—Michael Gangi

Art Dir.—Daniel Reeves
Designer—Mac Gawrych
SIC—2752; 2759; NAICS—323122; *Offset & digital printing & electronic prepress*
Employs—7; Estab.—1993
Sales—$500,000-$1Mil
Distrib.—Local
Privately owned corporation

### H & R WELDING, LLC

307 Drum Point Rd. (08723)
**Phone—(732) 920-4881**
Fax—(732) 920-6466
Email—hrwelding1@aol.com
Ptnr.—Justin Hager
Ptnr.—Jason Hager
Ptnr.—Bob Hager
Off. Mgr.—Gerri Stortz
SIC—3441; NAICS—332312; *Structural steel fabrication & erection*
Employs—7; Estab.—1968
Sales—$1.5Mil
Distrib.—Local
Privately owned partnership

### †INTERACTIVE COMPUTER CENTER, INC.

482 Brick Blvd. (08723)
**Phone—(732) 477-5800**
Fax—(732) 477-7796
www.iccicorp.com
Email—info@iccicorp.com
Owner—Steve Byrnes
Br. & IT Mgr.—Nick Cameron
Hum. Res. Mgr.—Lisa Lebar
Technician—Brian Bonder
SIC—5045; *Distributor of computer software*
Employs—10; Estab.—1983
Sales—$1Mil-$5Mil
Distrib.—Local
Privately owned corporation
AKA: ICCI

NEW ENTRY

### J & L BOAT CANVAS

190 Drum Point Rd. (08723)
**Phone—(732) 262-1535**
Owner—John Ribaudo
SIC—2394; *Boat canvas & awnings*
Employs—1
Sales—under $500,000 (est)

### J. C. ORTHOPEDIC, INC.

1680 Highway 88 (08724)
**Phone—(732) 458-7900**
Fax—(732) 458-7902
www.jcorthopedic.com
Email—jcorthoped@aol.com
Pres., CEO—Frank Digeronimo
Off. Mgr.—Amanda Doll
SIC—3842; *Artifical limbs & braces*
Employs—6
Sales—$500,000-$1Mil
Distrib.—Local
Privately owned corporation

### †K-C INTERNATIONAL, LLC

1608 Route 88, Ste. 301 (08724)
**Phone—(732) 202-9500**
Fax—(732) 202-9525
www.ekmanonline.com
Email—bj.dowlen@ekmangroup.com
CEO—Frank Crowley
SIC—5093; *Wholesaler of recycled paper, plastic & metal scrap materials*
Employs—30; Estab.—1976
Distrib.—Intl.
Limited Liability Company

### MARFORI FAMILY EYE CARE

20 Brick Plz. (08723)
**Phone—(732) 920-1775**
Fax—(732) 920-1381
Owner—Michelle Marfori
Optician—Ashley Ziegler

## Brick—(cont.)

SIC—3851; NAICS—339100; *Eyeglasses*
Employs—3; Estab.—2006
Sales—under $500,000
Distrib.—Local
Limited Liability Company

**MILLTEX MFG. CO.**
1101 Industrial Pkwy. (08724)
**Phone—(732) 840-3021**
Fax—(732) 840-3021
www.milltexcustomwindows.com
Email—milltexhome@verizon.net
Pres.—Martin Metzger, Sr.
V-P.—Martin Metzger, Jr.
Designer—Joan Townley
SIC—2392; 2391; NAICS—314121; *Comforters, draperies, window treatments, blinds & shutters; Brand name—Hunter Douglas; Norman Shutters; Horizon Shades Kravet; Duralee; Stout*
Employs—8; Estab.—1984
Sales—$500,000-$1Mil
4,000 sq ft site, Distrib.—Local
Privately owned corporation
AKA: Milltex Home Decorator

**NUNN & SON CUSTOM LETTERING**
10 Harding Dr. (08724)
**Phone—(732) 899-9682**
Email—nunnandson@yahoo.com
Pres.—James Nunn
SIC—3993; 2759; NAICS—323100; *Interior & exterior signs, banners, boat, truck & gold leaf lettering & large-format digital printing*
Employs—1; Estab.—1986
Sales—under $500,000
Distrib.—Regional
Sole ownership

**P I P PRINTING**
2960 Yorktowne Blvd. (08723)
**Phone—(732) 255-1980**
Fax—(732) 255-5808
www.pip.com
Email—tfazio@pip.com
Owner—Tim Fazio
Cust. Serv. Rep.—Jill Stroehlein
SIC—2752; NAICS—323100; *Offset printing*
Employs—2; Estab.—1984
Sales—under $500,000
Distrib.—Local
Sole ownership

**PARAMOUNT PRODUCTS, INC.**
1104 Industrial Pkwy. (08724)
**Phone—(732) 458-9200**
Fax—(732) 458-3942
www.paramountproductsco.com
Email—info@paramountproductsco.com
Pres.—H. C. Vogel
SIC—3469; 3679; *Custom, precision & drawn stampings for the photo-optic, defense, automotive, medical, aerospace, semiconductor & electronic tube industries*
Employs—10; Estab.—1945
Sales—$750,000
9,000 sq ft site, Distrib.—Intl.
Privately owned corporation

**PRO-COMM, INC.**
1105 Industrial Pkwy. (08724)
**Phone—(732) 206-0660**
Fax—(732) 458-1919
www.procomm222.com
Email—procomm222@aol.com
Pres.—Sheryl J. Visone
Prodn. Mgr.—Frank Visone
Administrator—Carol Butti

SIC—3699; 3663; 3829; 3812; *High-power, UHF, L-band, S-band, C-band, microwave frequency amplifiers, high-power miniature transmitters, radar simulators, triode & cavity oscillators, RF drivers, RF oscillator source systems & medical electronic & lab test equipment; Brand name—Pro-Comm; Micon*
Employs—11; Estab.—1989
Sales—$500,000-$1Mil
13,200 sq ft site, Distrib.—National
Privately owned sub-S corp.

**SALTY DOG, THE**
254 Brick Blvd., Ste. 1 (08723-7170)
**Phone—(732) 714-8400**
National—(888) 843-1585
Fax—(732) 477-9001
www.thesaltydog.com
Email—info@thesaltydog.com
Owner & Pres.—Art Peters
Off. Mgr.—Alexis Carter
SIC—2711; 2741; *Biweekly print & online boating shopper guide publishing*
Employs—5; Estab.—1985
Distrib.—Regional
Sole ownership

**SOUND ENVIRONMENTS, LLC**
1133 Industrial Pkwy., Ste. E (08724-2582)
**Phone—(732) 840-6600**
Fax—(732) 840-8845
Email—soundenv@aol.com
Pres.—Michael S. Conaccio
SIC—3651; NAICS—334310; *Custom high power nightclub, commercial & residential sound systems*
Employs—4; Estab.—1975
Sales—under $500,000
Distrib.—Intl.
Privately owned corporation

**SPAULDING FABRICATORS INC.**
1136 Industrial Pkwy. (08724)
**Phone—(732) 840-4433**
Fax—(732) 840-4970
www.spauldingfabricators.com
Email—spauldingfabricators@verizon.net
Pres.—Stephen Spaulding
V-P.—Michele Spaulding
SIC—2542; 3281; 3089; *Solid-surface, granite & engineered stone countertops; Brand name—Corian; Cambria; Silestone; Caesarstone*
Employs—21; Estab.—1988
Sales—$1Mil-$2.5Mil
Privately owned corporation

NEW ENTRY
**VAN HOLTEN'S HOMEMADE CANDY, INC.**
1893 Route 88 (08724)
**Phone—(732) 840-0888**
Fax—(732) 840-0888
www.vanholtenschocolates.com
Email—sales@vanholtenschocolates.com
Owner—Bob Meyer
SIC—2064; *Chocolates & fudge*
Employs—4; Estab.—1904
Sales—$1Mil-$2.5Mil (est)
Distrib.—Intl.
Privately owned corporation
AKA: Van Holten's Chocolates

## Bridgeport
### (Gloucester—S.W.)

†**ALBERT'S ORGANICS, INC.**
Div. of United Natural Foods, Inc.
200 Eagle Ct., P.O. Box 624 (08014)
**Phone—(856) 241-9090**
National—(800) 899-5944
Fax—(856) 241-9675
www.albertsorganics.com
Email—sdennis@albertsorganics.com
Pres.—Scott Dennis
V-P., Sales, Natl.—Rod Moyer
Corp. Comp.—Susan Roberts
Dir., Mktg.—Simcha Weinstein
Dir., Hum. Res.—Monica McClintock
IT Mgr.—Raymond Tan
SIC—5148; 5143; *Corporate headquarters & distributor of organic produce*
Employs—150
Company-wide: 500
Distrib.—National
Publicly owned corporation
Parent co.—United Natural Foods, Inc., Providence, RI
Phone—(401) 528-8634
See Parent Co. Section for full profile.

**CADDY CORP.**
509 Sharptown Rd., P.O. Box 345 (08014)
**Phone—(856) 467-4222**
Fax—(856) 467-5511
www.caddycorp.com
Email—caddycorp@caddycorp.com
Owner—Craig Cohen
Pres.—Harry Schmidt
Hum. Res. Mgr.—Al Scuderi
Cust. Serv. Mgr.—Roger Handy
Pur. Agt.—Robin Corma
SIC—3535; NAICS—333922; *Conveyor systems*
Employs—40; Estab.—1940
70,000 sq ft site, Distrib.—Intl.
Privately owned corporation

**CHELTEN HOUSE PRODUCTS, INC.**
607 Heron Dr., P.O. Box 434 (08014)
**Phone—(856) 467-1600**
Fax—(856) 467-4769
www.cheltenhouse.com
Email—info@cheltenhouse.com
CEO—Steve Dabrow
GM—Joseph Hoffman
Pur. Agt.—Charles Jackson
SIC—2033; 2035; *Organic & natural sauces, dressings & marinades for retail, foodservice & portion packaging applications; Brand name—Chelten House; Marinade Bay; Simply Natural*
Employs—150; Estab.—1960
135,000 sq ft site, Distrib.—Intl.
Privately owned sub-S corp.

**FEDERAL PRETZEL BAKING CO.**
Div. of J & J Snack Foods Corp.
300 Eagle Ct., P.O. Box 257 (08014)
**Phone—(215) 467-0505**
Fax—(909) 218-3907
www.federalpretzel.biz
Email—cust@federalpretzel.biz
GM—Tom Hunter
Bus. Mgr.—Jessica Ambruster
SIC—2096; NAICS—311919; *Soft pretzels*
Employs—20; Estab.—1922
45,000 sq ft site, Distrib.—Local
Publicly owned corporation
Parent co.—J & J Snack Foods Corp., Pennsauken, NJ
Phone—(856) 665-9534
See Parent Co. Section for full profile.

**FERRO CORP., DELAWARE RIVER PLT.**
Div. of Ferro Corp.
170 U.S. Route 130 S., P.O. Box 309 (08014)
**Phone—(856) 467-8216**
(800) 321-9942
Fax—(856) 467-8308
www.ferro.com
Email—investor@ferro.com
Plt. & Supply Chain Utility Mgr.—Bob Knighton
Env. & Safety Engr.—Karen Anthony
SIC—2899; NAICS—325199; *Commodity chemicals*
Employs—100; Estab.—1961
Distrib.—Intl.
Publicly owned corporation
Parent co.—Ferro Corp., Mayfield Heights, OH
Phone—(216) 875-5600
See Parent Co. Section for full profile.

**FLOWSERVE CORP.**
401 Heron Dr., P.O. Box 563 (08014)
**Phone—(856) 241-7800**
Fax—(856) 241-7801
www.flowserve.com
Email—info@flowserve.com
GM—Dave Siek
Application Engr.—Dan Barr
SIC—3053; NAICS—339991; *Mechanical seals*
Employs—40; Estab.—1998
20,000 sq ft site, Distrib.—National
Publicly owned corporation
Parent co.—Flowserve Corp., Irving, TX
Phone—(972) 443-6500
See Parent Co. Section for full profile.

**GODWIN, A XYLEM BRAND**
Div. of Xylem, Inc.
84 Floodgate Rd. (08014)
**Phone—(856) 467-3636**
National—(800) 247-8674
Fax—(856) 467-4841
www.godwinpumps.com
Email—sales@godwinpumps.com
Pres. & Sr. V-P., Dewatering—Colin Sabol
V-P. & Dir., Sales—Michael Delzingaro
Accts. Mgr., Natl.—Gregg Leslie
SIC—3561; NAICS—333911; *Company headquarters & automatic self-priming pumps for fast-paced emergency situations & temporary rental/permanent installations; Brand name—Dri-Prime; Heidra; Sub-Prime; NC Series; CD Series; HL Series; Wet-Prime*
Employs—260; Estab.—1976
Sales—$25Mil-$50Mil (est)
65,400 sq ft site, Distrib.—Intl.
Publicly owned corporation
AKA: Xylem Dewatering
DBA: Godwin Pumps
Parent co.—Xylem, Inc., Rye Brook, NY
Phone—(914) 323-5700
See Parent Co. Section for full profile.

**PANDROL USA L. P.**
501 Sharptown Rd., P.O. Box 367 (08014)
**Phone—(856) 467-3227**
National—(800) 221-2547
Fax—(856) 467-4031
www.pandrolusa.com
Email—a.reed@pandrolusa.com
Pres.—Frank Brady
Mktg. Mgr.—Breen Reardon
Qual. Assur. Mgr.—Mark Beale
SIC—3312; 3452; NAICS—332722; *Railroad joints & fasteners*
Employs—45; Estab.—1982
63,000 sq ft site, Distrib.—National
Limited Liability Partnership

GEOGRAPHICAL

## Bridgeport—(cont.)

**PENN JERSEY BUILDING MATERIALS, INC.**
247 Cedar Swamp Rd. (08014)
**Phone—(856) 467-0400**
Fax—(856) 467-6625
www.penn-jersey.net
Email—info@penn-jersey.net
Br. Mgr.—Bill Rhubart
SIC—3273; *Ready-mixed concrete*
Employs—12
Distrib.—Local
Privately owned corporation
Parent co.—Penn Jersey Building
Materials, Inc., Egg Harbor
Township, NJ
Phone—(609) 485-0068
See Parent Co. Section for full profile.

**PIERSON MATERIALS CO., INC., R. E.**
Div. of Pierson Construction Co., Inc., R. E.
860 Oak Grove Rd., P.O. Box 704 (08014)
**Phone—(856) 467-1421**
(856) 467-4199
National—(800) 608-6789
Fax—(856) 241-0136
www.repierson.com
Email—info@repierson.com
Sales Rep.—Fred Wietz
SIC—3273; NAICS—327320; *Ready-mixed concrete*
Employs—20; Estab.—2004
Sales—$500,000-$1Mil
Distrib.—Local
Privately owned corporation
Parent co.—Pierson Construction
Co., Inc., R. E., Pilesgrove, NJ
Phone—(856) 769-8244
See Parent Co. Section for full profile.

**PIERSON MATERIALS INC., R. E.**
Div. of Pierson Construction Co., Inc., R. E.
860 Oak Grove Rd., P.O. Box 704 (08014)
**Phone—(856) 467-4199**
National—(800) 608-6789
Fax—(856) 467-5360
www.repiersongroup.com
Email—smokienko@repierson.com
GM—Slavie Mokienko
Qual. Control Mgr.—Dan Karcher
Accountant—Michelle Miller
SIC—2951; NAICS—324121; *Asphalt paving materials, including sand, stone, crushed concrete*
Employs—35; Estab.—1989
Sales—$10Mil-$25Mil
Distrib.—Regional
Privately owned corporation
Parent co.—Pierson Construction
Co., Inc., R. E., Pilesgrove, NJ
Phone—(856) 769-8244
See Parent Co. Section for full profile.

**SEW-EURODRIVE, INC.**
2107 High Hill Rd., P.O. Box 481 (08014)
**Phone—(856) 467-2277**
Fax—(856) 845-3179
www.seweurodrive.com
Email—csbridgeport@
seweurodrive.com
Opers. Mgr.—Scott Bansky
Admn. Mgr.—Bernadette Jones
Cust. Serv. Rep.—Joshua Roselle
SIC—3566; NAICS—333612; *Motors & drives assembly*
Employs—55; Estab.—1986
100,000 sq ft site, Distrib.—National
Privately owned corporation
Parent co.—SEW-Eurodrive, Inc., Lyman, SC
Phone—(864) 439-7537
See Parent Co. Section for full profile.

**SULZER PUMPS (U.S.), INC.**
621 Haron Dr., P.O. Box 487 (08014)
**Phone—(856) 467-2400**
Fax—(856) 467-0072
www.sulzerpumps.com
Email—pumps.usa@sulzer.com
Serv. Ctr. Mgr.—Ginny Johnston
Cust. Serv. Mgr.—Curtis Samuels
Pur. Agt.—Wayne Pooley
Pur. Agt.—Dave Cook
Pur. Agt.—Mark Schneider
SIC—3561; NAICS—333911; *Industrial centrifugal pumps*
Employs—25; Estab.—1992
Distrib.—National
Privately owned corporation
Parent co.—Sulzer Pumps (U.S.), Inc., Portland, OR
Phone—(503) 205-3600
See Parent Co. Section for full profile.

**UPTOWN BAKERIES/J & J SNACK FOODS**
Div. of J & J Snack Foods Corp.
300 Eagle Ct., P.O. Box 257 (08014)
**Phone—(856) 467-9552**
Fax—(856) 467-9194
www.jjsnack.com
Email—webmaster@jjsnack.com
V-P, GM—Tom Hunter
Opers. Mgr.—David Mayer
Pur. Mgr.—Scott Ambruster
Off. Mgr.—Monica McMahon
Qual. Mgr.—John Politano
Maint. Engrg. Mgr.—Juan Perez
Hum. Res. Admn.—Jennifer Beck
SIC—2051; NAICS—311812; *Bakery products*
Employs—250; Estab.—1994
Sales—$40Mil
173,000 sq ft site, Distrib.—National
Publicly owned corporation
Parent co.—J & J Snack Foods
Corp., Pennsauken, NJ
Phone—(856) 665-9534
See Parent Co. Section for full profile.

---

# Bridgeton
## (Cumberland—S.W.)

**†ABC SUPPLY**
Div. of Alliance Vinyl Window Co., Inc.
41 N. Pearl St. (08302)
**Phone—(856) 455-4888**
Fax—(856) 453-7610
www.abcsupply.com
Email—sales@abcsupply.com
Br. Mgr.—Patrick Torinese
SIC—5021; 5033; *Distributor of vinyl, aluminum, wood & fiberglass windows, siding, doors, decking, columns & railings*
Employs—4; Estab.—1956
Sales—$500,000-$1Mil
Distrib.—Regional
Privately owned corporation
Parent co.—Alliance Vinyl Window
Co., Inc., Mount Ephraim, NJ
Phone—(856) 456-4954
See Parent Co. Section for full profile.

**ACKLEY'S SAWMILL**
98 W. Deerfield Rd. (08302)
**Phone—(856) 451-3704**
Ptnr.—Kenneth B. Ackley
Ptnr.—Brian Ackley
SIC—2421; *Lumber processing*
Employs—2; Estab.—1947
Sales—under $500,000
30,000 sq ft site, Distrib.—Regional
Privately owned partnership

**ADAMS PRINTING & GRAPHICS**
886 N. Pearl St. (08302)
**Phone—(856) 455-7177**
Fax—(856) 455-9695
Email—adams_printing@
verizon.net
Owner—Mary Swain
SIC—2752; 2759; NAICS—323100; *Commercial offset & digital printing*
Employs—3; Estab.—1972
Sales—under $500,000
3,500 sq ft site, Distrib.—Regional
Sole ownership

**ARDAGH GROUP**
443 S. East Ave., P.O. Box 400 (08302)
**Phone—(856) 455-2000**
Fax—(856) 455-3491
www.ardaghgroup.com
Email—sales@leoneglass.com
Sales Mgr., Natl.—John Orr
Pur. Mgr.—Frank Labletta
Hum. Res. Mgr.—James Economy
Accts. Payable Coord.—Gail Battle
SIC—3221; NAICS—327213; *Glass containers*
Employs—350; Estab.—1965
435,000 sq ft site, Distrib.—National
Privately owned sub-S corp.

**BORTON ENTERPRISES**
178 Woodruff Rd. (08302)
**Phone—(856) 453-9221**
Fax—(856) 453-9221
Email—tbaenterprises@
comcast.net
Pres.—Brad Borton
Editor—Corrine Borton
SIC—2721; *Equestrian magazine publishing*
Employs—10; Estab.—1998
Sales—$500,000-$1Mil (est)
Distrib.—National
Privately owned corporation

**BRIDGETON TROPHY & ENGRAVING**
641 Landis Ave. (08302)
**Phone—(856) 451-9007**
Fax—(856) 451-4966
Owner—Tom D'Agostino
Prodn. Mgr.—Nyla Errickson
SIC—3499; 3479; 3231; NAICS—327215; *Engraved trophies, glass etching & plaques*
Employs—10; Estab.—1956
Sales—under $800,000
25,000 sq ft site, Distrib.—National
Privately owned corporation

**BUONA VITA, INC.**
1 S. Industrial Blvd. (08302)
**Phone—(856) 453-7972**
Fax—(856) 453-7978
www.buonavitainc.com
Email—pjr@buonavitainc.com
Pres.—Paul InFranco
SIC—2011; NAICS—311611; *Italian beef braciola, meatballs, meatloaf, sausage & pizza toppings*
Employs—100; Estab.—1992
Sales—$6Mil-$10Mil
35,000 sq ft site, Distrib.—National
Privately owned corporation

**COBB'S MILL, LLC**
146 Cobbs Mill Rd. (08302)
**Phone—(856) 451-0671**
Fax—(856) 451-8314
www.cobbsmillllc.com
Treas.—Williams Cobb
SIC—2431; NAICS—321900; *Millwork*
Employs—2; Estab.—1705
Sales—under $500,000
Distrib.—Local
Privately owned corporation

**CUMBERLAND & SALEM GUIDE**
874 N. Pearl St., P.O. Box 735 (08302)
**Phone—(856) 451-1177**
Fax—(856) 451-5035
Publisher—James Kinkade
Off. Mgr.—Carol Kinkade
SIC—2711; *Newspaper publishing*
Employs—10; Estab.—1955
Sales—under $500,000 (est)
Distrib.—Local
Privately owned corporation

**CUMBERLAND DAIRY, INC.**
80 Edward Ave. (08302)
Mail addr: P.O. Box 308, Rosenhayn (08352)
**Phone—(856) 451-1300**
National—(800) 257-8484
Fax—(856) 451-1332
www.cumberlanddairy.com
Email—fcatalana@
cumberlanddairy.com
V-P, Opers.—Frank Catalana
Hum. Res. Mgr.—Kim Litchendorf
SIC—2026; 2023; NAICS—311500; *Milk & ice cream mixes*
Employs—65; Estab.—1933
100,000 sq ft site, Distrib.—Regional
Privately owned corporation
Parent co.—Cumberland Dairy, Inc., Rosenhayn, NJ
Phone—(856) 451-1300
See Parent Co. Section for full profile.

**CUMBERLAND ENGRAVING SERVICE**
127 W. Broad St. (08302)
**Phone—(856) 451-5052**
Fax—(856) 455-9660
Email—cumberlandengraving@
verizon.net
Owner—Wayne Rizzo
SIC—3479; *Trophy & plaque engraving*
Employs—2; Estab.—1973
Sales—under $500,000
1,500 sq ft site, Distrib.—Local
Sole ownership

**CUMBERLAND VALVE, INC.**
746 Shiloh Pike (08302)
**Phone—(856) 451-1324**
National—(800) 310-1324
Fax—(856) 451-0651
www.cumberlandvalve.com
Email—info@cumberlandvalve.com
GM—Thomas M. Davis
SIC—3492; 3052; *Hydraulic hose assemblies*
Employs—11; Estab.—1980
Sales—$2.6Mil-$5Mil
Distrib.—Regional
Privately owned corporation

**D AND S DESIGNS**
P.O. Box 1707 (08302)
**Phone—(856) 451-0954**
www.dandsdesigns.com
Email—sales@dandsdesigns.com
Owner—Sandra L. Rodriguez
Co-Pres.—Domenic A. Rodriguez
SIC—2396; 2395; 3993; 2759; *Custom screen printing & embroidery of wearables, non-wearables & promotional products; Brand name—Nike; Van Heusen; Izod; Gildan; Hanes; Jerzees; Bella; Canvas; adidas; Champion; Anvil; Augusta; Badger; Teamwork Athletic; Next Level; BIC; 3M; Leeds; Cross Pens; Holloway; Carhartt; Port Authority; UltraClub*
Employs—2; Estab.—1991
Sales—under $500,000
Distrib.—Regional
Sole ownership

**†F & H SUPPLY, INC**
1315 Route 77, P.O. Box 379 (08302)
**Phone—(856) 451-7080**
Fax—(856) 451-7076
www.fhsupply.net
Email—fhsupply@gmail.com
V-P—Harry Swistunow
GM—Frank Magazu

## Bridgeton—(cont.)

SIC—5084; 5085; *Wholesaler of industrial equipment & supplies, including nuts & bolts*
Employs—5; Estab.—2002
2,000 sq ft site, Distrib.—Local
Privately owned partnership

**GRIFFIN CARE, LLC**
80 Manheim Ave. (08302)
**Phone—(856) 455-6870**
National—(800) 366-6870
Fax—(856) 455-6849
www.griffincare.com
Email—info@griffincare.com
CEO—Mark Naim
COO—Shawn Naim
V-P., Mfg.—Jeffrey S. Basile
V-P., Engrg.—David J.Kenny
Hum. Res. Mgr.—Robert Krawiec
SIC—3842; 2399; *Absorbent disposable incontinence products, long term care absorbent burn pads & absorbent stretcher pads for EMTs; Brand name—Buddies; Passport; SuprAir; SupremeDri; Fresh Up; G & G Med Surge Products*
Employs—80; Estab.—1984
Sales—$14Mil
94,000 sq ft site, Distrib.—Intl.
Privately owned corporation

†**GROWMARK FS, LLC**
55 Silver Lake Rd. (08302)
**Phone—(856) 455-7688**
Fax—(856) 453-1130
www.growmarkfs.com
Email—info@growmarkfs.com
Plt. Mgr.—Rick Hatz
SIC—5191; *Distributor of agricultural pesticides & fertilizers*
Employs—15; Estab.—2005
Sales—$1Mil-$2.5Mil
Distrib.—Regional
Limited Liability Company
Parent co.—Growmark FS, LLC, Milford, DE
Phone—(302) 422-3002
See Parent Co. Section for full profile.

**JEM PRINT CO.**
36 Atlantic St. (08302)
**Phone—(856) 451-3885**
Fax—(856) 451-8390
Email—jemprint@aol.com
Pres., CFO—Herman Evans, Jr.
GM—Chuck Manupello
SIC—2759; 2791; NAICS—323122; *Commercial printing & typesetting*
Employs—4; Estab.—1971
Sales—under $500,000
4,800 sq ft site, Distrib.—Local
Sole ownership

**M K S, INC.**
7 N. Industrial Blvd. (08302)
**Phone—(856) 451-5545**
National—(800) 355-2677
Fax—(856) 451-9096
www.quantaflex.com
Email—sales@quantaflex.com
Pres.—Kennneth Brattlie
V-P.—William Miller
Off. Mgr.—Maryanne Moore
SIC—3646; NAICS—335122; *Electroluminescent lamps, membrane switches, DC/AC inverters & control panels; Brand name—Quantaflex; Quantaflex EL* Quantaflex M*
Employs—13; Estab.—1986
10,000 sq ft site, Distrib.—Intl.
Privately owned corporation

**MARTIN CORP.**
171 N. Pearl St. (08302)
**Phone—(856) 451-0900**
Email—jmartin@martindyeing.com
Pres., Treas.—Will Martin

V-P., Secy.—Judith S. Martin
SIC—2261; NAICS—313311; *Dyers & finishers; Brand name—Martexin Original Wax fabrics; Heavy Martexin WR fabrics*
Employs—16; Estab.—1948
Sales—$1.7Mil
90,000 sq ft site, Distrib.—National
Privately owned corporation

**NATIONAL REFRIGERANTS, INC.**
Div. of United Refrigeration, Inc.
661 Kenyon Ave. (08302)
**Phone—(856) 455-4555**
Fax—(856) 455-7626
www.refrigerants.com
Email—gloose@refrigerants.com
GM & Plt. Mgr.—John McDevitt
Hum. Res. Mgr.—Maritza Soto
Prod. Mgr.—Seth Barringer
SIC—2899; *Refrigerants blending & packaging*
Employs—70; Estab.—1983
8,400 sq ft site, Distrib.—Intl.
Privately owned corporation
Parent co.—United Refrigeration, Inc., Philadelphia, PA
Phone—(215) 698-9100
See Parent Co. Section for full profile.

**PALMETTO ADHESIVES CO., INC.**
Div. of Palmetto Adhesives Co.
1785 Burlington Rd. (08302)
**Phone—(856) 451-0405**
Fax—(856) 451-7710
www.palmettoadhesives.com
Email—kjordan@palmettoadhesives.com
Plt. Mgr.—Ray Charlton
Off. Mgr.—Kim Jordan
SIC—2891; NAICS—325520; *Adhesives*
Employs—15; Estab.—1983
Distrib.—National
Privately owned corporation
Parent co.—Palmetto Adhesives Co., Greenville, SC
Phone—(864) 232-8865
See Parent Co. Section for full profile.

**POOR BOY PALLET, LLC**
45 Finley Rd. (08302)
**Phone—(856) 451-3771**
www.poorboypallet.com
Email—poorboypallet@yahoo.com
Member—Dennis Macklin
Pres.—Garry Macklin
SIC—2448; *Wooden pallets*
Employs—20; Estab.—2006
Sales—$1Mil-$2.5Mil
Distrib.—Local
Limited Liability Company

**PREDATOR TOOLS (H Q)**
35 S. Woodruff Rd. (08302)
**Phone—(856) 455-3790**
Fax—(856) 455-6604
www.predatortools.com
Email—sales@predatortools.com
Owner—Pam Lesche
SIC—3599; 3499; *Company headquarters; digging tools & metal detectors (mfg. subcontracted)*
Employs—2; Estab.—1993
Sales—under $500,000
Distrib.—National
Privately owned corporation

**PRINT SIGN & DESIGN**
1791 S. Burlington Rd. (08302)
**Phone—(856) 451-8766**
Fax—(856) 451-8868
www.printsignanddesign.com
Email—speedyep@comcast.net
Pres.—Susan Lucas
Manager—Kelly Malitha
SIC—2759; 2791; NAICS—323122; *Commercial printing, typesetting & color separations*
Employs—8; Estab.—1962
4,500 sq ft site, Distrib.—Regional
Publicly owned corporation

**SOUTH STATE MATERIALS, LLC**
202 Reeves Rd., P.O. Box 68 (08302)
**Phone—(856) 451-5300**
Fax—(856) 455-3461
www.southstateinc.com
Email—kfrancis@southstateinc.com
Pres.—Chester Ottinger, Jr.
V-P.—Tim Larson
Cont.—Anthony Suppa
Accts. Payable Mgr.—Robin Mitchell
SIC—2951; NAICS—324121; *Company headquarters & asphalt paving compounds*
Employs—65; Estab.—1963
Sales—$50Mil-$100Mil
Distrib.—Local
Privately owned corporation

**SUNNY SLOPE FARMS**
400 Greenwich Rd. (08302)
**Phone—(856) 451-0022**
www.sunnyslopefarms.com
Pres.—Al Caggiano
SIC—2033; NAICS—311421; *Apples & peaches processing*
Employs—15; Estab.—1928
Seasonal: 15-100
Distrib.—Local
Privately owned corporation

**TERRIGNO'S BAKERY**
632 N. Pearl St. (08302)
**Phone—(856) 451-6368**
Owner—Cosmo Terrigno
SIC—2051; NAICS—311812; *Bread & cakes*
Employs—15; Estab.—1963
Sales—$1Mil-$2.5Mil (est)
Distrib.—Local
Sole ownership

**ULTRA CLEAN TECHNOLOGIES CORP.**
1274 Highway 77 (08302)
**Phone—(856) 451-2176**
National—(800) 791-9111
www.ultracleantech.com
Email—sales@ultracleantech.com
Sales Mgr., North America—Steve Roath
SIC—3569; *Pneumatic cleaning & sealing systems for hydraulic & fluid contamination control in hose, tube & pipe, including handheld & bench-mount launchers, nozzles, adapters & abrasive, grinding & foam projectiles; Brand name—Ultra Clean Tech*
Employs—100
Sales—$10Mil-$25Mil (est)
Distrib.—Intl.
Privately owned corporation

**W.W. MANUFACTURING CO., INC.**
60 Rosenhayn Ave. (08302)
**Phone—(856) 451-5700**
National—(800) 452-5547
Fax—(856) 451-4985
www.wwmfg.com
Email—info@wwmfg.com
Ptnr. & Pres.—Peter Lesche
Ptnr.—Ingrid Hawk
SIC—3546; 3524; 3423; NAICS—333991; *Steel landscaping & nursery hand tools, including steel spades, shovels, digging tools, rakes, ball carts & tracking trailers; Brand name—King of Spades; Dura Rakes; Lesche Digging Tool*
Employs—12; Estab.—1964
Sales—$1Mil-$5Mil
5,500 sq ft site, Distrib.—Intl.
Privately owned sub-S corp.

**WESTSIDE ENGRAVERS**
76 N. West Ave. (08302)
**Phone—(856) 455-4790**
Fax—(856) 453-1626

Email—westsideengravers@verizon.net
Owner & Operator—Dianne Johnson
SIC—3479; *Industrial & commercial engraving*
Employs—1; Estab.—1981
Sales—under $500,000
Distrib.—National
Sole ownership

**WHIBCO, INC. (H Q)**
87 E. Commerce St. (08302)
**Phone—(856) 455-9200**
     (856) 455-9203
National—(800) 631-8010
Fax—(856) 455-9009
www.whibco.com
Email—sales@whibco.com
Pres.—Wade R. Sjogren
Ex. V-P.—Walter Sjogren
Cont.—Bill Simcox
Asst. Cont.—Betty Whitelan
Dir., Admn. & MIS—Richard Bertonaczi
SIC—1442; NAICS—212321; *Corporate headquarters; sand & gravel processing*
Employs—30; Estab.—1841
Sales—$1Mil-$2.5Mil
Distrib.—Regional
Privately owned corporation
AKA: Whibco of NJ

**WHITEWAVE FOODS CO.**
70 Rosenhayn Ave. (08302)
**Phone—(856) 459-3890**
Fax—(856) 459-3502
www.whitewave.com
Email—white.wave@whitewave.com
Plt. Mgr.—John Bodrog
SIC—2099; *Soy milk*
Employs—100; Estab.—2004
Distrib.—National
Privately owned corporation
Parent co.—WhiteWave Foods Co., Broomfield, CO
Phone—(303) 635-4000
See Parent Co. Section for full profile.

**WOODROOF METAL SHOP**
73 Water St. (08302)
**Phone—(856) 455-1111**
Fax—(856) 455-5353
www.woodroofenergy.com
Owner—Bob Woodroof
Manager—Ron Cox
SIC—3444; *HVAC ducts*
Employs—2; Estab.—1930
Sales—$500,000-$1Mil
Distrib.—Regional
Privately owned corporation

**WOODRUFF ENERGY, INC.**
73 Water St., P.O. Box 777 (08302)
**Phone—(856) 455-1111**
Fax—(856) 455-4085
www.woodruffenergy.com
Pres.—Robert Woodruff, Jr.
SIC—1382; *Oil & natural gas exploration services*
Employs—50; Estab.—1869
Distrib.—Local
Privately owned corporation

## Bridgewater
(Somerset—N.E.)

**AMNEAL PHARMACEUTICALS, LLC**
400 Crossing Blvd., 3rd Fl. (08807-2863)
**Phone—(908) 947-3120**
Fax—(908) 947-3146
www.amneal.com
Email—businessdevelopment@amneal.com
Chrm., Co-CEO—Chirag Patel
Sr. V-P., Opers.—Sanjiv Patel
Sr. V-P., Global Opers. & Strategy—Joseph Todisco

GEOGRAPHICAL

## Bridgewater—(cont.)

SIC—2834; NAICS—325412; *Company headquarters & pharmaceuticals*
Employs—65; Estab.—2001
Distrib.—National
Limited Liability Company

**APPLEGATE FARMS (H Q)**
750 Route 202 S., Ste. 300 (08807)
**Phone—(866) 587-5858**
Fax—(800) 358-8289
www.applegatefarms.com
Email—help@applegate.com
Founder & CEO—Stephen McDonnell
V-P., Digital Media—Rob O'Donnell
IT Mgr.—Guy Lavalette
Hum. Res. Mgr.—Leah Pires
SIC—2013; *Company headquarters; natural & organic whole muscle meat processing (mfg. done in Philadelphia, PA & Baltimore, MD); Brand name—Applegate®*
Employs—50; Estab.—1987
Sales—$150Mil
Distrib.—National
Privately owned corporation

**B & A FLEX, INC.**
34 Charlotte Dr. (08807)
**Phone—(908) 722-2808**
National—(866) 722-2808
www.baflexhose.com
Email—info@baflexhose.com
GM—Dan Souza
SIC—3599; 3432; 3492; 3494; NAICS—332912; *Flexible metal hose, connectors & flow indicators*
Employs—14; Estab.—1990
Distrib.—Local
Privately owned corporation

**BRADDOCK HEAT TREATING CO., INC.**
Div. of Braddock Metallurgical, Inc.
123 Chimney Rock Rd. (08807)
**Phone—(732) 356-2906**
National—(800) 423-4328
Fax—(732) 356-2080
www.braddockmt.com
Email—wschultz@braddockmt.com
GM—W. J. Schultz, Jr.
Plt. Mgr.—Matthew Zichelli
Off. Mgr.—Duane Brikowski
Special Processing Mgr.—Stanley Lopacinski
Qual. Mgr.—Anthony Carratura
SIC—3398; NAICS—332811; *Metal heat treating*
Employs—20; Estab.—1952
Sales—$2Mil-$5Mil
20,000 sq ft site, Distrib.—National
Privately owned corporation
Parent co.—Braddock Metallurgical, Inc., Daytona Beach, FL
Phone—(386) 267-0955
See Parent Co. Section for full profile.

**BROTHER INTERNATIONAL CORPORATION**
200 Crossing Blvd. (08807)
**Phone—(908) 704-1700**
National—(888) 879-3232
Fax—(908) 704-8235
www.brother-usa.com
Email—jmiranda@brother.com
Chrm.—Tadashi Ishiguro
Pres.—Kaz Ikeda
CFO—Anthony Melfi
V-P., Chief Legal Officer—Henry J. Sacco, Jr.
Sr. V-P., Sales, Bus. Machine Group—Brian Vincent
Sr. V-P., Mktg., Bus. Machines—Don Cummins
Sr. V-P., Plng. & Prod.—Roger Nakagawa

Sr. V-P., Home Appliance Div. & Indl. Prods. Div.—Dean Shulman
V-P., Hum. Res.—Kim Miner
Corp. Pub. Rels. & Tradeshow Mgr.—Joann Miranda-Wallace
SIC—3579; *Corporate headquarters & office machinery, including printers, fax machines, P-touch labelers, typewriters, stamp creators, machine tools, gear motors/reducers & industrial sewing*
Employs—350; Estab.—1934
Company-wide: 1,100
Sales—$1.5Bil
Distrib.—Intl.
Privately owned corporation

**C TECHNOLOGIES, INC.**
757 U.S. Highway 202/206 (08807)
**Phone—(908) 707-1009**
Fax—(908) 707-1030
www.ctechnologiesinc.com
Email—info@ctechnologiesinc.com
Pres.—Craig D. Harrison
GM, MIS & Opers. Mgr.—Mark Salerno
Sales & Mktg. Mgr.—Larry Russo
Sales & Mktg. Mgr.—Mary Ann Vernieri
Acct. Mgr.—Joan Reich
Hum. Res. Mgr.—Loriann Pesci
SIC—3357; *Fiber-optic cable assembly; Brand name—SoloVPE*
Employs—40; Estab.—1986
Distrib.—National
Privately owned corporation

**CONVATEC, INC.**
CenterPoint II, Ste. 205, 1140 Route 22 E. (08807)
**Phone—(732) 412-5500**
        (908) 904-2200
National—(800) 422-8811
www.convatec.com
Email—mediarelations@convatec.com
CEO—Ken Berger
CFO—Nigel Clerkin
Sr. V-P., Opers.—Robbie Heginbotham
Sr. V-P., Comms. & Mktg.—Robert McKee
Sr. V-P., Hum. Res.—Joseph Baiunco
SIC—2834; 2844; NAICS—325412; *Corporate headquarters & health care products*
Employs—300; Estab.—1987
Worldwide: 8,000
Distrib.—Intl.
Privately owned corporation

**DEMAND, LLC**
36 S. Adamsville Rd. (08807)
**Phone—(908) 526-2020**
Fax—(908) 526-8012
www.demandllc.com
Email—demandllc@verizon.net
Owner—Joseph Kafara
Dir., Opers. & Hum. Res. & Off. Mgr.—Richelle Kafara
Shop Foreman—Vince Montone
SIC—3444; 3599; *Welding, machining & custom sheet metal fabrication shop*
Employs—16; Estab.—2002
Sales—$1Mil-$2.5Mil
16,000 sq ft site, Distrib.—Regional
Limited Liability Company

**DEWY MEADOW FOODS, INC.**
1018 Rector Rd. (08807)
**Phone—(908) 218-5655**
        (908) 966-3480
Fax—(908) 231-7556
Email—dewymeadowfoods@aol.com
Pres.—Randolph Krogoll

SIC—2037; 2038; 2053; NAICS—311411; *Frozen meat pies & bakery products*
Employs—20; Estab.—1929
Sales—$1Mil-$2.5Mil
Distrib.—National
Privately owned corporation

**DRAKA SPECIALTY TUBING**
111 Chimney Rock Rd. (08807)
**Phone—(732) 469-5902**
National—(866) 776-8823
Fax—(732) 469-6363
www.prysmiangroup.com
Dir., Opers. & Sales—Giovanni Calimani
SIC—3317; NAICS—331210; *Industrial stainless steel pressure tubes*
Employs—60; Estab.—2004
Sales—$10Mil-$25Mil (est)
Distrib.—Intl.
Publicly owned corporation

**DSPCON**
380 Foothill Rd., Ste. 101 (08807-2255)
**Phone—(908) 722-5656**
National—(888) 377-2668
Fax—(908) 722-3259
www.dspcon.com
Email—dspsales@dspcon.com
Dir., Engrg.—Clarke Ryan
Dir., Bus. Dev.—David Dixson
GM—Curt Allen
SIC—3825; NAICS—334500; *Data acquisition & test-end measurement systems*
Employs—30; Estab.—1990
Sales—$5Mil-$10Mil
Distrib.—Intl.
Publicly owned corporation

**†E & B DISTRIBUTORS, INC.**
400 Route 22 E. (08807)
**Phone—(732) 469-2266**
National—(800) 300-3106
Fax—(732) 469-3010
www.ebdist.com
Email—info@ebdist.com
Pres.—Brian Skowronek
V-P.—Barry Skowronek
SIC—5074; 5032; *Distributor of plumbing & heating supplies for bathrooms, including tile, stone, lighting, bath furniture, medicine cabinets, faucets & plumbing fixtures; Brand name—KOHLER; GROHE; HANSGROHE; ROHL; OMEGA CABINETRY; WOODPRO; EMPIRE INDUSTRIES; NUVO; NORWELL; ROBERN; GLASSCRAFTERS*
Employs—12; Estab.—1967
Sales—$2.5Mil-$5Mil
50,000 sq ft site, Distrib.—Local
Privately owned corporation

**ELI LILLY (H Q)**
Div. of Eli Lilly & Co.
440 Route 22 E. (08807)
**Phone—(908) 541-8100**
www.lilly.com
Email—egs@lilly.com
V-P., Global Qual.—Carole Beer
Assoc. V-P., Corp. Comms.—Tracy Henrikson
Sr. Dir., Portfolio Mktg., Oncology—Kim Aldridge
Assoc. Dir., Learning Tech.—Bob Guglielman
SIC—2834; *Divisional headquarters; oncology pharmaceutical drug candidates in Phase I, II & III clinical trials; Brand name—ERBITUX®*
Employs—350; Estab.—2001
Sales—$100Mil-$250Mil (est)
Publicly owned corporation
Parent co.—Eli Lilly & Co., Indianapolis, IN
Phone—(317) 276-2000
See Parent Co. Section for full profile.

**†FERGUSON ENTERPRISES, INC.**
830 Route 22 (08807)
**Phone—(908) 725-0666**
Fax—(908) 725-7950
www.ferguson.com
Email—eric.scott@ferguson.com
Br. Mgr.—Roger White
SIC—5074; *Wholesaler of plumbing & heating supplies*
Employs—10; Estab.—1982
Sales—under $500,000
Distrib.—Intl.
Publicly owned corporation
Parent co.—Ferguson Enterprises, Inc., Newport News, VA
Phone—(757) 874-7795
See Parent Co. Section for full profile.

**†GRIFFITH ELECTRIC SUPPLY CO., INC.**
4-W Chimney Rock Rd. (08807)
Mail addr: 5 2nd St., Trenton (08611-2231)
**Phone—(908) 203-1601**
Fax—(908) 203-1626
www.griffithelec.com
Email—pmauro@griffithelec.com
Br. Mgr.—Paul Mauro
SIC—5063; *Wholesaler of switches, boxes, panels & electrical breakers*
Employs—6
Distrib.—Local
Privately owned corporation
Parent co.—Griffith Electric Supply Co., Inc., Trenton, NJ
Phone—(609) 695-6121
See Parent Co. Section for full profile.

**HUMANCONCEPTS**
Div. of Saba Software, Inc.
1031 Route 22, Ste. 303 (08807)
**Phone—(908) 231-0204**
        (650) 581-2500
www.humanconcepts.com
Off. Mgr.—Patricia Wilder
SIC—7372; *Software development*
Employs—40; Estab.—1977
7,200 sq ft site, Distrib.—Intl.
Parent co.—Saba Software, Inc., Redwood City, CA
Phone—(650) 581-2500
See Parent Co. Section for full profile.

**HUNTER PRODUCTS, INC.**
792 Partridge Dr., P.O. Box 6795 (08807)
**Phone—(908) 526-8440**
National—(800) 524-0692
Fax—(908) 526-8348
www.hunterproducts.com
Email—phyllis@hunterproducts.com
Pres.—Phyllis Zelnick
Manager—Karen Russo
SIC—3559; *Ultra-compact electroplating pens & accessories*
Employs—18; Estab.—1986
Sales—$2.5Mil-$5Mil
Distrib.—Intl.
Privately owned sub-S corp.

**INGREDION INCORPORATED (H Q)**
Div. of Ingredion Inc.
10 Finderne Ave., Ste. C (08807)
**Phone—(908) 685-5555**
        (908) 685-5000
National—(866) 961-6285
Fax—(908) 685-5355
www.ingredion.com
Email—nsc.salessupport@nstarch.com
Global Dir., Innovation & Mktg. Excellence—Jill Schimmel
Dir. & Mktg. Comm. Mgr.—Marc Green
Hum. Res. Mgr.—John Mitolo

## Bridgewater—(cont.)

SIC—2046; NAICS—311200;
*Divisional headquarters;
specialty starches*
Employs—250; Estab.—1896
Worldwide: 2,250
Sales—$2.6Bil
Distrib.—Intl.
Privately owned corporation
Parent co.—Ingredion Inc.,
Westchester, IL
Phone—(708) 551-2600
See Parent Co. Section for full profile.

**INSMED, INC.**
10 Finderne Ave. (08807)
**Phone—(908) 977-9900**
www.insmed.com
Pres.—Will Lewis
CTO—Walter Perkins
Ex. V-P., Dev. & Chief Medical
Officer—Renu Gupta
Sr. V-P., Hum. Res.—Nicole
Schaeffer
SIC—2834; NAICS—325412;
*Inhaled pharmaceuticals for the
site-specific treatment of serious
lung diseases, including
pulmonary infections in cystic
fibrosis patients & cancers*
Employs—80; Estab.—2001
Distrib.—Intl.

**†INTERNATIONAL WIRE CO.**
27-E Kearney St. (08807)
**Phone—(732) 968-8122**
Fax—(732) 384-7509
GM—Mike Lee
SIC—5051; *Distributor of steel
products, including rods &
tubings*
Employs—15; Estab.—2000
Distrib.—Intl.
Privately owned corporation
AKA: IWC

**INTERSIL CORP.**
440 U.S. Highway 22 E., Ste. 100
(08807)
**Phone—(908) 685-6000**
Fax—(908) 685-6217
www.intersil.com
Email—webmaster@intersil.com
GM—Paul S. Ferrazza
Administrator—Pat Bishop
SIC—3674; NAICS—334413;
*High-performance analog
semiconductors*
Employs—24; Estab.—1999
Distrib.—National
Privately owned corporation
Parent co.—Intersil Corp., Milpitas,
CA
Phone—(408) 546-3300
See Parent Co. Section for full profile.

**LINES & LETTERS DESIGNS**
1386 Mount Vernon Rd. (08807)
**Phone—(732) 563-0909**
Fax—(732) 563-0005
www.linesandlettersdesigns.com
Email—lineletter@aol.com
Owner & Pres.—Brian Schofield
Off. Mgr.—Karen Levin
SIC—3993; *Interior & exterior
signs*
Employs—2
Sales—under $500,000 (est)
Distrib.—Regional

**LIQUIFLO, INC.**
7 Wilpert Rd. (08807)
**Phone—(732) 271-4600**
National—(800) 448-3646
Fax—(800) 445-4356
www.liquifloinc.com
Email—sales@liquifloinc.com
Pres.—Brian Atherton

SIC—3569; *Fluid handling filters &
pumps*
Employs—3; Estab.—1970
Sales—under $500,000
Distrib.—Intl.
Privately owned corporation

NEW ENTRY
**METAL FX FILMS, LLC**
27 Kearney St., Unit B (08807)
**Phone—(732) 560-1297**
National—(855) 547-5813
Fax—(732) 356-3643
www.metalfxfilms.com
Email—j.parker@metalfxfilms.com
Ptnr.—Charles Yetka
Ptnr.—Jim Parker
SIC—3081; *Polyester films*
Employs—5
Sales—$1Mil-$2.5Mil
10,000 sq ft site, Distrib.—Intl.
Limited Liability Company
DBA: Advanced Mfg. &
Development, Inc.

**NISTICA, INC.**
745 U.S. Highway 202-206, Ste.
201 (08807)
**Phone—(908) 707-9500**
Fax—(908) 707-9505
www.nistica.com
Email—info@nistica.com
Founder—Jefferson Wagener
CEO—Ashish Vengsarkar
CTO—Thomas Strasser
COO—Frank Smith
V-P., Fin. & Hum. Res. Mgr.—
Joanne Bisconti
Off. Mgr.—Lynn Hill
SIC—3669; NAICS—334290;
*Fiber-optic components*
Employs—55; Estab.—2005
Distrib.—Intl.
Privately owned corporation

**NITTA CASINGS INC.**
141 Southside Ave. (08807)
**Phone—(908) 218-4400**
(800) 526-3970
Fax—(908) 725-2835
www.nittacasings.com
Email—customerservice@
nittacasings.com
Pres., CEO—Rod Moore
COO—Francisco Sousa
CFO—Marcia Casas
V-P., Sales—Earle Mulrane
V-P., Sales, Asia Pacific—Vernon
Lee
V-P., New Bus. & Primary Opers.—
Rich Battersby
V-P., Hum. Res.—Roseann
Salerno
V-P., Engrg. & Special Projs.—Sho
Takagi
Mktg. Logistics Mgr.—Carol
Hoagland
SIC—2013; 3556; 2836; NAICS—
333294; *Edible collagen
sausage casings & collagen gel
for co-extrusion & sausage
linkers, z-linkers, cams & stuffing
tubes/horns; Brand name—
Bloom Fresh Sausage Casings;
Mahogany Sausage Casings;
Superfry Plus Fresh Sausage
Casings; Edible Artificial
Collagen Sausage Casings;
Clear Choice Sausage Casings;
Sausage Linkers; Z-Linkers*
Employs—192; Estab.—1962
Sales—$25Mil-$50Mil
175,000 sq ft site, Distrib.—Intl.
Privately owned corporation
ISO rating—9001:2008

**PIPING SOLUTIONS, INC.**
81 Chimney Rock Rd., Ste. 3
(08807)
**Phone—(732) 537-1009**
Fax—(732) 537-0911
www.pipingsolutionsinc.com
Email—psi_01@msn.com

Pres.—Ernest E. Stone III
SIC—3498; NAICS—332996;
*Process skid assemblies &
ASME B31.1 & B31.3 pipe
fabrication*
Employs—6; Estab.—2000
Sales—$500,000-$1Mil
12,000 sq ft site, Distrib.—National
Privately owned sub-S corp.

**QUARTZ TECHNOLOGY, INC.**
1355 Plymouth Rd. (08807)
Mail addr: P.O. Box 268, Liberty
Corner (07938)
**Phone—(908) 526-6362**
Fax—(908) 526-8838
www.quartztech.com
Email—quartz@quartztech.com
Pres.—Lothar Jung
SIC—3559; *Quartz processing
machinery*
Employs—2; Estab.—1972
Sales—under $500,000
Distrib.—Intl.
Privately owned corporation

**SAINT-GOBAIN PERFORMANCE
PLASTICS**
460 Milltown Rd. (08807)
**Phone—(908) 218-8888**
National—(800) 435-3992
Fax—(908) 218-9009
www.plastics.saint-gobain.com
Email—sgppl.marketing@saint-
gobain.com
Plt. Mgr.—Massimo Caiati
Hum. Res. Mgr.—Karen Arnott
Fin. Analyst—Rose Sebold
Cust. Serv. Rep.—Ted Zamorski
SIC—3052; 3084; 3052; 3312;
NAICS—326220; *Flexible
fluoropolymer hoses & fittings,
plastic pipe, silicone & food
grade rubber & stainless steel
hose assemblies*
Employs—60; Estab.—1980
54,000 sq ft site, Distrib.—National
Publicly owned corporation
Parent co.—Saint-Gobain
Performance Plastics, Aurora,
OH
Phone—(216) 245-0529
See Parent Co. Section for full profile.

**SANOFI U. S. (H Q)**
55 Corporate Dr. (08807)
**Phone—(908) 981-5000**
National—(800) 981-2491
www.sanofi.us
Email—mr@sanofi.com
Sr. V-P., Global Svcs.—Gregory
Irace
V-P., Hum. Res., Leadership &
Organizational Dev., N.
America—Nicolette Sherman
V-P., Animal Research, Disposition
& Safety—Marc Bonnefoi
Dir., Inv. Rels.—George Grosik
Head of Global Comms.—
Elizabeth Baxter
SIC—2834; NAICS—325412;
*Company headquarters;
pharmaceuticals*
Employs—2000
Country-wide: 16,900
Sales—$46Bil
Publicly owned corporation

**†SCHOFIELD CO., INC., GEORGE**
831 E. Main St. (08807)
Mail addr: P.O. Box 110, Bound
Brook (08805)
**Phone—(732) 356-0858**
National—(800) 827-6257
Fax—(732) 356-1137
www.schofieldstone.com
Email—sales@schofieldstone.com
Pres.—Bill Newell
Cont.—Bill Bittay
GM—Mike Gorman

SIC—5087; *Corporate
headquarters & distributor of
landscaping supplies*
Employs—34
Distrib.—National
Privately owned corporation
AKA: Schofield Stone * Stone
Center At Bridgewater

NEW ENTRY
**SERVICE APEX**
564-A Union Ave. (08807)
**Phone—(732) 560-2222**
Fax—(732) 560-1198
www.serviceapex.com
Email—bridgewater@
serviceapex.com
Pres.—Ken Griggs
SIC—2759; 2396; 2395; 3993;
*Commercial printing, t-shirt
screen printing & embroidery &
interior & exterior signage*
Employs—10; Estab.—1994
Sales—$1Mil-$2.5Mil
5,000 sq ft site, Distrib.—National
Privately owned corporation

**SOPHISTICATED STORAGE
SOLUTIONS, LLC**
7-W Chimney Rock Rd. (08807)
**Phone—(732) 356-4200**
Fax—(732) 356-4206
www.sophisticatedstorage.com
Email—information@
sophisticatedstorage.com
Owner—Jacki Melchior
Designer—Wendy Scott
SIC—2542; *Customized laminate
closets, storage shelving units,
entertainment centers & cabinets*
Employs—7; Estab.—2001
Sales—under $500,000
Distrib.—Local
Limited Liability Company

**THERMO FISHER SCIENTIFIC**
Div. of Thermo Fisher Scientific,
Inc.
755 U.S. Highway 202 (08807)
**Phone—(908) 526-1800**
Fax—(908) 526-3038
www.thermofisher.com
Email—info@thermofisher.com
Site Mgr.—Thomas Campbell
Hum. Res. Mgr.—John Farah
SIC—2899; 2835; 2833; NAICS—
325998; *Bioreagants & specialty
chemicals for research, analysis,
discovery & dingostic
applications*
Employs—162; Estab.—1975
Sales—over $1Bil
Distrib.—Intl.
Publicly owned corporation
Parent co.—Thermo Fisher
Scientific, Inc., Waltham, MA
Phone—(781) 622-1000
See Parent Co. Section for full profile.

**†TURTLE & HUGHES, INC.**
188 Foothill Rd. (08807)
**Phone—(732) 560-5575**
Fax—(732) 560-0847
www.turtle.com
Email—info@turtle.com
Ex. V-P., Br. Mgr.—Rick Reffler
Opers. Mgr.—Lisa Kwiatkowski
SIC—5063; 5084; 5085;
*Distributor of electrical &
industrial equipment & supplies*
Employs—100; Estab.—1991
Distrib.—Intl.
Privately owned corporation
Parent co.—Turtle & Hughes, Inc.,
Linden, NJ
Phone—(732) 574-3600
See Parent Co. Section for full profile.

**V-CUSTOM MILLWORK, INC.**
1480 Highway 22, P.O. Box 6842
(08807)
**Phone—(732) 469-9600**
Fax—(732) 469-8458

GEOGRAPHICAL

## Bridgewater—(cont.)

www.vcustommillwork.com
Email—sales@vcustom.com
Pres.—Susan Schumer
Hum. Res., IT & Off. Mgr.—Wendy
  Gromoich
SIC—2431; NAICS—321900;
  Millwork, including wall & stair
  wainscoting, interior & exterior
  trim & doors, crown mouldings,
  brickmolds, fireplaces, built-ins
  & library fixtures
Employs—10; Estab.—1992
Sales—$500,000-$1.5Mil
20,000 sq ft site, Distrib.—
  Regional
Limited Liability Company

## Brielle

(Monmouth—N.E.)

**COASTAL IMPORTS, INC.**

31 Mulberry Ct., Unit B (08730)
**Phone—(732) 223-4356**
Fax—(732) 223-8155
Email—coastalimports.inc@
  verizon.net
Pres.—Patricia Lusk
SIC—3556; New & used baking &
  restaurant equipment for retail &
  wholesale bakeries, including
  ovens, horizontal, vertical &
  spiral mixers, moulders, dividers,
  refrigeration, depositors & full
  production lines
Employs—2; Estab.—1986
1,500 sq ft site, Distrib.—Intl.
Privately owned corporation

**NEWMAN'S ORNAMENTAL
IRONWORKS, INC.**

207 Union Ave. (08730)
**Phone—(732) 223-9042**
Fax—(732) 223-6726
www.newmanironworks.com
Email—info@
  newmanironworks.com
Pres.—Rick Newman
Off. Mgr.—Brian Newman
Manager—Bill Newman
SIC—3441; NAICS—332312;
  Ornamental wrought iron
Employs—20; Estab.—1981
Sales—$2.5Mil-$5Mil
Distrib.—Local
Privately owned corporation

**RIES CO., INC., R. E.**

107 Lake Ave. (08730)
**Phone—(732) 892-1842**
Email—georgiegirl21021@
  gmail.com
Pres.—Raymond E. Ries
SIC—2394; NAICS—314912;
  Canvas boat covers &
  commercial upholstery
Employs—4; Estab.—1977
Sales—under $500,000
Distrib.—Regional
Privately owned corporation

## Brigantine

(Atlantic—S.E.)

NEW ENTRY
**JETEK ENTERPRISES, LLC**

4329 Atlantic Brigantine Blvd.
  (08203)
**Phone—(609) 266-4700**
www.jetekpwc.com
Email—ronnie@jetek.com
Owner—Ronnie Walker
SIC—3519; NAICS—336312;
  Rebuilt marine engines
Employs—3
Sales—under $500,000 (est)
Limited Liability Company

## Broadway

(Warren—N.W.)

**I S E FARMS, INC.**

Div. of ISE America, Inc.
110 Goodspring Rd., P.O. Box 567
  (08808)
**Phone—(908) 454-4148**
National—(800) 343-7926
Fax—(908) 454-9795
www.iseamerica.com
Email—ise@nac.net
Site Mgr.—Orlando Santiago Cruz
SIC—2015; Egg processing
Employs—85; Estab.—1988
Distrib.—Local
Privately owned corporation
Parent co.—ISE America, Inc.,
  Galena, MD
  Phone—(410) 755-6300
See Parent Co. Section for full profile.

## Brooklawn

(Camden—S.W.)

**AMERAL INTERNATIONAL, INC.**

7 Railroad Ln. (08030)
**Phone—(856) 456-9000**
National—(800) 222-5371
Fax—(856) 456-2522
www.ameral.com
Email—sales@ameral.com
Pres.—Louis Grieco
Sales Mgr.—Stan Tyska
Prodn. Mgr.—Steve Grieco
Administrator—Lisa Grieco
SIC—3679; 3699; 3648; NAICS—
  335129; Custom cable & wire
  harness assemblies, patch
  cords, data & voice cables,
  connectors, power supplies &
  LED lighting; Brand name—
  Pacific Transformer; Molex;
  Omron; Amphenol; Bogen;
  Osram; ITT Cannon; The LED
  Company
Employs—15; Estab.—1983
11,000 sq ft site, Distrib.—Intl.
Privately owned sub-S corp.
ISO rating—9001:2002

**C & L MACHINING CO.**

110 S. New Broadway, P.O. Box
  167 (08030)
**Phone—(856) 456-1932**
Fax—(856) 456-4401
www.candlmachine.com
Email—candlmach@aol.com
Pres.—George Cohen
SIC—3599; General machining,
  welding & gear cutting of large
  CNC, replacement &
  maintenance parts
Employs—6; Estab.—1968
Sales—under $1Mil
5,000 sq ft site, Distrib.—National
Privately owned corporation

**COLOSSUS GRANITE & MARBLE,
INC.**

416 Crescent Blvd. (08030)
**Phone—(856) 742-0090**
Fax—(856) 742-0092
www.colossusgranite.net
Email—colossusgranite@msn.com
Ptnr. & Pres.—Joe Franklin
Ptnr.—Kathy Franklin
SIC—3281; NAICS—327991;
  Custom granite & marble
  bathroom & kitchen countertops
  & vanity tops
Employs—8; Estab.—1999
Sales—$500,000-$1Mil
Distrib.—Regional
Privately owned corporation

**IMPRINT SPECIALTIES, INC.**

601 New Broadway (08030)
**Phone—(856) 456-2999**
Fax—(856) 456-6141
Email—rolferrys@gmail.com

Pres.—Francis Ferry
V-P.—Rolf Peiffer
SIC—2396; 2759; 2499; 3499;
  NAICS—323100; Commercial
  screen printing & awards for
  consumers & businesses
Employs—5; Estab.—1991
Sales—$500,000-$1Mil (est)
Distrib.—National
Privately owned corporation
AKA: Rolferry's

**†MATERIAL HANDLING SUPPLY, INC.**

1 Old Salem Rd. (08030)
**Phone—(856) 541-1290**
    (877) 647-9320
National—(800) 647-5438
Fax—(856) 742-0237
www.mhslift.com
Email—andy.levin@mhslift.com
Pres.—Andrew Levin
CFO—David Brown
V-P.—Brett Levin
Hum. Res. & Off. Mgr.—Amy
  Brown
SIC—5084; Wholesaler of material
  handling equipment & forklifts,
  including service, repair & parts
  inventory for support; Brand
  name—Crown Equipment
  Corporation; Nissan Forklift
  Corporation
Employs—110; Estab.—1970
60,000 sq ft site, Distrib.—Local
Privately owned sub-S corp.

## Budd Lake

(Morris—N.W.)

**AMERICAN SENSOR
TECHNOLOGIES, INC.**

450 Clark Dr., Ste. 4 (07828-4312)
**Phone—(973) 448-1901**
Fax—(973) 448-1905
www.astsensors.com
Email—info@astsensors.com
Pres., CEO—Richard Tasker
V-P., CFO—Michael Eldredge
V-P., Bus. Dev.—Karmjit Sidhu
Sales & Mktg. Mgr.—Samuel
  Franzblau
Mktg. Mgr.—Greg Montrose
SIC—3829; Corporate
  headquarters & industrial
  pressure transducers; Brand
  name—AST Sensors; AST;
  Macro Sensors
Employs—90; Estab.—1997
Sales—$5Mil-$20Mil
16,000 sq ft site, Distrib.—Intl.
Privately owned corporation
ISO rating—9001:2008

**CATHETER ROBOTICS, INC.**

500 International Dr., Ste. 255
  (07828)
**Phone—(973) 691-2000**
www.catheterrobotics.com
Email—info@catheterrobotics.com
Pres.—David A. Jenkins
Fin. Mgr.—Michelle Skurchak
SIC—3841; Remote catheter
  systems for cardiac & vascular
  applications
Employs—8; Estab.—2006
Sales—$1Mil-$2.5Mil (est)
Distrib.—Intl.
Privately owned corporation

NEW ENTRY
**FLOWONIX**

500 International Dr., Ste. 200
  (07828)
**Phone—(973) 426-9229**
Fax—(973) 426-0035
www.flowonix.com
Pres.—Steve Adler

SIC—3841; Medical devices,
  including implantable pumps &
  catheters; Brand name—
  Prometra ®
Employs—20; Estab.—2004
Sales—$2.5Mil-$5Mil (est)
10,000 sq ft site, Distrib.—Intl.
Privately owned corporation

**I C MACHINE, INC.**

199 U.S. Highway 46 (07828-
  3009)
**Phone—(973) 252-7083**
Fax—(973) 252-7084
Email—icmachine@live.com
Pres.—Ioan Comsulea
Off. Mgr.—Maria Comsulea
SIC—3599; Precision machining
  job shop
Employs—2; Estab.—1996
Sales—under $500,000
3,600 sq ft site, Distrib.—Local
Privately owned corporation

**KEFA NORTHEAST**

P.O. Box 88 (07828)
**Phone—(201) 664-5487**
www.kefanortheast.com
Email—regis@kefanortheast.com
Pres.—Regis Doucette
SIC—3479; Corrosion, thermal &
  anti-mold coatings
Employs—10; Estab.—1988
Sales—$500,000-$1Mil
Distrib.—Intl.
Privately owned corporation
AKA: Durable Solutions

**L-3 COMMUNICATIONS CORP.,
SPACE & NAVIGATION SYSTEMS**

Div. of L-3 Communications Corp.
450 Clark Dr. (07828)
**Phone—(973) 446-4000**
Fax—(973) 444-4256
www.l-3com.com
Email—sales@l-3com.com
Pres., Div.—Ted Trzesniowski
V-P., Contracts & Fin.—Judy
  DeSarro
Dir., Qual. Assur.—Tom Fabrizio
IT Mgr.—Paul Davis
Hum. Res. Mgr.—Susan Florio
SIC—3812; 3769; NAICS—
  334511; Inertial instruments &
  integrated fire control systems &
  pointing, guidance, control &
  positioning equipment for
  satellites, artillery & launch
  vehicles, including fiber optic
  gyros, ring laser gyros,
  momentum & reaction wheel
  assemblies
Employs—260; Estab.—2000
Distrib.—Intl.
Publicly owned corporation
Parent co.—L-3 Communications
  Corp., New York, NY
  Phone—(212) 697-1111
See Parent Co. Section for full profile.

**MEGASAFE**

8 Sunrise Ave. (07828)
**Phone—(973) 691-0382**
National—(800) 345-6552
Fax—(973) 691-1025
www.megasafe.com
Email—hookway@optonline.net
Pres.—Michael J. Hookway
SIC—3499; High security, jewelry,
  residential, office, restaurant &
  depository safes, fire-resistant &
  GSA file cabinets, vault rooms &
  vault doors
Employs—20; Estab.—1985
Sales—$1Mil-$2.5Mil
12,500 sq ft site, Distrib.—Intl.
Privately owned corporation
AKA: Hookway Enterprises

**SAN MAREL DESIGNS, INC.**

98 U.S. Highway 46, Ste. 10
  (07828)
**Phone—(973) 426-9554**
www.marellonline.com

## Budd Lake—(cont.)

Email—sales@mariellonline.com
CEO—Doug Landon
Pres.—Nan Derasmi
SIC—3961; 5137; NAICS—
339900; *Precious metal jewelry &
wholesaler of fashion
accessories, including special
occasion shawls, wraps,
evening bags & gloves; Brand
name—Mariell; San Marel
DEsigns*
Employs—8; Estab.—1986
Sales—$1.5Mil-$2Mil
4,000 sq ft site, Distrib.—Intl.
Privately owned sub-S corp.

## Buena
### (Atlantic—S.E.)

**COMAR, LLC**
1 Comar Pl. *(08310)*
**Phone—(856) 692-6100**
National—(800) 962-6627
Fax—(856) 692-9251
www.comar.com
Email—info@comar.com
CEO—Michael Ruggieri
V-P., Opers., N. America—Don
Hutchinson
V-P., Bus. Dev.—Richard Sica
Dir., Tech. Opers.—John Daly
Dir., Hum. Res.—Alan Dean
SIC—2834; 3089; NAICS—
325412; *Plastic pharmaceutical
packaging & liquid medication
delivery devices for the biotech,
ophthalmic, diagnostic &
medical packaging industries*
Employs—265; Estab.—1949
Sales—$100Mil-$250Mil (est)
Distrib.—Intl.
Privately owned corporation

**HANSON AGGREGATES NORTH
AMERICA**
Div. of Lehigh Hanson, Inc.
311 Unexpected Rd. (08310)
Mail addr: P.O. Box 338,
Newtonville (08346)
**Phone—(856) 697-1616**
Fax—(856) 697-2063
www.heidelbergcement.com
Email—enquiriesus@hanson.com
Plt. Mgr.—Frank Berghos
Foreman—Seymour Jones, Jr.
SIC—1442; NAICS—212321;
*Sand & gravel processing*
Employs—4; Estab.—1979
Sales—under $500,000
Distrib.—National
Publicly owned corporation
Parent co.—Lehigh Hanson, Inc.,
Irving, TX
Phone—(972) 653-5500
See Parent Co. Section for full profile.

**I G I LABORATORIES, INC.**
105 Lincoln Ave., P.O. Box 687
(08310)
**Phone—(856) 697-1441**
Fax—(856) 697-2259
www.igilabs.com
Email—info@igilabs.com
Pres., CEO—Jason Grenfell-
Gardner
Ex. V-P., Sales & Mktg.—Nadya
Lawrence
SIC—2834; NAICS—325412;
*Contract manufacturing of
pharmaceuticals*
Employs—45; Estab.—1977
Sales—$1Mil-$5Mil
25,000 sq ft site, Distrib.—National
Publicly owned corporation

**I-RON-X INDUSTRIES**
134 Wheat Rd. (08310)
**Phone—(856) 697-3518**
Fax—(856) 697-6225
www.i-ron-xindustries.com
Email—ptgmc@comcast.net

Pres., CFO—Paul Tomasello
SIC—3446; 3312; 3499; 3599;
NAICS—332323; *Wrought iron &
aluminum railings, steel &
aluminum fabrication &
aluminum welding; Brand
name—Jerith Fence Mfg. Co.;
Superior Aluminum Products;
Master Wire and Fence; Patio
Furniture by Winston Contract*
Employs—2; Estab.—1974
Sales—under $500,000
2,000 sq ft site, Distrib.—Regional
Limited Liability Company

**TRADE IMAGES**
701 S. Harding Hwy. (08310)
**Phone—(856) 697-2700**
Fax—(856) 697-3737
www.tradeimages.com
Email—davebird@tradeimages.com
Pres.—David Bird
Drafting Mgr.—Kip Russell
SIC—2431; 2434; NAICS—
337110; *Architectural millwork &
custom cabinetry*
Employs—25; Estab.—1995
Sales—$2.6Mil-$5Mil
Distrib.—Local
Privately owned corporation

**TRITON ASSOCIATED INDUSTRIES,
INC.**
North Brewster Rd., P.O. Box 627
(08310)
**Phone—(856) 697-3050**
Fax—(856) 697-9597
www.tritonglass.com
Email—sales@tritonglass.com
V-P.—Wayne Edwards
SIC—3231; NAICS—327215;
*Glass tube cutting*
Employs—20; Estab.—2000
Sales—$2.5Mil-$5Mil (est)
Distrib.—National

## Burlington
### (Burlington—S.E.)

**A. SMITH & SON, INC.**
300 W. Broad St., Ste. A (08016)
**Phone—(609) 747-0800**
National—(888) 738-3371
Fax—(609) 747-0818
www.asmith.biz
Email—sales@asmith.biz
Pres.—John R. Smith
SIC—2221; 2393; 2394; 2241;
NAICS—313210; *Nylon, canvas
& textile products, bags,
camping equipment, awnings &
web strap assemblies; Brand
name—SEVEER Stretchers*
Employs—7
4,200 sq ft site, Distrib.—National
Privately owned sub-S corp.

**A2Z EMBLEMS, LLC**
125 W. Route 130 N., Ste. C
(08016)
**Phone—(609) 239-9800**
Fax—(609) 239-9866
www.a2zemblems.com
Email—a2zemblems@aol.com
Owner—Annette Zelauskas
SIC—2396; 2395; *Apparel &
garment screen printing &
embroidery*
Employs—4
Sales—$500,000-$1Mil (est)
Distrib.—Regional
Limited Liability Company

**†ALLIED BUILDING PRODUCTS
CORP.**
11 Cadillac Rd., Box 1838 (08016)
**Phone—(609) 386-5500**
Fax—(609) 386-7650
www.alliedbuilding.com
Email—sales@alliedbuilding.com
Br. Mgr.—Bill Oratello

SIC—5033; *Distributor of
residential & commercial roofing*
Employs—15; Estab.—1987
Distrib.—National
Publicly owned corporation
Parent co.—Allied Building
Products Corp., East Rutherford,
NJ
Phone—(201) 507-8400
See Parent Co. Section for full profile.

**ALVA-TECH, INC.**
1208 Columbus Rd., Ste. G
*(08016-3439)*
**Phone—(609) 747-1133**
Fax—(609) 747-1136
www.alva-tech.com
Email—info@alva-tech.com
Pres.—Phillip Valenziano
V-P.—Frank J. Valenziano
SIC—2821; 2891; NAICS—
325211; *Intumescent firestop
products & joint fillers for
underground steel end ring
concrete pipe; Brand name—
FB-525 Fire Barrier; FB-725
Intumescent Composite Sheet;
Alva-Therm Intumescent Material*
Employs—20; Estab.—1973
Sales—$1Mil-$2.5Mil
Distrib.—Intl.
Privately owned corporation

**AMERICAN ASPHALT COMPANY,
INC.**
Div. of American Asphalt Co., Inc.
1701 River Rd. (08016)
Mail addr: 100 Main St., West
Collingswood Heights (08059-
1809)
**Phone—(856) 456-2899**
Fax—(856) 456-4398
www.americanasphaltcompany.co
m
Email—info@
americanasphaltcompany.com
Pres., CEO—Robert M. Brown
V-P., Sales & Mktg.—Dave Sulkin
V-P., Opers. & Prodn.—Jim Voytko
V-P., Construction—Robert A.
Moncrief
Plt. Mgr.—Chris Jennings
Contract Admn.—Marianne Busler
Dispatcher—George Mellon
SIC—2951; *Asphalt paving
materials & compounds &
asphalt paving contracting for
homebuilders, municipalities,
commercial clients, underground
utilities, site development &
general & asphalt paving
contractors, including street &
road construction; Brand
name—EZ Street High
Performance Cold Patch Asphalt*
Employs—10; Estab.—1903
Sales—under $500,000
Distrib.—Local
Privately owned corporation
Parent co.—American Asphalt Co.,
Inc., West Collingswood Heights,
NJ
Phone—(856) 456-2899
See Parent Co. Section for full profile.

**AMERICAN CASEIN CO., INC.**
109 Elbow Ln. (08016)
**Phone—(609) 387-3130**
Fax—(609) 387-7204
www.americancasein.com
Email—sales@109elbow.com
CEO—Adam Cabot

SIC—2824; 2023; *Powdered
protein ingredients for nutritional
beverages, food, health &
nutritional products & the
cosmetic & personal care
industries & protein polymers for
technical applications, including
custom spray drying & bulk
blending; Brand name—Mold-
Out™; Complete Milk Protein™;
CMP-I™; Casecrete™*
Employs—50; Estab.—1956
Sales—$10Mil-$25Mil (est)
Distrib.—Intl.
Privately owned corporation
Also see: American Custom
Drying Co., same loc.

**AMERICAN CUSTOM DRYING CO.**
109 Elbow Ln. (08016)
**Phone—(609) 387-3933**
Fax—(609) 387-7204
www.americancustomdrying.com
Email—acd@109elbow.com
CEO—Adam Cabot
V-P., Bus. Dev.—Martin Dansbury
Comp.—Roger Hare
SIC—2034; *Contract & toll
processing, including spray
drying, liquid & dry blending &
powder milling*
Employs—70; Estab.—1969
Distrib.—Intl.
Privately owned corporation
ISO rating—9008
Also see: American Casein Co.,
Inc., same loc.

**†BAKEMARK USA, LLC**
1815 Route 130 N. (08016)
**Phone—(609) 747-9000**
National—(800) 222-2454
Fax—(609) 747-8544
www.bakemark.com
Email—tlotito@bakemarkusa.com
GM—Anthony Lotito
SIC—5149; *Distributor of baking
ingredients, including flour &
baking & cake mixes*
Employs—50; Estab.—2002
Distrib.—Regional
Limited Liability Company
Parent co.—BakeMark USA, LLC,
Pico Rivera, CA
Phone—(562) 949-1054
See Parent Co. Section for full profile.

**BARTLETT PRINTING & GRAPHICS,
INC.**
4495 Route 130 S. (08016)
**Phone—(609) 386-1525**
Fax—(609) 386-0661
www.bartlettprinting.com
Email—bartlettprinting@verizon.net
CEO—Clifford Lewis
Pres., MIS Mgr.—Cynthia Lewis
SIC—2759; 2791; 2796; NAICS—
323122; *Offset printing &
typesetting*
Employs—3; Estab.—1983
Sales—under $500,000
6,000 sq ft site, Distrib.—Regional
Privately owned corporation

**BARTON & COONEY, LLC**
300 Richards Run (08016)
**Phone—(609) 747-9300**
National—(800) 368-8463
Fax—(609) 747-9700
www.bartoncooney.com
Email—llmalin@bartoncooney.com
Pres., COO—Patrick M. Doyle
CFO & Hum. Res. Mgr.—Linda
Malin
V-P.—Kathleen Doyle
GM—Steven Angel
Technical Svcs. Mgr.—Paul Kusiak

GEOGRAPHICAL

## Burlington—(cont.)

SIC—2759; 2752; NAICS—
323100; *Direct mail & digital
printing, variable print &
fulfillment*
Employs—110; Estab.—1969
Sales—$12Mil
85,000 sq ft site, Distrib.—National
Limited Liability Company
ISO rating—27002

**NEW ENTRY**
### BE & K PLASTICS

340 E. Broad St. (08016)
**Phone—(609) 386-3200**
Fax—(609) 386-3250
www.bekplastics.com
Email—info@bekplastics.com?
V-P.—Bob Shimmeng
SIC—3089; *Plastic food
containers*
Employs—12
Sales—$1Mil-$2.5Mil (est)

### †BURLINGTON COUNTY OVERHEAD DOOR CO., INC.

Div. of Overhead Door Corp.
444 Logan Ave., P.O. Box 127
(08016)
**Phone—(609) 387-9092**
Fax—(609) 387-7085
www.overheaddoor.com
Email—bcohd@verizon.net
Br. Mgr.—Tom Ballard
SIC—5031; *Distributor of hollow
metal overhead doors*
Employs—10; Estab.—1993
Distrib.—Local
Privately owned corporation
Parent co.—Overhead Door Corp.,
Lewisville, TX
Phone—(469) 549-7100
See Parent Co. Section for full profile.

### BURLINGTON PRESS

328 High St. (08016)
**Phone—(609) 387-0030**
Fax—(609) 387-4413
www.burlingtonpress.com
Email—experts@
burlingtonpress.com
CEO—Richard Lewis
CFO—Vivian Lewis
Creative Dir.—Scott Sutton
Prodn. Mgr.—George Taylor
Cust. Serv. Rep.—Roger Morris
SIC—2759; 2752; NAICS—
323122; *Digital, offset & large-
format printing & graphic design
for marketing campaigns &
visual communications,
including website development
& design & direct mail &
photographic services*
Employs—7; Estab.—1988
Sales—$500,000-$1Mil
5,000 sq ft site, Distrib.—Regional
Privately owned corporation

### BUTCO, INC.

2009 Route 130 N. (08016)
**Phone—(800) 872-8055**
Fax—(609) 387-3406
www.butco.us
Email—sales@butco.us
Pres., CFO & Webmaster—Peter
Senin
Manager—Bob Senin
SIC—3536; NAICS—333923;
*Portable tripod & tube hoists,
parts, supplies & equipment for
emergency rescue & confined
space access applications*
Employs—3; Estab.—1969
Sales—under $500,000
600 sq ft site, Distrib.—National
Privately owned sub-S corp.

### CELLUNET MFG. CO., INC.

460 Veterans Dr. (08016)
**Phone—(609) 386-3361**
Fax—(609) 386-8978

Email—cellunet@pics.com
Pres.—John Titone
V-P.—Robert Titone
SIC—3999; *Nylon hair nets*
Employs—11; Estab.—1988
Sales—$1Mil-$2.5Mil
Distrib.—National
Privately owned partnership

### CEMENTEX PRODUCTS, INC.

650 Jacksonville Rd., P.O. Box
1533 (08016)
**Phone—(609) 387-1040**
National—(800) 654-1292
Fax—(609) 386-8885
www.cementexusa.com
Email—info@cementexusa.com
Pres., CEO—Stephen H. Russo
COO—Jeffrey Russo
V-P.—Tracy Johnson
Fin. Mgr.—Carol Meredith
SIC—3423; *Double-insulated
hand tools, related tool
components for the utility,
industrial & telecommunication
markets & protective clothing &
equipment*
Employs—37; Estab.—1952
24,250 sq ft site, Distrib.—National
Privately owned sub-S corp.

### CENTRAL SAFETY EQUIPMENT, INC.

300 W. Broad St., P.O. Box 250
(08016)
**Phone—(609) 386-6448**
National—(800) 257-9537
Fax—(609) 386-6739
www.centryco.com
Email—info@centryco.com
Pres.—Mary Gordon
V-P., Sales—Bill Hartman
V-P., Tech.—Jack Jurechko
Cont.—Diane Rossi
Sales Mgr., Reg.—Jean Marie
IT Mgr.—John Kowalski
Hum. Res. Mgr.—Virginia Griffiths
SIC—3499; *Metal machine
protection parts & bellows*
Employs—30; Estab.—1946
Sales—$1Mil-$5Mil
27,000 sq ft site, Distrib.—Intl.
Privately owned corporation
AKA: Centryco, Inc.

### COAST RUBBER & GASKET, INC.

1208 Columbus Rd., Ste. G
(08016)
**Phone—(609) 747-0110**
Fax—(609) 747-0114
www.coastrubberandgasket.com
Email—vitoatcoastrubber@
earthlink.net
Pres., Plt. Mgr.—Vito Massa
SIC—3053; NAICS—339991;
*Gaskets & electrical insulators*
Employs—6; Estab.—1989
9,000 sq ft site, Distrib.—Local
Privately owned corporation

### COLGATE-PALMOLIVE CO.

400 Elbow Ln. (08016)
**Phone—(609) 239-2000**
Fax—(609) 386-9134
www.colgate.com
Email—investor_relations@
colpal.com
Cont.—Angelie George
Plt. Mgr.—Juan Montoya
SIC—2844; 2087; NAICS—
325600; *Fragrances & flavors*
Employs—30
Sales—$1Mil-$5Mil
30,000 sq ft site, Distrib.—Intl.
Publicly owned corporation
Parent co.—Colgate-Palmolive
Co., New York, NY
Phone—(212) 310-2000
See Parent Co. Section for full profile.

### COSTUME GALLERY

4451 Route 130 S. (08016)
**Phone—(609) 386-6601**
National—(800) 222-8125
Fax—(609) 386-0677

www.costumegallery.net
Email—info@costumegallery.net
Pres.—Linda Bradbury
Off. Mgr.—Kalie Krogulski
SIC—2389; *Dance recital
costumes; Brand name—
Costume Gallery*
Employs—120; Estab.—1958
Distrib.—Intl.
Privately owned corporation

### DYNATEC SYSTEMS, INC.

360 Connecticut Dr. (08016)
**Phone—(609) 387-0330**
Fax—(609) 387-2060
www.dynatecsystems.com
Email—info@dynatecsystems.com
Pres.—Thomas Doherty
Dir., Opers. & Opers. Mgr.—Bill
Fisher
Sales Mgr.—Archie Ross
Plt. Mgr.—Carl Shinn
Accts. Mgr.—Rosanne Fisher
SIC—3589; NAICS—333319;
*Wastewater treatment equipment*
Employs—15; Estab.—1978
10,000 sq ft site, Distrib.—Intl.
Privately owned corporation

### EASTERN SIGN TECH, LLC

112 Connecticut Dr., P.O. Box 564
(08016)
**Phone—(609) 261-2805**
Fax—(609) 386-9905
www.easternsigntech.com
Email—info@easternsigntech.com
Pres.—John Dunphy
V-P.—Rob Convery
Cont.—Jonathan Convery
Opers. Mgr.—Judith Bucci
Hum. Res. Mgr.—Dorothy Watson
SIC—3993; *Architectural signage
& LED displays*
Employs—40; Estab.—2000
Sales—$2.5Mil-$5Mil
Distrib.—National
Limited Liability Company
AKA: EST

### EMERSON INSTRUMENT & VALVE SERVICES

120 Kissel Rd. (08016)
**Phone—(609) 386-5000**
Fax—(609) 386-4310
www.emersonoffice.com
Email—rob.ruff@emerson.com
Acct. Mgr.—Mary Mallon
Cust. Serv. Rep.—Jeanine Mallon
SIC—3492; NAICS—332912;
*Control valves*
Employs—30
Sales—$5Mil-$10Mil (est)
Distrib.—Intl.
Privately owned corporation

### †FASTENAL CO.

921 Route 130 N. (08016)
**Phone—(609) 239-3016**
Fax—(609) 239-6983
www.fastenal.com
Email—njbur@stores.fastenal.com
GM—Tom Petruzzi
SIC—5072; 5084; 5085;
*Wholesaler of fasteners, safety
equipment, tools & abrasives*
Employs—3; Estab.—2007
5,000 sq ft site, Distrib.—Local
Publicly owned corporation
Parent co.—Fastenal Co., Winona,
MN
Phone—(507) 454-5374
See Parent Co. Section for full profile.

### FISHER CANVAS PRODUCTS, INC.

415 Saint Mary St. (08016)
**Phone—(609) 239-2733**
National—(800) 892-6688
Fax—(609) 239-2728
www.fishercanvas.com
Email—info@fishercanvas.com
Pres., Fin., MIS & R & D Mgr.—
Frederick Fisher
Off. Mgr.—Jennifer Mancini

SIC—2394; NAICS—314912;
*Canvas boat covers & bags,
awnings, tarps & custom sewn
textiles*
Employs—7; Estab.—1991
8,000 sq ft site, Distrib.—Regional
Privately owned corporation

### FRANKLIN ELECTRONIC PUBLISHERS, INC.

8 Terri Ln. (08016)
**Phone—(609) 386-2500**
National—(800) 266-5626
Fax—(609) 239-5990
www.franklin.com
Email—service@franklin.com
Pres., CEO—Barry Lipsky
SIC—3571; 2741; 3695; NAICS—
334111; *Electronic language
learning handheld devices,
including dictionaries,
translators, organizers, bibles &
games & electronic format
publishing*
Employs—30; Estab.—1981
Sales—$50Mil-$100Mil
Distrib.—Intl.
Privately owned corporation

### IFCO SYSTEMS

Div. of IFCO Systems North
America, Inc.
320 Dulty's Ln., P.O. Box 1333
(08016)
**Phone—(609) 386-5200**
National—(800) 355-7778
Fax—(609) 386-8300
www.ifcosystems.com
Email—brooks.curtis@
ifcosystems.com
GM—Taylor Thomas
Off. Mgr.—Jenna Berryman
SIC—2448; NAICS—321920;
*Wooden pallets*
Employs—79; Estab.—2003
Sales—$6Mil-$10Mil
Distrib.—Local
Privately owned corporation
AKA: Pallet Cos.
Parent co.—IFCO Systems North
America, Inc., Houston, TX
Phone—(713) 332-6145
See Parent Co. Section for full profile.

### INTERNATIONAL PRODUCTS CORP.

201 Connecticut Dr. (08016)
**Phone—(609) 386-8770**
Fax—(609) 386-8438
www.ipcol.com
Email—mkt@ipcol.com
Pres.—Kathy J. Wyrofsky
V-P., Quality—Thomas P.
McGuckin
Dir., Mktg.—Michele Christian
SIC—2842; 2992; 2841; NAICS—
325612; *Precision cleaners &
temporary assembly lubricants;
Brand name—Micro-90; P-80;
LF2100; Surface-Cleanse/930;
Zymit*
Employs—25; Estab.—1923
Distrib.—Intl.
Privately owned corporation
ISO rating—9001

### INTERPLAST, INC.

100 Connecticut Dr., P.O. Box
1328 (08016)
**Phone—(609) 386-4990**
Fax—(609) 386-9237
www.interplastinc.com
Email—sales@interplastinc.com
Pres.—Allen Langman
GM—Jared Langman
Hum. Res. & Off. Mgr.—Julie
Broueck

## Burlington—(cont.)

SIC—3082; NAICS—326121;
*Corporate headquarters & PTFE,
FEP, PFA, PCTFE fluropolymer
shapes, including rod, tube,
sheet, tape, film, bar, seals,
gaskets, valves seats, fabricated
parts & wear strips*
Employs—20; Estab.—1975
Distrib.—Intl.
Privately owned corporation

†**KEYIMPACT SALES & SYSTEMS,
INC.**

95 Connecticut Dr. (08016)
**Phone—(609) 265-8300**
National—(800) 524-1188
Fax—(609) 267-6662
www.kisales.com
Email—info@kisales.com
CEO—Daniel T. Cassidy
Pres.—Randy Wieland
Sr. V.-P., Reg. Presidents East—
Joe Hargadon
Ex. V.-P., Client Mgmt.—Rob
Monroe
SIC—5141; *Corporate
headquarters & wholesaler of
foodservice products for the
retail supermarket industry &
marketing services*
Employs—75; Estab.—2002
Distrib.—National
Privately owned corporation

**LOCKREY COMPANY LLC**

1280 Old York Rd. *(08016)*
**Phone—(856) 665-4794**
Fax—(856) 665-4166
Email—lockreycompany@
gmail.com
Pres.—George Eldredge
V.-P., Treas.—Hunter George
SIC—2992; NAICS—324191;
*Aerospace & industrial
lubricants; Brand name—Liqui-
Moly; Lockrey-Moly Products*
Employs—12; Estab.—1940
Sales—$1Mil-$5Mil
Distrib.—Intl.
Privately owned corporation
ISO rating—9000

**LYNCH EXHIBITS**

7 Campus Dr. (08016)
**Phone—(609) 387-1600**
National—(800) 343-1666
Fax—(609) 239-1666
www.lynchexhibits.com
Pres.—Michael Carrozza
V.-P., Fin.—John C. Seaver
Sales Mgr.—Brian Gozdan
Acct. Mgr.—Pat Roberts
Acctg. Admn.—Jenniffer Boyd
SIC—3993; 2541; *Trade show
displays*
Employs—110; Estab.—1926
Sales—over $1Bil
200,000 sq ft site, Distrib.—Intl.
Privately owned corporation

**NEW ENTRY**
**MAG SIGNS, INC.**

1208-F Columbus Rd. (08016)
**Phone—(609) 747-9600**
National—(888) 588-9057
Fax—(609) 747-9601
www.effectivesignworks.com
Email—bob@
effectivesignworks.com
Owner—Bob Persichetti
SIC—3993; 3599; *Interior &
exterior signs & welding job
shop*
Employs—12; Estab.—1999
Sales—$1Mil-$2.5Mil (est)
Distrib.—Regional
Privately owned corporation
AKA: Effective Signs

†**MCLANE BURLINGTON**

Div. of McLane Company, Inc.,
Foodservice Division
600 Commerce Dr. (08016)
**Phone—(609) 239-5000**
Fax—(800) 265-1992
www.mclaneco.com
Email—shane.falls@mclanefs.com
Dir., Opers.—Don Lenc
GM—Shane Falls
Hum. Res. Mgr.—Carol Thomas
Dist. Mgr.—Greg Pollard
Cust. Serv. Mgr.—Kim McGuire
Inventory Mgr.—Greg Renville
SIC—5141; *Distributor of general
line groceries to chain
restaurants*
Employs—150
192,000 sq ft site, Distrib.—
Regional
Privately owned corporation
Parent co.—McLane Company,
Inc., Foodservice Division,
Carrollton, TX
Phone—(972) 364-2000
See Parent Co. Section for full profile.

**MELTON SALES & SERVICE, INC.**

511 Elbow Ln. (08016)
**Phone—(609) 699-4800**
Fax—(609) 699-4819
www.meltons.com
Email—sales@meltons.com
V.-P., Prodn.—Chris Robles
Cont.—Ron Dillon
Ex. Dir.—Robert Melton
Ex. Dir.—John J. Melton
Pur. Mgr.—Lori Mlynarski
Sales Coord.—Michelle Owens
SIC—3519; 3621; 3714; NAICS—
335312; *Remanufactured diesel
engines, drive train components,
generators & ground support
equipment for military &
commercial applications; Brand
name—Cummins; Detroit Diesel;
Caterpillar; GM; AM General;
International; Komatsu; Isuzu;
John Deere; Hercules; Onan;
Lister Petter; Deutz; Allis
Chalmers; AxleTech; Meritor;
Funk; Clark; ZF*
Employs—85; Estab.—1949
150,000 sq ft site, Distrib.—Intl.
Privately owned sub-S corp.
DBA: Melton Industries

**MERCHANT & EVANS, INC.**

308 Connecticut Dr. *(08016)*
**Phone—(800) 257-6215**
      (609) 387-3033
Fax—(609) 387-4838
www.ziprib.com
Email—rjaconelli@ziprib.com
Chrm.—James R. Buck
Pres.—Steven J. Buck
V.-P.—Ronald L. Jaconelli, Jr.
Comp.—Lisa Purden
Sales Mgr., Natl.—James Webster
Mfg. Mgr.—Daniel McAuliffe
Pur. Mgr.—Paul Accordino
Engrg. Mgr.—Tony Thompson
Shop Foreman—Rob Major
SIC—3446; NAICS—332323;
*Structural & architectural metal
roofing products; Brand name—
ZIP-RIB; BD-1520; ZIP-LOK;
Classic Rib Series 305;
Traditional Rib Series 306; Flush
Lock Series 311*
Employs—35; Estab.—1866
Sales—$12Mil
45,000 sq ft site, Distrib.—National
Privately owned sub-S corp.

**MOTHER'S KITCHEN, INC.**

Div. of Rich Products Corp.
499 Veterans Dr. (08016)
**Phone—(609) 589-3033**
      (609) 589-3023
National—(800) 566-8437
Fax—(609) 386-5329
www.richs.com

Email—foodservice@rich.com
Plt. Mgr.—Scott Stone
Opers. Mgr.—Bryan Peterman
SIC—2051; NAICS—311812;
*Cheesecake & cakes*
Employs—220; Estab.—1971
110,000 sq ft site, Distrib.—
National
Privately owned corporation
AKA: Rich Products
Parent co.—Rich Products Corp.,
Buffalo, NY
Phone—(716) 878-8000
See Parent Co. Section for full profile.

**NATIONAL GYPSUM CO.**

1818 River Rd. (08016)
**Phone—(609) 499-3300**
Fax—(609) 499-1589
www.nationalgypsum.com
Email—nq@nationalgypsum.com
Plt. Mgr.—Terry Peterson
Off. Mgr.—Melissa Raynor
Off. Admn.—Cheryl Nolda
SIC—3275; NAICS—327420;
*Gypsum wallboard*
Employs—50; Estab.—1957
Distrib.—National
Privately owned corporation
Parent co.—National Gypsum Co.,
Charlotte, NC
Phone—(704) 365-7300
See Parent Co. Section for full profile.

**NORMAN'S GLASS & AUTO
SERVICES, INC.**

4482 Route 130 S. (08016)
**Phone—(609) 386-7100**
National—(800) 442-8869
Fax—(609) 387-3370
www.normansglass.com
Email—info@normansglass.com
Pres.—John Farfalla
V.-P., GM—John Farfalla, Jr.
Cont.—Fritz Denlinger
Store Mgr.—Robert Castiglia
SIC—3231; 3993; NAICS—
327215; *Automotive, residential
& commercial glass fabrication,
including mirrors, shower doors,
custom glass etching & signs;
Brand name—Kawneer; YKK;
US Aluminum; Alumax; PPG;
Drawtite; HiddenHitch; SnoWay*
Employs—10; Estab.—1973
18,000 sq ft site, Distrib.—
Regional
Privately owned corporation

**PENN METAL FINISHING CO., INC.**

700 Jacksonville Rd. (08016)
**Phone—(609) 387-3400**
Fax—(609) 387-3393
www.pennmetal.net
Email—info@pennmetal.net
Pres.—Louis Willa
GM—Steve Bartos
SIC—3479; NAICS—332813;
*Metal painting*
Employs—5; Estab.—1960
Sales—$500,000-$1Mil
Distrib.—Regional
Privately owned corporation

**PYROPTICS, INC.**

2015 Columbus Rd. (08016)
**Phone—(609) 386-6930**
Fax—(609) 386-6936
Pres.—Stephen Boyle
V.-P.—Jack Lake
SIC—3548; *Stud welding
equipment*
Employs—5; Estab.—1971
Distrib.—National
Privately owned corporation

**QUALITY PACKAGING SPECIALISTS
INTERNATIONAL, LLC**

5 Cooper St. (08016)
**Phone—(609) 239-0503**
Fax—(609) 239-0228
www.qpsiusa.com
Email—info@qpsiusa.com
Pres., CEO—Mike Ricketts

CFO—Dan Seniff
CIO—Jim Cleary
Chief Strategy Officer & Gen.
Counsel—Tom Belton
Sr. V.-P., Opers.—Will Hamilton
Ex. V.-P.—Derrick Ratleff
SIC—3089; *Company
headquarters & contract
packaging*
Employs—250; Estab.—1991
Sales—$10Mil-$25Mil
100,000 sq ft site, Distrib.—Intl.
Limited Liability Company
AKA: QPSI

**RIMTEC CORP.**

1702 Beverly Rd. (08016)
**Phone—(609) 387-0011**
National—(800) 272-0069
Fax—(609) 387-0282
www.rimtec.com
Email—info@rimtec.com
Pres.—Takara Fujii
Ex. V.-P.—Koichi Inoue
V.-P., Sales & Mktg.—Frank Hutzler
Hum. Res. Mgr.—Karen Kuder
SIC—2821; NAICS—325211;
*Polyvinyl chloride pellets*
Employs—100; Estab.—1983
50,000 sq ft site, Distrib.—National
Privately owned corporation

**RMI HOOBING**

460 Veterans Dr. (08016)
**Phone—(609) 387-1999**
Fax—(609) 387-7596
Email—awallace@rmihoobing.com
Pres.—Alan Wallace
SIC—2339; *Women's sportswear*
Employs—10; Estab.—1982
Sales—$1Mil-$2.5Mil (est)
Distrib.—National
Privately owned corporation

**SZABO SIGNS**

1108 Neck Rd. (08016)
**Phone—(609) 387-7213**
www.szabosigns.com
Email—szabosigns@verizon.net
Pres.—Joe Szabo, Jr.
SIC—3993; *Interior & exterior
signs, lettering, logos & decals*
Employs—1; Estab.—1990
Sales—under $500,000
Distrib.—Local
Privately owned corporation

**TECHNE, INC.**

3 Terri Ln., Ste. 10 (08016)
**Phone—(609) 589-2560**
National—(800) 225-9243
Fax—(609) 589-2571
www.bibby-scientific.com
Email—labproducts@tecneusa.com
Pres., Hum. Res. Mgr.—Peter
Lucas
V.-P., Prodn.—Chris Wunderlich
Cust. Serv. Mgr.—Mikki Stok
Buyer—Lesley Starr
SIC—3826; 3829; NAICS—
334516; *Manufacturer &
distributor of temperature
controlled & industrial laboratory,
molecular & chemistry
equipment; Brand name—
Techne; Jenway; Stuart; Electra
Thermal*
Employs—13; Estab.—1967
10,000 sq ft site, Distrib.—National
Privately owned corporation

**TIP INDUSTRIES, INC.**

340 W. Broad St. (08016)
**Phone—(609) 239-1900**
      (800) 847-8367
Fax—(609) 239-1911
www.tiptemp.com
Email—everydegreematters@
tiptemp.com
Owner, CEO & GM—Daniel E.
Farnan
Pres., Treas.—Judith H. Walls
Sales Mgr.—Neil Humphreys
Off. Mgr.—Kathy Paschall

GEOGRAPHICAL

## Burlington—(cont.)

SIC—3829; 3824; 3823; NAICS—334514; *Temperature sensors, alarm systems, thermal labels, control products & data loggers; Brand name—Temperature Guardian; Accsense; Omega; Marlin Mfg.; Doric Beckman; Skylink; Control Products; Athena; Madgetech; Henes; Cal Controls; Fuji; 3M; Avery Dennison; Inor; Oakton; TIPTEMP; Comark; Fluke*
Employs—10; Estab.—1997
Sales—$2Mil
5,000 sq ft site, Distrib.—National
Privately owned sub-S corp.
DBA: TIP TEMPerature Products

### TUSCAN DAIRY, INC.

Div. of Garelick Farms, LLC
117 Cumberland Blvd. (08016)
**Phone—(609) 499-2600**
National—(800) 648-0135
Fax—(609) 499-8083
www.deanfoods.com
Email—deanfoods@casupport.com
Plt. Mgr.—Eric Bayer
SIC—2026; 2023; NAICS—311411; *Dairy products*
Employs—200; Estab.—1998
Sales—$50Mil-$100Mil
Distrib.—Local
Privately owned corporation
AKA: Garelick Farms, LLC
Parent co.—Garelick Farms, LLC, Franklin, MA
Phone—(508) 528-9000
See Parent Co. Section for full profile.

### UNITED HOSPITAL SUPPLY CORP.

4422 Route 130 S. (08016)
**Phone—(609) 387-7580**
National—(800) 486-8484
Fax—(609) 387-0803
www.fencobankequipment.com
Email—mattjr@uhfenco.com
Pres.—Matthew Lyons
V-P.—Johnathon Lyons
SIC—2542; *Medical, laboratory, bank, security & undercounter steel cabinets for banks & credit unions; Brand name—Fenco Bank Equipment; Lab Design; UHSC*
Employs—85; Estab.—1958
Sales—$10Mil-$15Mil
89,000 sq ft site, Distrib.—Intl.
Privately owned corporation

### UNIVERSITY APPAREL, INC.

2501 Mount Holly Rd., Ste. 262 (08016)
**Phone—(609) 871-3601**
www.fraternalregalia.com
Email—support@fraternalregalia.com
Pres.—Jerry Hamm
V-P.—Wendi A. W. Hamm
SIC—2396; 2395; *Fraternal embroidery & lettering, Masonic apparel & accessories & specialty advertising*
Employs—2; Estab.—1988
Sales—under $500,000
1,200 sq ft site, Distrib.—National
Privately owned corporation

### WEST ELECTRONICS, INC.

5 Terri Ln., Ste. 15, P.O. Box 366 (08016)
**Phone—(609) 387-4300**
Fax—(609) 387-4304
Pres.—Bradford Brainard
Cont.—Vincent Bocchinfuso
Administrator—Mary Williamson

SIC—3679; 3823; NAICS—334513; *Guided missile power controls, communication equipment, flow & pressure recorders*
Employs—20; Estab.—1962
Sales—$2.6Mil-$5Mil
10,000 sq ft site, Distrib.—Intl.
Privately owned corporation

---

## Butler
### (Morris—N.W.)

### ACU-DATA BUSINESS PRODUCTS, INC.

1572 State Route 23, Ste. D (07405)
**Phone—(973) 838-5678**
National—(800) 535-6563
Fax—(973) 838-5229
www.acu-data78.com
Email—acudata78@aol.com
Pres.—Gerald J. Vinci
Secy., Pur. Agt.—Vivian M. Vinci
SIC—2761; 2759; 3993; NAICS—323116; *Business forms, advertising specialties & commercial printing*
Employs—2; Estab.—1978
Sales—$400,000
2,000 sq ft site, Distrib.—National
Privately owned corporation

### ADVANCED FASTENER INDUSTRIES

130 Main St. (07405)
Mail addr: 2711 Lowesville Rd., Arrington (22922)
**Phone—(973) 283-1013**
Fax—(973) 283-1173
www.advancedfastener.com
Email—advfastind@aol.com
Pres.—Don Manley
Off. Admn.—Christine Manley
SIC—3599; 3452; 3541; NAICS—332722; *Industrial machinery, fasteners & cutting tools*
Employs—7; Estab.—1982
Sales—$1Mil-$2.5Mil
Distrib.—Regional
Privately owned corporation

### BUSINESS GRAPHICS

22 Park Pl., P.O. Box 832 (07405)
**Phone—(973) 838-9553**
Fax—(973) 838-9554
Owner & Pres.—Robert Femia
SIC—2759; NAICS—323100; *Commercial printing*
Employs—1; Estab.—1976
Sales—under $500,000
Distrib.—Local
Sole ownership

### BUTLER PRINTING & LAMINATING

250 Hamburg Tpke., P.O. Box 836 (07405)
**Phone—(973) 838-8550**
National—(800) 524-0786
Fax—(973) 838-1767
www.butlerprinting.com
Email—sales@butlerprinting.com
Pres.—James Berezny
V-P. & Sales Mgr.—Gene Passalacqua
Plt. Mgr.—Andy Clark
Traf. Mgr.—Lou Bruno
SIC—2672; 2752; NAICS—322222; *Vinyl wall covering, printing & laminating*
Employs—55; Estab.—1988
150,000 sq ft site, Distrib.—Intl.
Privately owned corporation
AKA: Newco, Inc.

### C & S PRECISION PRODUCTS, LLC

22 Park Pl. (07405)
Mail addr: 23 Cedar St., Bloomingdale (07403)
**Phone—(973) 838-3644**
Fax—(973) 838-3898
Email—lmarion08@optonline.net
Member—Leonard Marion

SIC—3599; *Machine parts & CNC machining job shop*
Employs—4; Estab.—2001
Sales—under $500,000
Distrib.—National
Limited Liability Company

### DELTA SALES CO., INC.

1355 State Route 23 (07405-1726)
**Phone—(973) 838-0371**
Fax—(973) 838-2638
www.airoyal.com
Email—info@airoyal.com
Pres., Fin. & MIS Mgr.—Robert Infante
Off. Mgr.—Cristiane Jennings
SIC—3593; NAICS—333995; *Hydraulic & pneumatic cylinders & rotary actuators; Brand name—Airoyal*
Employs—2; Estab.—1985
Distrib.—Regional
Privately owned corporation
AKA: Airoyal Division of Delta Sales

### GAISER, INC., ROBERT F.

292 Main St., P.O. Box 807 (07405)
**Phone—(973) 838-0696**
Fax—(973) 838-3706
www.beauveste.com
Email—rfgaiser@optonline.net
Pres.—Stephen Gaiser
V-P. & Secy.—Lisa G. Dore
Foreman—Kurt Gaiser
SIC—2389; *Clerical vestments; Brand name—Beau Veste Brand*
Employs—18; Estab.—1940
Sales—$2.5Mil-$5Mil
Distrib.—Intl.

### GENERANT CO., INC.

1865 Route 23 S., P.O. Box 768 (07405)
**Phone—(973) 838-6500**
Fax—(973) 838-4888
www.generant.com
Email—gensales@generant.com
V-P.—Dino D'Onofrio
Pur. Mgr.—Darren Marino
Cust. Serv. Rep.—Jasmin Grant
Cust. Serv. Rep.—Todd Jamison
SIC—3492; 3089; NAICS—332912; *Pressure regulating valves & instrument tube fittings*
Employs—140; Estab.—1987
Distrib.—Intl.
Privately owned corporation

### GOFFCO INDUSTRIES, INC.

10 Park Pl., Bldg. 6-6 (07405)
**Phone—(973) 492-0150**
Fax—(973) 492-2154
www.goffco.com
Email—quotes@goffco.com
Pres.—Leslie Gough
Corp. Secy.—Charlene Gough
SIC—2759; NAICS—323100; *Commercial printing*
Employs—6; Estab.—1998
Distrib.—National
Privately owned corporation

### HAPPY CHEF UNIFORMS, INC.

22 Park Pl. (07405)
**Phone—(973) 492-2525**
National—(800) 347-0288
Fax—(973) 492-0303
www.happychefuniforms.com
Email—info@happychefuniforms.com
Ex. V-P.—Howard Curtin
V-P., Sales—David Barr
Dir., Dist., Hum. Res. & IT Mgr.—Mark Weaver
Off. Mgr.—Vanessa Petway
Cust. Serv. Rep.—Jessica Corley

SIC—2339; 2326; NAICS—315200; *Manufacturer & distributor of restaurant uniforms, professional cutlery & table linens*
Employs—40; Estab.—1975
Distrib.—National
Privately owned corporation

### HIGH POINT BREWING CO., INC.

22 Park Pl. (07405)
**Phone—(973) 838-7400**
Fax—(973) 838-3189
www.ramsteinbeer.com
Email—comments@ramsteinbeer.com
Pres.—Greg Zaccardi
Dir., Opers., Brewhouse—Alexis Bacon
SIC—2082; *Beer; Brand name—Ramstein Beer*
Employs—3; Estab.—1994
Sales—under $1Mil
7,000 sq ft site, Distrib.—Regional
Publicly owned corporation

### J M J PRINTING & GRAPHICS, INC.

1403 State Route 23, Ste. 8 (07405)
**Phone—(973) 838-3400**
Fax—(973) 838-2002
Email—printbyjmj@aol.com
Pres.—Debby Greenberg
V-P.—Bruce Greenberg
SIC—2752; 2759; 3089; NAICS—323100; *Printing & contract packaging*
Employs—20; Estab.—1990
5,000 sq ft site, Distrib.—National
Privately owned corporation

### JIGSAW PUBLISHING, LLC

8 Hemlock Ct. (07405)
**Phone—(973) 838-4838**
www.jigsawpub.com
Owner—Graham Fill
SIC—2731; *Children's novelty book publishing*
Employs—1
Sales—under $500,000 (est)
Distrib.—Intl.
Limited Liability Company

### KNORR ASSOCS., INC.

10 Park Pl., P.O. Box 400 (07405)
**Phone—(973) 492-8500**
Fax—(973) 492-0453
www.knorrassociates.com
Email—sales@knorrassociates.com
Pres.—Norman Dotti
Dir., Mktg.—Mark Odian
SIC—7372; *Environmental & health & safety management information collection software development; Brand name—DataPipe™*
Employs—10; Estab.—1977
Sales—under $500,000
Distrib.—Intl.
Privately owned corporation

### M. S. PLASTICS PACKAGING CO., INC.

10 Park Pl., Bldg. 2-1A-2 (07405-1371)
**Phone—(973) 492-2400**
National—(800) 593-1802
Fax—(973) 492-7801
www.msplastics.com
Email—keithh@msplastics.com
Pres.—Al Saraisky
V-P.—Ellen Saraisky
GM, Hum. Res. & IT Mgr.—Keith Howson
Bookkeeper—Maria Wieck
SIC—3089; *Plastic film & bag packaging*
Employs—15; Estab.—1992
8,500 sq ft site, Distrib.—National
Privately owned sub-S corp.

## Butler—(cont.)

**MESA LABORATORIES, INC.**
10 Park Pl., Ste. 3 (07405)
**Phone—(973) 492-8400**
National—(800) 663-4977
Fax—(303) 484-4992
www.mesalabs.com
Email—customerservice@
mesalabs.com
Dir., Opers.—Brian Roberts
Hum. Res. Mgr.—Shawna Neeley
Cust. Serv. Mgr.—Denise Cintron
Brand Mgr.—Dorel Nasso
Cust. Serv. Rep.—Jen Parisi
SIC—3829; *Portable primary gas flow measurement products for metrological & industrial process, industrial hygiene, environmental, analytical & laboratory applications*
Employs—22; Estab.—1990
13,000 sq ft site, Distrib.—Intl.
Publicly owned corporation
ISO rating—17025
Parent co.—Mesa Laboratories, Inc., Lakewood, CO
Phone—(303) 987-8000
See Parent Co. Section for full profile.

**MULLIN GLASS CO., INC.**
268 Main St. (07405)
**Phone—(973) 838-6767**
Fax—(973) 838-3398
www.mullinglass.com
Email—skip@mullinglass.com
Pres.—Gerald Mullin, Jr.
SIC—3231; NAICS—327215; *Glass fabrication*
Employs—2; Estab.—1953
Sales—under $500,000
2,400 sq ft site, Distrib.—Local
Privately owned corporation

**MY WAY PRINTS, INC.**
1376 Route 23 (07405)
**Phone—(973) 492-1212**
Fax—(973) 492-1567
www.pipbutler.com
Email—mail@pipbutler.com
Pres.—Myron Friedman
V.-P.—Gary Friedman
SIC—2752; 2791; NAICS—323122; *Offset printing & typesetting*
Employs—3; Estab.—1982
Sales—$500,000-$1Mil
3,000 sq ft site, Distrib.—Regional
Privately owned corporation
DBA: PIP Printing

**NANO'S, LLC**
22 Park Pl., P.O. Box 41 (07405)
**Phone—(973) 616-1515**
Fax—(973) 616-9666
www.nano-baby.com
Email—info@nano-baby.com
Ptnr.—Patricia Pienkowska
Ptnr.—Howard Balch
SIC—2369; NAICS—315200; *Children's clothing; Brand name—Nano*
Employs—2; Estab.—2002
Sales—under $500,000
1,800 sq ft site, Distrib.—National
Limited Liability Company

**OLYMPIC EDM & WATERJET, INC.**
20 Kiel Ave. (07405)
**Phone—(973) 492-0664**
Fax—(973) 492-9623
www.olympicedm.com
Email—info@olympicedm.com
Owner & Pres.—Don Ferrante
Off. Mgr.—Jody Laufer
SIC—3544; 3599; NAICS—333500; *Wire EDM, waterjet & tool & die shop*
Employs—8; Estab.—1980
6,000 sq ft site, Distrib.—National
Privately owned sub-S corp.

**PEERLESS CONCRETE PRODUCTS, INC.**
246 Main St. (07405)
**Phone—(973) 838-3060**
Fax—(973) 697-9009
www.peerlessconcrete.com
Email—sales@
peerlessconcrete.com
Ptnr.—Phil Monaco
Ptnr.—Clara Monaco
V.-P., Plt.—Paul Monaco, Jr.
Cont.—Steve McCann
Estimator—John Gardner
SIC—3272; *Precast concrete products, including concrete septic tanks, catch basins & custom products*
Employs—40; Estab.—1959
Distrib.—Regional
Privately owned corporation

**PRECISION FORMS, INC.**
97 Decker Rd. (07405)
**Phone—(973) 838-3800**
Fax—(973) 838-2296
www.precisionformsinc.com
Email—sales@
precisionformsinc.com
Pres., Hum. Res. & IT Mgr.—
William Sulski
V.-P.—Sandra Sulski
SIC—3599; 3544; NAICS—332997; *Long & short run production machining job shop, including fixtures, prototypes, gages, tooling, CNC turning & milling, Swiss screw machining, wire & sink EDM & laser marking*
Employs—36; Estab.—1955
Sales—$4Mil
11,000 sq ft site, Distrib.—National
Privately owned corporation

**R S MICROWAVE CO., INC.**
22 Park Pl., P.O. Box 273 (07405)
**Phone—(973) 492-1207**
Fax—(973) 492-2471
www.rsmicro.com
Email—queries@rsmicro.com
Pres.—Richard V. Snyder
MIS Mgr.—Valerie Santelli Snyder
SIC—3679; *Microwave filters multiplexers & subassemblies*
Employs—49; Estab.—1981
Sales—$9.8Mil
32,000 sq ft site, Distrib.—Intl.
Privately owned corporation

**RAILCO METALCRAFT, INC.**
22 Park Pl. (07405)
**Phone—(973) 838-2822**
Fax—(973) 838-3006
www.railcometalcraft.com
Email—info@railcometalcraft.com
Owner—Robert Williams
Estimator—Wes Shelton
SIC—3446; NAICS—332323; *Aluminum railings*
Employs—3; Estab.—1974
Sales—under $500,000
3,000 sq ft site, Distrib.—Local
Privately owned corporation

**RICH'S KITCHENS, INC.**
309 Hamburg Tpke. (07405)
**Phone—(973) 838-4026**
Fax—(973) 838-4040
www.richkitchens.com
Email—richkit309@aol.com
Pres.—Richard Palinski
V.-P., Fin.—Susan Palinski
Administrator—Janet Kissack
SIC—2541; *Plastic laminated countertops*
Employs—4; Estab.—1978
Sales—$500,000-$1Mil
2,500 sq ft site, Distrib.—Local
Privately owned corporation

**SQUIGGLY PRODUCTIONS, LLC**
164 Main St. (07405)
Mail addr: 11 Hazel Rd., West Milford (07480)
**Phone—(973) 838-7475**
Email—gsgraphics@optonline.net
Owner—Guy Scognamiglio
Off. Mgr.—Seana Scognamiglio
SIC—2752; 2759; 2791; 2789; NAICS—323122; *Offset & full-color digital printing, electronic prepress, graphic design & binding*
Employs—2; Estab.—1991
Sales—under $500,000
Distrib.—Regional
Limited Liability Company
AKA: G&S Graphics

**STANTON PRECISION PRODUCTS, LLC**
10 Park Pl., Bldg. 4 (07405)
**Phone—(973) 838-6951**
Fax—(973) 838-7341
www.swisscnc.com
Email—stantonprecision@msn.com
Member—Sean Stanton
Member—William Stanton
Pres., CFO—Charles J. Stanton
SIC—3599; *Screw machine job shop, including .060-inch to 1.250-inch diameter capacity & Swiss CNC machining*
Employs—7; Estab.—1988
Sales—over $1Mil
10,500 sq ft site, Distrib.—National
Limited Liability Company

**VALCAR PRECISION PRODUCTS, INC.**
22 Park Pl. (07405)
**Phone—(973) 838-7600**
    (973) 875-2371
Fax—(973) 838-3511
www.valcardirect.com
Email—valcar@nac.net
Pres., Fin., MIS, Opers. & R & D Mgr.—Carl Grossi
V.-P.—Andrew Grossi
SIC—3451; NAICS—332721; *Screw machine parts & CNC turning & milling job shop*
Employs—5; Estab.—1976
Sales—under $500,000
5,500 sq ft site, Distrib.—National
Privately owned corporation

---

## Caldwell

(Essex—N.E.)

**CALANDRA PRINTING**
491 Bloomfield Ave. (07006)
**Phone—(973) 228-1649**
National—(800) 834-3723
Fax—(973) 228-4894
www.calandraprinting.com
Email—keithcalandra@verizon.net
Owner—Keith Calandra
Sales Rep.—Maria Di Fabio
Graphic Designer—Edgar Santiago
SIC—2759; NAICS—323100; *Commercial printing*
Employs—4; Estab.—1979
Sales—under $500,000
Distrib.—Regional
Sole ownership

**COMPUTERIST, INC.**
15 Smull Ave., Ste. A (07006-5011)
**Phone—(973) 226-0100**
National—(877) 731-7979
Fax—(973) 226-0106
www.computerist.com
Email—sales@computerist.com
Pres.—Anthony Camilleri
V.-P.—Theresa Camilleri
SIC—3571; 7373; 5045; 5044; *Rebuilt computers & computer network systems integration & distributor of new computers & peripherals, including LANs, WANs, inkjet & multifunctional printers, home automation, audio & video products & software for businesses & consumers; Brand name—Dell; HP; Xerox; Citrix; Cisco; BlueCoat; OpenText; LifeSize Communication; Sonos; Lutron; Samsung; Microsoft; Adobe; VMware; Epson; Oki; Brother; Marantz; Denon; Nest*
Employs—5; Estab.—1992
1,500 sq ft site, Distrib.—National
Privately owned corporation

**†DEVON TRADING CORP.**
5 Fairfield Rd. (07006)
**Phone—(973) 812-9190**
www.devontrading.com
Email—info@devontrading.com
Pres.—Fran Orzech
SIC—5094; 5199; 5192; *Distributor of religious items, including precious metal rosaries, statues, pins & books*
Employs—22; Estab.—1951
Distrib.—National
Privately owned corporation

**LARSON-JUHL, LLC**
165 Clinton Rd. (07006)
**Phone—(973) 439-1801**
National—(800) 438-5031
Fax—(973) 227-2963
www.larsonjuhl.com
Email—lfey@larsonjuhl.com
Off. Mgr.—Nina Rivera
Manager—Nick Budzilovich
SIC—2499; *Wooden picture frames*
Employs—30; Estab.—1993
Distrib.—National
Publicly owned corporation
Parent co.—Larson-Juhl, LLC, Norcross, GA
Phone—(770) 279-5200
See Parent Co. Section for full profile.

**MERCURY COMMERCIAL ELECTRONICS**
Div. of Mercury Systems, Inc.
2 Henderson Dr., Ste. B (07006)
**Phone—(973) 244-1040**
Fax—(973) 244-1188
www.mrcy.com
Email—info@mrcy.com
Pres.—Tony Pospishil
SIC—3679; 3613; *Commercial electronics, including RF/microwave subsystems & components, attenuators, power switches, ferrites & detectors*
Employs—80
Sales—$10Mil-$25Mil (est)
Distrib.—National
Publicly owned corporation
Parent co.—Mercury Systems, Inc., Chelmsford, MA
Phone—(978) 256-1300
See Parent Co. Section for full profile.

**†MERCURY TIRE CO., INC.**
1 Fairfield Rd. (07006)
**Phone—(973) 785-0080**
National—(800) 526-1186
Fax—(973) 785-0084
Email—mercurytire@aol.com
Pres.—James Gilroy
Off. Mgr.—Roxanne Cogott
SIC—5014; *Distributor of tires; Brand name—COOPER; GOODYEAR; HANKOOK; CONTINENTAL*
Employs—15; Estab.—1974
Sales—$5Mil-$10Mil
10,000 sq ft site, Distrib.—Regional
Privately owned corporation

GEOGRAPHICAL

## Caldwell—(cont.)

**PROVOST SQUARE ASSOCS.**
6 Provost Sq. (07006)
**Phone—(973) 403-8755**
Fax—(973) 403-8755
Pres.—Barbara Mamchur
SIC—3911; NAICS—339911;
 Class rings
Employs—5
Distrib.—National
Privately owned corporation

**SIGNS & GRAPHIX**
433 Bloomfield Ave. (07006)
**Phone—(973) 226-8392**
Fax—(973) 226-8392
www.signsandgraphix.net
Email—stoppsign@gmail.com
Owner—Eric Sterru
SIC—3993; 2499; 3089; Big
 format interior, exterior & job site
 signs, vehicle lettering, banners,
 magnetics, vinyl graphics,
 lettering & design
Employs—1; Estab.—1990
Sales—under $500,000
Distrib.—Local
Sole ownership

**TECHNICAL PRODUCTS CO.**
264 Park Ave. (07006)
**Phone—(973) 228-2258**
Fax—(973) 228-0276
www.technicalproductsco.com
Email—dcmeserlian@
 voicesofsafety.com
Chrm.—Donald Meserlian
Pres.—Steve Meserlian
SIC—3829; Floor & footwear
 friction testers, force gages,
 expansion plugs & portable
 forced air heaters for health,
 safety & environmental
 applications
Employs—2; Estab.—1973
Sales—$1Mil
2,000 sq ft site, Distrib.—Intl.
Privately owned corporation

**WINDMILL HEALTH PRODUCTS, LLC**
6 Henderson Dr. (07006)
**Phone—(973) 575-6591**
National—(800) 822-4320
Fax—(973) 882-3256
www.windmillvitamins.com
Email—info@windmillvitamins.com
Pres.—Howard Munk
V-P., Sales, Special Market—
 Richard Lauritano
SIC—2833; 2844; 5122;
 Manufacturer & distributor of
 vitamin supplements, lifestyle
 formulations & beauty & health
 products, including nutritionally
 enhanced creams & lotions, anti-
 aging beauty formulas & 2-
 ounce to 1-gallon beverage
 grade & enhanced liquids;
 Brand name—Windmill Vitamins;
 Garden Greens; Hi Ener G;
 Super Juice; Vitabetic; Omega
 Works; Glucoflex Glucosamine;
 Focus Formula; Sleep Soundly;
 Sunshine
Employs—45; Estab.—1975
Sales—$10Mil-$25Mil
Distrib.—Intl.
Limited Liability Company

## Califon
(Hunterdon—N.W.)

**†AUTOMATION SALES CO.**
226 Beacon Hill Rd. (07830)
**Phone—(908) 832-7040**
National—(800) 468-8423
Fax—(908) 832-9735
www.automationsalesco.com
Email—jimp@feeders.biz
Pres.—James Powell

SIC—5084; Distributor of
 automation machinery, including
 vibratory & centrifugal feeders &
 feeder bowls; Brand name—
 Service Engineering Inc.
Employs—7; Estab.—1974
Distrib.—Regional
Privately owned corporation

**D & H CUTOFF CO., INC.**
412-I Trimmer Rd., Bldg. 11
 (07830)
**Phone—(908) 454-4961**
www.dandhcutoff.com
Email—dhcutoff@cutofftrimmer.com
Ptnr. & Pres.—Art W. DeSaules, Jr.
Ptnr.—Eric Smith
SIC—3599; Precision abrasive
 cutting
Employs—9; Estab.—1938
3,000 sq ft site, Distrib.—National
Privately owned corporation

**LOOMINARIES HANDWEAVING**
23 Big Spring Rd. (07830)
**Phone—(908) 832-6652**
Fax—(908) 832-6654
www.loominaries.com
Email—loominaries@comcast.net
Owner—Patricia Lukas
SIC—2273; NAICS—314110;
 Custom & production rag rugs
Employs—1; Estab.—1972
Sales—under $500,000 (est)
Distrib.—Intl.
Sole ownership

**PEDIATRX, INC. (H Q)**
90 Fairmount Rd. W., P.O. Box 423
 (07830)
**Phone—(908) 975-0753**
Fax—(866) 398-0816
www.pediatrx.com
Email—info@pediatrx.com
Founder, Chrm. & CEO—Cameron
 Durrant
Chief Admn. & Fin. Officer—David
 Tousley
SIC—2834; Corporate
 headquarters; specialty
 pharmaceuticals for the
 treatment of serious medical
 conditions treated in hospital,
 with an initial focus on oncology
 supportive care (mfg. done in
 Montreal, Canada); Brand
 name—Granisol
Employs—2; Estab.—2010
Sales—$1Mil-$2.5Mil (est)
Distrib.—National
Publicly owned corporation

**POWER BAG & FILM, LLC**
189 W. Valley Brook Rd. (07830)
**Phone—(908) 832-6648**
Fax—(908) 832-6526
www.powerbagandfilm.com
Email—tpower@
 powerbagandfilm.com
Manager—Trevor Power
SIC—2671; 2673; Polyethlene &
 polypropylene monolayer &
 coextruded flexible packaging,
 including general purpose bags,
 food & pharmaceutical box
 liners, shrink bags, bundling
 films, furniture & mattress bags &
 films & can liners
Employs—3; Estab.—2003
Sales—$3Mil
Distrib.—National
Limited Liability Company

**RAWCO, INC.**
452 Route 513 (07830)
**Phone—(908) 832-7700**
Fax—(908) 832-7784
www.rawcoprecision.com
Email—email@rawcoprecision.com
Pres.—Jeff Riley
Off. Mgr.—Lori Riley

SIC—3599; CNC turning, milling &
 machining job shop
Employs—7; Estab.—1972
Sales—under $500,000
5,000 sq ft site, Distrib.—Local
Privately owned corporation

**TRANSSTAR TRUCK BODY WELDING CO., INC.**
514 Route 513, P.O. Box 226
 (07830)
**Phone—(908) 832-2688**
Fax—(908) 832-5747
www.transstartruckbody.com
Pres.—Dominick Tranquilli
Off. Mgr.—Patricia Burke
SIC—3713; 3599; NAICS—
 336211; Truck bodies & welding
 job shop
Employs—5; Estab.—1977
Sales—under $500,000
Distrib.—Local
Privately owned corporation

## Camden
(Camden—S.W.)

**A & A SOFT PRETZEL CO.**
1100 N. 32nd St. (08105)
Mail addr: 211 Massachusetts
 Ave., Cherry Hill (08002)
**Phone—(856) 338-0208**
Pres.—Nicholas Panara
V-P.—Albert Panara
SIC—2051; NAICS—311812; Soft
 pretzels
Employs—2; Estab.—1929
Sales—under $500,000
Distrib.—Local
Privately owned corporation

**A-1 UNIFORMS, INC.**
721 Broadway (08103)
**Phone—(856) 963-7680**
Fax—(856) 963-0715
www.uniformcityinc.com
Pres.—Ralph Ishack
SIC—2326; 2339; 5136; 5137;
 NAICS—315225; Manufacturer
 & wholesaler of custom &
 standard police, correctional,
 security guard, fire department,
 school, industrial & maintenance
 uniforms & nurse scrubs,
 including screen printing &
 embroidery
Employs—3; Estab.—1939
Sales—under $500,000 (est)
Distrib.—Local
Privately owned corporation

**AMERINOX PROCESSING, INC.**
2201 Mount Ephraim Ave., Bldg.
 90 (08104)
**Phone—(856) 963-2200**
Fax—(856) 963-2201
www.amerinoxprocessing.com
Email—bcarter@
 amerinoxprocessing.com
Pres.—Seth Young
CFO—Bob Carter
Ex. V-P., Sales & Mktg.—Chris
 Fagan
Hum. Res. Mgr.—Paula Penta
SIC—3441; 3444; Stainless steel
 & aluminum processing,
 including hot-rolled & cold-rolled
 coil leveling & coil-to-coil
 polishing
Employs—40; Estab.—2003
Distrib.—National
Privately owned corporation
Also see: Midlantic Metals, same
 loc.

**ARCH CUSTOM MFG INC**
1215 S. 6th St. (08104)
**Phone—(856) 966-3835**
Fax—(856) 963-2092
Email—arpatinc@aol.com
Pres. & Fin. Mgr.—Donald Blair
MIS & R & D Mgr.—Ed Blair

SIC—3599; Precision machining
 job shop
Employs—4; Estab.—1968
Sales—under $500,000
55,000 sq ft site, Distrib.—National
Privately owned corporation

**ART METALCRAFT PLATING CO., INC.**
529 S. 2nd St. (08103)
**Phone—(856) 365-0001**
Fax—(856) 365-8539
Pres.—Roger Dolente
Corp. Secy.—Chance Moen
SIC—3471; NAICS—332813;
 Metal plating
Employs—12; Estab.—1949
Sales—under $500,000
Distrib.—Local
Privately owned corporation

**CAMDEN GLASS, INC.**
111 Marlton Ave. (08105)
**Phone—(856) 365-0142**
Fax—(856) 342-6710
www.camdenglass.com
Email—cgi@snip.net
Pres.—James Keller
SIC—3231; NAICS—327215;
 Glass cutting, glazing, beveling
 & fabrication
Employs—8; Estab.—1939
Sales—under $500,000
6,000 sq ft site, Distrib.—Local
Privately owned corporation

**CAMDEN PRINTWORKS**
1621 S. Broadway (08104)
**Phone—(856) 365-1424**
National—(888) 778-9675
www.camdenprintworks.net
Email—adam@
 camdenprintworks.net
GM—Adam Woods
SIC—2396; Custom t-shirt &
 sweatshirt screen printing
Employs—8; Estab.—1990
Sales—$750,000
5,000 sq ft site, Distrib.—National
Limited Liability Company

**CAMDEN YARDS STEEL CO., LLC**
2500 Broadway, Drawer 14
 (08104)
**Phone—(856) 342-7100**
National—(888) 373-9300
Fax—(856) 342-6677
www.camdenyardssteel.com
Email—info@
 camdenyardssteel.com
Ptnr.—Michael Amato
Ptnr.—Alan Kanoff
SIC—3312; Steel processing
Employs—25; Estab.—2001
Sales—$5Mil-$10Mil (est)
Distrib.—National
Limited Liability Company

**CAMPBELL SOUP CO. (H Q)**
1 Campbell Pl. (08103)
**Phone—(856) 342-4800**
 (856) 342-5982
Fax—(856) 342-3878
www.campbellsoup.com
Email—csr_feedback@
 campbellsoup.com
Chrm.—Paul Charron
CEO—Denise M. Morrison
Sr. V-P., CFO—Craig Owens
Sr. V-P., CIO—Joseph Spagnoletti
Dir., Hum. Res.—Pauline
 Ashworth
Hum. Res. Mgr.—Bob Morrisey
SIC—2032; 2033; 2098; NAICS—
 311421; Company headquarters;
 canned soups, stew, beans &
 spaghetti products; Brand
 name—Pepperidge Farm;
 Arnott's; V8
Employs—1200; Estab.—1869
Sales—$7.3Bil
Distrib.—Intl.
Publicly owned corporation

## Camden—(cont.)

**CATHOLIC STAR HERALD**
Div. of Diocese Of Camden
15 N. 7th St. (08102)
**Phone—(856) 583-6142**
Fax—(856) 756-7938
www.catholicstarherald.org
Email—csoper@
camdendiocese.org
Mng. Editor—Carl Peters
IT Mgr.—Joseph Torrieri
Hum. Res. Mgr.—John Raferty
Bus. Mgr.—Cynthia Soper
SIC—2711; 45 weeks per year
Catholic newspaper publishing
Employs—8; Estab.—1951
Sales—under $500,000
10,000 sq ft site, Distrib.—Local
Privately owned corporation
Parent co.—Diocese Of Camden,
Camden, NJ
Phone—(856) 756-7900
See Parent Co. Section for full profile.

**CENTRAL METALS, INC.**
1054 S. 2nd St. (08103)
**Phone—(856) 963-5844**
Fax—(856) 963-1789
www.centralmetals.com
Owner & Treas.—Maria Iannelli
GM—Anthony DeBlasio
SIC—3441; NAICS—332312;
Structural steel fabrication
Employs—75; Estab.—1969
Distrib.—Intl.
Privately owned corporation

**COLONIAL PROCESSING, INC.**
1930 S. 6th St. (08104)
**Phone—(856) 966-3313**
Fax—(856) 541-2409
www.colonialprocessing.com
Pres.—Steve Gove
Hum. Res., IT & Off. Mgr.—Brian
Gove
Bookkeeper—Bill Angnow
SIC—3325; NAICS—331513;
Steel processing
Employs—33; Estab.—1955
Distrib.—National
Privately owned corporation

**COMARCO PRODUCTS**
501 Jackson St. (08104)
**Phone—(856) 342-7557**
Fax—(856) 342-8448
www.comarco.net
Pres.—Tom Hoversen
GM—Eric Hoversen
Cust. Serv. Rep.—Liz Feliciano
SIC—2034; Vegetable processing
Employs—35; Estab.—1978
40,000 sq ft site, Distrib.—National
Privately owned corporation

**†CONTAINER RECYCLERS-CAMDEN,
INC.**
267 Jefferson St. (08104)
Mail addr: P.O. Box 563,
Blackwood (08012)
**Phone—(856) 963-5200**
Fax—(856) 963-4600
www.incinerationrecycling.com
Owner & Hum. Res. Mgr.—Ron
Fogel, Jr.
SIC—5093; Wholesaler of
recycled shipping containers,
including steel, plastic & fiber
drums & intermediate bulk
containers
Employs—30; Estab.—1970
Distrib.—Intl.
Privately owned corporation

**DURO PLATING CO., INC.**
273 Kaighns Ave. (08103)
**Phone—(856) 963-4967**
Pres.—Joe Minessale

SIC—3471; NAICS—332813;
Metal plating & finishing
Employs—3; Estab.—1950
Sales—under $500,000
Distrib.—Local
Privately owned corporation

**DYNAMIC BLENDING CO., INC.**
1475 S. 6th St. (08104)
**Phone—(856) 541-6626**
Fax—(856) 963-8841
Email—dblending@verizon.net
Pres.—Terence O'Reiley
Bookkeeper—Lori Creek
SIC—2841; NAICS—325611;
Detergents
Employs—11; Estab.—1970
Distrib.—Local
Privately owned corporation

**ELMCO TWO, INC.**
1045 Cambridge St. (08105)
Mail addr: P.O. Box 561,
Pennsauken (08110-0561)
**Phone—(856) 365-2244**
Fax—(856) 541-2168
www.elmcotwoinc.com
Email—info@elmcotwoinc.com
Pres.—Bernhard H. Kofoet
Manager—John Kofoet, Sr.
Bookkeeper—Rachael Kofoet
SIC—3444; Sheet metal
fabrication
Employs—3; Estab.—1960
Sales—$500,000-$1Mil
10,000 sq ft site, Distrib.—Local
Privately owned corporation

**ERICK INDUSTRIES, INC.**
837 S. 9th St. (08103)
Mail addr: P.O. Box 149, Bala-
Cynwyd (19004)
**Phone—(856) 966-2045**
Fax—(856) 966-2045
Pres.—Bill Patton
Asst. Mgr.—Fred Dunlap
SIC—3444; Sheet metal skylights
Employs—2; Estab.—1965
Sales—under $500,000
12,000 sq ft site, Distrib.—Local
Privately owned corporation

**EXTREME PAINTING & POWDER
COATING, LLC**
944 Reeves Ave. (08105)
**Phone—(856) 541-8733**
Fax—(856) 541-8022
www.expowder.com
Email—extremepowdercoating@
verizon.net
Pres.—Mike Pfeiffer
Manager—Judy Santos
SIC—3471; 3479; NAICS—
332813; Metal finishing &
powder coating
Employs—8; Estab.—1987
Sales—$500,000-$1Mil
6,000 sq ft site, Distrib.—Regional
Limited Liability Company

**F & R PALLETS, INC.**
1929 S. 4th St. (08104)
**Phone—(856) 964-8516**
Fax—(856) 635-1129
Email—jandrpallets02@yahoo.com
Pres.—Ronald Abate
Off. Mgr.—Jeniffer Abate
SIC—2448; NAICS—321920;
Wooden pallets
Employs—45; Estab.—1976
20,900 sq ft site, Distrib.—
Regional
Privately owned corporation
AKA: J & R Pallets

**FAST DOORS, LLC**
1800 Copewood St. (08103)
**Phone—(856) 966-3278**
National—(877) 682-7866
Fax—(856) 966-0293
www.fastdoors1.com
Email—fastdoors.sales@verizon.net
Pres.—Al Pooner
GM—John Jones

SIC—3442; NAICS—332321;
Metal storefront rolling & security
doors, gates & grilles
Employs—18; Estab.—1980
Sales—under $500,000
Distrib.—National
Privately owned corporation
Also see: Phil-Mar Industries,
same loc.

**†FCR CAMDEN, INC.**
2201 Mt. Ephraim Ave., Bldg. 10-A
(08104)
**Phone—(856) 342-7503**
Fax—(856) 342-7932
Pres.—Shawn Duffy
Regional Mgr.—Steven Gray
SIC—5093; Wholesaler of
recycled plastics, paper,
cardboard & metal scrap
materials
Employs—35; Estab.—1988
Distrib.—Local
Privately owned corporation
AKA: Re Community

**FOOTE & JENKS CORP.**
1420 Crestmont Ave. (08103)
**Phone—(856) 966-0700**
Fax—(856) 966-6137
www.footeandjenks.com
Pres.—Michael Baskin
Pur. Mgr.—Sherry Lemieux
Bookkeeper—Donna Demarco
SIC—2087; 2844; NAICS—
311900; Food flavorings &
fragrances
Employs—20; Estab.—1981
50,000 sq ft site, Distrib.—Intl.
Privately owned corporation

**GENERAL METAL & GLASS CO.**
613 Kaighn Ave. (08101)
**Phone—(856) 365-6323**
Fax—(856) 541-2553
Email—genmet613@aol.com
GM—Bill Tuling
Fin. Mgr.—Sandra Heaps
SIC—3231; 3442; NAICS—
327215; Glass & metal windows
Employs—3; Estab.—1996
Sales—under $500,000
3,000 sq ft site, Distrib.—Local
Sole ownership

**GEORGIA-PACIFIC GYPSUM, LLC**
Div. of Georgia-Pacific, LLC
1101 S. Front St. (08103)
**Phone—(856) 966-7600**
Fax—(856) 966-1475
www.gp.com
Email—info@gp.com
GM—Jermaine Jenkins
Facility Mgr.—George Garcia
SIC—3275; NAICS—327420;
Gypsum wallboards
Employs—20; Estab.—1995
Distrib.—Regional
Privately owned corporation
Parent co.—Georgia-Pacific, LLC,
Atlanta, GA
Phone—(404) 652-4000
See Parent Co. Section for full profile.

**HOLCIM U.S.**
Div. of Holcim (US), Inc.
595 Morgan Blvd. (08104)
**Phone—(856) 964-2555**
Fax—(856) 964-2660
www.holcim.com
Email—sales@holcim.com
Plt. Mgr.—Fred Hyatt
Dispatcher—Megan Madden
SIC—3241; NAICS—327310;
Cement
Employs—15; Estab.—2002
Distrib.—Intl.
Publicly owned corporation
Parent co.—Holcim (US), Inc.,
Bedford, MA
Phone—(781) 647-2501
See Parent Co. Section for full profile.

**HOWIE MFG. CO., INC.**
1227 Mechanic St. (08104)
**Phone—(856) 963-3560**
Fax—(856) 963-8538
Pres.—Jo Ann Howie
Sales Mgr.—Jean Howie
Qual. Control Mgr.—Rich Candy
SIC—3451; NAICS—332721;
Screw machine products
Employs—3; Estab.—1981
Sales—under $500,000 (est)

**INDUSTRIAL HYDRAULICS &
RUBBER, LLC**
458 Atlantic Ave. (08104)
**Phone—(856) 966-2600**
Fax—(856) 966-0044
www.indhr.net
Email—sales@indhr.net
GM—Michael Donahue
SIC—3593; 3599; NAICS—
333995; Rebuilt hydraulic
cylinders & machining job shop
Employs—7; Estab.—1907
Distrib.—Local
Privately owned corporation

**†JEN-CYN ENTERPRISES, INC.**
407 Atlantic Ave. (08104)
**Phone—(856) 541-7400**
Fax—(856) 541-7598
Pres.—Carol Clements
SIC—5051; Wholesaler of
galvanized & coated metal
sheets
Employs—45; Estab.—1982
Distrib.—Local
Privately owned corporation

**JONES & SON, INC., WILLIAM**
238 Liberty St. (08104)
**Phone—(856) 963-1199**
Fax—(856) 342-6807
www.jonesdrums.com
Email—wmjjonesinc@comcast.net
Pres.—John T. Williams
Treas.—Donna Williams
SIC—3412; NAICS—332439;
Reconditioned steel drums,
barrels, totes & pails
Employs—23; Estab.—1967
15,000 sq ft site, Distrib.—National
Privately owned sub-S corp.

**JOSEPH OAT CORP.**
2500 S. Broadway (08104)
**Phone—(856) 541-2900**
Fax—(856) 541-0864
www.josephoat.com
Email—rkaplan@josephoat.com
Pres., Opers.—Ron Kaplan
Pres., Engrg.—Michael Holtz
Cont.—Linda Brown
Cont., Doc.—Pat Dell
SIC—2819; Nuclear components
fabrication, including pressure
vessels, reactors, columns &
heat exchangers for the
chemical, petrochemical,
nuclear power & commercial
industries
Employs—100; Estab.—1788
Sales—$26Mil-$50Mil
140,000 sq ft site, Distrib.—Intl.
Privately owned sub-S corp.

**KAPLAN & ZUBRIN, INC.**
2nd & Kaighn Ave. (08103)
Mail addr: P.O. Box 1006, Camden
(08101)
**Phone—(856) 964-1083**
National—(800) 334-0002
Fax—(856) 964-0510
www.kzpickles.com
Email—kz.pickles@verizon.net
Pres.—Ronald Kaplan
Treas.—Richard Kaplan
Acct. Mgr.—Dawn Seternus Tuthill
Opers. Mgr.—Stu Taylor
Off. Mgr.—Sandy Dyer

GEOGRAPHICAL

## Camden—(cont.)

SIC—2035; *Pickles; Brand name—KZ; Garden State*
Employs—30; Estab.—1939
Sales—$3Mil
Distrib.—Local
Privately owned sub-S corp.

**KOHLDER MFG., INC.**
1001 Line St. (08103)
**Phone—(856) 342-8398**
National—(800) 220-2874
Fax—(856) 541-2378
www.kohlder.com
V-P.—Jeffery Kerber
Cont.—Mary Ann Rakus
Foreman—Joe Mooney
SIC—3585; *Commercial refrigeration*
Employs—6; Estab.—1982
Sales—$10Mil-$25Mil
12,000 sq ft site, Distrib.—National
Privately owned corporation

**L-3 COMMUNICATIONS CORP.**
1 Federal St. (08102)
**Phone—(856) 338-3000**
Fax—(856) 338-6014
www.l-3com.com
Email—info@l-3com.com
Pres.—Dave Micha
CIO—Ken Moritz
V-P., Opers.—John Tierney
V-P., Hum. Res.—Alison Courtial
Bus. Dev. Admn.—Colleen Kraus
SIC—3669; NAICS—334290; *Communications systems*
Employs—700
Sales—$25Mil-$100Mil
225,000 sq ft site,
Publicly owned corporation
ISO rating—9001
Parent co.—L-3 Communications Corp., New York, NY
  Phone—(212) 697-1111
  See Parent Co. Section for full profile.

**LERRO PRODUCTS, INC.**
1321 Walnut St. (08103)
Mail addr: P.O. Box 619, Camden (08101)
**Phone—(856) 203-3561**
Fax—(856) 246-1323
www.lerroproducts.com
Email—lerroproducts@aol.com
Pres.—Dan Albanese
Off. Mgr.—Peggy Crosby
SIC—2841; NAICS—325611; *Janitorial soap & chemicals*
Employs—20; Estab.—1946
20,000 sq ft site, Distrib.—Regional
Privately owned sub-S corp.

**MAFCO WORLDWIDE CORP.**
Div. of M & F Worldwide Corp.
300 Jefferson St. *(08104)*
**Phone—(856) 964-8840**
Fax—(856) 964-6029
www.magnasweet.com
Email—magnasweet@mafcolicorice.com
Sr. V-P., Gen. Counsel—Thomas Molchan
Sr. V-P.—Lee Collison
Dir., Acct., Audit & Hum. Res.—Lisa Armstrong
SIC—2087; 2111; NAICS—312221; *Corporate headquarters & tobacco flavors & extracts & sweetness enhancers; Brand name—Magnasweet*
Employs—150; Estab.—1850
Sales—$120Mil
390,000 sq ft site, Distrib.—Intl.
Publicly owned corporation
Parent co.—M & F Worldwide Corp., New York, NY
  Phone—(212) 572-8600
  See Parent Co. Section for full profile.

**MAGNETIC METALS CORP.**
1900 Hayes Ave. *(08105)*
**Phone—(856) 964-7842**
National—(800) 257-8174
Fax—(856) 365-8723
www.magmet.com
Email—khaley@magmet.com
Pres.—Frank A. Raneiro
Cont.—Wm. Pennington
Mktg. Mgr.—Kurt Haley
MIS Mgr.—Ken Johnston
Cust. Serv. & Export Mgr.—Lorraine Bock
Qual. Assur. Mgr.—Rodica Musat
Salesman—Dave Rollins
SIC—3469; 3399; *Metal stampings & high-grade nickel alloy laminations*
Employs—60; Estab.—1942
196,000 sq ft site, Distrib.—Intl.
Privately owned corporation

**MARKET STREET PRINTING, INC.**
122 N. 6th St. (08102)
**Phone—(856) 964-5995**
Fax—(856) 964-9385
www.marketstreetprinting.com
Email—msprinting@netzero.com
Pres.—Mookie Kamerkar
GM—Prakash Rao
SIC—2752; 2791; 2759; NAICS—323122; *Commercial offset printing & typesetting*
Employs—3; Estab.—1992
Sales—under $500,000
1,000 sq ft site, Distrib.—Local
Privately owned sub-S corp.

**†MIDLANTIC METALS**
2201 Mount Ephraim Ave., Ste. 90 (08104-3232)
**Phone—(856) 963-2822**
www.stainlesscenter.net
Email—dsharon@stainlesscenter.net
Pres.—Dean Sharon
SIC—5051; *Distributor of stainless steel flat & long products*
Employs—5; Estab.—2011
Sales—$1Mil-$2.5Mil
Distrib.—Local
Privately owned corporation
Also see: Amerinox Processing, Inc., same loc.

**MIGALI INDUSTRIES, INC.**
516 Lansdowne Ave. (08104)
**Phone—(856) 963-3600**
  (615) 907-2500
National—(800) 852-5292
Fax—(856) 963-3604
www.migali.com
Email—contact@migali.com
Pres.—Ernest Migali
Dir., Sales & Mktg.—Ernie Migali, Jr.
Dir., Opers.—Bruno Migali
SIC—3585; *Commercial refrigerators & freezers*
Employs—15; Estab.—1955
80,000 sq ft site, Distrib.—National
Privately owned corporation

**MILLER FABRICATORS**
1135 Mount Ephraim Ave. (08103)
**Phone—(856) 541-9499**
Fax—(856) 966-0790
www.millerfabricators.com
Email—millerfabricators@inbox.com
Owner, Pres. & CEO—Aaron Miller
Off. Mgr.—Madelon Still
SIC—2542; 2434; 2431; NAICS—337110; *Laminated countertops & custom cabinetry*
Employs—10; Estab.—1973
Sales—$2Mil-$3Mil
10,000 sq ft site, Distrib.—Regional
Privately owned corporation

**NEW JERSEY RIVET CO., LLC**
1785 Haddon Ave. (08103)
**Phone—(856) 963-2237**
Fax—(856) 963-2367
www.njrivet.com
Email—sales@njrivet.com
Sales Mgr., Inside—Kenneth Landgarten
Manager—Dennis Van Name
Asst. Mgr.—Steven Van Name
SIC—3452; 3599; NAICS—332722; *Semi-tubular rivets*
Employs—10; Estab.—1934
Sales—$1Mil-$5Mil
27,000 sq ft site, Distrib.—National
Limited Liability Company

**NJS SALES CORP.**
2840 Mount Ephraim Ave. (08104)
Mail addr: P.O. Box 2506, Cherry Hill (08034)
**Phone—(856) 619-1119**
Fax—(856) 337-0094
Email—lounjsteel@verizon.net
Pres.—Lou Cirignano
Pur. Mgr.—Bill Williams
SIC—3449; 5051; *Rebar fabrication & distributor of wire mesh & rebar*
Employs—15; Estab.—2005
18,000 sq ft site, Distrib.—National
Privately owned sub-S corp.

**NUTSCO, INC.**
1115 S. 2nd St. (08103)
**Phone—(856) 966-6400**
Fax—(856) 966-6544
www.nutsco.com
Email—info@nutsco.com
Owner & Pres.—Francisco Assis
V-P., Opers. & Dir., Acct.—Paulo Deoliveira
Off. Mgr.—Vickie Santana
SIC—2068; NAICS—311911; *Cashew processing*
Employs—12; Estab.—2001
Sales—$500,000-$1Mil
Distrib.—Regional
Privately owned corporation

**PATRICK J. KELLY DRUMS, INC.**
1810 River Ave. *(08105)*
**Phone—(856) 963-1795**
  (800) 963-1795
Fax—(856) 963-1788
www.kellydrums.com
Email—sales@kellydrums.com
Owner & Pres.—Patrick J. Kelly
V-P.—Lisa Kelly
Dir., Mktg.—Harold Aranow
SIC—2655; 3412; 3089; NAICS—322214; *New & reconditioned industrial steel, plastic & fiber drums, IBCs & totes; Brand name—Greif; Mauser; Schutz; General Steel; Ropak*
Employs—49; Estab.—1978
Sales—$11Mil
Distrib.—National
Privately owned corporation

**PHIL-MAR INDUSTRIES**
1800 Copewood St. (08103)
**Phone—(856) 966-0931**
Fax—(856) 966-0293
Email—aptondoor@verizon.net
GM—John Jones
SIC—3442; NAICS—332321; *Rolling steel doors*
Employs—2; Estab.—1988
Sales—$1Mil-$2.5Mil
Distrib.—Intl.
Privately owned corporation
Also see: Fast Doors, LLC, same loc.

**PLASTICS CONSULTING & MFG. CO.**
1431 Ferry Ave. (08104)
**Phone—(856) 963-7700**
National—(800) 222-0317
Fax—(856) 964-8977
www.pcmco.com
Email—sales@pcmco.com

Pres.—Steven Schwartz
V-P., Sales—Jonathan Sinrich
Opers. Mgr.—Kathy Parker
SIC—3795; 2851; NAICS—336992; *Tetrafluoroethylene, flouropolymer & epoxy coating systems for the chemical, pharmaceutical, adhesive, printing & laminating industries; Brand name—Edathon; Super-Poly-Off; Hi-S*
Employs—20
40,000 sq ft site, Distrib.—Intl.
Sole ownership

**PRIDE TEMPERED GLASS PRODUCTS, LLC**
2001 S. 6th St. (08104)
**Phone—(856) 365-1200**
Fax—(856) 365-1207
www.pridetemperedglass.com
Email—sales@pridetemperedglass.com
Pres.—John Galan
V-P., Opers.—Hugh Klein
Cust. Serv. Rep.—Jackie DePiano
SIC—3231; 3499; NAICS—327215; *Tempered & insulated glass & mirrors & metal storefronts, including glass fabrication*
Employs—10; Estab.—2008
Sales—$1Mil-$2.5Mil
Distrib.—Regional
Limited Liability Company

**RF PRODUCTS, INC.**
1500 Davis St. (08103)
**Phone—(856) 365-5500**
Fax—(856) 342-9757
www.rfproductsinc.com
Email—c.abbondante@rfproductsinc.com
Pres.—Robert M. Minke
Ex. V-P.—William E. Smith
V-P., Sales & Mktg.—Frank Arlotta
V-P., Opers.—Carmine Abbondante
V-P.—Rosanne Minke
V-P.—Eileen Minke
SIC—3663; 3669; NAICS—334220; *Radio frequency distribution systems, filters & multicouplers for military communications platforms*
Employs—38; Estab.—1979
Sales—$5Mil-$10Mil
90,000 sq ft site, Distrib.—Intl.
Privately owned corporation
ISO rating—9001:2008

**RIVER FRONT RECYCLING & AGGREGATES, LLC**
1301 N. 26th St. (08105)
Mail addr: 20 Maple Ave., Lumberton (08048)
**Phone—(856) 966-1100**
Fax—(856) 966-0008
www.riverfrontrecycling.com
Owner—Aaron Cave
SIC—3272; *Concrete, asphalt, dirt & wood recycling*
Employs—80; Estab.—2001
Sales—$1Mil-$2.5Mil
Distrib.—Local
Limited Liability Company

**SPRAY COAT FINISHING CO., INC.**
1125 Kaighn Ave. (08103)
**Phone—(856) 541-0950**
www.spraycoat.com
Email—spraycoatinc@gmail.com
Pres.—Chris Brown
V-P.—Jim Brown
SIC—3479; 3471; NAICS—332813; *Electronic component coating & furniture finishing*
Employs—5; Estab.—1980
Sales—under $500,000
10,000 sq ft site, Distrib.—National
Limited Liability Company

## Camden—(cont.)

**STANDARD MERCHANDISING CO. (HQ)**
1125 Wright Ave. (08103)
**Phone—(856) 964-9700**
National—(800) 526-2363
Fax—(866) 793-1150
www.standardmerchandisingco.com
Email—info@stanmerch.com
Pres., CFO—Jeff Tarnoff
V-P.—Lee Tarnoff
Sales Mgr.—Judy Lewis
Off. Mgr.—Donna Rogers
SIC—2252; 3949; 2389; NAICS—339920; *Company headquarters; men's & women's clothing, hosiery, socks, headbands, wristbands & athletic accessories; Brand name—Red Lion; b.ella; nouvella; Qtfeet; E.G. Smith; 2Brothers*
Employs—50; Estab.—1922
Sales—$10Mil
71,000 sq ft site, Distrib.—Intl.
Privately owned sub-S corp.

**STATE METAL INDUSTRIES, INC.**
941 S. 2nd St. (08103)
Mail addr.: P.O. Box 1407, Camden (08101)
**Phone—(856) 964-1510**
Fax—(856) 964-0233
www.statemetalindustries.com
Email—smialum@aol.com
Pres.—Yale Dorfmann
Cont.—Jim Marmion
Sales Mgr.—Jim Hennessy
Hum. Res. Mgr.—Alan Geer
SIC—3355; NAICS—331319; *Aluminum ingot & scrap aluminum*
Employs—100; Estab.—1948
Distrib.—Intl.
Privately owned corporation

**NEW ENTRY**
**VACORD SCREEN PRINTING**
1621 S. Broadway (08104)
**Phone—(888) 787-4587**
www.vacord.com
Email—order@vacord.com
Owner—Stuart Brent
SIC—2396; *Textile screen printing, including apparel & textile bags*
Employs—2; Estab.—2006
Distrib.—National
Privately owned corporation

**WATER SHOPPE, INC., THE**
112 N. 3rd St., 2nd Fl. (08102)
**Phone—(856) 964-4500**
Fax—(856) 969-9676
www.thewatershoppecorp.com
Email—thesourceh2o@gmail.com
Pres.—Carol Alexander
SIC—2086; *Bottled water*
Employs—4; Estab.—1984
Sales—$1Mil-$2.5Mil (est)
Distrib.—National
Privately owned corporation

**†WEINSTEIN SUPPLY CORP.**
Div. of Hajoca Corp.
1687 Haddon Ave. (08103)
**Phone—(856) 964-1700**
Fax—(856) 964-1278
www.weinsteinsupply.com
Email—prf409@hajoca.com
Profit Center Mgr.—Christopher Conte
SIC—5074; 5075; 5085; *Wholesaler of plumbing, heating & air conditioning supplies*
Employs—12; Estab.—1922
Distrib.—Local
Privately owned corporation
Parent co.—Hajoca Corp., Ardmore, PA
Phone—(610) 649-1430
See Parent Co. Section for full profile.

**WINTER, INC. & CO., F. W.**
Delaware Ave. & Elm St. (08102)
**Phone—(856) 963-7490**
Fax—(856) 963-7463
www.fwwinter.com
Email—fwwinter@fwwinter.com
Pres., CEO—Friedrich W. Winter
CFO—Clint Brown
Dir., Comm.—John Vickers
Plt. Mgr.—Dan Martelli
Maint. Mgr.—Russell Creech
Contract & Sales Administrator—Ginny Walsh
SIC—3399; *Metal & alloy powders*
Employs—22; Estab.—1983
Sales—$2.5Mil-$5Mil
60,000 sq ft site, Distrib.—Intl.
Privately owned corporation

---

## Cape May
(Cape May—S.E.)

**†ATLANTIC CAPES FISHERIES, INC.**
985 Ocean Dr. *(08204)*
**Phone—(609) 884-3000**
Fax—(609) 884-3261
www.atlanticcapes.com
Email—info@atlanticcapes.com
Pres.—Daniel Cohen
V-P., Sales—Jeff Bolton
V-P., Opers.—Sam Martin
SIC—5146; *Distributor of scallops & related seafoods; Brand name—Cape May Salt Oysters*
Employs—50; Estab.—1984
Sales—$175Mil
30,000 sq ft site, Distrib.—Intl.
Privately owned corporation

**CAPE PRINTING EXPRESS, INC.**
821 Shunpike Rd. (08204)
**Phone—(609) 884-8080**
Fax—(609) 884-4425
Email—printing821@comcast.net
Pres.—Richard Adelizzi
SIC—2752; 2791; NAICS—323122; *Offset printing & typesetting*
Employs—2; Estab.—1987
Sales—under $500,000
17,000 sq ft site, Distrib.—Local
Privately owned corporation
Also see: Great American Trolley Co., same loc.

**NEW ENTRY**
**CAPE PUBLISHING, INC.**
513 Washington St. (08204)
**Phone—(609) 898-4500**
www.capemay.com
Email—info@capemay.com
Owner—Bernar Haas
SIC—2721; *Magazine publishing*
Employs—5
Sales—under $500,000 (est)

**EXIT ZERO PUBLISHING**
109 Sunset Blvd., Ste. D (08204)
**Phone—(609) 770-8479**
Fax—(609) 770-8481
www.exitzero.us
Email—info@exitzero.us
Pres., Publisher & Editor—Jack Wright
Adv. Mgr.—Jason Black
SIC—2711; *Weekly newspaper publishing*
Employs—4; Estab.—2004
Distrib.—Local
Privately owned corporation

**FLYING FISH STUDIO**
130 Park Blvd. (08204)
**Phone—(609) 884-2760**
National—(800) 639-2085
Fax—(609) 884-9295
www.theflyingfishstudio.com
Email—flyingfishstudio@yahoo.com
Owner—Sue Lotozo
Sales Mgr.—Megan Magill

SIC—2396; *Textile screen printing*
Employs—4; Estab.—1991
Sales—$500,000-$1Mil
Distrib.—Local
Sole ownership

**GREAT AMERICAN TROLLEY CO. (HQ)**
821 Shunpike Rd. *(08204)*
**Phone—(609) 884-0450**
(609) 884-4076
National—(800) 487-6559
Fax—(609) 884-5980
www.gatrolley.com
Email—info@gatrolley.com
Pres.—Richard Adelizzi
Dir., Mktg.—Stephanie Schwartz
Proj. Mgr.—Damien Staples
SIC—3743; *Company headquarters; trackless trolleys*
Employs—50; Estab.—1981
Sales—$5Mil-$10Mil
17,000 sq ft site, Distrib.—Intl.
Also see: Cape Printing Express, Inc., same loc.

**HERITAGE TOWERS, INC.**
910 Shunpike Rd., Ste. B (08204)
**Phone—(609) 884-5999**
Fax—(609) 884-9744
www.heritagetowersinc.com
Email—htitower@comcast.net
Owner & Pres.—Michael Seaverns
Foreman—Mike Hollenback
SIC—3444; 3446; *Custom aluminum fabrication of fishing towers, t-towers, leaning posts, bow rails, rod holders & pilothouses for the sport fishing & marine industries & stairs, handrails, gates & fencing for residential & commercial projects*
Employs—2; Estab.—1989
Sales—$1Mil-$2.5Mil
Distrib.—Regional
Privately owned corporation

**INKWELL CORP.**
1414 Elmira St. (08204)
**Phone—(609) 884-0350**
Fax—(609) 884-0883
www.capemay4fun.com
Email—cyril@comcast.net
Pres.—Heide Cummings
SIC—2752; 2796; NAICS—323122; *Offset printing & textile screen printing*
Employs—3; Estab.—1979
Sales—under $500,000
Distrib.—Local
Privately owned corporation

**LUND'S FISHERIES CO.**
997 Ocean Dr., P.O. Box 830 *(08204)*
**Phone—(609) 884-7600**
Fax—(609) 884-0664
www.lundsfish.com
Email—info@lundsfish.com
Pres.—Jeffrey Reichle
V-P.—Wayne Reichle
Plt. Mgr.—John Hruska
SIC—2092; NAICS—311712; *Company headquarters & fish processing*
Employs—200; Estab.—1956
Sales—$25Mil-$50Mil
Distrib.—Intl.

**MARK I INDUSTRIES, INC.**
910 Shunpike Rd. (08204)
**Phone—(609) 884-0051**
Fax—(609) 884-0778
Owner—Robert Bartle
SIC—3599; *General machining job shop*
Employs—15; Estab.—1973
Sales—$1Mil-$2.5Mil (est)
Distrib.—Local
Privately owned corporation
Also see: T M U, Inc., same loc.
AKA: T M U, Inc.

**MURPHY FENCE CO., INC.**
507 Seashore Rd. (08204)
**Phone—(609) 886-1635**
Fax—(609) 898-0880
www.murphyfence.com
Email—info@murphyfence.com
CEO—Amy Litton
Pres.—Ryan Litton
SIC—2499; 3089; 3444; *Wooden, PVC & aluminum fencing & PVC railing*
Employs—25; Estab.—1962
Sales—under $500,000
Distrib.—Local
Privately owned corporation

**†NORTHEAST INDUSTRIAL, LLC**
661 Route 9 (08204)
**Phone—(609) 884-3510**
National—(800) 884-3152
Fax—(609) 884-3170
www.northeastindustrialnj.com
Email—contact@northeastindustrialnj.com
Pres., GM—Donald Carter
Secy-Treas.—Kyle Carter
SIC—5084; 5063; *Distributor of hydraulic, marine, industrial & electric winches & related equipment, including diesel generator sets, engines, power units & control stations*
Employs—2; Estab.—1987
Sales—under $1.5Mil
4,000 sq ft site, Distrib.—National
Limited Liability Partnership

**ROSEMAN'S BOAT YARD & CHARTER**
5 Roseman Ln. (08204)
**Phone—(609) 884-3370**
Fax—(609) 884-3311
Ptnr.—Joan Roseman
Ptnr.—Don Wiscott
SIC—3732; *Rebuilt boats*
Employs—2; Estab.—1975
Sales—under $500,000
Distrib.—Local
Sole ownership

**SEA GEAR MARINE SUPPLY, INC.**
1144 Route 109 (08204)
**Phone—(609) 884-2711**
National—(800) 627-4327
Fax—(609) 884-8467
www.seagearmarine.com
Email—info@seagearmarine.com
Owner, Pres. & CFO—Chuck Barto
Plt. Mgr.—Bruce Barto
IT Mgr.—Cindy Pierce
Manager—Sean Barto
SIC—3496; 3429; *Wire rope & sling assembly & hardware products*
Employs—14; Estab.—1985
25,000 sq ft site, Distrib.—National
Privately owned corporation

**SNOW'S**
Div. of Bumble Bee Foods, LLC
994 Ocean Dr. *(08204)*
**Phone—(609) 884-0440**
(800) 459-0396
Fax—(609) 898-2409
www.bumblebee.com
Email—larry.rossello@bumblebee.com
V-P., GM—Steve Veltman
Cont. & Hum. Res. Mgr.—Larry Rossello
SIC—2091; NAICS—311711; *Canned clams, clam chowder, broths & soups; Brand name—Snow's*
Employs—90
Sales—$10Mil-$25Mil
79,000 sq ft site, Distrib.—National
Limited Liability Company
Parent co.—Bumble Bee Foods, LLC, San Diego, CA
Phone—(858) 715-4000
See Parent Co. Section for full profile.

GEOGRAPHICAL

## Cape May—(cont.)

**T M U, INC.**
910 Shunpike Rd. (08204)
**Phone—(609) 884-7656**
Fax—(609) 884-0778
www.tmuinc.com
Email—tmu@comcast.net
Owner & Pres.—Robert Bartle
Plt. Mgr.—Mark Bartle
Off. Mgr.—Donna Bartle
SIC—3556; 3599; NAICS—
333294; *Food processing
machinery, precision machine
parts & CNC production job
shop*
Employs—10; Estab.—1965
18,000 sq ft site, Distrib.—National
Privately owned corporation
Also see: Mark I Industries, Inc.,
same loc.

**W J R B, INC.**
711 Town Bank Rd. (08204)
**Phone—(609) 884-1169**
Fax—(609) 884-5131
www.capemaywinery.com
Email—info@capemaywinery.com
Pres.—Toby Craig
V.-P.—Darren Heffington
SIC—2084; NAICS—312130;
*Wines*
Employs—5; Estab.—1995
Sales—$500,000-$1Mil
Distrib.—Local
Privately owned corporation
AKA: Cape May Winery

## Cape May Court House
(Cape May—S.E.)

NEW ENTRY
**BRIGHT SIDE NEWSPAPER**
1560 Route 83 (08210)
**Phone—(609) 861-2034**
www.brightsidenewspaper.com
Email—news@
brightsidenewspaper.com
Owner—Daniel Keen
Sales Mgr.—Rhonda Keen
SIC—2711; *Newspaper
publishing*
Employs—4; Estab.—1994
Sales—under $500,000
2,000 sq ft site, Distrib.—Local
Privately owned corporation

NEW ENTRY
**CAPE MINING & RECYCLING, LLC**
560 Goshen Rd., P.O. Box 246
(08210)
**Phone—(609) 465-3277**
Fax—(609) 463-1878
www.capeminingandrecycling.com
Owner—Phil Heun, Jr.
Off. Mgr.—Debbie Heun
SIC—1442; NAICS—331492;
*Stone recycling & sand & gravel
processing*
Employs—20; Estab.—2013
Distrib.—Local
Limited Liability Company

†**COLONIAL ELECTRIC SUPPLY CO.,
THE**
1143 S. Route 9 (08210)
**Phone—(609) 465-7144**
Fax—(609) 465-8456
www.colonialelectric.com
Email—info@colonialelectric.com
Br. Mgr.—Chris Brunetti
SIC—5063; *Distributor of electrical
equipment & supplies, including
lighting, wire & cable*
Distrib.—Local
Privately owned corporation
Parent co.—Colonial Electric
Supply Co., The, King of Prussia,
PA
Phone—(610) 312-8100
See Parent Co. Section for full profile.

**COMMERCIAL WATER SPORTS, INC.**
28 Clermont Dr. (08210)
**Phone—(609) 624-3404**
Fax—(609) 624-3402
www.cwsboats.com
Email—sales@cwsboats.com
Pres.—Rob Guarini
V.-P.—Pam Guarini
Prodn. Mgr.—Mark Larson
SIC—3732; 3089; *Custom
commercial fiberglass 31-foot &
35-foot parasail boats*
Employs—5; Estab.—2001
Sales—$500,000-$1Mil
Distrib.—Intl.
Privately owned corporation
AKA: CWS

**FLYING T-SHIRTS**
217 1st Ave. (08210)
**Phone—(609) 463-0397**
Fax—(609) 463-4643
Email—flyingtshirts4u@yahoo.com
Owner—Edward Donnelly
Off. Mgr.—Jeannette Donnelly
SIC—2396; *T-shirt screen printing*
Employs—2; Estab.—1976
Sales—under $500,000
Distrib.—Local
Sole ownership

**J & R PRINTING, INC.**
301 S. Main St. (08210)
**Phone—(609) 465-3530**
Fax—(609) 465-3530
Owner & Pres.—Jerry Gau
SIC—2759; NAICS—323100;
*Commercial printing*
Employs—1; Estab.—1976
Sales—under $500,000
Distrib.—Local
Sole ownership

**MITCHELL WELDING & IRON
WORKS, INC.**
7 Enterprise Dr. (08210)
**Phone—(609) 465-7510**
Fax—(609) 465-7337
www.mitchellironworks.com
Email—sales@
mitchellironworks.com
Pres., CFO—William Mitchell
V.-P., Fin.—Harry A. Mitchell, Jr.
SIC—3441; 3499; NAICS—
332312; *Structural steel & metal
fabrication*
Employs—8; Estab.—1949
Sales—$1Mil-$2.5Mil
13,000 sq ft site, Distrib.—Local
Privately owned corporation

**NATALI VINEYARDS, LLC**
221 N. Delsea Dr. (08210)
**Phone—(609) 465-0075**
www.natalivineyards.com
Email—natalivineyards@gmail.com
Pres.—Alfred Natali
Manager—Elizabeth Franco
SIC—2084; NAICS—312130;
*Wine*
Employs—6; Estab.—2000
Sales—under $500,000
Distrib.—Local
Privately owned corporation

**SHOEMAKER'S AUTOMOTIVE
MACHINE**
176 Kings Hwy. (08210)
**Phone—(609) 624-0847**
Fax—(609) 624-0655
Email—ishoemaker@comcast.net
Owner—Doug Shoemaker
SIC—3714; 3519; *Rebuilt
automotive engines*
Employs—1; Estab.—1979
Sales—under $500,000
Distrib.—Regional
Sole ownership

**SHROP'S SHOP**
1254 S. Route 9 (08210)
**Phone—(609) 465-1640**
Owner—Bill Shropshire

SIC—3312; *Steel fabrication*
Employs—1; Estab.—1977
Sales—under $500,000
Distrib.—Local

**THOMAS INSTRUMENTATION, INC.**
118 Kings Hwy. (08210)
Mail addr: 133 Landing Rd.,
Clermont (08210)
**Phone—(609) 624-7777**
Fax—(609) 624-8863
www.tiweb.net
Email—info@tiweb.net
CEO—Cassandra Gluyas
Sr. Techn.—Bill Riley
SIC—3672; NAICS—334412;
*Electronic circuit board
assembly for the industrial,
transportation, amusement park,
multimedia, consumer
electronics, biopharmaceutical,
medical, agricultural & defense
industries*
Employs—11; Estab.—1971
Sales—$1Mil-$2.5Mil
Distrib.—National
Sole ownership
Parent co.—Thomas
Instrumentation, Inc., Cape May
Court House, NJ
Phone—(609) 624-2630
See Parent Co. Section for full profile.

**THOMAS INSTRUMENTATION, INC.
(H Q)**
133 Landing Rd. (08210)
**Phone—(609) 624-2630**
Fax—(609) 486-6725
www.tiweb.net
Email—info@tiweb.net
CEO & Engr.—Cassandra Gluyas
Pres. & Engrg. Supv.—Thomas
Gluyas
CFO—Jan Gluyas
SIC—3625; 3672; NAICS—
335314; *Corporate
headquarters; custom
microcontrollers, including
design & electronic circuit board
assembly*
Employs—16; Estab.—1971
Sales—$2.6Mil-$5Mil
Distrib.—Intl.
Privately owned corporation

†**TRI-COUNTY BUILDING SUPPLIES,
INC.**
14 Reading Ave. (08210)
**Phone—(609) 465-5021**
Fax—(609) 465-5820
www.tcbsi.com
Email—webmaster@tcbsi.com
Br. Mgr.—Gary Rousseau
Asst. Mgr.—Randy Bakley
SIC—5031; 5033; *Distributor of
building supplies, including
lumber, plywood, roofing
shingles & coatings, insulation &
vinyl siding*
Employs—20; Estab.—1983
Distrib.—Regional
Privately owned corporation
Parent co.—Tri-County Building
Supplies, Inc., Pleasantville, NJ
Phone—(609) 646-0950
See Parent Co. Section for full profile.

†**TRI-COUNTY BUILDING SUPPLIES,
INC.**
211 Stites & Railroad Aves.
(08210)
**Phone—(609) 465-7839**
National—(800) 465-7838
Fax—(609) 465-4485
www.tcbsi.com
Email—webmaster@tcbsi.com
GM—Gary Rouseau
Inside Sales Agt.—Chris Kane
SIC—5033; 5032; *Wholesaler of
roofing, siding & sheet rock*
Employs—14; Estab.—1964
Distrib.—Regional
Privately owned corporation

Parent co.—Tri-County Building
Supplies, Inc., Pleasantville, NJ
Phone—(609) 646-0950
See Parent Co. Section for full profile.

## Carlstadt
(Bergen—N.E.)

**A & S PACKAGING & DISPLAY CORP.**
120 Kero Rd. (07072)
**Phone—(201) 531-1900**
Fax—(201) 531-1930
www.aspkg.com
Email—customer.service@
aspkg.com
Pres.—Roy Andersen
V.-P.—Brett Andersen
V.-P.—Eric Andersen
Corp. Secy.—Joanne Doupona
SIC—3086; 3089; NAICS—
326100; *Foam, EPS,
polystyrene, polyethylene &
urethane packaging,
architectural & display products,
floats & production sets*
Employs—15; Estab.—1959
Sales—over $2.5Mil
23,000 sq ft site, Distrib.—
Regional
Privately owned corporation

**ADVANTAGE PACKAGING
TECHNOLOGIES, LLC**
P.O. Box 301 (07072)
**Phone—(201) 832-1858**
Fax—(201) 939-0595
Email—grice@aarobotics.com
Ptnr.—Glenn Rice
Ptnr.—Mike Kavanagh
SIC—3565; NAICS—333993;
*Packaging machinery*
Employs—4; Estab.—1999
Distrib.—National
Privately owned partnership

†**AIRMATIC COMPRESSOR SYSTEMS,
INC.**
700 Washington Ave. (07072)
**Phone—(201) 342-1300**
National—(800) 864-7621
Fax—(201) 342-6241
www.airmaticcompressor.com
Email—service@
airmaticcompressor.com
Pres.—William N. Vowteras
SIC—5084; 5075; 5169;
*Distributor of air compressors,
compressed air treatment,
HVAC, boilers, chillers &
ductwork; Brand name—Atlas
Copco; Trane; Zeks; Carrier;
Aerco; Airtech; Fujitsu*
Employs—30; Estab.—1975
Sales—$8Mil-$11Mil
22,000 sq ft site, Distrib.—
Regional
Privately owned sub-S corp.

†**ALLIED BEVERAGE GROUP, LLC**
600 Washington Ave., P.O. Box
838 (07072)
**Phone—(201) 842-6200**
National—(800) 313-6767
Fax—(201) 842-6330
www.alliedbeverage.com
Email—jolynn.kawoczka@
alliedbeverage.com
Co-Chrm.—Eric M. Perlmutter
CIO—Brian Margolies
V.-P., Hum. Res.—Jolynn
Kawoczka
SIC—5182; 5181; *Company
headquarters & distributor of
wines, spirits & beers*
Employs—500; Estab.—1934
490,000 sq ft site, Distrib.—
Regional
Limited Liability Company

**ALLIED ENVELOPE CO., INC.**
33 Commerce Rd. (07072)
**Phone—(201) 440-2000**
Fax—(201) 507-8812

## Carlstadt—(cont.)

www.nowallied.com
Email—croyer@nowallied.com
Pres.—James Royer
V.-P., Sales—Jeff Miller
V.-P., E-Proc.—Chris Royer
GM—Andy Paretti
Plt. Mgr.—Dean Peragallo
Off. Mgr.—Roy Ward
Cust. Serv. Rep.—Sue Bana
SIC—2759; 2752; 2677; NAICS—
323100; *Full-service direct mail
& commercial printing of
business envelopes, letters,
forms & inserts*
Employs—50; Estab.—1932
Sales—$11Mil-$25Mil
65,000 sq ft site, Distrib.—National
Privately owned sub-S corp.
DBA: Allied Printing Resources

**AMERICAN GLASS CRAFTERS, INC.**
193 Veterans Blvd. (07072)
**Phone—(201) 525-1116**
National—(888) 683-1362
Fax—(201) 525-1117
www.glasscraftersinc.com
Email—sales@glasscraftersinc.com
Pres.—Joseph Cano
GM—Joseph Santolla
IT Mgr.—Bob Westervelt
SIC—3442; 3231; NAICS—
332321; *Frameless shower
doors*
Employs—35; Estab.—1994
Distrib.—Regional
Privately owned corporation

†**AMERICAN PAPER & SUPPLY CO.,
LLC**
10 Industrial Rd., P.O. Box 346
(07072)
**Phone—(201) 939-4200**
Fax—(201) 939-8668
www.apsjansan.com
Email—info@
americanpapertowel.com
Owner—Larry Shapiro
V.-P.—Jonathan Shapiro
V.-P.—Kevin Gray
Off. Mgr.—Judy Kostnicka
Cust. Serv. Rep.—Helen Montorio
SIC—5113; 5063; 5169; *Distributor
of maintenance/janitorial
supplies & equipment; Brand
name—GP; KC; Spartan
Chemical; Johnsons Wax;
Ecolab; Rubbermaid; Aluf
Plastic Bags; Techncial
Concepts; Gojo; Purell; 3M;
Tuway; Tornado; Kent; Bobrick;
ASI; Sylvania; GE*
Employs—45; Estab.—1932
90,000 sq ft site, Distrib.—
Regional
Privately owned corporation

**ARCY MFG. CO., INC.**
575 Industrial Rd. (07072)
**Phone—(201) 635-1910**
Fax—(201) 635-1911
www.arcy-mfg.com
Email—bob@arcymfg.com
Pres.—Bob Mattesky
V.-P.—Marc Mattesky
Off. Mgr.—Jackie Nievs
SIC—3053; NAICS—339991;
*Industrial gaskets & sealing
products; Brand name—
Flexitallic®; Garlock Sealing
Technologies®; Durlon® Sealing
Products; Theromseal®; JM
Clipper; elringklinger*
Employs—10; Estab.—1934
Sales—$3Mil-$4.5Mil
9,600 sq ft site, Distrib.—Intl.
Privately owned corporation

**ARDE BARINCO, INC.**
Div. of Arde, Inc.
875 Washington Ave. (07072)
**Phone—(201) 768-6070**
National—(800) 909-6070

Fax—(201) 784-0483
www.abmixer.com
Email—abmix@ardeinc.com
Engrg. & Sales Mgr.—Roy Scott
SIC—3559; *Mixing equipment,
high-shear rotor & stator mixers
& homogenizers for chemical,
personal care product, food,
pharmaceutical, cosmetic,
coating, paper & textile products
manufacturing & processing;
Brand name—Dispershear;
Double Helixx Mixer; DICON In-
Line Dispersing Grinder;
Reversible Homogenizing Mixer;
Cavitron Reactor System;
MAXIMIXER; MEGAGRINDER*
Employs—4; Estab.—1973
Sales—$2Mil
18,000 sq ft site, Distrib.—Intl.
Publicly owned corporation
Parent co.—Arde, Inc., Carlstadt,
NJ
Phone—(201) 784-9880
See Parent Co. Section for full profile.

**ARDE, INC.**
Div. of Aerojet Rocketdyne, Inc.
875 Washington Ave. (07072)
**Phone—(201) 784-9880**
Fax—(201) 784-9710
www.ardeinc.com
Email—admin@ardeinc.com
GM—Kirk Sneddon
SIC—3764; *Corporate
headquarters & guided missiles
& space vehicles pressure &
propellant tanks*
Employs—60; Estab.—1962
54,000 sq ft site, Distrib.—Intl.
Publicly owned corporation
Parent co.—Aerojet Rocketdyne,
Inc., Canoga Park, CA
Phone—(818) 586-1000
See Parent Co. Section for full profile.

**BAIK KWANG CORP.**
601 Commercial Ave., P.O. Box
7072 (07072)
**Phone—(201) 507-9985**
Fax—(201) 507-9980
www.cityhuntercapusa.com
Email—sales@cityhuntercap.com
Pres.—Sung Y. Park
Manager—Danny Lee
SIC—2353; *Skiing hats & baseball
caps*
Employs—10; Estab.—1991
Distrib.—Intl.
Privately owned corporation
DBA: City Hunter

**BETA PLASTICS CORP.**
Div. of Alpha Industries Corp.
120 Amor Ave. (07072)
Mail addr: P.O. Box 808, Lyndhurst
(07071)
**Phone—(201) 933-1400**
National—(800) 327-0672
Fax—(201) 933-0089
www.alpha-industries.com
Email—info@alpha-industries.com
Plt. Mgr.—Roland Teo
SIC—2673; *Plastic bags*
Employs—100; Estab.—1992
Distrib.—National
Privately owned corporation
Parent co.—Alpha Industries
Corp., Lyndhurst, NJ
Phone—(201) 933-6000
See Parent Co. Section for full profile.

**BETA SCREEN CORP.**
707 Commercial Ave. (07072)
**Phone—(201) 939-2400**
National—(800) 272-7336
Fax—(201) 939-7656
www.betascreen.net
Email—info@betascreen.com
Pres.—Arnold Serchuk
Cont., Fin. Mgr.—Sandy M. Titsch
GM—Klaus Wandschneider
Sales Mgr.—Stuart Serchuk
MIS Mgr.—Larry Goldberg

SIC—3555; NAICS—333293;
*Microscopes, prepress quality
control equipment, printer quality
control tools & densitometers for
the graphic arts industry*
Employs—9; Estab.—1957
20,000 sq ft site, Distrib.—Intl.
Privately owned corporation
AKA: Beta Industries

**BETTI INDUSTRIES, INC., H.**
303 Patterson Plank Rd. (07072)
**Phone—(201) 438-1300**
National—(800) 524-2343
Fax—(201) 438-4837
www.betson.com
Email—sales@betson.com
Chrm., CEO—Peter Betti
Pres., CFO—Bob Geschine, Sr.
IT Mgr.—Debra Wilson
Hum. Res. Mgr.—Linda Troy
SIC—3581; 3999; NAICS—
333311; *Corporate headquarters
& rebuilt vending & amusement
gaming machines*
Employs—140
Company-wide: 250
Sales—$10Mil-$25Mil (est)
Privately owned corporation
AKA: Betson Enterprises

**BIF NEW YORK, INC.**
465 Barell Ave. (07072)
**Phone—(201) 933-7777**
Fax—(201) 933-6261
www.bifnewyork.com
Email—info@bifnewyork.com
Pres.—Tommy Lee
SIC—2522; 2521; *Office furniture,
including chairs, tables, desks &
bookcases*
Employs—10; Estab.—2001
Sales—$1Mil-$2.5Mil (est)
Distrib.—Intl.
Privately owned corporation

**BURGER MAKER, INC.**
666 16th St. (07072)
**Phone—(201) 939-4747**
Fax—(201) 939-1965
www.burgermaker.com
Email—jschweid@burgermaker.com
Pres.—David Schweid
CFO—Mike Perchiacca
Ex. V.-P.—Jamie Schweid
Hum. Res. Mgr.—Migdalia Roman
SIC—2011; NAICS—311611;
*Gourmet hamburger patties for
foodservice distributors*
Employs—200; Estab.—1978
Distrib.—Regional
Privately owned corporation

**C & R PRINTING, INC.**
400 Gotham Pkwy. (07072)
**Phone—(201) 933-8000**
Fax—(201) 933-3589
GM—Dave Clarizio
SIC—2752; NAICS—323100;
*Offset printing*
Employs—10; Estab.—1964
Sales—$500,000-$1Mil
Distrib.—Regional
Privately owned corporation

**C T A MFG. CORP.**
263 Veterans Blvd. (07072)
**Phone—(201) 896-1000**
Fax—(201) 896-1378
www.ctatools.com
Email—info@ctatools.com
Pres.—Michael Borghard
V.-P.—Karen Borghard
Opers. Mgr.—Donna Reiff
Pur. Mgr.—Jamie Rubel
Traf. Mgr.—Mary Jane Tucker
SIC—3089; *Handtools*
Employs—40; Estab.—1977
25,000 sq ft site, Distrib.—Intl.
Privately owned corporation

**CARNEGIE DELI, INC.**
605 Washington Ave. (07072)
**Phone—(201) 507-5557**
National—(877) 898-3354
Fax—(201) 507-5584
www.carnegiedeli.com
Email—theplant@carnegiedeli.com
Pres., GM—James Jorgenson
Hum. Res. Mgr.—Gisela Moreno
SIC—2013; NAICS—311600; *Deli
products*
Employs—14; Estab.—1930
Distrib.—National
Privately owned corporation

**CERTIFIED BAKERY, INC.**
20 Universal Pl. (07072)
**Phone—(201) 635-9245**
Fax—(201) 635-9249
Email—certifiedbakery@
earthlink.net
Pres.—Sam Grunfeld
Sales Mgr.—Ron Grunfeld
SIC—2051; NAICS—311812;
*Breads & rolls*
Employs—75; Estab.—1983
Sales—$5Mil-$10Mil
Distrib.—National
Privately owned corporation

**CHANDLER MACHINE CO., INC.**
400 Veterans Blvd. (07072)
**Phone—(212) 741-2474**
Fax—(212) 741-2481
www.chandlermachineco.com
Email—sales@
chandlermachineco.com
V.-P., Opers.—Michael Feit
SIC—3552; NAICS—333292;
*Industrial hand-operated &
electrical sewing machines for
the garment trade, dry cleaning
establishments & laundries*
Employs—10; Estab.—1905
Sales—under $500,000
Distrib.—National
Privately owned corporation
Also see: Consolidated Sewing
Machine Corp., same loc.

**CITROMAX USA**
444 Washington Ave. *(07072)*
**Phone—(201) 933-8405**
Fax—(201) 933-8217
www.citromax.com
Email—cgonzabay@citroil.com
Pres.—Vivian Glueck
Dir., R & D—Elaine Kellman
Dir., Qual. Control—Joe Clark
SIC—2087; NAICS—311900;
*Citrus processing, including
natural & organic lemon oil &
lemon juice & sweet & fruit
flavors; Brand name—Citromax;
Citroil*
Employs—35; Estab.—1964
Sales—$25Mil-$50Mil (est)
45,000 sq ft site, Distrib.—Intl.
Privately owned sub-S corp.

**CITY THEATRICAL, INC.**
475 Barell Ave. (07072)
**Phone—(201) 549-1160**
National—(800) 230-9497
Fax—(201) 549-1161
www.citytheatrical.com
Email—info@citytheatrical.com
Pres.—Gary Fails
Mktg. Mgr.—Jennifer Tipton
Cust. Serv. Rep.—J. C. Moore
SIC—3648; NAICS—335129;
*Theatrical lighting accessories*
Employs—34; Estab.—1986
Sales—$500,000-$1Mil
40,000 sq ft site, Distrib.—Intl.
Privately owned sub-S corp.

**CLAUDE BAMBERGER MOLDING
COMPOUNDS CORP.**
111 Paterson Plank Rd., P.O. Box
67 (07072)
**Phone—(201) 933-6262**
Fax—(201) 933-8129

GEOGRAPHICAL

## Carlstadt—(cont.)

www.claudebamberger.com
Email—info@claudebamberger.com
Pres.—Claude Bamberger
V.-P.—Mo-Li Siow
Off. Mgr.—Mary Jethanamest
SIC—2821; 5162; *Manufacturer & distributor of purging compounds used for cleaning plastic machinery, including injection molding machines, extruders & blow molding equipment*
Employs—7; Estab.—1953
Distrib.—Intl.
Privately owned corporation

### COLORA HENNA

217 Washington Ave. (07072)
**Phone—(201) 939-0969**
National—(800) 989-0969
Fax—(201) 939-0516
Pres.—Esther Benattar
V.-P.—Nisso Benattar
Off. Mgr.—Donna Courter
SIC—2844; NAICS—325600; *Hair coloring preparations*
Employs—9; Estab.—1968
10,000 sq ft site, Distrib.—Intl.
Privately owned corporation

### COLOREDGE

Div. of Coloredge Visual
190 Jony Dr. (07072)
**Phone—(201) 716-5200**
National—(800) 321-8864
www.coloredgevisual.com
Email—sales@coloredge.com
Dir.—Tony Chester
SIC—2759; 2542; 3993; *Large-format printing & visual displays & exhibits & billboard finishing*
Employs—50
Sales—$5Mil-$10Mil (est)
Distrib.—National
Privately owned corporation
Parent co.—Coloredge Visual, New York, NY
Phone—(212) 594-4800
See Parent Co. Section for full profile.

**NEW ENTRY**
### COMP24, LLC

190 Jony Dr. (07072)
**Phone—(212) 502-6511**
(201) 716-5200
National—(800) 848-7716
www.comp24.com
Email—comp@comp24.com
Dir., Opers.—Paul Rosenblit
Sales Mgr.—Jim Buenayentetura
Hum. Res. Mgr.—Krishna Basedeo
SIC—2396; *Company headquarters & textile screen printing*
Employs—28; Estab.—1985
Sales—$2.5Mil-$5Mil
22,000 sq ft site, Distrib.—National
Limited Liability Company

### COMPONENTS & CONTROLS, INC.

495 Washington Ave., P.O. Box 437 (07072)
**Phone—(201) 438-9190**
Fax—(201) 438-3356
www.componentsandcontrols.com
Email—sales@componentsandcontrols.com
Pres., CEO—Jerry Orlando

SIC—3599; 3052; NAICS—326220; *Flexible metal & TFE hoses & industrial & instrumentation products; Brand name—Parker; Barksdale; McDaniel; Winters; Versa; 3 B Filter; Technitrace; Cameron; Contromatics; Adsco*
Employs—21; Estab.—1972
Sales—$1Mil-$10Mil
11,000 sq ft site, Distrib.—National
Privately owned corporation
AKA: Royal Instruments Div.

### CONSOLIDATED SEWING MACHINE CORP.

400 Veterans Blvd. (07072)
**Phone—(212) 741-7788**
National—(800) 221-8494
Fax—(212) 741-2150
www.consew.com
Email—consew@worldnet.att.net
Pres.—Murray Feit
V.-P., Opers.—Michael Feit
SIC—3559; *Corporate headquarters & industrial sewing machines, clutch motors & accessories*
Employs—29; Estab.—1898
30,000 sq ft site, Distrib.—Intl.
Privately owned corporation
Also see: Chandler Machine Co., Inc., same loc.

### CONTENT CRITICAL LLC

800 Central Blvd. (07072)
**Phone—(201) 528-2777**
Fax—(201) 804-6394
www.contentcritical.com
CEO—Fred VanAlstyne
COO—John Slaney
V.-P., Sales—Mitchell Koff
V.-P., Sales—Ronald Koff
SIC—2752; 2759; 2789; NAICS—323100; *Lithographic, wide-format & digital printing, mailing, fulfillment & binding*
Employs—203; Estab.—1916
Sales—$10Mil-$25Mil (est)
Distrib.—National
Privately owned corporation

### COORDINATED METALS CO., INC.

626 16th St. (07072)
**Phone—(201) 460-7280**
Fax—(201) 460-1821
www.cmi-metals.com
Email—sales@cmi-metals.com
Pres.—Frank Grippi
CFO—Scott Eisenberger
V.-P.—Paul Santo
SIC—3446; NAICS—332323; *Architectural & ornamental metal fabrication*
Employs—52; Estab.—1974
Sales—$14Mil-$17Mil
35,754 sq ft site, Distrib.—Local
Privately owned sub-S corp.

### COSMETIC COATINGS, INC.

219 Broad St., P.O. Box 95 (07072)
**Phone—(201) 438-7150**
Fax—(201) 438-7568
Pres.—Richard Gottesman
Off. Mgr.—Shari Skay
SIC—2844; NAICS—325600; *Nail polish*
Employs—20; Estab.—1991
Distrib.—Local
Privately owned corporation

### CUTTING TECHNIQUES, INC.

651 Industrial Rd. (07072)
**Phone—(201) 438-2222**
Fax—(201) 438-5151
www.cticando.com
Email—make@cticando.com
Pres.—Ron Radomski

SIC—3599; *General machining job shop, including abrasive waterjet cutting, wire EDM, CNC machining & blanchard grinding*
Employs—6; Estab.—1995
Sales—$500,000-$1Mil
6,000 sq ft site, Distrib.—Local
Privately owned corporation

### †DCI CHEESE CO.

861 Washington Ave. (07072)
**Phone—(201) 807-0999**
National—(800) 445-5496
Fax—(201) 807-9509
www.dcicheeseco.com
Email—moreinfo@dcicheeseco.com
Pres.—Kevin Therault
Cust. Serv. Rep.—Kerry McCarthy
Cust. Serv. Rep.—Angela Barrett
Cust. Serv. Rep.—Patty Tellian
SIC—5143; *Distributor of traditional, organic & specialty cheeses & related products*
Employs—30; Estab.—2008
Distrib.—National
Privately owned corporation
AKA: Sapuco Cheese
Parent co.—DCI Cheese Co., Richfield, WI
Phone—(262) 677-3407
See Parent Co. Section for full profile.

### DELTA MACHINE WORKS, INC.

257 Division Ave. (07072)
**Phone—(201) 935-7474**
Fax—(201) 935-5577
www.deltamachineworks.com
Email—mike@deltamachineworks.com
Pres., R & D Mgr.—Michael Alpos
MIS & Opers. Mgr.—John Marshall
Fin. Mgr.—Maria Alpos
SIC—3599; *General machining job shop*
Employs—3; Estab.—1981
Sales—under $500,000
3,000 sq ft site, Distrib.—Regional
Sole ownership

### DESIGN DISPLAY GROUP, INC.

105 Amor Ave. (07072)
**Phone—(201) 438-6000**
Fax—(201) 438-5599
www.designdisplaygroup.com
Email—sales@designdisplaygroup.com
Pres., CEO—Andrew Freedman
COO—John Bollbach
Ex. V.-P., Pur.—Harvinder Bedi
Ex. V.-P., Design & Engrg.—Jonathon Loew
Dir., Opers.—Steve Lorras
SIC—3993; 2541; 2542; *Custom point-of-purchase displays & store fixtures & interiors*
Employs—150; Estab.—1985
Sales—$26Mil-$29Mil
110,000 sq ft site, Distrib.—Intl.
Privately owned sub-S corp.

### DESIGNER SIGN SYSTEMS, LLC

352 Washington Ave. (07072)
**Phone—(201) 939-5577**
Fax—(201) 939-7043
www.dss-nj.com
Email—sales@dss-nj.com
Ptnr.—Danijel Farkas
Ptnr.—Kevin Hartnett
Ptnr.—James Hartnett
Ptnr.—Christine Considine
SIC—3993; *Healthcare, educational, corporate, institutional, municipal & residential sign systems, including sign planning & design services, design-build signage programs, budget development & feasibility studies*
Employs—11; Estab.—1979
Sales—$2Mil-$2.5Mil
10,000 sq ft site, Distrib.—National
Limited Liability Company

### DOHRMAN PRINTING CO., INC.

445 Industrial Rd. (07072)
**Phone—(201) 933-0346**
National—(800) 203-7746
Fax—(201) 933-0356
www.dohrmanprinting.com
Email—sales@dohrmanprinting.com
Pres., Fin., MIS & R & D Mgr.—Kenny Bell
V.-P.—Lisa Bell
SIC—2759; 2752; 3993; NAICS—323100; *Commercial offset 1-6 color, digital, instant & wide-format printing & promotional items*
Employs—6; Estab.—1918
Sales—over $500,000
6,000 sq ft site, Distrib.—National
Privately owned sub-S corp.

### †DREYCO, INC.

263 Veterans Blvd. (07072)
**Phone—(201) 896-9000**
Fax—(201) 896-1378
www.dreycoinc.com
Email—sales@dreycoinc.com
Pres.—Michael Borghard
Opers. Mgr.—Jamie Rubel
Traf. Mgr.—Mary Tucker
SIC—5013; 5169; 5087; 5046; *Distributor of automotive parts, tools, accessories, chemicals, garage & service station equipment, steam cleaners & pressure washers; Brand name—ACME; CTA; GSI; SCHUMACHER; JENNY; WALBRO; MECHANICS; MCKAY; THEXTON; ULLMAN; ZIM*
Employs—15; Estab.—1950
Distrib.—Intl.
Sole ownership

### EAGLE NUTRITIONALS

485 Washington Ave. (07072)
**Phone—(201) 964-1441**
Fax—(201) 964-1442
Owner—Marlon Durham
SIC—2834; *Vitamins*
Employs—45; Estab.—2001
Sales—$25Mil-$50Mil (est)
Distrib.—Local
Privately owned corporation

### ENER-G RUDOX, INC.

765 State Route 17 N., P.O. Box 467 (07072)
**Phone—(201) 438-0111**
National—(866) 783-6976
Fax—(201) 438-3403
www.energ-rudox.com
Email—info@energ-rudox.com
Pres.—Ryan Goodman
V.-P., Engrg.—Howard Goodman
Comp.—David Suarez
Proj. Mgr.—Jane Goodman
SIC—3621; NAICS—335312; *Diesel & natural gas generator sets & natural gas CHP co-generation generator sets for large government organizations, Fortune 500 companies & small businesses, including parts, service & rentals*
Employs—40; Estab.—1949
Sales—$5Mil-$10Mil
60,000 sq ft site, Distrib.—Intl.
Privately owned corporation

### FERRUM INDUSTRIES, INC.

735 Commercial Ave. (07072)
**Phone—(201) 935-1220**
National—(800) 624-8746
Fax—(201) 935-1824
www.textol.com
Email—rwolfin@textol.com
V.-P.—Richard Wolfin
V.-P.—Lawrence Wolfin

# Carlstadt—(cont.)

SIC—3451; NAICS—332721;
*Screw machine products*
Employs—10; Estab.—1950
Distrib.—National
Privately owned corporation

**GENERAL RUBBER CORP.**
850 Washington Ave., Front
(07072-3014)
**Phone—(201) 935-1900**
National—(800) 233-6294
Fax—(201) 935-1915
www.general-rubber.com
Email—sales@general-rubber.com
V.-P., Sales—Kelvin Mayrina
Sr. Sales Rep.—Catherin Goetzl
SIC—3053; 3494; NAICS—
339991; *Piping & ducting
expansion joints, vibration
connectors, penetration seals &
pinch valves*
Employs—10; Estab.—1957
Sales—$1Mil-$2.5Mil
Distrib.—Intl.
Privately owned corporation
Parent co.—General Rubber
Corp., Tucson, AZ
Phone—(520) 889-2979
See Parent Co. Section for full profile.

**GLOBE PACKAGING CO., INC.**
368 Paterson Plank Rd. (07072)
**Phone—(201) 939-3335**
National—(888) 211-0989
Fax—(201) 939-3325
www.globecasing.com
Email—sales@globecasing.com
Pres.—Issy Bank
V.-P., Fin.—David Knoebel
Plt. Mgr.—Bob Charles
Pur. Mgr.—Andy Huczak
SIC—2013; 2673; 3081; 2399;
NAICS—311600; *Plastic,
collagen, fibrous, cellulose,
textile & natural dimensional food
casings, including vac-pack &
shrink bags; Brand name—Kalle;
Oskuda; Viscofan; Walsroder;
Taikoh; Ennio International; DCW
Casing*
Employs—11; Estab.—1955
Sales—$1Mil-$5Mil
12,000 sq ft site, Distrib.—National
Privately owned corporation
AKA: Globe Casing Company

**GROBET FILE CO. OF AMERICA,
LLC.**
Div. of Dyson, Dyson & Dunn, Inc.
750 Washington Ave. (07072)
**Phone—(201) 939-6700**
National—(800) 847-4188
Fax—(201) 939-5067
www.grobetusa.com
Email—email@grobetusa.com
Pres.—John Canzoneri
CFO—Laurie Fisher
Plt. Mgr.—Randy Diamond
SIC—3423; *Company
headquarters & precision metal
tools; Brand name—Dixcel;
Procraft; Dixon; Mascot*
Employs—80; Estab.—1968
Sales—$10Mil-$25Mil
Distrib.—National
Privately owned corporation
AKA: Grobet USA
Parent co.—Dyson, Dyson &
Dunn, Inc., Winnetka, IL
Phone—(847) 441-5517
See Parent Co. Section for full profile.

**HACKENSACK STEEL CORP.**
645 Industrial Rd. (07072)
**Phone—(201) 935-0090**
Fax—(201) 935-4823
Pres.—Tony Fasciano
Proj. Mgr.—Mike Fasciano

SIC—3446; 3441; NAICS—
332323; *Structural steel stairs &
railings*
Employs—30; Estab.—1961
Sales—$1Mil-$2.5Mil
Distrib.—Local
Privately owned corporation

**HARTIN PAINT & FILLER CORP.**
14th & Broad Sts. (07072)
**Phone—(201) 438-3300**
Fax—(201) 438-7568
Pres.—Richard Gottesman
SIC—2851; NAICS—325510;
*Paints*
Employs—20; Estab.—1979
Sales—$5Mil-$10Mil (est)
Distrib.—National
Privately owned corporation

**HOLZER & ASSOCS., LLC, PHILIP**
350 Michelle Pl. (07072)
**Phone—(212) 691-9500**
Owner & Chrm.—Stuart Holzer
SIC—2752; NAICS—323100;
*Offset printing*
Employs—50; Estab.—1955
Distrib.—National
Limited Liability Company
Also see: Unimac Graphics, LLC,
same loc.

**HOUGHTON CHEMICAL CORP.**
30 Amor Ave. *(07072)*
**Phone—(800) 777-2466**
Fax—(617) 254-2713
www.houghton.com
Email—bhoughton@houghton.com
Plt. Mgr.—Roosevelt Boyd
SIC—2899; *Heat transfer fluids &
antifreeze; Brand name—SAFE-
T-THERM; WINTREX; GeoSafe;
Pah/Nol; Green Mountain*
Employs—4; Estab.—1929
Sales—$15Mil-$20Mil
Distrib.—National
Privately owned corporation
Parent co.—Houghton Chemical
Corp., Allston, MA
Phone—(617) 254-1010
See Parent Co. Section for full profile.

**HYCRETE, INC.**
462 Barell Ave. *(07072)*
**Phone—(201) 386-8110**
(866) 492-7383
Fax—(201) 386-8155
www.hycrete.com
Email—info@hycrete.com
Pres.—Jason Tuerack
Ex. V.-P. & Dir.—Philip Rhodes
Sales Rep., Inside—Joann Galinis
SIC—2899; *Concrete
waterproofing admixtures; Brand
name—Hycrete System W;
Hycrete W1000; Hycrete W500;
Hycrete V1000*
Employs—20; Estab.—2003
Distrib.—Intl.
Privately owned corporation

**NEW ENTRY**
**HYSO, LLC**
430 Gotham Pkwy., 2nd Fl.
(07072)
**Phone—(201) 635-9555**
Fax—(866) 682-8078
www.hyso.com
Email—sales@hyso.com
Owner—Simon Sassoon
SIC—3639; *Odor control & air
freshening devices with dual-fan
technology & automatic door
handle disinfecting devices;
Brand name—HYScent Dual;
HYScent Pod; D3 Micro*
Employs—6
Sales—$1Mil-$2.5Mil (est)
Limited Liability Company

**NEW ENTRY**
**IKEN MEDIA, LLC**
70 Triangle Blvd. (07072)
**Phone—(201) 372-0800**
Fax—(201) 372-0801
www.ikenmedia.com
Email—mail@ikenmedia.com
Owner—David Eichen
SIC—2759; 3993; *Commercial
printing & interior & exterior
signage & graphic design
services*
Employs—5
Sales—$500,000-$1Mil (est)
Distrib.—Regional
Limited Liability Company

**NEW ENTRY**
**IMPACT DISPLAYS GROUP, LLC**
310 13th St. (07072)
**Phone—(212) 842-1800**
Fax—(212) 842-1850
www.impactpop.com
Email—info@impactpop.com
CEO—Gill Horowitz
SIC—2541; 2542; 3993; *Point-of-
purchase displays*
Employs—32
Sales—$2.5Mil-$5Mil (est)
Distrib.—Regional
Limited Liability Company

**IMPRESSIVE PRINTING, INC.**
313 10th St. (07072)
**Phone—(201) 933-1650**
Fax—(201) 933-1387
www.impprinting.com
Email—rob@impprinting.com
Pres.—Robert Egan
Art Dir. & Manager—Dave Egan
SIC—2759; 2752; 3993; NAICS—
323100; *Commercial, full-color &
large-format printing of
continuous & carbonless forms,
envelopes, letterheads,
brochures, postcards, labels,
rigid signage, banners, mailers,
door hangers, sell sheets &
political materials*
Employs—2; Estab.—1989
Distrib.—Local
Privately owned corporation

**IMTECH GRAPHICS, INC.**
545 Dell Rd. (07072)
**Phone—(201) 933-8002**
Fax—(201) 804-0102
www.imtechgraphics.com
Email—imtech@
imtechgraphics.com
Pres.—Gary Cordovano
Prodn. Mgr.—Mike Vesia
Hum. Res. Mgr.—Gina Gonnella
SIC—2791; NAICS—323122;
*Electronic prepress, commercial
printing & typesetting*
Employs—130
30,000 sq ft site,
Privately owned corporation

**JA VISUAL GROUP**
150 Commerce Rd., Unit 3
(07072)
**Phone—(212) 463-0545**
www.javigital.com
Email—imaging@javigital.com
Pres.—Teri Uto
Off. Mgr.—Stacey Weissman
SIC—2759; NAICS—323100;
*Digital C-printing for the signage
industry*
Employs—20; Estab.—1991
Sales—$2.5Mil-$5Mil (est)
5,000 sq ft site, Distrib.—National
Privately owned corporation

**KISSLER & CO., INC.**
770 Central Blvd. (07072-3009)
**Phone—(201) 896-9600**
National—(800) 547-7537
Fax—(201) 896-9190
www.kissler.com

Email—sales@kissler.com
Pres.—Barry Kissler
V.-P.—Glenn Kissler
Sales Mgr., Natl.—Sean Kaplan
SIC—3432; NAICS—332900;
*Plumbing supplies; Brand
name—Dominion Faucets;
Rainflurry Showerheads; Kant
Burst Konnectors*
Employs—75; Estab.—1923
Sales—$10Mil-$25Mil
75,000 sq ft site, Distrib.—National
Privately owned sub-S corp.

**KNICKERBOCKER BED CO.**
770 Commercial Ave. (07072)
Mail addr: P.O. Box 65, Little Ferry
(07643)
**Phone—(201) 933-3100**
National—(800) 526-6294
Fax—(201) 933-6963
www.knickerbockerbedframes.com
Pres.—Milton Polevoy
V.-P., Admn.—George Milton
Off. Mgr.—Larry Davis
SIC—2514; *Metal bed frames*
Employs—30; Estab.—1919
Sales—$2.5Mil-$5Mil (est)
Distrib.—National
Privately owned corporation

**KRAZY KAT SPORTSWEAR, LLC**
100 Triangle Blvd. (07072)
**Phone—(201) 438-3399**
(212) 221-3040
Fax—(201) 438-0097
www.krazykat.com
Email—bansi@krazykat.com
CEO—Bansi Laknani
Pres.—Sidharth Lakhani
COO—Rohit Maharishi
Prodn. Mgr. & Analyst—Joan
Joseph
SIC—2331; 2339; 2389; NAICS—
315200; *Women's woven
blouses, dresses, skirts,
clothing, apparel & accessories;
Brand name—Girl Krazy; Sid &
Sandy; Skarf Krazy; Healing
Hands*
Employs—60; Estab.—1978
Distrib.—National
Limited Liability Company

**KROHN INDUSTRIES, INC.**
303 Veterans Blvd., P.O. Box 98
(07072)
**Phone—(201) 933-9696**
National—(800) 526-6299
Fax—(201) 933-9684
www.krohnindustries.com
Email—info@krohnindustries.com
Pres.—Nicholas Krohn
Plt. Mgr.—Alex Dominguez
SIC—3398; NAICS—332811;
*Brazing alloys*
Employs—10; Estab.—1955
Distrib.—Intl.
Privately owned corporation

**L V ADHESIVE, INC.**
341 Michele Pl. (07072)
**Phone—(212) 925-2600**
National—(800) 654-0090
Fax—(212) 226-5543
www.lvadhesive.com
Email—sales@lvadhesive.com
Pres., CEO—Linda Owen
V.-P.—Steve Owen
SIC—2672; NAICS—322222;
*Pressure-sensitive adhesive
papers & labels*
Employs—50; Estab.—1976
Sales—$10Mil-$25Mil (est)
20,000 sq ft site, Distrib.—Local
Privately owned corporation
AKA: Print & Peel

**MADA MEDICAL PRODUCTS, INC.**
625 Washington Ave. (07072)
**Phone—(201) 460-0454**
National—(800) 526-6370
Fax—(201) 460-3509
www.madamedical.com

GEOGRAPHICAL

## Carlstadt—(cont.)

Email—jeffreyadam@
madamedical.com
Pres.—Jeffrey Adam
CFO & Hum. Res. Mgr.—Robert
 Chasmar
Cust. Serv. Rep.—Gina Belmonte
SIC—3841; *Medical respiratory
 equipment*
Employs—35; Estab.—1969
40,000 sq ft site, Distrib.—National
Privately owned corporation

### MANHATTAN DOOR CORP.
109 Kero Rd. (07072)
**Phone—(718) 963-1111**
Fax—(718) 387-7941
www.manhattandoor.com
Email—info@manhattandoor.com
Owner—Michael Sklar
Chrm.—Martin Sklar
CFO—Laura Sklar
IT Mgr.—Vedim Sechlls
Hum. Res. Mgr.—Ricardo Ramos
SIC—2431; *Custom flush wooden
 doors*
Employs—40; Estab.—2009
Sales—$5Mil-$10Mil (est)
Distrib.—Regional
Privately owned corporation

### MARBLE SYSTEMS, INC.
610 Washington Ave. (07072)
**Phone—(201) 507-0111**
Fax—(201) 507-0888
www.marblesystems.com
Manager—Serafino Aprile
SIC—3281; *Natural stone
 fabrication, including
 countertops, vanity tops &
 fireplace surrounds*
Employs—10; Estab.—1982
Distrib.—Local

### †MARCOR DEVELOPMENT CORP.
341 Michele Pl. (07072)
**Phone—(201) 935-2111**
Fax—(201) 935-5223
www.marcordev.com
Email—marcordev@aol.com
Pres.—Tom Tchang
SIC—5169; 5122; *Distributor of
 bulk food ingredients &
 chemicals for the microbiology,
 fermentation & nutritional
 supplement markets*
Employs—12; Estab.—1977
Sales—$15Mil-$20Mil
Distrib.—Intl.
Privately owned sub-S corp.

### MASTER PRINTING, INC.
445 Industrial Rd. (07072)
**Phone—(201) 842-9100**
Fax—(201) 842-9393
www.masterprintinginc.com
Email—sales@
masterprintinginc.com
Pres.—John Aresta
COO—Joseph Aresta
SIC—2759; NAICS—323100;
 *Commercial printing*
Employs—25; Estab.—1969
28,000 sq ft site, Distrib.—
 Regional
Privately owned corporation

### †MICHAEL HALEBIAN & CO., INC.
557 Washington Ave. (07072)
**Phone—(201) 935-3535**
National—(800) 631-4115
Fax—(201) 935-4610
www.michaelhalebian.com
Email—info@michaelhalebian.com
Pres.—Michael Halebian, Jr.
V-P., GM—Joe Choflet
Cust. Serv. Mgr.—Robert Green
Sys. Admn.—Beth Dob

SIC—5162; 5031; 5023; 5169;
 *Distributor of floor coverings &
 related accessories, including
 resilient vinyl, hardwood, cork,
 adhesives & underlayment*
Employs—50; Estab.—1958
Distrib.—Local
Privately owned corporation

### MODERN SHOWCASE, INC.
610 Commercial Ave. (07072)
**Phone—(201) 935-2929**
www.modernshowcase.com
Email—modernsh@aol.com
Pres.—John Kang
Off. Mgr.—Will Kang
SIC—2541; 2542; *Metal &
 wooden store fixtures*
Employs—10; Estab.—1995
35,000 sq ft site, Distrib.—National
Privately owned corporation

### †MOMENI, INC.
60 Broad St. (07072)
**Phone—(212) 532-9577**
Fax—(212) 779-9568
www.momeni.com
Email—info@momeni.com
Pres.—Reza Momeni
Hum. Res. Mgr.—Vinny Bajaj
SIC—5023; *Corporate
 headquarters & distributor of
 area rugs & carpets*
Employs—35; Estab.—1975
Distrib.—Intl.
Privately owned corporation

### NATALE MACHINE & TOOL CO., INC.
339 13th St. (07072)
**Phone—(201) 933-5500**
National—(800) 883-8382
Fax—(201) 933-8146
www.circle-d.com
Email—cs@circle-d.com
Co-Pres.—Lynn Natale
Co-Pres.—Karen Natale
GM—John Cocozzo
SIC—3646; 3647; 3648; NAICS—
 335122; *Portable, permanent,
 industrial & marine lighting
 fixtures & accessories; Brand
 name—Circle-D Lights*
Employs—6; Estab.—1947
15,000 sq ft site, Distrib.—National
Privately owned sub-S corp.

### NES ENTERPRISES, INC.
513 Washington Ave. (07072)
Mail addr: P.O. Box 1377,
 Springfield (07081-5377)
**Phone—(201) 964-1400**
 (973) 820-5729
Fax—(201) 964-1406
www.nesenterprisesinc.com
Email—nesenterprises@aol.com
CEO—Sheldon Salkovitch
SIC—2353; *Men's hat linings*
Employs—9; Estab.—2006
Sales—$500,000-$1Mil
5,800 sq ft site, Distrib.—Intl.
Privately owned corporation

### †NISHIMOTO TRADING CO. LTD.
602 Washington Ave. (07072)
**Phone—(201) 804-1600**
Fax—(201) 635-9100
www.nishimototrading.com
Email—info@nishimotrading.com
Br. Mgr.—Pat Suguki
Sys. Mgr.—Lisa Harris
SIC—5141; *Distributor of general
 line Asian food products,
 including frozen foods*
Employs—120
Privately owned corporation
Parent co.—Nishimoto Trading Co.
 Ltd., Santa Fe Springs, CA
 Phone—(562) 802-1900
 See Parent Co. Section for full profile.

### NMN CLOSET, INC.
40 Veterans Blvd. (07072)
**Phone—(201) 964-9600**
National—(800) 293-3744

Fax—(201) 964-9622
www.closetsbydesign.com
Email—cbdnewjersey@aol.com
Pres.—Norman Holtz
SIC—2452; NAICS—321992;
 *Shelving products for closets,
 home offices & garage cabinets*
Employs—40; Estab.—2001
Sales—$5Mil-$10Mil
Distrib.—Regional
Privately owned corporation
DBA: Closets By Design

### NOVEL LITHOGRAPHERS, INC.
1 Kero Rd. (07072)
Mail addr: P.O. Box 998, Edison
 (08818)
**Phone—(201) 372-3900**
Fax—(201) 372-3878
Pres.—Martin Zarett
Off. Mgr.—Diane Osborne
SIC—2752; NAICS—323100;
 *Lithographic printing*
Employs—10; Estab.—1970
Distrib.—Regional
Privately owned corporation

### ORCHARD YARN & THREAD CO., INC.
135 Kero Rd. (07072)
**Phone—(201) 804-3999**
National—(800) 258-9276
Fax—(201) 804-3918
www.lionbrand.com
Email—support@lionbrand.com
CEO—David Blumenthal
Pres.—Dean Blumenthal
V-P., Sales—Hilary Tyor
V-P., Mktg.—Ilana Rabinowitz
Dir., IT—Brian Ramnarain
Dir., Hum. Res.—Lisa Maggi
SIC—2281; NAICS—313111;
 *Corporate headquarters & wool
 yarn; Brand name—Homespun;
 Vanna's Choice; Jiffy; Hometown
 USA; Wool-Ease; Fun Fur; LB
 Collection; Nature's Choice*
Employs—70; Estab.—1878
Sales—$5Mil-$10Mil
Distrib.—Intl.
Privately owned corporation
AKA: Lion Brand Yarn Co.

### OXBERRY, LLC
180 Broad St. (07072)
**Phone—(201) 935-3000**
Fax—(201) 935-0104
www.oxberry.com
Email—info@oxberry.com
Secy., Corp. Counsel—Anna
 Ferraro
SIC—3861; *Cameras & film
 scanners*
Employs—1; Estab.—1947
Sales—under $500,000
Distrib.—Intl.
Limited Liability Company

### PAN TECHNOLOGY
117 Moonachie Ave. (07072)
**Phone—(201) 438-7878**
National—(800) 722-3507
Fax—(201) 460-4546
www.pantechnology.com
Email—info@pantechnology.com
Pres.—Robert Rossomando
V-P., Sales—Michael Rossomando
IT Mgr.—Dave Barnwell
Off. Mgr.—Patty Protze
Accts. Rec. Mgr.—Michael Spero,
 Jr.
Cust. Serv. Rep.—Maureen Zoppi
SIC—2851; NAICS—325510;
 *Industrial paints, color
 concentrates & pigment
 dispersing agents*
Employs—48; Estab.—1948
60,000 sq ft site, Distrib.—Intl.
Privately owned corporation

### PANTONE LLC
Div. of X-Rite, Inc.
590 Commerce Blvd. (07072)
**Phone—(201) 935-5500**
 (888) 726-8663
Fax—(201) 896-0242
www.pantone.com
Email—corpnj@pantone.com
Sr. V-P., GM—Ron Potesky
V-P.—Laurie Pressman
V-P.—Andrew Hatkoff
V-P.—Brooks Tippett
Acct. Mgr., Cust. Rels.—Joanne
 Dingle
Hum. Res. Mgr.—Tracey Huffman
SIC—2752; NAICS—323100;
 *Standardized color matching
 systems, including color swatch
 books & software development*
Employs—100; Estab.—1963
80,000 sq ft site, Distrib.—Intl.
ISO rating—9001:2008
Parent co.—X-Rite, Inc., Grand
 Rapids, MI
 Phone—(616) 803-2100
 See Parent Co. Section for full profile.

### PENETONE CORP.
700 Gotham Pkwy., Ste. 2 (07072)
**Phone—(201) 567-3000**
National—(800) 631-1652
Fax—(201) 510-3973
www.west-penetone.com
Email—solutions@penetone.com
V-P., GM, Fin. & Pur. Mgr.—Bruce
 Muretta
V-P., Sales & Mktg.—Mike
 Bradford
V-P., R & D—Phillip Figdore
Cont., MIS Mgr.—Joyce Seccia
Opers. Mgr.—Charles Good
SIC—2842; 2843; NAICS—
 325612; *Industrial cleaning
 compounds; Brand name—
 Citrikleen; Wedac; Penkleen;
 Penblitz; Penpower; Penair;
 Pensolv*
Employs—27; Estab.—1932
Sales—$10Mil-$20Mil
Distrib.—Intl.
Privately owned sub-S corp.
Parent co.—Penetone Corp.,
 Princeton, NJ
 Phone—(609) 921-0501
 See Parent Co. Section for full profile.

### PERTECH INKS CORP.
140 Grand St. (07072)
**Phone—(908) 354-1700**
National—(800) 424-0038
Fax—(908) 354-1707
www.pertechcorporation.com
Email—info@
pertechcorporation.com
IT Mgr.—Joseph Benton
Off. Mgr.—Jeff Tusche
SIC—2893; NAICS—325910;
 *Printing inks*
Employs—25; Estab.—1989
Sales—$500,000-$1Mil
15,000 sq ft site, Distrib.—National
Privately owned corporation

### PETERSON STEEL RULE DIE CORP.
35 Broad St. (07072)
**Phone—(201) 935-6180**
Fax—(201) 935-9452
Pres.—Leonard Esposito
GM—Timothy Esposito
Off. Mgr.—Susan Jacob
SIC—3544; 2675; NAICS—
 333500; *Steel rule dies, die
 cutting & finishing*
Employs—10; Estab.—1963
13,000 sq ft site, Distrib.—Local
Privately owned corporation

### PICTORIAL OFFSET CORPORATION
111 Amor Ave. (07072)
**Phone—(201) 935-7100**
Fax—(201) 935-3254
www.pictorialoffset.com

## Carlstadt—(cont.)

Email—marketing@
pictorialoffset.com
Chairperson—Meryle Samuels
Mng. Dir.—Donald Samuels
Mng. Dir.—Gary Samuels
Mng. Dir.—Lester Samuels
Hum. Res. Mgr.—Mey Iriarte
SIC—2752; NAICS—323100;
*Sheet-fed & web printing,
including retouching, prepress,
fulfillment & mailing services*
Employs—300; Estab.—1938
Sales—$50Mil
200,000 sq ft site, Distrib.—Intl.
Privately owned corporation
ISO rating—9001

**POLYAIR NORTH EAST**
Div. of Polyair Inter Pack, Inc.
495 Meadow Ln. (07072)
**Phone—(201) 804-1700**
National—(800) 631-0281
Fax—(201) 804-1710
www.polyair.com
Email—marketing@polyair.com
Sales Mgr.—Jim Brennan
Plt. Mgr.—Joseph P. Hickey
Cust. Serv. Mgr.—Carol Seeley
SIC—3089; 2673; NAICS—
322232; *Packaging materials,
including bubble wrap, mailers &
foam packaging*
Employs—60; Estab.—1968
77,000 sq ft site, Distrib.—Regional
Privately owned corporation
Parent co.—Polyair Inter Pack, Inc.
Phone—(416) 679-6600
See Parent Co. Section for full profile.

**POTTERS INDUSTRIES, INC.**
600 Industrial Rd. (07072)
**Phone—(201) 460-0666**
National—(800) 552-3237
Fax—(201) 935-0752
www.pottersbeads.com
Email—customerservice@
pottersbeads.com
Plt. Mgr.—Glenn Evers
SIC—3231; NAICS—327215;
*Industrial glass beads*
Employs—15; Estab.—1950
Sales—$500,000-$1Mil
Distrib.—Intl.
Privately owned corporation
Parent co.—Potters Industries,
Inc., Malvern, PA
Phone—(610) 651-4700
See Parent Co. Section for full profile.

**PRECISION METAL MACHINING,
INC.**
800 Central Blvd., Ste. C (07072)
**Phone—(201) 843-7427**
Fax—(201) 843-9235
www.gopmmi.com
Email—sales@gopmmi.com
Pres.—Pat Fanicelli
Cont.—Judy Moceri
Dir., Sales—Larry Whitney
Dir., Opers.—Giovanni Riccardi
SIC—3599; 3471; 3479; *General
machining job shop, including
grinding, engraving, finishing,
wire EDM, CNC machining,
prototyping, TIG welding,
assembly, passivation, laser
marking & polishing*
Employs—40; Estab.—1986
Sales—$3.5Mil
34,000 sq ft site, Distrib.—Intl.
Privately owned corporation
ISO rating—9001:2008,
13485:2003
AKA: PMMI

**PREMIUM COLOR GRAPHICS, INC.**
651 Garden St. (07072)
**Phone—(973) 472-7007**
Fax—(973) 472-7601
www.premiumcolorgraphics.com
Email—outputpcg@aol.com
Pres.—John E. Watson

V-P.—Mark Fitzgerald
Cont. & Hum. Res. Mgr.—Pam
Megao
Cust. Serv. Rep.—Abbie Posner
SIC—2759; NAICS—323100;
*Commercial printing*
Employs—30; Estab.—1990
Distrib.—Regional
Privately owned corporation
AKA: PCG

**REGGIANI LIGHTING USA, INC.**
372 Starke Rd. (07072)
**Phone—(201) 372-1717**
Fax—(201) 372-1616
www.reggiani.net
Email—reggianilighting@aol.com
Pres.—John Savoretti
Dir., Tech.—Eric Silverman
SIC—3645; 3647; NAICS—
335121; *HID, low-voltage &
fluorescent lighting systems
assembly*
Employs—19; Estab.—2001
Sales—$1Mil-$2.5Mil
20,000 sq ft site, Distrib.—National
Privately owned corporation

**†SAFWAY ATLANTIC, LLC**
Div. of Safway Group Holding, LLC
700 Commercial Ave. (07072)
**Phone—(201) 636-5500**
National—(800) 558-4772
Fax—(201) 636-5542
www.safwayatlantic.com
Email—info_request@safway.com
Pres.—Greg Karas
Sales Mgr.—Jason Lynch
SIC—5084; *Wholesaler of
supported & suspended
scaffolds, including erection,
engineering, safety & project
management assistance & rental
service; Brand name—Safway
Systems Scaffold; QuikDeck
Suspended Access System*
Employs—20
Sales—$2Mil-$5Mil
18,000 sq ft site, Distrib.—National
Limited Liability Company
Parent co.—Safway Group
Holding, LLC, Waukesha, WI
Phone—(262) 523-6500
See Parent Co. Section for full profile.

**SAWITZ STORE FIXTURE, INC.**
130 Grand St. (07072)
**Phone—(201) 842-9444**
Fax—(201) 842-8812
www.sawitzstorefixture.com
Email—info@sawitzstorefixture.com
Pres.—Daniel Sawitz
Dir., Logistics & Sales—Carol
Weber
Fin. Mgr.—June Sawitz
SIC—2541; 2431; 2542; 2599;
NAICS—321900; *Wooden,
laminate & solid-surface store
fixtures, commercial furniture,
cabinetry & architectural millwork
for department stores, specialty
shops, vendors, museums, store
planners, architects, interior
designers & visual
merchandisers*
Employs—28; Estab.—1981
38,000 sq ft site, Distrib.—National
Privately owned corporation

**SCREEN REPRODUCTIONS CO.,
INC.**
850 Washington Ave. (07072)
**Phone—(201) 935-0830**
Fax—(201) 935-0471
Pres., Fin., GM & R & D Mgr.—
Larry Wiessenburg
SIC—2396; *Vinyl wallpaper
screen printing*
Employs—20; Estab.—1949
5,000 sq ft site, Distrib.—Intl.
Privately owned corporation

**SHOREWOOD DIGITAL DESIGN &
DEVELOPMENT CENTER**
Div. of International Paper Co.
1 Kero Rd. (07072)
**Phone—(201) 372-3900**
Fax—(201) 372-3878
www.shorewooddigital.com
Prodn. Mgr.—Dolores Jett
Off. Mgr.—Diane Osborne
Prepress Mgr.—Eric Demaille
SIC—2791; NAICS—323122;
*Electronic prepress*
Employs—35; Estab.—1970
Sales—$6Mil-$10Mil
Distrib.—Regional
Publicly owned corporation
Parent co.—International Paper
Co., Memphis, TN
Phone—(901) 419-9000
See Parent Co. Section for full profile.

**SHREEJI PRINTING CORP.**
55 Veterans Blvd. (07072)
**Phone—(201) 842-9500**
Fax—(201) 842-9502
www.sjprinting.com
Email—info@sjprinting.com
Pres.—Dilip Patel
SIC—2759; NAICS—323100; *Full
color printing of pressure-
sensitive labels & stickers*
Employs—16; Estab.—1996
9,000 sq ft site, Distrib.—Regional
Privately owned corporation

**SONAR PRODUCTS, INC.**
609-611 Industrial Rd. (07072)
**Phone—(201) 729-1116**
Fax—(201) 729-1066
Email—sonarsaurus@cs.com
Pres.—Mark Newman
Lab Dir.—Gerald Demenna
Off. Mgr.—Celia Cintron
Whse. Mgr.—Frank Rivera
Qual. Mgr.—Joel Rodriguiz
Pur. Agt.—Janet Soluso
SIC—3559; *Pharmaceutical
processing equipment &
supplies*
Employs—18; Estab.—1999
Distrib.—Regional
Privately owned corporation

**STANBEE CO., INC.**
70 Broad St., P.O. Box 436
(07072)
**Phone—(201) 933-9666**
Fax—(201) 933-7985
www.stanbee.com
Email—mberkson@stanbee.com
Pres.—Michael Berkson
V-P.—Robert Dalla Riva
Plt. Mgr.—Bruce Goldberg
Prodn. Mgr.—Frank Marinelli
SIC—2211; 3089; *Thermoplastic
counter & boxtoe materials &
coating of fabrics for the shoe
manufacturing industry*
Employs—40; Estab.—1948
55,000 sq ft site, Distrib.—Intl.
Privately owned corporation

**SUMMIT GROUP II**
333 16th St. (07072)
**Phone—(201) 460-8888**
Fax—(201) 460-0414
Email—jmonzo@
summitgroup2.com
Pres.—Tom Klein
V-P.—Jess Monzo
SIC—3446; 3449; 3231; NAICS—
332323; *Steel railings,
ornamental iron, structural steel,
glass window walls & partitions*
Employs—5; Estab.—1986
Distrib.—Regional
Limited Liability Company

**SUN CHEMICAL CORP.**
631 Central Ave. (07072)
**Phone—(201) 933-4500**
Fax—(201) 933-5658
www.sunchemical.com

Email—dave.quirk@
kohlmadden.com
Opers. Mgr.—Paul Haig
Lab Mgr.—Dave Quirk
SIC—2893; NAICS—325910;
*Printing ink*
Employs—30
Sales—$10Mil-$12Mil
22,000 sq ft site, Distrib.—Intl.
Publicly owned corporation
Parent co.—Sun Chemical Corp.,
Parsippany, NJ
Phone—(973) 404-6000
See Parent Co. Section for full profile.

**SWEET WATER SEAFOOD CORP.**
369 Washington Ave. (07072)
**Phone—(201) 939-6622**
Fax—(201) 939-4014
www.sweetwaterseafood.net
Email—plumpy1056@aol.com
Pres.—Joseph Niece
Off. Mgr.—Darren Kretzmer
SIC—2092; NAICS—311712; *Fish
processing*
Employs—5; Estab.—1965
Sales—$500,000-$1Mil
Distrib.—Local
Privately owned corporation

**TEC CAST, INC.**
440 Meadow Ln. (07072)
**Phone—(201) 935-3885**
Fax—(201) 933-7497
www.tec-cast.com
Email—l.biss@tec-cast.com
Pres.—Edgar Gotthold
CFO—Lynne Biss
V-P.—Robert Morehardt
SIC—3365; 3544; NAICS—
331524; *Aluminum investment
castings & casting molds*
Employs—70; Estab.—1970
Sales—$26Mil-$50Mil
35,000 sq ft site, Distrib.—National
Privately owned corporation

**THUMANN, INC.**
670 Dell Rd. (07072)
**Phone—(201) 935-3636**
Fax—(201) 935-2226
www.thumanns.com
Email—sales@thumanns.com
GM—Bob Burke, Sr.
Hum. Res. & Plt. Mgr.—Bill
Merkent
Payroll Mgr.—Richard Tillison
SIC—2011; NAICS—311611; *Meat
processing & packing*
Employs—210; Estab.—1953
Distrib.—National
Privately owned corporation

**TRAYCON MANUFACTURING
COMPANY**
555 Barell Ave. (07072)
**Phone—(201) 939-5555**
Fax—(201) 939-4180
www.traycon.com
Email—info@traycon.com
Pres.—Al Cialone
V-P., Opers.—Sandee M. Goldberg
SIC—3556; NAICS—333294;
*Food & tray handling conveyor
systems for the food service
industry; Brand name—Traycon*
Employs—25; Estab.—1962
Sales—$1Mil-$5Mil
50,000 sq ft site, Distrib.—National
Limited Liability Company

NEW ENTRY
**TRICO WEB, LLC**
75 Broad St. (07072)
**Phone—(201) 438-3860**
Fax—(201) 438-3861
www.tricowebprinting.com
Email—prepress@
tricowebprinting.com
Owner—Don Juliano

## Carlstadt—(cont.)

SIC—2759; *Commercial printing*
Employs—20; Estab.—2011
Sales—$2.5Mil-$5Mil (est)
Distrib.—Intl.
Limited Liability Company

### TUNNEL BARREL & DRUM CO., INC.

85 Triangle Blvd. *(07072)*
**Phone—(201) 933-1444**
Fax—(201) 933-3423
www.tunnelbarrel.com
Email—anthony@tunnelbarrel.com
Pres.—Anthony Urcioli
V-P.—Anthony J. Urcioli
Consultant—Joseph Binder
SIC—3089; 2655; 5085; NAICS—
322214; *Reconditioned fiber &
plastic drums & totes &
distributor of new drums, totes &
pails*
Employs—20; Estab.—1903
Sales—$4Mil-$5Mil
40,000 sq ft site, Distrib.—
Regional
Privately owned corporation

### UNIK INTERNATIONAL, INC.

40 Triangle Blvd. (07072)
Mail addr: P.O. Box 9, Hasbrouck
Heights (07604)
**Phone—(201) 531-1777**
National—(800) 766-8645
Fax—(201) 531-2676
www.unikinternational.com
Email—sales@unikleather.net
Pres.—Akmal Khilji
V-P.—Mohammed Khiji
SIC—2386; NAICS—315200;
*Leather clothing*
Employs—22; Estab.—1985
55,000 sq ft site, Distrib.—Intl.
Privately owned corporation

### UNIMAC GRAPHICS, LLC

350 Michele Pl. (07072)
**Phone—(201) 372-1000**
Fax—(201) 372-9745
www.unimacgraphics.com
Email—info@unimacgraphics.com
Pres.—Steven Rickett
V-P., Mktg.—Pamela Conover
Cont.—Nancy Disano
MIS Mgr.—Ben Nelson
Payroll & Hum. Res. Mgr—Leo
Scullion
Fin. Mgr.—Ron Joy
SIC—2759; 2789; NAICS—
323100; *Large-format, web &
sheet-fed commercial &
packaging printing, including die
cutting, embossing, foil
stamping, casting, curing & cold
foiling*
Employs—300; Estab.—1989
146,000 sq ft site, Distrib.—
National
Limited Liability Company
ISO rating—9001
Also see: Philip Holzer & Assocs.,
LLC, same loc.

### US INK CORP. (H Q)

Div. of Sun Chemical Corp.
631 Central Ave. (07072-1609)
**Phone—(201) 935-8666**
Fax—(201) 935-7305
www.usink.com
Pres.—Michael Dodd
V-P., Sales—John Corcoran
Dir., Hum. Res.—David Benson
Mktg. Mgr.—Todd Wheeler
SIC—2893; NAICS—325910;
*Corporate headquarters; printing
ink; Brand name—RealColor;
SpectraMAX; Spectra High
Strength; Ecosoy*
Employs—65; Estab.—1840
Sales—$10Mil-$25Mil
Distrib.—Intl.
Publicly owned corporation

Parent co.—Sun Chemical Corp.,
Parsippany, NJ
Phone—(973) 404-6000
See Parent Co. Section for full profile.

### VERNON DISPLAY GRAPHICS

Div. of Vernon Co., The
145 Commerce Rd. (07072)
**Phone—(201) 935-7117**
Fax—(201) 842-1598
www.vernondisplaygraphics.com
Email—info@
vernondisplaygraphics.com
Cont.—Todd Smith
GM—Andrew Gabriel
Hum. Res., IT & Off. Mgr.—Nancy
Whitchurch
SIC—2396; 2759; NAICS—
323100; *Screen printing &
grand-format digital printing*
Employs—34; Estab.—1997
35,000 sq ft site, Distrib.—National
Privately owned corporation
AKA: Vernon-Sal, Inc.
Parent co.—Vernon Co., The,
Newton, IA
Phone—(641) 792-9000
See Parent Co. Section for full profile.

### VISIPAK, A SINCLAIR & RUSH COMPANY

Div. of Sinclair & Rush, Inc.
640 Dell Rd., Ste. 1, P.O. Box 0188
(07072)
Mail addr: 123 Manufacturers Dr.,
Arnold (63010-4727)
**Phone—(800) 949-1141**
Fax—(636) 282-6888
www.visipak.com
Email—visipak@visipak.com
Dir., Sales & Mktg.—Jeff Barket
SIC—3089; 3081; 3082; *Plastic
tube packaging containers, caps
& plugs & plastic packaging &
containers; Brand name—
VisiPak*
Employs—90; Estab.—1946
Company wide: 500
Sales—$10Mil-$25Mil (est)
65,000 sq ft site, Distrib.—National
Privately owned corporation
Also see: Atlas Plastics, same loc.
Parent co.—Sinclair & Rush, Inc.,
Arnold, MO
Phone—(636) 282-6800
See Parent Co. Section for full profile.

### VISUAL GRAPHIC SYSTEMS, INC.

330 Washington Ave. (07072)
**Phone—(201) 528-2700**
National—(800) 203-0301
Fax—(201) 528-0890
www.vgsonline.com
Email—info@vgs-inc.com
Chrm.—Don Healy
Chrm.—Milton DiPietro
Pres.—Paul Theodore
V-P.—Matt Buksbaum
V-P.—Patrick Benasillo
Mktg. Mgr.—Anna Pambianchi
SIC—3993; 2541; 2542; *Custom
eco-friendly interior & exterior
signage & displays, menu
boards, drive-thru systems,
proprietary stock fixtures &
digital displays, including design
services, project management &
global implementation; Brand
name—Concurva®; Linea®;
AeroLinea®; MagaLens®;
CounterToppers®; Ovations®;
Magillum®; MenuView®
Menuboards; MagaFrame™;
Motivations®-Digital; Sign-O-
Matic™; EcoLogical™;
GripFlex®; Simplicity™*
Employs—155; Estab.—1981
85,000 sq ft site, Distrib.—Intl.
Privately owned sub-S corp.

### W & H SYSTEMS, INC.

120 Asia Pl. (07072)
**Phone—(201) 933-7840**
National—(800) 966-6993

Fax—(201) 933-2144
www.whsystems.com
Email—edempsey@
whsystems.com
Pres.—Don Betman
V-P., GM—Ken Knapp
Hum. Res. Mgr.—Joe Pollard
Mktg. Coord.—Elizabeth Dempsey
SIC—3537; 3569; 3535;
*Automated material handling
systems, including conveyor
systems, high-speed carton &
unit sortation systems,
palletizers, paperless picking &
packing systems & equipment
for merchandise distribution in
warehouses & design & support
services; Brand name—RSU -
Reliable Sortation Unit;
RapidPac-Automated Pick/Pack
System; Shiraz - Warehouse
Control System*
Employs—75; Estab.—1964
Sales—$25Mil-$40Mil
40,000 sq ft site, Distrib.—National
Privately owned corporation

### WATER-JEL TECHNOLOGIES

Div. of Riverside Partners, LLC
50 Broad St. (07072)
**Phone—(201) 507-8300**
National—(800) 275-3433
Fax—(201) 507-8325
www.waterjel.com
Email—info@waterjel.com
CFO—John McAndris
Sr. V-P. & Chief Mktg. Dir.—Stacy
Blatt
Sales Mgr., Eastern—Paul Slot
Hum. Res. Mgr.—Jerrilyn Eckardt
Mktg. Admn.—Ellen Jeseseke-
Woolsey
SIC—3842; 2231; 2844; 3999;
NAICS—325600; *Sterile burn
dressings, fire blankets, topical
muscle gels, creams, ointments,
sprays, hand sanitizers &
eyewashes*
Employs—80; Estab.—1980
Distrib.—Intl.
Privately owned corporation
Parent co.—Riverside Partners,
LLC, Cleveland, OH
Phone—(216) 344-1040
See Parent Co. Section for full profile.

### WEIR WELDING CO., INC.

316 12th St., P.O. Box 311 (07072)
**Phone—(201) 939-2284**
Fax—(201) 939-5525
www.weirwelding.com
Email—charlie@weirwelding.com
Pres.—Charles J. Weir
V-P.—Thomas Weir
SIC—3441; NAICS—332312;
*Corporate headquarters &
structural steel fabrication*
Employs—20; Estab.—1961
Sales—$2.5Mil-$5Mil (est)
18,000 sq ft site, Distrib.—
Regional
Privately owned corporation

### YOO-HOO CHOCOLATE BEVERAGE CORP.

Div. of Dr Pepper Snapple Group,
Inc.
600 Commercial Ave. (07072)
**Phone—(201) 933-0070**
Fax—(201) 933-5360
www.drpeppersnapple.com
Email—email@
drpeppersnapplegroup.com
Plt. Mgr.—William Pedoto
Qual. Assur. Mgr.—Ben Wilson
Hum. Res. Coord.—Marisol Rivera
SIC—2066; 2086; NAICS—
311300; *Noncarbonated
chocolate beverages*
Employs—64; Estab.—1908
Distrib.—Intl.
Publicly owned corporation

Parent co.—Dr Pepper Snapple
Group, Inc., Plano, TX
Phone—(972) 673-7000
See Parent Co. Section for full profile.

---

## Carneys Point

(Salem—S.W.)

### BRAVO PACKING

59 N. Gothwood Ave. (08069)
**Phone—(856) 299-1044**
National—(888) 272-8640
Fax—(856) 299-7102
www.bravosnaturalrearing.com
Email—bravopacking@starband.net
Owner—Joe Merola
SIC—2047; NAICS—311111;
*Natural pet food & treats*
Employs—5; Estab.—1960
Distrib.—National
Privately owned corporation

### CLEMENT PAPPAS & COMPANY, INC. (H Q)

Div. of Lassonde Industries, Inc.
1 Collins Dr., Ste. 200 (08069)
**Phone—(856) 455-1000**
www.clementpappas.com
Email—sales@clementpappas.com
CEO—Mark McNeil
Hum. Res. Bus. Ptnr.—Krystal
Reid
Chief Administrative Officer—
Dimitri Pappas
Sr. V-P., Sales—Bob Crawford
Sr. V-P., Mktg.—Patricia Nicolino
SIC—2033; 2086; 2099; NAICS—
311421; *Corporate headquarters;
bottled & canned fruit juice,
ready-to-drink tea, enhanced
water & cranberry sauce*
Employs—125; Estab.—1942
Company-wide: 550
Sales—$25Mil-$50Mil (est)
Distrib.—National
Privately owned corporation
Parent co.—Lassonde Industries,
Inc.
Phone—(866) 552-7643
See Parent Co. Section for full profile.

### †MCLANE NEW JERSEY

Div. of McLane Company, Inc.,
Grocery Div.
742 Courses Landing Rd. (08069)
**Phone—(856) 351-6200**
Fax—(856) 351-6208
www.mclaneco.com
Email—jim.tidmore@mclaneco.com
Pres.—Jim Tidmore
V-P., Dist.—Russell Gore
IT Mgr.—Tracy Krivan
Hum. Res. Mgr.—Ron Harvi
Cust. Serv. Mgr.—Vickie Savage
Hum. Res. Rep.—Kris Long
SIC—5141; *Distributor of general
line groceries to food &
convenience stores & military
commissaries*
Employs—413; Estab.—2004
210,000 sq ft site, Distrib.—Local
Privately owned corporation
Parent co.—McLane Company,
Inc., Grocery Div., Temple, TX
Phone—(254) 771-7500
See Parent Co. Section for full profile.

### PANPAC, LLC

212 N. Virginia Ave. (08069)
**Phone—(856) 376-3576**
Fax—(856) 299-0977
www.panpacusa.com
Email—info@panpacusa.com
Owner—Rahul Kaushik
SIC—3555; *Rebuilt offset printing
& postpress graphic arts
equipment*
Employs—14; Estab.—2005
50,000 sq ft site, Distrib.—Intl.
Limited Liability Company

## Carteret
(Middlesex—N.E.)

### †BERJE INC.
700 Blair Rd. (07008)
**Phone—(973) 748-8980**
Fax—(973) 680-9618
www.berjeinc.com
Email—berje@berjeinc.com
CEO—Kim Bleimann
Pres.—David Herbst
CFO—Brian Hart
V-P., Opers.—Frank Mara
Dir., Acctg.—Madhu Gandhi
SIC—5169; *Corporate headquarters & distributor of essential oils & aromatic chemicals for the pharmaceutical, flavor & fragrance industries*
Employs—100; Estab.—1949
250,000 sq ft site, Distrib.—Intl.
Sole ownership

### DR PEPPER SNAPPLE GROUP, INC.
1200 Milik St. (07008)
**Phone—(732) 969-1600**
Fax—(732) 969-9590
www.drpeppersnapple.com
Email—diana.perez@dpsg.com
Plt. Mgr.—Saul Cruz
Assoc. Hum. Res. Mgr.—Pamela Duncan
Hum. Res. Coord.—Diana Perez
SIC—2033; NAICS—311421; *Juices; Brand name—Snapple*
Employs—200; Estab.—1992
Sales—$10Mil-$25Mil
500,000 sq ft site,
Publicly owned corporation
Parent co.—Dr Pepper Snapple Group, Inc., Plano, TX
Phone—(972) 673-7000
See Parent Co. Section for full profile.

### FUJIPOLY AMERICA CORP.
900 Milik St., P.O. Box 119 (07008)
**Phone—(732) 969-0100**
Fax—(732) 969-3311
www.fujipoly.com
Email—info@fujipoly.com
Pres.—Frank Hobler
Prodn. Mgr.—Michael Goldshine
Acctg. Mgr.—Richard Potts
Qual. Assur. Mgr.—Jeffrey DeVries
SIC—3679; *Silicon rubber electronic components; Brand name—Zebra; Sarcon*
Employs—30; Estab.—1993
Sales—over $9Mil
24,500 sq ft site, Distrib.—Intl.
Privately owned corporation
ISO rating—9001:2008

### †JERSEY PAPER PLUS, INC.
600 Federal Blvd. *(07008)*
**Phone—(732) 750-1900**
Fax—(732) 750-2824
www.jerseypaper.com
Pres.—Steven Tabak
V-P.—Richard Beck
IT Mgr.—Rafael Guadalupe
Off. Mgr.—Kathleen Miller
SIC—5087; 5113; *Distributor of janitorial paper products*
Employs—50; Estab.—1983
Distrib.—Local
Privately owned corporation

### JO BELLA MACHINE MFG.
232 Washington Ave. (07008)
**Phone—(732) 541-7076**
www.jobellamachine.com
Owner—Izabella Skrzypko
Foreman—Eugene Skrzypko
SIC—3599; *General machining job shop*
Employs—4; Estab.—2011
Sales—under $500,000
1,350 sq ft site, Distrib.—Local
Privately owned corporation

---

**NEW ENTRY**
### LIFE A STITCH
37 Jackson Ave. (07008)
**Phone—(732) 969-0232**
Email—wolf646@aol.com
Owner—Ray Malivuk
SIC—2395; 2396; 3993; *Embroidery, t-shirt screen printing & interior & exterior signs*
Employs—2; Estab.—2000
Sales—under $500,000 (est)
Distrib.—Local
Sole ownership

### LM FOODS, LLC
100 Raskulinecz Rd. (07008)
**Phone—(732) 855-9500**
Fax—(732) 855-7474
www.lmfoods.com
Email—info@lmfoods.com
Pres.—Mark Olivito
CFO—Bong Ko
Sales Mgr.—Andrew Davidoff
Operation Mgr.—Scott Vansyckle
Off. Mgr.—Semi Cheon
Qual. Assur. Mgr.—Shirley Plazo
SIC—2092; NAICS—311712; *Surimi seafood products*
Employs—90; Estab.—1995
Distrib.—Intl.
Limited Liability Company

### MID JERSEY PET SUPPLY
296 Pershing Ave. (07008)
**Phone—(732) 541-2807**
Fax—(732) 969-8560
www.prosalt.com
Email—sales@midjerseypetsupply.com
Pres.—Ed Rutkowski
SIC—2048; *Frozen fish food*
Employs—5; Estab.—1977
Sales—under $500,000
Distrib.—Intl.
Privately owned corporation

### NU-WORLD CORP.
300 Milik St. (07008)
**Phone—(732) 541-6300**
Fax—(732) 541-8911
www.nuworldcosmetics.com
Email—info@nwcos.com
Cont.—Susan Pace
SIC—2844; NAICS—325600; *Cosmetics*
Employs—50; Estab.—1991
Sales—$1Mil-$2.5Mil
Distrib.—National
Privately owned corporation

### OXFORD INSTRUMENTS SUPERCONDUCTING TECHNOLOGY, INC.
Div. of Oxford Instruments America, Inc.
600 Milik St. (07008)
**Phone—(732) 541-1300**
Fax—(732) 541-7769
www.oxinst.com
Email—sales@ost.oxinst.com
Pres.—Jeff Parrell
V-P., Hum. Res.—Carol Durst
V-P., Fin.—Vivek Naidoo
Dir., Opers.—Chip Nelson
Acctg. Mgr.—Joseph Ingato
SIC—3357; 3679; 3264; NAICS—327113; *Corporate headquarters & superconductor wire & cable*
Employs—212; Estab.—1970
Sales—$70Mil
130,000 sq ft site, Distrib.—Intl.
Privately owned partnership
ISO rating—9000:2000
Parent co.—Oxford Instruments America, Inc., Concord, MA
Phone—(978) 369-9933
See Parent Co. Section for full profile.

### QUICK STRIP
1 Randolph St. (07008)
**Phone—(732) 969-3268**
www.quickstripnj.com
Email—info@quickstripnj.com

---

Pres.—Larry Fauci
SIC—3471; 3479; *Media blasting & powder coating for automobile restoration & body shops & do-it-yourself car enthusiasts*
Employs—1; Estab.—2004
Sales—under $500,000
Distrib.—Local
Limited Liability Company

### †TULNOY LUMBER, INC.
9-D Raskulinecz Rd. (07008-0009)
**Phone—(732) 634-4000**
Fax—(732) 634-0358
www.tulnoylumber.com
Email—tulnoyandj@aol.com
Br. Mgr.—Tony Ginese
Sales Rep.—Jerry Moncarz
SIC—5031; *Wholesaler of lumber*
Employs—25; Estab.—1920
Sales—$7Mil-$10Mil
100,000 sq ft site, Distrib.—Regional
Privately owned corporation
Parent co.—Tulnoy Lumber, Inc., Bronx, NY
Phone—(718) 583-3434
See Parent Co. Section for full profile.

---

## Cedar Brook
(Camden—S.W.)

### DUBELL LUMBER CO.
102 S. Route 73 (08018)
**Phone—(609) 567-2467**
Fax—(609) 567-9050
www.dubell.com
Email—info@dubell.com
Hum. Res. Mgr.—Pam Clow
SIC—2431; NAICS—321900; *Architectural millwork*
Employs—16; Estab.—1946
Sales—$500,000-$1Mil
7,500 sq ft site, Distrib.—Regional
Privately owned corporation
Parent co.—Dubell Lumber Co., Medford, NJ
Phone—(609) 654-4143
See Parent Co. Section for full profile.

---

## Cedar Grove
(Essex—N.E.)

### APEX MARBLE & GRANITE, INC.
998 Pompton Ave. (07009)
**Phone—(973) 857-3655**
Fax—(973) 857-3755
www.apextilegallery.com
Email—apex07009@aol.com
Pres.—Tom Tsatsaros
Off. Mgr.—Elena Tsatsaros
SIC—3281; NAICS—327991; *Marble & granite countertops*
Employs—7; Estab.—1992
Sales—$500,000-$1Mil (est)
Distrib.—Local
Privately owned corporation

### AQUA PRODUCTS, INC.
Div. of Fluidra USA, LLC
25 Rutgers Ave. (07009)
**Phone—(973) 857-2700**
National—(800) 221-1750
Fax—(973) 857-8981
www.aquaproducts.com
Email—icorbosiero@aquaproducts.com
Pres.—Tomer Porat
V-P., Mktg.—Steve Ferry
SIC—3589; 3679; NAICS—333319; *Robotic swimming pool cleaners for maintenance of residential, commercial & industrial aquatic facilities; Brand name—Aquabot; Pool Rover; Power Handi Vac; AquaMax; JetMax; UltraMax; DredgeVac*
Employs—200; Estab.—1982
100,000 sq ft site, Distrib.—Intl.
Privately owned corporation

---

Parent co.—Fluidra USA, LLC, Jacksonville, FL
Phone—(904) 378-0999
See Parent Co. Section for full profile.

### BELLEVILLE WIRE CLOTH CO., INC.
18 Rutgers Ave. (07009)
**Phone—(973) 239-0074**
National—(800) 631-0490
Fax—(973) 239-3985
www.bwire.com
Email—sales@bwire.com
Pres.—James Crowley
V-P.—Mike Crowley
Mktg. Mgr.—Dan Steele
SIC—3496; *Wire cloth, screens & filters*
Employs—35; Estab.—1919
Sales—$5Mil
30,000 sq ft site, Distrib.—National
Privately owned corporation
ISO rating—9001

### CARGILLE LABORATORIES
55 Commerce Rd. (07009)
**Phone—(973) 239-6633**
Fax—(973) 239-6096
www.cargille.com
Email—cargillelabs@aol.com
Pres., Tech.—William J. Sacher
Cont.—Cheryl Hosler
Hum. Res. & Pub. Rels. Mgr.—Catherine Cargille
SIC—3826; 3231; 2992; 3069; NAICS—334516; *Refractive index & sink-float standards & sets, including immersion oils, fiber optics, laser coupling, interfacing liquids & mounting media & disposable lab products*
Employs—22; Estab.—1924
16,000 sq ft site, Distrib.—National
Privately owned corporation

### CONTRACT FILLING, INC.
10 Cliffside Dr. (07009)
**Phone—(973) 239-6608**
Fax—(973) 239-6692
Email—contractfilling@aol.com
Pres.—William Lizzi
SIC—2844; NAICS—325600; *Deodorants & perfumes contract filling & packaging*
Employs—300; Estab.—1983
150,000 sq ft site, Distrib.—National
Privately owned sub-S corp.

### DEGREE DAY SYSTEMS, INC.
33 Village Park Rd., P.O. Box 510 (07009)
**Phone—(973) 239-7900**
National—(800) 233-4733
Fax—(973) 239-5442
www.degreeday.com
Email—info@degreeday.com
Pres., Treas.—Thomas Saczawa
V-P. & Dir., Mktg.—Mark Saczawa
SIC—2761; NAICS—323116; *Business forms & meter tickets for the fuel oil & propane gas industries; Brand name—All Weather Eze-Snap Meter Tickets*
Employs—10; Estab.—1926
8,700 sq ft site, Distrib.—Intl.
Privately owned corporation

### DIGITAL DESIGN, INC.
67 Sand Park Rd. (07009)
**Phone—(973) 857-0901**
National—(800) 967-7746
Fax—(973) 857-7906
www.evolutioninkjet.com
Pres., CEO—Ed Gerri
Cust. Serv. Mgr.—Ed McCarthy
SIC—3953; NAICS—339943; *Inkjet coding & marking systems*
Employs—30; Estab.—1980
Sales—$1Mil-$2.5Mil
Distrib.—Intl.
Privately owned corporation

GEOGRAPHICAL

## Cedar Grove—(cont.)

**ELNIK SYSTEMS, LLC**
107 Commerce Rd. (07009)
**Phone—(973) 239-6066**
Fax—(973) 239-3272
www.elnik.com
Email—elnik@elnik.com
Pres.—Claus Joens
V-P.—Stefan Joens
Pur. Mgr.—Inge Joens
Hum. Res. Mgr.—Patricia Plumb
SIC—3567; NAICS—333994;
*Sintering furnaces & debinding ovens for metal injection molding, including heating treating & vacuum furnaces, hot zones & retorts; Brand name—Elnik Systems*
Employs—35; Estab.—1969
Sales—$5Mil-$10Mil
22,000 sq ft site, Distrib.—Intl.
Limited Liability Company

**EMCO INDUSTRIAL PLASTICS, INC.**
99 Commerce Rd., P.O. Box 2503 (07009)
**Phone—(973) 559-5610**
Fax—(973) 239-1595
www.emcoplastics.com
Email—mailbox@emcoplastics.com
Pres.—William Egner
V-P.—Mark Mercadante
GM—Jim McNamara
Off. Mgr.—Jules Vahalla
SIC—3081; 3082; 3083; 5162;
NAICS—326113; *Plastic fabrication & distributor of plastic sheet, rod, tubing, film, profiles & machined parts, including CNC routing, milling, turning, bending, gluing & forming; Brand name—Plexiglas; Lucite; Lexan; Acrylite; Delrin; Nylatron; Teflon; Tuffak; Hyzod; Acetron; Vespel; Celazole; Victrex; Kydex; Micarta; Sintra; Spartech; Torlon; Trovidur; Tygon; Vivak; Zelux Zytel*
Employs—75; Estab.—1983
Sales—$10Mil-$25Mil
50,000 sq ft site, Distrib.—National
Privately owned corporation

**FAIRFIELD GOURMET FOOD CORP.**
11 Cliffside Dr. (07009)
**Phone—(973) 227-2800**
National—(800) 227-2800
Fax—(973) 882-6998
www.davidscookies.com
Email—corpsales@davidscookies.com
Pres., CEO—Ari Margulies
V-P., Sales—Lee Paguette
V-P., Natl. Accts.—Brent Maloy
Mktg. Mgr.—Aehee Park
SIC—2045; 2051; NAICS—311822; *Corporate headquarters & frozen cookie dough, ruggallech & pastries; Brand name—*
Employs—100
Company-wide: 350
Sales—$25Mil-$50Mil (est)
160,000 sq ft site, Distrib.—National
Privately owned corporation
AKA: David's Cookies

**INFOR METAL & TOOLING MANUFACTURING CORPORATION**
16 Commerce Rd. (07009)
**Phone—(973) 571-9520**
Fax—(973) 571-9630
www.informetal.com
Email—info@informetal.com
Pres.—Charles Insel
V-P.—Karl Insel
V-P.—George J. Insel

SIC—3469; 3465; 2782; 3544;
NAICS—339993; *Contract metal stamping, tool & die & machining of stationery fasteners for file folders & report covers for the office supply industry*
Employs—10; Estab.—1972
Sales—under $10Mil
15,500 sq ft site, Distrib.—Intl.
Privately owned corporation

**JENKINS & SONS, INC., M. W.**
444 Pompton Ave., P.O. Box 303 (07009)
**Phone—(973) 239-5150**
National—(800) 278-7437
Fax—(973) 239-8087
www.jenkinsbrush.com
Email—brushworks@jenkinsbrush.com
Pres. & V-P., Sales—Craig Sigler
V-P., Engrg.—Eric Eucker
SIC—3991; NAICS—339994;
*Industrial brushes; Brand name—METLKOR; LIFEWOOD*
Employs—7; Estab.—1877
Sales—$1Mil-$5Mil
Distrib.—National
Privately owned corporation

**JEWEL PRECISION SHEET METAL MACHINING, INC.**
200 Commerce Rd. (07009)
**Phone—(973) 857-5545**
Fax—(973) 857-5548
www.jewelprecision.com
Email—jerry@jewelprecision.com
Pres.—Ignazio Graziano
V-P.—Lorenzo Graziano
Qual. Assur. Mgr.—Gary Schenderger
SIC—3444; 3699; 3089; 3599;
*Sheet metal & plastic fabrication, thermoforming, laser marking & CNC machining job shop; Brand name—Surginizer ®*
Employs—75; Estab.—1984
47,500 sq ft site, Distrib.—National

**KING ENGINE BEARINGS**
371 Little Falls Rd., Ste. 5 (07009)
**Phone—(973) 857-0705**
National—(800) 772-3670
Fax—(973) 857-3228
www.kingbearings.com
Email—joseph@kingbearings.com
Owner & Pres.—Dalila Michel
Opers. Mgr.—May Sanchez
SIC—3562; NAICS—332991;
*Engine bearings*
Employs—15; Estab.—1981
Sales—$500,000-$1Mil
Distrib.—Intl.
Privately owned corporation

**LARACCA MFG., INC.**
395 Little Falls Rd. (07009)
**Phone—(973) 571-1452**
Email—laraccamfg@optonline.net
Pres.—Anthony Laracca
Plt. Mgr.—Pat Laracca
SIC—2452; NAICS—321992;
*Wooden storage sheds*
Employs—20; Estab.—1999
Sales—$500,000-$1Mil
Distrib.—Regional
Privately owned corporation

**†MCINTOSH CONTROLS CORP.**
218 Little Falls Rd., Unit 1 (07009)
**Phone—(973) 433-4700**
Fax—(973) 433-4704
www.mcintoshcontrols.com
Email—sales@mcintoshcontrols.com
Pres.—Harold Mattesky
V-P.—Richard Mattesky
Sales Rep.—Ryan Mattesky

SIC—5084; *Distributor of level, flow, pressure & temperature controls & instrumentation; Brand name—Gems Sensors; Warrick Controls; Fairchild; Mid-West Instruments; Bindicator; Kistler-Morse; King Engineering; Global Water; SymCom; SSAC; APG; Acromag; SmartCover*
Employs—9; Estab.—1950
Sales—$2.6Mil-$5Mil
6,000 sq ft site, Distrib.—National
Privately owned corporation

**METAL CUTTING CORP.**
89 Commerce Rd. (07009)
**Phone—(973) 239-1101**
National—(800) 783-6382
Fax—(973) 239-6651
www.metalcutting.com
Email—sales@metalcutting.com
Ex. V-P.—Joshua Jablons
Dir., Sales—Neal Day
Mktg. Mgr.—Evan Hardek
SIC—3499; 3471; NAICS—332813; *Burr-free cut-off tight-tolerance metal parts, cutting, grinding, lapping & polishing*
Employs—65; Estab.—1967
52,000 sq ft site, Distrib.—Intl.
Privately owned sub-S corp.

**MONITEUR DEVICES, INC.**
36 Commerce Rd. (07009)
**Phone—(973) 857-1600**
Fax—(973) 857-7289
www.moniteurdevices.com
Email—sales@moniteurdevices.com
Pres.—John Unoski
V-P., GM—Robert Unoski
Region Mgr.—Chris Carter
SIC—3669; NAICS—334290;
*Valve position transmitters, indicators & monitoring systems for automated valves; Brand name—Sentinel VPT; Watchman VPT; Sentinel S3 VPT; Survivor VPT; Companion VPT*
Employs—15; Estab.—1991
10,000 sq ft site, Distrib.—Intl.
Privately owned corporation
ISO rating—9001:2008

**OMEGA PRECISION CORP.**
1384 Pompton Ave., Ste. 3 (07009)
**Phone—(973) 256-3422**
Fax—(973) 256-6171
www.omegaprecision.com
Email—omega@omegaprecision.com
Pres.—Lawrence Niebling
MIS Mgr.—Mike Fisher
R & D Mgr.—Eric Evans
Bookkeeper—Jane Arlotta
SIC—3469; *Metal stampings*
Employs—20; Estab.—1973
20,000 sq ft site, Distrib.—National
Privately owned corporation

**OMNIA INDUSTRIES, INC.**
5 Cliffside Dr., P.O. Box 330 (07009)
**Phone—(973) 239-7272**
National—(800) 310-7960
Fax—(973) 239-5960
www.omniaindustries.com
Email—info@omniaindustries.com
Pres., CEO—Alberto R. Comini
Ex. V-P.—Denyse Comini Becker
Dir., Mktg.—Karen Andrews
SIC—3429; *Solid brass & stainless steel latch sets, mortise entry locksets, deadbolt locksets, narrow backset mortise locks, multipoint trim, hinges, cabinet hardware & architectural hardware*
Employs—50; Estab.—1964
Sales—$2.5Mil-$5Mil (est)
Distrib.—Intl.
Privately owned corporation

**PLAST-O-MATIC VALVES, INC.**
1384 Pompton Ave., Ste. 1 (07009)
**Phone—(973) 256-3000**
Fax—(973) 256-4745
www.plastomatic.com
Email—info@plastomatic.com
Pres.—Tim Delorenzo
V-P., Mfg.—Barry Nunno
Adv. & Mktg. Mgr.—Rick Bolger
Admn. Mgr.—Dana Delorenzo
SIC—3492; 3625; 3089; NAICS—332911; *Thermoplastic valves & controls for corrosive & ultra-pure liquid pressure & flow control*
Employs—60; Estab.—1967
Sales—$5Mil-$10Mil
52,000 sq ft site, Distrib.—Intl.
Privately owned corporation

**PRINT WRAP CORP.**
95 Sand Park Rd. (07009)
**Phone—(973) 239-1144**
Fax—(973) 239-1233
www.printwrap.com
Email—info@printwrap.com
V-P.—Roger Neiman
V-P.—Andrew Neiman
SIC—2759; NAICS—323100;
*Flexographic printing*
Employs—15; Estab.—1972
Distrib.—Regional

**RANDCASTLE EXTRUSION SYSTEMS, INC.**
220 Little Falls Rd., Unit 6 (07009)
**Phone—(973) 239-1150**
Fax—(973) 239-0830
www.randcastle.com
Email—sales@randcastle.com
Pres.—Keith Luker
GM—David Lorenc
SIC—3542; 3559; 3544; NAICS—333220; *Bench & floor screw extrusion machinery with 0.1cc to 200cc dominantly elongational batch mixers for compounding film, sheet, tubing, wire & production compounding screws, including lab size extruders & lines; Brand name—Microtruder; Taskmaster; Recirculator; Elongator*
Employs—5; Estab.—1987
8,000 sq ft site, Distrib.—Intl.
Sole ownership

**REPROMATIC PRINTING CO., INC.**
216 Little Falls Rd., Unit 3 (07009)
**Phone—(973) 239-7610**
Fax—(973) 239-7613
www.repromatic.com
Email—repromatic@optonline.net
Pres., GM—Paul Molinari
V-P.—Alyce Molinari
SIC—2759; NAICS—323100;
*Commercial printing*
Employs—4; Estab.—1973
Sales—under $1Mil
5,000 sq ft site, Distrib.—Regional
Privately owned corporation

**SAMA PLASTICS CORP.**
20 Sand Park Rd. (07009)
**Phone—(973) 239-7200**
www.samaplastics.com
Email—sales@samaplastics.com
Pres.—Mark Wolfberg
Cont. & Dir., Hum. Res.—Joy Martinek
SIC—3089; 2542; *Acrylic & wood display fixture & point-of-purchase displays*
Employs—45; Estab.—1944
44,000 sq ft site, Distrib.—National
Privately owned sub-S corp.

**SERVOMETER-PMG, LLC**
501 Little Falls Rd. (07009)
**Phone—(973) 785-4630**
Fax—(973) 785-0756
www.servometer.com
Email—info@servometer.com
Chrm.—Tony Penchuk

## Cedar Grove—(cont.)

Pres.—Glenn Weinrich
CFO—Gerry O'Donovan
Dir., Engrg. Svcs.—Paul Hazlitt
GM—Joe Madonna
Tech. Sales Mgr.—Fred Poelzing
Mktg. Mgr.—Lori Lyons
MIS Mgr.—Tony Gill
Bus. Dev. Mgr.—Jim Barkand
Engrg. Mgr.—Brent Caldwell
SIC—3471; 3599; NAICS—
332813; *Company headquarters
& custom miniature metal
bellows, bellows assemblies,
bellow-type flexible shaft
couplings, gold plated bellows
contacts & electroforms; Brand
name—Servometric;
Interconnectric*
Employs—72; Estab.—1957
Sales—$12Mil
26,000 sq ft site, Distrib.—Intl.
Limited Liability Company
ISO rating—9001:2000

### SPECTREX, INC.

218 Little Falls Rd., Unit 12
(07009)
**Phone—(973) 239-8398**
National—(800) 452-2107
Fax—(973) 239-7614
www.spectrex.net
Email—spectrex@spectrex.net
Pres.—Eric Zinn
V.-P.—Jay Cooley
Sales Mgr., Military—Barbara
Acocella
SIC—3829; *Open-path (line of
sight) gas detection systems,
including optical flame
detectors; Brand name—
SharpEye Flame Detectors;
SafEye Gas Detection Systems*
Employs—14; Estab.—1980
Sales—$12Mil
Distrib.—Intl.
Privately owned corporation
ISO rating—9001

### UNIT PACK CO., INC.

7 Lewis Rd. (07009)
**Phone—(973) 239-4112**
Fax—(973) 239-0429
www.unitpack.com
Email—elosser@unitpack.com
Pres.—Ernest Losser
Off. Mgr.—Cathy Lee
SIC—3089; *Plastic containers*
Employs—30; Estab.—1964
50,000 sq ft site, Distrib.—National
Privately owned sub-S corp.

### UNITED SUPPORT SOLUTIONS, INC.

134 Sand Park Rd. (07009-1240)
**Phone—(973) 857-2298**
Fax—(973) 857-4943
www.unitedss.com
Email—sales@unitedss.com
Pres.—Joe Ostering
V.-P.—John Ostering
Dir., Opers.—John Machnicki
Dir., Bus. Dev.—Melissa Spratt
SIC—3444; 3599; 3471; 3479;
NAICS—332710; *Sheet metal
fabrication, AWS & robotic
welding, 2-5 axis machining,
metal finishing, painting, powder
coating, silk-screening,
assembly & kitting*
Employs—80; Estab.—1980
Sales—$10Mil
75,000 sq ft site, Distrib.—National
Privately owned corporation
ISO rating—9001:2008

## Cedar Knolls

### (Morris—N.W.)

### †ARZEE SUPPLY CORP. OF NEW JERSEY

Div. of Allied Building Products
Corp.
15 E. Frederick Pl. (07927)
**Phone—(973) 267-1576**
National—(800) 988-7999
Fax—(973) 267-7650
www.arzee.com
Email—eddie.jacobus@arzee.com
Br. Mgr.—Ed Jacobus
SIC—5033; 5031; *Distributor of
building materials & supplies,
including roofing, siding,
windows & doors*
Employs—48; Estab.—1968
Distrib.—Local
Publicly owned corporation
Parent co.—Allied Building
Products Corp., East Rutherford,
NJ
Phone—(201) 507-8400
See Parent Co. Section for full profile.

### CARGILLE TAB-PRO CORP.

4 E. Frederick Pl. (07927)
**Phone—(973) 267-8888**
Fax—(973) 267-7998
Email—cargilletabpro@att.net
V.-P.—Catherine Cargille
Off. Mgr.—Scott Molinaro
Technical Mgr.—James Witanek
SIC—2899; *Contract chemical
tabletting & blending, including
fragrance carrier tablets &
grinding aids & pellet binders for
x-ray fluorescence spectrometry;
Brand name—Absorb-Tab;
Copolywax*
Employs—13; Estab.—1955
Sales—$1Mil
54,000 sq ft site, Distrib.—National
Privately owned corporation

### COMMERCIAL BUSINESS FORMS

240 Cedar Knolls Rd., Ste. 203
(07927-1621)
**Phone—(973) 682-9000**
National—(800) 243-9701
Fax—(973) 682-9559
www.printcbf.com
Email—info@printcbf.com
Pres.—Michael Gordon
Salesperson—Lauren Jester
SIC—2759; 2752; NAICS—
323100; *Commercial/business &
color printing of direct mail
marketing & promotional items,
membership cards, business
forms, checks, thermal labels &
tags & personalizing & remote
invoice & statement rendering;
Brand name—Cognitive
Solutions*
Employs—12; Estab.—1983
3,200 sq ft site, Distrib.—Regional
Privately owned corporation
AKA: Print C B F

### †CONSOLIDATED BEARINGS COMPANY

10 Wing Dr. (07927)
Mail addr: P.O. Box 1255,
Morristown (07962-1255)
**Phone—(973) 539-8300**
National—(877) 266-2744
Fax—(973) 539-5902
www.consbrgs.com
Email—sales@consbrgs.com
Pres.—Glenn R. Kuskin
Ex. V.-P.—Thomas O. Meerwarth
Dir., IT—Donald Vasta
Sales Mgr., Natl.—Wallace Krake

SIC—5085; *Company
headquarters & distributor of
standard & imported precision
bearings; Brand name—FAG;
Barden; INA; Schaeffler Group
Products*
Employs—30; Estab.—1933
70,000 sq ft site, Distrib.—National
Privately owned sub-S corp.
ISO rating—9001:2008

### ENERGIZER PERSONAL CARE

Div. of Energizer Holdings, Inc.
240 Cedar Knolls Rd., Ste. 401
(07927)
**Phone—(973) 753-3000**
National—(877) 277-4679
Fax—(973) 326-9005
www.personna.com
Email—asr@personna.com
CFO—Thomas Kasvin
CIO—Johnathan Beery
GM—Colin Hutchison
Mktg. Mgr.—John Jaeger
SIC—3421; NAICS—332200;
*Divisional headquarters & safety
razors & blades; Brand name—
Personna*
Employs—15; Estab.—1876
Distrib.—Intl.
Publicly owned corporation
Parent co.—Energizer Holdings,
Inc., St. Louis, MO
Phone—(314) 985-2000
See Parent Co. Section for full profile.

### FOSTER & CO., INC.

15 Wing Dr. (07927)
**Phone—(973) 267-4100**
National—(800) 526-0630
Fax—(973) 267-9842
www.fostercomfg.com
Email—info@fostercomfg.com
Pres., Fin. & MIS Mgr.—Richard
Foster
V.-P.—Kenneth Foster
Pur. Agt.—Karen Maffucci
Salesman—Robert Foster
SIC—2842; 3053; NAICS—
325612; *Cleaning & polishing
compounds, industrial fasteners,
brass fittings, hydraulic hose &
fittings, abrasives, cutting tools,
bin systems & service; Brand
name—Chem Power*
Employs—30; Estab.—1954
Distrib.—National
Privately owned corporation

### †MICRON OPTICS

14 Ridgedale Ave., Ste. 125
(07927-1115)
**Phone—(973) 267-5047**
Fax—(973) 267-6598
www.micron-optics.com
Email—micron@micron-optics.com
Pres.—Peter Burboeck
SIC—5049; 5043; 5065;
*Distributor of microscopes,
cameras & image analysis
equipment, including metrology
equipment, vision systems,
measuring microscopes,
comparators, 3D measuring
systems & x-ray inspection &
measuring systems; Brand
name—NIKON; SCIENSCOPE;
SHAPEGRABBER; DOLAN
JENNER; LUMENERA*
Employs—7; Estab.—1974
Sales—$2Mil
1,500 sq ft site, Distrib.—Local
Publicly owned corporation

### MORRIS FORMS CORP.

5 Saddle Rd. (07927)
**Phone—(973) 829-1200**
National—(800) 966-2367
Fax—(973) 829-1333
www.morrisforms.com
Email—sales@morrisforms.com
Pres.—Carl Badenhausen
Off. Mgr.—Dana A. Johnson

SIC—2759; 2752; 2761; 3993;
NAICS—323100; *Color, offset &
digital printing of multi-part,
continuous & bar-coded
business & school forms, labels,
catalogs, invoices, statements &
promotional products*
Employs—5; Estab.—1985
Sales—$500,000-$1Mil
Distrib.—National
Privately owned corporation

NEW ENTRY

### MYOS CORP. (H Q)

45 Horsehill Rd., Ste. 106 (07927)
**Phone—(973) 509-0444**
National—(888) 717-6967
Fax—(973) 348-5707
www.myoscorp.com
Email—jthomas@myoscorp.com
Pres.—Peter Levy
Hum. Res. & IT Mgr.—Joanne
Goodford
Tech. Mgr.—Maghsoud Dariani
SIC—2023; 2043; 2099;
*Corporate headquarters;
bionutritional supplements, bars,
meals & puddings (mfg.
subcontracted); Brand name—
Fortetropin™; MYO-X™*
Employs—10; Estab.—2011
Sales—$2.6Mil-$5Mil
5,000 sq ft site, Distrib.—National
Privately owned corporation

### †NEOPOST, INC.

Div. of Neopost USA, Inc.
2 Ridgedale Ave., 1st Fl. (07927-
1108)
**Phone—(973) 647-6700**
Fax—(973) 267-0103
www.neopostinc.com
Email—m.conway@neopost.com
GM—Steven Kaplan
Sales Mgr.—Nick Panagakos
Br. Admn.—Linda Wolf
SIC—5044; *Distributor of postage
& folding machines*
Employs—40; Estab.—2003
Distrib.—Regional
Privately owned corporation
Parent co.—Neopost USA, Inc.,
Milford, CT
Phone—(203) 301-3400
See Parent Co. Section for full profile.

### NUTRITION NORTH AMERICA

10 Saddle Rd. (07927)
**Phone—(973) 734-0023**
National—(800) 605-0410
Fax—(973) 734-0029
www.medicalfood.com
Email—info@medicalfood.com
Cust. Serv. Rep.—Tajah
Muhammad
Cust. Serv. Rep.—David Milmer
SIC—2099; 2096; NAICS—
311919; *Metabolic nutritional
drink formulas & mixes & food
products, including snacks*
Employs—26; Estab.—1993
Distrib.—Intl.
Privately owned corporation

### OLI SYSTEMS, INC.

240 Cedar Knolls Rd., Ste. 301
(07927)
**Phone—(973) 539-4996**
Fax—(973) 539-5922
www.olisystems.com
CEO—Marshall Rafal
COO—Andre Anderko
IT Mgr.—Chris Peter
SIC—7372; *Software
development*
Employs—20; Estab.—1971
4,578 sq ft site, Distrib.—National
Privately owned corporation

### TRUKMANN'S INC.

4 Wing Dr. (07927)
**Phone—(973) 538-7718**
Fax—(973) 285-4310

GEOGRAPHICAL

## Cedar Knolls—(cont.)

www.trukmannsrepro.com
Email—orders@trukmanns.com
CEO—Paul Korman
Pres.—Will Korman
SIC—2759; 2752; NAICS—
323100; *Commercial, large-
format, lithographic, color &
instant printing*
Employs—25; Estab.—1955
Distrib.—National
Privately owned sub-S corp.
AKA: Trukmann's Reprographics

**UNIQUE SYSTEMS, INC.**
4 Saddle Rd. (07927-1901)
**Phone—(973) 455-0440**
Fax—(973) 455-7214
www.uniquesystems.com
Email—sales@uniquesystems.com
Pres.—Olof A. Eriksen
V-P.—Kenneth Eriksen
Acctg. Mgr.—Carol McCarthy
SIC—3599; NAICS—333611;
*Machined replacement parts &
assemblies for steam turbines,
gears, rotating equipment &
centrifugal compressors; Brand
name—Elliott Process Vacuum
Systems; Elliott Turbines; Terry
Turbine & Gear Parts; Clark
Compressor Parts; Worthington
Turbine; Elliott Compressors*
Employs—20; Estab.—1973
25,000 sq ft site, Distrib.—Intl.
Privately owned sub-S corp.

## Cedarville

(Cumberland—S.W.)

**J & M ENTERPRISES**
32 North Ave. (08311)
**Phone—(856) 447-5090**
Fax—(856) 447-3306
www.jmentp.com
Email—jmelniczuk@comcast.net
Owner—John Melniczuk
SIC—3479; *Metal powder coating*
Employs—2; Estab.—1988
Sales—under $500,000 (est)
Distrib.—Regional
Sole ownership

**MILETTA BROTHERS, INC.**
194 Main St. *(08311)*
**Phone—(856) 447-4652**
Fax—(856) 447-4699
www.milettabrothers.net
Email—milettabrothersinc@
verizon.net
Pres.—Joseph Miletta, Jr.
Bookkeeper—Hilda Harris
SIC—3312; *Steel fabrication &
pipe fittings*
Employs—6; Estab.—1973
Sales—$500,000-$1Mil
Distrib.—Local
Privately owned corporation

**OWENS PLASTIC PRODUCTS, INC.**
393 Main St., P.O. Box 118 (08311-
0118)
**Phone—(856) 447-3500**
www.owensplasticproducts.com
Email—chris@
owensplasticproducts.com
Pres., CFO—Celeste Owens
GM—Chris Owens
SIC—3089; *Transfer, compression,
injection & insert molding of
thermo & thermoset plastics*
Employs—10; Estab.—1970
Sales—under $500,000
10,000 sq ft site, Distrib.—National
Privately owned corporation
ISO rating—9001:2000

## Chatham

(Morris—N.W.)

**ASHLAND, INC.**
116 Summit Ave. (07928)
**Phone—(973) 635-1551**
National—(800) 622-4423
Fax—(973) 635-4964
www.ashland.com
Email—jdevigili@ashland.com
V-P.—Sharrann Simmons
Site Mgr.—John Devigili
SIC—2899; *Specialty chemical
active ingredients & biopolymers
for the pharmaceutical & dietary
supplement industries*
Employs—22
Sales—$10Mil-$25Mil (est)
Distrib.—Intl.
Publicly owned corporation
Parent co.—Ashland, Inc.,
Covington, KY
Phone—(859) 815-3333
See Parent Co. Section for full profile.

**BURLING INSTRUMENTS, INC.**
16 River Rd., P.O. Box 298 (07928)
**Phone—(973) 635-9481**
Fax—(973) 635-9530
www.burlinginstruments.com
Pres., GM—Harry Bentas
Cust. Serv. Rep.—Elizabeth
Shields
SIC—3823; 3829; NAICS—
334513; *Temperature controls*
Employs—10; Estab.—1935
Sales—$1Mil-$2.5Mil
11,000 sq ft site, Distrib.—Intl.
Privately owned corporation

**CODFISH PARK DESIGN, LLC**
39 Commerce St. (07928)
**Phone—(646) 298-4050**
www.codfishpark.com
Email—info@
codfishparkdesign.com
Chief Cabinet Officer—Tyler
Merson
SIC—2434; 2511; NAICS—
337110; *Residential wooden
cabinets & furniture*
Employs—2; Estab.—2002
Sales—under $500,000
Distrib.—Local
Limited Liability Company

**DESKTOP ALERT, INC.**
346 Main St. (07928)
**Phone—(973) 727-0066**
Fax—(866) 689-9838
www.desktopalert.net
Email—info@desktopalert.com
Founder & Chief R & D Officer—
Howard Ryan
CTO—Justin Van Patten
SIC—7372; *IP-based emergency
notication software development*
Employs—5; Estab.—2001
Privately owned corporation

**EXELTIS**
1 Main St., Ste. 203 (07928)
**Phone—(973) 324-0200**
Fax—(973) 324-0795
www.exeltis.com
CEO—Maria Carell
SIC—2834; NAICS—325412;
*Pharmaceuticals*
Employs—25; Estab.—1977
Distrib.—Local
Privately owned corporation

**FERRITE WELDING PRODUCTS,
INC.**
31 S. Passaic Ave. (07928)
**Phone—(973) 377-6636**
          (973) 886-8455
Fax—(973) 377-0060
www.ferritewelding.com
Email—ferrite15@verizon.net
Pres.—Kevin Bukata

Sales Mgr., Inside—Adam
Sandeler
Mktg. Mgr.—Mark Serrittella
Fin. & MIS Mgr.—Jason Breland
SIC—3599; *Welding alloys &
accessories*
Employs—5; Estab.—1987
Sales—$500,000-$1Mil
4,000 sq ft site, Distrib.—National

**NATIONAL MFG. CO., INC.**
12 River Rd. (07928)
**Phone—(973) 635-8846**
Fax—(973) 635-7810
www.natlmfg.com
Email—websales@natlmfg.com
Pres., CEO—Robert Staudinger
V-P., Sales & Mktg.—Prasad
Mahadev
V-P., Fin.—Oliver Ibrahim
SIC—3469; *Deep-drawn &
shallow-drawn metal stampings*
Employs—190; Estab.—1944
Sales—$15Mil-$30Mil
65,000 sq ft site, Distrib.—Intl.
Privately owned corporation

**†RIZZO FINE ARTS INC., NICHOLAS F.**
32 Watchung Ave. (07928)
**Phone—(973) 635-7278**
Fax—(973) 635-7498
www.rizzofinearts.com
Email—info@rizzofinearts.com
Pres.—Nicholas F. Rizzo
V-P.—Brenda Rizzo
Dir.—Tony Dente
SIC—5199; *Wholesaler of fine
artwork, mirrors & framing*
Employs—10; Estab.—1981
7,200 sq ft site, Distrib.—Intl.
Privately owned corporation

**ROBBINS INSTRUMENTS, INC.**
2 N. Passaic Ave., P.O. Box 441
(07928)
**Phone—(973) 635-8972**
National—(800) 206-8649
Fax—(973) 635-8732
www.robbinsinstruments.com
Email—info@
robbinsinstruments.com
Pres.—George Mulvaney
Bookkeeper—Michelle Zeek
SIC—3841; *Surgical instruments,
including medical scissors,
needle holders & scalpels &
blade handles*
Employs—5; Estab.—1948
Sales—$500,000-$1Mil
Distrib.—Intl.
Privately owned sub-S corp.

**ROBERTSON PIPER SOFTWARE
GROUP, INC. (H Q)**
1500 Cardinal Dr. (07928)
**Phone—(973) 435-3640**
CEO—Doug Robertson
CFO—Tad Piper
V-P., Bus. Dev.—Kevin Kogler
SIC—6719; 7372; *Holding
company headquarters;
pharmacy management software
development*
Company-wide Emp.: 52 (est.)
Privately owned corporation

**ROTONDI & SONS, INC., S. (H Q)**
3 Watchung Ave. (07928)
Mail addr.—P.O. Box 1407, Summit
(07902)
**Phone—(973) 635-7799**
Fax—(973) 635-8006
Email—rotondi140@aol.com
Pres., CEO—Angelo Rotondi
CFO, Sales Mgr.—John Canace
Hum. Res. Mgr.—Mike Rotondi
SIC—2874; NAICS—325312;
*Corporate headquarters;
compost & yard waste recycling*
Employs—11; Estab.—1989
Sales—$5Mil-$10Mil (est)
Distrib.—Local
Privately owned corporation

**THEWAL, INC.**
12 Center St. (07928)
**Phone—(973) 635-1880**
Fax—(973) 635-1611
www.chathamprint.com
Email—info@chathamprint.com
Ptnr. & Pres.—Susan Kessel
Ptnr. & V-P.—Walter Francis
SIC—2759; 2752; 2791; 2789;
NAICS—323122; *Commercial &
digital printing, electronic
prepress & binding*
Employs—10; Estab.—1978
Sales—under $500,000
3,000 sq ft site, Distrib.—Regional
Privately owned corporation
AKA: Chatham Print & Design

**TODD ARCHITECTURAL MODELS**
54 Mountainview Rd., P.O. Box
1002 (07928)
**Phone—(973) 507-4072**
www.toddarchitecturalmodels.com
Email—toddmodel@mac.com
Pres.—Douglas Pitney
SIC—2499; 3499; 3089; *Wooden,
plastic & metal architectural
models*
Employs—7; Estab.—1968
Sales—under $750,000
4,000 sq ft site, Distrib.—Intl.
Privately owned sub-S corp.

**VINCHEM, INC.**
301 Main. St., P.O. Box 639
(07928)
**Phone—(973) 635-4841**
Fax—(973) 635-1459
www.vinchem.com
Email—vinchem@vinchem.com
Pres.—Vincent Ursino
V-P.—Paul Ursino
SIC—2899; *Chemical
preparations*
Employs—6; Estab.—1982
Sales—$2.5Mil-$5Mil (est)
Distrib.—National
Privately owned corporation

[NEW ENTRY]
**WATER ICE FACTORY, INC.**
15 Evergreen Rd (08084)
**Phone—(856) 627-6831**
www.thewatericefactory.com
Owner—Ralph Skidmore
SIC—2024; *Frozen ice cream
desserts*
Employs—5; Estab.—1987
Sales—$1Mil-$2.5Mil (est)
1,600 sq ft site, Distrib.—Local
Privately owned corporation

## Cherry Hill

(Camden—S.W.)

**ABRUZZI STONE & FLOORING, LLC**
1641 Marlton Pike E. (08034-1413)
**Phone—(856) 616-0800**
Fax—(856) 616-0801
www.abruzzistone.com
Email—abruzzistone@aol.com
Owner—Anthony DiGuglielmo
GM—Stephanie DiGuglielmo
SIC—3281; NAICS—327991;
*Custom fabrication of granite &
marble countertops & bathroom
design & remodeling*
Employs—10; Estab.—2009
Sales—$500,000-$1Mil
Distrib.—Local
Limited Liability Company

**ACB REPRODUCTION**
2060 Springdale Rd. (08003)
**Phone—(856) 751-0360**
Fax—(856) 751-5642
Email—cherryhill.planwell@e-
arc.com
Manager—Andy Bonachea

## Cherry Hill—(cont.)

SIC—2752; NAICS—323100; Instant printing
Employs—8; Estab.—1998
Sales—under $500,000
Distrib.—Local
Privately owned corporation

**ADMIRAL INTEGRATION, INC.**
1001 Marlton Pike W. (08002)
**Phone—(856) 429-6700**
Fax—(856) 427-0600
www.admint.com
Owner & Pres.—Katiusca McEntee
Opers. Mgr.—Chuck Yurek
Hum. Res. & IT Mgr.—Mike McEntee
SIC—7373; Computer network integration, including LANs & WANs
Employs—8
Sales—$500,000-$1Mil
Distrib.—Local
Privately owned corporation

**AIR DISTRIBUTION SYSTEMS, INC.**
1000 Astoria Blvd. (08003)
**Phone—(856) 874-1100**
Fax—(856) 874-1110
www.adsduct.com
Email—cdoyle@adsduct.com
Pres.—Charles Doyle
V-P.—Greg Doyle
SIC—3444; HVAC ducts
Employs—50; Estab.—2003
Sales—$5Mil-$10Mil (est)
Distrib.—Regional
Privately owned corporation
AKA: ADS

**ALL COVERED**
100 Dobbs Ln., Ste. 208 (08034)
**Phone—(856) 795-7330**
National—(800) 242-7403
Fax—(856) 795-4341
www.ucss.com
Email—jay@ucss.com
Pres.—Anthony Calabrese
SIC—7373; NAICS—541512; Computer LAN, WAN & internet integrated systems
Employs—25; Estab.—1983
Distrib.—Regional
Privately owned corporation

**ALPHAGRAPHICS**
5 N. Olney Ave., Ste. 200 (08003)
**Phone—(856) 761-8000**
Fax—(856) 761-8005
www.cherryhill.alphagraphics.com
Email—cherryhill@ alphagraphics.com
Owner—Dave Sanford
GM—Brian Manold
Graphic Designer—Don Almada
SIC—2752; 2759; NAICS— 323100; Digital & offset printing & graphic design
Employs—19; Estab.—1991
Sales—$500,000-$1Mil
17,000 sq ft site, Distrib.—Intl.
Privately owned corporation
AKA: SDALC

**AMERICAN IMAGES, LLC**
1910 Fairfax Ave. (08003)
**Phone—(856) 424-3944**
Fax—(856) 424-3894
www.americanimagesllc.com
Pres.—Wayne Baw
SIC—2396; Textile screen printing
Employs—4; Estab.—1991
Sales—under $500,000
3,300 sq ft site, Distrib.—Local
Privately owned corporation

**ARCHITECTURAL ACRYLICS**
5 Rockhill Rd., Ste. 3 (08003)
**Phone—(856) 751-2411**
Fax—(856) 751-1428
Owner—Scott Springman

SIC—2542; Acrylic store fixtures
Employs—10; Estab.—1987
Sales—$500,000-$1Mil
8,000 sq ft site, Distrib.—Regional
Sole ownership

**B&D MARKETING, INC.**
1879 Old Cuthbert Rd., Ste. 21 (08034-1431)
**Phone—(856) 354-2004**
National—(800) 873-3180
Fax—(856) 354-2104
www.bddonorrec.com
Email—info@bddonorrec.com
Pres.—Marlene Epworth
GM—Dona Farley
Hum. Res. Mgr.—Bernie Epworth
SIC—2499; 3479; 3231; 3089; NAICS—327215; Custom donor recognition wall displays, trees & plaques for healthcare organizations, houses of worship, charitable institutions, museums, libraries, foundations, professional associations, universities & local & state governments
Employs—5; Estab.—1995
Sales—$500,000-$1Mil
Distrib.—National
Privately owned corporation
AKA: B&D Donor Recognition Products

**BAYARD'S CHOCOLATE CO., INC.**
2325 Marlton Pike West (08002)
**Phone—(856) 663-2565**
www.bayardschocolates.com
Email—door21@ bayardschocolates.com
Pres.—Frank Glaser
SIC—2064; NAICS—311300; Candy
Employs—15; Estab.—1937
Distrib.—Regional
Privately owned corporation

**BEST DRAPERY & BLIND MFG. CO.**
1 Kresson Rd. (08034)
**Phone—(856) 429-2242**
Fax—(856) 429-2400
www.ebestdesign.com
Email—info@ebestdesign.com
Pres.—James Logan
SIC—2391; NAICS—337920; Custom draperies
Employs—2; Estab.—1987
Sales—$500,000-$1Mil
Distrib.—Local
Privately owned corporation
AKA: Best Drapery & Design, Inc.

**BESTWORK INDUSTRIES FOR THE BLIND, INC.**
1940 Almay Ave., Ste. 200 (08003)
**Phone—(856) 939-5220**
National—(800) 370-9560
Fax—(856) 939-5022
www.bestworkindustries.org
Email—bestwork@eticomm.net
Pres.—Belinda Moore
Hum. Res. Mgr.—Linda Parker
SIC—3842; 2326; 2393; 3089; Fabric safety vests, work aprons, tool bags & contract sewing, assembly & shrink packaging
Employs—100; Estab.—1981
Distrib.—Intl.
Privately owned corporation

**BLACK CAR NEWS**
714 Crestbrook Ave. (08003)
**Phone—(856) 751-0656**
National—(800) 723-9119
Fax—(856) 751-0657
www.blackcarnews.com
Email—neil@blackcarnews.com
Publisher—Neil Weiss

SIC—2711; Company headquarters & newsletter publishing for the car & livery markets
Employs—2
Sales—under $500,000 (est)
Distrib.—National
Privately owned corporation

**BREAD & BAGELS**
1600 Church Rd. (08002)
**Phone—(856) 667-2333**
Fax—(856) 667-3568
Owner—Heechul Bang
SIC—2051; NAICS—311812; Bread & bagels
Employs—4; Estab.—1999
Sales—$500,000-$1Mil (est)
Distrib.—Local
Sole ownership

**BROAD STREET MEDIA**
Div. of Broad Street Media, LLC
53 Haddonfield Rd., Ste. 306 (08002)
**Phone—(856) 779-3800**
Fax—(856) 667-0298
www.thenjwire.com
Email—wirenews@bsmphilly.com
Dir., Prodn.—Darwin Oordt
Hum. Res. Mgr.—Harriet Lakusiewicz
Bus. Mgr.—Darcy Oort
SIC—2711; Newspaper publishing
Employs—25; Estab.—1997
Sales—$500,000-$1Mil (est)
Distrib.—Local
Privately owned corporation
AKA: Wire Newspaper, The
Parent co.—Broad Street Media, LLC, Trevose, PA
Phone—(215) 355-9009
See Parent Co. Section for full profile.

NEW ENTRY
**CAROL'S CREATIONS, LLC**
112 Kipling Rd. (08003)
**Phone—(856) 428-0621**
www.carolscreationsllc.com
Email—info@carolscreationsllc.com
Owner—Carol Decuzzi
SIC—2396; Custom & one-off apparel & textile product embroidery
Employs—2; Estab.—1980
Sales—under $500,000 (est)
Distrib.—Local
Limited Liability Company

**CDK INDUSTRY, LLC**
900 Haddonfield Rd. (08002)
**Phone—(856) 488-5456**
Fax—(856) 488-5524
www.jockeystore.com
Pres., GM—James Walford
Export Mgr.—Mike E. Logan
SIC—3949; 2395; NAICS— 339920; Horse racing equipment & embroidery & jockey whips
Employs—3; Estab.—1972
4,800 sq ft site, Distrib.—Intl.
Limited Liability Company
AKA: Whips International

**CLASSIC CAKE CO., THE**
480 Evesham Rd. (08003)
**Phone—(856) 751-5448**
Fax—(856) 795-0891
www.classiccake.com
Email—info@classiccake.com
Owner—Barry Krachman
SIC—2051; 2052; 2066; 2038; NAICS—311812; Cakes, cookies, pastries, pies, artisan breads, chocolates, gelato & sorbets
Employs—70; Estab.—1998
Distrib.—Local
Privately owned corporation

†**COMMERCIAL HARDWARE, INC.**
5 Perina Blvd. (08003)
**Phone—(856) 810-0600**
Fax—(856) 810-0996
www.commercialhardware.com
Email—vic@ commercialhardware.com
CEO—Victor Palladino
Pres.—John D. DelCollo
V-P., Fin. & CFO—Dennis Barag
Collections Mgr.—Jenny Embaby
SIC—5072; 5031; Corporate headquarters & distributor of commercial finish hardware & hollow metal, architectural grade wooden & residential prehung wooden doors & trim & bathroom partitions
Employs—50; Estab.—1988
Publicly owned corporation

**COURIER-POST NEWSPAPER**
Div. of Gannett Co., Inc.
301 Cuthbert Rd. (08002)
Mail addr: P.O. Box 5300, Cherry Hill (08034)
**Phone—(856) 663-6000**
Fax—(856) 665-9503
www.courierpostonline.com
Email—cuserve@ courierpostonline.com
Dir., Sales & GM—Bill Janus
Dir., IT & Opers.—Ray McCandless
Hum. Res. Mgr.—Bonnie Still
Circ. Mgr.—Paul London
Newsroom Admn.—Cindy Grassia
SIC—2711; Newspaper publishing
Employs—200; Estab.—1875
178,000 sq ft site, Distrib.— National
Publicly owned corporation
Parent co.—Gannett Co., Inc., McLean, VA
Phone—(703) 854-6000
See Parent Co. Section for full profile.

**CUSTOM BRUSH CO. INC.**
1933 Owl Ct. (08003-2920)
**Phone—(856) 354-1673**
Fax—(856) 354-1603
www.cbbrushes.com
Email—rreisman@cbbrushes.com
Pres., Fin. & MIS Mgr.—Robin Reisman
Sales Mgr.—Ron Conyerrs
SIC—3991; NAICS—339994; Industrial brushes for the pharmaceutical, paper, bakery, labeling, printing, conveyor, battery & candy industries
Employs—3; Estab.—1967
Sales—over $500,000
20,000 sq ft site, Distrib.—National
Privately owned corporation

†**DAL-TILE SALES SERVICE CENTER 186**
Div. of Dal-Tile Corporation
2030 Springdale Rd., Ste. 100 (08003)
**Phone—(856) 489-3335**
Fax—(856) 489-0355
www.daltile.com
Email—cherryhill.ssc186@ daltile.com
Manager—John Huff
SIC—5032; Distributor of porcelain & ceramic tiles
Employs—9
Distrib.—Intl.
Publicly owned corporation
Parent co.—Dal-Tile Corporation, Dallas, TX
Phone—(214) 398-1411
See Parent Co. Section for full profile.

**DESIGNER T'S**
1165 Marlkress Rd., Ste. F (08003)
**Phone—(856) 751-4545**
National—(866) 364-4545
Fax—(856) 751-3767

GEOGRAPHICAL

## Cherry Hill—(cont.)

www.designerts.com
Email—jim@designerts.com
Owner—James Kelly
Art Dir.—Steve Wiggs
GM—Ray Jewusiak
Off. Mgr.—Sharon Kelly
SIC—2396; *T-shirt screen printing*
Employs—40; Estab.—1984
14,000 sq ft site, Distrib.—Local
Privately owned corporation

**DPI COPIES PRINTING & GRAPHICS, INC.**
2070 Route 70 E. (08003)
**Phone—(856) 874-1355**
National—(888) 374-0044
Fax—(856) 874-1699
www.dpicherryhill.com
Email—customersupport@
dpicherryhill.com
Pres.—Michael Jones
Off. Mgr.—Susane Jones
SIC—2752; NAICS—323100;
*Digital printing*
Employs—10; Estab.—2002
Sales—$500,000-$1Mil
Distrib.—Regional
Privately owned corporation

**†DUBELL LUMBER CO.**
731 Cuthbert Blvd. (08002)
**Phone—(856) 665-9100**
Fax—(856) 665-6924
www.dubell.com
Email—jcusick@dubell.com
Br. Mgr.—Jim Eaise
Sales Rep.—Bud Nicosia
SIC—5031; 5032; 5072;
*Wholesaler of building materials
& supplies, including lumber,
millwork, kitchen & bathroom
cabinets, decks, countertops,
doors, windows & hardware;
Brand name—Jeld-Wen;
Silverline; Masonite; Craftmaster;
Orac Decor; Fypon; Baldwin;
Schlage; Kwikset; Ecergrain;
Trex Dynasty; Decora; Hanstone;
Cambria*
Employs—20; Estab.—1991
Sales—$500,000-$1Mil
Distrib.—Local
Privately owned corporation
Parent co.—Dubell Lumber Co.,
Medford, NJ
Phone—(609) 654-4143
See Parent Co. Section for full profile.

**EAGLE ENTERPRISES, INC.**
11 W. Ormond Ave. (08002)
**Phone—(856) 427-0787**
National—(800) 361-9121
Fax—(856) 427-9050
www.eagleenterprises.logomall.co
m
Email—paul@eagleenter.com
Pres.—Paul Fisherkeller
Sales Rep.—Dee Fisherkeller
SIC—2759; NAICS—323100;
*Commercial printing*
Employs—5; Estab.—1996
Distrib.—National
Privately owned corporation

**†EDI DISTRIBUTORS, INC.**
20 Lakeside Ave., P.O. Box 501
(08003)
**Phone—(856) 429-2580**
National—(800) 433-2033
Fax—(856) 428-2549
www.edidistributors.com
Email—info@edidistributors.com
Pres.—Skip Markowitz
Off. Mgr.—Jessica Ruvo
SIC—5084; *Wholesaler of custom
high-pressure pump systems,
parts & accessories; Brand
name—CAT; Giant; General;
Comet; Udor; Legacy*
Employs—3; Estab.—1994
Distrib.—Intl.
Privately owned sub-S corp.

**EDWARDS CREATIVE PRODUCTS, INC.**
910 Beechwood Ave. (08002)
**Phone—(856) 665-3200**
Fax—(856) 665-3204
www.edwardscreative.com
Email—edwcreate@aol.com
Pres.—Charles S. Cohen
Corp. Secy.—Leona Z. Cohen
Opers. Mgr.—Matthew D. Cohen
SIC—2842; NAICS—325612;
*Household cleaning compounds*
Employs—10
9,500 sq ft site,
Privately owned corporation

**†EQUIPMENT MARKETERS**
100 Melrose Ave. (08003)
**Phone—(856) 428-3355**
National—(800) 223-1376
Fax—(856) 428-5477
www.equipmentmarketers.net
Email—maytag@
equipmentmarketers.net
Owner—Dick LaMaina
SIC—5087; *Distributor of
commercial laundry equipment*
Employs—15; Estab.—1945
Distrib.—Local
Sole ownership

**FEDEX OFFICE & PRINT CENTER**
Div. of FedEx Office & Print
Services, Inc.
1160 Marlton Pike E. (08034)
**Phone—(856) 427-0099**
National—(800) 463-3339
Fax—(856) 427-0328
www.fedex.com
Email—usa1220@fedex.com
Center Mgr.—John Shannon
Asst. Mgr.—Mary Chris Thompson
Proj. Coord.—Jason Sosa
SIC—2752; NAICS—323100;
*Instant printing*
Employs—10; Estab.—1983
Distrib.—Intl.
Publicly owned corporation
Parent co.—FedEx Office & Print
Services, Inc., Dallas, TX
Phone—(214) 550-7000
See Parent Co. Section for full profile.

**†FISHMAN FLOORING SOLUTIONS**
Div. of Fishman & Son, Inc., L.
621 Chapel Ave. E., Ste. A (08034)
**Phone—(856) 857-1141**
Fax—(856) 857-1143
www.lfishman.com
Email—service@lfishman.com
GM—Jason Edwards
SIC—5023; *Distributor of floor
coverings & installation supplies,
including vinyl flooring &
carpeting; Brand name—
Johnsonite; USG; Orcon Corp.;
Azrock; Domco*
Employs—4; Estab.—1998
Distrib.—Local
Privately owned corporation
Parent co.—Fishman & Son, Inc.,
L., Baltimore, MD
Phone—(410) 633-2500
See Parent Co. Section for full profile.

**FRIDAY MORNING QUARTERBACK**
1930 Marlton Pike E., Ste. F-36
(08003-4195)
**Phone—(856) 424-9114**
Fax—(856) 424-6943
www.fmqb.com
Email—fmqb@fmqb.com
Pres.—Kal Rudman
Cont.—Patricia Forster
Off. Mgr.—Lucille Rudman
SIC—2721; *Radio industry
magazine publishing*
Employs—15; Estab.—1968
Sales—$1Mil-$2.5Mil
Distrib.—National
Publicly owned corporation

**FRONTEND GRAPHICS**
1951 Old Cuthbert Rd., Ste. 414
(08034-1411)
**Phone—(856) 547-1600**
Fax—(856) 547-3837
www.frontendgraphics.com
Email—info@frontendgraphics.com
Owner, Pres. & Mktg. Mgr.—
Elizabeth Maul
V-P. & Sales Mgr.—Bob Maul
Prodn. Mgr.—Lisa Simon
SIC—2791; 2759; NAICS—
323122; *Digital direct mail
printing, large output, data
manipulation, large format &
electronic prepress*
Employs—6; Estab.—1973
Sales—$1Mil-$2.5Mil
4,500 sq ft site, Distrib.—National
Privately owned sub-S corp.

**GAC MODEL MAKING, LLC**
1879 Old Cuthbert Rd., Unit 38
(08034)
**Phone—(856) 857-9848**
Fax—(856) 857-9848
www.gacmodelmaking.com
Email—george@
gacmodelmaking.com
Ptnr.—Patricia Christoffersen
Ptnr.—George Christoffersen
SIC—3999; 3543; NAICS—
332710; *2D & 3D interactive
models for product development
projects, including display
fabrication & assembly,
prototypes & tooling patterns*
Employs—2; Estab.—2001
Distrib.—Regional
Limited Liability Company

**GARDEN STATE EMBROIDERY**
1879 Old Cuthbert Rd., Unit 10
(08034)
**Phone—(856) 616-9490**
www.gardenstateembroidery.com
Email—dave@
gardenstateembroidery.com
Owner—Dave Bewick
SIC—2395; *Embroidery*
Employs—5; Estab.—1999
Sales—under $500,000 (est)
Distrib.—Local
Privately owned corporation

**GARY'S GEM GARDEN**
404 Route 70 E. (08034)
Mail addr: 404 Marlton Pike E.,
Door 7, Cherry Hill (08034)
**Phone—(856) 795-5077**
Fax—(856) 795-0786
www.garysgemgarden.com
Email—info@garysgemgarden.com
Owner—Gary Weinstein
Off. Mgr.—Denise Weinstein
SIC—3911; 3915; NAICS—
339911; *Precious &
semiprecious gems & metal
jewelry*
Employs—3; Estab.—1973
Sales—under $500,000
Distrib.—Local
Sole ownership

**GAW ASSOCIATES, INC.**
670 Deer Rd., Unit A (08034)
**Phone—(856) 608-1428**
National—(877) 429-7225
Fax—(856) 608-1429
www.datacenterdepot.com
Email—kathy@gawtechnology.com
Pres.—Kathleen Gaw-Betz
V-P.—Charles Gaw
Qual. Mgmt. Sys. Rep.—Robyn
Crain

SIC—2542; 3679; 3699; 2599;
*Electronic cabinets/racks,
custom cable assemblies,
storage cabinets, educational
furniture & data room cabinets*
Employs—10; Estab.—1990
Distrib.—National
Privately owned corporation
ISO rating—TL9000, 9001:2008
AKAs: Data Center Depot & Gaw
Technology

**†GENERAL FLOOR, INC.**
Div. of General Floor Industries
2 Pin Oak Ln. (08003)
**Phone—(856) 424-0111**
Fax—(856) 424-6612
www.generalfloor.com
Email—info@generalfloor.com
Br. Mgr.—David Garro
Asst. Mgr.—Ed Becker
SIC—5023; 5031; *Wholesaler of
carpet, laminate, hardwood &
vinyl flooring*
Employs—3; Estab.—1980
Distrib.—Local
Privately owned corporation
Parent co.—General Floor
Industries, Bellmawr, NJ
Phone—(856) 931-0012
See Parent Co. Section for full profile.

**HOPPECKE BATTERYS, INC.**
1960 Old Cuthbert Rd., Ste. 130
(08034)
**Phone—(856) 616-0032**
Fax—(856) 616-0132
www.hoppecke-us.com
Email—info@hoppecke-us.com
V-P.—Larry Meisner
Sales Mgr., Transit—Robert
Magdule
SIC—3691; *Lead-acid batteries*
Employs—15; Estab.—1985
Sales—$2.5Mil-$5Mil (est)
Distrib.—Intl.
Privately owned corporation

[NEW ENTRY]

**ILKEM MARBLE & GRANITE**
2010 Springdale Rd., Ste. 200
(08003)
**Phone—(856) 433-8714**
Fax—(856) 433-8719
www.ilkemgranite.com/
Owner—Mustafa Kol
SIC—3281; *Granite & marble
countertops*
Employs—16; Estab.—1998
Sales—$1Mil-$2.5Mil (est)
Distrib.—Local
Privately owned corporation

**INSIGN, INC.**
1937 Olney Ave. (08003)
**Phone—(856) 424-1161**
National—(800) 332-6707
Fax—(856) 424-5778
www.insigninc.com
Email—insignincm@insigninc.com
Pres.—Samuel Miner
V-P., Fin. & Hum. Res. Mgr.—
Susan Weaver
GM—Ed McCann
IT Mgr.—Susan Miner
SIC—3993; *Vinyl signs*
Employs—30; Estab.—1990
Sales—$500,000-$1Mil
Distrib.—Local
Privately owned corporation

**INTERNATIONAL MICRO INDUSTRIES, INC.**
1951 Old Cuthbert Rd., Bldg. 404
(08034)
**Phone—(856) 616-0051**
Fax—(856) 616-0226
www.imi-corp.com
Email—sales@imi-corp.com
Pres., CEO—Christopher N.
Angelucci
Corp. Admn.—Gladys Pino
Accountant—Rose Cavaliere

© Copyright 2015 Manufacturers' News, Inc.

D61

## Cherry Hill—(cont.)

SIC—3559; 3471; NAICS—
332813; *Wafer electroplating &
bumping & contract MEMS*
Employs—23; Estab.—1971
10,000 sq ft site, Distrib.—Intl.
Privately owned corporation

**J M L COMPUTER PRODUCTS, INC.**
9 Wheelwright Ln. (08003)
**Phone—(856) 753-8500**
Fax—(856) 753-0355
www.jmlcable.com
Email—jjr@jmlcable.com
Pres.—John McLaughlin
SIC—3679; *Computer cable
assembly*
Employs—10; Estab.—1977
Sales—$1Mil-$2.5Mil
Distrib.—Intl.
Privately owned corporation

**J.B.A.T., INC.**
28 Coles Ave. (08002)
**Phone—(856) 667-7307**
Fax—(856) 667-5966
www.cherryhillprecision.com
Email—info@
cherryhillprecision.com
Pres.—John Schallenhammer
Corp. Secy.—Theresa
Schallenhammer
SIC—3599; *Precision machining
job shop*
Employs—22; Estab.—1968
7,200 sq ft site, Distrib.—Local
Privately owned corporation
AKA: Cherry Hill Precision

**JACE SYSTEMS, INC.**
5 Rockhill Rd., Ste. 2 (08003)
**Phone—(800) 800-4276**
Fax—(800) 236-2308
www.jacesystems.com
Email—salesinfo@jacesystems.com
Pres., CEO—Thomas Zieser
Hum. Res. Mgr.—Michaele
Narzikul
SIC—3845; NAICS—334500;
*Electrotherapy & continuous
passive motion devices (CPM's);
Brand name—K 100-A Knee
CPM; H-440 Hand CPM; W-550
Wrist CPM; T-300 Tpe CPM;
TriStim NMES Electrotherapy
Device*
Employs—15; Estab.—1985
Sales—$3Mil
16,000 sq ft site, Distrib.—Intl.
Limited Liability Company
ISO rating—9001, 13485
AKA: TGZ Acquisition Co.

**K R B PRINTING FOR BUSINESS**
1165 Marlkress Rd., Ste. G
(08003)
**Phone—(856) 751-5200**
Fax—(856) 751-6116
www.krbprinting.com
Email—krbart@krbprinting.com
Ptnr.—Kurt Barbera
Ptnr.—Bob Barbera
Bookkeeper—Sharon Decarlo
SIC—2759; 2791; NAICS—
323122; *Commercial printing &
electronic prepress*
Employs—12; Estab.—1988
Sales—$500,000-$1Mil
Distrib.—Regional
Privately owned partnership

**KEYSTONE INDUSTRIES**
616 Hollywood Ave. (08002)
Mail addr.: P.O. Box 2410, Cherry
Hill (08034)
**Phone—(856) 663-4700**
National—(800) 333-3131
Fax—(856) 663-0381
www.keystoneind.com
Email—info@keystoneind.com
CEO—Fred Robinson
Pres.—Cary Robinson
Ex. V.P., GM—Otto Voigt

Ex. V.P.—Gloria Berger
Dir., IT—Chuck Peterson
Hum. Res. Mgr.—June Cowger
SIC—3843; NAICS—339114;
*Company headquarters & dental
abrasives, carbides, chemicals,
brushes, crucibles, kiln furniture,
cement, paste & polymers*
Employs—130
Sales—$1Mil-$5Mil

**LINCOLN DENTAL SUPPLY, INC.**
616 Hollywood Ave. (08002)
Mail addr.: P.O. Box 2410, Cherry
Hill (08034)
**Phone—(856) 488-1333**
National—(800) 289-6678
Fax—(856) 663-3280
www.lincolndental.com
Email—jeff@lincolndental.com
Chrm. of the Board—Fred
Robinson
Pres.—Cary Robinson
V.-P.—Jeff Diblasi
Off. Mgr.—Marlene Mihiach
SIC—3843; NAICS—339114;
*Dental supplies, including
denture acrylic & teeth*
Employs—100; Estab.—1975
Distrib.—National
Privately owned corporation

**LRP & P GRAPHICS**
1165 Marlkress Rd. (08003)
Mail addr.: P.O. Box 1536, Cherry
Hill (08034)
**Phone—(856) 424-0158**
Fax—(856) 424-5730
www.padandpub.com
Email—artwork@padandpub.com
Pres.—Joan Buehler
Hum. Res. & Off. Mgr.—Gwyn
Andrews
SIC—2759; 2791; NAICS—
323122; *Offset & digital printing
& typesetting*
Employs—30; Estab.—1981
Distrib.—Regional
Privately owned corporation

**MAKING WAVES, INC.**
1916 Old Cuthbert Rd., Ste. B-20
(08034)
**Phone—(856) 795-9311**
Fax—(856) 795-5639
Pres.—Francine Keller
SIC—3961; NAICS—339900;
*Costume jewelry*
Employs—4; Estab.—1980
Sales—under $500,000 (est)
Distrib.—Local
Privately owned corporation

NEW ENTRY
**MANNING PUBLICATION CO.**
1233 Heartwood Dr. (08003)
**Phone—(856) 375-2597**
www.manning.com
Email—info@manning.com
Ptnr.—Marjan Bace
SIC—2731; *Book publishing*
Employs—12; Estab.—1990
Sales—$500,000-$1Mil (est)
Distrib.—Intl.
Sole ownership

**MARLTON PIKE PRECISION, LLC**
728 Beechwood Ave. (08002)
**Phone—(856) 665-1900**
Fax—(856) 665-8128
www.marltonpikeprecision.com
Email—mpprec@comcast.net
Pres.—Antonio Sala

SIC—3599; 3544; 3545; NAICS—
333500; *Precision machined
parts, fixtures, gages &
assemblies, including grinding,
CNC milling & turning, keyway
broaching, mold repair, industrial
tooling & repair, punches, dies &
shear blades*
Employs—18; Estab.—1948
Sales—$2Mil-$2.5Mil
10,000 sq ft site, Distrib.—National
Limited Liability Company
ISO rating—AS9100C, 9001

**MARTEK INDUSTRIES, INC.**
600 Deer Rd., Ste. 8 (08034)
**Phone—(856) 427-9411**
Fax—(856) 427-9295
www.safetybulb.com
Email—info@
martekindustriesinc.com
Pres.—Robert Anzalone
SIC—3641; NAICS—335110;
*Miniature light bulbs*
Employs—3; Estab.—1980
Sales—$500,000-$1Mil
Distrib.—National
Privately owned corporation

**MCELWEE & QUINN, LLC**
2070 E. Route 70, Ste. 4 (08003)
**Phone—(856) 229-7015**
Fax—(856) 520-8559
www.mcelweequinn.com
Email—production@
mcelweequinn.com
Pres.—Mary McElwee
SIC—2759; *Financial printing*
Employs—5; Estab.—1991
Sales—under $500,000
Distrib.—National
Limited Liability Company

**MELITTA U. S. A.**
1401 Berlin Rd. (08034)
**Phone—(856) 428-7202**
National—(800) 635-4882
Fax—(856) 428-7262
www.melitta.com
Email—consumerrelations@
melitta.com
Plt. Mgr.—Vinny Tagliaferro
Hum. Res. Mgr.—Michele Keys
Qual. Assur. Mgr.—Mark Kiczalis
SIC—2095; NAICS—311920;
*Coffee roasting & packing;
Brand name—Melitta*
Employs—50; Estab.—1964
90,000 sq ft site, Distrib.—National
Privately owned corporation

**METRO SIGNS**
410 Downs Dr., P.O. Box 865
(08003)
**Phone—(856) 428-9050**
Fax—(856) 428-5520
Email—metrosignschnj@
hotmail.com
Owner—Richard Lees
SIC—3993; *Signs*
Employs—3; Estab.—1884
Sales—under $500,000
Distrib.—National
Sole ownership

**MIEL PATISSERIE, LLC**
1990 Route 70 E., Ste. 14 (08003)
**Phone—(856) 424-6435**
Fax—(856) 424-6721
www.mielpatisserie.com
Email—wholesale@
mielpatisserie.com
Owner—Gelareh Nouri
SIC—2051; 2033; NAICS—
311812; *Fresh pastries, specialty
& wedding cakes, chocolates &
wedding & party favors*
Employs—12; Estab.—2010
5,500 sq ft site, Distrib.—Regional
Limited Liability Company

**MINUTEMAN PRESS**
2060 Springdale Rd., Ste. 700
(08003)
**Phone—(856) 817-8400**
Fax—(856) 817-8404
www.mmpch.com
Email—info@mmpch.com
Owner—Frank J. Bittner III
GM—Frank J. Bittner IV
SIC—2759; NAICS—323100;
*Commercial printing*
Employs—7; Estab.—1991
Distrib.—Regional
Privately owned corporation

**NEW JERSEY WIRE STITCHING
MACHINE CO.**
Div. of Precision Automation
Company, Inc.
1841 Old Cuthbert Rd. (08034)
**Phone—(856) 428-7400**
Fax—(856) 428-1270
www.newjerseywire.com
Email—info@newjerseywire.com
GM & Qual. Assur. Mgr.—Mike
Menaquale
Hum. Res. & IT Mgr.—Dan
Pomponio
SIC—3549; NAICS—333518; *Wire
stitching machinery*
Employs—50; Estab.—2001
Sales—under $500,000
Distrib.—Intl.
Privately owned corporation
Parent co.—Precision Automation
Company, Inc., Cherry Hill, NJ
Phone—(856) 428-7400
See Parent Co. Section for full profile.

**NORTHEAST MEDICAL SYSTEMS
CORP.**
901 Beechwood Ave. (08002)
**Phone—(856) 910-8111**
Fax—(856) 910-8112
www.northeastmedicalsystems.co
m
Email—j.conte@
northeastmedicalsystems.com
Pres.—Joseph Conte
V.-P.—David C. Oberg
Off. Mgr.—Maryanne Booker
SIC—3841; *Medical products*
Employs—5; Estab.—1988
Sales—$500,000-$1Mil
7,600 sq ft site, Distrib.—National
Privately owned sub-S corp.

**PANZAROTTI TARANTINI PIZZA, INC.**
2060 Springdale Rd., Ste. 300
(08003)
**Phone—(856) 489-0026**
Fax—(856) 489-0027
www.panzarotti.net
Email—leo@panzarotti.net
CEO—Leo Tarantini
V.-P.—Paul Tarantini
SIC—2099; *Pizza puffs*
Employs—12; Estab.—1960
Sales—$500,000-$1Mil
Distrib.—Regional
Privately owned corporation

**PAT PUBLICATIONS**
1165 Marlkress Rd., Ste. M, P.O.
Box 1536 (08003)
**Phone—(856) 424-0158**
Fax—(856) 424-5730
www.lrpandp.com
V.-P.—Carl Buehler
Hum. Res. Mgr.—Gwyn Andrews
Prepress Mgr.—Dominic Silvestro
SIC—2759; NAICS—323100;
*Commercial printing*
Employs—20; Estab.—1981
Distrib.—Local
Privately owned corporation
AKA: L R P & P Graphics

GEOGRAPHICAL

## Cherry Hill—(cont.)

**PINNACLE FOODS GROUP, LLC (H Q)**
Div. of Blackstone Group L. P., The
121 Woodcrest Rd. (08003)
**Phone—(856) 969-7100**
National—(800) 554-9458
Fax—(856) 969-7203
www.pinnaclefoods.com
Email—media_inquiries@
pinnaclefoods.com
CEO—Bob Gamgort
Pres., Frozen Div.—Mark Schiller
CFO—Craig Steeneck
Ex. V-P., CHRO—Mary Beth
DeNooyer
Ex. V-P., Chief Cust. Officer—Chris
Boever
Sr. V-P., Gen. Counsel & Secy.—
Kelly Maggs
SIC—2038; 2092; 2033; 2045;
NAICS—311412; *Company
headquarters; branded frozen
grocery foods, pickles, sauces &
syrups & baking mixes; Brand
name—Duncan Hines; Swanson;
Vlasic Pickles; Wish-Bone*
Employs—220; Estab.—2001
Sales—$25Mil-$50Mil (est)
Privately owned corporation
Parent co.—Blackstone Group L.
P., The, New York, NY
Phone—(212) 583-5000
See Parent Co. Section for full profile.

**PRECISION AUTOMATION
COMPANY, INC.**
1841 Old Cuthbert Rd. (08034)
Mail addr: P.O. Box 18,
Haddonfield (08033-0017)
**Phone—(856) 428-7400**
Fax—(856) 428-1270
www.precisionautomationinc.com
Email—sales@
precisionautomationinc.com
Pres., CEO—G. Frederick Rexon,
Jr.
V-P., COO—Daniel Pomponio
V-P. & Dir., Conveyor Sys. Div.—
Mark Petri
Dir., Sales & Mktg.—Gerry Renzi
GM & Qual. Assur. Mgr.—Michael
Menaquale
SIC—3559; 3535; 3599; 7373;
NAICS—333922; *Automation,
conveyor, control & complete
labeling systems, contract
manufacturing, machine
building, CNC precision
machining, fabrication, control
panel assembly & complete
systems integration; Brand
name—New Jersey Wire
Stitching Machines; Arca
Automation Labeling Systems*
Employs—50; Estab.—1946
Sales—$15Mil
45,000 sq ft site, Distrib.—National
Privately owned corporation
ISO rating—9001

**PRESSWORKS**
1879 Old Cuthbert Rd., Unit 28
(08034)
**Phone—(856) 427-9001**
National—(866) 427-9001
www.thinkipp.com
Email—info@thinkipp.com
Ptnr.—Diane Reilly
Ptnr.—Dennis Reilly
SIC—2759; NAICS—323100;
*Commercial printing &
promotional products*
Employs—10; Estab.—1989
Sales—$500,000-$1Mil
Distrib.—Intl.
Privately owned partnership

**PURATOS CORP.**
1941 Old Cuthbert Rd. (08034)
**Phone—(856) 428-4300**
National—(800) 654-0036

Fax—(856) 428-2939
www.puratos.us
Email—infous@puratos.com
Pres., U.S.—Frederic Duvauchelle
V-P., Sales—Michael Simone
V-P., Sales—Matt Crumpton
V-P., Opers. & Pur.—Brent Laurin
V-P., Fin. & IT—Marinela Maritescu
V-P., Hum. Res.—Robert Donegan
Reg. Dir., Americas—Karel
Zimmermann
Dir., Export, N. America—Pat Pilla
Comms. & Mktg. Mgr.—Kathryn
Power
SIC—2045; 2099; 2066; 2064;
NAICS—311822; *Corporate
headquarters & bread, bagel,
cake & doughnut mixes & dough
conditioners, icings, chocolates,
fruit fillings & glazes*
Employs—100; Estab.—1927
Sales—$12Mil-$15Mil
Distrib.—Intl.
Privately owned corporation

**R & R GRAPHICS, INC.**
1724 Route 70 E., Unit B (08003)
**Phone—(856) 751-7671**
Fax—(856) 751-8065
www.randrgraphics.net
Email—tom@randrgraphics.net
V-P.—Richard Risse
V-P.—Robert Risse
GM—Tom Ferry
SIC—2395; *Textile embroidery*
Employs—25; Estab.—2002
Sales—$1Mil-$2.5Mil (est)
Distrib.—Intl.
Privately owned corporation

**RAPID MODELS & PROTOTYPES,
INC.**
1311 Marlkress Rd. (08003)
**Phone—(856) 933-2929**
www.rapidmodels.net
Email—joe@rapidmodels.net
Ptnr. & Pres.—Angela A. Pizzo
Ptnr. & Sr. V-P.—Joseph A. Pizzo,
Sr.
SIC—3543; NAICS—332997;
*Rapid prototyping, CAD design
& digitized model making of
commercial products, including
toys, medical devices, laser
scanners, museum displays &
exhibits, scaled architectural
models & POP displays*
Employs—6; Estab.—1962
Sales—under $1Mil
5,000 sq ft site, Distrib.—Intl.
Privately owned partnership

**SANAKIRK, INC.**
1400 Berlin Rd., Ste. 123 (08003-
3191)
**Phone—(856) 429-0715**
Fax—(856) 429-0714
www.sjprinter.com
Email—info@sjprinter.com
CEO—Kirk R. Runton
V-P.—Oksana Kudina
SIC—2752; 2759; NAICS—
323100; *Commercial, digital,
small-format & large-format
printing & design of posters &
banners*
Employs—4; Estab.—1992
Sales—under $1Mil
1,500 sq ft site, Distrib.—Regional
Privately owned corporation
DBA: SJ Printer

**SPRINGDALE FARM MARKET, INC.**
1638 Springdale Rd. (08003)
**Phone—(856) 424-8674**
Fax—(856) 424-7074
www.springdalefarms.com
Email—sfm@juno.com
Pres.—Mary A. Jarvis
V-P.—John Ebert

SIC—2099; *Fruit & vegetable
processing*
Employs—45; Estab.—1989
Sales—$500,000-$1Mil
Distrib.—Local
Privately owned corporation

**†STE-LAR TEXTILES, INC.**
1301 Marlton Pike W. (08002)
**Phone—(856) 429-2245**
Fax—(856) 429-2251
www.ste-lartextiles.com
Email—steve@ste-lar.com
Pres.—Steven Bronstein
Secy-Treas.—Larry Per
Cont.—Kathryn Sutorius
SIC—5131; *Corporate
headquarters & distributor of
greige & finished textiles*
Employs—5; Estab.—1977
Sales—$10Mil
600,000 sq ft site, Distrib.—
National
Privately owned corporation

NEW ENTRY
**STONESHOP**
670 Deer Rd., Ste. 202 (08034)
**Phone—(856) 795-8900**
        (856) 428-2424
Fax—(856) 428-2224
www.stoneshop.com
Email—lindas@stoneshop.com
V-P.—Richard Holmes
SIC—3281; 3089; 3299; *Granite,
marble & engineered quartz
fabrication*
Employs—10
Sales—$500,000-$1Mil (est)

**SUBARU OF AMERICA, INC. (H Q)**
2235 Route 70 W., Subaru Plz.
(08002-6000)
Mail addr: P.O. Box 6000, Cherry
Hill (08034)
**Phone—(856) 488-8500**
National—(800) 782-2783
Fax—(856) 488-3137
www.subaru.com
Email—inquires@subaru.com
Chrm. & CEO—Tomomi
Nakamura
Pres., COO—Thomas Doll
Sr. V-P., CMO—Alan Bethke
Sr. V-P., Sales—Jeffrey Walters
V-P., Hum. Res.—Dan Dalton
V-P., Parts & Serv.—Gary
Palanjian
V-P., Legal—Sheila Galucci-Davis
V-P., Eastern Reg.—Mike
Hafertepe
V-P., Field & Distributor Opers.—
Mike Campbell
Dir., Corp. Comm.—Michael
McHale
Corp. Comms. Mgr.—Diane Anton
SIC—3711; *Corporate
headquarters; automobiles;
Brand name—Tribeca; Forester;
Impreza; Legacy; Outback*
Employs—450; Estab.—1968
Sales—$250Mil-$500Mil
Publicly owned corporation

**TECH-OPTICS INTERNATIONAL**
600 Deer Rd. (08034)
**Phone—(856) 795-8585**
National—(800) 257-5782
www.techopticsinternational.com
Email—info@
techopticsinternational.com
Dir., Sales & GM—Lisa Wassmer
SIC—3851; 3827; NAICS—
333314; *Hand & stand
magnifiers, loupes & binoculars
for ophthalmic, medical,
laboratory, industrial,
photographic & hobby
applications*
Employs—10
Sales—$1Mil-$2.5Mil
Distrib.—Intl.
Privately owned corporation

**TELEGENCE CORP.**
383 Kings Hwy. N., Ste. B-1
(08034)
**Phone—(856) 755-1717**
Fax—(856) 779-1245
www.telegence.com
Email—info@telegence.com
Owner—Mansour Kabirian
SIC—3571; *Business &
operational support systems (B/
OSS) solution provider for the
global telecommunications
market*
Employs—5
Sales—$2.5Mil-$5Mil (est)

**†TRI STATE HARDWARE, INC.**
Div. of Commercial Hardware, Inc.
5 Perina Blvd. (08003)
**Phone—(856) 810-0990**
Fax—(856) 810-0993
www.commercialhardware.com
Email—rose@
commercialhardware.com
Pres.—Rose Palladino
SIC—5031; 5072; *Distributor of
architectural doors, door frames
& door hardware*
Employs—6; Estab.—1997
Distrib.—Local
Privately owned corporation
Parent co.—Commercial
Hardware, Inc., Cherry Hill, NJ
Phone—(856) 810-0600
See Parent Co. Section for full profile.

**U.S. PULP & PAPER CORP.**
1930 Marlton Pike E., Ste. N-73
(08003-4203)
**Phone—(856) 489-3500**
Fax—(856) 489-5002
www.uspulpandpaper.com
Email—uspulp213@aol.com
Pres.—Arnold Cohen
Sales Mgr.—David Cohen
Off. Mgr.—Dana Roccia
SIC—2679; 5111; *Paper
converting & distributor of
packaging papers & boards,
including bleached & natural
kraft, towel, tissue, medium,
newsprint & printing papers,
bleached boards & linerboards*
Employs—20; Estab.—1986
Sales—$5Mil
Distrib.—Intl.
Privately owned corporation

**VEE DENNIS MFG. CO.**
620 Park Rd. (08034)
**Phone—(856) 428-7676**
Fax—(856) 795-4908
www.veedennis.net
Email—veedennis@verizon.net
Pres.—George D. Lymper
Qual. Control Mgr.—Steve
Schelpat
SIC—3444; 3599; *Sheet metal
fabrication & machining job shop*
Employs—25; Estab.—1961
21,000 sq ft site, Distrib.—Local
Privately owned corporation

**VICTOR'S PRINTING**
3 Perina Blvd. (08003)
**Phone—(856) 424-4600**
Fax—(856) 424-5439
CEO, CFO—Len Victor
COO—Jack Copeland
Treas. & Fin. Mgr.—Maureen
Victor
Off. Mgr.—Carol Funk
SIC—2759; NAICS—323100;
*Commercial printing*
Employs—35; Estab.—1972
24,000 sq ft site, Distrib.—
Regional
Privately owned sub-S corp.

**VICTORY REFRIGERATION**
110 Woodcrest Rd. (08003)
**Phone—(856) 428-4200**
National—(800) 523-5008

## Cherry Hill—(cont.)

Fax—(856) 428-7299
www.victory-refrig.com
Email—info@
victoryrefrigeration.com
Pres.—Richard Babboni
CFO—Eileen Kuriskin
V.-P., Sales—Mitchell Cohen
SIC—3585; *Commercial
refrigerators & freezers*
Employs—180; Estab.—1989
Sales—$35Mil-$40Mil
240,000 sq ft site, Distrib.—
National
Privately owned corporation

### WESTWARD PHARMACEUTICAL CORP.

2 Esterbrook Ln. (08003)
**Phone—(856) 424-3700**
National—(800) 631-2174
Fax—(856) 424-8747
www.west-ward.com
Email—info@west-ward.com
Cont.—George Muench
Sr. Dir., Plt. Opers.—Tom McDevitt
IT Mgr.—Rick Santora
SIC—2834; NAICS—325412;
*Injectable pharmaceuticals*
Employs—850
Sales—$25Mil-$100Mil
Distrib.—Intl.
Publicly owned corporation

### WORK OF ART CORP.

801 Olive Ave. (08002)
**Phone—(856) 488-1188**
Fax—(856) 488-8166
Email—woagrapics@aol.com
GM—Darren Winthrop
Fin. & MIS Mgr.—Sara Winthrop
SIC—2752; NAICS—323100;
*Offset printing*
Employs—3; Estab.—1987
Sales—under $500,000
800 sq ft site, Distrib.—Local
Privately owned corporation

## Chester

(Morris—N.W.)

### ANALYTICAL MEASUREMENTS

22 Mountain View Dr. (07930)
**Phone—(908) 955-7170**
National—(800) 635-5580
Fax—(908) 955-7170
www.analyticalmeasurements.com
Email—phmeter@verizon.net
Pres., CEO—W. Richard Adey
Off. Mgr.—Bob Smith
SIC—3829; *pH & ORP
instrumentation*
Employs—5; Estab.—1948
Sales—under $500,000
1,000 sq ft site, Distrib.—National
Privately owned sub-S corp.

### BRANDED SCREEN PRINTING, LLC

45 Warren St., P.O. Box 687
(07930)
**Phone—(908) 879-7411**
www.printablefashion/
branded.com
Pres.—Chris Smith
Shop Mgr.—Jay Smith
SIC—2396; *Textile screen printing*
Employs—5; Estab.—1990
Sales—under $500,000
Distrib.—Regional
Limited Liability Company

### J. EMANUEL CHOCOLATIER

461-B Main St. (07930-2526)
**Phone—(908) 955-7591**
        (908) 955-7592
Fax—(908) 955-7593
www.jemanuel.com
Email—info@jemanuel.com
Pres.—Alfred Michael Canzano
GM—Agata Maria Canzano

SIC—2066; 2064; NAICS—
311300; *Artisan chocolate
products, including wine-infused
& all-natural fruit & nut truffles,
almond butter crunch, assorted
barks, gift baskets, boxes &
towers, promotional chocolate
molds & party favors; Brand
name—Chester Crunch*
Employs—5; Estab.—1996
Sales—$100,000-$300,000
1,500 sq ft site, Distrib.—National
Limited Liability Company
AKA: AMC Family, LLC

### RECORDER NEWSPAPER CO.

Div. of Recorder Publishing Co.
530 E. Main St., P.O. Box 600
(07930)
**Phone—(908) 766-3900**
Fax—(908) 879-0799
www.newjerseyhills.com
Email—pgarber@
recordernewspapers.com
Mng. Editor—Mike Condon
Editor—Phil Garber
SIC—2711; *Weekly newspaper
publishing*
Employs—7; Estab.—1950
Sales—$500,000-$1Mil
Distrib.—Local
Privately owned corporation
Parent co.—Recorder Publishing
Co., Bernardsville, NJ
Phone—(908) 766-3900
See Parent Co. Section for full profile.

## Chesterfield

(Burlington—South)

### OMEGA METAL WORKS, INC.

41 Stelle Rd. (08515)
Mail addr: P.O. Box 224,
Bordentown (08505)
**Phone—(609) 298-5101**
        (609) 298-9100
Pres.—Ted B. Walker
SIC—3444; *Sheet metal
fabrication & HVAC ducts*
Employs—1; Estab.—1981
Sales—under $500,000
Distrib.—Local
Privately owned corporation

### TOWNSEND MACHINE, INC.

246 Sykesville Rd. (08515)
**Phone—(609) 298-0400**
Fax—(609) 723-3976
www.gotownsend.com
Pres.—Barclay A. Townsend
V.-P., Opers.—Dwayne Patterson
V.-P.—Barclay M. Townsend
Off. Mgr.—Cindy Vonschmidt
SIC—3451; 3599; NAICS—
332721; *Screw machine
products & machining job shop*
Employs—25; Estab.—1972
Sales—$1Mil-$5Mil
Distrib.—Local
Privately owned corporation

## Cinnaminson

(Burlington—S.E.)

### A & R RECYCLING CO.

1004 Union Landing Rd., P.O. Box
2440 (08077)
**Phone—(856) 829-1712**
Fax—(856) 829-2484
www.arrecyclinginc.com
Email—info@arrecyclinginc.com
Pres.—Anthony Tognini
Consultant—Micheal Groh
SIC—3312; 3341; *Metal recycling*
Employs—14
Sales—$2.5Mil-$5Mil (est)
Distrib.—Local
Privately owned corporation

### AQUA PRODUCTS, INC.

2703 River Rd., P.O. Box 231
(08077)
**Phone—(856) 829-8444**
National—(800) 446-6878
Fax—(856) 829-8482
Email—aquacleandish@aol.com
Pres.—Sam Jones, Sr.
V.-P. & Plt. Mgr.—Sam Jones, Jr.
SIC—2841; 2842; NAICS—
325611; *Laundry detergent,
cleaning compounds,
warewashing, sanitizers & car
wash products*
Employs—25; Estab.—1964
15,000 sq ft site, Distrib.—
Regional
Privately owned corporation

### AUTO SUN ROOF, INC. (H Q)

1305 Industrial Hwy., P.O. Box
2321 (08077)
**Phone—(856) 786-0600**
National—(800) 426-7663
Fax—(856) 786-7637
www.autosunroof.com
Email—sunroof@aol.com
Pres.—Richard W. Jones
SIC—3714; *Corporate
headquarters; car sunroof
assembly*
Employs—30; Estab.—1977
Sales—$5Mil-$10Mil (est)
Privately owned corporation

### BOSSEN ARCHITECTURAL MILLWORK, INC.

1818 Bannard St. (08077)
**Phone—(856) 786-1100**
Fax—(856) 786-3994
www.mouldings-etc.com
Email—jbsr@mouldings-etc.com
Pres.—Joseph H. Bossen
Proj. Mgr.—Paul Denyse
SIC—2431; 2499; NAICS—
321900; *Architectural millwork &
hardwood radius, arch, CNC,
rope & embossed mouldings &
corbels, bar & wine components
& fireplace mantels & surrounds*
Employs—30; Estab.—1947
23,000 sq ft site, Distrib.—National
Privately owned corporation

### CAPITAL LABEL & AFFIXING CO.

1100 Taylors Ln., Unit 5 (08077)
**Phone—(856) 786-1700**
Fax—(856) 786-7955
Email—capitallabel@verizon.net
Pres.—Frank Cooper
Hum. Res. & Off. Mgr.—Joan
Sheipe
Shpg. Mgr.—Ellen Waldman
R & D Mgr.—Jim Smith
SIC—2672; NAICS—322222;
*Pressure-sensitive labels*
Employs—4; Estab.—1985
Sales—$1Mil-$2.5Mil
15,000 sq ft site, Distrib.—National
Privately owned corporation

### CHAMBERLAIN'S VACU-BLAST SALES

1200 Bannard St., P.O. Box 225
(08077)
**Phone—(856) 829-6444**
Fax—(856) 829-4768
www.chamberlainsvacublast.com
Email—mv.cataline@
vacublastusa.com
Pres.—Mike Cataline, Jr.
V.-P.—Mike Cataline
SIC—3599; 5085; *Manufacturer of
abrasive blasting equipment &
supplies & wholesaler of
abrasives; Brand name—Vacu
Blast; Empire Abrasive; Potters;
Treibacher*
Employs—7; Estab.—1952
Sales—$1Mil-$2.5Mil
7,500 sq ft site, Distrib.—Intl.
Sole ownership

### CLOTHES HORSE, INC.

2200 Wallace Blvd., Ste. A (08077)
**Phone—(856) 829-8460**
Fax—(856) 829-8602
www.theclotheshorse.com
Email—katrina@
theclotheshorse.com
Pres., Fin. & MIS Mgr.—Katrina L.
Coldren
SIC—2399; *Horse blankets &
saddle cloths*
Employs—13; Estab.—1972
Sales—$1Mil-$2.5Mil
6,000 sq ft site, Distrib.—Intl.
Privately owned corporation

### DELVA TOOL & MACHINE CORP.

1603 Industrial Hwy., P.O. Box
2249 (08077)
**Phone—(856) 786-8700**
Fax—(856) 786-8708
www.delvatool.com
Pres.—Stephen J. Voellinger
V.-P.—Steve Griffith
Dir., Operation—Jim Valentine
Off. Mgr.—Lornajean Cann
SIC—3499; *Precision machining,
including low & high volume,
electromechanical assembly &
metrology services*
Employs—90; Estab.—1962
29,000 sq ft site, Distrib.—National
Privately owned corporation
ISO rating—9001:2000

### DU-MOR BLADE CO., INC.

1002 Union Landing Rd. (08077)
**Phone—(856) 829-9384**
        (856) 829-9166
Fax—(856) 829-9303
www.dumorblade.com
Email—info@dumorblade.com
CEO—Elaine M. Goralski
Chief Operating Officer—H.
Christopher Morris
Off. Mgr.—Alexandra Morris
SIC—3545; 3479; *Alloy & steel
machine tool blades for the
paper,printing & medical
industries; Brand name—Friction
Guard; Du-Mor Blade*
Employs—25; Estab.—1966
Sales—$26Mil-$50Mil
15,000 sq ft site, Distrib.—Intl.
Privately owned corporation

### EDKER INDUSTRIES, INC.

1401 Union Landing Rd. (08077)
**Phone—(856) 786-1971**
Fax—(856) 786-8258
www.edker.com
Email—edker@edker.com
Owner & Pres.—Tom Kerbaugh
SIC—3444; *Precision sheet metal
fabrication, including powder
coating & silk screening*
Employs—25; Estab.—1967
Sales—$1Mil-$5Mil
26,000 sq ft site, Distrib.—Intl.
Privately owned corporation

### GAB ELECTRONIC SERVICES, LLC

1703 Industrial Hwy., Unit 8
(08077)
**Phone—(856) 786-0108**
Fax—(856) 786-7444
www.gabelectronicservices.com
Email—greg@rhrtechnologies.com
Pres.—Greg Bogle
Off. Mgr.—Laura Bogle
SIC—3672; NAICS—334412;
*Printed circuit board assembly*
Employs—20; Estab.—1976
5,000 sq ft site, Distrib.—National
Privately owned corporation

### GRIFFIN SIGN CO., INC.

464 N. Randolph Ave. (08077)
**Phone—(856) 786-8517**
National—(888) 786-8517
Fax—(856) 786-3362
www.griffinhighway.com

GEOGRAPHICAL

## Cinnaminson—(cont.)

Email—griffinhighway@
griffinhighway.com
Pres.—Michelle Angerame
Ex. V.-P.—Ellen Angerame
Cont.—Dawn Gilbert
Off. Mgr.—Gwen De France
SIC—3993; *Traffic highway
signage*
Employs—50; Estab.—1984
Sales—$11Mil-$25Mil
Distrib.—Regional
Privately owned corporation

**†GROVE SUPPLY, INC.**
1818 Rowland St. (08077)
**Phone—(856) 303-2310**
Fax—(856) 303-2316
www.grovesupplyinc.com
Email—info@grovesupplyinc.com
Br. Mgr.—Tim Thompson
SIC—5074; 5075; *Wholesaler of
HVAC & kitchen & bathroom
equipment & supplies, including
sink & toilet fixtures; Brand
name—American Standard;
Comfortmaker; Delta; DuPont;
Honeywell; Moen*
Employs—7; Estab.—2005
Distrib.—Local
Privately owned corporation
Parent co.—Grove Supply, Inc.,
Warminster, PA
Phone—(215) 672-8666
See Parent Co. Section for full profile.

**HOEGANAES CORP. (H Q)**
1001 Taylors Ln. (08077)
**Phone—(856) 829-2220**
Fax—(856) 303-2720
www.hoeganaes.com
Email—ellen.rumpp@hoegcorp.com
Pres.—Abdul Butt
V.-P., Sales & Mktg.—Jim Shaul
V.-P., Hum. Res.—Marcey Wurst
V.-P., Fin.—Norman Mackey
Global Mktg. Mgr.—Tim Hale
SIC—3399; *Corporate
headquarters; iron & steel
powders for the automotive
industry*
Employs—100; Estab.—1953
Distrib.—Intl.
Publicly owned corporation

**INVENTORS SHOP, THE**
800 Industrial Hwy. (08077)
**Phone—(856) 303-8787**
Fax—(856) 829-8011
www.theinventorsshop.com
Off. Mgr.—Maryann Merritt
Prod. Mgr.—Mike Amato
SIC—3599; *General machining
job shop*
Employs—30; Estab.—1970
43,000 sq ft site, Distrib.—National
Privately owned corporation

**J.A.W. PRODUCTS, INC.**
835 Industrial Hwy., Unit 125
(08077)
**Phone—(856) 829-3210**
National—(888) 221-0671
Fax—(856) 829-3220
www.jawproducts.com
Email—info@jawproducts.com
Pres.—Earl Weightman
SIC—3843; 3496; NAICS—
333314; *Manufacturer &
distributor of orthodontic wire
products, including clasps,
labial bows, bonding pads,
straight lab wire & tubing,
flatbows, springs, mesh
strengtheners & silver soldering
supplies*
Employs—10
Sales—$1Mil-$2.5Mil (est)

**KOBOLAK & SON, INC.**
1818 Bannard St. (08077-1808)
**Phone—(856) 829-6106**
Fax—(856) 829-4190

Email—kobolakandson@
kobolak.com
Pres.—Erno Kobolak
Off. Mgr.—Dana Kobolak
SIC—2434; NAICS—337110;
*Custom cabinetry*
Employs—30; Estab.—1998
Sales—$1Mil-$2.5Mil
Distrib.—National
Sole ownership

**M. A. R. KIT, INC.**
1095 Cinnaminson Ave. (08077)
**Phone—(856) 829-5992**
Fax—(856) 829-5319
www.georgetti.com
Pres., GM—Michael Georgetti
SIC—2098; 2035; 2034; NAICS—
311823; *Italian pasta, sauces,
soups & prepared foods,
including catering services*
Employs—18; Estab.—1988
Sales—$1Mil-$2.5Mil
Distrib.—Local
Privately owned corporation
AKA: Georgetti Pasta

**MEREDITH PAVING CORP.**
1300 Union Landing Rd. (08077)
**Phone—(856) 829-4343**
Fax—(856) 829-3419
www.meredithpaving.com
Email—meredithpaving@aol.com
Pres.—Andrew Zorn
Treas.—Loretta Zorn
Bookkeeper—Bill Martin
SIC—2951; NAICS—324121;
*Asphalt paving compounds*
Employs—26; Estab.—1957
Sales—$6Mil-$10Mil
Distrib.—Regional
Privately owned corporation

**MICRO-TEK CORP.**
P.O. Box 2134 (08077)
**Phone—(856) 829-3855**
www.microtekcorp.com
Pres.—Ricki Rogers
Off. Mgr.—Mary Murphy
SIC—3357; *Teflon-insulated wire*
Employs—12; Estab.—1965
Sales—$500,000-$1Mil
Distrib.—Intl.
Privately owned corporation

**MID-ATLANTIC ENGINE SUPPLY**
Route 130 S. & Pennsauken St.,
P.O. Box 2270 (08077)
**Phone—(856) 829-7798**
National—(800) 257-8133
Fax—(856) 829-2776
www.maesco.com
Email—info@maesco.com
V.-P., Treas. & Cont.—Chuck Cook
SIC—3561; 3621; NAICS—
333911; *Marine & industrial
diesel engines & generators,
pump system assemblies &
industrial filters*
Employs—15; Estab.—1963
40,000 sq ft site, Distrib.—National
Sole ownership

**O & S RESEARCH, INC.**
1912 Bannard St., P.O. Box 221
(08077)
**Phone—(856) 829-2800**
Fax—(856) 829-0482
www.osresearch.com
Email—sales@osresearch.com
Pres.—Anderson L. McCabe
Cont., Fin. Mgr.—Lorraine Domask
Off. Mgr.—Ruth Anne Taylor
SIC—3231; 2899; NAICS—
327215; *Anti-glare optical
coatings & glass panels*
Employs—40; Estab.—1950
Sales—$1Mil-$5Mil
25,000 sq ft site, Distrib.—Intl.
Publicly owned corporation
ISO rating—9001:2008

**OLSEN MACHINE, LLC**
2504 Route 73 (08077)
**Phone—(856) 662-2121**
Fax—(856) 662-2080
Pres.—David Olsen
SIC—3599; *Machine parts*
Employs—3; Estab.—1973
Sales—under $500,000
Distrib.—Intl.
Limited Liability Company

**ONYX VALVE CO.**
835 Industrial Hwy., Ste. 4 (08077)
**Phone—(856) 829-2888**
Fax—(856) 829-3080
www.onyxvalve.com
Email—info@onyxvalve.com
Owner—David Gardellin
GM—Jim Campbell
Administrator—Rory Faden
SIC—3823; NAICS—334513;
*Industrial pinch valves &
pressure sensors*
Employs—20; Estab.—1994
Sales—under $500,000
20,000 sq ft site, Distrib.—Intl.
Privately owned corporation

**†PARTS CLEANING TECHNOLOGIES,
LLC**
835 Industrial Hwy., Ste. 1 (08077-
1929)
**Phone—(856) 786-8686**
Fax—(856) 786-8288
www.pct-1.com
Email—fatzingerd@aol.com
GM—Derrick Fatzinger
Off. Admn.—Una Bauso
SIC—5169; *Wholesaler of
chemicals, including
coordinated solvents*
Employs—5; Estab.—1925
Sales—$500,000-$1Mil
5,000 sq ft site, Distrib.—Local
Limited Liability Company
Parent co.—Parts Cleaning
Technologies, LLC, Redford, MI
Phone—(313) 952-2646
See Parent Co. Section for full profile.

**PHARMAKON CORP.**
2200 Wallace Blvd., Unit C, P.O.
Box 217 (08077)
**Phone—(856) 829-3161**
Fax—(856) 829-3609
www.pharmakondisplays.com
Email—william.shaffer@
pharmakondisplays.com
Pres.—William H. Shaffer, Sr.
GM—Bruce Shaffer
Sales Mgr.—William H. Shaffer, Jr.
SIC—3089; *Tabletop
pharmaceutical displays*
Employs—10; Estab.—1978
Sales—$1Mil-$2.5Mil
Distrib.—National
Privately owned corporation

**PHOENIX RESINS, INC.**
602 Union Landing Rd. (08077)
**Phone—(856) 303-9245**
National—(888) 627-3769
Fax—(856) 303-2889
www.greenacetone.com
Email—office@biobrands.net
Pres.—J. B. Currell
GM—MaryAnne McFarland
Sales Mgr., Inside—Andy Wilson
Off. Mgr.—Amanda Graham
SIC—2869; NAICS—325998; *Bio-
based cleaning solvents*
Employs—4; Estab.—1996
Sales—$2.5Mil-$5Mil
2,500 sq ft site, Distrib.—Intl.
Privately owned corporation

**QUICKIE MFG. CORP. (H Q)**
Div. of Jarden Corp.
1150 Taylors Ln., P.O. Box 156
(08077)
**Phone—(856) 829-7900**
National—(800) 257-5751
Fax—(856) 786-9318

www.quickie.com
Email—help@quickie.com
Ex. V.-P., Engrg.—Jace Weaver
Corp. Hum. Res. Mgr.—Diana
Lindh
Accts. Payable Mgr.—Susan Clark
Cust. Serv. Mgr.—Terry
Constantino
SIC—3991; 2392; 3089; NAICS—
339994; *Corporate
headquarters; cleaning products
for traditional in-home use &
commercial & contractor-grade
applications, including mops,
brooms, dusters, dustpans,
brushes, buckets & related
supplies; Brand name—Quickie
Original®; Quickie Home-Pro®;
Quickie Professional®; Quickie
Microban; Quickie Green
Cleaning®*
Employs—70; Estab.—1950
Sales—$200Mil
300,000 sq ft site, Distrib.—Intl.
Privately owned corporation
Parent co.—Jarden Corp., Boca
Raton, FL
Phone—(561) 447-2520
See Parent Co. Section for full profile.

**RAM ELECTRONIC INDUSTRIES INC.**
1704 Taylors Ln., Ste. 7 *(08077)*
**Phone—(856) 864-0999**
National—(888) 726-2440
Fax—(856) 786-2244
www.ramelectronics.net
Email—sales@ramelectronics.net
Pres.—Steve Misbin
Cont.—Eric Sklansky
Webmaster—Thomas Steves
SIC—3357; 3679; *Audio & video
cables & equipment, computer
accessories, OEM electronic
cables & wire harness
assemblies for computers, audio
& video & gaming; Brand
name—RAM Electronics*
Employs—60; Estab.—1980
Sales—$10Mil-$25Mil
20,000 sq ft site, Distrib.—Intl.
Privately owned corporation

**†SEA BOX, INC.**
700 Union Landing Rd., 1 Sea Box
Dr. (08077)
**Phone—(856) 303-1101**
National—(800) 732-2698
Fax—(856) 303-1501
www.seabox.com
Email—sales@seabox.com
V.-P., Sales—Nick Catanzariti
Off. Mgr.—Robin McMahon
SIC—5085; *Wholesaler of new &
used steel ISO shipping &
storage containers, including
shipping container modifications
into tool, communication &
storage shelters*
Employs—49; Estab.—1983
Sales—$1Mil-$5Mil
408,000 sq ft site, Distrib.—Intl.
Privately owned corporation
ISO rating—9001:2008

**TAMBURRI ASSOCS.**
1401 Industrial Hwy. (08077)
**Phone—(856) 829-4000**
Fax—(856) 829-1390
www.tamburri.com
Email—ta4steel@tamburri.com
Pres.—Phyllis Tamburri
V.-P.—Michael Tamburri
SIC—3441; 3448; NAICS—
332312; *Steel fabrication &
prefabricated steel buildings*
Employs—18; Estab.—1977
Sales—$2.5Mil-$5Mil (est)
Distrib.—Regional
Privately owned corporation

**T-M VACUUM PRODUCTS, INC.**
630 S. Warrington Ave. (08077)
**Phone—(856) 829-2000**
Fax—(856) 829-0990

## Cinnaminson—(cont.)

www.tmvacuum.com
Email—info@tmvacuum.com
Pres.—Fred Stuffer
V-P.—Rennie Wessner
Asst. Admn.—Roberta Hoyle
Pur. Agt.—Ken Schneider
SIC—3567; NAICS—333994;
Furnaces, ovens, environmental
chambers, thin film deposition
equipment & vacuum
components, including valves,
glove boxes & pumping systems
& accessories for the vacuum
furnace, vacuum oven,
environmental chamber & thin
film industries
Employs—35; Estab.—1965
Distrib.—Intl.
Privately owned corporation

### TRANSAXLE, LLC

Div. of Graham Partners, Inc.
2501 Route 73 S., P.O. Box 2306
(08077)
Phone—(856) 665-4445
National—(800) 257-0444
Fax—(856) 663-9072
www.transaxle.com
Email—info@transaxle.com
CEO—Dave Olsen
CFO—David Gordan
GM—John Ferry
GM, Off Hwy. Hydraulic Div.—John
Malley
IT Mgr.—Jason Matkowsky
SIC—3714; Company
headquarters & rebuilt truck
axles, rear ends & transmissions
Employs—70; Estab.—1979
Sales—$2.5Mil-$5Mil
Distrib.—National
Privately owned corporation
Parent co.—Graham Partners,
Inc., Newtown Square, PA
Phone—(610) 408-0500
See Parent Co. Section for full profile.

## Clark

(Union—N.E.)

### BUDGET PRINTING, LLC

70 Westfield Ave. (07066)
Phone—(732) 574-1330
Fax—(732) 574-0083
www.budgetprintnj.com
Email—info@budgetprintnj.net
Owner & Pres.—Robert Borg
Manager—Donny Mace
SIC—2759; 2752; 3993; NAICS—
323100; Full-color digital, offset
& screen printing & full-color
posters & banners
Employs—6; Estab.—1980
Sales—under $500,000
Distrib.—Regional
Limited Liability Company
AKA: Commercial Graphics

### CARTERET CODING, INC.

1431 Raritan Rd. (07066)
Phone—(732) 574-0900
Fax—(732) 574-9212
www.carteretcoding.com
Email—ccisales@
carteretcoding.com
Pres.—Charles Vill
V-P.—Sharon Vill
SIC—3559; Date & lot coding
systems for the packaging
industry
Employs—6; Estab.—1993
Sales—over $1Mil
Distrib.—Intl.
Privately owned corporation

### CLARK HOME SUPPLY

205 Westfield Ave. (07066)
Phone—(732) 388-5447
Fax—(732) 815-0049
Owner—Ray Meigs

SIC—3444; Aluminum awnings
Employs—1; Estab.—1954
Sales—under $500,000
Distrib.—Local
Sole ownership
AKA: Awnings Galore

### DIRECT CABINET SALES

265 Central Ave. (07066)
Mail addr: 4 Jeffrey Ln., Hamilton
(08619)
Phone—(732) 382-8080
Fax—(732) 382-1414
www.directcabinetsales.com
Off. Mgr.—Antonio Koutsouzos
SIC—2541; 2542; Custom
wooden & wire closets & shelves
Employs—8; Estab.—1991
Sales—under $500,000
Distrib.—Local
Privately owned corporation

### FIXTURECRAFT CORP.

1457 Raritan Rd., Ste. 201 (07066)
Phone—(908) 272-8145
   (908) 510-2753
National—(800) 275-1145
Fax—(908) 272-8149
www.fixturecraft.com
Email—sales@fixturecraft.com
Pres.—William P. Mooney
V-P., Warehousing—Michael
Rossetti
Acct. Mgr.—Debbi Fennes
SIC—3315; 3496; Portable &
folding wire display literature,
magazine & books racks for
teachers, libraries, trade shows,
conventions, exhibits & sales
presentations & public
warehousing; Brand name—
Fixturecraft
Employs—3; Estab.—1987
Sales—$500,000-$1Mil
125,000 sq ft site, Distrib.—
National
Privately owned corporation

### GAMCO INDUSTRIES, INC.

7 Walnut Ave. (07066)
Phone—(732) 381-0700
National—(800) 221-1367
Fax—(732) 381-6168
www.gamcofilters.com
Email—gamcoind@aol.com
Pres.—Fred Whiting
Off. Mgr.—Cindy Seng
SIC—3663; NAICS—334220;
Cable television filters
Employs—25; Estab.—1989
Sales—$1Mil-$2.5Mil
Distrib.—Intl.
Privately owned corporation

### HANSEN MACHINE & TOOL CO., INC.

27 Walnut Ave. (07066)
Phone—(732) 340-0466
Fax—(732) 340-0467
Email—Bob@
hansenmachine.comcastbiz.net
Pres.—Robert Hansen
SIC—3544; 3599; NAICS—
332710; Tooling & machining of
parts for the cosmetic industry
Employs—3; Estab.—1996
Sales—under $500,000
Distrib.—National
Privately owned corporation

### JABS PERSONAL STITCH, INC.

1120 Raritan Rd. (07066)
Phone—(732) 396-9699
Fax—(732) 396-3444
www.jabspersonalstitch.com
Email—jabspersonal@aol.com
Ptnr.—Joseph Arancio
Ptnr.—Andrea Arancio
SIC—2396; 2395; Textile screen
printing & embroidery
Employs—2; Estab.—2007
Sales—under $500,000
Distrib.—Local
Privately owned partnership

### KARNAK CORP.

330 Central Ave. (07066)
Phone—(732) 388-0300
National—(800) 526-4236
Fax—(732) 388-9422
www.karnakcorp.com
Email—info@karnakcorp.com
Pres., Chairwoman—Sarah J. Jelin
Vice Chrm. & CEO—James D.
Hannah
CFO—David Gritz
COO—Chris Salazar
IT Mgr.—Andy Ortiz
Matls. Mgr.—Mike Shubick
SIC—2952; NAICS—324122;
Corporate headquarters & roof
coatings
Employs—75; Estab.—1933
Sales—$25Mil-$35Mil
65,000 sq ft site, Distrib.—Intl.
Privately owned corporation

### KERRY INGREDIENTS & FLAVORS

Div. of Kerry, Inc.
160 Terminal Ave. (07066)
Phone—(732) 882-0202
Fax—(732) 499-7061
www.kerry.com
Email—sales@kerry.com
Cont.—Angel Albanese
Plt. Mgr.—Aidan O'Sullivan
Hum. Res. Mgr.—Jim Maas
Benefits Coord.—Nancy Cooney
Hum. Res. Rep.—Karen Novak
SIC—2844; 2087; 2869; NAICS—
325600; Flavorings & natural
products
Employs—135; Estab.—1860
Sales—$50Mil-$100Mil
140,000 sq ft site, Distrib.—Intl.
Privately owned corporation
Parent co.—Kerry, Inc., Beloit, WI
Phone—(608) 363-1200
See Parent Co. Section for full profile.

### L'OREAL U S A, INC.

222 Terminal Ave. (07066)
Phone—(732) 499-2838
Fax—(732) 499-2415
www.lorealusa.com
Email—media@us.loreal.com
V-P., Engrg.—Serge Pepin
Dir., Hum. Res.—Clarence Foster
SIC—2844; NAICS—325600; Hair
care products; Brand name—
Maybelline
Employs—400; Estab.—1976
Distrib.—Intl.
Publicly owned corporation
Parent co.—L'Oreal U S A, Inc.,
New York, NY
Phone—(212) 818-1500
See Parent Co. Section for full profile.

### MAJESTIC OPTICAL COATINGS

152 Willow Way (07066)
Phone—(732) 388-5604
National—(888) 278-8308
Fax—(732) 388-5826
www.majestic-coatings.com
Owner—Jeff Decker
SIC—3479; Reflective & anti-
reflective thin film optical
coatings
Employs—2; Estab.—1994
Sales—under $500,000
Distrib.—National
Privately owned corporation

### ORANGE MATTRESS

77 Central Ave. (07066)
Phone—(973) 761-1100
National—(800) 761-1100
www.mycustombedding.com
Email—custombedding@yahoo.com
Manager—Mindy Segal

SIC—2515; Mattresses & box
springs
Employs—15; Estab.—1902
Sales—$1Mil-$2.5Mil (est)
Distrib.—Intl.
Privately owned corporation
AKA: Custom Bedding of America,
Inc.

[NEW ENTRY]

### SHANGHAI OPTICS, INC. (H Q)

17 Brant Ave., Ste. 6 (07066-1548)
Phone—(732) 321-6915
Fax—(732) 875-0298
Email—info@shanghai-optics.com
V-P., Sales & Mktg.—Joanna Lee
SIC—3827; Corporate
headquarters; lens design &
assembly & optical & photonic
components, including
cylindrical lenses & prisms (mfg.
done in China)
Employs—7
Sales—$2Mil
Distrib.—Intl.
Privately owned corporation

### TANTER, INC.

151 Westfield Ave. (07066)
Phone—(732) 382-3555
Fax—(732) 388-4886
Email—h.horizon@verizon.net
Pres.—Walter Swierc
SIC—2759; NAICS—323100;
Commercial printing
Employs—2; Estab.—1983
Distrib.—Regional
Privately owned corporation
AKA: Horizon Printing

### TECHNOVISION, INC.

1119 Raritan Rd., Ste. 2 (07066)
Phone—(732) 381-0200
Fax—(732) 381-0207
www.etechnovision.com
Email—info@etechnovision.com
Hum. Res. Mgr.—Vanitha
Vasudevan
SIC—7373; NAICS—541512;
Computer systems integration
Employs—20; Estab.—1997
Sales—$1Mil-$2.5Mil
Distrib.—Local
Privately owned corporation

### THAL PRECISION INDUSTRIES, INC.

19-A Walnut Ave. (07066)
Phone—(732) 381-6106
Fax—(732) 381-5929
www.thalprecision.com
Email—paulthal@aol.com
Pres.—Jim Thal
V-P.—Paul Thal
SIC—3544; 3599; NAICS—
333500; Injection mold
fabrication, CNC & wire EDM,
EDM hole drilling & CNC
machining job shop
Employs—10; Estab.—1981
7,500 sq ft site, Distrib.—Regional
Privately owned sub-S corp.

## Clarksboro

(Gloucester—S.W.)

### DEWALT MFG. CO., INC.

88 W. Cohawkin Rd. (08020)
Phone—(856) 423-1207
National—(800) 439-1207
Fax—(856) 423-1409
www.dewalt-mfg.com
Email—dewalt-mfg@verizon.net
Pres.—Roger Dewalt
Prodn. Supv. & Machinist—Scott
Dewalt
SIC—3599; Precision & waterjet
machining job shop
Employs—7; Estab.—1960
Sales—under $1Mil
6,000 sq ft site, Distrib.—Local
Privately owned corporation

GEOGRAPHICAL

## Clarksboro—(cont.)

**REGO IRON CO.**
176 Cohawkin Rd. (08020)
**Phone—(856) 423-6779**
Fax—(856) 423-6779
Owner—Frank Rego
SIC—3446; NAICS—332323;
*Wrought iron railings*
Employs—1; Estab.—1986
Sales—under $500,000
Distrib.—Local
Sole ownership

---

## Clarksburg
### (Monmouth—N.E.)

**HYBRID-TEK, INC.**
Div. of Cetek, Inc.
9 Trenton Lakewood Rd., Ste. 1
(08510)
**Phone—(609) 259-3355**
Fax—(609) 259-3539
www.hybrid-tek.com
Email—bcatalano@hybrid-tek.com
IT Mgr.—Michael Murphy
Admn. Mgr. & Exec. Admn.—
Barbara A. Catalano
Hum. Res. Mgr.—Robert Catalano
Qual. Mgr.—Dana Ciardullo
Engr., Tech.—Brian T. Hammond
SIC—3674; NAICS—334413;
*Electronic thick film hybrids &
assemblies*
Employs—14; Estab.—1981
5,000 sq ft site, Distrib.—National
Privately owned corporation
Parent co.—Cetek, Inc.,
Poughkeepsie, NY
Phone—(845) 452-3510
See Parent Co. Section for full profile.

**RAMSEY MODEL DESIGN, DAVID A.**
P.O. Box 87 (08510)
**Phone—(609) 259-6757**
www.ramseymodeldesign.com
Email—david@
ramseymodeldesign.com
Owner—David A. Ramsey
SIC—3543; 3999; NAICS—
332997; *Models & prototypes*
Employs—1; Estab.—1980
Sales—under $500,000
Distrib.—Intl.
Sole ownership

---

## Clayton
### (Gloucester—S.W.)

**ALERIS MFG.**
Div. of Aleris International, Inc.
838 N. Delsea Dr. (08312)
**Phone—(856) 881-3600**
National—(800) 524-2558
Fax—(856) 881-9609
www.aleris.com
Email—info@aleris.com
Hum. Res. Mgr.—Michelle
Almeida
SIC—3353; NAICS—331315;
*Aluminum sheet & foil*
Employs—120; Estab.—1980
Distrib.—Regional
Privately owned corporation
AKA: Rolled Products
Parent co.—Aleris International,
Inc., Beachwood, OH
Phone—(216) 910-3400
See Parent Co. Section for full profile.

**COMP-SOLUTIONS & SERVICES**
621 N. Delsea Dr. (08312)
**Phone—(856) 863-1137**
Fax—(856) 307-0224
www.compsolutions.com
Email—anae@compsolutions.com
Pres.—Robert Errera
Comp. Techn.—Chazz Roman

SIC—3571; 3577; NAICS—
334111; *Computer parts*
Employs—8; Estab.—1995
Distrib.—Regional

**HUNGERFORD & TERRY, INC.**
226 N. Atlantic Ave., P.O. Box 650
(08312)
**Phone—(856) 881-3200**
Fax—(856) 881-6859
www.hungerfordterry.com
Email—sales@hungerfordterry.com
Pres. & V-P., Opers.—Thomas J.
Carrocino
V-P., Secy-Treas.—Joshua
Kastrava
V-P., Sales—Frank J. Caligiuri
SIC—3589; NAICS—333319;
*Water treatment equipment for
iron, manganese, arsenic,
radium, nitrates & hardness
removal & condensate polishers
& demineralizers; Brand name—
GreensandPlus*
Employs—50; Estab.—1909
9,000 sq ft site, Distrib.—Intl.
Privately owned corporation
Also see: Inversand Co., same loc.

**INVERSAND CO.**
226 N. Atlantic Ave., P.O. Box 650
(08312)
**Phone—(856) 881-2345**
Fax—(856) 881-6859
www.inversand.com
Email—mail@inversand.com
Pres.—Tom Carrocino
V-P., Sales—Ken Sayell
Sales Mgr.—Frank J. Caligiuri
SIC—1446; 3299; NAICS—
212322; *Manganese greensand
for municipal & industrial water
treatment applications; Brand
name—GreensandPlus*
Employs—50; Estab.—1925
5,000 sq ft site, Distrib.—Intl.
Privately owned corporation
Also see: Hungerford & Terry, Inc.,
same loc.

**K & C FUND RAISING &
EMBROIDERY**
101 S. Delsea Dr. (08312)
**Phone—(856) 881-6019**
National—(800) 882-6019
Fax—(856) 881-4423
Email—kandcemb@yahoo.com
Ptnr. & Hum. Res. Mgr.—Kathleen
Cromley
Ptnr.—Bill Cromley
SIC—2395; *Embroidery*
Employs—3; Estab.—1992
Sales—under $500,000
Distrib.—Local
Sole ownership

**MARLYN SHEET METAL, INC.**
606 N. Delsea Dr. (08312)
**Phone—(856) 863-6900**
Fax—(856) 863-6916
Pres.—Julius Brandt
SIC—3444; *HVAC sheet metal
fabrication*
Employs—15; Estab.—1996
6,500 sq ft site, Distrib.—National
Privately owned corporation

---

## Clementon
### (Camden—S.W.)

**CADPRO, INC.**
114 W. Atlantic Ave. *(08021)*
**Phone—(856) 435-0050**
Fax—(856) 435-0600
www.cadproinc.com
Email—elaine@cadproinc.com
Pres.—Elaine A. Bartie
V-P., Prodn.—Chris Kupczak

SIC—3599; 3444; *Machined &
sheet metal parts, assemblies &
fabrication for exhibit & museum
applications, including waterjet
cutting services*
Employs—10; Estab.—1985
Sales—$500,000-$1Mil
9,100 sq ft site, Distrib.—Regional
Privately owned corporation

**FREEDOM GLASS & METAL, INC.**
4 White Horse Pike, P.O. Box 868
(08021)
**Phone—(856) 627-3946**
Fax—(856) 627-6830
Email—jka@
freedomglassandmetal.com
Owner—Karen Arsenault
Pres.—Jim Arsenault, Jr.
Off. Mgr.—Dana Frail
SIC—3442; 3993; NAICS—
332321; *Aluminum windows &
storefronts*
Employs—20; Estab.—1983
Distrib.—Local
Privately owned corporation

**GAMBALE PRECAST, INC.**
1 Erial Rd. (08021)
**Phone—(856) 784-3399**
Fax—(856) 784-4565
www.gambale.com
Email—gci@gambale.com
Pres.—Nick Gambale, Sr.
Plt. Mgr.—Nick Gambale, Jr.
SIC—3272; *Precast concrete
products*
Employs—10; Estab.—1972
Sales—under $500,000
Distrib.—Local
Privately owned corporation

**GIAMBRI'S QUALITY SWEETS**
26 Brand Ave. (08021)
**Phone—(856) 783-1099**
Fax—(856) 783-6377
www.giambris.com
Email—info@giambris.com
Pres.—David Giambri
SIC—2064; NAICS—311300;
*Candy*
Employs—10; Estab.—1942
Distrib.—National
Privately owned corporation
AKA: Giambri's Candy

**KENDALL MFG. CO., INC.**
1366 Chews Landing Rd. (08021)
**Phone—(856) 227-2132**
Fax—(856) 374-8651
www.kendall-windows.com
Email—jstrater44@yahoo.com
Owner—James W. Strater
SIC—3089; 2431; 2394; 3444;
NAICS—314912; *Vinyl & wooden
windows & doors & retractable
awnings*
Employs—3; Estab.—1958
Distrib.—Local
Privately owned corporation

**†SYNTEX GROUP, INC.**
1838 Downs Ave. (08021)
**Phone—(856) 566-0058**
Fax—(609) 939-0233
www.syntexgroup.com
Email—syntexgroup@aol.com
Pres.—Eric Ezeiruaku
SIC—5084; 5072; *Distributor of
industrial machinery & tools*
Employs—5; Estab.—2002
Sales—under $2Mil
1,000 sq ft site, Distrib.—Intl.
Privately owned corporation

---

## Cliffside Park
### (Bergen—N.E.)

**CALVARUSO CLOTHING, G. & F.**
345 Palisade Ave. (07010)
**Phone—(201) 945-7118**
www.frankthetailornj.com
Email—gnfclothing@gmail.com

Owner—Frank Calvaruso
SIC—2339; *Custom made
women's clothing & alterations
for men & women*
Employs—2; Estab.—1973
Sales—under $500,000
Distrib.—Local
Sole ownership

**INTERSTATE ARCHITECTURAL &
IRON, INC.**
243 Laird Ave. (07010)
**Phone—(201) 941-0393**
Fax—(201) 941-5938
www.iai.50megs.com
Email—interstate243@gmail.com
Pres.—Richard Papp
SIC—3446; NAICS—332323;
*Architectural metalwork*
Employs—2; Estab.—1976
Sales—under $500,000
3,600 sq ft site, Distrib.—Local
Privately owned corporation

**NORTH BERGEN MARBLE &
GRANITE CORP.**
217 Palisade Ave. (07010)
**Phone—(201) 945-9988**
Fax—(201) 945-6644
Plt. Mgr.—Jim Markopolous
SIC—3281; NAICS—327991;
*Marble & granite countertops &
fireplaces*
Employs—4; Estab.—1972
Sales—$500,000-$1Mil
Distrib.—Local
Privately owned corporation

**ORTHO REMEDY, INC., THE**
522 Anderson Ave. (07010)
**Phone—(201) 943-3900**
National—(800) 662-7993
Fax—(201) 943-9055
www.orthoremedy.com
Email—orthorem@aol.com
Pres.—Thomas Velenti
Sales Mgr.—Victor Olson
SIC—3842; *Orthotics &
prosthetics*
Employs—7; Estab.—1976
Sales—$1Mil
12,000 sq ft site, Distrib.—Intl.
Privately owned corporation

**NEW ENTRY**

**P & M COMPUTERS, INC.**
97 Oakdene Ave., P.O. Box 270
(07010)
**Phone—(201) 943-0353**
Fax—(201) 943-0227
www.pandminc.com
Email—sales@pandminc.com
Pres., CTO—Francis Poeta
SIC—7373; *Computer systems
integration, including LANs &
WANs*
Employs—6; Estab.—1992
Distrib.—Intl.
Privately owned corporation

**ROYCE SIGNWORKS, INC.**
226 DeSoto Pl. (07010)
**Phone—(201) 945-5536**
www.roycesignworks.com
Email—sales@roycesignworks.com
Pres.—Richard Curasco
SIC—3993; *Interior & exterior
signs, truck lettering & gold leaf
& glass gilding services*
Employs—1; Estab.—1989
Sales—under $500,000
1,100 sq ft site, Distrib.—Local
Privately owned corporation

---

## Cliffwood
### (Monmouth—N.E.)

**D & W DIESEL**
423 County Rd. (07721)
**Phone—(732) 566-4970**
National—(888) 562-5391
Fax—(732) 566-0340

## Cliffwood—(cont.)

Opers. Mgr.—Craig Marcurano
Shop Foreman—Jim Wescott
SIC—3694; 3599; NAICS—
336322; *Rebuilt automotive
generators, starters, alternators,
diesel fuel injections &
turbochargers*
Employs—40; Estab.—1951
16,000 sq ft site, Distrib.—
Regional
Privately owned partnership

### ELKEM, INC.

443 County Rd. (07721)
**Phone—(732) 566-1700**
Fax—(732) 583-3076
www.elkem-inc.net
Email—twkent@elkem-inc.net
Pres.—Thomas W. Kent
V-P.—Jeffrey K. Lawrence
Off. Mgr.—Peggy Conrow
SIC—3471; NAICS—332813;
*Gold, silver, tin, copper, nickel &
tin-lead electroplating*
Employs—6; Estab.—1969
Sales—under $500,000
10,000 sq ft site, Distrib.—Intl.
Privately owned corporation
ISO rating—9001:2008

### MODERN INTERNATIONAL CORP.

145 Cliffwood Ave. *(07721)*
**Phone—(732) 696-9100**
National—(800) 322-9473
Fax—(732) 696-9111
www.moderninternational.net
Email—dstern@
moderninternational.net
Pres., GM—Daniel Stern
Fin. Mgr.—Karen Daube
Sales Rep.—Ira Halbfinger
Sales Rep.—Rick Stein
Bookkeeper—Diane Nieves
SIC—3496; 3089; 2241; NAICS—
313221; *Wire, steel & plastic
strapping, packaging products &
nonelectrical chains*
Employs—20; Estab.—1964
Sales—$1Mil-$2.5Mil (est)
30,000 sq ft site, Distrib.—Local
Privately owned corporation

### VPI INDUSTRIES, INC.

77 Cliffwood Ave., Ste. 3-B
(07721)
**Phone—(732) 583-6895**
www.vpiindustries.com
Email—sales@vpiindustries.com
Ptnr. & Co-Pres.—Mathew
Weisfeld
Co-Pres.—Harry Weisfeld
SIC—3651; NAICS—334310;
*Audio turntables, tonearms,
record cleaning machines &
accessories*
Employs—10; Estab.—1978
Sales—$1Mil-$2.5Mil
Distrib.—Intl.
Privately owned corporation

---

## Clifton

(Passaic—N.E.)

### A TO Z PRINTING & PROMOTIONS

1455 Main Ave. (07011)
**Phone—(973) 916-9995**
National—(888) 916-9995
www.printa2z.com
Email—info@printa2z.com
Pres.—Eyad Asmar
SIC—2752; NAICS—323100;
*Lithographic & commercial
printing*
Employs—7; Estab.—2000
Sales—$500,000-$1Mil
Distrib.—National
Privately owned corporation

### †ABC SUPPLY CO., INC., BRADCO DIV.

Div. of ABC Supply Co., Inc.
45 Samworth Rd. (07012)
**Phone—(973) 777-3663**
Fax—(973) 777-1113
www.bradcosupply.com
Email—info@bradcosupply.com
Br. Mgr.—Greg Anderson
SIC—5033; 5099; 5031;
*Distributor of roofing materials,
signs & windows*
Employs—10; Estab.—1967
Sales—$2.5Mil-$5Mil
10,000 sq ft site, Distrib.—National
Privately owned corporation
Parent co.—ABC Supply Co., Inc.,
Beloit, WI
Phone—(608) 362-7777
See Parent Co. Section for full profile.

### ACCURATE PLASTIC PRINTERS, LLC

30 Colfax Ave. (07013)
**Phone—(973) 591-0180**
National—(877) 222-7889
Fax—(973) 591-0811
www.accuplastic.com
Email—carlos@accuplastic.com
Pres.—Carlos Agudelo
V-P.—Jackie Agudelo
SIC—2752; 2759; *Plastic product
offset & digital printing of
business, membership, benefits,
ID & library cards, bookmarks,
schedules, shelf display signs,
door hangers & plastic rulers,
including laminating & die
cutting*
Employs—20; Estab.—1996
10,000 sq ft site, Distrib.—National
Limited Liability Company

### AERO MFG CO.

310 Allwood Rd., P.O. Box 1250
(07012)
**Phone—(973) 473-5300**
National—(800) 237-6634
Fax—(973) 473-3794
www.aeromfg.com
Email—sales@aeromfg.com
Pres.—Wayne Phillips
Ex. V-P.—Neil Pittman
Plt. Mgr.—Jim Hilton
SIC—3556; 3535; NAICS—
333294; *Stainless steel
foodservice, material handling &
medical equipment*
Employs—100; Estab.—1946
Sales—$5Mil-$10Mil
120,000 sq ft site, Distrib.—Intl.
Privately owned corporation

### ALCO SHEET METAL FABRICATORS, INC.

51 Chester St. (07011)
**Phone—(973) 772-7070**
Fax—(973) 772-4047
Pres.—Rick Coots
SIC—3444; *Sheet metal
fabrication*
Employs—2; Estab.—1966
Sales—under $500,000
Distrib.—Local
Privately owned corporation

### ALEXANDER, INC., SANDY

200 Entin Rd. (07014)
**Phone—(973) 470-8100**
(973) 472-2600
Fax—(973) 470-9269
www.sandyinc.com
Email—sandy@sandyinc.com
Pres., CEO—Michael Graff
CFO—Tim Fisher
Ex. V-P., Sales—Neal Alexander
Ex. V-P., Mktg.—Larry Westlake
Cont.—Tammy Youmans
Hum. Res. Mgr.—Alissa Macaluso

SIC—2759; NAICS—323100;
*Corporate headquarters &
commercial printing*
Employs—250
Sales—$100Mil
150,000 sq ft site, Distrib.—
National
Privately owned corporation
ISO rating—14001, 9001

### ALLSTATE PRINTING PACKAGING, INC.

791 Paulison Ave., Ste. 3 (07011)
**Phone—(973) 473-0700**
Fax—(973) 473-0022
www.allstateprint.com
Email—info@allstateprint.com
Owner & Pres.—Sam Zhong
Hum. Res. Mgr.—Tina Lee
SIC—2752; *Commercial offset
printing*
Employs—85; Estab.—1998
Sales—$10Mil-$25Mil (est)
Distrib.—National
Privately owned corporation
AKA: Crown Marketing Solution

### ALORIS TOOL TECHNOLOGY CO., INC.

397-407 Getty Ave. *(07011)*
Mail addr: P.O. Box 1529, Clifton
(07015-1529)
**Phone—(973) 772-1201**
(877) 772-1733
Fax—(973) 772-8606
www.aloris.com
Email—aloris@aloris.com
Pres.—Richard Roslowski
SIC—3545; 3541; 3544; *Quick-
change tooling, cutting tools, tool
posts & lathe accessories; Brand
name—Aloris/Yestool*
Employs—25; Estab.—1946
Sales—$1Mil-$5Mil
20,000 sq ft site, Distrib.—National
Privately owned corporation

### ALPHA PROCESSING CO. INC.

210 Delawanna Ave., P.O. Box 936
(07014)
**Phone—(973) 777-1737**
Fax—(973) 777-1891
www.alpha-processing.com
Email—info@alpha-processing.com
Pres.—Richard Jenny
Plt. Mgr.—Charlie Veneziano
Off. Mgr.—Kelly Rodrigues
SIC—3479; 2759; NAICS—
323100; *Metal products painting,
powder coating & commercial
screen printing*
Employs—50; Estab.—1979
20,000 sq ft site, Distrib.—National
Sole ownership

### AMERICAN HYGIENE INDUSTRIES, LLC

60 Page Rd. (07012)
**Phone—(973) 928-6533**
Fax—(973) 928-6539
www.ahindustries.com
Email—sales@ahindustries.com
Pres.—Chris Fuhrmann
V-P., Sales & Mktg.—Raj Prakash
Hum. Res. Mgr.—Virginia Leahy
SIC—2676; NAICS—322291; *Wet
wipes for baby, disinfecting,
antibacterial, surface, personal
care & pet applications; Brand
name—Go wipes; Smoke Mask;
Snuggies*
Employs—25; Estab.—2006
Distrib.—Intl.
Privately owned corporation

### AMERICAN MARKING SYSTEMS, INC.

1015 Paulison Ave. (07011)
Mail addr: P.O. Box 1677, Clifton
(07015-1677)
**Phone—(973) 478-5600**
National—(800) 782-6766
Fax—(973) 478-0039

www.ams-stamps.com
Email—info@ams-stamps.com
Pres.—John Collins
Cont.—John Newberger
Sales & Mktg. Mgr.—Ronald
Cochran
SIC—3953; 3993; 3089; NAICS—
339943; *Corporate headquarters
& custom office, marking &
identification products including
traditional & self-inking stamps,
inks, stamp pads, embossing
seals, daters, numbering
machines, nameplates, badges,
signs, plaques, banners & tags;
Brand name—ProMark;
Xstamper*
Employs—30; Estab.—1869
Sales—$5Mil-$10Mil
10,000 sq ft site, Distrib.—National
Privately owned corporation

[NEW ENTRY]

### ARISTON MULTIMEDIA, LLC

94 Valley Rd. (07013)
**Phone—(973) 553-2727**
Fax—(973) 553-2726
www.aristonmultimedia.com
Email—bernard@
aristonmultimedia.com
Owner—Bernard Williams
SIC—2759; 2395; 3993;
*Commercial printing, t-shirt
screen printing, embroidery &
signage*
Employs—4; Estab.—2010
Sales—under $500,000
2,200 sq ft site, Distrib.—National
Limited Liability Company

### †ATHENIA MASON SUPPLY, INC.

72 Mina Ave. (07011)
**Phone—(973) 253-0570**
Fax—(973) 253-0575
www.atheniamason.com
Email—sales@atheniamason.com
V-P.—Ken Kievit
V-P.—Tom Kievit
SIC—5032; *Distributor of masonry
supplies; Brand name—
Cambridge Pavers; Cultured
Stone; Grinnell Retaining Wall;
CST Retaining Wall; Robinson
Brick/Rock; R Stone - Stone
Veneer*
Employs—20; Estab.—1970
Distrib.—Regional
Privately owned corporation

### ATLANTIC CASTING & ENGINEERING

810 Bloomfield Ave. (07012)
**Phone—(973) 779-2450**
National—(800) 631-0135
Fax—(973) 779-2854
www.atlantic-ce.com
Email—sales@atlantic-ce.com
CEO—Jim Binns
V-P., Sales—Greg Rohrbacker
Plt. Mgr.—Rob Zevick
Hum. Res. Mgr.—Mila Jalbuena
Cust. Serv. Mgr.—Mechelle Coiro
SIC—3324; 3599; NAICS—
331512; *Investment castings &
CNC machining job shop*
Employs—100; Estab.—1937
75,000 sq ft site, Distrib.—National
Privately owned corporation

### ATLAS INDUSTRIAL MFG. CO.

81 Somerset Pl. (07012)
**Phone—(973) 779-3970**
Fax—(973) 779-7783
www.atlasindustrial.com
Email—info@atlasindustrial.com
Pres.—Frank G. De Lorenzo
Secy. & Pur. Agt.—Frank J. De
Lorenzo
Treas., Engrg. Mgr.—Ramsey
Mahadeen
Plt. Mgr.—Tom Ciampi
Hum. Res. & Off. Mgr.—Petey
Condron

GEOGRAPHICAL

## Clifton—(cont.)

SIC—3443; *Heat exchangers*
Employs—36; Estab.—1959
Sales—$500,000-$1Mil
Distrib.—Regional
Privately owned corporation
ISO rating—9001

**AUTOMATED FLEXIBLE CONVEYORS, INC.**
55 Walman Ave., 2nd Fl. (07011-3416)
**Phone—(973) 340-1695**
National—(800) 694-7271
Fax—(973) 340-8216
www.afcsolutions.com
Email—sales@afcsolutions.com
Pres.—Kevin Devaney
V-P.—Grace Faria
MIS Mgr.—Jeff Malenchek
Engr.—David Nadel
SIC—3535; 3559; NAICS—333922; *Spiral feeder conveyors, dump clean self- contained cartridge filter dust hood & bulk bag unloading stations*
Employs—20; Estab.—1983
Sales—$1Mil-$2.5Mil
30,000 sq ft site, Distrib.—Intl.
Privately owned corporation

**BARANTEC, INC.**
777 Passaic Ave., Ste. 345 (07012-1878)
**Phone—(973) 779-8774**
Fax—(973) 779-8768
www.barantec.com
Email—info@barantec.com
Pres.—Hillel Mordkowicz
V-P.—Diane Bersen
Sr. Prod. Engr.—Ted Bielitz
SIC—3625; 3613; NAICS—335314; *Standard & custom touch metal piezo switches, keypads & keyboards & industrial controls for indoor & outdoor applications; Brand name—EVERSWITCH*
Employs—10; Estab.—1985
Distrib.—National
ISO rating—9001

**BAY STATE MILLING CO.**
404 Getty Ave. (07011)
**Phone—(973) 772-1000**
National—(800) 647-3060
Fax—(973) 772-3542
www.bsm.com
Email—vincem.nj@bsm.com
Sales Mgr.—Vince Malara
Sales Rep.—Lucille Russo
SIC—2041; 2048; NAICS—311211; *Flour & animal feed milling*
Employs—60; Estab.—1879
Sales—under $500,000
Distrib.—Local
Privately owned corporation
Parent co.—Bay State Milling Co., Quincy, MA
Phone—(617) 328-4400
See Parent Co. Section for full profile.

**BEACON PUBLISHING CO., INC.**
Div. of Diocese Of Paterson
775 Valley Rd. (07013)
Mail addr: P.O. Box 1887, Clifton (07015-1887)
**Phone—(973) 279-8845**
Fax—(973) 279-2265
www.patersondiocese.org
Email—catholicbeacon@patersondiocese.org
Editor & GM—Richard A. Sokerka
SIC—2711; *Local Catholic newspaper publishing for the Diocese of Paterson*
Employs—7; Estab.—1967
Sales—$1Mil-$2Mil
Distrib.—Local
Privately owned corporation

Parent co.—Diocese Of Paterson, Clifton, NJ
Phone—(973) 777-8818
See Parent Co. Section for full profile.

**BERGEN METAL PRODUCTS, INC.**
120 Brighton Rd., Ste. 5 (07012)
**Phone—(973) 249-1500**
Fax—(973) 249-6500
Pres.—John Mottola
Off. Mgr.—Denise Scancereloa
SIC—3599; *Precision metal parts*
Employs—10; Estab.—1989
Sales—$1Mil-$2.5Mil (est)
Distrib.—Intl.
Privately owned corporation

**BIWAL MFG. CO., INC.**
48 Industrial St. W. (07012)
**Phone—(973) 778-0105**
Fax—(973) 778-0322
Pres.—Joseph J. Mrocka
SIC—3599; *General machining job shop*
Employs—22; Estab.—1967
Distrib.—Regional
Privately owned corporation

**BLACK PRINCE DISTILLERY, INC.**
691 Clifton Ave. (07011)
Mail addr: P.O. Box 1999, Clifton (07015-1999)
**Phone—(973) 365-2050**
Fax—(973) 365-0746
www.blackprincedistillery.com
Email—rickn@blackprincedist.com
V-P., Opers.—Richard Noone
SIC—2085; NAICS—312100; *Distilled liquors; Brand name—Llords Cordials; Devils Springs Vodka*
Employs—30; Estab.—1934
Sales—$10Mil-$25Mil (est)
Distrib.—National
Privately owned corporation

**BLANCHETTE TOOL & GAGE MFG.**
845 Bloomfield Ave., P.O. Box 1270 (07012)
**Phone—(973) 471-2100**
Fax—(973) 471-2104
www.blanchettetool.com
Email—info@blanchettetool.com
Pres.—R. Blanchette Garvey
V-P., GM—Tom Garvey
SIC—3545; 3824; 3829; NAICS—334514; *Visual gage comparators & dimensional measuring instruments, including air gages, fixtures & gage calibration & inspection services; Brand name—Sheffield Dimensional Instruments*
Employs—8; Estab.—1949
Sales—$500,000-$1Mil
8,500 sq ft site, Distrib.—Intl.
Privately owned corporation

**BLICKMAN, INC.**
500 U.S. Highway 46 (07011-1800)
**Phone—(973) 330-0557**
National—(800) 247-5070
Fax—(973) 330-0595
www.blickman.com
Email—info@blickman.com
Pres.—Rob Freedman
CFO—Paul Freedman
V-P., Mfg.—Dayne Smith
Cont.—Susan Schaub
SIC—2531; 3821; NAICS—339111; *Stainless steel & chrome hospital furniture; Brand name—Blickman Built*
Employs—85; Estab.—1975
71,000 sq ft site, Distrib.—Intl.
Privately owned corporation

**BOND PARADE FLOATS DISPLAYS, INC.**
111 Clifton Blvd. (07011)
**Phone—(973) 778-3333**
Fax—(973) 778-6950
www.bondparadefloats.com
Email—bondfloats@aol.com

Pres.—Robert DeVito
SIC—2499; *Parade floats*
Employs—20; Estab.—1942
Sales—$1Mil-$2.5Mil
Distrib.—National
Privately owned corporation

**BREURE SHEET METAL CO., INC.**
46 Walman Ave. (07011)
**Phone—(973) 772-6423**
Fax—(973) 772-7062
Email—darbreurehvac@optonline.net
Pres.—Matthew Breure
Off. Mgr.—Darlene Kalinowski
SIC—3444; *Sheet metal fabrication*
Employs—3; Estab.—1952
Sales—under $500,000
3,000 sq ft site, Distrib.—Regional
Privately owned corporation
AKA: Breure Heating & Air Conditioning

**BROTHERS QUALITY BAKERY OF ALLWOOD**
70 Market St. (07012)
**Phone—(973) 473-1467**
Fax—(201) 991-1590
Email—kearnybakery@aol.com
Co-Pres.—Michael Gencorelli
Co-Pres.—Thomas Gencorelli
SIC—2051; NAICS—311812; *Bakery products*
Employs—15; Estab.—1958
Sales—under $500,000
Distrib.—Local
Privately owned corporation

**BUDGET SIGNS**
8 Caroline Ave. (07011)
**Phone—(973) 340-2086**
www.truck-lettering.biz
Owner—Sandy Glogiewicz
SIC—3993; *Truck lettering*
Employs—1; Estab.—1982
Sales—under $500,000
Distrib.—Local
Sole ownership

**C & D CASES, INC.**
407 River Rd., Unit 9 (07014)
**Phone—(973) 473-4800**
Fax—(973) 473-4805
www.cdcaseco.com
Email—cdcaseco@horizon.net
Pres.—Coy Frisbee
SIC—2441; NAICS—321920; *Travel, sample & musical instrument cases*
Employs—4; Estab.—1982
Sales—under $500,000
5,000 sq ft site, Distrib.—Intl.
Privately owned sub-S corp.

**†CANGRO TRANSMISSION CO. OF NEW JERSEY**
Div. of Cangro Industries, Inc.
295 Crooks Ave. (07011)
**Phone—(973) 772-7662**
Fax—(973) 772-9446
www.cangroindustries.com
Email—cangrosales@ix.netcom.com
Br. Mgr.—Michael Thompson
Cust. Serv. Rep.—Joanne Smith
SIC—5084; 5085; *Distributor of industrial power transmission equipment, including bearings, pulleys, gears, sprockets, chains, reducers, variable speed drives & clutches*
Employs—10; Estab.—1983
Distrib.—Local
Privately owned corporation
Parent co.—Cangro Industries, Inc., Farmingdale, NY
Phone—(631) 454-9000
See Parent Co. Section for full profile.

**CENTURY ENGINEERING CO., INC.**
4 Orono St. (07013)
Mail addr: P.O. Box 737, Clifton (07015)
**Phone—(973) 779-3900**
Fax—(973) 778-9811
Email—cemailusa@erols.com
Pres.—Edward Haracz
Hum. Res. Mgr.—Susan Parris
Off. Mgr.—Linda Savage
SIC—3559; 3541; NAICS—333512; *Deburring & glass washer machinery*
Employs—15; Estab.—1950
Sales—$2.5Mil-$5Mil (est)
Distrib.—Intl.
Privately owned corporation

**CHALLENGE PRINTING CO., THE**
2 Bridewell Pl. (07014)
**Phone—(973) 471-4700**
National—(800) 654-1234
Fax—(973) 471-2562
www.challprint.com
Email—info@challengeprintingco.com
Pres.—Theodore Sasso
V-P.—Darrell Sasso
Acctg. & Hum. Res. Mgr.—Thomas Forrest
SIC—2752; NAICS—323100; *Company headquarters & labels, inserts & outserts printing for pharmaceuticals*
Employs—230; Estab.—1911
Sales—$15Mil
Distrib.—Intl.

**CHAMPION PLASTICS CORP.**
220 Clifton Blvd. (07011)
**Phone—(973) 777-9400**
(800) 526-1230
Fax—(800) 526-1238
www.championplastics.com
Email—sales@championplastics.com
GM—John Callaghan
Mktg. Mgr.—Denise Zangara
Hum. Res. Mgr.—Meryl Berrow
SIC—2673; 3081; NAICS—326113; *Polyethelene bags, liners, films, sheeting & shrink packaging; Brand name—Champtuf*
Employs—140; Estab.—1972
200,000 sq ft site, Distrib.—National
Privately owned partnership
ISO rating—9001:2000
Also see: X-L Plastics, Inc., same loc.

**CLARKSON & FORD CO.**
30 Industrial St. W. (07012)
**Phone—(973) 777-0300**
National—(800) 410-1965
Fax—(973) 777-3275
www.clarksonandford.com
Email—sales@clarksonandford.com
Pres.—Frank Johnson
Off. Mgr.—Cathy Johnson
SIC—2992; NAICS—324191; *Custom industrial lubricating, hydraulic, gear, compressor, cutting & soluble oils, drawing, stamping & metalworking fluids, coolants & slideway lubricants; Brand name—Banner Brand Lubricants*
Employs—10; Estab.—1883
Sales—$1Mil-$5Mil
Distrib.—Regional
Privately owned sub-S corp.

**CLIFTON FLUID POWER MACHINERY**
295 Allwood Rd. (07012)
Mail addr: P.O. Box 1827, Clifton (07015)
**Phone—(973) 778-3923**
Fax—(973) 778-9250
www.cliftonfluidpower.com
Email—cfp@cliftonfluidpower.com

## Clifton—(cont.)

GM—Richard Brodsky
SIC—3569; 3492; NAICS—
333995; Hydraulic machinery
Employs—9; Estab.—1980
Sales—under $500,000
Distrib.—Intl.
Privately owned corporation

**NEW ENTRY**
**CLIFTON MERCHANT MAGAZINE**
1288 Main Ave. (07011)
**Phone—(973) 253-4400**
www.cliftonmerchant.com
Owner—Tom Hawrylko
SIC—2721; Monthly magazine
publishing
Employs—4; Estab.—1990
Sales—under $500,000
800 sq ft site, Distrib.—Local
Sole ownership

**CLIFTON METAL PRODUCTS CO., INC.**
41 Clifton Blvd. (07011)
**Phone—(973) 777-6100**
Fax—(973) 473-3587
www.cliftonmetal.com
Email—cmp@simlab.net
Pres.—Dieter Kemmerich
Hum. Res., IT & Off. Mgr.—
Dorothy Grimes
SIC—3444; Sheet metal
fabrication
Employs—14; Estab.—1942
16,000 sq ft site, Distrib.—Local
Privately owned corporation

**CLIFTON MIRROR & GLASS CO., INC.**
188 Getty Ave. (07011)
**Phone—(973) 772-7770**
Fax—(973) 772-7637
www.cliftonglass.com
Cont.—Dale Calabro
SIC—3231; NAICS—327215;
Glass fabrication, table tops &
replacement windows
Employs—50; Estab.—1942
Sales—$5Mil-$10Mil (est)
Distrib.—Regional
Privately owned corporation

**COGESCO WATER TECHNOLOGIES CORP.**
891 Bloomfield Ave. (07012)
**Phone—(973) 249-9711**
National—(866) 264-6500
Fax—(973) 249-6911
www.cogescointl.com
Email—greche@cogescointl.com
Pres.—Gilles Reche
SIC—2899; Water treatment
chemicals
Employs—4; Estab.—2004
Sales—$1Mil-$2.5Mil
Distrib.—Local
Privately owned corporation

**COINING MFG., LLC**
35 Monhegen (07013)
**Phone—(973) 253-0500**
Fax—(973) 253-9611
www.coining.com
Email—mikew@coining.com
GM—Courtney Cromley
Mfg. Mgr.—Bob Mustegh
SIC—3469; Metal stampings
Employs—65; Estab.—1990
Sales—$10Mil
52,000 sq ft site, Distrib.—Intl.
Privately owned sub-S corp.
ISO rating—9001

**COLFAX CABINET CO., INC.**
86 Ackerman Ave. (07011)
**Phone—(973) 546-5422**
Fax—(973) 546-7222
Pres.—Martin Lovy
Off. Mgr.—Christiane Roghanian

SIC—2434; NAICS—337110;
Custom wooden kitchen
cabinets
Employs—15; Estab.—1969
Sales—over $1Mil
5,000 sq ft site, Distrib.—Regional
Privately owned corporation

**COMPOUNDING ENGINEERING SOLUTIONS, INC.**
473 Highway 46 W. (07011)
**Phone—(973) 340-4000**
Fax—(973) 340-4949
www.compounding.us
Email—piram473@gmail.com
Pres.—Arash Kiani
SIC—3087; NAICS—325991;
Plastic compound materials
Employs—10; Estab.—1999
Sales—under $500,000
Distrib.—Intl.
Privately owned corporation

**COMPUTOPRINT CORP.**
1360 Clifton Ave., Ste. 402 (07012)
**Phone—(973) 574-8800**
Fax—(973) 574-8887
Email—computopr@aol.com
Pres.—Marie Duplak
Sales Mgr.—Susan Skloo
Graphic Designer—Teresa
Czerhoniak
SIC—2759; NAICS—323100;
Commercial printing
Employs—10; Estab.—1972
Distrib.—Regional
Privately owned corporation

**COMUS INTERNATIONAL, INC.**
454 Allwood Rd. (07012)
**Phone—(973) 777-6900**
National—(800) 352-6687
Fax—(973) 777-8405
www.comus-intl.com
Email—info@comus-intl.com
Pres., CEO—Robert P. Romano
V.-P., COO—Joseph Perez
Sr. V.-P.—Joseph Romano
V.-P.—John Rollo
Hum. Res. Mgr.—Pat Galasso
SIC—3679; 3829; Tilt, tip-over,
float & reed switches, motion &
vibration sensors & solid state &
reed relays; Brand name—Oki
reed switches; Assemtech
Proximity Switches* Coto Reed
Switches
Employs—80; Estab.—1978
Sales—$12Mil
44,000 sq ft site, Distrib.—Intl.
Privately owned corporation
ISO rating—9001:2000

**CONVEYORS BY NORTH AMERICAN**
156 Huron Ave. (07013)
**Phone—(973) 777-6600**
Fax—(973) 614-1529
www.cbnaconveyors.com
Pres.—Gloria J. Kolodziej
SIC—3535; NAICS—333922;
Gravity conveyors
Employs—3; Estab.—1978
Sales—under $500,000
Distrib.—National
Privately owned corporation

**CORBO JEWELERS, INC.**
1055 Bloomfield Ave. (07012)
**Phone—(973) 777-1635**
Fax—(973) 777-0927
www.corbojewelers.com
Email—macorbo@aol.com
Pres.—Steven Corbo
V.-P.—Michael Corbo
Manager—Bill Ellinghausen
SIC—3911; NAICS—339911;
Jewelry, diamonds, color stones
& watches
Employs—10; Estab.—1952
Distrib.—Local
Privately owned sub-S corp.

**CRAFT LINE CABINET CORP.**
10 Walnut St. (07013)
**Phone—(973) 777-8808**
Fax—(973) 777-2305
www.craftlinecabinet.com
Email—craftline@erols.com
Owner—Gam Danziger
SIC—2452; 3083; NAICS—
321992; Laminated cabinets
Employs—10; Estab.—1989
Distrib.—Regional
Privately owned corporation

**CRAFTSMEN PRINTERS, THE**
855 Bloomfield Ave. (07012)
**Phone—(973) 773-8950**
National—(866) 734-1513
Fax—(973) 773-3160
www.craftsmenprinters.com
Email—inquiry@
craftsmenprinters.com
Pres.—Jaqueline Bischoff
V.-P.—Beverly Villata
Secy-Treas.—William H. Bischoff
Secy-Treas.—Richard Villata
GM—Russ Bischoff
SIC—2752; NAICS—323100;
Printing of package inserts (PIs),
booklets (IFUs) & packaging
related products for the medical
device, diagnostic,
pharmaceutical & cosmetic
industries
Employs—18; Estab.—1948
Sales—$4Mil
19,800 sq ft site, Distrib.—Intl.
Privately owned sub-S corp.
ISO rating—9001:2008
AKA: Brujan, Inc.

**CRYSTEX COMPOSITES, LLC**
125 Clifton Blvd. (07011)
**Phone—(973) 779-8866**
Fax—(973) 779-2013
www.crystexllc.com
Email—info@crystexllc.com
Pres., CEO—George Flores
V.-P., Opers.—Delvis Flores
Dir., Engrg. & Sales—Mike Brown
Hum. Res. Mgr.—Bridget Rivers
SIC—3299; 3264; Machinable &
moldable inorganic glass-mica
ceramics & stand-off insulators;
Brand name—Mykroy; Mycalex;
Mycalex Insulators
Employs—35; Estab.—2003
Sales—$1Mil-$5Mil
82,000 sq ft site, Distrib.—Intl.
Limited Liability Company
ISO rating—9001:2008

**CUSTOM & WASMUND BINDERY**
9 Sheridan Ave. (07011)
**Phone—(973) 815-1400**
National—(800) 229-6600
Fax—(973) 815-1439
www.cwbindery.com
Email—custombb@aol.com
Pres.—Lance Belostock
V.-P.—S. Belostock
Shpg. Mgr.—Glen Ong
Duplication Mgr.—Jamie Mitchel
SIC—2789; NAICS—323121;
Bookbinding & duplication
services
Employs—11; Estab.—1994
Sales—$500,000-$1Mil
Distrib.—Intl.
Privately owned corporation

**DATA DELAY DEVICES, INC.**
3 Mount Prospect Ave. (07013)
**Phone—(973) 773-2299**
Fax—(973) 773-9672
www.datadelay.com
Email—sales@datadelay.com
Pres.—Nino Lupi
GM & Sales Mgr.—Paul Kuper
Qual. Control Mgr.—Anthony
Domboroczky
Engrg. Mgr.—Victor Lupi

SIC—3679; Electronic
components, timing devices &
delay lines
Employs—8; Estab.—1964
12,000 sq ft site, Distrib.—Intl.
Privately owned sub-S corp.

**DELGEN PRESS, INC.**
250 Delawanna Ave. (07014)
**Phone—(973) 472-2266**
Fax—(973) 472-2276
www.delgenpress.com
Email—delgen.press@verizon.net
Pres.—Gregory E. Tolve
Off. Mgr.—Colleen Nielsen
SIC—2759; NAICS—323100;
Commercial printing
Employs—5; Estab.—1957
Sales—$500,000-$1Mil
Distrib.—Regional
Privately owned corporation

**DIKEMAN LAMINATING CORP.**
181 Sargeant Ave. (07013)
**Phone—(973) 473-5696**
Fax—(973) 473-2540
www.dikemanlaminating.com
Email—dikemanlam@aol.com
Pres.—Jeff Snyder
SIC—2679; 3083; NAICS—
326130; Corporate headquarters
& UV coating & film laminating
Employs—36; Estab.—1949
Sales—$5Mil-$10Mil (est)
Distrib.—Regional
Privately owned corporation

†**DRISCOLL FOODS**
174 Delawanna Ave. (07014)
**Phone—(973) 672-9400**
National—(877) 593-6637
Fax—(973) 883-8816
www.driscollfoods.com
Email—sales@driscollfoods.com
Pres.—Tim Driscoll
V.-P.—Ron Pereen
Sales Mgr.—John Levatino
Cust. Serv. Mgr.—Patty Volk
Whse. Mgr.—Helder Coelho
Jr. Accountant—Sapna Miah
SIC—5141; 5146; 5147; 5113;
Distributor of foodservice
products, including frozen foods,
fresh meats, poultry & fish,
produce, dairy, cleaning
supplies & paper goods
Employs—300; Estab.—1971
Distrib.—National
Privately owned corporation

**DRITAC FLOORING PRODUCTS, LLC**
60 Webro Rd. (07012)
**Phone—(973) 614-9000**
National—(800) 394-9310
Fax—(973) 614-9099
www.dritac.com
Email—info@dritac.com
Pres.—Yale Block
Ex. V.-P.—Myrna Block
V.-P., Sales—Chuck Hall
Dir., Mktg.—John Lio
SIC—2891; 2851; NAICS—
325520; Eco-friendly industrial
adhesives & coatings for the
leather & wood flooring
industries
Employs—20; Estab.—1960
Sales—$5Mil-$10Mil
Distrib.—Intl.

**DRIVE LINE SERVICE OF NEW JERSEY, INC.**
622 U.S. Highway 46 (07013)
**Phone—(973) 473-7900**
Fax—(973) 253-7132
www.drivelinenj.com
Email—drivelineservice@
hotmail.com
Pres.—Emmett Acocella

**GEOGRAPHICAL**

## Clifton—(cont.)

SIC—3714; *Automotive drive shafts*
Employs—3; Estab.—1980
Sales—$500,000-$1Mil
3,500 sq ft site, Distrib.—Regional
Sole ownership

**DYE INTO PRINT, INC.**
167 Fornelius Ave. (07013)
**Phone—(973) 772-8019**
National—(800) 422-2180
Fax—(973) 772-6519
www.dyeintoprint.com
Email—sales@dyeintoprint.com
Pres.—Mathew Lederman
Sales Mgr.—Agnes Witko
SIC—2269; 2399; NAICS—313300; *Wide-format dye sublimation textile & vinyl fabric printing & finished textile products, including banners, flags, backdrops, curtains & stage skirting*
Employs—62; Estab.—1999
Sales—$5Mil-$10Mil (est)
60,000 sq ft site, Distrib.—National
AKA: Something Different Linen

**DYNAMETRIC TOOL CO.**
27 Somerset Pl. (07012)
**Phone—(973) 471-8009**
Fax—(973) 471-8225
www.dynametrictool.com
Email—dynametric@optonline.net
Pres.—Frank Csapo
SIC—3599; *Precision machining job shop*
Employs—4; Estab.—1977
Sales—$150,000
6,000 sq ft site, Distrib.—National
Privately owned corporation

**DYNAMIC PRINTING & GRAPHICS, INC.**
250 Delawanna Ave. (07014)
**Phone—(973) 473-7177**
National—(877) 878-8088
Fax—(973) 473-7595
www.dynamic-inc.com
Email—lou@dynamic-inc.com
Pres., CEO—Lou Mascola
V-P., R & D & Hum. Res. & IT Mgr.—Paul Janacek
MIS & Off. Mgr.—Paola Janacek
Fin. Mgr.—Ira Geller
SIC—2752; 2796; 2791; NAICS—323122; *Offset printing, color separations & typesetting*
Employs—7; Estab.—1992
Sales—$1Mil-$2.5Mil
7,500 sq ft site, Distrib.—Local
Privately owned corporation

**E & M BINDERY, INC.**
11 Peekay Dr. (07014)
**Phone—(973) 777-9300**
National—(800) 736-2463
Fax—(973) 777-7991
www.embindery.com
Email—gary@embindery.com
Pres.—Gary Markovits
GM—Russell Starling
Plt. Mgr.—Deokumar Motiram
Hum. Res. Mgr.—Nakeisha Perea
Shpg. Mgr.—Andy Feierstein
Cust. Serv. Rep.—Donna Gassit
Estimator—Ken Deveo
SIC—2789; NAICS—323121; *Bookbinding*
Employs—100; Estab.—1963
Sales—$1Mil-$5Mil
50,000 sq ft site, Distrib.—Regional
Privately owned corporation

**E N G SCIENTIFIC, INC.**
82 Industrial St. E. (07012)
**Phone—(973) 472-7200**
National—(800) 922-0223
Fax—(973) 472-9460
www.engscientific.com
Email—engscientific@aol.com
Pres., CEO—Henry Eng
Lab Mgr.—Jane F. Purdy
Admn. Exec.—Kathy Pagani
SIC—2835; NAICS—325100; *Clinical diagnostic stains & reagents*
Employs—5; Estab.—1974
Sales—$800,000
11,000 sq ft site, Distrib.—Intl.
Privately owned corporation
AKA: A J P Scientific, Inc.

**ECSI INTERNATIONAL, INC.**
790 Bloomfield Ave., Bldg. C-1 (07012)
**Phone—(973) 574-8555**
Fax—(973) 574-8562
www.anti-terrorism.com
Email—ecsi@anti-terrorism.com
Pres., CEO—Arthur Birch
V-P., Proj.—Thomas Isdanavich
Dir., Sales & Mktg.—Richard Stern
IT Mgr. & Proj. Engr.—Yaser Hassan
Hum. Res. & Off. Mgr.—Natalie Schneider
Bookkeeper—Angie Foley
SIC—3651; 3827; NAICS—334310; *Infrared perimeter & intrusion detection systems*
Employs—24; Estab.—1976
13,000 sq ft site, Distrib.—Intl.
Privately owned sub-S corp.

**ELECTRO LIFT, INC.**
204 Sargeant Ave. (07013)
**Phone—(973) 471-0204**
National—(800) 338-9951
Fax—(973) 471-2814
www.electrolift.com
Email—info@electrolift.com
Pres.—David Erenstoft
Dir., Opers.—Deborah Erenstoft
MIS Mgr.—Steve Pilione
Administrator—Charlotte Grimes
Sales Rep.—George Davis
SIC—3537; *Material handling equipment*
Employs—30; Estab.—1932
25,000 sq ft site, Distrib.—Intl.
Privately owned sub-S corp.

**EONSMOKE, LLC (H Q)**
1500 Main Ave., Ste. 2 (07011)
**Phone—(800) 616-3711**
www.eonsmoke.com
Email—customerservice@eonsmoke.com
CFO—Gregory Grishayev
SIC—2111; 3699; *Company headquarters; electronic cigarettes, vapor products & accessories (mfg. subcontracted); Brand name—Eonsmoke; Miami Cigs; Spirit Vapor*
Employs—7; Estab.—2011
6,800 sq ft site, Distrib.—National
Limited Liability Company

**†ERIKA RECORD, LLC**
37 Atlantic Way (07012)
**Phone—(973) 614-8500**
National—(800) 682-8203
Fax—(973) 614-8503
www.erikarecord.com
Email—max@erikarecord.com
GM—Max Oehler
Sales Mgr.—Craig Kominiak
Sales Mgr.—Brian Woods
Sales Mgr.—Chris Houle
Financial Mgr.—Dan DaRocha

SIC—5046; *Wholesaler of commercial baking equipment, including ovens, mixers, cookie machines, roll & bread machines, bread, roll & cake slicers & dough sheeters; Brand name—ERIKA; KRUMBEIN; FORMATIC; MONO; NOVAPAN; EDHARD; CIBERPAN; JANSSEN*
Employs—10; Estab.—1991
Sales—$5Mil
8,500 sq ft site, Distrib.—Intl.
Privately owned partnership

**EXCELLENT PRINTING & GRAPHICS**
333 Hazel St. (07011)
**Phone—(973) 773-6661**
Fax—(973) 773-7602
www.excellent-printing.com
Owner & Hum. Res. Mgr.—Monty Abelghani
SIC—2759; *Commercial printing*
Employs—15
Sales—$1Mil-$2.5Mil (est)
Distrib.—National
Privately owned corporation

**EXELIS, INC.**
77 River Rd. (07014)
**Phone—(973) 284-0123**
Fax—(973) 284-4122
www.exelisinc.com
Email—media@exelisinc.com
Pres.—Rich Sorelle
V-P., Opers.—Arthur Smedberg
V-P., Hum. Res.—Rachelle Tucci
V-P., Strategy & Tech.—Mitchell Friedman
Dir., Comms.—Courtney Reynolds
Mktg. Comms. Mgr.—John C. Dench
Prod. Support Coord.—Ed Palacio
SIC—3812; 3669; 3663; NAICS—334511; *Aircraft self-protection, communications, radar & force protection systems, under sea sensors & sonar, reconnaissance & surveillance systems, aircraft composite components & weapon release systems*
Employs—1150
Sales—$2.1Bil
Distrib.—Intl.
Publicly owned corporation
ISO rating—9002

**FASTENATION, INC.**
120 Brighton Rd., Ste. 2 (07012)
**Phone—(973) 591-1277**
National—(800) 876-9922
Fax—(973) 591-1443
www.fastenation.com
Email—sales@fastenation.com
Owner & CEO—Jayne Petak
Ex. V-P.—David Petak
V-P.—Justin Ferdinand
SIC—3965; 2891; *Manufacturer & distributor of hook-&-loop & specialty fasteners, adhesive products, glue dots & foam tapes*
Employs—22; Estab.—1997
Distrib.—Intl.
Privately owned sub-S corp.

**FEDERAL DIRECT (H Q)**
95 Main Ave., Ste. 2 (07014-1749)
**Phone—(973) 667-9800**
National—(800) 927-5123
Fax—(973) 667-1677
www.feddirect.com
Email—sales@feddirect.com
CEO—Bernie Steins
Pres.—Angela Stubbs
COO—Bill Evans
IT Mgr.—Jim Von Dollen
Dir., Document Mgmt. & Cust. Serv. Mgr.—Sandra LoManto

SIC—2759; 2752; 2761; 2789; *Company headquarters; direct marketing services, including direct mail, digital & offset printing, business forms & fulfillment services*
Employs—45; Estab.—1942
Sales—$25Mil
Distrib.—National
Privately owned sub-S corp.

**†FERGUSON ENTERPRISES**
Div. of Ferguson Enterprises, Inc.
835 Bloomfield Ave. (07012)
**Phone—(973) 614-9464**
Fax—(973) 955-1794
www.ferguson.com
Email—joseph.proctor@ferguson.com
Br. Mgr.—Joseph Proctor
SIC—5074; *Wholesaler of industrial plumbing supplies, including PVC & metal pipe, valves, fittings & controls*
Employs—8; Estab.—2003
Distrib.—Local
Publicly owned corporation
Parent co.—Ferguson Enterprises, Inc., Newport News, VA
Phone—(757) 874-7795
See Parent Co. Section for full profile.

**FERROUS SAW WORKS**
345 Lakeview Ave. (07011)
**Phone—(973) 513-3936**
Fax—(973) 405-6066
Owner—Dominic Farino, Jr.
SIC—3541; 3425; NAICS—333512; *High-speed segmental & friction saws & blades*
Employs—1; Estab.—2005
Sales—$500,000-$1Mil
7,000 sq ft site, Distrib.—Regional
Sole ownership

**FINE ORGANICS CORP.**
420 Kuller Rd., P.O. Box 2277 (07015)
**Phone—(973) 478-1000**
National—(800) 526-7480
Fax—(973) 478-6120
www.fineorganicscorp.com
Email—custservice@fineorganicscorp.com
Pres., CEO & COO—Gary F. Straub
V-P.—Joseph Howanitz
Sales Mgr.—Lew Goldberg
Hum. Res. Mgr.—Barbara Haas
Cust. Serv. Mgr.—Dennis Esposito
SIC—2865; 2899; NAICS—325100; *Industrial chemical cleaning compounds*
Employs—14; Estab.—1939
Distrib.—Intl.
Privately owned corporation

**FORREST MFG. CO., INC.**
457 River Rd. (07014)
**Phone—(973) 473-5236**
National—(800) 733-7111
Fax—(973) 471-3333
www.forrestblades.com
Email—sales@forrestman.com
Pres.—James D. Forrest
V-P. & Hum. Res. Mgr.—Jay D. Forrest
Sales Mgr.—Tony Ferrato
SIC—3425; NAICS—332213; *Saw blades*
Employs—33; Estab.—1946
Sales—$5Mil-$10Mil
17,400 sq ft site, Distrib.—National
Privately owned sub-S corp.

**FRAGRANCE RESOURCES, INC.**
620 Route 3 W. (07014)
Mail addr: P.O. Box 4277, Clifton (07012)
**Phone—(973) 777-2979**
Fax—(973) 458-5234
www.fragranceresources.com
Email—clifton@fragranceresources.com

# Clifton—(cont.)

Mktg. Mgr.—Michael Simpson
SIC—2844; NAICS—325600;
*Corporate headquarters & perfumes*
Employs—5; Estab.—1987
Company-wide: 45
Distrib.—Intl.

## FUCHS AUDIO TECHNOLOGY, LLC

407 Getty Ave., 2nd Fl. (07011-2121)
**Phone—(973) 772-4420**
Fax—(973) 772-4460
www.fuchsaudio.com
Email—info@fuchsaudio.com
Pres.—Annette Fuchs
V.-P.—Andy Fuchs
SIC—3651; 3931; NAICS—334310; *Tube guitar & bass amplifiers, speaker cabinets, musical effects pedals & accessories, including modifications & repairs; Brand name—FUCHS; PLUSH FX PEDALS; FEITON SPEAKER CABINETS*
Employs—10; Estab.—1999
Sales—$1Mil-$2.5Mil
5,000 sq ft site, Distrib.—Intl.
Limited Liability Company

## FUJITEC AMERICA INC., NEW YORK REGION

Div. of Fujitec America, Inc.
215 Entin Rd. (07014)
**Phone—(973) 330-0100**
National—(800) 385-4832
Fax—(973) 365-4027
www.fujitecamerica.com
Email—sales@fujitecamerica.com
Opers. Mgr.—Joseph Smith
Payroll Admn.—Trish Pietrowitz
SIC—3534; NAICS—333921; *Elevators & escalators*
Employs—100; Estab.—2008
Sales—$10Mil-$25Mil (est)
Distrib.—Regional
Privately owned corporation
Parent co.—Fujitec America, Inc., Mason, OH
  Phone—(513) 932-8000
  See Parent Co. Section for full profile.

## GENAVITE, LLC

235 Clifton Blvd. (07011)
**Phone—(973) 779-1532**
Fax—(201) 343-3512
Owner—Bharat Patel
Lead Operator—Kirit Mistry
SIC—2834; NAICS—325412; *Vitamin coatings*
Employs—10; Estab.—1995
Sales—$5Mil-$10Mil (est)
Distrib.—Local
Limited Liability Company

## †GLEN MILLS INC.

220 Delawanna Ave. (07014)
**Phone—(973) 777-0777**
Fax—(973) 777-0070
www.glenmills.com
Email—staff@glenmills.com
Pres.—Peter Kendall
Dir.—S. Goldberg
Sr. Sales Engr.—E. Szwerc
Sales Exec.—D. Ahrens

SIC—5049; 3556; 3569; 3821; *Distributor of sample preparation laboratory equipment, including grinding beads & balls, sieves, wet & dry milling equipment & bioreactors for lab professionals, researchers & engineers; Brand name—Turbula®; Dyno®-Mill; Retsch; Zellwerk; Polytron; Z®RP; Bachofen; WAB; French Press G-M®*
Employs—10; Estab.—1980
Sales—over $5Mil
10,000 sq ft site, Distrib.—Intl.
Privately owned corporation
ISO rating—9002
AKA: IMPANDEX INC.

## GLOBE INDUSTRIES CORP.

48 Industrial St. W. (07012-1712)
**Phone—(973) 992-8990**
Pres.—Mark Melillo
SIC—3599; *Precision machining job shop*
Employs—7; Estab.—2000
Sales—$500,000-$1Mil (est)
Distrib.—Regional
Privately owned corporation

## GLUE-FOLD, INC., DIV. OF PERFECT FINISHING, INC.

Div. of Perfect Finishing, Inc.
40 Webro Rd. (07012)
**Phone—(973) 575-8400**
Fax—(973) 575-8401
www.gluefold.com
Email—info@gluefold.com
CFO—Isabel Garcia
SIC—2789; NAICS—323121; *Gluing, including affixing, attaching, pattern gluing, die cutting, laminating & converting of business forms, envelopes, labels, cards & two-way mailers for the trade*
Employs—6; Estab.—1973
12,000 sq ft site, Distrib.—National
Privately owned corporation
Parent co.—Perfect Finishing, Inc., Clifton, NJ
  Phone—(973) 472-7400
  See Parent Co. Section for full profile.

## GMPC PRINTING

1 Trenton Ave. (07011)
**Phone—(973) 894-1500**
Fax—(973) 546-6116
www.gmpcprinting.com
Email—info@gmpcprinting.com
Principal—Joseph Mulligan
Principal—Joe Genua
SIC—2752; 2791; NAICS—323122; *Offset printing & typesetting*
Employs—18; Estab.—1987
Sales—$2.6Mil-$5Mil
20,000 sq ft site, Distrib.—Regional
Privately owned corporation

## GOURMET DESSERT OUTLET, LLC

851 Van Houten Ave. (07013)
**Phone—(973) 815-1111**
Fax—(973) 815-1221
www.gdodesserts.com
Email—info@gdodesserts.com
Owner—Ezzat Tadros
SIC—2051; 2052; NAICS—311812; *Gourmet bakery products, including cakes & cookies*
Employs—6; Estab.—2004
Sales—$500,000-$1Mil
Distrib.—Local
Limited Liability Company

## GRAPHIC EXPRESS MENU CO., INC.

Div. of Centiv Services, LLC
200 Clifton Blvd., Ste. 6 (07011)
**Phone—(973) 685-0022**
Fax—(973) 685-0020
www.graphicexpressmenu.com
Email—sales@graphicexpressmenu.com

Cust. Serv. Rep.—Anissa High
Cust. Rep.—Kristina Smith
SIC—2759; 3089; NAICS—323100; *Menu covers*
Employs—30; Estab.—1994
Distrib.—National
AKA: Brand Muscle
Parent co.—Centiv Services, LLC, Chicago, IL
  Phone—(312) 235-5700
  See Parent Co. Section for full profile.

## HANDI-HUT, INC.

3 Grunwald St. *(07013)*
**Phone—(973) 614-1800**
  (800) 603-6635
Fax—(973) 614-8011
www.handi-hut.com
Email—staff@handi-hut.com
Pres.—Melvin Cohen
V.-P.—John S. Cozza
Administrator—Mary Cardy
SIC—3355; 3444; NAICS—331319; *Smoking & passenger waiting shelters, covered walkways, entrance vestibules & canopies; Brand name—Handi Hut*
Employs—25; Estab.—1971
Sales—$10Mil-$25Mil (est)
50,000 sq ft site, Distrib.—National
Privately owned corporation

## HIEMER & CO., EDWARD W.

141 Wabash Ave. (07011)
**Phone—(973) 772-5081**
Fax—(973) 772-0325
www.hiemco.com
Email—jevanwie@hiemco.com
Pres.—Judith Van Wie
V.-P.—James Van Wie
SIC—3231; NAICS—327215; *Fabrication & restoration of stained glass windows & etched & faceted glass, including aluminum frame replacement*
Employs—10; Estab.—1931
Sales—$500,000-$1Mil
Distrib.—National
Privately owned sub-S corp.

## HOWARD, INC., JAMES

1500 Main Ave., Ste. 3 (07011)
**Phone—(973) 928-1560**
Fax—(973) 928-1559
www.jameshoward.com
Email—info@jameshoward.com
Pres., CEO—Timothy James
SIC—2759; *Commercial & digital printing*
Employs—15
Sales—$1Mil-$2.5Mil (est)
Privately owned corporation

## HYGRADE BUSINESS GROUP, INC.

232 Entin Rd., P.O. Box 1099 (07014)
**Phone—(973) 249-6700**
National—(800) 836-7714
Fax—(973) 249-6109
www.hygradebusiness.com
Email—sales@hygradebusiness.com
Pres., CEO—Victor Albetta
CFO—Adam Horvath
COO—Joe Molinelli
SIC—2761; 2754; 2752; 3993; NAICS—323116; *Offset, digital & color printing of business forms, labels, promotional products & flexible packaging, including marketing & fulfillment services*
Employs—40; Estab.—1920
Sales—$25Mil
Distrib.—Regional
Privately owned corporation

## INNOVATIVE COSMETICS, INC.

270 Clifton Blvd. (07011)
Mail addr: 61 Kuller Rd., Clifton (07011)
**Phone—(973) 773-7700**
Fax—(973) 773-7007
www.incoco.com

Pres.—F. A. Park
SIC—2844; NAICS—325600; *Cosmetics*
Employs—40; Estab.—2006
Sales—$500,000-$1Mil
Distrib.—National
Privately owned corporation

## IN-PAK SERVICES, INC.

474 Getty Ave. (07011)
**Phone—(973) 595-5250**
Fax—(973) 595-1869
Pres.—Brian Billes
V.-P.—Greg Regina
Prodn. Mgr.—Elizabeth Wang
SIC—2211; NAICS—314912; *Cotton-cloth binder slip covers*
Employs—20; Estab.—1992
Sales—$500,000-$1Mil
Distrib.—National
Privately owned corporation
AKA: Walden Lang In-Pak

## INTERNATIONAL DELIGHTS BAKERY CO.

230 Brighton Rd. (07012)
**Phone—(973) 928-5582**
Fax—(973) 928-5589
www.intdelights.com
Email—info@intdelights.com
Pres.—Spiro Sayegh
SIC—2051; NAICS—311812; *Bakery products*
Employs—50
Privately owned corporation

## INTERNATIONAL VEILING CORP.

244 Hazel St., 2nd Fl. (07011)
**Phone—(973) 772-3100**
Fax—(973) 772-3863
V.-P.—David Wiley
Cust. Serv. Mgr.—Pamela Post
Bookkeeper—Debbie Wiley
SIC—2258; *Lace & net dyeing & finishing*
Employs—49; Estab.—1904
Distrib.—Intl.
Privately owned corporation

## J M MACHINE CO., LLC

5 Central Ave., Ste. 2, P.O. Box 1863 (07011)
**Phone—(973) 253-2188**
Fax—(973) 546-7727
Email—jmmachineshop@aol.com
Owner—Jerry Mazur
SIC—3599; *General machining job shop*
Employs—2; Estab.—1991
Sales—under $500,000 (est)
1,800 sq ft site, Distrib.—Local
Limited Liability Company

## JDS GRAPHICS, INC.

Div. of Kay Printing Co.
220 Entin Rd. (07014)
**Phone—(973) 330-3300**
Fax—(973) 330-3302
www.jdsgraphics.com
Email—bgenerale@jdsgraphics.com
Pres.—Debra Yuran
CFO—Bob Generale
V.-P.—Sheryl Heller
SIC—2759; NAICS—323100; *Commercial printing*
Employs—5; Estab.—1977
Distrib.—National
Privately owned corporation
Parent co.—Kay Printing Co., Clifton, NJ
  Phone—(973) 330-3000
  See Parent Co. Section for full profile.

## K & J ACCESSORIES, INC.

25 Ridgewood Rd. (07012)
**Phone—(973) 777-6741**
Fax—(973) 591-1191
Pres.—Karen Dicky
Sales Mgr.—Jacob Duma

GEOGRAPHICAL

## Clifton—(cont.)

SIC—3993; *Electric scoreboards*
Employs—2; Estab.—1999
Sales—under $500,000
Distrib.—Local
Privately owned corporation

### KAY PRINTING CO.

220 Entin Rd. (07014)
**Phone—(973) 330-3000**
Fax—(973) 330-3301
www.kayprinting.com
Email—info@kayprinting.com
Ptnr. & Pres.—Richard Kirschenbaum
Ptnr. & V-P.—Charlie Tuminello
V-P., Sales—Steven Tuminello
V-P.—Michael Costello
V-P.—Jeffrey Kirschenbaum
Cont.—Robert Generale
Sales Mgr.—Myron Kowal
SIC—2752; NAICS—323100; *Company headquarters & commercial printing*
Employs—60; Estab.—1974
Sales—$14.5Mil
50,000 sq ft site, Distrib.—National
Privately owned sub-S corp.

### LAMART CORP.

16 Richmond St. (07011)
Mail addr: P.O. Box 1648, Clifton (07015)
**Phone—(973) 772-6262**
Fax—(973) 772-3673
www.lamartcorp.com
Email—ahirsh@lamartcorp.com
Pres.—Steve Hirsh
V-P.—Alan Hirsh
Sales Mgr.—Kenneth Pace
Fin. Mgr.—Anthony Bonavita
Proj. Mgr.—Jonathan Hirsh
Logistics Mgr.—Todd Wellins
SIC—2672; NAICS—322222; *Paper coating & laminating*
Employs—80; Estab.—1956
40,000 sq ft site, Distrib.—Intl.
Privately owned corporation

### LAS PRINTING

1 Trenton Ave. (07011)
**Phone—(201) 991-5362**
Fax—(201) 991-7367
www.printparadigm.com
Email—joec@lasprinting.com
Pres.—Joe Conti
SIC—2752; 2791; NAICS—323122; *Commercial printing, electronic prepress & design*
Employs—10; Estab.—1951
6,000 sq ft site, Distrib.—National
Privately owned corporation
Also see: Minuteman Press, same loc.

### LENS CO., INC.

700 Route 46 W., Unit 7 (07013)
**Phone—(973) 546-0866**
National—(800) 546-0866
Fax—(973) 546-5367
www.lensco.net
Email—thelenscompany@aol.com
COO, Hum. Res. Mgr.—Prasad Umarye
Off. Mgr.—Amrita Umarye
SIC—3851; NAICS—339100; *Glass lenses*
Employs—4; Estab.—1989
Sales—$500,000-$1Mil
4,500 sq ft site, Distrib.—Intl.
Privately owned corporation

### LUBRIZOL ADVANCED MATERIALS, INC.

Div. of Lubrizol Corp.
1 Industrial W. (07012)
**Phone—(973) 471-1300**
Fax—(973) 471-3783
www.lubrizol.com
Email—info@lubrizol.com
Cont.—Jack Lewis
Plt. Mgr.—Nick Paolazzi
SIC—2869; 2844; NAICS—325600; *Personal care & industrial organic chemicals*
Employs—15; Estab.—1935
30,000 sq ft site, Distrib.—Intl.
Publicly owned corporation
AKA: Lubrizol Corp., The
Parent co.—Lubrizol Corp., Wickliffe, OH
Phone—(440) 943-4200
See Parent Co. Section for full profile.

### M & G FOOD, INC.

1295 Main Ave. (07011)
**Phone—(973) 340-0340**
www.homemadepirogi.com
Pres.—Michael Dutch
SIC—2038; NAICS—311412; *Homemade fresh & frozen pierogies*
Employs—6; Estab.—1986
Sales—under $500,000
Distrib.—Regional
Privately owned corporation

### M & P MACHINERY

1500 Main Ave., Ste. 31 (07011)
**Phone—(973) 253-1004**
Fax—(973) 253-1007
Email—mpmachinery@hotmail.com
Ptnr.—Marian Szuba
Ptnr.—Piotr Szuba
SIC—3552; *Rebuilt textile machinery & repair services*
Employs—2; Estab.—2004
Sales—$100,000
3,000 sq ft site, Distrib.—Local
Limited Liability Company

### MACTEX, LLC

489-A Getty Ave. (07011)
**Phone—(973) 340-3131**
Fax—(973) 340-3737
www.mactexinc.com
Email—mactex@yahoo.com
Owner—Rory McNamara
SIC—2241; *Tubular woven fabrics*
Employs—12; Estab.—1997
Sales—$6Mil-$10Mil
Distrib.—Local
Limited Liability Company

### MAJKA & SONS FUEL SERVICE, JOSEPH A.

568 Paulison Ave. (07011)
**Phone—(973) 777-8484**
Fax—(973) 777-0834
www.majkaoil.com
Email—majkaoil@gmail.com
Pres., GM—Scott Majka
SIC—1311; NAICS—211111; *Oil production*
Employs—15; Estab.—1971
Distrib.—Local
Sole ownership

### MARK LITHOGRAPHY, INC.

220 Entin Rd. (07014)
**Phone—(973) 538-5557**
Fax—(973) 330-3301
www.kmmedia.com
Email—info@kayprinting.com
Pres.—Charles Tumminello
Sales Mgr.—Fred Golden
IT Mgr.—Rob Natt
SIC—2752; 2796; NAICS—323122; *Offset printing & color separations*
Employs—35; Estab.—1990
27,000 sq ft site, Distrib.—National
Privately owned corporation

### MASTER BUSINESS FORMS CO.

195 Allwood Rd. (07012)
**Phone—(973) 594-8743**
National—(800) 216-1844
Fax—(973) 594-8748
www.masterbusinessforms.com
Email—print@masterbusinessforms.com
Owner & Pres.—Art Moloughney
V-P., Opers.—Mark Hennessey
Off. Mgr.—Pat Lamping
SIC—2761; 2759; NAICS—323116; *Business forms & digital printing*
Employs—50; Estab.—1989
Sales—$1Mil-$5Mil
13,000 sq ft site, Distrib.—Local
Privately owned corporation

### MASTERS INTERIORS, INC.

1500 Main Ave. (07011)
**Phone—(973) 253-0784**
Fax—(973) 253-0786
www.averyboardman.com
Email—lgentile@averyboardman.com
Owner—Kevin Costello
Pres.—Albert de Matteo
Hum. Res. Mgr.—Breda Costello
SIC—2512; 2515; NAICS—337121; *Upholstered wooden furniture, sofas & sofa beds*
Employs—30; Estab.—1984
Sales—$2.5Mil-$5Mil (est)
Distrib.—Regional
Privately owned corporation

### MAX GURTMAN & SONS, INC.

622 Lexington Ave. (07011)
Mail addr: P.O. Box 1849, Clifton (07015)
**Phone—(973) 478-7000**
Fax—(973) 478-0601
Shop Mgr.—Peter Dino
Bookkeeper—Susan Burleigh
SIC—3444; *Sheet metal fabrication*
Employs—4; Estab.—1925
Sales—under $500,000
Distrib.—Local
Privately owned corporation

### MEDIAGRAPHICS, INC.

25 Somerset Pl. (07012)
**Phone—(973) 777-2202**
Fax—(973) 777-2232
www.mediagraphics.net
Email—media55@aol.com
Pres.—Marge Offutt
V-P., Opers.—Jim Offutt
SIC—2752; 2759; NAICS—323100; *Large-format color printing of smart posters, video displays, construction & retail signage & event & golf graphics & magnets for displays & trade show booths*
Employs—12; Estab.—1988
7,000 sq ft site, Distrib.—Intl.
Privately owned corporation

### MERLIN GRAPHICS, INC.

194 Christie Ave. (07011)
**Phone—(201) 795-3330**
Fax—(973) 340-7070
www.merlingraphics.biz
Email—joe@merlingraphics.biz
Pres.—Joan Barbini
V-P.—Joseph Barbini
SIC—2759; NAICS—323100; *Commercial, business card & letterhead printing*
Employs—2; Estab.—1954
Sales—$500,000-$1Mil
Distrib.—National
Privately owned corporation

### METROPOLE, INC.

214 Clifton Blvd. (07011)
**Phone—(973) 473-2727**
Fax—(973) 473-2857
www.metropoleinc.com
Email—d.fin@metropoleinc.com
Pres.—David Finlay
SIC—3299; 3281; 3089; 3312; *Custom exterior terra cotta, granite, limestone, plastic, wood & steel architecture's molded forms & ornaments for facades of buildings & public monuments*
Employs—10; Estab.—1997
Sales—$500,000-$1Mil
Distrib.—Local
Sole ownership

### MINUTEMAN PRESS

1 Trenton Ave. (07011)
**Phone—(973) 894-1500**
(201) 659-9277
Fax—(973) 546-6116
www.minutemanpressnj.com
Email—info@minutemanpressnj.com
Principal—Joseph Mulligan
Principal—Joseph Genua
SIC—2752; 2759; 3993; 2675; NAICS—323100; *Offset & digital printing, promotional products, wide-format signs & banners, mailing services, die-cutting, custom packaging & graphic design & marketing*
Employs—18; Estab.—1987
Sales—$2.5Mil-$5Mil
20,000 sq ft site, Distrib.—Regional
Privately owned corporation
AKA: LAS Printing, same loc.

### NARAD MARKETING CORPORATION

200 Piaget Ave. (07011)
Mail addr: P.O. Box 1817, Clifton (07015-1817)
**Phone—(973) 881-0206**
(973) 223-4735
Fax—(973) 881-0207
www.naradmarketing.com
Email—nari@naradmarketing.com
Pres.—Narie Rekha
SIC—2865; 2861; 2869; NAICS—325191; *Synthetic organic & leak detection dyes, pure chemicals & herbal extracts; Brand name—Rekhaoil; Rekhaplast; Rekhafluor*
Employs—10; Estab.—1998
Sales—$5Mil-$10Mil
80,000 sq ft site, Distrib.—Intl.
Privately owned sub-S corp.

### †NATIONAL PUBLIC SEATING CORP.

149 Entin Rd. (07014)
**Phone—(973) 594-1100**
National—(800) 261-4112
Fax—(973) 594-1500
www.nationalpublicseating.com
Email—info@nationalpublicseating.com
Pres., Dir., Sales—Barry Stauber
Off. Mgr.—Mary Connolly
SIC—5021; 5084; *Distributor of upholstered & plastic stack chairs, steel, plastic & padded folding chairs, blow molded tables & chairs & storage dollies for educational, government & commercial institutional markets*
Employs—80; Estab.—1997
Distrib.—National
Privately owned corporation
Also see: Oklahoma Sound Corp., same loc.

### NEW JERSEY WIRE CLOTH CO., INC.

55 Park Slope (07011)
**Phone—(973) 340-0101**
Fax—(973) 340-9109
www.njwirecloth.com
Email—john@njwirecloth.com
Pres.—John Rafanello
SIC—3357; 3315; *Fine sewn, pin & brazed seams, endless back woven, screen packs & circles & screen & diaper belts for nonwoven machinery, including polyester, stainless steel & bronze spiral link water & press belts*
Employs—7; Estab.—1950
Sales—$1Mil-$5Mil
8,000 sq ft site, Distrib.—Intl.
Privately owned sub-S corp.

### NEWARK WIRE CLOTH CO., INC.

160 Fornelius Ave. (07013)
**Phone—(973) 778-4478**
(800) 221-0392
Fax—(973) 778-4481

## Clifton—(cont.)

www.newarkwire.com
Email—info@newarkwire.com
Pres.—Richard W. Campbell
V-P.—James L. Campbell
V-P.—Robert D. Lucki
SIC—3496; *Roll & cut wire cloth & fabricated wire cloth parts, including strainers, filters, baskets, test sieves, filter leaves, vessel internals & wedge wire; Brand name—SaniClean Strainers; Superlasieves*
Employs—30; Estab.—1911
Sales—$5Mil
30,000 sq ft site, Distrib.—Intl.
Privately owned sub-S corp.
ISO rating—9001:2008

**NORGUS SILK SCREEN CO.**
58 Sylvan Ave. (07011)
**Phone—(973) 365-0600**
National—(866) 442-7744
Fax—(973) 365-2749
www.gasolineadvertising.com
Email—info@gasolineadvertising.com
Owner & Pres.—Sanjay Thakker
Off. Mgr.—Shivani Papel
SIC—2759; 2396; 3499; NAICS—323100; *Screen, cylindrical, digital & large-format printing of price signs, banners, decals & graphics, including laser engraving, binding & die cutting for gas pumps & metal fabrication of sign frames, brackets & holders*
Employs—8; Estab.—1958
Sales—under $500,000
5,000 sq ft site, Distrib.—Local
Privately owned sub-S corp.
AKA: Gasoline Advertising Products

**NORTHEAST LOCK CORP.**
48 Oak St. (07014)
**Phone—(973) 777-7509**
National—(800) 524-2575
Fax—(973) 777-7551
www.northeastlock.com
Email—sales@northeastlock.com
Pres.—Kevin McCallen
Cont., Hum. Res.—Margarita Sambevski
Dir. & Manager—Shaun Polke
SIC—3429; *Lock assembly; Brand name—MEDECO; ILLINOIS LOCK; ROYAL LOCK; CCL; COMPX; PACIFIC LOCK*
Employs—30; Estab.—1956
Distrib.—Intl.
Privately owned sub-S corp.
ISO rating—9001:2000

†**NUTLEY HEATING & COOLING SUPPLY CO., INC.**
50 Page Rd. (07012)
**Phone—(973) 470-8844**
Fax—(973) 365-2171
www.nutleysupply.com
Email—richardcancelosi@nutleysupply.com
Pres.—Rick Cancelosi
V-P.—Susan Cancelosi
Pur. Mgr.—Joe Servidio
Cred. Mgr.—Karen Oliver
SIC—5075; 5074; 5084; *Corporate headquarters & distributor of HVAC equipment, boilers, radiators, industrial burners & accessories; Brand name—American Standard Heating & Air Conditioning; Weil McLain; Powerflame; A.O. Smith*
Employs—45; Estab.—1947
Distrib.—Regional
Privately owned corporation
AKA: NHCS

**OFFICE DEPOT BUSINESS SOLUTION DIV. OF NEW JERSEY**
Div. of Office Depot, Inc.
4 Brighton Rd. (07012)
**Phone—(973) 594-3000**
www.officedepot.com
Email—roberta.cramer@officedepot.com
Dir., Sales—Steve Cimilluca
Off. Mgr.—Roberta Cramer
SIC—2759; 5112; NAICS—323100; *Promotional & commercial printing & distributor of office supplies*
Employs—150
Sales—$10Mil-$25Mil (est)
Publicly owned corporation
Parent co.—Office Depot, Inc., Boca Raton, FL
Phone—(561) 438-4800
See Parent Co. Section for full profile.

**OKLAHOMA SOUND CORP.**
149 Entin Rd. (07014)
**Phone—(973) 594-9000**
Fax—(973) 594-9339
www.oklahomasound.com
Email—info@oklahomasound.com
V-P., Fin.—Barry Stauber
GM—Joe Lefkowitz
Hum. Res. Mgr.—Peggy Delvalle
Pur. Agt.—Joshua Gluck
SIC—3651; NAICS—334310; *Electronic sound systems*
Employs—30; Estab.—1982
Sales—$1Mil-$5Mil
30,000 sq ft site, Distrib.—National
Privately owned corporation
Also see: National Public Seating Corp., same loc.

**ONE SOURCE SOLUTIONS**
220 Encin Rd. (07014)
**Phone—(973) 242-4040**
Fax—(973) 242-8344
www.onesourcenj.com
Pres.—Roy Winters
V-P.—Sherri Winters
Off. Mgr.—Gwen Johnson
SIC—2752; 2791; NAICS—323122; *Offset printing & computerized typesetting*
Employs—12; Estab.—1984
Sales—$1Mil-$2.5Mil
Distrib.—Local
Privately owned corporation

**ONE STOP PACKAGING, LLC**
71-B Kingsland Ave. (07014)
**Phone—(973) 272-0170**
Fax—(973) 689-9538
www.1stoppackagingservice.com
Email—sales@1stoppackagingservice.com
Opers. Mgr.—Jason Werba
SIC—3999; *Contract packaging, including poly bagging, kitting & box service*
Employs—2; Estab.—1998
Sales—under $500,000
Distrib.—National
Limited Liability Company

†**PALLET EXPRESS, INC.**
70 Caroline Ave. (07011)
Mail addr: P.O. Box 70, Clifton (07015-0070)
**Phone—(973) 633-5858**
Fax—(973) 633-5027
Email—palletexpress@optonline.net
Pres., GM—Lenny Driesse
SIC—5085; *Distributor of wooden pallets*
Employs—7; Estab.—1998
Sales—$2Mil
Distrib.—Local
Privately owned corporation

**PALLMANN INDUSTRIES, INC.**
820 Bloomfield Ave. (07012)
**Phone—(973) 471-1450**
Fax—(973) 471-7152
www.pallmannindustries.com

Email—info@pallmannpulverizers.com
GM—Rolf Gren
Eqpt. Div. Mgr.—Kevin G. Moros
Acctg. Mgr.—Patricia Hanzo
SIC—3532; *Pulverizing & granulating machines*
Employs—12; Estab.—1961
Sales—$2.5Mil-$5Mil
50,000 sq ft site, Distrib.—Intl.
Privately owned corporation

**PARAMOUNT COSMETICS, INC.**
93 Entin Rd., Ste. 4 (07014)
**Phone—(973) 472-2323**
National—(800) 522-9880
Fax—(973) 472-5005
www.paramountcosmetics.net
Email—sales@paramountcosmetics.net
Pres.—Sanford Salzman
V-P.—Steve Schifrien
Dir., Sales—Alice Bavsa
Fin. Mgr.—Scott Mupo
SIC—2844; NAICS—325600; *Contract manufacturing & private label cosmetics & skin care products*
Employs—95; Estab.—1947
Sales—$5Mil-$10Mil
100,000 sq ft site, Distrib.—Intl.
Privately owned sub-S corp.

**PARIS LACE**
1500 Main Ave. (07011)
**Phone—(973) 478-9035**
National—(877) 599-5223
Fax—(973) 478-9186
www.parislace.com
Email—joparislace@optonline.net
Pres., Plt. Mgr.—Joseph Dickinson
SIC—2241; NAICS—313221; *Lace*
Employs—50; Estab.—1968
Distrib.—National
Privately owned corporation

†**PARK STEIN, INC.**
613 Route 46 E., P.O. Box 2399 (07013)
**Phone—(973) 340-3535**
Fax—(973) 340-9896
www.parksteinnj.com
Pres.—Steve Tendler
Off. Mgr.—Larry Freda
SIC—5093; *Wholesaler of recycled scrap metal*
Employs—28; Estab.—1984
Distrib.—Local
Privately owned corporation

**PATERSON STAMP WORKS**
Div. of American Marking Systems, Inc.
1015 Paulison Ave. (07011)
**Phone—(973) 478-5600**
Fax—(973) 478-0039
www.ams-stamps.com
Email—info@ams-stamps.com
Pres.—John Collins
Sales & Mktg. Mgr.—Ronald Cochran
SIC—3953; 3993; NAICS—339943; *Custom office & ID products, including rubber stamps, embossing seals, office signs, badges, plaques, banners, labels & tags; Brand name—Pro-mark; Xstamper*
Employs—17; Estab.—1869
Sales—$1Mil-$5Mil
8,000 sq ft site, Distrib.—National
Privately owned corporation
Parent co.—American Marking Systems, Inc., Clifton, NJ
Phone—(973) 478-5600
See Parent Co. Section for full profile.

**PERFECT FINISHING, INC.**
40 Webro Rd. (07012)
**Phone—(973) 472-7400**
Fax—(973) 472-7605
www.aladdinfinishing.com

Email—info@perfectfinishinginc.com
Co-Pres.—Bruce Flaim
Co-Pres.—Hank Ruggiero
Cont.—Elyse Stone
SIC—2675; 2789; NAICS—323121; *Corporate headquarters & paper die cutting, foil stamping, mounting & bookbinding*
Employs—50; Estab.—1970
Sales—$1Mil-$5Mil
60,000 sq ft site, Distrib.—Regional
Privately owned corporation
AKA: Aladdin Finishing

**PHYSITEMP INSTRUMENTS, INC.**
154 Huron Ave. (07013)
**Phone—(973) 779-5577**
National—(800) 452-8510
Fax—(973) 779-5954
www.physitemp.com
Email—info@physitemp.com
Pres.—Ronald Feller
V-P., Hum. Res. & IT Mgr.—Christopher Proffitt
Mktg. Mgr.—Michele Cantwell
SIC—3841; *Medical temperature measurement & control instruments*
Employs—19; Estab.—1983
5,500 sq ft site, Distrib.—Intl.
Privately owned corporation

NEW ENTRY
**POLINAS PLASTICS AMERICA, INC.**
98 Scoles Ave. (07012)
**Phone—(973) 777-8950**
www.polinas.com
Pres.—Ron Scardina
SIC—3081; *Plastic film for labels*
Employs—2
Sales—$500,000-$1Mil (est)
Distrib.—Intl.
Privately owned corporation

**POLYMER TECHNOLOGIES, INC.**
10 Clifton Blvd. (07011)
**Phone—(973) 778-9100**
Fax—(973) 778-9797
www.polymertechnologies.com
Email—info@polymertek.com
Pres.—Neal Goldenberg
Off. Mgr.—Louise Ecker
SIC—3089; *Custom plastic & metal injection molding, including modeling, prototype molds/sampling, feedstock compounding, toll sintering, production mold & material engineering & construction, product design & finite element & mold flow analysis*
Employs—70; Estab.—1987
143,000 sq ft site, Distrib.—Intl.
Privately owned corporation
AKA: PTI

**POLYTECH DESIGN, INC.**
26 W. 1st St. (07011)
**Phone—(973) 340-1390**
Fax—(973) 340-7444
www.polybelt.com
Email—info@polytechdesign.com
Pres., GM—Zak Shasha
SIC—3052; NAICS—326220; *Rubber & plastic timing belts*
Employs—13; Estab.—1992
Distrib.—National
Privately owned corporation

**PORTA-DISPLAY, INC.**
790 Bloomfield Ave., Ste. B-2 (07012)
**Phone—(973) 574-0057**
Fax—(973) 574-0059
Pres.—George Kruse
Exhibits Coord.—Aysha Kose

GEOGRAPHICAL

## Clifton—(cont.)

SIC—2541; 2542; *Convention exhibits*
Employs—2; Estab.—1965
Sales—under $500,000
Distrib.—National
Privately owned corporation

### POST EAGLE NEWSPAPER, INC.

800 Van Houten Ave. (07013)
Mail addr: P.O. Box 2127, Clifton (07015)
**Phone—(973) 473-5414**
Fax—(973) 473-3211
www.posteaglenewspaper.com
Email—posteagle@aol.com
Mng. Editor—Matt Grabowski
Editor, GM & Pur. Agt.—Christine Grabowski-Witmyer
Prodn. Mgr.—Ray Grabowski
SIC—2711; 2791; NAICS—323122; *Newspaper publishing*
Employs—3; Estab.—1963
Sales—under $500,000
Distrib.—National
Privately owned corporation

### PRECISE COMPONENTS & TOOL DESIGN, INC.

10 Clifton Blvd., Unit A-4 (07011)
**Phone—(973) 928-2928**
Email—hbenedikt@ precisecomponents.com
Pres.—Harry Benedikt
Hum. Res. Mgr.—Julie Jones
SIC—3599; 3543; NAICS—332997; *Industrial prototypes & precision machining job shop*
Employs—7; Estab.—1991
1,500 sq ft site, Distrib.—Local
Privately owned corporation

### PRECISION SAW & TOOL CORP.

56 Colfax Ave. (07013)
**Phone—(973) 773-7302**
Fax—(973) 773-0222
Pres.—James Montesano
Supervisor—Benn Deffalco
SIC—3544; NAICS—333500; *Tool & die job shop*
Employs—10; Estab.—2003
Sales—$500,000-$1Mil
Distrib.—Local
Privately owned corporation

### PREFERRED DISPLAY, INC.

310 Brighton Rd. (07012)
**Phone—(973) 405-5137**
Fax—(973) 405-5157
www.preferreddisplay.com
Email—service@ preferreddisplay.com
Pres.—Robert Rousseau
CFO—James Engler
Sales Mgr.—Bill Sysyn
Fin. Mgr.—Pat McAuley
SIC—2542; 2541; *Corporate headquarters & plastic, aluminum & wooden retail cosmetic displays, including wall units & counter displays*
Employs—250; Estab.—2005
Sales—$25Mil-$50Mil (est)
Distrib.—National
Privately owned corporation

### PRIDE GOURMET BAKERS, INC.

450 Getty Ave. (07011)
**Phone—(973) 340-3200**
Fax—(973) 340-3349
www.daisybakery.com
Email—daisybakery@yahoo.com
Owner & Pres.—Jose Cavan
Hum. Res. Mgr.—Diana Cavan
Accts. Payable Mgr.—Odalis Pena
SIC—2051; 2052; NAICS—311812; *Cakes, pastries & cookies*
Employs—50; Estab.—1999
Sales—$1Mil-$2.5Mil
Distrib.—National
Privately owned corporation
AKA: Daisy's Bakery

### PULSAR MICROWAVE CORP.

48 Industrial St. W. (07012)
**Phone—(973) 779-6262**
National—(800) 752-2790
Fax—(973) 779-2727
www.pulsarmicrowave.com
Email—sales@ pulsarmicrowave.com
Pres.—Charles Bobroski
Sales Mgr.—Patrick Claudio
Hum. Res. Mgr.—Sherry Tanbornino
SIC—3663; NAICS—334220; *Microwave components & subsystems*
Employs—25; Estab.—1987
Sales—$2.5Mil-$5Mil
1,400 sq ft site, Distrib.—Intl.
Privately owned corporation
ISO rating—9001:2008

### QUALITY INDUSTRIES, INC.

204 Getty Ave. (07011)
**Phone—(973) 478-4425**
Fax—(973) 478-0172
www.4qii.com
Email—wk@4qii.com
Pres.—Andrew Ponikowski
V-P. & Off. Mgr.—Michael Ponikowski
Prodn. Mgr.—Ziggy Maka
Off. Mgr.—Walter Kolbik
SIC—3599; 3499; 3089; *Fabrication & machining shop, including precision machining, machine building, welding, replacement machine parts rebuilding & repairing*
Employs—10; Estab.—1974
8,000 sq ft site, Distrib.—Regional
Privately owned corporation

### RANCO PRECISION SHEET METAL, INC.

40 Colorado St., P.O. Box 1101 (07014)
**Phone—(973) 472-8808**
Fax—(973) 773-0493
Email—sales@rancometal.com
Pres.—John C. Karpi, Sr.
V-P., Opers.—Longino Mendez
GM & MIS Mgr.—John Karpi, Jr.
SIC—3444; *Sheet metal fabrication & blind fasteners*
Employs—9; Estab.—1959
Sales—$500,000-$1Mil
10,000 sq ft site, Distrib.—Local
Privately owned corporation

### REGISTER LITHOGRAPHERS, LTD.

1155 Bloomfield Ave. (07012)
**Phone—(973) 916-2804**
Fax—(973) 916-2810
www.registerlitho.com
Email—info@registerlitho.com
Pres.—Joe Fishman
Off. Mgr.—Della Masin
SIC—2759; 2752; NAICS—323100; *Commercial & lithographic printing*
Employs—50; Estab.—1982
Distrib.—Local
Privately owned corporation

### R-PAC INTERNATIONAL CORP.

69 Kingsland Ave., Marino Plz. 1 (07014)
**Phone—(973) 916-1600**
Fax—(973) 916-1596
www.r-pac.com
Email—info.usa@r-pac.com
Plt. Mgr.—Daniel Rodriguez
SIC—2241; NAICS—313221; *Woven textile labels*
Employs—6; Estab.—1992
Sales—$1Mil-$2.5Mil (est)
Distrib.—Intl.
Privately owned corporation
AKA: Royal Woven Label, Inc.
Parent co.—R-Pac International Corp., New York, NY
Phone—(212) 465-1818
See Parent Co. Section for full profile.

NEW ENTRY
### S & Y NATURAL STONE, LLC

1000 Main Ave. (07011)
**Phone—(862) 200-5156**
Fax—(862) 200-5716
Email—sean.aziz@hotmail.com
Owner—Mehmet Caymaz
SIC—1429; *Broken marble quarrying*
Employs—4
Sales—under $500,000
6,000 sq ft site, Distrib.—Local
Limited Liability Company

### SAFAS CORP.

2 Ackerman Ave. (07011)
**Phone—(973) 772-5252**
National—(800) 472-6854
Fax—(973) 772-5858
www.safascorp.com
Email—info@safascorp.com
Pres.—Akbar Ghahary
Ex. V-P.—Fateme Ghahary
SIC—2821; NAICS—325211; *Sprayable polyester resin surfacing materials*
Employs—30; Estab.—1990
100,000 sq ft site, Distrib.—Intl.
Privately owned corporation

### SCHADLER & SONS, INC., JOHN

Div. of Schaff Piano Supply Co.
242 S. Parkway, P.O. Box 1068 (07014)
**Phone—(973) 777-5620**
National—(866) 842-4266
Fax—(973) 777-0481
www.schaffpiano.com
Email—apyziak@schaffpiano.com
Pres.—Herbert Johnson
GM—Andrew Pyziak
Whse. Mgr.—Cleve McCleod
SIC—3429; *Large diameter fasteners*
Employs—20; Estab.—1928
Sales—$1Mil-$2.5Mil
20,000 sq ft site, Distrib.—Intl.
Privately owned corporation
Parent co.—Schaff Piano Supply Co., Lake Zurich, IL
Phone—(847) 438-4556
See Parent Co. Section for full profile.

### SCIENTIFIC ALLOYS CORP.

5 Troast Ct. *(07011)*
**Phone—(973) 478-8323**
Fax—(973) 478-6780
www.bgaspheres.com
Email—bgaspheres@aol.com
Pres.—William Pian
Sales Mgr.—Christopher Pian
SIC—3356; NAICS—331491; *Solder, gold, silver & alloy spheres, washers, wire rings, discs, wire & bars; Brand name—Solderlloy Lead Free*
Employs—35; Estab.—1970
21,000 sq ft site, Distrib.—Intl.
Privately owned corporation
Also see: Semiconductor Mfg., same loc.

### SEMEL'S EMBROIDERY & SCREEN PRINTING, INC.

1078 U.S. Highway 46 (07013-2420)
**Phone—(973) 473-3959**
Fax—(973) 473-8895
www.semels.com
Email—embroideri@aol.com
Chrm.—Charlotte Semel
Fin. & MIS Mgr.—Dolly Semel
SIC—2395; 2396; *Contract vintage chain-stitch embroidery & screen printing of chenille, emblems, banners & high school jackets; Brand name—Hanes; Jerzees; Anvil; FOL; Gildan; American Apparel*
Employs—25; Estab.—1935
8,000 sq ft site, Distrib.—Intl.
Privately owned corporation

### SEMICONDUCTOR MFG.

5 Troast Ct. *(07011)*
**Phone—(973) 478-2880**
Fax—(973) 478-6780
www.bgaspheres.com
Email—bgaspheres@aol.com
Pres.—William Pian
Sales Mgr.—Christopher Pian
SIC—3469; 3496; 3356; *Metal stampings, spheres & wire, including solder, indium & gold alloys*
Employs—54; Estab.—1974
Sales—$5Mil-$10Mil
Distrib.—Intl.
Privately owned corporation
Also see: Scientific Alloys Corp., same loc.

### SHOWTECH, INC.

40 Entin Rd. (07014)
**Phone—(973) 249-6336**
Fax—(973) 249-6338
Owner—Dan Zazzali
Off. Mgr.—Barbare McGuire
SIC—2517; NAICS—337129; *Wooden audio & video cabinets*
Employs—7; Estab.—1972
Sales—under $500,000
10,000 sq ft site, Distrib.—Local
Privately owned corporation

### SIGNS OF 2000

421 Broad St. (07011)
**Phone—(973) 253-1333**
Fax—(973) 253-1958
www.signsof2000.com
Email—sign2000sa@aol.com
GM—Ray Salem
Manager—Abraham Salem
SIC—3993; 2394; NAICS—314912; *Interior & exterior signs & awnings*
Employs—10; Estab.—1997
Sales—$500,000-$1Mil
Distrib.—Regional
Privately owned corporation

NEW ENTRY
### SILIPOS, INC.

4 Brighton Rd., Ste. 320 (07012)
**Phone—(973) 928-5900**
National—(800) 229-7105
Fax—(212) 818-9873
www.silipos.com
Email—info@silipos.com
Pres., CEO—Bob Kuhn
SIC—3842; *Corporate headquarters & orthopedic mineral oil gel pads, sleeves & wraps*
Employs—8; Estab.—1989
Sales—$1Mil-$2.5Mil (est)
Distrib.—National
Privately owned corporation

### SMARTLITE, LLC

25 Madison Ave. (07011)
**Phone—(973) 470-9400**
National—(888) 830-8840
Fax—(973) 470-9424
www.smartlitech.com
Email—info@smartlitech.com
Manager—Gabor Lederer
SIC—3648; *Battery-operated electric votive & memorial candles*
Employs—7; Estab.—2003
Sales—$1Mil-$2.5Mil
Distrib.—National
Limited Liability Company

### SOMETHING DIFFERENT LINEN, INC.

167 Fornelius Ave. (07013-1845)
**Phone—(973) 772-8019**
National—(800) 422-2180
Fax—(973) 772-6519
www.somethingdifferentlinen.com
Email—msmith8939@aol.com
Co-Pres.—Mitchell Smith
Pres., Print—Matthew Lederman
V-P., Sales—Araceis Baez

## Clifton—(cont.)

Hum. Res. Mgr.—Karen Tyburczy
Cust. Serv. Rep.—Myra Ordiales
SIC—2392; *Tablecloths*
Employs—65; Estab.—1982
Sales—$1Mil-$5Mil
53,000 sq ft site, Distrib.—Intl.
Privately owned corporation

**SOMMERS PLASTIC PRODUCTS, INC.**
31 Styertowne Rd. (07012)
**Phone—(917) 696-3113**
     (973) 777-7888
National—(800) 225-7677
Fax—(973) 777-7890
www.sommers.com
Email—sales@sommers.com
Chrm.—Edward Schecter
V-P.—Fred Schecter
Comp., Cont. & Off. Mgr.—Dianne Dupray
Matls. Mgr.—Joann Novo
Cred. Mgr.—Anna Costenzo
SIC—3081; 2295; 2759; NAICS—326113; *Plastic & vinyl fabrics, including synthetic leather, skins, pleather, fake fur, clears, reflectives, frosty, lenticular & holographic novelties; Brand name—AgUARDIAN silver ion antimicrobial; Marshmallow; Roller Clear; Roller Patent; 4D Super Lenticular; Living Rubber*
Employs—20; Estab.—1947
Sales—over $10Mil
30,000 sq ft site, Distrib.—Intl.
Privately owned corporation

**SPARK WIRE PRODUCTS CO., INC.**
158 River Rd. (07014)
**Phone—(973) 773-6945**
Fax—(973) 773-0262
Pres.—Paul Fessak
V-P., Fin.—Michael Fessak
SIC—2542; *Wire display racks*
Employs—5; Estab.—1954
Sales—$500,000-$1Mil
10,000 sq ft site, Distrib.—Intl.
Privately owned corporation

**SPINK & GABOR, INC.**
11 Troast Ct. (07011)
**Phone—(973) 478-4551**
Fax—(973) 478-2446
Email—biged777@aol.com
Pres.—Edward R. Spink
SIC—2789; NAICS—323121; *Bookbinding*
Employs—3; Estab.—1911
Sales—under $500,000
6,500 sq ft site, Distrib.—National
Privately owned corporation

**†SST CORP.**
635 Brighton Rd. *(07012)*
Mail addr: P.O. Box 1649, Clifton (07015)
**Phone—(973) 473-4300**
     (800) 222-0921
Fax—(973) 473-4326
www.sst-corp.com
Email—info@sst-corp.com
Pres.—D. Gary Vassallo
V-P.—Bill Cain
V-P.—Mark Murray
Hum. Res. & IT Mgr.—Ray Curbelo
SIC—5122; 5169; *Distributor of pharmaceutical ingredients & chemicals*
Employs—36; Estab.—1948
Distrib.—Intl.
Privately owned corporation

**STAN CATERING TRUCKS, INC.**
15 Circle Ave. (07011)
**Phone—(973) 253-0556**
Fax—(973) 253-0176
Pres.—Stanley Bednarz

SIC—3444; *Sheet metal fabrication*
Employs—1; Estab.—1992
Sales—under $500,000
Distrib.—Local
Privately owned corporation

**STYLE RITE OF AMERICA, INC.**
118 Seger Ave. (07011)
**Phone—(973) 478-1100**
National—(800) 448-3667
Fax—(973) 478-7880
www.style-rite.com
Email—info@stylerite.com
Ptnr.—Jaime Galorenzo
Ptnr.—Jennifer Mass
V-P. & Off. Mgr.—Dianne Mass
SIC—3231; NAICS—327215; *Framed, frameless & heavy glass shower & bath enclosures & doors; Brand name—Duke; Duchess; Princess; Victoria; Clean-rite*
Employs—15; Estab.—1953
Sales—$1.5Mil-$2Mil
30,000 sq ft site, Distrib.—Local
Privately owned sub-S corp.

**SUBURBAN STEEL CRAFT**
22 W. 1st St. (07011)
**Phone—(973) 772-3430**
Fax—(973) 772-3430
Owner & Pres.—Robert C. Feiner
SIC—3446; NAICS—332323; *Railings & architectural metalwork*
Employs—2; Estab.—1970
Sales—under $500,000
800 sq ft site, Distrib.—Local
Sole ownership

**SWEPCO TUBE, LLC**
1 Clifton Blvd. (07011)
Mail addr: P.O. Box 1899, Clifton (07015)
**Phone—(973) 778-3000**
Fax—(973) 778-9289
www.swepcotube.com
Email—info@swepcotube.com
Pres.—Kenneth J. Schultz, Jr.
V-P., Fin.—Steve Oberhelman
Dir., Sales—Tim Schlicting
Sales Mgr., Export—Phill Lehr
IT Mgr.—Victor Drecchio
Hum. Res. Mgr.—John Cangialosi
Sales Rep., Inside—Barbara Gobrowolski
Sales Rep., Inside—Renee Degrotto
SIC—3317; NAICS—331210; *Stainless steel pipes & tubes*
Employs—120; Estab.—1949
Sales—$10Mil-$25Mil
200,000 sq ft site, Distrib.—Local
Limited Liability Company

**SYSTEMS HOUSE, INC., THE**
1033 U.S. Highway 46 (07013)
**Phone—(973) 777-8050**
National—(800) 637-5556
Fax—(973) 777-3063
www.tshinc.com
Email—sales@tshinc.com
Pres.—Seymour Fertig
V-P.—David Fertig
SIC—7372; 7373; *Cloud or in-house ERP systems for medical distribution, import management, e-commerce, sales, purchasing & warehouse management, drug pedigree & accounting software development & systems integration; Brand name—Master Distribution System; RemoteNet*
Employs—20; Estab.—1979
6,000 sq ft site, Distrib.—National
Privately owned corporation

**TAYLOR MICROWAVE, INC.**
48 Industrial W. (07012)
**Phone—(973) 890-7763**
Fax—(973) 890-7793
www.taylormicrowave.com

Email—sales@taylormicrowave.com
Pres.—Breni Saftre
SIC—3679; *Industrial microwave components*
Employs—8; Estab.—1986
Sales—$500,000-$1Mil
Distrib.—Intl.
Privately owned corporation

**TECH 21 USA, INC.**
790 Bloomfield Ave., Ste. B-1 (07012-1142)
**Phone—(973) 777-6996**
Fax—(973) 777-9899
www.tech21nyc.com
Email—info@tech21nyc.com
Pres.—Andrew Barta
V-P.—Dale Krevens
Sales Mgr.—Tyme Rogers
SIC—3651; 3931; 3679; NAICS—334310; *Electric guitar & bass amplifiers, signal processors, effects pedals & accessories; Brand name—SansAmp; Fly Rig; Character Series; Power Engine; Boost Series; Trademark Series; MIDI Moose; MIDI Mouse; Red Ripper; Roto Choir*
Employs—20; Estab.—1989
Sales—$2.5Mil-$5Mil
15,000 sq ft site, Distrib.—Intl.
Privately owned corporation

[NEW ENTRY]
**TITAN TECHNOLOGIES INTERNATIONAL, INC.**
222 Getty Ave. (07011)
**Phone—(973) 928-5222**
National—(866) 345-8484
Fax—(281) 449-9996
www.titanti.com
Email—info@titanti.com
Chrm.—John J. Staudinger
Secy., Cont.—Jerry Blas
GM—Ron Torretti
IT Mgr.—Jessica Torz
SIC—3544; 3546; 3599; NAICS—333500; *Hydraulic, pneumatic & electric industrial bolting, torque & tensioning tools for the oil & gas, mining, construction, off-road equipment, locomotive & crane industries, power plants, shipyards & steel mills*
Employs—20; Estab.—2000
Distrib.—Intl.
Privately owned corporation
ISO rating—9001

**TRIARCO INDUSTRIES, INC. (H Q)**
2 Brighton Rd., Ste. 404 (07012)
**Phone—(973) 942-5100**
www.triarco.com
Email—info@triarco.com
Pres.—Rodger R. Rhode, Jr.
CFO—Angelo R. Appierto
SIC—2833; NAICS—325411; *Corporate headquarters; herbal dietary supplements*
Employs—5; Estab.—1978
Distrib.—National
Privately owned corporation
ISO rating—9001:2000

**U. S. ARTISTIC MONUMENT CO., INC.**
262 Main Ave. (07014)
**Phone—(973) 777-7786**
Fax—(973) 777-7705
Pres.—Albert Manfredi
GM—Scottie Rullis
Off. Mgr.—Diana Rullis
SIC—3281; NAICS—327991; *Granite burial monuments*
Employs—3; Estab.—1986
Sales—under $500,000
Distrib.—Local
Privately owned corporation

**VALUE EYEWEAR, INC.**
1454 Main Ave. (07011)
Mail addr: P.O. Box 2029, Clifton (07015)
**Phone—(973) 478-6500**
National—(800) 631-0188
Fax—(800) 825-8064
www.valueeyewear.com
Email—frames@valueeyewear.com
Pres.—Richard Weiss
V-P.—Elliot Friedman
Off. Mgr.—Rosemarie Steed
SIC—3851; NAICS—339100; *Eyeglass & sunglass frames*
Employs—15; Estab.—1998
Sales—$1Mil-$2.5Mil
Distrib.—National
Privately owned corporation

**VAN NESS PLASTIC MOLDING CO.**
400 Brighton Rd. (07012)
**Phone—(973) 778-9500**
Fax—(973) 778-8588
www.vannessplastic.com
Email—office@vannessplastic.com
Pres.—William Van Ness
Sales & Mktg. Mgr.—Stephen Glassman
IT Mgr.—Fred Cowburn
Hum. Res. & Payroll Mgr.—Barbara Greco
SIC—3089; *Plastic injection molding*
Employs—150; Estab.—1945
170,000 sq ft site, Distrib.—National
Privately owned sub-S corp.

**VIP INDUSTRIES, INC.**
90 Brighton Rd. (07012)
**Phone—(973) 472-7500**
Fax—(973) 472-2404
www.vipindustriesinc.com
Email—e.sonatore@vipindustriesinc.com
Pres.—John Sonatore
V-P., Opers.—Mike Yannibelli
Off. Mgr.—Eric Sonatore
SIC—3679; *Wire harnesses, coaxial cable & electromechanical assemblies*
Employs—50; Estab.—1964
Sales—$3Mil-$6Mil
24,000 sq ft site, Distrib.—National
Privately owned corporation
ISO rating—9001:2008

**†W. W. GRAINGER, INC.**
308 Allwood Rd. (07012)
**Phone—(973) 777-7700**
National—(800) 472-4643
Fax—(973) 773-3080
www.grainger.com
Email—info@grainger.com
Br. Mgr.—Kevin Wojcicki
SIC—5169; 5072; 5084; 5063; *Wholesaler of commercial & industrial supplies, including adhesives, fasteners, hardware, filters & electrical lighting*
Employs—20; Estab.—1987
Distrib.—National
Privately owned corporation
Parent co.—W. W. Grainger, Inc., Lake Forest, IL
Phone—(847) 535-1000
See Parent Co. Section for full profile.

**WAGNER RACK, INC.**
2 Broad St. (07013)
**Phone—(973) 278-6966**
National—(888) 269-6966
Fax—(973) 278-9514
www.wagnerrack.com
Email—info@wagnerrack.com
Pres.—Ronald Wagner
SIC—2541; *Wooden magazine, book & retail display racks*
Employs—14; Estab.—1970
28,000 sq ft site, Distrib.—Intl.
Privately owned corporation

**GEOGRAPHICAL**

## Clifton—(cont.)

**WIEGERS, INC.**
181 Fornelius Ave. (07013)
Mail addr: P.O. Box 1528, Clifton
(07015-1528)
**Phone—(973) 778-8607**
Fax—(973) 778-6773
www.wiegersinc.com
Email—wiegersinc@aol.com
Pres. & Parts Mgr.—Ernest
Wiegers
V-P. & Serv. Mgr.—Kenneth
Wiegers
Treas., Sales Mgr.—Thomas
Wiegers
Off. Mgr., Acctg.—Jimmy Grieco
SIC—3713; 3714; 5012; 5013;
NAICS—336211; *Manufacturer &
distributor of custom-built truck
bodies & full-line liftgates; Brand
name—Anthony; Maxon; Interlift;
Thieman; Tommy Gate; Waltco;
Liftgate Dealer; Iroquois; Custom
Truck Bodies; Kidron; Reading;
Supreme; Truck Craft; Dorsey/Pitt
Trailers*
Employs—10; Estab.—1970
Sales—under $2Mil
Distrib.—Local
Privately owned corporation

**WIGGINS PLASTICS, INC.**
180 Kingsland Rd., P.O. Box 1077
*(07014)*
**Phone—(973) 667-7200**
Fax—(973) 667-3227
www.wigginsplastics.com
Email—info@wigginsplastics.com
Pres.—Isaac Weinberger
Cont., Hum. Res.—Gary Schick
Plt. Mgr.—George Mattingly
Cust. Serv. Rep.—Lucia Egoavil
SIC—3089; *Custom injection,
compression & transfer molding
of thermoplastics & thermosets*
Employs—65; Estab.—1948
Sales—$5Mil–$10Mil
60,000 sq ft site, Distrib.—Intl.
Privately owned corporation
ISO rating—9001:2008

**X-L PLASTICS, INC.**
220 Clifton Blvd. *(07011)*
**Phone—(973) 777-1888**
National—(800) 524-0781
Fax—(973) 777-1275
www.x-lplastics.com
Email—sales@x-lplastics.com
Pres.—Melvin Fischman
Cont. & Hum. Res. Mgr.—Meryl
Berow
Plt. Mgr.—Bob Laypan
IT Mgr.—Kenny Laypan
Off. Mgr.—Miriam Kahan
Pur. Agt.—Erwin Blum
SIC—2673; 3081; NAICS—
326113; *Plastic bags*
Employs—50; Estab.—1971
Distrib.—Intl.
Privately owned corporation
Also see: Champion Plastics
Corp., same loc.

**†XPEDX**
Div. of Veritiv Corp.
261 River Rd. (07014)
**Phone—(973) 405-2310**
Fax—(973) 405-2121
www.xpedx.com
Email—xpedx@ipaper.com
CFO—Jeffrey Patterson
V-P.—John May
Dir., Sales—Mark Mulvey
Br. Mgr.—Robert Stibitz
Cust. Serv. Mgr.—Diane
Nussbaum
SIC—5111; 5113; 5084; *Distributor
of paper, packaging materials &
equipment, labels & packaging
tapes*
Employs—120
Publicly owned corporation

Parent co.—Veritiv Corp.,
Loveland, OH
Phone—(513) 965-2900
See Parent Co. Section for full profile.

**†XPEDX**
Div. of Veritiv Corp.
261 River Rd. (07014)
**Phone—(973) 405-2300**
National—(888) 764-6965
Fax—(973) 405-2150
www.xpedx.com
Email—info@xpedx.com
Br. & Div. Mgr.—John Ransone
SIC—5111; 5085; 2791; NAICS—
323122; *Distributor of printing
paper & graphics supplies &
digital prepress*
Employs—50; Estab.—1997
Distrib.—Intl.
Publicly owned corporation
Parent co.—Veritiv Corp.,
Loveland, OH
Phone—(513) 965-2900
See Parent Co. Section for full profile.

---

## Clinton

(Hunterdon—N.W.)

**GULBRANDSEN TECHNOLOGIES,
INC. (H Q)**
2 Main St., P.O. Box 5523 (08809)
**Phone—(908) 735-5458**
www.gulbrandsen.com
Email—orders@gulbrandsen.com
Founder & CEO—Donald
Gulbrandsen
Pres.—David Drollinger
Cont.—Ray Jankowski
Hum. Res. Mgr. & Mktg. Rep.—
Rosa Lessa
Team Leader—Rose Bredael
SIC—2899; *Corporate
headquarters; water treatment
chemicals*
Employs—12; Estab.—1983
Sales—$5Mil–$10Mil
Distrib.—Intl.
Privately owned corporation
ISO rating—9001

**KRAMER ELECTRONICS USA, INC./
SIERRA VIDEO SYSTEMS (H Q)**
6 State Route 173 W. (08809)
**Phone—(908) 735-0018**
National—(888) 275-6311
Fax—(908) 735-0515
www.kramerus.com
Email—info@kramerus.com
Pres.—David Bright
V-P., Sales—Kent Cawthorne
V-P., Mktg.—Clint Hoffman
V-P., Fin.—Cathy Penyak
Hum. Res. Mgr.—Debbie Bright
SIC—3651; 5065; NAICS—
334310; *Corporate
headquarters; manufacturer &
distributor of analog & digital
audio, video & computer
graphics video signal, cables,
routing, processing &
interfacing; Brand name—
Kramer Electronics US; Sierra
Video Systems*
Employs—53; Estab.—1997
Distrib.—National
Privately owned partnership
ISO rating—9001

**MAIN STREET COMMUNICATIONS**
15 W. Main St. (08809)
**Phone—(908) 735-7570**
Fax—(908) 735-6564
Admn. Mgr.—Craig Reuter
SIC—2791; NAICS—323122;
*Typesetting & graphic design*
Employs—3; Estab.—1982
Sales—$500,000–$1Mil
Distrib.—Local
Sole ownership

**SPRUCE RUN PRINTING**
2005 Route 31 (08809)
**Phone—(908) 638-6464**
Fax—(908) 638-5966
www.sprucerunprinting.com
Email—sprucerunprinting@
gmail.com
Ptnr.—Tom Kowal
Ptnr.—Rob Lilly
Ptnr.—Jen Stas
SIC—2752; 2789; 3993; NAICS—
323100; *Offset printing & binding
of banners, invoices, letterheads,
brochures, every door direct
mailing materials, advertising
products & signs*
Employs—3; Estab.—1982
Sales—under $500,000
Distrib.—Local
Privately owned partnership

---

## Closter

(Bergen—N.E.)

**AMERICAN MONUMENT CO.**
50 Herbert Ave. (07624)
**Phone—(201) 750-1000**
Fax—(201) 750-0099
www.americanfamilyofcompanies.
com
Email—written2000@aol.com
Pres.—Ron Boyajian
Graphic Designer—Jim
McMannus
SIC—3281; 3365; 3366; NAICS—
327991; *Stone, natural rock,
granite, brick & concrete
engraving & aluminum & bronze
plaque carving; Brand name—
Written in Stone™*
Employs—20
Sales—$1Mil–$2.5Mil
Distrib.—Local
Privately owned corporation
AKAs: A-1 Written in Stone
Monuments & American Bronze
& Stone
Parent co.—American Monument
Co., Englewood, NJ
Phone—(201) 569-4455
See Parent Co. Section for full profile.

**ATLAS WOODWORKING, INC.**
15 Naugle St. (07624)
**Phone—(201) 784-1949**
Fax—(201) 784-7706
www.atlaswoodworking.com
Email—kenewald@
atlaswoodworking.com
Pres.—Kenneth J. Ewald
SIC—2431; NAICS—321900;
*Architectural woodworking*
Employs—15; Estab.—1995
Sales—$1Mil–$2.5Mil
5,000 sq ft site, Distrib.—Regional
Privately owned sub-S corp.

NEW ENTRY
**CALLAHAN JEWELERS, INC.**
86 Vervalen St. (07624)
**Phone—(201) 768-6136**
Fax—(201) 784-9218
www.callahanjewelers.com
Owner—Brian Callahan
Manager—Gene Tryde
SIC—3911; *Precious metal
jewelry, including diamond rings
& watches*
Employs—7; Estab.—1991
Sales—$1Mil–$2.5Mil (est)
2,200 sq ft site, Distrib.—Local
Privately owned corporation

**CARRINGTON CO., LLC (H Q)**
7 Reuten Dr. (07624)
**Phone—(800) 505-9546**
Fax—(201) 660-7455
www.carringtonfarms.com
Email—support@
carringtonfarms.com
CEO—Debbie Shandel
Pres.—Brad Miller

SIC—2099; *Company
headquarters; 100% organic,
non-genetically modified health
food products for health-
conscious customers, including
whole flax seeds, organic milled
& ground flax, flax meals & tea
blending & packing*
Employs—10
Sales—$1Mil–$2.5Mil (est)

**CARRINGTON TEA, LLC**
Div. of Carrington Co., LLC
7 Reuten Dr., P.O. Box 102 (07624)
**Phone—(201) 261-5517**
National—(800) 505-9546
Fax—(201) 261-1941
www.carringtontea.com
Email—support@carringtontea.com
CEO—David Eben
Pres.—Brad Miller
Ex. V-P., CMO—Debbie Shandel
SIC—2099; *Tea; Brand name—
Carrington Tea; Carrington
Farms; Nutra Tea; Lindsay
Gardens; Good Grains*
Employs—8; Estab.—1995
Sales—$1Mil–$2.5Mil (est)
Distrib.—National
Limited Liability Company
Parent co.—Carrington Co., LLC,
Closter, NJ
Phone—(800) 505-9546
See Parent Co. Section for full profile.

**ELGEN MFG. CO.**
10 Railroad Ave. (07624)
**Phone—(201) 964-0008**
National—(800) 503-9805
Fax—(201) 964-9030
www.elgenmfg.com
Email—info@elgenmfg.com
Pres.—David Young
Cont.—Susan Young
GM—John Cunha
IT Mgr.—Zoltan Orban
Hum. Res. Mgr.—Denise Sawey
SIC—3643; 3442; NAICS—
335931; *Flexible duct
connectors, galvanized, stainless
steel & aluminum access doors
& latches*
Employs—100; Estab.—1995
Sales—$5Mil–$10Mil
Distrib.—National
Privately owned corporation
AKA: Capital Hardware Supply

**EXTECH BUILDING MATERIALS**
100 Bogert St. (07624)
**Phone—(201) 768-2133**
(718) 852-7090
National—(800) 222-2133
Fax—(201) 768-5927
www.extechbuilding.com
Email—bfeury@extechbuilding.com
Br. Mgr.—Bob Lippe
SIC—3281; 5032; NAICS—
327991; *Custom natural stone
fabrication & distributor of
masonry products, supplies &
accessories for restoration &
mason contractors &
homeowners*
Employs—35; Estab.—1955
12,000 sq ft site, Distrib.—
Regional
Privately owned corporation
Parent co.—Extech Building
Materials, Long Island City, NY
Phone—(718) 786-2288
See Parent Co. Section for full profile.

**HARBRO CHURCH ARTS, INC.**
231 Herbert Ave., P.O. Box 776
(07624)
**Phone—(201) 768-5500**
National—(800) 223-0040
Fax—(800) 441-6655
www.judgesrobes.com
Email—harbro@verizon.net
Pres.—Robert J. Harrison
V-P.—Todd W. Harrison

## Closter—(cont.)

Corp. Secy-Treas.—Virginia H. Hall
SIC—2389; *Washable judicial robes for men & women*
Employs—3; Estab.—1921
Sales—$500,000
Distrib.—Intl.
Privately owned corporation

**INTECH CORP.**
250 Herbert Ave. (07624)
**Phone—(201) 767-8066**
National—(877) 218-2650
Fax—(201) 767-7797
www.intechpower.com
Email—info@intechpower.com
Pres.—Georg Bartosch
Engr. Mgr.—Tody Mihov
SIC—3089; 3566; *Self-lubricating plastic non-hygroscopic gears, rollers & cam followers for the packaging, printing, paper converting, medical, solar, semiconductor, cleanroom, automotive & aerospace equipment markets; Brand name—Power-Core™*
Employs—7; Estab.—1983
Distrib.—Intl.
Privately owned corporation

**INTEGRITY PRECISION PRODUCTS**
7 Reuten Dr. (07624)
**Phone—(201) 767-0700**
Fax—(201) 767-7088
Email—kc@intpp.com
Pres.—Ken Comorau
V-P.—Lesley Comorau
Off. Mgr.—Joann Hoffman
SIC—3452; NAICS—332722; *Stainless steel fasteners*
Employs—8; Estab.—1992
Sales—$500,000-$1Mil
Distrib.—National
Privately owned corporation

**J A MACHINE & TOOL CO., INC.**
84 Herbert Ave. (07624)
**Phone—(201) 767-1308**
Fax—(201) 767-3447
Email—ja.machine@verizon.net
Pres.—Andrew Petrinic
Off. Admn.—Vendula Hosek
SIC—3728; 3599; *Precision aircraft components & general machining job shop*
Employs—12; Estab.—1960
Sales—$1Mil-$2.5Mil
Distrib.—National
Privately owned corporation
ISO rating—AS9100

**†PRESSURE KING, INC.**
231 Herbert Ave., Ste. 1 (07624)
**Phone—(201) 768-1911**
National—(800) 468-1007
Fax—(201) 768-4811
www.pressureking.com
Email—pressurekg@aol.com
CEO—Harry McCormick
SIC—5087; *Distributor of commercial & industrial pressure cleaning equipment, including washers, trigger guns, wands, hoses, reels & nozzles; Brand name—Karcher; Sioux; KEW; Wap; Alto; Mi-T-m; Spraymart*
Employs—2; Estab.—1983
Distrib.—National
Privately owned corporation

**SUBURBAN GLASS & MIRROR, INC.**
231 Herbert Ave. (07624-1332)
**Phone—(201) 768-9586**
Fax—(201) 767-9131
www.suburbanglassandmirror.com
Email—info@suburbanglassandmirror.com
Pres.—Wayne Gangeri
V-P.—Jeffrey Gangeri
IT Mgr.—Matt Gangeri
Off. Mgr.—Christa Farrell
SIC—3231; 3211; NAICS—327215; *Corporate headquarters & glass & mirror fabrication, including replacement glass, framed & frameless shower enclosures & commercial storefronts*
Employs—20; Estab.—1961
Sales—$1Mil-$2.5Mil
Distrib.—Local
Privately owned corporation

**WOOD-O-RAMA, INC.**
100 67th St. (07624)
**Phone—(201) 768-1180**
Fax—(201) 768-1185
www.woodorama.com
Email—mouldings@woodorama.com
Pres.—Carlos Caronedo
SIC—2434; 2541; NAICS—337110; *Custom wooden kitchen cabinets & counters*
Employs—2; Estab.—1965
Sales—$500,000-$1Mil
Distrib.—Local
Privately owned corporation

## Collingswood
(Camden—S.W.)

**ALL STAR AWARDS & TROPHIES, INC.**
866 Haddon Ave. (08108)
**Phone—(856) 858-6600**
Email—ast858@aol.com
Pres.—Mary Anne Sonsini
V-P.—Bill Sonsini
SIC—3499; 3479; *Trophies & awards, including engraving services*
Employs—4; Estab.—1970
7,000 sq ft site, Distrib.—Regional
Privately owned corporation

**CATELLI BROS. VEAL & LAMB, INC.**
50 Ferry Ave. (08103)
**Phone—(856) 869-9293**
Fax—(856) 869-9488
www.catellibrothers.com
Email—llicht@catellibrothers.com
Pres.—Anthony Catelli
V-P., Opers.—Tom Thomson
Dir., Food Serv.—Louis Licht
Cust. Serv. Mgr.—Jack Womack
SIC—2011; NAICS—311611; *Corporate headquarters & veal & lamb processing*
Employs—225; Estab.—1981
Sales—$90Mil-$100Mil
Distrib.—National

**COLLINGSWOOD ARCHITECTURAL MILLWORK, INC.**
715 Taylor Ave. (08107)
**Phone—(856) 854-0440**
Fax—(856) 854-2897
www.collarch.com
Email—millwork@collarch.com
Pres.—Robert Engelke
Corp. Secy.—Margaret Engelke
SIC—2431; 2434; NAICS—337110; *Millwork, cabinets & countertops*
Employs—17; Estab.—1989
Sales—$1Mil-$2.5Mil
15,000 sq ft site, Distrib.—Local
Privately owned corporation

**LE MONDE DELUXE**
232 White Horse Pike (08107)
**Phone—(856) 854-5440**
Fax—(856) 854-5440
Owner—Pete D'Amico
SIC—3911; *Precious metal jewelry*
Employs—7; Estab.—1990
Sales—$1Mil-$2.5Mil (est)
Distrib.—Intl.
Sole ownership

**RETROSPECT, THE**
732 Haddon Ave., P.O. Box 296 (08108)
**Phone—(856) 854-1400**
Fax—(856) 854-8790
www.theretrospect.com
Email—editor@theretrospect.com
Owner—Brett Ainsworth
Editor—Mark Swanson
Cont.—Susan Ainsworth
Graphic Artist—Mark Zeigler
SIC—2711; *Newspaper publishing*
Employs—6; Estab.—1902
Sales—under $500,000
Distrib.—Local
Privately owned corporation

**STOUT'S METAL PRODUCTS**
222 Lincoln Ave. (08108)
**Phone—(856) 854-7938**
Fax—(856) 854-4709
www.stoutsmetal.com
Email—stoutsmetal@aol.com
Co-Pres.—Larry Stout, Sr.
Co-Pres.—Julianne Stout
SIC—3446; NAICS—332323; *Ornamental railings*
Employs—5; Estab.—1984
Sales—$500,000-$1Mil
Distrib.—Local
Privately owned sub-S corp.

**WARREN LIGHTNING ROD CO.**
2 Richey Ave. (08107)
**Phone—(856) 854-7000**
National—(800) 762-7637
Fax—(856) 854-1803
www.wlrc.net
Email—marketing@wlrc.net
Pres.—Stephen Humeniuk
Mktg. Mgr.—Janice Long
SIC—3643; NAICS—335931; *UL96A & NFPA 780 lighting protection systems, including installation*
Employs—24; Estab.—1950
Sales—$1Mil-$2.5Mil
Distrib.—Regional
Privately owned corporation

**WOODWORK & MORE, LLC**
24 W. Gorman Ave. (08108)
**Phone—(856) 986-3140**
Email—woodworkandmoore@yahoo.com
Owner—Edward Satkowski
SIC—2431; 2426; 2499; *Woodworking, including millwork, railing systems, wainscoting, wood trim & sanding & finishing of hardwood floors*
Employs—1; Estab.—2000
Sales—under $500,000
900 sq ft site, Distrib.—Regional
Limited Liability Company

## Cologne
(Atlantic—S.E.)

**ABSECON MILLS, INC.**
901 W. Aloe St., P.O. Box 672 (08213)
**Phone—(609) 965-5373**
National—(800) 255-7738
Fax—(609) 965-0938
www.absecon.com
Email—info@absecon.com
Pres., CEO—Randolph S. Taylor
Ex. V-P.—David Adair
V-P., Fin.—Patrick Zuno
SIC—2211; *Upholstery, ballistics & composite fabrics; Brand name—Sherpa; Shire; Durovay; Guardian; Stainless Steel; Grid Hercules; Ballistic Rip-stop; Ballistic Felt; Marquesa Lana*
Employs—200; Estab.—1978
100,000 sq ft site, Distrib.—Intl.
Privately owned corporation
AKA: Absecon Industries

**OLE HANSEN & SON, INC. (H Q)**
523 S. Leipzig Ave., P.O. Box 1020 (08213)
**Phone—(609) 965-3700**
www.olehanson.com
Email—dgoddard@olehansen.com
Chrm.—Roger B. Hansen
Pres., CEO—David Goddard
CFO & Corp. Treas.—Michael Lentz
SIC—1442; *Corporate headquarters; sand & gravel mining*
Employs—50
Distrib.—Local
Privately owned corporation

## Colonia
(Middlesex—N.E.)

**CUSTOM ENGRAVING**
29 Highland Rd. (07067)
Mail addr: P.O. Box 1214, Woodbridge (07095)
**Phone—(732) 574-1901**
Fax—(732) 574-1902
www.engraveditems.com
Email—john@engraveditems.com
Ptnr.—John Martelle
Ptnr.—Donna Martelle
SIC—3479; *Metal trophy engraving*
Employs—2; Estab.—1998
Sales—under $500,000
Distrib.—Local
Sole ownership

**MIDDLESEX ARMATURE SERVICE**
1155 Saint Georges Ave. (07067)
**Phone—(732) 634-3779**
Fax—(732) 229-0116
Owner—Kenneth Pittman
SIC—3694; *Rebuilt automotive starters & alternators*
Employs—8; Estab.—1954
Sales—$1Mil-$2.5Mil (est)
Privately owned corporation

## Colts Neck
(Monmouth—N.E.)

**CAMTEC INDUSTRIES, INC.**
28 Saddle Ridge Rd. (07722)
**Phone—(732) 332-9800**
Fax—(732) 332-9696
www.camtecindustries.com
Email—info@camtecindustries.com
Pres.—Anthony Mauro
SIC—3599; 3469; 3499; *CNC machining job shop, including metal fabrication, metal stamping, painting & powder coating*
Employs—16; Estab.—1995
Sales—$1Mil-$2.5Mil
Distrib.—National
Privately owned sub-S corp.

NEW ENTRY
**HERITAGE PUBLISHING, LLC**
620 High Bridge Rd. (07722)
**Phone—(732) 747-7770**
Fax—(732) 414-1736
www.homeimprovementguides.com
Email—info@homeimprovementguides.com
Co-Publisher—Nick Montalbano
Co-Publisher—Laura Montalbano
SIC—2741; *Home improvement guide publishing*
Employs—4
Sales—under $500,000 (est)
Distrib.—Local
Limited Liability Company

**LASER DIM GRAPHICS & PRINTING**
2 Parkwood Ln. (07722)
**Phone—(732) 821-9000**
Fax—(732) 821-0197
www.amprc.com

GEOGRAPHICAL

## Colts Neck—(cont.)

Email—artworks@amprc.com
Pres.—James Asghar
V-P.—Jeff Naqvi
SIC—2752; 2759; NAICS—
 323122; *Digital & offset printing*
Employs—10; Estab.—1994
Sales—$500,000-$1Mil
Distrib.—Regional
Privately owned corporation
AKA: American Printing

### MORAN POWER DYNAMICS

263 Route 537 E. (07722)
**Phone—(732) 544-8443**
Fax—(732) 389-8949
Pres.—Edward Moran
V-P.—Terri Moran
SIC—3593; NAICS—333995;
 *Seat actuators*
Employs—6; Estab.—1988
Sales—under $500,000
Distrib.—Local
Privately owned corporation

### †THE LINER CO., INC.

7 Meadows Run Dr. (07722)
**Phone—(732) 761-0700**
Fax—(732) 761-1525
www.linercompany.thebluebook.co
 m
Email—linerco@aol.com
Owner & Pres.—Carol Hartwell
V-P.—Jack Hartwell
SIC—5162; 5085; *Distributor of
 HDPE, PVC, geocomposite,
 geotextiles, grids, geosynthetics
 & erosion control materials,
 including installation; Brand
 name—GSE; Solmax;
 Watersaver; Colorado Linings;
 Strata; Willachoochee; Propex;
 Skaps*
Employs—2; Estab.—1976
Sales—$1Mil-$2.5Mil
7,000 sq ft site, Distrib.—National
Privately owned corporation

### VINCENT & CO., INC., J.

420 Route 34, Ste. 301, P.O. Box
 448 (07722)
**Phone—(732) 256-4410**
Fax—(732) 256-4410
Email—jbrando@jvincent.com
Pres.—Joseph V. Brando
Off. Mgr.—Meaghan Hughes
Sales Rep.—Veronica Baldini
SIC—3911; NAICS—339911;
 *Precious metal jewelry*
Employs—2; Estab.—1995
Sales—under $500,000
Distrib.—Local
Privately owned corporation

## Columbia

(Warren—N.W.)

### 10-31, INC.

2 W. Crisman Rd. (07832)
**Phone—(908) 496-4946**
Fax—(908) 496-4956
www.10-31.com
Email—wstender@10-31.com
Pres.—William Stender
IT Mgr.—Michael Labate
Off. Mgr.—Lynne Stender
SIC—2541; 2542; 3993; 3231;
 NAICS—337215; *Custom
 wooden, plastic & glass artwork
 displays, display cases &
 cabinetry & museum & gallery
 gueue products*
Employs—24; Estab.—1985
Sales—$3Mil-$3.5Mil
18,000 sq ft site, Distrib.—Intl.
Privately owned corporation

### COLUMBIA MACHINE

1 N. Riverview Ave. (07832)
**Phone—(908) 475-4057**
Owner—Alex Curtis

SIC—3599; *CNC machining job
 shop*
Employs—1; Estab.—1954
Sales—under $500,000
3,000 sq ft site, Distrib.—Local
Sole ownership

### CUSTOM HELIARC WELDING & MACHINE, INC.

49 Decatur St., P.O. Box 232
 (07832)
**Phone—(908) 496-8190**
Fax—(908) 496-8197
Email—customheliarc@
 embarqmail.com
Pres.—Michael D. Gannon
Foreman—Mike Gannon, Jr.
SIC—3613; 3643; NAICS—
 335313; *High voltage bus bar
 assemblies & connectors &
 welding & CNC machining job
 shop*
Employs—11; Estab.—1990
Distrib.—National
Privately owned sub-S corp.

### HOPE UNIFORM CO., INC.

4 Columbia St., P.O. Box 224
 (07832)
**Phone—(908) 496-4899**
Fax—(908) 496-4990
www.hopeuniform.com
Email—hopeuniforms@
 embarque.net
Pres.—Paul Lantz
Hum. Res. Mgr.—Amy Roberts
SIC—2311; NAICS—315200;
 *Police & firemen's uniforms*
Employs—16; Estab.—1966
Distrib.—National
Privately owned corporation
AKA: Hope Uniform & Security
 Products

### IMPERIAL MACHINE & TOOL CO.

8 W. Crisman Rd. (07832)
**Phone—(908) 496-8100**
Fax—(908) 496-8102
www.imperialmachine.com
Email—info@imperialmachine.com
Owner—Christian Joest
IT Mgr.—Jack Shelp
SIC—3599; *Contract
 manufacturing & CNC machining
 job shop*
Employs—35; Estab.—1943
27,000 sq ft site, Distrib.—Local
Privately owned partnership

### INTERTEST, INC.

303 State Route 94 (07832)
**Phone—(908) 496-8008**
National—(800) 535-3626
Fax—(908) 496-8004
www.intertest.com
Email—bginfo@intertest.com
Pres.—William Habermann
V-P., Sales—Tom Daly
Dir., Opers.—Larry N. Tourjee
Dir., Mktg.—Lana Santagata
SIC—3825; NAICS—334500;
 *Specialized vision products,
 remote visual inspection tools &
 non-destructive testing
 equipment; Brand name—iShot;
 Weld-i; XtendaCam; SeeUV;
 VIBES; WebViewer; MZ4;
 XBlock; Hawkeye Borescopes;
 Milliscope; Wohler; Sony;
 Toshiba; Sentech; FLIR; Watec;
 Hitachi; Panasonic; SnakeEye;
 Machida; FreedomView;
 Gopherscope*
Employs—40; Estab.—1981
12,000 sq ft site, Distrib.—Intl.
Privately owned corporation
ISO rating—9001:2008

### ORATON RUBBER STAMP CO., INC.

Div. of Taylor Corp.
407 Route 94 (07832)
**Phone—(908) 496-4161**
National—(800) 631-4454
Fax—(800) 635-6554

Plt. Mgr.—Vicky Finelli
SIC—3953; NAICS—339943;
 *Rubber stamps*
Employs—30
Sales—$1Mil-$2.5Mil (est)
Distrib.—National
Privately owned corporation
Parent co.—Taylor Corp., North
 Mankato, MN
 Phone—(507) 625-2828
 See Parent Co. Section for full profile.

## Columbus

(Burlington—S.E.)

### CREATIVE SCREEN DESIGN

531 Route 68, P.O. Box 369
 (08022)
**Phone—(609) 424-3334**
Fax—(609) 291-1035
Email—csdemb@aol.com
Owner—Cathy Cox
SIC—2396; 2395; *Textile screen
 printing, embroidery & trophy &
 plaque engraving*
Employs—2; Estab.—1987
Sales—under $500,000 (est)
Distrib.—Local
Sole ownership

### GT MILLWORK, LLC

2180 Hedding Rd. (08022)
**Phone—(609) 291-9222**
Fax—(609) 291-7003
www.gtmillwork.com
Email—gtmillwork@aol.com
Ptnr.—Gary Teyhen
Ptnr.—Mike Leming
Floor Mgr.—Jerry Littlejohn
SIC—2431; NAICS—321900;
 *Residential & commercial
 woodworking*
Employs—6; Estab.—2001
Sales—$500,000-$1Mil
6,500 sq ft site, Distrib.—Regional
Limited Liability Company

NEW ENTRY

### SQP, INC.

3206 Route 206, P.O. Box 248
 (08022)
**Phone—(609) 298-5111**
National—(800) 648-4789
Fax—(609) 298-0525
www.sqpartbooks.com
Pres.—Sal Quartuccio
SIC—2731; *Book publishing*
Employs—4
Sales—under $500,000 (est)

## Cookstown

(Burlington—S.E.)

### CLAYTON & SONS, LLC, RALPH

Div. of Clayton Block Co., Inc.
58 Goldman Dr. (08511)
Mail addr: P.O. Box 3015,
 Lakewood (08701)
**Phone—(609) 758-6900**
National—(800) 662-3044
www.claytonco.com
Email—kroe@claytonco.com
Plt. Mgr.—William Gangel
SIC—3273; *Ready-mixed
 concrete*
Employs—30; Estab.—1987
Distrib.—Regional
Privately owned corporation
AKA: Clayton Concrete
Parent co.—Clayton Block Co.,
 Inc., Neptune, NJ
 Phone—(732) 751-7600
 See Parent Co. Section for full profile.

### DRYTECH, INC.

54 Wrightstown Cookstown Rd.,
 P.O. Box 249 (08511)
**Phone—(609) 758-1794**
Fax—(609) 758-1774
www.drytechinc.com
Email—drytech@drytechinc.com

Pres., Fin. & R & D Mgr.—Tony
 Jones
Accountant & Hum. Res. Mgr.—
 Cynthia Borselli
Engr., Sys.—Doug Cooley
SIC—3599; 3634; 3564; *Cartridge
 dehydrators, moisture
 management & air purification
 equipment for defense,
 aerospace & elecronic
 applications*
Employs—24; Estab.—1991
15,000 sq ft site, Distrib.—National
Privately owned corporation

## Cranbury

(Middlesex—N.E.)

### ACCESS CONTROL GROUP, LLC

2555 U.S. Highway 130 S., Ste. 2
 (08512)
**Phone—(908) 789-8700**
Fax—(908) 789-2229
www.assetor.net
Email—info@assetor.net
Pres.—Arun Patel
SIC—3679; 3672; NAICS—
 334412; *Electronic assembly,
 wiring harnesses, printed circuit
 boards & material handling
 equipment*
Employs—25; Estab.—1987
Sales—$500,000-$1Mil
6,000 sq ft site, Distrib.—National
Limited Liability Company
ISO rating—9001

### ANTRONIX, INC. (H Q)

440 Forsgate Dr. (08512)
**Phone—(609) 395-1390**
Fax—(609) 395-1927
www.antronix.com
Email—info@antronix.net
Pres.—Danny Tang
Ex. V-P.—Neil Tang
GM—Tony DiPace
Dist. & Opers. Mgr.—Teresa Bell
Hum. Res. Mgr.—Christine Chen
SIC—3357; *Corporate
 headquarters; cable television
 products, including optical
 nodes, multitaps, line passives,
 amplifiers & grounding hardware
 (mfg. done in Taiwan & China)*
Employs—35; Estab.—1980
Sales—$5Mil-$10Mil (est)
Distrib.—Intl.
Privately owned corporation

### AVANTI

2650 U.S. Highway 130., Ste. I
 (08512)
**Phone—(609) 655-5333**
www.avantimfg.com
Email—sales@avantimfg.com
Engr.—Rajiv Toprani
SIC—2297; *Polypropylene &
 polyethylene spundbond
 nonwoven fabrics*
Employs—4
Distrib.—National
Privately owned corporation
Parent co.—Avanti, Clarksville, TN
 Phone—(931) 542-1039
 See Parent Co. Section for full profile.

### BETA CRAFT, INC.

2682 Route 130, P.O. Box 536
 (08512)
**Phone—(609) 655-1940**
Fax—(609) 655-0106
www.betacrafts.com
Pres.—Arthur Hasselbach
Corp. Secy.—Carol Hasselbach
SIC—3944; 2499; 3999;
 *Pinewood derby kits & supplies
 & orchid growing trays; Brand
 name—Humidi Grow; Pinewood
 Direct*
Employs—2; Estab.—1979
Sales—$2.5Mil-$5Mil
Distrib.—Intl.
Privately owned corporation

# Cranbury—(cont.)

**BROWN & PERKINS, INC.**
1193 Route 535, P.O. Box 412
(08512)
**Phone—(609) 655-1150**
Fax—(609) 655-1173
www.brownandperkins.com
Email—sales@
brownandperkins.com
Pres.—E. T. Comly
V-P., Treas.—William Comly
Plt. Mgr.—Michael Free
Qual. Assur. Mgr.—George
Woolley
Full Charge Bookkeeper—Diana
M. Bordetsky
SIC—3496; 3429; 2298; 5085;
Manufacturer & distributor of
wire rope, assemblies & slings,
chain, synthetic ropes & slings,
hardware & fittings; Brand
name—The Crosby Group; CM;
Acco Peerless; Muncy; Apex
Tool Group; Chicago Hardware;
Van Beest; Bridon America;
Wireco; Wire Rope Works;
Advantage; Worldwide; Frank
Winne; Tytan; Liftex
Employs—16; Estab.—1964
Sales—$1Mil-$2.5Mil (est)
30,000 sq ft site, Distrib.—National
Privately owned corporation

**CALIFORNIA CLOSET CO.**
2666 U.S. Highway 130 (08512)
**Phone—(609) 655-1899**
Fax—(609) 655-5171
www.californiaclosets.com
Email—anemeth@calclosets.com
Pres.—Dan Nili
IT Mgr.—Eric Nili
Hum. Res. Mgr.—Shiva Nili
Off. Mgr.—Alicia Nameth
SIC—2541; Wooden closets
Employs—15; Estab.—1986
Sales—$1Mil-$2.5Mil
Distrib.—Regional
Privately owned corporation

**†CARRERA OF AMERICA, INC.**
2 Corporate Dr., Ste. D (08512-
3604)
**Phone—(609) 409-8510**
Fax—(609) 409-8610
www.carrera-toys.com
Email—reception@carrera-toys.com
Pres.—Edward Gershowitz
Cont.—Irene Zaslavsky
Sales Mgr., Natl.—David Creed
Mktg. Mgr., N. America—David
Kennedy
Logistics & Whse. Mgr.—John
Seymour
SIC—5092; Wholesaler of
electronic toy cars, including slot
car racing sets & radio controlled
vehicles; Brand name—Carrera;
Carrera R/C; Pull N Speed;
Baufix
Employs—12; Estab.—2003
Distrib.—Intl.
Privately owned corporation

**CHAMBERLIN & BARCLAY, INC.**
2 Hightstown Cranbury Station Rd.
(08512)
**Phone—(609) 655-0700**
Fax—(609) 655-0838
Email—idbarclay@verizon.net
Pres.—David Barclay
Secy-Treas.—Ellen Deblois
Plt. Mgr.—David Deblois
SIC—2875; NAICS—325314;
Fertilizer blending
Employs—9; Estab.—1904
Sales—$2.5Mil-$5Mil
Distrib.—Regional
Privately owned corporation

**CHURCH & DWIGHT CO., INC.**
326 Half Acre Rd. (08512-0181)
**Phone—(609) 655-6000**
www.churchdwight.com
Email—james.craigie@
churchdwight.com
Hum. Res. Mgr.—Maria Moke
Sr. Admn.—Kim Roach
SIC—2835; NAICS—325400;
Pregnancy test kits
Employs—75; Estab.—1880
Sales—over $100Mil
Distrib.—Intl.
Publicly owned corporation
Parent co.—Church & Dwight Co.,
Inc., Ewing, NJ
Phone—(609) 683-5900
See Parent Co. Section for full profile.

**CMIC CMO USA CORP.**
3 Cedarbrook Dr., Ste. 3 (08512)
**Phone—(609) 395-9700**
Fax—(609) 395-8824
www.cmiccmousa.com
Email—bd@cmiccmousa.com
Ex. V-P. & Dir.—Gary Wada
Assoc. Dir., Hum. Res.—Rose B.
Hopkins
SIC—2834; NAICS—325412;
Pharmaceuticals
Employs—42; Estab.—1992
27,000 sq ft site, Distrib.—National
Privately owned corporation

**CONAGRA FOOD INGREDIENTS**
Div. of ConAgra Foods, Inc.
6 Santa Fe Way (08512)
**Phone—(609) 409-6200**
National—(800) 345-7742
Fax—(609) 409-6502
www.conagrafoods.com
Email—info@conagrafoods.com
GM—Joanna Holmes
Hum. Res. Mgr.—Jen Cloute
Pur. Agt.—Karen Wuelfing
SIC—2099; Spices
Employs—90; Estab.—1999
Sales—$10Mil-$25Mil (est)
Distrib.—Local
Publicly owned corporation
Parent co.—ConAgra Foods, Inc.,
Omaha, NE
Phone—(402) 240-4000
See Parent Co. Section for full profile.

**CORNERSTONE
PHARMACEUTICALS, INC.**
1 Duncan Dr. (08512)
**Phone—(609) 409-7050**
www.cornerstonepharma.com
Email—info@
cornerstonepharma.com
CEO—Robert Shorr
Pres., COO—Robert Rodriguez
CFO—Clifford H. Straub, Jr.
V-P., Clinical & Regulatory Affs.—
King C. Lee
V-P.—David A. Polinsky
Sr. Scientist—John Luddy
SIC—2834; Drug candidates in
Phase II clinical trials
Employs—15; Estab.—2001
Sales—$5Mil-$10Mil (est)
Distrib.—National
Privately owned corporation

**†COSMETIC ESSENCE, INC.**
1248 S. River Rd. (08512)
**Phone—(609) 395-1271**
Fax—(609) 395-1272
www.cosmeticessence.com
Email—sales@
cosmeticessence.com
GM—Gaetano Losito
Hum. Res. Mgr.—Janet Berrios
SIC—5122; Distributor of personal
care supplies, including
shampoos, creams & lotions
Employs—40; Estab.—2000
Sales—under $500,000
Distrib.—Intl.
Publicly owned corporation

Parent co.—Cosmetic Essence,
Inc., Holmdel, NJ
Phone—(732) 888-7788
See Parent Co. Section for full profile.

**CRP INDUSTRIES, INC.**
35 Commerce Dr. (08512)
**Phone—(609) 578-4100**
National—(800) 526-4066
Fax—(609) 655-5300
www.crpindustries.com
Email—info@crpindustries.com
Off. Mgr.—Fabine Gilson
SIC—3443; 3621; NAICS—
335312; Industrial housings,
motors & automotive aftermarket
parts
Employs—50; Estab.—1958
Sales—$5Mil-$10Mil (est)
Distrib.—National
Privately owned corporation

**DALER-ROWNEY U. S. A., LTD.**
7 Corporate Dr. (08512)
**Phone—(609) 655-5252**
Fax—(609) 655-5852
www.daler-rowney.com
Email—customer.service@
usa.daler-rowney.com
Pres., Sales Mgr.—Andrew Daler
Cont.—Jenny Rossi
Dir., Mktg.—Edouard Andre-
Hessig
SIC—3952; Fine art materials;
Brand name—Daler Rowney;
Robert Simmons
Employs—25; Estab.—1989
Sales—$11Mil-$25Mil
25,000 sq ft site, Distrib.—Intl.
Privately owned corporation

**DAN'S HEATING & AIR
CONDITIONING, INC.**
1007 Eastpark Blvd. (08512)
**Phone—(732) 297-9162**
Fax—(609) 395-6892
www.danshvac.net
Email—danshvac@aol.com
Pres.—Daniel Isbitski
Off. Mgr.—Linda Isbitski
Off. Mgr.—Dawn Doran
SIC—3444; HVAC ducts
Employs—40; Estab.—1972
Distrib.—Local
Privately owned corporation

**ENDO PHARMACEUTICAL, INC.**
Div. of Endo Pharmaceuticals, Inc.
8 Clarke Dr. (08512)
**Phone—(609) 409-9010**
National—(888) 262-8855
Fax—(609) 409-1650
www.endo.com
Email—info@valerapharma.com
Hum. Res. Coord.—Brooke
Reeder
SIC—3841; Drug delivery devices
Employs—27; Estab.—2005
12,000 sq ft site, Distrib.—Intl.
Publicly owned corporation
Parent co.—Endo
Pharmaceuticals, Inc., Malvern,
PA
Phone—(484) 216-0000
See Parent Co. Section for full profile.

**FITZPAK, INC.**
110 Melrich Rd., Ste. 2 (08512-
3524)
**Phone—(609) 860-0095**
Fax—(609) 860-8770
www.fitzpak.com
Email—info@fitzpak.com
Pres., CFO & Pers. Mgr.—Andrew
Fitzsimmons
V-P., Sales—Gene Kistler
Opers. Mgr.—Dan Pszonka
Off. Mgr.—Susan McCaffrey
SIC—3089; Plastic thermoforming
Employs—37; Estab.—1988
38,000 sq ft site, Distrib.—National
Privately owned corporation

**†HBC HOME & HARDWARE**
324-A Half Acre Rd. (08512-3254)
**Phone—(609) 860-9990**
National—(800) 523-1268
Fax—(609) 860-9991
www.hberger.com
Email—info@hberger.com
CEO—Donald C. Devine
CFO—Marc Friedant
V-P., Mktg. & Prod. Mgmt.—
Michele Hudec
Mktg. Coord.—Sommer
Zakrzewski
SIC—5074; 5198; 5072; 5085;
Company headquarters &
wholesaler of home
improvement products for
retailers, discount & hardware
stores & municipalities, including
security & builders' hardware,
plumbing products, paint
applicators & home
environmental products; Brand
name—Comfort Zone®; Guard®;
Stanley®; AquaPlumb®; Ultra®;
Wordlock®; Helping Hand®; KC
Tools®; Brightway®
Employs—170; Estab.—1971
Distrib.—Intl.
Privately owned corporation
DBA: HBC Home & Hardware
Products

**INFRAGISTICS, INC.**
2 Commerce Dr. (08512)
**Phone—(609) 448-2000**
National—(800) 231-8588
Fax—(609) 448-2017
www.infragistics.com
Email—sales@infragistics.com
Pres., CEO—Dean Guida
V-P., Prod. Mgmt.—Jason Beres
Dir., Opers.—Randy Miller
IT Mgr.—Pete Lombardo
Hum. Res. Mgr.—Debbie Gager
SIC—7372; Digital presentation
software development
Employs—150; Estab.—2003
Distrib.—National
Privately owned corporation

**INNOPHOS, INC. (H Q)**
259 Prospect Plains Rd., Bldg. A
(08512-3706)
**Phone—(609) 495-2495**
Fax—(609) 860-0138
www.innophos.com
Email—customerservice@
innophos.com
Chrm., Pres. & CEO—Randolph
Gress
CFO—Robert Harrer
V-P., IT & CAO—Charles Brodheim
V-P., Corp. Strategy & CRO—Louis
Calvarin
V-P., Gen. Counsel—William
Farren
V-P., Inv. Rels. & Treas., FP & A—
Mark Feuerbach
V-P., Mfg.—Yasef Murat
V-P., Dist., Logistics & Pur.—Iris
Alvarado
V-P., Hum. Res.—Gail Holler
V-P., Cust. Serv. & Plng.—Michael
Loverich
V-P., Qual. & Regulatory—Susan
Turner
V-P., Bus. Dev., Nutrition, Bus.
Global—Mark Thurston
V-P., Bus. Dev. & Research—
Francois Delprato
V-P., Specialty Ingredients—
Russell Kemp
V-P., Specialty Phosphate Bus.,
Global—Joseph Golowski

GEOGRAPHICAL

## Cranbury—(cont.)

SIC—2874; NAICS—325312; *Corporate headquarters; performance-critical & nutritional specialty ingredients for the food, beverage, dietary supplement, pharmaceutical, oral care & industrial end markets; Brand name—CAL-RISE®; Levair®; Perfection®; SAPP #4®; Regent 12XX®; V-90®; VersaCAL®; SuperBind™; Textur-Melt™; A-Tab®; Di-Tab®; TRI-TAB®; TCP-DC™; Calipharm®; INNOVALT®; ChelaMax; Aminogen®*
Employs—106
Sales—$25Mil-$50Mil
Distrib.—Intl.
Publicly owned corporation

### ITW COVID SECURITY GROUP
Div. of Illinois Tool Works, Inc.
32 Commerce Dr., Ste. 1 *(08512)*
**Phone—(609) 395-5600**
Fax—(609) 860-6401
www.itwcovid.com
Email—info@itw.com
Cont., IT Mgr.—Jim Violett
Dir., Hum. Res.—Louise Dohanish
GM—Bob Carey
Facilities Mgr.—Guenter Strahl
SIC—2821; 2759; NAICS—325211; *Holographic highly secure polymer materials & holographic printing for ID cards, travel & paper documents*
Employs—67; Estab.—2000
50,000 sq ft site, Distrib.—Intl.
Publicly owned corporation
Parent co.—Illinois Tool Works, Inc., Glenview, IL
Phone—(847) 724-7500
See Parent Co. Section for full profile.

### JILL'S THRILL, INC.
18 Hardley Dr. (08512)
**Phone—(609) 395-9900**
Fax—(609) 395-9920
www.companycasuals.com
Email—spusaprince@comcast.net
Pres.—John Wiegand
SIC—2396; 2395; *Apparel screen printing & embroidery*
Employs—2; Estab.—1997
Sales—under $500,000
Distrib.—Regional
Privately owned corporation
AKA: Screen Printing USA

### KEY INTERNATIONAL, INC.
4 Corporate Dr. *(08512)*
**Phone—(609) 619-3685**
Fax—(609) 619-3686
keyinternational.com
Email—sales@keyinternational.com
CEO—Valerie R. Ianieri
Pres.—Kevin Beenders
SIC—3565; 3556; NAICS—333993; *Food & pharmaceutical processing & packaging machinery; Brand name—Cora Butterfly Valves*
Employs—20; Estab.—1968
Sales—$8Mil-$10Mil
2,000 sq ft site, Distrib.—National
Privately owned sub-S corp.

### KRONOS WORLDWIDE, INC.
Div. of Valhi, Inc.
5 Cedarbrook Dr., Ste. 2 (08512)
**Phone—(609) 860-6200**
National—(800) 955-6318
Fax—(609) 860-6214
www.kronostio2.com
Email—kronos.marketing@kronosww.com
Co-Pres., Sales & Mktg.—H. Joseph Maas
Co-Pres.—Robert O'Brien
V-P., Sales & Mktg.—Jean-Pierre Gravel
Off. Admn.—Holly Wigdor

SIC—2816; NAICS—325100; *Titanium dioxide*
Employs—35; Estab.—2000
Sales—$10Mil-$25Mil
Distrib.—Intl.
Publicly owned corporation
Parent co.—Valhi, Inc., Dallas, TX
Phone—(972) 233-1700
See Parent Co. Section for full profile.

### LAMITECH, INC.
Div. of Texpack, Inc.
322 Half-Acre Rd. (08512)
**Phone—(609) 860-8037**
National—(800) 320-7456
Fax—(609) 860-8580
www.lamitech.com
Email—areiser@lamitech.com
GM—Adam Reiser
Hum. Res. Mgr.—Jerry Sarno
SIC—2672; NAICS—322222; *Paper & vinyl lamination*
Employs—25; Estab.—1994
35,000 sq ft site, Distrib.—Regional
Privately owned corporation
Parent co.—Texpack, Inc., Miami, FL
Phone—(305) 358-9696
See Parent Co. Section for full profile.

NEW ENTRY
### LEARNING LINKS, INC.
P.O. Box 326 (08512)
**Phone—(516) 437-9071**
Fax—(516) 437-5392
www.learninglinks.com
Email—learninglx@aol.com
Pres.—Russell Wagner
SIC—2741; *Educational literature study guide publishing for grades K-12; Brand name—Novel-ties; Swan books*
Employs—12; Estab.—1976
Sales—$500,000-$1Mil
Distrib.—National
Privately owned corporation

### LOVING PETS CORP.
110 Melrich Rd., Ste. 1 (08512)
**Phone—(609) 655-3700**
National—(866) 599-7387
Fax—(609) 655-3399
www.lovingpetsproducts.com
Email—admin@lovingpetsproducts.com
Owner—Eric Abbey
Hum. Res. Mgr.—Thomi Young
Proj. Mgr.—Dan Nagy
SIC—2047; 3469; *Natural pet treats & accessories, including stainless steel bowls*
Employs—20; Estab.—2006
Distrib.—Intl.

### MAIN TAPE CO., INC.
1 Capital Dr., Ste. 101 (08512)
**Phone—(609) 395-1704**
National—(800) 526-8273
Fax—(609) 395-3562
www.maintape.com
Pres.—Karen Olson
Plt. Mgr.—John Viotto
SIC—2672; 3081; NAICS—322222; *Pressure sensitive tapes & films; Brand name—PerfecTear; PreView; Screen Seal; Pallet Guard*
Employs—150; Estab.—2002
Distrib.—Intl.
Privately owned corporation

### MAINTAPE, INC.
1 Capital Dr., Ste. 101, Bldg. 1 (08512)
**Phone—(609) 395-1704**
National—(800) 526-8273
Fax—(609) 395-3562
www.maintape.com
Email—info@maintape.com
Pres.—Karen Olsen
Hum. Res. Mgr.—Joe Vanore
Off. Mgr.—Candy Ferguson

SIC—2672; 5113; NAICS—322222; *Manufacturer & distributor of adhesive-backed temporary surface protection films for moving, storage & construction applications*
Employs—100; Estab.—1990
Sales—$1Mil-$25Mil
16,000 sq ft site, Distrib.—National
Privately owned sub-S corp.

### MID STATE FILIGREE SYSTEMS, INC.
22 Brickyard Rd., P.O. Box 435 (08512)
**Phone—(609) 448-8700**
Fax—(609) 443-2833
www.filigreeinc.com
Email—questions@filigreeinc.com
Pres.—Harry Wise
V-P., Sales & Mktg.—Eugene McDermott
V-P., Opers.—Don Matthews
V-P., Engrg.—Ted Betz
Cont., Acct. Mgr.—Ron Notaro
SIC—3272; *Precast concrete filigree wideslab products*
Employs—20; Estab.—1980
697,000 sq ft site, Distrib.—Regional
Privately owned corporation

### MOTTAHEDEH & CO., INC.
5 Corporate Dr. (08512)
**Phone—(609) 409-1490**
National—(800) 443-8225
Fax—(609) 409-6702
www.mottahedeh.com
Email—customerservice@mottahedeh.com
Pres.—Wendy Kvalheim
V-P.—Lyle Stevens
Full Charge Bookkeeper—Carmen Chavarria
SIC—3269; NAICS—327112; *Porcelain dinnerware*
Employs—12; Estab.—1932
Sales—$5Mil-$6Mil
Distrib.—Intl.
Privately owned corporation

### NORLAND PRODUCTS, INC.
2540 Route 130, Ste. 100 (08512)
**Phone—(609) 395-1966**
Fax—(609) 395-9006
www.norlandproducts.com
Email—sales@norlandproducts.com
Pres.—Eric Norland
V-P.—Richard Norland
GM—Timothy Norland
Off. Mgr.—Joan Skibik
SIC—3826; NAICS—334516; *Interferometric microscopes for profiling fiber end faces, PC polished fiber optic connectors, fiber optic mechanical splices & UV & heat curing optical & electronic adhesives*
Employs—20; Estab.—1960
15,000 sq ft site, Distrib.—Intl.
Privately owned corporation

### NOSAJ DISPOSABLES, INC.
3 Security Dr., Ste. 312, P.O. Box 355 (08512)
**Phone—(800) 631-3809**
Fax—(800) 231-9222
www.ndiproducts.com
Pres.—Stanley Slosberg
V-P., Prodn.—David Morales
SIC—2679; NAICS—322200; *Disposable paper products, safety equipment & janitorial supplies*
Employs—20; Estab.—1971
Distrib.—Intl.
Privately owned corporation

### PALAYEKAR COS., INC.
101 Interchange Plz., Ste. 105 (08512)
**Phone—(609) 426-0564**
(609) 662-0509
Fax—(609) 426-9586

www.palnar.com
Email—info@palnar.com
Pres.—Supriya Palayekar
V-P., Opers.—Sachin Mandrekar
SIC—7372; *Software consulting & development*
Employs—49; Estab.—1997
Sales—$2.6Mil-$5Mil
Distrib.—National
Privately owned corporation
AKA: Palnar

### PAULAUR CORP.
105 Melrich Rd. *(08512)*
**Phone—(609) 395-8844**
Fax—(609) 395-8850
www.paulaur.com
Email—sales@paulaur.com
V-P., CFO—Mitchell Stefaniak
V-P., Sales & Mktg.—Alex Martello
V-P., Qual. Assur.—Scott Rodkey
Pur. Mgr.—Amanda Lewey
SIC—2064; 2099; NAICS—311300; *Contract blended food ingredients for the food, pharmaceutical & nutraceutical industries, including dessert toppings, pharmaceutical sugar spheres & NF & directly compressible sugars & fructose; Brand name—Baker's Palette; Colorful Craetions; Megatab Non-Gmo; Paulaur Sugar Spheres*
Employs—100; Estab.—1980
Sales—$10Mil-$25Mil
140,000 sq ft site, Distrib.—Intl.
Privately owned sub-S corp.

### PLANT FOOD CO., INC.
38 Hightstown Cranbury Station Rd. *(08512)*
**Phone—(609) 448-0935**
National—(800) 562-1291
Fax—(609) 443-8038
www.plantfoodco.com
Email—pfc@plantfoodco.com
Pres.—Ted Platz
V-P.—Grant Platz
SIC—2875; NAICS—325314; *Fertilizer blending; Brand name—Green-T® Fertilizers; Blu-Gro® Fertilizers; AdamsEarth® Soil Amendment*
Employs—35; Estab.—1946
Sales—$10Mil-$25Mil
27,000 sq ft site, Distrib.—National
Privately owned corporation

### PLYMOVENT CORPORATION (H Q)
115 Melrich Rd., Ste. 2 (08512-3526)
**Phone—(609) 395-3500**
National—(800) 644-0911
Fax—(609) 655-0569
www.plymovent.com/us/home.aspx
Email—info.usa@plymovent.com
Dir.—Jens Schlueter
Mktg. Mgr.—Carrie Selzone
SIC—3564; NAICS—333400; *Corporate headquarters; indoor pollution control systems for capturing & eliminating exhaust, smoke, dust, fumes & odors (mfg. done in Sweden); Brand name—Plymovent*
Employs—20; Estab.—1988
Distrib.—Intl.
Privately owned corporation
ISO rating—9001:2008

### PRINCETON CHROMATOGRAPHY, INC.
1206 Cranbury-S. River Rd. (08512)
**Phone—(609) 860-1803**
Fax—(609) 860-1805
www.pci-hplc.com
Email—sales@pci-hplc.com
Pres., CFO—Linda Caldwell
V-P.—Walton Caldwell
V-P.—Jeff Caldwell

## Cranbury—(cont.)

SIC—3826; NAICS—334516; *Chromatographic columns & bonded-phase silicas*
Employs—7; Estab.—1995
5,500 sq ft site, Distrib.—Intl.
Privately owned sub-S corp.

### PRINCETON LIGHTWAVE, INC.

2555 U.S. Highway 130, Ste. 1 (08512-3527)
**Phone—(609) 495-2600**
Fax—(609) 395-9113
www.princetonlightwave.com
Email—sales@ princetonlightwave.com
CEO—Mark Itzier
Pres.—Sabbir Rangwala
V-P., Bus. Opers.—Joseph Poekert
Dir., Sales—Ed McIntyre
SIC—3674; NAICS—334413; *Photon counting, dual band cameras, lasers, detectors, arrays & receivers*
Employs—40; Estab.—2000
Sales—$5Mil-$10Mil
Distrib.—Intl.
Privately owned corporation
ISO rating—9001:2008

### †ROBERT-JAMES SALES, INC.

9 Corporate Dr., P.O. Box B (08512)
**Phone—(609) 860-0900**
National—(800) 777-1858
Fax—(609) 860-0910
www.rjsales.com
Email—nj@rjsales.com
Br. Mgr.—Erin Motter
SIC—5074; 5085; *Distributor of stainless steel pipes, valves & fittings*
Employs—10; Estab.—1991
Distrib.—Regional
Privately owned corporation
Parent co.—Robert-James Sales, Inc., Buffalo, NY
Phone—(716) 651-6000
See Parent Co. Section for full profile.

### †SAMSON METAL SERVICE

2604 Route 130 N. *(08512)*
Mail addr: P.O. Box 421, Dayton (08810-0421)
**Phone—(609) 655-0777**
National—(800) 255-6166
Fax—(609) 655-3705
www.sam-metals.com
Email—info@sam-metals.com
Pres.—Jacques Capelluto
GM—Rick Markowitz
Admn. Mgr.—Pat Freels
SIC—5051; *Distributor of steel, metal & plastics*
Employs—19; Estab.—1978
Distrib.—Local
Limited Liability Company
ISO rating—9001:2008

### SASA DEMARLE, INC.

8 Corporate Dr. (08512)
**Phone—(609) 395-0219**
National—(888) 353-9726
Fax—(609) 395-1027
www.sasademarle.com
Email—info@sasademarle.com
CEO—Rudy Boussemart
V-P.—Pierre Bonnet
Sales Mgr., Retail—Arnaldo Miccoli
Acct. Mgr., Subway—Sam Makino
Admn. & Fin. Mgr.—Andrew Rozek
Sales & Mktg. Admn.—Brandon Iacometta
SIC—3089; *Nonstick flexible bakeware; Brand name—Flexipan; Silform; Silpat; Silpain; Flexipat; Roulpat; Siltray; Fiberlux; Fiberglass*
Employs—12; Estab.—1993
Sales—$10Mil-$20Mil
8,000 sq ft site, Distrib.—Intl.
Privately owned corporation

### SOLVAY U. S. A., INC.

Div. of Solvay America, Inc.
8 Cedar Brook Dr., CN-7500 (08512-7500)
**Phone—(609) 860-4000**
National—(888) 776-7337
Fax—(609) 860-2250
www.solvaychemicals.us
Email—solvayusacomm@ solvay.com
CFO—Mark Dahlinger
V-P., GM—John Foley
Dir., Comms.—John Klucsik
SIC—2819; 2869; *Corporate headquarters & industrial chemicals*
Employs—350; Estab.—1998
Sales—$1.5Bil
Distrib.—Intl.
Publicly owned corporation
AKA: Solvay
Parent co.—Solvay America, Inc., Houston, TX
Phone—(713) 525-6500
See Parent Co. Section for full profile.

### STE FABRICATION, INC.

28 Haypress Rd., Ste. 106 (08512)
**Phone—(732) 274-0024**
Fax—(732) 274-0043
Email—rj.stefabrication@verizon.net
Pres.—Rick Josephson
SIC—3312; *Stainless steel fabrication*
Employs—2; Estab.—2000
Sales—under $500,000
Distrib.—Local
Privately owned sub-S corp.

### SUN PHARMACEUTICAL INDUSTRIES, INC.

270 Prospect Plains Rd. (08512)
**Phone—(609) 495-2800**
Fax—(609) 495-2715
www.sunpharma.com
GM—Scott Randby
IT Mgr.—Chandulal Shah
Hum. Res. Rep.—Drastee Patel
SIC—2834; NAICS—325412; *Pharmaceutical preparations*
Employs—160; Estab.—2006
Sales—$50Mil-$100Mil (est)
275,000 sq ft site, Distrib.—Intl.
Privately owned corporation

### SYSTECH SOLUTIONS, INC.

2540 U.S. Highway 130, Ste. 128 (08512)
**Phone—(609) 395-8400**
National—(800) 847-7123
Fax—(609) 395-0064
www.systech-tips.com
Email—info@systech-tips.com
Pres., CEO—Robert DeJean
CFO—Peter Tantillo
IT Mgr.—Paul Juska
Hum. Res. Mgr.—Hope Hurley
SIC—3565; NAICS—333993; *Packaging systems for the pharmaceutical industry*
Employs—100; Estab.—1995
Distrib.—Intl.
Privately owned corporation

### †TRI-ED/NORTHERN VIDEO DISTRIBUTION

Div. of Tri-Ed Distribution, Inc.
7 Corporate Dr., Ste. 2 (08512-3634)
**Phone—(609) 860-0708**
National—(800) 366-4472
Fax—(609) 860-0864
www.tri-ed.com
Email—info@tri-ed.com
Reg. Dir.—Steve Chilimidos

SIC—5064; 5065; *Distributor of security, network video & surveillance equipment; Brand name—DSC; Panasonic; UTC Fire & Security; Pelco; Sony Electronics Inc.; Bosch Security; Speco Technologies; System Sensor*
Employs—20; Estab.—1986
Distrib.—National
Privately owned corporation
Parent co.—Tri-Ed Distribution, Inc., Woodbury, NY
Phone—(516) 941-2800
See Parent Co. Section for full profile.

### TRUMPF PHOTONICS, INC.

Div. of TRUMPF, Inc.
2601 US Route 130 S. *(08512)*
**Phone—(609) 925-8200**
Fax—(609) 409-7021
www.us.trumpf.com
Email—info@us.trumpf.com
Mng. Dir.—Georg Treusch
Dir., Operation—Carl Miester
Dir., RF Generator—Greg Charache
Off. Mgr.—Stacey Mignone
SIC—3699; 3542; 3827; NAICS—333513; *High-power semiconductor lasers, RF generators, optical components & laser mirrors*
Employs—150; Estab.—2002
Sales—$80Mil
Distrib.—Intl.
Privately owned corporation
ISO rating—9001
Parent co.—TRUMPF, Inc., Farmington, CT
Phone—(860) 255-6000
See Parent Co. Section for full profile.

### †UNITED STATIONERS SUPPLY CO.

Div. of United Stationers, Inc.
100 Liberty Way (08512)
**Phone—(609) 619-4000**
National—(866) 733-4894
Fax—(609) 409-9066
www.unitedstationers.com
Email—marketing@ussco.com
Br. Mgr.—Wayne Scott
Off. Mgr.—Joe LaBruna
Asst. Mgr.—Steve Leibowitz
SIC—5044; 5021; 5112; *Wholesaler of office equipment, furniture & supplies*
Employs—100; Estab.—2005
600,000 sq ft site, Distrib.—Local
Publicly owned corporation
Parent co.—United Stationers, Inc., Deerfield, IL
Phone—(847) 627-7000
See Parent Co. Section for full profile.

### WEST PATTERN WORKS, INC.

124 S. Main St. (08512)
**Phone—(609) 443-6241**
Fax—(609) 443-9466
www.westpatternworks.com
Email—westpattern@verizon.net
Pres.—Douglas Trendell
V-P.—Bill Davis
Secy.-Treas.—John Kwiatkowski
Off. Mgr.—Lauren A. Davis
Off. Mgr.—Teri Kwiatkowski
SIC—3543; NAICS—332997; *Foundry patterns*
Employs—15; Estab.—1972
Sales—$1Mil
Distrib.—National
Privately owned corporation

## Cranford

(Union—N.E.)

### AKRIMAX PHARMACEUTICALS, LLC (H Q)

11 Commerce Dr., 1st Fl., Ste. 100 (07016)
**Phone—(908) 372-0506**
New Jersey—(877) 509-3935
National—(888) 383-1733

Fax—(908) 282-7237
www.akrimax.com
Email—info@akrimax.com
Pres.—Donald C. Olsen
V-P., Opers.—Timothy Soule
SIC—2834; *Company headquarters; specialty pharmaceuticals for the treatment of metobolic diseases (mfg. subcontracted); Brand name—Tironsint®; Nitromist®; Inderal® LA; Lo/Ovral; Norgestrel ; Ethinyl Estradiol*
Employs—15; Estab.—2008
Sales—$5Mil-$10Mil (est)
Limited Liability Company

### ALL-STATE LEGAL

1 Commerce Dr. (07016)
**Phone—(908) 272-0800**
National—(800) 222-0510
Fax—(800) 634-5184
www.aslegal.com
Email—info@aslegal.com
Pres., CEO—Robert H. Busch
CFO & COO—Joe Fuzak
Dir., Sales—Maureen McDonnell
Dir., Mfg.—Jim Landis
Dir., Client Svcs. & Mktg.—Susan Jacobs
Dir., IT—Mark Scocco
Hum. Res. Mgr.—Rosemary Bashwiner
Mktg. Coord.—Lori Genzel
SIC—2752; 2759; 3479; 5112; NAICS—323100; *Full-color engraving & printing of stationery, business cards & marketing materials & distributor of legal specialty office supplies, including filing & mailing envelopes, fine paper, litigation products & general office supplies; Brand name—Fibre-Guard; Redweld; Case-Guard; Perfect Image; ALL-STATE Bond; Sheffield Linen; Counselor Linen; Color-Bands; Counselormark*
Employs—230; Estab.—1946
80,000 sq ft site, Distrib.—National
Privately owned corporation

### ARCADIAN CLOCK CO.

189 North Ave. E. (07016)
**Phone—(908) 276-0276**
www.arcadianclock.com
Email—munro@arcadianclock.com
Owner—David Munro
SIC—3873; NAICS—334518; *Precision regulator clocks*
Employs—1; Estab.—1999
Sales—under $500,000
Distrib.—Local
Sole ownership

### †BAILEY PACKAGING CO., INC.

217 Prospect Ave., Ste. 8-3B (07016-2256)
**Phone—(908) 759-0991**
Fax—(908) 709-1263
www.baileypackaging.com
Email—baileypackaging@att.net
Pres.—Vincent Bailey
V-P.—Erin Bailey Minio
SIC—5113; 5162; 5047; 5049; *Distributor of packaging materials, including plastic bottles, jars, caps, specimen cups, disposable pipettes, vials, microscope slides, transport & centrifuge tubes & laboratory supplies*
Employs—3; Estab.—1998
Distrib.—National
Privately owned corporation

### BERRY BUSINESS PROCEDURE CO.

6 Park St., P.O. Box 845 (07016)
**Phone—(908) 272-6464**
Fax—(908) 272-7607
www.berryprinting.com
Email—berryprint@aol.com
Pres.—David M. Cheek
Cust. Serv. Mgr.—Nancy Moss

GEOGRAPHICAL

## Cranford—(cont.)

SIC—2759; 2761; 2675; NAICS—323116; *Commercial & business form printing & die cutting for the trade*
Employs—4; Estab.—1956
Sales—$1Mil
6,000 sq ft site, Distrib.—National
Privately owned sub-S corp.

### BRITTEN & TRAVEL LITE GOLF, E. F.

22 South Ave. W., P.O. Box 246 (07016)
**Phone—(908) 276-4800**
National—(800) 898-1261
Fax—(908) 276-9153
www.efbritten.com
Email—info@efbritten.com
Pres.—Richard Stokes
V-P.—Marge Turner
Cust. Serv. Rep.—Denise Turner
SIC—3491; 3494; NAICS—332911; *Needle valves & pressure cylinders*
Employs—8; Estab.—1948
27,500 sq ft site, Distrib.—Intl.
Privately owned corporation

### †CHINOOK SCIENCES, LLC (H Q)

20 Commerce Dr., Ste. 350 (07016)
**Phone—(908) 272-5091**
Fax—(908) 272-6404
www.chinooksciences.com
Email—contact@chinooksciences.com
Co-Founder, Chrm. & CEO—Rifat Chalabi
Co-Founder & V-P., Admn.—Fanli Meng
Co-Founder & V-P., R & D—Harry Perry
Group Gen. Counsel—Zachary M. Barth
Sr. Dir., Fin.—Richard Galinkin
Dir., Bus. Dev.—Kenneth Foladare
SIC—5093; *Company headquarters; wholesaler of scrap metals*
Employs—15; Estab.—1998
Limited Liability Company

### COLTWELL INDUSTRIES, INC.

55 Winans Ave. (07016)
**Phone—(908) 276-7600**
Fax—(908) 276-2679
www.coltwell.com
Email—info@coltwell.com
V-P., Sales & Mktg.—Anthony Bengivenga
V-P., Fin.—George Bengivenga
Sales Rep., Inside—Alissa Bengivenga
SIC—3444; 3469; 3499; *Custom & standard extruded aluminum, stainless steel & metal components, shapes, parts, tubing, enclosures & heat sinks, including metal fabrication, cutting & stampings*
Employs—15; Estab.—1992
Sales—$1Mil-$2.5Mil (est)
25,000 sq ft site, Distrib.—Intl.
Privately owned sub-S corp.

### FAUST, INC., RUDOLPH

542 South Ave. E. (07016)
Mail addr: P.O. Box 335, Lambertville (08530)
**Phone—(908) 507-5104**
Email—faustink@faustink.com
Pres.—Peter Faust
Off. Mgr.—Valerie Budd
SIC—2893; 2796; NAICS—325910; *Engraving ink*
Employs—3; Estab.—1922
Distrib.—Intl.
Privately owned corporation

### FEDERAL PLASTICS CORP.

570 South Ave. E., Ste. F-1 (07016)
**Phone—(908) 272-5800**
National—(800) 541-4424
Fax—(908) 272-9021
www.federalplastics.com
Email—info@federalplastics.com
Pres.—Peter T. Triano
V-P.—Michael A. Triano
SIC—2821; 3089; NAICS—325211; *Compounder & distributor of thermoplastics; Brand name—Prism*
Employs—10; Estab.—1960
Sales—$500,000-$1Mil
80,000 sq ft site, Distrib.—Regional
Privately owned sub-S corp.

### GLITTEREX CORP.

7 Commerce Dr. (07016)
**Phone—(908) 272-9121**
Fax—(908) 272-9191
www.glitterex.com
Email—staff@glitterex.com
Pres.—Babu Shetty
V-P., Mktg. & Secy.—Roger Ertle
Cust. Serv. Mgr.—Lauren Dyer
Supt.—Ross Morrone
SIC—3089; 3497; *Plastic & aluminum glitters*
Employs—44; Estab.—1963
60,000 sq ft site, Distrib.—Intl.
Privately owned sub-S corp.

### GUARDTRAX, LLC

11 Commerce Dr., Lobby (07016)
**Phone—(908) 272-0114**
Fax—(908) 276-1088
www.guardtrax.com
Email—gtsales@guardtrax.com
CEO—Rich Pekmezian
Cust. Serv. Mgr.—Melissa Miller
SIC—3663; NAICS—335929; *Handheld GPS & wireless tracking devices for security companies; Brand name—NovaTracker; Maya; Kuva; GuardTrax; MapTrac; VCR; Visual Control Room; Verivision*
Employs—8; Estab.—2003
9,000 sq ft site, Distrib.—Intl.
Limited Liability Company

### J. J. ORLY, INC.

20 Commerce Dr., Ste. 128 (07016)
**Phone—(908) 276-9212**
www.jjorly.com
Email—rtf@jjorly.com
Pres.—William Herbert
V-P.—John Herbert
SIC—3469; *Deep-drawn stainless steel, cold-rolled steel, aluminum, brass & copper enclosures, cans, seamless boxes & cases in standard & custom shapes*
Employs—5
Sales—$500,000-$1Mil (est)

### JACLO INDUSTRIES

129 Dermody St. (07016)
**Phone—(908) 653-4433**
National—(800) 852-3906
Fax—(908) 653-1717
www.jaclo.com
Email—showerall@jaclo.com
Pres.—Larry Brodey
IT Mgr.—David Wolf
Hum. Res. Mgr.—Amanda Opperman
SIC—3432; NAICS—332900; *Showerheads & parts*
Employs—22; Estab.—1976
Sales—$2.6Mil-$5Mil
Distrib.—National
Privately owned corporation
AKA: Durst Corp.

### MADAN PLASTICS, INC.

Div. of Friend Skoler & Co., Inc.
108 N. Union Ave., Ste. 3 (07016)
**Phone—(908) 276-8484**
Fax—(908) 276-9483
www.madanplastics.com
Email—mail@madanplastics.com
GM—Michael Madan
Fin. & Hum. Res. Mgr.—Barbara Della Salla
Cust. Serv. Rep.—Renee Slater
SIC—3089; *Plastic injection molding, pizza dough trays & plastic containers; Brand name—DoughMate; Poly-Cons; BerryMate™*
Employs—50; Estab.—1955
60,000 sq ft site, Distrib.—National
Privately owned sub-S corp.
Parent co.—Friend Skoler & Co., Inc., Saddle Brook, NJ
Phone—(201) 712-0075
See Parent Co. Section for full profile.

### METALICO, INC. (H Q)

186 North Ave. E. (07016)
**Phone—(908) 497-9610**
Fax—(908) 497-1097
www.metalico.com
Email—info@metalico.com
Chrm., Pres. & CEO—Carlos E. Aguero
CFO—Eric W. Finlayson
Ex. V-P., Gen. Counsel—Arnold S. Graber
Ex. V-P.—Michael Drury
V-P. & Corp. Cont.—Kevin Whalen
V-P., Bus. Dev.—David DelBianco
SIC—3482; 3356; NAICS—332992; *Corporate headquarters; lead & lead products, ammunition & recycling*
Employs—12; Estab.—1997
Sales—$1Mil-$2.5Mil (est)
Distrib.—National
Publicly owned corporation

### NATIONAL CHRISTMAS PRODUCTS

2 Commerce Dr. (07016)
**Phone—(908) 709-4141**
National—(800) 280-8733
Fax—(908) 709-4145
www.nationaltree.com
Email—sales@nationaltree.com
Pres., CEO—Joseph A. Puleo
V-P., Secy.—Salvatore J. Puleo, Jr.
V-P., Fin. Mgr.—Richard Puleo
SIC—3999; NAICS—339999; *Artificial Christmas trees & related Christmas products*
Employs—35; Estab.—1990
Sales—$40Mil-$45Mil
100,000 sq ft site, Distrib.—Intl.
Privately owned corporation
AKA: National Tree Company

### NATIONAL MILL INDUSTRY, INC. (H Q)

22 Jackson Dr. (07016)
**Phone—(908) 862-8400**
www.carnivalbras.com
Pres.—Victor Shacalo
SIC—2341; *Corporate headquarters; lingerie (mfg. done overseas)*
Employs—40
Sales—$2.5Mil-$5Mil (est)

### NEWARK GROUP, INC., THE (H Q)

20 Jackson Dr. (07016)
**Phone—(908) 276-4000**
Fax—(908) 276-2888
www.newarkgroup.com
Email—fpapa3@gmail.com
Pres., CEO—Frank Papa
CFO—Gregg Kam
Sr. V-P., Hum. Res.—Manny Silva
V-P., Gen. Counsel—David Ascher
IT Mgr.—Tom Ritter

SIC—2679; NAICS—322200; *Corporate headquarters; paper converting*
Employs—60; Estab.—1912
Sales—$800Mil
Distrib.—National
Privately owned corporation

### NUTS.COM

125 Moen St. (07016)
**Phone—(908) 523-0333**
National—(800) 558-6887
Fax—(908) 272-3585
www.nuts.com
Email—care@nuts.com
Pres.—Jeff Braverman
V-P., Cust. Rels.—Dave Braverman
SIC—2068; 2064; NAICS—311911; *Nut roasting & dried fruits & candies*
Employs—40; Estab.—1929
Distrib.—National
Privately owned corporation
AKA: Nuts On Line

### ORIENT CORP. OF AMERICA (H Q)

6 Commerce Dr., Ste. 301 (07016)
**Phone—(908) 298-0990**
Fax—(908) 298-1833
www.orient-usa.com
Email—satok@orient-usa.com
Pres.—Akihiro Takahashi
V-P.—Koji Sato
Logistics Mgr.—Nadia Trindade
Manager—Keith T. Truzzolino
SIC—2899; *Corporate headquarters; chemical dyes*
Employs—5; Estab.—1979
Sales—under $500,000
Distrib.—Intl.
Privately owned corporation

### PARKER CHOMERICS

Div. of Parker Hannifin Corporation
135 Bryant Ave. (07016)
**Phone—(908) 272-5500**
Fax—(908) 272-2741
www.chomerics.com
Email—chomailbox@parker.com
Regional Mgr.—Eric Krohto
SIC—3679; *Electronic & magnetic interference shielding products*
Employs—50; Estab.—1959
30,000 sq ft site, Distrib.—Intl.
Publicly owned corporation
Parent co.—Parker Hannifin Corporation, Cleveland, OH
Phone—(216) 896-3000
See Parent Co. Section for full profile.

### PEM ALL FIRE EXTINGUISHER CORP.

39-A Myrtle St., P.O. Box 586 (07016)
**Phone—(908) 276-0211**
Fax—(908) 276-8074
www.pemall.com
Pres.—Tom Moskaluk
Off. Mgr.—Lisa Heims
SIC—3669; 2899; NAICS—334290; *Fire extinguishers & suppression systems*
Employs—15; Estab.—1947
10,000 sq ft site, Distrib.—Intl.
Privately owned corporation

### PETRO PACKAGING CO., INC.

16 Quine St., P.O. Box 546 (07016)
**Phone—(908) 272-4054**
Fax—(908) 272-2836
www.petropackaging.com
Email—info@petropackaging.com
Pres.—Rick Petrozziello
V-P.—John Petrozziello
Sales Mgr.—Don Ferrel

## Cranford—(cont.)

SIC—3082; NAICS—326121;
*Custom extruded CAB & PETG
tubing, rods & profiles for the
point-of-purchase, confectionary,
cosmetic, medical, hobby, toys,
industrial, arts/crafts &
pharmaceutical industries*
Employs—35; Estab.—1979
Sales—$5Mil-$10Mil (est)
Distrib.—Regional
Privately owned corporation

**PLYMOUTH PRINTING CO., INC. (H Q)**
450 North Ave., P.O. Box 68 (07016)
**Phone—(908) 276-8100**
National—(800) 450-8740
Fax—(908) 276-6566
www.plymouthprinting.com
Email—jmcmahon@
plymouthprintingcompany.com
CEO—H. D. Auerbach
Plt. Mgr.—Guy Vicari
Hum. Res. Mgr.—Jennifer McMahon
Pur. Agt.—Wendy Cenicoli
SIC—2759; NAICS—323100;
*Corporate headquarters;
pharmaceutical labels & inserts*
Employs—8; Estab.—1928
Sales—$12Mil-$15Mil
50,000 sq ft site, Distrib.—Intl.
Privately owned corporation

†**SALOMON BROS. EQUIPMENT CO., INC.**
P.O. Box 43 (07016)
**Phone—(908) 931-9311**
Fax—(908) 931-9312
www.salomonbros.com
Email—salomonbros@comcast.net
Pres.—David R. Salomon
Serv. Mgr.—Ron Salomon
SIC—5084; *Distributor of waste &
recycling equipment & supplies,
including consulting, national
equipment service & installation,
waste flow efficiency experts,
commodity brokerage & waste
audits; Brand name—Rudco;
Galbreath; Marathon; IBC; IPS;
Selco; Cooper; PTR; Accurate;
Piqua; WASP; US Wiretie; Cavert
Wire; American Baler; Allegheny;
Shred-Tech; Consolidated;
Wastequip; Kenbay; Orwalk;
BACE; AEP*
Employs—4; Estab.—1983
Sales—$1Mil-$2Mil
5,000 sq ft site, Distrib.—National
Privately owned sub-S corp.

†**SANZO LTD.**
35 Munsee Dr. (07016)
**Phone—(908) 276-6654**
Fax—(908) 276-2733
www.sanzoltd.com
Email—sales@sanzoltd.com
Owner & Pres.—Carol Sanzo
SIC—5046; 5084; 5074;
*Wholesaler of industrial,
commercial & plumbing
equipment*
Employs—5; Estab.—1988
Sales—$6.6Mil
1,500 sq ft site, Distrib.—National
Privately owned corporation

**SUNFLEX PACKAGERS, INC.**
2 Commerce Dr. (07016)
**Phone—(908) 709-1500**
Fax—(908) 708-1525
www.sunflexpackagers.com
Email—productinfo@
sunflexpackagers.com
Pres., CEO—Manoj Patel
V.-P., Admn.—Sandy Patel
Dir., Opers.—Manish Patel

SIC—3081; NAICS—326113;
*Plastic film & converting of
flexible packaging materials in
rolls & pouches*
Employs—10; Estab.—2001
50,000 sq ft site, Distrib.—National
Privately owned corporation

**T C GRAPHICS, INC.**
109 South Ave. W. (07016)
**Phone—(908) 276-7710**
Fax—(908) 276-5885
Email—tcgraphics.inc@verizon.net
Pres.—Tom Carvalho
Graphic Designer—Jeff Sowa
SIC—2752; 2791; 2796; NAICS—
323122; *Offset printing,
typesetting & color separations*
Employs—9; Estab.—1985
Sales—$500,000-$1Mil
Distrib.—Intl.
Privately owned corporation

**TOFUTTI BRANDS, INC.**
50 Jackson Dr. (07016)
**Phone—(908) 272-2400**
Fax—(908) 272-9492
www.tofutti.com
Email—info@tofutti.com
Pres., CEO—David Mintz
CFO—Steve Kass
Off. Mgr.—Terri Quinn
SIC—2024; 2051; 2052; NAICS—
311520; *Kosher soy-based ice
cream, dessert bars, cakes,
cookies & pastries*
Employs—15; Estab.—1981
Sales—$1Mil-$2.5Mil
Distrib.—Intl.
Privately owned corporation

**U. S. BLADE MFG.**
90 Myrtle St. (07016)
**Phone—(908) 272-2898**
National—(800) 252-3387
Fax—(908) 272-2717
www.usblade.com
Email—patcosgrove.usblade@
verizon.net
Pres.—Anthony Calenda
Sales Mgr.—Pat Cosgrove
SIC—3421; NAICS—332200;
*Industrial blades*
Employs—75; Estab.—1980
Sales—$6Mil-$10Mil
75,000 sq ft site, Distrib.—Intl.
Privately owned corporation

†**W. W. GRAINGER, INC.**
55 Jackson Dr. (07016)
**Phone—(908) 272-7156**
Fax—(908) 272-2074
www.grainger.com
Email—info@grainger.com
Br. Mgr.—Michael Crupe
SIC—5063; 5087; *Wholesaler of
electrical & janitorial supplies,
including lightbulbs, motors &
wire*
Employs—10; Estab.—1997
Distrib.—Intl.
Privately owned corporation
Parent co.—W. W. Grainger, Inc.,
Lake Forest, IL
Phone—(847) 535-1000
See Parent Co. Section for full profile.

**WEAVER ASSOCS. PRINTING SERVICE, INC.**
945 Lincoln Ave. E. (07016)
**Phone—(908) 272-6224**
Fax—(908) 272-9830
www.weaverprinting.com
Email—sales@weaverprinting.com
Owner & Pres.—John Weaver
Off. Mgr.—Sheryl Evers
SIC—2759; NAICS—323100;
*Commercial printing*
Employs—15; Estab.—1962
10,000 sq ft site, Distrib.—Local
Privately owned corporation
AKA: Weaver Printing & Digital
Copies

**Z I PARTS CO.**
215 Cristiani St. (07016)
**Phone—(908) 241-0109**
Fax—(908) 241-2558
Owner—Zbigniew Bielen
SIC—3499; 3599; *Metal
fabrication & machining job shop*
Employs—1; Estab.—1986
Distrib.—Local
Sole ownership

---

## Cream Ridge
(Monmouth—N.E.)

**A-1 J D K SPECIALTIES**
1 Millstream Rd. (08514)
**Phone—(732) 928-9495**
www.trophynj.com
Email—trophynj@aol.com
Owner—Gary Conk, Sr.
SIC—3089; 3479; *Plastic & metal
trophies, plaques & awards
engraving*
Employs—1; Estab.—2011
Sales—under $500,000
1,000 sq ft site, Distrib.—Regional
Limited Liability Company

**CENTRAL ART & ENGINEERING, INC.**
500 Goldman Dr., P.O. Box 289 (08514)
**Phone—(609) 758-5922**
(609) 758-5924
Fax—(609) 758-5923
www.centralartonline.com
Email—centralart22@yahoo.com
Pres., Hum. Res. Mgr.—John
Makkay
V.-P., GM & IT Mgr.—Eric Makkay
SIC—3089; 3993; NAICS—
325211; *Custom plastic
fabrication & cutting & interior &
exterior signage & graphics*
Employs—8; Estab.—1979
Sales—over $900,000
17,000 sq ft site, Distrib.—Intl.
Privately owned corporation
AKA: Plastics Concepts

**CREAM RIDGE WINERY**
145 Route 539 S., P.O. Box 98 (08514)
**Phone—(609) 259-9797**
Fax—(609) 259-1852
www.creamridgewinery.com
Email—crwinery@
creamridgewinery.com
Owner—Thomas R. Amabile
GM—Tim Schlitzer
SIC—2084; NAICS—312130;
*Wines*
Employs—8; Estab.—1988
Sales—$500,000-$1Mil
Distrib.—Regional
Privately owned corporation

**CUSTOM WOOD, LLC**
400 Goldman Dr. (08514)
**Phone—(609) 758-8288**
(609) 758-0366
Fax—(609) 758-0893
www.customwoodllc.com
Email—lisa@customwoodllc.com
Off. Mgr.—Lisa Zucatti
SIC—2434; 2431; 3281; NAICS—
337110; *Kitchen & bathroom
cabinets & granite countertops*
Employs—4; Estab.—1973
Sales—$1.5Mil-$2Mil
9,000 sq ft site, Distrib.—Local
Limited Liability Company

†**ENVIRONMENTAL SITE FURNISHINGS**
Div. of SIGMA Corp.
700 Goldman Dr. (08514)
**Phone—(281) 975-1776**
(201) 916-0730
National—(888) 367-1115
Fax—(281) 271-8410
www.esfbysigma.com

Email—sales@esfbysigma.com
Dir., Sales, Natl.—Kevin Mahoney
SIC—5031; 5021; 5091;
*Distributor of outdoor public site
furnishings & amenities,
including seating, benches,
bollards, cycle parking racks &
litter bins*
Employs—10; Estab.—1985
Sales—$5Mil-$10Mil
Distrib.—Intl.
Privately owned corporation
Parent co.—SIGMA Corp., Cream
Ridge, NJ
Phone—(609) 758-0800
See Parent Co. Section for full profile.

**JACKSON RACING ENGINES, INC., HENRY**
787 Route 537 (08514)
Mail addr: 787 Monmouth Rd.,
Cream Ridge (08514-2401)
**Phone—(609) 758-7476**
Fax—(609) 758-4991
www.henryjacksonracingengines.com
Email—hjackson1970@yahoo.com
Pres.—Henry Jackson
SIC—3519; 3714; *Automotive
racing engines*
Employs—2; Estab.—1995
Sales—under $500,000
Distrib.—Regional
Privately owned corporation

**NATIONAL ELECTRIC WIRE CO.**
100 Goldman Dr. (08514)
**Phone—(609) 758-3600**
Fax—(609) 758-6300
Email—gail@
nationalelectricwire.com
Pres.—Alan R. Keith
V.-P., Qual. Control—John Herr
Secy., Off. & Sales Mgr.—Gail C.
Keith
Dept. Mgr.—Steven Herr
SIC—3357; *Nickel chrome, nickel,
flat, strip, thermocouple &
copper-based alloy wire*
Employs—40; Estab.—1983
Sales—$10Mil
70,000 sq ft site, Distrib.—Intl.
Privately owned corporation
ISO rating—9001:2008

**RAKO MACHINE PRODUCTS, INC.**
845 Monmouth Rd. (08514)
**Phone—(609) 758-1200**
Owner—John Vanderduys
SIC—3599; *Prototypes & CNC
machining job shop*
Employs—6; Estab.—1965
Sales—$500,000-$1Mil (est)
4,500 sq ft site, Distrib.—Intl.
Privately owned corporation

†**SIGMA CORP. (H Q)**
700 Goldman Dr., P.O. Box 300 (08514)
**Phone—(609) 758-0800**
National—(800) 999-2550
Fax—(609) 758-1399
www.sigmaco.com
Email—engg@sigmaco.com
Chrm., CEO—Jim McGivern
Pres.—Larry Rybacki
CFO—Jeff Marcus
V.-P.—Mitchell Rona
V.-P.—S. Bhattacharji
Hum. Res. Mgr.—Dave Press
SIC—5051; *Corporate
headquarters; distributor of
underground pipe fittings for
drainage & sewer applications;
Brand name—SIGMA; ONELOK;
ZIP FLANGE*
Employs—90; Estab.—1985
Company-wide: 280
50,000 sq ft site, Distrib.—Intl.
Privately owned corporation

GEOGRAPHICAL

## Cream Ridge—(cont.)

**SIGNATURE SIGN**
31 Milaystown Rd. (08514)
Mail addr: P.O. Box 9993, Trenton
(08650)
**Phone—(609) 351-2231**
Fax—(609) 208-3234
www.signaturesignsanddesigns.net
Email—michele@
signaturesignsanddesigns.net
Owner—Michele Long
SIC—3993; *Interior & exterior
signs*
Employs—5; Estab.—2004
Sales—under $500,000
1,000 sq ft site, Distrib.—Regional
Privately owned corporation

## Cresskill
(Bergen—N.E.)

NEW ENTRY
**HENGSTENBERG GMBH**
90 Pershing Pl. (07626)
**Phone—(201) 568-6596**
Owner—Steffen Hengstenberg
SIC—2035; *Pickles*
Employs—4; Estab.—2001
Sales—$500,000-$1Mil (est)
10,000 sq ft site, Distrib.—Intl.
Privately owned corporation

**INNOVATIVE CARPETS**
45 Legion Dr. (07626)
**Phone—(201) 894-1008**
Fax—(201) 894-1067
www.innovativecarpets.com
Email—info@innovativecarpets.com
Owner—Robert Couri
Off. Admn.—Zach Mufson
SIC—2273; NAICS—314110;
*Carpets & rugs*
Employs—7; Estab.—1997
Sales—$1Mil-$2.5Mil
Distrib.—National
Privately owned corporation

**SILVER PALATE KITCHENS, INC.**
211 Knickerbocker Rd., P.O. Box
512 (07626)
**Phone—(201) 568-0110**
Fax—(201) 568-8844
www.silverpalate.com
Email—peter@silverpalate.com
Pres.—Peter Harris
SIC—2035; 2099; *Pasta &
cooking sauces, condiments,
oatmeal, chutneys, olives, ice
cream toppings, vinegars,
salsas, mustards & organic salad
dressings & mayonnaise*
Employs—10; Estab.—1977
Distrib.—National
Privately owned corporation

NEW ENTRY
**THETICA SYSTEMS, INC.**
145 13th St. (07626)
**Phone—(201) 399-7800**
Fax—(201) 266-6969
www.theticasystems.com
CEO—Ariel Yankilevich
CFO—Diti Yankilevich
SIC—7373; 7372; *Computer
systems integration &
prepackaged software
development; Brand name—
Thetica Explorer™; Thetica
Analytics Cloud Engine™;
Thetica Trader Tools™*
Employs—3; Estab.—2010
Distrib.—National
Privately owned corporation

**WILLRICH PRECISION
INSTRUMENT, INC.**
80 Broadway (07626)
**Phone—(201) 567-1411**
Fax—(201) 567-7470
www.willrich.com
Email—sales@willrich.com
Pres.—George Chitos
Off. Mgr.—Linda Eiter
SIC—3829; *Measuring
instrumentation*
Employs—10; Estab.—1986
4,500 sq ft site, Distrib.—National
Sole ownership

## Dayton
(Middlesex—N.E.)

**†AGFA CORP.**
400 Heller Park Ct. (08810)
**Phone—(973) 812-0400**
National—(888) 274-8626
Fax—(973) 812-1630
www.pitman.com
Email—info@pitman.com
CEO—Anthony P. Crupi
Ex. V-P., Opers.—James Sause
Dir., Hum. Res.—Vincent Lotano
SIC—5199; *Corporate
headquarters & distributor of
digital imaging products &
prepress & pressroom
consumable products for the
graphic communications
industry*
Employs—100; Estab.—1906
Distrib.—National
Privately owned corporation
Parent co.—Agfa Corp., Elmwood
Park, NJ
Phone—(201) 440-0111
See Parent Co. Section for full profile.

**ALLEGRA PRINCETON**
12 Stults Rd., Ste. 100 (08810)
**Phone—(609) 771-4000**
National—(800) 681-7446
Fax—(609) 228-5828
www.allegraprinceton.com
Email—sales@jlisigns.com
CEO—David Kovacs
SIC—2759; 3993; NAICS—
323100; *Printing, digital archiving,
finishing & mailing service*
Employs—30; Estab.—1980
15,000 sq ft site, Distrib.—National
Privately owned sub-S corp.

**ALLEGRA PRINT & IMAGING, INC.**
12 Stults Rd. (08810)
**Phone—(609) 771-4000**
Fax—(609) 228-5828
www.allegraprinceton.com
Email—info@allegraprinceton.com
Pres.—Ellis Galimidi
Sales Mgr.—Maurice Galimidi
Cust. Serv. Rep.—Matt Liss
SIC—2752; 2759; NAICS—
323122; *Offset, digital, instant &
color printing, large-format
imaging, graphic design &
mailing, fulfillment & marketing
services*
Employs—35; Estab.—1991
Sales—$6Mil-$10Mil
9,000 sq ft site, Distrib.—National
Privately owned corporation
AKAs: Allegra & Ellco Enterprises,
LTD

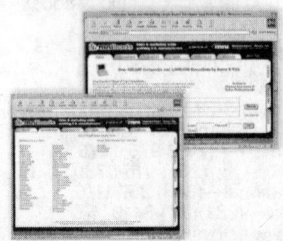
**mnileads.com**
*Looking for Quality Sales Leads
on the Internet? Look no Further!*

**ARCHTECH ELECTRONICS CORP.**
117 Docks Corner Rd., Ste. A
(08810-2529)
**Phone—(732) 355-1288**
National—(800) 288-1688
Fax—(732) 355-1008
www.archtech.net
Email—archtech@archtech.net
Owner—Peggy Foung
Pres.—Kirk Lee
V-P.—Paul Foung
Dir., Mfg.—Mike Wong
Dir., Operation—Austin Yang
Dir., Mktg.—George Tsao
Off. Mgr.—Jenny Sun
SIC—3643; 3669; 3678; 3679;
NAICS—335931; *Fiber-optic &
copper networking cable
assemblies & components for
the data telecom structured
cabling industry; Brand name—
NTW*
Employs—36; Estab.—1987
Sales—$10Mil
30,000 sq ft site, Distrib.—Intl.
Privately owned corporation

**CARY COMPOUNDS, LLC**
5 Nicholas Ct. (08810)
**Phone—(732) 274-2626**
National—(888) 358-4695
Fax—(732) 274-9003
www.carycompounds.com
Email—carycompounds@aol.com
Pres.—Charles Cary
Off. Mgr.—Abier Baynur
SIC—3089; *Plastic pellets*
Employs—25
Sales—$25Mil
66,000 sq ft site, Distrib.—Intl.
Limited Liability Company
ISO rating—9001:2008

**CENTRAL MILLS, INC.**
473 Ridge Rd. (08810)
**Phone—(732) 329-2009**
Fax—(732) 355-0233
www.freezecmi.com
Email—postmaster@freezecmi.com
Owner—Maurice Shalom
CEO—Charlie Tebele
Pres.—Lou Shalom
Whse. Mgr.—Ashuh Ooshi
SIC—2339; 2329; NAICS—
315228; *Men's & women's
sportswear*
Employs—200; Estab.—1986
187,000 sq ft site, Distrib.—
National
Privately owned corporation
AKA: Freeze

**EASY PAK SERVICES OF NEW
JERSEY**
6 Nicholas Ct., P.O. Box 676
(08810)
**Phone—(732) 274-2428**
Fax—(732) 274-2908
www.easypak.com
Pres.—Victor Veston
Hum. Res. Mgr. & IT Rep.—
Michelle Coia-Veston
SIC—2653; 3089; *Cardboard &
plastic packaging materials &
contract re-packaging of
consumer items*
Employs—28; Estab.—2004
70,000 sq ft site, Distrib.—National
Limited Liability Company

**FLINT GROUP**
6 Corn Rd. (08810)
**Phone—(732) 329-4627**
Fax—(732) 329-1428
www.flintgrp.com
Email—info@flintgrp.com

Opers. Mgr.—Don Witt
SIC—2893; NAICS—325910;
*Printing ink*
Employs—15; Estab.—1975
Distrib.—National
Privately owned corporation
Parent co.—Flint Group, Plymouth,
MI
Phone—(734) 781-4600
See Parent Co. Section for full profile.

**†FRANCO APPAREL GROUP**
231 Docks Corner Rd. (08810)
**Phone—(732) 438-5170**
www.francoapparel.com
Email—info@francoapparel.com
V-P., Dist.—Ronnie Blazer
SIC—5136; 5137; *Distributor of
children's clothing*
Employs—5; Estab.—1989
Distrib.—National
Privately owned corporation
Parent co.—Franco Apparel
Group, New York, NY
Phone—(212) 967-7272
See Parent Co. Section for full profile.

**†GARDEN STATE TILE
DISTRIBUTORS, INC.**
1290 Route 130 (08810)
**Phone—(732) 329-0860**
Fax—(732) 329-4636
www.gstile.com
Email—jfrance@gstile.com
Off. Mgr.—Jill France
Cust. Serv. Rep.—Jeff Strachan
SIC—5032; *Distributor of floor tile*
Employs—20; Estab.—1957
Distrib.—Regional
Privately owned corporation
Parent co.—Garden State Tile
Distributors, Inc., Farmingdale,
NJ
Phone—(732) 938-6675
See Parent Co. Section for full profile.

**GMB NORTH AMERICA, INC.**
100 Herrod Blvd. (08810)
**Phone—(609) 655-2422**
National—(800) 421-5019
Fax—(609) 655-2257
www.gmb.net
Email—gmbcorp@gmb.net
Pres.—Ben Koo
Cont.—Senya Nishijima
IT Mgr.—Hector Guevara
Hum. Res. Mgr.—Joyce Di Bari
Asst. Mgr.—Karen Antenucci
Administrator—Debby Waldron
Cust. Serv. Rep.—Laura Stowffer
SIC—3089; *Water pumps*
Employs—50; Estab.—1985
Sales—$11Mil-$25Mil
Distrib.—National
Privately owned corporation

**GRAPE ESCAPE, THE**
12 Stults Rd., Ste. 101 (08810)
**Phone—(609) 409-9463**
www.gograpes.com
Email—info@thegrapeescape.net
Pres.—Edward Ventura
SIC—2084; *Wines*
Employs—10; Estab.—2004
Sales—$750,000
Distrib.—Local
Privately owned corporation

**GRAPH CORR, LLC**
Div. of Rock-Tenn Co.
4 Corn Rd. (08810)
**Phone—(732) 355-0088**
Fax—(732) 274-9239
www.rocktenn.com
Email—lkrug@rocktenn.com
Cont.—John Daly
GM—Hugh Murphy
Cust. Serv. Mgr.—Lisa Krug
SIC—3089; 2653; NAICS—
322211; *Litho laminated sheets &
finished cartons*
Employs—26; Estab.—2001
55,000 sq ft site, Distrib.—National
Publicly owned corporation

## Dayton—(cont.)

Parent co.—Rock-Tenn Co.,
Norcross, GA
  Phone—(770) 448-2193
  See Parent Co. Section for full profile.

### GUARDIAN DRUG CO., INC.

2 Charles Ct. (08810)
**Phone—(609) 860-2600**
Fax—(609) 860-8008
www.guardiandrug.com
Email—info@guardiandrug.com
Pres.—Arvind B. Dhruv
Cont.—Jayshree Dixit
Hum. Res. & Opers. Mgr.—Bakul
  Doshi
Pur. Agt.—Samir Master
SIC—2834; NAICS—325412;
  *Over-the-counter pharmaceutical
  preparations*
Employs—110; Estab.—1988
Sales—$50Mil-$100Mil (est)
Distrib.—National
Privately owned corporation

### IMPACT UNLIMITED, INC.

250 Ridge Rd., P.O. Box 558
  (08810)
**Phone—(732) 274-2000**
National—(800) 321-1148
Fax—(732) 274-2417
www.impactunlimited.com
Email—sales@impactunlimited.com
Chrm.—Richard Nelson
Pres.—Kenneth R. Payne
V-P., Sales—Sandra Stransky
Cont.—Joseph Haggerty
IT Mgr.—Allen Hall
Hum. Res. Mgr.—Kim Coakley
SIC—2541; *Trade show exhibit,
  event & meeting solutions*
Employs—150; Estab.—1973
206,000 sq ft site, Distrib.—Intl.
Privately owned corporation

### INTERNATIONAL FLAVORS &
### FRAGRANCES, INC.

150 Docks Corner Rd. (08810)
**Phone—(732) 329-4600**
Fax—(732) 329-5635
www.iff.com
Email—xpressinformation@iff.com
Hum. Res. Bus. Ptnr., Flavors &
  Fragrances—Rebecca Force
Bus. & Hum. Res. Mgr.—Debra
  Cohen
SIC—2087; 2844; NAICS—
  311900; *Flavoring & fragrances*
Employs—300; Estab.—1964
Distrib.—Intl.
Publicly owned corporation
Parent co.—International Flavors &
  Fragrances, Inc., New York, NY
  Phone—(212) 765-5500
  See Parent Co. Section for full profile.

### IRVING RICE & CO.

161 Docks Corner Rd. (08810)
**Phone—(609) 655-6890**
National—(800) 366-7470
Fax—(609) 655-6895
www.suite-k.com
Email—info@suite-k.com
Pres.—Kathleen Molyneaux
Manager—Nonita Carroll
SIC—2844; NAICS—325600;
  *Cosmetics*
Employs—35; Estab.—1992
Distrib.—Intl.
Privately owned corporation
AKA: Suite-K Value Added
  Services, LLC

### L & L WELDING CONTRACTORS,
### INC.

3 Wheeling Rd. (08810)
**Phone—(609) 395-1600**
Fax—(609) 395-0109
Pres.—Frank Lagahuta
Foreman—Tom Lagahuta

SIC—3312; *Steel fabrication*
Employs—9; Estab.—1947
Sales—$1Mil-$2.5Mil
Distrib.—National
Privately owned corporation

### LIFEGAS, LLC

174 Ridge Rd., Ste. A (08810)
**Phone—(866) 543-3427**
Fax—(732) 438-9222
www.lifegas.com
Email—dayton@lifegas.com
GM—David Knight
Lead Filler—Alex Argenal
SIC—2813; NAICS—325120;
  *Medical compressed oxygen*
Employs—15; Estab.—2003
Sales—$5Mil-$10Mil (est)
Distrib.—Local
Limited Liability Company
AKA: Linde Group, The
Parent co.—LifeGas, LLC, Atlanta,
  GA
  Phone—(866) 543-3427
  See Parent Co. Section for full profile.

### LT APPAREL GROUP

Div. of Lollytogs, Ltd.
301 Herrod Blvd., P.O. Box 1001
  (08810)
**Phone—(732) 438-5500**
Fax—(732) 438-6979
www.ltapparel.com
Email—information@ltapparel.com
CEO—Morris Scotton
SIC—2325; 2339; NAICS—
  315200; *Children's clothing,
  including boys' & girls' casual
  shirts & pants*
Employs—100; Estab.—2003
Sales—$5Mil-$10Mil (est)
Distrib.—Intl.
Privately owned corporation
Parent co.—Lollytogs, Ltd., New
  York, NY
  Phone—(212) 502-6000
  See Parent Co. Section for full profile.

NEW ENTRY

### MEGA FORTRIS AMERICAS, INC.

3 Chris Ct., P.O. Box 934 (08810)
**Phone—(732) 230-3015**
Fax—(732) 909-2301
www.megafortrisusa.com
Email—sales@megafortrisusa.com
Owner—Claus Holmelund
SIC—3089; *Plastic security seals
  & boxes for the banking & casino
  industries*
Employs—7
Sales—$500,000-$1Mil (est)
Distrib.—Intl.
Privately owned corporation

### MINCING OVERSEAS SPICE CO.

10 Tower Rd., Bldg. KN (08810)
**Phone—(732) 355-9944**
Fax—(732) 355-9964
www.mincing.com
Email—mail@mincing.com
Pres.—M. Ruparelia
Administrator—Dawn Bryson
Administrator—Dawn Rey
SIC—2099; *Bulk spices*
Employs—30; Estab.—1927
50,000 sq ft site, Distrib.—Intl.
Privately owned corporation

### NETWORK ACCESS SYSTEMS

19 Isaac Dr. (08810)
**Phone—(732) 355-9770**
Fax—(732) 355-9774
www.naspc.com
Pres.—Bruce Lin
SIC—3571; *Computer assembly*
Employs—7
Sales—$2.5Mil-$5Mil (est)
Privately owned corporation

### NORTH AMERICA PACKAGING
### CORP. (NAMPAC)

Div. of BWAY Corporation
7 Wheeling Rd. (08810)
**Phone—(732) 997-4100**
Fax—(732) 997-4138
www.bwaycorp.com
Email—sales@nampac.com
Plt. Mgr.—Tamlin Ferguson
Hum. Res. Mgr.—Daniel Danson
SIC—3089; *Plastic pails & lids*
Employs—140; Estab.—1947
120,000 sq ft site, Distrib.—Local
Publicly owned corporation
Parent co.—BWAY Corporation,
  Atlanta, GA
  Phone—(770) 645-4800
  See Parent Co. Section for full profile.

### RICHMOND INDUSTRIES, INC.

1 Chris Ct. (08810)
**Phone—(732) 355-1616**
Fax—(732) 355-1617
www.richmond-industries.com
Email—kdigrazio@richmond-
  industries.com
Owner & Pres.—Keith DiGrazio
Sales Mgr.—James Reid
Opers. Mgr.—Jennifer Williams
Foundry Mgr.—Ed Chando, Jr.
SIC—3364; 3365; NAICS—
  331522; *Brass, bronze,
  manganese & aluminum bronze,
  aluminum & copper machined
  castings*
Employs—40; Estab.—1959
Sales—over $11Mil
40,000 sq ft site, Distrib.—National
Privately owned sub-S corp.

### ROBOTUNITS, INC.

5 Chris Ct., Ste. G (08810)
**Phone—(732) 438-0500**
Fax—(732) 438-0509
www.robotunits.com
Email—info.usa1@robotunits.com
Pres.—Juergen Roth
Engrg. Mgr.—Christopher
  Hollenstein
Administrator—Alisa Turner
SIC—3569; *Modular automation
  system, including luminum
  extrusions, conveyors, linear
  motion units, equipment
  enclosures & safety fencing*
Employs—15; Estab.—2000
Distrib.—Intl.
Sole ownership

### ROCK-TENN CO.

1 Corn Rd., P.O. Box 440 (08810)
**Phone—(732) 274-2500**
Fax—(732) 329-8461
www.rocktenn.com
Email—info@rocktenn.com
GM—Bob O'Connell
Sales Mgr.—Tim Kelly
Hum. Res. Mgr.—Jill Reilley
Administrator—Sue Scurato
SIC—2653; NAICS—322211;
  *Corrugated boxes*
Employs—120; Estab.—1982
Sales—$30Mil
Distrib.—Intl.
Publicly owned corporation
DBA: RockTenn
Parent co.—Rock-Tenn Co.,
  Norcross, GA
  Phone—(770) 448-2193
  See Parent Co. Section for full profile.

### SOMFY SYSTEMS, INC.

121 Herrod Blvd. *(08810)*
**Phone—(800) 647-6639**
       (609) 395-1300
Fax—(609) 395-1750
www.somfysystems.com
Email—marketing_us@somfy.com
CEO—Michael Lee
Dir., Mktg.—Tracy Christmann
Prod. Mktg. Mgr.—Deirdre Brower
Comm. & Mktg. Coord.—Jennifer
  Foster

SIC—3621; 3625; 3679; NAICS—
  335312; *Specialized motors &
  electronic controls for smart
  home interior & exterior window
  coverings, including awnings,
  rolling shutters, screens, solar
  shades, wood blinds &
  draperies; Brand name—Radio
  Technology Somfy RTS;
  Sonesse; Glydea; SIMU;
  WireFree*
Employs—80; Estab.—1977
Sales—$10Mil-$25Mil
Distrib.—Intl.
Publicly owned corporation

### SONOCO PRODUCTS CO.

Div. of Sonoco
5 Stults Rd. (08810)
**Phone—(609) 655-0300**
Fax—(609) 655-0745
www.sonoco.com
Email—info@sonoco.com
Plt. Mgr.—Russ Dean
SIC—2655; NAICS—322214;
  *Fiber cans*
Employs—60; Estab.—1945
Sales—$5Mil-$10Mil (est)
Distrib.—Intl.
Publicly owned corporation
Parent co.—Sonoco, Hartsville, SC
  Phone—(843) 383-7000
  See Parent Co. Section for full profile.

### STERLING FOOD FLAVORINGS, LLC

182 Ridge Rd., Ste. G (08810)
**Phone—(732) 438-1620**
Fax—(732) 438-1625
Email—rick@sterlingff.com
Ex. Dir.—Vitas Roman
Dir., Technical—Rick Englesbe
Whse. Mgr.—Tyler Englesbe
SIC—2099; *Savory food flavors,
  seasonings, HVP & yeast
  extracts*
Employs—10; Estab.—2003
10,000 sq ft site, Distrib.—National
Limited Liability Company

### SUNNY DELIGHT BEVERAGES CO.

10 Corn Rd. *(08810)*
**Phone—(732) 329-2391**
Fax—(732) 329-6560
www.sunnyd.com
Email—sales@sunnyd.com
Plt. Mgr.—Donald Ruddy
Hum. Res. Leader—Sangita
  Bhavsar
SIC—2033; NAICS—311421;
  *Juice bottling; Brand name—
  Sunny Delight; Bossa Nova; Fruit
  20; Elations; Very Fine; Fruit
  Simple*
Employs—130
Sales—$25Mil-$50Mil
Distrib.—Local
Publicly owned corporation
Parent co.—Sunny Delight
  Beverages Co., Cincinnati, OH
  Phone—(513) 483-3300
  See Parent Co. Section for full profile.

### †SUNSHINE BOUQUET CO.

3 Chris Ct., Ste. A, P.O. Box 892
  (08810)
**Phone—(732) 274-2900**
National—(800) 652-5006
Fax—(732) 274-3378
www.sunshinebouquet.com
Email—kstailey@
  sunshinebouquet.com
Owner—John Simko
CFO—Andrew Johnston
Dir., MIS—Mike Dawson
Sales Mgr.—Kellen Stailey
Acctg. Mgr.—Maria Ruiz
Hum. Res. Mgr.—Joel Cruz
SIC—5193; *Wholesaler of flowers
  & floral arrangements*
Employs—50; Estab.—1985
Sales—$1Mil-$2.5Mil
Distrib.—Local
Privately owned corporation

**GEOGRAPHICAL**

## Dayton—(cont.)

**UNITED PRODUCTS & INSTRUMENTS, INC. (H Q)**
182 Ridge Rd., Ste. E (08810)
**Phone—(732) 274-1155**
Fax—(732) 274-1151
www.unicosci.com
Email—sales@unicosci.com
Pres.—Albert Chang
SIC—3821; NAICS—339111; *Corporate headquarters; laboratory instruments (mfg. done overseas)*
Employs—10; Estab.—1991
Sales—$1Mil-$2.5Mil (est)
Distrib.—Intl.

**†UNITED SUPPLY CO., INC.**
7 Chris Ct., Ste. A (08810-1537)
**Phone—(732) 329-6301**
Fax—(732) 329-0337
www.unitedsupplynj.com
Email—kevinh@uscoinc.com
Br. Mgr.—Kevin Horn
SIC—5075; *Distributor of HVAC systems & accessories*
Employs—6; Estab.—1987
Sales—$500,000-$1Mil
20,000 sq ft site, Distrib.—Local
Privately owned corporation
Parent co.—United Supply Co., Inc., Plainfield, NJ
Phone—(908) 757-3232
See Parent Co. Section for full profile.

**†VICTORY PACKAGING, INC.**
8 Corn Rd., Ste. 2 (08810-2527)
**Phone—(732) 274-1745**
National—(800) 799-2176
Fax—(800) 840-4846
www.victorypackaging.com
Email—csnj@victorypackaging.com
Pres.—Robert Egan
GM—Brandon Egan
SIC—5113; 5162; *Distributor of packaging materials, including cardboard boxes, mailers, corrugated pads, cartons, bubble wrap, tapes, films & related materials*
Employs—75; Estab.—2001
Distrib.—Regional
Privately owned corporation
Parent co.—Victory Packaging, Inc., Houston, TX
Phone—(713) 961-3299
See Parent Co. Section for full profile.

**†WIN LABORATORIES, LTD.**
182 Ridge Rd., Ste. D (08810)
**Phone—(732) 355-1355**
Fax—(732) 355-1350
Email—jimmyw@winlab.com
Owner—Jimmy Wu
SIC—5093; *Wholesaler of recycled electronic scrap materials*
Employs—7; Estab.—1998
Distrib.—Local
Privately owned corporation

**†WORLDWIDE PARTS & ACCESSORIES CORP.**
Div. of WORLDPAC, Inc.
300 Herrod Blvd. (08810-1563)
**Phone—(732) 230-5000**
National—(800) 631-5544
Fax—(732) 438-3190
www.worldpac.com
Email—cf_admins@worldpac.com
Mktg. Progs. Mgr.—Sherry Blake
SIC—5013; *Distributor of automotive parts*
Employs—90; Estab.—1996
Distrib.—National
Privately owned corporation
DBA: WorldPac
Parent co.—WORLDPAC, Inc., Newark, CA
Phone—(510) 742-8900
See Parent Co. Section for full profile.

## Deal

(Monmouth—N.E.)

**INDEX SECURITY, INC. (H Q)**
500 Parker Ave., Ste. G (07723)
**Phone—(732) 531-9209**
National—(800) 983-8529
www.index-security.com
Email—info@index-security.com
Pres.—Ezra Hedaya
V-P.—Mark Hedaya
SIC—3577; *Corporate headquarters; biometric fingerprint verification hardware (mfg. subcontracted); Brand name—Biostik*
Employs—2; Estab.—2003
Sales—$2.6Mil-$5Mil
Distrib.—Intl.
Privately owned corporation

**SMART GEAR, LLC**
82 Norwood Ave., Ste. 2 (07723)
**Phone—(732) 663-0000**
www.smartgeartoys.com
Email—info@smartgeartoys.com
CEO—Sam Cohen
Pres.—Jason Cohen
SIC—3944; *Environmentally friendly educational toys, games, rockers, ride-ons, plush & balance bikes for childern ages birth & up; Brand name—Smart Gear; Wonderworld*
Employs—30; Estab.—2006
Distrib.—Intl.
Limited Liability Company

## Deepwater

(Salem—S.W.)

**E. I. DU PONT DE NEMOURS & CO., CHAMBERS WORKS PLT.**
Div. of E. I. du Pont de Nemours & Co.
67 Canal St. (08023)
**Phone—(856) 299-5000**
(856) 540-2200
Fax—(856) 540-4733
www.chambersworks.com
Email—moreinfo@chamberworks.com
Plt. Mgr.—Tim McDaniel
Hum. Res. Mgr.—Howard Brian Collings
Fin. Mgr.—Robert Ullo
Hum. Res. Consultant—Tenita Gibson
SIC—2899; *Chemical additives*
Employs—980
Publicly owned corporation
Parent co.—E. I. du Pont de Nemours & Co., Wilmington, DE
Phone—(302) 774-1000
See Parent Co. Section for full profile.

## Deerfield Street

(Cumberland—S.W.)

**HAMELIN PRODUCTS, INC.**
1616 Highway 77, P.O. Box 153 (08313)
**Phone—(856) 451-2935**
www.deerfieldmachine.com
Pres.—Don S. Kolbe
V-P.—Rudy Kolbe
Manager—Monika Tozer
SIC—3599; *General machining job shop, including CNC turning & milling*
Employs—14; Estab.—1980
Sales—$1Mil-$2.5Mil
12,000 sq ft site, Distrib.—Regional
Privately owned corporation
AKA: Deerfield Machine Parts

## Delair

(Camden—S.W.)

**ALUMINUM SHAPES, LLC**
9000 River Rd. (08110)
**Phone—(800) 242-7512**
Fax—(856) 662-6319
www.shapesllc.com
Email—sales@shapesllc.com
IT Mgr.—Joe Howards
Hum. Res. Mgr.—Wanda Johnson
SIC—3354; NAICS—331316; *Aluminum extrusions*
Employs—250; Estab.—1954
Sales—over $100Mil
1,500,000 sq ft site, Distrib.—National
Limited Liability Company

**OASIS RECORDING, INC.**
7905 N. Crescent Blvd. (08110)
**Phone—(888) 296-2747**
Fax—(866) 929-8402
www.oasiscd.com
Email—info@oasiscd.com
Pres.—Micah Solomon
Hum. Res. Mgr.—Sue Learn
SIC—3652; *Compact disc duplication*
Employs—10; Estab.—1987
Sales—$1Mil-$2.5Mil (est)
Distrib.—Intl.
Privately owned corporation
DBA: Oasis CD Mfg.

## Delanco

(Burlington—S.E.)

**ATCO PALLET CO.**
1000 Creek Rd., P.O. Box 5115 (08075)
**Phone—(856) 461-8141**
Fax—(856) 461-8146
www.atcopallet.net
Email—atcopallet@comcast.net
Pres. & Dir., Opers. & Sales—David Hajduk
Off. Mgr.—Stephanie Kolwicz
SIC—2448; NAICS—321920; *Company headquarters & wooden pallets*
Employs—28; Estab.—1970
Sales—$1Mil-$5Mil
Distrib.—Regional
Privately owned corporation

**COLD HEADED FASTENERS, INC.**
401 Creek Rd., P.O. Box 5488 (08075)
**Phone—(856) 461-3244**
National—(800) 233-1625
Fax—(856) 461-3299
www.coldheadedfasteners.com
Email—coldfast76@yahoo.com
Pres., Fin., Opers. & R & D Mgr.—Charles Massey
Treas., Off. Mgr.—MaryAnn Massey
SIC—3469; *Metal fasteners*
Employs—6; Estab.—1990
14,000 sq ft site, Distrib.—Intl.
Privately owned corporation

**FISHER & SONS, INC., HAROLD F.**
200 Ash St. (08075)
**Phone—(856) 461-2883**
National—(800) 624-2868
Fax—(856) 461-4519
Pres., CFO—Frank Fisher
V-P.—Barbara Fisher
SIC—2394; NAICS—314912; *Canvas products*
Employs—2; Estab.—1954
Sales—under $500,000
15,000 sq ft site, Distrib.—Local
Privately owned corporation

**G-O-METRIC, INC.**
215 Ash St. (08075)
**Phone—(856) 461-8080**
Fax—(856) 764-8956

Pres.—Paul Manion
SIC—3663; NAICS—334220; *EMI & RFI honeycomb ventilation panels*
Employs—6; Estab.—1970
7,000 sq ft site, Distrib.—Intl.
Privately owned corporation

**LAUREL MFRS., INC.**
620 Cooper St., P.O. Box 5306 (08075)
**Phone—(856) 461-6600**
Fax—(856) 461-6622
www.laurelmfg.com
Email—meyer@laurelmfg.com
Pres.—Dan Iosca
V-P.—Ted Gorczynski
Hum. Res. Mgr.—Tina Rowlands
SIC—2541; 2542; *Wooden & metal store fixtures*
Employs—40; Estab.—1984
Sales—$6Mil-$10Mil
60,000 sq ft site, Distrib.—Regional
Privately owned corporation
AKA: Med Laurel, LLC

**STYLEX**
740 Coopertown Rd., P.O. Box 5038 (08075)
**Phone—(856) 461-5600**
National—(800) 257-5742
Fax—(856) 461-5574
www.stylexseating.com
Email—info@stylexseating.com
Pres.—John Golden
V-P.—Bruce Golden
Cont.—Joseph Kowalonek
Hum. Res. Mgr.—Diane Fickes
Cred. Mgr.—Tina Anderson
Sr. Buyer—Steven Teller
SIC—2522; NAICS—337214; *Seating office furniture*
Employs—150; Estab.—1950
135,000 sq ft site, Distrib.—Intl.
Privately owned corporation

## Delmont

(Cumberland—S.W.)

**DELMONT SAWMILL**
4416 Route 47 (08314)
**Phone—(856) 785-1018**
Email—delmontsawmill@comcast.net
Owner—Peter Boyce
SIC—2421; *Lumber processing*
Employs—2; Estab.—1981
Sales—under $500,000 (est)
Distrib.—Local

## Delran

(Burlington—S.E.)

**ACTEGA KELSTAR, INC.**
950 S. Chester Ave., Ste. B-2 (08075-1272)
**Phone—(856) 829-6300**
www.actega.com
Email—info.actega.kelstar@altana.com
Pres., CEO—Mark Westwell
CFO & COO—Brian Long
V-P., Sales—Susan G. Kuchta
Mktg. Mgr.—Chris Calomino
SIC—2893; 2899; *Aqueous, UV & adhesive coatings, specialty inks, fountain solutions & pressroom chemicals for the graphic arts industry; Brand name—Starkote; Ultra Sheen; Scratch Kote; Starfount*
Employs—85
Distrib.—Intl.
Privately owned corporation

**BIOCLIMATIC AIR SYSTEMS**
600 Delran Pkwy., Ste. D (08075)
**Phone—(856) 764-4300**
National—(800) 394-3458
Fax—(856) 764-4301
www.bioclimatic.com

## Delran—(cont.)

Email—mail@bioclimatic.com
CEO—Stephen Zitin
SIC—3564; NAICS—333400; *Air purification equipment*
Employs—22; Estab.—1983
Sales—$500,000-$1Mil
24,000 sq ft site, Distrib.—Intl.
Limited Liability Company

**†CONVEYOR SYSTEMS & COMPONENTS**
21 Norman Ave., P.O. Box 343 (08075)
**Phone—(856) 461-8084**
National—(800) 255-4512
Fax—(856) 764-9367
www.conveyorsystems.com
Email—sales@conveyorsystems.com
GM & Sales Mgr.—Thomas McLarney
SIC—5084; *Distributor of conveyors & conveying equipment, including standard, special, power, roller, accumulating, belt, gravity, closet, roller & wheel conveyors, lift tables, ball transfers & motorized & standard pulleys; Brand name—Closet Conveyor; Automated Conveyor Systems; Omni Metal Craft; Van Der Graaf Motorized Pulleys; Interroll; Ralph Pugh; Bryant*
Employs—4; Estab.—1984
Sales—$1Mil
5,000 sq ft site, Distrib.—National
Privately owned corporation

**DAVOL, INC.**
Div. of C.R. Bard, Inc.
1822 Underwood Blvd. (08075)
**Phone—(856) 764-8158**
www.crbard.com
Email—info@crbard.com
Plt. Mgr.—Jose Nunez
Proj. Mgr.—Alan Grumbling
Off. Admn.—Christie Jensen
SIC—3841; 2261; NAICS—313311; *Medical textiles*
Employs—13; Estab.—1982
Sales—$500,000-$1Mil
Distrib.—Intl.
Publicly owned corporation
AKA: Davol-Delran, Inc.
Parent co.—C.R. Bard, Inc., New Providence, NJ
Phone—(908) 277-8000
See Parent Co. Section for full profile.

**HARLAND AMERICA**
1803 Underwood Blvd. (08075)
**Phone—(856) 764-9622**
Fax—(856) 764-9615
www.harlandamerica.com
Email—enquiries@harland-hms.com
Pres.—Jim Potter
Administrator—Linda Neel
SIC—3565; NAICS—333993; *Pressure sensitive labeling equipment; Brand name—Harland Sirius; Titan; Enterprise; Europa; Jupiter; Neptune; Proteus*
Employs—10; Estab.—1987
17,000 sq ft site, Distrib.—Intl.
Privately owned corporation

**†INDEPENDENT IMAGING**
1819 Underwood Blvd., Unit 1 (08075)
**Phone—(856) 764-9729**
National—(800) 543-4424
Fax—(856) 764-9745
www.independentimaging.org
Email—info@independentimaging.org
Owner & Hum. Res. Mgr.—John Thomas Walsh
IT Mgr.—Bill Walsh

SIC—5047; *Distributor of medical imaging equipment & supplies, including x-ray machines*
Employs—10; Estab.—1992
Sales—$1Mil-$2.5Mil
Distrib.—National
Privately owned corporation

**J & J RADIATOR SHOP**
71 St. Mihiel Dr. (08075)
**Phone—(856) 461-3533**
Fax—(856) 461-3533
www.jandjradiator.com
Email—info@jandjradiator.com
Owner—Joe Zeisweiss
SIC—3714; *Rebuilt automotive radiators*
Employs—1

**LIPPINCOTT MARINE**
74 Norman Ave. (08075)
**Phone—(856) 764-8282**
Fax—(856) 764-3672
Owner—Howard Lippincott
SIC—2394; NAICS—314912; *Canvas marine products*
Employs—2; Estab.—1980
Sales—under $500,000
2,000 sq ft site, Distrib.—Regional
Sole ownership

**LUCAS & SON, H. N.**
211 Carriage Ln. (08075)
**Phone—(856) 764-2400**
National—(866) 852-3592
Fax—(856) 764-2678
Email—hnlucas@hnlucas.com
Pres.—Steve Lloyd
Qual. Control Mgr.—Joe Chirico
SIC—3599; *General machining job shop*
Employs—12; Estab.—1950
7,200 sq ft site, Distrib.—National
Privately owned sub-S corp.

**MACHINE SHOP AT ENGINE SPECIALTIES, THE**
203 Carriage Ln. (08075)
**Phone—(856) 764-8701**
Fax—(856) 764-8702
GM—Scott Woodington
Off. Mgr.—Shannon Goodseller
Shop Supv.—Jami John
SIC—3599; 3714; *Automotive machining job shop*
Employs—7; Estab.—1998
Sales—$500,000-$1Mil
Distrib.—Local
Privately owned corporation

**MANCINE OPTICAL CO.**
2910 Route 130, Ste. 1 (08075-2599)
**Phone—(856) 764-0200**
National—(800) 887-3939
Fax—(856) 764-1414
www.mancineoptical.com
Email—info@mancineoptical.com
Pres.—Joseph Mancine
V-P., GM—Cliff Mancine
Off. Mgr.—Sharon Altadonna
SIC—3851; NAICS—339100; *Prescription safety glasses & specialty lenses*
Employs—20; Estab.—1952
Sales—$1Mil-$5Mil
6,400 sq ft site, Distrib.—National
Privately owned corporation

**†MCKESSON CORP.**
400 Delran Pkwy. (08075)
**Phone—(856) 461-7800**
National—(800) 279-9148
Fax—(856) 461-8064
www.mckesson.com
Email—inquire@mckesson.com
Dir., Opers.—Dan Montreuil
GM—Brian Ferreira
Hum. Res. Mgr.—Patty Dudinetz
Dist. Ctr. Mgr., Night—Lon Mietka
Dist. Ctr. Mgr., Day—Beth Robertson
Hum. Res. Coord.—Luceille Young

SIC—5122; *Wholesaler of pharmaceuticals*
Employs—200; Estab.—1912
Sales—$50Mil-$100Mil
Distrib.—Regional
Publicly owned corporation
Parent co.—McKesson Corp., San Francisco, CA
Phone—(415) 983-8300
See Parent Co. Section for full profile.

**SAILWORKS AT 43**
43 Norman Ave. (08075)
**Phone—(856) 764-0888**
Fax—(856) 393-7720
www.sailworksat43.com
Owner, Pres. & GM—Burt Geiges
SIC—2394; NAICS—314912; *Boat sails*
Employs—1; Estab.—2013
Sales—under $500,000
7,500 sq ft site, Distrib.—National
Privately owned corporation

**SARLO TOOL & MACHINE CO.**
62 Suburban Blvd. (08075)
**Phone—(856) 461-3206**
Fax—(856) 764-1899
Email—sarlotool@verizon.net
Pres.—Chris Sarlo
SIC—3599; *General machining job shop*
Employs—14; Estab.—1965
16,000 sq ft site, Distrib.—Regional
Privately owned sub-S corp.

**SIGN-A-RAMA**
4000 Route 130, Ste. 25 (08075)
**Phone—(856) 764-9777**
Fax—(856) 764-0305
www.signaramadelran.com
Email—delransignarama@comcast.net
Owner—Joann Davis
Sr. V-P.—Ron Davis
SIC—3993; *Interior & exterior signs*
Employs—4; Estab.—1995
Sales—under $500,000
1,000 sq ft site, Distrib.—Local
Limited Liability Company

**TOWN LINE TROPHIES**
2 Amberfield Dr. (08075)
**Phone—(856) 461-0540**
Fax—(856) 461-0860
www.townlinetrophies.com
Email—townlinetrophies@comcast.net
Ptnr. & Off. Mgr.—Nancy Hagmaier
Ptnr.—Bill Hagmaier
SIC—3499; 2396; *Trophies, plaques, bronze castings, crystal awards, textile screen printing, embroidery & advertising specialties*
Employs—3; Estab.—1979
Sales—under $500,000
Distrib.—Local
Sole ownership

---

## Dennisville
(Cape May—S.E.)

**BLUEWATER WELDING & FABRICATION, LLC**
1089 Route 47, P.O. Box 206 (08214)
**Phone—(609) 465-0680**
(609) 522-7352
National—(800) 709-0680
Fax—(609) 522-2500
www.bluewaterwelding.com
Email—office@bluewaterwelding.com
Owner—Ed Myland
Off. Mgr.—Marta Myland

SIC—3444; *Structural aluminum fabrication*
Employs—6; Estab.—2001
Distrib.—National
Limited Liability Company

---

## Denville
(Morris—N.W.)

**AEROSPACE PRECISION MFG. CO., INC.**
6 Hinchman Ave. (07834)
**Phone—(973) 625-2100**
Fax—(973) 625-0518
Pres.—Emile Ayli
SIC—3599; *Precision machining job shop*
Employs—4; Estab.—1980
Sales—under $500,000
Distrib.—National
Privately owned corporation

NEW ENTRY

**ALL STAR IDENTIFICATION**
400 Morris Ave., Ste. 241 (07834)
**Phone—(973) 625-4100**
National—(800) 831-5771
Fax—(973) 625-4104
www.allstarid.com
Owner—Art Evans
Hum. Res. Mgr.—Jackie Linehan
SIC—7373; *Computer systems integration*
Employs—15; Estab.—1990
3,000 sq ft site, Distrib.—Intl.
Privately owned corporation

**ALLIANCE TECHNOLOGIES GROUP, INC.**
3 Luger Rd., Ste. 4 (07834)
**Phone—(973) 664-1151**
Fax—(973) 664-1154
www.atgmfg.com
Email—customerservice@atgmfg.com
CEO—Phillip William Depalma
Pres.—Peter Depalma
SIC—3625; *Contract manufacturing of mechanical & electromechanical assemblies, including industrial controls*
Employs—6; Estab.—1996
Sales—$500,000-$1Mil
Distrib.—National
Privately owned corporation

**AMERICAN RADAR COMPONENTS, INC.**
39 Front St. (07834)
**Phone—(973) 627-5530**
Fax—(973) 627-4133
www.americanradarcomponents.com
Email—americanradar@optonline.net
Pres., CEO—John Maluk, Jr.
GM & IT Mgr.—Michael Maluk
Plt. Mgr.—John Maluk III
SIC—3679; *Microwave components*
Employs—8; Estab.—1953
Sales—$1Mil-$5Mil
10,000 sq ft site, Distrib.—Intl.
Privately owned sub-S corp.

**ANTHONY & SONS ITALIAN BAKERY**
20 Luger Rd. (07834)
**Phone—(973) 625-2323**
National—(866) 322-7323
Fax—(973) 625-7993
www.anthonyandsonsbakery.com
Email—info@anthonyandsonsbakery.com
GM—Phillip Dattolo
Hum. Res. Mgr.—Rhea Adler
Cust. Serv. Rep.—Chris March

GEOGRAPHICAL

# Denville—(cont.)

SIC—2051; NAICS—311812;
*Fresh artisan breads & sandwich
rolls, bagels & muffins for the
deli, restaurant, pizzeria, hotel,
school & foodservice markets*
Employs—55; Estab.—2003
Distrib.—Regional
Privately owned corporation

**BIZTECH, INC.**
3155 Route 10, Ste. 202 (07834)
**Phone—(973) 361-7666**
Fax—(973) 361-9677
www.biztechrp.com
Email—sales@biztechrp.com
Pres.—Louis Bizzarro
SIC—3543; NAICS—332997;
*Prototypes*
Employs—7; Estab.—1988
Sales—$500,000-$1Mil
Distrib.—National
Privately owned corporation

**†BOTTCHER AMERICA CORP.**
Div. of Bottcher America
Corporation
88 Ford Rd., Ste. 8 (07834)
**Phone—(973) 664-1241**
National—(800) 637-8120
www.bottcher.com
Email—support@boettcher-
systems.com
Sr. Sales Mgr.—Steve Foulds
SIC—5084; *Distributor of printing
press rollers*
Employs—18; Estab.—1984
10,000 sq ft site, Distrib.—Intl.
Privately owned corporation
AKA: Bottcher Systems
Parent co.—Bottcher America
Corporation, Belcamp, MD
Phone—(410) 273-7000
See Parent Co. Section for full profile.

**COMPONENTS CORP.**
6 Kinsey Pl. (07834)
**Phone—(973) 627-0290**
National—(800) 426-6726
Fax—(973) 361-5801
www.componentscorp.com
Email—sales@
componentscorp.com
Sales Mgr., Natl.—Chris Minter
SIC—3496; 3679; *Wire forms &
connectors*
Employs—17; Estab.—1943
Sales—$1Mil-$5Mil
15,000 sq ft site, Distrib.—Intl.
Privately owned corporation

**CO-PLANAR, INC.**
88 Ford Rd, P.O. Box 1115 (07834)
**Phone—(973) 625-3500**
Fax—(973) 625-1849
www.co-planar.com
Email—sales@co-planar.com
Pres.—James Cote
V-P., Mfg.—Mike Mullen
Dir., Sales & Mktg. Mgr.—Cal Cot
SIC—3469; 3081; NAICS—
326113; *Metal & polyester film
stampings*
Employs—28; Estab.—1978
Sales—$12Mil
33,500 sq ft site, Distrib.—Intl.
Privately owned sub-S corp.

**†CPR CONTAINER**
94 Ford Rd., Ste. 5 (07834-1353)
**Phone—(973) 625-0664**
Fax—(973) 625-0699
Email—cprdrums@msn.com
Owner—Nick Foglia
Off. Mgr.—Dana Miczak
SIC—5113; 5085; *Wholesaler of
plastic & steel packaging
containers, barrels, drums &
wooden crates*
Employs—5; Estab.—2002
Distrib.—Local
Sole ownership

**CUSTOM DECORATORS
WORKROOM**
415 E. Main St. (07834)
**Phone—(973) 625-0516**
Fax—(973) 625-3361
Ptnr.—Walter Kunzel, Jr.
Ptnr.—Lisa Conwell
SIC—2519; 2391; NAICS—
337125; *Custom furniture &
draperies*
Employs—5; Estab.—2009
Sales—under $500,000
Distrib.—National
Privately owned partnership

NEW ENTRY

**DSA GRAPHICS, LLC**
431 E. Main St., Ste. 3 (07834)
**Phone—(973) 625-7760**
Fax—(973) 625-8722
Owner—Dominic Santaite
SIC—2759; 2782; 2789;
*Commercial & promotional
screen printing & binding &
binders*
Employs—4
Sales—$500,000-$1Mil (est)
Limited Liability Company

**F G H SYSTEMS, INC.**
10 Prospect Pl. (07834)
**Phone—(973) 625-8114**
Fax—(973) 625-1442
www.fghsystems.com
Email—sales@fghsystems.com
Pres.—Frank Hohmann
Hum. Res., Off. & Pur. Mgr.—Rita
E. Hall
IT Mgr.—Eric Hohmann
SIC—3544; NAICS—333500; *Tool
& die job shop*
Employs—22; Estab.—1976
35,000 sq ft site, Distrib.—Intl.
Privately owned corporation

**FLOW SAFE, INC.**
30 Broad St. (07834)
**Phone—(973) 627-8553**
National—(888) 356-9723
Fax—(973) 627-8683
www.flowsafe.net
Email—info@flowsafe.net
COO—Eileen Klees
Bookkeeper—Teri Beresik
SIC—3822; NAICS—334512; *Air
flow control products assembly*
Employs—6; Estab.—1985
Sales—$500,000-$1Mil
Distrib.—Intl.
Privately owned corporation

**GENERAL RELIANCE CORP.**
88 Ford Rd., Ste. 20 (07834-1357)
**Phone—(973) 361-1400**
(973) 983-7800
Fax—(973) 361-3112
www.generalreliance.com
Email—mail@generalreliance.com
Pres.—Christopher Schmidt
Material Mgr.—Doreen Cornelius
Qual. Assur. Mgr.—Steve Stamper
SIC—3679; *Complex electronic
molded cable assemblies &
electromechanical assemblies*
Employs—29; Estab.—1960
Sales—over $10Mil
39,800 sq ft site, Distrib.—National
Sole ownership
ISO rating—AS9100C

**GENERAL STAMPING CO.**
451 E. Main St. (07834)
**Phone—(973) 627-9500**
National—(800) 627-6088
Fax—(973) 627-6012
www.generalstamping.com
Email—ddato@
generalstamping.com
Pres.—Damon Dato
Estimating, Sales & Mktg. Mgr.—
Samantha Corujo

SIC—3469; *Precision metal
stamping*
Employs—19; Estab.—1965
12,000 sq ft site, Distrib.—Intl.
Privately owned corporation

**GERARDI PRESS, INC.**
3 Luger Rd., Ste. 3, P.O. Box 545
(07834)
**Phone—(973) 627-2600**
Fax—(973) 627-2624
www.gerardipress.com
Email—kgerardi@gerardipress.com
Owner—Keith Gerardi
SIC—2759; *Commercial printing,
including brochures*
Employs—8; Estab.—1991
Sales—$1Mil-$2.5Mil
17,600 sq ft site, Distrib.—Regional
Privately owned corporation

**GLOCON, INC. (SWIFTER FANS)**
3-1 Luger Rd. (07834)
**Phone—(973) 463-7300**
Fax—(973) 463-1670
www.swifterfans.com
Email—swifter@glocon.net
V-P.—Arjun Agarwal
Mktg. Mgr.—Veena Agarwal
SIC—3564; NAICS—333400;
*Industrial axial fiberglass fans for
cooling towers, air-cooled heat
exchangers, exhausts &
agricultural application & hybrid
solar powered HVLS ceiling fans
for warehouses, assembly plants
& commercial buildings; Brand
name—Swifter®*
Employs—5; Estab.—1981
Sales—$500,000-$1Mil
Distrib.—Intl.
Privately owned corporation

**GUIDA SETTING CO.**
124 E. Main St. (07834)
**Phone—(973) 625-1225**
Fax—(973) 625-2122
www.guidajewelers.com
Email—info@guidajewelers.com
Owner—William D. Guida
Sales Rep.—Susan Guida
SIC—3911; NAICS—339911;
*Precious & semiprecious jewelry*
Employs—4; Estab.—1973
Sales—$500,000-$1Mil
Distrib.—National
Sole ownership

**INTEGRATED PACKAGING SYSTEMS**
3 Luger Rd., Ste. 5 (07834)
**Phone—(973) 664-0020**
Fax—(973) 664-0025
www.ipsnj.com
Email—info@ipsnj.com
Ptnr. & Pres.—Robert W. Fields
Ptnr. & V-P.—Michael McNeila
GM—Philip DePalma
Acctg. & Off. Mgr.—Janice
Mastropaolo
Tech. Mgr.—Michael Frusteri
SIC—3565; NAICS—333993;
*Packaging equipment for the
pharmaceutical, nutraceutical,
cosmetic, food & chemical
industries, including tablet
counters & liquid fillers*
Employs—10; Estab.—1992
16,000 sq ft site, Distrib.—Intl.
Privately owned corporation
AKA: IPS

**KATENA PRODUCTS, INC.**
4 Stewart Ct. (07834)
**Phone—(973) 989-1600**
National—(800) 225-1195
Fax—(973) 989-8175
www.katena.com
Email—globe@katena.com
CEO—William Friedberg
CFO—Jace Bender
V-P., Mktg.—Gordon Dahl

SIC—3841; *Eye surgery
instruments*
Employs—25; Estab.—1975
Distrib.—Intl.
Privately owned corporation

**LANE BOND TRADERS**
27 Cedar Lake Rd. (07834)
**Phone—(973) 586-2720**
National—(866) 586-2720
www.lanesystems.net
Email—pat@lanesystems.net
Owner—William Peer
SIC—3578; 7372; *Bond
calculating devices & trading
software development*
Employs—2; Estab.—1999
Sales—under $500,000
Distrib.—National
Privately owned corporation

**†LATICO LEATHER**
321 Palmer Rd., Ste. A (07834)
**Phone—(973) 442-9622**
National—(800) 969-8426
Fax—(973) 442-3073
www.laticoleathers.com
Email—info@laticoleathers.com
Owner—Paul Schreiber
Off. Mgr.—Tracey Smolder
SIC—5137; 5136; *Distributor of
women's & men's leather
handbags, briefcases,
backpacks, wallets, business
accessories & small leather
goods; Brand name—Latico*
Employs—10; Estab.—1987
Distrib.—National
Privately owned corporation

**LIBERTY ELECTRONICS**
465 Route 53 (07834)
**Phone—(973) 625-7966**
Fax—(973) 625-4689
www.libertyelectronicsinc.com
Email—sales@
libertyelectronicsinc.com
Pres.—Thomas Ferrante
SIC—3679; *Voice & data
products; Brand name—ICC;
Wiremold; Middle Atlantic;
Platinum Tools; Vanco; Caddy;
Arlington*
Employs—4; Estab.—1986
Sales—under $1Mil
2,500 sq ft site, Distrib.—National
Limited Liability Company

**LIBERTY ELECTRONICS, INC.**
465 E. Main St. (07834)
**Phone—(973) 625-7963**
Fax—(973) 927-4689
www.libertyelectronicsinc.com
Owner—Tom Ferrante
SIC—3357; 3679; *Wire & cable &
cable assemblies*
Employs—4; Estab.—1985
Distrib.—National
Privately owned corporation

**MECA ELECTRONICS, INC.**
459 E. Main St. (07834)
**Phone—(973) 625-0661**
National—(866) 444-6322
Fax—(973) 625-9277
www.e-meca.com
Email—sales@e-meca.com
Pres.—William C. Davo
GM—Thomas Hickey
Opers. Mgr.—Christine O'Shea
Bus. Dev. Mgr.—David Yatcilla
SIC—3679; *RF/microwave
components, including fixed
attenuators, directional & hybrid
couplers, isolators & circulators,
power divider & combiners, RF
loads & DC blocks for satellite,
radio, mobile radio, aviation & air
traffic communications; Brand
name—V-Line; M-Series; H-
Series*
Employs—45; Estab.—1961
10,000 sq ft site, Distrib.—Intl.
Privately owned corporation

## Denville—(cont.)

**OLMEC SYSTEMS, INC.**
255 W. Main St. (07834)
**Phone—(973) 586-6590**
Fax—(973) 586-6591
www.olmec.com
Email—info@olmec.com
Ptnr., Pres. & CEO—Chris Forte
Ptnr., Hum. Res. & IT—Jason
Montiego
SIC—7373; *Computer network
system integration, including
WANs*
Employs—10
Sales—under $500,000
Distrib.—Local
Privately owned corporation

**PLANITROI INC**
100-10 Ford Rd. (07834)
**Phone—(973) 664-0700**
Fax—(973) 664-0500
www.planitroi.com
Email—info@planitroi.com
Pres., CEO—Paul Baum
IT Mgr.—Anthony Trotta
SIC—3571; NAICS—334111;
*Rebuilt computers*
Employs—60; Estab.—2002
Sales—$25Mil-$50Mil (est)
Distrib.—Intl.
Sole ownership

**RUDOLPH INSTRUMENTS, INC.**
400 Morris Ave., Ste. 120 (07834)
**Phone—(973) 983-6700**
National—(800) 478-1877
Fax—(973) 983-6290
www.digipoltechnologies.com
Email—sales@
digipoltechnologies.com
Pres.—Kumar Utukuri
Sales Mgr.—Patrick O'Keefe
SIC—3826; NAICS—334516;
*Laboratory analytical
instruments, including
polarimeters, saccharimeters,
ellipsometers, polarographs &
refractometers; Brand name—
DigiPol*
Employs—5; Estab.—1961
Sales—under $500,000
1,300 sq ft site, Distrib.—Intl.
Privately owned sub-S corp.
DBA: DigiPol Technologies

**†TRI-K INDUSTRIES, INC.**
2 Stewart Ct., P.O. Box 10 (07834)
**Phone—(973) 298-8850**
National—(800) 526-0372
Fax—(973) 298-8940
www.tri-k.com
Email—info@tri-k.com
Pres.—Subhas Sen
CFO—Vikas Maheshwari
Dir., Global Bus. Dev.—Ben
Blinder
Mktg. Mgr.—Rebecca Morton
Hum. Res. Mgr.—Rita Simonian
Prod. Mgr.—Doug Krysiak
SIC—5122; *Corporate
headquarters & distributor of
specialty cosmetics ingredients
for the personal care industry;
Brand name—TRIglyphix Sense;
TRIquat; TRIsatin; TRIshield;
Panthequat; Glossamer; Fision
Soy Lift*
Employs—30; Estab.—1974
Sales—$10Mil-$25Mil
Distrib.—Intl.

**TRI-PLEX BUSINESS PRODUCTS,
INC / GRAPHIC SOLUTIONS**
400 Morris Ave., Ste. 220 (07834)
**Phone—(973) 627-5388**
　　　　(973) 627-5488
National—(888) 700-5454
Fax—(973) 627-5332
www.triplexbusiness.com
Email—walterl@tri-
plexbusiness.com

Pres.—Walter Lapham
V-P.—Frank Nardi
V-P.—James O'Neill
Major Acct. Mgr.—Marcelino Perez
Graphic Mgr.—Greg Trought
Cust. Serv. Mgr.—Lynelle Polye
SIC—2759; 2752; 2761; 3993;
NAICS—323116; *Digital color,
commercial, offset, large-format
& direct mail printing, including
business forms, cards, labels &
corporate ID images & indoor &
outdoor signs & contract
fulfillment & distribution services*
Employs—9; Estab.—1992
Sales—$2Mil
Distrib.—National
Privately owned corporation
AKA: Tri-Plex Graphic Solutions

**TX TECHNOLOGY CORP.**
100 Ford Rd., Unit 100-18 (07834)
**Phone—(973) 442-7500**
National—(800) 247-8567
Fax—(973) 442-7575
www.txindustrialmonitoring.net
Email—info@
txindustrialmonitoring.net
GM—Donald Black
Off. Mgr.—Nancy Neggers
Chief Engr.—Jim Herster
SIC—3661; 3829; NAICS—
334513; *Control monitoring
systems, sensors & air dryers;
Brand name—Sentinal; Hercules
940; Teleducer50; White Knight*
Employs—15; Estab.—1969
12,000 sq ft site, Distrib.—Intl.
Privately owned corporation

---

## Deptford

(Gloucester—S.W.)

**DEPTFORD PLATING**
Route 41 & Dein Ave., P.O. Box
5056 (08096)
**Phone—(856) 227-1144**
Lab Mgr.—Karen DeBellis
SIC—3471; NAICS—332813;
*Metal plating*
Employs—13; Estab.—1966
Sales—under $500,000
Distrib.—Regional
Privately owned corporation

**GTM SIGNS, INC.**
1298 Hurffville Rd. (08096)
Mail addr: 1960 Harris Dr.,
Deptford (08096-3863)
**Phone—(856) 227-2333**
Fax—(856) 227-8886
www.gtmsigns.com
Email—karl@gtmsigns.com
Ptnr.—Karl Baker
Ptnr.—Austin Galliger
Ptnr.—Anita Baker
SIC—2394; 3444; 3993; *Signs &
canvas & standing seam
awnings, including design &
installation; Brand name—
Durasol; Gemini; Omega Panel
Laminators Inc.; Merchant &
Evans Inc.; Zip Rib*
Employs—8; Estab.—1994
Sales—$500,000-$1Mil
Distrib.—National
Privately owned corporation

**LAMINATE CREATIONS, LLC**
1235 Hurffville Rd. (08096)
**Phone—(856) 232-8323**
Fax—(856) 232-8330
www.laminatecreations.com
Email—laminatecreations@
comcast.net
Member—James Martucci
Bookkeeper—Dawn Marini

SIC—2434; 2599; 2542; 3082;
NAICS—337110; *Wooden &
laminate kitchen cabinets,
casework, countertops, bars &
booths*
Employs—6; Estab.—1980
Sales—under $500,000
10,000 sq ft site, Distrib.—
Regional
Limited Liability Company

**PIN POINT CONTAINER CORP.**
669 Tanyard Rd. (08096)
**Phone—(856) 848-2115**
Fax—(856) 853-6865
www.pinpointpack.com
Email—bruce@pinpointpack.com
Pres.—Bruce Baelz
V-P.—Dustin Baelz
SIC—2657; NAICS—322212;
*Folding paperboard boxes,
packaging supplies, contract
packaging & fulfillment*
Employs—6; Estab.—1965
Distrib.—Regional
Privately owned corporation

**PRONTO PRINT**
1329 Hurffville Rd. (08096)
**Phone—(856) 232-7200**
Fax—(856) 232-6707
Email—prontopress@hotmail.com
Owner—Gene Duffy
Cust. Serv. Rep.—William
Gonzalez
SIC—2752; NAICS—323100;
*Offset printing*
Employs—3; Estab.—1986
Sales—under $500,000
Distrib.—National
Limited Liability Company

**SICA METAL PRODUCTS**
1775 Hurffville Rd., Route 41, P.O.
Box 5525 (08096)
**Phone—(856) 227-6616**
Fax—(856) 228-0738
www.sicametalproducts.com
Email—sicametalprods@msn.com
Owner & Fin. Mgr.—Ralph Sica,
Sr.
Foreman—Albert Sica
SIC—3499; 3398; NAICS—
332811; *Custom stainless steel &
metal fabrications, including
welding, bending & shearing of
countertops, hoods & boxes*
Employs—3; Estab.—1972
Sales—under $500,000
3,200 sq ft site, Distrib.—Regional
Sole ownership

**SOUTH JERSEY METAL, INC.**
1651 Hurffville Rd., Route 41, P.O.
Box 5148 (08096)
**Phone—(856) 228-0642**
Fax—(856) 228-8466
www.southjerseymetal.com
Email—jared@
southjerseymetal.com
Pres.—Joseph Wagner
COO—Jared Wagner
SIC—3444; 2542; *Commercial
stainless steel kitchen
equipment & products*
Employs—20; Estab.—1946
Sales—$1Mil-$5Mil
Distrib.—Regional
Privately owned corporation

**T & A METAL PRODUCTS, INC.**
1671 Hurffville Rd., P.O. Box 1805
(08096)
**Phone—(856) 227-1700**
Fax—(856) 227-1805
Pres.—Nick Demarco
Plt. Mgr.—Steve Demarco
Off. Mgr.—Fina Demarco
Off. Mgr.—Michelle D'Amelio

SIC—3556; NAICS—333294;
*Stainless steel kitchen
equipment*
Employs—6; Estab.—1964
Sales—$500,000-$1Mil
Distrib.—National
Privately owned corporation

---

## Dorchester

(Cumberland—S.W.)

**DORCHESTER SHIPYARD, INC.**
13 Front St., P.O. Box 600 (08316)
**Phone—(856) 785-8040**
Fax—(856) 785-8011
www.dorchestershipyard.com
Email—info@
dorchestershipyard.com
Pres.—John Kelleher
Hum. Res. Mgr.—Dan Pron
SIC—3731; *Shipbuilding & repairs*
Employs—16; Estab.—2005
Sales—$500,000-$1Mil
Distrib.—National
Privately owned corporation

**†JERSEY DIESEL**
Div. of Yank Marine, Inc.
487 Main St. (08316)
Mail addr: P.O. Box 271, Tuckahoe
(08250)
**Phone—(856) 785-8810**
Fax—(856) 785-1110
www.jerseydiesel.net
Email—jack487@comcast.net
GM—Bette Jeanyank
SIC—5084; *Distributor of diesel
engines*
Employs—4; Estab.—2005
Distrib.—Regional
Sole ownership
Parent co.—Yank Marine, Inc.,
Tuckahoe, NJ
Phone—(609) 628-2928
See Parent Co. Section for full profile.

---

## Dorothy

(Atlantic—S.E.)

NEW ENTRY
**HAPPLE PRINTING PARTNERSHIP,
INC.**
81 Cape May Ave., P.O. Box 36
(08317)
**Phone—(609) 476-2929**
Fax—(609) 476-2909
www.happleprinting.com
Email—info@happleprinting.com
Pres.—Ken Happle
SIC—2759; 2752; *Digital & offset
printing*
Employs—7; Estab.—1987
Sales—$500,000-$1Mil
Distrib.—Intl.
Sole ownership
AKA: Printing Gone Postal

**VIKING MOLD & TOOL, INC.**
64 Tuckahoe Rd. (08317)
**Phone—(609) 476-9333**
Fax—(609) 476-1000
Email—vikingmold@netzero.com
Pres.—James Sullivan
Hum. Res. & IT Mgr.—Susan
Sullivan
SIC—3089; *Plastic injection &
blow molding*
Employs—5; Estab.—1990
Sales—$500,000-$1Mil
Distrib.—National
Privately owned corporation

GEOGRAPHICAL

© Copyright 2015 Manufacturers' News, Inc. † Indicates wholesaler / distributor.

# Dover
## (Morris—N.W.)

## ALCOA
Div. of Alcoa, Inc.
9 Roy St. (07801)
**Phone—(973) 361-2310**
(973) 361-0300
Fax—(973) 989-5405
www.alcoa.com
Email—smv.afssales@alcoa.com
GM—William Miley
Sales Mgr.—Paul VonIpter
Pur. Mgr.—Paul Clarke
Hum. Res. Mgr.—Pilar Gilgorri
Hum. Res. Generalist—Lindsey Johnson
Payroll Specialist—Mini Gauther
SIC—3324; 3724; NAICS—331512; *Aircraft turbine engines*
Employs—675; Estab.—1945
Sales—$50Mil-$100Mil (est)
240,000 sq ft site, Distrib.—Intl.
Publicly owned corporation
ISO rating—9002
Parent co.—Alcoa, Inc., New York, NY
Phone—(212) 836-2600
See Parent Co. Section for full profile.

## AMSCOT STRUCTURAL PRODUCTS CORP.
241 E. Blackwell St. (07801)
**Phone—(973) 989-8800**
Fax—(973) 989-5651
www.amscotnj.com
Email—sales@amscotnj.com
Pres. & IT Mgr.—Peter Somogyi
V-P. & Hum. Res. Mgr.—Tracy Somogyi
Sales Mgr. & Engr.—Bob Furchak
Foreman—Jim Bruno
SIC—3568; NAICS—333613; *Structural slide bearings*
Employs—22; Estab.—1996
Distrib.—Intl.
Privately owned corporation

## ANTA ELECTRIC, INC.
32 Richboynton Rd. (07801)
**Phone—(973) 366-2222**
Fax—(973) 366-0075
www.antaelectric.com
Email—info@antaelectric.com
Owner & Hum. Res. Mgr.—Tanya Khazen
Sales Engr.—Justin Seara
SIC—3672; 3679; *Printed circuit board & wire harness assembly*
Employs—40; Estab.—1993
Sales—$5Mil-$10Mil (est)
50,000 sq ft site, Distrib.—Intl.
Privately owned corporation

## B.D. BRIGGS
31 Richboynton Rd. (07801)
**Phone—(973) 989-1950**
Fax—(973) 989-1959
www.bdbriggs.com
Email—sales@bdbriggs.com
Pres.—Ray Michael Gudelanis
SIC—3565; NAICS—333993; *Custom packaging machinery*
Employs—20; Estab.—2003
Distrib.—Intl.
Privately owned corporation

## BLANC DISPLAY GROUP, THE
88 King St., Ste. 1 (07801)
**Phone—(973) 537-0090**
National—(866) 559-4733
Fax—(973) 537-0906
www.blancind.com
Pres.—Didier Blanc
Mktg. Mgr.—Patricia Trento
SIC—2542; 3496; *Custom point-of-purchase displays, racks & wire parts*
Employs—100; Estab.—1950
Sales—$500,000-$1Mil
5,100 sq ft site, Distrib.—National
Privately owned corporation

## BLANC INDUSTRIES, INC.
88 King St. (07801)
**Phone—(973) 678-1200**
(973) 537-0090
Fax—(973) 537-0906
www.blancind.com
Email—info@blancind.com
Pres.—Didier Blanc
Sales Mgr.—Mike Snell
Mktg. Mgr.—Dave Lyons
IT Mgr.—Sean Flynn
Hum. Res. Mgr.—Laura Cuell
SIC—3993; 2542; 2541; NAICS—337215; *Corporate headquarters & point-of-purchase advertisement displays & commercial store fixtures*
Employs—60; Estab.—1997
Sales—$5Mil-$6Mil
120,000 sq ft site, Distrib.—Intl.
Privately owned sub-S corp.

## CASIO AMERICA, INC. (H Q)
570 Mount Pleasant Ave. (07801)
**Phone—(973) 361-5400**
National—(800) 706-2534
Fax—(973) 537-8926
www.casio.com
Chrm.—Shigenori Itoh
Ex. V-P., Fin.—Tomouyki Uchyama
Dir., Hum. Res.—Raymond Smith
GM, Mktg.—Peter Brinkman
Mktg. Mgr.—Sue Vander Schang
Pur. Agt.—Christine Pilczak
SIC—3571; 3679; NAICS—334111; *Corporate headquarters; computers & electronic components (mfg. done overseas)*
Employs—180; Estab.—1970
Sales—$350Mil
128,000 sq ft site, Distrib.—Intl.
Privately owned corporation

## COCOCARE PRODUCTS, INC.
85 Franklin Rd. (07801)
**Phone—(973) 989-8880**
Fax—(973) 989-1711
www.cococare.com
Email—info@cococare.com
Pres., CFO—Gerald Jay Dubin
MIS Mgr.—Joanne Schlesinger
Off. Mgr.—Gail Porfido
SIC—2844; NAICS—325600; *Health & beauty aids*
Employs—20; Estab.—1969
Distrib.—Intl.
Privately owned corporation

## DABURN ELECTRONICS & CABLE, INC.
44 Richboynton Rd. (07801)
**Phone—(973) 328-3200**
Fax—(973) 328-3130
www.daburn.com
Email—daburn@daburn.com
Pres., CEO—Ed Flaherty
SIC—3679; *Electronic wire, cable, heat shrinkable tubing & sleeving & porcelain insulators; Brand name—Daflex; Daflon; Danyon; Dalite; Stik-Klip; Stretch-N-Seal; Daburn CRT*
Employs—29; Estab.—1964
Sales—$5Mil-$15Mil
25,000 sq ft site, Distrib.—Intl.
Privately owned corporation

## DELTRONIC CRYSTAL INDUSTRIES
60 Harding Ave. (07801)
**Phone—(973) 328-7000**
Fax—(973) 361-0722
www.deltroniccrystal.com
Email—info@deltroniccrystal.com
Pres.—Stuart Samuelson
Off. Mgr.—Debbie Samuelson
Sales Admn.—Carol Sullivan
SIC—3679; *Laser crystals for optoelectronic materials & components*
Employs—20; Estab.—1986
Distrib.—Intl.
Privately owned corporation
Also see: ISOWAVE, 64 Harding Ave.

## DIVERSIFIED PRECISION TOOLING
143 Baker St. (07801)
**Phone—(973) 361-8545**
Pres.—Bob Minahan
SIC—3089; *Plastic injection molding & casting molds*
Employs—1; Estab.—1978
Sales—under $500,000
Distrib.—Local
Sole ownership

## FOX VALVE DEVELOPMENT CORP.
85 Franklin Rd., Hamilton Business Pk. (07801)
**Phone—(973) 328-1011**
Fax—(973) 328-3651
www.foxvalve.com
Email—info@foxvalve.com
Pres.—Lawrence Fox
V-P.—Steve Westaway
Off. Admn.—Joanne Lozesger
SIC—3491; 3494; NAICS—332911; *Valves, venturi eductors, ejectors & flow controls, including multi-stage vacuum systems, solids-conveying eductors & air, liquid & steam ejectors for the aerospace, industrial & research industries; Brand name—Fox Venturi Eductors*
Employs—23; Estab.—1961
Distrib.—Intl.
Privately owned corporation

## †GARDEN STATE TILE DISTRIBUTORS, INC.
267 Route 46 W. (07801)
**Phone—(973) 366-5035**
Fax—(973) 366-8478
www.gstile.com
Email—mnielsen@gstile.com
Opers. Mgr.—Mark Nielsen
SIC—5032; *Distributor of ceramic, porcelain & natural stone tiles*
Employs—4; Estab.—1987
Sales—$500,000-$1Mil
Distrib.—Regional
Privately owned corporation
Parent co.—Garden State Tile Distributors, Inc., Farmingdale, NJ
Phone—(732) 938-6675
See Parent Co. Section for full profile.

## H & W TOOL CO., INC.
22 Lee Ave. (07801)
**Phone—(973) 366-0131**
Fax—(973) 366-9347
www.hwtool.com
Email—rwinstead@hwtool.com
Pres., GM—Richard Winstead
V-P.—Henry Winstead
Off. Mgr.—Amy Winstead
Qual. Mgr.—Blevins Ford
Manager—Mike Gallager
SIC—3728; 3499; *Aeronautical & medical components*
Employs—18; Estab.—1966
7,500 sq ft site, Distrib.—Local
Privately owned sub-S corp.
ISO rating—13485

## HELRICKS PICTURE FRAMING, INC.
158 W. Clinton St., Ste. G (07801-3410)
**Phone—(973) 361-1301**
(973) 361-1300
National—(800) 659-8720
Fax—(973) 361-3511
www.helricks.com
Email—helricksinc@optonline.net
Pres.—Peter Harris
GM—Sandra Caron
SIC—2499; *Picture frames*
Employs—10; Estab.—1964
Sales—$825,000
5,000 sq ft site, Distrib.—National
Privately owned sub-S corp.

## INDUSTRIAL SERVICES ENTERPRISES
192 Franklin Rd. (07801)
**Phone—(973) 366-3939**
Fax—(973) 328-1307
www.isenj.com
Email—ise@isenj.com
Pres.—Sante D'Emidio
Ex. V-P.—Jennifer Donnelly
Plt. Mgr.—Kevin Donnelly
Off. Mgr.—Tracy Green
SIC—3441; 3312; NAICS—332312; *Structural steel fabrication*
Employs—30; Estab.—1970
Sales—$500,000-$1Mil
7,000 sq ft site, Distrib.—Local
Privately owned corporation

## INSTANT PRINTING, INC.
241 E. Blackwell St. (07801)
**Phone—(973) 366-6855**
Fax—(973) 366-2992
www.instantprintingdover.com
Email—instantprinting@att.net
Pres.—Ann Medore
Manager—Pete Medore
SIC—2759; 2752; NAICS—323100; *Commercial, offset & digital printing, design, plotting, outdoor signs & bindery*
Employs—4; Estab.—1969
Sales—$1Mil-$2.5Mil
Distrib.—Local
Privately owned corporation

## INTERNATIONAL FOODSOURCE, LLC
52 Richboynton Rd. (07801)
**Phone—(973) 361-7044**
(973) 607-1902
Fax—(973) 537-2917
www.valuednaturals.com
Email—customerservice@intlfoodsource.com
Pres.—David Lipson
Hum. Res. Mgr.—Leidy Ramirez
Proj. Mgr.—Jessica Brienza
SIC—2034; 2068; 2099; *Dried fruits, nuts & gourmet food products; Brand name—Valued Naturals*
Employs—120; Estab.—2004
Sales—$50Mil
7,000 sq ft site, Distrib.—National
Privately owned corporation
AKA: IFS, Inc.

## ISOWAVE
64 Harding Ave. (07801)
**Phone—(973) 328-7000**
Fax—(973) 328-7036
www.isowave.com
Email—info@isowave.com
Pres., CEO—Stuart Samuelson
GM—Sharon Kitts
Acctg. Mgr.—Debbie Cohn
Sales & Mktg. Admn.—Carol Sullivan
SIC—3674; NAICS—334413; *Optical isolators*
Employs—15; Estab.—1986
Sales—$5Mil-$10Mil
18,000 sq ft site, Distrib.—Intl.
Privately owned corporation
Also see: Deltronic Crystal Industries, 60 Harding Ave.

## JAN PACKAGING, INC.
100 Harrison St. *(07801)*
Mail addr: P.O. Box 448, Dover (07802-0448)
**Phone—(973) 361-7200**
National—(888) 452-6725
Fax—(973) 361-3306
www.janpackaging.com
Email—janpkg@janpackaging.com
Pres.—Karl Malavarca

## Dover—(cont.)

CFO—Kathy Caristia
Opers. Mgr.—Paula J. Smith
SIC—2449; NAICS—321920; *Wooden shipping crates for export packing*
Employs—80; Estab.—1952
Sales—$10Mil-$25Mil
250,000 sq ft site, Distrib.—Intl.
Privately owned corporation

**JDV EQUIPMENT CORP.**
1 Princeton Ave. (07801)
**Phone—(973) 366-6556**
Fax—(973) 366-3193
www.jdvequipment.com
Email—info@jdvequipment.com
Pres.—Robert T. Abbott
Sr. V-P.—Sean King
Acctg. Mgr.—Donna Abbott
SIC—3589; NAICS—333922; *Water & wastewater treatment equipment & services; Brand name—LEVEL LODOR™; TURBOMIXER*
Employs—8; Estab.—1990
Distrib.—Intl.
Privately owned corporation

**JERSEY SHEET METAL & MACHINE, INC.**
90 E. Dickerson St. (07801)
**Phone—(973) 366-0101**
Fax—(973) 989-7591
Email—jersey.sheetmetal@verizon.net
Pres.—Richard Hammond, Sr.
SIC—3444; *Sheet metal fabrication*
Employs—3; Estab.—1978
Distrib.—Regional
Privately owned corporation

**MANUFACTURERS' BRUSH CORP.**
69 King St. (07801)
**Phone—(973) 882-6966**
Fax—(973) 882-1226
www.manufacturersbrush.com
Email—info@manufacturersbrush.com
Pres.—Richard Draudt
SIC—3991; NAICS—339994; *Industrial & commercial brushes*
Employs—5; Estab.—1992
Sales—under $500,000
Distrib.—National

**MINITEC CORP.**
158 W. Clinton St., Ste. V (07801)
**Phone—(973) 989-1426**
Fax—(973) 989-1427
Email—smindlin@aol.com
Owner & Pres.—Scott Mindlin
Machine Operator—Gina Fisichelli
SIC—3469; *Metal stampings*
Employs—4; Estab.—1984
Sales—$500,000-$1Mil
5,000 sq ft site, Distrib.—National
Privately owned corporation

**MOTION CONTROL TECHNOLOGIES, INC.**
158 W. Clinton St., Ste. FF (07801)
**Phone—(973) 361-2226**
National—(888) 434-8077
Fax—(973) 361-3103
www.mctcable.com
Email—info@mctcable.com
Pres.—Frank Heidinger
SIC—3496; 3679; *Wire rope cable assemblies, including mechanical cable assemblies & cable lanyards & tethers*
Employs—10; Estab.—1998
Sales—$1Mil-$2.5Mil
Distrib.—Intl.
Privately owned corporation
AKA: MCT CABLE

**MPT INDUSTRIES**
85 Franklin Rd., Hamilton Bus. Park, Ste. 6-B (07801)
**Phone—(973) 989-9220**
www.autochic.com
Email—sales@autochic.com
Owner & Pres.—Michael Trueba, Jr.
Manager—John Little
SIC—2394; 2396; NAICS—314912; *Automotive covers & lubricants*
Employs—7; Estab.—1985
6,000 sq ft site, Distrib.—Intl.
Privately owned corporation
AKA: Auto Chic

**NEPTUNE PRODUCTS, INC.**
353 E. Blackwell St., P.O. Drawer 829 (07801)
**Phone—(973) 366-8200**
Fax—(973) 366-0398
www.neptuneproducts.com
Email—sales@neptuneproducts.com
Pres.—Richard Schroeder
SIC—3594; NAICS—333996; *Laboratory gas & air vacuum pumps; Brand name—NEPTUNE DYNA-PUMP*
Employs—5; Estab.—1953
Sales—$500,000-$1Mil
Distrib.—Intl.
Privately owned corporation

**NEW STANDARD PRINTING CORP.**
118 Lincoln Ave. (07801)
**Phone—(973) 366-0006**
www.newstandardprinting.com
Pres.—Michael Wetzel
SIC—2752; NAICS—323100; *Offset printing*
Employs—5; Estab.—1975
Distrib.—Regional
Privately owned corporation

**PRECISION SHAPE SOLUTIONS**
Div. of Service Metal Fabricating, Inc.
243 E. Blackwell St. (07801)
**Phone—(973) 989-7199**
Fax—(973) 989-7196
www.precisionshapes.com
Email—cory@precisionshapes.com
Site Mgr.—Cory Akers
SIC—3444; *Waterjet & laser cutting job shop*
Employs—5; Estab.—1982
37,000 sq ft site, Distrib.—National
Privately owned corporation
AKA: Service Metal Fabricating, Inc.
Parent co.—Service Metal Fabricating, Inc., Rockaway, NJ
Phone—(973) 625-8882
See Parent Co. Section for full profile.

**R & J CONTROL, INC.**
58 Harding Ave. (07801)
**Phone—(973) 328-6880**
Fax—(973) 328-0339
www.rjcontrol.com
Email—info@rjcontrol.com
Pres., MIS Mgr.—Robert Berry
Fin. Mgr.—Jeff Berry
SIC—3621; 3613; NAICS—335312; *Rebuilt diesel & gas generators & automatic transfer switches*
Employs—20; Estab.—1974
10,000 sq ft site, Distrib.—Regional
Privately owned corporation

**RIDGE PRECISION PRODUCTS INC.**
288 U.S. Highway 46, Ste. D (07801)
**Phone—(973) 361-3508**
Fax—(973) 361-4856
Email—mark@ridgeco.net
Pres., Sales & Mktg. Mgr.—Mark Leone
Matls. Mgr.—Fred Engelberger

SIC—3599; *Precision machining job shop*
Employs—10; Estab.—1982
Sales—$500,000-$1Mil
Distrib.—Local
Privately owned corporation

**SCIMEDX CORP.**
53 Richboynton Rd. (07801)
**Phone—(973) 625-8822**
National—(800) 221-5598
Fax—(973) 625-8796
www.scimedx.com
Email—info@scimedx.com
Pres.—Thomas L. Britten
SIC—3841; *Medical diagnostic test kits*
Employs—25; Estab.—1976
Distrib.—Intl.
Privately owned corporation
AKA: Ampcor Technology, Inc.

**SIGNS OF SENSE**
79 Bassett Hwy. (07801-3819)
**Phone—(973) 361-0037**
Fax—(973) 361-1717
www.signsofsense.com
Email—info@signsofsense.com
Owner & Pres.—Scott Rothbart
SIC—3993; 2759; 3089; NAICS—323100; *Full-color interior & exterior signs, banners, vinyl, vehicle, boat & window lettering & screen & digital printing*
Employs—3; Estab.—1992
Sales—under $500,000
5,000 sq ft site, Distrib.—Local
Sole ownership

**TECHNICAL GLASS PRODUCTS, INC.**
243 E. Blackwell St., Ste. B (07801)
**Phone—(973) 989-5500**
Fax—(973) 989-0121
www.technicalglassinc.com
Email—technicalglass@verizon.net
Pres.—Joseph Murray
SIC—3231; 3221; NAICS—327215; *Glassware, including viscometers, thermometers, hydrometers & petroleum testing glassware*
Employs—5; Estab.—1988
Sales—$100,000-$300,000
Distrib.—Intl.
Privately owned corporation

**TEE PEE PACKAGING CORP.**
85 Harrison St. (07801)
**Phone—(973) 328-6500**
Fax—(973) 328-7766
Pres.—Charles Deehan
V-P., Mktg.—Dennis Kwasnik
Sales Mgr.—Andrew Deehan
Bookkeeper—Donna Franchino
SIC—2673; *Plastic bags*
Employs—40; Estab.—1973
45,000 sq ft site, Distrib.—National
Privately owned corporation

**VERDEN TOOL & MFG., LLC**
121 E. Blackwell St. (07801)
**Phone—(973) 366-7510**
Fax—(973) 366-7510
Pres., Member & R & D Mgr.—Robert Denzer
Fin., MIS & Plt. Mgr.—Barry Birkholz
SIC—3544; NAICS—333500; *Tool & die job shop*
Employs—2; Estab.—1951
Sales—under $500,000
1,000 sq ft site, Distrib.—Local
Limited Liability Company

## Dumont

(Bergen—N.E.)

**K L M MECHANICAL CONTRACTORS, INC.**
109 W. Shore Ave. (07628)
**Phone—(201) 385-6965**
Fax—(201) 385-9497
Pres.—Ken Loehr
V-P.—Keith Loehr
SIC—3444; 3312; *Sheet metal fabrication & HVAC contracting, including steel ducts & mechanical contracting services*
Employs—8; Estab.—1967
Sales—$500,000-$1Mil
Distrib.—Local
Privately owned corporation

**KEYSTONE PRINTING, INC.**
21-C E. Madison Ave. (07628)
**Phone—(201) 387-7252**
Fax—(201) 387-2667
www.keystoneprintingnj.com
Email—jobs@keystoneprintingnj.com
Pres.—Janice Worner
V-P.—Michael Worner
Prod. Mgr.—Michael Dempsey
Bookkeeper—Janet Masio
SIC—2752; 2791; 3993; NAICS—323122; *Digital offset printing, typesetting & advertising specialties*
Employs—4; Estab.—1972
Sales—$500,000-$1Mil
4,000 sq ft site, Distrib.—Regional
Privately owned corporation

**KODAY PRESS, INC.**
69 Armour Pl. (07628)
**Phone—(201) 387-0001**
Fax—(201) 387-1117
www.kodaypress.com
Email—m_kaye@hotmail.com
Pres.—Eugene Koblantz
GM—Mark Koblantz
Off. Mgr.—Dave Kaye
SIC—2759; NAICS—323100; *Commercial printing*
Employs—12; Estab.—1934
Sales—$1Mil-$2Mil
16,000 sq ft site, Distrib.—National
Privately owned corporation

**P T L SHEET METAL, INC.**
70 Davies Ave. (07628)
**Phone—(201) 501-8700**
National—(877) 785-2337
Fax—(201) 385-0008
Email—ptlsheetmetal@optonline.net
Pres.—Candice MacWilliam
Plt. & Sales Mgr.—Robert MacWilliam
SIC—3444; *Sheet metal fabrication*
Employs—5; Estab.—1987
Sales—under $500,000
Distrib.—Local
Privately owned corporation

**SIGN ON, INC.**
149 Washington Ave., Apt. A (07628-2346)
**Phone—(201) 384-7714**
Fax—(201) 384-7741
www.signoninc.com
Email—signoninc@aol.com
Pres.—Manohar G. Massand
V-P.—Kiran Massand
SIC—3993; *Interior & exterior signs, banners & vehicle graphics, including installation & maintenance*
Employs—4; Estab.—1993
Sales—under $500,000
3,000 sq ft site, Distrib.—Regional
Privately owned sub-S corp.

GEOGRAPHICAL

## Dumont—(cont.)

### US CONCRETE MATERIALS, LLC
189 Berkley Pl. (07628)
Phone—(201) 385-6470
www.usconcretematerials.com
Email—uscmllc@yahoo.com
Pres.—Robert K. Bortnick
Sales Mgr., Intl.—Donna Russell
Mktg. Coord.—Linda Stetson
SIC—2821; 2899; 2891; NAICS—
325211; *Construction chemicals,
cold/hot weather admixtures,
floor shake-ons & granolithic
toppings & treatments for
concrete & masonry
waterproofing construction;
Brand name—Hydro;
HydroGuard; Hydrocel;
PowerBond; PowerPatch;
PowerGrout; Bond-Tec;
FerroTop; Florundum; DuraSeal;
Flow-Tec; Specure; Mason-Mate*
Employs—3; Estab.—1992
Sales—over $1Mil
Distrib.—Intl.
Limited Liability Company

## Dunellen
(Middlesex—N.E.)

### AVENEL PALLET CO., INC.
Foot Of S. 2nd St., P.O. Box 276
(08812)
Phone—(732) 752-0500
Fax—(732) 752-0533
Pres.—Vincent Colonna
GM—Michael Colonna
SIC—2448; NAICS—321920;
*Wooden pallets*
Employs—11; Estab.—1979
Distrib.—Local
Privately owned corporation

### BLACHER CANVAS PRODUCTS, INC.
604 Bound Brook Rd. (08812)
Phone—(732) 968-3666
Fax—(732) 968-0032
www.blachercanvas.com
Email—blachercanvas@aol.com
Pres.—George Rodoussakis
Manager—Manny Rodoussakis
SIC—2394; NAICS—314912;
*Canvas awnings*
Employs—7; Estab.—1947
Sales—under $500,000
Distrib.—Local
Privately owned corporation

### DOUBLE O MFG.
100 S. Washington Ave. (08812)
Phone—(732) 752-9423
Fax—(732) 752-0777
www.doubleomfg.com
Email—jeoslislo@verizon.net
Pres., CFO—Albert J. Oslislo
V-P., MIS & R & D—Jim Oslislo
SIC—3599; 3499; *Metal
fabrication & military standard
welding job shop*
Employs—9; Estab.—1986
9,000 sq ft site, Distrib.—National
Limited Liability Company

NEW ENTRY
### EDIGITAL GRAPHICS
326 U.S. Highway 22, Ste. 12-A
(08812)
Phone—(732) 968-1234
Fax—(732) 968-1233
www.edigitalgraphics.com
Email—info@edigitalgraphics.com
Owner—Elly Ezra
Manager—Ed Regan
SIC—2759; *Digital printing*
Employs—10; Estab.—2001
Sales—$500,000-$1Mil
3,000 sq ft site, Distrib.—Local
Sole ownership

### MISSRY ASSOCS., INC.
100 S. Washington Ave. (08812)
Phone—(732) 752-7500
National—(800) 336-4726
Fax—(732) 752-6820
www.miscohomeandgarden.com
Email—customerservice@
miscohomeandgarden.com
Pres.—Edward Missry
GM—Morris Moskowitz
Hum. Res. Mgr.—Christine
Wessner
SIC—3089; 2514; 2519; NAICS—
337125; *Home & garden
decorative accessories,
including planters, watering
cans, caddies, plant stands &
displays*
Employs—200; Estab.—1975
Distrib.—National
Privately owned corporation
DBA: Misco Enterprises

### PEDESTAL PALLET CO.
777 N. Avenue Ext., P.O. Box 450
(08812)
Phone—(732) 968-7488
Fax—(732) 968-7499
www.pedestalpallet.com
Email—info@pedestalpallet.com
Owner—John Ruotulo
V-P.—Anthony Defilipps
SIC—2448; NAICS—321920;
*Wooden pallets & skids*
Employs—15; Estab.—1975
Sales—$1Mil-$2.5Mil
Distrib.—Local
Privately owned corporation

### PRO-FORM PACKAGING, INC.
777 North Avenue Ext., P.O. Box
4231 (08812)
Phone—(732) 968-8123
National—(888) 377-8123
Fax—(732) 968-5242
www.proformpackaging.com
Email—info@
proformpackaging.com
Pres.—Kenneth Gibbs
Hum. Res. Mgr.—Russ Ropon
SIC—3082; 3089; NAICS—
326130; *Custom & contract
thermoformed packaging &
custom & stock display items,
including PET & RPET
clamshells, platforms & trays,
trifolds & point-of-purchase
display & robotic trays, reels,
vacuum forming & RF welding*
Employs—20; Estab.—1989
40,000 sq ft site, Distrib.—National
Privately owned corporation

### WEATHER TEK ALUMINUM CORP.
123 N. Washington Ave., P.O. Box
405 (08812)
Phone—(732) 752-0313
National—(800) 696-0313
Fax—(732) 752-0360
www.weathertek.net
Email—lindak@weathertek.net
Pres.—Charlie Ponti
V-P., Sales—David Wright
Off. Mgr.—Linda Krynski
SIC—3444; *Aluminum awnings &
siding*
Employs—15; Estab.—1968
Sales—$1Mil-$2.5Mil
Distrib.—Regional
Privately owned corporation

## East Brunswick
(Middlesex—N.E.)

### ACCUVIEW, INC.
40-C Cotters Ln., Ste. F (08816-
2037)
Phone—(201) 440-2225
National—(800) 275-4255
Fax—(201) 440-5655
www.accuview.com
Email—sales@accuview.com
Pres.—David H. Wu
SIC—3577; 3663; NAICS—
334220; *Flat panel LCD monitors
& touchscreens for security,
banking, industrial & marine
applications, medical systems &
digital signage; Brand name—
Accuview*
Employs—10; Estab.—1990
Sales—$5Mil
10,000 sq ft site, Distrib.—Intl.
Sole ownership
ISO rating—9001:2008

### ALL SEASONS DOOR & WINDOW, INC.
28 Edgeboro Rd. (08816)
Phone—(732) 238-7100
National—(800) 238-7001
Fax—(732) 238-7225
www.asdw.net
Email—customer@asdw.net
Pres., CFO—Steven Yu
GM—Angela Yu
Sales Mgr.—Yee Chin
MIS Mgr.—Jeff Chou
SIC—3089; 3442; NAICS—
332321; *Vinyl & aluminum
windows*
Employs—30; Estab.—1989
40,000 sq ft site, Distrib.—Local
Privately owned corporation

### †ALLIED ELECTRONICS, INC.
197 State Hwy. N-18 (08816)
Phone—(732) 846-4271
National—(800) 433-5700
Fax—(817) 595-3500
www.alliedelec.com
Email—manager@alliedelec.com
Off. Mgr.—Stan Duvall
SIC—5063; *Distributor of electrical
equipment*
Employs—5; Estab.—1992
Distrib.—National
Publicly owned corporation
Parent co.—Allied Electronics,
Inc., Fort Worth, TX
Phone—(817) 595-3500
See Parent Co. Section for full profile.

### †AMERICAN MACHINERY LIQUIDATORS, INC.
P.O. Box 6995 (08816-6995)
Phone—(732) 390-0006
Fax—(732) 390-0559
www.americanmachinery.com
Email—sales@
americanmachinery.com
Pres.—Marc Gallanter
V-P.—Deborah Gallanter
SIC—5084; *Distributor of new &
used toolroom & fabricating
equipment, including lathes,
milling machines, brakes,
shears, grinders & manual &
CNC machine tools &
accessories; Brand name—
Acer; Acu-Rite Digital Read Out;
Aloris; Birmingham; Cosen;
Disston; Dorian; Ercolina; Fagor;
Fortune; Manford; Newell Digital
Read Outs; Phase II; Royal
Products; Sharp Industries;
Vertech Soft Jaws*
Employs—2; Estab.—1992
Sales—$500,000-$1Mil
3,000 sq ft site, Distrib.—Intl.
Privately owned sub-S corp.

### ATLAS FASHIONS
148 Tices Ln. (08816)
Phone—(732) 254-6090
Fax—(732) 254-6095
Owner—Seo Shim
SIC—3961; NAICS—339900;
*Costume jewelry*
Employs—7; Estab.—1990
Sales—$500,000-$1Mil (est)
Distrib.—Intl.
Privately owned corporation

### AUMTECH, INC.
710 Old Bridge Tpke. (08816)
Phone—(732) 254-1875
Fax—(732) 254-2081
www.aumtech.com
Email—support@aumtech.com
Ex. V-P., COO—Tom Porter
V-P., Cust. Serv.—Fred Cook
SIC—7372; *Software
development, including
VoiceXml platform development,
speech recognition software
development, automated web
agent development, CRM
language accent neutralization
development & MRCP connector
development*
Employs—30; Estab.—1988
Distrib.—Intl.
Privately owned corporation

### †BLACKWELL ASSOCS., INC.
Div. of Adler, Inc., Kurt S.
15 Kimberly Rd. (08816)
Phone—(732) 238-8000
National—(800) 243-9627
Fax—(732) 238-8089
www.kurtadler.com
Email—info@kurtadler.com
GM, Opers. & Whse. Mgr.—John
Johnson
Off. Mgr.—Mary Crawford
Receiving Mgr.—Benny Rivera
Order Mgr.—John Urbanski
Asst. Whse. Mgr.—Michael
Beaudui
SIC—5199; *Wholesaler of
imported holiday decoration
items, including Christmas trees,
snow globes & handmade
ornaments*
Employs—65; Estab.—1946
Distrib.—Intl.
Privately owned corporation
Parent co.—Adler, Inc., Kurt S.,
New York, NY
Phone—(212) 924-0900
See Parent Co. Section for full profile.

### BLUESTAR SILICONES U.S.A. CORP. (H Q)
2 Tower Center Blvd., Ste. 1601
(08816)
Phone—(732) 227-2060
National—(866) 474-6342
Fax—(732) 249-7000
www.bluestarsilicones.com
Email—info@bluestarsilicones.com
Pres.—Chris York
CFO—Bertrand Mollet
Dir., Hum. Res.—Lisa Wheeler
SIC—2819; *Corporate
headquarters; industrial
chemicals*
Employs—20; Estab.—2007
Sales—$5Mil-$10Mil (est)
Distrib.—Intl.
Privately owned corporation

### C & A PRESS, INC.
636 State Route 18 (08816)
Phone—(732) 238-1150
Fax—(732) 238-3719
www.mmpeb.com
Email—art@mmpeb.com
Owner—Joe Kim
SIC—2759; *Commercial printing*
Employs—3; Estab.—2005
Sales—under $500,000 (est)
Distrib.—Regional
Privately owned corporation

### CENTURY PACKAGING, INC.
42 Edgeboro Rd. (08816)
Phone—(732) 249-6600
Fax—(732) 828-0558
www.centurypackaginginc.com
Email—cenpack@silk.net
Pres., CFO—Tom Picciolo, Jr.
V-P.—John Ranone
MIS & Off. Mgr.—Frank Picciolo
Bookkeeper—Pauline Giaccio

## East Brunswick— (cont.)

SIC—2652; 2657; NAICS—322213; *Paper boxes*
Employs—40; Estab.—1985
30,000 sq ft site, Distrib.—Regional
Privately owned corporation

**†CERMSOURCE, INC**
25 Kimberly Rd., Unit A, P.O. Box 6026 (08816)
**Phone—(732) 257-5002**
National—(800) 608-5828
Fax—(732) 257-5003
www.ceramsource.com
Email—sales@ceramsource.com
Mktg. Mgr.—Philip Kent
SIC—5085; *Wholesaler of refractories, including brick, ceramic foam filters, fiber insulation & graphite sheets; Brand name—TaoFibre; TaoFil*
Employs—10; Estab.—1999
Sales—$3Mil-$5Mil
Distrib.—Intl.
Privately owned sub-S corp.

**†CLASSIC CERAMIC TILE, INC.**
Div. of East Coast Tile Imports, Inc.
272 State Route 18, Ste. 3 (08816)
**Phone—(732) 390-7700**
Fax—(722) 390-6662
www.besttile.com
Email—showroom@besttile.com
Manager—Chris Martins
SIC—5032; *Wholesaler of ceramic tile & stone products*
Employs—4; Estab.—1990
Distrib.—Local
Privately owned corporation
Parent co.—East Coast Tile Imports, Inc., Ludlow, MA
Phone—(413) 583-4246
See Parent Co. Section for full profile.

**COILHOSE PNEUMATICS**
19 Kimberly Rd. (08816)
**Phone—(732) 432-7177**
National—(800) 852-1999
Fax—(732) 432-7425
www.coilhose.com
Email—info@coilhose.com
Pres.—Marvin Aaron
V-P., Div. & Cont.—Carmen Nunez-Oliviera
V-P., Engrg. & Opers.—Michael Khaitov
Sales Mgr., Natl.—Ray Demirjian
Mktg. Mgr.—Phillip Morris
Hum. Res. Mgr.—Joan DeSantis
SIC—3714; 3429; *Company headquarters & tire gages & repair products, pneumatic accessories & wheel hardware for the automotive afterrmarket industry; Brand name—Flexcoil®; Coilhose Cannon®; Typhoon Pro®; Flexeel®; Typhoon®; Flexeel Max®*
Employs—96; Estab.—1969
100,000 sq ft site, Distrib.—Regional
Privately owned corporation
DBA: Acme Automotive

**COMMERCE SIGN SOLUTIONS, LLC**
540 Cranbury Rd., Ste. 334 (08816)
**Phone—(732) 238-7000**
Fax—(732) 238-6999
www.commercesignsolutions.com
Email—info@commercesignsolutions.com
Owner—Linda Harrington

SIC—3993; 2759; 2541; 2542; NAICS—323100; *ADA & architectural signs, banners, trade show displays, window & truck lettering & large-format digital printing*
Employs—1; Estab.—2004
Sales—under $500,000
1,650 sq ft site, Distrib.—Regional
Limited Liability Company

**CORENTE, INC.**
758 Route 18, Ste. 110 (08816)
**Phone—(732) 254-0210**
National—(888) 783-0383
Fax—(732) 254-0221
www.corente.com
Email—techsupport@corente.com
Pres.—James Zucco
Cust. Network Engr.—Frank Lettieri
SIC—7373; NAICS—541512; *Computer network systems integration*
Employs—35; Estab.—1999
Sales—$5Mil-$10Mil
Distrib.—Intl.
Privately owned corporation

**†DADE PAPER CO.**
120 Tices Ln. (08816)
**Phone—(732) 254-3100**
National—(888) 946-2671
Fax—(732) 254-7342
www.dadepaper.com
Email—info@winansmcshane.com
V-P., Opers.—Mark Rogers
SIC—5087; 5113; *Distributor of janitorial supplies, industrial packaging, sanitary paper & plastic liners; Brand name—3M; Georgia-Pacific; Betco; Laidlaw; Procter & Gamble*
Employs—20; Estab.—1893
Distrib.—Regional
Privately owned corporation

**†DODSON GLOBAL, INC.**
27 Cotters Ln. (08816)
**Phone—(732) 238-7001**
Fax—(732) 238-7760
www.dodsonglobal.com
Email—sales@gffusa.com
Br. Mgr.—Allen Goodrich
Whse. Mgr.—Jamie Singo
SIC—5051; 5074; *Distributor of pipes & fittings*
Employs—7; Estab.—2006
Distrib.—National
Privately owned corporation
Parent co.—Dodson Global, Inc., Stone Mountain, GA
Phone—(404) 363-8900
See Parent Co. Section for full profile.

**DRAKE CORP.**
154 Tices Ln. (08816)
**Phone—(732) 254-1530**
         (732) 254-1808
Fax—(732) 254-1530
www.drakecorp.com
Email—alida@drakecorp.com
Pres.—Ralph Drake
Sales Mgr.—Karen Hanpp
SIC—2599; 3089; *Polymer-composite hotel furniture, including folding & stacking resin chairs*
Employs—8; Estab.—1983
Sales—$1Mil-$2.5Mil
Distrib.—National
Privately owned corporation

**†EAST BRUNSWICK SUPPLY, INC.**
413 State Route 18 (08816)
**Phone—(732) 254-1015**
Fax—(732) 254-1820
Email—eastbrunswicksupply@comcast.net
V-P.—Charles T. Lyons, Jr.

SIC—5074; 5075; *Wholesaler of plumbing & HVAC supplies*
Employs—11; Estab.—1949
Distrib.—Local
Privately owned corporation

**ECCE PANIS**
Div. of Campbell Soup Co.
3-B Brick Plant Rd. (08816)
**Phone—(732) 254-1770**
National—(888) 372-7323
Fax—(732) 254-1772
www.eccepanis.com
Email—ecce_panis_consumer_affairs@pepperidgefarm.com
Plt. Mgr.—Mike Vallen
SIC—2051; NAICS—311812; *Bread*
Employs—150; Estab.—2002
Distrib.—National
Publicly owned corporation
Parent co.—Campbell Soup Co., Camden, NJ
Phone—(856) 342-4800
See Parent Co. Section for full profile.

**ELITE PACKAGING CORP.**
40 Cotters Ln., Ste. E (08816)
**Phone—(732) 651-9955**
Fax—(732) 651-9958
Email—sales@elitepkg.net
Owner & Pres.—Mario Magali
Supervisor—Victor Martinez
SIC—2652; NAICS—322213; *Contract packaging & hand assembly*
Employs—100; Estab.—1996
Distrib.—National
Privately owned corporation

**FEDEX OFFICE & PRINT CENTER**
Div. of FedEx Office & Print Services, Inc.
212 State Route 18 (08816)
**Phone—(732) 249-9222**
National—(800) 463-3339
Fax—(732) 249-9315
www.fedex.com
Email—usa1212@fedex.com
Br. Mgr.—Andrew Takacs
Lead Consultant—Xavier Smalls
SIC—2752; NAICS—323100; *Instant printing & vinyl banners*
Employs—12; Estab.—1985
Distrib.—Regional
Publicly owned corporation
Parent co.—FedEx Office & Print Services, Inc., Dallas, TX
Phone—(214) 550-7000
See Parent Co. Section for full profile.

**GERARD SHEET METAL FABRICATORS, INC.**
385 Lexington Ave. (08816)
**Phone—(732) 257-4777**
Fax—(732) 257-7282
Email—gerardsmfi@aol.com
Pres.—Betty Hogan
V-P.—Derick S. Eastman
GM—Jerry Hogan III
Pur. Agt.—Tameerah Hines
SIC—3444; *HVAC sheet metal duct work fabricating*
Employs—30; Estab.—1982
Distrib.—Regional
Privately owned corporation

**INNERWORKINGS, INC.**
7 Joanna Ct., Ste. H (08816)
**Phone—(732) 651-8822**
         (732) 651-8181
Fax—(732) 651-8454
www.inwk.com
Email—info@inwk.com
Br. Mgr.—Sam Wilk
SIC—2759; 2396; *Screen printing of promotional items & embroidery*
Employs—30
Sales—$2.5Mil-$5Mil (est)
Distrib.—Intl.
Privately owned corporation

Parent co.—InnerWorkings, Inc., Chicago, IL
Phone—(312) 642-3700
See Parent Co. Section for full profile.

**J Z D, LLC**
733 Route 18 (08816-4904)
**Phone—(732) 257-2727**
Fax—(732) 257-7055
Email—jzdinc@aol.com
Pres.—David Loewenstein
SIC—2761; NAICS—323116; *Business form printing*
Employs—3; Estab.—1990
Sales—under $500,000
Distrib.—Local
Privately owned corporation

**J.M. FRY CO., INC.**
Div. of J. M. Fry Company, Inc.
124 Tices Ln., Ste. A (08816)
**Phone—(732) 238-1060**
Fax—(732) 238-1059
www.jmfryprintinginks.com
Email—sales.richmond@jmfryinks.com
Br. Mgr.—Nick Melillo
Off. Mgr.—Beverly Rodro
Floor Supv.—Kuan Rodriguez
SIC—2893; NAICS—325910; *Flexographic, offset & gravure printing ink*
Employs—8; Estab.—1989
Sales—under $500,000
Distrib.—Local
Privately owned sub-S corp.
Parent co.—J. M. Fry Company, Inc., Henrico, VA
Phone—(804) 236-8100
See Parent Co. Section for full profile.

**JB SIGNS**
23 Dorchester Dr., P.O. Box 454 (08816)
**Phone—(732) 613-3700**
Email—jbsigns@comcast.net
Owner—Leigh Baumann
SIC—3993; *Signs, magnets, banners & window, boat & vehicle lettering*
Employs—1; Estab.—2002
Sales—under $500,000
Distrib.—Local
Limited Liability Company

**JUDY LYNN SOFTWARE, INC.**
278 Dunhams Corner Rd., P.O. Box 373 (08816)
**Phone—(732) 390-8845**
www.judylynn.com
Pres.—Elliot Pludwinski
SIC—7372; *Downloadable switch software development*
Employs—2
Distrib.—Intl.

**LENG-D'OR USA, INC.**
50 W. Ferris St. (08816)
**Phone—(732) 254-4300**
Fax—(732) 254-4320
www.lengdor.com
Email—sales@lengdor.com
Dir., Plt.—Ricardo Mendoza
SIC—2096; NAICS—311919; *Potato pellet snacks, tortilla & corn chips & nachos*
Employs—15; Estab.—2006
Sales—$2.5Mil-$5Mil (est)
Distrib.—National
Privately owned corporation

**†MATRIX DISTRIBUTORS, INC.**
110 Tices Ln., Ste. 5-B (08816-2048)
**Phone—(732) 698-9991**
Fax—(732) 698-9994
www.matrixdistributors.com
Email—info@matrixdistributors.com
Ptnr.—Seth Grumet
Ptnr.—Chris Benevent
Compliance & Cust. Serv. Mgr.—Melissa Jones

GEOGRAPHICAL

## East Brunswick—(cont.)

SIC—5122; 5047; *Corporate headquarters & distributor of pharmaceuticals & medical products, including diabetic & diagnostic supplies, nutritional supplements & incontinence products*
Employs—50; Estab.—1999
Distrib.—Regional
Privately owned partnership

### MAUSER USA LLC

35 Cotters Ln., Ste. C *(08816-2032)*
**Phone—(732) 353-7000**
(732) 353-7100
National—(800) 626-1128
Fax—(732) 651-9777
www.mausergroup.com
Email—info.us@mausergroup.com
Pres., CEO—Jeff Simmonds
V-P., Fin. & Treas.—Elizabeth Miller
V-P., Sales & Mktg.—Anthony Piersanti
Dir., Hum. Res.—Ellen Sherman
Dir., Regulatory Affs. & Tech.—Christopher Lind
Assoc. Dir., Financial Reporting—Len DePinto
Plt. Controller—Brian Baughjmann
SIC—3089; 2653; 2411; 2449; *Company headquarters & plastic containers & drums; Brand name*—L1; L2; Delcon; Deldrum; Vanguard; EZH1; EZH2; Bulkdrum; Mauser SM; Delguard; Delloc; Delta; Polycon; ACT; Delcon; Repaltainer; LR
Employs—80; Estab.—1896
Worldwide: 4,000
Sales—$5Mil-$10Mil
97,000 sq ft site, Distrib.—Intl.
Publicly owned corporation
ISO rating—9001

### MON-ECO INDUSTRIES, INC.

5 Joanna Ct. (08816)
**Phone—(732) 257-7942**
National—(800) 899-6326
Fax—(732) 257-6525
www.mon-ecoindustries.com
Email—moneco.mei@verizon.net
Pres.—Phil Buzzerio
V-P.—Thomas Coscia
Plt. Mgr.—Dave St. Amour
Off. Mgr.—Mary Ann Vakos
SIC—2891; NAICS—325520; *Adhesives & sealants*
Employs—16; Estab.—1979
Sales—$500,000-$1Mil
24,000 sq ft site, Distrib.—Intl.
Privately owned corporation

### †QUALITY ELECTRIC MOTOR SERVICE, INC.

396 State Route 18 (08816)
**Phone—(732) 257-6655**
(732) 254-1343
Fax—(732) 257-7779
Email—qem396@aol.com
Pres., GM—Michael Quaglietta, Sr.
Manager—Mike Quaglietta, Jr.
SIC—5085; *Distributor of new & rebuilt electric motors, motor & pumps; Brand name*—Baldor; AO Smith; Fasco; General Electric; Little Giant; Magnetek; Hayward; Reliance; Leeson; Emerson; World-Wide; Hemco; Weg; Dayton;
Employs—3; Estab.—1976
Sales—over $660,000
8,000 sq ft site, Distrib.—National
Privately owned corporation

### RAPID PRINT & COPY SERVICE

78 Summerhill Rd. (08816)
**Phone—(732) 238-9056**
Fax—(732) 238-0141
Email—rapid.print@verizon.net
Pres.—Roly Kapoano
SIC—2752; 2791; NAICS—323122; *Offset printing & typesetting*
Employs—2; Estab.—1975
Sales—under $500,000
1,000 sq ft site, Distrib.—Local
Privately owned corporation

### RARITAN PHARMACEUTICALS, INC.

8 Joanna Ct. (08816)
**Phone—(732) 432-8200**
Fax—(732) 432-8255
www.raritanpharm.com
Email—info@raritanpharm.com
Pres.—Vin Nayak
SIC—2834; NAICS—325412; *Pharmaceuticals*
Employs—250; Estab.—2000
Sales—$101Mil-$1Bil
Distrib.—Intl.
Privately owned corporation

### RAZOR PRINTING

78 Summerhill Rd. (08816)
**Phone—(732) 238-7520**
Fax—(732) 238-9632
Email—razoreb@earthlink.net
Owner—Michael Sciara
SIC—2752; NAICS—323100; *Instant printing*
Employs—2; Estab.—1980
Sales—under $500,000
2,000 sq ft site, Distrib.—Regional
Sole ownership

### SUPREME MFG. CO., INC.

5 Connerty Ct. (08816)
**Phone—(732) 254-0087**
National—(800) 772-7632
Fax—(732) 254-5736
www.supreme-mfg.com
Email—supmfgco@aol.com
Pres.—Cliff Krause
SIC—2087; NAICS—311900; *Granita, frozen drinks mix, fruit juice concentrates, snow cone & flavored syrups & ice cream toppings*
Employs—34; Estab.—1974
Sales—$10Mil-$12Mil
47,800 sq ft site, Distrib.—Intl.
Privately owned corporation

### SUZIE MAC SPECIALTIES, INC.

12-B Connery Ct. (08816)
**Phone—(732) 238-3500**
National—(800) 221-2493
Fax—(732) 238-4106
www.suziemac.com
Email—gene@suziemac.com
Pres.—Suzanne MacDougall
GM & Sales Mgr.—Gene Mintz
SIC—3993; 2759; 2396; NAICS—323100; *Custom & screenprinted photoluminescent interior, exterior & political signs, banners & graphic design; Brand name*—SafeGlow; Prest-On-Products
Employs—9; Estab.—1984
25,000 sq ft site, Distrib.—National
Privately owned corporation

### VAHL, INC.

34 Kennedy Blvd. (08816)
**Phone—(718) 492-6655**
www.vahl.com
Email—info@vahl.com
Pres.—Henry G. Dieken
IT Mgr.—Tommy Ng
Hum. Res. Mgr.—Laura DiDomenico
SIC—3599; *Precision machining job shop*
Employs—40; Estab.—1938
Distrib.—Local
Privately owned corporation

### VENDING TRUCK, INC.

5 Litchfield Rd. (08816)
**Phone—(732) 969-5400**
Fax—(732) 257-0110
www.vendingtrucks.com
Email—vending@vendingtrucks.com
CEO—Howard Seasonwein
V-P., Bus. Dev.—Jamie Mannino
SIC—3713; NAICS—336211; *Custom new & used vending food trucks & concession trailers, including rental services*
Employs—20; Estab.—2003
Sales—$3Mil-$5Mil
Distrib.—Intl.
Privately owned corporation

NEW ENTRY
### VGS GROUP, INC.

197 State Route 18, Ste. 235 (08816)
**Phone—(732) 887-5912**
National—(888) 562-0021
Fax—(732) 783-0341
www.vgsgroup.net
Email—info@vgsgroup.net
Founder & Chrm.—Siva Coramutta
Founder & Pres.—Gaurav Tiwari
CFO—Puneet Gulat
SIC—1311; *Oil & gas production*
Employs—23
Publicly owned corporation

### VITAMIN RETAILER

431 Cranbury Rd., Ste. C (08816)
**Phone—(732) 432-9600**
Fax—(732) 432-9288
www.vitaminretailer.com
Email—russf@vitaminretailer.com
Owner & Publisher—Daniel McSweeney
Assoc. Publisher—Russ Fields
Sales Mgr.—Roy Kieffe
SIC—2741; *Vitamin supplement magazine publishing*
Employs—8; Estab.—1994
Sales—$500,000-$1Mil (est)
1,500 sq ft site, Distrib.—National
Privately owned corporation

### †Y & W INTERNATIONAL, INC.

16 Edgeboro Rd., Unit 5 (08816)
**Phone—(732) 390-7722**
Fax—(732) 390-7723
www.ywtoys.com
Email—lisa@ywtoys.com
Pres.—Yun Shun Yang
Manager—Lisa Li
SIC—5092; *Wholesaler of toy, novelties, die cast model cars & trucks; Brand name*—New-Ray Toys; Jada Toys; Kingsmart
Employs—5; Estab.—1988
Sales—$2.4Mil
15,000 sq ft site, Distrib.—Intl.
Privately owned corporation

## East Hanover

(Morris—N.W.)

### ANDEROL, INC.

Div. of Chemtura Corp.
215 Merry Ln. (07936)
**Phone—(973) 887-7410**
National—(800) 989-7692
Fax—(973) 887-6930
www.chemtura.com
Email—info@anderol.com
Pur. Mgr.—Linda Santos
SIC—2992; NAICS—324191; *Industrial lubricants & greases*
Employs—80; Estab.—1945
100,000 sq ft site, Distrib.—Intl.
Publicly owned corporation
Parent co.—Chemtura Corp., Philadelphia, PA
Phone—(215) 446-3911
See Parent Co. Section for full profile.

### BRUSSIAN STROKES SIGN CO.

15-A Melanie Ln., Ste. 3-A (07936)
**Phone—(973) 515-5151**
www.brussianstrokes.com
Email—david@brussianstrokes.com
Owner—David Gersham
SIC—3993; 2759; NAICS—323100; *Trade show, interior & exterior signs & graphics & large-format digital printing*
Employs—3; Estab.—1995
Sales—under $500,000
1,500 sq ft site, Distrib.—National
Sole ownership

### BUXTON BIOMEDICAL, INC. (H Q)

15-A Melanie Ln., Unit 7 (07936)
**Phone—(973) 560-4848**
National—(800) 427-5351
Fax—(973) 215-2922
www.buxtonbio.com
Email—info@buxtonbio.com
Pres.—Ed Schussler
Dir.—Alice M. Schussler
Opers. Mgr.—Annie Schussler
SIC—3841; *Corporate headquarters; surgical instruments (mfg. subcontracted)*
Employs—5; Estab.—1993
Sales—$500,000-$1Mil
3,200 sq ft site, Distrib.—Intl.
Privately owned sub-S corp.

### C & S TOOL CO., INC.

304 Ridgedale Ave. (07936)
**Phone—(973) 887-6865**
Fax—(973) 887-9567
Pres.—Robert Sadowski
SIC—3599; *Precision machining job shop*
Employs—7; Estab.—1959
Sales—$500,000-$1Mil
3,000 sq ft site, Distrib.—Intl.
Privately owned corporation

### CAPCO ENTERPRISES, INC.

34 DeForest Ave., Ste. 3 *(07936)*
Mail addr.: P.O. Box 335, Florham Park (07932-0335)
**Phone—(973) 884-0044**
(800) 252-1011
Fax—(973) 884-8711
www.capcoenterprisesinc.com
Email—sales@capcoenterprisesinc.com
Pres.—Carole Lapone
Plt. Mgr.—Brian T. Henry
Administrator—Jakki Goldberg
SIC—2064; 2068; NAICS—311300; *Roasted & sundae flavored Jordan almonds, toasted almonds & sugar coated licorice minis, peanuts, pistachios & chickpeas; Brand name*—Mia Rose Confections; Nutibles
Employs—13; Estab.—1991
Sales—over $1Mil
15,000 sq ft site, Distrib.—Intl.
Privately owned sub-S corp.

### CHEMSPA INDUSTRIES, INC.

22 Deforest Ave. (07936)
**Phone—(973) 386-1158**
National—(800) 243-6772
Fax—(973) 386-9055
www.spapartners.com
Email—central@spapartners.com
CEO—Jerome Rudy
V-P.—Miriam Rudy
Sales Mgr.—Kevin Kerrigan
SIC—2844; 2842; NAICS—325612; *Air fresheners, aromas & maintenance & personal care products, including shampoos, deodorants, conditioners & hair sprays*
Employs—6; Estab.—1981
10,000 sq ft site, Distrib.—Intl.
Privately owned corporation

## East Hanover—(cont.)

**COHERENT ADVANCED CRYSTAL GROUP**
Div. of Coherent, Inc.
31 Farinella Dr. (07936)
**Phone—(973) 240-6800**
Fax—(973) 581-1944
www.coherentinc.com
Email—coherent@coherentinc.com
GM—Dominic Loiacono
Sr. Admn. Mgr.—Donna Hahn
Buyer—Debbie Daniels
SIC—3827; NAICS—333314; *Optical crystals*
Employs—60; Estab.—1986
30,000 sq ft site, Distrib.—Intl.
Publicly owned corporation
Parent co.—Coherent, Inc., Santa Clara, CA
Phone—(408) 764-4000
See Parent Co. Section for full profile.

**CONTEMPORARY WALL SYSTEMS, INC.**
50 Williams Pkwy., Ste. F, P.O. Box 356 (07936)
**Phone—(973) 884-0474**
Fax—(973) 884-1606
www.cwswalls.com
Email—contemporaryinc@aol.com
Pres.—Robert Behringer
Sales Mgr.—Ed Michinski
SIC—2522; 2521; NAICS—337214; *Modular wall systems for commercial applications*
Employs—10; Estab.—1980
Sales—$1Mil-$2.5Mil (est)
Distrib.—Regional
Privately owned corporation

**CONTROL PRODUCTS**
280 Ridgedale Ave. (07936)
**Phone—(973) 887-9400**
Fax—(973) 887-5083
www.cpi-nj.com
Email—sales@cpi-nj.com
V-P.—Mac Stuhler
Cont.—Angelo DiGirolamo
Sales Rep.—Nancy Price
SIC—3643; 3679; NAICS—335931; *Waterproof & thermal switches & linear position sensors*
Employs—55; Estab.—1946
Sales—$10Mil-$25Mil
25,000 sq ft site, Distrib.—Intl.
Privately owned corporation

**D & F SCREW MACHINE PRODUCTS, INC.**
42 West St. (07936)
**Phone—(973) 887-1702**
Fax—(973) 887-5917
Pres.—David Moore
SIC—3451; NAICS—332721; *Screw machine products*
Employs—8; Estab.—1972
4,000 sq ft site, Distrib.—Regional
Privately owned corporation

**DILAURI STEEL FABRICATORS**
5 Merrys Ln. (07936)
**Phone—(973) 884-2414**
Fax—(973) 884-0752
www.dilauristeel.com
Pres.—Kathleen DiLauri
V-P.—Chris DiLauri
SIC—3312; 3599; *Steel fabrication & welding job shop*
Employs—2; Estab.—1975
Sales—$500,000-$1Mil
3,000 sq ft site, Distrib.—Local
Privately owned corporation

**DRISCOLL LABEL CO., INC.**
19 West St. (07936)
**Phone—(973) 585-7295**
Fax—(973) 585-7295
www.driscolllabel.com
Email—info@driscolllabel.com
Pres.—John Raguso, Jr.
Cust. Serv. Mgr.—Christy Raguso

Cust. Serv. Rep.—Gail Chill
SIC—2759; NAICS—323100; *Labels*
Employs—20; Estab.—1976
Distrib.—National
Privately owned corporation

**EBCO TOOL CO.**
8-B Great Meadow Ln. (07936)
**Phone—(973) 887-5255**
Email—ebco@optonline.net
Owner & GM—Edward Brown
SIC—3544; NAICS—333500; *Tool & die job shop*
Employs—1; Estab.—1986
Sales—under $500,000
5,000 sq ft site, Distrib.—Local
Sole ownership

**†FARMER ELECTRICAL SUPPLY**
16 Littell Rd. (07936)
**Phone—(973) 887-0510**
Fax—(973) 887-0587
Email—farmere16@optonline.net
Owner—Sam Farmer
Manager—Stanley Smith
SIC—5063; *Wholesaler of electrical equipment & supplies*
Employs—5; Estab.—1963
Distrib.—Regional
Privately owned corporation

**GIVAUDAN FLAVORS CORP.**
245 Merry Ln. (07936)
**Phone—(973) 386-9800**
Fax—(973) 463-8323
www.givaudan.com
Email—resources@givaudan.com
Hum. Res. Generalist—Tracey Mara
SIC—2087; 2869; NAICS—311900; *Flavors & flavoring materials*
Employs—200; Estab.—1957
150,000 sq ft site, Distrib.—Intl.
Publicly owned corporation
ISO rating—9002
Parent co.—Givaudan Flavors Corp., Cincinnati, OH
Phone—(513) 948-8000
See Parent Co. Section for full profile.

**JETTRON PRODUCTS, INC.**
56 Route 10 W., P.O. Box 337 (07936)
**Phone—(973) 887-0571**
Fax—(973) 887-4182
www.jettron.com
Email—info@jettron.com
Pres.—Ed Balzarotti
V-P.—Mark Balzarotti
Engrg. & Sales Mgr.—Karl Kott
SIC—3679; 3498; *High-voltage cable assemblies & precision, round & wave-guide rectangular tube bending*
Employs—20; Estab.—1959
12,000 sq ft site, Distrib.—Intl.
Privately owned sub-S corp.
ISO rating—9001:2008

**JULIUS MACHINE & TOOL CO.**
B-14 Merry Ln. (07936)
**Phone—(973) 515-8540**
(973) 417-3117
Email—tigru7@aol.com
Owner & Pres.—Julius Gaida
SIC—3599; 3499; *Precision CNC machining, turning & milling & metal fabrication of tube holders, hot air & positive shut-off nozzles, tube depressors, cooling rings, fittings, couplings, adapters, nuts & sleeves for aircraft, cosmetic & medical parts*
Employs—1; Estab.—1980
Sales—under $200,000
1,500 sq ft site, Distrib.—National
Sole ownership

**LOBELLO ARTS CORP.**
50 Route 10 W. (07936)
**Phone—(973) 887-6700**
Fax—(973) 887-0020
www.fastsigns.com/69
Email—69@fastsigns.com
Owner & Manager—Matt Lobello
V-P.—Kim Lobello
SIC—3993; *Interior & exterior signs*
Employs—5; Estab.—1990
Sales—$500,000-$1Mil
2,000 sq ft site, Distrib.—Intl.
Privately owned corporation
AKA: Fast Signs

**†M&J FRANK, INC.**
29 Eagle Rock Ave. (07936)
**Phone—(973) 887-1040**
Fax—(973) 887-8814
www.mjfrankinc.com
Email—office@mjfrankinc.com
Pres.—Andrew Becker
SIC—5046; 5078; *Wholesaler of foodservice & restaurant equipment & supplies*
Employs—13; Estab.—1939
Distrib.—Local
Sole ownership

**MENDEL CO. (H Q)**
12-C Great Meadow Ln. (07936-1708)
**Phone—(973) 599-1300**
Fax—(973) 599-0019
www.mendelco.com
Email—sales@mendelco.com
Pres.—Barry Fox
SIC—3559; *Company headquarters; pharmaceutical processing equipment parts (mfg. subcontracted)*
Employs—1; Estab.—2002
Sales—under $800,000
2,050 sq ft site, Distrib.—Intl.
Sole ownership

**NEW ADVENTURES, LLC (H Q)**
6 Deforest Ave., Ste. 7 (07936-2831)
**Phone—(973) 884-8887**
Fax—(973) 884-0108
www.newadventuresllc.com
Email—sales@newadventuresllc.com
Ptnr.—Beth Reiling
Ptnr.—Joseph Reiling
Mktg. Mgr.—Diane Friedman
Prod. Mgr.—Randy Zahorchak
SIC—3944; 3942; NAICS—339931; *Company headquarters; toys & dolls (mfg. done overseas)*
Employs—5; Estab.—2001
Sales—$500,000-$1Mil
Distrib.—Intl.
Limited Liability Company

**NEW JERSEY MEDIA GROUP**
Div. of Broad Street Media, LLC
11 Melanie Ln., Unit 22-A (07936)
**Phone—(973) 434-8888**
Fax—(973) 884-7493
Email—sales@njmarketeer.com
Dir., Adv.—Susan Papay
SIC—2721; *Monthly advertising magazine publishing*
Employs—10; Estab.—1993
Sales—under $500,000
Distrib.—Local
Privately owned corporation
AKA: Marketeer, The
Parent co.—Broad Street Media, LLC, Trevose, PA
Phone—(215) 355-9009
See Parent Co. Section for full profile.

**NOVARTIS PHARMACEUTICALS CORP. (H Q)**
Div. of Novartis Finance Corp.
1 Health Plz. (07936)
**Phone—(862) 778-8300**
National—(888) 644-8585

Fax—(973) 781-8265
www.pharma.us.novartis.com
Email—investor.relations@novartis.com
Pres.—Christi Shaw
Head of U.S. Med. & Chief Scientific Officer—Cathryn M. Clary
V-P. & Chief Admn. & Fin. Officer—Meryl Zausner
V-P., Chief Compliance Officer—Cynthia Cetani
V-P. & Head of Hum. Res.—Caryn Parlavecchio
V-P., Gen. Counsel—Thomas Kendris
V-P., Head of Diversity & Inclusion—Rhonda Crichlow
V-P., Head of Integrated Hospital Care Bus. Unit—Carol Lynch
V-P., Head of Mngd. Mkts., Mkt. Access, Primary Care & Estab. Meds.—Gregory Oakes
V-P. & Head of Multiple Sclerosis Bus. Unit—Dagmar Rosa-Bjorkeson
V-P. & Head of Critical Care Bus. Unit—Jesus Leal
V-P., Pub. Affs.—Kevin T. Rigby
V-P., Comms.—Anna Frable
SIC—2834; NAICS—325412; *Corporate headquarters; pharmaceuticals*
Employs—4390; Estab.—1940
Worldwide: 115,000
Sales—over $100Mil
Distrib.—National
Publicly owned corporation
Parent co.—Novartis Finance Corp., New York, NY
Phone—(212) 307-1122
See Parent Co. Section for full profile.

**PAPER MART, INC.**
151 Ridgedale Ave. (07936)
**Phone—(973) 884-2505**
National—(800) 772-2001
Fax—(973) 884-1982
www.papermartinc.com
Email—customerservice@papmar.com
IT & Off. Mgr.—Joseph Kramer
Hum. Res. Mgr.—June Walker
SIC—2752; NAICS—323100; *Offset printing*
Employs—100; Estab.—1951
Distrib.—Regional
Privately owned corporation

**PEGASUS GROUP PUBLISHING**
188 Route 10 W., Ste. 307 (07936)
**Phone—(973) 884-9100**
Pres.—Bruce Warren
SIC—2731; *Book publishing*
Employs—10
Sales—$500,000-$1Mil (est)
Distrib.—Intl.

**PRECISION ENGRAVING II, INC.**
13 Ridgedale Ave., P.O. Box 243 (07936)
**Phone—(973) 887-3350**
(973) 887-3351
Fax—(973) 887-1308
Email—preeng2@optimum.net
Pres.—Conrad Fiore
Manager—Karl Richardson
SIC—3479; *Industrial & comercial sign, control panels, dials & machine part engraving*
Employs—3; Estab.—1993
Sales—under $500,000
2,000 sq ft site, Distrib.—Regional
Privately owned sub-S corp.

**PRODUCT DEVELOPMENT ASSOCS., LLC**
12 Say Dr. (07936)
**Phone—(973) 267-0033**
Pres.—Stefan Bloom
V-P.—Sue Flower

GEOGRAPHICAL

## East Hanover—(cont.)

SIC—3543; NAICS—332997; *Industrial prototypes & models*
Employs—3; Estab.—1966
Sales—$500,000-$1Mil
Distrib.—National
Limited Liability Company

**PRO-MOTION ENGINES, LLC**
2 Great Meadow Ln., Apt. B (07936)
**Phone—(973) 884-5936**
Fax—(973) 884-5877
www.promotionengines.com
Email—promotionengines@aol.com
Owner—Larry Lempicki
SIC—3714; *High-performance engines, including automotive & truck engines*
Employs—2; Estab.—1995
Sales—under $500,000
Distrib.—National
Limited Liability Company

**PROTECTION ONE, INC.**
Div. of Protection One Alarm Monitoring, Inc.
50 Williams Pkwy., Ste. L (07936)
**Phone—(973) 227-3421**
National—(800) 438-4357
Fax—(973) 227-3974
www.protectionone.com
Email—frankbenna@protectionone.com
GM—Frank Benna
SIC—3669; 3679; NAICS—334290; *Burglar alarm, fire alarm, CCTV & access control systems*
Employs—18; Estab.—1991
Distrib.—National
Privately owned corporation
Parent co.—Protection One Alarm Monitoring, Inc., Lawrence, KS
Phone—(785) 856-5500
See Parent Co. Section for full profile.

**RESOURCE SYSTEMS, INC.**
7 Merry Ln. (07936)
**Phone—(973) 884-0650**
Fax—(973) 515-3166
www.rsipurifiers.com
Email—info@rsipurifiers.com
Pres.—Leonard R. Rubin
Proj. Engr.—Stephen Rubin
SIC—3826; 3569; NAICS—334516; *Industrial gas & palladium-alloy hydrogen purifiers & molecular sieve dryers*
Employs—3; Estab.—1974
Sales—under $500,000
5,800 sq ft site, Distrib.—Intl.
Privately owned sub-S corp.

**RONED PRINTING**
6 DeForest Ave., Ste. 2 (07936-2831)
**Phone—(973) 386-1848**
Fax—(973) 386-0969
www.roned.com
Email—info@roned.com
Owner—Ronald Russo
SIC—2759; NAICS—323100; *Commercial printing*
Employs—3; Estab.—1976
Sales—under $500,000
2,500 sq ft site, Distrib.—Local
Sole ownership

**SIGNALCRAFTERS TECH, INC.**
57 Eagle Rock Ave. (07936)
**Phone—(973) 781-0880**
National—(800) 523-5815
Fax—(973) 781-9044
www.signalcrafters.com
Email—sctgeneral@signalcrafters.com
Pres., Mfg. Mgr.—Al Vnencak
Sales Mgr.—Dave Jenkins

SIC—3825; NAICS—334500; *Frequency selective volt, impedance & power/SWR meters, signal sources & communications equipment*
Employs—6; Estab.—1978
8,000 sq ft site, Distrib.—Intl.
Privately owned corporation

**SIR SPEEDY PRINTING OF EAST HANOVER**
50 Route 10 W. (07936)
**Phone—(973) 884-0005**
Fax—(973) 503-0625
www.sirspeedy.com
Email—digitalservices@speedyeh.com
Owner—Perdipe Dave
SIC—2752; 2791; NAICS—323122; *Offset printing & typesetting*
Employs—10; Estab.—1982
Sales—$500,000-$1Mil
4,000 sq ft site, Distrib.—Regional
Privately owned corporation

**SNO SKINS, INC. (H Q)**
11 Melanie Ln., Ste. 3 (07936)
**Phone—(973) 884-8801**
National—(866) 840-7669
Fax—(973) 884-4495
www.snoskins.com
Email—customerservice@snoskins.com
Pres.—Steve Weiss
Creative Dir.—Janine Weiss
SIC—2339; *Corporate headquarters; women's sportswear & skiwear (mfg. subcontracted); Brand name—Sno Skins®*
Employs—6
Sales—$500,000-$1Mil (est)
Distrib.—National
Privately owned corporation

**TECHNIMETAL**
7 Melanie Ln., Ste. 3 (07936)
**Phone—(973) 428-2881**
Fax—(973) 428-3306
Email—tmetal@optonline.net
Pres.—Rich Ciatto
Secy.-Treas.—Richard Ferraiuolo
SIC—3444; *Sheet metal fabrication*
Employs—6; Estab.—1985
Sales—$1Mil-$2.5Mil
3,500 sq ft site, Distrib.—Local
Privately owned corporation

**TRIM BRUSH CO., INC.**
22 Littell Rd. (07936)
**Phone—(973) 887-2525**
Fax—(973) 887-8507
www.trimbrush.com
Email—info@trimbrush.com
CEO & Dir.—Diane Carton
Pres. & Dir.—Bruce Carton
Opers. Supv.—Newman H. Rochester
SIC—3991; *Scrubbing brushes*
Employs—5; Estab.—1981
Distrib.—Regional
Privately owned corporation

**V L V ASSOCS., INC.**
30-C Ridgedale Ave. (07936)
**Phone—(973) 428-2884**
Fax—(973) 428-2877
www.vlvassociates.com
Pres., Mfg. Mgr.—Michael J. Vaillancourt
Asst. Pres.—Cooky Dowling
Dept. Mgr.—Greg Dwyer
SIC—3842; *Medical devices*
Employs—30; Estab.—1982
Distrib.—National
Privately owned corporation

**VISCOT MEDICAL, LLC**
32 West St., P.O. Box 351 (07936)
**Phone—(973) 887-9273**
National—(800) 221-0658
Fax—(973) 887-3961

www.viscot.com
Email—store@viscot.com
Pres.—Gary J. Pieringer
V-P.—Sales—Jeff Lynch
SIC—3843; NAICS—339114; *Disposable medical, surgical & dental supplies, including surgical skin markers, waterproof permanent markers & medication marking labels*
Employs—25; Estab.—1974
10,000 sq ft site, Distrib.—Intl.
Limited Liability Company
ISO rating—13485

**WEISS-AUG CO. INC.**
220 Merry Ln. (07936)
**Phone—(973) 887-7600**
Fax—(973) 887-8109
www.weiss-aug.com
Email—marketing@weiss-aug.com
CEO—Dieter Weissenrieder
Mktg. Mgr.—Elisabeth Weissenrieder- Bennis
Pur. Agt.—Randy Pirrozzi
SIC—3089; 3469; *Custom insert molding, precision metal stamping & assembly solutions for the automotive, medical, electronic & semiconductor industries*
Employs—200; Estab.—1972
100,000 sq ft site, Distrib.—Intl.
Privately owned corporation
ISO rating—9001:2008, TS16949, 13485

**WIN-TECH PRECISION PRODUCTS, INC.**
5 Littell Rd. (07936)
**Phone—(973) 887-8727**
Fax—(973) 887-7971
www.wintechcorp.com
Email—wintechprecision@yahoo.com
Owner—Pravin Patel
Pres.—Rashmika Patel
SIC—3599; 3679; *CNC milling, turning, mechanical assembly & machined parts & kitting*
Employs—6; Estab.—1989
Sales—under $500,000
2,500 sq ft site, Distrib.—Local
Privately owned sub-S corp.

**ZINA'S SALADS, INC.**
11 Great Meadow Ln. (07936)
**Phone—(973) 428-0660**
Fax—(973) 503-1666
Email—zinasalads@optonline.net
Pres., R & D Mgr.—Igor Shaknovich
SIC—2099; *Prepared salads*
Employs—24; Estab.—1986
Sales—$2.6Mil-$5Mil
6,000 sq ft site, Distrib.—Local
Privately owned corporation

**ZYMET, INC.**
7 Great Meadow Ln. (07936)
**Phone—(973) 428-5245**
Fax—(973) 428-5244
www.zymet.com
Email—info@zymet.com
Pres.—Karl Loh
Cust. Serv. & Off. Mgr.—Kelly Nostrame
SIC—2891; NAICS—325520; *Electronic & fiber-optic adhesives, encapsulants, inks & coatings*
Employs—11; Estab.—1986
Distrib.—Intl.
Sole ownership

---

## East Orange
(Essex—N.E.)

**419 NEON, LLC**
364 Glenwood Ave. (07017)
**Phone—(732) 324-2445**
www.419neon.com
Email—419neon@gmail.com

Owner & Off. Mgr.—Roger Borg
SIC—3993; *Custom neon signs & lighting*
Employs—2; Estab.—1989
Sales—under $500,000
Distrib.—Regional
Limited Liability Company
DBA: World Neon

**AFRICAN TELECOM, INC.**
463 N. Arlington Ave., Ste. 17 (07017)
**Phone—(973) 675-9919**
www.africansuntimes.com
Email—africansuntimes@yahoo.com
Pres., Publisher—Chika Onyeani
Editor, Entertainment & Book Review—Abba Onyeani
SIC—2711; 2741; *Weekly Africa-themed print & online newspaper publishing; Brand name—The African Sun Times*
Employs—5
Distrib.—National

**AGRESTI CONSTRUCTION CO., INC.**
356 Glenwood Ave. (07017)
**Phone—(201) 825-8500**
Fax—(201) 825-3934
www.harringtonparker.com
Email—info@harringtonparker.com
Pres.—James Agresti
Administrator—Sandra Finizia
SIC—2431; 2541; *Architectural millwork & custom cabinetry*
Employs—12; Estab.—1989
Sales—$1Mil-$2.5Mil
Distrib.—Regional
Privately owned corporation
AKA: Harrington Parker

**ARCADE TILE & MARBLE CO.**
416 Central Ave. (07018)
**Phone—(973) 678-4600**
Fax—(973) 678-7370
www.arcaderoks.com
Email—arcaderoks@aol.com
Pres., Plt. Mgr.—John Gallo
SIC—3281; NAICS—327991; *Marble products*
Employs—5; Estab.—1979
Sales—under $500,000
20,000 sq ft site, Distrib.—Intl.
Privately owned sub-S corp.

**CARTER SOLUTION, INC., THE JANE**
45 S. 17th St. (07018)
**Phone—(973) 677-1008**
National—(877) 424-7227
Fax—(877) 919-5349
www.janecartersolution.com
Owner—Jane Carter
Bus. Consultant—Linda Carter
SIC—2844; NAICS—325600; *Hair care products, including shampoos & conditioners*
Employs—5; Estab.—2004
Sales—$1Mil-$2.5Mil (est)
Distrib.—Intl.
Limited Liability Company
AKA: Left-Handed Libra

**CROSS COUNTRY BOX CO., INC.**
2-8 Central Ave. (07018)
**Phone—(973) 673-8349**
Fax—(973) 673-8351
www.crosscountrybox.com
Email—dan@crosscountrybox.com
Pres.—Dan Goldman
SIC—2652; 2657; 2541; NAICS—322213; *Rigid paperboard boxes, folding cartons, inserts & partitions*
Employs—9; Estab.—1949
Sales—under $1Mil
11,000 sq ft site, Distrib.—National
Privately owned corporation

## East Orange—(cont.)

**HOSPI-TEL MFG. CO., INC.**
545 N. Arlington Ave. (07017)
Mail addr.: P.O. Box 7005,
Bloomfield (07003-7005)
**Phone—(973) 678-7100**
Fax—(973) 678-1482
www.hospitel.com
Email—info@hospitel.com
Pres.—David Freedland
Acctg. Mgr.—Frank Materia
SIC—2391; 2392; NAICS—
314121; *Shower & cubicle
curtains & mattress protectors*
Employs—80; Estab.—1976
50,000 sq ft site, Distrib.—Intl.
Privately owned sub-S corp.

**JUST US BOOKS, INC.**
P.O. Box 5306 (07019)
**Phone—(973) 672-7701**
Fax—(973) 677-7570
www.justusbooks.com
Email—justusbook@aol.com
Pres., CEO—Wade Hudson
V.-P.—Cheryl Hudson
SIC—2731; *Book publishing*
Employs—2; Estab.—1988
Distrib.—National
Privately owned corporation
AKA: Imprint

**KMBA FASHIONS, INC.**
272 Elmwood Ave., Bldg. 3
(07018)
**Phone—(973) 789-1652**
Email—kmbaclothing@aol.com
Pres.—William Cotton, Jr.
SIC—2396; 2395; *Screen printing
& embroidery of men's &
women's t-shirts & polo shirts*
Employs—6; Estab.—2001
Sales—$500,000-$1Mil (est)
Distrib.—National
Privately owned corporation

**†MED-X-RAY CO., INC.**
356 Glenwood Ave. (07017)
**Phone—(973) 673-8822**
Fax—(973) 678-2111
www.med-x-ray.com
Email—sales@med-x-ray.com
Pres.—Anthony Irwin
V.-P.—Tony Feeney
SIC—5047; *Distributor of x-ray
imaging equipment & film*
Employs—6; Estab.—1979
Sales—$1Mil-$2.5Mil
Distrib.—Regional
Privately owned corporation

**NEWARK AUTO TOP CO., INC.**
23 Centerway (07017)
Mail addr.: P.O. Box 4365, East
Orange (07019-4365)
**Phone—(973) 677-9935**
National—(800) 275-4695
Fax—(973) 677-9335
www.newark-auto.com
Email—ben@newark-auto.com
Pres.—Ben Hershkowitz
SIC—2273; 3069; NAICS—
314110; *Custom replacement
carpets for cars & trucks, custom
molded rubber mats for trucks,
vinyl heel pads & sewing
contractors; Brand name—
Perfect Parts*
Employs—20; Estab.—1907
Sales—$1Mil-$5Mil
20,000 sq ft site, Distrib.—National
Privately owned corporation
AKA: Newark Auto Products

**NOVAPAC LABORATORIES, INC.**
545 N. Arlington Ave. (07017)
**Phone—(973) 414-8800**
Fax—(973) 414-8888
www.novapaclabs.com
Email—novapaclab@aol.com
Owner—Gene Marc

SIC—2844; *Cosmetics, including
fragrances, night creams &
shampoos*
Employs—3
Sales—$1Mil-$2.5Mil (est)
Distrib.—Regional
Privately owned corporation

**PRINTING DELITE, INC.**
279 Sanford St. (07018)
**Phone—(973) 676-3033**
Fax—(973) 676-4845
Email—printingdelite@comcast.net
Pres.—Felipe Gomez
Manager—Abbie Gomez
SIC—2759; NAICS—323100;
*Offset printing*
Employs—4; Estab.—1972
Sales—under $500,000
Distrib.—Local
Privately owned corporation

**PROPS, DISPLAYS & INTERIORS,
INC.**
45 Glenwood Pl. (07017)
**Phone—(862) 704-6463**
www.pdiinc.com
Email—info@pdiinc.com
Pres., GM—Stephen Sebbane
SIC—3993; 2431; NAICS—
321900; *Retail displays, cabinets
& woodworking*
Employs—10; Estab.—1980
6,500 sq ft site, Distrib.—National
Privately owned sub-S corp.

**SACO & BIRNBAUM FINE
WOODWORKING**
71 Glenwood Pl. (07017)
**Phone—(973) 675-8999**
www.sbwoodworking.com
Owner—Danny Birnbaum
SIC—2511; *Residential &
commercial wooden furniture*
Employs—4; Estab.—2001
Sales—under $500,000 (est)
Distrib.—Intl.
Limited Liability Company

**SCI-BORE, INC.**
364 Glenwood Ave., Bldg. 18-E
(07017)
**Phone—(973) 414-9001**
Fax—(973) 414-9003
www.scibore.com
Email—sales@scibore.com
Pres., CFO—Nadiya Jinnah
Off. Mgr.—Della Lawton
Shop Mgr.—Doshawn Jackson
SIC—3498; 3312; NAICS—
332996; *High-carbon steel wire
guide nozzles for electronic coil
winding & small precision steel
parts*
Employs—7; Estab.—1991
Sales—$500,000-$1Mil
5,000 sq ft site, Distrib.—Intl.
Privately owned sub-S corp.

**SHEARMAN CABINETS, INC.**
195 N. Munn Ave. (07017)
**Phone—(973) 677-0071**
Pres.—Thomas Shearman
SIC—2434; NAICS—337110;
*Wooden cabinets*
Employs—5; Estab.—2004
Sales—under $500,000
Distrib.—Regional
Privately owned corporation

**STEVENS PRODUCTS, INC.**
128 N. Park St. (07017)
**Phone—(973) 672-2140**
Fax—(973) 672-2837
www.stevensproducts.net
Email—sales@stevensproducts.net
Pres., CFO—Ross S. Stevens, Jr.
MIS & Mktg. Mgr.—Robert
Cantalina
Off. Mgr.—Lisa Kihlberj

SIC—3644; *Electrical insulation*
Employs—30; Estab.—1937
Sales—$1Mil-$5Mil
12,000 sq ft site, Distrib.—Intl.
Privately owned corporation

**TAYLOR WINDOWS, INC.**
61 Central Ave. (07018)
**Phone—(973) 672-3000**
Fax—(973) 672-3036
Email—taylorwindow@verizon.net
Pres., CFO—Pat Taylor
Off. Mgr.—Cindy Digravina
SIC—3089; *Vinyl windows
assembly; Brand name—Taylor's
Weld Tuff*
Employs—5; Estab.—1984
20,000 sq ft site, Distrib.—Local
Privately owned sub-S corp.

**TECHNICAL AIDS, INC.**
219 S. 18th St. (07018)
**Phone—(973) 674-1082**
Fax—(973) 674-1085
www.techaids.com
Email—techi@techaids.com
Pres.—Alan Fenton
V.-P., Sales—John F. Fenton
Fin. Mgr.—Elfrieda Fenton
SIC—3672; 3679; NAICS—
334412; *Printed circuit boards,
cables & wire harnesses*
Employs—12; Estab.—1972
Sales—$500,000-$1Mil
10,000 sq ft site, Distrib.—National
Privately owned sub-S corp.

NEW ENTRY
**WAHIDA CLARK PUBLISHING, LLC**
60 Evergreen Pl., Ste. 904 (07018)
**Phone—(973) 678-9982**
Fax—(973) 678-9981
www.wclarkpublishing.com
Manager—Mia Evans
SIC—2731; *Book publishing*
Employs—10
Sales—$500,000-$1Mil (est)
Distrib.—Regional
Limited Liability Company

---

## East Rutherford

(Bergen—N.E.)

**ACCURATE METAL FABRICATION,
LLC**
28 John St. (07073)
**Phone—(201) 438-3733**
Fax—(201) 438-0530
Pres.—Stanley Patiro
Off. Mgr.—Rebecca Patiro
SIC—3444; *Sheet metal
fabrication*
Employs—2; Estab.—2006
Sales—under $500,000
Distrib.—Local
Limited Liability Company

**ALEX'S CUSTOM KITCHENS, LLC**
824 Paterson Ave. (07073)
**Phone—(201) 933-9359**
Owner—Louie Alexander Eliades
SIC—2434; 2431; 2499; NAICS—
337110; *Custom wooden kitchen
cabinets, vanities, wall units &
bars*
Employs—1; Estab.—2004
Sales—under $500,000
Distrib.—Regional
Sole ownership

**†ALLIED BUILDING PRODUCTS
CORP.**
Div. of Oldcastle, Inc.
15 E. Union Ave. (07073)
**Phone—(201) 507-8400**
National—(800) 541-2198
Fax—(201) 507-3842
www.alliedbuilding.com
Email—info@alliedbuilding.com
Chrm.—Michael Lynch
CEO—Bob Feury, Jr.
V.-P., IT—Allen Amtel

V.-P., Fin.—Frank Furia
SIC—5084; 5031; 5033;
*Corporate headquarters &
wholesaler of power actuated
tools & building supplies,
including windows, siding &
roofing*
Employs—200
Company-wide: 3,500
Distrib.—Intl.
Publicly owned corporation
Parent co.—Oldcastle, Inc.,
Atlanta, GA
Phone—(770) 804-3363
See Parent Co. Section for full profile.

**ALPINE GROUP, INC., THE (H Q)**
1 Meadowlands Plz., Ste. 801
(07073)
**Phone—(201) 549-4400**
Fax—(201) 549-4428
www.alpine-group.net
Chrm. & CEO—Steven S. Elbaum
Sr. V.-P. & Gen. Counsel—Stewart
H. Wahrsager
V.-P.—Dana P. Sidur
SIC—6719; 3993; 3496; 3351;
*Holding company headquarters;
nonilluminated fast-food menu
signs, scrap wire recycling &
metal tubing*
Employs—5
Distrib.—Intl.
Publicly owned corporation

**ARTMARK MOLD & TOOL CORP.**
742 Paterson Ave. (07073)
**Phone—(201) 935-3377**
Fax—(201) 933-2240
www.artmarkmold.com
Email—info@artmarkmold.com
Pres.—Ted Ura
V.-P.—Mark Ura
Off. Mgr.—Christine Ura
Designer—Arthur Ura
SIC—3544; NAICS—333500; *Tool
& molds*
Employs—7; Estab.—1990
Sales—$1.5Mil-$3Mil
15,000 sq ft site, Distrib.—National
Privately owned corporation
AKA: Art Mold & Tool Corp.

**†AZUMA FOODS INTERNATIONAL,
INC.**
Div. of Azuma Foods International,
Inc. U.S.A.
20 Murray Hill Pkwy., Ste. 130
(07073-2295)
**Phone—(201) 372-1112**
Fax—(201) 372-1118
www.azumafoods.com
Email—afiny@azumafoods.com
Br. Mgr.—Yoshi Sugiura
Administrator—Kaoru Ejiri
SIC—5146; 5142; *Distributor of
fresh & frozen seafood*
Employs—10
Distrib.—Regional
Sole ownership
Parent co.—Azuma Foods
International, Inc. U.S.A.,
Hayward, CA
Phone—(510) 782-1112
See Parent Co. Section for full profile.

**BALSCO CORRUGATED BOX &
DISPLAY, LLC**
160 Union Ave. (07073)
**Phone—(973) 546-0500**
Fax—(201) 507-8363
Pres.—Vincent Scolaro
SIC—2653; NAICS—322211;
*Corrugated boxes & displays*
Employs—5; Estab.—2008
Sales—$500,000-$1Mil
Distrib.—Local
Limited Liability Company

**BEACUT ABRASIVES CORP.**
788 Paterson Ave. (07073)
**Phone—(973) 249-1420**
(973) 249-1433
National—(800) 631-0063

GEOGRAPHICAL

## East Rutherford—(cont.)

Fax—(973) 249-1443
www.beacutabrasives.com
Email—beacut@att.net
Pres.—Vladimir Smilovic
Corp. Secy.—Grace Smilovic
SIC—3291; *Industrial abrasives;
Brand name—Beaflex;
EconoDiamond; Beacut*
Employs—11; Estab.—1984
Sales—$2Mil-$5Mil
12,000 sq ft site, Distrib.—National
Privately owned sub-S corp.

### BIG APPLE JEWELRY MFG.

62 Railroad Ave. (07073)
**Phone—(201) 531-1600**
National—(800) 987-0004
Fax—(201) 531-2227
www.braccio.com
Email—info@braccio.com
Pres.—Albert Sirazi
V-P.—Edward Sirazi
SIC—3911; 3915; NAICS—
339911; *Custom-designed gold,
sterling silver & diamond jewelry;
Brand name—Braccio*
Employs—7; Estab.—1982
Sales—$1Mil-$2.5Mil
2,500 sq ft site, Distrib.—National
Limited Liability Company
AKA: Braccio

### BLOOMFIELD DRAPERY CO., INC.

948 Paterson Ave. (07073)
**Phone—(973) 777-3566**
Fax—(973) 777-4402
www.bloomfielddrapery.com
Email—bloomfielddrapery@
earthlink.net
Pres.—Steve Gold
V-P.—Madeline Kannan
SIC—2391; 2591; 5023; NAICS—
314121; *Manufacturer &
distributor of theatrical stage &
window draperies, shades &
vertical & horizontal blinds,
including stage drapery cleaning
& flameproofing*
Employs—15; Estab.—1937
Sales—$1Mil-$2.5Mil
10,000 sq ft site, Distrib.—
Regional
Privately owned sub-S corp.

### C B FOOD, INC.

1 Madison St., Bldg. B (07073)
**Phone—(973) 773-9224**
National—(800) 524-2587
Fax—(973) 773-9225
www.customconcentrates.com
Email—info@
customconcentrates.com
Pres., Sales Mgr.—Milton Becker
SIC—2087; NAICS—311900;
*Drink mixes*
Employs—5; Estab.—1985
6,000 sq ft site, Distrib.—National
Privately owned sub-S corp.
DBA: Custom Concentrates

### CAMBREX CORP.

1 Meadowlands Plz., Ste. 1510
(07073-2214)
**Phone—(201) 804-3000**
Fax—(201) 804-9852
www.cambrex.com
Email—info@cambrex.com
Pres., CEO—Steven Klosk
Ex. V-P., Chief Operating Officer—
Shawn Cavanagh
Ex. V-P., CFO—Greg Sargen
Sr. V-P., Gen. Counsel—William
Haskel

SIC—2834; 2869; NAICS—
325412; *Corporate headquarters
& active pharmaceutical
ingredients (API), controlled
substances, chiral amines & fine
chemicals, including smoking
cessation products*
Employs—22; Estab.—1981
Worldwide: 1,063
Sales—$317Mil
Distrib.—Intl.
Publicly owned corporation

### CAPITAL FOAM PRODUCTS, INC.

75 E. Union Ave., P.O. Box 7564
(07073)
**Phone—(201) 933-5277**
National—(800) 526-4707
Fax—(201) 933-7684
Pres.—Bart Krupp
Off. Mgr.—Paulette Nedrow
SIC—3086; NAICS—326100;
*Foam fabrication*
Employs—45; Estab.—1966
95,000 sq ft site, Distrib.—Local
Privately owned corporation

### CCA INDUSTRIES, INC. (H Q)

200 Murray Hill Pkwy. (07073)
**Phone—(201) 935-3232**
               (800) 524-2720
Fax—(201) 935-0675
www.ccaindustries.com
Email—sales@ccaindustries.com
Pres., CEO—Richard Kornhauser
Pres., CFO—Steven Heit
COO—Drew Edell
Ex. V-P., IT—Elias Ciudad
V-P., Treas.—John Bingman
Dir., Hum. Res.—Ronnie Pouch
SIC—2844; 2023; *Corporate
headquarters; topical & OTC
health & beauty aids & dietary
supplement products (mfg. done
overseas); Brand name—Plus
White®; Nutra Nail®; Bikini Zone®*
Employs—135; Estab.—1983
Distrib.—Intl.
Publicly owned corporation

### D & M SHEET METAL CO., INC.

430 Central Ave. (07073)
**Phone—(201) 939-6300**
Fax—(201) 939-8038
Email—mpmdmsm@msn.com
Pres.—Mark Mihal
GM—Steven Mihal
SIC—3444; *Ductwork & sheet
metal fabrication*
Employs—15; Estab.—1969
20,000 sq ft site, Distrib.—Local
Privately owned corporation

### DAWN BIBLE STUDENTS ASSN.

199 Railroad Ave. (07073)
**Phone—(201) 438-6421**
National—(888) 440-3296
Fax—(201) 531-8333
www.dawnbible.com
Email—dawnbible@aol.com
Plt. Mgr.—Ken M. Fernets
Shpg. Mgr.—Janet Elbert
SIC—2732; 2791; NAICS—
323117; *Book printing &
typesetting*
Employs—6; Estab.—1932
Sales—under $500,000
7,000 sq ft site, Distrib.—Intl.
Privately owned corporation

### DCI METRO, INC.

1 Maple St., Unit 1 (07073)
**Phone—(201) 340-4329**
Fax—(201) 340-4318
www.dcimetro.net
Email—reception@dcimetro.net
Pres.—William Mihatov
V-P.—Joseph Pellagatti
Manager—Steve Tucholski
Bookkeeper—Carol Vitale

SIC—3442; 2431; 3429; NAICS—
332321; *Wood & metal doors &
frames & hardware*
Employs—28; Estab.—1995
Sales—$8Mil-$10Mil
Distrib.—Regional
Privately owned corporation

### DIAMOND CHEMICAL COMPANY, INC.

Union Ave. & DuBois St., P.O. Box
7428 (07073)
**Phone—(201) 935-4300**
National—(800) 654-7627
Fax—(201) 935-6997
www.diamondchem.com
Email—sales@diamondchem.com
Pres.—Harold Diamond
CFO—Dave Halpern
Cust. Serv. Mgr.—Kathy Ferguson
SIC—2841; NAICS—325611;
*Industrial & institutional
detergents, including organic
intermediates, warewashing,
floor care & housekeeping
products & car wash chemicals*
Employs—200; Estab.—1930
Sales—$100Mil-$250Mil (est)
160,000 sq ft site, Distrib.—Intl.
Privately owned sub-S corp.

### †EC HAIR IMPORT, INC.

99 Murray Hill Pkwy., Ste. B
(07073)
**Phone—(201) 933-8071**
National—(800) 216-5990
Fax—(201) 945-6649
Email—echairtopic@gmail.com
Pres.—Peter Lee
SIC—5122; *Wholesaler of hair
care supplies*
Employs—4; Estab.—2004
Sole ownership

### F X I, FOAMEX INNOVATIONS DIV.

Div. of FXI, Inc.
13 Manor Rd. (07073)
**Phone—(201) 933-8540**
National—(888) 896-3626
Fax—(201) 933-2125
www.fxi.com
Email—foamexinfo@foamex.com
Plt. Mgr.—Andrew Albanese
Scheduling Mgr.—Carmen Ramos
SIC—3086; NAICS—326100;
*Polyurethane foam*
Employs—80; Estab.—1998
Sales—$30Mil-$40Mil
210,000 sq ft site, Distrib.—Intl.
Publicly owned corporation
ISO rating—9000
Parent co.—FXI, Inc., Media, PA
Phone—(610) 744-2300
See Parent Co. Section for full profile.

### †FASTENAL CO.

33 Route 17 S. (07073)
**Phone—(201) 804-2228**
Fax—(201) 804-2699
www.fastenal.com
Email—njhac@stores.fastenal.com
Br. Mgr.—Mike Scrobel
Sales Rep.—Flavio Vento
SIC—5072; 5084; *Wholesaler of
fasteners, safety equipment,
tools & abrasives*
Employs—5; Estab.—2001
Distrib.—Regional
Publicly owned corporation
Parent co.—Fastenal Co., Winona,
MN
Phone—(507) 454-5374
See Parent Co. Section for full profile.

### GALAXY OF GRAPHICS LTD.

30 Murray Hill Pkwy., Ste. 300
(07073)
**Phone—(201) 806-2100**
National—(888) 464-7500
Fax—(201) 806-2050
www.galaxyofgraphics.com
Email—info@katgog.com
Asst. Cont.—Stewart Fredrik
Prodn. Coord.—Daniela Santiago

SIC—2741; *Art poster & print
publishing*
Employs—12; Estab.—2002
Distrib.—Intl.
Privately owned corporation

### GTBM

351 Paterson Ave. (07073)
**Phone—(201) 935-5090**
Fax—(201) 935-7022
www.info-cop.com
Email—sales@infocop.com
CEO—Richard Picolli
Dir., Strategic Plng.—Mike
Rubenstein
Acct. Mgr.—Nick Koval
Pur. Mgr.—Beth Weinberg
IT Mgr.—Lance Gober
SIC—7372; *Real-time database
search & communications
software development for
wireless law enforcement
applications*
Employs—21; Estab.—1999
Distrib.—Local
Privately owned sub-S corp.

NEW ENTRY
### HELIDEX, LLC (H Q)

186 Paterson Ave., Ste. 303
(07073)
**Phone—(201) 636-2546**
Fax—(201) 636-2548
www.helidex.com
Pres.—Chawki Bentetifa
Hum. Res. Mgr. & Off.
Administrator—Justin Russell
SIC—3441; NAICS—331312;
*Company headquarters;
structural aluminum fabrication
(mfg. done at co.-owned plant in
Spartanburg, SC)*
Employs—6
Sales—$1Mil-$2.5Mil (est)
Distrib.—Intl.
Limited Liability Company

### KANE-M, INC.

1 Madison St., Ste. F-9 (07073)
**Phone—(973) 777-2797**
National—(800) 346-2209
Fax—(973) 777-2739
www.kane-m.com
Email—sales@kane-m.com
Pres.—Masato Yamakawa
V-P., Sales—George Miranda
SIC—3965; NAICS—339993;
*Clothing snaps & fasteners*
Employs—4; Estab.—1983
Sales—$500,000-$1Mil
Distrib.—National
Publicly owned corporation
AKA: Morito

### KANSAI SPECIAL AMERICAN MACHINE CORP.

1 Madison St., Ste. F-11 (07073)
**Phone—(973) 470-8321**
Fax—(973) 470-8539
www.kansai-special.com
Email—chester@kansaispecial.net
Pres.—Hideo Koge
V-P.—Chester Hadyka
Tech. Mgr.—Michael Megnin
SIC—3639; NAICS—335200;
*Industrial sewing machines &
parts; Brand name—Kansai
Special*
Employs—5; Estab.—1997
Distrib.—National
Privately owned corporation

### LOGATTO BOOKBINDING, INC.

390 Paterson Ave., P.O. Box 7483
(07073)
**Phone—(201) 438-4344**
Fax—(201) 438-1775
www.logattobookbinding.com
Email—bookbindin@aol.com
Pres., Pur., Sales & Mktg. Mgr.—
Michael Logatto

## East Rutherford— (cont.)

SIC—2789; NAICS—323121; *Cloth & leather bookbinding, including restoration, rebinding & gold stamping*
Employs—4; Estab.—1967
Sales—under $500,000
1,200 sq ft site, Distrib.—National
Sole ownership

**NEW ENTRY**
**METROPOLITAN MFG., INC.**
450 Murray Hill Pkwy. (07073)
**Phone—(201) 933-8111**
Pres.—Tony Terrigno
SIC—2361; 2339; *Women's clothing, including blouses & pants*
Employs—60
Sales—$5Mil-$10Mil (est)

**MIL-COMM PRODUCTS CO., INC.**
2 Carlton Ave. (07073)
**Phone—(201) 935-8561**
National—(800) 743-4518
Fax—(201) 935-6059
www.mil-comm.com
Email—sales@mil-comm.com
Pres., CEO—Gordon Furlong
Ex. V.-P.—Charles Furlong
IT Mgr.—John Montenigro
SIC—2992; NAICS—324191; *Extreme performance, all-synthetic, non-hazardous lubricants & cleaners for industrial applications & military, aircraft, marine, hunting, fishing & security hardware & lock mechanisms*
Employs—10; Estab.—1985
Sales—$2Mil
26,000 sq ft site, Distrib.—Intl.
Privately owned corporation

**MUSHROOM WISDOM, INC.**
1 Madison St., Bldg. F (07073)
Mail addr: P.O. Box 1354, Paramus (07653)
**Phone—(973) 470-0010**
National—(800) 747-7418
Fax—(973) 470-0017
www.mushroomwisdom.com
Email—customerservice@mushroomwisdom.com
Pres.—Mike Shirota
V.-P., Sales—Shuji Matsubara
V.-P., Mktg.—Donna Noonan
V.-P., Education & Research—Mark J. Kaylor
Cust. Serv. Rep.—Megan McLaughlin
SIC—2833; NAICS—325411; *Dietary supplements, tea, skin cream, bulk extracts & powders from medicinal mushrooms*
Employs—13; Estab.—1991
Distrib.—National
Privately owned corporation

**OLIVERI PRINTING CORPORATION, CARL**
316 Main St., Ste. 1 (07073)
**Phone—(201) 438-0888**
Fax—(201) 438-6263
www.carloliveri.com
Email—copzap@aol.com
Owner & Pres.—Carl Oliveri
SIC—2752; 2759; NAICS—323119; *Commercial offset & digital printing & graphics*
Employs—10; Estab.—1977
10,000 sq ft site, Distrib.—National
Sole ownership

†**PAC TOOL & SUPPLY CO., INC.**
420 Paterson Ave., P.O. Box 7482 (07073)
**Phone—(201) 933-8550**
Fax—(201) 933-1771
Email—pactool@aol.com
Pres. & Sales Mgr.—Mike Pacala

SIC—5084; 5085; *Distributor of industrial metalworking, cutting & measuring tools, fasteners, hex bolts & abrasives & machine shop supplies & equipment; Brand name—Starrett; Armstrong; Holo-Krome; MK Morse; Morse Cutting Tools; United Abrasives; CGW Camel Grinding Wheels; Coilhose; Rustoleum; Norton Abrasives; Gd 8 Hex Bolts; Channellock*
Employs—3; Estab.—1965
4,000 sq ft site, Distrib.—Regional
Privately owned corporation

†**PRINTERS PARTS STORE**
82 Herman St. (07073)
**Phone—(201) 935-9595**
National—(800) 543-1117
Fax—(201) 935-5333
www.ppsnj.com
Email—info@ppsnj.com
Pres.—Barbara Pignato
SIC—5084; *Wholesaler of replacement parts, rollers, supplies & accessories for printing, prepress, pressroom & bindery equipment; Brand name—PRP™; Pamarco; Syn-Tac™; Chicago Manifold™; Lith-O-Roll™; Kompac; Crestline; AB Dick; Presstek; Ryobi; Itek; Heidelberg; Hamada; Multilith; ATF-Chief; Davidson; Toko; Townsend T-51; Baumfolder; Challenge; MBM*
Employs—4; Estab.—1985
Sales—$500,000-$1Mil
2,500 sq ft site, Distrib.—Intl.
Privately owned corporation

†**R.A.H. CARPET SUPPLIES, INC.**
80 Willow St. (07073)
**Phone—(973) 778-4759**
Fax—(973) 778-1316
Email—robkidnj@aol.com
Owner—Robert Holzberg
SIC—5049; *Distributor of carpet laying equipment & supplies*
Employs—9; Estab.—1986
Distrib.—Regional
Privately owned corporation

**REGAL STAMP & SIGN CO., INC.**
240 Park Ave., P.O. Box 342 (07073)
**Phone—(201) 939-0400**
Fax—(201) 939-5203
www.regalstampnj.com
Email—regalstamp@verizon.net
Owner & Pres.—Krista Brabston
SIC—3953; 3479; NAICS—339943; *Rubber stamps, marking devices & signs & seals engraving*
Employs—1; Estab.—1970
1,000 sq ft site, Distrib.—Local
Privately owned corporation

**ROYCE ASSOCS., L. P. (H Q)**
35 Carlton Ave. (07073)
**Phone—(201) 438-5200**
Fax—(201) 438-5207
www.royceintl.com
Email—info@royceintl.com
Pres.—Jay Royce
SIC—2865; NAICS—325100; *Company headquarters; textile & industrial organic dyes*
Employs—20; Estab.—1929
Sales—$30Mil
Distrib.—Intl.
Privately owned corporation

**RUSH INDEX TABS, INC.**
60 Willow St. (07073)
**Phone—(201) 531-1555**
National—(800) 231-7874
Fax—(866) 831-3200
www.rushindex.com
Email—rushindex@verizon.net
Pres.—Jay A. Cohen
Mktg. Mgr.—Scott Cohen

SIC—2672; 2675; NAICS—322222; *Plastic coated index tabs & dividers*
Employs—40; Estab.—1980
Distrib.—Local
Privately owned corporation

**RUTHERFORD SIGNRIGHT CO.**
769 Morton St. (07073)
**Phone—(201) 935-1511**
Fax—(201) 731-6248
Pres.—Steven Hanley
SIC—3993; *Vinyl, neon, wooden, graphic & plastic signs*
Employs—7; Estab.—1994
Sales—under $500,000
Distrib.—Regional
Privately owned corporation

**SHELTON, LLC, TODD**
450 Murray Hill Pkwy., Ste. C-2 (07073)
**Phone—(551) 655-4106**
National—(844) 626-6355
www.toddshelton.com
Owner—Todd Shelton
SIC—2326; *Men's casual clothing, including pants & shirts; Brand name—Todd Shelton*
Employs—6; Estab.—2012
Sales—under $500,000
6,000 sq ft site, Distrib.—National
Limited Liability Company

**SIEMENS INDUSTRY, INC., WATER TECHNOLOGIES**
Div. of Evoqua Water Technologies
20 Murray Hill Pkwy., Ste. 140 (07073)
**Phone—(201) 531-9338**
Fax—(201) 531-9450
www.evoqua.com
Email—information@evoqua.com
Br. Mgr.—Michael Schweiger
Off. Mgr.—Rosemary Ball
Serv. Mgr.—John Pelle
SIC—2899; *Water treatment & purification products, including ion exchange, reverse osmosis, carbon adsorbers, medias & emergency mobile & laboratory water systems*
Employs—50; Estab.—1991
Sales—$10Mil-$25Mil (est)
Distrib.—Regional
Publicly owned corporation
Parent co.—Evoqua Water Technologies, Alpharetta, GA
Phone—(978) 614-7111
See Parent Co. Section for full profile.

**STAR-GLO INDUSTRIES, LLC**
2 Carlton Ave. (07073)
**Phone—(201) 939-6162**
Fax—(201) 939-4054
www.starglo.com
Email—gthomas@starglo.com
Pres.—Edward Peterhoff
V.-P., Sales & Mktg.—Gene Thomas
Fin. & MIS Mgr.—Richard Wilz
Qual. Control Mgr.—Truman Slate
SIC—3089; 3069; 3599; *Swiss machining & rubber molding for the welding, electronics, packaging, aerospace, military & inflation components industries*
Employs—90; Estab.—1954
Sales—$10Mil-$25Mil (est)
180,000 sq ft site, Distrib.—National
Limited Liability Company

**STEAMIST, INC.**
25 E. Union Ave. (07073)
**Phone—(201) 933-5800**
National—(800) 969-9702
Fax—(201) 933-0746
www.steamist.com
Email—sales@steamist.com
Pres.—J. Noll
V.-P., Sales & Mktg.—J. Carney
Cont.—Robert Gerard

Dir., Opers.—D. Wostbrock
SIC—3621; *Steam generators for residential & commercial steam baths*
Employs—40; Estab.—1958
Distrib.—Intl.
Privately owned corporation
AKA: Steamaster

**STONE PLUS DESIGN, LLC**
21 Route 17 S. (07073)
**Phone—(201) 438-2725**
Fax—(201) 438-2726
www.stoneplusdesignllc.com
Email—stoneplusdesign@gmail.com
Owner—Roberto Palacios
SIC—3281; *Stone fabrication, including kitchen countertops, vanities, fireplaces & tub decks*
Employs—3; Estab.—2006
Sales—under $500,000 (est)
Distrib.—Regional
Limited Liability Company

**STONE SURFACES, INC.**
890 Paterson Plank Rd. (07073)
**Phone—(201) 935-8803**
Fax—(201) 935-8210
Email—stonesurfacesnj@yahoo.com
Pres.—Michael Sakosits
SIC—2542; 3281; NAICS—327991; *Solid surface & stone countertops*
Employs—30; Estab.—1986
Sales—$2.5Mil-$5Mil (est)
Distrib.—Local
Privately owned corporation

†**STYLEX IMPORTS & EXPORT CO., INC.**
425 Paterson Ave. (07073)
**Phone—(201) 964-1900**
Fax—(201) 964-9844
www.bachinternational.com
Email—styleximp@msn.com
Owner—Yogendra Chokshi
SIC—5131; *Wholesaler of imported India silk fabric*
Employs—1; Estab.—1983
Sales—under $200,000
Distrib.—National
Privately owned sub-S corp.
AKA: Bach International

**SUN CHEMICAL CORP.**
390 Central Ave. (07073)
**Phone—(201) 438-4041**
National—(800) 223-0717
Fax—(201) 896-9137
www.sunchemical.com
Email—info@usink.com
Maint. Supv.—George Rodriguez
SIC—2893; NAICS—325910; *Printing ink*
Employs—30
Sales—$5Mil-$10Mil (est)
Distrib.—Local
Publicly owned corporation
AKA: US Ink
Parent co.—Sun Chemical Corp., Parsippany, NJ
Phone—(973) 404-6000
See Parent Co. Section for full profile.

**TEL-INSTRUMENT ELECTRONICS CORP.**
1 Branca Rd. (07073-2121)
**Phone—(201) 933-1600**
Fax—(201) 933-7340
www.telinstrument.com
Email—sales@telinst.com
CEO—Jeffrey O'Hara
CFO & Dir., Fin.—Joseph P. Macaluso
V.-P., Mktg.—Chris Allen
R & D Mgr.—Ken Filardo
Engrg. Mgr.—Marc Perillo
Engrg. Mgr.—Lisa Schmidt

**GEOGRAPHICAL**

D100      © Copyright 2015 Manufacturers' News, Inc.      GEOGRAPHICAL SECTION

# Gain the Advantage in your Market with mni State-by-state Company Profiles!

## Discover the value in each company with 30 critical business facts
## Develop a cost-effective prospect database to generate sales

### State directories in print identify opportunities by 5 major sections:

- **By City:** pinpoint your target market by location. Each firm is listed alphabetically and complete company profiles contain up to 30 vital facts, including names of executives, # of employees, home office, etc.

- **By S.I.C. Number:** work your leads by what they make, using seven basic facts — key contact name, # of employees, address, phone, etc.

- **By Company Name:** an alphabetical index with address and phone for quick look-up.

- **By Parent Company:** to spot linked companies, this section gives name, address, phone and executives with all the branches, division and subsidiaries in the state.

- **By Product:** find all companies in each industry. Ideal for both buying and selling.

### EZSelect.com subscription databases come in three versions to fit any promotional budget:

**Full Version:** Contains all firms regardless of size. All the essential facts you need to determine your market potential are easily searchable and sortable by 12 criteria. You can export profiles, print address labels, print summary and detail reports, and browse all profiles.

**20+ Employees:** This version eliminates smaller manufacturers and contains only those firms employing 20 or more workers. Software features are identical to the Full Version.

**Basic Version:** Contains all firms for unlimited sorting as above. Print single profiles. Data exporting, merge and label printing are not available with this version.

**Manufacturers' News, Inc.**
Directories & Databases since 1912

**1633 Central St., Evanston, IL 60201**
**847-864-7000 • manufacturersnews.com**

---

## Burnham
(Cook—N.E.—Pop. 4,170)

**CALUMET LUBRICANTS CO.**
Div. of Calumet Specialty Products
  Partners
14000 S. Mackinaw Ave. *(60633)*
**Phone—(800) 437-3188**
        (708) 862-9100
Fax—(708) 862-4913
www.calumetlubricants.com
Email—joel@calumetlubricants.com
Sales Mgr., Export—Larry Buck
Sales Mgr., Base Oil—John
  Banach
Plt. Mgr.—Henry Banach
MIS Mgr.—Paul J. Ledbetter II
Tech. Serv. Mgr.—Anne Goldsmith
Tech. Sales Rep.—Joe Lapota, Jr.
SIC—2992; NAICS—324191;
*Lubricating oils; Brand name—
  Caltran; Caltech; Hydrocal;
  Calsol; Calpar; Penreco;
  Magiesol*
Employs—25; Estab.—1916
Sales—$10Mil-$25Mil
970,000 sq ft site, Distrib.—Intl.
Privately owned corporation
ISO rating—9002
Parent co.—Calumet Specialty
  Products Partners, Indianapolis,
  IN
Phone—(317) 328-5660
See Parent Co. Section for full profile.

## Features & Benefits:

1) Determine who to contact quickly & easily with names and titles

2) Pre-qualify companies with whom you'll do business through product descriptions

3) Find out how long a company has been in business and its number of employees

## East Rutherford— (cont.)

SIC—3825; NAICS—334500;
*Avionic test equipment; Brand
name—TIC*
Employs—58; Estab.—1947
Sales—$15Mil
28,000 sq ft site, Distrib.—Intl.
Publicly owned corporation
ISO rating—9001

**THEMAC, INC.**

405 Railroad Ave., P.O. Box 44
(07073)
**Phone—(201) 438-2313**
Fax—(201) 438-8647
www.themacinc-us.com
Email—jcremona@themacinc.com
Pres.—Joseph Cremona
V-P.—Barbara Cremona
Secy-Treas.—Laura Wilkins
Machinist—Ed Macon
SIC—3559; *Tool post grinding
machines; Brand name—themac
tool-post grinders*
Employs—7; Estab.—1976
Sales—$500,000-$1Mil
5,500 sq ft site, Distrib.—National
Privately owned sub-S corp.

**TOYO INK AMERICA, LLC**

30 Murray Hill Pkwy., Ste. 100
(07073)
**Phone—(201) 804-0616**
National—(866) 969-8696
Fax—(201) 804-0629
www.toyoink.com
Manager—Vito Vannetti
SIC—2893; *Commercial printing
inks & polymer chemicals*
Employs—8
Sales—$2.5Mil-$5Mil (est)
Privately owned corporation
Parent co.—Toyo Ink America,
LLC, Wood Dale, IL
Phone—(630) 930-5100
See Parent Co. Section for full profile.

**TRANS WORLD MARKETING CORP.**

360 Murray Hill Pkwy. (07073)
**Phone—(201) 935-5565**
Fax—(201) 935-3996
www.transworldmarketing.com
CEO—James Cavaluzzi
Sr. V-P., Sales—Peter Heil
V-P., Mktg.—Jerry Molatore
SIC—2541; 2542; *In-store retail
displays, fixtures, signage &
store environments*
Employs—300; Estab.—1967
Distrib.—National
Privately owned corporation

**US INK CORP.**

390 Central Ave. (07073)
**Phone—(201) 438-4041**
Fax—(201) 896-9137
www.usink.com
Email—info@usink.com
GM—Eddie Cabbell
Shpg. Supv.—Greg Gualdarama
SIC—2893; NAICS—325910;
*Printing ink*
Employs—21; Estab.—1990
Sales—$5Mil-$10Mil (est)
Distrib.—Intl.
Publicly owned corporation
Parent co.—US Ink Corp.,
Carlstadt, NJ
Phone—(201) 935-8666
See Parent Co. Section for full profile.

**WOODWARD JOGGER AERATORS, INC.**

45 Carlton Ave. (07073)
**Phone—(201) 933-6800**
Fax—(201) 933-6803
www.woodwardusa.com
Email—info@woodwardusa.com
Pres.—John Scillieri

SIC—3554; NAICS—333291;
*Paper & paperboard aerators*
Employs—20; Estab.—1950
Sales—$2.5Mil-$5Mil (est)
Distrib.—Intl.
Privately owned corporation

**ZENITH PRECISION, INC.**

536 Paterson Ave. (07073)
**Phone—(201) 933-8640**
Fax—(201) 933-0936
www.zenithprecision.com
Email—info@zenithprecision.com
Pres.—Matt de Gennaro
V-P.—Andrew de Gennaro
SIC—3599; *Precision & CNC
machining, including milling,
turning, grinding & jig boring for
the aerospace, commercial &
medical industries*
Employs—10; Estab.—1966
Sales—$500,000-$1Mil
4,000 sq ft site, Distrib.—National
Privately owned corporation

## East Windsor

(Mercer—N.E.)

**ELEMENTIS CHROMIUM, INC. (H Q)**

469 Old Trenton Rd. (08512)
**Phone—(609) 443-2000**
Fax—(609) 443-2422
www.elementis-chromium.com
Email—chromium.us@
elementis.com
Chrm.—Andrew Duff
CEO—David Dutro
Pres., Div.—Dennis Valentino
Dir., Hum. Res.—Frank Vavricka
SIC—2819; *Corporate
headquarters; chromium
chemicals, including
dichromate, chrome sulfate,
chromic acid, oxide & hydrate &
sodium sulfate*
Employs—130; Estab.—1998
Sales—$50Mil-$100Mil (est)
Privately owned corporation
Also see: Elementis Specialties,
Inc., same loc.

**ELEMENTIS SPECIALTIES, INC. (H Q)**

469 Old Trenton Rd. (08512)
**Phone—(609) 443-2000**
    (609) 443-2500
National—(800) 866-6800
Fax—(609) 443-2422
www.elementis-specialties.com
Email—contactus.web@
elementis.com
Pres.—Greg McClatchy
V-P., Global Supply Chain—
Gustavo Araujo
V-P., Fin.—Joe Budd
Dir., Mktg.—Clare Doyle
Dir., Bus., Coatings—Dave Brown
Dir., Global R & D—Ken Smith
Dir., Global Oilfield & Lubrication—
Jim Foley
Mktg. Mgr.—Eric Post
Tech. Mgr.—Homer Jamasbi
SIC—2851; 2869; NAICS—
325510; *Corporate
headquarters; paint, adhesive,
colorant & tint additives for oil
based drilling fluid rheology*
Employs—129
Sales—$500Mil
Distrib.—Intl.
Publicly owned corporation
ISO rating—9001

**HOVIONE, LLC**

40 Lake Dr. (08520)
**Phone—(609) 918-2600**
Fax—(609) 918-2615
www.hovione.com
Email—lemery@hovione.com
Hum. Res. Mgr.—Lavinia Emery

SIC—2834; NAICS—325412;
*Active pharmaceutical
ingredients*
Employs—50; Estab.—2000
Distrib.—National
Limited Liability Company

**ON-LINE SIGN**

2 Sheffield Rd. (08520)
Mail addr: P.O. Box 47, Cranbury
(08512-0047)
**Phone—(609) 443-1704**
    (732) 398-0300
National—(800) 891-7446
Fax—(609) 336-7437
www.on-linesign.com
Email—info@on-linesign.com
Pres.—Bernard Lerner
SIC—3993; *Interior & exterior
signs & banners*
Employs—3; Estab.—1990
Sales—$750,000
1,400 sq ft site, Distrib.—Intl.
Privately owned sub-S corp.

**SABINSA CORP.**

20 Lake Dr. (08520)
**Phone—(732) 777-1111**
Fax—(732) 777-1443
www.sabinsa.com
Email—info@sabinsa.com
Chrm.—M. Majeed
V-P., Bus. Dev.—Asha Ramesh
V-P.—Madhu Subramanian
IT Mgr.—Jaya Kumar Nair
Hum. Res. Mgr.—Mary Mlot
SIC—2834; NAICS—325412;
*Corporate headquarters &
phytonutrients, herbal extracts,
probiotics, mineral complexes &
specialty chemicals for the
nutritional, pharmaceutical &
food industries; Brand name—
SeleniumSelect; Curcumi C3
Complex; Bacopin; Picroliv;
Lactospore; Methyselene;
Forslean; Bioperine; Citrin;
Silbinol*
Employs—30; Estab.—1988
Sales—$30Mil
25,000 sq ft site, Distrib.—Intl.
Privately owned corporation

**SHISEIDO AMERICA, INC.**

366 Princeton Hightstown Rd.
(08520)
**Phone—(609) 371-5800**
Fax—(609) 371-8184
www.shiseido.com
Email—nwada@sai.shiseido.com
Pres., COO—Edward Houlihan
Sr. V-P., Tech.—Hiroto Morozumi
Ex. Dir., Mfg.—Ladio Hanzes
Ex. Dir., Opers.—Tom Halligan
Ex. Dir., Package Engrg. & Pur.—
Sandip Shah
Ex. Dir., Fin.—Bill Walsh
Ex. Dir., Package Engrg. & Pur.—
Sandip Shah
Ex. Dir., Plng.—Carol Billy
Ex. Dir., Qual. Assessment &
Improvement—Shyama Desai
SIC—2844; NAICS—325600;
*Cosmetics & fragrances; Brand
name—Shiseido; NARS; Bare
Escentuals*
Employs—160; Estab.—1989
Sales—$150Mil-$175Mil
215,000 sq ft site, Distrib.—Intl.
Privately owned corporation
Parent co.—Shiseido America,
Inc., New York, NY
Phone—(212) 805-2300
See Parent Co. Section for full profile.

**THERMO SYSTEMS, LLC (H Q)**

84 Twin Rivers Dr. (08520)
**Phone—(609) 371-3300**
Fax—(609) 371-3400
www.thermosystems.com
Email—info@thermosystems.com
Ptnr.—Greg Smith
Ptnr.—David Musto
Cont.—Phyllis Lasky

Hum. Res. Mgr.—Daneen
Spitaletto
SIC—3823; NAICS—334513;
*Company headquarters; direct
digital control systems*
Employs—50; Estab.—1998
Sales—$5Mil-$10Mil (est)
Distrib.—Intl.
Limited Liability Company

**TRIANGLE REPRO CENTER**

222 Dutch Neck Rd. (08520)
**Phone—(609) 448-8161**
Fax—(609) 448-9499
Email—info@trianglecopy.com
Owner & GM—Mike Cocciolillo
Manager—Joe Titi
SIC—2752; NAICS—323100;
*Large-format printing*
Employs—5; Estab.—1998
Sales—under $500,000
Distrib.—Regional
Privately owned corporation

## Eastampton

(Burlington—S.E.)

**EPICORE NETWORKS U.S.A., INC.**

4 Lina Ln. (08060)
**Phone—(609) 267-9118**
Fax—(609) 267-9336
www.epicorebionetworks.com
Email—information@
epicorebionetworks.com
CEO—Bill Long
Plt. Mgr.—Bill Cassler
Prodn. Mgr.—Sam Moore
Off. Mgr.—Michelle McCann Smith
SIC—2048; *Specialty feeds for
adult shrimp & marine animals;
Brand name—EPIFEED-MBF*
Employs—7; Estab.—1997
Sales—$1Mil-$2.5Mil (est)
Distrib.—Intl.

## Eatontown

(Monmouth—N.E.)

**AEROFLEX CONTROL COMPONENTS, INC.**

Div. of Aeroflex, Inc.
40 Industrial Way E. (07724)
**Phone—(732) 460-0212**
Fax—(732) 460-0214
www.aeroflex.com
Email—sales@aeroflex.com
Cont.—Jim Ebessen
Dir., Sales—John Ekis
GM—Charles S. Brand
Sales Admn.—Tracy Kavan
Sales Admn.—Chris Ann
McCallister
Pur. Agt.—Peggy Brand
SIC—3679; 3663; NAICS—
334220; *Radio frequency &
microwave components &
subsystems, detectors, limiters,
switches, attenuators, phase
shifters, amplifiers, synthesizers,
converters & switch matrices*
Employs—100; Estab.—1982
30,000 sq ft site, Distrib.—Intl.
Publicly owned corporation
Parent co.—Aeroflex, Inc.,
Plainview, NY
Phone—(516) 694-6700
See Parent Co. Section for full profile.

**ALKALINE CORP.**

20 Meridian Rd. (07724)
Mail addr: P.O. Box 306, Oakhurst
(07755)
**Phone—(732) 531-7830**
Fax—(732) 531-7830
www.morrowbrown.com
Email—allersearch@
allergyhelp.com
Pres.—Isadore Bale
Cust. Serv. Rep.—Noelle Scally

GEOGRAPHICAL

## Eatontown—(cont.)

SIC—3841; *Disposable allergy test needles*
Employs—5; Estab.—1981
Sales—$500,000-$1Mil (est)
Distrib.—National
Privately owned corporation

### ALLIED ENVIRONMENTAL SIGNAGE

556 Industrial Way W. (07724)
**Phone—(732) 578-1818**
Fax—(732) 578-1808
www.allied-signs.com
Pres.—Kevin White
Creative Dir.—Stephen Stacy
Off. Mgr.—Pat Pesapane
Proj. Mgr.—Kim Rasmussen
Proj. Mgr.—Natalie Carola
Sales Rep.—Rob Genz
SIC—3993; *Interior & exterior vinyl signs*
Employs—24; Estab.—1920
Sales—$500,000-$1Mil
Distrib.—National
Privately owned corporation

### ALTIOR

444 Route 35 S., Bldg. B (07724)
**Phone—(732) 440-1280**
Fax—(732) 212-9424
www.altior.com
Email—info@altior.com
Pres., CEO—Ramana Jampala
V-P., Sales—Jim Carlson
Dir., Mktg. & Prod.—Byron Rashad
SIC—3672; *Computer hardware protocol acceleration boards & IP cores for data networking & enterprise storage applications; Brand name—CebaFlex™; Ceba RIP Cores™*
Employs—55; Estab.—2004
Sales—$5Mil-$10Mil (est)
Distrib.—National
Privately owned corporation

### AOS THERMAL COMPOUNDS, LLC

22 Meridian Rd., Ste. 6 (07724)
**Phone—(732) 389-5514**
National—(888) 662-7337
Fax—(732) 389-6380
www.aosco.com
Email—sales@aosco.com
Pres., CEO—John Ziemski
V-P., Fin.—Jennifer Decker
V-P., R & D—Victor Papanu
Sales Mgr.—Lesley Maddalena
Hum. Res. Mgr.—Judith Ziemski
SIC—2992; 3679; 2821; NAICS—324191; *Heat sink compounds & thermal interface materials, including thermal pads, gap fillers & nonsilicone thermal greases; Brand name—Micro-faze; Sure-form; Absolute Zero*
Employs—12; Estab.—1895
Distrib.—Intl.
Limited Liability Company

### AUTOBAR SYSTEMS CORP.

1 Meridian Rd. (07724)
Mail addr: 20 Meridian Rd., Ste. 8, Eatontown (07724-2270)
**Phone—(732) 922-3355**
Fax—(732) 922-2221
Email—autobarcorp@aol.com
Pres.—Donald E. Ullery, Jr.
V-P.—Stephen Roman
Prod. Mgr.—John Armstrong
SIC—3581; 3559; NAICS—333311; *Liquor bottle dispensers & control equipment; Brand name—Autobar; Beermatic; Winematic; underbar*
Employs—5; Estab.—1947
Sales—under $500,000
6,000 sq ft site, Distrib.—Intl.
Privately owned corporation

### BIG CLIENT, LLC

1 Industrial Way W., Bldg. E (07724-2255)
**Phone—(732) 918-8221**
Fax—(732) 918-8331
www.big-client.com
Email—ben@big-client.com
CEO—Ben H. Zehavi
Prodn. Mgr.—Bob Clark
Qual. Mgr.—Ronni Zehavi
SIC—3571; 7373; *Thin client terminal computer & point-of-sale keyboard assembly & computer network systems integration*
Employs—30; Estab.—2010
Sales—$10Mil-$25Mil
5,000 sq ft site, Distrib.—Intl.
Limited Liability Company

NEW ENTRY
### BIOLOGICAL CONTROLS, INC.

749 Hope Rd. (07724)
**Phone—(732) 542-5822**
National—(800) 224-9768
Fax—(732) 389-8821
www.biologicalcontrols.com
Email—sales@biologicalcontrols.com
Owner—Gary Messina
SIC—3564; *Air purification systems; Brand name—Airphase*
Employs—5
Sales—$2Mil
20,000 sq ft site, Distrib.—Intl.
Privately owned sub-S corp.

### BRECOFLEX CO., L.L.C.

222 Industrial Way W. (07724)
**Phone—(732) 460-9500**
          (888) 463-1400
Fax—(732) 542-6725
www.brecoflex.com
Email—info@brecoflex.com
Pres.—Bernie Fuellemann
Sales Mgr.—Marc Slack
Sales Mgr.—Jorge Ferreira
Opers. Mgr.—Jonathan Weir
Acctg. & Hum. Res. Mgr.—Paula Newberry
Sr. Mktg. Coord.—Leticia Arce
SIC—3052; NAICS—326220; *Polyurethane timing & woven endless flat belts & metal pulleys*
Employs—70; Estab.—1989
Sales—$10Mil-$25Mil
60,500 sq ft site, Distrib.—Intl.
Limited Liability Company
ISO rating—9001

NEW ENTRY
### BURPEE MATERIAL TECHNOLOGY, LLC

15 Christopher Way (07724)
**Phone—(732) 544-8900**
Fax—(732) 544-8910
www.burpeetech.com
Email—info@burpeetech.com
CEO—Janet Burpee
SIC—3841; *Medical devices, including catheters & stents*
Employs—70
Sales—$10Mil-$25Mil (est)
Distrib.—Intl.
Limited Liability Company

### CENTER VOCATIONAL REHABILITATION

15 Meridian Rd., Ste. 1 (07724-4226)
**Phone—(732) 544-1800**
Fax—(732) 389-3453
www.cvrus.org
Email—drotondelli@cvrus.org
CEO—Russell Anderson
V-P., Cont.—Karen Cosenza
Sales & Mktg. Mgr.—Diane Rotondelli
Prodn. & Whse. Mgr.—William Bartok
IT Mgr.—Frank Marino

SIC—3089; *Contract packaging services, including shrink wrap, blister packaging, collating, hand packing & assembly, heat sealing, pick n' pack, re-packaging, labeling & bulk mail preparations*
Employs—150
Sales—$10Mil-$25Mil
25,000 sq ft site, Distrib.—Regional
Privately owned corporation

### CRITERION CHOCOLATES, INC.

125 Lewis St. (07724)
**Phone—(732) 542-7847**
Fax—(732) 542-0045
www.criterionchocolates.com
Email—criterion@criterionchocolates.com
V-P., GM—Ronald Boyadjian
V-P.—George Karagias
V-P.—James Samaras
SIC—2066; 2064; NAICS—311300; *Chocolate candy*
Employs—15; Estab.—1929
11,000 sq ft site, Distrib.—Regional
Privately owned corporation

### DSM ENTERPRISES, INC.

132 Lewis St., Unit B-5 (07724)
**Phone—(732) 380-9779**
National—(800) 974-2338
Fax—(732) 380-0725
www.dsmawnings.com
Email—wallymann@verizon.net
Pres.—Mark Donahue
V-P.—Wally Mann
SIC—3089; 2394; NAICS—314912; *Acrylic, vinyl & canvas awnings*
Employs—6; Estab.—2000
Sales—under $500,000
Distrib.—Regional
Privately owned corporation
AKA: DSM Awnings

### ELECTRONIC CONCEPTS, INC.

526 Industrial Way W. (07724)
**Phone—(732) 542-7880**
Fax—(732) 542-0524
www.ecicaps.com
Email—sales@ecicaps.com
Pres., CEO—Bernard Lavene
Ex. V-P.—Phillip Lepore
Cont.—Don Welker
GM—Joseph Bond
Pur. Mgr.—Mark Fitzpatrick
MIS Mgr.—Roger Manzella
Admn. Mgr.—Philip Maidlow
Hum. Res. Mgr.—Lisa Esposito
Qual. Control Mgr.—Jake Nugen
SIC—3675; NAICS—334414; *Corporate headquarters & electronic film capacitors*
Employs—150; Estab.—1969
Sales—$10Mil-$25Mil
100,000 sq ft site, Distrib.—Intl.
Privately owned corporation
ISO rating—AS9100

### ELLIS KUHNKE CONTROLS, INC.

132 Lewis St., Unit A-2 (07724)
**Phone—(732) 291-3334**
National—(800) 221-0714
Fax—(732) 291-8154
Email—ekcinc@aol.com
Pres.—Howard J. Boyce
V-P., Sales & Mktg.—John Ruane
V-P., Opers.—Frances Ruane
SIC—3625; 3824; 5084; 5085; NAICS—335314; *Manufacturer & distributor of pneumatic timers, counters, indicators, valves, fittings & pneumatic industrial controls & systems; Brand name—EKC; KUHNKE; AGASTAT*
Employs—8; Estab.—1969
Sales—$2Mil
4,000 sq ft site, Distrib.—Intl.
Privately owned corporation

### FARGO CONTROLS, INC.

P.O. Box 539 (07724)
**Phone—(732) 389-3376**
National—(800) 241-3755
Fax—(732) 542-3553
www.fargocontrols.com
Email—sales@fargocontrols.com
Pres.—E. Fargo
Sales & Mktg. Mgr.—Sharon Sullivan
SIC—3824; 3625; NAICS—334514; *Proximity sensors, counters, timers, hour meters & related industrial controls*
Employs—5; Estab.—1983
Distrib.—National
Privately owned corporation

### †FASTENAL CO.

22 Meridian Rd., Unit 2 (07724)
**Phone—(732) 542-7533**
Fax—(732) 542-7823
www.fastenal.com
Email—njeat@stores.fastenal.com
Br. Mgr.—Jan Humphrey
SIC—5072; 5084; *Wholesaler of fasteners, safety equipment, tools & abrasives*
Employs—3; Estab.—2003
Distrib.—National
Publicly owned corporation
Parent co.—Fastenal Co., Winona, MN
   Phone—(507) 454-5374
   See Parent Co. Section for full profile.

### †GREY OWL INDIAN CRAFT SALES CORP.

15 Meridian Rd., Ste. 5 (07724-4226)
**Phone—(732) 389-4626**
National—(800) 487-2376
Fax—(732) 389-4629
www.greyowlcrafts.com
Email—greyowlinc@aol.com
Pres.—Jim Feldman
SIC—5131; 5199; *Distributor of Native American crafts & craft products, including beads, head dresses, dance kits, peace pipes, feathers, shells & beading supplies*
Employs—2; Estab.—1947
Sales—under $500,000
Distrib.—Intl.
Privately owned sub-S corp.

### HAMPTON FORGE, LTD.

442 State Route 35 (07724)
**Phone—(732) 389-5507**
National—(877) 423-6743
Fax—(732) 389-5394
www.hamptonforge.com
Pres.—Felix Amar
Hum. Res. Mgr.—Susan Amar
SIC—3914; *Flatware & cutlery*
Employs—30; Estab.—1986
Sales—$2.5Mil-$5Mil (est)
Distrib.—Intl.
Privately owned corporation

### HERITAGE PHARMACEUTICALS, INC. (H Q)

12 Christopher, Ste. 300 (07724)
**Phone—(732) 429-1000**
Fax—(732) 429-1001
www.heritagepharma.com
Email—info@heritagepharma.com
CEO—Jeffrey Glazer
Dir., Fin.—Frank Petranich
SIC—2834; *Corporate headquarters; generic pharmaceuticals, including ethambutol, hydralazine, hydrochlorothiazide, sulindac & propranolol tablets & propoxyphene HCl & paromomycin capsules (mfg. subcontracted)*
Employs—15; Estab.—2006
Distrib.—Intl.
Privately owned corporation

## Eatontown—(cont.)

**†INDUSTRIAL CONTROLS DISTRIBUTORS, LLC**
17 Christopher Way (07724)
**Phone—(732) 918-9000**
National—(800) 631-2112
Fax—(732) 922-4417
www.industrialcontrolsonline.com
Pres.—Joe Eichelberger
V.-P., Mktg.—Mark Abraham
V.-P., Hum. Res.—Mary Windeler
SIC—5084; *Company headquarters & distributor of controls for HVAC, process control & industrial automation applications*
Employs—55; Estab.—1976
Distrib.—National
Limited Liability Company

**INNOVATIVE POWER SOLUTIONS, LLC**
373 South St. (07724)
**Phone—(732) 544-1075**
Fax—(732) 544-1078
www.ips-llc.com
Email—eliebermann@ips-llc.com
CEO—Eli Libermann
Dir., Opers.—Bill Schatzow
Buyer—Lisa Matiez
SIC—3621; NAICS—335312; *Generators*
Employs—40; Estab.—1999
Sales—$5Mil-$10Mil (est)
Distrib.—Intl.
Limited Liability Company

**IPKEYS TECHNOLOGIES**
1 Industrial Way W., Ste. E-1 (07724)
**Phone—(732) 389-4702**
Fax—(732) 389-8149
www.ipkeys.com
Email—info@ipkeys.com
Pres.—Mark Pappas
Manager—Robert Nawy
SIC—7373; 7372; *Computer & network systems integration & software development for the federal, Department of Defense, commercial & energy sectors, including LANs, WANs & consulting services*
Employs—117; Estab.—2005
10,000 sq ft site, Distrib.—National
Privately owned corporation

**KESSLER ELLIS PRODUCTS CO., INC.**
10 Industrial Way E., Ste. 6 (07724-3390)
**Phone—(732) 935-1320**
National—(800) 631-2165
Fax—(732) 935-9344
www.kep.com
Email—sales@kep.com
CEO—Corson Ellis III
Pres.—Peter Sabat
Acctg. Mgr.—Michelle Pulignano
SIC—3824; 3577; NAICS—334514; *Flowmeters, counting devices, timers & programmable logic controller peripherals*
Employs—50; Estab.—1962
24,000 sq ft site, Distrib.—Intl.
Privately owned corporation
ISO rating—9001:2008

**LAIRD & CO., INC.**
1 Laird Rd. (07724)
**Phone—(732) 542-0312**
Fax—(732) 542-2244
www.lairdandcompany.com
Email—sales@lairdandcompany.com
Pres.—Larrie Laird
Ex. V.-P., CFO—John E. Laird III
Sr. V.-P., Sales—Tom Alberico
V.-P., Prodn.—Janice Custer
V.-P.—Lisa Laird-Dunn
Cont.—Robert Reed
SIC—2085; 5182; NAICS—312100; *Corporate headquarters & manufacturer of distilled & blended liquors & distributor of imported wines & specialty products*
Employs—40; Estab.—1780
Sales—$50Mil-$100Mil
160,000 sq ft site, Distrib.—Intl.
Privately owned corporation

**M & M GRINDING, LLC**
132 Lewis St. (07724)
**Phone—(732) 542-1157**
Fax—(732) 542-1241
Email—mmgrinding@verizon.net
Owner & Pres.—John M. Dietz III
Bookkeeper—Sue Mitchell
SIC—3599; *Cylindrical grinding job shop*
Employs—3; Estab.—1998
Sales—$500,000
7,500 sq ft site, Distrib.—Intl.
Limited Liability Company

**MANFREDI ORTHOTIC & PROSTHETIC AFFILIATES, LLC**
749 Hope Rd. (07724)
**Phone—(732) 380-0366**
National—(800) 400-2580
Fax—(732) 380-0245
www.manfredioandp.com
Email—robertmanfredi@verizon.net
Pres.—Robert Manfredi
Corp. Secy.—Virginia Manfredi
GM—Jean Manfredi
SIC—3842; *Orthopedic, orthotic & prosthetic appliances*
Employs—8; Estab.—1958
Sales—$1Mil-$2.5Mil
Distrib.—Local
Limited Liability Company

**MANZI PRINTERS, INC.**
132 Lewis St., Ste. B-2 (07724)
**Phone—(732) 542-1927**
Fax—(732) 542-1977
www.manziprinting.com
Email—manziprinting@aol.com
Owner—Mike Manzi
V.-P.—Lou Manzi
SIC—2759; *Commercial printing*
Employs—3; Estab.—1985
Sales—under $500,000
2,005 sq ft site, Distrib.—Local
Privately owned corporation

**MASSTAR**
18 Heritage Rd. (07724)
**Phone—(732) 542-8004**
Fax—(732) 544-5044
www.masstar.com
Email—info@masstar.com
Owner—Charles Massa
SIC—7373; 3571; 3577; 7372; *Computer network systems integration, including LANs, WANs & custom computer hardware & software*
Employs—2; Estab.—1984
Sales—under $500,000
Distrib.—Local
Sole ownership

**MEGA PUMPS, L. P.**
611 Industrial Way W. (07724)
**Phone—(732) 578-9100**
Fax—(732) 578-9111
www.megapumps.com
Email—sales.info@mega-airless.com
Pres.—Lucyna Silberstein
V.-P.—Janice Swindlehurst
Accts. & Hum. Res. Mgr.—Michael Carle
IT Mgr.—Merle Crain
SIC—3569; *Cosmetic dispensing systems*
Employs—53; Estab.—1991
Sales—$1Mil-$2.5Mil
Distrib.—National
Limited Liability Partnership

**MOTION SYSTEMS CORP.**
600 Industrial Way W. (07724)
**Phone—(732) 222-1800**
Fax—(732) 389-9191
www.motionsystem.com
Email—applicationengineer@motionsystem.com
Pres.—William Wolf
SIC—3621; NAICS—335312; *Electromechanical actuators & gear motors for medical, handicap & material handling equipment, dental chairs, valve operators & ergonomic systems applications*
Employs—80; Estab.—1972
100,000 sq ft site, Distrib.—Intl.
Privately owned sub-S corp.

**NATIONAL PROTECTIVE SYSTEMS**
1 Meridian Rd. (07724)
**Phone—(732) 922-3609**
National—(800) 732-7978
Fax—(732) 922-2221
www.securesysteminc.com
Email—sales@securesysteminc.com
V.-P., Mfg.—Donald E. Ullery, Jr.
SIC—3669; NAICS—334290; *Portable personal & stationary equipment security alarm systems*
Employs—7; Estab.—1993
6,000 sq ft site, Distrib.—National
Privately owned corporation

**PACKETSTORM COMMUNICATIONS, INC.**
20 Meridian Rd. (07724)
**Phone—(732) 544-2434**
Fax—(732) 544-2437
www.packetstorm.com
Email—sales@packetstorm.com
Pres.—Bill Luthy
Test Engr.—Walt Rogers
SIC—3661; *Internet protocol network emulators & simulators for testing applications*
Employs—10; Estab.—1999
Distrib.—Intl.
Privately owned corporation

**PRECISION MIRROR & GLASS, INC.**
89 Route 35 N. (07724)
**Phone—(732) 389-8175**
Fax—(732) 389-8179
www.customshowerdoors.com
Email—info@customshowerdoors.com
Pres.—Tom Basile
GM—Larry Meyerson
Sales Mgr.—Jack Wingate
SIC—3231; 3211; NAICS—327215; *Frame-less tempered, laminated & etched glass shower doors & mirrors; Brand name—Precision Shower Doors Inc.*
Employs—5; Estab.—1984
40,000 sq ft site, Distrib.—Regional
Privately owned sub-S corp.

**†RONSTAN PAPER & PACKAGING**
72 James Way (07724)
**Phone—(732) 389-1040**
National—(877) 766-7826
Fax—(732) 389-9271
www.ronstanpaper.com
Email—sales@ronstanpaper.com
Pres.—William F. LaMorte
Opers. Mgr.—Chris LaMorte
SIC—5113; 5112; 5044; 5169; *Distributor of industrial & personal service paper, packaging materials & office & janitorial supplies, including cleaning chemicals & packaging machines*
Employs—12; Estab.—1946
Distrib.—Intl.
Privately owned sub-S corp.

**SHORE AWNING CO., INC.**
556 Industrial Way W. (07724)
Mail addr: P.O. Box 38, Avon by the Sea (07717-0038)
**Phone—(732) 578-1882**
National—(800) 747-1069
Fax—(732) 578-1885
www.shoreawning.com
Email—mm@shoreawning.com
Pres., CEO—Michael McClellan
SIC—2394; NAICS—314912; *Canvas awnings*
Employs—10; Estab.—1946
Sales—$500,000-$1Mil
5,000 sq ft site, Distrib.—Regional
Privately owned corporation

**SHORE P C**
3 Meridian Rd. (07724)
**Phone—(732) 380-0590**
Fax—(732) 380-0591
www.shore-pc.com
Email—sales@shore-pc.com
Owner & V.-P.—David Rose
Off. Mgr.—Michelle Hulsark
Prod. Mgr.—Steve Pierce
SIC—3672; NAICS—334412; *Printed circuit boards assemblies*
Employs—20; Estab.—1968
10,000 sq ft site, Distrib.—National
Privately owned corporation

**SPIRENT COMMUNICATIONS PLC**
Div. of Spirent Communications, Inc.
541 Industrial Way W. (07724)
**Phone—(732) 544-8700**
Fax—(732) 544-8347
www.spirent.com
Email—tas@spirent.com
V.-P., Fin.—Steve Clark
Sr. Dir., Hum. Res.—Phyllis Lockwood
Dir., Opers.—Ellis Bailey
MIS Mgr.—David Tieto
SIC—3825; NAICS—334500; *Telecommunication testing equipment*
Employs—150; Estab.—1984
54,000 sq ft site, Distrib.—Intl.
Privately owned corporation
Parent co.—Spirent Communications, Inc., Calabasas, CA
Phone—(818) 676-2300
See Parent Co. Section for full profile.

**STORAGE ENGINE, INC.**
1 Sheila Dr. (07724)
**Phone—(732) 747-6995**
National—(866) 734-8899
Fax—(732) 747-6542
www.storageengine.com
Email—info@storageengine.com
Pres., CEO—Gregg M. Azcuy
SIC—3571; NAICS—334111; *Computer data storage servers*
Employs—25; Estab.—1994
Sales—$1Mil-$2.5Mil
Distrib.—National
Privately owned corporation

**TECHNOL FUEL CONDITIONERS, INC.**
145 Wyckoff Rd., Ste. 300 (07724-1887)
**Phone—(732) 542-0111**
National—(800) 645-4033
Fax—(732) 542-0109
www.technol.com
Email—janis@technol.com
Owner—Odette Lichtman
Sales & Mktg. Mgr., Natl.—Janis Grundmann
SIC—2911; NAICS—324110; *Fuel additives; Brand name—STR 2+; DJR 3000 S1*
Employs—4; Estab.—2004
Sales—under $3Mil
Distrib.—National
Sole ownership

GEOGRAPHICAL

## Eatontown—(cont.)

**TRIDENT COMPUTER RESOURCES, INC.**

151 Industrial Way E., Ste. A-3 (07724-3323)
**Phone—(732) 544-9333**
Fax—(732) 544-1511
www.tridentusa.com
Email—information@tridentusa.com
Pres.—Scott Swain
CFO—Kathleen Iorio
SIC—7373; Computer network system integration
Employs—35; Estab.—1991
Distrib.—Intl.
Privately owned corporation

**TYCO ELECTRONICS SUBSEA COMMUNICATIONS, LLC (H Q)**

Div. of TE Connectivity
250 Industrial Way W. (07724)
**Phone—(732) 578-7000**
        (732) 578-7397
www.subcom.com
Email—info@subcom.com
Pres.—John Mitchell
V.-P., Sales & Mktg.—Mike Rieger
Hum. Res. Mgr.—Kristin Pasternack
SIC—3357; Divisional headquarters; underwater fiber-optic cables
Employs—129; Estab.—1955
Sales—$25Mil-$500Mil
Distrib.—Intl.
Publicly owned corporation
AKA: TE SubCom
Parent co.—TE Connectivity, Berwyn, PA
    Phone—(610) 893-9800
    See Parent Co. Section for full profile.

**WEST-WARD PHARMACEUTICAL CORP.**

401 Industrial Way W. (07724)
**Phone—(732) 542-1191**
National—(800) 631-2174
Fax—(732) 542-0940
www.west-ward.com
Email—ckriessler@west-ward.net
Pres., CEO—Michael Raya
V.-P., Hum. Res.—Stephen Kaplan
Area Mgr.—Seth Torphy
Mktg. Mgr.—Anthony Massero
Pur. Agt.—Colleen M. Kriessler
SIC—2834; NAICS—325412; Solid dose, injectible & generic pharmaceuticals
Employs—350; Estab.—1942
Company-wide: 800
70,000 sq ft site, Distrib.—National

## Edgewater

(Bergen—N.E.)

**C & S HOT STAMPING CO.**

20 Edgewater Pl. (07020)
**Phone—(201) 840-4004**
Fax—(201) 840-4028
www.cshotstamp.com
Email—orders@cshotstamp.com
Owner—Carmen Marino
Prodn. Mgr.—Adrian Garcia
SIC—2759; NAICS—323100; Contract commercial printing
Employs—5; Estab.—1989
Sales—under $500,000
Distrib.—National
Privately owned corporation

**CARTER CO., THE WILLIAM**

17 The Promenade (07020)
**Phone—(201) 313-1783**
www.carters.com
Email—contactus@carters.com
Owner—William Carter

SIC—2361; 2331; 2321; 2254; NAICS—315200; Children's shirts & under clothing
Employs—8
Sales—$500,000-$1Mil (est)
Distrib.—Regional
Privately owned corporation

**COFFEE ASSOCS., INC.**

178 Old River Rd., P.O. Box 240 (07020)
**Phone—(201) 945-1060**
Fax—(201) 945-4887
Pres.—William Callas
SIC—2095; NAICS—311920; Coffee roasting & packing
Employs—40; Estab.—1998
Sales—$25Mil-$50Mil (est)
Distrib.—Regional
Privately owned corporation

**POST OFFICE DIGITAL, INC.**

33 Hilliard Ave. (07020)
**Phone—(201) 945-8119**
Fax—(201) 945-8211
www.postofficedigital.com
Email—terrys@postofficedigital.com
Pres.—Achille Raspantini
V.-P., Sales—Terry Stoller
Post Prodn. Supv.—Scott Marchfeld
SIC—3695; NAICS—334613; DVD & media replication & production
Employs—10; Estab.—1999
Sales—$1Mil-$2.5Mil (est)
Distrib.—Intl.
Privately owned corporation

**SILKHOUSE INTERNATIONAL, INC.**

28 Garden Pl., Ste. 128 (07020)
**Phone—(201) 945-4569**
Fax—(201) 945-3975
Email—silkhouseinternational@yahoo.com
Pres.—Michael Liu
SIC—2331; 2335; 2337; 2339; NAICS—315200; Women's clothing
Employs—5; Estab.—1999
Sales—$500,000-$1Mil (est)
Distrib.—Intl.
Privately owned corporation

**SOLAR COLOR CHEMICAL CORP.**

180 River Rd. (07020)
**Phone—(201) 945-5775**
Fax—(201) 945-6778
Owner & Pres.—Randy Stasi
SIC—2893; NAICS—325910; Screen printing ink
Employs—1; Estab.—1978
Distrib.—Local
Privately owned corporation

**YIPPEE PRINTING & MARKETING**

115 River Rd., Bldg. 10 (07020)
**Phone—(201) 313-1900**
Fax—(201) 313-3377
www.epprinting.com
Manager—Shawn Spellbring
SIC—2396; 2395; NAICS—323100; Screen, offset & digital printing & embroidery
Employs—4; Estab.—2008
12,000 sq ft site, Distrib.—National
Privately owned corporation

## Edgewater Park

(Burlington—S.E.)

**INTERSTATE WELDING & MFG. CO., INC.**

1510 Village Ct. (08010)
**Phone—(609) 699-6950**
National—(800) 676-4666
Fax—(609) 699-6951
www.iwm3.com
Email—joseph@iwm3.com
Pres., CFO—Joseph N. Russomanno
Hum. Res. & Off. Mgr.—Rose Oakley

SIC—3444; 3499; 3498; 3548; Welding, tube, pipe & metal fabrication & installation of process plant & process equipment for the food, chemical & pharmaceutical industries
Employs—18; Estab.—1954
Sales—$1Mil-$5Mil
16,000 sq ft site, Distrib.—National
Privately owned sub-S corp.

**KEVIN'S SIGN CO.**

1212 Bridgeboro Rd. (08010)
**Phone—(609) 871-2385**
Email—kevinsignco@verizion.net
Owner—Kevin Liebner
SIC—3993; Interior & exterior signs
Employs—1; Estab.—1985
Sales—under $500,000 (est)
Distrib.—Regional
Sole ownership

**†PARK PUMPS & CONTROLS, INC.**

950 Mount Holly Rd., Ste. B (08010-1610)
**Phone—(609) 871-0944**
Fax—(609) 871-2987
www.parkpumps.com
Email—shirley@parkpumps.com
Owner—Calvin Stevenson
Pres.—Shirley A. Stevenson
SIC—5074; Distributor of sewage & wastewater pumps & controls
Employs—5; Estab.—1995
4,800 sq ft site, Distrib.—Local
Privately owned corporation

**SMARTPLAY INTERNATIONAL, INC.**

1550 Bridgeboro Rd. (08010)
**Phone—(609) 880-1860**
Fax—(609) 880-1865
www.smartplay.com
Email—info@smartplay.com
Pres.—David Michaud
Ex. V.-P.—Thomas Markert
IT Mgr.—Mike Rado
Hum. Res. Mgr.—Julie Markert
SIC—3999; Custom lottery number drawing machines
Employs—23; Estab.—1993
Sales—$2.5Mil-$4Mil
Distrib.—Intl.
Privately owned corporation

## Edison

(Middlesex—N.E.)

**AABHUSHAN EXPORTS PRIVATE LTD.**

155 Wood Ave. (08820)
**Phone—(732) 516-0800**
Fax—(732) 516-0813
www.aabhushanonline.com
Email—aabhushan@aol.com
Manager—Rachna Bhalla
SIC—3911; NAICS—339911; Precious metal jewlery
Employs—5; Estab.—1991
5,000 sq ft site, Distrib.—Local
Privately owned corporation
AKA: Aabhushan Family Jewelers

**AEROGROUP INTERNATIONAL, INC. (H Q)**

201 Meadow Rd. (08817)
**Phone—(732) 985-6900**
National—(800) 798-9478
Fax—(732) 985-3697
www.aerosoles.com
Email—customerservice@aerosoles.com
Pres.—Jules Schneider
CFO—Richard Morris
Dir., Prod.—Sharon Molfetta
Dir., Construction—Mike Bernard
IT Mgr.—Phillip Kinder
Hum. Res. Mgr.—Sue Cataudella

SIC—3144; NAICS—316214; Corporate headquarters; women's shoes (mfg. done in China)
Employs—120
Sales—$5Mil-$10Mil (est)
Distrib.—Regional
Privately owned corporation

**AFP TRANSFORMERS CORP.**

Div. of United Capital Corp.
206 Talmadge Rd. (08817)
**Phone—(732) 248-0305**
National—(800) 843-1215
Fax—(732) 248-0542
www.afp-transformers.com
Email—info@afp-transformers.com
Pres.—Greg Bongas
SIC—3677; NAICS—334416; Electrical cast coil, dry-type, control power & custom transformers
Employs—75; Estab.—1986
Distrib.—Intl.
Privately owned corporation
Parent co.—United Capital Corp., Great Neck, NY
    Phone—(516) 466-6464
    See Parent Co. Section for full profile.

**ALLEN FLAVORS, INC.**

23 Progress St. (08820)
**Phone—(908) 561-5995**
Fax—(908) 561-4164
www.allenflavors.com
Email—info@allenflavors.com
Pres.—Joseph Allen
V.-P., Admn. & Fin.—Michelle Allen
Assoc. V.-P.—Dana Allen
GM—Bruce Weber
Mktg. Mgr.—John Wilson
SIC—2087; NAICS—311900; Custom beverage pre-mixes & bases, including coffee & tea extracts & coffee roasting flavors; Brand name—Nestle Coffee and Tea Extracts
Employs—150; Estab.—1990
Sales—$100Mil-$250Mil (est)
225,000 sq ft site, Distrib.—National
Privately owned corporation

**ALPHAGRAPHICS 321**

90 Saw Mill Pond Rd., Heller Industrial Pk. (08817)
**Phone—(732) 985-6677**
Fax—(732) 985-2909
www.us321.alphagraphics.com
Email—us321@alphagraphics.com
Pres., CFO—Carl A. Venable
V.-P., Sales & Mktg.—Bernice P. Venable
SIC—2752; 2759; NAICS—323100; Digital & offset printing, promotional items & marketing services
Employs—4; Estab.—1990
Sales—$500,000-$1Mil
2,802 sq ft site, Distrib.—Regional
Privately owned corporation

**ALPINE METAL PRODUCTS**

7 Progress St. (08820)
**Phone—(908) 753-4543**
Fax—(908) 753-4377
www.alpinemetal.com
Email—engineering@alpinemetal.com
V.-P.—Keith Christian
V.-P.—Steve Bearden
SIC—3444; Sheet metal fabrication
Employs—19; Estab.—1965
23,000 sq ft site, Distrib.—Regional
Privately owned corporation

**AMERICAN RAILING DESIGN**

191 Vineyard Rd. (08817)
Mail addr: 326 Goodwin St., 1st Fl., Perth Amboy (08861)
**Phone—(732) 287-1122**
Fax—(732) 287-2306

## Edison—(cont.)

www.americanrailingdesign.com
Email—sales@
americanrailingdesign.com
Pres.—Andrew Martingano
SIC—3751; 3446; 3648; NAICS—
336991; *Commercial, residential
& industrial pipe bending &
fabrication, including bicycle
components, railings & lighting
fixtures*
Employs—10; Estab.—1996
Sales—$500,000-$1Mil (est)
Distrib.—Regional
Privately owned corporation

**ANTRON TECHNOLOGIES, INC.**
40 Brunswick Ave., Ste. 104
(08817-2589)
**Phone—(732) 205-0415**
Fax—(732) 205-0416
www.antron.com
Email—sales@antron.com
Pres.—Sing Hung
V-P.—Berkuei Hung
SIC—3679; *Power supplies*
Employs—5; Estab.—1992
Sales—$500,000-$1Mil (est)
2,200 sq ft site, Distrib.—National
Privately owned corporation

**AP DIAGNOSTIC LABORATORIES,
INC.**
1692 Oak Tree Rd., Ste. 17
(08820)
**Phone—(732) 906-7800**
    (732) 635-9729
Fax—(732) 906-7801
Email—apdiagedison@gmail.com
Pres.—Harshad Patel
Tech. Mgr.—Rajesh Bhagat
SIC—2835; NAICS—325413;
*Diagnostic test kits*
Employs—10; Estab.—2003
Sales—$1Mil-$2.5Mil
Distrib.—Local
Sole ownership

**APCO EXTRUDERS, INC.**
180 National Rd. (08817)
Mail addr: P.O. Box 556, Edison
(08818)
**Phone—(732) 287-5555**
National—(800) 942-8725
Fax—(732) 287-1421
www.apcoext.com
Email—apcoext@aol.com
Pres.—Emmanuel Parnes
Sales Mgr.—Charlie Grand
Plt. Mgr.—Dave Viera
Off. Mgr.—Renee Cedervall
SIC—3082; NAICS—326121;
*Plastic extrusions*
Employs—50; Estab.—1959
Distrib.—National
Privately owned corporation

**APPAREL DISTRIBUTION, INC.**
45 Saw Mill Pond Rd. (08817)
**Phone—(732) 287-1110**
Fax—(732) 287-4341
www.adi-logistics.com
Email—robertshaw@adi-
logistics.com
V-P.—Robert Shaw
Dir., Admn.—Cindy Aile
SIC—2399; 2759; 3999; NAICS—
323100; *Apparel label sewing,
pick ticket, invoice & UCC label
printing & assembly, repacking,
kitting, fulfillment, trucking,
reverse logistics & inventory
control services for the retail
apparel, electronics & office &
medical supply industries*
Employs—75; Estab.—2003
Distrib.—Intl.
Privately owned corporation
AKA: ADI Logistics

**ARCHON VITAMIN CORP.**
3775 Park Ave., Ste. 1 (08820)
**Phone—(973) 371-1700**
Fax—(973) 371-1277
www.archonvitamin.com
Dir., Pur.—Tracy Daniels
Dir., Tech.—A. Dieng
SIC—2834; NAICS—325412;
*Vitamins & nutritional
supplements*
Employs—65; Estab.—1995
50,000 sq ft site, Distrib.—National
Privately owned corporation

**ASHFAR ENTERPRISES, INC. (H Q)**
200 Metro Plex Dr., Ste. 275
(08817)
**Phone—(848) 202-1581**
Fax—(848) 202-1587
www.ashfar.com
Email—info@ashfar.com
Pres.—Farooq Sattar
CFO—Hanif Sattar
SIC—2282; NAICS—313112;
*Corporate headquarters;
polyester & nylon yarn warping*
Employs—9; Estab.—1980
Nationwide: 35
Sales—$1Mil-$2.5Mil (est)
Distrib.—National
Privately owned corporation

**ATLAS AUTO TRIM, INC.**
81 Highway 1 (08817)
**Phone—(732) 985-6800**
Fax—(732) 985-7888
www.atlasautotrim.com
Email—atlasautotrim@yahoo.com
Pres.—Sanford Dubin
SIC—2399; *Automotive seat
covers*
Employs—6; Estab.—1967
Sales—under $500,000
Distrib.—Local
Privately owned corporation

**AUTOMATIC ROLLS OF NEW
JERSEY, INC.**
Div. of Northeast Foods, Inc.
1 Gourmet Ln. (08837)
**Phone—(732) 549-2243**
National—(877) 222-2867
Fax—(732) 494-4980
www.nefoods.com
Email—humanresources@
nefoods.com
GM & Plt. Mgr.—Wayne Chandler
Hum. Res. Mgr.—Jackie Rivera
SIC—2051; NAICS—311812;
*Hamburger buns*
Employs—75; Estab.—1972
Sales—$6Mil-$10Mil
Distrib.—National
Privately owned corporation
Parent co.—Northeast Foods, Inc.,
Baltimore, MD
   Phone—(410) 558-3050
See Parent Co. Section for full profile.

**BELL SIGNS**
3125 Woodbridge Ave., Ste. 5-C
(08837-3259)
**Phone—(732) 738-0010**
Fax—(732) 738-6646
www.bellsignsnj.com
Email—ksbellsign@aol.com
Ptnr.—Stephen Bell
Ptnr.—Karen Bell
SIC—3993; 2759; NAICS—
323100; *Sandblasted, carved &
site interior & exterior signs, truck
& vehicle lettering, business
card, flyer & brochure printing &
logo design*
Employs—2; Estab.—1984
Sales—under $500,000
1,035 sq ft site, Distrib.—Local
Privately owned partnership

**BENNETT CABINETS, INC.**
1251 Highway 1 (08837)
**Phone—(732) 548-1616**
www.bennettcabinets.com

Email—bennettcabinets@
optonline.net
Pres.—Michael Bennett
SIC—2434; 2431; NAICS—
337110; *Custom wooden kitchen
cabinets & architectural
woodwork*
Employs—6; Estab.—1963
Sales—$500,000-$1Mil
5,000 sq ft site, Distrib.—Regional
Privately owned sub-S corp.

**BENTLEY LABORATORIES, LLC**
111 Fieldcrest Ave. (08837)
**Phone—(732) 512-0200**
Fax—(732) 512-0208
www.bentleylabs.com
Email—info@bentleylabs.com
CEO—Brian T. Fitzpatrick
Pres.—Gregory Torchiana
V-P., Bus. Dev.—Kathy Fitzpatrick
V-P., Fin.—James N. Slack
Off. Admn.—Linda Ramos
SIC—2844; 2834; NAICS—
325412; *Cosmetics &
pharmaceuticals*
Employs—200; Estab.—1988
125,000 sq ft site, Distrib.—
National
Limited Liability Company

**†BUCKHEAD BEEF CO.**
Div. of SYSCO Corp.
220 Raritan Ctr., P.O. Box 6988
(08837)
**Phone—(732) 661-4900**
National—(877) 282-4323
Fax—(661) 493-7732
www.buckheadbeefne.com
Email—contact@
buckheadbeefne.com
GM—Glenn Ermoian
Hum. Res. Mgr.—Nella Caterina
Trans. Mgr.—Michael Biancaniello
SIC—5147; *Distributor of meat,
including beef, pork, poultry &
seafood*
Employs—104; Estab.—1977
Sales—$250Mil-$500Mil
500,000 sq ft site, Distrib.—Local
Privately owned corporation
Parent co.—SYSCO Corp.,
Houston, TX
   Phone—(281) 584-1390
See Parent Co. Section for full profile.

**CAPUTO INTERNATIONAL, INC.**
112 Northfield Ave. (08837)
**Phone—(732) 225-5777**
Fax—(732) 225-0011
www.caputointernational.com
Email—info@
caputointernational.com
Owner—Paul Caputo
V-P.—Vincent Caputo
Accts. Mgr.—Samantha Caputo
SIC—3281; NAICS—327991;
*Marble, granite & stone slab
furniture, architectural highlights
& countertops; Brand name—
Caesarstone; Silestone*
Employs—6; Estab.—1864
10,000 sq ft site, Distrib.—Intl.
Privately owned sub-S corp.

**CELEBRITY INTERNATIONAL, INC.
(H Q)**
51 Saw Mill Pond Rd. (08817)
**Phone—(732) 476-2999**
Fax—(732) 476-2980
www.vitaminsbaby.com
Email—fliff@celebrityintl.com
Pres.—Eli Matalon
SIC—2369; NAICS—315200;
*Corporate headquarters;
children's clothing (mfg. done
overseas)*
Employs—50; Estab.—1965
Sales—$50Mil
Distrib.—Intl.
Privately owned corporation

**CHENOA INFORMATION SERVICE,
INC.**
10 Parsonage Rd., Ste. 312
(08837)
**Phone—(732) 549-6800**
www.chenoainc.com
Email—info@chenoainc.com
V-P.—Niku Trivedi
SIC—7372; *Financial service &
healthcare forms management &
completion software
development*
Employs—20; Estab.—2002
Distrib.—National
Privately owned corporation

**CINCO STAR, LLC**
2 Karnell Ct. (08820)
**Phone—(732) 744-1617**
National—(800) 654-4747
Fax—(732) 744-1615
www.cincostar.com
Owner—Vin Zaveri
SIC—3911; *Fine jewelry*
Employs—5; Estab.—1997
Sales—$500,000-$1Mil (est)
Distrib.—Regional
Limited Liability Company

**CLAUSEN CO., THE**
1055 King George Post Rd.
(08817)
Mail addr: P.O. Box 140, Fords
(08863-0140)
**Phone—(732) 738-1165**
Fax—(732) 738-1618
www.rustdefender.com
Email—clausenco@aol.com
Pres., CEO—Donald J. Peck
SIC—2821; 2851; NAICS—
325211; *Automotive refinishing
products; Brand name—Rust
Defender; Claw Glas Filler;
Gorilla Hair; Smoothout; All-U-
Need; Classic Plastic; Z-
Chrome; Z-Glas*
Employs—15; Estab.—1957
Sales—$1Mil-$5Mil
Distrib.—National
Privately owned corporation

**CLAYTON BLOCK CO., INC.**
1025 Route 1 S. (08837)
Mail addr: P.O. Box 3015,
Lakewood (08701-9015)
**Phone—(732) 549-1234**
National—(800) 662-3044
Fax—(732) 751-7630
www.claytonco.com
Email—kroe@claytonsonline.com
GM—Matt Emmert
Gen. Sales Mgr.—Joseph
Scaramuzzo
SIC—3271; NAICS—327331;
*Concrete block*
Employs—50; Estab.—1957
Distrib.—Regional
Privately owned corporation
Parent co.—Clayton Block Co.,
Inc., Neptune, NJ
   Phone—(732) 751-7600
See Parent Co. Section for full profile.

**COLONIAL WIRE & CABLE OF NJ,
INC.**
85 National Rd. (08817)
**Phone—(732) 287-1557**
National—(800) 982-8446
Fax—(732) 287-1586
www.colonialwire.com
Email—colonialwire@att.net
Pres.—Thomas Walsh
Mfg. Mgr.—Jake Saladino
SIC—3357; *Electrical wires &
cables*
Employs—100; Estab.—1992
Sales—$10Mil-$25Mil (est)
Distrib.—Local
Privately owned corporation

GEOGRAPHICAL

## Edison—(cont.)

**†COMAIRCO EQUIPMENT, INC.**
Div. of Comairco Equipment Ltd.
17 Progress St. (08820)
**Phone—(732) 331-1100**
(908) 756-1900
National—(877) 785-5247
Fax—(908) 756-1909
www.comairco.com
Email—sales@comairco.com
Sales Mgr.—Dave George
Hum. Res. Mgr.—Judy Cook
Off. Mgr.—Gary Symonds
Off. Mgr.—Drew Campbell
SIC—5084; *Wholesaler of air & gas compressors*
Employs—12; Estab.—1970
Sales—$500,000-$1Mil
Distrib.—Regional
Privately owned corporation
Parent co.—Comairco Equipment Ltd.
Phone—(450) 665-8780
See Parent Co. Section for full profile.

**†COMMUNICATIONS SUPPLY CORP.**
104 Sunfield Ave. (08837)
**Phone—(732) 346-1550**
National—(800) 886-9473
Fax—(732) 346-1750
www.gocsc.com
Email—info@gocsc.com
Br. Mgr.—Bill Dalton
Mgmt. Mgr.—Joe Smith
SIC—5065; *Wholesaler of communication equipment & low-voltage specialty wire & cable systems*
Employs—30; Estab.—1972
Sales—under $500,000
Distrib.—National
Publicly owned corporation
Parent co.—Communications Supply Corp., Carol Stream, IL
Phone—(630) 221-6400
See Parent Co. Section for full profile.

**COMTEL GLOBAL SERVICES, LLC**
105 Newfield Ave., Ste. K (08837)
**Phone—(732) 225-3055**
National—(877) 746-8311
Fax—(732) 225-3074
www.cgstogo.com
Email—info@cgstogo.com
Pres., CEO—Yossi Teichman
Sr. Admn. Mgr.—John Spadaccini
Logistics Mgr.—Kathy May
SIC—7373; *Computer network system integration, including LANs & WANs & IT services*
Employs—17
Distrib.—Intl.
Limited Liability Company
AKA: CGS

**CONHAGEN, INC., ALFRED (H Q)**
2035 Lincoln Hwy., Edison Sq. W., Ste. 3003 (08817)
**Phone—(732) 287-4565**
Fax—(732) 287-4956
www.conhagen.com
Email—newjersey@conhagen.com
Pres.—Alfred Conhagen, Jr.
Cont.—Vincent Kliesch
Hum. Res. & Off. Mgr.—Lynn Persing
SIC—3561; 3511; NAICS—333911; *Corporate headquarters; pump parts, turbines, compressors, rotors & rotating equipment*
Employs—5; Estab.—1942
Sales—$500,000-$1Mil (est)
Privately owned corporation

**CONSORTIUM COMPANIES**
400 Raritan Center Pkwy. (08837)
Mail addr.: P.O. Box 6444, Edison (08818)
**Phone—(732) 512-1777**
Fax—(732) 512-9444
www.e-consortium.com

Pres.—Lawrence Solomon
Proj. Coord.—Ann Granja
SIC—2759; 2752; NAICS—323100; *Commercial, offset & digital printing*
Employs—22; Estab.—1997
Distrib.—National
Privately owned corporation

**CONTI GROUP, THE (H Q)**
2045 State Route 27 (08817)
**Phone—(732) 520-5000**
Fax—(908) 755-5600
www.conticorp.com
Email—kconti@conticorp.com
Pres., CEO—Kurt G. Conti
CFO—Dominic Mustillo
V-P., Fin.—Richard Kenny
Hum. Res. Mgr.—Dawn Robinson
SIC—3272; 3441; 3599; NAICS—332312; *Company headquarters; precast concrete barriers, sound barrier walls & posts & fascia panels, structural metal fabrication & shearing, bending, drilling & welding job shop*
Employs—150; Estab.—1906
Sales—$10Mil-$25Mil (est)
Privately owned corporation

**COSMETIC ESSENCE, INC.**
50 Clearview Rd. (08837)
**Phone—(732) 225-2031**
Fax—(732) 225-3024
www.cosmeticessence.com
Email—sales@cosmeticessence.com
Plt. Mgr.—David Cassidy
SIC—2844; NAICS—325600; *Fragrance compounds*
Employs—90
Sales—$25Mil-$50Mil (est)
Publicly owned corporation
Parent co.—Cosmetic Essence, Inc., Holmdel, NJ
Phone—(732) 888-7788
See Parent Co. Section for full profile.

**COSPACK AMERICA CORP.**
3856 Park Ave. (08820)
**Phone—(732) 548-5858**
Fax—(732) 494-0339
www.cospackamerica.com
Email—cospack@cospackamerica.com
Pres.—Charles Hous
SIC—3089; *Contract cosmetics & skincare packaging services*
Employs—20
Sales—$2.5Mil-$5Mil (est)

**CPI USA INC.**
6 Doreen Ct. (08820)
**Phone—(732) 494-0007**
Fax—(732) 494-0028
www.cpiusainc.com
Email—info@cpiusainc.com
Founder & CEO—Isha Advani
Founder & Dir.—Deepak Advani
SIC—7373; *Computer network system integration, including LANs & WANs, custom software design, websites, mobile application design & web-based business intelligence reporting design; Brand name—CPI USA; HP; Dell; Lenovo; Cisco; Microsoft; VMware; EMC; Seagate; Western Digital; Intel*
Employs—4; Estab.—1997
Distrib.—National
Privately owned corporation

**CREATIVE COSTUME CO.**
61 Wilk Rd. (08837)
**Phone—(212) 564-5552**
www.creativecostume.com
Email—costume@creativecostume.com
Ptnr.—Susan Handler
Ptnr.—Linda Carcaci

SIC—2389; *Costumes*
Employs—2; Estab.—1982
Sales—under $500,000
Distrib.—National
Privately owned partnership

NEW ENTRY

**CREATIVE FURNITURE, INC. (H Q)**
240 Mill Rd. (08817)
**Phone—(732) 248-0255**
Fax—(732) 248-0093
www.creativefurniture.us
Email—info@creativefurniture.us
Owner—Leonid Kitovsky
SIC—2511; 2512; 2514; *Corporate headquarters; household furniture (mfg. done overseas)*
Employs—10
Sales—$500,000-$1Mil (est)
Distrib.—Local
Privately owned corporation

**CRODA, INC. (H Q)**
300 Columbus Cir., Ste. A (08837)
**Phone—(732) 417-0800**
Fax—(732) 417-0804
www.crodausa.com
Email—marketing-usa@croda.com
Pres.—Kevin Gallagher
CFO—Stephen Fish
Cont.—Joseph Aguero
Dir., Mktg.—Cara Eaton
Dir., Hum. Res.—Genevieve O'Donnel
SIC—2819; 2869; NAICS—325412; *Corporate headquarters; specialty chemicals*
Employs—100
Sales—$50Mil-$100Mil
Distrib.—Intl.
Publicly owned corporation

**CS APPAREL, INC. (H Q)**
3910 Park Ave., Ste. 2 (08820)
**Phone—(732) 906-9666**
National—(800) 430-6011
Fax—(732) 906-3275
www.casualstudio.com
Email—customer@casualstudio.com
Owner—Gopal Karnani
Sales Mgr.—Phillip Mulligan
SIC—2339; *Corporate headquarters; women's casual clothing, including sportswear (mfg. done overseas)*
Employs—5; Estab.—2005
Sales—$500,000-$1Mil (est)
Distrib.—Intl.
Privately owned corporation
AKA: Casual Studio

**CURRAN PFEIFF CORP.**
Liddle Ave. (08837)
Mail addr.: P.O. Box 527, Metuchen (08840-0527)
**Phone—(732) 225-0555**
Fax—(732) 225-5012
Pres., Hum. Res., Sales & Mktg. Mgr.—George Pfeiff, Jr.
V-P.—Eve Pfeiff
Off. Mgr.—Grace Wang
SIC—3269; NAICS—327112; *Ceramic products, including kiln posts & electric element holders, porcelain wire connectors, saggers, abrasive stone, dental laboratory items & dams for firing cart glass panels*
Employs—11; Estab.—1924
Sales—$1Mil
23,000 sq ft site, Distrib.—National
Privately owned corporation

**DIRORY INDUSTRIES, INC.**
39 Progress St. (08820)
**Phone—(908) 757-6650**
Fax—(908) 757-0012
Pres.—Roger Robinson
V-P.—Ryan Robinson
Secy-Treas.—Diane Robinson

SIC—3089; *Contract packaging*
Employs—15; Estab.—1982
Sales—under $500,000
Distrib.—National
Privately owned corporation
Also see: Progress Display, Inc., same loc.

**DRANETZ TECHNOLOGIES**
1000 New Durham Rd. (08818)
**Phone—(732) 287-3680**
National—(800) 372-6832
Fax—(732) 248-1834
www.dranetz.com
Email—sales@dranetz.com
Pres.—Bob Hart
V-P., Sales—Wieslaw Jerry Olechiw
Dir., Prod. Mgmt.—Ross Ignall
Opers. Mgr.—Robert Rodgers
Mktg. Mgr.—John Craig
Sales Admn. Mgr.—Patricia Guarraci
SIC—3825; NAICS—334500; *Company headquarters & electrical power analyzing equipment; Brand name—Dranetz HDPQ; Encore Series System; Dran-View 7*
Employs—50
Sales—$10Mil-$25Mil
50,000 sq ft site, Distrib.—Intl.
Privately owned corporation
ISO rating—9001

**DSO FLUID HANDLING CO., INC.**
Div. of Alfa Laval, Inc.
300 McGaw Dr., Ste. 2 (08837)
**Phone—(732) 225-9100**
National—(800) 527-6867
Fax—(732) 225-9101
www.dsofluid.com
Email—info@dsofluid.com
V-P., GM, Bus. Dev. & Sales—Ed Clark
SIC—3492; 3561; 3053; NAICS—332912; *Replacement parts for sanitary food, dairy & pharmaceutical processing equipment, including valve parts, pump parts, gaskets & o-rings*
Employs—15; Estab.—1995
Distrib.—Intl.
Privately owned corporation
Parent co.—Alfa Laval, Inc., Richmond, VA
Phone—(804) 222-5300
See Parent Co. Section for full profile.

**EDGE ORTHOTICS, INC.**
209 Pierson Ave. (08837)
**Phone—(732) 549-3343**
Fax—(732) 549-6555
www.edgeorthotics.com
Email—edgeorthotics@optonline.net
Owner & Pres.—James C. Bauman
SIC—3842; *Orthotics & prosthetics*
Employs—5
Sales—$1Mil-$2.5Mil
Distrib.—Regional
Privately owned corporation

**ENERGY OPTIONS, LLC**
256 Campus Dr. (08837)
**Phone—(732) 512-9100**
Fax—(732) 512-1500
www.energy-options.com
Email—sales@energy-options.com
Pres.—Bradley Freeman
V-P., Admn. & Fin.—Tracy Valle
Acctg. Specialist—Nancy Devenny
SIC—7373; 3569; NAICS—541512; *Automated HVAC systems & security monitoring systems integration; Brand name—Andover/Schneider Electric*
Employs—43; Estab.—1979
Distrib.—Regional
Limited Liability Company

## Edison—(cont.)

**ENTERIX, INC.**
Div. of Quest Diagnostics
236 Fernwood Ave. (08837)
**Phone—(732) 429-1899**
National—(800) 531-3681
Fax—(732) 429-1898
www.insuretest.com
Email—info@insuretest.com
V-P.—Robert Dachille
Cust. Serv. Rep.—Melissa Soto
SIC—2835; NAICS—325400;
*Colorectal cancer testing kits*
Employs—24; Estab.—1997
Sales—$500,000-$1Mil
Distrib.—Intl.
Publicly owned corporation
Parent co.—Quest Diagnostics,
Madison, NJ
Phone—(973) 520-2700
See Parent Co. Section for full profile.

**ENVIRO-PAK, INC.**
125 National Rd. (08817)
**Phone—(732) 248-1600**
Fax—(732) 248-1663
www.enviropakdrums.com
Email—info@enviropakdrums.com
Pres.—Edward Fitzpatrick
Sales Mgr.—Ralph Guliano
SIC—2655; NAICS—322214;
*Fiber drums*
Employs—25; Estab.—1991
Sales—$2.5Mil-$5Mil (est)
Distrib.—Local
Privately owned corporation

**EOS ENERGY STORAGE, LLC**
214 Fernwood Ave., Bldg. B
(08837)
**Phone—(732) 225-8400**
Fax—(732) 225-8425
www.eosenergystorage.com
Email—info@
eosenergystorage.com
CEO—Michael Oster
Pres.—Steve Hellman
V-P., R & D—George Adamson
Hum. Res. Mgr.—Emily Taubler
Chief Scientist & Inventor—Steven
Amendola
SIC—3691; 3692; NAICS—
335911; *Zinc-air battery system
for the electric utility, automotive,
transportation & commercial
industries*
Employs—30; Estab.—2008
Distrib.—Intl.
Privately owned corporation

**EXITFLEX USA, INC.**
254 Raritan Center Pkwy. (08837)
**Phone—(732) 512-9141**
National—(800) 932-0124
Fax—(732) 512-9145
www.exitflexusa.com
Email—mail@exitflexusa.com
Pres.—Joseph M. Medvecky
SIC—3492; *High-pressure hose,
tungsten carbide spray tips &
accessories for spray painting
equipment*
Employs—4; Estab.—1985
4,000 sq ft site, Distrib.—National
Privately owned corporation

**E-Z DO, INC.**
40 Executive Ave. (08817)
**Phone—(732) 287-8111**
Fax—(732) 287-0828
Pres., CEO—Mark S. Densen
CFO & Hum. Res. Mgr.—Brad
Gero
Cust. Serv. Rep.—Julie Paduano

SIC—2653; 2673; 3496; 3089;
NAICS—322211; *Houseware
products, including bath, shower
& closet accessories & storage
products, clothes hangers,
decorative shelving & shoe,
garment & travel bags*
Employs—150; Estab.—1954
83,000 sq ft site, Distrib.—National
Privately owned corporation

**†FASTENAL CO.**
55 Carter Dr. (08817)
**Phone—(732) 777-1029**
Fax—(732) 777-7892
www.fastenal.com
Email—njeds@stores.fastenal.com
Br. & Sales Mgr., Inside—Harrison
Jennings
SIC—5072; 5084; *Wholesaler of
fasteners, tools, abrasives &
safety equipment*
Employs—25; Estab.—2006
Distrib.—Local
Publicly owned corporation
Parent co.—Fastenal Co., Winona,
MN
Phone—(507) 454-5374
See Parent Co. Section for full profile.

**FASTSIGNS®**
485 Route 1 S., Crossroads Plz.
(08817)
**Phone—(732) 985-1166**
Fax—(732) 985-2290
www.fastsigns.com
Email—133@fastsigns.com
Owner—Sharad Patel
Graphic Designer—Sunny Patel
SIC—3993; *Interior & exterior
signs*
Employs—2; Estab.—2003
Sales—under $500,000
1,500 sq ft site, Distrib.—National
Sole ownership

**FERMAG TECHNOLOGIES**
80 Executive Ave. (08817)
Mail addr: P.O. Box 1364, Edison
(08818-1364)
**Phone—(732) 985-7300**
Fax—(732) 985-7566
www.fermagtechnologies.com
Email—pleddy@
fermagtechnologies.com
Pres.—John Perkins
V-P.—Pete Ledy
SIC—3264; NAICS—327113;
*Magnetic powders*
Employs—8; Estab.—1946
30,000 sq ft site, Distrib.—Intl.
Privately owned sub-S corp.
ISO rating—9001:2008

**FERRO CORP.**
54 Kellogg Ct. (08817)
**Phone—(732) 287-1930**
National—(800) 233-6712
Fax—(732) 287-8966
www.ferro.com
Email—info@ferro.com
Site Mgr.—Mike McKinney
Cust. Serv. Supv.—Roberta Wall
SIC—2865; 3253; 2851; NAICS—
325100; *Liquid & paste pigment,
polymer additives, tiles &
enamels*
Employs—30; Estab.—1985
Sales—$1Mil-$2.5Mil
Distrib.—Intl.
Publicly owned corporation
AKA: Ferro Liquid Colorants Div.
Parent co.—Ferro Corp., Mayfield
Heights, OH
Phone—(216) 875-5600
See Parent Co. Section for full profile.

**FIRST IMPRESSIONS SCREEN
PRINTING**
1703 State Route 27 (08817)
**Phone—(732) 777-7872**
National—(888) 498-7294
Fax—(732) 777-0488
www.first4tees.net

Email—first4tees@hotmail.com
Owner—Bill Miers
Prod. & Sales Mgr.—Karen Miers
SIC—2395; 2396; *Textile screen
printing & embroidery*
Employs—2; Estab.—1990
Sales—under $500,000
2,500 sq ft site, Distrib.—Intl.
Sole ownership

**FOREMOST WOOD PRODUCTS**
191 Vineyard Rd. (08817)
**Phone—(718) 447-5836**
Fax—(718) 447-5849
www.foremostwood.com
Email—sales@foremostwood.com
Pres.—John Autovino
SIC—2431; NAICS—321900;
*Wooden products, including
doors & door components*
Employs—5; Estab.—1990
Sales—$500,000-$1Mil
Distrib.—National
Privately owned corporation
AKA: Edison Finishing

**FUJIFILM U.S.A., INC.**
Div. of FUJIFILM Holdings
America Corp.
1100 King Georges Post Rd.
(08837)
**Phone—(732) 857-3000**
National—(800) 659-3854
Fax—(732) 857-3496
www.fujifilmusa.com
Email—spires@fujifilmusa.com
Facility Mgr.—Theresa Collins
SIC—3861; 3679; *Professional &
consumer films, cameras &
digital imaging equipment,
including printers*
Employs—60; Estab.—2000
Sales—$10Mil-$25Mil (est)
Distrib.—Local
Publicly owned corporation
Parent co.—FUJIFILM Holdings
America Corp., Valhalla, NY
Phone—(914) 789-8100
See Parent Co. Section for full profile.

**FULLER CONSTRUCTION
PRODUCTS, INC., H.B.**
Div. of Fuller Co., H.B.
59 Brunswick Ave. (08817)
**Phone—(732) 287-8330**
Fax—(732) 287-9495
www.hbfuller.com
Email—inquiry@hbfuller.com
Facility Mgr.—Michael Emery
SIC—2899; 3255; *High-tech
surface preparation mortar,
grout, adhesive products &
accessories for the tile industry;
Brand name—TEC®; CHAPCO®*
Employs—23; Estab.—1887
Distrib.—Regional
Publicly owned corporation
Parent co.—Fuller Co., H.B., St.
Paul, MN
Phone—(651) 236-5900
See Parent Co. Section for full profile.

**FUTURETECH SYSTEMS, INC.**
515 Plainfield Ave., Ste. 101
(08817-2598)
**Phone—(732) 777-7355**
National—(800) 275-4414
Fax—(732) 777-7385
www.futuretec.com
Email—info@futuretec.com
Pres.—Perry NeJappa
Prodn. Mgr.—Arun Annamalai
Mktg. Mgr.—Bob Perry
Admn. Mgr.—Pat Way
SIC—3577; *Document
management systems*
Employs—7; Estab.—1991
Sales—under $500,000
Distrib.—Intl.
Privately owned corporation

**GARRATT-CALLAHAN CO.**
306 Talmadge Rd. (08817)
**Phone—(732) 287-2200**
Fax—(732) 287-1439
www.g-c.com
Email—information@g-c.com
Off. Mgr.—Tina Decicco
SIC—2899; *Water treatment
chemicals*
Employs—5; Estab.—1904
Sales—$500,000-$1Mil
Distrib.—National
Privately owned corporation
Parent co.—Garratt-Callahan Co.,
Burlingame, CA
Phone—(650) 697-5811
See Parent Co. Section for full profile.

**†GENERAL FLOOR, INC.**
Div. of General Floor Industries
777 New Durham Rd. (08817)
**Phone—(732) 603-6100**
Fax—(732) 603-6160
www.generalfloor.com
Email—info@generalfloor.com
Br. Mgr.—Raul Corrales
SIC—5023; 5031; *Wholesaler of
carpet, laminate, hardwood &
vinyl flooring*
Employs—4
Privately owned corporation
Parent co.—General Floor
Industries, Bellmawr, NJ
Phone—(856) 931-0012
See Parent Co. Section for full profile.

**†GENERAL PLUMBING SUPPLY, INC.**
980 New Durham Rd. (08817)
Mail addr: P.O. Box 980, Edison
(08818-0980)
**Phone—(732) 248-1000**
National—(800) 225-5478
Fax—(732) 248-8795
www.generalplumbingsupply.net
Email—JustinF@
generalplumbingsupply.net
Pres.—Bruce Tucker
V-P., GM—Joe Novak
V-P., Fin.—Gary Kuperstein
Dir., Mktg.—Justin Freedman
Br. Mgr.—Pat Saverino
Showroom Mgr.—Scott Pashaian
SIC—5074; 5075; *Distributor of
HVAC & plumbing equipment &
supplies*
Employs—50; Estab.—1910
Sales—$50Mil-$100Mil
100,000 sq ft site, Distrib.—
Regional
Privately owned sub-S corp.
AKA: GPS

**GLENMORE PLASTIC INDUSTRIES,
INC.**
115 Newfield Ave. (08837)
**Phone—(718) 649-7800**
Fax—(718) 257-2661
Pres.—Harold Lebwohl
Ex. V-P.—Steven Shell
SIC—3083; NAICS—326130;
*Plastic laminating*
Employs—25; Estab.—1977
40,000 sq ft site, Distrib.—
Regional
Privately owned corporation

**GLOBAL GRAPHICS, INC.**
1945 State Route 27, Ste. 5
(08817)
**Phone—(732) 287-9390**
Fax—(732) 650-9889
Email—chiweekly@yahoo.com
Pres.—Chen-Li Fang
SIC—2759; NAICS—323100;
*Commercial printing*
Employs—2; Estab.—1985
Sales—under $500,000
Distrib.—National
Privately owned corporation

GEOGRAPHICAL

## Edison—(cont.)

### GRANT & SONS, INC., WILLIAM

130 Fieldcrest Ave. (08837)
**Phone—(732) 225-9000**
Fax—(732) 225-0950
www.grantusa.com
Email—info@wgrantusa.com
IT Mgr.—Ray Focht
Hum. Res. Mgr.—Tom Green
SIC—2085; NAICS—312100;
*Distilled & blended liquors*
Employs—70; Estab.—1970
90,000 sq ft site, Distrib.—National
Privately owned corporation
Parent co.—Grant & Sons, Inc.,
William, New York, NY
Phone—(212) 246-1760
See Parent Co. Section for full profile.

### †GRAYBAR ELECTRIC CO., INC.

105 E. Crest Ave., Ste. 207
(08837)
**Phone—(973) 404-5555**
National—(800) 472-9227
Fax—(973) 404-1965
www.graybar.com
Email—info@graybar.com
Br. Mgr.—Scott Kennedy
Fin. Mgr.—Raquel Simoes
Administrator—Allison Tidey
SIC—5063; *Distributor of electrical
supplies, including wires,
cables, switches & connectors*
Employs—60; Estab.—2005
Distrib.—National
Privately owned corporation
Parent co.—Graybar Electric Co.,
Inc., St. Louis, MO
Phone—(314) 573-9200
See Parent Co. Section for full profile.

### GUJARAT SAMACHAR

3 State Route 27, Ste. 307 (08820)
**Phone—(732) 452-1755**
Fax—(732) 452-1756
www.gujaratsamachar.com
Email—editor@
gujaratsamachar.com
Manager—Harshad Patel
SIC—2711; *Newspaper
publishing for the Indian
diaspora*
Employs—1
Sales—under $500,000 (est)
Distrib.—National
Privately owned corporation

### HANGER PROSTHETICS & ORTHOTICS, INC.

Div. of Hanger, Inc.
265 Fernwood Ave. (08837)
**Phone—(732) 417-0480**
Fax—(732) 417-4490
www.hanger.com
Email—info@hanger.com
Practice Mgr.—Robert Austin
Off. Admn.—Brittany Irizarry
SIC—3842; *Prosthetic & orthotic
appliances, including braces &
artificial arms & legs*
Employs—6; Estab.—1993
Distrib.—Local
Publicly owned corporation
Parent co.—Hanger, Inc., Austin,
TX
Phone—(512) 777-3800
See Parent Co. Section for full profile.

### HORIBA SCIENTIFIC

Div. of Horiba Instruments, Inc.
3880 Park Ave. (08820)
**Phone—(732) 494-8660**
National—(866) 562-4698
Fax—(732) 549-5125
www.horiba.com/scientific
Email—info.sci@horiba.com
Pres.—Steve Slutter
Chief Technical Officer—Sal Atzeni
V-P., Sales—Andrew Whitley
Mktg. Mgr.—Joanne Lowy
SIC—3826; NAICS—334516;
*Analytical instruments for
scientific research &
development & quality control,
including elemental analyzers,
fluorescence, forensics, particle
characterization, Raman,
spectroscopic ellipsometry,
sulfur-in-oil, XRF & OEM
spectrometers; Brand name—
HORIBA Scientific; HORIBA
Instruments; Jobin Yvon; SPEX;
IBH; HORIBA Jobin Yvon*
Employs—130; Estab.—1953
Sales—$10Mil-$25Mil
Distrib.—Intl.
Publicly owned corporation
ISO rating—9001
Parent co.—Horiba Instruments,
Inc., Troy, MI
Phone—(248) 689-9000
See Parent Co. Section for full profile.

### HOWMAN ASSOCS., INC.

12 Garden St. (08817)
Mail addr: P.O. Box 1365, Edison
(08818)
**Phone—(732) 985-7474**
National—(800) 526-2767
Fax—(732) 985-3164
www.howman.com
Email—sales@howman.com
Pres.—Howard Rood
Sales Mgr.—Andy Acton
Off. Mgr.—Jeff Rood
SIC—3613; NAICS—335313;
*Electrical control panels*
Employs—8; Estab.—1977
Sales—$1Mil-$2.5Mil
5,000 sq ft site, Distrib.—Intl.
Privately owned corporation
AKA: Howman Controls

### HUBER CORP., J.M. (H Q)

499 Thornall St., 8th Fl. (08837)
**Phone—(732) 549-8600**
www.huber.com
Email—webmaster@huber.com
Pres., CEO—Michael Marberry
CFO—Jeff Prosinski
CIO—Vincent Solano
Chief Comms. & Pub. Affs.
Officer—Robert Currie
Gen. Counsel—Carol Messer
Sr. Corp. Comms. Mgr.—Caroline
Langer
SIC—2499; 2899; 3295;
*Corporate headquarters;
hydrocolloids, specialty
chemicals & minerals &
engineered wood products*
Employs—65; Estab.—1883
Sales—$2.5Bil
Privately owned corporation

### †IBOCO CORP.

26 Northfield Ave. (08837)
**Phone—(732) 417-0066**
Fax—(732) 417-1166
www.iboco.com
Email—iboco@iboco.com
Pres.—Larry M. Darst
Mktg. Mgr.—Mark Keitel
Accountant—Jane Luo
SIC—5063; 5051; *Distributor of
wire duct, din rail & wire
management products*
Employs—12; Estab.—1986
Distrib.—Local
Privately owned corporation

### IMPORTERS SERVICE CORP.

65 Brunswick Ave. (08817)
**Phone—(732) 248-1946**
Fax—(732) 248-1949
www.iscgums.com
Email—iscgums@iscgums.com
Pres.—Eric Berliner
Hum. Res. Mgr.—Arlene Ramoo
SIC—2099; *Food ingredients*
Employs—40; Estab.—1995
Sales—$11Mil-$25Mil
Distrib.—National
Privately owned corporation

### ISOMETRIC MICRO FINISHING COATING

122 James St. (08820)
Mail addr: P.O. Box 2129, Edison
(08818-2129)
**Phone—(732) 906-8070**
www.isometriccoating.com
Email—leo@isometriccoating.com
Pres.—Roy Leo
SIC—3544; 3479; 3471; NAICS—
333500; *Metal coating & tool &
die polishing job shop*
Employs—6; Estab.—1953
Sales—$500,000-$1Mil
Distrib.—Intl.
Privately owned corporation

### IT AMERICA, INC.

100 Metroplex Dr., Ste. 207
(08817)
**Phone—(732) 985-5100**
Fax—(732) 909-2172
www.itamerica.com
V-P.—Praveen Thadakamalla
Hum. Res. Exec.—Bunty Arora
SIC—7373; NAICS—541512;
*Computer business operations
management integrated systems*
Employs—2; Estab.—2004
Sales—under $500,000
Distrib.—National
Privately owned corporation

### JOHNS MANVILLE

1000 Liddle Ave. (08837)
**Phone—(732) 225-9190**
National—(800) 255-6685
Fax—(732) 225-3539
www.jm.com
Email—webmaster@jm.com
Plt. Mgr.—Mark Sessler
Off. Mgr.—Jan Wierzbowski
SIC—3089; 3081; NAICS—
326113; *Fiberglass insulation &
plastic coverings*
Employs—50; Estab.—1958
Distrib.—Intl.
Publicly owned corporation
Parent co.—Johns Manville,
Denver, CO
Phone—(303) 978-2000
See Parent Co. Section for full profile.

### KAIZEN TECHNOLOGIES, INC.

1 State Route 27, Ste. 10 (08820)
**Phone—(732) 452-9555**
Fax—(732) 452-9559
www.kaizentek.com
Email—contact@kaizentek.com
Pres.—Ashok Krish
IT Mgr.—Vijay Patil
Hum. Res. Mgr.—Sandhya
Pramod
SIC—7373; NAICS—541512; *CAD
engineering computer integrated
systems*
Employs—72; Estab.—1995
Sales—$11Mil-$25Mil
Distrib.—Intl.
Privately owned corporation

### NEW ENTRY
### KEY JOY USA, LLC

3 Kellogg Ct., Ste. 12 (08817)
**Phone—(732) 339-0450**
Fax—(732) 339-0430
www.kjusa.net
Email—sales@kjusa.net
Regional Mgr.—Jerry Huang
SIC—3679; *Computer cable
assemblies & wire harnesses for
notebook PCs*
Employs—15
Sales—$1Mil-$2.5Mil (est)
Distrib.—Intl.
AKA: Key Joy International & KJ
USA

### †KTK CORP.

65 Midvale Rd. (08817)
Mail addr: P.O. Box 1394, Edison
(08818-1394)
**Phone—(732) 985-0447**
Fax—(732) 985-2006
www.ktkcorp.com
Email—ktk985@aol.com
Pres.—Joseph Kapler
V-P.—Carmella Toth
Bus. & Ex. Off. & Sales Mgr.—
Loretta Kapler
SIC—5085; *Distributor of steel,
fiber & plastic drums & pails*
Employs—5; Estab.—1971
Distrib.—Local
Privately owned corporation

### †KUMAR & KUMAR, INC.

57 Denise Dr. (08820)
**Phone—(732) 322-0435**
Fax—(270) 675-3896
www.kumarandkumar.net
Email—asood@kumarandkumar.net
Pres.—Ashish Sood
GM—Raj Kar
SIC—5013; *Distributor of
machined forging & casting
parts made from iron, steel &
aluminum for the railway & track
fitting, garage tools &
automobile, truck & trailer
suspension & exhaust; material
handling & agriculture machinery
parts industries*
Employs—5; Estab.—2001
Sales—$1Mil-$2.5Mil
Distrib.—National
Privately owned sub-S corp.

### KWALITY FOODS, LLC

1734 Oak Tree Rd. (08820)
**Phone—(732) 906-1941**
(888) 592-5489
Fax—(908) 757-2749
www.kwalityfoods.com
Email—kanti@kwalityfoods.com
Member—Kanti Parekh
Manager—Pankaj Patel
SIC—2024; *All-natural handmade
ethnic flavored ice cream in
cups, pints & half gallon, 1.5-
gallon & 3-gallon tubs; Brand
name—kwality*
Employs—5; Estab.—2002
Sales—$1Mil-$2.5Mil
Distrib.—National
Limited Liability Company

### †LABNET INTERNATIONAL, INC.

Div. of Corning, Inc.
31 Mayfield Ave. (08837)
Mail addr: P.O. Box 841,
Woodbridge (07095)
**Phone—(732) 417-0700**
National—(888) 522-6381
Fax—(732) 417-1750
www.labnetlink.com
Email—labnet@labnetlink.com
Pres.—Gerry Cooney
Off. Mgr.—Mark Zollar
Cust. Serv. Rep.—Megan
Chapman
SIC—5049; 5162; *Distributor of
laboratory centrifuges, plastics,
liquid handling instruments &
molecular biology products*
Employs—40; Estab.—1984
Sales—$25Mil-$50Mil
Distrib.—Intl.
Publicly owned corporation
Parent co.—Corning, Inc.,
Corning, NY
Phone—(607) 974-9000
See Parent Co. Section for full profile.

### LAIRD PLASTICS, INC.

135 Fieldcrest Ave., Ste. 135-F
(08837)
Mail addr: 1650 Republic Rd.,
Huntingdon Valley (19006-1808)
**Phone—(732) 593-2777**
Fax—(732) 593-2781

## Edison—(cont.)

www.lairdplastics.com
Email—edison@lairdplastics.com
GM—J. J. Duberville
Sales Mgr.—Stephen M. Biondy
Asst. Mgr.—John D. Compton
SIC—3081; 3082; 3089; NAICS—
326199; *Plastic see-thru,
mechanical & corrosive sheets,
rods, tubes & plastic digital
media & graphics products,
substrates & accessories*
Employs—20; Estab.—1955
Sales—$8Mil
42,000 sq ft site, Distrib.—National
Privately owned corporation
Parent co.—Laird Plastics, Inc.,
Boca Raton, FL
Phone—(561) 443-9100
See Parent Co. Section for full profile.

### LAWLER MFG. CORP.

7 Kilmer Ct. (08817)
**Phone—(732) 777-2040**
Fax—(732) 777-4828
www.lawlercorp.com
Email—info@lawlercorp.com
Pres., CFO—Mark Cekada
Sales Mgr.—Chris Maglasang
SIC—3829; *Fuels & lubricants
testing equipment*
Employs—15; Estab.—1945
8,300 sq ft site, Distrib.—Intl.
Privately owned corporation

### LIVINGSTON & W, INC.

973-B New Durham Rd. *(08817)*
Mail addr.—P.O. Box 496, Edison
(08818-0496)
**Phone—(732) 287-5790**
Fax—(732) 287-5793
Email—livwil@optimum.net
Pres.—Scott James
SIC—3599; *CNC & general
machining job shop*
Employs—4; Estab.—1946
Sales—$1Mil-$2Mil
10,000 sq ft site, Distrib.—Intl.
Privately owned sub-S corp.
ISO rating—9000

### LOOK OF LOVE INTERNATIONAL (H Q)

1795-B Route 27 S. (08817)
**Phone—(908) 687-9502**
National—(800) 526-7627
Fax—(908) 687-9509
www.lookoflove.com
Email—lookoflove@lookoflove.com
Pres.—Robert A. Anzivino
Dir., Adv.—Mo Hefnawy
SIC—3999; *Company
headquarters; women's
hairpieces & wigs (mfg. done in
China)*
Employs—15; Estab.—1967
Sales—under $500,000
4,000 sq ft site, Distrib.—National
Privately owned corporation

### LOTITO FOODS, INC./MRS. MAZZULA FOODS

240 Carter Dr. *(08817)*
**Phone—(732) 248-0222**
Fax—(732) 248-0442
www.lotitofoods.com
Email—info@lotitofoods.com
Pres.—Christopher Lotito
Cont.—Greg Natchez
Prodn. Mgr.—Patricia Sanchez
IT Mgr.—Carol LoPinto
Procurement Mgr.—Stephen
LoPinto
SIC—2022; 2034; NAICS—
311513; *Corporate headquarters
& cheese & sun-dried tomato
products*
Employs—200
Sales—$25Mil-$50Mil
52,000 sq ft site, Distrib.—Intl.

### LUMINAIRE LIGHTING CORP.

5 Sutton Pl. (08817)
Mail addr.—P.O. Box 2104, Edison
(08818)
**Phone—(732) 549-0056**
Fax—(732) 549-9737
www.luminairelighting.com
Email—info@luminairelighting.com
Ptnr.—Joe Lipson
Ptnr.—Ron Lipson
Cust. Serv. Rep.—Joyce
Wackenhut
SIC—3646; NAICS—335122;
*Industrial lighting fixtures*
Employs—10; Estab.—1976
Sales—$11Mil-$25Mil
Distrib.—Intl.
Privately owned corporation

### LYONDELLBASELL INDUSTRIES

340 Meadow Rd. (08817)
**Phone—(732) 777-2272**
Fax—(732) 777-2203
www.lyondellbasell.com
Email—info@lyondellbasell.com
Plt. Mgr.—David Schutka
Hum. Res. Mgr.—Josh Seidner
SIC—2819; 2869; *Chemicals*
Employs—65; Estab.—1984
Sales—$11Mil-$25Mil
Distrib.—Intl.
Publicly owned corporation
Parent co.—LyondellBasell
Industries, Houston, TX
Phone—(713) 652-7200
See Parent Co. Section for full profile.

### †M S INTERNATIONAL, INC.

Div. of MS International, Inc.
36 Brunswick Ave. (08817)
**Phone—(732) 650-1815**
Fax—(732) 650-1816
www.msistone.com
Email—msi_nj@msistone.com
Br. Mgr.—Kirit Shah
Manager—Loc Nguyen
SIC—5032; *Distributor of natural
stone, including granite, marble,
onyx & limestone*
Employs—15; Estab.—1975
Distrib.—National
Privately owned corporation
AKA: MSI
Parent co.—MS International, Inc.,
Orange, CA
Phone—(714) 685-7500
See Parent Co. Section for full profile.

### MACHINE TECH

3125 Woodbridge Ave., Ste. 4
(08837)
**Phone—(732) 738-6810**
Fax—(732) 738-6845
Email—mtigordon@yahoo.com
Owner—Gordon Scala
SIC—3599; *Precision & CNC
machining job shop*
Employs—4; Estab.—2003
Sales—$500,000-$1Mil
3,000 sq ft site, Distrib.—National
Sole ownership

### MAESTRO TECHNOLGIES, INC.

510 Thornall St., Ste. 375 (08837)
**Phone—(908) 458-8600**
www.maestro.com
Email—info@maestro.com
Mng. Dir.—Kamal S. Bathla
Hum. Res. Coord.—Ashmi Patel
SIC—7373; 7372; *Software
development & computer &
network systems integration,
including LANs, WANs & IT
consulting service*
Employs—54
Distrib.—Regional
Sole ownership

### MAIN ATTRACTIONS, INC.

85 Newfield Ave. (08837)
**Phone—(732) 225-3500**
National—(800) 394-3500
Fax—(732) 225-2110

www.mainattractions.com
Email—rsconda@
mainattractions.com
Pres.—Rocky Sconda
Off. Admn.—Theresa Ascolese
SIC—2394; NAICS—314912;
*Canvas products*
Employs—35; Estab.—1952
Distrib.—National
Privately owned corporation
AKA: Sconda Canvas Products

### MARK ARCHITECTURAL LIGHTING

Div. of Acuity Brands Lighting, Inc.
3 Kilmer Rd. (08817)
**Phone—(732) 985-2600**
National—(800) 526-6280
Fax—(732) 985-8441
www.marklighting.com
Email—info@marklighting.com
Pres.—Tim O'Brien
Cust. Serv. Mgr.—George Miller
Proj. Mgr.—Donna Sumner
SIC—3646; NAICS—335122;
*Commercial lighting fixtures*
Employs—120; Estab.—1979
150,000 sq ft site, Distrib.—Local
Publicly owned corporation
Parent co.—Acuity Brands
Lighting, Inc., Conyers, GA
Phone—(770) 922-9000
See Parent Co. Section for full profile.

### MAVERICK INDUSTRIES, INC.

94 Mayfield Ave. (08837)
**Phone—(732) 417-9666**
National—(800) 526-0954
Fax—(732) 417-9673
www.maverickhousewares.com
Email—info@
maverickhousewares.com
Pres.—Edward Mackin
Ex. V-P., Sales & Mktg.—Peter
Chapman
Opers. Mgr.—Darren Keller
Off. Mgr.—Jeanette Castro
Cust. Serv. Rep.—Nicki Deol
SIC—3631; 3634; NAICS—
335221; *Specialty kitchen &
barbecue appliances,
thermometers & accessories;
Brand name—Maverick*
Employs—10; Estab.—1981
Sales—$6Mil-$10Mil
900 sq ft site, Distrib.—National
Privately owned corporation

### MENTISSOFT, INC.

347 Plainfield Ave., Ste. 104
(08817)
**Phone—(732) 568-4715**
Fax—(732) 568-4763
www.mentissoft.com
Email—info@mentissoft.com
V-P.—Jeevesh Murthy
SIC—7372; *Software
development for retail,
healthcare & educational
applications*
Employs—3; Estab.—2009
Privately owned corporation

### METAL TEXTILES CORP.

Div. of United Capital Corp.
970 New Durham Rd. (08818)
**Phone—(732) 287-0800**
National—(800) 222-0969
Fax—(732) 248-8739
www.metexcorp.com
Email—sales@metexcorp.com
Pres.—Greg Vongas
V-P., Sales—Joseph Hodonski
Cont.—Rob Goldfarb
Dir., Prod.—George Walsh
IT Mgr.—Umesh Tevar
Hum. Res. Mgr.—Cathy Crawford
Benefits Mgr.—Gregory Edwards
SIC—3496; *Wire mesh filtration
gaskets*
Employs—190; Estab.—1981
Sales—$101Mil-$1Bil
55,000 sq ft site, Distrib.—Intl.
Privately owned corporation

Parent co.—United Capital Corp.,
Great Neck, NY
Phone—(516) 466-6464
See Parent Co. Section for full profile.

### MODEL RECTIFIER CORP.

80 Newfield Ave., P.O. Box 6312
(08837)
**Phone—(732) 225-2100**
Fax—(732) 225-0091
www.modelrectifier.com
Email—support@modelrectifier.com
Pres.—Frank Ritota
V-P.—Akiko Kimura
V-P.—Donald Boyce
SIC—3944; *Hobby & toy products
& remote control cars & train sets*
Employs—30; Estab.—1947
Sales—$2.5Mil-$5Mil (est)
Distrib.—National
Privately owned corporation

### †MODERN GROUP LTD.

75 New St. (08837)
**Phone—(800) 846-5840**
(732) 738-9200
Fax—(732) 738-4077
www.moderngroup.com
Email—webmaster@
moderngroup.com
Br. Mgr., Forklifts—Jerry Hagen
Serv. Mgr., Construction—Paul
Van Nocker
SIC—5052; 5084; *Distributor of
construction, industrial material
handling & warehouse
equipment*
Employs—25; Estab.—1946
Distrib.—Local
Privately owned corporation
Parent co.—Modern Group Ltd.,
Bristol, PA
Phone—(215) 943-9100
See Parent Co. Section for full profile.

### †MSC INDUSTRIAL SUPPLY CO.

Div. of MSC Industrial Direct Co.,
Inc.
105 Newfield Ave., Ste. E (08837)
**Phone—(732) 512-9555**
National—(800) 288-7270
Fax—(732) 512-9595
www.mscdirect.com
Email—branchken@mscdirect.com
Mktg. Mgr.—David Bothe
Sales Rep.—Kathleen Pryor
Sales Rep., Inside—Rosa Madera
SIC—5084; 5085; *Wholesaler of
industrial equipment & supplies*
Employs—15; Estab.—1967
Sales—$1Mil-$2.5Mil
Distrib.—Local
Publicly owned corporation
Parent co.—MSC Industrial Direct
Co., Inc., Melville, NY
Phone—(516) 812-2000
See Parent Co. Section for full profile.

### NETCOM SYSTEMS, INC.

200 Metroplex Dr. (08817)
**Phone—(732) 393-6100**
Fax—(732) 393-6190
www.netcom-sys.com
Pres.—Niten Ved
Cont.—Mona Ved
SIC—7372; *Software
development*
Employs—20; Estab.—1996
Distrib.—National
Privately owned corporation

### NEWARK WIRE WORKS, INC.

1059 King Georges Post Rd., Ste.
103 (08837)
**Phone—(732) 661-2001**
Fax—(732) 661-2003
www.newarkwireworks.com
Email—sales@
newarkwireworks.com
Pres.—JoAnn Spellman
V-P.—Joseph P. Spellman
V-P.—J. Michael Spellman

## Edison—(cont.)

SIC—3496; 3499; 3442; 3444; *Architectural wire mesh panels & fabricated metal products, including partitions, doors, sliding gates, railing in-fill panels, tenant storage cages, garage lockers & window guards*
Employs—16; Estab.—1910
Sales—$2.5Mil
24,000 sq ft site, Distrib.—Intl.
Privately owned partnership

### NOVEMBAL U. S. A., A TETRA PAK CO.

Div. of Tetra Pak, Inc.
3 Greek Ln. (08817)
**Phone—(732) 287-4949**
Fax—(732) 287-1053
www.novembal.com
Email—kathy.litchkowski@ tetrapak.com
Plt. Mgr.—John Famiglietti
Off. Mgr.—Denise Buzzelli
Cust. Serv. Supv.—Kathy Litchkowski
SIC—3089; *Plastic bottle closures (caps) for the major North American water companies*
Employs—62; Estab.—1997
82,000 sq ft site, Distrib.—National
Privately owned corporation
ISO rating—9001:2000
Parent co.—Tetra Pak, Inc., Denton, TX
Phone—(940) 565-8800
See Parent Co. Section for full profile.

### OFFICEMATE INTERNATIONAL CORP.

90 Newfield Ave. (08837)
Mail addr.: P.O. Box 6680, Edison (08818-6680)
**Phone—(732) 225-7422**
National—(800) 221-0400
Fax—(732) 225-0438
www.officemate.com
Email—oic@officemate.com
Cont.—Roger Ko
Cust. Serv. Rep.—Sharon Kiefer
SIC—2499; *Office supplies*
Employs—100; Estab.—1978
Sales—$10Mil-$25Mil
Distrib.—National
Privately owned corporation

### OMNI W.C., INC.

166 National Rd. (08817)
**Phone—(732) 248-0999**
Fax—(732) 248-0930
www.omniwcinc.com
Email—info@omniwcinc.com
Pres., Fin. & GM—Gary Tumminello
V-P., R & D—Nino Pasqua
MIS Mgr.—Yvette Kroh
Collections Mgr.—Ann Pagello
SIC—2621; 3089; NAICS—322100; *Paper & vinyl wall coverings*
Employs—18; Estab.—1983
33,000 sq ft site, Distrib.—National
Privately owned partnership

### OSI LASER DIODE, INC.

Div. of OSI Systems, Inc.
4 Olsen Ave. (08820)
**Phone—(732) 549-9001**
Fax—(732) 906-1559
www.laserdiode.com
Email—sales@osilaserdiodes.com
GM—Rollin Ball
Mfg. Mgr.—Larry Datel
Hum. Res. Mgr.—Bernie Parkhurst
Qual. Assur. Mgr.—Laura Vasilantone
Cust. Serv. Admn.—Christine Base

SIC—3674; NAICS—334413; *Semiconductor lasers & telecommunication receivers*
Employs—50; Estab.—1967
Sales—$12Mil
50,000 sq ft site, Distrib.—Intl.
Publicly owned corporation
Parent co.—OSI Systems, Inc., Hawthorne, CA
Phone—(310) 978-0516
See Parent Co. Section for full profile.

### OYSTAR USA, INC.

523 Raritan Centre S.W. (08837)
**Phone—(732) 343-7600**
National—(800) 722-8001
Fax—(732) 343-7601
www.oystarusa.com
Email—sales@oystarusa.com
IT Mgr.—Brian McNamara
Bookkeeper—Debbie Wallach
SIC—3565; NAICS—333993; *Packaging machinery*
Employs—47; Estab.—1988
Distrib.—Intl.
Privately owned corporation

### †PANZA & SONS, LTD., A.

141 Fieldcrest Ave. (08837)
**Phone—(732) 225-1314**
Fax—(732) 225-0021
www.icecreamproducts.com
Email—info@icecreamproducts.com
Pres.—Vito Panza
V-P., Opers.—Steven Panza
V-P., Pur.—Christopher Panza
Cust. Serv. Specialist—Wayne Happel
SIC—5143; *Stocking distributor of ice cream mixes, yogurt mixes, toppings, syrups & ingredients for making ice cream for the soft-serve & hard-serve ice cream industries; Brand name—Panza label; YoCream Yogurt; Honey Hill Yogurt; Jelly Belly Yogurt; Upstate Farms Yogurt*
Employs—70; Estab.—1965
Sales—$32Mil
80,000 sq ft site, Distrib.—Intl.
Privately owned sub-S corp.
AKA: The Ice Cream & Yogurt Professionals

### PHARMEDIUM

Div. of PharMEDium Services, LLC
43 Distribution Blvd. (08817)
**Phone—(732) 287-8655**
National—(800) 523-7749
Fax—(732) 287-8651
www.pharmedium.com
Email—wkelso@pharmedium.com
IT Mgr.—Chris Lee
Hum. Res. Mgr.—Nancy Brand
Center Mgr.—Walter Kelso
Cust. Serv. Specialist—Roger Hilton
Cust. Serv. Specialist—Mike Spoula
SIC—2834; NAICS—325412; *Sterile pharmaceutical compounding*
Employs—25; Estab.—1997
Distrib.—National
Privately owned corporation
Parent co.—PharMEDium Services, LLC, Lake Forest, IL
Phone—(847) 457-2300
See Parent Co. Section for full profile.

### PHOTON TECHNOLOGY INTERNATIONAL

3880 Park Ave. (08820)
**Phone—(732) 494-8660**
Fax—(732) 549-5125
www.pti-nj.com
Email—marketing@pti-nj.com
Chrm., Pres. & CEO—Charles G. Marianik
V-P., Secy.—Ronald J. Kovach

SIC—3825; NAICS—334500; *Fluorescence instrumentation for industry, medicine & research*
Employs—15; Estab.—1983
Sales—$5Mil-$10Mil
10,000 sq ft site, Distrib.—Intl.
Publicly owned corporation

### PICTURE-IT, INC.

1703 State Route 27 (08817)
**Phone—(732) 819-0420**
Fax—(732) 572-4216
www.pictureitawards.com
Email—service@ pictureitawards.com
Pres.—Roy Taetzsch
SIC—3089; 3231; 2499; 3479; NAICS—323100; *Acrylic, crystal, glass & wooden awards, plaques, signs & promotional products & engraving*
Employs—5; Estab.—1981
Sales—under $500,000
4,000 sq ft site, Distrib.—Regional
Privately owned sub-S corp.

### PROGRESS DISPLAY, INC.

39 Progress St. (08820)
**Phone—(908) 757-6650**
Ptnr.—Doug Forrestal
Pres.—Roger L. Robinson
Off. Mgr.—Diane Robinson
SIC—2653; NAICS—322211; *Corrugated paperboard displays*
Employs—10; Estab.—1992
Sales—under $500,000
Distrib.—National
Privately owned corporation
Also see: Dirory Industries, Inc., same loc.

### RAND DIVERSIFIED

3 Ethel Rd., Ste. 301 (08817)
**Phone—(732) 287-2525**
National—(888) 992-8200
Fax—(732) 287-2511
www.rand-div.com
Email—info@rand-div.com
Chrm.—Jack Wuensch
CEO—Stuart Sklovsky
Pres.—John Padovano
CFO—David Kauffman
COO—Don Garda
Ex. V-P., Sales—Brian Mumau
SIC—2541; 2542; 3993; *Company headquarters & point-of-purchase displays & packaging, including design, engineering, production, assembly, fulfillment, warehousing & distribution*
Employs—40; Estab.—1972
Sales—$110Mil
Distrib.—National
Limited Liability Company

### RIGHTANSWERS, INC.

333 Thornall St., Ste. 703 (08837)
**Phone—(732) 396-9010**
Fax—(732) 396-9011
www.rightanswers.com
Email—sales@rightanswers.com
Pres., CEO—Jeff Weinstein
V-P., Sales—Bill Pollie
V-P., Prof. Svcs.—Keith Berg
V-P., Prod. Mgmt.—Simon Yelsky
Dir., Mktg.—Veronica Mathieson
Dir., Client Success—Tom Policano
Mktg. Mgr.—Stefanie Lourenco
SIC—7372; *Software development*
Employs—50; Estab.—2002
Distrib.—Intl.
Privately owned corporation

### RIMEX METALS (USA) INC

2850 Woodbridge Ave. (08837)
**Phone—(732) 549-3800**
National—(800) 526-7600
Fax—(732) 549-6435
www.rimexmetals.com
Email—sales@rimexusa.com
Pres.—John Horbal
Sales Mgr.—Bruce Kardos

SIC—3479; *Metal finishes for architecture, interior, retail & industrial design applications; Brand name—Treadtex; Colourtex; Granex Bead Blast; MetalArt; 5-SM/5-WL; 6-OM/ 6WL; OneTex*
Employs—25; Estab.—1982
Sales—$20Mil
34,000 sq ft site, Distrib.—Intl.
Privately owned corporation

### ROCKWELL AUTOMATION, INC.

165 Fieldcrest Ave., Raritan Ctr. (08837)
**Phone—(732) 225-1360**
Fax—(732) 225-7833
www.rockwellautomation.com
Email—webmaster@rockwell.com
Regional Mgr.—Werny Castro
Proj. Mgr.—Joe Mendoker
SIC—3625; NAICS—335314; *AC & DC variable-speed drives*
Employs—15; Estab.—1978
Sales—$2.5Mil-$5Mil
Distrib.—Intl.
Publicly owned corporation
Parent co.—Rockwell Automation, Inc., Milwaukee, WI
Phone—(414) 382-2000
See Parent Co. Section for full profile.

### †ROMA MOULDING, INC.

115 Northfield Ave. (08837)
**Phone—(732) 346-0999**
National—(800) 554-0376
Fax—(732) 346-0223
www.romamoulding.com
Email—info@romamoulding.com
Manager—Barry Zimmerman
SIC—5199; *Distributor of picture frame moulding*
Employs—15; Estab.—1978
50,000 sq ft site, Distrib.— Regional
Privately owned corporation
Parent co.—Roma Moulding, Inc.
Phone—(905) 850-1500
See Parent Co. Section for full profile.

### S & S MFG., INC.

115 Fieldcrest Ave. (08837)
**Phone—(732) 698-2400**
Fax—(732) 662-5046
www.handrails.com
GM—Steve Silverman
SIC—3446; NAICS—332323; *Aluminum & brass railings*
Employs—45; Estab.—1985
Distrib.—Local
Privately owned corporation

### S L M MFG. CORP.

47 Langstaff Ave. (08817)
Mail addr.: P.O. Box 5607, Somerset (08875)
**Phone—(732) 469-7500**
National—(800) 526-3708
www.slmcorp.com
Email—tvajtay@slmcorp.com
Pres.—Thomas Vajtay
SIC—3089; *Transparent semi-rigid, collapsible plastic containers*
Employs—8; Estab.—1950
Sales—$1Mil-$5Mil
10,000 sq ft site, Distrib.—National
Privately owned corporation

### SAKAR INTERNATIONAL, INC. (H Q)

195 Carter Dr. (08817)
**Phone—(732) 248-1306**
Fax—(732) 248-1796
www.sakar.com
Email—sales@sakar.com
CEO—Charles Saka
Pres.—Jeff Saka
V-P., Sales & Mktg.—Stefan Betesh
Dir., Licensing—Liza Abrams
Mktg. Mgr.—Ralph Sasson

## Edison—(cont.)

SIC—3861; 3575; NAICS—334113; *Corporate headquarters; consumer electronics equipment & supplies, including digital cameras, MP3 players & computer accessories (mfg. done overseas)*
Employs—75; Estab.—1978
Sales—$25Mil-$50Mil (est)
Distrib.—Intl.
Privately owned corporation

**SCHAFFNER EMC, INC.**
52 Mayfield Ave. (08837)
**Phone—(732) 225-9533**
National—(800) 367-5566
Fax—(732) 225-4789
www.schaffnerusa.com
Email—usasales@schaffner.com
Pres.—Ken Bellero
Cont. & Hum. Res. Mgr.—Barbara Archiello
IT Mgr.—Phil Poland
Sales Admn.—Eileen Ayala
Sales Admn.—Amelia Gomez
SIC—3679; *Electronic components*
Employs—17; Estab.—1982
Distrib.—Intl.
Publicly owned corporation

**SCHUNDLER CO., INC.**
Div. of Normiska Corp.
150 Whitman Ave. (08817)
**Phone—(732) 287-2244**
          (732) 287-2246
Fax—(732) 287-4185
www.schundler.com
Email—info@schundler.com
Admn. & Sales Mgr.—Vikki Warman
Prodn. Mgr.—Grant Conaway
Opers. Mgr.—Mike Hellmann
SIC—3295; 1499; *Perlite & vermiculite aggregates & products, including special blends & mixes*
Employs—30; Estab.—1951
50,000 sq ft site, Distrib.—National
Privately owned corporation
Parent co.—Normiska Corp.
  Phone—(519) 780-0955
  See Parent Co. Section for full profile.

**SELECT ENTERPRISES, INC.**
71 Executive Ave. (08817)
Mail addr.: P.O. Box 1353, Edison (08818)
**Phone—(732) 287-8622**
Fax—(732) 287-8644
www.njpallet.com
Email—selectpallet@gmail.com
Pres.—Tom Lordi
SIC—2448; NAICS—321920; *Wooden pallets*
Employs—6; Estab.—1998
Sales—$500,000-$1Mil (est)
Distrib.—Local
Privately owned corporation

**SHEKIA GROUP, LLC, THE**
1130 King Georges Post Rd. (08837)
**Phone—(732) 372-7668**
Fax—(732) 372-7669
www.forevermarkcabinetry.com
Owner—Henry Linn
SIC—2434; *Wooden kitchen cabinets*
Employs—15
Sales—$1Mil-$2.5Mil (est)
Distrib.—National
Limited Liability Company

**SHIPSERV**
1090 King Georges Post Rd. (08837)
**Phone—(215) 862-3353**
www.marinersannual.com
Email—info@marinersannual.com
Editor—Don Staffin

SIC—2741; *International shipping & offshore drilling industries' product ordering guide publishing; Brand name—Mariner's Annual Ordering Guide*
Employs—6; Estab.—1958
Sales—under $500,000
Distrib.—Intl.
Privately owned corporation

**SILGAN CONTAINERS MFG. CORP.**
Div. of Silgan Containers, LLC
135 National Rd. (08817)
**Phone—(732) 287-0300**
Fax—(732) 287-5675
www.silgancontainers.com
Email—sales@silgancontainers.com
Off. Mgr.—Mayson Stewart
SIC—3411; NAICS—332431; *Steel cans*
Employs—120; Estab.—1987
180,000 sq ft site, Distrib.—National
Publicly owned corporation
Parent co.—Silgan Containers, LLC, Woodland Hills, CA
  Phone—(818) 710-3700
  See Parent Co. Section for full profile.

**SINO MONTHLY NEW JERSEY, INC.**
18 Sheppard Pl. (08817)
**Phone—(732) 650-0688**
Fax—(732) 650-7468
www.sino-monthly.com
Email—info@sino-monthly.com
Editor-in-Chief—Ivey Lee
Editor—May Lung
GM—Dana Wei
SIC—2721; *Chinese monthly magazine publishing*
Employs—5; Estab.—1991
Sales—under $500,000 (est)
Distrib.—Local
Privately owned corporation

**SIR SPEEDY PRINTING CENTER**
28 Campus Dr. (08837)
**Phone—(732) 225-2272**
Fax—(732) 225-2448
www.sirspeedy.com/edison
Email—orders@sirspeedyedison.com
Owner & Pres.—Robert Chido
Cust. Serv. Rep.—Jean Chido
Cust. Serv. Rep.—Charlene Wagner
SIC—2752; 2759; 2791; NAICS—323122; *Offset & digital printing & typesetting, including document services*
Employs—7; Estab.—1980
Sales—under $500,000
3,000 sq ft site, Distrib.—Local

**SMALL QUANTITIES NEW JERSEY, INC.**
66 Ethel Rd. *(08817)*
Mail addr.: P.O. Box 4167, Metuchen (08840-4167)
**Phone—(732) 248-9009**
Fax—(732) 248-9559
www.sqnji.com
Email—smallqnji@aol.com
Pres.—Harry Mathis
Cont.—Susan Hand
Plt. Mgr.—Wayne Bruck
Sales Rep.—Melissa Fazio
SIC—3321; NAICS—331511; *Metal stampings*
Employs—50; Estab.—1990
Sales—$5Mil-$10Mil
21,835 sq ft site, Distrib.—Intl.
Privately owned sub-S corp.

**SNOW JOE, LLC**
86 Executive Ave. (08817)
**Phone—(866) 766-9563**
Fax—(732) 248-1979
www.snowjoe.com
Email—service@snowjoe.com
Pres.—Joe Cohen

GM & Plt. Mgr.—Stephen Seldschuh
SIC—3524; *Lawn & garden equipment, including mowers, snow throwers, tillers, snow removal roof rakes, trimmers & edgers; Brand name—Snow Joe®; Sun Joe®*
Employs—25; Estab.—2001
Sales—$6Mil-$10Mil
Distrib.—Intl.
Limited Liability Company

**SPOTLESS SHADE, LLC**
1217 U.S. Highway 1 (08837)
**Phone—(732) 548-1714**
          (732) 548-1711
Fax—(732) 548-9782
www.spotlessshade.com
Email—spotlessshade@aol.com
Owner & GM—Scott Fitzgerald
SIC—2591; NAICS—337920; *Venetian & vertical blinds & window, pleated & cellular shades, including repair & cleaning services; Brand name—Hunter Douglas; Graber; Comfortex; GG Royal; Vista; Horizon Window Fashions*
Employs—5; Estab.—1946
Sales—$500,000-$1Mil
2,500 sq ft site, Distrib.—Local
Limited Liability Company

**STAPLES CONTRACT DIGITAL COPY SERVICES**
Div. of Staples, Inc.
258 Fernwood Ave. (08837)
**Phone—(732) 346-1377**
National—(866) 918-2679
Fax—(732) 346-1387
www.staplesdcs.com
Email—dcs2761@staplescopycenter.com
GM—Robert Zatorsky
SIC—2759; *Digital color, black & white & large-format printing*
Employs—20; Estab.—2006
Sales—$2.5Mil-$5Mil (est)
Distrib.—Local
Privately owned corporation
Parent co.—Staples, Inc., Framingham, MA
  Phone—(508) 253-5000
  See Parent Co. Section for full profile.

NEW ENTRY
†**STAR MICRONICS AMERICA, INC. (HQ)**
1150 King Georges Post Rd. (08837)
**Phone—(732) 623-5500**
National—(800) 782-7636
Fax—(732) 623-5590
www.starmicronics.com
Email—audiocomponents@star-us.com
Pres.—B. Aoki
Cont.—Steven Kowalek
Dir., Sales, Natl.—Christine Duffy
Dir., Opers.—Jeffrey St. John
IT Mgr.—Didoy Francisco
Hum. Res. Mgr.—Kim Coffey
SIC—5063; 5065; *Corporate headquarters; distributor of audio products & components, including microphones, speakers, receivers, headsets & transducers (mfg. done overseas)*
Employs—60; Estab.—1950
Sales—$6Mil-$10Mil
Distrib.—Intl.
Privately owned corporation

NEW ENTRY
**STEFANO FENCE SYSTEMS, INC.**
737 New Durham Rd. (08817)
**Phone—(732) 321-5050**
www.stefanofence.com
Owner—Stephen Smith
Off. Mgr.—Tina Tietchen

SIC—3444; 3089; *Aluminum architectural metalwork & vinyl fencing*
Employs—15
Sales—$1Mil-$2.5Mil (est)
Distrib.—Local
Privately owned corporation

**STERLING SYSTEM LLC**
22 Meridian Rd., Unit 10 (08820)
**Phone—(732) 452-1881**
Fax—(732) 767-0693
www.sterling-system.com
Email—nilesh@sterling-system.com
Pres. & Dir.—Sejal Dasondi
V-P.—Chuck Benvenuti
Dir.—Nilesh Dasondi
Acctg. Mgr.—Anu Prasad
SIC—7372; *Software development*
Employs—5; Estab.—2001
3,900 sq ft site, Distrib.—Intl.
Limited Liability Company

**STRIKEFORCE TECHNOLOGIES, INC.**
1090 King Georges Post Rd., Ste. 603 (08837)
**Phone—(732) 661-9641**
National—(866) 787-4542
Fax—(732) 661-9647
www.strikeforcetech.com
Email—info@strikeforcetech.com
CEO—Mark Kay
CTO—Ram Pemmaraju
Ex. V-P., Mktg.—George Waller
Software Developer—Ananth Rao
SIC—7372; *Identity protection software development*
Employs—7; Estab.—2001
Distrib.—Intl.

**SUPER STUD BUILDING PRODUCTS, INC.**
2960 Woodbridge Ave. (08837)
**Phone—(732) 662-6200**
Fax—(732) 548-6036
www.buysuperstud.com
Email—dkaiser@buysuperstud.com
Pres.—Ray Frobosilo, Sr.
V-P.—Ron Chase
Accts. Payable Mgr.—Linda Healy
Tech. Mgr.—Donna M. Kasier
SIC—3441; NAICS—332312; *Corporate headquarters & steel framing components*
Employs—200; Estab.—1973
Sales—$10Mil-$25Mil
Distrib.—Local
Privately owned corporation

†**SUPERIOR OFFICE SYSTEMS, INC.**
19 Gross Ave. (08837)
**Phone—(732) 738-0093**
Fax—(732) 738-4339
www.superiorofficenj.com
Email—apena@superiorofficenj.com
Pres.—Phil Blank
V-P.—Audra Pena
SIC—5044; 5045; 5065; *Distributor of office equipment, including copiers, printers & fax machines; Brand name—Canon; Sharp; KIP; Kyocera*
Employs—50; Estab.—1967
Sales—$9Mil
24,000 sq ft site, Distrib.—Regional
Privately owned corporation

**TCP RELIABLE, INC.**
551 Raritan Center Pkwy. (08837)
**Phone—(732) 346-9200**
Fax—(732) 346-0295
www.tcpreliable.com
Email—sales@tcpreliable.com
Pres., CEO—Maurice Barakat
Assoc. Technical Dir.—Anthony Alleva
Pur. Mgr.—Bernard Slaza
Qual. Assur. Mgr.—Rafael Forero
Fin. Mgr.—Anthony Spina

GEOGRAPHICAL

## Edison—(cont.)

SIC—3086; 2671; NAICS—326100; *Temperature control packaging; Brand name—Cryopak; DDL*
Employs—50; Estab.—1996
67,000 sq ft site, Distrib.—Intl.

**NEW ENTRY**

†**TELECO BUSINESS TELEPHONE SYSTEMS**
1883 State Route 27 (08817)
**Phone—(732) 777-7990**
National—(800) 835-3264
Fax—(800) 356-0953
www.teleco4.com
Email—info@teleco4.com
V-P. & Hum. Res. Mgr.—Andrew Taub
SIC—5065; *Distributor of business telephone systems*
Employs—15
Distrib.—National
Privately owned corporation

**TITAN CONVERTING**
150 Fieldcrest Ave., Ste. A (08837)
**Phone—(732) 225-2080**
Fax—(732) 225-0182
www.titanconverting.com
Email—carlmcnamara@titanconverting.com
Pres.—Carl McNamara
SIC—2952; NAICS—324122; *Asphalt & polyethylene-coated building facing papers, including asphalt-coated kraft, foil/kraft, foil/scrim/kraft & flangeless kraft papers*
Employs—10; Estab.—1995
Sales—$2.5Mil–$5Mil (est)
Distrib.—Intl.
Privately owned corporation

**UNIMED INTERNATIONAL, INC.**
105 Newfield Ave., Ste. F (08837-3825)
**Phone—(800) 754-6211**
Fax—(732) 417-5194
www.betterskintoday.com
Email—cs@unimedint.com
CEO—George Faltaous
V-P.—Sandy Faltaous
Opers. Mgr.—Christine Pileggi
SIC—2844; 2834; *All-natural antioxidant skin care & nutraceutical products*
Employs—20
Sales—$9Mil–$10Mil
Publicly owned corporation
AKA: Chamonix

**VICTORY INTERNATIONAL U. S. A., LLC**
75 Newfield Ave. (08837)
**Phone—(732) 417-1040**
Fax—(732) 417-5990
www.victoryinternational.net
Email—info@victoryinternational.net
Pres.—Anil K. Monga
Dir., Opers.—Gary Murphy
Ex. Admn.—April Conway
SIC—2844; NAICS—325600; *Perfumes*
Employs—10; Estab.—1985
Distrib.—National
Limited Liability Company

**VILS PHARMA, INC.**
135 Glendale Ave. (08817)
**Phone—(732) 777-6023**
Fax—(732) 777-9697
Co-Pres.—A. J. Upadhyay
Co-Pres.—Manju Upadhyay
SIC—2834; NAICS—325412; *Pharmaceutical coating*
Employs—5; Estab.—1995
Sales—$500,000–$1Mil
Distrib.—National
Privately owned corporation

**WOODSTOCK FARMS MFG.**
Div. of United Natural Foods, Inc.
96 Executive Ave. (08817)
**Phone—(732) 650-9905**
National—(800) 526-4349
Fax—(732) 650-9909
www.woodstockfarmsmfg.com
Hum. Res. Mgr.—Virginia Johnson
Cust. Serv. Rep.—Dawn Lewis
SIC—2034; 2068; NAICS—311911; *Organic, kosher & natural nuts, seeds, dried fruit & snacks*
Employs—120; Estab.—2002
Distrib.—National
Publicly owned corporation
Parent co.—United Natural Foods, Inc., Providence, RI
Phone—(401) 528-8634
See Parent Co. Section for full profile.

# Egg Harbor City
(Atlantic—S.E.)

**ACCENT FENCE, INC.**
1450 Bremen Ave., P.O. Box 656 (08215)
**Phone—(609) 965-6400**
Fax—(609) 965-6403
Email—jakeaccent@comcast.net
Pres.—Greg Carnasale
Corp. Secy.—Jake Shea
Proj. Mgr.—Abby Reyes
SIC—2499; 3499; NAICS—332323; *Wooden, metal & vinyl fences & ornamental ironwork*
Employs—20; Estab.—1990
Distrib.—Regional
Privately owned corporation

**ADVANCE TOOL & DIE, INC.**
1401 Bremen Ave. (08215)
**Phone—(856) 854-6329**
Fax—(856) 854-6263
Email—advanctool@aol.com
Pres., GM & Opers. Mgr.—Robert C. Sullivan
Machine Operator—Ricky Sullivan
SIC—3544; 3089; NAICS—333500; *Plastic injection molds & dies & plastic parts*
Employs—2; Estab.—1989
Sales—under $500,000
6,600 sq ft site, Distrib.—Intl.
Sole ownership

**COSTA MARINE CANVAS & ENCLOSURES, LLC**
1324 Moss Mill Rd. *(08215)*
**Phone—(609) 965-1538**
Fax—(609) 965-2625
www.costamarinecanvas.com
Email—info@costamarinecanvas.com
Owner—Donna Costa
GM—Chris Costa
SIC—2394; 2392; NAICS—314912; *Canvas boat covers, cushions, enclosures & coaming pads for marine interiors*
Employs—15; Estab.—1971
12,000 sq ft site, Distrib.—Intl.
Limited Liability Company

**DOLPHIN INDUSTRIES LTD.**
2141 River Rd., P.O. Box 344 (08215)
**Phone—(609) 965-5188**
Fax—(609) 965-5418
www.dolphinindustriesnj.com
Email—dolphinindustries@aol.com
Pres.—Antonio Pacheco
Off. Mgr.—Jimmy Brook
Off. Mgr.—Mary Lauer
SIC—3089; 3949; NAICS—339920; *Fiberglass swimming pools*
Employs—9; Estab.—1997
Sales—under $500,000
Distrib.—National
Privately owned corporation

**EGG HARBOR ROPE PRODUCTS, INC.**
5105 White Horse Pike, P.O. Box 294 (08215)
**Phone—(609) 965-2435**
Fax—(856) 547-6217
Pres.—Fred Good
SIC—2298; *Nylon rope & anchor & dock line for boats*
Employs—3; Estab.—1921
Sales—under $500,000
Distrib.—Regional
Privately owned corporation

**EGG HARBOR YACHTS**
801 Philadelphia Ave. (08215)
**Phone—(609) 965-2300**
www.silverton.com
Email—eggharborgroup@aol.com
Owner—Ira Trocki
Pres.—John Peterson
Sales & Mktg. Mgr.—Brett Marshall
SIC—3732; *33 feet-52 feet convertible, motor & sport bridge yachts; Brand name—Silverton Yachts; Ovation Yachts*
Employs—20; Estab.—1969
Distrib.—Intl.
Privately owned corporation
AKA: Silverton Marine

**JERSEY CAPE YACHTS**
2143 River Rd. (08215)
**Phone—(609) 965-8650**
Fax—(609) 965-7480
www.jerseycapeyachts.com
Email—info@jerseycapeyachts.com
Pres.—Wayne Puglise
Opers. Mgr.—Genine Puglise
SIC—3731; *Custom sportfishing yachts & marine dry-docking & yacht conversion, repair & storage; Brand name—Jersey Cape*
Employs—40; Estab.—1998
25,000 sq ft site, Distrib.—National
Privately owned corporation

**LAUREATE PRESS, INC.**
1336 W. Central Ave., P.O. Box 343 (08215)
**Phone—(609) 965-0447**
Fax—(609) 965-4032
Email—laureate@comcast.net
Pres.—Janet Rotellini
Corp. Secy.—Henry P. Sartorio
Treas.—Terry Rotellini
Cust. Serv. Mgr.—Robert Waldmann
SIC—2752; 2791; NAICS—323122; *Offset printing & typesetting*
Employs—6; Estab.—1925
Sales—under $500,000
4,500 sq ft site, Distrib.—Local
Privately owned corporation

**N.J. PLASTICS MACHINING & FABRICATING, INC.**
46 Liverpool Ave., P.O. Box 646 (08215)
**Phone—(609) 965-1550**
Fax—(609) 965-1546
www.njpm-fi.com
Email—njplastics@verizon.net
Pres.—Don Magdon
V-P.—Janice Magdon
SIC—3089; *Plastic products, including cup holders, windows, acrylic dessert displays, menu holders & industrial pumps & chemical tanks*
Employs—3; Estab.—1976
Sales—under $500,000
Distrib.—National
Privately owned corporation

**OCEAN YACHTS, INC.**
2713 Green Bank Rd. (08215)
**Phone—(609) 965-4616**
Fax—(609) 965-4914
www.oceanyachtsinc.com
Email—info@oceanyachtsinc.com

Pres.—John Leek III
GM—John Leek IV
SIC—3732; *Fishing & cruising boats*
Employs—30; Estab.—1977
Sales—$50Mil
95,000 sq ft site, Distrib.—Intl.
Privately owned sub-S corp.

**RENAULT WINERY**
72 N. Bremen Ave. (08215)
**Phone—(609) 965-2111**
National—(877) 473-6285
Fax—(609) 965-1702
www.renaultwinery.com
Email—webmaster@renaultwinery.com
Owner—Joseph Milza
Hum. Res. Mgr.—Doris Brown
SIC—2084; NAICS—312130; *Wines*
Employs—150; Estab.—2000
Sales—$50Mil–$100Mil
3,200 sq ft site, Distrib.—Intl.
Privately owned corporation

**SCHAIRER BROS.**
254 S. Bremen Ave. (08215)
**Phone—(609) 965-0996**
Fax—(609) 965-4040
Email—schairerbros@verizon.net
Ptnr.—Paul Schairer
Ptnr.—Anthony Schairer
SIC—2421; *Lumber processing & sawmilling*
Employs—8; Estab.—1936
Sales—under $500,000
Distrib.—Regional
Privately owned partnership
AKA: Schairer Tree Removal

**SWENSON WELDING & FABRICATION, BILL**
707 W. Duerer St. (08215)
Mail addr: P.O. Box 973, Pleasantville (08232)
**Phone—(609) 653-1177**
Fax—(609) 641-9354
Email—swensonwelding@comcast.net
Pres.—Bill Swenson
SIC—3499; 3599; *Metal fabrication & welding job shop*
Employs—3; Estab.—1993
Sales—under $500,000
Distrib.—Local
Privately owned corporation

**TF YACHTS, LLC**
801 Philadelphia Ave., P.O. Box 702 (08215)
**Phone—(609) 965-2300**
Fax—(609) 965-3517
www.eggharboryacht.com
Email—info@buddydavis.com
Pres.—Ira Trocki
COO—Robert Weidhaas
V-P., Sales & Mktg.—Robert Hazard
SIC—3731; 3732; *Pleasure & sport fishing yachts & boats; Brand name—Egg Harbor Yachts; Davis Yachts; Predator Yachts; Topaz Boats; Buddy Davis Edition Boats; Silverton Yachts; Ovation Yachts*
Employs—25; Estab.—1946
Sales—$15Mil
Distrib.—Intl.
Limited Liability Company

**TOMAD, INC.**
129 Cincinnati Ave. (08215)
**Phone—(609) 965-0808**
National—(800) 553-3104
Fax—(609) 965-5930
www.bctsouthersey.com
Email—bct2011@aol.com
Pres., Hum. Res. Mgr.—Brian Dagostino
Off. Mgr.—Madeline Dagostino
Off. Mgr.—Karen Dagostino

## Egg Harbor City— (cont.)

SIC—2752; 2791; NAICS—
323122; *Offset printing & typesetting*
Employs—12; Estab.—1980
5,000 sq ft site, Distrib.—Regional
Privately owned corporation
AKA: Business Cards Tomorrow

## Egg Harbor Township

(Atlantic—S.E.)

**NEW ENTRY**

**AKPHARMA, INC.**
6840 Old Egg Harbor Rd. (08234)
**Phone—(609) 645-5100**
Fax—(609) 645-0767
www.akpharma.com
Owner—Alan Kligerman
SIC—2023; *Dietary supplements; Brand name—Prelief* ®
Employs—5
Sales—$2.5Mil-$5Mil (est)
Distrib.—National

**†ANDLER SOUTH CORP.**
Div. of Andler Packaging Group
102 E. Parkway Dr. (08234)
**Phone—(609) 485-2000**
Fax—(609) 485-0391
www.andler.com
Email—sales@andler.com
Pres.—Richard Mclaughlin
Off. Mgr.—Ruth Nichols
SIC—5085; *Distributor of plastic & glass containers & closures for the food, chemical, pharmaceutical & cosmetics industries*
Employs—12; Estab.—1984
Distrib.—Intl.
Privately owned corporation
Parent co.—Andler Packaging Group, Everett, MA
Phone—(617) 387-5700
See Parent Co. Section for full profile.

**CATAMARAN MEDIA CO., LLC**
3120 Fire Rd. (08234)
**Phone—(609) 266-1860**
Fax—(609) 264-1555
www.thebeachcombernews.com
Email—adtro@
beachcombernews.com
Manager—James Miller
SIC—2759; 2711; NAICS—
323100; *Newspaper printing & publishing*
Employs—4; Estab.—1992
Sales—under $500,000
Distrib.—Local
Limited Liability Company
Parent co.—Catamaran Media Co., LLC, Marmora, NJ
Phone—(609) 624-8900
See Parent Co. Section for full profile.

**CATAMARAN MEDIA CO., LLC**
3120 Fire Rd. (08234)
Mail addr: P.O. Box 619, Northfield (08225)
**Phone—(609) 383-8994**
Fax—(609) 383-9072
www.catamaranmedia.com
Email—bob.fertsch@
shorenewstoday.com
Adv. Sales Mgr.—Bob Fertch
Sales Mgr., Classified—Chris Beasung
Graphic Artist—Christina Allentoff
SIC—2711; *Weekly print & online newspaper publishing; Brand name—The Current; The Wilwood Leader*
Employs—20; Estab.—1998
Sales—$500,000-$1Mil (est)
Distrib.—Local
Limited Liability Company

Parent co.—Catamaran Media Co., LLC, Marmora, NJ
Phone—(609) 624-8900
See Parent Co. Section for full profile.

**CLAYTON & SONS, RALPH**
103 Chestnut Ave. (08234)
Mail addr: P.O. Box 3015, Lakewood (08701)
**Phone—(609) 383-1818**
National—(800) 662-3044
Fax—(732) 751-7630
www.claytonco.com
Email—kroe@claytonco.com
Plt. Mgr.—Damian Haas
Dispatcher—Maurice Laub
Plt. Operator—Mike Wrobel
SIC—3273; NAICS—327320; *Ready-mixed concrete*
Employs—18; Estab.—1988
Sales—$500,000-$1Mil
Distrib.—Local
Privately owned corporation
Parent co.—Clayton & Sons, Ralph, Neptune, NJ
Phone—(732) 751-7600
See Parent Co. Section for full profile.

**COLLO ORNAMENTAL IRON, INC.**
1723 Somers Point Rd. (08234)
**Phone—(609) 926-8799**
Fax—(609) 926-9498
Owner & Pres.—Jim Collo, Sr.
Shop Foreman—Jim Collo, Jr.
Welder—Steve Schultz
SIC—3446; NAICS—332323; *Ornamental ironwork*
Employs—3; Estab.—1969
Sales—under $500,000
5,000 sq ft site, Distrib.—Local
Privately owned corporation

**†COOPER ELECTRIC SUPPLY CO.**
2727 Fire Rd. (08234)
**Phone—(609) 833-2115**
Fax—(609) 407-7215
www.cooper-electric.com
Email—jim.deangelis@cooper-electric.com
Br. Mgr.—Jim Deangelis
SIC—5063; *Distributor of electrical equipment & supplies, including connectors, wire & sockets*
Employs—10; Estab.—1992
Distrib.—Local
Privately owned corporation
Parent co.—Cooper Electric Supply Co., Monroe, NJ
Phone—(732) 747-2233
See Parent Co. Section for full profile.

**EASTERN SIGN CO.**
3011 Ocean Heights Ave., Ste. B (08234)
**Phone—(609) 927-0885**
Fax—(609) 927-8955
www.easternsignco.com
Email—mike@easternsignco.com
Ptnr.—Michael Franklin
Ptnr.—Wendy Franklin
Designer—Rob Hogan
SIC—3993; 2399; *Interior & exterior signs & banners*
Employs—5; Estab.—1995
Sales—$500,000-$1Mil
Distrib.—Local
Sole ownership

**FENCE MAX**
6514 Black Horse Pike (08234)
**Phone—(609) 646-2430**
Fax—(609) 646-6154
www.fencemaxnj.com
Owner & GM—Mark Amechi
SIC—2499; 3499; *Commercial, residential & industrial fencing*
Employs—26; Estab.—1973
Sales—under $500,000
Distrib.—Local
Privately owned corporation

**†FERGUSON ENTERPRISES, INC.**
2531 Tilton Rd. (08234)
**Phone—(609) 485-2266**
Fax—(609) 485-2180
www.ferguson.com
Email—kyle.lawton@ferguson.com
Br. Mgr.—Kyle Lawton
SIC—5074; *Distributor of plumbing supplies, including pipes, fixtures, valves, fittings, pumps & well supplies*
Employs—4; Estab.—2005
Distrib.—Local
Publicly owned corporation
Parent co.—Ferguson Enterprises, Inc., Newport News, VA
Phone—(757) 874-7795
See Parent Co. Section for full profile.

**GOTHAM GROUP, THE**
202 W. Parkway Dr., Ste. 2 (08234)
**Phone—(609) 645-2211**
Fax—(609) 645-3666
www.gothamgroup.com
Email—pete@gothamgroup.com
Pres.—Qiang Wang
CFO—Jack Gilbert
SIC—3993; 2541; 2542; NAICS—323100; *Large-format digital displays, specialty signage & accessories*
Employs—16; Estab.—1994
10,000 sq ft site, Distrib.—National
Privately owned sub-S corp.
AKA: Winsome Digital, Inc.

**INNOVATIVE CUTTING CONCEPTS, LLC**
203 Cates Rd. (08234)
**Phone—(609) 484-9960**
Fax—(609) 484-9960
www.innovativecuttingconcepts.com
Pres.—Ron Simone
Shop Foreman—Robert Martin
SIC—3281; NAICS—327991; *Marble & granite fabrication*
Employs—8; Estab.—2001
Distrib.—Local
Limited Liability Company

**†JOHNSON & TOWERS, INC.**
2701 Fire Rd. *(08234)*
**Phone—(609) 272-1415**
Fax—(609) 272-1868
www.johnsontowers.com
Email—pprior@johnsontowers.com
Dir., Bus. Dev.—Paul Apple
Br. Mgr.—Paul Prior
SIC—5084; 5013; *Distributor of diesel truck & marine engines, transmissions, generators & service; Brand name—Detroit Diesel; MTU; Volvo Penta; Mercedes Industrial; Allison Transmissions; Webasto*
Employs—20; Estab.—1928
Sales—$1Mil-$2.5Mil
Distrib.—Regional
Privately owned corporation
AKA: Johnson Truck Center
Parent co.—Johnson & Towers, Inc., Mount Laurel, NJ
Phone—(856) 234-6990
See Parent Co. Section for full profile.

**JOMAR CORP.**
Div. of Inductotherm Corp.
115 E. Parkway Dr. (08234)
Mail addr: P.O. Box 1020, Pleasantville (08232)
**Phone—(609) 646-8000**
Fax—(609) 645-9166
www.jomarcorp.com
Email—sales@jomarcorp.com
Ex. Admn.—Chris Acquaviva
SIC—3559; *Plastic injection blow molding machinery*
Employs—34; Estab.—1968
Distrib.—Intl.
Privately owned corporation

Parent co.—Inductotherm Corp., Rancocas, NJ
Phone—(609) 267-9000
See Parent Co. Section for full profile.

**†MALINCHO INC**
2545 Fire Rd., Ste. 3 (08234)
**Phone—(609) 677-6090**
National—(866) 203-3525
Fax—(609) 677-6092
www.malincho.com
Email—malincho@malincho.com
Ptnr.—Vladimir Natchev
CEO—Kalin Pentchev
SIC—5149; 5145; 5143; *Distributor of European food products, including feta cheese, German chocolate & vegetable spread; Brand name—Malincho*
Employs—6; Estab.—2001
Sales—$2Mil-$6Mil
5,000 sq ft site, Distrib.—Intl.
Privately owned sub-S corp.

**†MARY ELLEN MARYLAND CRABMEAT CO., INC.**
2613 Fire Rd. (08234)
**Phone—(609) 645-0161**
Fax—(609) 485-0110
Email—audmemd@comcast.net
Pres.—Audrey Jenkins
V-P.—Jack Jenkins
SIC—5146; 5149; *Distributor of fresh, pasteurized, frozen & smoked seafood, sushi items, soups & salads*
Employs—8; Estab.—1995
Sales—$3Mil-$5Mil
1,800 sq ft site, Distrib.—Regional
Privately owned sub-S corp.

**MID ATLANTIC GRAPHIX, INC.**
2558 Tilton Rd. (08234)
**Phone—(609) 569-9990**
National—(888) 722-4225
Fax—(609) 569-9993
www.signalgraphicprinting.com
Email—signal@comcast.net
CEO—J. Riley Gunnels
Pres.—Kathryn M. Gunnels
V-P., Admn.—Joseph S. Lacasse
SIC—2759; NAICS—323100; *Commercial & digital printing & graphic design*
Employs—14; Estab.—1999
6,000 sq ft site, Distrib.—Regional
Privately owned sub-S corp.
DBA: Signal Graphics

**OMEGA SPECIALTY PRODUCTS, LLC**
2511 Fire Rd., Ste. B-6 (08234)
**Phone—(609) 383-8835**
Fax—(609) 645-0017
www.omegaspecialties.com
V-P.—Walt Vayo
SIC—3993; NAICS—339950; *Interior & exterior signage*
Employs—9; Estab.—1997
Sales—$500,000-$1Mil
Distrib.—Local
Limited Liability Company

**PENN JERSEY BUILDING MATERIALS, INC.**
2819 Fire Rd. (08234)
Mail addr: P.O. Box 991, Pleasantville (08232)
**Phone—(609) 485-0068**
Fax—(609) 485-0350
www.penn-jersey.net
Email—info@penn-jersey.net
CEO—Dan Quade
CFO—William Sutton
SIC—3273; NAICS—327320; *Corporate headquarters & ready-mixed concrete*
Employs—20; Estab.—1989
Sales—$5Mil-$10Mil
6,000 sq ft site, Distrib.—Local
Privately owned sub-S corp.

GEOGRAPHICAL

## Egg Harbor Township— (cont.)

NEW ENTRY
**POST TO POST, LLC**
2545 Fire Rd., Ste. 1 (08234)
**Phone—(609) 646-9300**
Fax—(609) 646-9328
www.posttopost.com
Principal—Richard Sonsini
SIC—3446; 2499; 3089; *Architectural metalwork & wooden & vinyl fencing*
Employs—7
Sales—$500,000-$1Mil (est)
Distrib.—Local
Limited Liability Company

**PRINT ART, INC.**
6726 Delilah Rd. (08234)
**Phone—(609) 645-1940**
Fax—(609) 645-7762
www.print-art.net
Email—info@print-art.net
Pres.—Carl Blase
CFO & Hum. Res. Mgr.—Douglas E. Powell
SIC—2759; 2752; NAICS—323100; *Custom commercial, grand format & digital printing & design, fulfillment & direct mail services*
Employs—50; Estab.—1952
Sales—$8.5Mil
30,000 sq ft site, Distrib.—Intl.
Privately owned corporation

†**PUGGI CLASS B RECYCLING, A. J.**
6150 Mill Rd. (08234)
**Phone—(609) 926-6991**
Fax—(609) 926-6992
Pres.—A. J. Puggi
SIC—5093; *Wholesaler of recycled scrap paper, glass & metals*
Employs—10; Estab.—1989
Distrib.—Local
Privately owned corporation

†**QUALITY DISCOUNT PRESS PARTS & EQUIPMENT, INC.**
6088 Reega Ave. (08234)
**Phone—(609) 646-2212**
National—(800) 646-2212
Fax—(609) 646-2255
www.qualitydiscount.com
Email—sales@qualitydiscount.com
Pres.—Jeff Ludwig
Dir., Opers.—Bob Fudala
SIC—5084; *Wholesaler of new & used printing equipment & prepress, press & post press supplies for narrow web tag & label printers; Brand name—3M; Tesa; Praxair; Supercell Products; Webtron; Mark Andy; Arpeco; Nilpeter; Comco; Magpower; Fife*
Employs—20; Estab.—1993
34,000 sq ft site, Distrib.—Intl.
Privately owned sub-S corp.

**R S R FOOD SERVICE EQUIPMENT CORP.**
6574 Delilah Rd. (08234)
Mail addr: P.O. Box 1195, Pleasantville (08232-6195)
**Phone—(609) 646-5158**
www.rsrmetalartcreations.com
Email—rsrfsec@msn.com
Pres.—Rick Love
SIC—3556; 3499; NAICS—333294; *Food processing equipment & custom metal art fabrication*
Employs—3; Estab.—1977
Sales—$500,000-$1Mil
Distrib.—Intl.
Privately owned corporation

**RAILING DYNAMICS, INC. (H Q)**
135 Steelmanville Rd. (08234)
**Phone—(609) 601-1300**
National—(877) 420-7245
Fax—(609) 601-0180
www.rdirail.com
Email—cs@rdirail.com
Pres.—Chris Terrels
V.-P. & Dir., Fin.—Jon Gronow
Dir., Sales, Natl.—Jay Penney
Mktg. Comm. Mgr.—Carol Lyn Groce
SIC—3089; *Corporate headquarters; vinyl railings, composite railings & vinyl decking; Brand name— Endurance; Titan; RDI Metal Works*
Employs—30; Estab.—1989
Distrib.—Intl.
Privately owned corporation

**RHODES & RHODES MILLWORK CO., INC.**
3011 Ocean Heights Ave., Unit A (08234)
**Phone—(609) 653-3180**
Fax—(609) 653-3181
Email—rhodesandrhodes@gmail.com
Pres.—Scott Rhodes
Off. Mgr.—Kathy Rhodes
SIC—2431; NAICS—321900; *Millwork*
Employs—4; Estab.—1992
Distrib.—Regional
Privately owned corporation

**RSL, INC.**
3049 Fernwood Ave. (08234)
Mail addr: 3092 English Creek Ave., Egg Harbor Township (08234)
**Phone—(609) 645-9770**
Fax—(609) 645-8349
www.rslinc.com
Email—sales@rslinc.com
Plt. Mgr.—Steven Nixon, Sr.
SIC—2431; NAICS—321900; *Wooden & door inserts*
Employs—20; Estab.—1967
Sales—$11Mil-$25Mil
Distrib.—Local
Privately owned corporation
Parent co.—RSL, Inc., Egg Harbor Township, NJ
Phone—(609) 484-1600
See Parent Co. Section for full profile.

**RSL, INC. (H Q)**
3092 English Creek Ave. (08234-5245)
**Phone—(609) 484-1600**
National—(800) 257-8641
Fax—(609) 484-0422
www.rslinc.com
Email—sales@rslinc.com
Pres.—Ron Lewkowitz
V.-P.—Kevin Kavanaugh
Opers. Mgr.—Steve Nixon, Sr.
SIC—3211; NAICS—327211; *Corporate headquarters; vinyl door insert, injection molded doorlights sidelights, transoms & decorative glass*
Employs—12; Estab.—1964
Company-wide: 60
250,000 sq ft site, Distrib.—Intl.
Privately owned sub-S corp.

**S M COUNTER TOPS, LLC**
432 Boston Ave. (08234)
**Phone—(609) 926-9301**
Fax—(609) 926-9301
www.eggharbortownshipcontractor.com
Email—steve@thetopman.com
Pres.—Stephen Morin
SIC—2541; *Plastic laminated countertops*
Employs—1; Estab.—1995
Sales—under $500,000
Distrib.—Local
Sole ownership

**SEASHORE GLASS & MIRROR**
2547 Fire Rd., Ste. 2-B (08234)
**Phone—(609) 407-6032**
Fax—(609) 407-6034
www.seashoreglass.com
Email—seashoremirror@aol.com
Owner & Pres.—Joseph Pitzo
SIC—3231; NAICS—327215; *Heavy, frameless, framed & semi frameless color & pattern glass & mirror products, including shower doors, storefronts, mirror walls, vanity mirrors, shelves, tabletops & custom etching; Brand name—Century Shower Doors*
Employs—4; Estab.—1978
Sales—under $500,000
2,500 sq ft site, Distrib.—Regional
Sole ownership

NEW ENTRY
**STONE CRAFTERS, LLC**
6084 Reega Ave. (08234)
**Phone—(609) 646-0406**
Fax—(609) 646-6382
www.stonecraftersnj.com
Email—info@stonecraftersnj.com
Owner—Bill Millar
SIC—3281; 3089; 3299; *Granite, marble & cultured quartz countertops*
Employs—15
Sales—$1Mil-$2.5Mil (est)
Limited Liability Company

**STONE, INC., A. E.**
1435 Doughty Rd. (08234)
**Phone—(609) 641-2781**
Fax—(609) 641-0374
www.aestone.com
Email—info@aestone.com
CEO—Thomas K. Ritter
Pres. & IT Mgr.—Steven C. Kurtz
Fin. Cont.—Kellie Macom
Plt. Mgr.—Stanley Iwanowski
Hum. Res. Mgr.—Tracey Mitchell
Qual. Control Mgr.—Keith Sterling
Maint. Mgr.—Michael Dear
SIC—2951; NAICS—324121; *Corporate headquarters & asphalt paving compounds*
Employs—50; Estab.—1955
Sales—$10Mil-$25Mil
Distrib.—Regional
Privately owned corporation

**TWIN GLASS CO.**
6422 Black Horse Pike (08234)
**Phone—(609) 645-8834**
Fax—(609) 645-8806
www.twinglasscompany.com
Email—twinglass@comcast.net
V.-P.—Scott Summers
Off. Mgr.—Ann Minton
SIC—3231; NAICS—327215; *Glass, mirrors, storefronts, curtain walls, entrance doors & shower enclosures, including glazing*
Employs—6; Estab.—1949
Sales—under $500,000
Distrib.—Local
Limited Liability Company

†**WEINSTEIN SUPPLY CO.**
Div. of Hajoca Corp.
3187 Fire Rd. (08234)
**Phone—(609) 677-0666**
Fax—(609) 677-0648
www.weinsteinsupply.com
Email—prf404@hajoca.com
Br. Mgr.—Kevin Mooney
SIC—5074; *Wholesaler of plumbing & heating supplies*
Employs—12; Estab.—1983
Distrib.—Local
Privately owned corporation
Parent co.—Hajoca Corp., Ardmore, PA
Phone—(610) 649-1430
See Parent Co. Section for full profile.

**WHEELCHAIR GEAR**
126 Cindy Dr. (08234)
**Phone—(609) 653-6787**
www.wheelchairgear.com
Owner & Hum. Res. Mgr.—Leslie Snyder
SIC—2393; 3429; *Wheelchair convenience accessories, including textile backpacks & minibags, clip-on grommet attachments & wheelchair cup holders*
Employs—2; Estab.—2003
Sales—under $500,000
Distrib.—Intl.
Privately owned corporation

†**WMS GAMING, INC.**
Div. of WMS Industries, Inc.
2511 Fire Rd., Ste. A-10 (08234)
**Phone—(609) 569-0100**
National—(866) 967-4457
Fax—(609) 569-0101
www.wms.com
Email—customersupport@wms.com
GM—David Rifkin
Off. Mgr.—Robin Flood
SIC—5046; *Distributor of slot machines*
Employs—20; Estab.—1995
Distrib.—Local
Privately owned corporation
Parent co.—WMS Industries, Inc., Waukegan, IL
Phone—(847) 785-3000
See Parent Co. Section for full profile.

## Elizabeth
(Union—N.E.)

**814 AMERICAS**
814 2nd Ave. (07202)
**Phone—(908) 354-2674**
Fax—(908) 354-7170
www.814americas.com
GM—Michael Patracuolla
Off. Mgr.—Janet Fernandez
SIC—2011; NAICS—311611; *Meat packing & processing*
Employs—22; Estab.—1972
Distrib.—National
Privately owned corporation

**A & F TOOL**
930 Magnolia Ave. (07201)
**Phone—(973) 262-1792**
(516) 581-4485
Email—paramo_fernando@yahoo.com
GM—Fernando Paramo
SIC—3544; 3599; *Tool & die & general machining job shop*
Employs—6
Sales—under $500,000
Distrib.—National
Limited Liability Partnership

**ACTAVIS ELIZABETH, LLC**
Div. of Actavis, Inc.
200 Elmora Ave. (07202)
**Phone—(908) 527-9100**
Fax—(908) 284-1831
www.actavis.com
Email—actavis@actavis.com
Dir., Qual. Control—Scott Allen

## Elizabeth—(cont.)

SIC—2834; NAICS—325412; *Generic modified-release solid & oral dose tablets & capsules for cardiovascular, inflammatory, nervous & anti-anxiety disorders*
Employs—580
Sales—$25Mil-$100Mil
300,000 sq ft site, Distrib.— National
Privately owned corporation
Parent co.—Actavis, Inc., Parsippany, NJ
Phone—(862) 261-7000
See Parent Co. Section for full profile.

### ADCO SIGNS OF NEW JERSEY, INC.
57 Westfield Ave. (07208)
**Phone—(908) 965-2112**
National—(800) 548-0014
Fax—(908) 965-1379
www.adcosigns.net
Email—cmolski@aol.com
Owner—Clara D. Molski
SIC—3993; *Interior dimensional, silkscreen & vinyl signs*
Employs—40; Estab.—1986
Sales—$2.6Mil-$5Mil
Distrib.—National
Privately owned corporation

### AIR CLEAN CO., INC.
1135 Chestnut St. (07201)
**Phone—(908) 355-1515**
Email—airclean@aol.com
Pres.—Alex Drucker
SIC—3564; NAICS—333400; *Air pollution control equipment*
Employs—8; Estab.—1981
Sales—$500,000-$1Mil
Distrib.—Regional
Privately owned corporation

### †ALLIED BUILDING PRODUCTS CORP.
850 Flora St. (07201)
**Phone—(908) 820-9790**
National—(800) 969-3274
Fax—(908) 354-8028
www.alliedbuilding.com
Email—sales@alliedbuilding.com
Br. Mgr.—Thomas Meola
Opers. Mgr.—Anthony Michelini
SIC—5033; 5031; *Distributor of building materials & supplies, including roofing, insulation, drywall, siding, windows & doors*
Employs—10; Estab.—1950
Distrib.—National
Publicly owned corporation
Parent co.—Allied Building Products Corp., East Rutherford, NJ
Phone—(201) 507-8400
See Parent Co. Section for full profile.

### ALPHA WIRE CO.
Div. of Belden Inc.
711 Lidgerwood Ave., P.O. Box 711 (07207)
**Phone—(908) 925-8000**
National—(800) 522-5742
Fax—(908) 925-2238
www.alphawire.com
Email—info@alphawire.com
Dir., Sales—Tim Smith
Dir., Info. Sys.—Mayur Gohil
Hum. Res. Mgr.—Susan Cianci
Mktg. Comm. Mgr.—Justin Dubow
SIC—3496; *Divisional headquarters & cable & wire*
Employs—200; Estab.—1922
Distrib.—Intl.
Privately owned corporation
Parent co.—Belden Inc., St. Louis, MO
Phone—(314) 854-8000
See Parent Co. Section for full profile.

### AMERICAN CHEMICAL & ADHESIVE LLC
410 Division St. *(07201)*
**Phone—(908) 353-2260**
Fax—(908) 353-3641
Email—qzaman17@yahoo.com
Pres.—Qamar Zaman
V-P.—Osman Zaman
SIC—2851; NAICS—325510; *Plastic & metal coatings & flux*
Employs—5; Estab.—2013
Sales—under $500,000
7,000 sq ft site, Distrib.—National
Limited Liability Company

### AMERICAN CRANKSHAFT GRINDING CO., INC.
851-861 Fairmount Ave. (07201)
**Phone—(908) 352-5558**
Email—americancrank@optonline.net
Owner—Tony DiCosmo
SIC—3519; 3714; *Rebuilt engines & automotive machine shop, including rebuilt diesel cylinder heads*
Employs—3; Estab.—1984
Sales—under $500,000
Distrib.—Local
Sole ownership

### †ARZEE SUPPLY CORP. OF NEW JERSEY
Div. of Allied Building Products Corp.
450 York St. (07201)
**Phone—(908) 820-3700**
Fax—(908) 820-9001
www.arzeesupply.com
Email—paul.queijo@arzee.com
Sales Mgr.—John Esteves
Br. Mgr.—Paul Queijo
Opers. Mgr.—Ilidio Serra
SIC—5033; 5031; *Distributor of building materials & supplies, including roofing, siding, windows & doors*
Employs—7; Estab.—2001
Distrib.—Local
Publicly owned corporation
Parent co.—Allied Building Products Corp., East Rutherford, NJ
Phone—(201) 507-8400
See Parent Co. Section for full profile.

### †ATALANTA CORPORATION
1 Atalanta Plz. (07206)
**Phone—(908) 351-8000**
Fax—(908) 351-1978
www.atalantacorp.com
Email—info@atalanta1.com
Chrm., CEO—George Gellert
CFO—Charles Stough
CIO & CTO—Carl D'Angelo
Mktg. Mgr.—Jackie Folts
SIC—5141; 5147; 5143; *Corporate headquarters & distributor of general line groceries, including imported meats & cheeses*
Employs—150; Estab.—1982
Distrib.—Intl.
Privately owned corporation
AKA: Gellert Global Group

### ATTITUDES IN DRESSING, INC.
107 Trumbull St., Bldg. B-8 (07206)
**Phone—(908) 354-7218**
National—(800) 323-0786
Fax—(908) 354-4023
www.bodywrappers.com
Email—sales@bodywrappers.com
CEO—Michael Rubin
Pres.—Marie West
IT Mgr.—John Sinclair
Cred. Mgr.—Ligia Jorge
SIC—2339; *Women's & girls' clothing*
Employs—14; Estab.—1980
60,000 sq ft site, Distrib.—Intl.
Privately owned corporation

### BELL ARTE WOODWORKING, INC.
10 W. Mravlag Pl. (07201)
**Phone—(908) 355-1199**
Fax—(908) 355-6979
Pres.—Giusette Chillemi
GM—Sal Chillemi
SIC—2541; 2434; 2431; NAICS—337110; *Wooden store fixtures & cabinets & millwork*
Employs—12; Estab.—1991
Sales—$500,000-$1Mil
Distrib.—Local
Privately owned corporation

### BELLA PALERMO PASTRY SHOP, INC.
619 Elizabeth Ave. (07206)
**Phone—(908) 354-8610**
Fax—(908) 355-4830
www.bellapalermo.com
Email—info@bellapalermo.com
Pres.—Joe Oliver
V-P.—Maria Fatima
SIC—2051; NAICS—311812; *Custom wedding, birthday & Italian cakes, pastries & cookies*
Employs—10; Estab.—1952
15,000 sq ft site, Distrib.—Local
Privately owned sub-S corp.

### BLISS ELECTRICAL SUPPLY CO.
207 South St. (07202)
**Phone—(908) 289-9719**
(908) 352-2025
National—(800) 544-4887
Fax—(908) 353-5436
www.1800lightup.com
Email—vincicio@optonline.net
Owner & CEO—Vincent Cicio
CFO—Eric Ericson
Sales Mgr.—Laurence Melley
Off. Mgr.—Theadie White
SIC—3646; 3645; 3641; 3648; NAICS—335122; *Fluorescent indoor & outdoor lighting equipment for residential & commercial projects, including LED front runners, tubes, fixtures & light panels; Brand name—KB Lighting; Maxlight; Rab; Havells SLI Lighting; DrakaEP; Keystone Elec; East Coast Pnl Brd; Magnatron; TCP; Interelectric; Ushio; Bulbrite; Overdrive; Westinghouse; AAF Air Filters*
Employs—7; Estab.—1953
Sales—$1Mil-$2.5Mil
10,000 sq ft site, Distrib.—Local
Sole ownership

### †BUSINESS FURNITURE, INC.
133 Rahway Ave. (07202)
**Phone—(908) 355-3400**
Fax—(908) 355-8993
www.bfionline.com
CEO—Paul Gold
CFO—John Trotter
V-P., Opers.—John McClendon
Principal—Eric Gold
Hum. Res. Mgr.—Linda D'Adamo
SIC—5021; *Corporate headquarters & wholesaler of business furniture*
Employs—35
Distrib.—Regional
Privately owned corporation
AKA: BFI

### CAVALIER CHEMICAL CO.
26 Papetti Plz. (07206)
**Phone—(908) 558-0110**
National—(800) 228-2811
Fax—(908) 353-6752
www.cavalierchem.com
Owner—Norman Lubin
Plt. Mgr.—George Jaramillo
Hum. Res. Mgr.—Abbie Spohrer
SIC—2841; *Laundry detergents & kitchen cleaners*
Estab.—1960
Privately owned corporation

### CHILDREN'S APPAREL NETWORK LTD.
77 S. 1st St. (07206)
**Phone—(908) 351-4477**
Fax—(908) 352-6219
Pres.—Nathan Shalom
Off. Mgr.—Carol Scalzo
SIC—2369; NAICS—315200; *Baby clothing*
Employs—18; Estab.—1957
Sales—$11Mil-$25Mil
Distrib.—Intl.
Privately owned corporation
AKA: Nannette

### †CLASSIC TILE, INC.
325 Pine St., P.O. Box 1066 (07207)
**Phone—(908) 289-8400**
Fax—(908) 289-6266
www.classictile.com
Email—classictile@optonline.net
Pres.—Leah Glucroft
V-P.—Jack Teitel
SIC—5023; 5031; 5032; *Distributor of floor coverings, including rubber, cork, laminate, ceramic tile, wood & vinyl flooring*
Employs—25; Estab.—1977
5,000 sq ft site, Distrib.—Regional
Privately owned sub-S corp.

### COCKPIT USA, INC.
725 New Point Rd. (07201)
**Phone—(908) 558-9704**
Fax—(908) 558-9754
www.cockpitusa.com
Email—info@cockpitusa.com
Br. Mgr.—Andrew Baljeet
SIC—2386; NAICS—315200; *Men's & women's leather jackets*
Employs—12; Estab.—1942
Sales—$500,000-$1Mil
Distrib.—Intl.
Privately owned corporation
Parent co.—Cockpit USA, Inc., New York, NY
Phone—(212) 575-1616
See Parent Co. Section for full profile.

### †COMBINED SUPPLY CO., LLC
640 S. Broad St., P.O. Box 9192 (07202)
**Phone—(908) 353-8888**
Fax—(908) 353-6404
www.combinedsupply.net
Email—combinedsupply@optimum.net
Pres., GM—Patrick O'Grady III
SIC—5085; *Distributor of industrial hoses & fittings for process & transfer applications serving the petrochemical, pharmaceutical & food grade industries*
Employs—2; Estab.—1994
Sales—under $500,000
2,000 sq ft site, Distrib.—Local
Limited Liability Company

### CONSOLIDATED CONTAINER CO.
Div. of Consolidated Container Company
28-36 Slater Dr. (07206)
**Phone—(908) 351-7919**
Fax—(908) 351-7980
www.cccllc.com
Email—sales@cccllc.com
Plt. Admn. & Hum. Res. Rep.—Stephanie Cruz
SIC—3085; NAICS—326160; *Plastic bottles*
Employs—42; Estab.—1989
Sales—$1Mil-$5Mil
40,000 sq ft site, Distrib.—National
Privately owned corporation
Parent co.—Consolidated Container Company, Atlanta, GA
Phone—(678) 742-4600
See Parent Co. Section for full profile.

GEOGRAPHICAL

# Elizabeth—(cont.)

**CUEVA'S SIGNS**
853 Bayway Cir. (07201)
**Phone—(908) 820-5744**
Fax—(908) 820-5744
www.cuevassigns.com
Email—cuevassigns@live.com
Owner—Jose Miguel Cueva
SIC—3993; *Vinyl lettered signs*
Employs—2; Estab.—2003
Sales—under $500,000
Distrib.—Local
Sole ownership

**CYCLE CHEM, INC.**
201 S. 1st St. (07206)
**Phone—(908) 355-5800**
Fax—(908) 355-3495
www.cyclechem.com
Email—michaelpersico@
cleanventure.com
Pres.—Michael Persico
IT Mgr.—Chris Aranosian
Hum. Res. Mgr.—Suzanne
Czarnota
Sales Coord.—Debbie Scerbo
SIC—2865; NAICS—325100;
*Recycled-content oil*
Employs—60; Estab.—1984
Distrib.—Regional
Privately owned corporation

**DEB-EL FOOD PRODUCTS, LLC**
2 Papetti Plz., P.O. Box 876
(07206)
**Phone—(908) 351-0330**
National—(800) 421-3447
Fax—(908) 351-0334
www.debelfoods.com
Email—dgibber@debelfoods.com
Pres.—Elliot Gibber
GM—Oscar Reyes
R & D Mgr.—Alex Karmondi
SIC—2015; NAICS—312100;
*Dried eggs*
Employs—75; Estab.—1984
30,000 sq ft site, Distrib.—Intl.
Limited Liability Company

**DELTA FENCE CO.**
541 Spring St. (07201)
**Phone—(908) 355-9066**
Fax—(908) 355-9593
www.deltawholesalefence.com
Email—deltafence@aol.com
Owner—Carlos Milanes
SIC—3496; 2499; *Wooden, vinyl &
chain link fences*
Employs—4; Estab.—1995
Sales—under $500,000 (est)
Distrib.—Local
Privately owned corporation

**†DOZORTSEV & SONS ENTERPRISES**
411-415 John St. (07202)
**Phone—(908) 353-1234**
Fax—(908) 353-0660
www.winesandspiritsdcollection.co
m
Email—dozortsev.wines@
gmail.com
Owner—Eugene Dozortsev
SIC—5182; *Distributor of imported
& exported wines, distilled
spirits, cognacs, brandies,
liqueurs, single malts, vodkas &
tequilas from Argentina,
Armenia, Belarus, Chile, France,
Republic of Georgia, Germany,
Israel, Italy, Span, Ukraine &
Mexico*
Employs—6
Distrib.—National
Privately owned corporation

**DURO BAG MFG. CO.**
750 Dowd Ave. (07201)
**Phone—(908) 351-2400**
Fax—(908) 351-5102
www.durobag.com
Email—info@durobag.com
GM & Plt. Mgr.—Mike Davidson

Scheduler—Maritza Ramos
SIC—2674; NAICS—322224;
*Paper bags*
Employs—275; Estab.—2002
Sales—$25Mil-$50Mil (est)
Distrib.—Intl.
Privately owned corporation
Parent co.—Duro Bag Mfg. Co.,
Florence, KY
Phone—(859) 581-8200
See Parent Co. Section for full profile.

**EASTERN SILK MILLS, INC.**
212 Catherine St. (07201)
**Phone—(908) 355-6700**
Fax—(908) 351-9433
www.eastern-silk.com
Email—nj@eastern-silk.com
Pres., Hum. Res. Mgr.—Chong
Kim
SIC—2221; NAICS—313210; *Silk
dyeing, printing & finishing*
Employs—30; Estab.—1977
Sales—$6Mil-$10Mil
70,000 sq ft site, Distrib.—National
Privately owned corporation

**†ELIZABETH TRUCK CENTER**
878 North Ave. *(07201)*
**Phone—(908) 355-9200**
          (908) 355-8800
Fax—(908) 355-8801
www.elizabethtruckcenter.com
Email—spesceJr@
elizabethtruckcenter.com
Pres.—Steven Pesce
SIC—5013; *Distributor of truck
parts*
Employs—30; Estab.—1997
Distrib.—National
Privately owned corporation
AKA: ETC

NEW ENTRY
**EVOQUA WATER TECHNOLOGIES**
624 Evans St. (07201)
**Phone—(908) 353-7230**
Fax—(908) 353-8288
www.evoqua.com
Email—information.water@
evoqua.com
Br. Mgr.—Brian Frank
SIC—3589; *Wastewater treatment
equipment*
Employs—15
Sales—$2.5Mil-$5Mil (est)
Publicly owned corporation
Parent co.—Evoqua Water
Technologies, Alpharetta, GA
Phone—(978) 614-7111
See Parent Co. Section for full profile.

**FREEPORT-MCMORAN COPPER &
GOLD**
Div. of Freeport-McMoran Inc.
48-94 Bayway Ave. *(07202)*
**Phone—(800) 522-9929**
          (908) 558-4318
Fax—(908) 351-9475
www.fcx.com/metals/bayway.htm
Email—william_geissel@fmi.com
Sr. Sales & Mktg. Rep.—Michael
Prendergast
SIC—3366; 3351; NAICS—
331525; *Copper, copper alloys &
extruded, drawn & rolled
products, including rods, bars,
TBC, billets & round, flat & trolley
wire & components for
resistance welding; Brand
name—PD 135; PD 80EF; PD
35EF*
Employs—125; Estab.—1932
Sales—$10Mil-$25Mil (est)
Distrib.—Intl.
Publicly owned corporation
ISO rating—9001:2008
Parent co.—Freeport-McMoran
Inc., Phoenix, AZ
Phone—(602) 366-8100
See Parent Co. Section for full profile.

**GEMINI DJ & PRO AUDIO**
107 Trumbull St., Ste. F-8 (07206)
**Phone—(732) 346-0061**
Fax—(732) 346-0065
www.geminisound.com
Email—sales@geminisound.com
CEO—Artie Cabasso
V-P., Sales—Ikey Cabasso
V-P., Sales—Isaac Cabasso
V-P., Prod. Dev.—David Cabasso
SIC—3651; 3648; NAICS—
334310; *Disc jockey & pro audio
gear*
Employs—18; Estab.—1974
32,000 sq ft site, Distrib.—Intl.
Sole ownership

**GENERAL FILM PRODUCTS**
107 Trumbull St., Bldg. R-2
(07206)
**Phone—(908) 351-0454**
Fax—(908) 351-0482
Email—reisner@generalfilm.com
Hum. Res. & IT Mgr. & Prodn.
Coord.—Michael Eisner
Off. Mgr.—Rick DeRosa
SIC—3081; NAICS—326113; *Film
products*
Employs—50; Estab.—1982
Distrib.—Regional
Privately owned corporation

**GRAPHIRY PRINTING**
308 Morris Ave. (07208-3615)
**Phone—(908) 353-2223**
Fax—(908) 965-0509
www.graphiry.com
Email—graphiryinfo@optonline.net
Owner—Luis Arias
GM—Mary Arias
SIC—2759; NAICS—323100;
*Commercial printing*
Employs—6; Estab.—1986
Sales—$500,000-$1Mil
3,000 sq ft site, Distrib.—National
Sole ownership

**GRAY OVERHEAD DOOR CO.**
439 Third Ave. (07206)
**Phone—(908) 355-3889**
Fax—(908) 355-8449
GM—Eddie Acosta
Off. Mgr.—Gray Acosta
SIC—3442; NAICS—332321;
*Metal overhead garage doors*
Employs—5; Estab.—1963
10,000 sq ft site, Distrib.—
Regional
Privately owned corporation

**HAYWARD INDUSTRIES, INC.**
620 Division St. (07201)
**Phone—(908) 351-5400**
Fax—(908) 351-4492
www.haywardnet.com
Email—rdavis@haywardnet.com
Chrm.—Oscar Davis
Pres., CEO—Robert Davis
V-P., CFO—Andrew Diamond
V-P., Hum. Res.—Wayne Wilson
SIC—3949; 3433; 3561; 2842;
NAICS—339920; *Corporate
headquarters & swimming pool
equipment & supplies, including
heaters, lights, pumps &
cleaners*
Employs—100
Sales—$10Mil-$25Mil (est)
Distrib.—National
Privately owned corporation

**HEDAYA HOME FASHIONS, INC.**
1111 Jefferson Ave. (07201)
**Phone—(908) 352-0808**
National—(800) 223-1454
Fax—(908) 352-4060
www.nhhedayahomefashions.com
Email—info@hedayahome.com
Pres.—Nathan Hedaya
Accts. Mgr.—Sonya Pomoes

SIC—2399; 2392; *Aprons, towels,
oven mitts, place mats & pot
holders*
Employs—40; Estab.—1930
Sales—$11Mil-$25Mil
Distrib.—National
Privately owned corporation
AKA: Hedaya Bros.

**†HILLSIDE PAPER PRODUCTS, INC.**
20 Butler St. (07206)
**Phone—(908) 352-3300**
Fax—(908) 352-0770
www.hillsidepaper.com
Email—hillsidepaper@verizon.net
Pres.—Alan Lerner
SIC—5113; *Distributor of
corrugated boxes*
Employs—7; Estab.—1954
Distrib.—Regional
Privately owned corporation

**HISPANO PUBLISHING, LLC**
437 Linden Ave. (07208)
Mail addr: P.O. Box 972, Elizabeth
(07202-1709)
**Phone—(908) 351-9390**
          (908) 558-0951
Fax—(908) 351-9370
www.noticierohispano.com
Email—noticolomb@aol.com
Ex. Dir.—Nelson Franco
GM—Stella Ramirez
SIC—2711; *Spanish newspaper
publishing*
Employs—5; Estab.—1983
Sales—under $500,000
Distrib.—Regional
Limited Liability Company

**IMPERIAL WELD RING CORP.**
80-88 Front St., P.O. Box 6646
*(07206)*
**Phone—(908) 354-0011**
National—(800) 444-7356
Fax—(908) 354-9014
www.imperialweldringcorp.com
Email—imperialweldring@erols.com
Pres.—Calvin Sierra
SIC—3498; 3429; 3494; 3499;
*Precision metallic weld backing
rings, consumable weld inserts
& weld test coupons, including
specialty/custom machining*
Employs—15; Estab.—1959
Sales—$1Mil-$2.5Mil
Distrib.—Intl.
Privately owned corporation

**INDUSTRIAL ENVIRONMENTAL**
Div. of Fleetwash, Inc.
176 W. Westfield Ave. (07201)
**Phone—(908) 241-3830**
Fax—(908) 241-3837
www.foamatic.com
Email—info@foamatic.com
Opers. Mgr.—Frank Volpe
Logistics Mgr.—Dan Coyle
SIC—3589; NAICS—333319;
*Sanitation control systems &
pressure washing equipment*
Employs—5; Estab.—1968
10,000 sq ft site, Distrib.—National
Privately owned corporation
Parent co.—Fleetwash, Inc.,
Fairfield, NJ
Phone—(800) 847-3735
See Parent Co. Section for full profile.

**INDUSTRIAL RUBBER CO.**
938-940 S. Elmora Ave. *(07202)*
Mail addr: P.O. Box 359, Elizabeth
(07207-0359)
**Phone—(908) 351-1550**
Fax—(908) 351-8350
www.indrubber.com
Email—sales@indrubber.com
Pres.—Peter J. Dugett
GM—Dennis Szafran
Bookkeeper—Carol Harding

## Elizabeth—(cont.)

SIC—3052; 3053; NAICS—
326220; *Rubber hose, hydraulic
fittings, sheets & gaskets*
Employs—25; Estab.—1950
20,000 sq ft site, Distrib.—Local
Sole ownership

**INTERNATIONAL COCONUT CORP.**

225 W. Grand St. (07202)
Mail addr: P.O. Box 3326,
Elizabeth (07207)
**Phone—(908) 289-1555**
Fax—(908) 289-1556
www.internationalcoconut.com
Email—sales@
internationalcoconut.com
Pres.—Richard Kesselhaut
SIC—2099; *Sweetened coconut*
Employs—5; Estab.—1978
Distrib.—Intl.
Sole ownership

**JEROME INDUSTRIES CORP.**

Div. of Astrodyne Corp.
730 Division St. (07201)
**Phone—(908) 353-5700**
Fax—(908) 353-1021
www.jeromeindustries.com
Email—sales@
jeromeindustries.com
Graphic Designer—Ben Ahhi
SIC—3679; *Custom & military
grade low leakage switching
power supplies, including NiCad
& battery chargers &
transformers*
Employs—100; Estab.—1965
25,000 sq ft site, Distrib.—Intl.
Privately owned corporation
Parent co.—Astrodyne Corp.,
Mansfield, MA
Phone—(508) 964-6300
See Parent Co. Section for full profile.

**L & M ART GALLERY, LLC**

126 Elmora Ave. (07202)
**Phone—(908) 351-2633**
Fax—(908) 351-2633
www.lmartgallery.com
Email—lmartgallery@optonline.net
Pres.—Michael Sirotkin
SIC—2499; *Wooden & metal
picture frames*
Employs—3; Estab.—1957
Sales—under $500,000
Distrib.—Local
Limited Liability Company

**LAVOZ SPANISH NEWSPAPERS**

P.O. Box 899 (07207)
**Phone—(908) 352-6654**
Fax—(908) 352-9735
www.lavoznj.com
Email—lavoznj@aol.com
Publisher—Daniel Garcia
Pres.—Abel Berry
SIC—2711; *Newspaper
publishing*
Employs—5; Estab.—1969
Sales—under $500,000
Distrib.—Regional
Privately owned corporation

**LEHIGH PRECISION CO., INC.**

P.O. Box 214 (07207)
**Phone—(908) 351-6600**
(908) 884-3050
Fax—(908) 351-7380
www.lehighprecision.com
Email—lehprec@aol.com
Owner & Pres.—Mark Biederman
Off. Admn.—Sharon Waldron
SIC—3599; 3728; *General
machining of aircraft
components & parts*
Employs—5; Estab.—1978
10,000 sq ft site, Distrib.—National
Privately owned corporation

**LITHUANIAN BAKERY, INC., T. J.**

131 Inslee Pl. (07206)
**Phone—(908) 354-0970**
www.lithbake.com
Email—info@lithbake.com
Owner & Pres.—John Backiel
SIC—2051; NAICS—311812;
*Bakery products*
Employs—80; Estab.—1800
Sales—$10Mil-$25Mil (est)
Distrib.—Local
Privately owned corporation

**†LORCO PETROLEUM SERVICES**

450 S. Front St. (07202)
**Phone—(908) 820-8800**
Fax—(908) 820-8412
www.lorcopetroleum.com
Email—eblumetti@
lorcopetroleum.com
Pres.—John Lionetti
V-P.—Frank LoBello
Recycling Coord.—Gene Blumetti
SIC—5172; 5093; *Wholesaler of
recycled residual & used fuel oils
& antifreeze, retailer of antifreeze
& windshield washer fluids &
wastewater treatment, oil/water
separator cleaning & tank
cleaning & drum disposal*
Employs—150; Estab.—1957
Distrib.—Regional
Privately owned partnership

**MAGNOLIA BEEF CO., LLC**

1070 Magnolia Ave. (07201)
Mail addr: P.O. Box 220, Elizabeth
(07207)
**Phone—(908) 352-9412**
Fax—(908) 352-1576
www.magnoliabeefco.com
Email—magnoliabeef@aol.com
Pres.—Alan Simberloff
Bus. Mgr.—Gary Kepniss
Asst. Mgr.—Ray Smith
Asst. Mgr.—James Montefusco
SIC—2011; 2015; NAICS—311611;
*Meat & poultry processing*
Employs—25; Estab.—1941
Sales—$500,000-$1Mil
Distrib.—Regional
Privately owned sub-S corp.

**MARBLE FACTORY**

800 Magnolia Ave. (07201)
**Phone—(908) 353-2264**
Fax—(908) 353-1468
Email—themarblefactory@
yahoo.com
Pres.—Ilda Vitorino
V-P.—John Vitorino
GM & Sales Mgr.—Jennifer
Vitorino
SIC—3281; NAICS—327991;
*Marble countertops, stone
fabrication & ceramic tile*
Employs—12; Estab.—1991
22,000 sq ft site, Distrib.—Local
Privately owned corporation

**MASTER PRINTING CO.**

P.O. Box 9609 (07202)
**Phone—(908) 351-1568**
Email—master.printing@verizon.net
Pres.—Bill DePaolo
V-P.—Carmen DePaolo
SIC—2752; 3993; NAICS—
323100; *Offset printing, graphics
& copywriting*
Employs—3; Estab.—1974
Distrib.—Regional
Sole ownership

**MASTERCRAFT ELECTROPLATING**

801 Magnolia Ave. (07201)
**Phone—(908) 354-4404**
Fax—(908) 354-4405
Owner—Desmond Naraine
Supervisor—John Bell

SIC—3471; 3544; NAICS—
332813; *Vinyl record molds &
electroplating*
Employs—6; Estab.—1984
Distrib.—Regional
Sole ownership

**MICHAEL FOODS, INC.**

847 North Ave. (07201)
**Phone—(908) 282-7140**
Fax—(908) 354-8660
www.michaelfoods.com
Email—sales@michaelfoods.com
Dir., Hum. Res.—Jack Novak
Security Coord.—Elaine Rogers
SIC—2015; *Egg products*
Employs—75; Estab.—1924
Distrib.—Intl.
Publicly owned corporation
Parent co.—Michael Foods, Inc.,
Minnetonka, MN
Phone—(952) 258-4000
See Parent Co. Section for full profile.

**MINI PRECISION DEVICES, INC.**

615 Pennsylvania Ave. (07201)
**Phone—(908) 351-7423**
Fax—(908) 351-8362
Email—mini615@aol.com
Pres.—Tony Neto
Off. Mgr.—Dorinda Neto
SIC—3599; *General machining
job shop*
Employs—11; Estab.—1985
Distrib.—Local
Privately owned corporation

**NA-VET PRINTING CO.**

506 Elizabeth Ave. (07206)
**Phone—(908) 353-4441**
Fax—(908) 353-4759
Pres.—Larry Franchini
SIC—2752; 2759; 2791; 2396;
NAICS—323122; *Commercial,
digital & color printing of
business forms, cards, invoices
& envelopes, banners, signs &
silk-screened letters*
Employs—4; Estab.—1946
Sales—$500,000-$1Mil
Distrib.—Regional
Limited Liability Company

**NORTHEAST BINDERY, INC.**

419 Trumbull St. (07206)
**Phone—(908) 436-3737**
Fax—(908) 436-3738
Email—nebindery@aol.com
Owner & Pres.—Bel Romlochan
SIC—2789; NAICS—323121;
*Bookbinding*
Employs—22; Estab.—2000
Sales—$500,000-$1Mil
Distrib.—Local
Privately owned corporation

**NYP CORP.**

805 E. Grand St. (07201)
**Phone—(908) 351-6550**
National—(800) 524-1052
Fax—(908) 351-0108
www.nyp-corp.com
Email—sales@nyp-corp.com
Pres. & V-P., Sales—Gerald P.
Labelle
V-P., IT & Opers.—Christopher N.
Labelle
V-P.—Jerry Labelle
Cont.—Michael Slattery
SIC—2673; *Corporate
headquarters & polyester, burlap
& mesh bags*
Employs—50; Estab.—1946
Sales—$5Mil-$10Mil
60,000 sq ft site, Distrib.—National
Privately owned corporation

**OCEANIC ELECTRICAL MFG. CO.**

248-256 3rd St. (07206)
**Phone—(908) 355-1900**
Fax—(908) 355-0041
www.oceanicelectric.com
Email—info@oceanicelectric.com
Pres.—Hank Barnes

SIC—3646; NAICS—335122;
*Marine lighting fixtures*
Employs—15; Estab.—1922
Sales—$1Mil-$5Mil
15,000 sq ft site, Distrib.—Intl.
Privately owned partnership

**ON DEMAND MACHINERY, LLC**

150 Broadway (07206)
**Phone—(908) 351-6906**
Fax—(908) 351-7156
www.odmachinery.com
Email—info@odmachinery.com
Co-Pres.—John Jacobson, Sr.
Co-Pres.—John Jacobson, Jr.
Off. Mgr.—Aisha Belfield
SIC—3555; NAICS—333293;
*Bookbinding machinery*
Employs—16; Estab.—1995
Sales—$1Mil-$2.5Mil (est)
Distrib.—Intl.
Privately owned corporation
AKA: American Graphic Arts, Inc.

**†P & A CRANE & HOIST CO.**

369 Reuter Ave. (07202)
**Phone—(908) 527-6990**
Fax—(908) 527-6119
Email—pacrane369@aol.com
Pres.—Manny Pego
Off. Mgr.—Dean Anderson
SIC—5084; *Distributor of cranes*
Employs—2; Estab.—1994
Sales—under $500,000
Distrib.—Local
Privately owned sub-S corp.

**PABST ENTERPRISES EQUIPMENT
CO., INC.**

676 Pennsylvania Ave. (07201)
**Phone—(908) 353-2880**
Fax—(908) 353-1916
www.pabstenterprises.com
Email—info@pabstenterprises.com
Pres.—David Bechtold
GM—Jacek Jablonski
Off. Mgr.—Lidia Almeida
SIC—3599; *Sheet metal
fabrication & CNC & general
machining job shop*
Employs—20; Estab.—1934
Sales—$1Mil-$2.5Mil
25,000 sq ft site, Distrib.—
Regional
Privately owned corporation

**PAPETTI'S HYGRADE EGG
PRODUCTS, INC.**

Div. of Michael Foods, Inc.
877 North Ave. E. (07201)
Mail addr: P.O. Box 145, Elizabeth
(07205)
**Phone—(908) 282-7140**
National—(800) 223-7416
Fax—(908) 282-7140
www.michaelfoods.com
Email—info@michaelfoods.com
Acctg. Mgr.—Sanjeev Lund
SIC—2015; *Chicken egg
processing*
Employs—7; Estab.—1933
Sales—$500,000-$1Mil
Distrib.—Regional
Publicly owned corporation
Parent co.—Michael Foods, Inc.,
Minnetonka, MN
Phone—(952) 258-4000
See Parent Co. Section for full profile.

**PEACH BOUTIQUE, THE**

1139 E. Jersey St., Ste. 319
(07201)
**Phone—(908) 351-0739**
Fax—(908) 351-3493
www.peachboutique.com
Email—roslynpeach@aol.com
Pres., GM & Hum. Res. Mgr.—
Roslyn Rearden
Sales Mgr.—Phyllis Williams

GEOGRAPHICAL

## Elizabeth—(cont.)

SIC—2389; 2395; *Clerical & choir robes & embroidery*
Employs—6; Estab.—1988
Sales—under $500,000
1,200 sq ft site, Distrib.—National
Sole ownership

**PEGASUS HOME FASHIONS, INC.**
107 Trumbull St., Bldg. G-1, P.O. Box 9030 (07206)
**Phone—(908) 965-1919**
Fax—(908) 965-1883
www.pegasushomefashions.com
Email—contact@ pegasushomefashions.com
GM—Carmine Spinella
Sales Mgr.—Jerry Desposito
Accts. Rec. Mgr.—Maria Portalatin
SIC—2221; NAICS—313210; *Pillows, comforters, blankets, quilts & mattress pads*
Employs—70; Estab.—1985
Distrib.—Regional
Privately owned corporation
AKA: CNS Machinery

**†PERFORMANCE FOOD GROUP-AFI FOODSERVICE**
Div. of Performance Food Group, Inc.
1 Ikea Dr. (07207)
**Phone—(908) 629-1800**
National—(800) 275-9500
Fax—(908) 629-0500
www.pfgc.com
Email—info@pfgc.com
CEO—Chuck Cuomo
Pres.—Michael Irwin
V.-P., Hum. Res.—Kathy Stevens
V.-P., Bus. Admn.—Ronald Possumato
V.-P., Fin.—Susan Morgan
Opers. Mgr.—Joe Monteleone
Cust. Serv. Mgr.—Joanne Mancuso
SIC—5142; 5148; *Distributor of food products to restaurants, hospitals & schools, including meat, produce & canned & dry goods*
Employs—450; Estab.—1997
Distrib.—Regional
Publicly owned corporation
Parent co.—Performance Food Group, Inc., Richmond, VA
Phone—(804) 484-7700
See Parent Co. Section for full profile.

**PIPE GUARDS BOLLARDS, LLC**
478 Schiller St. (07206)
**Phone—(908) 354-2259**
Fax—(908) 353-0612
www.pipeguardsbollards.com
Email—sales@ pipeguardsbollards.com
Dir., Mktg.—Joe Zulewski
SIC—3498; *U-shaped pipe guards & bollards from fabricated steel pipe*
Employs—12; Estab.—1932
Sales—$1Mil-$2.5Mil
Distrib.—National
Limited Liability Company

**PRIDE PRODUCTS, INC.**
5 Slater Dr. (07206)
**Phone—(908) 353-6800**
Fax—(908) 353-6974
Pres.—Joseph Yen
Hum. Res. Mgr.—Yolanda Cardona
SIC—3942; NAICS—339931; *Contract assembly of toys*
Employs—23; Estab.—1983
Sales—$500,000-$1Mil
Distrib.—Regional
Privately owned corporation

**QUALITY SWISS SCREW MACHINE CO., INC.**
849 4th Ave. (07202)
**Phone—(908) 654-1881**
Fax—(908) 289-8451
Foreman—Juan Monserrate
SIC—3451; NAICS—332721; *Swiss screw machine products*
Employs—4; Estab.—1972
Sales—under $500,000 (est)
Distrib.—National
Privately owned corporation
Parent co.—Quality Swiss Screw Machine Co., Inc., Mountainside, NJ
Phone—(908) 654-1881
See Parent Co. Section for full profile.

**R V TECH, INC.**
801 Magnolia Ave., Bldg. 3-B (07201)
Mail addr: P.O. Box 39, Vauxhall (07088-0039)
**Phone—(908) 469-8701**
Fax—(908) 469-8707
Email—rvtechco@msn.com
Pres.—Mayur Shah
SIC—2851; 2891; NAICS—325510; *Industrial paints, coatings & adhesives*
Employs—5; Estab.—1997
Sales—$500,000-$1Mil
8,000 sq ft site, Distrib.—Intl.
Privately owned corporation

**RESOLV CORPORATION**
410 Division St. (07201)
Mail addr: 237 Worthen Rd. E., Lexington (02421-6129)
**Phone—(973) 676-5141**
(973) 220-2713
Fax—(973) 323-2581
www.resolvcorp.com
Email—alirizvi@aol.com
Plt. Mgr.—Robert Zaman
Admn. Mgr.—Mohan Selvaraj
SIC—2869; 2865; *Dyes & colors blending for plastics, inks, petroleum, gasoline, coatings, leather, tracers, markers, smoke, hair, food, solvent & specialty applications & pharmaceuticals, cosmetics & nutraceuticals; Brand name—RESOPLAST; RESONOL; RESOFLUOR; RESOBRIGHT; RESODIRECT; RESOBASIC; RESOVAT*
Employs—9; Estab.—1997
Sales—$5Mil-$10Mil
40,000 sq ft site, Distrib.—Intl.
Privately owned corporation
Parent co.—Resolv Corporation, Lexington, MA
Phone—(973) 676-5141
See Parent Co. Section for full profile.

**†STULZ SICKLES STEEL CO.**
929 Julia St. (07201)
Mail addr: P.O. Box 273, Elizabeth (07207)
**Phone—(908) 351-1776**
(800) 351-1776
Fax—(908) 351-8231
www.stulzsicklessteel.com
Email—stulzco@aol.com
Pres.—Philip DeStasio
V.-P., Sales—Robert Ogilvie
V.-P., Fin. & MIS Mgr.—Michael Harlan
Plt. Mgr.—Kevin Kolacki
Off. Mgr.—Lorraine Cuono
SIC—5051; *Wholesaler of steel products & steel cutting & fabrication; Brand name—Manganal Steel*
Employs—30; Estab.—1916
Sales—$15Mil
30,000 sq ft site, Distrib.—Intl.
Privately owned corporation

**SUPERIOR POWDER COATING, INC.**
600 Progress St. (07201)
**Phone—(908) 351-8707**
Fax—(908) 351-0870
www.superiorpowder.com
Email—info@superiorpowder.com
Pres.—Peter Markey
V.-P., Sales & Mktg.—Glenn Ashton
V.-P., Quality—John Elskamp
V.-P.—Charles Briggs
SIC—3479; *Metal finishing, including powder & electro coating*
Employs—150; Estab.—1989
112,000 sq ft site, Distrib.—National
Privately owned corporation
ISO rating—9001:2008

**SURVIVOR II, INC.**
919 Fairmount Ave. (07201)
**Phone—(908) 353-1155**
National—(800) 620-3743
Fax—(866) 968-3299
www.survivorwindowsii.com
Ptnr.—Tony Casas
SIC—3089; *Vinyl windows*
Employs—20; Estab.—2009
Sales—$2.5Mil-$5Mil (est)
Distrib.—Local
Privately owned corporation

**TOPCO, INC.**
107 Trumbull St. (07206)
**Phone—(908) 352-6720**
National—(800) 269-6720
Fax—(908) 352-9571
www.topcoinc.com
Email—topco@topcoinc.com
Pres.—Martin Gindoff
V.-P.—Jay Gindoff
Cont.—Jay Jeyarajah
Plt. Mgr.—Peter Palumbo
SIC—3469; *Deep drawn metal stampings*
Employs—60; Estab.—1895
100,000 sq ft site, Distrib.—National
Privately owned sub-S corp.

**TRI-STATE LEATHER, INC.**
504 4th Ave. (07202)
**Phone—(908) 275-3310**
(908) 994-1120
Email—tristateinc001@aol.com
Cont.—Walter Ramirez
SIC—2531; *Automotive seats*
Employs—14; Estab.—1990
Distrib.—Regional
Privately owned corporation

**†TRUE WORLD FOODS, LLC**
Div. of True World Group, LLC
32-34 Papetti Plz. (07206)
**Phone—(908) 351-1400**
National—(800) 486-3474
Fax—(908) 351-8485
www.trueworldfoods.com
Email—yi-suh@trueworldfoods.com
Hum. Res. Mgr.—Eve Roberts
Pub. Rels. Mgr.—Debbie Pike
SIC—5146; *Wholesaler of fresh & frozen seafood*
Employs—55; Estab.—1975
Distrib.—Intl.
Privately owned corporation
Parent co.—True World Group, LLC, Rockleigh, NJ
Phone—(201) 750-0024
See Parent Co. Section for full profile.

**UNION COUNTY PLATE GLASS CO. (H Q)**
1050 Elizabeth Ave., P.O. Box 9027 (07201)
**Phone—(908) 354-0380**
Fax—(908) 354-9321
www.ucpglass.com
Email—charlesjr@ucpglass.com
Pres.—Charles J. Komoroski, Jr.
V.-P.—Joseph S. Komoroski
Cont.—James S. Birmingham
Payroll Mgr.—Janet Bevan
SIC—3231; NAICS—327215; *Company headquarters; plate glass, including glass & glazing, aluminum curtain walls, skylights, storefronts & doors (mfg. subcontracted)*
Employs—60; Estab.—1946
Sales—$14Mil-$20Mil
Distrib.—Local
Privately owned sub-S corp.

**UNIVERSAL VALVE CO., INC.**
478 Schiller St. (07206)
**Phone—(908) 351-0606**
National—(800) 223-0741
Fax—(908) 351-0369
www.universalvalve.com
Email—inbox@universalvalve.com
Pres., CEO—Robert Milo
CFO—Amy A. Milo
Ex. V.-P.—Martin Pettesch
Dir., Mktg.—Joseph Zulewski
Opers. & Sales Mgr.—Peter Mascis
Pur. & Whse. Mgr.—Michael Farinha
SIC—3494; 3492; 3321; 3993; NAICS—332919; *Valves, fittings, vapor recovery equipment, manholes, banking signs, pipe guards, bollards, bollard covers, bike racks, retrofit sump covers & hose retrievers for gas stations & the service station industry*
Employs—30; Estab.—1932
60,000 sq ft site, Distrib.—Intl.
Privately owned sub-S corp.

**VARDA INTERNATIONAL CORP.**
41 S. Spring St. (07201)
**Phone—(908) 354-9090**
National—(800) 448-2732
Fax—(908) 354-9091
www.vardachocolatier.com
Email—sales@ vardachocolatier.com
Pres.—Varda Shamban
Prodn. Mgr.—Bololivar Valenaldivieso
Hum. Res. & Off. Mgr.—Michelle Hughes
SIC—2066; NAICS—311300; *Chocolates; Brand name—VARDA CHOCOLATIER*
Employs—3; Estab.—1987
Distrib.—National
Privately owned corporation

**†W. W. GRAINGER, INC.**
560-596 Bercik St., Ste. 1 (07201)
**Phone—(908) 787-1952**
Fax—(908) 787-1953
www.grainger.com
Email—info@grainger.com
GM—Phil Circelli
SIC—5084; 5085; *Wholesaler of industrial equipment & supplies*
Employs—12; Estab.—1992
Distrib.—Regional
Privately owned corporation
Parent co.—W. W. Grainger, Inc., Lake Forest, IL
Phone—(847) 535-1000
See Parent Co. Section for full profile.

## Elmer
(Salem—S.W.)

**†ARCHER PLASTICS, INC.**
1510 Jesse Bridge Rd. (08318)
**Phone—(856) 692-0242**
Fax—(856) 692-0243
www.archerseating.com
Email—archerseating@comcast.net
Pres.—Steve Archer
SIC—5021; *Wholesaler of modern & collectible wooden & plastic office, auditorium & stadium seating*
Employs—5; Estab.—1992
Distrib.—Intl.
Privately owned corporation

## Elmer—(cont.)

**BBK MACHINING, INC.**
429 Garrison Rd. (08318)
**Phone—(856) 358-8864**
Pres.—Edward Suess
V.-P.—Lynn Suess
SIC—3599; *General machining job shop*
Employs—2; Estab.—1987
Sales—under $500,000
Distrib.—Local
Privately owned corporation

**ELMER TIMES CO., INC.**
21 State St. (08318)
**Phone—(856) 358-6171**
Email—elmertimesco@aol.com
Pres.—Mark Foster
V.-P.—Preston Foster III
SIC—2711; *Weekly newspaper publishing*
Employs—4; Estab.—1885
Sales—under $500,000
Distrib.—Local
Privately owned corporation

**FAIRWAY PRODUCTS CO.**
265 Garden Rd., P.O. Box 611 (08318)
**Phone—(856) 358-6016**
National—(800) 323-2573
Fax—(856) 358-8055
www.fairwayproducts.com
Email—fairwayproducts@aol.com
Pres.—Edward Carman
Off. Mgr.—Paula Moore
SIC—3949; NAICS—339920; *Golf course equipment, including fairway yardage markers*
Employs—4; Estab.—1976
Sales—$500,000-$1Mil
Distrib.—Intl.
Privately owned corporation

**MANUTECH, INC.**
29 State St., P.O.Box 758 (08318)
**Phone—(856) 358-6136**
Fax—(856) 358-6279
Email—ed@manutechinc.net
Pres.—Edward P. Deinarowicz
SIC—3469; 3599; *Metal stampings & general machining job shop, including prototype, tool making & precision sheet metal fabrication*
Employs—4; Estab.—1982
Sales—under $500,000
5,000 sq ft site, Distrib.—National
Privately owned sub-S corp.

---

## Elmwood Park

(Bergen—N.E.)

**AGFA CORP. (H Q)**
611 River Dr. (07407)
**Phone—(201) 440-0111**
National—(800) 540-2432
www.agfapitman.com
Pres.—Peter Wilkens
CFO—Gunther Mertens
IT Mgr.—Joe Milici
Mktg. Comm. Mgr.—Lois Catala
SIC—2759; NAICS—323115; *Corporate headquarters; digital offset printing & equipment & supplies; Brand name—Agfa*
Employs—100; Estab.—1973
Sales—$50Mil-$100Mil
Publicly owned corporation
AKA: Agfa Graphics

**†BERGEN INDUSTRIAL SUPPLY A DIVISION OF F.W. WEBB**
30 Stefanic Ave. (07407)
**Phone—(201) 796-2600**
Fax—(201) 796-5603
www.fwwebb.com
Email—is66@fwwebb.com
GM—Tim Vandenburgh
Opers. Mgr.—Jeff Cortland
Off. Mgr.—Michael LaPorte
SIC—5074; *Distributor of plumbing supplies*
Employs—65; Estab.—1965
Distrib.—Local
Privately owned corporation

**BLOOMEX INTERNATIONAL, INC.**
295 Molnar Dr. (07407)
**Phone—(201) 703-9799**
Fax—(201) 703-9626
www.bloomex.com
Email—sales@bloomex.com
Pres.—Benjamin Laroux
SIC—3845; 3496; NAICS—334500; *Low-energy electronic muscle stimulators & insulated & uninsulated multicolored reusable carbon rubber medical grade accessories, including flexible electrodes & wire leads, sponges, adapters & related medical electronics; Brand name—Carbonflex; Medflex*
Employs—4; Estab.—1977
Sales—$500,000-$1Mil
3,500 sq ft site, Distrib.—Intl.
Privately owned corporation

**COLEX IMAGING, INC.**
55-57 Bushes Ln. (07407)
**Phone—(201) 265-5670**
Fax—(201) 265-7093
www.colex.com
Email—sales@colex.com
Pres.—Werner Waden
Administrator—Maureen Damato
SIC—3555; 5049; NAICS—333293; *Manufacturer & distributor of wide-format finishing equipment; Brand name—COLEX SHARPCUT FLATBED CUTTER; FOTOBA AUTOMATIC CUTTERS; ROLLSROLLER FLATBED APPLICATOR*
Employs—26; Estab.—1971
Sales—$5Mil
12,000 sq ft site, Distrib.—Intl.
Privately owned corporation

**CORBAN ENERGY GROUP**
418 Falmouth Ave. (07407)
**Phone—(201) 509-8555**
            (201) 509-8556
Fax—(201) 509-8550
www.corbanenergygroup.com
Email—howard.a@ corbanenergygroup.com
CEO—Daniel Chung
GM—Howard Adams
Consultant—John Schlosberg
SIC—3563; 3586; 3443; *Compressed natural gas (CNG) fueling compressors, stations, dispensers & tanks for truck fleets & consumer vehicles*
Employs—15
Sales—$1Mil-$5Mil
18,000 sq ft site, Distrib.—National
Sole ownership

**CROWN LIFT TRUCKS, INC.**
Div. of Crown Equipment Corp.
680 River Dr. (07407)
**Phone—(845) 753-5868**
www.crown.com
Email—contactus@crown.com
Manager—Paul Meda
SIC—3537; *Material handling equipment, including forklifts*
Employs—20
Sales—$2.5Mil-$5Mil (est)
Privately owned corporation
Parent co.—Crown Equipment Corp., New Bremen, OH
Phone—(419) 629-2311
See Parent Co. Section for full profile.

**DOR-WIN MFG. CO.**
109 Midland Ave. (07407)
**Phone—(201) 796-4300**
Fax—(201) 791-1962
www.dor-winmfg.com
Email—dorwin62@aol.com
Pres.—Marco Cangialosi
Manager—Roe Scaravilli
SIC—3089; 3442; NAICS—332321; *Vinyl windows & doors & steel & fiberglass entry doors, including new construction & replacement*
Employs—40; Estab.—1962
Sales—$5Mil
Distrib.—National
Privately owned corporation

**EASTERN CONCRETE MATERIALS, INC. (H Q)**
Div. of U. S. Concrete, Inc.
475 Market St., 3rd Fl. (07407)
**Phone—(201) 797-7979**
National—(800) 822-7242
Fax—(201) 791-9631
www.eastern-concrete.com
Email—pderosa@us-concrete.com
Pres.—Mike Gentoso
Dir., IT—Robert Osbahr
Sales Mgr.—Gary Graziano
Opers. Mgr.—Louis Petrollo
Hum. Res. Mgr.—Patricia Kotlowski
Qual. Control Mgr.—Paul DeRosa
SIC—3273; 3271; 3272; NAICS—327320; *Corporate headquarters; ready-mixed concrete, aggregates & landscape materials*
Employs—40
Sales—$5Mil-$10Mil
Distrib.—Regional
Publicly owned corporation
Parent co.—U. S. Concrete, Inc., Euless, TX
Phone—(817) 835-4105
See Parent Co. Section for full profile.

**ELMWOOD INDUSTRIES**
8 Paul Kohner Pl. (07407)
**Phone—(201) 703-1220**
Fax—(201) 794-8375
www.elmwoodindustries.com
Supervisor—Diane Zirpoli
SIC—2396; 2395; *Apparel screen printing & embroidery*
Employs—2; Estab.—2003
Sales—under $500,000 (est)
Distrib.—Local
Privately owned corporation

**ELMWOOD PRESS, INC.**
85 Main Ave. (07407)
**Phone—(201) 794-6273**
Fax—(201) 794-9085
www.elmwoodpress.net
Email—email@elmwoodpress.net
Owner & Off. Mgr.—Kimberly A. Murphy
GM—Al Cowie
SIC—2752; 2759; NAICS—323116; *Offset, digital & direct mail printing*
Employs—10; Estab.—1989
Distrib.—Regional
Privately owned corporation
Also see: Reliable Envelopes & Graphics, Inc., same loc.

**G & H SOHO, INC.**
413 Market St. (07407)
**Phone—(201) 216-9400**
Fax—(201) 216-1778
www.ghsoho.com
Email—sales@ghsoho.com
Pres.—James K. Harris
V.-P.—Gerald F. Burstein
Bus. Mgr.—Robert Tinkham
SIC—2759; 2791; NAICS—323122; *On demand digital printing & electronic prepress of books, catalogs, directories, newsletters & related bound products*
Employs—15; Estab.—1985
Sales—$2Mil
12,500 sq ft site, Distrib.—National
Privately owned corporation

**GRANT INDUSTRIES, INC.**
125 Main Ave. (07407)
**Phone—(201) 791-6700**
National—(800) 927-1187
Fax—(201) 791-0038
www.grantinc.com
Email—info@grantinc.com
Pres.—Michael Granatell
Acct. Mgr.—Brett Bullock
SIC—2843; 2844; NAICS—325613; *Textile chemicals & cosmetics*
Employs—85
Sales—$35Mil-$40Mil
Distrib.—National
Privately owned corporation

**JOHN WM. MACY CHEESESTICKS, INC.**
80 Kipp Ave. (07407)
**Phone—(201) 791-8036**
National—(800) 643-0573
Fax—(201) 797-5068
www.cheesesticks.com
Email—sales@cheesesticks.com
Pres., Hum. Res.—John Macy
V.-P., CFO & IT Mgr.—Tim Macy
SIC—2022; 2052; 2051; NAICS—311513; *Gourmet breadsticks, dessert twists & crisps*
Employs—60; Estab.—1985
38,000 sq ft site, Distrib.—National
Privately owned sub-S corp.

**K T S MACHINE SHOP**
60 Bushes Ln. (07407)
**Phone—(201) 791-2228**
Fax—(201) 791-7855
Owner—Stanley Darszcz
SIC—3599; *CNC & precision machining job shop*
Employs—2; Estab.—1987
Sales—under $500,000
Distrib.—Regional
Sole ownership

**KINGS CANDY CO., INC.**
55 Bank St., P.O. Box 264 (07407)
**Phone—(201) 791-4444**
Fax—(201) 791-2893
Pres.—Louis Lapone
V.-P.—Patrick Kaplan
Off. Mgr.—Marie Benkovic
SIC—2064; NAICS—311300; *Candy; Brand name—Lapone Jordan Almonds*
Employs—15; Estab.—1945
Sales—$500,000-$1Mil
Distrib.—National
Privately owned corporation

**KREISLER MFG. CORP.**
180 Van Riper Ave. (07407)
**Phone—(201) 791-0700**
Fax—(201) 791-8015
www.kreislermfg.com
Email—kreisler@kreisler-ind.com
Owner—Michael Stern
CFO—Ned Stern
Dir., Sales & Mktg.—Brad Barnes
Hum. Res. Mgr.—Lisa Sabrel
Hum. Res. Mgr.—Paul Lomelo
SIC—3317; 3498; NAICS—331210; *Tube & manifold fabrication for gas turbine engines*
Employs—150; Estab.—1962
50,000 sq ft site, Distrib.—Intl.

**†LOTUS EXIM INTERNATIONAL, INC.**
16 Leliarts Ln. (07407-3208)
**Phone—(201) 475-2810**
Fax—(201) 475-2817
www.lotusexim.com
Email—info@lotusexim.com
Pres.—Rajendra Kankariya
V.-P.—Jyoti Kankariya
Hum. Res. & Pers. Mgr. & Admn.—Rakesh K. Gupta

**GEOGRAPHICAL**

## Elmwood Park—(cont.)

SIC—5032; *Wholesaler of granite & marble*
Employs—15; Estab.—1998
Sales—$22Mil
16,000 sq ft site, Distrib.—National
Privately owned corporation

**MINIATURE FOLDING, INC.**
14 Wenzel St. (07407)
**Phone—(201) 773-6477**
Fax—(201) 773-6480
www.miniaturefolding.com
Email—info@miniaturefolding.com
Pres.—Christopher Taliercio, Sr.
V-P.—Christopher Taliercio, Jr.
SIC—3999; *Contract miniature folding of pharmaceutical & cosmetic printed materials, including hot melt tipping, precision cutting, RTA/ribbon outsets & padding*
Employs—25
Sales—$2.5Mil-$5Mil (est)
Distrib.—National
Privately owned corporation

**NITKA GRAPHICS, INC.**
355 E. 54th St. (07407)
Mail addr: 13-63 Henrietta Ct., Fair Lawn (07410)
**Phone—(201) 797-3000**
National—(800) 879-6482
Fax—(201) 797-3009
www.nitkainc.com
Email—nitka@mac.com
Pres.—Hayim Nitka
Sales Mgr.—Russ Spitzer
SIC—2752; 2759; NAICS—323110; *Annual report, newsletter, brochure & flyer printing*
Employs—12; Estab.—1980
10,200 sq ft site, Distrib.—Intl.
Privately owned corporation

**PAIGE PACKAGING**
1 Paul Kohner Pl. (07407)
**Phone—(973) 483-0505**
Fax—(201) 461-2677
www.paigecompany.com
Email—info@paigecompany.com
Owner—Allan Levine
Shpg. Mgr.—Mike Milan
SIC—2653; NAICS—322211; *Corrugated boxes*
Employs—35; Estab.—1960
55,000 sq ft site, Distrib.—Local
Privately owned corporation

**PENN COLOR, INC.**
30 Kohner Pl. (07407)
**Phone—(201) 791-5100**
Fax—(201) 791-2273
www.penncolor.com
Email—info@penncolor.com
Prodn. Mgr.—Bob Frei
Off. Mgr.—Beth Deleon
SIC—2816; 2865; NAICS—325910; *Plastic colorants, industrial coatings & printing inks*
Employs—80; Estab.—1985
Distrib.—Local
Privately owned corporation
Parent co.—Penn Color, Inc., Doylestown, PA
Phone—(215) 345-6550
See Parent Co. Section for full profile.

**PHILLIPS PRECISION, INC.**
7 Paul Kohner Pl. (07407)
**Phone—(201) 797-8820**
Fax—(201) 797-3039
www.phillipsprecisionmedicraft.com
Email—fphillips@phillipsprecision.com
Owner—Francis Phillips
Co-Pres., Medicraft—Michael Phillips
Co-Pres.—John Phillips

SIC—3842; 3841; *Orthopedic implants & instrumentation & sterilization cases & trays*
Employs—200; Estab.—1983
Sales—$11Mil-$25Mil
Distrib.—National
Privately owned corporation

**PHYTOCEUTICALS, INC.**
37 Midland Ave. (07407)
**Phone—(201) 791-2255**
Fax—(201) 791-2310
www.phyto-ceutical.com
Email—info@phyto-ceutical.com
Pres.—Mostafa Omar
SIC—2844; *Skin care products*
Employs—5
Sales—$1Mil-$2.5Mil (est)

**QUALITY REPRO CENTERS, INC.**
296 Route 46 E., P.O. Box 111 (07407)
**Phone—(201) 794-3905**
National—(800) 486-3930
Fax—(201) 794-3909
www.qrepro.com
Email—qrepro@optonline.net
Pres.—Joe DiGiaimo
V-P.—Michael DiGiaimo
SIC—2759; 2752; 2761; 5112; NAICS—323116; *Commercial & digital color printing of business forms & cards & commercial blueprinting, including CAD & digital plotting, scanning, mounting & laminating & distributor of media/toners & supplies for inkjet & digital wide-format plotters*
Employs—6; Estab.—1989
Sales—$500,000-$1Mil
3,000 sq ft site, Distrib.—Regional
Privately owned sub-S corp.

**RECYCLETECH CORP.**
418 Falmouth Ave. (07407)
**Phone—(201) 475-5000**
Fax—(201) 475-5001
www.recycletechno.com
Email—howard@recycletechno.com
Pres.—Dan Chung
GM—Howard Adams
Sales Mgr.—John Kim
SIC—3559; 5093; *Assembly of EPS (expanded polystyrene) recycling equipment, reverse vending machines & pyrolysis plants & wholesaler of recycled EPS*
Employs—15; Estab.—2004
Sales—$3Mil-$6Mil
18,000 sq ft site, Distrib.—Intl.
Sole ownership

**RELIABLE ENVELOPE & GRAPHICS, INC.**
85 Main Ave. (07407)
**Phone—(201) 794-7756**
National—(800) 776-2227
Fax—(201) 794-1319
www.reliableenvelope.com
Email—email@reliableenvelope.com
Chrm.—Gene Murphy
Pres.—Brian Murphy
Ex. V-P.—Kevin Murphy
Manager—Kim Murphy
SIC—2677; 2752; NAICS—323122; *Custom & standard envelopes, including offset printing, electronic prepress, binding, fulfillment & mailing services*
Employs—25; Estab.—1986
Distrib.—Regional
Privately owned corporation
Also see: Elmwood Press, Inc., same loc.

**†RICHARDS CO.**
437 Boulevard, P.O. Box 199 (07407)
**Phone—(201) 797-6300**
National—(800) 929-2992

Fax—(201) 797-2546
www.richardscompany.com
Email—dan.kleinrock@richardscompany.com
V-P., Opers. & CEO—Dan J. Kleinrock
V-P., Sales—Dave Kleinrock
SIC—5084; 5063; 5085; *Distributor of industrial equipment & supplies, including conveyors & components, adjustable speed drives, electric motors & controls, bearings & seals; Brand name—American Sleeve; Baldor Electric; Dayton; Diamond Chain; Danaher Motion; Lovejoy; Formsprag; Hub-City; Gates; Boston Gear; Martin Sprocket & Gear; NTN Bearings; RBC Bearings; Falk; Rexnord; Red Lion*
Employs—10; Estab.—1968
Distrib.—Intl.
Privately owned corporation

**SAWDUST DEPOT**
1 Boumar Pl. (07407)
**Phone—(201) 703-8400**
Fax—(201) 703-8405
Email—ippolitoid@gmail.com
Pres.—Vincent Ippolito
SIC—2421; *Sawdust & wood shavings*
Employs—8; Estab.—1917
Sales—$500,000-$1Mil
8,000 sq ft site, Distrib.—Local
Privately owned corporation

**SEALED AIR CORP. (H Q)**
200 Riverfront Blvd., 3rd Fl. (07407)
**Phone—(201) 791-7600**
National—(800) 346-5855
Fax—(201) 703-4205
www.sealedair.com
Email—tony.meola@sealedair.com
Pres., CEO—Jerome Peribere
Sr. V-P., CFO—Carol Lowe
Dir., Inv. Rels.—Lori Chaitman
Hum. Res. Mgr.—Norman Finch
Benefits Mgr.—Tony Meola
SIC—3089; 3086; NAICS—326100; *Corporate headquarters; food packaging containers, bubble wrap & envelopes*
Employs—100
Sales—$10Mil-$25Mil (est)
Publicly owned corporation

**SOUNDVIEW PAPER CO.**
1 Market St. (07407)
**Phone—(201) 796-4000**
National—(800) 631-8451
Fax—(201) 796-0470
www.marcalsmallsteps.com
Email—info@marcalsmallsteps.com
CEO—George Wurtz
CFO—Kim Knotts
Sr. V-P., Sales & Mktg.—John McLean
SIC—2621; NAICS—322100; *Company headquarters & eco-friendly paper tissue & towel products from recycled paper*
Employs—580
Sales—$100Mil-$250Mil (est)

**TROLEX CORP.**
20 Bushes Ln. (07407)
**Phone—(201) 794-8004**
National—(877) 604-1044
Fax—(201) 794-1359
www.zonefirst.com
Email—info@zonefirst.com
Pres.—Richard Foster
IT Mgr.—John Kraft
Hum. Res. & Off. Admn.—Lori Vanderkooy

SIC—3444; *Ventilation duct dampers*
Employs—30; Estab.—1965
Sales—$5Mil-$10Mil
26,000 sq ft site, Distrib.—Intl.
Privately owned corporation
AKA: Zonefirst

**UNGAR'S FOOD PRODUCTS, INC.**
9 Boumar Pl. (07407)
**Phone—(201) 703-1300**
National—(877) 772-3437
Fax—(201) 703-9333
www.drpraegers.com
Email—webquery@drpraegers.com
Pres.—Peter Praeger
CFO & COO—Jeff Cohen
Off. Mgr.—Ellen Somberg
Cust. Serv. Exec.—Rita Foster
SIC—2038; 2099; NAICS—311412; *Frozen kosher food products, including veggie burgers, pancakes & fish*
Employs—45; Estab.—1994
60,000 sq ft site, Distrib.—National
Privately owned sub-S corp.
AKA: Dr. Praeger's

**VANEA USA, INC.**
410 Market St. (07407)
**Phone—(201) 796-0722**
Fax—(201) 796-2313
www.vanea.us
Email—marchis@vanea.us
V-P.—Sandro Marchi
SIC—3253; 3261; NAICS—327122; *Italian-style ceramic tile & kitchen & bathroom fixtures*
Employs—10; Estab.—1976
Sales—under $500,000
Distrib.—National
Privately owned corporation

## Elwood
(Atlantic—S.E.)

**SPECIALTY RUBBER, INC.**
4500 White Horse Pike, P.O. Box 483 (08217)
**Phone—(609) 704-2555**
(800) 249-5848
Fax—(609) 704-8020
www.specialtyrubber.com
Email—specrub@yahoo.com
Pres.—Richard Orosz
V-P., Opers.—Kevin Orosz
Sales Mgr.—Christopher Orosz
SIC—3053; NAICS—339991; *Rubber gaskets*
Employs—5; Estab.—1985
Sales—$500,000-$1Mil
5,000 sq ft site, Distrib.—Intl.
Privately owned corporation

## Emerson
(Bergen—N.E.)

**ACCURATE DIAMOND TOOL CORP.**
1 Palisade Ave. (07630)
**Phone—(201) 265-8868**
National—(800) 631-0750
Fax—(201) 265-8865
www.accuratediamondtool.com
Email—accudiam@optonline.net
Pres.—Daniel Michael
SIC—3545; 3541; *Diamond dressing tools, diamond/CBN grinding wheels in resin bond, metal bond, electroplated, hybrid bond & vitrified bond & PCD/PCBN tipped inserts, end mills & cutting tools*
Employs—25; Estab.—1962
25,000 sq ft site, Distrib.—Intl.
Privately owned corporation

**AESYS, INC.**
27 Bland St. (07630)
**Phone—(201) 871-3223**
Fax—(201) 871-3239
www.aesysinc.com
Email—info@aesysinc.com

## Emerson—(cont.)

CFO—Evelyn McGregor
V-P., Mng. Dir.—Colin McGregor
SIC—3669; NAICS—334290;
*Pure LED signs for transit, coach
& highway applications*
Employs—5; Estab.—1977
Sales—$1Mil-$5Mil
Distrib.—National
Privately owned corporation

### AMERICAN INK JET SYSTEMS, INC.

34 Chestnut St. (07630)
**Phone—(201) 263-9177**
Fax—(201) 383-0120
www.ais-tech.us
Email—samples@
americaninkjetsystems.com
Pres.—Stephen Saltman
SIC—2893; 3085; 7372; 3571;
*Manufacturer of inkjet inks, bulk
ink refillable cartridges, RIP
software & graphic design
computer workstations for fine
art, photographic, textile &
signage printing & distributor of
color management software for
printing applications*
Employs—5
Sales—$1Mil-$2.5Mil (est)
Distrib.—Intl.
Privately owned sub-S corp.

### D R HANDMADE STRINGS, INC.

7 Palisade Ave. (07630)
**Phone—(201) 599-0100**
National—(800) 782-1901
Fax—(201) 599-0404
www.drstrings.com
Email—drstaff@drstrings.com
Pres.—Mark Dronge
MIS Mgr.—Tom Klukosky
SIC—3931; NAICS—339992;
*Guitar strings; Brand name—DR
HandMade Strings; EXTRA-Life
Strings*
Employs—35; Estab.—1986
12,000 sq ft site, Distrib.—Intl.
Privately owned corporation
AKA: D R Music

### EMERSON FENCE, INC.

10 Lincoln Blvd., P.O. Box 306
(07630)
**Phone—(201) 265-5150**
Fax—(201) 265-3449
www.emersonfence.com
Email—sales@emersonfence.com
Pres.—Robert Skrable, Jr.
V-P.—Donald Skrable
Cont., Fin. Mgr.—Kant Desai
SIC—2499; 3089; 3496; 5031;
NAICS—332618; *Manufacturer
& distributor of custom white &
red cedar, PVC, post, rail,
stockade, chain-link & aluminum
fencing*
Employs—20; Estab.—1957
Sales—$2Mil-$2.5Mil
4,000 sq ft site, Distrib.—Local
Privately owned corporation

### JAMOL LABORATORIES, INC.

13 Ackerman Ave., P.O. Box 313
(07630)
**Phone—(201) 262-6363**
Fax—(201) 262-2437
www.ponaris.net
Email—jamollab@aol.com
Pres.—Emil Scott Lucia
Administrator—Kay Carlson
SIC—2834; 2833; NAICS—
325412; *OTC botanical nose
drops for the treatment of
allergies, congestion, nose
bleeds & associated sinus
issues; Brand name—Ponaris
Nasal Emollient*
Employs—5; Estab.—1960
1,700 sq ft site, Distrib.—National
Privately owned corporation

### O&T-SUTER CONSERVATION, LLC

96 Hillside Ave. (07630)
**Phone—(201) 265-0262**
Email—millie@otsuter.com
Pres. & Manager—Millie Suter
V-P.—Deirdre Suter
SIC—2789; NAICS—323121;
*Hand bookbinding, including
paper & book restoration*
Employs—4; Estab.—1964
Sales—under $500,000
3,200 sq ft site, Distrib.—Local
Limited Liability Company

### RAY'S REPRODUCTIONS, INC.

39 Bland St. (07630)
**Phone—(201) 666-5650**
Fax—(201) 666-7784
www.raysreproductions.com
Email—irene@
raysreproductions.com
Pres.—Ray Stuart
V-P., Secy.-Treas.—Irene Stuart
SIC—2759; 2752; 3993; NAICS—
323100; *Digital, offset, large-
format & instant printing,
including graphics &
promotional products*
Employs—5; Estab.—1978
Sales—over $500,000
3,000 sq ft site, Distrib.—National
Privately owned corporation

### TOLIN DESIGN, INC.

16 Bland St. (07630)
**Phone—(201) 261-4455**
Fax—(201) 261-0018
www.tolindesign.com
Email—info@tolindesign.com
Pres., Plt. Mgr.—Tony Suarez
Foreman—Bill Anthony
SIC—3423; *Aircraft tools & ground
support equipment*
Employs—5; Estab.—1986
Sales—$500,000-$1Mil
Distrib.—Intl.
Privately owned corporation

### WEATHERCRAFT MFG. CO.

13 Emerson Plz. E. (07630)
**Phone—(201) 262-0055**
Fax—(201) 262-8860
www.weathercraftmfg.com
Email—info@weathercraftmfg.com
Pres.—Salvatore Gebbia
SIC—3444; 2394; *Aluminum
awnings & enclosures,
retractable fabric awnings &
loading dock & walkway covers*
Employs—15; Estab.—1976
Sales—$1Mil-$2.5Mil
Distrib.—Local
Privately owned corporation

---

## Englewood
(Bergen—N.E.)

### 3LAB, INC. (H Q)

100 W. Sheffield Ave. (07631)
**Phone—(201) 567-9100**
Fax—(201) 567-2280
www.3lab.com
Email—info@3lab.com
Pres.—David C. Chung
V-P.—Erica Chung
Mktg. Mgr.—Christina Oresajo
SIC—2844; NAICS—325600;
*Corporate headquarters; skin
care products, including body
lotion (mfg. subcontracted)*
Employs—10; Estab.—2003
Sales—$2.5Mil-$5Mil (est)
Distrib.—Intl.
Privately owned corporation

### †ACCURATE PRECISION FASTENERS CORP.

20 Honeck St. (07631)
**Phone—(201) 567-9700**
Fax—(201) 567-1965
Email—sales@
accurateprecision.com

Pres.—Michael Jacobs
Manager—Bruce Hendricksen
Manager—Marcia Wodka
SIC—5072; *Distributor of
aerospace fasteners*
Employs—25; Estab.—1947
Sales—$10Mil-$20Mil
20,000 sq ft site, Distrib.—Intl.
Privately owned corporation
ISO rating—9001

### ACME GEAR CO., INC.

130 W. Forest Ave., P.O. Box 779
(07631)
**Phone—(201) 568-2245**
Fax—(201) 568-0282
www.acmegear.com
Email—info@acmegear.com
Pres.—Joseph Gelles
Cont.—Rob Farrow
Mfg. Mgr.—Max Minder
SIC—3566; NAICS—333612;
*Gear machining job shop*
Employs—100; Estab.—1924
Sales—$6Mil-$10Mil
Distrib.—National
Privately owned corporation
ISO rating—9002

### [NEW ENTRY]

### ALEXANDER PUBLISHING, INC.

8 Depot Sq. (07631)
**Phone—(201) 569-5373**
www.alexanderpublishing.com
Email—sales@
alexanderpublishing.com
Pres.—Geoffrey Steck
SIC—2721; *Newsletter publishing*
Employs—4; Estab.—1986
Sales—$1Mil-$2.5Mil
1,000 sq ft site, Distrib.—Intl.
Privately owned corporation

### ALPINE TRADING CO., INC.

400 Overpeck Pl. (07631)
**Phone—(201) 871-6111**
National—(800) 938-0303
Fax—(800) 938-0228
www.imagefirstuniforms.com
Email—sales@
imagefirstuniforms.com
Pres.—Jacob Arden
V-P., Sales—Marlon Ortiz
Dir., Internet Opers.—David
Zilbershlag
Acct. Mgr.—Kevin Hedley
Cust. Serv. Rep.—Cynthia
Sanchez
SIC—2326; 2339; NAICS—
315200; *Police, security, airline &
corrections uniforms, work wear,
badges, patches & insignia;
Brand name—Image First
Uniforms*
Employs—40; Estab.—1991
50,000 sq ft site, Distrib.—National
Privately owned corporation

### AMD FINE LINENS, LLC

18 W. Forest Ave. (07631)
**Phone—(201) 568-5255**
Fax—(201) 568-0155
www.bellinofinelinens.com
Email—info@bellinofinelinens.com
Owner—Gianni Romagnolo
SIC—2392; *Bed linens*
Employs—7; Estab.—1986
Sales—$2Mil
Distrib.—Intl.
Limited Liability Company

### AMERICAN MONUMENT CO. (H Q)

479 N. Dean St. (07631)
**Phone—(201) 569-4455**
Fax—(201) 894-5540
www.800monument.com
Pres.—Ron Boyajian
V-P.—Greg Boyajian

SIC—3281; 3365; NAICS—
327991; *Company headquarters;
stone, natural rock, granite, brick
& concrete engraving &
aluminum & bronze plaque
casting; Brand name—Written in
Stone™*
Employs—3; Estab.—1978
Sales—under $500,000
Distrib.—National
Privately owned corporation

### APM HEXSEAL CORP.

44 Honeck St. (07631)
**Phone—(201) 569-5700**
National—(800) 498-9034
Fax—(201) 569-4106
www.apmhexseal.com
Email—info@apmhexseal.com
Pres.—David Morse
V-P., Prod.—Kenneth Foster
Billing Mgr.—Nancy Baron
SIC—3061; NAICS—326291;
*Rubber environmental seals for
the protection of switches, circuit
breakers, self-sealing fasteners,
screws, bolts, nuts & rivets*
Employs—40; Estab.—1950
15,000 sq ft site, Distrib.—Intl.
Privately owned corporation

### ARRO-MARK CO., LLC

158 W. Forest Ave. (07631)
**Phone—(201) 567-4112**
Fax—(201) 567-1373
www.arromark.com
Email—arromark@aol.com
Ptnr.—Stephanie Pappageorge
Pres.—George Pappageorge
SIC—3953; NAICS—339943;
*Metal, paint, permanent ink,
refillable, textile & water-based
markers*
Employs—22; Estab.—2001
Sales—$2.5Mil-$5Mil
Distrib.—Intl.
Limited Liability Company

### ARTUS CORP.

201 S. Dean St., P.O. Box 511
(07631)
**Phone—(201) 568-1000**
Fax—(201) 568-8865
www.artuscorp.com
Email—shims@artusworld.com
Pres.—Raphael Levi
Plt. Mgr.—Sam Levi
SIC—3499; *Shims & shim stock*
Employs—40; Estab.—1941
Sales—$2.5Mil-$5Mil (est)
Distrib.—Intl.
Privately owned corporation

### AUDIO DYNAMIX, INC.

170 Coolidge Ave. (07631)
**Phone—(201) 567-5488**
Fax—(201) 567-5411
www.cdxdvd.com
Email—info@cdxdvd.com
Pres.—Rich Gayed
SIC—3652; *CD & DVD duplication*
Employs—15; Estab.—1993
Sales—$1Mil-$2.5Mil
10,000 sq ft site, Distrib.—National
Privately owned corporation

### AYESHA STUDIO & GALLERY

21 N. Dean St. (07631)
**Phone—(201) 503-0073**
Fax—(201) 503-0046
www.ayeshastudio.com
Email—ayesha@ayeshastudio.com
Owner—Ayesha Mayadas
SIC—3911; *Gold jewelry,
including earrings, brooches &
necklaces*
Employs—2; Estab.—2000
Sales—under $500,000
Distrib.—National
Privately owned corporation

GEOGRAPHICAL

# Englewood—(cont.)

**BALTHAZAR BAKERY**

214 S. Dean St. (07631)
**Phone—(201) 503-9717**
Fax—(201) 503-9721
www.balthazarbakery.com
Owner—Keith McNally
GM—Paula Oland
GM—B. Young
Accts. Serv. Mgr.—Beth
  Blankenhorn
Cust. Serv. Rep.—Tina Cox
SIC—2051; NAICS—311812;
  Bakery products
Employs—60; Estab.—2000
Distrib.—Regional
Privately owned corporation

**BLITZ SAFE OF AMERICA, INC.**

33 Honeck St. (07631)
**Phone—(201) 569-5000**
National—(800) 597-7233
Fax—(201) 569-5042
www.blitzsafe.com
Email—blitzsafe@blitzsafe.com
Pres.—Ira Marlowe
Manager—Melanie Jerr
SIC—3679; Automobile stereos;
  Brand name—Skylink Direct
Employs—15; Estab.—1983
Distrib.—Intl.
Privately owned corporation

**BURGESS STEEL ERECTORS OF
NEW JERSEY, LLC**

200 W. Forest Ave., P.O. Box 5629
  (07631)
**Phone—(201) 871-3500**
  (212) 563-6000
National—(800) 871-3501
Fax—(201) 871-8750
www.burgesssteel.com
Email—estimating@
  burgesssteel.com
CFO—Thomas J. Parisi
V-P., Sales—Matthew J. Guerin
V-P., Mktg.—James P. Guerin
GM—Timothy Guerin
Chief Estimator—Gary James
SIC—3312; 3499; Steel fabrication
  & ornamental metals
Employs—85; Estab.—1976
Sales—$30Mil-$31Mil
50,000 sq ft site, Distrib.—
  Regional
Limited Liability Company

**C & C METAL PRODUCTS CORP.**

456 Nordhoff Pl., P.O. Box 7300
  (07631)
**Phone—(201) 569-7300**
Fax—(201) 569-4112
www.ccmetal.com
Email—sales@ccmetal.com
V-P., Secy.—Mitchell Chalfin
V-P., Pur.—Neal Liber
V-P.—Matthew Nathel
V-P.—Michael Nathel
Dir.—Daniel Nathel
SIC—3469; 3965; 3915; NAICS—
  339993; Corporate headquarters
  & metal stampings, eyelets,
  closures, buttons, buckles &
  findings; Brand name—Dyna-
  Line; Knobware; C & C Metal
  Products
Employs—50; Estab.—1914
Sales—$8Mil
150,000 sq ft site, Distrib.—Intl.
Privately owned corporation
ISO rating—9001:2008

**CANTONE PRESS, INC.**

161 Coolidge Ave. (07631)
**Phone—(201) 569-2288**
Fax—(201) 569-1747
www.pdqdigital.com
Email—joe@pdqdigital.com
Owner—Joe Cantone
Pres.—Frank Cantone
SIC—2791; 2752; NAICS—
  323122; Typesetting & offset
  printing
Employs—10; Estab.—1976
Sales—$500,000-$1Mil
Distrib.—National
Privately owned corporation
Also see: Contemporary, Inc.,
  same loc.

**CARTER PUMP**

326 S. Dean St. (07631)
**Phone—(201) 568-9798**
  (201) 568-4700
National—(800) 568-9798
Fax—(201) 568-1313
www.carterpump.com
Email—info@carterpump.com
Pres., CEO—Kevin Powers
Prodn. Mgr.—Roberto Lopez
MIS Mgr.—Michael Alessio
Fin. Mgr.—Brian Ready
SIC—3561; NAICS—333911;
  Company headquarters &
  plunger & diaphragm pumps &
  pneumatic ejectors; Brand
  name—Carter Pump
Employs—31; Estab.—1920
Sales—$5Mil-$10Mil
25,000 sq ft site, Distrib.—Intl.
Privately owned corporation

**CENTRAL ADMIXTURE PHARMACY
SERVICES**

Div. of B. Braun Medical, Inc.
160 W. Forest Ave. (07631)
**Phone—(201) 541-0080**
National—(800) 698-6759
Fax—(201) 541-0088
www.capspharmacy.com
Email—dan.buchner@bbraun.com
Br. Mgr.—Daniel Buchner
Buyer—Liz Gonzalez
SIC—2834; NAICS—325412;
  Pharmaceuticals
Employs—50; Estab.—1996
Distrib.—National
Privately owned corporation
AKA: CAPS
Parent co.—B. Braun Medical,
  Inc., Bethlehem, PA
  Phone—(610) 691-5400
See Parent Co. Section for full profile.

**CHICK MASTER INTERNATIONAL,
INC. (H Q)**

25 Rockwood Pl., Ste. 335 (07631)
**Phone—(201) 871-8810**
Fax—(201) 871-8814
www.chickmaster.com
Email—sales@chickmaster.com
Pres.—Robert Holzer
Sales Mgr.—Humberto Hernandez
Sales Mgr., Latin America—Pilar
  Garcia
SIC—3523; Corporate
  headquarters; poultry
  incubators; Brand name—Chick
  Master Incubation Systems
Employs—9; Estab.—1974
Distrib.—Intl.
Privately owned corporation

**CMYK PRINTING, INC.**

180 Coolidge Ave. (07631)
**Phone—(201) 458-1300**
Fax—(201) 458-1317
www.cmykprinting.com
Email—charles@cmykprinting.com
CEO—Charles Ambrogio
SIC—2759; NAICS—323100;
  Commercial printing, including
  brochures, business cards,
  letterheads & pocket folders
Employs—21; Estab.—1988
10,000 sq ft site, Distrib.—Local
Privately owned corporation

**CONTEMPORARY, INC.**

161 Coolidge Ave. (07631)
**Phone—(201) 569-3900**
Fax—(201) 569-9309
Pres.—Anthony Cantone
V-P.—Frank Cantone
Bookkeeper—Valerie Apsasform
SIC—2759; 2711; NAICS—
  323100; Electronic prepress &
  printing
Employs—22; Estab.—1976
Sales—under $500,000
Distrib.—Local
Privately owned corporation
Also see: Cantone Press, Inc.,
  same loc.

**D & I PRINTING CO., INC.**

23 Chestnut St. (07631)
**Phone—(201) 871-3620**
Fax—(201) 569-3134
Email—dandico@aol.com
Pres.—Gus Dovi
CFO—Diane Dovi
V-P.—Christine Dovi
SIC—2752; NAICS—323100;
  Offset printing
Employs—10; Estab.—1972
10,000 sq ft site, Distrib.—
  Regional
Privately owned corporation

**DECOR, INC.**

60 Cedar Ln. (07631)
**Phone—(201) 569-1900**
Fax—(201) 569-2166
www.decorinc.com
Email—decorinc@aol.com
Pres.—Richard Engel
V-P., Fin.—Peggy Napolitano
Hum. Res. Mgr.—Mercedes
  Fernandez
SIC—3229; NAICS—327212;
  Glass decorating
Employs—180; Estab.—1974
Sales—over $10Mil
130,000 sq ft site, Distrib.—Intl.

**DMG AMERICA, LLC**

242 S. Dean St. (07631)
**Phone—(201) 894-5505**
National—(800) 662-6383
Fax—(201) 894-0213
www.dmg-america.com
Email—info@dmg-america.com
Pres.—George Wolfe
SIC—3841; Dental materials;
  Brand name—Laxatemp;
  Laxacore; Honigan; Tempo
Employs—25; Estab.—1983
Sales—$2.5Mil-$5Mil (est)
Distrib.—Local
Limited Liability Company
ISO rating—9001

**EMPIRE TELECOMMUNICATIONS,
INC.**

15 S. Van Brunt St. (07631)
**Phone—(201) 569-3339**
www.empire-telecom.com
Pres.—Sid Kaplan
Design Engr.—Gary Wilt
SIC—3825; NAICS—334500;
  Electronic testing equipment
Employs—12; Estab.—1978
Sales—under $500,000
Distrib.—Intl.
Privately owned corporation

**ENGLEWOOD LAB, LLC**

88 W. Sheffield Ave. (07631)
**Phone—(201) 567-2267**
Fax—(201) 567-2280
www.englewoodlab.com
Email—info@englewoodlab.com
CEO—David Chung
Pres.—John Kim
V-P.—Vincent Penna
IT Mgr.—D. K. Lee
Hum. Res. Mgr.—Eunice Lee
Cust. Serv. Mgr.—Debbie Starr
Fin. Mgr.—Eliana Palacio
SIC—2844; NAICS—325600;
  Contract manufacturing of skin
  care products & cosmetics
Employs—50; Estab.—2003
28,000 sq ft site, Distrib.—Intl.
Limited Liability Company

**ENTERPRISE PRESS, INC.**

1 W. Forest Ave. (07631)
**Phone—(201) 894-0444**
Fax—(201) 894-0455
www.enterprise-press.com
Email—press@enterprise-
  press.com
Owner—Robert Hort
Pres.—Benjamin Hort
Cont.—Terri Francis
SIC—2759; NAICS—323100;
  Commercial printing
Employs—150; Estab.—1915
85,000 sq ft site, Distrib.—National
Privately owned corporation

**ERMENEGILDO ZEGNA CORP. (H Q)**

100 W. Forest Ave., Ste. A (07631)
**Phone—(201) 816-0921**
www.zegna.com
Email—customer.service@
  zegna.com
Pres.—Robert Aldrich
V-P., Fin.—Dorothy Montgomery
Hum. Res. Mgr.—Belen Garafola
SIC—2329; NAICS—315200;
  Corporate headquarters; men's
  clothing (mfg. done overseas)
Employs—50; Estab.—1975
Sales—$2.5Mil-$5Mil (est)
Distrib.—Intl.

**EZCOM SOFTWARE, INC.**

25 Rockwood Pl., Ste. 420 (07631-
  4971)
**Phone—(201) 883-1900**
National—(877) 765-3564
www.ezcomsoftware.com
Email—sales@ezcomsoftware.com
CEO—Carol Weidner
Dir., Cust. Support—Ted Cancila
Corp. Accts. Mgr.—John Bozza
Hum. Res. Mgr. & Coord.—Terry
  Reynolds
EDI Coord.—Dallas Richards
SIC—7372; EDI software
  development for manufacturers;
  Brand name—Lingo™
Employs—28; Estab.—2000
Distrib.—National
Privately owned corporation

**FORBO SIEGLING, LLC**

130 Coolidge Ave. (07631)
**Phone—(201) 567-6100**
National—(800) 255-5581
Fax—(201) 567-2981
www.forbo-siegling.com
Email—info@siegling-us.com
Br. Mgr.—Ron Supino
Hum. Res. Mgr.—Charlie Furr
SIC—3052; NAICS—326220;
  Conveyor belting
Employs—15; Estab.—1956
Sales—$500,000-$1Mil
Distrib.—Intl.
Limited Liability Company
Parent co.—Forbo Siegling, LLC,
  Huntersville, NC
  Phone—(704) 948-0800
See Parent Co. Section for full profile.

**FRENCH COLOR & FRAGRANCE CO.**

488 Grand Ave. (07631)
**Phone—(201) 567-6883**
National—(800) 762-9098
Fax—(201) 567-5749
www.frenchcolor.com
Email—sales@frenchcolor.com
Pres.—Peter A. French
SIC—2844; Fragrances & dyes for
  candles
Employs—17
Sales—$5Mil-$10Mil (est)
Privately owned corporation

**GEMINI CUT GLASS CO., INC.**

4 E. Forest Ave. (07631)
**Phone—(201) 568-7722**
Fax—(201) 568-7733
www.geminicutglass.com
Email—geminicutglass@nj.rr.com
Pres.—Eric Zelwian

## Englewood—(cont.)

Manager—Erika Zelwian
SIC—3645; 3646; NAICS—
335121; Custom chandeliers,
sconces & lighting fixtures
Employs—7; Estab.—1956
6,000 sq ft site, Distrib.—National
Privately owned corporation

**HOYT CORP.**
520 S. Dean St. (07631)
**Phone—(201) 894-0707**
National—(800) 255-4698
Fax—(201) 894-0916
www.hoyt-corp.com
Email—info@hoyt-corp.com
Pres.—Don Maguire
V.-P., Mktg.—Joe Finnerty
V.-P., Fin.—Dennis Maas
Cust. Serv. Mgr.—Barbara Hall
SIC—3699; 3499; 3399; 3799;
Custom & standard precious
metal electrical contact &
replacement contact kits for
industrial motor, mining
equipment & material handling
controls & light rail & diesel
electric locomotives
Employs—65; Estab.—1914
30,000 sq ft site, Distrib.—Intl.
Privately owned corporation

**INBEAU, INC.**
101 W. Palisade (07631)
**Phone—(201) 227-8875**
Fax—(201) 227-8865
www.inbeau.com
Email—info@inbeau.com
Owner—Simon Yang
Sales Mgr.—Andy Yang
SIC—3961; NAICS—339900;
Costume jewelry, including
necklaces & earrings
Employs—7; Estab.—2003
Sales—$500,000-$1Mil
Distrib.—National
Privately owned corporation

**IVYSKIN, LLC**
282 Grand Ave. (07631)
**Phone—(201) 266-5555**
www.ivyskin.com
Email—inquiry@ivyskin.com
Pres.—Mike Panahi
Sales Rep.—Chris Higgins
SIC—3172; Leather cellular
telephone cases
Employs—7; Estab.—2005
Sales—under $500,000 (est)
Distrib.—Intl.
Limited Liability Company

NEW ENTRY
**JEWISH VOICE**
73 Dana Pl., P.O. Box 8097
(07631)
**Phone—(201) 569-2845**
www.jewishvoiceandopinion.com
Email—advertising@
jewishvoiceandopinion.com
Editor—Susan Rosenbluth
SIC—2721; Magazine publishing
Employs—4; Estab.—1987
Sales—under $500,000
Distrib.—Local
Privately owned corporation

**KOSLOW SCIENTIFIC CO.**
172 Walkers Ln. (07631)
**Phone—(201) 541-9100**
Fax—(201) 541-9330
www.koslow.com
Email—sales@koslow.com
Pres.—Wolfgang Koslow
Sales Rep.—Donna Imhoff
SIC—3826; 2899; NAICS—
334516; Metal analyzing kits
Employs—30; Estab.—1966
Distrib.—Intl.
Privately owned corporation

**LA ESPERANZA BAKING**
148 W. Forest Ave. (07631)
**Phone—(201) 871-1934**
Fax—(201) 871-6733
Owner—Elena Queiruga
SIC—2051; NAICS—311812;
Hispanic, American & Italian
bread
Employs—40; Estab.—1949
Distrib.—Local

**LASTING IMPRESSION, INC.**
333 S. Dean St. (07631)
**Phone—(201) 871-7388**
Fax—(201) 871-4942
www.lastingimpressionusa.com
Email—info@
lastingimpressionusa.com
Owner—Darlene Story
SIC—2844; Cosmetics; Brand
name—Divon Cosmetics™;
Concealing Systems™; I Am
Cosmetics™
Employs—15; Estab.—1992
Sales—$5Mil-$10Mil
Distrib.—Intl.
Privately owned corporation

**LATTA GRAPHICS, INC.**
180 Cool Edge Ave. (07631)
**Phone—(201) 440-4040**
Pres., Hum. Res. Mgr.—Eileen
Latta
SIC—2759; NAICS—323100;
Commercial printing
Employs—18; Estab.—1978
Sales—$1Mil-$2.5Mil
Distrib.—Regional
Privately owned corporation

NEW ENTRY
**LORENZO FOOD GROUP, INC.**
196 Coolidge Ave. (07631)
**Phone—(201) 868-9088**
Owner—John Lorenzo
SIC—2099; NAICS—311991;
Fresh sandwiches, salads &
dessert cups
Employs—5
Sales—$500,000-$1Mil (est)
Distrib.—Local
Privately owned corporation
AKA: Lorenzo & Sons Provisions

**MARATHON ENTERPRISES, INC. (H
Q)**
9 Smith St. (07631)
**Phone—(201) 935-3330**
National—(800) 722-7388
Fax—(201) 935-5693
www.sabrett.com
Email—info@sabrett.com
Owner—Nikki Rosen
Pres.—Boyd Adelman
V.-P., Sales & Mktg.—Mark Rosen
Cred. Mgr.—Sandy Blumer
SIC—2013; NAICS—311600;
Corporate headquarters; hot
dogs; Brand name—Sabrett®
Employs—60
Sales—$10Mil-$25Mil (est)
Distrib.—Local
Publicly owned corporation
DBA: Sabrett Frankfurters

**MARGOLA CORP.**
232 S. Van Brunt St. (07631)
**Phone—(201) 816-9500**
Fax—(201) 816-0051
www.margola.com
Email—sales@margola.com
Owner—Neil Chalfin
V.-P.—Bernard Chalfin
Sales Mgr.—John Cardenelli

SIC—2396; 2399; 3499; 3089;
Manufacturer & distributor of
rhinestones, bead products,
metal & plastic apparel
ornaments, buckles & trimming,
including laser cutting
Employs—6; Estab.—1937
Sales—$1Mil-$5Mil
6,200 sq ft site, Distrib.—Intl.
Sole ownership

**MARINDUS CO., INC**
P.O. Box 663 (07631)
**Phone—(201) 567-8383**
National—(800) 869-8511
Fax—(201) 567-6055
www.airtectools.com
Email—info@airtectools.com
Pres.—Jim Bartis
SIC—3531; 3559; Concrete
surface preparation equipment,
including standard, compact &
vibration dampened needle
scalers, handheld & standup
rotary scarifiers & planers,
piston-type scrabblers &
pneumatic & ride-on power
scrapers
Employs—10; Estab.—1959
Distrib.—Intl.
Privately owned corporation

**MARLOW CANDY & NUT CO.**
65 Honeck St. (07631)
**Phone—(201) 569-7606**
Fax—(201) 569-9533
www.marlowcandyandnut.com
Email—akirk@marlowcandy.net
Owner—Mike Serpin
Off. Mgr.—Aideen Kirk
Bookkeeper—MaryAnn Santa
SIC—3089; NAICS—311330;
Contract & private label
packaging of candy & nuts;
Brand name—Marlow; Just
Goodies; Snack on the Go by
Marlow
Employs—25; Estab.—1976
Sales—under $500,000
Distrib.—Regional
Privately owned corporation

**MERCURY FLOOR MACHINES, INC.**
110 S. Van Brunt St. (07631)
Mail addr: 15571 Container Ln.,
Huntington Beach (92649)
**Phone—(201) 568-4606**
(714) 901-8400
National—(888) 568-4606
Fax—(201) 568-7962
www.mercuryfloormachines.com
Email—sales@
mercuryfloormachines.com
Pres.—Bill Allen
GM—Peter McGiffin
Opers. Mgr., W. Coast—Garry
Bocian
SIC—3589; NAICS—333319;
Commercial floor cleaning
equipment; Brand name—
LoBoy; Hecules; Boss; Ultra-DC
Employs—15; Estab.—1959
Sales—$1Mil-$5Mil
8,000 sq ft site, Distrib.—Intl.
Privately owned corporation

**METAL CITY FINDINGS CO.**
Div. of C & C Metal Products Corp.
456 Nordhoff Pl., P.O. Box 7300
(07631)
**Phone—(201) 569-7300**
Fax—(201) 569-4112
www.ccmetal.com
Email—sales@ccmetal.com
Pres.—Gerald Nathel
V.-P., Secy.—Mitchell Chalfin
V.-P., Treas.—Matthew Nathel
V.-P.—Michael Nathel
Pur. Agt.—Rod Sunga

SIC—3915; Costume jewelry
findings & metal stamping
Employs—40; Estab.—1914
150,000 sq ft site, Distrib.—
National
Privately owned corporation
Parent co.—C & C Metal Products
Corp., Englewood, NJ
Phone—(201) 569-7300
See Parent Co. Section for full profile.

**MICELI CABINET CORP.**
128 Madison Ave. (07631)
Mail addr: P.O. Box 1304,
Englewood Cliffs (07632)
**Phone—(201) 933-4004**
Fax—(718) 543-8232
Pres.—Joseph Schabes
SIC—2434; NAICS—337110;
Wooden cabinets
Employs—2; Estab.—1964
Sales—under $500,000
5,000 sq ft site, Distrib.—Local
Privately owned sub-S corp.

**MICROSURFACES, INC.**
1 W. Forest Ave. (07631)
**Phone—(201) 408-5596**
Fax—(201) 408-5797
www.proteinslides.com
Email—info@microsurfacesinc.com
Pres.—Athena Guo
SIC—2835; 3826; Protein
microarrays
Employs—6; Estab.—2000
Sales—$500,000-$1Mil
Distrib.—National
Privately owned corporation
AKA: MSI

**MUSIC TRADES MAGAZINE CORP.**
80 West St., P.O. Box 432 (07631)
**Phone—(201) 871-1965**
National—(800) 423-6530
Fax—(201) 871-0455
www.musictrades.com
Email—music@musictrades.com
Publisher—Paul Majeski
Editor—Brian Majeski
Bookkeeper—Juanita Hampton
SIC—2721; Music trade magazine
publishing
Employs—6; Estab.—1890
Sales—under $500,000
Distrib.—Intl.
Privately owned corporation

**NEW JERSEY BUSINESS FORMS
MFG. CORP.**
55 W. Sheffield Ave. (07631)
**Phone—(201) 569-4500**
National—(800) 466-6523
Fax—(201) 569-4650
www.njbf.com
Email—team@njbf.com
Pres.—David Harnett
SIC—2761; NAICS—323116;
Business form printing
Employs—65; Estab.—1971
Distrib.—Regional
Privately owned corporation

**NUVICO, INC.**
53 Smith St. (07631)
**Phone—(201) 541-1605**
National—(866) 523-1700
Fax—(201) 541-1620
www.nuvico.com
Email—admin@nuvico.com
CEO—I. J. Choi
CFO—Kiwhan Lee
V.-P., Sales & Mktg.—John Kwak
Sales Mgr.—Luke Lee
IT Mgr.—Royal Lee
Cust. Serv. Rep.—David Cho
SIC—3669; NAICS—334290; IP
surveillance closed-circuit
television equipment & video
surveillance products (mfg. done
South Korea)
Employs—20; Estab.—2001
15,000 sq ft site, Distrib.—Intl.
Privately owned corporation

GEOGRAPHICAL

## Englewood—(cont.)

**ORIVAL WATER FILTERS**
213 S. Van Brunt St. *(07631)*
**Phone—(201) 568-3311**
National—(800) 567-9767
Fax—(201) 568-1916
www.orival.com
Email—filters@orival.com
Pres.—Reuven Schwartz
SIC—3589; NAICS—333319;
*Automatic self-cleaning line
pressure powered water filters*
Employs—10; Estab.—1986
Sales—$1Mil-$2.5Mil (est)
5,000 sq ft site, Distrib.—Intl.
Privately owned corporation

**PALISADES DENTAL, LLC**
111 Cedar Ln., P.O. Box 5419
(07631)
**Phone—(201) 569-0050**
National—(800) 664-8000
Fax—(201) 569-0250
www.palisadesdental-llc.com
Cust. Serv. Rep.—Robin Rinker
SIC—3843; NAICS—339114;
*Dental drills*
Employs—15; Estab.—1993
Distrib.—Intl.
Limited Liability Company

**PRINT SOLUTIONS**
320 S. Dean St. (07631)
**Phone—(201) 567-9622**
Fax—(201) 567-9441
www.printsolutions.info
Email—mail@printsolutions.info
Pres.—Paul Vartanian
Plt. Mgr.—Ken Morrow
Graphic Designer—John
Rodriguez
SIC—2752; NAICS—323100;
*Offset printing*
Employs—6; Estab.—1989
Sales—under $500,000
Distrib.—Local
Sole ownership

**PROFESSIONAL IMAGES, LLC**
17 E. Linden Ave. (07631)
**Phone—(201) 569-4251**
www.123customprint.com
Email—123customprint@verizon.net
Owner—Steve Nicholson
SIC—2396; 2395; 2759; NAICS—
323100; *Screen printing &
embroidery of promotional t-
shirts, apparel, key chains, mugs
& magnets*
Employs—1; Estab.—1996
Sales—under $500,000
Distrib.—Regional
Limited Liability Company
AKA: Professional Images

**†RIVIERA PRODUCE CORP.**
205 Jackson St., P.O. Box 6065
(07631)
**Phone—(201) 227-7105**
Fax—(201) 227-7124
www.rivieraproduce.com
Email—sales@rivieraproduce.com
Pres.—Ben Friedman
SIC—5148; *Wholesaler of fresh
fruit & vegetables*
Employs—160; Estab.—1993
Distrib.—Regional
Privately owned corporation

**RUDY DI SIGNS & DISPLAYS**
169 N. Dean St. (07631)
**Phone—(201) 568-6160**
Owner—Ralph DiPasquale
SIC—3993; *Interior & exterior
signs*
Employs—1; Estab.—1958
Sales—under $500,000
Distrib.—Local
Sole ownership

**S. PARKER HARDWARE MFG.**
1 Parker Dr., P.O. Box 9882
(07631)
**Phone—(201) 569-1600**
National—(800) 772-7537
Fax—(201) 569-1082
www.sparker.com
Email—hardware@sparker.com
Pres.—Charles Silberman
Cont.—Sheldon Silver
Pur. Agt.—Loren Sellers
SIC—3429; *Commercial door
hardware*
Employs—25; Estab.—1899
Sales—over $10Mil
65,000 sq ft site, Distrib.—Intl.
Privately owned corporation

**SATESA CORP.**
154 W. Forest Ave. (07631)
**Phone—(201) 871-8989**
Fax—(201) 871-8686
www.satesa.com
Email—textiles@satesa.com
Pres.—Randy Loew
SIC—3081; 2295; 2395; 2399;
NAICS—326113; *Laminating,
coating & converting of fabrics
for the cleanroom, medical,
military, electronic & workwear
industries, including cutting &
sewing of finished garments &
special projects & high R-value
insulation for the construction
industry*
Employs—4; Estab.—1987
Sales—$5Mil-$10Mil
Distrib.—Intl.
Privately owned corporation

**SONALI ENERGEES USA, LLC (H Q)**
409 Grand Ave., Ste. 3 (07631)
**Phone—(201) 297-1177**
National—(888) 587-6527
Fax—(212) 906-1988
www.sonalisolar.com
Email—info@sonalisolar.com
Pres., CEO—Pankaj Desai
SIC—3674; *Company
headquarters; photovoltaic
modules (mfg. done in Gujarat,
India)*
Employs—100
Sales—$25Mil-$50Mil
Limited Liability Company

**SUPREME OIL CO., INC.**
80 S. Dean St. (07631)
**Phone—(201) 567-3177**
National—(800) 725-2364
Fax—(201) 567-1721
www.admirationfoods.com
Pres.—Seymour Unterman
Sales Mgr.—Steve Leff
Plt. Mgr.—Joe Abrassi
Off. Mgr.—Coleen Ryan
SIC—2079; NAICS—311200;
*Edible vegetable oil*
Employs—150; Estab.—1944
Sales—$6Mil-$10Mil
Distrib.—Regional
Privately owned corporation

**†TIME SYSTEMS INTERNATIONAL,
INC.**
142 S. Van Brunt St. (07631)
**Phone—(973) 472-2202**
National—(800) 224-2202
Fax—(973) 472-3744
www.timesystemsint.com
Email—info@timesystemsint.com
Pres.—Samuel Gleich
Off. Mgr.—Debbi Greenfield
SIC—5044; 5099; *Corporate
headquarters & distributor of
time & attendance management
equipment & software*
Employs—20; Estab.—1976
Sales—$500,000-$1Mil
2,100 sq ft site, Distrib.—Regional
Privately owned corporation
AKA: American Time Recorder,
Inc.

**UNITY GRAPHICS & ENGRAVING/
UNITY STEEL RULE DIE**
210 S. Van Brunt St., P.O. Box 88
(07631)
**Phone—(201) 569-6400**
Fax—(201) 569-2956
www.gounity.com
Email—unitypres@gounity.com
Ptnr.—Diane Iamartino
Ptnr.—Michael Iamartino, Jr.
Plt. Mgr.—Joe Lessa
SIC—2759; 3544; 2796; NAICS—
323122; *Rubber printing, plate
engraving & steel rule dies*
Employs—50; Estab.—1978
Sales—$5Mil-$10Mil (est)
Distrib.—Local
Privately owned corporation
AKA: Unity Steel Rule Die

---

# Englewood Cliffs
(Bergen—N.E.)

**AROMOR FLAVORS &
FRAGRANCES, INC.**
560 Sylvan Ave., Ste. 60 (07632)
**Phone—(201) 503-1662**
National—(866) 425-1660
Fax—(201) 503-1663
www.aromor.com
Email—sales@aromor-usa.com
Sales Mgr.—Carol Feldman
SIC—2819; 2869; *Aroma
chemicals for the fragrances &
flavors industries, including
natural, nature identical &
synthetic raw materials*
Employs—2; Estab.—2005
Distrib.—Intl.
Privately owned corporation

**AS SOFTWARE, INC.**
560 Sylvan Ave., Ste. 2052
(07632)
**Phone—(201) 541-1900**
National—(800) 613-4441
Fax—(201) 541-1199
www.as-software.com
Email—info@as-software.com
Pres.—Ari Sandman
Off. Mgr.—Sande Lewis
Support Rep.—Joseph Gabecki
SIC—7372; *Medical ultrasound
reporting & image management
software development for OB-
GYN, maternal fetal medicine
(MFM), perinatal, vascular
medicine & radiology*
Employs—21; Estab.—1991
Distrib.—National
Privately owned corporation

**BAUER PUBLISHING CO.**
270 Sylvan Ave., Ste. 210 (07632)
**Phone—(201) 569-6699**
National—(800) 216-6981
Fax—(201) 569-5303
www.bauerpublishing.com
Email—gdesantis@
bauerpublishing.com
CEO—Hubert Boehle
Sr. V-P.—Richard Parker
V-P., Fin.—Richard Teehan
SIC—2721; *Weekly cooking,
health & practical everyday tip
magazine publishing for
traditional, family-oriented
working women*
Employs—400; Estab.—1991
Distrib.—Intl.
Privately owned corporation

**CASTLE INDUSTRIES, INC.**
120 Sylvan Ave., Ste. 107 (07632)
**Phone—(201) 585-8400**
Pres.—Artie Schloss
IT Mgr.—Richard Kalc

SIC—3679; *Electrical components
& contract assembly for the
medical & telecommunication
industries*
Employs—20; Estab.—1972
Sales—$6Mil-$10Mil
Distrib.—Intl.
Privately owned corporation

**CONCORD PAPER MFG., INC.**
375 Sylvan Ave., Ste. 23 (07632)
**Phone—(201) 567-2529**
Fax—(201) 567-5616
www.concordpapermfg.com
Email—concordpap@aol.com
Dir., Sales & Mktg.—Donna Parker
SIC—2759; 2657; 5113; 5085;
NAICS—323100; *Shipping
boxes & folding cartons, printing
of pressure-sensitive labels,
forms, folders, flyers &
packaging inserts & distributor of
rope, twine, poly bags &
towelette paper for the
pharmaceutical, food, cosmetic
& chemical industries*
Employs—4; Estab.—1968
Distrib.—Regional
Privately owned corporation

**NEW ENTRY**
**†CROWN JEWEL IMPORTERS &
MARKETING CORP.**
140 Sylvan Ave., Ste. 109 (07632)
**Phone—(201) 461-3900**
Fax—(201) 461-3911
www.cjimporters.com
Email—crownjewel@verizon.net
Pres.—Zach Klein
SIC—5182; *Distributor of wines*
Employs—5
Privately owned corporation

**CUSTOM GASKET MFG.**
640 E. Palisade Ave. (07632)
**Phone—(201) 331-6363**
Fax—(201) 227-1407
Email—sales@
customgasketmfg.com
CEO—Eric Helf
SIC—3053; 3069; 3061; 3089;
*Custom molded rubber & die-cut
products, including rubber
gaskets, rubber seals, rubber
diaphragms, rubber grommets,
rubber bushings, rubber
bumpers, rubber stoppers,
rubber caps & rubber plugs*
Employs—15; Estab.—1967
Sales—$1Mil-$2.5Mil
20,000 sq ft site, Distrib.—National
Privately owned corporation

**E. T. BROWNE DRUG COMPANY,
INC.**
440 Sylvan Ave., P.O. Box 1613
(07632)
**Phone—(201) 894-9020**
(877) 725-6377
National—(888) 725-6377
Fax—(201) 894-5152
www.palmers.com
Email—info@etbrowne.com
Chrm.—Arnold H. Neis
Pres.—Robert C. Neis
V-P., Sales—Peter Augustine
Dir., Fin.—Susan Crook
SIC—2844; NAICS—325600;
*Corporate headquarters & skin &
hair care lotions; Brand name—
Palmer's; Black & Beautiful;
Parfums Lucien Lelong*
Employs—65; Estab.—1971
Sales—$150Mil
Distrib.—Intl.
Privately owned corporation

**GRAPHICTONE**
360 Sylvan Ave., Ste. 4 (07632)
**Phone—(201) 568-2008**
Fax—(201) 568-4754
www.graphictone.com
Email—mail@graphictone.us

## Englewood Cliffs— (cont.)

Pres.—Kirby Tan
SIC—2791; NAICS—323122; *Electronic prepress, including print-on-demand, digital photo magazine & perfect bound & saddle stitch bindery; Brand name—Graphictone; My i magazine*
Employs—5; Estab.—2010
2,500 sq ft site, Distrib.—Intl.
Privately owned corporation
DBA: Graphict One USA

**HI CLASS LIVING MAGAZINE**
120 Sylvan Ave., Ste. 209 (07632)
**Phone—(201) 363-0200**
Fax—(201) 363-0204
www.hiclass.com
Email—michael@hiclass.com
Owner & Publisher—Michael Raviv
Editor—Nava Raviv
SIC—2721; *Lifestyle magazine publishing*
Employs—4; Estab.—1984
Sales—under $500,000
Distrib.—Local
Privately owned corporation

**IVILLAGE, INC.**
Div. of NBCUniversal Media, LLC
900 Sylvan Ave. (07632)
**Phone—(212) 664-4444**
Fax—(212) 604-9133
www.ivillage.com
Email—info@ivillage.com
Editor—Jeff Cox
SIC—2721; 2731; *Magazine, journal & book publishing*
Employs—200; Estab.—1989
Sales—$10Mil-$25Mil (est)
Distrib.—Intl.
Publicly owned corporation
Parent co.—NBCUniversal Media, LLC, New York, NY
Phone—(212) 664-4444
See Parent Co. Section for full profile.

**KOREAN BERGEN NEWS**
210 Sylvan Ave., Ste. 23 (07632)
**Phone—(201) 894-9061**
Fax—(201) 894-9064
www.koreanbergennews.com
Email—koreanbergennews@gmail.com
Owner—Thomas Bae
SIC—2711; 2721; *Ethnic newspaper & magazine publishing*
Employs—15; Estab.—1999
Sales—$500,000-$1Mil
Distrib.—Local
Limited Liability Company

**LG ELECTRONICS USA, INC. (H Q)**
1000 Sylvan Ave. (07632)
**Phone—(201) 816-2000**
National—(800) 243-0000
Fax—(201) 816-0636
www.lg.com
Co-Pres., CEO—William Cho
Co-Pres., Home Entertainment—Thomas Lee
Co-Pres., AC & Energy Sols.—Ellen Kim
Co-Pres., Home Appliances—Chris Jung
V-P., Pub. Affs. & Comm.—John I. Taylor
SIC—3651; 3663; NAICS—334310; *Corporate headquarters; computer, home video & audio electronic products & home appliances; Brand name—LG*
Employs—500; Estab.—1978
Sales—$52Bil
Distrib.—Intl.
Privately owned corporation

**OCTAGON COMMUNICATIONS CORP.**
385 Sylvan Ave., Ste. 16 (07632)
**Phone—(201) 569-5870**
Fax—(201) 569-6684
www.mpdigest.com
Owner & Publisher—Douglas Markhouse
GM—Susan Gray
SIC—2721; *Magazine publishing for the aerospace & defense markets*
Employs—10
Sales—$500,000-$1Mil (est)
Distrib.—Intl.
Privately owned corporation
AKAs: Microwave Product Digest & MPD

**TRILOGY PUBLICATIONS, LLC**
560 Sylvan Ave., Ste. 1240 (07632)
**Phone—(201) 816-1211**
www.trilogypublications.com
Email—info@trilogypublications.com
Owner—Rose Reichman
Off. Mgr.—Lenore Clark
SIC—2731; *Children's book publishing*
Employs—6; Estab.—2001
Distrib.—National
Limited Liability Company

**UNILEVER NORTH AMERICA**
700 Sylvan Ave. (07632)
**Phone—(201) 567-8000**
www.unileverusa.com
Email—mediarelations.usa@unilever.com
Pres., N. America—Kees Kruythoff
Pres., Cust. Dev.—Todd Tillemans
Sr. V-P., Fin. & CFO—Henry Schirmer
Sr. V-P., Hum. Res.—Sumeet Salwan
Ex. V-P., Personal Care—Gina Boswell
V-P., Mktg. to Shoppers—Kathy O'Brien
V-P., Ice Cream & Beverages, U.S.—Alfie Vivian
V-P., Corp. Comms. & Sustainable Living—Jonathan Atwood
V-P., Gen. Counsel—Steve Rapp
SIC—2844; 2035; 2024; 2099; *Company headquarters & food & personal care products for consumers, including soaps, shampoos, deodorants, lotions, conditioners & body washes, teas, soups, mayonnaise, olive oil, pasta sauces, seasonings, instant side dishes & ice creams; Brand name—Axe; Ben & Jerry's; Breyers; Dove personal care products; Hellmann's; Knorr; TRESemmE; Vaseline*
Employs—1900; Estab.—1971
Sales—$9Bil
Distrib.—Intl.
Publicly owned corporation

---

## Englishtown

(Monmouth—N.E.)

†**AIR PRODUCTS & CHEMICALS, INC.**
405 State Route 33 (07726)
**Phone—(732) 446-5676**
Fax—(732) 446-2698
www.airproducts.com
Email—info@airproducts.com
Br. Mgr.—Ellen Hammer
SIC—5169; *Distributor of industrial chemicals & specialty gases, including amines & helium*
Employs—13; Estab.—1988
Distrib.—Intl.
Publicly owned corporation

Parent co.—Air Products & Chemicals, Inc., Allentown, PA
Phone—(610) 481-4911
See Parent Co. Section for full profile.

**BOWMAN TOOL**
147 Pinebrook Rd. (07726)
Mail addr.—P.O. Box 176, Keyport (07735)
**Phone—(732) 786-0770**
Fax—(732) 786-0880
www.bowmantool.net
Email—sales@bowmantool.net
Owner—Paul Bowman
SIC—3544; NAICS—333500; *Molds & tool & die job shop*
Employs—1; Estab.—1996
Sales—under $500,000 (est)
Distrib.—Local

**CARTRIDGE RENEWAL SYSTEMS**
13 Glendale Dr. (07726)
**Phone—(732) 845-9497**
National—(800) 459-2626
Fax—(732) 409-7335
www.cartridgerenewal.com
Email—info@cartridgerenewal.com
Ptnr.—Jacklyn Berman
Ptnr.—Craig Berman
SIC—3861; *Remanufactured toner cartridges*
Employs—2; Estab.—1993
Sales—under $500,000
Distrib.—National
Privately owned partnership

†**CHILDCARE SUPPLY CO. INC.**
77 Pension Rd., Ste. 13 (07726-5027)
**Phone—(732) 786-9888**
(732) 786-9595
National—(800) 269-8105
Fax—(732) 786-9895
www.childcaresupplycompany.com
Email—wegloveyoutoo@aol.com
Sales Mgr.—Shari Schwartz
SIC—5122; 5113; 5199; 5169; *Distributor of child care items, including gloves, paper towel supplies, disposable diapers, changing paper, baby wipes, shoe covers, changing table paper & janitorial products*
Employs—10; Estab.—1986
Distrib.—National
Sole ownership
DBA: Gloves Unlimited

**CLOSETTECH**
203 Woodward Rd. (07726)
**Phone—(732) 792-0088**
Fax—(732) 792-1110
www.closettechnj.com
Email—sales@closettechnj.com
Owner—Joe Adelfio
Sales Mgr.—Patty Jagemann
SIC—2541; 2542; *Wooden & plastic laminate custom closet systems & cabinets*
Employs—20; Estab.—1989
Sales—$1Mil-$2.5Mil
10,000 sq ft site, Distrib.—Local
Privately owned corporation

**COMTRON, INC.**
391 State Route 33 E. (07726-8306)
**Phone—(732) 446-7571**
National—(888) 266-8766
Fax—(732) 446-5768
www.comtroninc.com
Email—dlacross@comtroninc.com
Pres.—Gunther Wackerman
Duplexer Products Mgr.—Bob Pasino
Admn. Support Mgr.—Deborah LaCross

SIC—3661; 3679; *Electromechanical devices, cellular antennas & precision & CNC machining job shop*
Employs—14; Estab.—1961
Sales—$2.6Mil-$5Mil
13,000 sq ft site, Distrib.—Intl.
Privately owned sub-S corp.

**DIPASQUALE FENCE CO.**
196 Route 9 N. (07726)
**Phone—(732) 536-0660**
Fax—(732) 536-5208
www.dipasqualefence.com
Plt. Mgr.—Henry DiPasquale
Manager—Mike Chaglrin
SIC—2499; 3446; 3089; NAICS—332323; *Ornamental aluminum, wooden, PVC & vinyl fences, including installation*
Employs—12
Sales—$1Mil-$2.5Mil (est)
Distrib.—Local
Privately owned corporation

NEW ENTRY
†**EDESIA OIL, LLC**
225 County Road 522, Unit B (07726-8824)
**Phone—(732) 851-7979**
Fax—(732) 851-7980
www.edesiaoil.com
Email—celia@edesiaoil.com
Owner—Joseph Calcagno
Off. Mgr.—Celia Kost
SIC—5149; *Distributor of edible oils, including olive oils*
Employs—10; Estab.—2013
28,000 sq ft site, Distrib.—Regional
Limited Liability Company

**EMPIRE DESIGNS, INC.**
7 Main St. (07726)
**Phone—(732) 446-6447**
www.empire-designs.com
Email—knowmore@empire-designs.com
Pres.—Kathleen T. Bien
SIC—2395; 2396; 3993; 2389; *Embroidery, screen printing, promotional products & apparel manufacturing*
Employs—1; Estab.—1987
Distrib.—National
Privately owned corporation

**GOODMAN & CO., INC., BOB**
2 Steward Ln. (07726)
**Phone—(732) 446-0252**
National—(800) 909-6565
Fax—(732) 462-7082
www.bobgoodmanco.com
Email—bgtieman@aol.com
Pres.—Bob Goodman
Off. Mgr.—Jo Freud
SIC—2323; *Men's neckwear & cufflinks*
Employs—4; Estab.—1992
2,300 sq ft site, Distrib.—National
Privately owned corporation

**HAIR SYSTEMS, INC.**
30 Park Ave., P.O. Box 449 (07726)
**Phone—(732) 446-2202**
Fax—(732) 446-7968
www.hairsystemsinc.com
Email—info@hairsystemsinc.com
Pres., CEO—William E. Covey, Jr.
V-P., Sales & Mktg.—Michael Spano
V-P., Tech.—Mabel R. Covey
IT Mgr.—John Ruch
Hum. Res. Mgr.—Arlene Terea
Sales Rep.—Diana Deroian
SIC—2844; NAICS—325600; *Hair bleaches, dyes & liquids*
Employs—90; Estab.—1981
48,000 sq ft site, Distrib.—Intl.
Privately owned corporation

GEOGRAPHICAL

## Englishtown—(cont.)

**HUB SIGN CRANE CORP.**
67 Wood Ave. (07726)
**Phone—(732) 252-9090**
National—(800) 244-2339
Fax—(732) 252-9091
Principal—Chris Barber
SIC—3993; *Neon & vinyl signs*
Employs—5
Sales—under $500,000
Distrib.—Local
Privately owned corporation

NEW ENTRY
**JEWELRY DESIGN GALLERY, INC.**
357 U.S. Highway 9, Ste. 18
(07726)
**Phone—(732) 536-1184**
www.jewelrydesigngallery.com
Manager—Drew Cowit
SIC—3911; *Precious metal jewelry, including gold & silver jewelry*
Employs—4
Sales—$500,000-$1Mil (est)
Distrib.—Regional
Sole ownership

**MINUTEMAN PRESS**
349 U.S. Highway 9, Ste. 7
(07726)
**Phone—(732) 536-8788**
Fax—(732) 536-0579
www.mmpmanalapan.com
Email—info@mmpmanalapan.com
Pres.—Joe Lorenz
Manager—Jackie Yagla
SIC—2752; 2789; NAICS—323100; *Instant printing & mailing & bindery services*
Employs—6; Estab.—1988
Sales—$750,000
1,280 sq ft site, Distrib.—Local
Privately owned corporation

**NAL-PAK PAPER SPECIALTIES, LLC**
18 Monterey Ln. (07726)
**Phone—(732) 462-5196**
Fax—(732) 462-5196
Email—nalpakpaper@gmail.com
Pres.—Murray Kaplan
Manager—Jack Smith
SIC—2675; 3089; NAICS—322200; *Clear poly film & waxed paper die cutting*
Employs—5; Estab.—1947
Sales—$500,000-$1Mil
Distrib.—Intl.
Limited Liability Company

**QUADRANGLE PRODUCTS**
28 Harrison Ave., Bldg. 16-D
(07726)
**Phone—(732) 792-1234**
Fax—(732) 792-8305
www.quadrangleproducts.com
Email—craig@quadrangleproducts.com
Pres.—Michael Levine
GM—Craig Stamer
Prodn. Mgr.—Mike Ballantyne
Fin. Mgr.—Gayle Stamer
Engrg. Mgr.—Michael Babcock
Engr.—Vijay Budhan
SIC—3678; 3679; NAICS—334417; *Custom cable assemblies for interfacing to flat panel displays & associated peripherals*
Employs—31; Estab.—1985
8,500 sq ft site, Distrib.—Intl.
Privately owned corporation
ISO rating—9001:2008

**REISS MFG., INC.**
75 Mount Vernon Rd., P.O. Box 310 (07726-0310)
**Phone—(732) 446-6100**
Fax—(732) 446-1394
www.reissmfg.com
Email—reiss-corp@reissmfg.com
Pres.—Carl Reiss

Hum. Res. Mgr.—Doreen Santos
Qual. Assur. Mgr.—Lance Larsen
SIC—3089; *Corporate headquarters & plastic injection molding*
Employs—125; Estab.—1896
Sales—$60Mil
Distrib.—Intl.
Privately owned corporation
ISO rating—9001:2000

**REX LUMBER CO.**
1 Station St., P.O. Box 1776
(07726)
**Phone—(732) 446-4200**
National—(800) 631-2108
Fax—(732) 446-5036
www.rexlumber.com
Email—salesinfo@rexlumber.com
Owner & Opers. Mgr.—Ben Forester
Mill Mgr.—Larry Reitsma
SIC—2426; 2431; 2499; NAICS—321900; *FSC certified custom tropical & domestic hardwood mouldings & millwork*
Employs—85; Estab.—1946
Sales—$10Mil-$15Mil
12,000 sq ft site, Distrib.—Regional
Privately owned sub-S corp.
Parent co.—Rex Lumber Co., Acton, MA
Phone—(978) 263-0055
See Parent Co. Section for full profile.

**SILVI CONCRETE PRODUCTS, INC.**
470 State Highway 33 (07726)
**Phone—(267) 907-9150**
National—(800) 426-6273
Fax—(732) 446-4552
www.silvi.com
Email—trich@silvi.com
Plt. Mgr.—Frank King
SIC—3273; NAICS—327320; *Ready-mixed concrete*
Employs—20; Estab.—1977
Sales—$1Mil-$5Mil
40,000 sq ft site, Distrib.—Local
Privately owned corporation
Parent co.—Silvi Concrete Products, Inc., Fairless Hills, PA
Phone—(215) 295-0777
See Parent Co. Section for full profile.

**STAVOLA CONTRACTING CO., INC.**
120 Old Bergen Mill Rd. (07726)
**Phone—(732) 542-2328**
Fax—(732) 542-7519
www.stavola.com
Email—information@stavola.com
Owner & Manager—Joe Stavola
SIC—2951; *Asphalt*
Employs—4
Privately owned corporation
Parent co.—Stavola Contracting Co., Inc., Tinton Falls, NJ
Phone—(732) 542-2328
See Parent Co. Section for full profile.

**UNION HILL CORP. (H Q)**
34 Water St. (07726)
**Phone—(732) 786-9422**
Fax—(732) 786-9423
www.unionhillcorp.com
Email—info@uhcorp.com
CEO—Mike Conforth
SIC—3199; 2399; *Corporate headquarters; horse tack, saddle pads & equestrian accessories (mfg. done in China & India)*
Employs—4; Estab.—2005
Sales—under $500,000 (est)
Distrib.—Intl.
Privately owned corporation

**WOOD SHOP**
24 Water St. (07726)
**Phone—(732) 446-3377**
Fax—(732) 446-5009
Owner—Bruce Evano

SIC—2434; NAICS—337110; *Wooden kitchen cabinets*
Employs—1; Estab.—1976
Sales—under $500,000
Distrib.—Local
Sole ownership

## Erial
(Camden—S.W.)

**NATIONAL COLOR GRAPHICS**
1755 Williamstown Rd. (08081)
**Phone—(856) 435-6800**
Fax—(856) 435-0503
Owner—Jeffery Hughes
SIC—2759; NAICS—323100; *Commercial printing*
Employs—10; Estab.—1985
Sales—$500,000-$1Mil
Distrib.—Regional
Sole ownership

## Ewing
(Mercer—N.E.)

**ANTARES PHARMA, INC.**
100 Princeton S. Corporate Ctr., Ste. 300 (08628)
Mail addr: 100 Charles Ewing Blvd., Ste. 300, Trenton (08628-3458)
**Phone—(609) 359-3020**
Fax—(609) 359-3015
www.antarespharma.com
Email—info@antarespharma.com
Pres., CEO—Eamonn P. Hobbs
Pres., Parental Prods. Div., Ex. V-P. & CFO—Robert Apple
CTO—Peter Sadowski
V-P., Corp. Affs.—John 'Jack' Howarth
SIC—3841; *Corporate headquarters & needle-free drug delivery systems*
Employs—30; Estab.—1979
Sales—$20Mil-$25Mil
Distrib.—National
Publicly owned corporation

**ARCTIC ICE CREAM**
22 Arctic Pkwy. (08638)
**Phone—(609) 393-4264**
Fax—(609) 392-3663
Email—arcticicecream@hotmail.com
Pres.—Thomas Green
Plt. Mgr.—Faron Berkhalter
Off. Mgr.—Chris Green
SIC—2024; NAICS—311520; *Ice cream*
Employs—10
Sales—$1Mil-$2.5Mil
Distrib.—Local

**CHURCH & DWIGHT CO., INC. (H Q)**
500 Charles Ewing Blvd. (08628)
**Phone—(609) 683-5900**
www.churchdwight.com
Email—james.craigie@churchdwight.com
Chrm., CEO—James Craigie
V-P., CFO & Fin.—Matthew T. Farrell
V-P., Gen. Counsel—Patrick DeMaynagies
V-P., Sales—Lou Tursi
V-P., Global Opers.—Mark Conish
V-P., Mktg.—Bruce Fleming
SIC—2841; 3291; NAICS—325611; *Corporate headquarters; detergents, baking soda, steel wool products, fabric softener, sheets & latex condoms; Brand name—Arm & Hammer*
Employs—400
Sales—$1.6Bil
Publicly owned corporation

**DISCOVERY SEMICONDUCTORS, INC.**
119 Silvia St. (08628)
**Phone—(609) 434-1311**
Fax—(609) 434-1317
www.discoverysemi.com
Email—aberry@discoverysemi.com
Pres.—Abhay Joshi
V-P.—Sharon Joshi
SIC—3674; NAICS—334413; *Semiconductors*
Employs—20; Estab.—1993
14,000 sq ft site, Distrib.—Intl.
Privately owned corporation

**DUTCH'S MEATS, INC.**
30 Morse Ave. (08638)
**Phone—(609) 882-6650**
Fax—(609) 882-9370
Email—dutchsmeats@aol.com
Pres.—Dominic Granaldi, Jr.
V-P.—Dominic Granaldi III
Treas.—Albert Granaldi
SIC—2013; NAICS—311612; *Meat processing, including ground beef & single-portion cuts for restaurants & hotels*
Employs—10; Estab.—1972
Distrib.—Local
Privately owned corporation

**FEMTOTEK, INC.**
865 Lower Ferry Rd., Ste. B-9
(08628)
**Phone—(609) 406-9680**
Fax—(609) 406-9680
www.femtotek.com
Email—sales@femtotek.com
Pres.—David Edwards
SIC—7372; *High-performance test & instrumentation applications software development for the aerospace, chemical, life sciences, automotive & semiconductor industries; Brand name—FTI*
Employs—5; Estab.—1982
Distrib.—Intl.
Privately owned corporation

**FURNITURE MILL, INC., THE**
1536 Lower Ferry Rd. (08628)
**Phone—(609) 771-0274**
Fax—(609) 771-8087
www.furnituremill.com
Owner—Barb Conover
SIC—2511; *Furniture refinishing*
Employs—4; Estab.—1982
Sales—under $500,000
10,000 sq ft site, Distrib.—Local
Sole ownership

**GOUGH ENGRAVING & ADVERTISING SPECIALTIES**
1745 N. Olden Avenue Ext.
(08638)
**Phone—(609) 882-8700**
Fax—(609) 882-9163
www.goughengraving.com
Email—orders@goughengraving.com
Owner—Kathleen Gough
SIC—3479; 2395; 2396; 3993; *Brass & plastic engraving, award plaques, trophies, interior & exterior signage, screen printing, embroidery & imprinted advertising specialties, t-shirts & wearables*
Employs—4; Estab.—1980
Sales—$500,000-$1Mil
2,400 sq ft site, Distrib.—Regional
Sole ownership

**†HEATH LUMBER CO.**
1580 N. Olden Avenue Ext.
(08638)
**Phone—(609) 392-1166**
Fax—(609) 396-8050
www.heathlumber.com
Email—sales@heathlumber.com
Pres.—Gary Patricelli
Off. Mgr.—Barbara Staub

## Ewing—(cont.)

SIC—5031; 5072; 5169;
*Distributor of building materials &
supplies for homeowners,
professionals & do-it-yourselfers,
including framing & treated
lumber, plywood, windows,
doors & hardware*
Employs—30; Estab.—1857
Sales—$5Mil-$10Mil
36,000 sq ft site, Distrib.—
Regional
Privately owned corporation

### HEIGHTS USA, INC.

1445 Lower Ferry Rd. (08618)
**Phone—(609) 530-1300**
Fax—(609) 530-9430
www.heights-usa.com
Email—info@heights-usa.com
Opers. Mgr.—Tim Philburn
Hum. Res. Mgr.—Sheri Petrone
SIC—3555; 3552; NAICS—
333293; *Lithographic &
flexographic printing plate
equipment & parts & leather
testing equipment*
Employs—12; Estab.—1999
Distrib.—Intl.
Privately owned corporation

### HERMITAGE PRESS, INC.

1595 5th St. (08638)
**Phone—(609) 882-3600**
National—(800) 882-4376
Fax—(609) 882-1137
www.hermitagepress.com
Email—info@hermitagepress.com
Pres.—Michael Stoeckle
Sales Rep.—Tom Stoeckle
SIC—2759; NAICS—323100;
*Commercial printing; Brand
name—FSC & Rainforest
Alliance Certification;
Environmental Friendly Printing*
Employs—21; Estab.—1947
Distrib.—Regional
Privately owned corporation

### K W, INC.

1536 Lower Ferry Rd. (08618)
**Phone—(609) 882-6363**
Fax—(609) 882-6644
Email—kwincnj@aol.com
Pres.—Kurt Watson
V-P.—Patricia Watson
SIC—2521; 2541; 2431; NAICS—
337211; *Commercial casework,
architectural millwork &
residential cabinets*
Employs—3; Estab.—1989
Sales—$500,000-$1Mil
8,000 sq ft site, Distrib.—Regional
Privately owned sub-S corp.

### KINETICS INDUSTRIES, INC.

140 Stokes Ave. (08638)
**Phone—(609) 883-9700**
Fax—(609) 883-0025
www.kinetics-industries.com
Email—info@kinetics-
industries.com
Pres.—Ronald Secrest
V-P.—Keith Secrest
Pur. Agt.—Frank Antonowicz
SIC—3679; *Power rectifiers & field
excitation systems for
synchronous motors &
generators; Brand name—
KinetSync-SR; KinetSync-NB;
Stata-Flux Magnet Control
System; JVR Flux Forcing
Magnet Rectifier*
Employs—30; Estab.—1939
35,000 sq ft site, Distrib.—Intl.
Privately owned corporation

### KISTHARDT AUTO PRODUCTS, LLC

354 4th St. (08638)
**Phone—(609) 434-0700**
Fax—(609) 434-0702
www.kisthardts.com
Email—kapllc354@verizon.net

Pres., Fin., MIS & R & D Mgr.—
Kevin Burke
V-P.—Julie Burke
SIC—3714; *Upholstered
automobile seats, convertible
tops, vinyl roofs & automotive
glass*
Employs—4; Estab.—1926
Sales—under $500,000
5,200 sq ft site, Distrib.—Local
Limited Liability Company

### LAWRENCE CUSTOM DRAPERY SHOP

323 4th St. (08638)
**Phone—(609) 695-3877**
Fax—(609) 278-9059
www.shurenupholstery-
drapery.com
Email—info@shurenupholstery-
drapery.com
Pres.—Charlie Cullen
V-P.—Cathy Shuren
Sales Mgr.—Tom Edwards
SIC—2391; 2211; 2221; 2591;
NAICS—314121; *Custom
draperies, window treatments,
designer fabrics & upholstery for
homes, businesses & institutions*
Employs—20; Estab.—1963
Sales—$1Mil-$2.5Mil
Distrib.—Local
Privately owned corporation
AKAs: Shuren & Cullen, Inc. &
Shuren Upholstery

### MEDNET HEALTHCARE TECHNOLOGIES, INC.

275 Phillips Blvd. (08618)
**Phone—(609) 671-1790**
National—(800) 606-5511
Fax—(609) 671-1765
www.mednethealth.net
Email—info@mednethealth.net
Sales Mgr.—Janice Hardell
Hum. Res. Mgr.—Shawna Blustein
SIC—3845; *Ambulatory cardiac
monitors & electromedical
equipment*
Employs—50
Sales—$10Mil-$25Mil (est)
Distrib.—National
Privately owned corporation

### MINUTEMAN PRESS

35 Scotch Rd. (08628)
**Phone—(609) 883-0799**
National—(800) 774-6345
Fax—(609) 538-0701
www.minuteweb.minutemanpress.
com
Email—minuteweb@
minutemanpress.com
Pres.—Ted Blumenthal
V-P.—Susan Blumenthal
SIC—2759; 2752; NAICS—
323100; *Digital, offset, full color
& instant printing of booklets,
flyers, letterheads & envelopes &
advertising specialties*
Employs—4; Estab.—1985
Sales—$500,000-$1Mil
5,000 sq ft site, Distrib.—National
Privately owned sub-S corp.

### PFLAUMER BROS.

1008 Whitehead Road Ext.
(08638)
**Phone—(609) 883-4610**
Fax—(609) 883-1629
www.pflaumer.com
Email—dhamilton@pflaumer.com
Pres.—Harley McNair
Pur. Mgr.—Danielle Hamilton
SIC—2869; *Specialty chemicals
for coatings, paints & lubricants,
including additives, colorants,
dispersions & powdered
minerals*
Employs—15; Estab.—1984
Sales—$500,000-$1Mil
Distrib.—Intl.
Privately owned corporation

### PROFORMA UNLIMITED MARKETING EXPRESSIONS

36 Keswick Ave. (08638)
**Phone—(609) 882-0112**
www.marketingexpressions.net
Email—susan.barosko@
proforma.com
Ptnr.—Susan Barosko
Ptnr.—David R. Nettles
SIC—2759; 3993; NAICS—
323100; *Commercial printing,
stationery & promotional
products*
Employs—3; Estab.—2000
Sales—under $1Mil
Distrib.—Intl.
Limited Liability Company

### RIEGEL COMMUNICATION GROUP

One Graphics Dr., P.O. Box 7430
(08628)
**Phone—(609) 771-0555**
Fax—(609) 771-0947
www.riegelprintinginc.com
Email—info@riegelprintinginc.com
Pres.—Kathleen Atkins
CFO & Hum. Res. Mgr.—James B.
Eska
Ex. V-P.—Susan Heath
Acct. Exec. & Acct. Mgr.—Ellen
Wagner
Off. Mgr.—Peggy Tunney
SIC—2759; NAICS—323100;
*Commercial printing*
Employs—75; Estab.—1970
Sales—over $14Mil
42,000 sq ft site, Distrib.—
Regional
Privately owned sub-S corp.

### RJD MACHINE PRODUCTS, INC.

1424 Heath Ave. *(08638)*
**Phone—(609) 392-1515**
Fax—(609) 392-1098
www.rjdmachineproducts.com
Email—admin@
rjdmachineproducts.com
Pres.—Richard Roslowski
Secy-Treas.—Debra Roslowski
GM & Pur. Agt.—Julie Koveloski
SIC—3599; *Precision machining
job shop*
Employs—11; Estab.—1980
Sales—$1Mil-$5Mil
10,000 sq ft site, Distrib.—Intl.
Privately owned sub-S corp.

**NEW ENTRY**

### STATE WELDING

5 Industry Ct. (08638)
**Phone—(609) 882-3288**
www.weldingfabricationofnj.com
Email—amanofsteel@verizon.net
Owner—Donald Petrescu
SIC—3599; *Welding & general
machining job shop*
Employs—4; Estab.—1953
Sales—$500,000-$1Mil
10,000 sq ft site, Distrib.—Local
Sole ownership

### TRENTON JOE'S EMBROIDERY

4 Scotch Rd. (08628)
**Phone—(609) 538-9450**
Fax—(609) 538-9453
www.trentonjoe.net
Email—trentonjoenson@
comcast.net
Owner—Joseph Chiarello
Sales Mgr.—Nick Chiarello
Off. Mgr.—Beverly Chiarello
SIC—2395; 2396; *Embroidery,
screen printing & promotional
products*
Employs—7; Estab.—1980
Sales—under $500,000
Distrib.—Regional
Sole ownership

### TYGER SCIENTIFIC, INC.

324 Stokes Ave. (08638)
**Phone—(609) 434-0144**
National—(888) 329-8990

Fax—(609) 434-0143
www.tygersci.com
Email—sales@tygersci.com
Chrm., CEO—Adam Yuan
SIC—2819; 2869; 2899; *Organic
intermediates & specialty
chemicals for the
pharmaceutical, cosmetics,
electronic, photographic, rubber
& plastics industries*
Employs—10; Estab.—1992
Sales—$6Mil-$10Mil
7,000 sq ft site, Distrib.—Intl.
Privately owned corporation
ISO rating—9001:2008

### WASTE MANAGEMENT, INC.

107 Silvia St. (08628)
**Phone—(609) 587-1500**
Fax—(609) 434-5754
www.wm.com
Email—info@wm.com
Cont.—Tom Utermark
GM—Tara Hammer
Hum. Res. Mgr.—Larry Faschan
SIC—3089; 3341; *Glass, scrap
metal, plastic, paper, cardboard
& aluminum recycling*
Employs—120; Estab.—2000
Distrib.—Regional
Publicly owned corporation
Parent co.—Waste Management,
Inc., Houston, TX
Phone—(713) 512-6200
See Parent Co. Section for full profile.

---

## Fair Lawn

(Bergen—N.E.)

### ADVANCED PROTECTIVE PRODUCTS, INC.

17-12 River Rd. (07410)
**Phone—(718) 359-1315**
National—(800) 787-8007
Fax—(201) 548-5100
www.rust007.com
Email—tom@rust007.com
Owner & Pres.—Tom Heiss
SIC—2851; NAICS—325510;
*Rust-converting paint primers;
Brand name—Rust Knockout;
Rust Destroyer; Fast Dry Rust
Destroyer*
Employs—12; Estab.—1982
1,500 sq ft site, Distrib.—Intl.
Privately owned corporation

### AMERICAN FITTINGS CORP.

17-10 Willow St. (07410)
**Phone—(201) 664-0027**
Fax—(201) 664-1175
www.americanfittingscorp.com
Email—jkrawczyk@
americanfittingscorp.com
Pres.—Allen Fischbein
V-P., Sales & Mktg.—Joe
Krawczyk
Hum. Res. Mgr.—Heather
Fischbein
SIC—3644; 3643; NAICS—
335931; *Electrical fittings*
Employs—50; Estab.—1946
Sales—$500,000-$1Mil
Distrib.—National
Privately owned corporation
Also see: Edgewater Mfg. Co.,
Inc., same loc.

### AMERICAN GRAPHIC SYSTEMS, INC.

39-26 Broadway (07410)
**Phone—(201) 796-0666**
Fax—(201) 796-7997
www.americangraphics.com
Email—printandsign@aol.com
Pres.—Stan Schechter
Secy-Treas. & Graphic Artist—
Diane Schechter

GEOGRAPHICAL

## Fair Lawn—(cont.)

SIC—2752; 3993; NAICS—323122; *Offset printing & signs*
Employs—5; Estab.—1977
Sales—under $500,000
Distrib.—Local
Privately owned corporation

**ASSOCIATED FABRICS CORP.**
15-01 Pollitt Dr., Ste. 7 (07410)
**Phone—(800) 232-4077**
Fax—(866) 710-3850
www.afc-fabrics.com
Email—info@afcfabrics.com
Pres.—Martin Markowitz
Dir., Sales—Bruce Nocera
Off. Mgr.—Norman Horowitz
SIC—2299; 5131; *Fabric converting & distributor of fabrics; Brand name—Super Strech; Marvel Stretch; Double Stretch; Satin Stretch; Heavy Stretch*
Employs—6; Estab.—1928
Sales—$1Mil-$5Mil
6,000 sq ft site, Distrib.—Intl.
Privately owned corporation

**BEILIS DEVELOPMENT, LLC (H Q)**
20-21 Wagaraw Rd., Bldg. 31-B (07410)
**Phone—(973) 559-5670**
Fax—(973) 238-8686
www.ipbrandsllc.com
CTO—Kenneil Rey
Opers. Mgr.—Cheryl Gill
Hum. Res. Mgr.—Ricardo Anasarda
SIC—2844; *Company headquarters; cosmetics (mfg. subcontracted); Brand name—Intellectual Property Brands*
Employs—15; Estab.—2005
Sales—$5Mil-$10Mil (est)
Distrib.—Local
Limited Liability Company

**†BERGEN COUNTY MOTOR & TOOL CO.**
17-16 River Rd. (07410)
**Phone—(201) 796-3006**
Fax—(201) 796-0395
www.bergentool.com
Email—sales@bergentool.com
Pres.—David Rink
Bookkeeper—Doris Defino
SIC—5084; *Distributor of power tools & accessories & construction supplies; Brand name—Amana Tool; Bosch; Campion Cutting Tools; Dewalt; Delta; Diamond Products; Fein; Freud; General Wire Spring; Honda Engines; Husqvarna; Makita; Metabo; Milwaukee; Pacific Laser; Porter Cable; Ridgid; Sait; Tenryu; Voltec*
Employs—4; Estab.—1979
Sales—under $1Mil
4,500 sq ft site, Distrib.—National
Privately owned corporation

**BIOMET, INC.**
20-01 Pollitt Dr. (07410)
**Phone—(201) 797-7300**
Fax—(201) 797-0947
www.biomet.com
Email—custserv@biometmail.com
Prodn. Mgr.—Mike Shannon
Hum. Res. Mgr.—Peggy Noville
SIC—3369; 3842; NAICS—331528; *Orthopedic implants alloy castings*
Employs—50; Estab.—1979
Distrib.—Intl.
Privately owned corporation
Parent co.—Biomet, Inc., Warsaw, IN
Phone—(574) 267-6639
See Parent Co. Section for full profile.

**†BORO SUPPLY CO., INC.**
2-21 Banta Pl., P.O. Box 1034 (07410)
**Phone—(201) 794-3111**
National—(800) 622-1363
Fax—(201) 794-0347
www.borosupply.com
Email—sales@borosupply.com
Pres.—Stanley Romanek
V-P.—Susan Romanek
SIC—5084; *Wholesaler of machinery, equipment & supplies for metal fabricators & machine shops; Brand name—MARVEL; CLAUSING; SCOTCHMAN; KMT SAW; AMADA; DAKE; ERCOLINA*
Employs—7; Estab.—1982
Distrib.—Local
Privately owned corporation

**BUCHMANN CONTROL PANELS MFG., INC.**
5-18 Banta Pl. (07410)
**Phone—(201) 791-3161**
Fax—(201) 791-7143
Email—felock1201@aim.com
Owner—Red Buchman
Pres.—Fausto Lockhart
SIC—3613; NAICS—335313; *Control panels*
Employs—5; Estab.—1991
Sales—$500,000-$1Mil
2,000 sq ft site,
Privately owned corporation

**C & W SYSTEMS**
17-04 Split Rock Rd., P.O. Box 201 (07410)
**Phone—(201) 791-7892**
Fax—(201) 791-0953
Email—candw@erols.com
Owner—Walter Miller
SIC—2761; 2759; NAICS—323116; *Commercial business form & envelope printing*
Employs—1; Estab.—1981
Sales—under $500,000
Distrib.—Regional
Sole ownership

**CALMAC**
3-00 Banta Pl. (07410)
**Phone—(201) 797-1511**
Fax—(201) 797-1522
www.calmac.com
Email—info@calmac.com
CEO—Mark M. MacCracken
V-P., Engr.—Brian Silvetti
V-P., Sales & Mktg.—Paul Valenta
Mktg. Mgr.—Jasmine Williams
SIC—3585; *Ice storage & ice rink equipment, including thermal energy storage tanks for hybrid off-peak cooling systems & ice rink floors for permanent & temporary skating rinks; Brand name—IceBank; IceMat; HeatMat*
Employs—40; Estab.—1947
Distrib.—Intl.
Privately owned corporation

**CREATIVE INNOVATIONS, INC.**
20-21 Wagaraw Rd., Ste. 31-B (07410)
**Phone—(973) 636-9060**
Fax—(973) 636-9061
Email—metrocabinet@optimum.net
Pres.—Joseph Batavia
Off. Mgr.—Raj Loonkar
SIC—2434; 2431; NAICS—337110; *Wooden kitchen & bath cabinets & millwork*
Employs—8; Estab.—1996
Distrib.—National
Privately owned corporation

**†DE PASQUALE SALON SYSTEMS, INC.**
21-21 Broadway (07410)
**Phone—(201) 797-9101**
National—(800) 724-4247
Fax—(201) 797-0632
www.depasqualesalonsystems.com
Email—info@depasqualeco.com
Pres.—Joe Mastalia
CFO—Jim Savino
IT Mgr.—Rubin Morales
Hum. Res. Mgr.—Diane Messick
SIC—5087; 5122; *Distributor of beauty salon supplies, including skincare, bodycare & haircare products*
Employs—100; Estab.—1984
Distrib.—Regional
Privately owned corporation

**DESSAU CO., INC., MAURICE**
15-01 Pollitt Dr. (07410)
**Phone—(201) 791-2005**
Fax—(201) 791-2115
www.dessaudiamond.com
Email—sales@dessaudiamond.com
Pres.—Richard Dessau
Sales Mgr.—Travis Thompson
SIC—3423; *Industrial diamond tools*
Employs—25; Estab.—1841
Sales—$2.5Mil-$5Mil (est)
Distrib.—Intl.
Privately owned corporation
AKA: Dessau International

**EDGEWATER MFG. CO., INC**
17-10 Willow St. (07410)
**Phone—(201) 664-0022**
Fax—(201) 664-1175
www.americanfittingscorp.com
V-P., Opers.—Rachell Fischbein
Accts. Mgr.—Norman Sees
SIC—3679; *Electrical fittings*
Employs—12
Sales—$1Mil-$2.5Mil
Distrib.—National
Privately owned corporation
Also see: American Fittings Corp., same loc.

**EXCALIBUR BAGEL & BAKERY EQUIPMENT, INC.**
4-01 Banta Pl. (07410)
**Phone—(201) 797-2788**
Fax—(201) 797-2711
www.excalibur-equipment.com
Email—excaliburequip@aol.com
Pres.—Richard Zinn
V-P.—S. Kuo
SIC—3556; NAICS—333294; *Bagel & artisan bread making equipment & supplies, including triple action & spiral mixers, rack & revolving ovens, bagel formers & dividers, shredders, graters & bagel kettles*
Employs—14; Estab.—1994
Sales—$1Mil-$5Mil
45,000 sq ft site, Distrib.—Intl.
Sole ownership

**GEM SPORTS**
36-10 Broadway (07410)
**Phone—(201) 791-1776**
Fax—(201) 791-5472
www.gemsportsonline.com
Email—info@gemsportsonline.com
Pres.—Michael Cebulski
V-P.—Emiro Franco
Dir., Mktg.—Jennifer Cebulski
Off. Mgr.—Janice Pinto
SIC—2396; 2395; *Textile screen printing & embroidery of golf shirts, t-shirts, jackets & bags; Brand name—American Apparel; Bella; Gildan; Jerzee; Holloway; Soffe; Alleson; Augusta; High Five*
Employs—4; Estab.—1974
Sales—under $500,000
Distrib.—National
Limited Liability Company

**GERSON INDUSTRIES, INC.**
20-21 Wagaraw Rd., Bldg. 37, P.O. Box 12 (07410)
**Phone—(973) 423-6100**
(973) 626-3296
Fax—(973) 423-6130
Email—lgoldfond@aol.com
Pres.—Louis Goldfond
V-P.—Ruth Goldfond
SIC—2515; *Mattresses & box springs*
Employs—14; Estab.—1977
Sales—$1Mil-$2.5Mil (est)
Distrib.—Regional
Privately owned corporation
AKA: Gerson Mattress

**GILD, INC.**
18-02 River Rd., Ste. 5 (07410-1218)
**Phone—(201) 398-0030**
Fax—(201) 398-0018
www.gildsheetmetal.com
Email—gild@gildsheetmetal.com
Pres.—Lev Kulek
V-P.—Ely Kulek
SIC—3444; *Sheet metal fabrication*
Employs—10; Estab.—1984
Sales—$1Mil-$2.5Mil
500,000 sq ft site, Distrib.—Local
Sole ownership

**INDUSTRIAL CONSULTING & MARKETING**
20-21 Wagaraw Rd., Bldg. 38 (07410)
**Phone—(973) 427-2474**
National—(877) 405-5200
Fax—(973) 427-9899
www.icmstone.com
Email—info@icmstone.com
Pres.—Alfonso Bertoni
SIC—3281; NAICS—327991; *Kitchen & bathroom stone countertops*
Employs—40; Estab.—1996
Sales—$2.5Mil-$5Mil (est)
Distrib.—Local
Privately owned corporation
DBA: ICM

**JIMMY'S COOKIES, LLC**
18-01 River Rd. (07410)
**Phone—(201) 797-8900**
National—(800) 683-6648
Fax—(201) 797-2090
www.jimmyscookies.com
Pres.—Michael Pisani
Cust. Serv. Mgr.—Marie Kochanski
SIC—2052; 2045; NAICS—311822; *Gourmet cookies & cookie dough*
Employs—60; Estab.—1984
Distrib.—National
Privately owned corporation

**KA-LOR CUBICLE & SUPPLY CO., INC.**
P.O. Box 804 (07410)
**Phone—(201) 891-8077**
Fax—(201) 891-6331
Email—kalorcub@yahoo.com
Pres.—Dennis Brett
V-P.—Adele Brett
SIC—2391; 2392; 3429; 3841; *Hospital & institutional cubicle, shower & blackout curtains, liners & overhead tracks & hardware, including intravenous track & bottle holders; Brand name—Zip Trak*
Employs—21; Estab.—1962
Sales—$1Mil-$5Mil
3,000 sq ft site, Distrib.—Intl.
Privately owned corporation
AKA: Trakman, LLC

## Fair Lawn—(cont.)

**KUIKEN BROTHERS COMPANY, INC.**
6-02 Fair Lawn Ave., P.O. Box
1040 (07410-8040)
**Phone—(201) 796-2082**
Fax—(201) 475-2170
www.kuikenbrothers.com
Email—info@kuikenbrothers.com
Pres.—Douglas Kuiken
Cont.—Tom Tubridy
Plt. Mgr.—Phil Cerne
Hum. Res. Mgr.—Debbie Steyling
SIC—2421; *Corporate
headquarters & lumber
processing*
Employs—31; Estab.—1912
Company-wide: 240
Sales—$91Mil
Distrib.—Local
Privately owned sub-S corp.

**LANDZETTEL & SONS, INC.**
17-12 River Rd. (07410)
**Phone—(201) 796-3506**
Fax—(201) 797-5973
www.landzetteladsons.com
Email—office@
landzetteladsons.com
Pres.—Walter J. Landzettel
V.-P.—Robert W. Landzettel
Off. Mgr.—Marion R. Kotran
SIC—2851; 2899; NAICS—
325510; *Private label oil & latex
paints & waterproofing
compounds & additives*
Employs—8; Estab.—1932
15,000 sq ft site, Distrib.—Local
Privately owned corporation

**METRO BOWL**
37-02 Broadway (07410)
**Phone—(201) 791-2995**
Fax—(201) 797-3070
www.metrobowl.com
Owner—Miklos Heitler
SIC—3479; *Awards & engraving*
Employs—4; Estab.—1965
Sales—under $500,000
Distrib.—Local
Sole ownership

**MINUTEMAN PRESS**
23-51 Fair Lawn Ave. (07410)
**Phone—(201) 791-0550**
    (201) 791-1053
Fax—(201) 791-1456
www.fairlawn.minutemanpress.co
m
Email—fairlawn@
minutemanpress.com
Pres., CEO—Mitch Palin
Ex. V.-P.—Sandy Palin
V.-P., Graphic Design—Matt Palin
SIC—2759; 2752; 3993; NAICS—
323100; *Full-color & instant
printing & graphic design of
business cards, flyers,
brochures, newsletters,
letterheads, envelopes, social
invitations, signs, banners &
promotional merchandise,
including binding & laminating*
Employs—4; Estab.—1987
Sales—under $500,000
1,100 sq ft site, Distrib.—Regional
Privately owned sub-S corp.

**MITER BOX, LLC**
4-21 Banta Pl., Ste. B (07410)
**Phone—(201) 773-6209**
Fax—(201) 956-6780
Email—finserra@verizon.net
Owner—Frank Inserra
SIC—2434; NAICS—337110;
*Wooden cabinets*
Employs—7; Estab.—1994
Sales—$500,000-$1Mil
Distrib.—Regional
Sole ownership

**MJM IMPRESSIONS LLC**
20-10 Maple Ave., Bldg. 35-E, P.O.
Box 2 (07410)
**Phone—(973) 423-4999**
Fax—(973) 423-4155
Email—mjmprinting@optonline.net
Pres.—Mitchell Kempin
V.-P.—Jeffrey Kempin
SIC—2759; NAICS—323100;
*Commercial printing of
promotional products*
Employs—2; Estab.—1984
Sales—under $500,000
Distrib.—Regional
Limited Liability Company

**MONDELEZ INTERNATIONAL, INC.**
22-11 State Route 208 (07410-
2608)
**Phone—(201) 794-4000**
Fax—(201) 791-5710
www.mondelezinternational.com
Cont.—Jared Goldberg
Plt. Mgr.—Michael Wallace
Fin. Analyst—Leslie Glodava
SIC—2052; *Cookies & crackers*
Employs—500
Sales—$25Mil-$100Mil
Publicly owned corporation
Parent co.—Mondelez
International, Inc., Deerfield, IL
Phone—(847) 943-4000
See Parent Co. Section for full profile.

**NORITAKE CO., INC. (H Q)**
15-22 Fair Lawn Ave. (07410)
**Phone—(201) 796-2222**
Fax—(201) 796-9155
www.noritake.com
Email—ttomd2@n.noritake.co.jp
CEO—Satoru Shimazaki
Hum. Res. Mgr.—Kaz Kawamura
SIC—3291; *Corporate
headquarters; abrasive
products, including grinding
wheels & sandpaper disks*
Employs—20
Sales—$2.5Mil-$5Mil (est)
Distrib.—Intl.
Privately owned corporation

**POWERTECH**
0-02 Fair Lawn Ave. (07410)
**Phone—(201) 791-5050**
Fax—(201) 791-6805
www.power-tech.com
Email—info@power-tech.com
Mng. Ptnr.—Marty Lanning
SIC—3674; NAICS—334413;
*High-power NPN silicon
transistors*
Employs—9; Estab.—1969
14,000 sq ft site, Distrib.—Intl.
Privately owned corporation

**PRIVATE LABEL PRODUCTS, INC.**
20-21 Wagaraw Rd., Bldg. 34
(07410)
**Phone—(201) 791-1177**
Fax—(201) 791-0088
www.foodoodler.com
Email—info@foodoodler.com
Off. Mgr.—David Naor
SIC—3951; NAICS—339941;
*Specialty writing instruments*
Employs—12; Estab.—1995
10,000 sq ft site, Distrib.—Intl.
Privately owned corporation

**RANGECRAFT MFG. CO., INC.**
4-40 Banta Pl. (07410)
**Phone—(201) 791-0440**
National—(877) 724-6637
Fax—(201) 791-4494
www.rangecraft.com
Email—sales@rangecraft.com
Pres.—Ramona Panus
Dir., Mktg.—David Ryan

SIC—3444; 3366; *Custom-
designed decorative copper,
brass & stainless steel range
hoods for residential kitchens,
including buttons, bands & pot
rails*
Employs—19; Estab.—1990
11,500 sq ft site, Distrib.—National
Privately owned corporation

**REGEN & CO., INC.**
20-21 Wagaraw Rd., Bldg. 32
(07410)
**Phone—(973) 423-4236**
National—(800) 386-9555
Fax—(973) 423-5750
www.regenandcompany.com
Email—info@
regenandcompany.com
GM—Alan Regen
Sales Mgr., Natl.—Jed Regen
Manager—Joel Lewitz
SIC—2759; 3479; NAICS—
323100; *Commercial printing,
letterhead engraving, foil
stamping & embossing*
Employs—5; Estab.—1929
Sales—under $500,000
5,000 sq ft site, Distrib.—National
Privately owned corporation

NEW ENTRY
**RELIANCE PLASTIC & CHEMICAL
CORP.**
38-27 Wilson St., P.O. Box 395
(07410)
**Phone—(201) 797-8014**
Email—filco51@verizon.net
Pres.—Fred Levine
SIC—3052; 2541; 3089; *Flexible
down drains for erosion control &
garden hose & plastic floor
runners; Brand name—Reliance
Garden Hose; Reldrain
Downdrains; Relvin Carpet
Protectors*
Employs—10; Estab.—1953
Sales—$5Mil-$10Mil
Distrib.—Regional
Privately owned corporation

**RINKO ORTHOPEDIC APPLIANCES,
INC.**
2509 Broadway (07410)
**Phone—(201) 796-3121**
Fax—(201) 796-1551
www.rinko.com
Email—info@rinko.com
Pres.—Stephen Rinko
Off. Mgr.—Francisco Jimenez
SIC—3842; *Orthotic & prosthetic
appliances, including braces &
artificial limbs*
Employs—6; Estab.—1958
Sales—under $500,000
3,000 sq ft site, Distrib.—Regional
Privately owned corporation

**SANDVIK, INC. (H Q)**
1702 Nevins Rd., P.O. Box 428
(07410)
**Phone—(201) 794-5000**
National—(800) 726-3845
Fax—(201) 794-5257
www.sandvik.coromant.com/us
Email—us.coromant@sandvik.com
Pres., Market Area Americas—
Eduardo Martin
Mktg. Comms. Mgr., Market Area
Americas—Ester Codina
Mktg. Comms. Mgr., Market Area
Americas—Debby Oliveri
SIC—3541; NAICS—333512;
*Corporate headquarters; cutting
tools & tooling solutions for the
metalworking industry*
Employs—200; Estab.—1862
Sales—$1.2Bil
80,000 sq ft site,
Publicly owned corporation
AKA: Sandvik Coromant

**STEPPIN OUT MAGAZINE**
21-07 Maple Ave. (07410)
**Phone—(201) 703-0911**
Fax—(201) 703-0211
www.so-mag.com
Email—jeff@so-mag.com
Publisher—Jeff Trent
Editor—Dan Lorenzo
SIC—2721; *Magazine publishing*
Employs—5
Sales—under $500,000 (est)
Privately owned corporation

**TANIS & SONS, INC., JOEL**
17-68 River Rd. (07410)
**Phone—(201) 796-1556**
Fax—(201) 796-5553
www.tanisnj.com
Hum. Res., IT & Plt. Mgr.—Chris
Young
Qual. Control Mgr.—Todd Tages
Bookkeeper—Gail Rivera
SIC—3273; NAICS—327320;
*Ready-mixed concrete*
Employs—38; Estab.—1945
Distrib.—Local
Privately owned corporation

**TARGET COATINGS, INC.**
17-12 River Rd. (07410)
**Phone—(800) 752-9922**
Fax—(201) 797-5973
www.targetcoatings.com
Email—info@targetcoatings.com
Pres., Plt. Mgr.—Jeff Weiss
Off. Mgr.—Paula Newell
SIC—2851; NAICS—325510;
*Water-based wood coatings for
the furniture, architectural &
woodworking industries*
Employs—10; Estab.—2001
Distrib.—Local
Privately owned sub-S corp.

NEW ENTRY
**TEX PRINT USA, LLC**
20-21 Wagaraw Rd., Bldg. 37
(07410)
**Phone—(201) 773-6531**
Fax—(201) 773-6535
www.texprintusa.com
Email—orders@texprintusa.com
CEO—Edward Margarucci, Sr.
SIC—2269; *Textile dye
sublimation & heat transfer
printing*
Employs—20
Sales—$1Mil-$2.5Mil
Distrib.—National
Limited Liability Company

†**THERMO FISHER SCIENTIFIC INC.**
Div. of Thermo Fisher Scientific,
Inc.
1 Reagent Ln. (07410)
**Phone—(201) 796-7100**
National—(800) 766-7000
Fax—(201) 703-3102
www.fisherscientific.com
Email—webmaster@
thermofisher.com
V.-P., Global Sales & Mktg.—
Duane Talhouk
Global Dir., Dev. & Engrg.—Mark
Jasko
Dir., Opers.—Jason Stone
Dir., IT—Gene Holden
Dir., Hum. Res.—Marta Mazzola
Dir., Sourcing—Alan Polonsky
Dir., Qual. Assur.—Deva Puranam
Staff Accountant—Patricia Diaz
SIC—5169; *Wholesaler of
chemicals for pharmaceutical,
educational & research labs*
Employs—360; Estab.—1902
Sales—$25Mil-$100Mil
150,000 sq ft site, Distrib.—Intl.
Publicly owned corporation
ISO rating—9002
Parent co.—Thermo Fisher
Scientific, Inc., Waltham, MA
Phone—(781) 622-1000
See Parent Co. Section for full profile.

GEOGRAPHICAL

## Fair Lawn—(cont.)

**TIMBAR CORP.**
Div. of TimBar Packaging &
  Display
15-01 Pollitt Dr., Unit 9 (07410)
**Phone—(201) 568-7300**
National—(800) 572-6061
Fax—(201) 703-5559
www.timbar.com
Email—shinz@timbar.com
Proj. Mgr.—Stasi Hinz
Manager—Jose Cabrera
SIC—2653; 2541; *Point-of-
  purchase displays, corrugated
  boxes & graphic retail packaging*
Employs—12
Sales—$1Mil-$2.5Mil (est)
Distrib.—Intl.
Publicly owned corporation
Parent co.—TimBar Packaging &
  Display, Hanover, PA
  Phone—(717) 632-4727
  See Parent Co. Section for full profile.

**V H MACHINE TOOL CO.**
29 Smith Ave. (07410)
**Phone—(973) 427-8666**
Fax—(973) 427-8666
Owner—Dennis Van Houten
SIC—3599; *Machine parts*
Employs—1; Estab.—1985
Sales—under $500,000
Distrib.—Local
Sole ownership

**Y, INC.**
20-21 Wagaraw Rd., Bldg. 32
  (07410-1322)
**Phone—(201) 773-8425**
www.bodipure.com
Email—info@bodipure.com
Pres.—Dong Jin Yoon
Mng. Dir.—Jonathan Yoo
SIC—2844; 5122; *Manufacturer &
  distributor of professional natural
  skin & foot care & body treatment
  products for salons, spas &
  hotels; Brand name—
  BODIPURE®*
Employs—4; Estab.—2000
Company-wide: 8
Sales—$1Mil-$2.5Mil
Distrib.—Intl.
Publicly owned corporation
AKA: Bodipure

**ZEREGAS SONS, INC., A.**
20-01 Broadway, P.O. Box 241
  (07410-0241)
**Phone—(201) 797-1400**
National—(800) 797-1414
Fax—(201) 797-0148
www.zerega.com
Email—sales@zerega.com
Pres., GM—John B. Vermylen
V-P.—Rob Vermylen
V-P.—Mark Vermylen
Treas.—Nicholas Pugliesi
Plt. Mgr.—Joseph Anzalone
SIC—2098; NAICS—311823;
  *Corporate headquarters & pasta*
Employs—150; Estab.—1848
Sales—$85Mil
130,000 sq ft site, Distrib.—
  National
Privately owned sub-S corp.

**ZUMTOBEL LIGHTING, INC.**
17-09 Zink Pl., Unit 7 (07410)
**Phone—(973) 340-8900**
National—(800) 448-4131
Fax—(201) 796-4898
www.zumtobel.us
V-P.—Wolfgang Egger
IT Mgr.—Felix Toledo
Hum. Res. Mgr.—Cindy Geraphy
Mktg. Comm. Specialist—Ashley
  Marion

SIC—3646; NAICS—335122;
  *Commercial lighting fixtures*
Employs—25; Estab.—1992
Sales—$10Mil-$25Mil
80,000 sq ft site, Distrib.—Intl.
Privately owned corporation

---

## Fairfield
(Essex—N.E.)

**†A. H. HARRIS & SONS, INC.**
Div. of A.H. Harris & Sons, Inc.
160 Fairfield Rd. (07004)
**Phone—(973) 227-1600**
National—(800) 345-9055
Fax—(973) 227-0069
www.ahharris.com
Email—info@ahharris.com
GM—Dennis Orozco
SIC—5082; 5039; 5051; 5072;
  *Distributor of construction
  equipment & supplies, including
  concrete forming & shoring
  systems, geotextiles, wire mesh,
  steel rebar, hand & power tools &
  safety equipment*
Employs—10; Estab.—1983
Distrib.—Local
Privately owned corporation
Parent co.—A.H. Harris & Sons,
  Inc., West Hartford, CT
  Phone—(860) 216-9500
  See Parent Co. Section for full profile.

**A. V. BLUEBOOK**
Div. of VCOM International Multi-
  Media Corp.
80 Little Falls Rd. (07004)
**Phone—(800) 631-0868**
Fax—(800) 332-5871
www.avbluebook.com
Email—info@avbluebook.com
Sales Mgr., Natl.—Stephen Marino
SIC—3651; 3661; NAICS—
  334310; *Electronic audiovisual
  equipment & components,
  including control systems, CCTV
  cameras, speakers, mixers,
  cables, connectors,
  microphones & equipment racks*
Employs—1; Estab.—1958
Distrib.—National
Privately owned corporation
Parent co.—VCOM International
  Multi-Media Corp., Fairfield, NJ
  Phone—(201) 229-4270
  See Parent Co. Section for full profile.

**ACCURATE SCREW MACHINE CORP.**
Div. of MW Industries, Inc.
10 Audrey Pl., P.O. Box 1065
  (07004)
**Phone—(973) 244-9200**
National—(877) 285-2181
Fax—(973) 244-9177
www.accuratescrew.com
Email—sales@accuratescrew.com
GM—John Everett
Sales Mgr.—Gilbert Duke
IT Mgr.—Bill Marra
SIC—3451; NAICS—332721;
  *Screw machine products*
Employs—150; Estab.—1972
Sales—$14Mil
32,000 sq ft site, Distrib.—National
Privately owned corporation
Parent co.—MW Industries, Inc.,
  Rosemont, IL
  Phone—(847) 349-5780
  See Parent Co. Section for full profile.

**ACUATIVE (H Q)**
30 Two Bridges Rd., Ste. 240
  (07004-1550)
**Phone—(973) 227-8040**
Fax—(973) 556-1474
www.acuative.com
Email—rcarr@acuative.com
Pres., CEO—Vince Sciarra
CFO—Patrick Danna
COO—Rich Ackerman
Dir., Natl. Recruiting—Raymond
  Carr

SIC—3669; NAICS—334290;
  *Company headquarters;
  telecommunication systems*
Employs—40
Sales—$70Mil-$80Mil
Privately owned corporation

**ALISON CONTROL, INC.**
35 Daniel Rd. W. (07004)
**Phone—(973) 575-7100**
Fax—(973) 575-3647
www.alisoncontrol.com
Email—aci22@aol.com
Pres.—Gene E. Benzenberg
GM & Plt. Mgr.—Rob Roller
Manager—Paul Valentino
SIC—3829; 3669; NAICS—
  334290; *Fire detectors, fire
  detection control panels & high
  expansion foam fire protection
  systems; Brand name—A888
  Series Controls; 9090 Linear
  Thermal Sensor; HEF Systems*
Employs—20; Estab.—1964
13,500 sq ft site, Distrib.—Intl.
Privately owned corporation

**ALL METALS & FORGE GROUP, LLC**
75 Lane Rd. (07004)
**Phone—(973) 276-5000**
Fax—(973) 276-5050
www.steelforge.com
Email—sales@steelforge.com
Pres.—Lewis A. Weiss
CFO—John Andreacci
V-P.—Tim Grady
Opers. Mgr.—Jackie Lorianger
Logistics Mgr., Import & Export—
  Linda Hopler
SIC—3462; 3463; 5051; NAICS—
  332111; *Stainless, nickel,
  titanium, carbon & alloy steel &
  aluminum open die forgings,
  rolled seamless rings, shafts,
  blocks, discs & forged shapes*
Employs—39; Estab.—1984
39,000 sq ft site, Distrib.—Intl.
Limited Liability Company

**ALLIED PRINTING & GRAPHICS**
4 Madison Rd. (07004)
**Phone—(973) 227-0520**
Fax—(973) 227-7664
www.alliedpng.com
Email—alliedprnt@aol.com
Pres.—Domenick Pascarella
SIC—2759; NAICS—323100;
  *Commercial printing*
Employs—20; Estab.—1984
Distrib.—National
Privately owned corporation

**ALT GLOBAL, LLC**
3 Edison Pl., Ste. 2 (07004)
**Phone—(973) 287-6158**
National—(877) 354-3539
Fax—(973) 287-6168
www.altglobal.com
Manager—Eric Fischetti
SIC—2851; *Advanced cold
  applied liquid roofing,
  waterproofing & surfacing
  coatings*
Employs—10
Sales—$2.5Mil-$5Mil (est)
Distrib.—Intl.
Limited Liability Company

**AMARK INDUSTRIES, INC.**
18 Passaic Ave. (07004)
**Phone—(973) 992-8900**
Fax—(973) 992-9203
www.amarkwireco.com
Email—amarkindustries@aol.com
Pres., Qual. Assur. Mgr.—Mario
  Salerno

SIC—3451; 3496; NAICS—
  332721; *High precision
  escomatic screw machine
  products, medical wire,
  straightened & cut, wire drawing,
  wire forming, tapered wire &
  medical tubing, including
  stainless steel, copper, brass,
  aluminum & titanium*
Employs—5; Estab.—1980
23,500 sq ft site, Distrib.—Intl.
Privately owned corporation

**AMERICAN SHOWCASE &
FOODSERVICE EQUIPMENT, INC.**
19 Commerce Rd., Unit H (07004)
**Phone—(973) 227-1277**
National—(800) 965-6655
Fax—(973) 227-1678
Email—americanshowcase@
  verizon.net
Pres.—Tony Latallade
Prod. Mgr.—Efrain Latallade
SIC—3556; 3443; 3444; 5046;
  NAICS—333294; *Custom
  fabrication & distributor of
  commercial foodservice
  equipment*
Employs—6; Estab.—1989
Sales—$500,000-$1Mil
8,500 sq ft site, Distrib.—National
Privately owned corporation

**AM-MAC, INC.**
311 Route 46 W. (07004)
**Phone—(973) 575-7567**
National—(800) 829-2018
Fax—(973) 575-1956
www.am-mac.com
Email—ammac2@aol.com
Owner—Judith Spritzer
V-P.—Jon M. Spritzer
Sales Mgr.—Megan Link
SIC—3556; NAICS—333294;
  *Food preparation equipment*
Employs—12; Estab.—1992
Sales—over $10Mil
Distrib.—Intl.
Privately owned corporation

**ARETE DEVELOPMENT, INC.**
20 Industrial Rd. (07004)
**Phone—(973) 244-0037**
Fax—(973) 244-0054
www.bergensteel.com
Email—info@bergensteel.com
Owner—Jonathan Ettere
SIC—3441; *Structural steel
  fabrication*
Employs—4; Estab.—2011
Sales—$500,000-$1Mil
5,000 sq ft site, Distrib.—National
Limited Liability Company

**ARLINGTON MACHINE & TOOL CO.**
90 New Dutch Ln. (07004)
**Phone—(973) 276-1377**
Fax—(973) 276-1378
www.arlingtonmachine.com
Email—amt@arlingtonmachine.com
CEO—Susan Blanck
COO—John J. Staudinger
Sales Mgr.—Ron Lee
Cust. Serv. Mgr.—Carol Marques
Pur. Agt.—Hope Ennis
SIC—3599; 5084; *Contract close
  tolerance precision CNC
  machining & hydraulic actuator
  assemblies & manufacturer &
  distributor of hydraulic &
  pneumatic torque wrenches,
  tensioners & pumps*
Employs—90; Estab.—1963
80,000 sq ft site, Distrib.—Intl.
Privately owned corporation
AKA: TITAN Technologies
  International

**ARTHUR SCHUMAN, INC.**
40 New Dutch Ln. *(07004)*
**Phone—(973) 227-0030**
National—(800) 888-2433
Fax—(973) 227-1525
www.arthurschuman.com

## Fairfield—(cont.)

Email—info@arthurschuman.com
Pres.—Neal Schuman
CFO—Larry Schaefer
Dir., Mktg.—Melissa Shore
Dir., IT—Robert Castaldi
Plt. Mgr.—Vincent Angiolillo
SIC—2022; 2099; 2499; NAICS—311513; *Corporate headquarters & wedges, grated & shredded cheese & gourmet cheese boards; Brand name—Cello; Cello Riserva; Bella Rosa; Via del Gusto; Argitoni; Montforte; Messana; Imperia; Maggiore; Casa D'Angelo*
Employs—85; Estab.—1946
Sales—$505Mil-$525Mil
37,000 sq ft site, Distrib.—National
Privately owned corporation

**ASPE, INC.**
2 Daniel Rd. E. (07004)
**Phone—(973) 808-1155**
Fax—(973) 808-5666
Email—aspesales@aol.com
Pres.—Nancy Dam
Sales Mgr.—Trac Dam
Pur. Agt.—Mimi Prontnicki
SIC—3053; NAICS—339991; *Hermetic sealing devices*
Employs—20; Estab.—1971
18,000 sq ft site, Distrib.—National
Privately owned corporation

**ATLANTIC ENVELOPE CO.**
16 Passaic Ave., Unit 7 (07004)
**Phone—(973) 882-0436**
Fax—(973) 882-1035
www.atlanticenvs.com
Email—atlanticenvs@aim.com
Pres.—Christopher Molinari
V-P., Fin. Mgr.—Lauren Molinari
Prodn. Mgr.—Stephen Molinari
SIC—2759; NAICS—323100; *Envelope printing*
Employs—6; Estab.—1982
Sales—$1.5Mil
5,000 sq ft site, Distrib.—National
Privately owned sub-S corp.

**AUTO CLEAR, LLC**
2 Gardner Rd. (07004)
**Phone—(973) 276-6161**
National—(800) 231-6414
Fax—(973) 276-6166
www.a-clear.com
Email—info@a-clear.com
Pres., CEO—Brad Conway
Cont., Fin. & MIS Mgr.—Lou Tang
Hum. Res. Mgr.—Mary Beaman
Maint. Supv.—Ed Sunga
SIC—3844; 3829; NAICS—334517; *Hand-held, desktop, vehicle & walk-through security x-ray screening equipment & metal detectors, including narcotics & explosives trace detection equipment*
Employs—80; Estab.—1938
Sales—$10Mil-$15Mil
58,000 sq ft site, Distrib.—Intl.
Limited Liability Company

**AW MACHINERY, LLC**
7 Just Rd. (07004)
**Phone—(973) 882-3223**
Fax—(973) 882-3210
www.awmachinery.com
Email—awm@awmachinery.com
Ptnr. & Pres.—Nestor E. Gener
Ptnr. & Principal Electrical Engr.—Arthur K. Watson

SIC—3613; 3599; NAICS—333518; *Industrial equipment & integrated systems for the production of electrical wire & cable, including electrical control panels, wire & cable extrusion machinery, continuous vulcanizing & fiber optics extrusion & rewinding lines; Brand name—AW Machinery L.L.C.*
Employs—16; Estab.—2003
Sales—$2Mil-$4Mil
9,000 sq ft site, Distrib.—Intl.
Limited Liability Company

**AZCO CORP.**
26 Just Rd. (07004)
**Phone—(973) 439-1428**
Fax—(973) 439-9411
www.azcocorp.com
Email—cs@azcocorp.com
Pres.—Andrew Zucaro
Mktg. Admn.—Margie McKeon
SIC—3559; 3599; 3565; 3569; *Machinery for feeding, cutting, inserting & dispensing applications; Brand name—ACU-SERT; ACU-SLIT; AZCO SUR-FEED; AZCO SUR-PAK; SMARTKNIFE; SUR-CUT; SUR-FEED; SUR-PAK; SUR-SIZE; SUR-STAK; AZCO CORP.*
Employs—30; Estab.—1983
5,500 sq ft site, Distrib.—Intl.
Sole ownership
ISO rating—9001:2008

**BAR-LO CARBON PRODUCTS, INC.**
31 W. Daniel Rd., P.O. Box 10031 (07004)
**Phone—(973) 227-2717**
    (973) 303-1402
Fax—(973) 575-7164
www.barlocarbon.com
Email—barlo99@aol.com
Owner—Mohammed Yasin
Sales Mgr.—Chris Grillo
Plt. Mgr.—Winston James
Hum. Res. Mgr.—Kathline Jones
SIC—3624; NAICS—335991; *Graphite products, crucibles, jigs, fixtures, molds & dies*
Employs—32; Estab.—1965
Sales—$3Mil
Distrib.—National
Privately owned corporation

**BAXTER RUBBER CO.**
10 Spielman Rd. (07004)
**Phone—(973) 227-1956**
Fax—(973) 882-6873
www.baxterrubber.com
Email—baxter@baxterrubber.com
Owner & Cust. Sales Rep.—Dan Lambert
GM—Roy Weiss
Cust. Serv. Rep.—Kevin Hendricks
Cust. Serv. Rep.—John 'Rick' Ducharme
Bookkeeper—Paula Joana
SIC—3053; 3069; NAICS—339991; *Manufacturer & distributor of rubber parts, including grommets, o-rings, hoses, hose assemblies, clamps, couplings, tubing, sleeves & gaskets*
Employs—15; Estab.—1915
Sales—$2.6Mil-$5Mil
12,000 sq ft site, Distrib.—Intl.
Privately owned corporation

**BERGEN CABLE TECHNOLOGY, LLC**
343 Kaplan Dr. *(07004)*
**Phone—(973) 276-9596**
    (800) 237-4369
Fax—(973) 276-9566
www.bergencable.com
Email—sales@bergencable.com
Pres., GM—Peter Bartholomew
Cont.—Ronda Capilli
Sales Mgr.—Don Gorman
Pur. Mgr.—Debra Hillman

Qual. Control Mgr.—Surendra Patel
Engrg. Mgr.—Chid Mallipatna
SIC—3496; *Mechanical wire rope cable assemblies, including safety cables, threaded fastener retention systems, lockclad flight control assemblies, push-pull controls, microlin cable assembly & aircraft specific & commercial control cable assembly; Brand name—Safety Cable; Microline Cable; Lockclad*
Employs—30; Estab.—1942
Sales—$4Mil-$8Mil
15,000 sq ft site, Distrib.—Intl.
Limited Liability Company
ISO rating—9001:2008, AS9100:2009

**BILT-RITE TOOL & DIE CO., INC.**
29 Montesano Rd. (07004)
**Phone—(973) 227-2882**
Fax—(973) 808-1962
Pres., Fin., MIS & R & D Mgr.—Dennis George
Hum. Res. Mgr.—Dennis George, Jr.
SIC—3544; NAICS—333500; *Tool & die job shop*
Employs—12; Estab.—1956
Sales—$1Mil-$2.5Mil
4,000 sq ft site, Distrib.—National
Privately owned corporation

**BOARDS & BEAMS CO., LLC**
1275 Bloomfield Ave., Ste. 92 (07004)
**Phone—(973) 299-6100**
Fax—(862) 210-8135
www.woodboardsandbeams.com
Email—boards.beams@yahoo.com
Owner—Steve Djurasek
Ex. Mgr.—Jeff Steffl
SIC—2431; 2426; *Western red cedar & primed pine mouldings, MDF, wide plank flooring, reclaimed barn siding, hand-hewn timbers, planks, ceiling beams & decking lumber & hardwood products*
Employs—10; Estab.—2009
Sales—under $500,000
13,000 sq ft site, Distrib.—Regional
Privately owned corporation

**BUHL ELECTRIC, INC.**
Div. of VCOM International Multi-Media Corp.
80 Little Falls Rd. (07004)
**Phone—(201) 296-0600**
Fax—(201) 621-6110
www.buhl-electric.com
Email—sneckers@vcom-mm.net
Pres.—Sheldon Goldstein
Mng. Dir.—David Kyhl
Cust. Serv. Mgr.—Sharon Neckers
SIC—3643; NAICS—335931; *LED lighting products, including lighting fixtures & light sockets*
Employs—16; Estab.—1985
Distrib.—Intl.
Privately owned corporation
Parent co.—VCOM International Multi-Media Corp., Fairfield, NJ
   Phone—(201) 229-4270
See Parent Co. Section for full profile.

**C & M SHADE CORP.**
53 Dwight Pl. (07004)
**Phone—(201) 807-1200**
National—(800) 486-1116
Fax—(201) 807-1930
www.cmshade.com
Email—allen_francus@cmshade.com
Pres.—Allen Francus
Sales Mgr., Natl.—Blaise Domino

SIC—2591; 5023; NAICS—337920; *Manufacturer & distributor of motorized vertical, aluminum & wooden blinds, roller, pleated & cellular shades, shading systems & wood & faux wood shutters for residential & commercial applications; Brand name—Trends East; Norman Shutters; Coventry Woods; Shadow Woods; Shade Crest*
Employs—13; Estab.—1957
Sales—$1Mil-$5Mil
7,500 sq ft site, Distrib.—National
Privately owned sub-S corp.

**C & S MACHINE, INC.**
22 Commerce Rd., Ste. Q (07004-1604)
**Phone—(973) 882-1097**
National—(800) 394-1967
Fax—(973) 882-3242
Email—csmachine@verizon.net
Plt. & Sales Mgr.—Ron Woods
SIC—3552; NAICS—333292; *Textile & converting machinery*
Employs—4; Estab.—1989
Sales—$1Mil-$5Mil
12,000 sq ft site, Distrib.—Intl.
Sole ownership

**C N I CERAMICS NOZZLES, INC.**
23 Commerce Rd., Ste. L (07004-1609)
**Phone—(973) 276-1535**
National—(800) 645-7218
Fax—(973) 276-1537
www.ceramicnozzles.com
Email—cniceramic@comcast.net
Pres.—Thomas M. Calandrillo
SIC—3548; *Welding equipment*
Employs—6; Estab.—1955
5,000 sq ft site, Distrib.—Intl.
Privately owned corporation

**CAFFE BORBONE USA**
19 Commerce Rd., Ste. G (07004)
**Phone—(973) 227-7799**
Fax—(973) 227-7785
www.caffeborboneusa.com
Email—info@caffeborboneusa.com
Pres.—Antonio Amato
Off. Mgr.—Francesca Busciglio
SIC—2095; 5149; NAICS—311920; *Espresso coffee packing & distributor of single-dose espresso coffee pods*
Employs—8; Estab.—2003
Sales—$1Mil-$2.5Mil
10,000 sq ft site, Distrib.—National
Privately owned corporation

**CALIFORNIA CLOSETS**
4 Gardner Rd., Ste. 5 (07004-2297)
**Phone—(973) 882-3800**
Fax—(973) 882-9171
www.californiaclosets.com/north-jersey
Email—fairfieldcustserv@calclosets.com
Ptnr.—Marty Ginsberg
Mktg. Mgr.—Melanie Statlander
SIC—3089; 2493; 2542; *Melamine & MDF closets & related custom storage systems*
Employs—50; Estab.—1984
Sales—$4Mil-$7Mil
Distrib.—Local

**CARECAM INTERNATIONAL, INC.**
10 Plog Rd. *(07004)*
**Phone—(973) 227-0720**
Fax—(973) 227-7395
Email—carecaminc@hotmail.com
Co-Pres.—Mohit Jain
Co-Pres.—Haren Gupta
Co-Pres.—Ravinder Jain
SIC—2834; NAICS—325412; *Pharmaceuticals*
Employs—65; Estab.—1995
Sales—$6Mil-$10Mil
Distrib.—National
Privately owned sub-S corp.

GEOGRAPHICAL

## Fairfield—(cont.)

**†CAREMARK RX, INC.**
Div. of CVS/Caremark Corp.
180 Passaic Ave., Ste. 5 (07004)
**Phone—(973) 461-1550**
Fax—(973) 461-1750
www.caremark.com
Email—investorinfo@caremark.com
GM—Ed Ochoa
SIC—5122; *Distributor of medical pharmaceuticals*
Employs—20; Estab.—1995
Distrib.—Regional
Publicly owned corporation
Parent co.—CVS/Caremark Corp., Woonsocket, RI
Phone—(401) 765-1500
See Parent Co. Section for full profile.

**CARLEN MACHINE CO.**
1275 Bloomfield Ave., Bldg. 10, Door 89 (07004)
**Phone—(973) 808-1441**
Fax—(973) 808-1441
Owner—Carmine Zecca
SIC—3599; *General machining job shop*
Employs—1; Estab.—1988
Sales—under $500,000
Distrib.—Local
Sole ownership

**CARTRIDGE ACTUATED DEVICES, INC. (H Q)**
51 Dwight Pl. (07004-3311)
**Phone—(973) 575-1312**
        (973) 575-1313
Fax—(973) 575-6039
www.cartactdev.com
Email—info@cartactdev.com
Pres.—John Grant
Dir., Sales—Patrick M. Goudie
Admn. & Cust. Serv. Mgr.—Patty Kietrys
Hum. Res. Mgr.—Elizabeth Stichling
SIC—3559; *Corporate headquarters; pyrotechnic equipment*
Employs—40; Estab.—1960
Company-wide: 100
Sales—$5Mil-$10Mil
Distrib.—Intl.
Privately owned corporation
ISO rating—9001

**CBS OUTDOOR**
Div. of CBS Outdoor Americas, Inc.
185 Highway 46 (07004)
**Phone—(973) 575-6900**
National—(800) 966-9569
Fax—(973) 808-8316
www.cbsoutdoor.com
Email—george.wood@cbsoutdoor.com
V.-P., East Reg.—George Gross
Cont.—George Wood
SIC—3993; *Billboards & signs*
Employs—60; Estab.—1982
80,000 sq ft site, Distrib.—National
Publicly owned corporation
Parent co.—CBS Outdoor Americas, Inc., New York, NY
Phone—(212) 297-6400
See Parent Co. Section for full profile.

**CERAMIC MAGNETICS, INC.**
Div. of Thomas & Skinner, Inc.
16 Law Dr. (07004)
**Phone—(973) 227-4222**
Fax—(973) 227-6735
www.cmi-ferrite.com
Email—sales@cmi-ferrite.com
Dir., Tech. & Qual. Assur. Mgr.—John Ings
Prodn. Mgr., Grinding—Vincent DeFabrizio, Jr.
Prodn. Mgr., Powder—Thomas Muench, Jr.
MIS Mgr.—Amit Patel
Off. Mgr.—Patrice Ricciardi
Cust. Serv. Mgr.—Michele Ruiz
SIC—3264; NAICS—327113; *Ferrite cores*
Employs—42; Estab.—1965
Sales—$6Mil-$8Mil
72,000 sq ft site, Distrib.—Intl.
Privately owned corporation
ISO rating—9001:2008
Parent co.—Thomas & Skinner, Inc., Indianapolis, IN
Phone—(317) 923-2501
See Parent Co. Section for full profile.

**CHESAPEAKE PHARMACEUTICAL & HEALTHCARE PACKAGING**
Div. of Chesapeake Pharmaceutical Packaging Company, LLC
6 Commerce Rd. (07004)
**Phone—(973) 808-8000**
National—(800) 242-4657
Fax—(800) 521-1498
www.cortegra.com
Email—info@cortegra.com
GM—Jim Struhar
Prodn. Mgr.—James Smith
Opers. Mgr.—Gene Lepelletier
SIC—2759; 2672; NAICS—322222; *Label, insert & outsert printing for packaging application*
Employs—105
Distrib.—National
Limited Liability Company
Parent co.—Chesapeake Pharmaceutical Packaging Company, LLC, Hicksville, NY
Phone—(516) 277-8600
See Parent Co. Section for full profile.

**CHESNUT ENGINEERING, INC., W. R.**
14 Spielman Rd. (07004)
**Phone—(973) 227-6995**
Fax—(973) 227-7873
www.chesnuteng.com
Email—sales@chesnuteng.com
Pres.—Richard Chesnut
V.-P., Engr.—Dan Calligaro
Sales Admn.—Maria Cugliari
SIC—3555; NAICS—333293; *Gravure & flexographic printing presses*
Employs—10; Estab.—1973
Distrib.—Intl.
Privately owned corporation

**CHILTON LABORATORIES**
299-B Fairfield Ave. (07004)
Mail addr: P.O. Box 596, Caldwell (07007)
**Phone—(973) 575-1990**
National—(800) 443-8856
Fax—(973) 575-6164
www.enerjets.com
Email—info@enerjets.com
Pres.—Steven Heydt
Acctg. Mgr.—Candy Cousins
SIC—2064; 2833; NAICS—325411; *Caffeinated candy*
Employs—10; Estab.—1958
Sales—under $500,000
Distrib.—National
Privately owned corporation

**CK MANUFACTURING, INC.**
8 Gardner Rd. (07004)
**Phone—(973) 808-3500**
Fax—(973) 808-3511
Email—alliedplastics@verizon.net
Pres.—Richard Cafaro
V.-P.—Brian Kaltner
Bookkeeper & Off. Mgr.—Barbara DeAngelis
SIC—3544; 3089; NAICS—333500; *Plastic injection molds & molding*
Employs—20; Estab.—1953
12,500 sq ft site,
Privately owned sub-S corp.

**CLOSET BUTLER**
3 Spielman Rd. (07004)
**Phone—(973) 729-9222**
www.closetbutler.com
Email—info@closetbutler.com
Pres.—John Doyle
SIC—2392; *Wooden closets & storage systems*
Employs—10; Estab.—2004
Sales—$500,000-$1Mil
Distrib.—Local
Privately owned corporation

**COLUMBIA PRESS, INC.**
12 Industrial Rd., P.O. Box 10723 (07004)
**Phone—(973) 575-6535**
Fax—(973) 575-6344
www.columbiapress.com
Pres.—Charles Puleo
V.-P.—Alan Puleo
SIC—2759; NAICS—323100; *Commercial printing*
Employs—20; Estab.—1977
Sales—$500,000-$1Mil
Distrib.—National
Privately owned corporation
Also see: GMS Litho, Inc., same loc.

**COMMAND NUTRITIONALS, LLC**
10 Washington Ave., Ste. 1 (07004)
**Phone—(973) 227-8210**
Fax—(973) 227-2742
www.commandnutritionals.com
Email—info@commandnutritionals.com
Pres.—Scott Biedron
Off. Mgr.—Rosa Figueiredo
SIC—2834; NAICS—325412; *Contract manufacturer of nutritional supplements*
Employs—25; Estab.—1972
25,000 sq ft site, Distrib.—National
Limited Liability Company

**CONSTANT SERVICES, INC.**
17 Commerce Rd. (07004-1621)
**Phone—(973) 227-2990**
Fax—(973) 227-2705
www.constantservicesinc.com
Email—d.pepe3@verizon.net
Pres.—Vincent Pepe
V.-P., Opers.—Rosario Pepe
Cont., Fin. Mgr.—Dominick Pepe
Opers. Mgr.—Anthony V. Pepe
Traf. Mgr.—James A. Pepe
SIC—2754; NAICS—323111; *Rotogravure printing & laminating of vinyl & fabric substrates*
Employs—30; Estab.—1978
32,000 sq ft site, Distrib.—Intl.
Privately owned sub-S corp.
AKA: CSI

**CONTROL & POWER SYSTEMS, INC.**
17 Spielman Rd. (07004)
**Phone—(973) 575-3300**
National—(888) 305-1600
Fax—(973) 575-5300
www.c-p-s.com
Email—cps@c-p-s.com
Pres.—D. Shevich
V.-P.—D. Lyon
Cont.—E. Astman
Sales Mgr.—J. Lowell
SIC—3613; 3625; 7373; NAICS—335313; *Control & information systems integration, process equipment automation design & building, skid pump packages & industrial control panels*
Employs—36; Estab.—1979
Sales—$5Mil-$10Mil
16,000 sq ft site, Distrib.—Intl.
Privately owned corporation

**CONTROL INSTRUMENTS CORP.**
25 Law Dr. (07004)
**Phone—(973) 575-9114**
Fax—(973) 575-0013
www.controlinstruments.com
Email—sales@controlinstruments.com
Dir., Sales—Debra Hall
Mktg. Mgr.—Patty Gardner
SIC—3823; NAICS—334513; *Gas detection systems*
Employs—35; Estab.—1969
Sales—$5Mil-$10Mil
Distrib.—Intl.

**†COOPER ELECTRIC SUPPLY CORP.**
Div. of Cooper Electric Supply Co.
444 Route 46 E. (07004)
**Phone—(973) 278-8400**
Fax—(973) 227-8366
www.cooper-electric.com
Email—carol.kane@cooper-electric.com
Br. Mgr.—Randy Montgomery
Hum. Res. Mgr.—Georgia Nicolau
SIC—5063; *Distributor of electrical equipment & supplies, including connectors, wires & sockets*
Employs—12; Estab.—1982
Sales—$1Mil-$2.5Mil
Distrib.—Regional
Privately owned corporation
Parent co.—Cooper Electric Supply Co., Monroe, NJ
Phone—(732) 747-2233
See Parent Co. Section for full profile.

**CORPORATE WOODWORKING, INC.**
368 Passaic Ave., P.O. Box 10362 (07004)
**Phone—(973) 227-2211**
Fax—(973) 808-8276
www.corporatewoodworking.com
Email—mandersen@corporatewoodworking.com
Pres.—Dan Andersen
V.-P., Cont., Hum. Res. & IT Mgr.—Mike Andersen
GM—Bob Brennan
Accts. Rec. Mgr.—Lee O'Keefe
Estimator—Odir Castillo
SIC—2434; 2542; 3083; NAICS—337110; *Wooden & laminated cabinets*
Employs—15; Estab.—1989
25,000 sq ft site, Distrib.—Intl.
Privately owned corporation

**CREATIONS BY MARIOLA**
18 Riveredge Dr. (07004)
**Phone—(973) 808-9109**
Fax—(973) 808-9109
Email—creationsbymariola@yahoo.com
Owner—Mariola Dlugosh
SIC—2284; *Contract sewing*
Employs—1; Estab.—2003
Sales—under $500,000
Distrib.—Local
Sole ownership

**CRICKET HILL BREWING CO., INC.**
24 Kulick Rd. (07004)
**Phone—(973) 276-9415**
Fax—(973) 276-9452
www.crickethillbrewery.com
Email—info@crickethillbrewery.com
Pres.—Rick Reed
Opers. Mgr.—Ed Gangi
SIC—2082; *Microbrewery of lagers & ales; Brand name—East Coast Lager; American Ale; Hopnotic IPA; Colonel Blide's Bitter*
Employs—3; Estab.—2001
Sales—under $500,000
5,000 sq ft site, Distrib.—Regional
Privately owned corporation

**CUSTOM CUT METAL PRODUCTS, INC.**
7 Daniel Rd. E. (07004)
**Phone—(973) 808-6803**
Fax—(973) 808-6804
www.american-precision.com
Email—ccmp@ix.netcom.com
V.-P.—Gerhard Muller
Plt. Mgr.—Bernie Rausch

## Fairfield—(cont.)

SIC—3599; *Precision machining of stainless steel, aluminum, brass, plastics & castings for the biomedical, aerospace, telecommunication & commercial industries*
Employs—18; Estab.—1981
10,000 sq ft site, Distrib.—Intl.
Privately owned corporation
ISO rating—MIL-I-45208A
AKA: APCO

**DAA INTERNATIONAL LLC**

24 Commerce Rd., Ste. L (07004)
**Phone—(973) 575-7444**
National—(800) 631-0039
Fax—(973) 575-5751
www.daainternational.com
Email—dan@daainternational.com
Dir., Bus.—Daniel Dombrowski
SIC—2796; 3081; NAICS—323792; *Polyester laser printing, metal & ink jet plates, digital inks & masters & inkjet & laser films for screen printing applications; Brand name—Genie; Acorn*
Employs—5; Estab.—1981
5,000 sq ft site, Distrib.—Intl.
Limited Liability Company

**†DARON WORLDWIDE TRADING, INC.**

24 Stewart Pl., Ste. 4 (07004-1634)
**Phone—(973) 882-0035**
National—(800) 776-2324
Fax—(973) 882-8322
www.daronwwt.com
Email—ron@daronwwt.com
Pres.—Ronald Marx
V.-P., Sales & Mktg.—Eugene McKeown
V.-P.—David Marx
Cont.—Laura Harris
Dir., Operation—Paul Wettstein
Hum. Res. Mgr.—Linda Kormendi
SIC—5092; *Wholesaler of aviation, cruise ship & licensed NYC toys, including models & collectibles for the aviation industry & independent toy & hobby retailers; Brand name—Boeing; Airbus; Carnival; Royal Caribbean; United Airlines; American Airlines; Delta; Southwest Airlines; UPS; Chevron; Air Force One*
Employs—29; Estab.—1993
37,500 sq ft site, Distrib.—National
Privately owned corporation

**DAVEN INDUSTRIES, INC.**

55 Dwight Pl. (07004)
**Phone—(973) 808-8848**
National—(800) 834-8848
Fax—(973) 808-8777
www.davenindustries.com
Email—davenindustries@verizon.net
Pres.—Lou Lever
Sales Mgr.—Mike Mack
Bookkeeper—Gail Mason
SIC—3568; 3545; NAICS—333613; *Shafts, chucks, safety chucks, winders, idlers & spreader rolls*
Employs—30; Estab.—1976
Sales—$1Mil-$5Mil
Distrib.—National
Privately owned sub-S corp.

**DE LEO TEXTILES (H Q)**

53 Dwight Pl. (07004)
**Phone—(973) 439-6801**
National—(800) 443-6909
Fax—(973) 439-6815
www.deleoco.com
Email—info@deleoco.com
CEO & CFO—Craig E. De Leo
SIC—2211; 2221; NAICS—313210; *Company headquarters; automotive, upholstery & drapery textiles, including chenilles & velvets (mfg. done in Turkey)*
Employs—10; Estab.—1962
Sales—$1Mil-$2.5Mil (est)
Distrib.—National
Privately owned corporation

**DECKER TAPE PRODUCTS, INC.**

2 Stewart Pl. (07004)
**Phone—(973) 227-5350**
Fax—(973) 808-9418
www.deckertape.com
Pres.—Jack Decker
Mktg. Mgr.—Kelly Decker
SIC—2672; NAICS—322222; *Adhesive tapes*
Employs—90; Estab.—1969
30,000 sq ft site, Distrib.—National
Privately owned corporation

**DELTA CIRCUITS, INC.**

26 Spielman Rd. (07004)
**Phone—(973) 575-3000**
Fax—(973) 575-8682
www.deltacircuits-nj.com
Pres.—Pravin Bhuva
SIC—3672; NAICS—334412; *Printed circuit boards*
Employs—30; Estab.—1988
32,000 sq ft site, Distrib.—National
Privately owned corporation

NEW ENTRY
**DENTISTRY TODAY, INC.**

100 Passaic Ave., Ste. 220 (07004)
**Phone—(973) 882-4700**
www.dentistrytoday.com
Publisher—Paul Radcliffe
Editor-in-Chief—Damon C. Adams
SIC—2721; *Clinical news magazine publishing for dentists*
Employs—20
Sales—$1Mil-$2.5Mil (est)

**DESIGN OF TOMORROW, INC.**

24 Sherwood Ln. (07004)
**Phone—(973) 227-5676**
National—(800) 400-8396
Fax—(973) 227-5077
www.elssolutions.net
Email—info@elssolutions.net
Pres., GM—David Roitburg
Plt. Mgr.—Peter Wolak
SIC—2531; 2521; 3821; 2431; *Casework & millwork for schools & laboratories*
Employs—15; Estab.—1987
12,000 sq ft site, Distrib.—Regional
Privately owned corporation
Also see: National Precision Tool Co., Inc., same loc.
AKA: Educational & Laboratory Systems

**DIVERSITEX, INC. (H Q)**

376 Hollywood Ave., Ste. 203 (07004)
**Phone—(973) 808-4566**
Fax—(973) 808-6261
www.diversitexinc.com
Email—info@diversitexinc.com
Pres.—William C. Summers
SIC—2261; NAICS—313311; *Corporate headquarters; cotton fabric finishing (mfg. outsourced)*
Employs—16; Estab.—1970
Distrib.—National
Privately owned sub-S corp.

**DREW & ROGERS, INC.**

30 Plymouth St. (07004)
**Phone—(973) 575-6210**
    (800) 610-6210
Fax—(973) 575-7180
www.drewandrogers.com
Email—info@drew-rogers.com
Pres.—Thomas M. Rogers
V.-P.—Michael Monteleone

Cont.—Andy Miller
Accts. Mgr.—Craig McCaa
Hum. Res. Mgr.—Katie Gillgan
SIC—2759; 2761; NAICS—323116; *Commercial & business form printing*
Employs—35; Estab.—1944
Sales—$17Mil
40,000 sq ft site, Distrib.—National
Privately owned sub-S corp.

**DRIVE-MASTER CO., INC.**

37 Daniel Rd. West (07004-2521)
**Phone—(973) 808-9709**
Fax—(973) 808-9713
www.DriveMasterMobility.com
Email—info@DriveMasterMobility.com
Pres., CEO—Peter B. Ruprecht
V.-P., CFO—Adrienne M. Ruprecht
GM—Christina Knapik
SIC—3715; 3716; 3449; 3714; *Wheelchair accessible vans, lifts & driving controls; Brand name—Drive-Master; Braun; Vantage Mobility Eldorado; Accessable Vans of America; Bruno; Pride Mobility; EMC*
Employs—19; Estab.—1952
Sales—$3Mil-$5Mil
16,500 sq ft site, Distrib.—Intl.
Privately owned corporation

**EASY ABRASIVES, LLC (H Q)**

16 Passaic Ave., Unit 8 (07004)
**Phone—(973) 575-7879**
National—(800) 237-1186
Fax—(973) 575-7878
www.easyburs.com
Email—sales@easyburs.com
Owner—Quinn Hsu
Sales Mgr.—Lewis Zecchino
SIC—3291; *Company headquarters; carbide burs, wire brushes, tungsten electrodes & flap wheels & discs (mfg. done in China)*
Employs—5
Sales—$1Mil-$2.5Mil (est)
Distrib.—National
Limited Liability Company

**ED-MAR INDUSTRIES, INC.**

11 Ray Pl. (07004)
**Phone—(973) 808-9205**
Fax—(973) 808-9405
Email—edmarindust@verizon.net
Pres.—Edward Puchalski
Machinist—Steve Zonn
SIC—3599; *General machining job shop & packaging equipment*
Employs—4; Estab.—1980
Sales—$500,000-$1Mil
Distrib.—Local
Privately owned corporation

**ELMI MACHINE & TOOL CO., INC.**

1275 Bloomfield Ave., Bldg. 5, Unit 2-B (07004)
Mail addr: P.O. Box 1112, West Caldwell (07006)
**Phone—(973) 882-1277**
Fax—(973) 882-1257
www.elmimachine.com
Email—elmimachine@verizon.net
Pres.—Victor Vitencz
SIC—3599; *General machining job shop*
Employs—3; Estab.—1963
Sales—under $500,000
2,000 sq ft site, Distrib.—Local

**EMSE CORP.**

10 Plog Rd., Unit 1 (07004)
**Phone—(973) 227-9221**
National—(800) 935-3673
Fax—(973) 227-9223
www.emse.com
Email—info@emse.com
Pres.—Alex Rothenberg
Bookkeeper—Kim Dagostino

SIC—3563; NAICS—333912; *Medical vacuum pumps & compressors; Brand name—EMSECO; Hospair*
Employs—10; Estab.—1983
16,000 sq ft site, Distrib.—Intl.
Privately owned sub-S corp.

**†ESSENTIAL AMENITIES, INC.**

208 Passaic Ave., Ste. 1 (07004)
**Phone—(973) 882-8441**
National—(800) 541-6775
Fax—(937) 436-0202
www.essentialamenities.com
Email—customer.service@essentialamenities.com
Pres.—Mike Ware
Cust. Serv. Mgr.—Diana Johnson
SIC—5122; *Distributor of personal amenities, including shampoo, conditioner, lotion, soap, cologne & loofah mitts for hotels, spas, airlines, cruise lines & lodging establishments; Brand name—Tommy Bahama; Hermes; Pogessi; ECRU New York; Joseph Abboud; Dickens & Hawthorne*
Employs—25; Estab.—1988
Distrib.—National
Privately owned corporation

**ESTES CO., INC., CLIFFORD W.**

182 Fairfield Rd., Ste. 8 (07004-2453)
**Phone—(973) 575-4400**
National—(800) 962-5128
Fax—(973) 575-4481
www.estesco.com
Email—rdunnahoo@estesco.com
Chrm.—Douglas Estes
Cont.—Roxanne Catrambone
Sales Mgr., Natl.—Tom Catrambone
SIC—1446; 1429; *Corporate headquarters & aquarium gravel, colored decorative granules & colored quartz sand; Brand name—SpectraStone; Ceramaquartz; Perma Color Quartz*
Employs—6; Estab.—1960
Sales—$5Mil-$10Mil
3,500 sq ft site, Distrib.—Intl.
Privately owned corporation

**EXCELLENT BAKERY EQUIPMENT CO.**

315 Fairfield Rd. (07004)
**Phone—(973) 244-1664**
National—(888) 224-3571
Fax—(973) 244-1696
www.excellent-bagels.com
Email—karin@excellent-bagels.com
Pres.—Karin Seruga
SIC—3556; 5087; 5046; NAICS—333294; *Manufacturer & distributor of bakery machinery for the bagel, small bakery & foodservice markets & wholesale bakers, including bagel ovens/kettles, spiral & double arm mixers, bread/roll divider rounders & cheese graters/shedders; Brand name—ARTOFEX( R); DAUB; EXCELLENT; VMI*
Employs—15; Estab.—1995
Sales—$1Mil-$5Mil
30,000 sq ft site, Distrib.—National
Privately owned sub-S corp.

**EXCELLIUM PHARMACEUTICAL, INC.**

3 Oak Rd., Ste. G (07004-2903)
**Phone—(973) 276-9600**
Fax—(973) 276-9656
www.excellium.com
Email—excellium@aol.com
Pres.—Hasmukh Doshi

GEOGRAPHICAL

## Fairfield—(cont.)

SIC—2834; NAICS—325412;
*Generic prescription
pharmaceuticals*
Employs—35; Estab.—1997
Distrib.—Local
Privately owned sub-S corp.

**EXTREME DIGITAL GRAPHICS**

7 Kingsbridge Rd., Ste. 1 (07004)
**Phone—(973) 227-5599**
Fax—(973) 227-5699
www.extremedigital.net
Email—info@extremedigital.net
Pres.—Lynn Casile
Cust. Serv. Rep.—Alice Lynch
SIC—2759; *Commercial printing*
Employs—10; Estab.—2007
Sales—$1Mil-$2.5Mil (est)
Distrib.—Local
Privately owned corporation

**FABBIAN USA CORP.**

161 Dwight Pl. (07004)
**Phone—(973) 882-3824**
Fax—(973) 882-3826
www.fabbian.com
Email—usa@fabbian.com
Owner—Renato Fabbian
SIC—3645; 3646; NAICS—
335121; *Residential &
commercial decorative lighting
fixtures*
Employs—6; Estab.—2008
Sales—$500,000-$1Mil
Distrib.—Intl.
Privately owned corporation

**FAIRFIELD LAUNDRY MACHINERY**

5 Montesano Rd. (07004)
**Phone—(973) 575-4330**
Fax—(973) 575-8507
www.flmcorp.com
Email—halld@flmcorp.com
Pres., GM—Raymond Hall
V-P.—Raymond Tamburrino
Dir., Opers.—Dennis Hall
SIC—3582; NAICS—333312;
*Commercial laundry machines*
Employs—20; Estab.—1976
12,000 sq ft site, Distrib.—Intl.
Privately owned corporation

**FAIRFIELD LITHO II CORP.**

123 Lehigh Dr. (07004)
**Phone—(973) 575-7550**
Fax—(973) 575-7560
Email—brakowitz@flmgraphics.com
Pres.—William Rakowitz
SIC—2759; NAICS—323100;
*Commercial printing*
Employs—80; Estab.—1991
Sales—$5Mil-$10Mil
Distrib.—Regional
Privately owned sub-S corp.

**†FASTENAL CO.**

68-A Clinton Rd. (07004)
**Phone—(973) 244-0540**
Fax—(973) 244-0541
www.fastenal.com
Email—njfar@stores.fastenal.com
Br. Mgr.—Joe Bourlier
SIC—5072; 5084; *Wholesaler of
fasteners, safety equipment,
tools & abrasives*
Employs—4; Estab.—1967
Distrib.—Local
Publicly owned corporation
Parent co.—Fastenal Co., Winona,
MN
 Phone—(507) 454-5374
 See Parent Co. Section for full profile.

NEW ENTRY
**FATHER & SON DESIGN CENTER,
LLC**

111 Clinton Rd., Ste. 1 (07004)
**Phone—(973) 575-8635**
Fax—(973) 575-0644
www.fatherandsondesign.com

Email—sals@
 fatherandsondesign.com
GM—Sal Carramusa
SIC—3281; *Granite countertops*
Employs—4; Estab.—2014
Sales—$500,000-$1Mil
4,200 sq ft site, Distrib.—Local
Limited Liability Company

**†FCX PERFORMANCE, INC.**

333 Route 46 W., Ste. 130 (07004)
**Phone—(973) 575-8350**
National—(800) 253-6223
Fax—(973) 575-5228
www.fcxperformance.com
Email—info@fcxperformance.com
Br. Mgr.—John Ramey
Off. Mgr.—Ray Damato
SIC—5085; *Distributor of
automated valves for the
pharmaceutical industry*
Employs—10; Estab.—1997
Distrib.—National
Privately owned corporation
Parent co.—FCX Performance,
 Inc., Columbus, OH
 Phone—(614) 253-1996
 See Parent Co. Section for full profile.

**FISCHL MACHINE & TOOL CO.**

79 Clinton Rd. (07004)
**Phone—(973) 227-0767**
Fax—(973) 227-1867
Email—fmt21@verizon.com
Pres.—Rudolph Fischl
V-P.—Bob Fischl
SIC—3599; *General machining
job shop*
Employs—3; Estab.—1979
Sales—under $500,000
1,800 sq ft site, Distrib.—National
Sole ownership

**FLEETWASH, INC. (H Q)**

26 Law Dr., Unit E (07004)
Mail addr: P.O. Box 36014, Newark
 (07188)
**Phone—(800) 847-3735**
Fax—(973) 882-9390
www.fleetwash.com
Email—fleetwash@fleetwash.com
Co-Founder, Pres. & CEO—Vito
 DeGiovanni
CFO—Robert McDonald
CAO—Loraine Matarazzo
V-P.—Philip DeStafano
Env. Mgr.—Jim DiCarlo
SIC—3589; 3823; NAICS—
333319; *Corporate
headquarters; sanitation control
systems & pressure washing
equipment*
Employs—100
Sales—$10Mil-$25Mil (est)

**FLM GRAPHICS CORP.**

123 Lehigh Dr. *(07004)*
**Phone—(973) 575-9450**
Fax—(973) 575-6424
www.flmgraphics.com
Email—info@flmgraphics.com
CEO—Frank L. Misischia
Pres.—Frank M. Misischia
Sr. V-P. & Dir.—Peter Levine
Sr. V-P., Bus. Dev.—Peter Desbets
Ex. V-P., Sales—Anthony Gagliardi
Ex. V-P.—Vincent Gagliardi
V-P. & Dir., Access Images—Alex
 Piqueira
Hum. Res. Mgr.—Ro Sandor
SIC—2759; 2752; NAICS—
323100; *Commercial printing,
large-format digital imaging &
AEC reprographics*
Employs—65; Estab.—1972
Sales—$15Mil
44,000 sq ft site, Distrib.—National
Privately owned corporation

**FLORLIFT OF NEW JERSEY, INC.**

19 Gardner Rd., Ste. M (07004)
**Phone—(973) 484-1717**
 (800) 752-5438
Fax—(973) 484-1460

www.florlift.com
Email—florlift@yahoo.com
Pres.—Casper Vivona, Jr.
Off. Mgr.—Mary Vojnik
SIC—3534; NAICS—333921;
*Hydraulic invalid lifts & elevators
& commercial & industrial
elevators & lifting equipment for
personal residences, hospitals,
churchs, restaurants, bakeries,
manufacturing, material
handling, storage & warehouse
& funeral homes*
Employs—22; Estab.—1954
10,000 sq ft site, Distrib.—Intl.
Privately owned corporation

**FLOWSERVE CORP.**

142 Clinton Rd. (07004-2914)
**Phone—(973) 227-4565**
Fax—(973) 227-6615
www.flowserve.com
Email—mpatel@flowserve.com
Plt. Mgr.—M. Patel
SIC—3561; NAICS—333911;
*Rebuilt pumps*
Employs—25; Estab.—1969
Distrib.—Intl.
Publicly owned corporation
Parent co.—Flowserve Corp.,
 Irving, TX
 Phone—(972) 443-6500
 See Parent Co. Section for full profile.

**FOLEY CO.**

40 Pier Ln. W. (07004)
**Phone—(973) 575-8338**
Fax—(973) 808-2687
Pres.—Bill Hines
Off. Mgr.—Marge Hines
SIC—3471; NAICS—332813;
*Metal finishing*
Employs—2; Estab.—1980
Sales—under $500,000
Distrib.—Local
Privately owned corporation

**FOREMOST MACHINE BUILDERS,
INC.**

23 Spielman Rd. (07004)
**Phone—(973) 227-0700**
Fax—(973) 227-7307
www.foremostmachine.com
Email—sales@
 foremostmachine.com
Pres.—Marlena Heydenreich
Cont., Hum. Res. & IT Mgr.—C. J.
 Weinpel
Sales Engr.—Scott Polachek
Bookkeeper—Victoria Hayes
SIC—3599; *Machine parts for the
plastic industry*
Employs—45; Estab.—1982
Distrib.—Intl.
Privately owned corporation

**FRAMEWARE, INC.**

8 Audrey Pl. (07004)
**Phone—(973) 808-2022**
National—(800) 582-5608
Fax—(973) 808-0262
www.framewareinc.com
Email—dean@framewareinc.com
Pres.—Dean DeLuccia
Pur. Mgr.—Francklin Ermeus
Administrator—Tracy Deluccia
SIC—3429; 3334; NAICS—
331312; *Manufacturer &
distributor of picture & mirror
framing specialty hardware,
packaging, aluminum picture
frame mouldings & glass &
glazing for the picture framing
industry*
Employs—16; Estab.—1985
25,000 sq ft site, Distrib.—Intl.
Privately owned sub-S corp.

**GALAXY GLASS & STONE**

277 Fairfield Rd., P.O. Box 10154
 (07004)
**Phone—(973) 575-3440**
Fax—(973) 575-5235
www.galaxycustom.com

Email—info@galaxycustom.com
Pres., CEO—Eugene M. Negrin
Sr. V-P.—Steven Brenner
Dir., Mktg.—Lynda Portelli
SIC—3231; 2396; 2759; 3471;
NAICS—327215; *Custom &
decorative architectural glass for
hotels, restaurants, casinos,
museums & retail, fashion &
corporate applications, including
silk-screening, digital printing,
lamination & sandblasting;
Brand name—Silkglas®;
Silkmirror®; LeMystere®; Copper
Chainmail®; Galaxy WhiteCrystal*
Employs—35; Estab.—1977
45,000 sq ft site, Distrib.—Intl.
Privately owned corporation

**GARFIELD INDUSTRIES, INC.**

62 Clinton Rd. (07004)
Mail addr: P.O. Box 839, Caldwell
 (07006-0839)
**Phone—(973) 575-8800**
 (973) 575-8801
Fax—(973) 575-6840
www.garfieldbuff.com
Email—steve@garfieldbuff.com
Pres.—Debra Gladstone
Ex. V-P.—Steve Gelvan
Fin. Mgr.—Georgia Dontas
SIC—3291; *Buffing & polishing
wheels*
Employs—20; Estab.—1952
Sales—$1Mil-$5Mil
32,000 sq ft site, Distrib.—Intl.
Privately owned sub-S corp.

**GASFLO PRODUCTS, INC.**

19 Industrial Rd. (07004)
**Phone—(973) 276-9011**
Fax—(973) 276-9014
www.gasflo.com
Email—btowey@gasflo.com
Pres.—David Panetta
Dir., Sales & Mktg.—Bill Towey
SIC—3491; 3498; NAICS—
332911; *Cylinder connections,
valves, fittings & assemblies for
specialty gas applications*
Employs—40; Estab.—1997
Sales—$500,000-$1Mil
Distrib.—Intl.
Privately owned corporation

**GATOR COMMUNICATION GROUP**

175 Route 46 W. (07004)
**Phone—(973) 233-6700**
Fax—(973) 233-6701
www.gatorus.com
Pres.—Richard Bitetti
V-P.—Charles Stuto
SIC—2759; NAICS—323100;
*Commercial printing*
Employs—30; Estab.—2004
Distrib.—Local
Limited Liability Company
AKA: Harvard Printing

**GMS LITHO, INC.**

16 Passaic Ave. (07004)
**Phone—(973) 575-9400**
Fax—(973) 575-9401
Email—printit@gmslitho.com
Pres.—Greg Enright
Off. Mgr.—Sue Nappi
SIC—2759; NAICS—323100;
*Commercial printing*
Employs—10; Estab.—1992
Sales—$500,000-$1Mil
3,500 sq ft site, Distrib.—National
Privately owned corporation
Also see: Columbia Press, Inc.

**GPR CO., INC.**

22 Daniel Rd. (07004)
**Phone—(973) 227-6160**
Fax—(973) 808-8350
www.gprco.com
Email—sales@gprco.com
Pres.—George Verhoest
V-P., Sales & Mktg.—Gary Horman
Fin. Mgr.—Vicky Huynh
Qual. Assur. Mgr.—Anthony Gorga

## Fairfield—(cont.)

SIC—3599; 3543; NAICS—332997; *Production machining & contract manufacturing*
Employs—40; Estab.—1979
40,000 sq ft site, Distrib.—National
Privately owned corporation

**GRANULATION TECHNOLOGY, INC.**
12 Industrial Rd. (07004)
**Phone—(973) 276-0740**
Fax—(973) 276-0741
Pres.—Alka Nigalaye
SIC—2834; NAICS—325412; *Granulation pharmaceutical processing*
Employs—6; Estab.—1998
Sales—under $500,000
Distrib.—Regional
Privately owned corporation

**GRAPHIC MARKETING GROUP**
7 Kingsbridge Rd., Ste. 2 (07004)
**Phone—(973) 276-7901**
Fax—(973) 276-7902
www.graphicmg.com
Pres.—David Greene
Bookkeeper—Barbara Mazzaccaro
SIC—2759; 3993; *Commercial printing & vehicle wraps*
Employs—2; Estab.—2011
Sales—under $500,000 (est)
Distrib.—National
Limited Liability Company
AKA: BJG, Inc.

**H T STAMPING**
19 Gardner Rd., Ste. C (07004)
**Phone—(973) 227-4858**
Fax—(973) 227-4479
Email—info@htstamping.com
Pres.—Thomas Schall
GM—Tony Rodriguez
Off. Mgr.—Bernadette Mundrick
SIC—3469; 3544; NAICS—333500; *Metal stampings & tool & die job shop*
Employs—20; Estab.—1991
Distrib.—National
Privately owned corporation
ISO rating—9001:2000

**HAMILTON BUHL**
Div. of VCOM International Multi-Media Corp.
80 Little Falls Rd. (07004)
**Phone—(201) 229-9800**
National—(800) 631-0868
Fax—(800) 398-1812
www.hamiltonelectronics.com
Email—sales@hamiltonbuhl.com
V.-P.—Madeline Piccone
Sales & Mktg. Mgr.—Melissa Sopata
Sales Mgr., Natl.—Steve Marino
Prod. Mgr.—Israel Gautier
SIC—3861; 3679; 3663; 3669; NAICS—334220; *Technology & AV equipment for educational & industrial applications & government agencies, including media players, listening centers, headphones & headsets, AV carts & projection screens; Brand name—USB Transfer Express; Schoolmate; Hamilton Electronics; Buhl Industries; Mark IV Opus; Educator 90 Series; Educator 120 Series; SoundVision; Apple™; Mighty Mike; School Mate; Cadette*
Employs—19; Estab.—1970
Sales—$2.5Mil-$5Mil
Distrib.—Intl.
Privately owned corporation
AKA: V-Com
Parent co.—VCOM International Multi-Media Corp., Fairfield, NJ
Phone—(201) 229-4270
See Parent Co. Section for full profile.

**HANOVIA SPECIALTY LIGHTING LLC**
6 Evans St. (07004)
**Phone—(973) 651-5510**
National—(800) 229-3666
Fax—(973) 651-5550
www.hanovia-uv.com
Email—jsandrews@hanovia-uv.com
Ptnr.—Jeffrey S. Andrews
Ptnr.—Liming Du
SIC—3641; NAICS—335110; *Exposure & UV curing equipment; Brand name—Hanovia; Colight*
Employs—20; Estab.—1905
Sales—$1Mil-$5Mil
23,000 sq ft site, Distrib.—Intl.
Limited Liability Company

**†HAYES PUMP, INC.**
295 Fairfield Ave. *(07004)*
**Phone—(973) 808-0606**
        (800) 343-5020
National—(888) 778-5090
Fax—(973) 808-7311
www.hayespump.com
Email—Customerservice@hayespump.com
Ex. V.-P.—Joseph F. Larkin, Sr.
V.-P., GM—Joe Larkin
Opers. Mgr.—Mark Heckmann
IT Mgr.—Jason Marquis
SIC—5084; 5085; *Distributor of pumps & parts, including rotary gear, self-priming centrifugal & stainless steel pumps, controls, drives & filters; Brand name—Viking Pump; Goulds Pumps; Gorman-Rupp Pumps; Aurora Pumps; Grundfos Pumps; John Crane Seals; Moyno Pumps; Fairbanks Morse; Fybroc Pumps; Warren Rupp; Pump Smart Control Solutions*
Employs—22; Estab.—1992
Sales—$10Mil-$20Mil
Distrib.—National
Privately owned corporation
Parent co.—Hayes Pump, Inc., Concord, MA
Phone—(978) 369-8800
See Parent Co. Section for full profile.

**HEAT-TIMER CORP.**
20 New Dutch Ln. (07004)
**Phone—(973) 575-4004**
Fax—(973) 575-4052
www.heat-timer.com
Email—sales@heat-timer.com
Pres.—Michael Pitonyak
V.-P., Sales & Mktg.—Vincent Clerico
Hum. Res. Mgr.—Lucy Lucin
Sales Rep., Inside—Katie Caggiano
SIC—3822; NAICS—334512; *Heat timer controls*
Employs—50; Estab.—1937
Sales—$11Mil-$25Mil
Distrib.—Local
Privately owned corporation

**HEISLER INDUSTRIES, INC.**
224 Passaic Ave. (07004)
**Phone—(973) 227-6300**
Fax—(973) 227-7627
www.heislerind.com
Email—heislersales@heislerind.com
Pres.—Richard A. Heisler
CFO & Cont.—Dennis C. Walter
V.-P., Sales—James E. Lamb
Pur. Mgr.—Bob Gellner
MIS Mgr.—Ghan Senjalia
Sales Admn.—Judith M. Vinson

SIC—3565; 3569; 7373; NAICS—333993; *Packaging machines, automation & system integration services for the paint, petroleum, chemical, food & gypsum industries, including engineering, equipment, support & service; Brand name—Bail-O-Matic*
Employs—38; Estab.—1920
Sales—$5Mil-$10Mil
25,000 sq ft site, Distrib.—Intl.
Privately owned sub-S corp.

**HIGH PRECISION MACHINE SHOP, LLC**
1275 Bloomfield Ave., Ste. 63 (07004)
**Phone—(973) 227-5110**
Fax—(973) 227-4836
Email—petermitas@verizon.net
Pres.—Peter Mitas
V.-P.—George Mitas
SIC—3599; *Precision machining job shop*
Employs—6; Estab.—1989
4,200 sq ft site, Distrib.—Local
Limited Liability Company

**HUDSON INDUSTRIES CORP.**
271 U.S. Highway 46, Ste. F-207 (07004-2448)
**Phone—(973) 402-0100**
Fax—(973) 402-9520
www.milligan1868.com
Email—lkornbluh@milligan1868.com
Pres.—Lee Kornbluh
Off. Mgr.—Chris Hackney
SIC—2891; NAICS—325520; *Corporate headquarters & animal hide & bone glue, industrial & technical gelatins & proteins*
Employs—2; Estab.—1937
Sales—$1Mil-$5Mil
Distrib.—Intl.
Privately owned corporation

**HUNTER MFG. SERVICES, INC.**
19 Just Rd. *(07004)*
**Phone—(973) 365-5880**
Fax—(973) 365-0588
www.huntermfg.net
Email—khunter@huntermfg.net
Owner & Pres.—Kenneth C. Hunter
V.-P.—Tim Lang
Off. Mgr.—Linda Hunter
SIC—3565; 3599; 3728; NAICS—332997; *CNC machining of pharmaceutical packaging equipment & aerospace components, including prototypes & production runs*
Employs—12; Estab.—1998
Sales—$2Mil-$3Mil
4,000 sq ft site, Distrib.—National
Privately owned sub-S corp.

**IDP FILMS**
24 Commerce Rd., Ste. P (07004)
**Phone—(973) 227-1661**
Fax—(973) 227-4114
Owner—Jin Kim
SIC—2789; NAICS—332999; *Foil stamping*
Employs—4
Sales—under $500,000 (est)
Privately owned corporation

**IMPERIAL DAX CO., INC.**
120 New Dutch Ln. *(07004)*
**Phone—(973) 227-6105**
Fax—(973) 808-8533
www.daxhaircare.com
Email—lzawisha@imperialdax.com
Pres.—David Joy
GM—Donald Joy
Creative Dev. & Sales Mgr.—Michelle Rivera

SIC—2844; NAICS—325600; *Hair & skin care products, including pomades, waxes, shampoos & conditioners; Brand name—Imperial Dax; Dax Hair Care; DAX; Roots; High Life Pomade*
Employs—25; Estab.—1954
Sales—$5Mil-$10Mil
45,000 sq ft site, Distrib.—Intl.
Privately owned sub-S corp.
DBA: Dax Hair Care Products

**INDASA U. S. A., INC.**
23 Madison Rd. (07004)
**Phone—(800) 916-0090**
National—(800) 326-5909
Fax—(973) 227-1144
www.indasausa.com
Email—salesusa@indasausa.com
V.-P.—Alan Zaorski
SIC—3291; *Coated abrasives; Brand name—Indasa Abrasives*
Employs—9; Estab.—1999
15,000 sq ft site, Distrib.—Intl.
Privately owned corporation

**INDEPENDENT MACHINE CO.**
2 Stewart Pl. (07004)
**Phone—(973) 882-0060**
Fax—(973) 808-9505
www.independentusa.com
Email—imco@aol.com
Pres.—Jack Santa Lucia
V.-P., Sales—Bruce L. Butler
Sales & Mktg. Mgr.—Robin Ulanski
Fin. Mgr.—Anthony De Aquino
SIC—3599; *Industrial machinery*
Employs—20; Estab.—1968
Sales—$2.6Mil-$5Mil
34,000 sq ft site, Distrib.—Intl.
Privately owned corporation

**INDUSTRIAL BRUSH CO., INC.**
105 Clinton Rd. (07004)
**Phone—(973) 575-0455**
National—(800) 241-9860
Fax—(973) 575-6169
www.indbrush.com
Email—sales@indbrush.com
V.-P., Sales—Scott Enchelmaier
V.-P., Mfg. & IT Mgr.—Tim Enchelmaier
Plt. Mgr.—Kevin McCoy
Hum. Res. & Off. Mgr.—Holly Whittle
SIC—3991; NAICS—339994; *Industrial brushes*
Employs—25; Estab.—1946
Sales—$1Mil-$5Mil
35,000 sq ft site, Distrib.—Intl.
Privately owned corporation

**INDUSTRIAL FILTERS CO., INC.**
9 Industrial Rd. (07004)
**Phone—(973) 575-0533**
National—(800) 822-4778
Fax—(973) 575-9238
www.indfilco.com
Email—indfilco@aol.com
Pres.—Steven Donker
Off. Mgr.—Carol Centanni
SIC—3569; 2399; *Industrial water filters*
Employs—7; Estab.—1965
Sales—over $1Mil
Distrib.—Intl.
Privately owned corporation

**INDUSTRIAL LABELING SYSTEMS, INC.**
50 Kulick Rd. (07004)
**Phone—(973) 882-9688**
www.e-ilsi.com
Email—info@e-ilsi.com
Pres.—Yimin Shiuey
Acctg. Mgr.—Sherry Johnson
Hum. Res. Mgr.—Brad Mack

GEOGRAPHICAL

## Fairfield—(cont.)

SIC—2759; NAICS—323100;
*Label printing*
Employs—15; Estab.—1997
Sales—$1Mil-$2.5Mil
Distrib.—Regional
Privately owned corporation
Also see: Yellow Stone Distributing
Co., same loc.

**INNOVATIVE LABELING, INC.**
12 Gloria Ln., Ste. 4 (07004)
**Phone—(973) 227-4800**
Fax—(973) 227-4834
www.innovativelabeling.com
Email—innovative22@aol.com
Pres.—Cheryl Ziemba
V-P.—Richard Ziemba
SIC—2672; 3499; NAICS—
322222; *Indoor & outdoor
nameplates & labels &
polycarbonate overlays,
pressure-sensitive, digital, silk-
screened & military labels*
Employs—4; Estab.—1992
Sales—$1Mil-$2.5Mil
Distrib.—National
Privately owned corporation

**INTERNATIONAL CORD SETS, INC.**
6 Spielman Rd. (07004)
**Phone—(973) 227-2118**
Fax—(973) 882-8918
www.intlcordsets.com
Pres.—Dieter Baars
V-P., Mktg.—Ralph Mezza
Off. Mgr.—Mia Dewey
Qual. Control Mgr.—N. Patel
SIC—3699; 5063; *Manufacturer of
international cord sets &
distributor of wires, cables,
connectors & liquid-tight strain
reliefs*
Employs—18; Estab.—1981
12,500 sq ft site, Distrib.—National
Privately owned corporation

**INTERNATIONAL TOOL & MFG., INC.**
30 Sherwood Ln., Ste. 10 *(07004)*
**Phone—(973) 227-6767**
Fax—(973) 227-6711
www.international-inc.com
Email—sales@international-inc.com
Owner & Pres.—Susan Brock
V-P., Mfg.—Thomas Brock
V-P., Prodn.—Ryan Brock
SIC—3599; 3543; *Precision
machining job shop, including
prototypes*
Employs—10; Estab.—1990
Sales—$1Mil-$5Mil
5,500 sq ft site, Distrib.—National
Privately owned corporation
ISO rating—9001:2008

**J R C WEB ACCESSORIES, INC.**
46 Passaic Ave. (07004)
**Phone—(973) 625-3888**
Fax—(973) 226-4249
www.jrcweb.com
Email—support@jrcweb.com
Chrm., Pres. & Sales Rep.—Ralph
L. Ryan
V-P., Treas., Off.—Virginia L. Ryan
GM & Engrg. Mgr.—Todd A. Ryan
SIC—3429; 3555; NAICS—
333293; *Pneumatic &
mechanical chucks, shafts &
accessories*
Employs—12; Estab.—1975
Sales—under $500,000
8,000 sq ft site, Distrib.—Intl.
Privately owned corporation

**JASON INDUSTRIAL INC.**
340 Kaplan Dr., P.O. Box 10004
*(07004)*
**Phone—(973) 227-4904**
Fax—(973) 227-1651
www.jasonindustrial.com
Email—inquiries@
jasonindustrial.com
Pres.—Phillip Cohenca

V-P., Sales—Tom Tesoro
Dir., IT—James Messineo
MIS Mgr.—Chuck DePalmo
Hum. Res. Mgr.—Rosemary
Greene
SIC—3052; NAICS—326220;
*Corporate headquarters &
rubber timing belts*
Employs—50; Estab.—1957
Sales—$20Mil-$25Mil
30,000 sq ft site, Distrib.—National
Privately owned corporation

**JERSEY ARTISAN DISTILLING**
32 Pier Ln. W., Bldg. C (07004)
**Phone—(973) 521-7623**
Fax—(973) 521-7638
www.jerseyartisandistilling.com
Email—info@
jerseyartisandistilling.com
Owner—Krista Haley
SIC—2085; *Distilled spirits*
Employs—2; Estab.—2011
Sales—under $500,000
6,000 sq ft site, Distrib.—Regional
Privately owned corporation

**JERSEY MACHINE TOOL REPAIRING
& REBUILDING CO.**
1275 Bloomfield Ave., Bldg. 2, Unit
10 (07004)
**Phone—(973) 575-1044**
Fax—(973) 575-5948
Email—john@
jerseymachinetool.com
Owner—John Csiszar
Shop Mgr.—George Lako
SIC—3541; 3542; NAICS—
333512; *Rebuilt machine tools*
Employs—3; Estab.—1981
Sales—under $500,000
Distrib.—Regional
Sole ownership

**JMC DESIGN & GRAPHICS, INC.**
144 Fairfield Rd. (07004)
**Phone—(973) 276-9033**
Fax—(973) 276-9034
www.jmcprinting.com
Pres.—Joseph Caniano
Off. Admn.—Brielle Caniano
SIC—2759; NAICS—323100;
*Commercial printing & graphic
design*
Employs—7
Sales—under $500,000
Distrib.—Local
Privately owned corporation

†**KARL'S APPLIANCE, LLC**
65 Passaic Ave. (07004)
**Phone—(973) 227-1777**
National—(877) 695-2757
Fax—(973) 227-1801
www.karlsappliance.com
Email—customerservice@
karlsappliance.com
Pres.—Dan Schwartz
SIC—5078; 5064; *Wholesaler of
household appliances, including
refrigeration, cooking
equipment, dishwashers,
laundry machines, air
conditioners & vacuums; Brand
name—Aga; Amana; Bertazzoni;
Blomberg; Capital; Dancor;
Dandy; Electrolux; Five Star;
Frigidaire; General Electric;
Hoover; LG; Marvel; Samsung;
Premier; Lynx; Jenn-Air;
KitchenAid*
Employs—45; Estab.—1941
20,000 sq ft site, Distrib.—National
Limited Liability Company

**KATHY JEANNE, INC.**
7 Industrial Rd. (07004)
**Phone—(973) 575-9898**
Fax—(973) 575-7988
www.kathyjeanne.com
Email—jay@kathyjeanne.com
Pres.—Jeanne Gerish
V-P.—Jay Gerish
Off. Mgr.—Rosemary Thaler

SIC—2353; *Hats; Brand name—
Jack McConnell; Jeanne Marie;
Kathy Jeanne*
Employs—9; Estab.—1985
Sales—over $2Mil
12,000 sq ft site, Distrib.—National
Privately owned corporation

**KIDS OF AMERICA CORP.**
103 Route 46 W. (07004)
**Phone—(973) 808-8242**
Owner—Stephen Chan
SIC—3942; *Plush toys*
Employs—5
Sales—under $500,000 (est)
Distrib.—Intl.
Privately owned corporation

**KINETICS INFRARED**
40 Pier Ln. W. (07004)
**Phone—(973) 575-5332**
Fax—(973) 582-0442
www.kineticsir.com
Email—sales@gtckinetics.com
Pres.—Chris Hines
SIC—3567; NAICS—333994;
*Industrial electric infrared quartz
& panel heaters, infrared ovens
& process control systems*
Employs—6; Estab.—2000
Sales—$500,000-$1Mil
Distrib.—Intl.
Privately owned corporation

**KYOCERA DOCUMENT SOLUTIONS
AMERICA, INC. (H Q)**
225 Sand Rd. (07004)
**Phone—(973) 808-8444**
National—(800) 453-6482
Fax—(973) 882-6000
www.kyoceradocumentsolutions.c
om
Email—info@da.kyocera.com
Pres.—Norihiko Ina
Sr. V-P., Sales—Ed Bialecki
V-P., Mktg.—Peter Hendrick
V-P., Hum. Res.—Gary Bonomolo
Hum. Res. Mgr.—Kerri Fiore
SIC—3861; 3577; *Corporate
headquarters; office machines,
printers, fax & large-format
plotters & toner cartridges*
Employs—200; Estab.—1948
Sales—$50Mil-$100Mil (est)
Distrib.—Intl.
Publicly owned corporation

**L & M ARCHITECTURAL GRAPHICS,
INC.**
20 Montesano Rd. (07004)
**Phone—(973) 575-7665**
Fax—(973) 575-6709
www.lmsigns.com
Email—info@lmsigns.com
Pres.—Justin Lorenzo
V-P., Opers.—Paul Lorenzo
SIC—3993; *Interior & exterior
signs & environmental graphics*
Employs—15; Estab.—1999
Sales—$1Mil-$2.5Mil
Distrib.—National
Privately owned sub-S corp.

**LABEL GRAPHICS MFG.**
Div. of Label Graphics Mfg., Inc.
315 Fairfield Rd., Unit 1 (07004-
1930)
**Phone—(973) 890-5665**
National—(800) 845-2235
www.labelgraphicsmfg.com
Email—labels@
labelgraphicsmfg.com
V-P. & Off. Mgr.—Denise Silvano
SIC—2672; 3089; NAICS—
323100; *Pressure-sensitive
labels & flexible packaging,
including shrink sleeves*
Employs—10; Estab.—1988
Sales—$1Mil-$2.5Mil
Distrib.—National
Privately owned corporation

Parent co.—Label Graphics Mfg.,
Inc., Little Falls, NJ
Phone—(973) 890-5665
See Parent Co. Section for full profile.

**LACOUR, INC.**
36 Kulick Rd. (07004)
**Phone—(973) 227-4755**
Fax—(973) 227-3544
www.lacourinc.com
Email—sales@lacourinc.com
Pres.—Paul M. LaCour
GM—Tom Ruggieri
Sales Mgr.—Rick Stanaland
Proj. Coord.—Malinda Walker
SIC—2522; NAICS—337214;
*Composite trading & industrial
desks & office workstations*
Employs—20; Estab.—1972
Distrib.—National
Privately owned corporation

**LB BOOK BINDERY, LLC**
19 Gardner Rd., Ste. I (07004)
**Phone—(973) 244-0442**
Fax—(973) 244-0732
www.lbbookbinderyllc.com
Email—ralph@lbbookbinderyllc.com
Ptnr.—Frank Lozito
Ptnr.—Ralph Lozito
SIC—2789; *Bookbinding*
Employs—15; Estab.—1999
15,000 sq ft site, Distrib.—
Regional
Limited Liability Company

**LEVINE PACKAGING SUPPLY CORP.**
400 U.S. Highway 46 E. (07004)
**Phone—(973) 575-3383**
Fax—(973) 575-1141
www.levinebox.com
V-P.—L. Levine
SIC—2653; 5085; 5113; NAICS—
322211; *Manufacturer of
corrugated boxes & distributor of
packaging supplies, including
box & gum tape, bubble wrap,
strapping, loose fill & shipping
bags*
Employs—20
Sales—$2.5Mil-$5Mil (est)
DBA: Allied Paper Packaging

**LIBERTY SPORT, INC.**
107 Fairfield Rd. (07004)
**Phone—(973) 882-0986**
National—(800) 444-5010
Fax—(973) 575-1037
www.libertysport.com
Email—cfoliberty@aol.com
Pres.—Anthony DiChiara
CFO—Franco Tommasino
V-P.—Carmine DiChiara
MIS Mgr.—Al Guilarte
SIC—3851; 3949; NAICS—
339920; *Protective sports
eyewear; Brand name—Recs
Specs*
Employs—30; Estab.—1929
13,000 sq ft site, Distrib.—National
Privately owned sub-S corp.

**LINK COMPUTER GRAPHICS, INC.**
17-A Daniel Rd. (07004)
**Phone—(973) 808-8990**
www.linkinstruments.com
Email—sales@linkinstruments.com
Pres.—Hung-Wei Yeh
SIC—3825; 3829; 3679; 3826;
NAICS—334500; *Digital storage
oscilloscopes, logic & spectrum
analyzers & pattern generators*
Employs—10; Estab.—1986
Distrib.—Intl.
Privately owned corporation

**LITVANY PRINTING, LLC, STEVE**
1275 Bloomfield Ave., Ste. 13-R
(07004)
**Phone—(973) 244-0144**
Email—steves.printing@
hotmail.com
Pres.—Steve Litvany

# Fairfield—(cont.)

SIC—2759; *Commercial printing*
Employs—2; Estab.—2000
Sales—under $500,000
Distrib.—Local
Privately owned corporation

**LIZARD LABEL, INC.**
10-E Commerce Rd. *(07004-1617)*
**Phone—(973) 808-0098**
          (877) 807-0098
Fax—(973) 882-8829
www.lizardlabel.com
Email—sales@lizardlabel.com
Pres.—Joseph Winter
Prodn. Mgr.—Dominick Santise
Cust. Serv. Mgr.—Patricia
  Domozych
Label Specialist—Elaine Iacovone
SIC—2679; 2759; NAICS—
  322200; *Digitally printed
  pressure-sensitive labels*
Employs—10; Estab.—2004
Sales—$1Mil-$3Mil
Distrib.—National
Privately owned corporation

**LOGOTECH, INC.**
18 Madison Rd. (07004)
**Phone—(973) 882-9595**
National—(800) 988-5646
Fax—(973) 882-0902
www.logotech-inc.com
Email—labels@logotech-inc.com
Pres.—Leslie Gurland
Hum. Res. & IT Mgr.—Mary
  Monroe
Off. Mgr.—Anna Petras
SIC—2759; NAICS—323100;
  *Pressure-sensitive labels*
Employs—35; Estab.—1995
14,000 sq ft site, Distrib.—Intl.
Privately owned corporation

**LONT & OVERKAMP**
175 U.S. Highway 46 (07004)
**Phone—(973) 942-2243**
Fax—(973) 942-8203
www.lont.com
Email—ken@lont.com
CEO—Ken Lont
Pres.—Josh Lont
V-P.—Judy Lont
V-P.—Paul Pappas
Opers. Mgr.—Carol DePuy
Mktg. Mgr.—T. C. DeGeyter
Fin. & Hum. Res. Mgr.—Betty
  Moore
SIC—2752; 2791; 2789; 2759;
  NAICS—323122; *Offset, digital &
  direct mail printing &
  computerized typesetting &
  bookbinding*
Employs—50; Estab.—1902
22,000 sq ft site, Distrib.—Local
Privately owned corporation

**MAQUET**
Div. of Maquet Cardiovascular,
  LLC
15 Law Dr. (07004)
**Phone—(973) 244-6100**
National—(800) 777-4222
Fax—(973) 244-6279
www.maquet.com
Email—info@maquet.com
Dir., IT—Shen Lu
Hum. Res. Mgr.—Nancy Michael
SIC—3845; NAICS—334500;
  *Medical devices*
Employs—200; Estab.—1991
85,000 sq ft site, Distrib.—Intl.
Parent co.—Maquet
  Cardiovascular, LLC, Wayne, NJ
  Phone—(973) 709-7000
  See Parent Co. Section for full profile.

**MARKETING ADVERTISING
  PROMOTIONS, INC.**
4 Edison Pl. (07004)
**Phone—(973) 575-5656**
Fax—(973) 575-9175
www.themapworld.com

Email—map@themapworld.com
Pres.—John Litwinka
SIC—7372; *Medical coding &
  billing software development*
Employs—15; Estab.—1991
Sales—$500,000-$1Mil
Distrib.—Regional
Privately owned corporation

**†MELFAST, INC.**
18 Passaic Ave., Unit 4-5 (07004-
  3834)
**Phone—(973) 227-0045**
Fax—(973) 227-4024
www.melfast.com
Email—info@melfast.com
Pres.—Larry Melone
Pur. Mgr.—Jennifer Melone
  Schwanke
SIC—5072; *Distributor of inch &
  metric steel, stainless steel &
  exotic material fasteners, screws,
  nuts & bolts*
Employs—20; Estab.—1985
Sales—$2.5Mil-$5Mil
10,000 sq ft site, Distrib.—Intl.
Privately owned corporation

**MENNEKES ELECTRONICS, INC.**
277 Fairfield Rd. (07004)
**Phone—(973) 882-8333**
National—(800) 882-7584
Fax—(973) 882-5585
www.mennekes.com
Pres.—Walter Mennekes
SIC—3643; NAICS—335931;
  *Electronics equipment, including
  wiring devices & switches*
Employs—20; Estab.—1982
Sales—under $500,000
Distrib.—Regional
Privately owned corporation

**MERCURY LIGHTING PRODUCTS
  CO.**
20 Audrey Pl. (07004)
**Phone—(973) 244-9444**
National—(800) 637-2584
Fax—(973) 244-9522
www.mercltg.com
Email—sales@mercltg.com
Ptnr. & Opers. Mgr.—Brian
  Cunningham
Ptnr.—John Fedinec
Ptnr.—Scott Fleischer
Cont.—John Vittorio
SIC—3646; 3645; NAICS—
  335122; *Commercial &
  residential lighting fixtures*
Employs—130; Estab.—1982
100,000 sq ft site, Distrib.—
  Regional
Privately owned corporation

**†MG AMERICA, INC.**
31 Kulick Rd. *(07004)*
**Phone—(973) 808-8185**
Fax—(973) 808-8421
www.mgamerica.com
Email—sales@mgamerica.com
Pres.—Fabio Trippodo
Acctg. Mgr.—Nives Adamo
SIC—5084; *Wholesaler of
  packaging machinery, including
  pouches, cartonizers, palletizers
  & capsule fillers*
Employs—20; Estab.—1988
20,000 sq ft site, Distrib.—Intl.
Privately owned corporation

**MIDDLE ATLANTIC PRODUCTS, INC.**
Div. of Legrand North America
300 Fairfield Rd. (07004)
**Phone—(973) 839-1011**
Fax—(973) 839-1976
www.middleatlantic.com
Email—info@middleatlantic.com
Pres. & Dir., Sales & Mktg.—
  Michael Baker
V-P., Opers.—Bill Fuchs
Dir., Sales, S. Reg.—Bill Poling
Dir., Sales, N. Reg.—Robert
  Newhuis
Dir., IT—Dan Gitleman

Hum. Res. Mgr.—Dennise Tapia
Hum. Res. Generalist—Michelle
  Reed
SIC—3499; *Steel audio &
  broadcast racks; Brand name—
  Datatel; PopperStopper*
Employs—490; Estab.—1979
224,000 sq ft site, Distrib.—Intl.
Privately owned corporation
Parent co.—Legrand North
  America, West Hartford, CT
  Phone—(860) 233-6251
  See Parent Co. Section for full profile.

**MJG SCREEN PRINTING &
  EMBROIDERY**
24 Commerce Rd., Ste. K (07004)
**Phone—(973) 575-8877**
Fax—(973) 575-6677
www.mjgpromotions.com
Email—mjg129@gmail.com
Owner—Michael Garamella
SIC—2396; 2395; 3993; *T-shirt
  screen printing & embroidery &
  promotional products*
Employs—4; Estab.—1990
Sales—$1Mil-$3Mil
4,000 sq ft site, Distrib.—National
Sole ownership

**MODERN DRUMMER
  PUBLICATIONS, INC.**
271 Route 46 W., Ste. 212 (07004)
**Phone—(973) 239-4140**
National—(800) 551-3786
Fax—(973) 239-7139
www.moderndrummer.com
Email—mdinfo@
  moderndrummer.com
Pres.—Isabel Spagnardi
V-P.—Kevin Kearns
Editorial Dir.—Adam Budofsky
Adv., Sales & Mktg. Mgr.—Bob
  Berenson
Prodn. Mgr.—Scott Bienstock
SIC—2721; *Magazine publishing*
Employs—15; Estab.—1977
Sales—$1Mil-$2.5Mil
Distrib.—Intl.
Sole ownership
AKA: Modern Drummer

**MORGAN ADVANCED CERAMICS,
  INC.**
Div. of Morgan Technical Ceramics
26 Madison Rd. (07004)
**Phone—(973) 227-8877**
Fax—(973) 227-7135
www.wesgoduramic.com
Email—mtcussales@
  morganplc.com
GM—Jerry McConvery
Buyer—Barbara Rafiq
SIC—3269; NAICS—327113;
  *Ceramic parts*
Employs—30; Estab.—1927
32,000 sq ft site, Distrib.—Intl.
Publicly owned corporation
Parent co.—Morgan Technical
  Ceramics, Hayward, CA
  Phone—(510) 491-1100
  See Parent Co. Section for full profile.

**MOTIF INDUSTRIES, INC.**
8 Commerce Rd. (07004)
**Phone—(973) 575-1800**
Fax—(973) 575-1801
www.motif-industries.com
Email—info@motif-industries.com
Pres.—Al Elkay
GM—Peter Almeida
Off. Mgr.—Bonnie Patala
Manager—Bela Almeida
SIC—3851; 2672; NAICS—
  322222; *Ophthalmic products,
  including lens patterns, demo &
  sun lens edging & glazing, bar
  code labels & pad printing, drill
  charts, refurbishing, signs,
  banners & POP displays*
Employs—28; Estab.—1991
Sales—$1Mil-$2.5Mil
25,000 sq ft site, Distrib.—National
Privately owned sub-S corp.

**MULTI-PAK PACKAGING**
19 Spielman Rd. (07004)
**Phone—(973) 439-1182**
Fax—(973) 439-1235
www.multipaknj.com
Email—info@multipaknj.com
Pres.—John Culligan
Pur. Mgr.—Cathy Arm
Off. & Shpg. Mgr.—Melissa
  Dezabala
SIC—3089; *Contract packaging of
  pharmaceuticals, vitamins &
  supplements*
Employs—100; Estab.—1999
Sales—$1Mil-$2.5Mil
Distrib.—National
Limited Liability Company

**NATIONAL PRECISION TOOL CO.,
  INC.**
24 Sherwood Ln. (07004)
**Phone—(973) 227-5005**
Fax—(973) 227-5077
www.nptcinc.com
Email—sales@nptcinc.com
Pres., Fin., MIS & R & D Mgr.—
  Leon Roitburg
Off. Mgr.—Paulina Roitburg
SIC—3599; *Precision machining
  job shop*
Employs—20; Estab.—1984
20,000 sq ft site, Distrib.—
  Regional
Privately owned corporation
Also see: Design Of Tomorrow,
  Inc., same loc.

**NEW AGE METAL FABRICATING CO.**
26 Daniel Rd. (07004)
**Phone—(973) 227-9107**
Fax—(973) 227-6039
www.namf.com
Email—mcosta@namf.com
Pres.—Mario Costa
Ex. V-P.—Mario Costa, Jr.
Off. Mgr.—Marge Goble
Misc. Mgr.—Juliet Seymour
Fin. Mgr.—Joyce Gladstein
Engrg. Mgr.—Sanat Shah
SIC—3444; *Sheet metal
  fabrication*
Employs—60; Estab.—1979
33,000 sq ft site, Distrib.—National
Privately owned corporation

**NEW JERSEY BUSINESS MAGAZINE**
Div. of New Jersey Business &
  Industry Assn.
310 Passaic Ave., Ste. 201 (07004)
**Phone—(973) 882-5004**
Fax—(973) 882-4648
www.njbmagazine.com
Email—info@njbmagazine.com
Publisher—Vincent Schweikert
Editor—Anthony Biritterri
Dir., Adv.—Lisa Criscuolo
SIC—2791; 2721; NAICS—
  323122; *Electronic magazine
  prepress printing*
Employs—10; Estab.—1954
Sales—$500,000-$1Mil
2,400 sq ft site, Distrib.—Regional
Privately owned corporation
Parent co.—New Jersey Business
  & Industry Assn., Trenton, NJ
  Phone—(609) 393-7707
  See Parent Co. Section for full profile.

**NOMADIC DISPLAY**
4-6 Just Rd. (07004)
**Phone—(862) 210-8120**
National—(800) 336-5019
Fax—(862) 210-8123
www.nomadicdisplay.com
Email—exsv01@
  nomadicdisplay.com
Sales Mgr.—Michael Hurley
IT Mgr.—Gregory Whitmyre
Administrator & Prodn. Asst.—
  Ashley Occhifinto

GEOGRAPHICAL

## Fairfield—(cont.)

SIC—2542; *Portable & modular display systems*
Employs—10; Estab.—1987
Sales—$1Mil-$2.5Mil (est)
Distrib.—Intl.
Privately owned corporation
Parent co.—Nomadic Display, Springfield, VA
Phone—(703) 866-9200
See Parent Co. Section for full profile.

### NOUVEAUTES, INC.
70 Clinton Rd. (07004)
**Phone—(973) 882-8850**
Fax—(973) 882-8840
www.nouveautesusa.com
Email—info@nouveautesusa.com
Pres.—David Little
Accountant—Jack Oliver
SIC—2066; NAICS—311300; *Chocolate products*
Employs—15; Estab.—1992
10,000 sq ft site, Distrib.—National
Privately owned corporation
AKA: Incentive Gourmet

### O M P TECHNOLOGIES, INC.
24-H Commerce Rd. (07004)
**Phone—(973) 808-5543**
Fax—(973) 808-5618
www.omptech.com
Email—info@omptech.com
V-P.—Kanhan Hsiao
SIC—3599; *CNC machining job shop*
Employs—15; Estab.—1986
Sales—$1Mil-$2.5Mil
Distrib.—National
Privately owned corporation

### ON TARGET PRINTING & GRAPHICS, LLC
202 Fairfield Rd. (07004)
**Phone—(973) 287-6222**
Fax—(973) 287-6241
www.ontargetprinting.net
Email—info@ontargetprinting.net
Owner—Jeff Greulich
IT Mgr.—Alex Greulich
Hum. Res. Mgr.—Robyn Greulich
SIC—2759; *Commercial printing & graphic design*
Employs—5; Estab.—2007
Sales—under $500,000
Distrib.—Intl.
Limited Liability Company

### ORIENTAL AROMATICS, INC.
21 Spielman Rd. (07004)
**Phone—(973) 227-0400**
National—(888) 611-2727
Fax—(973) 227-9940
www.orientalaromatics.com
Email—dharmil@orientalaromatics.com
Pres., CEO—Dharmil Bodani
Acct. Mgr.—Mindy Buckner
SIC—2899; 2099; *Fragrances & flavors*
Employs—25; Estab.—1950
Sales—$10Mil-$25Mil (est)
Distrib.—Intl.
Privately owned corporation

### PACE PACKAGING CORP.
3 Sperry Rd. (07004)
**Phone—(973) 227-1040**
National—(800) 867-2726
Fax—(973) 227-7393
www.pacepackaging.com
Email—sales@pacepackaging.com
Pres.—Kenneth Regula
IT Mgr.—Sam Jarkas
Off. Mgr.—Marilyn Neubert

SIC—3569; 3085; *Automatic plastic bottle unscrambling systems for the dairy, juice, bottled water, food, detergents, industrial cleaners, soaps, lotions, motor oil, pharmaceutical, hair care, car care & bottling decorating industries*
Employs—48; Estab.—1968
30,000 sq ft site, Distrib.—Intl.
Privately owned corporation

### PANERA BREAD CO., LLC
Div. of Panera Bread Co., Inc.
5 E. Evans St. (07004)
**Phone—(973) 276-0250**
Fax—(973) 276-0280
www.panerabread.com
Email—comm126@panerabread.com
GM—Vince Chiappetta
SIC—2041; NAICS—311812; *Bread dough*
Employs—80; Estab.—2001
Sales—under $500,000
23,000 sq ft site, Distrib.—National
Privately owned corporation
Parent co.—Panera Bread Co., Inc., Sunset Hills, MO
Phone—(314) 984-1000
See Parent Co. Section for full profile.

### PARKER LABORATORIES, INC.
286 Eldridge Rd. (07004)
**Phone—(973) 276-9500**
National—(800) 631-8888
Fax—(973) 276-9510
www.parkerlabs.com
Email—parker@parkerlabs.com
Pres.—Neal Buchalter
Dir., Sales, Intl.—Martin King
Sales Mgr.—Tom Rodenberg
Mfg. Mgr.—Nick Economou
Adv. Mgr.—Joan Bartello
Pur. Mgr.—John O'Connor
Hum. Res. Mgr.—Diane Sharkey
SIC—3845; NAICS—334500; *Ultrasound lotions, gels & medical accessories; Brand name—Aquasonic 100; Aquasonic Clear; Sterile Aquasonic100; Aquaflex; Scan; Polysonic; Thermasonic Gel Warmer; Eclipse Probe Cover; Transeptic; Aquagel; Spectra 360; SignaSpray; SignaPad; SignaCreme; SignaGel; Tensive*
Employs—50; Estab.—1958
Sales—$10Mil-$25Mil (est)
Distrib.—Intl.
Privately owned corporation
ISO rating—13485:2003

### PAR-TROY SHEET METAL & CONDITIONING, LLC
122 Clinton Rd. (07004)
**Phone—(973) 227-1150**
Fax—(973) 227-2757
www.par-troy.com
Email—p.partroysm@verizon.net
Ptnr. & Pres.—Lino C. Rocha
Ptnr. & V-P.—Lino Rocha
Shop Mgr.—Juan Loasia
HVAC Mgr.—Marco Colon
SIC—3444; *Sheet metal fabrication & HVAC contracting, including architectural roofing, air conditioning & solar heating services*
Employs—7; Estab.—1975
Distrib.—Regional
Limited Liability Company

### PPI-TIME ZERO, INC.
11 Madison Rd. (07004)
**Phone—(973) 278-6500**
National—(800) 354-7298
Fax—(973) 278-2228
www.ppi-timezero.com
Email—sales@ppi-timezero.com
Chrm., Pres.—Dana Pittman
Ex. V-P., Qual. Control—Mike Shelor

Ex. V-P., Matls.—Walter Carter
Ex. V-P.—Joe Litavis
Dir., Opers.—Art Russo
Dir., Engrg.—Gene Ward
GM—Dwayne Waller
Fin. & Hum. Res. Mgr.—David Skinner
Traf. Mgr.—Larry Jones
Pur. Agt.—Trudy Ganguzza
SIC—3672; 3679; NAICS—334412; *Printed circuit board assemblies, sub-assemblies & system integration for military, aerospace, industrial controls, medical devices & homeland security products*
Employs—150; Estab.—1971
Sales—$450Mil-$500Mil
50,000 sq ft site, Distrib.—National
Privately owned corporation
ISO rating—9001:2008

### PRECISION MACHINED PRODUCTS, LLC
24 Kulick Rd. (07004)
**Phone—(973) 227-9538**
Fax—(973) 227-1233
Email—precisionmachined@verizon.net
Owner, Pres. & CFO—Kevin Blide
SIC—3599; *General machining, TIG welding, CNC lathe & milling job shop, including small-to-medium production runs*
Employs—4; Estab.—1970
Sales—under $500,000
2,100 sq ft site, Distrib.—Regional
Limited Liability Company

### PRESTIGE RUBBER MFG.
11 Spielman Rd. (07004)
**Phone—(973) 227-2505**
Fax—(973) 227-3306
www.prestigerubber.com
Email—prestigerubber@verizon.net
Pres.—Steve Kelley
SIC—3069; 3052; NAICS—326220; *Rubber tubing & expansion joints & specialty hose*
Employs—7; Estab.—1990
Sales—$1Mil-$2.5Mil
12,000 sq ft site, Distrib.—Intl.
Privately owned corporation

### PROFORMA SPECTRUM GRAPHICS
373 Route 46 W., Bldg. D, Ste. 130 (07004)
**Phone—(973) 882-8666**
Fax—(973) 882-9201
www.proforma.com
Pres.—John Vento
Hum. Res. Mgr.—Emma Nelson
SIC—2761; 2396; 2759; NAICS—323116; *Company headquarters & business form & textile screen & commercial printing*
Employs—20; Estab.—1987
Sales—$2.5Mil-$5Mil (est)
Distrib.—Regional
Privately owned corporation

### PROTECH POWDER COATING, INC.
Div. of Protech Chemicals Ltd.
21 Audrey Pl. (07004)
**Phone—(973) 257-0505**
Fax—(973) 257-0114
www.protechpowder.com
Email—sales@protechpowder.com
Cont.—Gilles Crotures
Plt. Mgr.—Louis Laurano
Off. Mgr.—Rvinya Roberts
SIC—3399; *Powder coatings; Brand name—Nuvocoat; PermaSlip; Thermolam; Heliocoat; E-bond; Velvacoat; Sterilcoat AM; Sol-ar; Clonecoat; Nanofoil*
Employs—27; Estab.—1992
50,000 sq ft site, Distrib.—Intl.
Privately owned corporation
ISO rating—9001:2000

Parent co.—Protech Chemicals Ltd.
Phone—(514) 745-0200
See Parent Co. Section for full profile.

### †PSS/WORLD MEDICAL, INC.
Div. of PSS World Medical, Inc.
208 Passaic Ave., Ste. 2 (07004)
**Phone—(973) 775-8600**
Fax—(973) 775-8520
www.pssd.com
Email—info@pssd.com
GM—Jason Bennett
Sales Mgr., Reg.—Blaine Nicholas
Sales Mgr., Reg.—Michael Meiners
Sales Mgr., Reg.—Darrell Justh
SIC—5047; 5122; *Distributor of medical supplies, equipment & pharmaceutical products*
Employs—50; Estab.—2001
Distrib.—Regional
Publicly owned corporation
Parent co.—PSS World Medical, Inc., Jacksonville, FL
Phone—(904) 332-3000
See Parent Co. Section for full profile.

### R & L SHEET METAL CO.
3 Kulick Rd. (07004)
**Phone—(973) 575-8448**
Fax—(973) 575-0993
www.randlsheetmetal.com
Email—rlmetal@verizon.com
Pres., Shop Mgr.—Jerry Grieco
SIC—3444; *Sheet metal fabrication*
Employs—12; Estab.—1950
22,000 sq ft site, Distrib.—Regional
Privately owned corporation

### R L E INDUSTRIES, LLC
35 Kulick Rd. (07004)
**Phone—(973) 276-1444**
National—(888) 895-0233
Fax—(973) 276-1453
www.rleindustries.com
Email—skoenig@rleindustries.com
CEO—Scott Koenig
Administrator—Elizabeth Henry
Pur. Agt.—Don Rozjabek
SIC—3646; NAICS—335122; *Lighting fixtures*
Employs—40; Estab.—1947
Distrib.—Intl.
Limited Liability Company
AKA: Robert Lighting & Energy Industries, LLC

### RACK DESIGN GROUP INC. / BARCODEAMERICA.COM
81 Clinton Rd. (07004)
Mail addr: P.O. Box 506, Madison (07940-0506)
**Phone—(973) 377-8182**
(973) 227-8622
National—(800) 734-4897
Fax—(973) 377-8183
www.barcodeamerica.com
Email—rrack@rdgguys.com
Pres.—Robert Rack
SIC—3577; 5045; 5065; *Manufacturer & distributor of custom machine & 3D vision systems, bar code verifiers, reading, inspection & printing systems, label & inkjet printers, label applicators & labels & ribbons; Brand name—RDGVision; Cab Technologies; Label Vision Systems; Datalogic; Microscan; Cognex; Matrox; Banner; Dalsa; Synrad; Motorola; Honeywell; Zebra; Datamax; Sato; Printronix; Opticon; Cognitive; ITW; Anviz; IIMAK*
Employs—10; Estab.—1993
Sales—$2.5Mil-$5Mil
5,000 sq ft site, Distrib.—Intl.
Privately owned sub-S corp.

## Fairfield—(cont.)

**RECTICO, INC.**
12 Gloria Ln., Unit 1 (07004)
**Phone—(973) 575-0009**
Fax—(973) 575-7117
www.rectico.com
Pres.—Scott Sandler
Off. Mgr.—Donna Bawer
SIC—3679; 2653; 3089; NAICS—322211; Crating, corrugated boxes & contract packaging
Employs—10; Estab.—1935
13,000 sq ft site, Distrib.—Regional
Sole ownership

**REDI-MAIL DIRECT MARKETING**
107 Little Falls Rd. (07004)
**Phone—(973) 808-4500**
Fax—(973) 808-5511
www.redimail.com
Email—sales@redimail.com
GM, BDO Opers.—Jay Menna
Hum. Res. Mgr.—Carol Pasquale
SIC—2759; Digital printing
Employs—100
5,500 sq ft site, Distrib.—Regional
Privately owned corporation

**RENEWABLE BIOSYSTEMS, LLC**
20 Spielman Rd. (07004)
**Phone—(973) 769-0600**
www.rbl.us.com
Email—pbehrle@rbl.us.com
CEO—Peter Behrle
SIC—3569; 3599; Organic oil extraction machinery for industrial waste recycling
Employs—15; Estab.—2008
Distrib.—Intl.
Limited Liability Company

**ROBINSON TECH INTERNATIONAL CORP.**
310 Fairfield Rd. (07004)
**Phone—(973) 287-6458**
Fax—(973) 287-6465
www.rti-abrasive.com
Email—sales@rticorporation.com
Owner—Mark Lin
SIC—3291; Abrasive supplies, including polishing discs, cutting wheels, grinding wheels & wire brushes
Employs—10; Estab.—1992
Distrib.—Intl.
Privately owned corporation

**ROCK-TENN CO.**
15 Garner Rd. (07004)
**Phone—(973) 594-6000**
www.rocktenn.com
Email—info@rocktenn.com
Off. Mgr.—Ashley Shiminsky
SIC—2542; 3543; NAICS—332997; Paperboard & corrugated display prototypes
Employs—40
Distrib.—Intl.
Publicly owned corporation
DBA: RockTenn
Parent co.—Rock-Tenn Co., Norcross, GA
　Phone—(770) 448-2193
　See Parent Co. Section for full profile.

**RUBBER & SILICONE PRODUCTS CO., INC.**
17 Montesano Rd. (07004)
Mail addr: P.O. Box 1215, Caldwell (07007)
**Phone—(973) 227-2300**
Fax—(973) 227-8747
Email—jeffdylla@aol.com
Pres.—Jeffery Dylla
Off. Mgr.—Deborah Dylla
SIC—3061; 2822; NAICS—326291; Molded rubber & urethane rollers & products
Employs—25; Estab.—1955
Distrib.—National
Privately owned corporation

**SAS STRESSTEEL, INC.**
100 New Dutch Ln. (07004)
**Phone—(973) 244-0507**
Fax—(973) 244-0544
www.stressteel.com
Email—sales@stressteel.com
V-P., CFO—Kevin J. Dowling
Sr. Opers. Mgr.—Nicholas J. Mauro, Sr.
Sales Mgr.—Tom Deysher
Supervisor—Lucrecia Valles
SIC—3449; Rebar fabrication
Employs—20; Estab.—2001
Sales—$2.5Mil-$5Mil (est)
Distrib.—Intl.
Privately owned corporation

**SCANDIA PACKAGING MACHINERY CO.**
15 Industrial Rd. (07004)
**Phone—(973) 473-6100**
Fax—(973) 473-7226
www.scandiapack.com
Email—wbb@scandiapack.com
Pres.—Wilhelm B. Bronander III
Ex. V-P.—Cecelia G. Bronander
Pur. Mgr.—Lew D'Allegro
Serv. Mgr.—Charles VanRiper
SIC—3565; NAICS—333993; Packaging machinery for overwrapping, cartoning & case packing
Employs—35; Estab.—1918
31,000 sq ft site, Distrib.—Intl.
Privately owned corporation

**†SCHRATTER FOODS, INC. (H Q)**
333 Fairfield Rd. (07004)
**Phone—(973) 575-3226**
National—(800) 592-4337
Fax—(973) 461-2439
www.ancofinecheese.com
Pres., CEO—Alain J. Voss
SIC—5143; Corporate headquarters; distributor of cheese
Employs—34
Privately owned corporation

**SCREEN PLAY, INC.**
1275 Bloomfield Ave., Ste. 5 (07004)
**Phone—(973) 227-9014**
Fax—(973) 227-8943
Email—screenplay@att.net
Pres.—Stephen Wacker
V-P.—James Hill
SIC—2396; T-shirt screen printing
Employs—4; Estab.—1992
Sales—$500,000-$1Mil
Distrib.—Regional
Privately owned corporation

**SENSOR SCIENTIFIC, INC.**
6 Kingsbridge Rd. (07004)
**Phone—(973) 227-7790**
National—(800) 524-1610
Fax—(973) 227-8063
www.sensorsci.com
Email—sales@sensorsci.com
Pres.—G. Robert Brinley
Sales Mgr.—Alena Svab
SIC—3823; NAICS—334513; Thermistors, RTD's & custom sensor assemblies for HVAC, medical, automotive, food service, data logger & appliance applications
Employs—22; Estab.—1983
15,000 sq ft site, Distrib.—Intl.
Privately owned corporation

**SIGN-A-RAMA**
400 Fairfield Rd., Ste. 5 (07004)
**Phone—(973) 227-6363**
Fax—(973) 227-5359
www.signarama-fairfield.com
Email—eric@signarama-fairfield.com
Owner & Mng. Member—Eric Bleezarde
Hum. Res. & IT Mgr.—Peter Smith

SIC—3993; 2759; NAICS—323100; Interior & exterior architectural signs, vehicle graphics & digital printing
Employs—7; Estab.—1995
Sales—under $500,000
1,500 sq ft site, Distrib.—National
Limited Liability Company

**SKYLINE STEEL FABRICATORS**
15 Just Rd. (07004)
**Phone—(973) 882-0234**
Fax—(973) 882-4922
www.skylinesteelllc.com
Email—sales@skylinesteelllc.com
Pres.—Mark Malick
V-P.—Bruce Thompson
Off. Mgr.—Steve Reynolds
SIC—3441; NAICS—332312; Structural steel fabrication
Employs—17; Estab.—2000
Sales—$2.6Mil-$5Mil
Distrib.—Regional
Privately owned corporation

**SOFRADIR EC, INC.**
373 U.S. Highway 46, Ste. E (07004-2442)
**Phone—(973) 882-0211**
Fax—(973) 882-0997
www.sofradir-ec.com
Email—info@sofradir-ec.com
Pres.—Frank Vallese
Mktg. Mgr.—Brooke Herbst
SIC—3861; 3827; NAICS—333314; Uncooled & cooled infrared & thermography cameras, night vision equipment & detectors; Brand name—HotShot; HotShot HD; AstroScope
Employs—42; Estab.—1969
10,000 sq ft site, Distrib.—Intl.
Privately owned corporation
ISO rating—9001:2000

**SOLBERN**
8 Kulick Rd. (07004)
**Phone—(973) 227-3030**
Fax—(973) 227-3069
www.solbern.com
Email—sales@solbern.com
Pres.—Tom Berger
V-P., Sales & Mktg., Intl.—Jorge Espino
Dir., Cust. Serv.—George Burrows
R & D Mgr.—John Walz
Fin. Mgr.—John Sokolowski
Cust. Serv. Rep.—Harry Pikemen
SIC—3565; NAICS—333993; Food processing equipment
Employs—35; Estab.—1950
Sales—$1Mil-$5Mil
24,000 sq ft site, Distrib.—Intl.
Privately owned corporation

**SPARKS BELTING CO.**
Div. of Sparks Belting Co., Inc.
5 Spielman Rd. (07004)
**Phone—(973) 227-4100**
National—(800) 426-1830
Fax—(973) 227-7369
www.sparksbelting.com
Email—sbcinfo@sparksbelting.com
Region Mgr.—David Engelhard
Opers. Mgr.—Rick Nash
Cust. Serv. Rep.—Chris Bryant
Cust. Serv. Rep.—Johnny Sample
SIC—3535; NAICS—333922; Industrial conveyor belting
Employs—18; Estab.—1945
Sales—$2.5Mil-$5Mil
20,000 sq ft site, Distrib.—Intl.
Privately owned corporation
Parent co.—Sparks Belting Co., Inc., Grand Rapids, MI
　Phone—(616) 949-2750
　See Parent Co. Section for full profile.

**STANDARD PRINTING & MAIL SERVICE**
30-A Plymouth St., P.O. Box 11021 (07004)
**Phone—(973) 790-3333**
National—(888) 836-4693
Fax—(973) 790-0315
www.standprint.com
Email—mail@standprint.com
Pres., GM—Kevin Walsh
Prodn. Mgr.—Tony Cordasco
SIC—2752; 2759; 2791; NAICS—323122; Offset & direct mail printing, electronic prepress & mail service
Employs—12; Estab.—1986
8,000 sq ft site, Distrib.—Regional

**SUN DIAL & PANEL CORP.**
2 Daniel Rd. (07004)
**Phone—(973) 226-4334**
Fax—(973) 808-6759
www.sundialandpanel.com
Email—info@sundialandpanel.com
Chrm., Pres. & CEO—Roger J. Lokker
Sales Mgr.—Julie Wilder
Prodn. & Qual. Control Mgr.—Jimmy Alinsug
Engr.—Liam Rafferty
SIC—3728; Aircraft components, including edgelit panels, keyboards & bezels
Employs—15; Estab.—1943
Sales—$1Mil-$5Mil
10,000 sq ft site, Distrib.—Intl.
Privately owned corporation

**SWITCH VISION**
103 Fairfield Rd. (07004)
**Phone—(973) 582-2304**
National—(800) 444-5010
www.switchvision.com
Email—webreply@libertysportonline.com
Owner—Anthony Dichiara
SIC—3851; Magnetic interchangeable optical lenses; Brand name—Magnetic Interchange Lens System™
Employs—60
Sales—$5Mil-$10Mil (est)
Distrib.—Intl.
Privately owned corporation

**TALLY DISPLAY CORP.**
19 Gardner Rd., Ste. A (07004)
**Phone—(973) 777-7760**
　　　　　(800) 758-2559
Fax—(973) 777-6220
www.tallydisplay.com
Email—info@tallydisplay.com
Pres.—Steve Rose
Sales Mgr.—Sheldon Hoffman
SIC—3993; LED, full-color & moving message signs, video, indoor & outdoor message centers, annunciators & modular components, including installation services; Brand name—DigiText; Lux Lite; Mini DigiText; TDC
Employs—5; Estab.—1991
Sales—over $2Mil
5,000 sq ft site, Distrib.—Intl.
Privately owned corporation

**NEW ENTRY**

**TECHNOGYM U. S. A. CORP.**
700 U.S. Highway 46 E. (07004)
**Phone—(206) 623-1488**
National—(800) 804-0952
Fax—(206) 623-1898
www.technogym.com
Email—info@technogym.com
CEO—Federico Foli
Pres.—Nerio Alessandri
Sales Mgr.—Ivo Grossi
Opers. Mgr.—Kim Mejer
Mktg. Mgr.—Kim Donohue
IT Mgr.—Luan Vuong
Acctg. & Hum. Res. Mgr.—Ronald Schaeffer

**GEOGRAPHICAL**

## Fairfield—(cont.)

SIC—3949; NAICS—339920;
*Commercial fitness equipment*
Employs—40; Estab.—1997
Sales—$6Mil-$10Mil
Distrib.—Intl.
Privately owned corporation

### TEVA PHARMACEUTICALS U.S.A., INC.

Div. of Teva Pharmaceuticals USA, Inc.
8-10 Gloria Ln. *(07004)*
**Phone—(973) 575-2775**
Fax—(973) 575-6089
www.tevapharmusa.com
Email—tevahr@tevapharm.com
Cont.—Ron Pisano
SIC—2834; NAICS—325412;
*Pharmaceuticals*
Employs—75; Estab.—1964
55,000 sq ft site, Distrib.—Intl.
Publicly owned corporation
Parent co.—Teva Pharmaceuticals USA, Inc., North Wales, PA
Phone—(215) 591-3000
See Parent Co. Section for full profile.

### THE FIREPLACE PLACE

264 U.S. Highway 46 E. (07004)
**Phone—(973) 227-8540**
National—(888) 377-5223
Fax—(973) 808-8553
www.thefireplaceplace.com
Email—joelfireplace@aol.com
Owner & GM—Joel Dolberg
SIC—3433; NAICS—333414;
*Wood, gas, pellet, electric & coal fireplaces, stoves & inserts*
Employs—15; Estab.—1976
7,600 sq ft site, Distrib.—Regional
Privately owned corporation

### THIN STONE SYSTEMS, LLC

23 Commerce Rd., Ste. O (07004)
**Phone—(973) 882-7377**
Fax—(973) 882-7726
www.thinstonesystems.com
Email—tssi@thinstonesystems.com
CEO—Anthony Tauriello
Pres.—Francisco Tauriello
Cont.—Dina Kaul
SIC—3281; NAICS—327991;
*Stone cutting*
Employs—15; Estab.—1988
Sales—$1Mil-$2.5Mil
Distrib.—Local
Privately owned corporation

### TILTON RACK & BASKET CORP.

66 Passaic Ave. (07004)
**Phone—(973) 226-6010**
Fax—(973) 227-4155
www.tiltonrackandbasket.com
Email—jtilton@tiltonrackandbasket.com
Pres.—Joseph Tilton
SIC—3496; *Industrial plating racks, fixtures & baskets*
Employs—25; Estab.—1974
20,000 sq ft site, Distrib.—Local
Privately owned corporation

### TIMECRUISER COMPUTING CORP.

9 Law Dr., Ste. 2 (07004)
**Phone—(973) 244-7856**
National—(877) 450-9482
Fax—(973) 244-7859
www.campuscruiser.com
Email—sales@campuscruiser.com
Pres.—Anthony Ma
Off. Mgr.—Lily Hsu
SIC—7372; *Prepackaged communications software development for colleges & universities*
Employs—25; Estab.—2000
Sales—$6Mil-$10Mil
Distrib.—National
Privately owned corporation

### TITANIUM FABRICATION CORP.

110 Lehigh Dr. (07004)
**Phone—(973) 227-5300**
      (973) 808-4968
Fax—(973) 227-2141
www.tifab.com
Email—bwilley@tifab.com
Pres., CEO—Brent Willey
V-P., Sales—Dan Williams
Corp. Cont.—Daniel Lefebvre
GM, Metal Svcs.—Bill Brownlee
Opers. Mgr.—Brian Brown
SIC—3463; 3364; 5051; NAICS—332112; *Custom titanium & reactive metal design & fabrication & distributor of metal*
Employs—45; Estab.—1972
120,000 sq ft site, Distrib.—Intl.
Privately owned corporation

### TORPAC, INC.

333 U.S. Highway 46 (07004)
**Phone—(973) 244-1125**
Fax—(973) 244-1365
www.torpac.com
Email—info@torpac.com
Pres.—Raj Tahil
Cust. Serv. Mgr.—Cynthia Caraballo
SIC—2834; 3565; NAICS—325412; *Custom & large-size two-piece empty soluble pharmaceutical capsules & capsule filling machinery*
Employs—10; Estab.—1989
Distrib.—Intl.
Privately owned corporation

### †TOTAL MACHINE SOLUTIONS, INC.

16 Spielman Rd. (07004)
**Phone—(973) 244-0017**
Fax—(973) 244-9118
www.totalmachinesolutions.com
Email—sales@totalmachinesolutions.com
Whse. Mgr.—Joe Vasquez
Sales Rep.—Tim Desmond
SIC—5063; 5084; *Distributor of electrical & mechanical power transmission equipment & supplies, including motors, bearings, variable speed drives & conveyor components*
Employs—7; Estab.—1996
Distrib.—National
Privately owned corporation
AKA: TMS
Parent co.—Total Machine Solutions, Inc., Plainview, NY
Phone—(516) 942-5125
See Parent Co. Section for full profile.

### TRIM & TASSELS, LLC (H Q)

204 Passaic Ave., Unit 3 (07004)
**Phone—(973) 808-1566**
National—(800) 477-3459
Fax—(973) 808-9196
www.trimandtassels.com
Owner—Pradeep Jalan
V-P.—Rashmi Jalan
SIC—2389; *Company headquarters; graduation caps & gowns & bookmark, program & home furnishing tassels, fringes & cordings (mfg. done overseas)*
Employs—3; Estab.—1998
Sales—$1Mil-$2.5Mil
Distrib.—Intl.
Limited Liability Company
AKA: Graduation Outlet

### ULTIMATE TRADING CORP.

4 Just Rd. (07004)
**Phone—(973) 228-7700**
Fax—(973) 228-7100
www.ultimatetrading.com
Email—customerservice@ultimatetrading.com
Pres.—Todd Knichel
Acct. Mgr.—Doug Roberts
SIC—3911; 5094; NAICS—339911; *Manufacturer & distributor of fine & costume jewelry*
Employs—60; Estab.—1982
21,000 sq ft site, Distrib.—Intl.
Privately owned sub-S corp.
AKA: Ultimate Trading

### UNIFOIL CORP.

12 Vanil Rd. E. (07004)
**Phone—(973) 244-9900**
Fax—(973) 244-5555
www.unifoil.com
Email—unifoil@unifoil.com
Sales Rep.—Brian Leverock
SIC—2657; NAICS—322212; *Metallized & holographic film laminated paperboard boxes for packaging*
Employs—3; Estab.—1978
100,000 sq ft site, Distrib.—Intl.
Privately owned sub-S corp.
Parent co.—Unifoil Corp., Fairfield, NJ
Phone—(973) 244-9900
See Parent Co. Section for full profile.

### UNIFOIL CORP.

12 Daniel Rd., Ste. 101 (07004-2536)
**Phone—(973) 244-9900**
Fax—(973) 244-5555
www.unifoil.com
Email—unifoil@unifoil.com
Pres., CEO—Joseph Funicelli
V-P., CFO—William Mulrooney
R & D Mgr.—Bob Gallino
SIC—3497; 3089; *Corporate headquarters & aluminum foil laminating, metallizing, coating & decorated plastics; Brand name—UniLustre; UltraLustre*
Employs—105; Estab.—1971
Sales—$50Mil
120,000 sq ft site, Distrib.—Intl.
Privately owned sub-S corp.
ISO rating—9000

### UNITED SPORT APPAREL

20 Gloria Ln. (07004)
**Phone—(973) 575-7840**
National—(800) 736-7342
Fax—(973) 882-6659
www.unitedsportapparel.com
Email—sales@unitedsportapparel.com
V-P.—Karen Morgan
Hum. Res. Mgr.—Christine Farruggia
Cust. Serv. Rep.—Tracy Fort
SIC—2389; *Athletic jackets*
Employs—45; Estab.—1933
25,000 sq ft site, Distrib.—National
Privately owned corporation

### V & L MACHINE TOOL CO., INC.

30 Sherwood Ln., Ste. 11 (07004)
**Phone—(973) 808-5858**
Fax—(973) 808-5848
www.vandlmachinetool.com
Email—vandlmachinetool@verizon.net
Pres.—Michael Sollitto
V-P.—George Vecchiet
Secy-Treas.—James Kirch
Off. Mgr.—Dolores Sollitto
SIC—3599; 3545; *Precision machine parts*
Employs—5; Estab.—1987
7,700 sq ft site, Distrib.—Local
Privately owned corporation

### V-COM

Div. of VCOM International Multi-Media Corp.
80 Little Falls Rd. (07004)
**Phone—(201) 229-9800**
National—(800) 526-0242
Fax—(201) 814-0510
www.comprehensivecable.com
Email—sales@comprehensivecable.com
Pres.—Scott Schaefer
Sales Mgr.—Martin Fensterstock
Hum. Res. & IT Mgr.—Steven Trabalka
Prod. Mgr.—Gary Winaker
SIC—3679; 3357; *Cable assemblies, connectors, switchers, splitters & converters*
Employs—25; Estab.—1980
Distrib.—National
Privately owned corporation
Parent co.—VCOM International Multi-Media Corp., Fairfield, NJ
Phone—(201) 229-4270
See Parent Co. Section for full profile.

### VCOM INTERNATIONAL MULTI-MEDIA CORP.

80 Little Falls Rd. (07004)
**Phone—(201) 229-4270**
Fax—(201) 440-6269
www.vcomimc.net
Email—smarino@vcom-mm.net
Pres., CEO—Sheldon Goldstein
Sales Mgr., Natl.—Stephen P. Marino
Cred. Mgr.—Eileen Graper
Pur. Agt.—Ronnie Turner
Pur. Agt.—Charlie Mena
SIC—3861; 3651; 5064; 5063; NAICS—334310; *Corporate headquarters & manufacturer of overhead projectors, AV furniture projection screens & lamps, lighting fixtures & lamp sockets & wholesaler of multimedia components, comprehensive cables & switches*
Employs—22
Sales—$5Mil-$10Mil (est)
Distrib.—Intl.
Privately owned corporation

### VICINITY MEDIA GROUP

165 Passaic Ave., Ste. 107 (07004)
**Phone—(973) 276-1688**
Fax—(973) 276-1466
Email—cblack@vicinitymediagroup.com
Founder & CEO—David Black
Pres., COO—Cathleen Black
Art Dir.—Michael Reidy
SIC—2721; *Magazine publishing; Brand name—Suburban Essex Magazine; Vicinity Magazine; North Jersey Woman Magazine*
Employs—8; Estab.—1994
Distrib.—Local
Privately owned corporation

### VIN-LAW MACHINE & TOOL CO., INC.

3 Kulick Rd., P.O. Box 10950 (07004)
**Phone—(973) 227-5100**
Fax—(973) 227-5177
www.vin-law.com
Email—vinlaw316@verizon.net
Pres.—Vincent Cirelli, Sr.
Shop Mgr.—Vincent Cirelli, Jr.
SIC—3599; *General machining job shop*
Employs—5; Estab.—1981
Sales—under $500,000
Distrib.—Local
Sole ownership

### †W. W. GRAINGER, INC.

277 Route 46 W. (07004)
**Phone—(973) 227-7220**
National—(800) 275-4994
Fax—(973) 227-8879
www.grainger.com
Email—info@grainger.com
Br. Mgr.—Damian Czirjak
SIC—5084; 5085; *Wholesaler of industrial equipment & supplies*
Employs—10; Estab.—2007
Distrib.—Intl.
Privately owned corporation
Parent co.—W. W. Grainger, Inc., Lake Forest, IL
Phone—(847) 535-1000
See Parent Co. Section for full profile.

## Fairfield—(cont.)

**WAVELINE, INC.**
160 Passaic Ave. (07004)
Mail addr: P.O. Box 718, West
Caldwell (07006)
**Phone—(973) 808-9113**
Fax—(973) 808-1524
www.wavelineinc.com
Email—sales@wavelineinc.com
Pres.—James McGregor
GM—Donato Morsillo
Hum. Res. Mgr.—Norman Schneitt
SIC—3679; *Waveguide
components & test equipment,
solid-state pin diode switches,
attenuators & phase shifters*
Employs—30; Estab.—1946
Sales—$1Mil-$2.5Mil
22,000 sq ft site, Distrib.—Local
Privately owned corporation

**WEST ESSEX GRAPHICS, INC.**
305 Fairfield Ave. (07004)
**Phone—(973) 227-2400**
Fax—(973) 227-2588
www.westessexgraphics.com
Email—sales@
westessexgraphics.com
Co-Pres.—Don Alldian
Co-Pres.—Tom Guth
Pur. Mgr.—Arlene Lombardi
IT Mgr.—Ron Rex
SIC—3555; NAICS—333293;
*Offset spot coating plates &
digital proofing, electronic
prepress & large-format digital
flexographic printing plates*
Employs—35; Estab.—1949
Sales—$5Mil-$10Mil
Distrib.—National
Privately owned corporation

**WINTER SCALE & EQUIPMENT**
20-A Kulick Rd. (07004-3308)
**Phone—(888) 808-3611**
Fax—(973) 808-3344
www.winterscale.com
Email—sales@winterscale.com
Pres.—John Winter
Off. Mgr.—Stephanie Preziosi
Serv. Mgr.—Rich Ianiello
Admn. Serv. Mgr.—Erick Gill
SIC—3556; NAICS—333294;
*Food processing equipment;
Brand name—Berkel; Biro;
Bizerba; CAS; Heat Seal;
Hobart; Hollymatic; Ishida;
Mettler Toledo; Ohaus;
Pattomatic; Promolux; Rice Lake;
Rollstock; Talsa; TEC*
Employs—25; Estab.—1986
Sales—$5Mil
Distrib.—Regional
Privately owned corporation

**WM. H. BREWSTER JR., INC.**
16 Kulick Rd. *(07004)*
**Phone—(973) 227-1050**
Fax—(973) 227-2363
www.brewster-washers.com
Email—info.mn@brewster-
washers.com
Pres.—Salvatore T. Freda, Jr.
Opers. Mgr.—Katherine Bayer
SIC—3452; NAICS—332722;
*Precision flat washers, shims,
stampings & discs from stainless
steel, brass, copper, phosphor,
bronze, nickel, nylon plastic &
PTFE*
Employs—8; Estab.—1919
Sales—$1Mil-$5Mil
10,000 sq ft site, Distrib.—Intl.
Privately owned sub-S corp.
ISO rating—9001:2008
AKA: Brewster Washers

**WRAPADE PACKAGING SYSTEMS,
LLC**
27 Law Dr., Ste. B (07004)
**Phone—(973) 773-6150**
National—(888) 815-8564

Fax—(973) 773-6010
www.wrapade.com
Email—sales@wrapade.com
Pres.—Bill Beattie
Secy-Treas.—Laurene Beattie
Opers. Mgr.—Greg Beattie
Off. Mgr.—Grace Pastore
Engr. Mgr.—Hugh Mallalieu
SIC—3565; NAICS—333993;
*Vertical & horizontal four side
seal pouch packaging machines
for the pharmaceutical, medical
device & nutraceutical
industries; Brand name—
Wrapade*
Employs—16; Estab.—1932
Sales—$1Mil-$5Mil
15,000 sq ft site, Distrib.—Intl.
Limited Liability Company

**YELLOW STONE DISTRIBUTING CO.**
50 Kulick Rd. (07004)
**Phone—(973) 808-8188**
Pres.—Yimin Shiuey
Cont.—Brad Mack
SIC—2672; *Pressure-sensitive
labels*
Employs—15
Sales—$2.5Mil-$5Mil (est)
Distrib.—Local
Privately owned corporation
Also see: Industrial Labeling
Systems, Inc., same loc.

## Fairton
(Cumberland—S.W.)

**FAIRFIELD PALLET CO., INC.**
282 Rockville Rd., P.O. Box 361
(08320)
**Phone—(856) 455-7999**
Fax—(856) 451-9059
www.fairfieldpallet.com
Email—pallets@fairfieldpallet.com
Pres.—Michael Smith
V-P., Sales—Dan Smith
V-P., Opers.—Herb Smith, Jr.
Corp. Secy.—C. Riley
Treas., Hum. Res.—Frederica
Smith
SIC—2875; 5093; NAICS—
325314; *Mulch & wholesaler of
rebuilt wooden pallets*
Employs—50; Estab.—1969
Sales—$6Mil-$10Mil
Distrib.—National
Privately owned corporation

**WOODCHUCKER, INC., THE**
42 Bridgeton-Fairton Rd., P.O. Box
380 *(08320)*
**Phone—(856) 575-0200**
Fax—(856) 575-0222
www.the-woodchucker.com
Email—omri@the-
woodchucker.com
Pres.—Karen Love Millul
V-P.—Omri Millul
SIC—2431; 2499; NAICS—
321900; *Commercial &
residential woodworking,
including wooden cabinets*
Employs—4; Estab.—1990
Sales—under $500,000
Distrib.—Regional
Privately owned corporation

## Fairview
(Bergen—N.E.)

**ALICE CORP.**
815 Fairview Ave., Unit 9-A
(07022)
**Phone—(201) 943-5877**
Fax—(201) 943-6594
www.alicecorporation.net
Email—alicecorporation@
yahoo.com
Pres.—Yoshi Yuyama
Manager—Yasu Tanaka

SIC—2024; *Japanese mochi ice
cream*
Employs—10; Estab.—1988
15,000 sq ft site, Distrib.—Local
Privately owned corporation

**AQL DECORATING CO., INC.**
215 Bergen Blvd. (07022)
**Phone—(201) 941-1610**
Fax—(201) 941-6450
www.aqldecorating.com
Email—info@aqldecorating.com
Pres.—Jim Sheehan
Prodn. Mgr.—George Wensenthal
SIC—2759; NAICS—323100;
*Plastic bottle screen printing*
Employs—85; Estab.—2003
Sales—$1Mil-$2.5Mil
Distrib.—National
Privately owned corporation

**ARTCRAFT CABINETS
WOODWORKING**
165 Broad Ave. (07022)
**Phone—(201) 943-6090**
Fax—(201) 943-3849
Owner—Hans Kraenclein
SIC—2431; NAICS—321900;
*Architectural woodwork*
Employs—2; Estab.—1962
Sales—under $500,000
Distrib.—Local
Sole ownership

**BERNHARD-LINK THEATRICAL, LLC**
815 Fairview Ave., Ste. 11 (07022-
1571)
**Phone—(201) 943-4190**
Fax—(201) 943-4191
www.bltprod.com
Email—blt@bltprod.com
Bus. Mgr.—Ruthie Burman
SIC—3999; 3646; 3648; *Custom
theatrical staging, scenery &
lighting for the special events
industry, including rentals*
Employs—18; Estab.—1976
Sales—$5Mil-$6Mil
Distrib.—National
Limited Liability Company

**CAMATRON SEWING MACHINE, INC.**
42 Bergenwood Rd., Ste. A
*(07022)*
**Phone—(201) 941-5116**
Fax—(201) 941-4566
www.camatron.com
Email—robertross@camatron.com
Pres.—Robert Ross
SIC—3559; 5084; NAICS—
333298; *Manufacturer &
distributor of specialized
industrial sewing machines &
parts for the apparel & non-
apparel markets; Brand name—
Juki; Brother; SINGER*
Employs—7; Estab.—1970
4,000 sq ft site, Distrib.—Intl.
Privately owned sub-S corp.

**CLIFFSIDE BODY CORP.**
130 Broad Ave., P.O. Box 206
(07022)
**Phone—(201) 945-3970**
Fax—(201) 945-7534
www.cliffsidebody.com
Email—sales@cliffsidebody.com
Pres.—Edward Greenwald
V-P.—Rob Greenwald
Treas.—Warren Greenwald
Sales Mgr.—John Burns
Off. Mgr.—Olga Greenwald
Bookkeeper—Dawn Glover
SIC—3713; NAICS—336211;
*Truck bodies & equipment, snow
plows, salt spreaders & liftgates*
Employs—30; Estab.—1919
30,000 sq ft site, Distrib.—
Regional
Privately owned corporation

**†COOPER ELECTRIC SUPPLY CO.**
217 Broad Ave. (07022)
**Phone—(201) 945-5900**
Fax—(201) 945-9126
www.cooper-electric.com
Email—brian.bertsch@cooper-
electric.com
Br. Mgr.—Brian Bertsch
SIC—5063; *Distributor of electrical
equipment & supplies, including
wire, cable & switches*
Employs—10; Estab.—2006
Distrib.—Local
Privately owned corporation
Parent co.—Cooper Electric
Supply Co., Monroe, NJ
Phone—(732) 747-2233
See Parent Co. Section for full profile.

**CUTLER BROS. BOX & LUMBER CO.**
711 W. Prospect Ave., P.O. Box
217 (07022)
**Phone—(201) 943-2535**
Fax—(201) 943-8532
www.cutlerpallets.com
Email—cutler711@aol.com
Owner—Gregory Cutler
SIC—2421; 2448; NAICS—
321920; *Pallets, skids, boxes &
lumber*
Employs—30; Estab.—1875
Sales—$11Mil-$25Mil
20,000 sq ft site, Distrib.—
Regional
Privately owned corporation

**DEARBROOK FABRICS, INC.**
430 Walker St., P.O. Box 338
(07022)
**Phone—(201) 945-4141**
Fax—(201) 945-8446
Pres.—Edward Parseghian
Prodn. Mgr.—Luis Pinas
Off. Mgr.—Patricia Alvarez
SIC—2397; NAICS—313222;
*Schiffli machine embroidery*
Employs—10; Estab.—1969
Sales—$500,000-$1Mil (est)
Distrib.—Intl.
Privately owned corporation

**EURO MECHANICAL, INC.**
16 Industrial Ave. (07022)
**Phone—(201) 313-8050**
Fax—(201) 313-8051
Email—euromechanical4@aol.com
Pres.—Ante Pestic
Admn. Mgr.—Monika Krol
SIC—3494; NAICS—332900;
*Rebuilt steam pipe fittings*
Employs—15; Estab.—1998
Sales—$1Mil-$2.5Mil (est)
Distrib.—Regional
Privately owned corporation

**FARAJ, INC.**
422 Cliff St. (07022)
**Phone—(201) 313-4480**
Fax—(201) 313-4485
www.usabeading.com
Email—farajinc@aol.com
Pres.—Zackary Faraj
Prodn. Mgr.—Moe Samman
Hum. Res. Mgr.—Raida Samman
SIC—2395; 2759; *100% domestic
mass-produced fabric
decorations, including patented
beading methods, embroidery,
laser cutting, rhinestones,
transfers & digital printing*
Employs—80; Estab.—1986
Sales—$6Mil
15,000 sq ft site, Distrib.—National
Privately owned corporation
AKA: USA Beading

**†FERGUSON ENTERPRISES, INC.**
369 Anderson Ave. (07022)
**Phone—(201) 945-3080**
Fax—(201) 945-8432
www.ferguson.com
Email—luis.rosa@ferguson.com
Br. Mgr.—Richard Aquimo

GEOGRAPHICAL

## Fairview—(cont.)

SIC—5074; *Distributor of HVAC & plumbing supplies, including pipes, fixtures, valves & fittings, kitchen & bath gallary & lighting appliances*
Employs—4; Estab.—1953
Distrib.—National
Publicly owned corporation
Parent co.—Ferguson Enterprises, Inc., Newport News, VA
Phone—(757) 874-7795
See Parent Co. Section for full profile.

**KRAUSE'S HOMEMADE CANDY CO.**

50 Bergen Blvd. *(07022)*
**Phone—(201) 943-4790**
Fax—(201) 943-4790
www.krausescandies.com
Email—krausescandies@gmail.com
Ptnr.—Nicole Cinquegrana
Ptnr.—William Cinquegrana
SIC—2066; NAICS—311300; *Chocolate candy*
Employs—15; Estab.—1950
Sales—$1Mil-$2.5Mil
Distrib.—Local
Sole ownership

**MARKO ENGRAVING & ART CORP.**

439 Fairview Ave. (07022)
**Phone—(201) 945-6555**
Fax—(201) 945-6546
Pres.—Marko Melnitchenko
Treas.—Luba Melnitchenko
SIC—3555; NAICS—333293; *Photo polymer printing plates*
Employs—20; Estab.—1972
12,000 sq ft site, Distrib.—Local
Privately owned corporation

**†NIKKO CERAMICS, INC.**

815 Fairview Ave., Ste. 9 (07022)
**Phone—(201) 840-5200**
Fax—(201) 840-5201
www.nikkoceramics.com
Email—custserv@nikkoceramics.com
Pres.—Kenji Anzai
V-P.—Kaz Suzuki
Acct. & Cred. Mgr.—Chen Cui
Acct. Exec.—Miyoko Jacobi
SIC—5023; *Distributor of chinaware*
Employs—11; Estab.—1968
Sales—$5Mil-$10Mil
60,000 sq ft site, Distrib.—National
Privately owned corporation

NEW ENTRY
**NORTH HUDSON PRESS**

429 Hancock Pl. (07022)
**Phone—(201) 941-2520**
Email—vpetrigliano@verizon.net
Owner—Vincent Petrigliano
SIC—2759; *Commercial printing*
Employs—3; Estab.—1968
Sales—under $500,000 (est)
12,000 sq ft site, Distrib.—Regional
Sole ownership

**POVINELLI & SONS, INC., M.**

318 9th St. (07022)
**Phone—(201) 943-0039**
Fax—(201) 943-0239
www.mpsnj.com
Email—matt@mpsnj.com
Pres.—Matthew Povinelli
SIC—3599; NAICS—333515; *Sharpening of professional cutlery for chefs, butchers, fish markets, delicatessens, sportsmen & consumers*
Employs—6; Estab.—1903
Sales—$500,000-$1Mil
Distrib.—National
Privately owned corporation

**PRIME FUR & LEATHER, INC.**

2931 Industrial Ave. (07022)
**Phone—(201) 941-9600**
Fax—(201) 941-7888
Email—primefur@yahoo.com
Pres.—Brian S. Han
SIC—2386; NAICS—315200; *Men's & women's leather jackets*
Employs—10
Sales—under $500,000
Distrib.—Local
Privately owned corporation

**PRINTING CRAFTSMAN, INC.**

130 Bergen Blvd. (07022)
**Phone—(201) 943-0276**
Fax—(201) 943-0278
Email—printer130@aol.com
Pres.—Kenneth Stueben
Prodn. Mgr.—John Ryan
Pressman—Jack Toppler
SIC—2759; 2752; 2791; NAICS—323122; *Commercial, offset, digital, & lithographic printing & electronic prepress*
Employs—10; Estab.—1942
Sales—$1Mil-$2.5Mil
Distrib.—Local

**PURCELL PRINTING CO., ROBERT**

244 Kamena St. (07022-1705)
**Phone—(201) 941-0375**
Pres.—Robert Purcell, Sr.
V-P.—Robert Purcell, Jr.
SIC—2752; 2759; NAICS—323100; *Offset & commercial printing*
Employs—3; Estab.—1946
Sales—under $500,000 (est)
Distrib.—Regional
Sole ownership

**QRS BEAUTY CORP.**

11 Commercial Ave. *(07022)*
**Phone—(201) 313-0305**
Fax—(201) 313-0316
www.qrsbeauty.com
Email—info@qrsbeauty.com
Pres.—Jang 'John' Park
SIC—2844; *Nail polishes, nail lacquers, color sets & nail art pens & brushes*
Employs—4; Estab.—2006
Sales—$1Mil-$2.5Mil (est)
Distrib.—National
Privately owned sub-S corp.

**SARACINO MONUMENTS, LLC, FRANK**

359 Bergen Blvd. (07022)
**Phone—(201) 945-1266**
Fax—(973) 702-1602
Email—saracino@nji.com
Ptnr.—Frank Saracino
Ptnr.—Tom Saracino
SIC—3281; 3499; NAICS—327991; *Granite upright monuments & markers, bronze plaques, marble statuary, candle holders, bronze, granite & marble vases & pet memorials & signs, including cemetery & mausoleum lettering & designing*
Employs—2; Estab.—1930
8,000 sq ft site, Distrib.—Regional
Limited Liability Company

**SCHREYER EMBROIDERY CO., INC.**

50 Industrial Ave. (07022)
**Phone—(201) 943-6221**
Fax—(201) 943-0827
Pres.—Christine Martin
GM—Carlos Arcila
SIC—2395; *Embroidery*
Employs—4; Estab.—1969
Sales—under $500,000
Distrib.—National
Privately owned corporation

**TONE EMBROIDERY, INC.**

333 Bergen Blvd. (07022)
**Phone—(201) 943-1082**
National—(800) 742-7506
Fax—(201) 943-7163
www.touchoflace.com
Pres.—Haim Sasson
Off. Mgr.—Gail Pang
SIC—2395; *Custom embroidery*
Employs—15; Estab.—1985
Sales—$500,000-$1Mil
Distrib.—National
Privately owned corporation

**WEISS & SONS, INC., I.**

815 Fairview Ave., Ste. 10 (07022)
**Phone—(201) 402-6500**
National—(888) 325-7192
Fax—(201) 402-6530
www.iweiss.com
Email—info@iweiss.com
Pres.—David Rosenberg
V-P.—Jennifer Tankleff
Off. Mgr.—Angie Micco
SIC—2391; 3999; NAICS—314121; *Theatrical draperies & rigging equipment*
Employs—33; Estab.—1900
13,000 sq ft site, Distrib.—Intl.
Privately owned corporation

---
## Fanwood
(Union—N.E.)

**GORSKY, INC., E.**

33 South Ave. (07023)
**Phone—(908) 322-8580**
Fax—(908) 322-5016
Pres. & Manager—Bill Gorsky
SIC—3599; *Machine parts fabrication*
Employs—5; Estab.—1970
Sales—under $500,000
Distrib.—National
Privately owned corporation

**†INNOVATIVE MARKING SYSTEMS, INC.**

105 Forest Rd. (07023)
**Phone—(908) 322-2900**
Fax—(908) 322-5995
www.imsmarking.com
Email—mario@imsmarking.com
Owner—Harry Fattenyatz
Pres.—Mario Passione
SIC—5045; *Distributor of marking, labeling & bar code dating systems; Brand name—Data Max; Printronix; Toshiba; Zebra; Sato; Motorola/Symbol Technologies; Datamax; Militags EPC; Leibinger; Paragon Labeling; OpenDate; AT Information Products; PackLeader Labelers; RFID*
Employs—5; Estab.—1995
Sales—$1Mil-$5Mil
Distrib.—Intl.
Privately owned corporation

**M & R DIAMOND QUILTING CO., INC.**

35 South Ave. (07023)
**Phone—(908) 322-4178**
    (877) 628-8322
Fax—(908) 322-4856
www.shovlinmattress.com
Email—mattressfac@aol.com
Pres., Fin. & MIS Mgr.—Ron Shovlin
Sales Mgr.—Stephen Winard
Off. Mgr.—Kara Shovlin
SIC—2515; *Mattresses & box springs*
Employs—10; Estab.—1979
Sales—over $1Mil
8,500 sq ft site, Distrib.—Regional
Privately owned sub-S corp.
DBA: Shovlin Mattress Factory

**†METRO AMERICA SALES, INC.**

137 South Ave. (07023)
**Phone—(908) 490-0001**
www.metroamericasalesinc.com
Email—metroamer@aol.com
Pres.—Harold Nevins
Fin. Mgr.—Joan Stumpf
SIC—5049; 5094; *Wholesaler of jewelry machinery, tools, sterling silver chains, findings & components*
Employs—3; Estab.—1995
Sales—$500,000
4,200 sq ft site, Distrib.—Intl.
Privately owned sub-S corp.
AKA: Metro Mold Components

---
## Far Hills
(Somerset—N.E.)

**ENGRAVED IMAGES**

Route 202 & Demun Pl., P.O. Box 966 (07931)
**Phone—(908) 234-0323**
Fax—(908) 234-0024
www.engravedimages.net
Email—engravedimages@comcast.net
Owner—Heidi Gammon
SIC—2759; 2752; 2789; 3479; NAICS—323100; *Offset & color printing & engraving of fine stationery, business cards, letterheads, corporate event materials, wedding invitations, menus & placards; Brand name—Crane; William Arthur; Checkerboard; Smock*
Employs—5; Estab.—1986
Sales—under $500,000
Distrib.—Regional
Sole ownership

**ZIMMER MACHINERY SYSTEMS**

19 Springcroft Rd. (07931)
**Phone—(908) 234-2560**
Fax—(908) 234-1391
Owner—Theodore Zimmer
SIC—3544; 3599; NAICS—333500; *Tool & die & precision machining job shop*
Employs—1; Estab.—1993
Sales—under $500,000
Distrib.—Local
Sole ownership

---
## Farmingdale
(Monmouth—N.E.)

**†ALLTEST INSTRUMENTS**

500 Central Ave. (07727)
**Phone—(732) 919-3339**
Fax—(732) 919-3332
www.alltest.us
Email—sales@alltest.us
Pres.—Nathan Nelson
SIC—5049; *Distributor of testing equipment, including amplifiers, analyzers, meters & oscilloscopes*
Employs—18; Estab.—2002
Distrib.—National
Privately owned corporation

**ALTO DEVELOPMENT CORP.**

5206 Asbury Rd., P.O. Box 758 (07727)
**Phone—(732) 938-2266**
Fax—(732) 938-2399
www.aemedical.com
Pres.—Tim Wojciechowicz
Plt. Mgr.—Charles Netterman
Off. Mgr.—Liz Campbell
Cust. Serv. Rep.—Loretta Allert
SIC—3841; *Surgical supplies, including electrosurgical instruments, cardiovascular pacing leads, neurology scalp clips, stainless steel sutures, illuminated vein harvest retractors, dissectors & industrial wire cables*
Employs—75; Estab.—1968
Distrib.—Intl.
Privately owned corporation
ISO rating—9001

## Farmingdale—(cont.)

**APPLICAD, INC.**
5029 Industrial Rd. (07727)
**Phone—(732) 751-2555**
www.aci-applicad.com
Email—sales@aci-applicad.com
Pres., CFO—John MacMillan
IT Mgr.—James Julian
SIC—3672; NAICS—334412;
 Printed circuit board design &
 assembly
Employs—30; Estab.—1988
20,000 sq ft site, Distrib.—Local
Privately owned sub-S corp.
ISO rating—9001:2000
AKA: ACI

**ATLANTA DRIVE SYSTEMS, INC.**
1775 State Route 34, Ste. D-10
 (07727)
**Phone—(732) 282-0480**
Fax—(732) 282-0450
www.atlantadrives.com
Email—info@atlantadrives.com
V-P.—Brad Donmoyer
SIC—3568; Rack & pinion drive
 systems
Employs—4

**ATLANTIS AROMATICS, INC.**
5047 Industrial Rd., Ste. 4 (07727)
**Phone—(732) 919-1112**
Fax—(732) 919-1211
www.atlantisaromatics.com
Email—info@atlantisaromatics.com
Pres.—Phillip Abbott
Pur. Agt.—Patti Averso
SIC—2844; NAICS—325600;
 Fragrances
Employs—6; Estab.—2002
Sales—under $500,000
Distrib.—National
Privately owned corporation

**BELFER GROUP**
10 Ruckle Ave. (07727)
Mail addr: P.O. Box 2079, Ocean
 (07712)
**Phone—(732) 493-2666**
Fax—(732) 493-2941
www.belfergroup.com
Email—jbelfer@belfer.com
Pres.—Bruce Belfer
Sales Mgr., Inside—Joe Belfer
SIC—3646; NAICS—335122;
 Lighting fixtures
Employs—47; Estab.—1975
Distrib.—Intl.
Privately owned corporation

**CENTRAL METAL FABRICATORS,
 INC.**
300 Central Ave. (07727)
**Phone—(732) 938-6900**
Fax—(732) 938-6902
www.centralmetalfab.com
Email—info@centralmetalfab.com
Pres.—Frank Cris
Off. Mgr.—Bonnie Alexander
SIC—3599; NAICS—332710;
 Precision machined components
 & assemblies for the
 commercial, industrial, military,
 medical, pharmaceutical,
 research & food preparation
 industries
Employs—20; Estab.—1980
Sales—$2.5Mil
35,000 sq ft site, Distrib.—National
Privately owned corporation

**CHAVANT, INC.**
5043 Industrial Rd. (07727)
**Phone—(732) 751-0003**
National—(800) 242-8268
Fax—(732) 751-1982
www.chavant.com
Email—mail@chavant.com
Pres.—Jack North
V-P.—Isaac Peng
Sales Mgr., Inside—Howard
 Cullen

SIC—3952; Clay, including
 modeling, hard styling, industrial
 design & sculpting; Brand
 name—Professional Plasteline;
 NSP; Le Beau Touche;
 AutoStyle; Castilene; Clayette
Employs—10; Estab.—1892
Distrib.—Intl.
Privately owned sub-S corp.

**CITYSAFE, INC.**
312 Squankum Yellowbrook Rd.
 (07727)
**Phone—(732) 751-0100**
Fax—(732) 751-1800
www.modulxusa.com
Email—sales@citysafe.com
Pres.—Karl Alizade
SIC—3499; Commercial safes,
 vaults, strong rooms, safe rooms
 & infrastructure protection;
 Brand name—MODUL-X
Employs—7; Estab.—1986
Sales—$500,000-$1Mil
Distrib.—Intl.
Privately owned corporation

**COLWOOD ELECTRONICS, INC.**
44 Main St. (07727)
**Phone—(732) 938-5556**
Fax—(732) 938-9037
www.woodburning.com
Email—colwood@woodburning.com
Pres.—Richard Colaguori
Shpg. Mgr.—Dennis Bozard
SIC—3553; NAICS—333210;
 Wood burning tools
Employs—4; Estab.—1979
Sales—under $500,000
Distrib.—Intl.
Privately owned corporation

**COMPOUNDERS, INC.**
15 Marl Rd., P.O. Box 413 (07727)
**Phone—(732) 938-5007**
Fax—(732) 938-5008
Email—comphs@aol.com
Pres.—Harold Saunders
Hum. Res. Mgr.—Jim Russell
Off. Mgr.—Kevin Russell
SIC—2891; NAICS—325520;
 Adhesives
Employs—6; Estab.—1961
Distrib.—Intl.
Privately owned corporation

**CUTTING EDGE GROWER SUPPLY
 LLC**
5033 Industrial Rd. (07727)
Mail addr: P.O. Box 554, Howell
 (07731)
**Phone—(732) 905-9220**
National—(866) 855-1442
Fax—(732) 905-9221
www.cuttingedgegrowersupply.co
 m
Email—info@
 cuttingedgegrowersupply.com
Pres.—Anthonie Barendregt
SIC—3084; PVC drip irrigation
 pipes
Employs—5; Estab.—2009
Sales—$1Mil-$2.5Mil
2,500 sq ft site, Distrib.—Intl.
Limited Liability Company

**DEAN TECHNOLOGY, INC.**
5027 Industrial Rd., Unit 4, P.O.
 Box 848 (07727)
**Phone—(732) 938-4499**
National—(800) 548-0344
Fax—(732) 938-4451
www.deantechnology.com
Email—info@hvca.com
Pres., Opers. Mgr.—Craig Dean
Cont.—Yvette Saenz
Sales Mgr.—Chris Robinson
Hum. Res. & Off. Mgr.—Judy
 Westerfield

SIC—3674; NAICS—334413;
 Corporate headquarters & high-
 voltage diodes & rectifier
 assemblies
Employs—10; Estab.—1987
Sales—$3Mil-$5Mil
9,000 sq ft site, Distrib.—Intl.
Privately owned corporation

**DEPOT AMERICA, INC.**
1495 Highway 34 (07727)
**Phone—(732) 919-0209**
National—(800) 648-6833
Fax—(732) 919-1929
www.depot-america.com
Email—dwfhr@dwfwholesale.com
Pres.—Eric Martin
SIC—3577; Computer printer
 parts
Employs—200; Estab.—1986
Sales—$50Mil-$100Mil (est)
Distrib.—Intl.
Privately owned corporation

**DIALIGHT CORPORATION (H Q)**
1501 State Highway 34 S. (07727)
**Phone—(732) 919-3119**
Fax—(732) 751-5778
www.dialight.com
Email—info@dialight.com
CEO—Roy Burton
CFO—Preston Wells
V-P., Sales—John Castner
V-P., Mktg.—Michael Schratz
V-P., Hum. Res.—David Myler
Dir., Corp. Qual.—Rich Liskoff
Dir., Sales, Obstruction &
 Hazloc—David Jennings
Dir., Cust. Serv.—Kathy Smith
SIC—3648; 3647; 3679; 3625;
 Corporate headquarters; solid-
 state warehouse, oil rig, tower,
 vehicle & traffic balls lighting
 equipment & controls for the oil &
 gas, petrochemical, pulp &
 paper, wastewater treatment,
 food processing & heavy
 manufacturing industries; Brand
 name—SafeSite
Employs—85; Estab.—1938
Sales—$100Mil-$150Mil
Distrib.—Intl.
Publicly owned corporation
ISO rating—9001:2000

NEW ENTRY
**DNE NUTRACEUTICALS, INC.**
700 Central Ave. (07719)
**Phone—(732) 806-9538**
Fax—(732) 806-9438
www.dnenutra.com
Email—michaelg@dnenutra.com
V-P.—Paul Kugielsky
SIC—2023; 2833; Contract
 manufacturing of dietary
 supplements & vitamins; Brand
 name—
Employs—50
Sales—$25Mil-$50Mil (est)
60,000 sq ft site, Distrib.—Intl.
Privately owned corporation

**DOLAN CREATION, INC.**
255 Squankum Rd., P.O. Box 693
 (07727)
**Phone—(732) 938-6656**
National—(800) 628-8320
www.dolancreations.com
Pres.—Douglas Dolan
SIC—3999; NAICS—332999;
 Refrigerator magnets, framed
 pictures & wall clocks
Employs—5; Estab.—1981
Sales—under $500,000
Distrib.—National
Sole ownership

**EASTERN AUTOMATION SYSTEMS**
1151 New Jersey Route 33, P.O.
 Box 2394 (07727)
**Phone—(732) 938-2002**
Fax—(732) 938-3140
www.easternautomation.net

Email—eastern@att.net
Pres.—Scott Bellows
Engrg. Mgr.—Ken Lippin
SIC—3569; Custom automated
 machinery
Employs—3; Estab.—1998
Sales—$500,000-$1Mil
7,500 sq ft site, Distrib.—Regional
Privately owned sub-S corp.

**ERNST FLOW INDUSTRIES**
116 Main St. (07727)
**Phone—(732) 938-5641**
National—(800) 992-2843
Fax—(732) 938-9463
www.ernstflow.com
Email—info@ernstflow.com
Sales Supv.—Susan Shanahan
Sales Rep.—Kelly Sziveri
SIC—3829; gages & flow
 indicators
Employs—14; Estab.—1990
Sales—$500,000-$1Mil
10,000 sq ft site, Distrib.—National
Privately owned corporation

**†EXTECH BUILDING MATERIALS,
 INC.**
Div. of Extech Building Materials
385 Asbury Rd. (07727)
**Phone—(732) 919-3340**
National—(800) 398-3242
Fax—(732) 919-3348
www.extechbuilding.com
Email—info@extechbuilding.com
Manager—Bob Lippe
Cred. Mgr., Reg.—Chris Cawley
Sales Rep.—John Costa
SIC—5032; 5085; Distributor of
 masonry materials & supplies,
 including brick, natural stone &
 tools
Employs—7; Estab.—1970
Distrib.—Local
Privately owned corporation
Parent co.—Extech Building
 Materials, Long Island City, NY
 Phone—(718) 786-2288
See Parent Co. Section for full profile.

**FARMINGDALE PRINTING**
70 Main St. (07727)
**Phone—(732) 938-2727**
Fax—(732) 938-4792
www.farmingdaleprintingandcopyc
 enter.com
Email—farmprinting@optonline.net
Pres.—Tom Trenholm
Manager—John McVey
Designer—Christie Trenholm
SIC—2752; 2759; 2791; NAICS—
 323122; Offset & digital printing
 & electronic prepress
Employs—3; Estab.—1987
Sales—$500,000-$1Mil
Distrib.—Local
Privately owned corporation
AKA: TNA Litho Group, Inc.

**FESTO DIDACTIC INC.**
1710 Highway 34, P.O. Box 686
 (07727)
**Phone—(732) 938-2000**
National—(800) 223-1057
Fax—(732) 774-8573
www.labvolt.com
Email—us@labvolt.com
CFO—Ralf Hermkens
Off. Mgr.—Teresa Curatolo
SIC—3699; Electronic educational
 training systems
Employs—54; Estab.—1934
Sales—$25Mil-$45Mil
23,000 sq ft site, Distrib.—Intl.
Privately owned corporation

**GARDEN STATE FOLIAGE, LLC**
600 Central Ave. (07727)
**Phone—(732) 751-0075**
National—(877) 426-6600
Fax—(732) 751-0020
Email—gsfoliageinc@aol.com
Ptnr.—Neil M. Roth
Ptnr.—Zsolt Kruppa

GEOGRAPHICAL

## Farmingdale—(cont.)

Ex. V-P., Opers.—Lisa L. Hill
SIC—3999; 2499; 3499; 3089;
*Christmas decorations, dried
foliage, floral accessory & home
decor*
Employs—20; Estab.—1977
Sales—over $3Mil
65,000 sq ft site, Distrib.—National
Limited Liability Company

†**GARDEN STATE TILE
DISTRIBUTORS, INC. (H Q)**
5001 Industrial Rd. (07727)
**Phone—(732) 938-6675**
Fax—(732) 938-4558
www.gstile.com
Email—info@gstile.com
Pres.—Stephen Fischer
V-P., Sales—Robert A. Fischer
IT Mgr.—Jose Rodriguez
Inventory Mgr.—Janet Bruno
SIC—5032; *Corporate
headquarters; distributor of floor
tile*
Employs—20; Estab.—1947
Company-wide: 80
Distrib.—National
Privately owned corporation

**GREEN TRAILERS, INC., STEPHAN
L.**
74 Squankum Yellowbrook Rd.
(07727)
**Phone—(732) 938-5663**
Fax—(732) 938-7646
www.stephangreentrailers.com
Email—sgreen1667@aol.com
Pres., Fin. & MIS Mgr.—Stephan L.
Green
Manager—Allen Green
SIC—3715; NAICS—336212;
*Equipment & flatbed trailers;
Brand name—Car Mate;
Integrity*
Employs—7; Estab.—1970
Sales—over $3Mil
50,000 sq ft site, Distrib.—National
Privately owned corporation
AKA: Green Enterprises, Stephan
L.

**HANGER PROSTHETICS &
ORTHOTICS, INC.**
Div. of Hanger, Inc.
5100 Belmore Blvd. (07727)
**Phone—(732) 919-7774**
National—(800) 582-2440
Fax—(732) 919-0188
www.hanger.com
Email—info@hanger.com
GM—Brian Kleiberg
Off. Mgr.—Colleen Carty
Administrator—Jazmine Paul
SIC—3842; *Orthotic & prosthetic
appliances*
Employs—8; Estab.—1995
Sales—under $500,000
Distrib.—National
Publicly owned corporation
Parent co.—Hanger, Inc., Austin,
TX
Phone—(512) 777-3800
See Parent Co. Section for full profile.

**HOWELL PRECISION TOOL CO.**
415 Cranberry Rd. (07727-3512)
**Phone—(732) 919-7300**
Fax—(732) 919-7750
www.howellprecision.com
Email—sales@howellprecision.com
Owner & Pres.—David Hanrahan
SIC—3544; 3599; NAICS—
333500; *Close tolerance CNC
milling, turning & wire EDM job
shop*
Employs—5; Estab.—1982
5,000 sq ft site, Distrib.—Intl.
Privately owned sub-S corp.

**INTERSPEC**
5025 Industrial Rd. (07727)
Mail addr: P.O. Box 705,
Allenwood (08720)
**Phone—(732) 938-4114**
National—(800) 526-2800
Fax—(732) 938-9083
www.interspec.com
Email—info@interspec.com
Owner—Richard P. Deacon
SIC—2824; *Flame-retardant
cubicle curtain fabrics for
hospitals & long-term care
facilities, including antimony-free
polyester fabrics*
Employs—7; Estab.—1963
Distrib.—Intl.
Privately owned corporation

†**JFD ASSOCIATES, INC.**
15 Railroad Ave. (07727)
**Phone—(732) 751-9041**
Fax—(732) 751-9044
www.jfdrecycling.com
Email—paperandie@optonline.net
Pres.—Andrea Holt
SIC—5093; *Wholesaler of
recycled paper & cardboard*
Employs—17
Distrib.—Local
Privately owned corporation

**KUNTZ CO., INC., R. T.**
5146 W. Hurley Pond Rd., P.O. Box
476 (07727)
**Phone—(732) 751-1770**
National—(800) 237-2120
Fax—(732) 751-1505
www.rtkuntz.com
Email—info@rtkuntz.com
Owner & Pres.—Rod Kuntz
GM—Scott Thompson
Off. Mgr.—Nina Levinstein
SIC—3559; 5084; *Manufacturer &
distributor of resin conveying,
material handling & scrap
reclaim systems for the plastics
industry*
Employs—7; Estab.—1975
Sales—$2.5Mil-$5Mil
7,500 sq ft site, Distrib.—Intl.
Privately owned sub-S corp.

**MASTER TOOL CORP.**
342 Squankum Yellowbrook Rd.,
P.O. Box 7 (07727)
**Phone—(732) 919-1010**
Fax—(732) 919-1010
Email—mastertoolcorp@yahoo.com
Pres.—Tom Di Donato
Off. Mgr.—Jane Di Donato
SIC—3599; *General machining
job shop*
Employs—4; Estab.—1988
Sales—under $500,000
Distrib.—Local
Privately owned sub-S corp.

**MECHANICAL COMPONENTS CORP.**
145 Yellowbrook Rd. (07727)
**Phone—(732) 938-3737**
Fax—(732) 938-3372
Email—mcccorp@hotmail.com
Owner & Pres.—Doel Burgos
V-P.—Ronald Fischer
SIC—3599; *General machining
job shop*
Employs—4; Estab.—1980
Sales—under $500,000
Distrib.—National
Privately owned corporation

**MR. DRIVE SHAFT**
5134-A Hurley Pond Rd. (07727)
**Phone—(732) 938-4118**
Fax—(732) 938-3545
Email—mr.driveshaft@gmail.com
Owner & MIS Mgr.—William
Everson

SIC—3714; *Automotive drive
shafts; Brand name—neapco®;
SPICER®; DANA; PowerTrain
Industries*
Employs—2; Estab.—1985
Sales—under $500,000
2,250 sq ft site, Distrib.—National
Sole ownership

**MUSCO SPORTS LIGHTING, LLC**
5146 W. Hurley Pond Rd. (07727)
**Phone—(732) 751-9114**
National—(866) 866-8232
Fax—(732) 751-9115
www.musco.com
Email—dan.shalloo@musco.com
Dist. Sales Mgr.—Dan Shalloo
Sales Coord.—Margaret Varela
SIC—3648; NAICS—335129;
*Sports lighting equipment*
Employs—2; Estab.—1970
Sales—under $500,000 (est)
Distrib.—Intl.
Limited Liability Company
Parent co.—Musco Sports
Lighting, LLC, Oskaloosa, IA
Phone—(641) 673-0411
See Parent Co. Section for full profile.

**NATIONAL EQUIPMENT CO.**
342 Squankum Yellowbrook Rd.,
P.O. Box 674 (07727)
**Phone—(732) 938-5084**
National—(800) 755-1706
Fax—(732) 938-5281
www.nationalequipmentcompany.n
et
Email—maurorac@aol.com
Pres.—Mauro R. Raccuglia
SIC—3559; 3544; 5084; NAICS—
333500; *Rebuilt production pipe
& bolt threading machinery &
wholesaler of grooving, cut-off &
fitting make on equipment,
associated parts, tooling &
consumables; Brand name—
Landis; Quality Chaser;
Continental Cut-Off Equipment;
Threading Tools Inc.; Swift/
Mercury; Kendall & Gent; Pace;
Victaulic; Ferguson*
Employs—4; Estab.—1962
Sales—under $500,000
20,000 sq ft site, Distrib.—National
Privately owned corporation

**NORTHEAST PALLET RECYCLING,
LLC**
133 Yellowbrook Rd. (07727)
**Phone—(732) 751-1919**
Fax—(732) 751-9009
Email—northeastpallet@
optonline.net
Pres.—Nicolas Martinez
Off. Mgr.—Heidi Schultz
SIC—2448; *Recycled wooden
pallets*
Employs—10; Estab.—2002
Sales—under $500,000
Distrib.—Regional
Limited Liability Company

**OSBORN'S MILL**
149 Yellowbrook Rd. (07727)
**Phone—(732) 751-0889**
Fax—(732) 751-9461
www.osbornsmill.com
Email—info@osbornsmill.com
GM—Mark Piccolo
Foreman—Gus Carlson
SIC—2431; NAICS—321900;
*Architectural millwork*
Employs—6; Estab.—1923
Sales—$500,000-$1Mil
10,000 sq ft site, Distrib.—Local

**P & E TECHNOLOGIES, INC.**
5140 W. Hurley Pond Rd. (07727)
**Phone—(732) 751-1515**
National—(800) 979-9801
Fax—(732) 751-1015
www.pecoingames.com
Email—pandegames@aol.com
Pres.—Phil Cornick

Opers. Mgr.—Edward Kaba
Prod. Mgr.—Al DeVivo
SIC—3581; 3944; NAICS—
333311; *Video games & vending
machines*
Employs—12; Estab.—1995
10,000 sq ft site, Distrib.—National
Privately owned corporation

**PATTY-O-MATIC, INC.**
Route 547, P.O. Box 404 (07727)
**Phone—(732) 938-2757**
National—(877) 938-5244
Fax—(732) 938-5809
www.pattyomatic.com
Email—info@pattyomatic.com
Pres.—Bernard Miles
SIC—3556; NAICS—333294;
*Food processing equipment*
Employs—12; Estab.—1974
Sales—$1Mil-$5Mil
10,000 sq ft site, Distrib.—Intl.
Privately owned sub-S corp.

**PEKAY INDUSTRIES, INC.**
Southard Ave., P.O. Box 559
(07727)
**Phone—(732) 938-2722**
Fax—(732) 919-0224
Pres., GM—Peter Kowalenko
Mfg. Mgr.—Bob Morton
SIC—3264; NAICS—327113;
*Electronics ceramic terminals*
Employs—12; Estab.—1971
Sales—$1Mil-$2.5Mil
Distrib.—Regional
Privately owned corporation

**PLASTASONICS, INC.**
5031 Industrial Rd. (07727)
**Phone—(732) 938-7694**
Fax—(732) 938-7695
www.plastasonics.com
Email—plastasonics@optonline.net
Pres.—Gary Young
V-P., Hum. Res. & IT Mgr.—Gary
Kuskin
SIC—3089; *Headphones,
handsets & headsets, including
plastic injection & insert molding,
welding & metal fabrication*
Employs—15; Estab.—1988
Sales—$1.5Mil-$2.5Mil
15,000 sq ft site, Distrib.—
Regional
Privately owned sub-S corp.
ISO rating—9001

**SELECTIVE COATINGS & INKS, INC.**
5008 Industrial Rd. (07727)
**Phone—(732) 938-7677**
Fax—(732) 938-2719
www.sci-inc-usa.com
Email—info@sci-inc-usa.com
Pres.—William Zak
Engrg. Mgr.—Michael Cuddy
Lab Mgr.—Scott Beriont
SIC—2893; NAICS—325910;
*Printing ink*
Employs—10; Estab.—1976
Sales—$2.5Mil-$5Mil (est)
Distrib.—Intl.
Privately owned corporation

**SPECIALTY STAIR & RAIL, LLC**
1717 State Route 34 Cliff St., Bldg.
8, P.O. Box 642 (07727)
**Phone—(732) 359-8174**
Fax—(732) 359-8175
Email—specialtystairs@
embarqmail.com
Ptnr.—Stacy Bloodgood, Jr.
Ptnr.—Lewis Griffin
SIC—2431; *Wooden stairs &
railings*
Employs—7; Estab.—2011
Sales—under $1Mil
2,000 sq ft site, Distrib.—National
Limited Liability Company

**STONE GRAPHICS CO., INC.**
5020 Industrial Rd. (07727)
**Phone—(732) 919-1111**
Fax—(732) 919-7888

## Farmingdale—(cont.)

www.signsbystone.com
Email—sales@signsbystone.com
Pres.—Raymond C. Stone
Off. Mgr.—Sherri Stone
SIC—2396; 2759; 3993; NAICS—
323100; *Screen printing, large-
format digital printing &
architectural, dimensional &
carved gold leaf interior &
exterior signs; Brand name—
GoldLeafSigns.com*
Employs—6; Estab.—1989
Sales—$1Mil-$2.5Mil
13,000 sq ft site, Distrib.—National
Privately owned corporation

### SURE DESIGN

5027 Industrial Rd., Unit 3 (07727)
**Phone—(732) 919-3066**
Fax—(732) 919-3071
www.sure-design.com
Email—info@sure-design.com
Ptnr.—Ken Thomas
Ptnr.—Fernando Irizarry
Ptnr.—Eric Thorson
SIC—3672; 3543; NAICS—
334412; *Printed circuit board
assemblies & prototypes*
Employs—11; Estab.—1997
Distrib.—Intl.
Limited Liability Partnership

### T J MFG., INC.

Allaire Airport, Bldg. 25, P.O. Box
2361 (07727)
**Phone—(732) 938-7325**
Fax—(732) 938-4634
Pres.—Tom Goski
SIC—2434; NAICS—337110;
*Wooden kitchen & bathroom
cabinets*
Employs—1; Estab.—1982
Sales—under $500,000
Distrib.—Local
Sole ownership

### TAYLOR FENCE CO.

1246 Route 33 (07727)
Mail addr: P.O. Box 126, Red Bank
(07701)
**Phone—(732) 747-5498**
Fax—(732) 938-5671
www.taylorfence.com
Email—info@taylorfence.com
Owner—Paul Crooks
Sales Rep.—Israel Garriga
SIC—3496; 2499; *Wooden, chain-
link & aluminum fencing*
Employs—50; Estab.—1959
Distrib.—Regional

### TEA & ELLE WOODWORKS, LLC

5004 Industrial Rd. (07727)
**Phone—(732) 938-9660**
Fax—(732) 938-3759
www.teaandelle.com
Email—teaelle@optonline.com
Owner—Todd Gleason
Bookkeeper—Carol Gleason
SIC—2431; 2541; 2511; NAICS—
321900; *CNC components &
parts*
Employs—7; Estab.—1998
Distrib.—Regional
Limited Liability Company

### †TEKRIS POWER ELECTRONICS, INC.

1675 State Route 34 (07727)
**Phone—(732) 938-4996**
Fax—(732) 938-5371
www.tekrispower.com
Email—chris@tekrispower.com
Pres.—Chris Hanrahan
V-P.—Laurie Hanrahan

SIC—5063; NAICS—335911;
*Distributor of inverters &
generators for the industrial,
alternative energy, marine & RV
industries; Brand name—
Xantrex; Magnum; Yamaha*
Employs—2; Estab.—1996
Sales—$1Mil
2,000 sq ft site, Distrib.—Intl.
Privately owned sub-S corp.

### TRI-STATE PUMP, INC.

5044 Industrial Rd., Ste. C (07727)
**Phone—(732) 223-3222**
National—(800) 810-1053
Fax—(732) 223-2587
www.pumps-parts.com
Email—sales@pumps-parts.com
Co-Pres.—Mike Caringi
Co-Pres.—Brian Atnes
SIC—3561; 3084; NAICS—
333911; *Industrial pumps*
Employs—10; Estab.—1962
Distrib.—Intl.
Privately owned corporation

### TROJAN TUBE CO.

Yellowbrook Rd., P.O. Box 496
(07727)
**Phone—(732) 938-5687**
National—(800) 394-5883
Fax—(732) 938-2363
www.trojantubecompany.biz
Email—trojantubecoinc@aol.com
Plt. & Sales Mgr.—Garry Hupser
SIC—3351; NAICS—331421;
*Brass, copper, nickel & copper
alloy tubing*
Employs—16; Estab.—1946
20,000 sq ft site, Distrib.—Intl.
Privately owned corporation

### †VIC GERARD GOLF CARS

281 Squankum Rd. (07727)
**Phone—(732) 938-4464**
National—(800) 339-4302
Fax—(732) 938-3211
www.vggc.net
Email—sales@vggc.net
Pres.—William Lynch
Cont., Off. Mgr.—Ted Wichmann
GM—Steve Gerard
SIC—5012; *Distributor of golf cars
& utility vehicles*
Employs—23; Estab.—1962
Sales—$4Mil-$6Mil
Distrib.—Regional
Privately owned corporation

## Fieldsboro

### (Burlington—S.E.)

### STEPAN CO.

220 4th St. (08505)
**Phone—(609) 298-1222**
Fax—(609) 298-7950
www.stepan.com
Email—order.placement@
stepan.com
Hum. Res. Specialist—Stacey
Santoleri
SIC—2843; NAICS—325613;
*Surfactants*
Employs—50; Estab.—1963
Distrib.—Intl.
Publicly owned corporation
ISO rating—9000
Parent co.—Stepan Co.,
Northfield, IL
Phone—(847) 446-7500
See Parent Co. Section for full profile.

## Flanders

### (Morris—N.W.)

### AMERICAN INSTANTS, INC.

117 Bartley Flanders Rd., P.O. Box
817 (07836)
**Phone—(973) 584-8811**
Fax—(973) 584-0444
www.americaninstants.com

Email—sales@
americaninstants.com
CEO—Christopher Roche
Pres.—Martin Wagner
V-P.—Jennifer Vilot
Dir., Lab Opers.—Kristin Truglio
Prodn. Mgr.—Debra Thomson
Opers. Mgr.—Chip Neice
SIC—2095; 2066; 2099; 2086;
NAICS—311920; *Instant
beverages, including
cappuccino, hot chocolate,
granita & chai drink mixes, fresh
brew & leaf tea & energy &
vitamin drinks; Brand name—
Cappuccino Supreme; Hot
Chocolate Supreme; Shivery
Shake; Deep Rich; D-Fib;
VaZoom*
Employs—60; Estab.—1961
70,000 sq ft site, Distrib.—Intl.
Privately owned corporation
ISO rating—9001:2008

### BON VENTURE, INC.

34 Ironia Rd., P.O. Box 850
(07836)
**Phone—(973) 584-5699**
National—(800) 883-4343
Fax—(973) 252-7403
www.bonventure.net
Email—info@bonventure.net
Pres.—Thomas Garde
V-P., Prodn.—Timothy Berdan
Hum. Res. Mgr.—Mary Beth
Piazza
SIC—2752; NAICS—323100;
*Offset printing*
Employs—40; Estab.—1976
Sales—$500,000-$1Mil
15,000 sq ft site, Distrib.—National
Privately owned corporation
DBA: Bon Venture Services, LLC

### †CHEF'S CORNER

178 U.S. Highway 206, Ste. B
(07836)
**Phone—(973) 691-1500**
Fax—(973) 691-3466
www.chefscornernj.com
Email—sales@chefscornernj.com
Store Mgr.—Theresa Berntsen
Sales & Mktg. Consultant—
Anthony LiPetri
Sales Consultant—James Padakis
SIC—5046; 5078; *Wholesaler of
restaurant & institutional
equipment & kitchen supplies*
Employs—5; Estab.—1996
Distrib.—Local
Privately owned corporation

### CHEROKEE RUBBER CO.

5 Laurel Dr., Unit 13 (07836)
Mail addr: P.O. Box 339, Chester
(07930-0339)
**Phone—(973) 584-3733**
Fax—(973) 584-2554
Email—cherokeerubber@
hotmail.com
Pres.—Gilbert J. Stroming II
Whse. Mgr.—Dennis Johnson
SIC—2822; NAICS—325212;
*Synthetic rubber tubing & cast
polyurethane sheet*
Employs—12; Estab.—1980
10,000 sq ft site, Distrib.—Intl.
Privately owned corporation

### †DANI LEATHER USA, INC.

37 Ironia Rd., Ste. 2 (07836-4422)
**Phone—(973) 598-0890**
Fax—(973) 598-0893
www.danileatherusa.com
Email—info@danileatherusa.com
Sales Mgr.—Mike Belluzzi
Sales Rep.—Michele Belluzzi
Off. Mgr.—Dawn Lemoncelli
Whse. Mgr.—John Calamusa

SIC—5199; *Distributor of Italian
leather for the furniture,
automotive, aircraft & fashion
markets; Brand name—Panama;
Box Land; Asolo; Florida; Aztec;
Manila; Lord; Nabuk; Garda;
Acquario; Como; New Lancaster*
Employs—5
Sales—over $4.5Mil
14,500 sq ft site, Distrib.—Intl.
Privately owned corporation
ISO rating—9001:2008
AKA: Gruppo Dani

### †DISTINCTIVE PROMOTIONS, INC.

268 U.S. Highway 206, Ste. 404
(07836)
**Phone—(973) 584-6800**
Fax—(973) 927-8485
www.distinctivepromotions.com
Email—loisp@
distinctivepromotions.com
Pres.—Lois Patrick
V-P., Sales—Michelle Patrick
V-P.—Dennis Patrick
Off. Mgr.—Lisa Pace
SIC—5199; 5122; *Distributor of
advertising promotional supplies*
Employs—10; Estab.—1984
1,300 sq ft site, Distrib.—National
Privately owned sub-S corp.

### ELECTRONIC MEASURING DEVICES, INC.

15 Mill Rd. (07836)
**Phone—(973) 691-4755**
www.emdsceptre.com
Email—emd@eclipse.net
COO—Klaus Ulbrich
SIC—3829; 7372; *Analog
coordinate measuring systems &
probing technology & software
for coordinate measuring
machines for the commercial
industries & government
agencies*
Employs—1; Estab.—1986
Sales—$500,000-$1Mil
3,000 sq ft site, Distrib.—Intl.
Privately owned corporation

### ESG, LLC

3 Gold Mine Rd. (07836)
**Phone—(973) 691-8517**
Fax—(973) 691-8321
www.eaglesystemgroup.com
Email—info@
eaglesystemgroup.com
Pres.—Vincent LoConte
Serv. Techn.—Nick Delre
SIC—3559; *Foil stamping
machinery for the printing
industry*
Employs—6; Estab.—2000
Sales—$500,000-$1Mil
Distrib.—Intl.
Privately owned corporation
AKA: Eagle System Group

### †FASTENAL CO.

186 Gold Mine Rd., Unit 1 (07836)
**Phone—(973) 691-0547**
Fax—(973) 347-4519
www.fastenal.com
Email—njmou@stores.fastenal.com
Br. Mgr.—Matthew Cohen
SIC—5072; 5084; 5085;
*Wholesaler of fasteners, safety
equipment, tools & abrasives*
Employs—5; Estab.—2005
Sales—$2.5Mil-$5Mil
3,000 sq ft site, Distrib.—Intl.
Publicly owned corporation
Parent co.—Fastenal Co., Winona,
MN
Phone—(507) 454-5374
See Parent Co. Section for full profile.

### HAAS LASER TECHNOLOGIES, INC.

37 Ironia Rd. (07836)
**Phone—(973) 598-1150**
Fax—(973) 598-1151
www.haaslti.com
Email—sales@haaslti.com

GEOGRAPHICAL

## Flanders—(cont.)

Pres.—Gilbert J. Haas
Bookkeeper—Sandy Laurent
SIC—3699; Industrial laser
systems, laser beam delivery
systems & components,
including custom machining
Employs—14; Estab.—1992
Sales—$1Mil-$5Mil
35,000 sq ft site, Distrib.—Intl.
Privately owned corporation

### JERSEY MICROWAVE, LLC

230 U.S. Highway 206, Ste. 407
(07836-9119)
Phone—(908) 684-2390
Fax—(908) 684-2391
www.jerseymicrowave.com
Email—sales@
jerseymicrowave.com
Pres.—Thanh Nguyen
Sales Mgr.—Tony Landaeta
Sales Admn.—Eileen Baer
SIC—3679; Microwave
components, including
receivers, amplifiers, switches,
phase-locked dielectric
resonator & free-running
dielectric oscillators, attenuators,
multipliers, switch & phase
shifters & block converters
Employs—28; Estab.—1994
Sales—$2.5Mil-$5Mil
11,332 sq ft site, Distrib.—Intl.
Limited Liability Company

### LA SIERRA COFFEE ROASTERS, LLC

42 Bartley Rd. (07836)
Mail addr: P.O. Box 568, Chester
(07930-0568)
Phone—(973) 927-9595
Email—ariascoffee@aol.com
Owner—Jorge Henao
Off. Mgr.—Daphne Mott
SIC—2095; NAICS—311920;
Coffee roasting & packaging
Employs—7; Estab.—1995
Sales—$2.5Mil-$5Mil
Distrib.—National
Limited Liability Company

### LENTRON CORP.

24 Ironia Rd. (07836)
Phone—(973) 252-9668
Fax—(973) 252-9554
Email—lentron@gti.net
Off. Mgr.—Anna Klett
SIC—3599; 3999; General
machining & assembly job shop
Employs—20; Estab.—1971
Sales—under $500,000
22,500 sq ft site, Distrib.—National
Privately owned sub-S corp.

### PHOENIX MACHINE

4 Gold Mine Rd. (07836)
Phone—(973) 691-8029
National—(888) 754-8932
Fax—(973) 691-8939
www.phoenixmach.com
Email—info@phoenixmach.com
Pres.—Michael Coulson
V.-P., Opers.—Phil Grippaldi
SIC—3554; NAICS—333291;
New & rebuilt paper & film
converting machinery, including
sifters, rewinders, coaters &
laminators
Employs—20; Estab.—1994
Distrib.—Intl.
Privately owned corporation
AKA: Phoenix Machine Rebuilders

### RUDOLPH TECHNOLOGIES, INC.

1 Rudolph Rd., P.O. Box 1000
(07836)
Phone—(973) 691-1300
Fax—(973) 691-4863
www.rudolphtech.com
Email—info@rudolphtech.com
Chrm., CEO—Paul F. McLaughlin
Sr. V.-P., CFO—Steven Roth

V.-P., Gen. Counsel—Bob Koch
SIC—3559; Corporate
headquarters & semiconductor
manufacturing equipment,
including software analysis &
review solutions for wafer
inspection & metrology
Employs—25; Estab.—1940
Nationwide: 400
Sales—$176.3Mil
40,000 sq ft site, Distrib.—Intl.
Publicly owned corporation

### SIEMENS HEALTHCARE DIAGNOSTICS, INC.

62 Flanders Bartley Rd. (07836)
Phone—(973) 927-2828
National—(800) 944-4146
Fax—(973) 927-2828
www.usa.siemens.com/
diagnostics
Email—usa.healthcare@
siemens.com
Head of R & D—David Stein
SIC—3826; NAICS—334516;
Blood & urine immunoassay
systems for laboratory
automation applications
Employs—450
Distrib.—Intl.
Publicly owned corporation
ISO rating—9001
Parent co.—Siemens Healthcare
Diagnostics, Inc., Deerfield, IL
Phone—(847) 267-5300
See Parent Co. Section for full profile.

### TRI-STATE QUIKRETE

Div. of QUIKRETE Cos., Inc., The
150 Gold Mine Rd. (07836)
Phone—(973) 347-4569
National—(800) 247-7334
Fax—(973) 347-7024
www.quikrete.com
Email—info@quikrete.com
Off. Mgr.—Sue Roach
Dispatcher—Keith Cooper
SIC—3272; Packaged cement
products; Brand name—
Quikrete; Specmix
Employs—35; Estab.—1982
Distrib.—National
Privately owned corporation
Parent co.—QUIKRETE Cos., Inc.,
The, Atlanta, GA
Phone—(404) 634-9100
See Parent Co. Section for full profile.

## Flemington

(Hunterdon—N.W.)

### 3M CO.

500 U.S. Highway 202 N. (08822)
Phone—(908) 788-4000
National—(800) 364-3577
Fax—(908) 782-1468
www.3m.com
Email—info@3m.com
Plt. Mgr.—Bob Silbernagel
Hum. Res. Coord.—Judi Anne
Cooke
SIC—3841; 3821; NAICS—
339111; Sterilization monitoring
devices
Employs—250
Sales—$25Mil-$50Mil (est)
Distrib.—Intl.
Publicly owned corporation
Parent co.—3M Co., St. Paul, MN
Phone—(651) 733-1110
See Parent Co. Section for full profile.

### ADVANCED SOLAR PRODUCTS, INC. (H Q)

270 S. Main St., Ste. 203 (08822)
Phone—(908) 751-5818
Fax—(908) 751-5819
www.advancedsolarproducts.com
Email—sales@
advancedsolarproducts.com
Pres., CEO—Lyle Rawlings
V.-P., COO—Edward Seliga
Dir., Opers.—Katie Hallock

SIC—3674; Corporate
headquarters; commercial solar
energy system design &
installation
Employs—27; Estab.—1991
Sales—$10Mil-$25Mil (est)
Distrib.—Local
Privately owned corporation

### AGILEACCESS™, LLC

23 Londonderry Dr. (08822)
Phone—(908) 788-7740
www.agileaccess.com
Email—contact@agileaccess.com
Founder & CTO—Syed Ahmed
SIC—7373; Hardware system
integration for the telecom
industry
Employs—3
Distrib.—Intl.
Limited Liability Company

### ALWAY, INC. (H Q)

440 U.S. Highway 202 (08822)
Phone—(908) 788-7220
Email—alwayinc@gmail.com
Pres.—Terry Hubscher
SIC—3429; 3499; NAICS—
339993; Corporate
headquarters; metal bed sheet
securing devices, including
suspenders & clips (mfg.
subcontracted); Brand name—
SLEEPSNUG; KEEPSNUG;
SNUGALL
Employs—1; Estab.—1983
Sales—under $500,000
Distrib.—Intl.
Privately owned corporation

### ANTI-HYDRO INTERNATIONAL, INC.

45 River Rd., Ste. 200 (08822)
Phone—(908) 284-9000
National—(800) 777-1773
Fax—(908) 284-9464
www.anti-hydro.com
Email—bruce@anti-hydro.com
Dir., Opers.—Bruce Kreielsheimer
Dir., Cust. Serv.—Howard Herr
SIC—2821; 2891; NAICS—
325211; Concrete admixtures,
coatings, industrial flooring,
hardeners, sealants, epoxies &
waterproofing products; Brand
name—Anti-Hydro; A-H Products
Employs—12; Estab.—1904
Sales—$1Mil-$5Mil
30,000 sq ft site, Distrib.—Intl.
Privately owned sub-S corp.

### AVID COMMUNICATIONS, INC.

27 Bluebird Ct., P.O. Box 2481
(08822)
Phone—(973) 625-7350
Fax—(908) 782-6768
www.avidcommunications.com
Email—info@
avidcommunications.com
Pres.—Thomas Chen
SIC—7373; Computer network
system integration, including
LANs & WANs
Employs—4
Privately owned corporation
AKA: ACI Msd

### CENTER FOR EDUCATIONAL ADVANCEMENT

11 Minneakoning Rd. (08822)
Phone—(908) 782-1480
Fax—(908) 782-5370
www.ceaemployment.com
Email—allstaff@
ceaemployment.com
Pres.—Michael Skoczek
V.-P., Opers.—Nancy A. Vargas
SIC—2834; 3089; NAICS—
325412; Contract
pharmaceutical packaging,
including specialty assembly,
inspection & mailing services
Employs—35; Estab.—1970
20,000 sq ft site, Distrib.—Local
Privately owned corporation

### CHARLES MACHINE SHOP SERVICE, ROB

24 Rake Rd. (08822)
Phone—(908) 806-8512
Owner—Rob Charles
SIC—3599; General machining
job shop
Employs—1; Estab.—1987
Sales—under $500,000
1,100 sq ft site, Distrib.—Regional
Sole ownership

### CHILDREN'S TECHNOLOGY REVIEW

120 Main St. (08822)
Phone—(908) 284-0404
Fax—(908) 284-0405
www.childrenstech.com
Pres.—Warren Buckleiter
Bookkeeper—Megan Billitti
SIC—2721; Monthly computer
software periodical publishing
Employs—5; Estab.—1985
Sales—under $500,000
Distrib.—Local
Privately owned corporation

### CONNECTOR TECHNOLOGY, INC.

5 Walter E. Foran Blvd., Ste. 4005
(08822)
Phone—(732) 745-2880
(800) 458-5646
Fax—(732) 828-9142
www.connectech.com
Email—info@connectech.com
Cont.—Judith Angiuoli
GM—William Mazur
Accts. Payable Rep.—Shelly Toavs
SIC—3678; NAICS—334417;
Electronic interconnect systems
for the industrial, commercial &
military markets
Employs—10; Estab.—1989
Sales—$1Mil-$2.5Mil (est)
Distrib.—National
Privately owned corporation
AKA: CTI

### †COOPER ELECTRIC SUPPLY CO.

19 Royal Rd. (08822)
Phone—(908) 782-3200
Fax—(908) 782-0998
www.cooper-electric.com
Email—cooperonline@cooper-
electric.com
Br. Mgr.—Jim Stevens
SIC—5063; Distributor of electrical
equipment & supplies, including
connectors, wires & sockets
Employs—15
Distrib.—Intl.
Privately owned corporation
Parent co.—Cooper Electric
Supply Co., Monroe, NJ
Phone—(732) 747-2233
See Parent Co. Section for full profile.

### CORNERSTONE PRINT & IMAGING, LLC

179 State Highway 31 (08822)
Phone—(908) 782-7966
Fax—(908) 782-1011
www.cornerstone-print.com
Email—info@cornerstone-print.com
Owner—Arthur Clarke
SIC—2759; NAICS—323100;
Commercial printing
Employs—6
Limited Liability Company

### CRETER VAULT CORP.

417 Highway 202 (08822)
Phone—(908) 782-7771
National—(800) 352-4890
Fax—(908) 782-4381
www.cretervault.com
Pres.—Richard E. Creter
V.-P.—Richard K. Creter
SIC—3272; Concrete burial vaults
Employs—45; Estab.—1985
30,000 sq ft site, Distrib.—Local
Privately owned corporation

## Flemington—(cont.)

**DIGITAL ARTS IMAGING, LLC**
105 State Route 31, Ste. 10 (08822)
**Phone—(908) 237-4646**
Fax—(908) 237-4644
www.digitalartsimaging.com
Email—info@digitalartsimaging.com
Pres.—Robert Vernon
SIC—3993; *Digital printing of signages, banners & window, vehicle & home graphics*
Employs—5; Estab.—2001
Distrib.—National
Limited Liability Company

**DMS LABORATORIES, INC.**
2 Darts Mill Rd. (08822)
**Phone—(908) 782-3353**
National—(800) 567-4367
Fax—(908) 782-0832
www.rapidvet.com
Email—dms@rapidvet.com
Pres.—Nicholas A. Gallo III
V-P.—Denise G. Darmanian
V-P.—Suzanne M. Reese
Cont.—Diane M. Rocchio
Admn. Mgr.—Dolores Bullock
SIC—2834; NAICS—325412; *Veterinary rapid test kits for canine & feline blood type determination, blood crossmatch compatibility & determination of dermatophytosis; Brand name—RapidVet-D; RapidVet-H; RapidVet-H IC; RapidVet-H Gel*
Employs—5; Estab.—1993
Sales—under $500,000
Distrib.—Intl.
Privately owned corporation

†**DURAWEAR GLOVE & SAFETY, INC.**
30 Royal Rd., Ste. 4 (08822)
**Phone—(908) 284-0776**
National—(800) 949-7233
Fax—(908) 284-1138
www.durawear.com
Email—ba@durawear.com
Pres.—William Archipoli
V-P.—Jeremy Archipoli
SIC—5136; 5137; 5049; *Distributor of industrial safety equipment, including gas monitor equipment, gloves, clothing, respiratory protection & rain gear; Brand name—MSA; 3M; Sperian; Uvex; Jackson; Bullard; Willson; Gerson; North Safety Products; Allegro; Perfect Fit Glove; Iron Clad; Ergodyne; DuPont; Kimberly-Clark; Miller; Bright Star; Pelican; Industrial Scientific; Dunlop Boots*
Employs—5; Estab.—1985
Sales—$2.5Mil
8,000 sq ft site, Distrib.—Intl.
Privately owned corporation

**FLEMINGTON ALUMINUM & BRASS, INC.**
24 Junction Rd. (08822)
**Phone—(908) 782-6317**
Fax—(908) 782-8078
www.fabonline.com
Email—fab@embarqmail.com
Pres.—James Kozicki
V-P.—Lynne Kozicki
SIC—3363; 3369; NAICS—331521; *Custom aluminum & brass castings, including traffic signals, brackets, poles & enclosures & plaques*
Employs—6; Estab.—1941
Distrib.—Regional
Privately owned corporation

**FLEMINGTON BITUMINOUS CORP.**
205 Pennsylvania Ave. (08822)
**Phone—(908) 782-2722**
Fax—(908) 782-6292
Pres.—Richard Mannon
Treas.—Hilda V. Mannon
SIC—2951; NAICS—324121; *Asphalt paving compounds*
Employs—6; Estab.—1978
Sales—$1Mil-$5Mil
Distrib.—Local
Privately owned corporation

**FLEMINGTON PRECAST & SUPPLY, LLC**
18 Allen St. (08822)
**Phone—(908) 782-3246**
Fax—(908) 718-1981
www.flemingtonprecast.com
Email—flemingb@precast.com
Ptnr.—Jeff Hoffman
Ptnr.—Susan Hoffman
SIC—3272; *Concrete precast supplies*
Employs—10; Estab.—1976
3,000 sq ft site, Distrib.—Local
Limited Liability Company

**G & C FAB CON, LLC**
5 Foster Ln., Bldg. A (08822)
**Phone—(908) 782-0526**
Fax—(908) 782-0188
www.gandcfabcon.com
Pres.—James C. Griffith
Comp.—Linda Langdon
SIC—3272; *Veterans cemeteries, including lawn crypts, columbariums, structural concrete & buildings & excavation, utility installation, roadway construction, interior renovations, irrigation & construction management*
Employs—41; Estab.—2005
Sales—$500,000-$1Mil
Distrib.—National
Limited Liability Company

**GENERAL PALLET, LLC**
97 River Rd. (08822)
Mail addr: P.O. Box 1000, Readington (08870)
**Phone—(908) 238-1000**
National—(888) 888-8778
Fax—(908) 806-5555
www.generalpallet.com
Email—customerservice@generalpallet.com
Ptnr.—Donald W. Baldwin
Ptnr.—Paula Baldwin
Cust. Serv. Rep.—Kathy Reich
SIC—2448; 3499; 3089; 3398; NAICS—321920; *New & reconditioned wooden, plastic, metal & heat-treated pallets, including pallets for export & ISPM-15*
Employs—7; Estab.—1954
Sales—$500,000-$1Mil
Distrib.—National
Limited Liability Company

**HITRAN CORP.**
362 Highway 31 (08822)
**Phone—(908) 782-5525**
Fax—(908) 782-9733
www.hitrancorp.com
Email—sales@hitrancorp.com
Pur. Mgr.—Deb Frey
IT Mgr.—John Hindle
Hum. Res. Mgr.—Mary Reese
Bookkeeper—Karen Bruns
SIC—3612; NAICS—335311; *Transformers*
Employs—80; Estab.—1965
50,000 sq ft site, Distrib.—National
Privately owned corporation

**HTD HEAT TRACE, INC.**
8 Bartles Corner Rd., Unit 104 (08822)
**Phone—(908) 788-5210**
Fax—(908) 788-5204
www.htdheattrace.com
Email—phaden@htdheattrace.com
Pres.—Michael Haden
Electrical Engr.—Derrike Hill
Food Engr.—Scott Brenneman
Administrator—Patricia Haden
SIC—3433; 3537; NAICS—333414; *Pipe tracing, tank & hopper heating & coal & material handling equipment*
Employs—10; Estab.—1996
Sales—$500,000-$1Mil
Distrib.—Intl.
Privately owned corporation

**INDUSTRIAL ELECTRONIC DEVICES, INC.**
8 Bartles Corner Rd., Bldg. 101 (08822)
**Phone—(908) 806-2255**
www.industrialdisplays.com
Email—info@industrialdisplays.com
Pres.—Jerry Kalajian
Prodn. Mgr.—Bill Sessler
Off. Mgr.—Ken Guinaw
SIC—3679; 3671; NAICS—334411; *Open frame, enclosed & watertight industrial, marine & military LCD monitors*
Employs—5; Estab.—1993
4,500 sq ft site, Distrib.—National
Privately owned corporation

**JERSEYCARTS, LLC**
6 Whiskey Ln. (08822)
**Phone—(908) 806-6400**
Fax—(908) 782-3123
www.jerseycarts.com
Email—greg@jerseycarts.com
Owner—Greg Merrigan
SIC—3993; 3089; *Golf carts, vinyl banners & signs*
Employs—1; Estab.—2005
Sales—under $500,000
Distrib.—Local
Limited Liability Company

**JOHANNA FOODS, INC.**
20 Johanna Farms Rd., P.O. Box 272 (08822)
**Phone—(908) 788-2200**
National—(800) 727-6700
Fax—(908) 788-2737
www.johannafoods.com
Email—info@johannafoods.com
Pres.—Robert Facchina
V-P., CFO—Richard A. Cook
Dir., Financial Acctg.—Bernardo Martinez
SIC—2033; 2024; NAICS—311421; *Corporate headquarters & fruit juices & yogurt; Brand name—La Yogurt; Tree Ripe; Ssips; Sabor Latino; Earth Wise*
Employs—580; Estab.—1927
Sales—$250Mil-$500Mil
560,000 sq ft site, Distrib.—National
Privately owned corporation

**KERRY INGREDIENTS**
Div. of Kerry, Inc.
26 Minneakoning Rd. (08822)
**Phone—(908) 782-4919**
Fax—(908) 782-6993
www.kerry.com
Email—sales@kerry.com
Plt. Mgr.—Jason Kehn
SIC—2087; NAICS—311900; *Seasonings*
Employs—48
53,000 sq ft site, Distrib.—National
Privately owned corporation
Parent co.—Kerry, Inc., Beloit, WI
Phone—(608) 363-1200
See Parent Co. Section for full profile.

**KUHL CORP.**
39 Kuhl Rd., P.O. Box 26 *(08822)*
**Phone—(908) 782-5696**
Fax—(908) 782-2751
www.kuhlcorp.com
Email—mjv@kuhlcorp.com
CEO—Kevin H. Kuhl
Pres.—Henry Kuhl
CFO, MIS Mgr.—Paul R. Kuhl, Jr.
COO—Jeffrey B. Kuhl
Sales Mgr.—Michael J. Vella
Hum. Res. Mgr.—Rick Kuhl
SIC—3556; NAICS—333294; *Washers, dryers, coolers & filters for the bakery, snack food, chips, chocolate, meat, poultry, egg, hatchery, dairy, beverage & animal research industries; Brand name—KUHL*
Employs—60; Estab.—1909
Distrib.—Intl.
Privately owned corporation

**MAGNA-POWER ELECTRONICS**
39 Royal Rd. (08822)
**Phone—(908) 237-2200**
Fax—(908) 237-2201
www.magna-power.com
Email—sales@magna-power.com
Pres.—Ira Pitel
Dir., Bus. Dev.—Adam Pitel
Dir., Engrg.—Grant Pitel
SIC—3629; NAICS—335999; *DC power supplies*
Employs—90; Estab.—1981
Distrib.—Intl.
Privately owned corporation

**MECHANICAL PRECISION, INC.**
11 Hopewell Ave. (08822)
**Phone—(908) 782-2511**
Fax—(908) 782-2361
www.mechanicalprecision.com
Email—wcullen@mechanicalprecision.com
Pres.—Wallace Cullen, Jr.
V-P.—Michael Cullen
Off. Mgr.—Cindy Cullen
SIC—3599; *Precision machining, including CNC machining, machine building, broaching, welding, grinding & CAD/CAM*
Employs—54; Estab.—1962
Sales—$6Mil-$10Mil
22,000 sq ft site, Distrib.—National
Privately owned corporation

**MEL CHEMICALS**
500 Barbertown Point Breeze Rd. (08822)
**Phone—(908) 782-5800**
National—(800) 366-9596
Fax—(908) 782-8378
www.zrchem.com
Opers. Mgr.—Gavin Edwards
Cust. Serv. Rep.—Donna Warner
SIC—2819; *Zirconium chemicals*
Employs—50; Estab.—1990
Distrib.—Regional
Privately owned corporation

†**NATIONAL PARTS SUPPLY CO., INC.**
56 State Route 31 (08822)
**Phone—(908) 782-3530**
Fax—(908) 782-1185
www.nationalpartssupply.net
Email—411.nps@gmail.com
Store Mgr.—Barry Higgins
Sales Rep.—Ken Silverthorne
SIC—5013; *Distributor of automotive parts, including ignitions*
Employs—20; Estab.—1967
6,000 sq ft site, Distrib.—Local
Privately owned corporation
Parent co.—National Parts Supply Co., Inc., North Brunswick, NJ
Phone—(732) 247-5171
See Parent Co. Section for full profile.

**NEMEC SIGN CO.**
114 Route 31 (08822)
**Phone—(908) 782-3175**
Fax—(908) 782-7515
Email—nemecsign@hotmail.com
Pres., GM—Bill Nemec
SIC—3993; *Interior & exterior signs*
Employs—1; Estab.—1970
Sales—under $500,000
Distrib.—Local
Sole ownership

GEOGRAPHICAL

## Flemington—(cont.)

**NJN PUBLISHING, INC. (H Q)**
8 Minneakoning Rd. (08822)
**Phone—(908) 782-4747**
Fax—(908) 782-9755
www.nj.com
Email—news@hcdemocrat.com
Publisher—Joe Gioioso
V.-P., Adv.—Al Kratzer
Ex. Editor—Craig Turpin
Cont.—Pamela Cahalan
Dir., Circ.—Judith Morgan
IT Mgr.—Robert Bell
Hum. Res. Mgr.—Sherry Ferello
SIC—2711; *Corporate headquarters; newspaper publishing; Brand name— Hunterdon County Democrat*
Employs—75; Estab.—1825
Sales—$1Mil-$2.5Mil
Distrib.—Regional
Privately owned corporation

**†PERROTTI SALES**
19 Woodside Ln. (08822)
**Phone—(908) 806-8899**
Owner—Ray Perrotti
SIC—5074; *Wholesaler of plumbing supplies*
Employs—4

NEW ENTRY
**POWERCOMM SOLUTIONS, LLC**
15 Minneakoning Rd., Ste. 311 (08822)
**Phone—(908) 806-7025**
Fax—(908) 806-4433
www.powercommsolutions.com
Manager—Raymond Fella
SIC—3829; 3825; NAICS— 334220; *Instrumentation products for the electric utility, railroad & transportation industries , including power communications monitors, analyzers, simulators & attenuators*
Employs—5
Sales—$500,000-$1Mil (est)
Limited Liability Company

**PRINT SHOPPE, INC.**
15 Minneakoning Rd., Ste. 305 (08822)
**Phone—(908) 782-9213**
Fax—(908) 782-2959
www.printshoppe.com
Email—psi@printshoppe.com
Pres.—Denise Hayes
V.-P.—Jason Hayes
Prodn. Mgr.—Jim Kennedy
SIC—2759; NAICS—323100; *Commercial printing*
Employs—9; Estab.—1991
Sales—$500,000-$1Mil
Distrib.—Local
Privately owned corporation

**PRINTECH**
35 Main St. (08822)
**Phone—(908) 782-9986**
Fax—(908) 806-7820
www.prin-tech.com
Email—mail@prin-tech.com
Pres.—Joseph Mastrull
Sales Rep.—Valerie Lezan
SIC—2759; NAICS—323100; *Commercial printing*
Employs—9; Estab.—1991
Sales—$500,000-$1Mil
3,500 sq ft site, Distrib.—Local
Privately owned corporation
AKA: Jem Printing

**PROGRAM DYNAMICS, INC.**
43 Pennsylvania Ave., P.O. Box 929 (08822)
**Phone—(908) 782-9398**
Pres., GM—Stephen Barrick
V.-P.—Pam Barrick

SIC—2721; 2741; *Automobile racing program & magazine publishing*
Employs—2; Estab.—1975
Sales—under $500,000
Distrib.—Regional
Privately owned corporation

**ROZANO SIGNS**
1005 County Road 523 (08822)
**Phone—(908) 788-5042**
Email—rozanosigns@gmail.com
Owner—Paul Rozano
SIC—3993; *Vinyl & hand lettered signs*
Employs—2; Estab.—1987
Sales—under $500,000
Distrib.—Regional
Sole ownership

**RSA ASSOCIATES**
812 County Road 579 (08822)
**Phone—(908) 806-4681**
www.rsa-assoc.com
Email—rsa@rsa-assoc.com
Pres.—Robert Alparone
SIC—7373; *Computer network systems integration, including EDI, ERP & CRM systems; Brand name—SAP; IBM; HP; Epson; Commvault; Symantec; Altova; HP; OKI; Intuit; Gentran; Sterling Integrator; Macola; Davinci WMS; Royal 4*
Employs—4; Estab.—1985
Distrib.—National
Sole ownership

**SOLSTICE MFG. CO.**
Div. of Advanced Solar Products, Inc.
270 S. Main St., Ste. 102 (08822)
**Phone—(908) 284-0096**
www.solsticemanufacturing.com
Email—info@ solsticemanufacturing.com
Dir., Opers.—Chris Rawlings
SIC—3429; *Ballasted solar panel mounting systems for flat commercial roofs, landfills & brownfields*
Employs—2; Estab.—2011
Sales—under $500,000 (est)
Distrib.—Local
Privately owned corporation
Parent co.—Advanced Solar Products, Inc., Flemington, NJ
Phone—(908) 751-5818
See Parent Co. Section for full profile.

**SPECIAL T'S**
12 Kings Ct. (08822-5555)
**Phone—(908) 806-8337**
Fax—(908) 806-2017
www.special-ts.com
Email—ryan@special-ts.com
Pres.—Ryan Amato
SIC—2395; 2396; *Custom & contract screen printing & embroidery on garments & textiles*
Employs—15; Estab.—1991
Sales—$1Mil
14,000 sq ft site, Distrib.—National
Privately owned sub-S corp.
AKA: Ambro Mfg.

**SUMMIT CHEMICAL SPECIALTY PRODUCTS**
45 River Rd., Ste. 300 (08822)
**Phone—(908) 782-9500**
Fax—(908) 782-5377
www.summitchem.com
Email—info@summitchem.com
Ptnr. & CEO—Richard Rosen
Ptnr. & CEO—Piyush J. Patel
Ptnr. & Ex. V.-P.—Milton K. Rosen
SIC—2819; 2899; *Aluminum compounds & industrial chemicals for wastewater treatment applications*
Employs—35
Distrib.—Intl.
Privately owned corporation

**TEES TO PLEASE SCREEN PRINTING**
15 Minneakoing Dr., P.O. Box 542 (08822)
**Phone—(908) 788-5508**
Fax—(908) 788-9448
www.tees2please.ws
Owner—Greg Legacki
Off. Mgr.—Karen Baron
SIC—2396; *T-shirt screen printing*
Employs—10; Estab.—1997
Sales—$1Mil-$2.5Mil
Distrib.—Regional
Sole ownership

**TRI-SEAL**
Div. of Tekni-Plex, Inc.
112 Church St. (08822)
**Phone—(908) 782-4000**
Fax—(908) 782-0990
www.tekni-plex.com
Email—info@tekni-plex.com
Plt. Controller—Sue Franson
Plt. Mgr.—James Khoury
R & D Mgr.—Randy Rounsaville
Cust. Serv. Rep.—Tara Rounsaville
SIC—2671; 3089; *Flexible packaging & cap liners*
Employs—120; Estab.—1998
Distrib.—Intl.
Privately owned corporation
Parent co.—Tekni-Plex, Inc., King of Prussia, PA
Phone—(484) 690-1520
See Parent Co. Section for full profile.

**UNITED STATES METAL POWDERS, INC.**
408 U.S. Highway 202 (08822)
**Phone—(908) 782-5454**
National—(800) 544-0186
Fax—(908) 782-3489
www.ampal-inc.com
Email—rhonda.kasler@ usbronzpowders.com
Pres., CEO—Clive Ramsey
V.-P., Tech.—Jessu Joys
V.-P. & Cust. Serv. Mgr.—Rhonda Kasler
Corp. Cont.—Barry Schmutter
SIC—3399; *Corporate headquarters & atomized aluminum powders for chemical, metallurgical & powder metallurgy applications*
Employs—12; Estab.—1918
Sales—$10Mil-$25Mil
Distrib.—Intl.
AKA: Ampal, Inc.

**VIVA MEXICAN RESTAURANT**
117 Broad St., Unit 1 (08822)
**Phone—(908) 788-0744**
www.restaurantevivamexico.com
Owner—Filiberto Arias
SIC—2099; *Frozen Mexican entrees*
Employs—10
Sales—$1Mil-$2.5Mil (est)

**WHITEHURST & CLARK, INC.**
1200 County Road 523 (08822)
**Phone—(908) 782-2323**
National—(800) 488-8040
Fax—(908) 237-2407
www.wcbks.com
Email—wcbooks@aol.com
Owner—Brad Seales
Plt. Mgr.—Elayne Suckno
IT Mgr.—Jay Makuch
SIC—2731; *Textbook publishing*
Employs—15; Estab.—1969
Sales—$2Mil
Distrib.—Intl.
Sole ownership

## Florence

(Burlington—S.E.)

**D C FABRICATORS, INC.**
801 W. Front St. (08518)
**Phone—(609) 499-3000**
Fax—(609) 499-4214
www.dcfab.com
Email—sales@dcfab.com
Pres., CEO—Gary Butler
Dir., Proj. Mgmt.—Lou Iszak
SIC—3443; *Steam condensers, heat exchangers, air ejectors, pressure vessels & filters*
Employs—130; Estab.—1995
Sales—$25Mil
125,000 sq ft site, Distrib.—Intl.
Privately owned sub-S corp.

**ENDURANCE NET, INC.**
763-B Railroad Ave. (08518)
Mail addr: P.O. Box 127, Roebling (08554-0127)
**Phone—(609) 499-3450**
National—(800) 808-6387
Fax—(609) 499-3520
www.endurancenetinc.com
Email—endurancenet@aol.com
Pres.—Anita Scarperia
V.-P.—Catherine Scarperia
SIC—2821; 3081; NAICS— 325211; *Barrier netting for schools, parks, zoos, animal protection, landfills & environmental agencies, game bird farms, vineyards, nurseries, tennis & baseball fields, golf courses & the construction & aquaculture industries*
Employs—15; Estab.—1966
6,500 sq ft site, Distrib.—National
Privately owned corporation
Also see: Tex-Net, Inc., same loc.

**MIDWAY MACHINE PRODUCT CORP.**
763-A Railroad Ave., P.O. Box 129 (08518)
**Phone—(609) 499-4377**
Fax—(609) 499-0084
www.midwaymachineproducts.com
Email—midway1987@verizon.net
Pres.—William Greene
V.-P.—Chris Greene
V.-P.—Scott Greene
Off. Mgr.—Dee Brecht
SIC—3599; *General machining job shop*
Employs—10; Estab.—1987
Sales—$500,000-$1Mil
Distrib.—Local
Privately owned corporation

**READY PAC PRODUCE, INC.**
700 Railroad Ave., P.O. Box 6 (08518-0006)
**Phone—(609) 499-1900**
National—(800) 567-1901
Fax—(609) 499-1406
www.readypac.com
Email—info@readypac.com
Cont.—Bernard Ganski
Dir., Plt.—Robert Nichols
Hum. Res. Mgr.—Christina Crowley
SIC—2099; *Packaged salads*
Employs—550; Estab.—1990
Sales—over $150Mil
106,000 sq ft site, Distrib.— National
Privately owned corporation
Parent co.—Ready Pac Produce, Inc., Irwindale, CA
Phone—(626) 856-8686
See Parent Co. Section for full profile.

## Florence—(cont.)

**TEX-NET, INC.**
763-B Railroad Ave. (08518)
Mail addr: P.O. Box 127, Roebling
(08554-0127)
**Phone—(609) 499-9111**
　　　　(609) 499-4545
National—(800) 541-1123
Fax—(609) 499-8227
www.texnetusa.com
Email—info@texnetusa.com
Pres.—John Scarperia
V.-P., Sales & Mktg.—Annette
　Scarperia
SIC—2821; 3081; NAICS—
　325211; *Polyester, polypropylene
　& nylon barrier netting systems
　for golf courses & driving ranges,
　baseball fields & indoor &
　outdoor sports training facilities*
Employs—20; Estab.—1986
Sales—$10Mil-$25Mil
Distrib.—Intl.
Privately owned corporation
Also see: Endurance Net, Inc.,
　same loc.

**TOTAL CONTROL ORTHOTIC LAB**
14 W. Front St. (08518)
**Phone—(609) 499-2200**
www.totalcontrolorthoticlab.com
Email—totalcontrolorthoticlab@
　verizon.net
Pres.—Dominic Ciccone, Jr.
SIC—3842; *Prosthetics &
　orthotics*
Employs—4; Estab.—1998
Sales—$500,000-$1Mil
Distrib.—Local
Privately owned sub-S corp.

---

# Florham Park
(Morris—N.W.)

NEW ENTRY
**ARMAC ASSOCS.**
71 Passaic Ave. (07932)
**Phone—(888) 422-3044**
Fax—(973) 328-3753
www.armac.us
Owner—Herb Etzold
SIC—3842; *Orthopedic devices*
Employs—20
Sales—$2.5Mil-$5Mil (est)

**ASCO POWER TECHNOLOGIES, L.P.
(H Q)**
Div. of Emerson Electric Co.
50 Hanover Rd. *(07932)*
**Phone—(800) 800-2726**
Fax—(973) 718-4333
www.emersonnetworkpower.com/
　asco
Email—customercare@asco.com
Pres.—Armand J. Visioli
V.-P., Sales & Mktg.—Donald
　Blackman
V.-P., Opers.—Mike Quinn
V.-P., Serv.—Allan Dunster
V.-P., Intl.—Amir Abouhasm
V.-P., Engrg.—Daniel Scheffer
SIC—3669; 3679; 3625; NAICS—
　334290; *Divisional headquarters;
　automatic transfer switches,
　power control systems,
　communications, industrial & fire
　pump products; Brand name—
　ASCO; Firetrol; Avtron
　Loadbanks; Surge Protection*
Employs—300; Estab.—1888
Sales—over $300Mil
300,000 sq ft site, Distrib.—Intl.
Privately owned corporation
ISO rating—9001:2000
Parent co.—Emerson Electric Co.,
　St. Louis, MO
Phone—(314) 553-2000
See Parent Co. Section for full profile.

**ASCO VALVE, INC.**
Div. of Emerson Electric Co.
50-60 Hanover Rd. (07932)
**Phone—(973) 966-2000**
Fax—(973) 966-2459
www.ascovalve.com
Email—info-valve@asco.com
Group Pres.—Jean Pierre
　Yaouanc
Ex. V.-P., Sales & Mktg.,
　Americas—Robert W. Kemple,
　Jr.
V.-P., Hum. Res.—Christopher
　Walsh
Corp. Secy.—Mary Ann Kranz
Dir., IT—Horst Braumann
Mktg. Comm. Mgr.—Kristen
　Walker
SIC—3491; NAICS—332911;
　*Corporate headquarters &
　miniature industrial valves*
Employs—220; Estab.—1888
Sales—$250Mil-$500Mil
Distrib.—National
Publicly owned corporation
Parent co.—Emerson Electric Co.,
　St. Louis, MO
Phone—(314) 553-2000
See Parent Co. Section for full profile.

NEW ENTRY
**ASCO VALVE, INC.**
50 Hanover Rd. (07932)
**Phone—(973) 966-2000**
Fax—(973) 966-2448
www.ascovalve.com
Email—info-valve@asco.com
Pres., Americas—John Meek
Ex. V.-P., Sales & Mktg.—Robert
　Kemple
V.-P., Sales, Fluid Power—Kent
　Brown
V.-P., Sales—Andy Duffy
Mktg. Coord., Social Media—
　Jenna Rebetje
SIC—3491; NAICS—332911;
　*Industrial valves*
Employs—500; Estab.—1888
Distrib.—Regional
Publicly owned corporation
Parent co.—ASCO Valve, Inc.,
　Florham Park, NJ
Phone—(973) 966-2000
See Parent Co. Section for full profile.

**BASF CORPORATION (H Q)**
100 Park Ave. (07932)
**Phone—(973) 245-6000**
National—(800) 526-1072
Fax—(973) 245-6714
www.basf.us
Email—kelley.white@basf.com
Chrm., CEO—Hans Engel
Pres., Ex. V.-P. & CFO—Andre
　Becker
Pres. & Ex. V.-P., Cust. & Market
　Dev.—Beate Ehle
Pres. & Ex. V.-P., Catalysts Div.—
　Kenneth Lane
Sr. V.-P., Gen. Counsel & CCO—
　Matthew Lepore
V.-P., Chief Comms. Officer—Robin
　Rotenberg
Sr. V.-P., Hum. Res.—Judy
　Zagorski
Corp. Media Rels. Mgr.—Kelley P.
　White
SIC—2899; *Corporate
　headquarters; industrial
　chemicals; Brand name—
　Ecovio; Elastopave;
　Luquafleece; Soluplus;
　Glysantin; Basotect; Green
　Sense; Sonneborn; Headline;
　Termidor; Phantom; Tonalin CLA*
Employs—1400; Estab.—1958
Worldwide: 112,000
Sales—$99Bil
325,000 sq ft site, Distrib.—Intl.
Publicly owned corporation

**BOOMERANG SYSTEMS, INC.**
30-A Vreeland Rd., Ste. 150
(07932)
**Phone—(973) 538-1194**
www.boomerangsystems.com
Email—info@
　boomerangsystems.com
CEO—Mark R. Patterson
Pres., Sales & Mktg. Mgr.—
　Christopher Mulvihill
CFO—Scott Shepherd
Treas.—Ryan Campbell
SIC—3569; *Corporate
　headquarters & automated
　robotic parking garage
　equipment & automated self
　storage systems*
Employs—8; Estab.—2008
Sales—$1Mil-$2.5Mil (est)
Distrib.—Intl.
Privately owned corporation

†**BRENT MATERIAL CO.**
325 Columbia Tpke., Ste. 308
(07932)
**Phone—(973) 325-3030**
　　　　(908) 686-3832
Fax—(973) 325-7360
www.brentmaterial.com
Email—info@brentmaterial.com
Pres.—Linda Gardner
SIC—5074; *Distributor of
　construction material for water,
　storm & sewer systems,
　including erosion control*
Employs—12; Estab.—1927
Distrib.—Local
Privately owned corporation

**FTI, INC. (H Q)**
Div. of Troy Corp.
8 Vreeland Rd. (07932)
**Phone—(973) 443-4200**
Fax—(973) 443-0263
www.tetraproducts.com
Email—ftiinfo@troycorp.com
V.-P.—William B. Smith
SIC—2992; 3312; NAICS—
　324191; *Corporate
　headquarters; gun lubricants,
　cleaning solvents & stainless
　steel cleaning rods (mfg.
　subcontracted)*
Employs—120; Estab.—1985
Sales—$1Mil-$2.5Mil
Distrib.—Intl.
Privately owned corporation
AKA: Tetra Products
Parent co.—Troy Corp., Florham
　Park, NJ
Phone—(973) 443-4200
See Parent Co. Section for full profile.

**GENERAL DYNAMICS ADVANCED
INFORMATION SYSTEMS**
Div. of General Dynamics Corp.
7-9 Vreeland Rd. (07932)
**Phone—(973) 514-4000**
Fax—(973) 765-5815
www.gd-ais.com
Email—ais.contact@gd-ais.com
Br. Mgr.—John Incera
SIC—3812; 7372; NAICS—
　334418; *Information systems for
　the aerospace, combat,
　technology & marine markets,
　including hardware & software*
Employs—25
Sales—$2.5Mil-$5Mil (est)
Distrib.—Local
Publicly owned corporation
Parent co.—General Dynamics
　Corp., Falls Church, VA
Phone—(703) 876-3000
See Parent Co. Section for full profile.

**HELLER INDUSTRIES, INC.**
4 Vreeland Rd., Ste. 1 (07932)
**Phone—(973) 377-6800**
Fax—(973) 377-3862
www.hellerindustries.com
Email—info@hellerindustries.com
CEO—David Heller

Pres.—Marc Peo
V.-P., Corp. Accts.—Don De Angelo
Cust. Serv. Rep.—Aubrey Ward
SIC—3569; *Reflow soldering
　ovens*
Employs—45; Estab.—1960
55,000 sq ft site, Distrib.—Intl.
Privately owned corporation

**LAPP USA**
29 Hanover Rd. *(07932)*
**Phone—(973) 660-9700**
　　　　(800) 774-3539
Fax—(973) 660-9330
www.lappusa.com
Email—sales@lappusa.com
Pres.—Marc Mackin
Ex. V.-P., Cable Div.—H. Keith
　Myrick
Mktg. Comms. Mgr.—Maureen
　Broe
SIC—3678; NAICS—334417;
　*Company headquarters &
　rectangular, pin & sleeve
　connectors, flexible cables,
　cable track, conduit, strain relief,
　remote access ports &
　assemblies; Brand name—
　OLFLEX; EPIC; CONTACT;
　SKINTOP; UNITRONIC; SILVYN;
　SILFLEX; FLEXIMARK;
　HITRONIC*
Employs—150; Estab.—1976
Sales—$50Mil
130,000 sq ft site, Distrib.—
　National
Privately owned corporation
ISO rating—9001:2000

**NESTLE HEALTHCARE NUTRITION,
INC. (H Q)**
12 Vreeland Rd., 2nd Fl., P.O. Box
697 (07932)
**Phone—(973) 593-7500**
　　　　(973) 593-7599
Fax—(973) 593-7600
www.nestle-nutrition.com
Email—mary.wade@us.nestle.com
Reg. Bus. Head, N. America—
　David Yates
Head of Infant Nutrition, Reg.
　Bus.—Gary Tickle
Head of Hum. Res., N. America—
　Georgina De La Pena
Head of Med. Affs.—Carol Siegle
Head of Med. Affs.—Jose
　Saavedra
SIC—2032; 3085; 3069; NAICS—
　326160; *Corporate
　headquarters; baby food &
　nutritional accessories, including
　infant bottles, cups & pacifiers;
　Brand name—BOOST®*
Employs—400; Estab.—1901
Sales—$100Mil-$250Mil (est)
Publicly owned corporation
AKA: Nestle Health Science

**SHIONOGI, INC. (H Q)**
300 Campus Dr. (07932)
**Phone—(973) 966-6900**
National—(855) 744-6664
www.shionogi.com
Email—medicalinformation@
　shionogi.com
Sales Mgr., District—Byron Brown
SIC—2834; NAICS—325412;
　*Corporate headquarters;
　pharmaceuticals (mfg.
　subcontracted)*
Employs—200; Estab.—1997
Sales—$100Mil-$250Mil (est)
Distrib.—National
Privately owned corporation

**SIEMENS INFRASTRUCTURE &
CITIES, BUILDING TECHNOLOGIES**
8 Fernwood Rd. (07932)
**Phone—(973) 593-2600**
National—(800) 222-0108
Fax—(973) 593-6670
www.usa.siemens.com/
　buildingtechnologies

GEOGRAPHICAL

## Florham Park—(cont.)

Email—fpkcustomerservice.us.sbt@
siemens.com
V.-P., Div.—Robert Suermann
Hum. Res. Mgr.—Diane Lancaster
Qual. Assur. Mgr.—Harry Lee
SIC—3669; NAICS—334290; *Fire
protection systems*
Employs—250; Estab.—1955
Sales—$50Mil-$100Mil
Distrib.—Intl.
Publicly owned corporation
Parent co.—Siemens
Infrastructure & Cities, Building
Technologies, Buffalo Grove, IL
Phone—(847) 215-1000
See Parent Co. Section for full profile.

### SUREPURE CHEMETALS, INC.

5 Nottingham Dr. (07932)
**Phone—(973) 377-4081**
Fax—(973) 377-5654
www.surepure.com
Email—sales@surepure.com
Pres.—Barry Vegter
MIS & Opers. Mgr.—Howard
Vegter
Fin. Mgr.—Stacey Klein
SIC—3357; *Gold, silver &
platinum wires*
Employs—8; Estab.—1979
Sales—$1Mil-$2.5Mil (est)
4,500 sq ft site, Distrib.—Intl.
Limited Liability Company

### TROPAR MFG. CO., INC.

5 Vreeland Rd. (07932)
**Phone—(973) 822-2400**
Fax—(973) 822-2891
www.airflyte.com
Email—gregd@airflyte.com
Pres.—Peter E. Ilaria
V.-P.—Gregory Della Badia
Pur. Mgr.—Stephen P.
Wannemacher
IT Mgr.—Bob O'Shea
Hum. Res. Mgr.—Rhonda
Samaniego
Cred. Mgr.—Phyllis Bosset
SIC—2499; 3499; 3873; 3089;
NAICS—334518; *Corporate
headquarters & plaques, clocks
& acrylic awards; Brand name—
AirFlyte*
Employs—60; Estab.—1959
Sales—$15Mil
50,000 sq ft site, Distrib.—Intl.
Privately owned corporation

### TROY CORP.

8 Vreeland Rd. (07932)
**Phone—(973) 443-4200**
Fax—(973) 443-0258
www.troycorp.com
Email—marketing@troycorp.com
Chrm., CEO—Daryl Smith
V.-P., Mktg.—David E. Faherty
V.-P., Admn. & Govt. Rels.—
Alexander Gerardo
V.-P., Hum. Res.—Robert Chance
V.-P., Dev.—Donald Shaw
SIC—2899; *Corporate
headquarters & biocides &
specialty additives; Brand
name—Polyphase; Troysan;
Mergal; Troykyd; Troysperse;
Troythix; Troyshield; Troysol;
Troymax; Troychem;
Powdermate® Homeshield*
Employs—70
Distrib.—Intl.
Privately owned corporation
ISO rating—9001:2000, 4001:2004

### VDM METALS USA, LLC

306 Columbia Tpke. (07932)
**Phone—(973) 437-1664**
National—(800) 227-8368
Fax—(973) 236-1960
www.thyssenkrupp-vdm-usa.com
Pres.—Tony Elfstrom
COO & Plt. Mgr.—George Kramer
CFO—Mike Risse

V.-P., Sales—Will Harbison
Sales Mgr., Inside—Jamie
Chesman
IT Mgr.—Louise Wood
Manager—Steve Chapman
SIC—3356; 3312; NAICS—
331491; *Company headquarters
& metal alloys & rolled steel
products*
Employs—80; Estab.—2001
Sales—$70Mil
130,000 sq ft site, Distrib.—Intl.
Privately owned corporation

### WASHINGTON STAMP EXCHANGE, INC.

2 Vreeland Rd. (07932)
**Phone—(973) 966-0001**
National—(877) 966-0001
www.washpress.com
Pres.—Michael August
Treas.—Tim Dvaney
SIC—2759; NAICS—323100;
*Commercial printing*
Employs—10; Estab.—1932
Sales—under $500,000
Distrib.—Regional
Privately owned corporation

### WORLD WIDE PACKAGING, LLC

15 Vreeland Rd. *(07932-1506)*
**Phone—(973) 805-6500**
National—(800) 950-0390
Fax—(973) 805-6512
www.wwpinc.com
Email—sales@wwpinc.com
Chrm.—Jeffrey S. Schneider
CEO—Barry Freda
Dir., Mktg. & Off. Mgr.—Holly
Benda
SIC—2844; 3089; *Contract
manufacturing of packaging
components for the cosmetic &
skin care industries, including
specialty decorating, finishing &
secondary packaging*
Employs—50; Estab.—1980
Sales—$2.5Mil-$5Mil
Distrib.—Intl.
Limited Liability Company

---

## Folsom

(Atlantic—S.E.)

### AMERICAN GALVANIZING CO., INC.

Div. of Virginia American
Industries, Inc.
1919 R.R. 54 *(08094)*
Mail addr.: P.O. Box 408,
Hammonton (08037-0408)
**Phone—(609) 567-2090**
Fax—(609) 567-2822
www.amergalv.com
Email—jgregor@amergalv.com
Pres.—John Gregor
Opers. Mgr.—George Cheesman
Off. Mgr.—Lillie Echevarria
Qual. Control Mgr.—Allen Ivins
Supply Chain Mgr.—Ian Gregor
Maint. Mgr.—Dave Powell
Sales Coord., Regional—Rick
Torres
Sales Coord., Regional—Jeff
Scagnelli
SIC—3443; 3479; *Hot dip
galvanizing & value-added
fabrication, assembly, masking &
painting*
Employs—70; Estab.—1982
Sales—$8Mil-$10Mil
70,000 sq ft site, Distrib.—National
Privately owned corporation
Parent co.—Virginia American
Industries, Inc., Richmond, VA
Phone—(804) 644-2611
See Parent Co. Section for full profile.

## Fords

(Middlesex—N.E.)

### BAI LAR INTERIOR SERVICES, INC.

554 New Brunswick Ave. (08863)
**Phone—(732) 738-0350**
National—(800) 481-0350
Fax—(732) 738-0074
www.bailarinteriors.com
Email—bailarinc@aol.com
Pres.—James E. Quinn
V.-P.—Patrick M. Quinn
SIC—2391; 2591; 5023; NAICS—
314121; *Manufacturer &
distributor of commercial stage
draperies, hospital cubicle
curtains & window shades &
blinds; Brand name—Springs
Window Fashions; Hunter
Douglas; Draper Inc.; Levolor;
Kirsch; Lutron; DaLite*
Employs—5; Estab.—1968
Sales—$800,000
Distrib.—Regional
Privately owned corporation

### CHEMTURA CORP., HATCO DIV.

Div. of Chemtura Corp.
1020 King George Post Rd.
(08863)
**Phone—(732) 738-1000**
Fax—(732) 738-1087
www.chemtura.com
Email—info@chemtura.com
Opers. Mgr.—Michael Goldberg
Hum. Res. Specialist—Shonagh
Stringfellow
SIC—2869; 2992; NAICS—
324191; *Synthetic lubricants &
intermediate organic chemicals*
Employs—145; Estab.—1957
Distrib.—Intl.
Publicly owned corporation
Parent co.—Chemtura Corp.,
Philadelphia, PA
Phone—(215) 446-3911
See Parent Co. Section for full profile.

### DATAMATICS MANAGEMENT SERVICES, INC.

330 New Brunswick Ave. (08863)
**Phone—(732) 738-9600**
National—(800) 673-0366
Fax—(732) 738-9603
www.datamaticsinc.com
Email—info@datamaticsinc.com
Chrm.—Norman C. Heinle, Jr.
Pres.—R. Kevin Heinle
V.-P., Dev. & Research—Raymond
Embry
Dir., Online Svcs.—Noah Heinle
Sales Coord.—Debbie Nelson
SIC—7372; *Time & attendance,
employee tracking & labor
management software
development, including
employee scheduling,
attendance record keeping,
benefit tracking, labor allocation
& access control; Brand name—
TC-1 Labor Management
System Enterprise Solution;
TimesheetPlus Web-based
Labor Management System*
Employs—20; Estab.—1966
Distrib.—National
Privately owned corporation

### MIDDLESEX INDUSTRIAL SALES, INC.

522 New Brunswick Ave. (08863)
**Phone—(732) 738-0537**
Fax—(732) 738-7077
www.middlesex.com
Pres.—Michael Amendola
SIC—3537; 3563; NAICS—
333912; *Material handling
equipment & air compressors*
Employs—3; Estab.—1967
Sales—under $500,000
2,500 sq ft site, Distrib.—Regional
Privately owned sub-S corp.

### MR. PRINTER

466 New Brunswick Ave. (08863)
**Phone—(732) 738-3977**
Fax—(732) 738-7569
Email—garymrp@aol.com
Owner—Gary Meyer
SIC—2759; NAICS—323100;
*Commercial printing*
Employs—2; Estab.—1990
Sales—under $500,000
Distrib.—Local
Sole ownership

---

## Forked River

(Ocean—S.E.)

### A B C MACHINERY CORP.

712-1 Old Shore Rd., P.O. Box
1212 (08731)
**Phone—(609) 971-0990**
Fax—(609) 971-1176
www.abcmachinerycorp.com
Email—abcmachinery@verizon.net
Prodn. Mgr.—Barry Cerino
SIC—3552; NAICS—333292;
*Textile machinery parts*
Employs—6; Estab.—1954
Sales—under $500,000
Distrib.—Intl.
Privately owned corporation

### APHRODITE MARBLE & GRANITE CO., INC.

700 Old Shore Rd. (08731)
**Phone—(609) 693-4450**
Fax—(609) 693-2244
www.aphroditemarbleandgranite.c
om
Email—spyro@
aphroditemarbleandgranite.com
Opers. Mgr.—Spyros Katsianis
Bookkeeper—Tara Katsianis
SIC—3281; NAICS—327991;
*Marble & granite fabrication*
Employs—6; Estab.—1980
Sales—$500,000-$1Mil
Distrib.—Regional
Privately owned corporation

### BILFINGER WATER TECHNOLOGIES

Div. of Weatherford International
Ltd.
708 Challenger Way (08731)
**Phone—(609) 693-9434**
National—(800) 935-5727
Fax—(609) 971-8708
www.bilfinger.com
Email—hank.leavitt@bilfinger.com
Plt. Mgr.—Hank Leavitt
Hum. Res. Mgr.—Skip Bolton
Cust. Serv. Rep.—Kathleen Ford
SIC—3084; 3083; NAICS—
326122; *PVC casings, fittings &
ground water monitoring
remediation products*
Employs—25; Estab.—1979
30,000 sq ft site, Distrib.—Intl.
Publicly owned corporation
Parent co.—Weatherford
International Ltd., Houston, TX
Phone—(713) 836-4000
See Parent Co. Section for full profile.

### BRICK-WALL CORP.

2215 Lacey Rd. (08731)
**Phone—(609) 693-6223**
Fax—(609) 971-7212
Email—lhesse@cjhesse.com
Plt. Mgr.—Jeff Grossman
SIC—2951; NAICS—324121;
*Asphalt paving compounds*
Employs—20
Distrib.—Local
Privately owned corporation
Parent co.—Brick-Wall Corp.,
Atlantic Highlands, NJ
Phone—(732) 787-0226
See Parent Co. Section for full profile.

## Forked River—(cont.)

**NEW ENTRY**
**C & C SIGNS & BANNERS**
812 Forepeak Dr. (08731)
**Phone—(609) 693-4667**
www.cncsigns.com
Owner—Paul Colucci
SIC—3993; 3089; 2759; *Interior & exterior signs & vinyl lettering & vehicle wraps*
Employs—1; Estab.—1997
Sales—under $500,000
2,000 sq ft site, Distrib.—Local
Sole ownership

**CORBCO, INC.**
40 Canterbury Dr. (08731)
**Phone—(908) 239-3279**
Email—corbcohpc@comcast.net
Pres.—Hipolito Paul Corbacho
V.-P.—Rose Corbacho
SIC—3089; *Plastic packaging prototyping*
Employs—3; Estab.—1978
Sales—$130,000-$300,000
800 sq ft site, Distrib.—National
Sole ownership

**CUSTOM AUTO RADIATOR, INC.**
441 S. Main St., Route 9 (08731)
**Phone—(609) 242-9700**
         (609) 242-1500
Fax—(609) 242-9793
www.customautoradiator.com
Email—carstreetrodpart@aol.com
Pres.—Charles Monjoy
Manager & Admn.—Kim Monjoy
SIC—3714; *Automotive radiators*
Employs—4; Estab.—1979
Sales—under $500,000
Distrib.—Intl.
Privately owned corporation

†**FERGUSON ENTERPRISES, INC.**
737 S. Main St. (08731)
**Phone—(609) 693-0077**
www.ferguson.com
Email—webmaster@ferguson.com
Br. Mgr.—Anthony D'Cone
Counter Mgr.—Mike Finley
SIC—5074; 5075; *Distributor of plumbing & HVAC equipment & supplies, including pipes, fixtures, valves, fittings, pumps & well supplies*
Employs—8; Estab.—1982
Sales—under $500,000
Distrib.—National
Publicly owned corporation
Parent co.—Ferguson Enterprises, Inc., Newport News, VA
   Phone—(757) 874-7795
See Parent Co. Section for full profile.

**GRANT BOAT WORKS**
120 Lakeside Dr., Ste. E, P.O. Box 597 (08731)
**Phone—(609) 971-1075**
Owner—Gregory Grant
SIC—3732; *Rebuilt boats*
Employs—2; Estab.—1927
Sales—under $500,000
Distrib.—Local
Sole ownership

**IACOVELLI STAIRS, INC.**
707 Challenger Way (08731)
**Phone—(609) 693-3476**
Fax—(609) 971-6766
Email—iacovellistairs@gmail.com
Pres.—Joseph Iacovelli
SIC—2431; NAICS—321900; *Wooden stairs & railings*
Employs—10; Estab.—1981
6,000 sq ft site, Distrib.—Regional
Privately owned corporation

**NEW ENTRY**
**LACEY CASH REGISTERS & BUSINESS MACHINES CO.**
2180 Llewellyn Pkwy., P.O. Box 1151 (08731)
**Phone—(609) 971-9494**
Fax—(609) 971-8111
Owner—Gene D'Alessandro
SIC—3578; NAICS—334419; *Rebuilt electronic cash registers*
Employs—2
Sales—under $500,000 (est)

**LOMBARDO GRAPHIC CONSULTANTS, INC.**
429 Lacey Rd., Ste. 8 (08731)
**Phone—(609) 693-1727**
Fax—(609) 971-5823
www.lgcprinting.com
Email—lombardographics@aol.com
Pres.—Eileen M. Lombardo
V.-P., Sales—John Paul Lombardo
Sales Mgr.—Jodi Lombardo
SIC—2759; NAICS—323100; *Commercial, business form & package printing*
Employs—7; Estab.—1989
Sales—$1Mil-$2.5Mil
5,500 sq ft site, Distrib.—National
Privately owned corporation

**ODD-IT-TEES**
405 S. Main St. (08731)
**Phone—(609) 693-8337**
Fax—(609) 693-6534
www.odditrees.logomall.com
Email—odditrees@verizon.net
Owner—William Austin
Off. Mgr.—Paula Austin
SIC—2396; *Textile screen printing*
Employs—4; Estab.—1981
Distrib.—Regional
Privately owned corporation

**PATRIOT MARINE FABRICATING**
708-4 Old Shore Rd. (08731-5903)
**Phone—(609) 693-5542**
Fax—(609) 693-9417
www.patriotmarinefab.net
Email—patriotmarine@comcast.net
Pres.—Nicole Spisak
SIC—3732; 3443; 3499; *Aluminum work boats, marine fuel tanks & metal fabrication*
Employs—3; Estab.—1990
Sales—under $500,000
3,500 sq ft site, Distrib.—National
Limited Liability Company
AKA: P/N Metalworks

**PLASTICS FOR CHEMICALS, INC.**
710 Old Shore Rd. (08731)
**Phone—(609) 242-9100**
National—(800) 230-1797
Fax—(609) 242-9137
Email—pfcfortfe@comcast.net
Pres., GM—John Donovan
SIC—3083; 3089; NAICS—326130; *Tetrafluoroethylene products*
Employs—5; Estab.—1980
Sales—$1Mil-$2.5Mil
4,500 sq ft site, Distrib.—National
Privately owned corporation

**REGAL PRINTERS, INC.**
707-3 Old Shore Rd. (08731)
**Phone—(609) 693-3533**
Fax—(609) 971-5962
Email—ttrenholm@regallithprinters.com
Pres.—Tom Trenholm
Proj. Mgr.—Beth Patterson
SIC—2752; NAICS—323100; *Lithographic printing*
Employs—4; Estab.—1985
Sales—under $500,000 (est)
Distrib.—Local
Privately owned corporation

**TRADEWIN SIGN, LLC**
699 Challenger Way, Unit D-7 (08731)
**Phone—(609) 488-5961**
Fax—(609) 488-5962
www.tradewinsign.com
Email—sales@tradewinsign.com
Owner—Darren Gibson
Asst. Off. Mgr.—Marni Renold
SIC—3993; *Signs, including neon & vinyl signs*
Employs—2; Estab.—2009
Sales—under $500,000
4,000 sq ft site, Distrib.—Regional
Limited Liability Company

**TRICO HOSE & GASKET CORP.**
700-2 Challenger Way, Lacey Business Pk. (08731)
**Phone—(609) 693-5301**
Fax—(609) 693-5304
www.tricohg.com
Email—adrian@tricohg.com
Owner—Adrian Seitz
SIC—3053; 3069; 5085; NAICS—339991; *Manufacturer of rubber gaskets & seals & distributor of industrial hoses & couplings*
Employs—4; Estab.—2004
Sales—$1Mil-$2Mil
3,000 sq ft site, Distrib.—National
Sole ownership

**TRYBUN ENGRAVING, LLC**
706 Old Shore Rd., Ste. 3 (08731)
**Phone—(609) 242-3105**
National—(800) 795-8757
Fax—(629) 242-3106
www.trybunengraving.com
Email—trybunengraving@aol.com
Pres.—Robert Trybun
GM—Michael Christopher
SIC—3479; *Plastic sign engraving*
Employs—3; Estab.—1999
Sales—under $500,000
Distrib.—Regional
Limited Liability Company

## Fort Dix

(Burlington—S.E.)

**UNICOR FEDERAL PRISON INDUSTRIES, INC.**
5835 Doughboy Loop, P.O. Box 38 (08640)
**Phone—(609) 723-1100**
Fax—(609) 723-8715
www.unicor.gov
Email—lawhorn@central.unicor.gov
Factory Mgr., Recycling—Jeff Eobstell
Factory Mgr., Textiles—Robert Ortiz
Warden—Donna Likefoose
Assoc. Warden—Glen Lawhorn
Assoc. Warden—Christine Dynan
SIC—2329; 2337; 2392; 2391; NAICS—314121; *Institutional & law enforcement clothing, computer recycling & textile repair*
Employs—600
Sales—$25Mil-$50Mil (est)
Distrib.—National
Publicly owned corporation
Parent co.—Unicor Federal Prison Industries, Inc., Washington, DC, MD
   Phone—(202) 305-3500
See Parent Co. Section for full profile.

## Fort Lee

(Bergen—N.E.)

**AJINOMOTO NORTH AMERICA, INC. (H Q)**
400 Kelby St., Ste. 18 (07024-2938)
**Phone—(201) 292-3200**
National—(800) 456-4666
Fax—(201) 346-5630
www.ajiusa.com
Email—lamendola@ajiusa.com
Pres.—Tomoya Yoshizumi
Dir., Hum. Res.—Sarah Lamendola
Hum. Res. Mgr.—Carol Killeen
SIC—2819; 2869; NAICS—311412; *Corporate headquarters; amino acids for pharmaceuticals, food & feed & food ingredients*
Employs—35; Estab.—1956
Sales—$1Mil-$5Mil
Distrib.—Intl.
Privately owned corporation

**NEW ENTRY**
**ALTIBASE, INC.**
1 Bridge Plz. N. (07024)
**Phone—(888) 837-7333**
www.altibase.com
Email—info@altibase.com
CEO—Chris Chung
SIC—7372; *Downloadable in-memory database management software development*
Employs—10; Estab.—1999
Sales—$11Mil-$25Mil
Distrib.—Intl.
Privately owned corporation

**AMERICAN BANKNOTE CORP. (H Q)**
2200 Fletcher Ave., Ste. 501 (07024)
**Phone—(201) 592-3400**
Fax—(201) 224-2762
www.abnote.com
Email—lisa@abnote.com
Chrm., CEO—Steven Singer
Sr. V.-P., CTO—Thomas Ziemkus
Ex. V.-P., COO—Patrick Gentile
Ex. V.-P., Gen. Counsel—David M. Kober
V.-P., Bus. Dev.—Richard Taylor
V.-P., R & D—Erik Mitterhofer
SIC—2759; NAICS—323100; *Corporate headquarters; stock certificate & bond printing*
Employs—10; Estab.—1795
Sales—$1Mil-$2.5Mil (est)
Privately owned corporation
AKA: Abnote

**BAETA CORP.**
1 Bridge Plz., Ste. 275 (07024)
**Phone—(201) 471-0988**
Fax—(201) 471-0988
www.baetacorp.com
Email—info@baetacorp.com
CEO—Len Pushkantser
SIC—3845; *Electronic hand-held health improvement recording devices & systems for consumers & healthcare professionals to monitor, treat & manage illnesses, including weight control, pain management, smoking cessation & pill/medication dispensing; Brand name—MyHealthTrends™*
Employs—5
Sales—$1Mil-$2.5Mil (est)
Distrib.—National
Publicly owned corporation

**BARRICADE BOOKS, INC.**
2037 Lemoine Ave. (07024)
**Phone—(201) 944-7600**
www.barricadebooks.com
Email—customerservice@barricadebooks.com
Pres.—Carole Stuart
SIC—2731; *Book publishing*
Employs—7; Estab.—1990
Sales—$500,000-$1Mil
2,500 sq ft site, Distrib.—National
Privately owned corporation

**GEOGRAPHICAL**

© Copyright 2015 Manufacturers' News, Inc.
† Indicates wholesaler / distributor.

## Fort Lee—(cont.)

**†BERLIN PACKAGING, LLC**
2050 Center Ave., Ste. 400
(07024)
**Phone—(201) 947-7744**
National—(800) 223-7546
Fax—(201) 947-7737
www.berlinpackaging.com
Email—marketing@
berlinpackaging.com
V.-P., Reg.—Jonathan Rabinowitz
Accts. Coord.—Beatrice Collazo
SIC—5085; *Distributor of
packaging materials, including
bottles*
Employs—20; Estab.—1988
2,000 sq ft site, Distrib.—Intl.
Limited Liability Company
Parent co.—Berlin Packaging,
LLC, Chicago, IL
Phone—(312) 876-9292
See Parent Co. Section for full profile.

**CADCAM-E.COM, INC.**
2115 Linwood Ave., Ste. 313
(07024)
**Phone—(201) 503-1881**
Fax—(201) 503-1886
www.cadcam-e.com
CEO—Kumar Rajan
V.-P., Sales & Mktg.—Vinay Wagle
SIC—7372; *CAD & MCAD
engineering platform & file
translation software development*
Employs—250; Estab.—2000
Distrib.—Intl.
Privately owned corporation
AKA: CCE

**COURISTAN, INC.**
2 Executive Dr., Ste. 400 (07024)
**Phone—(201) 585-8500**
National—(800) 223-6186
Fax—(201) 585-8552
www.couristan.com
Pres.—Ronald J. Couri
IT Mgr.—Steven Than
Hum. Res. Mgr.—Michelle Sapio
SIC—2273; NAICS—314110;
*Residential & commercial
carpets, including jacquards &
woolen rugs*
Employs—50; Estab.—1976
Sales—$1Mil-$2.5Mil
Distrib.—National
Privately owned corporation

**†EMPIRE RESOURCES**
1 Parker Plz. (07024)
**Phone—(201) 944-2200**
Fax—(201) 944-2226
www.empireresources.com
Pres., CEO—Nathan Kahn
CFO—Sandra Kahn
V.-P., Sales—Harvey Wrubel
Sales & Mktg. Mgr.—Eric Green
SIC—5051; *Distributor of
semifinished aluminum coil,
sheet, plate, treadplate, foil &
circles*
Employs—50
Distrib.—Local
Privately owned corporation

**FAST PRINT, LLC**
514 Main St. (07024)
**Phone—(201) 944-2350**
Fax—(201) 944-0065
www.fastprtllc.com
Email—fastprtllc@aol.com
Pres.—Anthony Clemente
V.-P.—Elaine Clemente
SIC—2752; 2791; NAICS—
323122; *Offset printing &
electronic prepress of municipal
forms, documents & related
materials*
Employs—2; Estab.—1987
Sales—under $500,000
Distrib.—National
Limited Liability Company

**GAVIN PRINTING, INC.**
1057 Glen Rd. (07024)
**Phone—(212) 721-9009**
(201) 755-6399
Fax—(201) 592-1557
Email—gavinprint@gmail.com
Ptnr.—Chang Shin
Ptnr.—June Shin
SIC—2752; NAICS—323100;
*Offset printing*
Employs—2; Estab.—1989
Sales—under $500,000
700 sq ft site, Distrib.—National
Privately owned sub-S corp.

**HUB PRINT & COPY CENTER, THE**
2037 Lemoine Ave. (07024)
**Phone—(201) 585-7887**
Fax—(201) 585-1560
www.hubprint.com
Email—staff@hubprint.com
Pres.—Gerard Tonner
V.-P.—Donna Tonner
SIC—2759; 2789; NAICS—
323112; *Commercial printing &
binding services*
Employs—2; Estab.—1989
Sales—$500,000-$1Mil
Distrib.—Local
Limited Liability Company

**†ICC CABLE CORP.**
2125 Center Ave., Ste. 401
(07024-5874)
**Phone—(201) 482-5750**
Fax—(201) 482-5751
www.icccable.com
Email—sales@icccable.com
Pres.—Jang Kim
Acctg. Mgr.—Sonya Park
SIC—5063; 5051; *Distributor of
cable & wire, including utility,
wind, marine, offshore &
industrial cables & electrical
components & accessories*
Employs—6; Estab.—2007
Distrib.—Intl.
Privately owned corporation

**†LION METALS, INC.**
2460 Lemoine Ave., Ste. 400-B
(07024)
**Phone—(201) 585-9191**
Fax—(201) 585-9872
Email—carrolldriskell@msn.com
Owner—Bob Blum
Member—Carrol Driskell
SIC—5093; *Wholesaler of scrap
metals*
Employs—3; Estab.—2001
Distrib.—Intl.
Privately owned corporation

**MORINAGA AMERICA, INC.**
400 Kelby St., 14th Fl. (07024)
**Phone—(201) 947-0408**
Fax—(201) 947-0465
www.morinaga-america.com
Email—kmorinaga@morinaga-
america.com
Br. Mgr.—Keita Morinaga
SIC—2064; *Japanese candy;
Brand name—Hichew*
Employs—3; Estab.—2012
Sales—$500,000-$1Mil (est)
Distrib.—Local
Privately owned corporation
Parent co.—Morinaga America,
Inc., Irvine, CA
Phone—(949) 732-1155
See Parent Co. Section for full profile.

**NADRI JEWELRY GROUP**
2 Executive Dr., Ste. 500 (07024)
**Phone—(201) 585-0088**
www.nadrijewelry.com
Owner—Young Choy
SIC—3911; NAICS—339911;
*Preciouis metal jewelry*
Employs—20
Distrib.—Local
Privately owned corporation

**PIONEER POWER SOLUTIONS, INC.
(H Q)**
400 Kelby St., 9th Fl. (07024)
**Phone—(212) 867-0700**
Fax—(212) 867-1325
www.pioneerpowersolutions.com
Email—info@
pioneerpowersolutions.com
Chrm. & CEO—Nathan J.
Mazurek
CFO & Dir.—Andrew Minkow
SIC—3612; *Corporate
headquarters; liquid-filled power
& dry-type electrical
transformers; Brand name—
Pioneer Transformers*
Employs—10; Estab.—2010
Sales—$1Mil-$2.5Mil (est)
Distrib.—Local
Publicly owned corporation
ISO rating—9001:2008

**NEW ENTRY**

**POSTCARDSRUS, INC**
440 West St., Ste. 2-S (07024)
**Phone—(201) 944-7070**
www.postcardsrus.com
Email—ir@postcardsrus.com
Pres.—Mark Kleinfeld
SIC—2759; *Commercial printing*
Employs—40
Sales—$5Mil-$10Mil (est)
Privately owned corporation
AKA: Print It

**PRG PACKING CORP. (H Q)**
2071 Lemoine Ave. (07024)
**Phone—(201) 242-5500**
Fax—(201) 242-5516
www.stahlmeyer.com
Email—info@stahlmeyer.com
Owner—Guillermo Gonzalez
Dir., Fin.—Anna Gonzalez
SIC—2013; *Corporate
headquarters; smoked meat
products, including pork & turkey
products*
Employs—125
Sales—$25Mil-$50Mil (est)
AKAs: Ferris & Stahl-Meyer
Foods, Inc.

**SHERMAN, INC. (H Q), NAT**
2200 Fletcher Ave. (07024)
**Phone—(201) 735-9000**
(800) 221-1690
Fax—(201) 735-9099
www.natsherman.com
Email—info@natsherman.com
Pres., CEO—Joel Sherman
CFO—Brendan Scott
V.-P., Sales—Matt Spillane
V.-P.—William Sherman
Dir., MIS—Lionel Legry
Dir., Hum. Res.—Al Detorre
SIC—2121; 2111; 2131; NAICS—
312229; *Corporate
headquarters; cigars, cigarettes
& pipe tobacco*
Employs—20; Estab.—1930
Distrib.—Local

**STAMM INTERNATIONAL CORP. (H
Q)**
1530 Palisade Ave., P.O. Box 1929
(07024)
**Phone—(201) 947-1700**
www.stamminternational.com
Email—stamminc@pobox.com
Pres.—Arthur Stamm
Ex. V.-P.—Marilyn Skony Stamm
SIC—6719; 3585; NAICS—
551112; *Holding company
headquarters; commercial &
industrial heating & A/C systems,
make-up air & commercial air
cleaning equipment & oil fired
unit heaters; Brand name—
Powermatic; SFL; Eltron; Rheem*
Employs—2; Estab.—1965
Distrib.—Intl.
Privately owned corporation

**UNITED ERP, LLC**
2460 Lemoine Ave., Ste. 503
(07024)
**Phone—(201) 567-6315**
www.unitederp.com
Email—efisher@unitederp.com
Owner, Member, Hum. Res. & IT
Mgr.—Judith Fisher
Pres. & IT Mgr.—Eric Fisher
SIC—7373; 7372; NAICS—
541512; *Computer integrated
systems & intellectual & property
rights accounting management
software development for
licensees, licensors & enterprise
resource planning*
Employs—11; Estab.—2003
1,200 sq ft site, Distrib.—Intl.
Limited Liability Company

**VICTORY WHITE METAL CO., INC.**
129 Victoria Pl. W. (07024-1807)
**Phone—(201) 585-0747**
(201) 914-4200
Fax—(201) 585-1977
www.vwmc.com
Email—ssmetalmaker@aol.com
V.-P.—Steven Salomon
SIC—3339; 3356; *Tin & lead
alloys in bar, ingot, wire & anode
form; Brand name—VWM
BRAND*
Employs—3; Estab.—1920
Sales—over $10Mil
Distrib.—Intl.
Privately owned corporation
ISO rating—9001:2008
Parent co.—Victory White Metal
Co., Inc., Cleveland, OH
Phone—(216) 271-1400
See Parent Co. Section for full profile.

**WILLIAMS PUBLICATIONS, INC., E.
W.**
2125 Center Ave., Ste. 305
(07024)
**Phone—(201) 592-7007**
Fax—(201) 592-7171
Pres.—Andy Williams
SIC—2721; *Magazine publishing*
Employs—8; Estab.—1938
Sales—$500,000-$1Mil (est)
Distrib.—National
Privately owned corporation

**WYSSMONT CO., INC.**
1470 Bergen Blvd. (07024)
**Phone—(201) 947-4600**
Fax—(201) 947-0324
www.wyssmont.com
Email—sales@wyssmont.com
Pres.—Ed Weisselberg
V.-P., Sales—Joseph Bevacqua
V.-P., Engr.—James Ulrich
Fin. Mgr.—L. Botcho
SIC—3567; 3559; 3556; 3823;
NAICS—333994; *Drying
equipment, feeders &
lumpbreakers for the chemical,
food, mining, plastic &
pharmaceutical applications;
Brand name—TURBO-DRYER;
ROTOSCOOP FEEDER;
ROTOCAGE Lumpbreaker*
Employs—25; Estab.—1932
Sales—$2.5Mil-$5Mil
21,000 sq ft site, Distrib.—Intl.
Privately owned sub-S corp.

## Franklin
(Sussex—N.W.)

**ACTION SCREEN PRINTING**
151 Main St. (07416)
**Phone—(973) 209-2491**
(973) 713-2320
Fax—(973) 209-7263
Email—jway44@hotmail.com
Ptnr.—Wayne Carney
Ptnr.—Raymond Carney
Div. Mgr.—Jack Wright

## Franklin—(cont.)

SIC—2396; *Textile screen & pad printing*
Employs—4; Estab.—1989
Sales—under $500,000
5,000 sq ft site, Distrib.—National
Privately owned sub-S corp.

**ADVANCED IMAGING ASSOCS., INC.**

190 Munsonhurst Rd., Ste. 6 (07416)
**Phone—(973) 823-8999**
Fax—(973) 823-8989
www.advancedimagingassoc.com
Pres.—Clifford Barker
SIC—3826; NAICS—334516; *Non-medical magnetic resonance imaging devices*
Employs—6; Estab.—2001
Sales—$1Mil-$2.5Mil (est)
Distrib.—Local
Privately owned corporation

†**ALLIED BUILDING PRODUCTS CORP.**

406 State Route 23 N. (07416)
**Phone—(973) 827-4113**
Fax—(973) 827-4363
www.alliedbuilding.com
Email—sales@alliedbuilding.com
Br. Mgr.—Jerome Newman
Sales Rep.—Jerel Dowdell
SIC—5033; 5031; *Distributor of building materials & supplies, including roofing, siding, windows & doors*
Employs—12; Estab.—2003
Distrib.—Regional
Publicly owned corporation
Parent co.—Allied Building Products Corp., East Rutherford, NJ
Phone—(201) 507-8400
See Parent Co. Section for full profile.

**B & C MACHINE CO., INC.**

22 Lasinski Rd. (07416-9715)
Mail addr.: P.O. Box 321, Sussex (07461)
**Phone—(973) 823-1120**
Fax—(973) 823-1119
Pres.—Robert Van Dyke
SIC—3599; *Precision machining job shop*
Employs—5; Estab.—1983
Sales—$500,000-$1Mil
2,000 sq ft site, Distrib.—Regional
Privately owned corporation

**CLAWSON MACHINE, DIV. OF TECHNOLOGY GENERAL CORP.**

Div. of Technology General Corp.
12 Cork Hill Rd. (07416)
**Phone—(973) 827-8209**
Fax—(973) 827-4613
www.clawsonmachine.com
Email—clawson@nac.net
Pres., Div.—Ryan Barbulescu
SIC—3569; *Commercial & industrial ice crushers & shavers*
Employs—5; Estab.—1883
10,000 sq ft site, Distrib.—Intl.
Publicly owned corporation
Parent co.—Technology General Corp., Franklin, NJ
Phone—(973) 827-4143
See Parent Co. Section for full profile.

**COLLAGEN MATRIX, INC.**

509 Commerce St. (07417)
**Phone—(201) 405-1477**
National—(888) 405-1001
Fax—(201) 405-1355
www.collagenmatrix.com
Email—admin@collagenmatrix.com
Dir., Mfg.—Greg Owens

SIC—2836; *Collagen & mineral-based extracellular materials for tissue & organ repair; Brand name—OssiMend™; OssiGuide™; TenoMend™; MatrixDerm; DuraMatrix; DuraMatrix Onlay; Collatene*
Employs—25
Sales—$5Mil-$10Mil (est)
6,000 sq ft site,
Privately owned corporation
Parent co.—Collagen Matrix, Inc., Oakland, NJ
Phone—(201) 405-1477
See Parent Co. Section for full profile.

**CREATIVE METAL WORK, INC.**

4 Park Dr., P.O. Box 509 (07416)
**Phone—(973) 823-0408**
Fax—(973) 823-0469
www.creativemetalworksnj.com
Email—zcmw@aol.com
Pres.—Zoran Grubic
SIC—3444; *Sheet metal fabrication*
Employs—10; Estab.—1987
Distrib.—Regional
Privately owned corporation

**EASTER SEAL SOCIETY OF NEW JERSEY**

Div. of Easter Seals New Jersey
133 Main St. (07416)
**Phone—(973) 827-9066**
Fax—(973) 827-3828
www.eastersealsnj.org
Email—essnj@nj.easterseals.org
Site Mgr.—Peggy Skipp
SIC—3089; *Contract packaging*
Employs—70; Estab.—1975
Distrib.—Regional
Privately owned corporation
Parent co.—Easter Seals New Jersey, New Brunswick, NJ
Phone—(732) 257-6662
See Parent Co. Section for full profile.

**FRANKLIN PRECAST**

20 Park Dr. (07416)
**Phone—(973) 827-7563**
Fax—(973) 827-4746
www.franklinprecast.com
Email—sales@franklinprecast.com
Pres.—Wendy Kovach
V-P.—Alex Kovach
SIC—3272; *Precast concrete septic tanks, seepage pits, d-boxes, risers, lids, septic related products, parking bumpers, custom boxes, custom slabs & catch basins, infiltrators, hoot aerobic tanks, pumps, polylok & peatmoss systems*
Employs—8; Estab.—1965
6,000 sq ft site, Distrib.—Local
Privately owned corporation

**LRB PERFORMANCE MACHINE CO.**

22-B Lasinski Rd. (07416)
**Phone—(973) 209-7770**
Fax—(973) 209-7780
www.lrbperformance.com
Email—lrbperf@aol.com
Owner—Lou Bengivenni
Off. Mgr.—Shawna Bengivenni
SIC—3519; 3714; 3599; *High performance & racing engines, including custom machining, fabrication & welding for street, strip, circle track & marine racing & antique tractor, car & boat motors restoration*
Employs—3; Estab.—1984
Sales—under $500,000
Distrib.—National
Sole ownership

**NEWTON PRINTING & EMBROIDERY**

75 Main St. (07416)
**Phone—(973) 827-2006**
National—(800) 874-4787
Fax—(973) 827-4001
www.newtonscreen.com
Email—frank@newtonscreen.com

Owner—Frank Newton
Pres.—Paula Lavorgna
SIC—3993; 2396; 2395; *Promotional & corporate branding products, including screenprinted t-shirts & embroidered golf shirts; Brand name—Hanes; Jerzees; Fruit of the Loom; Port Authority; Outer Banks; Nike; Ping; Champion; District Threads; Bella* Ogio; Devon & Jones; Gildan; Sport-Tek; Red House; Corner Stone; HYP; Anvil; Columbia; Harriton; Adidas*
Employs—10; Estab.—1979
Sales—$1Mil-$1.5Mil
3,500 sq ft site, Distrib.—National
Privately owned sub-S corp.

**NORTH AMERICAN STERILIZATION & PACKAGING COMPANY, INC.**

19 Park Dr. *(07416)*
**Phone—(973) 209-4388**
    (800) 392-6310
Fax—(973) 209-6374
www.naspco.com
Email—sales@naspco.com
Chief Operating Officer—Larry Partika
Dir., Mfg. Integration—Edward Wardell
Cust. Serv. & Prodn. Plng. Mgr.—Jill Nicholas
Accountant—Ryan Harris
SIC—3841; 3842; *Contract manufacturing of medical devices, including assembly, packaging, in-house 100% EtO sterilization & process, packaging & sterilization validations*
Employs—50; Estab.—1989
Sales—$10Mil
38,000 sq ft site, Distrib.—Regional
Privately owned corporation
ISO rating—13485:2003

**SMITH BROTHERS SERVICES, LLC**

3212 State Route 94, Ste. 9 (07416-9738)
**Phone—(973) 209-7569**
Fax—(973) 827-1163
www.smithbrothersservices.com
Email—sales@smithbrothersservices.com
Owner—Charles Smith
SIC—3561; 3823; 3713; NAICS—333911; *Rebuilt snowplow pumps, snowplow pump diagnostic tools, salt spreaders & work truck accessories, including welding & fabrication; Brand name—Meyer; Eureka Fluid Film; Buyers*
Employs—1; Estab.—2006
Sales—under $500,000
4,000 sq ft site, Distrib.—National
Limited Liability Company

**TECHNOLOGY GENERAL CORP. (H Q)**

12 Cork Hill Rd. (07416)
**Phone—(973) 827-4143**
Fax—(973) 827-4613
Email—eclipse@nac.net
Sales Mgr.—Diane Olsen
Opers. Mgr.—Jeff Fletcher
SIC—3569; 3585; 3563; 3599; NAICS—333999; *Corporate headquarters; electric & air-driven industrial mixers & commercial & industrial ice crushers & shavers*
Employs—5; Estab.—1957
Sales—$1.5Mil-$2.5Mil
Distrib.—Intl.
Publicly owned corporation

**UNITED SILICA PRODUCTS, INC.**

3 Park Dr. (07416)
**Phone—(973) 209-8854**
Fax—(973) 209-8864

www.unitedsilica.com
Email—quartzsales@unitedsilica.com
Pres., CFO—Lynnmarie Kane
SIC—3299; 3679; *Quartz plate, wafer carriers, process tubes & liners & custom quartzware*
Employs—20; Estab.—1989
7,200 sq ft site, Distrib.—Intl.
Privately owned corporation

**WILSON RECONDITIONING & DESIGN CO., LLC**

117 S. Rutherford Ave. (07416)
**Phone—(973) 823-6317**
Fax—(973) 823-6319
www.wilsonrecondition.com
Email—sales@wilsonrecondition.com
Pres.—Tim Wilson
Shop Foreman—George Valerius
SIC—3599; *Rebuilt tag finishing machinery*
Employs—4; Estab.—1989
Distrib.—Local
Privately owned corporation

†**WORLDWIDE SUPPLY, LLC**

1 Park Dr. (07416)
**Phone—(973) 823-6400**
Fax—(973) 823-6401
www.worldwidesupply.net
Email—info@worldwidesupply.net
Mng. Ptnr.—Jay Van Orden
Dir., Mktg.—Cheryl A. Stoyle
Sales & Mktg. Mgr.—Veronique Deblois
SIC—5045; 5065; *Wholesaler of new, excess, secondary & used network hardware & telecom equipment; Brand name—Cisco; Juniper; Arris; Motorola*
Employs—30; Estab.—2004
Distrib.—Intl.
Limited Liability Company

### Franklin Lakes
(Bergen—N.E.)

**BAXTER CORP., THE**

511 Commerce St., P.O. Box 645 (07417)
**Phone—(201) 337-1212**
Fax—(201) 337-9469
Email—gbowen@baxtercorp.com
Pres.—George Bowen
Cont.—Michael Kelly
Sales & Mktg. Mgr.—Elliot Newberg
SIC—3552; 2741; NAICS—333292; *Textile patterns & machinery, loom parts & jacquard accessories*
Employs—5; Estab.—1918
Sales—$2Mil-$5Mil
Distrib.—National
Sole ownership

**BECTON, DICKINSON & CO. (H Q)**

1 Becton Dr. (07417-1880)
**Phone—(201) 847-6800**
www.bd.com
Email—colleen_white@bd.com
Ex. Chrm.—Edward J. Ludwig
Pres., CEO—Vince Forlenza
Ex. V-P., CFO—David Elkins
Ex. V-P., COO—William A. Kozy
Ex. V-P.—Gary M. Cohen
V-P., Secy.—Gary M. DeFazio
V-P., Treas.—Richard K. Berman
V-P., Hum. Res.—Donna Boles
V-P., Medical Affs.—David T. Durack
Dir., Corp. Comm.—Colleen T. White
Dir., Worldwide Pub. Rels.—Alyssa Zeff

GEOGRAPHICAL

## Franklin Lakes—(cont.)

SIC—3841; *Company headquarters; medical equipment & diagnostic products*
Employs—1400; Estab.—1906
Sales—$7.37Bil
Distrib.—Intl.
Publicly owned corporation

**NEW ENTRY**

### C B PRINTING & GRAPHICS, INC.

795 Susquehanna Ave. (07417)
**Phone—(201) 445-6500**
Fax—(201) 445-7117
Owner—Craig Barbero
SIC—2759; *Commercial printing & graphic design services*
Employs—5
Sales—$500,000-$1Mil (est)
Distrib.—Local
Privately owned corporation

### †CARTRIDGE WORLD

830 Franklin Ave. (07417)
**Phone—(201) 891-0990**
Fax—(201) 891-6366
www.cartridgeworld.com/store634
Email—rbier@cartridgeworldusa.com
Pres.—Jeffrey W. Bier
V-P.—Randy S. Bier
Secy-Treas.—Ellen B. Bier
SIC—5112; 5044; *Distributor of ink & toner cartridges & printers; Brand name—HP; Brother; Canon; Dell; Lexmark; Epson; Xerox; Sharp; Samsung; Okidata; Kyocera/Mita; Pitney Bowes; Kodak*
Employs—3; Estab.—2006
Sales—under $500,000
1,240 sq ft site, Distrib.—National
Privately owned corporation
AKA: Cartridge World - Franklin Lakes

### DANAN DESIGN CORP.

599 Franklin Ave. (07417)
**Phone—(201) 891-5342**
Fax—(201) 891-5342
Email—woodart429@aol.com
Pres.—Ralph Jaffe
Prodn. Supv.—Ted Wilkins
SIC—2511; *Wooden & plastic laminate furniture*
Employs—2; Estab.—1982
Sales—under $500,000
Distrib.—Local
Limited Liability Company

### DIRECT COMPUTER RESOURCES, INC.

120 Birch Rd. *(07417)*
**Phone—(201) 848-0018**
(800) 878-4211
Fax—(201) 848-0064
www.datavantage.com
Email—info@datavantage.com
Pres., CEO—Joe Buonomo
Ex. V-P., Sales & Mktg.—Bill Vitiello
Ex. V-P., Tech.—George Lang
SIC—7372; *Prepackaged software for data masking, migration, extraction, obfuscation & encryption & application development; Brand name—DataVantage for IMS; DataVantage Global; DataVantage for DB2; DataVantage for MVS/VSAM; DataVantage AdVisEr; DataVantage Data Masking Express*
Employs—3; Estab.—1996
Sales—under $10Mil
2,000 sq ft site, Distrib.—Intl.
Privately owned sub-S corp.

### †FAGAN, INC., ED

769 Susquehanna Ave. (07417)
**Phone—(201) 891-4003**
National—(800) 335-6827
Fax—(201) 891-3207
www.edfagan.com
Email—sales@edfagan.com
Pres.—Edward Fagan
Sales Rep.—Patrick Frawley
SIC—5051; *Distributor of specialty metals & alloys for electronics, magnetic, electrical & industrial applications*
Employs—20; Estab.—1955
Distrib.—Intl.
Privately owned corporation

### FLEET EQUIPMENT CORP. (H Q)

567 Commerce St. (07417)
**Phone—(201) 337-7332**
National—(800) 631-0873
Fax—(201) 337-3294
www.fectrucks.com
Email—sales@fectrucks.com
Pres.—Rick Pearson
V-P.—Scott Pearson
SIC—3713; NAICS—336211; *Corporate headquarters; steel & aluminum truck bodies*
Employs—30; Estab.—1965
Sales—$500,000-$1Mil
Distrib.—National
Privately owned corporation
AKA: FEC

### GLEBAR CO.

527 Commerce St., P.O. Box 623 (07417)
**Phone—(201) 337-1500**
National—(800) 235-5122
Fax—(201) 337-6848
www.glebar.com
Email—info@glebar.com
Chrm.—Frederick Schumacher
CEO—Adam Cook
Pres.—John Bannayan
V-P., Sales & Mktg.—Mark Bannayan
V-P., Engrg.—Robert Gleason
V-P.—Nancy Schumacher
IT Mgr.—Josh Dejong
Off. Mgr.—Jean Marie Gatti
Pur. Agt.—Ronald Sietsma
SIC—3541; NAICS—333512; *Centerless grinding machines*
Employs—63; Estab.—1955
28,000 sq ft site, Distrib.—Intl.
Privately owned corporation
ISO rating—9001

### GLEN ROCK STAIR CORP.

551 Commerce St. (07417)
**Phone—(201) 337-9595**
Fax—(201) 337-3470
www.glenrockstairs.com
Email—office@glenrockstairs.com
Pres.—Nick Veenstra
Off. Mgr.—Kelly Faber
SIC—2431; NAICS—321900; *Wooden stairs*
Employs—25; Estab.—1950
Sales—$1Mil-$5Mil
16,000 sq ft site, Distrib.—Local
Privately owned corporation

**NEW ENTRY**

### GOLDEN RULE CREATIONS

250 Terrace Rd. (07417)
**Phone—(201) 337-4050**
www.goldenrulecreations.com
Owner—Fred Schiker
SIC—2399; *Custom emblems & patches*
Employs—4
Sales—$500,000-$1Mil (est)
Distrib.—Local
Privately owned corporation

### METO LIFT, INC.

556 Commerce St. (07417)
**Phone—(201) 405-0311**
Fax—(201) 405-0322
www.metolift.com

Email—sales@metolift.com
Pres.—William Rotenberry
V-P.—Susan Haas
Prodn. Mgr.—John Shepard
Engrg. Mgr.—Adam Baird
SIC—3559; 3444; *Stainless steel material handling equipment; Brand name—Metolift*
Employs—20; Estab.—1969
15,000 sq ft site, Distrib.—Intl.
Privately owned corporation

### ROMAR MACHINE & TOOL CO.

521 Commerce St. (07417)
**Phone—(201) 337-7111**
Fax—(201) 337-5385
www.romarmachine.com
Email—info@romarmachine.com
Pres.—Bob Thum
SIC—3565; 3499; 3599; NAICS—333993; *Packaging machinery tube holders, fill nozzles & sealing tools & general machining job shop*
Employs—12; Estab.—2006
Sales—$500,000-$1Mil
Distrib.—National
Privately owned corporation

### †U.S. TECH, INC.

P.O. Box 152 (07417)
**Phone—(800) 783-8187**
Fax—(800) 878-4876
www.ustechinc.com
Email—info@ustechinc.com
Pres.—Jeff Lerner
V-P.—Bruce Ford
Sales Engr.—Ken Murray
Sales Exec.—Sandy Bonfiglio
Sales Exec.—Bob Copeland
SIC—5063; *Distributor of uninterruptible power supply systems & electrical equipment for the military & medical, industrial, satellite & data room industries; Brand name—GE Power Quality; APC; Eaton/Powerware; Power Quality International (PQI); Accratech*
Employs—5; Estab.—1983
Sales—$3Mil
Distrib.—National
Privately owned sub-S corp.
ISO rating—9001

### VOZEH EQUIPMENT CORP.

509 Commerce St. (07417)
**Phone—(201) 337-4212**
Fax—(201) 337-3278
Email—sctcorp@aol.com
Owner—Karen Vozeh
Chrm., Pres.—Gregory Vozeh
V-P.—Christopher Vozeh
Off. Mgr.—Ann Wimberger
SIC—3545; 3841; 3842; *Industrial & medical cutting tools & surgical implants*
Employs—55; Estab.—1962
Sales—$1Mil-$2.5Mil
9,000 sq ft site, Distrib.—National
Privately owned corporation

### WALLACE EANNACE ASSOCIATES, INC.

779 Susquehanna Ave. *(07417)*
**Phone—(201) 891-9550**
(800) 932-4891
Fax—(201) 891-4298
www.wea-inc.com
Email—generalmailingnj@wea-inc.com
Manager—Hank Kunkel
Manager—Jim Collins
SIC—3443; *Heating specialties, including hot water & steam boilers & controls*
Employs—20; Estab.—1970
Sales—$5Mil-$7.5Mil
12,500 sq ft site, Distrib.—Local
Privately owned corporation

## Franklin Park

(Somerset—N.E.)

### JERSEY COW SOFTWARE CO., INC.

3031 State Route 27, Ste. A (08823)
**Phone—(732) 422-0101**
Fax—(732) 422-0110
www.jerseycow.com
Email—cow@jerseycow.com
Pres.—Bob Wickenden
Authority Assur. Mgr.—Andrew Adams
SIC—7372; *Educational software development*
Employs—4; Estab.—1983
Sales—under $500,000
Distrib.—Intl.
Privately owned corporation

## Franklinville

(Gloucester—S.W.)

### ADVERTISER, THE

235 Blackwood Ave., P.O. Box 54 (08322)
**Phone—(856) 694-0444**
Owner—Stanley Deininger
SIC—2752; NAICS—323100; *Offset & letterpress printing*
Employs—1; Estab.—1951
Sales—under $500,000
Distrib.—Local
Sole ownership

**NEW ENTRY**

### BA-TAMPTE PICKLE PRODUCTS, INC.

2660 Main Rd. (08322)
**Phone—(856) 697-9815**
www.batamptepickle.com
Email—customerrelations@batamptepickle.com
Owner—Howard Silberstein
SIC—2035; *Pickles*
Employs—12
Sales—$1Mil-$2.5Mil (est)
Distrib.—National
Privately owned corporation
Parent co.—Ba-Tampte Pickle Products, Inc., Brooklyn, NY
Phone—(718) 251-2100
See Parent Co. Section for full profile.

### EASTERN MACHINING CORP.

1197 Fries Mill Rd. (08322)
**Phone—(856) 694-3303**
Fax—(856) 694-2128
www.em-corp.us
Email—jdavis@em-corp.com
Pres.—Joe Davis
Off. Mgr.—Lisa Spera
SIC—3451; 3599; NAICS—332721; *Swiss screw machine products & general machining job shop*
Employs—5; Estab.—1990
Sales—$500,000-$1Mil
12,000 sq ft site, Distrib.—Intl.
Privately owned corporation

### PIONEER METAL FINISHING, INC.

2034 Coles Mill Rd., P.O. Box 387 (08322)
**Phone—(856) 694-0400**
www.pioneerpowdercoating.com
Email—fred@pioneerpowdercoating.com
Pres., Fin. & R & D Mgr.—Fred Trotz
SIC—3479; NAICS—332813; *Powder coating*
Employs—10; Estab.—1955
17,000 sq ft site, Distrib.—Regional
Privately owned corporation

### UPPER CASE PRINTING, LLC

752 Porchtown (08322)
**Phone—(856) 875-5000**
Fax—(856) 629-8554

## Franklinville—(cont.)

www.uppercaseprinting.com
Email—ucprinting@comcast.net
Owner—Richard Procida
SIC—2759; NAICS—323100;
  *Commercial printing*
Employs—1; Estab.—1993
Sales—under $500,000
Distrib.—Local
Limited Liability Company

## Freehold
### (Monmouth—N.E.)

### †ADVANCED BUSINESS MACHINES CO.
230 Randolph Rd. (07728)
**Phone—(732) 431-1464**
www.abmco.webs.com
Email—jrespler@superlink.net
Owner—J. Respler
SIC—5044; 5045; 5065;
  *Wholesaler of office equipment,
  printers & fax machines*
Employs—4; Estab.—1976
Sales—under $500,000
2,000 sq ft site, Distrib.—Intl.
Privately owned corporation

### APPLIED IMAGE, INC.
800 Business Park Dr. (07728)
**Phone—(732) 410-2444**
National—(800) 826-6545
www.bigres.com
Email—sales@bigres.com
Pres.—Allen Shanosky
Hum. Res. & IT Mgr.—John
  Toremy
Bookkeeper—Michelle Vavrence
SIC—2759; 3993; NAICS—
  323100; *Large-format graphic
  printing & environmental
  graphics*
Employs—20; Estab.—1998
22,000 sq ft site, Distrib.—National
Privately owned corporation

### AWNING CONCEPTS & DESIGN, INC.
916 Route 33 (07728)
**Phone—(732) 462-1131**
Fax—(732) 409-1423
www.awningdesign.net
Email—mark@awningdesign.net
Pres.—Mark Pedersen
GM—Alan Techner
SIC—2394; 3444; NAICS—
  314912; *Awnings*
Employs—8; Estab.—1997
Sales—$500,000-$1Mil
Distrib.—Local
Privately owned corporation

### BAILEY'S PRINTING, INC.
191 Throckmorton St. (07728)
**Phone—(732) 462-8010**
  　　(732) 462-6642
Fax—(732) 462-9672
www.baileysprinting.com
Email—baileys.printing@verizon.net
Pres.—Randy Bailey
V-P., Fin.—Sherry Bailey
SIC—2759; 2396; 2395; NAICS—
  323122; *Commerical & screen
  printing & custom embroidery*
Employs—2; Estab.—1985
Company-wide: 3
Sales—$500,000-$1Mil
6,500 sq ft site, Distrib.—Local
Privately owned corporation

### BERNARD, INC., DENNIS
142 Ely Harmony Rd. (07728)
**Phone—(800) 541-5456**
Fax—(732) 308-9608
www.dennisbernard.com
Email—info@dennisbernard.com
CEO—Dennis Bernard
V-P., Sales—Jeff Campanaro
Mktg. Mgr.—Eric Guffey
Off. Mgr.—Gina Davino

SIC—2844; *Hair care products,
  including shampoos &
  conditioners*
Employs—30
Distrib.—Intl.
Privately owned corporation

### CAMPUS COORDINATES
1711 Ginesi Dr., Ste. 1 (07728)
**Phone—(732) 866-6060**
Fax—(732) 866-6044
www.campuscoordinates.com
GM—Kevin Drake
SIC—2396; *Textile screen printing*
Employs—8; Estab.—1987
Sales—$500,000-$1Mil
4,000 sq ft site, Distrib.—Local
Limited Liability Company

### CHRIS INDUSTRIES, INC.
98 Industrial Ct. (07728)
**Phone—(732) 431-1800**
Fax—(732) 577-0101
Email—tci1@aol.com
Pres.—David A. Christie
SIC—2851; NAICS—325510;
  *Water-based coatings*
Employs—4; Estab.—1937
Sales—$500,000-$1Mil
7,000 sq ft site, Distrib.—Regional
Privately owned corporation

### CLAYTON BLOCK CO., INC.
225 Throckmorton St. (07728)
**Phone—(732) 462-1860**
National—(888) 763-8665
Fax—(732) 432-3287
www.claytonco.com
Email—bheffernan@
  claytonsonline.com
Off. Mgr.—Tom Boulter
Asst. Mgr.—James Mac
SIC—3271; *Concrete blocks*
Employs—7; Estab.—1946
Sales—$1Mil-$2.5Mil (est)
Distrib.—Local
Privately owned corporation
Parent co.—Clayton Block Co.,
  Inc., Neptune, NJ
  Phone—(732) 751-7600
See Parent Co. Section for full profile.

### COMPASS SIGNS, LLC
1 Market Yard (07728)
**Phone—(732) 294-7977**
Fax—(732) 294-7967
www.compasssigns.com
Email—jeff@compasssigns.com
Owner—Jeff Cherchia
SIC—3993; 2759; NAICS—
  323100; *Trade show & fleet
  graphics, interior & exterior
  signs, vinyl lettering, large-format
  printing & vehicle wraps*
Employs—4; Estab.—2004
Sales—under $500,000
Distrib.—National
Limited Liability Company

### †COOPER ELECTRIC SUPPLY CO.
3477 U.S. Highway 9 (07728)
**Phone—(732) 462-2424**
Fax—(732) 308-4604
www.cooper-electric.com
Email—tania.rodriguez@cooper-
  electric.com
Br. Mgr.—Tania Rodriguez
SIC—5063; *Distributor of electrical
  equipment & supplies, including
  connectors, wires & sockets*
Employs—12; Estab.—1961
Distrib.—National
Privately owned corporation
Parent co.—Cooper Electric
  Supply Co., Monroe, NJ
  Phone—(732) 747-2233
See Parent Co. Section for full profile.

### CROWN TROPHY, INC.
3443 Highway 9 (07728)
**Phone—(732) 462-3344**
Fax—(732) 462-4777
www.crowntrophy.com
Email—crownfreehold@verizon.net

Pres.—Christine Sansavera
SIC—3499; *Trophies & awards*
Employs—3; Estab.—2005
Sales—under $500,000
Distrib.—Local
Privately owned corporation

### D R TECHNOLOGY, INC.
73 South St. (07728)
**Phone—(732) 780-4664**
Fax—(732) 780-1545
www.drtechnologyinc.com
Email—sales@drtechnologyinc.com
Pres., CFO—Richard Schwartz
Secy., MIS Mgr.—Debbie Krueger
Engrg. Mgr.—Lucas Young
SIC—3559; *Pollution control
  scrubbers*
Employs—7; Estab.—1979
Sales—$1Mil-$2.5Mil
2,800 sq ft site, Distrib.—Intl.
Sole ownership

### DEPENDABLE MACHINING & STONE CO.
53 Weaverville Rd. (07728)
**Phone—(732) 462-0262**
Fax—(732) 462-0262
Email—stonecrvr@aol.com
Owner—Frank Minervini
SIC—3599; *Precision machining
  job shop*
Employs—3; Estab.—1969
Sales—under $500,000
Distrib.—Regional
Sole ownership

### DOLLY SCREEN PRINTING, INC.
1-19 Elm St. (07728)
**Phone—(732) 294-8979**
Fax—(732) 294-5599
www.dollyscreen.com
Email—dollyscreenprint@aol.com
Pres.—Mike Dolly
SIC—2396; 2395; *Textile screen
  printing & embroidery*
Employs—9; Estab.—1995
Sales—$1Mil-$2.5Mil
Distrib.—Local
Privately owned corporation

### FRANK'S ALUMINUM GLASS & MIRRORS CO.
588 Park Ave. (07728)
**Phone—(732) 462-8141**
Fax—(732) 462-6663
Pres.—Anthony Santoriello
SIC—3231; NAICS—327215;
  *Decorative mirrors*
Employs—4; Estab.—1960
Sales—$500,000-$1Mil (est)
Distrib.—Local
Privately owned corporation

### FREEHOLD GLASS & MIRROR, INC.
38 South St. (07728)
**Phone—(732) 462-6200**
Fax—(732) 462-8334
www.freeholdglass.com
Email—freeholdglass@yahoo.com
Pres.—David Gross
GM—Marina Gross
SIC—3231; NAICS—327215;
  *Custom frameless & framed
  shower & tub enclosures for
  residential projects & mirrors,
  storefronts & entrance doors for
  commercial properties*
Employs—6; Estab.—1930
Sales—under $1Mil
6,000 sq ft site, Distrib.—Regional
Privately owned corporation

NEW ENTRY
### GORDON INTERNATIONAL, INC.
6 Paragon Way (07728)
**Phone—(732) 431-3361**
National—(800) 446-9872
www.gordoninternational.com
Pres.—Peter Spaldaning
Hum. Res. Mgr.—Ruth Grijalda
Supervisor—David Urritia

SIC—2522; *Office furniture*
Employs—11; Estab.—1988
Sales—$500,000-$1Mil
18,000 sq ft site, Distrib.—Intl.
Privately owned corporation

### GRUMIUM LABS
4400 U.S. 9, Ste. 1000 (07728)
Mail addr: 18 Jason Ct.,
  Morganville (07751-2228)
**Phone—(732) 562-0001**
www.grumium.com
Email—naushad@grumium.com
Pres.—Regina Chitto
V-P.—Sherry Kader
V-P.—Junaid Nari
V-P.—Abdul Naushad
SIC—7372; *Custom software
  development for the financial
  services & healthcare industries*
Employs—28; Estab.—1997
Sales—$10Mil-$25Mil
Distrib.—National
Limited Liability Company

NEW ENTRY
### HAWK TECHNOLOGIES, INC.
3710 U.S. Highway 9 S., P.O. Box
  6685 (07728)
**Phone—(732) 577-8581**
National—(855) 225-9900
Fax—(732) 577-8581
www.hawktech.com
Email—info@hawktech.com
Pres.—Alex Sokolovski
SIC—2752; *Computer systems
  integration, including LANs &
  WANs*
Employs—10
Sales—$1Mil-$2.5Mil (est)
Distrib.—National
Privately owned corporation

### HOBBY PUBLICATIONS, INC.
83 South St., Unit 307 (07728)
**Phone—(732) 536-5160**
National—(800) 969-7176
Fax—(732) 536-5761
www.hobbypublications.com
Email—dgherman@hobbypub.com
Pres.—David Gherman
Off. Mgr.—Judy Silletti
SIC—2721; *Magazine publishing*;
  Brand name—DESIGN N.J.;
  PFM Production; Picture
  Framing Magazine; Hobby
  Merchandiser; West Coast Art &
  Frame Show; National
  Conference
Employs—25; Estab.—1945
10,000 sq ft site, Distrib.—National
Sole ownership

### INNODYNE ENGINEERING
1711 Ginesi Dr., Unit 2 (07728)
**Phone—(646) 240-0200**
www.innodyne.com
GM—Jim Mort
SIC—3679; *Electronic
  components & wires*
Employs—5; Estab.—1951
Distrib.—National
Privately owned corporation

### IVC INDUSTRIES, INC.
500 Halls Mill Rd. (07728)
**Phone—(732) 308-3000**
National—(800) 221-1208
Fax—(732) 761-2878
www.ivcinc.com
Email—ivcinquiries@ivcinc.com
Pres., CEO—Steven Dai
V-P., Mktg.—Steve Rosenman
Hum. Res. Mgr.—Jill Stambler
SIC—2833; NAICS—325411;
  *Corporate headquarters &
  pregnancy vitamins &
  supplements*
Employs—410; Estab.—1955
Sales—$100Mil
400,000 sq ft site, Distrib.—Intl.
Publicly owned corporation
AKA: International Vitamin Corp.

GEOGRAPHICAL

## Freehold—(cont.)

**J M T DESIGN, INC.**
914 Route 33, Fairfield Industrial Pk. (07728)
Mail addr: P.O. Box 40, Adelphia (07710)
**Phone—(732) 409-6661**
Fax—(732) 409-6662
www.jmtdesigninc.com
Email—gsw713@optonline.net
Pres.—Jerry Wojciehowski
Manager—Jerry Wojciehowski, Jr.
SIC—3599; *Precision machine parts, including welding & die & journal repair*
Employs—3; Estab.—1968
Sales—under $500,000
3,500 sq ft site, Distrib.—National
Privately owned corporation

**JDM ENGINEERING**
60 Jerseyville Ave. (07728)
**Phone—(732) 780-0770**
Fax—(732) 780-1715
www.teamjdm.com
Email—sales@teamjdm.com
Owner—James P. D'Amore
Off. Mgr.—Julie Marshal
SIC—3714; *Iron, steel & aluminum automotive performance parts, including pulleys & superchargers*
Employs—13; Estab.—1998
Sales—under $500,000
Distrib.—Intl.
Privately owned corporation

**JERSEY SHORE CPL, INC.**
301-C Commerce Dr. (07728)
**Phone—(732) 308-9990**
Fax—(732) 308-3046
Email—jamabile548@gmail.com
Supervisor—Gary Chlenber
SIC—2051; *Doughnuts*
Employs—60; Estab.—2006
Sales—$5Mil-$10Mil (est)
Distrib.—Local
Privately owned corporation

**KOLE DESIGN, LLC**
35 Cedar Ct. (07728)
**Phone—(732) 252-9365**
Owner—Terri Kolodny
SIC—3961; *Novelty & costume jewelry*
Employs—5; Estab.—1989
Sales—$500,000-$1Mil
Distrib.—National
Limited Liability Company

**LASER SAVE**
843 State Route 33, Ste. 11 (07728-8493)
**Phone—(732) 431-3339**
National—(800) 969-3339
Fax—(732) 431-3706
www.lasersave.com
Email—info@lasersave.com
Pres.—Alan D. Yoss
CFO, Sales & Mktg. Mgr.—Howard Topal
SIC—3861; 5044; 5112; *Remanufactured compatible color & monochrome toner cartridges for printers, copiers & fax machines & distributor of office supplies & equipment, including service; Brand name— HP; Okidata; Canon; Brother; Xerox; Tektronix; Samsung Sharp*
Employs—18; Estab.—1988
Sales—$2.5Mil-$5Mil
8,000 sq ft site, Distrib.—National
Privately owned corporation

NEW ENTRY
**LASER XPRESSIONS, INC.**
3710 Route 9 S., 2nd Fl. (07728)
**Phone—(732) 303-9530**
Fax—(732) 303-9531
www.laserxpressions.com
Email—info@laserxpressions.com

Pres.—Aco Sokolovski
SIC—3479; 3231; *Laser engraving of metal plaques & crystal awards*
Employs—14; Estab.—2004
Sales—$1Mil-$2.5Mil (est)
Distrib.—Intl.
Privately owned corporation

**LIGHTFIELD AMMUNITION CORP.**
912 Highway 33 (07728)
Mail addr: P.O. Box 162, Adelphia (07710)
**Phone—(732) 462-9200**
National—(800) 286-3114
www.litfld.com
Email—lacsabot@optonline.net
Owner—Peter Saker
SIC—3482; 3483; *Ammunition for hunting, wildlife control, home defense, police departments & local, state & federal agencies, including sabot shotgun slugs*
Employs—8; Estab.—1982
5,000 sq ft site, Distrib.—Local
Privately owned corporation

NEW ENTRY
**MEGASTRIKE, INC.**
331 Fairfield Rd., Ste. B-1 (07728)
**Phone—(732) 780-7383**
National—(866) 454-6487
Fax—(732) 298-6261
www.megastrike.com
Email—info@megastrike.com
Owner—Robert Uhrig
SIC—3949; *Fishing lures; Brand name—MegaStrike ™*
Employs—4; Estab.—2001
Sales—under $500,000
1,500 sq ft site, Distrib.—Intl.
Privately owned sub-S corp.

**MONMOUTH BIOPRODUCTS**
3 Industrial Ct., Ste. 4 (07728)
**Phone—(732) 863-0300**
National—(800) 692-5307
Fax—(732) 863-0534
www.monmouthbio.com
Email—info@monmouthbio.com
Owner—Sean M. Duddy
SIC—2836; NAICS—325414; *Bacteria & enzymes for wastewater, groundwater & soil remediation & composting*
Employs—6; Estab.—1998
7,500 sq ft site, Distrib.—Intl.
Limited Liability Company
ISO rating—9001

**MR. FENCE**
3468 U.S. Highway 9, Ste. 2 (07728)
**Phone—(732) 303-1614**
Fax—(732) 303-0358
www.cmrfence.com
Email—cmrfence@aol.com
Owner—Dan Caporellie
Bookkeeper—Annmarie Caporellie
SIC—2499; 2452; NAICS— 321992; *Vinyl, aluminum, wood & chain-link fencing, sheds, PVC maintenance free, pressure-treated & red wood & cedar swing sets, gazebos, pavilions, pergolas, decks & outdoor furniture*
Employs—8; Estab.—1983
Distrib.—Local
Sole ownership

**NESTLE' USA, INC., BEVERAGE DIV.**
Div. of Nestle USA, Inc.
61 Jerseyville Ave. (07728)
**Phone—(732) 462-1300**
Fax—(732) 431-3011
www.nestleusa.com
Email—info@nestleusa.com
Plt. Mgr.—Joe Rechtiene
GM—Ian Reed
IT Mgr.—Glenn Spadafore
Hum. Res. Mgr.—Wes Ikeda
Pur. Agt.—Patti Goldberg

SIC—2095; 2099; NAICS— 311920; *Coffee & tea blending*
Employs—315; Estab.—1980
Distrib.—National
Publicly owned corporation
Parent co.—Nestle USA, Inc., Glendale, CA
Phone—(818) 549-6000
See Parent Co. Section for full profile.

NEW ENTRY
**NETQ MULTIMEDIA**
919 State Route 33, Ste. 52 (07728)
**Phone—(732) 833-9300**
National—(800) 303-4782
Fax—(732) 833-1300
www.netqmedia.com
Owner—Rich Tillman
SIC—7373; *Computer network system integration, including LANs & WANs & structured cabling solutions*
Employs—4

**OLD MONMOUTH PEANUT BRITTLE CO.**
627 Park Ave. (07728)
**Phone—(732) 462-1311**
Fax—(732) 462-6820
www.oldmonmouthcandies.com
Email—sales@oldmonmouthcandies.com
Pres.—Hal Gunther
SIC—2064; NAICS—311300; *Peanut brittle*
Employs—4; Estab.—1939
Sales—$1Mil-$2.5Mil (est)
Distrib.—Local
Privately owned corporation
AKA: Old Monmouth Candies

**ONE SOURCE SOLUTIONS**
3 industrial Ct., Ste. 3 (07728)
**Phone—(732) 536-0702**
Fax—(732) 536-1347
www.onesourcesolutions.com
Email—sales@onesourcesolutions.com
Hum. Res. & IT Mgr.—Timothy O'Handley
Qual. Control Mgr.—Eric Bernstein
SIC—7372; 7373; NAICS— 541512; *Point-of-sale, inventory control & back office management software development & integrated systems*
Employs—12; Estab.—2004
Distrib.—National
Privately owned corporation

**PAUL-MARK PRINTING**
37 Stokes St. (07728)
**Phone—(732) 462-9110**
Fax—(732) 308-0014
www.paul-markprinting.com
Email—admin@paul-markprinting.com
Pres.—Mark Lamhut
SIC—2752; 2759; 2789; NAICS— 323122; *Offset & digital printing, letterpress, folding, numbering, die cutting, booklet making, pads, stationery, brochures, labels, postcards, business cards, envelopes & carbonless forms*
Employs—5; Estab.—1964
Sales—under $500,000
5,000 sq ft site, Distrib.—Local
Privately owned corporation

NEW ENTRY
**PI MAGAZINE**
4400 U.S. Highway 9, Ste. 1000 (07728)
**Phone—(732) 308-3800**
Fax—(732) 308-3314
www.pimagazine.com
Email—jim@pimagazine.com
Publisher—Jimmie Mesis

SIC—2721; *Trade magazine publishing*
Employs—2
Sales—under $500,000
Distrib.—Intl.
Privately owned sub-S corp.
AKA: Private Investigators Magazine

**PRECISION CABINETS**
410 E. Freehold Rd. (07728)
**Phone—(732) 462-3342**
Fax—(732) 462-8982
Owner—Robert Blatchley
SIC—2434; 2431; NAICS— 337110; *Wooden kitchen & office cabinets*
Employs—3; Estab.—1963
Sales—under $500,000
Distrib.—Regional
Sole ownership

**PRECISION FILAMENTS**
17 Bannard St., Ste. 30 (07728-1685)
**Phone—(732) 462-3755**
Fax—(732) 462-3758
Pres.—Robert McLean
SIC—3699; *CRT filaments*
Employs—5; Estab.—1955
Sales—$500,000-$1Mil
4,000 sq ft site, Distrib.—National
Privately owned corporation

**PRINCETON SEPARATION, INC.**
100 Commerce Dr. (07728)
Mail addr: P.O. Box 300, Adelphia (07710)
**Phone—(732) 431-3338**
National—(800) 223-0902
Fax—(732) 431-3768
www.prinsep.com
Email—info@prinsep.com
Pres.—Paul Nix
Dir., Engrg. & Mfg.—Kiran Desai
Fin. Mgr.—Regina Hatton
Cust. Serv. Mgr.—Wilma Crescente
Proj. Coord.—Lois Hart
SIC—2836; NAICS—325414; *Molecular separation products for proteins & DNA sequencing sample clean up*
Employs—19; Estab.—1984
15,000 sq ft site, Distrib.—Intl.
Privately owned corporation

**PRINTING TO GO**
578 Park Ave. (07728)
**Phone—(732) 462-0333**
Fax—(732) 462-5672
www.printingtogo.com
Email—order@printingtogo.com
Owner—Cindy Ziegler
Accountant—Charles Ziegler
Cust. Serv. Rep.—Sandra Quinones
SIC—2752; NAICS—323100; *Printing, including instant & large-format printing, blueprinting, laminating, scanning & binding*
Employs—5; Estab.—1994
Sales—under $500,000
1,000 sq ft site, Distrib.—National
Limited Liability Company

**PROMOTIONS & UNICORNS TOO, INC.**
71 W.Main St., Ste. 102 (07728)
**Phone—(732) 308-3444**
Fax—(732) 409-4744
www.promotionsandunicorns.com
Email—promotions.unicorns@verizon.net
Pres.—Robert Einhorn
SIC—2759; 2396; *Promotional item, apparel, garment & textile screen printing services*
Employs—5
Privately owned corporation

## Freehold—(cont.)

**SALKIN'S JEWEL CASE, INC.**
3585 Highway 9, South Freehold
Shopping Ctr. (07728)
**Phone—(732) 462-3311**
Fax—(732) 409-0638
www.salkinsjewelcase.com
Email—jewelcase5@aol.com
Pres.—Eric Salkin
V-P.—David Salkin
SIC—3911; NAICS—339911;
*Diamond, gold, silver & platinum
jewelry*
Employs—7; Estab.—1975
Sales—$500,000-$1Mil
1,500 sq ft site, Distrib.—Local
Privately owned corporation

**†SHORE POINT DISTRIBUTING CO.**
100 Shore Point Dr. *(07728)*
Mail addr.—P.O. Box 275, Adelphia
(07710)
**Phone—(732) 308-3334**
Fax—(732) 308-1610
www.shorepoint.com
Pres.—James Annarella
V-P., Sales—Jerry Fiorella
V-P., Opers.—Rick Lonardo
Dir., Fin.—William Gutierrez
Hum. Res. Mgr.—Kim Laman
SIC—5181; *Distributor of beer*
Employs—210
Distrib.—Local
Privately owned corporation

**†TARANTIN INDUSTRIES**
86 Vanderveer Rd. (07728)
**Phone—(732) 780-9340**
National—(866) 311-3371
Fax—(732) 780-5173
www.tarantin.com
Email—info@tarantin.com
Pres., CEO—Thomas Tarantin
CFO—James Tarantin
V-P., Sales—Richard Tarantin
Mktg. Mgr.—Diane Mullaney
Acctg. Mgr.—Rose Tirre
SIC—5084; 5085; *Company
headquarters & distributor of
propane & natural gas
equipment & supplies, including
tanks*
Employs—25
Distrib.—Regional
Privately owned corporation

**THE LIFESTYLE COMPANY, INC.**
6 Paragon Way, Ste. 112 (07728)
**Phone—(732) 303-7849**
National—(800) 622-0777
Fax—(732) 462-2351
www.purilens.com
Email—lenses@
lifestylecompany.com
Pres., CEO—Tom Seidner
Dir., Sales—Dan Cyriacks
SIC—3851; 2899; NAICS—
339100; *Plastic for contact
lenses & contact lens cleaners*
Employs—4; Estab.—1995
Sales—$1Mil
Distrib.—National
Privately owned corporation

**U.S. PROPACK, INC.**
341 Fairfield Rd. (07728)
Mail addr.—P.O. Box 298, Adelphia
(07710)
**Phone—(732) 294-4500**
Fax—(732) 294-4501
www.uspropack.com
Email—sales@uspropack.com
Pres.—Stephen Miller
Off. Mgr.—Linda Miller

SIC—2653; 3086; NAICS—
322211; *Industrial & promotional
packaging materials, including
corrugated boxes, die-cut
corrugated, custom foam inserts,
in-house handling trays & totes,
plastic bags & sheeting &
shipping cases with custom
foam inserts*
Employs—10; Estab.—1993
Sales—$1Mil-$2.5Mil
Distrib.—Intl.
Privately owned corporation

**VIGG DESIGNS, LLC**
584 Park Ave. (07728)
**Phone—(732) 683-9400**
Fax—(732) 683-9401
www.viggdesigns.com
Email—shop@viggdesigns.com
Owner—John Vigg
GM—Lily Pannella
SIC—3993; *Interior & exterior
signs*
Employs—5; Estab.—1997
Sales—$500,000-$1Mil
Distrib.—Intl.
Limited Liability Company

**W & E BAUM, INC.**
89 Bannard St. (07728)
**Phone—(732) 866-1881**
National—(800) 922-7377
www.webaum.com
Email—info@webaum.com
CEO—Maurice Zagha
Pres.—Richard Baum
V-P.—Heshy Spira
SIC—3499; 2499; 3281; 3231;
*Wooden, marble, metal, acrylic,
glass & brass donor walls, trees
of life, plaques, awards &
signage for churches,
synagogues, universities,
schools, hospitals, corporate
headquarters, nonprofit
organizations & government
institutions*
Employs—25; Estab.—1920
Sales—over $1Mil
13,000 sq ft site, Distrib.—Intl.
Privately owned sub-S corp.

[NEW ENTRY]
**WOODHUT, LLC**
339 Fairfield Rd. (07728)
**Phone—(732) 414-6440**
www.woodhutllc.com
Email—merrillhassell@aol.cut
Member—Merrill Hassell
SIC—2431; *Wooden doors &
windows*
Employs—10
Sales—$1Mil-$2.5Mil
Limited Liability Company

---

## Frenchtown
(Hunterdon—N.W.)

**ARCHITECTURAL WOODWORKING
ASSOCS., LLC**
4 7th St. (08825)
**Phone—(908) 996-7866**
Fax—(908) 996-7933
www.awacustomwood.com
Email—info@awacustomwood.com
Ptnr.—John Gehman
Ptnr.—Matthias Ritzmann
Opers. Mgr.—Patrick Hagerty
Off. Admn.—Cara Simonetta
SIC—2431; 2434; NAICS—
337110; *Architectural millwork &
wooden cabinets*
Employs—6; Estab.—1988
Sales—$500,000-$1Mil
9,000 sq ft site, Distrib.—National
Limited Liability Company

**CERBACO LTD.**
809 Harrison St. (08825)
**Phone—(908) 996-1333**
Fax—(908) 996-0023

www.cerbaco.com
Email—sales@cerbaco.com
Pres.—Alan Flash
Secy-Treas.—Michelle Flash
Opers. Mgr.—Keith McClean
SIC—3999; *Nonmetallic weld
backings*
Employs—20; Estab.—1977
Sales—$1Mil-$2.5Mil
Distrib.—Intl.
Privately owned corporation

**DESIGN PLAN LIGHTING, INC.**
79 Trenton Ave. (08825)
**Phone—(908) 996-7710**
Fax—(908) 996-7042
www.designplan.com
Email—klapper@designplan.com
V-P.—Richard Klapper
Administrator—Gerry Hudzik
SIC—3646; NAICS—335122;
*Lighting fixtures*
Employs—20; Estab.—1989
Sales—$1Mil-$2.5Mil
19,000 sq ft site, Distrib.—Intl.
Privately owned corporation

**F & R GRINDING, INC.**
138 County Road 513 (08825)
**Phone—(908) 996-0440**
Fax—(908) 996-0450
www.fandrgrinding.com
Email—ron@frgrinding.com
Pres.—Ron Nicolato
V-P.—Peter A. Nicolato
Plt. Mgr., Bar Stock Div.—Dave
Hughes
Off. Mgr.—Amanda Taglianetti
SIC—3599; *Centerless grinding*
Employs—15; Estab.—1984
Sales—$1Mil-$2.5Mil
16,500 sq ft site, Distrib.—National
Privately owned sub-S corp.

**METAL MASTERS**
1 Lower Oak Grove Rd. (08825)
**Phone—(908) 996-2555**
Fax—(908) 996-3456
www.metalmastersrestoration.com
Email—james@
metalmastersrestoration.com
Owner—James Sherron
Sales Mgr.—Josh Sherron
SIC—3471; NAICS—332813;
*Production-scale & custom metal
finishing & plating, including
refinishing of antiques*
Employs—5; Estab.—1977
Distrib.—Regional
Limited Liability Company

**RTS PACKAGING, LLC**
869 State Highway 12 (08825)
**Phone—(908) 782-0505**
National—(800) 526-1706
Fax—(908) 782-0583
www.rtspackaging.com
Email—rtspkg@rocktenn.com
GM—Greg Lawrence
SIC—2653; NAICS—322211;
*Fiberboard box partitions*
Employs—62; Estab.—2004
Distrib.—Intl.
Limited Liability Company
Parent co.—RTS Packaging, LLC,
Norcross, GA
Phone—(770) 448-2244
See Parent Co. Section for full profile.

**ZERO SURGE, INC.**
889 State Route 12, Ste. 2 (08825-
4223)
**Phone—(908) 996-7700**
National—(800) 996-6696
Fax—(908) 996-7773
www.zerosurge.com
Email—info@zerosurge.com
Pres.—Jack Harford
Dir., Sales & Mktg.—Donna
DeVico
MIS & R & D Mgr.—J. Rudy
Harford

SIC—3612; NAICS—335311;
*Power line surge suppressors;
Brand name—Spectrum WVR;
Total Surge Cancellation (TSC)
Technology*
Employs—10; Estab.—1989
4,500 sq ft site, Distrib.—National
Privately owned corporation

---

## Garfield
(Bergen—N.E.)

**A G F PRINTING, INC.**
92 Bogart Ave. (07026)
**Phone—(973) 253-8550**
Fax—(973) 253-8553
www.agfprinting.com
Ptnr.—Frank Elia
Pres.—Anthony D. Elia
V-P.—John Caravello
SIC—2759; NAICS—323100;
*Commercial printing*
Employs—5; Estab.—1925
Sales—$500,000-$1Mil
Distrib.—Local
Privately owned corporation

**ACON WATCH CROWN CO.**
260 Division Ave., P.O. Box 800
(07026)
**Phone—(973) 546-8585**
Fax—(973) 478-4067
www.aconwatch.com
Email—acohenacon@aol.com
Owner—Arnold K. Cohen
SIC—3873; NAICS—334518;
*Watch & watch band parts,
including watch crowns, strap
buckles, spring bars, spring-
loaded pins & glass crystals*
Employs—8; Estab.—1935
Sales—under $900,000
4,000 sq ft site, Distrib.—Intl.
Sole ownership

**ANATECH ELECTRONICS, INC.**
70 Outwater Ln., Ste. 3, P.O. Box
2217 (07026)
**Phone—(973) 772-4242**
Fax—(973) 772-4646
www.anatechelectronics.com
Email—sales@
anatechelectronics.com
V-P., Sales & Mktg.—Sam
Benzacar
SIC—3679; *Electronic
components & filters*
Employs—30; Estab.—1990
8,000 sq ft site, Distrib.—Intl.
Privately owned corporation

**APOLLO SIGN CO., INC.**
835 Midland Ave. (07026)
**Phone—(973) 772-7446**
(973) 772-7544
Fax—(973) 772-3798
Email—apollosign@gmail.com
Pres.—Valerie Vegliante
SIC—3993; *Trade show, neon &
magnetic interior & exterior
signs, banners, dimensional
displays, vehicle & window
lettering & logo design services
& bucket truck service*
Employs—5; Estab.—1984
Sales—under $500,000
Distrib.—Regional
Privately owned corporation

**APPLIED ENGINEERING, CORP.**
232 Palisade Ave. (07026)
**Phone—(973) 772-6022**
Fax—(973) 772-6023
www.appliedengineeringcorp.com
Email—appliedus@gmail.com
Pres.—Andre Savin

GEOGRAPHICAL

## Garfield—(cont.)

SIC—3565; 3569; 3559; 5084; NAICS—333993; *Manufacturer & distributor of custom & special packaging, production & automation machinery for the pharmaceutical, cosmetic & food industries, including filling machines & stand-up pouches with spouts; Brand name—PF8; B2FS; ALUFORM 2; BBFLEX*
Employs—5; Estab.—1997
Sales—$500,000-$1Mil
5,000 sq ft site, Distrib.—Intl.
Privately owned corporation

### ARTIC ICE MFG. & DRY ICE CO.
158 Semel Ave. (07026)
**Phone—(201) 370-3141**
Fax—(973) 772-7675
www.articiceco.com
Email—info@articiceco.com
Ptnr.—John Minichetti
Ptnr.—Steve Lengel, Jr.
Off. Mgr.—Gerri Minichetti
SIC—2097; NAICS—312113; *Dry & block ice & ice cubes*
Employs—5; Estab.—1923
Distrib.—Regional
Privately owned corporation
AKA: Arctic Ice

### ARTISTIC RAILINGS, INC.
500 River Dr. (07026)
**Phone—(973) 772-8540**
          (973) 772-7121
www.artisticrail.com
Email—info@artisticrail.com
Pres.—Tom Zuzik
SIC—3446; NAICS—332323; *Ornamental iron railings*
Employs—7; Estab.—1955
Sales—$500,000-$1Mil
Distrib.—National
Privately owned corporation

### ATLANTIC STONE II, LLC
98 Somerset St. (07026)
**Phone—(973) 928-1458**
Fax—(973) 928-1457
www.atlanticstone2.com
Email—service@atlanticstone2.com
Ptnr.—Michele Borrielli
SIC—3281; *Granite, marble & slate countertops, vanities & fireplace surrounds*
Employs—4; Estab.—2007
Sales—under $500,000
Distrib.—Local
Limited Liability Company

### BANKERS PEN CO., INC.
141 Lanza Rd. (07026)
**Phone—(718) 768-7107**
National—(800) 499-7367
Fax—(718) 768-7147
www.bankerspens.com
Email—sales@bankerspens.com
Pres.—Richard Danziger
Acctg. Mgr.—Elizabeth Ramirez
Cust. Serv. Mgr.—Bonnie Vaccaro
SIC—3951; 3993; NAICS—339941; *Promotional pens, pencils, key tags & tape measures; Brand name—Bankers*
Employs—30; Estab.—1981
20,000 sq ft site, Distrib.—Intl.
Privately owned sub-S corp.

**NEW ENTRY**
### BANKERS PEN, INC.
141 Lanza Ave., Bldg. 12 (07026)
**Phone—(800) 499-7367**
Fax—(888) 345-9102
www.bankerspens.com
Email—sales@bankerspens.com
Cust. Serv. Mgr.—Sandy Aubry

SIC—2759; *Promotional item screen printing, including pens & drinkware*
Employs—30
Sales—$1Mil-$2.5Mil
Distrib.—Intl.
Privately owned corporation

### BELMONT WHOLESALE FENCE MFG.
112-114 Monroe St. (07026)
**Phone—(973) 472-5121**
National—(800) 628-8928
Fax—(973) 472-9260
www.boundaryfence.net
Email—sales@boundaryfence.net
Manager—Joe Merchant
SIC—3089; *Vinyl fences & fencing materials; Brand name—Chainlink; Ornamental*
Employs—19; Estab.—1981
12,000 sq ft site,
Privately owned corporation
ISO rating—9001
AKA: Boundary Fence & Railing

### BRIMAR INDUSTRIES, INC.
64 Outwater Ln., 3rd Fl., P.O. Box 467 (07026)
**Phone—(973) 340-7889**
National—(800) 274-6271
Fax—(973) 340-7809
www.brimar.com
Email—sales@brimar.com
Pres.—Brian Costello
V-P., Prodn.—Gianni Gallorini
V-P., Opers.—Michael Schoenfeld
Prod. Dev. Mgr.—Mary Jimenez
SIC—2759; 3993; NAICS—323749; *Printed identification labels, decals, signs & nameplates*
Employs—60; Estab.—1988
30,000 sq ft site, Distrib.—Intl.
Privately owned corporation
Also see: Signs of Security, Inc., same loc.

### CLEAR PLUS WINDSHIELD WIPERS
100 Outwater Ln. (07026)
**Phone—(973) 546-8800**
Fax—(973) 546-0800
www.clearplus.com
Email—admin@clearplus.com
Owner—Raj Chawla
Mktg. Mgr.—Matt Beadling
Administrator—Daniella Toro
SIC—3714; *Windshield wipers*
Employs—10; Estab.—1996
Sales—$500,000-$1Mil
Distrib.—Intl.
Sole ownership

### CLYDE'S ICES & ICE CREAM, INC.
48 Gaston Ave. (07026)
**Phone—(973) 546-2760**
Fax—(973) 546-0285
Email—clydesitalianice@yahoo.com
Pres.—Tim Devens
SIC—2024; NAICS—311520; *Ice cream & frozen desserts*
Employs—8; Estab.—1909
Distrib.—Local
Privately owned corporation

### D A S INSTALLATIONS, INC.
176 Saddle River Rd., Bldg. D (07026)
**Phone—(973) 473-6858**
Fax—(973) 473-2626
www.dasinstallations.com
Email—dasinstallations@verizon.net
Pres.—Louis Skvarca
SIC—3535; NAICS—333922; *Belt conveyors*
Employs—10; Estab.—1986
Sales—under $500,000
Distrib.—Regional
Privately owned corporation

### DEJOHN MACHINE CO.
2 Elm St. (07026)
**Phone—(973) 478-1144**
Fax—(973) 478-6685
Email—dejohn190@cs.com
V-P., Fin.—Gino DiGiovanni
Shop Mgr.—Robert DiGiovanni
SIC—3599; *Precision & general machining job shop*
Employs—4; Estab.—1974
Sales—under $500,000
2,300 sq ft site, Distrib.—Local
Privately owned sub-S corp.

### DENNI'S STUDIO
169 Semel Ave. (07026)
**Phone—(973) 220-4898**
Email—dblatt4774@aol.com
Owner—Denise Blatt
SIC—2791; NAICS—323122; *Electronic prepress & graphic design*
Employs—1; Estab.—1982
Sales—under $500,000
400 sq ft site, Distrib.—Local
Sole ownership

### DENTAL MODELS & DESIGNS, INC.
20 Passaic St., Ste. 3 (07026)
**Phone—(973) 472-8009**
National—(888) 658-3660
Fax—(973) 472-8011
www.dentalmodelsanddesigns.com
Email—david@dentalmodelsanddesigns.com
Pres., Hum. Res.—David Lauchheimer
SIC—3843; *Dental models*
Employs—5; Estab.—1993
Sales—$500,000-$1Mil
Distrib.—Intl.
Privately owned corporation

### DIRECT SALES & SERVICES
141 Lanza Ave., Bldg. 8 (07026)
**Phone—(973) 340-4480**
National—(800) 422-6654
Fax—(973) 340-3501
www.auntgussies.com
Email—info@auntgussies.com
Pres.—David Caine
Cust. Serv. Rep.—Sandra Mendez
Cust. Serv. Rep.—Rosanna Perez
SIC—2052; *Cookies & crackers*
Employs—25; Estab.—1980
Sales—$2.5Mil-$5Mil
Distrib.—National
Privately owned corporation
AKA: Aunt Gussie's Cookies & Crackers

### ECLIPSE MFG., LLC
438 Lanza Ave. (07026)
**Phone—(973) 340-9939**
Fax—(973) 340-9962
www.eclipsemanufacturing.com
Email—mail@eclipsemanufacturing.com
Owner—Ziggy Nieradka
SIC—3599; *Industrial machine parts, CNC machining & welding job shop*
Employs—4; Estab.—2004
Sales—over $500,000
3,500 sq ft site, Distrib.—Local
Limited Liability Company

### ESCO INDUSTRIAL CORP.
141 Lanza Ave., Bldg. 3-B (07026)
**Phone—(973) 478-5888**
Hum. Res. Mgr.—Kathy Shu
SIC—3494; NAICS—332900; *Pipe fittings*
Employs—22; Estab.—1994
Sales—$2.5Mil-$5Mil (est)
Distrib.—Intl.
Privately owned corporation

### FANO MACHINE & TOOL CO.
20 Passaic St. (07026)
**Phone—(973) 773-9353**
Fax—(973) 773-9353

Pres.—Tony Cristofano
SIC—3599; *General machining job shop*
Employs—2; Estab.—1993
Sales—under $500,000
Distrib.—Local
Privately owned corporation

### FLUID FILTRATION CORP.
102 Van Winkle Ave. (07026)
**Phone—(973) 253-7070**
National—(888) 295-0408
Fax—(973) 253-0070
www.fluidfiltrationmfg.com
Email—fluidfiltr@aol.com
Pres.—Farzad Alborzi
Manager—Michael Alborzi
Shop Foreman—Armando Casillas
SIC—3569; 3494; 3498; 3589; NAICS—333319; *Pipeline & cone strainers, water filters, replacement baskets for basket strainers/bag & stainless steel filters, wire mesh, hastelloy & monel baskets, fabricated strainers, wye strainers & 'Y' strainer screens*
Employs—10; Estab.—1996
Sales—$1Mil-$5Mil
Distrib.—Intl.
Privately owned corporation

### FRAGALE'S BAKING CO.
68-74 Gaston Ave. (07026)
**Phone—(973) 546-0327**
Fax—(973) 546-0260
Owner—Andrew Fragale
Store Mgr.—Kevin Oleans
SIC—2051; NAICS—311812; *Bakery products*
Employs—12; Estab.—1950
5,000 sq ft site, Distrib.—Regional
Sole ownership

### GARFIELD CABINETS & MILLWORK, INC.
22 Garfield Ave. (07026)
**Phone—(973) 340-0507**
Fax—(973) 340-0507
Email—jdevito35@gmail.com
Pres.—James DeVito, Jr.
SIC—2434; 2431; NAICS—337110; *Wooden cabinets & millwork*
Employs—2; Estab.—1956
Sales—under $500,000
Distrib.—Local
Privately owned corporation

### †GARFIELD LUMBER & MILLWORK CO.
260 Lanza Ave. (07026)
**Phone—(973) 478-2160**
Fax—(973) 478-3164
www.garfieldlumber.com
Email—barry@garfieldlumber.com
Pres., CFO—Ray Sowa
MIS & Opers. Mgr.—Helen Schweighardt
R & D Mgr.—Barry Hinsinger
SIC—5031; 5072; *Distributor of lumber, millwork, hardware & power tools*
Employs—20; Estab.—1966
Sales—$1Mil-$5Mil
4,200 sq ft site, Distrib.—Local
Privately owned sub-S corp.

### GEMINI PLASTIC FILMS CORP.
535 Midland Ave., P.O. Box 360 (07026)
**Phone—(973) 340-0700**
National—(800) 789-4732
Fax—(973) 340-1045
www.geminiplasticfilms.com
Email—gemini-plastics@worldnet.att.net
CEO—Andrew Del Presto
Pres.—Richard Hulbert
Cont.—T. Murphy

## Garfield—(cont.)

SIC—2673; 3081; NAICS—
326113; *Plastic bags & films*
Employs—40; Estab.—1966
50,000 sq ft site, Distrib.—National
Privately owned corporation

**GENEVIEVE'S, INC.**
174 Ray St. (07026)
**Phone—(973) 772-8816**
Fax—(973) 772-5874
Pres.—David Dzwilewski
V-P.—Ann Dzwilewski
Plt. Mgr.—Genevieve Dzwilewski
Sales Rep.—Barbara Gorka
SIC—2066; NAICS—311300;
*Chocolate candy*
Employs—7; Estab.—1944
Sales—$500,000-$1Mil
Distrib.—National
Privately owned corporation

**GIORDANO, INC., PHILIP A.**
59 Garfield Ave. (07026)
**Phone—(973) 546-9267**
Fax—(973) 546-3084
www.computypenj.com
Email—production@
computypenj.com
Ptnr.—Robert Giordano
SIC—2759; 2791; *Commercial
printing, electronic prepress &
graphic design services*
Employs—3; Estab.—1978
Sales—under $500,000
2,000 sq ft site, Distrib.—Regional
Privately owned sub-S corp.
DBA: Computype

**†IBF CORP.**
44 Plauderville Ave. (07026)
**Phone—(973) 546-0055**
National—(800) 423-3456
Fax—(973) 546-1048
www.ibfcorp.com
Email—it@ibfcorp.com
Sr. V-P.—Amauri Augusto
Dir., IT—Darwin Z. A. Ferreira
Accountant—Ruben Amarante
SIC—5049; *Distributor of graphic
arts equipment, including
graphic arts film & x-ray offset
presensitized aluminum plates;
Brand name—IBF*
Employs—28; Estab.—1970
Sales—$5Mil-$10Mil
Distrib.—National
Privately owned corporation

**INTERNATIONAL CRYSTAL
LABORATORIES**
11 Erie St., Ste. 2 (07026)
**Phone—(973) 478-8944**
Fax—(973) 478-4201
www.internationalcrystal.net
Email—iclmail@
internationalcrystal.net
Pres.—Theresa Herpst
Dir., Crystal Tech.—Vladimir
Yakimovich
GM—Robert Herpst
Sales Mgr.—Irene Ascuitto
Catalog & Comms. Mgr.—Jill Ciffo
SIC—3827; 3826; 3674; 3821;
NAICS—333314; *Optical lenses,
lasers & spectroscopic &
laboratory equipment & supplies,
including crystal optics, lab
presses & dies, liquid, gas &
fluorescent cells & optics for
CO2 lasers & magneto-optical
materials*
Employs—20; Estab.—1962
Sales—$1Mil-$5Mil
6,500 sq ft site, Distrib.—National
Privately owned corporation

**†KUIKEN BROTHERS COMMERCIAL**
Div. of Kuiken Brothers Company,
Inc.
485 River Dr. (07026)
**Phone—(973) 772-0044**
Fax—(973) 772-4909

www.kuikenbrothers.com
Email—info@kuikenbrothers.com
Store Mgr.—Kenneth Kuiken
SIC—5031; 5072; *Distributor of
drywall, studs, acoustical ceiling
tile & grid, insulation, hollow
metal doors & frames &
architectural hardware, including
boom service*
Employs—25; Estab.—1912
Sales—$500,000-$1Mil
Distrib.—Regional
Privately owned sub-S corp.
AKA: Kuiken Brothers
Parent co.—Kuiken Brothers
Company, Inc., Fair Lawn, NJ
Phone—(201) 796-2082
See Parent Co. Section for full profile.

**LATIN PERCUSSION, INC.**
Div. of Fender Musical Instruments
Corp.
160 Belmont Ave. (07026)
**Phone—(973) 330-9103**
National—(888) 576-8742
Fax—(973) 772-3568
www.lpmusic.com
Email—customer_service@
lpmusic.com
Creative Dir.—Heidi Linsalata
Schaeffer
SIC—3931; NAICS—339992;
*Percussion instruments*
Employs—25; Estab.—1964
35,000 sq ft site, Distrib.—Intl.
Privately owned corporation
Parent co.—Fender Musical
Instruments Corp., Scottsdale,
AZ
Phone—(480) 596-9690
See Parent Co. Section for full profile.

**LONGO'S CABINET SHOP**
101 Monroe St. (07026)
**Phone—(973) 472-3567**
Fax—(973) 472-3567
Owner—Tom Esposito
SIC—2434; 2431; 2542; 3083;
NAICS—337110; *Wooden &
laminate cabinets*
Employs—1; Estab.—1955
Sales—under $500,000
Distrib.—Local
Sole ownership

**MEND TECH, INC.**
38 Irving Pl. (07026)
**Phone—(973) 340-9212**
Fax—(973) 340-1483
Email—mendtechinc@aol.com
Pres.—Eli Kaadan
Manager—Dan Haro
SIC—3843; NAICS—339114;
*Dental laboratory equipment*
Employs—5; Estab.—1996
Sales—$500,000-$1Mil
Distrib.—National
Privately owned corporation

**†METRO INDUSTRIAL SUPPLY, INC.**
200 Charles St. (07026-1238)
**Phone—(973) 546-5660**
Fax—(973) 546-5661
www.metroindustrialsupply.com
Email—info@
metroindustrialsupply.com
Pres.—Richard Dino
SIC—5084; 5085; *Wholesaler of
industrial equipment & supplies,
including power transmissions,
factory & mill supplies & safety &
gas detection equipment; Brand
name—Rexnord; Linkbelt; MB;
Koyo; Lumidor; Honeywell; SKF;
CR; Renold; Festo; Coilhose;
Baldor; Leeson; Elektrim;
Carlisle; Tribology; IKO; NB;
Lovejoy; Zellweger; AMI; FYH;
Jason; Champion; Maska;
Starcyl; All-Flo; Le*
Employs—5; Estab.—1983
Sales—$1Mil-$2.5Mil
5,000 sq ft site, Distrib.—National
Privately owned sub-S corp.

**MIDLAND RADIATOR SERVICE CO.**
420 Midland Ave. (07026)
**Phone—(973) 340-0533**
　　　(800) 605-8001
Fax—(973) 340-5941
www.midlandradiator.com
Email—midlandrad@aol.com
Pres.—Tom Peraino
SIC—3714; *Rebuilt heavy-duty
truck radiators & cooling systems*
Employs—8; Estab.—1964
Sales—under $500,000
Distrib.—Local
Privately owned corporation

**NORTH AMERICAN ILLUMINATION
CO.**
79 Commerce St. (07026)
**Phone—(973) 478-4700**
Fax—(973) 478-0152
www.americanlighting.com
Email—info@americanlighting.com
Co-Pres.—Paul Goldberg
SIC—3646; NAICS—335122;
*Commercial lighting fixtures*
Employs—16; Estab.—1994
Distrib.—Intl.
Privately owned corporation
AKA: American Lighting

**NORTH JERSEY RAVIOLI CO.**
65 Pacific Ave. (07026)
**Phone—(973) 772-5050**
Pres.—Anthony Apolito
SIC—2038; NAICS—311412;
*Ravioli*
Employs—2; Estab.—1977
Sales—under $500,000 (est)
Distrib.—Local
Privately owned corporation

**O'NEIL COLOR & COMPOUNDING
CORP.**
Div. of Primex Plastics Corp.
61 River Dr. (07026)
**Phone—(973) 777-8999**
National—(800) 282-7933
Fax—(888) 663-4565
www.oneilcolor.com
Email—dingram@oneilcolor.com
Sales Mgr.—David Sarkisian
Plt. Mgr.—Robert Hillyer
Off. Mgr.—Diane Ingram
Sales Rep.—Tim Talbott
Cust. Serv. Rep.—Linda Dojer
SIC—2816; NAICS—325100; *Dry
color compounding*
Employs—38; Estab.—1995
Distrib.—National
Privately owned corporation
Parent co.—Primex Plastics Corp.,
Richmond, IN
Phone—(765) 966-7774
See Parent Co. Section for full profile.

**†P & A AUTO PARTS, INC.**
396 Midland Ave. (07026)
**Phone—(973) 405-6068**
Fax—(973) 405-6072
www.paautoparts.com
Email—ljd25@optonline.net
Br. Mgr.—Louis Doto
SIC—5013; *Distributor of
automotive parts*
Employs—10; Estab.—2002
Distrib.—Local
Privately owned corporation
Parent co.—P & A Auto Parts, Inc.,
Hackensack, NJ
Phone—(201) 843-7156
See Parent Co. Section for full profile.

**PALMER ELECTRONICS, INC.**
156 Belmont Ave. (07026)
**Phone—(973) 772-5900**
Fax—(973) 772-6054
www.palmer-electronics.com
Email—victor@palmer-
electronics.com
Pres.—Victor R. Palmeri

SIC—3679; *Custom adaptors,
connectors, heads, pins &
terminals for the thermocouple
measurement industry, plastic &
porcelain thermocouple terminal
blocks & electrical porcelain
manufacturing*
Employs—4; Estab.—1953
Sales—$170,000-$180,000
8,000 sq ft site, Distrib.—Intl.
Privately owned corporation

**PAPERTEC, INC.**
141 Lanza Ave., Bldg. 29 (07026)
**Phone—(862) 591-1100**
National—(888) 444-9911
Fax—(862) 591-1103
www.papertecinc.com
Email—sales@papertecinc.com
Pres., CFO, Sales Mgr.—Ted
Bielen
V-P., Opers.—Kevin Bielen
V-P., Bus. Dev.—Todd Bielen
SIC—2679; NAICS—322200;
*Paper & film converting,
including slitting, rewinding,
sheeting, guillotine & die cutting
of substrates; Brand name—
Keena Tape*
Employs—15; Estab.—1977
Sales—$4Mil-$6Mil
50,000 sq ft site, Distrib.—Intl.
Limited Liability Company
AKA: WJJ & Company

**PENTA GLASS INDUSTRIES, INC.**
71 Hepworth Pl. (07026)
**Phone—(973) 478-2110**
Fax—(973) 478-2180
www.pentaglassindustries.com
Email—pentaglassind@
optonline.net
Pres.—Jim Huddleston
Off. Mgr.—Kathy Huddleston
Estimator—Pat Huddleston
SIC—3231; 3211; NAICS—
327215; *Glass store windows &
curtain walls, fabricated glass &
mirrors & custom laminated
glass*
Employs—6; Estab.—1986
10,000 sq ft site, Distrib.—Local
Privately owned corporation

**POLO MACHINE, INC.**
223 Banta Ave., P.O. Box 403
(07026)
**Phone—(973) 340-9984**
Email—polomill@verizon.net
Pres.—John Pszeniczny
SIC—3599; *General machining
job shop*
Employs—5; Estab.—1993
Sales—under $500,000
Distrib.—Local
Privately owned corporation

**POSTALOGIC, LLC**
64 Outwater Ln., Ste. 1 (07026-
3845)
**Phone—(973) 546-1400**
Fax—(973) 546-3297
www.postalogic.com
Email—data@postalogic.com
Pres.—Brian Parker
GM—Orin Redmond
Off. Mgr.—Maryann Magans
Mailing Svcs. Mgr.—Myron
Porochniak
SIC—2789; 2675; NAICS—
323121; *Binding & finishing
services for the printing industry,
including cutting, folding,
stitching, die-cutting, gluing,
drilling & collating*
Employs—40; Estab.—1983
Sales—$1Mil-$2.5Mil
Distrib.—Local
Privately owned corporation

**PRIMEX PLASTICS CORP.**
65 River Dr. (07026)
**Phone—(973) 470-8000**
National—(800) 631-7061

GEOGRAPHICAL

## Garfield—(cont.)

Fax—(973) 470-8728
www.primexplastics.com
Email—akepfinger@
primexplastics.com
GM & Sales Mgr.—Aaron Putnam
Opers. Mgr.—Dalo Chin
Hum. Res. Mgr.—Joann Call
Cust. Serv. Mgr.—Yasir Allatis
SIC—3081; NAICS—326113;
Polystyrene sheets & rolls
Employs—100; Estab.—1965
Distrib.—National
Privately owned corporation
Parent co.—Primex Plastics Corp.,
Richmond, IN
Phone—(765) 966-7774
See Parent Co. Section for full profile.

### PRODO-PAK CORP.

77 Commerce St., P.O. Box 363
(07026)
Phone—(973) 772-4500
Fax—(973) 772-0471
www.prodo-pak.com
Email—sales@prodo-pak.com
Pres.—John Mueller
Cont.—Lynda Schaller
GM—Ralph Isler
SIC—3565; NAICS—333993;
Automatic form/fill/seal
packaging machinery for flexible
three & four sided, fin & pillow
style & standup gusseted pouch
production; Brand name—
Prodo-Pak®
Employs—25; Estab.—1961
Sales—$1Mil-$5Mil
20,000 sq ft site, Distrib.—Intl.
Privately owned corporation

### PRODUCT IDENTIFICATION CO., INC.

141 Lanza Ave., Bldg. 19 (07026)
Phone—(973) 955-4747
National—(800) 419-4742
Fax—(973) 955-4750
www.alpack-pic.com
Email—info@alpack-pic.com
Pres.—Les Weinstock
Secy-Treas.—Arlene Weinstock
GM—Jeffrey Weinstock
Cust. Serv. Mgr.—Peter Pazumas
Qual. Control Mgr.—Edward
Kraemer, Sr.
SIC—3499; 3089; 2759; 3544;
NAICS—323100; Aluminum,
vinyl & polyester nameplates,
labels & decals & steel rule dies
Employs—20; Estab.—1964
Sales—over $1.5Mil
20,000 sq ft site, Distrib.—National
Privately owned sub-S corp.
AKA: Micro Steel Rule Die

### RONIC, INC.

173 Ray St. (07026)
Phone—(973) 772-2217
Fax—(973) 772-4385
Email—venicebakery@gmail.com
Pres., Hum. Res. & IT Mgr.—Nick
Aiello
SIC—2051; NAICS—311812;
Bakery products, including
breads, cakes & pastries
Employs—8
Distrib.—Local
Privately owned corporation

### ROYAL SLIDE SALES CO., INC.

42 Hepworth Pl. (07026)
Phone—(973) 777-1177
www.vinylbag.com
Email—royalnj@aol.com
V-P.—Lewis Neuman
V-P.—Abraham Levine

SIC—3089; 3965; NAICS—
339993; Home furnishings
packaging bags, cosmetics
packaging bags & zippers;
Brand name—Royal
Employs—15; Estab.—1943
Sales—$1Mil-$5Mil
45,000 sq ft site, Distrib.—Intl.
Privately owned corporation
ISO rating—9001

NEW ENTRY
### †RPL SUPPLIES, INC.

141 Lanza Ave., Bldg. 3-A (07026)
Phone—(973) 767-0880
National—(800) 524-0914
Fax—(973) 772-6601
www.rplsupplies.com
Email—information@
rplsupplies.com
Pres.—Michael Kaminski
SIC—5043; Wholesaler of printing
equipment & supplies for the
photo novelty industry
Employs—18

### S & M PRESS, INC.

169 Semel Ave., Ste. 2 (07026)
Phone—(973) 778-4405
(973) 546-6111
Fax—(973) 778-3609
Email—smpress219@aol.com
Owner—Maxine Bing
V-P.—Tracy Eliasof
Accountant—Melissa Eisenhower
SIC—2759; 3993; NAICS—
323100; Commercial printing,
promotional items & creative
marketing services
Employs—11; Estab.—1976
5,500 sq ft site, Distrib.—Regional
Privately owned corporation

### SAK TECHNOLOGIES, INC.

134 Gaston Ave. (07026)
Phone—(973) 340-8300
Fax—(973) 340-8388
www.saktech.com
Email—steven.karras@saktech.com
Pres.—Steven Karras
SIC—3679; 3672; Electronic
contract manufacturing,
including circuit boards
Employs—20
Sales—$2.5Mil-$5Mil (est)
Distrib.—Local
Privately owned corporation

### SIGNS OF SECURITY, INC.

64 Outwater Ln., 2nd Fl., P.O. Box
468 (07026)
Phone—(973) 340-8404
National—(800) 274-6271
Fax—(973) 779-3809
www.signsofsecurity.com
Email—sales@signsofsecurity.com
Pres.—Brian Costello
Plt. Mgr.—Juan Ventura
Mktg. Mgr.—Ruth Mery Jimenez
IT Mgr.—Michael Jenfield
Hum. Res. Mgr.—Joanna Pabelick
Cust. Serv. Rep.—John Janos
SIC—3993; Burglar & security
interior & exterior signs
Employs—60; Estab.—1999
Sales—$11Mil-$25Mil
Distrib.—Intl.
Privately owned corporation
Also see: Brimar Industries, Inc.,
same loc.

### STAR DYNAMIC CORP.

100 Outwater Ln. (07026)
Phone—(973) 340-3883
Fax—(973) 340-1530
www.stardynamic.com
Email—stardyn@aol.com
Pres.—Maria Vecchiotti
V-P.—Michelle Schartzman
V-P.—David I. Alster
Comp.—Hung Anqui
Pur. Mgr.—Joseph Elcavage

Qual. Assur. Mgr.—Anna
Haemmerle
SIC—3661; Military
telecommunications equipment
Employs—60; Estab.—1975
35,000 sq ft site, Distrib.—National
Privately owned corporation
ISO rating—9001:2008

### STEFAN ENTERPRISES, INC.

141 Lanza Ave., Bldg. 16-E
(07026)
Phone—(973) 253-6005
Fax—(973) 253-6006
www.stefanenterprises.com
Email—kspring@
stefanenterprises.com
Pres.—Stefan Missbrenner
Treas.—Kevin J. Spring
Hum. Res. Mgr.—Marilyn Basile
Accountant—Kelly Spreen
SIC—2396; Textile printing
Employs—20; Estab.—2001
Distrib.—Local
Privately owned corporation

### STRAVAL CO.

21 Columbus Ave. (07026)
Phone—(973) 340-9955
Fax—(973) 340-9933
www.straval.com
Email—info@straval.com
Pres.—Ed Simin
Corp. Secy.—Roseann Denoba
SIC—3491; 3494; NAICS—
332911; Industrial relief, back
pressure & bypass valves,
simplex strainers & high
pressure filters
Employs—15; Estab.—1989
Sales—$500,000-$1Mil
9,000 sq ft site, Distrib.—Intl.
Privately owned corporation

### SUMATIC CO., INC.

102 Dewitt St., P.O. Box 435
(07026)
Phone—(973) 772-1288
Fax—(973) 772-1927
Email—sumaticco@optonline.net
Pres.—Michel A. Sunier
GM—Terry Sunier
SIC—3599; Screw machine
products
Employs—5; Estab.—1985
Sales—$500,000-$1Mil
Distrib.—National
Privately owned corporation

### TECHNO DESIGN, INC.

11 Erie St., Front (07026)
Phone—(973) 478-0930
Fax—(973) 478-0575
Email—technodesigninc@
optonline.net
Pres., CFO—Ruben A. Diaz
SIC—3556; NAICS—333294;
Food processing machinery
Employs—4; Estab.—1976
8,000 sq ft site, Distrib.—Intl.
Privately owned corporation

### †TEES & NOVELTIES, INC.

P.O. Box 2059 (07026)
Phone—(973) 574-7591
National—(888) 386-7282
Fax—(973) 574-7590
www.teesandnovelties.com
Email—teesandnovelties@aol.com
Pres.—Sandy Ehrlich
SIC—5199; Distributor of
embroidered patches & slogan
novelty buttons, stickers & pins
Employs—6; Estab.—1989
Sales—$500,000
20,000 sq ft site, Distrib.—Intl.
Privately owned corporation

### TYPE-O-GRAPHICS, LLC

222 Outwater Ln., Ste. 1 (07026)
Phone—(973) 253-3333
Fax—(973) 253-3330
Pres.—Ruth Valdez
V-P.—John Valdez

Off. Mgr.—Rosie Valdez
SIC—2759; 2791; NAICS—
323122; Commercial printing &
typesetting
Employs—5; Estab.—1972
Distrib.—Regional
Privately owned corporation

### US MAGIC BOX, INC.

221 McArthur Ave. (07026)
Phone—(973) 772-2070
Fax—(973) 772-4033
www.usmagicbox.com
Email—info@usmagicbox.com
Pres.—Sam Omar
SIC—2675; 2759; NAICS—
322200; Die & laser cutting &
printing for packaging design
Employs—62; Estab.—1999
Sales—$10Mil-$25Mil (est)
Distrib.—National
Privately owned corporation

### VITAIRE CORP.

141 Lanza Ave., 4th Fl. (07026-
3538)
Phone—(973) 473-2244
National—(800) 552-5533
Fax—(201) 592-6612
www.vitaire.com
Email—info@vitaire.com
Pres.—Peter Vayda
Sales Mgr.—Janet Miller
SIC—3564; NAICS—333400;
HEPA air purification units for
allergy, asthma & respiratory
ailment relief; Brand name—
Vitaire
Employs—6; Estab.—1974
Distrib.—National
Privately owned sub-S corp.

### VOIGT LIGHTING

79 Commerce St. (07026)
Phone—(973) 928-2252
Fax—(973) 478-0152
www.voigtlighting.com
Email—paul@voigtlighting.com
Pres.—Paul Goldberg
Engr.—Matt Czwakil
SIC—3646; NAICS—335122;
Commercial & industrial lighting
fixtures
Employs—18; Estab.—1964
Distrib.—National
Privately owned corporation

### WEARBEST SIL-TEX MILLS, LTD.

325 Midland Ave., P.O. Box 589
(07026)
Phone—(973) 340-8844
Fax—(973) 340-2900
www.wearbest.com
Email—sales@wearbest.com
Pres.—Irwin Gasner
V-P., Admn. & CFO—Richard
Issacson
Dir., Hum. Res.—Barbara Warner
Plt. Mgr.—Bogdan Jamroz
SIC—2221; NAICS—313210;
Indoor & outdoor woven
jacquard fabrics & natural &
synthetic fibers for upholstery &
drapery applications; Brand
name—Wearbest; Bella-Dura®
Employs—90; Estab.—1980
70,000 sq ft site, Distrib.—Intl.
Sole ownership

NEW ENTRY
### WINDOW CREATIONS BY EMMY LTD.

103 Summerset St. (07026)
Phone—(917) 613-1491
(718) 965-3844
Fax—(718) 965-3844
Email—mottieisenberger@
yahoo.com
Pres.—Otto Eisenberger

## Garfield—(cont.)

SIC—2591; NAICS—337920;
*Window treatments*
Employs—4; Estab.—1988
Sales—under $500,000
Distrib.—National
Limited Liability Company

## Garwood
(Union—N.E.)

### ACCURATE BUSHING CO., INC./ SMITH BEARING DIV.

443 North Ave., 1st Fl. (07027)
**Phone—(908) 789-1121**
National—(800) 932-0076
Fax—(908) 789-9429
www.smithbearing.com
Email—info@accuratebushing.com
Pres.—Peter Dubinsky
Sales Mgr., Outside—John
  Columbo
Sales Mgr., Inside—Nancy Beanko
Mktg. Mgr.—Christina Froelick
SIC—3568; 3366; NAICS—
  333613; *Aircraft & industrial
  bearings, bushings & rollers*
Employs—50; Estab.—2001
Distrib.—National
Privately owned corporation

### †ADVANTAGE VACUUM LLC

110 South Ave., Ste. A (07027)
**Phone—(908) 228-5629**
National—(877) 777-6383
Fax—(908) 228-5991
www.advacnj.com
Email—info@
  advantagevacuum.com
Owner—Alan Schwartz
V.-P., Sales & Mktg.—Mark
  Schwartz
Off. Mgr.—Tracie Davis
Repair Dept. Supv.—Ken
  Schlossberg
SIC—5087; 5169; 5113; *Distributor
  of commercial vacuum cleaners
  & parts & janitorial supplies,
  including full-service vacuum
  repair; Brand name—Eureka;
  Sanitaire; Pro-Team;
  PerfectProducts; Malish;
  MagnetClean*
Employs—5; Estab.—2000
Sales—$1Mil-$2.5Mil
6,831 sq ft site, Distrib.—National
Limited Liability Company

### ALMARK TOOL & MFG. CO., INC.

27 South Ave., P.O. Box 189
  (07027)
**Phone—(908) 789-2440**
Fax—(908) 789-2465
www.almarktool.com
Email—mark@almarktool.com
Pres.—Mark Bowman
Secy-Treas., Off. Mgr.—Norma
  Bowman
SIC—3599; *Custom machined
  parts, including CNC production,
  prototyping & wire EDM*
Employs—10; Estab.—1973
Sales—$1Mil
6,000 sq ft site, Distrib.—Regional
Privately owned corporation
ISO rating—9001:2008

### CLASSIC COVES

P.O. Box 266 (07027)
**Phone—(908) 344-1776**
Fax—(908) 345-6176
www.classiccoves.com
Email—sales@classiccoves.com
Pres.—Mark Wellnitz

SIC—3299; 2431; NAICS—
  321900; *Indirect & accent cove
  lighting for lobbies, conference
  rooms, corridors, offices &
  schools*
Employs—2; Estab.—1993
Sales—$500,000-$1Mil
Distrib.—National
Limited Liability Company

### CREATIVE COLOR LITHOGRAPHERS, INC.

611 South Ave. (07027)
**Phone—(908) 789-2295**
Fax—(908) 789-2270
www.creativecolor.net
Email—zenon@creativecolor.net
Pres.—Chris Christopher
SIC—2752; 2791; NAICS—
  323122; *Offset printing &
  typesetting*
Employs—18; Estab.—1963
Sales—$500,000-$1Mil
Distrib.—Intl.
Privately owned corporation

### CROWN TROPHY CO., INC.

86 North Ave. (07027)
**Phone—(908) 789-0460**
Fax—(908) 654-0328
www.crowntrophyco.com
Email—crown.trophy@verizon.net
Pres.—Paul Todisco
Zone Coord.—Gloria Cyphers
SIC—3479; *Custom engraving of
  trophies & awards; Brand
  name—Airflyte; Barhill;
  Matthews Bronze*
Employs—4; Estab.—1967
Sales—under $500,000
6,000 sq ft site, Distrib.—Regional
Privately owned sub-S corp.

### †DELTA TOOL & POLISHING SUPPLIES CO., INC.

45 North Ave., P.O. Box 169
  (07027)
**Phone—(908) 518-7600**
Fax—(908) 518-1663
www.deltasupplies.com
Email—info@deltasupplies.com
Pres.—Jose Santos
Whse. Mgr.—Paulo Desousa
SIC—5085; *Distributor of mold
  polishing supplies; Brand
  name—Boride Stones; NSK
  America Tools; Kay Diamond;
  Foredom; Falcon Stones; SGS;
  Arc Abrasives; Ejector Pins*
Employs—3; Estab.—1997
Sales—under $500,000
1,000 sq ft site, Distrib.—National
Privately owned corporation

### KALIS METAL COMPONENTS CORP.

231 North Ave., P.O. Box 294
  (07027)
**Phone—(908) 789-0500**
Fax—(908) 789-0805
Email—garwoodevelyn@
  comcast.net
Hum. Res. & Off. Mgr.—Evelyn
  Archibald
Cust. Serv. Supv.—Cristopher
  Kalis
Shop Supv.—Jim Boettcher
Administrator—Charles Kalis
Administrator—Jamey Kalis
Expeditor—Chad Kalis
SIC—3444; 3499; *Sheet metal
  fabrication & precision metal
  parts*
Employs—30; Estab.—1972
Sales—$2.5Mil-$5Mil
Distrib.—National
Privately owned corporation
AKA: Garwood Metal Co.

### LIQUIFLO EQUIPMENT CO., INC.

443 North Ave., Ste. 2 (07027)
**Phone—(908) 518-0777**
Fax—(908) 518-1847
www.liquiflo.com
Email—sales@liquiflo.com

Pres.—Richard Picut
Cont., Fin. Mgr.—Ray Mattes
IT Mgr.—Keat Lin
Engr.—Jhon Hogg
Sales Coord.—Marienne
  Buccarelli
SIC—3561; NAICS—333911;
  *Centrifugal & external gear
  pumps*
Employs—30; Estab.—1975
60,000 sq ft site, Distrib.—Intl.
Privately owned corporation

### MEDRECON, INC.

257 South Ave. (07027)
**Phone—(908) 789-2050**
National—(800) 526-4323
Fax—(908) 789-3275
www.medrecon.com
Email—ortables@medrecon.com
Pres., CEO—Gary P. Sitcer
V.-P., Prodn.—Andy Kroszczynski
Accts. Mgr.—Wende Sitcer
Off. Mgr.—Cheryl Pizor
SIC—3841; 5047; *New & rebuilt
  OR & surgical tables &
  distributor of pre-owned OR
  tables for hospitals & surgery
  centers*
Employs—8; Estab.—1971
7,600 sq ft site, Distrib.—National
Privately owned sub-S corp.

### MOLD POLISHING CO., INC.

45 North Ave., P. O. Box 96
  (07027)
**Phone—(908) 518-9191**
Fax—(908) 518-9764
www.moldpolishing.com
Email—info@moldpolishing.com
Pres.—Joseph Guerrero
V.-P.—Jose Santos
Manager—Paulo DeSousa
SIC—3471; NAICS—332813;
  *Mold polishing*
Employs—4; Estab.—1980
Sales—$500,000-$1Mil
8,000 sq ft site, Distrib.—National
Privately owned corporation

### NEW JERSEY REPROGRAPHICS, INC.

110 Center St. (07027)
**Phone—(908) 789-1616**
Fax—(908) 789-2474
Email—jbprecisionpress@aol.com
Pres., CFO—Joseph Bizzarro
SIC—2752; 2759; NAICS—
  323100; *Offset & digital color
  printing of prescription blanks,
  forms, brochures & stationery*
Employs—4; Estab.—1980
Sales—under $500,000
3,100 sq ft site, Distrib.—Regional
Privately owned corporation
AKA: Precision Press

### NORCO, INC.

237 South Ave., P.O. Box 186
  (07027)
**Phone—(908) 789-1550**
National—(800) 358-6602
Fax—(908) 654-0812
www.norcopins.com
Email—customerservice@
  norcopins.com
Pres.—Michael Rosenberg
Ex. V.-P., Sales & Treas.—Marc
  Krattenstein
SIC—3961; 3499; 3993; 2395;
  NAICS—339900; *Lapel pins,
  dog tags, giant magnetic PVC
  paper clips, medals, buttons,
  silicone awareness bracelets,
  embroidered & photo patches &
  custom photo inserts*
Employs—15; Estab.—1980
12,000 sq ft site, Distrib.—Intl.
Privately owned sub-S corp.

### OCSIDOT, INC.

116 South Ave. (07027)
**Phone—(908) 789-3300**
Fax—(908) 789-0509

Owner—John Todisco
SIC—2759; NAICS—323100;
  *Commercial printing*
Employs—15; Estab.—1956
Distrib.—Regional
Privately owned corporation

### PETRO EXTRUSION TECHNOLOGIES, INC.

490 South Ave. (07027)
**Phone—(908) 789-3338**
National—(800) 229-3338
Fax—(908) 789-0434
www.petroextrusions.com
Email—rpetro@petroextrusions.com
Pres.—Robert Petrozziello
CFO, Secy. & Hum. Res. Mgr.—
  Frances Petrozziello
MIS Mgr.—Joe Petro, Jr.
Sales Rep., Inside—Julie Hanan
SIC—3089; *Plastic extrusions*
Employs—40; Estab.—1986
45,000 sq ft site, Distrib.—National
Privately owned corporation
Also see: Petro Plastics Co., Inc.,
  450 South Ave.

### PETRO PLASTICS

450 South Ave., P.O. Box 167
  (07027)
**Phone—(908) 789-1200**
Fax—(908) 789-1381
www.petroplastics.com
Email—petrosales01@aol.com
Pres.—Louis Petrozziello
SIC—3082; NAICS—326121;
  *Plastic extrusions*
Employs—45; Estab.—1957
55,000 sq ft site, Distrib.—Intl.
Privately owned corporation
Also see: Petro Extrusion
  Technologies, Inc., 490 South
  Ave.

### ROSCO, INC.

55 South Ave., P.O. Box 184
  (07027)
**Phone—(908) 789-1020**
Fax—(908) 789-1021
www.roscoincnj.com
Email—roscoincnj@verizon.net
Pres.—John Burton
SIC—3599; *Precision & CNC
  machining job shop*
Employs—6; Estab.—1941
Sales—$500,000-$1Mil
3,800 sq ft site, Distrib.—National
Privately owned corporation

### STANDARD PIPE PRODUCTS, INC.

15 North Ave. (07027)
**Phone—(908) 264-8284**
Fax—(908) 264-8290
www.standardpipeproducts.com
Email—info@
  standardpipeproducts.com
V.-P.—Henry Rudorfer
SIC—3498; *Carbon steel, red
  brass, stainless steel &
  aluminum pipe nipples & fittings*
Employs—10; Estab.—2011
Sales—$1Mil-$2.5Mil (est)
Distrib.—Intl.
Privately owned corporation

NEW ENTRY

### SUSPENDED AQUATIC MENTOR

628 South Ave. (07027)
**Phone—(973) 376-3335**
National—(888) 376-3335
Fax—(908) 889-1555
www.aquamentor.com
Email—info@aquamentor.com
Manager—Daniel Cynamon
SIC—3069; *Aquatic rescue tubes;
  Brand name—Super Rescue
  Tube™; Backboard Flotation
  Assist Device™*
Employs—4; Estab.—1983
Sales—$500,000-$1Mil
5,000 sq ft site, Distrib.—Intl.
Privately owned corporation

GEOGRAPHICAL

## Gibbsboro
(Camden—S.W.)

**HARBOR LINEN, LLC (H Q)**

2 Foster Ave. (08026)
**Phone—(856) 435-2000**
National—(800) 257-7858
Fax—(856) 346-4598
www.harborlinen.com
Email—info@harborlinen.com
Chrm.—Earl Waxman
V-P., Opers.—Ronald Brazzo
Cont.—Jim Malloy
Hum. Res. Mgr.—Michelle
  O'Donald
SIC—2392; 2389; 5023; 5136;
  NAICS—315200; *Company
  headquarters; manufacturer &
  distributor of textiles & apparel
  for the hospitality & long-term
  healthcare industries; Brand
  name—Global Textile
  Manufacturing; Harbor Linen
  Manufacturing; West Point
  Home; Thomaston; 1888 Mills;
  Pacific Coast Feather; The Pillow
  Factory; JS Fiber; VF
  Imagewear; Edwards Apparel*
Employs—100; Estab.—1973
Company-wide: 150
Sales—$10Mil-$25Mil (est)
Limited Liability Company

**MACFERREN'S PRINTING & CO.**

3 Democrat Rd. (08026)
**Phone—(856) 435-7066**
Fax—(856) 435-7144
Email—maceprintco@snip.net
Owner—Mike Macferren
SIC—2752; 2759; NAICS—
  323100; *Lithographic &
  commercial printing*
Employs—3; Estab.—2004
Sales—under $500,000
Distrib.—Regional
Limited Liability Company

NEW ENTRY
**PRAXIS DATA SYSTEMS, INC.**

4 Foster Ave., Ste. B & C (08026)
**Phone—(856) 679-2256**
National—(800) 337-7294
Fax—(856) 679-2266
www.praxisnet.com
Email—support@praxisnet.com
V-P.—Harry Srolovitz
Dir., Operation—Laura Yackle
Dir., Technical Svcs.—Robert
  Ferrara
Projects Mgr.—Emily Milby
SIC—7373; *Computer systems
  integration, including LANs,
  WANs, managed security &
  cloud services; Brand name—
  CISCO; HP; DELL; SONICWALL;
  Vmware; Microsoft; Riverbed;
  VEEAM; NEXSAN-IMATION;
  EMC*
Employs—17; Estab.—1993
Sales—$2.6Mil-$5Mil
5,000 sq ft site, Distrib.—Local
Privately owned sub-S corp.

**SSI CREATIVE GROUP**

20 E. Clementon Rd., Ste. 203-N
  (08026)
**Phone—(856) 663-2292**
Fax—(856) 663-2293
www.ssicreativegroup.com
Email—info@ssicreativegroup.com
Pres.—Chuck Jacques
Off. Admn.—Rachel Dibartolo
SIC—3993; *Interior & exterior
  signs*
Employs—70; Estab.—1992
40,000 sq ft site, Distrib.—National
Privately owned corporation

**SUPERIOR DRAPERY CO. &
HARBOR LINEN CO**

Div. of Harbor Linen, LLC
2 Foster Ave. (08026)
**Phone—(856) 435-2000**
National—(800) 257-7858
Fax—(856) 346-4598
www.harborlinen.com
Email—plieberman@
  harborlinen.com
Drapery Div. Mgr.—Paul J.
  Lieberman
SIC—2391; 2392; NAICS—
  314121; *Custom window
  treatments & bedding for hotels &
  healthcare industries*
Employs—50; Estab.—1970
Sales—$100Mil
10,000 sq ft site, Distrib.—National
Privately owned corporation
Parent co.—Harbor Linen, LLC,
  Gibbsboro, NJ
  Phone—(856) 435-2000
  See Parent Co. Section for full profile.

†**WILLIER ELECTRIC MOTOR REPAIR
CO., INC.**

1 Linden Ave., P.O. Box 98 (08026)
**Phone—(856) 627-3535**
Fax—(856) 627-5271
www.willierelectric.com
Email—sales@willierelectric.com
Pres.—Don Willier, Sr.
V-P.—Jim Willier
Secy-Treas.—Kathleen Willier
Opers. & Sales Mgr.—Don Willier,
  Jr.
SIC—5063; *Corporate
  headquarters & wholesaler of
  electric motors*
Employs—30; Estab.—1951
Sales—under $5Mil
Distrib.—Regional
Privately owned corporation

## Gibbstown
(Gloucester—S.W.)

**AIR LIQUIDE AMERICA L.P.**

A-Line Rd., P.O. Box 155 (08027)
**Phone—(856) 423-5220**
Fax—(856) 423-5025
www.airliquide.com
Email—webmaster@
  us.airliquide.com
Plt. Mgr.—Dan Dingman
SIC—2813; NAICS—325120; *Dry
  ice*
Employs—13; Estab.—1958
Sales—$5Mil-$10Mil (est)
Distrib.—National
Publicly owned corporation
Parent co.—Air Liquide America
  L.P., Houston, TX
  Phone—(713) 624-8000
  See Parent Co. Section for full profile.

**WAGNER PROVISIONS CO., INC.**

54 E. Broad St., P.O. Box 169
  (08027)
**Phone—(856) 423-1630**
  (856) 423-6481
Fax—(856) 423-6482
www.herbssnackfoods.com
Email—sales@
  herbssnackfoods.com
Pres., GM—Herb Wagner
SIC—2013; NAICS—311600; *Meat
  snack products*
Employs—10; Estab.—1938
Sales—under $500,000
Distrib.—National
Privately owned corporation

## Gillette
(Morris—N.W.)

**MITRONICS PRODUCTS, INC.**

239 Morristown Rd., P.O. Box 196
  (07933)
**Phone—(908) 647-5006**
Fax—(908) 647-7070
Pres.—Eric Bergman
SIC—2891; NAICS—325520;
  *Electronic ceramic seals*
Employs—6; Estab.—1970
Sales—$2.6Mil-$5Mil
Distrib.—National
Privately owned corporation

**PENDULUM AUDIO SYSTEMS, INC.**

P.O. Box 339 (07933)
**Phone—(908) 665-9333**
www.pendulumaudio.com
Email—info@pendulumaudio.com
Pres.—Gregory Gualtieri
SIC—3651; 3679; NAICS—
  334310; *Professional vacuum
  tube recording equipment*
Employs—10
Distrib.—National
Privately owned corporation

## Glassboro
(Gloucester—S.W.)

NEW ENTRY
**ACE SCREEN PRINTING, LLC**

24 High St. W. (08028)
**Phone—(856) 881-1188**
www.mimdesigns.com
Owner—Adam Szyfman
SIC—2396; 2395; *T-shirt screen
  printing & embroidery*
Employs—4
Sales—$500,000-$1Mil (est)
Limited Liability Company

**ART GRAPHICS**

54 Delsea Dr. N. (08028-1923)
**Phone—(856) 881-5029**
www.artgraphicsnj.com
Email—rtee2@verizon.net
Ptnr.—Art Dorn
Ptnr. & Off. Mgr.—Mary Ann Dorn
Prodn. Mgr.—David Dorn
SIC—2396; 2395; 3993; *Textile
  screen printing, embroidery,
  signs & decals, including
  digitizing services*
Employs—3; Estab.—1973
Sales—under $500,000
4,500 sq ft site, Distrib.—Regional
Privately owned partnership

**ASTRO SIGN CO.**

230 E. High St., Route 322
  (08028)
**Phone—(856) 881-4300**
Fax—(856) 881-2399
www.astrosignco.com
Email—info@astrosignco.com
Pres.—Christopher Painter
V-P., GM—Doug Painter
Pers. Mgr.—Joann Painter
SIC—3993; 3679; 2399; 3499;
  *Signs, vehicle lettering, banners,
  flags, flagpoles & traffic control &
  billboard advertising & billboard
  production*
Employs—16; Estab.—1983
Sales—$1Mil-$2.5Mil
5,500 sq ft site, Distrib.—Regional
Privately owned sub-S corp.
AKAs: Astro Outdoor Advertising,
  Inc. & Astro Outdoor & Astro
  Signs

**BELLIA PRINT & COPY CENTER**

190 William L. Dalton Dr. (08028)
**Phone—(856) 582-4004**
Fax—(856) 582-6001
www.bellia.net
Email—akbellia@bellia.net

Owner—Thomas Bellia
SIC—2759; *Commercial printing
  for small & large corporate,
  educational, healthcare,
  government, state, federal &
  residential customers, including
  forms, envelopes, letterheads,
  business cards & notecards*
Employs—4
Sales—$500,000-$1Mil (est)

**BORNMANN'S RV**

131 Delsea Dr. S. (08028)
**Phone—(856) 881-7979**
Fax—(856) 881-1611
www.bornmannsrv.com
Email—bornmannsrv@verizon.net
Owner—Eugene Bornmann
SIC—3716; *Recreational vehicle
  conversions & repair service*
Employs—4
Sales—$500,000-$1Mil (est)

†**BRIDA STONE, INC.**

555 Mullica Hill Rd. (08028)
**Phone—(856) 881-1700**
Fax—(856) 863-8531
www.bridastone.com
Email—sales@bridastone.com
Owner—Anthony Brida
Hum. Res. & IT Mgr.—Sandra
  Brida
Off. Mgr.—Sandra Baez
SIC—5032; 5083; *Wholesaler of
  natural stone & landscape
  supplies*
Employs—15; Estab.—2001
Sales—$1Mil
Distrib.—Regional
Privately owned corporation

**CWI ARCHITECTURAL MILLWORK,
LLC**

8 Deptford Rd., Dept. D (08028-
  2449)
**Phone—(856) 307-7900**
Fax—(856) 307-7500
www.cwimillwork.com
Email—cwimillwork@aol.com
Member—David N. Ganor
Member—Kim Ganor
SIC—2431; NAICS—321900;
  *Architectural millwork; Brand
  name—Wilson Art; Formica;
  Meganite*
Employs—7; Estab.—1993
Sales—$500,000-$1Mil
7,200 sq ft site, Distrib.—Regional
Limited Liability Company

**DEMOUNTABLE CONCEPTS, INC.**

200 Acorn Rd. (08028)
**Phone—(856) 863-0900**
National—(800) 254-3643
Fax—(856) 863-6704
www.demount.com
Email—sales@demount.com
Pres.—Rustin Cassway
V-P.—David Fisher
Sales Rep.—Michael Frett
SIC—3713; 3546; NAICS—
  336211; *Demountable truck
  body systems & equipment*
Employs—35; Estab.—1989
Sales—$6Mil-$10Mil
50,000 sq ft site, Distrib.—Intl.
Privately owned corporation

**ELRAY MFG. CO., INC.**

17 Liberty St. (08028)
**Phone—(856) 881-1936**
Fax—(856) 881-4928
www.elrayman.com
Email—elray@elrayman.com
Pres.—Ed Stopper
SIC—3469; *Metal stampings*
Employs—27; Estab.—1954
Distrib.—National
Privately owned corporation

## Glassboro—(cont.)

**FAZZIO MACHINE & STEEL**
3278 Glassboro Cross Keys Rd.,
   P.O. Box 232 (08028)
**Phone—(856) 881-2832**
Fax—(856) 881-4129
Email—fazziosteel@verizon.net
Pres.—Phil Fazzio
V-P.—Jamie Fazzio
SIC—3599; 5051; *General
   machining job shop & distributor
   of steel, galvanized, aluminum &
   stainless structural products*
Employs—6; Estab.—1940
Sales—$500,000-$1Mil
50,000 sq ft site, Distrib.—
   Regional
Privately owned corporation

**GLASSBORO PRINTING, INC.**
30 N. Academy St. (08028)
**Phone—(856) 881-2600**
Fax—(856) 881-0257
Pres.—Norman Murphy
Off. Mgr.—Satyra Oberfrank
SIC—2759; NAICS—323100;
   *Commercial printing*
Employs—3; Estab.—1970
Sales—under $500,000
Distrib.—Local
Privately owned corporation

**HI-PER TECH BRAKE PRODUCTS,
   INC.**
100 Delsea Dr., P.O. Box 770
   (08028)
**Phone—(856) 881-0900**
National—(800) 881-1488
www.hi-pertech.com
Email—info@hi-pertech.com
Pres.—Michael Carmolingo
SIC—3714; *Vehicle brakes*
Employs—20
Sales—$5Mil-$10Mil (est)
Distrib.—Local

**INDUSTRIAL DRUM CO.**
784 New Jersey Ave., P.O. Box
   586 (08028)
**Phone—(856) 881-2000**
Fax—(856) 881-4555
Email—tgd2000@comcast.net
Owner & Pres.—Ted Demiduke
SIC—3412; NAICS—332439;
   *Reconditioned 55-gallon steel &
   poly drums & 275 gallon IBC's*
Employs—8; Estab.—1980
Sales—$1Mil-$2.5Mil
Distrib.—Regional
Privately owned corporation

**NEW CENTURY BUILDING
   SYSTEMS, INC.**
70 Sewell St., P.O. Box 775
   (08028)
**Phone—(856) 863-8036**
Fax—(856) 863-8044
www.apgintl.com
Email—tsalzer@apgintl.com
Pres.—Thomas Salzer
V-P.—Eric Rosenberg
SIC—3442; 3231; NAICS—
   332321; *Aluminum windows &
   glass curtain walls*
Employs—8; Estab.—2004
25,000 sq ft site, Distrib.—
   Regional
Privately owned corporation

**S & W FABRICATORS, INC.**
100 S. Delsea Dr., Ste. 300, P.O.
   Box 664 (08028)
**Phone—(856) 881-8068**
National—(800) 772-4162
Fax—(856) 881-1605
Email—abjoffice@abjsprinkler.com
Pres.—Pattie Sebastiani

SIC—3498; NAICS—332996;
   *Metal pipe fabrication*
Employs—5; Estab.—1984
Sales—$500,000-$1Mil
Distrib.—Local
Privately owned corporation

**SMITH ENTERPRISES**
8-A Deptford Rd. (08028)
**Phone—(215) 416-9881**
Fax—(856) 608-9588
www.smithentpromos.com
Email—dstees@comcast.net
Owner—Damian Smith
SIC—2396; 2395; *Apparel screen
   printing & embroidery, including
   uniforms, staff shirts, hats &
   jackets;* Brand name—*Gildan;
   Hanes; American Apparel;
   SanMar; Bodek; Rhodes*
Employs—4; Estab.—1998
Sales—$500,000-$1Mil
Distrib.—National
Sole ownership

NEW ENTRY

**SPARK HOLLAND, INC.**
816 Delsea Dr. N. (08028)
**Phone—(609) 799-7250**
Fax—(609) 799-8250
www.ichromstore.com
Email—info@ichrom.com
Pres.—John Crutchfield
SIC—3826; *Analytical instruments
   for laboratories & scientific
   applications*
Employs—4
Sales—$500,000-$1Mil (est)

**WECOM, INC.**
20 Warrick Ave. (08028)
**Phone—(856) 863-8400**
National—(800) 628-4115
Fax—(856) 863-8408
www.wecom.com
Email—wecom@wecom.com
Pres.—Eric C. Sprengle, Sr.
V-P.—E. Carl Sprengle, Jr.
Corp. Secy.—Diana L. Pierce
SIC—3444; 3443; 3479; 3599;
   *Precision sheet metal aluminum
   & stainless steel fabrication,
   including laser cutting, CNC
   machining, punching, shearing,
   brake bending, MIG, TIG & spot
   welding, painting, powder
   coating, assembly, plating, silk
   screening & polishing*
Employs—27; Estab.—1961
Sales—over $3Mil
50,000 sq ft site, Distrib.—
   Regional
Privately owned corporation

## Glen Gardner
(Hunterdon—N.W.)

**EASTERN CONCRETE MATERIALS,
   INC.**
1 Railroad Ave. (08826)
**Phone—(908) 537-2135**
   (908) 537-2137
Fax—(908) 537-0939
www.eastern-concrete.com
Email—webmaster@
   easternconcrete.com
Plt. & Sr. Proj. Mgr.—Mike Guida
SIC—1429; NAICS—212319;
   *Crushed granite stone*
Employs—15; Estab.—1996
Distrib.—Regional
Publicly owned corporation
Parent co.—Eastern Concrete
   Materials, Inc., Elmwood Park,
   NJ
   Phone—(201) 797-7979
   See Parent Co. Section for full profile.

**E-HARVEST SYSTEMS (H Q)**
424 Little Brook Rd. (08826)
**Phone—(908) 832-0400**
www.e-harvest.com

Email—info@e-harvest.com
Owner—Robert Klein
SIC—3511; *Company
   headquarters; hydroelectric
   turbines (mfg. subcontracted)*
Employs—2; Estab.—2009
Sales—$500,000-$1Mil (est)
Distrib.—Intl.
Sole ownership

**SPACE POWER ELECTRONICS, INC.**
493 Westhill Rd. (08826)
**Phone—(908) 689-6547**
Fax—(908) 689-6549
Pres.—Ross J. Alestra
SIC—3674; NAICS—334413;
   *Semiconductors*
Employs—20; Estab.—1972
Sales—$1Mil-$2.5Mil
Distrib.—Intl.
Privately owned corporation

## Glen Ridge
(Essex—N.E.)

**O. R. COMFORT, LLC**
28 Appleton Rd. (07028)
**Phone—(973) 239-1950**
www.orcomfort.com
Email—sales@orcomfort.com
Pres., GM—Henry Marguet
SIC—3842; *Inflatable cushions &
   positioning devices for hospital
   operation rooms;* Brand name—
   *Shoulder-Float; Pelvic-Tilt;
   Delgado Inflatable Post*
Employs—4; Estab.—1998
Sales—$1Mil-$2.5Mil
Distrib.—National
Limited Liability Company

**SPACEMASTER, INC.**
855 Bloomfield Ave. (07028)
**Phone—(973) 429-1155**
Fax—(888) 817-8761
www.spacemaster.com
Email—space@spacemaster.com
Pres.—Raphael Badagliacca
Application & Dev. Mgr.—Keith
   Fossella
SIC—7372; *Software
   development*
Employs—15; Estab.—1990
Distrib.—Intl.
Privately owned corporation

## Glen Rock
(Bergen—N.E.)

**ARTIQUE GLASS STUDIO**
483 S. Broad St. (07452)
**Phone—(201) 444-3500**
Fax—(201) 444-7130
www.artiqueglassstudio.com
Email—info@
   artiqueglassstudio.com
Owner—Jay Demauro
SIC—3231; NAICS—327215;
   *Stained glass fabrication*
Employs—6; Estab.—1987
Sales—under $500,000
Distrib.—Local
Privately owned corporation

**COLEMAX GROUP, LLC / PRIMA
   CASES**
P.O. Box 103 (07452)
**Phone—(201) 489-1080**
Fax—(201) 301-7315
www.primacases.com
Email—sales@primacases.com
Mng. Dir.—Richard Flashenberg
Sales Mgr.—Janette Redfern
SIC—3172; 3089; 3069; *Leather,
   synthetic & molded carrying
   cases for cell phones,
   smartphones, tablets, PDAs,
   hand-held devices & portable
   wireless equipment*
Employs—6; Estab.—1996
Distrib.—Intl.
Limited Liability Company

**COX MERCHANDISING, LLC, FRED**
34 Radburn Rd. (07452)
**Phone—(201) 310-0740**
Fax—(201) 857-4154
www.fredcoxmerchandising.com
Email—fredcoxmerch@aol.com
CEO—Fred Cox
SIC—2395; *Embroidery*
Employs—2; Estab.—2003
Sales—under $500,000
Distrib.—National
Limited Liability Company

†**OPICI WINERY, INC.**
25 DeBoer Dr. (07452)
**Phone—(201) 689-1200**
Fax—(201) 689-1550
www.opici.com
Email—infonynj@opici.com
Pres.—Dina Opici
V-P.—Ron Gallo
Sales Mgr., Natl.—Angelo Serna
IT Mgr.—Steve Grayberg
SIC—5182; *Corporate
   headquarters & distributor of
   wine & spirits;* Brand name—
   *Beringer; Mondavi; St. Michelle*
   Opici; Sobieski; Maison Nicolas*
   Clicquot*
Employs—120; Estab.—1934
Distrib.—Regional
Privately owned sub-S corp.

**RC REPAIR**
526 Doremus Ave. (07452)
**Phone—(201) 445-0361**
Owner—John Deneke
SIC—3663; NAICS—334220;
   *Rebuilt radio control systems*
Employs—2; Estab.—1970
Distrib.—Local
Sole ownership

**SONOCO CORRFLEX, LLC**
Div. of Sonoco
Heritage Plaza II, 1st Fl., 65
   Harristow (07452)
**Phone—(201) 612-4008**
Fax—(201) 670-6919
www.sonoco.com
Email—cfdpsales@sonoco.com
Mktg. Svcs. Mgr.—Debra Koch
SIC—3993; *Display signs, graphic
   design & packaging*
Employs—18; Estab.—1997
Sales—under $500,000
Distrib.—Intl.
Publicly owned corporation
Parent co.—Sonoco, Hartsville, SC
   Phone—(843) 383-7000
   See Parent Co. Section for full profile.

**WORLD SOFTWARE CORP.**
266 Harristown Rd., Ste. 201
   (07452)
**Phone—(201) 444-3228**
National—(800) 962-6360
Fax—(201) 444-9065
www.worldox.com
Email—info@worldox.com
Dir.—Julie Camporini
SIC—7372; *Prepackaged
   document management software
   development;* Brand name—
   *Worldox*
Employs—25; Estab.—1991
Distrib.—Intl.
Privately owned corporation

## Glendora
(Camden—S.W.)

**DELAWARE VALLEY BOX &
   LUMBER CO.**
14 Austin Ave. (08029)
**Phone—(856) 939-1900**
Fax—(856) 939-1919
www.delvalbox.com
Email—marketing@delvalbox.com
Opers. Mgr.—Chris Gould
Admn. Mgr.—Linda Miller

GEOGRAPHICAL

## Glendora—(cont.)

SIC—2653; 2449; NAICS—
322211; *Corrugated boxes & wooden crates*
Employs—20; Estab.—1975
Sales—$2.5Mil-$5Mil (est)
Distrib.—Local
Parent co.—Delaware Valley Box & Lumber Co., Trenton, NJ
Phone—(609) 890-2900
See Parent Co. Section for full profile.

### †FASTENAL CO.

316 Black Horse Pike, Unit C (08029)
**Phone—(856) 939-2500**
Fax—(856) 939-2505
www.fastenal.com
Email—njbla@stores.fastenal.com
Store Mgr.—Blake Phillips
SIC—5072; 5084; *Wholesaler of fasteners, safety equipment, tools & abrasives*
Employs—4; Estab.—1965
Sales—under $500,000
Distrib.—Local
Publicly owned corporation
Parent co.—Fastenal Co., Winona, MN
Phone—(507) 454-5374
See Parent Co. Section for full profile.

### SIGNPROS

1215 Black Horse Pike (08029)
**Phone—(856) 939-1099**
Fax—(856) 939-2099
www.signprosnj.com
Email—info@signprosnj.com
Owner & Pres.—Nick Kappatos
SIC—3993; 2759; 3089; *LED channel letters, illuminated sign cabinets, pylon, monument, sandblasted & carved signs, awnings, vehicle graphics, digital printing, vinyl lettering & LED border lighting, including design, installation & service*
Employs—18; Estab.—1991
Sales—under $2.4Mil
9,500 sq ft site, Distrib.—Regional
Privately owned corporation

## Gloucester City

(Camden—S.W.)

### BLUEKNIGHT ENERGY PARTNERS L. P.

King & Jersey St., P.O. Box 31 (08030)
**Phone—(856) 456-6673**
　　　　(918) 237-4076
Fax—(856) 456-3331
www.bkep.com
Email—hr@bkep.com
Prod. Mgr.—Dave White
Terminal Mgr.—Ted Davis
SIC—2952; 2951; NAICS—
324122; *Asphalt products*
Employs—10; Estab.—1978
Distrib.—Regional
Privately owned corporation
Parent co.—Blueknight Energy Partners L. P., Tulsa, OK
Phone—(918) 237-4000
See Parent Co. Section for full profile.

### †CAPESPAN NORTH AMERICA

701 N. Broadway., Ste. 102 (08030-1034)
**Phone—(856) 742-0242**
Fax—(856) 742-0304
www.capespan.com
Email—info@capespan.com
Dir., Opers. & Sales—Stephen Stackhouse
Asst. Dir., Opers.—Stephen Vogt

SIC—5148; *Distributor of fruit*
Employs—13; Estab.—1992
Sales—$500,000-$1Mil
Distrib.—Local
Limited Liability Company
AKAs: Fisher Brother Sales & Fisher Capespan
Parent co.—Capespan North America
Phone—(514) 739-9181
See Parent Co. Section for full profile.

### D & N MACHINE MFG., INC.

334 Nicholson Rd., P.O. Box 67 (08030)
**Phone—(856) 456-1366**
Fax—(856) 456-5334
Email—dnnmachmfg@aol.com
Pres.—Robert Doble, Jr.
Plt. Mgr.—Kyle Davis
Hum. Res. Mgr.—Sandra Doble
SIC—3444; *Precision sheet metal fabrication*
Employs—6; Estab.—1949
Distrib.—Intl.
Privately owned corporation

### DUFFYS DELICIOUS CANDIES CO., INC.

29 N. Broadway (08030)
**Phone—(856) 456-2955**
Fax—(856) 456-2935
www.duffyscandies.com
Email—michelle@duffyscandies.com
Owner—Barbara Hall
Candymaker—Eric Sieg
SIC—2064; NAICS—311300; *Candy*
Employs—10; Estab.—1922
Sales—$500,000-$1Mil
12,000 sq ft site, Distrib.—Local
Privately owned corporation

### FLEXTRON SYSTEMS

85 Nicholson Rd. (08030)
**Phone—(856) 742-0550**
Fax—(856) 742-0554
www.flextronsystems.com
Email—info@flextronsystems.com
Pres.—Ish Chauhan
Sales Mgr.—Ron Thomas
SIC—3672; NAICS—334412; *Printed circuit boards & flexible printed circuits, including single, double-sided & multilayer*
Employs—11; Estab.—1964
Sales—$500,000-$1Mil
15,000 sq ft site, Distrib.—National
Privately owned corporation

### G & M PRINTWEAR

549 S. Broadway St. (08030)
**Phone—(856) 742-5551**
Fax—(856) 742-5549
www.gmprintwear.com
Email—rdill@gmprintwear.com
Owner—Robert Dill
Graphic Artist—Chris Mastrogiacomo
SIC—2396; *Textile screen printing*
Employs—5; Estab.—1993
Sales—$500,000-$1Mil
Distrib.—National
Privately owned corporation

### GLOUCESTER CITY BOX WORKS, LLC

775 Charles St. (08030)
**Phone—(856) 456-9032**
Fax—(856) 456-4317
www.gloucestercityworks.com
Email—gloucesterworks@aol.com
Pres.—Kathy White
SIC—2653; 3999; NAICS—
322211; *Contract packaging*
Employs—9; Estab.—2003
Sales—under $500,000
Distrib.—Local
Limited Liability Company

### GLOUCESTER CITY NEWS, INC.

34 S. Broadway, P.O. Box 151 (08030)
**Phone—(856) 456-1199**
Fax—(856) 456-1330
Email—gcneditor@verizon.net
Publisher—Albert J. Countryman, Jr.
Prodn. Mgr.—Michelle Festa
SIC—2711; 2791; NAICS—
323122; *Newspaper publishing*
Employs—4; Estab.—1927
Sales—under $500,000
1,000 sq ft site, Distrib.—Local
Privately owned corporation

### IMPERIAL DESIGN

729 Charles St. (08030)
**Phone—(856) 742-8480**
Owner—Derek Cohen
SIC—2541; *Wooden countertops*
Employs—3; Estab.—1997
Distrib.—Local
Sole ownership

### INDCO, INC.

511 Essex St., P.O. Box 109 (08030)
**Phone—(856) 456-6100**
Email—fredbinter@msn.com
Pres.—Fred Binter
SIC—2899; 2819; 2842; NAICS—
325612; *Contract blending of water-based chemicals for boiler & cooling tower water treating & janitorial supplies*
Employs—30; Estab.—1950
Sales—$6Mil-$10Mil
85,000 sq ft site, Distrib.—Intl.
Privately owned corporation

### MID-LANTIC PRECISION, INC.

940 Market St. (08030)
**Phone—(856) 456-3810**
Pres.—Lauri Wilke
SIC—3599; *General, precision & CNC machining job shop*
Employs—15
Sales—$1Mil-$2.5Mil (est)

### NASH ENGRAVING, INC.

528 Nicholson Rd. (08030)
**Phone—(856) 456-5656**
Fax—(856) 456-2106
www.nashind.com
Email—info@nashind.com
Owner—M. Nash
GM—T. Uibel
SIC—3479; 2796; NAICS—
323122; *Mechanical engraving of signs, nameplates & badges*
Employs—4; Estab.—1959
Sales—under $500,000
Distrib.—Regional
Privately owned corporation
AKA: Nash Industries

### REDKEYS DIES, INC.

1307 Market St. (08030)
**Phone—(856) 456-7890**
Fax—(856) 456-6393
www.redkeysdies.com
Email—redkeysdies@aol.com
Pres., CEO—Morgan F. Reichner
GM—Michael Kazmar
SIC—3544; NAICS—333500; *Steel rule, copper foil stamping & copper embossing dies & heat sealing boards*
Employs—6; Estab.—1969
4,000 sq ft site, Distrib.—Intl.
Privately owned sub-S corp.

### SHELBY CASTSTONE

600 Jersey Ave. (08030)
**Phone—(856) 456-0668**
Fax—(856) 456-0294
www.caststonebyshelby.com
Email—shelby@caststonebyshelby.com
Pres.—Fredrick M. Aziack
V-P.—Mike Palumbo
Plt. Mgr.—Luis Rodriquez

Off. Mgr.—Anthony Ruggiero
SIC—3281; NAICS—327991; *Stone products*
Employs—12; Estab.—2004
Distrib.—Regional
Limited Liability Company

### THERMOSEAL INDUSTRIES, LLC

400 Water St. (08030)
**Phone—(856) 456-3109**
National—(800) 456-7788
Fax—(856) 456-0989
www.thermoseal.com
Email—info@thermoseal.com
Pres.—Richard A. Chubb
CFO—Lisa A. Chubb
Cust. Accts. Mgr.—Karina Vigilante
Cust. Accts. Mgr.—Alexa Walter
Plt. Mgr.—David Kipphut
Maint. Supt.—Earl T. Grater
SIC—3231; NAICS—327215; *Glass insulating*
Employs—50; Estab.—1956
Distrib.—Intl.
Privately owned corporation

## Great Meadows

(Warren—N.W.)

### KENNY WILBERT VAULT CO.

40 Shades of Death Rd. (07838)
**Phone—(908) 637-4736**
　　　　(908) 812-0953
Pres.—Bruce Kenny
SIC—3272; *Concrete burial vaults*
Employs—4; Estab.—1968
Sales—under $500,000
Distrib.—Local
Privately owned corporation

### QUALITY COATINGS

Island Dragway Rd., P.O. Box 13 (07838)
**Phone—(908) 637-4556**
Fax—(908) 637-6101
Owner & GM—Paul Englehart
Prod. Mgr.—Lorraine Forsyth
SIC—2891; NAICS—325520; *Pressure-sensitive adhesives*
Employs—8; Estab.—1988
Sales—under $500,000
Distrib.—Regional
Privately owned corporation

### WICKI WHOLESALE STONE, INC.

17 Cemetery Rd., P.O. Box 104 (07838)
**Phone—(908) 637-6004**
National—(800) 504-7838
Fax—(908) 637-6282
www.wickistone.com
Email—info@wickistone.com
Pres.—Peter Wicki
V-P.—Al Kurnath
Off. Mgr.—Anne Luff
SIC—3281; NAICS—327991; *Stone fabrication*
Employs—20; Estab.—1980
Sales—$1Mil-$2.5Mil (est)
Distrib.—Regional
Privately owned corporation

## Green Brook

(Middlesex—N.E.)

### CASEY'S EXECUTIVE INTERIORS

152 Route 22 W., P.O. Box 7070 (08812)
**Phone—(732) 968-3236**
National—(888) 838-7647
Fax—(732) 968-5964
www.OfficeFurnitureNJ.com
Email—info@officefurniturenj.com
Ptnr.—Casey Chung
Principal—Huns Chung

## Green Brook—(cont.)

SIC—2521; 2522; NAICS—337211; *Wooden & metal office furniture*
Employs—10; Estab.—1984
Sales—$1Mil-$2.5Mil
Distrib.—Regional
Privately owned corporation

**EMBROIDME**
215 U.S. Highway 22 (08812)
**Phone—(732) 752-1871**
www.embroidme-greenbrook.com
Owner—Joann Karnila
SIC—2395; NAICS—314999; *Textile embroidery*
Employs—3; Estab.—2012
Distrib.—Local

**JABAT, INC., K.**
Div. of Jabat, Inc.
342 Highway 22 W. (08812)
Mail addr: P.O. Box 68, Middlesex (08846)
**Phone—(732) 469-8177**
Fax—(732) 271-1437
www.jabat.com
Email—sales@jabat.com
CEO—Susan McGill
Plt. Mgr.—Rich Ferrara
Off. Mgr.—Claudia Torma
SIC—3082; NAICS—326121; *Plastic tubing & profiles*
Employs—16; Estab.—1973
Sales—under $500,000
35,000 sq ft site, Distrib.—National
Privately owned sub-S corp.
Parent co.—Jabat, Inc., Olney, IL
Phone—(618) 392-3010
See Parent Co. Section for full profile.

**PAINTON STUDIOS, INC.**
299 U.S. Highway 22, Ste. 21 (08812)
**Phone—(732) 302-0200**
Fax—(732) 302-0327
www.painton.com
Email—output@painton.com
Pres.—Lisa J. Secula
SIC—2759; 3993; 2791; NAICS—323122; *4-color digital printing, signage, electronic prepress & graphic design*
Employs—3; Estab.—1978
Sales—under $500,000
2,000 sq ft site, Distrib.—Regional
Privately owned sub-S corp.

**SCHMIDT CO., INC., J. G.**
354 U.S. Highway 22, P.O. Box 880 (08812)
**Phone—(732) 563-9500**
Fax—(732) 563-4946
www.jgschmidt.com
Email—lhudkins@aol.com
Pres.—Thomas G. Schmidt
Cont.—Lynn Schmidt
Plt. Mgr.—Arthur Haas
Traf. Mgr.—Lisa Hudkins
SIC—3429; *Garage door hardware, including bottom, top & flag brackets, hinges, track clips, sheaves & center plates*
Employs—48; Estab.—1956
65,000 sq ft site, Distrib.—National
Privately owned corporation

**SERVICE APEX**
299 U.S. Highway 22 (08812)
**Phone—(732) 424-1616**
Fax—(732) 424-1601
www.serviceapex.com
Email—greenbrook@serviceapex.com
Owner—Ken Griggs
SIC—2759; 3993; NAICS—323100; *Digital commercial printing, signs, vehicle graphics & apparel screen printing*
Employs—6; Estab.—2001
Sales—$500,000-$1Mil (est)
Distrib.—Local
Sole ownership

**SIGNS BY TOMORROW**
326 U.S. Highway 22, Ste. 8-B (08812)
**Phone—(732) 424-9785**
Fax—(732) 424-9786
www.sbtgreenbrook.com
Email—greenbrook@signsbytomorrow.com
Owner—Rajesh Patel
Graphic Designer—Ed Schmid
SIC—3993; 3089; 2759; NAICS—323100; *Interior & exterior, trade show, architectural, dimensional, safety, real estate, ADA, contractor & vinyl signs, banners, magnetics, vehicle lettering & full color & wide-format digital printing*
Employs—4; Estab.—2003
Sales—under $500,000
Distrib.—Local
Privately owned corporation

**SKI JEWELERS CO.**
299 Route 22 (08812)
**Phone—(732) 752-6446**
Fax—(732) 752-6637
www.skijewelers.com
Email—info@skijewelers.com
Pres.—Joseph Sulovski
V-P.—James Ford
SIC—3911; NAICS—339911; *Precious metal jewelry*
Employs—6; Estab.—1980
Sales—$500,000-$1Mil
Distrib.—Local
Privately owned corporation
DBA: Greater New Jersey Diamond Exchange

## Green Village

(Morris—N.W.)

**KLEEMEYER & MERKEL, INC.**
68 Britten Rd., P.O. Box 204 (07935)
**Phone—(973) 377-0875**
Fax—(973) 377-5774
Email—nuge63@aol.com
Pres., GM—Tim Nugent
Secy-Treas.—Carl Kleemeyer
SIC—2011; NAICS—311611; *Pork, beef, lamb, goat & veal processing; Brand name—Green Village Packing Co. Hamburger Patties; Hatfield; IBP; National; Purdue; Rosen Lamb*
Employs—15; Estab.—1948
Distrib.—Regional
Privately owned corporation
DBA: Green Village Packing Co.

## Grenloch

(Gloucester—S.W.)

**HYDE CO., A. L.**
Div. of Ensinger, Inc.
1 Main St., P.O. Box 62 (08032)
**Phone—(856) 227-0500**
National—(800) 243-3221
Fax—(856) 232-1754
www.alhyde.com
Email—ekelly@alhyde.com
Cont.—Dennis Palludino
Sales Mgr.—Bruce Dickinson
Mfg. Mgr.—Gary Williams
SIC—3089; *Extruded plastic products*
Employs—90; Estab.—1930
120,000 sq ft site, Distrib.—National
Privately owned corporation
Parent co.—Ensinger, Inc., Washington, PA
Phone—(724) 746-6050
See Parent Co. Section for full profile.

## Guttenberg

(Hudson—N.E.)

**ARISTOCRAT EMBROIDERY CORP.**
7014 Jackson St. (07093)
**Phone—(201) 869-9126**
www.craigfabrics.com
Pres.—Craig Goldman
SIC—2395; *Embroidery*
Employs—5; Estab.—1957
Sales—under $500,000
Distrib.—National
Privately owned corporation
AKA: Craig Fabric

NEW ENTRY
**CPMAG, LLC**
6903 Jackson St. (07093)
**Phone—(201) 868-8585**
www.carrierpigeonmag.com
Email—info@carrierpigeonmag.com
CFO—Matt Barteluce
SIC—2721; *Magazine publishing; Brand name—Carrier Pigeon Illustrated Fiction & Fine Art; Carrier Pigeon Magazine*
Employs—3; Estab.—2014
Sales—under $500,000
4,000 sq ft site, Distrib.—National
Limited Liability Company
AKAs: Carrier Pigeon Illustrated Fiction & Fine Art & Carrier Pigeon Magazine

**DU-MATT CORP.**
111 71st St. (07093)
**Phone—(201) 861-4271**
Fax—(201) 861-3145
www.dumatt.com
Email—info@dumatt.com
Pres.—Adolf Manttillo
MIS Mgr.—Claudia Lauren
Fin. Mgr.—J. Sanders
SIC—3421; 3423; NAICS—332200; *Wax & wax-working tools; Brand name—Matt Waxes*
Employs—7; Estab.—1972
8,000 sq ft site, Distrib.—Intl.
Sole ownership

**G & S VALVES FITTINGS CO., INC.**
6910 Adams St. (07093-9069)
**Phone—(201) 868-8026**
Fax—(201) 868-4995
www.gs-valves.com
Pres.—Guido Scrivanich
Off. Mgr.—Sabrina Scrivanich
SIC—3491; NAICS—332911; *Rebuilt valves, including repair & service*
Employs—9; Estab.—1974
Sales—$500,000-$1Mil
10,000 sq ft site, Distrib.—Regional
Privately owned corporation

**SUMMIT BRASS & BRONZE WORKS, INC.**
112 71st St. (07093)
**Phone—(201) 861-2080**
Fax—(201) 861-6883
Pres.—Robert Francin
SIC—3914; *Brass & bronze ecclesiastical ware*
Employs—4; Estab.—1920
Sales—under $500,000
Distrib.—National
Privately owned corporation

## Hackensack

(Bergen—N.E.)

NEW ENTRY
**A M GRAPHY**
95 Myer St. (07601)
**Phone—(201) 488-0360**
www.amgraphy.com
Email—info@amgraphy.com
Ptnr.—Leandro Morales

Ptnr.—Tony Morales
SIC—2791; NAICS—323122; *Electronic prepress*
Employs—3; Estab.—1969
3,000 sq ft site, Distrib.—Local
Privately owned corporation

†**A.C.T. LIGHTING, INC.**
122 John St. (07601)
**Phone—(201) 996-0884**
Fax—(201) 996-0811
www.actlighting.com
Email—sales@actlighting.com
V-P., Sales—Brian Dowd
Ex. V-P.—Ben Saltzman
Whse. Mgr.—Jon Venable
SIC—5063; *Distributor of lighting fixtures*
Employs—20
Distrib.—National
Privately owned corporation
Parent co.—A.C.T. Lighting, Inc., Agoura Hills, CA
Phone—(818) 707-0884
See Parent Co. Section for full profile.

**ADVANCE FIBER TECHNOLOGIES**
344 Lodi St. (07601)
**Phone—(201) 488-2700**
National—(800) 631-1930
Fax—(201) 489-5656
www.aftthread.com
Email—custsvc@ast3.com
Pres.—Peter Phillips
Sales Mgr., Natl.—Rick Brumfield
Off. Mgr.—Nancy Babcock
Cust. Serv. Rep.—Tammy Wilson
Cust. Serv. Rep.—Nicole Ramirez
SIC—2284; *Industrial sewing & fiberglass threads*
Employs—50; Estab.—1982
Sales—$11Mil-$25Mil
Distrib.—Intl.
Privately owned corporation

**APOLLO QUIK PRINT CO., INC.**
49 Orchard St. (07601)
**Phone—(201) 488-1101**
Fax—(201) 488-0974
Email—print@apolloprintinginc.com
Pres.—Kevin Bliss
SIC—2752; 2791; NAICS—323122; *Offset printing & typesetting*
Employs—4; Estab.—1970
Sales—under $500,000
1,500 sq ft site, Distrib.—National
Privately owned corporation

**ARCADIA EQUIPMENT, INC.**
140 Lawrence St. (07601)
**Phone—(201) 342-3308**
Fax—(201) 342-3334
www.arcadiaequipment.com
Email—info@arcadiaequipment.com
Pres.—Doug White
SIC—3561; NAICS—333911; *Pump systems for the pharmaceutical, personal care, food & chemical industries*
Employs—12
Sales—$1Mil-$2.5Mil (est)
Distrib.—Regional
Privately owned corporation

NEW ENTRY
**ATHENS PRINTING CO., INC.**
95 Myer St. (07601)
**Phone—(201) 342-1771**
Fax—(201) 342-1773
Email—athensprinting@verizon.net
CEO—Spyros Papathanasiou
SIC—2759; NAICS—323100; *Commercial printing*
Employs—1; Estab.—1962
Sales—under $500,000
10,000 sq ft site, Distrib.—Local
Privately owned sub-S corp.

GEOGRAPHICAL

# Hackensack—(cont.)

**AUTO COOL RADIATOR SERVICE**

10 Terhune Pl. (07601)
**Phone—(201) 343-3099**
Fax—(201) 343-3113
Email—autocool@verizon.net
Owner—Tom Meek
SIC—3714; *Rebuilt automotive & truck radiators*
Employs—15; Estab.—1977
Sales—under $500,000
Distrib.—Regional
Privately owned corporation

**AUTOMATED BUSINESS PRODUCTS, INC. (H Q)**

50 Clinton Pl., Mail Slot 1 (07601)
**Phone—(201) 489-1440**
National—(800) 334-1440
Fax—(201) 489-9443
www.abpdirect.com
Pres.—Robert Mahalik
Sales Mgr.—Michael Roberts
Sales Mgr.—John Yeck
SIC—3578; 3559; *Corporate headquarters; money & document processing equipment (mfg. done overseas)*
Employs—9; Estab.—1972
Sales—under $500,000
Distrib.—Intl.
Privately owned corporation

**†AUTOPART INTERNATIONAL, INC.**

260 Hudson St. (07601)
**Phone—(201) 488-4187**
Fax—(201) 488-4501
www.autopartintl.com
Email—info@autopartintl.com
Br. Mgr.—John Lopez
SIC—5013; *Distributor of automotive parts*
Employs—2; Estab.—2006
Distrib.—Regional
Publicly owned corporation
Parent co.—Autopart International, Inc., Norton, MA
Phone—(781) 784-1111
See Parent Co. Section for full profile.

**B & S TOOL & CUTTER SERVICE, INC.**

99 John St. (07601)
**Phone—(201) 488-3545**
(201) 487-4444
National—(800) 334-1420
Fax—(201) 488-3861
www.cncsharptools.com
Email—cncsharptools@juno.com
Pres.—Fred Lindenau
V-P.—Thomas Lindenau
SIC—3545; *Cutting tools & sharpening, including end mills, step drills, cutters, saws & form tools*
Employs—7; Estab.—1959
Sales—$500,000-$1Mil
4,500 sq ft site, Distrib.—Intl.
Privately owned corporation

**BCG MARBLE & GRANITE FABRICATORS CO., INC.**

167 Sussex St. (07601)
**Phone—(201) 343-8487**
Fax—(201) 343-8273
www.bcggranite.com
Owner & Pres.—Giuseppe Guerini
SIC—3281; NAICS—327991; *Corporate headquarters & limestone, slate, marble & granite fabrication*
Employs—15; Estab.—1990
Sales—$500,000-$1Mil
10,000 sq ft site, Distrib.—Local
Privately owned corporation

**BEACON OFFSET CO., INC.**

204 Russell Pl. (07601)
**Phone—(201) 488-4241**
Fax—(201) 488-6776
Email—beaconptg@verizon.net
Pres.—Vivian Hollenbeck

SIC—2752; NAICS—323100; *Offset printing*
Employs—6; Estab.—1959
Sales—under $500,000
Distrib.—Local
Limited Liability Company

NEW ENTRY

**BERGEN WHOLESALE MEATS CORP.**

154 Hackensack Ave. (07601)
**Phone—(201) 342-2138**
Fax—(201) 342-1288
Owner—Ernest W. Hanabergh III
SIC—2011; *Meat processing*
Employs—10
Sales—$2.5Mil-$5Mil (est)
Distrib.—Local
Privately owned corporation

**BIOGENESIS, INC.**

296 Washington Ave. (07601)
**Phone—(201) 678-1992**
Fax—(201) 678-1993
www.biogenesis-labs.com
Email—info@biogenesis-labs.com
Pres.—Ann Rabbani
SIC—2844; NAICS—325600; *Skin care products*
Employs—10; Estab.—1997
Sales—$2.5Mil-$5Mil (est)
Distrib.—National
Privately owned corporation

**BLUE DOG GRAPHICS**

222 River St. (07601)
**Phone—(201) 343-3343**
Fax—(201) 343-4491
www.gobluedog.com
Email—info@bluedognj.com
Pres.—Donald Perlman
Graphic Designer—Elaine Rosales
Pressman—Francis Guzman
SIC—2759; 3993; NAICS—323100; *Printing & promotional products*
Employs—5; Estab.—1984
2,800 sq ft site, Distrib.—Local
Privately owned corporation

NEW ENTRY

**BONGO VISTA PUBLISHING, LLC**

32 Catalpa Ave. (07601)
**Phone—(201) 343-0252**
www.greatgodbongo.com
Owner—Mario Sen
SIC—2731; *Book publishing*
Employs—2; Estab.—2007
Sales—under $500,000 (est)
Distrib.—Intl.
Limited Liability Company

NEW ENTRY

**BRUNO THE KING OF RAVIOLI CO.**

174 Union St. (07601)
**Phone—(201) 646-0505**
www.brunoscatering.com
Email—ravking@aol.com
Pres.—Glen Rassam
SIC—2098; *Pasta products*
Employs—18; Estab.—1905
Sales—$500,000-$1Mil (est)
Distrib.—Local
Privately owned corporation

**BUYERS LABORATORY LLC**

20 Railroad Ave. (07601)
**Phone—(201) 488-0404**
Fax—(201) 488-0461
www.buyerslab.com
Email—info@buyerslab.com
CEO—Gerry Stoia
Mng. Editor—Daria Hoffman
Mng. Dir.—Anthony Polifrone
Interim Opers. Consultant—Carrie Plantamura

SIC—2721; 2741; 7372; *Newsletter & test report publishing & software development*
Employs—40; Estab.—1961
14,000 sq ft site, Distrib.—Intl.
Privately owned corporation

**C & K PUNCH & SCREW MACHINE PRODUCTS**

160 Hobart St. (07601)
**Phone—(201) 343-6750**
National—(800) 440-5635
Fax—(201) 343-1814
www.candkpunches.com
Email—sales@candkpunches.com
Pres., GM—Don Kuder
V-P.—Al Conrad
SIC—3599; 3544; NAICS—333500; *Punches for steel rule dies & precision CNC lathe parts*
Employs—8; Estab.—1943
Sales—$500,000-$1Mil
4,000 sq ft site, Distrib.—Intl.
Privately owned sub-S corp.

**CAD SIGNS**

169 Lodi St. (07601)
**Phone—(201) 267-0457**
Fax—(201) 525-5415
www.cadsigns.net
Email—alex@cadsigns.net
Pres.—Alex Galiano
SIC—3993; 2394; *Signs, banners, vinyl letters & graphics & fabric awnings*
Employs—30; Estab.—2005
Sales—$2.5Mil-$5Mil (est)
Distrib.—Local
Privately owned corporation

**CALIFORNIA STUCCO PRODUCTS CORP.**

85 Zabriskie St. (07601)
**Phone—(201) 457-1900**
National—(888) 455-1300
Fax—(201) 342-2114
www.californiastucco.net
Email—calstucco@californiastucco.net
Pres.—Edwin D. Gorter
Off. Mgr.—Edwin Gorter, Jr.
SIC—3299; *Stucco*
Employs—10; Estab.—1927
Sales—$1Mil-$2.5Mil
10,000 sq ft site, Distrib.—Intl.
Sole ownership

**CAVALLA, INC.**

111 Union St. (07601)
**Phone—(201) 343-3338**
Fax—(201) 487-1096
www.cavalla.net
Email—apisani@cavalla.net
Pres.—Arthur Pisani
GM—Bob Pisani
SIC—3559; 3565; NAICS—333993; *Equipment for manufacturing & packaging cosmetic, personal care & pharmaceuticals products*
Employs—18; Estab.—1925
20,000 sq ft site, Distrib.—Intl.
Privately owned corporation

**CERAMIC PRODUCTS, INC.**

221 Park St. (07601)
**Phone—(201) 342-8200**
National—(800) 887-3622
Fax—(201) 342-3040
www.ceramicproductsinc.com
Email—info@ceramicproductsinc.com
Pres.—Tony Vidaic
Opers. Mgr.—Mark Vidaic
Off. Mgr.—Vanessa Bulice
SIC—3264; NAICS—327113; *Ceramic fixtures, wear pins & insulators; Brand name—Macor; Aluminas*
Employs—8; Estab.—1990
6,000 sq ft site, Distrib.—Intl.
Privately owned corporation

**CLIP STRIP CORP.**

343 S. River St. (07601)
**Phone—(201) 342-9155**
(800) 425-4778
Fax—(201) 342-1438
www.clipstrip.com
Email—info@clipstrip.com
Pres.—Edward D. Spitaletta
Ex. V-P., CFO—Anthony Mickolajczyk
CBO—John Spitalertta
V-P., Sales—Robert Spitaletta
Asst. V-P., Sales—Darnelle Holliday
Mktg. Mgr.—Arc Shelichach
SIC—2542; 3089; 3499; 3496; *Point-of-purchase merchandise & store displays, including merchandisers, ceiling/countertop/shelf edge & wire fixture sign holders, literature holders, hangtags, power panels, fasteners & display hooks; Brand name—Clip Strips® Merchandisers; Roto Clips; Econo Strips™; Sticky Strips*
Employs—6; Estab.—1980
Sales—$5Mil-$15Mil
25,000 sq ft site, Distrib.—Intl.
Privately owned corporation
Also see: The Fifty/Fifty Group, Inc., same loc.
AKA: CSC

**CONTINENTAL COOKIES, INC.**

185 S. Newman St. (07601)
**Phone—(201) 498-1966**
Fax—(201) 498-1969
www.continentalcookies.com
Email—info@continentalcookies.com
Pres., Fin. & MIS Mgr.—Stefan Gavosto
Off. Mgr.—Natalie Franco
SIC—2052; *Cookies*
Employs—15; Estab.—1967
Sales—$500,000-$1Mil
15,000 sq ft site, Distrib.—Regional
Privately owned corporation

**CONTRACT COATINGS, INC.**

161 Beech St. (07601)
**Phone—(201) 343-3131**
Fax—(201) 343-3512
www.contract-coating.com
Email—info@contract-coating.com
Owner—Bob Patel
Pres.—Bharat Patel
SIC—2834; NAICS—325412; *Pharmaceuticals, including table coatings, film, sugar & enteric & soft gel coating*
Employs—15; Estab.—1984
Sales—under $500,000
4,500 sq ft site, Distrib.—National
Privately owned corporation

**COUNTY GLASS & METAL INSTALLERS, INC.**

80 Dewitt Pl. (07601)
**Phone—(201) 343-7417**
Fax—(201) 343-7469
www.countyglass.com
Pres.—Eugene Vanbert
Comp.—Susan Wong
SIC—3499; 3312; 3444; NAICS—332999; *Metal, steel & aluminum fabrication of curtain & slope walls, window systems, entrances & interiors*
Employs—6; Estab.—1990
Sales—under $500,000
18,000 sq ft site, Distrib.—Local
Privately owned corporation

**COUNTY SEAT, LLC**

77 Hudson St. (07601)
**Phone—(201) 488-5795**
Fax—(201) 343-8720
www.cntyseat.com
Email—info@cntyseat.com

## Hackensack—(cont.)

Publisher—Gail Zisa
Editor-in-Chief—Lauren Zisa
SIC—2711; 2741; *Monthly print & online newspaper publishing*
Employs—6; Estab.—2003
Sales—$500,000-$1Mil
Distrib.—Local
Limited Liability Company

**CREATIONS IN GLASS**
344 Main St. (07601)
**Phone—(201) 488-0229**
Fax—(201) 488-2188
www.createinglass.com
Owner—Joe Henchewski
SIC—3231; *Custom stained glass windows, etched glass, storefronts & frameless shower doors*
Employs—2; Estab.—1984
Sales—under $500,000
1,984 sq ft site, Distrib.—Regional
Privately owned corporation

**DDS, INC.**
100 Commerce Way, Ste. 5 (07601)
**Phone—(888) 495-7440**
Fax—(201) 880-7799
www.ddsbelt.com
Email—info@ discdiseasesolutions.com
Sr. V.-P.—Paul Kim
Logistics Coord.—James Kim
SIC—3842; *Spinal & neck braces*
Employs—10; Estab.—2005
Sales—$1Mil-$2.5Mil
Distrib.—Regional
Privately owned corporation
AKA: Disc Disease Solutions, Inc.

**DESIGN-N-STITCH, INC.**
194 Atlantic St. (07601)
**Phone—(201) 488-1314**
Fax—(201) 488-1335
www.design-n-stitch.com
Email—fitz@design-n-stitch.com
Ptnr. & Pres.—John Fitzpatrick
Ptnr. & Treas.—Robert Fitzpatrick
SIC—2396; 2395; *Screen printing & embroidery of t-shirts, polo shirts & hats*
Employs—8; Estab.—1995
2,500 sq ft site, Distrib.—National
Privately owned corporation

**DIE TECH, LLC**
58 McKinley St. (07601)
**Phone—(201) 343-8324**
Fax—(201) 489-0803
Email—james@die-techllc.com
Pres.—James Galbreath
SIC—3544; NAICS—333500; *Steel rule dies*
Employs—15; Estab.—2003
Sales—$1Mil-$2.5Mil
Distrib.—Regional
Limited Liability Company

**DISCOUNT OFFICE SUPPLY**
146 Hudson St. (07601)
**Phone—(201) 342-3030**
Fax—(201) 342-7272
www.barrofficesupply.com
Email—barrofficesupply@ verizon.net
Pres.—Larry Barr
V.-P.—Sean Barr
SIC—2759; 2752; 2741; 2796; NAICS—323122; *Pamphlet, brochure, stationery & business card printing & embroidery*
Employs—5; Estab.—1994
Sales—$500,000-$1Mil (est)
Distrib.—Regional
Privately owned corporation

**DIVELY MODELS, INC., BOB**
540 Hudson St. (07601)
**Phone—(201) 310-2340**
www.bobdivelymodels.com
Email—s2flyer@aol.com

Pres.—William Stevick
SIC—3944; *Scale model airplane kits, including plastic vacuum forming & resin cast parts*
Employs—1; Estab.—1995
Sales—under $500,000
1,500 sq ft site, Distrib.—National
Privately owned corporation

**DUCT MATE, INC.**
190 Lexington Ave. (07601)
**Phone—(201) 488-8002**
Fax—(201) 488-1427
www.ductmatehvac.com
Email—ductmate@covad.net
Owner & Pres.—Joseph Tasca
Corp. Secy.—Patricia Tasca
GM—Brian Becker
SIC—3444; *HVAC ductwork*
Employs—7; Estab.—1992
Sales—$1Mil-$2.5Mil
2,000 sq ft site, Distrib.—Local
Privately owned corporation

**ELCAM MEDICAL, INC.**
2 University Plz., Ste. 620 (07601-6224)
**Phone—(201) 457-1120**
National—(800) 530-2441
Fax—(201) 457-1125
www.elcam-medical.com
Email—info@elcam-medical.com
Pres.—Amir Halperin
V.-P., Sales—Willer Ghelfi
Cont.—Geri Hernandez
Dir., Mktg.—Lisa Gulich
Cust. Serv. Mgr.—Miriam Lerner
Cust. Serv. Mgr.—Candi Longo
SIC—3841; 3842; *OEM disposable medical devices for IV therapy, patient monitoring & drug delivery & hemodialysis products, including stopcocks, manifolds, needless & monitoring devices, interventional cardiology & radiology accessories & auto-injectors*
Employs—6; Estab.—2000
2,150 sq ft site, Distrib.—Intl.
Privately owned corporation

**ELECTRO CERAMIC INDUSTRIES**
75 Kennedy St. (07601)
**Phone—(201) 342-2630**
Fax—(201) 342-1823
www.electroceramic.com
Email—sales@electroceramic.com
Pres.—Frank Floystad
Off. Admn.—Pam Rocco
SIC—3264; NAICS—327113; *Metal & ceramic seals*
Employs—20; Estab.—1970
8,000 sq ft site, Distrib.—National
Privately owned corporation

**FIELDS, INC., SAMUEL H.**
197 Union St. (07601)
**Phone—(201) 343-4626**
www.samfieldslab.com
V.-P.—Robert Fields
GM—Richard Fields
SIC—3843; NAICS—339114; *Dental prosthetics*
Employs—25; Estab.—1930
Sales—$2.5Mil-$5Mil (est)
Distrib.—Local
AKA: Fields Labs, Sam

†**FORD FASTENERS, INC.**
110 S. Newman St. (07601)
**Phone—(201) 487-3151**
National—(800) 272-3673
Fax—(201) 487-1919
www.fordfasteners.com
Email—info@fordfasteners.com
CEO—Christopher Cellary
Pres.—Stephen Cellary
Sales Mgr., Natl.—Robert Dickenson
Cred. & Hum. Res. Mgr.—Rosanne Palatucci

SIC—5072; NAICS—332722; *Distributor of industrial, self-drilling, self-tapping, cutting, self-sealing & sheet metal fastener screws, nuts & bolts*
Employs—10; Estab.—1963
Sales—$5Mil-$10Mil
27,000 sq ft site, Distrib.—National
Privately owned corporation

**FORDION PACKAGING LTD.**
185 Linden St. (07601)
**Phone—(201) 692-1344**
Fax—(201) 836-3275
Owner—Francis Harvey
SIC—3089; *Plastic bags*
Employs—15; Estab.—1983
Sales—$500,000-$1Mil
Distrib.—Local
Privately owned corporation

**FORMS MANAGEMENT SERVICES, INC.**
162 Lodi St. (07601)
**Phone—(201) 336-3200**
Fax—(201) 336-3206
www.fmsgraphics.com
Pres.—Frank Rizzo
SIC—2759; *Commercial printing*
Employs—5; Estab.—1971
Sales—$500,000-$1Mil
Distrib.—Regional
Privately owned corporation
AKA: FMS Graphics

**FOSTER ENGRAVING AND LASER CO.**
174 S. Main St., Ste. B (07601)
**Phone—(201) 489-5979**
Fax—(201) 489-0112
www.fosterengraving.net
Email—fosterengraving@ verizon.net
Pres.—Giovanni Osorio
GM—Joe Payne
SIC—3479; *Laser, mechanical, YAG & CO2 engraving*
Employs—5; Estab.—1956
Sales—under $500,000
2,000 sq ft site, Distrib.—National
Privately owned corporation

**GENERAL AVIATION & ELECTRONICS MFG. CO., INC.**
30 Jersey Pl. (07601)
Mail addr: P.O. Box 2245, South Hackensack (07606-0845)
**Phone—(201) 487-1700**
Fax—(201) 487-8606
www.generalae.com
Email—john.baker@generalae.com
Pres.—John Baker
Dir., Sales—George Alexandrakis
Accts. Mgr.—Nancy Detoma
Cust. Serv. Mgr.—Bella Baker
SIC—3499; *Precision sheet metal fabrication, including welded & dip brazed assemblies*
Employs—35; Estab.—1954
25,000 sq ft site, Distrib.—Intl.
Privately owned corporation
ISO rating—AS9100C

**GEOGRAPHIA MAP CO., INC.**
75 Moore St. (07601-7107)
**Phone—(201) 488-4411**
Fax—(201) 488-4401
www.geographiamaps.com
Email—info@geographiamaps.com
Pres.—Israel Polak
Off. Mgr.—Steven Polak
SIC—2741; 5199; NAICS—339150; *Publisher & distributor of maps; Brand name—Geographia; Rand McNally*
Employs—15
Sales—$1Mil-$2.5Mil
8,750 sq ft site, Distrib.—Regional
Privately owned corporation

NEW ENTRY
**GRAPHIC SOLUTIONS & SIGNS, LLC**
82 Burlews Ct. (07601)
**Phone—(201) 343-7446**
Fax—(201) 203-5254
www.signgss.com
Member—Felipe Alarcon
Pres.—Jorge Lara
SIC—3993; 3089; 2759; *Interior & exterior signs & vinyl lettering & vehicle wraps & graphic design services*
Employs—18; Estab.—2006
Sales—$1Mil-$2.5Mil
8,000 sq ft site, Distrib.—Local
Limited Liability Company
AKA: GSS

**GREAT NOTCH INDUSTRIES, INC.**
140 Liberty St. (07601)
**Phone—(201) 343-8110**
Fax—(201) 343-8327
Email—pcgalinski@optonline.net
Pres.—Paul Galinski
V.-P.—James Galinski
SIC—3599; *Precision machining job shop*
Employs—2; Estab.—1984
Sales—under $500,000
3,200 sq ft site, Distrib.—Regional
Privately owned corporation

**HAROUT TOOL & MACHINE CORP.**
9-11 Dyatt Pl. (07601)
**Phone—(201) 646-0664**
Fax—(201) 646-1381
Email—harouttool@opton.net
Pres.—Harry Terjanian
Operating Mgr.—Garo Terjanian
SIC—3599; *General machining job shop*
Employs—3; Estab.—1972
Sales—under $500,000
5,000 sq ft site, Distrib.—Local
Privately owned corporation

**HELM DENTAL, INC.**
111 Troast St. (07601)
**Phone—(201) 342-2915**
Email—mmteeth@yahoo.com
Ptnr. & Pres.—Albert Helm
Ptnr.—Mike Melillo
SIC—3843; NAICS—339114; *Dentures*
Employs—4; Estab.—1945
Distrib.—Local
Privately owned corporation

**HIGH TECHNOLOGY CORP.**
144 South St. (07601)
**Phone—(201) 488-0010**
Fax—(201) 488-4318
www.screenchanger.com
Email—aalroy@screenchanger.com
V.-P., Sales—Aline Alroy
Opers. Mgr.—Michael Yannai
SIC—3559; *Plastics machinery*
Employs—20; Estab.—1969
20,000 sq ft site, Distrib.—Intl.
Privately owned corporation

**HOFFMAN/NEW YORKER, INC. (H Q)**
46 Clinton Pl. (07601)
**Phone—(201) 488-1800**
Fax—(201) 488-4480
www.hoffman-newyorker.com
Email—info@hoffman-newyorker.com
V.-P.—Terry Rothlisberger
Sales Mgr., Natl.—Jeff Rabinowitz
Sales Mgr., Natl.—Richard Greco
Sales Mgr., Export—Thomas Bolan
SIC—3582; 3589; 3559; NAICS—333312; *Corporate headquarters; steam finishing presses & electric high-pressure boilers; Brand name—HOFFMAN; NEW YORKER*
Employs—10; Estab.—1904
95,000 sq ft site, Distrib.—Intl.
Privately owned sub-S corp.

GEOGRAPHICAL

# Hackensack—(cont.)

**HUDSON UNITED GLASS & WINDOW CORP.**
476 Hudson St. (07601)
**Phone—(201) 440-3937**
Fax—(201) 440-1876
www.hudsonunitedglass.com
Email—webmaster@
hudsonunitedglass.com
Pres.—John Monacchio
SIC—3231; NAICS—327215;
*Glass cutting & fabrication*
Employs—3; Estab.—2001
Sales—under $500,000
2,500 sq ft site, Distrib.—Local
Privately owned corporation

**HUTCHTON & SIMON, INC.**
140 Atlantic St. (07601)
**Phone—(201) 487-1033**
Fax—(201) 487-6332
Email—danc@
hutchtonandsimoninc.com
Pres.—Dan Cubicciotti
SIC—3444; 3599; *Sheet metal
fabrication, welding & precision
machining job shop*
Employs—25; Estab.—1976
17,000 sq ft site, Distrib.—Local
Privately owned corporation
AKA: Danson Sheet Metal, Inc.

**NEW ENTRY**
**INTERIOR ART & DESIGN, INC.**
59 Oak St. (07601)
**Phone—(201) 488-8855**
Fax—(201) 487-4488
www.interiorart.com
Owner—Ori Katzin
SIC—2391; *Custom window
coverings, including draperies*
Employs—20
Sales—$1Mil-$2.5Mil (est)
Distrib.—Local

**JM CUSTOM DESIGN MILLWORK**
101 Hobart St. (07601)
**Phone—(201) 487-8990**
Fax—(201) 487-1907
www.jmmillwork.com
Email—jmmillwork@aol.com
Owner—Joseph Marrella
SIC—2431; 2499; NAICS—
321900; *Custom millwork,
including wooden doors,
molding & components*
Employs—2; Estab.—1980
Sales—under $500,000
4,500 sq ft site, Distrib.—Regional
Privately owned partnership

**JOHNSON & MAYER, INC.**
58 Hobart St. (07601)
**Phone—(201) 646-1717**
Fax—(201) 646-1115
www.thetattoosource.com
Email—jmtat@optonline.net
Pres.—Mitchell Perdue
V-P.—Jake Johnson
SIC—2672; 2759; NAICS—
322222; *Decals*
Employs—20; Estab.—1992
Distrib.—Intl.
Privately owned corporation

**KAYDEN MFG., INC.**
83-A Burlews Ct. (07601)
**Phone—(201) 880-9898**
Fax—(201) 880-9897
www.kaydenmfg.com
Email—sales@kaydenmfg.com
Owner & Pres.—Jeff Kayden
SIC—3089; 3444; *Vinyl swimming
pool liners & sheet metal pool
step & bench inserts; Brand
name—Kayden Liners™;
ZipStep™*
Employs—5; Estab.—2006
Sales—$500,000-$1Mil
Distrib.—Intl.
Privately owned sub-S corp.

**NEW ENTRY**
**†KEEHN POWER PRODUCTS**
132 Johnson Ave. (07601)
**Phone—(201) 489-4454**
Fax—(201) 489-0731
www.keehnpower.com
Owner—Charles Keehn
SIC—5083; *Distributor of lawn &
garden power equipment*
Employs—20; Estab.—1979
Distrib.—Local
Privately owned corporation

**KRAISSL CO., INC.**
299 Williams Ave. *(07601)*
**Phone—(201) 342-0008**
National—(800) 572-4775
Fax—(201) 342-0025
www.strainers.com
Email—kraissl2@aol.com
Pres.—Richard C. Michel
Asst. Cont.—Angela Di Palma
Sales Mgr.—William Henderson
Opers. Mgr.—Michael Phillips
Pur. Agt.—Irma Campbell
SIC—3494; 3561; 3491; NAICS—
333911; *Heavy-duty industrial
valves, pumps & strainers for
pipeline service; Brand name—
Sea-view*
Employs—21; Estab.—1926
14,000 sq ft site, Distrib.—Intl.
Privately owned corporation

**LECO PLASTICS, INC.**
130 Gamewell St. (07601)
**Phone—(201) 343-3330**
Fax—(201) 343-0558
www.lecoplastics.com
Email—sales@lecoplastics.com
Pres.—Barry Schwartz
SIC—3089; 3544; NAICS—
333500; *Plastic extrusions &
molding*
Employs—9; Estab.—1946
Distrib.—National
Privately owned corporation

**NEW ENTRY**
**LIVEU, INC.**
2 University Plz., Ste. 505 (07601)
**Phone—(201) 742-5229**
Fax—(201) 623-4838
www.liveu.tv
Email—info_us@liveu.tv
Pres.—Avichai Cohen
SIC—3663; NAICS—335929;
*Portable video equipment &
software development for the
news industry, including 3G/4G
bonded uplink field units, mobile
apps & external antennae; Brand
name—LU-Lite Series® & LiveU
Xtender®*
Employs—60
Sales—$10Mil-$25Mil (est)

**LOSURDO FOODS, INC.**
20 Owens Rd. (07601)
**Phone—(201) 343-6680**
Fax—(201) 343-8652
www.losurdofoods.com
Email—info@losurdofoods.com
Founder—Michael Losurdo
Pres., CEO—Marc J. X. Losurdo
V-P., Sales—Vincenza Migliorelli
Corp. Secy.—Mary Losurdo
Treas., Hum. Res. Mgr.—Maria
Losurdo
Sales Mgr.—Greg Luciano
SIC—2022; 2045; 2023; NAICS—
311513; *Corporate headquarters
& dairy products including fresh
mozzarella, mozzarella curd,
ricotta, impastata & grated
cheese & frozen pizza dough;
Brand name—Losurdo; Bel
Capri; Caprese; Monte Maria;
Augustus*
Employs—100; Estab.—1959
Sales—$50Mil-$100Mil
75,000 sq ft site, Distrib.—National
Privately owned corporation

**M B C FOOD MACHINERY CORP.**
78 McKinley St. (07601)
**Phone—(201) 489-7000**
Fax—(201) 489-0614
www.mbcfoodmachinery.com
Email—jbattaglia@
mbcfoodmachinery.com
Pres.—John Battaglia
Opers. Mgr.—Gary Brugger
SIC—3556; NAICS—333294;
*Food processing equipment*
Employs—7; Estab.—1965
Sales—$1Mil-$2.5Mil
7,000 sq ft site, Distrib.—National
Privately owned sub-S corp.

**MARBLE & STONE CRAFTERS, LLC**
50 Johnson Ave., Ste. F (07601)
**Phone—(201) 343-2840**
Fax—(201) 342-2845
Email—ccmarble59@yahoo.com
Owner, Pres. & CEO—Christopher
Caruso
SIC—3281; NAICS—327991;
*Granite & marble countertops*
Employs—8; Estab.—2004
Sales—$1Mil-$2.5Mil
Distrib.—Regional
Privately owned corporation

**†MARCONE SUPPLY**
Div. of Marcone Appliance Parts
Center
180 Main St. (07601)
**Phone—(201) 489-6444**
National—(866) 256-9093
Fax—(201) 489-4648
www.marcone.com
Email—customerservice@
marcone.com
Sales Rep.—Gaston Hinton
SIC—5064; *Wholesaler of
appliance parts*
Employs—10; Estab.—2008
Sales—under $500,000
Distrib.—National
Privately owned corporation
Parent co.—Marcone Appliance
Parts Center, St. Louis, MO
Phone—(314) 993-9196
See Parent Co. Section for full profile.

**MASTER BOND, INC.**
154 Hobart St. *(07601)*
**Phone—(201) 343-8983**
Fax—(201) 343-2132
www.masterbond.com
Email—main@masterbond.com
Pres.—James Brenner
Cust. Serv. & Sales Mgr.—Lori
Silvano
Online Mktg. Mgr.—Dmitriy
Zhitomirskiy
Cust. Serv. & Sales Rep.—Sandy
Sobel
SIC—2891; 2821; NAICS—
325520; *Custom adhesives,
sealants, coatings, potting
compounds & encapsulants for
the electronic, medical, optical,
aerospace & hi-tech industries*
Employs—20; Estab.—1976
Sales—$2.5Mil-$5Mil
25,000 sq ft site, Distrib.—Intl.
Privately owned corporation

**MATTHEWS ENGRAVERS, EDWARD R.**
61 S. State St. (07601)
**Phone—(201) 342-4644**
Fax—(201) 488-1140
Email—matthews.engravers@
gmail.com
Owner & Engraver—Nick
Lontemuro
SIC—3993; *Engraved interior &
exterior signs*
Employs—1; Estab.—1977
Sales—under $500,000
Distrib.—Regional
Sole ownership

**MEDCO WEST**
Div. of Medco Manufacturing Co.
25-21 Di Carolis Ct. (07601)
**Phone—(201) 457-9260**
Fax—(201) 457-9265
www.mdjco.com
Email—sales@mdjco.com
V-P., Sales—Don Hahn
Prodn. Mgr.—Alfonso Agudelo
SIC—3679; *Contract electronic,
through-hole, box build &
electromechanical assembly*
Employs—25; Estab.—2009
Sales—$500,000-$1Mil
Distrib.—National
Privately owned corporation
Parent co.—Medco Manufacturing
Co., Brentwood, NY
Phone—(631) 667-9699
See Parent Co. Section for full profile.

**MERC USA, INC.**
41 Newman St. (07601)
**Phone—(201) 489-3527**
National—(800) 777-9599
Fax—(201) 489-7636
www.inserch.com
Email—mercusainc@yahoo.com
Pres.—Jahan Astaneha
SIC—2321; 2325; NAICS—
315200; *Men's shirts & trousers*
Employs—10; Estab.—1986
Sales—under $500,000
18,000 sq ft site, Distrib.—Local
Privately owned corporation

**MERIT TROPHIES & ENGRAVING, INC.**
184 Main St. (07601)
**Phone—(201) 487-5780**
Fax—(201) 487-6586
Email—meritaward@aol.com
V-P., GM—Jim Dolack
SIC—3479; 3499; 3993; 3089;
*Laser engraving of signs,
plaques, gavels, acrylic & crystal
awards & cast bronze tablets*
Employs—5; Estab.—1948
Sales—$500,000-$1Mil
Distrib.—National
Privately owned corporation

**METROPOLITAN RUBBER CO.**
135 Lawrence St. (07601)
**Phone—(201) 489-0909**
Fax—(201) 489-9341
www.metrorubber.com
Email—metrorubber@aol.com
Pres.—Jerry Simmons
V-P.—Brian Simmons
Corp. Secy.—Renee Abramas
SIC—3069; *Industrial rubber
products, including rubber
hoses & rubber matting*
Employs—8; Estab.—1978
Sales—under $500,000
10,000 sq ft site, Distrib.—National
Privately owned corporation

**†MINGOLO PRECISION PRODUCTS, INC.**
174 S. Main St., Ste. 1 (07601)
**Phone—(201) 488-6300**
Fax—(201) 488-9020
www.surveyors-shop.com
Email—mingoloprecision@
covad.net

# Hackensack—(cont.)

Pres.—Louis Mingolo
SIC—5049; *Wholesaler of surveying equipment & supplies*
Employs—22
Distrib.—Local
Privately owned corporation

## MODI SYSTEMS, INC.

88 S. State St. (07601)
**Phone—(201) 525-0775**
National—(800) 222-6634
Fax—(201) 525-0771
www.modisystems.com
Email—msi@modisystems.com
V-P., GM—Theresa Esposito
Sales Mgr.—Laurie Esposito
SIC—3531; *Roofing torches*
Employs—10; Estab.—1980
Sales—$1Mil-$2.5Mil (est)
Distrib.—Intl.
Privately owned corporation

## MULTI-PAK CORP.

180 Atlantic St. (07601)
**Phone—(201) 342-7474**
Fax—(201) 342-6525
www.compactors1.com
Email—sales@compactors1.com
Chrm.—Neil Cavanaugh
Pres.—Phil Cahill
SIC—3639; NAICS—335200; *Trash compactors, including repair & chute & duct cleaning; Brand name—Multi-Pak*
Employs—25; Estab.—1968
Distrib.—Intl.
Privately owned sub-S corp.

## MUL-T-LOCK USA, INC.

Div. of ASSA, Inc.
100 Commerce Way, Ste. 2 (07601)
**Phone—(973) 778-3222**
National—(800) 562-3511
Fax—(973) 778-4007
www.mul-t-lockusa.com
Email—info@mul-t-lockusa.com
Pres.—Micha Kimchi
Cont., Fin. Mgr.—Anna Gimuriman
SIC—3429; *High-security lock assembly*
Employs—35; Estab.—1985
12,001 sq ft site, Distrib.—National
Publicly owned corporation
Parent co.—ASSA, Inc., New Haven, CT
   Phone—(203) 603-5958
   See Parent Co. Section for full profile.

## N. B. C. ENGRAVING CO., INC.

228 Park St. (07601)
Mail addr: P.O. Box 1036, Hackensack (07602)
**Phone—(201) 387-8011**
Fax—(201) 387-9602
www.nbcengraving.com
Email—info@nbcengraving.com
Pres.—John Scagliotti
Engraver—Danny Lamberti
SIC—3479; *Mechanical engraving*
Employs—4; Estab.—1932
Sales—under $500,000
Distrib.—National
Privately owned corporation

## NEI GROUP, INC.

44 Burlews Ct. (07601)
**Phone—(201) 488-5858**
National—(800) 223-5820
Fax—(201) 488-1926
www.neigroup.com
Pres.—John Nanasi
GM—Andy Kardos
Sales Mgr.—Ernie Reinitz
SIC—3911; NAICS—339911; *Corporate headquarters & gold jewelry & diamonds*
Employs—40; Estab.—1965
12,000 sq ft site, Distrib.—National
Privately owned corporation

## NORTH JERSEY WINDOW TREATMENTS, LLC

164 South St. (07601)
**Phone—(201) 487-2121**
www.dsworkroom.com
Email—draperyman@aol.com
Pres.—Martin Gutman
SIC—2391; 2591; NAICS—314121; *Draperies & window treatments*
Employs—12; Estab.—1945
Sales—$500,000-$1Mil
Distrib.—Regional
Limited Liability Company

## NU E-Z CUSTOM BINDERY, LLC

111 Essex St. (07601)
**Phone—(201) 488-4140**
Fax—(201) 488-4116
Email—nuez@optonline.net
Pres.—Julia Paulucci
V-P., Sales—Louis Paulucci
SIC—2789; NAICS—323121; *Die cutting, gluing, wire-o-binding, saddle stitching, shrink packaging, hand work & fulfillment & padding*
Employs—40; Estab.—2003
Sales—$3.3Mil
26,000 sq ft site, Distrib.—Regional
Limited Liability Company

## OCEANIC GRAPHIC PRINTING USA

105 Main St., 3rd Fl. (07601)
**Phone—(201) 883-1816**
Fax—(201) 883-1826
www.ogprinting.com
Email—nj@ogprinting.com
Pres.—David Li
Off. Mgr.—Jean Blandino
Proj. Mgr.—Dustin Li
SIC—2759; NAICS—323100; *Commercial printing*
Employs—10; Estab.—1989
Distrib.—Intl.
Privately owned corporation

## ORPAK USA

100 1st St., Ste. 200 (07601)
**Phone—(201) 441-9820**
National—(800) 776-4462
Fax—(201) 441-9830
www.orpakusa.com
Email—info@orpakusa.com
Pres.—Shlomo Slotwiner
V-P., Sales—Moshe Shaked
Cont., Hum. Res. Mgr.—Vito Cantatore
SIC—3829; *Fuel management systems*
Employs—10; Estab.—1991
Sales—$1Mil-$2.5Mil
Distrib.—National
Privately owned corporation

## O'SHEA'S PRINTING SERVICES CO., INC.

483 Main St. (07601)
**Phone—(201) 343-8668**
Fax—(201) 343-2105
www.osheaprinting.com
Email—info@osheaprinting.com
Pres.—William Bracken
Manager—Brian Meadows
SIC—2759; NAICS—323100; *Commercial printing & related services*
Employs—3; Estab.—1972
Sales—$500,000-$1Mil
1,200 sq ft site, Distrib.—Local
Privately owned corporation

## †P & A AUTO PARTS, INC.

530 River St. (07601)
**Phone—(201) 843-7156**
           (201) 655-7117
Fax—(201) 655-7322
www.paautoparts.com
Email—m.agnello@paautoparts.com
Pres., CFO—Joe Cupoli
Sales Mgr.—Russell Guarciello

Opers. Mgr.—Michael Agnello
SIC—5013; *Corporate headquarters & distributor of automotive parts*
Employs—30; Estab.—1977
Privately owned corporation

## PAPERBOARD PRODUCTS CO.

21 Shafer Pl. (07601)
**Phone—(201) 440-1600**
Fax—(201) 440-6740
Pres.—Jonathan Marks
SIC—2652; NAICS—322213; *Paperboard containers & boxes*
Employs—22; Estab.—1956
Distrib.—Intl.
Privately owned corporation
AKA: International Container Co.

## PAPSON PRINTING CORP.

115 Hudson St. (07601)
**Phone—(201) 342-2860**
Fax—(201) 342-4927
www.rediprint.net
Email—info@rediprint.net
Pres., Off. Mgr.—Chris Papson
SIC—2752; 2791; NAICS—323122; *Offset printing & typesetting*
Employs—3; Estab.—1984
Sales—$500,000-$1Mil
Distrib.—Local
Privately owned corporation
AKA: Redi Print

## PATCHAMP, INC.

20 E. Kennedy St. (07601)
**Phone—(201) 457-1504**
Fax—(201) 457-1507
www.patchamp.com
Email—sales@patchamp.com
Pres.—Virginia Connors
SIC—3663; *Prewired video & audio distribution amplifiers & systems for digital broadcast & communications facilities*
Employs—7
Sales—$1Mil-$2.5Mil (est)
6,000 sq ft site,
Privately owned corporation

## PEARCE WELDING CO., LLC

155 S. River St. (07601)
**Phone—(201) 488-0434**
Fax—(201) 440-9132
Pres.—John F. Pearce
Bookkeeper—Anna Pearce
SIC—3441; *Structural steel fabrication*
Employs—2; Estab.—1973
Sales—under $500,000
Distrib.—Local
Limited Liability Company

## PIONEER INDUSTRIES, INC.

171 S. Newman St. (07601)
**Phone—(201) 933-1900**
Fax—(201) 933-9580
www.pioneerindustries.com
Email—ecarlson@pioneerindustries.com
Pres.—Mitchell Dorf
Hum. Res. Mgr.—Maureen Caratenuto
Cust. Serv. Rep.—Eric Carlson
SIC—3442; NAICS—332321; *Steel doors & door frames*
Employs—60
140,000 sq ft site,
Privately owned corporation

## PLENUM SCIENTIFIC RESEARCH, INC.

210 Lee Pl. (07601)
**Phone—(201) 489-2771**
Fax—(201) 489-8035
www.plenumusa.com
Email—plenum@usa.com
Pres., R & D Mgr.—Shajadi Parvin
V-P., MIS—Geecee Pat
Fin. Mgr.—Ahsan Ahmed
Consultant—Abdullah Lakeeb

SIC—2899; 2819; *Biochemicals & chemical reagents*
Employs—10; Estab.—1992
Sales—$500,000-$1Mil
5,000 sq ft site, Distrib.—Intl.
Privately owned corporation
AKAs: American Institute Of Pharmaceutical Technologies & AIPT

## PMC INDUSTRIES

275 Hudson St. *(07601)*
**Phone—(201) 342-3684**
Fax—(201) 342-3568
www.pmc-industries.com
Email—pmcindustries@verizon.net
Pres.—Kazmier Wysocki
V-P., R & D—Peter Wysocki
Sales Mgr.—James J. Harris
SIC—3565; NAICS—333993; *Special screw capping machines & plug inserters, including sorter handling caps & plugs with dip tubes & aerosol valves & trigger & pump caps, orienting units & servo, electronic control & special inspection systems*
Employs—25; Estab.—1955
Sales—$1Mil-$5Mil
20,000 sq ft site, Distrib.—National
Privately owned corporation
Also see: Progressive Machine Co., 293 Hudson St.

## PRISMATIX DECAL, INC.

324 Railroad Ave. (07601)
**Phone—(201) 525-2800**
National—(800) 222-9662
Fax—(201) 525-2828
www.prismatixinc.com
Email—prismatix@optonline.net
Pres., CEO—Miriam Salomon
Sales Mgr.—Ira Salomon
SIC—2399; 3499; 3479; *Decals, emblems, trophies & engraving*
Employs—10; Estab.—1976
Sales—$1Mil-$2.5Mil
8,000 sq ft site, Distrib.—National
Privately owned corporation

## PROGRESSIVE MACHINE CO.

293 Hudson St. (07601)
**Phone—(201) 342-3636**
Fax—(201) 342-7366
www.progressivemc.com
Email—info@progressivemc.com
Pres.—Peter Wysocki
SIC—3599; *Machining job shop*
Employs—6; Estab.—1919
Sales—$1Mil-$2.5Mil
Distrib.—Local
Privately owned corporation
Also see: PMC Industries, 275 Hudson St.

## ROLL FLEX LABEL CO., LLC

199 Lee Pl. (07601)
**Phone—(201) 489-3330**
Fax—(201) 489-8831
Email—rollflex@rollflex.com
Owner—William Zink
Pres.—William Zink, Jr.
MIS Mgr. & Cust. Serv. Rep.—Karlo Endaya
SIC—2759; NAICS—323100; *Pressure-sensitive label printing*
Employs—7; Estab.—1983
Sales—$1.4Mil
8,000 sq ft site, Distrib.—Intl.
Limited Liability Company

## RUFFINO PACKAGING, INC.

63 Green St. (07601)
**Phone—(201) 487-1260**
Fax—(201) 487-3926
www.ruffinopackaging.com
Email—joe@ruffinopackaging.com
Pres.—Joseph Ruffino

GEOGRAPHICAL

# Hackensack—(cont.)

SIC—2657; NAICS—322212; *Folding cartons, including blisters, display packaging & e-flute & micro-flute corrugated*
Employs—18; Estab.—1953
15,000 sq ft site, Distrib.—Regional
Privately owned corporation

**S & P TEES**

14 Frederick St. (07601)
Mail addr: P.O. Box 4012, South Hackensack (07606)
**Phone—(201) 996-1411**
Fax—(201) 996-1791
www.sptees.com
Email—paul@sptees.com
Owner & Pres.—Paul Tortorici
SIC—2396; *Textile screen printing*
Employs—1; Estab.—1988
2,400 sq ft site, Distrib.—National
Limited Liability Company

**S. GOLDBERG & CO., INC.**

3 University Plz., Ste. 400 (07601-6222)
**Phone—(201) 342-1200**
Fax—(201) 342-4405
www.thesgcompanies.com
Email—info@thesgcompanies.com
Pres.—Bernie Leifer
CFO—Stan Altscher
V-P., Sales—Thomas O'Brien
V-P., Opers.—Paul Kingslow
Licensing Mgr.—Jerry Giarrusso
SIC—3142; NAICS—316212; *Corporate headquarters & men's & women's footwear (mfg. overseas)*
Employs—73
Sales—$25Mil-$50Mil
Privately owned corporation
DBA: S. G. Footwear

**SEDTEK, INC.**

113 Meadow St. (07601)
**Phone—(201) 489-4040**
Fax—(201) 489-4949
www.sedtek.com
Email—info@sedtek.com
Pres., R & D Mgr.—Gerald Danker
Opers. Mgr.—Robert Ragusa
Off. Mgr.—Donna Ragusa
SIC—3544; 3599; NAICS—326291; *Metal bar soap molds, rubber products & machining job shop*
Employs—15; Estab.—1905
Sales—$500,000-$1Mil
3,000 sq ft site, Distrib.—National
Privately owned corporation

**SIGN-A-RAMA, INC.**

379 Main St. (07601)
**Phone—(201) 489-6969**
Fax—(201) 489-1429
www.sign-a-rama.com
Email—signaramasales@aol.com
Pres.—Michael Fried
V-P.—Johnathon Sklar
SIC—3993; *Interior & exterior signs & vinyl sign letters*
Employs—3; Estab.—1992
Sales—under $500,000
3,000 sq ft site, Distrib.—Regional
Privately owned corporation

**SJA JEWELRY, INC.**

Div. of NEI Group, Inc.
44 Burlews Ct. (07601)
**Phone—(201) 837-0990**
National—(800) 257-4109
Fax—(201) 488-1827
www.yolante.com
Bookkeeper—Roseann Bonito
SIC—3911; NAICS—339911; *Precious metal jewelry*
Employs—40; Estab.—1978
2,000 sq ft site, Distrib.—National
Privately owned corporation

Parent co.—NEI Group, Inc., Hackensack, NJ
Phone—(201) 488-5858
See Parent Co. Section for full profile.

**SLINGO, INC.**

411 Hackensack Ave., 8th Fl. (07601)
**Phone—(201) 489-6727**
www.slingo.com
Founder—Sal Faloiglia
Pres., CEO—Rich Roberts
GM—Eric Lamendola
SIC—7372; *Online casual game software development*
Employs—18; Estab.—1995
Distrib.—National
Privately owned corporation

**SOME'S WORLD-WIDE UNIFORMS**

314 Main St. (07601)
**Phone—(201) 843-1199**
National—(800) 631-7077
Fax—(201) 843-3014
www.somes.com
Email—someunif@somes.com
CEO—Andrea Some
COO—Heschel Some
Dir., Sales—Jason Some
SIC—2389; NAICS—315200; *Governmental uniforms & accessories*
Employs—30; Estab.—1959
Sales—$1Mil-$5Mil
30,000 sq ft site, Distrib.—Intl.
Privately owned corporation

**TANGENT GRAPHICS**

151 Hobart St. (07601)
**Phone—(201) 488-2840**
Fax—(201) 489-1254
Email—tangraph@optonline.net
Pres.—John Wehle
SIC—2759; NAICS—323100; *Commercial printing*
Employs—8; Estab.—1980
Sales—under $500,000
Distrib.—Local
Privately owned corporation

**TARGET PRINTING & GRAPHICS**

9 E. Passaic St. (07601)
**Phone—(201) 883-0200**
Fax—(201) 883-0242
www.targetprinting.com
Email—tonyflaim@targetprinting.com
Pres.—Tony Flaim
SIC—2752; 2759; NAICS—323100; *Offset & digital printing, signs, banners & window lettering*
Employs—9; Estab.—1987
Sales—$1Mil-$2.5Mil (est)
3,500 sq ft site, Distrib.—Regional
Privately owned corporation

**TECH REPRO, INC.**

65 Zabriskie St. (07601)
**Phone—(201) 489-1333**
Fax—(201) 489-0674
www.techrepro.com
Email—sales@techrepro.com
Pres.—Kevin Tremble
Bookkeeper—J. Hand
SIC—2752; 2759; 2791; 2789; NAICS—323122; *Large-format, instant & color printing, typesetting & binding*
Employs—10; Estab.—1961
Sales—$500,000-$1Mil
Distrib.—Local
Privately owned corporation

**TESTRITE INSTRUMENT CO.**

216 S. Newman St. (07601)
**Phone—(201) 543-0240**
National—(888) 873-2735
Fax—(201) 543-2195
www.testrite.com
Email—info@testrite.com
Pres.—Larry Rubin
IT Mgr.—Yos Reyes
Off. Mgr.—Nigi Olivio

SIC—3444; 2542; *Telescopic aluminum tube educational & visual presentation products, including banner stands, pop-ups, sign frames, hanging sign & poster holders & flipchart easels*
Employs—120; Estab.—1919
Sales—$500,000-$1Mil
90,000 sq ft site, Distrib.—Local
Privately owned corporation
AKA: Testrite Visual Products

**THE FIFTY/FIFTY GROUP, INC**

343 S. River St. (07601)
**Phone—(201) 343-1243**
National—(800) 524-2822
Fax—(201) 489-6477
www.lolaproducts.com
Email—info@lolaproducts.com
Chrm. of the Board—Edward D. Spitaletta
Pres.—Richard Spitaletta
COO—Charles Spitaletta
V-P., Admn., Fin. & Hum. Res. Mgr.—Buddy Mickolajczyk
Plt. & Shpg. Mgr.—Ed Francke
SIC—3991; NAICS—339994; *Mop, broom & brush assemblies*
Employs—25; Estab.—1969
Sales—over $10Mil
50,000 sq ft site, Distrib.—National
Privately owned sub-S corp.
Also see: Clip Strip Corp., same loc.
DBA: Lola Products

**TOTAL INK SOLUTIONS**

200 S. Newman St., Unit 4 (07601-3124)
**Phone—(201) 487-9600**
(877) 937-6400
Fax—(201) 487-9620
www.totalinksolutions.com
Email—marc@totalinksolutions.com
Pres.—Luis Uribe
GM—Marc Jelinsky
SIC—2893; NAICS—325910; *Plastisol, water-based, solvent-based & UV curable screen printing inks, photo emulsions & prepress supplies; Brand name—Total Ink Solutions*
Employs—6; Estab.—1990
Sales—$2.5Mil-$5Mil
19,000 sq ft site, Distrib.—National
Limited Liability Company
AKA: CRS Ink International

**TRIUMPH KNITTING, INC.**

18-20 Di Carolis Ct. (07601)
**Phone—(201) 646-0022**
Fax—(201) 646-1198
www.triumphknittinginc.com
Email—sgerber@triumphknittinginc.com
Pres.—Steve Gerber
Bookkeeper—John Ladolcetta
SIC—2259; 2257; 2254; 2253; *Industrial & polyester fabrics, apparel, fillers & wiping rags*
Employs—19; Estab.—1972
20,000 sq ft site, Distrib.—Local
Privately owned corporation

**TYZ-ALL PLASTICS, LLC**

130 Gamewell St. (07601)
**Phone—(201) 343-1200**
National—(800) 645-6334
Fax—(201) 343-0558
www.tyzall.com
Email—customerservice@tyzall.com
Pres.—Betty Ballin
V-P., Opers.—Susan D'Alessandro
Plt. Mgr.—Jose Tuesta
Off. Mgr.—Lisa Sumner
SIC—3089; *Plastic products*
Employs—10; Estab.—1975
15,000 sq ft site, Distrib.—Intl.
Privately owned corporation

**UNIVERSAL ELECTRIC MOTOR SERVICE, INC.**

131 S. Newman St. (07601)
**Phone—(201) 968-1000**
Fax—(201) 678-9511
Email—uemotor@verizon.net
Pres.—Stephen Stagg
Shop Mgr.—John Pinkus
SIC—3621; NAICS—335312; *Rebuilt electric motors*
Employs—35; Estab.—1945
Sales—$5Mil-$10Mil
Distrib.—National
Privately owned corporation

**VISUAL RETAIL PLUS, INC.**

540 Hudson St., 4th Fl. (07601)
**Phone—(201) 678-9888**
National—(888) 767-4004
Fax—(201) 678-1440
www.visualretailplus.com
Email—sales@visualretailplus.com
Owner—Dafna Halevy
Dir., Bus. Dev.—Hili Shrem
SIC—7372; *Point-of-sale & inventory management software development for the vertical retail markets*
Employs—11; Estab.—1991
Distrib.—National
Sole ownership

**WHAT A TEE 2, INC.**

82 Sussex St. (07601)
**Phone—(201) 457-0060**
Fax—(201) 457-0064
www.whatatee.com
Email—info@whatatee.com
Pres.—Harry Poulas
Off. Mgr.—Sophia Pappas
SIC—2396; 2395; *T-shirt screen printing & embroidery*
Employs—10; Estab.—2000
Sales—$500,000-$1Mil
Distrib.—National
Privately owned corporation

**WIDMER TIME RECORDER CO., INC.**

228 Park St. (07601)
Mail addr: P.O. Box 588, Hackensack (07602-0588)
**Phone—(201) 489-3810**
National—(800) 424-4459
Fax—(201) 489-3478
www.widmertime.com
Email—widmer@widmertime.com
Pres.—Robert J. Widmer
CIO & CTO—Stephen Widmer
Ex. V-P., COO—Tim Carney
Dir., Sales—James Carney
Off. Mgr.—Donna Siegler
Export Mgr.—Robert Thompson
SIC—3579; *Time recorders, including time clocks, time stamp, embossing & numbering machines & check signers; Brand name—Widmer Time Recorder*
Employs—25; Estab.—1933
Sales—$5Mil-$10Mil (est)
15,000 sq ft site, Distrib.—Intl.
Privately owned corporation

NEW ENTRY

**WORLD SCIENTIFIC PUBLISHING CO., INC.**

27 Warren St., Ste. 401-402 (07601)
**Phone—(201) 487-9655**
Fax—(201) 487-9656
www.worldscientific.com
Pres.—Doreen Phua
SIC—2731; *Book publishing*
Employs—10; Estab.—1981
Sales—$500,000-$1Mil (est)
Distrib.—Intl.
Privately owned corporation

**ZAIYA, INC.**

185 Kenneth St. (07601)
**Phone—(201) 343-3988**
Fax—(201) 343-3477
Pres.—Yoko Sano

## Hackensack—(cont.)

SIC—2051; NAICS—311812;
*Bread*
Employs—20
Sales—$2.5Mil-$5Mil (est)
Distrib.—Local
Privately owned corporation

## Hackettstown

(Warren—N.W.)

### ALMETEK INDUSTRIES, INC.

2 Joy Dr. (07840)
**Phone—(908) 850-9700**
National—(800) 248-2080
Fax—(908) 850-9618
www.almetek.com
Email—csr@almetek.com
CEO—Lori McMahon
Pres.—Michael Quagliana
V-P.—Donna Quagliana
Mktg. Mgr.—Kacy Salas
Hum. Res. Mgr.—Lori Otto
Accts. Rec. Coord.—Pat Bracaglia
Billing Coord.—Sharon
Vanheteren
SIC—2672; 2759; 3629; 3993;
NAICS—322222; *Metal &
polyethelene safety signs,
pressure-sensitive labels &
identification systems*
Employs—75; Estab.—1975
42,000 sq ft site, Distrib.—National
Privately owned corporation

### ANDREX, INC.

101 Bilby Rd., Ste. E (07840)
**Phone—(908) 852-4377**
      (908) 852-4376
National—(800) 527-3361
Fax—(908) 852-4367
www.andrex-usa.com
Email—sales@andrex-usa.com
Pres.—William T. Pote
Prod. Mgr.—Brian Barends
SIC—3643; 3679; NAICS—
335931; *Brass, nickel & stainless
steel flexible metal hose &
conduits*
Employs—20; Estab.—1983
Sales—$1Mil-$5Mil
20,000 sq ft site, Distrib.—Intl.
Privately owned corporation
ISO rating—9001:2008

### †COMPUTER WHOLESALERS, INC.

715 Willow Grove St., Ste. 5
(07840)
**Phone—(908) 684-0802**
Fax—(908) 684-0599
www.gocwi.com
Email—info@gocwi.com
Pres.—Ivan Somyk
GM—Taras Somyk
Sales Mgr.—Jeff Wurst
IT Mgr.—Anthony Prestia
Off. Mgr.—Tara Lake
Tech. Mgr.—Andy Bickley
Asset Mgr.—Kelley Biggiotti
Software Developer—Rich Oswald
SIC—5045; *Wholesaler of
computer equipment & supplies,
including notebooks, desktops,
monitors & printers; Brand
name—Apple; Dell; HP/
Compaq; IBM; Cisco*
Employs—25; Estab.—1994
Sales—$12Mil
35,000 sq ft site, Distrib.—Intl.
Privately owned corporation
ISO rating—9001:2008
AKA: CWI

### CUSTOM PRODUCTS MFG., INC.

430 Sand Shore Rd., Ste. 4 & 5
(07840)
**Phone—(908) 852-2078**
Fax—(908) 852-5118
www.museumstoreproducts.com
Pres.—Haywood Huntley

SIC—2499; *Museum gift items*
Employs—15
3,500 sq ft site, Distrib.—Regional
Privately owned corporation

### EDHARD CORP.

279 Blau Rd. (07840)
**Phone—(908) 850-8444**
National—(888) 334-2731
Fax—(908) 850-8445
www.edhard.com
Email—meter@edhard.com
Pres.—Edgar Bars
Cont.—Joseph Englert
Off. Mgr.—Nancy Neri
SIC—3556; 3589; 3565; 3824;
NAICS—333294; *Liquid &
viscous product filling &
depositing systems for the
bakery, foodservice, cosmetic &
packaging industries*
Employs—27; Estab.—1970
Sales—$1Mil-$5Mil
33,000 sq ft site, Distrib.—Intl.
Privately owned corporation

### FILTRATION SOLUTIONS, INC.

432 Sand Shore Rd., Ste. 8
(07840)
**Phone—(908) 684-4000**
Fax—(908) 684-4100
www.filtsol.com
Email—sales@filtsol.com
Pres.—Chang Jen
GM—Vin Ardizzone
SIC—3714; *Fuel, oil, wastewater
treatment & aqueous filtration
equipment*
Employs—5; Estab.—2000
Sales—$1Mil-$5Mil
Distrib.—Intl.
Privately owned sub-S corp.

### GP PRECISION, INC.

434 Sand Shore Rd. *(07840)*
**Phone—(908) 850-1940**
Fax—(908) 850-5926
www.gpsheetmetal.com
Email—sales@gpsheetmetal.com
Pres.—W. Arthur Cubbage
V-P., Sales—Dennis Collinson
V-P., Opers.—Seth Cubbage
Sales Engr.—Peter Samp
SIC—3444; *Precision metal
fabrication*
Employs—40; Estab.—1966
Sales—$8Mil-$10Mil
25,000 sq ft site, Distrib.—National
Privately owned corporation
ISO rating—9001:2000

### GRAPHIC IMAGE, INC.

445 Route 46 (07840)
**Phone—(908) 852-7007**
Fax—(908) 850-1999
www.graphicimageinc.com
Email—info@graphicimageinc.com
Pres.—Claudia Ehrgott
SIC—2759; 3993; NAICS—
323100; *Commercial printing,
signs, posters, displays,
promotional items, graphic
design & project management*
Employs—4; Estab.—1978
Sales—$500,000-$1Mil
Distrib.—Local
Privately owned corporation

### GREENE BROS. SPECIALTY COFFEE ROASTERS, INC.

313 High St. (07840)
**Phone—(908) 979-0022**
Fax—(908) 979-0526
www.greenesbeans.com
Email—bubba42@
greenesbeans.com
Pres.—David Greene
V-P.—Brian Greene
Acct. Mgr.—Gizella Meert

SIC—2095; NAICS—311920;
*Coffee roasting*
Employs—12; Estab.—1995
Sales—$500,000-$1Mil
2,000 sq ft site, Distrib.—Regional
Privately owned corporation

### HACKETTSTOWN SHEET METAL, INC.

1 Stiger St. (07840)
Mail addr: P.O. Box 2491,
Branchville (07826)
**Phone—(908) 852-3752**
Fax—(908) 852-9498
GM—Ken Nakowski
Mechanic—Chris Nakowski
SIC—3444; *Sheet metal
fabrication*
Employs—3; Estab.—1989
Sales—under $500,000
Distrib.—Local
Privately owned corporation

### HOLLIE STUDIOS

200-C Valentine, P.O. Box 530
(07840)
**Phone—(908) 852-7263**
www.holliestudios.com
Owner—John Mandick
SIC—2396; *Textile screen printing*
Employs—4; Estab.—1976
Sales—under $500,000
Distrib.—Local
Limited Liability Company

### KINGWOOD INDUSTRIAL PRODUCTS, INC.

261 Main St., Unit 1 & 2 (07840)
**Phone—(908) 852-8655**
Fax—(908) 852-8668
www.kingwoodindustrial.com
Email—info@
kingwoodindustrial.com
Pres.—Kevin Smith
SIC—3842; 3821; 3291;
*Audiology equipment &
supplies, including hearing aids
& laboratory & grinding &
polishing equipment & supplies*
Employs—4; Estab.—1990
Sales—$500,000-$1Mil
22,000 sq ft site, Distrib.—Intl.
Privately owned corporation

### LAMB PRINTING, INC.

700 Grand Ave. (07840)
**Phone—(908) 852-5354**
Fax—(908) 813-0906
Email—lamb@lambprinting.com
Pres.—Michael Lamb
SIC—2752; NAICS—323100;
*Offset printing*
Employs—6; Estab.—1985
Sales—under $500,000
2,500 sq ft site, Distrib.—Regional
Privately owned corporation

### LORDON, INC.

453 Route 46, Ste. 1-A (07840)
**Phone—(908) 813-1143**
National—(888) 521-8800
Fax—(908) 813-1610
www.britesidepanels.com
Email—csr@britesidepanels.com
Pres.—Donna Quagliana
V-P.—Lori McMahon
SIC—3648; 3993; NAICS—
335129; *Reflective traffic sign
panels & strips*
Employs—5; Estab.—1997
Sales—$500,000-$1Mil
Distrib.—National
Privately owned corporation

### MANGO CUSTOM CABINETS, INC.

216 W. Stiger St. (07840)
**Phone—(908) 813-3077**
Fax—(908) 813-1101
www.mangocustominc.com
Email—kim@
mangocustomcabinets.com
Owner—Richard Mango
Off. Mgr.—Kimberly Gang

SIC—2431; 2434; 2541; NAICS—
337110; *Architectural millwork,
including custom cabinetry &
commercial store fixtures*
Employs—20; Estab.—1992
Sales—$4Mil
Distrib.—Intl.
Privately owned corporation

### MARS CHOCOLATE NORTH AMERICA

Div. of Mars, Incorporated
800 High St. (07840)
**Phone—(908) 852-1000**
Fax—(908) 850-2734
www.mars.com
Email—info@mars.com
Hum. Res. Bus. Ptnr.—Nicholas
Miele
Dir.—Mary Myers
Sr. Corp. Affs. Mgr.—Lee Andrews
SIC—2064; NAICS—311300;
*Divisional headquarters & candy*
Employs—1480
Sales—$250Mil-$500Mil (est)
Privately owned corporation
Parent co.—Mars, Incorporated,
McLean, VA
Phone—(703) 821-4900
See Parent Co. Section for full profile.

### MOBILE POWER, INC.

392 Watters Rd. (07840)
**Phone—(908) 852-3117**
National—(800) 433-0781
Fax—(908) 852-2941
www.mobilepowerinc.com
Email—mobilepowerinc@
comcast.net
Pres.—Paul Mitchell
Off. Mgr.—Sharon Cerny
Shpg. & Rec. Mgr.—David Frontier
SIC—3694; 3629; NAICS—
336322; *Mobile heavy output
alternators & current inverters,
DC to AC inverters, AC power
supply & industrial hybrid power
systems; Brand name—Xantrex;
Schneider Electric; Victron
Energy*
Employs—5; Estab.—1977
Sales—$500,000-$1Mil
1,000 sq ft site, Distrib.—Intl.
Privately owned corporation

### †MORAK, INC.

3 Janice Dr. (07840-5512)
**Phone—(973) 527-7470**
National—(800) 564-4206
Fax—(908) 441-9803
www.approvedwindowsales.com
Email—winsales2@gmail.com
Owner—Thomas Byrnes
SIC—5031; *Distributor of windows
& doors; Brand name—Marvin;
Andersen; Masonite; Kolbe;
Trimline; Skyline; Optimum;
Crystal; WeatherGuard; Okna;
Starmark*
Employs—4; Estab.—1981
Sales—$500,000-$1Mil
Distrib.—Regional
Privately owned corporation
AKA: Marvin Window Sales

### MULTIMODE FIBER OPTICS, INC.

432 Sand Shore Rd., Unit 1
(07840)
**Phone—(908) 684-5802**
Fax—(908) 684-5803
www.multimodefo.com
Email—sales@multimodefo.com
Pres., CFO—Roger Berkowitz
SIC—3357; *Fiber-optic cables,
including fiber optic bundles,
collimators, fiber optic vacuum
feedthroughs & raw optical fiber*
Employs—8; Estab.—1997
4,000 sq ft site, Distrib.—Intl.
Privately owned sub-S corp.

GEOGRAPHICAL

## Hackettstown—(cont.)

**NEW ENTRY**
**MY PRIVATE LABEL, LLC**
112 East Ave., Ste. 5 (07840)
**Phone—(908) 441-2375**
www.myprivatelabel.com
Owner—John Salvia
SIC—2759; *Custom label printing*
Employs—5; Estab.—2000
Sales—$500,000-$1Mil (est)
Distrib.—National
Limited Liability Company

**NATIONAL ENVIRONMENTAL SERVICES CO.**
Div. of National Environmental
Service Co.
700 Grand Ave. (07840)
**Phone—(908) 813-1195**
National—(800) 237-3878
Fax—(908) 813-1124
www.drdust.com
Email—info@drdust.com
CFO—Paul Kestner
V-P., Prodn.—Peter Foley
SIC—3532; *High-pressure water
spray dust control systems for
the mining industry*
Employs—6; Estab.—1989
Sales—$1.5Mil-$2Mil
5,000 sq ft site, Distrib.—Intl.
Privately owned corporation
Parent co.—National
Environmental Service Co.,
Mendham, NJ
Phone—(973) 543-4586
See Parent Co. Section for full profile.

**OMNITEK, INC.**
20 Newburgh Rd. (07840)
**Phone—(908) 852-8500**
Fax—(908) 852-8507
www.omnitek-usa.com
Pres.—Forrest Vander Vliet
IT & Prodn. Mgr.—James Momary
SIC—3821; NAICS—339111;
*Organic & inorganic
photoconductors*
Employs—12; Estab.—1978
30,000 sq ft site, Distrib.—National
Privately owned corporation

**PT OF VU, LLC**
52 Edinborough Ct. (07840)
**Phone—(908) 979-1360**
Fax—(908) 979-1361
www.coldemar.com
Email—info@coldemar.com
Ptnr.—Louis Strauss
Ptnr.—Lisa Strauss
SIC—3199; *Natural sea (Tilapia
fish) leather wallets & credit &
debit card & smart phone cases*
Employs—5; Estab.—2005
Sales—$500,000-$1Mil
Distrib.—Intl.
Limited Liability Company
AKA: Col De Mar

**QUINCAS CORP.**
112 East Ave., Unit 7-A (07840)
**Phone—(908) 850-3914**
www.quincas.com
Email—quincas@verizon.net
Pres.—Bill DeMarco
SIC—3599; *CNC & general
machining job shop, including
custom prototypes & production*
Employs—3; Estab.—2003
Sales—under $500,000
2,500 sq ft site, Distrib.—Local
Privately owned sub-S corp.

**ROLLON CORP.**
101 Bilby Rd., Ste. B *(07840)*
**Phone—(973) 300-5492**
National—(877) 976-5566
Fax—(908) 852-2714
www.rolloncorp.com
Email—info@rolloncorp.com
Cont.—Shelly Connolly
Mng. Dir.—Rick Wood

SIC—3562; *Linear bearings,
actuators & linear motion
products assembly; Brand
name—Compact Rail; Easy Rail;
ActuatorLine; Telescopic Rail*
Employs—25; Estab.—1997
Sales—$8Mil-$9.5Mil
22,500 sq ft site, Distrib.—National
Privately owned corporation
ISO rating—9001

**RUDOLPH RESEARCH ANALYTICAL**
55 Newburgh Rd. (07840)
**Phone—(973) 584-1558**
Fax—(973) 584-5440
www.rudolphresearch.com
Email—info@rudolphresearch.com
Pres., Mktg. Mgr.—Richard C.
Spainer
V-P., IT—Robert Taggart
Hum. Res. Mgr.—Elizabeth Mintz
Sales Coord.—Kathy Green
SIC—3826; NAICS—334516;
*Automatic polarimeters,
refractometers & density meters
for the pharmaceutical, sugar,
food, flavor & fragrance,
chemical, beverage &
petrochemical industries; Brand
name—Autopol; TempTrol*
Employs—55; Estab.—1996
Sales—$11Mil-$25Mil
25,000 sq ft site, Distrib.—Intl.
Privately owned corporation

**S & W CUSTOM SCREEN PRINTING**
147 Main St. (07840)
**Phone—(908) 852-4808**
Pres., GM—Justin Weiss
SIC—2396; *T-shirt screen printing*
Employs—5; Estab.—1999
Sales—under $500,000
Distrib.—Local

**S.S.P. MANUFACTURING, INC.**
83 Spring Ln. (07840)
**Phone—(908) 852-3125**
Fax—(908) 852-3425
www.sspseals.com
Email—rrom@sspseals.com
Pres., Sales Mgr.—Ray Romanick
V-P., Hum. Res. & IT Mgr.—Kathy
Fitzpatrick
SIC—3089; 3053; NAICS—
339991; *CNC lathe-cut custom
plastic goods & molded parts,
including PTFE, HPU & oil seals
& water-cut gaskets*
Employs—9; Estab.—1995

**SMR RESEARCH CORP.**
300 Valentine St. (07840)
**Phone—(908) 852-7677**
Fax—(908) 852-6884
www.smrresearch.com
Email—marie.sheard@
smrresearch.com
Pres.—Stuart Feldsein
Admn. Mgr.—Marie Sheard
SIC—2741; *Research study
publishing, including home
equity, mortgage, life insurance
& credit risk/collections studies*
Employs—10
Sales—$500,000-$1Mil
Distrib.—National
Privately owned sub-S corp.

**TCS TECHNOLOGIES, INC.**
430 Sand Shore Rd., Unit 1
(07840)
**Phone—(908) 852-7555**
Fax—(908) 852-7216
www.tcsuv.com
Email—sales@tcsuv.com
Pres.—Gerard Fitzgerald
Plt. Mgr.—Pat Ward
Engrg. Mgr.—Jason Fitzgerald
SIC—3641; NAICS—335110;
*Ultraviolet lamps for digital inkjet
& wide-format UV printers*
Employs—12; Estab.—1976
5,100 sq ft site, Distrib.—Intl.
Privately owned sub-S corp.

**TDI POWER**
36 Newburgh Rd. (07840)
**Phone—(908) 850-5088**
Fax—(908) 850-0540
www.tdipower.com
Email—heather.maguire@
tdipower.com
CEO—James Feely
IT Mgr.—John Schmidt
Hum. Res. Mgr.—Janet Ennis
Mktg. Comms. Mgr.—Heather
Maguire
Prod. Safety Mgr.—Robert Stewart
SIC—3674; NAICS—334413; *High
technology power conversion
products, including DC & AC
power systems, power supplies,
rectifiers, converters &
accessory equipment*
Employs—225; Estab.—1960
150,000 sq ft site, Distrib.—Intl.
Privately owned corporation
AKA: Transistors Devices

**THOMAS & BETTS CORP.,
ELASTIMOLD DIV.**
Div. of Thomas & Betts Corp.
1 Esna Pk. (07840)
**Phone—(908) 852-1122**
Fax—(908) 813-2163
www.tnb.com
Email—media@tnb.com
GM—Allan Bordstrom
SIC—3643; NAICS—335931;
*High-voltage underground
connectors*
Employs—300; Estab.—1996
Distrib.—Intl.
Publicly owned corporation
Parent co.—Thomas & Betts
Corp., Memphis, TN
Phone—(901) 252-5000
See Parent Co. Section for full profile.

**WOERNER MACHINE & TOOL CO.**
700 Grand Ave., Bldg. 7 (07840)
Mail addr: 76 N. Mount Lebanon,
Port Murray (07865)
**Phone—(908) 979-0042**
Fax—(908) 979-0056
Pres., Fin., MIS & R & D Mgr.—
Edgar W. Woerner
SIC—3534; NAICS—333921;
*Elevator & escalator parts*
Employs—2; Estab.—1946
Sales—under $500,000
3,750 sq ft site, Distrib.—Local
Privately owned corporation

**WOODTEC, INC.**
300 Stiger St. (07840)
**Phone—(908) 979-0180**
Fax—(908) 979-0181
Pres.—John Marra
V-P., Opers.—Paul Wzorek
SIC—2431; NAICS—321900;
*Millwork*
Employs—7; Estab.—1991
Sales—$500,000-$1Mil
4,000 sq ft site, Distrib.—Regional
Privately owned corporation

## Haddon Heights
(Camden—S.W.)

**DEL BUONO BAKING CO.**
319 Black Horse Pike (08035)
**Phone—(856) 546-9585**
www.delbuonobaking.com
Pres.—Tom Witman
Manager—Dori Rogers
SIC—2051; NAICS—311812;
*Bakery products*
Employs—25; Estab.—1937
Sales—under $500,000
Distrib.—Local
Privately owned corporation

**SENSONICS, INC.**
125 White Horse Pike, P.O. Box
112 (08035)
**Phone—(800) 547-8838**
Fax—(856) 547-5665
www.sensonics.com
Email—sales@sensonics.com
Pres., CEO—Richard Doty
Acctg. Mgr.—Elise Dinetz
SIC—2835; *Corporate
headquarters & quantitative
human olfactory sense test strips
to assess smell & taste (mfg.
subcontracted)*
Employs—9; Estab.—1982
Distrib.—Intl.
Privately owned corporation

## Haddon Township
(Camden—S.W.)

**EXPRESS IT, INC.**
61 Haddon Ave. (08108)
**Phone—(856) 854-1888**
www.expressitsite.com
Email—expressitnj@comcast.net
Pres.—Steve Jones
SIC—2759; NAICS—323100;
*Commercial printing*
Employs—4; Estab.—1991
Sales—under $500,000
Distrib.—Local
Privately owned corporation

## Haddonfield
(Camden—S.W.)

**A TASTE OF OLIVE, LLC**
106 Kings Hwy. E., Ste. A (08033)
**Phone—(856) 795-0043**
www.atasteofolive.com
Email—contact@atasteofolive.com
Manager—Fabio Auguadro
Sales Assoc.—Morgan Leone
SIC—2079; 2099; *Olive oils &
vinegars*
Employs—10
Distrib.—Local
Limited Liability Company
Parent co.—A Taste Of Olive, LLC,
West Chester, PA
Phone—(610) 429-0292
See Parent Co. Section for full profile.

**NEW ENTRY**
**AMPHIBIAN PRESS, LLC**
309 Hutchinson Ave. (08033)
**Phone—(856) 547-3022**
Owner—Margaret Westermaier
SIC—2731; *Chapbook publishing*
Employs—1
Sales—under $500,000
Distrib.—Local
Limited Liability Company

**DORADO SYSTEMS, LLC**
8 Kings Hwy. E. (08033)
**Phone—(856) 354-0048**
www.doradosystems.com
Email—info@doradosystems.com
Dir.—Michael Matt
SIC—7373; *Healthcare EDI
system integration, including
VANs*
Employs—4
Limited Liability Company

**OUR NAME IS MUD**
Div. of Enesco, LLC
15 Potter St., Ste. 1 (08033)
**Phone—(856) 375-2098**
National—(877) 683-7867
www.ournameismud.com
Email—info@ournameismud.com
Pres.—Kip Veasey

## Haddonfield—(cont.)

SIC—3269; NAICS—327112;
*Pottery products*
Employs—1; Estab.—1997
Sales—under $500,000 (est)
Distrib.—National
Limited Liability Company
AKA: Our Name Is Mud.com
Parent co.—Enesco, LLC, Itasca,
IL
Phone—(630) 875-5300
See Parent Co. Section for full profile.

### PROFESSIONAL PRINTING SERVICES

116 N. Haddon Ave. (08033)
**Phone—(856) 429-8644**
Fax—(856) 429-8522
Email—proprinting@comcast.net
Owner & Pres.—Joe McElroy
SIC—2752; NAICS—323100;
*Instant printing*
Employs—3; Estab.—1992
Sales—under $500,000
1,000 sq ft site, Distrib.—Local
Privately owned sub-S corp.

### REVIVA LABS, INC.

705 Hopkins Rd. (08033)
**Phone—(856) 428-3885**
Fax—(856) 429-0767
www.revivalabs.com
Email—stephen.strassler@
revivalabs.com
Pres.—Stephen Strassler
Cont.—Tracey Tetreault
Adv. Mgr.—Casey McCormick
Adv. Mgr.—John Levins
Hum. Res. Mgr.—Shirley Levins
SIC—2844; NAICS—325600; *Skin care products; Brand name—Aesthetics Unique; InterCell; Reviva Labs*
Employs—32; Estab.—1973
Sales—$7Mil
10,000 sq ft site, Distrib.—Intl.
Privately owned corporation

NEW ENTRY
### ROSS & PERRY, INC.

203 Chews Landing Rd. (08033)
**Phone—(856) 429-5752**
Fax—(856) 427-6136
www.rossperry.com
Manager—George Ross Fisher
SIC—2731; *Book publishing*
Employs—3; Estab.—2004
Sales—$500,000
4,000 sq ft site, Distrib.—Intl.
Privately owned corporation

### VETERANO WARD COMMERCIAL PRINTING

301 Bradshaw Ave. (08033)
**Phone—(856) 429-5460**
Fax—(856) 429-5490
Email—fward@lvlrealtors.com
Owner—Frank Ward
SIC—2752; 2791; NAICS—
323122; *Offset printing & typesetting*
Employs—4; Estab.—1987
Sales—under $500,000
Distrib.—Regional
Sole ownership

## Hainesport

(Burlington—S.E.)

### ALTERNATIVE AIR & STORE FIXTURES

3-C Mary Way (08036-2729)
**Phone—(609) 261-5870**
Fax—(609) 261-5531
www.aafixtures.com
Email—aainfo@aafixtures.com
Ptnr.—James Lunstead
Ptnr.—Michael Banks

SIC—3585; 2541; 2542; 3993;
*Refrigerated & dry custom & standard display cases & store fixtures for the food display industry*
Employs—6; Estab.—1994
Sales—$1Mil-$2.5Mil
Distrib.—Intl.
Limited Liability Company
AKA: alternative air llc

### B & L INDUSTRIAL SERVICES, INC.

700 Park Ave., Unit 7 (08036)
Mail addr: P.O. Box 98, Burlington
(08016)
**Phone—(609) 386-9500**
Fax—(609) 386-1190
Pres.—Richard Lodwig
Off. Mgr.—Sue McMullen
SIC—3312; 3564; NAICS—
333400; *Steel fabrication, rebuilt fans & blowers & mechanical maintenance*
Employs—4; Estab.—1971
Sales—$1Mil-$2.5Mil
20,000 sq ft site, Distrib.—
Regional
Privately owned corporation

### COX INDUSTRIES

Div. of Cox Industries, Inc.
1517 Route 38 W., P.O. Box 507
(08036)
**Phone—(609) 267-4700**
Fax—(609) 267-8974
www.coxwood.com
Email—ptaylor@coxwood.com
Plt. Mgr.—Phil Taylor
Off. Supv.—Carol Pallante
SIC—2491; NAICS—321114;
*Wood preservation*
Employs—10; Estab.—1960
Company-wide: 400
Sales—$2.5Mil-$5Mil (est)
Distrib.—Regional
Privately owned corporation
Parent co.—Cox Industries, Inc.,
Orangeburg, SC
Phone—(803) 534-7467
See Parent Co. Section for full profile.

### CRYOVATION, LLC

9-B Mary Way (08036)
**Phone—(609) 914-4792**
Fax—(239) 337-2796
www.cryovation.com
Email—info@cryovation.com
Pres.—Ric Boyd
Dir., Mktg.—Chelsea D'Ariano
Pur. Mgr.—Rachel Boyd
Design & Engrg. Mgr.—Nate Boyd
SIC—3569; *Gas cylinder filling systems*
Employs—25; Estab.—2000
Sales—under $500,000
Distrib.—Intl.
Limited Liability Company

NEW ENTRY
### FRINTON LABORATORIES, INC.

4204 Sylon Blvd. (08036)
**Phone—(856) 722-7037**
Fax—(856) 439-1977
www.frinton.com
Email—sales@frinton.com
Pres.—George Inglessis
Dir., Sales—Jason Inglessis
SIC—2834; *Pharmaceuticals*
Employs—4; Estab.—1962
Sales—under $500,000
Distrib.—Intl.
Privately owned corporation

### HADDON FENCE CO., INC.

1460 Route 38 (08036)
**Phone—(609) 261-1286**
www.haddonfence.com
Pres.—Roger Miller
Off. Mgr.—Joyce Miller

SIC—2499; *Wooden fencing*
Employs—6; Estab.—1985
Sales—under $500,000
Distrib.—Local
Privately owned corporation

### HAINESPORT TOOL & MAINTENANCE

1924 Ark Rd. *(08036)*
**Phone—(609) 261-0016**
Fax—(609) 261-2105
www.hainesporttool.com
Email—rich@hainesporttool.com
Owner & Pres.—Gary Zwick
Manager—Richard Parziale
SIC—3542; 3531; NAICS—
333513; *Rebuilt machine tools & earth moving & foundry equipment, including maintenance & repair*
Employs—18; Estab.—1961
Sales—$1Mil-$2.5Mil
12,000 sq ft site, Distrib.—Intl.
Privately owned corporation

### †INDEPENDENT METAL SALES, INC.

Park & Delaware Aves.,
Hainesport Industrial Pk., P.O.
Box 17 (08036)
**Phone—(609) 261-8090**
Fax—(609) 261-7319
www.independentmetalsales.com
Email—info@
independentmetalsales.com
Pres.—Edward Kligerman
Off. Mgr.—Coleen Spector
SIC—5051; *Steel service center*
Employs—17; Estab.—1992
Distrib.—Local
Privately owned corporation
ISO rating—9001:2000

### MINUTEMAN PRESS

1299 Route 38, Ste. 2 (08036)
**Phone—(609) 261-1024**
Fax—(609) 261-2625
www.mmphport.com
Email—csr@mmphport.com
Pres. & Cust. Serv. Rep.—Frank
Bittner
SIC—2752; 2791; NAICS—
323122; *Offset printing & graphic design*
Employs—7; Estab.—1990
Sales—$500,000-$1Mil
3,000 sq ft site, Distrib.—National
Privately owned corporation

### NTH DEGREE PRODUCTS, LLC

404 Laurel Ridge Rd. (08036)
**Phone—(609) 518-9447**
Fax—(609) 518-9445
www.nthdegreeproducts.com
Email—nthdegreeproducts@
yahoo.com
CEO—Donald G. Lopata
SIC—3255; 3297; 3259; 3299;
NAICS—327124; *High-temperature ceramic refractories for pottery, china, dinnerware, military, electronics, industrial & glass applications, including refractory kiln furniture, alumina, AZS, coriderite & bricks*
Employs—2; Estab.—2000
Sales—$500,000-$1.5Mil
Distrib.—Intl.
Privately owned corporation
ISO rating—9001

### PERRY PRODUCTS CORP.

25 Hainesport-Mount Laurel Rd.
(08036)
**Phone—(609) 267-1600**
(609) 288-4052
Fax—(609) 267-8724
www.perryvidex.com
Email—jcoia@perryvidex.com
Pres.—Gregg P. Epstein
V-P., Sales—John Coia
V-P., Opers.—Robert Parrish

SIC—3443; *Heat exchangers, including pressure vessels & retubing of heat exchangers*
Employs—15; Estab.—1932
Sales—$6Mil-$8Mil
15,000 sq ft site, Distrib.—Intl.
Privately owned partnership

### SIGN-A-RAMA

1459 Highway 38, P.O. Box 360
(08036)
**Phone—(609) 702-1444**
National—(800) 379-3213
Fax—(609) 702-0300
www.signaramahainesport.com
Email—sarhainesport@comcast.net
Owner—Gary Kuffer
Prodn. Mgr.—C. Morales
Graphic Artist—Kristine Kuffer
SIC—3993; 3089; 2759; 2542;
NAICS—323100; *Interior & exterior, ADA & project signs, vehicle lettering, digital printing & trade show displays*
Employs—4; Estab.—1996
Sales—under $500,000
3,000 sq ft site, Distrib.—Local
Limited Liability Company

### SOLV-TEC, INC.

3860 Sylon Blvd. (08036)
**Phone—(609) 261-4242**
National—(888) 254-0150
Fax—(609) 261-4498
www.solv-tec.com
Pres.—Patrick O'Brien
SIC—2899; *Leak repair sealant additives for automotive antifreeze & coolants*
Employs—8; Estab.—2008
Sales—$500,000-$1Mil
Distrib.—Intl.
Privately owned corporation

### UNITED NATIONAL MACHINE TOOL, INC.

2404 Sylon Blvd., P.O. Box 608
(08036)
**Phone—(609) 265-2269**
Fax—(609) 265-3684
Email—unmt@verizon.net
Pres.—Robert Donahue
Off. Mgr.—Maureen Donahue
Shpg. Mgr.—Alex Donahue
SIC—3544; 3599; NAICS—
333500; *Rotary tooling*
Employs—14; Estab.—1998
18,000 sq ft site, Distrib.—Intl.
Privately owned corporation

## Haledon

(Passaic—N.E.)

### APPAREL GROUP AMERICA, INC.

250 Belmont Ave. (07508)
**Phone—(973) 942-6800**
Fax—(973) 942-0600
www.apparelgroup.net
Email—eguerrero@
apparelgroup.org
Pres.—Vincent Musarra
IT Mgr.—Steven Musarra
Hum. Res. Mgr.—Damarys
Gonzalez
SIC—2396; 3089; *Apparel screen printing & packaging*
Employs—120; Estab.—1997
Distrib.—Local
Privately owned corporation

### E & W TEXTILE PROCESSORS, INC.

293 Morrissee Ave. (07508)
**Phone—(973) 942-8718**
Fax—(973) 942-5554
Pres., Cont.—Joseph Pizzoli
SIC—2261; NAICS—313311;
*Textile dyeing*
Employs—30; Estab.—1992
Varies: 30-40
Distrib.—Regional
Privately owned corporation

GEOGRAPHICAL

## Haledon—(cont.)

**HALEDON AUTO PARTS**
269 Haledon Ave. (07508)
**Phone—(973) 595-8200**
Fax—(973) 790-9224
www.haledonautoparts.com
Email—hap4parts@hotmail.com
Pres., Hum. Res. & IT Mgr.—
  Howard T. Wilson
V-P.—Steve Vanderwerf
GM—Carl Gugliotta
Off. Mgr.—Gisela Weber
SIC—3599; 3714; 5013; 5014;
  *Automotive machine shop &
  distributor of automotive parts*
Employs—23; Estab.—1936
Sales—$1Mil-$2.5Mil
6,600 sq ft site, Distrib.—Local
Privately owned sub-S corp.

NEW ENTRY
**INTEGRATED MICRO SYSTEMS, INC.**
74 Lee Ave. (07508)
**Phone—(973) 904-9700**
Fax—(973) 904-0401
www.imicrosys.com
Pres.—Jeffery Durante
SIC—7373; *Computer network
  system integration, including
  LANs & WANs*
Employs—6
Distrib.—Local
Privately owned corporation

**JP ROTELLA CO., INC.**
20 E. Barbour St. (07508)
Mail addr: P.O. Box 8438, Haledon
  (07538-0438)
**Phone—(973) 942-2559**
Fax—(973) 942-5135
Email—jprotellaco@optimum.net
Pres.—John Rotella, Jr.
Off. Mgr.—Adrienne Schuler
SIC—3679; 3469; *Electronic
  components, including
  subassemblies, precision spot
  welding, short-run metal
  stampings, lapping & wire form
  straight & headed pins*
Employs—7; Estab.—1960
Sales—$500,000-$1Mil
3,600 sq ft site, Distrib.—National
Sole ownership

**M R L MFG. CORP.**
59 Lee Ave., P.O. Box 8440
  (07508)
**Phone—(973) 790-1744**
Fax—(973) 790-1414
www.mrlmfg.com
Email—mrlmfg@aol.com
Pres.—John De Napoli
Sales & Mktg. Mgr.—David
  Morales
Fin. Mgr. & Bookkeeper—
  Elizabeth Gordon
SIC—3452; NAICS—332722;
  *Commercial nuts*
Employs—17; Estab.—1977
19,500 sq ft site, Distrib.—National
Privately owned corporation

**MINI FROST FOODS CORP.**
1237 Belmont Ave. (07508)
**Phone—(973) 427-4258**
National—(800) 835-6464
Fax—(973) 427-0973
www.minifrostfoods.com
Email—minifrostfoods@verizon.net
Pres.—Katherine Kelly
SIC—2053; NAICS—311813;
  *Frozen fruit-filled pastries*
Employs—15; Estab.—1975
Sales—$1Mil-$2.5Mil
Distrib.—Local
Privately owned corporation

NEW ENTRY
**PRO MACHINE CO.**
5 Sicomac Rd. (07508)
**Phone—(973) 855-9935**
Fax—(973) 238-0019
www.promachinecompany.com
Email—agpromachine@yahoo.com
Owner—Eddie Demetro
IT Mgr.—Ed Green
SIC—3566; 3561; 3545; 3599;
  *Rebuilt gear boxes, pumps &
  shear blades & precision
  machining job shop*
Employs—18; Estab.—1999
Sales—$2.5Mil-$5Mil (est)
Distrib.—Regional
Privately owned corporation

**STONE INDUSTRIES, INC.**
400-402 Central Ave. (07508)
Mail addr: P.O. Box 8310, Haledon
  (07538-8310)
**Phone—(973) 595-6250**
        (973) 595-6130
Fax—(973) 595-7087
www.braenstone.com
Email—info@braenstone.com
Chairwoman & CEO—Janet Braen
Pres.—Scott Braen
CFO—Rob Kranznoski
V-P., Sales & Mktg.—Thomas
  Lynch
V-P., Hum. Res.—Samantha Braen
IT Mgr.—Ray Scott
SIC—2951; NAICS—324121;
  *Corporate headquarters &
  crushed stone, sand, asphalt &
  paving, landscape & mason
  supplies*
Employs—150; Estab.—1904
Sales—$5Mil-$10Mil (est)
Distrib.—Regional
Privately owned sub-S corp.

---

## Hamburg
(Sussex—N.W.)

**ABATE FENCE, INC.**
3619 Route 23 (07419)
**Phone—(973) 827-4167**
Fax—(973) 827-4571
www.abatefence.com
Email—fencehunter@aol.com
Pres.—Dominick Rotolo
SIC—2499; 3496; *Wooden, wire,
  aluminum & PVC fences*
Employs—5; Estab.—1978
Sales—under $500,000
Distrib.—Local
Privately owned corporation

**ACCURATE FORMING**
24 Ames Blvd. (07419)
**Phone—(973) 827-7155**
Fax—(973) 827-3678
www.accurateforming.com
Email—info@accurateforming.com
Pres.—Chuck Segar
Pur. Mgr.—Martina Tuevas
Hum. Res. Mgr.—Sandy Caravela
Cust. Serv. Mgr.—Eileen
  Stevenfield
SIC—3499; *Metal stampings*
Employs—50; Estab.—1967
70,000 sq ft site, Distrib.—National
Privately owned corporation

**AMES RUBBER CORP.**
19 Ames Blvd. (07419)
**Phone—(973) 827-9101**
Fax—(973) 827-8893
www.theamescorp.com
Email—info@amesrubber.com
Pres., CEO—Charles Roberts
V-P., CFO—William Kovach
V-P., Quality—James E. Sistler, Jr.
V-P., Matls. & Prod. Dev.—Chris
  del Rosario
Sales Mgr., Inside—Derek
  Eversdyke
Hum. Res. Mgr.—Karen Hartman
Accts. Payable Mgr.—Linda Donat

Payroll Supv.—Louise McChesney
SIC—3069; *Molded & non-
  molded rubber products for the
  office automation, aerospace,
  aircraft, alternative energy,
  industrial & automotive
  industries; Brand name—
  AmesSeal*
Employs—110; Estab.—1949
Sales—$20Mil-$25Mil
175,000 sq ft site, Distrib.—Intl.
Privately owned corporation
ISO rating—AS9100

**CAVA WINERY & VINEYARD, INC.**
3619 State Route 94 (07419-9651)
**Phone—(973) 823-9463**
Fax—(973) 300-4816
www.cavawinery.com
Email—info@cavawinery.com
CEO—Anthony Riccio
CFO & COO—Larry Ciccarelli
Hospitality Mgr.—Nikki Smithhart
SIC—2084; *Wines; Brand name—
  Vini di Riccio; Ceci Bella;
  Skylands; Cava*
Employs—30; Estab.—2006
Sales—$1Mil-$2.5Mil
Distrib.—Local
Privately owned sub-S corp.

**EASTERN CONCRETE MATERIALS,
INC.**
3620 Route 23 N. (07419)
**Phone—(973) 827-7625**
National—(888) 913-7625
Fax—(973) 827-0652
www.us-concrete.com
Email—webmaster@us-
  concrete.com
V-P.—David Besaw
Sales Mgr.—Gregg Wall
Dispatcher—Lynn Kemenczy
SIC—1429; 1423; NAICS—
  212319; *Crushed stone & granite
  quarrying*
Employs—20; Estab.—2002
Sales—$500,000-$1Mil
Distrib.—Regional
Publicly owned corporation
AKA: Hamburg Stone Quarry
Parent co.—Eastern Concrete
  Materials, Inc., Elmwood Park,
  NJ
  Phone—(201) 797-7979
  See Parent Co. Section for full profile.

**TRILLIUM, INC.**
3627 Route 23 S. (07419)
**Phone—(973) 827-1661**
National—(888) 742-7202
Fax—(973) 827-8883
www.trilliumus.com
Email—info@unitedvacuum.com
Pres.—Al Citarella
SIC—3563; NAICS—333912;
  *Industrial rotary piston vacuum
  pumps & lobe blowers*
Employs—20
Limited Liability Company
AKA: United Vacuum Pumps, Inc.

**WANTAGE STONE, LLC**
80 State Route 23 (07419)
**Phone—(973) 702-7866**
Fax—(973) 702-7877
Cont.—Christina Fama
Hum. Res. Mgr.—Matt Maxer
Weighmaster—Tori Waite
SIC—1499; *Dolomite dimension
  quarrying*
Employs—6
Distrib.—Local
Limited Liability Company

**WEB-COTE INDUSTRIES, INC.**
141 Wheatsworth Rd., P.O. Box
  120 (07419)
**Phone—(973) 827-2299**
Fax—(973) 827-0069
www.web-cote.com
Pres.—James Cowen
Off. Mgr.—Pat Deboon
Off. Admn.—Susan Masciaielli

SIC—2675; NAICS—322200;
  *Paper label tapes*
Employs—20; Estab.—2006
Distrib.—National
Privately owned corporation

**WILCOX PRESS**
6 Main St. (07419)
**Phone—(973) 827-7474**
Fax—(973) 827-5373
Owner—Jody Palmasano
SIC—2759; NAICS—323100;
  *Commercial printing*
Employs—4; Estab.—1930
Sales—$500,000-$1Mil
Distrib.—Local
Sole ownership

---

## Hamilton
(Mercer—N.E.)

**ARMSTRONG INDUSTRIAL HOSE
PRODUCTS, LLC**
1400 E. State St. (08609)
**Phone—(609) 989-5161**
Fax—(609) 989-5165
www.armstrongindustrialhose.com
Email—salesinfo@
  armstrongindustrialhose.com
Pres., CEO—Brian Logue
Plt. Mgr.—Mike J. Logue
Cust. Serv. Mgr.—Lori Costelow
SIC—3052; 3069; NAICS—
  326220; *Rubber & plastic tubing
  & hose*
Employs—14; Estab.—1947
60,000 sq ft site, Distrib.—National
Limited Liability Company

NEW ENTRY
**BROWN & CO., INC., BILL**
275 Whitehead Rd. (08619)
**Phone—(609) 396-9191**
National—(800) 221-0519
Fax—(609) 586-1654
www.billbrowninc.com
Email—info@billbrowninc.com
Off. Mgr.—Ken Bruce
SIC—2396; 2759; *T-shirt & textile
  & promotional item screen
  printing, including drinkware &
  pens*
Employs—2
Sales—under $500,000 (est)
Privately owned corporation

†**CAOLA & CO.**
2 Crossroads Dr., P.O. Box 8772
  (08691)
**Phone—(609) 890-7331**
        (800) 792-8626
Fax—(609) 588-5247
www.caolacompany.com
Email—kcaola@caolacompany.com
CEO—John Caola
SIC—5072; 5063; 5065;
  *Wholesaler of locks & electronic
  security systems & card access,
  including CCTV, biometrics,
  replacement doors, hardware &
  automatic door closers; Brand
  name—Schlage; Rixson; Gantz;
  Honeywell; Kantech; HID; Yale;
  Locknetics; Ilco; Corbin/
  Russwin; Adamsrite; Master;
  Detex; AlarmLock; HES;
  Kwickset Galaxy; Bosch; Ilco
  Kaba; Unitek; Pelco; Corbin
  Russwin; Kwikse; CBC Cameras*
Employs—18; Estab.—1913
28,000 sq ft site, Distrib.—Intl.
Privately owned corporation

**CAPITOL CITY ALUMINUM
PRODUCTS**
407 Rutgers Ave. (08619)
**Phone—(609) 587-3653**
Fax—(609) 587-3655
www.capitolcityaluminum.com
Email—capitolcityalum@gmail.com
Pres.—Louis Battaglia

## Hamilton—(cont.)

SIC—3442; 2591; 2394; 3444;
NAICS—332321; *Canvas &
aluminum awnings & entries,
storefronts, blinds, commercial
windows, doors & canopies,
including commercial &
residential construction*
Employs—5; Estab.—1946
Sales—under $2Mil
Distrib.—Local
Privately owned corporation
AKA: Battaglia Contracting, Louis

**CARPENTER EMERGENCY
LIGHTING, INC.**
2 Marlen Dr. (08691)
**Phone—(609) 689-3090**
National—(888) 884-2270
Fax—(609) 689-3091
www.carpenterlighting.com
Email—sales@
carpenterlighting.com
Owner—Avinash C. Diwan
Sales Mgr., Natl.—Philip Salvatore
SIC—3648; 3993; NAICS—
335129; *Emergency lighting &
exit signs; Brand name—
Carpenter Emergency Lighting;
Atek*
Employs—30; Estab.—1996
Distrib.—National
Limited Liability Company
Also see: East-West Service Co.,
Inc., same loc.

**†CERTIFIED STEEL CO.**
Div. of Certified Steel Company
199 Whitehead Rd. (08619)
**Phone—(609) 890-7000**
Fax—(609) 890-9904
www.certifiedsteel.com
Email—info@certifiedsteel.com
CFO—Dante Germano
V.-P., Opers.—Tim Boyd
V.-P., Flat Rolled Prods.—Jerry
Katelhon
SIC—5051; *Full-line steel service
center, including hot rolled
carbon & structural steel, plates,
coils, sheets & merchant bars,
plate burning, shearing & saw
cutting; Brand name—Herr Voss
Leveling Line*
Employs—82; Estab.—1989
330,000 sq ft site, Distrib.—
Regional
Sole ownership
Parent co.—Certified Steel
Company, Lawrenceville, NJ
Phone—(609) 396-7600
See Parent Co. Section for full profile.

**EAST-WEST SERVICE CO., INC.**
2 Marlen Dr. (08691)
**Phone—(609) 631-9000**
Fax—(609) 689-3091
www.carpenterlighting.com
Email—sales@
carpenterlighting.com
Owner—Avinash C. Diwan
Off. Mgr.—Cindy Verdi
SIC—3993; 3648; 3643; NAICS—
335129; *Exit signs, emergency
lights & power strips*
Employs—17; Estab.—1977
6,000 sq ft site, Distrib.—National
Privately owned corporation
Also see: Carpenter Emergency
Lighting, Inc., same loc.

**GENESIS BIOTECHNOLOGY GROUP
(H Q)**
1000 Waterview Dr. (08691)
**Phone—(609) 786-2800**
National—(877) 269-0090
Fax—(609) 570-1050
www.genesisbiotech.org
CEO—Eli Mordechai
Chief Opers. Officer—Martin E.
Adelson
V.-P., Corp. Dev. & Opers.—
Michael Gale

V.-P., Sales—Valerie Tharnish
Dir., IT—Janet Cohen
Dir., Acctg. & Fin.—Joseph
Donovan
Dir., Hum. Res.—Christin Knox
SIC—3089; *Company
headquarters; disposable plastic
injection-molded components for
medical research, clinical
diagnostic & biotech
environments, including
centrifuge tubes & strip caps*
Employs—950
Sales—$100Mil-$250Mil (est)
120,000 sq ft site, Distrib.—
National
Privately owned corporation

**HORIZON SIGN CO.**
340 Patterson Ave., Ste. C (08610)
Mail addr: P.O. Box 3394, Trenton
(08619-0394)
**Phone—(609) 586-0041**
National—(800) 520-7446
Email—horizonsignco@
optimum.net
Owner—Thomas R. Barbieri
SIC—3993; 3499; *Illuminated
interior & exterior signs, cast
metal plaques, dimensional
letters & vinyl graphics, including
service & installation*
Employs—1; Estab.—1976
Sales—under $500,000
1,950 sq ft site, Distrib.—Local
Sole ownership

**HOTFOIL-EHS, INC.**
2960 E. State Street Ext. (08619)
**Phone—(609) 588-0900**
Fax—(609) 588-8333
www.hotfoilehs.com
Email—dap@hotfoilehs.com
Pres.—Neville Richards
V.-P.—Matt Richards
GM—Mike Macomber
Mktg. Mgr.—Dean A. Prassas
Engrg. Mgr.—Bob Damiano
SIC—3567; 3444; 3548; 3612;
NAICS—333994; *Industrial
heating equipment, including
hopper heaters, heating
blankets, coal handling chutes,
furnaces, burners, resistor-
controlled welders, heavy-duty
transformers, equipment controls
& heat treatment equipment*
Employs—35; Estab.—1993
Sales—$5Mil-$10Mil
Distrib.—Intl.
Privately owned corporation

**HOUZER, INC.**
2605 Kuser Rd. (08691-1805)
**Phone—(609) 584-1900**
National—(800) 880-3639
Fax—(609) 584-1930
www.houzersink.com
Email—info@houzersink.com
Owner—Tyler Byun
SIC—3431; *Corporate
headquarters & stainless steel
kitchen & bathroom sinks (mfg.
done overseas); Brand name—
HOUZER®*
Employs—25; Estab.—1992
Sales—$10Mil-$50Mil
Distrib.—National
Sole ownership

**INTERNATIONAL PROCESS PLANTS**
17-A Marlen Dr. (08691)
**Phone—(609) 586-8004**
Fax—(609) 586-0002
www.ippe.com
Email—sales@ippe.com
Pres.—Ron Gale
Ex. V.-P.—Jan Gale
V.-P., Counsel—Harold Bogatz
Dir., Global Sales—Keith West
GM—Tony Chiarella

SIC—3585; 3443; *Refrigeration &
air conditioning equipment,
chillers, heat exchangers &
vapor recovery*
Employs—25; Estab.—1985
Sales—$1Mil-$5Mil
37,000 sq ft site, Distrib.—Intl.
Privately owned corporation

**INTERSTATE PANEL, LLC**
67 Benson Ave. (08610)
**Phone—(609) 586-4411**
Fax—(609) 586-4422
www.ultraseam.com
Email—melissa@interstatepanel.net
CEO—Donald Anderson
CFO—Mark Berube
COO—Jerry Turner
SIC—3444; *Metal roofing panels*
Employs—29; Estab.—2001
Distrib.—Local
Limited Liability Company

**KRAFTWORK CUSTOM DESIGN**
1837 S. Broad St. (08610)
**Phone—(609) 848-0578**
www.kraftwork.net
Email—info@kraftwork.net
Owner—Michael K. Sylvester
SIC—3993; 2394; 2396; 2395;
NAICS—314912; *Dimensional,
carved, gold, neon, channel
letter, vinyl, logo & vehicle signs,
commercial backlit & canvas
awnings, large-format digital
printing of forms, cards &
banners & screen printing &
embroidery of shirts, jackets &
hats*
Employs—4; Estab.—1984
Sales—under $500,000 (est)
Distrib.—Regional
Sole ownership

**LINEAR PHOTONICS, LLC**
3 Nami Ln., Ste. 7-C (08619)
**Phone—(609) 584-5747**
Fax—(609) 631-0177
www.linphotonics.com
Email—info@linphotonics.com
Pres.—Allen Katz
V.-P., Engrg. & Opers.—John
MacDonald
Mktg. Mgr.—Therese Ulrich
Hum. Res. Mgr.—Patricia Voral
Bus. Mgr.—Debbie Kamens
SIC—3671; 3679; NAICS—
334411; *Fiber-optic detectors,
receivers, photonics & electronic
equipment*
Employs—10; Estab.—2004
Sales—$1Mil-$2.5Mil (est)
Distrib.—Intl.
Limited Liability Company
Also see: Linearizer Technology,
Inc., same loc.

**LINEARIZER TECHNOLOGY, INC.**
3 Nami Ln., Ste. 9-C (08619-1285)
**Phone—(609) 584-8424**
Fax—(609) 631-0177
www.lintech.com
Email—info@lintech.com
Pres.—Allen Katz
V.-P., Prodn. & Qual.—Eugene
Hoffman
V.-P., Engrg.—Roger Dorval
Cont.—Michelle Rybinski
Mktg. Mgr.—Therese Ulrich
SIC—3663; NAICS—334220;
*Amplifier distortion control
modules for radio & satellite
communications; Brand name—
Linearizer; Distortion correction
solutions*
Employs—75; Estab.—1992
Sales—$10Mil-$25Mil
12,000 sq ft site, Distrib.—Intl.
Privately owned corporation
ISO rating—9001
Also see: Linear Photonics, LLC,
same loc.

**MEDICAL INDICATORS, INC.**
16 Thomas J. Rhodes Industrial
Dr. (08619)
**Phone—(609) 737-1600**
Fax—(609) 737-0588
www.medicalindicators.com
Email—customerservice@
medicalindicators.com
V.-P., GM—Paul Baker
SIC—3841; *Custom promotional
single-use, reusable & wearable
clinical thermometers; Brand
name—NexTemp Single-Use
Thermometers; NexTemp
Reusable Thermometers;
NexTemp Plus Rectal
Thermometer; NexTemp Ultra-
Extended Signal Thermometers;
TraxIt Wearable Thermometers;
TraxIt Children's Thermometers*
Employs—50; Estab.—1997
Sales—$6Mil-$10Mil
15,000 sq ft site, Distrib.—Intl.
Privately owned corporation
ISO rating—13485:2003

**MERLIN INDUSTRIES, INC.**
2904 E. State Street Ext. (08619)
**Phone—(609) 807-1000**
National—(800) 289-1836
Fax—(609) 807-1001
www.merlinindustries.com
Email—emailus@merlinind.com
Pres.—Andrew Maggion
SIC—3081; 3089; NAICS—
326113; *Vinyl pool covers, liners
& safety fences*
Employs—200; Estab.—1988
Distrib.—National
Privately owned corporation

**MILLNER KITCHENS, INC.**
200-B Whitehead Rd., Ste. 108
(08619)
**Phone—(609) 890-7300**
Fax—(609) 890-7301
www.millnerkitchens.com
Pres.—John Millner
SIC—2434; NAICS—337110;
*Wooden kitchen cabinets*
Employs—8
Sales—$500,000-$1Mil (est)
Distrib.—Local
Privately owned corporation

**MINUTEMAN PRESS, INC./WINDSOR
GRAPHICS**
2100 Nottingham Way (08619)
**Phone—(609) 586-3838**
(609) 586-8088
Fax—(609) 584-0274
www.gominutemanpress.com
Email—print@
gominutemanpress.com
Owner—Anthony Loffredo
SIC—2759; 2752; 3993; 2396;
NAICS—323100; *Offset, screen
& digital color printing of
letterheads, envelopes, business
cards, pocket folders, brochures,
flyers, newsletters, mailings,
pads, instruction sheets, signs,
banners, t-shirts & promotional
products*
Employs—4; Estab.—1994
Sales—under $500,000
2,200 sq ft site, Distrib.—Local
Privately owned corporation

**PRINCETEL, INC.**
2560 E. State Street Ext. *(08619)*
**Phone—(609) 588-8801**
(609) 895-9890
Fax—(609) 895-9552
www.princetel.com
Email—info@princetel.com
Pres.—Barry Zhang
Sales Mgr.—Brian Horsford

**GEOGRAPHICAL**

## Hamilton—(cont.)

SIC—3678; 3643; 3679; NAICS—334417; *Fiber-optic rotary joints, electrical sliprings & video/data MUX/DMUX fiber media converters for the geophysical, military, biomedical, wind energy, broadcasting, robotic & communications market*
Employs—40; Estab.—2000
Sales—$6Mil
41,500 sq ft site, Distrib.—Intl.
Privately owned corporation
ISO rating—9001

### PRINTWORX

2103 Whitehorse Mercerville Rd. (08619)
Phone—**(609) 586-3006**
Fax—(609) 586-6168
www.printworxnj.com
Email—inbox @ printworxnj.com
Owner—Carolyn D'Amico
SIC—2759; NAICS—323100; *Graphic design & blueprints, including wide-format color & instant printing*
Employs—4; Estab.—1982
Sales—under $500,000
2,200 sq ft site, Distrib.—Local
Limited Liability Company

### STERLING HOME PRODUCTS, INC.

127 U.S. Highway 206, Ste. 22 (08610)
Phone—**(609) 585-8941**
National—(800) 729-5960
Fax—(609) 585-0114
www.sterlinghomeproducts.com
Email—info @ sterlinghomeproducts.com
V-P., Fin., MIS & Opers.—Roger DeAngelis
V-P., Mktg.—Arthur DeAngelis
Off. Mgr.—Mary Ann DeAngelis
SIC—3596; 3873; NAICS—333997; *Bathroom, kitchen, parcel, postal & counting scales & timers; Brand name—Sterling*
Employs—4; Estab.—1976
Sales—$500,000-$1Mil (est)
Distrib.—Intl.
Privately owned corporation

### TEXTILE CREATIONS, INC. (H Q)

8-B S. Gold Dr. (08691)
Phone—**(609) 631-4433**
Fax—(609) 631-4434
www.textilecreations.com
Email—info @ textilecreations.com
Pres.—Jim Hankin
SIC—2269; NAICS—313300; *Corporate headquarters; cotton textile dyeing & finishing (mfg. done in China & India)*
Employs—10; Estab.—1990
Sales—under $500,000
Distrib.—Intl.
Privately owned corporation

### US LOGIC, LLC

2885 E. State Street Ext. (08619)
Phone—**(609) 530-0005**
Fax—(609) 528-2604
www.uslogic.com
Email—sales @ uslogic.net
Pres. & Member Mgr.—Seth Jackson
Cont.—Stacy Leigh
SIC—7373; *Computer network systems integration, including LANs, WANs & server consolidation & value-added reseller of data center level computer hardware & network systems components*
Employs—17; Estab.—2003
Distrib.—Intl.
Limited Liability Company
AKA: Legacy System

### VOXWARE, INC.

300 American Metro Blvd., Ste. 155 (08619)
Phone—**(609) 514-4100**
National—(877) 483-7239
Fax—(609) 514-4101
www.voxware.com
Email—sales @ voxware.com
Pres., CEO—Keith Phillips
SIC—3669; NAICS—334290; *Voice-recognition systems, including hardware, software & services*
Employs—30; Estab.—1996
8,000 sq ft site, Distrib.—Intl.
Privately owned corporation
AKA: Verbex Acquisition Corp.

### WHITE EAGLE PRINTING CO.

2550 Kuser Rd. (08691)
Mail addr: P.O. Box 8307, Trenton (08650)
Phone—**(609) 586-2032**
Fax—(609) 586-8052
www.whiteeagleprinting.com
Email—ericb @ whiteeagleprinting.com
Pres.—Eric Bielawski
Bookkeeper—Linda Badick
SIC—2759; NAICS—323100; *Commercial printing*
Employs—20; Estab.—1928
15,000 sq ft site, Distrib.—Regional
Privately owned corporation

### WOODLAND MFG. CO., INC.

1936 E. State St. (08619)
Phone—**(609) 587-4180**
Fax—(609) 587-1880
www.woodlandmfg.com
Email—info @ woodlandmfg.com
Pres., Prodn. Mgr.—L. A. Marcinkus, Jr.
Off. Mgr.—Steve Asch
SIC—2653; NAICS—322211; *Corrugated boxes*
Employs—13; Estab.—1980
110,000 sq ft site, Distrib.—Local
Privately owned corporation

---

## Hamilton Square

(Mercer—N.E.)

### ADV PROMOS & MORE, LLC

12 Baltusrol St. (08690)
Phone—**(609) 587-7500**
Fax—(609) 587-7502
www.advisionpromo.com
Email—advpromos @ verizon.net
Owner—Andrea M. Anepete
SIC—2396; 2395; 2759; 3993; *Custom printed promotional products, including screen printing & embroidery*
Employs—1; Estab.—1989
Sales—under $500,000
1,600 sq ft site, Distrib.—National
Sole ownership

### WORD CENTER PRINTING

1905 Highway 33, Ste. 10 (08690)
Phone—**(609) 586-5825**
Fax—(609) 586-5835
www.wordcenterprinting.com
Email—info @ wordcenterprinting.com
Owner, Fin., GM & MIS Mgr.—Marilyn Silverman
Prodn. Mgr.—Jerry Silverman

SIC—2759; 2752; NAICS—323100; *Full-color & high-speed printing of envelopes & forms with in-line variable data & numbering & handmade custom invitations & design services; Brand name—Checkerboard; Carlson Craft; Natural Impressions; Winsted; McPherson; Tatex; Birchcraft; Neenah; Stardream*
Employs—4; Estab.—1982
Sales—under $500,000
1,500 sq ft site, Distrib.—Regional
Sole ownership

---

## Hammonton

(Atlantic—S.E.)

### APPLE PRINTING CO., INC.

5 Weymouth Rd., P.O. Box 574 (08037)
Phone—**(609) 561-4411**
Fax—(609) 561-9172
Email—sales @ apple20.com
Pres.—Michael Crescenzo
GM—Marie Crescenzo
SIC—2759; NAICS—323100; *Commercial printing*
Employs—3; Estab.—1983
Sales—under $500,000
Distrib.—Regional
Privately owned corporation

### ARAWAK PAVING COMPANY

7503 Weymouth Rd. (08037)
Phone—**(609) 561-4100**
Fax—(609) 567-4750
www.arawakpci.com
Email—info @ arawakpci.com
Pres.—John M. Barrett
V-P.—Susan Barrett
Hum. Res. Mgr.—Dan MacDonnell
SIC—2951; NAICS—324121; *Company headquarters & asphalt paving compounds*
Employs—80
Sales—$1Mil-$5Mil
Distrib.—Local

### ASPHALT PAVING SYSTEMS

500 N. Egg Harbor Rd., P.O. Box 530 (08037)
Phone—**(609) 561-4161**
Fax—(609) 561-0920
Email—apsi @ comcast.net
Owner—Robert Caposerri
GM—John Constantino
SIC—2951; NAICS—324121; *Asphalt paving mixtures & blocks*
Employs—15; Estab.—1982
Sales—$500,000-$1Mil (est)
Distrib.—Local
Sole ownership

### BLUE ANCHOR FENCE, LLC

314 Arrowood Ave. (08037)
Phone—**(609) 561-1874**
Fax—(609) 561-1897
www.blueanchorfence.com
Pres.—Raymond Reyes
SIC—2499; *Wooden fences*
Employs—6; Estab.—2003
Sales—$500,000-$1Mil (est)
Distrib.—Regional
Limited Liability Company

### BUCCI MANAGEMENT CO., INC.

603 N. 1st Rd. (08037)
Phone—**(609) 561-1888**
Pres.—Guy Bucci
SIC—3944; *Children's games & marbles*
Employs—1; Estab.—1981
Sales—$500,000-$1Mil
Distrib.—National
Privately owned corporation

### C & E CANNERS, INC.

1249 Mays Landing Rd., P.O. Box 229 (08037)
Phone—**(609) 561-1078**
Fax—(609) 567-2776
Email—bobcap @ pics.com
Pres.—Robert Cappuccio
V-P.—Stephen Cappuccio
Dir. & Plt. Mgr.—David Cappuccio
Dir.—Joseph F. Cappuccio II
Dir.—Paul Cappuccio
Cust. Serv. Rep.—Christina Olivo
SIC—2033; 2035; NAICS—311421; *Canned cranberry sauce, ketchup, lemon juice & bag-in-a box juices*
Employs—26; Estab.—1934
Sales—$3Mil
100,000 sq ft site, Distrib.—National
Privately owned corporation

### CARTCO, INC.

621 Grape St. (08037)
Phone—**(978) 692-7070**
Owner—Carl Tillstrom
SIC—3599; *General machining job shop*
Employs—50; Estab.—1976
Sales—$1Mil-$2.5Mil
Distrib.—Local
Privately owned corporation

### CENTER METAL FABRICATORS, INC.

1026 Black Horse Pike, P.O. Box 29 (08037)
Phone—**(609) 567-1808**
Fax—(609) 567-0649
Email—cmf1026 @ comcast.net
Pres.—Michele McDonough
SIC—3444; *Aluminum storefronts & windows*
Employs—5; Estab.—1992
6,800 sq ft site, Distrib.—Local
Privately owned corporation

### †COLONIAL ELECTRIC SUPPLY CO., THE

469 S. White Horse Pike (08037)
Phone—**(609) 704-9950**
Fax—(609) 704-9955
www.colonialelectric.com
Email—info @ colonialelectric.com
Br. Mgr.—Fred Snyder
Hum. Res. Mgr.—Joseph Perry
SIC—5063; *Distributor of electrical equipment & supplies, including lighting, wire & cable*
Employs—6
Distrib.—Local
Privately owned corporation
Parent co.—Colonial Electric Supply Co., The, King of Prussia, PA
Phone—(610) 312-8100
See Parent Co. Section for full profile.

### CUSTOM SALES & SERVICE, INC.

275 S. 2nd Rd., P.O. Box 635 (08037)
Phone—**(609) 561-6900**
National—(800) 257-7855
Fax—(609) 567-9318
www.foodcart.com
Email—lynda.sikora @ foodcart.com
Pres.—William Sikora
V-P.—Lynda Sikora
Dir., Sales—Guy Selph
SIC—3556; 3799; NAICS—333294; *Food carts, trailers & trucks*
Employs—50; Estab.—1958
Distrib.—Regional
Privately owned corporation

### DIVERSIFIED MILLWORK, INC.

420 N. 2nd Rd., Unit C (08037)
Phone—**(609) 270-7385**
Fax—(609) 270-7443
Email—tim @ diversified-millwork.com
Pres.—Don McFaul
V-P.—Tim McFaul

## Hammonton—(cont.)

SIC—2431; 2434; 2542; NAICS—337110; *Wooden, plastic laminate & solid-surface cabinets & custom trim & millwork*
Employs—10; Estab.—1996
12,000 sq ft site, Distrib.—Regional
Privately owned sub-S corp.

**†DONIO, INC., FRANK**
692 N. Egg Harbor Rd., P.O. Box 529 (08037)
**Phone—(609) 561-2466**
Fax—(609) 561-2543
www.donio.com
Email—info@donio.com
Pres.—David F. Arena
CFO—Brian Anderson
V-P.—Bob Donio
Corp. Secy.—Judy Pape
GM—Pat Aloisio
SIC—5148; *Distributor of fresh fruits & vegetables; Brand name—Top Crop*
Employs—120; Estab.—1933
150,000 sq ft site, Distrib.—Intl.
Privately owned corporation

**EAGLE EMBROIDERY & GRAPHIX**
587 White Horse Pike (08037)
**Phone—(609) 561-1457**
www.eagleesa.com
Email—info@eagleesa.com
Owner—Phyllis Mazzeo
SIC—2396; 2395; *Textile screen printing & custom embroidery*
Employs—1; Estab.—1995
Sales—under $500,000
Distrib.—Local
Sole ownership

**†EQUIPMENT XCHANGE, LLC**
309 Columbia Rd. (08037)
**Phone—(609) 561-0500**
Fax—(609) 561-0510
www.exllc.com
Email—sales@exllc.com
Ptnr.—Scott Tarzy
Ptnr.—Jack DeStefano
Sales Mgr.—Jim Ricci
SIC—5084; *Wholesaler of used processing equipment, including centrifuges, filters, tanks, reactors, heat exchangers, mills & mixers for the pharmaceutical, food & chemical industries; Brand name—Sharples; Alfa Laval; Westfalia; Pfaudler; Paterson Kelly*
Employs—8; Estab.—1999
Sales—$3Mil
Distrib.—Intl.
Limited Liability Company

**GARVEY CORP.**
208 S. Route 73 (08037)
**Phone—(609) 561-2450**
Fax—(609) 561-2328
www.garvey.com
Email—infinity@garvey.com
Pres.—William J. Garvey
V-P., GM—Steven Ferrante
Sales Mgr.—Michael Earling
SIC—3535; 3443; NAICS—333922; *Table top conveyors & accumulators*
Employs—80; Estab.—1926
Sales—$10Mil-$25Mil
Distrib.—National
Privately owned corporation

**HAMMONTON GAZETTE, INC.**
233 Bellevue Ave., P.O. Box 1228 (08037)
**Phone—(609) 704-1939**
Fax—(609) 704-1938
www.hammontongazette.com
Email—editor@hammontongazette.com
Pres.—Gabriel Donio
Editor-in-Chief—Gina Rullo

Editor, Sports—Dan Russoman
SIC—2711; *Newspaper publishing*
Employs—5; Estab.—1997
Sales—under $500,000
Distrib.—Local
Privately owned corporation

**HAMMONTON NEWS & ATLANTIC COUNTY NEWSPAPER GROUP**
Div. of Gannett Co., Inc.
115 12th St. (08037)
**Phone—(609) 561-2300**
Fax—(609) 567-2249
www.thehammontonnews.com
Email—ngrasso@gannett.com
Ex. Editor—Nora Grasso
GM—Joe Calchi
Accts. Exec., Retail—Wendy Armington
SIC—2711; *Newspaper publishing*
Employs—3; Estab.—1964
Sales—$500,000-$1Mil
Distrib.—Local
Publicly owned corporation
Parent co.—Gannett Co., Inc., McLean, VA
Phone—(703) 854-6000
See Parent Co. Section for full profile.

**KELLOGG CO.**
322 S. Egg Harbor Rd. (08037)
**Phone—(609) 567-2300**
Fax—(609) 567-4948
www.kellogg.com
Email—info@kellogg.com
Hum. Res. Mgr.—Monica Raker
SIC—2038; NAICS—311412; *Frozen waffles*
Employs—120
Distrib.—Local
Publicly owned corporation
Parent co.—Kellogg Co., Battle Creek, MI
Phone—(269) 961-2000
See Parent Co. Section for full profile.

**MASSARELLI'S LAWN ORNAMENTS**
500 S. Egg Harbor Rd. (08037)
**Phone—(609) 567-9700**
Fax—(609) 567-8844
www.massarelli.com
Email—sales@massarelli.com
Pres.—Mario Massarelli
Cont.—Christine Massarelli
Admn. Mgr.—Cheryl Tamagni
Cust. Serv. Mgr.—Lisa Puentes
SIC—3272; *Precast concrete & terrazzo fountains*
Employs—100; Estab.—1972
Distrib.—Regional
Privately owned corporation

**MASTER WIRE MFG., INC.**
1019 Black Horse Pike, Route 322, P.O. Box 328 (08037)
**Phone—(609) 567-1616**
Fax—(609) 561-0673
www.masterwirefence.com
Email—mwmfginc@msn.com
Pres.—Geraldine Hefferon
V-P.—Brian Hefferon
Sales Mgr.—Chris Hefferon
Comml. Estimator—Rob Battece
Dispatcher, Counter Sales—C. R. Derringer
SIC—3496; 3089; *Chain-link & PVC fencing & ornamental aluminum; Brand name—Kroy Vinyl Fencing & Railings; Ultra Ornamental Aluminum*
Employs—16; Estab.—1983
14,400 sq ft site, Distrib.—Regional
Privately owned corporation
AKA: Premier Vinyl

**NINSA VINYL FENCE, LLC**
125 Lincoln St. (08037)
**Phone—(609) 561-5397**
Fax—(609) 561-6294
www.ninsallc.com
Email—rfisher@ninsallc.com

Owner—Greg Fondacaro
Cont.—Olga Applegate
Sales Rep.—Amy Sprouse
SIC—3089; *Vinyl fence sections, posts, gates & railings*
Employs—8; Estab.—1998
Distrib.—Local
Limited Liability Company

**PLAGIDO'S WINERY**
570 N. 1st Rd. (08037)
**Phone—(609) 567-4633**
Fax—(619) 567-3448
www.plagidoswinery.com
Email—christine@plagidoswinery.com
Owner—Ollie Tomasello
SIC—2084; *Wines*
Employs—3; Estab.—1999
Sales—under $500,000
5,000 sq ft site, Distrib.—Intl.
Privately owned corporation

**POLYVEL, INC.**
100 9th St. (08037)
**Phone—(609) 567-0080**
Fax—(609) 567-9522
www.polyvel.com
Email—info@polyvel.com
Pres.—Brian Tidwell
V-P.—Gary LoSasso
Dir., Sales—John Bassetti
Dir., Opers.—Scott Lam
SIC—2821; NAICS—325211; *Plastic additive concentrates; Brand name—Hydropel; Polyscent*
Employs—20; Estab.—1984
Sales—$10Mil-$25Mil (est)
46,000 sq ft site, Distrib.—Intl.
Privately owned sub-S corp.
ISO rating—9001:2000
Also see: ROWA Group USA, LLC, same loc.

**†RODIO TRACTOR SALES, INC.**
717 White Horse Pike *(08037)*
**Phone—(609) 561-0141**
Fax—(609) 561-4344
www.rodiotractor.com
Email—sales@rodiotractor.com
Pres.—Butch Rodio
Sales Mgr.—Aaron Biehl
Off. Mgr.—Sallie Belmont
SIC—5083; *Distributor of agricultural equipment, including tractors, tillers, cutters, sprayers & mowers; Brand name—Massey Ferguson; Kubota; LandPride; Chambers American Products; Hustler; Wright; Walker; Echo; RedMax*
Employs—10; Estab.—1963
Sales—$3Mil
Distrib.—Regional
Privately owned sub-S corp.

**ROWA GROUP USA, LLC**
100 9th St. (08037)
**Phone—(609) 567-8600**
Fax—(609) 567-9522
www.rowainc.net
Email—sales@rowainc.net
Pres.—Dave Baglia
Cont.—Donna Wittenberg
Cust. Serv. Rep.—Alicia Olson
SIC—2821; NAICS—325211; *Plastic resins*
Employs—13; Estab.—2003
Distrib.—Intl.
Limited Liability Company
Also see: Poylvel, Inc., same loc.
AKA: Rowa, Inc.

**SIGNARAMA**
655 S. White Horse Pike (08037)
**Phone—(609) 878-3375**
Fax—(609) 878-3376
www.signshammonton.com
Email—rich@signsham.com
Owner—Richard Matteo

SIC—3993; 2759; 2395; 2396; NAICS—323100; *Illuminated & non-illuminated full-color, wide-format, ADA, neon & political signs, banners, posters, magnets, digital printing, window lettering, vehicle graphics & wraps, silk screening, apparel embroidery & promotional items*
Employs—3; Estab.—2003
Sales—under $500,000
2,000 sq ft site, Distrib.—Local
Limited Liability Company

**T G MFG., INC.**
299 Old Forks Rd. (08037)
**Phone—(609) 561-0022**
National—(800) 847-4302
Fax—(609) 561-2972
www.tgmmarine.com
Email—tgarvey@tgmmarine.com
Pres.—Tom Garvey
SIC—3949; NAICS—339920; *Overhead mounted aluminum big game fishing reels*
Employs—15; Estab.—1977
Sales—$1Mil-$2.5Mil (est)
Distrib.—National

**TOMASELLO WINERY, INC.**
225 White Horse Pike (08037)
**Phone—(609) 561-0567**
National—(800) 666-9463
Fax—(609) 561-8617
www.tomasellowinery.com
Email—info@tomasellowinery.com
Chrm., Pres., CFO—Charles J. Tomasello, Sr.
V-P., R & D—John K. Tomasello
Secy-Treas.—Steve Smith
Sales Mgr.—James Potter
Sales Mgr.—Laurie Milby
Info. Serv. Mgr.—Lisa McClelland
SIC—2084; NAICS—312130; *Wines*
Employs—8; Estab.—1933
25,000 sq ft site, Distrib.—Intl.
Privately owned corporation

**WINSLOW HOT MIX, LLC**
Div. of Stone, Inc., A. E.
784 Piney Hollow Rd. (08037)
**Phone—(609) 561-2100**
Fax—(609) 561-2540
www.aestone.com
Email—mgooch@winslowhotmix.com
Opers. Mgr.—Mike Gooch
SIC—2952; 2951; NAICS—324122; *Asphalt products*
Employs—4; Estab.—1980
Distrib.—Local
Privately owned corporation
Parent co.—Stone, Inc., A. E., Egg Harbor Township, NJ
Phone—(609) 641-2781
See Parent Co. Section for full profile.

## Hampton
(Hunterdon—N.W.)

**NEW ENTRY**
**CELLDEX THERAPEUTICS, INC.**
53 Frontage Rd., Ste. 200 (08827)
**Phone—(908) 200-7500**
Fax—(908) 454-1911
www.celldextherapeutics.com
Email—info@celldextherapeutics.com
CEO—Anthony S. Marucci
SIC—2836; *Pharmaceuticals*
Employs—50
Sales—$10Mil-$25Mil (est)

**FOSTER WHEELER CORP. (H Q)**
53 Frontage Rd., P.O. Box 9000 (08827)
**Phone—(908) 730-4000**
(908) 713-3206
Fax—(908) 730-5300
www.fwc.com
Email—fw@fwc.com

GEOGRAPHICAL

© Copyright 2015 Manufacturers' News, Inc. † Indicates wholesaler / distributor.

## Hampton—(cont.)

CEO—Gary Nedelka
Ex. V.-P., Sales & Mktg.—Dave
  Parham
V.-P., Cont.—Lisa Z. Wood
V.-P., Corp. Comm. & Inv. Rels.—
  W. Scott Lamb
IT Mgr.—Tibor Menyhert
SIC—3443; 3585; *Corporate
  headquarters; industrial boilers &
  heaters*
Employs—500; Estab.—1891
Sales—$50Mil-$100Mil
Distrib.—Intl.
Publicly owned corporation

### IKARIA, INC. (H Q)

Div. of Madison Dearborn
  Partners, LLC
53 Frontage Rd., P.O. Box 9001
  (08827)
**Phone—(908) 238-6600**
Fax—(908) 238-6468
www.ikaria.com
Email—info@ikaria.com
Chrm., CEO—Daniel Tasse
Sr. V.-P., CFO—Tasos Konidaris
Sr. V.-P., CMO—Joseph Stauffer
Sr. V.-P., Global Mfg. & Logistics—
  L. L. Sheu
Sr. V.-P., Comml. Opers.—Stephen
  Ross
Sr. V.-P., Hum. Res.—James Briggs
Sr. V.-P., Corp. Dev. & Legal—
  Matthew Bennett
Ex. V.-P., R & D—Douglas Greene
Sr. Dir., Comms.—Samina Bari
SIC—6719; 2834; 2819; NAICS—
  551112; *Holding company
  headquarters; pharmaceutical
  blending for clinical trials & bulk
  production & nitric oxide for
  inhalation therapy*
Employs—175; Estab.—2003
Distrib.—Intl.
Publicly owned corporation
Parent co.—Madison Dearborn
  Partners, LLC, Chicago, IL
  Phone—(312) 895-1000
  See Parent Co. Section for full profile.

### KAPPUS PLASTICS CO., INC.

61-65 Route 31 S., P.O. Box 151
  (08827)
**Phone—(908) 537-2288**
National—(800) 537-1175
Fax—(908) 537-7192
www.kappusplastics.com
Email—kpsales@
  kappusplastics.com
GM—Kathleen Herbert
Sales Rep.—Rosemarie Houck
SIC—3089; 3081; NAICS—
  326113; *Plastic sheeting*
Employs—50; Estab.—1970
Sales—under $500,000
Distrib.—Local
Privately owned corporation

### MONITORING SOLUTIONS, INC.

78 Route 173, Ste. 7 (08827)
**Phone—(908) 713-0172**
National—(888) 380-5226
Fax—(908) 713-0221
www.monsol.com
Email—sales@monsol.com
Pres.—Mike Sroka
Sales Mgr., Natl.—Jim Nowak
Software Mgr.—Macklin Williams
SIC—3823; NAICS—334513;
  *Corporate headquarters &
  emissions monitoring equipment
  & services*
Employs—25; Estab.—1996
Distrib.—National
Privately owned corporation

### PENDERGAST SIGNS

566 Charlestown Rd. (08827)
**Phone—(908) 735-9295**
www.pendergastsigns.com
Email—tom@pendergastsigns.com
Pres.—Thomas Pendergast

Artist—Ralph Ralsenthy
SIC—3993; *Carved, gold leafed,
  sandblasted & painted signs*
Employs—4; Estab.—1975
Sales—under $500,000
Distrib.—Regional
Sole ownership

### T M INDUSTRIES, INC.

729 Route 625 S. (08827)
**Phone—(908) 730-7674**
National—(800) 647-7674
Fax—(908) 730-6501
Pres., CFO—Gerda A. Tietje
Sales & Mktg. Mgr.—Arno Tietje
SIC—3569; *Automatic grease
  lubricators*
Employs—8; Estab.—1979
Distrib.—Intl.
Privately owned sub-S corp.

### TECHNATRON, INC.

78 Route 173 W., Ste. 9 (08827)
**Phone—(908) 238-1122**
Fax—(908) 238-1123
Email—technatron@earthlink.net
Pres.—Jose Medeiros
Secy-Treas.—Donna Medeiros
Foreman & Shop Supv.—Ralph
  McHale
SIC—3599; *CNC & precision
  machining job shop*
Employs—5; Estab.—1995
Sales—$500,000-$1Mil
Distrib.—National
Privately owned corporation

## Hardwick

(Warren—N.W.)

### IMPERIAL BILLIARDS CORP.

2 Sandy Ln. (07825)
**Phone—(908) 459-4825**
Fax—(908) 459-5878
www.imperialbillards.com
Email—info@imperialbillards.com
Pres.—Valerio Vindici
V.-P.—Anthony DeFillippis
SIC—3949; NAICS—339920;
  *Billiard & poker tables*
Employs—3; Estab.—1966
Sales—under $500,000
Distrib.—Regional
Privately owned corporation

## Harrington Park

(Bergen—N.E.)

### A M GRAPHICS CO., INC.

68 Schraalenburgh Rd. (07640)
**Phone—(201) 767-5320**
Fax—(201) 767-5321
www.amgraphics.com
Pres., Plt. Opers., Sales & Mktg.
  Mgr.—John Motta
Manager—Sal Motta
SIC—2752; NAICS—323100;
  *Offset printing & graphics*
Employs—3; Estab.—1967
2,000 sq ft site, Distrib.—Regional
Privately owned corporation

NEW ENTRY
### HAGUE ACADEMIC PRESS LTD.

75 Lohs Pl. (07640)
**Phone—(201) 750-9091**
Pres.—Marsha Cohen
SIC—2721; *Trade magazine
  publishing*
Employs—2
Sales—under $500,000 (est)

## Harrison

(Hudson—N.E.)

### BARNETT MACHINE TOOL CORP.

401 Supor Blvd., P.O. Box 189
  (07029)
**Phone—(973) 482-6222**
Fax—(973) 482-6012

www.barnett-machine.com
Email—sales@barnett-
  machine.com
Pres.—Antonio Ferreira
V.-P.—Angelo Tamburri
Asst. Mgr.—Steve Ferreira
SIC—3599; 3545; *Precision
  machine tools & general
  machining job shop, including
  heavy parts machining*
Employs—24; Estab.—1997
Sales—$1Mil-$1.5Mil
20,000 sq ft site, Distrib.—National
Privately owned corporation

### CAMPBELL FOUNDRY CO.

800 Bergen St. (07029)
**Phone—(973) 483-5480**
Fax—(973) 483-1843
www.campbellfoundry.com
Email—johnc3@
  campbellfoundry.com
Pres.—Chris Campbell
V.-P., Secy.—John R. Campbell III
V.-P., Treas.—Greg Campbell
Cont.—John Burguillos
SIC—3321; NAICS—331511;
  *Company headquarters &
  manhole covers*
Employs—20; Estab.—1921
Sales—over $25Mil
Distrib.—Regional
Privately owned corporation

### †CONTINENTAL-AERO (H Q)

530 Bergen St., P.O. Box 354
  (07029)
**Phone—(973) 481-3000**
National—(800) 631-7999
Fax—(973) 485-6464
www.continental-aero.com
Email—sales@continental-
  aero.com
Pres.—William Giddins
Cont.—Kathy Heller
Sales Mgr.—Anthony Blasi
SIC—5072; *Company
  headquarters; distributor of
  nylon-insert & all-metal locknuts
  & finished hex nuts; Brand
  name—Purple Color Nylon Tork
  LokNuts*
Employs—6; Estab.—1948
Distrib.—Intl.
Privately owned sub-S corp.
ISO rating—9001:2000

### DOLCE VITA INTIMATES, LLC (H Q)

1000 1st St. (07029)
**Phone—(973) 482-8400**
Fax—(973) 482-8485
Email—customerservice@
  moviestarinc.com
Ptnr.—Jack Thekkekara
Ptnr.—Diana Baradarian
SIC—2341; 2342; 2384; NAICS—
  315200; *Corporate
  headquarters; women's
  nightgowns, lingerie &
  loungewear (mfg. done in Italy)*
Employs—30
Sales—$1Mil-$2.5Mil (est)
Distrib.—National
Publicly owned corporation

NEW ENTRY
### EASTERN GLASS RESOURCES, INC.

770 Supor Blvd. (07029)
**Phone—(973) 483-8411**
Fax—(973) 482-2717
www.eglassr.com
Email—info@eglassr.com
Owner—Phil Phisher
IT Mgr.—Harris Derner
SIC—3231; 3446; *Insulated &
  tempered glass & architectural
  aluminum panels*
Employs—30; Estab.—1986
Sales—$2.5Mil-$5Mil (est)
Distrib.—Regional
Sole ownership

### F M B, INC.

70 Supor Blvd. (07029)
**Phone—(973) 485-5544**
National—(800) 362-0006
Fax—(973) 485-3005
www.fmbsteel.com
Email—company@fmbsteel.com
Pres.—Bradley A. Yount
CFO & IT Mgr.—Timothy Smith
V.-P., Opers.—Gary Payliss
Cont.—Tom Pleasic
SIC—3446; *Metal railing
  fabrication*
Employs—30; Estab.—1969
60,000 sq ft site, Distrib.—
  Regional
Privately owned corporation

### FARINHAS BAKERY, INC.

301 Harrison Ave. (07029)
**Phone—(973) 482-5640**
Manager—Clara Estrada
Salesperson—Lena Garcia
  Alvarez
SIC—2051; NAICS—311812;
  *Bread & doughnuts*
Employs—18; Estab.—1968
Sales—$500,000-$1Mil
Distrib.—Local
Privately owned partnership

### FEDERAL CASTERS CORP.

785 Harrison Ave. (07029)
**Phone—(973) 483-6700**
Fax—(973) 483-5030
www.sedcosteel.com
Pres.—Charles Camella
V.-P.—Sal Camella
Cont.—Hal Delaney
Opers. Mgr.—John Tritto
Sales Agt.—Vincent Romito
SIC—3429; *Casters*
Employs—80; Estab.—1970
50,000 sq ft site, Distrib.—National
Privately owned corporation

### FLEXO CRAFT PRINTS, INC.

1000 1st St. (07029)
**Phone—(973) 482-7200**
Fax—(973) 482-9574
www.flexocraft.com
Email—abe@flexocraft.com
Pres.—Mendel Klein
V.-P.—Hershel Klein
Accts. Mgr.—Abe Klein
SIC—2759; 3861; NAICS—
  323100; *Gift wrap printing, heat
  transfer paper & packaging &
  distributor of gift wrapping
  supplies, including paper, boxes,
  gift bags, bows & tissue paper*
Employs—15; Estab.—1980
Sales—$11Mil-$25Mil
250,000 sq ft site, Distrib.—Intl.
Privately owned corporation

### GEO SPECIALTY CHEMICALS, INC.

1st & Essex St. (07029)
**Phone—(973) 484-8400**
Fax—(973) 485-3834
www.geosc.com
Email—info@geosc.com
Plt. Mgr.—Jorge Tena
Material Handling Mgr.—James
  Toney
Prod. Mgr.—Thil Dispenza
SIC—2899; *Chemicals*
Employs—8; Estab.—1992
Sales—$2.5Mil-$5Mil (est)
Distrib.—National
Publicly owned corporation
Parent co.—GEO Specialty
  Chemicals, Inc., Ambler, PA
  Phone—(215) 773-9280
  See Parent Co. Section for full profile.

### †HARRISON EQUIPMENT CORP.

500 Essex St. (07029)
**Phone—(973) 485-1448**
National—(800) 400-1448
Fax—(973) 485-4563
Email—harrisonrental@aol.com
Owner—Robert Koones

## Harrison—(cont.)

Cont.—Steven Berger
SIC—5084; *Distributor of welding & compaction equipment, generators, excavators, air tools, compressors & pumps, including service & rental*
Employs—11; Estab.—1962
Sales—$2Mil
60,000 sq ft site, Distrib.—Regional
Privately owned sub-S corp.

**HOCKMEYER EQUIPMENT CORP.**
610 Supor Blvd., Ste. 1 (07029)
**Phone—(973) 482-0225**
Fax—(973) 484-6114
www.hockmeyer.com
Email—sales@hockmeyer.com
Cont.—Maureen Jetter
Pur. Agt.—Walter Audersch
SIC—3556; NAICS—333294; *Grinding & dispersion equipment & industrial mixers & blenders*
Employs—4; Estab.—1940
Distrib.—Intl.
Privately owned corporation

†**KELLY, INC., MYLES F.**
43-57 Harrison Ave. (07029)
**Phone—(973) 481-0600**
Fax—(973) 481-3725
www.mylesfkelly.com
Email—jkellymfk@aol.com
Pres.—Jeff Kelly
SIC—5033; 5031; *Corporate headquarters & distributor of residential & commercial roofing products, including windows & doors*
Employs—20; Estab.—1935
Distrib.—Regional
Privately owned corporation

**MAZA & MAZA WELDING**
28 Mulock Pl. (07029)
**Phone—(973) 481-4441**
Fax—(973) 481-7310
www.mazarail.com
Owner—Luis Maza
SIC—3599; *Welding job shop*
Employs—2; Estab.—1976
Sales—under $500,000
Distrib.—Local
Sole ownership

**OSBORNE CO., INC., C. S.**
125 Jersey St. (07029)
**Phone—(973) 483-3232**
Fax—(973) 484-3621
www.csosborne.com
Email—cso@csosborne.com
Owner & Pres.—Jake Angell
Sales Rep.—Tyrone Nirvaez
SIC—3423; *Nonelectric hand tools*
Employs—75; Estab.—1826
Distrib.—National
Privately owned corporation

**PLAQUE ART CREATIONS CO.**
401 S. 2nd St. (07029)
**Phone—(973) 482-2536**
Fax—(973) 482-1405
www.plastercraft.com
Email—info@plastercraft.com
Pres.—Belinda Kalthoff
SIC—3299; *Plaster products*
Employs—9; Estab.—1962
Sales—$1Mil-$2.5Mil
Distrib.—National
Privately owned corporation

**PRECISE CONTINENTAL**
1 Cape May St. (07029)
**Phone—(973) 350-0330**
National—(800) 392-2496
Fax—(973) 350-0211
www.precisecorp.com
Email—info@precisecorp.com
Pres.—Jim Donnelly
Cont.—Leonard Nangoe

Manager—Sheila Donnelly
SIC—2678; NAICS—322233; *Company headquarters & engraved stationery, business cards, invitations, point-of-purchase advertising displays & commercial printing*
Employs—38; Estab.—1883
Sales—$6Mil-$10Mil
32,500 sq ft site, Distrib.—Intl.
Privately owned corporation

**R. P. BAKING CO.**
Div. of Rockland Bakery, Inc.
840 Jersey St. (07029)
**Phone—(973) 483-3374**
National—(800) 525-5779
Fax—(973) 483-1600
www.pechters.com
Email—sales@pechters.com
Plt. Mgr.—Angel Santos
Billing Mgr.—Vev Malde
Shpg. Mgr.—John Costolve
Shpg. Dispatcher—Manny Dellivira
SIC—2051; NAICS—311812; *Bread & bakery products*
Employs—400; Estab.—1888
Distrib.—Local
Privately owned corporation
AKA: Pechter's Bakery
Parent co.—Rockland Bakery, Inc., Nanuet, NY
Phone—(845) 623-5800
See Parent Co. Section for full profile.

†**ROVER & SON IRON & STEEL CO., F.**
516 Central Ave. *(07029)*
**Phone—(973) 484-7668**
Fax—(973) 484-9496
Pres.—John Rover
Off. Mgr.—Donna Jimmerson
SIC—5093; *Wholesaler of recycled iron & metal*
Employs—10; Estab.—1918
Sales—under $500,000
Distrib.—National
Privately owned corporation
AKA: FRSCO Corp.

**VO-TOYS, INC.**
400 S. 5th St. (07029)
**Phone—(973) 484-0088**
National—(800) 272-0088
Fax—(973) 484-9569
www.vo-toys.com
Email—info@vo-toys.com
Pres.—Arthur Hirschberg
V-P.—Gary Hirschberg
Cont., Accts. Rec. & Fin. Mgr.—Andres Penabad
IT Mgr.—Greg Telesky
SIC—3089; 3499; 3999; *Pet accessories & products, including toys, apparel, shampoo, grooming products, chews & carriers*
Employs—125; Estab.—1953
200,000 sq ft site, Distrib.—Intl.
Privately owned sub-S corp.

**ZARALO, LLC**
1 Cape May St. *(07029)*
**Phone—(862) 902-5220**
Fax—(862) 902-5291
Owner—David Lomita
Hum. Res. Mgr.—Shirley Aspiazu
SIC—2339; NAICS—315239; *Women's clothing*
Employs—28; Estab.—2006
Sales—$2.5Mil-$5Mil (est)
Distrib.—National
Limited Liability Company

## Hasbrouck Heights
(Bergen—N.E.)

**BERGEN INTERNATIONAL, LLC**
411 Route 17 S., Ste. 100 (07604)
**Phone—(201) 299-4499**
National—(866) 554-4951
Fax—(201) 335-5909
www.bergeninternational.com

Email—info@bergeninternational.com
Ptnr.—Dick Leahy
CFO—Richard Long
Off. Mgr.—Linda O'Donovan
SIC—2899; *Company headquarters & chemical foaming agents for the plastics industry; Brand name—Foamazol*
Employs—30; Estab.—1999
Distrib.—Intl.
Limited Liability Company

**EDGESYS, INC.**
411 State Route 17, Ste. 310 (07604)
**Phone—(201) 727-1663**
Fax—(312) 884-7945
www.edgesys.com
Email—info@edgesys.com
CEO—Emanuell James
V-P.—Galvina Mukund
SIC—7373; NAICS—541512; *Business process outsourcing & knowledge transfer computer integrated systems & consulting services*
Employs—15; Estab.—1997
Distrib.—Intl.
Privately owned corporation
AKA: Edgesys Consulting

NEW ENTRY
**MEADOWLANDS SIGNS**
58 State Route 17 (07604)
**Phone—(201) 426-0420**
Fax—(201) 426-0419
www.meadowlandsigns.com
Email—meadowlandsigns@msn.com
Owner—Jose Fuentes
SIC—3993; 2394; *Interior & exterior signs & canvas awnings*
Employs—4; Estab.—1999
Sales—under $250,000
2,600 sq ft site, Distrib.—Local
Privately owned corporation

**MINUTEMAN PRESS, INC.**
216 Boulevard (07604)
**Phone—(201) 288-7787**
Fax—(201) 288-3476
www.nj.minutemanpress.com
Email—tcolletti@minutemanpress.com
Manager—Tom Colletti
Graphic Designer—John Kennedy
SIC—2752; 2791; NAICS—323122; *Offset printing & typesetting*
Employs—4; Estab.—2009
Sales—under $500,000
1,000 sq ft site, Distrib.—Regional
Limited Liability Company
AKA: Eco Printing, LLC

†**MODERN GROUP LTD.**
112-128 Route 17 N. (07604)
**Phone—(201) 288-1441**
(800) 233-0197
Fax—(201) 288-6264
www.moderngroup.com
Email—frassaj@moderngroup.com
Br. Mgr.—Joe Frassa
SIC—5084; 5082; *Wholesaler of industrial machinery & construction equipment*
Employs—35; Estab.—2000
Distrib.—Regional
Privately owned corporation
Parent co.—Modern Group Ltd., Bristol, PA
Phone—(215) 943-9100
See Parent Co. Section for full profile.

**OBSERVER**
P.O. Box 445 (07604)
**Phone—(201) 288-0333**
Email—theobsnews@verizon.net
Editor—Constance Doheny
Mng. Dir.—Kathleen Hoffman
Off. Mgr.—Carina Ruggiero

Circ. Mgr.—Kelly Kasper
SIC—2741; *Newspaper publishing*
Employs—7; Estab.—1925
Sales—under $500,000
Distrib.—Local
Privately owned corporation
AKA: Hasbrouck Heights Publication Co.

**TATRA EAGLE, INC.**
31 Madison Ave. (07604)
**Phone—(201) 288-3815**
Email—tatraeagle@verizon.net
Pres.—Jane Kedron
Technical Editor & Dir.—Henry Kedron
SIC—2721; *Periodical publishing*
Employs—3; Estab.—1948
Sales—under $500,000 (est)
Distrib.—National
Privately owned corporation

## Haskell
(Passaic—N.E.)

**AMERICAN BERYLLIA, INC.**
16 1st Ave. (07420)
**Phone—(973) 248-8080**
Fax—(973) 248-8012
www.americanberyllia.com
Email—info@americanberyllia.com
CEO—Nussy Brauner
V-P., Bus. Dev.—Jeffrey Brundage
SIC—1459; NAICS—212325; *Beryllium oxide ceramic parts, including heat sinks, crucibles, washers, thermocouple tubing & custom substrates for aerospace, defense, electronic & commercial applications*
Employs—25; Estab.—1988
Sales—$500,000-$1Mil
Distrib.—Intl.
Privately owned corporation

**ARROW SHED, LLC**
1 3rd Ave. (07420)
**Phone—(973) 835-3200**
National—(800) 851-1085
Fax—(973) 835-1006
www.arrowsheds.com
Email—custserv@arrowsheds.com
V-P., Hum. Res.—Joanne Trezza
IT Mgr.—Peter Moore
Manager—Edward Paisker
Hum. Res. Benefits Admn.—Mary Ellen Cappuccio
SIC—3479; NAICS—332812; *Steel coating of storage units, panels & related products*
Employs—45; Estab.—1984
Sales—$2.5Mil-$5Mil (est)
Distrib.—Intl.
Privately owned corporation
Parent co.—Arrow Shed, LLC, Breese, IL
Phone—(618) 526-4546
See Parent Co. Section for full profile.

**INTERNATIONAL FORGE, LLC**
14 Doty Rd. (07420)
Mail addr.—P.O. Box 134, Bloomingdale (07403)
**Phone—(973) 729-0359**
Fax—(973) 729-4364
www.ironandstone.com
Email—joan@ironandstone.com
Pres., Sales—Michael Nestico
Bookkeeper—Joan Shuhnicki
SIC—3446; NAICS—332323; *Architectural iron railings, doors, gates, tables, chairs & statues*
Employs—7; Estab.—1956
Sales—$1Mil-$5Mil
Distrib.—Local
Limited Liability Company

**MACHINE PLUS, INC.**
97 4th Ave. (07420)
**Phone—(973) 839-8884**
Fax—(973) 835-5361
www.machineplusinc.com

GEOGRAPHICAL

## Haskell—(cont.)

Pres.—Ford Robbins
V-P.—Allen Pittelkow
Off. Mgr.—Joyce Robbins
SIC—3599; *Precision machine parts*
Employs—7; Estab.—1987
Sales—$500,000-$1Mil
6,000 sq ft site, Distrib.—National
Privately owned corporation

**POLY MOLDING, LLC**

96 4th Ave. (07420)
**Phone—(973) 835-7161**
National—(800) 229-7161
Fax—(973) 835-2438
www.polymoldingcorp.com
Email—admcorn@
 polymoldingllc.com
Pres.—Adam Corn
Plt. Mgr.—Richard Smith
Off. Mgr.—Joanne Doty
SIC—3086; NAICS—326100; *Expanded polystyrene insulation*
Employs—19; Estab.—1957
Distrib.—Regional
Limited Liability Company

**POMPTON MILLWORK, INC.**

1458 Ringwood Ave. (07420)
**Phone—(973) 835-0585**
Fax—(973) 835-4837
Email—pomptonmillwork@
 gmail.com
Pres.—William Kealy
SIC—2431; 2499; NAICS—321900; *Millwork & wooden products*
Employs—2; Estab.—1991
Sales—$500,000-$1Mil
Distrib.—Regional
Privately owned corporation

**PROGASKET AEROSPACE & AUTOMOTIVE, LLC**

14 Doty Rd. (07420)
**Phone—(973) 831-4533**
National—(888) 776-4275
Fax—(973) 831-4532
www.progasketaerospace.com
Email—mprodani@aol.com
Pres.—Mitch Prodani
V-P.—Mitch Prodani, Jr.
SIC—3469; 3053; NAICS—332116; *Metal stampings for the aerospace & automotive industries, including precision machined parts, washers & gaskets*
Employs—10; Estab.—1997
Distrib.—Intl.
Limited Liability Company

**SICO SYSTEMS CONTROL, INC.**

1263 Ringwood Ave. (07420)
**Phone—(973) 831-9110**
Fax—(973) 831-8112
Email—acct@sicocontrol.net
Pres., CFO—Gary Sigal
Bookkeeper—Svetlana Sigal
SIC—3625; NAICS—335314; *System integration & industrial controls*
Employs—6; Estab.—1986
4,000 sq ft site, Distrib.—National
Privately owned sub-S corp.

**STAMPEX TOOL&DIE, INC.**

75 4th Ave. (07420)
**Phone—(973) 839-4040**
Fax—(973) 616-1707
Email—stampex@aol.com
Owner—Thomas Nieshalla
Opers. Mgr.—Detmar Nieshalla

SIC—3469; 3544; NAICS—333500; *Precision metal stampings, including progressive dies & tooling for the medical/ surgical, electronic, recreational & commercial industries*
Employs—6; Estab.—1973
12,000 sq ft site, Distrib.—Regional
Privately owned corporation

**TECHLINE EXTRUSION SYSTEMS**

89 4th Ave. (07420)
**Phone—(973) 831-0317**
Fax—(973) 831-7923
Email—vnorman@optonline.net
Ptnr.—Wilma Norman
Pres.—Victor Norman
SIC—3599; *Extrusion machinery*
Employs—15; Estab.—1984
Sales—$500,000-$1Mil
Distrib.—Intl.
Privately owned corporation

**VAN DYK TRIM STONE, LLC**

85 4th Ave. (07420)
**Phone—(973) 831-1802**
Fax—(973) 831-0503
Email—vtrimstone@optimum.net
Pres.—David Van Dyk
Off. Mgr.—Janice Van Dyk
SIC—3272; *Cast stone*
Employs—5; Estab.—2006
Sales—$1Mil-$2.5Mil
Distrib.—Regional
Privately owned corporation

**VISUAL PACKAGING CORP.**

91 4th Ave. (07420)
**Phone—(973) 835-7055**
Fax—(973) 835-0445
www.visualpackagingcorp.com
Email—visualpackaging@
 optimum.net
Pres.—Don Stackhouse
V-P.—Brian Stackhouse
SIC—3089; *Plastic boxes*
Employs—6; Estab.—1982
Sales—$500,000-$1Mil
50,000,000 sq ft site, Distrib.—National
Privately owned corporation

# Haworth

(Bergen—N.E.)

**EVER-READY MEDIA PACKAGING**

P.O. Box 40 (07641)
**Phone—(973) 566-9333**
www.erpack.com
Email—packages@erpack.com
Pres.—Marshall Weingarden
SIC—2671; 3089; 3086; *Contract media packaging, including CD/ DVD hubs & dots, spiders, security pockets & custom foam products; Brand name— ClearGripz; SureGripz CD/DVD hubs; QuickLoad CD/DVD hubs; Velcro® Brand hook & loop; Texacro hook & loop; 3M Dual Lock*
Employs—5; Estab.—1963
Sales—under $500,000
Distrib.—Intl.
Privately owned corporation

# Hawthorne

(Passaic—N.E.)

**AEROSPACE NYLOK**

Div. of Marmon Group, LLC, The
11 Thomas Rd. S. (07506)
Mail addr: P.O. Box 651,
 Hawthorne (07507-0651)
**Phone—(973) 427-8555**
National—(800) 276-9565
Fax—(973) 427-4723
www.nylok.com
Email—sales@nylok.com
Opers. Mgr.—Hans Dorflinger

Admn. Mgr.—Karen Solka
SIC—3452; NAICS—332722; *Self-locking industrial fasteners*
Employs—24; Estab.—1962
Sales—$5Mil-$10Mil
Distrib.—Intl.
Privately owned corporation
Parent co.—Marmon Group, LLC, The, Chicago, IL
 Phone—(312) 372-9500
 See Parent Co. Section for full profile.

**AKADEMA, INC.**

140 5th Ave. (07506)
**Phone—(973) 304-1470**
Fax—(973) 636-6375
www.akademapro.com
Email—info@akademapro.com
CEO—Joe Gilligan
Pres.—Lawrence Gilligan
V-P.—Kris Totten
SIC—3949; NAICS—339920; *Baseball & softball equipment for professional, college, high school & youth players; Brand name—Ken Wel; Reach; Pro Player Baseball*
Employs—21; Estab.—1997
Distrib.—Intl.
Privately owned sub-S corp.

**AMERICAN ELECTROPLATING CO.**

342 Lincoln Ave. (07506)
**Phone—(973) 427-2300**
Fax—(973) 427-2612
Pres., V-P. & Secy-Treas.—Glenn M. Mulzet
SIC—3471; NAICS—332813; *Electroplating*
Employs—6; Estab.—1930
5,000 sq ft site, Distrib.—Local
Privately owned corporation

**ARMOUR PRODUCTS**

176-180 5th Ave. (07506)
**Phone—(973) 427-8787**
Fax—(973) 427-8823
www.armourproducts.com
Email—armourprod@aol.com
Co-Pres.—Sydney St. James
Co-Pres.—Terrence F. Picone
SIC—3423; *Glass etching & mirror decorating tools & products for the craft, hobby & stained glass industries; Brand name—Armour Etch; Rub N Etch; Sand Etch; Inflate A Booth; Over N Over; Made to Order Stencils*
Employs—15; Estab.—1972
Sales—$1Mil-$2.5Mil
Distrib.—Intl.
Privately owned corporation

**ARTISTIC MARBLE & GRANITE SURFACES, INC.**

269 Goffle Rd. *(07506)*
**Phone—(973) 304-2001**
Fax—(973) 427-9142
www.artisticmarbleandgranitesurfa
ces.com
Email—artistic269@aol.com
Pres.—Mark Marzandarani
Dir., Client Serv.—Sean Chavis
Manager—Affie Marzandarani
SIC—3281; NAICS—327991; *Marble & granite countertop fabrication*
Employs—22; Estab.—1997
Sales—$1Mil-$2.5Mil (est)
15,000 sq ft site, Distrib.—Regional
Privately owned corporation

**ARTISTIC METAL WORKS CORP.**

199 7th Ave. (07506)
**Phone—(973) 304-0600**
Fax—(973) 304-0602
www.artisticmetalnj.com
Email—info@artisticmetalnj.com
V-P.—Julius Minervini
GM—Domenick Minervini

SIC—3446; *Architectural & ornamental metalwork, including stairs, railings, gates & fences*
Employs—4; Estab.—2006
Sales—$500,000-$1Mil
10,000 sq ft site, Distrib.—National
Privately owned corporation

**B & S SHEET METAL CO., INC.**

60 5th Ave. (07506)
**Phone—(973) 427-3739**
Fax—(973) 427-5981
Pres.—Robert Buchmann
V-P.—Gary Buchmann
SIC—3444; *Sheet metal fabrication*
Employs—14; Estab.—1959
Sales—$500,000-$1Mil
19,000 sq ft site, Distrib.—Local
Privately owned corporation

**BASSANO PRINTERS & LITHOGRAPHERS**

67 Royal Ave. (07506)
**Phone—(973) 423-1400**
Fax—(973) 427-0810
www.bassanoprinting.com
Pres., MIS Mgr.—Ronald C. Bassano
Opers. Mgr.—Matthew Bassano
Fin. Mgr.—Donna Bossano
SIC—2752; NAICS—323100; *Lithographic printing*
Employs—5; Estab.—1978
3,000 sq ft site, Distrib.—National
Privately owned sub-S corp.

**†BLACKHAWK INDUSTRIAL, ATLANTIC TOOL SYSTEMS DIV.**

170 5th Ave. (07506)
**Phone—(973) 238-0009**
National—(800) 524-0890
Fax—(973) 238-0010
www.blackhawkid.com
Email—sales@blackhawkid.com
GM—J. F. Montague
GM—John Baker
SIC—5084; 5085; 5172; 5198; *Wholesaler of pneumatic tools, abrasives, cutting tools, pneumatic & power tool accessories, electric & hand tools, hoists, spray paints, lubricants, band saw blades & specialty machinery; Brand name—Carborundum; Norton; Standard Abrasives; Abmast; Sait; Ingersoll-Rand; Sioux Tools; Bahco/Sandvik Saws and Tools; Williams; Urrea*
Employs—8; Estab.—1977
Sales—under $5Mil
6,000 sq ft site, Distrib.—Regional
Privately owned corporation
ISO rating—9001:2008
AKA: Duncan Industrial Equipment

**BLANCO ASSOCS., INC., J.**

280 9th Ave., Unit 1 (07506)
**Phone—(973) 427-0619**
Fax—(973) 427-0670
www.jblanco.com
Email—info@jblanco.com
Pres.—Victor Ramos
SIC—3494; 3446; NAICS—332323; *Pipe hangers & supports & architectural metal fabrication, including metal decking, stairs, handrails & grating*
Employs—15; Estab.—1984
10,000 sq ft site, Distrib.—Regional
Privately owned corporation

**BRAWER BROS., INC. (H Q)**

375 Diamond Bridge Ave., P.O. Box 640 (07506)
**Phone—(973) 238-1800**
Fax—(973) 238-1545
www.brawerbros.com
Email—sales@brawerbros.com
CEO—Skip Smith
Dir., MIS—John Italia

## Hawthorne—(cont.)

Opers. Mgr.—Larry Haney
Accts. Payable Mgr.—Rose Angito
SIC—2281; NAICS—313111;
*Corporate headquarters; yarn*
Employs—8; Estab.—1946
Distrib.—Intl.
Privately owned corporation
Also see: Middleburg Yarn
Processing Co., Inc., same loc.

### BROADHURST SHEET METAL WORKS

230 Warburton Ave. (07506)
**Phone—(973) 427-3972**
Fax—(973) 427-1323
www.broadhurstindustries.com
Email—kris@
broadhurstindustries.com
Pres.—Kristopher Lill
SIC—3444; *Stainless steel sheet metal fabrication*
Employs—8; Estab.—1946
11,000 sq ft site, Distrib.—Local
Privately owned corporation

### CAKE SPECIALTY, INC.

255 Goffle Rd. (07506)
**Phone—(973) 238-0500**
Fax—(973) 238-1829
www.cakespecialty.net
Email—info@cakespecialty.net
Secy-Treas.—Mike Despirto
Plt. Mgr.—Nicholas Despirto
SIC—2051; 2052; NAICS—
311812; *Cakes, cookies & baked goods*
Employs—9; Estab.—1964
Sales—under $500,000
7,700 sq ft site, Distrib.—Local
Privately owned corporation

[NEW ENTRY]

### CAST LIGHTING, LLC

1120-A Goffle Rd. (07506)
**Phone—(973) 423-2303**
Fax—(973) 423-2304
www.cast-lighting.com
Owner—David Beausoleil
SIC—3645; 3646; *Lighting fixtures & transformers for the residential & commercial markets*
Employs—4
Sales—$500,000-$1Mil (est)
Limited Liability Company

### †COLONIAL COMMERCIAL CORP.

275 Wagaraw Rd. (07506)
**Phone—(973) 427-8224**
        (973) 427-3320
Fax—(973) 427-6981
www.colonialcomm.com
Email—pgasiewicz@
colonialcomm.com
Chrm.—Michael Goldman
Pres., CEO—William Pagano
V.-P., Sales—Peter Gasiewicz
Sales Mgr., Comml.—Nick Conte
Whse. Mgr.—Joe Ferrier
SIC—5074; 5075; 5063; *Corporate headquarters & distributor of commercial HVAC, plumbing & electrical equipment, supplies & accessories & climate control systems for professional contractors*
Employs—50
Distrib.—Regional
Privately owned corporation
DBA: Universal Supply Group

### COMMERCIAL PRODUCTS CO. U. S. A.

117 Ethel Ave., P.O. Box 504
(07507)
**Phone—(973) 427-6887**
Fax—(973) 427-0549
www.commercial-products.com
Email—info@commercial-products.com
Pres.—Charles Arnaldi
Ex. V.-P.—Elaine Arnaldi

Sales Rep.—Tom Shephard
SIC—2821; 2822; NAICS—
325211; *Textile resins & softeners*
Employs—5; Estab.—1944
11,700 sq ft site, Distrib.—Intl.
Privately owned corporation

### COMPUTER CRAFTS, INC.

57 Thomas Rd. (07506)
Mail addr: P.O. Box 644,
Hawthorne (07507)
**Phone—(973) 423-3500**
Fax—(973) 423-1231
www.computer-crafts.com
Email—usa-info@computer-crafts.com
Pres.—Donald Harkins
V.-P.—Robert Harkins
Prodn. Mgr.—Allen Pomante
IT Mgr.—Yefim Gorelik
Fin. & Hum. Res. Mgr.—Joan Fenners
Prodn. Planner—Jim Milore
SIC—3679; *Computer cable assemblies*
Employs—80; Estab.—1966
Distrib.—Intl.
Privately owned corporation

### CONNECTION PRINTING, INC.

86 5th Ave. (07506)
**Phone—(973) 423-2004**
Fax—(973) 423-1363
www.connectionprinting.com
Email—info@
connectionprinting.com
Pres.—Bob Rino
V.-P.—Elliot Montalvo
Off. Mgr.—Robert Brown
Designer—Rick Shields
SIC—2759; 2791; NAICS—
323122; *Commercial printing & typesetting*
Employs—4; Estab.—1992
Sales—under $500,000
Distrib.—Local
Privately owned corporation

### CONTINENTAL AROMATICS

1 Thomas Rd. S. (07506)
**Phone—(973) 238-9300**
Fax—(973) 238-9301
www.continentalaromatics.com
Email—information@
continentalaromatics.com
Owner—Ira Schneider
Pres.—Stephen W. Reynolds
SIC—2844; NAICS—325600;
*Fragrances*
Employs—30; Estab.—1977
Distrib.—Intl.
Privately owned corporation

### EPPLEY BUILDING & DESIGN, INC.

220-B Goffle Rd. (07506)
**Phone—(973) 636-9499**
Fax—(973) 636-9808
www.ebandd.com
Email—rrampersad@ebandd.com
Pres.—Paul Eppley
IT Mgr.—Rudy Rampersad
Off. Mgr., Hum. Res.—Laurie Wheathley
SIC—2434; 2431; NAICS—
337110; *Custom cabinets & architectural millwork*
Employs—35; Estab.—1984
Sales—$1Mil-$2.5Mil
12,500 sq ft site, Distrib.—Regional
Privately owned corporation

### FISK ALLOY WIRE, INC.

10 Thomas Rd., P.O. Box 26
(07507)
**Phone—(973) 427-7550**
Fax—(973) 825-8501
www.fiskalloy.com
Email—sales@fiskalloy.com
Pres.—Eric Fisk
V.-P., Sales & Mktg.—Micheal Geiser
Dir., Sales—Glenn Davidson
Dir., IT—Michael Bhatt

Dir., Hum. Res.—Donna Golden
SIC—3351; NAICS—331421;
*Bare & electroplated wire*
Employs—175; Estab.—1973
100,000 sq ft site, Distrib.—Intl.
Privately owned sub-S corp.

### FREZZOLINI ELECTRONICS, INC.

7 Valley St. (07506)
**Phone—(973) 427-1160**
Fax—(973) 427-0934
www.frezzi.com
Email—info@frezzi.com
Pres.—James Crawford
V.-P., Sales—Ed Kuhn
V.-P., Engrg.—Kevin Crawford
SIC—3663; 3669; 3679; 3648;
NAICS—334220; *Professional portable powered lighting gear, accessories & service for TV news, including high output solid-state COB LED lighting kits & on-cam lights with high capacity portable rechargeable batteries; Brand name—Frezzi; SkyLight; HyLight; EyLight; HMI Super Sun-Gun; Mini-Fill; Micro-Fill*
Employs—15; Estab.—1935
Sales—$1.5Mil-$3Mil
15,000 sq ft site, Distrib.—Intl.
Privately owned corporation

### HAWTHORNE PAINT CO., INC.

66 5th Ave. (07506)
Mail addr: P.O. Box 157,
Hawthorne (07507-0157)
**Phone—(973) 423-2335**
Fax—(973) 423-9363
www.paintsforcars.com
Email—hawthpaint@aol.com
Pres., Fin. & MIS Mgr.—Murray Greene
SIC—2851; NAICS—325510;
*Commercial, residential, industrial & automotive paint*
Employs—9; Estab.—1982
Sales—$1Mil-$5Mil
16,000 sq ft site, Distrib.—National
Privately owned corporation

### HAWTHORNE PRESS

463 Lafayette Ave., P.O. Box 1
(07507)
**Phone—(973) 427-3330**
Email—hawthornepress@
optonline.net
Pres.—Linda C. Missonellie
SIC—2711; NAICS—323122;
*Weekly newspaper publishing*
Employs—10; Estab.—1924
Sales—$500,000-$1Mil
Distrib.—Local
Privately owned corporation

### HAWTHORNE RUBBER MFG. CORP.

35 4th Ave., P.O. Box 171 (07507)
**Phone—(973) 427-3337**
National—(800) 643-2580
Fax—(973) 427-8233
www.hawthornerubber.com
Email—mike@
hawthornerubber.com
Chrm., Pres., CFO—Michael Morton
V.-P., Secy., Cred.—John Morton
GM—Dennis Dec
Adv. Mgr.—Jim Ticchio
Off. & Pers. Mgr.—Coreen Michelson
SIC—3069; *Molded rubber parts*
Employs—30; Estab.—1947
12,500 sq ft site, Distrib.—Intl.
Privately owned corporation

### †HEEREMA CO.

200 6th Ave. (07506)
Mail addr: P.O. Box 568,
Hawthorne (07507-0568)
**Phone—(973) 423-0505**
Fax—(973) 427-8672
www.heeremacompany.com
Email—heerema@
heeremacompany.com

Pres.—William C. Heerema
Bookkeeper—Steve Baker
SIC—5084; 5078; 5065;
*Wholesaler of industrial pumps, refrigeration equipment, tanks & fittings for the dairy, beverage & pharmaceutical industries, including digital pasteurization controls, sanitary positive displacement pumps & pharmaceutical & biotech tanks*
Employs—25; Estab.—1922
Distrib.—Regional
Privately owned corporation

### INDEPENDENT SHEET METAL CO., INC.

233 Central Ave. (07506)
Mail addr: P.O. Box 649,
Hawthorne (07507)
**Phone—(973) 423-1150**
Fax—(973) 423-2722
Pres.—Ed Redenack
SIC—3444; *Sheet metal fabrication*
Employs—25; Estab.—1901
31,000 sq ft site, Distrib.—Regional
Privately owned corporation

### INTEK PLASTICS, INC.

150 5th Ave. *(07506)*
**Phone—(973) 427-7331**
Fax—(973) 427-2616
www.intekplastics.com
Email—sales@intekplastics.com
GM & Sales Mgr.—Joseph S. Ganguzza
Prodn. Mgr.—Mike Voelker
Opers. Mgr.—Stevee Tingle
Cust. Serv. & Off. Mgr.—Barbara Britton
Design & Proj. Engr.—Pedro Panana
SIC—3089; *Custom & stock plastic profile extrusions*
Employs—35; Estab.—1992
Sales—$2.5Mil-$5Mil (est)
130,000 sq ft site, Distrib.—Intl.
Privately owned corporation
AKA: Intek/Elite Plastics
Parent co.—Intek Plastics, Inc., Hastings, MN
Phone—(651) 437-7700
See Parent Co. Section for full profile.

### JET PRECISION METAL, INC.

7 Schoon Ave. (07506)
**Phone—(973) 423-4350**
Fax—(973) 423-1570
www.jetprecision.com
Pres.—Nick DiMaggio
SIC—3469; *Punching, forming, welding & precision sheet metal component assembly*
Employs—37; Estab.—1986
20,000 sq ft site, Distrib.—Regional
Privately owned corporation

### JO-DE MACHINE CO., INC.

43 Ethel Ave. (07506)
**Phone—(973) 427-9555**
Fax—(973) 304-0166
www.jodemachine.com
Pres.—Joseph D'Angelo
SIC—3565; NAICS—333993;
*Packaging machinery*
Employs—4; Estab.—1967
Sales—under $500,000
5,000 sq ft site, Distrib.—Intl.
Privately owned corporation

### LIPARI'S SAUSAGE, INC.

220 6th Ave. *(07506)*
**Phone—(973) 304-0137**
Fax—(973) 304-0728
www.liparisausage.com
Email—lipsaus@aol.com
V.-P., CEO & COO—Joe Manganella
Pres.—Marilynn Manganella

GEOGRAPHICAL

## Hawthorne—(cont.)

SIC—2011; NAICS—311611; *Meat & sausage processing, cutting & packing*
Employs—25; Estab.—1997
Sales—$5Mil-$10Mil
Distrib.—Regional
Privately owned corporation

**MAGNATROL VALVE CORP.**
67 5th Ave. *(07506)*
Mail addr: P.O. Box 17, Hawthorne (07507-0017)
**Phone—(973) 427-4341**
　　　　(800) 711-0017
Fax—(973) 427-7611
www.magnatrol.com
Email—info@magnatrol.com
Pres.—Raymond A. Kretschmer, Sr.
COO, Opers. Mgr.—David Kretschmer
Cont., Fin. & Hum. Res. Mgr.—Bob Malzacher
GM—David DeCara
Adv., Sales & Mktg. Mgr.—David J. Calafiore
Sales Mgr.—Raymond Kretschmer, Jr.
Cred. Mgr.—Dot Stierli
SIC—3491; 3492; NAICS—332911; *Corporate headquarters & industrial & commercial solenoid valves; Brand name—Magnatrol Solenoid Valves*
Employs—30; Estab.—1936
Sales—$1Mil-$5Mil
14,240 sq ft site, Distrib.—Intl.
Privately owned corporation

**MIDDLEBURG YARN PROCESSING CO., INC. (H Q)**
375 Diamond Bridge Ave., P.O. Box 640 (07507)
**Phone—(973) 238-1800**
Fax—(973) 238-1544
www.brawerbros.com
Email—brawerbros@aol.com
CEO—Skip Smith
V-P., Admn.—John Italia
Cont.—Adolpho Castillo
Billing Supv.—Sally Nigito
SIC—2281; NAICS—313111; *Corporate headquarters; yarn processing*
Employs—12
Sales—$1Mil-$2.5Mil (est)
Privately owned corporation
Also see: Brawer Bros., Inc., same loc.

**MID-STATE ENTERPRISES, INC.**
155 Van Winkle Rd. (07506)
Mail addr: P.O. Box 25, Hawthorne (07507)
**Phone—(973) 427-6040**
Fax—(973) 427-9750
Pres., CFO—David C. Humphreys
V-P., Sales—Nicholas Ligosh
SIC—3061; NAICS—326291; *Industrial rubber bellows*
Employs—6; Estab.—1946
Sales—$500,000-$1Mil
6,000 sq ft site, Distrib.—National
Privately owned corporation

**MINIATURE FOLDING**
300 9th Ave. (07506)
**Phone—(201) 773-6477**
Fax—(201) 773-6480
www.miniaturefolding.com
Email—chris@miniaturefolding.com
Pres.—Christopher Taliercio, Sr.
Qual. Control Mgr.—Christopher Taliercio, Jr.

SIC—2789; NAICS—322212; *Miniature folding, padding, tipping & placement of pharmaceutical, promotional & cosmetic printed materials*
Employs—20; Estab.—1989
Sales—$1Mil-$2.5Mil (est)
Distrib.—Regional
Privately owned corporation

**NEXUS PLASTICS, INC.**
1 Loretto Ave. (07506)
Mail addr: P.O. Box 667, Hawthorne (07507-0667)
**Phone—(973) 427-3311**
National—(800) 486-3987
Fax—(973) 427-4847
www.nexusplastics.com
Email—sales@nexusplastics.com
Pres., CEO—Marwan Sholakh
CFO—Leslie Plaskon
GM—Tamer Sholakh
Sales Mgr.—Joe Polise
Accts. Mgr., Natl.—Joseph R. Esak
Plt. Mgr.—Tariq Yaqoob
Hum. Res. Mgr.—Kari Sholakh
Qual. Assur. Mgr.—Wayne Dzierenowski
SIC—2673; 3081; 3089; NAICS—326113; *Corporate headquarters & poly packaging materials, including plastic bags, sheets, single wound & centerfold sheeting, tubing & center slit tubing*
Employs—90; Estab.—1982
Sales—$10Mil-$25Mil
82,000 sq ft site, Distrib.—Intl.
Privately owned sub-S corp.
ISO rating—9001:2008

**PEERLESS COATINGS, LLC**
220-A Goffle Rd. *(07506)*
**Phone—(973) 427-8771**
Fax—(973) 427-8779
www.peerlesscoatings.com
Email—peerless1@verizon.net
GM—Joe Hyer
SIC—3479; 3089; *Metal & plastic coatings*
Employs—45; Estab.—2000
Sales—$2.5Mil-$5Mil (est)
Distrib.—Regional
Limited Liability Company

**PREMIO FOODS, INC.**
50 Utter Ave. *(07506)*
**Phone—(973) 427-1106**
Fax—(973) 427-5251
www.premiofoods.com
Email—info@premiofoods.com
Pres.—Mark Cinque
Hum. Res. Mgr.—Nina Rehrer
SIC—2013; NAICS—311600; *Sausages*
Employs—100; Estab.—1992
Distrib.—National
Privately owned corporation

**PRINTMASTERS**
1108 Goffle Rd. (07506)
**Phone—(973) 427-6598**
Fax—(973) 427-6598
www.printmasters1108.com
Email—info@printmasters1108.com
Pres.—Paula Cornett
SIC—2752; 2759; 3993; 2396; NAICS—323122; *Business printing, graphics & design, wedding & social invitations, promotional signs & screen printing of t-shirts*
Employs—4; Estab.—1996
1,000 sq ft site, Distrib.—Regional
Sole ownership

**PROMOTIONAL GRAPHICS ETC., INC.**
85 Wagaraw Rd. (07506)
Mail addr: 81 E. 26th St., Paterson (07514-1615)
**Phone—(973) 423-3900**
Fax—(973) 423-3989

www.promo-graphics.com
Email—rodney@promo-graphics.com
Pres.—Dianne Dopp
V-P.—Rodney Dopp
SIC—2759; NAICS—323100; *Printed labels, including ESD static dissipative, thermal transfer, direct thermal & VIP inkjet labels & hang tags*
Employs—10; Estab.—1993
Sales—$2Mil
15,000 sq ft site, Distrib.—Regional
Privately owned corporation

**RADIANT ENERGY SYSTEMS, INC.**
175 N. Ethel Ave. (07506)
**Phone—(973) 423-5220**
National—(800) 720-5256
www.radiantenergy.com
Email—info@radiantenergy.com
Sales & Mktg. Coord.—Jim Margiotta
SIC—3567; NAICS—333994; *Custom electrical & gas-fired infrared, hot air impingement & flotation dryers & combination systems for the process heating industry; Brand name—Versa Heat*
Employs—20; Estab.—1985
Sales—$5Mil
25,000 sq ft site, Distrib.—Intl.
Privately owned corporation

**RAINBOW SPECIALTY COLORS, INC.**
27 Utter Ave., Ste. B (07506)
**Phone—(973) 304-0912**
Fax—(973) 304-0913
www.rainbowspecialtycolors.com
Email—info@rainbowspecialtycolors.com
Owner—Dayana Dill
Whse. Mgr.—John Dill
SIC—2865; *Dyes & color concentrates*
Employs—10; Estab.—2001
10,000 sq ft site, Distrib.—National
Privately owned corporation

**RUSH GRAPHICS, INC.**
1122 Goffle Rd. (07506)
**Phone—(973) 427-9393**
Fax—(973) 427-1901
www.rushgraphics.com
Email—production@rushgraphics.com
Pres.—Zora Agheli
V-P., Fin.—Sam Kassaii
Off. Coord.—Mariam Razani
SIC—2791; 2796; 2752; NAICS—323122; *Electronic prepress & commercial printing*
Employs—10; Estab.—1984
10,000 sq ft site, Distrib.—Intl.
Privately owned sub-S corp.

**SIGNATURE MARKETING & MFG.**
301 Wagaraw Rd. (07506)
**Phone—(973) 427-3700**
National—(800) 856-7238
Fax—(973) 427-2906
www.signaturecrafts.com
Email—info@signaturecrafts.com
Owner & Pres.—Michael Assile
SIC—2891; 5169; NAICS—325520; *Manufacturer & wholesaler of adhesives*
Employs—6; Estab.—1986
Sales—under $500,000
Distrib.—National
Privately owned corporation

**SIGNS BY TOMORROW**
1108 Goffle Rd., Ste. 1 (07506)
**Phone—(973) 423-4600**
　　　　(973) 423-4601
Fax—(973) 423-4602
www.signsbytomorrow.com/paramus
Email—paramus@signsbytomorrow.com

Owner—Joe Sevean
Prodn. Mgr.—Victor Soto
SIC—3993; *Interior & exterior signs*
Employs—2; Estab.—1995
Sales—$500,000-$1Mil
2,000 sq ft site, Distrib.—Intl.
Sole ownership

**TREMONT CO., INC., I. W.**
18 Utter Ave. (07506)
**Phone—(973) 427-3800**
Fax—(973) 427-3778
www.iwtremont.com
Pres.—Sal Averso
GM—James Averso
Prodn. Mgr.—Andrew Averso
Acct. Coord.—Josh Cejong
SIC—3621; NAICS—335312; *Packaging converters*
Employs—25; Estab.—1978
Distrib.—Intl.
Privately owned corporation

**ULMA FORM WORKS, INC.**
58 5th Ave. (07506)
**Phone—(973) 636-2040**
Fax—(973) 636-2045
www.ulma-c.us
Corp. Secy.—Mary Raichelson
Bookkeeper—Willeta Jazwinski
SIC—3444; *Steel concrete forms*
Employs—50; Estab.—2000
Sales—$5Mil-$10Mil (est)
Distrib.—National
Privately owned corporation

**VALENTA & SONS, INC., JERRY**
40 Schoon Ave. (07506)
**Phone—(973) 423-2220**
Fax—(973) 423-9590
Pres.—Jerry Valenta
GM & Textile Designer—Rich Valenta
SIC—2675; NAICS—322200; *Jacquard card cutting*
Employs—6; Estab.—1964
Distrib.—Intl.
Privately owned corporation

**VANDEREEMS MFG. CO., INC.**
40 Schoon Ave. (07506)
**Phone—(973) 427-2355**
Fax—(973) 427-2356
Pres.—John Vandereems
SIC—2449; 2441; 2448; NAICS—321920; *Wooden crates, boxes & custom pallets*
Employs—6; Estab.—1930
Sales—under $500,000
7,000 sq ft site, Distrib.—Regional
Privately owned corporation

**XENOPORE CORP.**
299 Wagaraw Rd. (07506)
Mail addr: P.O. Box 505, Hawthorne (07507)
**Phone—(973) 423-2400**
National—(800) 356-6296
Fax—(973) 423-2401
www.xenopore.com
Email—xenopore@xenopore.com
Pres.—Allan Douglas
SIC—3089; 3231; NAICS—327215; *Plastic & glass laboratory plates & slides*
Employs—8; Estab.—1988
Sales—$500,000-$1Mil
Distrib.—Intl.
Privately owned corporation

---

## Hazlet

(Monmouth—N.E.)

**AAEON ELECTRONICS, INC. (H Q)**
11 Crown Plz., Ste. 208 (07730-2496)
**Phone—(732) 203-9300**
Fax—(732) 203-9311
www.aaeon.com
Email—sales@aaeon.com
Pres.—Yuhmin Hwang
Hum. Res. Mgr.—Nancy Hung

## Hazlet—(cont.)

Off. Mgr.—Trish Longo
SIC—3571; 3577; NAICS—
334111; *Corporate headquarters;
single board computers & panel
monitors (mfg. done overseas);
Brand name—AAEON*
Employs—20; Estab.—1992
Sales—$10Mil-$25Mil (est)
Distrib.—National
Privately owned corporation

### ADVANCED MARINE TECHNOLOGY

12 Crown Plz., Unit 204 (07730)
**Phone—(732) 888-8248**
Fax—(732) 739-5445
Email—adme@att.net
Pres., GM—Anatoly Nemiroski
SIC—3824; NAICS—334514; *Oil
content meters*
Employs—7; Estab.—1983
Sales—under $500,000
Distrib.—Intl.
Privately owned corporation

NEW ENTRY
### DIRECT DEVELOPMENT, LLC

1338 State Route 36 (07730)
**Phone—(732) 739-8890**
Fax—(732) 739-3262
www.marketmeprinting.com
Email—info@marketmeprinting.com
Owner—Vinod Gopal
SIC—2759; 2396; *Commercial,
promotional & apparel screen
printing*
Employs—8
Sales—$1Mil-$2.5Mil (est)
Distrib.—Intl.
Limited Liability Company

### ELECTRIC FAN ENGINEERING CO.

8 Crown Plz., Unit 105 (07730)
**Phone—(732) 203-0320**
National—(800) 338-4121
Fax—(732) 203-1199
www.electricfanengineering.com
Email—roger@
electricfanengineering.com
Pres.—Roger Clemente
Manager—John Smith
SIC—3564; NAICS—333400;
*Electric & hydraulic fan cooling
systems*
Employs—5; Estab.—1987
Sales—$1Mil-$2.5Mil
Distrib.—Local
Privately owned corporation

### INDUSTRIAL WATER
### TECHNOLOGIES, INC.

6 Village Ct. (07730)
**Phone—(732) 888-1233**
Fax—(732) 888-9441
www.iwtnj.com
Pres., CFO—Richard Demartino
Opers. Mgr.—Joy Lacy
SIC—2899; *Specialty chemicals
for wastewater, boiler & cooling
water treatment*
Employs—9; Estab.—1991
Sales—$500,000-$1Mil
Distrib.—National
Privately owned corporation

### INTERNATIONAL FLAVORS &
### FRAGRANCES, INC.

600 Highway 36 (07730)
**Phone—(732) 264-4500**
National—(800) 433-4472
www.iff.com
Email—xpressinformation@iff.com
Plt. Mgr.—David Smith
SIC—2087; 2844; NAICS—
311900; *Flavors & fragrances*
Employs—250; Estab.—1958
200,000 sq ft site, Distrib.—Local
Publicly owned corporation
ISO rating—9002

Parent co.—International Flavors &
Fragrances, Inc., New York, NY
Phone—(212) 765-5500
See Parent Co. Section for full profile.

### †KOPO INTERNATIONAL, INC.

100 Village Ct., Ste. 202 (07730)
**Phone—(732) 203-1505**
Fax—(732) 203-1506
Email—steelusa@aol.com
Pres., CEO—Stephen Cucih
Off. Mgr.—Terry Mellica
SIC—5051; *Distributor of steel*
Employs—3; Estab.—1980
Distrib.—Intl.
Privately owned corporation

### LAZAR TECHNOLOGIES, INC.

39 Evergreen St. (07730)
**Phone—(732) 739-9622**
Fax—(732) 739-9610
www.lazartechnologies.com
Email—carlos@lazarcapper.com
Pres.—Carlos Gaviria
Treas.—Isabel Gaviria
Sales Mgr.—Sabrina Gaviria
SIC—3565; 3535; NAICS—
333993; *Bottle capping
equipment, inspection, placing,
sorting & bottle handling &
conveying systems & filling &
labeling systems, including line
integration, end of line robotics,
palletizers & pallet shrink
wrappers; Brand name—Lazar
Cappers; Nita Labeler*
Employs—9; Estab.—1993
Sales—$1.5Mil
10,000 sq ft site, Distrib.—Intl.
Privately owned corporation

### MID STATE CONTROLS, INC.

8 Crown Plz., Ste. 102 (07730)
**Phone—(732) 335-0500**
Fax—(732) 335-0500
Email—msc1936@aol.com
Opers. & R & D Mgr.—Robert
Rosko
Fin. & Off. Mgr.—Karen Lazarus
SIC—3613; NAICS—335313;
*Electric control panels*
Employs—7; Estab.—1984
Sales—$1Mil-$1.5Mil
8,000 sq ft site, Distrib.—Local
Privately owned corporation

### NOUVEAU PROSTHETICS &
### ORTHOTICS

984 State Route 36 (07730)
**Phone—(732) 739-0888**
National—(800) 316-8330
Fax—(732) 739-5351
www.artificiallimbs.com
Email—info@artificiallimbs.com
Pres.—Stuart Weiner
Hum. Res. & Off. Mgr.—Camille
Levin
SIC—3842; *Prosthetic & orthotic
appliances*
Employs—10; Estab.—1998
Sales—$500,000-$1Mil
Distrib.—Local
Privately owned corporation

### PETER J. MORLEY LLC

21 Village Ct. (07730)
**Phone—(732) 264-0010**
Fax—(732) 264-2275
www.gosafeguard.com
Email—pmorley-88@comcast.net
Pres.—Pete Morley
Bus. Specialist—Diane Waitt
SIC—2759; 3993; NAICS—
323100; *Business printing &
promotional products*
Employs—3; Estab.—2004
Sales—$500,000-$1Mil
Distrib.—Regional
Limited Liability Company

### SCHREIBER, INC., EARLE C.

1 Bethany Rd., Bldg. 1, Ste. 13
(07730)
**Phone—(732) 335-1424**
Fax—(732) 335-1420
Email—ecsinc13@msn.com
Pres.—Margery Schreiber Wright
SIC—3851; NAICS—339100;
*Artificial eyes*
Employs—4; Estab.—1931
Sales—under $500,000
1,250 sq ft site, Distrib.—Local
Privately owned corporation

### TRETINA PRINTING, INC.

1301 State Route 36, Concord Ctr.
(07730)
**Phone—(732) 264-2324**
Fax—(732) 264-0180
www.tretinaprinting.com
Email—sales@tretinaprinting.com
Pres.—Jan Tretina, Sr.
Sales Mgr.—Jan Tretina, Jr.
Off. Mgr.—Jane Dovolla
Bookkeeper—Olga Tretina
SIC—2759; 2752; NAICS—
323100; *Commercial & offset
printing & mailing & fulfillment
services*
Employs—8; Estab.—1972
Sales—$500,000-$1Mil
Distrib.—National
Privately owned corporation

## Hewitt

### (Passaic—N.E.)

### A & A IRONWORKS, INC.

955 Burnt Meadow Rd. (07421)
**Phone—(973) 728-4300**
Fax—(973) 728-4302
www.aaironwork.com
Email—davev@aaironwork.com
Pres.—Adam G. Muzer
V-P.—Adam E. Muzer
V-P.—Mark M. Muzer
Shop Foreman—Raymond Teague
SIC—3441; 3312; 3446; NAICS—
332312; *Ironwork & structural
steel fabrication & erection;
Brand name—SPACE STAIR
INC.*
Employs—15; Estab.—1963
12,000 sq ft site, Distrib.—National
Privately owned corporation

### COYOTE PALLET CO.

13 Oradell Rd. (07421)
**Phone—(973) 853-7266**
Fax—(973) 853-7266
Owner—Donald Coyote
SIC—2448; *Wooden pallets*
Employs—3
Sales—under $500,000 (est)
Distrib.—Local
Privately owned corporation

### INNOVATION CONCEPTS, INC. (H Q)

870 Warwick Tpke. (07421)
Mail addr: P.O. Box 11, Chester
(10918)
**Phone—(973) 853-5300**
Fax—(973) 853-5300
www.poochietreats.com
Email—info@poochietreats.com
Pres.—Robert Tolve
Hum. Res. Mgr.—Judy Tolve
SIC—2047; *Corporate
headquarters; dog treats &
chews (mfg. subcontracted);
Brand name—Poochie Chews;
Chicken On A Bone; Nutter
Pops; Poochie Shampoo Infused
Bath Sponge; Poochie Burritos;
Poochie Naturals*
Employs—5; Estab.—2001
Sales—$1Mil-$2Mil
Distrib.—National
Privately owned corporation

### J. R.'S SCREEN PRINTING

1930 Greenwood Lake Tpke., P.O.
Box 561 (07421)
**Phone—(973) 728-7802**
Fax—(973) 728-2331
Owner, Hum. Res. & IT Mgr.—
John Reape, Jr.
Manager—Danielle Reape
SIC—2396; 2395; *Textile screen
printing & embroidery*
Employs—2; Estab.—1995
Sales—under $500,000
Distrib.—Local
Sole ownership

NEW ENTRY
### JOURNAL AMERICA

1950 Greenwood Lake Tpke., P.O.
Box 459 (07421)
**Phone—(973) 728-8355**
Fax—(973) 728-7128
Email—prjournalamerica@
yahoo.com
Owner—George Malmgren
SIC—2721; *Journal publishing*
Employs—10
Sales—$500,000-$1Mil
Distrib.—Regional
Privately owned corporation

### NORTHEAST CONCRETE
### PRODUCTS, LLC

937 Burnt Meadow Rd., P.O. Box
963 (07421)
**Phone—(973) 728-1667**
Fax—(973) 728-2662
www.northeastconcrete.net
Email—johnvitale@
northeastconcrete.net
Pres.—John Vitale
Hum. Res. Mgr.—Liv Vitale
Qual. Control Mgr.—Amanda
Vitale
SIC—3272; *Concrete catch
basins, tanks, lightpole bases &
water retention systems*
Employs—8; Estab.—2000
Sales—$500,000-$1Mil
Distrib.—Local
Limited Liability Company

### NORTHEAST SHEET METAL, LLC

870 Warwick Tpke. (07421)
**Phone—(973) 853-0500**
Fax—(973) 853-4552
Owner—Nicole Amado
SIC—3444; *Sheet metal
fabrication*
Employs—8; Estab.—1995
Sales—$2.6Mil-$5Mil
Distrib.—Regional
Privately owned corporation

### WILEY'S LAKE PRESS, INC.

1902 Greenwood Lake Tpke.
(07421)
**Phone—(973) 728-9231**
Fax—(973) 728-6722
Email—dwiley2@optonline.net
Pres.—Richard Wiley
V-P.—Theresa Wiley
SIC—2752; 2759; NAICS—
323100; *Offset & color printing of
brochures, booklets, letterheads,
envelopes, business cards &
invoices*
Employs—2; Estab.—1950
Sales—under $500,000
Distrib.—Regional
Privately owned corporation

### YOUNG ASPHALT PAVING
### MATERIALS, ROBERT

830 Burnt Meadow Rd. (07421)
**Phone—(973) 728-8133**
Fax—(973) 728-7708
Pres.—Bill Young
Off. Mgr.—Karen Young

GEOGRAPHICAL

## Hewitt—(cont.)

SIC—2951; NAICS—324121;
*Asphalt paving compounds*
Employs—10; Estab.—1956
Sales—under $500,000 (est)
Distrib.—Local
Privately owned corporation

## High Bridge

(Hunterdon—N.W.)

**B & B ULTRA-SONIC, INC.**
10 E. Main St. (08829)
**Phone—(908) 638-5775**
Pres.—Richard N. Baumann
Corp. Secy.—Harriet L. Lutz
SIC—3599; *General machining
job shop*
Employs—10; Estab.—1986
Sales—$1Mil-$2.5Mil (est)
Distrib.—Regional

**CUSTOM ALLOY CORP.**
3 Washington Ave., Ste. 6 (08829-
2108)
**Phone—(800) 453-1724**
(908) 638-6200
Fax—(908) 638-4499
www.customalloy.us
Email—dpalmer@customalloy.us
Pres.—Adam M. Ambielli
V-P., Fin. & Cont.—Greg Owens
V-P.—Donald M. Burns
Corp. Admn.—Dee Palmer
SIC—3494; NAICS—332900;
*Butt-weld pipe fittings & near net
shape forgings*
Employs—260; Estab.—1968
Sales—$75Mil
275,000 sq ft site, Distrib.—Intl.
Privately owned corporation

**ENVIRO-CLEAR CO., INC.**
152 Cregar Rd. (08829)
**Phone—(908) 638-5507**
Fax—(908) 638-4636
www.enviro-clear.com
Email—info@enviro-clear.com
Pres.—C. Meyer
V-P.—K. N. Muldowney
Sales Mgr.—James Grau
Plt. Mgr.—Bob Herder
SIC—3532; 3559; *Liquid/solid
clarifiers, thickeners, filters &
drives; Brand name—ENVIRO-
CLEAR; PRONTO*
Employs—19; Estab.—1970
Sales—$10Mil
Distrib.—Intl.
Privately owned corporation

**GLASSMAN HIGH VOLTAGE, INC.**
124 W. Main St., P.O. Box 317
(08829-0317)
**Phone—(908) 638-3800**
Fax—(908) 638-3700
www.glassmanhv.com
Email—sales@glassmanhv.com
Owner—Sanford H. Glassman
GM—John Belden
Sales Mgr.—Scott Jarmicki
IT Mgr.—Lee Thornton
Hum. Res. Mgr.—Jeannie Fleck
SIC—3612; NAICS—335311; *High
voltage power supplies*
Employs—70; Estab.—1977
Distrib.—Intl.
Privately owned corporation

**J & M MFG., INC.**
54 Main St., P.O. Box 43 (08829)
**Phone—(908) 638-6727**
Fax—(908) 638-5077
Email—jmmachine@
embarqmail.com
CEO—John Gargas
V-P.—Maureen Gargas
SIC—3599; *Precision machining
job shop*
Employs—10; Estab.—1970
8,500 sq ft site, Distrib.—Local
Privately owned corporation

**NORSAL DISTRIBUTION ASSOCS.**
150 Cregar Rd. (08829)
**Phone—(908) 638-8900**
Fax—(908) 638-4205
www.norsalnda.com
Email—russell.lown@
norsalnda.com
Owner—Norma Moscato
CEO—Sal Moscato
Opers. Mgr.—Russell Lown
SIC—3613; NAICS—335313;
*Custom switchgear, switchboard
& motor control lineups*
Employs—10; Estab.—1986
Sales—$1Mil-$2.5Mil
14,000 sq ft site, Distrib.—
Regional
Privately owned corporation

## Highland Park

(Middlesex—N.E.)

**BIRNN CHOCOLATES, INC.**
314 Cleveland Ave. (08904)
**Phone—(732) 545-4400**
Fax—(732) 545-4494
www.birnnchocolates.com
Email—info@birnnchocolates.com
Pres.—John Cunnell
SIC—2066; 2064; NAICS—
311300; *Chocolate confectionery*
Employs—4; Estab.—1932
Sales—$300,000
5,000 sq ft site, Distrib.—National
Privately owned corporation

**GEEBEE MARKETING, INC.**
300 Raritan Ave., 2nd Fl. (08904)
**Phone—(732) 777-6033**
Fax—(732) 777-0526
www.pressmantoy.com
Email—gbm@aol.com
Pres.—Robert N. Kersey
V-P.—Gayle Brill Mittler
Cont.—April Kapland
Mktg. Mgr.—Linzey Lockwood
SIC—3944; *Games & puzzles*
Employs—4; Estab.—1997
Sales—$500,000-$1Mil
Distrib.—Intl.
Privately owned corporation

**WHITE LOTUS HOME**
431 Raritan Ave. (08904)
**Phone—(732) 828-2111**
National—(877) 426-3623
Fax—(732) 828-4159
www.whitelotus.net
Email—sales@whitelotus.net
Pres.—Marlon Pando
SIC—2515; *Natural & organic
mattresses & bedding*
Employs—20; Estab.—1981
Sales—$500,000-$1Mil
5,000 sq ft site, Distrib.—National
Limited Liability Company

## Highlands

(Monmouth—N.E.)

**CERTIFIED CLAM CORP.**
190 Bay Ave., P.O. Box 383
(07732)
**Phone—(732) 872-6650**
Fax—(732) 872-6653
www.certifiedclam.com
Email—sales@certifiedclam.com
Pres.—Kathy Armstrong
SIC—2092; NAICS—311712;
*Fresh clam processing*
Employs—12; Estab.—1992
Sales—$1Mil-$2.5Mil (est)
Distrib.—Intl.
Privately owned corporation

## Hightstown

(Mercer—N.E.)

**BUCK MINING & MATERIALS, INC.**
P.O. Box 1386 (08520)
**Phone—(732) 446-9336**
Email—buckmining@gmail.com
Owner—Maureen Stone
Pres.—Lesley Buck
V-P.—Kevin Buck
SIC—1442; 1499; NAICS—
212321; *Sand & gravel
processing & dirt mining*
Employs—5; Estab.—1982
Sales—$500,000-$1Mil
Distrib.—Local
Privately owned corporation

**C & S SCIENTIFIC CORP.**
P.O. Box 1056 (08520)
**Phone—(609) 448-7037**
National—(877) 448-7037
Fax—(267) 200-0430
www.csscientific.com
Email—jsava@csscientific.com
Pres.—Jerome Sava
V-P.—Pat Cerminaro
SIC—2899; *Heating oil & diesel
fuel additives, including
biodiesel & bioheat blends &
boiler water treatment
chemcials; Brand name—Treat
Now; Biotreat; Diesel-Add;
Antigel; Tank-Shield; Organoban;
Sludgeban; Injectrol*
Employs—10; Estab.—1993
Distrib.—National
Privately owned sub-S corp.

**CCL LABEL, INC.**
Div. of CCL Industries Corp.
120 Stockton St. (08520)
**Phone—(609) 443-3700**
Fax—(609) 443-0617
www.cclind.com
Email—webmaster@cclind.com
V-P., Sales, North America—
Robert Ryckman
Cont.—Ralph Petagna
Hum. Res. Mgr.—Dennis
Richardson
Maint. Mgr.—Frank Higgins
Cust. Serv. Rep.—Melissa Giblin
SIC—2672; NAICS—322222;
*Pharmaceutical & consumer
product pressure-sensitive
labels*
Employs—100; Estab.—1951
Sales—$50Mil-$100Mil
Distrib.—Intl.
Publicly owned corporation
Parent co.—CCL Industries Corp.,
Boston, MA
Phone—(508) 872-4511
See Parent Co. Section for full profile.

**CORE TECH SOLUTIONS, INC.**
50 Lake Dr. E. Windsor (08520)
**Phone—(609) 443-1400**
Email—kirtivalia@yahoo.com
Pres.—Kirti H. Valia
V-P.—Manjari Valia
SIC—2834; NAICS—325412;
*Pharmaceutical preparations*
Employs—10; Estab.—1998
Sales—under $500,000
Distrib.—National
Privately owned corporation

NEW ENTRY
**MCGRAW-HILL CONSTRUCTION**
Div. of McGraw-Hill Financial, Inc.
148 Princeton Hightstown Rd.
(08520)
**Phone—(800) 393-6343**
Fax—(866) 794-5065
www.construction.com
Email—andreakerwin@mcgraw-
hill.com
Power Source Mgr.—Andrea
Kerwin
Cust. Serv. Rep.—Raymond
Engeles
Cust. Care Prod. Specialist—
Edwin Belgera
SIC—2721; 2741; *Bimonthly print
& online magazine publishing for
the construction industry*
Employs—3; Estab.—1900
Sales—under $500,000
Distrib.—National
Publicly owned corporation
AKA: Constructor - Magazine of
the Associated General
Contractors of America
Parent co.—McGraw-Hill Financial,
Inc., New York, NY
Phone—(212) 512-2000
See Parent Co. Section for full profile.

**OLD HIGHTS PRINT SHOP, INC.**
133 S. Main St. (08520)
**Phone—(609) 443-4700**
Fax—(609) 443-8053
Email—old.hights@verizon.net
Pres.—Cathy M. Simmons
V-P.—Richard J. Simmons
SIC—2759; 2396; 2752; NAICS—
323122; *Commercial, digital &
screen printing of t-shirts,
wearables & advertising
specialties*
Employs—3; Estab.—1973
Sales—$250,000
1,000 sq ft site, Distrib.—Regional
Privately owned corporation

**PRINCETON BOOK CO.**
614 U.S. Highway 130, Ste. 1-C
(08520)
**Phone—(609) 426-0602**
National—(800) 220-7149
Fax—(609) 426-1344
www.dancehorizons.com
Email—pbc@dancehorizons.com
Pres.—Charles H. Woodford
SIC—2731; *Dance book
publishing*
Employs—3; Estab.—1997
Sales—under $500,000
Distrib.—Intl.
Privately owned corporation

**RKM ENTERPRISES, INC.**
177 Mercer St. (08520)
**Phone—(609) 448-7539**
National—(800) 636-4478
Fax—(609) 448-1105
www.rkment.com
Email—daverkm@ent.com
Pres.—Dave Babcock
Manager—Kim Lemmon
SIC—2396; 2395; *Textile screen
printing & embroidery*
Employs—4; Estab.—1988
Sales—$500,000-$1Mil (est)
Distrib.—National
Privately owned corporation

**ROOF DECK, INC.**
80 Twin Rivers Dr., P.O. Box 295
(08520)
**Phone—(609) 448-6666**
Fax—(609) 443-0784
www.roofdeckinc.com
Email—info@roofdeckinc.com
Comp., GM & Pur. Agt.—Frank
LaCava
Opers. Mgr.—Fred Gettings
SIC—3444; 3441; NAICS—
332312; *Metal roof & floor decks*
Employs—10; Estab.—1972
Sales—$500,000-$1Mil
20,000 sq ft site, Distrib.—
Regional
Privately owned sub-S corp.

## Hillsborough

(Somerset—N.E.)

**3D BIOTEK, LLC**
1 Ilene Ct. (08844)
**Phone—(732) 729-6270**
Fax—(978) 382-3165

## Hillsborough—(cont.)

www.3dbiotek.com
Email—info@3dbiotek.com
CEO—Qing Liu
COO—Wing K. Lau
Sr. Ex. V.-P.—James Fay
SIC—2835; 3841; NAICS—
325410; *3D in-vitro cell culture
scaffolds & contract
manufacturing & rapid
prototyping for medical devices
& biodegradable stent
fabrication*
Employs—3; Estab.—2007
Sales—under $500,000
1,200 sq ft site, Distrib.—Intl.
Limited Liability Company

**ADAM, GATES & CO., LLC**
249 Homestead Rd. (08844)
**Phone—(908) 829-3386**
Fax—(908) 829-3387
www.adamgatescompany.com
Email—sales@
adamgatescompany.com
Member—Abdelhamid Ramadan
SIC—2899; 2865; *Fine & specialty
chemicals & near-infrared dyes*
Employs—10; Estab.—2011
Sales—$2.5Mil-$5Mil (est)
Distrib.—Intl.
Limited Liability Company

**AEROPRES CORP.**
318 Valley Rd. (08844)
**Phone—(908) 722-2571**
National—(800) 233-4001
Fax—(908) 722-8752
www.aeropres.com
Email—sales@aeropres.com
Plt. Mgr.—Gordon Sammis
Off. Mgr.—Eileen McGuire
Qual. Control Mgr.—Patrick
Caulfield
SIC—2911; NAICS—324110;
*Liquid petroleum gas processing*
Employs—8; Estab.—1979
Distrib.—Regional
Privately owned corporation
Parent co.—Aeropres Corp.,
Shreveport, LA
Phone—(318) 221-6282
See Parent Co. Section for full profile.

**AGINCOURT FINE WOOD**
212 E. Mountain Rd. (08844)
**Phone—(908) 874-4737**
Fax—(908) 874-5217
Email—agincourt.fm@earthlink.net
Owner—Francis Martin
Sales Mgr.—Barbara Martin
Mill Mgr.—Kyle Martin
SIC—2421; 2431; NAICS—
321900; *Lumber processing &
millwork*
Employs—3; Estab.—1987
Sales—under $500,000
4,000 sq ft site, Distrib.—Local
Privately owned corporation

**ALPHAGRAPHICS, INC.**
173 Route 206 N. (08844)
**Phone—(908) 281-9476**
Fax—(908) 359-7260
www.us207.alphagraphics.com
Email—us207@alphagraphics.com
Pres.—Thomas Hopkins
SIC—2752; NAICS—323100;
*Offset & digital printing*
Employs—10; Estab.—1988
Sales—$500,000-$1Mil
Distrib.—Local
Privately owned corporation

**AMERICAN BY-PRODUCTS
RECYCLERS, LLC**
301 Roycefield Rd. (08844)
**Phone—(973) 267-0109**
National—(800) 825-0630
Fax—(908) 722-5901
www.americanby-products.com
Email—info@americanby-
products.com

Owner—Robert Soracco
SIC—2899; *Biodiesel fuel from
recycled cooking oil*
Employs—10
Distrib.—Local
Limited Liability Company
AKA: Planet Earth Biodiesel

**ANDERSON MACHINE CO.**
109 Stryker Ln., Unit 10 (08844)
**Phone—(908) 281-7153**
Fax—(908) 281-9688
www.andersonmachinecompany.c
om
Email—andersonmachine@
yahoo.com
Ptnr.—John Anderson
Ptnr.—Rick Anderson
Machinist—Eric Anderson
SIC—3599; *General machining
job shop*
Employs—3; Estab.—1980
Sales—under $500,000
3,125 sq ft site, Distrib.—Local
Privately owned sub-S corp.

**APEX PRINTING SERVICES, INC.**
6 Ilene Ct., Bldg. 6, Unit 16
(08844)
**Phone—(908) 281-9221**
Fax—(908) 281-0934
www.apexprintingservices.com
Owner & Pres.—Dave Nazarenko
SIC—2752; NAICS—323100;
*Offset printing*
Employs—5; Estab.—1989
Sales—under $500,000
Distrib.—National
Sole ownership

**B & L PRINTING CO., INC.**
46 Old Camplain Rd. (08844)
**Phone—(908) 707-1311**
Fax—(908) 707-4067
www.blprinting.com
Email—sales@blprinting.com
Pres., CFO—Gerald Harris
SIC—2752; 2759; NAICS—
323100; *Commercial offset,
digital color, instant, wide-format
& variable printing, binding,
graphic design & mailing*
Employs—4; Estab.—1988
Sales—$500,000-$1Mil
2,500 sq ft site, Distrib.—Regional
Privately owned sub-S corp.
AKA: Premium Service Printing

**BELLE MEAD PRINTING, LLC**
42 Old Camplain Rd. (08844)
**Phone—(908) 595-9500**
Fax—(908) 595-9502
Email—bellemeadprinting@
verizon.net
Owner—Thomas E. Lemore
SIC—2752; 2759; NAICS—
323100; *Offset, digital &
promotional printing*
Employs—3; Estab.—1998
Sales—under $500,000
Distrib.—Local
Limited Liability Company

**BLUE CHIP INDUSTRIES, INC.**
50 Old Camplain Rd. (08844)
**Phone—(908) 704-1466**
Pres.—Carl Imhoff
SIC—3599; *General machining
job shop*
Employs—1; Estab.—1966
Sales—$500,000-$1Mil
Distrib.—National
Privately owned corporation

**C & C TOOL CO., LLC**
216 U.S. Highway 206, Ste. 2
(08844)
**Phone—(908) 431-0330**
Fax—(908) 431-0332
Email—cctoolllc@embarqmail.com
Owner & Pres.—Steven A. Calello
Machinist—Steven A. Calello, Jr.
Machinist—Patrick Anderson
Toolmaker—Robert Apisa

SIC—3544; NAICS—333500;
*Plastic injection molds for the
plastic industry*
Employs—4; Estab.—1988
Sales—$500,000
2,400 sq ft site, Distrib.—Local
Limited Liability Company

**CAPUS AUTOMATION SERVICES,
INC.**
856 Highway 206 (08844)
Mail addr: P.O. Box 1269, Belle
Mead (08502)
**Phone—(908) 281-0227**
National—(800) 678-2777
Fax—(908) 281-7882
Email—capusauto@aol.com
Pres.—Joseph B. Vautier
Accountant—Steve Brilliant
SIC—3559; *Automated material,
storage & retrieval equipment for
document & inventory
applications*
Employs—4; Estab.—1990
Sales—$1Mil-$2.5Mil
Distrib.—Intl.
Privately owned corporation

**CERTIFIED LABELING SOLUTIONS**
51 Old Camplain Rd. (08844)
**Phone—(908) 704-9997**
Fax—(908) 704-8188
www.cdpnj.com
Email—info@cdpnj.com
Pres.—Joseph F. Braun
Plt. Mgr.—Rich Pokorny
Hum. Res. & IT Mgr.—Marie Gaz
Off. Mgr.—Jennifer Walter
SIC—2672; NAICS—322222;
*Pressure-sensitive labels*
Employs—30; Estab.—1986
Sales—$5.5Mil
20,000 sq ft site, Distrib.—National
Privately owned corporation
AKA: Distributor Label Products,
Inc.

**CLANTECH, INC.**
198 Highway 206 S. (08844)
**Phone—(908) 281-7667**
Fax—(908) 281-7671
www.clantech.com
GM—David Gracie
Technician—Jason Klett
SIC—3679; *Electronic
components & equipment*
Employs—2
Sales—under $500,000 (est)

**DATATEST, INC.**
300 Valley Rd. (08844)
Mail addr: P.O. Box 801, Belle
Mead (08502)
**Phone—(908) 369-1590**
Fax—(908) 369-1594
www.datatest-inc.com
Email—sales@datatest-inc.com
Pres.—Paul Ford
Acct. & Fin. Mgr.—Bob Prendeville
SIC—3822; 3829; NAICS—
334512; *Air pollution &
combustion monitoring
equipment & process control
monitors*
Employs—25; Estab.—2002
15,000 sq ft site, Distrib.—Intl.
Privately owned corporation
AKA: Redkoh
Also see: Redkoh Industries, Inc.,
same loc.

**DEC'S METAL FABRICATION, LLC**
198 U.S. Highway Route 206,
Bldg. 4, Ste. E (08844)
**Phone—(908) 281-0283**
www.decsmetal.com
Email—decsmetal@
embarqmail.com
Owner—Adrien Dec

SIC—3444; *Sheet metal
fabrication for HVAC applications*
Employs—3; Estab.—1998
Sales—under $500,000 (est)
Distrib.—Local
Limited Liability Company

**DIE-TECH, INC.**
677 Amwell Rd. (08844)
**Phone—(908) 369-6756**
Fax—(908) 369-8875
Pres.—Joe Welches
V.-P.—Glenn Welches
SIC—3599; *Precision machining
job shop*
Employs—2; Estab.—1980
Sales—under $500,000
Distrib.—National
Privately owned corporation

**ELEMCO BUILDING CONTROLS**
14 Ilene Ct., Bldg. 11, Unit 1
(08844)
**Phone—(908) 281-2201**
Fax—(908) 359-2290
www.ebcsystemsnj.com
Email—info@ebcsystemsnj.com
Pres.—Joe Wozniak
Operation Mgr.—Christopher
Wozniak
Off. Mgr.—Kim Mackie
Engr.—David Glaser
SIC—3679; 3822; NAICS—
334512; *Mechanical HVAC,
process automation & energy
management systems for the
commercial building & IT data
center markets; Brand name—
Teletrol; Opto22; Inductive
Automation; Allen Bradley;
Sensaphone*
Employs—8; Estab.—1982
Sales—$1Mil-$5Mil
3,000 sq ft site, Distrib.—National
Privately owned sub-S corp.

**ESCO PRECISION, INC.**
71 Old Camplain Rd. (08844)
**Phone—(908) 722-0800**
Fax—(908) 722-0802
www.escoprecision.com
Email—selkholy@aol.com
Pres.—Samy Elkholy
Sales Mgr.—Abby Elkholy
SIC—3451; 3469; NAICS—
332721; *Screw machine
products & metal stampings*
Employs—17; Estab.—1981
Sales—$1Mil-$5Mil
Distrib.—Intl.
Privately owned corporation

**G & J STEEL & TUBING, INC.**
406 Roycefield Rd. (08844)
**Phone—(908) 526-4445**
National—(800) 322-8823
Fax—(908) 526-9487
www.gjsteel.com
Email—sales@gjsteel.com
Pres.—John Tursky
Cont.—Gary Borowicz
Sales Mgr.—Elizabeth Brady
Qual. Control Mgr.—Peter
Narczykiewicz
Pur. Agt.—Susan Tursky
SIC—3498; 3312; NAICS—
331210; *Fabricated metal tubing*
Employs—45; Estab.—1976
Sales—over $5Mil
25,000 sq ft site, Distrib.—Intl.
Privately owned corporation
ISO rating—9001:2000

**GENERAL TOOL SPECIALTIES, INC.**
284 Sunnymead Rd. (08844)
**Phone—(908) 874-3040**
National—(888) 436-3487
Fax—(908) 874-5777
www.generaltoolinc.com
Email—engineering@
generaltoolinc.com
Pres.—John Domici
Off. Mgr.—Susan Bittle

GEOGRAPHICAL

# Hillsborough—(cont.)

SIC—3544; NAICS—333500;
*Plastic molds*
Employs—13; Estab.—1977
Sales—$1Mil-$5Mil
Distrib.—Intl.
Privately owned corporation

**HANKIN ENVIRONMENTAL
SYSTEMS, INC.**
1 Harvard Way, Ste. 6, P.O. Box
5759 (08844)
**Phone—(908) 722-9595**
Fax—(908) 722-9514
www.hankinenv.com
Email—hankin@hankines.com
Pres.—David Chou
Ex. V-P., Opers.—Harshad Modi
MIS Mgr.—Milan Berec
Acctg. & Fin. Mgr.—Richard Sun
Doc. Coord.—Robert Dmochowski
SIC—3567; NAICS—333994;
*Multiple hearth industrial &
municipal furnaces & rotary kilns*
Employs—12; Estab.—1973
Sales—$4Mil
6,000 sq ft site, Distrib.—Intl.
Privately owned corporation

**HERCULES ENTERPRISES, LLC**
321 Valley Rd. (08844)
**Phone—(908) 369-0000**
Fax—(908) 369-0626
Pres.—Karl Massaro
Cont.—Bernard Gautier
Plt. Mgr.—Richard Libertore
Pur. Agt.—Al Alexander
SIC—3715; NAICS—336212;
*Steel container chassis for the
trucking industry*
Employs—65; Estab.—2002
Distrib.—Intl.
Privately owned corporation

**HEROFLON USA CORP.**
Home State Road 249 (08844)
**Phone—(908) 829-4949**
Fax—(908) 241-7357
www.heroflonusa.com
Email—heroflon@aol.com
Off. Mgr.—Jennifer Dockweiler
SIC—2821; NAICS—325211;
*Plastic raw materials, including
PTFE*
Employs—4; Estab.—1999
Sales—$2.5Mil-$5Mil (est)
Distrib.—National
Privately owned corporation

**INDOFINE CHEMICAL CO., INC.**
121 Stryker Ln. (08844)
**Phone—(908) 359-6778**
National—(888) 463-6346
Fax—(908) 359-1179
www.indofinechemical.com
Email—chemical@
indofinechemical.com
Pres.—Vigi Bezwada
V-P.—Sujata Moton
Dir.—Ramesh Mandadi
SIC—2899; *Organic & inorganic
chemical processing for the
pharmaceutical, biotechnology,
flavor & fragrance & agricultural
industries*
Employs—30; Estab.—1981
Sales—$10Mil-$25Mil
Distrib.—Intl.
Privately owned corporation

**INDUSTRIAL TUBE CORP.**
297 Valley Rd. (08844)
Mail addr: P.O. Box 957, Somerville
(08876)
**Phone—(908) 369-3737**
Fax—(908) 369-8805
www.industrialtubecorp.com
Email—sales@
industrialtubecorp.com
Owner & Pres., IT—Lydia
Imhauser
Corp. Secy.—Marian Imhauser
Plt. Mgr.—Matthew Gutman

Pur. Mgr.—Kenneth Imhauser
Hum. Res. Mgr.—Walter Havens
SIC—3351; NAICS—331421;
*Brass tubing*
Employs—50; Estab.—1970
Sales—$11Mil-$25Mil
Distrib.—National
Privately owned corporation

**INMAT INC.**
216 U.S. Highway 206, Ste. 7
(08844)
Mail addr: P.O. Box 7, Raritan
(08869)
**Phone—(908) 874-7788**
www.inmat.com
Email—contact@inmat.com
Pres., CEO—Harris Goldberg
Off. Mgr.—Patti Plytynski
SIC—2851; NAICS—325510;
*Specialty nanocomposite barrier
coatings; Brand name—
Nanolok™; Air D-Fense™*
Employs—6; Estab.—1999
Sales—$2.5Mil-$5Mil
4,000 sq ft site, Distrib.—Intl.
Privately owned corporation

**INNOVATIVE MFG., INC.**
198 U.S. Highway 206, Ste. 4
(08844)
**Phone—(908) 904-1884**
Fax—(908) 904-6433
www.innomfg.com
Email—innovativemfg@earthlink.net
Owner—Kevin Lovell
Hum. Res. Mgr.—Jessica Villa
Qual. Assur. Inspector—Dan
Lovell
SIC—3599; *General machining
job shop*
Employs—17; Estab.—1999
Sales—$1Mil-$2.5Mil (est)
Distrib.—Regional
Privately owned corporation

**J K DESIGN, INC.**
465 Amwell Rd. (08844)
**Phone—(908) 428-4700**
Fax—(908) 428-4701
www.jkdesign.com
Pres.—Jerome Kaulius
Off. Mgr.—Jennifer Simone
SIC—2791; 2796; NAICS—
323122; *Computerized
typesetting & color separations*
Employs—45; Estab.—1992
Distrib.—Local
Privately owned corporation

**J N R MACHINE & TOOL**
12 Ilene Ct., Bldg. 12, Unit 2
(08844)
**Phone—(908) 281-6603**
Fax—(908) 281-7418
Pres.—John Radecsky
Pur. Agt.—Neal Tabor
SIC—3599; *Precision machining
job shop*
Employs—2; Estab.—1979
Sales—under $500,000
2,000 sq ft site, Distrib.—Local
Privately owned partnership

**KLEIN RECYCLING**
2156 Camplain Rd. *(08844)*
**Phone—(908) 722-2288**
Fax—(908) 722-9052
www.kleinrecycling.com
Email—rsant@kleinrecycling.com
Pres.—Richard Santaniello
Buyer—Lori Treier
Buyer—Nick Santaniello
SIC—3312; 3341; *Scrap metal
recycling*
Employs—15; Estab.—2002
Sales—$2.5Mil-$5Mil (est)
Distrib.—Local
Privately owned corporation

**KWG INDUSTRIES, LLC**
330 Roycefield Rd., Unit B (08844)
**Phone—(908) 218-8900**
Fax—(908) 218-1888

www.kwgindustries.com
Email—sales@kwgindustries.com
Pres., CEO—Kurt W. Grimm
Cont.—Margaret Peterson
SIC—3599; 5051; NAICS—
331312; *Manufacturer of
precision machined parts for
OEMs & stocking distributor of
aluminum, stainless steel, metal,
carbon steel, copper & steel;
Brand name—Sapa Extruded
Products; Crucible Stainless
Steels*
Employs—15; Estab.—1996
Sales—$5Mil-$10Mil
20,000 sq ft site, Distrib.—Intl.
Limited Liability Company
ISO rating—9001:2008
DBA: Peterson & Marsh Metals
AKA: Jersey Machine & Tool

**LI'L INSPIRATIONS, LLC**
P.O. Box 5754 (08844)
**Phone—(908) 369-5840**
www.lil-inspirations.com
Email—shop2@lil-inspirations.com
Pres.—Sandra Kircher
SIC—2395; *Custom embroidery of
personalized wedding
handkerchiefs, throw blankets &
gifts*
Employs—2; Estab.—1992
Sales—under $500,000
Distrib.—Intl.
Limited Liability Company

**LITTLE JOE INDUSTRIES**
10 Ilene Ct., Ste. 4 (08844)
**Phone—(908) 359-5213**
Fax—(908) 359-5724
www.littlejoe.com
Email—info@littlejoe.com
Owner—Michael Engel
SIC—3826; *Ink testing equipment*
Employs—4; Estab.—1965
Sales—under $500,000
3,000 sq ft site, Distrib.—Intl.
Privately owned corporation

**LOUMARC SIGNS**
178 Route 206 (08844)
**Phone—(908) 575-4000**
Fax—(908) 575-4010
www.loumarcsigns.com
Email—sales@loumarcsigns.com
Pres.—Larry Gliozzi
Prodn. Mgr.—Diana Diaz
Off. Mgr.—Laura Shreve
SIC—3993; *Interior & exterior
signs, including design,
production, installation, service
& permit service*
Employs—6; Estab.—1984
Sales—$500,000-$1Mil
1,900 sq ft site, Distrib.—National
Privately owned sub-S corp.

**†M & A RECYCLING**
65 Old Camplain Rd. (08844)
**Phone—(908) 218-9191**
Fax—(908) 218-1139
www.marecycling.com
Email—ma-recycling@yahoo.com
Owner—Jake Fiedler
SIC—5093; *Wholesaler of
recycled scrap metals*
Employs—10; Estab.—1989
Distrib.—Local
Privately owned sub-S corp.

**†MEL-PAK EQUIPMENT CO.**
649 U.S. Highway 206, Ste. 9-303
(08844-1520)
**Phone—(201) 825-2624**
www.mel-pak.com
Email—sales@mel-pak.com
Pres., GM—Mike Mellone

SIC—5084; *Wholesaler of
packaging machinery &
automation for the cosmetic,
pharmaceutical, personal care,
food & medical device
industries; Brand name—Omega
Design Corp; Filamatic; MGS
Machinery; UAC Packaging;
McBrady; CSI; Clear
Automation; LSI*
Employs—2; Estab.—1968
2,000 sq ft site, Distrib.—Regional
Privately owned corporation

**MENCO BUSINESS PRODUCTS**
178 Route 206 S. (08844)
**Phone—(908) 281-0911**
Fax—(908) 281-0711
www.mencotech.com
Pres.—Ozzie Mendez
V-P.—Richard Lattanzi
Art Dir.—Mark Raskin
SIC—2752; 2791; 2796; NAICS—
323122; *Offset printing,
typesetting & color separations*
Employs—15; Estab.—1984
Distrib.—Local
Privately owned corporation

**†MINERAIS U. S., LLC**
105 Raider Blvd., Ste. 104 (08844)
**Phone—(908) 874-7666**
Fax—(908) 874-7725
www.mineraisus.com
Email—sales@mineraisus.com
CEO—Tom Mayrides
SIC—5051; *Distributor of metal
alloys*
Employs—13
Distrib.—Intl.
Limited Liability Company

**MOLECU-WIRE CORP.**
56 Old Camplain Rd. (08844)
Mail addr: P.O. Box 5426,
Somerset (08875)
**Phone—(732) 296-9473**
Fax—(732) 296-9683
www.molecu.com
Email—piczar@aol.com
Pres.—Vinod Barot
V-P., Opers.—Hung Chan
Dir., Mktg.—Stephen Tetorka
Sales Mgr.—Nancy Roake
Plt. Mgr.—Edward Clark
Qual. Assur. Mgr.—Steve Mabil
SIC—3357; *Copper & insulated
wires*
Employs—80; Estab.—1958
70,000 sq ft site, Distrib.—Intl.
Privately owned corporation

**NATURAL DENTAL STUDIOS, INC.**
216 U.S. Highway 206, Ste. 23
(08844)
**Phone—(908) 281-0089**
National—(800) 223-0811
Fax—(908) 281-9562
Email—naturaldental@aol.com
Pres.—Charles Palmieri
SIC—3843; *Dental restoration
products*
Employs—5; Estab.—1978
Sales—$500,000-$1Mil (est)
1,800 sq ft site, Distrib.—Regional
Privately owned corporation

**OLSON MOTOR & CONTROL CO.,
INC.**
100 Old Camplain Rd. (08844)
Mail addr: P.O. Box 55, Manville
(08835)
**Phone—(908) 231-1500**
Fax—(908) 231-9557
Email—wolson@olsonmc.com
Pres.—William Olson
V-P., Opers.—Eric Olson
GM & Bus. Mgr.—Ann Olson
Off. Mgr.—Victoria Malfitano
Control Sys. Designer—Mike
Ostaszewski

## Hillsborough—(cont.)

SIC—3613; NAICS—335313;
*Custom electrical panels &
enclosures*
Employs—15; Estab.—1984
Distrib.—Intl.
Privately owned corporation

**PERMADUR INDUSTRIES, INC.**
186 U.S. Highway 206 S. (08844-
4123)
**Phone—(908) 359-9767**
National—(800) 392-0146
Fax—(908) 359-9773
www.permadur.com
Email—info@permadur.com
Pres.—William A. Schneider
CFO—Mary Emily Schneider
SIC—3536; NAICS—333923;
*Hoists, cranes, table & vehicle
lifts, hot stamping machines &
lifting magnets; Brand name—
Permadur*
Employs—63; Estab.—1972
32,000 sq ft site, Distrib.—Intl.
Privately owned corporation
Also see: Sissco Material
Handling, same loc.

**PRESTIGE MILLWORK, LLC**
152 U.S. Highway 206, Bldg. 17-A
*(08844)*
**Phone—(908) 526-5100**
Fax—(908) 526-5109
www.prestigemillworkllc.com
Email—mindyz@
prestigemillworkllc.com
Owner, Pres. & Sales Mgr.—Dan
Bugasch
Off. Mgr.—Mindy L. Zankel
Estimator—James Hoyte
SIC—2431; 2499; NAICS—
321900; *Architectural woodwork
& casework*
Employs—25; Estab.—1987
50,000 sq ft site, Distrib.—Local
Sole ownership

†**PROVEN TECHNOLOGY, INC.**
5 Woodshire Way (08844)
**Phone—(908) 359-7888**
www.industrialblowmolding.com
Email—rslawska@aol.com
Pres.—Robert Slawska
SIC—5084; *Wholesaler of plastics
machinery & equipment*
Employs—5; Estab.—1994
Sales—under $500,000
Distrib.—National
Privately owned corporation

**RC FINE FOODS, INC.**
139 Stryker Ln. (08844)
Mail addr: P.O. Box 236, Belle
Mead (08502-0236)
**Phone—(908) 359-5500**
National—(800) 526-3953
Fax—(908) 359-6957
www.rcfinefoods.com
Pres.—Susan Goldman
V-P.—Gary Cohen
Secy-Treas.—Barbara Cohen
SIC—2034; 2035; 2087; 2099;
NAICS—311900; *Soup, sauce,
gravy, salad dressing & dessert
mixes, soup bases, extracts &
specialty foods*
Employs—70; Estab.—1972
Sales—$5Mil–$10Mil
48,000 sq ft site, Distrib.—National
Privately owned sub-S corp.

**RECKITT BENCKISER, LLC**
Div. of Reckitt Benckiser, Inc.
799 U.S. Highway 206, P.O. Box
5817 (08844)
**Phone—(908) 533-2000**
Fax—(908) 533-2066
www.reckittbenckiser.com
Email—info@reckittbenckiser.com
Plt. Mgr.—Cal Smedberg
Hum. Res. Mgr.—Berniece
Jennifer

SIC—2842; NAICS—325612;
*Household & professional
cleaning supplies*
Employs—230; Estab.—1976
400,000 sq ft site, Distrib.—Intl.
Publicly owned corporation
Parent co.—Reckitt Benckiser,
Inc., Parsippany, NJ
Phone—(973) 404-2600
See Parent Co. Section for full profile.

**REDKOH INDUSTRIES, INC.**
300 Valley Rd. (08844)
Mail addr: P.O. Box 801, Belle
Mead (08502)
**Phone—(908) 369-1590**
Fax—(908) 369-1594
www.redkoh.com
Email—redkoh@redkoh.com
Pres.—Paul Ford
Plt. Mgr.—John Jannone
Off. Mgr.—Belinda Halloran
Fin. Mgr.—Robert Prendeville
Engrg. Mgr.—Neil Flynn
SIC—3679; *Electronic pollution
control components*
Employs—23; Estab.—1982
Sales—$6Mil–$10Mil
3,200 sq ft site, Distrib.—Intl.
Privately owned corporation
Also see: Datatest, Inc., same loc.

**ROYAL CABINET CO., INC.**
152 U.S. Highway 206, Unit 14-D
(08844-4128)
**Phone—(908) 203-8000**
Fax—(908) 203-8400
www.royalcabinet.com
Email—info@royalcabinet.com
Pres.—Paul Y. McDonald
Pur. Agt.—Maciej Podstawski
SIC—2434; 2542; NAICS—
337110; *Wooden, laminated &
commercial kitchen cabinets*
Employs—30; Estab.—1962
Sales—$4Mil
44,000 sq ft site, Distrib.—
Regional
Privately owned sub-S corp.

**SC ENGINEERING CO., INC.**
115 Stryker Ln., Bldg. 4 (08844)
**Phone—(908) 874-5955**
Fax—(908) 874-6349
www.scpumps.com
Email—info@scpumps.com
Pres.—Tom Arias
V-P.—Howard Lacks
SIC—3561; 3566; NAICS—
333911; *Vertical turbine pumps,
pumping equipment, gear
drives, drive shaft & supplies,
including millwright service &
alignments*
Employs—7; Estab.—1980
Sales—$1Mil–$2.5Mil
Distrib.—Regional
Privately owned corporation

**SISSCO MATERIAL HANDLING**
186 Route 206 S. (08844)
**Phone—(908) 359-9767**
National—(800) 392-0146
Fax—(908) 359-9773
www.sisscohoist.com
Email—info@sisscohoist.com
Pres.—William Schneider, Sr.
SIC—3536; NAICS—333923;
*Hoists, cranes, jib cranes &
monorails; Brand name—
Permadur*
Employs—49; Estab.—1972
32,000 sq ft site, Distrib.—Intl.
Privately owned corporation
Also see: Permadur Industries,
Inc., same loc.
AKA: PermaDur Industries

**SNYDER MACHINE CO.**
214 Sunnymead Rd. (08844)
**Phone—(908) 359-2745**
Fax—(908) 359-2745
Email—smceric@earthlink.net
Owner—Eric Snyder

SIC—3599; *General machining
job shop*
Employs—1; Estab.—1983
Sales—under $500,000
1,200 sq ft site, Distrib.—Regional
Sole ownership

**SOUND MANAGEMENT GROUP**
5 Ilene Ct., Bldg. 7, Unit 3, P.O. Box
6060 (08844)
**Phone—(908) 874-7826**
National—(800) 221-0580
Fax—(908) 874-4525
www.smg-corp.com
Email—info@smg-corp.com
Pres.—Arthur P. Barkman
V-P., Sales—Michael E. Barkman
V-P., Mktg.—Keith P. Barkman
V-P.—Paul R. Barkman
SIC—3446; NAICS—332323;
*Sound-masking systems,
including acoustical wall panels,
blinds & barrier systems &
ceiling treatments; Brand
name—Sound Shadow®;
SoundElite®; SoundDelete®*
Employs—6; Estab.—1993
Sales—$500,000–$1Mil
3,000 sq ft site, Distrib.—National
Limited Liability Company

**SWISS ORTHOPEDIC CO., INC.**
188 Highway 206 (08844)
**Phone—(908) 874-5522**
Fax—(908) 874-8821
www.swiss-orthopedic.com
Email—swissortho@
embarqmail.com
Pres.—Peter Seitz
V-P.—Holger Drallmayer
Technician—Bill Koster Bocco
SIC—3842; *Artificial limbs &
braces*
Employs—4; Estab.—1989
2,500 sq ft site, Distrib.—Local
Privately owned corporation

**THINFILMS, INC.**
15 Ilene Ct., Ste. 6 (08844)
**Phone—(908) 359-7014**
Fax—(908) 359-7015
www.thinfilmsinc.com
Email—am@thinfilmsinc.com
Pres.—Arshad Mumtaz
Administrator—Meryl Seigel
SIC—3479; 2821; *Thin film
coatings*
Employs—11; Estab.—1988
Sales—$2Mil–$2.5Mil
6,000 sq ft site, Distrib.—Intl.
Privately owned sub-S corp.
ISO rating—9001:2008

**TOP KNOBS USA, INC.**
170 Township Line Rd., Bldg. D
(08844)
Mail addr: P.O. Box 779, Belle
Mead (08502)
**Phone—(908) 359-6174**
National—(800) 499-9095
Fax—(888) 486-7566
www.topknobs.com
Email—customerservice@
topknobs.com
Pres.—Warren Ramsland
Hum. Res. Mgr.—Paul Mulhern
Sales Admn.—David Tyler
Cust. Serv. Specialist—Brian
Lancsak
SIC—3429; *Kitchen & bath drawer
& cabinet knobs, handles &
accessories*
Employs—35; Estab.—1998
Distrib.—National
Privately owned corporation

**TRI-DELTA PLASTICS, INC.**
208 Cougar Ct. (08844)
**Phone—(908) 722-6021**
Fax—(908) 725-8824
www.tridelplastics.com
Email—info@tridelplastics.com
Pres.—Thomas Dolan
V-P., Sales & Mktg.—Brian Dolan

V-P., Opers.—Paul Rolando
Acct. & Hum. Res. Mgr.—Karen
Cipolloni
Cust. Serv. Mgr.—Peggy
Masterson
SIC—3085; NAICS—326160;
*Plastic bottles*
Employs—90; Estab.—1989
88,000 sq ft site, Distrib.—Intl.
Privately owned sub-S corp.

**TUR MACHINE, LLC**
198 U.S. Highway 206, Ste. 5
(08844)
**Phone—(908) 874-0235**
Fax—(908) 874-9589
www.turmachine.com
Email—info@turmachine.com
Ptnr.—Zbigniew Richard Rolka
Ptnr.—Lucjan Wiercinski
Pres.—Richard Rolka
SIC—3599; 3429; 3449; 3499;
*General machining shop*
Employs—6; Estab.—2000
Sales—under $500,000
Distrib.—National
Limited Liability Company

†**UAC PACKAGING, LLC**
330 Roycefield Rd., Unit C *(08844)*
**Phone—(908) 595-6890**
Fax—(908) 595-6893
www.uacpackaging.com
Email—cappers@
uacpackaging.com
Pres.—Charles Bernius
SIC—5084; *Distributor of
automatic capping machinery &
parts*
Employs—10; Estab.—2001
Sales—$1Mil–$2.5Mil
6,000 sq ft site, Distrib.—Intl.
Limited Liability Company

**ZALA MACHINE CO., INC.**
109 Stryker Ln., Ste. 11 (08844-
1911)
**Phone—(908) 431-9106**
Fax—(908) 431-9430
www.zalamachine.com
Email—sales@zalamachine.com
Owner & Pres.—Stanley Zala
Cont.—Joanna Zala
Manager—Martin Zala
SIC—3599; *Medium & large
machining, including turning,
milling, gundrilling, honing,
grinding & weldments of
precision machine parts for the
oil & gas, power generation,
automotive & plastic & rubber
extrusion industries*
Employs—15; Estab.—2001
Sales—$1.7Mil
10,000 sq ft site, Distrib.—
Regional
Privately owned corporation

## Hillsdale

(Bergen—N.E.)

**BUILDING PERFORMANCE
EQUIPMENT, INC.**
80 Broadway, Ste. 101 (07642)
**Phone—(201) 722-1414**
Fax—(201) 722-0999
www.lowkwh.com
Email—jackie@lowkwh.com
CEO—Klas Haglid
Off. Mgr.—Jackie McGrath
SIC—3564; NAICS—333400;
*High-efficiency energy recovery
ventilation systems for
commercial & residential
applications*
Employs—10; Estab.—1998
Sales—$1Mil–$2.5Mil
Distrib.—Intl.
Privately owned corporation

**GEOGRAPHICAL**

## Hillsdale—(cont.)

**JAN-MAR INDUSTRIES**
568 Hillsdale, P.O. Box 314 (07642)
**Phone—(201) 664-3930**
Email—janmarind@optonline.net
Pres.—Mark Biddelman
SIC—3931; NAICS—339992; *Musical instrument accessories; Brand name—Eddie Bell Guitar Accessories*
Employs—1; Estab.—1971
Sales—under $500,000
Distrib.—National
Privately owned corporation

**NEW ENTRY**
**MILLER CORP., CAROL S.**
98 Saddlewood Dr., Ste. A (07642)
**Phone—(201) 406-4578**
www.carolsmillerhandbags.com
Email—carolmiller@gmail.com
Pres.—Carol Schepker
SIC—3171; *Women's handbags*
Employs—4
Sales—under $500,000 (est)

**UNIMADE METALS, INC.**
115 Patterson St. (07642)
**Phone—(201) 666-7747**
Fax—(201) 666-3611
www.unimade.com
Email—eng@unimade.com
Pres.—F. Borosch
Treas., GM—Steven Vajay
Dir., Admn.—Marion C. Vajay
SIC—3444; 3599; *Precision sheet metal & machined products*
Employs—12; Estab.—1980
12,000 sq ft site, Distrib.—Regional
Privately owned corporation

---

## Hillside
(Union—N.E.)

**ABBA PRODUCTS CORP.**
1301 Central Ave. (07205)
**Phone—(908) 353-0669**
Fax—(908) 353-2065
www.abbaseed.com
Email—mike@abbaseed.com
Pres., GM—Mike Abbate
Opers. Mgr.—Hubert Tonealbes
SIC—2048; *Bird feed*
Employs—100; Estab.—1973
Sales—$6Mil-$10Mil
85,000 sq ft site, Distrib.—Intl.
Privately owned corporation

**ABELES & HEYMANN KOSHER PRODUCTS**
739 Ramsey Ave. (07205)
**Phone—(908) 206-8886**
Fax—(908) 206-8632
www.abeles-heymann.com
Email—sl@aandh.us
Pres., CEO—Micha Rakaby
Hum. Res. Mgr.—Martin Word
R & D Mgr.—Seth Leavitt
Bookkeeper—Arlene Yelverton
SIC—2013; NAICS—311600; *Kosher deli foods & packaging*
Employs—25; Estab.—1997
2,500 sq ft site, Distrib.—National
Limited Liability Company

**†ADDRESSING MACHINE SUPPLY**
1290 Central Ave. (07205)
**Phone—(908) 289-7900**
Fax—(908) 289-7911
www.amsstore.net
Email—sales@amsstore.net
Pres.—Herbert Singe
V.-P., Sales & Serv. & GM—David Stackewicz
SIC—5044; *Distributor of new, refurbished & pre-owned mailing machines & supplies*
Employs—13; Estab.—1961
Sales—$500,000-$1Mil
15,000 sq ft site, Distrib.—Regional
Privately owned corporation

**ALL AMERICAN GRAPHIC ARTS**
763 Ramsey Ave. (07205)
**Phone—(908) 686-1479**
Fax—(908) 686-2815
Owner—Ed Rodriguez
GM—Connie Rodriguez
SIC—2759; 3497; NAICS—323100; *Foil stamping & embossing & stationery engraving*
Employs—2; Estab.—1981
Sales—under $500,000
Distrib.—Local
Privately owned corporation

**ALL BRIGHT METAL FINISHING, LLC**
760 Ramsey Ave. (07205)
**Phone—(908) 206-9411**
Fax—(908) 206-9412
www.allbrightmetalnj.com
Email—allbrightmetalfinishing@msn.com
Owner—Mario Cerva
SIC—3471; NAICS—332813; *Metal finishing*
Employs—1; Estab.—2010
Sales—under $500,000
Distrib.—Local
Limited Liability Company

**AMERICAN STONE, INC.**
215 Route 22 W. (07205)
**Phone—(973) 318-7707**
Fax—(973) 318-7667
Email—amerstone@aol.com
V.-P.—Steve Young
Off. Mgr.—Kaitlynn Safonie
SIC—3281; NAICS—327991; *Marble & granite products*
Employs—9; Estab.—1995
Sales—$500,000-$1Mil (est)
Distrib.—Regional
Privately owned corporation

**ARCH CROWN, INC.**
460 Hillside Ave., Ste. 1 (07205-1100)
**Phone—(973) 731-6300**
National—(800) 526-8353
Fax—(973) 731-2228
www.archcrown.com
Email—info@archcrown.com
CEO—Norman Liebman
Pres.—Craig Meadow
IT Mgr.—Luke Ayd
Bookkeeper & Hum. Res. Mgr.—Judy Buttle
Off. Mgr.—Sandy Desai
SIC—2759; 2675; 2789; 3577; NAICS—323100; *Tags & labels, including die cutting, foil stamping & bar coding systems & supplies*
Employs—32; Estab.—1907
Distrib.—National
Privately owned corporation

**ARNOLD DESKS, INC.**
Div. of Arnold Furniture Mfrs., Inc.
1409 Chestnut Ave., P.O. Box 842 (07205)
**Phone—(908) 686-5656**
Fax—(908) 686-9401
www.thearnoldgroup.com
Email—mat@thearnoldgroup.com
Steel Mgr.—Matt Stoffers
Bookkeeper—Donna Weeks
Estimator—John Smith
SIC—2522; NAICS—337214; *Contemporary & traditional case goods*
Employs—18; Estab.—1977
Distrib.—National
Privately owned corporation

Parent co.—Arnold Furniture Mfrs., Inc., Irvington, NJ
Phone—(973) 399-0505
See Parent Co. Section for full profile.

**ARROW ENGINEERING CO.**
260 Pennsylvania Ave. (07205)
**Phone—(908) 353-5233**
Fax—(908) 353-8362
www.arroweng.com
Email—sales@arroweng.com
Pres.—Raymond Fluet
Bookkeeper—Ragaa Messieh
SIC—3821; NAICS—339111; *Laboratory equipment, including laboratory mixers*
Employs—20; Estab.—1945
Sales—$1Mil-$5Mil
10,000 sq ft site, Distrib.—National
Privately owned corporation
Also see: Fluets Corp., same loc.

**AWARDS TROPHY CO.**
611 U.S. Highway 22 (07205)
**Phone—(908) 687-5775**
Fax—(908) 687-3451
www.awardstrophy.com
Email—rene@awardstrophy.com
Owner—Ed Gallo
SIC—3993; 3479; *Trophies, plaques, pins, medals & advertising specialties*
Employs—5; Estab.—1968
2,800 sq ft site, Distrib.—National
Privately owned corporation

**AYERS PRINTING**
1413 Chestnut Ave. (07205)
**Phone—(908) 687-2891**
Fax—(908) 687-1203
www.ayersco.com
Email—sales@ayersco.com
Pres.—James L. Ayers
SIC—2759; NAICS—323100; *Commercial printing*
Employs—5; Estab.—1923
Sales—under $500,000
6,000 sq ft site, Distrib.—National
Privately owned sub-S corp.

**BANNER DESIGN**
600 N. Union Ave., P.O. Box 5343 (07205)
**Phone—(908) 687-5335**
National—(800) 426-9744
Fax—(908) 687-7447
www.800-4-any-sign.com
Email—solutions@800-4-any-sign.com
Sales Mgr.—Bill Levy
SIC—3993; *Graphic & industrial design, signs, displays, exhibits & wood, metal & plastic fabricating*
Employs—40; Estab.—1986
Sales—$5Mil-$10Mil
78,000 sq ft site, Distrib.—Intl.
Privately owned corporation
ISO rating—9001:2000

**BASIC TOOL & DIE CORP.**
752 Ramsey Ave. (07205)
**Phone—(908) 688-9155**
Fax—(908) 688-0335
www.press-brake-dies.com
Email—basictool@att.net
Pres.—James Tollar
Secy.-Treas.—Robert Wuerthner
SIC—3469; 3544; NAICS—333500; *Metal stampings & press brake dies; Brand name—Johanna Roller Shade Brackets*
Employs—4; Estab.—1977
Sales—$500,000
4,000 sq ft site, Distrib.—Regional
Privately owned sub-S corp.

**BEAU LABEL LLC**
385 Hillside Ave. (07205)
**Phone—(973) 318-7800**
National—(800) 523-2328
Fax—(973) 318-7808
www.beaulabel.com
Email—vjmelapioni@beaulabel.com

Pres.—Vincent J. Melapioni
Cont.—Charina Affronti
Plt. Mgr.—Tom Savona
Estimator—Carlene Lewis
SIC—2672; NAICS—322222; *Pressure-sensitive labels*
Employs—80; Estab.—1967
Distrib.—National
Limited Liability Company

**BROOK METAL PRODUCTS, INC.**
6 Evans Terminal (07205)
**Phone—(908) 355-1601**
Fax—(908) 527-0305
Email—brookmetal@mindspring.com
Pres., Off. Mgr.—Wendy Merendino
SIC—3444; 3599; NAICS—332312; *Welding & sheet metal fabrication*
Employs—8; Estab.—1987
Sales—$2.5Mil-$5Mil
Distrib.—National
Privately owned corporation

**BUTLER ENGINEERING ASSOCS., INC.**
764 Ramsey Ave. (07205)
**Phone—(908) 688-3300**
Fax—(908) 688-1903
Email—sales@butlerwc.com
Pres.—Chad Hetzel
Supervisor—Bob Wood
SIC—2899; *HVAC water treatment products*
Employs—12; Estab.—1938
Sales—$500,000-$1Mil
10,000 sq ft site, Distrib.—National
Privately owned corporation

**CAMEO NOVELTY & PEN**
400 Hillside Ave. (07205)
**Phone—(973) 923-1600**
National—(800) 832-2636
Fax—(973) 923-8480
www.cameoline.com
Email—sol@cameoline.com
Pres.—Sol Oberlander
Hum. Res. & IT Mgr.—Sam Oberlander
Cust. Serv. Rep.—Stephanie Jimenez
SIC—2759; 2396; NAICS—323100; *Promotional product screen printing, including pens, pencils, mugs, bags & key chains*
Employs—20; Estab.—2006
Sales—$500,000-$1Mil
Distrib.—Local
Privately owned corporation

**†CASINGS OF NJ, INC.**
Div. of Casings, Inc.
711 Ramsey Ave. (07205)
**Phone—(908) 851-7766**
www.casingsinc.com
Email—info@casingsinc.com
Br. Mgr.—Bill Evans
SIC—5093; 5014; *Wholesaler of recycled tires*
Employs—30; Estab.—1973
Distrib.—National
Privately owned corporation
Parent co.—Casings, Inc., Catskill, NY
Phone—(518) 943-9404
See Parent Co. Section for full profile.

**CERTIFIED PROCESSING CORP.**
184 Route 22 E. (07205)
**Phone—(973) 923-5200**
Pres.—Paul P. Iacono
SIC—2833; NAICS—325411; *Caffeine refining*
Employs—2; Estab.—1960
Sales—under $500,000
35,000 sq ft site, Distrib.—National
Privately owned corporation

## Hillside—(cont.)

**COCOA PROCESSING CORP.**
Div. of Mecca & Sons Trucking Corp.
650 Ramsey Ave. (07205)
Mail addr: 580 Luis Munoz Marin Blvd, Jersey City (07310-1416)
Phone—**(201) 792-5866**
Fax—(201) 792-7090
www.meccatrucking.com
Email—anthony.hodge@meccatrucking.com
V-P.—Michael Mecca
GM—Anthony Hodge
SIC—2066; NAICS—311300; *Cocoa & sugar processing*
Employs—10; Estab.—1987
Sales—$1Mil-$2.5Mil
Distrib.—Intl.
Privately owned corporation
Parent co.—Mecca & Sons Trucking Corp., Jersey City, NJ
Phone—(201) 792-5866
See Parent Co. Section for full profile.

**†COOPER ALLOY CORP.**
201 Sweetland Ave. (07205)
Phone—**(908) 688-4216**
Fax—(908) 686-9314
www.vanton.com
Email—mkt@vanton.com
Pres.—Stuart Cooper
Hum. Res. Mgr.—Barbara Riscinti
SIC—5093; *Wholesaler of scrap metal*
Employs—15; Estab.—1950
Distrib.—National
Privately owned corporation
Also see: Vanton Pump & Equipment Corp., same loc.

**DEITZ & SONS, INC., M.**
490 Hillside Ave. (07205)
Phone—**(908) 686-8800**
(908) 686-6601
National—(888) 300-5790
Fax—(908) 686-6602
www.mdeitz.com
Email—info@mdeitz.com
Pres.—Ken Deitz
V-P.—Steve Deitz
SIC—2531; 2599; *Wooden restaurant chairs & barstools & metal table bases & tabletops*
Employs—15; Estab.—1921
Sales—$1Mil-$2.5Mil
45,000 sq ft site, Distrib.—Intl.
Privately owned sub-S corp.

**DIVERSIFIED DISPLAY PRODUCTS, LLC**
777 Ramsey Ave., P.O. Box 913 (07205)
Phone—**(908) 686-2200**
Fax—(908) 686-3984
www.ddpmsc.com
Email—info@ddpmsc.com
Owner—David Rosen
Off. Mgr.—Jacqui Wolf
SIC—2672; NAICS—322222; *Coated paper products*
Employs—24; Estab.—1985
25,000 sq ft site, Distrib.—Local
Limited Liability Company

**DORAN SLING & ASSEMBLY CORP.**
1285 Central Ave. (07205)
Phone—**(908) 351-7800**
Fax—(908) 355-5544
www.bilcogroup.com
Email—sales@bilcogroup.com
CEO—Barry Lemberg
Pres.—Michael Cuccinello
Comp.—Carla Ferreira
SIC—3496; 3429; 2298; *Wire rope, chain, nylon & wire rope slings, shackles, turnbuckles & rigging hardware*
Employs—24; Estab.—1981
55,000 sq ft site, Distrib.—Intl.
Privately owned corporation
AKA: Bilco Wire Rope

**FEDERAL LABEL SYSTEMS, INC.**
385 Hillside Ave. (07205)
Phone—**(917) 331-7979**
(718) 899-6000
Fax—(973) 318-7808
www.federal-label.com
Email—prothchild@federallabel.com
Pres.—Paul E. Rothchild
SIC—2759; NAICS—323100; *Instant redeemable coupons & extended text labels*
Employs—40; Estab.—1904
Sales—$6Mil-$10Mil
45,000 sq ft site, Distrib.—Regional
Privately owned corporation

**FLUETS CORP.**
260 Pennsylvania Ave. (07205)
Phone—**(908) 353-5229**
Fax—(908) 353-8362
www.fluetscorp.com
Pres.—Ray Fluet
Off. Mgr. & Admn.—Roger Fluet
Bookkeeper—Ragaa Messieh
SIC—3599; *Precision machining job shop*
Employs—30; Estab.—1965
Sales—$500,000-$1Mil
10,000 sq ft site, Distrib.—National
Privately owned corporation
Also see: Arrow Engineering Co., same loc.

**G & H SHEET METAL WORKS, INC.**
1423 Chestnut Ave. *(07205)*
Phone—**(973) 923-1100**
Fax—(973) 923-8501
www.ghsmw.com
Email—info@ghsmw.com
Pres. & Proj. Mgr.—Eric Heide
V-P., Engrg.—Donald G. Shaffer
SIC—3444; *Sheet metal fabrication*
Employs—12; Estab.—1938
Sales—$500,000-$1Mil
16,000 sq ft site, Distrib.—Local
Privately owned sub-S corp.

**†GLENWOOD OFFICE FURNITURE II, INC.**
561 U.S. Highway 22 (07205-1914)
Phone—**(908) 687-3770**
(201) 401-7005
National—(888) 449-3375
Fax—(908) 687-4111
www.glenwoodoffice.com
Email—ravi@glenwoodoffice.com
Owner & V-P.—Ravi Uppal
SIC—5021; *Distributor of new & used commercial-grade office furniture, including installation & moving services; Brand name—Office Star; AIS; First Office; OFS; Jofco; Compatico; National; Farifield; Arnold; Nucraft; Pre-owned Steelcase; Knoll; Herman Miller*
Employs—7; Estab.—2005
Sales—over $1.5Mil
10,000 sq ft site, Distrib.—Regional
Privately owned corporation

**H & H SWISS SCREW MACHINE PRODUCTS CO., INC.**
1478 Chestnut Ave. *(07205)*
Phone—**(908) 688-6390**
National—(800) 826-9985
Fax—(908) 688-3503
www.hhswiss.com
Email—bhardman@hhswiss.com
Pres.—Darryl Stacy
V-P., Fin.—Diane C. Lucas
Dir., Sales & Mktg.—Brett Hardman

SIC—3451; 3499; 3599; NAICS—332721; *Precision custom CNC Swiss screw machine parts & components for the aerospace, communications, electrical/electronics, insert molding, instrumentation, medical, military & vehicle controls industries, including Swiss automatics & escomatics*
Employs—55; Estab.—1940
Sales—$5Mil-$10Mil
28,500 sq ft site, Distrib.—National
Privately owned corporation
ISO rating—AS9100, 9001

**HELLER TRUCK BODY CORP.**
138 U.S. Highway 22 (07205)
Phone—**(973) 923-9200**
Fax—(973) 923-9269
www.hellertruck.com
Email—contactus@hellertruck.com
Pres., CEO—Darryl Novak
SIC—3713; NAICS—336211; *Custom aluminum & fiberglass reinforced plastic refrigerated, city delivery, platform, stake & moving van bodies, including liftgates installation*
Employs—3; Estab.—1948
Sales—$1Mil
Distrib.—Local
Privately owned sub-S corp.

**HILLSIDE BOTTLING CORP.**
1 Evans Terminal (07205)
Phone—**(908) 353-6773**
Fax—(908) 353-3213
Email—hillsidebev@aol.com
Plt. Mgr.—Frank Zurawel
Off. Admn.—Jenny Lopez
SIC—2086; NAICS—312100; *Soft drinks*
Employs—10; Estab.—1996
Distrib.—National
Privately owned corporation

**HILLSIDE CANDY CO.**
35 Hillside Ave. *(07205)*
Phone—**(973) 926-2300**
National—(800) 524-1304
Fax—(973) 926-4440
www.hillsidecandy.com
Email—info@hillsidecandy.com
Owner—Ted Cohen
V-P., Sales—Jim Hutchins
V-P., Export & Mktg.—Sandy Gencarelli
Plt. Mgr.—Henry Adamkowski
SIC—2064; NAICS—311300; *Organic, sugar & sugar-free candy; Brand name—GoLightly; GoNaturally; Hillside Sweets; GoOrganic*
Employs—37; Estab.—1980
Sales—under $10Mil
15,000 sq ft site, Distrib.—National
Limited Liability Company

**HILLSIDE PLASTICS CORP.**
125 Long Ave., P.O. Box 609 *(07205)*
Phone—**(800) 837-7731**
Fax—(973) 923-2056
www.hillsideplasticscorp.com
Email—maria@hillsideplastics.net
Pres.—Harold Kaufman
V-P., Bus. Dev.—Maria Silva
GM—Les Frazier
Hum. Res., IT & Off. Mgr.—Ira Sussman
SIC—3082; 3081; NAICS—326121; *Plastic extrusions of shrink bundling, postal, freezer grade, converter grade & multi-layer films & pallet, furniture & mattress covers & drum & box liners*
Employs—85; Estab.—1994
75,000 sq ft site, Distrib.—Intl.
Privately owned corporation

**INTERNATIONAL TOOL & MACHINE, LLC**
446 Hillside Ave. (07205)
Phone—**(908) 687-5580**
Fax—(908) 687-5368
Email—itm446@aol.com
Pres.—Chris Hoeker
Off. Mgr.—Bridget Lippert
SIC—3599; *Precision machining job shop*
Employs—5; Estab.—1976
Sales—$500,000-$1Mil
Distrib.—National
Privately owned corporation

**J R ENGINEERING & MACHINE CORP.**
663 Ramsey Ave. (07205)
Phone—**(908) 810-6300**
National—(800) 349-8429
Fax—(908) 810-1666
www.jrengr.com
Email—sales@jrengr.com
Pres., CEO—F. Joseph Kilroy
V-P., Sales & Mktg.—D. Wakeman
Treas.—Joe Clark
MIS Mgr. & Bookkeeper—Barbara Rap
Shop Foreman—John Kozke
SIC—3561; 3559; NAICS—333911; *Rebuilt centrifugal pump parts & machining job shop*
Employs—15; Estab.—1967
Sales—$1Mil-$2.5Mil
12,000 sq ft site, Distrib.—Regional
Privately owned corporation

**†KAMAN INDUSTRIAL TECHNOLOGIES CORP.**
502 Bloy St. (07205)
Phone—**(908) 687-0004**
Fax—(908) 687-9691
www.kamandirect.com
Email—newp01@kaman.com
GM—John Marra
SIC—5084; 5085; *Distributor of industrial equipment & supplies*
Employs—8; Estab.—1985
Sales—$1Mil-$2.5Mil
Distrib.—National
Publicly owned corporation
Parent co.—Kaman Industrial Technologies Corp., Bloomfield, CT
Phone—(860) 687-5000
See Parent Co. Section for full profile.

**LALLY-PAK, INC.**
1209 Central Ave. (07205)
Phone—**(908) 353-3344**
Fax—(908) 351-4411
www.lallypak.com
Email—sales@lallypak.com
Pres.—Henry Herbst
GM—David Rubin
MIS & Opers. Mgr.—Eric Garber
Fin. Mgr.—Eli Salomon
SIC—2673; *Plastic bags*
Employs—55; Estab.—1973
110,000 sq ft site, Distrib.—National
Privately owned corporation

**LOVE PALLET COMPANY, LLC.**
460 Mundet Pl., P.O. Box 774 *(07205)*
Phone—**(908) 964-3385**
Fax—(908) 688-1525
www.lovepallet.com
Ptnr.—Brenda Cardoza
Ptnr.—Susanne Lanzafama
Off. Mgr.—Marian Love
SIC—2448; NAICS—321920; *Wooden pallets*
Employs—16; Estab.—1970
Sales—$500,000-$1Mil
Distrib.—Local
Privately owned partnership

GEOGRAPHICAL

## Hillside—(cont.)

**MANHATTAN DRUG CO., INC.**
225 Long Ave., Bldg. 15, 3rd Fl.
(07205)
**Phone—(973) 926-0816**
Fax—(973) 926-1735
www.ibiopharma.com
Email—c.laureta@ibopharma.com
CEO—E. Gerald Kay
CFO—Dina Masi
V.-P., Mfg.—Riva Sheppard
V.-P., Logistics—Christina Kay
SIC—2834; NAICS—325412;
Nutritional supplements &
vitamin preparations
Employs—90; Estab.—1980
40,000 sq ft site, Distrib.—National
Privately owned corporation

**MICHAELIAN & KOHLBERG (H Q)**
100 Hoffman Pl. (07205)
**Phone—(908) 522-1004**
Fax—(908) 522-1006
www.michaelian.com
Email—info@michaelian.com
Owner & Designer—Teddy
Sumner
SIC—2273; Company
headquarters; hand-knotted
rugs, Oriental rugs & handmade
carpets (mfg. done overseas)
Employs—4; Estab.—1921
Sales—$1Mil-$2.5Mil
Distrib.—National

**NEW YORK BLACKBOARD OF NJ,
INC.**
83 U.S. Highway 22 (07205)
**Phone—(973) 926-1600**
National—(800) 652-6273
Fax—(973) 926-3440
www.nyblackboard.com
Email—info@nyblackboard.com
Pres.—Henry Ruggiero
V.-P., Mktg.—Kevin Ruggiero
Corp. Secy.—Regina Ruggiero
Prod. Mgr.—Brian Ruggiero
SIC—3281; 2499; NAICS—
327991; Markerboards,
chalkboards, bulletin boards &
photo infused/imprinted writing
boards; Brand name—
Polyvision; Forbo Cork; Da-Lite
Screen
Employs—6; Estab.—1944
12,000 sq ft site, Distrib.—National
Privately owned corporation

**OASIS FOODS CO.**
635 Ramsey Ave., P.O. Box 697
(07205)
**Phone—(908) 964-0477**
National—(800) 275-0477
Fax—(908) 964-1369
www.oasisfoods.com
Pres., CEO—William Gillingham
Dir., Sales—Leo Nigro
Sales Mgr.—Ivonne Teixeria
IT Mgr.—David White
Hum. Res. Mgr.—Evelyn Nieves
SIC—2035; 2079; 2099; 2084;
NAICS—312130; Vegetable oils,
salad dressings, sauces,
mayonnaise, margarines, butter
substitutes, shortenings,
vinegars, cooking wines &
maraschino cherries for the
foodservice industry
Employs—150; Estab.—1975
Distrib.—Intl.
Privately owned corporation

**POLISHED METALS LTD.**
487 Hillside Ave., Ste. 5 (07205)
**Phone—(908) 688-1188**
National—(800) 526-7051
Fax—(908) 688-2418
www.polishedmetals.com
Email—david@polishedmetals.com
V.-P. & Sales Mgr.—David Lazarus
V.-P.—Andrew Lazarus
V.-P.—Don Williams

Sales Rep.—Lorna Dellomo
SIC—3471; NAICS—332813;
Architectural & ornamental metal
polishing, including stainless
steel, bronze, brass,copper &
aluminum for the construction,
elevator, furniture & automotive
industries
Employs—60; Estab.—1979
65,000 sq ft site, Distrib.—Intl.
Privately owned sub-S corp.
ISO rating—9002

**QUEST INDUSTRIES, LLC**
480 Mundet Pl. (07205)
**Phone—(908) 851-9070**
Fax—(908) 851-9060
www.questllc.com
Email—ingridcornehl@questllc.com
CEO—Ravi Reddy
CFO—Ayesha Dabholkar
V.-P., Bus. Dev.—Ingrid Cornehl
Bus. Dev. Exec.—Chris Tubertine
SIC—3231; 3229; NAICS—
327215; Company headquarters
& decorative glassware for the
wine, spirits, beverage,
consumer & cosmetics/personal
care markets
Employs—90; Estab.—1999
Sales—$10Mil-$25Mil
Distrib.—Intl.
Limited Liability Company

**RAMCO EQUIPMENT CORP.**
32 Montgomery St. (07205)
**Phone—(908) 687-6700**
Fax—(908) 687-0653
www.ramkleen.com
Owner & Pres.—Fred Randall
V.-P., Chief Engr.—Al Raven
Cont. & Off. Mgr.—Genny Randall
Sales Mgr., Natl.—Robert
Peterson
Sales Mgr.—Ana Neves
Shop Foreman—Mirek Mroz
Pur. Agt.—Oretta Tigges
SIC—3559; Industrial parts
washers & parts washers
systems
Employs—20; Estab.—1927
15,000 sq ft site, Distrib.—Intl.
Privately owned corporation

**RINGEL BROS., INC.**
7 W. Shelton Ter., P.O. Box 727
(07205)
**Phone—(908) 688-9222**
Fax—(908) 688-9221
www.ringelbrothers.com
Email—sales@ringelbrothers.com
Pres.—Doug Eppel
Sales Mgr.—Frank Vogt
SIC—2679; 2671; NAICS—
322200; Paper converting
Employs—14; Estab.—1907
Sales—$500,000-$1Mil
27,000 sq ft site, Distrib.—Regional
Privately owned sub-S corp.

**RONALD-MARK ASSOCS., INC.**
1227 Central Ave., P.O. Box 776
(07205)
**Phone—(908) 558-0011**
Fax—(908) 558-9366
www.ronaldmark.com
Email—plastics@ronaldmark.com
Pres., CEO—Les Satz
V.-P., PVC Film & Supported
Fabrics—Charles Riotto
V.-P., Trading—Ron Satz
V.-P.—Michael Satz

SIC—3081; 3089; 3069; NAICS—
326113; Corporate headquarters
& vinyl, film & sheet fabrication,
including supported fabrics,
PVC resins, surface materials &
caviar beads; Brand name—
Kinon; XTRMPLY
Employs—50; Estab.—1974
Sales—$60Mil
120,000 sq ft site, Distrib.—Intl.
Privately owned sub-S corp.
AKA: Engineered Polymer
Technologies

**SKY FRAME & ART, INC.**
28 Evans Terminal (07205)
**Phone—(908) 354-5656**
Fax—(908) 354-0303
www.skyframeinc.com
Email—info@skyframeinc.com
Pres.—Robert Benrimon
SIC—2499; 3089; Corporate
headquarters & custom picture
frames & mouldings
Employs—20; Estab.—1982
Sales—$1Mil-$2.5Mil (est)
Distrib.—National
Privately owned corporation

**SNAPCO MFG. CORP.**
140 Central Ave. (07205)
**Phone—(973) 282-0300**
Fax—(973) 282-7627
www.snapcofasteners.com
Email—snapcomfg@aol.com
Chrm., Pres., CFO & R & D Mgr.—
Jeffrey G. Spitz
COO, Mktg. Mgr.—Philip Iuliano
Sales Mgr.—Ed Ganek
Sales Mgr.—Bill Smith
Chief Engr. & Plt. Mgr.—Edwardo
Gomes
Cust. Serv. Mgr.—Ray Addison
SIC—2241; 3069; 3965; NAICS—
313221; Snap, fastener tape,
eyelets, grommets, button &
buckle molds & shoe ornaments
Employs—25; Estab.—1946
34,000 sq ft site, Distrib.—Intl.
Privately owned sub-S corp.

**THOMAS MFG., INC.**
630 Ramsey Ave. (07205)
**Phone—(908) 810-0030**
Fax—(908) 810-1551
www.tmiwindows.com
Email—info@tmiwindows.com
Pres.—Tom Lukowiak
V.-P., Sales—Jeff Lukowiak
SIC—3442; NAICS—332321;
Commercial aluminum windows
Employs—25; Estab.—1992
Distrib.—Regional
Privately owned corporation

**UNION BEVERAGE PACKERS, LLC**
600 N. Union Ave. (07205)
**Phone—(908) 206-9111**
Fax—(908) 206-9430
www.unionbevnj.com
Email—sales@unionbevnj.com
CEO—Yaron Gohar
Plt. Mgr.—Gary Cummings
Maint. Mgr.—Arek Tarniowy
SIC—2086; NAICS—312100;
Beverage bottling
Employs—190; Estab.—2003
Distrib.—Local
Limited Liability Company

**UNIQUE WIRE WEAVING CO., INC.**
762 Ramsey Ave. (07205)
**Phone—(908) 688-4600**
Fax—(908) 688-4601
www.uniquewire.com
Email—cheryl@uniquewire.com
Pres.—Ken Beyer
Mktg. Mgr.—Cheryl Beyer
Off. Mgr.—Maryann Gibki

SIC—3496; Industrial woven wire
cloth & filter cloth, including
custom weaving, fabrication &
prototypes
Employs—20; Estab.—1946
Sales—$1Mil-$5Mil
10,000 sq ft site, Distrib.—National
Privately owned sub-S corp.

**UNITED FORMS FINISHING**
1413 Chestnut Ave., 1st Fl.
(07205)
**Phone—(908) 687-0494**
Fax—(908) 687-9211
www.uffcorp.com
Email—uffcorp@uffcorp.com
Pres., Fin. & Sales Mgr.—Liz
Demkin
V.-P., Fin., MIS, R & D & Sales—
Paul A. Dick Jr.
Hum. Res. & Off. Mgr.—Janice
Phemsint
Administrator—Madeline Yochum
SIC—2759; NAICS—323100;
Commercial offset & laser
printing
Employs—20; Estab.—1981
Sales—$2.5Mil-$5Mil
35,000 sq ft site, Distrib.—Intl.
Privately owned corporation

**VANGUARD PACKAGING, INC.**
620 Ramsey Ave. (07205)
Mail addr: 15 Stratford Dr.,
Livingston (07039)
**Phone—(973) 391-9200**
Fax—(973) 391-9201
www.vanguardpkg.net
Email—michaelw@vanguardpkg.net
Pres.—Michael Wische
SIC—2657; NAICS—322212;
Custom packaging materials,
including printed folding cartons,
blister cards & e-flute
Employs—3; Estab.—1996
Sales—$2.5Mil-$5Mil
Distrib.—National
Privately owned corporation

**VANTON PUMP & EQUIPMENT
CORP.**
201 Sweetland Ave. (07205)
**Phone—(908) 688-4216**
Fax—(908) 686-9314
www.vanton.com
Email—mkt@vanton.com
Ex. V.-P.—Larry Lewis
V.-P., Sales—K. Comerford
Treas., Cont.—Barbara Riscinti
Engr. Mgr.—Alvin Labar
SIC—3561; NAICS—333911;
Nonmetallic chemical pumps
Employs—50; Estab.—1950
Sales—$11Mil-$25Mil
60,000 sq ft site, Distrib.—Intl.
Privately owned corporation
Also see: Cooper Alloy Corp.,
same loc.

**WIREWORKS CORP.**
380 Hillside Ave. (07205)
**Phone—(908) 686-7400**
National—(800) 642-9473
Fax—(908) 686-0483
www.wireworks.com
Email—sales@wireworks.com
Pres.—Gerald Krulewicz
CFO—Larry Williams
Sales Mgr.—Richard Chilvers
Administrator—Brenda Daughtry
SIC—3663; NAICS—334220;
Audio & video cable systems
Employs—20; Estab.—1974
4,000 sq ft site, Distrib.—Intl.
Privately owned corporation

**XEVEE CORP.**
27 Montgomery St., P. O. Box
5277 (07205)
**Phone—(908) 964-0444**
Fax—(908) 964-0453
Email—xevee@aol.com
Pres.—Zev Sluzak
Off. Mgr.—Raina Warner

## Hillside—(cont.)

SIC—3599; *Welding job shop*
Employs—4; Estab.—2004
Sales—under $500,000
Distrib.—Intl.
Privately owned corporation

**YALE HOOK & EYE CO., INC.**
33 Race St. (07205)
**Phone—(973) 824-1440**
National—(800) 562-9459
Fax—(973) 824-3136
www.yhe.com
Email—sales@yhe.com
Pres.—Ann Roseman
Sales Mgr.—Morton Roseman
SIC—3965; NAICS—339993;
*Hooks, eye & snap fastener
tapes*
Employs—15; Estab.—1914
Distrib.—Intl.
Privately owned corporation

---

# Hoboken
(Hudson—N.E.)

**ANTIQUE BAKERY & PIZZERIA, INC.**
122 Willow Ave. (07030)
**Phone—(201) 714-9323**
Fax—(201) 714-4823
Pres.—Ivan Rodriguez
SIC—2051; NAICS—311812;
*Italian bread*
Employs—6; Estab.—1990
Sales—under $500,000
Distrib.—Local
Privately owned corporation

**BURGISS GROUP, LLC, THE**
111 River St., Ste. 10 (07030-5773)
**Phone—(201) 427-9600**
Fax—(201) 795-9237
www.burgiss.com
Email—sales@burgiss.com
Pres.—James M. Kocis
Cont.—Fuhchun Tsay Ramirez
Dir., Bus. Dev. & Sales—Stephen
　Bruhns
SIC—7372; *Company
headquarters & private equity
software development*
Employs—80
Limited Liability Company

†**CARPATHIAN INDUSTRIES, LLC**
51 Newark St., Ste. 508 (07030)
**Phone—(201) 798-8883**
Fax—(201) 850-1280
www.carpathianinc.com
Email—info@carpathianinc.com
Owner & Pres.—Paul Lichstein
SIC—5162; 5051; *Wholesaler of
plastic & metal parts*
Employs—9; Estab.—2001
Sales—$17Mil
Distrib.—Intl.
Limited Liability Company

**CHAMBORD PRINTS, INC.**
38 Jackson St. (07030)
**Phone—(201) 795-2007**
Fax—(646) 619-4112
Email—dennis@
　chambordprints.com
Pres.—Dennis Shah
Off. Mgr.—Rose Robertson
SIC—2671; *Hand-printed
wallpaper*
Employs—12; Estab.—1947
Sales—$500,000-$1Mil
Distrib.—Regional
Privately owned corporation

**NEW ENTRY**
**DILLISTONE SYSTEMS, INC.**
50 Harrison St., Ste. 201-A (07030)
**Phone—(201) 653-0013**
Fax—(201) 221-7518
www.dillistone.com
Email—sales@dillistone.com
Pres.—Jason Starr

SIC—7372; *Prepackaged
software development; Brand
name—FileFinder*
Employs—10
Distrib.—Local
Privately owned corporation

**FULL HOUSE PRINTING, INC.**
60 Newark St. (07030)
**Phone—(201) 798-7073**
www.fullhouseprinting.com
Email—larry@fullhouseprinting.com
Pres.—Larry Weiss
Manager—Rose Catti
SIC—2752; NAICS—323100;
*Offset printing*
Employs—7; Estab.—1979
Sales—under $500,000
1,500 sq ft site, Distrib.—Regional
Privately owned corporation

**GIBSON DESIGNS, INC., KATHY**
1416 Willow Ave. (07030)
**Phone—(201) 420-0088**
National—(800) 517-7222
Fax—(201) 656-4732
www.ansoniabridal.com
Email—bridalveil@aol.com
Pres.—Ruth Wiener
SIC—2353; *Bridal veils &
accessories*
Employs—20; Estab.—1999
Sales—$500,000-$1Mil
Distrib.—Local
Privately owned corporation

**HARRISON SCOTT PUBLICATIONS,
INC.**
5 Marine View Plz., Ste. 400
　(07030)
**Phone—(201) 659-1700**
Fax—(201) 695-4141
www.hspnews.com
Email—info@hspnews.com
Publisher—Andrew Albert
Cont.—Nestor Charriez
Dir., Mktg.—Barbara Eannace
GM—Daniel Cowles
Prodn. Mgr.—Michelle Lebowitz
Cust. Serv. Rep.—Pat Pugliese
SIC—2721; *Newsletter publishing*
Employs—25; Estab.—1988
Sales—$1Mil-$2.5Mil
Distrib.—Intl.
Privately owned corporation

**HUDSON REPORTER ASSOCS., LP**
1400 Washington St., P.O. Box
　3069 (07030)
**Phone—(201) 798-7800**
Fax—(201) 798-0018
www.hudsonreporter.com
Email—editorial@
　hudsonreporter.com
Co-Publisher—Lucha Malato
Co-Publisher—David Unger
SIC—2711; *Newspaper
publishing*
Employs—25; Estab.—1983
Sales—$1Mil-$2.5Mil
Distrib.—Local
Limited Liability Company

**MAZZANTI, INC.**
701 Grand St. (07030)
**Phone—(201) 360-4400**
Fax—(201) 360-4500
www.emazzanti.net
Owner & Pres.—Carl Mazzanti
SIC—7373; *Computer network
systems integration, including
LANs & WANs*
Employs—14
Distrib.—Intl.
Privately owned corporation

**MODELSMITH INTERNATIONAL, INC.**
66 Willow Ave., 2nd Fl. (07030)
**Phone—(201) 714-9519**
Fax—(201) 217-0666
Pres.—Karol Popek

SIC—3312; 2499; 3089; 3543;
　NAICS—332997; *Steel, wood &
acrylic fabrication, furniture,
fixtures & prototypes*
Employs—5; Estab.—1984
Sales—$500,000-$1Mil
5,000 sq ft site, Distrib.—National
Privately owned corporation

**MOLA IRON WORKS**
61 Patterson Ave. (07030)
**Phone—(201) 963-3485**
Fax—(201) 963-2265
Owner—Tony Mola
V-P.—John Mola
Welder—Frank Ratto
SIC—3599; *Welding job shop*
Employs—3; Estab.—1979
Sales—under $500,000
Distrib.—Local
Privately owned corporation

**MOSSFAUSET WOODWORKING**
49 Harrison St., 13th Fl. (07030)
**Phone—(201) 714-9797**
Fax—(201) 714-4836
www.mossfauset.com
Email—office@mossfauset.com
Owner—Kelly Fauset
SIC—2599; NAICS—337122;
*Handcrafted custom high-end
residential wood furniture for
architects, designers &
architectural interiors*
Employs—3; Estab.—1987
Sales—under $500,000
Distrib.—Local
Sole ownership

**PAN AMERICAN COFFEE CO., LLC**
500 16th St. (07030)
**Phone—(201) 963-2329**
Fax—(201) 659-1883
Pres.—Roy Montes
V-P.—Ruth Montes
SIC—2095; NAICS—311920;
*Coffee roasting*
Employs—40; Estab.—1966
Distrib.—Intl.
Privately owned corporation

**POGGI PRESS, THE**
1501 Adams St., P.O. Box M-668
　(07030)
**Phone—(201) 659-0837**
Fax—(201) 659-7834
Email—poggipress@aol.com
Pres.—Charles Poggi
V-P.—Bob En
SIC—2759; 2752; NAICS—
　323100; *Commercial, offset &
digital printing*
Employs—21; Estab.—1928
80,000 sq ft site, Distrib.—Local
Privately owned corporation

**RADII, INC.**
66 Willow Ave., 3rd Fl. (07030)
**Phone—(201) 420-4700**
Fax—(201) 420-4750
www.radiiinc.com
Email—wood@radiiinc.com
Pres.—Ed Wood
V-P.—Lescek Stefanski
SIC—3999; *Architectural models*
Employs—12; Estab.—1999
Sales—$500,000-$1Mil
Distrib.—Intl.
Privately owned corporation

**RELATIONAL ARCHITECTS**
33 Newark St., Ste. 3-A (07030)
**Phone—(201) 420-0400**
www.relarc.com
Email—admi@relarc.com
Mng. Dir.—Max Gartner
SIC—7372; *Software
development*
Employs—30; Estab.—1987
Distrib.—Intl.
Privately owned corporation

**SIMS PUMP VALVE CO., INC.**
1314 Park Ave., P.O. Box 3338
　(07030)
**Phone—(201) 792-0600**
National—(800) 746-7303
Fax—(201) 792-4803
www.simsite.com
Email—simspump@aol.com
Pres.—John A. Kozel
Acct. Mgr.—Dorey Bauer
SIC—3561; NAICS—333911;
*Structural composite pumps &
pump parts*
Employs—22; Estab.—1919
Distrib.—Intl.
Privately owned corporation

**SKYLINE GRAPHIC MANAGEMENT**
601 Adams St., P.O. Box 6147
　(07030)
**Phone—(201) 798-1919**
Fax—(201) 798-9099
www.skylinegraphic.com
Owner—Al Festa
Graphic Designer—Jessica
　Rosaro
SIC—3993; *Interior & exterior vinyl
signs*
Employs—2; Estab.—1989
Distrib.—Local
Privately owned corporation

**TERMINAL PRINTING CO.**
94 River St., P.O. Box 30 (07030)
**Phone—(201) 659-5924**
Fax—(201) 795-1580
Owner—John A. Bado III
Secy-Treas.—Virginia Bado
SIC—2752; 2791; NAICS—
　323122; *Offset printing &
typesetting*
Employs—20; Estab.—1924
Distrib.—Local
Sole ownership

**TYPEWORKS**
228 Jefferson St., Apt. 4 (07030)
**Phone—(201) 653-8380**
Fax—(201) 331-2911
Email—typeworkinc@optimum.net
Pres.—Janice Weiss
SIC—2791; NAICS—323122;
*Computerized typesetting,
graphic design & promotional
items*
Employs—4; Estab.—1985
Sales—under $500,000
Distrib.—Regional
Privately owned sub-S corp.

**UNION DRY DOCK & REPAIR CO.,
INC.**
901 Sinatra Dr., P.O. Box M-1539
　(07030)
**Phone—(201) 792-9090**
Fax—(201) 792-4977
Pres.—Robert J. Burke
V-P.—Bruce Southern
V-P.—Robert Ferry
SIC—3731; *Marine dry-docking &
barge & vessel conversion &
repair*
Employs—75; Estab.—1908
Sales—$5Mil-$10Mil
Distrib.—National
Privately owned corporation

**WILEY & SONS, INC., JOHN**
111 River St. (07030-5773)
**Phone—(201) 748-6000**
National—(800) 225-5945
Fax—(201) 748-6088
www.wiley.com
Email—opportunities@wiley.com
Pres., CEO—Stephen M. Smith
Ex. V-P., CFO—John Kritzmacher
Ex. V-P., CMO—Clay Stobaugh
Ex. V-P., CTO—Patrick Dyberg
Sr. V-P., Treas.—Vincent Marzano
Sr. V-P., Corp. Cont.—Edward J.
　Melando
Ex. V-P., Gen. Counsel—Gary M.
　Rinck

**GEOGRAPHICAL**

## Hoboken—(cont.)

Ex. V.-P., Hum. Res.—M. J. O'Leary
SIC—2721; 2731; *Corporate headquarters & scientific & technical periodical & book publishing; Brand name— Frommer Travel Guides; Dummies Guides; Cliffsnotes; Betty Crocker*
Employs—2000; Estab.—1807
Sales—$1Bil
Distrib.—Intl.
Privately owned corporation

## Ho-Ho-Kus

(Bergen—N.E.)

**ALAN BAIRD INDUSTRIES, INC.**
1 Hollywood Ave., Ste. 9 (07423)
**Phone—(201) 652-6335**
(201) 652-1741
Fax—(201) 652-3653
www.bairdindustries.com
Email—info@bairdindustries.com
Pres.—Michael Cseh
GM—David Holmes
Qual. Assur. Mgr.—James Lake
Off. Admn.—Yajaira Laucell
SIC—3315; *Wire, mechanical cable & cable assembly for the medical device industry, including stainless steel, tungsten, nitinol & titanium*
Employs—75; Estab.—1973
23,000 sq ft site, Distrib.—Intl.
Privately owned corporation
DBA: Baird Industries

**ATOMIZING SYSTEMS INC.**
1 Hollywood Ave., Ste. 1 (07423-1438)
**Phone—(201) 447-1222**
Fax—(201) 447-6932
www.coldfog.com
Email—atomizingsystems@coldfog.com
Pres., CEO—Michael V. Elkas
Prodn. Mgr.—Thomas Pagliaroni
Off. Mgr.—Lisa Vliet
Engrg. Mgr.—John Zhang
SIC—3585; *Patented ruby-orifice, non-wearing fog nozzles & fog systems for humidification, cooling, chemical injection, dust & odor control & special effects; Brand name—Cold Fog*
Employs—16; Estab.—1979
Sales—$10Mil
8,500 sq ft site, Distrib.—Intl.
Privately owned corporation
ISO rating—9002

**INDUSTRIAL PRODUCTS CORP.**
1 Hollywood Ave., Ste. 30 (07423-1438)
**Phone—(201) 652-5913**
National—(800) 472-5913
Fax—(201) 652-2494
Email—jkdjr@cometlink.com
Owner & Pres.—J. K. Dohner, Jr.
Off. Mgr.—Jane Keeley
SIC—3423; *Industrial machine knives*
Employs—2; Estab.—1967
8,100 sq ft site, Distrib.—Intl.
Sole ownership

**MAYOS SPORTSWEAR, INC.**
1 Hollywood Ave., Bldg. 2-D (07423)
**Phone—(201) 652-8570**
Fax—(201) 652-2199
www.mayosportswear.com
Email—mayo.sports@verizon.net
Pres.—Bob Mainenti
Corp. Secy.—Renee Barbatallo

SIC—2396; 2395; *Textile screen printing & embroidery*
Employs—6; Estab.—1988
Sales—$500,000-$1Mil
Distrib.—Local
Privately owned corporation

**MINUTEMAN PRESS**
19 Sheridan Ave. (07423)
**Phone—(201) 444-0236**
Fax—(201) 445-6660
www.hohokus.minutemanpress.com
Email—emailus@minutemanpress.com
Member—Suzanne Seise
Pres.—Donald A. Seise
Art Dir.—Kyle Barker
SIC—2759; 2752; 2789; 3993; NAICS—323100; *Digital, offset & high-speed printing, promotional items, graphic design & direct mail & binding services*
Employs—3; Estab.—1977
Sales—over $400,000
1,700 sq ft site, Distrib.—Regional
Limited Liability Company

**SIRIUS TECHNOLOGY LLC**
1 Hollywood Ave., Ste. 19-A (07423)
**Phone—(201) 493-1414**
National—(888) 394-1414
Fax—(201) 493-8494
www.powersolution.com
Email—nj@powersolution.com
CEO—David Dadian
CTO—David Ruchman
V.-P., Web Opers.—Dina Dadian
V.-P.—Peter Sierra
SIC—7373; *Computer network system integration & management IT services*
Employs—10; Estab.—1996
3,000 sq ft site, Distrib.—National
Privately owned corporation
DBA: powersolution.com

**TAGE PUBLISHING SERVICE, INC.**
5 Brownstone Way (07423)
**Phone—(201) 445-3050**
Pres.—Tony Caruso
Secy.-Treas.—Maria Caruso
SIC—2731; *Book publishing*
Employs—2; Estab.—1985
Sales—under $500,000 (est)
Distrib.—National
Privately owned corporation

## Holmdel

(Monmouth—N.E.)

**COSMETIC ESSENCE, INC. (H Q)**
2182 Route 35 S. (07733)
**Phone—(732) 888-7788**
www.cosmeticessence.com
Email—sales@cosmeticessence.com
Pres., CEO—Peter Martin
CFO—Tom Nelson
Sr. V.-P., Global Sales & Mktg.— Matt Heuer
Sr. V.-P., Hum. Res.—Brian Laperriere
IT Mgr.—Rick Hopkins
Accts. Payable Mgr.—Jeannine Callahan
SIC—2844; NAICS—325600; *Corporate headquarters; fragrance blending, compounds & cosmetics*
Employs—350
Nationwide: 3,000
Sales—$100Mil-$250Mil (est)
Publicly owned corporation

†**DESIGNER SOURCE, INC.**
2139 State Route 35 (07733)
**Phone—(732) 264-7775**
Fax—(732) 264-8990
www.designersourceinc.com
Email—info@designersourceinc.com

Ptnr.—Laura Beglin
Ptnr.—Larry Beglin
GM—Dave Troland
SIC—5031; 5032; *Distributor of architectural mouldings, including wood, plaster & polyurethane doors, columns, medallions, niches & fireplace surrounds*
Employs—6; Estab.—2003
Sales—under $500,000
Distrib.—Local
Privately owned corporation

**JG MACHINE WORKS**
2182 State Route 35 *(07733)*
**Phone—(732) 203-2077**
Fax—(732) 203-2078
www.jgmachine.com
Email—dnelson@jgmachine.com
GM—Donald Nelson
Fin. Mgr.—Charlie Avery
SIC—3565; NAICS—333993; *Packaging machinery*
Employs—4; Estab.—1953
Sales—$1Mil-$5Mil
5,200 sq ft site, Distrib.—Intl.
Limited Liability Company

**METUCHEN CAPACITORS, INC.**
2139 Highway 35, Ste. 2, P.O. Box 399 (07733)
**Phone—(732) 888-9700**
National—(800) 899-6969
Fax—(732) 888-7811
www.metcaps.com
Email—sales@metcaps.com
Pres.—Gary Ficsor
Cont.—Joan Onori
Sales Mgr.—Todd Bernstein
Adv. Mgr.—Kim Applegate
Cred. Mgr.—Cathy Hoehl
Qual. Control Mgr.—Mauro Bellifemine
Pur. Agt.—Sharon Petyo
SIC—3675; 3676; 3678; 5063; NAICS—334414; *Manufacturer & distributor high-voltage & high-temperature ceramic & tantalum capacitors, EMI/RFI filters, ferrites, magnetics & filtered connectors; Brand name—API (Spectrum Control); Kemet; Oxley; Metuchen Capacitors; ASC; Electronic Film Capacitor*
Employs—26; Estab.—1972
13,000 sq ft site, Distrib.—Intl.
Privately owned corporation
ISO rating—9001, AS9100

**TROPP PRINTING CORP.**
8 Woodhollow Dr. (07733)
**Phone—(212) 233-4519**
Fax—(212) 791-2953
www.troppprinting.com
Email—info@troppprinting.com
Pres.—William Tropp
Off. Mgr.—Michael Tropp
SIC—2752; 2759; 2791; NAICS—323110; *Offset & color printing & electronic prepress*
Employs—5; Estab.—1953
Sales—under $500,000
Distrib.—Local
Privately owned corporation

**UREACH TECHNOLOGIES, INC.**
Div. of Genband, Inc.
2137 State Highway 35, 1st Fl. (07733)
**Phone—(732) 335-5400**
Fax—(732) 335-8129
www.ureach.com
Email—techsupport@ureachtech.com
CEO & Dir.—David Ittner
IT Mgr.—Michael Stanton

SIC—7372; *Prepackaged software development for telecommunications service providers; Brand name—Mobile PBX*
Employs—45; Estab.—1999
Sales—$11Mil-$25Mil
Distrib.—National
Privately owned corporation
Parent co.—Genband, Inc., Frisco, TX
Phone—(972) 521-5800
See Parent Co. Section for full profile.

## Hopatcong

(Sussex—N.W.)

**ENVIRONMENTAL SERVICES GROUP/GREEN POWER**
151 Sparta Stanhope Rd. (07843)
Mail addr: P.O. Box 507, Stanhope (07874)
**Phone—(201) 569-2020**
Fax—(973) 770-1158
www.greenpowerchemical.com
Email—info@greenpowerchemical.com
CEO—August D'Angelo
V.-P., Opers.—Jake Wilson
Cont.—Tom Hawkins
Pur. & Sales Mgr.—Peter D'Angelo
SIC—3699; *Environmentally friendly cleaners, including aqueous parts washers, solvent parts washers, adhesive resin removers, wax removers & silicone removers*
Employs—15; Estab.—1996
Distrib.—Intl.
Limited Liability Company
AKA: Green Power Chemical

**INNOVATIVE NETWORK SOLUTIONS**
29 Cove Rd. (07843)
**Phone—(973) 299-8800**
www.insnj.com
Email—sales@insnj.com
Pres.—Garry Manz
Pur. Mgr.—Chris Palazzi
SIC—7373; *Computer network system integration, including LANs & WANs*
Employs—5; Estab.—1991
Distrib.—Intl.
Privately owned corporation

## Hope

(Warren—N.W.)

**SOUTHLAND MFG. CO.**
316 Great Meadows Rd., P.O. Box 350 (07844)
**Phone—(908) 459-5858**
Fax—(908) 459-5058
Email—ketrumpore@yahoo.com
Pres.—L. R. Trumpore
V.-P.—Kevin E. Trumpore
SIC—3069; *Custom industrial molded rubber products, including compression & transfer molding, in-house tool shop, sample & small production runs, research & development*
Employs—2; Estab.—1964
Distrib.—National
Privately owned corporation

## Hopewell

(Mercer—N.E.)

**FANCY THREADS**
31 Railroad Pl. (08525)
**Phone—(609) 466-0050**
Email—fancythreads2@aol.com
Owner—Debbie Varbasse

## Hopewell—(cont.)

SIC—2395; 2396; *Embroidery & textile screen printing*
Employs—1; Estab.—1989
Sales—under $500,000
Distrib.—Regional
Sole ownership

**HOPEWELL POTTERY**
18 Burton Ave. (08525)
**Phone—(609) 466-9048**
www.hopewellpottery.net
Owner—Constance McIndoe
SIC—3269; *Pottery*
Employs—1; Estab.—1975
Sales—under $500,000
Distrib.—National
Sole ownership

**NXLEVEL SOLUTIONS**
57 Hamilton Ave., Ste. 303 (08525)
**Phone—(609) 466-2828**
Fax—(609) 466-4322
www.nxlevelsolutions.com
Email—info@nxlevelsolutions.com
Pres.—Robert Christensen
Ex. V-P.—Peter Sandford
Sr. Acct. Mgr.—Sean Murphy
SIC—7372; *E-learning software development*
Employs—15; Estab.—2004
Sales—$1Mil-$2.5Mil
Distrib.—National
Privately owned corporation

**PAMCO PRINTERS & STATIONERS**
P.O. Box 567 (08525)
**Phone—(609) 309-5025**
www.pamcoprinters.com
Owner—Vincent Mistretta
SIC—2759; NAICS—323100; *Commercial printing*
Employs—3; Estab.—1983
Distrib.—Local
Privately owned corporation

**REID PLUMBING PRODUCTS, LLC**
371 Route 31 N. (08525)
**Phone—(609) 466-1785**
National—(800) 211-8070
Fax—(609) 466-3982
www.wellmanager.com
Email—info@wellmanger.com
Owner—John Reid
GM—Andy Reid
SIC—3561; NAICS—333911; *Well management equipment for maintaining water levels of low-yield wells*
Employs—7; Estab.—1993
Sales—under $500,000
Distrib.—Intl.
Limited Liability Company

## Howell

(Monmouth—N.E.)

**†ADVANCED FILTRATION CO.**
25-A Arnold Blvd., P.O. Box 324 (07731)
**Phone—(732) 901-6676**
Fax—(732) 901-6677
www.advancedfiltration.com
Email—sales@advancedfiltration.com
Pres.—John Woods
Sales Mgr.—John McHugh
SIC—5084; 5085; *Distributor of water, air, gas, fuel, oil, hydraulic & turbine air intake filters & lube oil filtration systems; Brand name—Kaydon Filtration; Islip Flow Controls; Van Air; Nowata Filtration; Shawndra; Mahle*
Employs—3; Estab.—1993
Distrib.—Intl.
Privately owned corporation
AKA: Advanced Filtration

**ALL-STATE FENCE, INC.**
1389 Route 9 N. (07731)
**Phone—(732) 431-4944**
National—(855) 336-2365
Fax—(866) 209-0281
www.allstatefence.com
Email—customerservice@allstatefence.com
Pres.—Scott Skrable
V-P.—Michael Skrable
SIC—3496; 3089; 3446; 2499; *Residential & commercial chain-link, vinyl, aluminum & custom board fencing; Brand name—ActiveYards*
Employs—8; Estab.—1978
Sales—$500,000-$1Mil
Distrib.—Regional
Privately owned sub-S corp.
Parent co.—All-State Fence, Inc., Howell, NJ
Phone—(732) 431-4944
See Parent Co. Section for full profile.

**ALL-STATE FENCE, INC.**
1389 Highway 9 N. (07731)
**Phone—(732) 431-4944**
National—(855) 226-2486
Fax—(732) 683-1523
www.allstatefence.com
Email—customerservice@allstatefence.com
Pres.—Scott Skrable
SIC—2499; *Corporate headquarters & wooden fences*
Employs—10; Estab.—1979
Sales—under $500,000
Distrib.—Local
Privately owned corporation

**AMERICAN BRAIDING & MFG., INC.**
247 Old Tavern Rd. (07731)
Mail addr: P.O. Box 426, Farmingdale (07727)
**Phone—(732) 938-6333**
National—(800) 597-6555
Fax—(732) 938-6377
www.abmco.com
Email—info@abmco.com
Pres.—Gerald Bailey
Off. Mgr.—Lara Nelson
SIC—3089; *Mechanical compression packing*
Employs—10; Estab.—1978
26,000 sq ft site, Distrib.—Intl.
Privately owned corporation
ISO rating—9001:2000

**AQUARIAN WHAT'S YOUR SIGN, LLC**
37 Newtons Corner Rd. (07731)
**Phone—(732) 206-0726**
Fax—(732) 785-0771
Email—whatsyoursign2@aol.com
Owner—Bill McCarrick
SIC—3993; *Vinyl signs*
Employs—2
Sales—under $500,000
Distrib.—Local
Privately owned corporation

**ARNOLD STEEL CO., INC.**
79 Randolph Rd. (07731)
**Phone—(732) 363-1079**
Fax—(732) 905-7460
www.arnoldsteel.com
Email—tpflaster@arnoldsteel.com
Chrm. of the Board—Felix Pflaster
Pres.—Leon Pflaster
V-P. & Secy.—Tina Pflaster
Hum. Res. Mgr.—Nancy Stanch
SIC—3441; NAICS—332312; *Structural steel fabrication & erection, including multi-story, commercial, residential, industrial & institutional buildings*
Employs—50; Estab.—1961
Sales—$20Mil-$25Mil
70,000 sq ft site, Distrib.—Regional
Privately owned sub-S corp.

**BR WELDING & INDUSTRIAL SERVICES, INC.**
3 Brook Rd. (07731)
**Phone—(732) 363-8253**
National—(888) 898-9353
Fax—(732) 363-0155
www.brwelding.com
Email—info@brwelding.com
Pres.—Brandon Reo
Hum. Res. & Off. Mgr.—Stephanie Krill
Shop Foreman—Jeff Zimba
SIC—3441; 3599; NAICS—332312; *Structural metal fabrication & welding job shop*
Employs—20; Estab.—1984
Distrib.—Regional
Privately owned corporation

**CONFECTION COLLECTION**
6754 Route 9 (07731)
**Phone—(732) 905-3039**
National—(800) 905-3039
Fax—(732) 905-9968
www.confectioncollection.com
Email—ben@confectioncollection.com
Owner—Sarah Cywiak
Manager—Benjamin Spira
Designer—Esther Spira
SIC—2064; 3999; NAICS—311300; *Chocolates, nuts, dried fruit, candy, gifts, baskets, favors & balloons*
Employs—3; Estab.—1998
Sales—$500,000-$1Mil
Distrib.—Local
Privately owned corporation

**CROWN ENGINEERING CORP.**
550 Squankum Yellowbrook Rd. (07731)
Mail addr: P.O. Box 846, Farmingdale (07727)
**Phone—(732) 938-3600**
National—(800) 631-2153
Fax—(732) 938-3969
www.crownengineering.com
Pres.—Michael J. Palmer
Secy-Treas.—Jackie Palmer
SIC—3822; NAICS—334512; *Electrodes, flame rods, igniters & terminal connectors for ignition oil & gas fired equipment & grain drying equipment*
Employs—20
2,200 sq ft site,

**CUSTOM WINDOW TREATMENTS BY WAYNE LUBIN**
1029 U.S. Highway 9 (07731-3367)
**Phone—(732) 462-4961**
Fax—(732) 308-3310
www.lubinswindowtreatments.com
Email—cwtlubins@optimum.net
Owner—Wayne Lubin
SIC—2591; NAICS—337920; *Custom window treatments for commercial, retail & wholesale applications*
Employs—5; Estab.—1953
Sales—$500,000-$1Mil
6,000 sq ft site, Distrib.—Regional
Privately owned corporation

**†CUTTER, DRILL & MACHINE, INC.**
175 Ramtown Greenville Rd., Unit 701 (07731)
Mail addr: P.O. Box 140, Lakewood (08701-0140)
**Phone—(732) 206-1112**
Fax—(732) 206-1114
www.cutterdrill.com
Email—cutterdrill@optonline.net
Pres.—Michael C. Tellier
Secy-Treas.—Darren W. Ryan
Off. Mgr.—Debbie Tellier

SIC—5084; 5085; *Distributor of water pipeline tapping equipment & materials; Brand name—Romac; AY McDonald; North American Pipe; American Flow Control; MultiFittings; Reed Tools; US Pipe; Wachs Tools*
Employs—4; Estab.—1986
Sales—$2Mil
Distrib.—National
Privately owned sub-S corp.

**DEPENDABILITIES SCREEN PRINTING**
632 Hulses Corner Rd. (07731)
**Phone—(732) 886-0800**
Fax—(732) 367-2802
Owner—Don Green
SIC—2396; *T-shirt & school uniform screen printing*
Employs—4; Estab.—2002
Sales—under $500,000
Distrib.—Local
Sole ownership

**ECS, LLC**
1827 U.S. Highway 9 (07731)
**Phone—(732) 462-5530**
Fax—(732) 462-4181
www.ecsconveyors.com
Email—ecs@ecsconveyors.com
Owner—Virginia Sena
Pur. Mgr.—Leslie Hunt
SIC—3535; NAICS—333922; *Conveyors & truck loaders*
Employs—15; Estab.—2004
Sales—$1Mil-$2.5Mil
Distrib.—National
Limited Liability Company

**FENCES BY TAYLOR, INC.**
1246 Highway 33 (07731)
Mail addr: P.O. Box 126, Red Bank (07701)
**Phone—(732) 349-8626**
Fax—(732) 938-5671
www.taylorfence.com
Email—webmaster@taylorfence.com
Pres.—Paul Taylor
SIC—2499; *Wooden fences*
Employs—20; Estab.—1966
Sales—$1Mil-$2.5Mil (est)
Distrib.—Local
Privately owned corporation

**G & G STAIRS**
2559 U.S. Highway 9 (07731)
**Phone—(732) 905-3083**
www.ggstairs.com
Email—ggstairs@optonline.net
Pres.—Sean Coffey
Off. Admn.—Shannon Coffey
SIC—2431; NAICS—321900; *Wooden stairs & railings*
Employs—2; Estab.—1972
Sales—under $500,000
Distrib.—Regional
Privately owned corporation

**GARDEN STATE SIGN CO.**
4880 U.S. Highway 9 (07731)
**Phone—(732) 363-7645**
Fax—(732) 363-7655
www.gardenstatesign.com
Email—gardenstatesign@ymail.com
Pres.—Joseph E. Ervin
SIC—3993; NAICS—335129; *Interior & exterior signs, electronic message centers & information displays & carved gold leaf & wayfinding signage*
Employs—7; Estab.—1951
Sales—under $1Mil
4,000 sq ft site, Distrib.—Regional
Privately owned sub-S corp.

**GARON PRODUCTS, INC.**
256 Maxim Rd. (07731)
**Phone—(732) 828-6400**
National—(800) 631-5380
Fax—(732) 828-6597
www.garonproducts.com

GEOGRAPHICAL

## Howell—(cont.)

Email—customercare@
garonproducts.com
V.-P., Pur. & Whse. Opers.—
Michael Crowley
Manager—Christine Martinez
SIC—2899; 2891; 2851; *Concrete
floor repair products & concrete
floor coatings, including grouts,
urethane mortars & adhesives*
Employs—4
Sales—$1Mil-$2.5Mil (est)
Distrib.—National
Privately owned corporation
Parent co.—Garon Products, Inc.,
Manasquan, NJ
Phone—(732) 223-2500
See Parent Co. Section for full profile.

### GREEN & SONS, INC., JONATHAN
48 Squankum-Yellowbrook Rd.
(07731)
Mail addr: P.O. Box 326,
Farmingdale (07727)
**Phone—(732) 938-7007**
National—(800) 526-2303
Fax—(732) 938-5788
www.jonathangreen.com
Email—email@jonathangreen.com
CEO—Barry Green
V.-P.—Todd Pretz
Fin. & MIS Mgr.—Keith Decher
SIC—2041; 2875; 2879; NAICS—
311211; *Grass seeds, fertilizers &
turf chemicals*
Employs—30; Estab.—1957
40,000 sq ft site, Distrib.—National
Privately owned corporation

### †HADDON HOUSE FOOD PRODUCTS, INC.
433 Oak Glen Rd. (07731)
**Phone—(732) 367-7901**
National—(800) 257-6174
Fax—(732) 363-5294
www.haddonhouse.com
Email—merchandiser@
haddonhouse.com
Opers. Mgr.—Ken Wilkinson
SIC—5149; 5143; *Distributor of
gourmet, frozen, ethnic, dairy &
natural food products, including
teas, seasonings & sauces*
Employs—225; Estab.—1978
Distrib.—Intl.
Privately owned corporation
Parent co.—Haddon House Food
Products, Inc., Medford, NJ
Phone—(609) 654-7901
See Parent Co. Section for full profile.

### HAMILLTIME ENTERPRISES, INC.
1761 U.S. Highway 9 (07731)
**Phone—(732) 303-5998**
Owner—John Hamill
SIC—2833; *Contract packaging of
herbal products*
Employs—2; Estab.—2008
Sales—$500,000-$1Mil (est)
Distrib.—Local
Privately owned corporation

### HARMONY PRINTING
504 Aldrich Rd., Ste. 22 (07731)
**Phone—(732) 987-9040**
Fax—(732) 987-9041
www.harmonyprintingonline.com
Email—info@
harmonyprintingonline.com
Owner & CEO—Bill Blake
SIC—2759; 2396; *Promotional
item & apparel, garment & textile
screen printing*
Employs—4; Estab.—2001
Sales—under $500,000
Distrib.—National
Privately owned corporation

### †IDEAL TILE IMPORTING CO., INC.
2232 Route 9 S. (07731)
**Phone—(732) 308-1008**
National—(888) 433-1198
Fax—(732) 308-1008

www.idealtile.com
Pres.—Mario Grillo
Cont.—Vita Romano
Manager—John Alexandar
SIC—5032; *Distributor of floor &
wall tiles*
Employs—11; Estab.—1986
Sales—under $500,000
Distrib.—National
Privately owned corporation

### LAWLER WOODWORK, LLC
938 Lakewood Farmingdale Rd.
(07731)
**Phone—(732) 942-7204**
Fax—(732) 942-7205
www.lawlerwoodwork.com
Email—jl@lawlerwoodwork.com
Owner—John Lawler
SIC—2541; 2434; *Commercial &
residential wooden cabinets,
counters & display cases,
including information & sales
kiosks & kitchen cabinets*
Employs—10; Estab.—2002
5,000 sq ft site, Distrib.—Local
Limited Liability Company

### †MAJESTIC FENCE CO., INC.
6839 US Highway 9 (07731)
**Phone—(732) 363-8181**
Fax—(732) 370-8131
www.majesticfencecompany.com
Email—kenny@
majesticfencecompany.com
Pres.—Ken Gorlin
V.-P.—Harvey Tooter
SIC—5031; 5039; *Distributor of
residential & commercial
wooden, aluminum & iron
fencing, accessories & guard
rails*
Employs—10; Estab.—1983
Sales—$1Mil-$2.5Mil
Distrib.—Local
Privately owned sub-S corp.

### MARK-O-LITE SIGN CO.
1420 U.S. Highway 9 (07731-3331)
**Phone—(732) 462-8530**
Fax—(732) 409-3772
www.markolitesignco.com
Email—markolitesign@aol.com
Pres., Sales Mgr.—Howard Mark
SIC—3993; *Interior & exterior
signs*
Employs—5; Estab.—1965
Sales—$500,000-$1Mil
3,000 sq ft site, Distrib.—Regional
Privately owned corporation

### NATIONAL SHRINKWRAP
6220 U.S. Highway 9 (07731)
**Phone—(732) 942-4554**
National—(800) 423-7971
Fax—(732) 942-9562
www.nationalshrinkwrap.com
Email—nationalshrinkwrap@
gmail.com
Owner & Pres.—Art Marko
SIC—3565; 3081; NAICS—
333993; *Shrink-wrapping
machinery & film; Brand name—
Biolefin™ Biodegradeable
Polyolefin*
Employs—2; Estab.—1984
Sales—under $500,000
Distrib.—Intl.
Privately owned corporation
AKA: National Sales Of Central NJ

### PRINT HOUSE, INC., THE
6535 U.S. Highway 9 (07731)
**Phone—(732) 364-4254**
Fax—(732) 886-5915
Email—info@theprinthouseinc.com
Pres.—Leah Kovalenko
SIC—2759; *Commercial printing*
Employs—4; Estab.—1998
Sales—under $500,000
1,800 sq ft site, Distrib.—National
Privately owned corporation

### PUGLISI EGG FARMS, INC.
75 Easy St. (07731)
**Phone—(732) 938-2373**
Fax—(732) 938-2232
Pres.—John Puglisi
V.-P.—Paul Puglisi
Secy-Treas.—Mike Puglisi
SIC—2015; *Egg production &
processing*
Employs—40; Estab.—1940
Distrib.—Local
Privately owned corporation

### S J PRINT SOLUTIONS
257 Ford Rd. (07731)
**Phone—(732) 363-7711**
Fax—(732) 905-3875
Email—sjprint@optonline.net
Pres.—Adeline McGovern
Graphic Designer—Dona Romeu
SIC—2759; NAICS—323100;
*Commercial, digital & color
printing & graphic design*
Employs—4; Estab.—1990
Sales—under $500,000
Distrib.—Local
Privately owned corporation

### †SCHROTH, INC., EMIL A.
Yellowbrook Rd. & Copper Ave.
(07731)
Mail addr: P.O. Box 496,
Farmingdale (07727-0496)
**Phone—(732) 938-5015**
Fax—(732) 938-2363
Email—eschrothinc@aol.com
Pres.—Emil A. Schroth, Jr.
V.-P.—Benjamin U. Jackson
Sales Mgr.—Stephen C. Samaha
Plt. Mgr.—Benjamin U. Jackson,
Jr.
SIC—5093; *Wholesaler of copper
& aluminum*
Employs—15; Estab.—1931
Sales—$25Mil-$40Mil
Distrib.—Intl.
Privately owned sub-S corp.

### SHANGRI LA FARM, LLC
1055 Maxim Southard Rd. (07731)
**Phone—(732) 901-8777**
www.shangrilafarmllc.com
Email—shangrilafarmllc@aol.com
Owner—Elaine Taylor
SIC—2395; *Embroidery*
Employs—1; Estab.—1976
Sales—under $500,000
Distrib.—Local
Limited Liability Company

### SHURTS FRAMES & MOLDING, DON
294 Lanes Mill Rd. (07731)
**Phone—(732) 363-1323**
Fax—(732) 363-1323
Owner—Don Shurts
SIC—2499; *Wooden picture
frames & mouldings*
Employs—2; Estab.—1973
Sales—under $500,000
Distrib.—Local
Privately owned corporation

### SUBURBAN BUILDING PRODUCTS
1178 Lakewood Farmingdale Rd.
(07731)
**Phone—(732) 901-8900**
Fax—(732) 901-2155
www.suburbanbuildingproducts.co
m
Email—info@
suburbanbuildingproducts.com
Owner—Vincent Bochario
SIC—3444; *Vinyl fabrication*
Employs—55; Estab.—1971
Sales—$11Mil-$25Mil
Distrib.—Local
Privately owned corporation

### SUPERIOR GRAPHICS & SIGNS, INC.
576 Casino Dr. (07731)
**Phone—(732) 625-0101**
www.edecals.com

Email—help@edecals.com
Pres.—Ken Barnaby
Shpg. Mgr.—Nick Fink
SIC—3993; *Car & boat vinyl
decals & commercial truck
lettering*
Employs—3; Estab.—2001
Sales—under $500,000 (est)
Distrib.—National
Sole ownership

### TUERS ALUMINUM, LLC
2562 Lakewood-Allenwood Rd.
(07731)
**Phone—(732) 458-2031**
Fax—(732) 840-9637
www.tuersaluminumllc.com
Ptnr.—Nick Tsoukalis
Ptnr.—Susan Tsoukalis
SIC—3444; *Aluminum awnings*
Employs—2; Estab.—1971
Sales—under $500,000
Distrib.—Regional
Limited Liability Company

### UNITED ENERGY CORP.
3526 U.S. Highway 9 S., Ste. 103
(07731)
**Phone—(732) 994-5225**
National—(800) 327-3456
Fax—(732) 994-5226
www.unitedenergycorp.net
Email—lramos@
unitedenergycorp.net
Chrm.—Jack Silver
Off. Mgr.—Lillian Ramos
SIC—2842; 2899; *Specialty
chemicals for the oil & gas
industry & petroleum refineries,
including dispersants,
degreasers, viscosity reducers &
corrosion inhibitors for pipeline,
flow line & well cleaning &
preservation*
Employs—5; Estab.—1996
Sales—under $500,000
Distrib.—Local
Publicly owned corporation

## Hurffville
(Gloucester—S.W.)

### WELD-DONE WELDING, INC.
20 Woodland Ave. (08080)
Mail addr: P.O. Box 5616, Deptford
(08096)
**(856) 582-7080**
Fax—(856) 582-2002
Pres.—Jeff Podesek
Opers. Mgr.—Harry Harding
SIC—3499; 3446; NAICS—
332323; *Structural steel
fabrication, metal stairs, railings,
catwalks, mezzanines & ladders*
Employs—15; Estab.—1986
Sales—$1Mil-$2.5Mil (est)
Distrib.—Regional
Privately owned corporation

## Irvington
(Essex—N.E.)

### ALBERT PAPER PRODUCTS CO.
464 Coit St. (07111)
Mail addr: P.O. Box 989, Hillside
(07205)
**Phone—(973) 373-0330**
Fax—(973) 373-5868
www.albertpaperproducts.com
Email—rmksr@aol.com
Pres.—Richard M. Kenah
V.-P.—Mark Kenah
Plt. Mgr.—Thomas Lampo

## Irvington—(cont.)

SIC—2653; NAICS—322211; *Corrugated & paperboard boxes, including cosmetic liners for the cosmetic & medical industries & candy & food packaging*
Employs—25; Estab.—1944
Sales—$1Mil-$5Mil
36,000 sq ft site, Distrib.—Regional
Privately owned corporation

**ALBOUM HAT CO., INC., W.**
1439 Springfield Ave. (07111)
**Phone—(973) 371-9100**
Fax—(973) 399-4110
www.rodeoking.com
Pres.—W. Alboum
Manager—Justin Alboum
SIC—2353; *Hats & caps*
Employs—20; Estab.—1921
Distrib.—Intl.
Privately owned corporation

**AMERICAN ALUMINUM CASTING CO.**
324 Coit St. (07111)
**Phone—(973) 372-3200**
Fax—(973) 375-4958
www.americanalum.com
Email—rhartl@aacco.net
Pres.—Robert W. Hartl
V-P.—Clifford Hartl
Opers. Mgr.—Dave Janosz
IT Mgr.—Tom Ivan
Chief Engr.—Bill Berner
SIC—3365; NAICS—331524; *Aluminum castings*
Employs—50; Estab.—1921
Sales—$5Mil-$8Mil
130,000 sq ft site, Distrib.—Intl.
Privately owned sub-S corp.

**AMERICAS BAKERY**
32-50 Buffington St., P.O. Box 5099 (07111)
**Phone—(973) 372-0700**
Fax—(973) 372-0707
Email—americasbakery@hotmail.com
Ptnr.—Tony Vicente
Ptnr.—Henry Rocha
SIC—2051; NAICS—311812; *Bread rolls*
Employs—55; Estab.—1984
Sales—$5Mil-$10Mil
Distrib.—Regional
Privately owned partnership

**ARNOLD FURNITURE MFRS., INC.**
400 Coit St. (07111)
**Phone—(973) 399-0505**
Fax—(973) 399-7638
www.arnoldfurniture.com
Email—info@arnoldfurniture.com
Pres.—Julius Arnold
Sr. V-P.—Glenn Arnold
GM—Mark Lipka
Special Projs. Mgr.—Barbara Arnold
SIC—2521; 2522; NAICS—337110; *Corporate headquarters & conference room furniture & case goods*
Employs—23; Estab.—1962
Sales—$1Mil-$2.5Mil (est)
150,000 sq ft site, Distrib.—Intl.
Privately owned corporation

**ARNOLD KOLAX FURNITURE, INC.**
Div. of Arnold Furniture Mfrs., Inc.
146 Coit St. (07111)
**Phone—(973) 375-3344**
Fax—(973) 375-6024
www.arnoldkolax.com
Email—eric@arnoldgroupsales.com
Pres.—Eric Arnold
Bookkeeper—Roxana Zamora

SIC—2531; 2521; NAICS—337211; *Fine wooden library & office furniture, including tables, chairs, bookcases & desks*
Employs—12; Estab.—2004
Sales—$500,000-$1Mil
Distrib.—National
Privately owned corporation
Parent co.—Arnold Furniture Mfrs., Inc., Irvington, NJ
Phone—(973) 399-0505
See Parent Co. Section for full profile.

**ARNOLD RECEPTION DESKS, INC.**
120 Coit St. (07111)
**Phone—(973) 375-8101**
National—(800) 306-0076
Fax—(973) 375-8090
www.ardesk.com
Email—william@ardesk.com
Pres.—William Kolax
Cont.—Margaret Kolax
GM—Benjamin Kolax
Sales Mgr.—Peter Branigan
Proj. Mgr.—Melissa Nieves
Proj. Mgr.—Jose Gonsalez
SIC—2521; NAICS—337211; *Reception desks, workstations & courtroom furniture*
Employs—27; Estab.—1989
Sales—$1Mil-$2.5Mil
Distrib.—Intl.
Privately owned sub-S corp.

**ASIA TRADING**
390 Nye Ave. (07111)
**Phone—(973) 577-1300**
Fax—(973) 622-1446
www.uniprouniforms.com
Email—sales@uniprouniforms.com
Pres.—Meir Frei
V-P.—David Find
Hum. Res. & IT Mgr.—Ari Brin
SIC—2326; 2337; 5136; 5137; NAICS—315200; *Manufacturer & distributor of security uniforms, including shirts, sweaters, vest, suit jackets, blazers & pants*
Employs—20; Estab.—2009
Sales—$500,000-$1Mil
Distrib.—National
Privately owned corporation
AKA: Unipro Uniforms

**B & B IRON WORKS**
300 Coit St. (07111)
**Phone—(973) 375-9000**
Fax—(973) 375-9087
www.bbironworksinc.com
Pres.—Mauro Belgiovine
Off. Mgr.—Sarah Annese
SIC—3446; *Architectural & ornamental ironwork*
Employs—50; Estab.—2004
Sales—$1Mil-$2.5Mil
Distrib.—National
Privately owned corporation

**BIERMAN EVERETT FOUNDRY CO.**
133 S. 20th St. (07111)
**Phone—(973) 373-8800**
          (973) 407-0628
Fax—(973) 373-3949
Email—befcofdry@aol.com
Pres.—Robert Julius
SIC—3321; 3365; 3366; NAICS—331511; *Gray iron, ductile iron & aluminum sand castings*
Employs—2; Estab.—1913
Sales—$1.5Mil-$3.5Mil
42,000 sq ft site, Distrib.—Regional
Privately owned sub-S corp.

**BISTIS PRESS**
1310 Clinton Ave. (07111)
**Phone—(973) 373-8033**
Ptnr.—Nick Bistis
Ptnr.—Matthew Bistis

SIC—2759; 2791; NAICS—323122; *Commercial printing & typesetting*
Employs—2; Estab.—1986
Sales—under $500,000
12,800 sq ft site, Distrib.—Local
Privately owned partnership

**CHASEN & SONS, INC., M.**
123 S. 20th St. (07111)
**Phone—(973) 589-8700**
Fax—(973) 589-7325
Email—mchasen@live.net
Pres., CEO—Alan Schachman
V-P.—David Schachman
SIC—2299; *Corporate headquarters & mattress filling & insulator pads & cotton & synthetic furniture stuffing & filling*
Employs—20; Estab.—1936
Sales—$1Mil-$2.5Mil
40,000 sq ft site, Distrib.—Regional
Privately owned sub-S corp.

**CHASEN & SONS, INC., M.**
117 S. 20th St. (07111)
**Phone—(973) 374-8956**
GM—David Schachman
SIC—2299; *Mattress components, including filling & insulator pads*
Employs—15
Sales—$500,000-$1Mil
Distrib.—Local
Privately owned corporation
Parent co.—Chasen & Sons, Inc., M., Irvington, NJ
Phone—(973) 589-8700
See Parent Co. Section for full profile.

**DAIRYLAND ICE CREAM**
487 Chancellor Ave. (07111)
**Phone—(973) 923-7625**
Fax—(973) 923-2557
www.dairylandicecream.com
Email—dairyland7@cs.com
Pres.—Arthur Anastasia
GM—Richard Patton
SIC—2024; NAICS—311520; *Ice cream*
Employs—20; Estab.—1903
11,000 sq ft site, Distrib.—Regional
Privately owned corporation

**DIVERSIFIED IMPRESSIONS, INC.**
119 Coit St. (07111)
**Phone—(973) 399-9041**
Fax—(973) 399-8431
Email—divimp@earthlink.net
Pres.—Richard Feldman
SIC—2759; 2791; NAICS—323122; *Commercial printing & typesetting*
Employs—6; Estab.—1981
Sales—$500,000-$1Mil
3,600 sq ft site, Distrib.—Regional
Privately owned corporation
Also see: Stuyvesant Press, Inc., same loc.

**ELECTRONIC TECHNOLOGY, INC.**
511 Lyons Ave. (07111)
**Phone—(973) 371-5160**
Fax—(973) 371-1929
www.eti-nj.com
Email—sales@eti-nj.com
Pres.—Victor Mohl
Engr., Electrical—Joe Dealeo
Buyer—Maureen Trapp
SIC—3625; NAICS—335314; *Electronic controls & computers*
Employs—80; Estab.—1989
25,000 sq ft site, Distrib.—Local
Privately owned corporation

**FRONTLINE INDUSTRIES, INC.**
990 Chancellor Ave. (07111)
**Phone—(973) 373-7211**
National—(800) 890-7325
Fax—(973) 374-0365
www.frontlineindustries.com
Email—sales@frontlineindustries.com

Pres.—Alfredo Ciotola
Dir.—Chris Ciotola
Off. Mgr.—Luisa Patino
Proj. Mgr.—Alfred Ciotola
SIC—3053; 3061; 3561; NAICS—339991; *Custom mechanical seals, flexible shaft couplings & pumps for the chemical, food & beverage, marine, petrochemical, pharmaceutical & industrial industries, hospitals, hotels, municipalities, power plants, utility companies & high risers*
Employs—15; Estab.—1980
15,000 sq ft site, Distrib.—Local
Privately owned corporation

**IMPERIAL SEWING MACHINE CO., INC.**
584 S. 21st St. (07111)
**Phone—(973) 374-3405**
Fax—(973) 374-1185
www.imperialsewingmachine.com
Email—imperialsewing@aol.com
Pres.—Philip Pantusco
SIC—3559; *Industrial sewing machines, including pleating machinery, slitters, winders & bias equipment; Brand name—Imperial*
Employs—6; Estab.—1952
Sales—$500,000-$1Mil
15,000 sq ft site, Distrib.—Intl.
Privately owned sub-S corp.
AKA: Chandler

**INFINITE MANUFACTURING GROUP, INC.**
171 Coit St. *(07111)*
**Phone—(973) 649-9950**
Fax—(973) 649-9951
www.infinitegroupusa.com
Email—info@infinitesign.com
Founder & CEO—Bernard Alloysius
Dir., Opers.—Michael Nasto
Dir., Mktg.—Moses Antony
SIC—3993; 2542; 2531; 2599; NAICS—339950; *Indoor & outdoor architectural signage, channel letters, displays, window lettering, custom fixtures & designer furniture for the retail & wholesale industries*
Employs—20; Estab.—2002
Sales—$1Mil-$2.5Mil
Distrib.—Intl.
Privately owned corporation

**INTERGEL VITAMIN CO.**
Div. of IVC Industries, Inc.
191 40th St. (07111)
**Phone—(973) 371-4400**
National—(800) 221-1208
www.ivcinc.com
Email—ivcinquiries@ivcinc.com
Dir., Opers.—Eric Sylvester
SIC—2834; NAICS—325412; *Pharmaceutical & nutritional products*
Employs—100; Estab.—1995
Sales—$50Mil-$100Mil (est)
Distrib.—Intl.
Parent co.—IVC Industries, Inc., Freehold, NJ
Phone—(732) 308-3000
See Parent Co. Section for full profile.

**JESSE J. HEAP & SONS, INC.**
576 S. 21st St. (07111)
**Phone—(973) 372-1559**
Fax—(973) 372-1929
www.jesseheap.com
Email—info@jesseheap.com
Pres.—Jesse Heap
V-P.—William Heap

GEOGRAPHICAL

## Irvington—(cont.)

SIC—3559; *Industrial sewing machine attachments, fusing & laminating machinery, material handling & dye sublimation equipment, rolling racks, carts, trucks, storage devices & heat transfer printing*
Employs—8; Estab.—1930
Sales—$500,000-$1Mil
22,000 sq ft site, Distrib.—Intl.
Privately owned corporation

### MONDO INTERNATIONAL, INC.

464 Coit St., P.O. Box 894 (07111)
**Phone—(973) 256-6123**
Fax—(973) 256-2370
www.mondollc.com
Email—rraimondo@mondollc.com
Pres.—Robert Raimondo
V-P.—Richard Kenah
SIC—2657; NAICS—322212; *Paperboard products, including cartons, die cuts, pads, U-boards, narrow rolls, slip sheets, inserts, liners & partitions*
Employs—10; Estab.—1974
27,000 sq ft site, Distrib.—Intl.
Limited Liability Company

### MPM DISPLAY, INC.

74 Woolsey St. *(07111)*
**Phone—(973) 374-3477**
Fax—(973) 374-0078
Email—michaelmpm@mac.com
Pres., Plt. Opers. Mgr.—Michael Bertko
Bookkeeper—Kathy Mattera
SIC—2541; *Point-of-purchase displays*
Employs—10; Estab.—1986
Sales—$500,000-$1Mil
Distrib.—National
Privately owned corporation

### P A K MFG., INC.

704 S. 21st St. (07111)
**Phone—(973) 372-1090**
Fax—(973) 372-1091
www.pakmanufacturing.com
Email—info@pakmanufacturing.com
Pres.—Alex Even-Esh
SIC—3841; *Surgical instruments*
Employs—38; Estab.—1996
28,000 sq ft site, Distrib.—National
Privately owned corporation

### QUALITY PAPER CONVERTERS OF NEW JERSEY, INC.

673 S. 21st St. (07111)
**Phone—(973) 399-1200**
Pres.—John Cumming
Opers. & Sales Mgr.—Steve Protzo
Off. Mgr.—Michael Cumming
SIC—2679; NAICS—322200; *Paper converting*
Employs—20; Estab.—1996
Distrib.—Regional
Privately owned corporation

### RICHARDS MFG.

517 Lyons Ave. (07111)
**Phone—(973) 371-1771**
Fax—(973) 371-4304
www.richards-mfg.com
Email—richardsales@richards-mfg.com
Ptnr. & Pres.—Joseph Bier
Ptnr.—Adam Bier
CEO—Bruce Bier
IT Mgr.—Spencer Fox
SIC—3679; 3643; NAICS—335931; *Electric cable connectors*
Employs—150; Estab.—1940
Sales—$10Mil-$25Mil (est)
Distrib.—National
Privately owned corporation

### ROSA-LY PIROGI

256 Madison Ave. (07111)
**Phone—(973) 371-0650**
www.rosalypirogi.com
Email—rosalypierogi@gmail.com
Owner—Gregory Baran
SIC—2098; NAICS—311823; *Pasta products*
Employs—1; Estab.—1982
Sales—under $500,000
Distrib.—Local
Sole ownership

### STUYVESANT PRESS, INC.

119 Coit St. (07111)
**Phone—(973) 399-3880**
Fax—(973) 399-0480
www.stuyvesantpress.com
Email—mroesch@stuyvesantpress.com
Pres., CEO—Michael Roesch
Plt. Mgr.—John Roesch
Prepress Mgr.—Joram Freudenfelds
Accountant—Lisa Lance
SIC—2752; 2759; 3993; 2791; NAICS—323122; *Offset, commercial, digital, color & wide-format printing, electronic prepress, signs & banners*
Employs—10; Estab.—1977
Sales—$1Mil-$2.5Mil
15,000 sq ft site, Distrib.—National
Privately owned sub-S corp.
Also see: Diversified Impressions, Inc., same loc.
AKA: Green Earth Press

### TOUCH DYNAMIC, INC.

17 Camptown Rd. (07111)
**Phone—(732) 382-5701**
National—(888) 508-6824
Fax—(732) 382-5777
www.touchdynamic.com
Pres.—Craig Paritz
Sales Mgr.—Dave Graber
Hum. Res. Mgr.—Robyn Ketz
SIC—3571; 3577; NAICS—334111; *Book-size PCs & touch-screen flat-panel monitors*
Employs—30; Estab.—1984
Sales—$10Mil-$25Mil (est)
Distrib.—Intl.
Privately owned corporation
AKA: TD

### WAYNE COUNTY FOODS, INC.

360 Coit St. (07111)
**Phone—(973) 399-0101**
Fax—(973) 399-2070
www.waynecountyfoods.com
Email—info@wcfds.com
Pres.—Peter Nemeth
Bookkeeper—Sharon Frigerio
Cust. Serv. Rep.—Nickey Nemeth
SIC—2033; NAICS—311421; *Private label fruit blend, grape & lemon juice, vinegar & apple cider bottling, including hot & cold glass filling, glass & plastic packaging & sleeve, cut, stack & pressure-sensitive labeling*
Employs—30; Estab.—1963
Distrib.—Local
Privately owned corporation

### WESTCO FRUIT & NUT PRODUCTS CO., INC.

93-97 Coit St. (07111)
**Phone—(973) 373-1866**
Fax—(973) 373-7900
www.westconutsonline.com
Email—westcottnut@gmail.com
Pres., Hum. Res. Mgr.—Rivka F. Moradi
Plt., Sales & Mktg. Mgr.—Jacob Moradi
Plt. Mgr.—Natan Moradi
SIC—2068; 2064; 2034; NAICS—311911; *Nuts, dried fruit & candy*
Employs—3; Estab.—1992
Sales—$500,000-$1Mil
7,000 sq ft site, Distrib.—National
Privately owned corporation

### WHEELER INDUSTRIAL CORP.

485 Lyons Ave. *(07111)*
**Phone—(973) 926-0551**
Fax—(973) 926-0984
www.wheelermetal4u.com
Email—pd.coates@wheelermetal4u.com
Chrm., Pres. & CEO—Paul Coates
V-P., Special Prods.—Michael Halleran
GM—John Vazquez
IT Mgr.—Bill Dorney
Engrg. Mgr.—Chris Shouln
Traf. Mgr.—Tom Ford
Plating Mgr.—George Burbank
Sales Rep., Midwest IN, IL, MN & WI—Jeff Moe
SIC—3351; 3315; NAICS—331421; *Corporate headquarters & copper & brass base alloys & round, flat, shaped, beryllium copper & medical grade wires; Brand name—Super Strip; Flat Wires; Live Wire; Spring Wires Copper Knight; Fort Knox; Silver Bullet*
Employs—21; Estab.—1989
20,000 sq ft site, Distrib.—National
Privately owned sub-S corp.

---

## Iselin

(Middlesex—N.E.)

NEW ENTRY
### 925NY

200 Middlesex Tpke., Ste. 202 (08830)
**Phone—(732) 404-4400**
Fax—(732) 404-1179
www.925ny.com
Email—robert@925co.com
Pres.—John LaBarbera
V-P.—Rosy LaBarbera
Off. Mgr.—Maria Tina
SIC—3911; *Sterling silver jewelry; Brand name—Silver Safari*
Employs—5; Estab.—2013
2,600 sq ft site, Distrib.—Intl.
Privately owned sub-S corp.

NEW ENTRY
### ADVANSTAR COMMUNICATIONS, INC.

485 U.S. Highway 1 S., Ste. 200 (08830)
**Phone—(732) 346-3000**
www.advanstar.com
Email—info@advanstar.com
Publisher—Mike Tracey
SIC—2721; *Magazine publishing*
Employs—50
Sales—$2.5Mil-$5Mil (est)
Distrib.—Intl.
Privately owned corporation
Parent co.—Advanstar Communications, Inc., Santa Monica, CA
Phone—(310) 857-7500
See Parent Co. Section for full profile.

### AERGO SOLUTIONS, INC.

33 Wood Ave. S., 5th Fl. (08830)
**Phone—(732) 321-1500**
Fax—(732) 321-1501
www.aergo.com
Email—info@aergo.com
Pres.—Michael Fetteducati
Analyst—Stephan Heckel
SIC—7372; *Software development*
Employs—12; Estab.—1996
Distrib.—National
Privately owned corporation

### ALLEGRA MARKETING PRINT MAIL

665 State Route 27 (08830-1820)
**Phone—(732) 404-0665**
Fax—(732) 404-0668
www.allegraprintonline.com
Email—allegraprint@yahoo.com
Pres.—Alkesh Shah
SIC—2759; 2791; 2789; NAICS—323122; *Digital color, instant, direct mail & large-format printing, electronic prepress, graphic design & binding of corporate identity & promotional items*
Employs—3; Estab.—1995
Sales—under $500,000
2,000 sq ft site, Distrib.—Local
Privately owned sub-S corp.

### ANSELL HEALTHCARE PRODUCTS, LLC (H Q)

111 Wood Ave. S., Ste. 210 *(08830-2700)*
**Phone—(732) 345-5400**
     (800) 800-0444
National—(800) 232-1309
Fax—(732) 219-5114
www.ansell.com
Email—info@ansell.com
Chrm.—Glenn Barnes
CEO—Magnus Nicolin
Pres., GM, Med. Bus. Unit—Anthony Lopez
CFO—Neil Salmon
Sr. V-P., CIO—Giri Peddinti
Sr. V-P., Gen. Counsel—Bill Reilly
Sr. V-P., Opers.—Steve Genzer
Sr. V-P., N. America—Bob Gaither
V-P., Branding & Global Comm.—Frank Mantero
SIC—2259; 2381; 3069; *Company headquarters; industrial work, latex & knit gloves*
Employs—200
Worldwide: 14,000
Sales—$1.5Bil
Privately owned corporation

### BASF CORPORATION, CATALYSTS DIV.

Div. of BASF Corporation
25 Middlesex-Essex Tpke., P.O. Box 770 (08830)
**Phone—(732) 205-5000**
National—(800) 631-9505
Fax—(732) 205-7136
www.catalysts.basf.com
Email—joseph.jones@basf.com
Dir., Hum. Res.—Krisanne Pook
Dir., Corp. Comm.—Joseph Jones
Dir., Env. Catalysis Research—Mikhail Rodkin
SIC—2819; 2816; NAICS—325100; *Divisional headquarters & environmental & process catalysts, technologies & material services*
Employs—400; Estab.—2006
Sales—$7Bil
Distrib.—Intl.
Publicly owned corporation
Parent co.—BASF Corporation, Florham Park, NJ
Phone—(973) 245-6000
See Parent Co. Section for full profile.

NEW ENTRY
### COUNSEL PRESS, LLC

517 U.S. Highway 1 S., Ste. 1160 (08830)
**Phone—(732) 750-9229**
National—(800) 527-7325
Fax—(732) 750-2770
www.counselpress.com
Manager—Robert L. Pincu
SIC—2731; *Book publishing for the law profession*
Employs—2
Sales—under $500,000 (est)
Distrib.—Local
Limited Liability Company

## Iselin—(cont.)

### FEDEX OFFICE & PRINT CENTER
Div. of FedEx Office & Print
Services, Inc.
1 Quality Way (08830)
**Phone—(732) 636-3580**
National—(800) 463-3339
Fax—(732) 636-3581
www.fedex.com
Email—usa1040@fedex.com
Off. Mgr.—Kathleen Murray
Ctr. Consultant—Ashley Lopez
Ctr. Consultant—Tamatha Schultz
SIC—2759; 3993; NAICS—
323100; *Commercial & instant
printing, signs, banners &
laminating*
Employs—4; Estab.—1971
Sales—$500,000-$1Mil
Distrib.—Intl.
Publicly owned corporation
Parent co.—FedEx Office & Print
Services, Inc., Dallas, TX
Phone—(214) 550-7000
See Parent Co. Section for full profile.

### IMPACT PRINTING
762 Green St. (08830)
**Phone—(732) 636-8893**
Fax—(732) 636-0067
www.impactprintjob.com
Owner—Eugene Lucas II
SIC—2752; 2791; NAICS—
323122; *Offset printing &
typesetting*
Employs—2; Estab.—1985
Sales—under $500,000 (est)
Distrib.—Local
Sole ownership

### L P B GRAPHICS, INC.
512-514 Route 27 (08830)
**Phone—(732) 283-4333**
National—(888) 303-3363
Fax—(732) 283-4339
www.letsprintbaby.com
Email—info@lpbgraphics.com
Pres.—Lisa Berg
Prod. Mgr.—John D. Burke
Bookkeeper—Kathy Introne
SIC—2752; 2791; NAICS—
323122; *Commercial offset
printing & typesetting, interior &
exterior signs & advertising
specialties*
Employs—8; Estab.—1985
Sales—$1Mil-$2.5Mil
5,000 sq ft site, Distrib.—National
Privately owned corporation

### MAGLIONE'S ITALIAN ICES
111 Madison St. (08830)
**Phone—(732) 283-0705**
Fax—(732) 283-3290
www.maglione-ices.com
Email—michael.maglione@
italianice.net
Ptnr. & GM—Michael Maglione
Ptnr.—George Maglione
Off. Mgr.—Toni Maglione
SIC—2024; NAICS—311520;
*Italian ices*
Employs—12; Estab.—1957
Sales—$500,000-$1Mil
Distrib.—Regional
Limited Liability Company

### MAIDENFORM BRANDS, INC.
Div. of Hanesbrands, Inc.
485 U.S. Highway 1 S., Bldg. F
(08830)
**Phone—(732) 621-2500**
National—(800) 292-2895
Fax—(732) 621-2510
www.maidenform.com
Email—websupport@
maidenform.com
Sr. V-P. & Mng. Dir., Intl.—Patricia
J. Royak
Dir., IT—Robert Russo

SIC—2341; 2342; NAICS—
315200; *Lingerie*
Employs—225; Estab.—1920
Distrib.—Intl.
Publicly owned corporation
Parent co.—Hanesbrands, Inc.,
Winston-Salem, NC
Phone—(336) 519-8080
See Parent Co. Section for full profile.

NEW ENTRY
### OPHTHALMOLOGY TIMES
485F U.S. Highway 1 S., Ste. 1
(08830)
**Phone—(732) 346-3060**
Fax—(732) 596-0016
Publisher & Editor—Leo Avila
SIC—2721; *Monthly magazine
publishing*
Employs—4
Sales—under $500,000 (est)

### SHOWCASE PRINTING OF ISELIN
181 E. James Pl. (08830)
**Phone—(732) 283-0438**
Fax—(732) 283-4988
Email—showcsprnt@aol.com
Pres.—Vivian Hoppock
V-P.—Glenn Hoppock
SIC—2759; NAICS—323100;
*Commercial printing*
Employs—2; Estab.—1987
Sales—under $500,000
Distrib.—Regional
Sole ownership

### SIGNS BY TOMORROW
825 Highway 1 S., Ste. 6 (08830)
**Phone—(732) 602-7878**
National—(800) 550-1818
Fax—(732) 602-0889
www.signsbytomorrow.com/iselin
Email—iselin@
signsbytomorrow.com
Pres.—Rajeev Krishna
Administrator—Bindu Krishna
SIC—3993; *Interior & exterior
signs*
Employs—7; Estab.—1992
Sales—$750,000-$1.2Mil
Distrib.—Regional
Privately owned corporation

### THROMBOGENICS, INC.
101 Wood Ave. S., Ste. 600
(08830)
**Phone—(732) 590-2900**
Fax—(212) 201-0921
www.thrombogenics.com
Email—info@thrombogenics.com
Head of N. American Opers.—
Keith Stewaid
Coordinator—Keisha Scott
SIC—2834; *Ophthalmic
pharmaceutical drug candidates
in Phase III clinical trials*
Employs—20
Sales—$10Mil-$25Mil (est)
Distrib.—National
Publicly owned corporation

### VIOLIN MEMORY, INC.
33 Wood Ave. S., 3rd Fl. (08830)
Mail addr: 510 Thornall St., Ste.
240, Edison (08837)
**Phone—(650) 396-1492**
National—(888) 984-6546
www.violin-memory.com
Email—support@vmem.com
Off. Mgr.—Mary Martis
Principal Engr.—Evan Chen
SIC—3674; NAICS—334413;
*Semiconductor devices*
Employs—57; Estab.—2005
Sales—$10Mil-$25Mil (est)
Distrib.—National
Privately owned corporation
Parent co.—Violin Memory, Inc.,
Santa Clara, CA
Phone—(650) 396-1500
See Parent Co. Section for full profile.

### VITECH SYSTEMS GROUP, INC.
111 Wood Ave. S. (08830)
**Phone—(646) 344-5282**
www.vitechinc.com
Email—info@vitechinc.com
Pres.—Frank Vitiello
SIC—7372; *Insurance, investment
& benefit administration software
development*
Employs—80
Distrib.—Intl.
Privately owned corporation
Parent co.—Vitech Systems
Group, Inc., New York, NY
Phone—(212) 868-0900
See Parent Co. Section for full profile.

## Island Heights
### (Ocean—S.E.)

### BEACHWOOD CANVAS WORKS, LLC
39 Lake Ave., P.O. Box 137
(08732)
**Phone—(732) 929-3168**
Fax—(732) 929-3479
www.beachwoodcanvas.com
Email—beachwoodcanvas@
comcast.net
Pres. & Bookkeeper—Dan
Janquitto
SIC—2394; NAICS—314912;
*Canvas products*
Employs—10; Estab.—1971
8,000 sq ft site, Distrib.—Intl.
Limited Liability Company

### SIGNDESIGN, LLC
206 Lake Ave., P.O. Box 892
(08732)
**Phone—(732) 929-3700**
Email—signmediainc@comcast.net
Pres.—Stephan Mueller
SIC—3993; *Nonelectric signs*
Employs—1; Estab.—1988
Sales—under $500,000
Distrib.—Regional
Privately owned corporation

## Jackson
### (Ocean—S.E.)

### BCG MARBLE & GRANITE CO.
Div. of BCG Marble & Granite
Fabricators Co., Inc.
370 Whitesville Rd. (08527)
**Phone—(732) 367-3788**
Fax—(732) 367-2849
www.bcggranite.com
Email—bcggranite@gmail.com
Ptnr.—Pasquale Petrocelli
Off. & Sales Mgr.—Gabriella
Carrasco
SIC—3281; NAICS—327991;
*Marble & granite countertops,
vanities & tub surrounds*
Employs—20; Estab.—1997
Distrib.—Regional
Privately owned corporation
Parent co.—BCG Marble & Granite
Fabricators Co., Inc.,
Hackensack, NJ
Phone—(201) 343-8487
See Parent Co. Section for full profile.

NEW ENTRY
### BROWBANDS WITH BLING & OTHER THINGS
985 Farmingdale Rd. (08527)
**Phone—(732) 740-8300**
Fax—(732) 276-5221
www.browbandswithbling.com
Email—kagriffin@optonline.net
Owner—Katherine Griffin

SIC—3199; 3172; *Custom
handcrafted leather products
embellished with Swarovski
crystals, including browbands,
stock pins, dog collars, belts,
bracelets, spurs & spur straps*
Employs—1; Estab.—2005
Sales—$133,000
2,200 sq ft site, Distrib.—National
Privately owned corporation

### †CAMPBELL FOUNDRY, MATERIALS DIV.
Div. of Campbell Foundry Co.
630 S. Hope Chapel Rd. *(08527)*
**Phone—(732) 408-1111**
Fax—(732) 408-1105
www.campbellfoundry.com
Email—sales@
campbellfoundry.com
Br. Mgr.—Leon Theodorou
SIC—5162; *Wholesaler of PVC,
HDPE, RCP, CMP & DIP pipe &
fittings*
Employs—5; Estab.—1999
Company-wide: 10
Sales—over $5Mil
Distrib.—Intl.
Privately owned corporation
Parent co.—Campbell Foundry
Co., Harrison, NJ
Phone—(973) 483-5480
See Parent Co. Section for full profile.

### CLEANZONES, LLC
640 Herman Rd., Ste. 2 (08527-
3068)
**Phone—(732) 534-5590**
National—(888) 399-2464
Fax—(732) 534-5589
www.cleanzones.com
Email—sales@cleanzones.com
Pres.—David McClelland
V-P., Sales & Mktg.—Toni
Shamsky
SIC—3564; 3821; NAICS—
339111; *Air filtration equipment
for the cleanroom industry,
including air showers, softwall &
hardwall cleanrooms &
polypropylene fume exhaust &
filtered exhaust hoods &
casework*
Employs—10; Estab.—2000
Sales—$5Mil
5,000 sq ft site, Distrib.—National
Limited Liability Company

### CREATIVE WOOD PRODUCTS, INC.
370 Whiteville Rd. (08527)
**Phone—(732) 370-0051**
Fax—(732) 370-2442
Pres.—George Tomaszewicz
V-P.—Jeff Tomaszewicz
Fin. Mgr.—Jess Tomaszewicz
SIC—2431; NAICS—321900;
*Millwork*
Employs—8; Estab.—1992
Sales—$500,000-$1Mil
15,000 sq ft site, Distrib.—
Regional
Privately owned corporation

### CURTIS SIGN DESIGN
640 Herman Rd., Ste. 1 (08527)
**Phone—(732) 928-9494**
Fax—(732) 928-9227
www.curtissign.com
Email—sales@curtissign.com
Pres.—Ed Kronenthal
SIC—3993; *Nonelectric signs*
Employs—2; Estab.—1985
Sales—under $500,000
Distrib.—Local
Sole ownership

### DESIGNERS KITCHENS, INC.
250 Faraday Ave. (08527)
**Phone—(732) 370-5500**
Fax—(732) 363-2929
www.designerskitchens.net
Email—designerskitchens@
optimum.net
Pres.—Edwin Rivera

GEOGRAPHICAL

## Jackson—(cont.)

GM—Hector Rivera
CAD Designer—David Seme
Bookkeeper—Lisa Curcoran
SIC—2431; 2434; NAICS—337110; *Architectural woodwork & wooden cabinets*
Employs—15; Estab.—1980
Sales—$500,000-$1Mil
8,000 sq ft site, Distrib.—Local
Privately owned sub-S corp.

**DMD STAIRS & RAILS, LLC**
370 Whitesville Rd., Ste. 8 (08527)
**Phone—(732) 901-0102**
Fax—(732) 730-3886
www.dmdstairsandrails.com
Email—dmdstairandrails@comcast.net
Pres.—Douglas Diani
Off. Mgr.—Brianne Johnson
SIC—2431; 3446; NAICS—332323; *Wooden & metal stairs & railings*
Employs—20; Estab.—2004
Sales—$500,000-$1Mil
Distrib.—Regional
Limited Liability Company

**I DID IT METAL ART, INC.**
53 Gables Way (08527)
**Phone—(732) 866-8481**
www.ididitart.com
Email—ididitart@aol.com
Owner—Dale Pilling
SIC—3911; *Precious metal jewelry*
Employs—1; Estab.—1999
Sales—under $500,000
Distrib.—National
Sole ownership

**JERSEY SHORE STEEL, INC.**
636 Herman Rd. (08527)
**Phone—(732) 833-8855**
Fax—(732) 833-8866
Ptnr.—Gary Loveland
Ptnr.—Randall Loveland
SIC—3444; 3443; *Sheet & plate steel fabrication*
Employs—18; Estab.—2000
Sales—$1Mil-$2.5Mil (est)
12,000 sq ft site, Distrib.—Regional
Privately owned corporation

**LATINOS UNIDOS DE NUEVA JERSEY, LLC**
190 Hickory Rd. (08527)
**Phone—(732) 534-5959**
Fax—(732) 987-4677
www.lunj.net
Pres.—Jorge Rod
Hum. Res. & IT Mgr.—Betty Rod
SIC—2711; *Latin monthly newspaper printing & publishing*
Employs—6; Estab.—2003
Sales—$1.5Mil
1,400 sq ft site, Distrib.—Local
Limited Liability Company

**NEW HORIZON LIGHTING, INC.**
632 Cedar Swamp Rd. (08527)
**Phone—(732) 833-8086**
Fax—(732) 833-8085
www.newhorizonlighting.com
Email—sales@newhorizonlighting.com
Pres.—Michael Stoddard
Sales Rep.—Tom Szeszko
SIC—3646; *Energy-efficient light fixtures for commercial applications, including commercial buildings, warehouses & offices*
Employs—15; Estab.—2006
Sales—$1Mil-$2.5Mil
Distrib.—National
Privately owned corporation

**NEW JERSEY IRON, INC.**
905 Patterson Rd. (08527)
**Phone—(732) 928-7242**
Fax—(732) 928-7247

Email—njiron@optonline.net
Pres.—Larry Karpinsky
Off. Mgr.—Doreen Lewis
Administrator—Tony Ritchie
SIC—3441; NAICS—332312; *Structural iron fabrication*
Employs—20; Estab.—1980
Sales—$1Mil-$2.5Mil
Distrib.—Local
Privately owned corporation

**PEDECO PRINTING, INC.**
12 Summers Dr. (08527)
**Phone—(732) 363-0510**
Pres.—Tom Degliomini
SIC—2752; NAICS—323100; *Offset & lithographic printing*
Employs—12; Estab.—1927
Distrib.—National
Privately owned corporation

**PRESENTATION SOLUTIONS, INC.**
432 Clearstream Rd. (08527)
**Phone—(732) 961-1960**
National—(888) 517-4189
Fax—(732) 961-1962
www.presentationsolution.com
Email—msweeney@presentationsolution.com
Pres.—Margo Sweeney
Sales Rep.—Mark Landers
SIC—2542; NAICS—337215; *Trade show exhibits*
Employs—4; Estab.—1995
Sales—$500,000-$1Mil
4,000 sq ft site, Distrib.—National
Privately owned corporation

**†S & R SALES, INC.**
1 Sandart Plz. (08527)
**Phone—(732) 905-0278**
National—(800) 270-7263
Fax—(732) 905-6926
www.s-rsales.com
Email—s-rsales@juno.com
Pres.—Stu Pancer
V-P.—Rochelle Pancer
Off. Mgr.—Simone Pancer
SIC—5199; *Distributor of sand & candle art & spin art supplies*
Employs—12; Estab.—1967
Sales—$500,000-$1Mil
Distrib.—National
Privately owned corporation

**†T & B SPECIALTIES, INC.**
479 Wright Debow Rd. (08527)
**Phone—(732) 928-4500**
Fax—(732) 928-1819
Email—tombtbs@optonline.net
Pres.—Thomas E. Barchie
Sales Mgr.—Tom Blonder
Off. Mgr.—Cathy Niman
SIC—5084; 5085; *Wholesaler of industrial equipment & supplies & janitorial supplies*
Employs—3; Estab.—1985
Sales—$2.5Mil
3,500 sq ft site, Distrib.—Regional
Privately owned corporation

**UNEX MANUFACTURING, INC.**
50 Progress Pl. (08527)
**Phone—(732) 928-2800**
National—(800) 695-7726
Fax—(732) 928-2828
www.unex.com
Email—span@unex.com
Pres.—Brian Neuwirth
V-P., Opers.—Howard McIlvaine
IT Mgr.—Norbert Danecker
Hum. Res. Mgr.—Maria Bird
SIC—3535; 3537; NAICS—333922; *Carton flow track & material handling equipment*
Employs—65; Estab.—1964
55,000 sq ft site, Distrib.—National
Privately owned corporation

**V E P MANUFACTURING INC.**
575 S. Hope Chapel Rd. (08527)
**Phone—(732) 657-0666**
Fax—(732) 657-2580
www.vepmfg.com

Email—vepmfg@aol.com
Pres., CFO—Robert Pfluger
V-P., MIS & Dir., Qual. Control—Thomas Pfluger
Plt. Mgr.—Ryan V. Pfluger
Mktg. Mgr.—Timothy Pfluger
SIC—3599; *Precision CNC machining job shop*
Employs—22; Estab.—1973
8,000 sq ft site, Distrib.—National
Privately owned partnership

**WALTER R. EARLE CORPORATION**
Div. of Earle Asphalt Company
655 S. Hope Chapel Rd. (08527)
Mail addr.—P.O. Box 757, Farmingdale (07727-0757)
**Phone—(732) 657-8551**
Fax—(732) 657-9230
www.earleco.com
Email—info@earleco.com
V-P.—Thomas J. Earle
Corp. Secy.—Michael Earle
Hum. Res. Mgr.—Darlene Rasmussen
Dispatcher—Robert Schue
SIC—2951; NAICS—324121; *Asphalt paving compounds*
Employs—35; Estab.—1968
Sales—$10Mil
Distrib.—Local
Limited Liability Company
Parent co.—Earle Asphalt Company, Wall, NJ
Phone—(732) 308-1113
See Parent Co. Section for full profile.

## Jamesburg
(Middlesex—N.E.)

**†AUTO KING PARTS & SUPPLIES**
67 E. Railroad Ave. (08831)
**Phone—(732) 521-0474**
www.autokingparts.com
Email—autokingparts@aol.com
Owner—Joseph Donnelly
SIC—5013; *Distributor of automotive parts & supplies, including brakes*
Employs—10; Estab.—1974
9,000 sq ft site, Distrib.—Local
Sole ownership

**JAMESBURG PRESS MADISON PRINTING, INC.**
9 E. Railroad Ave. (08831)
**Phone—(732) 521-0262**
Fax—(732) 521-0262
Pres.—Fred Voza
Plt. Mgr.—Chris Voza
SIC—2752; 2791; NAICS—323122; *Offset printing & typesetting*
Employs—2; Estab.—1962
Distrib.—Local
Sole ownership
AKA: Madison Printing Service

**MENDOKER'S QUALITY BAKERY, INC.**
34 W. Railroad Ave. (08831)
**Phone—(732) 521-0056**
Fax—(732) 521-2590
Email—mendokersqualitybakery@gmail.com
Pres.—Edward Mendoker
Sales Mgr.—Nicole Mendoker
SIC—2051; NAICS—311812; *Bakery & deli products*
Employs—50; Estab.—1932
Sales—$2.6Mil-$5Mil
Distrib.—Regional
Privately owned corporation

**SWEET SIGN SYSTEMS, INC.**
9 Davison Ave., Ste. 4 (08831)
**Phone—(732) 521-9300**
(732) 309-0245
Fax—(732) 521-1892
www.sweetsign.com
Email—sweetsign1920@aol.com
Pres., CEO & CFO—Richard Dawson

V-P.—Christine Dawson
Proj. Mgr.—Jeremy Slappey
Acctg. Supv.—Diane Tanner
Graphic Designer—Dan Scheffler
SIC—3993; *Architectural interior & exterior signs, banners & vehicle graphics; Brand name—SignComp Extrusions; 3M vinyl*
Employs—5; Estab.—1920
Sales—$600,000
900 sq ft site, Distrib.—National
Sole ownership

## Jersey City
(Hudson—N.E.)

**A & R SEWING CO., INC.**
451 Communipaw Ave. (07304)
**Phone—(201) 332-0622**
Fax—(201) 332-8538
www.arsewing.com
Email—arsewingco@aol.com
Pres.—Jerry Ragoobir
V-P.—Morris Stone
SIC—2399; *Contract sewing*
Employs—12; Estab.—1991
Sales—$1Mil-$2.5Mil
Distrib.—Local
Privately owned corporation

**A.B. TEES SCREEN PRINTING, LLC**
7 Sherman Ave., 3rd Fl. (07307)
**Phone—(201) 239-0022**
Fax—(201) 221-8453
www.abtees1.com
Email—order4abtees@verizon.net
Pres.—Anthony Blunda, Jr.
SIC—2396; *Custom & contract textile screen printing of apparel & promotional items*
Employs—4; Estab.—1986
10,000 sq ft site, Distrib.—National
Limited Liability Company

**ACADIA SCENIC, INC.**
130 Bay St. (07302)
Mail addr.—P.O. Box 197, Jersey City (07303)
**Phone—(201) 653-8889**
Fax—(201) 653-4717
Pres.—David Lawson
Foreman—Nick Depaola
SIC—2499; 3448; 2399; NAICS—332311; *Theatrical scenery buildings*
Employs—25; Estab.—1982
Distrib.—Local
Privately owned corporation

**ACRILEX, INC.**
230 Culver Ave. (07305)
**Phone—(201) 333-1500**
National—(800) 222-4680
Fax—(201) 333-1237
www.acrilex.com
Email—info@acrilex.com
Pres.—Steven R. Sullivan
Dir., New Prod. Dev.—Dan Rustin
GM & Plt. Mgr.—Orlando Alcantara
R & D Mgr.—Dominec Procopio
SIC—3089; *Corporate headquarters & acrylic sheet & plastic fabrication*
Employs—50; Estab.—1972
Sales—$15Mil-$20Mil
50,000 sq ft site, Distrib.—Intl.

**AL QUICK QUALITY PRINTERS, INC.**
77 Tuers Ave. (07306)
**Phone—(201) 659-4003**
Fax—(201) 659-5331
Pres.—Al Gonzalez
Administrator—Darlene Sanchez
SIC—2759; NAICS—323100; *Commercial printing*
Employs—3; Estab.—1988
Sales—under $500,000
Distrib.—Regional
Privately owned corporation

## Jersey City—(cont.)

**ALL AMERICAN RECYCLING CORP.**
2 Hope St. (07307)
**Phone—(201) 656-3363**
Fax—(201) 656-8188
www.allamericanrecyclingcorp.co
m
Email—mf_stocks@hotmail.com
Pres.—Vincent M. Ponte
CFO—Charles C. Jacobson
V-P.—Vincent F. Ponte
GM—William Gannon
SIC—2611; 3089; 5093; NAICS—
322100; *Paper & plastic
recycling, including paper
shredding & book destruction*
Employs—137; Estab.—1996
Sales—$25Mil-$35Mil
Distrib.—Regional
Privately owned corporation

**ALLIED BIAS PRODUCTS CORP.**
430 Communipaw Ave., Ste. 3
(07304)
**Phone—(201) 432-6050**
Fax—(201) 432-8881
Email—lenny@alliedbias.com
Pres.—Leonard Staloff
Plt. Opers. Mgr.—Steve Moskovitz
SIC—2269; NAICS—313300;
*Textile converting, slitting &
cutting*
Employs—12; Estab.—1963
Sales—$1Mil-$5Mil
15,000 sq ft site, Distrib.—Intl.
Privately owned sub-S corp.
AKA: Star Binding

**ALLWELD IRON**
160 Culber Ave. (07305)
**Phone—(201) 434-8750**
Owner—Jose Nedrano
SIC—3312; *Steel fabrication*
Employs—1; Estab.—1996
Sales—under $500,000
Distrib.—Local
Sole ownership

NEW ENTRY
**AMDOCS, INC.**
34 Exchange Pl. (07311)
**Phone—(201) 631-3200**
www.amdocs.com
Email—care@amdocs.com
Dir.—Amy McLean
SIC—7373; *Computer systems
integration, including LANs &
WANs*
Employs—8; Estab.—2005
Sales—$2.5Mil
Distrib.—Intl.
Publicly owned corporation
Parent co.—Amdocs, Inc.,
Chesterfield, MO
Phone—(314) 212-7000
See Parent Co. Section for full profile.

**ANDERSON INTERNATIONAL
FOODS, INC.**
95 Burma Rd. (07305)
**Phone—(516) 747-2210**
Fax—(201) 333-8735
Email—andersonfoods@aol.com
Pres.—Bridgitte Mizrahi
V-P.—Martin Esquenazi
Prodn. Coord.—Ozzy Perdomo
SIC—2022; NAICS—311513;
*Cheese*
Employs—30; Estab.—1996
Distrib.—Regional
Privately owned corporation

**BANNON GROUP**
629 Grove St. (07310)
**Phone—(201) 451-6500**
Fax—(201) 451-5697
Email—scott.merrill@
bannongroup.com
Pres.—Michael Falcone
V-P., Prodn.—Scott Merrill
Bookkeeper—Benita Kasper

SIC—2759; 2752; NAICS—
323100; *Color, offset, direct mail
& digital printing of promotional,
corporate, financial,
pharmaceutical & sales
materials, package inserts &
branded, sales & media kits &
fulfillment service*
Employs—3; Estab.—1974
Distrib.—Regional
Limited Liability Company

†**BASS, INC., RUDOLF**
45 Halladay St. (07304)
**Phone—(201) 433-3800**
Fax—(201) 433-6853
www.rudolfbassinc.net
Email—rbassmachy@aol.com
Pres.—Richard H. Bass
SIC—5084; *Distributor of
industrial woodworking
machinery*
Employs—4; Estab.—1918
Sales—under $500,000
Distrib.—Regional
Privately owned corporation

**BEL FUSE, INC. (H Q)**
206 Van Vorst St. (07302)
**Phone—(201) 432-0463**
Fax—(201) 432-9542
www.belfuse.com
Email—belfuse@belf.com
Pres., CEO—Daniel Bernstein
V-P., Opers.—Dennis Ackerman
Fin. Cont.—Jerold Kimmel
Dir., Fin.—Craig Brosious
Pur. Mgr.—Kevin Meehan
IT Mgr.—Mike Grosso
SIC—3679; 3613; NAICS—
335313; *Corporate
headquarters; electronic
components for the networking,
telecommunications, high-speed
data transmission, commercial
aerospace, transportation &
consumer products industries &
the military; Brand name—Bel;
Signal Transformer; Stewart
Connector; Cinch Connector;
Bel Power Solutions; Cinch
Connectivity Solutions; TRP
Connector*
Employs—22; Estab.—1949
Sales—$349Mil
5,000 sq ft site, Distrib.—Intl.
Publicly owned corporation
ISO rating—9001, AS9100

**BETHEL INDUSTRIES, INC.**
3423 John F. Kennedy Blvd.
(07307)
**Phone—(201) 656-8222**
Fax—(201) 656-6620
Email—bethkim@verizon.net
Pres.—Sun Kim
SIC—2337; 2311; NAICS—
315200; *Women's jackets &
men's & women's military
uniforms*
Employs—110
Sales—$10Mil-$25Mil (est)
Distrib.—National
Privately owned corporation

**BETTER PLASTICS, INC.**
1 Mallory Ave. (07305)
**Phone—(201) 332-6777**
National—(866) 330-6777
Fax—(201) 332-4223
www.betterplastics.com
Email—betterplastics@comcast.net
Pres.—Debra Fiore
V-P.—Joseph Santo, Jr.
SIC—2542; *Plastic laminated
solid surface countertops &
cabinets*
Employs—10; Estab.—1980
10,000 sq ft site, Distrib.—Local
Privately owned corporation

**BURNS BROS. & MCCABE, INC.**
787 Tonnele Ave. (07307-3916)
**Phone—(201) 795-0800**
Fax—(201) 795-0121
www.burns-bros.com
Email—customerservice@burns-
bros.com
Pres.—John M. Burns, Jr.
V-P.—Neil Burns
SIC—3281; NAICS—327991;
*Cemetery monuments*
Employs—8; Estab.—1987
2,500 sq ft site, Distrib.—Regional
Privately owned sub-S corp.

**C.A.M.E. MACHINE & METAL
WORKS, INC.**
181 Pacific Ave. (07304)
**Phone—(201) 309-0005**
Fax—(201) 309-0055
www.servimego.com
Email—ciromed@aol.com
Pres.—Ciro Medina
SIC—3599; *Machining job shop,
including general metalworking,
milling, gearing, grinding,
lathing, CNC equipment &
specialty welding, rim repair &
custom designing*
Employs—4; Estab.—2001
Sales—under $500,000
2,000 sq ft site, Distrib.—National
Privately owned corporation

**CARLASCIO INC. ORTHOTICS,
PROSTHETIC, CUSTOM SHOES**
283 Grove St. (07302)
**Phone—(201) 333-8716**
                    (201) 434-7150
Fax—(201) 200-9391
www.carlascioorthopedics.com
Email—sales@
carlascioorthopedics.com
Owner—Louis Carlascio
Dir., Opers.—Midred Elaine
Carlascio
Manager—Jackie Raynodo
SIC—3842; 3143; 3144; 3149;
NAICS—316213; *Custom
handmade orthotics, prosthetics
& custom prescription molded &
orthopedic shoes for men,
women & children, including
corrective footwear & alterations
for deformities & mastectomy
fittings & supplies; Brand
name—SAS; PW MINOR; New
Balance; Dr. Comfort; Drew
Shoes*
Employs—11
Sales—$1Mil-$2.5Mil
Distrib.—Local
Privately owned sub-S corp.
AKA: Carlascio Orthopedics

**CENVEO, INC.**
25 Linden Ave. E. (07305)
**Phone—(201) 434-2100**
National—(800) 526-3020
Fax—(201) 434-4048
www.cenveo.com
Email—info@cenveo.com
Plt. Mgr.—Vito Mazza
Graphic Artist & Supv.—Joe
Miranda
SIC—2677; NAICS—322232;
*Envelope printing*
Employs—96; Estab.—1992
100,000 sq ft site, Distrib.—Intl.
Publicly owned corporation
Parent co.—Cenveo, Inc.,
Stamford, CT
Phone—(203) 595-3000
See Parent Co. Section for full profile.

†**CERTIFIED PRODUCTS CO.**
269 Kearney Ave. *(07305)*
**Phone—(201) 433-0013**
                    (800) 654-2436
Fax—(201) 433-1482
www.cerprodnjhydraulics.com
Email—info@
cerprodnjhydraulics.com

Owner—Cosimo Ferretti
SIC—5085; 5169; *Distributor of
hose assemblies & lubricants*
Employs—15; Estab.—1933
Sales—$1Mil-$5Mil
Distrib.—Regional
Privately owned corporation

**CITY PRINT SHOP, INC.**
157 Sip Ave. (07306)
**Phone—(201) 792-6699**
Fax—(201) 792-0214
Email—zodams@aol.com
Owner & Pres.—Craig Olsen
SIC—2759; NAICS—323100;
*Commercial printing*
Employs—1; Estab.—1978
Sales—under $500,000
Distrib.—Local
Sole ownership

**COLUMBIA PAINT LAB, INC.**
452 Communipaw Ave. (07304)
**Phone—(201) 435-4884**
Fax—(201) 435-0440
Pres.—George Pahiakos
SIC—2851; NAICS—325510;
*Paints*
Employs—17; Estab.—1905
Distrib.—Local
Privately owned corporation

**COMPOSITION PRINTING**
P.O. Box 55 (07303)
**Phone—(201) 798-0531**
Fax—(201) 798-0501
Email—lfgradin@verizon.net
Pres., Fin. & R & D Mgr.—Allen
Gradin
MIS Mgr.—Lynn Fox
SIC—2759; NAICS—323100;
*Commercial & color printing of
business forms & manifold books*
Employs—6; Estab.—1987
Sales—$500,000-$1Mil
7,500 sq ft site, Distrib.—National
Privately owned corporation
AKA: Logomania, Inc.

**COMPUTER SHARE, INC.**
480 Washington Blvd. (07310)
**Phone—(201) 680-5307**
www.computershare.com
Pres.—Bernie O'Connor
Cust. Serv. Rep.—Rob Chillemi
SIC—2752; NAICS—323100;
*Offset printing of business &
financial documents & materials
for public & private companies &
organizations*
Employs—120; Estab.—1997
Sales—$1Mil-$2.5Mil
Distrib.—National
Publicly owned corporation

†**COOPER ELECTRIC SUPPLY CO.**
1521 John F. Kennedy Blvd.
(07305)
**Phone—(201) 434-8575**
Fax—(201) 434-4636
www.cooper-electric.com
Email—scott.macdonald@cooper-
electric.com
Br. Mgr.—Scott MacDonald
SIC—5063; *Distributor of electrical
equipment & supplies, including
connectors, wires & sockets*
Employs—8; Estab.—1998
Distrib.—Intl.
Privately owned corporation
Parent co.—Cooper Electric
Supply Co., Monroe, NJ
Phone—(732) 747-2233
See Parent Co. Section for full profile.

**DAVID AUBREY, INC**
186 Griffith St. (07307)
**Phone—(201) 653-2200**
Fax—(201) 653-6344
www.davidaubrey.com
Email—info@davidaubrey.com
Pres.—Jennifer Arago
Dir., Admn.—V. J. Curtis
Accts. Mgr.—Kera Partei

## Jersey City—(cont.)

SIC—3961; NAICS—339900;
*Costume jewelry*
Employs—25; Estab.—1996
Sales—$1Mil-$2.5Mil
Distrib.—Intl.
Privately owned corporation

**DELEON PRINTING & SUPPLY, INC.**

311 Palisade Ave. (07307)
**Phone—(201) 798-8440**
Fax—(201) 798-1283
Email—deleonprinting@gmail.com
Pres.—Paul Deleon
SIC—2759; 2752; *Commercial
printing, including blueprinting*
Employs—3; Estab.—1999
Sales—under $500,000
1,300 sq ft site, Distrib.—National
Privately owned corporation

**DELOITTE**

3 2nd St., Harborside Plaza 10,
Ste. 300 (07311)
**Phone—(212) 937-8200**
Fax—(212) 937-8298
www.deloitte.com
Email—info@deloitte.com
Co-Founder & COO—Samuel
Goldman
CEO—William Karl
IT Mgr.—Mike Harrison
Hum. Res. Mgr.—Priya Borana
SIC—7373; NAICS—541512;
*Business process & technology
computer integrated systems*
Employs—120; Estab.—1996
Distrib.—Intl.
Privately owned corporation

**DG3 NORTH AMERICA, INC.**

100 Burma Rd. (07305)
**Phone—(201) 793-5000**
Fax—(201) 333-8428
www.dg3.com
CFO, The CGI Group—L. J.
Baillargeon
Sr. V.-P., Major Accts. & Sales—
Fred Gorra
Sr. V.-P., Offshoring & Opers.—
Andy Manning
Dir. & Sr. Mktg. Specialist—Joe
Lindfeldt
Plt. Mgr.—Patrick Caragliano
IT Mgr.—John Kondratowicz
Hum. Res. Mgr.—Otto Garcia
Maint. Mgr.—Peter Manetakis
SIC—2752; 2759; NAICS—
323100; *Offset & digital printing,
including document
management*
Employs—400; Estab.—1989
167,000 sq ft site, Distrib.—Intl.
Privately owned corporation

**DIAMOND DIE CUTTERS &
EMBOSSERS**

629 Grove St., 6th Fl. (07310)
**Phone—(201) 876-8540**
Email—diamondie@verizon.net
GM—Moon Mui
Off. Mgr.—Anna Mendez
SIC—3544; 2796; 3469; NAICS—
323122; *Die cutting, metal
stamping & embossing*
Employs—15; Estab.—1999
Sales—$5Mil-$10Mil
Distrib.—Intl.
Privately owned corporation

NEW ENTRY
**DISCOUNT DIGITAL PRINT, LLC**

629 Grove St., 16th Fl. (07310)
**Phone—(201) 659-9600**
Fax—(212) 994-5391
Email—info@
discountdigitalprint.com
Owner—Jim Dilworth

SIC—2759; *Digital printing*
Employs—8; Estab.—2005
Sales—$500,000-$1Mil
3,000 sq ft site, Distrib.—National
Limited Liability Company

**DOWNTOWN INTERIORS, LLC**

629 Grove St., 8th Fl. (07310)
**Phone—(201) 798-4728**
Fax—(201) 798-6528
www.downtowninteriors.com
Email—info@
downtowninteriors.com
Pres.—Hertzel Abraham
SIC—2431; NAICS—321900;
*Custom cabinets*
Employs—12; Estab.—2005
Sales—$500,000-$1Mil
4,000 sq ft site, Distrib.—Regional
Privately owned corporation

**EASTERN MILLWORK, INC.**

18 Chapel Ave. (07305)
**Phone—(201) 451-9510**
Fax—(201) 451-9511
www.easterncompanies.com
Email—info@
easterncompanies.com
Pres.—Andrew Campbell
Cont., Hum. Res. & Off. Mgr.—
Thomas Titus
GM—Marko Herzig
IT Mgr.—Jordan Mrazek
Pur. Agt.—Fred Rodrigo
SIC—2434; 2431; 2499; NAICS—
337110; *Commercial wooden
cabinets, stairs & mouldings &
architectural millwork*
Employs—60; Estab.—1992
17,000 sq ft site, Distrib.—National
Privately owned corporation

**EIGEN ARTS, INC.**

150 Bay St. (07302)
**Phone—(201) 798-7310**
Fax—(201) 798-4962
www.eigenarts.com
Email—info@eigenarts.com
Pres.—Paul Brothe
Off. Mgr.—Airena Yates
SIC—3269; NAICS—327112;
*Ceramic dinnerware, vases,
planters & bathroom accessories*
Employs—6; Estab.—1989
Distrib.—Intl.
Privately owned corporation

NEW ENTRY
**ELECTROHEAT INDUCTION**

9 Spruce St. (07306)
**Phone—(908) 494-0726**
www.electroheatinduction.com
Email—sales@
electroheatinduction.com
Proj. Engr.—Charlie Parsana
SIC—3567; 3548; *Induction
heating & melting equipment,
including melting & smelting
furnaces, hardening, pipe
heating & welding equipment*
Employs—10
Sales—$1Mil-$2.5Mil
Distrib.—National
Limited Liability Company

**ELEMENTIS SPECIALTIES, INC.**

400 Claremont Ave. (07304)
**Phone—(201) 395-5108**
National—(800) 418-5191
Fax—(201) 432-2962
www.elementis-specialties.com
Email—info@elementis-
specialties.com
Plt. Mgr.—Parkash Patel
Cust. Serv. Rep.—Judy Smith
SIC—2899; *Rheological additives*
Employs—40; Estab.—2000
Distrib.—Intl.
Publicly owned corporation
Parent co.—Elementis Specialties,
Inc., East Windsor, NJ
Phone—(609) 443-2000
See Parent Co. Section for full profile.

†**EMPIRE RECYCLING, INC.**

3 New York Ave., P.O. Box 17398
(07307)
**Phone—(732) 393-0200**
Fax—(732) 393-0808
www.galaxyrecycling.com
Email—galaxyrecycling@aol.com
Pres., GM—Gary Giordano
GM—Don Arrighetta
SIC—5093; *Wholesaler of scrap
paper for the recycling industry*
Employs—35; Estab.—1988
Distrib.—Regional
Privately owned corporation
DBA: Garden State Recycling

**FABRIC CHEMICAL CORP.**

61 Cornelison Ave. (07304)
**Phone—(201) 432-0440**
Fax—(201) 432-7997
Pres.—Andrew Jacobson
Bookkeeper—Barbara Smith
SIC—2819; *Laboratory chemicals*
Employs—9; Estab.—1968
Sales—$2.5Mil-$5Mil (est)
Distrib.—National
Privately owned corporation

**FELDMAN STAINED GLASS**

401 Halladay St. (07304)
Mail addr: 26 Cornelia St., Ste. 4,
New York (10014)
**Phone—(201) 434-2887**
(646) 416-2432
Fax—(201) 434-2887
www.feldmanstainedglass.com
Email—larry@
feldmanstainedglass.com
Proprietor—Larry A. Feldman
SIC—3231; 3645; 3211; NAICS—
327215; *Custom stained glass
windows, skylights, lamps &
lighting for homes, churches &
synagogues, including repair &
restoration work; Brand name—
Feldman Stained Glass*
Employs—3; Estab.—1987
Sales—under $500,000
Distrib.—Intl.
Sole ownership

†**FERGUSON ENTERPRISES, INC.**

1 Colony Rd. (07305)
**Phone—(201) 369-5120**
Fax—(201) 536-3580
www.ferguson.com
Email—fenton.harpster@
ferguson.com
Br. Mgr.—Chad Leland
SIC—5074; *Distributor of
plumbing & heating supplies*
Employs—20
Distrib.—Local
Publicly owned corporation
Parent co.—Ferguson Enterprises,
Inc., Newport News, VA
Phone—(757) 874-7795
See Parent Co. Section for full profile.

**FILIPINO EXPRESS NEWSPAPER,
INC.**

2711 John F. Kennedy Blvd.
(07306-5712)
**Phone—(201) 434-1114**
Fax—(201) 434-0880
www.filipinoexpress.com
Email—filexpress@aol.com
Publisher & GM—Lito Gajilan
SIC—2711; 2791; NAICS—
323122; *Newspaper publishing*
Employs—7; Estab.—1986
Sales—under $500,000
Distrib.—Local
Sole ownership

**FINE WRAP INDUSTRY, INC.**

123 Town Square Pl. (07310)
**Phone—(732) 960-9602**
National—(888) 390-1666
Fax—(732) 907-1854
www.finewrapind.com
Email—info@finewrapind.com
Pres.—Bob Jones

V.-P.—Jack Veck
SIC—2673; *Flexible plastic food
product bags*
Employs—10
Sales—$1Mil-$2.5Mil (est)
Distrib.—National
Privately owned corporation

†**FINISHMASTER, INC.**

700 Garfield Ave. (07305)
**Phone—(201) 435-1555**
National—(800) 840-1358
Fax—(201) 432-1921
www.finishmaster.com
Email—info@finishmaster.com
GM—Cliff White
SIC—5198; 5013; *Distributor of
automotive paints & coatings*
Employs—4; Estab.—1967
Distrib.—Local
Publicly owned corporation
Parent co.—FinishMaster, Inc.,
Indianapolis, IN
Phone—(317) 237-3678
See Parent Co. Section for full profile.

**FLEX MOULDING, INC.**

112 Wells Ave. (07306)
**Phone—(201) 360-3634**
(201) 487-8080
National—(800) 307-3357
Fax—(201) 360-3834
www.flexiblemoulding.com
Email—info@flexiblemoulding.com
GM—Al Smith
SIC—3089; *Cast polyester
mouldings, preformed & flexible
millwork & cast architectural
ornamental, including custom
replication & restoration casting;
Brand name—Flex Moulding;
Flex Mould; Superflex*
Employs—15; Estab.—1960
10,000 sq ft site, Distrib.—National
Privately owned corporation

**FLUITEC INTERNATIONAL (H Q)**

333 Washington St., Ste. 201
(07302-3095)
**Phone—(201) 946-4584**
Fax—(201) 434-2768
www.fluitec.com
Email—info@fluitec.com
Pres., CEO—Frank Magnotti
Ex. V.-P., Bus. Dev.—Greg
Livingstone
Ex. V.-P., Bus. Dev.—Brian
Thompson
V.-P., Engrg. & Opers.—Simon
Bard
Cont.—April Pannell
Dir., Sales, Global Inside—Deanna
Komuves
SIC—3569; 3823; *Company
headquarters; lubricant
conditioning monitoring &
contamination control equipment
for turbines (mfg. subcontracted)*
Employs—50; Estab.—2011
Sales—$5Mil-$10Mil
Distrib.—Intl.
Privately owned corporation

†**FORTUNE PLASTIC & METAL, INC.**

20 Carbon Pl. (07035)
**Phone—(201) 333-3339**
Fax—(201) 333-7662
www.fortunegroup.net
Email—recycler@fortunegroup.net
CEO—Norman Ng
V.-P.—Victor Ng
SIC—5093; *Corporate
headquarters & wholesaler of
recycled nonferrous metals &
plastics & materials reclaimed
from recycled electronics*
Employs—40; Estab.—1994
Distrib.—Regional
Privately owned corporation

## Jersey City—(cont.)

**GARDEN STATE AWARDS**
3516 John F. Kennedy Blvd. (07307-4128)
**Phone—(201) 795-9420**
Fax—(201) 795-0099
www.gardenstateawards.com
Email—sky3516@gmail.com
Pres.—Michael Sky
SIC—3479; *Trophy & award engraving; Brand name—8 lines*
Employs—5; Estab.—1992
Sales—under $500,000
2,200 sq ft site, Distrib.—National
Privately owned corporation

**GENERAL PENCIL CO.**
67 Fleet St. (07306)
**Phone—(201) 653-5351**
Fax—(201) 653-2298
www.generalpencil.com
Email—sales@generalpencil.com
Chrm.—James S. Weissenborn
Pres., CEO—Kate Vanoncini
V-P. & IT Mgr.—Helmut Bode
SIC—3952; *Wooden-cased art & school pencils & art & craft school products; Brand name— General's; Kimberly; Multichrome; The Masters; KISS-OFF; Charcoal White; All-Art; Semi Hex; Layout; Sketch & Wash; PRIMO; Cedar Pointe* All-Art; Peel and Sketch; Sketchmate*
Employs—42; Estab.—1889
Sales—$5Mil-$10Mil (est)
50,000 sq ft site, Distrib.—Intl.
Privately owned corporation

**GEORGE TAUB PRODUCTS**
277 New York Ave. (07307)
**Phone—(201) 798-5353**
National—(800) 828-2634
Fax—(201) 659-7186
www.taubdental.com
Email—sales@taubdental.com
Owner, Pres. & Fin. Mgr.— Lawrence Taub
IT & Sales Mgr.—Jordan Taub
Off. Mgr.—Steven Taub
SIC—3843; NAICS—339114; *Dental coatings & stains for acrylic, dental die spacers & die hardeners & visible light veneer & dual cured cements; Brand name—Minute Stain; Fusion; Fusion Zr cements; RubberSep; Hydroxyline; Perfectone Molds; InstaGlaze; TruFit; Tru Paque; Smart Spacer; SalDri; Bright Spot; Blazer Torches; Permabond; Aron Alpha; HiGloss; Trident Dental Instruments*
Employs—6; Estab.—1950
Sales—over $900,000
3,800 sq ft site, Distrib.—Intl.
Privately owned corporation
Also see: Perfectone Mold Co., same loc.

**GINN CO.**
812 Jersey Ave. (07310)
**Phone—(201) 216-1660**
National—(888) 216-1711
Fax—(201) 216-1668
Email—prepress-dept@verizon.net
Pres.—Robert Glickenhaus
V-P., Treas.—John Caime
SIC—2752; 2771; NAICS— 323100; *Christmas, wedding, social, business announcement & greeting cards; Brand name— Elgin Vellum*
Employs—20; Estab.—1947
Sales—$1Mil-$2.5Mil
30,000 sq ft site, Distrib.—National
Privately owned sub-S corp.

**GL CONSULTING, INC.**
1000 Plaza Three (07311)
**Phone—(201) 451-9121**
Fax—(201) 451-0849
www.smp-ag.com
Email—info@smp-ag.com
Sr. V-P.—Roger Elwell
Cont.—Dino Panayio
Off. Mgr.—Amelia Ortiz
SIC—7372; *General ledger database software development, including SAP & Oracle transformation solutions*
Employs—45; Estab.—1980
Distrib.—Intl.
Privately owned corporation
AKA: GL Assocs.

**GREENVILLE COLORANTS (H Q)**
20 Linden Ave. E. (07305)
**Phone—(201) 595-0200**
National—(800) 832-8985
Fax—(201) 332-0444
www.greenvillecolorants.com
Email—info@ greenvillecolorants.com
Owner & Co-Chrm.—Ronald M. Weiss
CFO—Joseph Lynch
SIC—2865; NAICS—325100; *Company headquarters; industrial colorants*
Employs—8; Estab.—2005
Distrib.—Regional
Privately owned corporation

**GREENWICH GRAPHICS, LLC**
234 16th St., 8th Fl. (07310)
Mail addr: 1238 48th St., Brooklyn (11219)
**Phone—(201) 420-7100**
(212) 727-1116
Fax—(212) 965-8282
Email—gwich@mindspring.com
Owner, Pres. & MIS Mgr.—Wolfe Gluck
SIC—2796; 2791; 2759; NAICS— 323122; *Printing plates, computerized typesetting, electronic prepress & commercial & poster printing*
Employs—8; Estab.—1988
2,400 sq ft site, Distrib.—National
Sole ownership

**GUMRUNNERS, LLC**
333 Washington St., P.O. Box 392 (07303-0392)
**Phone—(201) 678-9300**
Fax—(201) 221-7997
www.gumrunners.com
Email—info@gumrunners.com
Co-Founder—Laurence Molloy
Co-Founder—Kevin Gass
SIC—2067; NAICS—311340; *Caffeinated & noncaffeinated chewing gum; Brand name— Jolt; Nutri-Trim*
Employs—4; Estab.—2002
Sales—$500,000-$1Mil
Distrib.—Local
Limited Liability Company

**H M S MONACO, INC.**
629 Grove St., 5th Fl. (07310-1249)
**Phone—(201) 533-0007**
National—(800) 777-0901
Fax—(201) 533-8939
www.hmsmonaco.com
Email—hmsmonaco@hotmail.com
Pres., CEO—Ira Erstling
Bookkeeper & Hum. Res. Mgr.— Jose Redriguez
SIC—3961; 3999; 3942; NAICS— 339931; *Costume jewelry, stuffed toys & novelties*
Employs—40; Estab.—1984
Sales—$3Mil
30,000 sq ft site, Distrib.—National
Privately owned sub-S corp.

**HALSTED CORP.**
78 Halladay St. (07304)
**Phone—(201) 433-3323**
National—(800) 843-5184
Fax—(201) 333-0670
www.halstedbag.com
Email—ud@bhalstedsandbags.com
Pres.—Michael J. Murphy
SIC—2393; 2673; NAICS— 314911; *Manufacturer & distributor of industrial woven polypropylene bulk & textile bags for the chemical, mining, agriculture & feed/grain industries*
Employs—35; Estab.—1876
Distrib.—National
Privately owned sub-S corp.

**HANSEN CO., INC., JOSEPH C.**
629 Grove St., Ste. 26 (07310)
**Phone—(201) 222-1677**
National—(866) 988-8055
Fax—(201) 222-1699
www.josephchansen.com
Email—info@josephchansen.com
Pres.—Barney Simon
SIC—2391; NAICS—314121; *Manufacturer of stage & theater draperies, drapery track & hardware & drapery & dance floor rental services*
Employs—3; Estab.—1927
Sales—$500,000-$1Mil
Distrib.—Intl.
Privately owned corporation

**HUDSON COMMUNITY ENTERPRISES**
780 Montgomery St. (07306)
**Phone—(201) 432-5959**
Fax—(201) 432-6227
www.hudsoncommunity.org
Email—jbrown@ hudsoncommunity.org
Pres.—Joe Brown
SIC—3089; *Contract packaging*
Employs—65; Estab.—1954
Distrib.—Local
Privately owned corporation

**INFINITE PRINT**
225 New York Ave. (07307)
**Phone—(862) 668-3094**
Fax—(973) 571-9552
Email—infiniteprint@yahoo.com
Owner—Robert Pracht
SIC—2396; *Textile screen printing*
Employs—1; Estab.—2005
Sales—under $500,000
Distrib.—Regional
Privately owned corporation

**INSURANCE SERVICES OFFICE, INC.**
Div. of Verisk Analytics, Inc.
545 Washington Blvd. (07310)
**Phone—(201) 469-2000**
National—(800) 888-4476
Fax—(201) 469-4006
www.iso.com
Email—info@iso.com
Chrm.—Frank J. Coyne
Pres., CEO—Scott Stephenson
Ex. V-P., CFO & Group Exec., Risk Assessment—Mark Anquillare
Sr. V-P., CIO & Group Ex., Supply Chain Risk Analytics—Perry F. Rotella
V-P., CMO—Christopher H. Perini
Hum. Res. Mgr.—Robert Orr

SIC—7372; *Risk evaluation & management software development; Brand name— ISO; AISG; AIR Worldwide; A-PLUS; AscendantOne; BCEGS; COA; Coverage Verifier; FireLine; iiX; ISO ClaimSearch; ISO HomeValue; Intellicorp; Integrator; InterThinx; ISO MarketWatch; ISO Participation Plus; ISO Suite+*
Employs—1200; Estab.—1971
Sales—$557Mil
Distrib.—Intl.
Privately owned corporation
Parent co.—Verisk Analytics, Inc., Jersey City, NJ
Phone—(201) 469-2000
See Parent Co. Section for full profile.

**IPC SYSTEMS, INC. (H Q)**
Harborside Financial Ctr., 3 2nd St., Plz. 10, 15th Fl. (07311)
**Phone—(201) 253-2000**
Fax—(201) 253-2361
www.ipc.com
Email—ipcsubs@quadrantsubs.com
CEO—Neil Barua
Sr. V-P., Gen. Counsel & Chief Admn. Officer—John McSherry
Sr. V-P., Sales & Support—Joseph Smolarski
Sr. V-P. & Mng. Dir., Trading Comm. Sys.—Michael Speranza
Sr. V-P. & Mng. Dir., Enhanced Svcs.—Marianne Leitch
SIC—3669; NAICS—334290; *Corporate headquarters; telephone systems*
Employs—130; Estab.—1973
Sales—$10Mil-$25Mil (est)
Distrib.—Intl.

**JENSON & MITCHELL, INC.**
880 Communipaw Ave. (07304)
**Phone—(201) 332-4140**
Fax—(201) 332-2439
www.jensonandmitchell.com
Email—springrepair@aol.com
Pres.—Frank Mitchell
Plt. Mgr.—Charles Blotchock
SIC—3493; 3714; NAICS— 332611; *Automotive springs & truck suspension systems*
Employs—3; Estab.—1928
Sales—under $500,000
Distrib.—Local
Privately owned corporation

**†JETRO CASH & CARRY, INC.**
Div. of Restaurant Depot, LLC
1 Amity St. (07304)
**Phone—(201) 434-4334**
Fax—(201) 434-8912
www.restaurantdepot.com
Email—sales@restaurantdepot.com
GM—Tom Desciscio
SIC—5141; *Wholesaler of general line groceries to restaurants & caterers*
Employs—50
Limited Liability Company
Parent co.—Restaurant Depot, LLC, College Point, NY
Phone—(718) 762-8700
See Parent Co. Section for full profile.

**JON-DA PRINTING CO.**
234 16th St., 8th Fl. (07310)
**Phone—(201) 653-6200**
Fax—(201) 653-0027
GM—Melody Serra
SIC—2752; NAICS—323100; *Offset printing*
Employs—14; Estab.—1969
Sales—under $500,000
Distrib.—Local
Privately owned corporation

**JORGENSEN-CARR LTD.**
50 Dey St., 4th Fl. (07306)
**Phone—(201) 792-2278**
Fax—(201) 792-1916
www.jorgensencarrllc.com

GEOGRAPHICAL

# Jersey City—(cont.)

Email—jorgcarr@msn.com
Pres.—Mike Jorgenson
V.-P.—Kenneth Carr
SIC—2431; 2511; NAICS—321900; *Furniture & architectural woodworking, including frame & panel doors*
Employs—5; Estab.—1987
Sales—$500,000-$1Mil
Distrib.—Regional
Privately owned sub-S corp.

## KNF FLEXPAK CORPORATION.
Div. of KNF Corp.
44 Howell St. (07306)
Phone—(201) 656-4012
Fax—(201) 656-5194
www.knfcorporation.com
Email—sales@knfcorporation.com
GM—Paul Bellantonio
Sales Mgr.—Ray Glenn
SIC—2673; 3082; NAICS—326121; *Plastic bag extrusions*
Employs—40
Distrib.—National
Privately owned corporation
Parent co.—KNF Corp., Tamaqua, PA
  Phone—(570) 386-3550
  See Parent Co. Section for full profile.

## KOBRICK COFFEE CO., INC.
693 Luis Marin Blvd. (07310)
Phone—(201) 656-6313
National—(800) 562-7491
Fax—(201) 656-3665
www.kobricks.com
Email—info@kobricks.com
Pres.—Steve Kobrick
Dir., Mktg.—Nikole Kobrick
Sales Mgr.—Kevin Lane
SIC—2095; NAICS—311920; *Coffee roasting*
Employs—30; Estab.—1920
Distrib.—Intl.

## LANGENDORFF CORP.
633 Grove St. (07310)
Phone—(201) 659-6300
Fax—(201) 659-6311
www.langendorffcorp.com
Pres.—Frank Langendorff
SIC—2759; 2752; NAICS—323100; *Commercial offset printing*
Employs—6; Estab.—1956
Sales—under $500,000
Distrib.—Regional
Privately owned corporation

## LEE SIMS CHOCOLATES
743 Bergen Ave. (07306)
Phone—(201) 433-1308
Fax—(201) 433-0288
www.leesimschocolates.com
Email—leesims743@aol.com
Pres., CEO—Nicholas Vlahakis
Manager—Valerie Vlahakis
Manager—Susan Coviello
SIC—2066; 2068; 2052; NAICS—311911; *Assorted chocolate candy, mixed nuts & butter cookies*
Employs—8; Estab.—1950
Distrib.—Regional
Sole ownership

## LINDER & CO., INC.
1183 W. Side Ave. (07306)
Phone—(201) 386-8788
Fax—(201) 386-1222
www.lindergraphics.com
Email—csr@lindergraphics.com
Pres.—George R. Linder
V.-P., Sales & Mktg.—George-Michael Linder
Plt. Foreman—Brian Medlin

SIC—2752; 2759; 2789; NAICS—323100; *Commercial offset, conventional & digital printing, foil stamping, die cutting, binding & finishing*
Employs—18; Estab.—1852
Sales—$1.5Mil-$4Mil
32,000 sq ft site, Distrib.—National
Privately owned corporation

## M & F MACHINE WORKS
243-245 Custer Ave. (07305)
Phone—(201) 433-4085
Fax—(201) 433-4085
Owner—Alexander Salazar
SIC—3599; *General machining job shop*
Employs—3; Estab.—1941
Sales—under $500,000
Distrib.—Local
Sole ownership

NEW ENTRY
## MAGAZINE OF FANTASY & SCIENCE FICTION, THE
105 Leonard St. (07307)
Mail addr: P.O. Box 3447, Hoboken (07030)
Phone—(201) 876-2551
Fax—(201) 876-2551
www.fandsf.com
Email—sitemaster@fandsf.com
Publisher & Editor—Gordon Van Gelder
SIC—2721; *Magazine publishing*
Employs—4; Estab.—2006
Sales—$500,000-$1Mil
1,800 sq ft site, Distrib.—Intl.
Privately owned corporation

## MECCA & SONS TRUCKING CORP. (H Q)
580 Luis Munoz Marin Blvd. (07310-1416)
Phone—(201) 792-5866
Fax—(201) 792-7090
www.meccatrucking.com
Email—sales@meccatrucking.com
Pres.—Helen Mecca
CFO—Sandy Anest
Sales Mgr.—Paul Kish
SIC—2066; NAICS—311300; *Corporate headquarters; cocoa & sugar processing*
Employs—30; Estab.—1950
Company-wide: 100
Sales—$10Mil-$25Mil
Distrib.—Local
Privately owned sub-S corp.

## METAL MANAGEMENT NORTHEAST, INC.
Div. of Sims Metal Management
1 Linden Ave. E. (07305)
Phone—(201) 577-3110
     (201) 577-3200
Fax—(201) 432-5332
www.simsmm.com
Email—generalquestions@sims-groupusa.com
GM—Joe Payaso
IT Mgr.—Nuno Cascais
Comml. Mgr.—Michael Barkhorn
SIC—3341; 3399; 2821; 3449; *Metal recycling*
Employs—250; Estab.—1972
Sales—$50Mil-$100Mil
Distrib.—National
Privately owned corporation
AKA: Sims Metal Management
Parent co.—Sims Metal Management, New York, NY
  Phone—(212) 604-0710
  See Parent Co. Section for full profile.

## MITSUBISHI TANABE PHARMA AMERICA, INC. (H Q)
525 Washington Blvd., Ste. 400 (07310)
Phone—(908) 607-1980
Fax—(908) 607-1956
www.mitsubishi-pharma.com
Pres.—Takashi Nagago

Hum. Res. Mgr.—Nancy Sharko
SIC—2834; *Corporate headquarters; pharmaceutical drug candidates for chronic kidney disease in Phase I & III clinical trials (mfg. subcontracted)*
Employs—75
Sales—$25Mil-$50Mil (est)
Distrib.—Intl.
Privately owned corporation

## NESTLE WATERS NORTH AMERICA, INC.
Div. of Nestle' Waters North America, Inc.
111 Thomas McGovern Dr. (07305)
Phone—(201) 451-4000
National—(800) 950-9396
Fax—(201) 356-1876
www.nestlewatersnorthamerica.com
Email—contactus@waters.nestle.com
Factory Mgr.—Djenane Fleurentin
SIC—2086; NAICS—312100; *Bottled water*
Employs—13; Estab.—1921
45,000 sq ft site, Distrib.—Regional
Privately owned corporation
Parent co.—Nestle' Waters North America, Inc., Stamford, CT
  Phone—(203) 531-4100
  See Parent Co. Section for full profile.

## NEW YORK DAILY NEWS
Div. of Daily News L. P.
125 Theodore Conrad Dr. (07305)
Phone—(201) 946-6000
Fax—(212) 210-1861
www.nydailynews.com
Email—voicers@nydailynews.com
Sr. Mng. Editor—Robert Moore
Cont.—Michael Piccirillo
Plt. Mgr.—Chris Baker
IT Mgr.—Naren Prasath
Hum. Res. Mgr.—Arlen Bell
Benefits Admn.—Paula Buffington
SIC—2711; *Newspaper publishing*
Employs—600
Sales—$10Mil-$25Mil
430,000 sq ft site, Distrib.—Local
Parent co.—Daily News L. P., New York, NY
  Phone—(212) 210-2100
  See Parent Co. Section for full profile.

## NEW YORK SAMPLE CARD CO., INC.
812 Jersey Ave., 3rd Fl. (07310)
Phone—(201) 526-9040
Fax—(201) 526-9047
www.nysample.com
Email—info@nysample.com
Pres., MIS Mgr.—Kenneth Ehrlich
V.-P.—R. Ehrlich
SIC—2782; 2789; 2675; 2752; NAICS—323121; *Sample cards & books, including color standards, swatches, binding, die cutting, printing & yarn/ thread winding*
Employs—25; Estab.—1912
Sales—$1Mil-$2.5Mil
38,000 sq ft site, Distrib.—National
Privately owned corporation

## NICHOLAS GALVANIZING CO.
120 Duffield Ave. (07306)
Phone—(201) 795-1010
Fax—(201) 217-4258
Email—nicholasgalvanizing@verizon.net
Owner—Robert Gregory
GM—Angel Torres
Hum. Res., IT & Maint. Mgr.—Severino Canama
Off. Mgr.—Maria Martinez

SIC—3479; *Galvanized steel engraving*
Employs—29; Estab.—1949
Distrib.—Local
Privately owned corporation
AKA: Five Roses

## OFFICE PRINTS, THE
30 Journal Sq. (07306)
Phone—(201) 222-5555
Fax—(201) 217-6637
www.theofficeprints.com
Email—journalsquareoffice@gmail.com
Art Dir.—Ashley Centeno
GM—Kevin Sanders
SIC—2752; NAICS—323114; *Instant printing & graphic design services*
Employs—9; Estab.—1995
Sales—$500,000-$1Mil
Distrib.—Local
Privately owned corporation

## OSCAR PRINTING SERVICES
549 Newark Ave. (07306)
Phone—(201) 659-1588
Fax—(201) 659-1351
Email—oscarprint2000@yahoo.com
Pres.—Oscar Fernando
SIC—2759; NAICS—323100; *Commercial printing*
Employs—1; Estab.—2000
Sales—$500,000-$1Mil
Distrib.—Local
Privately owned corporation

## PEGASYSTEMS, INC.
111 Town Square Pl. (07310)
Phone—(201) 239-2300
National—(888) 723-2832
Fax—(201) 239-2315
www.antennasoftware.com
Email—cservice@antennasoftware.com
Pres., CEO—James Hemmer
Chief Mktg. & Strategy Officer—Jim Somers
CFO—Bill Smith
CTO—Dan Zeck
Ex. V.-P., Hum. Res.—Peter Watts
Ex. V.-P., Prof. Svcs. & Sols. Delivery—Gregg Plekan
Off. Mgr.—Paulette David
SIC—7372; *Mobile platform software development; Brand name—AMP™ Solution*
Employs—30
Distrib.—Intl.
Privately owned corporation
AKA: Antenna Software, Inc.
Parent co.—Pegasystems, Inc., Cambridge, MA
  Phone—(617) 866-6000
  See Parent Co. Section for full profile.

## PERFECTONE MOLD CO.
277 New York Ave. (07307)
Phone—(201) 798-5353
National—(800) 828-2634
Fax—(201) 659-7186
www.perfectonemolds.com
Email—sales@taubdental.com
Pres., Engr.—Lawrence Taub
Dir., Mktg.—Jordan Taub
SIC—3843; 3544; NAICS—339114; *Rubber dental molds for making wax pontics, including dental wax, wax heaters, wax glossing liquid & provisional resin restorations & arts & crafts molds for small figurines for school & Sunday school projects; Brand name—Perfect Wax; Perfect Mold Material; Perfectone Molds*
Employs—5; Estab.—1952
Sales—under $100,000
800 sq ft site, Distrib.—Intl.
Privately owned corporation
Also see: George Taub Products, same loc.

© Copyright 2015 Manufacturers' News, Inc.

## Jersey City—(cont.)

**†PLASTIC SERVICES, INC.**
200 Pacific Ave. (07304)
**Phone—(201) 200-1200**
Fax—(201) 200-9979
www.plasticservicesinc.com
Email—info@plasticservicesinc.com
Pres.—Jeff Turner
V-P.—Todd Howard
SIC—5093; 3089; *Plastic reprocessing & wholesaler of recycled scrap plastic*
Employs—20; Estab.—1992
Distrib.—Intl.
Privately owned corporation

**POLY-VERSION, INC.**
49 Fisk St. (07305)
**Phone—(201) 451-0600**
Fax—(201) 451-5712
www.poly-version.com
Email—pgoldschmiedt@poly-version.com
Pres., CEO—Philip Goldschmiedt
V-P.—Teresa Mert
Opers. Mgr.—Patty Reese
SIC—3089; *Disposable plastic gloves laminated to printed instruction sheets*
Employs—35; Estab.—1967
25,000 sq ft site, Distrib.—Local
Privately owned sub-S corp.

**PRIMARY COLORS GRAPHICS**
629 Grove St., 7th Fl. (07310)
**Phone—(201) 526-9300**
Fax—(201) 526-9298
Pres.—Cindy Wong
Prod. Mgr.—See Chin
SIC—2752; NAICS—323100; *Offset printing*
Employs—20; Estab.—2012
Sales—under $500,000
Distrib.—Regional
Privately owned sub-S corp.

**R WORLD ENTERPRISES**
197 Congress St. (07307)
**Phone—(201) 795-2428**
Fax—(201) 795-0708
Email—rworldenterprises@yahoo.com
Ptnr.—Marian Pacailler
SIC—2048; *Birdseeds*
Employs—3; Estab.—1971
Sales—under $500,000
8,000 sq ft site, Distrib.—National
Sole ownership

**R. B.'S RUBBER STAMP, INC.**
551 W. Side Ave. (07304)
**Phone—(201) 547-9955**
Fax—(201) 547-3599
www.rbsent.com
Email—raj@rbsent.com
Pres.—Leila Bahadur
GM—Raj Bahadur
SIC—3953; 2321; 2331; 3993; NAICS—339943; *Rubber stamps, marking devices, signs, custom printed t-shirts & promotional products*
Employs—2; Estab.—1987
Sales—under $500,000
600 sq ft site, Distrib.—Local
Privately owned corporation

**RAMBUSCH COMPANY**
160 Cornelison Ave. *(07304)*
**Phone—(201) 333-2525**
Fax—(201) 433-3355
www.rambusch.com
Email—info@rambusch.com
Chrm.—Martin V. Rambusch
Pres., CEO—Edwin P. Rambusch
Cont.—Nancy Hirsch

SIC—3648; 3231; NAICS—335129; *Standard & custom lighting fixtures, including restoration & replication of historic lighting fixtures & stained glass & church furnishings*
Employs—43; Estab.—1898
Sales—$5Mil-$10Mil
38,000 sq ft site, Distrib.—Intl.
Privately owned corporation
AKA: Rambusch Lighting

**RUSSO & SONS, INC., THOMAS**
854 Communipaw Ave. (07304)
**Phone—(201) 332-4159**
Fax—(201) 332-1940
Pres., CFO—Thomas Russo
SIC—3312; *Steel fabrication*
Employs—3; Estab.—1919
Sales—under $500,000
6,000 sq ft site, Distrib.—Local
Privately owned sub-S corp.

**SANDKAMP WOODWORKS, LLC**
430 Communipaw Ave. (07304)
**Phone—(201) 200-0101**
Fax—(201) 215-2225
www.sandkampwoodworks.com
Email—mail@sandkampwoodworks.com
Owner & Pres.—Anthony Sandkamp
SIC—2431; 2434; 2511; NAICS—337110; *Wooden kitchen & custom built-in cabinets, libraries, furniture & millwork*
Employs—3; Estab.—1991
Sales—under $500,000
Distrib.—Regional
Limited Liability Company

**SIGNS & CUSTOM METAL, INC.**
62 Monitor St. (07304)
**Phone—(201) 200-0110**
National—(800) 579-4100
Fax—(201) 200-1717
www.signscm.com
Email—sales@signscm.com
Pres.—Shan Kumar
Designer—Joe Perez
SIC—3993; *Custom architectural signs*
Employs—10; Estab.—1994
Distrib.—National
Privately owned corporation

**SKY PRINTING CO.**
338 Montgomery St. (07302)
Mail addr: P.O. Box 442, Jersey City (07303)
**Phone—(201) 433-3133**
Fax—(201) 433-0005
www.skyprinting.org
Owner—Laurie Benjamin
SIC—2761; 2759; NAICS—323119; *Business format digital printing*
Employs—1; Estab.—1908
Sales—$1Mil-$2.5Mil
Distrib.—Regional
Privately owned corporation

**SOCIETY OF NAVAL ARCHITECTS & MARINE ENGINEERS**
601 Pavonia Ave., Ste. 400 (07306)
**Phone—(201) 798-4800**
National—(800) 798-2188
Fax—(201) 798-4975
www.sname.org
Ex. Dir.—Erik Seither
Hum. Res., IT & Off. Mgr.—Joe Caggiano
Administrator—Erlinda Sauspino
SIC—2721; *Architectural & engineering journal publishing*
Employs—18; Estab.—1893
Sales—$2.6Mil-$5Mil
Distrib.—Intl.
Privately owned corporation
AKA: SNAME

**SPOO, INC.**
225 NY Ave., Ste. 1 (07307)
**Phone—(201) 420-0075**
www.spooprinting.com
Pres.—Chris Norelli
SIC—2396; *Screen printing*
Employs—1; Estab.—1987
Sales—under $500,000
Distrib.—Local
Privately owned corporation

**STALOFF BROS.**
22 Lewis Ave. (07306)
**Phone—(201) 653-6479**
Fax—(201) 604-0194
www.staloffbrothers.com
Email—staloffbrothers@verizon.net
Ptnr.—Glenn Brownstein
Ptnr.—Mary Brownstein
SIC—3499; *Architectural metal fabrication*
Employs—3; Estab.—1892
Sales—under $500,000
Distrib.—Local
Privately owned partnership

**STAR SNACKS, LLC**
105 Harbor Dr. (07305)
**Phone—(201) 200-9820**
National—(800) 775-9909
Fax—(201) 200-9827
www.starsnacks.net
Email—info@starsnacks.net
Mng. Ptnr.—Mendel Brachfeld
V-P., Sales, Natl.—Joseph Weinreich
Plt. Mgr.—J. J. Fleischer
SIC—2068; 2034; NAICS—311911; *Nuts & dried fruit*
Employs—200; Estab.—1954
Distrib.—Intl.
Limited Liability Company

**STATEWIDE GRANITE & MARBLE**
3257 Kennedy Blvd. (07306)
**Phone—(201) 653-1700**
Fax—(201) 653-9496
www.statewidestone.com
Email—statewidegranite@aol.com
GM—Linda Coviello
SIC—3281; NAICS—327991; *Marble & granite countertops*
Employs—7; Estab.—1988
Sales—$500,000-$1Mil (est)
Distrib.—National
Privately owned corporation

**†SUMMIT IMPORT CORP.**
100 Summit Pl. (07305)
**Phone—(201) 985-9800**
National—(800) 888-8228
Fax—(201) 985-8055
www.summitimport.com
Email—info@summitimport.com
Pres., CEO—Whiting Wu
Secy-Treas. & Cont.—Larry Chiu
Off. Mgr.—Tony Lee
SIC—5149; *Distributor of Asian food products, including canned foods*
Employs—80; Estab.—1950
120,000 sq ft site, Distrib.—National
Privately owned corporation

**†SYSCO FOOD SERVICES OF METRO NEW YORK, LLC**
Div. of SYSCO Corp.
20 Theodore Conrad Dr. (07305)
**Phone—(201) 433-2000**
National—(800) 275-4100
Fax—(201) 451-5604
www.syscometrony.com
Email—sales@sysco.com
Pres.—Phillip Lahm
Dir., Hum. Res.—Shelly Budhar
IT Mgr.—Dan Pentland
Prod. Dev. Mgr.—Frank Recine
Cust. Serv. Rep.—David Wood

SIC—5141; 5087; *Wholesaler of general line groceries & restaurant supplies*
Employs—530; Estab.—1970
Sales—$450Mil
300,000 sq ft site, Distrib.—National
Privately owned corporation
Parent co.—SYSCO Corp., Houston, TX
Phone—(281) 584-1390
See Parent Co. Section for full profile.

**NEW ENTRY**

**TESSIE'S SOAP BOX**
65 South St. (07307)
**Phone—(201) 533-8337**
Owner—Teresa Cooper
SIC—2841; *Laundry detergent*
Employs—2
Sales—$1Mil-$2.5Mil (est)

**UNIVERSAL PRINTS, INC.**
625 Newark Ave. (07306)
**Phone—(201) 656-7878**
Fax—(201) 659-9070
Email—upi656@aol.com
Pres.—David Gabriel
SIC—2759; 2752; NAICS—323100; *Commercial & instant printing*
Employs—2
Sales—under $500,000
1,000 sq ft site, Distrib.—Local
Privately owned corporation

**WALL STREET GROUP, INC.**
1 Edward Hart Dr. (07305)
**Phone—(201) 333-4784**
National—(800) 344-0280
Fax—(201) 332-1597
www.wallstreetgroup.com
Pres.—Phillip J. McGee
Off. Mgr.—Marge Mottola
Pur. Agt.—John Nitti
SIC—2759; NAICS—323100; *Commercial printing*
Employs—35
Distrib.—Local
Privately owned corporation

**WALTER MACHINE CO., INC., THE**
84-98 Cambridge Ave., P.O. Box 7700 (07307)
**Phone—(201) 656-5654**
Fax—(201) 656-0318
www.waltergear.com
Email—info@waltergear.com
Pres.—Don Chatrnuck
SIC—3566; NAICS—333612; *Gear drives*
Employs—40; Estab.—1927
Distrib.—Intl.
Privately owned corporation

**NEW ENTRY**

**WHOLESALE PRINT HOUSE**
1757 John F. Kennedy Blvd. (07305)
**Phone—(201) 333-7746**
Fax—(201) 706-7628
Email—takeoverprint@gmail.com
Owner—Omar Gordon
Prodn. Mgr.—Bernard Gordon
Ex. V-P.—Roshawn Gordon
SIC—2759; *Commercial printing , including business forms, cards, letterheads & invitations*
Employs—3; Estab.—2007
Sales—$100,000-$200,000
1,500 sq ft site, Distrib.—Local
Sole ownership

**WILLOW IRON WORKS**
67 Pollock Ave. (07305)
**Phone—(201) 659-7266**
Fax—(201) 432-0227
Pres.—Michael Zaccaria

## Jersey City—(cont.)

SIC—3446; NAICS—332323; *Ornamental ironwork, including fences, gates, stairs & railings*
Employs—7; Estab.—1988
Sales—$500,000-$1Mil (est)
Distrib.—Local
Privately owned corporation

**XCEEDIUM, INC.**
30 Montgomery St., Ste. 1020 (07302)
Mail addr: 2214 Rock Hill Rd., Ste. 100, Herndon (20170)
**Phone—(201) 536-1000**
National—(877) 636-5803
Fax—(201) 536-1200
www.xceedium.com
Email—info@xceedium.com
CFO—Rick Rose
Sr. V.-P., Engrg.—Brian McCullough
Ex. V.-P., Global Sales—Jay Zimmet
Ex. V.-P., Bus. Dev.—Mordecai Rosen
V.-P., Mktg.—Patrick McBride
Dir., Sales, Inside—Diann Murphy
Dir., IT—Luis Guzman
SIC—3577; *All-in-one computer network hardened appliances for access control & high-risk user auditing & privileged identity & access management*
Employs—50; Estab.—1992
Distrib.—Intl.
Privately owned corporation

## Johnsonburg

(Warren—N.W.)

**RUBBER FABRICATION & MOLDING, INC.**
1100 Route 519, P.O. Box 412 (07846)
**Phone—(908) 852-7725**
Fax—(908) 813-2577
www.rubber-fab.com
Email—rubberfab@verizon.net
Pres.—Bill Washer, Sr.
V.-P., Mfg.—Bill Washer, Jr.
SIC—3052; NAICS—326220; *Rubber hose & fittings*
Employs—5; Estab.—1990
Sales—$500,000-$1Mil
Distrib.—Intl.
Privately owned corporation

## Keansburg

(Monmouth—N.E.)

**AWNING SHOPPE, THE**
190 Highway 36 (07734)
**Phone—(732) 787-4246**
Fax—(732) 787-4245
Email—awningshoppe@verizon.net
Ptnr.—Tom McCarthy
Ptnr.—Kevin Gallagher
Off. Mgr.—Mariann St. Johns
SIC—2394; NAICS—314912; *Canopies, awnings & outdoor canvas products*
Employs—8; Estab.—1986
Sales—under $500,000
Distrib.—Local
Privately owned partnership

**KENCO WIRE & IRON PRODUCTS, INC.**
425 Carr Ave. (07734)
**Phone—(732) 495-3000**
Fax—(732) 495-6605
www.kencowire.com
Email—info@kencowire.com
Pres.—Mary Urban
V.-P.—Stephen G. Kennedy
Treas.—Paul Kennedy

SIC—3496; 3316; NAICS—331221; *Wire mesh partitions, window guards, jell cells & detention equipment*
Employs—15; Estab.—1978
Sales—under $500,000
27,000 sq ft site, Distrib.—Regional
Privately owned corporation

**SMITTEEZ SPORTSWEAR**
224 Main St., P.O. Box 274 (07734)
**Phone—(732) 787-5500**
Fax—(732) 471-6730
www.smitteez.com
Email—smitteesez@smitteez.com
Owner—James Smith
SIC—2396; 2395; *Apparel & athletic uniform screen printing & embroidery*
Employs—4; Estab.—1993
Sales—$500,000-$1Mil (est)
Distrib.—Regional
Privately owned corporation

## Kearny

(Hudson—N.E.)

**A. L. WILSON CHEMICAL CO.**
1050 Harrison Ave., P.O. Box 207 (07032)
**Phone—(201) 997-3300**
National—(800) 526-1188
Fax—(201) 997-5122
www.alwilson.com
Email—lynnmills@alwilson.com
Pres.—Fred Schwarzmann
Ex. V.-P.—Randy Schwarzmann
Off. Mgr.—Christina Lang
SIC—2819; 2842; 2843; 2899; *High-performance chemical products for removing stains from textiles for professional launderers & drycleaners; Brand name—RustGo; YellowGo; Laundry TarGo; TarGo EF; TarGo Dry; InkGo; 'G'Go; EasyGo; RiteGo; SpotsGo; BonGo; QwikGo; SoGo; CreaseGo; PermaGo; ColorGo; DroGo; ExGo; Fluoride Free RustGo*
Employs—20; Estab.—1928
Distrib.—Intl.
Privately owned corporation

**†ACE AUTO SALVAGE**
34 Stover Ave. (07032)
**Phone—(201) 997-6178**
Fax—(201) 997-0855
Owner—Frances Reilly
SIC—5013; 5015; *Wholesaler of rebuilt & used automotive parts*
Employs—2
Distrib.—Local
Privately owned corporation

**AMERIFILM CONVERTERS**
85 Lincoln Hwy. (07032)
**Phone—(973) 690-5900**
National—(800) 966-7200
Fax—(973) 817-8663
www.amerifilm.net
Email—info@amerifilmcorp.com
Dir., Sales—Peter Campisi
GM—Matteo Vandoni
Plt. Mgr.—Cesare Vandoni
Mktg. Mgr.—Joanne Kowal
SIC—2759; NAICS—323100; *Flexographic printing*
Employs—25; Estab.—2003
40,000 sq ft site, Distrib.—Intl.
Privately owned corporation

**ARRAY MFG. TECH CORP.**
100 Arlington Ave. (07032)
**Phone—(201) 997-1333**
Fax—(201) 997-7920
www.arraysolders.com
Email—sales@arraysolders.com
Pres.—Frank Garcia
V.-P.—John Corio
Mfg. Mgr.—Tony Williams
Off. Mgr.—Billy Volek

SIC—3469; *Metal stampings*
Employs—7; Estab.—1990
Sales—$1Mil-$2.5Mil
Distrib.—Local
Privately owned corporation

**BELLEVILLE CORP.**
328 Belleville Tpke. (07032)
**Phone—(201) 991-6222**
Fax—(201) 991-6203
www.gildnsonwindows.com
Email—info@gildnsonwindows.com
Chrm., Pres.—Alan Gildenberg
V.-P., Secy. & MIS Mgr.—Angie Gildenberg
SIC—3089; *Vinyl windows & doors*
Employs—7; Estab.—1946
Sales—$1Mil
10,000 sq ft site, Distrib.—Local
Privately owned corporation
AKA: Gild & Son

**BERGEN BARREL & DRUM CO.**
43 O'Brien St., Ste. 45 (07032)
**Phone—(201) 998-3500**
Fax—(201) 998-0414
www.dixiepolydrum.com
Email—dixiepolydrum@aol.com
Off. Mgr.—Mary Mecka
SIC—3089; *Polyethylene drums*
Employs—15; Estab.—1963
Distrib.—Intl.
Privately owned corporation

**BINDI NORTH AMERICA, INC. (H Q)**
630 Belleville Tpke. (07032)
**Phone—(973) 812-8118**
Fax—(973) 812-5020
www.bindiusa.com
Email—info@bindiusa.com
Pres., CEO—Attilio Bindi
Dir., Operation—Christopher Klemensowicz
Hum. Res. Mgr.—Kelly Cespebes
Sales & Mktg. Coord.—Belda Apolinario
SIC—2024; *Corporate headquarters; frozen desserts*
Employs—40; Estab.—1946
Sales—$5Mil-$10Mil
Distrib.—National
Privately owned corporation

**BROTHER'S QUALITY BAKERY**
365 Kearny Ave. (07032)
**Phone—(201) 991-4364**
Fax—(201) 991-1590
Email—kearnybake@aol.com
Chrm.—Michael Gencarelli
Pres.—Thomas Gencarelli
SIC—2051; NAICS—311812; *Bread, muffins, pastries & cakes*
Employs—20; Estab.—1977
5,000 sq ft site, Distrib.—Local
Privately owned partnership

**BUNGE NORTH AMERICA, INC.**
125 Sanford Ave. (07032)
**Phone—(201) 467-0200**
National—(800) 966-1645
Fax—(201) 991-4310
www.bunge.com
Email—info@bunge.com
Sales Mgr., Inside—C. C. Petford
Plt. Mgr.—Steve Dobyna
Hum. Res. Mgr.—Jenny Augustine
Trans. Coord.—Elvin Rodrigues
SIC—2034; *Spices, shortenings, oils, margarines & pan releases*
Employs—65; Estab.—1983
Sales—$500,000-$1Mil
20,000 sq ft site, Distrib.—Local
Publicly owned corporation
Parent co.—Bunge North America, Inc., St. Louis, MO
Phone—(314) 292-2000
See Parent Co. Section for full profile.

**CALBAR, LLC**
307 Bergen Ave. (07032)
**Phone—(201) 246-1555**
Fax—(201) 246-1449
www.calbarllc.com

Email—calbar2005@yahoo.com
Pres.—Vincent J. Caldaro
Supervisor—Maria Barbosa
SIC—3911; NAICS—339911; *Gold & silver jewelry, including casting & finishing*
Employs—5; Estab.—2005
Sales—under $500,000
8,000 sq ft site, Distrib.—National
Privately owned corporation

**†CALI CARTING, INC.**
450 Bergen Ave., P.O. Box 440 (07032)
**Phone—(201) 991-5400**
Fax—(201) 991-1038
www.calicarting.com
Email—john.cali@calicarting.com
Owner—John Cali
SIC—5093; *Wholesaler of recycled scrap plastic, metal & glass materials*
Employs—10; Estab.—1998
Distrib.—Local
Privately owned corporation

**COASTAL PACKAGING**
48 Sellers St. (07032)
**Phone—(201) 955-4414**
Fax—(201) 955-4415
Email—coastalpak@chejnet.com
Pres.—Morris Lefkowitz
V.-P.—Edward Lefkowitz
SIC—2657; NAICS—322212; *Folding boxes*
Employs—16; Estab.—1995
Distrib.—Local

**CONTINENTAL ROLLER CO., INC.**
75 Arlington Ave. (07032)
**Phone—(201) 997-7999**
Fax—(201) 998-5650
www.continentalroller.com
Email—sales@continentalroller.com
Owner—Carmine Bruzzesi
GM—Vince Bruzzesi
SIC—3555; 3069; *Printing rollers for sheetfeed & web presses & rubber rollers for industrial applications*
Employs—6
Sales—under $500,000 (est)

**CRYSTAL BEVERAGE CORP.**
174 Sanford Ave., P.O. Box 393 (07032)
**Phone—(201) 991-2342**
Fax—(201) 991-1882
Pres., Plt. Mgr.—John Apolinario
Off. Mgr.—Victor Apolinario
SIC—2086; NAICS—312100; *Soft drinks*
Employs—13; Estab.—1982
Distrib.—National
Privately owned corporation

**CUSTOM STEEL CONTRACTORS, INC.**
17 Eastern Rd. (07032)
**Phone—(973) 344-4449**
Fax—(973) 344-1413
www.customsteelcontractors.com
Email—danmoran@customsteelcontractors.com
Pres.—Dan Moran
Estimator—Martin Turek
SIC—3312; *Steel fabrication*
Employs—20; Estab.—1986
Sales—$1Mil-$5Mil
21,000 sq ft site, Distrib.—Regional
Privately owned corporation

**DOLLFUS MIEG CO., INC.**
10 Basin Dr., Ste. 130 (07032)
**Phone—(973) 589-0606**
Fax—(973) 589-8931
www.dmc-usa.com
Email—dmcusa@dmcus.com
CEO—Joseph McCabe
CFO—Joseph Zawadzki
V.-P., Sales—Sharlene Bell
V.-P., Mktg.—Steve Mancuso

## Kearny—(cont.)

SIC—2284; *Needlework & embroidery threads & fabrics, crochet products & needlework accessory items; Brand name— DMC; Variations; PRISM*
Employs—25; Estab.—1934
Distrib.—National
Privately owned corporation
AKA: DMC, Inc., Charles Craft Fabrics

### †EXCEL PLASTICS RECYCLING, INC.
996 Belleville Tpke. *(07032)*
**Phone—(201) 991-2500**
Fax—(201) 991-2526
www.excelrecycling.net
Email—brian@excelrecycling.net
Owner—Brian Chen
SIC—5093; *Wholesaler of recycled plastic materials*
Employs—20
Sales—under $500,000
Distrib.—Regional
Privately owned corporation

### †FEDERAL WINE & LIQUOR CO.
56 Hackensack Ave., P.O. Box 519 (07032)
**Phone—(973) 624-6444**
National—(800) 433-3929
Fax—(973) 589-3556
www.fedway.com
Pres.—Richard Leventhal
SIC—5182; *Company headquarters & distributor of wine & liquor*
Employs—40; Estab.—1920
Distrib.—Regional
Privately owned corporation

### G & S MOTOR EQUIPMENT CO.
1800 Harrison Ave., P.O. Box 493 (07032)
**Phone—(201) 998-9244**
Fax—(201) 998-3349
www.gstechnologies.com
Email—customercare@ gstechnologies.org
Pres.—Gabor Newmark
Hum. Res. Mgr.—Anabella Perfeito
SIC—3612; NAICS—335311; *Rebuilt electrical transformers & oil-filled electrical equipment dismantling & EPA-approved disposal services*
Employs—55; Estab.—1977
Sales—$11Mil-$25Mil
Distrib.—Intl.
Privately owned corporation

### †GAMS POWER TOOLS & SUPPLIES, INC.
133-135 Schuyler Ave. (07032)
**Phone—(201) 955-0222**
      (201) 955-0268
Fax—(201) 955-0310
Email—tonygams@hotmail.com
Pres.—Margaret Servidio
Secy.-Treas.—Anthony J. Servidio
SIC—5084; 5085; *Distributor of contractor's tools & supplies, including repair & rental services; Brand name—Bosch; DeWalt; Hitachi; Milwaukee; Porter-Cable; Sinclair; MMM; Freud; RIDGID; DAP; Strong-Man; NSS; IRWIN; Minwax; Rust-Oleum; Stanley; USG; Filmtech; RectorSeal; Tyco; Kidde; Shop-Vac; Robin/Subaru*
Employs—5; Estab.—1985
Sales—$800,000
8,500 sq ft site, Distrib.—Local
Privately owned sub-S corp.

### HONEYWARE, INC.
244 Dukes St. (07032)
**Phone—(201) 997-5900**
National—(800) 525-5905
Fax—(201) 997-4420
www.honeyware.com
Email—ray@honeyware.com

Chrm. & CEO—Tony Sheng
Pres., COO—Ray Sheng
SIC—3089; 3544; NAICS— 333500; *Plastic injection molding, tooling & assembly, including product development & international sourcing; Brand name—Honeyware; Geni; Wilpak Inks; Handi*
Employs—60; Estab.—1977
86,000 sq ft site, Distrib.—Intl.
Privately owned sub-S corp.
Also see: Wilpak Industries, Inc., same loc.

**NEW ENTRY**

### HOUSE PRINTING, LLC
311 Kearny Ave. (07032)
**Phone—(201) 772-5988**
Email—jdshouseprinting@ hotmail.com
Owner—Juan Calva
SIC—2396; 2395; 3993; *T-shirt screen printing & embroidery & interior & exterior signage & graphic services*
Employs—1
Sales—under $500,000 (est)
Limited Liability Company

### HUDSON & BERGEN CO.
350 Belleville Tpk. (07032)
**Phone—(201) 991-4900**
Fax—(201) 998-4949
Email—hbblinds@aol.com
Pres., CFO—Steven C. Boyd
SIC—2591; NAICS—337920; *Venetian blinds & window shades*
Employs—4; Estab.—1948
6,000 sq ft site, Distrib.—Local
Privately owned corporation

### HUMMEL MACHINE & TOOL CO.
580 Davis Ave. (07032)
**Phone—(201) 991-5200**
Fax—(201) 991-2904
Email—eevans580@aol.com
Mfg. Mgr.—Edward Evans
Off. Mgr.—Mary Wendower
SIC—3599; *CNC machining job shop*
Employs—15; Estab.—1950
Distrib.—National
Privately owned corporation

### JED DISPLAY, LLC
55 Arlington Ave. (07032)
**Phone—(201) 340-2329**
Fax—(201) 340-2021
www.jeddisplay.com
Email—contactus@jeddisplay.com
Owner, Cont. & Manager—James B. Howell, Jr.
Supervisor—J. R. Howell
SIC—2542; *Point-of-purchase displays & specialty carts*
Employs—5; Estab.—2007
Sales—$500,000-$1Mil
Distrib.—National
Limited Liability Company

### †JET LINE PRODUCTS, INC.
55 Jacobus Ave. (07032)
**Phone—(973) 690-2999**
Fax—(973) 690-2944
www.jetlineprod.com
Email—help@jetlineprod.com
Pur. Agt.—Laura Meola
SIC—5091; 5084; *Corporate headquarters & distributor of swimming pool equipment & supplies, including pumps & chlorine*
Employs—20; Estab.—1971
Sales—$6Mil-$10Mil
Distrib.—Regional
Privately owned corporation

### KEARNY SCREW MACHINE CO.
554 Elm St. (07032)
**Phone—(201) 998-4363**
Owner—Otto Carchia

SIC—3451; NAICS—332721; *Screw machine products*
Employs—1; Estab.—1994
Sales—under $500,000
Distrib.—Local
Sole ownership

### KEARNY SHEET METAL WORKS, INC.
579 Davis Ave. (07032)
**Phone—(201) 991-4745**
Fax—(201) 991-0836
Email—ksmetals@aol.com
Pres.—Mike Smolensky
Off. Mgr.—Cindy Smolensky
SIC—3444; 3599; *24-gage to 1/4-inch sheet metal & aluminum fabrication & welding of steel frames, platforms & beams*
Employs—6; Estab.—1927
Sales—$500,000-$1Mil
Distrib.—Local
Privately owned corporation

### KEARNY SMELTING & REFINING, INC.
936 Harrison Ave., Ste. 5 (07032)
**Phone—(201) 991-7276**
Fax—(201) 998-1274
Email—ksrcorp@aol.com
Pres.—Francine Rothschild
Fin. & Off. Mgr.—Melba Walsh
SIC—3341; *Brass & bronze smelting, refining & extruding*
Employs—25; Estab.—1945
Distrib.—Local
Privately owned corporation
Also see: Mac Metals, Inc., same loc.

### KENNEY STEEL TREATING CORP.
100 Quincy Pl. (07032)
**Phone—(201) 998-4420**
National—(800) 576-7790
Fax—(201) 998-4429
www.kennysteel.com
Email—kennysteel@verizon.net
Pres.—James Dumphy
Corp. Secy.—Carla Peso
Plt. Mgr.—Francis Toner
Prodn. Mgr.—James Dumphy, Jr.
SIC—3398; NAICS—332811; *Steel brazing*
Employs—20; Estab.—1959
Sales—$1Mil-$2.5Mil
Distrib.—Local
Privately owned corporation

### KUEHNE CO.
86 Hackensack Ave. (07032)
**Phone—(973) 589-0700**
Fax—(973) 589-4866
www.kuehnecompany.com
Email—info@kuehnecompany.com
Pres., CEO—Don Nicolai
CFO—William Paulin
V-P.—Boyd Hunnaman
Dir., Mktg.—Dave Zilberfarb
Plt. Mgr.—Manny Cunha
SIC—2819; *Company headquarters & bleach*
Employs—80; Estab.—1988
Varies: 80-100
Sales—$25Mil-$50Mil (est)
Distrib.—Intl.
Privately owned corporation

### L & R MFG. CO., INC.
577 Elm St., P.O. Box 607 *(07032)*
**Phone—(201) 991-5330**
National—(800) 572-5326
Fax—(201) 991-5870
www.lrultrasonics.com
Email—info@lrultrasonics.com
Pres.—Robert J. Lazarus
Cont.—Robert R. Rothe
Dir., Sales & Mktg.—Bruce Letsch
Dir., Pur.—Carmen Distano
Dir., IT—Jay Fleischauer

SIC—3841; 3699; 2899; 5084; *Manufacturer & distributor of ultrasonic cleaning equipment, solutions & accessories; Brand name—UltraDose; Ellanar; Quantrex; SweepZone; Ink-Out; Effica; Barrier Spray*
Employs—100; Estab.—1930
Sales—$10Mil-$25Mil
Distrib.—Intl.
Privately owned corporation
ISO rating—9001:2000

### M & G TOOL & DIE CO.
936 Harrison Ave. (07032)
**Phone—(201) 997-0506**
Fax—(201) 997-8510
Email—giovanni@nac.net
Owner—Giovanni Millocca
SIC—3544; NAICS—333500; *Tool & die job shop*
Employs—4; Estab.—1987
Sales—under $500,000
6,500 sq ft site, Distrib.—Regional
Sole ownership

### MAC METALS, INC.
936 Harrison Ave., CN 670 (07032)
**Phone—(201) 997-8001**
National—(800) 631-9510
Fax—(201) 997-7457
www.macmetals.com
Email—sales@macmetals.com
Pres.—Francine Rothschild
Comp.—Karen Karp
Sales Mgr.—Mark Sisson
Sales Rep.—Marion Barnes
SIC—3356; NAICS—331491; *Brass & bronze extrusions*
Employs—34; Estab.—1982
Sales—$500,000-$1Mil
Distrib.—Intl.
Privately owned sub-S corp.
Also see: Kearny Smelting & Refining, Inc., same loc.

### MAC PRODUCTS, INC.
60 Pennsylvania Ave., P.O. Box 469 (07032)
**Phone—(973) 344-0700**
Fax—(973) 344-5891
www.macproducts.net
Email—info@macproducts.net
Pres.—Edward Russnow
V-P., Opers.—Jerry Bianco
Dir., Engrg.—Peter Michaels
Sales Mgr.—Mike Pereira
IT Mgr.—Otto Acosta
Sales Engr.—David Zuercher
Sales Rep., Inside—Robert Adornati
SIC—3613; 3643; 3599; 3443; NAICS—335313; *Electrical control panels, connectors, switchgear & high-voltage cable accessories, diesel electric locomotive components, traction power & overhead contact systems components, heat exchangers & custom fabricated industrial equipment*
Employs—135; Estab.—1968
Sales—$50Mil
170,000 sq ft site, Distrib.—Intl.
Privately owned corporation
ISO rating—9001:2008

### METRO-CHEM, INC.
24 Pennsylvania Ave., P.O. Box 401 (07032)
**Phone—(973) 589-2800**
National—(800) 332-7627
Fax—(973) 589-8444
www.metro-chem.com
Email—metrochemoffice@aol.com
Owner—Pete Potocki
Plt. Mgr.—Phil Adamo
Hum. Res. & IT Mgr.—John Cowan

## Kearny—(cont.)

SIC—2841; NAICS—325611;
*Industrial laundry detergent*
Employs—14; Estab.—1980
Distrib.—Regional
Privately owned corporation

### MID-CONTINENT PACKAGING CO., INC. (H Q)

55 Jacobus Ave., 1st Fl. (07032)
**Phone—(973) 589-3544**
National—(800) 883-1883
Fax—(973) 589-5093
www.midcontinentpkg.com
Email—help@midcontinentpkg.com
Pres.—Mark Epstein
V-P.—Larry Epstein
V-P.—Andrew Epstein
Cont.—Stephen Epstein
SIC—3089; *Corporate
headquarters; chemical
packaging*
Employs—60
Sales—$5Mil-$10Mil (est)
Distrib.—National
Privately owned corporation
AKA: Alden Leeds

### MILLAR SHEET METAL

39 Rizzolo Rd. (07032)
**Phone—(201) 997-1990**
Fax—(201) 997-2240
Pres.—Maggie Millar
V-P.—Peter Millar
SIC—3444; *Sheet metal
fabrication*
Employs—5; Estab.—1987
Distrib.—Local
Privately owned corporation

### MULTI-TEX PRODUCTS CORP.

54 2nd Ave. (07032)
**Phone—(201) 991-7262**
Fax—(201) 991-4509
Email—multitexproducts@
yahoo.com
Pres.—Michaelene Dwulet
Plt. Mgr.—Tom Harabedian
SIC—2281; NAICS—313111;
*Metallic yarns, including
braiding & microslitting*
Employs—8; Estab.—1943
Distrib.—Intl.
Privately owned corporation

### NATIONAL PACKAGING CORP.

14 Campus Dr. *(07032)*
**Phone—(973) 344-0100**
Fax—(973) 344-0220
www.nationalpack.com
Email—info@nationalpack.com
Pres.—Martin Schlesinger
V-P.—Jay Schlesinger
Sales & Mktg. Mgr.—Ira Matyas
Cust. Serv. Supv.—Sam Akerman
SIC—2653; NAICS—322211;
*Corrugated cartons & packaging
materials*
Employs—25; Estab.—1978
Distrib.—Intl.
Sole ownership

### NEW ENGLAND BEDDING TRANSPORT

102 3rd Ave. (07032)
**Phone—(201) 997-2337**
Fax—(201) 997-7378
www.newenglandbedding.org
Email—nebt@aol.com
Pres., Hum. Res. & IT Mgr.—
Douglas Daly
SIC—2515; *Mattresses*
Employs—8; Estab.—2010
Distrib.—Local
Privately owned corporation

### ONE STOP PRINTING, LLC

135 Kearny Ave., Ste. B (07032)
**Phone—(201) 991-3320**
            (201) 283-4235
www.onestopprintingllc.com
Email—onestopprinting.dy@
gmail.com

Owner—Darwin Yamuca
SIC—2759; 2396; 3993;
*Commercial printing, t-shirt
screen printing & interior &
exterior signs*
Employs—2; Estab.—2006
Sales—under $500,000 (est)
2,000 sq ft site, Distrib.—Local
Limited Liability Company

### OWENS CORNING

1249 Newark Tpke. (07032)
**Phone—(201) 998-5666**
Fax—(201) 998-0530
www.owenscorning.com
Email—info@owenscorning.com
Plt. Mgr., Asphalt—Raul Martinez
SIC—2951; NAICS—324121;
*Asphalt paving compounds*
Employs—90; Estab.—1977
Sales—$2.5Mil-$5Mil (est)
Distrib.—Intl.
Publicly owned corporation
DBA: Trumbull Asphalt Co.
Parent co.—Owens Corning,
Toledo, OH
Phone—(419) 248-8000
See Parent Co. Section for full profile.

### PARAGON STEEL & TOOL CO., INC.

339 Bergen Ave. (07032)
**Phone—(201) 997-1676**
Fax—(201) 997-4744
Pres.—William Fisher
SIC—3599; *Tool sharpening*
Employs—3; Estab.—1924
Sales—under $500,000
Distrib.—National
Privately owned corporation

### PHARMACHEM LABORATORIES, INC.

265 Harrison Ave. (07032)
**Phone—(201) 246-1000**
National—(800) 526-0609
Fax—(201) 246-8105
www.pharmachemlabs.com
Email—sales@
pharmachemlabs.com
Pres.—Dave Holmes
V-P., GM—Colin MacIntyre
V-P., Sales—Paul Borrell
Treas.—Andrea Bauer
Dir., New Prod. Dev.—Mitch Skop
IT Mgr.—Marco Lipps
Hum. Res. & Payroll Mgr.—
Maritere Velazquez
SIC—2833; NAICS—325411;
*Corporate headquarters &
nutritional ingredients for the
herbal supplement,
pharmaceutical, food &
beverage & pet product
industries; Brand name—Phase
2 Carb Controller; Lactium;
Perluxan; Benexia Chia;
Celadrin; CranMax*
Employs—50; Estab.—1978
Sales—$10Mil-$25Mil (est)
Distrib.—Intl.
Privately owned corporation

### PICASSO LIGHTING INDUSTRIES, LLC

46 Sellers St. (07032)
**Phone—(201) 246-8188**
Fax—(201) 246-8122
www.picassoltg.com
Email—bbregman@picassoltg.com
Owner—Boris Bregman
SIC—3646; 3648; *LED, recessed,
suspended, surface mount,
perimeter, cove & specialty
lighting equipment for the
commercial, architectural & high-
end markets*
Employs—20; Estab.—2007
Sales—$500,000-$1Mil
Distrib.—National
Limited Liability Company

### PROFESSIONAL ENVIRONMENT SYSTEMS

49 O'Brien Rd. (07032)
**Phone—(201) 991-3000**
Fax—(201) 991-3700
www.pesworldwide.com
Pres.—Percy Mentor
V-P.—Robert Mentor
Off. Mgr.—Angela Gamarra
SIC—3444; *HVAC ductwork*
Employs—15; Estab.—1977
Sales—$1Mil-$2.5Mil (est)
Distrib.—National
Privately owned corporation

### PRO-SCREEN PRINTING, INC.

590 Belleville Tpke., Bldg. 24
(07032)
**Phone—(201) 246-7600**
Fax—(201) 246-8992
Pres.—Dilip Lavani
V-P., Sales & Mktg.—Hasmukh
Lavani
Plt. Mgr.—Anagat Patel
SIC—2759; 3085; NAICS—
326160; *Plastic bottles & silk
screen printing of plastic bottles
& plastic jars*
Employs—8; Estab.—2000
12,000 sq ft site, Distrib.—National
Privately owned sub-S corp.

### ROYAL LUMBER & MILLWORK CO., INC.

455 Schuyler Ave., P.O. Box 443
(07032)
**Phone—(201) 991-8550**
Fax—(201) 998-5658
V-P.—Arthur Rogoff
Secy-Treas.—Howard Mehr
SIC—2431; 2421; NAICS—
321900; *Millwork & lumber
processing*
Employs—5; Estab.—1944
1,000 sq ft site, Distrib.—Local
Privately owned corporation

### SCHUYLER PRINTING CO., INC.

71 Kearny Ave. (07032)
**Phone—(201) 997-8083**
Fax—(201) 991-3754
Pres.—Edward A. Conlon
V-P., Fin.—Vera Conlon
SIC—2752; 2791; NAICS—
323122; *Offset printing &
typesetting*
Employs—4; Estab.—1981
Sales—under $500,000
2,200 sq ft site, Distrib.—Local
Sole ownership

### SIGNS BY LYNN

329 Kearny Ave., Ste. A (07032-
2668)
**Phone—(201) 998-4273**
            (201) 572-1839
Fax—(201) 998-0038
www.signsbylynn.com
Email—info@signsbylynn.com
Owner—Lynn Oelz
SIC—3993; 2394; 3499; NAICS—
314912; *Commercial, residential,
ADA & architectural interior &
exterior signs, banners, awnings,
digital graphics & truck lettering*
Employs—3; Estab.—1982
Sales—under $500,000
Distrib.—Local
Sole ownership

### †SOS GASES, INC.

1100 Harrison Ave. *(07032)*
**Phone—(201) 998-7800**
            (800) 626-7998
Fax—(201) 998-5243
www.sosgasesinc.com
Email—sosgasesinc@msn.com
Pres.—Steve Defilipps, Sr.
Sales Rep., Inside—Steve
Defilipps, Jr.
Bookkeeper—Marlene Lago

SIC—5172; 5084; *Distributor of
industrial & specialty gases,
including oxygen, nitrogen &
liquified petroleum & welding
equipment & systems*
Employs—23; Estab.—1961
Sales—$10Mil-$25Mil
Distrib.—Regional
Privately owned corporation

### SPECTRA COLORS CORP.

25 Rizzolo Rd. *(07032)*
**Phone—(201) 997-0606**
National—(800) 527-8588
Fax—(201) 997-0504
www.SpectraColors.com
Email—Dyes@SpectraColors.com
Pres., Mktg. Mgr.—Luis B. Marrero
Chief Operating Officer—Ray
McCreary
Mktg. Mgr.—Alexis Capik
SIC—2893; 2899; 2087; NAICS—
325910; *Colorants & dyes for the
ink, food, drug, toiletries &
candle industries; Brand name—
Spectracid; Spectramine;
Spectrasol; Specandle; Spectra;
SpectraWash; SpectraRinse*
Employs—30; Estab.—1987
Sales—over $9Mil
27,000 sq ft site, Distrib.—Intl.
Privately owned corporation

### STANSON CORP.

2 N. Hackensack Ave. (07032)
**Phone—(973) 344-8666**
Fax—(973) 344-8505
www.stanson.com
Email—stanson@stanson.com
Pres.—Robert Holuba
V-P., COO—Stanley Holuba
SIC—2841; NAICS—325611;
*Powder & liquid detergents,
softeners, cleaners & polishes*
Employs—100; Estab.—1949
500,000 sq ft site, Distrib.—Intl.

### THE OBSERVER

39 Seeley Ave. (07032)
**Phone—(201) 991-1600**
Fax—(201) 991-8941
www.theobserver.com
Email—robertpez@hotmail.com
Pres.—Mary Tortoreti
GM—Robert Pezzolla
SIC—2711; *Weekly newspaper
publishing*
Employs—12; Estab.—1887
Distrib.—Local
Privately owned sub-S corp.

### UNITED DIE CO., INC.

199 Devon Ter. (07032)
**Phone—(201) 997-0250**
National—(800) 428-5462
Fax—(201) 997-3297
www.uniteddie.com
Email—sales@uniteddie.com
Pres.—Jim Kontra
Hum. Res. Mgr.—Ed Martin
Bookkeeper—Marion Martin
SIC—3544; NAICS—333500;
*Tungsten carbide, steel &
ceramic tooling & draw, forming,
extrusion, swaging, shaving &
sectional dies, mandrels & draw
bench parts*
Employs—30; Estab.—1940
Distrib.—Intl.
Privately owned corporation

### †UNIVERSAL CHEMICALS INC.

100 N. Hackensack Ave. *(07032)*
**Phone—(973) 589-1525**
Fax—(973) 589-8013
www.universalchem.com
Email—info@universalchem.com
Pres.—Jerry Kaplan

## Kearny—(cont.)

SIC—5169; *Distributor of water treatment & swimming pool chemicals, including sodium hypochlorite, sodium hydroxide, alum, hydrogen peroxide & hydrochloric acid*
Employs—10; Estab.—1968
Sales—$3Mil
15,000 sq ft site, Distrib.—Local
Privately owned sub-S corp.

†VECKRIDGE CHEMICAL CO., INC.

60 Central Ave. (07032)
**Phone—(973) 344-1818**
Fax—(973) 690-5936
www.veckridge.com
Email—rv@veckridge.com
Pres.—Mark Veca
V-P.—Bob Veca
SIC—5169; *Wholesaler of industrial chemicals*
Employs—20; Estab.—1949
Sales—$25Mil
20,000 sq ft site, Distrib.— Regional
Privately owned corporation
ISO rating—2001

WATSON GRAPHICS, INC.

578 Kearny Ave. (07032)
**Phone—(201) 955-0283**
Fax—(201) 955-2909
www.watsongraphicsinc.com
Email—watsongraphicsinc@ verizon.net
Pres.—Marlene Watson
SIC—2752; 2759; NAICS— 323100; *Offset, instant, color & thermographic printing of invitations, signs, banners & promotional items & window & truck lettering*
Employs—1; Estab.—1987
Sales—under $500,000
Distrib.—Regional
Privately owned corporation

WELDON ASPHALT CO.

Div. of Weldon Materials, Inc.
1100 Harrison Ave. (07032)
**Phone—(201) 991-3200**
Fax—(201) 991-5607
www.weldonmat.com
Email—sales@weldonmat.com
Plt. Mgr.—Jerome Mars
Dept. Mgr.—Adrian Sharp
SIC—2951; NAICS—324121; *Asphalt paving compounds*
Employs—4; Estab.—1991
Distrib.—Regional
Privately owned corporation
Parent co.—Weldon Materials, Inc., Westfield, NJ
Phone—(908) 233-4444
See Parent Co. Section for full profile.

WEST HUDSON MILLWORK, INC.

60 Arlington Ave. (07032)
**Phone—(201) 991-7191**
Fax—(201) 991-4987
Email—jhonnycayso@aol.com
Pres.—Jonathan David Giordano
SIC—2511; 2431; NAICS— 321900; *Wooden & laminated cabinets, furniture & millwork*
Employs—2; Estab.—1945
Sales—under $500,000
7,500 sq ft site, Distrib.—Intl.
Privately owned corporation

†WILLIAMS SCOTSMAN, INC.

35 Ford Ln. (07032)
**Phone—(973) 589-1234**
National—(800) 782-1500
Fax—(973) 589-3434
www.willscot.com
Email—info@willscot.com
GM—Greg Downing

SIC—5039; *Wholesaler of modular buildings, mobile offices & storage containers*
Employs—100; Estab.—1955
Sales—$500,000-$1Mil
Distrib.—National
Privately owned corporation
Parent co.—Williams Scotsman, Inc., Baltimore, MD
Phone—(410) 931-6000
See Parent Co. Section for full profile.

WILPAK INDUSTRIES, INC.

244 Dukes St. (07032)
**Phone—(201) 997-7600**
Fax—(201) 997-4420
www.honeyware.com
Email—wilpak_inks@hotmail.com
Pres.—Tony Sheng
V-P., Fin. & Opers.—Ray Sheng
Opers. & Sales Mgr. & Administrator—Joy Speakes
Bookkeeper—Carmen Roman
Chemist—Elliott Leibowitz
SIC—2899; *Inks for writing instruments & writing systems*
Employs—5; Estab.—1980
66,000 sq ft site, Distrib.— Regional
Privately owned corporation
Also see: Honeyware, Inc., same loc.

## Keasbey
(Middlesex—N.E.)

†BAYSHORE RECYCLING CORP.

75 Crows Mill Rd., P.O. Box 290 (08832)
**Phone—(732) 738-6000**
Fax—(732) 738-9150
www.bayshorerecycling.com
Email—info@ bayshorerecycling.com
Pres.—Valerie Montecalvo
CFO—Lee Becker
COO—Frank Montecalvo
Adv. & Mktg. Coord.—Elena Bagarozza
SIC—5093; *Wholesaler of recycled concrete, asphalt, brick & block & construction/ demolition debris & petroleum-contaminated soil remediation services; Brand name— Bayshore Recycling Corp; Bayshore Soil Management; Coastal Metal Recycling Corp; Montecalvo Disposal Services; Montecalvo Material Recovery Facility; Montecalvo Contracting; Port Raritan Marine Terminal*
Employs—160; Estab.—1995
Distrib.—Local

CARRINI, INC. (H Q)

140 Smith St., 5th Fl. (08832)
**Phone—(732) 650-1775**
Fax—(732) 650-1688
www.carrini.com
Email—info@carrini.com
Pres.—Eli Chabot
SIC—3143; 3149; 3144; NAICS— 316213; *Corporate headquarters; men's, women's & children's fashion shoes (mfg. done overseas)*
Employs—18; Estab.—1983
Distrib.—Intl.
Privately owned corporation

NEW ENTRY
COMPUTER SQUARE, INC.

330 Mac Ln. (08832)
**Phone—(732) 346-0200**
Fax—(732) 346-0209
www.csitech.com
Email—sales@csitech.com
Pres., CEO—Chen C. Yeh
Accts. Mgr.—Rich Norcross

SIC—7372; *Web-based e-government software development; Brand name— InfoShare*
Employs—33; Estab.—1990
Sales—$2.6Mil-$5Mil
Distrib.—Regional
Privately owned corporation

JESSUP, INC., CHARLES

177 Smith St. (08832-0158)
**Phone—(732) 324-0430**
National—(800) 573-2529
Fax—(732) 324-1616
www.jessupinc.com
Email—info@jessupinc.com
Pres.—Jay Jessup
SIC—3555; 3569; NAICS— 333293; *OEM manual screen printing equipment, including hinge clamps, kick legs & register bars & fabric protectors for roller frames; Brand name— Roller-Rap*
Employs—6; Estab.—1969
Sales—$500,000-$1Mil
7,000 sq ft site, Distrib.—Intl.
Privately owned sub-S corp.
Also see: Jessup, Inc., Charles M., same loc.

†JESSUP, INC., CHARLES M.

177 Smith St. (08832)
**Phone—(732) 324-0430**
    (732) 324-0431
National—(800) 525-4657
www.jessupinc.com
Email—info@jessupinc.com
Pres., CEO & CFO—Charles M. Jessup
SIC—5084; 5065; *Distributor of commercial & textile screen printing equipment & supplies, digital imaging systems & direct-to-garment inkjet printers; Brand name—Sea Jay Mfg.; Brother International; International Coatings; Coates Screen; SunChemical; Naz Dar; Chromaline; Kiwo; Sefar; Ulano; Image Armor; i-Group; American M & M; Cudner & O'Connor; Direct2Shirt; Tuflon; DTG; ICC; IGT*
Employs—9; Estab.—1948
Sales—$1Mil-$5Mil
10,000 sq ft site, Distrib.—Intl.
Privately owned sub-S corp.
Also see: Jessup, Inc., Charles, same loc.
AKA: Screen And Digital Supply

†MAINETTI USA, INC.

300 Mac Ln. (08832)
**Phone—(201) 215-2900**
National—(800) 762-1167
Fax—(732) 738-7210
www.mainetti.com
Email—info.usa@mainetti.com
Pres., Mainetti Americas—Roberto Peruzzo
Pres., Mainetti USA—Steven Regino
Mktg. Mgr.—Leslie Mercado
Acctg. & Hum. Res. Mgr.—Hilton Lambert
Client Svcs. Mgr.—Ginna Cristian
SIC—5113; *Corporate headquarters & distributor of garment hangers & packaging, including polybags, garment bags & gift bags & boxes; Brand name—A&E™; Randy; Mainetti™*
Employs—30; Estab.—1962
Sales—$1Mil-$5Mil
Distrib.—Intl.
Privately owned corporation
ISO rating—9001

†OILMATIC SYSTEMS, LLC

155 Smith St., P.O. Box 185 (08832)
**Phone—(732) 324-9890**
National—(800) 645-6284
Fax—(732) 324-9895
www.oilmatic.com
Email—system@oilmatic.com
Acct. Mgr.—Deena Allora
SIC—5149; *Distributor of bulk cooking oil systems for restaurants*
Employs—20; Estab.—1998
Distrib.—Local
Limited Liability Company

PRAXAIR, INC., RAIRATAN BAY, PLT. 907

Div. of Praxair, Inc.
60 Crows Mill Rd. (08832)
**Phone—(732) 738-4150**
www.praxair.com
Email—info@praxair.com
GM—Mike Beaudrow
SIC—2813; NAICS—325120; *Nitrogen & oxygen processing*
Employs—8
Sales—$2.5Mil-$5Mil (est)
Distrib.—Local
Publicly owned corporation
Parent co.—Praxair, Inc., Danbury, CT
Phone—(203) 837-2000
See Parent Co. Section for full profile.

TRAP ROCK INDUSTRIES

Div. of Trap Rock Ind., LLC
Foot of Crows Mill Rd. (08832)
**Phone—(732) 738-4222**
National—(800) 789-7625
Fax—(732) 738-7054
www.traprock.com
Email—barbara.hutchins@ traprockind.com
V-P.—Wayne Bryant
SIC—2951; NAICS—324121; *Asphalt paving compounds*
Employs—10; Estab.—2004
Sales—under $500,000
Distrib.—Local
Privately owned corporation
Parent co.—Trap Rock Ind., LLC, Kingston, NJ
Phone—(609) 924-0300
See Parent Co. Section for full profile.

†WAKEFERN FOOD CORP. (H Q)

5000 Riverside Dr. (08832)
**Phone—(732) 906-5932**
www.wakefern.com
Email—joe.sheridan@ wakefern.com
Chrm., CEO—Joseph S. Colalillo
Pres., COO—Joe Sheridan
CFO—Doug Wille
Sr. V-P., Perishables—Bill Mayo
Sr. V-P., Non-Perishable—Chris Lane
Sr. V-P.—Jeff Reagan
V-P., eCommerce—Cheryl Williams
V-P., Consumer & Corp. Comms.— Karen Meleta
SIC—5143; *Corporate headquarters; distributor of perishables & non-perishable food products & milk; Brand name—Shop Rite; Price Rite; Durling Farms*
Employs—400; Estab.—1957
Privately owned corporation

## Kendall Park
(Middlesex—N.E.)

†ABRAZIL, LLC

1 Jacques Ave. (08824)
**Phone—(732) 297-9262**
    (732) 297-5500
    (732) 658-5191
National—(800) 227-2945
www.abrazil.net

GEOGRAPHICAL

## Kendall Park—(cont.)

Email—sales@abrazil.net
Owner—Tony Chuang
SIC—5122; 5199; *Wholesaler of dietary supplements, botanicals, herbs & bee propolis extract*
Employs—4; Estab.—2002
Distrib.—Intl.
Limited Liability Company

**KEMM GRAPHICS**

94 Providence Blvd. (08824)
**Phone—(732) 718-3449**
Email—kemmgraphics@comcast.net
Owner—Eric Sichel
Manager—Aaron Marx
SIC—2759; NAICS—323100; *Commercial printing*
Employs—5; Estab.—1997
Sales—$500,000-$1Mil
Distrib.—Local
Privately owned corporation

## Kenilworth

(Union—N.E.)

**ABBEY/WATCHUNG, LLC**

16 N. 26th St. (07033)
**Phone—(908) 241-7717**
www.abbeywatchung.com
Email—abbeylam@aol.com
Pres. & Member—Margaret A. Beute
Off. Admn.—Bob Boak
SIC—3081; 2789; 3479; NAICS—326113; *Film, archival & vinyl laminating, engraving, bookbinding, custom engraving, document preservation & book repair*
Employs—5; Estab.—1947
Sales—$500,000-$1Mil
Distrib.—Intl.
Limited Liability Company

**†ABCO REFRIGERATION SUPPLY CORP.**

395 N. 14th St. (07033)
Mail addr: 49-70 31st St., Long Island City (11101)
**Phone—(908) 931-0700**
National—(877) 937-2226
Fax—(908) 931-0707
www.abcorefrigeration.com
Email—kenilworth@abcorefrigeration.com
Opers. Mgr.—John Canetti
SIC—5075; *Distributor of air conditioning systems*
Employs—5; Estab.—2000
Sales—$2.5Mil-$5Mil
Distrib.—Local
Privately owned corporation
Parent co.—ABCO Refrigeration Supply Corp., Long Island City, NY
Phone—(718) 937-9000
See Parent Co. Section for full profile.

**AIR CENTER, INC.**

270 Monroe Ave. (07033)
**Phone—(908) 276-1992**
National—(800) 273-5421
Fax—(908) 276-3466
www.aircentercompressor.com
Email—aircenter@skyweb.net
Pres.—Matthew W. Ruggiero
Fin. Mgr.—Bill Fitzell
Off. Admn.—Rose Gianquitto
SIC—3563; NAICS—333912; *Rebuilt air compressors*
Employs—15; Estab.—1998
6,500 sq ft site, Distrib.—Regional
Privately owned corporation

**ALLOY CAST PRODUCTS, INC.**

700 Swenson Dr. (07033)
**Phone—(908) 245-2255**
Fax—(908) 245-3267
www.alloycastproducts.com

Email—fpanico@alloycastproducts.com
Pres.—Frank S. Panico
V-P.—Ann M. Panico
Off. Mgr.—Patty Agudo
Qual. Assur. Mgr.—Vincent Contini
SIC—3324; NAICS—331512; *Precision alloy castings; Brand name—REXALLOY*
Employs—15; Estab.—1959
Sales—$2.5Mil-$3.5Mil
15,000 sq ft site, Distrib.—Intl.
Privately owned corporation

**ARC DOCUMENT SOLUTIONS**

Div. of ARC Document Solutions, Inc.
844 Fairfield Ave. (07033)
**Phone—(973) 372-5200**
Fax—(973) 372-7066
www.e-arc.com
Email—irvington.cservice@e-arc.com
Dir., Sales—Jeffrey Jimenez
Acct. Exec.—Jeffrey Young
SIC—2752; NAICS—323100; *Blueprinting, including reprographic services, color digital output, scanning, document management, large-format color & instant plotters, managed print services, cost recovery solutions, cloud storage & online plan rooms; Brand name—Abacus PCR; Planwell; IshipDocs; Planwell collaborate*
Employs—40; Estab.—1927
Sales—$10Mil
25,000 sq ft site, Distrib.—National
Publicly owned corporation
Parent co.—ARC Document Solutions, Inc., Walnut Creek, CA
Phone—(925) 949-5100
See Parent Co. Section for full profile.

**ASSEMBLIES UNLIMITED, INC.**

530 N. Michigan Ave. (07033)
**Phone—(877) 273-6259**
www.assemblies.com
Email—sales@assemblies.com
Pres.—Randy Shaw
Sales Mgr.—Jim DeKosta
SIC—3089; *Full turnkey contract packaging & fulfillment services, including shrink & cellophane wrapping, POP display & manual assembly, blister packaging, repackaging, labeling & reworking*
Employs—100; Estab.—1980
Sales—$500,000-$1Mil
150,000 sq ft site, Distrib.—National
Privately owned sub-S corp.
Parent co.—Assemblies Unlimited, Inc., Bloomingdale, IL
Phone—(630) 980-0200
See Parent Co. Section for full profile.

**ATLANTIC COAST CRUSHERS, INC.**

128 Market St. (07033)
**Phone—(908) 259-9292**
Fax—(908) 259-9280
www.gocrushers.com
Email—info@gocrushers.com
Pres.—Jack Paddock
Engr.—Jim Herdman
SIC—3559; *Industrial particle size reduction equipment, including crushers & shredders; Brand name—Flow-Sentry Crusher; Flow-Smasher Crusher Lumpbreaker; Flow-Sizer Crusher Lumpbreaker; Particle Sizer Crusher*
Employs—10; Estab.—1989
Sales—$1Mil-$2.5Mil
5,000 sq ft site, Distrib.—Intl.
Privately owned sub-S corp.

**B & B MILLWORK**

333 Monroe Ave. (07033)
**Phone—(973) 249-0300**
Fax—(973) 249-0303

www.bbmillwork.com
Email—bb@bbmillwork.com
Owner—Mel Krause
Pur. Agt.—Manny Jacobowiez
SIC—2431; NAICS—321900; *Wooden doors & mouldings*
Employs—20; Estab.—2003
Distrib.—Regional
Sole ownership

**B & M FINISHERS, INC.**

201 S. 31st St. (07033)
**Phone—(908) 241-5640**
Fax—(908) 241-5061
www.bmfinishers.com
Email—prsm69@aol.com
Pres.—Robert Bramson
Plt. Mgr.—Diane Staubach
Sr. Technical Advisor—Tony Caroselli
SIC—3471; NAICS—332813; *Aluminum anodizing & colored & embossed stainless steel; Brand name—Prismatic Stainless Steel; Kalon - Hard Anodize impregnated with teflon*
Employs—30; Estab.—1956
Sales—$1Mil-$5Mil
20,000 sq ft site, Distrib.—Intl.
Privately owned corporation
ISO rating—9001, AS9100
AKA: Kenilworth Anodizing

**B & W PRINTING CO., INC.**

730 Fairfield Ave. (07033)
**Phone—(908) 241-3060**
Fax—(908) 298-9248
www.bwprinting.com
Email—bwprinting@att.net
Sales Mgr.—Gary Butler
SIC—2752; 2791; NAICS—323122; *Instant digital & commercial printing & mailing services*
Employs—5; Estab.—1951
Sales—under $500,000
3,000 sq ft site, Distrib.—National
Privately owned corporation

**BELTING INDUSTRIES CO., INC.**

20 Boright Ave., P.O. Box 310 (07033)
**Phone—(908) 272-8591**
National—(800) 843-2358
Fax—(908) 272-3825
www.beltingindustries.com
Email—info@beltingindustries.com
Owner—Scott Cooper
Pres.—Jeff Smith
Cont.—Paul West
Sales Mgr., Inside—Yvonne Chin
Mktg. Mgr.—Rita J. Kae
Hum. Res. Mgr.—Kathy Tomasula
SIC—3052; NAICS—326220; *Corporate headquarters & industrial belting*
Employs—23; Estab.—1958
Sales—$5Mil-$10Mil
35,500 sq ft site, Distrib.—Intl.
Privately owned corporation

**†BENEDICT-MILLER, LLC**

123 N. 8th St. (07033)
**Phone—(908) 497-1477**
National—(800) 526-6372
Fax—(908) 497-1480
www.benedict-miller.com
Email—info@benedict-miller.com
Pres.—Jerry Shaw
Sales Mgr. & Mgr. of Alloy Sheet, Plate & Bars—Ed Halpin
Mktg. Mgr.—Walter Las
SIC—5051; *Wholesaler of aircraft sheet & plate steel*
Employs—40; Estab.—1940
48,000 sq ft site, Distrib.—Intl.
Limited Liability Company
ISO rating—9001:2008

**BERKELEY CONTRACT PACKAGING, LLC**

530 N. Michigan Ave. (07033)
**Phone—(908) 810-4000**
Fax—(908) 810-4646

www.berkeleypackaging.com
Email—dserebrenik@bpack.com
Pres.—Jack Concannon
Dir., Mktg.—Don Serebrenik
Sales Mgr.—Theresa M. Plant
Plt. Mgr.—Paul Cuartas
Hum. Res. Mgr.—Kathy Amiano
SIC—3089; *Company headquarters & contract packaging & promotional packaging, including blister packaging, fin-seal overwrapping, shrink wrapping/banding, glue tip-ons, hand & kit assembly, trap blisters, auto bagging, rework & culling*
Employs—158; Estab.—1992
Sales—$25Mil-$50Mil
80,000 sq ft site, Distrib.—Intl.
Limited Liability Company

**BLUE BLADE STEEL**

123 N. 8th St., P.O. Box 40 (07033)
**Phone—(908) 272-2620**
Fax—(908) 272-8252
www.bluebladesteel.com
Email—bbsales@bluebladesteel.com
Pres.—Jeremiah H. Shaw
V-P., Mfg.—Don Lindeworth
Sales Mgr., Inside—Jeff King
Hum. Res. & IT Mgr.—Gail Snyder
Traf. Mgr.—Kathy Poland
SIC—3398; NAICS—332811; *High carbon, stainless & alloy strip heat treating, slitting & edging*
Employs—40; Estab.—1978
45,000 sq ft site, Distrib.—Intl.
Privately owned corporation
ISO rating—9001:2000

**†BONEHAM METAL PRODUCTS, INC.**

327 N. 14th St. (07033)
**Phone—(908) 272-1200**
National—(800) 631-7852
Fax—(800) 526-9494
www.bonehamusa.com
Email—sales@bonehamusa.com
Assoc. V-P.—Doreen Guenther
SIC—5085; *Wholesaler of bushings & dowel pins*
Employs—7; Estab.—1972
10,000 sq ft site, Distrib.—National
Privately owned corporation

**CENTURION PRINTING**

761 Lexington Ave. (07033)
**Phone—(908) 241-9839**
Fax—(908) 241-8667
www.centurionprinting.com
Email—prepress@centurionprinting.com
Owner—Anthony Caccavale
Prodn. Mgr.—Joseph Quinn
SIC—2752; NAICS—323100; *Offset printing*
Employs—4; Estab.—1986
Sales—under $500,000
Distrib.—Local
Limited Liability Company

**CONSOLIDATED STEEL & ALUMINUM FENCE**

316 N. 12th St., P.O. Box 643 (07033)
**Phone—(908) 272-6262**
Fax—(908) 272-0494
www.consolidatedfencecompany.com
Email—jderosa@csafinc.com
Pres.—Paul Cacicedo
Ex. V-P.—John DeRosa
Comp.—Armando Orsini

## Kenilworth—(cont.)

SIC—3496; 3444; 3446; 3679; *Commercial chain-link, steel, aluminum & ornamental iron fences, gate operators & access control systems, including installation*
Employs—60; Estab.—1958
Sales—$9Mil-$12Mil
Distrib.—Local
Privately owned corporation
Also see: Security Fabricators, Inc., same loc.

### CRYOFAB, INC.
540 N. Michigan Ave., P.O. Box 485 (07033)
Phone—(908) 686-3636
National—(800) 426-8126
Fax—(908) 686-9538
www.cryofab.com
Email—sales@cryofab.com
Owner & Co-Pres.—Vincent J. Grillo
Off. Supv.—Lynn Pradke
SIC—3679; 3443; 3499; *Cryogenic equipment & accessories*
Employs—49; Estab.—1971
Sales—$8Mil-$10Mil
30,000 sq ft site, Distrib.—Intl.
Privately owned sub-S corp.

### DAYSOL INDUSTRIES
40 Boright Ave. (07033)
Phone—(908) 272-5900
Fax—(908) 272-8320
www.daysol.com
Email—info@daysol.com
Pres.—Dennis Polvere
V-P.—Greg Gannon
Shpg. Mgr.—Judy Hertzberg
Accountant—Shirley Cook
SIC—3089; *Plastic vacuum forming, hot stamping, packing & assembly*
Employs—25; Estab.—1958
40,000 sq ft site, Distrib.—National
Privately owned corporation
Also see: Unified Resources In Display, Inc./Display Pro Manufacturing, same loc.
AKA: Display Pro Mfg.

### DESIRON
820 Colfax Ave. (07033)
Phone—(908) 241-7776
Fax—(908) 241-5885
www.desiron.com
Email—soho@desiron.com
Pres.—Frank Carsaro
Off. Mgr.—Linda Rox
SIC—2511; 2514; *Residential wooden & metal furniture*
Employs—10; Estab.—1997
30,000 sq ft site, Distrib.—National
Limited Liability Company

### DIGITRON ELECTRONIC CORP.
144 Market St. (07033)
Phone—(908) 245-7200
Fax—(908) 245-0555
www.digitroncorp.com
Email—aschwartz@digitroncorp.com
Pres.—Joe Schwartz
Off. Mgr.—Alex Schwartz
Accts. Rep.—Nadia Trindade
SIC—3674; NAICS—334413; *Semiconductors & diodes*
Employs—9
Distrib.—Intl.
Privately owned corporation

### EXOTHERMIC MOLDING, INC.
50 Lafayette Pl. (07033)
Phone—(908) 272-2299
Fax—(908) 272-3355
www.exothermic.com
Email—paul@exothermic.com
Pres., R & D Mgr.—Paul K. Steck
Mfg. Mgr.—Caonabo Delgado
Off. Mgr.—Jessica Sarnicki

Mktg. Rep.—Joe Passarella
SIC—3089; *Reaction injection molding, contract manufacturing, custom instrument housings & finishing, mold making & value-added assembly*
Employs—17; Estab.—1983
10,400 sq ft site, Distrib.—National
Privately owned sub-S corp.

### F & G TOOL & DIE, INC.
195 Sumner Ave. (07033)
Phone—(908) 241-5880
Fax—(908) 241-6831
www.toplineseating.com
Email—norman@toplineseating.com
CEO—Carl Friedrich
Pres.—Norman Friedrich
V-P.—John Friedrich
SIC—3544; NAICS—333500; *Stamping dies & CNC machining job shop*
Employs—10; Estab.—1969
Sales—$1Mil-$2Mil
14,000 sq ft site, Distrib.—Local
Privately owned corporation

### F & M MACHINE CO., INC.
751 Lexington Ave. (07033)
Phone—(908) 245-8830
Fax—(908) 245-0239
www.fmmachineco.com
Email—fmmachineco@aol.com
Pres., Plt. Mgr.—Dick Rutledge
V-P.—Norman Radick
SIC—3469; 3599; *Metal stamping & machining job shop*
Employs—6; Estab.—1947
Sales—$500,000-$1Mil
11,000 sq ft site, Distrib.—National
Privately owned sub-S corp.

### GAUER METAL PRODUCTS, INC.
175-179 N. Michigan Ave. (07033)
Phone—(908) 241-4080
National—(877) 428-3763
Fax—(908) 245-2325
www.gauermetal.com
Email—sales@gauermetal.com
CEO—Dennis J. Schultz
Pres.—Dennis P. Schultz
V-P.—John Gotsch
SIC—3499; 3599; *Metal storage rack frames, gravity flow conveyors, deburring machines, cut-to-length strip lines & bar edgers, including stamping, punching, bending, welding & machining; Brand name—Flo-Rak; Gauer Deburring Machines; Gauer Bar Edgers & Cut to Length Lines*
Employs—40; Estab.—1946
Sales—$2.5Mil-$5Mil (est)
70,000 sq ft site, Distrib.—Intl.
Privately owned corporation

### †GENERAL FLOOR, INC.
Div. of General Floor Industries
125 Market St. (07033)
Phone—(908) 241-4888
National—(800) 664-3624
Fax—(908) 241-4860
www.generalfloor.com
Email—info@generalfloor.com
Br. Mgr.—Marcio Nescia
SIC—5023; 5031; *Wholesaler of carpet, laminate, hardwood & vinyl flooring*
Employs—4; Estab.—1998
Sales—under $500,000
20,000 sq ft site, Distrib.—Local
Privately owned corporation
Parent co.—General Floor Industries, Bellmawr, NJ
Phone—(856) 931-0012
See Parent Co. Section for full profile.

### GREGORY PRESS, INC.
7 Mark Rd., Ste. A (07033-1000)
Phone—(908) 686-0030
Fax—(908) 686-6473
www.gregorypress.com

Email—quotes@gregorypress.com
Pres.—Gregory P. Loessel
V-P.—Erika Loessel
V-P.—Victoria Loessel
GM—Jeff Loessel
SIC—2759; NAICS—323100; *Commercial printing*
Employs—23; Estab.—1978
7,500 sq ft site, Distrib.—Regional
Privately owned corporation

### HENRY MACHINE SHOP, INC.
345 Market St. (07033)
Phone—(908) 925-2218
Fax—(908) 333-4196
Email—mlee@henryprecision.com
Pres.—Henry Lee
V-P.—Kit Lee
V-P.—Michael Lee
SIC—3599; *Precision CNC machine shop*
Employs—6; Estab.—2004
Sales—under $500,000
Distrib.—Intl.
Privately owned partnership

### HI-GRADE PRODUCTS MFG. CO.
752 Jefferson Ave., P.O. Box 273 (07033)
Phone—(908) 245-4133
Fax—(908) 241-1260
Email—hi-gradeproducts@verizon.net
Pres.—Jeffrey Pfingst
Treas.—Donna Pfingst
SIC—3451; NAICS—332721; *Screw machine products*
Employs—12; Estab.—1963
Sales—$500,000-$1Mil
5,000 sq ft site, Distrib.—National
Privately owned corporation

### IDL TECHNIEDGE, LLC
30 Boright Ave. (07033)
Phone—(908) 497-9818
National—(888) 764-7487
Fax—(908) 497-9828
www.techniedge.com
Email—info@techniedge.com
Pres., CEO—Sean Quinn
CFO—Michael Donath
V-P., Sales—Kevin Quinn
V-P., Sales, Specialty—Deb Williams
V-P., Engrg.—Eric Carmichael
SIC—3421; 3423; 3841; NAICS—332200; *Hand blades & tools, including utility & razor blades & knives for consumer, industrial & specialty applications; Brand name—Techni Edge; IDL Tools; Work Tough; ViperGrip; ToolHook; MOD Level; T Tools; Sliver*
Employs—125; Estab.—1979
30,000 sq ft site, Distrib.—Intl.
Limited Liability Company
AKA: TechniEdge

### INK WELL PRINTERS INC.
38 S. 21st St. (07033-1626)
Phone—(908) 272-8090
Fax—(908) 272-7934
Email—mail@theinkwellusa.com
Pres.—Elizabeth Ensslin
Off. Mgr.—Sue Gillespie
SIC—2752; 2791; NAICS—323122; *Offset printing & typesetting*
Employs—4; Estab.—1973
Sales—under $500,000
Distrib.—Regional
Privately owned corporation

### J M C TOOL & MFG. CO.
845 Fairfield Ave. (07033)
Phone—(908) 241-8950
Fax—(908) 241-8965
Email—jmctoolco@hotmail.com
Pres.—Charles Giamo
V-P.—Mike Giamo

SIC—3599; *Precision & CNC machining job shop*
Employs—8; Estab.—1965
Sales—$500,000-$1Mil
6,400 sq ft site, Distrib.—National
Privately owned corporation

### JEWELRY TOOL & DIE CO.
4 Mark Rd., Ste. G (07033)
Phone—(908) 686-3500
Fax—(908) 684-0801
Email—jlytooldie@comcast.net
Owner—Peter Ehmann
SIC—3911; 3469; NAICS—339911; *Jewelry, metal stampings & dies*
Employs—3; Estab.—1961
Sales—under $500,000
7,000 sq ft site, Distrib.—Local
Sole ownership

### J-MAC PLASTICS, INC.
40 Lafayette Pl. *(07033)*
Phone—(908) 709-1111
Fax—(908) 709-8908
Email—service@jmacplastics.com
Pres.—John McNamara
Plt. Mgr.—Dan McNamara
Fin., Hum. Res. & Off. Mgr.—Jill E. Farawell
SIC—3089; *Plastic injection molding*
Employs—17; Estab.—1980
Sales—$500,000-$1Mil
22,500 sq ft site, Distrib.—National
Privately owned corporation
Also see: Kratt Pitch Pipe Co., Wm, same loc.

### JOHNSON ENGINEERING, WELTON V.
22 N. 26th St. (07033)
Phone—(908) 241-3100
Fax—(908) 241-3101
Email—johnsonengg@verizon.net
Owner & Pres.—Paul Damjanovic
SIC—3451; NAICS—332721; *Screw machine products*
Employs—20; Estab.—1947
Sales—under $500,000
8,000 sq ft site, Distrib.—National
Sole ownership

### KD ENVELOPES & PRINTING, LLC
7 Mark Rd. (07033)
Phone—(908) 686-1798
Fax—(908) 686-6473
www.kdenv.com
Email—john@kdenv.com
Owner—Donna Loessel
Secy-Treas.—Vickie Loessel
SIC—2759; *Envelope printing*
Employs—3; Estab.—2007
Sales—under $500,000
Distrib.—Local
Limited Liability Company

### KELLES, INC.
20 Hoiles Dr. (07033)
Phone—(908) 241-9300
Fax—(908) 241-9654
www.kelles.com
Email—mjpatrick@kelles.com
Pres., CEO—Michael J. Patrick
V-P., COO—Anthony J. Pace
Off. Mgr.—Georgeann Caponegro
Shop Supt.—George Emme
IT Specialist—Mike Andrews
SIC—3599; *General machining job shop*
Employs—14; Estab.—1978
7,000 sq ft site, Distrib.—Regional
Privately owned sub-S corp.

### KENECO, INC.
123 N. 8th St., P.O. Box 121 (07033)
Phone—(908) 241-3700
National—(800) 932-0121
Fax—(908) 272-0344
www.kenecoinc.com
Email—mail@kenecoinc.com
Pres.—William Van Loan
MIS Mgr.—Tom Hoefenkrieg

GEOGRAPHICAL

## Kenilworth—(cont.)

R & D Mgr.—Mike Wood
SIC—3535; NAICS—333922;
*Gravity flow racks; Brand name—Kenrail; Roller Runways; Beamtrack*
Employs—3; Estab.—1979
Distrib.—National
Privately owned corporation

**KENNEDY OPTICIANS**

552 Boulevard (07033)
**Phone—(908) 276-2020**
Email—contact@
kennedyopticians.com
Owner—James Kennedy
SIC—3851; NAICS—339100;
*Optic lens grinding & contact lenses*
Employs—3; Estab.—1966
Sales—under $500,000
2,600 sq ft site, Distrib.—Local
Sole ownership

**KNA GRAPHICS, INC.**

303 N. 14th St. (07033)
**Phone—(908) 272-4232**
Fax—(908) 272-2233
www.signarama-kenilworth.com
Email—info@signarama-
kenilworth.com
Pres.—Kamal Assad
V-P.—Nada Assad
SIC—3993; *Wide-format digital printing, light boxes, channel letters, carved signs, vehicle lettering, graphics, banners, magnets & window lettering*
Employs—6; Estab.—2010
4,000 sq ft site, Distrib.—Local
Privately owned corporation
DBA: Sign-A-Rama

**KRATT PITCH PIPE CO., WM**

40 Lafayette Pl. (07033)
**Phone—(908) 709-8901**
Fax—(908) 709-8908
www.krattpitchpipe.com
Email—service@krattpitchpipe.com
Plt. Mgr.—Robert McNamara
Off. Mgr.—Jill Farawell
SIC—3931; NAICS—339992;
*Musical pitch pipes; Brand name—The Master Key Chromatic Pitch Instrument*
Employs—7; Estab.—2001
Sales—$500,000-$1Mil
Distrib.—National
Privately owned corporation
Also see: J-Mac Plastics, Inc., same loc.

**LMK WATERJET**

835 Fairfield Ave. (07033)
**Phone—(908) 241-8113**
Fax—(908) 241-2836
www.lmkwaterjet.com
Email—jotool835@yahoo.com
Pres.—Herbert J. Olbrich
SIC—3599; *Contract & custom waterjet cutting of stainless steel, aluminum, steel, brass, titanium, plastics, wood & gasket materials for the manufacturing sectors; Brand name—LMK Waterjet*
Employs—2; Estab.—1960
Sales—under $500,000
4,000 sq ft site, Distrib.—Regional
Privately owned corporation

**†MARCONE SUPPLIES**

Div. of Marcone Appliance Parts Center
870 Boulevard, Ste. 4 (07033)
**Phone—(973) 371-8800**
Fax—(973) 371-3735
www.marcone.com
Email—mail@jacobyparts.com
Br. Mgr.—Denin Burke
SIC—5064; *Wholesaler of appliance parts*
Employs—5; Estab.—1958
Distrib.—National
Privately owned corporation
Parent co.—Marcone Appliance Parts Center, St. Louis, MO
Phone—(314) 993-9196
See Parent Co. Section for full profile.

**MASTER DRAPERY WORKROOM, INC.**

220 N. 14th St. (07033)
**Phone—(908) 272-4404**
Pres., Sales Mgr.—Phil Ricca
SIC—2391; NAICS—314121;
*Draperies*
Employs—4; Estab.—1968
Sales—under $500,000 (est)
Distrib.—Local

**MERCK & CO., INC.**

2000 Galloping Hill Rd. (07033)
**Phone—(908) 298-4000**
www.merck.com
Email—merck@merck.com
Ex. Dir., Global Benefits—Mary Weber
SIC—2834; NAICS—325412;
*Pharmaceuticals, for allergies, skin care, oncologists & acute coronary disorders*
Employs—2600; Estab.—1947
Sales—$12.7Bil
Distrib.—Intl.
Publicly owned corporation
Parent co.—Merck & Co., Inc., Whitehouse Station, NJ
Phone—(908) 423-1000
See Parent Co. Section for full profile.

**†MOTION INDUSTRIES, INC.**

141 Market St., Ste. 8 (07033)
**Phone—(908) 241-1047**
National—(800) 526-9328
Fax—(908) 354-1061
www.motionindustries.com
Email—john.velit@motion-ind.com
Br. Mgr.—John Velit
Opers. Mgr.—Nancy Salt
SIC—5085; *Distributor of industrial maintenance, repair & operation (MRO) parts including bearings, power transmission, electrical & indl. automation, material handling, hydraulic & pneumatic components, hydraulic & indl. hose & safety/indl. supplies; Brand name—Altra; Baldor; Eaton; Emerson Industrial Automation; Gates; Lovejoy; Martin; Nexen; NSK; NTN; Rexnord; Schaeffler Group; SEW Eurodrive; SKF; SMC; Sumitomo; THK; Thomson; Timken; Tsubaki; US Motors; Vacon; Webster*
Employs—20
Distrib.—National
Privately owned corporation
Parent co.—Motion Industries, Inc., Birmingham, AL
Phone—(205) 951-1154
See Parent Co. Section for full profile.

**MS TOOL CO., INC.**

500 S. 31st St. (07033)
**Phone—(908) 245-7989**
Fax—(908) 245-7997
Owner—Eberhard Schweitzer
SIC—3544; NAICS—333500; *Tool & die job shop*
Employs—2; Estab.—1965
Sales—$500,000-$1Mil
Distrib.—National
Privately owned corporation
AKA: Schweitzer Special Machines

**NETWORKING TECHNOLOGIES & INTEGRATION**

50 Boright Ave. (07033)
**Phone—(908) 276-1200**
Fax—(908) 276-7120
www.networkingtec.com
Email—sales@networkingtec.com
Pres.—John Azzinaro
SIC—7373; *Computer network system integration, including LANs & WANs*
Employs—10
Distrib.—Local
Privately owned corporation

**NORDIC METAL, LLC**

500 S. 31st St. (07033)
Mail addr.: P.O. Box 43203, Montclair (07043)
**Phone—(908) 245-8900**
Fax—(908) 245-5345
www.nordicmetal500.com
Email—nordicmetal500@aol.com
Pres.—Bo L. Johansson
V-P. & Plt. Mgr.—Bob Deuel
SIC—3444; *Sheet metal fabrication*
Employs—8; Estab.—1977
8,000 sq ft site, Distrib.—National
Limited Liability Company

**OSTLUND, INC., CAL**

555 N. Michigan Ave. (07033)
**Phone—(908) 688-4466**
Fax—(908) 687-5833
www.calostlund.com
Email—info@calostlund.com
Pres., CEO—Cal Ostlund, Jr.
V-P.—Steven Ostlund
SIC—2541; 2542; *Trade show exhibits*
Employs—50; Estab.—1978
Sales—$10Mil-$15Mil
40,000 sq ft site, Distrib.—National
Privately owned corporation

**PETERSON STAMPING & MFG. CO.**

75 N. Michigan Ave., P.O. Box 190 (07033)
**Phone—(908) 241-0900**
Fax—(908) 241-0706
www.petersonstamping.com
Email—support@
petersonstamping.com
Pres.—Robert Olsen, Sr.
Off. Mgr.—Robert Olsen, Jr.
Bookkeeper—Erika Sullivan
SIC—3469; *Metal stampings*
Employs—10; Estab.—1947
Sales—$500,000-$1Mil
10,000 sq ft site, Distrib.—National
Privately owned corporation

**PINNACLE COSMETICS PACKAGING, LLC**

80 Market St., P.O. Box 733 (07033)
**Phone—(908) 241-7777**
Fax—(908) 241-9449
Owner—Ed Halsch
SIC—2844; NAICS—325600;
*Perfume packaging*
Employs—15; Estab.—2002
Sales—$5Mil-$10Mil (est)
Distrib.—National
Limited Liability Company

**PRECISION BLINDS PRODUCTS, INC.**

637 Boulevard (07033)
**Phone—(908) 245-7766**
Fax—(908) 245-8915
www.theblinddept.com
Email—blindwonder@verizon.net
Pres.—Robert Schreiber
Sales Rep.—Frank DiCosmo
SIC—2391; 2591; NAICS—
314121; *Window treatments, flooring & wall coverings*
Employs—3; Estab.—1986
Sales—$1Mil-$5Mil
Distrib.—Local
Privately owned corporation

**PRECISION ESCALATORS**

147 N. Michigan Ave. (07033)
**Phone—(908) 259-9017**
National—(800) 233-0838
Fax—(908) 259-9013

www.optimumprecision.net
Email—webmaster@
optimumprecision.net
Pres.—Gregory Maroukian
SIC—3082; NAICS—326121;
*Precision urethane parts*
Employs—7; Estab.—1995
Sales—under $500,000
2,400 sq ft site, Distrib.—National
Privately owned corporation

**PROGRESSIVE TOOL & MFG. CO.**

708 Fairfield Ave. (07033)
**Phone—(908) 245-7010**
Fax—(908) 245-7011
Pres.—Gunter Heim
SIC—3469; 3544; NAICS—
333500; *Metal stampings & tool & die job shop*
Employs—6; Estab.—1977
Sales—$500,000-$1Mil
2,500 sq ft site, Distrib.—National
Privately owned corporation

**R L TOOL & DIE CO.**

739 Fairfield Ave. (07033)
**Phone—(908) 245-7710**
Fax—(908) 245-7712
Email—rl.tool@verizon.net
Owner & Pres.—Dennis Heucke
SIC—3544; NAICS—333500;
*Precision tooling of medical products & devices, including EDM machining & dies*
Employs—3; Estab.—1957
6,000 sq ft site, Distrib.—National
Privately owned corporation

**RAMCO MFG. CO., INC.**

365 Carnegie Ave. (07033)
**Phone—(908) 245-4500**
Fax—(908) 245-3142
www.ramco-safetyshields.com
Email—info@ramco-
safetyshields.com
Pres.—Kevin J. Nee
SIC—3494; 3089; NAICS—
332900; *Flanges, expansion & threaded pipe joints, valves & safety shields*
Employs—25; Estab.—1942
15,000 sq ft site, Distrib.—Intl.
Privately owned sub-S corp.

**ROTECH TOOL & MOLD CO., INC.**

824 Fairfield Ave. (07033)
**Phone—(908) 241-9669**
Fax—(908) 241-9128
www.rotechtool.com
Email—rotech@verizon.net
Pres.—Terry Leschinski
V-P., Shop Foreman—Bob Leschinski, Jr.
SIC—3544; NAICS—333500;
*Plastic injection molds, including pharmaceutical fabrication & stamping die work*
Employs—7; Estab.—1979
Distrib.—Local
Privately owned corporation

**ROYAL PRIME WINDOW SPECIALIST, INC.**

742 Fairfield Ave. (07033)
**Phone—(908) 354-7600**
National—(800) 354-7676
Fax—(908) 354-6341
www.royalprime.com
Email—ainelli@royalprime.com
Pres. & IT Mgr.—Andrew Inelli
Ex. Mgr.—Andy Inelli, Jr.
Hum. Res. & Off. Mgr.—Cila Pereirra
Bookkeeper—Ana Miranda
SIC—3089; 3442; 3231; NAICS—
332321; *High-end vinyl replacement windows & decorative glass, including installation*
Employs—6; Estab.—1978
90,000 sq ft site, Distrib.—Regional
Privately owned corporation

## Kenilworth—(cont.)

**SEAGRAVE COATINGS CORP.**
209 N. Michigan Ave. (07033)
**Phone—(201) 933-1000**
Fax—(201) 933-3646
www.seagravecoatings.com
Email—hptepperman@
seagravecoatings.com
Pres.—Peter Tepperman
SIC—2851; NAICS—325510;
*Paints & industrial coatings*
Employs—20; Estab.—1846
30,000 sq ft site, Distrib.—Intl.
Privately owned corporation

**SECURITY FABRICATORS, INC.**
316 N. 12th St., P.O. Box 643
(07033)
**Phone—(908) 272-9171**
Fax—(908) 272-6089
www.securityfabricators.com
Pres.—Paul Cacicedo
Bookkeeper—Maria Galvao
SIC—3496; *Chain link fencing*
Employs—15; Estab.—1948
Sales—$1Mil-$2.5Mil (est)
Distrib.—National
Privately owned corporation
Also see: Consolidated Steel &
Aluminum Fence, same loc.

**SHIRA ESTHETICS, INC.**
65 S. 21st St., Ste. 2 (07033)
**Phone—(908) 497-9497**
National—(800) 957-4472
Fax—(908) 497-9420
www.shiraesthetics.com
Email—info@shiraesthetics.com
Pres.—Yair Nezaria
V-P.—Bob Churchill
SIC—2844; *Beauty, body & skin
care products, including toners,
cleansers & moisturizers; Brand
name—Shir-Organic Skin Care;
Shir-Radiance; Boto-Derm Rx
Skin Care; Omega 3 Skin Care;
Glyco-C skin care; Chamomile
Azulene skin care; Sea Weed
skin care; Solar Energy skin care*
Employs—21; Estab.—1990
Sales—$2.5Mil-$5Mil
Distrib.—Intl.
Privately owned corporation

**STOLLEN MACHINE & TOOL CO.,
INC.**
761 Lexington Ave. (07033)
**Phone—(908) 241-0622**
www.stollentool.com
Email—doug@stollenmachine.com
Pres., Fin. & R & D Mgr.—Douglas
Stollen
MIS & R & D Mgr.—Tom Terpos
Off. Mgr.—Wendy Solomon
SIC—3599; *CNC machining job
shop*
Employs—5; Estab.—1954
Sales—under $500,000
10,000 sq ft site, Distrib.—Local
Privately owned sub-S corp.

**SYNRAY CORP.**
209 N. Michigan Ave. (07033)
**Phone—(908) 245-2600**
Fax—(908) 245-2460
www.synray.com
Email—info@synray.com
Pres.—Stan Lesniewski
GM—Joe Petronella
Plt. Mgr.—Al Banks
Off. Mgr.—Colleen Merendino
SIC—2821; NAICS—325211;
*Alkyd & acrylic resins &
saturated polyesters; Brand
name—Syncone; Synacryl;
Synaqua; Synpoxy; Synplex*
Employs—30; Estab.—1981
25,535 sq ft site, Distrib.—National
Privately owned corporation

**TASTE IT PRESENTS, INC.**
200 Sumner Ave. (07033)
**Phone—(908) 241-9191**
Fax—(908) 241-9410
www.tasteitpresents.com
Email—sales@tasteitpresents.com
Pres.—John Alair
V-P.—Larry DiMurro
SIC—2053; NAICS—311813;
*Frozen desserts*
Employs—50; Estab.—1997
Distrib.—Intl.
Privately owned corporation

**TELEDEX, INC. (H Q)**
1 Atlas St. (07033)
**Phone—(908) 964-8109**
Fax—(908) 964-8252
www.datexx.com
Email—mei@datexx.com
Owner & CEO—Mei Nogochi
Off. Mgr.—Eddy Nogochi
SIC—3648; NAICS—335129;
*Corporate headquarters; LED
lighting equipment (mfg. done in
China)*
Employs—6; Estab.—1994
Sales—under $500,000
Distrib.—National
Privately owned corporation

**TOP LINE SEATING, INC.**
540 S. 31st St. (07033)
**Phone—(908) 241-9051**
Fax—(908) 241-6831
www.toplineseating.com
Email—sales@toplineseating.com
CEO—Carl Friedrich
Pres.—Norman Friedrich
Off. Mgr.—John Friedrich
SIC—2599; 2531; *Bar stools &
chairs for the casino gaming,
hotel, restaurant & banquet
industries*
Employs—15; Estab.—1998
Sales—$1Mil-$2.5Mil
Distrib.—Intl.
Privately owned corporation

**T-RIFIC TEES, LLC**
100 N. 12th St., Ste. 2 (07033)
**Phone—(908) 272-5140**
Fax—(908) 272-5170
www.t-rifictees.com
Email—sales@t-rifictees.com
Pres.—Victor Herman
SIC—2396; *Custom silk screen
printing*
Employs—12; Estab.—1985
Sales—$1Mil-$2.5Mil
12,500 sq ft site, Distrib.—Intl.
Privately owned corporation

**ULTIMATE TOOL & MFG. CO.**
360-A Carnegie Ave. (07033)
**Phone—(908) 241-4575**
Fax—(908) 241-4576
Email—ultiworks@aol.com
Owner, GM & Plt. Mgr.—Paul
Plante
SIC—3544; 3599; 3543; NAICS—
333500; *Tool & die & CNC
machining job shop, including
prototypes & development*
Employs—5; Estab.—1976
Sales—under $500,000
3,500 sq ft site, Distrib.—Local
Sole ownership

**UNIFIED RESOURCES IN DISPLAY,
INC./DISPLAY PRO
MANUFACTURING**
40 Boright Ave. (07033)
**Phone—(908) 272-1112**
Fax—(908) 272-1024
www.ur-indisplay.com
Email—cbrother@ur-indisplay.com
Pres., GM—Dennis Polvere
Hum. Res. Mgr.—John Pillarella
Off. Mgr.—Judith Hertzberg

SIC—2541; 2542; *Point-of-
purchase displays, assembly,
injection, molding, metal, wood
& laser cutting*
Employs—20; Estab.—1986
Sales—$18Mil-$22Mil
105,000 sq ft site, Distrib.—
National
Privately owned corporation
Also see: Daysol Industries, same
loc.

**UNION COUNTY SEATING & SUPPLY
CO., INC.**
121 N. Michigan Ave., Ste. E
(07033-1261)
**Phone—(908) 241-4949**
(732) 522-3886
Fax—(908) 241-2979
www.unioncountyseating.com
Email—bruce@
unioncountyseating.com
Owner & Pres.—Bruce Bussell
SIC—2531; *New &
remanufactured transit & coach
seating for the transportation
industry, including stock
replacement parts, custom
design, leather & embroidery;
Brand name—Bostrom;
National; Sears MFG.; USSC
Recaro; Freedman; AMSECO;
Kab Seating; Isringhausen*
Employs—26; Estab.—1986
Sales—$1.5Mil
13,000 sq ft site, Distrib.—National
Privately owned sub-S corp.

**†V.S. SYSTEMATICS, INC.**
300 S. Michigan Ave., 1st Fl.
(07033-2036)
**Phone—(908) 241-5110**
(908) 391-4344
Fax—(908) 241-0052
www.vssystematics.com
Email—testeves@
vssystematics.com
Owner—Sarah Esteves
V-P.—Silverio Esteves
Hum. Res. Mgr.—Tony Esteves
SIC—5084; 5063; *Wholesaler of
industrial automation equipment,
including motors, sensors &
controls & standard gear box &
pneumatics; Brand name—
Wenglor; Baldor; Lesson;
Bodine; Bonfiglioli Gear Box;
MGM Motor & Brakes; Lafert
Motors; Salima /Motor Power;
Lion Precision/Banner; Turk;
Sick; Omron; Wenglor; Boston
Gear; Dodge; WindSmith;
Bonfiglioli Motor; STM*
Employs—3
4,500 sq ft site, Distrib.—National
Privately owned corporation

**VENTRONICS, INC.**
346 Monroe Ave., P.O. Box 142
(07033)
**Phone—(908) 272-9262**
Fax—(908) 272-7630
www.ventronicsinc.com
Email—ventronics@verizon.net
Pres.—Joseph C. Venerus
MIS Mgr.—Peter Evans
Fin. Mgr.—Pattie Johnstone
R & D Mgr.—Barry Burbank
Dept. Mgr.—Jim Hill
SIC—3677; 3672; 3678; 3679;
NAICS—334416; *Transformers,
inductors, chokes, coils, printed
circuit boards, adapters &
passive components; Brand
name—Mutronics; Ventronics;
Camelion*
Employs—19; Estab.—1972
60,000 sq ft site, Distrib.—Intl.
Sole ownership
ISO rating—9002

**WAAGE ELECTRIC, INC.**
720 Colfax Ave., P.O. Box 337
(07033)
**Phone—(908) 245-9363**
(800) 922-4365
Fax—(908) 245-8477
www.waage.com
Email—info@waage.com
Pres., R & D Mgr.—Marc Waage
V-P.—Bruce Waage
SIC—3567; NAICS—333994;
*Commercial & industrial electric
heating equipment for wax & soft
melting systems, including
industrial electric furnaces, hot
plates, immersion, duct, SX-strip,
digitally controlled & custom
heaters & wax & solder pots;
Brand name—Waage®*
Employs—6; Estab.—1908
Sales—$1Mil-$5Mil
12,000 sq ft site, Distrib.—Intl.
Privately owned corporation

**WAGNER FOTO SCREEN PROCESS**
4 Mark Rd. (07033)
**Phone—(908) 624-0800**
Fax—(908) 624-0801
Email—wagnerfoto@aol.com
Pres.—Bob Masucci
Off. Mgr.—Donna Masucci
SIC—2396; *Screen printing of
clothing*
Employs—2; Estab.—1939
Sales—under $500,000
Distrib.—Local
Limited Liability Company

**WESTFIELD SHEET METAL WORKS,
INC.**
261 Monroe Ave., P.O. Box 128
(07033)
**Phone—(908) 276-5500**
Fax—(908) 276-6808
www.westfieldsheetmetal.com
Email—wsmwinc@aol.com
Pres.—Campbell Johnstone
V-P.—Thomas D. Johnstone
Comp.—Gregg Wheatley
SIC—3444; 3312; 3591; *Custom
stainless & carbon steel,
aluminum & metal products,
including design, fabrication &
installation*
Employs—25; Estab.—1928
50,000 sq ft site, Distrib.—National
Sole ownership

**WHITE CONVEYORS, INC.**
10 Boright Ave. (07033)
**Phone—(800) 524-0273**
Fax—(908) 686-9317
www.white-conveyors.com
Email—sales@white-conveyors.com
Ex. V-P.—Mark Speckhart
V-P., Sales & Mktg.—Paul Mullen
V-P., Opers.—Steven Wilp
Pur. Mgr.—Caroline Ordner
Hum. Res. Mgr.—John Speckhart
SIC—3535; 3582; NAICS—
333922; *Garment conveyors for
dry cleaners, hotels, retail & jails;
Brand name—U-Pick-It; ADC
Dry Cleaning Conveyors; Jail
Conveyors; Home Closet
Conveyors*
Employs—100; Estab.—1946
82,000 sq ft site, Distrib.—National
Privately owned corporation

**YOUR TOPS, INC.**
101 S. 21st St. (07033)
**Phone—(908) 272-0011**
Fax—(908) 709-2044
www.yourtopsinc.net
Pres.—Gary Wiese
Manager—Garrett Wiese
SIC—2396; *Screen printing*
Employs—2; Estab.—1985
Sales—under $500,000
Distrib.—Regional
Privately owned corporation

GEOGRAPHICAL

## Kenilworth—(cont.)

### YUHL PRODUCTS, INC.

15 N. 7th St. (07033)
**Phone—(908) 276-5180**
Fax—(908) 276-0535
Email—yuhlproducts@msn.com
Pres.—Ron Yuhl
SIC—3089; *Plastic injection molding, including prototype & production molds, assembly & packaging*
Employs—3; Estab.—1976
Sales—under $500,000
1,000 sq ft site, Distrib.—Intl.
Privately owned sub-S corp.

### †Z & Z HOLDING CO INC

Div. of Johnstone Supply, Inc.
370 Market St., P.O. Box 239 (07033)
**Phone—(908) 298-1212**
Fax—(908) 298-1290
www.johnstonenj.com
Email—customer.service@ johnstonenj.com
Pres.—Robert Zimmermann
V-P.—Bud Zimmermann
Cont.—Mary B. Holt
Dir.—C. M. Zimmermann
SIC—5075; 5078; *Wholesaler of HVAC/R equipment & supplies, including heating, ventilation, air conditioning, refrigeration, plumbing, hydronics & electrical products; Brand name— Coleman; Fujitsu; Rinnai; Evcon; Crown; Honeywell; Taco; AO Smith; Emerson; Nu-Calgon; Parker; White Rodgers; UEI; ICM Controls; NTI; Grundfos; Fluke; Fieldpiece; Turbotorch; Ridgid; JB; Giant; Fasco; ICM Controls*
Employs—57; Estab.—1987
Company-wide: 95
Distrib.—Intl.
Privately owned corporation
AKA: Johnstone Supply
Parent co.—Johnstone Supply, Inc., Portland, OR
Phone—(503) 419-9100
See Parent Co. Section for full profile.

## Kenvil

(Morris—N.W.)

### COUNTY CONCRETE CORP.

50 Railroad Ave., P.O. Box F (07847)
**Phone—(973) 584-7122**
Fax—(973) 584-4370
www.countyconcretenj.com
Email—info@countymaterials.com
Pres.—John C. Crimi
Ex. V-P.—Peter Crimi
V-P., Sales—John Post
V-P.—Ron Sutton
Cont.—Sam DeSteno
Dir., Hum. Res.—John Skelly
Maint. Mgr., Fleet—Ed Gaffney
SIC—3272; 3281; NAICS— 327991; *Corporate headquarters & concrete, sand & gravel processing*
Employs—90
Sales—$5Mil-$10Mil
Privately owned corporation

### PRO IMAGE PROMOTIONS, INC.

489 U.S. Highway 46 (07847)
**Phone—(973) 252-8000**
Fax—(973) 252-8871
www.proimagenj.com
Email—brian@proimagenj.com
Pres.—Brian Hewitt
Cust. Serv. Rep.—Kim Agrusti

SIC—2396; 2395; *Promotional textile screen printing & embroidery, including golf shirts, t-shirts & towels*
Employs—4; Estab.—1995
Sales—under $500,000
Distrib.—Regional
Privately owned corporation

### TROY-ONIC, INC.

90 Dell Ave., P.O. Box 494 (07847)
**Phone—(973) 584-6830**
Fax—(973) 584-7205
www.troyonic.com
Email—info@troyonic.com
Pres.—Mike Murphy
Dir., Opers.—Jason Gillen
SIC—3671; NAICS—334411; *Electron tubes*
Employs—20; Estab.—1962
5,000 sq ft site, Distrib.—National
Privately owned corporation

## Keyport

(Monmouth—N.E.)

### †AIR & GAS TECHNOLOGIES, INC.

42 Industrial Dr. *(07735)*
**Phone—(732) 566-7227**
      (800) 716-5550
Fax—(732) 566-0535
www.airgastech.com
Email—bkeelen@airgastech.com
Pres.—Vince Tomasso
V-P.—Brian Keelen
SIC—5084; *Wholesaler of industrial air & breathing air compressors & process & natural gas compressors for natural gas vehicle refueling & technical rescue dive equipment; Brand name— CompAir; Bauer Compressors; Sullivan-Palatek; Domnick-Hunter; Rix; Chicago-Pneumatic; Interspiro; ANGI; Boge Compressors; BRC FuelMaker; Cubo Gas CNG Compressors*
Employs—18; Estab.—1995
Distrib.—Regional
Privately owned corporation

### AMP CUSTOM RUBBER, INC.

3 Cass St., Ste. 8 *(07735)*
Mail addr: P.O. Box 377, Hazlet (07730-0377)
**Phone—(732) 888-2714**
      (888) 888-2714
Fax—(732) 739-2715
www.ampcustomrubber.com
Email—amprubber@aol.com
Pres., Sales Mgr.—John Petrizzo
SIC—3053; NAICS—339991; *Gaskets*
Employs—15; Estab.—1987
15,000 sq ft site, Distrib.—National
Privately owned sub-S corp.

### BAYSHORE METAL PRODUCTS, INC.

120 Francis St., Ste. 6 (07735)
**Phone—(732) 739-9260**
Fax—(732) 739-4236
www.bayshoremetal.com
Email—bayshoremetal@ hotmail.com
Pres.—Richard Walker
GM—Richard Walker, Jr.
Supervisor—Joe Walker
SIC—3444; *Precision sheet metal fabrication*
Employs—4; Estab.—1986
Sales—$500,000-$1Mil
Distrib.—National
Privately owned corporation

### CRAFTSMEN RAILING, INC.

3 Cass St. (07735)
**Phone—(732) 264-1080**
Fax—(732) 264-0191
www.craftsmenrailing.com
Pres.—Ray Cottone
Off. Mgr.—Pat Simmer

SIC—3446; 3444; NAICS— 332323; *Iron & aluminum railings*
Employs—5; Estab.—1972
Sales—under $500,000
2,800 sq ft site, Distrib.—Local
Privately owned corporation

### ENCUR, INC.

200 Division St., P.O. Box 92 (07735)
**Phone—(732) 264-2098**
Fax—(732) 264-0126
www.encur.com
Email—info@encur.com
Pres.—Mark M. Curcio
Off. Mgr.—Maureen Del Popolo
Prod. Mgr.—Otto Gigantino
SIC—3585; *Induction heating equipment*
Employs—7; Estab.—1972
Sales—$2.6Mil-$5Mil
10,000 sq ft site, Distrib.—Intl.
Privately owned sub-S corp.

### FAST COPY PRINTING CENTER

81 Broad St. (07735)
**Phone—(732) 739-4646**
Fax—(732) 739-8862
Email—fastcopyprinting@msn.com
Owner, Fin. & MIS Mgr.—William Sacks
SIC—2752; 2791; NAICS— 323122; *Offset & instant printing & typesetting*
Employs—4; Estab.—1988
Sales—under $500,000
6,500 sq ft site, Distrib.—Regional
Privately owned corporation

### FRAGRANCE RESOURCES, INC.

275 Clark St., P.O. Box 110 (07735)
**Phone—(732) 264-6767**
Fax—(732) 264-1389
www.fragranceresources.com
Email—clifton@ frangeresources.com
V-P.—Larry Zakreski
SIC—2844; NAICS—325600; *Fragrance compounds*
Employs—60; Estab.—1987
60,000 sq ft site, Distrib.—Intl.
Privately owned corporation
Parent co.—Fragrance Resources, Inc., Clifton, NJ
Phone—(973) 777-2979
See Parent Co. Section for full profile.

### FRIEDLAND & BROS., INC., RALPH

17 Industrial Dr. (07735)
**Phone—(732) 290-9800**
National—(800) 631-2162
Fax—(732) 290-2933
Pres.—Ely Tawil
SIC—2591; NAICS—337920; *Window shades*
Employs—30
Sales—$2.5Mil-$5Mil (est)
Distrib.—Regional
Privately owned corporation

### G & M CUSTOM FORMICA WORK

120 Francis St., Bldg. C (07735)
**Phone—(732) 888-0360**
Fax—(732) 888-4450
Email—gmmica@aol.com
Ptnr.—George Macchia
Ptnr.—Michael Macchia
Ptnr.—James Macchia
SIC—2541; 2542; *Plastic laminated countertops*
Employs—3; Estab.—1985
Sales—under $500,000
Distrib.—Local
Privately owned partnership

### G A F MACHINE TOOL CO., INC.

39 Maple Pl., P.O. Box 18 (07735)
**Phone—(732) 264-8717**
Fax—(732) 739-8847
www.gafmachine.com
Email—info@gafmachine.com
Pres.—George Fernandez
Foreman—Charlie Desaules

SIC—3599; *Precision & CNC machining job shop*
Employs—6; Estab.—1971
Sales—under $500,000
3,000 sq ft site, Distrib.—National
Privately owned corporation

### INTERNATIONAL RIDING HELMETS, INC.

21 Industrial Dr., Old Bridge Township (07735)
**Phone—(732) 290-3000**
National—(800) 435-6380
Fax—(732) 290-3024
www.irhhelmets.com
Email—ridinghelmets@ optonline.net
Pres., GM—Frank Plastino
SIC—3949; NAICS—339920; *Equestrian helmets*
Employs—10; Estab.—1983
Sales—$1Mil-$2.5Mil (est)
Distrib.—Intl.
Privately owned corporation
AKA: Intec, Inc.

### J.R.M. PRODUCTS, INC.

701 Locust St. (07735)
Mail addr: 15 Philips Mill Dr., Middletown (07748)
**Phone—(732) 495-3092**
Fax—(732) 495-1144
www.jrmclips.com
Email—jrmprodinc@aol.com
Pres.—Robert Wichowski
V-P.—Marianne Wichowski
SIC—3444; 3366; 3496; 3469; *American-made custom steel, stainless steel, nickel plate & brass holster, belt & buckle clips, military buckles, thumb break stiffeners, holster shanks & snap hooks, including metal stamping & wire forming*
Employs—4; Estab.—1972
Sales—under $500,000
3,000 sq ft site, Distrib.—Intl.
Privately owned corporation

### MARMUS, INC.

51 E. Front St. (07735)
**Phone—(732) 264-3681**
Fax—(732) 264-3681
Pres.—Terry Musson
SIC—2759; 2752; 2396; NAICS— 323100; *Textile screen, commercial, digital & wide-format printing; Brand name— Photo Offset Printing; Terry's Tees*
Employs—1; Estab.—1953
Sales—under $500,000
1,700 sq ft site, Distrib.—Local
Privately owned corporation

### METHOD ASSOCS., INC.

120 Francis St., Ste. 2 (07735)
**Phone—(732) 888-0444**
Fax—(732) 264-8769
www.methodassociates.com
Email—methodpax@ methodassociates.com
Pres., Plt. Mgr.—Malcom Will
SIC—3089; *Contract packaging*
Employs—20; Estab.—1963
Sales—$1Mil-$2.5Mil
Distrib.—Intl.
Privately owned corporation

<u>NEW ENTRY</u>

### MR. GREEN TEA ICE CREAM CO.

25 Church St., Unit 104 (07735)
**Phone—(732) 446-9800**
www.mrgreentea.com
Email—info@mrgreentea.net
CEO—Richard Emanuel
SIC—2024; *Ice cream; Brand name—Mr. Green Tea ®*
Employs—21; Estab.—1968
Sales—$5Mil-$10Mil (est)
Distrib.—National
Sole ownership

## Keyport—(cont.)

**REEDY INTERNATIONAL CORP.**
25 E. Front St., Ste. 200 (07735-1564)
Mail addr: 9301-A Forsyth Park Dr., Charlotte (28273)
**Phone—(732) 264-1777**
Fax—(732) 264-1189
www.reedyintl.com
Email—thealy@reedyintl.com
Sr. Prod. Mgr.—Theresa Healy
SIC—2869; *Plastic foaming & nucleating agents & plastic processing additives; Brand name—SAFOAM; SAFTEC; SEKUR*
Employs—12; Estab.—1989
Sales—$3Mil-$5Mil
5,000 sq ft site, Distrib.—Intl.
Privately owned sub-S corp.
ISO rating—9001:2000
Parent co.—Reedy International Corp., Charlotte, NC
Phone—(980) 819-6930
See Parent Co. Section for full profile.

**TASK U. S. A.**
3 Cass St. (07735)
**Phone—(732) 739-0377**
Fax—(732) 739-0144
Email—taskusa@hotmail.com
V-P.—Tom Saporita
SIC—3585; *Commercial air conditioners*
Employs—20; Estab.—1991
12,000 sq ft site, Distrib.—Regional
Privately owned corporation

## Kingston
### (Somerset—N.E.)

**CIVIC RESEARCH INSTITUTE, INC.**
4478 Route 27, P.O. Box 585 (08528)
**Phone—(609) 683-4450**
Fax—(609) 683-7291
www.civicresearchinstitute.com
Email—cri.customer.service@comcast.net
Pres.—Mark Peel
Cust. Serv. Mgr.—Sandi Hill
Cust. Serv. Rep.—Heather Laspino
SIC—2721; *Periodical publishing*
Employs—3; Estab.—1993
Sales—$500,000-$1Mil
Distrib.—National
Privately owned corporation

**TRAP ROCK IND., LLC**
4415 Route 27, P.O. Box 419 (08528)
**Phone—(609) 924-0300**
Fax—(609) 252-8929
www.traprock.com
Email—gmorgan@traprock.com
Pres.—Wiliam H. Stavola
V-P.—Michael Crowley
Sales Mgr.—Michael Conti
Plt. Opers. Mgr.—Gilbert Girard
Hum. Res. Mgr.—Jerry Myers
Cred. Mgr.—Gloria Morgan
SIC—2951; NAICS—324121; *Company headquarters & crushed stone & hot mix asphalt*
Employs—350; Estab.—1966
Sales—over $1Mil
Distrib.—Regional
Privately owned corporation
AKA: Trap Rock Industries

## Kinnelon
### (Morris—N.W.)

**†BSTC GROUP, INC.**
135 Kinnelon Rd., Rm. 201 (07405)
**Phone—(973) 492-5220**
Fax—(973) 492-1176

Pres.—Andrew Berardinelli
SIC—5051; *Distributor of nails*
Employs—4; Estab.—1980
Sales—$500,000-$1Mil
Distrib.—Intl.
Privately owned corporation

**PRINTERS PLACE NORTH, LLC**
2 Kiel Ave., Ste. 154 (07405-2572)
**Phone—(973) 838-3741**
Email—printersplace@optonline.net
Pres.—Mary Murphy
V-P.—Frank Pron
SIC—2752; NAICS—323100; *Offset printing*
Employs—2; Estab.—2005
Sales—under $500,000
Distrib.—Regional
Limited Liability Company

**TYPE-N-GRAPHIC**
170 Kinnelon Rd., Ste. 12 (07405)
**Phone—(973) 838-6544**
Fax—(973) 838-8161
Email—tng@170kr.net
V-P.—Jim Kapotes
Off. Mgr.—Jim Hill
SIC—2791; NAICS—323122; *Commercial typesetting*
Employs—5; Estab.—1976
Sales—$500,000-$1Mil
Distrib.—Local
Privately owned corporation
AKA: TNG Creative

## Lafayette
### (Sussex—N.W.)

**A B STAMP**
10 Mill Pine Dr. (07848)
**Phone—(973) 383-1683**
Fax—(973) 383-0885
Pres.—Fred Thornton
Bookkeeper—Geri Runyon
SIC—3993; 3953; NAICS—339943; *Interior & exterior signs, rubber stamps, marking & identification products*
Employs—3; Estab.—1972
4,000 sq ft site, Distrib.—National
Privately owned corporation

**BEAVER RUN FARMS**
300 Beaver Run Rd. (07848)
**Phone—(973) 875-5555**
Fax—(973) 875-2924
www.beaverrunform.com
Email—kjones@shotmeyerbros.com
GM—Tim Shotmeyer
SIC—2951; 3281; NAICS—324121; *Asphalt paving compounds & crushed stone products*
Employs—15
Sales—$500,000-$1Mil
Distrib.—Local
Privately owned corporation

**BON CHEF, INC.**
205 State Route 94 (07848)
**Phone—(973) 383-8848**
          (973) 968-7138
National—(800) 331-0177
Fax—(973) 383-1827
www.bonchef.com
Email—info@bonchef.com
Pres., R & D Mgr.—Sal Torre
CFO—Denise Cosentino
V-P.—Jeremy Mottola
Dir., Sales Admn.—Amy Passafaro
Dir., IT—Jody Torre
SIC—3365; 3589; NAICS—331524; *Flatware, chafing dishes, sandstone, coffee urns, juice dispensers, mobile banquet buffet & hollowware*
Employs—90; Estab.—1972
Sales—$25Mil
63,000 sq ft site, Distrib.—Intl.
Privately owned corporation

**BRAEN STONE**
217 Limecrest Rd. (07848)
**Phone—(973) 383-7100**
Fax—(973) 383-1408
www.braenstone.com
Email—pkronyak@comcast.net
Off. Mgr.—Pam Kronyak
SIC—1411; NAICS—212311; *Aggregate quarrying*
Employs—12; Estab.—2012
Sales—$1Mil-$2.5Mil
Distrib.—Regional
Privately owned corporation

**CLASSIC MARKING PRODUCTS, INC.**
10 Millpond Dr., Unit 9 (07848)
**Phone—(973) 383-2223**
Fax—(973) 383-0885
www.classicmarking.com
Email—fred@classicmarking.com
Pres.—Fred Thornton, Sr.
V-P.—William Thornton
SIC—3953; 3993; NAICS—339943; *Rubber stamps, markers, signs & promotional gift items*
Employs—9; Estab.—1984
Sales—$500,000-$1Mil
Distrib.—Regional
Privately owned corporation

**FREDON WELDING & IRON WORKS CO.**
52 State Route 15, P.O. Box 260 (07848)
**Phone—(973) 383-6768**
Fax—(973) 383-8018
www.fredonwelding.com
Email—jim@fredonwelding.com
Pres.—James Zylstra
Bus. Admn.—Terry Sipley
SIC—3446; 3599; NAICS—332323; *Ironwork & welding job shop*
Employs—28; Estab.—1965
Distrib.—Local
Privately owned corporation

**JORDAN MFG., LLC**
Div. of Carl Stahl Sava Industries, Inc.
28 Randazzo Rd., P.O. Box 226 (07848)
**Phone—(973) 383-8363**
Fax—(973) 579-6607
www.jordanstamping.com
Email—info@jordanstamping.com
GM—Gary Wilson
Prod. Mgr.—Jerry Whitney
SIC—3469; 3544; NAICS—333500; *Metal stampings, tooling, CNC turning & screw machining*
Employs—8; Estab.—1995
15,000 sq ft site, Distrib.—National
Privately owned corporation
Parent co.—Carl Stahl Sava Industries, Inc., Riverdale, NJ
Phone—(973) 835-0882
See Parent Co. Section for full profile.

**LAMSON AIRTUBES, LLC**
10 Millpond Dr., Unit 4 (07848-3825)
**Phone—(973) 300-4267**
National—(866) 247-8823
Fax—(973) 300-1932
www.airtubes.com
Email—service@airtubes.com
CEO—Scott Begraft
Ex. V-P.—Bryan Neuman
SIC—3535; NAICS—333922; *Pneumatic tube conveyor systems; Brand name—Eagle Pneumatic; Lamson; Airtubes*
Employs—10; Estab.—1898
Distrib.—Intl.
Limited Liability Company

**NEW JERSEY MACHINE & TOOL CO.**
257 Houses Corner Rd. (07848)
**Phone—(973) 383-6102**
Email—njmtool@ptd.net
Pres.—Tom Hegyi
SIC—3599; *General machining job shop*
Employs—1; Estab.—1980
Sales—under $500,000
Distrib.—Intl.
Sole ownership

**TEESING USA, LLC**
10 Millpond Dr., Unit 7 (07848)
**Phone—(973) 383-0691**
Fax—(973) 383-4672
www.teesingusa.com
Email—teesingusa@teesing.com
Sales Acct. & Sales Mgr.—John Sparnon
Acct. Admn.—Faith Healy
SIC—3492; 3674; NAICS—332912; *Quick-connect hydraulic & pneumatic compressed natural gas hoses & accessories, including ultra high-purity semiconductor components; Brand name—Rectus; TEMA; Nycoil; Serto; C-Matic; Rotarex; Parflex*
Employs—3; Estab.—1952
Sales—$4Mil
10,000 sq ft site, Distrib.—Intl.
Limited Liability Company
ISO rating—9001:2000

## Lake Como
### (Monmouth—N.E.)

**PHOTO ART STENCIL & SIGN CORP.**
701 17th Ave., P.O. Box 127 (07719)
**Phone—(732) 681-7300**
Email—fjtanis@aol.com
Pres.—Frederick J. Tanis
SIC—2396; 2759; 3993; NAICS—323100; *Industrial & yard signs & screen printing of decals, posters & special shapes*
Employs—2; Estab.—1949
Sales—$150,000
7,000 sq ft site, Distrib.—Local
Privately owned corporation

## Lake Hiawatha
### (Morris—N.W.)

**BOZZONE CUSTOM WOODWORK, INC.**
77 N. Beverwyck Rd. (07034)
**Phone—(973) 334-5598**
Fax—(973) 402-8738
Pres.—Lou Bozzone
SIC—2434; 2542; 3083; NAICS—337110; *Wooden & laminate cabinets*
Employs—4; Estab.—1977
Sales—under $500,000
3,000 sq ft site, Distrib.—Local
Privately owned corporation

**CLASS ACT EMBROIDERY**
86 N. Beverwyck Rd., Ste. A (07034)
**Phone—(973) 394-0045**
Fax—(973) 394-0090
www.classactembroidery.com
Email—clasact123@aol.com
Owner—Kathy Breslow
SIC—2396; 2395; *Textile screen printing & embroidery, including sweats, hats, sweaters, t-shirts, gym bags, team uniforms & jackets*
Employs—5; Estab.—1993
Sales—$1Mil-$2.5Mil
Distrib.—Local
Privately owned partnership

GEOGRAPHICAL

## Lake Hiawatha—(cont.)

**EMPIRICAL LABS, INC.**
41 N. Beverwyck Rd. (07034)
**Phone—(973) 541-9446**
Fax—(973) 541-9448
www.empiricallabs.com
Email—empiricallabs@gmail.com
Pres.—David Derr
V-P., Opers.—Judith Derr
SIC—3651; 7372; NAICS—
334310; *Professional audio
processing equipment & digital
audio software development,
including audio compressors &
frequency filtering devices*
Employs—7; Estab.—2001
Sales—$1Mil-$2.5Mil
5,000 sq ft site, Distrib.—Intl.
Privately owned corporation

## Lake Hopatcong
### (Morris—N.W.)

**BATTEN THE HATCHES**
70 State Route 181 (07849)
**Phone—(973) 663-1910**
Email—battenhatches@yahoo.com
Owner—Maria Pappas
SIC—2394; NAICS—314912;
*Canvas boat covers*
Employs—2; Estab.—1990
Sales—under $500,000
Distrib.—Local
Sole ownership

**DIGITIZE, INC.**
158 Edison Rd. (07849)
**Phone—(973) 663-1011**
National—(800) 523-7232
Fax—(973) 663-4333
www.digitize-inc.com
Email—info@digitize-inc.com
Pres.—Abraham Brecher
V-P., Sales—Arnon Amir
V-P.—Linda Brecher
SIC—3663; 3669; 3651;
*Proprietary, ETL listed, FM
approved fire/security alarm
monitoring systems for large
campus applications, including
interfaces with most FACPs &
communicates via wire, fiber,
Ethernet & RF; Brand name—
Digitize SYSTEM 3505; Remote
Annunciator; Text-2-Cell; DGM-8/
16LS; DGM-32/64; MUXPAD II;
CAPS II; CGRMS; iLNX;
VersAlarm; MeshSetnry; D-LAN;
AlarmLAN*
Employs—18; Estab.—1977
Sales—$1Mil-$5Mil
7,200 sq ft site, Distrib.—Intl.
Privately owned corporation
ISO rating—9001:2008
AKA: Digitize International

**JEFFERSON LUMBER & MILLWORK CORP.**
298 Espanong Rd. (07849)
**Phone—(973) 663-3100**
Fax—(973) 663-1499
www.jeffersonlumberandmillwork.com
Email—lrlumber@verizon.net
Pres.—Mary Lytle
V-P.—Marie Quaranta
GM—Anthony Lytle
GM—Ralph Quaranta
Off. Mgr.—Lisa Lytle Ranft
Off. Mgr.—Sandra Quarabta Guido
Buyer—Vincent Quaranta
SIC—2421; 2431; NAICS—
321900; *Lumber processing &
millwork; Brand name—
Timbertech; Trex; Jeld-Wen;
Marvin; L. J. Smith; Garden State
Lumber; Boise Cascade*
Employs—15; Estab.—1947
Sales—$1Mil-$5Mil
7,500 sq ft site, Distrib.—Local
Privately owned corporation

**NEW ENTRY**
**LAKE HOPATCONG NEWS**
37 Nolans Point Park Rd. (07849)
**Phone—(973) 663-2800**
www.lakehopatcongnews.com
Email—editor@
lakehopatcongnews.com
Publisher & Editor-in-Chief—Karen
Fucito
SIC—2711; *Newspaper
publishing*
Employs—1; Estab.—2012
Sales—under $500,000
Distrib.—National
Privately owned corporation

**NEW ENTRY**
**WATER MARK TECHNOLOGIES, INC.**
762 State Route 15 S., Ste. 2-B
(07849)
**Phone—(973) 663-3438**
www.watermark-tech.com
Email—info@watermark-tech.com
Pres.—Phil Reilly
SIC—2869; 2819; NAICS—
325199; *Organic & inorganic
chemicals for the oil & gas &
construction industries*
Employs—8
Sales—$2.5Mil-$5Mil (est)

**WELDON MATERIALS, INC.**
181 Route 181 (07849)
Mail addr: 141 Central Ave.,
Westfield (07090)
**Phone—(973) 663-1800**
Fax—(973) 663-0909
www.weldonmat.com
Email—sales@weldonmat.com
V-P.—Bill Weldon
Acct. Mgr.—Beth Rotella
Plt. Mgr.—Steve Champion
Recpt. Admn.—Debbie Lear
SIC—2951; 3281; NAICS—
324121; *Asphalt paving
compounds & crushed stone*
Employs—40; Estab.—1900
Distrib.—Local
Privately owned corporation
Parent co.—Weldon Materials,
Inc., Westfield, NJ
Phone—(908) 233-4444
See Parent Co. Section for full profile.

## Lakehurst
### (Ocean—S.E.)

**MICROMEDIA PUBLICATIONS, INC.**
15 Union Ave., P.O. Box 521
(08733)
**Phone—(732) 657-7344**
Fax—(732) 657-7388
www.micromediapubs.com
Email—bricktimes@comcast.net
Publisher—Stewart Swann
Mng. Editor—Robyn Weber
Treas.—Alice Swann
GM—Linda Siemon
SIC—2711; *Newspaper
publishing*
Employs—12; Estab.—1992
Sales—under $500,000
Distrib.—Local
Privately owned corporation

## Lakewood
### (Ocean—S.E.)

**1 STOP WRAPS, LLC**
1525 Prospect St., Ste. 602
(08701)
**Phone—(732) 363-7800**
Fax—(732) 363-7500
www.1stopwraps.com
Email—sales@1stopwraps.com
Owner & Pres.—Frank Mele

SIC—3993; 2759; NAICS—
323100; *Signs & large-format
digital printing, including vinyl
banners & vehicle wraps*
Employs—4; Estab.—2005
Sales—under $500,000
2,500 sq ft site, Distrib.—National
Limited Liability Company

**†ABC SUPPLY CO., INC., BRADCO DIV.**
Div. of ABC Supply Co., Inc.
691 New Hampshire Ave. (08701)
**Phone—(732) 905-9355**
Fax—(732) 505-1841
www.bradcosupply.com
Email—info@bradcosupply.com
Dir., Sales—Larry Gelber
Br. Mgr.—Jill Criage
SIC—5033; 5072; *Distributor of
roofing materials, including
shingles, felt, waterproofing &
hardware*
Employs—50; Estab.—2001
Distrib.—Local
Privately owned corporation
Parent co.—ABC Supply Co., Inc.,
Beloit, WI
Phone—(608) 362-7777
See Parent Co. Section for full profile.

**ACKERSON DRAPERY & DECORATING SERVICES, INC.**
500 James St., Ste. 14 (08701)
**Phone—(732) 905-4433**
National—(800) 282-4433
Fax—(732) 905-9606
www.ackersondrapery.com
Email—ackersondrapery@aol.com
Pres., CFO—Ronni Leddy
V-P., Secy. & Plt. Mgr.—Michael K.
Leddy
Off. & Traf. Mgr.—June E. Overbey
Qual. Control Mgr.—Sharon
Basket
SIC—2391; 2591; NAICS—
314121; *Theatrical stage curtains
& window treatments; Brand
name—Graber; Hunter Douglas;
Draper; Levolor*
Employs—8; Estab.—1962
Sales—$600,000
2,500 sq ft site, Distrib.—Local
Privately owned sub-S corp.

**ACTION OFFICE SUPPLIES, INC.**
687 Prospect St., Ste. 480 (08701)
Mail addr: P.O. Box 277, Adelphia
(07710)
**Phone—(732) 534-3000**
National—(800) 298-1000
Fax—(732) 534-3016
www.actoff.com
Email—sonny@actoff.com
Pres.—Sonny Arora
CFO—Helen Menyhart
CTO & MIS Mgr.—Vincent
Robinson
SIC—2759; 5112; NAICS—
323119; *Commercial printing &
distributor of office supplies &
furniture*
Employs—21; Estab.—1994
Sales—under $5Mil
17,000 sq ft site, Distrib.—National
Privately owned sub-S corp.

**AGF BURNER, INC.**
1955 Swarthmore Ave., Unit 2
(08701-4557)
**Phone—(732) 730-8090**
Fax—(732) 730-8060
www.agfburner.com
Email—sales@agfburner.com
Pres.—Christopher T. Keogh
Off. Mgr.—Jacqueline Gromosaik

SIC—3433; NAICS—333414;
*Gas, industrial, furnace, fishtail,
ribbon & ring burners, venturi
(tube) mixers, torches & blast
tips for glass working, flame
treating plastics & metal heating
applications & the coffee
roasting, baking & special
effects industries; Brand name—
AGF Burner; AGF*
Employs—10; Estab.—1878
Distrib.—Intl.

**NEW ENTRY**
**ALEX REAL, LLC**
501 Prospect St., Ste. 107 (08701)
**Phone—(732) 730-8770**
www.superbagline.com
Email—superbag@
superbagline.com
Pres.—Alexander Vorhand
SIC—2759; *Promotional printing,
including towels, blankets &
bags*
Employs—11
Sales—$1Mil-$2.5Mil (est)
Limited Liability Company
AKA: Super Bags

**ALPHA ASSOCS., INC.**
145 Lehigh Ave. (08701)
**Phone—(732) 730-1800**
National—(800) 631-5399
Fax—(732) 634-1430
www.alphainc.com
Email—doug@alphainc.com
Chrm., CEO—A. Louis Avallone
Pres., COO—Christopher Avallone
Ex. V-P.—John Baxter
V-P., Mfg.—Kevin Burton
V-P., Pur.—Bob Orecchio
Hum. Res. Mgr.—Joyce Rzepka
Prodn. Planner—Fran Copeland
SIC—2295; 3299; 3069; *Coated &
impregnated high-temperature
fabrics, engineered composite
insulation facings & rubber
composite elastomers for
aerospace, military, construction
& industrial applications,
including silicone,
fluoroelastomer, neoprene &
EPDM*
Employs—100; Estab.—1968
Distrib.—National
Privately owned corporation

**AMERICAN STAIR & RAIL ARTISANS, LLC**
687 Prospect St., Ste. 420 (08701)
**Phone—(732) 363-3734**
National—(800) 782-4770
Fax—(732) 363-1120
www.stairsnj.com
Email—sales@stairsnj.com
Owner—Renee Brown
SIC—2431; NAICS—321900;
*Interior stairs, rails &
replacement millwork*
Employs—15; Estab.—1979
Sales—$1Mil-$2.5Mil
Distrib.—Local
Limited Liability Company

**AMERICAN VAN EQUIPMENT, INC.**
149 Lehigh Ave. (08701)
**Phone—(800) 526-4743**
Fax—(732) 905-2749
www.americanvan.com
Email—salesservice@
amvanequip.com
Pres.—Charles Richter
Ex. V-P.—Richard Gebbia
V-P., Sales—Joseph Fallon
V-P., Fin.—Marc C. Richter
Cont.—Robert Caswell

© Copyright 2015 Manufacturers' News, Inc. D215

## Lakewood—(cont.)

SIC—3444; 3499; 2542; 3496; *Aluminum, steel & hot dipped galvanized form & book, job specific & ladder racks, cargo carriers, shelf & bin systems, bulkhead partitions & small part & floor storage systems & drawer units for commercial vans & trucks*
Employs—95; Estab.—1978
130,000 sq ft site, Distrib.—National
Privately owned sub-S corp.

### AMETEK GLASSEAL, INC.
Div. of AMETEK, Inc.
485 Oberlin Ave. S. (08701)
**Phone—(732) 370-9100**
Fax—(732) 370-7107
www.glasseal.com
Email—bill.hubbard@ametek.com
Hum. Res. Mgr.—Emma Tardiff
Cust. Serv. Rep.—Janet Bass
SIC—3679; *Hermetic seals*
Employs—160; Estab.—1946
Sales—$1Mil-$2.5Mil
Distrib.—Intl.
Publicly owned corporation
Parent co.—AMETEK, Inc., Berwyn, PA
Phone—(610) 647-2121
See Parent Co. Section for full profile.

### AQUATHERM INDUSTRIES, INC.
1940 Rutgers University Blvd. (08701)
**Phone—(732) 905-9002**
National—(800) 535-6307
Fax—(732) 905-9899
www.aquathermindustries.com
Email—info@ aquathermindustries.com
Pres., CEO—Dave Sizelove
SIC—3433; NAICS—333414; *Unglazed poylmer solar thermal collectors, system components & solar pool heaters for residential & commercial swimming pools & spas; Brand name—Solar Industries; Ecosun; Ultrasun; Ultra-Swim; Sun-Swim; Sun-Swim Plus; Ecolite; Sunlite*
Employs—25; Estab.—1989
50,000 sq ft site, Distrib.—Intl.
Privately owned corporation
ISO rating—9001:2008

### †ARDEN SALES
128 14th St. (08701)
**Phone—(732) 730-1418**
Fax—(732) 367-0253
Email—ysaltz8@gmail.com
Owner—Charles Saltz
SIC—5169; *Distributor of cleaning supplies*
Employs—1; Estab.—1958
Sales—under $500,000
Distrib.—Regional
Privately owned corporation

### †ARDOM BEARING GROUP
1000 Bennett Blvd., Ste. 7 (08701)
**Phone—(732) 370-2310**
Fax—(732) 364-5013
www.ardombearing.webs.com
Email—ardombearing@hotmail.com
Owner & Pres.—Dominick Commesso
SIC—5084; 5063; *Company headquarters & wholesaler of bearings & power transmission equipment; Brand name— Baldor; Boston; Leason; GE; Marithon; Motors martin Gear Hub City; Goodyear; Rexnord; FAG; SKF; Timken; Consolidated; Royersford; Smith; Styer; Sealmaster; Torrington*
Employs—5; Estab.—1976
Sales—under $500,000
Distrib.—National
Privately owned corporation

### ART'S WINDOWS, INC.
199 Ocean Ave. (08701)
**Phone—(732) 367-1770**
National—(800) 822-8920
Fax—(732) 367-5177
www.artswindows.com
Email—sales@ artswindows.com
Pres.—Art Engel
V-P.—Michael Engel
SIC—2591; NAICS—337920; *Window treatments*
Employs—9; Estab.—1985
3,700 sq ft site, Distrib.—Regional
Privately owned corporation

### †ARZEE SUPPLY
Div. of Allied Building Products Corp.
1905 Swarthmore Ave. (08701)
**Phone—(201) 935-0800**
Fax—(732) 370-3838
www.arzee.com
Email—paul.maslanek@arzee.com
Br. Mgr.—Paul Maslanek
Br. Admn.—Mary Burns
SIC—5033; 5031; *Distributor of building materials & supplies, including roofing, siding, windows & doors*
Employs—20
Publicly owned corporation
Parent co.—Allied Building Products Corp., East Rutherford, NJ
Phone—(201) 507-8400
See Parent Co. Section for full profile.

### ASTOR CHOCOLATE CORP.
651 New Hampshire Ave. (08701)
**Phone—(732) 901-1001**
Fax—(732) 901-1003
www.astorchocolate.com
Email—info@astorchocolate.com
Chrm.—David Grunhut
SIC—2064; 2066; NAICS— 311300; *Gourmet Belgian chocolates & specialty, novelty, seasonal & themed confectionary products for the foodservice, catering & gourmet retail markets & souvenir gift shops, including truffles, liquor cups, dessert shells & wedding & party favors; Brand name— Astor Chocolates; Lebelge Chocolatier; Paramount Chocolate*
Employs—150; Estab.—1950
Distrib.—National
Privately owned sub-S corp.

### †ATLAS WELDING SUPPLY CO., INC.
808 Brook Rd. (08701)
**Phone—(732) 363-1148**
Fax—(732) 364-1298
www.atlasweldingsupplyinc.com
Email—atlweb@aol.com
Corp. Secy.—Dina Pincus
GM—Harry Berlin
Off. Mgr.—Daniel Altstadter
SIC—5084; 5085; 5169; *Distributor of welding equipment & supplies, including gases*
Employs—7; Estab.—1956
Sales—$1Mil-$5Mil
2,000 sq ft site, Distrib.—Regional
Privately owned corporation

### AVCON
1915 Swarthmore Ave., Ste. 3 (08701-4567)
**Phone—(732) 286-9496**
National—(800) 242-8266
Fax—(732) 286-0526
www.avcon.com
Email—info@avcon.com
CEO—Larry Stanley
Pres.—Klint Stanley
V-P.—Andrew Davidson

SIC—3089; 3444; *Structural maintenance-free thermoplastic architectural aluminum railings & systems; Brand name—AVCON; Majestic Series Aluminum*
Employs—35; Estab.—1991
35,000 sq ft site, Distrib.—Intl.
Privately owned corporation

### AVIV BIOMEDICAL, INC.
750 Vassar Ave. (08701)
**Phone—(732) 370-1300**
Fax—(732) 370-1303
www.avivbiomedical.com
Email—info@avivbiomedical.com
Pres.—Jack Aviv
Ex. Admn.—Rosemarie Arch
Administrator—Flo Aviv
SIC—3841; 3826; NAICS— 334516; *Scientific & clinical instruments; Brand name—AVIV*
Employs—14; Estab.—1974
Distrib.—Intl.
Privately owned corporation

**NEW ENTRY**
### BGS, INC.
910 E. County Line Rd., Ste. 101 (08701)
**Phone—(732) 442-5000**
CEO—Elkana Tombak
SIC—3823; *Boiler controls*
Employs—15
Sales—$1Mil-$2.5Mil (est)
Distrib.—Local
Privately owned corporation

### BLINDS TO GO, INC.
1800 Cedar Bridge Ave. (08701)
**Phone—(732) 901-2001**
Fax—(732) 901-1453
www.blindstogo.com
Email—sales@blindstogo.com
Plt. Mgr.—Alfredo Fuentes
Hum. Res. Mgr.—Glenroy Burke
SIC—2591; NAICS—337920; *Vertical & venetian window blinds & pleated shades*
Employs—150; Estab.—1954
Distrib.—National
Privately owned corporation
Parent co.—Blinds To Go, Inc., Paramus, NJ
Phone—(732) 321-5000
See Parent Co. Section for full profile.

### BONLAND INDUSTRIES, INC.
890 Towbin Ave. (08701)
**Phone—(732) 886-7127**
Fax—(732) 858-8683
www.bonlandhvac.com
Email—dparent@bonlandhvac.com
Br. Mgr.—Dan Parent
Prodn. Mgr.—Chuck Diou
Br. Admn.—Sue Strauss
SIC—3444; *Sheet metal fabrication*
Employs—75; Estab.—1997
12,000 sq ft site, Distrib.— Regional
Privately owned corporation
Parent co.—Bonland Industries, Inc., Wayne, NJ
Phone—(973) 694-3211
See Parent Co. Section for full profile.

**NEW ENTRY**
### BOUND TO LAST
144 E. 9th St. (08701)
**Phone—(732) 942-0423**
Owner—Joseph Apfel
SIC—2789; *Bookbinding*
Employs—1; Estab.—2001
Sales—$60,000
200 sq ft site, Distrib.—Local
Privately owned corporation

### BP GRAPHICS & PRINTING
315 4th St. (08701-3231)
**Phone—(732) 905-9830**
Fax—(732) 905-1320
www.bpgraphics.biz
Email—info@bpgraphics.biz

Pres.—Ben Heineman
SIC—2752; 2791; 2796; NAICS— 323122; *Instant printing & typesetting*
Employs—15; Estab.—1991
5,000 sq ft site, Distrib.—Local
Sole ownership

### BRAND AROMATICS, INC.
1600 Oak St., P.O. Box 3033 (08701)
**Phone—(732) 363-8080**
National—(800) 363-2080
Fax—(732) 363-8041
www.brandaromatics.com
Email—flavors@ brandaromatics.com
Pres.—Karl E. Brand
V-P.—Dennis Shea, Jr.
SIC—2099; *Concentrated savory flavoring ingredients*
Employs—40; Estab.—1998
Sales—$5Mil-$10Mil (est)
Distrib.—Intl.
Privately owned sub-S corp.

### BRIGHT IDEAS USA, LLC
890 Morris Ave. (08701)
**Phone—(732) 886-8865**
National—(877) 232-5100
Fax—(866) 370-1367
www.dontgethit.com
Email—info@dontgethit.com
Mng. Member & GM—Deena Leiman
Pur. Mgr.—Eli Leiman
SIC—3842; 2329; 2339; 3648; *Company headquarters & safety & nighttime visibility items, including reflective wear & bicycle lights for pedestrians, cyclists, first responders, construction workers & school children (mfg. subcontracted); Brand name—Bright ideas; Xsight*
Employs—4; Estab.—2004
Sales—$500,000-$1Mil
Distrib.—Intl.
Limited Liability Company
AKA: DontGetHit.com

### CBS OUTDOOR
Div. of CBS Outdoor Americas, Inc.
1245 Towbin Ave. (08701)
**Phone—(732) 901-1100**
Fax—(732) 901-1104
www.cbsoutdoor.com
Email—info@cbsoutdoor.com
Opers. Supv.—Bill Fredricks
SIC—3993; *Advertising billboards*
Employs—25; Estab.—1997
Sales—$1Mil-$2.5Mil (est)
Distrib.—National
Publicly owned corporation
Parent co.—CBS Outdoor Americas, Inc., New York, NY
Phone—(212) 297-6400
See Parent Co. Section for full profile.

### CENTURY SPORTS
1715 Oak St., Ste. 1 (08701-6105)
**Phone—(732) 905-4422**
(800) 526-7548
Fax—(732) 901-7766
www.centurysportsinc.com
Email—centurysportsinc@cs.com
Opers. Mgr.—Sandy Hunt
SIC—3949; NAICS—339920; *Tennis court equipment, gymnasium padding, baseball field padding, fencing, ball machines & court accessories; Brand name—Wilson; Royale; Regency; Revolution; Har-Tru*
Employs—20; Estab.—1972
22,000 sq ft site, Distrib.—Intl.
Privately owned sub-S corp.

GEOGRAPHICAL

# Lakewood—(cont.)

## CET FILMS, INC.
Div. of R Tape Corporation
1650 Corporate Rd. W. (08701)
**Phone—(732) 367-5511**
National—(877) 926-2876
Fax—(732) 367-2908
www.cetfilms.com
Email—szagami@cetfilms.com
Sales Mgr.—Guy Leigh
Acct. Mgr.—Julie Villa
Opers. Mgr.—Ken Graver
Tech. Mgr.—George Masi
Supply Chain Mgr.—Jim Prem
SIC—3081; 3083; NAICS—
326113; *Metallized, acrylic &
polycarbonate laser engravable
security, protective overlaminate,
supported & unsupported films
for the financial & smart card
industries, POP displays,
packaging, signage, theatrical
lighting gels & graphic overlays*
Employs—14; Estab.—1973
42,000 sq ft site, Distrib.—Intl.
Privately owned corporation
AKA: Custom Extrusion
Technologies
Parent co.—R Tape Corporation,
South Plainfield, NJ
Phone—(908) 753-5570
See Parent Co. Section for full profile.

## CHURCH & DWIGHT CO., INC.
800 Airport Rd. (08701)
**Phone—(732) 730-3100**
Fax—(732) 730-3191
www.churchdwight.com
Email—investorrelations@
churchdwight.com
Plt. Mgr.—Timothy O'Farrell
Hum. Res. Mgr.—Joann
Louizides-Spates
SIC—2812; *Sodium bicarbonate;
Brand name—Arm & Hammer*
Employs—200
Distrib.—Intl.
Publicly owned corporation
Parent co.—Church & Dwight Co.,
Inc., Ewing, NJ
Phone—(609) 683-5900
See Parent Co. Section for full profile.

## CLAYTON ASSOCS., INC.
1650 Oak St. (08701)
**Phone—(732) 363-2100**
National—(800) 248-8650
Fax—(732) 364-6084
www.jclayton.com
Email—sales@jclayton.com
Pres., MIS Mgr.—James Clayton
V-P., GM—Brad Clayton
V-P., Fin.—Jan Clayton
Accountant—Vita Gasile
SIC—3714; 3589; NAICS—
333319; *Automotive & industrial
brake washing equipment &
dustless vacuum sanding system*
Employs—20; Estab.—1985
Sales—$2.6Mil-$5Mil
18,500 sq ft site, Distrib.—Intl.
Privately owned sub-S corp.

## COASTAL AMUSEMENTS, INC.
1950 Swarthmore Ave. (08701)
**Phone—(732) 905-6662**
Fax—(732) 905-6815
www.coastalamusements.com
Email—sales@
coastalamusements.com
Pres.—Lenny Dean
Ex. V-P.—Sal Mirando
SIC—3999; *Corporate
headquarters & coin operated
arcade & redemption video
games; Brand name—Micro GT*
Employs—35; Estab.—1988
Distrib.—Intl.
Privately owned corporation

## COMPONENT HARDWARE GROUP, INC.
1890 Swarthmore Ave., P.O. Box
2020 (08701)
**Phone—(732) 363-4700**
National—(800) 526-3694
Fax—(732) 364-8110
www.componenthardware.com
Email—sales@
componenthardware.com
Pres., CEO—Harry Franze
CFO—Frank Probst
Ex. V-P., Sales & Mktg.—Ed
Whartnaby
V-P., Opers.—Marty Burns
V-P., Engrg.—Brion Gompper
Dir., Mktg.—Lois Schneck
Dir., Matls. Mgmt.—Allan Smith
SIC—3429; 3432; NAICS—
332900; *Plumbing & specialty
hardware & components,
including die casting, investment
casting, forging, stamping,
machining & injection molding
for the foodservice, commercial
& institutional industries; Brand
name—Encore plumbing; Flame
Gard; TOP-LINE plumbing; Keil
Refrigeration; SANIGUARD;
Quick-Tite; Brite Gard;
Drainmaster; Quik-Wash;
SaniShower; Regal Ride casters*
Employs—85; Estab.—1981
Sales—$70Mil-$80Mil
80,000 sq ft site, Distrib.—Intl.
Privately owned corporation

## COTTRELL GRAPHICS, LLC
1525 Prospect St., Unit 314
(08701)
**Phone—(732) 349-7430**
Fax—(732) 349-2920
Pres.—David F. Cottrell
Cont. & Off. Mgr.—Janet Heller
SIC—2752; NAICS—323100;
*Instant printing*
Employs—4; Estab.—2001
Distrib.—Local
Privately owned corporation

## CREOH U. S. A.
910 E. County Line Rd., Ste. 202-
A (08701)
**Phone—(718) 821-0570**
Fax—(718) 821-0571
www.creoh.com
Email—info@creoh.com
Pres., CEO—Joe Zicherman
COO—Mo Rothstein
SIC—2653; NAICS—322211;
*Corrugated boxes*
Employs—5; Estab.—2004
Sales—$1Mil-$2.5Mil
Distrib.—Intl.
Privately owned corporation

NEW ENTRY
## †CRYSTALWARE
601 Prospect St. (08701-9997)
**Phone—(732) 367-4444**
Fax—(718) 301-9779
www.ligimports.com
Email—sales@ligimports.com
Ptnr.—Nisson Kugler
Ptnr.—Joshua Lipschutz
Ptnr.—Tzali Gombo
SIC—5113; *Distributor of
disposable plastic cutlery for the
foodservice industry, including
spoons, knives & forks; Brand
name—CrystalWare; Sterex;
SafeGuard; Sip N Joy; Green
Soft; Softowel; Silky Soft; Sani-
Swipes*
Employs—50; Estab.—2004
Distrib.—National
Limited Liability Company

## CUISINE INNOVATIONS, LLC
1920 Swarthmore Ave., Ste. 1
(08701)
**Phone—(732) 730-9310**
National—(800) 248-3399

Fax—(732) 730-9913
www.cuisineinnovations.com
Email—info@
cuisineinnovations.com
Ptnr.—Paul Bensabat
Ptnr.—Alain Bankier
Sr. V-P., Sales—Richard Kahn
Dir., Mktg.—Michele Adams
GM—Philip Decker
Sales Mgr., Reg.—Ken Peterson
Opers. Mgr.—Bill Byrne
IT Mgr.—Jarppi Piroj
Hum. Res. Mgr.—Maria Colon
Asst. Qual. Control Mgr.—Kim
Fazekas
SIC—2092; NAICS—311712;
*Seafood processing*
Employs—75; Estab.—1998
Varies: 75-150
16,000 sq ft site, Distrib.—National
Privately owned corporation

## D.E.B. MFG., INC.
850 Towbin Ave. (08701)
**Phone—(732) 364-7007**
National—(800) 334-2027
Fax—(732) 364-7299
www.debmfg.com
Email—info@debmfg.com
Pres.—Hollis T. Mueller
V-P.—David Armstrong
Secy-Treas., Fin. & MIS Mgr.—Ron
Lyons
Hum. Res. & Off. Mgr.—Kim Citron
SIC—3444; *Rotary viscous
dampers; Brand name—D.E.B.
Manufacturing Rotary Viscous
Dampers*
Employs—12; Estab.—1989
Sales—$1.6Mil-$1.8Mil
8,500 sq ft site, Distrib.—Regional
Privately owned corporation
ISO rating—AS9100C

## DALEMARK INDUSTRIES, INC.
575 Prospect St., Ste. 211 (08701-
5040)
**Phone—(732) 367-3100**
Fax—(732) 367-7031
www.dalemark.com
Email—sales@dalemark.com
GM—Michael DelliGatti
Sales & Mktg. Mgr.—Maria Rau
Acct. Mgr.—Kathy Scalzo
Proj. Mgr.—Thurman Becker
SIC—3559; 3565; NAICS—
333993; *Industrial coding,
labeling & imprinting systems &
accessories for the packaging
industry; Brand name—DOT-
MARK; CODAIRE; INCA-ROL;
NUMER-CODE; HDT; SPARKS;
FLASH; HANDI-CODA; POP;
OP; CP; CPT; TA; 975;
CONVEYOR PRINTER;
COMPACT; MINI; SRR; D; HD;
985; 950; CODITHERM;
XXTREME; TDI*
Employs—10; Estab.—1955
Sales—$1Mil-$5Mil
12,000 sq ft site, Distrib.—Intl.
Privately owned sub-S corp.
AKA: Algene Marking

## DASH INDUSTRIES, INC.
639 5th St. (08701)
**Phone—(732) 364-5850**
Fax—(732) 364-8413
Owner—Alan Dirshawitz
SIC—3089; 2759; NAICS—
323100; *Disposable plastic bags
& tablecloths & screen printing*
Employs—2; Estab.—2003
Sales—under $500,000
Distrib.—Local
Privately owned corporation

## DINASO BUILDING SUPPLIES
Div. of DiNaso Staten Island, LLC
133 Ocean Ave. (08701)
**Phone—(732) 886-6666**
Fax—(732) 886-6660
www.dinasoandsons.com

Email—contact@
dinasoandsons.com
Br. Mgr.—Billy Epp
SIC—2431; NAICS—321900;
*Prime trim wooden doors &
windows*
Employs—50; Estab.—1995
Sales—$6Mil-$10Mil
Distrib.—Local
Limited Liability Company
Parent co.—DiNaso Staten Island,
LLC, Staten Island, NY
Phone—(718) 559-5855
See Parent Co. Section for full profile.

## DISPERSION TECHNOLOGY, INC.
1885 Swarthmore Ave. (08701)
**Phone—(732) 364-4488**
Fax—(732) 364-1018
Email—dtcolors@aol.com
Pres.—Yogesh Parikh
IT Mgr.—Melissa Cruse
Off. Mgr.—Kim Sertico
SIC—2816; 2865; NAICS—
325100; *Pigment dispersion of
silicones & silicone products*
Employs—10; Estab.—1992
12,000 sq ft site, Distrib.—Intl.
Privately owned corporation
AKA: DTI

## DIVERSIFIED FIXTURE, INC.
1930 Swarthmore Ave. (08701)
**Phone—(732) 886-0600**
National—(877) 348-3499
Fax—(732) 886-0911
www.diversifiedfixture.com
Email—jerry@diversifiedfixture.com
Pres., CEO—Jerry Vitillo
Dir., Automated Machining—Jerry
Castoral
SIC—2541; 2542; *Wood & plastic
store fixtures, medical casework
& wall cladding; Brand name—
DIVTEC*
Employs—10; Estab.—1985
Sales—$1Mil-$2.5Mil
22,000 sq ft site, Distrib.—National
Privately owned corporation

## DPT LAKEWOOD, LLC
Div. of DPT Laboratories Ltd.
1200 Paco Way, Bldg. 19 (08701)
**Phone—(732) 367-9000**
Fax—(732) 364-5266
www.dptlabs.com
Email—dptlabs.sales@dptlabs.com
Site Mgr.—Gene Ciolfi
SIC—2834; 3089; 2819; NAICS—
325412; *Pharmaceuticals, health
care & chemical products
blending & packaging*
Employs—700
Sales—$250Mil-$500Mil (est)
Distrib.—Intl.
Privately owned corporation
Parent co.—DPT Laboratories
Ltd., San Antonio, TX
Phone—(210) 476-8100
See Parent Co. Section for full profile.

## DUDLEY CHEMICAL CORP.
125 Kenyon Dr., Ste. 1 (08701)
**Phone—(732) 886-3100**
Fax—(732) 886-3688
www.dudley-chem.com
Owner—Art Foulsham
Cust. Serv. Mgr.—Doris Schneir
SIC—2865; *Biological stains &
dyes*
Employs—18; Estab.—1987
Sales—$10Mil-$25Mil (est)
Distrib.—National
Privately owned corporation

## EAST COAST COUNTER TOPS, INC.
166 Main St., P.O. Box 645 (08701)
**Phone—(732) 363-7734**
Fax—(732) 367-4060
Email—eastcoastcountertops@
hotmail.com
Pres.—Ofer Malhi
Bookkeeper—Patty Paxton

## Lakewood—(cont.)

SIC—2541; 2434; NAICS—
337110; *Wooden countertops &
cabinets*
Employs—10; Estab.—1997
Sales—under $500,000
Distrib.—Local
Privately owned corporation

**ELCO GLASS INDUSTRIES CO., INC.**
1855 Swarthmore Ave. (08701)
Mail addr: P.O. Box 425,
Perrineville (08535)
**Phone—(732) 363-6550**
Fax—(732) 905-2086
Pres.—E. Bavarsky
SIC—3211; NAICS—327211; *Flat
glass*
Employs—25; Estab.—1960
Sales—$5Mil-$10Mil (est)
Distrib.—National
Privately owned corporation

**†FERGUSON ENTERPRISES, INC.**
190 Oberlin Ave. N. (08701)
**Phone—(732) 905-1000**
Fax—(732) 905-9628
www.ferguson.com
Email—jim.golini@ferguson.com
GM—Jim Golini
Br. Mgr.—Joe Noone
SIC—5051; 5074; *Wholesaler of
industrial pipe & valves,
plumbing supplies, HVAC
equipment, pumps & well
supplies, including PVC & metal
pipe, valves, fittings & controls*
Employs—100
Distrib.—Intl.
Publicly owned corporation
Parent co.—Ferguson Enterprises,
Inc., Newport News, VA
Phone—(757) 874-7795
See Parent Co. Section for full profile.

**FINESSE & LUCAS**
40 Chestnut St., Ste. 14 (08701)
**Phone—(732) 367-0839**
          (732) 367-6822
Email—lucasfinesse@hotmail.com
Pres.—Luz A. Fredes
V-P.—Carlos Fredes
SIC—2395; 2396; *Embroidery &
screen printing*
Employs—2; Estab.—1978
Sales—under $500,000
Distrib.—National
Privately owned corporation
AKA: Finesse Custom Embroidery

**FLEXABAR CORP.**
1969 Rutgers Blvd. (08701)
**Phone—(732) 901-6500**
Fax—(732) 901-6504
www.flexabar.com
Email—andy@flexabar.com
CEO—Andrew Guglielmo
Pres.—Richard J. Guglielmo
V-P.—Danny Guglielmo
SIC—2851; NAICS—325510;
*Marine paints & coatings; Brand
name—Flexabar®*
Employs—21; Estab.—1942
Sales—$10Mil-$14Mil
40,000 sq ft site, Distrib.—Intl.
Privately owned corporation

**FLEXDEL CORP.**
1969 Rutgers University Blvd.
(08701)
**Phone—(732) 901-7771**
National—(888) 353-9335
Fax—(732) 901-6504
www.aquagardboatpaint.com
Email—flexabar@sprintmail.com
Pres.—Richard J. Guglielmo, Jr.
Hum. Res. & IT Mgr.—Andy
Guglielmo
Administrator—Stacey Tuvey

SIC—2851; NAICS—325510;
*Environmentally friendly water-
resistant, waterproof &
antifouling paints & coatings for
marine applications*
Employs—20; Estab.—1967
Sales—under $500,000
Distrib.—Intl.
Privately owned corporation

**FRANCIS METALS CO., INC.**
687 Prospect St., Ste. 430 (08701-
4648)
**Phone—(732) 761-0500**
Fax—(732) 761-0538
www.franciscablesystems.com
Email—info@
franciscablesystems.com
Pres.—Matt Deiner
GM—John McLaughlin
Off. Mgr.—Alice Dean
SIC—3357; 3679; *Armored
electronic cable & commercial
cable systems*
Employs—20; Estab.—1992
Sales—$1Mil-$2.5Mil
Distrib.—National
Privately owned corporation

**GAR PRODUCTS**
170 Lehigh Ave. (08701)
**Phone—(732) 364-2100**
National—(800) 424-2477
Fax—(732) 370-5021
www.garproducts.com
Email—service@garproducts.com
Owner—Jay Garfunkle
CEO—Ellen Garfunkle
Pres.—Sam Garfunkle
COO—Fred Durand
Dir., Pur.—Mark Hone
Fin. & Hum. Res. Mgr.—Karen
Schweining
SIC—2599; *Commercial,
hospitality, outdoor & health care
seating*
Employs—140; Estab.—1956
100,000 sq ft site, Distrib.—Intl.
Privately owned corporation

**GELBSTEIN BAKERY**
415 Clifton Ave. (08701)
**Phone—(732) 363-3636**
Fax—(732) 363-1124
Owner—Louie Friedman
GM—Bob Gruenebaum
SIC—2051; NAICS—311812;
*Bread*
Employs—20; Estab.—1993
Sales—$1Mil-$2.5Mil
Distrib.—Local
Sole ownership

**GIOIA SAILS INC.**
1951 Rutgers University Blvd.
(08701-4538)
**Phone—(732) 901-6770**
          (732) 901-0840
Fax—(732) 901-9987
www.gioiasails.com
Email—donnie@gioiasails.com
Owner & Sales Mgr.—Don Gioia
V-P., Sales—Dawn Gioia
Hum. Res. Mgr.—Janice Stewart
SIC—2394; NAICS—314912;
*Corporate headquarters &
canvas products for residential &
commercial applications,
including boat covers &
upholstery; Brand name—
ANINA*
Employs—30; Estab.—1966
Distrib.—National
Privately owned corporation

**GLOBAL PRINT MEDIA**
421 W. County Line Rd. (08701)
**Phone—(732) 886-0505**
www.globalprintmediausa.com
Email—info@
globalprintmediausa.com
Pres.—Jacob Stendig

SIC—2759; NAICS—323100;
*Commercial printing*
Employs—6; Estab.—1996
Sales—under $500,000
Distrib.—Local
Privately owned corporation

**GOLDEN FLUFF, INC.**
118 Monmouth Ave. (08701)
**Phone—(732) 367-5448**
Fax—(732) 367-1028
www.goldenfluff.com
Pres.—Ephraim Schwinder
GM—Sshlomo Schwinder
SIC—2096; NAICS—311919;
*Popcorn*
Employs—9; Estab.—1982
Sales—$500,000-$1Mil
Distrib.—National
Privately owned corporation

**†GOYEN VALVE CORP.**
Div. of Tyco
1195 Airport Rd. (08701)
**Phone—(732) 364-7800**
National—(800) 542-0110
Fax—(732) 364-1356
www.cleanairsystems.com
Email—lsheridan@goyen.com
Pres.—Steven O'Neill
SIC—5085; *Distributor of dust
collector pilot solenoid &
diaphragm valves & brass,
aluminum & plastic industrial
valves*
Employs—15; Estab.—1935
Distrib.—Intl.
Publicly owned corporation
Parent co.—Tyco, Princeton, NJ
Phone—(609) 720-4200
See Parent Co. Section for full profile.

**GRIFF DECORATIVE FILMS LTD.**
Div. of Griff Paper & Film
700 Vassar Ave. (08701)
**Phone—(732) 367-2166**
Fax—(732) 367-6203
www.tapeandlabel.com
Email—gene.silvestro@
tapeandlabel.com
GM—Gene Silvestro
SIC—3081; NAICS—326113;
*Decorative thin plastic film,
including holographic & self-
adhesive*
Employs—10; Estab.—2002
Sales—$1Mil-$2.5Mil
20,000 sq ft site, Distrib.—Intl.
Privately owned sub-S corp.
Parent co.—Griff Paper & Film,
Levittown, PA
Phone—(215) 428-1075
See Parent Co. Section for full profile.

**H & S STONE, INC.**
705 Cross St. (08701)
**Phone—(732) 364-2265**
Fax—(732) 364-5010
Email—hsstone1@msn.com
Pres.—Nicolas Hernandez
SIC—3281; NAICS—327991;
*Stone fabrication*
Employs—6; Estab.—2001
Distrib.—Local
Privately owned corporation

**HALO SHEET METAL, INC.**
140 Lehigh Ave. (08701)
**Phone—(732) 901-0080**
Fax—(732) 901-9571
Pres.—Patricia Pellegrino
V-P.—Robert Gumnick
Cont.—Paul Pellegrino
Estimator—Darren Hook
SIC—3444; *Sheet metal
fabrication & installation*
Employs—40; Estab.—1998
Distrib.—Local
Privately owned corporation

**HAR-TRU SPORTS**
Div. of Har-Tru Sports Corp.
1715 Oak St., Ste. 1 (08701)
**Phone—(800) 526-7548**
          (434) 295-6167
National—(877) 442-7878
www.hartru.com
Email—info@hartru.com
Dir., Sales—Tracy Lynch
Opers. Mgr.—Sandy Hunt
SIC—3949; 2211; NAICS—
339920; *Netting products &
knitted industrial fabrics,
including tennis nets, posts, line
tape & windscreen & indoor
divider curtains; Brand name—
Courtmaster; Tenex; Royale;
Regency; Mastershade; Quik
Fence; Har-Tru*
Employs—30; Estab.—1967
Distrib.—Intl.
Privately owned sub-S corp.
Parent co.—Har-Tru Sports Corp.,
Charlottesville, VA
Phone—(434) 295-6167
See Parent Co. Section for full profile.

**HENRICH, INC., HAROLD R.**
300 Syracuse Ct. (08701)
**Phone—(732) 370-4455**
Fax—(732) 370-5566
www.haroldhenrich.com
Email—sales@haroldhenrich.com
Pres.—Tom Henrich
SIC—3499; *Metal fabrication*
Employs—48; Estab.—1927
40,000 sq ft site, Distrib.—Local
Privately owned corporation

**HOMIEK SHEET METAL
FABRICATION & HVAC SUPPLIES,
INC.**
1352 Route 9 (08701)
**Phone—(732) 364-7644**
National—(800) 343-9975
Fax—(732) 364-5806
www.ephomiek.com
Pres.—Edward P. Homiek
Cont. & Bookkeeper—Beth
Homiek
SIC—3444; *HVAC ducts*
Employs—20; Estab.—1989
Distrib.—Local
Privately owned corporation

**HOUSE OF GRANITE & MARBLE,
INC.**
1920 Swarthmore Ave., Ste. 4
(08701)
**Phone—(732) 367-7211**
Fax—(732) 987-4044
www.houseofgranite.biz
Email—gitty@houseofgranite.biz
Pres.—Joel Reisman
SIC—3281; *Custom fabrication of
natural stone, including marble &
granite*
Employs—10; Estab.—2009
Sales—$500,000-$1Mil (est)
5,000 sq ft site, Distrib.—Regional
Privately owned corporation

**ID-TECH SOLUTIONS, INC.**
505 E. County Line Rd. *(08701)*
**Phone—(718) 408-9199**
Fax—(718) 504-4042
www.idtechsolutions.com
Email—sales@idtechsolutions.com
Pres.—Isaac Deutsch
COO—Abe Tobal
Cont.—Abe Seidenfeld
SIC—7373; *Computer network
system integration, including
LANs & WANs*
Employs—25; Estab.—2001
Sales—$1Mil-$5Mil
3,000 sq ft site, Distrib.—Regional
Privately owned corporation

**†INDUSTRIAL WELDING SUPPLY, INC.**
999 Airport Rd., Ste. 1 *(08701)*
**Phone—(732) 367-7100**
Fax—(732) 367-6953

GEOGRAPHICAL

## Lakewood—(cont.)

www.weldingsupplynj.com
Email—indweldsup@aol.com
Pres.—Jim Cusick
V-P.—Scot Cusick
Secy-Treas.—Linda Cusick
SIC—5084; *Distributor of welding equipment & supplies, including welders, tanks & gases*
Employs—4; Estab.—1976
Distrib.—Local
Privately owned corporation
Parent co.—Industrial Welding Supply, Inc., Sayreville, NJ
Phone—(732) 721-1150
See Parent Co. Section for full profile.

### INKIT DESIGN N' PRINT LLC

644 Cross St., Unit 2 (08701)
**Phone—(732) 363-8098**
Fax—(732) 363-7098
www.inkitdesign.com
Email—sales@inkitdesign.com
Pres.—Aaron Dembinsky
V-P.—Liav Barshishat
SIC—3993; *Interior & exterior signs & banners, vehicle lettering & full color printing; Brand name—Avery; 3M; LG*
Employs—6; Estab.—2007
15,000 sq ft site, Distrib.—National
Limited Liability Company

### †INNOVATIVE GLASS & MIRROR, INC.

15 Chambersbridge Rd. (08701)
**Phone—(732) 961-2267**
Fax—(732) 961-2236
www.igmnj.com
Email—igmnj@yahoo.com
Pres.—Dave Panebianco
SIC—5039; *Distributor of architectural glass & mirrors, custom shower & tub enclosures & doors, storefronts, tabletops & insulated, fireproof & ornamental glass & beveling*
Employs—4; Estab.—1988
Sales—$1Mil
9,000 sq ft site, Distrib.—Regional
Privately owned corporation

### ITW PROFESSIONAL BRANDS

Div. of Illinois Tool Works, Inc.
1295 Towbin Ave. (08701)
**Phone—(732) 363-9281**
National—(800) 242-7374
Fax—(732) 363-4302
www.itwprofessionalbrands.com
Email—cservice@itwprobrands.com
Cont.—Michael Mont'Etna
Bus. Unit Mgr.—Michael O'Connell
Assoc. Mktg. Mgr.—Tara Millar
SIC—2299; *Disposable wiping products for the foodservice, industrial, janitorial & healthcare industries; Brand name—Klean Microbe Guard; Simple Solutions; Atlantic Mills*
Employs—300; Estab.—1983
90,000 sq ft site, Distrib.—Intl.
Publicly owned corporation
Parent co.—Illinois Tool Works, Inc., Glenview, IL
Phone—(847) 724-7500
See Parent Co. Section for full profile.

### JACQUARD FABRICS CO., INC.

1965 Swarthmore Ave. (08701)
**Phone—(732) 905-4545**
Fax—(732) 905-5334
www.jacquardfabricsinc.net
Email—jacqfab@aol.com
Owner & Pres.—Leonard Gliner
Bookkeeper & Hum. Res. Mgr.—Delores Hannah
Whse. Mgr.—Shelton Cagle
Order Entry Rep.—Barbara Sanders
SIC—2211; *Upholstery fabrics*
Employs—40; Estab.—1982
35,000 sq ft site, Distrib.—National
Sole ownership

### JERSEY JACK PINBALL, INC.

1645 Oak St. (08701)
**Phone—(732) 364-9900**
Fax—(732) 987-6842
www.jerseyjackpinball.com
Email—jack@jerseyjackpinball.com
Pres., CEO—Jack Guarnieri
CFO—Michael Carle
Opers. Mgr.—Larry Appice
Off. Mgr.—Katie English
SIC—3999; *Coin-operated pinball arcade games*
Employs—60; Estab.—2011
Sales—$5Mil-$10Mil (est)
Distrib.—Intl.
Privately owned corporation

### JESEL, INC.

1985 Cedar Bridge Ave., Ste. 2 (08701-7031)
**Phone—(732) 901-1800**
Fax—(732) 901-6777
www.jesel.com
Email—info@jesel.com
Pres.—Dan Jesel
V-P. & Dir., Bus.—D. W. Grob
Hum. Res. Mgr.—Karen Grob
SIC—3714; *Race car engine parts*
Employs—50; Estab.—1980
68,000 sq ft site, Distrib.—Intl.
Privately owned corporation

### KOMO MACHINE, INC.

Div. of PMC, Inc.
1 Komo Dr. (08701)
**Phone—(732) 719-6222**
National—(800) 255-5670
Fax—(732) 579-5443
www.komo.com
Email—info@komo.com
Pres.—Mike Kolibas
Ex. V-P.—Jeff Erickson
Sales Mgr., Natl.—Joseph Donatelli
Sales Mgr., Inside—Brian Stier
SIC—3569; 3541; 3542; 3544; NAICS—333512; *High speed CNC routing machining centers*
Employs—40; Estab.—1966
Distrib.—Intl.
Privately owned corporation
Parent co.—PMC, Inc., Sun Valley, CA
Phone—(818) 896-1101
See Parent Co. Section for full profile.

### KRAEMER KOATING, INC.

1925 Swarthmore Ave. (08701)
**Phone—(732) 886-6315**
Fax—(732) 886-6417
www.kraemerkoating.com
Email—info@kraemerkoating.com
Pres. & Software Techn.—Paul Kraemer
Plt. Mgr.—Demetri Regas
Bookkeeper—Barbara Kraemer
SIC—3559; *Research machinery coating equipment*
Employs—5; Estab.—1980
12,000 sq ft site, Distrib.—Intl.
Privately owned corporation

### L. S. SOFTWARE SYSTEMS, INC.

419 12th St. (08701)
**Phone—(732) 367-7164**
Fax—(732) 370-9083
www.jewelrysoftware.net
Email—sales@jewelrysoftware.net
Pres.—Adele Yoffe
SIC—7372; *Jewelry pricing calculation & inventory management software development for retail, wholesale & manufacturing applications; Brand name—Magical Jeweler*
Employs—6
Privately owned corporation

### LAMINETICS, INC.

1263 River Ave. (08701)
**Phone—(732) 367-1116**
Fax—(732) 367-7717
Pres.—Robert Kicak

SIC—2542; 2434; NAICS—337110; *Wooden & laminated countertops & cabinets*
Employs—3; Estab.—1993
8,000 sq ft site, Distrib.—Regional
Privately owned corporation

### LARDIERI'S CUSTOM WOODWORKING, INC.

1830 Swarthmore Ave., Ste. 6 (08701)
**Phone—(732) 905-6334**
Fax—(732) 370-2186
www.lardieriscustomwoodworking.com
Email—rlardieri@aol.com
Co-Pres., Off. Mgr.—Robert Lardieri, Sr.
Co-Pres.—Don Lardieri
GM—Adam Arpaio
GM & Bookkeeper—Gayle Hutchinson
SIC—2431; 2499; NAICS—321900; *Custom wooden kitchen cabinets, entertainment centers, libraries, bath vanities, fireplace mantles & closets*
Employs—6; Estab.—1992
Sales—$1Mil-$2.5Mil
Distrib.—Local
Privately owned corporation

### LEGACY STAIRS & MILLWORK, INC.

1000 Airport Rd., Ste. 104 (08701)
**Phone—(732) 905-7705**
Fax—(732) 905-7750
www.legacystairs.com
Email—sales@legacystairs.com
Owner—Stephen Hasse
Off. Mgr.—Linda Esposito
SIC—3446; 3444; 2499; 3231; NAICS—332323; *Custom wooden, steel & aluminum conventional, curved, spiral, elliptical & winder stairs & wooden, steel, iron, brass, bronze, nickel, aluminum, glass & cable rails*
Employs—6; Estab.—2006
Sales—$1Mil-$2Mil
Distrib.—National
Privately owned corporation

### LIFE SCIENCE LABORATORIES, LLC

170 Oberlin Ave. N., Ste. 26 (08701)
**Phone—(732) 367-1900**
Fax—(732) 367-4146
Email—az@lslabs.net
Owner—Yochanan Bulka
Ex. V-P.—Adeena Zabrowsky
SIC—2834; NAICS—325412; *Nutritional supplements*
Employs—10; Estab.—2002
Distrib.—National
Limited Liability Company

**NEW ENTRY**

### LIFE SCIENCE LABS SUPPLEMENTS, LLC

170 Oberlin Ave. (08701)
**Phone—(732) 367-1749**
Ex. V-P.—Adeena Zabrowsky
SIC—2834; *Nutritional supplements*
Employs—14
Sales—$5Mil-$10Mil (est)
Limited Liability Company

### LILO MATERNITY, LLC

1526 Laguna Ln. (08701)
**Phone—(732) 370-5456**
National—(877) 545-6932
www.lilomaternity.com
Email—info@lilomaternity.com
Owner—Neal Benedek

SIC—2331; 2337; *Maternity clothing, including t-shirts, sweaters & skirts*
Employs—6; Estab.—2007
Sales—$500,000-$1Mil
Distrib.—Intl.
Privately owned corporation

### LUMINER CONVERTING GROUP, INC.

1925 Swarthmore Ave., Ste. 5 (08701)
**Phone—(732) 886-6557**
Fax—(732) 886-6692
www.luminer.com
Email—luminer@luminer.com
Pres., Hum. Res. & IT Mgr.—Thomas Spina
Sales Mgr.—Gary Price
Plt. Mgr.—John Borrelli
Pur. Agt.—Gail Cannizzaro
SIC—2672; NAICS—322222; *Corporate headquarters & pressure-sensitive labels*
Employs—25; Estab.—1991
26,000 sq ft site, Distrib.—Intl.
Privately owned corporation

### M T I PRECISION PRODUCTS, LLC

730 Airport Rd. (08701)
**Phone—(732) 905-7440**
National—(800) 367-9290
Fax—(732) 905-7445
www.mti-dental.com
Email—info@mti-dental.com
Ptnr.—Joe DeLuca
Ptnr.—Rob Reisley
Pres.—Haye Hinrichs
Accountant—J. Abrahamsen
SIC—3843; NAICS—339114; *Dental handpieces, including nose cones, contra attachments, scalers, tips & replacement cartridges; Brand name—Lynx*
Employs—12; Estab.—1989
Sales—$1Mil-$2.5Mil
4,000 sq ft site, Distrib.—Local
Limited Liability Company

### M&S CANADA CORP.

8 Arosa Hill (08701)
**Phone—(732) 901-6636**
Fax—(732) 901-0436
Pres.—Malkie Mosokowitz
SIC—2339; 2369; *Women's & girl's sportswear*
Employs—3; Estab.—2003
Sales—under $500,000
Distrib.—Intl.
Privately owned corporation

### MACHON BEER HATORAH, INC.

41 E. 8th St. (08701)
**Phone—(732) 364-9638**
Fax—(732) 901-0621
Pres.—Rabbi Lazar Apter
SIC—2731; *Hebrew-language book publishing*
Employs—3; Estab.—1994
Sales—$1Mil-$2.5Mil
Distrib.—Regional
Privately owned corporation

### MAGNA INDUSTRIES, INC.

1825 Swarthmore Ave., Ste. 1 (08701-4570)
**Phone—(732) 905-0957**
National—(800) 510-9856
Fax—(732) 367-2989
www.magnaindustries.com
Email—sales@magnaindustries.com
Pres.—Walter Ostrowicki
GM—Jerry Krzeminski
Sales Mgr.—Jeff Simmons
Off. Mgr.—Robert Figiela

## Lakewood—(cont.)

SIC—3556; NAICS—333294; *Bakery equipment, including baking, oven & transportation racks, tables & foodservice equipment*
Employs—27; Estab.—1979
Sales—$4Mil-$10Mil
44,000 sq ft site, Distrib.—National
Privately owned corporation

**MANLEY PERFORMANCE PRODUCTS, INC.**
1960 Swarthmore Ave. (08701)
**Phone—(732) 905-3366**
National—(800) 526-1362
Fax—(732) 905-3010
www.manleyperformance.com
Email—sales@manleyperformance.com
Pres.—Henry Manley
Hum. Res. & IT Mgr.—Gil Morejon
SIC—3519; 3592; 3714; NAICS—336311; *High-performance internal engine components*
Employs—115; Estab.—1966
40,000 sq ft site, Distrib.—National
Sole ownership

**MDI MFG., INC.**
100 Syracuse Ct. (08701)
**Phone—(732) 994-5599**
Fax—(732) 994-5598
www.mdiman.com
Email—mdiman@aol.com
Pres.—Mark Daugherty
SIC—3599; *Precision machining job shop*
Employs—24; Estab.—1985
Sales—$1Mil-$5Mil
25,000 sq ft site, Distrib.—Intl.
Privately owned corporation

**MILSPRAY, LLC**
845 Towbin Ave. (08701)
**Phone—(732) 886-2223**
Fax—(732) 886-2250
www.milspray.com
Email—customerservice@milspray.com
Pres., CEO—Brian Feser
V.-P., Contracts & Fin.—Elizabeth DeSerio
Dir., Comms. & Mktg.—Chantel Robinson
Staff Accountant—Janet Armett
SIC—2851; 3559; 3589; *Mil-spec paint, renewable energy, corrosion repair & vehicle wash systems for DOD, government & commercial agencies; Brand name—MILSPRAY; Scorpion Energy Hunter™*
Employs—40; Estab.—2007
Distrib.—National
Limited Liability Company

**MISTER COOKIE FACE, LLC**
Div. of Fieldbrook Foods Corp.
1989 Rutgers University Blvd. (08701)
**Phone—(732) 370-5533**
National—(888) 350-5533
Fax—(732) 370-4015
Plt. Controller—Suzanne Crovo
Plt. Mgr. & Pur. Agt.—Mahesh Khemrej
SIC—2024; NAICS—311520; *Private label contract manufacturing of ice cream novelties*
Employs—100; Estab.—1992
40,000 sq ft site, Distrib.—National
Sole ownership
Parent co.—Fieldbrook Foods Corp., Dunkirk, NY
Phone—(716) 366-5400
See Parent Co. Section for full profile.

**MOUNTAIN MILLWORK**
14 Clifton Ave. S. (08701)
**Phone—(732) 901-9400**
Manager—Nathan Joseph

SIC—2431; 2434; *Architectural millwork & wooden kitchen cabinets*
Employs—3
Sales—under $500,000 (est)
Distrib.—Local
Privately owned corporation

**NITTO DENKO AMERICA AUTOMOTIVE, INC.**
Div. of Nitto Denko America, Inc.
1990 Rutgers Blvd. (08701)
**Phone—(732) 901-7905**
Fax—(732) 901-9354
www.nittousa.com
Email—sales@nitto.com
Dir., Opers.—Eric G. Pike
Hum. Res. Mgr.—Susan Herbert
Opers. Admn. Coord.—Denise Ulrich
SIC—2672; 3069; NAICS—322222; *Pressure-sensitive tapes & foam rubber*
Employs—100; Estab.—1954
Distrib.—Intl.
Publicly owned corporation
Parent co.—Nitto Denko America, Inc., Fremont, CA
Phone—(510) 445-5400
See Parent Co. Section for full profile.

**OCEANA DESIGNS, INC.**
450 Oberlin Ave. S. (08701-6903)
**Phone—(732) 987-6944**
Fax—(732) 987-6947
www.oceanadesigns.net
Email—sales@oceanadesigns.net
Owner—George Gavallas
SIC—3281; *Granite & marble countertops; Brand name—DuPont; Cambria*
Employs—20
Sales—$500,000-$1Mil
Distrib.—Local
Privately owned corporation

**OLD FASHIONED KITCHEN, INC.**
1045 Towbin Ave. (08701)
**Phone—(732) 364-4100**
Fax—(732) 905-7352
www.oldfashionedkitchen.com
Email—info@oldfashionedkitchen.com
Pres.—Jay Conzen
V.-P., Cont.—Joann Lemasvewski
SIC—2038; NAICS—311412; *Frozen foods*
Employs—85; Estab.—1950
30,000 sq ft site, Distrib.—National
Privately owned corporation

NEW ENTRY
**ON THE LEVEL COUNTER TOP, INC.**
825 Brook Rd. (08701)
**Phone—(732) 370-4186**
Fax—(732) 370-9747
www.otlcountertops.com
Pres.—Vito G. Paratore
SIC—2434; 2542; *Wooden kitchen cabinets & formica countertops*
Employs—1
Sales—under $500,000 (est)
2,000 sq ft site, Distrib.—Local
Privately owned corporation

†**R. E. MICHEL CO., INC.**
895 Towbin Ave. (08701)
**Phone—(732) 886-3592**
Fax—(732) 886-3595
www.remichel.com
Email—customerservice@remichel.com
Manager—John Manning
SIC—5075; *Wholesaler of heating & air conditioning equipment*
Employs—3; Estab.—2006
Distrib.—Local
Privately owned corporation
Parent co.—R. E. Michel Co., Inc., Glen Burnie, MD
Phone—(410) 760-4000
See Parent Co. Section for full profile.

**RED THE UNIFORM TAILOR, INC.**
475 Oberlin Ave. S. (08701)
**Phone—(848) 299-0100**
National—(800) 272-7337
Fax—(848) 299-0150
www.rtut.com
Email—info-rtut@rtut.com
CEO—Patricia Klein
V.-P., Sales—Tracy Gluck
Prodn. Mgr.—Tom Hoffenson
IT Mgr.—Bob Entrekin
SIC—2326; 2329; 2331; 2337; NAICS—315200; *Corporate headquarters & men's & women's uniforms for the police, hospitality, chef, corporate, healthcare & industrial industries*
Employs—60; Estab.—1977
Sales—$10Mil-$12Mil
43,000 sq ft site, Distrib.—National
Privately owned sub-S corp.

**ROBEN MFG. CO., INC.**
760 Vassar Ave. (08701)
**Phone—(732) 364-6000**
National—(800) 220-9122
Fax—(732) 905-9703
www.robenmfg.com
Email—nev@robenmfg.com
Pres.—Gary R. Huhn
V.-P., MIS & Sales—Kelly E. Wyrough
Bookkeeper & Hum. Res. Mgr.—Nev Heimall
Qual. Control Mgr.—Akhlesh K. Mathur
SIC—3443; *Custom nickel alloy fabrication of processing equipment, pressure vessels & heat exchangers*
Employs—32; Estab.—1955
40,000 sq ft site, Distrib.—Intl.
Privately owned corporation

**ROELYN LITHO, INC.**
687 Propect St., Unit 410 (08701)
**Phone—(732) 942-9650**
National—(800) 886-8564
Fax—(732) 942-9655
www.roelynn.com
Email—vincentpraino@roelynn.com
Pres.—Vincent Praino
Off. Mgr.—Rosemarie Praino
Graphic Artist—Craig Como
SIC—2761; NAICS—323116; *Business form printing*
Employs—8; Estab.—1986
5,000 sq ft site, Distrib.—National
Privately owned corporation

**ROYAL SEAMLESS CORP.**
1000 Airport Rd., Ste. 202 (08701)
**Phone—(732) 901-9595**
Fax—(732) 901-9029
www.royalseamless.com
Email—basia13@me.com
Pres.—Barbara Kusmierczyk
SIC—3444; *Aluminum & copper gutters & downspouts*
Employs—6; Estab.—2007
Sales—$1Mil-$2.5Mil
4,000 sq ft site, Distrib.—Local
Privately owned corporation

**RUBBERECYCLE, LLC**
1985 Rutgers Blvd. (08701)
**Phone—(732) 363-0600**
National—(888) 436-6846
Fax—(732) 363-4247
www.rubberecycle.com
Email—info@rubberecycle.com
Ptnr.—Robert Gestetner
Ptnr.—Morris Hassan
V.-P., Sales—Keith Sacks
Sales Mgr.—Sandy Gartner
SIC—3069; *Recycled tire rubber mulch & curbs for playgrounds, landscaping & equestrian arenas*
Employs—40; Estab.—1996
Sales—$1Mil-$2.5Mil
Distrib.—National
Privately owned corporation

†**SCP DISTRIBUTORS, LLC**
Div. of Pool Corporation
1985 Rutgers University Blvd., Ste. A (08701)
**Phone—(732) 730-1451**
Fax—(732) 730-1525
www.scppool.com
Email—webmaster@scppools.com
Br. Mgr.—Jeff Delmastero
SIC—5091; *Distributor of swimming pools, spas & accessories*
Employs—7
Distrib.—Local
Publicly owned corporation
Parent co.—Pool Corporation, Covington, LA
Phone—(985) 892-5521
See Parent Co. Section for full profile.

**SHACHIHATA, INC., U. S. A.**
Div. of Shachihata, Inc.
525 Oberlin Ave. S. (08701)
**Phone—(732) 370-4770**
Fax—(732) 370-2646
www.xstamper.com
Email—mforte@xstamper.com
GM—Young Sin Park
Hum. Res. Mgr.—Maureen McGurk
SIC—3953; 3993; NAICS—339943; *Rubber stamps & engraved signs; Brand name—Xstamper; Classix; Xecutives; Artline*
Employs—30; Estab.—1988
Distrib.—National
Privately owned corporation
Parent co.—Shachihata, Inc., Torrance, CA
Phone—(310) 530-4445
See Parent Co. Section for full profile.

**SHORE POINT COMMUNICATIONS**
160 Lehigh Ave., Ste. B (08701)
**Phone—(732) 961-7936**
National—(800) 458-0990
Fax—(732) 961-7939
www.shorepointcomm.com
Email—info@shorepointcomm.com
Pres.—David Francis
SIC—2759; NAICS—323100; *Commercial printing & direct mailing services*
Employs—9; Estab.—1982
Sales—$500,000-$1Mil
Distrib.—National
Privately owned corporation

**SIKA CORP.**
995 Towbin Ave. (08701)
**Phone—(973) 473-3330**
Fax—(732) 886-5440
www.usa.sika.com
Off. Mgr.—Kathy Murphy
SIC—2891; NAICS—325520; *Sealants, adhesives & primers; Brand name—Bondaflex; Ucolor; Silbridge; Silfast; Paracryl; Parathane; Parasil*
Employs—30; Estab.—1984
Distrib.—Intl.

**SILVER STONES INTERNATIONAL, LLC**
902 E. County Line Rd., Ste. 200 (08701)
**Phone—(732) 886-0011**
National—(866) 745-8373
Fax—(732) 886-3637
www.silverstonesusa.com
Email—info@silverstonesusa.com
Off. Mgr.—Cindy Kallus
SIC—3911; NAICS—339911; *Silver jewelry*
Employs—10
Sales—$1Mil-$2.5Mil (est)
Distrib.—Intl.
Limited Liability Company

**GEOGRAPHICAL**

## Lakewood—(cont.)

**SKRIPAK METAL FABRICATORS, INC.**
170 Oberlin Ave. N., Unit 17 (08701)
**Phone—(732) 364-9662**
National—(800) 662-2823
Fax—(732) 364-8345
www.skripakmetal.com
Email—jskripak@skripakmetal.com
Pres., CFO—John Skripak, Jr.
MIS & Pers. Mgr.—Kim Skripak
Engr.—Mike Hill
SIC—3443; 3444; 3537; NAICS—332999; *Metal carts & tables, catwalks, hoods, machine guards & platforms*
Employs—10; Estab.—1991
Sales—$500,000-$1Mil
5,500 sq ft site, Distrib.—National
Privately owned sub-S corp.

**SMARTPOOL, INC.**
687 Prospect St., Ste. 460 (08701)
**Phone—(732) 730-9880**
Fax—(732) 730-9881
www.smartpool.com
Email—info@smartpool.com
Pres.—Lewis Dubrofsky
Hum. Res. & IT Mgr.—Bill Baker
SIC—3589; *Robotic swimming pool cleaners*
Employs—20
Distrib.—Intl.
Privately owned corporation

**SPAR-TEX CO., INC.**
200 Lehigh Ave. (08701)
**Phone—(732) 367-4400**
Fax—(732) 367-4172
www.spartex.biz
Owner—Charles Sparacino
Prod. Mgr.—Manny Polostri
SIC—2399; NAICS—315211; *Contract sewing of home textiles & decorative pillows*
Employs—100; Estab.—1963
Sales—$10Mil-$25Mil (est)
93,000 sq ft site,

**SS WHITE BURS, INC.**
1145 Towbin Ave. (08701)
**Phone—(800) 535-2877**
Fax—(732) 905-0987
www.sswhiteburs.com
Email—info@sswhiteburs.com
Pres.—Tom Gallop
V-P., Mfg.—Wayne Boylan
Qual. Assur. Mgr.—Dereck Gladden
SIC—3843; NAICS—339114; *Carbide dental burs; Brand name—Piranha®; GreatWhite®; Fissurotomy®; ExpressLine®; Revelation®; TDA®*
Employs—250; Estab.—1887
40,000 sq ft site, Distrib.—Intl.
Privately owned corporation
ISO rating—9001

**STAG BROS. CAST STONE**
720 Vassar Ave. (08701)
**Phone—(732) 363-6582**
Fax—(732) 363-6877
Pres.—Bill Stagliano
V-P.—Sal Stagliano
Plt. Mgr.—Bob Lensky
SIC—3272; 3281; NAICS—327991; *Precast concrete & stone products*
Employs—10; Estab.—1992
Sales—$1Mil-$2.5Mil
Distrib.—Regional
Privately owned corporation

**STEF'S PERFORMANCE PRODUCTS**
693 Cross St. (08701)
**Phone—(732) 367-8700**
Fax—(732) 367-8793
www.stefs.com
Email—joestef99@aol.com
Pres.—Joe Stefanacci

SIC—3714; *Race car oil system components*
Employs—22; Estab.—1990
Sales—$5Mil-$10Mil (est)
Distrib.—Intl.
Privately owned sub-S corp.

NEW ENTRY
**STICH N' SEW CENTRE**
123 E County Line Rd. (08701)
**Phone—(732) 363-2220**
Fax—(732) 363-2200
www.stitchnsewcentre.com
Owner—Beth Fisher
SIC—2391; *Custom window treatments, including draperies, sheers, valances & cornices & custom upholstery services*
Employs—40; Estab.—1950
Sales—$2.5Mil-$5Mil (est)

**†STICKEL PACKAGING SUPPLY**
1991 Rutgers University Blvd., Lakewood Industrial Pk. *(08701)*
**Phone—(732) 905-2811**
National—(888) 784-2535
Fax—(732) 364-6909
www.stickelpackaging.com
Email—info@stickelpackaging.com
Founder—Hal Stickel
CFO—Jeanne Stickel
Sr. V-P.—Christopher Borriello
V-P.—Peter Borriello
GM—Tom Schmiegel
SIC—5113; 5087; *Wholesaler of packaging, janitorial & safety supplies; Brand name—Stick Tape; Stick True Gauge Stretch Film; Sealed Air; Poly Air; Intertape; Primetac; Sigma; Paragon; Polychem; Dubose; Laminations; Simoniz*
Employs—31; Estab.—1987
50,000 sq ft site, Distrib.—Regional
Privately owned corporation

**†SUPREME ASSET MANAGEMENT & RECOVERY, INC.**
1950 Rutgers University Blvd. (08701)
**Phone—(732) 370-4100**
National—(866) 509-7267
Fax—(732) 370-5116
www.samrecovery.com
Email—mrunko@samrecovery.com
Pres.—Albert Boufarah
Dir., Opers.—Mitch Runko
Facility Mgr.—Robert Brown
Mktg. Mgr.—Bob Reilly
SIC—5093; 5094; *Corporate headquarters & distributor of recycled computers & electronics & silver reclamation*
Employs—35; Estab.—2007
Distrib.—Regional
Privately owned corporation

**SYMRISE PURESCENTS**
Div. of Symrise, Inc.
1715 Oak St., Ste. 3 (08701)
**Phone—(732) 922-2520**
Fax—(732) 922-2590
www.symrise.com
Email—tsalsso@symrisepurescents.com
Pres.—Jack Corley
Opers. Mgr.—Tony Salsso
SIC—2844; NAICS—325600; *Fragrance oils*
Employs—17; Estab.—1986
Distrib.—Intl.
Privately owned corporation
Parent co.—Symrise, Inc., Teterboro, NJ
Phone—(201) 288-3200
See Parent Co. Section for full profile.

**†TC PETROLEUM**
575 Prospect St., Ste. 264 (08701-5040)
**Phone—(732) 367-2116**
National—(800) 560-2116

Fax—(732) 367-2067
Email—carol@tcpetroleum.com
Pres.—Dennis Schurgin
Off. Mgr.—Carol Brunt
Technical Mgr.—John Bianchi
SIC—5172; *Wholesaler of lubricants; Brand name—Shell Oil; Cam 2*
Employs—5; Estab.—1978
Distrib.—Local
Privately owned sub-S corp.

**TIPICO PRODUCTS, INC.**
490 Oberlin Ave. S. (08701)
**Phone—(732) 942-8820**
Fax—(732) 942-8837
www.tipicoproducts.com
Email—tipicoproducts@aol.com
GM—Bob Castellano
SIC—2022; NAICS—311513; *Processed cheese*
Employs—150; Estab.—1993
Distrib.—National
Privately owned corporation

**†TOWN & COUNTRY LINEN CORP.**
475 Oberlin Ave. S. (08701)
**Phone—(732) 364-2000**
Fax—(732) 364-0243
www.tncliving.com
Email—skeingarsky@tncliving.com
V-P., Cust. Serv. & Dist.—Susan Keingarsky
SIC—5023; *Distributor of domestic & imported table linens, kitchen textile & bedding products & coordinated bathroom supplies, including oven mitts, scrubbers, aprons, runners, placemats, shower curtains, lotion pumps, rugs, duvets, sheets & shams; Brand name—kate spade new York; Calvin Klein; Fiesta®; Vera; KitchenAid; Duck Dynasty; Disney*
Employs—32; Estab.—1973
Distrib.—Regional
Privately owned corporation

**VINYLAST, INC.**
1830 Swarthmore Ave. (08701)
**Phone—(732) 367-7200**
Fax—(732) 370-4659
www.vinylast.com
Email—stevenj@vinylast.com
Pres., GM—Steven J. Leary
Off. Mgr.—Christine Knapp
SIC—3442; 3089; NAICS—332321; *Aluminum & vinyl windows, doors, railings, fencing & decks fabrication*
Employs—20; Estab.—1973
52,000 sq ft site, Distrib.—National
Privately owned sub-S corp.

**VOGELSANG FASTENER CORP**
1790 Swarthmore Ave. (08701)
**Phone—(732) 364-0444**
          (732) 364-4422
National—(800) 526-2376
Fax—(732) 364-8111
www.vogelsangfastener.com
Email—sales@vogelsangfastener.com
V-P., GM—Dale Stuban
Bus. Dev. Mgr.—Nick Penney
Bus. Dev. Mgr.—Bill Pappas
SIC—3429; 3452; 3498; NAICS—332722; *Slotted, coiled & metric tension pins, roll pins, slotted spring pins, spiral pins, split tension bushings, compression limiters & tubular products; Brand name—Rollpin*
Employs—50; Estab.—1981
Sales—$5Mil-$10Mil
54,000 sq ft site, Distrib.—Intl.
Privately owned corporation
ISO rating—9001

**WEBCO GRAPHICS/W.G.I. CORP.**
1875 Swarthmore Ave. (08701)
**Phone—(732) 370-2900**
Fax—(732) 367-4621
www.webcographics.com
Email—webcographics@aol.com
Pres.—Glenn Davis
Off. Mgr.—Maureen Davis
SIC—2711; 2759; 2791; NAICS—323122; *Newsprint printing of newspapers, brochures, booklets & coupon books*
Employs—12; Estab.—1983
Sales—$1Mil-$2.5Mil
Distrib.—Regional
Privately owned corporation
AKA: Webco Graphics

**WOODHAVEN LUMBER & MILLWORK, INC.**
200 James St., P.O. Box 870 (08701)
**Phone—(732) 901-0030**
          (732) 901-5518
National—(800) 325-8623
Fax—(732) 901-5562
www.woodhavenlumber.com
Email—info@woodhavenlumber.com
Pres.—Alan Robinson
V-P.—David Robinson
Cont.—Peter Lavin
Dir., Mktg.—Tom London
SIC—2431; 2421; 2499; 3429; NAICS—321900; *Millwork, including decks, railings, doors, drywall, insulation, lumber, plywood, moulding, siding, stairs, trusses, windows, kitchen cabinetry & flooring, hardware & tools & painting & design services; Brand name—Andersen; SilverLine; TimberTech; Trex; TruStile; Therma Tru; Medallion Cabinetry*
Employs—152; Estab.—1976
Sales—over $50Mil
Distrib.—Regional
Privately owned corporation

**WORTHINGTON BIOCHEMICAL CORP.**
730 Vassar Ave. (08701)
**Phone—(732) 942-1660**
National—(800) 445-9603
Fax—(732) 942-9270
www.worthington-biochem.com
Pres.—Von Worthington
V-P.—Jim Zacka
Hum. Res. Mgr.—Marti Bookstein
Cust. Serv. Rep.—Christina Edwards
SIC—2835; NAICS—325400; *Highly purified enzymes*
Employs—50; Estab.—1947
Distrib.—Intl.
Privately owned corporation

---

## Lambertville
(Hunterdon—N.W.)

**ADVANCED CERAMETRICS, INC.**
245 N. Main St., P.O. Box 128 (08530)
**Phone—(609) 397-2900**
National—(800) 261-1208
Fax—(609) 397-2708
www.advancedcerametrics.com
Email—advcer@advancedcerametrics.com
V-P., COO—Michael Hendricks
Cust. Serv. Mgr.—Tanya Catanzareti
Qual. Control Mgr.—Kim Williamson

## Lambertville—(cont.)

SIC—3264; NAICS—327113; *Advanced ceramic fibers & shapes & energy harvesting systems, including transducers, actuators, active structural controls & vibration damping*
Employs—20; Estab.—1947
Sales—$1Mil-$5Mil
19,300 sq ft site, Distrib.—Intl.
Privately owned corporation

**AIRMED BIOTECH, LLC**
510 Titus Rd. (08530)
**Phone—(215) 378-9114**
Fax—(815) 550-2228
www.airmedbio.com
Pres., CEO—Jack Kerins
V-P., Bus. Dev., Intl.—Tony Ortiz
SIC—2835; *Saliva, blood & urine test devices for drug testing programs for employers, law enforcement & the military & malaria, HIV & related diagnostic tests for rapid detection; Brand name—OraScreen Saliva Drug Screen; Airmed Keyless Urine Dual Specimen Cup; Airmed Saliva Sampler*
Employs—5; Estab.—2007
Sales—$500,000-$1Mil
2,500 sq ft site, Distrib.—Intl.
Privately owned sub-S corp.
AKA: Airmed Advisory

**BREEN COLOR CONCENTRATES, INC.**
11 Kari Dr. (08530)
**Phone—(609) 397-8200**
Fax—(609) 397-2551
www.breencolor.com
Email—info@breencolor.com
Pres.—Howard DeMonte
V-P., Tech.—Paul Legnetti
Hum. Res. Mgr.—Tracy Muskatell
Cust. Serv. Mgr.—Helen Goodman
Cust. Serv. Rep.—Jeannie Hartman
Cust. Serv. Rep.—Dianna Sands
SIC—2816; NAICS—325100; *Color concentrates*
Employs—60; Estab.—1977
Sales—$15Mil-$20Mil
42,000 sq ft site, Distrib.—Intl.
Privately owned corporation

**CASTOR JEWELRY**
13 N. Union St. (08530)
**Phone—(609) 397-0809**
www.castorjewelry.com
Email—info@castorjewelry.com
Ptnr.—Tom Castor
Ptnr.—Sandra Castor
SIC—3911; NAICS—339911; *Precious metal jewelry*
Employs—3; Estab.—1994
Sales—under $500,000 (est)
Distrib.—National
Sole ownership

**J W S COMPUTERS, INC.**
20 S. Main (08530)
**Phone—(908) 730-6628**
Fax—(908) 730-8140
www.jwscomputers.com
Email—sales@jwscomputers.com
Ptnr.—Jeff Sailer
Ptnr.—Pam Sailer
SIC—3571; NAICS—334111; *Computers*
Employs—7; Estab.—1989
Sales—$500,000-$1Mil
1,800 sq ft site, Distrib.—Regional

**L S P INDUSTRIAL CERAMICS**
34 Mount Airy Village Rd., P.O. Box 302 (08530)
**Phone—(609) 397-8330**
National—(800) 543-8217
Fax—(609) 397-4660
www.lspceramics.com
Email—lspceramics@aol.com
Pres.—Frank D. Smith

Sales Mgr.—Phill Lewis
Off. Mgr.—Joan Smith
Salesman—John Johnson
SIC—3299; *Electronic & industrial ceramics*
Employs—5; Estab.—1983
Sales—$500,000-$1Mil
Distrib.—Intl.
Privately owned corporation

**LEHIGH FLUID POWER, INC.**
1413 Route 179 (08530)
**Phone—(609) 397-3487**
National—(800) 257-9515
Fax—(609) 397-0932
www.lehighfluidpower.com
Email—sales@lehighfluidpower.com
Pres.—Frank McGonigle
Sales Mgr., Global—Carl Blasina
SIC—3593; NAICS—333995; *Custom & standard NFPA-styled hydraulic & pneumatic actuators, stainless steel, brass & steel booster cylinders, pressure intensifiers & accessories; Brand name—Miracalube Self-Lube Air Cylinder; JHD; JHDH; HP; LSSE; LSSW*
Employs—30; Estab.—1946
Sales—$3.5Mil-$8Mil
Distrib.—Intl.
Privately owned corporation

**RUGGIERI PRECISION MACHINE, LLC**
1404 Route 179 (08530-3414)
**Phone—(609) 397-4378**
Fax—(609) 397-3974
www.ruggierimachine.com
Email—ruggierimachine@verizon.net
Owner—John Ruggieri
Off. Mgr.—Marian Larowe
SIC—3599; *General machining job shop*
Employs—5; Estab.—1990
Distrib.—Regional
Limited Liability Company

---

## Landing
(Morris—N.W.)

**A. B. SCANTLEBURY CO.**
112 Kings Hwy. (07850)
**Phone—(973) 770-3000**
Fax—(973) 770-3002
www.absco.com
Email—john.spinelli@absco.com
Off. Mgr.—John Spinelli
Assembly Mgr.—Steve Getz
Bookkeeper—Elaine Laiacoma
SIC—3444; 3599; 3679; *Sheet metal fabrication, precision machining & electromechanical assembly*
Employs—8; Estab.—1963
5,000 sq ft site, Distrib.—National
Privately owned corporation

**AMERICAN ADVERTISING**
131 Landing Rd. (07850)
**Phone—(973) 398-6200**
Pres.—Clark Wheeler
V-P.—Shelly Wheeler
Graphic Designer—Jill Gellene
SIC—2759; NAICS—323100; *Direct mail printing*
Employs—5; Estab.—1989
Sales—under $500,000
Distrib.—National
Privately owned sub-S corp.

**AMHERST SCIENTIFIC, LLC**
112 Kings Hwy. (07850)
**Phone—(973) 770-7772**
Fax—(973) 770-5521
www.amherstscientific.com
Email—chris.grant@amherstscientific.com
Pres.—Chris Grant

SIC—3671; NAICS—334411; *Cooled photomultiplier vacuum tube housings, including TEC & TEC A/C*
Employs—6; Estab.—1988
2,500 sq ft site, Distrib.—Intl.

**CORRVIEW INTERNATIONAL, LLC**
P.O. Box 8513 (07850)
**Phone—(973) 770-7764**
Fax—(973) 770-6576
www.corrview.com
Email—sales@corrview.com
Pres., CEO—William Duncan
SIC—3829; 3429; *Metal pipe corrosion monitoring plugs & ultrasonic pipe testing*
Employs—2; Estab.—2000
Sales—under $500,000
Distrib.—Intl.
Limited Liability Company

**E & J MACHINE AND TOOL, LLC**
12 Orben Dr., Unit 1 (07850)
**Phone—(973) 810-2312**
　　　　　(973) 810-2313
Fax—(973) 601-7953
www.ejmachine.com
Email—sales@ejmachine.com
Owner—Edmund Kiss
Administrator—Attila Kiss
SIC—3599; 3541; *CNC lathe & milling job shop, including screw machines & small parts under 1 5/8-inches*
Employs—5; Estab.—1984
Sales—$1Mil-$2.5Mil
6,000 sq ft site, Distrib.—National
Limited Liability Company

**PRC LASER**
Div. of ROFIN-SINAR, Inc.
350 N. Frontage Rd. (07850)
**Phone—(973) 347-0100**
Fax—(973) 347-8932
www.prclaser.com
Email—sales@prclaser.com
Pres.—James G. Rickert
Hum. Res. Mgr.—Nancy McNamara
SIC—3699; *Industrial lasers*
Employs—60; Estab.—1975
30,000 sq ft site, Distrib.—Intl.
Privately owned corporation
Parent co.—ROFIN-SINAR, Inc., Plymouth, MI
　　Phone—(734) 455-5400
　　See Parent Co. Section for full profile.

**PRUDENT PUBLISHING CO.**
400 N. Frontage Rd. (07850)
**Phone—(973) 347-4554**
National—(800) 772-1144
Fax—(973) 347-5855
www.gallerycollection.com
Email—support@gallerycollection.com
Plt. Mgr.—Sharon Ruthnan
SIC—2771; *Greeting cards publishing; Brand name—Gallery Collection*
Employs—100; Estab.—1929
Distrib.—Intl.
Privately owned corporation
Parent co.—Prudent Publishing Co., Ridgefield Park, NJ
　　Phone—(201) 641-7900
　　See Parent Co. Section for full profile.

---

## Landisville
(Atlantic—S.E.)

**BELLVIEW WINERY**
150 Atlantic St. (08326)
**Phone—(856) 697-7172**
Fax—(856) 697-7183
www.bellviewwinery.com
Email—winery@bellviewwinery.com
Pres.—Jim Quarella
COO—Scott Quarella
Winemaker—David Gardner

SIC—2084; NAICS—312130; *Dry & sweet red & white wines; Brand name—Bellview*
Employs—6; Estab.—2000
6,000 sq ft site, Distrib.—Local
Privately owned corporation

**NORELL, INC.**
314 Arbor Ave., P.O. Box 307 (08326)
**Phone—(856) 697-0020**
National—(800) 519-3688
Fax—(856) 697-0021
www.nmrtubes.com
Pres.—Greg Norell
SIC—3826; NAICS—334516; *Test tubes*
Employs—20; Estab.—1967
Sales—$2.6Mil-$5Mil
Distrib.—Intl.
Privately owned corporation

---

## Laurel Springs
(Camden—S.W.)

**J & R REBUILDERS, INC.**
330 Washington Ave. (08021)
**Phone—(856) 627-1414**
National—(800) 428-0583
Fax—(856) 627-9801
Email—jrrebuilders@juno.com
Pres.—Robert Visconti
SIC—3694; NAICS—336322; *Rebuilt alternators & starters*
Employs—1; Estab.—1975
Sales—under $500,000
Distrib.—Local
Privately owned sub-S corp.

**†MONKEY JOE'S BIG NUT CO.**
205 N. White Horse Pike (08021)
**Phone—(856) 627-4600**
Fax—(856) 435-1796
www.bignutco.com
Email—mjbncustomerservice@bignutco.com
Owner—Joe Bush
SIC—5149; 5159; *Wholesaler of dried fruits & salted & unsalted nuts*
Employs—18; Estab.—1997
Sales—over $1Mil
Distrib.—Regional
Sole ownership

**ROYER GRAPHICS, INC.**
101 Lincoln Dr. (08021)
**Phone—(856) 344-7935**
Fax—(856) 344-7936
Email—royergraph@aol.com
Pres.—Tony Cannuli
SIC—2752; 2759; NAICS—323122; *Offset, digital & web printing & graphic design*
Employs—8; Estab.—1981
Sales—$500,000-$1Mil
20,000 sq ft site, Distrib.—Regional
Privately owned corporation

---

## Laurence Harbor
(Middlesex—N.E.)

**KEYVALET**
15 Industrial Dr., P.O. Box 1099 (08879)
**Phone—(732) 521-1394**
National—(800) 947-0304
Fax—(732) 521-1396
www.keyvaletinc.com
Email—info@keyvaletinc.com
Owner—Nancy Teufel
Pres.—Kenneth Biba

GEOGRAPHICAL

## Laurence Harbor—(cont.)

SIC—3429; 3499; 3599; *Standard & specialty security locks & key boxes & machine job shop; Brand name—Key FOB Disabler; Mercedes Style Key Locks; Operating Master Keys; Medi-Locks; EternaLock Motorcycle Lock; EternaLock Bicycle Lock; EternaLock Cable Lock; EternaLock Chain Lock*
Employs—4; Estab.—1988
Sales—under $500,000
2,500 sq ft site, Distrib.—National
Limited Liability Company

**VOLTA CORP.**
11 Industrial Dr., P.O. Box 1027 (08879)
**Phone—(732) 583-3300**
Fax—(732) 583-4900
www.voltacorp.com
Email—sales@voltacorp.com
Acctg. Mgr.—James Brown
SIC—3678; NAICS—335999; *Electrical connectors*
Employs—10; Estab.—1967
Distrib.—National
Privately owned corporation

## Lavallette
(Ocean—S.E.)

**LAVALLETTE PRINTING**
301 Grand Central (08735)
**Phone—(732) 793-8303**
Fax—(732) 793-4179
Owner—Bruno Hornung
SIC—2752; NAICS—323100; *Instant printing*
Employs—1; Estab.—1992
Sales—under $500,000
Distrib.—Local
Sole ownership

**VANNOTE CUSTOM CANVAS**
1904 Grand Central Ave. (08735)
**Phone—(732) 830-6555**
Fax—(732) 240-6021
Owner—Thomas Vannote
SIC—2394; NAICS—314912; *Marine canvas*
Employs—1; Estab.—1993
Sales—under $500,000
Distrib.—Local
Sole ownership

## Lawrence Township
(Mercer—N.E.)

**DIGITAL SURROUNDINGS, LLC**
11 Princess Rd., Ste. E (08648)
**Phone—(609) 912-1800**
Fax—(609) 912-1801
www.digitalsurroundings.com
Email—info@digitalsurroundings.com
Pres.—Chris D. Erdman
Bus. Opers. Mgr.—Lisa Ilaria
SIC—7373; *Commercial & residential audio/visual system integration & installation*
Employs—10; Estab.—2002
Distrib.—Regional
Limited Liability Company

**LMT MERCER GROUP, INC.**
690 Puritan Ave. (08648)
**Phone—(609) 989-0399**
National—(888) 570-5252
Fax—(609) 989-1199
www.lmtproducts.com
Email—orders@lmtproducts.com
Pres.—Anthony Lesensky
IT Mgr.—Peter Fischer
Hum. Res. Mgr.—Alane Barnick

SIC—3089; *Vinyl fence, deck & railing components*
Employs—45; Estab.—1987
Sales—$5Mil-$10Mil (est)
Distrib.—Intl.
Privately owned corporation

**RAMCO SYSTEMS CORP.**
3150 U.S. Highway 1, Ste. 130 (08648)
**Phone—(609) 620-4871**
Fax—(609) 620-2860
www.ramco.com
Email—info@ramco.com
CEO—Virender Agarwal
V-P.—Venkatesh Viswanathan
IT Mgr.—Karthikeyan Seetharaman
Hum. Res. Mgr.—K. V. Subramanian
Reg. Implementation Mgr.—Bala Vaidyanathan
SIC—7372; *Software development & implementation for trading services, manufacturing & logistics applications*
Employs—30; Estab.—1989
Distrib.—Intl.
Privately owned corporation

## Lawrenceville
(Mercer—N.E.)

**ALBRIDGE SOLUTIONS, INC.**
1009 Lenox Dr., Bldg. 4, Ste. 204 (08648)
**Phone—(609) 620-5800**
Fax—(609) 620-5801
www.albridge.com
Email—info@albridge.com
CEO—John Brett
COO & Mng. Dir.—Marc Butler
Mng. Dir., Tech.—Pete Antonucci
SIC—7372; *Computer network systems integration; Brand name—Albridge Data Warehouse; AdvisoryWorld; Albridge Applink; Albridge Wealth Desktop*
Employs—230

**ALMA OFFSET CO., INC.**
225 Bakers Basin Rd., P.O. Box 6487 (08648)
**Phone—(609) 587-5480**
Fax—(609) 587-7846
Email—almaink@bellatlantic.net
Pres.—Dan Markowski
Off. Mgr.—Sherry Lloyd
SIC—2752; NAICS—323100; *Offset printing*
Employs—7; Estab.—1948
Sales—$1Mil-$2.5Mil
Distrib.—Regional
Privately owned corporation

**BRITTON INDUSTRIES, INC.**
227 Bakers Basin Rd., P.O. Box 6499 *(08648)*
**Phone—(609) 588-8225**
   (844) 274-8866
Fax—(609) 588-8965
www.brittonindustries.com
Email—sales@brittonindustries.com
Pres.—James Britton
CFO—Pat Flannery
GM—Jim Mangarella
Mktg. Mgr.—Carrie Kulak
SIC—2421; 2875; NAICS—327331; *Bulk organic triple ground root & color enhanced mulch & related products for residential, commercial, municipal & equine applications*
Employs—80; Estab.—1989
Sales—$10Mil-$25Mil (est)
Distrib.—Regional
Privately owned corporation

**†CERTIFIED STEEL COMPANY (H Q)**
1333 Brunswick Ave., Ste. 200 *(08648)*
**Phone—(609) 396-7600**
   (800) 466-7660
Fax—(609) 392-6372
www.certifiedsteel.com
Email—info@certifiedsteel.com
CEO—Sydney Sussman
Pres.—Diane Kane
Cont.—Jo Ellen Boyd
IT Mgr.—Michael Ciesialka
Hum. Res. Mgr.—Kathy Finch
SIC—5051; *Company headquarters; steel service center, including cut-to-length services*
Employs—25
330,000 sq ft site,
Privately owned corporation

**COMMUNITY NEWS SERVICE, LLC**
15 Princess Rd., Ste. K (08648)
**Phone—(609) 396-1511**
Fax—(609) 396-1132
www.mercerspace.com
Email—jgriswold@mercerspace.com
Co-Publisher—James Griswold
Co-Publisher—Thomas Valeri
Mng. Editor—Joseph Emanski
Dir., Sales—Thomas Fritts
Dir., Prodn.—Stacey Micallef
Off. Mgr.—Brittany Bayo
Traf. Coord.—Norine Longo
SIC—2711; *Community newspaper publishing*
Employs—14; Estab.—2001
1,700 sq ft site, Distrib.—Local
Limited Liability Company

**DATACOLOR**
5 Princess Rd. (08648)
**Phone—(609) 924-2189**
National—(800) 433-1885
Fax—(609) 895-7472
www.datacolor.com
Email—marketing@datacolor.com
Pres., CEO—Albert Busch
Dir., Mktg.—Scott Helias
Mktg. Mgr.—Kim Nusser
SIC—3827; NAICS—333314; *Spectrophotometers, software, instruments, textile laboratory equipment, production solutions, digital color control, home theater solutions, lightbooths & conditioning cabinets; Brand name—Datacolor Certified; Datacolor Paint; Spyder; Datacolor Match Textile; Datacolor Tools; Datacolor Check; Datacolor 600; Datacolor Match Pigment; Datacolor Autolab*
Employs—120; Estab.—1971
Sales—$50Mil-$75Mil
70,000 sq ft site, Distrib.—Intl.
Publicly owned corporation
ISO rating—9001:2000

**HALO FARM, INC.**
970 Spruce St. (08648)
**Phone—(609) 695-3311**
Fax—(609) 695-3372
Email—halofarm@horizon.net
Pres.—Jerry Reilly
GM—Rick Monteserin
Off. Mgr.—Christina Hayes
SIC—2024; 2026; NAICS—311520; *Ice cream, milk & fruit drinks*
Employs—20; Estab.—1974
Sales—under $500,000
Distrib.—Local
Privately owned corporation

**HARWILL CORP.**
3175 Princeton Pike (08648)
Mail addr: P.O. Box 1645, East Windsor (08520)
**Phone—(609) 895-1955**
Fax—(609) 895-1963

www.harwillexpresspress.com
Email—hep@harwillexpresspress.com
Pres.—Steve Portrude
Secy.-Treas.—Harriet Portrude
SIC—2759; 2791; 2796; NAICS—323122; *Commercial & digital printing, typesetting, graphic design & color separations*
Employs—6; Estab.—1973
Sales—under $500,000
3,500 sq ft site, Distrib.—Regional
Privately owned corporation
AKA: Harwill Express Press

**LAWRENCE MOLD AND TOOL CORP.**
1412 Ohio Ave. *(08648)*
**Phone—(609) 392-5422**
Fax—(609) 392-5861
www.lawrencemoldandtool.com
Email—glesenskyj@lawrencemold.net
Owner—George Lesenskyj
V-P., Sales—Mark L. Board
Hum. Res. Mgr.—Alane Barnick
Tooling Engr.—Roy Glenn
Tooling Engr.—Ken Brown
SIC—3089; 3544; *Plastic injection molding & tool & die shop*
Employs—25; Estab.—1998
Sales—$1Mil-$5Mil
Distrib.—Intl.
Privately owned corporation

**NATIONAL REPROGRAPHICS, INC.**
Div. of NRI
3175 Princeton Pike (08648)
**Phone—(609) 896-4100**
Fax—(609) 896-0829
www.nrinet.com
Email—csr.3175@nrinet.com
GM—Kathy Dotta
SIC—2752; NAICS—323100; *Instant printing & blueprinting*
Employs—2; Estab.—1939
1,470 sq ft site, Distrib.—Regional
Privately owned corporation
AKA: Rethink Color
Parent co.—NRI, New York, NY
   Phone—(212) 366-7000
   See Parent Co. Section for full profile.

**PRINCETON POWER SYSTEMS, INC.**
3175 Princeton Pike, Ste. C (08648-2331)
**Phone—(609) 955-5390**
Fax—(609) 751-9225
www.princetonpower.com
Email—info@princetonpower.com
Co-Founder & Ex. CSO—Darren Hammell
Pres., CEO—Kenneth McCauley
CFO—Matthew Rosner
Hum. Res. Mgr.—Rebecca Goodman
SIC—3823; 3511; 3534; 3612; NAICS—334513; *Electric power converting equipment, including AC-link motor controllers, solar panel arrays & small wind turbines, ropeless elevators & lightweight active transformers*
Employs—48; Estab.—2001
Sales—$10Mil
30,000 sq ft site, Distrib.—Intl.
Privately owned corporation

**REFINERY SYSTEMS, A DIV. OF CORE LAB**
Div. of Core Laboratories, Inc.
11 Princess Rd. (08648)
**Phone—(609) 896-2673**
Fax—(609) 520-1224
www.refinerysystems.com
Email—sales@refinerysystems.com
GM—Craig Tournay
Order Processing Coord.—Joy Lysaght
SIC—3829; *Octane/cetane, CFR engine testing equipment*
Employs—12; Estab.—1967
10,000 sq ft site, Distrib.—Intl.
Privately owned corporation

## Lawrenceville—(cont.)

Parent co.—Core Laboratories,
Inc., Houston, TX
Phone—(713) 328-2673
See Parent Co. Section for full profile.

**RETHINK COLOR, A DIVISION OF
NRI**
Div. of NRI
3175 Princeton Pike (08648)
**Phone—(609) 896-4100**
National—(800) 357-3776
Fax—(609) 896-0829
www.nrinet.com
Email—csr.3175@nrinet.com
Reg. V-P.—Frank Plum
Br. Mgr.—Kathy Dotta
IT Mgr.—Richard Ziegler
Digital Press Mgr.—Lisa Trosko
Large Format Mgr.—Dana Vogel
Asst. Mgr.—Mary Wertz
Cust. Serv. Rep. & Dispatcher—
Ramon Correa
SIC—2759; 2752; NAICS—
323100; *Blueprinting & digital,
color, instant, large-format &
small-format color & 3D printing*
Employs—20; Estab.—1898
Sales—$2.5Mil-$5Mil (est)
20,000 sq ft site, Distrib.—
Regional
Privately owned corporation
AKA: National Reprographics, Inc.
Parent co.—NRI, New York, NY
Phone—(212) 366-7000
See Parent Co. Section for full profile.

**U.S. 1 PUBLISHING CO.**
15 Princess Rd. (08648)
**Phone—(609) 452-7000**
Fax—(609) 452-0033
www.princetoninfo.com
Email—info@princetoninfo.com
Publisher—Richard K. Rein
Special Proj. Mgr.—Sarah
Hastings
Writer—Bill Sans
SIC—2711; *Newspaper
publishing*
Employs—10; Estab.—1984
Sales—$500,000-$1Mil
Distrib.—Local
Privately owned corporation

## Lebanon

(Hunterdon—N.W.)

**AIRSCAN, INC.**
291 Route 22 E., Ste. 12 (08833)
**Phone—(908) 823-9425**
Fax—(908) 823-9428
www.airscan1.com
Email—airscan1@airscan1.com
Pres., CEO—Stephen Shoemaker
Opers. Mgr.—Karla Biondi
R & D Mgr.—Alina Casian
SIC—3826; NAICS—334516; *Gas
monitors for OSHA compliance*
Employs—8; Estab.—1991
Sales—$500,000-$1Mil
3,200 sq ft site, Distrib.—Intl.
Privately owned corporation

**ARTISAN KITCHEN STUDIO, LLC**
26 Cokesbury Rd., P.O. Box 151
(08833)
**Phone—(908) 236-7233**
Fax—(908) 236-7683
www.kitchenstudioinc.com
Email—info@kitchenstudioinc.com
Pres.—Richard Butler
Off. Mgr.—Debra Butler
SIC—2434; 2542; NAICS—
337110; *Wooden & laminate
cabinets & custom kitchen
design services*
Employs—2; Estab.—1987
Sales—$500,000-$1Mil
8,000 sq ft site, Distrib.—Regional
Privately owned corporation

**B & B PRESS, INC.**
24 Cokesbury Rd., Ste. 11 (08833-
2218)
**Phone—(908) 840-4323**
Fax—(908) 840-4358
www.bbpress.com
Email—printit@bbpress.com
Pres., GM—Mark Bistis
V-P. & Prodn. Mgr.—John Bistis
SIC—2752; 2759; NAICS—
323100; *Offset & digital printing,
graphic design & mailing*
Employs—6; Estab.—1922
Sales—$1Mil-$2.5Mil
3,560 sq ft site, Distrib.—Regional
Privately owned corporation

**CLORDISYS SOLUTIONS, INC.**
291 Route 22 E., Salem Industrial
Park 5 (08833)
**Phone—(908) 236-4100**
Fax—(908) 236-2222
www.clordisys.com
Email—info@clordisys.com
Dir., Opers.—Paul Lorcheim
Tech. Mgr.—Mark Czarneski
Engr.—Dan Paznek
Engr.—Kevin Lorcheim
SIC—2899; *Chlorine dioxide
sterilization & decontamination
equipment & services*
Employs—25; Estab.—2001
20,000 sq ft site, Distrib.—Intl.
Privately owned sub-S corp.

**CONSTRUCTION SPECIALTIES, INC.**
3 Werner Way (08833)
**Phone—(908) 236-0800**
National—(800) 972-7214
www.c-sgroup.com
Email—info@c-sgroup.com
Co-Chrm.—Ellen Hallock Hakes
Co-Chrm.—Thomas Hakes
Pres., CEO—Ronald Dadd
V-P., Fin. & CFO—Edward Altieri
CIO—Charles Brown
Ex. V-P.—R. Gordon Stewart
V-P., Sales—Ken Major
Cont.—Frank Clark
Dir., Adv.—Julian Stearns
Dir., Hum. Res.—Marian
Scharnikow
SIC—3354; NAICS—331316;
*Corporate headquarters &
architectural specialty products;
Brand name—Acrovyn; Pedigrid;
Explovent; Pedisystems; APC
Dayliter; Location Smart Louvers;
Zip Block Parking Joint;
Pedimat; PediTred*
Employs—48; Estab.—1948
Worldwide: 1,400
Sales—$200Mil
500,000 sq ft site, Distrib.—Intl.
Privately owned corporation

**CUTTING BOARD CO.**
291 Highway 22 (08833)
Mail addr: 2 Dreahook Rd.,
Branchburg (08876)
**Phone—(908) 725-0187**
National—(866) 247-2409
Fax—(908) 725-6074
www.cuttingboardcompany.com
Email—tony@
cuttingboardcompany.com
Ptnr. & Reg. Mgr.—Anthony
Pizzelanti
Ptnr.—Theresa Pizzelanti
SIC—3231; 2499; 3089; 3083;
NAICS—327215; *Standard,
custom, glass, plastic &
polyethylene sheet cutting
boards*
Employs—3; Estab.—1999
Distrib.—National
Privately owned partnership

**DOGGETT CORP., THE**
30 Cherry St. *(08833)*
**Phone—(908) 236-6335**
(800) 448-1862
Fax—(908) 236-7716

www.doggettcorp.com
Email—mellickr@cs.com
Pres., CEO—Roger D. Mellick
Secy-Treas., MIS & Off. Mgr.—
Pamela Springstun
SIC—2875; NAICS—325314; *Tree
& specialty fertilizers*
Employs—6; Estab.—1935
15,000 sq ft site, Distrib.—Intl.
Privately owned sub-S corp.

**EAST PERFORMANCE EXHAUST**
1050 U.S. Highway 22, Bldg. B
(08833)
**Phone—(908) 236-2820**
www.eastexhaust.com
Email—eastexhaust@aol.com
Pres.—Steve Babinsky
Off. Mgr.—Elizabeth Rajno
SIC—3714; *Automotive exhaust
systems*
Employs—3; Estab.—1988
Sales—$500,000-$1Mil
Distrib.—National
Privately owned corporation

**ENERGY KINETICS, INC.**
51 Molasses Hill Rd. (08833)
**Phone—(908) 735-2066**
National—(800) 735-2066
Fax—(908) 735-2068
www.energykinetics.com
Email—info@energykinetics.com
Pres.—Roger Marran
Sales Mgr., Natl.—Paul Owen
Cust. Serv. Rep.—Missy Urion
SIC—3433; NAICS—333414;
*Boilers & hot water heaters;
Brand name—System 2000;
EKpak*
Employs—45; Estab.—1979
Sales—$1Mil-$2.5Mil
Distrib.—National
Privately owned sub-S corp.

**ENPRO, INC.**
1401 U.S. Highway 22, P.O. Box
418 (08833)
**Phone—(908) 236-2137**
Fax—(908) 236-2137
www.enproinc.biz
Email—enproinc@embarqmail.com
Pres.—Vincent R. Cioffi
Opers. Mgr.—Tom Vincent
SIC—3589; NAICS—333319;
*Deaearators for the power
industry*
Employs—15; Estab.—1961
Sales—$2.5Mil-$5Mil
Distrib.—Intl.
Privately owned corporation

**FROGWORKS.COM, LLC**
48 Sutton Rd. (08833)
**Phone—(908) 832-6704**
Fax—(908) 832-6704
www.frogworks.com
Email—manager@frogworks.com
Pres.—Rolf Margenau
SIC—2731; *Book publishing*
Employs—2; Estab.—1998
Sales—under $500,000
Distrib.—Intl.
Limited Liability Company
AKA: Frogworks Publishing

**HARY MFG., INC.**
24 Cokesbury Rd. (08833)
Mail addr: P.O. Box 187,
Woodbridge (07095-0187)
**Phone—(908) 722-7100**
Fax—(908) 947-0035
www.hmiprinters.com
Email—sales@hmiprinters.com
Pres.—Paul Hary

SIC—3555; NAICS—333293;
*Fully automated screen & stencil
printing equipment for precision
deposition applications,
including thick-film & hybrid &
surface mounts for the
automotive, aerospace,
education, medical &
photovoltaic/solar industries;
Brand name—AMI; Presco;
Affiliated Manufacturers Inc.;
Shami Wipe*
Employs—12; Estab.—1957
Sales—$5Mil-$10Mil
15,000 sq ft site, Distrib.—Intl.
Privately owned corporation

**HEMATECHNOLOGIES, INC.**
291 U.S. Highway 22, Ste. 12
(08833)
**Phone—(908) 823-9430**
Fax—(908) 823-9428
www.hematek.com
Email—hematek@hematek.com
Pres.—Stephen M. Shoemaker
SIC—3826; NAICS—332710;
*Medical laboratory instruments*
Employs—4

**JONATHAN LEASING CORP.**
17 Water St. (08833)
**Phone—(908) 226-3434**
Fax—(908) 226-3435
www.donschreiber.com
Email—info@donschreiber.com
Pres.—Barry A. Reed
V-P., Sales & Mktg.—Nathan
Connell
Fin. Mgr.—Paul Flax
SIC—2782; NAICS—323100;
*Loose-leaf binders, index tabs,
media replication & turned edge
& poly products*
Employs—3; Estab.—1961
30,000 sq ft site, Distrib.—
Regional
Privately owned sub-S corp.
AKA: Schreiber Co., Don

**LEBANON CHEESE CO., INC.**
3 Railroad Ave., P.O. Box 63
(08833)
**Phone—(908) 236-2611**
Pres.—Joe Lotito
Off. Mgr.—David Fredericks
SIC—2022; NAICS—311513;
*Ricotta cheese*
Employs—5; Estab.—1929
Sales—$2.5Mil-$5Mil (est)
Distrib.—Regional
Privately owned corporation

**MOUNTAIN TOP LOGGING, LLC**
P.O. Box 324 (08833)
**Phone—(908) 413-2982**
Pres.—Matthew Good
SIC—2411; *Logging*
Employs—1; Estab.—1996
Sales—under $500,000
Distrib.—Regional
Limited Liability Company

**NODECO MACHINE SERVICE**
5 Wayside Ln. (08833)
**Phone—(908) 236-7996**
Fax—(908) 437-1228
Owner—Richard Nodes
SIC—3599; *CNC machining job
shop*
Employs—1; Estab.—1980
Sales—under $500,000
Distrib.—Regional
Sole ownership

**OPS DIAGNOSTICS, LLC**
291 U.S. Highway 22 E., Bldg. 6
(08833)
**Phone—(908) 253-3444**
Fax—(908) 575-1660
www.opsdiagnostics.com
Email—info@btc-bti.com
Pres.—David Burden

GEOGRAPHICAL

## Lebanon—(cont.)

SIC—3821; 2899; NAICS—
339111; *Laboratory equipment &
reagent prototyping*
Employs—3; Estab.—1989
Sales—$500,000-$1Mil
Distrib.—Intl.
Limited Liability Company

**†PLATE CONCEPTS, INC.**
1221 U.S. Highway 22, Ste. 3
(08833-2228)
**Phone—(908) 236-9570**
Fax—(908) 236-9575
www.plateconcepts.com
Email—info@plateconcepts.com
Pres.—James Gooch
Engr.—Karl Duerwald
SIC—5084; *Wholesaler of plate
heat exchangers*
Employs—10; Estab.—1995
10,000 sq ft site, Distrib.—Intl.
Privately owned corporation

**STAVOLA CONSTRUCTION
MATERIALS, INC.**
Div. of Stavola Contracting Co.,
Inc.
30 Rockaway Rd. (08833)
Mail addr: P.O. Box 482, Tinton
Falls (07724)
**Phone—(908) 439-2800**
Fax—(732) 356-2175
www.stavola.com
Email—information@stavola.com
Plt. Supt.—Juan Berrios
SIC—3281; NAICS—327991;
*Crushed stone*
Employs—5; Estab.—2001
Distrib.—Regional
Privately owned corporation
Parent co.—Stavola Contracting
Co., Inc., Tinton Falls, NJ
Phone—(732) 542-2328
See Parent Co. Section for full profile.

**WEBER & SCHER MFG. CO., INC.**
1231 US Highway 22 E., P.O. Box
366 (08833)
**Phone—(908) 236-8484**
Fax—(908) 236-7001
www.webscher.com
Email—webscher@webscher.com
Chrm., CEO—J. William Scher
Pres.—Gregory Scher
V-P., Fin. & Pers. Mgr.—J. Douglas
Scher
Sales Mgr.—David Brown
Plt. Opers. Mgr.—Jim Kling
MIS Mgr.—Gregory Bogut
SIC—3643; 3549; NAICS—
335931; *Machinery & equipment
for the manufacturing of
nonferrous wire & cables*
Employs—35; Estab.—1915
30,000 sq ft site, Distrib.—Intl.
Privately owned sub-S corp.

## Ledgewood
(Morris—N.W.)

**ADAM METAL PRODUCTS**
7 Orben Dr., P.O. Box 450 (07852)
**Phone—(973) 770-1100**
Fax—(973) 770-1105
www.adammetal.com
Email—info@adammetal.com
Pres.—Raymond B. Bentley
Cont.—Asha Shah
GM—Robert H. Smith
Sales Mgr.—Christopher Newman
Plt. Mgr.—Ed Bentley
Cust. Serv. Rep.—Paul Groover
SIC—3646; 3645; NAICS—
335122; *Commercial &
residential lighting fixtures,
suspended linear products &
proprietary units*
Employs—50; Estab.—1948
75,000 sq ft site, Distrib.—National
Privately owned corporation

**ALL QUALITY FENCE**
1266 Route 46, P.O. Box 85
(07852)
**Phone—(973) 927-0722**
Fax—(973) 927-1094
www.allqualityfencenj.com
Email—allqualityfence@yahoo.com
Owner—John Johnson
Pres., Hum. Res. Mgr.—Tom
Lemma
V-P.—Chris Lemma
SIC—3496; 2499; 3089; NAICS—
332323; *Aluminum, red & white
cedar, chain-link & PVC fencing;
Brand name—Jerith; Alumi
Guard; Bufftech; Homeland*
Employs—6; Estab.—1960
3,600 sq ft site, Distrib.—Local
Sole ownership

**CASTLE PRINTING, INC.**
1501 U.S. Highway 46 (07852)
**Phone—(973) 584-0990**
(973) 584-1660
Fax—(973) 584-6996
www.castleprinters.com
Email—info@castleprinters.com
Ptnr. & Pres.—Kevin Ebner
Ptnr. & V-P.—James M. Storms,
Sr.
SIC—2752; 2759; NAICS—
323100; *Offset, instant, wide-
format & digital color printing,
binding & UV coating*
Employs—9; Estab.—1990
Sales—under $1Mil
8,000 sq ft site, Distrib.—National
Privately owned sub-S corp.

**CHESHIRE STUDIO, INC.**
261 Main St., 2nd Fl. (07852)
**Phone—(973) 240-7360**
Fax—(973) 240-7363
www.cheshirestudioinc.com
Email—cheshirestudio@
optimum.net
Pres.—Jack Hurdes
V-P.—Nancy Hurdes
SIC—2759; 3993; NAICS—
323100; *Commercial printing,
advertising specialties & graphic
design*
Employs—2; Estab.—1987
3,000 sq ft site, Distrib.—Local
Privately owned sub-S corp.

**†CINTAS FIRE PROTECTION**
Div. of Cintas Corp.
1705 U.S. Route 46 W. (07852)
**Phone—(973) 347-3901**
Fax—(973) 347-3905
www.cintas.com
Email—info@cintas.com
Off. Mgr.—Paula Cincotta
SIC—5099; 5087; *Distributor of
fire extinguishers & sprinkler
systems*
Employs—30; Estab.—2004
Distrib.—National
Publicly owned corporation
Parent co.—Cintas Corp., Mason,
OH
Phone—(513) 459-1200
See Parent Co. Section for full profile.

**DEZINE LINE, INC.**
1104 Route 46 E. (07852)
**Phone—(973) 989-1009**
National—(800) 240-8337
Fax—(973) 989-1150
www.dezineline.com
Email—info@dezineline.com
Pres.—Steve Mattero
SIC—2396; 2395; *Textile screen
printing & embroidery*
Employs—6; Estab.—1983
3,000 sq ft site, Distrib.—Regional
Privately owned sub-S corp.

**KENVIL WELDERY & MACHINE, INC.**
15 Kings Pkwy. (07852)
**Phone—(973) 584-1729**
Fax—(973) 584-4041

www.kenvilweldery.com
Email—gary@kenvilweldery.com
Pres.—Gary Magura
SIC—3599; 3444; *Metal
fabrication & machining &
welding job shop*
Employs—3; Estab.—1946
Sales—under $500,000
3,800 sq ft site, Distrib.—Regional
Privately owned corporation

**SIGN-A-RAMA LEDGEWOOD**
244 Main St. (07852)
**Phone—(973) 584-9301**
National—(888) 584-9301
Fax—(973) 584-9332
Email—sarledgewood@aol.com
Pres., Sales—Michael Grivalsky
V-P., Prodn.—Steven Grivalsky
SIC—3993; *Electric signs,
monuments & specialty projects,
including in-house fabrication,
service & installation*
Employs—6; Estab.—1990
Sales—$500,000-$1Mil (est)
8,500 sq ft site, Distrib.—Regional
Privately owned corporation

## Leesburg
(Cumberland—S.W.)

**ALLEN STEEL CO.**
202 High St. (08327)
**Phone—(856) 785-1171**
Pres.—James P. Allen III
SIC—3732; 3556; NAICS—
333294; *Commercial fishing
boats & food processing
equipment*
Employs—5; Estab.—1952
Sales—$2.6Mil-$5Mil
Distrib.—Regional
Privately owned corporation

## Leonardo
(Monmouth—N.E.)

**JERSEY SHORE COFFEE
ROASTERS, LLC**
64 Thompson Ave., Ste. B (07737)
**Phone—(732) 291-0505**
Fax—(732) 291-0505
www.jerseyshorecoffeeroasters.co
m
Email—info@
jerseyshorecoffeeroasters.com
Manager—Greg Martinez
SIC—2095; NAICS—311920;
*Coffee roasting*
Employs—4; Estab.—2004
Sales—$2.5Mil-$5Mil (est)
Distrib.—Intl.
Limited Liability Company

## Leonia
(Bergen—N.E.)

**†APPLE FOOD SALES CO., INC.**
117 Fort Lee Rd., Ste. B-7 (07605)
**Phone—(201) 592-0277**
Fax—(201) 585-7244
Email—agrusa@agrusainc.com
Pres.—Jill Bush
Manager—Donna Bush
SIC—5149; *Distributor of Italian
food products, including vinegar*
Employs—15; Estab.—1987
Distrib.—National
Privately owned sub-S corp.

**†INDUKEY NORTH AMERICA, LLC**
329 Moore Ave. (07605)
**Phone—(877) 588-2172**
National—(866) 463-8539
Fax—(877) 588-2172
www.indukey-na.com
Email—info@indukey-na.com
Pres.—Roland Weimer
Sales Mgr.—Andrea Ebersbach

SIC—5045; *Distributor of
industrial, medical & rugged
computer keyboards & input
devices; Brand name—InduKey;
InduProof; InduProofmed;
InduMedical; InduMoose;
InduStyle; InduMousemed;
InduSteel; InduDur; InduSense*
Employs—2; Estab.—2007
Distrib.—Intl.
Limited Liability Company

**KULITE SEMICONDUCTOR
PRODUCTS, INC.**
1 Willow Tree Rd. (07605)
**Phone—(201) 461-0900**
Fax—(201) 461-0990
www.kulite.com
Email—info-kulite@kulite.com
Chrm. of the Board & CEO—Nora
Kurtz
Vice Chrm.—Lou DeRosa
Pres.—Dick Martin
CFO—Abraham Morcos
V-P., Miniature Transducer Sales—
George Boctor
Cont.—Steve Masciale
Dir., Adv. & Creative—Ira Levine
Pur. Mgr.—Glenn Hric
MIS Mgr.—Omar Gonzalez
Qual. Control Mgr.—Eileen
McMorrow-Ricca
SIC—3829; *Miniature high
frequency & flight qualified
pressure transducers, wind
tunnel engine pressure probes,
turbine blade implants &
transducers for process &
manufacturing control & the
automotive test industry*
Employs—750; Estab.—1959
Sales—$25Mil-$100Mil
200,000 sq ft site, Distrib.—Intl.
Privately owned corporation
ISO rating—9001

**OZONIA NORTH AMERICA, LLC**
600 Willow Tree Rd. (07605)
**Phone—(201) 676-2525**
Fax—(201) 346-5460
www.ozonia.com
Email—sales@ozonia.com
CEO—Anthony Dusovic
Sales Mgr.—Gaspar Lesznik
SIC—3589; NAICS—333319;
*Water & wastewater treatment
equipment, ozone generators &
ultraviolet disinfection systems*
Employs—50
Sales—$1Mil-$5Mil
35,000 sq ft site, Distrib.—Intl.
Privately owned corporation

**PACICCO & CO. JEWELERS**
331 Broad Ave. (07605)
**Phone—(201) 947-1106**
Fax—(201) 947-7414
Email—paciccocompany@aol.com
Pres.—Robert Pacicco
Mktg. Mgr.—Kate Moran
Pers. Mgr.—Katherine Pacicco
SIC—3911; NAICS—339911;
*Precious metal jewelry*
Employs—5; Estab.—1920
2,000 sq ft site, Distrib.—National
Privately owned corporation

**SOLGAR, INC.**
500 Willow Tree Rd. (07605)
**Phone—(201) 944-2311**
National—(800) 645-2246
Fax—(201) 944-7351
www.solgar.com
Email—publicrelations@solgar.com
Hum. Res. Mgr.—Rose Asvala
SIC—2833; NAICS—325411;
*Nutritional supplements*
Employs—100; Estab.—1947
Sales—$50Mil-$100Mil
Distrib.—Intl.
Privately owned corporation

## Leonia—(cont.)

**TEKKOTE CORP.**
Div. of Mondi Akrosil, LLC
580 Willow Tree Rd. (07605)
**Phone—(201) 585-8875**
National—(800) 252-2203
Fax—(201) 585-9122
www.tekkote.com
Dir., Fin.—Ron Saia
GM—Paul Ortiz
Hum. Res. Mgr.—Beth Arp
SIC—2671; NAICS—322222;
*Corporate headquarters &
silicone-coated release liner
finishing for pressure-sensitive
adhesive products*
Employs—90; Estab.—1988
Sales—$10Mil-$25Mil (est)
65,000 sq ft site, Distrib.—National
Publicly owned corporation
Parent co.—Mondi Akrosil, LLC,
Pleasant Prairie, WI
Phone—(262) 997-3000
See Parent Co. Section for full profile.

## Liberty Corner
(Somerset—N.E.)

**NEW HORIZON PRESS, INC.**
34 Church St. (07938)
Mail addr: P.O. Box 669, Far Hills
(07931-0669)
**Phone—(908) 604-6311**
Fax—(908) 604-6330
www.newhorizonpressbooks.com
Email—nhp@
newhorizonpressbooks.com
Pres., Publisher—Joan Dunphy
Asst. Editor—Caroline
Russomanno
SIC—2731; *Book publishing*
Employs—4; Estab.—1983
Sales—under $500,000
Distrib.—National
Privately owned corporation

**SEAL SPOUT CORP.**
50 Allen Rd., P.O. Box 74 (07938)
**Phone—(908) 647-1900**
Fax—(908) 647-0648
www.sealspout.com
Email—info@sealspout.com
Prodn. Mgr.—Frank Lombardo
Engr.—Peter Janocik
SIC—3565; NAICS—333993;
*Packaging machinery*
Employs—12; Estab.—1944
Sales—$1Mil-$2.5Mil
15,000 sq ft site, Distrib.—Intl.
Privately owned corporation

## Lincoln Park
(Morris—N.W.)

**ABOX AUTOMATION CORP.**
2 Frassetto Way, Unit 2 (07035)
**Phone—(973) 659-9611**
Fax—(973) 659-9811
www.aboxautomation.com
Email—cs@aboxautomation.com
Mng. Ptnr.—Steve Kanthan
Mng. Ptnr.—Sean Keogh
Pres.—Harish Tailor
V-P.—Dave Pfaff
SIC—3569; *Precision feeding,
cutting & dispensing machinery*
Employs—4; Estab.—2004
4,000 sq ft site, Distrib.—National
Privately owned corporation

**ACTION GRAPHICS, INC.**
600 Ryerson Rd., Ste. G (07035)
**Phone—(973) 633-6500**
National—(800) 365-6687
Fax—(973) 633-0660
www.actiongraphicsnj.com
Email—actiongrnj@aol.com
Pres., CFO & Treas.—Dale E. Park
Bookkeeper—Judy Steves

SIC—2759; 2796; NAICS—
323122; *Commercial printing &
mailing services*
Employs—24; Estab.—1972
20,000 sq ft site, Distrib.—
Regional
Privately owned corporation

**AIRGAS EAST, INC.**
1-D Frassetto Way (07035)
**Phone—(973) 633-9666**
National—(866) 924-7427
Fax—(973) 633-9669
www.airgas.com
Email—info@airgas.com
Br. Mgr.—Alex Jimenez
Opers. Mgr.—Jack Denning
Off. Mgr.—Janice Walson
SIC—2813; NAICS—325120;
*Medical gases*
Employs—25; Estab.—1972
Sales—$1Mil-$2.5Mil
6,400 sq ft site, Distrib.—Regional
Publicly owned corporation
Parent co.—Airgas East, Inc.,
Salem, NH
Phone—(603) 890-4600
See Parent Co. Section for full profile.

**†APRIA HEALTHCARE, INC.**
1 Frassetto Way, Ste. F (07035)
**Phone—(973) 305-0099**
National—(800) 672-1946
Fax—(973) 305-8780
www.apria.com
Email—contact_us@apria.com
Br. Mgr.—Rosemary Berkowitz
SIC—5047; 5169; *Distributor of
durable medical equipment &
supplies, including oxygen
cylinders, wheelchairs & hospital
beds*
Employs—30; Estab.—1993
Distrib.—National
Publicly owned corporation
Parent co.—Apria Healthcare, Inc.,
Lake Forest, CA
Phone—(949) 639-2000
See Parent Co. Section for full profile.

**ERL EMBROIDERY & SCREEN
PRINTING**
8 Evergreen Dr. (07035)
**Phone—(973) 633-7428**
Email—promogear@optonline.net
CEO—Michael Hackett
Pres.—Elizabeth Hackett
SIC—2395; 2396; *Textile
embroidery & screen printing*
Employs—2; Estab.—2004
Sales—under $500,000 (est)
Distrib.—Local
Privately owned corporation

**HISHI PLASTICS U. S. A., INC.**
600-F Ryerson Rd. (07035)
**Phone—(973) 633-1230**
Fax—(973) 872-8381
www.hishiplastics.com
Email—customerservice@
hishiplastics.com
Cont., Hum. Res. Mgr. &
Accountant—Maiko Kishinaka
Cust. Serv. Mgr.—Lisa Silvano
Cust. Serv. Rep.—Kathy Ricker
SIC—3082; NAICS—326121; *PVC
heat shrinkable tubing &
electronic condensers for the
food/beverage, pharmaceutical,
health/beauty, battery &
sportings goods industries*
Employs—62; Estab.—1985
Sales—$5Mil-$10Mil
20,000 sq ft site, Distrib.—Intl.
Privately owned corporation

NEW ENTRY
**JHDS, LLC**
107 Beaverbrook Rd., Ste. 3
(07035)
**Phone—(973) 782-4086**
Fax—(800) 762-8201
www.jhdsllc.com

Email—estimating@jhdsllc.com
Ptnr.—Santosh Salvi
Ptnr.—Jorge Hermida, Sr.
Ptnr.—Jorge Hermida, Jr.
SIC—3441; *Structural steel
fabrication*
Employs—15
Sales—$2.5Mil-$5Mil (est)
1,000 sq ft site,
Limited Liability Company

NEW ENTRY
**LIFE & LEISURE, LLC**
234 Main St., Ste. 2 (07035)
**Phone—(973) 696-8009**
Fax—(973) 556-1991
www.lifeandleisurenj.com
Email—info@lifeandleisurenj.com
Publisher & Editor—Joe Pellegrino
SIC—2711; *Newpaper publishing*
Employs—8; Estab.—2003
Sales—$500,000-$1Mil
Distrib.—Local
Limited Liability Company

**NASA MACHINE TOOLS, INC.**
1-B Frassetto Way (07035)
Mail addr: P.O. Box 157, Pompton
Plains (07444-0157)
**Phone—(973) 633-5200**
Fax—(973) 633-5727
www.nassamachine.com
Email—sales@nassamachine.com
Pres.—Bob DeGeorge
V-P.—Bob DeGeorge, Jr.
GM—Bob Mancinelli
Foreman—Dwayne DiBuono
SIC—3541; NAICS—333512;
*Precision & CNC machine tools*
Employs—25; Estab.—1979
Sales—$5Mil-$10Mil
12,000 sq ft site, Distrib.—Intl.
Privately owned sub-S corp.

**TEKNICS INDUSTRIES, INC.**
170 Beaver Brook Rd. (07035)
**Phone—(973) 633-7575**
www.teknics.com
Pres.—Bruce Robertson
Cont.—Dennis Diaz
Opers., Sales & Mktg. Mgr.—David
Robertson
Off. Mgr.—Dan Koester
Acting Off. Mgr.—Michael
Gallagher
SIC—3542; 3599; NAICS—
333513; *Industrial automation &
heavy truck Class 8 frame rail
manufacturing systems,
automotive, special built
machines & CNC machine tools*
Employs—24; Estab.—1978
30,000 sq ft site, Distrib.—Intl.
Privately owned corporation

**TRANSMISSION TECHNOLOGY
CORP.**
1 High Mountain Trl. (07035)
**Phone—(973) 305-3600**
Email—djfolenta@optonline.net
Pres.—Dezi Folenta
SIC—3728; 3732; *Helicopter &
marine vessel transmission &
power systems prototypes*
Employs—1; Estab.—1970
Sales—$500,000-$1Mil
Distrib.—Intl.
Privately owned corporation

**UNGERER & CO.**
4 Bridgewater Ln., P.O. Box U
(07035)
**Phone—(973) 628-0600**
Fax—(973) 628-0251
www.ungererandcompany.com
Email—na@
ungererandcompany.com
Pres.—Kenneth G. Voorhees
CFO—Richard Dambres, Jr.
Sales Mgr.—Kenneth G. Voorhees
III
Hum. Res. Mgr.—Marie English

SIC—2844; 2869; NAICS—
325600; *Company headquarters
& fragrances & flavors*
Employs—135
Distrib.—Intl.

## Lincroft
(Monmouth—N.E.)

**MCKNIGHT DRAPERY SERVICES**
126 Majestic S. (07738)
**Phone—(732) 741-3655**
Fax—(732) 741-3516
Owner—Gail McKnight
SIC—2391; NAICS—314121;
*Draperies*
Employs—1; Estab.—1976
Sales—$500,000-$1Mil
Distrib.—Local
Privately owned partnership

## Linden
(Union—N.E.)

**A & C CATALYSTS, iNC.**
1600 W. Blancke St. (07036)
**Phone—(908) 474-9393**
(908) 636-2273
www.ac-catalysts.com
Email—info@ac-catalysts.com
Dir., Mktg., Consumer—John
Wolfe
Dir., Indl. Mktg.—Doug Sober
Dir.—Abraham Goldstein
Info. Mgr.—Dave Rawlins
Cust. Serv. Rep.—Linnaea Nowold
SIC—2821; NAICS—325211;
*Plastic resins; Brand name—
Aminopearl™; Resicure™;
Technicure™; Technirez™*
Employs—35; Estab.—1987
Sales—$10Mil-$25Mil
44,000 sq ft site, Distrib.—Intl.
Privately owned sub-S corp.
ISO rating—9001:2008

**A&M INDUSTRIAL, INC.**
325 Commerce Rd. (07036)
Mail addr: P.O. Box 1044, Rahway
(07065-3282)
**Phone—(908) 862-1800**
Fax—(732) 574-2081
www.am-ind.com
Email—sales@am-ind.com
Ex. V-P.—David Young
Br. Mgr.—John Smickenbecker
SIC—3492; 3829; 5084; NAICS—
332912; *Manufacturer of
industrial & hydraulic hose
assemblies & measurement &
testing equipment for the
petrochemical industry &
distributor of gas detection
equipment & SCBAs; Brand
name—Petro-Marine; MSA;
Honeywell Safety; Goodyear;
Aeroquip; Dixon*
Employs—10; Estab.—1975
Sales—$1Mil-$2.5Mil
Distrib.—Regional
Privately owned corporation
AKA: Petro Marine
Parent co.—A&M Industrial, Inc.,
Rahway, NJ
Phone—(732) 574-1111
See Parent Co. Section for full profile.

**AB PRECISION CO.**
1506 E. Elizabeth Ave. (07036)
**Phone—(908) 925-1356**
Fax—(908) 925-9756
www.abprecisionco.com
Email—abprecisionco@verizon.net
Pres.—Puzant Duznatian
SIC—3544; NAICS—333500;
*Plastic injection molds & tool &
die job shop*
Employs—2; Estab.—1980
Sales—under $500,000
7,500 sq ft site, Distrib.—National
Privately owned corporation

GEOGRAPHICAL

# Linden—(cont.)

**ACE NEON FACTORY, LLC**

2101 Grier Ave. (07036)
**Phone—(908) 486-6366**
Fax—(908) 486-6366
www.aceneonfactory.com
Email—scott@aceneonfactory.com
Pres.—Scott Fedor
SIC—3993; *Custom neon signs & neon sign repair services*
Employs—3; Estab.—1955
Sales—$1Mil-$2.5Mil
Distrib.—National
Limited Liability Company

**ADVANCE MACHINE, INC.**

531 Pennsylvania Ave. (07036)
**Phone—(908) 486-7244**
Fax—(908) 925-3267
Email—advancemachine1@verizon.net
Pres.—Richard Walano, Sr.
V-P. & Prodn. Mgr.—Carl M. Walano
Plt. Mgr.—Richard Walano, Jr.
SIC—3599; *Precision machining job shop*
Employs—7; Estab.—1971
Sales—$1Mil-$2.5Mil
Distrib.—National
Privately owned corporation

**ADVANCED ORIENTATION SYSTEMS, INC.**

2525 E. Brunswick Ave., Ste. 205 (07036)
**Phone—(908) 474-9595**
Fax—(908) 474-9090
www.aositilt.com
Email—sales@aositilt.com
Pres., Fin. & Opers. Mgr.—Marty Berger
V-P., MIS & R & D—Eli Marianovsky
SIC—3825; 3812; NAICS—334511; *Electrolytic tilt sensors, inclinometers, tilt alarms & electronic compasses*
Employs—9; Estab.—1995
1,440 sq ft site, Distrib.—Intl.
Privately owned sub-S corp.

**AJAY METAL FABRICATORS, INC.**

355 Dalziel Rd. (07036)
**Phone—(908) 523-0558**
      (908) 523-0557
Fax—(908) 523-0560
www.ajaymetal.com
Email—ajaymetal@aol.com
Pres.—Tony Zambell
Off. Mgr.—Jeanette Zambell
Off. Mgr.—Carolyn Zambell
SIC—3443; 3444; 3446; 3537; NAICS—332999; *Steel, aluminum, stainless, copper & titanium fabrication of hydraulic tanks, machine guards, railings, platforms, hoppers, racks & stands*
Employs—9; Estab.—1977
Sales—$500,000-$1Mil
13,500 sq ft site, Distrib.—Local
Privately owned corporation

**ALPHA PRECISION MOLD**

8 Roselle St. *(07036)*
**Phone—(908) 587-9090**
Fax—(908) 587-9020
www.alphaprecisionmold.com
Email—info@alphaprecisionmold.com
Owner—Hugo Daniel Santos

SIC—3544; 3543; 3479; *Custom high-precision plastic molds & prototypes, including injection molds, rapid prototyping, mold revision & engineering & 3D surface machining of soft & hard metal, hard milling, polishing & CNC EDM services & artwork*
Employs—3; Estab.—2009
Sales—$750,000
4,000 sq ft site, Distrib.—National
Limited Liability Company

**AMERICAN MICA CORP.**

1015 Pennsylvania Ave. (07036)
**Phone—(908) 587-5237**
Fax—(908) 587-5238
Email—americanmicacorp@yahoo.com
Pres.—Ray Bailey
Off. Mgr.—Eileen Bailey
SIC—2431; NAICS—321900; *Architectural millwork*
Employs—3; Estab.—1979
Sales—under $500,000
6,000 sq ft site, Distrib.—Local
Privately owned sub-S corp.

**B & B ELECTROPLATING CO.**

559 Pennsylvania Ave. *(07036)*
**Phone—(908) 925-5044**
Fax—(908) 925-1936
www.bbplating.com
Email—r2thistle@aol.com
Owner & Co-Pres.—Russell Thistle
Co-Pres.—Edwin Wristen
Hum. Res., IT & Off. Mgr.—Kathy Markle
SIC—3471; NAICS—332813; *Electroplating, including tin, silver, nickel, barrel, rack, bus bar & aluminum*
Employs—15; Estab.—1960
Sales—$1Mil-$2.5Mil
23,000 sq ft site, Distrib.—Intl.
Privately owned corporation

[NEW ENTRY]
**†BAG FACTORY, INC., THE**

726 N. Stiles St. (07036)
**Phone—(908) 925-7122**
National—(800) 242-4640
Fax—(908) 925-0023
www.nationalbingoonline.com
Email—sales@nationalbingoonline.com
Owner—Charlie Klein
SIC—5113; *Distributor of bingo bags, papers, ink markers, balls, cages, lottery balls & chips*
Employs—4

**BAKERS BOUNTY**

7 Maple Ave. (07036)
**Phone—(908) 587-1602**
www.bakersbounty.net
Owner—Gerry LaPrete
SIC—2051; NAICS—311812; *Baked goods, including cakes & pies*
Employs—7; Estab.—1979
Sales—$500,000-$1Mil (est)
Distrib.—Local
Privately owned corporation

**†BEISLER AMERICA, LLC**

1841 E. Elizabeth Ave., P.O. Box 1683 (07036)
**Phone—(908) 925-4040**
Fax—(908) 925-3052
www.beisleramerica.com
Email—beisler@aol.com
Pres.—Ron Liang

SIC—5084; 5046; *Distributor of industrial & commercial sewing machines & pressing, fusing, iron, vacuum table & industrial knitting equipment; Brand name—Beisler America; Strobel; Duerkopp Adler; Japsew; Pfaff; Pegasus; Weishi; Efka Motoers; Beckmann; Clinton Industries; Lucas Textile Machines; Juki; Brother; German Guetermann Thread*
Employs—5; Estab.—1986
Sales—$2Mil
8,000 sq ft site, Distrib.—Intl.
Privately owned corporation
AKA: Lucas America Inc.

**BRODIE SYSTEM, INC.**

1539 W. Elizabeth Ave. *(07036)*
**Phone—(908) 862-8620**
Fax—(908) 862-8632
www.brodiesystem.com
Email—customerservice@brodiesystem.com
Opers. Mgr.—John Farrell
Manager—Nicholas Lloyd
SIC—3599; *General machining job shop*
Employs—15; Estab.—1929
Distrib.—Regional
Privately owned corporation

**CALTEX INDUSTRIES, INC.**

1301 W. Elizabeth Ave., Ste. E-1 (07036)
**Phone—(973) 273-1707**
Fax—(973) 923-8000
www.caltexindustries.com
Email—caltexind@verizon.net
Pres.—Arnold Gottfried
SIC—2299; *Wiping cloths from recycled apparel & nonapparel closeouts*
Employs—20; Estab.—2003
Sales—$1Mil-$2.5Mil
Distrib.—Intl.
Privately owned corporation

**CAMIN CARGO CONTROL, INC. (H Q)**

230 Marion Ave. (07036)
**Phone—(908) 523-0616**
Fax—(908) 862-1622
www.camincargo.com
Email—sales@camincargo.com
Pres.—Carlos Camin
CFO—Claudio Camin
IT Mgr.—Marcelo Remotti
SIC—1389; *Corporate headquarters; oilfield services*
Employs—60

**CAPITAL FOODS, INC.**

1701 E. Elizabeth Ave. (07036)
**Phone—(908) 587-9050**
Fax—(908) 587-9052
www.capitalfoods.com
Email—capitalfoods@comcast.net
Pres.—Joseph Falcone
Secy., Bookkeeper—Virginia Connors
SIC—2022; NAICS—311513; *Ricotta cheese*
Employs—22; Estab.—1992
Sales—$500,000-$1Mil
Distrib.—National
Privately owned corporation

**CDI GROUP, INC.**

1135 W. Elizabeth Ave. *(07036)*
**Phone—(908) 862-1493**
      (800) 339-8246
Fax—(908) 862-9018
www.cdigroupinc.com
Email—info@cdigroupinc.com
CEO—Jordan Ruddy
Pres.—Bart Shulman
Sales Mgr. & Pur. Agt.—Richard Constant

SIC—2541; 5199; *Manufacturer of custom modular trade show exhibits, including design/build & distributor of portable trade show displays; Brand name—Laarhoven; Classic; Moss; Metalli*
Employs—20; Estab.—1943
Sales—$1Mil-$5Mil
32,000 sq ft site, Distrib.—Intl.
Privately owned corporation

**CENTRAL POLY CORP.**

2400 Bedle Pl. (07036)
**Phone—(908) 862-7570**
Fax—(908) 862-9019
www.centralpoly.com
Email—dave@centralpoly.com
Pres.—Andrew Hoffer
V-P., GM—David Freier
Administrator—Nicole Lawson
SIC—2673; *Plastic bags*
Employs—10; Estab.—1993
Sales—$1Mil-$2.5Mil
Distrib.—Local
Privately owned corporation

**COLORCO, INC.**

1261 W. Elizabeth Ave. (07036)
**Phone—(908) 862-3010**
Fax—(908) 862-7443
www.colorco-flo.com
Email—diane@colorco-flo.com
Pres.—Christopher Bates
V-P.—Art Howard
Treas.—Diane Galgoci
Technical Dir.—Robert Patton
Plt. Mgr.—Mike Penson
SIC—2851; NAICS—325510; *Custom dry color & color concentrates for plastic components manufacturers*
Employs—34; Estab.—1962
15,000 sq ft site, Distrib.—Intl.
Privately owned corporation
Also see: Colorflo, Inc., same loc.

**COLORFLO, INC.**

1261 W. Elizabeth Ave. (07036)
**Phone—(908) 862-3010**
Fax—(908) 862-7443
www.colorco-flo.com
Email—diane@colorco-flo.com
Pres.—Harold Penson
Treas.—Diane Galgoci
SIC—2851; NAICS—325510; *Liquid colorants & PVC dispersions for injection, blow, rotational & compression molding, profile & sheet extrusions, blown film, ribbon & thermoforming*
Employs—5; Estab.—1984
Sales—$500,000-$1Mil
5,000 sq ft site, Distrib.—Regional
Also see: Colorco, Inc., same loc.

**COMPLY, INC.**

330 Dalziel Rd. (07036)
**Phone—(908) 862-6600**
National—(800) 836-4750
Fax—(908) 862-6004
www.complyinc.com
Email—info@immonline.com
Off. & Sales Mgr.—Shari Klein-Katz
SIC—2761; NAICS—323116; *Commercial business form printing*
Employs—10; Estab.—1988
Sales—$1Mil-$2.5Mil (est)
Distrib.—National
Privately owned corporation
Also see: Integrated Media Management, LLC, same loc.

**†COOPER ELECTRIC SUPPLY CO.**

1805 Lower Rd. (07036)
**Phone—(732) 340-0346**
Fax—(732) 340-0187
www.cooper-electric.com
Email—cooperonline@cooper-electric.com
Br. Mgr.—Anthony Merola

## Linden—(cont.)

SIC—5063; *Distributor of electrical equipment & supplies, including connectors, wires & sockets*
Employs—10; Estab.—1981
Distrib.—Local
Privately owned corporation
Parent co.—Cooper Electric Supply Co., Monroe, NJ
Phone—(732) 747-2233
See Parent Co. Section for full profile.

### COUNTY GRAPHICS FORMS MANAGEMENT CO.

2 Stercho Rd. (07036)
**Phone—(908) 474-9797**
Fax—(908) 474-5232
www.countygraphics.com
Email—webmaster@countygraphics.com
Pres.—Robert Gaudiosi
SIC—2761; NAICS—323116; *Business form printing*
Employs—20; Estab.—1998
Sales—$2.5Mil-$5Mil (est)
Distrib.—Regional
Privately owned corporation

### COX PRINTERS

1634 E. Elizabeth Ave. (07036)
**Phone—(908) 928-1010**
Fax—(908) 928-1212
www.coxprinters.com
Email—info@coxprinters.com
Pres.—Michael Kaufman
CFO—Sally Kaufman
Off. Mgr.—Cindy Pumar
SIC—2759; 2752; NAICS—323122; *Commercial, offset & digital printing, direct mail & warehouse fulfillment services*
Employs—28; Estab.—1907
18,000 sq ft site, Distrib.—National
Privately owned corporation
Also see: SpectraMedia, same loc.

### CREATIVE DESIGN PLUS

1634 E. Elizabeth Ave. (07036)
**Phone—(732) 287-3336**
Fax—(732) 287-3293
www.cdpmarketing.com
Email—sales@cdpmarketing.com
GM—Ping Larrabee
SIC—2759; 3993; 2542; 2541; NAICS—323100; *Commercial printing, advertising specialties, signs, banners, trade show displays & graphic design*
Employs—8; Estab.—2002
Sales—$1Mil
4,000 sq ft site, Distrib.—National
Limited Liability Company

### CUSTOM BANDAG, INC.

401 E. Linden Ave. (07036)
**Phone—(908) 862-2400**
Fax—(908) 862-2761
www.custombandag.com
Email—service@custombandag.com
Chrm., Pres.—Fernando de Jesus
V.-P., Secy.—Maria E. de Jesus
GM—Jack Ventura
Sales Mgr.—Anthony Spurdis
Cred. Mgr.—Isilda Barata
Pers. & Pub. Rels. Mgr.—Margareth de Jesus
SIC—3011; NAICS—326211; *Tire retreading*
Employs—40; Estab.—1975
35,000 sq ft site, Distrib.—Regional
Privately owned sub-S corp.

### CUSTOM FABRICATORS, INC.

400 Commerce Rd. (07036)
**Phone—(908) 862-4244**
Fax—(908) 862-4245
www.metalfab.net
Email—amada245@aol.com
Pres.—Joseph Bonanno

SIC—3444; 3581; NAICS—333311; *Sheet metal fabrication & coin-operated machine component parts*
Employs—8; Estab.—1987
Distrib.—Local
Privately owned corporation

### CUTTING EDGE CASTING, INC.

1233 W. Saint Georges Ave. (07036)
**Phone—(908) 925-7500**
Fax—(908) 925-9240
www.cuttingedgecatalog.com
Email—sales@cuttingedgecatalog.com
Pres.—Steven Filler
V.-P.—Thomas Hazel
Hum. Res. Mgr.—Bilka Martinz
SIC—3325; 3322; NAICS—331513; *Metal castings & stampings*
Employs—30; Estab.—1993
40,000 sq ft site, Distrib.—Local
Privately owned corporation

### D & G PRECISION

709 Louis Ave. (07036)
**Phone—(908) 925-1578**
Owner—Jesse Lesniak
SIC—3599; *Precision machining job shop*
Employs—2
Sales—under $500,000 (est)
Distrib.—Local
Sole ownership

### DANA POLY INC.

1301 W. Elizabeth Ave. (07036)
**Phone—(908) 474-0600**
      (800) 474-1020
Fax—(908) 474-0604
www.danapoly.com
Email—sales@danapoly.com
CEO—Mendy Rosner
SIC—2673; *Plastic & polyethylene bags*
Employs—40; Estab.—1992
Sales—$4Mil-$10Mil
Distrib.—National

### D'ANGELO METAL PRODUCTS CO., INC.

360 Dalziel Rd. (07036)
**Phone—(908) 862-8220**
Email—dampco@hotmail.com
Pres.—John D'Angelo
Plt. Mgr.—Tony Scamarzella
Pkg. Mgr.—Kathleen Matlaga
SIC—3432; NAICS—332900; *Shower arms, nipples, plumbing supplies & contract nickel & chrome plating*
Employs—14; Estab.—1946
Sales—$1Mil-$5Mil
25,000 sq ft site, Distrib.—National
Privately owned corporation

### EAGLE STEEL & IRON, LLC

7 Garfield St. (07036)
**Phone—(908) 587-1025**
Fax—(908) 587-1023
Email—eaglesteel_7@hotmail.com
Owner—Karol Kulik
SIC—3441; *Structural steel fabrication & erection*
Employs—15; Estab.—2001
Distrib.—Regional
Limited Liability Company

### EPICOR, INC.

1414 E. Linden Ave., P.O. Box 1608 (07036)
**Phone—(908) 925-0800**
Fax—(908) 925-7795
www.epicorinc.com
Email—epicorinc@aol.com
Pres.—R. M. Bussiculo
Hum. Res. Admn.—Judy Thompson
Pur. Agt.—Arlene Totka

SIC—2899; *Powdered ion-exchange resins & mixtures*
Employs—20; Estab.—1972
Sales—$5Mil-$10Mil
35,000 sq ft site, Distrib.—Intl.
Privately owned corporation
ISO rating—9001:2008

### EVERGARD STEEL CORP.

1825 Pennsylvania Ave. (07036)
**Phone—(908) 925-6800**
Fax—(908) 925-6802
Email—evergard3@gmail.com
Pres.—Connie Frances Macellara
V.-P.—Catherine Marie Smith
SIC—3315; *Steel wire*
Employs—10; Estab.—1961
Sales—$1Mil
10,000 sq ft site, Distrib.—National
Privately owned sub-S corp.

### EXCEL DIE CORP.

19 Grant St. (07036)
**Phone—(908) 587-2606**
Fax—(908) 587-2607
Email—exceldiecorp@gmail.com
Pres.—Hanna Krysa
Manager—Jerry Kosc
SIC—3469; 3544; 2431; NAICS—333500; *Metal stamping, millwork & tool & die job shop*
Employs—4; Estab.—1990
Sales—under $500,000
Distrib.—National
Privately owned corporation

### EXPRESS PRINTING, INC.

209 W. Saint Georges Ave. (07036)
**Phone—(908) 925-6300**
Fax—(908) 925-6302
Email—expresslinden@yahoo.com
Pres.—Sam Kamdar
SIC—2752; 2791; NAICS—323122; *Offset printing & typesetting*
Employs—4; Estab.—1984
Sales—under $500,000
1,500 sq ft site, Distrib.—National
Privately owned corporation

### †FASTENAL CO.

1026 W. Elizabeth Ave., Unit 2 (07036)
**Phone—(908) 862-8880**
Fax—(908) 862-8881
www.fastenal.com
Email—njlin@stores.fastenal.com
Br. Mgr.—Alex Klinga
SIC—5072; 5084; 5085; *Wholesaler of fasteners, safety equipment, tools & abrasives*
Employs—3; Estab.—1967
Sales—$500,000-$1Mil
2,000 sq ft site, Distrib.—Intl.
Publicly owned corporation
Parent co.—Fastenal Co., Winona, MN
   Phone—(507) 454-5374
See Parent Co. Section for full profile.

### FAUST THERMOGRAPHIC, INC.

325 Cantor Ave., P.O. Box 1277 (07036)
**Phone—(908) 474-0555**
National—(800) 447-2473
Fax—(908) 474-8042
www.faustusa.com
Email—sales@faustusa.com
Pres.—Craig Schwartzer
V.-P.—Earl Walker
SIC—3087; NAICS—325991; *Thermographic printing powders*
Employs—8; Estab.—2005
23,000 sq ft site, Distrib.—Intl.
Privately owned corporation

### GALVANOTECH

330-A Dalziel Rd. (07036)
**Phone—(908) 241-3900**
www.galvanotech.com
Pres.—Gerry Volkov
V.-P.—Sofia Volkov

SIC—3559; *Electroplating equipment*
Employs—12; Estab.—1990
12,000 sq ft site, Distrib.—Intl.
Privately owned sub-S corp.

### GENERAL MAGNAPLATE CORP.

1331 U.S. Route 1 (07036)
**Phone—(908) 862-6200**
National—(800) 852-3301
Fax—(908) 862-6110
www.magnaplate.com
Email—info@magnaplate.com
CEO & Board Chair—Candida Aversenti
Pres., COO—Edmund Aversenti
V.-P., GM—Wayne R. Cromwell
Asst. V.-P. & Mktg. Coord.—Valerie Corigliano
SIC—3471; NAICS—332813; *Corporate headquarters & industrial metal plating; Brand name—Tufram; Nedox; Plasmadize; Lectrofluor*
Employs—50; Estab.—1952
Sales—$10Mil
70,000 sq ft site, Distrib.—Intl.
Privately owned corporation
ISO rating—9001:2008

### HAMMER MFG. CO., INC.

417 Commerce Rd., P.O. Box 1340 (07036)
**Phone—(908) 862-1730**
Fax—(908) 862-1733
www.hammermfg.com
Email—sales@hammermfg.us
Pres.—William J. Fig
Bookkeeper—Susanne Keicher
SIC—3469; *Metal stampings & light mechanical assembly*
Employs—35; Estab.—1955
15,000 sq ft site, Distrib.—Intl.
Privately owned sub-S corp.
AKA: WGJF Mfg. Corp.

### HANSOME ENERGY SYSTEMS, INC.

365 Dalziel Rd. (07036)
**Phone—(908) 862-9044**
Fax—(908) 862-8195
Email—han317@aol.com
Chrm.—Al Reposi
Pres.—Selma Rossen
V.-P.—Thomas Costello
Administrator—Shannon McIntire
SIC—3621; NAICS—335312; *Electric motors*
Employs—32; Estab.—1969
30,000 sq ft site, Distrib.—Intl.
Privately owned corporation

### HARSCO CORP.

1800 Lower Rd. (07036)
**Phone—(732) 396-1269**
National—(877) 203-8755
Fax—(732) 396-1369
www.aluma.com
Email—swright@aluma.com
GM—Scott Wright
Opers. Mgr., N.E. District—John Thomas
SIC—3272; NAICS—332323; *Concrete forming & shoring*
Employs—25; Estab.—1964
Sales—$1Mil-$2.5Mil
Distrib.—Regional
Publicly owned corporation
AKA: Harsco Infrastructure
Parent co.—Harsco Corp., Camp Hill, PA
   Phone—(717) 763-7064
See Parent Co. Section for full profile.

### IFC PRODUCTS, INC.

568 E. Elizabeth Ave., P.O. Box 2175 (07036)
**Phone—(908) 587-1221**
National—(800) 395-0099
Fax—(908) 587-1661
www.ifcproducts.com
Email—ifcproducts@aol.com
Pres.—Joseph Christiano
V.-P.—Maria Christiano

GEOGRAPHICAL

## Linden—(cont.)

SIC—2087; 2844; *Flavorings, extracts, essential oils & liquid colors for the baking, ice cream, ices & candy industries*
Employs—4
Sales—$2.5Mil-$5Mil
Distrib.—National
Privately owned sub-S corp.

### IFC SOLUTIONS

1601 E. Linden Ave. (07036)
**Phone—(908) 862-8810**
National—(800) 875-9393
Fax—(908) 862-8825
www.intlfoodcraft.com
Email—info@intlfoodcraft.com
Pres.—David J. Dukes
Dir.—Judith E. Grossman
Sales Rep.—Billy Alosco
Cust. Serv. Rep.—Abby Kustin
SIC—2087; NAICS—311900; *Food color concentrates, food-grade anti-stick lubricants & contract organic ingredient blending for the food, confectionery & cosmetic industries*
Employs—22; Estab.—1939
Distrib.—Intl.
Privately owned sub-S corp.

### IK CONSTRUCTION, INC.

1118 E. Baltimore Ave. (07036)
Mail addr: P.O. Box 944, South Orange (07079-0944)
**Phone—(908) 925-5200**
  (201) 306-3161
Fax—(908) 925-5211
www.ikconstruction.com
Email—ikatw@aol.com
Pres.—Ian Katwaroo
SIC—3441; 3312; 3446; 3599; NAICS—332312; *Steel, ornamental iron & structural steel fabrication, erection & pipe welding of stairs, hand railings, catwalks & ladders*
Employs—8; Estab.—1998
Sales—$1Mil-$4.5Mil
Distrib.—National
Privately owned sub-S corp.

### INDUSTRIAL MACHINE & ENGINEERING CO.

1807 W. Elizabeth Ave. (07036)
**Phone—(908) 862-8874**
Fax—(908) 862-1061
Owner—Valerie Peti
GM—Jack Carlos
Off. Mgr.—Lois Burns
SIC—3599; *General machining job shop*
Employs—10; Estab.—1975
Sales—$500,000-$1Mil
Distrib.—Local
Privately owned corporation

### INFANTI BRAND CHAIR & STOOLS

1153 W. Elizabeth Ave. (07036)
**Phone—(718) 447-5632**
National—(877) 875-8593
Fax—(718) 447-5667
www.infantiseating.com
Email—info@infanti.com
V-P., Sales & Mktg.—Jack Douglass
SIC—2531; 2599; NAICS—337127; *Stacking aluminum banquet chairs, barstools, tables, gaming stools & restaurant furniture, including refurbishing & reupholstering services; Brand name—Infanti; Versi-Chair*
Employs—10; Estab.—2002
Sales—$1Mil-$2.5Mil
Distrib.—Intl.
Limited Liability Company
AKA: Infanti Seating

### INTEGRATED MEDIA MANAGEMENT, LLC

330 Dalziel Rd. (07036)
**Phone—(908) 862-6600**
National—(800) 836-4750
Fax—(908) 862-6004
www.immonline.com
Email—info@immonline.com
Pres.—Charles Klein
V-P., Bus. Dev. & Sales—John Levy
Off. Mgr.—Shari Klein
SIC—7372; *Document management software development*
Employs—60; Estab.—1988
Sales—$26Mil-$50Mil
Distrib.—National
Limited Liability Company
Also see: Comply, Inc., same loc.
AKA: IMM

### INTERLINK PRODUCTS INTERNATIONAL, INC.

1315 E. Elizabeth Ave. (07036)
**Phone—(908) 862-8090**
National—(888) 869-4010
Fax—(908) 862-8191
www.itlk.com
Email—interlink1025@aol.com
Pres.—Eli Zhadanov
Off. Mgr.—Anna Zhadanov
SIC—3089; *Plastic injection molding*
Employs—10; Estab.—1996
Sales—over $9Mil
10,000 sq ft site, Distrib.—National
Publicly owned corporation

### J & D TOOL, LLC

5 Grant St. (07036)
**Phone—(908) 486-5353**
Fax—(908) 486-5358
Email—jimdidyoung.jdtool@yahoo.com
Owner—James Didyoung
SIC—3599; *General machining job shop*
Employs—2; Estab.—2003
Sales—under $500,000
Distrib.—Regional
Limited Liability Company

### J.V.M. SALES, INC.

3401-A Tremley Point Rd. *(07036)*
**Phone—(908) 862-4866**
Fax—(908) 862-4867
www.gratedcheeseusa.com
Email—jsales.jvm@verizon.net
Pres., CEO—Marybeth Tomasino
Off. Mgr.—Cathy Summa
SIC—2022; *Cheese*
Employs—70; Estab.—1983
Sales—$25Mil-$50Mil (est)
Distrib.—Intl.
Privately owned corporation

### †JFC INTERNATIONAL, INC.

55 Wildcat Way (07036)
**Phone—(908) 525-4400**
Fax—(908) 474-0401
www.jfc.com
Email—info@jfc.com
Br. Mgr.—Shoso Ota
Whse. Mgr.—Tony Altavilla
SIC—5146; 5149; 5141; *Wholesaler of packaged Japanese foods, including sushi*
Employs—60; Estab.—1906
230,000 sq ft site, Distrib.—Intl.
Publicly owned corporation
Parent co.—JFC International, Inc., Los Angeles, CA
Phone—(323) 721-6100
See Parent Co. Section for full profile.

### JOBE INDUSTRIES, INC. (H Q)

1600 W. Elizabeth Ave., P.O. Box 1367 (07036)
**Phone—(908) 862-0400**
National—(800) 222-5623
Fax—(908) 862-1039
www.jobe-industries.com

Email—sales@jobe-industries.com
CEO—Sheila Reicher
Pres.—Joe Beer
V-P.—Charlene Rosenberg
SIC—2841; NAICS—325611; *Corporate headquarters; industrial cleaners, including soap & detergents for automotive applications (mfg. subcontracted); Brand name—Dafna Automotive Specialty Products; Jobe Industries Inc.; BioSudz*
Employs—19; Estab.—1950
Distrib.—Regional
Privately owned corporation

### JOCO PRECISION, INC.

333 Dalziel Rd. (07036)
**Phone—(908) 862-1611**
Fax—(908) 862-3055
Co-Pres.—Peter Korcusko
Co-Pres.—Nick Cereste
Off. Mgr.—Linda Zielny
SIC—3599; *Precision grinding*
Employs—6; Estab.—2000
Sales—$500,000-$1Mil
Distrib.—Regional
Privately owned corporation

### JOHNSTON LETTER CO., INC.

1634 E. Elizabeth Ave. (07036)
**Phone—(908) 928-1217**
Fax—(908) 928-1212
Email—johnstonletter@verizon.net
Pres.—Michael Kaufman
IT & Prod. Mgr.—Dieter Beutel
SIC—2759; NAICS—323100; *Commercial printing, including variable data printing, mailing & fullfillment services*
Employs—25; Estab.—1926
Sales—under $500,000
15,000 sq ft site, Distrib.—Local
Privately owned corporation

### KASHMIR CROWN BAKERY

710 W. Linden Ave. (07036)
**Phone—(908) 474-1470**
Fax—(908) 474-1159
www.kcbusa.com
Email—kcbusa@hotmail.com
Owner—Z. Ahmed
Corp. Mgr.—Sohail Ahmed
SIC—2051; NAICS—311812; *Bakery products*
Employs—60; Estab.—1997
Distrib.—Intl.
Privately owned corporation
Also see: 1030 W. Linden Ave. loc.

NEW ENTRY
### KASHMIR CROWN BAKING, LLC

1030 W. Linden Ave. (07036)
**Phone—(908) 474-0970**
Fax—(908) 474-1159
www.kcbusa.com
Email—kcbusa@hotmail.com
Pres.—Sajjad Ahmed
Hum. Res. Mgr.—Sohail Ahmed
SIC—2051; 2052; *Bakery products, including breads, cake & cookies*
Employs—70
Sales—$5Mil-$10Mil (est)
Distrib.—National
Limited Liability Company
Also see: 710 W. Linden Ave. loc.
AKA: KCB Bakery & Food Distribution

### †KEMPERLE, INC., ALBERT

626 E. Elizabeth Ave. (07036)
**Phone—(908) 925-6133**
Fax—(908) 925-4344
www.kemperle.com
Email—ron@akemperle.com
Br. Mgr.—Terry Gardner
Cust. Serv. Rep.—Tony Lourenco

SIC—5198; 5084; *Wholesaler of automotive body shop equipment & supplies, including paint, coatings & spray guns*
Employs—20; Estab.—1993
12,000 sq ft site, Distrib.—Regional
Privately owned corporation
Parent co.—Kemperle, Inc., Albert, Amityville, NY
Phone—(631) 842-5300
See Parent Co. Section for full profile.

### KORNSPAN JEWELRY, INC.

1131 W. Saint Georges Ave. (07036)
**Phone—(908) 925-1101**
Fax—(908) 925-9227
www.kornspanjewelry.com
Email—info@kornspanjewelry.com
Co-Pres.—Albert Kornspan
Buyer—Craig Kornspan
Jeweler—Darren Kornspan
SIC—3911; NAICS—339911; *Gold, platinum & diamond jewelry*
Employs—3; Estab.—1983
Sales—$500,000-$1Mil
Distrib.—Local

### L J ENGRAVING & SIGNS

409 N. Wood Ave., P.O. Box 1039 (07036)
**Phone—(908) 925-3510**
National—(888) 557-4467
Fax—(908) 925-4844
www.lj-engravingandsigns.com
Email—ljes@verizon.net
Owner—Leonard Neuringer
Opers. Mgr.—Linda Hundley
Engraver—Bob Patrick
SIC—3479; 3993; *Interior & exterior signs, engraving & award recognition products*
Employs—3; Estab.—1987
Sales—under $500,000
3,000 sq ft site, Distrib.—National
Privately owned corporation

### LAEGER METAL SPINNING CO., INC.

1514 E. Elizabeth Ave. (07036)
**Phone—(908) 925-5530**
Fax—(908) 486-4684
Email—sales@laegerspinning.com
GM—Leo Zuckerman
SIC—3469; *Hydroforming & metal stampings*
Employs—5; Estab.—1951
Sales—$500,000-$1Mil
7,000 sq ft site, Distrib.—National
Privately owned corporation

### LAMINATED INDUSTRIES, INC.

2000 Brunswick Ave. (07036)
**Phone—(908) 862-5995**
Fax—(908) 862-5891
Email—orders@laminated-industries.com
Pres.—Mendel Schwimmer
SIC—2679; NAICS—322200; *Paper converting*
Employs—40; Estab.—1985
Distrib.—Regional
Privately owned corporation

### LEIZ CUSTOM WOODWORK, DAVID

2301 E. Edgar Rd., Bldg. 5-A (07036)
**Phone—(908) 486-1533**
Fax—(908) 486-1631
www.dleizwoodworking.com
Email—dleiz@verizon.net
Owner & Pres.—David Leiz
Foreman—Danny Scelzo
SIC—2431; 2434; NAICS—337110; *Wooden kitchen, built-in & entertainment cabinets, libraries, mantels & high end closets*
Employs—4; Estab.—1975
7,000 sq ft site, Distrib.—Regional
Privately owned corporation

## Linden—(cont.)

**LENTINE SHEET METAL, INC.**
1210 E. Elizabeth Ave. (07036)
**Phone—(908) 486-8974**
Fax—(908) 486-8751
www.andersensheetmetal.com
Pres.—John Lentine
SIC—3444; Sheet metal
fabrication
Employs—7; Estab.—1983
Sales—under $500,000
Distrib.—Local
Privately owned corporation

**LIBERTY MACHINE TOOL & DIE, INC.**
903 E. Elizabeth Ave. (07036)
**Phone—(908) 925-0300**
Fax—(908) 925-0300
Email—lmtdms@hotmail.com
Co-Pres.—Michael Elzahr
Co-Pres.—Billy Elzahr
SIC—3544; 3599; NAICS—
333412; Tool & die & general
machining job shop
Employs—2; Estab.—2003
Sales—under $500,000
Distrib.—Local
Privately owned corporation

**LIPO CHEMICALS, INC.**
1515 W. Blancke St. (07036)
**Phone—(973) 926-0331**
National—(800) 274-7843
Fax—(973) 926-4921
www.lipochemicals.com
Cont.—Anthony Vicale
Hum. Res. Mgr.—Steve Young
Qual. Control Mgr.—Robert Dowd
Cust. Serv. Rep.—Natasha
Salerno
SIC—2834; 2869; NAICS—
325412; Cosmetic ingredients &
pharmaceutical chemicals,
including emulsifiers,
surfactants, emollients,
humectants & excipients
Employs—35; Estab.—2002
Distrib.—Intl.
Parent co.—Lipo Chemicals, Inc.,
Paterson, NJ
Phone—(973) 345-8600
See Parent Co. Section for full profile.

**†LUCA LAUNDRY EQUIPMENT, INC.**
Div. of Super Laundry Equipment
Corp.
1500 W. Blancke St. (07036)
**Phone—(908) 862-2200**
National—(800) 992-7269
Fax—(908) 862-0591
www.superlaundry.com
Email—dluca@superlaundry.com
V-P., Reg.—Richard R. Luca
Off. Mgr.—Joanne Luca
Parts Mgr.—Chris Canzius
Installation Mgr.—Serf Monteiro
Serv. Mgr.—Ray Fusco
Sales Exec., Indl.—Ray Fusco, Sr.
SIC—5087; 5046; Distributor of
commercial & industrial laundry
& dry-cleaning machinery &
related equipment, including
installation & service; Brand
name—ALLIANCE; UNIMAC;
SPEED QUEEN; HUEBSCH;
WASCOMAT; CONSOLIDATED;
TRITON (WASHEX);
MULTIMATIC; UNI-PRESS;
FULTON; MIURA STEAM;
ELECTROLUX
Employs—14; Estab.—1967
Distrib.—Local
Privately owned corporation
Parent co.—Super Laundry
Equipment Corp., Woodbury, NY
Phone—(516) 678-4404
See Parent Co. Section for full profile.

**MAGNALUBE, INC.**
1331 W. Edgar Rd., P.O. Box 1250
(07036)
**Phone—(718) 729-1000**
Fax—(718) 729-2690
www.magnalube.com
Email—info@magnalube.com
Pres.—Kerby Saunders
SIC—2992; Specialty lubricants
Employs—8
Sales—$2.5Mil-$5Mil (est)
Distrib.—Intl.
Privately owned corporation

**MATCHLESS UNITED CO.**
Div. of Matchless Metal Polish Co.
801 E. Linden Ave. (07036)
**Phone—(908) 862-7300**
Fax—(908) 862-7305
www.matchlessmetal.com
Email—matchlesslinden@aol.com
GM—Ricki Patchkiewitz
SIC—2842; NAICS—325612;
Polishing compounds, aqueous
cleaners, buffing wheels &
diamond crosscut contact
wheels
Employs—8; Estab.—1885
Distrib.—Intl.
Privately owned corporation
Parent co.—Matchless Metal
Polish Co., Chicago, IL
Phone—(773) 924-1515
See Parent Co. Section for full profile.

**MERCER COATING & LINING CO., INC.**
1410 E. Linden Ave., P.O. Box
1656 (07036)
**Phone—(908) 925-5000**
(908) 406-0260
Fax—(908) 925-9091
www.mercercoating.com
Email—mercercoating@aol.com
CEO—R. Bussiculo
Pres.—Michael Powers
Hum. Res. Mgr.—Linda Tatarynw
SIC—3069; 3479; Rubber linings,
sandblasting & painting of
structural steel, manufacturing
equipment, tanks & tank trailers
Employs—12; Estab.—1956
Sales—over $1Mil
30,000 sq ft site, Distrib.—
Regional
Privately owned sub-S corp.

**MICROCAST TECHNOLOGIES CORP.**
1611 W. Elizabeth Ave. (07036)
**Phone—(908) 523-9503**
Fax—(908) 374-7967
www.mtcnj.com
Email—sales@mtcnj.com
Pres.—Dean Fuschetti
V-P.—Richard Fuschetti
Pur. Mgr.—Margaret Honko
IT Mgr.—Steven Fuschetti
Hum. Res. Mgr.—Elaine Struening
Cust. Serv. Mgr.—Kasia Kozlowski
SIC—3471; 3089; NAICS—
332813; Metal plating, plastic
injection molding, prototypes &
die castings
Employs—120; Estab.—1995
150,000 sq ft site, Distrib.—
National
Privately owned corporation
Also see: Paramount Metal
Finishing Co., 1515 W. Elizabeth
Ave.

**†MID-ATLANTIC TRUCK CENTER, INC.**
525 W. Linden Ave. (07036)
**Phone—(908) 862-8181**
National—(800) 257-0093
Fax—(908) 862-9141
www.internationaltrucks.com
Email—sswift@mid-
atlantictrucks.com
GM—Fred Berger
Sales Mgr.—Bill Hanley

Hum. Res. & IT Mgr.—Shaune
Swift
SIC—5012; Distributor of flatbeds,
custom semi, utility & delivery
trucks, tri-axle dump trucks, long
haulers & 50-ton highway rigs;
Brand name—International
Employs—48; Estab.—1991
Distrib.—Local
Privately owned corporation

**MONUMENTS ARE FOREVER, INC.**
200 E. Edgar Rd., Ste. 1-A (07036)
**Phone—(908) 862-0220**
Fax—(908) 862-7834
www.monumentsareforever.com
Email—acleffi@
monumentsareforever.com
Pres.—Andrew Cleffi
Salesperson—John Smith
SIC—3281; NAICS—327991;
Granite burial monuments &
signage & engraved stone
products
Employs—2; Estab.—1916
Sales—under $500,000
Distrib.—Intl.
Privately owned corporation

**NATIONAL STEEL RULE CO., INC.**
750 Commerce Rd. (07036)
**Phone—(908) 862-3366**
National—(800) 922-0885
Fax—(908) 862-5339
www.steelrule.com
Email—e.mucci@steelrule.com
Pres.—Eddie Mucci, Jr.
Plt. Mgr.—Robert Versprill
SIC—3541; NAICS—333512;
Industrial cutting blades
Employs—90; Estab.—1997
Distrib.—Intl.
Privately owned corporation

**NEW CRUSHED TOAST CORP.**
625 Pennsylvania Ave. (07036)
**Phone—(908) 925-2920**
Fax—(908) 925-2921
www.newcrushedtoast.com
Email—newcrushed@aol.com
Ptnr. & Pres.—Carlito Perez
Ptnr.—Nancy Perez
SIC—2099; NAICS—311812; 50-
lb. bags- 2,000-lb bags of
breadcrumbs
Employs—8; Estab.—2005
Sales—$500,000-$1Mil
4,000 sq ft site, Distrib.—Local
Privately owned corporation

**NEW YORK POULTRY CO., INC.**
3351 Tremley Point Rd. (07036)
**Phone—(908) 523-1600**
National—(866) 361-3600
Pres.—John Nasary
SIC—2015; Poultry processing
Employs—15; Estab.—2003
Sales—$1Mil-$2.5Mil
Distrib.—Local
Privately owned corporation

**NORTH AMERICAN ELEVATOR, INC.**
609 W. Elizabeth Ave. (07036)
**Phone—(908) 523-1234**
National—(866) 274-8700
Fax—(908) 523-0722
www.northamericanelevator.com
Email—info@
northamericanelevator.com
Pres.—Tommy Curran
Hum. Res. Mgr.—Synthia Noda
SIC—3534; NAICS—333921;
Elevators; Brand name—Hollister
Whitney; G.A.L. MCE; Smart
Rise
Employs—20; Estab.—2004
Sales—$2.5Mil-$5Mil (est)
10,000 sq ft site, Distrib.—National
Privately owned corporation

**PARAMOUNT METAL FINISHING CO.**
1515 W. Elizabeth Ave. (07036)
**Phone—(908) 862-0772**
Fax—(908) 862-9477

www.pmf1.com
Email—bnegrin@pmfnj.com
Pres.—Michael Fuschetti
Sales Mgr.—Martin Levy
Off. Mgr.—Wilma Villani
Prod. Mgr.—Mark Andres
Qual. Assur. Mgr.—Joseph Boyd
Sales Rep.—Bernard R. Negrin
SIC—3471; NAICS—332813;
Electroless nickel, bright tin,
silver, gold, zinc nickel,
manganese phosphate, zinc
phosphate & black nickel
plating, including hardcoating,
anodizing, chemical film, solid
film lubrication, CARC & powder
coating & wet painting
Employs—130; Estab.—1949
75,000 sq ft site, Distrib.—
Regional
Privately owned corporation
ISO rating—9001:2008
Also see: Microcast Technologies
Corp., 1611 W. Elizabeth Ave.

**PATWIN PLASTICS, INC.**
2300 E. Linden Ave. (07036)
**Phone—(908) 486-6600**
National—(800) 225-0957
Fax—(908) 486-6605
www.patwin.com
Email—info@patwin.com
Pres.—Tom Hannen
IT Mgr.—Tim Hannen
Hum. Res. Mgr.—Allen Hannen
Off. Mgr.—Kim Biggs
Traf. Mgr.—Arvis Jackson
SIC—3082; NAICS—326121;
Plastic extrusions
Employs—30; Estab.—1972
Sales—$500,000-$1Mil
Distrib.—National
Privately owned corporation

**PHILLIPS 66 BAYWAY REFINERY**
Div. of Phillips 66 Co.
1400 Park Ave. (07036)
**Phone—(908) 523-5000**
Fax—(908) 523-5425
www.phillips66.com
Email—media@phillips66.com
Refinery Mgr.—Brian Coffman
Engrg. Mgr.—Phil Anderson
SIC—2999; 2821; NAICS—
324199; Oil refining & refined fuel
& plastic resins
Employs—800; Estab.—1909
Sales—over $5Bil
Distrib.—Regional
Publicly owned corporation
Parent co.—Phillips 66 Co.,
Houston, TX
Phone—(281) 293-6000
See Parent Co. Section for full profile.

**PIC CORP.**
1101 W. Elizabeth Ave., P.O. Box
4258 (07036)
**Phone—(908) 862-7977**
National—(800) 799-7302
Fax—(908) 862-8063
www.pic-corp.com
Email—info@pic-corp.com
Pres.—Allen Rubel
COO—Eric Rubel
Administrator—Geri Franlin
SIC—2879; NAICS—325320;
Pesticides & insect & rodent
control
Employs—24; Estab.—1953
44,000 sq ft site, Distrib.—National
Privately owned sub-S corp.

**PRAXAIR**
Div. of GTS-Welco
515 E. Edgar Rd. (07036)
**Phone—(908) 862-7200**
National—(800) 942-1148
Fax—(908) 862-7271
www.gts-welco.com
Email—info@gts.com
Opers. Mgr.—Mike Anuszeniski

GEOGRAPHICAL

## Linden—(cont.)

SIC—3548; 2813; NAICS—
325120; *Welding equipment & specialty gases*
Employs—2; Estab.—1989
17,500 sq ft site, Distrib.—National
Privately owned corporation
Parent co.—GTS-Welco,
Allentown, PA
Phone—(610) 398-2211
See Parent Co. Section for full profile.

### PRECISION SHOE BRACE & LIMB, LLC

618 W. Elizabeth Ave., P.O. Box 1213 (07036)
**Phone—(908) 523-0026**
Fax—(908) 523-0036
Pres.—Paul Goodman
SIC—3842; *Artificial limbs & orthotic braces*
Employs—8; Estab.—1986
Sales—$1Mil-$2.5Mil (est)
Distrib.—Local

### PRINCE DONUT CO., INC.

2345 E. Linden Ave. (07036)
**Phone—(908) 925-2262**
Fax—(908) 925-4057
GM—Fernando Inahuazo
SIC—2051; NAICS—311812; *Bakery products*
Employs—50; Estab.—1994
Sales—$5Mil-$10Mil (est)
Distrib.—Local
Privately owned corporation

### PRO PLASTICS, INC.

1190 Sylvan St., P.O. Box 1489 (07036)
**Phone—(908) 925-5555**
National—(866) 925-5000
Fax—(908) 862-8364
www.proplasticsinc.com
Email—sales@proplasticsinc.com
Pres.—George Sievewright
V-P.—Dennis Krokosz
Pur. Agt.—Lynn Fullem
SIC—3089; 5162; *Manufacturer of custom plastic parts & distributor of plastic sheet, rod & tubing; Brand name—Tecaform; Tecamid; Hydlar; Tecast; Tecanat; Tecason; Tecanyl; Tecapet; Hydex; PVC; Acrylic*
Employs—12; Estab.—1972
Sales—$1Mil-$2.5Mil
Distrib.—Intl.
Privately owned corporation

### PULASKI MEAT PRODUCTS CO.

123 N. Wood Ave. (07036)
**Phone—(908) 925-5380**
Fax—(908) 925-6547
www.pulaskimeats.com
Pres.—Ron Pulaski
Manager—Jared Pulaski
SIC—2013; NAICS—311600; *Prepared meat products*
Employs—20; Estab.—1959
Distrib.—Local
Privately owned corporation

### REPUBLIC MOLD & TOOL CO., INC.

109 Bradford Ave. (07036)
**Phone—(908) 862-3344**
Fax—(908) 862-2247
www.republicmold.com
Email—info@republicmold.com
Pres.—Werner Brandl
SIC—3544; NAICS—333500; *Plastic injection molds*
Employs—2; Estab.—1965
Sales—under $500,000
4,500 sq ft site, Distrib.—National
Privately owned corporation

### RESEARCH & MFG. CORP. OF AMERICA

1130 W. Elizabeth (07036)
**Phone—(908) 862-6744**
Fax—(908) 862-6748
www.ramcoa.com

Email—aaronfils@ramcoa.com
Pres.—Charles Semah
Off. Mgr.—Murray Dayan
SIC—3089; *Plastic injection molding*
Employs—25; Estab.—1985
60,000 sq ft site, Distrib.—National
Privately owned sub-S corp.

### REX TOOL & MFG. CO.

544 E. Elizabeth Ave., P.O. Box 1423 (07036)
**Phone—(908) 925-2727**
Pres.—John Haydu
SIC—3544; NAICS—333500; *Tool & die job shop*
Employs—3; Estab.—1955
Sales—under $500,000
Distrib.—Local
Privately owned corporation

### ROTUBA EXTRUDERS, INC.

1401 S. Park Ave. (07036)
**Phone—(908) 486-1000**
Fax—(908) 486-0874
www.rotuba.com
Email—info@rotuba.com
Pres., CEO—Adam Bell
V-P., Opers.—Jim Blumenfeld
V-P., Fin.—Mark Littwin
Dir., Sales, Extrusion—Patrick J. McEvoy
Dir., Sales, Compounding—Hugh O'Neill
SIC—3082; NAICS—326121; *Plastic extrusions for lighting & point-of-purchase displays & compounding for cellulosics; Brand name—Auracell; Naturacell; Snifty*
Employs—120; Estab.—1967
Sales—$25Mil-$100Mil
150,000 sq ft site, Distrib.—Intl.
Privately owned corporation

### †ROYAL DELUXE ACCESSORIES, LLC

2563 Brunswick Ave., Bldg. O (07036)
**Phone—(908) 523-0550**
Fax—(908) 523-0556
www.royaldeluxeny.com
Email—info@royaldeluxeny.com
Pres.—Elliot Zeitoune
Sales Assoc.—Lourdes Lamort
SIC—5094; 5199; 5139; *Wholesaler of costume jewelry, ladies' & girls' hair accessories & seasonal footwear for department stores, discount stores, drug stores & supermarkets*
Employs—18; Estab.—1995
1,000 sq ft site, Distrib.—Intl.
Privately owned corporation

### S S TOOL & MFG. CO., INC.

1 Garfield St. (07036)
**Phone—(908) 486-5497**
Fax—(908) 486-8864
Pres.—Steven Kanyo
SIC—3599; *Precision machining job shop*
Employs—6; Estab.—1979
Sales—under $500,000
Distrib.—Local
Privately owned corporation

### SAFETY-KLEEN SYSTEMS, INC.

1200 Sylvan St. (07036)
**Phone—(908) 862-2000**
Fax—(908) 862-2384
www.safety-kleen.com
Email—info@safety-kleen.com
Facility Mgr.—Andrea Martone
SIC—3599; *Industrial recycling*
Employs—50; Estab.—1965
Distrib.—National
Privately owned corporation
Parent co.—Safety-Kleen Systems, Inc., Richardson, TX
Phone—(972) 265-2000
See Parent Co. Section for full profile.

### SCREEN TECH OF NEW JERSEY, INC.

1800 W. Blancke St. (07036)
**Phone—(908) 862-8000**
Fax—(908) 862-2629
Pres.—Bob Barron
V-P.—John Schofield
Off. Mgr.—Lisa Barron
Bookkeeper—Terri Krawec
SIC—2396; *Glass silk screening*
Employs—30
Sales—$2.5Mil-$5Mil (est)
Distrib.—Local

### SENTREX INGREDIENTS, LLC

350 Cantor Ave. (07036)
**Phone—(908) 862-4440**
Fax—(908) 862-4415
www.sentrexingredients.com
Email—sales@sentrexingredients.com
Member—Arthur Gurerrera
SIC—2087; 2099; *Extracts, concentrates, essences & food flavoring ingredients*
Employs—5
Sales—$5Mil-$10Mil (est)
Limited Liability Company

### †SHALLCROSS BOLT & SPECIALTIES CO.

1 McCandless St. *(07036)*
**Phone—(908) 925-4700**
Fax—(908) 925-8451
www.shallcrossbolt.com
Email—info@shallcrossbolt.com
Owner & Pres.—Jeff Kaden
GM—William Weeks
Sales Mgr.—Brian Hathaway
Cust. Sales Rep.—Todd Kaden
Cust. Sales Rep.—Mike Golia
SIC—5072; *Distributor of steel, steel plated, steel HD galvanized, stainless steel, brass, silicon bronze, monel, titanium, alloy C276 & aluminum fasteners, including ASTM A193 B7, B7M, B8 CLI & CLII & B8M CLI & CLII*
Employs—25; Estab.—1972
Sales—$2Mil
20,000 sq ft site, Distrib.—National
Privately owned sub-S corp.

### SHELVING DEPOT, INC.

419 W. Elizabeth Ave. (07036)
**Phone—(908) 474-8000**
National—(800) 647-4353
Fax—(908) 474-1219
www.shelvingdepot.com
Email—richard@shelvingdepot.com
Pres.—Richard Kurland
Sales Mgr.—Greg Attanasio
Pur. Mgr.—Susan Krane
Acctg. Mgr.—Steven H. Kurland
Sales Rep., Inside—Joe Malinowski
SIC—2541; 3429; 2542; 3499; *Shelving, store fixtures, metal, wooden & acrylic displays & packaging, including printed bags & gift boxes; Brand name—Handy Store Fixtures*
Employs—12; Estab.—1958
Sales—$2.5Mil-$5Mil
Distrib.—National
Privately owned sub-S corp.
AKA: Rite Packaging

### SHORT RUN STAMPING CO., INC., THE

925 E. Linden Ave. (07036)
**Phone—(908) 862-1070**
Fax—(908) 862-6260
www.shortrun.com
Email—srsnj@shortrun.com
Pres.—Randy Speir
Plt. Mgr.—Jeff Hewett

SIC—3469; *Corporate headquarters & custom metal stampings & related assemblies*
Employs—26; Estab.—1951
Sales—$1Mil-$5Mil
20,000 sq ft site, Distrib.—National
Privately owned sub-S corp.

### SOLAR COMPOUNDS CORP.

1201 W. Blancke St., P.O. Box 1097 (07036)
**Phone—(908) 862-2813**
Fax—(908) 862-8061
www.solarcompounds.com
Email—sales@solarcompounds.com
Ex. V-P.—Joseph Barbanel
Dir., Tech.—Joseph Faccone
Plt. Mgr.—Tom Noble
Fin. & Hum. Res. Mgr.—Paula Kopcho
Qual. Control Mgr.—Alice Thomsen
Matls. Mgr.—John Englert
Administrator—Diane Scheuer
SIC—2891; NAICS—325520; *Wire, cable, flooding & filling compounds, adhesives, sealants, coatings, potting, encapsulants, flame retardants, epoxies, RTV silicones & hot melts, including toll manufacturing, blending, specialty coatings & acrylic resins*
Employs—30; Estab.—1920
Sales—$6Mil-$10Mil
Distrib.—Intl.
Privately owned sub-S corp.

### SPECTRAMEDIA

1634 E. Elizabeth Ave. (07036)
**Phone—(908) 928-1220**
Fax—(908) 928-1212
www.spectramedia.us
Email—mrubin@spectramedia.us
Owner—Mike Kaufman
GM—Marty Rubin
IT Mgr.—David Creighton
Sales Rep.—Todd Pifher
Cust. Serv. Rep.—Melissa Parisi
SIC—2759; NAICS—323100; *Financial printing, including finance forms, classification folders & related bank products*
Employs—25; Estab.—1929
Sales—$500,000-$1Mil
21,000 sq ft site, Distrib.—National
Privately owned corporation
Also see: Cox Printers, same loc.

### STAR METAL PRODUCTS, INC.

1125 W. Elizabeth Ave. (07036)
**Phone—(908) 474-9860**
Fax—(908) 474-9868
Pres., Fin., GM & R & D Mgr.—Donald Eckloff
SIC—3444; *Sheet metal fabrication*
Employs—32; Estab.—1980
48,000 sq ft site, Distrib.—National
Privately owned sub-S corp.

### STYLUS CUSTOM APPAREL, INC.

729 E. Elizabeth Ave. (07036)
**Phone—(908) 587-0800**
Fax—(908) 587-1777
www.stylusapparel.com
Pres.—Domenic Muscillo
SIC—2395; 2396; *Custom embroidery & apparel screen printing*
Employs—4
Sales—under $500,000 (est)
Privately owned corporation

### SUBURBAN SIGN MFG., LLC

210 Marion Ave. (07036)
**Phone—(908) 862-7222**
Fax—(908) 862-2541
Email—info@suburbansign.com
Pres.—Thomas Testa
Manager—Nancy Testa

## Linden—(cont.)

SIC—3993; *Wholesale interior & exterior signs for the trade*
Employs—18; Estab.—1948
10,000 sq ft site, Distrib.—National
Privately owned corporation

### SWISHER HYGIENE INC.

Div. of Swisher Hygiene, Inc.
1805 Lower Rd. (07036)
**Phone—(800) 221-0806**
Fax—(908) 353-6752
www.swsh.com
Email—customercare@swsh.com
CEO—William Pierce
COO—Blake Thompson
CFO—William Nanovsky
SIC—2842; NAICS—325612; *Cleaning compounds*
Employs—20; Estab.—1986
Distrib.—National
Publicly owned corporation
Parent co.—Swisher Hygiene, Inc., Charlotte, NC
Phone—(704) 364-7707
See Parent Co. Section for full profile.

### TAF TOOLING, LLC

1100 E. Linden Ave. (07036)
**Phone—(908) 474-0294**
Fax—(908) 474-0365
www.taftooling.com
Email—taftooling@hotmail.com
Owner—Hector Aboal
Programmer—Louise Aboal
SIC—3544; NAICS—333500; *Molds for vacuum thermoforming applications*
Employs—3; Estab.—2006
Sales—under $500,000
Distrib.—Local
Limited Liability Company

### TOTAL SPECIALTIES USA, INC.

5 N. Stiles St. (07036)
**Phone—(908) 862-9300**
Fax—(908) 862-4961
www.total.com
Email—info@total.com
Pres.—Mark Neustead
V.-P., Admn. & Fin.—Jean Luc Courtin
V.-P., Hum. Res.—Steve Daubert
Dist. Mgr.—Daryl Foley
SIC—2992; NAICS—324191; *Corporate headquarters & petroleum & synthetic lubricating & metalworking fluids, greases, engine oils & NSF H1 lubricants for glass bottle manufacturers & the food processing, metalworking & marine industries; Brand name—TOTAL; ELF; Nevastane*
Employs—65; Estab.—1868
Sales—$25Mil-$50Mil
Distrib.—Intl.
Publicly owned corporation
ISO rating—9002

### TRIPLE S INDUSTRIES

1108 E. Linden Ave., P.O. Box 1293 (07036)
**Phone—(908) 862-0110**
National—(877) 862-0111
Fax—(908) 862-9257
Email—triplesind@aol.com
Pres.—Robert Schulte
V.-P., Qual. Control—John Schulte
Corp. Secy.—Bozena Daukszewicz
Treas.—Walter Bradshaw
Pur. Mgr.—John Milone III
SIC—3599; *General machining job shop*
Employs—10; Estab.—1970
Sales—$1Mil-$2.5Mil
8,500 sq ft site, Distrib.—Regional
Privately owned corporation

### †TURTLE & HUGHES, INC.

1900 Lower Rd. (07036)
**Phone—(732) 574-3600**
Fax—(732) 574-2365
www.turtle.com
Email—info@turtle.com
Chrm.—Suzanne T. Millard
Pres.—Jayne Millard
CFO—Trevor Barnett
Opers. Mgr.—Chuck Noll
Hum. Res. Mgr.—Lucy Liana
SIC—5063; *Corporate headquarters & distributor of electrical equipment & supplies*
Employs—150; Estab.—1983
Company-wide: 540
Distrib.—National
Privately owned corporation

### U. S. BRASS & COPPER, CORP.

641 E. Elizabeth Ave., P.O. Box 1052 (07036)
**Phone—(908) 486-3322**
(908) 486-6171
Fax—(908) 486-3352
www.flexline.com
Email—sales@flexline.com
Pres.—Jeff Scheininger
Cust. Serv. Mgr.—Lori Battaglia
SIC—3492; NAICS—332912; *Metal hose fittings & assemblies*
Employs—10; Estab.—1950
10,000 sq ft site, Distrib.—National
Privately owned corporation
DBA: Flexline

### UNIQUE SCREEN PRINTING CORP., INC.

1016 McKinley St. (07036)
**Phone—(908) 925-3773**
Fax—(908) 925-3087
www.uniquescreenprinting.com
Email—jose@uniquescreenprinting.com
Pres.—Jose Grajeda
SIC—2396; *Textile screen printing & novelties*
Employs—30; Estab.—1930
15,000 sq ft site, Distrib.—Regional
Privately owned corporation

### VIP OPTICAL LABORATORIES, INC.

325 Dalziel Rd. (07036)
**Phone—(908) 523-1422**
Fax—(908) 523-1423
www.vipopticallabs.com
Email—customerservice@vipopticallabs.com
Owner—Richard Robbins
SIC—3851; NAICS—339100; *Optical lens grinding*
Employs—10
Sales—$1Mil-$2.5Mil (est)
Distrib.—National
Privately owned corporation

NEW ENTRY
### †W&O SUPPLY, INC.

7 W. Baltimore Ave. (07036)
**Phone—(908) 486-5338**
National—(800) 995-1161
Fax—(908) 486-4350
www.wosupply.com
Email—linden.nj@wosupply.com
Regional Mgr.—Bill Duffy
Whse. Mgr.—Abraham Williams
SIC—5085; *Distributor of marine piping, valves & fittings; Brand name—*
Employs—5
Distrib.—Intl.
Privately owned corporation
Parent co.—W&O Supply, Inc., Jacksonville, FL
Phone—(904) 354-3800
See Parent Co. Section for full profile.

### WALDEN FARMS, INC.

1209 W. Saint Georges Ave. (07036)
**Phone—(908) 925-9494**
National—(800) 229-1706

Fax—(908) 925-9537
www.waldenfarms.com
Email—waldenfarms@aol.com
Pres., CFO—Mitchell Berko
V.-P.—Paul Berko
Dir., Opers. & Opers. & R & D Mgr.—Brian Sherwood
SIC—2035; 2033; 2087; NAICS—311421; *Salad dressings, condiments, syrups, pasta sauces & fruit spreads; Brand name—Walden Farms*
Employs—20; Estab.—1966
16,000 sq ft site, Distrib.—National
Privately owned corporation

### WELDON ASPHALT CORP.

Div. of Weldon Materials, Inc.
2000 Marshes Dock Rd. (07036)
Mail addr: 141 Central Ave., Westfield (07090)
**Phone—(908) 862-0646**
National—(888) 322-2231
Fax—(908) 862-4631
www.weldonmaterials.com
Email—sales@weldonmat.com
Br. Mgr.—Dominic Mileto
SIC—2951; NAICS—324121; *Hot mix asphalt for driveway, parking lot, interstate highway & airport runway paving contractors*
Employs—4; Estab.—1908
Sales—under $500,000 (est)
Distrib.—Local
Privately owned corporation
Parent co.—Weldon Materials, Inc., Westfield, NJ
Phone—(908) 233-4444
See Parent Co. Section for full profile.

### WELLBILT INDUSTRIES

2 Maple Ave. (07036)
**Phone—(908) 486-6002**
Fax—(908) 486-4236
www.wellbiltind.com
Email—info@wellbiltind.com
Owner & IT Mgr.—Les Zalewski
Off. Mgr.—Renee Grine
SIC—3499; 3469; 3599; *Custom metal fabrication & stamping, welding & CNC turning & machining*
Employs—15; Estab.—1980
Sales—$1Mil-$2.5Mil
Distrib.—National
Privately owned sub-S corp.

### WILLIAMS BERELL, INC.

612 E. Elizabeth Ave., P.O. Box 1341 (07036)
**Phone—(908) 486-4952**
Fax—(908) 486-3411
Pres.—Barry Boydman
V.-P.—Craig Boydman
SIC—2759; NAICS—323100; *Commercial printing*
Employs—2; Estab.—1968
Sales—under $500,000
6,000 sq ft site, Distrib.—Regional
Privately owned corporation

### WILL'S CUSTOM DISPLAYS & WOODWORK

1202 E. Elizabeth Ave. (07036)
**Phone—(908) 925-0008**
Fax—(908) 925-2942
www.willsdisplay.com
Owner—Will Alicea
SIC—2434; 2541; NAICS—337110; *Wooden cabinets, displays & store fixtures*
Employs—1; Estab.—1995
Sales—under $500,000
Distrib.—Regional
Sole ownership

### WYLD GRAND FORMAT IMAGING, LLC

1618 E. Elizabeth Ave. (07036)
**Phone—(908) 587-2995**
www.wyldgfi.com
Email—wyldgfi@comcast.net
Member—William J. DiStaso

SIC—2893; *Inks for the commercial printing markets*
Employs—3; Estab.—2005
Sales—$500,000-$1Mil (est)
4,500 sq ft site, Distrib.—Regional
Limited Liability Company

---

## Lindenwold

(Camden—S.W.)

### ATHLETIC IMPRINTERS, INC.

775 Ashbourne Ave. (08021)
**Phone—(856) 346-4545**
Email—athimp@comcast.net
Owner, Pres. & CEO—Dennis Tallman
Manager—Eileen Tallman
SIC—2395; 3479; *Embroidery & heat press, tackle twill, trophies & plaques*
Employs—2; Estab.—1984
Sales—under $500,000
Distrib.—Regional
Privately owned sub-S corp.

### DUNBAR MFG., LLC

2400 Egg Harbor Rd. (08021)
**Phone—(856) 346-0666**
Fax—(856) 346-0016
www.dunbarusa.com
Email—info@dunbarusa.com
Owner—Sheila Santarpio
Bookkeeper—Charles North
SIC—3714; *Truck-mounted cranes & hydrostatic equipment*
Employs—2; Estab.—1998
Sales—under $500,000
Distrib.—National
Privately owned corporation

### HALL CO. ABRASIVES, WILLIAM R.

901 E. Gibbsboro Rd. (08021)
**Phone—(856) 784-6700**
National—(800) 448-0954
Fax—(856) 784-6701
Email—rmpluese@aol.com
Pres.—George Aho
Opers. Mgr.—Richard M. Pluese
Shpg. Mgr.—Mike Warchel
SIC—3843; 3291; NAICS—339114; *Rubber bonded abrasives for the dental, jewelry & hobby industries & thin cut off wheels for industrial applications*
Employs—30; Estab.—1882
Distrib.—Intl.
Privately owned corporation

### INTERNATIONAL WELDING TECHNOLOGIES, INC.

2650 Egg Harbor Rd. (08021)
**Phone—(856) 435-8004**
Fax—(856) 435-4004
www.internationalwelding.com
Email—info@internationalwelding.com
GM—Neil Wilkinson
Off. Mgr.—Jennifer Wilkinson
SIC—3548; 5084; 5085; *Manufacturer & wholesaler of welding equipment & supplies*
Employs—10; Estab.—1990
Sales—$500,000-$1Mil
Distrib.—Intl.
Privately owned corporation

### PAVERART, LLC

2512 Egg Harbor Rd., Ste. C (08021)
**Phone—(856) 783-7000**
Fax—(856) 783-7033
www.paverartllc.com
Email—mail@paverartllc.com
Pres.—Mick Seroka
CFO—Kenneth Bull
V.-P., Sales & Mktg.—Michael K. Bull

GEOGRAPHICAL

## Lindenwold—(cont.)

SIC—3271; NAICS—327331; *Decorative interlocking concrete paving blocks, including artistic designs, commercial logos & streetscapes*
Employs—5; Estab.—2003
Sales—$1Mil-$2.5Mil
Distrib.—National
Limited Liability Company

### SEIDMAN PRODUCTIONS, INC.

254 E. Gibbsboro Rd., Ste. C (08021)
**Phone—(856) 627-1356**
Fax—(856) 435-7021
www.spboxing.com
Email—seidmanproductions@ spboxing.com
Pres.—Jay Seidman
SIC—2741; *Monthly boxing program publishing*
Employs—3; Estab.—1986
Sales—under $500,000
Distrib.—Regional
Privately owned corporation

### SIGNS & LINES PRINTING

242 Gibbsboro Rd. (08021)
**Phone—(856) 784-0400**
Fax—(856) 627-1901
Owner, Hum. Res. & IT Mgr.—Dan Krug
SIC—3993; 2396; *Vinyl letter signs & textile screen printing*
Employs—2; Estab.—1984
Sales—under $500,000
Distrib.—Local
Sole ownership

### VACUUM SALES, INC.

51 Stone Rd. (08021)
**Phone—(856) 627-7790**
National—(800) 547-7790
Fax—(856) 627-3044
www.vacuumsalesinc.com
Email—jredstreake@ vacuumsalesinc.com
Pres.—James Redstreake
Fin. Mgr.—Carolyn Redstreake
Parts Mgr.—Bill Bax
SIC—3443; *Vacuum truck tanks, street sweeper trucks & combination vacuum-jetting trucks*
Employs—20; Estab.—1981
Sales—$10Mil
10,000 sq ft site, Distrib.—National
Privately owned corporation

## Linwood

(Atlantic—S.E.)

### AD PLUS

111 Cambridge Ave. (08221)
**Phone—(609) 653-7007**
Fax—(609) 653-1706
Owner—Leonard Demingo
SIC—3231; NAICS—327215; *Glass fabrication*
Employs—1; Estab.—1980
Sales—under $500,000
Distrib.—Local
Sole ownership

### ATLANTIC PROSTHETIC & ORTHOTIC SERVICES, INC.

199 New Rd., Ste. 56 (08221)
**Phone—(609) 927-6330**
Fax—(609) 927-6366
Email—atpro@bachanach.org
Pres.—Rich Kathrins
Billing Mgr.—Joan Gatti
Prosthetist—Roy Aungst
SIC—3842; *Custom prosthetic & orthotic devices*
Employs—5; Estab.—2009
Sales—under $500,000
Distrib.—Regional
Privately owned corporation

### CLOFINE DAIRY & FOOD PRODUCTS, INC.

1407 New Rd., P.O. Box 335 (08221)
**Phone—(609) 653-1000**
National—(800) 441-1011
Fax—(609) 653-0127
www.clofinedairy.com
Email—lclofine@clofinedairy.com
Chrm.—Larry Clofine
Pres.—Fred Smith
SIC—2026; 2023; NAICS—311500; *Manufacturer & distributor of dried & fluid dairy products & proteins, custom blended formulations, soy milk & tofu powders & dried specialty products for industrial food manufacturers; Brand name— Soyfine; Fine-Mix*
Employs—17; Estab.—1900
Sales—$50Mil
Distrib.—Intl.
Privately owned corporation

### HANGER CLINIC

Div. of Hanger, Inc.
210 New Rd., Ste. 7 (08221)
**Phone—(609) 653-8323**
Fax—(609) 653-4295
www.hanger.com
Email—info@hanger.com
GM—Brian Kleiberg
SIC—3842; *Prosthetics & orthotics*
Employs—4; Estab.—2002
Sales—$500,000-$1Mil (est)
Distrib.—National
Publicly owned corporation
Parent co.—Hanger, Inc., Austin, TX
Phone—(512) 777-3800
See Parent Co. Section for full profile.

## Little Egg Harbor

(Ocean—S.E.)

### INDEPENDENCE CRYOGENIC ENGINEERING, LLC

891 Route 9 N., P.O. Box 527 (08087)
**Phone—(609) 294-0012**
Fax—(609) 294-0163
www.cryopumper.com
Email—frankhughes@ cryopumper.com
Pres.—Susan Hughes
SIC—3443; 3585; *Rebuilt cryogenic refrigeration systems & parts, including cold heads, compressors, oil absorbers & ancillary devices*
Employs—16; Estab.—1994
Sales—$1Mil-$2.5Mil (est)
Distrib.—Intl.
Limited Liability Company

### OCEAN GRANITE MARBLE, LLC

140 7th Ave., Unit 9 (08087)
**Phone—(609) 296-1800**
Fax—(609) 296-6373
www.oceangraniteandmarble.com
Email—oceangranite@yahoo.com
Ptnr.—Dustin Bodony
Ptnr.—Emily Bodony
SIC—3281; NAICS—327991; *Marble & granite fabrication & countertops*
Employs—4; Estab.—1999
Sales—under $500,000
Distrib.—Regional
Limited Liability Company

### SPECTRUM FOILS, INC.

68 Ivy Creek Dr. (08087)
**Phone—(973) 481-0808**
Fax—(973) 482-7393
Email—mrplbi@yahoo.com
Pres.—Bill Pack
SIC—3497; *Hot stamping & printing foils*
Employs—6; Estab.—2008
Sales—under $500,000
12,000 sq ft site, Distrib.—Intl.
Privately owned corporation

## Little Falls

(Passaic—N.E.)

### ANDON BRUSH CO., INC.

1 Merrit Ave. (07424)
**Phone—(973) 256-6611**
National—(800) 875-2636
Fax—(973) 256-7965
www.andonbrush.com
Email—info@andonbrush.com
Pres., GM—Robert Newell
V.-P., Sales & Sales Mgr.—Joan Marck
SIC—3843; 3991; 3221; NAICS—339114; *Dental, pharmaceutical, cosmetic, commercial, artistic & industrial brushes, applicators, daubers, bottles, jars & containers; Brand name— Cobra® Brush; CA Brush®; Salon Stix; Color Stix*
Employs—15; Estab.—1990
Sales—$5Mil-$10Mil
12,000 sq ft site, Distrib.—National
Privately owned corporation

### ARTS WEEKLY, INC.

52 Sindle Ave., P.O. Box 1140 (07424)
**Phone—(973) 812-6766**
Fax—(973) 812-5420
www.theaquarian.com
Email—dianec@theaquarian.com
Publisher—Chris Farinas
Ad Dir.—Michelle Denholtz
Opers. Mgr.—Diane Casazza
SIC—2711; *Weekly newspaper publishing*
Employs—10; Estab.—1998
Sales—$500,000-$1Mil
Distrib.—Regional
Privately owned corporation
AKA: Aquarian Weekly, The

### BOIARDI PRODUCTS CORP.

Div. of Q. E. P. Co., Inc.
453 Main St., Ste. 4 (07424)
**Phone—(973) 256-1100**
National—(800) 352-8668
Fax—(973) 256-5744
www.boiardiproducts.com
Email—jmezzone@qep.com
Plt. Mgr.—Peter Klotz
SIC—2899; *Tile grouting material; Brand name—Elastiment*
Employs—7; Estab.—1981
Sales—$500,000-$1Mil
Distrib.—Regional
Privately owned corporation
Parent co.—Q. E. P. Co., Inc., Boca Raton, FL
Phone—(561) 994-5550
See Parent Co. Section for full profile.

### CANTEL MEDICAL CORP. (H Q)

150 Clove Rd., 9th Fl. (07424)
**Phone—(973) 890-7220**
Fax—(973) 890-7270
www.cantelmedical.com
Email—akrakauer@ cantelmedical.com
Chrm.—Charles M. Diker
Pres., CEO—Andrew Krakauer
V.-P., Corp. Dev.—Seth M. Yellin
Cont.—Steve Anaya
Hum. Res. Mgr.—Chris Geschickter
SIC—3841; 3842; *Corporate headquarters; dialysis equipment, water filters, sterilants, cleaners & cardiovascular surgery products*
Employs—23
Sales—$2.5Mil-$5Mil (est)
Distrib.—Intl.
Publicly owned corporation

### CHEM FLOWTRONICS, INC.

195 Paterson Ave. (07424)
Mail addr: P.O. Box 4635, Wayne (07474)
**Phone—(973) 785-0001**
          (800) 486-3356
Fax—(973) 785-8051
www.chem-flowtronics.com
Email—info@chem-flowtronics.com
Pres., CEO—Kevin Mooney
V.-P., Sales—Gavin Mooney
V.-P., Prod. Dev.—Bill Davidson
Sr. Dir., Mktg.—Cathy Williams
Dir.—Ann Mooney
Sr. Prodn. Mgr.—Ray French
Engrg. & Qual. Control Mgr.—Art Baxter
Engrg. Mgr.—Joe Brunden
Sr. Admn.—Lisa Snyder
SIC—3559; *Pharmaceutical, biotechnical & chemical process equipment, sight flow indicators, mixers, vessel systems, valves & custom fabrication; Brand name—Chem Flow Corp; Borodrain; CFL Mixer*
Employs—10; Estab.—1947
15,000 sq ft site, Distrib.—Intl.
Sole ownership

### COMPUTER EASE, LLC

153 Newark Pompton Tpke., Ste. A (07424)
**Phone—(973) 812-6626**
www.computer-ease-llc.com
Email—webmaster@computer-ease-llc.com
Owner—Matt Aquino
Computer Tech.—Joe Cucuzza
SIC—7373; *Computer networrk systems integration*
Employs—5
Distrib.—Local
Limited Liability Company

### FALLS SCREEN PRINTING, INC.

25 Amity St. (07424)
**Phone—(973) 812-0555**
Fax—(973) 812-1214
Email—jayfalls@verizon.net
Pres.—Jay Brady
Manager—Pete Muniz
SIC—2396; 2395; *Textile screen printing & embroidery*
Employs—4; Estab.—1998
Sales—under $500,000
2,600 sq ft site, Distrib.—Local
Privately owned corporation

### ILL-EAGLE ENTERPRISES LTD.

385 Main St. (07424)
**Phone—(973) 237-1111**
Fax—(973) 237-1112
www.illeagle.com
Email—designationname@ illeagle.com
Pres.—Darryl Sage
Prodn. Mgr.—Paul Carroll
Prodn. Dev. Mgr.—Peter Kavka
Cust. Serv. Rep.—Kelly Punne
SIC—3499; 2499; *Trophies, awards & picture frames*
Employs—44; Estab.—1990
20,000 sq ft site, Distrib.—National
Privately owned corporation

### †INTEGRATED DOCUMENT TECHNOLOGIES

1 Cardinal Dr. (07424)
**Phone—(973) 237-1200**
Fax—(973) 237-1274
www.idtofficesolutions.com
Email—gperillo@idtoffice.com
Ptnr. & Treas.—Gerard Perillo
Ptnr.—Liz Perrillo

## Little Falls—(cont.)

SIC—5044; *Distributor of office equipment, including managed print services, installation, service & support; Brand name—Xerox; Konica Minolta*
Employs—20; Estab.—1998
Sales—$3.5Mil
8,000 sq ft site, Distrib.—National
Privately owned sub-S corp.

**IT MANAGEMENT**
195 Browertown Rd., Ste. 2 (07424)
**Phone—(973) 389-1200**
Fax—(973) 904-1945
www.itmanagement.cc
Email—admin@itmanagement.cc
Owner—Marc Caruso
SIC—7373; *Computer network system integration, including LANs & WANs*
Employs—1; Estab.—2003
Sales—under $500,000
Distrib.—Local
Sole ownership

**KBM KITCHEN & BATH**
75 Harrison St. (07424)
**Phone—(973) 890-4900**
Fax—(973) 890-5063
Email—sales@kbmusa.com
Pres.—Boris Karpovski
V-P.—Ela Karpovski
Off. Mgr.—Ali Karpovski
SIC—2434; NAICS—337110; *Kitchen & bathroom cabinets*
Employs—8; Estab.—1982
Sales—$500,000-$1Mil (est)
Distrib.—Regional
Privately owned sub-S corp.

**KEARFOTT CORPORATION, GUIDANCE & NAVIGATION DIV.**
Div. of Astronautics Corp. Of America
1150 McBride Ave. (07424-2564)
**Phone—(973) 785-6000**
Fax—(973) 785-6025
www.kearfott.com
Email—marketing@kearfott.com
Pres.—Craig Scott
Dir., Sales—Edward Kelly
Dir., Opers.—Greg Ryan
Dir., Contracts & Prog. Mgmt.—Mary Ann Piazza
Dir., Engrg.—Brian Fly
Dir., Qual. Assur.—Paul Schatteman
Mfg. Mgr.—David Cardy
Hum. Res. Mgr.—Patricia Santana
SIC—3812; NAICS—334511; *Corporate headquarters & inertial guidance & navigation components & equipment, including gyroscopes for military & commercial applications*
Employs—200; Estab.—1917
Sales—$50Mil-$100Mil
300,000 sq ft site, Distrib.—Intl.
Privately owned corporation
ISO rating—9001:2000
Parent co.—Astronautics Corp. Of America, Milwaukee, WI
Phone—(414) 449-4000
See Parent Co. Section for full profile.

**LABEL GRAPHICS MFG., INC.**
175 Paterson Ave. (07424)
**Phone—(973) 890-5665**
Fax—(973) 890-1164
www.labelgraphicsmfg.com
Email—info@labelgraphicsmfg.com
Pres.—Thomas Silvano
V-P.—Denise Silvano
GM—Ali Kahn
Pur. Mgr.—Jake Ritz

SIC—2759; 2671; NAICS—323100; *Corporate headquarters & pressure-sensitive labels & flexible packaging*
Employs—50; Estab.—1979
Sales—$8Mil
26,000 sq ft site, Distrib.—Intl.
Privately owned sub-S corp.

**LITTLE FALLS TROPHY CO.**
555 Route 46 E., P.O. Box 1050 (07424)
**Phone—(973) 256-5222**
Fax—(973) 256-8497
www.awardmakers.com
Email—lftoffice@aol.com
Ptnr. & V-P.—Ellen Riccobono
Pres., GM—Dennis Messineo
SIC—3499; 3479; *Trophy engraving*
Employs—7; Estab.—1967
Sales—under $500,000
Distrib.—Regional
Privately owned corporation
AKA: Award Makers

**OVADIA CORP.**
101 E. Main St., 2nd Fl. (07424)
**Phone—(973) 256-9200**
National—(800) 776-8234
Fax—(973) 256-7346
www.ovadia.com
Email—fran@ovadia.com
V-P.—Steven Ovadia
Pur. Agt.—Fran Meriwether
SIC—3089; *Plastic jewelry display trays*
Employs—40; Estab.—1994
Distrib.—Intl.
Privately owned corporation

**PAPERCLIP COMMUNICATIONS, INC.**
125 Paterson Ave. (07424)
**Phone—(973) 256-1333**
National—(866) 295-0505
Fax—(973) 256-8088
www.paper-clip.com
Email—info@paper-clip.com
Pres.—Andy McLaughlin
SIC—2721; 2741; 2759; 2752; *Specialty printing & online information publishing of newsletters, brochures, manuals, training kits & binders for higher education & K-12 administrators*
Employs—20; Estab.—1992
Sales—$1Mil-$2.5Mil
Distrib.—Intl.
Privately owned corporation

**PARR LEADBURNING CO., J. W.**
87 Parkway (07424)
**Phone—(973) 256-8093**
Fax—(973) 256-0965
Pres.—Gary Parr
SIC—3444; *Sheet metal fabrication*
Employs—2; Estab.—1968
Sales—$500,000-$1Mil
3,200 sq ft site, Distrib.—Regional
Sole ownership

**PRINTFLEX**
1250 U.S. Highway 46 (07424-1810)
**Phone—(973) 256-5900**
Fax—(973) 256-1360
Email—arminio5941@juno.com
Owner—Trish Arminio
Prodn. Mgr.—Ralph Arminio
SIC—2759; NAICS—323100; *Commercial & instant printing, including layout, typography & design services*
Employs—3; Estab.—1949
Sales—under $500,000
Distrib.—Local
Sole ownership

**PROMEDIA TECHNOLOGY SERVICES, INC.**
535 U.S. Highway 46 (07424)
**Phone—(973) 253-7600**
Fax—(973) 253-5601
www.promedianj.com
Email—egomez@promedianj.com
Pres.—Gene Murphy
Hum. Res. Mgr.—Jessica Ciccarelli
Sales Rep., Inside—Edwin Gomez
SIC—7373; *Computer network system integration, including LANs & WANs*
Employs—50; Estab.—1991
Privately owned corporation

**SUN TEE, LLC**
25 Amity St., Ste. 1 (07424)
**Phone—(973) 812-0349**
Fax—(973) 812-0492
www.sunteespro.com
Email—mmbsun@aol.com
Pres.—Mark Babin
Art Designer—Ron Gega
SIC—2396; 2395; *Screen printing & embroidery*
Employs—11; Estab.—1995
6,500 sq ft site, Distrib.—National
Privately owned corporation

**TAURUS PRECISION, INC.**
129 Paterson Ave. (07424)
**Phone—(973) 785-9254**
Fax—(973) 785-9223
Email—taurusprecision@aol.com
Pres.—Michael Jakubas
Fin. & Off. Mgr.—Kathleen Jakubas
SIC—3599; *Precision machining of medical & defense instruments; Brand name—Drumlok*
Employs—18; Estab.—1983
Sales—$1Mil-$5Mil
5,000 sq ft site, Distrib.—National
Privately owned corporation

**TECHNICAL SYSTEMS GROUP, INC.**
28 Muller Pl. (07424)
**Phone—(973) 785-1118**
Fax—(973) 785-4585
www.tompat.com
Email—tompat@tompat.com
Pres.—Peter Y. Chin
V-P.—Mary Chin
SIC—3679; NAICS—334418; *Custom factory automation, safety & industrial electronics & electronic assembly for governmental, commercial & consumer applications*
Employs—7; Estab.—1983
7,000 sq ft site, Distrib.—National
Privately owned sub-S corp.
Also see: TomPat Technologies, Inc., same loc.

**TOMPAT TECHNOLOGIES, INC.**
28 Muller Pl. (07424)
**Phone—(973) 785-1118**
Fax—(973) 785-4585
www.tompat.com
Email—tompat@tompat.com
Pres.—Peter Chin
GM—Mary A. Chin
SIC—3669; NAICS—334290; *Factory automation, safety & consumer electronics*
Employs—9; Estab.—1988
Sales—$1Mil-$2.5Mil (est)
Also see: Technical Systems Group, Inc., same loc.

**UTZ, LLC**
4 Peckman Rd. (07424)
**Phone—(973) 339-1100**
Fax—(973) 256-2581
www.utz.com
Email—sales@utz.com
Plt. Mgr.—Jonah Bilotta
Opers. Mgr.—Lisa Guider

SIC—3679; *Wire mesh thick film screens, laser & chemically cut stencils*
Employs—25; Estab.—2008
Sales—$7Mil
14,000 sq ft site, Distrib.—Intl.
Limited Liability Company
ISO rating—9002

---

## Little Ferry
(Bergen—N.E.)

**ALTONA BLOWER & SHEET METAL WORK, INC.**
23 N. Washington Ave. (07643)
**Phone—(201) 641-3520**
Fax—(201) 641-1509
www.altonametal.com
Pres.—Walter Martin
Off. Mgr.—Kelly Battaglia
Opers. Specialist—Katie Hilder
SIC—3444; *Sheet metal fabrication*
Employs—8; Estab.—1965
Sales—$500,000-$1Mil
6,000 sq ft site, Distrib.—Local
Privately owned corporation

**BASSIL BOOKBINDING & FINISHING, INC.**
2 Alsan Way (07643)
**Phone—(201) 440-4925**
Fax—(201) 440-4975
Email—ebassil1@aol.com
Pres.—Eli Bassil
Off., Sales & Mktg. Mgr.—Christine Fleming
SIC—2789; NAICS—323121; *Bookbinding*
Employs—15; Estab.—1985
Distrib.—National
Privately owned corporation

**BEAR HANDS LTD.**
38 Main St. (07643)
**Phone—(201) 807-9898**
National—(877) 805-9898
Fax—(201) 807-9808
www.bearhands.net
Email—info@bearhands.net
Owner—Jeffrey Golden
Cust. Serv. Mgr.—Jody Feinstein-Cohen
SIC—2389; 2353; 2259; 2253; *Fleece hats, mittens & scarves; Brand name—BearHands & Buddies*
Employs—5; Estab.—2002
Sales—$500,000-$1Mil (est)
Distrib.—National
Privately owned sub-S corp.

**CLASSIC MARBLE & TILE**
11 Main St. (07643)
**Phone—(201) 440-8848**
Fax—(201) 440-3869
www.classicmarbletile.com
Email—classicmarble@nj.com
Owner—Michael Timarchi
Secy-Treas.—Isabella Timarchi
Hum. Res. & IT Mgr.—David Timarchi
SIC—3281; NAICS—327991; *Marble & granite products*
Employs—12; Estab.—1984
Sales—$1Mil-$2.5Mil
Distrib.—Local
Privately owned corporation

**CLINTON INDUSTRIES, INC.**
207 Redneck Ave. (07643)
**Phone—(201) 440-0400**
National—(800) 899-2546
Fax—(201) 440-5040
www.clintonind.com
Email—general@clintonind.com
COO—Larry Paricio
Sales Mgr.—Hajdar Hoxholli
Hum. Res. Mgr.—Dara Silper

GEOGRAPHICAL

## Little Ferry—(cont.)

SIC—3552; NAICS—333292; *Industrial sewing machine motors & attachments*
Employs—15; Estab.—1954
10,000 sq ft site, Distrib.—Intl.
Privately owned corporation

**DASSAULT FALCON JET CORP. (HQ)**
Teterboro Airport, 200 Riser Rd. (07643)
Mail addr: P.O. Box 2000, South Hackensack (07606-0620)
**Phone—(201) 440-6700**
National—(800) 526-7071
Fax—(201) 541-4515
www.falconjet.com
Email—resumes@falconjet.com
Pres., CEO—John Rosanvallon
V-P., Gen. Counsel—James Marks
V-P., Hum. Res.—Susan Wetzel
V-P., Fin.—Claude Draillard
Corp. Secy.—Peter S. Rothwell
Treas.—Robert Gogerty
SIC—3721; *Corporate headquarters; aircraft, including aircraft sales, service & after sales support of Falcon business jets in the Western Hemisphere & Pacific Rim; Brand name—Falcon*
Employs—420; Estab.—1969
Sales—over $500Mil
130,000 sq ft site, Distrib.—Intl.
Privately owned corporation
ISO rating—9001:2008

**DREW-WAL MACHINE & TOOL CORP.**
76 Monroe St. (07643)
**Phone—(201) 641-3887**
Fax—(201) 641-3888
Email—drewwal@n.j.r.r.com
Pres.—Andrew J. Kovach
Foreman—Peter Occhiogross
SIC—3599; 3544; NAICS—333500; *General machining & tool & die job shop*
Employs—4; Estab.—1961
Sales—$500,000-$1Mil
3,000 sq ft site, Distrib.—Local
Privately owned sub-S corp.

**EVENTIDE, INC.**
1 Alsan Way (07643)
**Phone—(201) 641-1200**
Fax—(201) 641-1640
www.eventide.com
Email—info@eventide.com
Bookkeeper—Phyllis Wasserman
SIC—3663; NAICS—334220; *Broadcasting equipment*
Employs—70; Estab.—1978
Distrib.—Intl.
Privately owned corporation

**FERRY MACHINE CORP.**
75 Industrial Ave. (07643)
**Phone—(201) 641-9191**
Fax—(201) 641-7320
www.ferrymachine.com
Email—lferretti@ferrymachine.com
Pres., MIS & R & D Mgr.—Louis Ferretti
SIC—3599; 3842; 3728; *Precision military & medical machining job shop*
Employs—30; Estab.—1952
Sales—$4Mil-$5Mil
12,000 sq ft site, Distrib.—National
Privately owned corporation

**FIDELIS GROUP, INC.**
223 Gates Rd., Unit A (07643)
**Phone—(201) 641-4701**
www.thefidelisgroup.com
Pres.—Lizleen Singh

SIC—2752; NAICS—323110; *Commercial offset printing & direct mail production*
Employs—80; Estab.—1997
Sales—under $500,000
8,000 sq ft site, Distrib.—National
Privately owned corporation

**GLOBE PHOTOENGRAVING CO., LLC**
19 N. Washington Ave. *(07643)*
**Phone—(201) 489-2300**
National—(877) 726-4498
Fax—(201) 641-7682
www.globeengraving.com
Email—magdies1@verizon.net
V-P.—Alan Soojian
Secy.-Treas.—Greg Chrisman
Bookkeeper—Beth Coleman
Bookkeeper—Rosemarie Cariglia
SIC—2796; NAICS—323122; *Photoengraving*
Employs—12; Estab.—1952
Sales—$500,000-$1Mil
7,000 sq ft site, Distrib.—National
Limited Liability Company

**JNT TECHNICAL SERVICES, INC.**
85 Industrial Ave. (07643)
**Phone—(201) 641-2130**
Fax—(201) 641-2309
Pres.—Glenn F. Jorgensen
Off. Mgr.—Elena Rose
SIC—3621; NAICS—335312; *Power plant equipment*
Employs—20; Estab.—1976
Sales—$500,000-$1Mil
Distrib.—Regional
Privately owned corporation

**†MACHINE SHOP DISCOUNT SUPPLY**
P.O. Box 16 (07643)
**Phone—(201) 518-8472**
National—(800) 388-0459
Fax—(201) 596-3425
www.msdiscount.com
Email—sales@msdiscount.com
Pres.—Hy Ash
GM—Paul Billig
Pur. & Sales Mgr.—Mike Raghu
Manager—Neil Bacharach
SIC—5084; 5085; 5072; *Distributor of cutting & measuring machine tools, machine accessories, abrasives & fasteners; Brand name—MEDA*
Employs—15; Estab.—1948
Distrib.—Intl.
Privately owned corporation

**MARTIN PRINTING SERVICE, INC.**
63 Liberty St. (07643)
**Phone—(201) 440-0410**
Fax—(201) 440-6772
Email—gmartinkus@aol.com
Pres.—Al Martin
Corp. Secy.—N. Martinkus
Plt. Mgr.—Gene Martinkus
SIC—2759; NAICS—323100; *Commercial printing*
Employs—3; Estab.—1974
Sales—under $500,000
7,000 sq ft site, Distrib.—Local
Privately owned corporation

**RIEDEL SIGN CO., INC.**
15 Warren St. (07643)
**Phone—(201) 641-9121**
Fax—(201) 641-8338
www.riedelsignco.com
Email—bill@riedelsignco.com
Pres.—William C. Riedel
SIC—3993; 2759; NAICS—323100; *Interior & exterior signs, vehicle graphics & large-format printing*
Employs—5; Estab.—1954
Distrib.—Regional
Privately owned corporation

**SCIENTIFIC DESIGN CO., INC.**
49 Industrial Ave. (07643)
**Phone—(201) 641-0500**
Fax—(201) 641-6986
www.scidesign.com
Email—info@scidesign.com
Pres.—Paul Lamb
Ex. V-P.—Robert V. Schneider III
Dir., Catalyst Sales—Ashok S. Padia
Dir., Acctg., Fin. & Tax—James J. Farley
Dir., Licensing—Allan S. West
Dir., R & D—Tom Giroux
Dir., Engrg.—Pradip Chakravarti
Hum. Res. Mgr.—Eric Schreier
EHS Mgr.—Marc Levine
Cred. & Collections Mgr.—Terry L. Baglieri
SIC—2819; *Chemical catalysts; Brand name—Syn Dox; Syn Dol*
Employs—135; Estab.—1987
Sales—$75Mil-$100Mil
Distrib.—Intl.
Privately owned corporation
ISO rating—9001:2008

## Little Silver
(Monmouth—N.E.)

**ENDO OPTIKS, INC.**
39 Sycamore Ave. (07739)
**Phone—(732) 530-6762**
National—(800) 756-3636
Fax—(732) 530-5344
www.endooptiks.com
Email—info@endooptiks.com
Founder—Martin Uram
Chief Opers. Mgr.—Paula Ender
SIC—3841; *Ophthalmic laser & endoscopy instruments & systems*
Employs—6
Sales—$4Mil
5,000 sq ft site, Distrib.—Intl.
Privately owned sub-S corp.

**FREEHOLD MFG. ASSEMBLY, INC.**
86 Birch Ave., P.O. Box 269 (07739)
**Phone—(732) 224-9066**
Fax—(732) 224-9077
Pres.—Trudy Lane
V-P.—Greg Cook
SIC—3444; *Sheet metal fabrication*
Employs—10; Estab.—1978
Sales—$1Mil-$2.5Mil
Distrib.—National
Privately owned corporation

**NOVATECH GRAPHICS**
54 Birch Ave., Ste. A (07739)
**Phone—(732) 469-1887**
Fax—(732) 530-1288
www.novadirect.com
Email—djm@novadirect.com
Owner—David J. McCartney
SIC—2759; NAICS—333293; *Full-color printed envelopes for the trade*
Employs—3; Estab.—1971
Sales—under $500,000
1,250 sq ft site, Distrib.—Regional
Sole ownership

**SIMTRONICS CORP.**
50 Birch Ave., Ste. 100, P.O. Box 38 (07739)
**Phone—(732) 747-0322**
National—(800) 730-0760
Fax—(732) 224-0009
www.simtronics.com
Email—info@simtronics.com
Pres.—Thomas Judge

SIC—7372; *Prepackaged software development, including operator training simulators for the process industry & educational institutions; Brand name—DSS-100 Dynamic Simulator System*
Employs—25; Estab.—1992
Distrib.—Intl.
Privately owned sub-S corp.

## Livingston
(Essex—N.E.)

**ACL EQUIPMENT CORP.**
257 E. Northfield Rd., P.O. Box 620 (07039)
**Phone—(973) 740-9800**
　　　　(973) 740-1040
Fax—(973) 535-6005
www.aclequipment.com
Email—sales@aclequipment.com
Pres.—Martin Reinfeld
SIC—3993; *Interior signs & assembly; Brand name—Tell-R-Lite; Sing-L-Line; Sell-N-Serv; Pag-N-Serv*
Employs—3; Estab.—1968
Sales—under $500,000
Distrib.—Intl.
Privately owned corporation

NEW ENTRY

**†ACROSS INTERNATIONAL, LLC**
111 Dorsa Ave. (07039)
**Phone—(888) 988-0899**
www.acrossinternational.com
Email—info@acrossinternational.com
Member—Rentian Huang
SIC—5049; *Distributor of laboratory equipment & supplies, including induction heaters, drying ovens, ball mills, lab furnaces & pellet presses*
Employs—5
Distrib.—Intl.
Limited Liability Company

**ALL THE BEST INVITATIONS**
123 W. Mount Pleasant Ave. (07039)
**Phone—(973) 992-4033**
National—(866) 992-4033
www.allthebestinvitations.com
Email—bestinvitations@aol.com
Owner—Peter Turkell
SIC—2759; *Invitation printing*
Employs—2; Estab.—1999
Sales—$500,000-$1Mil
1,300 sq ft site, Distrib.—National
Sole ownership

**†BERLISS BEARING CO.**
644 W. Mount Pleasant Ave., P.O. Box 45 (07039)
**Phone—(973) 992-4242**
Fax—(973) 992-6669
www.berliss.com
Email—info@berliss.com
Pres.—Darin Vogt
Chief Engr.—Michael Carbone
SIC—5085; *Distributor of roller bearings*
Employs—20; Estab.—1930
Sales—$5Mil-$10Mil
58,800 sq ft site, Distrib.—Intl.
Privately owned corporation

**CAMPAK, INC.**
119 Naylon Ave. (07039)
**Phone—(973) 597-1414**
Fax—(973) 992-4713
www.campak.com
Email—info@campak.com
CEO—Thomas Miller
Sales Mgr.—Brian Oliver
Off. Admn.—Donna Anderson

## Livingston—(cont.)

SIC—3565; *Packaging equipment*
Employs—11; Estab.—1991
Sales—under $500,000
25,000 sq ft site, Distrib.—Intl.
Privately owned corporation

**CROWN ASSOCS. U. S. A., INC.**
19 Winged Foot Dr. (07039)
**Phone—(973) 785-3477**
Fax—(973) 422-1126
www.proforma.com/crown
Email—linda.hart@proforma.com
Pres.—Linda Hart
GM—Ken Kohn
SIC—2759; 2771; NAICS—
323100; *Business & greeting
card printing*
Employs—3; Estab.—1991
Sales—$500,000-$1Mil
800 sq ft site, Distrib.—Regional
Privately owned sub-S corp.

**CUSTOM CONVERTERS, INC.**
115 Naylon Ave. (07039)
**Phone—(973) 994-9000**
Fax—(973) 994-6679
www.customconverters.com
Email—info@customconverters.com
Pres.—Mark Krause
Bus. Mgr.—Maria Moore
SIC—2679; 3081; 2399; 3497;
NAICS—326113; *Paper, plastic
film, aluminum foil & textile
converting*
Employs—10; Estab.—1980
Sales—$2.5Mil-$5Mil
Distrib.—Regional
Privately owned corporation
Also see: David Krause
Associates, same loc.

**FORMOSA PLASTICS CORP. U.S.A.
(H Q)**
9 Peach Tree Hill Rd. (07039-
2090)
**Phone—(973) 992-2090**
National—(800) 716-7200
Fax—(973) 422-7851
www.fpcusa.com
Email—corporate-
communications@fpcusa.com
V.-P., GM, Vinyl—Dick Heinle
V.-P., GM, Polyolefins—Ken
Mounger
V.-P., GM, Chlor Alkali—Philip
Chen
V.-P., Comm., Env. & Safety—
Robert Kelley
Corp. Comms. Mgr.—Steve Rice
Hum. Res. Mgr.—Peter Limone
SIC—3087; NAICS—325991;
*Corporate headquarters; plastic
resins, including PVC, PP, PE,
LLDPE & caustic for pipe, film,
bags, autos, containers, fixtures
& industrial applications; Brand
name—Formolon; Formolene*
Employs—265; Estab.—1990
Sales—$30Bil
Distrib.—Intl.
Privately owned corporation
ISO rating—14001, 9001

**FRANKLIN MILLER, INC.**
60 Okner Pkwy., P.O. Box 070663
(07039)
**Phone—(973) 535-9200**
Fax—(973) 535-6269
www.franklinmiller.com
Email—info@franklinmiller.com
V.-P., Sales—Dave Schuppe
Apps. Engr.—Greg Singh
Webmaster—Jennifer Ceruto

SIC—3569; 3531; *Size reduction
processors for wet/dry industrial
applications, wastewater
grinding & screening & solid
waste reduction including
crushers, shredders, grinders &
screens; Brand name—
Delumper®; Taskmaster®; Super
Shredder®*
Employs—35; Estab.—1918
Sales—$10Mil-$20Mil
20,000 sq ft site, Distrib.—Intl.
Privately owned corporation

**G L TOOL & MFG. CO., INC.**
26 Okner Pkwy. (07039)
**Phone—(973) 740-0001**
Fax—(973) 740-9243
www.gl-tool.com
Email—info@gl-tool.com
Pres.—Gerhard Liepold
Acct. Mgr.—Julie Liepold
SIC—3544; NAICS—333500; *Tool
& die job shop*
Employs—12; Estab.—1975
Distrib.—Intl.
Privately owned corporation

**HEALTHTRONICS, INC.**
354 Eisenhower Pkwy., Ste. 2150
(07039)
**Phone—(973) 994-3220**
National—(877) 411-4367
Fax—(973) 994-0027
www.healthtronics.com
Email—info@healthtronics.com
Ex. V.-P., Sales & Mktg.—Lawrence
G. Drappi
Dir., Sales—Lisa C. Grills
Dir., Cust. Support—Barbara
D'italia
Hum. Res. Rep.—Elizabeth Ballew
SIC—7372; *Interoperable EHR
software development for mobile
devices; Brand name—
UROAnalytics™*
Employs—22; Estab.—2003
Privately owned corporation
Parent co.—HealthTronics, Inc.,
Austin, TX
Phone—(512) 328-2892
See Parent Co. Section for full profile.

**I T I ELECTRONICS, INC.**
32 Stonewall Dr. (07039-1822)
**Phone—(973) 890-7888**
Email—itielect@aol.com
Pres.—Robert Stein
SIC—3661; *Telecommunications
equipment*
Employs—2; Estab.—1947
500 sq ft site, Distrib.—National
Privately owned corporation

**INTEPLAST GROUP LTD. (H Q)**
9 Peach Tree Hill Rd. (07039)
**Phone—(973) 994-8000**
Fax—(973) 716-7456
www.inteplast.com
Email—info@inteplast.com
Founder & Pres.—John Young
V.-P., Admn.—Joseph Wang
Assets & Bus. Dev. Mgr.—J. T.
McGrath
SIC—2673; 3081; NAICS—
326113; *Company headquarters;
BOPP, stretch, XF cross-
laminated, construction films,
grocery, merchandise & garment
bags, stretch wraps, trash can
liners, fluted plastic & clear, rigid,
free-form & celuka PVC sheets;
Brand name—IntePro®;
IntePlus®; Barrier-Bac®; Pelliko®;
TUF board®; InteFoam®;
InteCel®; InteClear®*
Employs—237; Estab.—1991
Company-wide: 2,486
Sales—$1Bil
Distrib.—Intl.
Privately owned partnership

**MILESTONE SCIENTIFIC, INC. (H Q)**
220 S. Orange Ave., Ste. 102
(07039)
**Phone—(973) 535-2717**
National—(800) 862-1125
Fax—(973) 535-2829
www.milestonescientific.com
Email—info@
milestonescientific.com
Chrm.—Leslie Bernhard
CEO—Leonard A. Osser
CFO—Joseph D'Agostino
Off. Mgr.—Laura Kaunitz
SIC—3841; *Corporate
headquarters; computer-
controlled local anesthetic
delivery systems for medical &
dental applications (mfg. done in
China); Brand name—
CompuDent; CompuMed; STA*
Employs—10; Estab.—1989
Sales—$2.5Mil-$5Mil
Distrib.—Intl.
Publicly owned corporation

**MINUTEMAN PRESS OF
LIVINGSTON, LLC**
47 E. Northfield Rd. (07039)
**Phone—(973) 992-3136**
Fax—(973) 535-1371
www.livingston-
nj.minutemanpress.com
Email—livingston@
minutemanpress.com
Pres.—Bhuman Patel
SIC—2759; 3993; NAICS—
323100; *Instant printing, signs,
banners & promotional proudcts*
Employs—2; Estab.—1989
Sales—$500,000-$1Mil
2,000 sq ft site, Distrib.—Regional
Limited Liability Company

**P I P PRINTING OF LIVINGSTON**
465 W. Mount Pleasant Ave.
(07039)
**Phone—(973) 533-9330**
Fax—(973) 533-9311
www.pip.com
Email—pipliv@pip.com
Pres.—Georgia Solofoff
Secy-Treas.—Steve Solofoff
SIC—2759; 2752; NAICS—
323100; *Commercial & instant
printing*
Employs—9; Estab.—1990
Sales—$1Mil-$2.5Mil
4,700 sq ft site, Distrib.—Local
Privately owned sub-S corp.

**REVICCI, INC.**
25 Sycamore Ter. (07039)
**Phone—(973) 994-1421**
Fax—(973) 994-1421
Email—ctshin7@gmail.com
Co-Pres.—Theresa Choi
Co-Pres.—John Shin
SIC—2844; NAICS—325600; *Skin
care products; Brand name—
Revicci Cosmetics Skin Care*
Employs—2; Estab.—1990
Sales—under $500,000
Distrib.—Regional
Privately owned corporation

**ROSEVILLE TOOL & MFG.**
22 Okner Pkwy. (07039)
**Phone—(973) 992-5405**
Fax—(973) 992-1183
GM—David Miller
SIC—3469; 3544; *Metal
stampings & tool & die job shop*
Employs—30; Estab.—1966
Distrib.—National
Privately owned corporation

**SIGNAL SIGN CO.**
105 Dorsa Ave. (07039)
**Phone—(973) 535-9277**
Fax—(973) 535-9276
www.signalsign.com
Email—info@signalsign.com
Mng. Member—Bruce J. Fish

Sales Mgr.—Scott Baird
Prodn. Supv.—Peggy Johnson
SIC—3993; *Architectural interior &
exterior signs & fleet graphics*
Employs—12; Estab.—1956
Sales—$2.5Mil
15,000 sq ft site, Distrib.—National
Limited Liability Company

**UTILITY DEVELOPMENT CORP.**
112 Naylon Ave. (07039)
**Phone—(973) 994-4334**
Fax—(973) 994-3341
www.udccorp.com
Email—udcliv@msn.com
Pres.—Harry S. Katz
V.-P. & Dir., Research—Radha
Agarwal
Engr., Plastics—David Perese
Sr. Chemist—Jason Fitzgerald
SIC—3086; 2891; NAICS—
325520; *Plastic foam, adhesives,
polymer composite products &
coatings*
Employs—6; Estab.—1987
Sales—$1Mil-$2.5Mil
5,000 sq ft site, Distrib.—Intl.
Privately owned corporation

**VANCO MILLWORK, INC.**
18 Microlab Rd. (07039)
**Phone—(973) 992-3061**
Fax—(973) 992-3253
Email—lyn@vancomillwork.com
CEO—Lyn Vanadia
SIC—2434; 2431; NAICS—
337110; *Custom cabinetry,
millwork & architectural
woodworking*
Employs—8; Estab.—1990
10,000 sq ft site, Distrib.—
Regional
Privately owned sub-S corp.

**VANDERMOLEN CORP.**
119 Dorsa Ave. (07039)
**Phone—(973) 992-8506**
National—(877) 992-8506
Fax—(973) 992-4219
www.vandermolencorp.com
Email—info@vandermolencorp.com
Pres.—Aldo H. Vandermolen
Manager—Irene Shea
SIC—3499; 3524; 3699; 3559;
*Electric indoor & outdoor insect
control equipment, wood
chipping machines, brush &
hedge chippers & lawn line
trimmers; Brand name—AVP®;
Woodpro®; Bugkill®; Windmill;
Flykil*
Employs—3; Estab.—1953
Distrib.—Intl.
Privately owned corporation
AKA: VC Marketing

**WEST ESSEX TRIBUNE, INC.**
495 S. Livingston Ave., P.O. Box
65 (07039)
**Phone—(973) 992-1771**
Fax—(973) 992-7015
www.westessextribune.net
Email—wetribune@gmail.com
Publisher—Jennifer Cone Chciuk
Editor—Nancy Dinar
Bus. Mgr.—Ellen Harte
SIC—2711; *Community
newspaper publishing*
Employs—10; Estab.—1929
Sales—under $500,000
Distrib.—Local
Privately owned corporation

---

## Lodi
(Bergen—N.E.)

**AERONAUTICAL INSTRUMENT &
RADIO, INC.**
234 Garibaldi Ave. (07644)
**Phone—(973) 473-0034**
Fax—(973) 473-8748
www.airco-international.com
Email—airco234@aol.com

GEOGRAPHICAL

## Lodi—(cont.)

Pres.—Wilfrid Burke
V.-P.—Eugene Beregi
Import & Export Mgr.—Liana Luciano
SIC—3728; *Aircraft equipment*
Employs—28; Estab.—1970
20,000 sq ft site, Distrib.—Intl.
Privately owned corporation

**ALL STATE MEDAL CO., INC.**
16 Adams Pl. (07644)
**Phone—(973) 458-1458**
Fax—(973) 458-1678
www.allstatemedal.com
Email—magicmedal@aol.com
Pres.—Richard J. Micucci, Jr.
Sales Rep.—Martin Phillips
SIC—3479; *Standard & laser engraving of trophies, plaques, corporate pins & jewelry*
Employs—5; Estab.—1920
Sales—under $500,000
2,500 sq ft site, Distrib.—National
Privately owned corporation

**ALLURE VISUALS & PRINTING**
9 1st St. (07644)
**Phone—(201) 288-1111**
Fax—(201) 288-3311
Manager—Joe Soleck
SIC—2759; *Commercial printing, including letterheads, business cards & journals*
Employs—2
Sales—under $500,000 (est)
Privately owned corporation

**AMERIFAB CORP., INC.**
196 Garibaldi Ave. (07644)
**Phone—(973) 777-2120**
Fax—(973) 777-9242
www.amerifabcorp.com
Pres.—Tom Castell
Off. Mgr.—Marge Castell
SIC—3444; *Sheet metal fabrication*
Employs—7; Estab.—1981
Sales—under $500,000
Distrib.—Local
Privately owned corporation

**ANTHONY QUALITY PRINTING, MARK**
187 Garibaldi Ave. (07644)
**Phone—(973) 815-1113**
Fax—(973) 815-2113
Owner—Mark Anthony
SIC—2752; NAICS—323100; *Offset printing*
Employs—7
Distrib.—Local

**AVENTA SYSTEMS, LLC**
40 Arnot St., Unit 7 (07644)
**Phone—(973) 246-4853**
Fax—(201) 461-4007
www.aventallc.com
Email—info@aventallc.com
Member—Felix Gorohovsky
Manager—Conrad Palka
SIC—7373; *Computer network system integration, including LANs & WANs*
Employs—3
20,000 sq ft site, Distrib.—National
Limited Liability Company

**AVIANNE HEALTH CARE SYSTEMS**
115 1st St. (07644)
**Phone—(201) 288-4100**
Fax—(201) 288-5601
www.avianne.com
Email—avianne@avianne.com
Pres.—Robert Siconolfi
SIC—2841; *Soap*
Employs—1; Estab.—1976
Sales—$500,000-$1Mil (est)
Distrib.—National
Privately owned corporation

**†B & B SUPPLY CORP.**
40 Arnot St., Unit 14 (07644)
**Phone—(201) 313-9021**
Fax—(201) 313-9389
www.bbtoolsupply.com
Email—sales@bbtoolsupply.com
Pres.—Slobodan Ristovic
Sales & Mktg. Mgr.—Alex Ristovic
SIC—5084; *Wholesaler of machine cutting tools*
Employs—5; Estab.—1993
Distrib.—National
Privately owned corporation

**BETA IRON WORKS, INC.**
31 Pasadena Ave. (07644)
**Phone—(973) 815-2730**
Fax—(973) 815-2731
www.betaironwork.com
Email—betaironwork@msn.com
Owner—Aharon Elperin
SIC—3446; *Architectural metalwork, including wrought iron railings, gates, window bars & grilles*
Employs—2; Estab.—1992
Sales—under $500,000
Distrib.—Local
Privately owned corporation

**BRIM ELECTRONICS, INC.**
120 Home Pl. (07644)
**Phone—(201) 796-2886**
Fax—(973) 778-2792
www.brimelectronics.com
Email—info@brimelectronics.com
Pres.—Barry Danziger
Corp. Secy.—I. Danizer
GM—B. Brown
Opers. Mgr.—Tom Barry
Off. Mgr.—M. Aaron
Foreman—James Ocello
SIC—3357; 3356; 3429; NAICS—331491; *Insulated electronic wires & cables, tubing, sleeving, shielded braiding, fastening devices & ceramic insulators; Brand name—Brim Crom; Brim Lite; Bryon; Mini Flyx; CHV; Brim Flyx; Brim Flex*
Employs—25; Estab.—1975
Sales—$1Mil-$5Mil
Distrib.—Intl.
Privately owned sub-S corp.

**COLOR FLO GRAPHICS CORP.**
10 Dell Glen Ave., Ste. 1 (07644)
**Phone—(201) 525-0105**
Fax—(201) 525-0761
www.colorflographics.com
Owner & GM—Peter Young
Accts. Mgr.—Carlos Quintanilla
Graphic Artist—Larry Stover
SIC—2396; *Textile screen printing*
Employs—15; Estab.—1960
Sales—$500,000-$1Mil
Distrib.—Local
Privately owned corporation

**D.W.L INTERNATIONAL TRADING CO.**
65 Industrial Rd. (07644)
**Phone—(973) 916-9958**
National—(888) 946-2682
Fax—(973) 916-9959
www.wincous.com
Email—sales@wincous.com
Pres., CEO—David Li
V.-P., CFO—Peggy Ding
V.-P., Sales—Steve Chang
IT Mgr.—Frank Haug
Hum. Res. Mgr.—Michael Chen
SIC—3589; 3914; 5087; 5094; *Company headquarters & restaurant supplies for the foodservice industry, including flatware, bakeware, cutlery, professional cookware, steam table pans, pizza & bar supplies, chafers, dispensers, coffee urns & tabletop service ware*
Employs—150; Estab.—1991
Sales—$6Mil-$10Mil
Distrib.—National
Privately owned corporation
AKA: Winco

**DUX PAINTS, INC.**
18 Mill St. (07644)
**Phone—(973) 473-2376**
Fax—(973) 473-1648
www.duxpaint.com
Email—howard@duxpaint.com
Pres.—Howard Goldstein
SIC—2851; NAICS—325510; *Paints; Brand name—Dux Paints*
Employs—10; Estab.—1947
Sales—$6Mil-$10Mil
15,000 sq ft site, Distrib.—Local
Privately owned corporation

**EVERBIND MARCO BOOK CO., INC.**
60 Industrial Rd., P.O. Box 695 (07644)
**Phone—(973) 458-0485**
National—(800) 842-4234
Fax—(973) 458-5289
www.everbind.com
Pres.—Stewart Penn
V.-P., Sales & Mktg.—Chuck Davis
Prodn. Mgr.—Bennett Primeva
Cust. Serv. Rep.—Yani Roman
SIC—2789; NAICS—323121; *Bookbinding*
Employs—50; Estab.—2000
Distrib.—Regional
Privately owned corporation

**FAB DOG, INC.**
160 Gregg St., Unit 7 (07644)
**Phone—(973) 472-5555**
National—(877) 322-3647
Fax—(973) 472-0009
www.fabdog.com
Email—info@fabdog.com
COO—Michael Becher
Off. Mgr.—Wendy Schuler
SIC—3999; *Dog accessories*
Employs—5; Estab.—2002
Sales—$1Mil-$2.5Mil
Distrib.—Intl.
Privately owned corporation

**GALLERIA ENTERPRISES, INC.**
300-3 State Route 17 S., Ste. E (07644)
**Phone—(646) 416-6683**
National—(800) 301-5424
Fax—(646) 290-5754
www.galleria-us.com
Email—sales@galleria-us.com
Ptnr. & CEO—Joe Simeone
Ptnr.—Tony Margulis
SIC—3999; 2394; *Folding & stick umbrellas & canvas tote & satchel bags*
Employs—7; Estab.—1999
Sales—$500,000-$1Mil (est)
Distrib.—Intl.
Privately owned corporation

**GFC COATINGS & CHEMICALS**
18 Mill St. (07644)
**Phone—(973) 272-0257**
Fax—(973) 272-0260
www.glossflo.com
Email—info@glossflo.com
Pres.—Jeffrey Klein
V.-P.—Steve Eilenberg
SIC—2851; NAICS—325510; *Custom industrial paints, lacquers, urethanes & water reducible coatings*
Employs—9; Estab.—1940
Distrib.—Intl.
Privately owned sub-S corp.

**H & S GRAPHICS**
196 Garibaldi Ave., Ste. 3 (07644)
**Phone—(973) 779-5880**
Fax—(973) 779-5859
www.h-sgraphics.com
Email—info@h-sgraphics.com
Pres., Emeritus—John Santangelo
Pres.—Thomas Santangelo
Ex. V.-P., Sales & Mktg.—John A. Santangelo
Ex. V.-P., Fin.—Mike Santangelo
Bookkeeper—Stan Wysocki
SIC—2752; NAICS—323100; *Color commercial offset printing*
Employs—8; Estab.—1986
6,500 sq ft site, Distrib.—National
Privately owned corporation

**HK METAL CRAFT MFG. CORP.**
35 Industrial Rd. (07644)
**Phone—(973) 471-7770**
Fax—(973) 471-9666
www.hkmetalcraft.com
Email—webmaster@hkmetalcraft.com
Chrm., Pres.—Joshua Hopp
V.-P., COO—Dominick Federici
Treas., Hum. Res. Mgr.—Nancy Hopp
Sales Mgr.—Brian Bishop
Pur. Mgr.—Jim Kehoe
IT & Info. Serv. Mgr.—William Brutzman
Cust. Serv. Mgr.—Richard Richelieu
SIC—3452; 3053; NAICS—332722; *Metal washers & gaskets, spring washers & shallow drawn parts, including custom stampings*
Employs—36; Estab.—1926
56,000 sq ft site, Distrib.—Intl.
Privately owned corporation

**LABEL MASTER, INC.**
89 Dell Glen Ave. (07644)
**Phone—(973) 546-3110**
Fax—(973) 546-7482
Email—labelmaster89@aol.com
Pres.—Robert Mazzella
SIC—2759; NAICS—323100; *Pressure-sensitive labels*
Employs—10; Estab.—1978
Distrib.—National
Privately owned corporation

**MCCAIN FOODS USA, INC.**
11 Gregg St. (07644)
**Phone—(201) 368-0600**
Fax—(201) 368-8771
www.mccainusa.com
Email—info@mccainusa.com
Hum. Res. Mgr.—Barbara German
Prod. Mgr.—Kim Tung
SIC—2038; NAICS—311412; *Frozen pizza; Brand name—Ellio's*
Employs—120
Distrib.—Intl.
Privately owned corporation
Parent co.—McCain Foods USA, Inc., Lisle, IL
Phone—(630) 955-0400
See Parent Co. Section for full profile.

**MINT PRINTING & DESIGN**
475 Westminster Pl. (07644)
**Phone—(973) 546-2060**
Fax—(973) 546-2063
Ptnr.—Tom Davis
Ptnr.—Mark Davis
Off. Mgr.—Bill Davis
SIC—2759; NAICS—323100; *Commercial printing & graphic design*
Employs—4; Estab.—1992
Sales—under $500,000
Distrib.—Local
Limited Liability Company

## Lodi—(cont.)

**NEVERENDING NEON**
91 Dell Glen Ave. (07644)
**Phone—(973) 772-4840**
Fax—(973) 772-4840
www.neverendingneon.com
Email—neverendingneon@aol.com
Owner & Pres.—Mark Provenzano
SIC—3993; *Neon interior & exterior signs, LED lighting & light boxes*
Employs—1; Estab.—1990
Sales—under $500,000
Distrib.—National
Limited Liability Company

**ORLANDO BAKERY**
236 Harrison Ave. (07644)
**Phone—(973) 772-8883**
Fax—(973) 772-5788
Salesperson—Daniel Cartel
SIC—2051; NAICS—311812; *Bakery products*
Employs—15
Sales—$1Mil-$2.5Mil (est)
Distrib.—Intl.

**PACI PRESS, INC.**
25 First St., Rear Bldg. (07644)
**Phone—(973) 478-6550**
Fax—(973) 478-6891
Pres.—William Lorusso
SIC—2752; NAICS—323100; *Offset & letterpress printing*
Employs—1; Estab.—1941
Sales—under $500,000
1,000 sq ft site, Distrib.—Regional
Privately owned corporation

**PRESTO PRINT & COPY**
79 S. Main St., Ste. 3 (07644)
**Phone—(973) 777-8377**
Fax—(973) 777-8339
www.prestoprintandcopy.com
Email—gnpresto@aol.com
Pres.—George Nigito
Sales Mgr.—Kathleen Nigito
SIC—2752; NAICS—323100; *Offset printing*
Employs—3; Estab.—1990
Distrib.—Local
Sole ownership

**RENNIE MFG. & METAL FINISHING CO., INC.**
12-14 Rennie Pl., P.O. Box 285 (07644)
**Phone—(973) 773-9175**
Fax—(973) 773-1004
Pres.—Alan Kessinger
Off. Mgr.—Sue Kessinger
SIC—3471; NAICS—332813; *Metal finishing*
Employs—12; Estab.—1982
11,000 sq ft site, Distrib.—National
Privately owned corporation

**ROMANO & SON, INC.**
501 Baldwin Ave. (07644)
**Phone—(973) 472-3240**
Fax—(973) 472-0265
www.romanoandson.com
Email—primo501@aol.com
Owner—Paul Romano
Off. Mgr.—Maria Rodriguez
Sales Rep.—David Deino
SIC—3281; NAICS—327991; *Granite & marble countertops & floor tiles*
Employs—5; Estab.—1970
Sales—under $500,000
Distrib.—Local
Privately owned corporation

**SPECTRACHEM**
10 Dell Glen Ave., Ste. 3-A (07644-1759)
**Phone—(973) 253-3553**
National—(800) 524-2806
Fax—(973) 253-6663
www.spectrachem.net
Email—sales@spectrachem.net

Pres.—Zaghary Kousoulis
Fin. Mgr.—Peggy Emord
SIC—2893; 2865; 2851; NAICS—325910; *Water-based pigment dispersions & textile & wallcovering inks; Brand name—Pigment Dispersions; Plastique Inks; Spectrasperse Dispersions; Dyfast Low Crock for Textile; Ready For Use Textile Inks; Inks for Wallcoverings*
Employs—10; Estab.—1998
Sales—$1Mil-$2Mil
25,000 sq ft site, Distrib.—Intl.
Privately owned sub-S corp.

**STAINED GLASS DESIGN, INC.**
87 Dellglen Ave. (07644)
**Phone—(973) 772-5070**
Email—ggeswaldo@mac.com
Pres., Sales Mgr.—George Geswaldo
SIC—3231; NAICS—327215; *Stained glass*
Employs—3; Estab.—1967
Sales—under $500,000
5,000 sq ft site, Distrib.—Local
Privately owned corporation

†**STEWART & STEVENSON POWER PRODUCTS, LLC- ADDA DIV.**
Div. of Stewart & Stevenson, LLC
180 Route 17 S., P.O. Box 950 (07644)
**Phone—(201) 489-5800**
Fax—(201) 368-1071
www.atlanticdda.com
Email—rmangs@atlanticdda.com
CEO—John F. Farmer
Sr. V-P.—Timothy E. Meade
Sr. V-P.—Michael McGovern
V-P., Admn.—Megan Hollberg
SIC—5084; 5013; *Company headquarters & distributor of diesel engines & automatic transmissions; Brand name—Detroit Diesel; Allison; MTU; Mobile Climate Control*
Employs—90; Estab.—2013
Sales—over $100Mil
45,000 sq ft site, Distrib.—Regional
Limited Liability Company
DBA: Atlantic Detroit Diesel-Allison
Parent co.—Stewart & Stevenson, LLC, Houston, TX
Phone—(713) 751-2700
See Parent Co. Section for full profile.

**STEWART & STEVENSON POWER PRODUCTS, LLC, ADDA DIV.**
Div. of Stewart & Stevenson Power Products, LLC- ADDA Div.
33 Gregg St. (07644)
**Phone—(201) 291-8415**
Fax—(201) 845-3288
www.atlanticdda.com
Email—dbellesheim@atlanticdda.com
Serv. Mgr.—Scott Brandstetter
SIC—3621; NAICS—336211; *Gas open, weatherproof, sound-attenuated & trailer mounted standby, emergency, continuous power & on-site utility combined heat & power generator sets for the power generation, energy, marine, construction, industrial & retail industries*
Employs—200; Estab.—1980
Sales—$25Mil-$50Mil (est)
Distrib.—Intl.
Limited Liability Company
DBA: Atlantic Detroit Diesel-Allison, LLC
Parent co.—Stewart & Stevenson Power Products, LLC- ADDA Div., Lodi, NJ
Phone—(201) 489-5800
See Parent Co. Section for full profile.

†**SUBURBAN AUTO SEAT CO., INC.**
35 Industrial Rd. (07644)
**Phone—(973) 778-9227**
National—(866) 666-3336
Fax—(973) 777-8564
www.suburbanseats.com
Email—sales@suburbanseats.com
Pres.—Amy Winfield
SIC—5013; *Distributor of aftermarket replacement seating, custom seating, cab accessories & safety equipment for commercial trucks, buses, agricultural & construction vehicles, ground support & material handling equipment & ferry boats; Brand name—National Seating; Bostrom Seating; Sears Seating; ISRI; HO Bostrom; Seats Inc.; Wise Seating; Knoedler Seating; Freedman Seating; Grammer; KAB; USSC; Brigade Electronics; Coverall; InnerSpace*
Employs—13; Estab.—1947
Distrib.—Intl.
Privately owned corporation
AKA: Suburban Seating

**SUFFERN PLATING CO.**
210 Garibaldi Ave., P.O. Box 755 (07644)
**Phone—(973) 473-4404**
Fax—(973) 473-7096
www.suffernplating.com
Email—info@suffernplating.com
GM—Carlos Arguello
Shpg. & Rec. Mgr.—Lisa Ortega
SIC—3471; NAICS—332813; *Nickel, bronze & brass plating*
Employs—25; Estab.—1949
Distrib.—Local
Privately owned corporation

**THE STAR GROUP**
80-A Industrial Rd. (07644)
**Phone—(973) 778-8600**
Fax—(973) 778-8623
www.starnj.com
Email—sales@starnj.com
Pres.—Michael Friedman
V-P., Sales—Marc Rosenstrauch
Cont.—Marge Trovato
Pur. Mgr.—Mayda Plescia
SIC—2241; 3089; NAICS—313221; *Woven & fabric labels, hang tags & packaging*
Employs—10; Estab.—1982
Distrib.—Intl.
Limited Liability Company

**TONY JONES APPAREL, INC.**
300-1 Route 17 S., Unit C (07644)
**Phone—(973) 773-6200**
Fax—(973) 773-6210
Email—sales@clench.com
Pres.—John Yi
Acctg. Mgr.—Rachel Seo
SIC—2321; 2311; NAICS—315200; *Men's apparel*
Employs—7; Estab.—1996
Distrib.—Intl.
Privately owned corporation

**UVITEC PRINTING INK, INC.**
14 Mill St. (07644)
**Phone—(973) 778-0737**
Fax—(973) 778-5981
www.uvitec.com
Email—sales@uvitec.com
Pres.—George A. Dakos
V-P., Sales—Andrew Wasserman
Fin., Hum. Res. & MIS Mgr.—Angela Badillo
Cust. Serv. Rep.—Janet Acquafredda
Sr. Chemist—John Donaleski

SIC—2893; NAICS—325910; *Ultraviolet curable printing inks & coatings*
Employs—18; Estab.—1980
11,000 sq ft site, Distrib.—Intl.
Privately owned corporation

**V. TECH INSTRUMENTS, INC.**
171 Burns Ave. (07644)
**Phone—(973) 546-7635**
Fax—(973) 546-7651
Email—sales@vtechinstrumentsinc.com
Pres.—Jaw Wu
Asst. Mgr.—Lisa Wu
SIC—3825; NAICS—334500; *Portable electronic spectrum analyzers*
Employs—5; Estab.—1994
Sales—under $500,000
Distrib.—Intl.
Privately owned corporation

**VERSATILE DISTRIBUTORS, INC.**
80 Industrial Rd. (07644)
**Phone—(973) 779-1400**
National—(800) 466-5777
Fax—(973) 473-1788
www.americanjewelwindow.com
Email—information@americanjewelwindows.com
Pres.—Joel Cuccio
SIC—2431; 3442; NAICS—332321; *Vinyl windows, entry & storm doors & canopies for residential & new construction commercial apartment buildings*
Employs—55; Estab.—1937
Distrib.—Regional
Privately owned corporation
DBA: American Jewel Window Systems
AKA: Grove Home Products

**VITAMIA & SONS**
206 Harrison Ave. (07644)
**Phone—(973) 546-1140**
National—(800) 930-2553
Fax—(973) 546-3882
www.pastaboy.com
Email—vitamiapastaboy@aol.com
Pres.—Anthony Vitamia
V-P.—Joseph Vitamia
GM—Francesco 'Paul' Vitamia
Off. Mgr.—Nancy Spiehler
SIC—2098; 2033; 2051; 2022; NAICS—311823; *Ravioli, pasta, sauces, bread, cheese & party trays*
Employs—12; Estab.—1976
Sales—under $500,000
Distrib.—Regional
Privately owned corporation

**WOOD & LAMINATES, INC.**
102 Route 46 E. (07644)
**Phone—(973) 773-7475**
Fax—(973) 773-8344
www.wlbars.com
Email—gabriels@wlbars.com
Pres.—Gabriel Salazar
Art Dir., Architect—Julio Botero
SIC—3083; 2541; 2426; 2431; NAICS—326130; *Custom bars & interiors for homes, restaurants, hotels & country clubs; Brand name—WL BARS*
Employs—20; Estab.—1988
Distrib.—National
Privately owned corporation
AKA: WL Interiors

## Logan Township
(Gloucester—S.W.)

**ADVANCED DRAINAGE SYSTEMS, INC.**
300 Progress Ct. (08085)
**Phone—(856) 467-4779**
(866) 705-6578
Fax—(856) 467-4861
www.ads-pipe.com
Email—info@ads-pipe.com

**GEOGRAPHICAL**

## Logan Township— (cont.)

Plt. Accountant—Jerri Haas
SIC—3084; *Corrugated plastic pipes*
Employs—64; Estab.—1964
Sales—$11Mil-$25Mil
Distrib.—Local
Privately owned corporation
Parent co.—Advanced Drainage Systems, Inc., Hilliard, OH
Phone—(614) 658-0050
See Parent Co. Section for full profile.

### AMERICAN INFINITY COMPOUNDING CORP.

2079 Center Square Rd. (08085)
**Phone—(856) 467-3030**
Fax—(856) 467-3033
www.infinitycompounding.com
Email—ccarreno@ infinitycompounding.com
Pres.—Carlos Carreno
Opers. Mgr.—Don Knabb
Cust. Serv. Mgr.—Tracy Little
Fin. Mgr.—Chris Carreno
SIC—3089; *Custom compounded plastic resins*
Employs—17; Estab.—2005
Distrib.—Intl.
Privately owned corporation

### CUSTOM BUILDING PRODUCTS, INC.

2115 High Hill Rd. (08085)
**Phone—(856) 467-9226**
National—(800) 272-8786
Fax—(856) 467-1928
www.custombuildingproducts.com
Email—contactus@cbpmail.com
Plt. Mgr.—Joan Clugsten
Traf. Coord.—Sue Winterborne
SIC—2891; 2899; NAICS— 325520; *Flooring grout & mortar*
Employs—180; Estab.—1994
Distrib.—National
Privately owned corporation
Parent co.—Custom Building Products, Inc., Seal Beach, CA
Phone—(562) 598-8808
See Parent Co. Section for full profile.

### EARLY CHILDHOOD RESOURCES, LLC

2165 Center Square Rd. (08085)
**Phone—(856) 638-1170**
Fax—(856) 638-1171
www.ecr4kids.com
Email—customerservice@ ecr4kids.com
Pres.—Mitchell Lynn
SIC—2531; *Stackable school chairs, wooden children's furniture & play products (mfg. subcontracted)*
Employs—6; Estab.—2003
Sales—$1Mil-$2.5Mil
Distrib.—National
Privately owned corporation

### POWELL ELECTRONICS, INC.

200 Commodore Dr. (08085)
**Phone—(856) 241-8000**
National—(800) 235-7880
Fax—(856) 241-8630
www.powell.com
Email—info@powell.com
Pres.—E. J. Schilling
CFO—Schawn Beatty
Sr. V-P., Mktg.—John Barringtonn
V-P., Central—Albert Fiorillo
Cont.—Eugene Regruto
Hum. Res. Mgr.—Diane Lombardo

SIC—3678; 5065; NAICS— 334417; *Corporate headquarters & distributor of electronic connectors, switches & value-added service; Brand name— AAO; Airborn; Glenair; Honeywell; Raychem; Winchester; Tyco*
Employs—150; Estab.—1946
Company-wide: 205
Sales—$77Mil
20,000 sq ft site, Distrib.—Intl.
Privately owned corporation
ISO rating—9002

### RADIO SYSTEMS DESIGN, INC.

601 Heron Dr. (08085)
**Phone—(856) 467-8000**
Fax—(856) 467-3044
www.radiosystems.com
Email—sales@radiosystems.com
Pres.—Daniel Braverman
Sales Mgr.—Jo-Ann Dunn
Mfg. Mgr.—Dennis Greben
SIC—3663; NAICS—334220; *Radio broadcasting equipment; Brand name—Radio Systems; StudioHub+; Talking House; iAM Radio*
Employs—15; Estab.—1976
Sales—$1Mil-$5Mil
13,000 sq ft site, Distrib.—Intl.
Privately owned sub-S corp.

### †RANSOME INTERNATIONAL

Div. of Navistar International Corp.
2320 High Hill Rd. (08085)
**Phone—(856) 241-8890**
Fax—(856) 241-8891
www.ransomrest.com
Email—ransominternational@ gmail.com
GM—Brian Walsh
Off. Mgr.—Susan Mourar
Serv. Mgr.—Leo McCaffrey
Parts Mgr.—David Bigelow
SIC—5013; *Wholesaler of truck parts*
Employs—20; Estab.—2005
Distrib.—Regional
Publicly owned corporation
Parent co.—Navistar International Corp., Lisle, IL
Phone—(331) 332-5000
See Parent Co. Section for full profile.

---

## Long Branch

(Monmouth—N.E.)

### ABRAHAM'S NATURAL FOODS

9 Long Branch Ave., P.O. Box 89 (07740)
**Phone—(732) 229-5799**
National—(800) 327-9903
Fax—(732) 571-0890
www.abrahamsnatural.com
Email—info@abrahamsnatural.com
Owner—Louis Fellman
GM—Audrey Almantrading
SIC—2099; *Hummus dip*
Employs—5; Estab.—1985
Sales—$500,000-$1Mil (est)
Distrib.—Regional

### BAXTER CO., INC., E. L.

70 S. 7th Ave., P.O. Box 277 (07740)
**Phone—(732) 229-8219**
(908) 415-0295
Fax—(732) 229-8457
www.elbaxter.com
Email—sales@elbaxter.com
CEO—Elwood Baxter
Pres.—Ronald M. Eberhardt
Plt. Mgr.—Richard Braun

SIC—2653; 2448; 2449; 3081; NAICS—322211; *Packaging, shipping & handling supplies, including corrugated boxes, foam end caps, tapes, stretch & shrink wraps, pallets, wood crates, industrial packaging & antistatic materials*
Employs—14; Estab.—1971
Sales—$1Mil-$5Mil
20,000 sq ft site, Distrib.—National
Privately owned corporation

### BRITTON CABINETS

199 Westwood Ave. (07740)
**Phone—(732) 222-2232**
Fax—(732) 222-5383
Owner & Pres.—Tim Britton
SIC—2434; *Wooden kitchen cabinets*
Employs—10
Sales—$500,000-$1Mil (est)
Distrib.—Local
Privately owned corporation

### C D M DUST CONTROL OF NEW JERSEY

15-17 S. 7th Ave. (07740)
**Phone—(732) 222-3694**
Fax—(732) 222-0265
Pres.—Robert G. Koenig
Bookkeeper—Cheryl Crawford
SIC—3564; NAICS—333400; *Dust control systems*
Employs—11; Estab.—1972
Sales—$500,000-$1Mil
7,200 sq ft site, Distrib.—Regional
Privately owned sub-S corp.

### COMFORT MECHANICAL CORP.

420 Division St., P.O. Box 4135 (07740)
**Phone—(732) 870-2292**
Fax—(732) 870-0140
Email—comfortmech6@ comcast.net
Pres.—Alexander Dohme
Off. Mgr.—Philip Dohme
SIC—3444; *Sheet metal ductwork*
Employs—15; Estab.—1978
Distrib.—Regional
Privately owned corporation

### COOPER NOTIFICATION

Div. of Cooper Industries, Inc.
273 Branchport Ave. (07740)
**Phone—(732) 222-6880**
National—(800) 631-2148
Fax—(732) 222-8707
www.coopernotification.com
Email—info@cooperwheelock.com
Pres.—Scott Hearn
V-P., Sales, Wheel Locks—Todd Pelland
V-P., Mktg.—Ted Milburn
V-P., Fin.—David Lowry
Cust. Serv. Rep.—Maryellen Azarian
Cust. Serv. Rep.—Margie Hudnik
SIC—3669; NAICS—334290; *Fire alarm signals & voice systems*
Employs—350; Estab.—1923
70,000 sq ft site, Distrib.—Intl.
Publicly owned corporation
Parent co.—Cooper Industries, Inc., Houston, TX
Phone—(713) 209-8400
See Parent Co. Section for full profile.

### JAMM LITHO, INC.

Div. of Accucolor, LLC
185 Broadway (07740)
**Phone—(732) 870-1999**
Fax—(732) 870-1414
www.jammprinting.com
Email—jammprinting.lb@verizon.net
Owner—Robert LaBella
Br. Mgr.—Jason Haney

SIC—2759; NAICS—323100; *Commercial printing*
Employs—9; Estab.—1973
Sales—$500,000-$1Mil
Distrib.—Local
Privately owned corporation
AKA: Jamm Printing
Parent co.—Accucolor, LLC, Shrewsbury, NJ
Phone—(732) 741-4594
See Parent Co. Section for full profile.

### JERSEY JOB GUIDE, INC.

422 Morris Ave., Ste. 5 (07740)
**Phone—(732) 263-9675**
Fax—(732) 263-0494
www.guidepubs.net
Pres.—Mike Beson
Editor & Acct. Mgr.—Rebecca Kopp
Off. Mgr.—Cathy Harlow
SIC—2741; *Employment advertising publishing*
Employs—6; Estab.—2001
Sales—under $500,000
Distrib.—Regional
Privately owned corporation
AKA: Guide Publications

### KOLL MACHINE & TOOL CO., FRANK G.

390 Warburton Pl., P.O. Box 464 (07740)
**Phone—(732) 870-2966**
Fax—(732) 870-1594
Owner—Richard Koll
SIC—3566; NAICS—333612; *Model boat radio controls, gearboxes, speed drives & changers*
Employs—3; Estab.—1940
Sales—under $500,000
5,200 sq ft site, Distrib.—Intl.
Sole ownership

### L.A. CHAMPON & CO., INC. (H Q)

266 Broadway (07740)
**Phone—(732) 923-0003**
Fax—(732) 923-0322
www.lachampon.com
Email—staff@lachampon.com
Owner—Charles Champon
Off. Mgr.—Kim Champon
SIC—2861; *Corporate headquarters; cedar oil*
Employs—10
Sales—$2.5Mil-$5Mil (est)
Distrib.—Intl.
Privately owned corporation

### LINK NEWS INC., THE

176 Broadway, P.O. Box 120 (07740)
**Phone—(732) 222-4300**
Fax—(732) 870-6800
www.thelinknews.com
Email—editor@thelinknews.com
Owner—Patty O'Neill
SIC—2711; *Weekly newspaper publishing*
Employs—3
Sales—under $500,000 (est)
Distrib.—Local
Privately owned corporation

### †MHE, INC.

47 Atlantic Ave. (07740)
**Phone—(732) 571-6112**
Fax—(732) 263-9485
www.mheincnj.com
Email—mheinc@comcast.net
Pres., GM—Dave Stickle

## Long Branch—(cont.)

SIC—5084; *Wholesaler of material handling equipment, including racking, shelving, mezzanines, wire partitions & perimeter security bollards; Brand name—Ridg-U-Rak; Cogan; Wildeck; Nexel; Allied Modular; Inplant Offices; Wireway-Huskey; WireCrafters; Ideal Shield; Hyster; DLM; Bluff; Advanced Tabco; Comtec; PortaFab; Vestil*
Employs—4; Estab.—1997
Sales—$500,000-$1Mil
2,600 sq ft site, Distrib.—Regional
Privately owned corporation

**MONMOUTH RUBBER & PLASTICS CORP.**
75 Long Branch Ave. (07740)
**Phone—(732) 229-3444**
National—(800) 375-1960
Fax—(732) 229-0711
www.rubberplastics.com
Email—sales@monmouthrubber.com
Pres. & Sales Mgr.—John M. Bonforte, Jr.
GM—John M. Bonforte, Sr.
Off. Mgr.—Jo Ann Buonomo
SIC—3086; NAICS—326100; *Closed cell sponge rubber & plastic foam, including buns, sheets, rolls, plain & PSA; Brand name—Durafoam; Bondaflex*
Employs—47; Estab.—1964
Sales—$5Mil-$10Mil
40,000 sq ft site, Distrib.—Intl.
Privately owned corporation
ISO rating—9001:2008

**PERRY'S**
11 N. 5th Ave. (07740)
**Phone—(732) 222-5040**
Fax—(732) 222-5021
www.perrystrophy.com
Email—ptcawards@aol.com
Owner, Pres., Fin. & MIS Mgr.—Carl DeCesare
Secy-Treas.—Theresa DeCesare
SIC—3479; *Metal & laser engraving, glass etching & signs*
Employs—4; Estab.—1970
Sales—under $500,000
2,500 sq ft site, Distrib.—National
Privately owned sub-S corp.

**POANDL BROTHERS WOODWORKING, INC.**
20 N. 7th Ave., P.O. Box 4015 (07740)
**Phone—(732) 229-8585**
www.lbmdesign.net
Email—sales@lbmdesign.net
Pres.—William Poandl
SIC—2431; 3089; *Architectural millwork, including solid wood interior & exterior custom doors, windows, mouldings, brackets, standing & running trim, custom cabinetry & wainscot*
Employs—4; Estab.—1985
Sales—$500,000-$1Mil
8,000 sq ft site, Distrib.—Regional
Privately owned corporation
DBA: LBM Design
AKA: Long Branch Mfg. & Design

**QUALITY REBUILDERS**
617 Broadway (07740)
**Phone—(732) 222-9100**
Fax—(732) 222-0837
Owner—Manuel Azevedo
SIC—3694; NAICS—336322; *Rebuilt automotive starters & alternators*
Employs—1; Estab.—1979
Sales—under $500,000
Distrib.—Local
Sole ownership

**RICCI TOOL & DIE CO.**
122 Myrtle Ave. (07740)
**Phone—(732) 222-2777**
Fax—(732) 222-2213
Email—riccitoolanddie@verizon.net
Pres.—John Ricci, Sr.
GM—John Ricci, Jr.
Off. Mgr.—Bob Koshko
SIC—3544; 3469; 3499; 3599; NAICS—333500; *Tool & die job shop, including metal stampings & fabrication, prototypes, CNC machining, EDM & research & development*
Employs—9; Estab.—1965
Sales—$500,000-$1Mil
Distrib.—National
Privately owned corporation

**SHORE MICROSYSTEMS, INC.**
45 Memorial Pkwy. (07740)
**Phone—(732) 870-0800**
National—(800) 600-9656
Fax—(732) 870-1912
www.shoremicro.com
Email—sales@shoremicro.com
Pres.—Gordon Elam
Dir., Sales & Mktg.—Scott Bald
SIC—3661; *Computer networking redundant Ethernet switches*
Employs—10; Estab.—1984
Sales—$1Mil-$5Mil
10,000 sq ft site, Distrib.—Intl.
Privately owned corporation

**STELAIR DESIGN CORP.**
570 Broadway (07740)
**Phone—(732) 571-3391**
Fax—(732) 571-3390
www.stelairdesigncorp.com
Email—stelair@aol.com
Pres.—Howard Steel
SIC—2396; *Textile screen printing*
Employs—1; Estab.—1990
Distrib.—National
Sole ownership

## Long Valley
(Morris—N.W.)

**CARFARO RAILINGS COMPANY, FRANK**
70 Hackelbarney Rd. *(07853)*
**Phone—(908) 879-7312**
Fax—(908) 879-8870
www.carfarorailings.com
Email—fcarfarorailings@yahoo.com
Pres.—Frank Carfaro
SIC—3446; 3444; NAICS—332323; *Iron & aluminum railings*
Employs—1; Estab.—1993
Sales—under $500,000
Distrib.—Regional
Privately owned corporation

**COOPER CHEMICAL CO.**
20 Parker Rd. (07853)
**Phone—(908) 876-3231**
Fax—(908) 876-3857
www.cooperchemical.com
Email—officemanager@cooperchemical.com
Pres., MIS Mgr.—Hugo L. Kleinhans
Fin. & Off. Mgr.—Nancy Kleinhans
SIC—2819; *Pharmaceutical intermediate chemicals*
Employs—8; Estab.—1946
Sales—$1Mil-$5Mil
Distrib.—National
Privately owned corporation

**FRAZIER INDUSTRIAL CO.**
91 Fairview Ave., P.O. Box F (07853)
**Phone—(908) 876-3001**
National—(800) 614-4162
Fax—(908) 876-3615
www.frazier.com
Email—frazier@frazier.com
CEO—William Mascharka
Pres.—Carlos Oliver

V-P., Engrg.—Rocco Spano
Comp., MIS Mgr.—Charlie Milazzo
Plt. Mgr.—Ken Backer
Pur. Agt.—Dana Ansel
SIC—2542; 3441; NAICS—332312; *Company headquarters & structural steel pallet racking, including pallet, push-back, cantilever & carton flow racks; Brand name—Sentinel; Glide-In; Klamp/Fast Cantilever; SelecDeck*
Employs—100; Estab.—1949
Sales—$10Mil-$25Mil (est)
50,100 sq ft site, Distrib.—Intl.
Privately owned corporation

**LONG VALLEY EQUIPMENT**
165 Fairview Ave. (07853)
**Phone—(908) 876-1022**
www.longvalleyequip.com
Email—longvalleyequip@gmail.com
Owner—Doug Underdahl
SIC—3861; *Photographic equipment*
Employs—6; Estab.—1996
Sales—under $500,000
Distrib.—Intl.
Privately owned corporation

**SYENCE SKINCARE LABORATORIES INC.**
99 W. Mill Rd. (07853)
**Phone—(908) 791-0044**
www.syence.com
Email—info@syence.com
Owner & Dir.—Sean Campbell
COO—Hugh Campbell
SIC—2844; NAICS—325600; *High-end skincare preparations, including face creams & body lotions*
Employs—6; Estab.—1992
Sales—$1Mil-$2.5Mil
Distrib.—Intl.
Privately owned corporation

**VALLEY SHEPHERD CREAMERY**
50 Fairmount Rd. (07853)
**Phone—(908) 876-3200**
Fax—(908) 916-5269
www.valleyshepherd.com
Email—info@valleyshepherd.com
Owner—Eran Wajswol
Shpg. Mgr.—Amanda Bancroft
SIC—2026; *Cheeses*
Employs—6; Estab.—2003
Sales—$1Mil-$2.5Mil (est)
Distrib.—Local
Limited Liability Company

**NEW ENTRY**
**WINDOWSCAPES**
5 Winay Ter. (07853)
**Phone—(908) 850-0678**
Owner—Kathy Sheola
SIC—2391; *Draperies*
Employs—1; Estab.—1994
Sales—under $500,000
Distrib.—Local
Privately owned corporation

## Lumberton
(Burlington—S.E.)

**CCL LABEL TUBEDEC**
92 Ark Rd. (08048)
**Phone—(609) 953-5050**
Fax—(856) 273-2710
www.sancoa.com
CEO—Joseph T. Sanski
SIC—2672; 2759; NAICS—322222; *Pressure-sensitive labels*
Employs—320; Estab.—1987
65,000 sq ft site, Distrib.—Intl.
Publicly owned corporation

**CHAMPION FASTENERS, INC.**
707 Smithville Rd. (08048)
**Phone—(609) 267-5222**
National—(800) 755-2693

Fax—(609) 267-2745
www.champfast.com
Email—sales@champfast.com
CEO—Aldo Magazzeni
V-P., Sales & Mktg.—Stan Lippincott
Plt. Mgr.—J. Lallo
SIC—3452; NAICS—332722; *Welding studs & specialty fasteners*
Employs—25; Estab.—1990
Sales—$1Mil-$5Mil
30,000 sq ft site, Distrib.—Intl.
Privately owned corporation

**DISTINCTIVE WOOD WORK, INC.**
70 Stacy Haines Rd., Ste. D (08048-4107)
**Phone—(609) 714-8505**
Fax—(609) 714-8544
www.distinctivewoodwork.net
Email—jcherubino@verizon.net
Owner—Jim Cherubino
SIC—2431; 2521; 2531; 2599; NAICS—337129; *Custom residential & commercial millwork & furniture, including entertainment centers, bars, offices, wall units, medical cabinetry, reception areas & bank interiors*
Employs—3; Estab.—1995
Sales—under $500,000 (est)
Distrib.—Local
Privately owned corporation

†**ENVIROPORE, INC.**
P.O. Box 443 (08048)
**Phone—(609) 261-1588**
National—(800) 874-6270
Fax—(609) 953-0702
www.enviropore.com
Email—sales@enviropore.com
Pres.—Tom Bintliff
SIC—5084; 5049; *Distributor of industrial environmental air sampling equipment & laboratory filtration supplies*
Employs—5; Estab.—1989
Distrib.—National
Privately owned sub-S corp.

**FINAS FINISHING, INC.**
50 Stacy Haines Rd. (08048)
Mail addr: P.O. Box 1206, Bellmawr (08099)
**Phone—(609) 267-4836**
Fax—(609) 267-5707
Email—finasfinishing@comcast.net
Pres.—John Fina
MIS & Off. Mgr.—Joann Fina
SIC—2752; 3993; 3471; NAICS—332813; *Metal & plastic screen printing, industrial painting & engraving & advertising specialties*
Employs—8; Estab.—1971
8,000 sq ft site, Distrib.—Local
Privately owned corporation

†**FRANKLIN MACHINE PRODUCTS, INC.**
101 Mount Holly By Pass (08048)
**Phone—(609) 267-3700**
National—(800) 257-7737
Fax—(800) 255-9866
www.fmponline.com
Email—sales@fmponline.com
Owner & Pres.—Joe Grato
V-P.—Michael A. Conte, Sr.
Cont.—Michael Cooper
Dir., Sales & Mktg.—Arnold Kimmons
Sales Mgr.—Carol Adams
Mktg. Mgr.—Steve Domzalski
Hum. Res. Mgr.—Janice M. Klumpp
SIC—5087; *Distributor of food service parts & accessories*
Employs—150; Estab.—1918
Distrib.—National
Privately owned sub-S corp.
AKA: FMP

**GEOGRAPHICAL**

## Lumberton—(cont.)

**†INTERSTATE CONNECTING COMPONENTS, INC.**
Div. of Heilind Electronics, Inc.
120 Mount Holly Byp. (08048)
**Phone—(856) 722-5535**
Fax—(856) 722-9425
www.connecticc.com
Email—info@connecticc.com
Pres.—Scott Jacobs
SIC—5065; *Distributor of industrial, military-spec. & communications connectors, including audio, video, fiber-optic & RF connectors*
Employs—60; Estab.—1986
Distrib.—Intl.
Privately owned corporation
ISO rating—9001:2000
Parent co.—Heilind Electronics, Inc., Wilmington, MA
Phone—(978) 657-4870
See Parent Co. Section for full profile.

**METAL ETCHING TECHNOLOGY ASSOCS., INC.**
140 Mount Holly Bypass, Unit 10 (08048)
Mail addr: P.O. Box 660, Hainesport (08036)
**Phone—(609) 261-2670**
Fax—(609) 261-4007
www.metassocs.com
Email—sales@metassocs.com
Pres.—Ting Shi
Ex. V-P.—Fred Cox
Sales Mgr., Natl.—John Reed
Cust. Serv. Rep.—Angela Alexander
SIC—3953; NAICS—339943; *Solder paste stencils*
Employs—20; Estab.—1992
7,000 sq ft site, Distrib.—Intl.
Privately owned corporation

**MOORHOUSE SAILMAKERS, INC.**
52 Stacy Haines Rd. (08048)
**Phone—(609) 654-7819**
Fax—(609) 518-0010
www.mandmsailing.com
Email—info@mandmsailing.com
Owner—John MacCausland
Bookkeeper—Beth Reitinger
Consultant—Skip Moorhouse
SIC—2394; NAICS—314912; *Boat sails*
Employs—3; Estab.—1976
Sales—under $500,000
Distrib.—Intl.
Privately owned corporation

**ONPATH TECHNOLOGIES**
100 Mount Holly Bypass (08048)
**Phone—(609) 518-4100**
Fax—(609) 518-4361
www.onpathtech.com
Email—info.request@onpathtech.com
Founder—Peter Dougherty
CEO—Brian McCann
V-P., CTO—Larry Cantwell
V-P., Global Sales—David I. White
Sales Mgr., Inside—Eileen Branmley
Hum. Res. Mgr.—Susan Devault
SIC—3663; 7372; NAICS—334220; *Data communications hardware & software development*
Employs—90; Estab.—2006
Sales—$10Mil-$25Mil (est)
Distrib.—Intl.
Privately owned corporation

**TREK CONNECT**
120 Mount Holly Bypass (08048)
**Phone—(856) 608-0901**
Fax—(856) 608-0902
www.trekconnect.com
Email—sales@trekconnect.com
Dir.—Craig Jacobs

SIC—3679; 3613; NAICS—335313; *Cable & harness assemblies & switching systems*
Employs—30; Estab.—1997
Distrib.—Regional
Privately owned corporation

**NEW ENTRY**
**WINDOW COVERING CONCEPTS**
29 Bella Rd. (08048)
**Phone—(609) 261-1181**
National—(800) 220-8491
Fax—(609) 678-0684
www.windowcoveringinc.com
Email—info@windowcoveringinc.com
Owner—Damien Latini
SIC—2591; *Custom draperies*
Employs—1; Estab.—1990
Sales—under $500,000
Distrib.—Local
Privately owned corporation

**YESTERWEAR PRODUCTIONS, INC.**
705 Smithville Rd. (08048)
**Phone—(609) 567-2544**
Email—anthony@yesterwear.net
Pres.—Cary Chasky
Hum. Res. Mgr.—Joan Lapenta
SIC—2396; *T-shirt screen printing*
Employs—50; Estab.—1985
25,000 sq ft site, Distrib.—Local
Privately owned corporation

---

## Lyndhurst
(Bergen—N.E.)

**ALPHA INDUSTRIES CORP. (H Q)**
P.O. Box 808 (07071)
**Phone—(201) 933-6000**
Fax—(201) 933-6429
www.sigmaplasticsgroup.com
Email—info@alpha-industries.com
CEO—Alfred Teo
CFO—John Reier
Hum. Res. Mgr.—Debra Barbour
SIC—2673; *Corporate headquarters; plastic bags & film*
Employs—20
Sales—$2.5Mil-$5Mil
Distrib.—Intl.
Privately owned corporation

**AMERIGEN PHARMACEUTICALS, INC. (H Q)**
9 Polito Ave., Ste. 900 (07071)
**Phone—(732) 993-9827**
www.amerigenpharma.com
Email—mvalsera@amerigenpharma.com
Pres.—John Lowry
CFO—Dennis Potter
Dir., Opers.—Michelle Valsera
SIC—2834; *Corporate headquarters; generic pharmaceuticals (mfg. done in China); Brand name—BYSTOLI®*
Employs—20; Estab.—2007
Sales—$10Mil-$25Mil (est)
Distrib.—Intl.
Privately owned corporation

**CAMBRIDGE PAVERS, INC.**
Jerome Ave., P.O. Box 157 (07071)
**Phone—(201) 933-5000**
Fax—(201) 933-5532
www.cambridgepavers.com
Email—linda@cambridgepavers.com
Owner, Chrm., Pres. & CEO—Charles H. Gamarekian
Hum. Res. Mgr.—Lauren Conte
Cust. Serv. Rep.—Jamie Berry
SIC—3271; NAICS—327331; *Interlocking concrete paving stones; Brand name—Armortec*
Employs—150; Estab.—1993
Distrib.—Regional
Privately owned sub-S corp.

**CASE-IT**
1050 Valley Brook Ave. (07071)
**Phone—(201) 804-5556**
Fax—(201) 804-5558
www.caseit.com
Email—bmicaseit@aol.com
Pres.—Adam Merzon
Sales Mgr.—Howard Kaminski
Hum. Res. Mgr.—Vince Vigil
SIC—3161; NAICS—316991; *Carrying cases*
Employs—10; Estab.—1991
Sales—$1Mil-$2.5Mil (est)
Distrib.—Intl.
Privately owned corporation

**CHASE MACHINE CO., INC.**
127 Park Ave., P.O. Box 148 (07071)
**Phone—(201) 438-2218**
(201) 438-2214
Fax—(201) 438-8590
Email—chasemachine@comcast.net
Pres.—Donald Lascola
SIC—3561; NAICS—333911; *Industrial pump parts for the water, chemical, oil & gas industries*
Employs—13; Estab.—1951
Sales—$1Mil-$5Mil
4,000 sq ft site, Distrib.—National
Privately owned corporation

**†DAL-TILE CORPORATION**
1250 Valley Brook Ave. (07071)
**Phone—(201) 729-0203**
(201) 729-9169
National—(866) 344-0723
Fax—(201) 729-0207
www.daltile.com
Email—newyorkstone.ssc379@daltile.com
Stone Mgr.—Peter Chomyszak
Tile Mgr.—Marc Frank
SIC—5032; *Distributor of ceramic, porcelain & stone tile & mosaics*
Employs—15; Estab.—2003
40,000 sq ft site, Distrib.—National
Publicly owned corporation
Parent co.—Dal-Tile Corporation, Dallas, TX
Phone—(214) 398-1411
See Parent Co. Section for full profile.

**DELTA PRINTING CO.**
1000 Wall Street W. (07071)
**Phone—(201) 935-0036**
Fax—(201) 935-0037
www.deltaprinting.com
Email—info@deltaprinting.com
GM—Vick Mazbanian
SIC—2759; NAICS—323100; *Commercial, instant, offset & digital printing*
Employs—8; Estab.—2000
Sales—$1Mil-$2.5Mil
Distrib.—Regional
Sole ownership

**DRAWBASE SOFTWARE**
1099 Wall St. W., Ste. 269 (07071-3617)
**Phone—(973) 927-6814**
Fax—(973) 387-9777
www.drawbase.com
Email—info@drawbase.com
Pres., CEO—Evan Kontos
Dir., Sales—David Connors
Administrator—Cynthia Kontos
SIC—7372; *Integrated workplace management software development; Brand name—Drawbase®; Move Manager™; DataCenter Manager™; DecisionBase®; MaximoLink™; MEP Manager™; Projector™; Drawbase Web Viewer™; Infor EAM Link™*
Employs—10; Estab.—1986
Distrib.—Intl.
Limited Liability Company

**ELEGANT DESSERTS**
275 Warren St. (07071)
**Phone—(201) 933-0770**
National—(800) 933-0770
Fax—(201) 933-7309
www.elegantdesserts.com
Email—sales@elegantdesserts.com
Owner—John Mazur
Sales Mgr.—Cindy Mazur
Off. Mgr.—Linda Schifano
SIC—2051; NAICS—311812; *Cakes, pastries & tortes*
Employs—20; Estab.—1994
Sales—$1Mil-$2.5Mil
Distrib.—Regional
Privately owned corporation

**FABIAN COUTURE GROUP INTERNATIONAL**
205 Chubb Ave., Ste. 1 (07071)
**Phone—(201) 460-7776**
National—(800) 367-6251
Fax—(800) 367-7017
www.fabiancouture.com
Email—sales@fabiancouture.com
Pres.—Allan Weiss
V-P.—Dan Gindea
Sales Rep.—Brian Reedinger
Cust. Serv. Rep.—Marsha Rosenthal
SIC—2311; 2321; 2323; NAICS—315200; *Men's tuxedos, shirts & ties*
Employs—35; Estab.—1992
Sales—under $500,000
Distrib.—Intl.
Privately owned corporation

**G & G SIGNS, INC.**
323 2nd Ave. (07071)
**Phone—(201) 939-4099**
National—(800) 341-7446
Fax—(201) 939-0889
www.ggsigns.com
Email—ggdesignsinc@gmail.com
Pres.—Joe Garofalo
SIC—3993; *Interior & exterior signs*
Employs—2; Estab.—1978
Sales—under $500,000
Distrib.—Local
Privately owned corporation
AKA: G & G Designs, Inc.

**†IESI RECYCLING CORP. (H Q)**
Div. of IESI Corp.
1099 Wall St. W., Ste. 250 (07071)
**Phone—(201) 443-3000**
Fax—(201) 443-3020
www.iesi.com
Email—eapuzzi@iesi.com
V-P. & Reg. Mgr.—Ed Apuzzi
SIC—5093; *Divisional headquarters; wholesaler of recycled paper*
Employs—15; Estab.—2001
Distrib.—Local
Privately owned corporation
Parent co.—IESI Corp., Fort Worth, TX
Phone—(817) 632-4000
See Parent Co. Section for full profile.

**IMPERIAL ELECTRO PLATING**
52 Park Ave. (07071)
**Phone—(201) 438-9450**
(201) 438-1010
Fax—(201) 438-2341
Email—imperialplating@verizon.net
Pres.—Fred Englehardt
V-P.—Ed Englehardt
Off. Mgr.—Nicole Lacorie
SIC—3471; NAICS—332813; *Electroplating*
Employs—20; Estab.—1977
Sales—$1Mil-$2.5Mil
Distrib.—Local
Privately owned corporation

## Lyndhurst—(cont.)

**JMA SAUSAGE AND MEAT COMPANY, INC.**
205 Stuyvesant Ave., Ste. 211 (07071-1704)
**Phone—(201) 636-2022**
Fax—(201) 842-6649
www.jmasausage.com
Email—jaragona5@verizon.net
Pres.—Joe Aragona, Jr.
SIC—2013; NAICS—311600; *Italian sausage, breakfast sausage, chorizo sausage & poultry sausage; Brand name— Torino Sausag; Gina Sausage; Country Maid Sausage; Aragona Chorizo; Manga Bene*
Employs—5; Estab.—1994
Sales—$1Mil-$2.5Mil
Distrib.—National
Privately owned sub-S corp.
AKA: JMA
DBA: Torino Sausage Co.

**LINK THEORY**
Div. of Link Theory Holdings (US), Inc.
165 Polito Ave. (07071)
Mail addr.—38 Gansevoort St., New York (10014)
**Phone—(201) 728-5700**
Fax—(201) 896-1041
www.theory.com
Email—theoryjobs@theoryjobs.com
Hum. Res. Mgr.—Emma Morgan
Cust. Serv. Mgr.—Rose Salerno
SIC—2329; 2339; NAICS— 315200; *Men's & women's clothing*
Employs—100; Estab.—2006
Distrib.—National
Privately owned corporation
AKA: Theysken's
Parent co.—Link Theory Holdings (US), Inc., New York, NY
Phone—(212) 300-0800
See Parent Co. Section for full profile.

[NEW ENTRY]
**MEGAS YEEROS, LLC**
165 Chubb Ave. (07071)
**Phone—(212) 777-6342**
www.megasyeeros.com
Email—info@megasyeeros.com
Pres., GM—Nikos Stergiou
Principal—George Vanis
SIC—2011; 2015; *Lamb, beef, pork & chicken gyros meat processing; Brand name— Megas Yeeros™*
Employs—20; Estab.—2014
Sales—$5Mil-$10Mil (est)
32,000 sq ft site, Distrib.— Regional
Limited Liability Company

**MIZRAK**
288 Livingston Ave., 1st Fl. (07071)
**Phone—(973) 622-0328**
Fax—(973) 504-8575
www.mizrak.com
Email—mizrak@mizrak.com
Pres.—Yalcin Mizrak
SIC—2339; 2369; NAICS— 315200; *Women's & children's sportswear*
Employs—2; Estab.—2008
Distrib.—Local
Sole ownership

**NEILL SUPPLY CO., INC.**
700 Schuyler Ave. (07071)
**Phone—(201) 939-1100**
National—(800) 526-6376
Fax—(201) 939-6095
www.lipipe.com
Email—sales@lipipe.com
Pres.—Robert Moss
GM—Brad Moss

SIC—3569; 5051; 5085; 5074; *Manufacturer of fire sprinklers & distributor of welded pipes, valves & fittings*
Employs—60; Estab.—1955
Sales—$5Mil-$10Mil (est)
Distrib.—Regional
Privately owned corporation

**OMEGA PLASTICS CORP.**
Div. of Alpha Industries Corp.
Page & Schuyler Ave., Bldg. 3, P.O. Box 808 (07071-2611)
**Phone—(201) 933-5353**
National—(800) 663-4283
Fax—(201) 933-8921
www.sigmaplastics.com
Email—info@alpha-industries.com
Pres.—Ed Miller
CFO—John Reier
GM—Bill Silori
Hum. Res. Mgr.—Debra Barbour
SIC—2673; *Divisional headquarters & plastic bags*
Employs—50
Sales—$5Mil-$10Mil
Distrib.—National
Sole ownership
Parent co.—Alpha Industries Corp., Lyndhurst, NJ
Phone—(201) 933-6000
See Parent Co. Section for full profile.

**OTIS GRAPHICS, INC.**
290 Grant Ave. (07071)
**Phone—(201) 438-7120**
Fax—(201) 438-5546
www.otisgraphics.com
Email—printing@otisgraphics.com
Pres.—Patricia Motisi
V-P.—Ronald Kist, Jr.
SIC—2759; NAICS—323100; *Commercial printing*
Employs—5; Estab.—1968
Sales—$1Mil-$2.5Mil
Distrib.—Intl.
Privately owned corporation

**POLYURETHANE SPECIALTIES CO.**
624 Schuyler Ave. (07071)
**Phone—(201) 438-2325**
National—(800) 348-2553
Fax—(201) 507-1367
www.polyurethanespecialties.com
Email—sales@ polyurethanespecialties.com
Owner—Phil Gianatasio
SIC—2821; NAICS—325211; *Polyurethane processing*
Employs—30; Estab.—1972
Distrib.—Intl.
Privately owned corporation

**RAMSEY PRINT CORP.**
1000 Wall St. W., Ste. 2 (07071)
**Phone—(201) 460-1008**
Fax—(201) 340-4056
www.ramsbeeprint.com
Email—jeff@ramsbeeprint.com
CFO—Jeffrey Beecher
Pressman—Wally Mehan
SIC—2752; 2791; NAICS— 323122; *Offset printing & computerized typesetting*
Employs—6; Estab.—1983
5,000 sq ft site, Distrib.—National
Privately owned corporation

**RIDGE CARBIDE TOOL CO.**
595 New York Ave., P.O. Box 497 (07071)
**Phone—(201) 438-8777**
National—(800) 443-0992
Fax—(888) 728-8665
www.ridgecarbidetool.com
Email—rattool@verizon.net
Pres. & Shpg. Mgr.—John Ferrie
SIC—3541; NAICS—333512; *Carbide cutting tools*
Employs—8; Estab.—1970
Sales—$1Mil-$2.5Mil (est)
Distrib.—Local
Privately owned corporation
AKA: Apex Ridge

**ROSA PEN CORP.**
155 Park Ave., Ste. 101 (07071-1462)
**Phone—(201) 939-1112**
National—(800) 386-2367
Fax—(201) 939-3301
www.acepens.com
Email—info@acepens.com
Owner & Pres.—Anthony J. Rosa
SIC—3951; NAICS—339941; *Custom manufacturing of bent chiropractic & advertising & promotional ballpoint pens; Brand name—ACE; Spun-tip refills; Binder-Mate; Aro-Sharp; Sweet 16 Lollipop Pens*
Employs—5; Estab.—1925
10,000 sq ft site, Distrib.—National
Privately owned corporation
DBA: ACE Pens

**SAMPLE MARSHALL LABORATORIES, INC.**
63 Park Ave. *(07071)*
**Phone—(201) 933-0570**
National—(800) 323-7695
Fax—(201) 933-9157
www.samplemarshall.com
Email—sales@samplemarshall.com
Pres.—James Sample
GM—Joseph Pulzone
Opers. Mgr., Plating—Michael Memoli
Off. Mgr.—Barbara Gabriel
Bookkeeper—Zoila Robles
SIC—3291; *Diamond & CBN abrasive grinding tools & wheels; Brand name—Tuff-Kote*
Employs—11; Estab.—1947
15,000 sq ft site, Distrib.—Intl.
Privately owned corporation
ISO rating—9001:2000

**SIGMA PLASTICS GROUP (H Q)**
Div. of Alpha Industries Corp.
Page & Schuyler Aves., Bldg. 5, P.O. Box 808 (07071)
**Phone—(201) 933-6000**
Fax—(201) 933-6429
www.sigmaplastics.com
Email—info@alpha-industries.com
Ex. V-P.—Alan Teo
Pur. Mgr., Resin—Lisa Muccilo
Hum. Res. Mgr.—Debra Barbour
SIC—3081; NAICS—326113; *Company headquarters; plastic sheeting & film*
Employs—200
Sales—$50Mil-$100Mil (est)
Privately owned corporation
Parent co.—Alpha Industries Corp., Lyndhurst, NJ
Phone—(201) 933-6000
See Parent Co. Section for full profile.

**SIGMA STRETCH FILM**
Div. of Sigma Plastics Group
Page Ave., Bldg. 5 & 8, P.O. Box 808 (07071)
**Phone—(201) 507-9100**
National—(800) 672-9727
Fax—(201) 507-0447
www.sigmastretchfilm.com
Email—info@sigmastretchfilm.com
Cust. Serv. Rep.—Sabrina Protomastro
Cust. Serv. Rep.—Sunday Korteling
SIC—3081; NAICS—326113; *Plastic stretch film*
Employs—100; Estab.—1989
Distrib.—Intl.
Privately owned corporation
Parent co.—Sigma Plastics Group, Lyndhurst, NJ
Phone—(201) 933-6000
See Parent Co. Section for full profile.

**SIKA CORPORATION**
201 Polito Ave. (07071-3601)
**Phone—(201) 933-8800**
National—(800) 933-7452
Fax—(201) 933-6225

www.sikaconstruction.com
Email—info@sika-corp.com
Pres., CEO—Christoph Ganz
Ex. V-P., Opers.—Herbert Zwartkruis
Ex. V-P., Hum. Res.—Nick Romano
Ex. V-P., Refurbishment—Rick Montani
Brand Dev. Mgr.—Rosa Romualdo
SIC—3272; 2891; 3996; NAICS— 325520; *Corporate headquarters & concrete materials & restoration technology & epoxy flooring materials; Brand name— Sikaflex; Sikagard; SikaWrap; SikaGrout; Sikadur; Sikafloor; SikaRepair; SikaQuick; SikaTop; SikaLatex; SikaSil; Sika MonoTop; SikaPronto; SikaBond; Sika CarboDur*
Employs—107; Estab.—1937
Company-wide: 900
Distrib.—National
Privately owned corporation
ISO rating—9000:2000

**SIR SPEEDY PRINTING CENTER**
122 Ridge Rd. (07071)
**Phone—(201) 896-2727**
Fax—(201) 896-0121
www.sirspeedynj.com
Email—info@sirspeedynj.com
Dir.—Tom Penisch
GM—Joanne Penisch
SIC—2759; 2752; 3993; 2396; NAICS—323119; *Full-color digital, traditional offset & instant printing of legal documents, marketing & training materials, posters, signs & banners & custom imprinted apparel, including graphic design, website design & marketing & direct mail services*
Employs—5; Estab.—1995
Sales—$500,000-$1Mil
Distrib.—National
Privately owned corporation

**STORKDELIVERY.COM**
232 Webster Ave. (07071)
**Phone—(201) 933-7721**
www.storkdelivery.com
Email—info@storkdelivery.com
Owner—Dennis Mazza
SIC—3993; *Lawn signs, wooden exterior signs, stork & baby announcements, vinyl banners & custom window painting*
Employs—2; Estab.—2001
Sales—under $500,000
Distrib.—Local
Limited Liability Company

**STRIVE GROUP, LLC, THE**
Div. of Menasha Packaging Company, LLC
160 Chubb Ave., Ste. 101 (07071)
**Phone—(973) 893-1300**
Fax—(773) 227-6000
www.strivegroup.com
Email—sales@strivegroup.com
Owner—Jeff Schuoski
SIC—2542; 3993; NAICS— 337215; *Point-of-purchase displays*
Employs—50; Estab.—2002
Sales—$5Mil-$10Mil (est)
Distrib.—National
Limited Liability Company
Parent co.—Menasha Packaging Company, LLC, Chicago, IL
Phone—(312) 880-4620
See Parent Co. Section for full profile.

**TRYLON METAL WORKS INC.**
136 Park Ave. (07071)
**Phone—(201) 939-8282**
Fax—(201) 939-0799
www.trylonrailing.com
Email—info@trylonrailing.com
Pres.—Ralph Marchione
Off. Mgr.—Barbara Marchione

GEOGRAPHICAL

## Lyndhurst—(cont.)

SIC—3446; NAICS—332323;
*Architectural handrails*
Employs—15; Estab.—1984
Sales—$1Mil-$2.5Mil
Distrib.—Local
Privately owned corporation
AKAs: Trylon & Trylon Railing

**VERINT SYSTEMS, INC.**
9 Polito Ave., 9th Fl. (07071)
**Phone—(201) 559-3788**
Fax—(201) 933-6820
www.verint.com
Email—sales@verint.com
Off. Admn.—Sasha Matthews
SIC—3669; NAICS—334290;
*Voice recording & archiving
systems; Brand name—Audiolog*
Employs—50; Estab.—1997
Distrib.—Intl.
Privately owned corporation
Parent co.—Verint Systems, Inc.,
Melville, NY
Phone—(631) 962-9600
See Parent Co. Section for full profile.

NEW ENTRY
**VSPLASH TECHLABS, INC. (H Q)**
1050 Wall St. W., Ste. 630 (07071)
**Phone—(201) 355-0066**
www.vsplash.com
Email—social@vsplash.com
Pres.—Umesh Tibrewal
SIC—7372; *Corporate
headquarters; internet-based
software development
(development done in India);
Brand name—vSplash*
Employs—27; Estab.—1999
Distrib.—Intl.
Privately owned corporation

**WACOAL AMERICA, INC.**
1 Wacoal Plz. (07071)
**Phone—(201) 933-8400**
National—(800) 526-6286
Fax—(201) 933-8296
www.wacoalamerica.com
Email—customerservice@wacoal-
america.com
Plt. Mgr.—Ismael Vicens
SIC—2341; 2342; 2339; NAICS—
315200; *Intimate apparel*
Employs—200; Estab.—1985
131,000 sq ft site, Distrib.—Intl.
Privately owned corporation
Parent co.—Wacoal America, Inc.,
New York, NY
Phone—(212) 532-6100
See Parent Co. Section for full profile.

## Madison
(Morris—N.W.)

**ALFRED'S SPORT SHOP**
32 Main St. (07940)
**Phone—(973) 377-0051**
Fax—(973) 966-1889
www.alfredssportshop.com
Email—hhisports@yahoo.com
GM—Chuck Bleakley
SIC—2329; 2339; 2396; 2759;
NAICS—313210; *Baseball,
softball & lacrosse equipment,
uniforms, apparel & footwear,
including silk screening &
printing*
Employs—6; Estab.—1980
Sales—$500,000-$1Mil
Distrib.—Local
Privately owned corporation

**AMERICAN
MICROSEMICONDUCTOR, INC.**
133 Kings Rd., P.O. Box 104
(07940)
**Phone—(973) 377-9566**
Fax—(973) 377-3078
www.americanmicrosemi.com

Email—rm@
americanmicrosemi.com
Pres.—William Foley
Sales Mgr.—Rose Marie
Memmolo
Opers. Mgr.—Sean Michael
Hum. Res. Mgr.—Sharon Justus
SIC—3674; NAICS—334413;
*Semiconductors & devices*
Employs—15; Estab.—1957
Distrib.—Intl.
Privately owned corporation

**BARCODEAMERICA.COM**
144 Shunpike Rd., P.O. Box 506
(07940)
**Phone—(973) 377-8182**
National—(800) 734-4897
Fax—(973) 377-8183
www.barcodeamerica.com
Email—rrack@rdgguys.com
Pres.—Robert W. Rack
SIC—7373; 5045; 5065; *Systems
integration & distributor of
readers & bar code quality
verification systems, labels &
thermal ribbon, inkjet & laser
printing systems, mobile data
collection & label applicators &
2D & 3D machine vision; Brand
name—RDGVision; Cognex;
Datalogic; Microscan; Keyence;
Anviz; Label Vision Systems;
Cab Technologies; Zebra;
Datamax; Sato; Cognitive; DNP;
ITW; Sony; IIMAK; Armor; Epson;
Honeywell; Motorola; Opticon;
Unitech; GoCator*
Employs—10; Estab.—1993
Sales—$1Mil-$10Mil
5,000 sq ft site, Distrib.—Intl.
Privately owned sub-S corp.

**CALDWELL CONSUMER HEALTH,
LLC (H Q)**
8 Elmer St., Ste. 1 (07940)
**Phone—(973) 360-1090**
National—(888) 317-4402
Fax—(973) 360-1091
www.revivepersonalproducts.com
Email—info@thenaturaldentist.com
CEO—Michael Lesser
Pres., COO—Kelly Kaplan
SIC—2844; 2834; *Company
headquarters; personal
healthcare products, including
vaginal contraceptives,
spermicide, dental plaque
remover & mouthwash (mfg.
subcontracted); Brand name—
Stim-U-Dent; Conceptrol; Gynol
II; Fresh 'n Brite; Healthy
Woman; The Natural Dentist*
Employs—6; Estab.—2008
Sales—$2.5Mil-$5Mil (est)
Distrib.—Intl.
Limited Liability Company
DBA: Revive Personal Products

**HANSEN'S CABINET SHOP, INC.**
42 Park Ave. (07940)
**Phone—(973) 377-2444**
Fax—(973) 377-0659
Email—arfst7@aol.com
Pres.—A. Hansen
V-P.—Barry Gonnelli
Corp. Secy.—Theresa Gonnelli
SIC—2434; 2542; 2431; NAICS—
337110; *Custom wooden &
plastic laminated cabinets*
Employs—4; Estab.—1965
Sales—under $500,000
4,000 sq ft site, Distrib.—Local
Limited Liability Company
AKA: Achbjc, LLC

**HELLER CO., E. P.**
21-25 Samson Ave., P.O. Box 26
(07940)
**Phone—(973) 377-2878**
Fax—(973) 514-1022
www.ephco.com
Email—ephburs@aol.com
Chrm., CEO—Eugene Heller

Pres.—A. Daub, Jr.
V-P.—Douglas Heller
V-P.—Peter Heller
Hum. Res. Mgr.—Catherine Heller
Fin. Mgr.—Z. Mansouri
SIC—3545; *Solid carbide cutting
& pneumatic tools &
resharpening service*
Employs—25; Estab.—1962
6,000 sq ft site, Distrib.—Intl.
Privately owned corporation

**QUEST DIAGNOSTICS (H Q)**
3 Giralda Farms (07940)
**Phone—(973) 520-2700**
Fax—(973) 520-2136
www.questdiagnostics.com
Email—mediacontact@
questdiagnostics.com
Non-Exec. Chrm.—Daniel C.
Stanzione
Pres., CEO—Stephen H.
Rusckowski
Sr. V-P., Chief Med. Officer—Jon
R. Cohen
Sr. V-P., Chief Legal Counsel—
Michael Prevoznik
V-P., Corp. Comms.—Gary
Samuels
Ex. Dir., Investor Rels.—Kathleen
Valentine
SIC—7372; *Company
headquarters; healthcare
medical information collection,
storage, retrieval & management
software development*
Employs—300
Distrib.—National
Publicly owned corporation

**RED FEATHER MARKETING GROUP**
332 Main St. (07940)
**Phone—(973) 966-1399**
          (973) 769-8149
www.red-feather.com
Email—info@red-feather.com
Ptnr.—Steve Becker
Ptnr.—Jeff Roberts
SIC—3993; 2542; 2759;
*Advertising specialties, including
outdoor signage, banners,
displays, commercial printing,
promotional item screen printing
& events graphics*
Employs—7; Estab.—1990
Sales—$2.5Mil
3,000 sq ft site, Distrib.—National
Privately owned corporation

**SENSOR PRODUCTS, INC.**
300 Madison Ave., Ste. 100
(07940)
**Phone—(973) 884-1755**
National—(800) 755-2201
Fax—(973) 884-1699
www.sensorprod.com
Email—sales@sensorprod.com
Off. Mgr.—Evan Worthing
Prod. Mgr.—Carlos Bais
SIC—3829; 3825; NAICS—
334514; *Tactile pressure
sensors; Brand name—
Pressurex; Topaq; Tactilus; IDEA;
E-Nip; AutoNIS; Pointscan*
Employs—25; Estab.—1990
Distrib.—Intl.
Privately owned corporation

**SHOR INTERNATIONAL CORP.**
77 Fairwood Rd. (07940)
**Phone—(973) 520-8777**
Fax—(973) 520-8779
www.ishor.com
Email—service@ishor.com
Pres., CFO—Peter Shor
V-P., GM—Nathan Shor
GM—John Scott
SIC—3423; *Jewelry tools &
refining systems*
Employs—36; Estab.—1918
Sales—$1Mil-$2.5Mil
Distrib.—Intl.
Privately owned corporation
AKA: I Shor

**STEWART-MORRIS, INC.**
71 Kings Rd. (07940)
**Phone—(973) 822-2777**
www.stewart-morris.com
Email—stewartmorris@aol.com
Pres.—John W. Morris
V-P.—Virginia M. Williams
SIC—3499; 3993; *Awards, gifts,
flags & promotional products*
Employs—6; Estab.—1972
Sales—$500,000-$1Mil
2,500 sq ft site, Distrib.—National

**TEMPERATURE HUMIDITY
INSTRUMENTS LLC**
235 Main St., Ste. 281 (07940-
2288)
**Phone—(908) 354-8236**
Fax—(908) 354-9564
www.check-it-electronics.com
Email—checkit@check-it-
electronics.com
Pres.—Richard Bettle
SIC—3829; *Temperature &
humidity indicators &
temperature sensors; Brand
name—Check-It*
Employs—5; Estab.—2012
Sales—over $1Mil
1,000 sq ft site, Distrib.—Intl.
Limited Liability Company
DBA: Check-It Electronics

## Magnolia
(Camden—S.W.)

**SAPPHIRE ENVELOPE & GRAPHICS
CO., INC.**
214 W. Davis Rd. (08049)
**Phone—(856) 782-2227**
Fax—(856) 782-8479
Pres.—Anthony Mellaca
V-P., GM—Stephen A. Bressi
SIC—2759; NAICS—323100;
*Commercial printing*
Employs—10; Estab.—1996
20,000 sq ft site, Distrib.—Local
Privately owned corporation

## Mahwah
(Bergen—N.E.)

**A T INFORMATION PRODUCTS, INC.**
575 Corporate Dr. (07430)
**Phone—(201) 529-0202**
Fax—(201) 529-5603
www.atip-usa.com
Pres.—Joseph Traut
Sales & Mktg. Mgr.—Roger
Angrick
Cust. Serv. Mgr.—Steve Sentowski
SIC—3565; 2759; NAICS—
333993; *Inkjet printing & labeling
systems*
Employs—9; Estab.—1987
Distrib.—National
Privately owned corporation

**†ACE JANITORIAL SUPPLY, INC.**
164 Franklin Tpke., Ste. 2 (07430)
**Phone—(201) 529-1750**
Fax—(201) 529-1463
www.acesupplynj.com
Email—customerservice@
acesupplynj.com
Pres.—H. Mike Timpone
SIC—5113; 5169; 5063; *Distributor
of janitorial & electrical supplies,
including paper towels, cleaning
chemicals & fluorescent light
bulbs; Brand name—Brulin; Bay
West; Heritage; Georgia Pacific;
Technical Concepts; Oreck;
Mercury Floor Machine*
Employs—4; Estab.—1992
7,500 sq ft site, Distrib.—Regional
Privately owned sub-S corp.

## Mahwah—(cont.)

**ACUPAC PACKAGING, INC.**
Div. of Kolmar Laboratories, Inc.
55 Ramapo Valley Rd. (07430)
**Phone—(201) 529-3434**
Fax—(201) 529-1319
www.acupac.com
Email—acupac@acupac.com
GM—Stephanie Hayano
Plt. Mgr.—Tom Kilroy
Hum. Res. Mgr.—Athina Krassas
Process Engr.—Katie Lillis
Cust. Serv. Rep.—Rich D'Andra
SIC—3089; Contract packaging
Employs—200; Estab.—1979
80,000 sq ft site, Distrib.—
Regional
Privately owned corporation
Parent co.—Kolmar Laboratories,
Inc., Port Jervis, NY
Phone—(845) 856-5311
See Parent Co. Section for full profile.

**AIR WORLD, INC.**
126 Christie Ave. (07430)
**Phone—(201) 831-0700**
www.airworldtads.com
Email—airworld@gmail.com
Pres.—Sam Oh
V-P.—John Rizzuto
Manager—Michael Oh
SIC—2394; NAICS—314912;
Cloth covers for apparel cleaning
presses
Employs—20; Estab.—2002
Sales—$500,000-$1Mil
Distrib.—National
Privately owned corporation

**†ALLIED BUILDING PRODUCTS
CORP.**
27-33 Franklin Tpke. (07430)
**Phone—(201) 529-3300**
Fax—(201) 512-0313
www.alliedbuilding.com
Email—sales@alliedbuilding.com
Br. Mgr.—John Rogan
SIC—5033; 5031; Distributor of
building materials & supplies,
including roofing, siding,
windows & doors
Employs—10; Estab.—1958
Distrib.—Regional
Publicly owned corporation
Parent co.—Allied Building
Products Corp., East Rutherford,
NJ
Phone—(201) 507-8400
See Parent Co. Section for full profile.

**ALPHAGRAPHICS OF MAHWAH**
1 Lethbridge Plz., Route 17 N.
(07430)
**Phone—(201) 327-2200**
Fax—(201) 529-3392
www.us713.alphagraphics.com
Email—johnchris@
alphagraphics.com
Pres.—John Chrisostomou
Cust. Serv. Mgr.—Cecilia Bino
SIC—2759; 2752; 3993; NAICS—
323100; Digital, direct mail &
business printing, signs,
banners, posters, graphic
design & marketing services;
Brand name—AlphaGraphics
Employs—6; Estab.—2012
Sales—$1Mil-$5Mil
2,500 sq ft site, Distrib.—Regional
Privately owned corporation

**†ARCO, INC.**
300 State Route 17, Unit K (07430)
**Phone—(201) 828-9808**
Fax—(201) 828-5955
www.arcoinc.com
Email—info@arcoinc.com
CEO—Adil Ansari
Pres.—Rick Kapoor
Qual. Assur. Mgr.—Joan De
Angelis

SIC—5065; Distributor of memory
products & supply chain
services; Brand name—Alliance
Memory; AMIC; Analog Power;
Anovay; ATO; Bellnix; Chiplus;
DOMINANT; Edison Opto; Eon;
Eorex; ESMT; Etron; Fidelix;
Fortasa; Giantec; gaDevice;
Jauch; LEDIL; Maida;
MarsLEDS; Maximus;
Memoright; RunCore
Employs—25; Estab.—1994
Distrib.—Intl.
Privately owned corporation
ISO rating—9001:2008

**ARIES PRECISION TOOL, INC.**
300 State Route 17, Ste. H (07430)
**Phone—(201) 252-8550**
Fax—(201) 252-8551
Email—apt1444@yahoo.com
Pres.—Stephen Bachman
SIC—3599; Precision machining
& CNC turning & milling job shop
Employs—6; Estab.—1986
Sales—under $1Mil
3,000 sq ft site, Distrib.—Regional
Privately owned sub-S corp.

**BIONOMIC INDUSTRIES, INC.**
777 Corporate Dr. (07430)
**Phone—(201) 529-1094**
Fax—(201) 529-0252
www.bionomicind.com
Email—info@bionomicind.com
Pres.—John Enhoffer
GM—Linda Babcock
SIC—3564; Air pollution control
equipment
Employs—12
Sales—$1Mil-$2.5Mil (est)
Privately owned corporation

**†BLACKMAN PLUMBING SUPPLY
CO., INC.**
270 Route 17 S. (07430)
**Phone—(201) 529-5500**
National—(888) 802-7866
Fax—(201) 252-8098
www.blackman.com
Email—marketing@blackman.com
Br. Mgr.—Randy Gillies
Wholesale Mgr.—Laurie Hanley
SIC—5074; 5075; Distributor of
plumbing, heating & air
conditioning equipment &
supplies; Brand name—
American Standard; Delta
Faucet; ELKAY; Grohe;
Insinkerator; Jacuzzi
Employs—30; Estab.—1921
Distrib.—Regional
Privately owned corporation
Parent co.—Blackman Plumbing
Supply Co., Inc., Bayport, NY
Phone—(631) 823-4300
See Parent Co. Section for full profile.

**BUHLER INC**
Div. of Buhler Inc.
40 Whitney Rd. (07430)
**Phone—(201) 847-0600**
Fax—(201) 847-0606
www.buhler.com
Email—patrik.maeder@
buhlergroup.com
Pres.—Steve Jacobson
Sales Mgr.—Korkmaz Oz
Opers. Mgr.—Daniel Flannery
Cust. Serv. Mgr.—Diane
Yaskoweak
Head of Tech.—Edward Casama

SIC—3599; 3559; 3556; 2841;
NAICS—335311; Processing
equipment for the chemical,
pharmaceutical, recycling,
building & plastic materials,
paper coatings, provisions, fine
foods, detergents & soaps
industries, including dispersing
mills, mixers, reactors & plastic
compounders; Brand name—
Perl Mill; Gelimat; Turbulent
Superflusher; NanoStar
Employs—15; Estab.—1970
35,000 sq ft site, Distrib.—Intl.
Privately owned corporation
Parent co.—Buhler Inc., Plymouth,
MN
Phone—(763) 847-9900
See Parent Co. Section for full profile.

**CASES BY SOURCE, INC.**
215 Island Rd. (07430)
**Phone—(201) 831-0005**
National—(888) 665-9768
Fax—(201) 831-0009
www.casesbysource.com
Email—contact@
casesbysource.com
V-P.—Matthew Adler
Opers. & Prodn. Mgr.—Joe
Hughes
IT Mgr.—Paul Lavigne
Cust. Serv. Mgr.—Renee Gordon
SIC—2441; 3089; NAICS—
321920; Aluminum, plastic &
wood SKB, ATA, pelican,
seahorse & underwater kinetics
stock & custom cases for
commercial, military & industrial
applications; Brand name—
EuroCase; Spectra Case; Trans
Case; Versa Case; Pelican;
Zarges; SKB; Hardigg; Zero
Employs—25; Estab.—2000
13,000 sq ft site, Distrib.—Intl.
Privately owned corporation
Also see: Source Packaging, Inc.,
same loc.

**CELCO, INC.**
14 Industrial Ave., 3rd Fl. (07430)
**Phone—(201) 327-1123**
Fax—(201) 327-7047
www.celco.com
Email—info@celco.com
V-P.—John Constantine, Jr.
SIC—3679; Corporate
headquarters & electronic
components
Employs—3; Estab.—1945
Distrib.—National
Privately owned corporation

**†CENTRAL PET**
Div. of Central Garden & Pet Co.
301 Island Rd. (07430)
**Phone—(201) 529-5050**
Fax—(201) 529-1285
www.centralpet.com
Email—info@centralpet.com
Pres.—Neill Hines
SIC—5199; Distributor of pet
supplies
Employs—50; Estab.—1989
Distrib.—National
Publicly owned corporation
Parent co.—Central Garden & Pet
Co., Walnut Creek, CA
Phone—(925) 948-4000
See Parent Co. Section for full profile.

**CODA, INC.**
30 Industrial Ave. (07430)
**Phone—(201) 825-7400**
Fax—(201) 825-8133
www.codamount.com
Email—sales@codamount.com
Pres.—Lee Coda
V-P.—Sally Becker

SIC—3861; Laminating
equipment & graphic finishing
supplies
Employs—30; Estab.—1992
55,000 sq ft site, Distrib.—Intl.
Privately owned corporation

**COURIER CORP.**
1 International Blvd., Ste. 400
(07495)
**Phone—(201) 934-7100**
National—(800) 631-7795
Fax—(201) 934-8971
www.alternateplans.com
Email—customerservice@
courier.com
CEO—James Conway III
SIC—2731; Book publishing
Employs—5; Estab.—1985
Sales—under $500,000
Distrib.—National
Publicly owned corporation
Parent co.—Courier Corp., North
Chelmsford, MA
Phone—(978) 251-6000
See Parent Co. Section for full profile.

**D&M HOLDINGS US, INC. (H Q)**
100 Corporate Dr. (07430)
**Phone—(201) 762-6500**
Fax—(201) 762-6670
www.dmglobal.com
Email—info@dmglobal.com
CEO—Jim Caudill
Pres., Sales, N. America—Brian
Poggi
Global CFO—Amy O'Keefe
Sr. Hum. Res. Mgr.—Antoinette
Landsman
SIC—6719; 3651; 3714; 5064;
NAICS—551112; Holding
company headquarters; home
entertainment components,
including residential &
automotive speakers,
professional audio & audiovisual
equipment distribution &
computer software development
Employs—100
Distrib.—National
Privately owned corporation

**DIMENSIONAL COMMUNICATIONS
INC.**
1595 MacArthur Blvd. (07430)
**Phone—(201) 767-1500**
Fax—(201) 767-9696
www.dimcom.com
Email—info@dimcom.com
Pres.—Douglas Fixell
V-P., Prodn.—Steve Wietzke
Dir., Acct. Mgmt.—Burt Galbraith
Dir., Multimedia Technologies—
Bob Sneed
Sr. Acct. Mgr.—Kathleen Consigli
SIC—2541; 2542; Trade show
displays & booths
Employs—70; Estab.—1973
Sales—over $20Mil
121,000 sq ft site, Distrib.—
National
Privately owned corporation

**†EXECUTIVE BINDING SYSTEMS,
INC.**
330 Franklin Tpke. (07430)
**Phone—(201) 642-0011**
Fax—(201) 642-0012
www.executivebinding.com
Email—info@executivebinding.com
CFO—Bob Kronenberger
SIC—5084; Distributor of
document binding equipment &
supplies; Brand name—GBC;
Powis Parker; Fastback;
Channelbind; Pro-Bind; Bind
Rite; MBM; Masterbind; Akiles;
Rhino-O-Tuff
Employs—6; Estab.—1972
3,000 sq ft site, Distrib.—Regional
Privately owned sub-S corp.

GEOGRAPHICAL

## Mahwah—(cont.)

**F & M EXPRESSIONS UNLIMITED**
211 Island Rd. (07430)
**Phone—(201) 512-3338**
National—(800) 225-9634
Fax—(201) 512-3240
www.fmexpressions.com
Email—frank@fmexpressions.com
Pres., CEO—Frank Flanagan
Comp.—Joe Endres
Sales Mgr.—Joe Dotson
SIC—2759; 3993; NAICS—323100; *Heat transfer & decal printing*
Employs—100; Estab.—1981
40,000 sq ft site, Distrib.—Intl.
Privately owned sub-S corp.

**FECKEN-KIRFEL AMERICA, INC.**
6 Leighton Pl., Ste. 1 (07430)
**Phone—(201) 891-5530**
Fax—(201) 891-0129
www.fecken-kirfel.com
Email—info@fk-am.com
Bookkeeper—Laurie Weis
Cust. Serv. Rep.—Pat Kenyon
Technician—Steve Debonte
Technician—Chris Haliniak
SIC—3541; NAICS—333512; *Foam & plastic cutting blades*
Employs—9; Estab.—1871
Sales—$500,000-$1Mil
Distrib.—Intl.
Privately owned corporation

**FLAVOR & FRAGRANCE SPECIALTIES, INC. (H Q)**
3 Industrial Ave. (07430)
**Phone—(201) 825-2025**
National—(800) 998-4337
Fax—(201) 825-2070
www.ffs.com
Email—info@ffs.com
Pres.—Michael Bloom
Dir., IT—Richard Dolinsky
Acctg. Mgr.—Ken Bagnuolo
Hum. Res. Mgr.—Joyce Delaney
SIC—2087; 2844; NAICS—311900; *Corporate headquarters; food flavorings, enhancers, perfumes & fragrances*
Employs—50; Estab.—1983
70,000 sq ft site, Distrib.—Intl.

**FLOXITE COMPANY, INC.**
31 Industrial Ave., Ste. 2 (07430-3591)
**Phone—(201) 529-2019**
(201) 529-3768
National—(888) 378-3332
Fax—(201) 529-1349
www.floxitemirrors.com
Email—floxite@aol.com
Pres.—Bruce Pitot
Dir., New Bus.—Andrea Fasolo
Sales Coord.—Pat Ely
SIC—3231; NAICS—327215; *Cosmetic vanity, wall, travel, lighted & unlighted make-up mirrors; Brand name—Floxite; Rialto*
Employs—8; Estab.—1984
Sales—under $500,000
Distrib.—National
Privately owned corporation

**FLUORAMICS, INC.**
18 Industrial Ave. (07430)
**Phone—(201) 825-8110**
National—(800) 922-0075
Fax—(201) 825-7035
www.tufoil.com
Email—pdouglas@fluoramics.com
Pres.—Franklin G. Reick
Dir., Sales, Intl., Adv. Mgr. & Coord.—Paula Douglas
Off. Mgr.—Rina Digioia
SIC—2992; 2899; NAICS—324191; *Industrial lubricants, engine oil additives & oxygen compatible thread sealants*
Employs—7; Estab.—1968
Sales—$1Mil-$5Mil
28,000 sq ft site, Distrib.—Intl.
Privately owned corporation

**FMDK TECHNOLOGIES, INC.**
63 Ramapo Valley Rd., Lobby 4 (07430)
**Phone—(201) 828-9822**
Fax—(201) 828-9810
www.merlincontrols.com
Email—information@fmdkinc.com
Pres.—Frank Gallo
Off. Mgr.—Ruth Morton
Engr.—Joe Sagal
SIC—3679; 3613; 3625; NAICS—335313; *Electronic control system spare parts & light rail EBCU repair services & electrostatic precipitators, HV, rapper & general process controls, including title V EPA ESP reporting; Brand name—Merlin*
Employs—4; Estab.—1998
Sales—$300,000-$500,000
4,000 sq ft site, Distrib.—National
Privately owned sub-S corp.
AKA: Merlin Controls

**FOLSOM CORP. (H Q)**
43 McKee Dr., Ste. 1, P.O. Box 6660 (07430)
**Phone—(201) 529-3550**
National—(800) 688-3481
Fax—(201) 529-0258
www.biminibayoutfitters.com
Email—customerservice@bimini-bay.com
Pres., CEO—Robert Feldscott
IT Mgr.—Tim Smith
Hum. Res. Mgr.—Howard Diamond
SIC—3949; 2329; 2339; *Corporate headquarters; sport fishing tackle (mfg. done in Asia) & men's & women's outdoor clothing, including shirts, pants & rainwear (mfg. subcontracted)*
Employs—20
Sales—$2.5Mil-$5Mil (est)
Distrib.—Intl.
Privately owned corporation
AKA: Bimini Bay Outfitters, Ltd.

**FORTHMANN MACHINES, INC.**
1495 MacArthur Blvd. (07430)
**Phone—(201) 818-1221**
Fax—(201) 818-9756
www.forthmann.com
Email—customerservice@forthmann.com
Pres.—James Beezer
Plt. Mgr.—David Christiansen
Asst. Plt. Mgr.—Mike Ottensoser
SIC—3599; *Label cutting machines; Brand name—ZEFFFCO*
Employs—50; Estab.—1960
Sales—$2.5Mil-$5Mil
118,000 sq ft site, Distrib.—Intl.
Privately owned corporation
Also see: Stelron Cam Co., same loc.

**†GENERAL REPRODUCTION PRODUCTS**
23 McKee Dr. (07430)
**Phone—(201) 934-0027**
National—(800) 477-8402
Fax—(201) 934-8368
www.grprod.com
Email—info@grprod.com
Owner—Wayne Alexander
Pres.—William Alexander
Cust. Serv. Mgr.—Susan Rahner
Cust. Serv. Rep.—Sheila Miller
SIC—5044; *Wholesaler of large-format copiers*
Employs—13; Estab.—1963
Sales—$500,000-$1Mil
Distrib.—Regional
Privately owned corporation

**GLASCO UV, LLC**
126 Christie Ave., Ste. 1 (07430)
**Phone—(201) 934-3348**
Fax—(201) 934-3388
www.glascouv.com
Pres.—Julie Donnellan
SIC—3589; *Ultraviolet water disinfection equipment for residential, commercial, industrial & wastewater applications*
Employs—7; Estab.—2008
Distrib.—Intl.
Limited Liability Company

**†GLENMARK GENERICS INC., USA**
750 Corporate Dr. (07430)
**Phone—(877) 273-1194**
(201) 684-8000
Fax—(201) 831-0080
www.glenmark-generics.com
Email—info@glenmarkpharma.com
Pres., CEO—Terry Coughlin
Ex. V-P.—Paul Dutra
Secy. & Assoc. Dir., Fin.—Biplab Mazumdar
SIC—5122; NAICS—325412; *Distributor of generic pharmaceuticals*
Employs—50; Estab.—2005
Sales—$150Mil-$200Mil
65,000 sq ft site, Distrib.—Regional
Privately owned corporation

**GLOBAL SOFT DIGITAL SOLUTIONS, INC.**
500 Corporate Dr. (07430)
**Phone—(201) 684-0900**
Fax—(201) 670-1004
www.globalsoftdigital.com
Email—info@globalsoftdigital.com
Pres.—Christopher Petro
Ex. Admn.—Dawn Davis
SIC—2759; NAICS—323100; *Digital & large-format printing, fleet graphics & fulfillment services for digital & electronic marketing*
Employs—50; Estab.—1998
Distrib.—Intl.
Privately owned corporation

**IMAGINATION ARTS PUBLICATIONS**
57 Thunderhead Pl., P.O. Box 103 (07430)
**Phone—(201) 529-5105**
Fax—(201) 529-5105
www.iapbooks.com
Email—iapbooks@optonline.net
Owner—Judith Peck
SIC—2741; *Creative art book publishing*
Employs—1; Estab.—2003
Distrib.—Local
Sole ownership

**†JAGUAR LAND ROVER NORTH AMERICA**
555 MacArthur Blvd. (07430)
**Phone—(201) 818-8500**
Fax—(201) 818-9781
www.jaguarlandrover.com
Pres.—Andy Goss
SIC—5012; *Distributor of automobiles*
Employs—250
Privately owned corporation

**LENETA CO., INC.**
15 Whitney Rd. (07430)
**Phone—(201) 847-9300**
National—(800) 663-6324
Fax—(201) 848-8833
www.leneta.com
Email—sales@leneta.com
Pres.—Dan Schaeffer
V-P.—Joseph Schaeffer
Corp. Secy.—Neta Schaeffer
Tech. Standards Mgr.—Joe Peters
SIC—3829; 3559; *Paint test charts & draw down equipment for the coatings, ink & cosmetic industries*
Employs—115; Estab.—1956
Sales—$2Mil
23,000 sq ft site, Distrib.—Intl.
Privately owned corporation

**LEVER MFG. CORP.**
420 State Route 17 (07430)
**Phone—(201) 684-4400**
(201) 684-1615
National—(800) 526-5265
Fax—(201) 529-0188
www.levercorp.com
Email—bcorbett@levercorp.com
Ex. V-P.—William M. Corbett
Prodn. Mgr.—Joseph Oram
Off. Mgr.—Sue Isidori
Parts Mgr.—Don Bower
R & D Mgr.—Neven Grgurev
SIC—3549; NAICS—333518; *Slitting machinery for tapes, foams, foils, textiles, nonwovens, rubber, films, graphite & felt*
Employs—25; Estab.—1910
30,000 sq ft site, Distrib.—National
Limited Liability Company
Also see: Thermwell Products Co., Inc., same loc.

**MICRO LOGIC, INC.**
31 Industrial Ave., Ste. 6 (07430)
**Phone—(201) 962-7512**
Fax—(201) 962-7508
www.miclog.com
Email—alex@emachineshop.com
CEO—Jim Lewis
Hum. Res. & IT Mgr.—Alex Dimitrovski
SIC—3672; *Corporate headquarters & printed circuit board assembly*
Employs—17; Estab.—1978
Sales—$1Mil-$2.5Mil (est)
Distrib.—Intl.
Privately owned corporation

**MICROMAT CO.**
185 State Route 17 (07430)
**Phone—(201) 529-3738**
Fax—(201) 529-5942
Email—micromat1@optonline.net
Pres.—Erwin Eibert
IT Mgr.—Peter Eibert
SIC—3491; 3492; *Safety valves*
Employs—5; Estab.—1963
Sales—$500,000-$1Mil
Distrib.—National
Privately owned corporation

**MINDRAY NORTH AMERICA**
800 MacArthur Blvd. (07430)
**Phone—(201) 995-8000**
National—(800) 777-4222
Fax—(201) 995-8002
www.mindray.com
Dir., Opers.—George Soloman
Hum. Res. Mgr.—Michele Thompson
SIC—3845; NAICS—334500; *Patient monitoring devices*
Employs—200; Estab.—1990
Sales—$11Mil-$25Mil
Distrib.—Intl.

**MYAT, INC.**
360 Franklin Tpke. (07430)
**Phone—(201) 684-0100**
Fax—(201) 684-0104
www.myat.com
Email—sales@myat.com
Pres.—Philip Cindrich
Plt. Mgr.—Bob Hilfdorf
Hum. Res. Mgr.—Robert Miano

## Mahwah—(cont.)

SIC—3663; NAICS—334220; *Electronic transmission equipment*
Employs—25; Estab.—2006
Distrib.—Intl.
Privately owned corporation

### PAULIST PRESS

997 MacArthur Blvd. (07430)
**Phone—(201) 825-7300**
National—(800) 218-1903
Fax—(201) 825-6921
www.paulistpress.com
Email—info@paulistpress.com
Pres.—Father Mark-David Janus
V-P., GM—Kevin Maguire
Prodn. Supv.—Kimberly Bernard
Cust. Serv. Supv.—Dawn Hoffman
Cust. Serv. Rep.—Joyce Somers
SIC—2731; *Religious book publishing*
Employs—50; Estab.—1866
Distrib.—Intl.
Privately owned corporation

### PHILLIPS SCIENTIFIC

31 Industrial Ave., Ste. 1 (07430-2210)
**Phone—(201) 934-8015**
Fax—(201) 934-8269
www.phillipsscientific.com
Email—sales@phillipsscientific.com
Pres.—Thomas Phillips
V-P. & Off. Mgr.—Sue Phillips
GM—Rob Ehrhart
SIC—3829; 3679; NAICS—334519; *Data acquisition electronics*
Employs—15; Estab.—1980
Sales—$1Mil-$5Mil
9,000 sq ft site, Distrib.—Intl.
Privately owned sub-S corp.

### POLYTYPE AMERICA CORP.

10 Industrial Ave. (07430)
**Phone—(201) 995-1000**
Fax—(201) 995-1080
www.wifag-polytype.com
Email—info@polytypeamerica.com
Pres., CEO—Peter Andrich
Hum. Res. Mgr.—Melissa Pagano
SIC—3555; 3559; NAICS—333293; *Digital grand-format printers & dry offset printing equipment for plastic containers, cups, lids, buckets, tubes & metal cans & coating & laminating machines for paper, film & foil*
Employs—25; Estab.—1950
Sales—$10Mil-$20Mil
30,000 sq ft site, Distrib.—Intl.
Privately owned corporation

### PRINTING & SIGNS EXPRESS, INC.

634 Wyckoff Ave. (07430)
**Phone—(201) 368-1255**
Fax—(201) 368-1464
www.signguys.net
Email—sales@signguys.net
Pres.—Joe Busto
SIC—3993; *Interior & exterior signs*
Employs—4; Estab.—1993
Sales—$500,000-$1Mil
Distrib.—Local
Privately owned corporation

### †PTC ELECTRONICS, INC.

45 Whitney Rd., Ste. B-9 *(07430)*
Mail addr: P.O. Box 72, Wyckoff (07481-0072)
**Phone—(201) 847-0500**
National—(800) 989-9518
Fax—(201) 847-1394
www.ptcelectronics.com
Email—sales@ptcelectronics.com
Pres.—Alan Kicks
V-P.—John Kicks

SIC—5065; *Distributor of electronic weighing, pressure & force measurement equipment; Brand name—SCAIME; AST Sensors; London Instruments; PTC Electronics; Mantracourt*
Employs—7; Estab.—1978
Sales—$1Mil
2,500 sq ft site, Distrib.—Intl.
Privately owned corporation

### RAD DATA COMMUNICATIONS, INC.

900 Corporate Dr., Ste. 1 (07430-3611)
**Phone—(201) 529-1100**
National—(800) 444-7234
Fax—(201) 529-5777
www.radusa.com
Email—market@radusa.com
Pres.—Uri Zilberman
V-P., Fin.—Paul Sweeney
Cust. Serv. Mgr.—Hala Dollari
Sales Coord.—Erin Connelly
SIC—3577; *Network communication equipment for carrier ethernet, SONET, TDM & ATM applications, including ethernet demarcation, routers, rate/media converters, gateways & multiplexers*
Employs—55; Estab.—1981
Sales—$10Mil-$25Mil (est)
Distrib.—Intl.
Privately owned corporation

### RUTAN POLY INDUSTRIES, INC.

39 Siding Pl. *(07430)*
**Phone—(201) 529-1474**
(800) 872-1474
Fax—(201) 529-4440
www.rutanpoly.com
Email—sales@rutanpoly.com
Pres.—Arnold Tanowitz
V-P., Secy., Fin.—Esther Tanowitz
V-P., Opers.—Sandra Meyers
Sales Mgr.—Lou Papaccioli
Off. Mgr.—Joy Ferracane
SIC—2673; 3083; 3081; 3082; NAICS—326130; *Plastic bags, films, tubing & sheeting*
Employs—32; Estab.—1966
Sales—$1Mil-$6Mil
23,200 sq ft site, Distrib.—National
Privately owned sub-S corp.

### SEIKO CORP. OF AMERICA (H Q)

1111 MacArthur Blvd. (07430-2038)
**Phone—(201) 529-5730**
National—(800) 722-4452
Fax—(201) 529-4543
www.seikousa.com
Email—custserv@seikousa.com
Pres., CEO—Yoshikatsu Kawada
Sr. V-P., Sales & Mktg.—Martin Gormley
Sr. V-P., Corp. Opers. & Plng.—Nozomu Oshima
SIC—3873; NAICS—334518; *Corporate headquarters; watches & clocks (mfg. done overseas)*
Employs—150; Estab.—1970
Sales—$10Mil-$25Mil
Distrib.—Intl.

### SEIKO OPTICAL PRODUCTS OF AMERICA, INC. (H Q)

Div. of SEIKO Corp. Of America
575 Corporate Dr., Ste. 205 (07430)
**Phone—(201) 529-9099**
National—(800) 992-2895
Fax—(201) 529-9019
www.seikoeyewear.com
Email—csmail@seikoeyewear.com
Pres.—Yoshito Kataoka
Sr. V-P., Sales & Mktg.—Michael J. Rybacki
Sales Mgr.—Lori Mitchell
Hum. Res. Mgr.—Michelle O'Connell

SIC—3851; *Divisional headquarters; optical lenses & frames*
Employs—50; Estab.—1981
Sales—$5Mil-$10Mil (est)
Distrib.—Intl.
Privately owned corporation
Parent co.—SEIKO Corp. Of America, Mahwah, NJ
Phone—(201) 529-5730
See Parent Co. Section for full profile.

### SHARP ELECTRONICS CORP. (H Q)

1 Sharp Plz. (07430)
**Phone—(201) 529-8200**
National—(800) 237-4277
Fax—(201) 529-8425
www.sharpusa.com
Email—sharpsolar@sharpusa.com
Chrm., CEO—Toshiyuki Osawa
Pres.—John Herrington
Sr. V-P., CFO—Bill Flynn
V-P., Branding & Mktg.—Mark Viken
Assoc. V-P., Pro AV/IT Sales—John Sheehan
Assoc. Dir., Mktg. Comms.—Terri Siebert
Asst. Comms. Mgr.—Martha Harvey
SIC—3634; 3639; 3651; NAICS—334310; *Corporate headquarters; microwave ovens, toners, copiers, solar panels & LCD televisions*
Employs—900; Estab.—1962
Sales—$30Bil
Publicly owned corporation

### SOURCE PACKAGING, INC.

215 Island Rd. (07430)
**Phone—(201) 831-0005**
National—(888) 665-9768
Fax—(201) 831-0009
www.casesbysource.com
Email—info@sourcepac.com
Pres.—Allen Adler
V-P.—Matthew Adler
Mktg. Mgr.—Jeff Chookazian
SIC—3089; 2652; NAICS—322213; *Presentation & protective packaging, displays & cases*
Employs—20; Estab.—1985
Distrib.—Intl.
Privately owned corporation
Also see: Cases by Source, Inc., same loc.
AKA: Cases By Source

### SPECTRO ANALYTICAL INSTRUMENTS, INC.

Div. of AMETEK, Inc.
91 McKee Dr. (07430)
**Phone—(201) 642-3000**
National—(800) 548-5809
Fax—(201) 642-3091
www.spectro.com
Email—info@spectro.com
V-P., Sales & Mktg.—Tom Blumer
IT Mgr.—Michael Tedesci
Hum. Res. Mgr.—Roberta Burns
SIC—3827; NAICS—333314; *Emission spectrometers*
Employs—20; Estab.—1981
Sales—$5Mil-$10Mil
1,500 sq ft site, Distrib.—Local
Publicly owned corporation
Parent co.—AMETEK, Inc., Berwyn, PA
Phone—(610) 647-2121
See Parent Co. Section for full profile.

### STARNET BUSINESS SOLUTIONS, INC.

46 Industrial Ave. (07430)
**Phone—(201) 760-2600**
Fax—(201) 252-8356
www.starnet-media.com
Email—studio@starnet-media.com
CEO—John S. Brink
Off. Mgr.—Lynn Wiggers
Manager—Linda Tonnessen

SIC—2759; NAICS—323100; *Digital offset & commercial printing & graphic design, including posters, banners & books*
Employs—30; Estab.—2010
Sales—$500,000-$1Mil
15,000 sq ft site, Distrib.—Regional
Privately owned corporation

### STELRON CAM CO.

1495 MacArthur Blvd. (07430)
**Phone—(201) 529-5450**
Fax—(201) 529-5493
www.stelron.com
Email—customerservice@stelron.com
Ptnr.—James Beezer
Ptnr.—William Beezer
Engr.—Dan Sullivan
SIC—3599; *Manufacturing machinery components, including index drives, pick/place, rotary & linear CAM actuators, machine chassis, precision link conveyors, anti-friction slides & custom cams*
Employs—85; Estab.—1959
Sales—$5Mil-$10Mil
120,000 sq ft site, Distrib.—National
Privately owned sub-S corp.
ISO rating—9001
Also see: Forthmann Machines, Inc., same loc.
AKA: Stelron Components, Inc.

NEW ENTRY
### STITCH-IT-UP EMBROIDERY

151 Fisher Rd. (07430)
**Phone—(201) 512-9881**
Fax—(201) 512-9882
Email—chris@stitch-it-up.com
Principal—Christine D. Domizio
SIC—2395; 2396; *Custom embroidery & apparel screen printing*
Employs—1; Estab.—2004
Sales—under $500,000
Distrib.—Local
Privately owned corporation

### STRYKER ORTHOPAEDICS

Div. of Stryker Corporation
325 Corporate Dr. (07430)
**Phone—(201) 831-5000**
National—(800) 447-7836
Fax—(201) 831-4000
www.stryker.com
Email—contactus@stryker.com
Group Pres.—David Floyd
Pres., Hip Reconstruction—Bill Huffnagle
V-P., Advanced Opers.—Jack Czajkowski
SIC—3842; *Divisional headquarters & orthopedic & prosthetic devices*
Employs—1300; Estab.—1980
Sales—$250Mil-$500Mil (est)
Publicly owned corporation
Parent co.—Stryker Corporation, Portage, MI
Phone—(269) 385-2600
See Parent Co. Section for full profile.

### TAM METAL PRODUCTS, INC.

55 Whitney Rd. (07430)
**Phone—(201) 848-7800**
Fax—(201) 848-8479
www.tam-ind.com
Email—info@tam-ind.com
Co-Pres.—Frank Cariddi
Co-Pres.—Mark Cariddi
V-P.—Jason Cariddi
Off. Mgr.—Maria Polatz
Bookkeeper—Marianne Miller

GEOGRAPHICAL

## Mahwah—(cont.)

SIC—3444; 3599; *Precision sheet metal fabrication & machining for the aerospace, electronics, defense, communications & medical industries*
Employs—50; Estab.—1958
50,000 sq ft site, Distrib.—National
Privately owned corporation

### TELEMETRICS, INC.

6 Leighton Pl., Ste. 4 *(07430)*
**Phone—(201) 848-9818**
Fax—(201) 848-9819
www.telemetricsinc.com
Email—marketing@
telemetricsinc.com
Pres. & V.-P.—Anthony Cuomo
SIC—3663; NAICS—334220; *Robotic television camera systems*
Employs—29; Estab.—1973
14,000 sq ft site, Distrib.—Intl.
Privately owned sub-S corp.

### THERMWELL PRODUCTS CO., INC.

420 State Route 17 (07430-2135)
**Phone—(201) 684-4400**
National—(800) 526-5265
Fax—(201) 684-1660
www.frostking.com
Email—support@frostking.com
Pres.—David B. Gerstein
Ex. V.-P.—Vincent Giarratana
V.-P., Secy.-Treas.—Mel Gerstein
V.-P., IT—Jeff Adler
Hum. Res. & Off. Mgr.—Sue Isidori
Pur. Agt.—Tim Popiela
SIC—3069; 3442; NAICS—332321; *Weatherstripping & sealing products, including soft foam tape & gutter, AC & garage door seals*
Employs—350; Estab.—1910
500,000 sq ft site, Distrib.—National
Privately owned corporation
Also see: Lever Mfg. Corp., same loc.

### TRAFFIC SAFETY & EQUIPMENT CO.

457 State Route 17 (07430)
**Phone—(201) 327-6050**
National—(888) 260-3246
Fax—(201) 327-4807
www.trafficsafetydirect.com
Email—sales@
trafficsafetydirect.com
Pres.—Peter J. Simpson
Sales Mgr.—Kevin Cunningham
Off. Mgr.—Nicole Drake
SIC—3993; *Interior & exterior signs & vinyl lettering; Brand name—Western; Snoway*
Employs—9; Estab.—1968
16,000 sq ft site, Distrib.—National
Privately owned sub-S corp.

### TURNKEY SOLUTIONS, INC.

45 Whitney Rd. (07430)
**Phone—(201) 848-7676**
Fax—(201) 345-4555
www.turnkey-solutions-inc.com
Email—davel@turnkey-solutions-inc.com
Pres.—David Lyman
SIC—3589; NAICS—333319; *Industrial wastewater treatment equipment*
Employs—9; Estab.—1993
Sales—under $500,000
2,000 sq ft site, Distrib.—Intl.
Privately owned corporation

### UNEX CORP.

333 Route 17 N. (07430)
**Phone—(201) 512-9500**
National—(800) 367-4986
Fax—(201) 512-9615
www.hytorc.com
Email—dricca@hytorc.com
CEO—John Junkers
Pres.—Joe Paul
IT Mgr.—Jan Agay
Hum. Res. Mgr.—Joann Masiello
SIC—3569; *Hydraulic tools & bolting systems*
Employs—80; Estab.—1970
Distrib.—Intl.
Privately owned corporation
DBA: Hytorc

### †VISH CORP.

200 State Route 17, Ste. 200-A (07430-1243)
**Phone—(201) 529-2900**
Fax—(201) 529-1919
www.vishgroup.net
Email—info@vishgroup.net
Pres.—Mahesh T. Kukreja
SIC—5093; *Wholesaler of recycled scrap metal, plastic & paper*
Employs—20; Estab.—1980
Distrib.—Intl.
Privately owned corporation

### VITAL SIGNS

50 Bedford Rd. (07430)
**Phone—(201) 723-8488**
www.vitalsigns2.com
Email—vitalsigns2@msn.com
Pres.—David Treadwell
SIC—3993; *Interior & exterior signs*
Employs—3; Estab.—2000
Sales—under $500,000
Distrib.—Regional
Privately owned sub-S corp.

NEW ENTRY

### VOICECOM PLUS, INC.

63 Ramapo Valley Rd., Ste. 201-A (07430)
**Phone—(201) 760-2260**
National—(800) 538-0025
Fax—(201) 760-2255
www.voicecomplus.com
Email—info@voicecomplus.com
Owner—Tina Lyding
SIC—3661; *Rebuilt voice & communications telephone equipment*
Employs—20; Estab.—1992
Sales—$5Mil-$10Mil (est)
Distrib.—National
Privately owned corporation

---

## Malaga
### (Gloucester—S.W.)

### CINDY MERCKX PUBLICATIONS, LLC

330 Oak Ave. (08328)
Mail addr: P.O. Box 367, Franklinville (08322)
**Phone—(856) 694-1600**
Fax—(856) 694-0469
www.thenjsentinel.com
Email—ftsentinel@comcast.net
Owner & Publisher—Cindy Merckx
SIC—2711; *Newspaper publishing*
Employs—2; Estab.—2008
Distrib.—Local
Limited Liability Company
AKA: Sentinel Gloucester County, The

---

## Manahawkin
### (Ocean—S.E.)

### ASAP COASTAL PRINTING AND SIGNS

775 N. Main St. (08050)
**Phone—(609) 597-7421**
    (609) 597-2727
Fax—(609) 597-3715
www.atsignsandprints.com
Email—asapcoastal@comcast.net
Pres.—Jovi M. Flores
Sr. V.-P.—William DeBernardis
V.-P. & Prodn. Mgr.—Rhett Yap
Off. Mgr.—Laura Mury
SIC—2759; NAICS—323100; *Offset & direct mail market printing & fulfillment services*
Employs—5; Estab.—1975
Sales—$1Mil-$1.4Mil
3,000 sq ft site, Distrib.—Local
Privately owned corporation

### †COOPER ELECTRIC SUPPLY CO.

317 E. Bay Ave. (08050)
**Phone—(609) 978-4666**
Fax—(609) 978-4673
www.cooper-electric.com
Email—bruce.whitley@cooper-electric.com
Br. Mgr.—Bruce Whitley
Counter Sales Rep.—Howard Ferdine
Counter Sales Rep.—Paul Scott
SIC—5063; *Distributor of commercial, industrial & residential electrical supplies, including cable, conduit & distribution & lighting equipment*
Employs—3; Estab.—1998
Distrib.—Local
Privately owned corporation
Parent co.—Cooper Electric Supply Co., Monroe, NJ
Phone—(732) 747-2233
See Parent Co. Section for full profile.

### COPY-RITE PRINTING

378 N. Main St. (08050)
**Phone—(609) 597-9182**
Fax—(609) 597-1311
Owner—Gail Moro
GM—John Moro
SIC—2759; NAICS—323100; *Commercial printing*
Employs—4; Estab.—1977
Sales—under $500,000
1,200 sq ft site, Distrib.—Local
Sole ownership

### FORKED RIVER GAZETTE, INC.

119 Voyager Rd. (08050)
Mail addr: P.O. Box 898, Forked River (08731)
**Phone—(609) 693-7490**
www.forkedrivergazette.com
Email—info@forkedrivergazette.com
Pres., Publisher—Jennifer Grazioso
SIC—2711; *Newspaper publishing*
Employs—1; Estab.—1971
Sales—under $500,000
Distrib.—Local
Privately owned sub-S corp.

### LUCILLE'S OWN MADE CANDY CO.

156 E. Route 72 (08050)
**Phone—(609) 597-7300**
Fax—(609) 597-7393
www.lucillescandies.com
Ptnr.—Janice M. Eismann
Ptnr.—Carl Eismann
Ptnr.—Nathaniel Eismann
SIC—2064; NAICS—311300; *Chocolate candy*
Employs—10; Estab.—1927
Sales—$500,000-$1Mil
Distrib.—Regional
Privately owned partnership

NEW ENTRY

### NEW JERSEY LOGOWEAR

100 McKinley Ave., Ste. 6 (08050)
**Phone—(609) 597-9400**
Fax—(609) 597-9440
www.njlogowear.com
Email—njlogowear@comcast.net
Ptnr.—Keith Anderson
Ptnr.—Randy Campoli
SIC—2759; 2396; 2395; 3479; *Promotional item, apparel & textile screen printing, embroidery, trophy & plaque engraving & custom signs*
Employs—7; Estab.—2009
Sales—$100,000-$250,000
Distrib.—Regional
Limited Liability Company

### TAYLOR MADE CABINETS

516 E. Bay Ave. (08050)
**Phone—(609) 978-6900**
Fax—(609) 978-6764
www.taylormadecabinets.com
Email—sales@
taylormadecabinets.com
Ptnr. & Plt. Mgr.—Dave Taylor
Ptnr.—Christopher Taylor
Accountant—Lynn Taylor
SIC—2434; 2542; 3083; NAICS—337110; *Wooden & laminate cabinets*
Employs—15; Estab.—1985
Sales—$4Mil
8,000 sq ft site, Distrib.—Local
Privately owned corporation

### †WOODHAVEN LUMBER & MILLWORK, INC.

725 E. Bay Ave. (08050)
**Phone—(609) 597-1118**
Fax—(609) 597-8727
www.woodhavenlumber.com
Email—info@
woodhavenlumber.com
Br. Mgr.—John Cadanatre
SIC—5031; *Distributor of lumber, windows, doors & architectural millwork*
Employs—15
Distrib.—National
Privately owned corporation
Parent co.—Woodhaven Lumber & Millwork, Inc., Lakewood, NJ
Phone—(732) 901-0030
See Parent Co. Section for full profile.

---

## Manalapan
### (Monmouth—N.E.)

### †AIRGAS RETAIL SOLUTIONS

Div. of Airgas, Inc.
270 U.S. Highway 9 (07726)
**Phone—(732) 431-0288**
National—(800) 421-5070
Fax—(732) 431-4084
www.airgas.com
Email—info@airgas.com
Opers. Mgr.—Christine Zrebiec
Supervisor—Melissa Sheffer
SIC—5169; *Wholesaler of compressed helium & carbon dioxide gases*
Employs—12; Estab.—1957
Distrib.—National
Publicly owned corporation
AKA: Cylinder Central
Parent co.—Airgas, Inc., Radnor, PA
Phone—(610) 687-5253
See Parent Co. Section for full profile.

### ALL POLY MFG., LLC

200 Craig Rd., Ste. 201 (07726)
**Phone—(732) 431-6630**
Fax—(732) 431-6680
www.allpolymfg.com
Email—allpoly@aol.com
Off. Mgr.—Jennifer Thomas
Manager—Kevin Thomas
Bookkeeper—Jeff Gier
SIC—3089; *Plastic packaging materials*
Employs—7; Estab.—2002
Distrib.—National
Limited Liability Company
AKA: All Poly

## Manalapan—(cont.)

**AMBASSADOR UNIFORM GROUP, INC.**
289 Highway 33 E. (07726)
Mail addr: P.O. Box 91, Marlboro (07746-0091)
**Phone—(732) 792-1111**
National—(800) 711-5885
Fax—(732) 792-0111
www.ambassadoruniform.com
Email—ambassunif@aol.com
Pres.—Allan Behm
SIC—2389; 2339; 5136; 5137; *Manufacturer & wholesaler of service apparel for the foodservice & hospitality industries, including vests, pants, shirts, jackets, polo shirts & ties; Brand name—Edwards; Van Heusen; Sanmar; Blue Gen; Alain; 15*
Employs—8; Estab.—1993
Sales—$3Mil
Distrib.—National
Privately owned sub-S corp.

**CCARD, INC.**
17 Belleterre Dr. (07726)
**Phone—(732) 303-8264**
Fax—(732) 303-8264
Pres.—Chris Cardinale
SIC—3679; 3672; *Electronic cable assemblies & printed circuit boards*
Employs—6; Estab.—1995
Sales—$500,000-$1Mil (est)
1,000 sq ft site, Distrib.—Local
Privately owned corporation

**†CENTRAL CONNECTORS, INC.**
4 Bridge Plaza Dr., Ste. 1 (07726-1747)
**Phone—(732) 972-3456**
Fax—(732) 972-3455
www.centralconnectors.com
Email—cenconnect@aol.com
Owner & Pres.—Maureen Ledbetter
GM—Kevin Ledbetter
SIC—5065; *Distributor of electronic connectors for aerospace, military, communications & industrial applications; Brand name—ADI; AMPHENOL AEROSPACE; CROWN CONNECTORS; DEUTSCH; DETORONICS; KINGS; TROMPETER; RHIMCOCONNECTORS*
Employs—3; Estab.—1995
Distrib.—National
Privately owned corporation
ISO rating—9001

**CHAMPION MARBLE & GRANITE, INC.**
4 Kinney Rd. (07726)
**Phone—(732) 409-3200**
Fax—(732) 409-3202
www.championmarble.com
Email—championmarble@aol.com
Owner—Fero Gjonbalaj
SIC—3281; *Stone fabrication*
Employs—5; Estab.—1988
Sales—$500,000-$1Mil
Distrib.—Local
Privately owned corporation

**COBYCO, INC.**
65 Wilson Ave. (07726)
**Phone—(732) 446-4448**
Fax—(732) 446-9110
www.cobyembroidery.net
Email—sales@cobyembroidery.net
Pres.—Elana Keinan
SIC—2395; *Embroidery*
Employs—2; Estab.—1993
Distrib.—National
Privately owned corporation

**EWC CONTROLS, INC.**
385 State Route 33 (07726)
**Phone—(732) 446-3110**
National—(800) 446-3110
Fax—(732) 446-5362
www.ewccontrols.com
Email—info@ewccontrols.com
Pres.—Mike Reilly
Comp. & Treasurer—Anne Reilly
Plt. Mgr.—Wayne Koehler
Hum. Res. Mgr.—Jessica Dreskin
Matls. Mgr.—David Dreskin
Qual. Control Mgr.—Ric Kostbar
SIC—3822; NAICS—334512; *HVAC controls & zoning systems for forced air heating & cooling & humidifiers for residential buildings; Brand name—Ultra-Zone*
Employs—53; Estab.—1961
Sales—$15Mil-$20Mil
28,000 sq ft site, Distrib.—National
Privately owned corporation

**EXCELSIOR METAL PRODUCTS, LLC**
151 State Route 33, Ste. 201 (07726)
**Phone—(732) 651-9914**
National—(800) 919-4422
Fax—(732) 651-9980
www.excelsiorlockers.com
Email—sales@excelsiorlockers.com
Mng. Ptnr.—Jordan Cayne
Ptnr.—Suzan Cayne
V-P.—Howard Blum
SIC—2542; 2541; *Contract manufacturing of electronic & standard lockers*
Employs—13; Estab.—2003
Sales—$2.6Mil-$5Mil
Distrib.—Intl.
Limited Liability Company

**†FAITH GROUP CO. (H Q)**
195 Route 9, Ste. 205 (07726)
**Phone—(732) 431-1326**
Fax—(732) 431-1673
www.faith-group.com
Email—info@faith-group.com
Pres.—Yong Liu
GM—Chris Jiang
SIC—5093; *Company headquarters; wholesaler of recycled plastic*
Employs—15; Estab.—1993
Sales—$500,000-$1Mil
Distrib.—National
Privately owned corporation

**G M REPAIR, INC.**
90 Millhurst Rd. (07726)
Mail addr: P.O. Box 363, Tennent (07763)
**Phone—(732) 350-0304**
Fax—(732) 350-0137
Owner—Henry Gutzan
SIC—3499; *Industrial & commercial metal fabrication*
Employs—1; Estab.—1986
Sales—under $500,000
Distrib.—Regional
Sole ownership

**GREATER MEDIA NEWSPAPERS**
Div. of Greater Media, Inc.
198 Route 9 N., P.O. Box 950 (07726)
**Phone—(732) 358-5200**
Fax—(732) 780-4257
www.gmnews.com
Email—dkenyon@gmnews.com
Publisher & GM—Ben Cannizzaro
Mng. Editor—Mark Rosman
IT Mgr.—Gene Lennon
Hum. Res. Mgr.—Linda Vinci
SIC—2711; *Weekly print & online newspaper publishing*
Employs—74; Estab.—1958
Distrib.—Local
Privately owned corporation

Parent co.—Greater Media, Inc., Braintree, MA
Phone—(781) 348-8600
See Parent Co. Section for full profile.

**M & J CONTRACTING, INC.**
85 Tracey Station (07726)
**Phone—(732) 446-1112**
Fax—(732) 446-3292
www.jemco.com
Pres.—Doris Grillo
SIC—3441; NAICS—332312; *Structural steel fabrication*
Employs—3; Estab.—2005
Sales—$500,000-$1Mil (est)
Distrib.—Local
Privately owned corporation

**MARLO PLASTIC PRODUCTS, INC.**
289 State Route 33 (07726-8364)
**Phone—(732) 792-1984**
　　　　　(732) 792-1988
National—(800) 400-1128
Fax—(732) 792-1996
www.marloplastics.com
Email—info@marloplastics.com
Pres., R & D Mgr.—Arthur Livingston
Off. Mgr.—Amanda Livingston
Off. Mgr.—Terry Derham
SIC—3089; *Soft vinyl plastic products*
Employs—40; Estab.—1948
Sales—$2.6Mil-$5Mil
22,000 sq ft site, Distrib.—National
Privately owned corporation
Also see: G. G. Tauber Co., LLC, same loc.

**NUTRI PET RESEARCH, INC./NUPRO SUPPLEMENTS**
227 State Route 33 E. (07726)
**Phone—(732) 786-8822**
National—(800) 360-3300
Fax—(732) 786-8181
www.nuprosupplements.com
Email—nupro@skyweb.net
Pres.—Janis Gianforte-Horner
V-P., Sales—Robert Bruce Horner
GM—Teri Leon
SIC—2834; 2833; NAICS—325412; *Holistic pet vitamin supplements & nutritional supplements for pets; Brand name—NUPRO All Natural Dog Supplement; NUPRO Joint & Immunity Support Dog Supplement; NUPRO Health Nuggets for Cats; NUPRO All Natural Ferret Supplement; NUPRO Custom Electrolyte Formula*
Employs—7; Estab.—1989
Sales—$2.5Mil-$5Mil
Distrib.—Intl.
Privately owned corporation

**ONWARDS, INC. (H Q)**
10 Connor Dr. (07726)
**Phone—(732) 309-7348**
Fax—(732) 446-4966
Email—yangsupcha@yahoo.com
Pres.—Yang-Sup Cha
SIC—2329; 2339; NAICS—315200; *Corporate headquarters; men's, women's & children's jackets, jerseys & shirts (mfg. subcontracted); Brand name—Onwards*
Employs—3; Estab.—2000
Sales—under $500,000
Distrib.—National
Privately owned corporation

**SIGNARAMA**
349 U.S. Highway 9, Ste. 6 (07726-5105)
**Phone—(732) 536-7575**
Fax—(732) 536-7576
www.signarama-manalapan.com
Email—signarama@optonline.net
Ptnr. & Pres.—Jackie Barber
Ptnr.—Chris Barber

SIC—3993; 2759; NAICS—323100; *Full-service commercial & residential interior & exterior signs, banners, trade show & promotional products, vehicle graphics & digital printing; Brand name—Gemini brand letters*
Employs—4; Estab.—2013
Sales—under $500,000
1,300 sq ft site, Distrib.—Local
Limited Liability Partnership

**TAUBER CO., LLC, G. G.**
289 State Route 33, Ste. 12 (07726-8365)
**Phone—(301) 881-3567**
National—(800) 638-6667
Fax—(301) 881-1909
www.ggtauber.com
Email—cservice2@ggtauber.com
Pres.—Becky Livingston
V-P. & Off. Mgr.—Corrie Froseth
SIC—3089; *Vinyl badge holders, promotions & awards; Brand name—IDENTA CLIP; IDENTA PIN; IDENTA SNAP; IDENTA FOLD; IDENTA STIC*
Employs—4; Estab.—1946
Sales—$1.5Mil
Distrib.—Intl.
Privately owned corporation
Also see: Marlo Plastic Products, Inc., same loc.

---

## Manasquan
(Monmouth—N.E.)

**AHERN'S PRINTING & GRAPHICS**
231 Parker Ave. (08736)
**Phone—(732) 223-1476**
Fax—(732) 223-0594
www.aherncopy.com
Owner—Matthew Ahern
SIC—2752; NAICS—323100; *Blueprinting*
Employs—8; Estab.—2002
Distrib.—Regional
Privately owned corporation

**ARMSTRONG & SONS, INC.**
2335 Highway 34 (08736)
**Phone—(732) 223-1555**
Fax—(732) 223-1063
www.armstrongandsons.com
Email—sales@armstrongandsons.com
Pres.—Linda Pietsch
GM—Michael Pickell
SIC—3545; *Tube cutting tools for replacing thin or leaking tubes in steam condensers, heat exchangers & chillers; Brand name—Airetool; Kris*
Employs—3; Estab.—1939
Sales—under $500,000
2,900 sq ft site, Distrib.—National
Privately owned corporation

**DELAIRE U. S. A., INC.**
1913 Atlantic Ave., Ste. R-1 (08736-1029)
**Phone—(732) 528-4520**
Fax—(732) 528-4521
www.delaireusa.com
Email—sales@delaireusa.com
Pres.—Lorraine Hallock
SIC—3679; *Custom RF & fiber optic cable assemblies & subsystems for military & commercial applications*
Employs—20; Estab.—1994
8,000 sq ft site, Distrib.—Intl.
Privately owned sub-S corp.

**DESIGN 446**
2411 Atlantic Ave., Ste. 4 (08736)
**Phone—(732) 223-0100**
Fax—(732) 223-9740
www.design446.com
Email—info@design446.com
Owner & Hum. Res. Mgr.—Tom Vialne

GEOGRAPHICAL

## Manasquan—(cont.)

SIC—2752; 2759; NAICS—323122; *Offset & digital printing & typesetting, signs, banners & promotional products*
Employs—40; Estab.—1917
Distrib.—Local
Privately owned corporation

### DR. T-SHIRT

221 Parker Ave. (08736)
**Phone—(732) 223-3866**
National—(800) 435-0066
Fax—(732) 223-3565
www.drt-shirt.com
Email—gio50@aol.com
Pres.—Robert Giaquinto
V-P.—Mary O'Brien
SIC—2396; 2395; *T-shirt screen printing & embroidery*
Employs—3; Estab.—1987
2,000 sq ft site, Distrib.—National
Sole ownership

### GARON PRODUCTS, INC.

2430 Route 34, Ste. B-12 (08736)
Mail addr: P.O. Box 1924, Wall (07719-1924)
**Phone—(732) 223-2500**
National—(800) 631-5380
Fax—(732) 223-2002
www.garonproducts.com
Email—customercare@garonproducts.com
Pres.—Arthur Crowley
V-P., Mktg.—Tara Crowley
V-P., New Bus. Dev.—John Crowley
Cust. Serv. Exec.—Pamela Weir
SIC—2851; NAICS—325510; *Corporate headquarters & floor coatings & concrete repair products*
Employs—15; Estab.—1960
Distrib.—National
Privately owned corporation
ISO rating—9001:2008

### INTERCAT, INC. (H Q)

Div. of Johnson Matthey, Inc.
2399 Highway 34, Ste. C-1 (08736)
**Phone—(732) 223-4644**
National—(800) 346-5425
Fax—(732) 223-3447
www2.intercatinc.com
Email—info@intercatinc.com
Corp. Cont.—Dawn Serani
Hum. Res. Mgr.—Geri Fiore
SIC—2899; *Corporate headquarters; fuel additives*
Employs—8; Estab.—1986
Distrib.—Intl.
Publicly owned corporation
Parent co.—Johnson Matthey, Inc., Wayne, PA
  Phone—(610) 341-8300
  See Parent Co. Section for full profile.

### MANASQUAN SIGHT SAVER OPTICAL

1407 W. Atlantic Ave. (08736)
**Phone—(732) 223-4242**
Fax—(732) 223-5472
www.sightsaveroptical.com
Email—sightsaver@hotmail.com
Owner—Bruce Ziegler
Optician—Dean Purdy
SIC—3841; *Prescription eyeglasses*
Employs—6; Estab.—1981
Sales—under $500,000
Distrib.—Local
Sole ownership

### MR. PAUL'S CUSTOM CABINETS

2416 Highway 35 (08736)
**Phone—(732) 528-9427**
Fax—(732) 528-6131
www.mrpaulscabinets.com
Pres.—Paul Waltsak
Corp. Secy.—Claire Waltsak

SIC—2434; NAICS—337110; *Wooden kitchen & bath cabinets*
Employs—3; Estab.—1965
2,400 sq ft site, Distrib.—Local
Privately owned corporation

### NORTH SAILS NEW JERSEY

2422 Highway 34 (08736)
**Phone—(732) 528-8899**
Fax—(732) 528-6565
www.northsails.com
Email—henryb@sales.northsails.com
Owner & Pres.—Henry Bossett
SIC—2394; 2399; NAICS—314912; *Polyester, aramid fiber, carbon, canvas, laminate & woven fabric sails, banners & related products, including custom sewing; Brand name—North Sails*
Employs—3; Estab.—1972
Sales—under $500,000
7,500 sq ft site, Distrib.—Intl.
Sole ownership

### PDEC, INC.

2101 Atlantic Ave. (08736)
**Phone—(732) 223-5995**
Fax—(732) 223-8812
www.pdeconline.com
Pres.—Joseph Sodano
Asst. Mgr.—Kathy Applegate
SIC—2752; NAICS—323100; *Offset printing*
Employs—15; Estab.—1992
Sales—$500,000-$1Mil
Distrib.—Local
Privately owned corporation

### PL CUSTOM BODY & EQUIPMENT CO.

2201 Atlantic Ave. (08736)
**Phone—(732) 223-1411**
National—(800) 752-8786
Fax—(732) 223-8456
www.plcustom.com
Email—info@plcustom.com
Chrm., CEO—Jean S. Smock
Pres.—Robert L. Stevenson
V-P., Sales & Mktg.—Deborah Smock Thomson
V-P., Rescue Sales & Sales—Mike Marquis
IT Mgr.—Don Miller
Hum. Res. Mgr.—Terri Bower
Administrator—Debbie Bailey
SIC—3711; *Ambulances, heavy rescue vehicles & first responders*
Employs—140; Estab.—1946
110,000 sq ft site, Distrib.—National
Privately owned corporation
AKAs: PL Custom & Rescue 1 & NJEV

### SHERMAN & SON, INC., W. F.

84 Broad St. (08736)
**Phone—(732) 223-1505**
Fax—(732) 223-1508
www.wfsherman.com
Email—wfsherman@verizon.net
Pres.—Donald F. Sherman, Jr.
Corp. Secy.—Jamie Furlong
SIC—2511; 2431; *Wooden furniture & architectural millwork*
Employs—10; Estab.—1878
Sales—$500,000-$1Mil (est)
Distrib.—Regional
Privately owned corporation

### STAR NEWS GROUP

13 Broad St. (08736)
**Phone—(732) 223-0076**
Fax—(732) 528-1212
www.starnewsgroup.com
Email—editor@thecoaststar.com
Pres., Publisher—James Manser
Mng. Editor—Jamie Biesiada
Editor—Doug Paviluk
GM—Alison Manser Ertl

SIC—2711; *Newspaper publishing*
Employs—35; Estab.—1877
Distrib.—Local
Privately owned corporation

### T P S MACHINING

204 E. Main St. (08736)
**Phone—(732) 223-9305**
Fax—(732) 223-8720
Pres.—Ken C. Ludwig
V-P.—Charles Ware
SIC—3599; *General machining job shop*
Employs—3; Estab.—1990
Sales—under $500,000
3,000 sq ft site, Distrib.—Regional
Privately owned corporation
AKA: Maritime Tool

### THERMAL INNOVATIONS CORP.

2220 Landmark Pl., Ste. 1 (08736)
**Phone—(732) 223-1812**
  (732) 223-5533
National—(800) 756-5772
Fax—(732) 223-9495
www.thermalinnovations.com
Email—sales@thermalinnovations.com
Pres.—Nicholas Fusilli
SIC—3567; NAICS—333994; *Infrared, convection & ultraviolet oven systems*
Employs—4; Estab.—1988
6,000 sq ft site, Distrib.—Intl.
Privately owned corporation

### WINE PRODUCTS, INC.

2416 Highway 35, Ste. B (08736)
Mail addr: 118 Racquet Rd., Wall (07719)
**Phone—(732) 528-5222**
Fax—(732) 528-5139
Pres.—John Kuntz
Corp. Secy.—Kim Kuntz
SIC—2499; 3499; *Wooden & metal wine racks*
Employs—2; Estab.—1979
Sales—under $500,000 (est)
Distrib.—National
Privately owned corporation

---

## Manchester

(Ocean—S.E.)

### FIRST PRIORITY EMERGENCY VEHICLES, INC.

2444 Ridgeway Blvd., Bldg. 500 (08759)
**Phone—(732) 657-1104**
National—(800) 247-7725
Fax—(732) 657-7955
www.emergencyvehiclecenter.com
Email—fpev@aol.com
Pres.—Robert J. Freeman
V-P.—Greg DeForge
Sales Mgr., Specialty Vehicle Div.—Chris Vallat
Sales Mgr., Fire Apparatus—Bob Emery
Sales Mgr., Ambulance—Ken Clark
Sales Mgr., Law Enforcement—Ken Wilson
SIC—3711; 5012; *Manufacturer & distributor of emergency medical, rescue, firefighting & homeland security vehicles & mobile health clinics for domestic & international marketplaces; Brand name—KME Fire Apparatus; Road Rescue; Braun; Marque; McCoy Miller ambulances; First Priority First Responder Units; BQR Compact Fire Apparatus; Custom Truck & Body Works*
Employs—47; Estab.—1998
Sales—$25Mil
52,000 sq ft site, Distrib.—Intl.
Privately owned corporation
AKA: International Emergency Vehicles

### MID JERSEY BUILDING SUPPLY

2486 Ridgeway Blvd. (08759)
**Phone—(732) 657-2000**
Fax—(732) 657-2215
www.mjbs.us
Email—bob@mjbs.com
Owner, Pres., CEO, GM & Off. Mgr.—Robert Jeffers
V-P.—Bob Jeffers, Jr.
Manager—Bonnie Jeffers
SIC—3444; *Aluminum patio covers, enclosures, screen rooms, windows, aluminum & vinyl railings, dock covers & awnings; Brand name—Silverline; Reeb; Mason; Therma Tru; Transistion Railings; Elite; M & W Windows; PGT Windows; Versa Tex; Azek; Timber Teck Decking; Simpson; Velux; Larson; NPC; Alum Railing*
Employs—12; Estab.—1976
10,000 sq ft site, Distrib.—Regional
Limited Liability Company

### ORGO-THERMIT, INC.

3500 Colonial Dr. N. *(08759-5799)*
**Phone—(732) 657-5781**
Fax—(732) 657-5899
www.orgothermit.com
Email—info@orgothermit.com
Pres.—Dave Randolph
Dir., Qual. & R & D—Frik Hefer
Dir., Bus. Dev.—GeorgeAnne Tutunjian
Dir., Field Svcs.—Randy Dry
SIC—3548; 3599; *Aluminothermic welding products, kits & tools for the railroad & transit industries, including training & precision grinding corrugation of rail profiles*
Employs—30; Estab.—1900
Sales—$5Mil-$10Mil
Distrib.—National
Privately owned corporation
ISO rating—9001:2008

### READE MANUFACTURING CO.

2590 Ridgeway Blvd. (08759)
**Phone—(732) 657-6451**
Fax—(732) 657-6628
Pres.—James Gardella
V-P., Sales—Brad Ford
V-P., Opers.—John McConaghie
Bookkeeper—Juliet Deak
SIC—2819; *Magnesium grinding*
Employs—30; Estab.—1957
Distrib.—Intl.
Privately owned corporation

---

## Mantoloking

(Ocean—S.E.)

### MILITARY EQUIPMENT CORP. OF AMERICA (H Q)

P.O. Box 181 (08738)
**Phone—(908) 769-1000**
  (201) 919-6000
Email—militaryequip@aol.com
Pres.—Robert C. Mehlin, Sr.
Corp. Secy.—Barbara B. Mehlin
SIC—2329; 2339; NAICS—315200; *Corporate headquarters; military nylon & wool sweaters & dress swords (mfg. done overseas)*
Employs—2; Estab.—1969
Distrib.—National
Privately owned corporation

---

## Mantua

(Gloucester—S.W.)

### HANGSTERFER'S LABORATORIES, INC.

175 Ogden Rd. *(08051-1615)*
**Phone—(856) 468-0216**
National—(800) 433-5823
Fax—(856) 468-0200

# Manufacturers Directories & Databases for all 50 states

## Call 800-221-2172
visit ManufacturersNews.com
or use order form on reverse

mni®

Get Real-Time Access to the freshest industrial info

Visit EZSelect.com for more info

# mni's DIRECTORIES & DATABASES

## Call (800) 221-2172 for national, regional, metro & industry databases

Circle price of product you wish; fill out order form below

| State | # of Firms | Local Execs | Web & Email | Pages | Book Price | 1-Year Subscription to EZSelect.com Full version | 20+ version | Basic version | State | # of Firms | Local Execs | Web & Email | Pages | Book Price | 1-Year Subscription to EZSelect.com Full version | 20+ version | Basic version |
|---|---|---|---|---|---|---|---|---|---|---|---|---|---|---|---|---|---|
| Alabama | 6,204 | 15,274 | 8,845 | 696 | $113 | $512 | $352 | $179 | New Jersey | 10,778 | 26,279 | 17,820 | 1,140 | $145 | $642 | $472 | $225 |
| Alaska | 1,091 | 2,241 | 1,739 | 182 | $72 | $232 | $126 | $97 | New Mexico | 2,490 | 5,147 | 3,447 | 302 | $89 | $331 | $192 | $116 |
| Arizona | 6,116 | 13,303 | 9,855 | 640 | $112 | $507 | $328 | $177 | New York | 18,966 | 43,944 | 29,004 | 1,776 | $209 | $823 | $631 | $288 |
| Arkansas | 3,924 | 9,595 | 5,497 | 464 | $102 | $413 | $271 | $144 | N. Carolina | 11,812 | 29,561 | 18,292 | 1,232 | $149 | $663 | $487 | $232 |
| California | 27,489 | 66,283 | 45,571 | 2,544 | $221 | $968 | $848 | $339 | N. Dakota | 1,633 | 3,596 | 2,348 | 246 | $79 | $272 | $165 | $97 |
| Colorado | 7,667 | 16,283 | 11,727 | 782 | $119 | $548 | $337 | $192 | Ohio | 19,369 | 52,639 | 29,716 | 1,992 | $211 | $838 | $659 | $293 |
| Connecticut | 6,177 | 14,849 | 9,613 | 660 | $112 | $500 | $336 | $175 | Oklahoma | 6,253 | 14,381 | 8,561 | 672 | $112 | $503 | $326 | $176 |
| Delaware | 909 | 2,068 | 1,455 | 166 | $71 | $215 | $131 | $97 | Oregon | 6,621 | 15,438 | 10,482 | 698 | $114 | $515 | $335 | $180 |
| Florida | 16,010 | 37,002 | 25,854 | 1,548 | $192 | $774 | $518 | $271 | Pennsylvania | 19,652 | 49,215 | 29,066 | 1,956 | $211 | $836 | $633 | $293 |
| Georgia | 11,715 | 27,575 | 17,477 | 1,200 | $149 | $665 | $473 | $233 | Rhode Island | 2,037 | 4,839 | 3,137 | 268 | $87 | $308 | $205 | $108 |
| Hawaii | 1,515 | 2,987 | 2,281 | 184 | $79 | $272 | $148 | $97 | S. Carolina | 5,673 | 13,862 | 8,573 | 648 | $111 | $478 | $328 | $167 |
| Idaho | 2,467 | 5,619 | 3,639 | 308 | $89 | $333 | $196 | $116 | S. Dakota | 1,562 | 3,736 | 2,334 | 236 | $81 | $270 | $166 | $97 |
| Illinois Mfrs. | 18,367 | 48,572 | 28,207 | 2,052 | $211 | $815 | $612 | $285 | Tennessee | 8,204 | 20,064 | 12,376 | 888 | $122 | $570 | $408 | $200 |
| Illinois Svcs. | 26,548 | 62,915 | 41,197 | 2,388 | $207 | $920 | $710 | $322 | Texas | 25,230 | 60,739 | 39,198 | 2,436 | $211 | $932 | $742 | $326 |
| Indiana | 10,745 | 28,320 | 16,363 | 1,188 | $146 | $648 | $484 | $227 | Utah | 4,311 | 10,207 | 6,714 | 494 | $102 | $428 | $291 | $150 |
| Iowa | 6,108 | 15,151 | 9,324 | 736 | $112 | $494 | $336 | $173 | Vermont | 1,657 | 3,897 | 2,622 | 238 | $82 | $277 | $162 | $97 |
| Kansas | 5,079 | 11,998 | 7,417 | 552 | $107 | $462 | $300 | $162 | Virginia | 7,473 | 18,392 | 11,613 | 804 | $119 | $542 | $380 | $190 |
| Kentucky | 5,800 | 15,083 | 8,425 | 656 | $111 | $488 | $345 | $171 | Washington | 7,718 | 18,261 | 12,616 | 808 | $118 | $554 | $366 | $194 |
| Louisiana | 6,162 | 14,143 | 9,049 | 648 | $111 | $498 | $331 | $174 | W. Virginia | 2,194 | 5,202 | 2,865 | 300 | $87 | $319 | $209 | $112 |
| Maine | 2,591 | 5,719 | 3,946 | 322 | $92 | $340 | $201 | $119 | Wisconsin | 12,857 | 33,428 | 20,069 | 1,464 | $151 | $693 | $516 | $243 |
| Maryland/DC | 5,700 | 13,303 | 8,932 | 618 | $111 | $481 | $326 | $168 | Wyoming | 1,337 | 2,770 | 1,885 | 208 | $78 | $253 | $142 | $97 |
| Mass. | 9,307 | 22,587 | 14,976 | 944 | $141 | $605 | $443 | $212 | | | | | | | | | |
| Michigan | 15,702 | 38,385 | 24,015 | 1,576 | $191 | $752 | $557 | $263 | | | | | | | | | |
| Minnesota | 10,627 | 26,843 | 16,601 | 1,184 | $145 | $635 | $448 | $222 | | | | | | | | | |
| Mississippi | 3,322 | 8,224 | 4,561 | 416 | $99 | $387 | $256 | $136 | | | | | | | | | |
| Missouri | 9,347 | 23,139 | 13,814 | 1,008 | $141 | $606 | $423 | $212 | | | | | | | | | |
| Montana | 2,178 | 4,280 | 2,926 | 274 | $87 | $318 | $153 | $111 | | | | | | | | | |
| Nebraska | 3,375 | 7,957 | 4,897 | 420 | $97 | $385 | $242 | $135 | | | | | | | | | |
| Nevada | 2,133 | 4,565 | 3,422 | 286 | $86 | $305 | $191 | $107 | | | | | | | | | |
| New Hamp. | 2,882 | 7,020 | 4,651 | 356 | $93 | $355 | $227 | $124 | | | | | | | | | |

**EZSelect.com** databases: Tap into the **mni** database on a real-time basis. Choose your database from any of the subscriptions listed here or create your own custom subscription by providing your criteria. Powerful functions let you research companies and contacts, build lists of prospects, print reports and mailing labels, save and share profiles, or export to your favorite CRM software. Offered in 12 month subscriptions for live 24x7 access. Runs on PC, Mac, tablet, or smart phone. The Full & 20+ employees versions include all advanced features, such as the ability to export profiles, print address labels, print summary and detail reports, bulk exclude and browse all profiles. The Basic version allows you to view & print one profile at a time, and does not include the advanced features of the Full version. *All counts & prices subject to change.* Learn more and start your free demo at **EZSelect.com**

**Company** _____

**Your Name (please print)** _____

**Street Address** _____

**City** _____ **State** _____ **Zip** _____

**Phone (** ) _____ **Fax (** ) _____
(to give us permission to keep you up to date.)

**Email** _____
required on EZSelect Subscription orders

**Signature** _____ **Date** _____

## Mail, Fax, Email, or Phone Your Order to:

**Sales Total:** $ _____

**Shipping** (books only): $ _____
($9.45 first book, $5 each additional book)

**GRAND TOTAL:** $ _____

*All mni data is copyrighted & its use is subject to certain terms & conditions.*

### METHOD OF PAYMENT

☐ **Check enclosed** (Add 9.0 % sales tax on books delivered to Illinois)

☐ **Charge to my credit card:**

☐ American Express   ☐ Visa   ☐ MC   ☐ Discover

**Acct.#** _____

**Expires:** _____

 **Manufacturers' News, Inc.**
*Identify & contact U.S. manufacturers*

**1633 Central Street • Evanston, IL 60201-1569 • Order Toll Free: 800-221-2172 • Fax: 847-332-1100**
**Order online: mnistore.com • EZSelect.com • mnileads.com • sales@manufacturersnews.com** 5/14

## Mantua—(cont.)

www.hangsterfers.com
Email—sales@hangsterfers.com
CEO—Ann Jones
Sales Mgr.—L. C. Skip Wolford
Export Mgr.—Cynthia Brake
Sales Coord., Inside—Lorraine Romano
SIC—3569; *Metal working lubricants & coolants*
Employs—40; Estab.—1942
Sales—$10Mil-$25Mil
Distrib.—Intl.
Privately owned corporation
ISO rating—9001

### KINNARNEY RUBBER CO., INC.

450 Main St., P.O. Box 37 (08051)
**Phone—(856) 468-1320**
Fax—(856) 468-7438
www.kinnarney.com
Email—jimk@kinnarney.com
Pres.—Jim Kinnarney
V-P.—Jack Kinnarney
V-P.—Luke Kinnarney
SIC—3061; NAICS—326291; *Molded rubber products, including masking boots that protect electronic components on printed circuit boards*
Employs—10; Estab.—1960
8,000 sq ft site, Distrib.—Intl.
Privately owned corporation

**NEW ENTRY**

### MANTUA SIGN & LIGHTING

550 Bridgeton Pike, Ste. 5 (08051)
**Phone—(856) 415-0022**
Fax—(856) 415-0032
www.mantuasign.com
Email—info@mantuasign.com
Owner—Jay Glaser
GM—Ashley Cannon
SIC—3993; 2759; *Interior & exterior signs, channel & dimensional lettering, large-format digital printing & graphic design services*
Employs—3; Estab.—2008
Sales—$500,000-$1Mil
4,000 sq ft site, Distrib.—Regional
Privately owned corporation

### SPARKLE EMBROIDERY MONOGRAMS

550 Bridgeton Pike, Ste. 12 (08051)
**Phone—(856) 468-0304**
Fax—(856) 468-1915
Owner—Teri Warming
V-P.—Bill Warming
SIC—2395; 2396; *Apparel embroidery, monogramming & screen printing*
Employs—5; Estab.—1987
Sales—under $500,000 (est)
Distrib.—Local
Sole ownership

## Manville

(Somerset—N.E.)

### ALJAY TOOL & DIE CORP.

1213 Kennedy Blvd. (08835)
**Phone—(908) 722-2403**
Fax—(908) 704-0124
www.aljay.net
Email—aljay59@aol.com
Pres.—Albert Fischer, Sr.
V-P., R & D—Al Fischer, Jr.
SIC—3544; NAICS—333500; *Tool & die job shop*
Employs—4; Estab.—1959
Sales—under $500,000
2,400 sq ft site, Distrib.—National
Privately owned corporation

### †ESTRIN CALABRESE SALES AGENCY

17 S. Main St., Ste. 3 (08835)
**Phone—(908) 722-9980**
www.estrincalabrese.com
Pres.—Michael Estrin
SIC—5063; *Distributor of commercial & residential lighting, components & fixtures*
Employs—7
Privately owned corporation

### HARRISON SEAL CORP.

1201 Kennedy Blvd. (08835)
**Phone—(908) 722-3322**
Fax—(908) 722-3964
www.harrisonseal.com
Email—jargento@harrisonseal.com
Pres.—Jack Argento
SIC—3679; *Hermetic seals*
Employs—4; Estab.—1985
Sales—$500,000-$1Mil
Distrib.—Intl.
Privately owned corporation

### MANVILLE RUBBER PRODUCTS, INC.

1009 Kennedy Blvd. (08835)
**Phone—(908) 526-9111**
Fax—(908) 526-7123
www.manvillerubber.com
Email—mgajewski@manvillerubber.com
Pres.—Sophia Gajewski
V-P.—Mark Gajewski
SIC—3069; *Rubber products, including molded rubber components, rubber-to-metal bonded assemblies & rubber covered rollers for the electrical, electronics, automotive, fiber optics, railroad, medical, aerospace, military, computer appliance industries*
Employs—35; Estab.—1969
Sales—$500,000-$1Mil
Distrib.—Intl.
Privately owned corporation

**NEW ENTRY**

### MOLECU-WIRE CORP.

1215 Kennedy Blvd. (08835)
Mail addr: P.O. Box 5426, Somerset (08873)
**Phone—(908) 429-0300**
Fax—(908) 429-0700
Email—piczar@aol.com
Pres., CEO—Vinod K. Barot
SIC—3679; NAICS—331422; *Wire & cable harness assemblies, including copper & nickel*
Employs—12; Estab.—1958
Sales—$1Mil-$2.5Mil (est)
25,000 sq ft site, Distrib.—Intl.
Privately owned corporation

### SIGN-A-RAMA

32 S. Main St. (08835)
**Phone—(908) 203-8005**
Fax—(908) 203-8115
www.signaramaonline.com
Email—sales@signaramaonline.com
Pres.—Deepak Changrani
SIC—3993; *Vinyl, lawn & carved signs, banners, light cabinets, channel letters & vehicle lettering*
Employs—2; Estab.—2004
Distrib.—National
Sole ownership
AKA: JMM Signs, LLC

## Maple Shade

(Burlington—S.E.)

### 2 FOR 1 MACHINERY GROUP, THE

30 N. Pine Ave. (08052)
Mail addr: P. O. Box 251, Moorestown (08057)
**Phone—(856) 321-0474**
www.2for1machinery.com
Email—ropeman1956@gmail.com

Pres.—Wayne Bancroft
Machinist—Wayne Ramos
SIC—3552; NAICS—333292; *Remanufactured spindle machinery & related parts for the textile industry*
Employs—4; Estab.—1989
Sales—under $500,000
2,000 sq ft site, Distrib.—Intl.
Privately owned corporation

**NEW ENTRY**

### AEROCOAT SOURCE, LLC

11 Morris Ave. (08052)
**Phone—(856) 428-8145**
National—(877) 546-7305
Fax—(856) 428-4713
www.aerocoat.com
Owner—Richard Creek
SIC—3479; 3471; *Metal coating for aviation applications*
Employs—15
Sales—$1Mil-$2.5Mil (est)
Distrib.—Intl.
Limited Liability Company

### ARIZONA SIGNS & TRUCK LETTERING

3121 Route 73 S. (08052)
**Phone—(856) 482-2288**
National—(800) 600-1412
Fax—(856) 482-6644
www.arizonadesigninc.com
Email—sales@arizonadesigninc.com
Owner—Jeffrey Chudoff
Off. Mgr.—Lisa Hannah
SIC—3993; 3089; NAICS—323100; *Vinyl interior & exterior signs, lettering, banners & vehicle graphics, business card & stationery printing, graphic designs & logos*
Employs—5; Estab.—1985
Sales—under $500,000
Distrib.—Regional
Sole ownership
AKA: Arizona Signs & Glass Tints Specialists

### C P S METALS, INC.

450 S. Fellowship Rd. (08052)
**Phone—(856) 779-0846**
Fax—(856) 779-0905
Pres.—Edwin Pelczarski
V-P., Fin., MIS & R & D—Paul Pelczarski
SIC—3444; *Sheet metal fabrication*
Employs—17; Estab.—1975
Sales—$1Mil-$2.5Mil
16,000 sq ft site, Distrib.—Regional
Privately owned corporation

### †EASTERN LIFT TRUCK CO., INC.

549 E. Linwood Ave., Route 73 N., P.O. Box 307 (08052)
**Phone—(856) 779-8880**
National—(888) 779-8880
Fax—(856) 482-8804
www.easternlifttruck.com
Email—sales@easternlifttruck.com
Pres.—Mike Pruitt
V-P.—Dan Pruitt
Cont.—Ed Gallagher
Corp. Parts Mgr.—Ed Henry
Corp. Serv. Mgr.—Derf Remington
Sales Admn. Mgr.—Jackie DeNote

SIC—5084; 5014; *Corporate headquarters & distributor of material handling equipment, including new & used forklifts, replacement parts, tires, warehouse products, hydraulic hose assemblies & fittings, golf carts, scissor lifts & compactor & baler repair; Brand name—Yale; Combilift; Lift Loader; JLG; Taylor-Dunn*
Employs—370; Estab.—1974
40,000 sq ft site, Distrib.—Regional
Privately owned sub-S corp.
Parent co.—Eastern Lift Truck Co., Inc., York, PA
Phone—(717) 764-1161
See Parent Co. Section for full profile.

### EPOPLEX

Div. of Stonhard, A Div. Of StonCor Group
1000 E. Park Ave., P.O. Box 308 (08052)
**Phone—(856) 667-8399**
National—(800) 822-6920
Fax—(856) 779-2963
www.epoplex.com
Email—epoplex@epoplex.com
GM—Kent Stough, Jr.
Off. Mgr.—Cindi Westlund
SIC—2851; NAICS—325510; *Epoxy paint & adhesives*
Employs—87; Estab.—1983
Distrib.—Intl.
Privately owned corporation
Parent co.—Stonhard, A Div. Of StonCor Group, Maple Shade, NJ
Phone—(856) 779-7500
See Parent Co. Section for full profile.

### FRANK'S UPHOLSTERY & DRAPERIES

49 S. Boulevard Ave. (08052)
**Phone—(856) 779-8585**
Fax—(856) 779-8007
Owner—Frank Troso
MIS Mgr.—Kevin Bergen
Fin. Mgr.—Theresa Troso
SIC—2512; 2391; NAICS—337121; *Upholstered furniture & draperies*
Employs—5; Estab.—1976
Sales—under $500,000
2,900 sq ft site, Distrib.—Local
Sole ownership

### HOLMAN ENTERPRISES, INC. (H Q)

244 E. Kings Hwy. (08052)
**Phone—(856) 663-5200**
Fax—(856) 665-3444
www.holmanenterprises.com
Chrm.—Joseph Holman
V-P., Dealership Opers.—William Cariss
Hum. Res. Mgr.—Brandon Renous
SIC—3713; NAICS—336211; *Corporate headquarters; truck bodies*
Employs—30
Sales—$5Mil-$10Mil (est)
Distrib.—Regional
Privately owned corporation

### INNOVATIVE SOFTWARE SOLUTIONS, INC. (H Q)

3000 S. Lenola Rd. (08052)
**Phone—(856) 910-9190**
Fax—(856) 910-9192
www.issisystems.com
Email—jbarling@issisystems.com
Ptnr.—Steve Webb
Ptnr.—Larry Goldstein
Pres.—James Barling
IT Mgr.—Rich Henderson
SIC—7372; *Corporate headquarters; software development*
Employs—90
Distrib.—National

**GEOGRAPHICAL**

## Maple Shade—(cont.)

**KAPLAN INDUSTRIES, INC.**

10 Morris Ave., Route 73 (08052)
**Phone—(856) 779-8181**
National—(800) 257-8299
Fax—(856) 779-8242
www.kaplanindustries.com
Email—kaplan@
kaplanindustries.com
Dir., Opers.—Jim Johnston
Plt. Mgr.—John Carson
Pur. Agt.—Barbara Leone
SIC—3443; 3494; NAICS—
332900; *High & low pressure
compressed gas cylinders,
aluminum cylinders & valves*
Employs—15; Estab.—1991
Sales—$1Mil-$2.5Mil
Distrib.—Intl.
Privately owned corporation

**MAIN STREET GRAPHICS, INC.**

30 W. Main St. (08052)
**Phone—(856) 755-3523**
Fax—(856) 755-3524
www.mainstreetgraphics.net
Email—mike@
mainstreetgraphics.net
Pres.—Eileen Cusumano
Hum. Res. & Prod. Mgr.—Mike
Cusumano
SIC—2759; *Commercial offset
printing*
Employs—4; Estab.—2000
Sales—under $500,000
Distrib.—National
Privately owned corporation

**OAKWOOD UNIFORM & EQUIPMENT CO.**

400 E. Main St. (08052)
**Phone—(856) 429-4534**
      (856) 779-7680
Fax—(856) 779-0176
Pres.—Sally Corson
Corp. Secy.—Carol Corson
SIC—2326; 2337; NAICS—
315200; *Police, firefighter, postal
& public safety uniforms*
Employs—15; Estab.—1959
Sales—$500,000-$1Mil
Distrib.—Local
Privately owned corporation

**PIONEER MACHINE & TOOL CO.**

425 E. Broadway, P.O. Box 8
(08052)
**Phone—(856) 779-8800**
Fax—(856) 779-9233
Email—gczuzak@
pioneermachine.net
Ptnr.—George Czuzak, Jr.
Ptnr.—Michael Czuzak
Plt. Mgr.—John Cuthbert
Off. Mgr.—Denise Schaeffer
SIC—3728; 3444; *Aerospace
components*
Employs—30; Estab.—1953
20,000 sq ft site, Distrib.—National
Privately owned corporation
ISO rating—9001

**QUICK CUT STAMPING & EMBOSSING, INC.**

815 E. Main St. (08052)
**Phone—(856) 321-0050**
Fax—(856) 755-9669
Email—office@aquickcut.com
Pres.—Holly Zahradnick
V-P.—John Zahradnick
Off. Admn.—Lissette Acevedo
Estimator—Jim Ford
SIC—2675; 2789; NAICS—
322200; *Die cutting, foil
stamping & embossing of pocket
folders, door hangers, rotary
business file index cards, file
folders, business & holiday
greeting cards, including
polyester film reinforcing,
transfer tapping, tabbing & hand
binding work; Brand name—
CCM (Channel Creasing Matrix)*
Employs—10; Estab.—1998
Sales—$500,000
3,500 sq ft site, Distrib.—Regional
Privately owned sub-S corp.
AKA: A Quick Cut

**SIR SPEEDY PRINTING CENTER**

300 S. Lenola Rd., Ste. 22 (08052)
**Phone—(856) 866-0588**
Fax—(856) 273-8631
www.sirspeedy.com/mapleshade
Email—speedymaple@aol.com
Pres.—Dennis Marks
V-P.—Darlene A. Marks
Manager—William Kaisla
SIC—2759; 2752; 3993; NAICS—
323100; *Offset, single, multicolor
& color digital printing, signs,
banners, posters, graphic
design, promotional products &
mailing & document services*
Employs—8; Estab.—1982
Sales—$500,000-$1Mil
4,000 sq ft site, Distrib.—Regional
Privately owned sub-S corp.

**SMALL BUSINESS SERVICE CENTER**

122 E. Kings Hwy., Ste. 504
(08052)
**Phone—(856) 234-8059**
National—(800) 615-6245
Fax—(856) 234-3702
www.sbsconline.com
Email—john@sbsconline.com
CEO—Sandy Testa
COO & Dir.—John Testa
MIS Mgr.—Lauren Testa
Data Proc. Mgr.—Trish Reichert
SIC—2759; 2752; NAICS—
323100; *Laser, inkjet, digital,
lettershop & offset printing,
fulfillment & direct mail
preparation services*
Employs—20; Estab.—1985
10,000 sq ft site, Distrib.—National
Privately owned sub-S corp.
AKAs: All Mail Service Center &
SBSC

**SOUTH JERSEY CUSTOM SCREEN PRINTING**

481 W. Route 38 (08052)
**Phone—(856) 482-1500**
Owner—Stan Jay
SIC—2396; 2759; NAICS—
323100; *Custom screen printing*
Employs—2; Estab.—1987
Sales—under $500,000
Distrib.—Regional
Sole ownership

**†SOUTH JERSEY WELDING SUPPLY CO.**

496 Route 38 E. (08052)
**Phone—(856) 778-4440**
Fax—(856) 778-9661
www.sjwelding.com
Email—sales@sjwelding.com
Pres.—Robert Thornton, Jr.
V-P.—David Thornton
SIC—5084; 5085; *Company
headquarters & wholesaler of
welding equipment & supplies*
Employs—35; Estab.—1962
Distrib.—National
Privately owned corporation

**STONHARD, A DIV. OF STONCOR GROUP**

Div. of RPM International, Inc.
1000 E. Park Ave., P.O. Box 308
(08052-0308)
**Phone—(856) 779-7500**
National—(800) 854-0310
Fax—(856) 321-7525
www.stonhard.com
Email—marketing@stonhard.com
Pres.—David Reif
V-P., Mktg., Intl.—Peggy Fynan
V-P., R & D—Fred Gelfant
V-P., Prod. Dev.—Mike Jewell
Dir., Dev. & Training—Mike Galie
Dir.—Rick Neill
Mktg. Mgr.—Kendall Ellis
SIC—2891; NAICS—325520;
*Company headquarters &
seamless, resilient & polymer
epoxy flooring*
Employs—500
Sales—$200Mil
100,000 sq ft site, Distrib.—Intl.
Privately owned corporation
ISO rating—9002
Parent co.—RPM International,
Inc., Medina, OH
Phone—(330) 273-5090
See Parent Co. Section for full profile.

**SUPERIOR PRINTING INK CO., INC.**

666 E. Linwood Ave. (08052)
**Phone—(856) 482-9066**
Fax—(856) 482-1078
www.superiorink.com
Email—jkissinger@superiorink.com
Br. Mgr.—Joe Kissinger
SIC—2893; *Printing inks*
Employs—8
Sales—$2.5Mil-$5Mil (est)
Distrib.—National
Privately owned corporation
Parent co.—Superior Printing Ink
Co., Inc., Teterboro, NJ
Phone—(201) 478-5600
See Parent Co. Section for full profile.

**THOMSON LAMINATION CO., INC.**

504 E. Linwood Ave. (08052)
**Phone—(856) 779-8521**
Fax—(856) 779-8819
www.tlclam.net
Email—mgrove@tlclam.net
Chrm.—Sterling A. Martin
Pres.—Sterling A. Martin III
V-P., Sales—Milan Grove
V-P., Fin.—John Borden
V-P.—Debra Vernier
Dir., Qual.—Daniel O'Connor
Prodn. Control Mgr.—Keith
Boswick
Shpg. Mgr.—James Feigenbutz
Tool Engrg. Mgr.—Charles Frame
SIC—3469; 3479; 3544; NAICS—
333500; *Motor laminations &
assemblies, including stamping,
precision carbide dies & high
temperature annealing services
for aerospace, medical, machine
tool, military & commercial
applications*
Employs—100; Estab.—1964
70,000 sq ft site, Distrib.—Intl.
Sole ownership
ISO rating—AS9100

**†VAN AIR & HYDRAULICS, INC.**

Div. of RG Group
612 E. Woodlawn Ave. (08052)
**Phone—(856) 779-7300**
National—(800) 526-2708
Fax—(856) 779-8507
www.vanairhydraulic.com
Email—vanair@vanairhyd.com
GM—Barb Fox
SIC—5084; *Distributor of
industrial motion control
electronic equipment & fluid
handling systems*
Employs—10; Estab.—1977
Distrib.—National
Privately owned corporation
Parent co.—RG Group, York, PA
Phone—(717) 846-9300
See Parent Co. Section for full profile.

## Maplewood

(Essex—N.E.)

**ACME RUBBER STAMP WORKS**

6 Burnett Ave. (07040)
**Phone—(973) 761-7146**
Fax—(973) 761-1608
www.acmerubberstampworks.com
Email—acmers@verizon.net
Pres.—Lori Bierman
SIC—3953; NAICS—339943;
*Rubber stamps & seals*
Employs—3; Estab.—1973
Sales—under $500,000
Distrib.—National
Privately owned corporation

**BARRASSO & BLASI, INC.**

1581 Springfield Ave. (07040)
**Phone—(973) 761-0595**
Fax—(973) 761-4999
Pres.—Robert Blasi
V-P.—Buddy Mazzo
SIC—3911; NAICS—339911;
*Precious metal jewelry & pins*
Employs—3; Estab.—1916
Sales—under $500,000
Distrib.—National
Privately owned corporation

**†CAC INTERNATIONAL**

30 Camptown Rd. (07040)
**Phone—(973) 371-4300**
National—(800) 788-7756
Fax—(973) 371-4611
www.cacchinausa.com
Email—cacbang@yahoo.com
Owner—Kevin Deng
SIC—5023; *Wholesaler of
chinaware*
Employs—10; Estab.—1996
Distrib.—National
Sole ownership

**COLUMBIA MARKETING CORP.**

221 Rutgers St. (07040)
**Phone—(973) 275-1700**
National—(800) 429-6374
Fax—(973) 275-3998
www.gayosphere.com
Pres.—Alan H. Beck
Graphic Designer—Brian Pelton
SIC—2721; 2741; *Tourist guides &
travel map & magazine
publishing*
Employs—2; Estab.—1995
Sales—under $500,000
Distrib.—National
Privately owned corporation

**DIPIETRO FOODS, INC.**

1701 Springfield Ave. (07040)
**Phone—(973) 762-4077**
Fax—(973) 762-7734
Email—dipietrofoods@verizon.net
Pres.—Lucy DiPietro Manzella
SIC—2098; NAICS—311823;
*Uncooked pasta*
Employs—3; Estab.—1960
Sales—$500,000-$1Mil (est)
Distrib.—Regional
Privately owned corporation

**ELECTRONIC MFG. CO.**

71 Newark Way (07040)
**Phone—(973) 762-1300**
Fax—(973) 762-4540
www.elecmfgco.com
Email—info@elecmfgco.com
Pres.—Martin Peterson
V-P.—Chris McKee
MIS Mgr.—Leo Zuckerman
Engrg. Mgr.—Jesse Kakstys

## Maplewood—(cont.)

SIC—3469; 3599; *Metal stampings & CNC turning & milling*
Employs—25; Estab.—1989
Sales—$2.5Mil-$5Mil
Distrib.—National
Privately owned partnership

### GREGORY SIGNS, LLC
1453 Springfield Ave., P.O. Box 671 (07040)
**Phone—(973) 761-0165**
National—(866) 744-6634
Fax—(973) 763-8863
www.signmfg.com
Email—gregorysign@comcast.net
Ptnr.—Gregory Rabinovich
Pres.—Victor Gregory
SIC—3993; *Interior & exterior signs*
Employs—2; Estab.—1980
Sales—under $500,000
Distrib.—Local
Limited Liability Company

### IDEAL-JACOBS CORP.
515 Valley St. (07040)
**Phone—(973) 275-5100**
National—(877) 873-4332
Fax—(973) 275-5161
www.idealjacobs.com
Email—info@idealjacobs.com
Pres.—Andrew C. Jacobs
V-P.—Vincent Santoro
V-P.—Mike Valentine
Graphic Designer—Igor Lebre
SIC—2759; NAICS—323100; *Commercial screen printing*
Employs—30; Estab.—1921
Distrib.—Intl.
Privately owned corporation

### KAUPP & SONS, INC., C. B.
6 Newark Way (07040)
**Phone—(973) 761-4000**
Fax—(973) 761-0253
www.kaupp.com
Email—custserv@kaupp.com
CEO—Clem Kaupp, Jr.
Pres., MIS Mgr.—William Kaupp
SIC—3599; 3469; *Corporate headquarters & precision machining & hydroforming job shop*
Employs—25; Estab.—1924
Sales—$1Mil-$5Mil
40,000 sq ft site, Distrib.—National
Privately owned sub-S corp.
ISO rating—9001:2000

### MAPLEWOOD BEVERAGE PACKERS, LLC
Div. of Arizona Beverages USA, LLC
45 Camptown Rd. (07040)
**Phone—(973) 416-4582**
Fax—(973) 416-4583
www.drinkarizona.com
Email—info@drinkarizona.com
GM—Nick DiMirio
Hum. Res. & Off. Mgr.—Roseanne Semler
Admn. Officer—Janice Roman
SIC—2086; NAICS—312100; *Beverage bottling*
Employs—175; Estab.—1992
Distrib.—National
Limited Liability Company
Parent co.—Arizona Beverages USA, LLC, Woodbury, NY
Phone—(516) 812-0300
See Parent Co. Section for full profile.

### NERSESIAN PUBLISHING, ROY
10 Maryland Rd. (07040)
**Phone—(973) 762-8604**
www.nerses.com
Email—nerses1@verizon.net
Principal—Roy L. Nersesian
SIC—2731; *Book publishing*
Employs—1
Privately owned corporation

### †NEW JERSEY PLUMBING, HEATING & INDUSTRIAL SUPPLY, LLC
Div. of Bayonne Plumbing Supply, Inc.
91 Newark Way (07040)
**Phone—(973) 761-4567**
Fax—(973) 761-0395
www.thebathconnection.com
Email—info@thebathconnection.com
Ptnr.—Jim Buggy
Showroom Mgr., Fanwood—Ralph Yeager
Sales Rep., Inside—Ryan McPeek
SIC—5074; *Wholesaler of plumbing supplies, including pipes, valves & fittings*
Employs—5; Estab.—1968
Distrib.—Local
Privately owned corporation
AKA: Bath Connection, The
Parent co.—Bayonne Plumbing Supply, Inc., Bayonne, NJ
Phone—(201) 339-8000
See Parent Co. Section for full profile.

### PENN TOOL CO.
1776 Springfield Ave. (07040)
**Phone—(973) 761-4343**
National—(800) 526-4956
Fax—(973) 761-1494
www.penntoolco.com
Email—info@penntoolco.com
Owner—Gene Elson
V-P., Sales—Mike Elson
SIC—3423; 3545; *Hand tools & measuring instruments*
Employs—8; Estab.—1967
Sales—$500,000-$1Mil
Distrib.—National
Privately owned corporation

### RAILS CO.
101 Newark Way (07040)
**Phone—(973) 763-4320**
National—(800) 217-2457
Fax—(973) 763-2585
www.railsco.com
Email—rails@railsco.com
Chrm., Pres. & CEO—G. N. Burwell
Secy-Treas., CFO—M. Kinda
Sales Mgr.—Darby Burwell
MIS Mgr.—Ed Oksienik
SIC—3743; 3569; *Railroad heaters, controls & lubrication equipment*
Employs—35; Estab.—1932
Sales—$5Mil-$10Mil
35,000 sq ft site, Distrib.—National
Privately owned sub-S corp.

### RESTAURANT GRAPHICS, INC.
67 Newark Way (07040)
**Phone—(973) 763-4036**
National—(800) 622-6368
Fax—(973) 763-6128
www.rgmenus.com
Email—macmenu@aol.com
Pres.—Tom Stravakis
SIC—2752; 2759; 2791; NAICS—323100; *Lithographic & commercial printing of restaurant menus, including electronic prepress, laminating & graphic design*
Employs—7; Estab.—1981
Sales—$650,000
6,000 sq ft site, Distrib.—Regional
Privately owned corporation

### R-S RESTAURANT EQUIPMENT MFG. CORP.
40 Camptown Rd. (07040)
**Phone—(973) 375-3388**
National—(800) 628-3388
Fax—(973) 375-3768
www.rsrestaurantequipment.com
Email—redstaronbowery@rsrestaurantequipment.com
Off. Mgr.—Andrew Lee

SIC—3589; NAICS—333319; *Restaurant equipment*
Employs—14
Distrib.—Local

### TRIMARCO JEWELERS, INC.
1847-1849 Springfield Ave. (07040)
**Phone—(973) 762-7380**
Fax—(973) 762-5772
www.trimarcojewelers.com
Email—info@trimarcojewelers.com
GM—Ken Trimarco
SIC—3911; NAICS—339911; *Precious metal jewelry*
Employs—4; Estab.—1951
Distrib.—Local
Privately owned corporation

### UNION TOOL & MOLD CO.
220 Rutgers St. (07040)
**Phone—(973) 763-6611**
Fax—(973) 763-7643
www.uniontool-mold.com
Email—info@uniontool-mold.com
Pres.—Robert Arrighi
Off. Mgr.—Alison Arrighi
SIC—3544; NAICS—333500; *Plastic molds & metal dies*
Employs—30; Estab.—1956
Sales—$1Mil-$2.5Mil
Distrib.—Regional
Privately owned corporation

### VISUAL IMPACT ADVERTISING, INC.
9 Highland Pl. (07040)
**Phone—(973) 763-4900**
www.mattersmagazine.com
Email—joanne@mattersmagazine.com
Owner—Karen Duncan
Supervising Editor—Joanne Di Pasquale
SIC—2711; *Magazine publishing, including recipes & social & local issues*
Employs—7
Sales—under $500,000 (est)
Distrib.—Local

### VITALI, INC., UBALDO
188-190 Hilton Ave. (07040)
**Phone—(973) 763-9310**
Fax—(973) 763-5715
Email—ubaldo@mindspring.com
Pres.—Ubaldo Vitali
SIC—3341; *Silver products*
Employs—3; Estab.—1977
Sales—under $500,000
3,000 sq ft site, Distrib.—National
Privately owned corporation

---

## Marlboro
### (Monmouth—N.E.)

### A+ PRODUCTS, INC.
8 Timber Ln., Marlboro Industrial Pk. (07746)
**Phone—(732) 866-9111**
National—(888) 275-8728
Fax—(732) 866-0191
www.aplusproducts.net
Email—info@aplusproducts.net
Founder & Pres.—Mike Schreiber
Dir., Fin.—Sabrena Watkins
Opers. Mgr.—Randy Hamill
Mktg. Mgr.—Donna Lloyd
SIC—3429; 3089; 3499; 3082; NAICS—332510; *Corporate headquarters & custom & standard metal & plastic hardware for the promotional, shooting, hunting, hospitality & medical markets, including grommets, washers, snap sets, rivets/eyelets, key rings/fobs, buckles & holster clips*
Employs—40; Estab.—1992
Sales—$20Mil
25,000 sq ft site, Distrib.—Intl.
Privately owned corporation
AKAs: A+ Products & A+ Group & A+

### EFCO FORMS
Div. of EFCO Corp.
77 Vanderburg Rd. (07746)
**Phone—(732) 308-1010**
Fax—(732) 409-2426
www.efcoforms.com
Email—info@efcoforms.com
Sales Mgr.—Joe Capozzi
SIC—3444; *Concrete forms*
Employs—15; Estab.—1988
Sales—$1Mil-$2.5Mil
Distrib.—National
Privately owned corporation
Parent co.—EFCO Corp., Des Moines, IA
Phone—(515) 266-1141
See Parent Co. Section for full profile.

### EXPRESS TAG & LABEL CO.
52 N. Main St. (07746)
**Phone—(718) 965-1400**
www.garmenthangtags.com
Email—expresstag@aol.com
Owner—Gerald Tomaselli
SIC—2752; 2759; 3993; NAICS—323100; *Printed labels & tags, postcards & promotional products & office printed products*
Employs—4; Estab.—1982
Sales—$500,000-$1Mil
Distrib.—Local
Limited Liability Company

### HILMAN ROLLERS
12 Timber Ln., P.O. Box 45 *(07746)*
**Phone—(732) 462-6277**
(888) 276-5548
Fax—(732) 462-6355
www.hilmanrollers.com
Email—sales@hilmanrollers.com
Pres., CEO—Jeff Hill
V-P., CFO—Susan Montgomery
COO & Pur. Mgr.—Chris Hill
Sales Mgr.—Charles Holzapfel
Qual. Assur. Mgr.—John Hendricks
Mktg. Rep.—Jeff Hill
SIC—3537; *Roller dollies for moving very heavy equipment & systems*
Employs—70; Estab.—1953
Sales—$15Mil-$20Mil
75,000 sq ft site, Distrib.—Intl.
Privately owned corporation
ISO rating—9001:2008
AKA: Hilman, Incorporated

### INTERNATIONAL CUSHIONING CO.
240 Boundary Rd. (07746)
**Phone—(732) 683-9600**
National—(866) 311-9600
Fax—(732) 683-9911
www.internationalcushioning.com
Email—iccbud@verizon.net
Pres.—Buddy Bussey
SIC—3086; *Company headquarters & polystyrene foam, EPS loose-fill & packaged bean-bag fill*
Employs—25
Sales—$1Mil-$2.5Mil
Distrib.—National
Limited Liability Company

### †J & J METALS TRADING, LLC
26 Edie Dr. (07746)
**Phone—(732) 617-0500**
Manager—Ralph Borenstein
SIC—5093; *Wholesaler of recycled nonferrous metals*
Employs—2
Limited Liability Company

### JD GRAPHICS, INC.
6 Richardson Ct. (07746)
**Phone—(732) 972-7790**
Fax—(732) 972-3907
Email—jdmrsign@gmail.com
Pres., Fin. & MIS Mgr.—Jay Davis
V-P., Opers.—Gail Davis

GEOGRAPHICAL

## Marlboro—(cont.)

SIC—3993; *Interior & exterior signs*
Employs—3; Estab.—1987
Sales—$500,000-$1Mil
Distrib.—Local
Privately owned sub-S corp.
AKA: Mr. Sign

**JERSEY GRANITE & TILE, LLC**

234 Boundary Rd., Ste. 4 (07746)
**Phone—(732) 683-1600**
Fax—(732) 683-1616
www.jerseygranitetile.com
Email—jerseygranitetile@gmail.com
Pres.—Martin Hronchich
SIC—3281; *Granite & marble countertops & vanities & installation services*
Employs—8; Estab.—2001
Sales—$500,000-$1Mil
Distrib.—Local
Limited Liability Company

**†KALDOR EMERGENCY LIGHTS, LLC**

19 Vanderburg Rd. (07746)
**Phone—(732) 780-6707**
Fax—(732) 780-0210
www.kaldoremergency.com
Email—kaldorlights@aol.com
Owner—Ilana Gases
SIC—5063; *Distributor of automotive emergency & lighting equipment, including light bars, sirens, speakers & switchboxes*
Employs—5; Estab.—1989
Distrib.—Regional
Limited Liability Company

**MILLENNIUM GRAPHICS, INC.**

35 Vanderburg Rd. (07746)
**Phone—(732) 431-0440**
National—(877) 543-9742
Fax—(732) 431-0455
www.schoolphotoonline.com
Owner—Robert Klepner
Cont.—George Lorme
Sales Mgr.—Nanette Ross
SIC—2791; NAICS—323122; *Electronic prepress*
Employs—13; Estab.—1999
15,000 sq ft site, Distrib.—National
Privately owned corporation
AKA: School Photo Marketing

**MULTI TECH INDUSTRIES CORP.**

64 S. Main St., P.O. Box 159 (07746)
**Phone—(732) 431-0550**
Fax—(732) 409-6695
www.multi-tech-industries.com
Email—jimbernard47@gmail.com
Pres.—James Bernard
Plt. Mgr.—Eric Lamorte
SIC—3643; 3644; 3496; NAICS—335931; *Rotary switches, cord strain-reliefs & ground fault locators*
Employs—11; Estab.—1933
Sales—$500,000-$1Mil
16,000 sq ft site, Distrib.—National
Sole ownership

**PARKWAY PRINTING, INC.**

52 N. Main St., Ste. C-11 (07746)
**Phone—(732) 308-0300**
Email—parkwayprinting@aol.com
Pres., Off. Mgr.—Robin Meringolo
Off. Mgr.—Steve Meringoldo
Asst. Off. Mgr.—Freddy Jones
SIC—2759; 2791; NAICS—323122; *Commercial printing, computerized typesetting & electronic prepress*
Employs—5; Estab.—1973
Sales—under $500,000
Distrib.—National
Privately owned corporation

**PLASMA POWDERS & SYSTEMS, INC.**

228 Boundary Rd., Ste. 2, P.O. Box 132 (07746)
**Phone—(732) 431-0992**
National—(800) 358-4287
Fax—(732) 308-1075
www.plasmapowders.com
Email—info@plasmapowders.com
Pres.—Peter Foy
GM—William Sibree
SIC—3399; 3315; *Metal powders & wire & thermal spray equipment, including new & used, repair, demonstration, training & coating development; Brand name—Bondrite Wire*
Employs—8; Estab.—1980
Sales—under $3Mil
6,000 sq ft site, Distrib.—Intl.
Privately owned sub-S corp.

**†QLT.COM**

238 Boundary Rd., Unit 304 (07746)
**Phone—(732) 431-0740**
National—(800) 221-9832
Fax—(914) 668-2080
www.qlt.com
Email—sales@qlt.com
Owner—Ken Kendes
V-P.—Chris Zdanowitz
SIC—5043; 5112; *Distributor of photographic heat transfer equipment & supplies, including paper posters & frames; Brand name—Chroma Crystal; Chroma Fusion; Photo Creations; EZ Peel; SuperSoft; Can't Miss;;Photo Fusion*
Employs—25; Estab.—1977
50,000 sq ft site, Distrib.—Intl.
Privately owned corporation

**SINE-TRU TOOL CO., INC.**

238 Boundry Rd. (07746)
Mail addr: P.O. Box 280, Morganville (07751)
**Phone—(732) 591-1100**
Fax—(732) 591-0386
www.sinetrutool.com
Email—noreaster427@msn.com
Pres.—Ken Klawunn
Bookkeeper—Jennifer Kingsland
SIC—3544; 3599; NAICS—333500; *Rebuilt industrial tooling, knives & general machining & welding job shop*
Employs—6; Estab.—1952
Sales—$500,000-$1Mil
12,000 sq ft site, Distrib.—Local
Privately owned corporation

**TOP NOTCH PLASTICS**

217 Bradwick Way (07746)
**Phone—(732) 946-0049**
Fax—(732) 946-2035
Owner—Ted Green
V-P.—Edward Green
SIC—3081; 2673; *Plastic bags*
Employs—25; Estab.—1982
Sales—$5Mil-$10Mil (est)
Distrib.—National
Privately owned corporation

---

## Marlton

(Burlington—S.E.)

**ACSIS, INC.**

9 E. Stow Rd., Ste. D (08053-1504)
**Phone—(856) 673-3000**
Fax—(856) 810-3597
www.acsisinc.com
Email—info@acsisinc.com
CEO—Jeremy Coote
CFO—Stephanie Siebel
CSO—John Di Palo
Sr. Dir., Opers.—Feroz Khan
Dir., Hum. Res.—Maureen Konecky
SIC—7372; *Cloud-based software development for brand protection, enterprise serialization & end-to-end supply chain visibility*
Employs—60; Estab.—1996
Distrib.—Intl.
Privately owned corporation

**†ADEMCO DISTRIBUTION, INC.**

1000 Lincoln Dr. E., Unit 4 (08053)
**Phone—(856) 985-9050**
Fax—(856) 985-9094
www.adi-dist.com
Email—info@adi-dist.com
Sales Mgr.—Marion Longaker
Br. Mgr.—Kathie McBride
SIC—5063; *Distributor of security products, including fire alarms & closed circuit television equipment & systems*
Employs—10; Estab.—1980
Distrib.—Intl.
Publicly owned corporation
DBA: ADI
Parent co.—Ademco Distribution, Inc., Melville, NY
    Phone—(631) 692-1000
See Parent Co. Section for full profile.

**ASCO POWER TECHNOLOGIES, INC.**

Div. of ASCO Power Technologies, L.P.
5000 Sagemore Dr., Ste. 200 (08053)
**Phone—(856) 810-9600**
National—(800) 800-2726
Fax—(856) 810-9601
www.ascopower.com
Email—robert.groben@emerson.com
Opers. Mgr.—Jeff Dunn
SIC—3679; *Backup power equipment*
Employs—10; Estab.—1987
Sales—$500,000-$1Mil
Distrib.—Regional
Privately owned corporation
Parent co.—ASCO Power Technologies, L.P., Florham Park, NJ
    Phone—(800) 800-2726
See Parent Co. Section for full profile.

**ASCO VALVE, INC.**

13000 Lincoln Dr. W., Ste. 106 (08053)
**Phone—(856) 985-8700**
Fax—(856) 985-5030
www.ascovalve.com
Email—asconortheast@asco.com
Dir., Sales, N.E. Reg.—John Matro
Sr. Sales Engr., Inside—William Kohler
SIC—3492; *Pneumatic valves & fittings; Brand name—ASCO Red Hat*
Employs—5
Sales—$47Mil
Publicly owned corporation
Parent co.—ASCO Valve, Inc., Florham Park, NJ
    Phone—(973) 966-2000
See Parent Co. Section for full profile.

**BUDGET PRINTING CENTER**

300 E.Greentree Rd., Unit 14 (08053)
**Phone—(856) 596-2980**
Fax—(856) 596-5580
www.budgetprintingcenter.com
Email—bo@budgetprintingcenter.com
Owner—Bo Sidhu
Manager—Jazz Sidhu
SIC—2759; NAICS—323100; *Commercial printing, including wedding invitations*
Employs—2; Estab.—1986
Sales—under $500,000
1,200 sq ft site, Distrib.—Local
Sole ownership

**BUSINESS CARD EXPRESS**

8 E. Stow Rd., Ste. 140, P.O. Box 728 (08053)
**Phone—(856) 596-3150**
National—(800) 628-6203
Fax—(856) 596-1448
www.bcex.com
Email—johnsr@bcex.com
Pres.—John McTigue
Off. Mgr.—Jane Derman
SIC—2752; 2791; NAICS—323122; *Offset printing & computerized typesetting*
Employs—38; Estab.—1989
Distrib.—Regional
Privately owned sub-S corp.

**COMPLIANCE EDUCATIONAL SYSTEMS, INC.**

P.O. Box 669 (08053)
**Phone—(856) 793-0137**
Fax—(856) 793-0139
www.cesiep.com
Email—info@cesiep.com
Pres.—Christine Castile
SIC—7372; *Regular & special education management software development*
Employs—5; Estab.—1999
Distrib.—Regional
Privately owned corporation
AKA: CES

**EASTMED ENTERPRISES, INC.**

11 Brandywine Dr. (08053)
**Phone—(856) 797-0131**
Fax—(856) 797-0151
www.discountlaryngoscope.com
Email—mona_eastmed06@yahoo.com
Pres.—Supti M. Putatunda
SIC—3841; *Corporate headquarters & surgical instruments for emergency medical services, anesthesiologists, hospital & military medical facilities & surgical centers (mfg. done overseas); Brand name—Eastmed; SunMed; Yeescope*
Employs—4; Estab.—1987
Sales—$500,000-$1Mil
Distrib.—National
Privately owned corporation
ISO rating—9001:2000

**FASTSIGNS®**

906 Greentree Sq., Route 73 N. (08053)
**Phone—(856) 985-8730**
Fax—(856) 985-8531
www.fastsigns.com/64
Email—64@fastsigns.com
Pres.—Kevin Rose
Opers. Mgr.—Paul Rose
SIC—3993; *Interior & exterior signs*
Employs—8; Estab.—1990
2,400 sq ft site, Distrib.—National
Limited Liability Company

**GLOBAL - THE TOTAL OFFICE (H Q)**

17 W. Stow Rd., P.O. Box 562 (08053)
**Phone—(856) 596-3390**
National—(800) 220-1900
Fax—(856) 596-5684
www.globaltotaloffice.com
Email—corphq@globalindustries.com
Pres.—Jon Abraham
Ex. V-P., Sales—Alan Breslow
Ex. V-P., Opers.—Jon Soll
V-P., Opers.—Brian Kennedy
Dir., Design & Mktg.—Michael Fishman
Dir., IT—Adam White
Dir., IT—Ed Ainsworth
Dir., Hum. Res.—Mary Schultz

## Marlton—(cont.)

SIC—2521; 2522; 2531; 2599; NAICS—337211; *Company headquarters; metal, plastic & wooden office, healthcare, educational, industrial & hospitality furniture (mfg. done in Canada); Brand name—Offices To Go; Evolve Furniture Group; GLOBALcare*
Employs—175; Estab.—1966
Nationwide: 475
Sales—$10Mil-$25Mil (est)
Distrib.—Intl.
Privately owned corporation
ISO rating—14001

### GREENTREE PRINTING

9004 Lincoln Dr. W., Ste. G (08053-3206)
**Phone—(856) 596-2330**
Fax—(856) 596-0308
www.greentreeprinting.net
Email—billing@ greentreeprinting.net
Ptnr. & Pres.—Paul Barbera
Ptnr.—Joseph Nolan
SIC—2752; 2759; 2789; NAICS—323100; *Offset, instant & full-color printing of flyers, brochures, postcards, carbonless & custom forms, letterheads, envelopes, business cards, magnets, stamps & labels, including binding & numbering*
Employs—3; Estab.—1983
Sales—under $500,000
Distrib.—Local
Privately owned sub-S corp.

### HOLTEC INTERNATIONAL (H Q)

555 Lincoln Dr. W., Ste. 1 (08053)
**Phone—(856) 797-0900**
Fax—(856) 797-0909
www.holtecinternational.com
Email—j.russell@holtec.com
Pres., CEO—Kris Singh
Sr. V.-P., CFO—Frank Bongrazio
Sr. V.-P., CNO—Pierre Oneid
Sr. V.-P., Intl. Projs.—William Woodward
Ex. V.-P.—Alan Soler
V.-P., Opers., N. America—Pankaj 'P. K.' Chaudhary
V.-P., Mfg. & Supply—Alan Hickman
V.-P., Contracts, Fin., Hum. Res. & IT—Nick Abraczinskas
V.-P., Corp. Bus. Dev.—Joy Russell
V.-P., Qual. Assur.—Mark Soler
Proposal Mgr.—Patty Tsilimidos
SIC—3499; 3312; 3443; 2542; *Company headquarters; steel fabrication, heat exchangers, storage racks, air-cooled condenser, wet & dry nuclear waste transport & storage containers & casks; Brand name—HI-STAR; HI-STORM; HI-SAFE; MULTI-PURPOSE CANISTERS (MPC); HOLTITE; HOMER; HI-SHIELD; HI-COOL; HI-TRAC; DOUBLE WALL CANISTER; VECASP; HI-PACK 75*
Employs—170; Estab.—1986
Sales—$255Mil
32,000 sq ft site, Distrib.—Intl.
Privately owned corporation

### LONG REACH HIGH REACH, LLC

890 E. Rte. 70, Ste. B (08053)
**Phone—(856) 797-6999**
Fax—(856) 797-6994
www.longreachhighreach.com
Email—longreachhighreach@ gmail.com
Owner—Percy Ransome

SIC—3531; *Construction equipment attachments, including long-reach & high-reach construction equipment attachments*
Employs—6
Sales—$1Mil-$2.5Mil (est)
Distrib.—Intl.
Limited Liability Company
AKA: LRHR, LLC

### LYDIA'S LAND, LLC

P.O. Box 852 (08053)
**Phone—(856) 983-7258**
www.lydiasland.com
Email—lydia@lydiasland.com
Owner—Lydia Land
SIC—2771; *Handmade greeting cards*
Employs—1
Sales—under $500,000
Distrib.—National
Limited Liability Company

### †MBO AMERICA

4 E. Stow Rd., Ste. 12 (08053-3150)
**Phone—(609) 267-2900**
Fax—(609) 267-1477
www.mboamerica.com
Email—info@mboamerica.com
Pres., CEO—Frank Bahmer
V.-P., Opers.—Werner King
SIC—5084; *Distributor of printing industry machinery, including high speed folders, automated delivery & digital finishing solutions & mailing equipment; Brand name—MBO; MBO Digital; Herzog & Heymann; Palamides; Bograma; Ibis*
Employs—20; Estab.—1985
Distrib.—Intl.
Privately owned corporation

### PACKAGING CORP. OF AMERICA, CRANBURY CREATIVE DESIGN CENTER

Div. of Packaging Corp. Of America
8 E. Stow Rd., Ste. 100 (08053)
**Phone—(856) 596-5020**
Fax—(856) 596-5021
www.packagingcorp.com
Email—info@packagingcorp.com
GM, Packaging Engrg. & Design Ctr. Mgr.—Paul Freeman
Proj. Mgr.—Jeanine Carr
Design Mgr.—Chris Azzarano
SIC—2653; NAICS—322211; *Corrugated boxes & displays*
Employs—10; Estab.—1976
Sales—$500,000-$1Mil
Distrib.—National
Publicly owned corporation
Parent co.—Packaging Corp. Of America, Lake Forest, IL
Phone—(847) 482-3000
See Parent Co. Section for full profile.

### PIRAMAL GLASS-USA, INC. (H Q)

401 Route 73 N., Bldg. 10, Ste. 202, Lake Center Executive Pk. (08053)
**Phone—(856) 293-6400**
Fax—(856) 293-6401
www.piramalglassusa.com
Email—ggi@piramalglassusa.com
CEO—Niraj Tipre
Dir., IT—Swanandesh Rane
Hum. Res. Mgr.—Dean Harding
Cust. Serv. Mgr.—Andrea Mulkey
Cred. Mgr.—Diane Thacker
SIC—3221; NAICS—327213; *Corporate headquarters; glass containers & plastic-coated decorative glass containers for pharmaceutical & cosmetic products packaging*
Employs—25
Sales—$2.5Mil-$5Mil (est)
Distrib.—Intl.
Privately owned corporation

### PLAZA 70 BAGELS

65 Highway 70 E. (08053)
**Phone—(856) 983-5151**
Fax—(856) 983-7119
Pres.—Tony Naimoli
SIC—2051; NAICS—311812; *Bagels*
Employs—2; Estab.—1976
Sales—under $500,000 (est)
Distrib.—Local
Privately owned corporation
AKA: Blue Plaza, Inc.

### PROSTHETIC ORTHOTIC SOLUTIONS INTERNATIONAL

Div. of Physiotherapy Assocs., Inc.
100 Brick Rd., Ste. 315 (08053)
**Phone—(856) 810-7900**
Fax—(856) 810-2580
www.physiocorp.com
Email—info@physiocorp.com
Manager—Kevin Towers
Administrator—Maria Giordano
SIC—3842; *Prosthetics*
Employs—5; Estab.—2001
Sales—under $500,000
Distrib.—Local
Privately owned corporation
AKA: Freedom Management Services
Parent co.—Physiotherapy Assocs., Inc., Exton, PA
Phone—(610) 644-7824
See Parent Co. Section for full profile.

NEW ENTRY

### QED FINANCIAL SYSTEMS, INC.

10000 Sagemore Dr., Ste. 10201 (08053)
**Phone—(856) 797-1200**
Fax—(856) 797-9719
www.qedfs.com
Email—solutions@qedfs.com
CEO—Joseph Potesta
SIC—7372; *Prepackaged software development; Brand name—QED*
Employs—30
Privately owned corporation

### REPCO, INC.

6 Eves Dr. *(08053)*
**Phone—(800) 822-9190**
Fax—(800) 424-9224
www.repcoinc.com
Email—sales@repcoinc.com
Pres. & Fin. Mgr.—Ann Braytenbah
Dir., Mktg.—Chuck Gillin
Sales Mgr.—William Hill
SIC—3679; 3589; NAICS—333319; *Replacement electrical contacts, coils & carbon brushes*
Employs—11; Estab.—1976
20,000 sq ft site, Distrib.—Intl.
Privately owned corporation

### S & R DESIGNS, INC.

36 W. Route 70, Ste. 213 (08053)
**Phone—(856) 985-0303**
Fax—(856) 985-7491
www.srdesignsonline.com
Pres.—Steve Billig
SIC—3911; NAICS—339911; *Precious metal jewelry*
Employs—2; Estab.—1997
Distrib.—Intl.
Privately owned corporation

## Marmora

(Cape May—S.E.)

### ALLEGRA MARKETING PRINT & MAIL

533 S. Shore Rd. (08223)
**Phone—(609) 390-1400**
Fax—(609) 390-0217
www.allegramarmora.com
Email—info@allegramarmora.com
Owner—Nicholas Wieand
Cust. Serv. Rep.—Joe Smith

SIC—2752; 2791; NAICS—323122; *Offset printing & typesetting*
Employs—10; Estab.—1976
Sales—$500,000-$1Mil
4,500 sq ft site, Distrib.—Regional
Privately owned corporation

### CATAMARAN MEDIA CO., LLC

507 S. Shore Rd. (08223)
**Phone—(609) 624-8900**
Fax—(609) 624-3470
www.shorenewstoday.com
Email—gazette@ catamaranmedia.com
Publisher—Rick Travers
Pres.—Curt Travers
Editor—James Fitzpatrick
Editor—Bill Barlow
Comp.—John Cavaretti
Adv. & Sales Mgr.—Steve Mehl
SIC—2711; *Company headquarters & newspaper publishing; Brand name—Upper Township Gazette; Gazette Leader; Beachcomber; Middle Township Gazette; Wildwood Leader; Lower Katy May Gazette; The Current Of Absecon/Pleasantville; The Current Of Hamilton & Egg Harbor City*
Employs—50
Sales—$1Mil-$5Mil
Distrib.—National

## Martinsville

(Somerset—N.E.)

### STEVE'S SCREEN PRINTING

660 Mitchell Ln. *(08836)*
**Phone—(732) 469-7670**
www.stevesscreenprinting.com
Email—ssp469@yahoo.com
Owner—Stephen Niederle
SIC—2396; 2395; *Textile, metal, plastic & wood screen printing & embroidery*
Employs—1; Estab.—1982
Sales—under $500,000
2,000 sq ft site, Distrib.—Local
Sole ownership

## Matawan

(Monmouth—N.E.)

### A. L. DON

1 Dock St. (07747)
**Phone—(732) 574-1441**
National—(800) 458-5722
Fax—(732) 574-9191
www.atlantic-group.com/aldon
Email—sales@aldonladders.com
CEO—Peter Gronbeck
COO—Arthur Jeronimo
V.-P.—Thomas Burns
SIC—2499; 3089; *Wooden & synthetic pilot & debarkation ladders*
Employs—8; Estab.—1949
Sales—$500,000-$1Mil
Distrib.—Intl.
Privately owned corporation

### †ATAK TRUCKING, INC.

1341 Route 34 *(07747)*
**Phone—(917) 912-2900**
Fax—(718) 227-9833
www.ataktrucking.com
Email—tommyatak@yahoo.com
Pres.—Sharon Torocco
V.-P.—Tommy Torocco
SIC—5032; *Wholesaler of building materials, including sand, gravel, crushed stone & dirt*
Employs—2; Estab.—1986
Sales—under $500,000
Distrib.—Local
Privately owned corporation

GEOGRAPHICAL

## Matawan—(cont.)

**B GREEN INNOVATIONS, INC.**
750 State Route 34, Ste. 8 (07747-4600)
**Phone—(732) 696-9333**
National—(877) 996-9333
Fax—(732) 441-9895
www.bgreeninnovations.com
Email—information@
bgreeninnovations.com
Pres., CEO—Jerome Mahoney
Off. Mgr.—Dolores Serafin
SIC—3069; *100% recycled rubber-based anti-vibration pads for front load washing machines & dryers, compressors & commercial condensers; Brand name—EcoPod™; VibeAway™*
Employs—4; Estab.—1997
Sales—$1Mil
1,500 sq ft site, Distrib.—National
Publicly owned corporation

**CERONICS, INC.**
5 Dock St., P.O. Box 75 (07747)
**Phone—(732) 566-5600**
Fax—(732) 566-9317
www.ceronicsinc.com
Email—ceronics@verizon.net
Pres.—Richard Patton
SIC—2851; NAICS—325510; *High temperature ceramic coatings*
Employs—7; Estab.—1959
Sales—$500,000-$1Mil
Distrib.—Intl.
Privately owned corporation

**D & C BAGEL BOYS, INC.**
1055-C Highway 34 (07747)
**Phone—(732) 566-4523**
Fax—(732) 566-1715
www.elishotbagels.com
Pres.—David Glasser
SIC—2051; NAICS—311812; *Bagels*
Employs—11; Estab.—1973
Sales—$500,000-$1Mil
Distrib.—Local
Privately owned corporation

**DIGIVAC CO.**
105-B Church St. *(07747)*
**Phone—(732) 765-0900**
Fax—(732) 765-1800
www.digivac.com
Email—sales@digivac.com
Pres.—Timothy Collins
Off. Mgr.—J. T. Matthews
SIC—3625; 3829; *Vacuum instrumentation & scientific controls; Brand name—DigiVac; Bullseye Precision Gauge; Filter Alert; TracVac Meter; StrataVac; ReAct browser; Multi-ReAct software*
Employs—14; Estab.—1983
Sales—$1Mil-$2Mil
4,000 sq ft site, Distrib.—Intl.
Privately owned corporation

**DUFERCO STEEL, INC. (H Q)**
100 Matawan Rd., Ste. 400 (07747)
**Phone—(732) 566-3130**
National—(888) 783-3588
Fax—(732) 583-9406
www.duferco.com
Email—duferco@dufercoinj.com
Pres.—Joe Deverter
Sr. V.-P.—Mike Vignale
V.-P., Fin.—John O'Brien
V.-P., Raw Matls.—Jack Palmer
SIC—3312; 3462; 3325; NAICS—332111; *Corporate headquarters; steel slabs, sheets, beams, plates, pipes, panels & coated products*
Employs—30
Sales—$5Mil-$10Mil (est)
Distrib.—National
Privately owned corporation

**ENDLESS GAMES, INC.**
35 Main St., Ste. B (07747)
**Phone—(732) 414-2213**
Fax—(732) 414-2219
www.endlessgames.com
Pres.—Michael Gasser
Sales Mgr.—Brian Turtle
Cust. Serv. Rep.—Jennifer Watters
SIC—3944; *Family board games*
Employs—5; Estab.—1996
Sales—under $500,000
Distrib.—National
Privately owned corporation

**GEMTOR, INC.**
1 Johnson Ave. (07747)
**Phone—(732) 583-6200**
National—(800) 405-9048
Fax—(732) 290-9391
www.gemtor.com
Email—sales.info@gemtor.com
Pres.—Craig Neustater
Off. Mgr.—Ruth Ullrich
SIC—3842; *Safety, fall protection & confined-space & fire rescue & retrieval equipment*
Employs—30; Estab.—1985
Sales—over $5Mil
16,000 sq ft site, Distrib.—Intl.
Privately owned corporation
ISO rating—9001

**KITCHEN KRAFTSMAN, THE**
343 State Route 34 (07747)
**Phone—(732) 583-3321**
Fax—(732) 583-3351
www.kitchenkraftsman.com
Email—mrkraftsman@aol.com
Owner—Jimmy Kuck
Designer—April Smith
SIC—2434; *Custom & semicustom wooden kitchen cabinets*
Employs—2; Estab.—2006
Sales—under $500,000 (est)
Distrib.—Local
Privately owned corporation

**†LYMPHEDEMA PRODUCTS, LLC**
750 State Route 34, Ste. 7 (07747)
**Phone—(732) 290-2888**
   (866) 445-9674
Fax—(866) 854-7800
www.lymphedemaproducts.com
Email—info@
lymphedemaproducts.com
Owner & COO—Max Salas
SIC—5047; *Distributor of medical supplies, including gauze bandages, compression wraps, soft casts & slings; Brand name—BiaCare; Bellisse; BSN-Jobst; CirAid Medical Products; Farrow Medical; Juzo; Lohmann & Rauscher; Medi; Peninsula Medical*
Employs—5
Distrib.—National
Limited Liability Company

**MATAWAN STAINED GLASS**
77-A Main St. (07747)
**Phone—(732) 583-1030**
Fax—(732) 583-1030
Owner & Pres.—Jim Wallace
SIC—3231; NAICS—327215; *Stained glass*
Employs—2; Estab.—1978
Sales—under $500,000
500 sq ft site, Distrib.—Regional
Sole ownership

**NEW JERSEY STAIR & RAIL, INC.**
746 Lloyd Rd. (07747)
**Phone—(732) 583-8400**
National—(877) 940-9663
Fax—(732) 583-6303
www.usmahogany.com
Pres.—Robert Barrett
Manager—Richard Barrett

SIC—3446; NAICS—332323; *Wooden handrails & stairs*
Employs—5; Estab.—1986
Sales—$500,000-$1Mil
Distrib.—Local
Privately owned corporation

**OEG BUILDING MATERIALS**
395 State Route 34 (07747)
**Phone—(732) 667-3636**
Fax—(732) 667-3637
www.oegusa.com
Email—info@oegusa.com
Owner—Oscar Rosner
SIC—3444; *Metal drywall studs & steel framing components*
Employs—45; Estab.—2007
Sales—$5Mil-$10Mil (est)
Distrib.—Local
Privately owned corporation

**PRINT SHOPPE**
1077-M Highway 34 (07747)
**Phone—(732) 583-4343**
Fax—(732) 583-3340
www.printshoppenj.com
Email—printshoppe@earthlink.net
Pres.—Paul Silvergold
Prod. Mgr.—Roger Silvergold
SIC—2759; NAICS—323100; *Commercial printing*
Employs—15; Estab.—1982
Sales—$1Mil-$2.5Mil
3,000 sq ft site, Distrib.—Local
Privately owned corporation

**RYAN INDUSTRIAL SERVICE, INC.**
80 Freneau Ave. (07747)
**Phone—(732) 566-9538**
Email—ryancustommachine@
yahoo.com
Pres.—Chris Ryan
SIC—3599; *General machining job shop*
Employs—3; Estab.—1969
Sales—under $500,000
4,000 sq ft site, Distrib.—National
Privately owned corporation
AKA: Ryan Custom Machine

**TELMARK PACKAGING CORP.**
30 Freneau Ave., Ste. 2-B (07747-3392)
**Phone—(732) 739-9100**
Fax—(732) 739-9130
www.telmarkpkg.com
Email—info@telmarkpkg.com
Pres.—Eric Ludwig
Prodn. Coord.—Craig Frost
SIC—2844; 2833; 2834; 3999; *Contract formulation, manufacturing & packaging of sample products for the health & beauty, pharmaceutical, nutritional & pet products industries*
Employs—8; Estab.—1994
Sales—$6Mil-$10Mil
Distrib.—Intl.
Privately owned corporation

**TIELMANN, INC., D. R.**
1208 State Route 34, Ste. 1 (07747)
**Phone—(732) 332-1860**
www.fibercontrol.com
Email—info@fibercontrol.com
Pres.—D. R. 'Debbie' Tielmann
SIC—3357; *Fiber-optic cable*
Employs—5; Estab.—1995
Sales—$1Mil-$2.5Mil (est)
Distrib.—Intl.
Privately owned corporation

**TILES UNLIMITED**
1016 State Route 34, Ste. 9 (07747)
**Phone—(732) 566-3886**
Fax—(732) 583-6456
www.tilesunlimited.net
Email—tilesunlim@aol.com
Manager—Vito Mancini
Manager—Theresa Mancini

SIC—3281; *Stone fabrication, including marble, granite, onyx & slate & marketing, showroom display & design services*
Employs—10
Sales—$500,000-$1Mil
Privately owned corporation

## Mauricetown
(Cumberland—S.W.)

**U.S. SILICA CO.**
Div. of U.S. Silica Company
9035 Noble St., P.O. Box 254 (08329)
**Phone—(856) 785-0720**
National—(800) 257-7034
Fax—(856) 785-1492
www.ussilica.com
Email—sales@ussilica.com
Plt. Mgr.—Justo Lucena
Pur. Mgr.—Dave Mason
Maint. Supv.—Bill Davis
Sales Rep.—Mike Barnette
SIC—1446; NAICS—212322; *Industrial silica sand; Brand name—FilPro® Filtration Sands & Gravels; SURE PLAY® Top Dressing Sand; Lighthouse Filter Sand; TriBlend; Optijump Volleyball Sand*
Employs—50; Estab.—1947
Distrib.—Intl.
Privately owned corporation
Parent co.—U.S. Silica Company, Frederick, MD
Phone—(301) 682-0600
See Parent Co. Section for full profile.

## Mays Landing
(Atlantic—S.E.)

**†AMERICAN AUTO SALVAGE & RECYCLING, INC.**
3113 Route 50 (08330)
**Phone—(609) 965-2900**
National—(888) 398-4274
Fax—(609) 965-6997
www.americanscrapmetal.net
Email—recycle3113@aol.com
Pres.—Joe Silipena
Sales & Mktg. Mgr.—Ed Silipena
SIC—5093; *Wholesaler of scrap metals*
Employs—45; Estab.—1945

**AMERICAN YOUTH ENTERPRISES, INC.**
120 Marlin Ln., P.O. Box 653 (08330)
**Phone—(609) 909-1900**
National—(800) 837-7280
Fax—(609) 909-8860
www.goaye.com
Email—info@goaye.com
Pres.—David Hagan
Off. Mgr.—Kelly Hagan
SIC—2396; 2759; NAICS—323100; *Promotional products screen printing*
Employs—8; Estab.—1994
Sales—under $500,000
Distrib.—National
Privately owned corporation

**BALIC WINERY, INC.**
6623 Harding Hwy. (08330)
**Phone—(609) 625-2166**
Fax—(609) 625-1904
www.balicwinery.com
Email—info@balicwinery.com
Pres.—Bojan Balic
Ex. V.-P.—Jay Jobani
V.-P.—Charles McMurtry
Hum. Res. Mgr.—Toni Fabrizi
SIC—2084; NAICS—312130; *Wines*
Employs—4; Estab.—1966
Sales—$500,000-$1Mil
Distrib.—Intl.
Privately owned sub-S corp.

## Mays Landing—(cont.)

**CASTELLANE MFG. CO.**
1405 Cantillion Blvd., P.O. Box 921 (08330)
**Phone—(609) 625-3427**
Fax—(609) 625-3428
Pres.—Nicholas Castellane
GM—Greg Schmidt
SIC—2353; *Uniform hats*
Employs—15; Estab.—1983
Distrib.—Intl.
Privately owned corporation

**GEM REFRIGERATOR CO., INC.**
176 Blvd. Route 50 (08330-4322)
**Phone—(609) 625-2500**
Fax—(609) 625-2299
www.gemref.com
Email—info@gemref.com
Plt. Mgr.—Tony Iacono
Off. Mgr.—Tracy Murray
Asst. Mgr.—Joe Walker
SIC—3632; NAICS—335222; *Refrigerators & freezers for pharmacies, blood banks & hospitals*
Employs—17; Estab.—1944
Sales—$2.5Mil-$5Mil
Distrib.—National
Privately owned corporation

**JERSEY PAW PRINTS**
P.O. Box 26 (08330)
**Phone—(609) 909-5100**
Owner, Publisher & Editor—Carol Ruck
SIC—2711; 2791; NAICS— 323122; *Newspaper publishing*
Employs—1; Estab.—2000
Sales—under $500,000
Distrib.—Regional
Sole ownership

[NEW ENTRY]
**LANDSMAN UNIFORMS, INC.**
4450 Black Horse Pike, Ste. 3958 (08330)
**Phone—(609) 909-1000**
National—(888) 822-4981
Fax—(609) 909-9968
www.landsmanuniforms.com/ index.cfm
Email—lusales@comcast.net
Owner—Janet Smith
SIC—2395; *Custom embroidery*
Employs—15; Estab.—1964
Sales—under $500,000
2,000 sq ft site, Distrib.—Local
Privately owned corporation

**SOUTH JERSEY LUMBERMANS, INC.**
6268 Holly St. (08330)
**Phone—(609) 965-1411**
Fax—(609) 965-5554
www.sjlumbermans.com
Pres., GM—Stephen Pinkos
Off. Mgr.—Joan Anthony
SIC—2431; 2499; NAICS— 321900; *Wooden boat & deck components & millwork*
Employs—3; Estab.—1973
Sales—$500,000-$1Mil
Distrib.—Local
Privately owned corporation

---

## Maywood

(Bergen—N.E.)

**CIRCUIT REPRODUCTION CO., INC.**
219 Hergesell Ave. (07607)
**Phone—(201) 712-9292**
Fax—(201) 712-9155
Email—crcplot@aol.com
Pres.—Paul Kabaria
V-P.—Praful Kabaria
V-P.—Amit Kabaria
GM—Ashok Kabaria
SIC—3672; NAICS—334412; *Printed circuit boards*
Employs—11; Estab.—1985
Sales—$1Mil-$2.5Mil
20,000 sq ft site, Distrib.—National
Privately owned corporation
Also see: Precision Products Co., same loc.
AKA: CRC

**COOPER PANELS, LLC, JOHN**
250 Maywood Ave., Ste. C (07607)
**Phone—(201) 487-4018**
Fax—(201) 487-2819
Email—jcoopercooper@verizon.net
Pres.—Darby Diedrich
SIC—3448; NAICS—332311; *Metal roof & wall panels; Brand name—Centria; Fabral; Firestone; Atas; Metlspan*
Employs—6; Estab.—1914
Distrib.—Regional
Privately owned corporation

**CORPORATE GRAPHICS & ENVELOPE MFG., INC.**
29 Brook Ave. (07607)
**Phone—(201) 880-4006**
Fax—(201) 880-4003
www.corporateenvelope.com
Email—info@ corporateenvelope.com
Pres.—Peter Levenson
Prod. Coord.—Anne Earley
Bookkeeper—Oksana Konyk
SIC—2759; NAICS—323100; *Commercial envelope printing*
Employs—5; Estab.—2007
Sales—under $500,000
85,000 sq ft site, Distrib.—National
Privately owned corporation
ISO rating—9001

**DESAUSSURE EQUIPMENT CO., INC.**
23 W. Howcroft Rd. (07607)
**Phone—(201) 845-4242**
National—(800) 238-6797
Fax—(201) 845-4586
www.maywood.com
Email—sales@maywood.com
CEO—William Desaussure
Pres., COO—Jack DeSaussure
CFO—Barbara Jenkins
V-P., Sales & Mktg.—Ken Perrson
SIC—2511; *Wooden, laminated & folded banquet tables*
Employs—40; Estab.—1918
Sales—$5Mil-$10Mil
50,000 sq ft site, Distrib.—Intl.
Privately owned corporation
AKA: Maywood Furniture Corp.

**DOLCE BROS. PRINTING**
29 Brook Ave. (07607)
**Phone—(201) 843-0400**
Fax—(201) 843-0404
www.dolceprint.com
Email—estimates@dolceprint.com
CEO—James Dolce
Pres.—Glenn Dolce
GM—Bill Comarco
Off. Mgr.—Aimee Cuevas
Estimator—Dan Shapiro
SIC—2759; NAICS—323100; *Commercial printing*
Employs—35; Estab.—1986
Sales—$10Mil
38,000 sq ft site, Distrib.—Local
Privately owned sub-S corp.

**ENCORE POLY CORP.**
240 W. Passaic St., Ste. 7 (07607)
**Phone—(201) 845-4510**
Fax—(201) 845-7045
www.encorepoly.com
Plt. & Sales Mgr.—Sandy Stevens
SIC—3673; *Polybags*
Employs—10; Estab.—2000
Sales—$1Mil-$2.5Mil
Distrib.—National
Privately owned corporation

**F I P GRAPHICS, INC.**
P.O. Box 952 (07607)
**Phone—(201) 362-3194**
Email—fipublish@aol.com
Pres., GM—Larry Eisen
Art Dir.—Kathy Dames
SIC—2759; NAICS—323100; *Commercial printing & graphic design services*
Employs—5; Estab.—1976
5,000 sq ft site, Distrib.—National
Sole ownership

**JACLYN, INC.**
197 W. Spring Valley Ave., Ste. 1 (07607-1729)
**Phone—(201) 909-6000**
Fax—(201) 226-7866
www.jaclyninc.com
Email—laura.calabria@ jaclyninc.com
Chrm.—Allan Ginsburg
Pres.—Robert Chestnov
CFO—Anthony Christon
V-P., Sales—Howard Ginsburg
Hum. Res. Mgr.—Laura Calabria
SIC—3171; NAICS—316992; *Corporate headquarters & handbags & apparel*
Employs—100
Sales—$65Mil-$70Mil
Distrib.—National
Publicly owned corporation

**JIMCAM PUBLISHING, INC.**
19 W. Pleasant Ave. (07607)
**Phone—(201) 843-5700**
Fax—(201) 843-5781
www.ourtownnewsonline.com
Email—rtownmaywoodrp@aol.com
Co-Publisher—Jim Hornes
Co-Publisher—Camille Hornes
SIC—2711; 2752; NAICS— 323100; *Newspaper publishing & invitation printing*
Employs—2; Estab.—1947
Sales—under $500,000
Distrib.—Local
Privately owned corporation
AKAs: Invitations By Camille & Our Town Printing

**JOSEPH CASTINGS, INC.**
25 Brook Ave. (07607)
**Phone—(201) 712-0717**
National—(877) 220-1346
Fax—(201) 712-0818
www.josephcastings.com
Off. Mgr.—Paul Low
SIC—3914; *Jewelry castings*
Employs—15; Estab.—1989
Sales—$1Mil-$2.5Mil
Distrib.—National
Privately owned corporation
Also see: Victor's Three-D, Inc., same loc.

**KOVCO PUBLISHING, INC.**
230 W. Passaic St. (07607)
**Phone—(201) 843-7277**
          (201) 843-9099
Fax—(201) 843-0715
www.kovatsschool.com
Email—njrekovats@aol.com
Pres.—Frank W. Kovats
SIC—2731; *Real estate textbook publishing*
Employs—2; Estab.—1973
Sales—under $500,000
Distrib.—Local
Privately owned corporation

**MALT PRODUCTS CORP.**
121 E. Hunter Ave. (07607)
Mail addr: P.O. Box 898, Saddle Brook (07663)
**Phone—(201) 845-9106**
National—(800) 250-7501
Fax—(201) 845-0643
www.maltproducts.com
Email—info@maltproducts.com
Plt. Mgr.—Chuck Stewart
Hum. Res. & IT Mgr.—Lu Mone

Tech. Mgr.—Harb Singh
SIC—2082; *Malt extracts*
Employs—16; Estab.—1988
Sales—$1Mil-$2.5Mil
Distrib.—National
Privately owned corporation
Parent co.—Malt Products Corp., Saddle Brook, NJ
Phone—(201) 845-4420
See Parent Co. Section for full profile.

**METRO TAG & LABEL, INC.**
25 E. Spring Valley Ave., Ste. 200 (07607)
**Phone—(201) 845-4747**
          (201) 913-6414
Fax—(201) 845-9447
www.metrotagandlabel.com
Email—rick@metrotagandlabel.com
Pres.—Phil Glassman
Off. & Sales Mgr.—Sandy Kats
SIC—2752; 2672; 2759; 5112; NAICS—322222; *Commercial offset & digital printing of custom & thermal transfer labels, tags, forms, small folding boxes, posters & plastic bags & distributor of thermal ribbons*
Employs—3; Estab.—1997
Distrib.—National
Sole ownership

**MYRON CORP.**
205 Maywood Ave. (07607)
**Phone—(201) 843-6464**
www.myron.com
Email—service@myron.com
CEO—Jim Adler
COO—David Chun
Ex. V-P., Prod. & Sales & Mktg.— Jim O'Dowd
V-P., Global Cash Mgmt. & Treas.—Robert Lack
V-P., Supply Chain—Steve Kjekstad
V-P., IS—Ed Hohnecker
V-P., E-Commerce—Mark Pepin
Sr. Mgr.—Barbara Chrencik
Hum. Res. Mgr.—Jenny Supple
Hum. Res. Rep.—Louisa Kutniewski
SIC—3578; 3951; 3873; 2782; NAICS—339941; *Imprinted personalized business gifts, including desk clocks, calculators, pocket calendars & pens; Brand name—Myron Smarter Business Gifts; Adler Business Gifts*
Employs—450; Estab.—1949
Sales—$50Mil-$100Mil
Distrib.—Intl.
Privately owned corporation

**PRECISION PRODUCTS CO.**
219 Hergesell Ave. (07607)
**Phone—(201) 712-5757**
Fax—(201) 712-5760
Email—ppcplot@aol.com
Pres.—Amit Kabaria
V-P. & Tech. Dir.—F. J. Lamanna
Hum. Res. Mgr.—Ashok Kabaria
SIC—3672; NAICS—334412; *Printed circuit boards*
Employs—15; Estab.—1955
30,000 sq ft site, Distrib.—National
Privately owned corporation
Also see: Circuit Reproduction Co., Inc.

**STEPAN CO.**
100 W. Hunter Ave. (07607)
**Phone—(201) 845-3030**
National—(800) 523-3614
Fax—(201) 712-7235
www.stepan.com
Email—techserv@stepan.com
V-P., Specialty Prods.—Robert Peacock

GEOGRAPHICAL

## Maywood—(cont.)

SIC—2869; 2099; NAICS—
311200; *Food products
chemicals, oils & emulsifiers;
Brand name—NEOBEE;
WECOBEE; DREWPOL;
DREWMULSE; Clarinol; Marinol;
Pinnothin*
Employs—95; Estab.—1959
Distrib.—Intl.
Publicly owned corporation
ISO rating—9002
Parent co.—Stepan Co.,
Northfield, IL
Phone—(847) 446-7500
See Parent Co. Section for full profile.

### VICTOR'S THREE-D, INC.

25 Brook Ave. (07607)
**Phone—(201) 845-4433**
National—(800) 322-9008
Fax—(201) 845-3058
www.victorsettings.com
Email—feedback@
victorsettings.com
Pres., GM—Robert Hess
IT Mgr.—Paul Low
Billing Mgr.—Rosie Milette
SIC—3915; *High-precision, die-
struck jewelry settings*
Employs—100; Estab.—1958
Distrib.—National
Privately owned corporation
Also see: Joseph Castings, Inc.,
same loc.
AKA: Victor Settings, Inc.

---

## Medford

(Burlington—S.E.)

### ACE STEEL RULE DIE CO.

251 Atsion Rd. (08055)
**Phone—(609) 654-4161**
www.acesteelruledies.com
Email—acedies@gmail.com
Ptnr.—Joe Schoel
Ptnr.—Paul Schoel
SIC—3544; NAICS—333500;
*Steel rule dies*
Employs—2; Estab.—1965
Sales—under $500,000
Distrib.—Local
Privately owned partnership

### ACS CANVAS & AWNINGS

83 Union St. (08055)
**Phone—(609) 953-9700**
Owner—Alan C. Schwarzwalder
Fabricator—Michael
Schwarzwalder
SIC—2394; NAICS—314912;
*Residential & commercial
awnings, canopies & patio
covers*
Employs—2; Estab.—1987
Sales—under $500,000
1,500 sq ft site, Distrib.—Local
Sole ownership

### ALENCO FENCE & SUPPLY CORP.

167 Route 70, Bldg. B (08055)
**Phone—(609) 654-6060**
Fax—(609) 654-6537
www.alencofence.com
Email—alencofence@yahoo.com
Owner—Chris Murphy
V-P.—Maureen Murphy
Sales Rep.—Doreen Blake
SIC—2499; 3446; 3496; 3089;
NAICS—332323; *Wooden,
aluminum, chain-link & vinyl
posts, fencing & railings; Brand
name—EP Henry Pavers and
wall systems*
Employs—10; Estab.—1978
Sales—$1Mil-$2.5Mil
Distrib.—Local
Privately owned corporation
AKA: Alenco Fence & Pavers

### CENTRAL RECORD CORP., THE

Div. of Digital First Media
32 S. Main St., Ste. A, P.O. Box
1027 (08055)
**Phone—(609) 654-9221**
Fax—(609) 654-8237
www.jerseylocalnews.com
Email—news@
medfordcentralrecord.com
Publisher—Edward Condra
V-P., Sales—Eric Mayberry
Mng. Editor—Susan Miller
Editor, Sports—Bill Kile
SIC—2711; *Weekly print & online
newspaper publishing; Brand
name—The Medford Central
Record*
Employs—30; Estab.—1908
Sales—$1Mil-$2.5Mil (est)
Distrib.—Local
Publicly owned corporation
Parent co.—Digital First Media,
Fairless Hills, PA
Phone—(215) 504-4200
See Parent Co. Section for full profile.

### †DUBELL LUMBER CO.

148 Route 70 E., P.O. Box 1449
(08055)
**Phone—(609) 654-4143**
Fax—(609) 953-1783
www.dubell.com
Email—info@dubell.com
Owner—Gene DiMediao
GM—Carmen Chappine
Sales Mgr.—John Cusick
Hum. Res. Mgr.—Pam Shepard
SIC—5031; 5072; *Company
headquarters & wholesaler of
building materials & supplies,
including lumber, millwork,
kitchen & bathroom cabinets,
decks, countertops, doors,
windows & hardware*
Employs—35
Distrib.—Local
Privately owned corporation

### †HADDON HOUSE FOOD PRODUCTS, INC. (H Q)

250 Old Marlton Pike (08055)
**Phone—(609) 654-7901**
National—(800) 257-6174
Fax—(609) 654-0412
www.haddonhouse.com
Email—merchandiser@
haddonhouse.com
CEO—David Anderson
CFO—Dave Landis
Ex. V-P.—David Anderson, Jr.
V-P., Investor Svcs.—Donna
Nelson
SIC—5149; 5143; *Corporate
headquarters; distributor of
gourmet, frozen, ethnic, dairy &
natural food products, including
teas, seasonings & sauces*
Employs—30; Estab.—1960
Company-wide: 1,300
Distrib.—National
Privately owned corporation

### INFORMATION TODAY, INC.

143 Old Marlton Pike (08055)
**Phone—(609) 654-6266**
National—(800) 300-9868
Fax—(609) 654-4309
www.infotoday.com
Email—custserv@infotoday.com
Pres., Publisher—Thomas H.
Hogan
CFO—John Brokenshire
V-P., Bus. Dev. & Mktg.—Thomas
H. Hogan, Jr.
V-P., IT—William C. Spence
V-P., Admn.—John Yersak
Dir., Hum. Res.—Sue Hogan
SIC—2721; 2731; *Corporate
headquarters & magazine &
book publishing*
Employs—30; Estab.—1980
Distrib.—National

### J & S PRECISION CO.

16 Medford Evesboro Rd. (08055)
**Phone—(609) 654-0900**
Fax—(609) 654-7098
www.jsprecision.thomasregister.co
m
Email—jsprec@comcast.net
Pres.—Stephen Janssen
Sales Mgr.—James Chapman
Engrg. Mgr.—Rita Deebee
SIC—3451; NAICS—332721;
*Screw machine products*
Employs—50; Estab.—1963
47,000 sq ft site, Distrib.—Local
Privately owned corporation
ISO rating—9002

### JANTEK INDUSTRIES, LLC

230 Route 70 (08055-9522)
**Phone—(609) 654-1030**
National—(800) 770-1030
Fax—(609) 654-1083
www.jantekllc.com
Email—sales@jantekllc.com
CEO—Keith Kailian
V-P., COO—Frank Giuseppini
Acctg. Mgr.—Barbara Makarowski
Info. Serv. Mgr.—Anthony
Makarowski
Pur. Agt.—Russell Modica
SIC—3231; 3444; 2431; 2499;
NAICS—327215; *Windows,
doors & related products for
single family & multi-family
residential applications; Brand
name—Appleby; American
Classic*
Employs—40; Estab.—1995
Sales—$5Mil-$10Mil
76,000 sq ft site, Distrib.—National
Limited Liability Company

### JOURNAL REGISTER CO., THE

Div. of Digital First Media
32 S. Main St., Ste. A (08055)
**Phone—(609) 654-5000**
Fax—(609) 654-8237
www.southjerseylocalnews.com
Email—news@
medfordcentralrecords.com
Editor—Jenn Lucas
Ex. Editor—Suzanne Miller
Assoc. Editor, The Record Breeze
& Community News—Drew
Berner
GM—Matt Grisafi
SIC—2711; 2741; *Weekly print &
online newspaper publishing;
Brand name—The Newsweekly*
Employs—12; Estab.—1967
Sales—under $500,000
Distrib.—Local
Publicly owned corporation
AKAs: Central Record Publications
& South Jersey News & Central
Record
Parent co.—Digital First Media,
Fairless Hills, PA
Phone—(215) 504-4200
See Parent Co. Section for full profile.

### LEO'S FAMOUS YUM YUM

7 Tomlinson Mill Rd., Ste. 5
(08055)
**Phone—(856) 797-8771**
www.leosicecream.net
Email—leosicecream@aol.com
CEO—Rick Cirelli
SIC—2024; *Ice cream & frozen
desserts*
Employs—7
Distrib.—Local
Privately owned corporation

### LIMO DIGEST

3 Reeves Station Rd. (08055)
**Phone—(609) 953-4900**
Fax—(609) 953-4905
www.limodigest.com
Email—info@limodigest.com
Assoc. Publisher—Dawn Sheldon
Dir., Creative Art—John Crawford

SIC—2721; *Magazine publishing*
Employs—10; Estab.—1990
Sales—$2.5Mil-$5Mil
Distrib.—Intl.
Privately owned corporation

### MEDFORD CONCRETE CO.

4 Tidswell Ave., P.O. Box 273
(08055)
**Phone—(609) 654-2200**
GM—Bob Brick
SIC—3272; *Precast concrete
products, parking bumpers,
septic tank components & slabs*
Employs—1; Estab.—1911
Sales—under $500,000
Distrib.—Local
Sole ownership

### †MEDFORD SILICONES, INC.

P.O. Box 2072 (08055)
**Phone—(609) 953-1092**
Email—medfordsilicones@
hotmail.com
Owner & Pres.—Eric Ley
SIC—5162; *Wholesaler of silicone
resins*
Employs—2; Estab.—1980
Sales—$500,000-$1Mil
Distrib.—National
Privately owned corporation

### †MODERN TECHNOLOGIES GROUP, INC.

3 Reeves Station Rd. (08055)
**Phone—(609) 714-8900**
Fax—(609) 714-8985
www.mtgparts.com
Pres.—Ric Cohen
V-P., Opers.—Ryan Weiss
SIC—5013; 5065; 5039; *Corporate
headquarters & distributor of
limousine parts & accessories,
including engine parts, GPS
units & window glass*
Employs—30; Estab.—1994
Distrib.—Intl.
Privately owned corporation

### POLYMER SOLUTIONS INTERNATIONAL, INC.

9 Roxbury Dr. (08055)
Mail addr: P.O. Box 310, Newtown
Square (19073)
**Phone—(609) 714-2899**
National—(877) 444-7225
Fax—(610) 356-6327
www.prostackpallets.com
Email—info@prostack.com
Pres.—D. Kelly
Ex. V-P.—G. Daly
Dir., Sales, North America—Steve
Kurth
Dir., Sales, Intl.—C. Scott
SIC—3089; *Plastic material
handling equipment, including
pallets; Brand name—ProStack;
ProGenic*
Employs—15; Estab.—1997
Distrib.—Regional
Privately owned corporation

### REGAL-PINNACLE MFG., INC.

220 Route 70, Ste. A (08055)
**Phone—(609) 714-2330**
Fax—(609) 714-2331
www.regalpinnacle.com
Email—regalpinnacle@
regalpinnacle.com
Pres.—Peter C. Palko
Off. Mgr.—Diane Cullman
SIC—2541; 2542; *Wooden &
metal display fixtures &
refrigerated & non-refrigerated
display cases*
Employs—75; Estab.—1984
Sales—$5Mil
Distrib.—Intl.
Privately owned corporation

## Medford—(cont.)

### ROSELLI'S FOOD SPECIALTIES, INC., L. E.
155 Church Rd. (08055)
**Phone—(609) 654-4816**
Fax—(609) 953-5673
www.rosellisfood.com
Email—laurar@rosellisfood.com
Pres.—Laura Roselli
V.-P. & Hum. Res. Mgr.—Ed De Lorenzo
SIC—2038; 2098; 2033; NAICS—311412; *Frozen pasta products & pasta sauces*
Employs—12; Estab.—1969
Sales—$1Mil-$2.5Mil
10,000 sq ft site, Distrib.—Regional
Privately owned sub-S corp.
DBA: Roselli Co., L. E.

### SIRCHIE FINGER PRINT LABS, INC., VEHICLE DIV.
Div. of Sirchie Finger Print Labs, Inc.
612 Gravelly Hollow Rd., P.O. Box 789 (08055)
**Phone—(609) 654-0777**
National—(800) 545-7375
Fax—(609) 654-7869
www.sirchienj.com
Email—sirchie-vehicle-division@erols.com
CEO—Anthony A. Saggiomo
Off. Mgr.—Regina Dudley
SIC—3711; *Crime scene investigation & forensic evidence collection vehicles*
Employs—35; Estab.—1927
Distrib.—Intl.
Privately owned corporation
AKA: Sirchie Acquisition Co.
Parent co.—Sirchie Finger Print Labs, Inc., Youngsville, NC
Phone—(919) 554-2244
See Parent Co. Section for full profile.

### STAUTS PRINTING & GRAPHICS
12 Maine Trl. (08055)
**Phone—(609) 654-5382**
www.stautsprinting.com
Email—office@stautsprinting.com
Bus. Mgr.—W. Stauts
SIC—2759; 2791; NAICS—323122; *Commercial printing & typesetting*
Employs—5; Estab.—1958
Distrib.—Local
Privately owned corporation

## Medford Lakes
(Burlington—S.E.)

### ENTITE PRESS, INC.
139 Stokes Rd. (08055)
**Phone—(609) 714-9213**
National—(800) 459-4221
Fax—(609) 714-9214
www.entitepress.com
Email—bill@entitepress.com
Pres.—William M. Frame
SIC—2759; NAICS—323100; *Commercial printing*
Employs—1; Estab.—1921
6,000 sq ft site, Distrib.—Regional
Privately owned corporation

## Mendham
(Morris—N.W.)

### ALLIED GROUP, INC.
5 Coldhill Rd., Bldg. 19, P.O. Box 209 (07945)
**Phone—(973) 543-5404**
National—(800) 728-8311
Fax—(973) 543-9737
www.alliedfilters.com
Email—info@alliedfilters.com
Pres.—Ed Thomas
V.-P.—Robert J. Probst
SIC—2679; 3569; NAICS—322200; *Coalescing filters, mist eliminators, fiberglass filter tubes, air/oil & liquid/liquid separators*
Employs—24
Distrib.—Intl.
Privately owned corporation

### †BIO-MEDICAL PRODUCTS CORP.
10 Halstead Rd. (07945)
**Phone—(973) 543-7434**
National—(800) 543-7427
Fax—(973) 543-7497
Email—biomedicalproductscorp@msn.com
Manager—John G. Geppert
SIC—5122; *Distributor of medical products for hospitals, clinics, labs, physician offices, nursing homes & health department clinics, including urinalysis transport tubes, pocket-size can hand degerming foam & diagnostic test kits; Brand name—Safety-Soft; Double-Check; Uri-Tube*
Employs—2; Estab.—1987
Sales—$500,000-$1Mil
Distrib.—National
Privately owned corporation

### †FORTRAD INSTRUMENTS, LLC
8 Franklin Rd. (07945)
**Phone—(973) 543-2371**
Fax—(973) 543-5446
www.fortrad.com
Email—sales@fortrad.com
Pres.—Karl H. Grohn
SIC—5047; *Distributor of hand-held ophthalmic surgical instruments, including forceps, scissors, needle holders, hooks, manipulators, cannulas, sterilizing cases & trephines*
Employs—2; Estab.—1979
Distrib.—Intl.
Privately owned corporation

### JEWELER'S GALLERY CORP.
9 W. Main St. (07945)
**Phone—(973) 543-6117**
www.jewelersgallerycorp.net
Pres., GM—Robert West
SIC—3911; NAICS—339911; *Precious metal jewelry*
Employs—3; Estab.—1974
Sales—under $500,000
Distrib.—Local
Privately owned corporation

### MERCER INTERNATIONAL, INC.
39 W. Main St., P.O. Box 540 (07945)
**Phone—(973) 543-9000**
National—(800) 463-7237
www.oil-water-separators.com
Email—dgoding@mercerows.com
Pres.—David Goding
Off. Mgr.—Rachelle Goding
SIC—3589; NAICS—333319; *Custom oil/water separators, including aboveground, below ground, concrete & existing equipment retrofits & rentals; Brand name—Mult-Pack; Compliance Master; Chimney Zone*
Employs—10; Estab.—1985
Sales—$1Mil-$2.5Mil
Distrib.—Intl.
Privately owned corporation

### NATIONAL ENVIRONMENTAL SERVICE CO. (H Q)
7 Hampshire Dr. (07945)
**Phone—(973) 543-4586**
National—(800) 227-3878
Fax—(973) 543-4588
www.drdust.com
Email—info@drdust.com
Pres.—Mark Kestner
CFO—Paul Kestner
SIC—3532; *Company headquarters; high-pressure water spray dust control systems for the mining industry; Brand name—Dr Dust; DustPro; DustBoy; DirtSquirt Wheel Wash*
Employs—2
Sales—$1.5Mil
Distrib.—Intl.
Privately owned corporation
AKA: NESCO

### PEGGNET COMPUTERS, LLC
4 E. Main St., Ste. 3 (07945)
**Phone—(973) 543-1222**
Fax—(815) 642-4884
www.peggnet.com
Email—arivers@peggnet.com
Pres.—Christopher McManus
Opers. Mgr.—Anthony Rivers
SIC—7373; *Computer network system integration*
Employs—10
Distrib.—Local
Limited Liability Company

NEW ENTRY
### ROTH STUDIO COLLECTION, LLC, THE JUDITH
3 Stone House Rd. (07945)
**Phone—(973) 543-4455**
www.jrcal.com
Pres.—Judith Roth
SIC—2741; *Calendar printing*
Employs—6
Sales—under $500,000 (est)
Limited Liability Company

### VAN DESSEL SPORTS, LLC
15 W. Main St., Ste. 2 (07945)
**Phone—(973) 543-2599**
National—(866) 835-5454
Fax—(973) 543-2744
www.vandesselsports.com
Email—info@vandesselsports.com
Pres.—Edwin Bull
Off. Mgr.—Tracy Ander
SIC—3751; NAICS—336991; *Bicycles*
Employs—2; Estab.—2000
Distrib.—National
Limited Liability Company

## Mercerville
(Mercer—N.E.)

### CLARICI DIGITAL
88 Youngs Rd. (08619)
**Phone—(609) 587-7204**
Fax—(609) 587-5932
www.clarici.com
Email—gene@clarici.com
Owner & Pres.—Gene Clarici, Jr.
V.-P., Digital Prodn.—Allan Ramcharan
V.-P., Prepress—Chris Rodkey
Off. Mgr.—Meg Leone
SIC—2396; 2759; NAICS—323100; *Screenprinted graphics, digital printing & laser imaging*
Employs—25; Estab.—1923
18,000 sq ft site, Distrib.—National
Privately owned sub-S corp.

### CONGOLEUM CORP.
3500 Quakerbridge Rd., P.O. Box 3127 (08619)
**Phone—(609) 584-3000**
Fax—(609) 584-3685
www.congoleum.com
Email—ringram@congoleum.com
Pres., CEO—Robert Moran
Sr. V.-P., Sales & Mktg.—Dennis Jarosz
Sr. V.-P., Opers.—Dan Garson
Sr. V.-P., Admn.—Tom Sciortino
V.-P., Mfg.—Greg Guynn
Dir., IT—Ron Duchesneau
Dir., Hum. Res.—Robert Ingram
SIC—3996; 3089; NAICS—326192; *Corporate headquarters & resilient flooring; Brand name—Duraceramic; Ultima; Evolution*
Employs—354; Estab.—1993
Sales—$200Mil
50,000 sq ft site, Distrib.—National
Privately owned corporation

### CONGOLEUM CORP., PLT. 2
Div. of Congoleum Corp.
3500 Quakerbridge Rd., P.O. Box 3127 (08619)
**Phone—(609) 584-3000**
National—(800) 234-8811
Fax—(609) 584-3830
www.congoleum.com
Email—wneville@congoleum.com
Plt. Mgr.—Wayne Neville, Sr.
SIC—3996; NAICS—326192; *Vinyl laminate floor coverings*
Employs—200; Estab.—1989
300,000 sq ft site, Distrib.—National
Privately owned corporation
Parent co.—Congoleum Corp., Mercerville, NJ
Phone—(609) 584-3000
See Parent Co. Section for full profile.

### CREATIVE MACHINING SYSTEMS, INC.
124 Youngs Rd. (08619)
**Phone—(609) 586-3932**
Fax—(609) 586-5633
www.creativemachining.com
Email—jsmith@creativemachining.com
Co-Pres., CEO—Victor Scharko
Co-Pres.—Antonina Scharko
Cont. & Off. Mgr.—Jacklene Scharko
GM—Victor Gorin
SIC—3599; *Precision machining job shop*
Employs—15; Estab.—1973
12,000 sq ft site, Distrib.—Regional
Privately owned corporation

### JOHNSON ATELIER
60 Sculptors Way (08619)
**Phone—(609) 890-7777**
Fax—(609) 890-1816
Pres.—J. Seward Johnson, Jr.
Ex. Dir.—Charles Haude
SIC—3325; NAICS—331513; *Metal sculpture castings*
Employs—25
Sales—$2.5Mil-$5Mil (est)
Distrib.—Intl.

### LASER ENERGETICS, INC.
3535 Quakerbridge Rd., Ste. 700 (08619)
**Phone—(609) 587-8250**
National—(800) 763-6275
Fax—(609) 587-9315
www.laserenergetics.com
Email—info@laserenergetics.com
Founder, Pres. & CEO—Robert D. Battis
Sr. Laser Engr.—Tom Frobose
SIC—3699; *Industrial lasers*
Employs—12; Estab.—1991
Sales—$1Mil-$2.5Mil
9,100 sq ft site, Distrib.—Intl.
Publicly owned corporation

### PRESS ROOM, INC., THE
100 Youngs Rd., Ste. 2 (08619)
Mail addr: P.O. Box 2989, Hamilton Square (08690)
**Phone—(609) 689-3817**
Fax—(609) 689-1166
www.thepressroominc.com
Email—matt@thepressroominc.com
Pres., Hum. Res. Mgr.—Ted Altomari
GM, IT & Press Mgr.—Matthew L. Altomari
Manager—Tara Lavin

GEOGRAPHICAL

## Mercerville—(cont.)

SIC—2759; 2752; 2791; NAICS—323122; Commercial offset, digital & instant printing & electronic prepress
Employs—8; Estab.—1986
Distrib.—National
Privately owned corporation

### SIR SPEEDY PRINTING

3100 Quakerbridge Rd. (08619)
Phone—(609) 586-8222
(609) 452-8860
Fax—(609) 586-8512
www.sirspeedy.com/mercerville
Email—info@sirspeedymercer.com
Pres.—David A. Kaplan
Treas.—Joanne M. Kaplan
GM—Ira Katz
Asst. Mgr.—Ron Applegate
SIC—2759; NAICS—323100; Printing, mailing, fulfillment & marketing services
Employs—9; Estab.—1983
Sales—$1Mil-$5Mil
5,000 sq ft site, Distrib.—Local
Privately owned corporation

## Merchantville

(Camden—S.W.)

### BUDGET PRINT CENTER

177 S. Centre St., Ste. 200-K (08109)
Phone—(856) 438-6204
Fax—(856) 438-6221
www.bpc-graphics.com
Email—mail@bpc-graphics.com
Owner—Thomas Jenkins
SIC—2759; NAICS—323100; Commercial printing, marketing, graphic design, direct mail & promotional products
Employs—3; Estab.—1981
Sales—under $500,000
1,500 sq ft site, Distrib.—Regional
Sole ownership

### CREATIVE PRINT GROUP, INC., THE

7905 Browning Rd., Ste. 112 (08109)
Phone—(856) 486-1700
www.creativeprintgroup.com
Email—info@cpgi.net
Pres.—Howard Friedman
SIC—2759; Commercial printing
Employs—16
Sales—$1Mil-$2.5Mil (est)
Distrib.—National
Privately owned corporation

### MONARCH MFG. WORKS, INC.

7249-B Browning Rd. (08109-4602)
Phone—(856) 241-1500
National—(800) 394-7377
Fax—(856) 324-0313
www.monarchnozzles.com
Email—info@monarchnozzles.com
Pres., CEO—Harry D. Beccari
Dir., Mfg.—Craig Cesare
Dir., Hum. Res.—Margaret Devillasanta
SIC—3599; 3523; 3524; 3432; NAICS—332919; Precision spray nozzles for the industrial oil, agricultural water & residential markets; Brand name—Monarch; Eclipse; Premimum; Doorwin
Employs—25; Estab.—1916
70,000 sq ft site, Distrib.—Intl.
Sole ownership

NEW ENTRY
### †THANKS FOR BEING GREEN, LLC

5070-B Central Hwy. (08109)
Phone—(856) 333-0991
www.magnum-llc.us
Pres.—John Martorano, Jr.

SIC—5045; 5065; Distributor of parts reclaimed from used computers & electronics
Employs—10
Limited Liability Company
AKA: MagnumComputer Recycling

### WEIDNER PUBLISHING GROUP

114 Woodbine Ave. (08109)
Phone—(856) 486-1755
www.arlhs.com
Email—weidner@waterw.com
Pres.—James Weidner
SIC—2731; Medical textbook publishing
Employs—7; Estab.—1967
Sales—$500,000-$1Mil (est)
Distrib.—Intl.
Privately owned corporation

NEW ENTRY
### ZENITH PRINTING

7440 Baxter Ave. (08109)
Phone—(856) 662-6275
Owner—Mark Wintermute
SIC—2759; Commercial printing, including business cards & specialty printing
Employs—1
Sales—under $500,000
800 sq ft site, Distrib.—Local
Sole ownership

## Metuchen

(Middlesex—N.E.)

### A-AAABACUS PRINTING & PROMOTIONAL SPECIALTIES OF METUCHEN

243 Amboy Ave. (08840)
Phone—(732) 767-9204
www.aaabacus.com
Email—samv9@juno.com
Owner—Sam H. Van Chama
SIC—2759; 2396; 2395; NAICS—323122; Commercial printing, binding & graphic design & screen printing & embroidery of garments
Employs—2; Estab.—1989
Sales—under $500,000
Distrib.—Local
Sole ownership

### ABILITEES UNLIMITED, INC.

23 Adams St. (08840)
Phone—(732) 494-1513
Fax—(732) 494-5358
www.abilitees.com
Email—abilitees@cs.com
Owner & Pres.—Helen Lenihan
SIC—2395; 2396; 2752; Textile embroidery & screen & offset printing of business cards & advertising specialty items
Employs—8; Estab.—1984
Sales—$500,000-$1Mil
Distrib.—Local
Privately owned corporation

### ACE ELECTRONICS, INC.

235 Liberty St. (08840)
Phone—(732) 603-9800
Fax—(732) 603-9767
www.aceelectronics.com
Email—info@aceelectronics.com
Pres.—Ed Divila
V-P., GM—Vinu Patel
Off. Mgr.—Chrissi Serio
SIC—3679; Corporate headquarters & cable assemblies, bulk wire & cable connectors
Employs—65; Estab.—1976
Sales—over $15Mil
15,000 sq ft site, Distrib.—National
Privately owned corporation
ISO rating—9001:2008

### BERKELEY VARITRONICS SYSTEMS, INC.

255 Liberty St. (08840)
Phone—(732) 548-3737
National—(888) 737-4287
Fax—(732) 548-3404
www.bvsystems.com
Email—info@bvsystems.com
Pres., CEO—Scott N. Schober
Sr. CTO—Gary Schober
V-P. & Media Dir.—Craig Schober
Sales Mgr., Regional—Carmine Caferra
Sales Mgr., Regional—Janet Jaracz
Off. Mgr.—Cynthia Corcino
SIC—3829; 3663; 3669; NAICS—334220; Wireless telecommunications test equipment, including handheld transmitters, receivers, analyzers, cellphone detectors & security tools; Brand name—Yellowjacket; YellowFin; PocketHound; Wolfhound-PRO; Manta Ray
Employs—30; Estab.—1973
Sales—$4Mil-$7Mil
5,000 sq ft site, Distrib.—Intl.
Privately owned sub-S corp.

### BLUE PARACHUTE

263 Amboy Ave., Ste. 1 (08840-2477)
Phone—(732) 767-1320
Fax—(732) 767-1340
www.bluechute.com
Email—angela@bluechute.com
Pres.—David Friedberg
V-P.—Angela Pineiro
SIC—2759; 3993; NAICS—323100; Commercial printing, large-format signage, promotional materials, graphic design & packaging, mailing & fulfillment services
Employs—4; Estab.—2011
Sales—$1Mil-$2.5Mil
Distrib.—National
Limited Liability Company

### C & K PLASTICS, INC.

159 Liberty St. (08840)
Phone—(732) 549-0011
Fax—(732) 549-1889
www.candkplastics.com
Email—info@candkplastics.com
Pres.—Robert Carrier
GM—Sandeep Amin
Sales Mgr.—Rodney Whittier
SIC—3089; Plastic thermoforming, including vacuum, twin sheet & pressure forming & secondary operations
Employs—58; Estab.—1963
85,000 sq ft site, Distrib.—Intl.
Privately owned corporation
ISO rating—9001

### CHEM-IS-TRY, INC.

160-1 Liberty St. (08840)
Phone—(732) 372-7311
National—(800) 243-6123
Fax—(732) 372-7312
www.chem-is-try.com
Email—info@chem-is-try.com
Pres.—Praful K. Porwal
SIC—2899; Contract manufacturing of specialty chemicals & custom organic synthesis
Employs—3; Estab.—2004
Sales—$1Mil-$2.5Mil
Distrib.—Intl.
Privately owned corporation

### CHINESE NEWSWEEK CORP.

32 Bridge St. (08840)
Phone—(732) 744-1000
Fax—(732) 744-1185
www.new-new.com
Owner—Meilun Lee
Editor-in-Chief—Ivy Lee

Editor—Jasmine Huang
SIC—2711; Weekly online newspaper publishing
Employs—5
Sales—under $500,000 (est)

### CRITERION PUBLISHING CO.

87 Forrest St., P.O. Box 4278 (08840)
Phone—(732) 548-8300
Fax—(732) 548-8338
www.criterionnews.com
Email—info.criterion@verizon.net
V-P., GM—Christopher M. Crane
V-P., Fin.—Priscilla Hudson
SIC—2711; 2791; NAICS—323122; Newspaper publishing; Brand name—The Criterion News Advertiser; The Criterion; Mailing Service; The Criterion Publishing Company; The Crit
Employs—7; Estab.—1952
Sales—$500,000-$1Mil
Distrib.—Local
Limited Liability Company

### DIAGNOSTIC SPECIALTIES

4 Leonard St. (08840)
Phone—(732) 549-4011
Fax—(732) 549-4711
Email—info@ds-nj.com
Pres., MIS Mgr.—Praful Raja
Fin. Mgr.—Nagin Patel
SIC—3841; 2835; NAICS—325400; Medical diagnostic test kits, including blood test kits, pregnancy test kits, analytical & regeant chemicals & in vitro & in vivo diagnostic substances
Employs—6; Estab.—1976
Sales—$1Mil-$2Mil
15,000 sq ft site, Distrib.—Intl.
Privately owned corporation

### DIVINE PRINTING, INC.

131 Liberty St. (08840)
Phone—(732) 632-8800
Fax—(732) 632-8844
www.c2cprint.com
Pres.—David Silbiger
Cust. Serv. Mgr.—Leah Delgadillo
Shpg. Coord.—Michael Tritto
SIC—2759; NAICS—323100; Commercial printing
Employs—15; Estab.—2000
Sales—$1Mil-$2.5Mil
Distrib.—Intl.
Privately owned corporation

NEW ENTRY
### EASY PRINTS, INC.

172 Main St. (08840)
Phone—(848) 229-2410
www.theswanbrothers.com
Owner—Darren Swan
SIC—2396; 2395; T-shirt screen printing & embroidery
Employs—5; Estab.—2009
Sales—$500,000-$1Mil (est)
Distrib.—Intl.
Privately owned corporation
AKA: Swan Brothers

### EDISON MACHINE

25 Liberty St. (08840)
Phone—(732) 494-5011
www.edisonmachine.com
Email—info@edisonmachine.com
Ptnr.—Joshua Leo
Sales Mgr.—Joe Andrews
SIC—3599; General machining job shop
Employs—10; Estab.—2001
Sales—$500,000-$1Mil
Distrib.—National
Privately owned partnership

### FRANCO MFG. CO., INC. (H Q)

555 Prospect St. (08840-2271)
Phone—(732) 494-0500
National—(800) 631-4663
Fax—(732) 494-8270
www.francomfg.com

## Metuchen—(cont.)

Email—web.admin@francomfg.com
Pres.—Louis D. Franco
CFO—Michael Kaplan
Ex. V-P.—Morris Franco
Ex. V-P.—Jack Franco
V-P., Sales & Mktg.—David Franco
V-P., Sourcing—Howard Bernstein
Dir., IT—Ren Cui
Hum. Res. Mgr.—Cheryl Nishiura
SIC—2392; *Corporate headquarters; textile towels*
Employs—100; Estab.—1952
72,000 sq ft site, Distrib.—Intl.

**GLOBE DIE CUTTING PRODUCTS**
76 Liberty St., P.O. Box 4339 (08840)
**Phone—(732) 494-7744**
Fax—(732) 548-9755
www.globediecuttingproducts.com
Email—sales@globediecutting.com
Cont., Sales Mgr.—Joel Nagler
Dir., Pers.—Joe Mahoney
Hum. Res. Exec. & Off. Mgr.—JoAnne Katz
SIC—2789; NAICS—322200; *Print finishing for the folding carton, point-of-purchase display & commercial printing industries, including die cutting, perforating, punching, gluing, CAD/CAM services & mounting*
Employs—110; Estab.—1978
Distrib.—Regional
Privately owned corporation

**GRAPHIC EQUIPMENT CORP.**
55 Wester Ave. (08840)
**Phone—(732) 494-5350**
Fax—(732) 494-4596
www.gecorp.com
Email—info@gecorp.com
Pres.—Karl Kuehnrich
V-P.—Michael Greenlaw
Secy-Treas.—Barbara Kuehnrich
GM—Ken Kuehnrich
Plt. Mgr.—Charles Carson
Bookkeeper—Nancy Superak
SIC—3555; NAICS—333293; *Printing press rewinders, machinery & machine shop*
Employs—55; Estab.—1968
Sales—$11Mil-$25Mil
100,000 sq ft site, Distrib.—Intl.
Privately owned corporation
AKA: Charter Machinery Corp.

**HOLLER METAL FABRICATORS, INC.**
215 Liberty St. (08840)
**Phone—(732) 635-9050**
Fax—(732) 635-9052
Email—hollermetalfab@aol.com
Pres., Plt. Mgr.—Dan Holler
Proj. Mgr.—Mike Thor
SIC—3499; *Metal fabrication*
Employs—7; Estab.—1967
Sales—$1Mil-$2.5Mil
Distrib.—Regional
Privately owned corporation

**HYPERTECH, INC.**
279 Central Ave., Ste. B (08840)
**Phone—(732) 635-1755**
www.hypertechusa.com
Email—hypertechann@yahoo.com
Pres.—Ann Hsu
V-P.—Derek Chen
IT Mgr.—Fred Chen
SIC—7373; 5045; *Computer network systems integration, including LANs & WANs & wholesaler of computers & accessories*
Employs—10; Estab.—1996
Sales—under $500,000
Distrib.—Local
Privately owned corporation

**J & E METAL FABRICATORS, INC.**
1 Coan Pl. *(08840)*
**Phone—(732) 548-9650**
Fax—(732) 548-9589

www.metalfab.com
Email—je@metalfab.com
Pres.—Mark Brazina
V-P., Opers.—Eric Webb
SIC—3444; *Precision sheet metal fabrication*
Employs—25; Estab.—1975
40,000 sq ft site, Distrib.—National
Privately owned corporation

**NEW ENTRY**
**JCW ROLLING & FABRICATION**
60 Liberty St. (08840)
**Phone—(732) 548-7636**
Fax—(732) 548-5251
www.jcwrolling.com
Email—ken@jcwrolling.com
Owner—Kenneth Greiff
SIC—3599; 3498; *CNC & machining job shop & metal pipe fabrication*
Employs—20; Estab.—1995
Sales—$500,000-$1Mil
12,000 sq ft site, Distrib.—Local
Limited Liability Company

**KIDS AT OUR HOUSE**
47 Stoneham Pl. (08840)
**Phone—(732) 548-1779**
www.dannyandkim.com
Email—info@dannyandkim.com
Ptnr.—Danny Adlerman
Ptnr.—Kim Adlerman
SIC—2731; *Picture book & novel publishing*
Employs—2
Sales—under $250,000
Distrib.—Intl.
Privately owned sub-S corp.

**LEARY HEATING & AIR CONDITIONING, INC., BILL**
6 Green St. (08840)
**Phone—(732) 494-9200**
Fax—(732) 632-9898
www.billleary.net
Email—info@billleary.net
Pres.—Bill Leary
Bookkeeper—Carolyn Laketos
SIC—3444; *HVAC sheet metal fabrication*
Employs—8; Estab.—1988
6,000 sq ft site, Distrib.—Regional

**NEW ENTRY**
**NURSEJOE.COM**
11 Plainfield Ave. (08840)
**Phone—(848) 250-9900**
www.nursejoe.com
Email—nursejoe.com@nursejoe.com
Owner—Jose Mancheno
SIC—2389; *Men's & women's medical scrubs for military applications*
Employs—2; Estab.—2003
Sales—under $500,000 (est)
Distrib.—National
Privately owned corporation

**NEW ENTRY**
**POWERSPEC, INC.**
1 Linsley Pl. (08840)
**Phone—(732) 494-9490**
Fax—(732) 494-9494
www.powerspecinc.com
Manager—Peter Elkoury
SIC—3679; *Contract manufacturing & assembly of electronic products, including wire harnesses & adapters*
Employs—7; Estab.—2005
Sales—$500,000-$1Mil (est)
Distrib.—Local
Privately owned corporation

**REID BOOK BINDING, D.**
543 New Durham Rd. (08840)
**Phone—(732) 494-9589**
Fax—(732) 494-9589
www.reidbookbinding.com
Email—reidbookbinding@aol.com

Owner—David Reid
SIC—2789; NAICS—323121; *Bookbinding*
Employs—2; Estab.—1979
Sales—under $500,000
500 sq ft site, Distrib.—Regional
Privately owned corporation

**RIBER, INC.**
15 Liberty St. (08840)
**Phone—(732) 603-0680**
Fax—(732) 603-8611
www.riber.com
Off. Mgr.—Karima Javios
Serv. Mgr.—Kenna Aikens
SIC—3674; 3679; NAICS—334413; *Semiconductor equipment*
Employs—5; Estab.—1996
Distrib.—Intl.
Privately owned sub-S corp.

**S & S VALVE SERVICE, INC.**
105 Liberty St. (08840)
**Phone—(732) 548-2040**
(610) 693-6360
Fax—(732) 549-9550
www.ssvalveserviceinc.com
Email—ssvalve@aol.com
Pres.—David Stanski
Off. Mgr.—Maria Oliveira
SIC—3491; 3492; 5085; NAICS—332911; *Rebuilt boiler safety valves, including ball, butterfly, boiler stop, control & blow down valves & distributor of safety, steam reducing & regulating, gate & globe valves & valve actuators & limit switches; Brand name—APOLLO/Conbraco; Hydroseal; Aquatrol; EIM Electric Actuator; Moniteur Limit Switches; Keckley*
Employs—10; Estab.—1960
Sales—$2.5Mil-$5Mil
10,000 sq ft site, Distrib.—National
Sole ownership

**S G MFG. CORP.**
15 Oliver St. (08840)
**Phone—(732) 494-6520**
Fax—(732) 494-5395
Foreman—George Roma
SIC—3568; NAICS—333613; *Nuclear submarine universal joints*
Employs—4; Estab.—1957
Sales—$1Mil-$2.5Mil
Distrib.—Local
Privately owned corporation

**SHAMAN SYSTEMS, INC.**
402 Main St., Ste. 100-330 (08840)
**Phone—(908) 429-0542**
www.shamansys.com
Email—info@shamansys.com
Pres.—Ketan Shah
SIC—7373; *Computer network systems integration, including LANs & WANs & custom software development*
Employs—6; Estab.—1997
Sales—under $500,000
Distrib.—National
Privately owned sub-S corp.

**SPEX CERTIPREP, INC.**
203 Norcross Ave. *(08840)*
**Phone—(732) 549-7144**
(800) 522-7139
Fax—(732) 603-9647
www.spexcertiprep.com
Email—crmsales@spexcsp.com
Chrm.—Neil Stein
Chrm.—Ralph Obenauf
Pres.—Yvonne Cangelosi
V-P., Inorganic Mfg.—Huifang Lang
V-P., IS—Lisa Petro
Dir., Sales—Tim Osborne-Jones
Dir., Organic Mfg.—Julian Burton
Acct. Mgr.—Debbie Huzar
Mktg. Mgr.—Amy Williams

Pers. Mgr.—Laura Van Malden
SIC—3826; 2833; NAICS—334516; *Organic & inorganic certified reference materials & reagents & sample grinding & preparation equipment for spectroscopy, chromatography & related analytical instrumentation; Brand name—Assurance; Claritas PPT; SPEXFusionFlux; Katanax; Geno/Grinder; Mixer/Mill; Shatter/Box; Freezer/Mill; X-Press; QuEChERS*
Employs—80; Estab.—1954
30,000 sq ft site, Distrib.—Intl.
Privately owned corporation
ISO rating—9001

**NEW ENTRY**
**SPEX FORENSICS**
203 Norcross Ave. (08840)
**Phone—(732) 549-7144**
National—(800) 657-7739
Fax—(913) 764-4021
www.spexforensics.com
GM—Lisa Petro
SIC—3821; 3826; NAICS—339111; *Forensic laboratory equipment*
Employs—3; Estab.—1980
Sales—$500,000-$1Mil
Distrib.—Intl.
Privately owned corporation
AKA: Spex Criminalistics

**SRS, INC.**
74 Liberty St., P.O. Box 4277 (08840)
**Phone—(732) 548-6630**
Fax—(732) 548-6885
www.srs-metals.com
Email—contact@srs-metals.com
Pres.—Rich Blatman
V-P., Cont.—Marliyn Russo
Sr. Proj. Mgr.—Kevin Metz
Lead Engr.—Michael Kessell
Lead Estimator—Lin Huang
SIC—3444; 3366; 3231; NAICS—332323; *Stainless steel, bronze & glass guardrails & handrails, including helical rails*
Employs—22; Estab.—1965
19,000 sq ft site, Distrib.—National
Privately owned sub-S corp.

**TRINITY MFG., LLC**
60 Leonard St. (08840)
**Phone—(732) 549-2866**
National—(866) 450-6654
Fax—(732) 549-7828
www.trinityinstore.com
Ptnr.—Randy Riley
SIC—2542; 3089; *Plastic thermoformed displays for retail stores*
Employs—10; Estab.—2001
Sales—$10Mil-$25Mil
Distrib.—Intl.
Limited Liability Company
AKA: Grenite Sustainability Fushions

**WEST MACHINE WORKS, INC.**
101 Liberty St. (08840)
**Phone—(732) 549-2183**
Fax—(732) 549-2930
Pres.—Jan Van Hoesen
Hum. Res. Mgr.—Cathy Van Hoesen
Welder—Erick Van Hoesen
SIC—3599; *Precision machining job shop*
Employs—8; Estab.—1954
Distrib.—Local
Privately owned corporation

**WINCUP**
Div. of New WinCup Holdings, Inc.
190 Liberty St. (08840)
**Phone—(732) 494-1999**
Fax—(732) 494-6210
www.wincup.com

**GEOGRAPHICAL**

## Metuchen—(cont.)

Email—sales@wincup.com
Plt. Mgr.—Mike Revier
Hum. Res. Mgr.—Gloria Rizzolo
SIC—3086; NAICS—326100;
*Foam cups & containers*
Employs—120; Estab.—1996
Sales—$10Mil-$25Mil
80,000 sq ft site, Distrib.—National
Privately owned corporation
Parent co.—New WinCup
Holdings, Inc., Stone Mountain,
GA
Phone—(770) 493-8568
See Parent Co. Section for full profile.

### WINDOW SHAPES, INC.

225 Liberty St. (08840)
**Phone—(848) 229-2431**
Fax—(848) 229-2432
www.windowshapes.com
Email—tchange@
windowshapes.com
Owner & V-P.—Tom Change
Off. Mgr.—Margie Rosado
Cust. Serv. Rep.—Diane Cruz
SIC—3089; 3231; NAICS—
327215; *Vinyl architectural
shaped windows, garden
windows, patio & French doors,
operating octagons & curved
jamb extensions & casings*
Employs—25; Estab.—1997
45,000 sq ft site, Distrib.—Intl.
Privately owned corporation

### WORLD JOURNAL, INC.

Div. of World Journal
41-A Bridge St. (08840)
**Phone—(732) 632-8890**
Fax—(732) 632-9595
www.worldjournal.com
Email—webmaster@
worldjournal.com
Off. Mgr.—Allen Chang
SIC—2711; *Newspaper
publishing*
Employs—5; Estab.—1998
Distrib.—Regional
Privately owned corporation
Parent co.—World Journal,
Whitestone, NY
Phone—(718) 746-8889
See Parent Co. Section for full profile.

---

## Mickleton

(Gloucester—S.W.)

### ATLAS FLASHER & SUPPLY CO., INC.

430 Swedesboro Ave., P.O. Box
488 (08056)
**Phone—(856) 423-3333**
National—(877) 933-8299
Fax—(856) 423-3313
www.atlasflasher.com
Email—info@atlasflasher.com
CEO—Karenanne Brown
Pres.—Ryan Brown
V-P.—Jason Morse
Opers. Mgr.—James Montgomery
Off. Mgr.—Cynthia Sabol
SIC—3993; *Corporate
headquarters & traffic control
signs*
Employs—40; Estab.—1950
Distrib.—Local
Privately owned corporation

### DIGITAL PRODUCTIONS, INC.

410 Southgate Ct. (08056)
**Phone—(856) 224-1111**
Pres.—Charles Budd
SIC—2759; *Digital printing &
point-of-purchase (POP) display
printing*
Employs—12
Sales—$1Mil-$2.5Mil (est)

### MARTIN'S SPECIALTY SAUSAGE CO.

150 Harmony Rd. (08056)
**Phone—(856) 423-4000**
National—(800) 882-1698
Fax—(856) 423-5130
www.martinssausage.com
Email—martin@
martinssausage.com
Pres.—Martin Guinta
Cont.—Joe Pasquarello
Off. Mgr.—Agnes DeMarco
SIC—2013; NAICS—311600;
*Sausage*
Employs—30; Estab.—1991
Sales—under $500,000
Distrib.—Regional
Privately owned corporation

### SAINT-GOBAIN PERFORMANCE PLASTICS

210 Harmony Rd. (08056)
**Phone—(856) 423-6630**
National—(800) 543-8823
Fax—(856) 423-8182
www.saint-gobain.com
Email—sgppl.marketing@saint-
gobain.com
Plt. Mgr.—Regan Gallo
Market Mgr.—Rich Mason
SIC—3082; NAICS—326121;
*Plastic tubing*
Employs—80; Estab.—1982
Distrib.—Intl.
Publicly owned corporation
Parent co.—Saint-Gobain
Performance Plastics, Aurora,
OH
Phone—(216) 245-0529
See Parent Co. Section for full profile.

NEW ENTRY
### †TRICO LIFT, INC.

418 Southgate Ct. (08056)
**Phone—(800) 468-7426**
www.tricolift.com
Email—dsander@tricolift.com
Br. Mgr.—Chuck Turner
Mktg. Mgr.—Dana Sander
SIC—5084; *Distributor of
industrial lifts, including boom,
scissor & vertical mast lifts;
Brand name—Genie; JLG; MEC*
Employs—100; Estab.—1952
30,000 sq ft site, Distrib.—National
Privately owned corporation
Parent co.—Trico Lift, Inc., Millville,
NJ
Phone—(856) 776-2350
See Parent Co. Section for full profile.

---

## Middlesex

(Middlesex—N.E.)

### ADM CORP.

100 Lincoln Blvd. *(08846)*
**Phone—(732) 469-0900**
Fax—(732) 469-0785
www.admcorporation.com
Email—info@admcorporation.com
Chrm., CEO—Mary Mota
V-P., CFO—Michael Turner
V-P., Sales & Mktg.—Ed Yarber
V-P., Opers.—Susan Mota
Plt. Mgr.—Gene Potts
SIC—2677; NAICS—322232;
*Pressure-sensitive envelopes*
Employs—150; Estab.—1964
Sales—$10Mil-$25Mil
100,000 sq ft site, Distrib.—
National
Privately owned sub-S corp.

### ADVANCED PROCESS TECHNOLOGY, INC.

200 Egel Ave. (08846)
**Phone—(732) 356-4438**
Fax—(732) 356-4005
www.advancedprocess.com
Pres.—Henry Phillips
Bookkeeper—Debbie Lipari

SIC—3559; *Processing
equipment*
Employs—15; Estab.—1969
Sales—$500,000-$1Mil
Distrib.—National
Privately owned corporation
Also see: Newbold, Inc., same loc.

### ADVANCED SPECIALTY GAS EQUIPMENT

Div. of Air Liquide America
Specialty Gases, LLC
241 Lackland Dr. (08846)
**Phone—(732) 271-9300**
National—(888) 999-2743
Fax—(732) 271-1630
www.asge-online.com
GM—Jackie Flatky
SIC—3559; NAICS—333132;
*High-purity specialty gas
equipment*
Employs—15; Estab.—1992
Sales—$500,000-$1Mil
Distrib.—Intl.
Privately owned corporation
Parent co.—Air Liquide America
Specialty Gases, LLC,
Plumsteadville, PA
Phone—(215) 766-8860
See Parent Co. Section for full profile.

### AGATE LACQUER TRI-NAT, LLC

824 South Ave. (08846)
**Phone—(732) 968-1080**
National—(800) 452-4735
Fax—(732) 968-1269
www.agatelacquer.com
Email—jamesnatalini@
agatelacquer.com
Owner—James Natalini
Off. Mgr.—Cindy Lenner
SIC—2851; NAICS—325510;
*Clear coat, air dry, baking &
water solvent lacquer coatings*
Employs—2; Estab.—2003
Sales—under $500,000
15,000 sq ft site, Distrib.—Intl.
Limited Liability Company

### AMERICAN PRECISION SHEET METAL CORP.

84 Baekeland Ave. (08846)
**Phone—(732) 356-4306**
(732) 356-5225
Fax—(732) 356-0075
Email—mikejr@apsheetmetal.com
Pres.—Michael Wood
V-P.—Paul Wood
SIC—3444; *Sheet metal
fabrication*
Employs—70; Estab.—1974
Sales—$5Mil-$10Mil (est)
Distrib.—Local
Privately owned corporation

### AVON FABRICS, INC.

484 Lincoln Blvd. (08846)
**Phone—(732) 764-9700**
Fax—(732) 764-8899
www.avonfabrics.com
Email—avonfabrics123@gmail.com
Owner—D. J. Jain
SIC—2221; 2241; 2392; *Woven,
embroidered & novelty silk
fabrics & ready made silk
drapery panels for interior fabrics
retailers, major jobbers &
manufacturers of furniture,
bedding, lampshades & pillows
& custom decorative silk pillows
for interior designers*
Employs—3
Sales—under $500,000 (est)
Distrib.—National
Privately owned corporation

### BAMCO, INC.

30 Baekeland Ave. (08846)
**Phone—(732) 302-0889**
Fax—(732) 302-9456
www.bamcoinc.org
Email—info@bamcoinc.org
Pres.—Michael Biviano
Sales Mgr.—Bob Balaam

Hum. Res. Mgr.—Elaina Oiler
Accts. Payable Mgr.—Rusty Eppa
SIC—3448; NAICS—332311;
*Architectural metal wall panels*
Employs—100; Estab.—1985
Sales—$10Mil-$25Mil (est)
Distrib.—National
Privately owned corporation

### †BEARING DEPOT & SUPPLY, INC.

819 Lincoln Blvd., Ste. 1 (08846-
2270)
**Phone—(732) 563-2225**
National—(800) 860-1922
Fax—(732) 563-2224
www.bearingdepot.com
Email—george@bearingdepot.com
Pres.—Donna Hardgrove
V-P.—George Hardgrove
SIC—5085; 5169; *Distributor of
metric & inch ceramic bearings,
mechanical seals, sprockets,
roller chains & gears &
lubricants; Brand name—NTN;
NACHI; Martin; US Seal; FYH;
Bando; Goodyear; IKO; Timken
Seals; HKK; Daido; Bower; BCA;
SNR; OTC; Consolidated; THK;
AMI; Koyo; Smith; FBJ*
Employs—5; Estab.—1996
Sales—$1Mil-$2.5Mil
4,500 sq ft site, Distrib.—National
Privately owned sub-S corp.

### BOMAR CRYSTAL CO.

201 Blackford Ave., P.O. Box 10
(08846)
**Phone—(732) 356-7787**
National—(800) 526-3935
Fax—(732) 356-7362
www.bomarcrystal.com
Email—sales@bomarcrystal.com
Off. & Sales Mgr.—Minnie Lirio
Engr.—David Miskov
SIC—3679; *Electronic
components, including quartz
crystal, clock oscillator, VCXO,
TCXO & OCXO*
Employs—10; Estab.—1963
12,700 sq ft site, Distrib.—National
Privately owned sub-S corp.

### CAPITAL PRINTING CORP.

420 South Ave. (08846)
**Phone—(732) 560-1515**
Fax—(732) 560-9633
www.capitalprintingcorp.com
Email—info@
capitalprintingcorp.com
Pres.—Nolan Russo
V-P.—Ron Schulwitz
Admn., Hum. Res. & IT Mgr.—Toni
Petty
SIC—2759; 2761; NAICS—
323116; *Commercial & business
form printing*
Employs—120; Estab.—1983
Distrib.—National
Privately owned corporation

### CENTRAL COMPONENTS MFG., LLC (H Q)

440 Lincoln Blvd. (08846)
**Phone—(732) 469-5720**
National—(888) 288-5152
Fax—(732) 469-1919
www.centralcm.com
Email—info@centralcm.com
Pres.—Marion Weldon
Sales & Mktg. Mgr.—Tom
Winfough
Opers. Mgr.—Greg Lane
IT Mgr.—Jeff Demos
Acctg. Mgr.—Tom Stiff
Hum. Res. Mgr.—Mary Fisher

## Middlesex—(cont.)

SIC—3678; NAICS—334417;
*Company headquarters;
electronic connectors, custom
PCB connectors, fiber optic
connectors, wire harnesses,
power supplies & electronic
interconnection devices (mfg.
done in Taiwan)*
Employs—20; Estab.—1995
Sales—$5Mil-$10Mil
50,000 sq ft site, Distrib.—National
Limited Liability Company
ISO rating—9001

### CENTRAL SHEET METAL FABRICATORS, INC.

897 South Ave., Ste. A (08846)
**Phone—(732) 968-6100**
Fax—(732) 968-6108
www.centralsheetmetal.com
Email—sales@
centralsheetmetal.com
Pres.—Gerard Ezyske
Secy-Treas.—Dawn Pascale
Pur. Mgr.—Bryan Pascale
Bookkeeper—Elisa Rubiano
SIC—3444; *Custom sheet metal &
HVAC ductwork fabrication &
installation*
Employs—45; Estab.—1986
30,000 sq ft site, Distrib.—
Regional
Privately owned corporation

### CONTAINER MFG., INC.

50 Baekeland Ave., P.O. Box 428
(08846)
**Phone—(732) 563-0100**
Fax—(732) 563-0704
www.containermfg.com
Email—djennings@
containermfg.com
Pres.—David Jennings
V.-P., Sales—Robert Jennings
SIC—3085; NAICS—326160;
*Plastic bottles*
Employs—42
Sales—$6Mil-$10Mil
48,000 sq ft site, Distrib.—Intl.
Privately owned corporation

### COREPHARMA, LLC

215 Wood Ave. (08846)
**Phone—(732) 868-1090**
National—(800) 850-2719
Fax—(732) 868-1091
www.corepharma.com
Email—cs@corepharma.com
CEO—Christopher Worrell
SIC—2834; NAICS—325412;
*Contract generic prescription
pharmaceuticals*
Employs—200; Estab.—1998
Sales—$50Mil-$100Mil
55,000 sq ft site, Distrib.—National
Limited Liability Company

### CROTON PRODUCTS

514 Wellington St. (08846)
**Phone—(732) 560-9223**
Fax—(732) 469-7956
www.dripnet.com
Owner—David Jablonski
SIC—3081; *Two-ply reinforced
polyethylene tarps for leaking
ceilings*
Employs—1; Estab.—1998
Sales—under $500,000
Distrib.—National
Sole ownership

### CRT INTERNATIONAL, INC.

260 Wagner St. (08846)
**Phone—(973) 887-7737**
Fax—(973) 887-7331
www.crt-inc.com
Email—ctarantino@crt-inc.com
V.-P., Hum. Res. & IT—Carmine
Tarantino
GM—Mario Schiavone

SIC—2752; 2759; 2761; 2789;
NAICS—323116; *Commercial &
packaging printing of set boxes,
displays, e-flute packaging,
blister cards, press kits,
brochures, catalogs, posters,
flyers, pocket folders & snap-out
& computer forms, including 4-6
color printing & binding*
Employs—8; Estab.—1981
Distrib.—National
Privately owned corporation

### DIAGNOSTIC SERVICES, INC.

220 Mountain Ave. (08846)
**Phone—(732) 271-9199**
    (732) 718-9051
www.diagnostic-services-inc.com
Email—info@diagnostic-services-
inc.com
Pres.—Mike Molner
V.-P.—Pam Molner
Prod. Mgr.—Tony Pacelli
SIC—3861; *New & rebuilt
overhead & rail-mounted nuclear
medicine imaging & equine
scintigraphy systems for
veterinarians, universities &
private clinics, including gamma
camera detectors, imaging
computers & gantry systems*
Employs—4; Estab.—1984
Sales—$500,000-$1Mil
Distrib.—Intl.
Privately owned corporation

### DIAMOND BRITE METAL PROCESSING

333 Cedar Ave., Ste. 1 (08846-
2400)
**Phone—(732) 564-1164**
Fax—(732) 564-1169
www.diamondbritemetal.com
Email—ssexc@aol.com
Pres.—George Karpus
SIC—3471; NAICS—332813;
*Metal polishing of pipe, strip,
plate, angle & fittings & slitting,
buffing & sawing*
Employs—10; Estab.—1981
Sales—$1.5Mil
13,000 sq ft site, Distrib.—Intl.
Sole ownership

### DYNAFLOW ENGINEERING

106 Egel Ave. (08846)
**Phone—(732) 356-9790**
National—(800) 801-3962
Fax—(732) 356-9794
www.dynafloweng.com
Email—4sales@dynafloweng.com
Pres.—Ross Block
SIC—3561; 3398; 3089; NAICS—
333911; *Stainless, alloy & plastic
gear pumps; Brand name—
Dynaflow*
Employs—5; Estab.—1994
Sales—$1Mil-$5Mil
Distrib.—National
Privately owned corporation

### EMBROIDERY CONCEPT & DESIGN, LLC

201 Pond Ave. (08846)
**Phone—(732) 926-9400**
National—(877) 664-6900
Fax—(732) 926-9401
www.ecdinc.com
Email—ecdinc@aol.com
Pres., CEO—Wahid Sattar
SIC—2395; *Embroidery*
Employs—15; Estab.—1990
Distrib.—Local
Limited Liability Company

### EXPORT CONSULTANTS CORP.

250 Lackland Dr., Ste. 6, P.O. Box
308 (08846)
**Phone—(732) 469-0700**
Email—eccsly@att.net
Pres.—Mary Ann Althausen
Off. Mgr.—Mary Brinson
Off. Admn.—Barbara Roberts

SIC—3728; *Aircraft parts*
Employs—7; Estab.—1975
Sales—under $500,000
Distrib.—Intl.
Privately owned corporation

### F & A MACHINE CO., INC.

133 Lincoln Blvd. (08846)
**Phone—(732) 356-5777**
Fax—(732) 356-4102
www.fandamachineco.com
Email—info@fandamachineco.com
Pres.—Frank Adami
Plt. Mgr.—Dan Adami
SIC—3599; *General machining
job shop*
Employs—3; Estab.—1974
Sales—$500,000-$1Mil
Distrib.—Local
Privately owned corporation

### F S T PRINTING, INC.

1324 Bound Brook Rd. (08846)
**Phone—(732) 560-3749**
Fax—(732) 560-0938
www.fstprinting.com
Email—sales@fstprinting.com
Pres.—Sal Buonocore
V.-P.—Tim Hurley
V.-P.—Frank Buonocore
SIC—2752; 2791; NAICS—
323122; *Offset & instant printing
& electronic prepress of labels,
envelopes & wedding invitations*
Employs—5; Estab.—1983
Sales—under $500,000
2,500 sq ft site, Distrib.—National
Privately owned partnership

### †FASTENAL CO.

550 Lincoln Blvd. (08846)
**Phone—(732) 748-0140**
Fax—(732) 748-0141
www.fastenal.com
Email—njmid@stores.fastenal.com
Store Mgr.—Derek Dandy
Sales Rep., Outside—Donald
Kumah
SIC—5072; 5084; *Wholesaler of
fasteners, safety equipment,
tools & abrasives*
Employs—5; Estab.—1998
Sales—under $500,000
Distrib.—Intl.
Publicly owned corporation
Parent co.—Fastenal Co., Winona,
MN
    Phone—(507) 454-5374
See Parent Co. Section for full profile.

### FRAM TRAK INDUSTRIES, INC.

205 Hallock Ave. (08846)
**Phone—(732) 424-8400**
Fax—(732) 424-8811
www.framtrak.com
Email—info@framtrak.com
Pres., CEO—Al Santelli, Sr.
V.-P.—Al Santelli, Jr.
Cust. Serv. Mgr.—Deborah Myers
SIC—3089; 3082; 3544; NAICS—
326121; *Custom & stock plastic
extrusions & plastic injection
moldings; Brand name—Wire
Trak; E-Stat; Fram Trak; Farm Trak*
Employs—50; Estab.—1977
70,000 sq ft site, Distrib.—Intl.
Privately owned corporation

### GENERAL MACHINE CO. OF NEW JERSEY

301 Smalley Ave. (08846)
**Phone—(732) 752-7900**
National—(800) 654-3626
Fax—(732) 752-5857
www.okgemco.com
Email—sales@okgemco.com
Chrm.—John Muench
Pres.—Casey Muench
Prod. Line Mgr.—David Levine

SIC—3559; *Industrial laboratory,
portable production, porta-
hopper blenders & gemcomatic
drum loading/unloading systems
for the pharmaceutical,
nutraceutical, food, chemical &
powdered metal industries*
Employs—30; Estab.—1916
60,000 sq ft site, Distrib.—Intl.
Privately owned corporation

### GRANITE SURFACES, LLC

368 Lincoln Blvd. (08846)
**Phone—(732) 627-9200**
Fax—(732) 627-9204
www.granite-surfaces.com
Email—brian@granite-surfaces.com
Owner—Rocca Lavecchia
Sales Mgr.—Brian Salas
SIC—3281; *Stone kitchen
countertops, bathroom vanity
tops & jacuzzi & fireplace
surrounds*
Employs—5; Estab.—2007
Sales—under $500,000
6,000 sq ft site, Distrib.—Local
Limited Liability Company

### GRAPHIC PRINTING CO., INC.

283 Lincoln Blvd. (08846)
**Phone—(732) 627-9000**
Fax—(732) 627-9001
Email—billgraphic@netscape.net
Pres.—William Gazi
Off. Mgr.—Isabelle Hackel
SIC—2759; NAICS—323100;
*Commercial printing*
Employs—2; Estab.—1947
Sales—under $500,000
Distrib.—Local
Privately owned corporation

### GRAPHIX ONE, LLC

725 Lincoln Blvd. (08846)
**Phone—(732) 560-4700**
Fax—(732) 560-4702
www.graphixonenj.com
Email—info@graphixonenj.com
Ptnr.—Jeff Yingling
SIC—2759; 2752; 3993; NAICS—
323100; *Commercial, screen &
offset printing of brochures,
booklets & signs*
Employs—3; Estab.—2003
Sales—under $500,000
Distrib.—Intl.
Limited Liability Company

### HOOD FINISHING PRODUCTS, INC.

9 Factory Ln. (08846)
**Phone—(732) 805-0088**
National—(800) 229-0934
Fax—(732) 805-4042
www.hoodfinishing.com
Email—info@hoodfinishing.com
Pres.—Erick Kasner
Cust. Serv. Mgr.—Dolores Bristol
SIC—2851; 2842; NAICS—
325510; *Wood finishing &
refinishing products, spray
equipment & furniture restoration
systems, including lacquers,
stains, varnishes, polyurethanes,
finish removers & sandpaper*
Employs—6; Estab.—1980
12,000 sq ft site, Distrib.—National
Privately owned sub-S corp.
AKA: Hydrocote

### IMAGE SCREEN PRINTING, INC.

532 Lincoln Blvd. (08846)
**Phone—(732) 560-1817**
Fax—(732) 560-0795
www.imagescreenprintingembroid
ery.com
Email—imagescreen@yahoo.com
Pres., CFO—Gary Mangee
SIC—2396; 2395; *Textile screen
printing & embroidery*
Employs—8; Estab.—1987
5,700 sq ft site, Distrib.—Regional
Privately owned sub-S corp.

GEOGRAPHICAL

## Middlesex—(cont.)

**JAFCO INDUSTRIES, LLC**

136 Lincoln Blvd. (08846)
**Phone—(732) 356-1502**
Fax—(732) 356-3542
Email—jafco@jafcollc.com
Pres.—Abe Werczberger
V-P.—Naftali Weiser
Prodn. Mgr.—Jim Reilly
Hum. Res. & Off. Mgr.—Dorothy Mikruk
SIC—2542; 3083; 2431; NAICS—326130; *Architectural millwork & plastic laminate casework*
Employs—20; Estab.—1969
Sales—under $500,000
12,000 sq ft site, Distrib.—Regional
Limited Liability Company

**JEMA-AMERICAN, INC.**

824 South Ave. (08846)
**Phone—(732) 968-5333**
Fax—(732) 968-1269
www.jema-american.com
Email—jema.american@verizon.net
Pres.—James Natalini
GM—April Morlock
Off. Mgr.—Rosa Rodriguez
SIC—2851; NAICS—325510; *Specialty coatings for the vacuum metallizing, cosmetic packaging & automotive aftermarket industries*
Employs—8; Estab.—1956
Sales—$2Mil-$5Mil
15,000 sq ft site, Distrib.—Intl.
Privately owned sub-S corp.

**KAVANGO, INC.**

544 Lincoln Blvd. (08846)
**Phone—(732) 424-2430**
www.kavangohome.com
Email—r.rigg@kavangohome.com
Manager—Peter Rigg
SIC—2842; *Fragrance gels, sachets & beads & air fresheners*
Employs—20; Estab.—2005
Sales—$1Mil-$2.5Mil (est)
Distrib.—National
Privately owned corporation

**KOBA CORP.**

60 Baekeland Ave. (08846)
**Phone—(732) 469-0110**
National—(800) 289-5622
Fax—(732) 469-0835
www.kobacorp.com
Email—info@kobacorp.com
Pres.—Franz Bach
Bookkeeper—Ursula Mooney
SIC—3089; *Plastic flower pots*
Employs—17; Estab.—1966
Sales—$1Mil-$5Mil
Distrib.—Intl.
Privately owned corporation

**L & D'S SAPORE RAVIOLI & CHEESE, INC.**

429-B Lincoln Blvd. (08846)
**Phone—(732) 563-9190**
Fax—(732) 563-9195
www.saporeravioli.com
Email—anthony@saporeravioli.com
Mng. Ptnr.—Anthony Florano
Founder—Domenick F. Discenza
Sales Mgr., Natl.—Jerry Dresher
Prodn. Mgr.—Michael Discenza
SIC—2098; 2035; NAICS—311412; *Handmade fresh & frozen Italian ravioli, pastas, gourmet sauces & cheeses*
Employs—15; Estab.—1998
Sales—$2.5Mil-$5Mil (est)
Distrib.—Local
Privately owned corporation

**MATRIX TEST EQUIPMENT, INC.**

200 Wood Ave. (08846)
**Phone—(732) 469-9510**
Fax—(732) 469-0418
www.matrixtest.com
Email—sales@matrixtest.com
Sales Mgr.—Charles Kouzoujian
SIC—3825; NAICS—334500; *Cable television test equipment & distortion test equipment*
Employs—10; Estab.—1973
16,000 sq ft site, Distrib.—Intl.
Privately owned corporation

**MICROTUBE FABRICATORS, INC.**

Div. of Handy & Harman Ltd.
250 Lackland Dr. (08846)
**Phone—(732) 469-7420**
Fax—(732) 469-4314
www.handytube.com
Email—info@hhmtf.com
Div. Mgr.—Rick Kreppel
Hum. Res. Mgr.—Jane Gulliver
SIC—3498; NAICS—332996; *Metal medical tubing*
Employs—50; Estab.—1988
Sales—$500,000-$1Mil
Distrib.—National
Publicly owned corporation
Parent co.—Handy & Harman Ltd., White Plains, NY
Phone—(914) 461-1300
See Parent Co. Section for full profile.

**MONTER LITE CO., INC.**

560 Lincoln Blvd., Ste. 2 (08846)
**Phone—(732) 748-1288**
National—(888) 887-4233
Fax—(732) 748-0178
www.monterlite.com
Email—monterlite@aol.com
V-P.—Jerry Lin
SIC—3999; 5199; *Manufacturer & wholesaler of handmade & imported lampshades*
Employs—10; Estab.—1995
Sales—$1Mil-$2.5Mil
Distrib.—National
Privately owned corporation

**MR. SIGN, INC.**

319 Bound Brook Rd. (08846)
**Phone—(732) 560-0606**
Fax—(732) 560-0616
www.mrsign.com
Email—marketing@mrsign.com
Pres.—Ron Gengoult
V-P.—Michael Gengoult
SIC—3993; *Interior & exterior signs*
Employs—3; Estab.—1989
Sales—under $500,000
800 sq ft site, Distrib.—Local
Privately owned corporation

**NATIONAL METAL FINISHINGS CORP., INC.**

897 South Ave., P.O. Box 486 (08846)
**Phone—(732) 752-7770**
Fax—(732) 752-6579
www.natmetfin.com
Email—natmetfin@att.net
Pres.—Lou Fahsbender
V-P., Opers.—Thomas Finkle
Engr.—Thomas Cornelson
Bookkeeper—Linda Mickus
SIC—3471; 3499; NAICS—332813; *Chill rolls, including design, overlay, fabrication, grinding & chromium plating & polishing for the sheet & film industries*
Employs—12; Estab.—1971
Distrib.—National
Privately owned corporation

**†NEW BRUNSWICK SAW SERVICE, INC.**

400 Lincoln Blvd. (08846)
**Phone—(908) 755-2366**
Fax—(908) 755-2377
www.nbssfoodequipment.com
Email—sales@nbssfoodequipment.com
Pres.—Michael Schaefer
Ptnr.—Robert Bonapace
SIC—5046; *Distributor of meat processing equipment, including slicers, saws, grinders & knife sets*
Employs—20; Estab.—1945
Distrib.—National
Privately owned corporation

NEW ENTRY

**NEW CENTURY WOOD PRODUCTS**

131 Lincoln Blvd. (08846)
**Phone—(732) 271-2557**
Email—newcenturymillwk@aol.com
Owner—David Lomonte
SIC—2431; 2434; *Millwork & casework*
Employs—10; Estab.—2000
Sales—$1Mil-$2.5Mil (est)
5,000 sq ft site, Distrib.—Local
Privately owned corporation

**NEWBOLD, INC.**

200 Egel Ave. (08846)
**Phone—(732) 469-5654**
Fax—(732) 356-4005
www.newboldtargets.com
Pres.—Henry A. Phillips
Bookkeeper—Debbie Lipari
SIC—3949; *Polymer handgun & pistol targets*
Employs—5; Estab.—2000
Sales—under $500,000
Distrib.—Intl.
Privately owned corporation
Also see: Advanced Process Technology, Inc., same loc.

**PETERSON BROS. MFG.**

10 Baekeland Ave. (08846)
**Phone—(732) 271-8240**
Fax—(732) 271-8230
www.petebrosmfg.com
Email—glpb515@aol.com
Pres., Mktg. Mgr.—Gary B. Lewis
Secy-Treas.—Marlys Lewis
GM—Gary Lewis
Pur. Agt.—Patricia Hudak
SIC—3469; 3599; *Metal stampings & machine products*
Employs—25; Estab.—1950
Sales—$1Mil-$5Mil
15,000 sq ft site, Distrib.—National
Privately owned corporation

**PHILLIPS SAFETY PRODUCTS, INC.**

123 Lincoln Blvd. (08846)
**Phone—(732) 356-1493**
National—(800) 221-0036
Fax—(732) 356-7127
www.phillipssafetyproducts.com
Email—info@phillipssafetyproducts.com
Pres.—Robert Phillips
V-P.—Ryan Phillips
Hum. Res. Mgr.—Jeanne Nickl
SIC—3827; 3231; NAICS—333314; *Lead glass windows, glass etching, x-ray protection & optical lens grinding*
Employs—10; Estab.—2001
Sales—under $500,000
Distrib.—Intl.
Privately owned corporation

**PHOENIX FRICTION PRODUCTS, INC.**

276-278 Lincoln Blvd. (08846)
**Phone—(732) 667-7937**
National—(877) 570-5630
Fax—(732) 667-7942
www.phoenixfriction.com
Email—sales@phoenixfriction.com
Pres.—Lou Rivieccio
V-P.—Bill Sanders
Cont.—Sally Rivieccio
SIC—3714; *Automotive, truck & all-terrain vehicle brakes & clutches; Brand name—Phoenix Friction; Aisin; Centric; Dayton Parts; Eaton Fuller; Exedy (Daikin) Clutch; Lipe Clutch; Precision (Bearing Technologies); RunCool Rotors; Sachs (ZF) Clutch; SKF (Chicago Rawhide); Valeo*
Employs—10; Estab.—1986
Sales—$5Mil-$10Mil
Distrib.—Intl.
Privately owned corporation

**†PIPELINE SUPPLY CO.**

203 Egel Ave. *(08846)*
**Phone—(732) 560-1509**
     (800) 354-4244
Fax—(732) 560-0064
www.pipelinesupplynj.com
Email—office@pipelinesupplynj.com
COO—James Westerman
V-P., Fin.—James Koval
Inside Sales Specialist—Peter Walters
SIC—5084; *Distributor of pipeline equipment, tools & supplies; Brand name—Advance Brushes; Crosby; Cooper Tools; Liftex Slings; Norton Abrasives; Sawyer Mfg.; KC Welding; Reed Manufacturing; Pipeline Inspection*
Employs—10; Estab.—1970
Distrib.—Intl.
Privately owned corporation

**PRECISE PRINTING**

748 Lincoln Blvd. (08846)
**Phone—(732) 271-8626**
     (732) 939-5901
Fax—(732) 271-5901
Email—preciseprinting@aol.com
Pres.—Frank Tredici
SIC—2752; NAICS—323100; *Offset printing*
Employs—3; Estab.—1986
Sales—under $500,000
2,000 sq ft site, Distrib.—Local
Sole ownership

**PRECISE TOOL & MOLD CO., INC.**

240 E. Lackland Dr. (08846)
**Phone—(732) 469-3062**
Fax—(732) 469-0159
www.precise-tool-mold.com
Email—info@precise-tool-mold.com
Pres.—George Peppe, Sr.
Off. Mgr.—Karyn Orashen
SIC—3544; NAICS—333500; *Plastic injection molds*
Employs—20; Estab.—1970
Distrib.—National
Privately owned corporation

**PREMIER SPECIALTIES, INC.**

236 Blackford Ave. *(08846)*
**Phone—(732) 469-6615**
Fax—(732) 469-6772
www.premierfragrances.com
Email—info@premierfragrances.com
Pres., Hum. Res. Mgr.—Roger Rich
Qual. Control Mgr.—Odila Zocca
Cust. Serv. Supv.—Karla Arevalo
SIC—2844; 2087; NAICS—325600; *Fragrances & flavors*
Employs—21; Estab.—1998
14,000 sq ft site, Distrib.—Intl.
Privately owned corporation

**R & R STAIRS, INC.**

131 Wood Ave. (08846)
**Phone—(732) 752-9400**
Fax—(732) 752-6500
Email—rrstairs@optonline.net
Pres.—Rich Kaminski
Off. Mgr.—Vicky Riley
Sys. Admn.—Bruce St. Laurent

## Middlesex—(cont.)

SIC—2431; 3446; NAICS—
332323; *Interior wooden &
ornamental metal stairs & railings*
Employs—20; Estab.—1996
Distrib.—Local
Privately owned corporation

### R T B FABRICATORS, INC.
220 Lincoln Blvd. (08846)
**Phone—(732) 469-4127**
Fax—(732) 469-4135
Owner & Pres.—Tom Gillen
SIC—3444; *Aluminum, stainless
steel & sheet metal fabrication*
Employs—3; Estab.—1987
Sales—under $500,000 (est)
Distrib.—Regional
Privately owned corporation

### SCIENTIFIC MACHINE
700 Cedar Ave., P.O. Box 67
(08846)
**Phone—(732) 356-1553**
National—(800) 641-7940
Fax—(732) 356-2569
www.scimac.com
Email—info@scimac.com
Pres.—Elizabeth Landau
Lawrence
V-P.—Virginia Landau
Treas.—Roger Landau
Accts. Payable & Rec. Mgr.—Lisa
Czislowski
SIC—3821; NAICS—339111;
*PTFE laboratory ware &
accessories, including stoppers,
sleeves, OEM parts, quartz &
glass threaded components &
stainless steel reaction
equipment*
Employs—25; Estab.—1956
Sales—$1Mil-$5Mil
10,000 sq ft site, Distrib.—Intl.
Privately owned sub-S corp.

### SERVICE MACHINE CO.
311 Lincoln Blvd. (08846)
**Phone—(732) 356-9021**
Fax—(732) 563-9753
Pres.—Peter Delia
SIC—3599; *General machining
job shop*
Employs—4; Estab.—1990
4,000 sq ft site, Distrib.—Intl.
Privately owned sub-S corp.

### SIGMA DESIGN COMPANY
200 Pond Ave. *(08846)*
**Phone—(732) 629-7555**
Fax—(732) 629-7556
www.sigmadesign.net
Email—info@sigmadesign.net
Pres.—Gerard J. Lynch
SIC—3841; 3999; 3599; 3826;
*Contract manufacturing &
assembly of new products,
complex electromechanical
machinery & specialty filtration
equipment for the aerospace,
automotive, biotech, consumer
products, electronics, medical
device & pharmaceutical
industries*
Employs—10; Estab.—1999
Sales—$1Mil-$2.5Mil
20,000 sq ft site, Distrib.—Intl.
Sole ownership

### SIGMA ENGINEERING &
### CONSULTING ASSOCS.
220 Lincoln Blvd. (08846)
**Phone—(732) 356-3046**
Fax—(732) 356-7360
www.sigmaeca.com
Email—bob@sigmaeca.com
Pres.—Robert P. Bruno
SIC—3599; *General machining
job shop*
Employs—10; Estab.—1976
10,000 sq ft site, Distrib.—Intl.
Privately owned corporation

### SOMA LABS, INC.
252 Wagner St. (08846)
**Phone—(732) 271-3444**
Fax—(732) 271-3446
www.somalabs.com
Email—sales@somalabs.com
Pres.—John Botzolakis
SIC—2833; NAICS—325411;
*Private label vitamins &
nutritional supplements*
Employs—56; Estab.—1999
Distrib.—Regional
Privately owned corporation

### SPADIX TECHNOLOGIES, INC.
110 Egel Ave. (08846)
**Phone—(732) 356-6906**
Fax—(732) 356-6907
www.spadixtechnologies.com
Email—sales@
spadixtechnologies.com
Pres.—Albert Simone
Off. Mgr.—Ann Marie Wolliver
SIC—3559; *Automation machinery*
Employs—10; Estab.—1993
6,000 sq ft site, Distrib.—National
Privately owned sub-S corp.

### SPRAY-TEK, INC.
344 Cedar Ave. (08846)
**Phone—(732) 469-0050**
Fax—(732) 302-0866
www.spray-tek.com
Email—dennis.monaghan@spray-
tek.net
Mng. Ptnr., Pres. & CEO—David A.
Brand
Acct. Mgr.—Dennis Monaghan
Prodn. Mgr.—Paulo Cardoso
IT Mgr.—Ashish Gujral
Hum. Res. & Off. Mgr.—Michelle
Brower
SIC—2087; 2833; NAICS—
325411; *Corporate headquarters
& food flavorings, vitamins,
cosmetics & chemicals*
Employs—40; Estab.—1980
Sales—$6Mil-$10Mil
22,000 sq ft site, Distrib.—Intl.
Privately owned corporation

### STANDARD TECH APPLIED
### RESOURCE
824 South Ave. (08846)
**Phone—(732) 968-6776**
Fax—(732) 968-4144
Pres.—Carmine Spatola
Prodn. Mgr.—James Wilkins
Manager—Kathy Mayo
SIC—3479; *Wire coating*
Employs—6; Estab.—1985
Sales—$500,000-$1Mil
Distrib.—Intl.
Privately owned corporation

### STONE KING, INC.
900 Lincoln Blvd., Ste. 1 (08846)
**Phone—(732) 868-8687**
Fax—(732) 868-8612
www.stonekingusa.com
Email—services@
stonekingusa.com
Pres.—Tommy Sie
SIC—3281; NAICS—327991;
*Granite & marble kitchen
countertops & bathroom vanities*
Employs—10; Estab.—2005
Sales—$500,000-$1Mil
Distrib.—Local
Privately owned corporation

### SUMMIT HILL FLAVORS
253 Lackland Dr. W. (08846-2510)
**Phone—(732) 805-0335**
Fax—(732) 805-1994
www.summithillflavors.com
Email—info@summithillflavors.com
Pres.—Robert Delin
V-P., GM, Sales & Mktg.—Dwight
C. Grenawalt
Cust. Serv. Coord.—Lee Poole
SIC—2087; 2099; NAICS—
311900; *Savory natural & organic
food flavors; Brand name—
Summit Hill Flavors*
Employs—30; Estab.—1990
30,000 sq ft site, Distrib.—National
Privately owned sub-S corp.
AKA: ACTIV International

### TECHNICAL FABRICATORS, INC.
203 Wood Ave., Ste. A (08846)
**Phone—(732) 469-7373**
Fax—(732) 469-9199
www.technicalfabricators.com
Email—info@
technicalfabricators.com
Ptnr.—Keith Ball
Ptnr.—Vera Ball
GM—Brian Ball
SIC—3569; *Industrial filters*
Employs—10; Estab.—1959
16,000 sq ft site, Distrib.—Intl.
Privately owned corporation

### TESS-COM, INC.
400 South Ave., Ste. 11 (08846)
**Phone—(732) 560-8100**
Fax—(732) 560-9544
www.tess-com.com
Email—salesnj@tess-com.com
V-P., GM—David Colonna
Engr.—Joe Skodak
SIC—3826; 3829; *Gas analyzers
& continuous emission
monitoring equipment, including
analyzer shelters & sample
systems*
Employs—10; Estab.—1979
12,000 sq ft site, Distrib.—National
Privately owned corporation
Parent co.—Tess-Com, Inc.,
Clairton, PA
Phone—(412) 233-5782
See Parent Co. Section for full profile.

### TOOLING ETC., LLC
250 Hallock Ave., Ste. C (08846)
**Phone—(732) 752-8080**
Fax—(732) 752-8209
www.toolingetc.com
Email—info@
wagnercarbidesaw.com
Pres.—Markus Jesacher
V-P.—Ernest Jesacher
SIC—3425; 3599; NAICS—
332213; *Segmental, solid,
circular & hot friction blades,
carbide tipped circular cold saw
blades & thread cutting
equipment*
Employs—12; Estab.—1980
Sales—$1Mil-$2.5Mil
6,800 sq ft site, Distrib.—National
Limited Liability Company
DBA: Wagner Carbide Saw Div.

### UNIQUE ALUMINUM EXTRUSION,
### LLC
333 Cedar Ave., Ste. 6 (08846)
**Phone—(732) 271-0006**
(732) 271-1160
National—(800) 218-6004
Fax—(732) 271-8327
www.unalext.com
Email—info@unalext.com
CFO—Selim Uzel
COO—Theodore Malinowski
SIC—3354; NAICS—331316;
*Aluminum extrusions*
Employs—20; Estab.—2007
Distrib.—Regional
Limited Liability Company

### UNLIMITED STEEL FABRICATORS,
### INC.
840 Lincoln Blvd. (08846)
**Phone—(732) 356-7534**
Fax—(732) 356-7489
Pres., GM—Richard Stokes
SIC—3312; *Steel fabrication*
Employs—2; Estab.—1979
Sales—under $500,000
Distrib.—Regional
Privately owned corporation

### VAN-CON, INC.
123 William St. (08846)
**Phone—(732) 356-8484**
Fax—(732) 805-9661
www.vanconbus.com
Email—info@vanconbus.com
Pres.—James Anderson
Salesman—Gordon Horst
SIC—3713; NAICS—336211;
*School buses*
Employs—18; Estab.—1973
Sales—$5Mil-$10Mil
Distrib.—National
Privately owned corporation

### VEOLIA ES TECHNICAL
### SOLUTIONS, LLC
Div. of Veolia Environmental
Services North America Corp.
125 Factory Ln. *(08846)*
**Phone—(732) 469-5100**
Fax—(732) 469-1957
www.veoliaes.com
Email—ray.clark@veolia.com
Cont.—Ray Clark
GM—Dave Flood
Facility Mgr.—Mike Pikulin
IT Mgr.—Derek S. Artz
SIC—2869; *Solvent recycling*
Employs—90; Estab.—1962
Sales—$20Mil
Distrib.—Regional
Publicly owned corporation
Parent co.—Veolia Environmental
Services North America Corp.,
Chicago, IL
Phone—(312) 552-2800
See Parent Co. Section for full profile.

### WELDON MACHINE & BORING, INC.
134 Wood Ave. (08846)
**Phone—(732) 356-1887**
Fax—(732) 356-3285
Pres.—Weldon Brantley
SIC—3599; *General machining
job shop*
Employs—3; Estab.—1974
4,500 sq ft site, Distrib.—Local
Privately owned corporation

### WEST SIDE PRECISION MACHINE
### PRODUCTS, INC.
280 Lincoln Blvd. (08846)
**Phone—(732) 560-9006**
Fax—(732) 560-9090
www.westsideprecision.com
Email—westside1@verizon.net
Pres.—David Gizzi
SIC—3599; 3451; 3452; 3494;
NAICS—332721; *Precision
machining, including Swiss
CNC, magnet & plastic
machining, CNC milling &
turning, screw machine products
& long & short run production of
hydraulic & cable fittings,
aerospace components, medical
products & pneumatic devices*
Employs—5; Estab.—1987
Sales—$500,000-$1Mil
Distrib.—Intl.
Privately owned corporation
ISO rating—9001:2000

## Middletown
(Monmouth—N.E.)

### ALLIANCE WOODWORK CORP.
19 Ogden Ct., P.O. Box 684
(07748)
**Phone—(732) 671-6884**
Fax—(732) 671-6565
Pres.—Jean Brandel
SIC—2431; NAICS—321900;
*Architectural woodwork &
moulding*
Employs—6; Estab.—1998
Sales—$500,000-$1Mil (est)
Distrib.—Regional

GEOGRAPHICAL

## Middletown—(cont.)

**†COOPER ELECTRIC SUPPLY CO.**
666 State Route 35 (07748)
**Phone—(732) 671-5000**
Fax—(732) 671-1218
www.cooper-electric.com
Email—cooperonline@cooper-electric.com
Br. Mgr.—Chris Schuman
SIC—5063; *Distributor of electrical equipment & supplies*
Employs—5
Distrib.—National
Privately owned corporation
Parent co.—Cooper Electric Supply Co., Monroe, NJ
Phone—(732) 747-2233
See Parent Co. Section for full profile.

**ENGINEERED PRECISION CASTING CO.**
952 Palmer Ave. (07748)
**Phone—(732) 671-2424**
Fax—(732) 671-8615
www.epcast.com
Email—info@epcast.com
Owner—Walter Dubovick
SIC—3324; NAICS—331512; *Investment castings*
Employs—70; Estab.—1946
Sales—$5Mil-$10Mil (est)
Distrib.—National
Privately owned corporation
AKA: EPCO

**GUTTENPLAN'S FROZEN DOUGH SPECIALISTS, INC.**
100 Highway 36 (07748)
**Phone—(732) 495-9480**
National—(888) 422-4357
Fax—(732) 495-2415
www.guttenplan.com
Pres.—Abraham Littenberg
IT Mgr.—Chad Kineski
Hum. Res. Mgr.—Shar Seshadri
SIC—2051; NAICS—311812; *Frozen dough*
Employs—90; Estab.—1908
Sales—over $1Bil
Distrib.—National
Privately owned corporation

**RIVERSIDE PRINTS LLC**
11 Lawrence Cir. (07748-2704)
**Phone—(732) 671-8222**
National—(800) 783-7474
Fax—(732) 671-8207
www.riversideprints.com
Email—info@riversideprints.com
Pres., CEO—Howard Kirschner
SIC—2759; 2752; 2791; 3993; *Large-format digital & offset printing of giclees, displays, signs & posters, electronic prepress, mounting, lamination, graphic design, document & film imaging & large-format & document scanning; Brand name—Adobe; Quark; Microsoft; Corel; Epson; HP; Contex; PantherPro; Okidata; Seal; Macintosh; Windows*
Employs—2; Estab.—1987
Sales—under $500,000
1,800 sq ft site, Distrib.—National
Limited Liability Company
AKA: Riverside Image

**STETZ MACHINE SHOP, JOHN**
17 Highway 36 (07748)
**Phone—(732) 495-0847**
Fax—(732) 495-5929
Email—jstetz2@verizon.net
Owner—John Stetz
Shop Foreman—Keith Grove
Sr. Admn.—Gary Smith
Expeditor—Donna Olivera
SIC—3599; 3728; *Aerospace machining job shop*
Employs—7; Estab.—1973
2,000 sq ft site, Distrib.—National
Sole ownership

## Midland Park
(Bergen—N.E.)

**†ABS BRAKE SYSTEMS LTD.**
445 Godwin Ave. (07432)
**Phone—(201) 689-6893**
National—(866) 784-3302
Fax—(201) 689-6894
www.absbrakesystems.com
Email—info@absbrakesystems.com
Pres., CEO—Ronald P. Torriani
GM—Paul Lim
SIC—5013; *Company headquarters & wholesaler of automotive brake systems & parts*
Employs—5; Estab.—1983
Sales—$500,000-$1Mil
Distrib.—Intl.
Privately owned corporation

**ALPHA GRAPHICS**
95 Greenwood Ave. (07432)
**Phone—(201) 447-4800**
Fax—(201) 447-4300
www.masterrepro.com
Email—info@masterrepro.com
Pres.—Mark Shishmanian
SIC—2752; 2789; NAICS—323121; *Offset printing, graphic design & binding*
Employs—7; Estab.—1981
Sales—$500,000-$1Mil
Distrib.—National
Privately owned corporation
AKA: Master Repro, Inc.

**ALTECH MACHINE & TOOL, INC.**
230 Bank St., Ste. 1 (07432)
**Phone—(201) 652-4409**
Fax—(201) 652-9440
www.altechmachine.com
Email—is@altechmachine.com
Pres., Hum. Res. Mgr.—Ismael Sierra
Treas.—Pam Sierra
SIC—3544; 3599; NAICS—333500; *Tool & die & CNC machining job shop, including production stamping, prototypes & special machinery*
Employs—5; Estab.—1995
Sales—$500,000-$1Mil
3,000 sq ft site, Distrib.—Regional
Privately owned sub-S corp.
ISO rating—9001:2008

**†AMERICAN FILTER & TANK CO., INC.**
231 Greenwood Ave., Ste. 2 (07432)
**Phone—(201) 857-5056**
Fax—(201) 857-5057
www.american-filter.com
Email—sales@american-filter.com
Owner & Pres.—John Spanedda
SIC—5088; 5085; *Distributor of spray nozzles & air & liquid filters; Brand name—BEX; Delavan; Spraying Systems; US Filter; Pentair Filtration; Rosedale; Parker Filtration*
Employs—3; Estab.—1989
Sales—$1Mil-$2.5Mil
1,000 sq ft site, Distrib.—National
Privately owned corporation

**†ARTIQUE, INC.**
P.O. Box 44 (07432)
**Phone—(201) 444-8989**
www.artiqueinc.com
Email—info@artiqueinc.com
GM—Jack Reeman
SIC—5199; *Wholesaler of handmade seasonal gift items, including custom glass ornaments, 19th century engraving reproductions & Grandma Moses prints*
Employs—12; Estab.—1964
Distrib.—Intl.
Privately owned corporation

**AVIATION INTERNATIONAL NEWS**
214 Franklin Ave. (07432)
**Phone—(201) 444-5075**
Fax—(201) 444-4647
www.ainonline.com
Email—rpadfield@ainonline.com
Pres.—Wilson Leach
COO—R. Randall Padfield
Editor-in-Chief—Charles Alcock
Mng. Editor, Monthly Edition—Annmarie Yannaco
Prodn. Editor, Monthly Edition—Jane Campbell
Editor, Bus. Jet Traveler—Jeff Burger
Creative Dir.—John Manfredo
Mfg. & Prodn. Mgr.—Tom Hurley
SIC—2721; *Company headquarters & magazine publishing*
Employs—23; Estab.—1972
Sales—$1Mil-$5Mil
Distrib.—Intl.
Privately owned corporation

**COMPLETE HYDRAULIC WORKS, INC.**
140 Greenwood Ave. (07432)
**Phone—(201) 444-7877**
National—(800) 640-7162
Fax—(201) 444-4651
www.chwinc.com
Email—chwinc@msn.com
Pres.—Daniel J. Fano
Off. Mgr.—Rosie Gaffney
Technician—Jerome Keizh
SIC—3593; NAICS—333995; *Hydraulic systems*
Employs—5; Estab.—1987
4,700 sq ft site, Distrib.—National
Privately owned corporation

**CUSTOM DESIGNERS, LLC**
80 Greenwood Ave., Ste. 14 (07432)
**Phone—(201) 652-5219**
Fax—(201) 652-9129
www.customdesigners.info
Email—customdesigners@optonline.net
Owner—Harry E. Parker
CFO—Kathy Partker
Bookkeeper—Joseph Nobile
SIC—2394; NAICS—314912; *Custom canvas boat covers, car & boat interiors & commercial & residential awnings*
Employs—4; Estab.—1979
Sales—under $500,000
1,200 sq ft site, Distrib.—Local
Limited Liability Company

**FORREST SIGNS**
281 Greenwood Ave. (07432)
**Phone—(201) 670-7760**
Fax—(201) 670-9050
www.forrestsignsonline.com
Email—forgraphix@aol.com
Owner—Norman Forrest
SIC—3993; *Interior & exterior signs*
Employs—1; Estab.—1969
Sales—under $500,000
Distrib.—Local
Limited Liability Company

**†FRANZEN INTERNATIONAL, INC.**
23 Birch St., Ste. 1 (07432-1718)
**Phone—(201) 405-2228**
Fax—(201) 405-1963
www.franzenint.com
Email—tim@franzenint.com
Pres.—Michaela Franzen
Sales Mgr., Natl.—Timothy Mann
SIC—5072; *Distributor of firearm security products, luggage hardware & case hardware*
Employs—3
Sales—$1Mil-$1.5Mil
Distrib.—Regional
Privately owned corporation

**HAFCO FOUNDRY, INC.**
301 Greenwood Ave., Front (07432)
**Phone—(201) 447-0433**
Fax—(201) 447-1065
www.hafcovac.com
Email—info@hafcofoundry.com
Pres.—Michael Fornaci
GM—John Rodriguez
SIC—3589; NAICS—333319; *Heavy-duty industrial vacuum cleaners, parts & accessories*
Employs—6; Estab.—1969
Sales—$1Mil-$2.5Mil
Distrib.—Intl.
Privately owned corporation

**IRON MOUNTAIN PLASTICS, INC.**
112 Greenwood Ave. (07432)
**Phone—(201) 445-0063**
Fax—(201) 445-1115
www.implastic.com
Email—info@implastic.com
Pres.—Richard Ver Hage
GM—Henry Ver Hage
SIC—3089; *Laboratory plastics*
Employs—19; Estab.—1987
Sales—$2.5Mil-$5Mil
Distrib.—National
Privately owned corporation

**J & R LAMB STUDIOS, INC.**
190 Greenwood Ave. (07432)
**Phone—(201) 891-8585**
National—(877) 700-5262
Fax—(201) 891-8855
www.lambstudios.com
Email—lambstudios@optonline.net
Pres.—Donald Samick
Secy-Treas.—Donna Samick
SIC—3231; NAICS—327215; *Stained glass windows & restoration*
Employs—7; Estab.—1857
Sales—$1Mil-$2.5Mil
4,000 sq ft site, Distrib.—National
Privately owned sub-S corp.

**†KUIKEN BROTHERS COMPANY, INC.**
145 Lake Ave. (07432)
**Phone—(201) 652-1000**
Fax—(201) 447-0567
www.kuikenbrothers.com
Email—info@kuikenbrothers.com
Dir., Mktg.—Ryan Mulkeen
SIC—5031; *Wholesaler of lumber*
Employs—70; Estab.—1998
Distrib.—Intl.
Privately owned sub-S corp.
Parent co.—Kuiken Brothers Company, Inc., Fair Lawn, NJ
Phone—(201) 796-2082
See Parent Co. Section for full profile.

**MR. QUICK SIGN**
30 Dairy St. (07432)
**Phone—(201) 670-1690**
(201) 447-3463
Fax—(201) 444-8162
Email—mrquicksign@verizon.net
Pres.—Trena Greenfield
V-P.—Bernard Greenfield
SIC—3993; *Vinyl interior & exterior signs*
Employs—3; Estab.—1986
Sales—under $500,000
950 sq ft site, Distrib.—Regional
Sole ownership

**OFF THE HOOK SEAFOOD, LLC**
126-A Greenwood Ave. (07432)
**Phone—(201) 444-8895**
Fax—(201) 444-8896
www.othseafood.com
Email—john@othseafood.com
Ptnr.—John Sclafani
Ptnr.—Peter Sclafani

## Midland Park—(cont.)

SIC—2092; *Seafood processing for hotels, stadiums, restaurants & caterers*
Employs—4; Estab.—2006
Sales—$500,000-$1Mil
Distrib.—Regional
Limited Liability Company

**PINNACLE PRESS, INC.**
41 Prospect St. (07432)
**Phone—(201) 652-0500**
Fax—(201) 652-0503
www.printatpinnacle.com
Email—hsiegel@bellatlantic.net
Owner—Howard Siegel
SIC—2752; NAICS—323100; *Offset printing*
Employs—7; Estab.—1976
Sales—$500,000-$1Mil
1,500 sq ft site, Distrib.—National
Privately owned corporation

**PRECISION MULTIPLE CONTROLS, INC.**
33 Greenwood Ave. (07432)
**Phone—(201) 444-0600**
National—(800) 775-5862
Fax—(201) 445-8575
www.precisionmulticontrols.com
Email—precision@pmcontrols.com
Pres.—Peter Zecher
V-P.—Darren Lilley
Cred. Mgr.—Gloria Bernardine
SIC—3625; 3648; NAICS—335314; *Industrial timers, low-voltage & defrost controls, flashing warning lights & photo cells*
Employs—50; Estab.—1957
35,000 sq ft site, Distrib.—Intl.
Privately owned corporation

**TECH PRODUCTS CO., INC.**
300 Greenwood Ave. (07432)
**Phone—(201) 444-7777**
Fax—(201) 444-1909
www.techproductsco.com
Email—techproducts@optonline.net
Owner—Robert White
Off. Mgr.—Margaret White
SIC—3559; *Precision machinery job shop & pharmaceutical machinery parts*
Employs—10; Estab.—1994
Distrib.—Local
Privately owned corporation

**VERMONT STORE FIXTURE CORPORATION**
Div. of Vermont Store Fixture Corp.
265 Greenwood Ave. (07432)
**Phone—(201) 652-3401**
Fax—(201) 652-3460
www.vsfc.com
Email—vsfixture@aol.com
GM—Joseph Motisi
SIC—2541; *Wooden store fixtures*
Employs—9; Estab.—1970
9,000 sq ft site, Distrib.—Intl.
Privately owned sub-S corp.
Parent co.—Vermont Store Fixture Corp., Danby, VT
Phone—(802) 293-5126
See Parent Co. Section for full profile.

**VILLADOM TIMES, THE**
333 Godwin Ave., P.O. Box 96 (07432)
**Phone—(201) 652-0744**
Fax—(201) 670-4745
www.villadom.com
Email—editorial@villadom.com
Ptnr. & Co-Publisher—Albert Vierheilig
Ptnr. & Co-Publisher—Ester Vierheilig
Classified Rep.—Karen Rau
Graphic Designer—Karl Vierheilig

SIC—2711; *Newspaper publishing*
Employs—20; Estab.—1987
Distrib.—Local
Privately owned corporation

**WOSTBROCK EMBROIDERY, INC.**
11 Paterson Ave. (07432)
**Phone—(201) 445-3074**
Fax—(201) 444-2114
www.chiefneckerchief.com
Email—info@chiefneckerchief.com
Pres.—Henry Wostbrock
SIC—2395; *Embroidery*
Employs—4; Estab.—1898
Sales—under $500,000
Distrib.—Intl.
Privately owned corporation
AKA: Chief Neckerchief

---

## Milford
### (Hunterdon—N.W.)

**ALBA VINEYARD**
269 Route 627 (08848)
**Phone—(908) 995-7800**
Fax—(908) 995-7155
www.albavineyard.com
Email—vineyard@albavineyard.com
Owner & Pres.—Thomas Sharko
SIC—2084; NAICS—312130; *Wines*
Employs—4; Estab.—1981
14,500 sq ft site, Distrib.—National
Limited Liability Company

**GEORGIA PACIFIC, INC.**
Div. of Georgia-Pacific, LLC
623 Riegelsville Rd. (08848)
**Phone—(908) 995-2228**
National—(800) 524-2642
Fax—(908) 995-9143
www.gp.com
Email—info@gp.com
GM—David Bailey
Plt. Mgr.—Brian Ibach
SIC—2679; 2653; NAICS—322211; *Corrugated paper sheets*
Employs—68; Estab.—1992
Distrib.—Local
Privately owned corporation
Parent co.—Georgia-Pacific, LLC, Atlanta, GA
Phone—(404) 652-4000
See Parent Co. Section for full profile.

**STEVENS CABINET & MILLWORK**
776 Frenchtown Rd. (08848)
**Phone—(908) 996-6290**
Fax—(908) 996-6291
Owner—Paul Stevens
Cabinetmaker—Aragorn Bromberg
SIC—2434; 2541; 2431; NAICS—337110; *Wooden kitchen & office cabinets & millwork*
Employs—3; Estab.—1977
Sales—under $500,000
Distrib.—Local
Sole ownership

---

## Millburn
### (Essex—N.E.)

**†BATH CONNECTION, THE**
Div. of Bayonne Plumbing Supply, Inc.
183 Millburn Ave. (07041)
**Phone—(973) 467-7888**
Fax—(973) 467-9647
www.thebathconnection.com
Email—nancym@thebathconnection.com
Br. Mgr.—Nancy Malchi
Sales Rep.—Ada Saharig

SIC—5031; 5063; *Wholesaler of bathroom accessories, including cabinets, decorative lighting, towel racks & shower faucets*
Employs—7; Estab.—1983
Distrib.—Local
Privately owned corporation
Parent co.—Bayonne Plumbing Supply, Inc., Bayonne, NJ
Phone—(201) 339-8000
See Parent Co. Section for full profile.

**BLUE PLANET SOLUTIONS, INC.**
116 Millburn Ave., Ste.108 (07041)
**Phone—(973) 597-4555**
Fax—(973) 597-4558
www.blueplanetsolutions.com
Email—info@blueplanetsolutions.com
Co-Pres.—Avinash Kulkarni
Co-Pres.—Pratibha Kulkarni
Secy., Off. Mgr.—Seema Darbhe
Bus. Analyst—Prakash Pathak
SIC—7372; *IT recruiting & consulting software development*
Employs—30; Estab.—1997
Distrib.—National
Privately owned corporation

**†GOTHAM SALES CO.**
302 Main St. (07041)
**Phone—(973) 912-8412**
National—(800) 237-2527
Fax—(973) 912-0814
www.gothamsales.com
Email—sales@gothamsales.com
Pres.—Daniel Schwartzstein
V-P., Sales—Jeffrey Dahl
SIC—5074; 5083; 5072; 5064; *Distributor of household appliances, lawn & garden power equipment, power tools & consumer electronics; Brand name—MTD; New Leaf; Haier; Sharp; Snow Joe; Black & Decker; Toro; Midea*
Employs—8; Estab.—1991
Sales—$7Mil
2,500 sq ft site, Distrib.—National
Privately owned sub-S corp.

**GRASSMANN-BLAKE, INC.**
58 E. Willow St. (07041)
**Phone—(973) 379-6170**
National—(800) 842-2881
Fax—(973) 379-5333
www.gbclasp.com
Email—sales@gbclasp.com
Pres.—Richard Blake
SIC—3915; *Precious metal jewelry clasps*
Employs—25; Estab.—1995
Sales—$2.5Mil-$5Mil (est)
Distrib.—Intl.
Privately owned corporation

**KASON CORP.**
67-71 E. Willow St. (07041)
**Phone—(973) 467-8140**
Fax—(973) 258-9533
www.kason.com
Email—info@kason.com
Pres.—Henry Alamzad
Plt. Mgr.—Trevor Burry
Pur. Mgr.—Alissa Moore
Acctg. Mgr.—Isabel Filipe
Off. Mgr.—Tanya Duarte
Cust. Serv. Mgr.—Brian Sullivan
Chief Engr.—William Zhao
SIC—3569; *Screening & processing equipment & related products for bulk solid materials, slurries & related products*
Employs—40; Estab.—1967
40,000 sq ft site, Distrib.—Intl.
Privately owned corporation

**LENS MODE, INC.**
150 Main St., Ste. 1 (07041)
**Phone—(973) 467-2000**
National—(800) 852-5880
Fax—(888) 852-5880
www.lensmodecontacts.com
Email—lensmode@aol.com

Pres.—Daniel Strulowitz
Secy., Bookkeeper—Jesse Strulowitz
SIC—3851; NAICS—339100; *Contact lenses*
Employs—5; Estab.—1986
Distrib.—National
Privately owned corporation

**†MCT DAIRIES, INC.**
15 Bleeker St. (07041)
**Phone—(973) 258-9600**
National—(877) 258-9600
Fax—(973) 258-9222
www.mctdairies.com
Email—info@mctdairies.com
Pres., CEO—Kenneth Meyers
CFO—Vincent McCann
Ex. V-P.—David Raff
SIC—5143; 3089; *Corporate headquarters & wholesaler of dairy products & contract cheese packaging*
Employs—11; Estab.—1980
Distrib.—Intl.
Privately owned corporation

**NEW ENTRY**

**NORTH JERSEY MEDIA GROUP, INC.**
181 Milburn Ave., Ste. 201 (07041)
**Phone—(973) 921-6451**
Fax—(973) 921-6458
www.northjersey.com/millburn-shorthills
Editor & Manager—Harry Trumbore
SIC—2711; *Weekly newspaper publishing; Brand name—The Record; Herald News*
Employs—5
Sales—under $500,000 (est)

**SPORTS INFORMATION MEDIA, INC.**
343 Millburn Ave., Ste. 208 (07041)
**Phone—(973) 564-5014**
National—(800) 733-0543
Fax—(973) 564-5601
www.sportsinfomedia.com
Email—sales@sportsinfomedia.com
Ptnr. & Pres.—Mark Furman
SIC—2759; NAICS—323122; *Commercial printing of lineup cards, dugout charts, coaching aids & related game management tools for coaches of collegiate, high school, amateur & youth sports teams*
Employs—5; Estab.—2006
Sales—under $500,000
Distrib.—National
Privately owned corporation

---

## Millington
### (Morris—N.W.)

**AUTODRILL, LLC**
50 Division Ave., Ste. 18 (07946)
**Phone—(908) 542-0244**
National—(800) 871-5022
Fax—(908) 542-0242
www.autodrill.com
Email—info@autodrill.com
Ptnr.—Joe Agro, Sr.
Ptnr.—Joe Agro, Jr.
SIC—3541; 5084; NAICS—333512; *Manufacturer & distributor of automatic drilling equipment, automatic tapping equipment & multi-spindle heads; Brand name—AutoDrill; AutoTap*
Employs—6; Estab.—1999
Sales—$1.5Mil
3,000 sq ft site, Distrib.—Intl.
Limited Liability Company

**BARRETT CO.**
33 Stonehouse Rd., P.O. Box 421 (07946)
**Phone—(908) 647-0100**
National—(800) 647-0100

**GEOGRAPHICAL**

## Millington—(cont.)

Fax—(908) 647-0278
www.barrettroofs.com
Email—info@barrettroofs.com
Pres.—Timothy Barrett
V.-P.—R. C. Forish
V.-P.—B. T. Barrett
Sales Mgr.—William M. White
Mktg. Mgr.—Rachel Verrill
Tech. Svcs. Mgr.—Guido Capolino
SIC—2952; NAICS—324122;
 High-performance roofing &
 waterproofing systems for green
 vegetative roofs, plaza deck
 reconstructions & re-roofing
 solutions; Brand name—Ram
 Tough; Greenroof Roofscapes;
 Ram ColdTar; Polyfelt; Black
 Pearl Waterproofing; RamCold
Employs—8; Estab.—1928
Sales—$25Mil-$50Mil
30,000 sq ft site, Distrib.—National
Privately owned corporation

### GARDEN STATE FIREWORKS, INC.

383 Carlton Rd., P.O. Box 403
 (07946)
**Phone—(908) 647-1086**
National—(800) 999-0912
Fax—(908) 647-6258
www.gardenstatefireworks.com
Email—info@
 gardenstatefireworks.com
V.-P.—August Nunzio Santore
Secy.-Treas.—Frances Desmelyk
SIC—2892; 5092; NAICS—
 325920; Manufacturer &
 distributor of fireworks & displays
Employs—24; Estab.—1890
Sales—$1Mil-$2.5Mil
Distrib.—Intl.
Privately owned corporation

### JENCKS SIGNS CORP.

50 Division Ave., Ste. 14 (07946)
**Phone—(908) 542-1400**
Fax—(908) 542-1406
www.jencksigns.com
Email—jencksigns@verizon.net
Pres.—Barry Herman Jencks
SIC—3993; Interior & exterior
 signs
Employs—5; Estab.—1957
Sales—under $500,000
Distrib.—National
Privately owned corporation

### RW DELIGHTS, INC.

50 Division Ave., Ste. 44 (07946)
**Phone—(718) 683-1038**
National—(866) 892-1096
Fax—(646) 558-0343
www.rwdelights.com
Email—info@rwdelights.com
Pres., CEO—Roxanne Kam
SIC—2024; Frozen souffles
Employs—4; Estab.—2006
Sales—$500,000-$1Mil
5,000 sq ft site, Distrib.—National
Privately owned corporation

### WATTLOTS, LLC

1932 Long Hill Rd. (07946)
**Phone—(908) 626-1555**
National—(877) 928-8568
Fax—(908) 626-9197
www.wattlots.com
Email—kkaufman@wattlots.com
Founder & CEO—William E. S.
 Kaufman
CTO—Tom Russell
Sr. V.-P., Sales—William
 Jungermann
Dir., Bus. Dev.—Chris Connor

SIC—3674; 3648; Solar-generated
 parking lot canopy systems &
 exterior wall mounted systems,
 including power arbors, solar
 media stations & solar lighting;
 Brand name—The WATTLOTS
 Power Arbor™; LiteBeams™
Employs—5; Estab.—2009
Sales—$1Mil-$2.5Mil
Distrib.—Intl.
Limited Liability Company

### Z & R CUTTER SERVICE, INC.

50 Division Ave., Ste. 21 (07946)
**Phone—(908) 647-6757**
Email—zrcutters@comcast.net
Owner—Dennis Zetterstrom
SIC—3599; General machining &
 grinding job shop
Employs—2; Estab.—1970
Sales—under $500,000 (est)
Distrib.—Local
Privately owned corporation

---

## Millstone Township

### (Monmouth—N.E.)

### ARMFIELD, INC.

9 Trenton Lakewood Rd., Ste. 2
 (08510)
**Phone—(609) 208-2800**
www.discoverarmfield.co.uk
Email—info@armfieldinc.com
GM, U.S.—Mike Di Leo
SIC—3556; NAICS—333294;
 Laboratory equipment for
 engineering education &
 miniature scale research &
 development machinery for the
 food processing, pharmaceutical
 & cosmetics industries
Employs—8; Estab.—1877
Distrib.—Intl.
Privately owned corporation

### GREIF, INC.

200 Rike Dr. (08535)
**Phone—(609) 448-5300**
National—(800) 535-3293
Fax—(609) 448-7106
www.greif.com
Email—bill.guttridge@greif.com
Plt. Supv.—William Guttridge
Hum. Res. Admn.—Andrea Kara
SIC—2655; NAICS—322214;
 Fibre drums
Employs—35; Estab.—2000
Sales—$2Mil-$3.5Mil
Distrib.—Intl.
Publicly owned corporation
ISO rating—9001:2000
Parent co.—Greif, Inc., Delaware,
 OH
 Phone—(740) 549-6000
 See Parent Co. Section for full profile.

---

## Milltown

### (Middlesex—N.E.)

### BANNISTER CO., INC.

126 N. Main St. (08850)
**Phone—(732) 828-1353**
Fax—(732) 545-0846
www.bannistercompany.com
Email—banni126@aol.com
Pres.—Lionel E. Bannister
V.-P.—Thomas Bannister
SIC—3479; 3993; Metal
 engraving & signs
Employs—4; Estab.—1955
Sales—under $500,000
12,000 sq ft site, Distrib.—Intl.
Privately owned corporation

### HEADS UP INDUSTRIES

132 Van Liew Ave., Ste. 4 (08850)
**Phone—(732) 846-3388**
Owner—Wayne Celko

SIC—3599; General machining &
 welding job shop
Employs—1; Estab.—1992
Sales—under $500,000
Distrib.—Local
Sole ownership

### INTERNATIONAL PAPER CO.

101 Ford Ave. (08850)
**Phone—(732) 828-1700**
National—(800) 352-4955
Fax—(732) 828-7623
www.internationalpaper.com
Email—info@ipaper.com
GM—Rob Marquis
Prodn. Mgr.—Vincent Morico
Acctg. Mgr.—Dorian Pincus
Cust. Serv. Rep.—Robin Allen
SIC—2653; NAICS—322211;
 Corrugated boxes
Employs—40; Estab.—1979
Distrib.—Local
Publicly owned corporation
Parent co.—International Paper
 Co., Memphis, TN
 Phone—(901) 419-9000
 See Parent Co. Section for full profile.

### JASON MILLS, LLC

440 S. Main St. (08850-1727)
**Phone—(732) 651-7200**
Fax—(732) 651-7222
www.jasonmills.com
Email—info@jasonmills.com
Pres.—Michael Lavroff
Dir., Sales & Mktg.—Brenda
 Stamboulian
SIC—2258; Knitted mesh fabrics
 for the military, law enforcement
 agencies, industrial applications,
 medical products, safety, high
 visibility vests, outdoor gear,
 substrates, pool skimmers &
 filters, sports netting & apparel
Employs—5; Estab.—2007
Sales—$1Mil-$5Mil
Distrib.—Intl.
Limited Liability Company

### MILLER, LLC, SALLY (H Q)

30 N. Main St. (08850)
**Phone—(732) 729-4840**
Fax—(732) 729-9899
www.sallymiller.biz
Member—Sally Miller
Off. Mgr.—Raluca Vatan
SIC—2361; 2335; Company
 headquarters; preteen & teen
 girls' casual clothing, including
 dresses & tops (mfg.
 subcontracted)
Employs—13
Sales—$1Mil-$2.5Mil (est)

NEW ENTRY
### R & D PROMOTIONS, LTD.

164 Van Liew Ave. (08850)
**Phone—(732) 828-7408**
Owner—Rick Dadika
SIC—2396; T-shirt screen printing
Employs—3
Sales—under $500,000 (est)
Distrib.—Local
Privately owned corporation

---

## Millville

### (Cumberland—S.W.)

### AAVOLYN CORP.

207 Bogden Blvd., P.O. Box 1097
 (08332)
**Phone—(856) 327-8040**
National—(888) 228-6596
Fax—(856) 327-9595
www.aavolyn.com
Email—sales@aavolyn.com
Pres.—Lynn Farrell
V.-P.—Gerard D. Farrell
IT Mgr.—Karen Sims
Hum. Res. Mgr.—Susan Gilbert
Off. Mgr.—Carolyn Shourds
Engrg. Mgr.—Venkat Koganti

Pur. Agt.—Melissa Dion
SIC—3563; NAICS—333912;
 Compressor replacement parts,
 including compressor rod
 packing, piston rings, rider rings,
 compressor packing cases,
 pistons, rods & valve
 components
Employs—32; Estab.—1996
Sales—$1Mil-$5Mil
25,000 sq ft site, Distrib.—Intl.
Privately owned corporation

### ACTION SIGNS & AWARDS

305 N. 11th St. (08332)
**Phone—(856) 825-2454**
Fax—(856) 825-1359
www.actionsignsandawards.com
Email—engravables@aol.com
CEO—Irene Inferrera
Ptnr.—Dean Inferrera
SIC—3993; 3499; Vinyl lettered
 signs, trophy engraving, awards,
 t-shirts imprinting & advertising
 speciality items
Employs—2; Estab.—1982
Sales—under $500,000
2,400 sq ft site, Distrib.—National
Sole ownership

### †ADVANCED METAL PROCESSING NJ, LLC

Div. of Chinook Sciences, LLC
326 S. Wade Blvd. (08332)
**Phone—(856) 327-0048**
Fax—(856) 327-0038
Br. Mgr.—Patricia Campbell
SIC—5093; Wholesaler of scrap
 metals
Employs—20
Distrib.—Local
Limited Liability Company
Parent co.—Chinook Sciences,
 LLC, Cranford, NJ
 Phone—(908) 272-5091
 See Parent Co. Section for full profile.

### AMCOR RIGID PLASTICS

625 Sharp St. (08332)
**Phone—(856) 327-1540**
Fax—(856) 327-0157
www.amcor.com
Email—info@amcor.com
Cont.—Kara Carland
Plt. Mgr.—Jim Kallicragas
Safety Coord.—Brenda Saxton
SIC—3089; Plastic caps &
 closures
Employs—175
Distrib.—Intl.
Publicly owned corporation
Parent co.—Amcor Rigid Plastics,
 Manchester, MI
 Phone—(734) 428-9741
 See Parent Co. Section for full profile.

### †AMERICAN IRON & METAL INTERNATIONAL, LLC

301 S. 12th St., P.O. Box 965
 (08332)
**Phone—(856) 825-2950**
Fax—(856) 825-2918
Mng. Member—Lori A.
 Winterbottom
Hum. Res. & IT Mgr.—Janice
 Myers
SIC—5093; Wholesaler of scrap
 metals
Employs—40; Estab.—2012
Distrib.—Intl.
Limited Liability Company

### ARCHITECTURAL METAL DESIGNS, INC.

1505 Pineland Ave. (08332)
**Phone—(856) 765-3000**
National—(877) 310-3506
Fax—(856) 765-3350
www.amdnj.com
Email—info@amdnj.com
Pres.—Martin Schlembach

## Millville—(cont.)

SIC—3448; 3444; *Aluminum composite wall panel systems & metal roofing fabrication*
Employs—20; Estab.—2001
Sales—$2.5Mil-$5Mil (est)
30,000 sq ft site, Distrib.—National
Privately owned corporation

**BIG 3 PRECISION MOLD SERVICES**
Div. of Big 3 Precision Products
30 Gorton Rd. (08332)
**Phone—(856) 293-1400**
Fax—(856) 825-6970
www.big3precision.com
Email—robert.dzwonar@
big3precision-nj.com
Plt. Mgr.—Joe Klaudi
Off. Mgr.—Jennifer Caine
SIC—3544; NAICS—333500;
*Injection blow molds & injection stretch blow molds for the plastic bottle industry*
Employs—50; Estab.—2003
50,000 sq ft site, Distrib.—Intl.
Privately owned corporation
Parent co.—Big 3 Precision Products, Centralia, IL
Phone—(618) 533-3251
See Parent Co. Section for full profile.

**BREWSTER VAULTS & MONUMENTS, INC.**
1017 Steeprun Rd. (08332)
**Phone—(856) 785-1412**
National—(800) 754-1412
Fax—(856) 785-0939
Pres.—Joseph Brewster
V-P.—Barbara Brewster
Secy-Treas.—F. Asa Brewster
SIC—3272; *Concrete burial vaults*
Employs—10; Estab.—1945
Sales—$1Mil-$2.5Mil
Distrib.—Local
Privately owned corporation

**CAIN MACHINE, INC.**
1501 Oakland Ave. *(08332)*
**Phone—(856) 825-7225**
Fax—(856) 825-3126
Email—dcain124@comcast.net
Pres., GM—Douglas Cain
Bookkeeper—Cheryl Adams
SIC—3499; 3599; *Metal parts, scientific glass machinery & tetrafluoroethylene products*
Employs—6; Estab.—1940
Sales—under $600,000
Distrib.—National
Privately owned corporation

**CARLISLE MACHINE WORKS, INC.**
412 S. Wade Blvd., Bldg. 5, P.O. Box 746 (08332)
**Phone—(856) 825-0627**
National—(800) 922-1167
Fax—(856) 825-5510
www.carlislemachine.com
Email—carlisle@
carlislemachine.com
Pres.—Mary Dougherty
V-P., Mfg.—Frank Dougherty III
Off. Mgr.—Judi Doran
SIC—3433; 3231; 3569; 3599;
NAICS—333414; *Custom fabrication & machining of industrial gas burners, combustion systems, ignition systems & artistic & scientific glass products & automation machine process & systems for the plastic & glass industries*
Employs—23; Estab.—1917
Sales—$1Mil-$5Mil
20,000 sq ft site, Distrib.—Intl.
Privately owned corporation

**CREAMER GLASS, LLC**
411 N. 10th St. (08332)
Mail addr: 2201 Quince Ln., Millville (08332)
**Phone—(856) 327-2023**
Fax—(856) 327-2077
www.creamerglass.com
Email—creamer@
creamerglass.com
Owner & GM—Todd Miskelly
SIC—3231; NAICS—327215;
*Glass fabrication*
Employs—5; Estab.—1919
Sales—under $500,000
Distrib.—Intl.
Limited Liability Company

**DELTRONICS CORP.**
224 Bogden Blvd., P.O. Box 446 (08332)
**Phone—(856) 825-8200**
Fax—(856) 825-3906
Email—deltronicscorp@aol.com
Pres.—Bob Hignutt
V-P., GM—Ken Hignutt
Asst. GM—Diana Hignutt
SIC—3561; NAICS—333911;
*Rebuilt sewage pumps*
Employs—12; Estab.—1964
7,500 sq ft site, Distrib.—Regional
Privately owned corporation

**DURAND GLASS MFG. CO.**
901 S. Wade Blvd. (08332)
**Phone—(856) 327-4800**
(856) 825-5620
Fax—(856) 691-1245
www.arcinternational.com
Email—info@arcinternational.com
CEO—Fred Dohn
CFO—Fabian Klimsza
V-P., Hum. Res.—Tom Reed
IT Mgr.—Samuel Buttner
Hum. Res. Mgr.—Stephanie Ojeda
SIC—3229; 3231; NAICS—327212; *Glass tableware*
Employs—700; Estab.—1982
Sales—$25Mil-$100Mil
2,000,000 sq ft site, Distrib.—Intl.

**EAGLE PALLET**
108 S. Wade Blvd. (08332)
**Phone—(856) 765-9444**
Fax—(856) 765-9553
Email—eaglepallet@aol.com
Pres.—Ken Giaccio
Sales Mgr.—Ron Leider
SIC—2448; NAICS—321920;
*New, recycled, re-manufactured, custom sized & heat treated wooden pallets*
Employs—15; Estab.—2003
Sales—$1Mil-$2.5Mil
Distrib.—Local
Limited Liability Company

**ESPOMA CO.**
6 Espoma Rd. (08332)
**Phone—(856) 825-0542**
National—(800) 634-0603
Fax—(856) 825-1385
www.espoma.com
Pres.—Serge Brunner
V-P.—Jeremy Brunner
SIC—2875; NAICS—325314;
*Organic plant food*
Employs—25; Estab.—1929
Sales—under $500,000
Distrib.—National
Privately owned corporation

**FRIEDRICH & DIMMOCK, INC.**
2127 Wheaton Ave., P.O. Box 230 (08332)
**Phone—(856) 825-0305**
National—(800) 524-1131
Fax—(856) 327-4299
www.fdglass.com
Email—sales@fdglass.com
CEO—Joseph A. Plumbo
GM—Brent Thorn

SIC—3229; 5049; NAICS—327212; *Manufacturer of precision glass & quartz components for industrial, science, research & fiber optics applications & distributor of glass tubing, rod & reusable glassware; Brand name—Kavalier Simax Glass*
Employs—45; Estab.—1919
Sales—$4Mil
62,131 sq ft site, Distrib.—Intl.
Privately owned sub-S corp.
ISO rating—9001:2008
AKA: F & D

**GENERAL POLYGON SYSTEMS, INC.**
203 Peterson St. (08332)
**Phone—(856) 825-3300**
National—(800) 825-1655
Fax—(856) 825-7720
www.generalpolygon.com
Email—joepitassi@
generalpolygon.com
Owner & Pres.—Joseph Pitassi
V-P.—Michael Sormanti
Dir., Opers.—Gina Barber
SIC—3545; *Machined polygon profiles for precision machining applications*
Employs—11; Estab.—1996
Sales—$1Mil-$2.5Mil
7,000 sq ft site, Distrib.—Intl.
Sole ownership

**GERRESHEIMER, INC.**
Div. of Gerresheimer Glass, Inc.
1300 Wheaton Ave. (08332)
**Phone—(856) 506-0501**
Fax—(856) 327-5887
www.gerresheimer.com
Email—info@gerresheimer.com
V-P., Molded Glass Div., U.S.A.—Norman Angel
Dir., Hum. Res. & Safety—Michelle Hoffman
Technical Dir.—Thomas Maiberger
SIC—3221; NAICS—327213; *Glass pharmaceutical & cosmetic bottles*
Employs—230; Estab.—2004
Distrib.—National
Privately owned corporation
Parent co.—Gerresheimer Glass, Inc., Vineland, NJ
Phone—(856) 692-3600
See Parent Co. Section for full profile.

**GIFFORD & CO., BRIAN L.**
514 Bogden Blvd. (08332)
**Phone—(856) 327-0011**
Fax—(856) 327-8706
Email—giffords13@aol.com
Owner—Brian L. Gifford
SIC—3272; *Dry mix concrete for on-site jobs & projects*
Employs—9; Estab.—1981
Sales—$500,000-$1Mil (est)
Distrib.—Local
Privately owned corporation

**GROUPE SEB USA**
2121 Eden Rd. (08332)
Mail addr: 1 Boland Dr., Ste. 1, West Orange (07052)
**Phone—(856) 825-6300**
National—(800) 395-8325
Fax—(856) 825-6321
www.groupeseb.com
Email—sstephens@
us.groupeseb.com
Sr. V-P., Hum. Res.—Martin Falkenberg
V-P., IT & Opers.—Manny Cortez
Dir., Dist.—Ray Dudek
Hum. Res. Mgr.—Sheri Stephens
Qual. Mgr., C.S.S.—Rick Place
SIC—3443; 3469; *Cookware & small appliances*
Employs—210; Estab.—1960
750,000 sq ft site, Distrib.—Intl.
Privately owned corporation

**HENDERSON AQUATIC, INC.**
1 White Hall (08332)
**Phone—(856) 825-4771**
National—(800) 222-0347
Fax—(856) 825-6378
www.hendersonusa.com
Email—info@hendersonusa.com
Pres.—Allan Edmund
SIC—3069; *Wet suits for water sports*
Employs—45; Estab.—1954
35,000 sq ft site, Distrib.—Intl.
Privately owned sub-S corp.

**INTEX MILLWORK SOLUTIONS, LLC**
20 Bogden Blvd. (08332)
**Phone—(856) 293-4100**
Fax—(856) 293-4102
www.intexmillwork.com
Email—info@intexmillwork.com
Owner—Joe Umosella
Web Designer—Michael Alvertson
Estimator—Darren Midgette
SIC—3089; *Custom PVC millwork, including pergola & railing systems & window & door surrounds*
Employs—20; Estab.—2004
Distrib.—Regional
Limited Liability Company

**†KAFFE MAGNUM OPUS**
500 S. Wade Blvd. (08332)
**Phone—(856) 327-9962**
National—(800) 652-5282
Fax—(856) 327-9975
www.kmocoffee.com
Email—terry@kmocoffee.com
Pres., CEO—Bob Johnson
Dir., Opers.—Paul Johnson
Sales & Mktg. Mgr.—Heidi McDonough
Off. Mgr.—Terry Kolonich
SIC—5149; *Wholesaler of coffee*
Employs—18; Estab.—1997
Sales—$1Mil-$3.5Mil
Distrib.—National
Privately owned corporation

**KRUYSMAN CO., RON**
7100 W. Buckshutem Rd. (08332)
**Phone—(856) 327-0605**
Email—rkruysman@mac.com
Owner & Pres.—Ron Kruysman
SIC—3446; NAICS—332323;
*Architectural & ornamental metalwork*
Employs—1; Estab.—1984
Sales—under $500,000
Distrib.—Local
Sole ownership

**LAMONICA FINE FOODS**
48 Gorton Rd., P.O. Box 309 *(08332)*
**Phone—(856) 825-8111**
National—(800) 922-1141
Fax—(856) 825-9354
www.lamonicafinefoods.com
Email—info@
lamonicafinefoods.com
Pres.—Danny LaVecchia
CFO—Tom Considine
V-P., Sales & Mktg.—Chris Douthett
V-P., Opers.—Michael A. LaVecchia
Plt. Mgr.—Ken Carroll
SIC—2092; NAICS—311712; *Wild caught clam products, including fresh, frozen, canned, breaded, value-added, seafood soups, sauces & chowders; Brand name—LaMonica; Cape May; Maryland House; Ocean Chef; Sea Cove; Tender Harvest; Atlantic Treasure*
Employs—200; Estab.—1923
96,000 sq ft site, Distrib.—National
Limited Liability Company

GEOGRAPHICAL

## Millville—(cont.)

**LLOYD'S OF MILLVILLE, INC.**
208 S. Wade Blvd. (08332)
Phone—(856) 825-0345
Fax—(856) 825-7666
www.lloydsofmillville.com
Pres., Fin. & R & D Mgr.—Ben Lloyd, Jr.
V.-P., Fin. & MIS—Linda Lloyd
SIC—2394; 3444; NAICS—314912; *Canvas goods, sewing & retractable & backlit awnings & canopies*
Employs—3; Estab.—1930
Sales—under $500,000
1,800 sq ft site, Distrib.—Regional
Privately owned corporation
AKA: Lloyd's Awnings

**LRC ASSOCIATES, INC.**
328 S. 2nd St. (08332)
Phone—(215) 244-1150
Fax—(215) 639-5568
www.lrcassociates.com
Email—lclements@lrcassociates.com
Pres.—Lawrence R. Clements
Off. Mgr.—Joan Thompson
Chief Engr.—Daniel Guaragno
SIC—3569; NAICS—333298; *Custom & engineered production automation machinery & systems, including robotic welding, assembly, grinding & machine loading & unloading, vision guided robotics & CNC plasma cutting machines & equipment*
Employs—35; Estab.—1986
20,000 sq ft site, Distrib.—Regional
Privately owned corporation

**MARLEEN, INC.**
1101 N. 10th St., P.O. Box 70 (08332)
Phone—(856) 327-8281
Fax—(856) 327-8460
Email—accounting@marleenincl.com
Pres.—Preston Hickman
Cont., Fin. Mgr.—Harold L. Krawiec
SIC—3089; *Contract packaging*
Employs—15; Estab.—1994
Sales—$1Mil-$5Mil
Distrib.—Local
Privately owned corporation

**MITCHELL PRODUCTS, LLC**
1205 W. Main St. (08332)
Phone—(856) 327-2005
National—(866) 436-0500
Fax—(856) 327-6881
www.tricure.com
Email—dmitchell@tricure.com
Member—Dave Mitchell
Dir., Mktg.—Sarah Weaver
Sales Mgr., Natl.—Karen Plumley
Off. Mgr.—Sandy McDermott
SIC—2879; NAICS—325320; *Soil & turf conditioning chemicals for golf courses*
Employs—6; Estab.—1999
Sales—$2.5Mil-$5Mil (est)
Distrib.—Intl.
Limited Liability Company

**N. M. KNIGHT CO., INC.**
1001 S. 2nd St., P.O. Box 1099 (08332)
Phone—(856) 327-4855
Fax—(856) 825-9142
www.nmknight.com
Email—info@nmknight.com
Pres.—Jack Narbut
V.-P.—Andrew Sarclette
V.-P.—John Custer
Dir., Mktg. & Sales Mgr.—C. Scott Nagao

SIC—3433; 3559; NAICS—333414; *Gas burners, custom machinery & polarizing instruments*
Employs—50; Estab.—1965
Distrib.—Intl.
Sole ownership

**NCS ENTERPRISES, INC.**
300 M St. (08332)
Phone—(856) 825-3275
Fax—(856) 327-3732
Email—chris@cckingrebar.com
Pres., Hum. Res. Mgr.—Chris Shropshire
Off. Mgr.—Anna Shea
SIC—3441; NAICS—332312; *Structural steel fabrication*
Employs—9; Estab.—1990
Sales—$500,000-$1Mil
Distrib.—Local
Privately owned corporation
AKA: KING, C. C.

**PARAGON PRINTING SHOP**
600 Columbia Ave. (08332)
Phone—(856) 825-2497
Fax—(856) 825-4360
www.paragonprintshop.com
Email—todd@paragonprintshop.com
Owner—Todd Cimino
SIC—2759; 2791; NAICS—323122; *Commercial printing, electronic prepress & t-shirt screen printing*
Employs—5; Estab.—2012
Sales—under $500,000
4,200 sq ft site, Distrib.—National
Privately owned corporation

**PROJECTS, INC.**
310 Orange St. (08332)
Phone—(856) 825-7312
Fax—(856) 825-0352
Pres.—Anees Hanna
Shop Mgr.—Tom Sheppard
Engr.—Paul Minz
SIC—3599; *Rebuilt injection molding machines*
Employs—6; Estab.—1988
Sales—$500,000-$1Mil (est)
Distrib.—Intl.
Privately owned corporation

**RAILING DYNAMICS, INC.**
1201 N. 10th St. (08332)
Phone—(856) 327-1698
National—(800) 488-7245
Fax—(856) 327-6811
www.railingdynamics.com
Email—cs@ridirail.com
Dir., Opers.—Wayne Batchelder
IT Mgr.—Bob Howe
Hum. Res. Mgr.—Lora Johnson
Administrator—Kathy Aragon
SIC—3089; *Vinyl railings*
Employs—70; Estab.—1990
Sales—$5Mil-$10Mil (est)
Distrib.—National
Privately owned corporation
Parent co.—Railing Dynamics, Inc., Egg Harbor Township, NJ
  Phone—(609) 601-1300
  See Parent Co. Section for full profile.

**RARITAN ENGINEERING CO., INC.**
530 Orange St. (08332)
Phone—(856) 825-4900
Fax—(856) 825-4409
www.raritaneng.com
Email—sales@raritaneng.com
Pres.—Arthur J. Bretnall, Jr.
CFO—Kim Shinn
Plt. Mgr.—Greg Morales
Chief Engr.—Vinod Mehta
Pur. Agt.—Dale Nichols

SIC—3999; *Corporate headquarters & pleasure boats equipment, including marine toilets, waste treatment systems, ice makers & water heaters; Brand name—Atlantes Freedom; Icer-Ette; Electro Scan; SeaEra; Crown Head; PHII; 1700 Series Water Heater; Marine Elegance*
Employs—20; Estab.—1958
Sales—$5Mil
40,000 sq ft site, Distrib.—Intl.
Privately owned sub-S corp.

**RAYBOLD MFG., INC.**
102 S. 8th St. (08332)
Phone—(856) 327-7733
Fax—(856) 327-7737
www.raybold.net
Email—sales@raybold.net
Pres.—William Riland
SIC—2759; 2675; 3231; 3089; NAICS—323100; *Screen printing of glass bottles & plastic sheets, die cutting of plastics, metal, paper, film & gasket materials, laminating of glass, plastics, foam, fabrics & metals & die cut disposable paper slippers*
Employs—9; Estab.—2003
Sales—$500,000-$1Mil
8,000 sq ft site, Distrib.—Intl.
Privately owned sub-S corp.
Also see: Raybold Mfg., Inc., Disposable Products Div., same loc.

**RAYBOLD MFG., INC., DISPOSABLE PRODUCTS DIV.**
102 S. 8th St. (08332)
Phone—(856) 327-7733
Fax—(856) 327-7737
www.disposablepaperslippers.com
Email—sales@raybold.net
Pres.—Bill Riland
SIC—3142; 2621; NAICS—316212; *Disposable paper slippers*
Employs—10; Estab.—2003
Sales—$500,000-$1Mil
8,000 sq ft site, Distrib.—National
Privately owned sub-S corp.
Also see: Raybold Mfg., Inc., same loc.

**REMINDER NEWSPAPER**
2 W. Vine St., P.O. Box 1600 (08332)
Phone—(856) 825-8811
Fax—(856) 825-0011
www.reminderusa.net
Email—editor@remindernewspaper.net
Pres., Publisher—Darrell Kopp
Editor—Dan Podehl
SIC—2711; *Weekly online & printed newspaper publishing*
Employs—15
Sales—$500,000-$1Mil (est)
Distrib.—Local
Privately owned corporation

**†SCIENTIFIC LABORATORY SUPPLIES, INC.**
Div. of Finneran Assocs., J. G.
1401 Wade Blvd. (08332)
Phone—(856) 327-4410
Fax—(856) 327-4642
www.slslux.com
Email—slslux@aol.com
Dir.—Cliff Hitchner
Sales & Mktg. Mgr.—Rick Ordile
SIC—5085; *Distributor of glass & plastic containers for environmental testing*
Employs—12; Estab.—1992
Distrib.—Intl.
Privately owned corporation
AKA: SLS, Inc.
Parent co.—Finneran Assocs., J. G., Vineland, NJ
  Phone—(856) 696-3605
  See Parent Co. Section for full profile.

**SELOVER CO., LLC, R. N.**
17 Wolf Rd. (08332-3508)
Phone—(856) 293-9009
Fax—(856) 293-9080
www.seloverprinting.com
Owner & Pres.—Richard Selover
SIC—2759; NAICS—323100; *Commercial printing*
Employs—1; Estab.—1962
Sales—under $500,000
Distrib.—Local
Limited Liability Company

**SHURE-PAK CORP.**
1500 N. 10th St., P.O. Box 105 (08332)
Phone—(856) 825-0808
National—(877) 825-0808
Fax—(856) 825-1562
www.shure-pak.com
Email—shure-pak@msn.com
Pres.—Aaron Sheppard
Off. Mgr.—Sherry Bodine
SIC—2652; 2657; NAICS—322213; *Paperboard folding cartons*
Employs—4; Estab.—1980
Sales—under $1Mil
20,000 sq ft site, Distrib.—Regional
Privately owned corporation

**SILVER CLOUD MFG. CO.**
525 Orange St. (08332)
Phone—(856) 825-8900
www.silver-cloud.com
Email—info@silver-cloud.com
V.-P., Sales & Mktg.—Robert Cowperthwait
Bus. Mgr.—Bob Foster
SIC—3679; *Display filters, lenses, EMI/RFI shielding & display enhancements; Brand name—Duralan II*
Employs—50; Estab.—1993
Sales—under $10Mil
72,000 sq ft site, Distrib.—Intl.
Privately owned corporation
ISO rating—9001:2000

**†TRICO LIFT, INC. (H Q)**
1101 Wheaton Ave. (08332)
Phone—(856) 776-2350
National—(800) 468-7426
Fax—(856) 776-2365
www.tricolift.com
Pres.—Ken Pustizzi
Cont.—Stephan Cattle
Dir., Mktg.—Terry Cardenter
IT Mgr.—Bob McClellan
Hum. Res. Mgr.—Andrea Jaworski
Dispatch Mgr.—Micki McCue
SIC—5084; *Corporate headquarters; distributor of industrial lifts, including boom, scissor & vertical mast lifts*
Employs—25; Estab.—1952
Sales—$500,000-$1Mil
Distrib.—National
Privately owned corporation

**TROUT PRINTING LLC**
33 Reeves St. (08332-4817)
Phone—(856) 327-8366
Fax—(856) 327-8308
www.troutprinting.net
Email—bo@troutprinting.net
Owner—Bo Novakowski
SIC—2759; 2752; NAICS—323100; *Commercial offset printing*
Employs—5; Estab.—1983
Sales—under $500,000
2,000 sq ft site, Distrib.—Regional
Sole ownership

**WHEATON GLASS WAREHOUSE**
1501 N. 10th St. (08332)
Phone—(856) 327-5228
National—(800) 833-0410
Fax—(856) 825-9014
www.glass-warehouse.com
Email—pez.dutton@wheaton.com

## Millville—(cont.)

Pres.—Steve Drozdow
IT Mgr.—Tony Verna
Hum. Res. Mgr.—Mike Eyler
SIC—3231; NAICS—327215;
*Glass fabrication*
Employs—60; Estab.—1959
Sales—$5Mil-$10Mil (est)
Distrib.—Intl.
Privately owned corporation

### WHEATON INDUSTRIES, INC.

1501 N. 10th St. (08332)
**Phone—(856) 825-1100**
National—(800) 225-1437
Fax—(856) 825-1368
www.wheaton.com
Email—marcom@wheaton.com
Pres., CEO—Wayne L. Brinster
CFO—Thomas E. Kohut
V-P., Sales, North America—Chris Gildea
V-P., Opers.—Jeff Schempp
V-P., IT—Tonya M. Verna
V-P., Org. Dev.—Michael Eyler
Dir., Global Mktg.—Traci Neri-Luciano
Cust. Serv. Rep.—Kim Dare
SIC—3229; NAICS—327212;
*Corporate headquarters & scientific glassware & instrumentation, including glass, glass containers, glass & plastic vials, packaging & packaging development*
Employs—300; Estab.—1954
Sales—$50Mil-$75Mil
Distrib.—Intl.
Privately owned corporation

## Milmay
### (Atlantic—S.E.)

### PALMONARI, INC., J. V.

1234 Tuckahoe Rd., P.O. Box 68 (08340)
**Phone—(609) 476-2642**
Fax—(609) 476-2318
Email—palmonari@comcast.net
Pres.—Michael Flem
V-P.—Joseph Palmonari, Jr.
Bookkeeper—Ellen Plummer
SIC—3441; NAICS—332312;
*Structural steel fabrication*
Employs—15; Estab.—1977
Distrib.—Regional
Privately owned corporation

## Mine Hill
### (Morris—N.W.)

### FIABILA, INC.

114 Iron Mountain Rd. (07803)
**Phone—(973) 659-9510**
Fax—(973) 659-9504
Pres.—Pierre Miasnik
V-P.—Benard Bonneau
Cont.—Oksana Combs
Prodn. Mgr.—Bob Capitani
Cust. Serv. Coord.—Javier Abreu
SIC—2844; NAICS—325600; *Nail polish*
Employs—15; Estab.—2001
Distrib.—Intl.
Privately owned corporation

### †TRINITY RECYCLING OF NEW JERSEY

116 Iron Mountain Rd. (07803)
**Phone—(973) 366-9199**
Fax—(973) 366-9169
V-P.—John Mroz
Off. Mgr.—Sharon Millo
SIC—5093; *Wholesaler of recycled newspaper, cardboard & mixed paper & metal*
Employs—10; Estab.—2002
Distrib.—Local
Privately owned corporation

### WIRE CLOTH MFRS., INC.

110 Iron Mountain Rd. (07803)
**Phone—(973) 328-1000**
Fax—(973) 328-0919
www.wireclothman.com
Email—newjerseysales@ wireclothman.com
Pres.—Kathleen Hegarty
COO—Kathy Blaber
V-P., Opers.—Jim Hegarty
Qual. Control Mgr.—Mike George
SIC—3496; *Corporate headquarters & wire mesh products*
Employs—25; Estab.—1965
Sales—$10Mil-$20Mil
90,000 sq ft site, Distrib.—Intl.
Privately owned corporation

## Monmouth Junction
### (Middlesex—N.E.)

### ACTIVE IMPRINTS

4266 U.S. Highway 1 (08852)
**Phone—(732) 329-2613**
National—(800) 515-8337
Fax—(732) 329-2454
www.activeimprints.com
Email—sales@activeimprints.com
Pres.—Duane Watlington
Accts. Exec.—Diane Reznick
SIC—2396; 2395; *Custom imprinted promotional products, including screen-printed & embroidered wearables & apparel; Brand name—Nike; Champion; Cutter & Buck; Hanes; Gildan; Jerzees; Anvil; Port Authority; Ultraclub; District Threads; Next Level; Ogio; Red House; Sport Tek; Corner Stone; Columbia; Dickies; Hyp; Bella; Alo; Badger; Bayside*
Employs—9; Estab.—1983
3,000 sq ft site, Distrib.—Intl.
Privately owned sub-S corp.

### AGIN SIGNS & DESIGN

Route 1 S. (08852)
Mail addr: 45 Stillwell Rd., Kendall Park (08824)
**Phone—(732) 297-9007**
Fax—(732) 297-2153
www.aginsigns.com
Email—aginsigns@yahoo.com
Owner—Rick Agin
SIC—3993; *Interior & exterior signs*
Employs—2; Estab.—1984
Sales—under $500,000
Distrib.—Local
Sole ownership

### ALFA MACHINE CO., INC.

2154 Highway 130 N. (08852)
**Phone—(732) 821-0044**
Fax—(732) 821-8915
www.alfamach.com
Email—alfamach@aol.com
Pres.—Louis Pall
Off. Mgr.—Gabriella Pall
Shop Mgr.—Bill Szilagyi
SIC—3559; 3599; *Holography equipment, including special machine design, fabrication & integration for the industrial, automation, packaging & pharmaceuticals industries*
Employs—4; Estab.—1970
Sales—$500,000-$1Mil
15,000 sq ft site, Distrib.—Intl.
Privately owned corporation

### AU'SOME INC. (H Q)

2031 Highway 130, Ste. E., Bldg. A (08852)
**Phone—(732) 951-8818**
National—(877) 287-6639
Fax—(732) 951-8828
www.ausomecandy.com
Email—info@ausome.com
CEO—David Tsu

V-P.—Carlos Yeung
Hum. Res. Mgr.—Rose Araneo
SIC—2064; NAICS—311300;
*Corporate headquarters; candy & fruit snacks (mfg. done overseas); Brand name—Florida's Natural; Nintendo Candies; Marvel Candies; Bratz Candies; Betty Boop Candies*
Employs—10; Estab.—1998
Sales—$2.5Mil-$5Mil (est)
10,000 sq ft site, Distrib.—National
Privately owned corporation
AKA: Au'some LLC

### †BUNZL NEW JERSEY, INC.

Div. of Bunzl USA, Inc.
27 Distribution Way (08852)
Mail addr: P.O. Box 668, Dayton (08810)
**Phone—(732) 821-7000**
Fax—(732) 821-3150
www.bunzldistribution.com
Email—resumemc@bunzlusa.com
GM—Mike Schilling
SIC—5113; 5087; 5169; *Distributor of paper bags & janitorial supplies, including cleaning chemicals*
Employs—30; Estab.—1981
Distrib.—Regional
Privately owned corporation
Parent co.—Bunzl USA, Inc., St. Louis, MO
　Phone—(314) 997-5959
See Parent Co. Section for full profile.

### DOLPH CO., JOHN C.

Div. of Von Roll USA, Inc.
320 New Rd. (08852)
**Phone—(732) 329-2333**
Fax—(732) 329-1143
www.dolphs.com
Email—info@dolphs.com
Site Mgr.—Thomas Wacker
SIC—2851; 2899; NAICS—325510; *Electrical insulating varnishes & resins; Brand name—Synthite®; Hi Therm®; Aqua Therm®; Dolph's®; Dolphon®; XL®*
Employs—24; Estab.—1910
50,000 sq ft site, Distrib.—Intl.
Privately owned corporation
ISO rating—9001:2000
Parent co.—Von Roll USA, Inc., Schenectady, NY
　Phone—(518) 344-7100
See Parent Co. Section for full profile.

### DOW JONES & CO., INC.

4300 N. Route 1 (08852)
Mail addr: P.O. Box 300, Princeton (08543)
**Phone—(609) 520-4000**
National—(800) 369-5663
www.dj.com
Email—service@dowjones.com
Proj. Specialist—Carissa Salvatore
SIC—2711; *Newspaper publishing; Brand name—Wall Street Journal*
Employs—1200; Estab.—1882
Distrib.—Intl.
Publicly owned corporation
Parent co.—Dow Jones & Co., Inc., New York, NY
　Phone—(212) 416-2000
See Parent Co. Section for full profile.

### †FILTER TECHNOLOGIES, INC.

45 Stouts Ln., Unit 3 (08852)
**Phone—(732) 329-2500**
Fax—(732) 329-2600
Email—sales@filterselect.com
Dir.—Peter Wojnarowicz

SIC—5085; 5063; *Distributor of industrial water & air filters & ultraviolet light equipment for the pharmaceutical & bottling industries; Brand name—Shelco; Aquafine; Air Sentry; Eaton; Air Guard; batchmasterfilters.com; winefiltercity.com; bagfiltercity.com*
Employs—5; Estab.—2000
Sales—$2Mil-$5Mil
10,000 sq ft site, Distrib.—National
Privately owned sub-S corp.
AKA: Filter & Water Technologies

### †HIGH GRADE BEVERAGE

891 Georges Rd. (08852-3097)
Mail addr: P.O. Box 7092, North Brunswick (08902)
**Phone—(732) 821-7600**
Fax—(732) 821-5953
www.hgbev.com
Email—info@hgbev.com
Corp. V-P.—Guy Battaglia
V-P., Corp. Fin.—Herbert J. Schloss
Corp. Cont.—Jeffrey Epstein
Dir., Hum. Res.—William Calcagno
Opers. Mgr.—John Morra
SIC—5181; 5149; *Company headquarters & distributor of beverages, including beer & soft drinks*
Employs—150; Estab.—1940
Distrib.—Regional
Privately owned corporation

### INFINOVA

51 Stouts Ln. (08852)
**Phone—(732) 355-9100**
National—(888) 685-2002
Fax—(732) 355-9101
www.infinova.com
Email—sales@infinova.com
Pres.—Jeffrey Liu
Opers. Mgr.—Brian Zhou
Hum. Res. Mgr.—Kathy Lui
Accts. Rec. Rep.—Susan Kravcov
SIC—3663; 3669; NAICS—334220; *Megapixel, IP & analog surveillance systems, including access control & fiber-optic communications systems*
Employs—20; Estab.—1993
Distrib.—Intl.
Privately owned corporation

### INNOVATIVE PHOTONIC SOLUTIONS

4250 U.S. Highway 1, Ste. 1 (08852)
**Phone—(732) 355-9300**
Fax—(732) 355-9300
www.innovativephotonics.com
Email—sales@ innovativephotonics.com
Pres.—John Connolly
V-P.—Nancy Morris
V-P.—Scott Rudder
SIC—3699; 3674; NAICS—334413; *High-technology wavelength-stabilized lasers & semiconductor light sources*
Employs—20; Estab.—2003
Sales—$2.5Mil-$5Mil (est)
Distrib.—Intl.
Privately owned corporation

NEW ENTRY
### INTELLECT TECHNOLOGIES, INC.

4301 U.S. Highway 1, Ste. 120 (08852)
**Phone—(609) 454-3170**
Fax—(609) 454-3272
www.intellecttech.com
Email—sales@intellecttech.com
Dir., Global Sales—John LeDuc
SIC—7372; *Prepackaged software development; Brand name—Intellect eFreight; Intellect eShip; Intellect eCustoms*
Employs—20

GEOGRAPHICAL

## Monmouth Junction— (cont.)

### MASTERGRAPHX, INC.
45 Stouts Ln., Ste. 14, P.O. Box 567 (08852)
**Phone—(732) 329-0088**
National—(800) 675-9819
Fax—(732) 329-0024
www.mgxprint.com
Email—mgxprint@aol.com
Pres.—Robert Copeland
GM—Peter Cownsend
Manager—James Copeland
SIC—2752; 2791; NAICS— 323122; *Offset printing & typesetting*
Employs—10; Estab.—1980
Distrib.—Local
Privately owned corporation

### NANONEX CORP.
1 Deerpark Dr., Ste. O (08852)
**Phone—(732) 355-1600**
Fax—(732) 355-1608
www.nanonex.com
Email—sales@nanonex.com
Chrm. & Founder—Stephen Y. Chou
Pres.—Lin Chou
V-P., Bus. Opers. & CTO—Hua Tan
SIC—3674; 3559; NAICS— 334413; *Nano/microstructure manufacturing equipment, materials & processes for semiconductors, magnetic disks, displays, solar cells, light emitting diodes, optics & optical communication & biotechnology applications; Brand name—Air Cushion Press; NX3000; NX2600BA; NX2600; NX2500; NX2000; NX1000; NXB200; NXB100; NXR1000; NXR2000; NXR3000; Ultra100; Lumina210; Lumina200; NX-M200; NX-A20; NX-A15; NX-A10; NX-SP100*
Employs—30; Estab.—1999
Sales—over $3Mil
5,000 sq ft site, Distrib.—Intl.
Privately owned corporation

### NCH CORP.
34 Stouts Ln., P.O. Box 25 (08852)
**Phone—(732) 329-8111**
Fax—(732) 329-0946
www.nch.com
Email—info@nch.com
Plt. Mgr.—Julie Kormos
SIC—2842; NAICS—325612; *Cleaning chemicals*
Employs—12; Estab.—1971
Sales—$1Mil-$2.5Mil (est)
Distrib.—Intl.
Privately owned corporation
AKAs: Chemsearch & Mohawk Laboratories
Parent co.—NCH Corp., Irving, TX
Phone—(972) 438-0211
See Parent Co. Section for full profile.

### OMNICOMM SYSTEMS, INC.
1100 Cornwall Rd., Ste. 111 (08852)
**Phone—(732) 960-2820**
www.omnicomm.com
Email—sales@omnicomm.com
Ex. V-P., Opers. & Svcs.—Ken Light
SIC—7372; *eClinical software development for pharmaceutical, biotechnology & medical device organizations that conduct clinical trial research*
Employs—20; Estab.—1997
Distrib.—National
Publicly owned corporation
Parent co.—Omnicomm Systems, Inc., Fort Lauderdale, FL
Phone—(954) 473-1254
See Parent Co. Section for full profile.

### PHARMASEQ, INC.
11 Deerpark Dr., Ste. 104 (08852)
**Phone—(732) 355-0100**
Fax—(732) 355-0102
CEO—Richard J. Morris
Pres.—Wlodek Mandecki
Off. Mgr.—Dorris Murphy
SIC—2835; NAICS—325400; *Commercial physical research laboratory diagnostic substances*
Employs—5; Estab.—1997
Sales—$1Mil-$2.5Mil (est)
Distrib.—Regional
Privately owned corporation

### PRINCETON BIOMEDITECH CORP.
4242 U.S. Highway 1 (08852)
Mail addr: P.O. Box 7139, Princeton (08543-7139)
**Phone—(732) 274-1000**
Fax—(732) 274-1010
www.pbmc.com
Email—info@pbmc.com
Pres.—Jemo Kang
Chief Administrative Officer— Sunny Suh
V-P., Bus. Dev.—Roger Kang
V-P.—Walter Kang
SIC—2835; 3841; 3826; NAICS— 325413; *One-step advanced rapid diagnostic products & test kits for the areas of fertility, infectious diseases, drugs of abuse, cardiac markers, veterinary, food & environmental diagnostics & consumer, laboratory & professional point-of-care use; Brand name— BioSign®; LifeSign®; AccuSign®; OvuSign®; BioStrip®; BioStrep; StatusFirst™; DXpress™*
Employs—70; Estab.—1988
Distrib.—Intl.
Privately owned corporation
ISO rating—13485

### PRINCETONIAN GRAPHICS, INC.
45 Stouts Ln., Ste. 4 (08852)
**Phone—(732) 329-8282**
Fax—(732) 329-6441
www.pringraph.com
Email—pg@pringraph.com
Pres.—Joseph Menig
Art Dir.—Tony Catania
Sales Mgr.—Hillarey Sbivak
Bookkeeper—Joanne Maraviglia
Designer—Brandy Fidel
SIC—2752; 2759; NAICS— 323122; *Offset & digital printing & graphic design*
Employs—14; Estab.—1969
10,000 sq ft site, Distrib.— Regional
Privately owned corporation

### RIDGE DOORS
335 New Rd., P.O. Box 180 (08852)
**Phone—(732) 329-2311**
National—(800) 631-5656
Fax—(732) 329-2313
www.ridgedoors.com
Email—ridgedoors@msn.com
Pres., GM—Marcelle Bouvier
V-P.—Diane Bouvier
V-P.—Rejean Bouvier
SIC—2431; 3429; NAICS— 321900; *Custom wooden garage doors & replacement wood sections, including swingout wood doors with architectural details & related hardware*
Employs—5; Estab.—1948
70,000 sq ft site, Distrib.—National
Privately owned corporation

### SCIECURE PHARMA, INC.
11 Deerpark Dr., Ste. 120 (08852)
**Phone—(732) 329-8089**
Fax—(732) 329-8083
Pres.—Nolan Wang
Hum. Res. Mgr.—Christine Wang
SIC—2834; *Generic pharmaceutical prototypes & research & development*
Employs—20; Estab.—2010
Sales—$10Mil-$25Mil (est)
Distrib.—National
Privately owned corporation

### SUVEN LIFE SCIENCES LTD.
1100 Cornwall Rd. (08852)
**Phone—(732) 274-0037**
Fax—(732) 274-0501
www.suven.com
Email—feedback@suven.com
CEO—Venkat Jasti
Dir., R & D—Padmakumar R. Kaimal
Proj. Coord.—Mike Easted
SIC—2836; NAICS—325414; *Pharmaceutical development carbohydrate-based chiral compounds*
Employs—10; Estab.—1989
Sales—$1Mil-$2.5Mil (est)
Distrib.—National
Privately owned corporation
AKA: Asian Clinical Trials

### SYSCO GUEST SUPPLY (H Q)
Div. of SYSCO Corp.
4301 Highway 1, P.O. Box 902 (08852)
**Phone—(609) 514-9696**
National—(800) 772-7676
Fax—(609) 514-2692
www.guestsupply.com
Email—eservice@guestsupply.com
Pres., COO—Paul T. Xenis
V-P., CFO—Michael Louro
Dir., Mktg.—Kathy Hatrak
Hum. Res. Mgr.—Barbara Moran
SIC—2844; 2819; 3089; NAICS— 325600; *Divisional headquarters; personal care cosmetics & amenities, housekeeping & laundry chemicals, cups, lids, glassware, kitchenware, can liners & paper products for hotels/motels*
Employs—140
Sales—$50Mil-$100Mil (est)
Distrib.—Intl.
Privately owned corporation
Parent co.—SYSCO Corp., Houston, TX
Phone—(281) 584-1390
See Parent Co. Section for full profile.

### TAMIR BIOTECHNOLOGY, INC. (H Q)
11 Deer Park Dr. (08852)
**Phone—(732) 823-1003**
www.tamirbio.com
Email—info@tamirbio.com
Pres., CEO—Charles Muniz
SIC—2834; *Corporate headquarters; biopharmaceutical drug candidates in Phase III clinical trials (mfg. subcontracted); Brand name—Onconase*
Employs—5; Estab.—2010
Sales—$2.5Mil-$5Mil (est)
Distrib.—Intl.
Publicly owned corporation

### TRIS PHARMA, INC.
2033 U.S. Highway 130, Ste. D (08852)
**Phone—(732) 940-2800**
Fax—(732) 940-2855
www.trispharma.com
Email—info@trispharma.com
Pres., CEO—Ketan Mehta
Pres.—Janet Penner
V-P., Bus. Dev.—Jonathan Berlent
SIC—2834; *Over-the-counter, branded & generic pharmaceuticals in liquid, chewable/ODT & strip dosage forms*
Employs—300
Sales—$100Mil-$250Mil (est)
Privately owned corporation

### TYRX, INC.
Div. of Medtronic, Inc.
1 Deer Park Dr., Ste. G (08852)
**Phone—(732) 246-8676**
Fax—(732) 246-8677
www.tyrx.com
Email—info@tyrx.com
Dir., Mktg.—Randy Mansfield
Principal Fin. Analyst—Pamela Amsbaugh
SIC—2834; 2836; NAICS— 325412; *Implantable combination drug & device medical products, including bioresorbable polymer-coated mesh products*
Employs—34; Estab.—2003
Distrib.—National
Publicly owned corporation
Parent co.—Medtronic, Inc., Minneapolis, MN
Phone—(763) 514-4000
See Parent Co. Section for full profile.

### VALEUR CORP., OILCO U. S. A. DIV.
596 Ridge Rd., P.O. Box 226 (08852)
**Phone—(732) 329-4666**
National—(800) 526-3171
Fax—(732) 329-9422
www.oilco-usa.com
Email—sales@oilco-usa.com
Pres.—R. C. Slawinski, Jr.
Treas.—Marge Salinski
MIS Mgr.—Kevin R. Skochil
Fin. Mgr.—M. A. Slawinski
SIC—3559; *Liquid handling systems*
Employs—10; Estab.—1974
25,000 sq ft site, Distrib.—Intl.
Privately owned corporation

## Monroe
(Middlesex—N.E.)

### ACCENT KITCHEN & BATH CENTER & COUNTERTOPS
510 Englishtown Rd. (08831)
**Phone—(732) 786-1001**
Fax—(732) 786-0998
Off. Mgr.—Christopher John
Manager—Joseph Citro
SIC—2542; *Plastic laminate & high-density board kitchen countertops*
Employs—3; Estab.—1993
Sales—under $500,000
Distrib.—Local
Privately owned corporation

### BROADWAY INDUSTRIES
1 S. Middlesex Ave. (08831)
**Phone—(609) 662-3970**
National—(800) 342-5113
Fax—(609) 662-3971
www.shipmasterbags.com
Email—sales@broadwayind.com
Pres.—Albert S. Kohn
COO—Steve Kohn
Hum. Res. Mgr.—Marina Gorel
Cust. Serv. Rep.—Peggy Rehill
SIC—3089; 2673; *Plastic upholstery & mattress covers & shipping bags*
Employs—22; Estab.—1945
Distrib.—National
Privately owned corporation

### †COOPER ELECTRIC SUPPLY CO.
Div. of Sonepar USA
1 Matrix Dr. (08831)
**Phone—(732) 747-2233**
(732) 945-1249
Fax—(732) 576-8779
www.cooper-electric.com
Email—linda.maia-lopes@cooper-electric.com
Pres.—Mike Dudas
Ex. V-P.—David Cooper
Corp. V-P.—Ronald Reffler
Dir., Pur.—Jim Walsh

## Monroe—(cont.)

Corp. Cred. Mgr.—Diane Beresford
Regional Mgr.—Tom Brady
Mktg. Mgr.—Linda Maia-Lopes
Hum. Res. Mgr.—Georgia Nicolaou
SIC—5063; Company headquarters & distributor of electrical supplies, commercial lighting & generator & power systems; Brand name—Sylvania; SquareD; Hubbell; Lutron; Southwire; Pass& Seymour; 3M
Employs—160; Estab.—1961
Distrib.—Regional
Privately owned corporation
Parent co.—Sonepar USA, Philadelphia, PA
Phone—(215) 399-5900
See Parent Co. Section for full profile.

### COSMETICS & PERFUME FILLING & PACKAGING, INC.

30 Engelhard Dr. (08831)
Phone—(973) 680-8900
Fax—(973) 680-0020
www.cpfpi.com
Email—info@cpfpi.com
Pres.—Devraj Vaghani
V-P., Sales & Mktg. & IT Mgr.—Ashvin Vaghani
V-P., Mfg.—Vijay Vaghani
Hum. Res. Mgr.—Micki Perez
SIC—2844; 3089; NAICS—325600; Contract manufacturing & packaging services, including fragrances, deodorant sticks & liquid skin care products
Employs—100; Estab.—1991
95,000 sq ft site, Distrib.—Intl.
Privately owned corporation

### R & M MFG., INC.

20 Abeel Rd. (08831)
Phone—(609) 495-8032
Fax—(609) 495-8038
www.randmmfg.com
Email—drudolph@randmmfg.com
Pres.—Tom Marvel
V-P.—David Rudolph
Plt. Mgr.—Gary Taylor
Off. Mgr.—Karen Mulvihill
Designer—Anna Zylikovich
SIC—3083; NAICS—326130; Plastic laminate architectural casework
Employs—25; Estab.—1991
Distrib.—Regional
Privately owned corporation

## Monroe Township

(Middlesex—N.E.)

### AMERINEX APPLIED IMAGING, INC.

P.O. Box 6473 (08831)
Phone—(609) 944-8855
National—(877) 664-8772
Fax—(609) 944-8855
www.amereximaging.com
Email—sales@amereximaging.com
Pres.—Richard Kretschmann
V-P., Sales & Mktg.—Bruno Lay
SIC—7372; Two dimensional & three dimesional imaging processing & analysis software development; Brand name—Aphelion™ Developer; Aphelion™ Lab; Aphelion™ Optional Modules
Employs—8
Distrib.—Intl.
Privately owned corporation

### BERRY PLASTICS

Div. of Berry Plastics Corp.
34 Engelhard Dr. (08831)
Phone—(609) 655-4600
Fax—(609) 655-0225
www.berryplastics.com
Email—info@berryplastics.com
Plt. Mgr.—Bob Loftus
Hum. Res. Mgr.—Wendy Hornish
Inventory Control Mgr.—Teresa Morris
SIC—3085; NAICS—326160; Plastic bottles
Employs—300; Estab.—1982
320,000 sq ft site, Distrib.—Intl.
Privately owned corporation
Parent co.—Berry Plastics Corp., Evansville, IN
Phone—(812) 424-2904
See Parent Co. Section for full profile.

### BLUE STREAK SCREEN PRINTING CO.

33 E. Railroad Ave. (08831)
Phone—(732) 656-0400
Fax—(732) 521-1634
www.bluestreakuniforms.com
Email—bluestreaknj@aol.com
Pres.—James Craparotta
SIC—2396; 2395; Textile screen printing & custom embroidery
Employs—3; Estab.—2003
Sales—under $500,000
Distrib.—Local
Sole ownership
AKA: Blue Streak Uniforms, LLC

### BRACCO DIAGNOSTICS, INC.

259 Prospect Plains Rd., Bldg. H (08831)
Phone—(609) 514-2200
National—(800) 631-5245
Fax—(609) 514-2424
www.bracco.com
Email—braccootc@diag.bracco.com
Pres., CEO—Vittorio Puppo
CFO—Joseph Vaughn
COO—Anthony A. Lombardo
V-P., Hum. Res.—Lori Fochesato
IT Mgr.—Robert Covello
SIC—2819; 2835; NAICS—325400; Corporate headquarters & barium & radiological materials for medical diagnostic testing
Employs—175; Estab.—1936
Sales—$112Mil
100,000 sq ft site, Distrib.—Intl.
Privately owned corporation

### CONSOLIDATED CONTAINER CO., LLC

Div. of Consolidated Container Company
4 Pleasant Hill Rd. (08831)
Phone—(609) 655-0855
Fax—(609) 655-0520
www.cccllc.com
Email—sales@cccllc.com
Plt. Mgr.—Tom Walker
Qual. Control Mgr.—Sarah Gerkes
SIC—3089; Plastic containers
Employs—37; Estab.—1995
Sales—$1Mil-$2.5Mil
Distrib.—National
Privately owned corporation
DBA: New Jersey Plastics
Parent co.—Consolidated Container Company, Atlanta, GA
Phone—(678) 742-4600
See Parent Co. Section for full profile.

### DAVLYN INDUSTRIES, INC.

Div. of Shiseido America, Inc.
7 Fitzgerald Ave. (08831)
Phone—(609) 860-5100
Fax—(609) 860-5175
www.shiseido.com
Email—customerservice@shiseidousa.com
Ex. Dir., Opers.—Tom Halligan
SIC—2844; NAICS—325600; Cosmetics & skin care products
Employs®—180; Estab.—1980
150,000 sq ft site, Distrib.—Intl.
Privately owned corporation
Parent co.—Shiseido America, Inc., New York, NY
Phone—(212) 805-2300
See Parent Co. Section for full profile.

### EASTERN TEA CORP.

1 Engelhard Dr. (08831)
Phone—(609) 860-1100
National—(800) 221-0865
Fax—(609) 860-1105
www.bromleytea.com
Email—beth@bromleytea.com
Pres.—Paul Barbakoff
V-P.—Ira Barbakoff
V-P.—Glenn Barbakoff
Cont., Traf.—Barbara Uttan
Qual. Control Mgr.—Narmada Boppana
Bookkeeper—Rohona Paul
Cust. Serv. Rep.—Kathy Pajak
SIC—2099; Tea; Brand name—Bromley
Employs—50; Estab.—1947
89,000 sq ft site, Distrib.—National
Privately owned corporation

### ICICLE, INC.

341 School House Rd. (08831)
Phone—(732) 521-4223
Fax—(732) 521-4223
www.icicleseafoods.com
Pres.—Richard Lamont
Off. Mgr.—Lorane Lamont
SIC—3421; NAICS—332200; Scissors
Employs—2; Estab.—2001
Sales—under $500,000
Distrib.—Local
Privately owned corporation

### LAGGREN'S, LLC

P.O. Box 7173 (08831)
Phone—(609) 235-9883
Fax—(609) 235-9873
Email—dlasser@comcast.net
Pres.—David Lasser
SIC—2394; 2591; 2399; NAICS—314912; Canvas awnings, window shades, blinds, window treatments, flags & banners; Brand name—Graber; Sunbrella; Dickson; Para; Freedom; B & W Horizon; Annin
Employs—10; Estab.—1906
Sales—$500,000-$1Mil
Distrib.—Regional
Limited Liability Company

### †MAIN ELECTRIC SUPPLY CO., INC.

24 Public Rd., P.O. Box 7323 (08831)
Phone—(609) 860-8500
Fax—(609) 860-1067
Email—mainelec@mainelectricsupplyco.com
Pres.—Perry Sablosky
SIC—5063; Distributor of electrical supplies & equipment
Employs—35; Estab.—1987
Sales—over $20Mil
23,500 sq ft site, Distrib.—Local
Privately owned corporation

### MONROE MACHINE & DESIGN, INC.

566 Buckelew Ave. (08831)
Phone—(732) 521-3434
Fax—(732) 521-3050
www.monroemachine.com
Email—info@monroemachine.com
Pres.—Susan Kovacs
MIS, Prod. & R & D Mgr.—Mozes Kovacs
CNC Machinist—Victor Nikolov
SIC—3565; 3569; NAICS—333993; Packaging & automation machinery, including machining, fabrication, welding, short & long run production, design services & research & development support
Employs—5; Estab.—1970
Sales—$500,000-$1Mil
4,800 sq ft site, Distrib.—Regional
Privately owned sub-S corp.

### NULAB FURNITURE CORP.

11 Federal Rd. (08831)
Phone—(732) 792-0050
Fax—(732) 792-0721
www.nulab.com
Email—nulab@earthlink.net
CEO—Fran Ditringo
Pres., R & D Mgr.—Anthony Ditringo
Engr. Mgr.—Bob Pelosi
Estimator—Arkady Leyzerov
SIC—2542; Laboratory furniture
Employs—20; Estab.—1989
Sales—$500,000-$1Mil
8,000 sq ft site, Distrib.—Intl.
Privately owned corporation

### †O'NEAL FLAT ROLLED METALS

Div. of O'Neal Steel, Inc.
1 Fitzgerald Ave. (08831)
Phone—(609) 395-7007
Fax—(609) 395-9555
www.ofrmetals.com
Email—newjersey@ofrmetals.com
GM—Jeff Katz
Sales Mgr., Inside—Bill Blake
SIC—5051; NAICS—332322; Steel service center, including stainless steel, aluminum & coated carbon steel coils, cut-to-length sheets, bars, pipe & tubing
Employs—34
Sales—$3Bil
100,000 sq ft site, Distrib.—National
Privately owned corporation
ISO rating—9001:2008
Parent co.—O'Neal Steel, Inc., Birmingham, AL
Phone—(205) 599-8000
See Parent Co. Section for full profile.

### PROCESS COMPONENTS

301 John Wall Rd. (08831)
Phone—(732) 786-1500
National—(888) 388-4321
Fax—(732) 786-9511
www.procompstainless.com
Email—insidesales@procompstainless.com
Pres.—David Zimmerman
Opers. Mgr.—Doug Campbell
Off. Mgr.—Randi Risley
SIC—3569; 3823; NAICS—334513; High purity flow components
Employs—8; Estab.—1997
Sales—$1Mil-$2.5Mil
Distrib.—National
Privately owned corporation
DBA: Procomp, Inc.

### QUAD/GRAPHICS, INC.

28 Engelhard Dr. (08831)
Phone—(609) 495-1200
Fax—(609) 860-5854
www.qg.com
Email—info@qg.com
GM & Plt. Mgr.—George Lane
Plt. Mgr.—Steven Flood
Hum. Res. Mgr.—Angel Egozcue
SIC—2759; NAICS—323100; Direct marketing print production
Employs—169; Estab.—1999
Distrib.—Local
Publicly owned corporation
Parent co.—Quad/Graphics, Inc., Sussex, WI
Phone—(414) 566-6000
See Parent Co. Section for full profile.

### †TW METALS, INC.

27 Engelhard Dr. (08831)
Phone—(609) 655-4120
National—(800) 203-8000
Fax—(609) 655-4195
www.twmetals.com
Email—sales@twmetals.com
V-P.—Bill Schmit
Acct. Mgr.—Mike Scarnici
Qual. Control Mgr.—Ken Perrine

GEOGRAPHICAL

## Monroe Township—(cont.)

SIC—5051; *Distributor of specialty metals*
Employs—100; Estab.—1998
Distrib.—Intl.
Privately owned corporation
Parent co.—TW Metals, Inc., Exton, PA
Phone—(610) 458-1300
See Parent Co. Section for full profile.

## Monroeville

(Salem—S.W.)

**AURA BADGE CO.**
264 Clayton Ave. (08343)
Mail addr: P.O. Box 655, Clayton (08312)
**Phone—(856) 881-9026**
National—(800) 333-2872
Fax—(856) 881-7359
www.aurabadge.com
Email—sales@aurabadge.net
Owner & IT Mgr.—Phil Barbaro
Hum. Res. Mgr.—Jonas Barbaro
SIC—3993; 2399; *Promotional & identification products, including badges, buttons, bumper stickers, decals, magnets, ribbons, tote bags, backpacks, blankets, hats & shirts*
Employs—70; Estab.—1952
Sales—$11Mil-$25Mil
30,000 sq ft site, Distrib.—National
Privately owned sub-S corp.

**FOOTE'S SLAUGHTER HOUSE**
28 Swedesboro Rd. (08343)
**Phone—(856) 358-8550**
Owner—Gerald B. Thomas
SIC—2011; NAICS—311611; *Meat processing*
Employs—1; Estab.—1947
Sales—under $500,000
Distrib.—Local
Sole ownership

NEW ENTRY
**MONROEVILLE VINEYARD & WINERY, LLC**
314 Richwood Rd. (08343)
**Phone—(856) 521-0523**
www.monroevillewinery.net
Email—debrabasile@monroevillewinery.comcastbiz.net
GM—Debra Basile
SIC—2084; *Wines; Brand name—Monroeville Winery*
Employs—4
Sales—$1Mil-$2.5Mil (est)
1,000 sq ft site, Distrib.—Local
Limited Liability Company

## Montague

(Sussex—N.W.)

**ROBERTSON INDUSTRIES**
19 State Route 23 (07827)
**Phone—(973) 293-8666**
Fax—(973) 293-8601
www.foamfab.com
Email—info@foamfab.com
Owner—Craig Robertson
SIC—3086; NAICS—326100; *Foam fabrication for packaging*
Employs—7; Estab.—1988
Sales—$1Mil-$2.5Mil
Distrib.—Intl.
Privately owned corporation

**TYMAC CONTROLS CORP.**
432 U.S. Highway 206, Ste. C (07827)
**Phone—(973) 293-3339**
www.tymac.com
Email—us@tymac.com
Pres., CEO—John Mickowski

SIC—3823; NAICS—334513; *Process sensors & control instruments, systems integrators & die casting & plastic molding equipment*
Employs—25; Estab.—1973
Sales—$3Mil-$10Mil
Distrib.—Intl.
Privately owned corporation

**WESTFALL WINERY, LLC**
141 Clove Rd. (07827)
**Phone—(973) 293-3428**
Fax—(973) 293-7453
www.westfallwinery.com
Email—westfallwinery@gmail.com
Ptnr.—Loren Mortimer
Ptnr.—Georgene Mortimer
SIC—2084; NAICS—312130; *Company headquarters & wines*
Employs—4; Estab.—2001
Sales—$1Mil-$2.5Mil
Distrib.—Local
Limited Liability Company

## Montclair

(Essex—N.E.)

**ALCARO & ALCARO PLATING CO., INC.**
112 Pine St., P.O. Box 1215 (07042)
**Phone—(973) 746-1200**
Fax—(973) 744-6177
www.alcaro.com
Email—info@alcaro.com
Pres.—Tony Alcaro
GM—Michelle Kendall
SIC—3471; NAICS—332813; *Electroplating*
Employs—20; Estab.—1987
Sales—$1Mil-$2.5Mil (est)
Distrib.—Local
Privately owned corporation

**APPLEGATE FARM HOMEMADE ICE CREAM, INC.**
616 Grove St. (07043)
**Phone—(973) 744-5900**
Fax—(973) 744-0334
www.applegatefarm.com
Email—info@applegatefarm.com
Pres., CEO—Jason Street
SIC—2024; NAICS—311520; *Ice cream*
Employs—15; Estab.—1848
Sales—under $500,000
8,000 sq ft site, Distrib.—Local
Privately owned corporation

**BUDGET PRINT CENTER**
590 Valley Rd. (07043)
**Phone—(973) 744-5520**
Fax—(973) 744-3853
www.sirspeedy.com
Email—bpcum2004@verizon.net
Owner—Dave Pradip
Typesetter—Ken Ward
Cust. Serv. Rep.—Erica Feegan
SIC—2752; 2791; NAICS—323122; *Offset printing & typesetting*
Employs—3; Estab.—1977
Sales—under $500,000
2,000 sq ft site, Distrib.—Local
Sole ownership
AKA: Sir Speedy

**CALIMA JEWELS**
215 Glen Ridge Ave. (07042)
**Phone—(973) 746-2976**
Fax—(973) 746-2976
Email—calima1@verizon.net
Owner—George Lugo
GM—Patricia Lugo
SIC—3911; NAICS—339911; *Precious metal jewelry*
Employs—2; Estab.—1996
Sales—under $500,000
Distrib.—Local
Sole ownership

NEW ENTRY
**GLOBAL METALS SALES CORP.**
196 Inwood Ave. (07043)
**Phone—(212) 813-3100**
Fax—(212) 813-3101
www.globalmetals.com
Email—sales@globalmetals.com
Pres.—Michael John Van Rhyn
SIC—3339; NAICS—331419; *Nonferrous metals*
Employs—10; Estab.—1964
Sales—$2.5Mil-$5Mil (est)
Distrib.—National
Privately owned corporation

**ITALIAN TRIBUNE PUBLISHING CO.**
7 N. Willow St., Ste. 8-C (07042-3591)
**Phone—(973) 860-0101**
Fax—(973) 860-0106
www.italiantribune.com
Email—mail@italiantribune.com
Publisher—A. J. Buddy Fortunato
Mng. Editor—Joan Alagna
Editor—Marion Fortunato
Assoc. Editor—Annemarie Casella
SIC—2711; *Newspaper publishing*
Employs—8; Estab.—1931
Sales—$500,000-$1Mil
3,000 sq ft site, Distrib.—National
Privately owned corporation
AKA: Italian Tribune

**LINCOLN MONUMENT CO., INC.**
405 Orange Rd. (07042)
**Phone—(973) 744-1800**
National—(800) 854-1330
Fax—(973) 744-1871
www.lincolnmonument.com
Email—sales@lincolnmonument.com
Owner & Pres.—Ralph Rullis, Jr.
SIC—3281; NAICS—327991; *Burial monument engraving*
Employs—5; Estab.—1919
Sales—under $500,000 (est)
Distrib.—Regional

**MP TECHNOLOGIES, LLC (H Q)**
345 Claremont Ave., Ste. 26 (07042)
**Phone—(646) 366-1155**
Fax—(718) 482-7136
Email—mpt4220@aol.com
Chrm.—John Mahdessian
Pres.—Robert Saks
Dir., IT—George Barek
SIC—2393; 2499; 2842; 3999; NAICS—314911; *Company headquarters; pocket stain removal kits, wooden & plastic hangers, plastic & garment bags & gift wrap products & boxes, including custom designing & manufacturing (mfg. done overseas); Brand name—Madame Paulette*
Employs—15; Estab.—1954
Sales—$8Mil
5,000 sq ft site, Distrib.—Intl.
Limited Liability Company

**NICOLOS ITALIAN BAKERY & DELI, INC.**
6 Baldwin St. (07042)
**Phone—(973) 746-1398**
Fax—(973) 509-9389
www.nicolosbakery.com
Pres.—Nicolos Zecchino, Sr.
SIC—2051; NAICS—311812; *Bakery products, including bread & deli products*
Employs—9; Estab.—1967
Sales—$1Mil-$2.5Mil
Distrib.—Local
Privately owned corporation

**NORTHWEST ESSEX COMMUNITY HEALTHCARE NETWORK, INC.**
83 Walnut St. (07042)
**Phone—(973) 744-7733**
Fax—(973) 744-3744

Email—nwechn@verizon.net
GM & Prod. Mgr.—William Delorenzo
Hum. Res. Mgr.—Phyllis Gerber
SIC—3089; 2759; 2759; NAICS—323100; *Contract assembly, packaging & screen printing*
Employs—125; Estab.—1958
30,000 sq ft site, Distrib.—Local

**PRINTER'S PLACE, INC., THE**
8 S. Fullerton Ave. (07042)
**Phone—(973) 744-8889**
Fax—(973) 744-7201
www.theprintersplace.com
Email—quality@theprintersplace.com
Pres.—Francis Michael Lami
Graphic Designer—Darlene Zalewski
SIC—2759; NAICS—323100; *Commercial printing*
Employs—6; Estab.—1975
13,000 sq ft site, Distrib.—Local
Privately owned corporation

**STUDIO 042**
423 Bloomfield Ave. (07042)
**Phone—(973) 509-7591**
Fax—(888) 290-2382
www.studio042.com
Email—quality@studio042.com
CEO—Scott F. Kennedy
Pres.—Pilar P. Kennedy
Manager—Colleen Vandorn
SIC—2759; 2752; NAICS—323100; *Commercial & instant printing*
Employs—10; Estab.—1989
3,800 sq ft site, Distrib.—Regional
Privately owned corporation

**VERONA-CEDAR GROVE TIMES**
Div. of North Jersey Media Group, Inc.
130 Valley Rd. (07042)
**Phone—(973) 233-5048**
Fax—(973) 233-5032
www.vcgtimes.com
Email—vcgtimes@northjersey.com
Publisher—Mike Lawson
Mng. Editor—Joshua Jongsma
Editor—Lillian Ortiz
SIC—2711; 2741; *Weekly print & online community newspaper publishing*
Employs—5; Estab.—1948
Sales—under $500,000 (est)
Distrib.—Local
Privately owned corporation
Parent co.—North Jersey Media Group, Inc., Woodland Park, NJ
Phone—(973) 569-7000
See Parent Co. Section for full profile.

**WISH FACTORY, INC., THE**
21 Church St., Ste. 2 (07042)
**Phone—(973) 744-3131**
www.thewishfactoryinc.com
Email—joel@thewishfactoryinc.com
Owner—Scott Bachrach
SIC—3944; *Children's toys*
Employs—13
Distrib.—Intl.

## Montvale

(Bergen—N.E.)

**AEP INDUSTRIES INC. (H Q)**
95 Chestnut Ridge Rd. (07645)
**Phone—(201) 641-6600**
National—(800) 999-2374
Fax—(201) 807-2567
www.aepinc.com
Email—feeneyp@aepinc.com
Chrm., Pres. & CEO—J. Brendan Barba
Ex. V-P, Fin. & CFO—Paul Feeney
Ex. V-P, Mfg.—David J. Cron
Ex. V-P, Opers.—Paul C. Vegliante
V-P, Treas.—James Rafferty
V-P, Cont.—Linda Guerrera

## Montvale—(cont.)

V-P., Hum. Res.—Karen Aloia
SIC—3081; NAICS—326113;
*Corporate headquarters;
polyethylene film & bags*
Employs—200; Estab.—1970
Sales—$50Mil-$100Mil
Publicly owned corporation

NEW ENTRY

**†BAOSTEEL AMERICA, INC.**

85 Chestnut Ridge Rd., Ste. 210
(07645)
**Phone—(201) 307-3355**
Fax—(201) 307-3358
www.baosteelamerica.com
Email—bai@baosteelusa.com
Pres.—Ye Meng
SIC—5051; *Metal service center*
Employs—25

**BENJAMIN MOORE & CO. (H Q)**

Div. of Berkshire Hathaway, Inc.
101 Paragon Dr. (07645)
**Phone—(201) 573-9600**
National—(800) 344-0400
Fax—(201) 573-0046
www.benjaminmoore.com
Email—info@benjaminmoore.com
CEO—Mike Searles
Sr. V-P., Opers.—Barry Chadwick
V-P., Gen. Counsel—Mark
Boyland
V-P., Mfg.—Ken Marino
V-P., Mktg.—Nick Harris
V-P., Fin.—Robert Pettel
Dir., Corp. Comm.—Kimberlee
Bradshaw
Comms. Mgr.—Kelly Sinatra
SIC—2851; NAICS—325510;
*Divisional headquarters; paints &
coatings; Brand name—
Benjamin Moore; Coronado;
Insl-x; Corotech; Lenmar*
Employs—400; Estab.—1883
Sales—$1Bil
138,500 sq ft site, Distrib.—Intl.
Privately owned corporation
Parent co.—Berkshire Hathaway,
Inc., Omaha, NE
Phone—(402) 346-1400
See Parent Co. Section for full profile.

**BLUESPIRE STRATEGIC
MARKETING**

110 Summit Ave., Ste. B (07645)
**Phone—(201) 740-6100**
National—(800) 727-6397
Fax—(201) 740-6136
www.bluespiremarketing.com
Email—bluespiremarketing@
bluespiremarketing.com
Pres., CEO—Kathryn Hammond
SIC—2721; 2741; NAICS—
323122; *Contract medical
magazine publishing as part of
marketing & communications
services for healthcare
organizations*
Employs—35; Estab.—1987
Distrib.—National
Privately owned corporation
AKA: Medical Decision Point

**BOB'S TROPHY**

6 Hamilton St. (07645)
**Phone—(201) 391-3790**
Fax—(201) 391-7473
www.btspecialties.com
Email—btspecialties@gmail.com
Owner—Mitch Cumstein
SIC—3914; *Trophies & plaques*
Employs—3; Estab.—1968
Sales—under $500,000
Distrib.—Intl.
Sole ownership
AKA: BT Specialty

**CHARLES G.G. SCHMIDT & CO., INC.**

301 W. Grand Ave. (07645)
**Phone—(201) 391-5300**
(800) 724-6438
Fax—(201) 391-3565
www.cggschmidt.com
Email—sales@cggschmidt.com
Pres.—Richard I. Paul
SIC—3553; 3544; NAICS—
333210; *Woodworking
machinery, knives, cutters &
heads & tooling for shapers,
moulders, CNC routers, planers,
tenoners & saws*
Employs—20; Estab.—1926
Sales—$1Mil-$5Mil
10,000 sq ft site, Distrib.—National
Privately owned corporation

**COINING, INC.**

Div. of AMETEK, Inc.
15 Mercedes Dr. (07645)
**Phone—(201) 791-4020**
Fax—(201) 791-1637
www.coininginc.com
Email—sales@coininginc.com
V-P., Sales & Mktg.—Julie Scelzo
V-P., Field Sales—Vito Tanzi
V-P., Mfg. & Opers.—Peter
Pachella
V-P.—Ken Whited
Cont.—John Bailey
Opers. Mgr.—Martin Mott
R & D Mgr.—Martin Oud
Qual. Assur. Mgr.—Joseph
DePalma
SIC—3356; 3469; NAICS—
331491; *Preformed solder &
brazing*
Employs—75; Estab.—1997
21,000 sq ft site, Distrib.—Intl.
Publicly owned corporation
ISO rating—9001:2000
Parent co.—AMETEK, Inc.,
Berwyn, PA
Phone—(610) 647-2121
See Parent Co. Section for full profile.

**CUSTOM INTERIORS, INC.**

47 W. Grand Ave. (07645)
**Phone—(201) 573-9702**
Fax—(201) 573-0605
Pres.—Keith D. Wright
SIC—2434; 2431; NAICS—
337110; *Wooden cabinets &
custom woodworking*
Employs—2; Estab.—1971
Sales—under $500,000
Distrib.—Local
Privately owned corporation

NEW ENTRY

**DATA CENTRUM COMMUNICATIONS,
INC.**

135 Chestnut Ridge Rd., 2nd Fl.
(07645)
**Phone—(201) 391-1911**
Fax—(201) 225-1440
www.healthmonitor.com
Pres., CEO—Eric Jensen
SIC—2721; *Magazine publishing;
Brand name—Health Monitor
Network*
Employs—30
Sales—$2.5Mil-$5Mil (est)
AKA: Health Monitor Network

**FARBEST-TALLMAN FOODS CORP.
(H Q)**

160 Summit Ave., Ste. 200 (07645)
**Phone—(201) 573-4900**
New Jersey—(800) 897-6096
Fax—(201) 573-0404
www.farbest.com
Email—info@farbest.com
Pres.—Daniel M. Meloro
Sr. V-P.—Chip Jackson
Sr. V-P.—Robert Claire

SIC—2099; *Corporate
headquarters; food blending;
Brand name—Farbest Brands;
FarMax; Bake-Mate; Mato-Mate*
Employs—17; Estab.—1955
Distrib.—Intl.
Privately owned sub-S corp.

**HAMILTON BELL CO., INC.**

30 Craig Rd. (07645)
**Phone—(201) 391-4100**
National—(800) 526-0864
Fax—(201) 391-5994
www.hamiltonbell.com
Email—hamiltonbell@
mindspring.com
GM—Linda Luciano
SIC—3821; NAICS—339111;
*Laboratory centrifuges*
Employs—7; Estab.—1948
Sales—$1Mil-$5Mil
10,000 sq ft site, Distrib.—
Regional
Privately owned corporation

**IPACESETTERS**

135 Chestnut Ridge Rd., Ste. 2
(07645)
**Phone—(201) 391-1500**
(630) 243-9783
Fax—(201) 391-3266
www.callargi.com
Email—tsearcy@ipacesetters.com
Pres., CEO—Tim Searcy
CFO—Michael Kennedy
SIC—7372; *Marketing &
subscription fulfillment software
development*
Employs—25; Estab.—1980
Sales—$500,000-$1Mil
Distrib.—Intl.
Privately owned corporation

**KAYPENTAX**

Div. of PENTAX Of America, Inc.
3 Paragon Dr. (07645)
**Phone—(973) 628-6200**
National—(800) 289-5297
Fax—(201) 391-2063
www.kaypentax.com
Email—sales@kaypentax.com
Pres.—David Woods
Dir., Sales—Steve Crump
Dir., IT—Vito Micciolo
Mfg. Mgr.—Joe Mulligan
SIC—3841; *Medical instruments*
Employs—50; Estab.—1947
44,000 sq ft site, Distrib.—Intl.
Privately owned corporation
Parent co.—PENTAX Of America,
Inc., Montvale, NJ
Phone—(201) 571-2300
See Parent Co. Section for full profile.

**KIDDE FIRE TRAINERS, LLC**

17 Philips Pkwy. (07645)
**Phone—(201) 300-8100**
National—(800) 288-3973
Fax—(201) 300-8101
www.kiddeft.com
Email—info-us@kiddeft.com
Pres., CEO—Rob Lane
Dir., Serv. & Upgrade Sales—
James Gould
Mktg. & Proposal Specialist—
Delana Peralta
SIC—3699; *Firefighter training
simulator systems; Brand
name—FireTrainer®*
Employs—65; Estab.—1979
Sales—$10Mil-$25Mil (est)
Distrib.—Intl.
Limited Liability Company

**PENTAX OF AMERICA, INC.**

3 Paragon Dr., Ste. 1 (07645)
**Phone—(201) 571-2300**
National—(800) 431-5880
Fax—(201) 391-3925
www.pentaxmedical.com
Email—sales@pentaxmedical.com
Pres.—David Woods
Ex. V-P.—Gene Merente

V-P., Hum. Res.—Adrienna
Messina
Hum. Res. Mgr.—Chris Casteline
SIC—3845; NAICS—334500;
*Corporate headquarters &
medical endoscopes*
Employs—180; Estab.—1979
Sales—$20Mil-$50Mil
40,000 sq ft site,
Privately owned corporation
AKA: Pentax Medical Co.

**TATA GLOBAL BEVERAGES (H Q)**

155 Chestnut Ridge Rd., 2nd Fl.
(07645)
**Phone—(201) 571-0300**
National—(800) 728-0084
Fax—(201) 571-0358
www.tataglobalbeverages.com
Email—communication.team@
tataglobalbeverages.com
CFO—Tom Corcoran
Sr. V-P., Sales & Mktg.—David
Allen
Sr. V-P.—Daniel Smith
V-P., Hum. Res.—Liesel Bell
Dir., IT—Jeff Howard
SIC—2095; NAICS—311920;
*Company headquarters; coffee
roasting & packing; Brand
name—Tetley USA; Eight
O'Clock Coffee*
Employs—50
Sales—$25Mil-$50Mil (est)
Distrib.—National
Publicly owned corporation
AKA: Tetley Harris Food Group

**WAINSCOT MEDIA**

110 Summit Ave. (07645)
**Phone—(201) 571-2244**
Fax—(201) 782-5319
www.wainscotmedia.com
Cont.—Agnes Salves
Dir., Adv.—Jacquelynn Fischer
Hum. Res., IT & Off. Mgr.—
Cathryn Valentine
SIC—2721; *Custom regional
health & lifestyle magazine
publishing*
Employs—50; Estab.—2005
Sales—$1Mil-$2.5Mil
Distrib.—Regional
Limited Liability Company

**†WINEBOW, INC.**

75 Chestnut Ridge Rd., Ste. 1
(07645)
**Phone—(201) 445-0620**
Fax—(201) 445-9869
www.winebow.com
Email—info@winebow.com
Founder & Chrm.—Leonardo
LoCascio
Pres., CEO—Jon Moramarco
Group Pres., Dist.—Frank Shobe
Group Pres., Fin. & Opers.—Scott
Ades
CFO—Mark Nowicki
Sr. V-P., CIO—Michael Levine
Dir., Pub. Rels.—Marilyn Krieger
GM, Sales, NJ—Robert Barry
SIC—5182; *Corporate
headquarters & distributor of
wine & distilled beverages*
Employs—100; Estab.—1980
Distrib.—Regional
Privately owned corporation

## Montville
(Morris—N.W.)

**ASHTON FOOD MACHINERY CO.,
INC.**

P.O. Box 60 (07045)
**Phone—(973) 521-7603**
Fax—(973) 521-7603
www.ashtonfood.com
Email—ashtonfood@aol.com
Pres., Fin. & R & D Mgr.—
Lawrence Oberman
MIS Mgr.—David Oberman

GEOGRAPHICAL

## Montville—(cont.)

SIC—2064; NAICS—311300; Peanut processing machinery, blanchers, roasters & packaging; Brand name—Ashton; Golden Eagle
Employs—10; Estab.—1946
Sales—$1Mil-5Mil
26,000 sq ft site, Distrib.—Intl.
Privately owned sub-S corp.

### †AST BEARINGS, LLC

Div. of Motion Industries, Inc.
115 Main Rd. (07045)
**Phone—(973) 335-2230**
National—(800) 526-1250
Fax—(973) 335-6987
www.astbearings.com
Email—sales@astbearings.com
Pres.—Mike Pelehach
V-P., Sales & Mktg.—Dan Fox
SIC—5085; Distributor of ball bearings & related bearing products; Brand name—AST; GRW; EZO/Sapporo; IKO; IGUS; IJK; INA; JAF; KBC; KSK; NACHI; NTN; ORS; URB; SMT; GMN; FYH
Employs—60; Estab.—1963
Sales—$30Mil
Distrib.—Intl.
Privately owned corporation
ISO rating—AS9100, 9001:2008
Parent co.—Motion Industries, Inc., Birmingham, AL
Phone—(205) 951-1154
See Parent Co. Section for full profile.

### DRUG DELIVERY TECHNOLOGY, LLC

219 Changebridge Rd. (07045)
**Phone—(973) 299-1200**
Fax—(973) 299-7937
www.drug-dev.com
Email—info@drug-dev.com
Pres., Publisher—Ralph Vitaro
Editor-in-Chief—Dan Marino
Creative Dir.—Shalamar Eagel
SIC—2721; Pharmaceutical & biological delivery systems magazine publishing
Employs—25; Estab.—2001
Sales—$1Mil-$2.5Mil
Distrib.—Intl.
Limited Liability Company
AKA: Drug Development & Delivery

### FAT MURRAY'S DOGGY TREATS

3 Deer Hill Dr., P.O. Box 32 (07045)
**Phone—(973) 299-2968**
Fax—(973) 334-3481
www.fatmurrays.com
Email—info@fatmurrays.com
Owner—Ronda Fliss
SIC—2047; Gourmet baked dog treats; Brand name—Fat Murray's Doggy Treats
Employs—3; Estab.—2003
Sales—$1Mil-$2.5Mil
1,000 sq ft site, Distrib.—National
Limited Liability Company

### HICKOK MATTHEWS CO.

337 Main Rd. (07045)
**Phone—(973) 335-3400**
Fax—(973) 335-7964
www.hickokmatthews.com
Email—info@hickokmatthews.com
Pres.—W. Schroth
Sales Rep.—Susan Schoth
SIC—3499; Metal picture frames
Employs—10; Estab.—1957
Sales—under $500,000
Distrib.—National
Privately owned corporation

### MAROTTA CONTROLS, INC.

78 Boonton Ave., P.O. Box 427 (07045)
**Phone—(973) 334-7800**
Fax—(973) 334-1219

www.marotta.com
Email—sales@marotta.com
Pres.—Patrick Marotta
CFO—Kevin Price
V-P., CSO—Michael J. Leahan
V-P., Engrg.—Steve Fox
Dir., Opers.—Walter Gilmore
Dir., Comms. & Mktg.—Tara J. Collazo
Hum. Res. Mgr.—John McKinley
SIC—3492; 3592; 3728; 3769; NAICS—332912; High-performance & specialty motion & flow control products & systems for aerospace, defense & space applications, including valves, manifolds, hydraulic systems, electronic controllers & power supplies; Brand name—M-PACT Pure Air Compression Technologies; M-CRAFT Corrosion Resistant Advanced Fluid Technologies; M-CONTROL Electronic Control Equipment; Flo-Fuse; Flo-Fit
Employs—200; Estab.—1943
Sales—$25Mil-$50Mil
115,000 sq ft site, Distrib.—Intl.
Privately owned corporation
ISO rating—9001:2008

### PJ MURPHY FOREST PRODUCTS CORP. (H Q)

150 River Rd., Bldg. L, Ste. 1, P.O. Box 300 (07045)
**Phone—(973) 316-0800**
Fax—(973) 316-9455
www.pjmurphy.net
Email—info@pjmurphy.net
Pres.—Fred Faehner
Mng. Dir.—Josh Faehner
Off. Mgr.—Tim Faehner
SIC—2421; Corporate headquarters; sanitized animal bedding, wood chips, meat smokers, woodflour & hardwood flavoring sawdust
Employs—5; Estab.—1895
Sales—$1Mil-$2.5Mil (est)
Privately owned corporation

### ROCKLINE INDUSTRIES, INC.

1 Kramer Dr., P.O. Box 189 (07045)
**Phone—(973) 257-9346**
Fax—(973) 257-9672
www.rocklineind.com
Email—sales@rocklineind.com
Plt. Mgr.—Chris Bruno
Pur. Agt.—John O'Sullivan
SIC—2679; NAICS—322200; Coffee filters
Employs—160; Estab.—1976
80,000 sq ft site, Distrib.—National
Privately owned corporation
Parent co.—Rockline Industries, Inc., Sheboygan, WI
Phone—(920) 452-3004
See Parent Co. Section for full profile.

### SPERRO METAL PRODUCTS, LLC

2 Skyline Dr., P.O. Box 397 (07045)
**Phone—(973) 335-2000**
Fax—(973) 335-2656
www.sperro.com
Email—sales@sperro.com
Owner—James Fernandez
Off. Mgr.—Shirley Putnam
Proj. Mgr.—Ed Fernandez
SIC—3444; Sheet metal fabrication for the construction, architectural, industrial & power industries
Employs—25; Estab.—1970
20,000 sq ft site, Distrib.—Intl.
Limited Liability Company

### †SULLIVAN DENTAL PRODUCTS, INC.

Div. of Henry Schein, Inc.
45 U.S. Highway 46 (07058)
**Phone—(973) 227-3533**
Fax—(973) 227-3680
www.henryschein.com

Email—custserv@henryschein.com
Manager—George Khoury
Inventory Coord.—Mike Eain
SIC—5047; Distributor of dental, medical & veterinarian equipment & supplies
Employs—60; Estab.—2004
Distrib.—Intl.
Publicly owned corporation
Parent co.—Henry Schein, Inc., Melville, NY
Phone—(631) 843-5500
See Parent Co. Section for full profile.

### WEB INDUSTRIES, INC.

5 Mars Ct., P.O. Box 237 (07045)
**Phone—(973) 335-1200**
National—(800) 449-8692
Fax—(973) 335-7054
Email—webindustries@aol.com
Pres.—William Burgoyne
Secy-Treas.—Anne Marie Burgoyne
SIC—3291; Superabrasive grinding & slicing products for industrial applications
Employs—11; Estab.—1969
Sales—$1Mil-$2Mil
11,000 sq ft site, Distrib.—National
Privately owned sub-S corp.

---

## Moonachie

(Bergen—N.E.)

### †ABBEY METAL CORP.

59 Grand St. (07074)
**Phone—(201) 438-0330**
Fax—(201) 438-6002
www.abbeymetal.com
Email—mail@abbeymetal.com
Pres.—Burton G. Zuckerman
CFO—Kenneth O. Zuckerman
Corp. Secy.—Arthur M. Zuckerman
Plt. Mgr.—Arthur Hoizer
SIC—5093; Wholesaler of nonferrous, high temperature & specialty metals
Employs—10; Estab.—1947
Sales—$5Mil-$10Mil
15,000 sq ft site, Distrib.—National
Privately owned corporation

### ACRISON, INC.

20 Empire Blvd. (07074)
**Phone—(201) 440-8300**
Fax—(201) 440-4939
www.acrison.com
Email—informail@acrison.com
Dir., Mktg.—John T. Shaw
Asst. Sales Mgr., Natl.—Sam Berry
SIC—3559; 3589; 3625; NAICS—333319; Volumetric & weight-loss feeders & blenders & wastewater treatment equipment & controls; Brand name—Acri Data; Acri-lok; Batch-lok; MD-II 2000; SBC-2000
Employs—140; Estab.—1963
Sales—$25Mil-$50Mil
Distrib.—Intl.
Privately owned corporation

### ALGAR-THE DISPLAY CONNECTION INC.

131 W. Commercial Ave. (07074)
**Phone—(201) 438-1000**
Fax—(201) 438-2224
www.display-connection.com
Email—bonnie@displayconnection.com
Pres.—Deian Urso
Plt. Mgr.—Ed Chudkowski
Off. Mgr.—Bonnie Kachidurian
Shpg. Mgr.—Cliff Goldberg

SIC—2541; Point-of-purchase displays
Employs—65; Estab.—1981
Varies: 65-80
Sales—$5Mil-$10Mil
Distrib.—National
Privately owned corporation
DBA: The Display Connection

### ALU, INC.

240 Anderson Ave. (07074)
**Phone—(201) 617-2000**
Fax—(201) 617-2001
www.alu.com
Email—daniele.cincotti@alu.com
CFO & COO—Daniele Cincotti
Cust. Serv. Rep.—Elizabeth Oquendo
Cust. Serv. Rep.—Myrna Colondres
Cust. Serv. Rep.—Paul Maldonado
SIC—2542; Aluminum store display fixtures
Employs—15; Estab.—1986
Sales—$1Mil-$2.5Mil (est)
Distrib.—Intl.
Privately owned corporation

### AMKO DISPLAYS, LLC (H Q)

4 Barrett Ave. (07074)
**Phone—(201) 460-7199**
National—(800) 503-7199
Fax—(201) 460-7197
www.amkodisplay.com
Email—info@amkodisplay.com
Pres.—Douglas Lim
Manager—Eric Um
SIC—2542; Company headquarters; display cases (mfg. subcontracted)
Employs—3; Estab.—1991
Sales—$500,000-$1Mil
Distrib.—Intl.
Limited Liability Company

### AVANTI LINENS, INC.

234 Moonachie Rd. (07074)
**Phone—(201) 641-7766**
National—(800) 360-0836
Fax—(201) 641-1712
www.avantilinens.com
Email—info@avantilinens.com
Chrm.—Arthur Tauber
CFO & Hum. Res. Mgr.—Patricia Grisolia
COO—Jeff Kaufman
SIC—2392; 2399; Embellished & bordered towels & kitchen textiles
Employs—165; Estab.—1969
Sales—$6Mil-$10Mil
125,000 sq ft site, Distrib.—Intl.
Privately owned corporation

### BIO COMPRESSION SYSTEMS, INC.

120 W. Commercial Ave. (07074)
**Phone—(201) 939-0716**
National—(800) 888-0908
Fax—(201) 939-4503
www.biocompression.com
Email—biosystems@biocompression.com
CEO, Sales Mgr.—Robert G. Freidenrich
Pres., Sales Mgr.—Jonathan Ross
Ex. V-P., Mktg. & Prod. Dev.—John Motherwell
Comp.—Kathy Finley
Dir., Mktg.—Laureen Baccaro
Dir., Qual. Assur. & Regulatory Affs.—Barbara Whitman
IT & Matls. Mgr.—Amanda Riley
Cust. Serv. Rep.—Carolyn Depascale
Cust. Serv. Rep.—Gloria Rozema
Cust. Serv. Rep.—Toni Ann D'Agnese
SIC—3841; Medical equipment
Employs—15; Estab.—1973
Sales—over $10Mil
10,000 sq ft site, Distrib.—Intl.
Sole ownership

## Moonachie—(cont.)

**BYLADA FOODS, LLC**
140 W. Commercial Ave. (07074)
**Phone—(201) 933-7474**
Fax—(201) 933-1530
www.byladafoods.com
Email—info@byladafoods.com
GM—Eric Silverman
SIC—2038; NAICS—311412;
 *Miniature pizza bagels*
Employs—35
Distrib.—National
Limited Liability Company

**C C S STONE**
9-11 Caesar Pl. (07074)
**Phone—(201) 933-1515**
National—(800) 227-7785
Fax—(201) 933-5744
www.ccsstone.com
Email—info@ccsstone.com
Pres.—Don Mitnick
V-P.—Jonathan Mitnick
V-P.—Bryan Mitnick
Cont.—Corey Mitnick
SIC—3281; 2531; NAICS—
 327991; *Marble, granite, slate &
 limestone products, including
 slabs, tiles & cut-to-size projects*
Employs—25; Estab.—1963
53,000 sq ft site, Distrib.—National
Privately owned corporation

**CAPCO SPORTSWEAR INC. (H Q)**
100 W. Commercial Ave. (07074)
**Phone—(201) 939-9228**
National—(800) 322-7267
Fax—(201) 939-8858
www.kccaps.com
Email—nj@kccaps.com
GM—Wally Richards
Cust. Serv. Rep.—J. Delgado
SIC—2353; 2329; 2392; 2395;
 NAICS—315200; *Corporate
 headquarters; stock blank
 baseball caps, knitted ribbed
 toques & beanies, blankets &
 aprons, including domestic
 embroidery (mfg. done
 overseas); Brand name—KC
 Caps; Head Shots; KC Sport;
 NU-FIT; Napa*
Employs—10; Estab.—1987
Distrib.—Intl.
Privately owned corporation
AKA: KC Caps

**CARTER MFG. CO., INC.**
55 Anderson Ave. *(07074)*
**Phone—(201) 935-0770**
Fax—(201) 935-2812
www.carterstampings.com
Email—sales@carterstampings.com
Pres.—John Scholz
Prodn. Mgr.—Mark Casatelli
Qual. Assur. Mgr.—M. Patel
SIC—3469; *Metal stampings*
Employs—30; Estab.—1954
20,000 sq ft site, Distrib.—Intl.
Privately owned corporation

**COGNATI CHEESE CO., INC.**
Div. of Schratter Foods, Inc.
205 Moonachie Rd., 2nd Fl.
 (07074)
**Phone—(201) 807-9100**
Fax—(201) 807-9696
Email—alvino.daddio@
 cognaticheese.com
Pres.—Alain Voss
Cont.—Sunit Patel
Plt. Mgr.—Al Daddio
SIC—2022; NAICS—311513;
 *Cheese*
Employs—45; Estab.—1995
Distrib.—Regional
Privately owned corporation
Parent co.—Schratter Foods, Inc.,
 Fairfield, NJ
 Phone—(973) 575-3226
 See Parent Co. Section for full profile.

**COLUMBIA NUT & BOLT, LLC**
Div. of Supply Technologies, LLC
50 Graphic Pl. (07074)
**Phone—(201) 641-7600**
Fax—(201) 641-4200
Pres.—William Laufer
SIC—3452; NAICS—332722;
 *Fasteners*
Employs—50; Estab.—1955
Sales—$5Mil-$10Mil (est)
Distrib.—Intl.
Limited Liability Company
Parent co.—Supply Technologies,
 LLC, Cleveland, OH
 Phone—(440) 947-2100
 See Parent Co. Section for full profile.

**DU TECHNOLOGIES, INC.**
300 W. Commercial Ave. (07074)
**Phone—(201) 729-0070**
Fax—(201) 328-9555
www.dutechnologies.com
Email—info@dutechnologies.com
Pres.—Marcel Branis
Opers. Mgr.—John Andronici
Sales Rep.—Tom Slaughter
SIC—3089; *Insulated flexible
 plastic ductwork*
Employs—25; Estab.—1999
Sales—$2.5Mil-$5Mil (est)
Distrib.—Intl.
Privately owned corporation

**DV8 ENTERPRISES, LLC**
141 W. Commercial Ave. (07074)
**Phone—(201) 641-4944**
Fax—(201) 641-3468
www.dv8foamfabrication.com
Email—mike3@dv8.com
Pres., CEO—Michael Mozeika III
COO—Robert J. Virella
Cust. Serv. Mgr.—Tara Stendari
SIC—3086; NAICS—326100;
 *Reticulated polyurethane foams
 & flexible plastic foam products
 for consumer products, military
 vehicles, waste treatment
 installations, home improvement
 stores & medical devices*
Employs—25; Estab.—2012
35,000 sq ft site, Distrib.—Intl.
Privately owned corporation

**EARTHDIGITAL**
Div. of EarthColor, Inc.
77 Moonachie Ave. (07074)
**Phone—(551) 497-5400**
National—(888) 282-4141
Fax—(201) 896-8049
www.earthcolor.com
Email—bandino@earthcolor.com
Pres.—Nicholas Brusco
V-P., Mktg.—Carin Mifsud
V-P., Mailing—Barbara Andino
SIC—2759; NAICS—323100;
 *Digital printing & fulfillment &
 mailing services, including web-
 to-print services & data
 management*
Employs—175; Estab.—1965
125,000 sq ft site, Distrib.—
 National
Privately owned partnership
Parent co.—EarthColor, Inc.,
 Parsippany, NJ
 Phone—(973) 884-1300
 See Parent Co. Section for full profile.

**ELECTRO-MINIATURES CORP.**
68 W. Commercial Ave. (07074)
**Phone—(201) 460-0510**
Fax—(201) 935-8153
www.electro-miniatures.com
Email—info@emcsales.com
Pres.—Mark Pollack
Dir., Admn. & Opers.—Laurie
 Edelman
Sales Mgr.—Barbara Triolo
Pur. Agt.—Renee Campbell

SIC—3621; NAICS—335312;
 *Electrical slip rings & slip ring
 assemblies*
Employs—70; Estab.—1974
20,000 sq ft site, Distrib.—
 Regional
Privately owned corporation

**FLEXI PRINTING PLATE CO., INC.**
50 Commercial Ave. (07074)
**Phone—(201) 939-3600**
Fax—(201) 460-7866
www.flexiplate.com
Email—flexi@flexiplate.com
Pres.—John Moss
SIC—2796; NAICS—323122;
 *Printing plates, commercial
 printing & photo engravings*
Employs—50; Estab.—1956
27,000 sq ft site, Distrib.—Regional
Privately owned corporation
AKA: FlexiGalvanic

**GRACIS, INC.**
25 Graphic Pl. (07074)
**Phone—(201) 296-0700**
Fax—(201) 296-0701
Email—gracisprint2@aol.com
Pres.—Robert Powell
Secy-Treas.—Diane Powell
SIC—2752; 2791; NAICS—
 323122; *Offset printing &
 typesetting*
Employs—2; Estab.—1901
Sales—under $500,000
Distrib.—Regional
Privately owned corporation

**GRAND DISPLAYS, INC.**
12 Empire Blvd. (07074)
**Phone—(201) 994-1500**
Fax—(201) 994-1180
www.grand-display.com
Email—susan@edisonlitho.com
Pres.—Susan Ostreicher
CFO—Joe Ostreicher
Mng. Dir.—Peggy Sacino
Hum. Res. Mgr.—Anna Bagnato
SIC—2675; 2541; 2542; 3993;
 NAICS—322200; *Paper die
 cutting & displays*
Employs—60; Estab.—1983
Distrib.—Intl.
Privately owned corporation

**H. CROSS CO.**
150 W. Commercial Ave. (07074)
**Phone—(201) 964-9380**
Fax—(201) 964-9385
www.hcrosscompany.com
Email—info@hcrosscompany.com
Pres.—Edward McClary
Administrator—Diane McClary
SIC—3356; NAICS—331491;
 *Rhenium, molybdenum,
 tungsten, tantalum & precious
 metals ribbons, strips, foils &
 wires, including metal slitting &
 processing*
Employs—36; Estab.—1939
28,000 sq ft site, Distrib.—Intl.
Privately owned corporation

**HAIN CELESTIAL GROUP, INC., THE**
50 Knickerbocker Rd. (07074)
**Phone—(201) 935-4500**
National—(800) 958-3772
Fax—(201) 935-8264
www.terrachips.com
Email—consumerrelations@hain-
 celestial.com
Plt. Mgr.—Yoses Brecher
Hum. Res. Mgr.—Nidia Trotta
SIC—2034; *Vegetable chips*
Employs—100
Sales—$5Mil-$10Mil (est)
Distrib.—Intl.
Privately owned corporation
AKA: Terra Chips
Parent co.—Hain Celestial Group,
 Inc., The, New Hyde Park, NY
 Phone—(516) 587-5000
 See Parent Co. Section for full profile.

NEW ENTRY
**HIGHROAD PRESS**
220 Anderson Ave. (07074)
**Phone—(201) 708-6900**
Fax—(201) 636-4088
www.highroadpress.com
Email—info@highroadpress.com
Owner & CEO—Hallie Satz
Pres.—Eric Tepfer
SIC—2759; 2789; NAICS—
 323100; *Commercial, digital,
 sheet-fed & web printing,
 including prepress, bindery &
 fulfillment services*
Employs—45; Estab.—2004
Sales—$11Mil
38,000 sq ft site, Distrib.—
 Regional
Limited Liability Company

**INOAC - CREST FOAM**
100 Carol Pl. (07074)
**Phone—(201) 807-0809**
Fax—(201) 229-1344
www.crestfoam.com
Email—info@crestfoam.com
V-P., Mfg.—Jay Patel
Dir., Safety & Hum. Res. Mgr.—
 Eric Reyes
Sales & Mktg. Mgr.—Dimitri
 Dounis
Cust. Serv. Mgr.—Cristian Tapia
Plt. Controller—Tess Sun
SIC—3086; NAICS—326100;
 *Polyurethane reticulated ester &
 ether foam; Brand name—
 Filtercrest; EZ-Dri; JetCrest;
 Feltcrest; SafeCrest; HydroCrest*
Employs—75; Estab.—1991
Sales—$25Mil-$30Mil
130,000 sq ft site, Distrib.—Intl.
Privately owned corporation
ISO rating—9001

**INTERNATIONAL AROMATICS, INC.**
200 Anderson Ave. (07074)
**Phone—(201) 964-0900**
Fax—(201) 964-0807
Email—customercare@
 iaromatics.com
Pres.—Gary Gerardi
Hum. Res. Mgr.—Tareeza Acosta
Cust. Serv. Rep.—Linda Lieng
Fragrance Evaluator—Christina
 Vega
SIC—2844; NAICS—325600;
 *Fragrances*
Employs—15; Estab.—1984
Sales—under $500,000
Distrib.—National
Privately owned corporation

**JADE EASTERN TRADING, INC.**
245 Moonachie Rd. (07074)
**Phone—(201) 440-8500**
www.marquisny.com
Email—marquis@marquisny.com
Pres.—J. R. Lee
IT Mgr.—Byung Seo
SIC—2321; NAICS—315200;
 *Men's polo, dress, denim &
 woven shirts*
Employs—15; Estab.—1975
Distrib.—Intl.
Privately owned corporation
AKA: Marquis

**†LA FE FOODS, INC.**
230 Moonachie Ave. (07074)
**Phone—(201) 329-6260**
Fax—(201) 329-6272
www.lafe.com
Pres.—Juan Carlos Pena
V-P., Sales—Marino Roa
Pur. Agt.—Aaron Soca
Hum. Res. Exec.—Latisha Martin
Fin. Exec.—Julio Wexler
Telecommunication Exec.—Linda
 Colon

## Moonachie—(cont.)

SIC—5141; 5143; 5142;
*Distributor of groceries from the
Caribbean, Central America,
South America & Europe,
including dairy, beverages &
frozen food products*
Employs—85; Estab.—2001
Distrib.—Local
Privately owned corporation
AKA: Gonzalez & Tapanes, Inc.

### LPS INDUSTRIES, INC.

10 Caesar Pl. (07074)
**Phone—(201) 438-3515**
National—(800) 275-4577
Fax—(201) 438-0040
www.lpsind.com
Email—info@lpsind.com
CEO—Madeleine Robinson
V-P., Sales—Phil Pasqualone
Dir., IT—Stephen Tansey
Hum. Res. Mgr.—Beth Senzer
SIC—2652; 2655; 2621; 2673;
NAICS—322213; *Paperboard
boxes & tubes, paper & foil
packaging; Brand name—
Vaporflex; PresQuick; Top-Loc;
Loc-Top*
Employs—225; Estab.—1959
200,000 sq ft site, Distrib.—Intl.
Limited Liability Company
ISO rating—9001:2008

### MEADOWLANDS BINDERY, INC.

146 W. Commercial Ave. *(07074)*
**Phone—(201) 935-6161**
Fax—(201) 935-9014
www.meadowlandsbindery.com
Email—frank@mbibindery.com
Pres.—Carmine Idone
V-P.—Frank Idone
Corp. Secy.—Maria Molfetas
Off. Mgr.—Terri Corriston
SIC—2789; NAICS—323121;
*Bookbinding*
Employs—40; Estab.—1978
Distrib.—Regional
Privately owned corporation

### MOVEABLE FEAST, INC.

99 Grand St., Ste. 8 (07074)
**Phone—(201) 939-4500**
Fax—(201) 939-5444
www.chefalains.com
Owner—Alain Quirin
Bus. Mgr.—Denise Quirin
SIC—2092; NAICS—311712;
*Smoked fish, including salmon,
trout, tuna & sturgeon; Brand
name—Chef Alain's*
Employs—5; Estab.—1998
Sales—$500,000-$1Mil
3,000 sq ft site, Distrib.—National
Privately owned corporation

### †NATIONAL TILE & MOSAIC

175 Moonachie Rd. (07074)
**Phone—(201) 807-9800**
Fax—(201) 807-9020
www.nationaltileandmosaic.com
Email—nationaltileandmosaic@
gmail.com
Pres.—Leila Mehrnia
SIC—5032; *Wholesaler of
limestone, stone & marble tile;
Brand name—Magnolia
Collection; British Ceramic;
Codicer; Castel*
Employs—3; Estab.—2010
Sales—$500,000-$1Mil
17,000 sq ft site, Distrib.—National
Limited Liability Company

### PERFECT PEARL CO., INC.

100 State St. (07074)
**Phone—(201) 705-5200**
Fax—(201) 641-5055
Email—info@ppearlco.com
Pres.—Albert Spitzer
Corp. Secy.—Eli Spitzer
Opers. Mgr.—Moshe Tyner
Off. Mgr.—Galina Ruvin

SIC—3961; NAICS—339900;
*Costume jewelry; Brand name—
'Majestic'; 'Menorca'*
Employs—40; Estab.—1956
10,000 sq ft site, Distrib.—Intl.
Privately owned corporation

### PERMA GRAPHICS, INC.

25 Graphic Pl. (07074)
**Phone—(201) 814-1200**
Fax—(201) 814-1600
www.permagraphicsinc.com
Email—perma.graphics@
verizon.net
Pres.—Rita Caloni
V-P.—Michael Caloni
Prodn. Mgr.—Michael Pagano
SIC—2752; NAICS—323100;
*Offset printing*
Employs—15; Estab.—1988
Sales—$3Mil-$5Mil
25,000 sq ft site, Distrib.—Intl.
Privately owned corporation

### PRESIDENT CONTAINER GROUP

200 W. Commercial Ave. (07074)
Mail addr: P.O. Box 387, Wood
Ridge (07075)
**Phone—(201) 933-7500**
Fax—(201) 933-8990
www.presidentcontainer.com
Email—pcsales@
presidentcontainer.com
Pres.—Marvin Grossbard
Sr. V-P.—Richard Grossbard
V-P., Sales—John Kasztan
V-P., Prodn.—Joe Restifo
V-P., Opers.—Richard Goldberg
V-P.—Larry Grossbard
IT Mgr.—Trevor Smith
SIC—2653; NAICS—322211;
*Company headquarters &
corrugated paperboard
containers & point-of-purchase
displays*
Employs—100; Estab.—1947
Company-wide: 400
Sales—$50Mil-$100Mil
Distrib.—National

### RAFFETTO'S CORP.

62 W. Commercial Ave. (07074)
**Phone—(201) 372-1222**
Fax—(201) 935-4619
Pres.—Richard Raffetto
Off. Admn.—John Papa
SIC—2098; NAICS—311823;
*Fresh macaroni, spaghetti &
fettuccini*
Employs—15; Estab.—1906
Sales—$1Mil-$2.5Mil
Distrib.—Local
Privately owned corporation

### †RONDO INC. USA

51 Joseph St. (07074)
**Phone—(201) 229-9700**
National—(800) 882-0633
Fax—(201) 229-0018
www.rondo-inc.com
Email—info@us.rondo-online.com
Pres.—Jerry Murphy
V-P., Sales—Andrea Henderson
SIC—5046; 5084; *Distributor of
commercial & industrial bakery
equipment & parts & repair
services; Brand name—
RONDO; Benier; Diosna*
Employs—15; Estab.—1964
Distrib.—National
Privately owned corporation

### ROYAL BAKING CO.

8 Empire Blvd. (07074)
**Phone—(201) 296-0888**
Fax—(201) 296-0950
Owner & Pres.—Jack Dipiazza
Plt. Mgr.—Carmen Dipiazza

SIC—2051; NAICS—311812;
*Bakery products, including
bread & cakes*
Employs—80; Estab.—1963
Distrib.—National
Privately owned corporation
AKA: Leonard Novelty Bakery

### †RUGBY ABP CORP.

Div. of Rugby IPD Corp.
60 Joseph St. (07074)
**Phone—(201) 807-9701**
National—(800) 447-7578
Fax—(201) 807-9719
www.rugbyabp.com
Email—aalvarez@rugbyabp.com
Regional Mgr.—Arsenio Alvarez
IT Mgr.—Greg Shinn
Hum. Res. Mgr.—Adriane Ramos
Cust. Serv. Rep.—Jose Iglesias
SIC—5031; 5074; 5072; 5169;
*Wholesaler of industrial building
materials, including hardwood
veneer & plywood, melamine
board, butcher block tops, solid
wood cabinets & parts, stainless
steel sinks & faucets, hand tools
& adhesives; Brand name—
Rugby; Staron; Samsung;
Flakeboard of Canada; Michigan
Maple Block; Veneer Tech;
Columbia Forest*
Employs—20; Estab.—1983
Sales—$1Mil-$2.5Mil
Distrib.—Local
Privately owned corporation
Parent co.—Rugby IPD Corp.,
Concord, NH
Phone—(603) 369-6004
See Parent Co. Section for full profile.

### SANKAR ASSOCS., INC.

14 Empire Blvd. (07074)
**Phone—(201) 994-1700**
Fax—(201) 994-1708
www.sankarassociates.com
Email—sankar@
sankarassociates.com
Pres.—Burton Kreindel
V-P.—Jeffrey Weinstein
SIC—2022; 3089; NAICS—
311513; *Contract cheese
packaging for the dairy industry*
Employs—30; Estab.—1994
Distrib.—National
Privately owned corporation

### SCREEN-TRANS DEVELOPMENT CORP.

100 Grand St. (07074)
**Phone—(201) 933-7800**
National—(800) 338-7437
Fax—(201) 804-6371
www.screentrans.com
Email—info@screentrans.com
Pres.—Robert DeVries
Bookkeeper—Barbara Moran
SIC—2399; *Fabric banners,
including textile screen, table &
rotary digital inkjet & dye
sublimation printing on fabrics;
Brand name—Accu-Trans®; Foil-
On®*
Employs—25; Estab.—1958
Sales—$2.5Mil-$3Mil
18,800 sq ft site, Distrib.—National
Privately owned corporation

### SLEEPABLE SOFAS LTD.

6 Empire Blvd. (07074)
**Phone—(973) 546-4502**
Fax—(973) 546-9347
www.sleepablesofas.com
Email—info@sleepablesofas.com
Pres., CEO—Darren DeMatteo
Pres.—Donna DeMatteo
Cont., MIS Mgr.—Susan Roman
Plt. Mgr.—Gerald Shortino
Plt. Mgr.—Robert Roman
Pur. Mgr.—Bud Randle

SIC—2512; 2392; NAICS—
337121; *Company headquarters
& custom upholstered furniture,
seating & down & feather
products; Brand name—Avery
Boardman Ltd; Carlyle Custom
Convertibles; Lodi Down &
Feather*
Employs—65; Estab.—1971
Sales—$1Mil-$5Mil
Distrib.—National
Privately owned corporation

### STAR RAVIOLI MFG. CO., INC.

2 Anderson Ave. (07074)
**Phone—(201) 933-6427**
Fax—(201) 933-0484
www.starravioli.com
Email—sales@starravioli.com
Pres., CFO—Laurence Piretra
V-P.—Eileen Pisani
V-P.—Michael Piretra
Sales Mgr.—Richard Pisani
SIC—2098; 2038; NAICS—
311823; *Fresh & frozen gourmet
Italian ravioli, stuffed shells,
manicotti, gnocchi & tortellini*
Employs—12; Estab.—1946
Distrib.—Regional
Privately owned corporation

### STATE CONTAINER CORP.

111 W. Commercial Ave. (07074)
Mail addr: P.O. Box 502,
Rutherford (07070)
**Phone—(201) 933-5200**
Fax—(201) 933-0968
www.statecontainer.com
GM—Carmine Barresi
Plt. Mgr.—Jose Lugo
Cust. Serv. Rep.—Dawn Vantile
SIC—2653; NAICS—322211;
*Corrugated boxes & containers*
Employs—60; Estab.—1955
85,000 sq ft site, Distrib.—
Regional
Privately owned corporation

### SWINTEC EAST (H Q)

320 W. Commercial Ave. (07074)
Mail addr: P.O. Box 356, Wood
Ridge (07075-0356)
**Phone—(201) 935-0115**
National—(800) 225-0867
Fax—(201) 935-6021
www.swintec.com
Email—customerinfo@swintec.com
Pres.—Dominic Vespia
V-P.—Matt Arki
Sales Mgr.—Ed Michaels
SIC—3579; *Company
headquarters; typewriters,
calculators & cash registers
(mfg. done overseas)*
Employs—10; Estab.—1978
Sales—$1Mil-$2.5Mil
Distrib.—Intl.

### TRI-LON COLOR GRAPHICS, INC.

220 Anderson Ave. (07074)
**Phone—(201) 708-6900**
Fax—(201) 708-6901
www.trilongraphics.com
Email—info@trilongraphics.com
Pres.—David Strickler
V-P.—Mark Strickler
SIC—2759; NAICS—323122;
*Digital printing*
Employs—35
Distrib.—Local
Privately owned corporation

### †TUBE LIGHT CO., INC. (H Q)

300 Park St. (07074-1139)
**Phone—(201) 641-6660**
(201) 641-1011
National—(800) 631-0778
Fax—(800) 637-1011
www.tubelite.com
Email—dbrown@tubelite.com
Pres.—Leon Jaffe
V-P., Fin.—Sharon Schwartz
Cont.—Steve Able
GM—Don Brown

## Moonachie—(cont.)

Cust. Serv. Mgr.—Lois Stibely
Whse. Mgr.—Rocco Della Luna
SIC—5099; 5199; *Corporate headquarters; distributor of sign, screen printing & digital imaging supplies; Brand name—Hewlett-Packard; 3m; Avery; Oracal; Laminators; Sign Foam; Aluminum Sheets; Cut Vinyl; Gerber; Digital Printers; UV Printers; Flatebed Printers; Alcan; Jain; Plotters; Thermal Printers; Sericol; Mimaki; Graphtec*
Employs—180; Estab.—1964
Sales—$5Mil-$30Mil
Distrib.—Intl.
Privately owned corporation
AKA: Tubelite Co., Inc.

### ULTIMATE SPINNING & TURNING CORP.

9 Willow St. (07074)
**Phone—(201) 372-9740**
Fax—(201) 372-9742
www.ultimatespinning.com
Email—info@ultimatespinning.com
Pres.—Mike Novack
Off. Mgr.—Diane Van Blarcom
SIC—3541; 3599; NAICS—333512; *Metal, stainless steel & brass spinning & turning*
Employs—12; Estab.—1947
Sales—$1.5Mil
6,000 sq ft site, Distrib.—National
Privately owned corporation

---

## Moorestown
(Burlington—S.E.)

### ACKLEY MACHINE CORP.

1273 N. Church St., Ste. 106 (08057-1194)
**Phone—(856) 234-3626**
Fax—(856) 234-8657
www.ackleymachine.com
Email—accounting@ackleymachine.com
Pres.—Michael Ackley
Global Sales Mgr. & Chief Design Engr.—Sam Louden
Sales Mgr.—Phillip Gulotta
Pur. Agt.—David Pressler
Bookkeeper—Betty Bollinger
SIC—3555; NAICS—333293; *Printing machinery*
Employs—32; Estab.—1976
Sales—$1Mil-$5Mil
20,000 sq ft site, Distrib.—Intl.
Sole ownership

### ALBION ENGINEERING CO.

1250 N. Church St. (08057)
**Phone—(856) 235-6688**
Fax—(856) 235-9460
www.albioneng.com
Email—service@albioneng.com
Owner—Mark Schneider
GM—Robert E. Reynolds
Hum. Res. & Off. Mgr.—Lucinda Schneider
SIC—3423; *Professional caulking guns & adhesive dispensers; Brand name—Albion; DDT; Backer Rod; Hot Pot*
Employs—19; Estab.—1929
42,000 sq ft site, Distrib.—Intl.
Privately owned sub-S corp.

### AMERICAN BILTRITE, INC.

105 Whittendale Dr. (08057)
**Phone—(856) 778-0700**
National—(888) 224-6325
Fax—(856) 778-7485
www.abitape.com
Email—info@abitape.com
V-P., GM—Michel Merky
V-P., Opers.—Rob Scheader
V-P., Hum. Res.—Bonnie Posnak
V-P., Fin.—Art Carr
V-P., R & D—John Poulton

Plt. Mgr.—Joseph Derr
Pur. Mgr.—Stan Male
MIS & IT Mgr.—Joseph Mariani
Hum. Res. Mgr.—Fran Venneri
Qual. Assur. Mgr.—Jim August
SIC—2672; NAICS—322222; *Pressure-sensitive tape, including film & paper products for the sign industry & automotive & industrial applications*
Employs—100; Estab.—1908
Sales—$40Mil-$50Mil
250,000 sq ft site, Distrib.—Intl.
Publicly owned corporation
Parent co.—American Biltrite, Inc., Wellesley, MA
Phone—(781) 237-6655
See Parent Co. Section for full profile.

### ANDEK CORPORATION

850 Glen Ave., P.O. Box 392 (08057)
**Phone—(856) 786-6900**
National—(800) 800-2844
Fax—(856) 786-0580
www.andek.com
Email—info@andek.com
Pres.—Harvey Liss
Ex. V-P.—Neil Shearer
V-P.—Andrew Liss
Opers. Mgr.—Thomas Taylor
Financial Mgr.—Hans Braun
Qual. Control Mgr.—Joanne Pizzillo
SIC—2891; 2851; NAICS—325520; *High-performance coatings & sealant systems for the commercial, industrial & residential construction industries; Brand name—Andek; Polaroof; Polafloor; Polagard; Polaseal; Polajoint; Polaprime; RoofdX; Flashband; COCOON*
Employs—20; Estab.—1973
20,000 sq ft site, Distrib.—Intl.
Privately owned corporation
ISO rating—9001

### AUTOMATION & CONTROL, INC.

1491 Lancer Dr. (08057)
**Phone—(856) 234-2300**
Fax—(856) 234-5223
www.automation-control.com
Email—info@automation-control.com
Pres.—Ron Iannacone
Off. Mgr.—Darra Hansken
Bus. Dev. Mgr.—Janet Marie Patel
SIC—3625; 7372; 7373; NAICS—335314; *Custom industrial automation control panel fabrication & industrial electrical contracting, including electrical engineering, software development & systems integration; Brand name—Factory Intelligence Network-FIN*
Employs—30; Estab.—1994
Sales—$5Mil-$10Mil (est)
Distrib.—National
Privately owned sub-S corp.
AKA: ACI

### BARLOW TYRIE, INC.

1263 Glen Ave., Ste. 230 (08057)
**Phone—(856) 273-7878**
National—(800) 451-7467
Fax—(856) 273-9199
www.teak.com
Email—ussales@teak.com
Ex. V-P.—C. W. Hessler
SIC—2511; *High-end residential & commercial outdoor furnishings*
Employs—8; Estab.—1920
Sales—$5Mil-$10Mil
35,000 sq ft site, Distrib.—Intl.
Privately owned corporation

### BIOMEDICON

30 E. Central Ave. (08057)
**Phone—(856) 778-1880**
Fax—(856) 778-1880

www.biomedicon.com
Email—msinger@biomedicon.com
Pres., GM & Opers. Mgr.—Mark Singer
SIC—3841; 3842; *Hospital operating room & procedure room instruments & equipment; Brand name—BioMediCon*
Employs—19; Estab.—1984
Sales—under $1.5Mil
Distrib.—Intl.
Sole ownership

### BODINE TOOL & MACHINE CO., INC.

1273 N. Church St., Ste. 103 (08057)
**Phone—(856) 234-7800**
Fax—(856) 234-4281
www.bodinetool.com
Email—bodine@bodinetool.com
Pres.—William Lauth
V-P., GM—Brian Lauth
Off. Mgr.—Sarah Uff
SIC—3544; NAICS—333500; *Tool & die job shop*
Employs—30; Estab.—1937
Sales—$2.5Mil-$5Mil (est)
20,000 sq ft site, Distrib.—Local
Privately owned corporation

### C. R. LAURENCE CO., INC.

1511 Lancer Dr. (08057)
**Phone—(856) 727-1022**
Fax—(866) 727-3299
www.crlaurence.com
Email—info@crlaurence.com
Br. Mgr.—Jason Kee
Asst. Mgr.—Kelly Perkins
SIC—3429; *Hardware for glass mirrors, displays, windows & doors*
Employs—15; Estab.—1992
Distrib.—Intl.
Privately owned corporation
Parent co.—C. R. Laurence Co., Inc., Los Angeles, CA
Phone—(323) 588-1281
See Parent Co. Section for full profile.

### CHEMIQUE, INC.

315 N. Washington Ave. (08057)
**Phone—(856) 235-4161**
National—(800) 225-4161
Fax—(856) 273-0917
www.chemique.com
Email—chemique@aol.com
Pres.—Edward Drazga
Sales Mgr.—Jennifer Drazga
Prodn. Mgr.—Perry Lafferty
Sales Coord.—JoAnn Roadside
SIC—2842; 2851; NAICS—325612; *Kitchen & bathroom cleaners, marble & stone care, car detailing & building restoration products, deck & wood strippers & cleaners, paver cleaners & sealers, paint removers & graffiti solutions; Brand name—KRC-7®; Artisan®; DWR®; Bac-2-Nu®; Strip-It®; New England®*
Employs—10; Estab.—1976
Sales—$2.2Mil
15,000 sq ft site, Distrib.—National
Privately owned sub-S corp.

### CIRCUIT TECH ASSEMBLY, LLC

341 New Albany Rd., Ste. 130 (08057)
**Phone—(856) 231-0777**
Fax—(856) 231-7878
www.circuittechassembly.com
Email—bsherlock@circuittechassembly.com
Pres.—Bill Sherlock, Jr.
Cust. Serv. Mgr.—Dotti Lippincott

SIC—3672; 3679; NAICS—334412; *Contract electronic manufacturing services, including SMT & PTH printed circuit board assemblies, box builds & testing*
Employs—12; Estab.—2004
Sales—over $3Mil
Distrib.—Intl.
Limited Liability Company
ISO rating—9001:2000

### CLONDALKIN PHARMA & HEALTHCARE

1224 N. Church St. (08057)
**Phone—(856) 439-1700**
www.clondalkin.com
Email—info@clondalkingroup.com
Dir., Opers.—Chris Lengthorn
Hum. Res. Mgr.—Lisa Monte Carlo
SIC—2759; NAICS—323100; *Inserts, labels & stickers printing for pharmaceutical companies*
Employs—177; Estab.—1999
Sales—$26Mil-$50Mil
Distrib.—Intl.
Privately owned sub-S corp.
Parent co.—Clondalkin Pharma & Healthcare, Greensboro, NC
Phone—(336) 292-4555
See Parent Co. Section for full profile.

### COM-PAK, INC.

Div. of Riverside Acquisition Group, LLC
365 New Albany Rd. (08057)
**Phone—(856) 802-1900**
Fax—(856) 787-4001
www.com-pak.com
Email—info@com-pak.com
CEO—Clif McDougall
Hum. Res. Mgr.—Dianne Daniels
Client Serv. Mgr.—Andrea Giordano
SIC—2759; 2789; *Commercial & digital printing & binding & direct mail services*
Employs—280
Sales—$25Mil-$50Mil (est)
Limited Liability Company
AKA: Com-Pak Services
Parent co.—Riverside Acquisition Group, LLC, Moorestown, NJ
Phone—(856) 802-1900
See Parent Co. Section for full profile.

### COMTREX SYSTEMS CORP.

1247 N. Church St., Ste. 7 (08057)
**Phone—(856) 778-0090**
Fax—(856) 778-9322
www.comtrex.com
Email—info@comtrex.com
Pres.—Jeffrey Rice
Prodn. & R & D Mgr.—Duane Reed
IT Mgr.—Charles Hardin
Acctg. & Hum. Res. Mgr.—Jill Barbera
SIC—3578; *Computer cash registers*
Employs—13; Estab.—1981
Distrib.—Intl.
Privately owned corporation

### CURBELL, INC., PLASTICS DIV.

Div. of Curbell Plastics, Inc.
844 N. Lenola Rd., Ste. 6 (08057)
**Phone—(856) 778-1100**
National—(800) 831-2550
Fax—(856) 778-1131
www.curbellplastics.com
Email—mcranston@curbellplastics.com
Admn. Mgr.—Nicole Weiss
Bus. Mgr.—Mike Cranston
SIC—3089; *Plastic fabrication*
Employs—10; Estab.—1943
Sales—$500,000-$1Mil
Distrib.—Regional
Privately owned corporation
Parent co.—Curbell Plastics, Inc., Orchard Park, NY
Phone—(716) 667-3377
See Parent Co. Section for full profile.

**GEOGRAPHICAL**

## Moorestown—(cont.)

### CVC THERMOSET SPECIALTIES, INC.

Div. of Emerald Performance Materials, LLC
844 N. Lenola Rd., Ste. 1 (08057)
Phone—(856) 533-3000
Fax—(856) 533-3003
www.emeraldmaterials.com
Email—czarnitz@cvcchem.com
V.-P., Sales & Mktg.—Charles Zarnitz
Cont.—Kristy Putnam
Plt. Mgr.—Rich Santo
Cust. Serv. Mgr.—Traci Dunn
Matls. Mgr.—Marty Kelly
SIC—2821; NAICS—325211; Plastic resins & monomers; Brand name—Epalloy; Erisys; Omicure; HyPox
Employs—50; Estab.—1986
35,000 sq ft site, Distrib.—Intl.
Privately owned corporation
ISO rating—9001:2000
Parent co.—Emerald Performance Materials, LLC, Cuyahoga Falls, OH
Phone—(330) 916-6700
See Parent Co. Section for full profile.

### DENTON VACUUM, LLC

1259 N. Church St., Bldg. 3 (08057)
Phone—(856) 439-9100
Fax—(856) 439-9111
www.dentonvacuum.com
Email—info@dentonvacuum.com
Chrm.—Peter Denton
Pres.—Vincent McGinty
V.-P., Fin.—Ellen Carson
SIC—3821; 3559; NAICS—339911; Vacuum thin film coating deposition systems
Employs—45; Estab.—1964
Sales—$17Mil
53,000 sq ft site, Distrib.—Intl.
Limited Liability Company
Also see: Quantum Coating, Inc., same loc.

### DYNAMIC MACHINING, INC.

876 N. Lenola Rd., Ste. 9-A (08057)
Phone—(856) 273-9830
Fax—(856) 273-0393
www.dynamicmachining.com
Email—hbudman@aol.com
Pres.—Harold Budman
V.-P.—Irv Budman
SIC—3599; Precision machining job shop
Employs—25; Estab.—1993
11,000 sq ft site, Distrib.—Local
Privately owned corporation

### ELECTRO MAGNETIC PRODUCTS, INC.

355 Crider Ave. (08057)
Phone—(856) 235-3011
Fax—(856) 722-0566
www.empmags.com
Email—emason@empmags.com
Pres.—Eric Mason
Sales Mgr.—Paul Pachuta
SIC—3469; Metal stampings, transformer & motor laminations
Employs—40; Estab.—1972
35,000 sq ft site, Distrib.—Intl.
Privately owned sub-S corp.

### EMS AVIATION

Div. of Honeywell Aerospace
121 Whittendale Dr., Ste. A (08057)
Phone—(856) 234-5020
National—(800) 220-1209
Fax—(856) 234-5242
www.emsaviation.com
Email—george.evans@emsaviation.com
V.-P., Opers.—John Serazio
Cont.—Charles Worthman
IT Mgr.—George 'Buck' Evans
Hum. Res. Mgr.—Kathy Cava
SIC—3577; Computer peripherals & components for commercial & military aircraft
Employs—100; Estab.—1970
Distrib.—Intl.
Publicly owned corporation
ISO rating—AS9100B
Parent co.—Honeywell Aerospace, Phoenix, AZ
Phone—(602) 436-2311
See Parent Co. Section for full profile.

### EXACTA V & H CORP.

107 Whittendale Dr. (08057)
Phone—(856) 235-7379
Pres.—Wayne Hubler
SIC—3599; General machining job shop
Employs—9; Estab.—1973
Sales—under $500,000
Distrib.—Local
Privately owned sub-S corp.

### FORTUNA ENTERPRISE USA, INC.

235 Country Club Dr. (08057)
Phone—(856) 778-7588
Fax—(856) 778-7539
www.vulcancasters.com
Pres.—Huichuan C. Liao
SIC—3562; Casters
Employs—2; Estab.—1990
Distrib.—National
Privately owned corporation

### GARDEN STATE DIESEL

97 Foster Rd., Ste. 4 (08057)
Phone—(856) 914-9797
Fax—(856) 914-0007
Email—gstatediesel@aol.com
Owner & GM—Rich Carragher
SIC—3519; 3714; Rebuilt diesel engine fuel injection parts for trucks
Employs—8; Estab.—1996
Sales—$1Mil-$2.5Mil
Distrib.—Regional
Privately owned corporation

### H. G. SCHAEVITZ LLC

102 Commerce Dr., Ste. 8 (08057-4205)
Phone—(856) 727-0250
Fax—(856) 727-0251
www.alliancesensors.com
Email—sales@alliancesensors.com
CEO—Harold Schaevitz
COO—John Matlack
CTO—Ed Herceg
SIC—3674; Industrial position, linear & rotary in-cylinder sensors
Employs—14; Estab.—2012
Sales—$5Mil-$10Mil
Distrib.—Intl.
Limited Liability Company
DBA: Alliance Sensor Group

### HARRIS TEA CO.

Div. of Harris Freeman & Co., Inc.
344 New Albany Rd. (08057)
Phone—(856) 793-0290
National—(888) 561-5017
Fax—(856) 793-0283
www.harristea.com
Email—richard@harrisfreeman.com
Sr. V.-P.—Robert Hackel
V.-P., Contract Sales—Richard P. Haas
Opers. Mgr.—Jim Gebre
SIC—2099; Company headquarters & tea, tea bags, instant tea & iced tea mix, including blending & packing; Brand name—Harris; Tea India; Newman's Own Organic Teas; Glenmere; Dorsett
Employs—80; Estab.—1982
Sales—under $50Mil
90,000 sq ft site, Distrib.—Intl.
Privately owned corporation

Parent co.—Harris Freeman & Co., Inc., Anaheim, CA
Phone—(714) 765-1190
See Parent Co. Section for full profile.

### IMCO REINFORCED PLASTICS, INC.

858 N. Lenola Rd. (08057)
Phone—(856) 235-7254
National—(800) 899-4626
Fax—(856) 234-3964
Email—imcofrp@netzero.net
GM & MIS Mgr.—Henry W. Regan
Off. Mgr.—Ginny Zimmer
SIC—3083; 3089; NAICS—326130; Fiberglass products
Employs—20; Estab.—1977
Sales—$1Mil-$5Mil
20,000 sq ft site, Distrib.—National
Privately owned corporation
Also see: Imco, Inc., same loc.

### IMCO, INC.

858 N. Lenola Rd., Bldg. 1 (08057)
Phone—(856) 499-2214
Fax—(856) 499-2523
www.imco-inc.net
Email—customerservice@imco-inc.net
Pres.—A. Ross Davis
Dir., Bus. Dev. & Hum. Res. Mgr.—Kim Shutt
SIC—3599; 3444; Sheet metal fabrication & precision machining job shop & supply chain management
Employs—40; Estab.—1944
Sales—$5Mil-$10Mil
Distrib.—National
Privately owned corporation
ISO rating—AS9100
Also see: Imco Reinforced Plastics, Inc., same loc.

### IT'S EXCITING LIGHTING, LLC

1270 Glen Ave. (08057)
Phone—(856) 727-5200
National—(800) 381-3919
Fax—(856) 727-4040
www.itsexcitinglighting.com
Email—jmurphy@itsexcitinglighting.com
CEO—John Murphy
Hum. Res. Mgr.—Lewis Setzer
Qual. Control Mgr.—Axel Cordero
SIC—3645; NAICS—335121; Battery operated wireless wall sconces
Employs—8; Estab.—2006
Sales—$1Mil-$2.5Mil
Distrib.—National
Limited Liability Company

### JET PULVERIZER CO., INC.

1255 N. Church St. (08057)
Phone—(856) 235-5554
National—(800) 670-9695
Fax—(856) 778-7712
www.jetpulverizer.com
Email—blist@jetpul.com
Pres.—Ed Fay
Ex. V.-P.—William S. Henry
V.-P.—Jeff Conn
Sr. Acct. Mgr.—Brian List
Plt. Mgr.—Daryl Bear
Prodn. Mgr.—Rick Pottieger
Fin. Mgr.—Christine Henry
SIC—3559; 3599; Jet pulverizers, including jet energy milling & grinding equipment & custom toll processing for the abrasives, minerals, pharmaceuticals, pigments, cosmetics & aerospace industries; Brand name—Micron-Master® Jet Pulverizers; Pharma-Master® Jet Pulverizers
Employs—30; Estab.—1947
Sales—$6Mil
20,000 sq ft site, Distrib.—Intl.
Privately owned sub-S corp.
ISO rating—9001:2000

### KERN & SZALAI MACHINE, LLC

351 Crider Ave. (08057)
Phone—(856) 802-1500
Fax—(856) 802-1522
Email—angela@kernszalai.com
Pres.—Erwin Vermes
V.-P.—Michael Vermes
Off. Mgr.—Angela Rathgeb
SIC—3599; CNC machining job shop, including production runs, lathe/milling & prototyping
Employs—45
Sales—$6Mil-$10Mil
Distrib.—Intl.
Limited Liability Company
Also see: Vermes Machine Co., Inc., same loc.

### KETEC, INC.

1256 N. Church St., Ste. A (08057-1146)
Phone—(856) 778-4343
Fax—(856) 778-8337
www.ketec.com
Email—info@ketec.com
Pres.—George Kaltner
Opers. Mgr.—Charles Romeyn
SIC—3669; 3089; NAICS—334290; Theft-prevention tags & detection systems; Brand name—Ketec
Employs—14; Estab.—1988
Sales—$1Mil-$5Mil
15,000 sq ft site, Distrib.—Intl.
Privately owned corporation

### LEGRAND ASSOCS.

214 W. Main St., Ste. 102 (08057)
Mail addr: 1601 Walnut St., Ste. 616, Philadelphia (19102)
Phone—(800) 273-8565
National—(800) 523-4314
Fax—(215) 496-1693
www.legrandeyes.net
Email—joelgrand@gmail.com
Pres.—Joseph LeGrand
Off. Mgr.—Madeline Vasquez
Dept. Mgr.—Susan Shore
SIC—3851; NAICS—339100; Artificial eyes
Employs—3; Estab.—1950
Sales—under $500,000 (est)
Distrib.—National
Privately owned corporation
Parent co.—LeGrand Assocs., Philadelphia, PA
Phone—(215) 496-1307
See Parent Co. Section for full profile.

### LOCKHEED MARTIN

Div. of Lockheed Martin Corp.
199 Borton Landing Rd., Rm. 108-108, P.O. Box 1027 (08057)
Phone—(856) 722-4100
Fax—(856) 722-4170
www.lockheedmartin.com
Email—jeffrey.adams@lmco.com
V.-P., GM—Jeff Bantle
V.-P., Fin.—Charlie Hubbs
Dir., U.S. Navy Aegis Progs.—Jim Sheridan
Comm. Mgr.—Kathy Baier
SIC—3679; Electronic components
Employs—4500
Sales—$500Mil-$1Bil (est)
1,000,000 sq ft site, Distrib.—Local
Publicly owned corporation
ISO rating—9001
Parent co.—Lockheed Martin Corp., Bethesda, MD
Phone—(301) 897-6000
See Parent Co. Section for full profile.

NEW ENTRY
### LUM TECH LIGHTING, INC.

201 Commerce Dr., Ste. 5 (08057)
Phone—(856) 234-2211
www.lum-techlighting.com
Email—sales@lum-techlighting.com
Owner—Joseph Ma

## Moorestown—(cont.)

SIC—3645; 3646; *Lighting supplies, including incandescent, fluorescent, halogen & LED fixtures for commercial & residential applications*
Employs—10
Sales—$1Mil-$2.5Mil (est)

**MCLEAN PACKAGING CORP.**
1504 Glen Ave. (08057)
**Phone—(856) 359-2600**
National—(800) 523-3153
Fax—(856) 359-2910
www.mcleanpackaging.com
Email—jeff.besnick@mcleanpackaging.com
Pres.—Joseph Fenkel
GM, Sales & Mktg.—Jeff Besnick
Engrg. Mgr.—R. J. Howarth
SIC—2652; NAICS—322213; *Corporate headquarters & paper set-up boxes & corrugated containers*
Employs—80; Estab.—1961
Sales—$45Mil
Distrib.—National
Sole ownership

**NW SIGN INDUSTRIES, INC.**
360 Crider Ave. (08057)
**Phone—(856) 802-1677**
National—(800) 998-6366
Fax—(856) 802-0412
www.nwsignindustries.com
Email—hr@nwsignindustries.com
Chrm. & CEO—Ronald Brodie
Sr. V.-P.—Karl Kaelin
Recruiting & Training Mgr.—Carol Mackin
SIC—3993; *Corporate headquarters & interior & exterior signage & signage programs for corporate, retail, private, commercial & municipal applications, including design & project management, installation & service*
Employs—60; Estab.—1992
Sales—$40Mil-$50Mil
Distrib.—National
Privately owned corporation

**OLDCASTLE BUILDINGENVELOPE®**
1500 Glen Ave. (08057)
**Phone—(866) 653-2278**
Fax—(856) 234-6105
www.oldcastlebe.com
Email—sales@oldcastlebe.com
Sales Mgr.—Brian Moore
Hum. Res. Mgr.—Tracy Moore
SIC—3231; 3499; NAICS—327215; *Glass & metal fabrication*
Employs—100; Estab.—1997
Sales—$50Mil-$100Mil
Distrib.—Regional
Publicly owned corporation
Parent co.—Oldcastle BuildingEnvelope®, Dallas, TX
Phone—(214) 273-3400
See Parent Co. Section for full profile.

**OMNIMED, INC.**
Div. of Briggs Healthcare
800 Glen Ave. (08057)
**Phone—(856) 359-2231**
National—(800) 257-2326
Fax—(856) 359-2249
www.omnimedbeam.com
Email—info@omnimedbeam.com
Pres.—Steve Heffernen
Asst. Hum. Res. Mgr.—Darlene Vrancik
Cust. Serv. Rep.—Sharon Herron

SIC—3841; *Medical products, including privacy screens, narcotic cabinets, wall desks, bedpan racks, glovebox holders, IV stands, power lifter, patient charting products & computer workstations*
Employs—30; Estab.—1992
Distrib.—National
Privately owned corporation
Parent co.—Briggs Healthcare, West Des Moines, IA
Phone—(515) 327-6400
See Parent Co. Section for full profile.

**OPEX CORPORATION**
305 Commerce Dr. *(08057)*
**Phone—(856) 727-1100**
Fax—(856) 727-1955
www.opex.com
Email—info@opex.com
Pres., CEO—Dave Stevens
Tradeshow Coord.—Kristen Stevens
SIC—3579; *Incoming & outgoing mail processing & imaging products, including mail extraction & sorting equipment with image capture & payment processing capabilities; Brand name—OPEX; Omation; Perfect Pick*
Employs—400; Estab.—1975
Distrib.—Intl.
Privately owned corporation

**PARKEON, INC.**
40 Twosome Dr., Ste. 7 (08057)
**Phone—(856) 234-8000**
National—(800) 732-6868
Fax—(856) 234-7178
www.parkeon.com
Email—ussales@parkeon.com
Pres., N. Amer.—Chris Octon
V.-P., Sales—Jim Dufon
Asst. Dir., Mktg.—Sean Renn
IT Mgr.—Darren Cusano
Hum. Res. Mgr.—April Apfelbaum
Tech. Support Rep.—Nicholas McLaren
SIC—3824; NAICS—334514; *On & off integrated street parking systems*
Employs—40; Estab.—1974
Sales—$11Mil-$25Mil
Distrib.—Intl.
Privately owned corporation

†**PARTS DISTRIBUTORS, LLC**
Div. of Uni-Select USA, Inc.
901 N. Lenola Rd., P.O. Box 832 (08057)
**Phone—(856) 778-1400**
Fax—(856) 439-5900
www.uniselectusa.com
Email—hrjobs@uniselectusa.com
Hum. Rels. Mgr.—Denise Esposito
SIC—5013; *Distributor of automotive parts*
Employs—200; Estab.—2003
Distrib.—National
Privately owned corporation
Parent co.—Uni-Select USA, Inc., Amherst, NY
Phone—(716) 531-9200
See Parent Co. Section for full profile.

**PERFECT PRINTING, INC.**
1533 Glen Ave. (08057)
**Phone—(856) 787-1877**
Fax—(856) 787-0054
www.perfectprinting.com
Email—annolivo@perfectprinting.com
Pres., GM—Joe Olivo
V.-P.—Ann Olivo
SIC—2759; 2791; NAICS—323122; *Commercial offset & digital printing & computerized typesetting*
Employs—50; Estab.—1979
Sales—$5Mil-$10Mil (est)
Distrib.—Local
Privately owned corporation

**PIONEER RESEARCH CO.**
97 Foster Rd., Ste. 5 (08057)
**Phone—(856) 866-9191**
National—(800) 257-7742
Fax—(856) 866-8615
www.pioneer-research.com
Email—info@pioneer-research.com
Pres.—W. Harms
Sales Coord.—Donna Walls
SIC—3861; *Underwater cameras & photographic equipment for scuba diving & marine & outdoor enthusiasts*
Employs—40; Estab.—1977
15,000 sq ft site, Distrib.—Intl.
Privately owned corporation

**POPLAR BINDERY, INC.**
300 Mill St. (08057)
**Phone—(856) 727-8030**
Fax—(856) 727-1677
www.poplarbindery.com
Email—steve@poplarbindery.com
Pres.—Steve Heisler
Day Shift Mgr.—Michael Heisler
SIC—2789; *Print finishing & binding of pharmaceutical pamphlet folders*
Employs—16; Estab.—1994
Sales—$1Mil-$2.5Mil (est)
Distrib.—National
Privately owned corporation

**PRISM COLOR CORP.**
31 Twosome Dr., Ste. 1 (08057)
**Phone—(856) 234-7515**
Fax—(856) 234-7516
www.prismcolorcorp.com
Email—chrisbrown@prismcolorcorp.com
Co-Pres.—Edward Brown
Co-Pres.—Ronald Krankowski
Cont., Fin. Mgr.—Chris Brown
SIC—2759; NAICS—323100; *Commercial printing*
Employs—70; Estab.—1984
37,420 sq ft site, Distrib.—Local
Privately owned corporation

**QUALITY CONCEPTS, INC.**
730 Marne Hwy. (08057)
**Phone—(856) 235-0909**
National—(800) 745-6120
Fax—(856) 235-9937
www.qualityconcepts.com
Email—sales@qualityconcepts.com
Ptnr. & V.-P., Sales & Mktg.—Michael Santori
Ptnr. & V.-P., Sales & Mktg.—Thomas S. Wagner
Fin. Mgr.—Cindy Herd
SIC—2759; 3993; NAICS—323100; *Commercial printing & promotional items*
Employs—15; Estab.—1987
Sales—under $500,000
12,000 sq ft site, Distrib.—Regional
Privately owned corporation

**QUANTUM COATING, INC.**
1259 N. Church St., Bldg. 1 (08057)
**Phone—(856) 231-0706**
Fax—(856) 231-0709
www.quantumcoating.com
Email—danp@quantumcoating.com
Pres.—D. Patriarca
Dir., Cust. Serv. & Off. Mgr.—Linda Costello
Dir., Coating—Ian Stevenson

SIC—3231; NAICS—327215; *Anti-reflective coated display panels, multilayer all-dielectric filters, transparent conductive & broadband anti-reflection glass coating on flat panels for aerospace & aviation applications*
Employs—34; Estab.—1990
Distrib.—National
Privately owned corporation
ISO rating—9001:2008
Also see: Denton Vacuum, LLC, same loc.

**RAMSAY CABINETMAKERS, INC., DAVID**
310 Mill St. (08057)
**Phone—(856) 234-7776**
Fax—(856) 234-2618
www.ramsaycabinetmakers.com
Email—contact@ramsaycabinetmakers.com
Pres.—David Ramsay III
Off. Mgr.—Sarah Harbold
Proj. Mgr.—Rob Bishop
SIC—2431; 2511; NAICS—337110; *High-end custom cabinetry, furniture & woodwork*
Employs—8; Estab.—1980
Distrib.—Regional
Privately owned corporation

**RIVERSIDE ACQUISITION GROUP, LLC (H Q)**
365 New Albany Rd. (08057)
**Phone—(856) 802-1900**
Fax—(856) 787-4001
www.com-pak.com
Email—info@com-pak.com
Pres.—Cliff McDuggle
CFO—Scott Mangan
COO—Russ Stewart
Cont.—Joan Rose
SIC—6719; 2759; 2789; *Company headquarters & private investment firm; commercial & digital printing & binding & direct mail services*
Employs—7
Limited Liability Company

**SCHINDLER ELEVATOR CORP.**
840 N. Lenola Rd., Ste. 4 (08057-1055)
**Phone—(856) 234-2220**
Fax—(856) 437-2322
www.us.schindler.com
Email—uswebmaster@us.schindler.com
Site Mgr.—Kyle Rainwater
SIC—3534; NAICS—333921; *Escalators & elevators*
Employs—20; Estab.—1898
Distrib.—National
Privately owned corporation
Parent co.—Schindler Elevator Corp., Morristown, NJ
Phone—(973) 397-6500
See Parent Co. Section for full profile.

†**SHINGLE & GIBB COMPANY**
845 Lancer Dr. (08057)
**Phone—(856) 234-8500**
National—(800) 989-8500
Fax—(856) 273-7640
www.shingle.com
Email—info@shingle.com
Pres.—Drew Pfleger
COO—Brian Lepsis
V.-P., Opers.—Rich Hoffman
Sr. Opers. Mgr.—Fred Wudarski
SIC—5084; 5085; *Company headquarters & distributor of automation & motion controls & hydraulic & pneumatic valves & actuators*
Employs—25; Estab.—1933
Distrib.—Local
Privately owned corporation

GEOGRAPHICAL

## Moorestown—(cont.)

**SHOWCASE GRAPHICS, LLC**

33 E. Main St., Ste. 4 (08057)
**Phone—(856) 722-5400**
Fax—(856) 722-0890
www.showcase-graphics.com
Email—dmarsdale@showcase-
graphics.com
Owner—Debra Marsdale
Graphic Designer—Sarah
Ramadori
SIC—2759; 2752; 2396; 3993;
NAICS—323100; *Commercial &
digital printing of packaging, ad
specialties & apparel*
Employs—3; Estab.—2001
Sales—under $1Mil
Distrib.—Local
Limited Liability Company

**SIPP SILK**

216 Hedgeman Rd. (08057)
**Phone—(856) 234-6224**
Fax—(856) 234-6295
www.sippsilks.com
Email—angelasipp@comcast.net
Ptnr.—George Sipp
Ptnr.—Angela Sipp
SIC—2389; *Jockey uniforms, silks,
blinkers, helmet covers & pants*
Employs—2; Estab.—1977
Sales—under $500,000
1,600 sq ft site, Distrib.—Intl.
Sole ownership

**SJ MAGAZINE**

1223 N. Church St. (08057)
**Phone—(856) 722-9300**
Fax—(856) 234-9912
www.sjmagazine.net
Email—sales@sjmagazine.net
Publisher & Editor—Marianne
Aleardi
SIC—2721; *Magazine publishing*
Employs—7
Sales—$500,000-$1Mil (est)
Privately owned corporation

**SWEMCO**

1215 N. Church St. (08057)
**Phone—(856) 222-9900**
Fax—(856) 222-0700
www.swemco.net
Email—sales@swemco.net
Pres., COO—Richard P.
Szczepkowski
Dir., Engrg.—Steve Sangillo
Hum. Res. Mgr.—Jackie
Szczepkowski
Qual. Mgr.—Michael Galvin
SIC—3672; NAICS—334412;
*Contract manufacturing of
printed circuit board & full box
build assemblies*
Employs—90; Estab.—1965
36,000 sq ft site, Distrib.—National
Privately owned corporation

**SYSCOM TECH**

1537 Glen Ave. (08057)
**Phone—(856) 642-7661**
National—(800) 255-1203
Fax—(856) 642-1111
www.syscomtechusa.com
Owner—Peter Aninnos
V-P.—Larry Leary
SIC—3679; *Wire harness & cable
assemblies*
Employs—60; Estab.—1978
Sales—under $500,000
Distrib.—National
Privately owned corporation

**TAURUS DISPLAY CORP.**

1249 Glen Ave. (08057)
**Phone—(856) 793-3500**
Fax—(856) 793-3545
www.tdcinstore.com
Email—sales@tdcinstore.com
Pres.—Thomas Petroni
Cont., Hum. Res. & Off. Mgr.—
Stephanie Metoff

Off. Mgr.—Lorri Mealey
SIC—2653; NAICS—322211;
*Corrugated displays*
Employs—25; Estab.—1991
Sales—under $500,000
Distrib.—Intl.
Privately owned corporation
AKA: TDC Instore

**TITANSEAL, INC.**

876 N. Lenola Rd., Ste. 3-E
(08057)
**Phone—(856) 582-7725**
National—(888) 294-7325
Fax—(856) 581-8915
www.titanseal.com
Email—titanseal@verizon.net
Pres.—Denise Danyliw
SIC—3429; *Air-purged shaft seals
for industrial processing
equipment*
Employs—2; Estab.—2002
Sales—$500,000-$1Mil
Distrib.—Intl.
Privately owned corporation

**VERMES MACHINE CO., INC.**

351 Crider Ave. (08057)
**Phone—(856) 642-9300**
Fax—(856) 642-9302
www.vermesmachine.com
Email—lynn@vermesmachine.com
Ptnr.—Mike Vermes
Ptnr.—Erwin Vermes
Hum. Res., IT & Off. Mgr.—Lynn
Kite
SIC—3599; *CNC machining job
shop*
Employs—50; Estab.—1977
Distrib.—National
Privately owned corporation
Also see: Kern & Szalai Machine,
LLC, same loc.

**XERIMIS INC.**

102 Executive Dr. (08057)
**Phone—(856) 727-9940**
National—(866) 937-4647
Fax—(856) 727-9942
www.xerimis.com
Email—general.information@
xerimis.com
CEO—Carol Sue Bernardo
Pres.—Peter D. Bernardo
V-P., Opers.—Gary Savvas
V-P., Fin. & Hum. Res.—Ann
Flanigan
V-P., Tech. Svcs.—Eric
Roncskevitz
V-P., Proj. Mgmt.—Thomas
McLoughlin
Dir., Corp. Affs.—Georgianna
Dickson
Dir., Qual. Assur.—Jason Bissey
Sales & Mktg. Exec.—James
LoCascio
Bus. Dev. Exec.—Kevin Clover
SIC—2834; 2836; 5122; *Custom
primary & secondary clinical
packaging for pharmaceutical,
biotechnology & clinical research
organizations & distributor of
clinical supplies &
pharmaceutical kits for clinical
studies*
Employs—100; Estab.—2000
64,000 sq ft site, Distrib.—Intl.
Privately owned corporation

---

## Morganville

(Monmouth—N.E.)

**†A D S SALE CO., INC.**

1010 Campus Dr. (07751)
**Phone—(732) 591-0500**
Fax—(732) 591-2765
www.rsaroomservice.com
Email—sales@rsaroomservice.com
Pres.—Marshall Summer
Dir., Sales—C. J. Burgher

SIC—5023; 5122; *Distributor of
hotel products, including ice
buckets, soap, shampoo,
toothpaste, toothbrushes, combs
& shower caps*
Employs—21; Estab.—2003
5,000 sq ft site, Distrib.—National
Privately owned corporation

**APPAREL ZONE, INC.**

165 Amboy Rd., Ste. 505 (07751)
**Phone—(732) 441-7780**
Fax—(732) 441-7784
www.apparelzone.net
Email—shirtmen@aol.com
Pres.—Todd Berman
SIC—2395; 2396; *Apparel
embroidery & screen printing*
Employs—5; Estab.—2000
Sales—$500,000-$1Mil
Distrib.—National
Privately owned corporation

**AURORA MULTIMEDIA CORP.**

205 Commercial Ct. (07751)
**Phone—(732) 591-5800**
Fax—(732) 591-5801
www.auroramultimedia.com
Email—sales@
auroramultimedia.com
CEO—Paul Harris
COO—Michael Twerdak
SIC—3651; 3577; NAICS—
334310; *Audio visual
processors, controls &
automation*
Employs—30; Estab.—1997
Distrib.—Intl.
Privately owned corporation

NEW ENTRY
**BROOKE BUSINESS FORMS &
SUPPLIES, INC.**

50 U.S. Highway 9, Ste. 303
(07751)
**Phone—(732) 617-7550**
Fax—(732) 617-7553
www.brookebusiness.com
Email—info@brookebusiness.com
Pres.—Neil Rosen
SIC—2759; *Commercial printing*
Employs—8
Sales—$1Mil-$2.5Mil (est)

**BRY-PAT ADVERTISING SPECIALTY
& SIGNS**

Tennent Rd., Route 79, P.O. Box
369 (07751)
**Phone—(732) 591-0999**
Fax—(732) 591-2791
Owner—Gary Birne
SIC—3993; *Custom interior &
exterior signs*
Employs—4; Estab.—1985
Sales—under $500,000 (est)
Distrib.—National
Sole ownership

**CENOGENICS CORP.**

100 Route 520, P.O. Box 308
(07751)
**Phone—(732) 536-6457**
National—(800) 747-9457
Fax—(732) 972-8527
www.cenogenics.net
Email—cenogenics@verizon.net
Pres.—Michael Katz
V-P., Prodn.—Nitza Katz
Cont.—Susan Nothstein

SIC—2835; 3842; NAICS—
325400; *Contract medical stool,
blood, urinalysis, pregnancy, LH,
CRP, RF, IM, ASO, syphilis
serology & brucella diagnostic
tests & febrile antigens; Brand
name—TriSlide; Stool Blood Test;
Accunate Pregnancy Test;
Monodex IM test; Acculysin ASO*
Employs—15; Estab.—1981
Sales—$1Mil-$5Mil
20,000 sq ft site, Distrib.—Intl.
Privately owned corporation
ISO rating—13485, 9001
Also see: Laboratory Diagnostics
Co., Inc., same loc.

**IN STITCHES EMBROIDERY, INC.**

1020 Campus Dr. (07751)
**Phone—(732) 460-2660**
    (732) 241-5368
Fax—(732) 460-2662
www.institchesnj.com
Email—sales@institchesnj.com
Pres.—Harry Harkavy
SIC—2395; *Custom embroidery*
Employs—10; Estab.—1997
Sales—under $500,000
Distrib.—National
Privately owned corporation

**INDUSTRIAL BRAKE & CLUTCH
EXCHANGE**

2 U.S. Highway 9, Ste. 4 (07751)
**Phone—(732) 970-0090**
    (732) 970-0092
Fax—(732) 970-0094
www.industrialbrakeclutch.com
Email—chris@
industrialbrakeclutch.com
Pres.—Chris Makrilos
SIC—3714; *Industrial &
automotive clutches & brakes,
including relining, fabrication &
powder coating*
Employs—3; Estab.—1976
Sales—$500,000-$1Mil
Distrib.—National
Privately owned corporation

NEW ENTRY
**INTUITIVE TECHNOLOGY
PARTNERS**

102 Serpentine Dr. (07751)
Mail addr: 2137 Route 35,1st Fl.,
Holmdel (07733)
**Phone—(201) 993-7799**
Fax—(201) 731-5526
www.itp-inc.com
Email—sales@itp-inc.com
Pres.—Jay Modh
SIC—7373; *Computer network
system integration, including
LANs & WANs for finance &
insurance companies*
Employs—48; Estab.—2012
Sales—$6Mil-$10Mil
3,000 sq ft site, Distrib.—Intl.
Privately owned corporation

**LABORATORY DIAGNOSTICS CO.,
INC.**

100 Route 520, P.O. Box 160
(07751)
**Phone—(732) 536-6300**
National—(800) 747-9457
Fax—(732) 972-8527
www.cenogenics.com
Email—inquiry@cenogenics.com
Pres.—Michael Katz
Accountant—Susan Notastein

## Morganville—(cont.)

SIC—2835; 3842; NAICS—325400; *Medical diagnostic test kits, including brucella diagnostic, stool blood, pregnancy, LH, CRP, RF, IM, syphilis serology & urinalysis tests & febrile antigens*
Employs—15; Estab.—1981
Distrib.—Intl.
Privately owned corporation
Also see: Cenogenics Corp., same loc.
AKA: Cenogenics Corp.

### PRECISION NUMERICAL TECHNOLOGY, INC.

31 Ardsley Pl. (07751)
Mail addr: P.O. Box 64, Wickatunk (07765)
**Phone—(732) 591-4884**
Fax—(732) 591-4882
www.pntmachining.com
Email—sales@pntmachining.com
Pres.—Carol Barfield
SIC—3599; *Precision machining job shop*
Employs—3; Estab.—1997
Sales—$500,000-$1Mil
Distrib.—National
Privately owned corporation

### SCREW MACHINE SPECIALTIES

50 U.S. Highway 9, Ste. 305 (07751-1558)
**Phone—(732) 972-5400**
Fax—(732) 972-1801
www.smspecialties.com
Email—info@smspecialties.com
Dir., Sales & Mktg.—Avi Tobias
SIC—3451; 3592; NAICS—332724; *Precision machined parts for OEMs, including screw machine, CNC turned, Swiss automatic & micro machining, broaching, precision thread rolling, milling, tapping, drilling, plating, knurling & heat treating*
Employs—25; Estab.—1995
Distrib.—Intl.
Privately owned corporation
ISO rating—9001

### TOWN & COUNTRY PLASTICS, INC.

P.O. Box 269 (07751)
**Phone—(732) 780-5300**
Fax—(732) 294-0001
www.tandcplastics.net
Email—tandcplastics@aol.com
Pres., Sales Mgr.—Harold Marmel
SIC—3089; 3599; *Plastic pollution control & chemically resistant equipment, including tanks, interceptors, sumps, sinks, countertops, drains, pipes, valves, fittings & hoods & rainwater & gray water harvesting systems, including plastic welding; Brand name—T & C*
Employs—18; Estab.—1974
Distrib.—National
Privately owned corporation

### UNITED BLOWER CO., INC.

22 Westbrook Dr. (07751)
**Phone—(201) 601-5700**
Fax—(201) 601-4743
www.unitedblowerco.com
Email—unitedblowerco@yahoo.com
Pres.—Howard Spitzer
Off. Mgr.—Steven Warren
SIC—3564; NAICS—333400; *Food safe pressure & explosion-proof, material handling & corrosion resistant blowers & centrifugal & pedestal fans*
Employs—3; Estab.—1937
5,000 sq ft site, Distrib.—Intl.
Privately owned corporation

### VYTRAN, LLC

1400 Campus Dr. (07751)
**Phone—(732) 972-2880**
Fax—(732) 972-4410
www.vytran.com
Email—info@vytran.com
Pres., CEO—Ed Connor
Sales Mgr.—Dan Bowden
Hum. Res. Mgr.—Larry Wineberg
SIC—3559; *Precision fiber splicing & glass processing equipment for research & development & manufacturing applications*
Employs—50
Sales—$10Mil-$25Mil
Distrib.—Intl.
Limited Liability Company

### WATERDOCTOR, INC.

1030-C Campus Dr. (07751)
**Phone—(732) 972-4510**
National—(888) 407-7010
Fax—(732) 972-8492
www.waterdoctorusa.com
Email—info@waterdoctorusa.com
Pres.—Joe Lee
GM—Elizabeth Lee
Bookkeeper—Sue Choy
SIC—3589; NAICS—333319; *Water purification equipment*
Employs—9; Estab.—1986
Sales—$1Mil-$2.5Mil (est)
Distrib.—Regional
Privately owned corporation

## Morris Plains
(Morris—N.W.)

### AIRES JEWELRY CO.

3 Harrison Ave. (07950)
**Phone—(973) 292-0950**
Fax—(973) 292-2719
www.airesjewelers.com
Email—info@airesjewelers.com
Pres.—Ronald W. Arends
V-P.—Chris Arends
SIC—3911; NAICS—339911; *Gold, silver & platinum jewelry*
Employs—8; Estab.—1946
Sales—$1Mil-$2.5Mil
Distrib.—Local
Privately owned corporation

### CHARMANT GROUP, INC.

400 American Rd. (07950)
**Phone—(973) 538-1511**
National—(800) 645-2121
Fax—(800) 443-2238
www.charmant-usa.com
Email—info@charmant-usa.com
Pres.—Harry Aida
IT Mgr.—Debbie Kacerek
Hum. Res. Mgr.—Kieth Andretta
Prod. Mgr.—Michele Ziss
SIC—3851; NAICS—339100; *Eyeglasses*
Employs—60; Estab.—1956
Distrib.—Intl.
Privately owned corporation

### CORFACTS, INC.

P.O. Box 10 (07950)
**Phone—(973) 998-6935**
Fax—(973) 998-6936
www.corfactsonline.com
Email—corfacts@optonline.net
Principal—John Ford
SIC—2731; *Online business-to-business directory publishing*
Employs—7
Sales—$500,000-$1Mil (est)
Distrib.—National
Privately owned corporation

**NEW ENTRY**
### EUROIMMUN US, INC.

1100 The American Rd., Ste. 1 (07950)
**Phone—(973) 656-1000**
National—(800) 913-2022
Fax—(973) 656-1098
www.euroimmun.us
Email—info@euroimmun.us
Mng. Dir.—Hamid Erfanian
SIC—2835; NAICS—325413; *Diagnostic test kits, including autoimmune & molecular diagnostics kits*
Employs—13
Sales—$5Mil-$10Mil (est)
Distrib.—National
Privately owned corporation

### IMMUNOMEDICS, INC.

300 The American Rd. (07950-2460)
**Phone—(973) 605-8200**
Fax—(973) 605-8282
www.immunomedics.com
Email—info@immunomedics.com
Pres., CEO—Cynthia L. Sullivan
V-P., Fin. & CFO—Peter P. Pfreundschuh
Sr. Dir., Inv. Rels. & Grant Mgmt.—Chau Cheng
Dir., Hum. Res.—Amy Baker
SIC—2834; NAICS—325412; *Humanized monoclonal antibody-based cancer treatment medicines*
Employs—125; Estab.—1982
Sales—$1Mil-$5Mil
Distrib.—Local
Publicly owned corporation

### PETITTS INK CORP.

1745 State Route 10, Ste. 4 (07950)
**Phone—(973) 984-2400**
Fax—(973) 984-2410
www.cartridgeworld.com
Email—petitts.ink@gmail.com
CEO—Kathleen Petitt
Co-Pres.—Art Petitt
GM—Bryan Petitt
SIC—3955; 3861; *Remanufactured inkjet & laser toner printer cartridges*
Employs—3; Estab.—2006
Sales—under $500,000
Distrib.—National
Privately owned corporation
AKA: Cartridge World In Morris Plains

### SEWMATIC ATTACHMENTS

39 E. Hanover Ave. (07950)
**Phone—(973) 290-9174**
Fax—(973) 290-9176
www.sewmatic.com
Owner—Richard Rivera
V-P.—Richard Koppinger
SIC—3639; NAICS—335200; *Industrial sewing machine attachments, including repair & sales*
Employs—15; Estab.—1932
Sales—$500,000-$1Mil
Distrib.—Intl.
Sole ownership
Also see: Wire & Cable Fabricating Devices, same loc.

### SKILA, A SELA2 CO.

201 Littleton Rd., 2nd Fl. (07950)
**Phone—(973) 889-1300**
Fax—(973) 889-5455
www.qforma.com
Email—knowledgesolutions@qforma.com
CEO—Kilian Weiss
CFO—Ed Mendham
COO, Europe & V-P., Global Mktg.—Andy Rankin
Hum. Res. Mgr.—Sona Ravani
Staff Accountant—Ditendra Thakuri
SIC—7372; *Pharmaceutical software development*
Employs—25; Estab.—1995
Distrib.—Intl.
Privately owned corporation

### TEMPTIME CORP.

116 The American Rd., 2nd Fl. (07950)
**Phone—(973) 984-6000**
Fax—(973) 984-1520
www.temptimecorp.com
Email—info@temptimecorp.com
Pres.—Renaat Van den Hooff
Sr. V-P.—Thaddeus Prusik
V-P., Facilities & Mfg.—Brad Mataczynski
Ex. Dir.—William Smiley
Ex. Dir.—Christopher Caulfield
IT Mgr.—Matt Webb
SIC—2759; NAICS—323100; *Time & temperature sensitive indicator labels*
Employs—70; Estab.—1987
Sales—$28Mil
40,000 sq ft site, Distrib.—Intl.
Privately owned corporation

**NEW ENTRY**
### TEMPTIME CORP.

116 The American Rd. (07950)
**Phone—(973) 984-6000**
Fax—(973) 984-1520
www.temptimecorp.com
Pres.—Renaat Van den Hooff
SIC—3826; 3842; NAICS—334516; *Non-reversible temperature indicators for health care applications, blood banks, pharmaceuticals & umbilical stump disinfectants*
Employs—70; Estab.—1976
Distrib.—Intl.
Privately owned corporation

### WALPOLE WOODWORKERS, INC.

540 Tabor Rd. (07950)
**Phone—(973) 539-3555**
Fax—(973) 539-2796
www.walpolewoodworkers.com
Email—sales@walpolewoodworkers.com
GM—Barry Stegenga
SIC—2499; *Wooden fences*
Employs—12; Estab.—1933
Varies: 3-20
Sales—$1Mil-$2.5Mil (est)
Distrib.—Regional
Privately owned corporation
AKA: Walpole Outdoors
Parent co.—Walpole Woodworkers, Inc., Walpole, MA
Phone—(508) 668-2800
See Parent Co. Section for full profile.

### WIRE & CABLE FABRICATING DEVICES

39 E. Hanover Ave., Ste. 1 (07950)
**Phone—(973) 290-9069**
Fax—(973) 290-9104
Ptnr.—Richard Koppinger
Ptnr.—William Stergio
Ptnr.—Richard Rivera
SIC—3423; *Stainless steel electrical wiring tools*
Employs—4; Estab.—1992
Sales—under $500,000
Distrib.—Intl.
Privately owned partnership
Also see: Sewmatic Attachments, same loc.

### XYBION MEDICAL SYSTEMS

201 Littleton Rd. (07950)
**Phone—(973) 538-5111**
Fax—(973) 540-9712
www.xybion.com
Email—xmscustserv@xybion.com
CEO—Pradip K. Banerjee
CFO—Steven L. Porfano
Hum. Res. Mgr.—Fran Mink

GEOGRAPHICAL

## Morris Plains—(cont.)

SIC—7372; *Toxicology & pathology data management software development for preclinical safety assessment laboratories, life sciences product companies & contract research organizations*
Employs—50; Estab.—1976
Distrib.—Intl.
Sole ownership

---

## Morristown

(Morris—N.W.)

### ALPHAGRAPHICS, INC.

60 Speedwell Ave. (07960)
**Phone—(973) 984-0066**
Fax—(973) 984-9755
www.us293.alphagraphics.com
Email—us293@alphagraphics.com
Owner—Brian Harrigan
GM—Janine Myer
SIC—2759; 2752; 2791; NAICS—323100; *Commercial offset & instant printing, typesetting & mailing services*
Employs—7; Estab.—1989
Sales—$500,000-$1Mil
4,000 sq ft site, Distrib.—Local
Privately owned corporation
ISO rating—9000
AKA: Alphagraphics Of Morristown

### ART CULINAIRE MAGAZINE

40 Mills St. (07963)
Mail addr: P.O. Box 238, Madison (07940)
**Phone—(973) 993-5500**
Fax—(973) 993-8779
www.getartc.com
Email—artculinaire@verizon.net
Pres., Publisher—Franz Mitterer
SIC—2721; *Magazine publishing; Brand name—Art Culinaire Magazine*
Employs—4; Estab.—1986
2,500 sq ft site, Distrib.—Intl.

### BERTOT INDUSTRIES, INC.

23 Malcolm St., Ste. 1 (07960)
**Phone—(973) 267-0006**
Fax—(973) 267-1922
Email—bertot@optonline.net
Pres.—Harold Jelonnek
V-P.—Curtiss Jelonnek
Contract Admn.—Frank Gaden
SIC—3599; *General machining job shop*
Employs—10; Estab.—1969
Sales—$750,000-$1Mil
10,000 sq ft site, Distrib.—National
Privately owned corporation
ISO rating—9001:2008

### BLUE SAGE SOFTWARE

35 Lord William Penn Dr. (07960)
**Phone—(973) 366-1900**
Fax—(973) 366-7450
www.bluesagesoftware.com
Pres.—Roger Moyers
SIC—3571; NAICS—334111; *Computer systems*
Employs—10; Estab.—1970
Sales—$5Mil-$10Mil (est)
Distrib.—Intl.
Privately owned corporation

### CAPSUGEL (H Q)

412 Mount Kemble Ave., Ste. 200-C (07960-6674)
**Phone—(862) 242-1700**
National—(800) 845-6973
www.capsugel.com
Email—capsugelcommunications@capsugel.com
Pres., CEO—Guido Driesen
CFO—John Shroyer
CMO—Erasmo Schutzer
Sr. V-P., Hum. Res. & CHRO—Patricia Kelly

Sr. V-P., Global Opers.—Anthony Macci
Gen. Counsel—John de Grandpre
Dir., Hum. Res.—Sherri Weiland
SIC—2899; *Company headquarters; hard gelatin & plant-based capsules for healthcare applications & custom dosage forms for the pharmaceutical industry; Brand name—Plantcaps™*
Employs—67
Sales—$25Mil-$50Mil (est)
Privately owned corporation

### CITY DIECUTTING, INC.

1 Cory Rd., Ste. C (07960)
**Phone—(973) 270-0370**
Fax—(973) 270-0369
www.bookdisplays.com
Email—info@bookdisplays.com
Pres.—Eric DeVos
SIC—2541; 2542; *Semi-gloss, water resistant, black & high quality corrugated counter & floor displays; Brand name—CityStands*
Employs—18; Estab.—1989
Sales—$1Mil-$5Mil
43,000 sq ft site, Distrib.—Intl.
Privately owned corporation
ISO rating—9002
AKA: bookdisplays.com

### COLAS, INC. (H Q)

163 Madison Ave., Ste. 500 (07960)
**Phone—(973) 290-9082**
www.colas.com
Email—dgacolas@aol.com
Pres.—Georges Ausseil
CFO—Jean Luc Begasse
Sr. V-P.—Jim Weeks
V-P., Hum. Res.—Paul Pischko
V-P.—Victor A. Serri
SIC—2951; 3272; NAICS—324121; *Corporate headquarters; asphalt paving compounds & ready-mixed concrete*
Employs—10
Sales—under $500,000 (est)
Privately owned corporation

### COLGATE-PALMOLIVE CO.

191 E. Hanover Ave. (07960)
Mail addr: P.O. Box 1928, Morristown (07962)
**Phone—(973) 630-1500**
Fax—(973) 630-1476
www.colgate.com
Email—investor_relations@colpal.com
Dir., Plt.—Tia Pillers
Hum. Res. Mgr.—Yuri Baz
SIC—2844; NAICS—325600; *Soft soap & deodorants; Brand name—Soft Soap; Mennen Speed Stick Deodorants*
Employs—568; Estab.—1940
Sales—$25Mil-$100Mil
575,000 sq ft site, Distrib.—Intl.
Publicly owned corporation
Parent co.—Colgate-Palmolive Co., New York, NY
Phone—(212) 310-2000
See Parent Co. Section for full profile.

### COUNTY CONCRETE CORP.

145 Ridgedale Ave. (07960)
**Phone—(973) 538-3113**
Fax—(973) 538-3281
www.countyconcretenj.com
Email—info@countyconcretenj.com
Dispatch Supv.—Bill Space
SIC—3273; NAICS—327320; *Ready-mixed concrete*
Employs—10; Estab.—1979
Distrib.—Regional
Privately owned corporation
Parent co.—County Concrete Corp., Kenvil, NJ
Phone—(973) 584-7122
See Parent Co. Section for full profile.

### COVER-ALL TECHNOLOGIES, INC.

412 Mount Kemble Ave., Ste. 110-C (07960)
**Phone—(973) 461-5200**
Fax—(973) 461-5257
www.cover-all.com
Email—supportcenter@cover-all.com
Pres., CEO—Manishy Shah
Ex. V-P., COO—Maryanne Gallagher
Sr. V-P., Bus. Dev. & Comm.—Alex Ker
SIC—7372; *Policy administration, data capture, rating, policy issuance & transactional workflow software development for the property & casualty insurance industry; Brand name—My Insurance Center; NexGen Business Intelligence Suite*
Employs—50; Estab.—1981
Distrib.—National

[NEW ENTRY]
### DATASCAN GRAPHICS, INC.

55 Madison Ave., Ste. 400 (07960)
**Phone—(973) 543-4800**
National—(866) 389-6711
Fax—(973) 543-4803
www.datascangraphics.com
Email—rhouse@datascangraphics.com
Pres.—Roy House
SIC—2541; 2542; 3993; *Point-of-purchase displays*
Employs—25; Estab.—1987
Sales—$2Mil-$5Mil
3,500 sq ft site, Distrib.—Intl.
Privately owned corporation

### DAYBROOK HOLDINGS, INC. (H Q)

161 Madison Ave., 2nd Fl. (07960)
Mail addr: P.O. Box 1931, Morristown (07962)
**Phone—(973) 538-6766**
Fax—(973) 538-1065
www.daybrook.com
Email—info@daybrook.com
Pres., CEO—Gregory F. Holt
CFO—Steve Morganstern
Sr. V-P., Sales & Mktg.—Glenn R. Speakman
Dir., Corp. Comms.—Lauren Holt
SIC—2047; 2048; NAICS—311111; *Corporate headquarters; fish meal & oil for pet food & aquaculture feed*
Employs—6; Estab.—1990
Sales—$25Mil
Distrib.—Intl.
Privately owned corporation

### DELPHUS, INC.

152 Speedwell Ave. (07960)
**Phone—(973) 267-9269**
www.delphus.com
Email—info@delphus.com
Owner & Pres.—Hans Levenbach
SIC—7372; *Demand forecasting & order replenishment planning systems software development for manufacturers, distributors & retailers; Brand name—PEER Planner®; PEERForecaster*
Employs—8; Estab.—1988
Sales—$500,000-$1Mil
Distrib.—Intl.
Privately owned sub-S corp.

### DUSENBERY ENGINEERING CO.

309 E. Hanover Ave., P.O. Box 1001 (07962)
**Phone—(973) 539-2200**
Fax—(973) 538-5186
www.dusenberyeng.com
Email—dusenberyeng@cs.com
Pres.—Philip Williams
V-P.—William Janus

SIC—3443; *Industrial pressure vessels*
Employs—13; Estab.—1948
Sales—$1Mil-$5Mil
8,000 sq ft site, Distrib.—Intl.
Privately owned corporation

### ENJOU CHOCOLATE, INC.

8 Dehart St. (07960)
**Phone—(973) 993-9090**
www.enjouchocolat.com
Email—sales@enjouchocolat.com
Pres.—Wendy Taffet
SIC—2066; NAICS—311300; *Chocolate candy*
Employs—10; Estab.—1986
Distrib.—Regional
Privately owned corporation

### GARDEN STATE ORTHOPEDIC, INC.

Div. of Garden State Orthopaedic Center, Inc.
95 Mount Kemble Ave. *(07960)*
**Phone—(973) 538-4948**
Fax—(973) 605-8481
www.gsortho.com
Email—gsoc@gsortho.com
Off. Mgr.—Jennifer Cordileone
SIC—3842; *Orthopedic, orthotic & prosthetic appliances & supplies*
Employs—5; Estab.—1982
Sales—$500,000-$1Mil
Distrib.—Regional
Privately owned corporation
Parent co.—Garden State Orthopaedic Center, Inc., Oakland, NJ
Phone—(201) 337-5566
See Parent Co. Section for full profile.

### GORDON MILLS MFG., INC. (H Q)

68 Sherwood Dr. (07960-6381)
**Phone—(973) 359-1080**
Fax—(973) 359-1095
Email—gordonmillsmfg@aol.com
Pres.—Bernard Factor
V-P.—William Factor
SIC—3144; 2251; 5139; 5137; NAICS—316214; *Corporate headquarters; manufacturer & distributor of slippers & women's hosiery (mfg. done overseas)*
Employs—3; Estab.—1982
Distrib.—National
Privately owned corporation

### HOMES & ESTATES MAGAZINES

173 Morris St. (07960)
**Phone—(973) 605-1877**
Fax—(973) 605-1883
www.homesandestatesonline.com
Email—homesandestates@gmail.com
Publisher—Pete Best
SIC—2721; *Real estate magazine publishing*
Employs—4; Estab.—1993
Sales—$1Mil
Distrib.—Local
Privately owned corporation

### HONEYWELL INTERNATIONAL, INC. (H Q)

101 Columbia Rd. (07962)
**Phone—(973) 455-2000**
National—(800) 601-3099
Fax—(973) 455-4807
www.honeywell.com
Email—prestone.information@honeywell.com
Chrm., CEO—David M. Cote
Pres., CEO, Performance Matls. & Technologies—Andreas Kramvis
Pres., Trans. Sys.—Terrence Hahn
Sr. V-P., CFO—David J. Anderson
Sr. V-P., Gen. Counsel—Kate Adams
Sr. V-P., Hum. Res.—Mark James
V-P., Chief Mktg. & Strategy Officer—Rhonda Germany
V-P., Info. Sys.—Michael Lang
V-P., Inv. Rels.—Elena Doom
Dir., New Bus. Dev. & Strategy—Phil Wojcik

## Morristown—(cont.)

**Weatherization Prods. & Svcs.**
Bus. Mgr.—Bryan Magnus
SIC—3822; 2899; 2891; 2389;
NAICS—334512; *Corporate
headquarters; control & energy
management systems, electronic
chemicals, adhesives, fire-
resistant clothing, incinerators,
security systems, aircraft lighting
fixtures & engine parts*
Employs—1500; Estab.—1899
Company-wide: 22,909
Sales—$38Bil
Distrib.—Intl.
Publicly owned corporation

**JENKINS, INC., BRAD**
291 Mount Kemble Ave. (07960)
**Phone—(973) 331-1995**
Fax—(973) 331-1602
www.bradjenkinsinc.com
Email—info@bradjenkinsinc.com
Pres. & Principal—Brad Jenkins
SIC—2599; 2511; 2514; NAICS—
337110; *Architectural & interior
design, including restaurant &
residential furniture*
Employs—4; Estab.—1993
Sales—under $500,000
Distrib.—National
Privately owned sub-S corp.

**KAHLE AUTOMATION**
89 Headquarters Plz., Ste. 355
(07960)
**Phone—(973) 993-1850**
www.kahleautomation.com
Email—kahle@
kahleautomation.com
Pres.—Julie Logothetis
SIC—3559; *Assembly machinery
for pharmaceutical & medical
device industries*
Employs—10; Estab.—1920
22,000 sq ft site, Distrib.—Intl.
Privately owned corporation
AKA: Kahle Engineering Corp.

**MARA'S GOURMET CHEESECAKE**
281 Speedwell Ave. (07960)
**Phone—(973) 682-9200**
Fax—(973) 682-9553
www.marasdesserts.com
Email—info@marasdesserts.com
Pres.—Glenn Magley
GM & Plt. Mgr.—Mara Magley
Sales Mgr.—Ian Magley
SIC—2051; NAICS—311812;
*Cakes & pies*
Employs—4; Estab.—1986
Sales—under $500,000
Distrib.—Local
Privately owned corporation

**MINUTEMAN PRESS**
120 Speedwell Ave. (07960)
**Phone—(973) 539-0610**
Fax—(973) 539-6879
www.morristown.minutemanpress.
com
Email—mmpmorristown@aol.com
Owner—John Volpecello, Jr.
Graphic Designer—Claudia
Salinas
Pressman—Moises Martinez
SIC—2759; NAICS—323100;
*Commercial & instant printing*
Employs—3; Estab.—1996
Sales—under $500,000
Distrib.—Local
Privately owned corporation

**†MOE DISTRIBUTORS, INC.**
55 Abbett Ave. (07960)
**Phone—(973) 539-8200**
Fax—(973) 539-0327
www.moedistributors.com
Email—info@moedistributors.com
V-P.—Jeff Doremus
V-P.—Art Thompson

SIC—5072; 5074; *Distributor of
decorative bathroom fixtures &
faucets & door & cabinet
hardware; Brand name—
Baldwin; Schlage; Omnia;
Fusion; Emtek; Nostalgic
Warehouse; Rocky Mountain;
Ashley Norton; Hamilton; Norton;
PDQ; Falcon; Ives; Deltana;
Amerock; Allison; Top Knobs;
Schaub; Rk International; Atlas;
Hansgrohe; Grohe*
Employs—7; Estab.—1983
Distrib.—Regional
Privately owned corporation

**MORRIS COUNTY DUPLICATING
CORP.**
1 Lafayette Ave. (07960)
**Phone—(973) 993-8484**
Fax—(973) 605-8828
www.mcdsolutions.com
Email—copies@mcdsolutions.com
Pres.—Ernie D'Angelo
Off. Mgr.—Nancy Cerefice
Sales Rep.—Edna M. Payrett
SIC—2759; 2752; NAICS—
323100; *Full-service document
imaging, scanning & support,
including color, instant & digital
color printing of posters,
banners, invitations &
announcements*
Employs—30; Estab.—1985
Sales—$1Mil-$2.5Mil
25,000 sq ft site, Distrib.—
Regional
Privately owned corporation
AKA: MCD Print & Document
Solutions

**MORRIS MAGNETOS, INC.**
103 Washington St. (07960)
**Phone—(973) 540-9171**
National—(800) 237-8624
www.morrismagneto.com
Email—info@morrismagneto.com
Pres.—David Shaw
SIC—3694; NAICS—336322;
*Motorcycle magnetos*
Employs—4; Estab.—1969
Sales—under $500,000
Distrib.—Intl.
Privately owned corporation

**NEW JERSEY MONTHLY MAGAZINE,
INC.**
55 S. Park Pl., P.O. Box 920
(07963)
**Phone—(973) 539-8230**
Fax—(973) 538-2953
www.njmonthly.com
Pres., Publisher—Keith Tomlinson
Editor—Ken Schlager
Billing Mgr.—Jim Dennison
SIC—2721; *Magazine publishing*
Employs—40; Estab.—1975
Sales—$6Mil-$10Mil
Distrib.—Local
Privately owned corporation

**†PLUS PACKAGING, INC.**
10 Mount Pleasant Rd. (07960)
Mail addr: P.O. Box 12, Madison
(07940-0012)
**Phone—(973) 538-2216**
National—(800) 535-9550
Fax—(973) 538-5502
www.pluspackaging.com
Email—packaging@
pluspackaging.com
Pres.—Lee Dornfeld
Sales Rep.—Lynn Voinier
SIC—5113; *Distributor of
corrugated boxes for packaging*
Employs—6; Estab.—1977
Sales—$500,000-$1Mil
Distrib.—Intl.
Privately owned corporation

**PORTASEAL, LLC**
1 John St., P.O. Box 1203 (07962)
**Phone—(973) 539-0100**
Fax—(973) 539-4101

www.portaseal.com
Email—portaseal@earthlink.net
Pres.—Stanley D. Grabowy
SIC—3069; *Weatherstripping*
Employs—10; Estab.—1957
Sales—$500,000-$1Mil
4,000 sq ft site, Distrib.—Regional
Limited Liability Company
AKA: Portaseal Weatherstripping

**POSITIVE PUBLICATIONS, LLC**
65 Madison Ave., Ste. 510 (07960)
**Phone—(973) 218-0310**
Fax—(973) 455-0205
www.industrytoday.com
Email—corporate@
industrytoday.com
COO—Susan Poeton
Administrator—Diane Jones
SIC—2721; *Magazine publishing
for the manufacturing sector*
Employs—21; Estab.—1998
Distrib.—Intl.
Limited Liability Company
AKA: Industry Today

**POWERS & CO., M. J.**
65 Madison Ave., Ste. 220 (07960)
**Phone—(973) 898-1200**
Fax—(973) 898-1201
www.alertpubs.com
Email—psych@alertpubs.com
Pres., Publisher—Michael Powers
Assoc. Editor—Trish Elliott
Asst. Editor—Krista Strobel
SIC—2721; *Medical newsletter
publishing*
Employs—3; Estab.—1976
Sales—$500,000-$1Mil
Distrib.—Intl.
Privately owned corporation

NEW ENTRY
**R A C SYSTEMS CORP.**
1-B Glimpsewood Ln. (07960)
**Phone—(973) 292-3200**
Fax—(973) 292-9565
www.racsystems.com
Pres.—Walter Rodriguez
SIC—7373; *Computer systems
integration, including LANs &
WANs*
Employs—2; Estab.—1989
Sales—under $500,000
900 sq ft site, Distrib.—Regional
Privately owned corporation

**RIOS ENGRAVING**
1 Maple Ave. (07960)
**Phone—(973) 539-5749**
(973) 538-7650
National—(888) 539-5749
Fax—(973) 285-9755
www.riosengraving.com
Email—rolando6@optonline.net
Owner, Plt. Opers. & Sales & Mktg.
Mgr.—Rolando G. Rios
SIC—3089; 3499; 3231; 2759;
*Custom & laser engraving of
plastic & metal signs, panels &
glassware & vinyl letters, signs,
banners, rubber stamps,
trophies, awards & watch
batteries & sublimation/digital
printing*
Employs—3; Estab.—1965
Sales—under $500,000
20,000 sq ft site, Distrib.—National
Sole ownership

**SCHINDLER ELEVATOR CORP. (H Q)**
20 Whippany Rd. (07960)
Mail addr: P.O. Box 1935,
Morristown (07962)
**Phone—(973) 397-6500**
National—(800) 225-0140
Fax—(973) 397-3710
www.us.schindler.com
Email—kathi.rucki@
us.schindler.com
Chrm.—Alfred N. Schindler
CEO—Jakob Zueger
Corp. Comms. Mgr.—Kathy Rucki

Dist. Mgr.—Jeremiah Heller
SIC—3534; NAICS—333921;
*Corporate headquarters;
elevators, escalators,
replacement parts, signal
fixtures, controls & components*
Employs—240
Sales—$25Mil-$50Mil
Distrib.—National
Privately owned corporation

**SIGN-A-RAMA**
166 Ridgedale Ave. (07962)
**Phone—(973) 605-8313**
National—(888) 508-5088
Fax—(973) 605-8306
www.sign-a-rama.com
Email—signpro@earthlink.net
Owner—David Fan
SIC—3993; *Interior & exterior
signs*
Employs—4; Estab.—1991
Sales—under $500,000
3,000 sq ft site, Distrib.—Local
Sole ownership

**†THOMAS & CO., INC., P. L.**
119 Headquarters Plz. (07960)
**Phone—(973) 984-0900**
Fax—(973) 984-5666
www.plthomas.com
Pres.—Paul M. Flowerman
SIC—5122; *Distributor of vitamins,
minerals & nutritional
supplements*
Employs—18; Estab.—1948
Distrib.—Intl.
Privately owned corporation

**TYBER MEDICAL, LLC (H Q)**
89 Headquarters Plz. N., Ste. 1464
(07960)
**Phone—(866) 761-0933**
Fax—(866) 889-9914
www.tybermedical.com
Email—sales@tybermed.com
Pres., CEO—Jeff Tyber
Dir., Sales & Mktg.—Steve Zieger
SIC—3842; *Company
headquarters; orthopedic
implants (mfg. subcontracted)*
Employs—12
Sales—$2.5Mil-$5Mil (est)
10,000 sq ft site, Distrib.—Intl.
Limited Liability Company
ISO rating—13485:2003

**WELLCARE TODAY, LLC**
89 Headquarters Plz., Ste. 1461
(07960)
**Phone—(866) 656-1188**
Fax—(866) 219-6741
www.wellcaretoday.com
Email—d.ferrara@
wellcaretoday.com
Pres.—Dan Ferrara
V-P.—Michael Carr
SIC—7372; *Healthcare mobile
phone application software
development; Brand name—
HealthAssist*
Employs—10; Estab.—2009
Distrib.—National
Limited Liability Company

**WORK 'N' WEAR STORE**
73 Market St. (07960)
**Phone—(973) 267-2373**
Fax—(973) 267-1121
Owner—Bob Hellreisel
SIC—2396; *Textile screen printing*
Employs—2; Estab.—1984
Sales—under $500,000
Distrib.—Local
Sole ownership

GEOGRAPHICAL

## Mount Arlington
(Morris—N.W.)

NEW ENTRY

**AZDEN CORP.**
200 Valley Rd., Ste. 101 (07856-1320)
**Phone—(973) 810-3070**
National—(800) 247-4501
Fax—(973) 810-3076
www.azden.com
Email—sales@azden.com
CEO—Motonori Sato
Pres.—Sho Torii
V-P.—Wayne Alonso
Bookkeeper—Renate Alonso
SIC—3651; NAICS—334310; *Wireless microphone systems, powered speakers, shotgun microphones & portable mixers*
Employs—10; Estab.—1984
Sales—over $6Mil
4,000 sq ft site, Distrib.—Intl.
Privately owned corporation

**GRAY STAR, INC.**
200 Valley Rd., Ste. 200 (07856)
**Phone—(973) 398-3331**
www.graystarinc.com
Email—graystarnj@aol.com
Pres.—Martin Stein
V-P.—Russell Stein
SIC—3844; 3556; NAICS—334517; *Food irradiation equipment*
Employs—4; Estab.—1989
Distrib.—Intl.
Privately owned corporation

## Mount Ephraim
(Camden—S.W.)

**ALLIANCE VINYL WINDOW CO., INC.**
301 Crescent Blvd. (08059)
**Phone—(856) 456-4954**
Fax—(856) 456-2920
www.alliancevinylwindows.com
Email—alliance@avw.cc
Pres., GM & Sales Mgr.—Jeff Hersh
Maint. Mgr.—Jim Pierce
SIC—3089; *Corporate headquarters & vinyl replacement windows & patio doors*
Employs—45; Estab.—1956
28,460 sq ft site, Distrib.—Regional
Privately owned sub-S corp.

**CABINET WORKS CORP.**
511 W. Kings Hwy. (08059)
**Phone—(856) 931-7289**
Fax—(856) 931-7286
Pres.—Frank Cavallaro
Corp. Secy.—Nancy Cavallaro
SIC—2434; 2542; 3083; NAICS—337110; *Wooden & laminate cabinets & architectural millwork*
Employs—3; Estab.—1982
Sales—under $500,000
3,000 sq ft site, Distrib.—Local
Privately owned corporation

**GADREN MACHINE CO.**
108 Main St., P.O. Box 117 (08059)
**Phone—(856) 456-4329**
National—(800) 822-4233
Fax—(856) 456-2238
www.gadrenmachine.com
Email—gmachine@comcast.net
Pres.—George S. Gadren, Jr.
V-P., Prodn.—Gary Gadren
Treas.—Frank Gadren
Sales Mgr.—Connie Wozinak
Sales Mgr., Outside—David Borton
Off. Mgr.—Laura Beck
SIC—3599; 3491; 3494; NAICS—332911; *Valves & CNC machining job shop; Brand name—Gade Valves*
Employs—15; Estab.—1937
12,500 sq ft site, Distrib.—Intl.
Privately owned sub-S corp.

**J T GRAPHICS**
34 Mt. Ephraim Ave. (08059)
**Phone—(856) 931-3548**
Fax—(856) 931-3548
Owner & GM—John Thompson
SIC—3993; *Interior & exterior signs & lettering*
Employs—1; Estab.—1991
Sales—under $500,000
Distrib.—Local
Privately owned corporation

**SELECT MACHINE TOOL, INC.**
19 Thompson Ave. (08059)
**Phone—(856) 933-2100**
Fax—(856) 933-2101
Pres.—Jay Brad
SIC—3599; *Precision machining job shop*
Employs—7; Estab.—1975
Sales—$1Mil-$2.5Mil
Distrib.—Local
Privately owned corporation

## Mount Freedom
(Morris—N.W.)

**GRAPHIC CENTER, THE**
P.O. Box 595 (07970)
**Phone—(973) 366-6676**
Fax—(973) 984-1800
www.graphiccenterdigital.com
Email—info@graphiccenterdigital.com
Owner & CFO—Sandra Guido
Off. Mgr.—Louise Manniello
SIC—2759; 2752; NAICS—323100; *Commercial & digital printing of booklets, brochures, business cards, envelopes, flyers, forms, invitations, labels, letterheads, pads, pocket folders & restaurant menus*
Employs—12; Estab.—1982
Sales—$2.5Mil
Distrib.—Local
Privately owned corporation
AKA: Graphic Center Digital

**LEONARD PUBLICATIONS, INC.**
10 W. Hanover Ave., P.O. Box 553 (07970)
**Phone—(973) 895-6000**
www.leopub.com
Email—leonardpub@aol.com
Pres.—Pat Leonard
SIC—2721; *Quarterly informational magazine publishing for volunteer EMTs certified by the state of New Jersey; Brand name—The Gold Cross*
Employs—2; Estab.—1985
Sales—under $500,000 (est)
Distrib.—Regional
Privately owned corporation

**MOUNT FREEDOM PRINTING**
P.O. Box 285 (07970)
**Phone—(908) 362-9299**
Fax—(908) 362-5493
www.mountfreedomprinting.com
Email—jobs@mountfreedomprinting.com
Graphic Design Mgr.—Barbara Connolly
SIC—2752; 2791; NAICS—323122; *Color offset printing, typesetting & graphic design of business forms, business & post cards, promotional products, banners, signage, labels, brochures, checks, stationery, wedding annoucements & t-shirts*
Employs—3; Estab.—2001
Sales—under $500,000 (est)
1,100 sq ft site, Distrib.—Local
Privately owned corporation

## Mount Holly
(Burlington—S.E.)

**AMCOR FLEXIBLES, INC.**
220 Shreve St. (08060)
**Phone—(609) 267-5900**
Fax—(609) 267-7437
www.amcor.com
Email—media.relations@amcor.com
GM—Greg Dubler
Process Engr.—Karen Berman
Qual. Coord.—Melissa Clemens
SIC—3081; NAICS—326113; *Sterilized medical packaging*
Employs—30; Estab.—1954
Sales—over $1Bil
Distrib.—Intl.
Privately owned sub-S corp.
Parent co.—Amcor Flexibles, Inc., Mundelein, IL
Phone—(847) 362-9000
See Parent Co. Section for full profile.

**†APRIA HEALTHCARE, INC.**
118 Burrs Rd., Ste. C (08060)
**Phone—(609) 265-2190**
National—(800) 338-8039
Fax—(609) 265-2087
www.apria.com
Email—contact_us@apria.com
Br. Mgr.—Christopher Lange
SIC—5047; *Distributor of medical equipment & supplies*
Employs—50
Distrib.—Local
Publicly owned corporation
Parent co.—Apria Healthcare, Inc., Lake Forest, CA
Phone—(949) 639-2000
See Parent Co. Section for full profile.

**BREAKER GROUP, INC., THE**
32-34 Mill St. (08060)
**Phone—(609) 267-1330**
Fax—(609) 267-1433
www.breakergroup.com
Email—sales@breakergroup.com
Pres.—Tony Minervini
CFO—David Haniebnik
V-P., Sales & Mktg.—Bill McFeeley
V-P.—Randy Weaver
SIC—7373; 3661; NAICS—541512; *Computer integrated systems, including LAN/WAN, security, IP telephony, wireless communications integration & PBX & IP phone systems; Brand name—ShoreTel; Brocade; Ruckus; Aruba*
Employs—14; Estab.—2006
Sales—$3Mil
1,800 sq ft site, Distrib.—Regional
Limited Liability Company

**DEANS GRAPHICS**
16 Mill St., P.O. Box 809 (08060)
**Phone—(609) 261-8817**
National—(800) 963-3267
Fax—(609) 261-9372
www.deansgraphics.com
Email—steve@deansgraphics.com
Pres.—Stephen Deans
Sales Rep.—Mark Deans
SIC—2752; 2791; NAICS—323122; *Web & sheetfed offset printing & graphic design*
Employs—5; Estab.—1983
3,000 sq ft site, Distrib.—Regional
Limited Liability Company

**GLOBAL SPECIALTY PRODUCTS USA, INC.**
10 Eagle Ave., Ste. 500 (08060)
**Phone—(609) 518-7577**
Fax—(609) 518-5277
www.gsp-usa-inc.com
Email—info@gsp-usa-inc.com
Pres.—Theresa Wansiki
Manager—Anthony Faghani
SIC—2842; NAICS—325612; *Environmentally safe, nonhazardous, nonflammable biodegradable aqueous & solvent-based degreasers, paint strippers, rust inhibitors & industrial cleaning products*
Employs—12; Estab.—1993
Distrib.—Intl.
Privately owned corporation

**JAN L, INC.**
26 Mill St., Ste. 26 (08060)
**Phone—(609) 261-1133**
Fax—(609) 261-1167
www.janlinc.com
Email—janco@aol.com
Pres.—Bruce Levinson
Off. Mgr.—Teresa Evans
SIC—3841; 3999; 3291; *Hand drill dust collection systems, rotary tools & abrasive bits for podiatry, nail salon, dental lab & jewelry-making applications*
Employs—7; Estab.—1983
Sales—$1Mil-$2.5Mil (est)
Distrib.—Intl.
Privately owned corporation

**MAPLE MACHINE CO., INC.**
Mount Holly Industrial Commons, Unit 9 (08060)
Mail addr: 424 Landing St., Lumberton (08048-4522)
**Phone—(609) 702-0975**
Fax—(609) 702-0976
Email—maplemc@voicenet.com
Pres.—Ernie Mellon
SIC—3451; 3599; NAICS—332721; *Screw machine products & precision machining job shop*
Employs—6; Estab.—1993
Sales—under $500,000
4,500 sq ft site, Distrib.—National
Privately owned corporation

**MECH-TRONICS**
100 Campus Dr. (08060)
**Phone—(609) 267-0680**
National—(800) 856-7699
Fax—(609) 267-7621
www.mech-tronics.net
Email—sales@mech-tronics.net
Pres.—Peter Reed
Prodn. & Sales Supv.—Kevin Summer
SIC—3677; NAICS—334416; *Custom electronic transformers & inductors*
Employs—7; Estab.—1975
Sales—$500,000-$1Mil
Distrib.—Intl.
Privately owned corporation

**MONICK MFG. CORP.**
2619 Route 206 (08060)
Mail addr: P.O. Box 2713, Vincentown (08088-2713)
**Phone—(609) 267-0777**
Fax—(609) 267-0777
Email—monickmfg@aol.com
Pres.—Monte Hauser
V-P.—Richard Gerke

## Mount Holly—(cont.)

SIC—3569; 3599; *Machine parts & welding job shop*
Employs—5; Estab.—2002
Sales—$500,000-$1Mil
4,000 sq ft site, Distrib.—Regional
Privately owned corporation

### NATIONAL PIPE HANGER CORP.

200 Campus Dr., R.R. 30 (08060)
**Phone—(609) 261-5353**
Fax—(609) 261-3249
www.nationalpipehanger.com
Email—williammccabe@
nationalpipehanger.com
Pres., CEO—William McCabe
V-P., Fin.—Marystelle Bruckner
V-P.—Mike Spegel, Sr.
IT Mgr.—Mike Spegel, Jr.
Sheet Metal Mgr.—Butch Reed
Shpg. Mgr.—Darlene Schilling
SIC—3444; *Corporate headquarters & metal pipe hangers & sheet metal fabrication*
Employs—60; Estab.—1986
Sales—$5Mil-$10Mil (est)
50,000 sq ft site, Distrib.—National
Privately owned corporation

### PIERSON MATERIALS, INC., R. E.

Div. of Pierson Construction Co., Inc., R. E.
1550 Route 38 (08060)
Mail addr: P.O. Box 704, Bridgeport (08014)
**Phone—(609) 267-2257**
         (856) 740-2400
National—(800) 608-6789
Fax—(609) 267-5848
www.repiersongroup.com
Email—info@repierson.com
Manager—Bruce Scandlin
SIC—3273; NAICS—327320; *Ready-mixed concrete*
Employs—20; Estab.—1952
Sales—under $500,000
Distrib.—Local
Privately owned corporation
Parent co.—Pierson Construction Co., Inc., R. E., Pilesgrove, NJ
Phone—(856) 769-8244
See Parent Co. Section for full profile.

### PUREST COLLOIDS, INC.

600 Highland Dr., Ste. 602 (08060)
**Phone—(609) 267-2112**
National—(866) 233-4633
Fax—(609) 267-2250
www.purestcolloids.com
Email—info@purestcolloids.com
Pres.—Frank S. Key
GM—Robert Kroelinger
SIC—2833; NAICS—325411; *Colloidal silver supplements*
Employs—6; Estab.—2005
Sales—$2.5Mil-$5Mil (est)
4,000 sq ft site, Distrib.—Intl.
Privately owned corporation

### SAM'S CUSTOM WOODWORKING

14 Dunham Ln. (08060)
**Phone—(609) 267-4962**
Owner—Samuel Sortino
SIC—2434; *Wooden cabinets*
Employs—1

### SIR SPEEDY PRINTING

897 Rancocas Rd. (08060)
**Phone—(609) 267-1232**
National—(800) 406-7312
Fax—(609) 267-8289
www.sirspeedy.com/mountholly
Email—speedy7113@verizon.net
Pres.—Joseph Barlam
SIC—2752; 2791; NAICS—323122; *Commercial printing & typesetting*
Employs—2; Estab.—1990
Sales—under $500,000
Distrib.—Local
Privately owned corporation

### TRAP ROCK

Div. of Trap Rock Ind., LLC
27 Maple Ave. (08060)
Mail addr: P.O. Box 419, Kingston (08528)
**Phone—(609) 265-8500**
Fax—(609) 497-0135
www.traprock.com
Email—gmorgan@traprock.com
Sales Mgr.—Michael Conti
SIC—2951; 3272; NAICS—324121; *Asphalt paving compounds & concrete*
Employs—5; Estab.—1966
Distrib.—Regional
Privately owned corporation
Parent co.—Trap Rock Ind., LLC, Kingston, NJ
Phone—(609) 924-0300
See Parent Co. Section for full profile.

### WEL-FAB, INC.

124 Burrs Rd. (08060)
Mail addr: P.O. Box 86, Lumberton (08048-0086)
**Phone—(609) 261-1393**
Fax—(609) 261-7336
www.wel-fab.com
Email—paulelstone@wel-fab.com
Chrm. of the Board & V-P.—Paul J. Elstone, Sr.
Pres.—Dan O'Connor
V-P., Military Sales—Paul J. Elstone, Jr.
Off. Mgr.—Bonnie Sheppard
Off. Mgr.—Sam Young
SIC—3599; 3448; *Steel fabrication & welding of collapsible container systems & lightweight inflatable decontamination systems; Brand name—LIDS - Lightweight Inflatable Decontamination Systems; CCS - Collapsible Container Systems*
Employs—18; Estab.—1981
Sales—$5Mil-$8Mil
4,800 sq ft site, Distrib.—Regional
Privately owned sub-S corp.

---

## Mount Laurel

(Burlington—S.E.)

### ACTEON, INC.

124 Gaither Dr., Ste. 140 (08054-1712)
**Phone—(856) 222-9988**
National—(800) 289-6367
Fax—(856) 222-4726
www.acteongroup.com
Email—info@us.acteongroup.com
V-P., COO—Tim Long
Qual. Mgr.—Rick Rosati
SIC—3843; 3861; NAICS—339114; *Electronic dental equipment & supplies, including osteotomes, polishers, surgery units, curing lights, anesthetic, endo treatment, hygiene & impression products, intraoral cameras & medical & surgical endoscopy equipment; Brand name—Satelec; Sopro; Pierre Roland; Sopro-Comeg*
Employs—25; Estab.—1998
9,866 sq ft site, Distrib.—National
Privately owned corporation
ISO rating—9001
AKA: ACTEON North America

### AHB FOODS INTERNATIONAL

823 E. Gate Dr., Unit 3 (08054)
**Phone—(856) 642-9955**
Fax—(856) 642-9904
www.ahbfoods.com
Email—info@ahbfoods.com
Pres.—Jay Roseman
Cont. & Hum. Res. Mgr.—Betty Ann Pier

SIC—2051; NAICS—311812; *Artisan baked goods & breads*
Employs—30; Estab.—2005
Sales—$500,000-$1Mil
Distrib.—Local
Privately owned corporation

### †ALLIED BEVERAGE GROUP, LLC

901 Plesant Valley Ave., P.O. Box 5090 (08054)
**Phone—(856) 234-4111**
Fax—(856) 234-7932
www.alliedbeverage.com
Email—webmaster@
alliedbeverage.com
V-P.—Ed Feldman
SIC—5182; *Wholesaler of wine*
Employs—50; Estab.—1996
Sales—$11Mil-$25Mil
Distrib.—Local
Limited Liability Company
Parent co.—Allied Beverage Group, LLC, Carlstadt, NJ
Phone—(201) 842-6200
See Parent Co. Section for full profile.

### ALLIED ORTHOTICS & PROSTHETICS

813 E. Gate Dr., Ste. A (08054)
**Phone—(856) 273-6400**
Fax—(856) 273-0506
www.alliedop.com
Ex. V-P.—Howard Brand
SIC—3842; *Orthotic & prosthetic devices, including braces & artificial limbs*
Employs—14; Estab.—1990
20,000 sq ft site, Distrib.—Local
Privately owned corporation

### ARCTICCOOLERS, INC.

135 Gaither Dr., Ste. A (08054)
**Phone—(856) 231-0262**
Fax—(856) 231-0264
www.arcticcoolers.com
Pres.—Andrew Pearl
Off. Mgr.—Renee Naplins
SIC—3585; *Water coolers*
Employs—15; Estab.—1997
Sales—$2.5Mil-$5Mil (est)
Distrib.—Regional
Privately owned corporation

### AUTOMOTIVE RENTALS, INC.

Div. of Holman Enterprises, Inc.
4001 Leadenhall Rd., P.O. Box 5039 (08054)
**Phone—(856) 778-1500**
National—(800) 227-2273
Fax—(856) 273-1568
www.arifleet.com
Email—rdeeck@arifleet.com
Pres.—Carl Ortell
V-P., Sales—Gene Welsch
V-P., IT—Steve Haindle
Dir., Fleet Sols.—Richard Deeck
Hum. Res. Mgr.—Rob Kimner
SIC—3714; *Corporate headquarters & truck bodies*
Employs—900
Sales—$250Mil-$500Mil (est)
Distrib.—National
Privately owned corporation
Parent co.—Holman Enterprises, Inc., Maple Shade, NJ
Phone—(856) 663-5200
See Parent Co. Section for full profile.

### CAMPUS CLASSICS

3206 Route 38, P.O. Box 757 (08054)
**Phone—(856) 234-7474**
National—(800) 360-7570
Fax—(856) 234-0284
GM—Gerald Duncan
SIC—2329; NAICS—315200; *Silk screening & computerized embroidery*
Employs—2; Estab.—1966
Sales—under $500,000
Distrib.—Local
Sole ownership

### CUT MARK, INC.

801 S. Church St., Ste. 6 (08054)
**Phone—(856) 234-3428**
Fax—(856) 273-2837
www.cutmark.com
Email—sales@cutmark.com
Owner—George Gibson
Off. Mgr.—Laurie Middleman
SIC—3599; 3451; NAICS—332721; *Precision & CNC milling & turning job shop, automated screw machining, metal stamping & sheet metal fabrication*
Employs—7
Sales—under $500,000
500 sq ft site, Distrib.—Local
Sole ownership

### DYNTEK SERVICES, INC.

Div. of DynTek, Inc.
1120 Route 73, Ste. 100 (08054)
**Phone—(856) 834-1100**
Fax—(856) 834-1111
www.dyntek.com
Email—info@dyntek.com
Sr. Dist. Mgr.—Orlando Lima
Sr. Sales Rep., Inside—Debora Hartman
Sales Rep., Inside—Loretta Kushner
SIC—7373; NAICS—541512; *Advanced networking & IP communications computer integrated systems for commerce, education & government*
Employs—10; Estab.—1989
Distrib.—National
Parent co.—DynTek, Inc., Newport Beach, CA
Phone—(949) 271-6700
See Parent Co. Section for full profile.

### E & T PLASTICS

Div. of E & T Plastics Mfg. Co., Inc.
824 E. Gate Dr., Ste. E (08054)
**Phone—(856) 787-0900**
National—(800) 328-5871
Fax—(856) 787-9414
www.e-tplastics.com
Email—info@e-tplastics.com
Sales Mgr.—Ed Godshalk
Asst. Mgr.—Bernie Delaney
SIC—3089; *Plastic fabrication*
Employs—8; Estab.—1983
15,000 sq ft site, Distrib.—Intl.
Privately owned corporation
Parent co.—E & T Plastics Mfg. Co., Inc., Long Island City, NY
Phone—(718) 729-6226
See Parent Co. Section for full profile.

### †FEDERAL WINE & LIQUOR CO.

1 Central Ave. (08054)
**Phone—(856) 234-3200**
Opers. Mgr.—John Longa
SIC—5182; 5181; *Distributor of wine, liquor & beer*
Employs—150
Parent co.—Federal Wine & Liquor Co., Kearny, NJ
Phone—(973) 624-6444
See Parent Co. Section for full profile.

### FEDEX OFFICE & PRINT CENTER

Div. of FedEx Office & Print Services, Inc.
1211 Route 73 (08054)
**Phone—(856) 273-5959**
Fax—(856) 273-6535
www.fedexoffice.com
Email—usa1281@fedex.com
GM & Br. Mgr.—Seth Stocking
Asst. Mgr.—Carri Sykes
SIC—2759; NAICS—323100; *Laser printing*
Employs—8; Estab.—1994
Sales—$1Mil-$2.5Mil (est)
Distrib.—Local
Publicly owned corporation

GEOGRAPHICAL

## Mount Laurel—(cont.)

Parent co.—FedEx Office & Print
Services, Inc., Dallas, TX
Phone—(214) 550-7000
See Parent Co. Section for full profile.

**FOOD SCIENCES CORPORATION**
821 E. Gate Dr. (08054)
**Phone—(856) 778-8080**
Fax—(856) 778-4192
www.foodsciences.com
Email—hr@foodsciences.com
Pres.—Robert Schwartz
Dir., Mktg.—Lynda Lewis
SIC—2834; NAICS—325412;
*Weight loss meal replacements
& protein & nutritional
supplements; Brand name—
New Direction; NutriMed;
Advanced Health System*
Employs—150; Estab.—1976
Sales—$50Mil-$100Mil
Distrib.—Intl.
Privately owned corporation

**†FRANK WINNE & SON, INC.**
521 Fellowship Rd., Ste. 115
(08054)
**Phone—(913) 321-1983**
        (931) 212-3720
National—(888) 266-7590
Fax—(888) 266-9555
www.frankwinne.com
Email—info@frankwinne.com
Pres.—Doug Coath
Cont.—Rob Adelizzi
Sales Rep.—Mark Taylor
SIC—5085; *Wholesaler of rope,
tape, twine, safety supplies &
rubber products; Brand name—
Tubbs Rope; Clover and
Winmore Baler Twines; Winmore
Net Wrap; Tarp Straps; Winmore
Rubber Bands*
Employs—25; Estab.—1895
Distrib.—National
Privately owned corporation

**FRANKFORD UMBRELLAS**
824 E. Gate Dr. (08054)
Mail addr.—110 Gaither Dr., Mount
Laurel (08054)
**Phone—(856) 222-4134**
Fax—(856) 222-4712
www.frankfordumbrellas.com
Email—info@
frankfordumbrellas.com
Pres.—Marc Kaufer
Sales Mgr.—Angela Rampson
MIS & Sales Mgr.—Shawn
MacDonald
Sales Rep.—Bill Kenny
SIC—3999; *Patio & beach
umbrellas & chaise lounges*
Employs—15; Estab.—1898
Sales—$500,000-$1Mil
18,000 sq ft site, Distrib.—National
Privately owned corporation

**GIBSON, INC., GEORGE**
801 S. Church St., Ste. 6 (08054)
**Phone—(856) 234-5502**
Fax—(856) 273-2837
Pres.—George Gibson
Off. Mgr.—Lorri Middleman
SIC—3599; NAICS—332710;
*General machining job shop*
Employs—3; Estab.—1980
Sales—under $500,000
Distrib.—Local
Privately owned corporation

NEW ENTRY
**GLASTON AMERICA, INC.**
600-D Commerce Pkwy. (08054)
**Phone—(856) 786-1200**
Fax—(856) 234-4331
www.glaston.net
Email—usa@glaston.net
V.-P.—Scott Steffy

SIC—3231; *Architectural glass
fabrication, including beveling &
straight line edging*
Employs—60
Sales—$5Mil-$10Mil (est)
Distrib.—Intl.
Privately owned corporation

**GRAYHAIR SOFTWARE, INC.**
124 Gaither Dr., Ste. 160 (08054)
**Phone—(856) 727-9372**
National—(866) 507-9999
Fax—(856) 727-1315
www.grayhairsoftware.com
Email—sales@
grayhairsoftware.com
Pres.—Cameron Bellamy
V.-P., Prod. Mgmt. & Mktg.—
Raymond Chin
V.-P.—Jeff Stangle
Dir., Bus. Dev.—Josh McCaully
Hum. Res. Mgr.—Debbie Lemon
Prod. Mgr.—Stephanie Miracle
SIC—7372; *Direct mail
production, preparation,
payment & postage
reconciliation software
development, including
intelligent mail bar codes,
address hygiene, CASS, NCOA,
ACS & PCOA*
Employs—35; Estab.—2000
Distrib.—National
Privately owned corporation

**HONEYWELL HBS**
Div. of Honeywell International,
Inc.
534 Fellowship Rd. (08054)
**Phone—(856) 437-1832**
Fax—(856) 437-2730
www.honeywell.com
Email—info@honeywell.com
GM—Ed Neary
Administrator—Ava Harrison
Opers. Coord.—Cathy Foote
SIC—3585; *Heating & air
conditioning equipment*
Employs—50; Estab.—1920
Distrib.—National
Publicly owned corporation
Parent co.—Honeywell
International, Inc., Morristown,
NJ
Phone—(973) 455-2000
See Parent Co. Section for full profile.

**HUSSMANN CORP.**
3001 Irwin Rd., Ste. D (08054)
**Phone—(856) 793-7050**
National—(800) 879-9142
Fax—(856) 793-7099
www.hussmann.com
Email—hussman-info@irco.com
Reg. Sales Mgr., Northeast—Tony
Saggiomo
SIC—3585; NAICS—333415;
*Stationary refrigeration
equipment*
Employs—10; Estab.—2002
Publicly owned corporation
Parent co.—Hussmann Corp.,
Bridgeton, MO
Phone—(314) 291-2000
See Parent Co. Section for full profile.

**INFORMATICA CORP.**
309 Fellowship Rd. (08054)
**Phone—(856) 642-4080**
Fax—(856) 642-4079
www.informatica.com
Email—support@informatica.com
GM—Scott Seifried
SIC—7372; *Data integration
software development; Brand
name—Application Information
Lifecycle Management*
Employs—15
Privately owned corporation
Parent co.—Informatica Corp.,
Redwood City, CA
Phone—(650) 385-5000
See Parent Co. Section for full profile.

**INJECTION WORKS, INC.**
104 Gaither Dr. (08054)
**Phone—(856) 802-6444**
National—(888) 378-3241
Fax—(856) 778-8214
www.injectionworks.com
Email—info@injectionworks.com
Owner—Chris Rapacki
Opers. Mgr.—Dan Ferrante
Fin. & Pers. Mgr.—Rose Connolly
SIC—3089; *Plastic injection
molding*
Employs—25; Estab.—1988
Sales—$6Mil-$10Mil
50,000 sq ft site, Distrib.—Intl.
Privately owned sub-S corp.

**†INTERLINE BRANDS, INC. (H Q)**
Div. of Interline Brands, Inc.
804 Eastgate Dr., Ste. 100 (08054)
**Phone—(856) 439-1222**
National—(800) 345-3000
Fax—(800) 220-3291
www.interlinebrands.com
Email—aricciuti@
interlinebrands.com
V.-P., Hum. Res.—Annette Ricciuti
V.-P., Application Dev.—Jay
Polekoff
Payroll Mgr.—Shannon Eastwick
SIC—5074; 5075; 5063; 5064;
*Divisional headquarters;
distributor of standard &
specialty plumbing, hardware,
lighting, electrical & janitorial
supplies, HVAC heating & air
conditioning equipment &
appliances & appliance parts*
Employs—250; Estab.—1996
Distrib.—National
Privately owned corporation
DBA: Interline New Jersey
Parent co.—Interline Brands, Inc.,
Jacksonville, FL
Phone—(904) 421-1400
See Parent Co. Section for full profile.

**INTEST CORP.**
804 E. Gate Dr., Ste. 200 (08054)
**Phone—(856) 505-8800**
National—(800) 501-6886
www.intest.com
Email—postmaster@intest.com
Ex. Chrm.—Alyn Holt
Pres.—Robert E. Matthiessen
CFO—Hugh Regan, Jr.
Dir., Hum. Res.—Gina Floyd
GM—Daniel Graham
SIC—3829; *Corporate
headquarters & semiconductor
docking equipment*
Employs—50; Estab.—1981
Sales—$50Mil
120,000 sq ft site, Distrib.—Intl.
Privately owned corporation

**INVENTEK COLLOIDAL CLEANERS,
LLC (USA)**
106 Gaither Dr. *(08054)*
**Phone—(856) 206-0058**
Fax—(856) 206-0094
www.inventekcleaners.com
Email—info@inventekcleaners.com
Pres.—Yasmin Andrecola
V.-P.—Paul N. Andrecola
Plt. Supv.—Kelly Warrick
Prodn. Supv.—Carol Hulmes

SIC—2841; 2842; 2879; NAICS—
325611; *Nontoxic & eco-friendly
colloidal cleaning compounds
for oil & gas well services, the
foodservice industry, carpets,
drains, grease traps & natural
pest control products; Brand
name—Inventek; InventeK
Beyond Green; Green Genie;
Eco Green; EnviroLogik; DelVel
Eliminator; CSI; Skeet-R-Gone;
Perf Go Green; Car Planet;
Green Earth Technologies*
Employs—25; Estab.—1978
Sales—$125Mil-$230Mil
160,000 sq ft site, Distrib.—Intl.
Limited Liability Company

**JERSEY TEMPERED GLASS, INC.**
2035 Briggs Rd., P.O. Box 205
(08054)
**Phone—(856) 273-8700**
Fax—(856) 273-1999
www.jerseytemperedglass.com
Email—sales@
jerseytemperedglass.com
Pres.—Nicholas Concio
Treas.—William Southwick
Plt. Mgr.—John Latko
SIC—3229; 3211; 3231; NAICS—
327212; *Tempered glass,
including beveled, V-grooved,
Victorian antique & insulating
units*
Employs—30; Estab.—1976
47,000 sq ft site, Distrib.—National
Privately owned corporation

**JOHNSON & TOWERS, INC.**
2021 Briggs Rd., P.O. Box 4000
(08054)
**Phone—(856) 234-6990**
National—(800) 394-6996
Fax—(856) 234-5518
www.johnsontowers.com
Email—shink@johnsontowers.com
Chrm.—Walter Johnson III
GM—Bob Shomo, Jr.
Hum. Res. Mgr.—Shelley Hink
SIC—3519; 3714; 5084; *Corporate
headquarters & rebuilt truck
engines & distributor of diesel
engines & transmissions; Brand
name—MTU; DDC; Allison;
Freightliner*
Employs—75; Estab.—1926
Sales—$70Mil
100,000 sq ft site, Distrib.—
Regional
Privately owned corporation

**JW INDUSTRIES, INC.**
21 Elbo Ln. (08054)
**Phone—(856) 235-9285**
National—(800) 344-4843
Fax—(856) 235-9295
www.jwindustriesinc.net
Email—jwindustries@comcast.net
V.-P.—Jack Fecher
SIC—3061; 3069; NAICS—
326291; *Custom molded rubber
parts, rubber-to-metal parts,
rubber molded hoses, rubber
extrusions & industrial rubber
sheet in neoprene, nitrile, SBR,
butyl, EPDM, silicone & viton for
the marine, automotive &
industrial OEM industries*
Employs—2; Estab.—1984
Sales—$1Mil-$2.5Mil
10,000 sq ft site, Distrib.—Intl.
Privately owned corporation

**†KENNEDY COS., THE**
8000 Midlantic Dr., Ste. 200-N
(08054)
**Phone—(856) 813-5000**
Fax—(856) 813-5001
www.kennedy-companies.com
Pres., Hum. Res. Mgr.—Robert
Kennedy, Jr.

## Mount Laurel—(cont.)

SIC—5051; 5087; *Company headquarters & distributor of pipes & erosion control, sewer, water & storm equipment*
Employs—20; Estab.—2002
Distrib.—Local
Privately owned corporation

### KUBIK MALTBIE, INC.

7000 Commerce Pkwy., Ste. C (08054)
**Phone—(856) 234-0052**
Fax—(856) 234-0760
www.maltbie.com
Email—bspillane@maltbie.com
Pres.—Charles M. Maltbie, Jr.
V-P., Sales—George Mayer
V-P.—Gary Brooks
Cont. & Dir., Hum. Res.—Lisa Rice
Dir., Bus. Dev.—Ryan Skorch
Off. Admn.—Briety Spillane
Pur. Agt.—Duane Binkley
SIC—2542; *Glass & metal museum showcases & displays*
Employs—40; Estab.—1965
Sales—$2.5Mil-$5Mil (est)
Distrib.—Intl.
Privately owned corporation
DBA: Maltbie

### LTS / LT SECURITY INC. (H Q)

109 W. Park Dr., Ste. C (08054)
**Phone—(856) 780-9888**
National—(855) 835-8889
Fax—(856) 780-9889
www.ltsecurityinc.com
Email—sales@ltsnj.com
Pres.—Wing Pang
SIC—3663; *Corporate headquarters; full-line professional-grade surveillance equipment (mfg. done in China); Brand name—LTS; Platinum*
Employs—32
Sales—over $15Mil
Distrib.—Intl.
Privately owned corporation

### LUX PRODUCTS CORP. (H Q)

6000 Commerce Pkwy., Ste. I (08054)
Mail addr: 13113 Spivey Dr., Laredo (78045)
**Phone—(856) 234-7905**
National—(800) 628-4309
Fax—(856) 234-7825
www.luxproducts.com
Email—dmcbain@luxproducts.com
Pres.—Paul Balon
MIS Mgr.—Roger Milley
Hum. Res. Mgr.—MaryAnn Turra
Pur. Agt.—Diane McBain
SIC—3823; 3822; NAICS—334513; *Corporate headquarters; thermostats, timers & range replacement parts for home appliances*
Employs—23; Estab.—1991
40,000 sq ft site, Distrib.—National
Privately owned corporation

### †MACRO EQUIPMENT CO.

205 Hartford Rd., Route 38 (08054)
**Phone—(856) 235-4235**
Fax—(856) 778-0927
www.macroequip.com
Email—info@macroequip.com
Owner & Pres.—Paul J. Panarello
Sales Mgr.—Craig Cunningham

SIC—5082; 5083; *Distributor of outdoor power equipment for commercial, residential, industrial, construction, farm & landscape applications, including chainsaws, line & hedge trimmers, brush cutters, blowers, cut-off & pole saws, augers & power hand tools*
Employs—7; Estab.—1971
Sales—over $950,000
2,600 sq ft site, Distrib.—Regional
Privately owned corporation

### METAL DYNAMIX, LLC

709 Fellowship Rd. (08054)
**Phone—(856) 235-4559**
National—(877) 429-9199
www.metaldynamix.com
Email—sales@metaldynamix.com
Pres.—Charles Gaw
SIC—3444; 3599; *Sheet metal fabrication & CNC machining job shop*
Employs—9
Limited Liability Company

### †MIDLANTIC SUPPLY, LLC

8000 Midlantic Dr., Ste. 200-N., P.O. Box 506 (08054)
**Phone—(856) 813-5014**
Fax—(856) 778-4933
www.midlanticsupply.com
Email—info@midlanticsupply.com
Owner—Diane Disanto
SIC—5051; 5084; 5085; 5032; *Distributor of waterworks & sewer equipment & supplies, including steel, iron, PVC, sewer & drain pipe, fittings, valves, meters, backflow preventers & reinforced concrete pipe*
Employs—5; Estab.—2005
Distrib.—Regional
Limited Liability Company

### NEW ENTRY
### MJ CORPORATE SALES, INC.

109 W. Park Dr., Unit B (08054)
**Phone—(856) 778-0055**
Fax—(856) 778-8871
www.mjcorp.com
Email—sales@mjcorp.com
Owner—John Dikmak
Pres.—Robert Madosky
Off. Mgr.—Kathy Warwick
SIC—2396; 2395; 2759; 3993; *Apparel screen printing & embroidery, signs, banners, vehicle graphics, large-format printing, graphic design & award engraving*
Employs—25
Sales—$2.5Mil-$5Mil (est)

### MNEMONICS, INC.

P.O. Box 877 (08054-0877)
**Phone—(856) 234-0970**
www.mnemonicsinc.com
Email—contact@mnemonicsinc.com
Pres.—Michael Negin
SIC—3599; *Computer-automated proofreading, machine & vision systems for the pharmaceutical, printing & automated manufacturing industries; Brand name—AVIA; AVIA Private Eye; AVIA Color Matching*
Employs—4; Estab.—1979
Sales—$500,000-$1Mil (est)
1,600 sq ft site, Distrib.—Intl.
Privately owned sub-S corp.

### MONARCH ART PLASTICS, LLC

3838 Church Rd. (08054)
**Phone—(856) 235-5151**
Fax—(856) 778-9032
www.monarchplastics.com
Email—mplastic@monarchplastics.com
CEO—William Shanley
Sales Mgr.—Becky Marsh

SIC—3089; 2759; NAICS—323100; *Custom plastics printing & fabrication, including screening, laminating & fulfillment of clipboards, brochure holders & dry erase boards*
Employs—25; Estab.—1995
Distrib.—National
Limited Liability Company
AKA: Monarch Plastics

### NETQUEST CORP.

523 Fellowship Rd., Ste. 205 (08054)
**Phone—(856) 866-0505**
Fax—(856) 866-2852
www.netquestcorp.com
Email—info@netquestcorp.com
CEO—Jesse Price
V-P., Sales—Richard Moulder
Off. Mgr.—Karin Jandoli
SIC—3661; 7372; *High speed broadband optical & copper telecommunication monitoring & access systems*
Employs—20; Estab.—1985
Sales—$5Mil
Distrib.—Intl.
Privately owned corporation

### OKI DATA AMERICAS, INC.

2000 Bishops Gate Blvd. (08054)
**Phone—(856) 235-2600**
National—(800) 654-3282
www.okidata.com
Email—support@okidata.com
Pres., CEO—Masahiko Morioka
Pres., Oki Data do Brasil—Sergio Horikawa
Ex. V-P., CFO—Kazutaka Onodera
Sr. V-P., Fin.—Joseph Reilly
Ex. V-P.—Mitsuaki Takahara
V-P., U.S. Sales—Greg Van Acker
V-P., Engrg., Sales Support—Kazuhido Nagaoka
V-P., Bus. Plng. & Opers.—Koichiro Fukano
V-P., Mktg., N. America—Carl Taylor
GM, Canada—Mario Pallotta
Sr. Mktg. Mgr., Mktg. Comms.—Sue Kirvan
SIC—3577; 3861; *Digital color & monochrome printers & MFP products, serial impact dot matrix printers, thermal label printers, POS printers & digital color products for the graphic arts & production market; Brand name—OKI; proColor*
Employs—350; Estab.—1972
Sales—$100Mil-$250Mil
Distrib.—Intl.

### ORACLE CORP.

330 Fellowship Rd., Ste. 100 (08054)
**Phone—(856) 359-2999**
Fax—(856) 638-1245
www.oracle.com
Email—info@oracle.com
Facility Mgr.—Scott Goldberg
SIC—7372; *Software development*
Employs—20
Distrib.—Intl.
Publicly owned corporation
Parent co.—Oracle Corp., Redwood City, CA
Phone—(650) 506-7000
See Parent Co. Section for full profile.

### ORIGIO, INC.

Div. of CooperSurgical, Inc.
77 Elbo Ln. (08054)
**Phone—(856) 762-2000**
National—(800) 648-1151
Fax—(888) 847-7266
www.origio.com
Email—us.customerservice@origio.com
Ex. V-P., Mfg.—Allan Toft Jacobsen

Chief Exec.—Bob Hanley
SIC—2835; *In-vitro fertilization (IVF) substances; Brand name—SAGE Media™*
Employs—30
Sales—$10Mil-$25Mil (est)
Distrib.—Local
Publicly owned corporation
Parent co.—CooperSurgical, Inc., Trumbull, CT
Phone—(203) 601-5200
See Parent Co. Section for full profile.

### PENNY PLATE, LLC (H Q)

14000 Horizon Way, Ste. 300 (08054)
Mail addr: P.O. Box 3003, Haddonfield (08033)
**Phone—(856) 429-7583**
National—(800) 527-9909
Fax—(856) 429-7166
www.pennyplate.com
Email—info@pennyplate.com
Pres.—Paul Cobb
Dir., Hum. Res.—Sharon Fitzpatrick
SIC—3497; *Company headquarters; aluminum foil containers*
Employs—12
Sales—$10Mil-$25Mil
Distrib.—National
Privately owned corporation

### PMC GROUP, INC. (H Q)

1288 Route 73 (08054)
**Phone—(856) 533-1866**
Fax—(856) 533-1867
www.pmc-group.com
Email—spiccone@pmc-group.com
Pres., COO—Debtash Chakrabarti
IS Mgr.—Wei Chen
Pub. Rels. Mgr.—Sheila Piccone
SIC—2819; 2869; 3089; 3695; NAICS—334613; *Corporate headquarters; industrial chemicals, compounds, plastic injection molding & pipe fabrication*
Employs—35; Estab.—1994
Sales—$10Mil-$25Mil (est)
Privately owned corporation

### PRC-DESOTO INTERNATIONAL, INC.

Div. of PPG Aerospace
823 E. Gate Dr., Unit 4 (08054)
**Phone—(856) 234-1600**
(856) 437-2105
Fax—(856) 234-5515
www.ppg.com
Email—corporateinfo@ppg.com
Cust. Serv. Mgr.—Mary Ready
Cust. Serv. Rep.—Joyce Jones
Cust. Serv. Rep.—Kim Kerr
SIC—2891; NAICS—325520; *Aerospace sealants & coatings blending & packaging*
Employs—30; Estab.—1977
24,000 sq ft site, Distrib.—Regional
Privately owned corporation
AKA: PPG Aerospace
Parent co.—PPG Aerospace, Sylmar, CA
Phone—(818) 362-6711
See Parent Co. Section for full profile.

### PROBUILD CO., LLC

Div. of ProBuild Holdings, Inc.
817 Eastgate Dr., Ste. 101 (08054)
**Phone—(856) 505-1100**
National—(800) 883-8800
Fax—(856) 505-1158
www.probuild.com
Email—info@probuild.com
Area V-P.—Rob Gaites
IT Mgr.—Don Chucas
SIC—2421; *Lumber processing*
Employs—50
Sales—$1Mil-$2.5Mil
Distrib.—Local
Privately owned corporation

GEOGRAPHICAL

## Mount Laurel—(cont.)

Parent co.—ProBuild Holdings, Inc., Denver, CO
Phone—(303) 262-8500
See Parent Co. Section for full profile.

**PRODUCTIVE PLASTICS, INC.**

103 W. Park Dr. (08054)
Phone—(856) 778-4300
Fax—(856) 234-3310
www.productiveplastics.com
Email—respond@
productiveplastics.com
Pres.—Hal Gilham
Ex. V-P., Sales—John Zerillo
V-P., Opers.—Evan J. Gilham
V-P., Fin.—Todd Mitchell
Corp. Qual. Mgr.—Doug Peters
Cust. Serv. Admn.—Debbie Curatolo
SIC—3089; Thermoformed plastic components including vacuum, pressure & twin-sheet forming & value added assembly of sheet metal & injection molded plastic parts
Employs—60
Sales—$8Mil-$12Mil
83,000 sq ft site, Distrib.—National
Privately owned corporation
ISO rating—9001:2000

**QAD, INC.**

10000 Midlantic Dr., Ste. 100 W. (08054)
Phone—(856) 273-1717
Fax—(630) 719-4930
www.qad.com
Email—info@qad.com
Hum. Res. Bus. Ptnr.—Stephanie Derman
Dir., Hum. Res.—Rich Montgomery
Coordinator—John Curcio
SIC—7372; Warehouse management system software development
Employs—140; Estab.—1979
Distrib.—Intl.
Publicly owned corporation
Parent co.—QAD, Inc., Santa Barbara, CA
Phone—(805) 566-6000
See Parent Co. Section for full profile.

**ROOSEVELT PAPER CO.**

1 Roosevelt Dr. (08054)
Phone—(856) 303-4100
(800) 523-3470
Fax—(856) 642-1949
www.rooseveltpaper.com
Email—degan@rooseveltpaper.com
Chrm., CEO—Ted Kosloff
Pres.—David Kosloff
CFO—Tony Janulewicz
V-P., Sales & Mktg.—Dean Egan
Sales Mgr.—Dennis Carney
IT Mgr.—John Gordon
SIC—2679; NAICS—322200; Company headquarters & printing paper converting for printers & packaging companies
Employs—132; Estab.—1932
Sales—$10Mil-$25Mil
465,000 sq ft site, Distrib.—National
Privately owned sub-S corp.

**S. FRANKFORD & SONS, INC.**

110 Gaither Dr. (08054)
Phone—(856) 222-4134
Fax—(856) 222-4712
www.umbrellasusa.com
Email—info@
frankfordumbrellas.com
Pres.—Mark Kaufer
SIC—3999; Umbrellas, including commercial-grade beach & cart umbrellas
Employs—6
Sales—$500,000-$1Mil (est)
Distrib.—Intl.
Privately owned corporation

**SENSIGRAPHICS, INC.**

105 W. Park Dr. (08054)
Phone—(856) 853-9100
Fax—(856) 853-6966
www.sensigraphics.com
Email—info@sensigraphics.com
Pres.—Harold Gilham
Mktg. Mgr.—Shawn DePasquale
SIC—3679; 3577; Custom membrane switches, keypads, graphic overlays, control panels & contract electronic assembly, including design services
Employs—30; Estab.—1994
Sales—$2.5Mil-$5Mil (est)
Distrib.—National
ISO rating—9001:2008

**SL INDUSTRIES, INC. (H Q)**

520 Fellowship Rd., Ste. A-114 (08054)
Phone—(856) 727-1500
Fax—(856) 727-1683
www.slindustries.com
Email—info@slindustries.com
Pres., CEO—William T. Fejes, Jr.
CFO, Secy-Treas.—Louis J. Belardi
Dir., Hum. Res.—Maryann Cassidy
SIC—3669; NAICS—334290; Corporate headquarters; power electronics, motion, protection, teleprotection & communication equipment
Employs—10; Estab.—1987
Company-wide: 2,000
Sales—$100Mil
Publicly owned corporation

**SQUARE ONE, INC.**

111 Gaither Dr., Ste. 104 (08054)
Phone—(856) 234-6999
Fax—(856) 234-4550
www.sqone.net
Email—jillt@sqone.net
Pres.—Colin Townsend
V-P.—Jill Townsend
Accountant—Grace M. Barr
SIC—2759; 2752; 2789; 2791; NAICS—323121; Commercial, offset & digital printing, binding, electronic prepress, mailing & fulfillment
Employs—45; Estab.—1993
15,000 sq ft site, Distrib.—Regional
Privately owned sub-S corp.

**SYCAMORE NETWORKS, INC.**

Div. of Coriant America, Inc.
100 Century Pkwy, Ste. 120 (08054)
Phone—(856) 359-9301
National—(800) 337-4374
Fax—(856) 359-9302
www.sycamorenet.com
Email—contactsales@
sycamorenet.com
Opers. Mgr.—Joan Gianiotis
SIC—3669; NAICS—334290; Communications equipment
Employs—110; Estab.—1991
Sales—$10Mil-$25Mil (est)
Distrib.—Intl.
Publicly owned corporation
Parent co.—Coriant America, Inc., Chelmsford, MA
Phone—(978) 250-2900
See Parent Co. Section for full profile.

**ULYSSES MACHINE CO.**

41 Lancelot Ln. (08054)
Phone—(856) 979-3674
(856) 658-9239
National—(800) 625-7154
Fax—(856) 931-5573
www.ulyssesmachine.com
Email—ulysses6373@comcast.net
Owner—Ulysses Xenophontos

SIC—3559; 3829; Rope twisting, wire braider & ballistic testing equipment; Brand name—Whirlwind Twister Parts; Wardwell Wire; Braider Parts
Employs—2; Estab.—1987
Sales—under $500,000
3,000 sq ft site, Distrib.—National
Sole ownership

**VENTRAQ, INC.**

Div. of Genband, Inc.
817 E. Gate Dr., Ste. 101 (08054-1208)
Phone—(856) 866-1000
National—(800) 225-0191
Fax—(856) 866-0185
www.ventraq.com
Email—salesinfo@ventraq.com
Dir., Opers., N. American—Bruce Kasian
Dir., Software Dev.—Sameer Rele
SIC—7372; Telecommunication billing mediation, customer self-service & revenue assurance systems software development; Brand name—EventDynamics Mediation Software; C3C Customer Self-Serve Software; BIAS Business Analytics Software
Employs—40; Estab.—1967
20,000 sq ft site, Distrib.—Intl.
Privately owned corporation
ISO rating—9001:2000
Parent co.—Genband, Inc., Frisco, TX
Phone—(972) 521-5800
See Parent Co. Section for full profile.

**†W. W. GRAINGER, INC.**

819 E. Gate Dr. (08054)
Phone—(856) 234-8550
Fax—(856) 234-2524
www.grainger.com
Email—info@grainger.com
GM—Ron Schomo
Cust. Serv. Rep.—Greg Milakovic
SIC—5084; 5085; Wholesaler of industrial equipment & supplies
Employs—15; Estab.—1958
Distrib.—Local
Privately owned corporation
Parent co.—W. W. Grainger, Inc., Lake Forest, IL
Phone—(847) 535-1000
See Parent Co. Section for full profile.

**WALK THE TECHNOLOGY SOLUTION**

9000 Commerce Pkwy., Ste. H (08054)
Phone—(856) 222-0643
National—(800) 427-2674
Fax—(856) 222-0653
www.wachter.com
V-P., Engrg. & IT Mgr.—Marty Roselli
SIC—3661; Data communications equipment
Employs—30
Distrib.—Intl.
Privately owned corporation

**†WASHINGTON PROFESSIONAL SYSTEMS, INC.**

109 Gaither Dr., Ste. 301 (08054)
Phone—(856) 273-8688
Fax—(856) 273-8558
www.wpsworld.com
Email—sales@wpsworld.com
Br. Mgr.—Joe Hondros
Documentation Coord.—Darryl Turner
SIC—5065; Distributor of audiovisual equipment & systems
Employs—4; Estab.—1989
Distrib.—National
Privately owned corporation

Parent co.—Washington Professional Systems, Inc., Wheaton, MD
Phone—(301) 942-6800
See Parent Co. Section for full profile.

**WEIL-MCLAIN**

Div. of SPX Corporation
17000 Commerce Pkwy., Ste. B (08054-2267)
Phone—(856) 866-7400
Fax—(856) 866-8828
www.weil-mclain.com
Email—bprice@weil-mclain.com
Reg. Mgr., Mid Atlantic—William Price, Jr.
SIC—3443; High efficiency gas & oil boilers
Employs—11; Estab.—1886
Sales—$1Mil-$2.5Mil (est)
Distrib.—Regional
Publicly owned corporation
ISO rating—9001
Parent co.—SPX Corporation, Charlotte, NC
Phone—(704) 752-4400
See Parent Co. Section for full profile.

**WHITTLE & MUTCH, INC.**

712 Fellowship Rd. (08054)
Phone—(856) 235-1165
Fax—(856) 235-0902
www.wamiflavor.com
Email—sales@wamiflavor.com
Pres.—John C. Mutch, Jr.
V-P., Secy.—John C. Mutch III
V-P., Treas.—Richard L. Mutch
Plt. Mgr.—Joe Grubb
SIC—2087; NAICS—311900; Flavoring extracts
Employs—14; Estab.—1892
Sales—$10Mil-$25Mil (est)
17,000 sq ft site, Distrib.—Intl.
Privately owned corporation

**XTREME TECHNOLOGIES GROUP, LLC**

135 Gaither Dr., Ste. F (08054)
Phone—(856) 273-7800
Fax—(856) 273-7838
www.xtechs.com
Owner—Louis Passareola
Off. Mgr.—Kristie Keilyk
SIC—7373; NAICS—541512; Network systems integration & custom software development
Employs—20; Estab.—1999
Distrib.—National
Limited Liability Company

**ZIMMER TRI-STATE, INC.**

Div. of Zimmer Holdings, Inc.
1001 Briggs Rd., Ste. 275 (08054)
Phone—(856) 778-8300
National—(800) 582-5911
Fax—(856) 778-0894
www.zimmer.com
Email—sales@zimmer.com
Opers. Mgr.—Stan Smoyer
Hum. Res. Mgr.—Joyce Stitt
Cust. Serv. Rep.—Kathy Haussman
SIC—3842; Orthopedic joint implants
Employs—60; Estab.—1986
Distrib.—National
Publicly owned corporation
Parent co.—Zimmer Holdings, Inc., Warsaw, IN
Phone—(574) 267-6131
See Parent Co. Section for full profile.

---

## Mount Olive

(Morris—N.W.)

**GIVAUDAN FRAGRANCES CORP.**

Div. of Givaudan Flavors Corp.
300 Waterloo Valley Rd. (07828)
Phone—(973) 448-6500
Fax—(973) 448-6517
www.givaudan.com
Email—corp.communications@
givaudan.com

## Mount Olive—(cont.)

V-P., Opers.—John Trombley
Engrg., Facility & Maint. Mgr.—
Joseph Ciccone
Security Mgr.—Tom Allen
SIC—2844; 2869; NAICS—
325600; *Perfumes, fragrances &
personal care products*
Employs—200; Estab.—1820
Sales—$50Mil-$100Mil
210,000 sq ft site, Distrib.—Intl.
Publicly owned corporation
Parent co.—Givaudan Flavors
Corp., Cincinnati, OH
Phone—(513) 948-8000
See Parent Co. Section for full profile.

### INTEGRATED MICROWAVE TECHNOLOGIES, LLC

200 International Dr. (07828)
**Phone—(908) 852-3700**
National—(800) 968-2666
Fax—(908) 813-0399
www.imt-solutions.com
Email—sales@imt-solutions.com
CFO—Robert Chiarulli
COO—Todd Hansen
Dir., Mktg.—Elena Waldhuber
Bus. Dev. Mgr.—Sean Drew
SIC—3679; 3663; *Digital
microwave video equipment &
systems for broadcast, sports,
defense, security & law
enforcement applications,
including portable & ultra
compact transmitters &
receivers; Brand name—IMT;
Nucomm; RF Central*
Employs—80; Estab.—1990
65,000 sq ft site, Distrib.—Intl.
Limited Liability Company
ISO rating—9001:2008

### ROBERTET-NOVAROME FRAGRANCES, INC.

400 International Dr. (07828)
**Phone—(973) 575-4550**
Fax—(973) 575-5965
Prodn. Mgr.—Sterling Lutz
Pur. Mgr.—Melanie De Ritter
Hum. Res. Mgr.—Marie Saracino
SIC—2844; NAICS—325600;
*Perfume & essential oils*
Employs—85
Distrib.—Intl.
Privately owned corporation

### TRONEX INTERNATIONAL, INC.

300 International Dr. (07828)
**Phone—(973) 335-2888**
National—(800) 833-1181
Fax—(973) 335-2900
www.tronexcompany.com
Email—information@
tronexcompany.com
Pres., CEO—Donald L. Chu
Ex. V-P. & Chief Bus. Dev.
Officer—Poyee L. Tai
Asst. V-P., Bus. Dev. & Govt. Div.—
Bob Domenech
Natl. Dir., Healthcare Div.—
Edmund S. Tai
Dir., Safety Sols. Div.—Steve
Rummel
Mktg. Prog. Mgr.—Luann Padden

SIC—3841; 3842; 2389; NAICS—
325412; *Advanced medical,
hospital health & safety products
& supplies, including disposable
gloves, bandages & apparel;
Brand name—Tronex; The
Choice; NEW AGE; SynTech;
CLEANnSAFE; Air Touch; Safety
Through Education; Quality Is a
Journey Not a Destination;
'Making a Positive Difference
and the World a Better Place'*
Employs—69; Estab.—1989
200,000 sq ft site, Distrib.—
National
Privately owned corporation
ISO rating—13485, 9001
AKAs: Tronex Healthcare & Tronex
Safety Solutions & Tronex
Government

## Mount Royal

(Gloucester—S.W.)

### BROWN & CO., C. W.

161 Kings Hwy. (08061)
**Phone—(856) 423-3700**
Fax—(856) 423-8894
Pres.—Robert Botto
SIC—2011; NAICS—311611; *Meat
processing*
Employs—6; Estab.—1998
Sales—$1Mil-$2.5Mil (est)
Distrib.—Regional
Privately owned corporation

## Mount Tabor

(Morris—N.W.)

### A-1 ADVANCED MARKING TECHNOLOGIES, LLC

1420 Route 53, P.O. Box 485
(07878)
**Phone—(973) 627-0155**
Fax—(973) 627-7469
www.a1marking.com
Email—sales@a1marking.com
Pres., Off. & Plt. Mgr.—Cynthia
Hopping
Sales Mgr.—Frank Swiontkowski
SIC—2396; 2759; NAICS—
323100; *Hot stamping, screen
printing & pad printing*
Employs—12; Estab.—2000
Sales—$1Mil-$2.5Mil
Distrib.—National
Privately owned corporation

## Mountain Lakes

(Morris—N.W.)

### ACCESSIT GROUP, INC.

115 Route 46 W., Bldg. E, Ste. 35
(07046)
**Phone—(973) 316-6016**
Fax—(973) 394-5602
www.accessitgroup.com
Email—training@accessitgroup.com
CEO—Joe Luciano
Off. Mgr.—Valerie Golbieri
IT Mgr.—Nathan Brown
SIC—7373; NAICS—541512;
*Computer security integrated
systems*
Employs—10; Estab.—2000
Distrib.—Local
Privately owned corporation

### CIRE TECHNOLOGIES, INC.

251 Boulevard (07046)
**Phone—(973) 402-8301**
National—(800) 388-8301
Fax—(973) 402-8302
www.ciretechnologies.com
Email—sales@
ciretechnologies.com
Pres.—Eric Becht

SIC—3559; NAICS—333292;
*Industrial dryers for the
converting industry & fume
oxidizers for VOC abatement*
Employs—3; Estab.—1990
Sales—under $2Mil
Distrib.—Intl.
Privately owned sub-S corp.

### DATABASE ACCESS SYSTEMS, INC.

60 Midvale Rd., Ste. 206, P.O. Box
126 (07046)
**Phone—(973) 335-0800**
Fax—(973) 335-1956
www.dbasinc.com
Email—info@dbasinc.com
Pres., CEO—Michael Palazzi
GM—Joe Ferraro
Engr.—Tony Amelia
Technician—Nick Bazin
SIC—3679; 3229; NAICS—
327212; *Fiber-optic network
cards & switches; Brand name—
Codenet; CodeStar; CodeLink*
Employs—4; Estab.—1980
Sales—$500,000-$1Mil
Distrib.—Intl.
Privately owned corporation
AKAs: Codenoll Access &
Codenoll

### DELUXE MFG. OPERATIONS, INC.

Div. of Deluxe Corp.
105 U.S. Highway 46 (07046)
**Phone—(973) 334-8000**
National—(800) 335-8931
Fax—(973) 334-4292
www.deluxe.com
Email—feedback@deluxe.com
Plt. Mgr.—Steve Penna
IT Mgr.—Mark Powne
SIC—2761; 2782; NAICS—
323116; *Check printing*
Employs—200; Estab.—1920
Distrib.—Intl.
Publicly owned corporation
Parent co.—Deluxe Corp.,
Shoreview, MN
Phone—(651) 483-7111
See Parent Co. Section for full profile.

### FLAROMA, INC.

96 Fanny Rd., P.O. Box 325
(07046)
**Phone—(973) 316-8185**
Fax—(973) 316-8949
Pres.—Bob Amaducci
SIC—2087; NAICS—311900;
*Food flavorings*
Employs—30; Estab.—1985
Distrib.—National
Privately owned corporation

### RED OAK SOFTWARE, INC.

115 U.S. Highway 46, Ste. F-1000
(07046)
**Phone—(973) 316-6064**
National—(877) 660-4688
Fax—(973) 394-5625
www.redoaksw.com
Email—info@redoaksw.com
Pres., CEO—George Cummings
V-P., Sales—Bill Muscato
V-P., Opers.—Johanna Haltmeier
SIC—7372; *Enterprise software
development; Brand name—The
Transaction Integration™ Experts*
Employs—5; Estab.—1999
Distrib.—Intl.
Privately owned corporation

### †SPECIALTY DISPOSAL SERVICES, INC.

115 Route 46, Bldg. E-37-38
(07046)
**Phone—(973) 402-9246**
Fax—(973) 335-5833
www.specialtydisposal.com
Email—snesteriak@
specialtydisposal.com
Opers. Mgr.—Stephen Nesteriak

SIC—5093; *Wholesaler of
recycled cardboard, plastic,
paper & metal*
Employs—50; Estab.—1990
Distrib.—Intl.
Publicly owned corporation
AKA: SDS

### VITROCOM, INC.

8 Morris Ave., P.O. Box 125
(07046)
**Phone—(973) 402-1443**
Fax—(973) 402-1445
www.vitrocom.com
Email—sales@vitrocom.com
Plt. Mgr.—Phill Motyka
Opers. Mgr.—Paul Motyka
Off. Mgr. & Pur. Agt.—Sue
Christiansen
Cust. Serv. Rep.—Heather Bruer
SIC—3231; NAICS—327215;
*Fiber-optic components &
technical glass products*
Employs—30; Estab.—1968
Sales—$2.6Mil-$5Mil
28,000 sq ft site, Distrib.—Intl.
Publicly owned corporation
AKA: VitroCom FBN NJ Mfg.

### WESTERN SCIENTIFIC COMPUTERS, INC.

28 W. Shore Rd. (07046)
**Phone—(973) 263-9311**
Fax—(973) 263-1976
Email—wsc_inc@verizon.net
Pres.—Joe Lutz
Off. Mgr.—Jody Klinghoffer
SIC—7373; NAICS—541512;
*Systems integration for CAD/
CAM*
Employs—14; Estab.—1980
Sales—$500,000-$1Mil
Distrib.—Intl.
Privately owned corporation

## Mountainside

(Union—N.E.)

### A. K. STAMPING CO., INC.

1159 Highway 22 E. (07092)
**Phone—(908) 232-7300**
Fax—(908) 232-1593
www.akstamping.com
Email—sales@akstamping.com
CEO—Arthur Kurz
V-P.—Marlene Kurz
Sales Mgr.—Josh Kurz
Payroll Coord.—Diana Diaz
Pur. Agt.—Linda Bonnel
SIC—3469; 3429; *Metal
stampings & circuit board
brackets*
Employs—45; Estab.—1947
Sales—$6Mil-$10Mil
100,000 sq ft site, Distrib.—Intl.
Privately owned corporation
AKA: Globe Mfg. Sales, Inc.

### A.K. DE RAMA INDUSTRIAL CONTROL SYSTEMS, INC.

253 Sheffield St. (07092)
**Phone—(908) 789-1600**
Fax—(908) 789-1609
www.akderama.net
Email—derama@aol.com
Pres.—Antonio K. De Rama
V-P.—Felisa V. De Rama
Off. Mgr.—Rosalina G. Antao
SIC—3823; NAICS—334513;
*Industrial control systems*
Employs—12; Estab.—1991
Sales—$4Mil
5,500 sq ft site, Distrib.—Regional
Privately owned sub-S corp.

### AIR & SPECIALTIES SHEET METAL

276 Sheffield St. (07092)
**Phone—(908) 233-8306**
Fax—(908) 233-8323
www.airspecialtiesnj.com
Email—airspecialties@
airspecialtiesnj.com
Pres.—Kim Deitrich

GEOGRAPHICAL

## Mountainside—(cont.)

V-P.—Bruce Deitrich
Off. Mgr.—Rose Runes
SIC—3444; *HVAC ducts & sheet metal fabrication*
Employs—15; Estab.—1987
Sales—$2.5Mil-$5Mil
Distrib.—Regional
Privately owned corporation

**ALPHAGRAPHICS**

1111 U.S. Highway 22 E. (07092)
**Phone—(908) 233-5553**
Fax—(908) 363-1012
www.alphagraphics.com/us644
Email—us644@alphagraphics.com
Owner & Pres.—Patrick Rotondo
SIC—2759; NAICS—323100; *Digital large-format & offset printing, including variable data marketing, CD/DVD duplication, multi-part forms, training manuals, books, brochures & personalized mailing & fulfillment services*
Employs—3; Estab.—1992
2,800 sq ft site, Distrib.—National
Privately owned corporation

**AMERICAN ALUMINUM CO. (AMALCO)**

230 Sheffield St. *(07092)*
**Phone—(908) 233-3500**
Fax—(908) 233-3241
www.amalco.com
Email—info@amalco.com
Pres.—Andrew Brucker
Sales Mgr.—Ronald R. King
Prodn. Mgr.—Eldar Sukurlu
Pur. Mgr.—Karen Alifante
Fin. & MIS Mgr.—Nancy Irslinger
Maint. Mgr.—Rick Turner
SIC—3469; 3499; *Metal fabrication, including hydroforming & deep drawing of standard & specialty metals for the defense, aerospace, communications, medical, dental, pump, ordnance & security industries*
Employs—60; Estab.—1910
Sales—$7Mil-$12Mil
60,000 sq ft site, Distrib.—Intl.
Privately owned sub-S corp.

**AMERICAN TELETIMER CORP.**

1167 Globe Ave. (07092)
**Phone—(908) 654-4200**
Fax—(908) 653-1155
www.teletimer.com
Email—theoffice@teletimer.com
Pres.—Joel Rosenzweig
Ex. V-P., Engrg.—Ron Couturier
SIC—3625; 3949; NAICS—335314; *Horse race timing equipment*
Employs—3; Estab.—1938
Sales—$500,000-$1Mil (est)
Distrib.—Intl.
Privately owned corporation

**CSM WORLDWIDE, INC.**

1100 Globe Ave. *(07092)*
**Phone—(908) 233-2882**
Fax—(908) 233-1064
www.csmworldwide.com
Email—mtorstrup@
csmworldwide.com
CEO—Atul Shah
Pres.—Michael Torstrup
Pur. Agt.—Andre Chase
SIC—3564; NAICS—333400; *Air pollution control equipment*
Employs—20; Estab.—1971
16,000 sq ft site, Distrib.—Intl.

**DANFOSS HAGO, INC.**

Div. of Danfoss, Inc.
1120 Globe Ave. (07092)
**Phone—(908) 232-8687**
Fax—(908) 232-7246
www.hago.danfoss.com
Email—hago@danfoss.com

GM—Rich Sthil
Prodn. Mgr.—Andrew Kozdon
Hum. Res. Mgr.—Tara Cichetti
Cust. Serv. Mgr.—Todd Vitali
SIC—3432; NAICS—332900; *Stainless steel spray atomizing nozzles; Brand name—Hago Precision Nozzles*
Employs—110; Estab.—1937
9,000 sq ft site, Distrib.—Intl.
Privately owned sub-S corp.
ISO rating—9000
Parent co.—Danfoss, Inc., Baltimore, MD
Phone—(410) 931-8250
See Parent Co. Section for full profile.

**DE DIETRICH U. S. A., INC. (H Q)**

244 Sheffield St. (07092)
Mail addr.: P.O. Box 345, Union (07083)
**Phone—(908) 317-2585**
Fax—(908) 889-4960
www.ddpsinc.com
Email—sales@ddpsinc.com
Pres.—Don Doell
CFO—Gary Kaplan
Sr. Proj. Mgr.—Kenneth Leivanen
SIC—3559; 3231; NAICS—327215; *Corporate headquarters; glass lining process systems & equipment for the pharmaceutical chemical & biopharmaceutical industries*
Employs—30
Worldwide: 1,100
Distrib.—Intl.
AKA: DDPS, Inc.

**DIGITAL COLOR CONCEPTS, INC.**

256 Sheffield St. (07092)
**Phone—(908) 264-0504**
Fax—(908) 264-0514
www.dccnyc.com
Email—info@dccnyc.com
Pres.—Don Terwilliger
IT Mgr.—Tom Scholl
Hum. Res. Mgr.—Patty Taylor
SIC—2759; NAICS—323100; *Corporate headquarters & commercial printing*
Employs—80; Estab.—1987
Sales—$10Mil-$25Mil (est)
Distrib.—National
Privately owned corporation

**ELENA CONSULTANTS**

1175 Globe Ave., P.O. Box 1339 (07092)
**Phone—(908) 654-8309**
Fax—(908) 654-0333
Owner—Karen Miller
SIC—3543; NAICS—332997; *Industrial prototypes*
Employs—10; Estab.—1959
Distrib.—National
Sole ownership

**FISHER CO., INC., ROBERT**

280 Sheffield St. (07092)
**Phone—(908) 928-0002**
 (908) 928-0330
National—(800) 526-8052
Fax—(908) 928-0092
www.rsfisher.com
Email—fisherktgold@yahoo.com
Pres.—David Roth
Off. Mgr.—JoAnne Tseytlin
SIC—3911; NAICS—339911; *Fine handmade 14K gold & silver jewelry*
Employs—3; Estab.—1903
Sales—$1Mil-$5Mil
Distrib.—National
Privately owned corporation

**GUSMER ENTERPRISES, INC. (H Q)**

1165 Globe Ave. (07092)
**Phone—(908) 301-1811**
Fax—(908) 301-1812
www.gusmerenterprises.com
Email—sales@
gusmerenterprises.com
Pres.—Marla G. Jeffrey

Cont.—Janet De la Torre
IT & Opers. Mgr.—Alicia Alexander
SIC—3556; NAICS—333294; *Corporate headquarters; beverage production supplies & filtering equipment; Brand name—Gusmer Filter Sheets; Micro Essentials Yeast Nutrients; Millipore Cartridges; Chr. Hansen Yeast; Chr Hansen Cultures; Novozymes Enzymes*
Employs—18; Estab.—1918
Sales—$40Mil
Distrib.—Intl.
Privately owned corporation
ISO rating—9001

**JOCELY, INC.**

280 Sheffield St. (07092)
**Phone—(800) 526-4597**
Fax—(908) 654-4613
www.jabel.com
Email—sales@jabel.com
Pres.—David Connolly
Opers. Mgr.—Katie Smith
Sales Rep.—Liza Connolly
SIC—3911; NAICS—339911; *Precious metal jewelry*
Employs—35; Estab.—1916
30,000 sq ft site, Distrib.—National
Privately owned corporation
AKA: Jabel

**†KLINGELHOFER CORP.**

165 Mill Ln. (07092)
**Phone—(908) 232-7200**
National—(800) 879-5546
Fax—(908) 232-1841
www.klingelhofer.com
Email—klingelhofercorp@aol.com
Pres.—Al Klingelhofer
V-P.—Fred E. Schaefer
Sales & Serv. Mgr.—Wolfgang Mahr
Parts Mgr.—Daniel McCauley
Saw Blade Mgr.—Bob Klingelhofer
SIC—5084; 5072; *Distributor of metal sawing, deburring & cutting machines, parts & saw blades; Brand name—KASTO; RSA; VERSA-KUT; WAGNER; LAZZARI; OTT + HEUGEL; Bimax*
Employs—11; Estab.—1929
Distrib.—National
Privately owned corporation

**MAZMET**

1050 Bristol Rd. (07092)
**Phone—(908) 654-7686**
Fax—(908) 654-7898
www.mazmet.com
Pres.—Dennis Maziekin
SIC—3446; NAICS—332323; *Architectural metal products*
Employs—10; Estab.—1947
Sales—$1Mil-$2.5Mil
Distrib.—Regional
Privately owned corporation

**METROPOLITAN CORPORATE COUNSEL**

1180 Wychwood Rd. (07092)
**Phone—(908) 654-4840**
Fax—(908) 842-9175
www.metrocorpcounsel.com
Email—info@
.metrocorpcounsel.com
CIO & IT Mgr.—Mag Smith
Editor—Martha Driver
Editor—Robert Parillo
SIC—2711; *Legal newspaper publishing*
Employs—13; Estab.—1998
Sales—$500,000-$1Mil
Distrib.—National
Privately owned corporation

**MP TUBE WORKS, INC.**

237 Sheffield St. *(07092)*
**Phone—(908) 317-2500**
Fax—(908) 317-2969
www.mptubeworksinc.com
Email—mptube@aol.com

Pres.—Michael J. McGinley
V-P.—Paul W. Kelman
SIC—3599; 3498; NAICS—332996; *Tube fabrication & general machining job shop*
Employs—8; Estab.—1980
20,000 sq ft site, Distrib.—National
Privately owned corporation

**NEW JERSEY PRECISION TECHNOLOGIES, INC.**

1081 Bristol Rd. (07092)
**Phone—(908) 232-8847**
National—(800) 409-3000
Fax—(800) 409-3022
www.njpt.com
Email—sales@njpt.com
Pres., Sales Mgr.—Bob Tarantino
Fin. Cont.—Dominic Lacalamita
SIC—3599; 3544; 3841; 3842; NAICS—333500; *Wire & ram EDM & small hole drilling for the orthopedics/medical device, instrumentation, aerospace, plastic extrusion tooling & tool & die industries & full service CNC machining & vertically integrated contract manufacturer*
Employs—45; Estab.—1995
Sales—$5Mil-$10Mil
10,500 sq ft site, Distrib.—National
Privately owned sub-S corp.
ISO rating—13485:2003, 9001:2008

**NEW LINE PRINTING & TECHNOLOGY, INC.**

1011 Route 22 E. (07092)
**Phone—(973) 232-5003**
Fax—(973) 232-6332
Pres.—John Luciano
Bookkeeper—Michele Krieger
SIC—2759; NAICS—323100; *Commercial printing*
Employs—7
Sales—$1Mil-$2.5Mil (est)
Distrib.—National
Privately owned corporation

**PAGLIA & SON, INC., D.**

280 Sheffield St. (07092)
**Phone—(908) 654-5999**
National—(800) 372-4542
Fax—(908) 654-5553
www.dpaglia.com
Email—support@dpaglia.com
Pres.—Daniel Paglia
SIC—3911; NAICS—339911; *Ladies' jewelry*
Employs—4; Estab.—1998
Sales—under $500,000
Distrib.—Local
Privately owned corporation

**PRINCETON CASE CO., INC.**

615 Sherwood Pkwy. (07092)
**Phone—(908) 687-1750**
Fax—(908) 687-1755
www.princetoncase.com
V-P.—Steve Parker, Jr.
SIC—3089; 3086; NAICS—326100; *Plastic carrying cases & foam fabrication*
Employs—21; Estab.—1964
Distrib.—Intl.
Privately owned corporation

[NEW ENTRY]

**PRISM DIGITAL COMMUNICATIONS, LLC**

1011 U.S. Highway 22, Ste. 1 (07092)
**Phone—(908) 789-7747**
Fax—(973) 232-5054
www.prismdc.com
Ptnr. & Mng. Dir.—Brian Dewitt
Hum. Res. Mgr.—Jack Ayan
SIC—2759; *Commercial printing*
Employs—10; Estab.—2006
Sales—$1Mil-$2.5Mil (est)
10,000 sq ft site, Distrib.—Intl.
Limited Liability Company

## Mountainside—(cont.)

**PUTNUM STAINLESS TUBES, INC.**
1163 Route 22 E. (07092)
Mail addr: P.O. Box 477, Westfield (07091-0477)
**Phone—(908) 232-9200**
National—(800) 631-7330
Fax—(908) 232-6709
Email—putnum@cobat.net
Pres.—James Schlenker
V-P.—Robert Schlenker
SIC—3444; *Stainless steel tubing*
Employs—14; Estab.—1969
Sales—$1Mil-$2.5Mil
Distrib.—Regional
Privately owned corporation

**QUALITY SWISS SCREW MACHINE CO., INC.**
960 Mountain Ave. (07092)
**Phone—(908) 654-1881**
National—(800) 211-7114
Fax—(908) 654-4409
www.qualityswiss.com
Email—qual.swis@verizon.net
Pres.—Andrew Cangelosi
Prodn. Mgr.—Todd Luetters
Hum. Res. Mgr.—Isabella Cangelosi
SIC—3451; NAICS—332721; *Corporate headquarters & Swiss screw machine products*
Employs—28; Estab.—1970
18,000 sq ft site, Distrib.—National
Privately owned corporation
ISO rating—9001

**REMINGTON INDUSTRIES, INC., CORDES MACHINE DIV.**
269 Sheffield St. (07092)
**Phone—(908) 233-2600**
www.cordesmachine.com
Email—info@cordesmachine.com
Plt. Mgr.—Doug West
Off. Mgr.—Deanna Devito
SIC—3599; 3559; *Stair building equipment for wood stair builders & custom industrial machinery & replacement parts for the adhesives, aerospace, automation, baking, chemicals, coating, earthmoving construction & panels industries; Brand name—Stair-Rout™; Wedgit™; Kerf-It™; Stair-Clamp™; Tread-Saw™; Stair-Template™*
Employs—120; Estab.—1947
Distrib.—Intl.
Privately owned corporation

**RPR GRAPHICS, INC.**
1136 U.S. Highway 22, P.O. Box 1159 (07092)
**Phone—(908) 654-8080**
Fax—(908) 301-1213
www.rprgraphicsinc.com
Email—downloads@rprgraphicsinc.com
Pres., CEO—Laura Ruocco
CFO—Susan J. Arlington
Dir., Client Svcs. & Sales—Frank DeCarlo
Dir., IT—Luis A. Velez
SIC—2791; 2796; NAICS—323122; *Digital asset management, electronic prepress, color separations & high-resolution digital imaging & pre-media services*
Employs—20; Estab.—1985
Sales—$1Mil-$5Mil
13,000 sq ft site, Distrib.—National
Privately owned sub-S corp.

**SNAP ACTION, INC.**
1260 Route 22 W. (07092)
**Phone—(908) 654-4380**
www.snapaction.net
Email—info@snapaction.net
GM—Doreen Dauria
SIC—3613; NAICS—335313; *Circuit breakers*
Employs—25; Estab.—1977
10,000 sq ft site, Distrib.—Intl.
Privately owned corporation

**SPRINGFIELD HEATING & AIR CONDITIONING CO., INC.**
217 Sheffield St. (07092)
**Phone—(908) 233-8400**
Fax—(908) 233-0404
www.springfieldhvac.com
Pres.—Louis Gallini
V-P.—Joseph Gallini
SIC—3312; *Steel fabrication*
Employs—13; Estab.—1943
7,000 sq ft site, Distrib.—Local
Sole ownership

**VERREX CORP.**
1130 Route 22 (07092-2888)
**Phone—(908) 232-7000**
National—(800) 303-8170
Fax—(908) 232-7991
www.verrex.com
Email—verrex@verrex.com
Pres.—Thomas Berry, Jr.
V-P., Sales—Bill Chamberlin
V-P., Hum. Res.—Matthew Smith
Treas.—Michelle Capolino
Comp.—Nancy Bowe
Dir., Opers.—Mark Mogila
Dir., Bus. Dev. & Mktg.—Theresa Hahn
Dir., Pur.—Pat Corcoran
Dir., MIS—George Bird
Dir., Proj. Mgmt.—Jaime Callejo
SIC—3663; 7373; NAICS—334220; *Corporate audiovisual & conferencing systems, including design, integration, service & support; Brand name—GMS; Verrex*
Employs—70; Estab.—1947
Sales—$40Mil
35,000 sq ft site, Distrib.—Intl.
Privately owned corporation

## Mullica Hill
(Gloucester—S.W.)

**ACTION SIGN CO., INC.**
217 Ewan Rd. (08062-2903)
**Phone—(856) 478-0404**
Fax—(856) 478-6889
Email—actionsign@verizon.net
Pres.—John V. Secatore
SIC—3993; *Interior & exterior signs*
Employs—4; Estab.—1984
Sales—under $500,000
1,800 sq ft site, Distrib.—Local
Privately owned corporation

**DETAIL MODEL & MACHINE**
61 Woodstown Rd. (08062)
**Phone—(856) 223-0184**
Owner—David Rose
SIC—3999; 3993; 2541; 2542; *Training & trade show models & trade show displays*
Employs—4; Estab.—1991
Sales—under $500,000
Distrib.—National
Privately owned corporation

**EDUCATIONAL INFORMATION & RESOURCE CENTER**
107 Gilbreth Pkwy. (08062)
**Phone—(856) 582-7000**
Fax—(856) 582-4206
www.eirc.org
Email—civory@eirc.org
Ex. Dir.—Charles Ivory
SIC—3993; *Vinyl lettering & education-related programs & services for parents, schools, communities, nonprofit organizations & privately held businesses*
Employs—70; Estab.—1968
Distrib.—Intl.
AKA: EIRC

**HERITAGE VINEYARDS OF RICHWOOD, LLC**
480 Mullica Hill Rd. (08062)
**Phone—(856) 589-4474**
(856) 589-6090
Fax—(856) 589-9344
www.heritagewinenj.com
Email—heritagestation@snip.net
Ptnr.—William H. Heritage
Ptnr.—Penni Heritage
Hum. Res. & IT Mgr.—Rich Heritage
SIC—2084; NAICS—312130; *Wines*
Employs—15; Estab.—1851
Distrib.—Local
Limited Liability Company

## Murray Hill
(Union—N.E.)

**ALCATEL-LUCENT (H Q)**
600 Mountain Ave. (07974-0636)
**Phone—(908) 582-8500**
Fax—(908) 508-2576
www.alcatel-lucent.com
Email—execoffice@alcatel-lucent.com
Chrm.—Phillippe Camus
CEO—Michel Combes
CMO—Tim Krause
SIC—3661; 3357; *Company headquarters; telecommunication & networking equipment*
Employs—4000
Worldwide: 70,000
Sales—$9.44Bil
Publicly owned corporation

**FABLOK MILLS, INC.**
140 Spring St. (07974-1194)
**Phone—(908) 464-1950**
Fax—(908) 464-6520
www.fablokmills.com
Email—info@fablokmills.com
Pres.—Alex Fisher
Sales Mgr.—Joe Sutton
Hum. Res. Mgr.—Nancy Gabby
Fin. Mgr.—Jim Malure
Cust. Serv. Mgr.—Silvia Koeller
SIC—2221; 2259; 2297; NAICS—313210; *Nylon, polyester & polypropylene knitted mesh fabrics*
Employs—45; Estab.—1951
50,000 sq ft site, Distrib.—Intl.
Privately owned corporation
ISO rating—9001:2008

**FLODYNE CONTROLS, INC.**
48 Commerce Dr. (07974)
**Phone—(908) 464-6200**
Fax—(908) 464-1553
www.flodynecontrols.com
Email—sales@flodynecontrols.com
Pres., Adv. Mgr.—Carol Perrin
V-P., GM—Michael Perrin
SIC—3494; 3492; NAICS—332912; *Cryogenic, high-pressure & high-speed ball, solenoid & butterfly valves & controls*
Employs—12; Estab.—1960
Sales—$1Mil-$2Mil
30,000 sq ft site, Distrib.—National
Privately owned corporation

**GLOWPOINT, INC.**
430 Mountain Ave., Ste. 301 (07974-2764)
**Phone—(973) 855-3411**
National—(866) 456-9764
Fax—(908) 464-2482
www.glowpoint.com
Email—contactme@glowpoint.com
Pres., CEO—Joe Laezza
Ex. V-P., CFO—John R. McGovern
Sr. V-P., Sales & Mktg.—Stephen K. Vobbe
Sr. V-P., Opers.—Thomas P. Schroeder
Sr. V-P., Prod. & Strategy—Anil Balani
Sr. V-P., Bus. Dev.—Peter Holst
V-P., Mktg.—Darren Podrabsky
V-P., Info. Sys. & Tech.—Shane Bouslough
V-P., Engrg.—Lou Chiorazzi
V-P., Corp. Dev. & Strategy—Tolga Sakman
Gen. Counsel & Secy.—Michael Hubner
Dir., Mktg. Comms.—Michael Croker
SIC—7372; *Cloud-managed SaaS software development with videoconferencing & telepresence features; Brand name—Glowpoint; OpenVideo™*
Employs—80; Estab.—2000
Distrib.—Intl.
Publicly owned corporation

**PAGEWORKS, LLC**
P.O. Box 892 (07974)
**Phone—(908) 665-0607**
Fax—(908) 665-2052
www.kidsguide.com
Email—kids@kidsguidenj.com
Pres.—Jean Unger
SIC—2741; 2721; *Children's places & events guide publishing*
Employs—3; Estab.—1987
Sales—under $500,000
Distrib.—Regional
Limited Liability Company

## National Park
(Gloucester—S.W.)

**SIGNS UNLIMITED, INC.**
601 Hessian Ave. (08063)
**Phone—(856) 848-4942**
Fax—(856) 848-8535
Email—signsunl@verizon.net
Pres.—Cecilia B. Chinai
Secy., Hum. Res. & IT Mgr.—Kays B. Chinai
SIC—3993; *Interior & exterior signs, name & photo ID badges & engraving*
Employs—4; Estab.—1995
Sales—under $500,000
Distrib.—National
Privately owned corporation

## Neptune
(Monmouth—N.E.)

**ALL-STAR PRO & SPORT STORE**
642 State Route 35 N. (07753)
**Phone—(732) 774-3444**
Fax—(732) 774-0567
Owner—Joe Storzieri
SIC—2395; 3499; 2499; 3089; *Trophies, plaques & textile embroidery*
Employs—2; Estab.—1996
Distrib.—Local
Sole ownership

**ASBURY PARK PRESS**
Div. of Asbury Park Press, Inc.
3600 Highway 66 (07753)
Mail addr: P.O. Box 1550, Neptune (07754)
**Phone—(732) 922-6000**
National—(800) 822-9770
Fax—(732) 643-4013
www.app.com
Email—newstips@app.com
GM, Adv., Retail—Regan Apo
Leader—Tamara Wilder
SIC—2711; *Newspaper publishing*
Employs—500; Estab.—1977
Sales—$10Mil-$25Mil (est)
Distrib.—Local
Privately owned corporation

GEOGRAPHICAL

# Neptune—(cont.)

Parent co.—Asbury Park Press, Inc., Neptune, NJ
Phone—(732) 922-6000
See Parent Co. Section for full profile.

## ASBURY PARK PRESS, INC. (H Q)

Div. of Gannett Co., Inc.
3600 Highway 66, P.O. Box 1550 (07754-1550)
**Phone—(732) 922-6000**
　　　　　(732) 643-4120
National—(800) 822-9770
Fax—(732) 643-4112
www.app.com
Email—glongo@app.com
Pres., Publisher—Thomas M. Donovan
V-P., Editor—Hollis Townes
V-P., IT—Wayne Peragallo
V-P., Hum. Res.—Kathy Abatemarco
V-P., Fin.—Kevin Huff
V-P., Prod.—Jack Roth
V-P., Circ.—Jane Pettigrew
Dir. & Mktg. Mgr.—Gina Longo
SIC—2711; *Corporate headquarters; newspaper printing*
Employs—450; Estab.—1879
Sales—$25Mil-$100Mil
198,000 sq ft site, Distrib.—Regional
Publicly owned corporation
Parent co.—Gannett Co., Inc., McLean, VA
Phone—(703) 854-6000
See Parent Co. Section for full profile.

## AUTOMATED CONTROL CONCEPTS, INC.

3535 State Route 66, Ste. 14 (07753)
**Phone—(732) 922-6611**
Fax—(732) 922-9611
www.automated-control.com
Email—info@automated-control.com
Pres.—Michael Blechman
Sr. V-P. & Technical Dir.—Victor Ronchetti
Ex. V-P.—Kevin Hannigan
V-P., Sales & Mktg.—Arlene Weichert
Sales & Mktg. Coord.—Kathleen Accorsi
SIC—7373; NAICS—541512; *Systems integration services, including PLC programming, HMI/SCADA configuration & manufacturing execution system implementation for manufacturing, process control & information technology; Brand name—ProcessRecords; bioRecords; bioStation; OP/Station; microOP*
Employs—40; Estab.—1983
Sales—$15Mil-$20Mil
17,500 sq ft site, Distrib.—National
Privately owned sub-S corp.

## BECKER PLATING, INC.

121 Highway 35 N. (07753)
**Phone—(732) 775-8945**
Fax—(732) 775-0169
www.beckerplating.com
Email—beckerplatinginc@aol.com
Pres.—Norman Becker
SIC—3471; NAICS—332813; *Electroplating*
Employs—2; Estab.—1946
6,400 sq ft site, Distrib.—Regional

## CLAYTON & SONS, RALPH (H Q)

1355 Campus Pkwy. (07753)
Mail addr: P.O. Box 3015, Lakewood (08701-9015)
**Phone—(732) 751-7600**
　　　　　(800) 662-3044
Fax—(732) 751-7630
www.claytonco.com
Email—kroe@claytonsonline.com

Pres.—William Clayton
V-P.—Douglas Clayton
V-P.—Dan Clayton
V-P.—Casey Clayton
Dir., Tech. Svcs., Qual. Control—Matthew Savona
Gen. Sales Mgr.—Joseph M. Scaramuzzo
SIC—3272; *Company headquarters; ready-mixed concrete*
Employs—15; Estab.—1951
Sales—$1Mil-$2.5Mil
Distrib.—Local
Privately owned corporation
Also see: Clayton Block Co., Inc., same loc.

## CLAYTON BLOCK CO., INC.

1355 Campus Pkwy. (07753)
Mail addr: P.O. Box 3015, Lakewood (08701-9015)
**Phone—(732) 751-7600**
　　　　　(800) 662-3044
Fax—(732) 751-7630
www.claytonco.com
Email—kroe@claytonsonline.com
Owner—William Clayton, Jr.
V-P.—Douglas Clayton
V-P.—Casey Clayton
V-P.—Dan Clayton
Dir., Mktg.—Kathy Roe
Gen. Sales Mgr.—Joseph M. Scaramuzzo
Hum. Res. Mgr.—Wayne Tart
SIC—3273; NAICS—327320; *Corporate headquarters & ready-mixed concrete & concrete block*
Employs—25; Estab.—1962
Distrib.—Local
Privately owned corporation
Also see: Clayton & Sons, Ralph, same loc.

## CONTAINER GRAPHICS CORP.

3535 Highway 66, Parkway 100, Bldg. 2 (07753)
**Phone—(732) 922-1180**
Fax—(732) 922-1696
www.containergraphics.com
Email—neptunecad@containergraphics.com
Site Mgr.—Dominick Georgiano
Cust. Serv. Rep.—Jake Smith
SIC—3544; NAICS—333500; *Flat & rotary laser cutting dies*
Employs—13; Estab.—1962
Sales—$1Mil-$2.5Mil (est)
Distrib.—Intl.
Privately owned corporation
Parent co.—Container Graphics Corp., Cary, NC
Phone—(919) 481-4200
See Parent Co. Section for full profile.

## COTTAGE LACE & RIBBON CO.

21 TFH Plaza Union & 3rd Ave. (07753)
**Phone—(732) 776-9353**
www.ribbonbazaar.com
Email—contact@ribbonbazaar.com
Pres.—Shahid Waseem
Webmaster—Noman Waseem
SIC—2241; 5131; NAICS—313221; *Manufacturer of wired ribbons & distributor of decorative & holiday ribbons*
Employs—2; Estab.—1996
Sales—under $500,000
Distrib.—National
Privately owned corporation
AKA: Novum Industries, Inc.

## CRAFTMASTER PRINTING, INC.

2024 Corlies Ave. (07753)
**Phone—(732) 775-0011**
Fax—(732) 775-1771
www.craftmasterprinting.com
Email—curtb@craftmasterprinting.com
Pres.—Curtis Baumgartner

SIC—2759; 2752; 2395; 2396; NAICS—323100; *Corporate headquarters & single-color, full-color, high-speed instant & wide-format printing of raffle tickets & signage & embroidery & screen printing of advertising specialties, including scanning, faxing & email services*
Employs—4; Estab.—1990
Sales—under $500,000
Distrib.—Regional
Privately owned corporation

## †CREATIVE DISPLAYS & DESIGNS, INC.

349 Essex Rd. (07753)
**Phone—(732) 918-8010**
Fax—(732) 918-8999
www.cdi25.com
Email—info@cdi25.com
Pres.—Danette Bussey
Bookkeeper—Patricia Dasaro
SIC—5193; 5021; *Wholesaler of home dÉcor products, including artificial & preserved plants & accent furniture*
Employs—22; Estab.—1986
Sales—$2.5Mil-$5Mil
Distrib.—Regional
Privately owned corporation

## ELECTRO IMPULSE LABORATORY, INC.

1805 Route 33 (07753)
Mail addr: P.O. Box 278, Neptune (07754)
**Phone—(732) 776-5800**
Fax—(732) 776-6793
www.electroimpulse.com
Email—sales@electroimpulse.com
Pres.—Mark Rubin
Sales Mgr.—Thomas J. McNicholas
IT Mgr.—Brett Beach
Hum. Res. Mgr.—P. J. Rubin
SIC—3585; 3825; 3663; 3679; NAICS—332323; *Custom closed-loop cooling systems & RF dummy loads & calorimeters for hospitals, the aircraft, aerospace & electronic industries & the military*
Employs—41; Estab.—1949
Sales—$5Mil-$10Mil
60,000 sq ft site, Distrib.—Intl.
Privately owned corporation

## EXCELSIOR MEDICAL CORP.

1933 Heck Ave. (07753)
**Phone—(732) 776-7525**
National—(800) 487-4276
Fax—(732) 776-7600
www.excelsiormedical.com
Email—info@excelsiormedical.com
CEO—Steve Thornton
V-P., Hum. Res.—Lynette Bowman
Hum. Res. Mgr.—Derrick Moodey
SIC—3559; *Pharmaceutical pumps*
Employs—400; Estab.—1987
Sales—$50Mil-$100Mil (est)
Distrib.—Intl.
Privately owned corporation

## GERIN CORP.

1109 7th Ave. (07753)
**Phone—(732) 774-3256**
Fax—(732) 774-0274
www.gerincorp.com
Email—gerincorp@optimum.net
Pres.—Robert N. Gerin
Manager—Patricia Brennan
SIC—3829; *Oil testing equipment*
Employs—10; Estab.—1947
Sales—$500,000-$1Mil
4,000 sq ft site, Distrib.—Intl.
Privately owned corporation

## GLUEFAST CO., INC.

3535 State Route 66, Ste. 1 (07753)
**Phone—(732) 918-4600**
National—(800) 242-7318

Fax—(732) 918-4646
www.gluefast.com
Email—info@gluefast.com
Pres.—Lester Mallet
GM—Joe Benenati
Cust. Serv. Rep.—Melissa Shomo
SIC—2891; 3599; NAICS—325520; *Glue & gluing equipment for the packaging, graphics, picture framing & converting industries & acrylic coatings for wall art; Brand name—Label Pro 5.5 Label Gluer; SKID-LOCK; Colonel Label Gluer; Captain B Label Gluer; Solo Glue Riter*
Employs—10; Estab.—1939
Sales—$1Mil-$5Mil
15,500 sq ft site, Distrib.—Intl.
Privately owned sub-S corp.

## GOURMET KITCHEN, INC.

1238 State Route 33 (07753)
**Phone—(732) 775-5222**
National—(800) 492-3663
Fax—(732) 775-5225
www.gourmetkitcheninc.com
CEO—Raymond Walsh
Co-Pres.—Patricia Duffy
Co-Pres.—Michael B. Lacey
V-P., Cust. Serv.—Patricia Craig
Corp. Secy.—Ryan Walsh
Cust. Serv. Rep.—Amy Kelly
SIC—2099; 2038; NAICS—311412; *Manufacturer & distributor of frozen hors d'oeuvres; Brand name—Gourmet Kitchen*
Employs—80; Estab.—1986
14,000 sq ft site, Distrib.—National
Privately owned sub-S corp.

## GROEZINGER PROVISION, INC.

1200 7th Ave. (07753)
**Phone—(732) 775-3220**
National—(800) 927-9473
Fax—(732) 775-3223
www.alexianpate.com
Email—informationrequest@alexianpate.com
Pres.—Laurie Cummins
Acct. Mgr.—John Stevens
Mktg. Mgr.—Donna Kutz
SIC—2013; NAICS—311600; *Gourmet pates, mousses, terrines & specialty meat products*
Employs—20; Estab.—1982
20,000 sq ft site, Distrib.—National
Privately owned corporation

## HEALTH CARE SOFTWARE, INC.

1350 Campus Pkwy. (07753)
Mail addr: P.O. Box 2430, Farmingdale (07727)
**Phone—(732) 938-5600**
National—(800) 524-1038
Fax—(732) 938-5380
www.hcsinteractant.com
Email—marketing@hcsinteractant.com
Pres.—Tom Fahey
Dir., Hum. Res.—Janice Dewski
IT Mgr.—Darren Yonkin
SIC—7372; 7373; NAICS—541512; *Computer software development & system integration*
Employs—50; Estab.—1969
Sales—$11Mil-$25Mil
Distrib.—National
Privately owned corporation

## HINCK'S TURKEY FARM, INC.

3930 Belmar Blvd. (07753)
Mail addr: 1414 Atlantic Ave., Manasquan (08736)
**Phone—(732) 681-0508**
　　　　　(732) 223-5622
Fax—(732) 528-8247
www.hincksfarm.com
Email—hincksfarm@monmouth.com
Pres.—Robert L. Longo

## Neptune—(cont.)

GM—Richard Orozco
Plt. Mgr.—Bill Young
SIC—2015; *Turkey processing*
Employs—9; Estab.—1935
Sales—$500,000-$1Mil
Distrib.—Regional
Privately owned corporation

**JAMM PRINTING**
Div. of Accucolor, LLC
108 W. Sylvania Ave. (07753)
**Phone—(732) 502-0110**
Fax—(732) 502-0255
www.jammprinting.com
Email—jammprinting.nc@
verizon.net
Owner—Robert LaBella
Manager—Mike Kelemen
SIC—2759; 2791; NAICS—
323122; *Commercial printing &
typesetting*
Employs—7; Estab.—1957
Sales—$1Mil-$2.5Mil
Distrib.—Local
Privately owned corporation
Parent co.—Accucolor, LLC,
Shrewsbury, NJ
Phone—(732) 741-4594
See Parent Co. Section for full profile.

**KIRMS PRINTING CO., INC.**
1520 Washington Ave., P.O. Box
1067 (07753)
**Phone—(732) 774-8000**
National—(800) 631-5803
Fax—(877) 536-5153
www.schoolpub.com
Email—info@schoolpub.com
Pres.—Albert Kirms
Bookkeeper—Linda Moldach
SIC—2759; NAICS—323100;
*School newspaper & leisure
guide printing*
Employs—20; Estab.—1987
Sales—under $500,000
Distrib.—National
Privately owned corporation
Also see: School Publications Co.,
Inc., same loc.
AKAs: Senior Publishing & School
Publishing

**LAGER GLASS CO., INC.**
1913 Heck Ave., P.O. Box 426
(07753)
**Phone—(732) 775-9220**
National—(800) 287-9220
Fax—(732) 775-1021
Pres.—Dean Lager
V.-P., CFO—Arnold Giles
Shop Foreman—Wayne Galus
Bookkeeper—Marie Pagliuca
SIC—3231; NAICS—327215;
*Glass fabrication*
Employs—8; Estab.—1947
Sales—under $500,000
20,000 sq ft site, Distrib.—Local
Privately owned corporation

**MACKEY'S PRINT XPRESS**
1107 7th Ave. (07753)
**Phone—(732) 775-1730**
Fax—(732) 774-7625
www.mackeyprint.com
Email—mackeyprint@aol.com
Owner & Pres.—Ron Mackey
SIC—2759; 2752; 3953; 3993;
NAICS—339943; *Single,
multicolor offset & digital printing
of large-format posters,
envelopes, cards, booklets,
magnetic vehicle & window
signs & corporate & notary seals,
rubber stamps & banners &
binding services*
Employs—3; Estab.—1970
Sales—under $500,000
Distrib.—Regional
Limited Liability Company

**MALLETECH, LLC**
1107 11th Ave. (07753)
Mail addr: P.O. Box 467, Asbury
Park (07712-0467)
**Phone—(732) 774-0011**
Fax—(732) 774-0033
www.mostlymarimba.com
Email—malletech@
mostlymarimba.com
CEO—Leigh H. Stevens
GM—Tom Meyers
SIC—3931; 2731; 2741; NAICS—
339992; *Keyboard percussion
instruments, marimbas,
xylophones, vibes,
glockenspiels, mallets, bags &
accessories & percussion music
CD & method book publishing;
Brand name—Malletech; M-
Tech; Keyboard Percussion
Publications; Studio4 Music*
Employs—15; Estab.—1982
Sales—$1Mil-$2Mil
20,000 sq ft site, Distrib.—Intl.
Limited Liability Company

**MASTERCRAFT IRON, INC.**
1111 10th Ave. (07753)
Mail addr: P.O. Box 748, Neptune
(07754)
**Phone—(732) 988-3113**
Fax—(732) 988-3321
Email—pstagaard@mciron.com
Plt. Mgr.—Frank Morton
Proj. Mgr.—Bob Vannorman
SIC—3441; NAICS—332312;
*Structural steel fabrication*
Employs—15; Estab.—1976
Distrib.—Regional
Privately owned corporation

**†SCAASIS ORIGINALS, INC./
OCEANIC TRADING CO.**
1006 11th Ave. (07753)
**Phone—(732) 775-7474**
      (212) 290-8585
National—(800) 942-2139
Fax—(732) 775-7535
www.scaasis.com
Email—pbrown@scaasis.com
CEO—Neil Saada
CFO—Patricia Brown
SIC—5199; 5136; 5137;
*Wholesaler of souvenirs,
novelties & giftware, including
miniature polyresin lighthouse
replicas & scrimshaw &
distributor of men's, women's &
children's apparel; Brand
name—Scaasis Originals
Lighthouses; 6th Man; Game
Time; Rapid-Dry Tech; Victoria
Jeans; Paulina Jeans*
Employs—20; Estab.—1990
Distrib.—National
Privately owned sub-S corp.

**SCHOOL PUBLICATIONS CO., INC.**
1520 Washington Ave., P.O. Box
1067 (07753)
**Phone—(732) 988-1100**
National—(888) 637-3200
Fax—(800) 336-6996
www.schoolpub.com
Email—info@schoolpub.com
Pres.—Albert G. Kirms
V.-P., GM—William Kirms
Bookkeeper—Linda Moldoch
SIC—2752; NAICS—323100;
*School newspaper, yearbook &
literary magazine printing*
Employs—20; Estab.—1930
Distrib.—Regional
Privately owned corporation
Also see: Kirms Printing Co., Inc.,
same loc.
AKAs: Kirms & Kirms Printing

**SEAJAY MFG. CO.**
9 Memorial Dr., Ste. 1 (07753-
5083)
**Phone—(732) 774-0900**
National—(800) 221-0535

Fax—(732) 774-7287
Email—seajay_mfg@verizon.net
Pres.—Jeffrey Finn
Engr.—Marc Coccio
SIC—3544; 3599; NAICS—
333500; *Plastic bottle molds &
industrial molds for the blow
molding industry & trimming &
deflashing machines for the blow
molded parts industry*
Employs—8; Estab.—1961
Sales—$1Mil
6,500 sq ft site, Distrib.—National
Privately owned corporation

**STERLING SEAL & SUPPLY, INC.**
1105 Green Grove Rd. (07753)
**Phone—(732) 918-8004**
National—(800) 631-5580
Fax—(732) 918-8114
www.sterlingseal.com
Email—dderosa@sterlingseal.com
Pres.—Angelo Derosa
Fin. Cont.—Svetlana Azimova
Hum. Res. Mgr.—Fred Zink
SIC—3053; NAICS—339991;
*Corporate headquarters & o-
rings & bonded seals for
engineering & manufacturing;
Brand name—Dowty*
Employs—13; Estab.—1998
Sales—$6Mil-$10Mil
30,000 sq ft site, Distrib.—Intl.
Privately owned corporation

**STREIT & SON CO., INC., CARL**
703 Atkins Ave. (07753)
Mail addr: P.O. Box 157, Neptune
(07754)
**Phone—(732) 775-0803**
Fax—(732) 775-2274
Pres.—Jim Robinson
GM—Terry Daniels
Off. Mgr.—Jennifer Robinson
Bookkeeper—Judy Robinson
SIC—2011; 2015; NAICS—311611;
*Meat, poultry & pork processing*
Employs—5; Estab.—1955
Sales—under $500,000
Distrib.—Local
Privately owned corporation

**SYSTEMS SALES CORP.**
1345 Campus Pkwy. (07753)
**Phone—(732) 751-0600**
Fax—(732) 751-0489
www.sscnj.com
Email—info@sscnj.com
Pres.—John Ventrella
SIC—3669; *Fire alarm systems*
Employs—20; Estab.—1981
Sales—$2.5Mil-$5Mil (est)
Distrib.—Local
Privately owned corporation

**TDK-LAMBDA, INC.**
Div. of TDK-Lambda Americas,
Inc.
405 Essex Rd. (07753)
**Phone—(732) 922-9300**
Fax—(732) 922-9334
www.us.tdk-lambda.com
Email—bonnie.west@us.tdk-
lambda.com
Pres.—Pascal Chausson
V.-P., Mfg.—Wayne Morrison
Sales Mgr., Inside—Bonnie West
SIC—3679; *Power supplies*
Employs—165; Estab.—1947
97,000 sq ft site, Distrib.—Intl.
Privately owned corporation
ISO rating—9001
Parent co.—TDK-Lambda
Americas, Inc., San Diego, CA
Phone—(619) 575-4400
See Parent Co. Section for full profile.

**TOLL COMPACTION GROUP, LLC**
14 Memorial Dr. (07753)
**Phone—(732) 776-8225**
Fax—(732) 776-8306
www.tollcompaction.com
Email—rpritchard@
tollcompaction.com

Mng. Ptnr. & Pres., IT—Rod
Pritchard
Mng. Ptnr.—Tyson Pritchard
Hum. Res. & Off. Mgr.—Janet
Deramos
SIC—2833; NAICS—325411;
*Company headquarters &
granulation, blending, milling &
screening for chemicals, food &
nutritional supplements*
Employs—46; Estab.—2004
25,000 sq ft site, Distrib.—Intl.
Privately owned partnership
ISO rating—9001

**UNISERV ADVERTISING, INC.**
37 State Route 35 N. (07753)
**Phone—(732) 774-1010**
Fax—(732) 774-3311
www.uniservinc.com
Email—info@uniservinc.com
Pres.—Glen Suchecki
SIC—2396; 2759; 2395; *Apparel
& promotional item screen
printing, embroidery, commercial
printing, graphic design & web
development*
Employs—11
Sales—$1Mil-$2.5Mil (est)

**VIAMENTE, INC.**
3600 State Route 66, Ste. 400
(07753)
**Phone—(732) 686-7843**
www.viamente.com
Email—info@viamente.com
Pres.—Chris Sullens
SIC—7372; *Cloud-based SaaS
software development for vehicle
fleet routing optimization
applications*
Employs—1

---

## Neptune City
(Monmouth—N.E.)

**†ALL HANDS FIRE EQUIPMENT, LLC**
7 3rd Ave. (07753)
Mail addr: P.O. Box 1245, Wall
(07719-1245)
**Phone—(732) 502-8060**
National—(888) 681-1009
Fax—(732) 502-8064
www.allhandsfire.com
Email—sales@allhandsfire.com
Ptnr. & Pres.—Don Colarusso
Ptnr. & GM—Scott T. Colarusso
SIC—5099; 5136; 5139;
*Wholesaler of firefighting
equipment, including fire
extinguishers, fire blankets,
boots & gloves, water rescue &
technical rescue & firefighter
escape systems & training*
Employs—4; Estab.—2001
Distrib.—National
Limited Liability Company

**J & J MATERIALS, INC.**
49 Laurel Ave., P.O. Box 2128
(07753)
**Phone—(732) 988-3300**
National—(800) 331-9560
Fax—(732) 774-1807
www.jandjmaterials.com
Email—sales@jandjmaterials.com
Pres.—Stephen J. Zschiegner
Bookkeeper—Diane Koppenal
SIC—2899; *Precious metal
chemicals, compounds &
powders*
Employs—10; Estab.—2002
Sales—$2.5Mil-$5Mil (est)
Distrib.—Regional

**NEPTUNE AUTO SUPPLY, INC.**
51 TFH Plz. (07753)
**Phone—(732) 774-0002**
National—(800) 379-2886
Fax—(732) 774-0600
www.neptuneauto.com
Email—neptuneauto1@aol.com
Chrm.—John Giganti

GEOGRAPHICAL

## Neptune City—(cont.)

Pres.—Dave Blaess
Opers. Mgr.—Scott Blaess
SIC—3714; *Automotive hydraulic & air conditioning hoses*
Employs—20; Estab.—1988
Distrib.—Local
Privately owned corporation

**NYLABONE PRODUCTS**
Div. of Central Garden & Pet Co.
1 TFH Plz., 3rd & Union Ave., P.O. Box 427 (07753)
**Phone—(732) 988-8400**
National—(855) 273-7527
Fax—(732) 988-1700
www.nylabone.com
Email—info@nylabone.com
Ex. V-P.—Mark E. Johnson
Dir., Engrg. & Maint.—John Collazo
Hum. Res. Mgr.—Erin Carr
SIC—3999; 2731; *Pet chew toys & pet book publishing*
Employs—250; Estab.—1952
250,000 sq ft site, Distrib.—Intl.
Publicly owned corporation
Parent co.—Central Garden & Pet Co., Walnut Creek, CA
Phone—(925) 948-4000
See Parent Co. Section for full profile.

**PARK STEEL & IRON CO. (H Q)**
9 Evergreen Ave. (07753)
Mail addr: P.O. Box 365, Bradley Beach (07720)
**Phone—(732) 775-7500**
Fax—(732) 776-8494
Email—parksteel1@verizon.net
Pres., GM—Scott Pilling
Off. Mgr.—Elan Palmer
SIC—3312; *Company headquarters; structural, ornamental & restoration steel fabrication*
Employs—7; Estab.—1910
Sales—$1Mil-$2.5Mil
Distrib.—Regional
Privately owned sub-S corp.

**REX SIGN CO.**
60 Steiner Ave. (07753)
**Phone—(732) 774-1377**
National—(800) 640-1377
Fax—(732) 988-1509
www.rexsigns.net
Email—info@rexsigns.net
Pres.—Jacqueline Janocha
SIC—3993; *Signs*
Employs—8; Estab.—1925
5,000 sq ft site, Distrib.—Regional
Privately owned corporation

---

## Neshanic Station

(Somerset—N.E.)

**WESTCON ORTHOPEDICS, INC.**
4 Craig Rd. (08853)
Mail addr: P.O. Box 337, Three Bridges (08887-0337)
**Phone—(908) 806-8981**
National—(800) 382-4975
Fax—(908) 806-6664
www.westconortho.com
Email—info@westconortho.com
Chrm.—Patti Merwin
Pres.—Donn Gordon
V-P., Sales—Sean Gordon
SIC—3842; *Orthopedic products & surgical devices; Brand name—K-Cap-ES; K-Cap-E; K-Cap-P; K-Cap-I; S&S 15; S&S 120; S&S 240; Total Support*
Employs—4; Estab.—1989
Sales—$250,000-$500,000
Distrib.—Intl.
Privately owned sub-S corp.
AKA: Diversified Medical Group

## New Brunswick

(Middlesex—N.E.)

**A N S PLASTICS CORP.**
625 Jersey Ave., Ste. 11 (08901)
**Phone—(732) 247-2776**
National—(888) 660-2247
Fax—(732) 247-1594
www.shopping-bags.net
Email—ansplastics@ansplastics.com
V-P.—Ramy Samuel
Off. Mgr.—Corey Paganelli
SIC—2673; *Plastic & HDPE shopping, custom printed & grocery bags*
Employs—18; Estab.—1991
Sales—$500,000-$1Mil
Distrib.—Regional
Privately owned corporation

**A. P. DEAUVILLE, LLC**
594 Jersey Ave. (08901)
**Phone—(732) 545-0200**
Fax—(732) 545-0111
www.apdeauville.com
Email—info@apdeauville.com
Pres., CEO—Frederick Horowitz
V-P., Mktg.—Bruce Lazare
V-P. & IT Mgr.—Michael Allen
Plt. Mgr.—Robert Stanley
Pur. Mgr.—Jose Escobar
Hum. Res. Mgr.—Alfred Efremoff
Accountant—Jaya Sivaprakasam
SIC—2844; NAICS—325600; *Deodorants, anti-perspirants, body wash & shampoo*
Employs—35; Estab.—2001
Distrib.—Intl.
Privately owned corporation

**ACCU-SEAL RUBBER, INC.**
18-F Home News Row (08901)
**Phone—(732) 246-4333**
National—(800) 315-4761
Fax—(732) 246-4609
www.accusealrubber.com
Email—sales@accusealrubber.com
Pres.—Pravin Tejani
V-P.—Dinesh Tejani
SIC—3069; *Extruded, molded & fabricated rubber products*
Employs—4; Estab.—2000
Sales—under $500,000
5,000 sq ft site, Distrib.—Intl.
Privately owned sub-S corp.

**AKCROS CHEMICALS, INC.**
500 Jersey Ave. (08901)
**Phone—(732) 247-2202**
National—(800) 500-7890
Fax—(732) 247-8416
www.akcros.com
Email—info-nb@akcros.com
Site Mgr.—George Turk
IT & Safety Mgr.—Joe Trilone
Hum. Res. Mgr.—Erin Wachenheim
Cust. Serv. Rep.—Melissa Waluk
SIC—2821; NAICS—325211; *PVC, oxide & coating additives*
Employs—45
250,000 sq ft site, Distrib.—Intl.
ISO rating—9002

**ALANDA SOFTWARE**
391 George St. (08901)
**Phone—(201) 386-2007**
Fax—(201) 386-9044
www.alandasoftware.com
Founder & Pres.—Dean Rossi
Dir., Opers.—Allen Oliver
SIC—7372; *Software development*
Employs—20; Estab.—2005
Distrib.—Local
Privately owned corporation

**ALPHAGRAPHICS**
401 Jersey Ave., Ste. F (08901-3293)
**Phone—(732) 247-0809**
Fax—(732) 247-0840
www.us347.alphagraphics.com
Email—us347@alphagraphics.com
Pres.—H. J. Kim
SIC—2752; NAICS—323100; *Offset printing*
Employs—5; Estab.—1992
Sales—over $500,000
2,200 sq ft site, Distrib.—Regional
Privately owned corporation

**ART MATERIAL SERVICE CO., INC.**
625 Joyce Kilmer Ave. (08901)
**Phone—(732) 545-8888**
National—(888) 522-5526
Fax—(732) 545-9166
www.artmaterialsservice.com
Email—sales@artmaterialsservice.com
Pres.—Joe Eichert
GM—Gerald Lee
SIC—3429; *Picture frame hardware*
Employs—50; Estab.—1976
Distrib.—Intl.
Privately owned corporation

**BIELEN GRAPHIC ARTS, R. J.**
6 Jules Ln. (08901-3636)
**Phone—(732) 545-3501**
(732) 545-3502
Fax—(732) 545-9842
Email—rjbielenboxconve@aol.com
Pres.—Robert J. Bielen
V-P.—Robert V. Bielen
Estimator—Jane Smith
SIC—2657; 2675; 2789; NAICS—322212; *Laser die cutting & gold stamping of printed paperboard, boxes, holiday & business cards & invitations for the pharmaceutical & cosmetic industries*
Employs—11; Estab.—1986
Sales—$2Mil-$3.5Mil
15,000 sq ft site, Distrib.—National
Privately owned corporation

**CB&I**
502-B Jersey Ave. (08901)
**Phone—(732) 435-0777**
Fax—(732) 435-0888
www.cbi.com
Opers. Mgr.—Dan Frana
SIC—3494; NAICS—332900; *Industrial pipe fittings, including iron, chrome, carbon & stainless*
Employs—15; Estab.—2004
155,000 sq ft site, Distrib.—National
Publicly owned corporation
AKA: Alloy Piping Products
Parent co.—CB&I, Baton Rouge, LA
Phone—(225) 932-2500
See Parent Co. Section for full profile.

**CENMED ENTERPRISES**
121 Jersey Ave. (08901)
**Phone—(732) 447-1100**
National—(800) 470-3570
Fax—(732) 249-0008
www.cenmed.com
Email—info@cenmedonline.com
Sales Mgr.—Rizwan Chaudhry
Acct. Exec.—Larry Bitacolo
SIC—2835; 5047; 5122; NAICS—325400; *Manufacturer of diagnostic drug tests & distributor of medical, surgical, laboratory & safety supplies*
Employs—12; Estab.—1992
Distrib.—National
Privately owned corporation

**†CHALMERS & KUBECK, INC.**
8 Jules Ln. (08901)
**Phone—(732) 993-1251**
National—(800) 242-5637
Fax—(732) 993-1252
www.candk.com
Email—wsalvi@candk.com
Sales Mgr.—Jim Heuer
Br. Mgr.—Wayne Salvi
SIC—5085; *Distributor of pump, turbine, gearbox, compressor, pressure relief & industrial valves*
Employs—25; Estab.—1950
Sales—$1Mil-$2.5Mil
Distrib.—Regional
Privately owned corporation
Parent co.—Chalmers & Kubeck, Inc., Aston, PA
Phone—(610) 494-4300
See Parent Co. Section for full profile.

**CONSOLIDATED CHEMEX CORP.**
235 Jersey Ave. (08901)
**Phone—(732) 828-7676**
Fax—(732) 828-8677
www.chemexcorp.com
Email—sales@chemexcorp.com
Pres.—Walter M. Geslak
Sales Mgr.—Dave Mason
Off. Mgr.—Debra Rabner
Qual. Control Mgr.—Mike Evans
SIC—3589; 2843; NAICS—333319; *Pressure washers & cleaning chemicals, toll blending & contract manufacturing; Brand name—Chemex*
Employs—18; Estab.—1971
Sales—$1Mil-$5Mil
50,000 sq ft site, Distrib.—National
Privately owned corporation

**CREATION FLAVORS INTERNATIONAL LLC**
1 Richmond St., Ste. 3038 (08901)
**Phone—(732) 763-8622**
Fax—(978) 246-5610
www.creationflavors.com
Email—info@creationflavors.com
Manager—Rick Kamdem
SIC—2869; *Flavors for dog & cat food formulas; Brand name—TasteGuard; SavorGuard; Natural Functional Savory Flavors (NFSF)*
Employs—12; Estab.—2005
Sales—$100,000
Distrib.—National
Limited Liability Company
AKAs: Kamdem Group & Creation Flavors

**DOWNTOWN PRINTING CENTER, INC.**
46 Paterson St. (08901)
**Phone—(732) 246-7990**
Fax—(732) 246-3425
www.downtownprint.com
Email—grafix@downtownprint.com
Pres.—Juan Ruiz
SIC—2752; 2791; NAICS—323122; *Offset printing & typesetting*
Employs—14; Estab.—1977
Sales—$500,000-$1Mil
Distrib.—Local
Privately owned corporation

**EASTER SEALS NEW JERSEY (H Q)**
9 Terminal Rd. (08901)
**Phone—(732) 257-6662**
(732) 828-2032
Fax—(732) 220-2964
www.easterealsnj.org
Email—essnj@nj.easterseals.com
CEO—Brian Fitzgerald
COO—Charles Perry
Dir., Mktg.—Vanessa Holden
IT Mgr.—Curt Butler
Bus. Dev. Mgr.—Colleen Ward
SIC—3089; *Company headquarters; contract assembly*
Employs—55; Estab.—1948
Sales—$5Mil-$10Mil
Distrib.—Local

## New Brunswick—(cont.)

**ENERGY RECYCLING CO., LLC**
409 Joyce Kilmer Ave. (08901)
**Phone—(732) 545-6619**
Fax—(732) 249-4249
www.energyrecyclingco.com
Email—info@
energyrecyclingco.com
Pres.—Larry Schrager
SIC—3589; NAICS—333319;
*Wheeled metal recycling &
janitorial carts & recycling &
trash bins; Brand name—CartX;
EZ-Hauler; Barrel Buddy;
LobbyMate; TerraBin; TerraBin
Station*
Employs—5; Estab.—1995
Sales—under $500,000
Distrib.—National
Limited Liability Company

**EPIC INDUSTRIES**
1007 Jersey Ave. (08901)
**Phone—(732) 249-6867**
National—(800) 221-3742
Fax—(732) 249-7683
www.epicindustries.com
Email—sales@epicindustries.com
V.-P.—Sam Levine
Pur. Mgr.—Priyam Desai
Fin. Mgr.—Rich Davis
Cust. Serv. Mgr.—Sandi
MacDougall
Salesman—Tony Massol
SIC—2841; NAICS—325611;
*Cleaners, detergents, sanitizers,
deodorizers, disinfectants & dish
machine & laundry detergents
for commercial & institutional
markets*
Employs—60; Estab.—1921
Sales—$5Mil–$10Mil
75,000 sq ft site, Distrib.—National
Privately owned corporation

**EXCEL DISPLAY CORP.**
100 Jersey Ave., Ste. A206
(08901)
Mail addr: P.O. Box 10028, New
Brunswick (08906)
**Phone—(732) 246-3728**
Fax—(732) 246-3753
www.excel-display.com
Email—excelix@excel-display.com
Pres., CFO & GM—Tom K. Shih
SIC—3679; *Electronic
components, including liquid
crystal displays & modules;
Brand name—Excelix LCD;
Excel-Display; Excel-Tech;
Excel-Technology*
Employs—5; Estab.—2003
Sales—$1Mil–$1.5Mil
4,500 sq ft site, Distrib.—Intl.
Privately owned sub-S corp.

**†FASTENAL CO.**
987 Jersey Ave., Ste. C (08901)
**Phone—(732) 246-0248**
Fax—(732) 246-3054
www.fastenal.com
Email—njsom@stores.fastenal.com
Br. Mgr.—Mike Kane
SIC—5072; 5084; 5085;
*Wholesaler of fasteners, safety
equipment, tools & abrasives*
Employs—3; Estab.—2006
Distrib.—Intl.
Publicly owned corporation
Parent co.—Fastenal Co., Winona,
MN
Phone—(507) 454-5374
See Parent Co. Section for full profile.

**FCS FLUIDAIRE CLEANING
SERVICES, INC.**
11 Industrial Dr. (08901)
**Phone—(732) 964-1700**
Fax—(732) 249-7220
www.fluidaire.com
Email—mail@fluidaire.com
V.-P., Sales—Robert P. Lasky

SIC—3569; 3567; NAICS—
333994; *Thermal fluidized bed
cleaning equipment & burn-off &
atmospheric furnaces for the
plastics industry, including
furnace service & repair &
contract cleaning services;
Brand name—Economite*
Employs—30; Estab.—1996
Sales—$2.5Mil–$5Mil
60,000 sq ft site, Distrib.—Intl.
Privately owned corporation
Also see: Procedyne Corp., same
loc.

**GALAXY II, INC.**
235 Jersey Ave., Unit A (08901)
**Phone—(732) 828-2686**
Fax—(732) 828-2606
Pres.—Earl Creighton
SIC—3599; *Precision machining
job shop*
Employs—5; Estab.—1976
Sales—under $500,000
5,000 sq ft site, Distrib.—Local
Privately owned corporation

**†GLOBEPHARMA, INC.**
2-B Janine Pl. (08901)
Mail addr: P.O. Box 7307, North
Brunswick (08902-7307)
**Phone—(732) 296-9700**
Fax—(732) 777-5129
www.globepharma.com
Email—sanni@globepharma.com
Pres.—Sanni Raju
V.-P.—Venkat Raju
SIC—5047; 5084; *Wholesaler of
pharmaceutical solid dosage
form equipment; Brand name—
MaxiBlend; SimpleBlend;
MiniPress; Miniblend; PowderEx;
Sift-N-Blend*
Employs—10; Estab.—1993
Distrib.—Intl.
Privately owned corporation

**HEALTHY FOOD BRANDS, LLC**
122 Quentin Ave. (08901)
**Phone—(212) 444-9909**
Fax—(212) 444-9914
www.hfbusa.com
Email—info@healthy-food-
brands.com
GM—Joe Eckstein
SIC—2064; NAICS—322211;
*Candy & confectionery
packaging*
Employs—105; Estab.—1992
Sales—$50Mil–$100Mil
Distrib.—National
Sole ownership
ISO rating—9000
Parent co.—Healthy Food Brands,
LLC, Commack, NY
Phone—(631) 543-9600
See Parent Co. Section for full profile.

**HEMISPHERX BIOPHARMA, INC.**
783 Jersey Ave. (08901)
**Phone—(732) 249-3250**
Fax—(732) 249-6895
www.hemispherx.net
Email—info@hemispherx.net
V.-P., Opers.—Wayne Springate
SIC—2834; NAICS—325412;
*Pharmaceuticals*
Employs—30; Estab.—1980
44,000 sq ft site, Distrib.—National
Privately owned corporation
Parent co.—Hemispherx
BioPharma, Inc., Philadelphia,
PA
Phone—(215) 988-0080
See Parent Co. Section for full profile.

**ILLUMINATING EXPERIENCES, LLC**
625 Jersey Ave., Unit 7 (08901)
**Phone—(732) 745-5858**
National—(800) 734-5858
Fax—(732) 745-9710
www.illuminatingexperiences.com
Owner—Claire Vitale
Hum. Res. Mgr.—Don Whittaker

Pur. Agt.—Jose Cubas
Cust. Serv. Rep.—Debbie Graffeo
SIC—3646; 3645; NAICS—
335122; *Commercial &
residential lighting fixtures*
Employs—10; Estab.—1970
80,000 sq ft site, Distrib.—National
Limited Liability Company

**†INTERNATIONAL MERCANTILE
AGENCIES, INC.**
18 Home News Row (08901)
**Phone—(732) 246-3900**
National—(800) 272-7748
Fax—(732) 246-8040
www.brass4u.com
Email—info@brass4u.com
Pres.—Aman Kapur
V.-P.—Amita Kapur
SIC—5023; 5099; *Wholesaler of
imported decorative home
furnishings & event & rental
decor for weddings, parties &
special events*
Employs—10; Estab.—1974
Distrib.—Intl.
Privately owned sub-S corp.
AKA: I.M.A. Brass

**INTERNATIONAL SWIMMING
POOLS, INC.**
14-C Van Dyke Ave. (08901)
**Phone—(732) 565-9229**
Fax—(732) 565-1203
www.internationalswimmingpools.
com
Email—info@
internationalswimmingpools.com
Pres.—Brad Korbel
V.-P., Cust. Serv.—Mary Vargas
Mktg. Mgr.—Danielle Wehrle
SIC—3444; *Custom sheet metal
fabrication, including swimming
pool panels; Brand name—
Super Steel; Excalibur; Venture
Inground Swimming Pools*
Employs—19; Estab.—1993
53,000 sq ft site, Distrib.—National
Privately owned corporation

**JOHNSON & JOHNSON (H Q)**
1 Johnson & Johnson Plz. (08933)
**Phone—(732) 524-0400**
National—(800) 526-3967
Fax—(732) 214-0332
www.jnj.com
Email—info@jnj.com
Worldwide Chrm., Consumer
Div.—Jesse Wu
CEO—Alex Gorsky
V.-P., Fin. & CFO—Dominic J.
Caruso
V.-P., Inv. Rels.—Louise Mehrotra
SIC—3842; 2834; NAICS—
325412; *Company headquarters;
surgical instruments, including
medical monitoring devices &
disposable contact lenses &
pharmaceuticals; Brand name—
Tylenol; BandAid; Johnson's
Baby Powder*
Employs—900; Estab.—1886
Statewide: 1,300
Sales—$100Mil–$250Mil (est)
Publicly owned corporation

**K V K U S A, INC.**
Div. of Sun Chemical Corp.
19-A Home News Row (08901)
**Phone—(732) 846-2355**
Fax—(732) 846-2335
www.sunchemical.com
Email—info@sunchemical.com
GM—Gregory McMorray
Acctg. Mgr.—Nancy Malik
SIC—2816; NAICS—325100; *Ink
pigment dispersions*
Employs—6; Estab.—1978
Distrib.—Regional
Publicly owned corporation
Parent co.—Sun Chemical Corp.,
Parsippany, NJ
Phone—(973) 404-6000
See Parent Co. Section for full profile.

**LE PAPILLON**
120 Albany St., Ste. 300 (08901)
**Phone—(732) 843-6116**
Fax—(732) 843-6118
Owner—Watson Warriner
SIC—3231; NAICS—327215;
*Glass perfume vials*
Employs—20; Estab.—1999
Distrib.—National
Privately owned corporation

**†MATERIALS RECLAIM INDUSTRIES**
409 Joyce Kilmer Ave., Ste. 3
(08901)
**Phone—(732) 979-3479**
Fax—(732) 937-4605
www.materialsreclaim.com
Pres.—Ted Kasternakis
SIC—5093; *Wholesaler of
recycled industrial & commercial
plastic & electronic scrap
materials*
Employs—4; Estab.—1991
Distrib.—National
Sole ownership

**†MCNICHOLS CO.**
2 Home News Row (08901)
**Phone—(732) 509-3092**
National—(800) 237-3820
Fax—(732) 846-5555
www.mcnichols.com
Email—sales@mcnichols.com
GM—Mike Davidson
Sales Mgr.—David Willauer
Opers. Mgr.—Paul Carey
SIC—5051; *Metal service center,
including perforated & expanded
metals, wire mesh, bar, plank &
fiberglass grating, matting,
handrail components, fiberglass
structurals, ladder rungs, stair
treads & infill panels & partitions;
Brand name—McNichols; The
Hole Story; The Hole Book*
Employs—28; Estab.—1952
Sales—$175Mil
Distrib.—National
Privately owned corporation
ISO rating—9001:2008
Parent co.—McNICHOLS Co.,
Tampa, FL
Phone—(813) 282-3828
See Parent Co. Section for full profile.

**MEGA ELECTRONICS, INC.**
4-B Jules Ln. (08901)
**Phone—(732) 249-2656**
Fax—(732) 249-7442
www.megaelectronics.com
Email—sales@
megaelectronics.com
Pres.—Elfie Schwarzinger
V.-P., Sales & Mktg.—Guy Francfort
SIC—3679; *Power supplies,
including AC/DC & DC/DC
power converters, international &
UL/CSA power cords & cord
sets; Brand name—MEGA*
Employs—15; Estab.—1994
10,000 sq ft site, Distrib.—National
Privately owned corporation

**METALLO GASKET CO., INC.**
16 Bethany St. (08901)
**Phone—(732) 545-7223**
Fax—(732) 545-9848
www.metallogasket.com
Email—info@metallogasket.com
Pres., CEO—Frederick Haleluk
GM—Rati Zardiashvili
Off. Mgr.—Joan Nagel
SIC—3053; 3599; NAICS—
339991; *Gaskets, shims,
washers, raschig rings & tower
packings, including waterjet
cutting*
Employs—10; Estab.—1919
18,000 sq ft site, Distrib.—Intl.
Privately owned corporation

GEOGRAPHICAL

## New Brunswick—(cont.)

**MILESTONE PHARMTECH USA, INC.**
100 Jersey Ave., Bldg. D, Box D-4
(08901)
**Phone—(732) 579-8201**
Fax—(732) 579-8252
www.milestonepharmtech.com
Email—services@
milestonepharmtech.com
CEO—Eric Zhang
SIC—2834; NAICS—325412;
*Chemical intermedia for the
pharmaceuticals industry*
Employs—5; Estab.—2008
Sales—$2.5Mil-$5Mil (est)
Distrib.—Intl.
Privately owned corporation

**†MOTION INDUSTRIES, INC.**
12-D Jules Ln. (08901)
**Phone—(732) 828-8711**
National—(800) 526-9328
Fax—(732) 828-3597
www.motionindustries.com
Email—john.velit@motion-ind.com
Br. Mgr.—John Velit
SIC—5085; *Distributor of
industrial maintenance, repair &
operation (MRO) parts including
bearings, power transmission,
electrical & indl. automation,
material handling, hydraulic &
pneumatic components,
hydraulic & indl. hose & safety/
indl. supplies; Brand name—
Altra; Baldor; Eaton; Emerson
Industrial Automation; Gates;
Lovejoy; Martin; Nexen; NSK;
NTN; Rexnord; Schaeffler Group;
SEW Eurodrive; SKF; SMC;
Sumitomo; THK; Thomson;
Timken; Tsubaki; US Motors;
Vacon; Webster*
Employs—5
Distrib.—National
Privately owned corporation
Parent co.—Motion Industries,
Inc., Birmingham, AL
Phone—(205) 951-1154
See Parent Co. Section for full profile.

**MR. ICE BUCKET, LLC**
345 Sandford St. (08901-2320)
**Phone—(732) 545-0420**
Fax—(732) 846-3383
www.mricebucket.com
Email—sales@mricebucket.com
Pres.—Fred Haleluk
V-P., Sales—Sudesh Rajpal
Sales Mgr., Reg.—George
Bitsadze
SIC—3089; *Vinyl cover ice
buckets & trays; Brand name—
Mr. Ice Bucket; Shelton-ware;
Paperworks*
Employs—5; Estab.—1965
Sales—$6Mil-$10Mil
25,000 sq ft site, Distrib.—Intl.
Limited Liability Company

**NEW BRUNSWICK LAMP SHADE CO.**
7 Terminal Rd. *(08901)*
**Phone—(732) 545-0377**
Fax—(732) 545-6993
www.nbls.com
Email—shades@nbls.com
CEO—Paul Zankel
Pres.—Nathan Zankel
COO—Richard Zankel
SIC—3229; 3645; 3089; NAICS—
327212; *Lampshades*
Employs—20; Estab.—1943
16,000 sq ft site, Distrib.—Intl.
Privately owned corporation

**NEW BRUNSWICK PLATING, INC.**
1010 Jersey Ave. (08901)
Mail addr: P.O. Box 7280, North
Brunswick (08902)
**Phone—(732) 545-6522**
Fax—(732) 846-9779
www.nbplating.com

Email—info@nbplating.com
Pres.—Anthony Melchione
CFO, Cont. & Hum. Res. Mgr.—
Bobbi Sica-Gumbinger
V-P., Pur. & CPO—Michael Sica
Plt. Mgr.—Brian Patterson
IT Mgr.—Walter Gumbinger
SIC—3559; *Metal finishing*
Employs—52; Estab.—1932
77,000 sq ft site, Distrib.—Intl.
Privately owned sub-S corp.

**OHM LABORATORIES, INC.**
Div. of Ranbaxy, Inc.
14 Terminal Rd. (08901)
**Phone—(732) 514-4380**
www.ohmlabs.com
Email—info.unitedstates@
ranbaxy.com
V-P., GM—Bob Patton
Head of Opers. & Qual.—Dan
Martins
SIC—2834; *Pharmaceuticals*
Employs—400
Sales—$100Mil-$250Mil (est)
Distrib.—National
Privately owned corporation
Parent co.—Ranbaxy, Inc.,
Princeton, NJ
Phone—(609) 720-9200
See Parent Co. Section for full profile.

**OMEGA CIRCUITS & ENGINEERING
CORP.**
8 Terminal Rd. (08901)
**Phone—(732) 246-1661**
Fax—(732) 246-1643
www.omegacircuits.com
Email—sales@omegacircuits.com
Pres.—James C. Genes, Jr.
Dir., Sales—Tyler Genes
MIS & Off. Mgr.—Lash Ramen
SIC—3672; NAICS—334412;
*Printed circuit boards*
Employs—24; Estab.—1980
18,000 sq ft site, Distrib.—National
Privately owned sub-S corp.
ISO rating—9002

**†PRIMESOURCE BUILDING
PRODUCTS, INC.**
20 Van Dyke Ave (08901)
**Phone—(732) 296-0600**
National—(800) 745-3318
Fax—(732) 296-8797
www.primesourcebp.com
Email—jobs@primesourcebp.com
GM—Scott Simmel
Prod. & Sales Mgr.—Alan Bloom
SIC—5072; 5033; 5031; 5169;
*Distributor of building materials,
including fasteners, roofing
shingles, coatings, sealants,
adhesives, air vents, kitchen &
bathroom cabinets & acoustical
ceilings*
Employs—30; Estab.—1990
Sales—$1Mil-$2.5Mil
Distrib.—Local
Publicly owned corporation
Parent co.—PrimeSource Building
Products, Inc., Irving, TX
Phone—(972) 999-8500
See Parent Co. Section for full profile.

**PROCEDYNE CORP.**
11 Industrial Dr. (08901)
**Phone—(732) 249-8347**
Fax—(732) 249-7220
www.procedyne.com
Email—mail@procedyne.com
Pres., COO—Thomas Parr
V-P., Opers.—Bob Schulz
Sales Mgr., Process Tech.—Frank
Fisher

SIC—3567; NAICS—333994;
*High-temperature industrial &
heat treating furnaces, calciners
& fluid bed dryers; Brand
name—Mikrodyne Filter*
Employs—35; Estab.—1961
60,000 sq ft site, Distrib.—Intl.
Privately owned corporation
Also see: FCS Fluidaire Cleaning
Services, Inc., same loc.
AKA: Fluidaire Cleaning Services

**RARITAN PACKAGING INDUSTRIES,
INC.**
570 Jersey Ave. (08901)
Mail addr: P.O. Box 7237, North
Brunswick (08902-7237)
**Phone—(732) 246-7200**
Fax—(732) 246-4942
www.raritancontainer.com
Email—rarcon@aol.com
CEO, CFO—Sandy Newman
Pres.—Bernie Newman
SIC—2653; NAICS—322211;
*Corrugated boxes, packaging
supplies & packaging design*
Employs—2; Estab.—1974
Sales—$500,000
2,500 sq ft site, Distrib.—Local
Privately owned corporation

**RARITAN VALLEY WORKSHOP**
Div. of Easter Seals New Jersey
9 Terminal Rd. (08901)
**Phone—(732) 828-8080**
Fax—(732) 828-5374
www.eastersealsnj.org
Email—essnj@nj.easterseals.com
Plt. Mgr.—Andy Scisorek
SIC—3999; 3089; *Contract
packaging & assembly*
Employs—250; Estab.—1967
Sales—$25Mil-$50Mil (est)
Distrib.—Regional
Privately owned corporation
Parent co.—Easter Seals New
Jersey, New Brunswick, NJ
Phone—(732) 257-6662
See Parent Co. Section for full profile.

**RESEARCH DIETS, INC.**
20 Jules Ln. (08901)
**Phone—(732) 247-2390**
Fax—(732) 247-2340
www.researchdiets.com
Email—info@researchdiets.com
Pres.—E. Ulman
V-P., Fin.—Steven Goldschmidt
SIC—2048; *Laboratory animal
feed*
Employs—50; Estab.—1984
Distrib.—Intl.
Privately owned sub-S corp.

**ROYALE COSMETICS CORP.**
4-A Jules Ln. (08901)
**Phone—(732) 246-7275**
Fax—(732) 246-0578
www.royalcosmetics.com
Email—royalcosmetics@
optonline.net
Pres.—Steve Tulshi
Sales Mgr.—Bobby Rossi
Bus. Admn.—Bonnie Tulshi
SIC—2844; NAICS—325600;
*Cosmetics*
Employs—12; Estab.—1990
Sales—$500,000-$1Mil
25,000 sq ft site, Distrib.—National
Privately owned corporation

**RUTGERS UNIVERSITY PRESS**
106 Somerset St., 3rd Fl. (08901)
**Phone—(848) 445-7781**
National—(800) 848-6224
Fax—(732) 745-7039
www.rutgerspress.rutgers.edu
Email—rupbrooks@rutgers.edu
Dir., Sales & Mktg.—Elizabeth
Scarpelli
Dir., Press—Marlie Wasserman

SIC—2731; *Nonfiction book
publishing*
Employs—17; Estab.—1936
Distrib.—Intl.
Privately owned corporation

**SCHELLER PRINTING CO., LEWIS**
2275 Old Georges Rd. (08902)
**Phone—(732) 843-5050**
Fax—(732) 214-1541
www.lewprint.com
Email—lewprint@gmail.com
Pres.—Lewis Scheller
V-P.—Peggy Scheller
SIC—2759; NAICS—323100;
*Commercial printing*
Employs—3; Estab.—1984
Sales—under $500,000
Distrib.—Local
Privately owned corporation

**SMITH FILTER CORP.**
16 Van Dyke Ave. (08901)
**Phone—(732) 745-2600**
National—(800) 447-4009
Fax—(309) 764-6816
www.smithfilter.com
Email—jana@smithfilter.com
Plt. Mgr.—Wiley Hargrove III
SIC—3564; NAICS—333411;
*Permanent & disposable
building ventilation air filters*
Employs—28; Estab.—1939
Sales—$5Mil-$10Mil
30,000 sq ft site, Distrib.—National
Privately owned corporation
Parent co.—Smith Filter Corp.,
Moline, IL
Phone—(309) 764-8324
See Parent Co. Section for full profile.

**SOUTHEASTERN PLASTICS CORP.**
Div. of Alpha Industries Corp.
15 Home News Row (08901)
**Phone—(732) 846-8500**
National—(800) 966-2247
Fax—(732) 846-9795
www.alpha-industries.com
Email—info@sigmaplastics.com
GM—Greg Gallo
SIC—2673; *Plastic garment &
laundry bags*
Employs—57; Estab.—1960
Sales—$5Mil-$10Mil (est)
Distrib.—Regional
Privately owned corporation
Parent co.—Alpha Industries
Corp., Lyndhurst, NJ
Phone—(201) 933-6000
See Parent Co. Section for full profile.

[NEW ENTRY]
**SPECTRUM CHEMICAL MFG. CORP.**
769 Jersey Ave. (08901)
**Phone—(732) 214-1300**
Fax—(732) 220-6553
www.spectrumchemical.com
Email—sales@
spectrumchemical.com
Cont.—Steve Toigo
SIC—2899; *Laboratory chemicals,
including steroids & sugars*
Employs—110
Sales—$50Mil-$100Mil (est)
ISO rating—9001:2008
Parent co.—Spectrum Chemical
Mfg. Corp., Gardena, CA
Phone—(310) 516-8000
See Parent Co. Section for full profile.

**STONE SURFACES OF CENTRAL
JERSEY, INC.**
690 Jersey Ave., Unit 13 (08901)
**Phone—(732) 745-1727**
Fax—(732) 745-1728
www.stonesurfacescj.com
Email—info@stonesurfacescj.com
Pres.—Daniel Sakosits

## New Brunswick—(cont.)

SIC—3281; NAICS—327991;
Granite countertops
Employs—22; Estab.—1997
Sales—$1Mil-$2.5Mil (est)
Distrib.—Regional
Privately owned corporation

**T/MAC, INC.**
100 Jersey Ave., Bldg. D-6 (08901)
**Phone—(732) 247-0022**
Fax—(732) 247-4622
www.tmacinc.com
Email—tmac@tmacinc.com
Pres.—Marvin Wurtzelman
Off. Mgr.—Cathy Leveson
SIC—3679; Radio frequency &
microwave power amplifiers
Employs—10; Estab.—1992
5,000 sq ft site, Distrib.—National
Privately owned corporation

**TARGUM PUBLISHING CO.**
126 College Ave., Ste. 431 (08901)
**Phone—(732) 932-7051**
Fax—(732) 932-0079
www.dailytargum.com
Email—webmaster@
dailytargum.com
Opers. Mgr.—Liz Katz
SIC—2711; Daily newspaper
publishing
Employs—80; Estab.—1869
Sales—$1Mil-$2.5Mil
Distrib.—Local
Privately owned corporation

**TREK II PRODUCTS, INC.**
570 Jersey Ave. (08901)
**Phone—(732) 214-9200**
Fax—(732) 214-9257
www.trekii.com
Email—contact@trekii.com
Pres.—Michael Smokowicz
SIC—3931; NAICS—339992;
Musical instruments
Employs—10; Estab.—1993
Sales—$500,000-$1Mil
Distrib.—Intl.
Privately owned corporation

**UNIVERSAL LABORATORIES, INC.**
3 Terminal Rd. (08901)
**Phone—(732) 545-3130**
National—(800) 872-0101
Fax—(732) 214-1210
www.universalnutrition.com
Email—info@universalnutrition.com
Pres., CEO—Mike Rockoff
V-P.—Clyde Rockoff
IT Mgr.—Bob Gluckin
Hum. Res. Mgr.—Carol Milazzo
Cust. Serv. Rep.—James
Cammarano
SIC—2834; NAICS—325412;
Vitamin preparations & food
supplements
Employs—200; Estab.—1980
Sales—$25Mil-$40Mil
150,000 sq ft site, Distrib.—Intl.
Privately owned corporation
AKA: Universal Nutrition, Inc.

**WOODLINE WORKS CORP.**
625 Jersey Ave. (08901)
**Phone—(732) 828-9100**
Fax—(732) 828-9102
www.woodlineworks.net
Owner, GM & Hum. Res. Mgr.—
Song Wu
SIC—2499; Unfinished pine wood
crafts
Employs—30; Estab.—1993
34,000 sq ft site, Distrib.—National
Privately owned corporation

## New Egypt
### (Ocean—S.E.)

**C & C JETRONIC, INC.**
126 Evergreen Rd. (08533)
**Phone—(609) 758-3553**
Fax—(609) 758-6600
www.ccjetronic.com
Email—ccjetronic@verizon.net
Pres.—Cheng J. Chiang
SIC—3677; 3672; NAICS—
334416; Electronic contract
manufacturing of electronic coils,
printed circuit boards & battery
chargers (mfg. done in Taiwan &
China)
Employs—3; Estab.—1986
Sales—under $500,000 (est)
Distrib.—Regional
Privately owned corporation

**CRAFTMASTER PRINTING, INC.**
3 Main St. (08533)
**Phone—(609) 758-5990**
Fax—(609) 758-1300
www.craftmasterprinting.com
Email—info@
craftmasterprinting.com
Manager & Graphic Artist—Sherry
Nepulis
SIC—2759; 2752; NAICS—
323100; Instant & color printing
& blueprinting
Employs—1; Estab.—2002
Sales—under $500,000
Distrib.—Regional
Privately owned corporation
Parent co.—Craftmaster Printing,
Inc., Neptune, NJ
Phone—(732) 775-0011
See Parent Co. Section for full profile.

**LITTLE HOUSE CANDLES**
20 Province Line Rd. (08533)
Mail addr: P.O. Box 181, Cream
Ridge (08514)
**Phone—(609) 758-2996**
Fax—(609) 758-4619
www.littlehousecandles.com
Email—sales@
littlehousecandles.com
Owner—Jennifer Ingalls
SIC—3999; Scented candles
Employs—5; Estab.—1995
Sales—$500,000-$1Mil
Distrib.—National
Privately owned sub-S corp.

## New Gretna
### (Burlington—S.E.)

**STAIN-LESS WATER FILTERS, LLC**
51 Munion Field Rd., P.O. Box 219
(08224)
**Phone—(609) 296-2564**
Fax—(609) 296-2564
www.stainlesswaterfilters.com
Email—stainlesswf@comcast.net
Owner—Jill Pennella
SIC—3589; NAICS—333319;
Portable water softeners & filters
Employs—2; Estab.—2000
Sales—under $500,000
Distrib.—Local
Limited Liability Company

**VIKING YACHT CO.**
5738 U.S. Highway 9 N., P.O. Box
308 (08224)
**Phone—(609) 296-6000**
Fax—(609) 296-3956
www.vikingyachts.com
Email—gwaldron@
vikingyachts.com
Co-Pres., CEO—Patrick Healey
Co-Pres.—William Healey
V-P., Mfg.—Al Uhl
V-P., Hum. Res.—Drew Davala
Dir., Comm. & Mktg.—Peter
Frederiksen
Hum. Res. Admn.—Nancy Darby

Benefit Coord.—Marilyn Acosta
SIC—3732; 3731; Yachts; Brand
name—Viking Yachts; Viking
Sport Cruisers
Employs—750; Estab.—1964
Sales—over $150Mil
550,000 sq ft site, Distrib.—Intl.
Sole ownership

NEW ENTRY
**VIKING YACHTING CENTER, INC.**
5724 N. Route 9 (08224)
**Phone—(609) 296-2388**
Fax—(609) 296-0076
www.vikingyachtingcenter.com
Email—marina@vikingyachts.com
GM—Eugene R. McCann
Off. Mgr.—Cheri Ginsberg
SIC—3599; 3732; General
machining job shop for
fiberglass boats
Employs—3
Sales—under $500,000 (est)

## New Milford
### (Bergen—N.E.)

**MACY CUSTOM IRON RAILINGS CO.,
J.**
116 River Rd. (07646)
**Phone—(201) 262-4302**
Ptnr.—John Zielen
Ptnr.—Mark Zielen
SIC—3446; NAICS—332323; Iron
railings
Employs—2; Estab.—1970
Sales—under $500,000
Distrib.—Local
Sole ownership

NEW ENTRY
**METRO PUBLISHING GROUP, INC.**
626 McCarthy Dr. (07646)
**Phone—(201) 385-2000**
www.travelwritersjournal.net
Email—metropub@aol.com
Owner—Bob Nesoff
SIC—2741; Travel guide
publishing
Employs—5
Sales—under $500,000 (est)
Distrib.—Intl.
Privately owned corporation

**SCOTT GRAPHICS PRINTING, INC.**
690-D River Rd. (07646)
**Phone—(201) 262-0473**
Fax—(201) 262-0210
www.scottgraphicsprinting.com
Email—sales@
scottgraphicsprinting.com
Pres.—Scott McNiff
Prod. Mgr.—Christie McNiff
SIC—2759; 2752; NAICS—
323100; Commercial, offset,
textile screen & lithographic
printing
Employs—15; Estab.—1987
Sales—$2.6Mil-$5Mil
Distrib.—Intl.
Privately owned corporation

**SIGNS BY BLOHM, INC.**
230 River Rd. (07646)
**Phone—(201) 262-3172**
Fax—(201) 262-3157
www.blohmsigns.com
Email—wblohmsigns@aol.com
Pres.—Wayne Blohm
SIC—3993; Carved, sandblasted,
plastic, metal, gold leaf & rigid
substrate signs & banners,
dimensional letters & truck
lettering
Employs—4; Estab.—1935
Sales—under $500,000
2,400 sq ft site, Distrib.—Regional
Privately owned sub-S corp.

## New Providence
### (Union—N.E.)

**ALPHAGRAPHICS**
558 Central Ave. (07974)
**Phone—(908) 277-3000**
Fax—(908) 277-0404
Owner—Michael Tan
SIC—2759; NAICS—323100;
Commercial printing
Employs—10; Estab.—1989
3,500 sq ft site, Distrib.—Local
Privately owned sub-S corp.
ISO rating—9002

**APPLIED SURFACE TECHNOLOGIES**
15 Hawthorne Dr. (07974)
**Phone—(908) 464-6675**
Fax—(908) 464-7475
www.co2clean.com
Email—roberts@co2clean.com
Owner—Robert Sherman
SIC—3599; NAICS—333912;
Carbon dioxide snow cleaning
equipment for metals, polymers,
glass & optic, ceramics,
scanning probe microscopy,
surface analysis & vacuum
systems, fire recovery & art
restoration applications
Employs—1; Estab.—1991
Sales—under $500,000
1,000 sq ft site, Distrib.—Intl.
Sole ownership

**C.R. BARD, INC. (H Q)**
730 Central Ave. (07974)
**Phone—(908) 277-8000**
Fax—(908) 277-8098
www.crbard.com
Email—ecommerce@crbard.com
Chrm., CEO—Timothy M. Ring
Pres., COO—John H. Weiland
Sr. V-P., CFO—Christopher S.
Holland
V-P., Gen. Counsel & Secy.—Sam
Khichi
V-P., Hum. Res.—Bronwen K.
Kelly
Group V-P.—Timothy P. Collins
Group V-P.—Brian P. Kelly
Group V-P.—Sharon M. Alterio
Mktg. Progs. Mgr.—Jacqueline
Ference
SIC—3841; Corporate
headquarters; vascular, urology,
oncology & surgical specialty
products
Employs—300; Estab.—1907
Company-wide: 12,000
Sales—$2.9Bil
Distrib.—Intl.
Publicly owned corporation

**CARTRIDGE WORLD NEW
PROVIDENCE, LLC**
1310 Springfield Ave. (07974)
**Phone—(908) 771-9696**
Fax—(908) 771-9699
www.cartridgeworldusa.com
Email—cartridgeworldnp@
yahoo.com
Owner—John T. Figueiredo
SIC—3955; NAICS—339944;
Rebuilt ink cartridges
Employs—3; Estab.—2004
Sales—under $500,000
1,000 sq ft site, Distrib.—Local
Limited Liability Company

**CHEMETALL**
675 Central Ave. (07974)
**Phone—(908) 464-6900**
National—(800) 526-4473
Fax—(908) 464-7914
www.chemetallna.com
Email—duane.fudge@
chemetall.com
Pres., CEO—Ron Felber
V-P., CFO—Kevin Filipski
V-P., Mktg. & Tech.—Julia Murray
Dir., Mktg.—Duane Fudge

GEOGRAPHICAL

## New Providence— (cont.)

SIC—2819; 3823; *Company headquarters & surface treatment chemicals, chemical management systems & process equipment, including service programs, dispensing, controlling & monitoring; Brand name*—Gardobond; Gardocool; Gardoclean; Tech Cool; Permatreat; Oxsilan
Employs—100; Estab.—1909
Sales—$200Mil-$300Mil
Distrib.—Intl.
Privately owned corporation

**FRC ELECTRICAL INDUSTRIES**
Div. of Filter Research Corp.
705 Central Ave. (07974)
**Phone—(908) 464-3200**
Fax—(908) 464-7619
www.frccorp.com
Email—dking@frccorp.com
Sales & Mktg. Mgr.—Dennis King
Traf. Mgr.—Fouad Sqalli
SIC—3679; *Hermetic seals*
Employs—50; Estab.—1994
40,000 sq ft site, Distrib.—Intl.
Privately owned corporation
Parent co.—Filter Research Corp., Palm Bay, FL
Phone—(321) 676-3300
See Parent Co. Section for full profile.

**GRAVER WATER SYSTEMS, LLC**
Div. of Berkshire Hathaway, Inc.
675 Central Ave., Ste. 3 (07974)
**Phone—(908) 516-1400**
National—(877) 472-8379
Fax—(908) 516-1401
www.graver.com
Email—sales@graver.com
Pres.—Michael O'Brien
Mktg. Mgr.—Robert Applegate
SIC—3589; NAICS—333319; *Water & wastewater treatment equipment & condensate polishing systems*
Employs—35; Estab.—1948
Sales—$30Mil-$35Mil
Distrib.—Intl.
Publicly owned corporation
ISO rating—9001:2008
Parent co.—Berkshire Hathaway, Inc., Omaha, NE
Phone—(402) 346-1400
See Parent Co. Section for full profile.

**LAWYERS DIARY AND MANUAL**
890 Mountain Ave. (07974)
Mail addr: P.O. Box 1027, Summit (07902-1027)
**Phone—(973) 642-1440**
Fax—(973) 242-1905
www.lawdiary.com
Email—mail@lawdiary.com
COO & Publisher—Ed Denne
IT Mgr.—Vic Kanwar
Hum. Res. Mgr.—Millie Diaz
SIC—2721; 2741; *Legal information resource & lawyer, law firm, judge, court & agency directory publishing & software development, including diary, calendar, case register & cash account register software; Brand name*—LDMoffice; LDMonline; LDMreference; The Lawyers Diary & Manual®; New Jersey Legislative Manual; eLaw.com; New Jersey Lawyers Service; American Clerical Service; Fitzgerald's Legislative Manual; LegaList; Legal Pages®
Employs—50; Estab.—1929
Sales—$2.5Mil-$5Mil (est)
Distrib.—Regional
Privately owned corporation

**LEXISNEXIS MARTINDALE-HUBELL**
Div. of Reed Elsevier, Inc.
121 Chanlon Rd. (07974)
**Phone—(908) 464-6800**
(908) 673-5052
National—(800) 526-4902
www.martindale.com
Email—info@martindale.com
Dir., Sales—Greg Schraft
SIC—2741; *Directory publishing*
Employs—500; Estab.—1998
Sales—$70Mil
Distrib.—Intl.
Publicly owned corporation
Parent co.—Reed Elsevier, Inc., New York, NY
Phone—(212) 309-8100
See Parent Co. Section for full profile.

**LINDE NORTH AMERICA, INC. (H Q)**
575 Mountain Ave. (07974-2097)
**Phone—(908) 464-8100**
(908) 771-1491
National—(800) 755-9277
Fax—(908) 771-1460
www.lindeus.com
Email—sales.lg.us@linde.com
Pres.—Patrick F. Murphy
V-P., Gen. Counsel—Mark Weller
V-P., Supply—Ken Flessner
V-P., Energy Sols.—Earl Lawson
V-P., Corp. Comm.—Peter Gavigan
V-P., Electronics & Markets—Cliff Caldwell
Head of Hum. Res., Americas—Peter Vermeulen
Mktg. Support Mgr.—Janice Lamb
SIC—2813; 2869; NAICS—325120; *Corporate headquarters; industrial & medical gases for cryogenic freezing, inert atmospheres, pH control, ozone, medical oxygen, metal & electronic applications; Brand name*—Cryoline; Ecovar; REBOX
Employs—575; Estab.—1880
Sales—$1Bil-$2Bil
Distrib.—Intl.
Publicly owned corporation
AKA: Linde, LLC

**NEW PRINT SHOP, INC.**
558 Central Ave. (07974)
**Phone—(609) 392-0782**
Fax—(609) 392-7766
www.njprinting.com
Email—orders@njprinting.com
Pres.—Mike Tan
Acct. Exec.—Lou Salerno
SIC—2759; NAICS—323100; *Commercial & medical printing*
Employs—6; Estab.—1960
Sales—under $500,000
6,000 sq ft site, Distrib.—Regional
Privately owned corporation

**NJN PUBLISHING INDEPENDENT PRESS, INC.**
Div. of NJN Publishing, Inc.
309 South St. (07974)
Mail addr: 8 Minneakoning Rd., Flemington (08822)
**Phone—(908) 464-1025**
Fax—(908) 464-9085
www.nj.com
Email—ipeditors@njnpublishing.com
Hum. Res. Rep.—Lindsey Gartner
Reporter—Barbara Rybolt
SIC—2711; *Newspaper publishing*
Employs—15; Estab.—1998
Sales—$500,000-$1Mil (est)
Distrib.—Local
Privately owned corporation
Parent co.—NJN Publishing, Inc., Flemington, NJ
Phone—(908) 782-4747
See Parent Co. Section for full profile.

**R. R. BOWKER**
Div. of ProQuest, LLC
630 Central Ave. (07974)
**Phone—(908) 795-3500**
National—(888) 269-5372
www.bowker.com
Email—techsupport@bowker.com
V-P., Bus. Dev.—Angela D'Agostino
Sr. Off. Mgr.—Joan Huff
SIC—2741; *Bibliographical information directory publishing*
Employs—95; Estab.—1872
Distrib.—Intl.
Privately owned corporation
Parent co.—ProQuest, LLC, Ann Arbor, MI
Phone—(734) 761-4700
See Parent Co. Section for full profile.

**REEVES ENTERPRISES, INC.**
571 Central Ave. (07974)
**Phone—(908) 665-9511**
National—(800) 883-6752
Fax—(908) 665-9122
www.icedtea.com
Email—info@icedtea.com
Pres.—Edward Reeves
V-P.—Michael Murray
Shpg. Mgr.—Ken Flynn
Lab Mgr.—Trudy Jenna
SIC—2099; *Tea blending & packaging*
Employs—7; Estab.—1971
Sales—under $500,000
Distrib.—Intl.
Privately owned corporation
AKA: Templar Food Products

**SAFEGUARD**
Div. of Safeguard Business Systems, Inc.
1253 Springfield Ave., Ste. 258 (07974)
**Phone—(973) 887-9500**
Fax—(973) 887-1580
www.gosafeguard.com
Email—customerservice@gosafeguard.com
Pres.—Anthony 'Tony' De Paola
SIC—2752; 3993; NAICS—323122; *Offset printing, vinyl signs & advertising layout, brochure design & typesetting services*
Employs—1; Estab.—1969
Sales—under $500,000
2,000 sq ft site, Distrib.—Local
Privately owned corporation
Parent co.—Safeguard Business Systems, Inc., Dallas, TX
Phone—(214) 905-3935
See Parent Co. Section for full profile.

**VENUS KNITTING MILLS, INC.**
140 Spring St., Bldg. 1 (07974)
**Phone—(908) 464-2400**
Fax—(908) 464-5108
www.vkmsports.com
Pres.—Bob Fermach
SIC—2321; 2329; NAICS—315200; *Sporting goods*
Employs—20; Estab.—1956
Distrib.—Local
Privately owned corporation

---

## Newark

(Essex—N.E.)

**24 HORAS-PORTUGUESE DAILY NEWSPAPER**
68 Madison St. (07105)
**Phone—(973) 817-7400**
Fax—(973) 817-8383
www.24horasnewspaper.com
Email—imalves@24horasnewspaper.com
Pres.—Victor Alves
Dir., Mktg. & Opers.—Igor Alves

SIC—2711; *Newspaper publishing*
Employs—10; Estab.—1999
Sales—$500,000-$1Mil
Distrib.—Regional
Privately owned corporation

**A C TRANSFORMER CORP.**
89 Madison St. (07105)
**Phone—(973) 589-8574**
National—(800) 940-1033
Fax—(973) 589-3155
www.actransformer.com
Email—acinfo@actransformer.com
Pres.—Robert Giangrande
V-P.—Irene Giangrande
SIC—3612; NAICS—335311; *Electrical & specialty transformers, including repair*
Employs—6; Estab.—1947
Sales—$500,000
10,000 sq ft site, Distrib.—Intl.
Privately owned sub-S corp.

**A-1 PLASTICS**
136 Tichenor St. (07105)
**Phone—(973) 344-4441**
National—(800) 435-2247
Fax—(973) 344-4411
Email—a1plastic@kewnet.com
Pers. Mgr.—Sam Rosenburg
SIC—2673; *Plastic bags*
Employs—40; Estab.—1988
Sales—$5Mil-$10Mil (est)
Distrib.—Intl.
Privately owned corporation

**AARHUS UNITED USA, INC.**
131 Marsh St. (07114)
**Phone—(973) 344-1300**
Fax—(973) 344-9049
www.aak.com
CFO—Peter Maulbeck
Plt. Mgr.—Nigel Glover
Off. Admn.—Terri Simon
Benefit & Payroll Admn.—Susan DelGrosso
SIC—2079; NAICS—311200; *Edible oils*
Employs—80
140,000 sq ft site, Distrib.—Intl.
Privately owned corporation
AKA: A A K

**ABBY BINDERY, LLC**
121 Christie St. (07105)
**Phone—(973) 690-5509**
Fax—(973) 690-5876
Member—Jeff Maida
Sales Mgr.—Marc Girard
Off. Mgr.—Gina Jaime
SIC—2789; NAICS—323121; *Bookbinding*
Employs—30
22,000 sq ft site, Distrib.—Local
Privately owned corporation

**ABCO DIE CASTERS, INC.**
39 Tompkins Point Rd. (07114)
**Phone—(973) 624-7030**
Fax—(973) 624-7425
www.abcodiecasters.com
Email—sales@abcodiecasters.com
Pres.—Joseph R. Vitollo
V-P.—Fred Vitollo
V-P.—Stephen Vitollo
SIC—3364; 3479; NAICS—331522; *Die casting & powder coating*
Employs—70; Estab.—1971
55,000 sq ft site, Distrib.—National
Privately owned sub-S corp.
ISO rating—9001:2008

**†ACB PRODUCE, INC.**
135-137 Pacific St. (07105)
**Phone—(973) 522-1141**
Fax—(973) 522-1160
Email—acbproduce@aol.com
Pres.—Anibal Bota
Off. Mgr.—Maria Bota

## Newark—(cont.)

SIC—5148; *Wholesaler of fruits & vegetables*
Employs—7; Estab.—1976
Distrib.—Local
Privately owned corporation

### ACE TOOL & MFG. CO., INC.
532 Mulberry St., Ste. 1 (07114)
**Phone—(973) 824-0222**
(973) 824-0223
Fax—(973) 242-2974
Email—acetoolmfg@aol.com
Pres.—Charles Kolarsick
Plt. Mgr.—George Holan
Bookkeeper—Linda Fedorka
SIC—3089; *Plastic injection molding*
Employs—9; Estab.—1929
Sales—under $1Mil
10,000 sq ft site, Distrib.—Regional
Privately owned corporation

### †ACTION LIFT TRUCKS, INC.
35 Avenue C *(07114)*
**Phone—(973) 589-2320**
Fax—(973) 824-4768
www.actionlifttrucks.com
Email—actionlift@optonline.net
Owner—Sid Litvack
SIC—5082; *Distributor of forklift trucks*
Employs—5; Estab.—1971
Distrib.—Regional
Privately owned corporation

### ADVANCED CABINETS
654 4th St. (07107)
**Phone—(973) 481-3441**
Fax—(973) 481-3441
Owner—Pompeo Leone
Manager—Michael Leone
SIC—2434; NAICS—337110; *Wooden kitchen cabinets*
Employs—2; Estab.—1975
Sales—under $500,000
Distrib.—Local
Sole ownership

### †ADVANCED RECOVERY, INC.
50 Grafton Ave. (07104)
**Phone—(973) 485-9100**
National—(866) 794-8050
Fax—(973) 485-8844
www.advancedrecovery.com
Email—infonorth@ advancedrecovery.com
Pres., GM—Mark Rea
Dir., Opers.—Mark Rea, Jr.
SIC—5065; 5045; 5093; *Wholesaler of used electronic & computer parts & metals from recycled electronic equipment*
Employs—15; Estab.—1991
Sales—$3Mil
120,000 sq ft site, Distrib.—Intl.
Privately owned sub-S corp.
ISO rating—14001

### ADVOCATE PUBLISHING CORP.
171 Clifton Ave., P.O. Box 9500 (07104)
**Phone—(973) 497-4200**
(973) 497-4201
Fax—(973) 497-4192
www.rcan.org/advocate
Email—pearsoma@rcan.org
Assoc. Publisher & Editor—Deacon Al Frank
Dir., Adv. & Opers.—Margaret Pearson-McCue
Dir., Comm.—Jim Goodness
SIC—2711; 2721; 2741; NAICS—323122; *Print & online newspaper, magazine, annual directory & almanac publishing for the Archdiocese of Newark*
Employs—5; Estab.—1951
7,500 sq ft site, Distrib.—National
Privately owned corporation

### AFFORDABLE COPIES CENTER
55 Halsey St. (07102)
**Phone—(973) 802-1007**
Fax—(973) 802-1015
Email—nobelnj2010@gmail.com
Owner—Jaman Monir
SIC—2752; 2791; NAICS—323100; *Instant printing & electronic prepress*
Employs—2; Estab.—1982
Sales—under $500,000
Distrib.—Local
Sole ownership

### †AIDIL WINES & LIQUORS
Div. of Seabra Group
574 Ferry St. (07105)
**Phone—(973) 712-0950**
Fax—(973) 344-2816
www.aidilwines.com
Email—ligia.santos@aidilwines.com
GM—Pedro Carvalho
Admn. Mgr.—Ligia Santos
SIC—5182; *Distributor of wine*
Employs—15; Estab.—2007
Distrib.—Local
Privately owned corporation
Parent co.—Seabra Group, Newark, NJ
Phone—(973) 491-0399
See Parent Co. Section for full profile.

### AIRMET, INC.
671 N. 3rd St. (07107)
**Phone—(973) 481-5550**
Fax—(973) 481-5551
www.airmetmetalworks.com
Email—info@airmetmetalworks.com
Pres.—Stephen A. Yavorski, Sr.
V-P.—Cindy Yavorski
SIC—3312; 3444; 3499; 3599; *Metal fences, gates, railings, steel & sheet metal fabrication & welding job shop*
Employs—6; Estab.—1971
Sales—$500,000-$1Mil
11,000 sq ft site, Distrib.—Regional
Privately owned corporation

### ALL METAL POLISHING & PLATING, INC.
23 George St. (07105)
**Phone—(973) 589-8070**
Fax—(973) 589-0035
www.acemetalfinishing.com
Email—acepci@optonline.net
Pres.—Ailton Lima
Plt. Mgr.—Antonio Najarro
SIC—3471; 3479; NAICS—332813; *Metal polishing, plating, powder coating & media blasting*
Employs—10; Estab.—1968
Sales—$500,000-$4Mil
40,000 sq ft site, Distrib.—Regional
Privately owned corporation
DBA: Ace Powder Coating

### †ALLIED STEEL DISTRIBUTION & SERVICE CENTER
118-144 Harper St. (07114)
**Phone—(973) 824-7347**
National—(888) 289-7833
Fax—(973) 642-8404
www.alliedsteel.com
Email—sales@alliedsteel.com
Pres.—Don DeFaria, Jr.
Sales Mgr.—Dan Connolly
Plt. Mgr.—Lou Calderon
SIC—5051; 3443; 3444; 3599; *Steel service center, including plate & sheet fabrication, metal forming, production saw cutting, plasma & flame cutting, shearing, punching, bending, burning & welding*
Employs—14; Estab.—1969
Sales—$5Mil-$6Mil
Distrib.—Local
Privately owned corporation

### ALLSTATE PAPER BOX CO., INC.
223 Raymond Blvd. (07105)
**Phone—(973) 589-2600**
Fax—(973) 817-9326
www.allstatepaperbox.com
Email—sales@ allstatepaperbox.com
Pres.—Matt Elias
Sales Mgr.—Howard Greenberg
Acct. Mgr.—Bruce Konecky
SIC—2652; 2674; 2657; NAICS—322213; *Set-up paperboard, folding & vinyl boxes & shopping bags, including pre-tied ribbons, stretch loops & bows*
Employs—70; Estab.—1967
Sales—$12Mil
100,000 sq ft site, Distrib.—Intl.
Privately owned corporation

### ALPHATEC COMPUTER COMMUNICATIONS
41 Merchant St. (07105)
**Phone—(973) 344-8736**
www.eztechcomputers.com
Email—info@eztechcomputers.com
Owner—Viton Nascimendo
SIC—3571; NAICS—334111; *Computers*
Employs—2; Estab.—1993
Sales—under $500,000
Distrib.—Local
Sole ownership

### AMERICAN ADHESIVES & COATINGS, INC.
470 Mulberry St. (07114)
**Phone—(973) 623-7070**
Fax—(973) 824-5106
Pres., Hum. Res. & IT Mgr.—Joanne Hayo
GM—John Torres
SIC—2891; NAICS—325520; *Adhesives & adhesive coatings*
Employs—10; Estab.—1977
Sales—$1Mil-$2.5Mil
Distrib.—Intl.
Privately owned corporation

### AMERICAN FUR FELT, LLC
53 Rome St. (07105)
**Phone—(973) 344-3026**
Fax—(973) 344-1607
Email—americanfurfelt@aol.com
Pres.—Lucilio Pereira
V-P., Mfg.—Maria DaSilva
SIC—2371; 2399; NAICS—315200; *Fur felt cutting*
Employs—11; Estab.—2001
Sales—$1Mil-$2.5Mil
Distrib.—Intl.
Limited Liability Company

### AMERICAN HALAL SLAUGHTER HOUSE
270 Raymond Blvd. (07105-4620)
**Phone—(973) 817-8444**
Fax—(973) 817-8003
Email—meccahalal1@aol.com
Pres.—Omar Mady
V-P.—Susie Mady
SIC—2011; NAICS—311611; *Halal meat processing & packing for the wholesale & retail meat markets*
Employs—17; Estab.—1995
Sales—under $500,000
Distrib.—National
Privately owned corporation
DBA: Mecca Halal Wholesale

### AMERICAN LAWYER'S MEDIA, INC.
238 Mulberry St., 2nd Fl. (07102)
**Phone—(973) 642-0075**
Fax—(973) 642-0920
www.njlj.com
Publisher & Hum. Res. Mgr.—Robert Speinbaum
Editor—Ronald Fleury
SIC—2721; *Law journal publishing*
Employs—30; Estab.—1878
Distrib.—National
Privately owned corporation

### AMERICAN WASTE & TEXTILE, LLC
73 Vesey St. (07105)
**Phone—(973) 589-6252**
National—(877) 724-7948
Fax—(973) 589-7549
www.ragsrus.com
Email—americanwaste@ mindspring.com
Ptnr., CEO & MIS Mgr.—Jeffrey Belfer
Pres., CFO—Leonard Belfer
SIC—2299; 2621; NAICS—322100; *Wiping cloths, industrial work gloves, oil absorbent paper towels, janitorial supplies, packaging supplies, cheesecloth & terry towels*
Employs—10; Estab.—1948
Sales—$1Mil-$5Mil
20,000 sq ft site, Distrib.—Regional
Limited Liability Company

### AMERI-TEX, INC.
461 Frelinghuysen Ave. (07114)
**Phone—(973) 286-0102**
Fax—(973) 286-0140
Email—jforg33@aol.com
Pres.—Greg Opiola
V-P.—Jerry Kulminski
Off. Mgr.—Nicole Opiola
Technician—John London
SIC—2339; 2329; NAICS—315200; *Knit goods, including sweaters, scarves, blankets & hats*
Employs—8; Estab.—1985
Sales—under $500,000
Distrib.—Regional
Privately owned corporation

### AMROD CORP.
305-A Craneway St. (07114)
**Phone—(973) 344-2978**
Fax—(973) 344-0365
www.amrod.com
Email—info@amrod.com
Pres.—Mark Woehnker
Operation Mgr.—David Arp
Traf. Mgr.—Jene Gibson
Fin. Mgr.—Michael Ustupski
SIC—3351; NAICS—331421; *Copper rods*
Employs—45; Estab.—1985
40,000 sq ft site, Distrib.—National
Privately owned sub-S corp.

### ANHEUSER-BUSCH COS., INC.
Div. of Anheuser-Busch InBev Worldwide, Inc.
200 U.S. Highway 1 & 9 (07114)
Mail addr: P.O. Box 879, Newark (07101)
**Phone—(973) 645-7700**
(973) 645-7736
Fax—(973) 645-8950
www.anheuser-busch.com
Email—stl@anheuser-busch.com
Hum. Res. Mgr.—Fran Justin
Resource Mgr.—Kathy Corbel
SIC—2082; *Malt beverages*
Employs—500
Sales—$50Mil-$100Mil (est)
Distrib.—Intl.
Publicly owned corporation
Parent co.—Anheuser-Busch InBev Worldwide, Inc., St. Louis, MO
Phone—(314) 577-2000
See Parent Co. Section for full profile.

### ANHYDRIDES & CHEMICALS, INC.
7-33 Amsterdam St. (07105)
**Phone—(973) 465-0077**
Fax—(973) 465-7713
www.broadview-tech.com
Email—prhodes@broadview-tech.com

GEOGRAPHICAL

© Copyright 2015 Manufacturers' News, Inc.

# MANUFACTURERS DIRECTORIES &

**AL** — 6,204 companies • 20,772 execs.
Published each April

**AK** — 999 companies • 2,907 execs.
Published each January

**AZ** — 6,116 companies • 17,585 execs.
Published each April

**AR** — 3,700 companies • 12,974 execs.
Published each October

**CA** — 27,489 companies • 78,827 execs.
Published each March

**CO** — 7,407 companies • 21,156 execs.
Published each June

**CT** — 5,776 companies • 17,167 execs.
Published each June

**DE** — 824 companies • 2,848 execs.
Published each June

**FL** — 16,010 companies • 44,853 execs.
Published each April

**GA** — 10,859 companies • 34,741 execs.
Published each May

**HI** — 1,515 companies • 3,829 execs.
Published each April

**ID** — 2,385 companies • 7,094 execs.
Published each November

**IL** — 18,071 companies • 57,586 execs.
Published each January

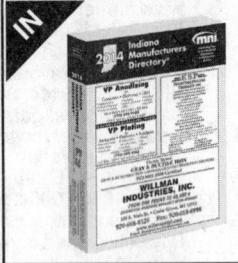
**IN** — 10,745 companies • 36,982 execs.
Published each April

**IA** — 6,108 companies • 20,259 execs.
Published each February

**KS** — 5,079 companies • 16,344 execs.
Published each May

**KY** — 5,560 companies • 19,914 execs.
Published each October

**LA** — 6,162 companies • 18,898 execs.
Published each May

**ME** — 2,350 companies • 6,808 execs.
Published each January

**MD/DC** — 5,276 companies • 16,328 execs.
Published each June

**MA** — 8,976 companies • 27,163 execs.
Published each August

**MI** — 15,702 companies • 45,828 execs.
Published each March

**MN** — 10,135 companies • 32,069 execs.
Published each November

**MS** — 3,322 companies • 11,652 execs.
Published each April

**MO** — 8,940 companies • 28,860 execs.
Published each August

## All in the same easy-to-use format as this directory!
## To order, call 800-221-2172 or visit mnistore.com

# DATABASES FOR OTHER STATES

**MT**

2,024 companies • 5,210 execs.
Published each August

**NE**

3,181 companies • 10,563 execs.
Published each July

**NV**

2,030 companies • 6,520 execs.
Published each November

**NH**

2,695 companies • 8,526 execs.
Published each November

**NJ**

10,183 companies • 30,023 execs.
Published each February

**NM**

2,490 companies • 6,975 execs.
Published each February

**NY**

18,274 companies • 50,013 execs.
Published each September

**NC**

11,812 companies • 38,612 execs.
Published each February

**ND**

1,501 companies • 4,818 execs.
Published each May

**OH**

18,965 companies • 63,095 execs.
Published each September

**OK**

5,927 companies • 18,253 execs.
Published each August

**OR**

6,351 companies • 18,912 execs.
Published each November

**PA**

18,666 companies • 58,463 execs.
Published each July

**RI**

1,826 companies • 5,466 execs.
Published each January

**SC**

5,473 companies • 18,775 execs.
Published each September

**SD**

1,562 companies • 5,107 execs.
Published each December

**TN**

7,693 companies • 26,288 execs.
Published each October

**TX**

25,626 companies • 76,533 execs.
Published each May

**UT**

4,402 companies • 13,782 execs.
Published each September

**VT**

1,526 companies • 4,516 execs.
Published each January

**VA**

7,027 companies • 23,136 execs.
Published each November

**WA**

7,718 companies • 23,065 execs.
Published each March

**WV**

2,063 companies • 7,021 execs.
Published each July

**WI**

12,368 companies • 40,647 execs.
Published each July

**WY**

1,337 companies • 4,205 execs.
Published each November

## Industrial directories for Canada & Mexico also available.
## For pricing, call 800-221-2172 or visit mnistore.com

## Newark—(cont.)

V-P.—Phillip Rhodes
Sales Mgr.—Jason Tuerack
SIC—2899; *Anhydrides for curing epoxy resins, flame retardants & unsaturated liquid anhydrides for epoxy filament winding, pultrusion, resin infusion & electrical potting of ignition coils, high-voltage transformers & printed circuit boards*
Employs—7; Estab.—1970
Sales—$500,000-$1Mil
Distrib.—Local
Privately owned corporation
AKA: Broadview Technologies, Inc.

### ANTONIO MOZZARELLA FACTORY, INC.

631 Frelinghuysen Ave. (07114)
**Phone—(973) 353-9411**
Fax—(973) 353-0996
Email—antoniomozz@verizon.net
Pres.—Tom Tugliese
SIC—2022; NAICS—311513; *Mozzarella cheese*
Employs—22; Estab.—1991
Sales—under $500,000
Distrib.—Local
Privately owned corporation

### APEX GEAR & MACHINE CO.

938 Lake St. (07104)
**Phone—(973) 482-5542**
Fax—(973) 482-8706
www.apexgearandmachine.com
Email—apexgear@aol.com
Pres.—Steve Ciocci
Off. Mgr.—Mary Jones
Foreman—Keith Ermilio
SIC—3566; 3599; NAICS—333612; *Precision gears, racks & grinding, broaching & machining job shop*
Employs—6; Estab.—1946
Distrib.—National
Privately owned corporation

### ARCHIVE DESIGNS, INC.

238 Emmet St. (07114)
**Phone—(973) 242-6400**
National—(888) 352-8345
Fax—(973) 242-0928
www.archivedesignsinc.com
Email—info@archivedesignsinc.com
Pres.—John Olaya
SIC—2542; *Large steel document storage systems & flat files*
Employs—5
Sales—$500,000-$1Mil
Distrib.—Local
Privately owned corporation

### ARDMORE, INC.

29 Riverside Ave., Bldg. 14 (07104)
**Phone—(973) 481-2406**
Fax—(973) 481-2637
Pres., CFO—Albert Sharphouse
SIC—2843; NAICS—325613; *Personal care product intermediate chemicals*
Employs—8; Estab.—1958
18,000 sq ft site, Distrib.—National
Privately owned corporation

### AROL CHEMICAL PRODUCTS CO.

649 Ferry St. (07105)
**Phone—(973) 344-1510**
Fax—(973) 344-7127
Pres.—Salvatore Coppola
V-P.—Juliet Coppola
SIC—2841; NAICS—325611; *Textile washing & base maintenance chemicals*
Employs—6; Estab.—1965
Distrib.—National
Privately owned corporation

### ARROW MACHINE CO.

117 Norfolk St. (07103)
**Phone—(973) 642-2430**
Fax—(973) 642-2431
Owner & Corp. Pres.—George Ambandos
SIC—3519; *Rebuilt engines*
Employs—6; Estab.—1925
Sales—$500,000-$1Mil
Distrib.—Local
Privately owned corporation

### ASCOT TAG & LABEL CO., INC.

577 3rd St. (07107)
**Phone—(973) 482-0900**
National—(800) 826-7268
Fax—(973) 482-1212
Email—ascottag@aol.com
Pres. & V-P.—Charles DeFranza
V-P.—Charles DeFranza, Jr.
V-P.—Michale DeFranza
Logistic Mgr.—Jason Paternina
Estimator—Frank Marinella
Bookkeeper—Dora Pancun
SIC—2752; 2759; NAICS—323100; *Tags, labels & commercial printing*
Employs—45; Estab.—1976
Sales—$5Mil-$10Mil
Distrib.—Intl.
Privately owned corporation

### ATLAS DESK & OFFICE EQUIPMENT CORP.

185-193 Central Ave., 2nd Fl. (07103)
**Phone—(973) 242-8989**
Fax—(973) 623-7838
www.atlasdesk.com
Email—cbright@atlasdesk.com
Pres.—Mark Parra
Cont., Hum. Res. & IT Mgr.—Nancy Henderson
SIC—2521; 3577; NAICS—337211; *Office furniture & equipment*
Employs—12; Estab.—1966
Sales—$500,000-$1Mil
Distrib.—Regional
Privately owned corporation

### ATLAS REFINERY, INC.

142 Lockwood St. (07105)
**Phone—(973) 589-2002**
Fax—(973) 589-7377
www.atlasrefinery.com
Email—info@atlasrefinery.com
CEO—Steve B. Schroeder
Pres.—Steven B. Schroeder, Jr.
Dir., Admn. & Fin.—Joe Gargano
Opers. Mgr.—Bill Boumann
Lab Mgr.—Massimiliano La Falce
SIC—2843; NAICS—325613; *Lubricants for leather & leather finishing compounds; Brand name—Atlas; Atlasol; Atlastan; Eureka*
Employs—21; Estab.—1887
90,000 sq ft site, Distrib.—Intl.
Privately owned corporation
ISO rating—9001:2000

### ATLAS WOODWORK

212 Wright St. (07114)
**Phone—(973) 621-9595**
Fax—(973) 621-0395
Email—atlaswoodwork@aol.com
Pres.—Antonio Martins
Hum. Res. Mgr.—Rachel Martins
Asst. Proj. Mgr.—Anna Eades
SIC—2434; 2431; 2541; NAICS—337110; *Wooden kitchen cabinets & commercial fixtures*
Employs—10; Estab.—2002
Sales—$500,000-$1Mil (est)
Distrib.—Regional
Privately owned corporation

### BANANAFISH

250 Passaic St. (07104)
**Phone—(212) 686-4666**
National—(800) 899-8689
www.bananafishinc.com
Email—info@bananafish.com
Owner—Steven Betesh
SIC—2392; *Infant bedding*
Employs—30; Estab.—1995
3,000 sq ft site, Distrib.—National
Privately owned corporation

### BELL CONTAINER CORP.

615 Ferry St., P.O. Box 5728 (07105)
**Phone—(973) 344-4400**
Fax—(973) 344-0817
www.bellcontainer.com
Email—sales@bellcontainer.com
Pres.—Arnold Kaplan
Sales Mgr.—Matthew Rosten
SIC—2653; NAICS—322211; *Corrugated boxes & containers*
Employs—175; Estab.—1890
Sales—$90Mil
Distrib.—Local
Privately owned corporation
ISO rating—9001:2008

### BENJAMIN MOORE & CO.

134 Lister Ave. (07105)
**Phone—(973) 344-1200**
Fax—(201) 949-6245
www.benjaminmoore.com
Email—info@benjaminmoore.com
Plt. Mgr.—Ward Bubeck
Process Mgr.—Rod Caldwell
EHS Process Mgr.—Ron DeFroscia
Shpg. & Rec. Foreman—Keith Roberts
Facility Admn.—Joanne Egan
SIC—2851; NAICS—325510; *Commercial & industrial paints & coatings*
Employs—55; Estab.—1925
Distrib.—National
Privately owned corporation
Parent co.—Benjamin Moore & Co., Montvale, NJ
Phone—(201) 573-9600
See Parent Co. Section for full profile.

### BENNETT HEAT TREATING & BRAZING CO., INC.

690 Ferry St. *(07105)*
**Phone—(973) 589-0590**
Fax—(973) 589-6518
www.bennetheat.com
Email—pciulla@bennetheat.com
Pres., CFO—David Quaglia
V-P.—John DiTrapano
Cont.—Pete Ciulla
Qual. Control Mgr.—John Quaglia
Manager—Mark Fiore
SIC—3398; NAICS—332811; *Corporate headquarters & metal heat treating & brazing*
Employs—40; Estab.—1954
Sales—$1Mil-$7Mil
45,000 sq ft site, Distrib.—National
Privately owned corporation

### BEST PROVISION CO., INC.

144 Avon Ave. (07108)
**Phone—(973) 242-5000**
National—(800) 631-4466
Fax—(973) 648-0041
www.bestprovision.com
Email—bestprovco@aol.com
CEO—Len Karp
V-P., Treas.—Kevin Karp
Corp. Secy.—Richard Dolinko
Dir., Hum. Res.—Clara Belle Mendez
Plt. Mgr.—Al Silver
SIC—2011; 2015; NAICS—311611; *Beef & deli meat processing & packing*
Employs—100; Estab.—1938
Distrib.—Intl.
Privately owned corporation

### BOYKO'S METAL FINISHING CO.

100 Poinier St. (07114)
**Phone—(973) 623-4254**
Fax—(973) 623-3529
Pres.—John Boyko
GM—Jeff Schultz

SIC—3479; *Powder coating*
Employs—30; Estab.—1959
Sales—$1Mil-$5Mil
30,000 sq ft site, Distrib.—Regional
Publicly owned corporation

### BRAZILIAN VOICE

412 Chestnut St., P.O. Box 5686 (07105)
**Phone—(973) 491-6200**
Fax—(973) 491-6287
www.brazilianvoice.com
Email—roberto@brazilianvoice.com
CEO—Roberto Leman
SIC—2711; *Newspaper publishing*
Employs—5
Sales—under $500,000 (est)

### BRISTOL-DONALD CO., INC.

50 Roanoke Ave. (07105)
**Phone—(973) 589-2640**
Fax—(973) 589-2610
www.bristoldonald.com
Email—sales@bristoldonald.com
Pres.—Robert Greeley, Jr.
Secy-Treas.—Daniel Greeley
Sales Mgr.—John Silva
SIC—3714; *Truck equipment*
Employs—25; Estab.—1946
Sales—$1Mil-$5Mil
30,000 sq ft site, Distrib.—Regional
Privately owned corporation

### BUSH TANK FABRICATORS, INC.

222 Thomas St. (07114)
**Phone—(973) 596-1121**
Fax—(973) 596-1662
Email—bushtank@aol.com
Pres.—Thomas Horenburg
SIC—3444; 3312; *Custom aluminum, steel & stainless steel fabrication of process equipment, tanks, ribbon, v & double cone blenders & related products for the food, pharmaceutical & chemical industries*
Employs—10; Estab.—1980
Sales—$500,000-$1Mil
10,000 sq ft site, Distrib.—Intl.
Privately owned corporation

### C W C INDUSTRIES, INC.

185 Foundry St. (07105)
**Phone—(973) 344-1434**
Fax—(973) 589-1617
Pres.—Stan Acroman
GM—Baldwin Chan
Prodn. Mgr.—Steve Chan
SIC—2789; NAICS—323121; *Hot stamping foil*
Employs—10; Estab.—1969
32,000 sq ft site, Distrib.—Intl.
Privately owned corporation

### CALANDRA'S ITALIAN & FRENCH BAKERY

204 1st Ave. W. (07107)
**Phone—(973) 484-5598**
Fax—(973) 484-7999
www.calandras.net
Email—calandras@aol.com
Pres.—Luciano Calandra
V-P.—Engim Aktas
GM—Gino Ciselli
SIC—2051; NAICS—311812; *Italian & French baked goods, including bread, cakes & pastries*
Employs—60; Estab.—1964
Sales—$5Mil-$10Mil (est)
Distrib.—Regional
Privately owned corporation

### CAMBRIDGE INDUSTRIES OF AMERICA CO., INC.

7-33 Amsterdam St. (07105)
**Phone—(973) 465-0077**
Fax—(973) 465-7713
www.broadview-tech.com

# Newark—(cont.)

Email—prhodes@broadview-tech.com
Pres.—Phillip Rhodes
SIC—2821; NAICS—325211;
*Epoxy resins & plastercicers*
Employs—8; Estab.—1987
Sales—$1Mil-$2.5Mil
Distrib.—Local
Privately owned corporation
AKA: Broadview Technologies

## CAPORASO SALES CORP.

144 Emmet St. *(07114)*
**Phone—(973) 824-7286**
Fax—(973) 824-3837
Email—capsalesco2@aol.com
Pres.—Nicholas F. Caporaso
Treas., CFO—Nicholas D. Caporaso
V-P.—Joseph Caporaso
SIC—3499; *Trophy & plaque supplies*
Employs—3; Estab.—1962
Sales—under $500,000
5,000 sq ft site, Distrib.—National
Privately owned corporation

## CARDOLITE CORP.

500 Doremus Ave. (07105)
**Phone—(973) 344-5015**
Fax—(973) 344-1197
www.cardolite.com
Email—contactus@cardolite.com
Pres.—Anthony Stonis
Dir., Opers.—Angel Soto
Cust. Serv. Rep.—Maria Ruiz
Cust. Serv. Rep.—Laiza Calis
SIC—2821; NAICS—325211;
*Epoxy resins*
Employs—80; Estab.—1998
Distrib.—Local
Privately owned corporation
ISO rating—9002

## CHEMTRADE

Div. of Chemtrade Chemical, LLC
330 Doremus Ave. (07105)
**Phone—(973) 589-5300**
Fax—(973) 465-4359
www.chemtradelogistics.com
Email—mcusmano@chemtradelogistics.com
Plt. Mgr.—Mathew Cusmano
SIC—2819; *Aluminum sulfate*
Employs—4
Distrib.—National
Publicly owned corporation
Parent co.—Chemtrade Chemical, LLC, Parsippany, NJ
Phone—(973) 515-0900
See Parent Co. Section for full profile.

## COBON PLASTICS CORP.

90 South St., Dock 5 (07114)
**Phone—(973) 334-6330**
National—(800) 360-1324
Fax—(973) 344-6335
www.cobonplastics.com
Email—cbco101@aol.com
Pres., CEO—Michael F. Nelson
V-P.—C. Mans
Bookkeeper—Nancy Holmes
SIC—3082; NAICS—326121;
*Plastic tubing for the medical & laboratory industries*
Employs—11; Estab.—1949
Sales—$1Mil-$1.5Mil
18,000 sq ft site, Distrib.—National
Privately owned corporation
Also see: Couse & Bolten Co., same loc.

## COLANTUONO & KLURMAN ASSOCS., INC.

225 Clifford St., P.O. Box 5150 (07105)
**Phone—(973) 589-5445**
Fax—(973) 589-8141
Email—lourdes@ckscrap.com
Pres.—Sanford Klurman
Cont.—Lourdes Najarro

Dir., Sales & Sales Mgr.—Joe Blandino
Opers. Mgr.—Ross Cerini
SIC—3341; *Scrap metal recycling*
Employs—40; Estab.—1970
Distrib.—Regional
Privately owned corporation

## COLONIAL CONCRETE CO.

1196 McCarter Hwy. (07104)
**Phone—(973) 482-1920**
Fax—(973) 482-7524
www.colonialconcrete.com
Email—sales@colonialconcrete.com
Pres.—Martin Lucibello
Dir., Comms. & Tech.—Jerry Jansen
Dir., Qual. Control—John Serro
Sales Mgr.—Richard Shoop
Plt. Opers. Mgr.—James Bizarro
SIC—3273; NAICS—327320;
*Company headquarters & ready-mixed concrete*
Employs—30; Estab.—1952
Sales—$5Mil-$10Mil (est)
Distrib.—Local

## COLONY, LLC

852 S. Orange Ave., P.O. Box 6444 (07106)
**Phone—(973) 375-4315**
Fax—(973) 375-4315
www.colonyllc.net/home
Email—colonypress@optonline.net
Off. Mgr.—Todd Glass
Consultant—William Gooding
SIC—2752; NAICS—323100;
*Offset printing*
Employs—2; Estab.—1958
Sales—under $500,000
Distrib.—Local
Privately owned corporation

## COLOR SCREEN PROS

100 Verona Ave. (07104)
**Phone—(973) 268-5080**
National—(800) 774-6869
Fax—(973) 350-0300
www.colorscreenpros.com
Email—printmyt@aol.com
Owner—Oscar Cano
Manager—Ursula Espinoza
SIC—2396; 2759; 2395; 2752;
*Apparel & promotional item screen printing, custom embroidery, commercial & offset printing & signs, banners & vinyl graphics*
Employs—8; Estab.—1999
Sales—$1Mil-$2.5Mil
10,000 sq ft site, Distrib.—Local
Privately owned corporation

## CORTE PROVISIONS

Div. of Seabra Group
574 Ferry St. (07105)
**Phone—(973) 712-0970**
Fax—(973) 589-7320
www.cortesfamous.com
Opers. Mgr.—Rui Serra
SIC—2013; NAICS—311600;
*Sausage processing*
Employs—14; Estab.—1922
20,000 sq ft site, Distrib.—National
Privately owned corporation
Parent co.—Seabra Group, Newark, NJ
Phone—(973) 491-0399
See Parent Co. Section for full profile.

## COUSE & BOLTEN CO.

90 South St., Dock 5 (07114)
**Phone—(973) 344-6330**
National—(800) 360-1324
Fax—(973) 344-6335
Email—cbco101@aol.com
Owner, CEO & COO—Michael Nelson

SIC—3052; 3089; 5085; 5072;
NAICS—326220; *Manufacturer & distributor of hydraulic, rubber, metal, stainless steel, bronze & PTFE hose assemblies, belting & fittings, plastic tubing, exhaust ducts & conveyor belt fasteners; Brand name—Gates Corp; Hi Tech/Duravent; Flexaust; Flexco; Dixon Valve & Coupling*
Employs—7; Estab.—1899
Sales—$1Mil-$2.5Mil
Distrib.—Regional
Privately owned corporation
Also see: Cobon Plastics Corp., same loc.

NEW ENTRY

## CREATIVE EMBROIDERY CORP.

305 3rd Ave. W., Ste. 3 (07107)
Mail addr: P.O. Box 1485, Bloomfield (07003)
**Phone—(973) 497-5700**
Fax—(973) 497-5520
Pres.—Steve Diamond
SIC—2396; 2395; *Custom apparel screen printing & embroidery*
Employs—20; Estab.—1975
Sales—under $500,000
10,000 sq ft site, Distrib.—National
Privately owned corporation

## CREATIVE PATTERNS & MFG., INC.

54 Freeman St., P.O. Box 5549 (07105)
**Phone—(973) 589-1391**
Fax—(973) 589-1392
Email—creativepattern@msn.com
Co-Pres.—David Cummins
Co-Pres.—James Generoso
Co-Pres.—Robert Jenkins
SIC—3089; *Plastic fabrication*
Employs—9; Estab.—1993
Sales—$500,000-$1Mil
5,500 sq ft site, Distrib.—Local
Privately owned sub-S corp.

NEW ENTRY

## CSI FABRICATORS

15 Lexington St. (07105)
**Phone—(973) 344-0955**
(610) 923-6543
www.csifabricators.com
Email—info@csifabricators.com
Manager—Kiran Pagarey
SIC—3441; 3446; 3599; *Sheet metal fabrication, architectural metalwork & CNC machining job shop*
Employs—7
Sales—$1Mil-$2.5Mil (est)
ISO rating—9001:2008

NEW ENTRY

## D & H PALLETS, LLC

45 Verona Ave. (07104)
**Phone—(973) 481-2981**
Owner—Ramon Munoz
SIC—2448; *Wooden pallets*
Employs—6
Sales—$500,000-$1Mil (est)
Limited Liability Company

## D M STEEL

279 Sherman Ave. (07114)
**Phone—(973) 732-4763**
Fax—(973) 732-4768
Email—marcducate@yahoo.com
Pres., CFO—Marc Ducate
Secy-Treas., MIS & Off. Mgr.—Judy Ducate
SIC—3312; *Steel slitting, round edging, shearing & leveling*
Employs—15; Estab.—2009
32,000 sq ft site, Distrib.—National
Privately owned corporation

## DALFEN UNLIMITED

27 1/2 Lentz Ave. (07105)
**Phone—(973) 344-4006**
Fax—(973) 344-4006
www.dalfenunlimited.com

Email—dalfen@aol.com
Owner—Ed Norton
SIC—2759; NAICS—323100;
*Commercial printing*
Employs—5; Estab.—1984
Sales—under $500,000
Distrib.—Local
Sole ownership

## DARLING INGREDIENTS, INC.

825 Wilson Ave. *(07105)*
**Phone—(973) 465-1900**
(800) 842-5927
Fax—(973) 465-9247
www.darlingii.com
Email—sales@darlingii.com
Pres.—Neil Katchen
V-P.—Billy Frish
Cont.—Ron Hine
GM—Edward Schlagenhaft
Plt. Mgr.—Tom Miller
SIC—2899; *Inedible tallow*
Employs—200; Estab.—1989
Sales—$50Mil-$100Mil (est)
Distrib.—Intl.
Publicly owned corporation
Parent co.—Darling Ingredients, Inc., Irving, TX
Phone—(972) 717-0300
See Parent Co. Section for full profile.

## DAVION, INC.

29-75 Riverside Ave., Bldg. 10 (07104)
**Phone—(973) 485-0793**
Fax—(973) 485-0025
www.davion.com
Pres.—James Placa
V-P.—James Placa III
Cust. Serv. Rep.—Victoria Ruan
SIC—2844; NAICS—325600;
*Cosmetics & baby care products*
Employs—30; Estab.—1987
30,000 sq ft site, Distrib.—Intl.
Privately owned corporation

## DCI SIGNS & AWNINGS, INC.

110 Riverside Ave. (07104)
**Phone—(973) 350-0400**
Fax—(973) 350-0401
www.dcisigns.com
Email—info@dcisigns.com
Pres.—Danny Castillo
SIC—3993; 3444; *Interior & exterior signs & custom awnings*
Employs—25; Estab.—1998
Distrib.—National
Privately owned corporation

## DEBORAH SALES, LLC

109 Meeker Ave. (07114)
**Phone—(973) 344-8466**
Fax—(973) 344-3981
www.deborahsales.us
Email—crei@deborahsales.us
Pres.—Jacira Rei
V-P.—Carlos Rei
SIC—3559; 3479; 3993; *Metal imprinting, advertising specialties, paint can openers & ladder hooks*
Employs—2; Estab.—1957
Sales—under $500,000
3,000 sq ft site, Distrib.—Intl.
Limited Liability Company

## DEL SOL SIGNS

119 New Jersey Railroad Ave. (07105)
**Phone—(973) 589-8655**
Fax—(973) 589-2885
Email—delsolsigns@verizon.net
Owner—Jose DelSol
SIC—3993; *Interior & exterior signs & vinyl lettering*
Employs—2; Estab.—1968
Sales—under $500,000
Distrib.—Local
Sole ownership

## DELISA PALLET CORP.

91-97 Blanchard St. (07105)
**Phone—(973) 344-8600**
Fax—(973) 344-0689

GEOGRAPHICAL

## Newark—(cont.)

www.delisapallet.com
Email—delisapal8@aol.com
Pres.—John Delisa
Cont., Fin. & MIS Mgr.—James A. Chichelo
SIC—2448; NAICS—321920; *New, used & reconditioned wooden pallets & scrap wood removal*
Employs—15; Estab.—1958
Sales—over $5Mil
Distrib.—Regional
Privately owned corporation

**DELTECH RESIN CO.**
Div. of Deltech Corp.
49 Rutherford St. *(07105)*
**Phone—(973) 589-0880**
(973) 589-3331
New Jersey—(800) 785-4415
Fax—(973) 589-7231
www.deltechcorp.com
Email—danderson@deltechresins.com
Prodn. Mgr.—Haresh Kothari
Opers. Mgr.—Robert Betz
Admn. Mgr.—Pravin Dalal
Tech. Mgr.—Alex Neymark
SIC—2821; NAICS—325211; *Polyurethane dispersions, including acrylic emulsions, oil modified urethanes, short, medium & long oil specialty alkyds, water reducible alkyds & co-polymer emulsions; Brand name—Thibaut; Walker/UR-CRYL Polymer*
Employs—20
Sales—$10Mil-$25Mil
Distrib.—National
Privately owned corporation
Parent co.—Deltech Corp., Baton Rouge, LA
Phone—(225) 775-0150
See Parent Co. Section for full profile.

**DIAMOND HARD CHROMIUM CO., INC.**
463 NJ Railroad Ave. (07114)
**Phone—(973) 824-9412**
Fax—(973) 824-9412
Pres.—Adolf Dobbs
V-P.—Richard Dobbs
SIC—3471; NAICS—332813; *Hard chrome plating*
Employs—2; Estab.—1956
Sales—under $500,000
Distrib.—Local
Privately owned corporation

**DURAAMEN ENGINEERED PRODUCTS, INC.**
457 Frelinghuysen Ave. (07114)
**Phone—(973) 230-1301**
National—(866) 835-6595
Fax—(973) 241-7830
www.duraamen.com
Email—info@duraamen.com
Pres.—Victor Pachade
SIC—2851; *Epoxy & decorative concrete floor coatings, including self-leveling concrete & micro-toppings, self-leveling epoxy coatings, polyurethane concrete flooring systems & concrete sealers*
Employs—10; Estab.—2006
Sales—$2.5Mil-$5Mil (est)
Distrib.—Intl.
Privately owned corporation
Parent co.—Duraamen Engineered Products, Inc., New York, NY
Phone—(212) 386-7609
See Parent Co. Section for full profile.

**DYNAMIC DIE CUTTING & FINISHINGS**
104-110 South St. (07114)
**Phone—(973) 589-8338**
Fax—(973) 589-4123

Email—diecut1@verizon.net
Pres.—Emilio Esteva
V-P.—George Esteva
Treas.—John Esteva
SIC—2675; NAICS—322200; *Paper die cutting*
Employs—10; Estab.—1958
Sales—$900,000
13,000 sq ft site, Distrib.—Local
Limited Liability Company

**DYNA-VEYOR, INC.**
10 Hudson St. (07103)
**Phone—(973) 484-1119**
National—(800) 326-5009
Fax—(973) 484-7790
www.dyna-veyor.com
Email—dynaveyor@aol.com
Pres., CEO—Steve Ayre
V-P.—B. J. Ayre
Off. Admn.—Leslie Ayre
SIC—3535; 3052; 3568; NAICS—333922; *Plastic conveyor chains, belting, sprockets, idlers & related conveyor components for the food processing & product packaging industries*
Employs—18; Estab.—1969
29,000 sq ft site, Distrib.—Intl.
Privately owned corporation

**ELAN CHEMICAL COMPANY, INC.**
268 Doremus Ave. *(07105)*
**Phone—(973) 344-8014**
Fax—(973) 344-1948
www.elan-chemical.com
Email—sales@elan-chemical.com
Pres., CEO—Jocelyn Kapp-Manship
Ex. V-P., COO—Julie Weisman
V-P., CFO—Lou Shragher
Dir., Cust. Serv.—Isabel M. Couto
SIC—2087; 2844; NAICS—311900; *Food flavorings & fragrance ingredients*
Employs—60; Estab.—1968
Sales—$10Mil-$25Mil
15,000 sq ft site, Distrib.—Intl.
Privately owned corporation
Also see: Natural Flavors, Inc., same loc.

**EMPIRE LUMBER & MILLWORK CO.**
377 Frelinghuysen Ave. (07114)
**Phone—(973) 242-2700**
Fax—(973) 242-3970
Email—iraskent@aol.com
Chrm.—Ira Kent
Pres., Millwork Opers.—Charles Shields
Pres.—Wayne Kent
V-P., Sales—Ross Weinick
V-P., Mktg.—Brad Caplan
Secy., Comp.—Arlene Appelbaum
GM & Opers. Mgr.—John Derose
SIC—2431; 2421; 5031; 5072; NAICS—337212; *Architectural millwork, dimension lumber & distributor of metal frames, wooden & metal doors & hardware; Brand name—Pioneer Products; Ceco Steel Products*
Employs—35; Estab.—1948
Sales—$7Mil-$9Mil
60,000 sq ft site, Distrib.—Regional
Privately owned sub-S corp.

**ENGRAVER'S BENCH & GREEK UNIQUE, INC.**
1212 Raymond Blvd. (07102)
**Phone—(973) 297-1810**
Fax—(973) 297-1302
Email—engraversbench@aol.com
Owner & Pres.—Willie J. Williams

SIC—3479; 2796; 2395; 2396; NAICS—323122; *Metal, wood, plastic & glass engraving, sandblasting, embroidery, screen printing, plaques, trophies, sublimation, rubber stamps, seals, business cards, letterheads, stationery & Greek college paraphernalia*
Employs—3; Estab.—1996
Sales—under $500,000
Distrib.—National
Limited Liability Company

**EPOLIN**
358-364 Adams St. (07105)
**Phone—(973) 465-9495**
Fax—(973) 465-5353
www.epolin.com
Email—epolin@epolin.com
CEO—Greg Amato
Hum. Res. & Off. Mgr.—Clarena Pena
SIC—2865; 2869; 2821; NAICS—325100; *Organic, infrared & absorbing dyes; Brand name—Epolight Dyes; Epolight Inks; Spectre Inks; Luminate*
Employs—11; Estab.—1984
Sales—$2Mil-$8Mil
20,000 sq ft site, Distrib.—Intl.
Limited Liability Company

**EVERTILE FLOORING CO., INC.**
127 Frelinghuysen Ave. (07114)
**Phone—(973) 242-7474**
National—(888) 562-5845
Fax—(973) 242-0303
www.locktileusa.com
Email—info@locktileusa.com
Owner & Pres.—Nigel Mandel
Dir., Sales—David Webber
Off. Mgr.—Meryl Kruper
SIC—3996; NAICS—326192; *PVC flooring tiles*
Employs—8; Estab.—1996
Sales—under $500,000
Distrib.—National
Privately owned corporation

**†EXTECH BUILDING MATERIALS, INC.**
Div. of Extech Building Materials
61-89 Ave. K (07105)
**Phone—(973) 274-3340**
Fax—(973) 274-3348
www.extechbuilding.com
Email—info@extechbuilding.com
Pres.—Timothy Feury
Br. Mgr.—Tina Nocera
SIC—5032; 5033; 5085; 5082; *Distributor of brick, stone, construction tools & equipment & roofing*
Employs—50; Estab.—1998
Distrib.—National
Privately owned corporation
Parent co.—Extech Building Materials, Long Island City, NY
Phone—(718) 786-2288
See Parent Co. Section for full profile.

**EXTREME PALLET**
301-317 Astor St. (07114)
**Phone—(973) 596-1400**
Fax—(973) 756-4071
Email—extremepallet@yahoo.com
Pres.—Eddie Sanchez
SIC—2448; NAICS—321920; *Wooden pallets*
Employs—3; Estab.—1990
45,000 sq ft site, Distrib.—Local

**EXTREME PALLET, INC.**
315 Astor St. (07114)
**Phone—(973) 286-1717**
Fax—(973) 756-4071
www.extremepallet.com
Email—extremepallet@yahoo.com
Pres.—Eddie Sanchez

SIC—2448; NAICS—321920; *ISPM 15 certified custom wooden pallets*
Employs—11; Estab.—2004
Sales—$500,000-$1Mil (est)
Distrib.—Local
Privately owned corporation

**FAIRFIELD INDUSTRIES, INC.**
827 N. 6th St. (07107)
**Phone—(973) 483-0100**
National—(800) 207-7265
Fax—(973) 483-5333
www.fairfield-industries.com
Email—dclover@optonline.net
Pres., Plt. Mgr.—Daniel Clover
Off. Mgr.—Joann Clover
SIC—3441; 3321; NAICS—332312; *Pre-cast metal manholes & spill containers*
Employs—20; Estab.—1951
Distrib.—Regional
Privately owned corporation

**FEDERAL BRONZE CASTING INDUSTRIES**
9 Backus St. (07105)
**Phone—(973) 589-7575**
Fax—(973) 589-7078
www.onesourcecc.com
Email—fbci@aol.com
Pres.—Doug Reichard
Off. Mgr.—Irene Pallitto
Shpg. & Rec. Mgr.—Carla Rodriguez
SIC—3366; 2499; NAICS—331525; *Brass, bronze & aluminum castings & wood patterns*
Employs—42; Estab.—1945
30,000 sq ft site, Distrib.—Regional
Privately owned sub-S corp.

**FIRMENICH, INC.**
150 Firmenich Way *(07114-3124)*
**Phone—(973) 589-3443**
www.firmenich.com
Email—ron.kurtz@firmenich.com
Dir., Chem. Mfg.—Claudio Barbosa
Health, Safety & Env. Mgr.—Ron Kurtz
SIC—2869; NAICS—325600; *Encapsulated flavors for the beverages & savory & sweet foods industries & ingredients for the fine fragrance, body care & home care industries*
Employs—185; Estab.—1985
Sales—$50Mil-$100Mil
Distrib.—Intl.
Privately owned corporation
AKA: Chem Fleur
Parent co.—Firmenich, Inc., Plainsboro, NJ
Phone—(609) 452-1000
See Parent Co. Section for full profile.

**FLEXCRAFT INDUSTRIES, INC.**
390 Adams St., P.O. Box 2098 (07114)
**Phone—(973) 589-3403**
Fax—(973) 589-0015
Email—info@flexcraftindustries.com
Pres.—Bruce Machlader
Off. Mgr.—Heidi Bello
SIC—2891; NAICS—325520; *Electronic packaging sealants*
Employs—15; Estab.—1930
Sales—$500,000-$1Mil
Distrib.—Intl.
Privately owned corporation

**FLEXON INDUSTRIES CORP.**
1 Flexon Plz. (07114)
**Phone—(973) 824-5530**
National—(800) 327-4673
Fax—(973) 824-1208
www.flexonhose.com
Email—drauch@flexonhose.com
CEO—Alex Folkman
Pres.—David Rauch
Cont.—Henry Rosenbaum

## Newark—(cont.)

Plt. Mgr.—Tony Ruiz
SIC—3052; NAICS—326220;
*Garden hoses*
Employs—100; Estab.—1978
320,000 sq ft site, Distrib.—Intl.
Privately owned corporation
Also see: U. S. Wire & Cable, Inc.,
33 Queen St. loc.
AKA: US Wire & Cable

**FOREM PACKAGING, INC.**
2-44 Cornelia St., P.O. Box 50090
(07105)
**Phone—(973) 589-0402**
Fax—(973) 589-0453
Email—sales@forempackaging.com
V-P., GM—Howard N. Slade
Off. Mgr.—Maronda Pierce
Asst. Mgr.—Julisa Rosario
SIC—3089; NAICS—323100;
*Flexible packaging materials*
Employs—18; Estab.—1988
Sales—over $8.5Mil
Distrib.—Intl.
Privately owned corporation

**FORM CUT INDUSTRIES, INC.**
197 Mount Pleasant Ave. (07104)
**Phone—(973) 483-5154**
Fax—(973) 483-4512
www.formcut.com
Email—info@formcut.com
Pres.—Charles Alberto
Ex. V-P., Comp.—Steve Alberto
V-P., Mfg. & Plt.—John Frey
Corp. Secy.—Joan Alberto
GM—Ken De Graaf
MIS Mgr.—Bruce Ballard
Pur. Agt.—Isa Mancini
SIC—3451; 3452; 3965; NAICS—
332721; *Precision wire forms,
leads, pins, Swiss screw
machine & cold headed
products*
Employs—50; Estab.—1963
Sales—$5Mil-$10Mil
33,000 sq ft site, Distrib.—Intl.
Privately owned corporation

**†FREEDOM METALS, LLC**
960 Frelinghuysen Ave. (07114)
**Phone—(973) 242-2119**
Fax—(973) 242-2407
Email—freedommetal1@aol.com
Ptnr.—Peter Bartolomeo
Ptnr.—Roger Vroom
SIC—5093; *Wholesaler of
nonferrous scrap metals*
Employs—5; Estab.—2005
Distrib.—Local
Limited Liability Company

**G.J. CHEMICAL CO., INC.**
128 Doremus Ave. (07105)
**Phone—(973) 589-4176**
Fax—(973) 589-3072
www.gjchemical.com
Email—customerservice@
gjchemical.com
Pres.—Diana Colonna
Off. Mgr.—Sonia Lannitelli
SIC—2869; 2819; *Laboratory
chemicals*
Employs—25; Estab.—1974
Sales—$5Mil-$10Mil (est)
Distrib.—Local
Privately owned corporation
Parent co.—G.J. Chemical Co.,
Inc., Somerset, NJ
Phone—(973) 589-1450
See Parent Co. Section for full profile.

**GAMBERT SHIRTS, LLC, L.**
61 Freeman St., 5th Fl. (07105)
**Phone—(973) 344-3440**
Fax—(973) 344-3441
www.gambertshirts.com
Email—mitchg@gambertshirts.com
Owner & Pres.—Lorraine Gambert
COO—Mel Gambert
Opers. Mgr.—Jamie Anderson
Opers. Supv.—Mitch Gambert

SIC—2321; 2331; NAICS—
315200; *Custom & private label
ready-to-wear woven shirts for
men & women*
Employs—90; Estab.—1994
Sales—$6Mil-$10Mil
16,000 sq ft site, Distrib.—National
Limited Liability Company

**GANN LAW BOOKS, INC.**
1 Washington Pk., Ste. 1300
(07102)
**Phone—(973) 268-1200**
Fax—(973) 268-1330
www.gannlaw.com
Pres.—Michael Protzel
Cust. Serv. Rep.—R. Connly
SIC—2731; *Law book publishing*
Employs—19
Sales—$1Mil-$2.5Mil (est)
Distrib.—Local
Privately owned corporation

**†GEORGE A. MATHEWSON CO.**
9-11 Foundry St. (07105)
**Phone—(973) 344-0081**
Fax—(973) 344-8376
Email—dave.gam@verizon.net
Pres.—Dave Czachur
V-P.—Stan Pearson
SIC—5051; 5084; *Wholesaler of
bearings & power transmission
equipment*
Employs—2; Estab.—1948
Sales—$300,000-$500,000
2,500 sq ft site, Distrib.—Local
Privately owned corporation

**GE-RO DESK CO.**
334 N. 5th St. (07107)
**Phone—(973) 485-0505**
Fax—(973) 485-9003
Owner—Rolf J. Hoppe
SIC—2521; *Wooden office
furniture*
Employs—9; Estab.—1968
12,500 sq ft site, Distrib.—
Regional
Privately owned corporation
AKA: R J Hoppe Store
Construction

**GLASSROOTS, INC.**
10 Bleeker St. (07102)
**Phone—(973) 353-9555**
Fax—(973) 353-9551
www.glassroots.org
Dir., Hum. Res.—Katie Witzig
Prog. Dir.—Jenny Pollack
SIC—3961; 3915; 3231; 3253;
*Glass jewelry, beadmaking &
mosaics*
Employs—20; Estab.—2001
Sales—$1Mil-$2.5Mil (est)
Distrib.—Local
Privately owned corporation

**GLOBE PLATING, INC.**
220 Miller St. (07114)
**Phone—(973) 623-1116**
Fax—(973) 623-8870
Email—globeplating@gmail.com
Pres.—Michael Maykish
SIC—3471; 3479; NAICS—
332813; *Metal finishing & plating*
Employs—6; Estab.—1991
Sales—$500,000-$1Mil
16,000 sq ft site, Distrib.—Local
Sole ownership

**GLORIN PRINTING, INC.**
258 Clifton Ave. (07104)
**Phone—(973) 481-3233**
Fax—(973) 481-6807
Email—glorin@optonline.net
Pres., Hum. Res. & IT Mgr.—Irving
Linares
SIC—2759; 2791; NAICS—
323122; *Commercial printing &
electronic prepress*
Employs—3; Estab.—1977
Sales—under $500,000
Distrib.—Local
Privately owned corporation

**GOLDEN PLATTER FOODS, INC.**
37 Tompkins Point Rd. (07114)
**Phone—(973) 242-0290**
Fax—(973) 465-7580
www.goldenplatter.com
Email—goldenplatterfoods@
hotmail.com
V-P.—Scott Bennett
GM—Lee Barr
Bookkeeper—Twang Nguyen
SIC—2015; 2011; NAICS—311611;
*Poultry & meat processing*
Employs—40; Estab.—1987
Sales—$5Mil-$10Mil (est)
Distrib.—Intl.
Privately owned corporation

**GRAMMER, DEMPSEY & HUDSON
CO.**
212 Rome St. (07105)
Mail addr: P.O. Box 1059, Newark
(07101)
**Phone—(973) 589-8000**
Fax—(973) 589-2551
Email—jhudson.gdh@yahoo.com
Pres.—James Hudson
Ex. V-P.—Morgan Hudson
GM—Nick Demidon
Hum. Res. & IT Mgr.—Jack Jaquin
SIC—3312; 3599; 5051; *Carbon,
alloy, stainless & tool bar & plate
steels, including cast iron, drill
rod & flat ground stock*
Employs—8; Estab.—1960
2,100 sq ft site, Distrib.—Regional
Privately owned corporation

**GRAVER TECHNOLOGIES, LLC**
72 Lockwood St. (07105)
**Phone—(973) 690-5290**
National—(800) 533-6623
Fax—(973) 690-5808
www.gravertech.com
Email—info@gravertech.com
Dir., Opers. & Plt. Mgr.—Jim
Sheridan
Prodn. Mgr.—John Almeida
Mktg. & Tech. Mgr.—Al Tavares
SIC—2821; 2899; NAICS—
325211; *Ion exchange resins &
water treatment chemicals*
Employs—40; Estab.—1946
Sales—$6Mil-$10Mil
55,000 sq ft site, Distrib.—Intl.
Privately owned corporation
Parent co.—Graver Technologies,
LLC, Newark, DE
Phone—(302) 731-1700
See Parent Co. Section for full profile.

**GREAT AMERICAN VEAL CO., INC.**
50 Avenue L, Ste. 5 (07105-3841)
**Phone—(973) 589-6363**
Fax—(973) 589-1188
Email—gafoods@optonline.net
Pres.—Zarko Grgas
Plt. Mgr.—Lisa Velasquez
Off. Mgr.—Tatiana Ramos
Bookkeeper—Joe Montefusco
SIC—2011; 2013; 2015; *Meat
processing, including veal rib
chops, racks & loins & beef &
poultry patties, sausages &
meatballs*
Employs—50; Estab.—1981
Sales—$6Mil-$10Mil
Distrib.—Intl.
Privately owned corporation

**GREEN & SON, INC., CHARLES E.**
625 3rd St. (07107)
Mail addr: P.O. Box 8277, Glen
Ridge (07028)
**Phone—(973) 485-3630**
Fax—(973) 485-6510
www.charlesegreen.com
Email—sales@charlesegreen.com
Pres.—John V. Green III
V-P.—Rebecca Green Sullivan
Off. Mgr.—Kaitlin Green
Prod. Mgr.—Lenny Fishman

SIC—3991; NAICS—339994;
*Metal paint brush ferrules & paint
rollers, including wire forming &
metal stampings for the paint
brush industry*
Employs—40; Estab.—1876
80,000 sq ft site, Distrib.—Intl.
Privately owned corporation

**GREGORY PACKAGING, INC.**
247 Rome St., P.O. Box 5188
(07105)
**Phone—(973) 465-1113**
Fax—(973) 465-7307
www.suncupjuice.com
Pres.—Ed Gregory
Cont.—Jeffrey Marcus
Hum. Res. Mgr.—Roseanne
Gorski
SIC—2033; NAICS—311421;
*Juice packaging*
Employs—49
Sales—$10Mil-$25Mil (est)
Privately owned corporation

**GREWE PLASTICS, INC.**
123 S. 15th St. (07107)
**Phone—(973) 485-7602**
Fax—(973) 485-7650
www.greweco.com
Email—greweco@gmail.com
Dir., Sales & Mktg.—Allen Blum
IT Mgr.—Susan Blum
Off. Mgr.—Judy Schwartz
SIC—3089; *Plastic fabrication*
Employs—10; Estab.—1947
Sales—$1Mil-$2.5Mil
Distrib.—Intl.
Privately owned corporation

**†GTS-WELCO**
425 Avenue P (07105)
**Phone—(973) 589-7895**
National—(877) 935-2624
Fax—(973) 589-0427
www.gts-welco.com
Email—info@gts-welco.com
Chrm. of the Board—Robert
D'Alessandro
V-P., Sales & Mktg.—Michael
Finley
Hum. Res. Mgr.—Christina
Thacther
SIC—5084; 5085; *Wholesaler of
welding equipment & supplies,
including gases*
Employs—100; Estab.—1990
Distrib.—National
Privately owned corporation
Parent co.—GTS-Welco,
Allentown, PA
Phone—(610) 398-2211
See Parent Co. Section for full profile.

**GUARDIAN FENCE CO., INC.**
180 Wright St., P.O. Box 2009
(07114)
**Phone—(973) 824-1850**
National—(866) 836-3367
Fax—(973) 824-5862
Email—info@guardianfence.com
Pres.—Nancy Maccarelli
GM—J. A. Feldman
Bookkeeper—Joseph Carmevali
SIC—3496; 2499; 3089; *Chain-
link, wooden & vinyl fencing &
highway guide rails*
Employs—20; Estab.—1953
40,000 sq ft site, Distrib.—National
Privately owned sub-S corp.

**GUARDRITE STEEL DOOR CORP.**
81 Springdale Ave. (07107)
**Phone—(973) 481-4424**
Fax—(973) 482-5347
www.guardritedoor.com
Pres.—William Santana
SIC—3442; NAICS—332321;
*Rolling steel doors & gates*
Employs—5; Estab.—1985
Sales—$500,000-$1Mil
29,000 sq ft site, Distrib.—Intl.
Privately owned corporation

GEOGRAPHICAL

# Newark—(cont.)

**†H & C METALS, INC.**
91 Malvern St., P.O. Box 5150
(07105)
**Phone—(973) 589-7778**
Fax—(973) 589-5879
Pres.—Frank Colantuono
SIC—5093; *Wholesaler of scrap metal*
Employs—15; Estab.—1978
Distrib.—Local
Privately owned corporation

**HAENSSLER SHEET METAL WORKS, INC.**
592 Hawthorne Ave. (07112)
**Phone—(973) 373-6360**
Fax—(973) 373-6022
www.haensslersm.com
Email—w.haenssler@
haensslersm.com
Pres.—Wendy Haenssler
V-P.—Richard Haenssler
SIC—3444; *Custom sheet metal & stainless steel fabricated products*
Employs—12; Estab.—1957
Sales—$1Mil-$2.5Mil
Distrib.—Regional
Privately owned corporation

**HAL-O MFG. CO.**
137 Meeker Ave. (07114)
**Phone—(973) 824-6122**
Fax—(973) 824-4047
www.halochain.com
Email—hal@halochain.com
Pres.—Harold Roth
V-P.—Cornelis Brokling
Fin. Mgr.—Lois E. Roth
SIC—3646; 3462; NAICS—335122; *Lighting components & chains*
Employs—13; Estab.—1990
Sales—$1Mil-$5Mil
20,000 sq ft site, Distrib.—Intl.
Privately owned sub-S corp.

**HANDY STORE FIXTURES, INC.**
337 Sherman Ave. (07114)
**Phone—(973) 242-1600**
National—(800) 631-4280
Fax—(973) 642-6222
www.handystorefixtures.com
Email—sales@
handystorefixtures.com
Pres.—Paul Kurland
V-P.—Richard Kurland
V-P.—Joe O'Brien
SIC—2542; *Steel shelving*
Employs—100; Estab.—1960
Distrib.—Intl.
Privately owned corporation

**HEADWEAR CREATIONS, INC.**
200 Wright St. (07114)
**Phone—(973) 622-1144**
Fax—(973) 622-4309
www.headwearcreations.com
Email—headwearcreations@
aol.com
Pres.—Ruben Spitz
SIC—2353; *Casual hats & caps for men & women*
Employs—45; Estab.—1960
Distrib.—National
Privately owned corporation

**HERAEUS PRECIOUS METALS NORTH AMERICA, LLC**
Div. of Heraeus, Inc.
65 Euclid Ave. *(07105)*
**Phone—(973) 817-7878**
Fax—(973) 578-2786
www.heraeus.com
Email—refiningnj@heraeus.com
V-P. & Site Mgr.—Alan Semko
SIC—3339; NAICS—331419; *Precious metal refining & trading*
Employs—23; Estab.—1851
Sales—$10Mil-$100Mil
10,000 sq ft site, Distrib.—Intl.
Privately owned corporation
Parent co.—Heraeus, Inc., New York, NY
Phone—(212) 752-2705
See Parent Co. Section for full profile.

**†HIGH BRIDGE STONE CO., INC.**
187 Marsh St. (07114)
**Phone—(973) 344-5522**
www.highbridgestoneco.com
Email—info@
highbridgestoneco.com
Chrm.—John Bitow
CFO—Greg Marshall
SIC—5032; *Wholesaler of Indian Belgian block granite*
Employs—10; Estab.—1980
Sales—$1Mil-$2.5Mil
Distrib.—Regional
Privately owned corporation

**HILIN LIFE PRODUCTS, INC.**
211 Warren St., Ste. 211 *(07103)*
**Phone—(973) 648-0265**
National—(877) 456-6943
Fax—(973) 648-0267
www.knowhen.com
Email—info@hilinlife.com
CEO—Helen Denise
SIC—2835; *Fertility management test kits; Brand name—KNOWHEN™ Saliva Fertility Monitor & Educational Kit*
Employs—6; Estab.—2009
Sales—$1Mil-$2.5Mil (est)
Distrib.—Intl.
Privately owned corporation

**HOLBY VALVE, INC.**
24 Ferdon St. (07105)
**Phone—(973) 465-7400**
Fax—(973) 465-7475
www.holby.com
Email—sales@holby.com
V-P.—Thomas Lentine
SIC—3494; 3492; NAICS—332900; *1/2-inch to 4-inch thermostatic mixing valves for tempering domestic hot water; Brand name—Holby Tempering Valve*
Employs—10; Estab.—1930
6,000 sq ft site, Distrib.—National
Sole ownership

**HOPPE CO., INC., R. J.**
340 N. 5th St. (07107)
**Phone—(973) 485-5665**
National—(800) 530-1280
Fax—(973) 485-9003
www.rjhoppeinc.com
Email—ge-rodesk@att.net
Pres.—Rolf B. Hoppe, Jr.
SIC—2521; NAICS—337211; *Wooden office furniture, specialty desks & command centers*
Employs—10; Estab.—1968
Sales—$1Mil-$2.5Mil
12,500 sq ft site, Distrib.—National
Privately owned corporation
AKA: Gero Desk

**HUDSON DISPLAY CORP.**
831 Frelinghuysen Ave. (07114)
**Phone—(973) 623-8255**
Fax—(973) 623-8332
Email—contact@
hudsondisplays.com
Pres.—Maggie Marin
SIC—2542; *Plastic display fixtures*
Employs—4; Estab.—1993
Sales—under $500,000
Distrib.—Local
Privately owned corporation

**INDUSTRIAL HARD CHROMIUM CO.**
7 Rome St. (07105)
**Phone—(973) 344-2265**
Fax—(973) 344-2812
www.ihcco.com
Email—craig@ihcco.com
V-P.—Craig Foote
V-P., Cont.—Nancy Lanzalotto
SIC—3471; NAICS—332813; *Chrome plating*
Employs—16; Estab.—1992
Sales—$1Mil-$2.5Mil (est)
Distrib.—Local

**INDUSTRIAL WELDING CO.**
655 Ferry St. (07105)
**Phone—(973) 589-3100**
Fax—(973) 589-2449
Email—industrial_welding@
hotmail.com
Pres.—Brian Hollfelder
Acctg. Mgr.—Silvana Enriquez
SIC—3499; 3599; *Metal fabrication & welding job shop*
Employs—6; Estab.—1987
Sales—$500,000-$1Mil
10,000 sq ft site, Distrib.—Local
Privately owned corporation

**INERGETICS, INC.**
550 Broad St., 12th Fl. (07102)
**Phone—(908) 604-2500**
National—(888) 412-9179
Fax—(908) 604-2545
www.inergetics.com
Email—info@inergetics.com
Opers. Mgr.—Sherman Fan
SIC—2023; 2834; NAICS—325412; *Nutritional drink mixes for cancer patients*
Employs—10; Estab.—2000
Sales—$1Mil-$2.5Mil
Distrib.—National
Publicly owned corporation

**INNOVATIVE RESIN SYSTEMS, INC.**
257 Wilson Ave. *(07105)*
**Phone—(973) 465-6887**
Fax—(973) 465-0592
www.rez-cure.com
Email—info@rez-cure.com
Pres.—Pinakin Patel
Sales Mgr.—Manny Nerantzoulis
Opers. Mgr.—Sachin Patel
SIC—2891; 2821; 3089; NAICS—325520; *Custom epoxy, polyurethane & acrylic structural adhesives, coatings, pottings & encapsulating compounds; Brand name—Rez-Cure; UV-Cure; Acrylic-Cure; Poly-Cure*
Employs—15; Estab.—1997
Sales—$5Mil-$10Mil
30,000 sq ft site, Distrib.—Intl.
Privately owned corporation
ISO rating—9001

**INTERNATIONAL COMPRESSOR CO., INC.**
361 Jelliff Ave. (07108)
Mail addr: P.O. Box 42, Mountain Lakes (07046-0042)
**Phone—(973) 824-7170**
Fax—(973) 824-5575
Email—sales@
intlcompressorco.com
Pres.—Clarence Wilson
Manager—Val Ray
SIC—3563; 5063; 5084; NAICS—333912; *Rebuilt air compressors & distributor of new air compressors & parts, compressed air system components & new electric motors & motor starters; Brand name—Curtis Toledo; Saylor-Beall; Marathon Electric Motors; Square D; Rustoleum Paint; Manchester Tank; Baldor; Maska-V-Belts & Sheaves; Conrader Values*
Employs—7; Estab.—1983
Sales—$2.5Mil-$5Mil
20,000 sq ft site, Distrib.—National
Privately owned corporation

**IRON BOUND METAL, INC.**
238 Emmet St. (07114)
**Phone—(973) 242-5704**
Fax—(973) 242-0928
www.ironboundmetalinc.com
Email—info@
ironboundmetalinc.com
Pres.—John Olaya
Off. Mgr.—Jill Clementi
SIC—3599; 3499; *General machining & fabrication job shop*
Employs—5; Estab.—1997
Sales—under $500,000
10,000 sq ft site, Distrib.—Local
Privately owned corporation

**IRONBOUND TROPHY CENTER**
289 Lafayette St., Ste. A (07105-2132)
**Phone—(973) 344-3872**
Fax—(973) 344-6989
www.ironboundtrophycenter.com
Email—rob@
ironboundtrophycenter.com
Owner—Christine Naia
GM—Robert Naia
Manager—Jon Dasilva
SIC—3499; 2499; 3089; 3479; *Trophies & plaques & acrylics, corporate gifts, clocks, nameplates, medals, neck ribbons & engraving*
Employs—3; Estab.—1962
Sales—under $500,000
1,500 sq ft site, Distrib.—Local
Sole ownership

**IRONBOUND WELDING, INC.**
156 Walnut St. (07105)
**Phone—(973) 589-3128**
Fax—(973) 589-1183
Email—iflamecutting@optimum.net
Pres.—Louis Tamasco
Sales Mgr.—Joseph Aulisi
SIC—3599; *Welding job shop*
Employs—2; Estab.—1958
Sales—under $500,000
Distrib.—Local
Privately owned corporation

**ISPEECH**
211 Warren St. (07103)
**Phone—(917) 338-7723**
www.ispeech.org
Email—info@ispeech.org
Founder & CEO—Heath Ahrens
V-P., Opers.—Vanessa Rose
SIC—7372; *Speech recognition software development for mobile & web applications*
Employs—30; Estab.—2007
Distrib.—Intl.
Privately owned corporation
DBA: iSpeech.org

**J T D SALES, LLC (H Q)**
71 Bloomfield Ave. (07104)
**Phone—(973) 482-5070**
National—(800) 445-6601
Fax—(973) 482-0725
www.fleetwoodequipment.com
Email—mike@skyfoods.us
Pres., CEO—Michael Fortanascio
Opers. Mgr.—Joe Miano
Off. Mgr.—Virginia Lowensten

## Newark—(cont.)

SIC—3556; NAICS—333294;
*Company headquarters; meat
slicing & grinding machines
(mfg. done overseas)*
Employs—5; Estab.—1923
Sales—$500,000-$1Mil
Distrib.—National
Limited Liability Company

**†J.D. BEVERAGE CO.**
10 Richards St. (07105)
**Phone—(973) 344-8149**
Fax—(973) 589-8981
Email—lapbeer@optonline.net
Pres.—Joe D'Orazio
V-P.—James D'Orazio
SIC—5149; *Wholesaler of
nonalcoholic beverages*
Employs—12; Estab.—1972
Sales—$2Mil
Distrib.—Local
Privately owned corporation

**JADE APPAREL, INC.**
133 Kossuth St. (07105)
**Phone—(973) 522-1003**
Fax—(973) 522-1155
www.jadeapparelinc.com
Email—sales@jadeapparelinc.com
Pres.—Teddy Maroulis
Cont.—Ajay Watts
Payroll Supv.—Maria Xavier
SIC—2389; NAICS—332710;
*Contract manufacturing for the
apparel industry, including
sample & pattern making,
cutting, fusing, sewing,
embroidery, hangtag & label
application & packaging*
Employs—400; Estab.—1982
Sales—$50Mil-$100Mil (est)
Distrib.—Regional
Privately owned corporation

**JARCHEM INDUSTRIES, INC.**
414 Wilson Ave. (07105)
**Phone—(973) 344-0600**
Fax—(973) 344-5743
www.jarchem.com
Email—info@jarchem.com
V-P., Sales & Mktg.—Dennis Boyd
Cont.—David Honig
Mng. Dir.—Art Hein
Dir., Operation—Joe Rotunno
Sales Mgr., Personal Care—David
Humphrey
Sales Mgr., Acetates—Rich
Germain
Acctg. Mgr. & ISO Internal
Auditor—Mary Ellen Fitzgerald
Technical Sales Specialist—
Brendon Bohnert
SIC—2869; 2819; 2843; *Acetate
salts, specialty branched &
unsaturated alcohols, branched
acids, acrylamide, acrylate &
pyrrolidone monomers, poly-vinyl
pyrrolidone polymers, alkyl
polyglucosides, sarcosinates,
specialty butters/oils &
surfactants; Brand name—
JarCal; Jarcol; Jarplex;
Jarfactant; JarGrip; JarTherm;
Jarpol; Jaric; Aminosyl;
Sucranov; Jarxotic*
Employs—50; Estab.—1978
Sales—$20Mil-$30Mil
50,000 sq ft site, Distrib.—Intl.
Privately owned sub-S corp.
ISO rating—9001:2008

NEW ENTRY
**JEFFERSON PRINTING SERVICE**
184 Jefferson St. (07105)
**Phone—(973) 491-0019**
Fax—(973) 491-0032
www.jeffersonprint.com
Pres.—Julio DePaula

SIC—2759; 3993; *Commercial
printing, signage & vehicle
wraps*
Employs—10
Sales—$1Mil-$2.5Mil (est)

**JERSEY STEEL DOORS, INC.**
95 N. 11th St. (07107)
**Phone—(973) 482-4020**
Fax—(973) 482-1148
www.jerseysteeldoors.com
Email—info@jerseysteeldoors.com
Pres.—Roland Gonzalez
SIC—3442; NAICS—332321;
*Steel overhead rolling doors*
Employs—10; Estab.—1986
Sales—$1Mil-$2.5Mil
Distrib.—Regional
Sole ownership

**JERSEY WINDOWS & BUILDING
SUPPLIES**
831 Broadway (07104)
**Phone—(973) 482-3614**
National—(888) 353-7739
Fax—(973) 482-3992
www.jerseywindowfactory.com
Store Mgr.—Will Zapata
SIC—3089; 3444; *Vinyl &
aluminum windows & vinyl siding
for commercial & residential
applications*
Employs—2; Estab.—1999
Sales—under $500,000
Distrib.—Local
Privately owned corporation

**JOC GROUP, INC.**
2 Penn Plz. E., 12th Fl. (07105)
**Phone—(973) 776-8660**
National—(800) 952-3839
www.joc.com
Email—cbrooks@joc.com
CEO—Gavin Carter
V-P., Hum. Res.—Cindy Mevorah
V-P., Directory Group—Amy
Middlebrook
Sr. Editor—Peter Leach
Sr. Editor—Joseph Bonney
Sr. Editor—William B. Cassidy
Ex. Editor—Chris Brooks
Mng. Editor—Barbara Wyker
Research Editor—Marsha
Salisbury
SIC—2721; *Corporate
headquarters & magazine
publishing; Brand name—
Breakbulk; Journal of Commerce*
Employs—120
Sales—$10Mil-$25Mil (est)
Privately owned corporation

**JOEY'S FINE FOODS, INC.**
135 Manchester Pl. (07104)
**Phone—(973) 482-1400**
Fax—(973) 482-1597
www.joeysfinefoods.com
Email—sales@joeysfinefoods.com
Pres.—Joseph Aihini
V-P.—Ed Scoppa
SIC—2051; 2052; NAICS—
311812; *Cakes, cookies &
pastries*
Employs—60; Estab.—1984
35,000 sq ft site, Distrib.—National
Privately owned corporation

NEW ENTRY
**JUST NATION, LLC**
359 Central Ave. (07103)
**Phone—(973) 485-5878**
Fax—(973) 485-5335
www.justnationllc.com
Email—info@justnationllc.com
Owner—S. Crespo
SIC—2448; *Wooden pallets*
Employs—4
Sales—under $500,000 (est)
Distrib.—Local
Limited Liability Company

**†K C S METAL PRODUCTS, INC.**
415 Ferry St. (07105)
**Phone—(973) 578-2688**
National—(866) 533-2688
Fax—(973) 578-2788
Email—kcsmetal@hotmail.com
Pres.—Carmen Khuu
SIC—5046; *Wholesaler of wire
shelving*
Employs—5; Estab.—2005
Sales—$500,000-$1Mil
Distrib.—National
Privately owned corporation

**KAMPACK, INC.**
Div. of KapStone Paper And
Packaging Corp.
100 Frontage Rd. (07114)
**Phone—(973) 589-7400**
National—(800) 766-3812
Fax—(973) 465-6851
www.kampackinc.com
Email—contactus@
kampackinc.com
CEO—Karen Mehiel
V-P., Fin.—Randy Baer
Dir., Hum. Res.—Jackie Simmons
SIC—2653; NAICS—322211;
*Corporate headquarters &
corrugated boxes*
Employs—125; Estab.—1959
Sales—$40Mil-$60Mil
185,000 sq ft site, Distrib.—Local
Publicly owned corporation
Parent co.—KapStone Paper And
Packaging Corp., Northbrook, IL
Phone—(847) 239-8800
See Parent Co. Section for full profile.

**KEARNY STEEL CONTAINER CORP.**
401 South St. (07105)
**Phone—(973) 589-2070**
Fax—(973) 589-1770
www.kearnysteel.com
Email—ksc401@aol.com
Pres.—Michael Verzaleno
V-P.—Michael Verzaleno, Jr.
Plt. Mgr.—William Gegan
Opers. Mgr.—George Sheridan
Hum. Res. & Off. Mgr.—Susan
Carrano
Health & Safety Mgr.—Craig
Goodman
Maint. Engr.—Paul Adamson
Env. Consultant—Jerry Pica
Dispatcher—Andrew DeStefano
SIC—3412; 2655; 3089; NAICS—
332439; *Reconditioned & new
steel, fiber & plastic containers,
container disposal & destruction
& plastic regrind*
Employs—75; Estab.—1951
Sales—$8Mil-$10Mil
Distrib.—Intl.
Privately owned sub-S corp.

**†KEITH INDUSTRIES, INC.**
248 Astor St. (07114)
**Phone—(973) 642-3332**
Fax—(973) 733-9453
www.keithindustries.com
Email—sales@keithindustries.com
Pres.—Jay Weiss
CFO—Charlotte Williams
V-P., Sales—Lee Ross
SIC—5085; *Distributor of plastic,
steel & fibre drums, pails, cans &
totes*
Employs—50; Estab.—1961
Sales—$5Mil-$10Mil
Distrib.—National
Publicly owned corporation

**KEYSTONE FOLDING BOX CO., INC.**
367 Verona Ave. (07104)
**Phone—(973) 483-1054**
Fax—(973) 483-5853
www.keyboxco.com
Email—sales@keyboxco.com
Pres.—Wade E. Hartman

SIC—2657; NAICS—322212;
*Folding paperboard boxes &
child resistant blister cards*
Employs—65; Estab.—1908
Sales—$1Mil-$2.5Mil
80,000 sq ft site, Distrib.—Intl.
Privately owned corporation

NEW ENTRY
**KRAFTAPE PRINTERS, INC.**
124 Orchard St. (07102)
**Phone—(973) 824-3005**
Fax—(973) 824-3364
www.kraftape.com
V-P.—Robert Hirtler
Off. Mgr.—Luv Acosta
SIC—2759; *Commercial printing,
including sealing tapes for boxes*
Employs—6; Estab.—1989
Sales—$500,000-$1Mil (est)
Distrib.—National
Privately owned corporation

**L M C PRECISION, INC.**
91 Rome St., Ste. 93 (07105)
**Phone—(973) 522-0005**
Fax—(973) 522-0007
Pres.—Manuel Lobo
V-P.—Jose Cruz
Opers. Mgr.—Carla Lobo
SIC—3599; *CNC machining job
shop*
Employs—12; Estab.—1999
Sales—$1Mil-$2.5Mil
Distrib.—Local
Privately owned sub-S corp.

**LEATHER HANDLE MFG. CO.**
44 Dickerson St. (07103)
**Phone—(973) 485-2866**
Fax—(973) 485-2037
Email—leatherhandle@aol.com
Pres.—Walter Robak
Bookkeeper—Irene Robak
SIC—3199; NAICS—316999;
*Leather handles*
Employs—7; Estab.—1960
Sales—$500,000-$1Mil
4,000 sq ft site, Distrib.—National
Privately owned corporation

**LIBERTY MECHANICAL
CONTRACTORS, INC.**
330 Raymond Blvd. (07105)
**Phone—(973) 344-6131**
Fax—(973) 344-7307
www.liberty-contractors.com
Email—rroberti@liberty-
mechanical.com
Pres., CFO—Frank P. Zurica
Off. Mgr.—Elizabeth M. Grasso
Bus. Dev. Mgr.—Robert Roberti
SIC—3599; 3441; 3498; NAICS—
332312; *Welding job shop &
industrial mechanical contractor,
including welded & threaded
piping, conveyor line, boiler &
chiller installation & steel
fabrication services*
Employs—25; Estab.—1973
Sales—$6Mil-$10Mil
6,000 sq ft site, Distrib.—Regional
Privately owned sub-S corp.

**LOPES CO.**
304 Walnut St. (07105)
**Phone—(973) 344-3063**
Fax—(973) 344-8048
Pres.—Hermino Lopes
SIC—2013; NAICS—311600;
*Sausage*
Employs—4; Estab.—1967
Sales—under $500,000
Distrib.—Regional
Privately owned corporation

**LOUIS IRON WORKS**
218 Lackawanna Ave. (07103)
**Phone—(973) 624-2700**
Fax—(973) 624-0706
Email—louisironworkinc@aol.com
Pres.—Louis Velasco

GEOGRAPHICAL

# Newark—(cont.)

SIC—3446; NAICS—332323; *Ornamental ironwork, including gates, fire escapes & window bars*
Employs—2; Estab.—2006
Sales—under $500,000 (est)
Distrib.—Regional
Privately owned corporation

## LUBRIPLATE LUBRICANTS CO.

129 Lockwood St. *(07105)*
**Phone—(973) 589-9150**
(800) 733-4755
Fax—(973) 589-4432
www.lubriplate.com
Email—info@lubriplate.com
Pres., CEO—Richard McCluskey
V.-P., CFO—Michael McCluskey
V.-P., CMO—James Girard III
Ex. V.-P., Secy.—Robert A. Reh, Sr.
V.-P., Sales—Steve Morrow
Dir., IT—Dan Moroses
SIC—2911; 2992; NAICS—324110; *Company headquarters & industrial lubricants & oils; Brand name—Lubriplate®; Fiske*
Employs—20; Estab.—1870
37,000 sq ft site, Distrib.—Intl.
Privately owned corporation
ISO rating—9001

## LUSO MACHINE, INC.

29 Avenue C (07114)
**Phone—(973) 242-1717**
Fax—(973) 242-1728
www.lusomachine.com
Email—quotes@lusomachine.com
Pres.—Adriano Remelgado
V.-P.—Sergio Remelgado
Manager—Filipe S. Remelgado
Manager—Harold Smith
SIC—3599; *Machine parts*
Employs—8; Estab.—1998
Sales—$2.6Mil-$5Mil
Distrib.—National
Privately owned corporation

## LUSO-AMERICANO CO., INC.

88 Ferry St. (07105)
**Phone—(973) 589-4600**
Fax—(973) 344-4201
www.lusoamericano.com
Email—lpires@lusoamericano.com
Pres.—Tony Matinho
Editor—Luis Pires
Dir., Opers.—Paul Matinho
SIC—2711; *Newspaper publishing*
Employs—16; Estab.—1928
Sales—$500,000-$1Mil (est)
Distrib.—National
Privately owned corporation

## LYONDELLBASELL INDUSTRIES

300 Doremus Ave. (07105)
**Phone—(973) 578-2200**
Fax—(973) 578-2235
www.lyb.com
Email—info@lyondellbasell.com
Site Mgr.—Jim Hilliard
Accountant—Annalynn Zak
SIC—2869; *Industrial ethanol products*
Employs—6
2,600 sq ft site, Distrib.—National
Publicly owned corporation
Parent co.—LyondellBasell Industries, Houston, TX
Phone—(713) 652-7200
See Parent Co. Section for full profile.

## MACHINE PARTS, INC.

17 Ferdon St. (07105)
**Phone—(973) 491-5444**
Fax—(973) 491-0114
Email—mpinj@aol.com
Pres.—Ricardo Cruz
V.-P.—Douglas J. Reichard
Comp.—Raj Mittal
GM—Michael Lameiras
Manager—John Reichard
Machinist—Joe Lopes

SIC—3599; *CNC machining job shop*
Employs—7; Estab.—1995
Sales—under $500,000
7,500 sq ft site, Distrib.—Local
Privately owned sub-S corp.

NEW ENTRY
## MAINSOURCE METALFAB, LLC

59 Poinier St., Unit 61 (07114)
**Phone—(973) 353-0988**
Fax—(973) 353-0994
www.mainsourcemetal.com
Email—ldlu@mainsourcemetal.com
Owner—Eldie Lu
SIC—3441; *Structural steel fabrication*
Employs—20; Estab.—2006
Sales—$2.5Mil-$5Mil (est)
Distrib.—Local
Limited Liability Company

## MANCO PLATING, INC.

390 Park Ave., P.O. Box 7025 (07107)
**Phone—(973) 485-6800**
Fax—(973) 485-8444
Email—mancoplating@verizon.net
Pres.—Luis Garcia
Plt. Mgr.—David Munoz
Off. Mgr.—Lissette Garcia
SIC—3471; NAICS—332813; *Electroplating*
Employs—12; Estab.—1965
Sales—$1Mil
Distrib.—Local
Privately owned corporation

## MANISCHEWITZ CO., THE (H Q)

80 Avenue K (07105)
**Phone—(201) 553-1100**
Fax—(973) 589-5298
www.manischewitz.com
Email—deborah.ross@manischewitz.com
Pres.—Mark Weinstein
CFO—Tom Keogh
V.-P., Sales—Kevin O'Brien
V.-P., Pur.—Yossi Ostreicher
V.-P., Admn. & Hum. Res.—Beatrice Scotti
Opers. Mgr.—Randall Copeland
Consumer Affs. Mgr.—Deborah Ross
SIC—2052; 2099; 2024; 2033; NAICS—311520; *Company headquarters; kosher cookies, pasta, crackers, soups, matza, pudding & fruit juices*
Employs—65
Sales—$10Mil-$25Mil (est)
Limited Liability Company

## MARA POLISHING & PLATING CORP.

105-107 W. Peddie St. *(07112)*
**Phone—(973) 242-0800**
Fax—(973) 242-5205
www.marametalpolishingplating.com
Email—maraplater105@verizon.net
Ptnr.—Louis Galarza
Ptnr.—Eugene R. Maykish
SIC—3471; NAICS—332813; *Metal plating & polishing*
Employs—4; Estab.—1969
Sales—$500,000-$1Mil
Distrib.—National
Privately owned corporation

## †MARJAM SUPPLY CO.

6 International Way (07114)
**Phone—(973) 491-6030**
Fax—(973) 824-4140
www.marjam.com
Email—carmen@marjam.com
Sales Rep.—Steve Hartler
SIC—5031; 5033; *Distributor of building materials, including flooring, insulation, windows, roofing, siding & lumber*
Employs—60; Estab.—1966
Distrib.—National
Privately owned corporation

Parent co.—MarJam Supply Co., Farmingdale, NY
Phone—(631) 249-4900
See Parent Co. Section for full profile.

## MARKBILT TECHNICAL FABRICS CORP.

Div. of Safer Holding Corp.
1875 McCarter Hwy. (07104)
**Phone—(973) 482-6400**
Fax—(973) 424-7179
www.markbilt.com
Email—mwoltin@markbilt.com
Pres.—Mark Woltin
SIC—2257; *Stretch knit, 3D & upholstery fabrics, jacquards & fabrics with copper, silver & carbon for the medical, sports & technical textile markets*
Employs—100; Estab.—1974
250,000 sq ft site, Distrib.—National
Privately owned corporation
Parent co.—Safer Holding Corp., Newark, NJ
Phone—(973) 482-6400
See Parent Co. Section for full profile.

## MEADOWS KNITTING CORP.

Div. of Safer Holding Corp.
1875 McCarter Hwy. (07104)
**Phone—(973) 482-6400**
Fax—(973) 484-7179
www.safertextiles.com
Email—marketing@safertextiles.com
V.-P.—Marty Sohn
IT Mgr.—Bill Garrity
Hum. Res. Mgr.—Richard Wachsman
Off. Mgr.—Bebi Khan
SIC—2257; *Knit textile products*
Employs—100; Estab.—1977
Sales—over $1Bil
125,000 sq ft site, Distrib.—Local
Privately owned corporation
Parent co.—Safer Holding Corp., Newark, NJ
Phone—(973) 482-6400
See Parent Co. Section for full profile.

NEW ENTRY
## MEDITERRANEAN STUCCO CORP.

111 Main St. (07105)
**Phone—(973) 491-0160**
National—(800) 589-8281
Fax—(973) 491-0162
www.mediterraneanstucco.com
Pres.—Ernesto Andrade
SIC—3299; *Stucco materials*
Employs—5
Sales—$500,000-$1Mil (est)

## METAL GRAPHICS, INC.

49 Empire St. (07114)
**Phone—(973) 242-0300**
Fax—(973) 242-6750
Email—metalgraphics@gmail.com
Pres.—Peter Parmar
Plt. Mgr.—Navdeep Pargar
SIC—3471; NAICS—332813; *Metal finishing*
Employs—9; Estab.—1983
20,000 sq ft site, Distrib.—Regional
Privately owned sub-S corp.

## †METALS USA, PLATES & SHAPES GROUP

Div. of Metals USA, Inc.
182 Frelinghuysen Ave. *(07114)*
**Phone—(973) 242-1000**
(800) 524-1203
Fax—(973) 242-2246
www.metalsusa.com
Email—tcreanza@metalsusa.com
GM—Thomas Creanza
Plt. Mgr.—Greg Pirrone
Buyer—Paula Malave

SIC—5051; 3312; *Steel service center, including steel fabrication*
Employs—31; Estab.—1904
Sales—$20Mil-$22Mil
85,000 sq ft site, Distrib.—Regional
Privately owned corporation
Parent co.—Metals USA, Inc., Fort Lauderdale, FL
Phone—(954) 202-4000
See Parent Co. Section for full profile.

## †METRO HYDRAULIC JACK CO.

1271 McCarter Hwy., P.O. Box 9410 (07104)
**Phone—(973) 350-0111**
National—(800) 649-5797
Fax—(973) 350-0112
www.metrohydraulic.com
Email—info@metrohydraulic.com
Pres.—Michael Storch
V.-P.—Steven Storch
Hum. Res., IT & Off. Mgr.—Ilene McPherson
SIC—5084; *Distributor of jacks, cylinders, pumps, hydraulic & mechanical tools & lubrication equipment, including repair services; Brand name—Power Team; NORCO; Simplex; Lincoln; ENERPAC; Greenlee; Gardner Bender; Graco; Hein Werner; Omega; AFF*
Employs—17; Estab.—1941
Sales—$3Mil-$3.5Mil
20,000 sq ft site, Distrib.—Intl.
Privately owned sub-S corp.

## MINUTEMAN PRESS CORP.

55 Commerce St. (07102)
**Phone—(973) 624-6907**
Fax—(973) 624-2066
www.minutemanpressnewark.com
Email—sales@mmpnewark.com
Pres.—Holly Kaplansky
Designer—Alexis Mobley
SIC—2759; 2752; NAICS—323100; *Commercial offset & instant printing*
Employs—4; Estab.—1994
Sales—$500,000-$1Mil
1,500 sq ft site, Distrib.—Regional
Privately owned corporation

## N & J MACHINE PRODUCTS CORP.

52 Bruen St. (07105)
**Phone—(973) 589-0031**
Fax—(973) 589-0222
Pres.—Nino Pereira
SIC—3599; *General machining job shop*
Employs—5; Estab.—1988
Sales—under $500,000
5,000 sq ft site, Distrib.—Local
Privately owned corporation

## NARCISO PRINTING, INC.

120-22 Malvern St. (07105)
**Phone—(973) 578-2088**
Fax—(973) 578-2083
www.narcisos.com
Email—info@narcisos.com
Pres.—Felix Narciso
V.-P.—Maria Narciso
Plt. & Prodn. Mgr.—Carlos Nunes
SIC—2759; NAICS—323100; *Commercial printing*
Employs—6; Estab.—1987
Sales—$500,000
3,000 sq ft site, Distrib.—Regional
Privately owned sub-S corp.

## NASTO'S ICE CREAM CO., INC.

236 Jefferson St. (07105)
**Phone—(973) 589-3333**
Fax—(973) 589-6232
www.nastoicecream.com
Email—nastos@optonline.net
Pres., CEO—Frank Nasto III
V.-P., Prodn.—Dean J. Nasto
Secy.-Treas.—Frank Nasto, Jr.

## Newark—(cont.)

SIC—2024; NAICS—311520; *Ice cream; Brand name—Nasto's Ice Cream*
Employs—19; Estab.—1939
10,000 sq ft site, Distrib.—Local
Privately owned corporation

**NATURAL FLAVORS, INC.**
268 Doremus Ave. (07105)
**Phone—(973) 589-1230**
Fax—(973) 589-0016
www.flavor.com
Pres.—Herb Stein
V-P.—Jason Stein
Off. Mgr. & Pur. Agt.—Libera Armenti
SIC—2087; NAICS—311900; *Natural flavorings*
Employs—25
Sales—$25Mil-$50Mil (est)
Distrib.—Intl.
Also see: Elan Chemical Company, Inc., same loc.

**N-C CARPET BINDING & EQUIPMENT CORP.**
858 Summer Ave. (07104)
**Phone—(973) 481-3500**
National—(800) 526-1184
Fax—(973) 481-0839
www.n-ccarpet.com
Email—sales@nccarpet.com
Pres., CEO & Principal, Sales & Mktg.—Mel Maher
V-P.—Mark Caplan
SIC—3559; *Machinery for the carpeting & flooring industry, including carpet binders, sergers, fringers, carvers, bevelers & cutters*
Employs—14; Estab.—1956
30,000 sq ft site, Distrib.—Intl.
Privately owned corporation
Also see: Newark Caplan Sewing Machine, Inc., same loc.

**NEMA ASSOCIATES, INC.**
57 Bruen St. (07105-1424)
**Phone—(973) 274-0052**
Fax—(973) 274-9259
www.nemadesign.com
Email—sales@nemadesign.com
Pres., CEO—Juan Carlos Lopez
V-P., CFO—Claudia Lopez
SIC—2759; 2752; 3993; 2542; NAICS—323121; *Full-service digital, large-format, specialty & web printing, retail store decorative signs & danglers, banners, decals, point-of-purchase displays & sampling units & trade show hardware & graphics; Brand name—HP; OCE; EPSON; XEROX; HEIDELBERG; PROMOTOR*
Employs—14; Estab.—1991
Sales—$4Mil
6,500 sq ft site, Distrib.—National
Privately owned sub-S corp.
AKA: Network Marketing Associates

**NEW JERSEY GALVANIZING & TINNING WORKS, INC.**
139 Haynes Ave., 1st Fl. (07114)
**Phone—(973) 242-3200**
National—(800) 631-9044
Fax—(973) 242-6461
www.newjerseygalvanizing.com
Email—njgalvanizing@aol.com
Pres., GM—Robert E. Gregory
SIC—3479; *Hot dip galvanizing*
Employs—50; Estab.—1902
Distrib.—Regional
Privately owned corporation

**NEW JERSEY MICROSYSTEMS, INC.**
211 Warren St., Ste. 31 (07103)
Mail addr: 251 S. Mountain Ave., Montclair (07042)
**Phone—(973) 297-1450**
Fax—(973) 297-1125

www.rfidsensorsystems.com
Email—customerservice@jerseymicro.com
Pres.—Frederick D. Chichester
CEO—William Carr
Engr.—Prasanna Ramakrishnan
SIC—3663; 3829; NAICS—334220; *RFID tags & sensor systems*
Employs—12; Estab.—1996
Sales—$2.5Mil-$5Mil (est)
Distrib.—Intl.
Privately owned corporation

**NEWARK ASPHALT CORP.**
30 Passaic St. (07104)
**Phone—(973) 268-3636**
National—(800) 773-5127
Fax—(973) 268-3639
www.napp-grecco.com
Email—ngc@napp-grecco.com
GM—Joseph Biggica
SIC—2951; NAICS—324121; *Asphalt paving compounds*
Employs—6; Estab.—1965
Distrib.—Local
Privately owned corporation

**NEWARK CAPLAN SEWING MACHINE, INC.**
858 Summer Ave. (07104)
**Phone—(973) 481-4400**
 (973) 481-4401
National—(800) 526-1184
Fax—(973) 481-0839
www.n-ccarpet.com
Email—sales@nccarpet.com
Pres., CEO, CFO, Principal & MIS Mgr.—Mel Maher, Sr.
MIS Mgr.—Maliad Maher
R & D Mgr.—Al Hajjar
SIC—3559; NAICS—333292; *Industrial sewing machinery, spare/replacement parts, needles & attachments, including repair; Brand name—N-C; NC; N C*
Employs—14; Estab.—1946
Sales—$1Mil-$5Mil
30,000 sq ft site, Distrib.—National
Privately owned corporation
Also see: N-C Carpet Binding & Equipment Corp., same loc.

**NEWARK GROUP, INC., THE**
60 Lockwood St. (07105)
**Phone—(973) 465-3900**
National—(800) 366-8685
Fax—(973) 589-2062
www.newarkgroup.com
Email—info@thenewarkgroup.com
V-P., GM—Charles M. Stone
SIC—2611; NAICS—322100; *Recycled paper*
Employs—40; Estab.—1928
Sales—$10Mil-$25Mil (est)
Distrib.—Local
Privately owned corporation
AKA: Newark Recycled Fibers
Parent co.—Newark Group, Inc., The, Cranford, NJ
 Phone—(908) 276-4000
 See Parent Co. Section for full profile.

**NEWARK INDUSTRIAL SPRAYING, INC.**
12 Amsterdam St. (07105)
**Phone—(973) 344-6855**
Fax—(973) 344-1773
www.newarkindustrialspray.com
Pres.—Richard D. Wantz
SIC—3479; 2759; NAICS—323100; *Industrial powder coating, spray painting & silk screening*
Employs—15; Estab.—1948
Sales—$1Mil-$2.5Mil
Distrib.—Local
Privately owned corporation

**NEWARK LINER & WASHER, INC.**
819 Broadway (07104)
**Phone—(973) 482-5400**
Fax—(973) 482-1127

www.newarklinerandwasher.com
Email—avelina2@verizon.net
Pres.—Avelina Figueroa
GM—Antonio Acevedo
Sys. Mgr.—Nuel Lopez
SIC—3089; *Bottle cap liners*
Employs—28; Estab.—1988
10,000 sq ft site, Distrib.—National
Privately owned corporation

**NEWARK MOLD & TOOL, INC.**
147 New Jersey Railroad Ave. (07104)
**Phone—(973) 578-2881**
Fax—(973) 578-2978
Email—newarkmold@aol.com
Pres., Hum. Res. & IT Mgr.—Joe Cerejo
Machinist—Carlos Cerejo
SIC—3544; NAICS—333500; *Injection molds & tooling for the plastic & scientific research industries*
Employs—2; Estab.—1990
Sales—under $500,000
3,000 sq ft site, Distrib.—National
Privately owned corporation

**NEWARK MORNING LEDGER CO.**
Div. of Staten Island Publications, Inc.
1 Star Ledger Plz. (07102)
**Phone—(973) 392-4141**
National—(888) 782-7533
Fax—(973) 392-7886
www.nj.com
Email—info@starledger.com
Publisher—Rich Vezza
Dir., Mktg.—Robert C. Provost
Dir., IT—Pat Riccio
Dir., Circ.—Dennis Carletta
Opers. Mgr.—Steve Leotsakos
SIC—2711; *Divisional headquarters & newspaper publishing; Brand name—The Star Ledger*
Employs—400; Estab.—1912
Company-wide: 1,700
Sales—$10Mil-$25Mil (est)
Distrib.—Regional
Privately owned corporation
Parent co.—Staten Island Publications, Inc., Staten Island, NY
 Phone—(718) 981-1234
 See Parent Co. Section for full profile.

**NEWARK STAMP & DIE WORKS, INC.**
35 Verona Ave. (07104)
**Phone—(973) 485-7111**
Fax—(973) 485-6905
www.newarkstampdie.com
Pres.—Bruce McNab
Off. Mgr.—Roger Bautista
SIC—3953; NAICS—339943; *Rubber & metal stamps*
Employs—9; Estab.—1917
10,000 sq ft site, Distrib.—Intl.
Privately owned corporation

**†NEWARK STEEL & ORNAMENTAL SUPPLY**
41-43 Frelinghuysen Ave. (07114)
**Phone—(973) 424-9790**
Fax—(973) 424-9791
Owner—Jose Martinez
GM—Jose Pinero
SIC—5051; *Wholesaler of hot-rolled steel supplies*
Employs—8; Estab.—1995
1,000 sq ft site, Distrib.—Local
Privately owned corporation

**NEWARK STEEL FABRICATORS, INC.**
104 Albert Ave. (07105)
**Phone—(973) 344-2904**
 (973) 725-2418
Fax—(973) 344-2905
Email—newarksteel@optonline.net
Pres.—Luis Martinez
V-P.—Manny Martinez
Estimator—Victor Perea

SIC—3446; 3312; NAICS—332323; *Steel & ornamental iron railings & stairs*
Employs—5; Estab.—2001
Sales—under $500,000
Distrib.—Local
Privately owned corporation

**NEWARK WELDING CO.**
47 Morris Ave. (07103)
**Phone—(973) 642-6479**
Owner—Richard Dellatorre
SIC—3599; *Welding job shop*
Employs—1
Sales—under $500,000 (est)
Sole ownership

**NORPAK CORP.**
70 Blanchard St. (07105-4702)
**Phone—(973) 589-4200**
National—(800) 631-6970
Fax—(973) 578-8845
www.norpak.net
Email—sales@norpak.net
V-P., GM—James G. Coraci
Sales Mgr.—Mike Pacyna
Plt. Mgr.—Pedro Oliveira
Pur. Mgr.—Louis Rebol
SIC—2679; NAICS—322200; *Paper converting*
Employs—60; Estab.—1954
Sales—$10Mil-$15Mil
100,000 sq ft site, Distrib.—Regional
Privately owned corporation

**OMAVI CLOTHING CO. (H Q)**
701-703 McCarter Hwy., Ste. 102 (07102)
**Phone—(973) 642-2000**
Fax—(973) 642-2001
www.redtagbrand.com
Pres.—Hakim Stevens
Off. Mgr.—Nerisa Singh
SIC—2321; 2329; NAICS—315200; *Company headquarters; men's clothing (mfg. subcontracted)*
Employs—5; Estab.—2010
Sales—under $500,000 (est)
Distrib.—Local
Privately owned corporation
AKA: Red Tag Brand

**OZER INTERNATIONAL, LLC**
145 Manchester Pl. (07104)
**Phone—(973) 497-5656**
National—(877) 257-5656
Fax—(973) 497-5655
www.ozermarblegroup.com
Email—gonca@ozermarblegroup.com
Pres.—Sualp Yurteri
V-P.—F. Gonca Yurteri
SIC—3281; 1411; NAICS—327991; *Manufacturer of granite & marble kitchen countertops & distributor of natural stone, marble, travertine & limestone tiles, granite slabs, mosaics & cut-to-size stone products*
Employs—25; Estab.—1998
Sales—$2.6Mil-$5Mil
30,000 sq ft site, Distrib.—National
Limited Liability Company

**P B A PRINTING**
170 Malvern St. (07105)
**Phone—(973) 817-9712**
Fax—(973) 817-7338
www.pbaprinting.com
Email—contat@pbaprinting.com
Owner—Joe Figueiredo
Graphic Designer—Eli Castro
SIC—2752; 2791; NAICS—323122; *Offset printing & typesetting*
Employs—4; Estab.—1993
Distrib.—Local
Privately owned corporation

GEOGRAPHICAL

# Newark—(cont.)

## PANASONIC CORP. OF NORTH AMERICA (H Q)

2 River Front Plz. (07102)
**Phone—(201) 348-7500**
National—(800) 211-7262
Fax—(201) 348-8164
www.panasonic.com
Email—daguetl@us.panasonic.com
Chrm., CEO—Joseph M. Taylor
Pres., Enterprise Sols. Div.—James Doyle
Sr. Corp. V-P.—Yoshi Yuasa
Dir., Hum. Res. Serv.—Isabell Daguet
Hum. Res. Mgr.—Lara Braca
Prod. Mgr., Comm.—Jamie Lawson
SIC—3679; 3621; 3728; 3651; NAICS—335312; *Corporate headquarters; electric motors & electronic products, including in-flight entertainment systems, televisions, displays & vacuum cleaners; Brand name—Panasonic*
Employs—800
Sales—$88Bil
340,000 sq ft site, Distrib.—National
Privately owned corporation

## PANASONIC INDUSTRIAL DEVICES SALES CO. OF AMERICA (H Q)

2 River Front Plz., 7th Fl. (07102)
**Phone—(908) 464-3550**
Fax—(908) 464-8513
Cont.—Kane Inoue
Dir., Mktg. & Tech.—Steve Cummins
Head of Mktg. Group—Nick DeGaetano
SIC—3679; *Company headquarters; electronic components, including vision, measurement & connect sensors, touch screens, signal & power relays, timers, GPS equipment & wiring devices (mfg. done in Japan)*
Employs—180; Estab.—1986
Distrib.—Intl.

## PARAMOUNT BAKERIES, INC.

61 Davenport Ave. (07107-2533)
**Phone—(973) 482-6638**
Fax—(973) 482-3285
www.paramountbakeries.com
Email—orders@paramountbakeries.com
Pres.—Shraga Zabludovsky
SIC—2051; NAICS—311812; *Baked goods; Brand name—Paramount; Bread City; Sweet City*
Employs—50; Estab.—1924
40,000 sq ft site, Distrib.—Regional
Privately owned corporation

## PARAMOUNT FIXTURE CORP.

175 Mount Pleasant Ave. (07104)
**Phone—(973) 485-8261**
            (973) 485-1585
National—(800) 244-1076
Fax—(973) 485-3366
www.paramountfixturecorp.com
Email—fixtureman175@aol.com
Owner & Pres.—Stephen Porcelli
V-P.—Danniel Moore
Off. Mgr.—Len Lendensky

SIC—2541; 2542; 3281; 2431; NAICS—321900; *Custom wooden & metal store fixtures, plastic laminate millwork, granite, marble & solid-surface countertops & stock kitchen cabinets for commercial & residential applications*
Employs—35; Estab.—1992
Sales—$6Mil-$10Mil
45,000 sq ft site, Distrib.—Regional
Privately owned corporation

## PARKWAY WIRE FRAME CO., INC.

249 Astor St. (07114)
**Phone—(973) 242-5220**
Email—nash.mark@ymail.com
Pres.—Mark Hoglund
SIC—2541; *Window displays*
Employs—9; Estab.—2002
Sales—$500,000-$1Mil
Distrib.—Regional
Sole ownership

## PAUL DYEING CO.

626 Orange St. (07107)
**Phone—(973) 484-1121**
National—(800) 950-7285
Fax—(973) 484-4822
www.pauldyeing.com
Email—pauldyeing@optimum.net
Pres.—Laurie Braun
Off. Mgr.—Mary McDermott
SIC—2261; 2262; NAICS—313311; *Dyeing of fashion apparel, table linens, uniforms & towels for industrial laundries, hotels & restaurants*
Employs—17; Estab.—1932
Sales—$1Mil-$5Mil
Distrib.—National
Privately owned sub-S corp.

## PEERLESS UMBRELLA CO., INC.

427 Ferry St. (07105)
**Phone—(973) 578-4900**
Fax—(973) 578-2626
www.peerlessumbrella.com
Email—info@peerlessumbrella.com
Pres.—Gene Moscowitz
V-P.—Rosalind Leonessa
Sales Mgr., Natl.—Daniel Edge
SIC—3999; 5136; 5199; *Manufacturer & distributor of umbrellas, folding chairs & pop-up gazebos*
Employs—120; Estab.—1929
Sales—$15Mil-$20Mil
120,000 sq ft site, Distrib.—National
Privately owned corporation

## PENN JERSEY PAINT CO., INC.

1255 McCarter Hwy. (07104)
**Phone—(973) 482-5430**
Fax—(973) 482-1347
www.pennjerseypaintco.com
Pres.—Ernest Castroaro
SIC—2851; NAICS—325510; *Paints*
Employs—4; Estab.—1925
Sales—$500,000-$1Mil
Distrib.—Regional
Privately owned corporation

## PERLEN STEEL CORP.

265 Passaic St. (07104)
**Phone—(973) 485-5522**
National—(800) 775-5698
Fax—(973) 485-1667
Email—sales@perlensteelcorp.com
Pres.—Richard Perlen
Hum. Res. & Off. Mgr.—Candy Johnson
Manager—Richard Azzarone

SIC—3441; 5051; NAICS—332312; *Structural steel fabrication & distributor of wire, cable, sub & test weights, rails, wire rope, slings, counterweight frames, buffers, buffer inspection platforms, rail brackets, machine beams & bed plates; Brand name—Iph wire rope; volstahl rails*
Employs—13; Estab.—1982
Sales—$6Mil-$7Mil
40,000 sq ft site, Distrib.—Regional
Privately owned sub-S corp.

## PHARMACEUTICAL INNOVATIONS

897 Frelinghuysen Ave. (07114)
**Phone—(973) 242-2901**
Fax—(973) 242-0578
www.pharminnovations.com
Email—info@pharminnovations.com
Pres.—Gilbert Buchalter
Plt. Mgr.—Nelson Carvalho
SIC—2899; *Ultrasound & electromedical gels & detergent sprays; Brand name—After-Tens; D-Foam; Electro Mist; Evron Gel; For Play; Gamma Gel; Gentle Gel; Lean On Me; Lectron II; M-Spray 2000; Other-Sonic; Photon; Pre-Tac; Prep N' Stay; Prep Trode; Q.R. Quick Recovery; Res-Off; Slo-Dry; Spraytrode*
Employs—20; Estab.—1971
55,000 sq ft site, Distrib.—Intl.
Privately owned corporation
ISO rating—9001

## POLY ONE CORP.

Div. of PolyOne Corp.
297 Ferry St. (07105)
**Phone—(973) 522-2800**
National—(888) 721-4242
Fax—(973) 344-7952
www.polyone.com
Email—info@polyone.com
Sales Mgr., Natl.—Joe Herres
SIC—3081; NAICS—326113; *Plastic sheet & film*
Employs—100; Estab.—1988
100,000 sq ft site, Distrib.—Intl.
Publicly owned corporation
Parent co.—PolyOne Corp., Avon Lake, OH
Phone—(440) 930-1000
See Parent Co. Section for full profile.

## POOKA, INC.

87 Halsey St. (07102)
**Phone—(973) 954-2471**
National—(866) 245-1403
Fax—(973) 954-2512
www.pookapureandsimple.com
Email—info@pookapureandsimple.com
Pres.—Dawn Fitch
Off. Mgr.—Cathy Simmons
SIC—2844; *Natural bath & body care products, including shower gels, body sprays & moisturizers*
Employs—3; Estab.—2000
Sales—under $500,000
Distrib.—National
Privately owned corporation

## PORTUGUESE STRUCTURAL STEEL, INC.

255 South St. *(07114)*
**Phone—(973) 344-1342**
Fax—(973) 344-1730
www.portuguesesteel.com
Email—paula@portuguesesteel.com
Pres.—Paula Cabral
SIC—3441; NAICS—332312; *Structural steel fabrication, including welding & installation services*
Employs—10
Sales—$3.5Mil-$5Mil
15,000 sq ft site, Distrib.—Local

## PRINTERS' SERVICE, INC.

26 Blanchard St. (07105)
**Phone—(973) 589-7800**
Fax—(973) 589-3225
www.prisco.com
Email—inquiries@prisco.com
Chrm.—Richard B. Liroff
Pres.—Bruce D. Liroff
CFO, MIS Mgr.—Russ Mantione
V-P., Mktg.—Eric Gutwillig
Sales Mgr.—Tom Latchford
SIC—3555; 2893; NAICS—333293; *Corporate headquarters & pressroom chemicals & process control & environmental equipment, including printing blankets, coatings, adhesives & supplies & wide-format inkjet printing; Brand name—Prisco; Priscolith; PriscoTech; AquaFlo; AquaChill; AquaMix; PriscoBond; PriscoDigital; HP Scitex; Hostert; Esko; Caldera*
Employs—100; Estab.—1900
75,000 sq ft site, Distrib.—Intl.
Privately owned sub-S corp.
AKA: Deleet Merchandising

## †PROPANE POWER CORPORATION, A DIV. OF SUBURBAN PROPANE

Div. of Suburban Propane Partners, L.P.
915 Delancy St. (07105)
**Phone—(973) 589-3030**
Fax—(973) 817-7241
www.propanepower.com
Email—egiron@propanepower.com
Manager—Tom Raulinavich
Administrator—Velvet Anderson
SIC—5172; *Distributor of propane gas*
Employs—40; Estab.—1965
Sales—$2.5Mil-$5Mil
Distrib.—Regional
Publicly owned corporation
Parent co.—Suburban Propane Partners, L.P., Whippany, NJ
Phone—(973) 887-5300
See Parent Co. Section for full profile.

## PURE H2O TECHNOLOGIES, INC.

211 Warren St., Ste. 318 (07103)
**Phone—(973) 622-0440**
Fax—(973) 859-7889
www.ipureh2o.com
Email—sales@ipureh2o.com
CEO—John Edwards
Engr.—Matt Rela
Engr.—Mark Jones
SIC—3589; NAICS—333319; *Water treatment & purification equipment, including reverse osmosis units*
Employs—20; Estab.—1997
20,000 sq ft site, Distrib.—Intl.
Privately owned corporation

## Q-PAK, INC.

2145 McCarter Hwy. (07104)
**Phone—(973) 483-4404**
Fax—(973) 484-7896
www.qpakcorp.com
Email—qpak@earthlink.net
Pres.—Michael Formica
V-P.—Tony Formica
SIC—3085; NAICS—326160; *Plastic bottles*
Employs—20
Privately owned sub-S corp.

## R.A.B. FOOD GROUP, LLC

Div. of Manischewitz Co., The
80 Avenue K (07105)
**Phone—(201) 553-1100**
Fax—(973) 589-5298
www.manischewitz.com
Email—customerservice@rabfoodgroup.com
Plt. Mgr.—Randall Copeland
IT Mgr.—Jarpi Pirog
Hum. Res. Mgr.—Beatrice Scotti
Payroll Admn.—Elizabeth Rosario
Pur. Agt.—Elvira Miranda

## Newark—(cont.)

SIC—2052; 2099; 2034; *Kosher cookies, noodles, dry soup mix & matzos*
Employs—200; Estab.—1888
Sales—$50Mil-$100Mil
Distrib.—National
Limited Liability Company
Parent co.—Manischewitz Co., The, Newark, NJ
Phone—(201) 553-1100
See Parent Co. Section for full profile.

**†RAGONESE & SONS, INC., PATSY**
331 Adams St. (07105)
**Phone—(973) 344-7411**
Fax—(973) 344-7418
Email—shredd18@aol.com
Pres.—Gerald Ragonese, Jr.
Off. Mgr.—Maria Clara Fernandes
SIC—5093; *Wholesaler of shredded recycled paper*
Employs—20; Estab.—1920
Distrib.—Local
Privately owned corporation

**RAMELSON CO., INC., U. J.**
165 Thomas St. (07114)
**Phone—(973) 589-5422**
Fax—(973) 589-5429
www.ramelson.com
Email—ujramelson1937@verizon.net
Pres.—John L. Ramella
V-P.—Daniel J. Ramella
SIC—3423; *Woodcarving tools*
Employs—4; Estab.—1937
Sales—$500,000-$1Mil
Distrib.—National
Privately owned corporation

**RANDALL MFG. CO., INC.**
200 Sylvan Ave. (07104)
**Phone—(973) 484-7600**
National—(800) 631-8688
Fax—(973) 482-9318
www.randallmanufacturing.com
Pres.—Cary Tinfow
SIC—3442; 2431; NAICS—332321; *Metal & wood building products*
Employs—22; Estab.—1954
Distrib.—Local
Privately owned corporation

**RAZAC PRODUCTS CO., INC.**
25 Brenner St. (07108)
**Phone—(973) 622-3700**
National—(800) 600-1022
Fax—(973) 353-9330
www.razacproducts.com
CEO—William Dowdy
Pres., CFO—Darren Dowdy
V-P., MIS—Jalil Dowdy
V-P.—Devvan Dowdy
SIC—2844; NAICS—325600; *Hair care products*
Employs—35; Estab.—1981
Sales—$2.6Mil-$5Mil
23,000 sq ft site, Distrib.—National
Privately owned corporation

**REAL KOSHER LLC**
146 Christie St. (07105)
**Phone—(973) 690-5394**
Fax—(973) 690-5397
www.realkosherfoods.com
Email—sales@realkosherfoods.com
Dir., Mktg.—Jerry Abramson
Mng. Member—Irving Braun
SIC—2013; 2011; NAICS—311600; *Kosher fresh meats, sausages & provisions; Brand name—999; Real Kosher; Lower East Side; Jacks Gourmet*
Employs—20; Estab.—1930
Sales—$2Mil-$5Mil
15,000 sq ft site, Distrib.—Intl.
Limited Liability Company

**REDDAWAY MFG. CO., INC.**
32 Euclid Ave. (07105)
**Phone—(973) 589-1410**
Fax—(973) 589-8223
www.redcoproducts.com
Email—redcoproducts@earthlink.net
CEO—William T. Walker
V-P., Fin.—Daisy Gonzalez
SIC—3069; *Industrial brake linings, friction materials & products; Brand name—RNAW; Redco Non Asbestos Woven Brake Lining*
Employs—14; Estab.—1890
Distrib.—Intl.
Privately owned corporation

**REGENCY ELEVATOR PRODUCTS**
870 Mount Prospect Ave. (07104)
**Phone—(973) 481-1400**
Fax—(973) 481-3444
www.regencyelevator.com
V-P.—Jack Guarino
Engr.—Ernest Schneck
SIC—3534; NAICS—333921; *Elevator cars, fixtures & fronts*
Employs—20; Estab.—1985
Sales—$500,000-$1Mil
Distrib.—National
Privately owned corporation

**REUTHER ENGINEERING & MACHINING CO., INC.**
126 S. 14th St. (07107)
**Phone—(973) 485-5800**
Fax—(973) 482-6005
www.reutherengineering.com
Email—customersupport@reutherengineering.com
Owner—Ken Rys
SIC—3599; *General machining job shop*
Employs—24; Estab.—1939
Sales—$2.5Mil-$5Mil
Distrib.—Local
Privately owned corporation

**REX WINE VINEGAR CO.**
828-830 Raymond Blvd. (07105)
**Phone—(973) 589-6911**
Pres.—Vincent Carlesimo
Shop Foreman—Gordon Buynes
SIC—2084; 2099; NAICS—312130; *Cooking wines & vinegars*
Employs—8; Estab.—1946
Distrib.—National
Privately owned corporation

**REXELL FOODS CORP.**
120 Orchard St. (07102)
**Phone—(973) 741-0404**
Fax—(973) 741-0401
www.pampangofoods.com
Email—info@pampangofoods.com
Off. Mgr.—Violet Engalla
Manager—Edsel Engalla
SIC—2011; NAICS—311611; *Meat processing; Brand name—Pampango; Tito Al's*
Employs—6; Estab.—2004
Sales—under $500,000
Distrib.—Regional
Privately owned corporation

**RIMMEL ROGERS, INC.**
250 Passaic St. (07104)
**Phone—(201) 998-4700**
Fax—(201) 998-3066
Email—rimmelrogers@hotmail.com
Pres.—Manoj Doshi
SIC—3089; 5136; 5137; *Contract packaging & distributor of hosiery, including socks*
Employs—7; Estab.—1997
Distrib.—National
Privately owned corporation

**ROBERT YOUNG & SONS, INC.**
25 Grafton Ave. (07104)
**Phone—(973) 483-0451**
Fax—(973) 483-0185

www.ryoungandsons.com
Email—ryoungandsons@aol.com
Pres.—David A. Young
Off. Mgr.—Rachel Young
Fin. Mgr.—Nancy Z. Young
SIC—3281; NAICS—327991; *Dimensional-cut limestone, marble & granite fabrication & installation*
Employs—5; Estab.—1885
Sales—$1Mil
18,500 sq ft site, Distrib.—Local
Privately owned sub-S corp.

**ROCK-TENN CO.**
2013 McCarter Hwy. (07104)
**Phone—(973) 268-4938**
Fax—(973) 484-8628
www.rocktenn.com
Email—sales@rocktenn.com
Pres.—Steven Grossman
V-P.—Jim Porter
SIC—2653; NAICS—322211; *Corrugated cardboard packaging & point-of-sale displays*
Employs—200; Estab.—1895
200,000 sq ft site, Distrib.—National
Publicly owned corporation
DBA: RockTenn
Parent co.—Rock-Tenn Co., Norcross, GA
Phone—(770) 448-2193
See Parent Co. Section for full profile.

**ROYAL ALUMINUM CO., INC.**
620 Market St. (07105)
**Phone—(973) 589-8880**
National—(800) 526-2747
Fax—(973) 589-3954
www.royalaluminum.net
Pres.—John Inelli
V-P.—Jeff Papa
Off. Mgr.—Joanne Acevado
SIC—3442; NAICS—332321; *Vinyl & aluminum windows & doors*
Employs—50; Estab.—1957
Sales—$5Mil-$10Mil
60,000 sq ft site, Distrib.—Local
Privately owned corporation

**RUGGIERO SEAFOOD, INC.**
474 Wilson Ave., P.O. Box 5369 (07105)
**Phone—(973) 589-0524**
National—(866) 225-2627
Fax—(973) 589-5690
www.ruggieroseafood.com
Email—james@ruggieroseafood.com
Pres.—Rocco Ruggiero
V-P.—Frank Ruggiero
Natl. Dir., Sales & Mktg.—James Magee
SIC—2092; NAICS—311712; *Frozen seafood, including calamari, mussels, clams, swai, tilapia, flounder, conch, salads, scallops, cuttlefish, octopus & smelts; Brand name—Fisherman's Pride; Ocean Tides; Asian Pearl; Sea Devil; Ocean Majesty; Fruit of the Sea*
Employs—50; Estab.—1980
Sales—$25Mil-$30Mil
Distrib.—Intl.
Privately owned corporation

**RUST-OLEUM CORP.**
480 Frelinghuysen Ave. (07114)
**Phone—(732) 469-8100**
Fax—(973) 824-2210
www.rustoleum.com
Email—rnanes@rustoleum.com
Plt. Mgr.—Robert Nanes
SIC—2851; NAICS—325510; *Specialty paint*
Employs—50; Estab.—1847
Distrib.—National
Publicly owned corporation

Parent co.—Rust-Oleum Corp., Vernon Hills, IL
Phone—(847) 367-7700
See Parent Co. Section for full profile.

**S & G TOOL AID CORP.**
43 E. Alpine St. (07114)
**Phone—(973) 824-7730**
Fax—(973) 621-7132
www.toolaid.com
Email—info@toolaid.com
Sales Mgr., Natl.—Wayne Hutchings
Plt. Mgr.—Robert Von Nessi
Mktg. Mgr.—Robert Platt
SIC—3589; 3546; 3423; NAICS—336399; *Automotive & auto body repair shop tools & equipment, including diagnostic, electrical, hand tools, air tools & accessories, suspension & alignment; Brand name—Tool Aid; S & G Tool Aid*
Employs—75; Estab.—1971
Distrib.—National
Privately owned corporation

**S H P C, INC.**
187 Christie St., P.O. Box 5328 (07105)
**Phone—(973) 589-5242**
Fax—(973) 589-2163
www.starheelplate.com
Pres. & V-P.—Paul Sacks
GM—Fred Foreman
SIC—3325; 3321; 3469; NAICS—331513; *Iron & steel castings & stampings*
Employs—20; Estab.—1950
Sales—$1Mil-$2.5Mil (est)
Distrib.—National
Privately owned corporation
AKA: Star Heel Plate

**SAFER HOLDING CORP.**
1875 McCarter Hwy. (07104)
**Phone—(973) 482-6400**
Fax—(973) 482-5694
www.safertextiles.com
Email—bobbypetrenko@safertextiles.com
Pres., CEO—Albert Safer
CFO—Richard Wachsman
COO—Niso Barokas
Plt. Mgr.—Ami Inbal
SIC—2262; 2261; NAICS—313311; *Corporate headquarters & textile dyeing, printing, finishing & knitting of wovens & warp knits*
Employs—150; Estab.—1982
Sales—$10Mil-$25Mil
Distrib.—National
Privately owned corporation

NEW ENTRY
**SAN MIGUEL LIVE POULTRY, LLC**
499 Orange St. (07107)
**Phone—(973) 482-1007**
Manager—Alex Montalbo
SIC—2015; *Poultry processing*
Employs—3; Estab.—2010
Sales—under $500,000 (est)
Publicly owned corporation

**SANTOS BAKERY**
123 Hudson St. (07103)
**Phone—(973) 732-7200**
Fax—(973) 732-7222
Owner—Ablio Santos
Off. Mgr.—Jose Brico
SIC—2051; NAICS—311812; *Bakery products*
Employs—12; Estab.—1950
Sales—under $500,000
Distrib.—Local
Privately owned corporation

**SCHTILLER & PLEVY, INC.**
695 S. 12th St. (07103)
**Phone—(973) 242-4600**
Fax—(973) 242-1235
www.schtiller-plevy.com

GEOGRAPHICAL

# Newark—(cont.)

Email—info@schtiller-plevy.com
Pres., R & D Mgr.—Lawrence Plevy
Proj. Mgr.—Wanda Cabrera
SIC—3446; NAICS—332323; *Architectural metalwork & historic restoration*
Employs—24; Estab.—1920
Sales—over $4Mil
6,500 sq ft site, Distrib.—Regional
Privately owned sub-S corp.

## SCIENTIFIC LABELING SYSTEMS, INC.
339 6th Ave. W. (07107)
**Phone—(973) 722-8229**
Fax—(717) 505-8662
Pres.—Richard D. Powers
SIC—2672; NAICS—322222; *Pressure-sensitive labels*
Employs—7; Estab.—1972
Distrib.—Regional
Sole ownership

## SCORIES, INC.
28 Vassar Ave., P.O. Box 4223 (07112)
**Phone—(973) 923-1372**
Fax—(973) 705-9624
www.scories.com
Email—scorieshair@gmail.com
Pres.—William Hall
Bus. Mgr.—Shan-Tai Hall
SIC—2844; NAICS—325600; *Natural hair care products for dandruff, dry & damaged hair, including shampoos, conditioners, hairdress & treatments & cremes for locks, twists & naturally curly & kinky hair; Brand name—Natural Elegance Hair Care Line*
Employs—15; Estab.—1984
Distrib.—Local
Privately owned corporation

## SEABRA GROUP (H Q)
574 Ferry St. (07105)
**Phone—(973) 491-0399**
Fax—(973) 344-4930
www.seabragroup.com
Email—triunfofoods@triunfofoods.com
Pres.—Antonio Seabra
IT Mgr.—Pedro Cardoso
SIC—2013; NAICS—311600; *Company headquarters; sausage processing*
Employs—26
Sales—$5Mil-$10Mil
Distrib.—National
Limited Liability Company

## †SEIDLER CHEMICAL & SUPPLY CO.
537 Raymond Blvd. *(07105)*
**Phone—(973) 465-1122**
Fax—(973) 465-4469
www.seidlerchem.com
Email—sales@seidlerchem.com
Pres.—Richard Seidler
V.-P., Acctg. & Hum. Res.—Martha R. Seidler
Pur. Mgr.—John Zalesky
IT Mgr.—Dion Morreale
Shpg. & Rec. Mgr.—Bob Foley
SIC—5169; *Distributor of specialty & industrial chemicals & ingredients for the biotech, pharmaceutical, food, plating, water treatment & construction industries, including acids, solvents, salts & high-purity chemicals; Brand name—Avantor; Spectrum; Domino; Armand; Inolex; Sensient; ISP; Staley; General; Eka; Baker; Mallinckrodt; Tate & Lyle; ADM*
Employs—18; Estab.—1896
Sales—$10Mil-$15Mil
36,500 sq ft site, Distrib.—National
Privately owned corporation
AKA: Seidler Chemical Co.

## SERRATELLI HAT CO., INC.
418-26 Central Ave., P.O. Box 7069 (07107)
**Phone—(973) 623-4133**
National—(888) 335-8428
Fax—(973) 622-3358
www.serratellihatcompany.com
Email—customerservice@serratellihatcompany.com
Pres.—Dean Serratelli
Off. Mgr.—Christina Serratelli
SIC—2353; 2386; NAICS—315200; *Cowboy hats*
Employs—49; Estab.—1878
Distrib.—National
Privately owned corporation

## SHAMROCK TECHNOLOGIES, INC.
255 Pacific St. (07114)
**Phone—(973) 242-2999**
National—(800) 349-1822
Fax—(973) 242-8074
www.shamrocktechnologies.com
Email—marketing@shamrocktechnologies.com
Chrm.—William B. Neuberg
CFO & V.-P., Hum. Res.—Joe Shade
V.-P., Sales, Worldwide—John J. Gallagher
V.-P., Mktg.—Joon S. Choo
V.-P., Tech.—Manshi Sui
Cont.—Anthony Moscicki
Pur. Mgr.—Bob Diehm
Hum. Res. Mgr.—Mohammed Elmonayery
SIC—2843; 2869; NAICS—325613; *Corporate headquarters & micronized wax powders, dispersions, emulsions & compounds, including PTFE, polytetrafluoroethylene, polyethylene, polypropylene & fluoropolymers, custom wax alloys, natural waxes & specialty additives*
Employs—100; Estab.—1945
100,000 sq ft site, Distrib.—Intl.
Privately owned corporation

## SHEET METAL PRODUCTS, INC.
794 N. 6th St. (07107)
**Phone—(973) 482-0450**
Fax—(973) 482-0180
Email—sales@s-m-p-inc.com
Pres.—William F. Kovacs
Bus. Dev. Mgr.—Brad Gray
SIC—3444; 3443; 3499; *Contract manufacturing & industrial metal fabrication of sheet metal products & ASME code pressure vessels, including welding, punching, plasma burning, bending, polishing, blasting, painting & electromechanical & mechanical assembly*
Employs—30; Estab.—1935
Sales—$3Mil-$4Mil
27,000 sq ft site, Distrib.—Regional
Privately owned sub-S corp.
AKAs: SMP & SMP, Inc.

## SHERI'S COOKERY, INC.
33 Delancy St. (07105)
**Phone—(973) 589-2060**
Fax—(973) 589-3260
CEO—Murray Forman
Pres.—Thomas M. Kochanowski
Manager—Chris Young
SIC—2099; *Mixed potato, macaroni & pasta salads*
Employs—20; Estab.—1985
Distrib.—National
Privately owned corporation

## SIGNODE PACKAGING GROUP
Div. of Illinois Tool Works, Inc.
151 Fabyan Pl. (07112)
**Phone—(800) 235-4066**
Prodn. Mgr.—Jorge Jarrin
Off. Mgr.—Val Brown
SIC—2653; 2655; NAICS—322211; *Fiberboard & corrugated packaging materials & solutions; Brand name—Angle Board*
Employs—35
Distrib.—National
Publicly owned corporation
Parent co.—Illinois Tool Works, Inc., Glenview, IL
Phone—(847) 724-7500
See Parent Co. Section for full profile.

## SIMS METAL MANAGEMENT
8-18 Noble St. (07114)
**Phone—(973) 824-8900**
Fax—(973) 824-8077
www.simsmm.com
Email—keithbologno@simsmm.com
GM—Keith Bologno
SIC—3444; *Sheet metal recycling*
Employs—10; Estab.—1945
Sales—under $500,000
Distrib.—Local
Privately owned corporation
Parent co.—Sims Metal Management, New York, NY
Phone—(212) 604-0710
See Parent Co. Section for full profile.

## SKIP GAMBERT & ASSOCS., INC.
436 Ferry St., Ste. 2 (07105)
**Phone—(973) 344-3373**
Fax—(973) 344-3581
www.skipgambert.com
Email—customerservice@skipgambert.com
Pres.—David Gambert, Jr.
GM—David Gambert, Sr.
Sales Mgr.—Louis Ricart
Cust. Serv. Rep.—Elizabeth Cunag
SIC—2321; NAICS—315200; *Custom shirts for men*
Employs—140; Estab.—1992
22,000 sq ft site, Distrib.—National
Privately owned sub-S corp.

## SMITH TOOL & MFG., R. G.
245 South St. (07114)
**Phone—(973) 344-1395**
Fax—(973) 344-1387
Pres.—Edgar Blaus, Jr.
Corp. Secy.—Chris Blaus
Machinist—Michael Ferreira
SIC—3599; 3544; NAICS—333500; *General machining & tool & die job shop*
Employs—9; Estab.—1930
Sales—$1Mil-$2.5Mil (est)
Distrib.—Regional
Privately owned corporation

## SOLMOR MFG. CO., INC.
164 Emmet St. (07114)
**Phone—(973) 824-7203**
Fax—(973) 424-0983
www.solmor.com
Email—rulmel999@verizon.net
Pres.—Robert Ulmer
SIC—3914; *Earring findings*
Employs—5; Estab.—1933
Sales—$500,000-$1Mil
Distrib.—National
Privately owned sub-S corp.

## SOWA CORP.
223 Murray St. (07114)
**Phone—(973) 297-0008**
Fax—(973) 297-1210
www.sowacorp.com
Email—sowacorp@gmail.com
Pres.—Adam Garstka
SIC—3469; *Metal stampings*
Employs—4; Estab.—1996
Sales—under $500,000
5,000 sq ft site, Distrib.—Regional
Privately owned corporation

## SPACENOW! CORPORATION
234 Emmet St. (07114)
**Phone—(973) 504-8585**
National—(800) 504-8585
Fax—(973) 504-8330
www.spacenowcorp.com
Email—info@spacenowcorp.com
Pres., R & D Mgr.—Bernard Morcheles
Sales Mgr.—Julisa Aguilar
Factory Mgr.—Manuel Ricardo
Asst. Factory Mgr.—Randolph Coleman
SIC—2542; *High density mobile filing & storage systems; Brand name—DuoGlider; TrioGlider; ArtGlider; NoTrac Moving-Aisle; NoTrac DuoGlider; SlatGrid Mobile Display & Storage System*
Employs—5; Estab.—1993
15,000 sq ft site, Distrib.—Intl.
Privately owned sub-S corp.

## STANDARD EMBOSSING PLATE
129 Pulaski St. (07105)
**Phone—(973) 344-6670**
Fax—(973) 344-6730
www.standardembossing.com
Email—standardembossing@yahoo.com
Ptnr. & Pres.—Chris Fleissner
Ptnr. & CFO—Richard Fleissner
SIC—2796; NAICS—323122; *Leather embossing & embossing plates*
Employs—3; Estab.—1888
Sales—under $500,000
10,000 sq ft site, Distrib.—Intl.
Privately owned corporation

## STAR EMBROIDERY CORP.
305 3rd Ave. W. (07107)
**Phone—(973) 481-4300**
National—(800) 435-5397
Fax—(973) 481-1267
www.star-embroidery.com
Email—sembroider@aol.com
Owner, GM, Hum. Res. & IT Mgr.—Dean Gannet
Factory Mgr.—Jacqueline Spence
SIC—2395; *Embroidery*
Employs—20; Estab.—1992
Sales—$1Mil-$2.5Mil (est)
Distrib.—Local
Privately owned corporation

## STATE TOOL GEAR CO., INC.
211 Camden St. (07103)
**Phone—(973) 642-6181**
Fax—(973) 642-0649
www.statetoolgear.com
Email—sales@statetoolgear.com
Pres.—Michael Insabella
Off. Mgr.—Camille Tedesco
SIC—3566; 3599; NAICS—333612; *Gears & gear cutting*
Employs—14; Estab.—1962
Sales—$500,000-$1Mil
8,500 sq ft site, Distrib.—Regional
Privately owned sub-S corp.

## STIRRUP METAL PRODUCTS CORP.
215 Emmet St. (07114)
**Phone—(973) 824-7086**
Fax—(973) 824-7088
www.stirrupmetal.com
Email—sales@stirrupmetal.com
Pres.—Todd Stirrup
V.-P.—George Stirrup
Off. Mgr.—Dave Kold
SIC—3469; 3499; *Metal stampings & fabrication*
Employs—20; Estab.—1900
Sales—$1Mil-$2.5Mil
Distrib.—Local
Privately owned corporation

## SUBURBAN MONUMENT & VAULT
203 Sherman Ave., P.O. Box 2370 (07114)
**Phone—(973) 242-7007**
National—(800) 804-6803
Fax—(973) 242-2035
Owner—Clyde Brooks

## Newark—(cont.)

SIC—3281; 3272; NAICS—
327991; *Granite monuments &
concrete burial vaults*
Employs—6; Estab.—1967
Sales—$500,000-$1Mil
Distrib.—Local
Sole ownership

**SUPREME INK CO., INC.**

65 McWhorter St. (07105)
**Phone—(973) 344-2922**
Fax—(973) 344-3888
www.supremeinkcompany.com
Email—info@
supremeinkcompany.com
Pres.—John Ahmed
Prod. Mgr.—Abraham Tawadros
Shpg. Mgr.—Noah Ahmed
SIC—2893; NAICS—325910;
*Printing ink*
Employs—12; Estab.—1970
Sales—$1Mil-$2.5Mil
Distrib.—Intl.
Privately owned corporation

**†TAYLOR AUTO PARTS**

222 Pacific St. (07114)
Mail addr: P.O. Box 5218, Newark
(07105-0218)
**Phone—(973) 465-4345**
Fax—(973) 465-4823
Email—taylorauto@optimum.net
Pres.—Frederick Taylor
Off. Mgr.—Andrea Taylor
SIC—5015; 5093; *Wholesaler of
used automotive parts & scrap
metals*
Employs—3; Estab.—1998
Distrib.—Local
Privately owned corporation

**TEAM U. S. A.**

200 Badger Ave. (07108)
**Phone—(973) 596-2800**
National—(888) 872-9999
Fax—(973) 732-5350
www.teamusauniforms.com
Email—shivthapar@aol.com
Pres.—Shiv Thapar
V-P.—Veena Thapar
Prod. Mgr.—Zoila Naches
SIC—2253; 2329; 2339; 2258;
NAICS—315200; *Team sports
uniforms; Brand name—TEAM-
USA*
Employs—20; Estab.—1995
Sales—$1Mil-$5Mil
20,000 sq ft site, Distrib.—National
Sole ownership

**TEIXEIRA'S BAKERY**

113-129 Kossuth St., P.O. Box
5550 (07105)
**Phone—(973) 589-8875**
Fax—(973) 589-6510
CEO—Manuel Teixeira
MIS Mgr.—Mark Vendreyes
Off. Supv.—John Rio
SIC—2051; NAICS—311812;
*Bakery products*
Employs—280; Estab.—1976
68,000 sq ft site, Distrib.—
Regional
Privately owned corporation

**TENAX FINISHING PRODUCTS CO.**

390 Adams St. (07114)
**Phone—(973) 589-9000**
Fax—(973) 589-7067
Email—office@tenaxfp.com
Pres., MIS Mgr.—James O'Neill
V-P.—John O'Neill
SIC—2851; NAICS—325510;
*Paints*
Employs—11; Estab.—1948
20,000 sq ft site, Distrib.—
Regional
Privately owned corporation

**TOVLI, INC.**

49 Hunter St. (07114)
**Phone—(718) 417-6677**
Fax—(718) 417-0932
Pres.—Abraham Osterichner
GM—Trudy Osterichner
SIC—2038; NAICS—311411;
*Specialty frozen food products*
Employs—25; Estab.—1995
Distrib.—National
Privately owned corporation

**TRI STATE STONE, INC.**

111 Rome St., Ste. 2 (07105)
**Phone—(973) 344-7220**
Fax—(973) 344-7240
www.tristatestone.us
Email—tristatestone@hotmail.com
Pres.—Gene Gonsalves
SIC—3281; *Stone fabrication*
Employs—10; Estab.—2005
Sales—$500,000-$1Mil (est)
Distrib.—Local
Privately owned corporation

**TROY CHEMICALS**

Div. of Troy Corp.
1 Avenue L (07105)
**Phone—(973) 589-2500**
Fax—(973) 589-0490
www.troycorp.com
Email—troychemical@troycorp.com
IT Mgr.—Tregg Favoy
SIC—2869; 2851; NAICS—
325510; *Paint additives*
Employs—100; Estab.—1957
Distrib.—Intl.
Privately owned corporation
AKA: Troy Corp.
Parent co.—Troy Corp., Florham
Park, NJ
Phone—(973) 443-4200
See Parent Co. Section for full profile.

**U. S. S. CORP.**

780 Frelinghuysen Ave. (07114)
**Phone—(973) 242-1110**
Fax—(973) 242-5755
COO—Carlos Matos
Hum. Res. Mgr.—Elizabeth
Caseillo
Fin. Supv.—Julia Isabel
SIC—2759; NAICS—323100;
*Glass screen printing*
Employs—200; Estab.—1962
Distrib.—Intl.
Privately owned corporation

**U. S. WIRE & CABLE, INC.**

33 Queen St. (07114)
**Phone—(973) 824-5529**
National—(800) 327-4673
Fax—(973) 824-1208
www.flexonhose.com
Email—drauch@flexonhose.com
Pres.—David Rauch
SIC—3496; 2298; 3357; *Wire,
cables, cords & accessories*
Employs—100; Estab.—1987
320,000 sq ft site, Distrib.—
National
Privately owned corporation
Also see: Flexon Industries Corp.,
1 Flexon Plz. loc.
AKA: Flexon Industries

**ULANET CO., GEORGE**

413-415 Market St. (07105)
**Phone—(973) 589-4876**
Fax—(973) 589-6922
www.ulanet.com
Email—info@ulanet.com
Pres.—Jon Ulanet
SIC—3634; 3822; NAICS—
334512; *Heating elements,
including immersion heaters &
bimetal thermostats*
Employs—9; Estab.—1931
Sales—$1Mil-$5Mil
18,000 sq ft site, Distrib.—Intl.
Privately owned sub-S corp.

**UNIONWEAR/NEW JERSEY
HEADWEAR CORP.**

305 3rd Ave. W., Ste. 5 (07107)
**Phone—(973) 497-0102**
National—(877) 932-7864
Fax—(973) 497-7708
www.unionwear.com
Email—resource@unionwear.com
Pres.—Mitchell Cahn
GM—Colin Greene
IT Mgr.—Adam Hammond
Hum. Res. Mgr.—Gloria Montoya
SIC—2353; 2396; 2395; *Custom
embroidered, screenprinted &
blank baseball, military, winter &
work caps, hats, t-shirts & bags*
Employs—50; Estab.—1992
Sales—$6Mil-$10Mil
20,000 sq ft site, Distrib.—Intl.
Privately owned sub-S corp.

**UNITED EQUIPMENT &
FABRICATORS**

175 Orange St. (07103)
**Phone—(973) 242-2737**
Fax—(973) 242-2738
www.unitedef.com
Email—unitedef@unitedef.com
Manager—Robert Ayars
SIC—3089; 3444; 3599; NAICS—
332998; *Custom plastic,
fiberglass, stainless & carbon
steel & aluminum fabrication for
tanks, exhaust hoods, ductwork,
lab workstations, sinks, piping,
grating/structurals, liners &
valves, including general
machining & repair*
Employs—5; Estab.—2005
Distrib.—Regional
Limited Liability Company

**UNITED LABEL CORP.**

65 Chambers St. (07105)
**Phone—(973) 589-6500**
Fax—(973) 589-4465
www.unitedlabelcorp.com
Email—josie1@unitedlabelcorp.com
V-P., Sales—John T. O'Connor
Bookkeeper—Josie Stewart
SIC—2679; 2759; NAICS—
322200; *Pressure-sensitive
paper labels*
Employs—10; Estab.—1968
Sales—$1Mil-$2.5Mil
100,000 sq ft site, Distrib.—
National
Privately owned corporation

**UNITED STATES BOX CORP.**

1296 McCarter Hwy. (07104)
**Phone—(973) 481-2000**
National—(800) 221-0999
Fax—(973) 481-2002
www.usbox.com
Email—manager@usbox.com
Pres.—Alan Kossoff
V-P.—Tom Kossoff
SIC—2652; 2657; NAICS—
322213; *Folding & setup
paperboard boxes*
Employs—65; Estab.—1948
50,000 sq ft site, Distrib.—Intl.
Privately owned corporation

**UNITED STATES SPRAY FINISHING
CO., INC.**

70 Blanchard St. (07105)
**Phone—(973) 589-3490**
Ptnr.—Brad Newton
Pres.—Frank Del Mastro
SIC—3471; NAICS—332813;
*Metal finishing*
Employs—9; Estab.—1976
Sales—under $500,000
Distrib.—Local
Privately owned corporation

**UNITY BRAND HALAL PRODUCTS**

94 Orange St. (07102)
**Phone—(973) 624-4847**
Fax—(973) 624-0118
Email—unityhalal@aol.com

Owner & Pres.—Akbar Salam
SIC—2011; NAICS—311611; *Meat
processing*
Employs—6; Estab.—1985
Sales—under $500,000
Distrib.—Local
Privately owned corporation

**UNIVERSAL UNIFORM**

1015 Broad St., P.O. Box 637
(07102)
**Phone—(973) 622-5700**
Fax—(973) 622-7934
www.universal-uniform.com
Email—contactus@universal-
uniform.com
Pres.—Paul Marchese
SIC—2311; NAICS—315200;
*Police & firemen uniforms*
Employs—13; Estab.—1974
Sales—under $500,000
Distrib.—Regional
Privately owned sub-S corp.

**VEHICLE SAFETY MFG., LLC**

408 Central Ave. (07107)
**Phone—(973) 643-3000**
National—(800) 832-7233
Fax—(973) 643-2167
www.vehiclesafetymfg.com
Email—ernies@
vehiclesafetymfg.com
Pres.—Ernest Scherler
V-P., GM—Rebecca Kirschman
V-P., Sales, OEM—Fernando
Columbro
Dir., Fin.—Daviel Rivera
SIC—3647; 3625; 3613; NAICS—
336321; *Heavy-duty vehicle
safety & lighting equipment,
including turn signal switches,
LED & auxiliary lighting, stop,
tail, turn signal, clearance,
backup & dome lamps & reflux
reflectors; Brand name—VSM*
Employs—52; Estab.—1979
Sales—$10Mil-$15Mil
150,000 sq ft site, Distrib.—Intl.
Limited Liability Company
ISO rating—14000, 9001:2000,
TS16949:2009

**VIEIRA'S BAKERY**

34-48 Avenue K (07105)
**Phone—(973) 589-7719**
Fax—(973) 589-5144
www.vieirasbakery.com
Pres.—Carlos Vieira
SIC—2051; NAICS—311812;
*Portuguese bread*
Employs—70; Estab.—1968
Sales—$5Mil-$10Mil (est)
90,000 sq ft site, Distrib.—National
Privately owned corporation

**VIEIRAS BAKERY, INC.**

34 Avenue K, Ste. 48 (07105)
**Phone—(973) 465-1212**
Fax—(973) 589-5144
www.vieirasbakery.com
Owner—Carlos Vieira
SIC—2051; *Fresh & frozen
Portuguese breads*
Employs—10
Sales—$1Mil-$2.5Mil (est)

**W & E SALES CO., INC.**

370 Elizabeth Ave. (07112-2708)
**Phone—(973) 824-2000**
National—(800) 932-9009
Fax—(973) 824-7382
www.wesales.com
Email—wemail@wesales.com
GM—R. Carr
SIC—3452; 3429; 5013; 5072;
NAICS—336399; *Manufacturer
& wholesaler of automotive
fasteners, hardware &
specializes body tools for auto
body & auto glass shops*
Employs—15; Estab.—1932
Sales—$1Mil-$2.5Mil (est)
Distrib.—Intl.
Privately owned corporation

GEOGRAPHICAL

## Newark—(cont.)

**W.B. LAW & SON, INC.**
280 Wilson Ave., Unit B (07105)
**Phone—(973) 344-2270**
National—(800) 675-0627
Fax—(973) 344-1917
www.lawcoffee.com
Email—info@lawcoffee.com
Owner—David M. Mendez
Secy-Treas.—Antoinette Marmora
SIC—2095; NAICS—311920;
Coffee & coffee related products
Employs—38; Estab.—1909
Sales—$9Mil-$10Mil
Distrib.—National
Privately owned corporation
DBA: Law Coffee Co.

**WELCO ACETYLENE CORP.**
321 Roanoke Ave. (07105)
**Phone—(973) 465-1043**
Fax—(973) 589-7438
Email—john_j_smith@praxair.com
V.-P.—John Smith
SIC—2813; NAICS—325120;
Acetylene gas
Employs—14; Estab.—1985
Sales—under $500,000
Distrib.—Local
Privately owned corporation

**WIRE FORMING CORP. OF NEW JERSEY**
109 Meeker Ave., Ste. 135 (07114)
**Phone—(973) 824-5558**
Fax—(973) 824-4358
Email—njwire@verizon.net
Pres.—Donato Iannascolio
SIC—3496; Custom wire displays & four slide products
Employs—20; Estab.—1967
Sales—$1Mil-$2.5Mil
20,000 sq ft site, Distrib.—National
Sole ownership

**WOODWORK 4 U, LLC**
205 Frelinghuysen Ave. (07114)
**Phone—(973) 643-3044**
Fax—(973) 643-3034
www.woodwork4ullc.com
Email—woodwork4ullc@yahoo.com
Pres.—Michal Jenicek
SIC—2434; 2541; NAICS—337110; Wooden kitchen cabinets & showcases, including installation
Employs—5; Estab.—1990
Sales—$500,000-$1Mil
16,000 sq ft site, Distrib.—Regional
Privately owned partnership

**WORKSHOP STONE**
281 Mount Pleasant Ave. (07104)
**Phone—(973) 230-9212**
Fax—(973) 230-9213
www.workshopstone.com
Email—sales@workshopstone.com
Owner—Carlos Jaramallo
SIC—3281; Marble & granite countertop fabrication
Employs—2; Estab.—2009
Sales—under $500,000
Distrib.—National
Sole ownership

**ZAGO MFG. CO., INC.**
21 E. Runyon St. (07114)
**Phone—(973) 643-6700**
Fax—(973) 643-4433
www.sealingscrews.com
Email—info@zago.com
Pres.—Harvey Rottenstrich
SIC—3452; 3053; NAICS—332722; Self-sealing fasteners, nuts, toggle switch boots & panel bushing seals
Employs—24; Estab.—1993
Distrib.—Local
Privately owned corporation

**ZVONKO STULIC & SON, INC.**
21 Main St. (07105)
**Phone—(973) 589-3773**
www.zssfabrication.com
Email—ziggy@zssfabrication.com
Pres.—Zvonko Stulic
SIC—3444; 3443; Plate & sheet metal fabrication, welding & general machining job shop
Employs—5; Estab.—1986
Sales—under $500,000
5,000 sq ft site, Distrib.—National
Privately owned sub-S corp.

## Newfield
(Gloucester—S.W.)

**ART STONE PRODUCTS**
113 Church St., P.O. Box 10 (08344)
**Phone—(856) 697-5895**
Fax—(856) 697-5897
Pres.—Thomas Paul
Off. Mgr.—Jenna Rizzo
SIC—3281; NAICS—327991; Cast stone products
Employs—25; Estab.—1986
Sales—$1Mil-$2.5Mil (est)
Distrib.—Local

**GRAPHIC TECHNIQUES, LLC**
10 S. West Blvd., P.O. Box 4 (08344)
**Phone—(856) 697-2480**
Fax—(856) 697-9214
Email—graphictechniques@comcast.net
Pres.—Darryl Erickson
GM—Michelle Meehan
SIC—2759; 2791; NAICS—323122; Commercial printing & typesetting
Employs—3; Estab.—2005
Sales—under $500,000
Distrib.—National
Limited Liability Company

**NEW ERA ENTERPRISES, INC.**
208 N. West Blvd., Rear (08344)
Mail addr: P.O. Box 747, Vineland (08362)
**Phone—(856) 794-2005**
Fax—(856) 697-8727
www.newera-spectro.com
Email—cs@newera-spectro.com
Pres.—Frank Bosco
GM—Stephanie L. Bosco
SIC—3821; NAICS—339111; Scientific glassware
Employs—7; Estab.—1984
2,000 sq ft site, Distrib.—Intl.
Privately owned sub-S corp.

## Newfoundland
(Passaic—N.E.)

**ATLANTIC RUBBER ENTERPRISES**
35 Union Valley Rd. (07435)
**Phone—(973) 697-5900**
Fax—(973) 208-0709
Email—atlanticrubber@verizon.net
Pres.—Phillip Corbae
Fin. Mgr.—Jo Corbae
SIC—3052; NAICS—326220; Hose assemblies
Employs—3; Estab.—1973
8,000 sq ft site, Distrib.—National
Privately owned corporation
DBA: Hercules World Industries

**FIBER-LITE MFG. CO., INC.**
1152 Greenpond Rd. (07435)
**Phone—(973) 208-1300**
Fax—(973) 208-1313
www.fiberliteawnings.com
Email—sales@fiberliteawnings.com
Owner—Joe Taranto
SIC—2394; NAICS—314912; Custom canvas awnings & canopies
Employs—5; Estab.—1980
Sales—$500,000-$1Mil
Distrib.—Regional
Privately owned corporation

**PHOENIX PRECISION, INC.**
2963 Route 23 (07435)
**Phone—(973) 208-8877**
Pres.—Edward F. Wolos III
Off. Mgr.—Pam Cavallaro
SIC—3599; Precision machining job shop
Employs—12; Estab.—1992
8,400 sq ft site, Distrib.—National
Privately owned corporation

**R G I, INC.**
27 Union Valley Rd. (07435)
**Phone—(973) 697-2624**
Fax—(973) 697-0550
Email—rgiinc@optonline.net
Pres.—Barry Maloney
V.-P.—Ray Christian
SIC—3599; 3494; 3492; 3561; NAICS—332912; CNC machining of valves, pumps & manifolds
Employs—16; Estab.—1977
16,000 sq ft site, Distrib.—National
Privately owned corporation

## Newport
(Cumberland—S.W.)

**HANSON AGGREGATE BMC**
Div. of Lehigh Hanson, Inc.
1101 Railroad Ave. (08345)
**Phone—(856) 447-4294**
Fax—(856) 447-4298
www.hanson.com
Email—dhergert@lehighcement.com
Sales Mgr.—Dave Hergert
Gen. Supt.—Al Lorenzo
SIC—1442; NAICS—212321; Sand & gravel processing
Employs—25; Estab.—1981
Distrib.—Regional
Publicly owned corporation
Parent co.—Lehigh Hanson, Inc., Irving, TX
Phone—(972) 653-5500
See Parent Co. Section for full profile.

**NOVAK CO., TONY**
185 Bayview Rd., P.O. Box 333 (08345)
**Phone—(856) 649-4171**
National—(800) 609-0783
Fax—(888) 581-0788
www.tonynovak.com
Email—tonynovakcpa@gmail.com
Owner—Tony Novak
SIC—2741; Financial & tax planning guide publishing; Brand name—Employer's Guide to Health Reimbursement Arrangements; Small Business Owners Guide to Employee Benefit Plans
Employs—1; Estab.—1987
Distrib.—National
Sole ownership

## Newton
(Sussex—N.W.)

**A & L PLASTICS CO., INC.**
2 Municipal Rd., P.O. Box 160 (07860)
**Phone—(973) 383-2221**
National—(888) 385-5031
Fax—(973) 383-3203
www.alplastics.com
Email—mike@alplastics.com
Pres.—Michael O'Shea
SIC—3089; Custom plastic extrusion, raised floor grommets, molding & trim edge
Employs—10; Estab.—1961
33,000 sq ft site, Distrib.—Intl.
Privately owned corporation

**ADVANTAGE SIGNS, FLAGS & BANNERS/ COUNTRY CROSSINGS**
130 Newton Sparta Rd. (07860)
**Phone—(973) 579-3880**
Fax—(973) 579-7327
Owner—Glenn Gerard
SIC—3993; Interior & exterior signs & banners
Employs—1; Estab.—1986
Sales—under $500,000
Distrib.—Regional
Sole ownership
AKA: Advantage Flags

**ALESSANDRA MISCELLANEOUS METALWORKS, INC.**
75-B Mill St. (07860)
**Phone—(973) 786-6805**
Fax—(973) 786-7302
www.alessandra-metalworks.com
Email—ammwinc@yahoo.com
Owner—Scott Alessandra
SIC—3446; 3599; NAICS—332323; Steel stair, rail & ladder fabrication & welding job shop
Employs—7; Estab.—1990
Distrib.—Local
Privately owned corporation

**ARTISAN AWNING CO.**
17 Jefferson St., P.O. Box 387 (07860)
**Phone—(973) 383-5608**
Fax—(973) 300-3099
www.artisanawnings.com
Owner—Randall R. De Groat
SIC—2394; Custom canvas awnings & canopies
Employs—2; Estab.—1982
Sales—under $500,000 (est)
2,000 sq ft site, Distrib.—Local
Privately owned corporation

**AUTOMATIC MACHINE PRODUCTS**
56 Paterson Ave. (07860)
**Phone—(973) 383-9929**
Fax—(973) 383-5569
Owner—Don Schanstra
GM—Tina Schanstra
SIC—3599; General machining job shop
Employs—5; Estab.—1977
Sales—$500,000-$1Mil
Distrib.—Intl.
Sole ownership

**BILL MARTIN MACHINE, LLC**
56 Paterson Ave., Ste. 112 (07860)
**Phone—(973) 300-5052**
Fax—(973) 300-5053
Email—billmartinmachine@yahoo.com
Owner—Bill Martin
SIC—3599; CNC machining job shop
Employs—1; Estab.—2007
Sales—under $500,000
Distrib.—Local
Limited Liability Company

**CARSTENS PUBLICATIONS, INC.**
108 Phil Hardin Rd. (07860)
**Phone—(973) 383-3355**
Fax—(973) 383-4064
www.carstens-publications.com
Email—carstens@carstenspublications.com
Pres.—Henry R. Carstens
Adv. Mgr.—John Early
SIC—2721; Magazine publishing
Employs—20; Estab.—1931
Sales—$500,000-$1Mil
Distrib.—Local
Privately owned corporation

© Copyright 2015 Manufacturers' News, Inc.

## Newton—(cont.)

**CUSTOM WOOD FURNITURE, INC.**
37 E. Clinton St., P.O. Box 3034 (07860)
**Phone—(973) 579-4880**
Fax—(973) 579-0070
www.cwfinc.biz
Email—jd@customwoodfurnitureinc.com
Pres.—John Kweselait
V-P., Opers.—Arkadius Wysocki
Off. Mgr.—Janice Denning
SIC—2434; 2542; 3083; NAICS—337110; *Wooden & laminated cabinets*
Employs—15; Estab.—1989
Sales—over $1Mil
10,000 sq ft site, Distrib.—National
Privately owned corporation

**ENGINEERED SILICONE PRODUCTS, LLC**
75 Mill St., Ste. 2 (07860)
**Phone—(973) 300-5120**
National—(888) 932-7377
Fax—(973) 300-5125
www.wearesp.com
Email—sales@wearesp.com
Opers. Mgr.—Lynn Haberman
Sales Rep.—Matt Doering
SIC—3842; *Silicone medical devices, including silicone gel orthotic distal end pads, gel discs, suction valves, knee sleeves & joint alignment devices*
Employs—5; Estab.—1996
Distrib.—Intl.
Limited Liability Company

**FOUR STAR REPRODUCTION, INC.**
52 Paterson Ave., Ste. 2 (07860-2308)
**Phone—(862) 268-8200**
National—(800) 635-7351
Fax—(862) 268-8201
www.fourstarcolor.com
Email—johns@fourstarcolor.com
Pres.—Charles Cioppa
Cont.—John Stropole
Opers. Mgr.—Dennis Bittleman
SIC—2759; 2752; 2657; 2791; NAICS—323122; *Commercial offset & digital printing, electronic prepress & binding for the pharmaceutical, food & cosmetic industries & paper folding boxes for the packaging industry*
Employs—35; Estab.—1966
Sales—$5Mil-$6Mil
28,000 sq ft site, Distrib.—National
Privately owned corporation
AKA: Four Star Color

**FREDON DEVELOPMENT INDUSTRIES**
393 State Route 94 S. (07860)
**Phone—(973) 383-7576**
Fax—(973) 383-5982
www.fredondevelopment.com
Email—pmatonis@fredondevelopment.com
Pres.—Jerry Wildrick
Off. Mgr.—Patricia Matonis
SIC—3544; 3543; NAICS—332997; *Plastic custom component prototype molds for the automotive, cosmetics, electrical, electronics, medical & safety industries*
Employs—11; Estab.—1973
Distrib.—National
Privately owned corporation

**HORIZON TOOL & MOLD, INC.**
56 Paterson Ave. (07860)
**Phone—(973) 300-0393**
Fax—(973) 300-5697
Co-Pres.—Don Van De Moere
Co-Pres.—Jim O'Donnell
SIC—3544; NAICS—333500; *Molds & tool & die job shop*
Employs—2; Estab.—1997
Sales—under $500,000
Distrib.—Local
Privately owned sub-S corp.

**IMAGEPOINT SCREEN PRINTING**
69 Water St. (07860)
**Phone—(908) 684-1768**
National—(888) 727-5615
www.myimagepoint.com
Email—customerservice@myimagepoint.com
Owner & Pres.—John Fernicola
SIC—2396; *Custom imprinted apparel*
Employs—12
Sales—$500,000-$1Mil
Distrib.—National
Limited Liability Company

**MINISINK PRESS, INC.**
2 Water St., P.O. Box 278 (07860)
**Phone—(973) 383-1350**
Fax—(973) 383-7504
www.minisinkpress.com
Email—info@minisinkpress.com
Pres.—Tom Delaney, Jr.
SIC—2759; NAICS—323100; *Commercial printing*
Employs—2; Estab.—1959
Sales—under $500,000
1,800 sq ft site, Distrib.—Local
Privately owned corporation

**MIRA PLASTICS CO., INC.**
1 Mira Ave., Fredon Twp., P. O. Box 399 (07860)
**Phone—(973) 383-6380**
Fax—(973) 383-3803
www.miraplastics.com
Email—sales@miraplastics.com
Pres.—Anthony Miragliotta
V-P.—Anthony P. Miragliotta
Treas.—Tina Miragliotta
SIC—3089; 2759; 3599; NAICS—323100; *Thermoplastic injection molding, hot stamping, screen printing, ultrasonic welding & heat transfer indexing*
Employs—25; Estab.—1955
Sales—$1Mil-$5Mil
62,000 sq ft site, Distrib.—Intl.
Privately owned sub-S corp.

**MRI INTERNATIONAL**
44-50 Clinton St. (07860)
**Phone—(973) 383-3645**
Fax—(973) 383-6672
www.mri-diazo.com
Email—mridiazo@goes.com
Pres.—William Foltyn
Dir.—Cynthia Foltyn
Corp. Mgr.—Diane Apostola
SIC—3861; 3552; NAICS—333293; *Sensitizers for the offset lithographic & screen printing industries; Brand name—Diazon-7; Diazon-7LZ; CMI-18; Diazo Oil SS*
Employs—7; Estab.—1969
Sales—$1Mil-$2.5Mil
12,000 sq ft site, Distrib.—Intl.
Privately owned corporation
AKA: Molecular Rearrangement, Inc.

**NATIONAL LECITHIN, INC. (H Q)**
93 Spring St., Ste. 303 (07860)
**Phone—(973) 940-8920**
Fax—(973) 940-8921
www.nationallecithin.com
Email—info@nationallecithin.com
Pres.—Patricia Bruno
SIC—2075; *Corporate headquarters; soybean lecithin (mfg. done at company-owned facility in Easton, PA)*
Employs—2; Estab.—1976
Sales—$2.5Mil-$5Mil (est)
Distrib.—Regional
Privately owned corporation

**NEW JERSEY HERALD, THE**
Div. of Quincy Newspapers, Inc.
2 Spring St., P.O. Box 10 (07860)
**Phone—(973) 383-1500**
National—(800) 424-3725
Fax—(973) 383-8477
www.njherald.com
Email—newsroom@njherald.com
Interim Publisher & Dir., Adv. & Mktg.—Keith Flinn
Editor & GM—Bruce Tomlinson
Adv. Mgr.—Nicole Hammer
SIC—2711; *Newspaper publishing*
Employs—60; Estab.—1829
Sales—$1Mil-$5Mil
Distrib.—Local
Privately owned corporation
Parent co.—Quincy Newspapers, Inc., Quincy, IL
Phone—(217) 223-5100
See Parent Co. Section for full profile.

**NEWCO, INC.**
1 Hicks Ave. (07860)
**Phone—(973) 383-7777**
Fax—(973) 383-0506
www.newcoprinting.com
Email—newco@nac.net
Pres.—James Berezny
V-P., Mfg. & GM—Jesse Alexander
Off. Mgr.—Loraine Mcintosh
Pur. Agt.—Linda Berezny
SIC—2679; NAICS—322200; *Vinyl wall coverings*
Employs—62; Estab.—1978
Sales—$10Mil-$25Mil
Distrib.—National
Privately owned corporation

**NEWTON T & M CORP.**
119 Fredon Springdale Rd. (07860)
**Phone—(973) 383-1232**
Fax—(973) 383-3819
Pres., Plt. Mgr.—Ralph Meola
SIC—3089; 3544; NAICS—333500; *Plastic injection molding & molds*
Employs—8; Estab.—1962
Sales—$1Mil-$2.5Mil
Distrib.—Regional
Privately owned corporation

**POWER MIST RACING, LLC**
67 Stickles Pond Rd. (07860)
**Phone—(973) 383-1061**
Fax—(973) 579-5185
www.powermist.com
Pres.—Rick Fales
SIC—2911; NAICS—324110; *Racing oils, lubricants & fuels; Brand name—Power Mist*
Employs—1; Estab.—1954
5,000 sq ft site, Distrib.—Intl.
Limited Liability Company

**SCHNEIDER & MARQUARD, INC.**
112 Phil Hardin Rd., P.O. Box 39 (07860)
**Phone—(973) 383-2200**
Fax—(973) 383-6529
www.schneidermarquard.com
Email—info@schneidermarquard.com
Pres.—Michael J. O'Shea
V-P. & Prodn. Mgr.—Michael P. O'Shea
Sales Mgr.—Laura O'Brien
Engrg. Mgr.—Ian Bates
Qual. Control Mgr.—Colleen Rice
SIC—3544; NAICS—333500; *Retaining rings & tool & die job shop & micro-hole punching machine*
Employs—22; Estab.—1931
Distrib.—Intl.
Privately owned sub-S corp.

**SCHRADER & CO., INC.**
188 Halsey Rd. (07860)
**Phone—(973) 579-2700**
Fax—(973) 579-1806
www.schraderandcoinc.com
Email—sales@schraderandcoinc.com
Pres.—David Lake
Sales Mgr.—Dan Kovach
SIC—3444; 3599; NAICS—332322; *Precision sheet metal & machined components*
Employs—10; Estab.—1980
Sales—$1Mil-$2.5Mil
14,000 sq ft site, Distrib.—National
Privately owned sub-S corp.

**SCREEN CREATIONS PLUS**
8 Hillside Ave. (07860)
**Phone—(973) 579-5015**
Owner—Dawn Alvarez
SIC—2396; 2395; *Textile screen printing & embroidery*
Employs—2; Estab.—1993
Sales—under $500,000
Distrib.—Local
Sole ownership

**SIMPLE STEP, LLC**
12 W. Owassa Tpke. *(07860)*
**Phone—(973) 948-2938**
Fax—(973) 948-0182
www.simplestep.com
Email—sales@simplestep.com
Pres.—Charles Grenz
V-P.—Toni Ree
SIC—3823; NAICS—334513; *Motion controllers for the automation, instrumentation & robotic industries; Brand name—Simple Step; SSNEMA17; SSMicro; SSXYMicro; SSXYZMicro; SSMicroMC; SSXYQE; SSXYZMicroMC; SSCBGecko; SSXYGecko; SSXYZGecko*
Employs—10; Estab.—1999
Sales—$500,000-$1Mil
Distrib.—Intl.
Privately owned sub-S corp.

**SKYLANDS PRESS**
57 Trinity St., P.O. Box 809 (07860)
**Phone—(973) 383-5006**
Owner—John Daly
SIC—2759; *Commercial printing*
Employs—3; Estab.—1991
Sales—$500,000-$1Mil
Distrib.—Local
Privately owned corporation

**SPECTRUM TOOL**
56 Paterson Ave. (07860)
**Phone—(973) 579-0087**
Fax—(973) 579-0089
Pres., CFO—Steve Denison
V-P., Fin.—Scott Martin
SIC—3599; *General machining job shop*
Employs—3; Estab.—1993
Sales—under $500,000
2,500 sq ft site, Distrib.—Regional
Privately owned corporation

**STUART MILLS, INC.**
25 Stillwater Rd. (07860)
**Phone—(973) 579-5717**
Fax—(973) 579-2507
www.millsplastics.com
Email—smillsco@earthlink.net
Pres.—Stuart Mills
GM—Charles Wolfrum
Acct. & MIS Mgr.—John LaFiura
Prodn. Mgr.—Frank Suydan
R & D Mgr.—Joe Costa
Fin. Mgr.—John Michaels
SIC—3599; 3089; 3444; 5162; *CNC milling & turning, sheet metal & plastic fabrication & distributor of plastic*
Employs—6; Estab.—1993
3,000 sq ft site, Distrib.—National
Limited Liability Company

**THORLABS, INC.**
56 Sparta Ave. (07860)
**Phone—(973) 300-3000**
Fax—(973) 300-3600

GEOGRAPHICAL

## Newton—(cont.)

www.thorlabs.com
Email—sales@thorlabs.com
Pres., CEO—Alex Cable
CFO—Robert Regimbal
COO—Carmine Lencsak
Strategic Mktg. Mgr.—Tyler Morgus
Mktg. Comms. Mgr.—Laurie Morgus
SIC—3674; 3826; 3827; 3829; NAICS—334413; *Corporate headquarters & optomechanical, motion control, nanopositioning, fiber alignment & fiber & optical components, including fiber, adaptive, polarization & IR optics, IR detectors, optical isolators & laser power meters & systems*
Employs—850; Estab.—1987
Sales—$100Mil-$250Mil
36,700 sq ft site, Distrib.—Intl.
Privately owned corporation

---

## Norma

(Salem—S.W.)

**B & B POULTRY CO., INC.**
Almond Rd., P.O. Box 307 (08347)
**Phone—(856) 692-8893**
Fax—(856) 692-0438
Email—information@bandbpoultry.com
Pres.—Mark Fisher
GM—Josh Fisher
Opers. & Qual. Control Mgr.—Louis Rothman
Off. Mgr.—Maria Guedara
SIC—2015; *Poultry processing*
Employs—150; Estab.—1945
Sales—$10Mil-$25Mil (est)
Distrib.—Local
Privately owned corporation

---

## North Arlington

(Bergen—N.E.)

**ARISTA CUSTOM TAPES, INC.**
20 Argyle Pl. (07031)
**Phone—(201) 997-7610**
Fax—(201) 997-7175
Pres.—Thoms Lefkowitz
SIC—2752; NAICS—323100; *Label & tape printing*
Employs—7
Sales—$500,000-$1Mil (est)
Distrib.—Regional

**ATLANTIC KENMARK ELECTRIC, INC.**
11 Ewing Ave. (07031)
**Phone—(201) 991-2117**
Fax—(201) 991-1752
www.atlantickenmark.com
Email—atlantickenmark@comcast.net
Pres., Fin., MIS & R & D Mgr.—Salvatore Gaccione
V-P.—Frank Gaccione
Treas. & Foreman—Vince Gaccione
SIC—3621; NAICS—335312; *Rebuilt electric motors*
Employs—15; Estab.—1978
Sales—$1Mil-$5Mil
5,090 sq ft site, Distrib.—Regional
Privately owned corporation

**BAYWAY LUMBER**
43 Porete Ave. (07031)
Mail addr: P.O. Box 368, Kearny (07032)
**Phone—(201) 991-4200**
Fax—(201) 991-6500
www.baywaylumber.com
Email—todd@baywaylumber.com
Pres. & V-P.—Todd Anderson

SIC—2421; *Lumber processing*
Employs—8; Estab.—1926
70,000 sq ft site, Distrib.—Local
Limited Liability Company

**C & F BURNER CO.**
39 River Rd., P.O. Box 7189 (07031)
**Phone—(201) 998-8083**
Fax—(201) 955-0858
Pres.—Elizabeth Dunn
Off. Mgr.—Jackie Semaca
SIC—3823; *Heating controls for boilers & water heaters*
Employs—34; Estab.—1959
Sales—$5Mil-$10Mil (est)
Distrib.—Regional
Privately owned corporation

**CLAYTON BLOCK CO., INC**
Div. of Clayton Block Co., Inc.
2 Porete Ave. (07031)
Mail addr: P.O. Box 3015, Lakewood (08701-9015)
**Phone—(201) 955-6292**
Fax—(201) 998-3637
www.claytonco.com
Email—katroeclay@aol.com
Gen. Sales Mgr.—Joseph Scaramuzzo
SIC—3271; NAICS—327331; *Concrete block & architectural precast*
Employs—32
Distrib.—Regional
Privately owned corporation
Parent co.—Clayton Block Co., Inc., Neptune, NJ
Phone—(732) 751-7600
See Parent Co. Section for full profile.

**HAWARD CORPORATION**
29 Porete Ave. (07031)
**Phone—(201) 991-8777**
Fax—(201) 991-1903
www.haward.com
Email—sales@haward.com
Pres.—Dean Ward, Jr.
V-P.—Keith J. Schumacher
Cont.—Athens Zambalis
Hum. Res. Mgr.—Anne Zames
SIC—3471; 3479; NAICS—332813; *Metal finishing, including electropolishing, passivation, solid film lubricants & fluorocarbon & powder coatings*
Employs—42; Estab.—1947
40,000 sq ft site, Distrib.—National
Privately owned sub-S corp.
ISO rating—9001:2000

**MINUTEMAN PRESS OF NORTH ARLINGTON**
75 Ridge Rd. (07031)
**Phone—(201) 991-1030**
Fax—(201) 991-0139
www.na.minutemanpress.com
Email—djabini@minutemanpress.com
V-P.—Amir Djabini
SIC—2752; 2791; 2789; 2771; NAICS—323100; *Instant printing, electronic prepress, binding & greeting cards*
Employs—5; Estab.—1980
Sales—under $500,000
Distrib.—Regional
Limited Liability Company
AKA: iKreative VC

**MR. PASTA**
159 Ridge Rd. (07031)
**Phone—(201) 991-5959**
Fax—(201) 991-1011
Owner & GM—Silvano Masiero
SIC—2098; NAICS—311823; *Pasta*
Employs—5; Estab.—1974
Sales—under $500,000
1,000 sq ft site, Distrib.—Local
Privately owned corporation

**PAR-METAL, INC.**
29 Ewing Ave. (07031)
**Phone—(201) 955-0800**
National—(800) 747-1209
Fax—(201) 955-2332
www.par-metal.com
Email—sales@par-metal.com
Pres.—John Ango
SIC—3469; 3444; *Steel & aluminum electronic enclosures, housings & chassis*
Employs—10; Estab.—1983
Sales—$500,000-$1Mil
16,000 sq ft site, Distrib.—Intl.
Publicly owned corporation

**TEMPERATURE PROCESSING CO., INC.**
228 River Rd. (07031)
**Phone—(201) 991-8000**
Fax—(201) 991-8014
Email—willtpc@verizon.net
Pres.—William J. Engelhard
Contract Review Specialist—Veronica Morales
SIC—3398; NAICS—332811; *Metal heat treating*
Employs—10; Estab.—1956
10,000 sq ft site, Distrib.—Local
Privately owned corporation

**WHITE EAGLE MONUMENTAL CO., INC.**
257 Ridge Rd. (07031)
**Phone—(201) 991-0094**
National—(800) 214-1822
Fax—(201) 991-0008
www.whiteeaglemonument.com
Email—weagle1@verizon.net
Pres.—Florence Dean
V-P.—Joseph A. Dean
SIC—3281; NAICS—327991; *Burial grave monuments & sandblast lettering*
Employs—2; Estab.—1926
Distrib.—Local
Privately owned corporation

---

## North Bergen

(Hudson—N.E.)

**†A & A IRON & METAL CO., LLC**
2006 40th St. (07047)
**Phone—(201) 865-1370**
www.njscrapmetals.com
Email—info@njscrapmetals.com
Member—Robert Albericci
Member—Deborah Albericci
SIC—5093; *Wholesaler of recycled scrap metals, ferrous & nonferrous metals, copper, aluminum, stainless steel, brass, iron & steel, including roll-off container service*
Employs—7; Estab.—1954
Distrib.—Regional
Limited Liability Company

**ALL LACE PROCESSING CORP.**
1109 Grand Ave., Unit 4 (07047)
**Phone—(201) 867-8795**
Fax—(201) 867-7008
www.alllace.com
Email—key@alllace.com
Pres.—Key Gaetano
V-P., Opers.—Frank Gaetano
SIC—2241; NAICS—313221; *Lace cutting & separating*
Employs—15; Estab.—1981
20,000 sq ft site, Distrib.—Local
Privately owned corporation

**ALLIED PUMP CORPORATION**
1109 Grand Ave., Bldg. 5 *(07047)*
**Phone—(201) 798-3277**
Fax—(201) 798-8781
www.allied-pump.com
Email—alliedpumps@gmail.com
Pres.—Benjamin Miller
Bookkeeper—Maria Raia

SIC—3561; 5084; NAICS—333911; *Manufacturer & distributor of boiler feed, booster, condensate, HVAC, sump & sewage pumps & systems, including float balls, switches & rods, alternator, pressure, disconnect & safety switches, relays, solenoid vlaves & magnetic starters; Brand name—AO Smith; Armstrong; ASCO; Ashcroft; Aurora; Baldor; Barnes; Burks; Cla-Val; Crane; Dunham Bush; Dwyer; Furnas Controls; Gast; Grundfos; Hayward; Hoffman; Honeywell; Johnson Controls; Kraissl; Liberty; Little Giant*
Employs—15; Estab.—1963
Sales—$2.5Mil-$5Mil
Distrib.—National
Privately owned corporation

**ALLIED SPECIALTY GROUP, INC.**
3114 Tonnelle Ave. (07047)
**Phone—(201) 223-4600**
Fax—(201) 863-5701
www.alliedmetal.com
Email—info@alliedmetal.com
Pres.—Henry H. Bilge
Opers. Mgr.—Barry Sloan
SIC—3448; NAICS—337215; *Aluminum composite panels systems & column cover systems for building structures; Brand name—Estolga Attachment*
Employs—5; Estab.—2007
Distrib.—National
Privately owned corporation

**NEW ENTRY**
**ALVARO STAIRS, LLC**
4201 Tonnelle Ave., Ste. 12 (07047)
**Phone—(201) 864-6754**
Email—alvarostairs@yahoo.com
Principal—Enrique Bernar
SIC—2431; *Wooden stairs*
Employs—5
Sales—$500,000-$1Mil (est)
Limited Liability Company

**AMPERITE CO.**
Div. of Olympic Controls Corp.
4201 Tonnelle Ave., Ste. 6 (07047)
**Phone—(201) 864-9503**
National—(800) 752-2329
Fax—(201) 864-3955
www.amperite.com
Email—info@amperite.com
V-P., Admn. & Sales & Hum. Res. Mgr.—Judith Johnson
V-P., Engrg. & Pur. & Mfg. Mgr.—Frank Kretkowski
SIC—3679; 3625; NAICS—335314; *Time delay relays, flashers & industrial controls*
Employs—20; Estab.—1922
Sales—$2.6Mil-$5Mil
6,000 sq ft site, Distrib.—Intl.
Privately owned corporation
Parent co.—Olympic Controls Corp., Elgin, IL
Phone—(847) 742-3566
See Parent Co. Section for full profile.

**ARAM, INC., MICHAEL**
2102 83rd St. (07047)
**Phone—(201) 758-2551**
National—(866) 792-2726
Fax—(201) 758-2553
www.michaelaram.com
Email—info@michaelaram.com
Pres.—Michael Wolohojis
IT Mgr.—Myra Banzuela
Hum. Res. Mgr.—Armando Dabalus
Cust. Serv. Mgr.—Tom Cribbin

## North Bergen—(cont.)

SIC—3499; 3429; 2514; *Hand-crafted metal tableware, hardware & furniture*
Employs—7; Estab.—1997
Sales—under $500,000
Distrib.—Regional
Privately owned corporation

### ARC PLASMET CORP.

4131 Bergen Tpke. (07047)
**Phone—(201) 867-8533**
Fax—(201) 867-7023
www.arcplasmet.com
Email—arcplasmet@gmail.com
Pres.—Tony Calana
SIC—3089; *Plastic fabrication & machining job shop*
Employs—9; Estab.—1970
Sales—$500,000-$1Mil
7,500 sq ft site, Distrib.—Local
Privately owned corporation

### ARMCO COMPRESSOR PRODUCTS CORP.

2042 46th St. *(07047)*
**Phone—(201) 866-6766**
Fax—(201) 866-0360
www.armcocompressor.com
Email—sales@armcocompressor.com
Pres.—Ara Zadourian
SIC—3563; NAICS—333912; *Air & process compressor components*
Employs—11; Estab.—1970
Sales—$4Mil-$5Mil
Distrib.—National

### ARMEL ELECTRONICS, INC.

1601 75th St. (07047)
**Phone—(201) 869-4300**
National—(800) 840-0666
Fax—(201) 869-4304
www.armel.us
Email—info@armel.us
Pres.—Edward D. Johnsen
Sales Mgr.—Linda Mercado
Qual. Control Mgr.—Ole Flandrup
SIC—3679; 3643; NAICS—335931; *Electronic components for military & commercial enterprises; Brand name—Armel KELVIN Socket; Armel Miniature Stand-Off terminals*
Employs—19; Estab.—1949
26,000 sq ft site, Distrib.—National
Privately owned corporation
ISO rating—9001:2008

### BAL TOGS INDUSTRIES

6605-09 Smith Ave. (07047)
**Phone—(201) 866-0201**
National—(800) 992-6629
Fax—(201) 861-1177
www.baltogs.com
Email—ed@baltogs.com
Pres.—Bruce Kopelman
V-P., Sales—Edward McDaniel
Mktg. Mgr.—John Maher
Bookkeeper—Joann Lindsey
SIC—2339; *Dance & exercise clothing*
Employs—100; Estab.—1984
Distrib.—Intl.
Privately owned corporation
AKA: B T Industries

### BERGEN MFG. & SUPPLY CO., INC.

2025 85th St. (07047)
**Phone—(201) 854-3461**
National—(800) 829-7730
Fax—(201) 662-1967
Pres.—Steven Petrone
SIC—3069; *Rubber products*
Employs—10; Estab.—1977
Sales—$1Mil-$2.5Mil (est)
Distrib.—National
Privately owned corporation

### BUDGET PALLET, INC.

3225 Dell Ave. (07047)
**Phone—(201) 330-2800**
Pres.—Ernest Parodi
SIC—2448; NAICS—321920; *Wooden pallets*
Employs—15; Estab.—1987
Sales—$1Mil-$2.5Mil (est)
Distrib.—Local
Privately owned corporation

### C & P EMBROIDERY, LLC

6602 Smith Ave. (07047)
**Phone—(201) 854-0388**
Fax—(201) 854-8092
Pres., Fin. & MIS Mgr.—Ivonne Heguy
SIC—2395; *Military emblems*
Employs—5; Estab.—1981
Sales—under $500,000
2,000 sq ft site, Distrib.—National
Privately owned corporation

### CAPITOL BOX CORP.

1300 6th St. *(07047)*
**Phone—(201) 867-6018**
Fax—(201) 867-4159
www.capitolbox.com
Email—capitolbox@verizon.net
Pres.—Edward Maleh
V-P., Treas.—Edward B. Maleh
Corp. Secy.—Shirley Maleh
Bookkeeper—Kate Carroll
SIC—2652; NAICS—322213; *Rigid set-up paper board boxes*
Employs—26; Estab.—1936
Sales—$1Mil-$5Mil
12,500 sq ft site, Distrib.—National
Privately owned corporation

### CHAMPION INK CO., INC.

2045 88th St. (07047)
**Phone—(201) 868-4100**
Fax—(201) 868-3449
Email—championink@aol.com
Pres.—Ray Czorniewy
Manager—Lenny Porcoro
SIC—2893; NAICS—325910; *Screen printing ink*
Employs—3; Estab.—1965
Sales—$1Mil-$2.5Mil
Distrib.—National
Privately owned corporation

### COLONIAL CONCRETE CO.

9301 Railroad Ave. (07047)
**Phone—(201) 435-9200**
Fax—(201) 869-2504
www.colonialconcrete.com
Email—sales@colonialconcrete.com
V-P., Br. Mgr.—Frank Rizzo
Plt. Mgr.—Bob Daddario
Acctg. Mgr.—Pam Johnson
SIC—3273; NAICS—327320; *Ready-mixed concrete*
Employs—7; Estab.—1970
Sales—$1Mil-$2.5Mil (est)
Distrib.—Local
Privately owned corporation
Parent co.—Colonial Concrete Co., Newark, NJ
Phone—(973) 482-1920
See Parent Co. Section for full profile.

### COLONNA BROTHERS, INC.

4102 Bergen Tpke., P.O. Box 808 *(07047)*
**Phone—(201) 864-1115**
     (800) 626-8384
Fax—(201) 864-0144
www.colonnabrothers.com
Email—customerservice@colonnabrothers.com
Pres.—Peter Colonna
V-P., Opers., Sales & Mktg., Natl.—Elizabeth Cerenov
V-P.—Mark Colonna
Secy-Treas.—Diane Maniscalco
Dir., Logistics—Janelle Colonna

SIC—2022; 2099; NAICS—311513; *Private label & branded grated & shredded cheeses, spices, sprinkles, bread crumbs & Italian specialties; Brand name—Colonna; Spice Farms; Herakles; Risparmio*
Employs—100; Estab.—1918
Varies—100-125
Sales—$60Mil
52,000 sq ft site, Distrib.—National
Privately owned sub-S corp.

### DERMARITE INDUSTRIES, LLC

7777 W. Side Ave., P.O. Box 7209 (07047)
**Phone—(973) 569-9000**
National—(800) 337-6296
Fax—(973) 569-9001
www.dermarite.com
Email—info@dermarite.com
Pres.—Naftali Minzer
V-P., Plt. Opers.—Dominick Palmieri
V-P.—Mark Friedman
Dir., Hum. Res. & Off. Svcs.—Stephanie Turiano
SIC—2834; 2844; NAICS—325412; *Skin, wound & personal care products; Brand name—SilvaKollagen; DermaSyn; DermaGinate; DermaView Foam Levin Guaze Dress Klenz Wash; DermaSeptin*
Employs—98; Estab.—1995
40,000 sq ft site, Distrib.—National
Limited Liability Company

### DRAPERY & MORE, INC.

2321 Kennedy Blvd., Ste. 2401-B-1 (07047)
**Phone—(201) 271-9661**
Fax—(201) 271-9776
Pres.—Ally Espana
V-P.—Marcelino Espana
Bookkeeper—Maria Espana
SIC—2391; 2591; NAICS—314121; *Custom window treatments, including valances, draperies, roman shades, balloons & inter, blackout & regular linings*
Employs—9; Estab.—2003
Sales—under $500,000
Distrib.—Regional
Privately owned corporation

### E.W.E. AUTO SEAT COVER CO.

8431 Kennedy Blvd. *(07047)*
**Phone—(201) 869-6470**
Fax—(201) 868-8491
Email—eweauto@yahoo.com
Pres.—Walter Somick
V-P.—Peter Somick
SIC—3714; *Leather, fabric & vinyl automotive seat covers*
Employs—3; Estab.—1947
Sales—$1Mil-$2.5Mil
Distrib.—Local
Privately owned corporation

### EDISON LITHOGRAPHING CORP.

3725 Tonnelle Ave. (07047)
**Phone—(201) 902-9191**
Fax—(201) 902-0475
www.edisonlitho.com
Email—george@edisonlitho.com
Pres.—George Gross
V-P.—Joseph Ostreicher
Comp.—Joseph Gross
GM—Mel Schwerts
SIC—2759; 2789; NAICS—323122; *Large-format printing & finishing*
Employs—80; Estab.—1958
80,000 sq ft site, Distrib.—National
Privately owned corporation

### FIVE STAR BUILDING PRODUCTS, INC.

2012 86th St. (07047)
**Phone—(201) 869-4181**
Fax—(201) 869-1658
Pres.—Daniel Politi

Prodn. Mgr.—Fred Van Duyne
SIC—3442; 3089; NAICS—332321; *Aluminum & vinyl doors & windows*
Employs—15; Estab.—1976
Sales—$500,000-$1Mil
Distrib.—Local
Privately owned corporation

### FRUTAROM USA, INC.

Div. of ICC Industries, Inc.
9500 Railroad Ave. (07047)
**Phone—(201) 861-9500**
National—(800) 526-7147
Fax—(201) 861-8711
www.frutarom.com
Email—info@frutarom.com
Plt. Mgr.—Gary Bath
IT Mgr.—Shai Lavie
SIC—2087; NAICS—311900; *Flavorings, flavoring extracts, pharma/nutraceuticals & cosmetic ingredients*
Employs—125; Estab.—1933
150,000 sq ft site, Distrib.—Intl.
Privately owned corporation
Parent co.—ICC Industries, Inc., New York, NY
Phone—(212) 521-1700
See Parent Co. Section for full profile.

### GOLD ATTACHMENTS SEWING SUPPLY, INC.

7051 Kennedy Blvd. (07047)
**Phone—(201) 854-0320**
Fax—(201) 854-0320
Pres.—Elsayed Elsamra
V-P.—Wafaa Elsamra
GM—Sayed Elsamra
SIC—2339; 2329; NAICS—315200; *Men's & women's clothing*
Employs—3; Estab.—2001
Sales—under $500,000
Distrib.—Local
Privately owned corporation

### GP CHEMICALS, INC. (H Q)

7225 Bergenline Ave. (07047)
**Phone—(201) 869-2200**
Fax—(201) 869-2209
www.gpchemicals.com
Email—michael@gpchemicals.com
Pres.—Michael Politopoulos
SIC—2869; *Corporate headquarters; specialty & fine chemicals for the rubber, adhesive, aerospace, electronics & coating industries (mfg. subcontracted)*
Employs—2; Estab.—1982
Sales—$500,000-$1Mil (est)
Distrib.—Intl.
Privately owned corporation

### H2L, LLC

4201 Tonnelle Ave., Ste. 2 (07047)
**Phone—(201) 864-0060**
Fax—(201) 864-2467
www.h2ldesign.com
Off. Mgr.—Michelle Bastiar
SIC—2431; 2541; 2542; *Commercial & residential wooden millwork & wooden & laminate cabinets, casework & store fixtures*
Employs—9
Sales—$1Mil-$2.5Mil (est)
12,000 sq ft site, Distrib.—Local
Limited Liability Company

### HICKORY INDUSTRIES, INC.

4900 W. Side Ave. (07047)
**Phone—(201) 223-0050**
National—(800) 732-9153
Fax—(201) 223-0950
www.hickorybbq.com
Email—customerservice@hickorybbq.com
Pres.—Steven Amroti

GEOGRAPHICAL

## North Bergen—(cont.)

SIC—3589; 3559; NAICS—333319; *Rotisseries, pizza ovens, warmers & specialty grills*
Employs—30; Estab.—1946
Sales—$10Mil-$25Mil
46,000 sq ft site, Distrib.—Intl.
Privately owned sub-S corp.

**HIGHWAY BODY WORKS, INC.**
8600 Tonnelle Ave. (07047)
**Phone—(201) 869-0900**
Fax—(201) 869-4402
Email—highwaybody@aol.com
Pres.—Raymond Koeppel
V-P., GM—Steve Koeppel
SIC—3713; NAICS—336211; *Rebuilt truck bodies*
Employs—8; Estab.—1948
Sales—$500,000-$1Mil
Distrib.—Local
Privately owned corporation

**HUDSON BREAD**
5601-5711 Tonnelle Ave. (07047)
**Phone—(201) 422-7900**
Fax—(201) 422-0199
www.hudsonbread.com
Email—info@hudsonbread.com
Pres.—Mariusz Kolodziej
V-P., Sales—Rafal Bieluch
V-P., Prodn.—Raymond Million
Cont.—Lucy Lubrano
Accountant—Anna Sledz
SIC—2051; NAICS—311812; *Artisan bread; Brand name—Hudson Breads; Hudson Bread South; Prestige Bread; Breadman*
Employs—90; Estab.—1994
60,000 sq ft site, Distrib.—Regional
Privately owned corporation

†**HUDSON HEATING WHOLESALER, INC.**
1109 Grand Ave., Ste. 1 (07047)
**Phone—(201) 348-6700**
Fax—(201) 348-8906
www.hudsonheatingwholesaler.com
Email—info@hudsonheatingwholesaler.com
Pres.—Chris Connell
Secy-Treas.—Thomas Halleran
Sales Mgr.—David Vaccaro
SIC—5075; *Distributor of HVAC supplies*
Employs—12; Estab.—1963
Sales—$6Mil-$8Mil
Distrib.—Local
Privately owned sub-S corp.

†**HUDSON NEWS DISTRIBUTORS, LLC**
5903 W. Side Ave. (07047)
**Phone—(201) 867-3600**
National—(888) 648-3766
Fax—(201) 867-0067
www.hudsongroupusa.com
Email—info@hudsongroup.com
Corp. V-P., IS—David Blish
Cont.—Roy Feliciano
Dist. Mgr.—Ronald Clark
SIC—5192; *Company headquarters & distributor of magazines & books*
Employs—645; Estab.—1926
Distrib.—Regional
Privately owned corporation

**J & J CORP., INC.**
8607 River Rd. (07047)
**Phone—(201) 313-0900**
Fax—(201) 313-3205
www.jandjcorp.com
Email—jjgranitemarble@optonline.net
Owner—Carlos Godoy
Supervisor—Nigel Perez

SIC—3281; NAICS—327991; *Granite & marble kitchen countertops & bathroom vanity tops*
Employs—7; Estab.—1998
Sales—$500,000-$1Mil (est)
Distrib.—Local
Privately owned corporation

**K H MACHINE WORKS**
4322 Grand Ave. (07047)
**Phone—(201) 867-2338**
Fax—(201) 867-8783
Email—khcando@optonline.net
Pres.—Shereelynn Koehler
Shop Mgr.—Jeremiah Koehler
SIC—3599; *General machining job shop*
Employs—5; Estab.—1918
Sales—under $500,000
Distrib.—Regional
Privately owned corporation

NEW ENTRY
**MAYABEQUE PRODUCTS CORP.**
7424 Bergenline Ave., Ste. 1 (07047)
**Phone—(201) 869-0531**
Pres.—Andre Idavoy
SIC—2011; *Meat processing*
Employs—7
Sales—$2.5Mil-$5Mil (est)
Privately owned corporation

**METRO WEB CORP.**
5901 Tonnelle Ave. (07047)
**Phone—(201) 553-0700**
Fax—(201) 553-7840
www.metrowebnj.com
Email—production@metrowebnj.com
Chrm. of the Board & Pres.—William Vogel
Hum. Res. Mgr.—Chris Henson
SIC—2759; *Financial document printing for the trade*
Employs—65; Estab.—1991
Sales—$1Mil-$2.5Mil
Distrib.—Local
Privately owned corporation

**NEW JERSEY BEER CO., LLC**
4201 Tonnelle Ave. (07047)
**Phone—(201) 758-8342**
www.njbeerco.com
Email—info@njbeerco.com
Manager—Kevin Napoli
SIC—2082; *Beer*
Employs—5; Estab.—2009
Sales—$500,000-$1Mil (est)
Distrib.—Local
Limited Liability Company
AKA: NJ Beer Co.

**NEW YORK SEWING MACHINE, INC.**
8555 Tonnelle Ave., Unit 301 (07047)
Mail addr: 2011 85th St., Ste. 15, North Bergen (07047-4714)
**Phone—(201) 809-2009**
National—(800) 225-2852
Fax—(201) 861-9201
www.nysmac.com
Email—machines@nysmac.com
Pres.—Sheldon Rothstein
Secy-Treas., CFO—Lester Rosenberg
Engrg., MIS & Plt. Mgr.—Michael Reese
SIC—3639; 3559; 5064; 5084; *Manufacturer & distributor of sewing machines & parts; Brand name—U S Blindstitch; NYSMAC Machinery; Juki; Pegasus; Yamato; Merrow; Highlead; Sheffield cutting; Ace Cutting*
Employs—5; Estab.—2001
4,000 sq ft site, Distrib.—Intl.
Privately owned corporation

**OCEANIC METALS LLC**
8555 Tonnelle Ave., Ste. 404 (07047)
**Phone—(201) 662-1192**
Fax—(201) 662-7418
oceanicllc.tripod.com
Email—crete14@verizon.net
Owner—Demetris Orfanos
SIC—3599; 3498; 3446; NAICS—331111; *Steel, aluminum & cast iron cutting, bending, twisting & hole-punching*
Employs—1; Estab.—1987
Sales—under $500,000
Distrib.—Local
Limited Liability Company

†**OLIVERI & SONS, INC., A.**
4401 Dell Ave., P.O. Box 88 (07047)
**Phone—(201) 319-9112**
Fax—(201) 319-9720
www.aoliveriandsons.com
Email—nickd@aoliveriandsons.com
Ptnr.—Iggy DePalma
Ptnr.—Nicholas DePalma
Collection Mgr.—Clara Bini
SIC—5149; *Wholesaler of baking flour & ingredients*
Employs—12; Estab.—1907
Distrib.—Regional
Privately owned corporation

**RELIABLE RUBBER & PLASTIC MACHINERY CO.**
2008 Union Tpke. (07047)
**Phone—(201) 865-1073**
(201) 865-2850
Fax—(201) 865-6878
www.reliable-machinery.com
Email—info@reliable-machinery.com
Pres.—Helga Liccardo
V-P. & Sales Mgr.—Thomas Liccardo
V-P. & Engrg. Mgr.—Joseph Liccardo III
SIC—3559; *Processing machinery for the rubber, plastics & related industries & machine shop for repair & overhauling of equipment; Brand name—Reliable*
Employs—40; Estab.—1935
Sales—$1Mil-$5Mil
250,000 sq ft site, Distrib.—Intl.
Privately owned corporation

**REUTHER MATERIAL CO., INC.**
5303 Tonnelle Ave. (07047)
**Phone—(201) 863-3550**
Fax—(201) 863-0950
www.reuthermaterial.com
Email—info@reuthermaterial.com
V-P., Opers.—Douglas Reuther
V-P.—Lois Marrone
V-P.—Robert Diehl
Bookkeeper—Bernadette Martinez
SIC—3271; NAICS—327331; *Concrete block*
Employs—20; Estab.—1933
Distrib.—Local
Privately owned corporation

**SCHRIPPS EUROPEAN BREAD, INC.**
5410 Tonnelle Ave. (07047)
**Phone—(201) 867-0909**
Fax—(201) 867-5310
www.schripps.com
Email—information@schripps.com
Pres., CFO, MIS Mgr.—Dan Marcus
SIC—2051; 2052; NAICS—311812; *European bread, rolls & pretzels*
Employs—40; Estab.—1985
20,000 sq ft site, Distrib.—Regional
Privately owned corporation

NEW ENTRY
**SEQUINS CITY**
1302 13th St. (07047)
**Phone—(201) 348-8111**
Fax—(201) 348-8812
www.sequincity.com
Email—contact@sequincity.com
Pres.—Raymond Hill
SIC—2395; *Fabric & textile embroidery*
Employs—6
Sales—under $500,000 (est)

**TWO BROTHERS IRON WORKS**
3709 Liberty Ave. (07047-2534)
**Phone—(201) 866-7970**
Fax—(201) 866-7755
www.twobrothersironworks.com
Email—fernando@twobrothersironworks.com
Proj. Mgr.—Fernando Reyes
Shop Mgr.—Paul Reyes
SIC—3446; 3444; *Ornamental metalwork, including interior & exterior aluminum, stainless steel & iron railings*
Employs—10; Estab.—2005
4,000 sq ft site, Distrib.—Local
Limited Liability Company

†**UNITED CANDY & TOBACCO CO.**
7408 Tonnelle Ave. (07047)
**Phone—(201) 943-8675**
Email—united7408@yahoo.com
Pres.—Joseph Choi
Off. Mgr.—Raymond Epifano
SIC—5194; *Wholesaler of cigarettes*
Employs—10; Estab.—1960
Sales—under $500,000
Distrib.—Local
Privately owned corporation

**W Y PLASTIC INDUSTRY, INC.**
2500 Secaucus Rd. (07047)
**Phone—(201) 617-8000**
Fax—(201) 617-7688
www.wyindustries.com
Email—support@wyindustries.com
GM—Bill Cheng
Manager—Henry Cheng
SIC—3089; *Plastic products*
Employs—6; Estab.—2000
Sales—$500,000-$1Mil
Distrib.—Regional
Privately owned corporation

**W. R. GRACE & CO.**
2133 85th St. (07047)
**Phone—(201) 869-5220**
Fax—(201) 869-7160
www.grace.com
Email—concrete@grace.com
Regional Mgr.—Atom Saverse
Plt. Mgr.—Chris Troyano
SIC—3272; *Concrete additives*
Employs—6
Sales—$500,000-$1Mil
49,000 sq ft site, Distrib.—Regional
Publicly owned corporation
Parent co.—W. R. Grace & Co., Columbia, MD
Phone—(410) 531-4000
See Parent Co. Section for full profile.

---

## North Branch
(Somerset—N.E.)

**AESTHETIC PRESS, INC.**
P.O. Box 5306 (08876)
**Phone—(908) 369-3777**
Fax—(908) 369-3777
www.aestheticpress.com
Email—info@aestheticpress.com
Pres.—Susan Choroszewski
Secy-Treas.—Walter Choroszewski

## North Branch—(cont.)

SIC—2731; 2741; Book, calendar & card publishing & graphic design services
Employs—3; Estab.—1985
Sales—under $500,000
Distrib.—Regional
Privately owned sub-S corp.

### KAUTEX MACHINES, INC.

201 Chambers Brook Rd., P.O. Box 5329 (08876)
**Phone—(908) 252-9350**
National—(800) 445-8206
Fax—(908) 253-9565
www.kautex-group.com
Email—kautexmachines@kautex-group.com
V-P., Sales, North America—Chuck Flammer
Cont.—Ed Schneider
Bus. Dev. Mgr.—Bill Farrant
SIC—3559; Plastic extrusion blow molding machinery
Employs—20; Estab.—2005
11,000 sq ft site, Distrib.—Intl.
Privately owned corporation

### RATHGIBSON, LLC

100 Aspen Hill Rd. (08876)
**Phone—(908) 218-1400**
Fax—(908) 218-0008
www.rathgibson.com
Email—sales@rathgibson.com
V-P.—Joe Waldinger
IT Mgr.—Chris Hannemann
Hum. Res. Mgr.—Rita Schuler
Sales Rep., Inside—Char Dropp
SIC—3317; NAICS—331210; Welded stainless steel & titanium tubing for the oil & gas, power generation, food, beverage & pharmaceutical industries
Employs—110; Estab.—1962
Sales—$26Mil-$50Mil
255,000 sq ft site, Distrib.—Intl.
Publicly owned corporation
Parent co.—RathGibson, LLC, Janesville, WI
Phone—(608) 754-2222
See Parent Co. Section for full profile.

### SCHUTZ CONTAINER SYSTEMS, INC.

200 Aspen Hill Rd., P.O. Box 5950 (08876)
**Phone—(908) 526-6161**
National—(877) 724-8389
Fax—(908) 526-0550
www.schuetz.net
Email—annethorn@schuetz.net
Pres., CEO—Frederik Wenzel
CFO—Ian Miller
Plt. Mgr.—Ricardo Gonzalez
Hum. Res. Mgr.—Eric Bayda
Accts. Payable Mgr.—Anne Thorn
SIC—3089; Corporate headquarters & plastic containers
Employs—65
Sales—$5Mil-$10Mil
64,000 sq ft site, Distrib.—Intl.
Privately owned corporation

### ULTIMATE TRAINING MUNITIONS

Div. of Bihler Of America, Inc.
55 Readington Rd. (08876)
**Phone—(908) 725-9000**
Fax—(908) 725-0457
www.utmworldwide.com
Email—sales@utmworldwide.com
Opers. Mgr.—Steve Cassidy
Hum. Res. Mgr.—Elyssa Borden

SIC—3482; 3842; NAICS—332992; Ammunition & training blanks for small arms, small arm conversion kits & safety goggles, face masks & ballistic gloves
Employs—30; Estab.—2005
Sales—$2.5Mil-$5Mil (est)
120,000 sq ft site, Distrib.—National
Privately owned corporation
DBA: UTM, Inc.
Parent co.—Bihler Of America, Inc., Phillipsburg, NJ
Phone—(908) 213-9001
See Parent Co. Section for full profile.

---

## North Brunswick

(Middlesex—N.E.)

### ABB INC., BUSINESS UNIT TURBOCHARGER

Div. of ABB Inc.
1460 Livingston Ave., P.O. Box 6005 (08902)
**Phone—(732) 932-6000**
Fax—(732) 932-6378
www.abb.com/turbocharging
Email—turbo@us.abb.com
Pres.—Chuck Noddin
Opers. Mgr.—Mike Huh
Bus. Admn.—Nadine Kuntz
SIC—3511; NAICS—333611; Rebuilt turbochargers
Employs—12; Estab.—1978
Sales—$2.5Mil-$5Mil (est)
Distrib.—Intl.
Publicly owned corporation
Parent co.—ABB Inc., Cary, NC
Phone—(919) 856-2360
See Parent Co. Section for full profile.

### ABP INDUCTION, LLC

1460 Livingston Ave. (08902)
**Phone—(732) 932-6400**
Fax—(732) 828-7274
www.abpinduction.com
V-P., Melting Foundry Div.—David Decker
SIC—3567; Induction melting furnaces for foundry applications
Employs—22; Estab.—2006
Sales—$2.5Mil-$5Mil (est)
Distrib.—Intl.
Limited Liability Company

### †AC COMPACTING, LLC

1577 Livingston Ave., P.O. Box 7266 (08902)
**Phone—(732) 249-6900**
National—(800) 524-0183
Fax—(732) 249-6909
www.accompacting.com
Email—info@accompacting.com
Pres.—Paul Schaa
CFO, Cont.—John Nowatkowski
Sales Mgr.—Paul Bick
SIC—5084; Distributor of pharmaceutical processing equipment, including PIV variable speed drives for the pharmaceutical manufacturing & development industries
Employs—10; Estab.—1999
Sales—$3Mil-$6Mil
Distrib.—Intl.
Limited Liability Company

### AFLEX EXTRUSION TECHNOLOGIES, INC.

1600 Livingston Ave. (08902)
**Phone—(732) 752-0048**
Fax—(732) 752-3795
www.aflexinc.com
Email—sales@aflexinc.com
Co-Pres.—Daryl Little
Co-Pres.—Gary M. Fredrick

SIC—3082; 3052; NAICS—326121; Plastic extruded products, including decorative moldings, poster frames & vacuum hoses
Employs—10; Estab.—1997
Sales—$1Mil-$2.5Mil (est)
Distrib.—National
Privately owned corporation
AKA: Princeton Molding Group

### ARTEGRAFT, INC.

220 N. Center Dr. (08902)
**Phone—(732) 422-8333**
National—(800) 631-5264
Fax—(732) 422-8647
www.artegraft.com
Email—info@artegraft.com
Pres., CEO—Richard A. Gibson
CFO—Norris J. Horn
V-P., Sales—Warren Kirschbaum
V-P., Opers. & Hum. Res. Mgr.—Cathleen VanDerVeer
V-P., Scientific Affs.—Laurence A. Potter
Cust. Serv. Rep.—Casey Gillingham
SIC—3842; Vascular grafts & thrombectomy devices
Employs—18; Estab.—1992
9,000 sq ft site, Distrib.—National
Privately owned sub-S corp.

### ATLANTIC PRECISION TECHNOLOGY, LLC

432 Quarry Ln. (08902)
**Phone—(732) 648-7786**
Email—cpatrick6@comcast.net
CEO—Richard Slacum
Pres.—Carol Patrick
Administrator—Victoria Marx
SIC—3599; Precision machining job shop
Employs—5; Estab.—1987
Sales—under $500,000
Distrib.—Intl.
Limited Liability Company

### AXLETREE SOLUTIONS, INC.

2 King Arthur Ct., Lakeside W., Ste. A-1 (08902)
**Phone—(732) 296-0001**
www.axletrees.com
Email—info@axletrees.com
Pres.—Mohan Murali
Chief Operating Officer—Martin Lightman
Sr. V-P., Infrastructure—Gopal Ganji
Off. Mgr.—Sandy Halabi
SIC—7372; Bank communication & treasury automation SaaS software development
Employs—15; Estab.—2002
Distrib.—Intl.
Privately owned corporation

### BEDDING INDUSTRIES OF AMERICA

1375 Jersey Ave. (08902)
**Phone—(732) 628-0800**
Fax—(732) 628-0803
www.therapedic.com
Email—bedshop@cs.com
Pres.—Stuart Carlitz
Cont.—Steve Berezwik
Off. Mgr.—Mike Campbell
SIC—2515; 2392; Mattresses
Employs—100; Estab.—1990
Sales—$6Mil-$10Mil
90,000 sq ft site, Distrib.—Local
Privately owned corporation

### BENANTI, INC., D. F.

420 Quarry Ln. (08902-4727)
**Phone—(732) 422-3102**
Pres.—Dominick Benanti
Off. Mgr.—Marie Fisher
SIC—3273; NAICS—327320; Ready-mixed concrete
Employs—5; Estab.—1961
Sales—under $500,000
Distrib.—Local
Privately owned corporation

### BLUE STAR GLASS, INC.

2300 U.S. Highway 1, Bldg. 31 (08902)
**Phone—(732) 422-1272**
Fax—(732) 422-1274
www.bluestarglass.net
Email—info@bluestarglass.net
GM—MeMelida Mavric-Halkic
Fin., Hum. Res. & IT Mgr.—Scott Jeffreis
Off. Mgr.—Rebecca Muehlbauer
Staff Accountant—Sylwia Malkinska
SIC—3231; Commercial glass tempering & fabrication, including monolithic insulated glass units, frameless shower doors & glass shelves
Employs—15; Estab.—2009
57,000 sq ft site, Distrib.—Regional
Privately owned corporation

### BRUNSWICK SIGN & EXHIBIT CORP.

1510 Jersey Ave. (08902)
**Phone—(732) 246-2500**
Fax—(732) 246-7789
www.brunswicksign.com
Email—btalan@brunswicksign.com
GM—Bruce Talan
Graphic Designer—Jeff Boguski
SIC—3993; Interior & exterior vinyl & neon signs
Employs—4; Estab.—1963
Sales—$500,000-$1Mil
10,000 sq ft site, Distrib.—Local
Sole ownership

### BWAY CORP.

Div. of BWAY Corporation
1202 Airport Rd. (08902)
**Phone—(732) 247-6700**
Fax—(732) 247-0502
www.bwaycorp.com
Email—sales@bwaycorp.com
Sales Mgr.—Leslie Sammarco
Opers. Mgr.—Daniel Martin
Hum. Res. Mgr.—Eyvonda Queen
SIC—3412; NAICS—332439; Metal pails
Employs—110; Estab.—1997
Varies: 110-140
Sales—$10Mil-$25Mil
100,000 sq ft site, Distrib.—National
Publicly owned corporation
Parent co.—BWAY Corporation, Atlanta, GA
Phone—(770) 645-4800
See Parent Co. Section for full profile.

NEW ENTRY
### CHEMSPEED, INC.

113 N. Center Dr. (08902)
**Phone—(732) 329-1225**
Fax—(732) 329-1226
www.chemspeed.com
Email—chemspeed@chemspeed.com
GM—Mark Meyers
SIC—7372; Automated workflow application software development; Brand name—SWING; ISYNTH; MULTIPLANT; AUTOPLANT; EMULSIFIER; FORMAX; FLEX; FLEXSHUTTLE
Employs—10; Estab.—1999
Distrib.—Intl.
Privately owned corporation

### CHIROMATIC, INC.

1375 Jersey Ave. (08902)
Mail addr: 190 Sayre Dr., Princeton (08540)
**Phone—(800) 526-5116**
National—(800) 406-1713
www.chiromatic.com
Email—chiromatic1@gmail.com
Pres.—Debbie Carlitz

GEOGRAPHICAL

## North Brunswick—(cont.)

SIC—2515; 2392; 3086; *Firm & pressure relieving visco-elastic memory foam & latex foam mattresses, pillows & foam mattress toppers for chiropractic patients; Brand name— Chiromatic*
Employs—2; Estab.—1977
Sales—under $500,000 (est)
Privately owned corporation

### CUSTOM CRAFT PLASTICS

Div. of Silver Line Building Products, LLC
100 King Arthurs Ct., P.O. Box 6029 (08902)
**Phone—(732) 843-3000**
Fax—(732) 843-5680
Email—info@custcraft.com
Off. Mgr.—Tracy Geraci
SIC—3089; *Plastic injection molding*
Employs—100
50,000 sq ft site, Distrib.—Intl.
Privately owned corporation
Parent co.—Silver Line Building Products, LLC, North Brunswick, NJ
Phone—(732) 435-1000
See Parent Co. Section for full profile.

### CUSTOM LINERS, INC.

1555 Ruth Rd., Ste. 7 (08902)
**Phone—(201) 569-1889**
Fax—(732) 940-0085
Owner—John Boag
SIC—2653; *Corrugated liners & partitions for packaging applications*
Employs—4; Estab.—2007
Sales—$500,000-$1Mil (est)
Distrib.—Intl.
Privately owned corporation

### DISTEK, INC.

121 N. Center Dr. (08902)
**Phone—(732) 422-7585**
National—(888) 234-7835
Fax—(732) 422-7310
www.distekinc.com
Email—info@distekinc.com
Pres.—Gerald Brinker
Admn. Mgr.—Gail Rayner
SIC—3826; NAICS—334516; *Pharmaceutical testing instruments*
Employs—63; Estab.—1976
Distrib.—Intl.
Privately owned corporation
ISO rating—9001:2000

### EMI YOSHI, INC.

1200 Jersey Ave. (08902)
**Phone—(732) 248-5533**
Fax—(732) 248-5552
www.emiyoshi.com
Email—info@emiyoshi.com
Ptnr.—Harry Meisels
SIC—3089; *Premium disposable plastic servingware for caterers, restaurants, schools, hotels & retailers*
Employs—21
Distrib.—Intl.
Privately owned partnership

### †FORKLIFT HEADQUARTER, LLC

975 Joyce Kilmer Ave. (08902)
**Phone—(732) 821-1413**
Fax—(732) 821-7189
www.forkliftqs.com
Email—forkman0614@aol.com
Pres.—Mark Gabel
SIC—5084; *Distributor of used forklifts & racking; Brand name— Caterpillar; Clark; Yale; Daewoo; Crown; Interlake; USP; Frazier; Wire Deck*
Employs—1; Estab.—1995
Distrib.—Local
Privately owned sub-S corp.

### GENERAL FOUNDRIES, INC.

1 Progress Rd. (08902)
**Phone—(732) 697-9000**
National—(800) 222-9555
Fax—(732) 376-9000
www.generalfoundriesinc.com
Email—sales@generalfoundriesinc.com
Pres.—Rita J. Todani
V-P., Opers. & Sales—Sam Chowdhuri
V-P., Sales—A. J. Narang
SIC—3321; NAICS—331511; *Corporate headquarters & iron castings, manhole frames & covers*
Employs—16; Estab.—1998
Sales—$1Mil-$2.5Mil (est)
Distrib.—Regional
Privately owned corporation

### GOODYEAR RUBBER PRODUCTS CORP.

1583 Livingston Ave., Ste. 4 (08902-1833)
**Phone—(732) 448-1111**
Fax—(732) 448-0564
www.goodyearinternational.com
Email—sales@goodyearinternational.com
Pres.—Andrew Warga
SIC—3069; 3089; *Rubber & plastic hose, conveyor belting, v belting, chemical, petroleum, air & fluoropolymer hose assemblies; Brand name— Boston hose; Freeaire Refrigeration; Tygon Tubing; Jason Hose; Jason V-Belts; Kuriyama Hose Tubing; Dixon Fittings*
Employs—6; Estab.—1886
Sales—$500,000-$1Mil
Distrib.—National
Privately owned corporation

### †GRANT SUPPLY CO., INC.

901 Joyce Kilmer Ave. (08902)
**Phone—(732) 545-1018**
Fax—(732) 545-9879
www.grantsupply.com
Email—bills@grantsupply.com
Pres.—Bill Stanbach
V-P.—Joseph Nastus
Hum. Res. Mgr.—Grace Desantis
SIC—5074; *Corporate headquarters & distributor of plumbing supplies; Brand name—American Standard; AO Smith; Bradley; Chicago Faucets; Cuno@Delany@Delta; Elkay; Fluidmaster; Gerber; Grohe; Insinkerator; Lasco; Moen; Mustee; Panasonic Bath Fans; B&G*
Employs—55; Estab.—1933
Distrib.—Local
Privately owned corporation

### †HERAEUS SENSOR TECHNOLOGY USA

1901 U.S. Highway 130 (08902)
**Phone—(732) 940-4400**
National—(888) 777-7396
Fax—(732) 940-4445
www.heraeus-sensor-technology-us.com
Email—info.hst-us@heraeus.com
GM—Douglas Joy
Sales Mgr.—Thomas Ferron
Prod. Mgr.—Robert Gliniecki
SIC—5065; *Distributor of platinum RTD temperature sensor elements, including technical support*
Employs—6; Estab.—2009
Distrib.—Intl.
Limited Liability Company
ISO rating—9001

### HESS CORP.

2800 U.S. Highway 1 (08902)
**Phone—(732) 940-3705**
www.hess.com
Email—investorrelations@hess.com
Manager—Roman Ozhogan
SIC—1382; 1311; *Oil & gas exploration & production*
Employs—35; Estab.—1937
Distrib.—Intl.
Publicly owned corporation
Parent co.—Hess Corp., New York, NY
Phone—(212) 997-8500
See Parent Co. Section for full profile.

### INTENSE-US

1200 Airport Rd., Ste. A (08902)
**Phone—(732) 249-2228**
Fax—(732) 249-8139
www.intenseco.com
Email—sales@intenseco.com
Dir., Mktg.—Kevin Laughlin
SIC—3674; NAICS—334413; *Semiconductor lasers*
Employs—40; Estab.—1995
25,000 sq ft site, Distrib.—Intl.
Privately owned corporation

### INTERSTATE CONTAINER BRUNSWICK, LLC

Div. of Interstate Resources, Inc.
501 Finnegan Ln. (08902)
**Phone—(732) 821-8100**
Fax—(732) 821-4040
www.iripaper.com
Email—sales@interstatecontainer.com
Opers. Mgr.—Dave McQade
Proj. Mgr.—Lisanne Destefano
SIC—2653; NAICS—322211; *Corrugated boxes, die cuts & displays*
Employs—300; Estab.—1990
Distrib.—Regional
Privately owned corporation
Parent co.—Interstate Resources, Inc., Arlington, VA
Phone—(703) 243-3355
See Parent Co. Section for full profile.

### LIFE OF THE PARTY, LLC

832 Ridgewood Ave., Ste. 4 (08902-2200)
**Phone—(732) 828-0886**
Fax—(732) 828-0980
www.soapplace.com
Email—info@soapplace.com
Pres.—Carole Krinsky
Opers. Mgr.—Debra Rodriguez
Mktg. & Prod. Mgr.—JoAnn Soltis
SIC—3544; 3089; NAICS—333500; *Plastic candy & craft molds*
Employs—15; Estab.—1985
Sales—$2.6Mil-$5Mil
20,000 sq ft site, Distrib.—National
Limited Liability Company

### MALTESE IRON WORKS, INC., JOHN

1453 Jersey Ave., P.O. Box 7161 (08902)
**Phone—(732) 249-4350**
Fax—(732) 249-9182
www.jmiw.com
Email—l.kokinos@jmiw.com
Pres.—Laurence Danza
Secy.-Treas.—Mary Danza
Plt. Mgr.—Ed Boris
Hum. Res. Mgr.—Lauren Kokinos
SIC—3312; *Steel fabrication*
Employs—18; Estab.—1954
Sales—$1Mil-$2.5Mil
Distrib.—Local
Privately owned corporation

### MERIAL LTD.

631 U.S. Highway 1 (08902)
**Phone—(732) 729-5700**
National—(888) 637-4251
www.merial.com
Email—info@merial.com
Opers. Mgr.—Heidi Tomenehok
SIC—2834; NAICS—325412; *Pharmaceuticals*
Employs—75; Estab.—1997
Sales—$25Mil-$50Mil (est)
Distrib.—Regional
Privately owned corporation
Parent co.—Merial Ltd., Duluth, GA
Phone—(678) 638-3000
See Parent Co. Section for full profile.

### MIDDLESEX PUBLICATIONS, INC.

850 Carolier Ln. (08902)
**Phone—(732) 435-0005**
Fax—(732) 435-0677
www.njcoups.com
Email—productions@njparentweb.com
Owner—Mark Chelton
Sr. Editor—Helene Simon
Prod. Mgr.—Matthew White
SIC—2721; 2741; *Monthly print & online parenting & shopper guide magazine publishing*
Employs—12; Estab.—1982
Sales—$500,000-$1Mil
Distrib.—Local
Privately owned corporation
AKA: Pennysaver

### MODERN FENCE & CONSTRUCTION, LLC

1527 Livingston Ave. (08902)
**Phone—(732) 238-5588**
National—(877) 312-2300
Fax—(732) 238-8088
www.modernfenceco.com
Email—sales@modernfenceco.com
Pres.—Kenneth Walewski
Treas.—Beata Suski-Walewski
SIC—3089; 5039; *Manufacturer & wholesaler of PVC & vinyl fences & railings*
Employs—3; Estab.—2004
Sales—$1.9Mil
12,000 sq ft site, Distrib.—Local
Limited Liability Company

### †MONARCH ELECTRIC SUPPLY CO.

Div. of US Electrical Services, Inc.
1527 Livingston Ave. (08902)
**Phone—(732) 249-1616**
Fax—(732) 249-1981
www.monarchelectric.com
Email—jrivera@usesi.com
Manager—Fred Brutko
SIC—5063; *Distributor of electrical supplies*
Employs—5; Estab.—1996
Distrib.—Local
Privately owned corporation
Parent co.—US Electrical Services, Inc., Hartford, CT
Phone—(860) 522-3232
See Parent Co. Section for full profile.

### NATIONAL PAINT INDUSTRIES

1999 Elizabeth St. (08902)
**Phone—(732) 821-3200**
National—(800) 432-4333
Fax—(732) 821-8180
www.ipaint.us
Email—dschnurr@gmail.com
Co-Pres.—Michael Schnurr
Co-Pres.—Donald Schnurr
V-P., Sales—Bruce Bernard
Hum. Res. Mgr.—Sandy Lipesky

## North Brunswick— (cont.)

SIC—2851; NAICS—325510; *Company headquarters & paints & coatings for marine, industrial, residential & commercial applications; Brand name—Blue Water Marine Paint; Harco; Garco; Wilson Imperial; National Paint*
Employs—45; Estab.—1959
65,000 sq ft site, Distrib.—National
Privately owned corporation

### †NATIONAL PARTS SUPPLY CO., INC.

535 Milltown Rd. (08902)
**Phone—(732) 247-5171**
Fax—(732) 247-4118
Email—411.ncs@gmail.com
Owner—John Salasko
Comp.—Joe Mesquite
Sales Mgr.—John Warren
IT Mgr.—Pete Garcia
SIC—5013; *Corporate headquarters & wholesaler of automotive parts*
Employs—100; Estab.—1967
Distrib.—Local
Sole ownership

### NATURAL STONE KITCHEN & BATH

2280 U.S. Highway 130 (08902)
**Phone—(732) 297-5450**
Fax—(732) 297-5465
www.naturalstonegranite.com
Email—allnj@ naturalstonegranite.com
Pres.—Manuel Angamarca
Manager—Diego Salinas
SIC—3281; *Natural stone fabrication*
Employs—3; Estab.—2006
Sales—$500,000-$1Mil
Distrib.—Local
Privately owned corporation

### NORCIA CORP.

451 Black Horse Ln. (08902)
**Phone—(732) 297-1101**
National—(800) 882-1081
Fax—(732) 297-8129
www.norciacorp.com
Email—norciacorp@gmail.com
Pres.—Pat Norcia
Secy-Treas.—John Norcia
Off. Mgr.—Sereniti Norcia
SIC—3713; NAICS—336211; *Truck bodies & equipment*
Employs—8; Estab.—1957
Sales—$500,000-$1Mil
Distrib.—Local
Privately owned sub-S corp.

### OHM LABORATORIES, INC.

Div. of Ranbaxy, Inc.
1385 Livingston Ave., P.O. Box 7397 (08902)
**Phone—(732) 418-2235**
Fax—(732) 418-7208
www.ohmlabs.com
Email—info.unitedstates@ ranbaxy.com
CFO—Manjeet Bindra
V.-P., Prodn.—Ganpat Desai
Pur. Mgr.—Shobha Sanade
Engrg. Mgr.—Narendra Bhojra
SIC—2834; NAICS—325412; *Pharmaceuticals*
Employs—160; Estab.—1982
Sales—$10Mil-$25Mil
33,000 sq ft site, Distrib.—National
Privately owned corporation
Parent co.—Ranbaxy, Inc., Princeton, NJ
Phone—(609) 720-9200
See Parent Co. Section for full profile.

### OPTICAL INSIGHT, LLC

778 Highway 1 (08902)
**Phone—(732) 828-3937**
www.opticalinsightnj.com
Owner—Joseph Grodman
SIC—3851; NAICS—339100; *Eyeglasses*
Employs—2; Estab.—1980
Sales—under $500,000
Distrib.—Local
Limited Liability Company

### OSHKO INTERNATIONAL CORP.

115 Riverbend Dr. (08902)
**Phone—(732) 821-8222**
Pres.—Michael Oh
SIC—3942; NAICS—339931; *Stuffed animals*
Employs—1; Estab.—1923
Sales—under $500,000
Distrib.—National
Privately owned corporation

### PARKWAY-KEW CORP.

2095 Excelsior Ave. (08902)
**Phone—(732) 398-2100**
www.parkwaykew.com
Email—sales@parkwaykew.com
Pres., Plt. Mgr.—Eugene E. Klein, Sr.
V.-P., Engrg.—Eugene E. Klein, Jr.
Sales Mgr.—Mark Patrizzia
Off. Mgr.—Rosemary Wick
SIC—3479; 3599; *HVOF, plasma & thermal spray coatings, including CNC machining, grinding & super finishing & fracking plungers & wheels for container shipping; Brand name—Colmonoy; Praxair; Sulzer Metco; Fracking; Festoon*
Employs—15; Estab.—1952
Sales—$1Mil-$5Mil
23,000 sq ft site, Distrib.—National
Privately owned corporation

### PLASMATIC SYSTEMS, INC.

1327 Aaron Rd. (08902)
**Phone—(732) 297-9107**
Fax—(732) 297-3306
www.plasmapreen.com
Email—aribner@optonline.net
Pres.—Aaron Ribner
SIC—3629; NAICS—335999; *Electronics plasma cleaning equipment; Brand name—Plasma-Preen*
Employs—1; Estab.—1987
Sales—under $500,000
1,000 sq ft site, Distrib.—Intl.
Privately owned sub-S corp.

### PRO-TAPES & SPECIALTIES

621 Route 1 S. (08902)
Mail addr: P.O. Box 640, Milltown (08850)
**Phone—(732) 346-0900**
National—(800) 345-0234
Fax—(732) 729-7373
www.protapes.com
Email—sales@protapes.com
Ptnr.—Barry Hart
Ptnr.—Arnold Silver
Ptnr.—Barney Silver
Ptnr.—Ed Miller
V.-P., Mktg.—Christopher Hart
Dir., Operation—Mike Harned
Dir., Acctg. & Fin.—Robert Marshall
Hum. Res. Admn.—Rosanne McGovern
SIC—2891; NAICS—322222; *Tapes & adhesives*
Employs—96; Estab.—1976
Sales—over $30Mil
Distrib.—Intl.
Privately owned sub-S corp.
ISO rating—9001:2008

### SCALA PASTRY

1896 U.S. Highway 130 (08902)
**Phone—(732) 398-9808**
Fax—(732) 398-8583
www.scalapastry.com
Owner—Paul Scala
SIC—2051; *Fresh bakery products, including bread & pastries*
Employs—5; Estab.—1986
Sales—under $500,000
Distrib.—Local
Privately owned corporation

### SILVER LINE BUILDING PRODUCTS, LLC

Div. of Andersen Corp.
1 Silver Line Dr., P.O. Box 6029 (08902)
**Phone—(732) 435-1000**
National—(800) 234-4228
www.silverlinewindows.com
Email—hr@silverlinewindow.com
V.-P., Sales—Al Worthing
V.-P., Mktg.—Andrew Karr
Dir., Engr.—Andrew Obst
Mktg. Mgr.—Sharon Gifford
SIC—3089; *Company headquarters & vinyl windows & doors*
Employs—3000; Estab.—1947
Sales—over $100Mil
880,000 sq ft site, Distrib.—National
Privately owned corporation
Parent co.—Andersen Corp., Bayport, MN
Phone—(651) 264-5150
See Parent Co. Section for full profile.

NEW ENTRY
### SOMERSET GLASS CO., INC.

2086 U.S. Highway 130 (08902)
**Phone—(732) 297-7444**
Fax—(732) 297-1409
www.somersetglass.net
Email—somersetglass2@aol.com
Pres.—Bill Hand
SIC—3211; 3231; *Frameless shower door enclosures for residential & commercial applications*
Employs—10; Estab.—1984
Sales—$1Mil-$2.5Mil (est)
6,000 sq ft site, Distrib.—Local
Privately owned corporation

### †SUMMIT STAINLESS STEEL, LLC

2001 Elizabeth St. (08902)
**Phone—(732) 297-9505**
(800) 326-9505
Fax—(732) 422-1370
www.summitstainless.com
Pres.—Frank Tairaue
V.-P.—Rich Husar
Dir., Hum. Res.—Lee Fredericks
SIC—5051; *Wholesaler of stainless steel*
Employs—25; Estab.—1974
Distrib.—Local
Limited Liability Company

### TALON PAINT PRODUCTS, INC.

Div. of National Paint Industries
1999 Elizabeth St. (08902)
**Phone—(732) 821-3200**
Fax—(732) 821-8180
www.ipaint.us
Email—sales@ nationalpaintsupply.net
Pres.—Michael Schnurr
V.-P.—Don Schnurr
Sales Mgr.—George Pica
SIC—2851; NAICS—325510; *Paints*
Employs—45; Estab.—1959
Sales—$25Mil
Distrib.—National
Privately owned corporation
Parent co.—National Paint Industries, North Brunswick, NJ
Phone—(732) 821-3200
See Parent Co. Section for full profile.

### TIFFANEES TOYS, INC.

601 Nassau St., Ste. 593 (08902)
**Phone—(732) 828-6333**
Fax—(732) 828-4575
www.tiffaneestoys.com
Email—tiffstoys@aol.com
Pres.—Mirta D'Amaro
Ex. Off. Mgr.—Jacqueline Bracero
SIC—3942; 2399; 2392; NAICS—339931; *Stuffed toys, pet beds, pillow cushions, airline pillows & home textiles*
Employs—13; Estab.—1994
Sales—under $500,000
11,000 sq ft site, Distrib.—Regional
Privately owned corporation

### URVESH GRANITE (USA), INC.

1777 Route 130 S. (08902)
**Phone—(201) 369-3934**
Email—urveshinc@aol.com
Pres.—Bharat Patel
SIC—3281; 2434; *Granite countertops & wooden kitchen cabinets*
Employs—8
Sales—$500,000-$1Mil (est)
Privately owned corporation

### †UTILITY TRAILER SALES OF NEW JERSEY

589 Nassau St. (08902)
**Phone—(866) 957-2787**
(732) 745-1222
Fax—(732) 745-2699
www.utilityofnj.com
Email—utility4@utilityofnj.com
Pres.—Larry Dwyer, Sr.
Bookkeeper—Beverly Donnamaria
SIC—5012; 5013; *Distributor of new & used trailers & aftermarket parts, including service repair shop*
Employs—16; Estab.—1985
Sales—under $500,000
24,000 sq ft site, Distrib.—Regional
Privately owned corporation

### WARWICK MFG. & EQUIPMENT CO., LLC

1112 12th St. (08902)
**Phone—(732) 729-0400**
(732) 241-9263
Fax—(732) 729-1235
www.warwickequipment.com
Email—sales@ warwickequipment.com
Mng. Dir.—Greg Pantchenko
SIC—3565; 3556; 3537; NAICS—333993; *Food, packaging, chemical, cosmetic, construction, rubber & material handling machinery*
Employs—3; Estab.—1970
Sales—$2Mil
40,000 sq ft site, Distrib.—Intl.
Limited Liability Company

## North Caldwell

(Essex—N.E.)

### HILLTOP HONEY, LLC

15 Hill St. (07006)
**Phone—(201) 953-0198**
www.hilltophoneynj.com
Email—klutch.cargo@verizon.net
Pres.—Joseph Lelinho
SIC—2099; 2844; *Honey, beeswax, pollen, propolis, hand creams & lip balms, including residential hive rentals & swarm retrieval; Brand name—Hilltop Honey; Honeylips Lip Balm*
Employs—3; Estab.—1995
Sales—under $500,000
Distrib.—Regional
Limited Liability Company

### SPECIALTY PAPER BOX CO.

14 Highland Dr. (07006)
**Phone—(973) 396-8556**
Fax—(973) 396-8557
Email—specialty201@aol.com
Pres.—Harry Engel III

GEOGRAPHICAL

## North Caldwell—(cont.)

SIC—2652; 2653; 3089; NAICS—322213; *Setup, corrugated & plastic boxes*
Employs—4; Estab.—1946
Sales—under $2Mil
Distrib.—National
Privately owned sub-S corp.

## North Haledon

### (Passaic—N.E.)

**HOFER MACHINE & TOOL CO., INC.**
126 Linda Vista Ave. (07508)
**Phone—(973) 427-1195**
Fax—(973) 427-6906
Email—hmt111@aol.com
Pres.—Alan P. Hofer
SIC—3643; NAICS—335931; *Electrical cable connectors*
Employs—19; Estab.—1947
Sales—$4Mil
15,000 sq ft site, Distrib.—National
Privately owned sub-S corp.

**PHOENIX SYSTEMS, LLC**
39 Morningside Ave. (07508)
**Phone—(201) 857-3901**
National—(888) 282-6446
Fax—(201) 857-3904
www.phoenixsg.com
Email—info@phoenixsg.com
Owner—Andrew Vaccaro
Off. Mgr.—Kristy Ruiz
SIC—3651; 7373; NAICS—334310; *Audiovisual equipment & systems for homes, businesses & corporations, including lighting systems, automation, digital signs & displays, home entertainment centers & boardroom & video conferencing*
Employs—5; Estab.—1987
Sales—$1Mil-$2.5Mil
Distrib.—Intl.
Sole ownership

## North Plainfield

### (Union—N.E.)

**DEAD END SCREEN PRINTS, INC.**
266 Lewis St. (07060)
**Phone—(908) 754-4552**
National—(800) 204-4545
www.deadendscreen.com
Email—descreen@att.net
Pres.—Rudy Basso
V-P.—Alex Basso
SIC—2396; *T-shirt, hat, sweatshirt, jacket & bag screen printing*
Employs—3; Estab.—1977
Sales—under $500,000
1,000 sq ft site, Distrib.—Local
Sole ownership

**GORKIN GLASS CO., INC.**
26 Race St. (07060)
**Phone—(908) 756-0544**
Fax—(908) 756-0228
www.gorkinglass.com
Email—sales@gorkinglass.com
Pres.—William Schultz
Cust. Serv. Mgr.—Stacy Manfredo
SIC—3231; NAICS—327215; *Glass shower doors & mirrors*
Employs—15; Estab.—1918
Sales—under $500,000
Distrib.—Local
Privately owned corporation

**SIGN-A-RAMA**
1030 U.S. Highway 22 (07060)
**Phone—(908) 561-4167**
Fax—(908) 561-4114
www.signarama-northplainfield.com
Email—info@signarama-northplainfield.com
Owner & Pres.—Paul Janulis

SIC—3993; *Interior & exterior signs, banners, vehicle & window lettering & digital prints*
Employs—2; Estab.—1989
Sales—under $500,000
Distrib.—Regional
Limited Liability Company

**T N R TOOL & MACHINE CO.**
2 Coddington Ave. (07060)
**Phone—(908) 754-4010**
Email—tnrtool@comcast.net
Owner—Rudy Romani, Sr.
Foreman—Richard Davis
SIC—3599; *Precision machining job shop*
Employs—3; Estab.—1975
Sales—under $500,000
Distrib.—Local
Sole ownership

## Northfield

### (Atlantic—S.E.)

**ATLANTIC CITY SHADE SHOP, INC.**
500 Tilton Rd., P.O. Box 217 (08225)
**Phone—(609) 641-8700**
National—(800) 439-7423
Fax—(609) 645-3918
www.acshade.com
Email—info@acshade.com
Owner, MIS Mgr. & Chief Engr.—Howard Markman
CEO, CFO—Barry Markman
SIC—2391; 2591; 5023; NAICS—314121; *Manufacturer & distributor of pleated window shades, motorized window treatments, shutters, draperies, curtains, horizontal, vertical & wooden blinds, bedding & valances; Brand name—Lutron; Comfortex; Norman International; Springs; Levolor; Kirsch; Draper; Hunter Douglas; Graber; Bali; Somfy; B & W; Waverly; Kravett; Fabricut; Makita*
Employs—16; Estab.—1947
Sales—$4Mil
5,400 sq ft site, Distrib.—Regional
Privately owned corporation
AKA: Wallace Blinds

**EDMUNDS & ASSOCS.**
301-A Tilton Rd. (08225)
**Phone—(609) 645-7333**
National—(800) 220-3754
Fax—(609) 645-3111
www.edmundsassoc.com
Email—support@edmundsassoc.com
Pres.—Bob Edmunds
SIC—7372; *Financial, accounting & billing software development*
Employs—30; Estab.—1982
Distrib.—Local
Privately owned corporation

**FEDEX OFFICE & PRINT CENTER**
Div. of FedEx Office & Print Services, Inc.
450 Tilton Rd. (08225)
**Phone—(609) 569-8100**
National—(800) 463-3339
Fax—(609) 569-8149
www.fedex.com
Email—usa1817@fedex.com
Center Mgr.—Brian Sherr
Asst. Mgr.—Marta Vant
Ctr. Specialist—Dave Cager
SIC—2752; NAICS—323100; *Instant printing*
Employs—7; Estab.—1972
Sales—$500,000-$1Mil
Distrib.—Local
Publicly owned corporation
Parent co.—FedEx Office & Print Services, Inc., Dallas, TX
Phone—(214) 550-7000
See Parent Co. Section for full profile.

## Northvale

### (Bergen—N.E.)

**ADM TRONICS UNLIMITED, INC.**
224 Pegasus Ave. (07647)
**Phone—(201) 767-6040**
www.admtronics.com
Email—sales@admtronics.com
Pres.—Andre DiMino
Dir., Sales & Mktg.—Tom Kistler
Plt. Mgr.—Tim Gilmartin
Lead Engr.—Matthew Drummer
SIC—3845; 2899; 2844; *Contract manufacturing of medical electronic devices & components for human & veterinary applications & water-based industrial adhesives, coatings, resins & additives, skin adhesives & topical dermatological & cosmetic products; Brand name—Polaqua; Aquaforte; Pros-Aide; Aurex-3; Santel; Ottimo; Flo-Med*
Employs—14; Estab.—1969
Sales—$1Mil-$5Mil
16,000 sq ft site, Distrib.—Intl.
Publicly owned corporation
ISO rating—13485
Also see: Antistatic Industries, same loc.
AKAs: Mark's Adhesive Co. & Aqua Based Technologies

**ALEX MACHINE SHOP, INC.**
267 Livingston St., P.O. Box 268 (07647)
**Phone—(201) 768-9110**
Fax—(201) 768-9132
Pres.—Alex Aleksich
Foreman—Joe Poeic
SIC—3599; 3556; NAICS—333294; *General machining job shop & food products machinery parts*
Employs—5; Estab.—1970
Sales—under $500,000
10,000 sq ft site, Distrib.—Local
Privately owned corporation

**AMERICAN GAS & CHEMICAL CO.**
220 Pegasus Ave. (07647)
**Phone—(201) 767-7300**
National—(800) 288-3647
Fax—(201) 767-1741
www.amgas.com
Email—info@amgas.com
Pres.—Gerald Anderson
CFO—Jim Zanosky
COO—M. Kershaw
Sales Techn.—Nick Armendinger
SIC—3823; NAICS—334513; *Leak detectors, gas monitors & detection technology; Brand name—Leak-Tec; Gaz-Tec; Flaw Finder; CGT-501; TSI-301*
Employs—75; Estab.—1957
Sales—$25Mil
26,000 sq ft site, Distrib.—Intl.
Privately owned corporation
ISO rating—9000

**ANTISTATIC INDUSTRIES, A DIV. OF ADM TRONICS, INC.**
224 Pegasus Ave. (07647)
**Phone—(201) 767-6040**
National—(800) 214-7900
Fax—(201) 784-0620
www.antistaticindustries.com
Email—aexstatic@aol.com
Pres., CEO—Andre DiMino
Dir., Sales—Thomas Kistler

SIC—2851; 3955; NAICS—325510; *Static dissipative products, including conductive paints, shielding & transparent coatings, wrist straps, transparent conductive films & shielding bags & cartridges for jet priners; Brand name—STATICPAINT®; STATICVEIL®; STATICTAPE; STATICSTIC; STATICNYLON CABLE TIES*
Employs—15; Estab.—1980
20,000 sq ft site, Distrib.—Intl.
Limited Liability Company
Also see: ADM Tronics Unlimited, Inc., same loc.

**ARMS GRAPHICS**
169 Paris Ave. (07647)
**Phone—(201) 767-6504**
National—(888) 784-5905
Fax—(201) 767-6471
www.minutemannorthvale.com
Email—info@minutemannorthvale.com
Pres.—Allan Schneider
Cust. Serv. Rep.—Deborah Free
SIC—2752; 2791; NAICS—323122; *Offset & instant printing & typesetting*
Employs—3; Estab.—1980
1,200 sq ft site, Distrib.—Regional
Privately owned corporation
DBA: Minuteman Press, Inc.

**AZZURRO GROUP, LLC**
100 Stonehurst Ct. (07647)
**Phone—(201) 767-0850**
Fax—(201) 767-5840
www.azzurrohd.com
Email—bcordo@azzurrogroup.com
CEO—Frank Luperella
Pub. Rels. Mgr.—Jennifer Park
SIC—7373; *Broadcast system integration*
Employs—15; Estab.—2007
24,000 sq ft site, Distrib.—Intl.
Limited Liability Company

**BIPORE, INC.**
31 Industrial Pkwy. (07647)
**Phone—(201) 767-1993**
Fax—(201) 767-0435
Email—bipore@msn.com
Pres.—Durmus Koch
Engr.—Jenna Koch
SIC—3841; 3089; *Plastic medical devices*
Employs—50; Estab.—1988
Sales—$1Mil-$5Mil
Distrib.—Intl.
Privately owned corporation

**DATA TECHNOLOGIES, INC.**
224 N. Pegasus Ave., Ste. A (07647)
**Phone—(201) 784-3225**
Fax—(201) 784-3319
www.data-tech.com
Chrm.—Rachel Peleg
Pres.—Ami Peleg
Tech. Engr.—Tom Cautterl
SIC—3629; NAICS—335999; *Battery chargers*
Employs—10; Estab.—1989
Distrib.—Intl.
Privately owned corporation

**ELITE PHARMACEUTICALS, INC.**
165 Ludlow Ave. (07647)
**Phone—(201) 750-2646**
Fax—(201) 750-2755
www.elitepharma.com
Email—eliteinfo@elitepharma.com
Chrm.—Jerry Treppel
Pres., CEO—Nasrat Hakim
CFO—Carter Ward
V-P., Qual. & Regulatory Affs.—Barbara Ellison
SIC—2834; NAICS—325412; *Oral controlled-release pharmaceuticals*
Employs—40
Sales—$10Mil-$25Mil (est)

## Northvale—(cont.)

**ENOR CORP.**
245 Livingston St. (07647)
**Phone—(201) 750-1680**
Fax—(201) 750-1418
www.enor.com
Email—mail@enor.com
CEO—Steven Udwin
Pres.—Dave Tarica
Cont., Opers. Mgr.—Roy Udwin
SIC—3949; *Sporting goods for children*
Employs—100; Estab.—1997
Distrib.—National
Privately owned corporation

**FILLO FACTORY, INC.**
10 Fairway Ct. (07647)
**Phone—(201) 439-1036**
National—(800) 653-4556
Fax—(201) 385-0012
www.fillofactory.com
Email—denise@fillofactory.com
CEO—Ron Rexroth
Ex. V-P.—Denise LeBrun
Plt. Mgr.—Phil Digateano
Prodn. Mgr.—Mike Gilles
SIC—2038; 2045; 2099; NAICS—311412; *Private label fillo doughs, organic & natural appetizers, chili, entrees, desserts & pocket sandwiches; Brand name—Hors d'oeuvres Unlimited; Aunt Trudy's; Yia Yia's*
Employs—150; Estab.—1996
Sales—$5Mil-$10Mil
85,000 sq ft site, Distrib.—Intl.
Privately owned corporation
AKA: Fillo Factory, The

**GEA MECHANICAL EQUIPMENT US, INC.**
100 Fairway Ct. (07647)
**Phone—(201) 767-3900**
National—(800) 722-6622
Fax—(201) 767-3901
www.gea.com
Email—sales@gea.com
Pres.—Michael J. Vick
CFO—Norbert Breuer
Dir., Process Div.—Derek Ettie
Hum. Res. Mgr.—Pam Pekar
Parts Mgr.—Rob Donohue
Repair Mgr.—Mike Ebenhack
SIC—3569; 3599; 3556; 3533; NAICS—333294; *Corporate headquarters & centrifuges & separators for the food, beverage & oil industries*
Employs—175; Estab.—1950
Sales—$10Mil-$25Mil
Distrib.—Intl.
Privately owned corporation
ISO rating—9001

**GLOBTEK, INC.**
186 Veterans Dr. (07647)
**Phone—(201) 784-1000**
Fax—(201) 784-0111
www.globtek.com
Email—sales@globtek.com
CEO—Anna Kaplan
V-P., Sales—Ed Seaman
Mktg. Coord.—Gene LoCascio
SIC—3643; 3621; 5063; NAICS—335931; *Manufacturer & distributor of power supplies, including adapters, cord sets & battery packs*
Employs—65; Estab.—1984
Sales—$30Mil
35,000 sq ft site, Distrib.—Intl.
Privately owned corporation

**GMB (USA), INC.**
190 Veterans Dr., Ste. B *(07647-2313)*
**Phone—(201) 768-3577**
Fax—(201) 221-8338
www.gmb-usa.com
Email—usa@gmb-usa.com
Pres.—Bryant Kang

GM—Joo H. Kim
Acctg. Mgr.—Diane So
SIC—7373; *Systems integration for the shipbuilding, marine & energy development industries*
Employs—23
Distrib.—Intl.
Privately owned corporation

**GNUTTI CARLO**
140 Ludlow Ave. (07647)
**Phone—(201) 768-8200**
Fax—(201) 768-5470
www.gnutticarlo.it
Email—sales@gnutti.ca
CFO—Renato Bampa
SIC—3714; *Company headquarters & automotive parts*
Employs—120; Estab.—1986
Distrib.—Intl.
Sole ownership
This company plans relocating to Jacksonville, AL early 2015

**GRAND EQUIPMENT OF AMERICA**
267 Livingston St. (07647)
**Phone—(201) 784-1101**
Fax—(201) 784-1116
Pres.—Neil White
Opers. Mgr.—Bill Young
Serv. Mgr.—Herb Fish
SIC—3599; *Company headquarters & dairy equipment & packaging*
Employs—21; Estab.—2001
Sales—$6Mil-$10Mil
Distrib.—Intl.
Privately owned corporation

**HAUSMANN INDUSTRIES, INC.**
130 Union St. (07647)
**Phone—(201) 767-0255**
National—(888) 428-7626
Fax—(201) 767-1369
www.hausmann.com
Email—sales@hausmann.com
CEO—David Hausmann
Cont.—Adam Heminover
Dir., Sales & Mktg.—George Batchelor
Prod. Mgr.—Abhay Jain
Cust. Serv. Mgr.—Cecelia Lubeck
Sales & Mktg. Admn.—Julie Skoda
SIC—3842; 2599; 2531; *American-made healthcare products, including medical treatment tables, rehabilitation & physical therapy equipment & athletic training equipment; Brand name—PROTEAM by Hausmann; S&W By Hausmann*
Employs—100; Estab.—1955
Distrib.—National
Privately owned corporation

**INDUSTRIAL RIVET & FASTENER CO.**
200 Paris Ave. (07647)
**Phone—(201) 750-1040**
National—(800) 289-7483
Fax—(201) 750-1050
www.rivet.com
Email—info@rivet.com
Pres.—Bill Goodman
V-P., Opers.—Juan Sanchez
V-P.—Steve Sherman
Cont.—Doris Banzuela-Goldberg
Special Accts. Mgr.—Michelle Zaret
Qual. Control Mgr.—Emry Yildiz
SIC—3452; NAICS—332722; *Blind, solid, semitubular, collar, shoulder, structural & specialty cold-headed rivets, screws, sems, pins, studs & nails*
Employs—60; Estab.—1912
Sales—$500,000-$1Mil
30,000 sq ft site, Distrib.—National
Privately owned corporation

**INRAD OPTICS, INC.**
181 Legrand Ave. (07647)
**Phone—(201) 767-1910**
Fax—(201) 767-9644

www.inradoptics.com
Email—sales@inradoptics.com
Chrm.—Jan Winston
Pres., CEO—Amy Eskilson
CFO—William J. Foote
V-P., Sales & Mktg.—George Murray
V-P., Hum. Res.—Bill Brucker
IT Mgr.—Ed Barrett
SIC—3229; 3471; 3827; NAICS—327212; *OEM custom optics, laser accessories & thin film optical coatings; Brand name—Inrad; Laser Optics; MRC Optics*
Employs—65; Estab.—1973
Sales—$11Mil
42,000 sq ft site, Distrib.—Intl.
Publicly owned corporation

**INTERPLEX NAS INC., BETA DIV.**
Div. of Interplex Industries, Inc.
232 Pegasus Ave. (07647)
**Phone—(201) 367-1300**
Fax—(201) 768-8988
www.interplex.com
Email—info@nasinterplex.com
Dir., Bus. Dev.—Joe Praino
GM—Ken Beller
Asst. Mgr.—Roman Herman
SIC—3469; 3089; *Metal stampings & plastic injection molding*
Employs—95; Estab.—1958
18,000 sq ft site, Distrib.—National
Privately owned corporation
Parent co.—Interplex Industries, Inc., College Point, NY
Phone—(718) 961-6212
See Parent Co. Section for full profile.

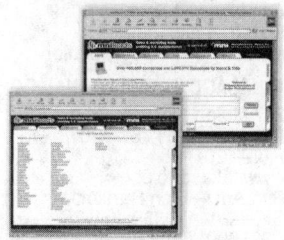

mnileads.com
Looking for Quality Sales Leads on the Internet? Look no Further!

**†JOANNOU CYCLE CO., INC., G.**
151 Ludlow Ave. (07647)
**Phone—(201) 768-9050**
National—(800) 222-0570
Fax—(201) 768-9520
www.jamisbikes.com
Email—dekiert@jamisbikes.com
CEO—Carine Joannou
V-P.—Madeline Joannou
Opers. Mgr.—Denise Ekiert
IT Mgr.—Dave Rosen
Hum. Res. Mgr.—Justin Flax
SIC—5091; *Corporate headquarters & wholesaler of bicycles*
Employs—100; Estab.—1940
Distrib.—Intl.
Privately owned corporation
AKA: Jamis Bicycle

**†LAB-TECH, INC.**
103 Stonehurst Ct. (07647)
**Phone—(201) 784-1093**
Fax—(800) 627-7280
www.lab-tech.net
Email—sales@lab-tech.net
Pres., CEO—Michael Pildes
Hum. Res. & IT Mgr.—Eileen Becker
Cust. Serv. Rep.—Nicole Moraski

SIC—5048; *Distributor of ophthalmic lenses & lab supplies for optical practitioners & retailers*
Employs—8; Estab.—1997
Distrib.—Regional
Privately owned corporation

**MULTIMATIC**
162 Veterans Dr., P.O. Box 156 (07647)
**Phone—(201) 767-9660**
Fax—(201) 767-7037
www.multimatic-usa.com
Email—multdc@aol.com
COO—Ron Velli
Cont. & Hum. Res. Mgr.—Frank Janssen
Plt. & Pur. Mgr.—Joseph Cincotta
Parts Mgr.—George Jessen
SIC—3582; NAICS—333312; *Dry cleaning machines*
Employs—10; Estab.—1960
40,000 sq ft site, Distrib.—Intl.
Limited Liability Company

**†NASSAU LENS CO., INC.**
160 LeGrand Ave. (07647)
**Phone—(201) 767-8033**
National—(800) 526-0313
Fax—(800) 637-3415
www.nassau247.com
Email—nassau1@nassauvisiongroup.com
Pres.—Maureen Cavanaugh
Dir., Sourcing—Ralph Dalo
Key Acct. Mgr.—Sue Vitez
SIC—5048; *Corporate headquarters & distributor of ophthalmic lenses*
Employs—50
Privately owned corporation

**OORI TRADING, INC.**
230 Union St., P.O. Box 154 (07647)
**Phone—(201) 367-3030**
National—(800) 597-0029
Fax—(201) 564-9221
www.oorifashion.com
Email—sales@oorifashion.com
CEO—Ku Tae Yi
IT Mgr.—Ed Change
Acctg. Mgr.—Sebastian Noh
SIC—3961; NAICS—339900; *Corporate headquarters & costume jewelry, including bangle bracelets, earrings & pins*
Employs—15; Estab.—1995
Sales—$1Mil-$2.5Mil
Distrib.—National
Privately owned corporation

**ORTHOFEET, INC.**
152-A Veterans Dr. (07647)
**Phone—(201) 767-6224**
National—(800) 524-2845
Fax—(201) 767-6748
www.orthofeet.com
Email—mb@orthofeet.com
Pres.—Aaron Bar
V-P., Mfg.—Mike DiSotto
Dir., Scientific Affs.—Dennis Janisse
SIC—3842; *Custom orthotics & therapeutic shoes for medical practitioners & providers of othropedic footwear & orthotics*
Employs—20; Estab.—1980
Distrib.—Intl.
Privately owned corporation

**PANLINE USA, INC.**
251 Union St. (07647)
**Phone—(201) 750-8010**
National—(800) 666-2539
Fax—(201) 750-8030
www.alextoys.com
Email—info@alextoys.com
Pres.—Fred Keeler
Hum. Res. Mgr.—Dennis Gutierrz

GEOGRAPHICAL

## Northvale—(cont.)

SIC—3944; 3961; 2511; 3999; NAICS—339900; *Juvenile toys, including bathtub play, imaginative & dramatic play, fashion, jewelry, beach & pool playthings & whimsical children's furniture*
Employs—66; Estab.—1985
100,000 sq ft site, Distrib.—Intl.
Privately owned corporation
AKA: Alex Toys

### PAPAILIAS CO., INC., J. G.

245 Pegasus Ave. (07647)
**Phone—(201) 767-4027**
Fax—(201) 767-7870
www.papailias.com
Email—gpapailias@papailias.com
Pres., Cont.—George Papailias
V-P., Opers.—David Bittman
GM & Engr.—Robert Surovich
SIC—3823; NAICS—334513; *Variable process control equipment*
Employs—40; Estab.—1959
18,000 sq ft site, Distrib.—Intl.
Privately owned corporation
Also see: Papco Industries, Inc., same loc.

### PAPCO INDUSTRIES, INC.

245 Pegasus Ave. (07647)
**Phone—(201) 767-9051**
Fax—(201) 767-7870
www.papcoindustries.com
Email—info@papcoindustries.com
Pres.—George Papailias
V-P., Opers.—David Bittman
GM & IT Mgr.—Robert Surovich
Opers. Mgr.—David Wexler
Hum. Res. Mgr.—Claudia Monticelli
Manager—Karen Ramos
SIC—3441; NAICS—332312; *Expansion joints*
Employs—20; Estab.—1985
20,000 sq ft site, Distrib.—Intl.
Sole ownership
Also see: Papailias Co., Inc., J. G., same loc.

### POWER SHADE CO., INC.

112 Paris Ave. (07647)
**Phone—(201) 767-3727**
Fax—(201) 767-3877
www.powershade.com
Email—info@powershade.com
Pres.—Greg Powers
SIC—2591; NAICS—337920; *Window blinds & shades*
Employs—10
Sales—$1Mil-$2.5Mil (est)
Distrib.—Regional

### RAB LIGHTING, INC.

170 Ludlow Ave. (07647)
**Phone—(201) 784-8600**
National—(888) 722-1000
Fax—(201) 784-0077
www.rabweb.com
Email—custserv@rabweb.com
CEO—Ross Barna
COO—Ken Brown
V-P., Mktg.—Terri Dumas
IT Mgr.—Eric Hannon
Cust. Serv. Rep.—Karen Martin
SIC—3648; NAICS—335129; *Outdoor commercial & residential lighting fixtures*
Employs—100; Estab.—1946
Sales—over $1Bil
100,000 sq ft site, Distrib.—Intl.
Sole ownership

### REMA TIP TOP/NORTH AMERICA, INC. (H Q)

119 Rockland Ave. (07647)
**Phone—(201) 768-8100**
Fax—(201) 768-0946
www.rematiptop.com
Email—jxu@rematiptop.com
Pres.—Olafur Gunnarsson
CFO—Jeffrey Xu
Hum. Res. Mgr.—Jack Renahan
Accts. Payable Mgr.—Richard Orcilla
SIC—3069; 3089; 3532; 3052; NAICS—326220; *Corporate headquarters; rubber, epoxy & polyurethane industrial tank linings & liners, mining machinery & splice belts & pulleys*
Employs—25
Sales—$2.5Mil-$5Mil (est)
Distrib.—Intl.
Privately owned corporation

### RICH ART COLOR CO., INC.

202 Pegasus Ave. (07647)
**Phone—(201) 767-0009**
Fax—(201) 767-0567
www.richartcolor.com
Email—orders@richartcolor.com
Pres.—Marc Jennings
CFO—Charlie Generelli
Off. Mgr.—Toni Corrigan
SIC—3952; 2851; *Washable & non-washable paints & decorative glues for teachers, students, artists, parents & children, crafters & businesses*
Employs—15; Estab.—1926
Sales—$1Mil-$2.5Mil
Distrib.—Local
Privately owned corporation

### STAY FOCUSED MARKETING

157 Veterans Dr. (07647)
**Phone—(201) 750-5050**
National—(855) 370-5050
Fax—(201) 750-5051
www.stayfocusedmkt.com
Email—sue@stayfocusedmkt.com
Pres.—Marvin Levy
Off. Mgr.—Susan Franco
Bookkeeper—Jeff Michael
SIC—3914; *Titanium & ceramic knives*
Employs—5; Estab.—1999
Distrib.—National
Privately owned corporation

### TAKASAGO INTERNATIONAL CORP.

267 Union St. (07647)
**Phone—(201) 767-9001**
Fax—(201) 784-7110
www.takasago.com
Pur. Agt.—Rich Bartilotti
SIC—2844; 2869; NAICS—325600; *Fragrances*
Employs—60; Estab.—1988
Distrib.—National
Privately owned corporation
Parent co.—Takasago International Corp., Rockleigh, NJ
Phone—(201) 767-9001
See Parent Co. Section for full profile.

### VIZ MOLD & DIE LTD.

210 Industrial Pkwy. (07647)
**Phone—(201) 784-8383**
Fax—(201) 784-4420
www.vizmold.com
Email—info@vizmold.com
Pres.—Dimitrios Lymberis
Off. Mgr.—Viola Kadlubowski
SIC—3544; NAICS—333500; *Plastic injection molds, tools & dies*
Employs—5; Estab.—1994
62,600 sq ft site, Distrib.—Local
Privately owned corporation
Also see: Viz Plastic Products Ltd., same loc.

### VIZ PLASTIC PRODUCTS LTD.

210 Industrial Pkwy. (07647)
**Phone—(201) 784-4442**
Fax—(201) 784-4420
www.vizmold.com
Email—info@vizmold.com
Pres., Hum. Res., IT & Off. Mgr.—Dimitrios Lymberis
Off. Mgr.—Viola Kadlubowski
SIC—3089; *Plastic products, including baskets, bowls, dishes, stock vases, vases, party accessories & water picks*
Employs—5; Estab.—1987
Sales—$1Mil-$2.5Mil
62,600 sq ft site, Distrib.—Local
Privately owned corporation
Also see: Viz Mold & Die Ltd., same loc.

---

# Norwood

(Bergen—N.E.)

### AMERICA OGGI

475 Walnut St. (07648)
**Phone—(201) 358-6697**
Fax—(201) 358-9212
www.americaoggi.info
Pres., Editor—Andrea Mantineo
V-P. & Deputy Editor—Massimo Jaus
Cont., Hum. Res. & Off. Mgr.—Francesco Totino
Adv. Mgr.—Maria Pirraglia
Bus. Mgr.—Domenico Delli Carpini
Circ. Mgr.—Tina Sasso
SIC—2711; 2741; *Daily print & online Italian language newspaper publishing*
Employs—40; Estab.—1988
12,000 sq ft site, Distrib.—Regional
Privately owned corporation
Also see: JB Offset Printing Corp., same loc.

### BON-JOUR GROUP, LLC

1100 Blanch Ave. (07648)
**Phone—(201) 646-1070**
Fax—(201) 646-1080
www.bon-jourpromos.com
Email—miket@bon-jour.com
Owner & Pres.—Michael Tchertchian
GM & Prodn. Mgr.—Christine Soto
Off. Mgr.—Donna Colasuono
SIC—2395; 2396; 2759; 3993; *Embroidery & screen printing of promotional items & packaging, fulfillment & heat transfers; Brand name—Change Is Good*
Employs—17; Estab.—1991
Sales—$4Mil-$5Mil
20,000 sq ft site, Distrib.—National
Privately owned corporation

### CONTROL GROUP, THE

500 Walnut St. (07648)
**Phone—(201) 768-1900**
Fax—(201) 784-1527
www.controlgroupusa.com
Email—control@controlgroupusa.com
Ptnr.—William Cheringal
Ptnr.—Jeffrey Levine
IT Mgr.—Curtis Burns
Hum. Res. Mgr.—Rob Taglieri
Floor Mgr.—Jim Imburgia
Cust. Serv. Rep.—Jean Bischer
Cust. Serv. Rep.—Lynne Levine
SIC—2752; 2754; NAICS—323111; *Pressure-sensitive label printing*
Employs—50; Estab.—1970
Sales—$1Mil-$2.5Mil
Distrib.—National
Privately owned partnership
AKA: Norwood Printing

### CREATIVE CONCEPTS CORP.

70 Oak St., Ste. 202 (07648)
**Phone—(201) 750-1234**
Fax—(201) 750-1940
www.creaconcepts.com
Email—info@creaconcepts.com
Pres.—Jean P. Subrenat
Dir., Opers.—Brett Guinta
SIC—2844; NAICS—325600; *Perfumes & fragrances*
Employs—5; Estab.—1997
Distrib.—Intl.
Privately owned corporation

### EARTH FRIENDLY PRODUCTS, INC.

Div. of Earth Friendly Products
380 Chestnut St. (07648)
**Phone—(201) 750-7701**
National—(800) 875-5999
Fax—(201) 750-7720
www.venuslabs.com
Email—venusnj@venuslabs.com
Pur. Mgr.—Keith Dutter
SIC—2842; NAICS—325612; *Cleaning compounds*
Employs—20; Estab.—1967
15,000 sq ft site, Distrib.—Intl.
Privately owned corporation
Parent co.—Earth Friendly Products, Addison, IL
Phone—(630) 595-1900
See Parent Co. Section for full profile.

### EMABOND SOLUTIONS, LLC

Div. of T. A. Systems, Inc.
49 Walnut St., Ste. 2 (07648-1390)
**Phone—(201) 767-7400**
Fax—(201) 767-3608
www.emabond.com
Email—info@emabond.com
V-P., Sales—Steve Chookazian
V-P., Opers. & Technical—Drew LaMarca
Matls. Mgr.—Cynthia Robertson
SIC—3559; *Plastic bonding machinery; Brand name—Emabond; Emaweld; Exoweld*
Employs—18; Estab.—1968
20,000 sq ft site, Distrib.—Intl.
Limited Liability Company
ISO rating—TS16949
Parent co.—T. A. Systems, Inc., Rochester Hills, MI
Phone—(248) 656-5150
See Parent Co. Section for full profile.

### †FERGUSON ENTERPRISES, INC.

444 Livingston St. (07648)
**Phone—(201) 768-6080**
Fax—(201) 768-8135
www.ferguson.com
Email—kerry.hampton@ferguson.com
Br. Mgr.—Kerry Hampton
Showroom Consultant—Doug Lamantia
SIC—5074; *Distributor of plumbing supplies, including pipe, fixtures, valves & fittings*
Employs—10; Estab.—1971
Distrib.—Local
Publicly owned corporation
Parent co.—Ferguson Enterprises, Inc., Newport News, VA
Phone—(757) 874-7795
See Parent Co. Section for full profile.

### FLAVOR DEVELOPMENT CORP.

388 Chestnut St. *(07648)*
**Phone—(201) 784-8188**
Fax—(201) 784-5501
www.flavordev.com
Email—sales@flavordev.com
Pres.—Joseph Staffieri
Opers. Mgr.—Ned Brennan
Off. Mgr.—Linda Staffieri
Pur. Agt.—Kathy Shubert
SIC—2099; *Flavors*
Employs—12; Estab.—1998
Sales—$6Mil
Distrib.—Intl.
Privately owned corporation

### GALOW CO., INC., H.

15 Maple St. (07648)
**Phone—(201) 768-0547**
Fax—(201) 768-2311
www.hgalowco.com
Email—info@hgalowco.com
Pres.—Michael Galow
Engr., Mfg.—Robert Galow
SIC—3599; *Precision machine parts, including CNC & EDM machining & assembly*
Employs—45; Estab.—1981
40,000 sq ft site, Distrib.—Intl.
Privately owned corporation

## Norwood—(cont.)

**INTAROME FRAGRANCE & FLAVOR CORP.**
370 Chestnut St. (07648)
**Phone—(201) 767-8700**
National—(800) 631-1566
Fax—(201) 767-8757
www.intarome.com
Email—info@intarome.com
Pres., CEO—Daniel G. Funsch
CFO, MIS Mgr.—Judith A. Dugan
Plt. Mgr.—Ernesto Aponte
Lab Mgr.—Gregory Husar
Accts. Payable Mgr.—Andrea Fleshman
Accts. Rec. Mgr.—Deborah Britten
Pur. Agt.—Carl Wolfson
SIC—2844; 2087; NAICS—325600; *Fragrances & flavors*
Employs—53; Estab.—1969
40,000 sq ft site, Distrib.—Intl.
Privately owned corporation

**JB OFFSET PRINTING CORP.**
475 Walnut St. (07648)
**Phone—(201) 664-4400**
Fax—(201) 750-1630
Pres.—Andrea Mantineo
Off. Mgr.—Carol Kearns
SIC—2752; 2711; NAICS—323100; *Offset newspaper printing*
Employs—9; Estab.—1978
Sales—under $500,000
Distrib.—Local
Privately owned corporation
Also see: American OGGI, same loc.

**LIVING INTELLIGENT, INC.**
70 Oak St., Ste. 103 (07648)
**Phone—(201) 784-0500**
Fax—(201) 750-6400
www.livingintelligent.com
Email—info@livingintelligent.com
CEO—Mitchell Arthur
Manager—Mike Johnson
SIC—7373; *Computer, communications & audiovisual network systems integration, including LANs, VoIP & videoconferencing*
Employs—8; Estab.—2008
3,000 sq ft site, Distrib.—Local
Privately owned corporation

**M J H GEAR & TOOL CO., INC.**
15 Maple St. (07648)
**Phone—(212) 246-3800**
Fax—(212) 265-4053
Pres.—John M. Halkias
Treas.—M. A. Halkias
SIC—3566; 3599; NAICS—333612; *Precision gears*
Employs—3; Estab.—1951
Sales—$500,000-$1Mil
8,000 sq ft site, Distrib.—National
Privately owned corporation

**MITSUI FOODS, INC.**
Div. of Mitsui & Co. U. S. A., Inc.
35 Maple St. (07648)
**Phone—(201) 750-0500**
Fax—(201) 750-0148
www.mitsuifoods.com
Email—t.osada@mitsui.com
Pres., CEO—Tom Osada
CFO—Albert Caamic
Sr. V-P., Traditional Bus., COO—Jeff Lacy
Sr. V-P., Coffee Div.—Toru Miyake
V-P., Sales Admn.—Maureen Marcason
V-P., IT—Phil Demarest
V-P., Hum. Res.—Ann Murphy
V-P., New Prod. Dev.—Paul Labell
V-P., Logistics & Supply Chain Mgmt.—Daniel Kochenash
V-P., Global Proc.—Johns Thampan
Sr. Logistics Mgr.—Gary Sweeney

Bus. Mgr., Bus. Plng. & Mktg.—Agata Skowronska
SIC—2098; 2038; 5149; NAICS—311999; *Manufacturer of frozen pasta products & distributor of canned food products*
Employs—60; Estab.—1998
Sales—$10Mil-$25Mil (est)
Distrib.—National
Publicly owned corporation
AKA: Mitsui International
Parent co.—Mitsui & Co. U. S. A., Inc., New York, NY
Phone—(212) 878-4000
See Parent Co. Section for full profile.

**PRECISION TECHNOLOGY, INC.**
50 Maple St., P.O. Box 422 (07648)
**Phone—(201) 767-1600**
Fax—(201) 767-6739
www.ptiplastics.com
Email—customerservice@ptiplastics.com
Pres., CEO—Ira Housman
V-P., Sales & Mktg. & IT Mgr.—Charles Plesher
V-P. & Qual. Analyst—Chistopher Clegg
Asst. Cont. & Hum. Res. Mgr.—Patrick Vargas
Logistics & Pur. Mgr.—Harry Ocasio
Cust. Serv. Mgr.—Chuck Plesher
Cust. Serv. Rep.—Jaime Deluisa
SIC—3842; 3089; *Plastic components for orthopedic body implants, trials & instruments*
Employs—40; Estab.—1971
52,000 sq ft site, Distrib.—National
Privately owned sub-S corp.

**RAINMEN U. S. A., INC.**
10 Maple St. (07648)
**Phone—(201) 784-3244**
National—(800) 426-7446
Fax—(201) 784-3242
www.rainmenusa.com
Email—sales@satchelsnewyork.com
Owner—Jeff Nanus
Plt. Mgr.—Liz Sutherland
Cust. Serv. Rep.—Giovanni Violino
Cust. Serv. Rep.—Diane Daly
SIC—3499; 2394; NAICS—314912; *Umbrellas, canvas bags & accessories*
Employs—200; Estab.—1922
Sales—$50Mil-$100Mil
Distrib.—Intl.
Privately owned corporation
AKAs: AAA Umbrella Co. & Satchels

**SPORTS TIME**
40 Oak St. (07648)
**Phone—(201) 768-1101**
Fax—(201) 768-2662
Email—info@sportstimenj.com
Pres.—Evan Baumgarten
SIC—2396; 2395; *Textile screen printing & embroidery*
Employs—6; Estab.—1985
Sales—$500,000-$1Mil (est)
Distrib.—Regional
Privately owned corporation

**STREETGLOW, INC. (H Q)**
57 Oak St. (07648)
**Phone—(973) 709-9000**
National—(800) 787-3384
Fax—(973) 709-1000
www.streetglow.com
Email—sales@streetglow.com
Pres., CEO, CFO & COO—Jack Panzarella
Cont.—Paul Bonanno

SIC—3647; 3714; NAICS—336321; *Corporate headquarters; automotive neon & LED accessories (mfg. done in China)*
Employs—5; Estab.—1991
220,000 sq ft site, Distrib.—Intl.
Privately owned corporation

**TELESCRIPT, INTERNATIONAL LLC**
55 Walnut St., Ste. 101-A (07648-1332)
**Phone—(201) 767-6733**
Fax—(201) 784-0323
www.telescript.com
Email—info@telescript.com
Ptnr.—Christopher O'Brien
Ptnr.—James O'Brien
SIC—3663; NAICS—334220; *Teleprompter systems; Brand name—Telescript*
Employs—12; Estab.—1957
5,000 sq ft site, Distrib.—Intl.
Limited Liability Company
DBA: Telescript International

**TRU MFG., INC.**
40 Oak St. (07648)
**Phone—(201) 768-4050**
Fax—(201) 768-3057
www.trumfg.com
Email—info@trumfg.com
Pres.—Paul Mastropietro
GM—Bill Carlos
Off. Mgr.—Pat Caparelli
SIC—3599; *Precision machining job shop*
Employs—12; Estab.—1972
13,000 sq ft site, Distrib.—Local
Privately owned corporation

**WOOD ARTISANS, INC.**
49 Oak St. (07648)
**Phone—(201) 768-1663**
Fax—(201) 768-1071
Pres.—Harland Reese
V-P.—Robert H. Reese
SIC—2431; 2434; NAICS—337110; *Wooden cabinets & millwork*
Employs—2; Estab.—1961
Sales—$500,000-$1Mil
7,000 sq ft site, Distrib.—Local
Privately owned corporation

**ZENITH ULTRASONICS**
85 Oak St., P.O. Box 412 (07648)
**Phone—(201) 767-1332**
National—(800) 432-7664
Fax—(201) 768-6999
www.zenith-ultrasonics.com
Email—sales@zenith-ultrasonics.com
Pres., Sales & Mktg. Mgr.—Michael Pedzy
Cont.—Maggie Miller
SIC—3559; *Ultrasonic cleaning equipment, including small tabletop/benchtop systems, large single cleaning tanks & multi-tank clean/rinse/dry systems & optional equipment, including filtration systems & wastewater evaporators; Brand name—Crossfire; Ultramatic; Transtar; Vortex; Omega-HF; Pulse-Sonic; MBT; Meridian; MBT Advantage*
Employs—15; Estab.—1935
15,000 sq ft site, Distrib.—Intl.

# Nutley
(Essex—N.E.)

**ADM CUSTOM METAL FABRICATION, INC.**
263 Hillside Ave., Ste. 2 (07110-1169)
**Phone—(973) 284-0088**
www.admmetal.com
Email—info@admmetal.com
Pres., CEO—Andrew K. Mihal

SIC—3444; 3599; *Precision sheet metal & frame fabrication, including prototypes, production runs, laser cutting & robotic welding*
Employs—14; Estab.—1983
Sales—$1Mil-$5Mil
14,000 sq ft site, Distrib.—Regional
Privately owned corporation

**ASTRO TOOL CORP.**
90 Washington Ave. (07110)
**Phone—(973) 661-1299**
Fax—(973) 661-0743
www.astrotool.com
Email—sales@astrotool.com
Sales Mgr., Eastern—John Nosti
Acct. Mgr.—Neena Studebaker
SIC—3546; 3423; NAICS—333991; *Pneumatic, hand crimp, insertion & extraction tools*
Employs—2; Estab.—1987
Sales—$3.5Mil-$4.5Mil
16,000 sq ft site, Distrib.—Intl.
Privately owned corporation
Parent co.—Astro Tool Corp., Beaverton, OR
Phone—(503) 642-9853
See Parent Co. Section for full profile.

**BAUM DRAPERIES**
666 Passaic Ave. (07110)
**Phone—(973) 661-1841**
Fax—(973) 661-1851
Ptnr.—Robert Baum
Ptnr.—Muriel Baum
SIC—2391; NAICS—314121; *Draperies & curtains*
Employs—5; Estab.—1951
Distrib.—Local
Privately owned partnership

**BAUMAR INDUSTRIES, INC.**
29 E. Centre St. (07110)
**Phone—(973) 667-5490**
Fax—(973) 667-2552
www.baumarindustries.com
Email—thomas@baumar.net
Pres., CFO—Arthur Bautis
Manager—Frank Jones
SIC—2834; NAICS—325412; *Contract chemical tablets*
Employs—10; Estab.—1979
5,000 sq ft site, Distrib.—National
Privately owned sub-S corp.
ISO rating—9001:2000

**DESIGNMECHA, INC.**
73 Race St. (07110)
**Phone—(973) 493-8146**
www.designmecha.com
Email—jkiney@optonline.net
Pres.—Joseph Kinney
SIC—3559; *Ultrasonic nanocrystal surface modification equipment for ferrous & nonferrous metal cold forging for the construction, manufacturing, medical & military applications*
Employs—3; Estab.—2004
Sales—under $500,000
Distrib.—National
Privately owned corporation

**EMBROIDERY BY COZY, INC.**
695 Passaic Ave. (07110)
**Phone—(973) 661-9781**
National—(800) 851-5009
Fax—(973) 661-1736
Email—emb@cozytux.com
Pres.—Ralph Savastano
GM—Jeff Savastano
Off. Mgr.—Susan Savastano
SIC—2395; *Embroidery*
Employs—15; Estab.—1993
Sales—$500,000-$1Mil
Distrib.—Local
Privately owned corporation

GEOGRAPHICAL

## Nutley—(cont.)

**GRIFFITH SHADE CO.**
308 Washington Ave., Ste. 1 (07110)
**Phone—(973) 667-1474**
(800) 487-1066
Fax—(973) 667-0496
www.griffithshade.com
Email—jgriffith@griffithshade.com
Pres. & Shop Mgr.—John K. Griffith
V-P.—Mary Ann Griffith
Cont.—Glen Peckel
SIC—2591; NAICS—337920; *Venetian & vertical blinds, cellular window shades, motorized window shades, transparent sun shades, stage drapes, commercial carpet & layout & design services*
Employs—4; Estab.—1950
Sales—$500,000-$1Mil
10,000 sq ft site, Distrib.—Regional
Privately owned sub-S corp.

**INS TECHNOLOGIES**
P.O. Box 615 (07110)
**Phone—(973) 808-6400**
National—(800) 770-7163
www.insti.com
Pres.—Steve Melillo
Manager—Judy Prendergast
SIC—7373; NAICS—541512; *Computer telephone network integrated systems & installation*
Employs—10; Estab.—1987
Sales—$500,000-$1Mil
Distrib.—Regional
Privately owned corporation

**J & G ENTERPRISES, INC.**
182 High St. (07110-4402)
**Phone—(973) 667-7673**
(973) 667-7675
Fax—(973) 667-3597
www.jngenterprises.com
Email—info@jngenterprises.com
Principal & Manager—John Mancini
SIC—2395; 2396; 2759; 3479; *Custom apparel embroidery & screen printing of police equipment & uniforms & laser engraving of metal tags & plaques*
Employs—1; Estab.—2007
Sales—under $500,000
1,000 sq ft site, Distrib.—National
Privately owned corporation
AKA: 911 Specialties

**†J & J INDUSTRIAL SUPPLY, INC.**
113 E. Centre St., P.O. Box 110174 (07110)
**Phone—(973) 235-0100**
Fax—(973) 235-0129
Email—jj.industrial@verizon.net
Pres.—Joe Damore, Sr.
Sales Mgr.—Joseph Damore
SIC—5084; 5085; *Wholesaler of industrial equipment & supplies*
Employs—7; Estab.—1987
Sales—under $500,000
3,000 sq ft site, Distrib.—National
Privately owned corporation

**KODEX INC.**
160 Park Ave., Ste. 1 (07110)
**Phone—(973) 235-0606**
National—(800) 325-6339
Fax—(973) 235-0132
www.kodexray.com
Email—kodex@kodexray.com
Pres., CEO, CFO—Donna Korkala
V-P., Engrg. & R & D & Chief Engr.—Gary Korkala
MIS Mgr.—Garrett Sollitto
SIC—3844; NAICS—334517; *Digital x-ray imaging systems for industrial quality control & high resolution systems for museums & universities specializing in ichthyology & archaeological applications, laboratory & portable battery operated systems; Brand name—ImageXi; Imagex20*
Employs—5; Estab.—1980
Sales—$3Mil
8,500 sq ft site, Distrib.—Intl.
Privately owned corporation

**PNC, INC.**
115 E. Centre St. *(07110)*
**Phone—(973) 284-1600**
Fax—(973) 284-1925
www.pnconline.com
Email—sales@pnconline.com
Pres.—Sam Sangani
SIC—3672; 3953; NAICS—334412; *Printed circuit boards & assemblies for the high frequency RF/microwave, audio, defense & medical industries, including PCB design & SMT stencils; Brand name—ACCUFRAME*
Employs—80; Estab.—1969
Sales—$15Mil-$20Mil
38,000 sq ft site, Distrib.—Intl.
Privately owned corporation
ISO rating—9001:2008

**PRINTING TECHNIQUES, INC.**
48 Franklin Ave. (07110)
**Phone—(973) 667-2606**
Fax—(973) 667-9517
Email—manvapt3@aol.com
Pres.—Joseph Vitiello, Jr.
V-P.—Richard Vitiello
Corp. Secy.—Daniel Vitiello
Graphic Designer—Dan Vitiello
SIC—2759; 2752; NAICS—323100; *Commercial sheetfed, offset & digital printing & graphic design*
Employs—11; Estab.—1976
Sales—$1Mil-$2.5Mil
3,500 sq ft site, Distrib.—Regional
Privately owned corporation

**ROCHE NUTLEY**
Div. of Roche Holdings, Inc.
340 Kingsland St. (07110-1199)
**Phone—(973) 235-5000**
National—(800) 526-6367
Fax—(973) 235-7605
www.rocheusa.com
Email—nutley.medinfo@roche.com
V-P. & Head of Medicinal Chemistry—Karen Lackey
Pub. Affs. Officer—Darien Wilson
SIC—2834; NAICS—325412; *Pharmaceutical drug candidates in Phase II & III clinical trials for cancer treatment, inflammatory diseases & virology; Brand name—Xeloda; Fuzeon; Pegasys; CellCept; Tamiflu*
Employs—1000; Estab.—1905
Distrib.—Local
Publicly owned corporation
Parent co.—Roche Holdings, Inc., South San Francisco, CA
Phone—(650) 225-1000
See Parent Co. Section for full profile.

**RULE ONE, INC.**
68 E. Centre St. (07110)
**Phone—(973) 661-4563**
Fax—(973) 661-4111
Email—ruleone@attglobal.net
Pres.—Roger Emil
Corp. Secy-Treas.—Eric Emil
SIC—3544; NAICS—333500; *Steel rule cutting dies & die cutting*
Employs—3; Estab.—1977
Sales—under $500,000
5,000 sq ft site, Distrib.—National
Privately owned sub-S corp.

**SPEEDPRO IMAGING**
52 E. Centre St., Ste. 3-B (07110)
**Phone—(973) 542-8384**
Fax—(973) 542-8385
www.speedproessex.com
Email—speedproessex@speedpro.com
Pres.—Doug Nixon
CMO—Jerry Gainey
SIC—2759; 2542; 2541; 3993; NAICS—323119; *Large-format graphic printing, including vehicle wraps, trade show displays & event, indoor & outdoor signage*
Employs—4; Estab.—2010
Sales—$500,000-$1Mil
2,900 sq ft site, Distrib.—National
Privately owned corporation

**THOMAS GRECO PUBLISHING INC.**
244 Chestnut St., Ste. 202 (07110-4318)
**Phone—(973) 667-6922**
Fax—(973) 235-1963
www.grecopublishing.com
Email—alicia@grecopublishing.com
Pres., Publisher—Tom Greco
V-P. & Dir., Sales—Alicia Figurelli
Art Dir.—Lea Velocci
SIC—2721; *Automotive trade magazine publishing*
Employs—7; Estab.—1986
Sales—under $500,000
Distrib.—Regional
Privately owned corporation

**NEW ENTRY**
**THOMSON REUTERS CORP.**
Div. of Thomson Reuters Holdings, Inc.
492 River Rd. (07110)
**Phone—(973) 662-3070**
www.thomsonreuters.com
Email—general.info@thomsonreuters.com
Br. Mgr.—Jim McHugh
SIC—2711; NAICS—323119; *Newspaper publishing*
Employs—15
Sales—$500,000-$1Mil (est)
Distrib.—Intl.
Privately owned corporation
Parent co.—Thomson Reuters Holdings, Inc., New York, NY
Phone—(646) 223-4000
See Parent Co. Section for full profile.

**UNILITE CO., INC.**
151 River Rd. (07110)
**Phone—(973) 667-1674**
Fax—(973) 667-1728
Pres.—Mario Foti
V-P.—Michael Foti
V-P.—John Foti
SIC—3599; *Electronic devices & machining job shop*
Employs—9; Estab.—1972
Distrib.—Regional
Privately owned corporation

**ZINICOLA BAKING CO.**
127 King St. (07110)
**Phone—(973) 667-1306**
Pres.—George Zinicola
V-P.—William Zinicola
SIC—2051; NAICS—311812; *Italian bread & rolls*
Employs—11; Estab.—1921
Sales—$1Mil-$2.5Mil (est)
Distrib.—Local
Privately owned corporation

---

## Oak Ridge
(Passaic—N.E.)

**A. GIMENEZ TRADING, LLC**
5 Wegmann Way (07438)
**Phone—(973) 697-2240**
www.manilasihawan.com
Email—info@manilasihawan.com
Mng. Member—Melissa Laserna
SIC—2011; 2013; 2015; *Beef, pork, sausage & chicken processing*
Employs—8; Estab.—2007
Sales—$2.5Mil-$5Mil (est)
Distrib.—National
Limited Liability Company

**DURA-CARB, INC.**
204 Chamberlain Rd., P.O. Box 407 (07438)
**Phone—(973) 697-6665**
National—(800) 526-1081
Fax—(973) 697-0279
www.dura-carb.com
Email—scott@dura-carb.com
Pres.—Donald Biermeister
V-P.—Scott Biermeister
Off. Mgr.—Joan Sardo
SIC—3544; NAICS—333500; *Carbide die components*
Employs—10; Estab.—1977
5,000 sq ft site, Distrib.—Intl.
Privately owned corporation

**ESCO OPTICS**
1 Tideland Rd., P.O. Box 308 (07438)
**Phone—(973) 697-3700**
National—(800) 922-3726
Fax—(973) 697-3011
www.escooptics.com
Email—sales@escooptics.com
Pres.—Lee Steneken
Cont.—Chuck Vincent
Sales Mgr.—Fred Keglovits
SIC—3827; 2821; NAICS—333314; *American-made custom & standard optical components, including fused silica, BK-7 & borofloat lenses, windows, prisms, filters & optical coatings*
Employs—33; Estab.—1955
Sales—$5Mil-$7Mil
14,000 sq ft site, Distrib.—Intl.
Privately owned corporation

**†JEFFERSON MEDICAL & IMAGING, INC.**
5470 Berkshire Valley Rd., P.O. Box 254 (07438)
**Phone—(973) 697-5077**
National—(800) 935-0427
Fax—(973) 697-5170
www.jeffmed.com
Email—sales@jeffmed.com
Pres., CEO—Susan E. Kurylo
CFO & COO—Brian J. Kurylo
V-P., Sales—Carmen Criscione
SIC—5047; *Distributor of medical imaging equipment & medical supplies*
Employs—15; Estab.—1974
Distrib.—Regional
Privately owned corporation

**JET INDUSTRIAL ELECTRONICS CORP.**
104 Ridge Rd. (07438)
**Phone—(973) 697-2300**
Fax—(973) 697-1793
Email—jet@nac.net
Pres.—John Boyce
SIC—3541; 3543; 3599; NAICS—333512; *Roller grinding machinery & CNC machining job shop, including machine tools retrofitting & industrial electrical services*
Employs—25; Estab.—1978
2,000 sq ft site, Distrib.—Regional
Privately owned corporation

**M&R DESIGNS & PROMOTIONS**
21 Stone Oak Ln. (07438)
**Phone—(908) 928-9400**
Fax—(908) 928-9490
www.mrdesignspromotions.com
Email—orders@mrpromotions.com
Owner—Doreen Scott

## Oak Ridge—(cont.)

SIC—2396; 2395; *Promotional products screen printing & embroidery*
Employs—4; Estab.—1985
Sales—$500,000-$1Mil
Distrib.—National
Limited Liability Company

**NOVA SYSTEMS**
246 Cozy Lake Rd. (07438)
Mail addr: P.O. Box 684, Newfoundland (07435)
**Phone—(973) 697-3281**
Fax—(973) 208-0125
Email—bob@group2tech.com
Owner—Bob Deutsch
SIC—3625; 3569; NAICS—334519; *Custom control systems & equipment for ground support for the aviation industry*
Employs—3; Estab.—1978
Sales—$500,000-$1Mil
Distrib.—National
Privately owned corporation

**OXBOW TOOL & DIE CORP.**
44 Fremont Ter. (07438)
Mail addr: P.O. Box 181, Newfoundland (07435)
**Phone—(973) 697-6647**
Pres.—John G. Tulp
SIC—3544; NAICS—333500; *Precision & CNC tool & die machining job shop*
Employs—1; Estab.—1979
Sales—under $500,000
Distrib.—National
Privately owned corporation

**RAUE SCREW MACHINE PRODUCT CO.**
173 Oak Ridge Rd., P.O. Box 207 (07438)
**Phone—(973) 697-7500**
Fax—(973) 697-7010
Email—cindyraue@verizon.net
Pres.—Carl Raue
V-P.—Guy Raue
Off. Mgr.—Cindy Raue
SIC—3599; *Precision machining job shop*
Employs—3; Estab.—1973
Sales—under $500,000
Distrib.—National
Privately owned corporation

**SERVICE CONCRETE CO.**
173 Oak Ridge Rd., P.O. Box 235 (07438)
**Phone—(973) 697-4040**
(973) 827-0035
National—(800) 266-2738
Fax—(973) 697-7457
www.serviceconcrete.com
Email—bknorr@serviceconcrete.com
Pres., Fin. & R & D Mgr.—Anthony Dellechiaie
GM & Off. Mgr.—William Knorr
Sales Mgr.—Sid Crum
Plt. Mgr.—Chris Young
Driver—Jason Howard
SIC—3273; NAICS—327320; *Ready-mixed concrete*
Employs—34; Estab.—1963
Sales—$5Mil-$10Mil (est)
7,200 sq ft site, Distrib.—Regional
Privately owned sub-S corp.

## Oakhurst

(Monmouth—N.E.)

**ANNA SOIREE**
2005 State Route 35, Ste. 19 (07755)
**Phone—(732) 686-9570**
www.annasoiree.com
Email—annasoiree@yahoo.com
Owner—Nicole Chambers
SIC—2759; *Invitation printing*
Employs—2
Distrib.—Local
Sole ownership

**CARTRIDGE WORLD OAKHURST**
1815 State Route 35 (07755)
**Phone—(732) 531-4232**
Fax—(732) 676-7890
www.cartridgeworldusa.com/store47
Email—gotink1@verizon.net
Owner—Joe Betesh
Mktg. Mgr.—Joy Betesh
SIC—3955; 3861; 5043; *Remanufactured inkjet & toner printer cartridges & distributor of new inkjet & toner printer cartridges*
Employs—2; Estab.—2005
Sales—under $500,000
Distrib.—National
Sole ownership

**DOGSTAR DIGITAL, LLC**
429 Redmond Ave. (07755)
**Phone—(732) 768-3699**
www.dogstardigital.com
Email—info@dogstardigital.com
Owner—Jay Armbrust
SIC—2752; 2759; NAICS—323100; *Full-service offset, color & digital printing of visual communications for sales & marketing campaigns/programs, including graphic design, mailing & fulfillment services & photography*
Employs—2; Estab.—2001
Sales—$500,000-$1Mil
5,000 sq ft site, Distrib.—National
Limited Liability Company

NEW ENTRY
**DREYER'S LUMBER & HARDWARE, INC.**
348 Elberon Blvd. (07755)
**Phone—(732) 531-0220**
www.dreyerslumber.com
Email—customerservice@dreyerslumber.com
Owner—Walter Dreyer
SIC—2421; 2431; 5031; 5072; *Lumber processing & millwork & distributor of lumber & hardware*
Employs—4
Sales—$500,000-$1Mil (est)

**G & S FELDMAN, INC.**
P.O. Box 1136 (07755)
**Phone—(732) 918-8838**
Fax—(866) 461-8056
www.gsfeldman.com
Email—info@gsfeldman.com
Pres., Sales Mgr.—Kenny Feldman
SIC—2653; NAICS—322211; *Corrugated boxes*
Employs—12; Estab.—1920
Distrib.—Regional

NEW ENTRY
**R. K. INDUSTRIES, INC.**
259 Overbrook Ave. (07755)
**Phone—(732) 531-1123**
National—(800) 841-7246
Fax—(732) 531-1142
www.waterloov.com
Email—info@waterloov.com
Pres.—Richard Kuhns
SIC—3444; *Aluminum gutter covers*
Employs—10; Estab.—1989
Sales—$1Mil-$2.5Mil (est)
Distrib.—National
Privately owned corporation
AKA: Waterloov & Mark of Perfection

**VITAMINS FOR LIFE, LLC**
1806 Bellmore St., P.O. Box 853 (07755)
**Phone—(732) 663-1559**
Fax—(732) 663-1569
www.vitaminsforlife.net
Email—sales@vitaminsforlife.net
Pres.—Mark Gruberg
V-P.—Bernard Gruberg
SIC—2833; NAICS—325412; *Nutritional supplements*
Employs—35; Estab.—1989
40,000 sq ft site, Distrib.—Intl.
Limited Liability Company

## Oakland

(Bergen—N.E.)

**†AIRGAS, INC.**
5 Iron Horse Rd. (07436)
**Phone—(201) 337-5891**
Fax—(201) 337-5892
www.airgas.com
Email—info@airgas.com
Facility Mgr.—Larry Myers
Store Mgr.—Kirk Johnson
SIC—5172; *Wholesaler of propane gas*
Employs—20; Estab.—1982
Distrib.—National
Publicly owned corporation
Parent co.—Airgas, Inc., Radnor, PA
Phone—(610) 687-5253
See Parent Co. Section for full profile.

**ALPHA PROFESSIONAL TOOLS (HQ)**
103 Bauer Dr. (07436)
**Phone—(800) 648-7229**
Fax—(201) 337-2216
www.alpha-tools.com
Email—orderdesk@alpha-tools.com
Pres.—Nao Takahashi
Hum. Res. Mgr.—Ellen Burke
Off. Mgr.—Mindy Wessel
SIC—3546; *Company headquarters; power hand tools & accessories, including polishers, grinders & profiling wheels (mfg. done overseas)*
Employs—25; Estab.—1986
Sales—$500,000-$1Mil
Distrib.—National
Privately owned corporation

**†AMEREX CORP.**
128 Bauer Dr., Ste. 4 (07436-3111)
**Phone—(201) 337-1616**
Fax—(800) 526-3738
www.amerex-fire.com
Email—jmiller@amerex-fire.com
V-P., Sales, NJ & NY & Br. Mgr.—Jack Miller
SIC—5099; *Distributor of hand portable & wheeled fire extinguishers for commercial & industrial applications*
Employs—5; Estab.—1990
Sales—$500,000-$1Mil
Distrib.—National
Privately owned corporation
Parent co.—Amerex Corp., Trussville, AL
Phone—(205) 655-3271
See Parent Co. Section for full profile.

**AMERLUX, LLC**
178 Bauer Dr. (07436)
**Phone—(973) 882-5010**
Fax—(973) 882-2605
www.amerlux.com
Email—rferdico@amerlux.com
Chrm.—Frank P. Diassi
Pres., CEO—Charles Campagna
Sr. V-P., CFO—Frank Weston
V-P., Opers.—Chris McQuillan
V-P., Hum. Res. & IT—Aimee Vadyak
V-P., Bus. Dev.—Joseph Manning
Mktg. Mgr.—Russ Ferdico
SIC—3646; NAICS—335122; *Company headquarters & architectural grade, energy-efficient lighting fixtures for the retail, hospitality, supermarket, commercial & exterior markets; Brand name—Evoke; Cylindrix; Gruv; SmartSite; Imperia; Contour; Hornet; Fino; Mesa; Fiatto; LS35*
Employs—250; Estab.—1982
Sales—$100Mil
190,000 sq ft site, Distrib.—Intl.
Sole ownership
AKA: Amerlux Global Lighting Solutions

**CAPTIVE FASTENER CORP.**
19 Thornton Rd. (07436)
**Phone—(201) 337-6800**
Fax—(201) 337-1012
www.captive-fastener.com
Email—jkinlin@captive-fastener.com
V-P., Sales—Jim Kinlin
Chief Exec.—Randolph Carbora
Chief Engr.—Joe Alderisio, Jr.
SIC—3452; NAICS—332722; *Metal fasteners; Brand name—Captive*
Employs—100; Estab.—1974
Sales—$20Mil-$25Mil
150,000 sq ft site, Distrib.—Intl.
Privately owned corporation
ISO rating—9001:2008

**COLLAGEN MATRIX, INC.**
15 Thornton Rd. (07436)
**Phone—(201) 405-1477**
National—(888) 405-1001
Fax—(201) 405-1355
www.collagenmatrix.com
Email—admin@collagenmatrix.com
Pres., CEO—Shu-Tung Li
V-P., COO—Debbie Yuen
V-P., CRO—Peggy Hansen
Cont.—Keith Westpy
Sr. Sales & Mktg. Mgr.—Margo Lane
Sr. Pur. Mgr. & Cust. Serv. Admn.—Liesa DeNardo
SIC—2836; *Corporate headquarters & collagen & mineral-based extracellular materials for tissue & organ repair; Brand name—OssiMend™; OssiGuide™; TenoMend™; MatrixDerm; DuraMatrix; DuraMatrix Onlay; Collatene*
Employs—80; Estab.—1997
Sales—$10Mil-$25Mil
28,000 sq ft site,
Privately owned corporation

**CONCRETE ON DEMAND, INC.**
45 Edison Ave., Ste. 1 (07436)
**Phone—(201) 337-0005**
Fax—(201) 337-0080
CEO—Moshe Engel
Corp. Secy.—Lori Rotella
SIC—3273; NAICS—327320; *Ready-mixed concrete*
Employs—8; Estab.—2008
Sales—under $500,000
Distrib.—Local
Privately owned corporation

**CROWN LIFT TRUCKS**
Div. of Crown Equipment Corp.
104 Bauer Dr. (07436)
**Phone—(201) 337-1211**
Fax—(201) 337-5868
www.crown.com
Email—paul.almeida@crown.com
Br. Mgr.—Paul Almeida
Coordinator—Donna Marinna
SIC—3537; *New & rebuilt material handlings lift trucks & forklift trucks*
Employs—80; Estab.—1950
41,000 sq ft site, Distrib.—Intl.
Privately owned corporation

**GEOGRAPHICAL**

## Oakland—(cont.)

Parent co.—Crown Equipment
Corp., New Bremen, OH
Phone—(419) 629-2311
See Parent Co. Section for full profile.

**D B M CORP., INC.**
32-A Spruce St. (07436)
**Phone—(201) 677-0008**
Fax—(201) 688-9444
www.dbmcorp.com
Email—info@dbmcorp.com
Pres.—Dale Sybnor
V-P., Sales & Mktg.—Mike Cagney
V-P.—William Pastor
Buyer—Steve Dann
SIC—3825; *Wireless
communication radio frequency
& satellite test equipment*
Employs—15; Estab.—1999
Distrib.—Intl.
Privately owned sub-S corp.

**DEWEY ELECTRONICS CORP.**
27 Muller Rd. (07436)
**Phone—(201) 337-4700**
National—(800) 526-5174
Fax—(201) 337-3976
www.deweyelectronics.com
Email—dewey@
deweyelectronics.com
Pres., CEO—John H. D. Dewey
Sr. V-P.—Edward L. Proskey
Treas.—Stephen P. Krill
Dir., Hum. Res. & Off. Mgr.—Carol
F. Grofsik
SIC—3679; *Electronic
components, 2kW diesel
generator sets*
Employs—30; Estab.—1955
Sales—$7Mil
48,000 sq ft site, Distrib.—National
Publicly owned corporation

**EKATO CORP.**
48 Spruce St. (07436)
**Phone—(201) 825-4684**
Fax—(201) 825-9776
www.ekato.com
Email—usa@ekato.com
V-P., Hum. Res. & IT Mgr.—Don
Rowen
SIC—3559; *Fluid mixing systems,
mixers, agitators & blenders*
Employs—20; Estab.—1985
Sales—$2.5Mil-$5Mil (est)
Distrib.—Intl.
Privately owned corporation

**ENGINEERING LABORATORIES,
INC.**
360 W. Oakland Ave. (07436)
**Phone—(201) 337-8116**
National—(800) 941-2525
Fax—(201) 337-2467
www.plasticballs.com
Email—sales@plasticballs.com
Pres.—Daniel S. Mason
V-P., Prodn.—Jason J. Mason
Sales Mgr.—Adam Mason
Hum. Res., IT & Off. Mgr.—Marge
Mason
Shpg. Mgr.—Lisa Delvecchio
SIC—3089; *Plastic industrial balls,
beads & small components*
Employs—30; Estab.—1935
35,000 sq ft site, Distrib.—Intl.
Sole ownership

**FIMS MFG. CORP.**
8 Allerman Rd. *(07436)*
**Phone—(201) 845-7088**
Fax—(201) 845-8287
www.fimsmfg.com
Email—fimsmfg@optonline.net
Pres., CFO—Sergio Facchini
V-P., MIS—Michael Facchini
Inventory Mgr.—Melissa Walsh
Off. Admn.—Jennifer Kramer

SIC—3599; *Machine parts,
including CNC milling & turning,
EDM, waterjet cutting services &
MIG & TIG welding*
Employs—20; Estab.—1962
Sales—$1Mil-$6Mil
20,000 sq ft site, Distrib.—National
Privately owned corporation

**GARDEN STATE ORTHOPAEDIC
CENTER, INC.**
9 Post Rd., Ste. OP-1 (07436-
1690)
**Phone—(201) 337-5566**
Fax—(201) 337-1456
www.gsortho.com
Email—gsocinc@aol.com
Pres.—Louis J. Haberman
SIC—3842; *Corporate
headquarters & orthopedic,
orthotic & prosthetic appliances
& supplies*
Employs—3; Estab.—1976
Sales—$500,000
2,500 sq ft site, Distrib.—Regional
Privately owned corporation

**ID TECHNOLOGY**
Div. of Pro Mach, Inc.
48 Spruce St. (07436)
**Phone—(888) 405-4574**
Fax—(201) 405-1179
www.labelingsystems.com
Email—lsi@labelingsystems.com
V-P., GM—Jack Roe
Hum. Res. Mgr.—Vickie Bonetter
Application Engr.—Steve Huth
SIC—3565; NAICS—333993;
*Pressure sensitive labeling
machinery*
Employs—25; Estab.—1998
45,000 sq ft site, Distrib.—Intl.
Privately owned corporation
Parent co.—Pro Mach, Inc.,
Loveland, OH
Phone—(513) 831-8778
See Parent Co. Section for full profile.

**†KANEBRIDGE CORP.**
153 Bauer Dr. (07436)
**Phone—(201) 337-3200**
National—(800) 222-9221
Fax—(201) 337-2301
www.kanebridge.com
Email—sales@kanebridge.com
Pres.—Joseph McGrath
Cont.—Mike Sutphin
Pur. Mgr.—Nick Pelez
IT Mgr.—Jim Kierstead
Hum. Res. Mgr.—Joanne
Vandunck
SIC—5072; *Corporate
headquarters & distributor of
industrial fasteners, nuts & bolts*
Employs—45; Estab.—1997
Company-wide: 70
Distrib.—National
Privately owned corporation

**KINESYS AUTOMATION, INC.**
5 Fir Ct., Unit 3 (07436)
**Phone—(201) 337-5000**
Fax—(201) 337-5200
www.kinesysauto.com
Email—sales@
kinesysautomation.com
Pres.—Diana Manoussakis
V-P., Opers.—Terry Kipriadis
SIC—3535; 3565; NAICS—
333922; *Packaging, conveying,
filling, capping & indexing
machinery*
Employs—8; Estab.—1989
8,000 sq ft site, Distrib.—National
Privately owned corporation

**MERIDIAN SURFACES**
677 Ramapo Valley Rd. (07436)
**Phone—(201) 337-7888**
www.meridiansurfaces.com
Owner—Dan Lazzara
Off. Mgr.—Lulu Lazzara

SIC—2541; *Countertops*
Employs—2; Estab.—1997
Sales—under $500,000
Distrib.—Local
Sole ownership

**METROPOLITAN VACUUM CLEANER
CO., INC.**
5 Raritan Rd. (07436)
**Phone—(201) 405-2225**
National—(800) 822-1602
Fax—(201) 405-2660
www.metrovacworld.com
Email—david.stern@
metrovacworld.com
Pres.—Jules Stern
V-P., Sales, Natl.—Kenneth Stern
V-P., Mktg.—David Stern
GM—Robert Stevenson
IT Mgr.—David Bernstein
Off. Mgr.—Rosella Margiotta
Fin. Mgr.—Sam Jarona
SIC—3635; 3423; NAICS—
335212; *Household vacuum
cleaners, electric air pumps, pet
& motorcycle dryers & computer
cleaning systems*
Employs—75; Estab.—1939
60,000 sq ft site, Distrib.—Intl.
Privately owned sub-S corp.

**MULHERN BELTING, INC.**
148 Bauer Dr., P.O. Box 620
(07436)
**Phone—(201) 337-5700**
National—(800) 253-6300
Fax—(201) 337-6540
www.mulhernbelting.com
Email—jbouley@
mulhernbelting.com
CEO—Patrick Mulhern
Pres.—Michael Mulhern
V-P., Fin. & Opers.—Dennis
Dubatowka
Br. Mgr.—Steve Stoner
Acctg. Mgr.—Jeannie Bouley
SIC—3535; NAICS—333922;
*Corporate headquarters &
conveyor belting*
Employs—45; Estab.—1932
Sales—$25Mil
50,000 sq ft site, Distrib.—
Regional
Privately owned corporation
ISO rating—9001

**†NATIONAL ELECTRONIC ALLOYS,
INC.**
3 Fir Ct. (07436)
**Phone—(201) 337-9400**
National—(888) 524-4309
Fax—(201) 337-9698
www.nealloys.com
Email—sales@nealloys.com
Pres.—Richard Geoffrion
Sales Mgr.—Ed Post
Off. Mgr.—Winnie Bellinger
Sales Rep.—Mike Sancetta
SIC—5051; *Metal service center*
Employs—20; Estab.—1991
Distrib.—Intl.
Privately owned corporation
ISO rating—9001:2000

**ND INDUSTRIES, INC.**
128 Bauer Dr., Ste. 2 (07436)
**Phone—(201) 651-1500**
National—(800) 634-8699
Fax—(201) 651-1400
www.ndindustries.com
Email—info@ndindustries.com
GM—Bill Lang
SIC—3452; NAICS—332722;
*Locking elements on screws*
Employs—30; Estab.—1955
Distrib.—Local
Privately owned corporation
Parent co.—ND Industries, Inc.,
Clawson, MI
Phone—(248) 288-0000
See Parent Co. Section for full profile.

NEW ENTRY
**P M C DINERS, INC.**
56 Spruce St. (07436)
**Phone—(201) 337-6146**
Fax—(201) 337-1286
Pres.—Herbert G. Enyart
SIC—3448; *Prefabricated metal
buildings*
Employs—6
Sales—$500,000-$1Mil (est)

**RAPID TAG & LABEL, INC.**
5 Fir Ct., Ste. 4 (07436)
**Phone—(201) 337-5551**
National—(877) 438-8247
Fax—(201) 337-5514
www.rapidtags.com
Email—sales@rapidtags.com
Pres.—Lester Szajna
V-P., Sales & Mktg.—Denise
Newton
V-P., Prodn.—Ursula Szajna
V-P.—Francine Bradley
Bookkeeper—Cathy Cook
SIC—2759; NAICS—323100; *Bar
code label printing*
Employs—5; Estab.—2002
Sales—under $500,000
Distrib.—Intl.
Privately owned partnership

**†RELAY SPECIALTIES, INC.**
17 Raritan Rd., P.O. Box 7000
(07436)
**Phone—(201) 337-1000**
National—(800) 526-5376
Fax—(201) 337-1862
www.relayspec.com
Email—sales@relayspec.com
Pres.—Barry Sauer
V-P.—Steve Gershberg
Sales Mgr., Natl.—Ken Cohen
Hum. Res. Mgr.—Nicole Voss
SIC—5065; *Wholesaler of
electromechanical & electronic
components*
Employs—35; Estab.—1963
18,000 sq ft site, Distrib.—Intl.
Privately owned corporation

**ROYAL MASTERS GRINDERS, INC.**
143 Bauer Dr., P.O Box 630
(07436)
**Phone—(201) 337-8500**
Fax—(201) 337-2324
www.royalmaster.com
Email—mailbox@royalmaster.com
Pres.—John Memmelaar
V-P.—John Memmelaar, Jr.
SIC—3541; NAICS—333512;
*Centerless grinding machines*
Employs—48; Estab.—1950
Distrib.—Intl.
Privately owned corporation

**ROYLE SYSTEMS GROUP, LLC**
111 Bauer Dr., Ste. 2 (07436)
**Phone—(201) 644-0345**
Fax—(201) 644-0346
www.roylesystems.com
Email—sales@roylesystems.com
Pres.—Greg Ramsey
Sr. V-P.—Peter Ramsey
V-P., Mfg.—Jim Carbone
SIC—3559; *Rubber & plastic
extrusion equipment for the wire
& cable industry*
Employs—30; Estab.—1855
40,000 sq ft site, Distrib.—Intl.
Limited Liability Company

**TOPCON MEDICAL SYSTEMS, INC.**
111 Bauer Dr. *(07436)*
**Phone—(201) 599-5100**
National—(800) 223-1130
Fax—(201) 599-5250
www.topcon.com
Email—tmsmarketing@topcon.com
Pres., CEO—Dave Mudrick
Cont.—Tracy Brandenburg
IT Mgr.—Gus Jarrous
Hum. Res. Mgr.—Paula Louzeiro
Media Coord.—Linda Dunlea

## Oakland—(cont.)

SIC—3841; *Medical diagnostic equipment, including imaging, delivery & lens processing*
Employs—133; Estab.—1989
Distrib.—Intl.
Privately owned corporation

**TRACER TOOL & MACHINE CO., INC.**

32 Iron Horse Rd. (07436)
**Phone—(201) 337-6184**
Fax—(201) 337-3156
www.tracermed.com
Email—lconner@tracermed.com
Pres.—D. Lindsay Conner
Plt. Mgr.—Oscar Castillo
Off. Mgr.—Tina L. Tomat
SIC—3599; *Precision & CNC machining, milling & turning of orthopedic instruments & implants for the aerospace, pharmaceutical & food industries*
Employs—22; Estab.—1964
7,500 sq ft site, Distrib.—National
Sole ownership
ISO rating—9001, 13485

## Oaklyn

(Camden—S.W.)

**DUBIN BROS. LUMBER CO., INC.**

710 Newton Ave., P.O. Box 85 (08107)
**Phone—(856) 854-4675**
National—(800) 989-4675
Fax—(856) 854-4704
www.dubinlumber.com
Email—customerservice@dubinlumber.com
Pres.—Richard Dubin
V-P.—Michael Dubin
SIC—2426; *Dimensional lumber*
Employs—5; Estab.—1996
Sales—under $500,000 (est)
Distrib.—Local
Privately owned corporation

**HUBLER & ASSOCS.**

146 E. Holly Ave. (08107)
**Phone—(856) 906-5341**
Owner—Richard G. Hubler
SIC—2759; *Commercial printing*
Employs—2; Estab.—2001
Sales—under $500,000
Distrib.—Intl.
Sole ownership

**PENN JERSEY WEEKEND DIRECTIONALS**

208 W. Clinton Ave. (08107)
**Phone—(856) 858-8888**
www.pennjerseysigns.com
Email—contact@weekenddirectionalsigns.com
Owner—Ann Marie Bauman
V-P.—Paul Schlimme
Graphic Designer—Michelle Griffin
SIC—3993; *Signs, including weekend directional & yard signs, banners & mini billboards; Brand name—Coroplast; Peachtree; Foamcraft; Firesprint; Oracal; 3m*
Employs—10; Estab.—2003
Sales—$3Mil
4,600 sq ft site, Distrib.—National
Limited Liability Company
AKA: Salem Oak Homes

## Ocean

(Monmouth—N.E.)

**A W EUROSTILE**

736 Route 35 (07712)
**Phone—(732) 493-1883**
Fax—(732) 530-0372
www.aweurostile.com
Email—aweurostile@aol.com
Pres.—Andrea Wyman

Acct. & Sales Mgr.—Elizabeth Wyman
SIC—3281; 3231; 5032; NAICS—327991; *Manufacturer & distributor of marble, granite, quartz, limestone, slate & recycled glass countertops, ceramic, custom, mosaic, metal & glass tile & stone ledgers for exterior & interior applications & exterior pavers for pools & patios*
Employs—10; Estab.—1987
36,000 sq ft site, Distrib.—Regional
Privately owned corporation

**ACD CUSTOM GRANITE, INC.**

1304 Roller Rd. (07712)
**Phone—(732) 695-2400**
Fax—(732) 695-2401
www.acdcustomgranite.com
Email—cynthia@acdcustomgranite.com
Pres.—Cynthia Schomaker
SIC—3281; 2542; NAICS—327991; *Natural & engineered stone fabrication & countertops; Brand name—Cambrian; Vetrazzo; Quartzmaster; Caesarstone; IceStone; Hanstone; Silestone*
Employs—13; Estab.—2001
Sales—$2Mil-$2.5Mil
11,000 sq ft site, Distrib.—Regional
Privately owned corporation

**ADPRO IMPRINTS, INC.**

3411 Rose Ave. (07712)
Mail addr: 1206 State Route 35, Ocean (07712)
**Phone—(732) 493-8555**
(732) 531-2133
Fax—(732) 531-2142
www.adproimprints.com
Email—info@adproimprints.com
Pres.—Peter L. Demaree, Jr.
V-P.—Anthony L. Lugo
Art Dir.—Jessica Renna
SIC—2396; 2395; 3993; *Textile screen printing, embroidery, promotional items, signage & graphic design & branding services*
Employs—5; Estab.—1983
2,800 sq ft site, Distrib.—Regional
Privately owned sub-S corp.

**ANDANTEX U.S.A., INC.**

1705 Valley Rd. (07712)
**Phone—(732) 493-2812**
National—(800) 713-6170
Fax—(732) 493-2949
www.andantex.com
Email—info@andantex.com
Pres.—Michael G. Munn
V-P., Sales—Bruce Bradley
V-P., Mfg.—Paul Drescher
V-P., Mktg.—Pat Drescher
V-P., Fin.—Mary Vaccarelli
V-P., Chief Engr.—Dave Regiec
V-P.—Mary Ann Bradley
SIC—3566; NAICS—333612; *Right-angle gearboxes, servo worm & planetary reducers, industrial racks& pinions & web tension products; Brand name—Anglgear; ROTOMISSION; MEROBEL*
Employs—20; Estab.—1980
Sales—$5Mil-$10Mil
13,000 sq ft site, Distrib.—Intl.
Privately owned corporation

**ATLANTIC PRINTING & GRAPHICS, LLC**

1301 W. Park Ave. (07712)
**Phone—(732) 493-4222**
Fax—(732) 493-0279
Email—atlprnt@comcast.net
Owner—Ed Lawrence
Pressman—Ed Ulstein

SIC—2759; 2752; NAICS—323100; *Commercial & instant printing*
Employs—5; Estab.—1983
Sales—under $500,000
Distrib.—Local
Privately owned corporation

**ATMOS TECH INDUSTRIES**

1108 Pollack Ave. (07712)
**Phone—(732) 493-8400**
Fax—(732) 493-8954
www.atmostech.com
Email—sales@atmostech.com
Mktg. Mgr.—Shaun Brower
Off. Mgr.—Michelle Webster
Shpg. Mgr.—Joyce Criscuolo
Sales Rep.—Tom McCarthy
SIC—3564; 3499; NAICS—333400; *Cleanroom filters, air showers, stainless steel console equipment, cleanrooms & pharmaceutical equipment*
Employs—48; Estab.—1971
20,000 sq ft site, Distrib.—Intl.
Limited Liability Company

**CHOICE SIGNS**

3407 Rose Ave., Ste. 3 (07712-3969)
**Phone—(732) 493-1644**
Fax—(732) 493-5656
www.choicesigns.com
Email—choicesigns99@aol.com
V-P., Opers.—Daniel Kowalski
SIC—3993; 2759; 2541; NAICS—323100; *ADA braille, vinyl & magnetic interior & exterior signs, banners, trade show displays, digital printing & vehicle lettering*
Employs—3; Estab.—1992
Sales—under $500,000
2,200 sq ft site, Distrib.—National
Privately owned sub-S corp.

**CROWN PRODUCTS, INC.**

1302 Roller Rd. (07712)
**Phone—(732) 493-0022**
Fax—(732) 493-0099
Email—c1rown@aol.com
Pres., GM—Joseph Tagliareni
SIC—3949; 3993; NAICS—339920; *Promotional golf accessories*
Employs—25; Estab.—1980
Distrib.—National
Privately owned corporation

**HERRING CO., INC., D. C.**

1750 Brielle Ave., Ste. B-2 (07712-3953)
**Phone—(732) 695-2272**
Fax—(732) 695-2275
www.dcherring.com
Email—dherr10123@aol.com
Founder—Daniel C. Herring
Pres.—Daniel A. 'Drew' Herring
V-P., Opers.—Thomas Pedrazzo
SIC—3069; NAICS—326220; *Extruded cellular rubber products*
Employs—6; Estab.—1959
Sales—$3.5Mil-$4.5Mil
6,500 sq ft site, Distrib.—Intl.
Privately owned corporation

**IMMUNOSTICS, INC.**

3505 Sunset Ave. (07712)
**Phone—(732) 918-0770**
National—(800) 722-7505
Fax—(732) 918-0618
www.immunostics.com
Email—sales@immunostics.com
Pres.—Kenneth Kupits
V-P.—Vincent LaStella
Sales Coord.—Andrea Geffon

SIC—3841; *Medical diagnostic kits; Brand name—Hema-Screen; Colon Alert; Immuno Detector*
Employs—30; Estab.—1985
Sales—$6Mil-$10Mil
18,000 sq ft site, Distrib.—National
Privately owned corporation
ISO rating—13485

**KINETRON, INC.**

1416 S. Roller Rd. (07712)
**Phone—(732) 918-7777**
National—(888) 854-6387
Fax—(732) 493-8277
www.kinetron.com
Email—kinetron@aol.com
Pres.—Judith Gogan
V-P.—Timothy Labrecque
SIC—3444; *Precision sheet metal fabrication, plasma cutting & machining job shop*
Employs—8; Estab.—1962
5,000 sq ft site, Distrib.—National
Privately owned sub-S corp.

**LOGO KNITS, INC.**

42-A Cindy Ln. (07712)
**Phone—(732) 382-6961**
National—(800) 874-5646
Fax—(732) 382-9479
www.logoknits.com
Email—sales@logoknits.com
Pres.—Paul Van Anda
Manager—Bryan Finley
SIC—2392; 2395; *Knitted blankets & embroidery*
Employs—12; Estab.—1904
Sales—$500,000-$1Mil
Distrib.—National
Privately owned corporation

**MILLER & SONS, INC., I. V.**

15 Cindy Ln. (07712-7249)
**Phone—(732) 493-4040**
Fax—(732) 493-4044
Email—george@ivmiller.com
Pres., CFO—George H. Miller
Ex. V-P.—Jack V. Miller
Secy-Treas.—Juni M. Fraser
SIC—3089; 3999; *Metallizing of plastic packaging components, closures & aerosol covers*
Employs—18; Estab.—1949
10,000 sq ft site, Distrib.—National
Privately owned sub-S corp.

**ORYCON CONTROL TECHNOLOGY, INC.**

3407 Rose Ave. (07712)
**Phone—(732) 922-2400**
Fax—(732) 922-2403
www.orycon.com
Email—support@orycon.com
Pres. & GM, Hum. Res.—Sal Benenati
IT & Prodn. Mgr.—Tom Siverson
Off. Mgr.—Colleen Benenati
SIC—3823; NAICS—334513; *Plastics working hot runner systems*
Employs—20; Estab.—1981
Sales—$1Mil-$2.5Mil
20,000 sq ft site, Distrib.—Intl.
Privately owned corporation

**PHIL-LU, INC.**

1206 Herbert Ave. (07712)
**Phone—(732) 531-6338**
www.phil-luinc.com
Email—philluinc@aol.com
Pres.—Lucille Petillo
V-P.—Phillip J. Pettillo
Engr.—David Petillo

GEOGRAPHICAL

## Ocean—(cont.)

SIC—3842; 3841; *Custom spinal, ophthalmic, microsurgical & neurological medical & surgical devices, including fuel cells, hydrogen generators, new product development & electronic prototypes for the medical industry*
Employs—3; Estab.—1971
Sales—$500,000-$1Mil
3,000 sq ft site, Distrib.—Intl.
Privately owned corporation

### PHOENIX MFG., INC.

1306 Brielle Ave. (07712)
**Phone—(732) 380-1666**
National—(866) 887-2457
Fax—(732) 380-1501
www.phoenixpvcrails.com
Email—info@phoenixpvcrails.com
Pres.—Richard Sheridan
CFO—Kerry Sheridan
V-P., Sales & Mktg.—Jennifer Sheridan
SIC—3089; 3444; *PVC & aluminum railings & PVC pergolas, shower enclosures & fences*
Employs—10; Estab.—1991
Sales—$1Mil-$5Mil
Distrib.—Regional
Privately owned corporation

### QP2000, LLC

Div. of Quikie Print & Copy Shops
827 W. Park Ave. (07712)
**Phone—(732) 531-8860**
Fax—(732) 517-0417
www.quikieprint.com
Email—ocean@quikieprint.com
GM—John Thompson
Shop Mgr.—Darleen Colgan
SIC—2752; 2759; NAICS—323100; *Offset & instant printing, digital graphics, print on demand & mailing services*
Employs—5; Estab.—1976
Sales—over $500,000
2,000 sq ft site, Distrib.—Regional
Privately owned corporation
AKA: Quikie Print & Copy Shop
Parent co.—Quikie Print & Copy Shops, Shrewsbury, NJ
Phone—(732) 933-1010
See Parent Co. Section for full profile.

### QUIKIE PRINT & COPY SHOP

Div. of Quikie Print & Copy Shops
827 W. Park (07712)
**Phone—(732) 531-8860**
Fax—(732) 517-0417
www.quikieprint.com
Email—ocean@quikieprint.com
Manager—Darleen Calgon
Manager—John Thompson
Asst. Mgr.—Jodie Rossi
SIC—2752; NAICS—323100; *Instant printing*
Employs—4; Estab.—1990
Sales—$500,000-$1Mil
600,000 sq ft site, Distrib.—Regional
Privately owned corporation
Parent co.—Quikie Print & Copy Shops, Shrewsbury, NJ
Phone—(732) 933-1010
See Parent Co. Section for full profile.

### REFLECTIVE METALS, INC.

1001 Hopewell Ave. (07712)
**Phone—(732) 918-7490**
National—(800) 448-6556
Fax—(732) 918-7495
Email—reflectivemetals@hotmail.com
Pres.—Joseph Lodato
Off. Mgr.—Rose Lodato
Foreman—John Ray

SIC—3471; NAICS—332813; *Architectural metal finishing & polishing*
Employs—4; Estab.—1992
Sales—under $500,000
10,000 sq ft site, Distrib.—National
Privately owned corporation

### SCHALL MFG., INC.

3501 Rose Ave. (07712)
**Phone—(732) 918-8800**
Fax—(732) 918-2318
Pres.—Martin Schall
SIC—3599; *General machining job shop*
Employs—5; Estab.—1991
Sales—$500,000-$1Mil (est)
Distrib.—Regional
Privately owned corporation

### SPECIALTY LIGHTING INDUSTRIES, INC.

1306 Doris Ave. (07712)
**Phone—(732) 517-0800**
Fax—(732) 517-0971
www.specialtylightingindustries.com
Email—sales@specialtylightingindustries.com
Pres.—Ben Salomon
V-P., Bus. Dev.—Awi Salomon
Cust. Serv. Rep.—Kimberley Nutlie
SIC—3646; 3645; NAICS—335122; *Commercial & residential lighting equipment*
Employs—25; Estab.—1993
10,000 sq ft site, Distrib.—Intl.
Privately owned corporation

### SPRAY POWDERS, INC.

23 Cindly Ln. *(07712)*
Mail addr: P.O. Box 76, Oakhurst (07755-0076)
**Phone—(732) 493-1311**
Fax—(732) 493-0140
Email—somabhai@aol.com
Owner—Yadu M. Patel
Pres.—Mahesh S. Patel
SIC—3479; *Powder coatings*
Employs—2; Estab.—2000
Sales—under $250,000
Distrib.—National
Sole ownership

### UTE MICROWAVE, INC.

3500 Sunset Ave., Ste. D-1 (07712-3956)
**Phone—(732) 922-1009**
Fax—(732) 922-1848
www.utemicrowave.com
Email—info@utemicrowave.com
Pres.—L. Nilson
Prod. Mgr.—J. Gross
Fin. Mgr.—S. Zboyan
R & D Mgr.—A. Owens
SIC—3679; *High-powered microwave ferrite & low-powered octave & common band isolators & circulators*
Employs—20; Estab.—1963
Sales—$1Mil-$5Mil
7,000 sq ft site, Distrib.—Intl.
Privately owned sub-S corp.

## Ocean City

(Cape May—S.E.)

### BROWN'S AWNING CO.

628 West Ave. (08226)
**Phone—(609) 398-6262**
Fax—(609) 398-6264
www.brownsawning.com
Pres.—Christina Russick
SIC—2394; NAICS—314912; *Canvas awnings*
Employs—7; Estab.—1984
Sales—$500,000-$1Mil (est)
Distrib.—National
Privately owned corporation

### COFFEE CO., LLC, THE

928 Boardwalk (08226)
**Phone—(609) 399-5533**
Fax—(609) 398-2564
www.oceancitycoffee.com
Email—coffee@oceancitycoffee.com
Owner—Joan Williamson
Manager—Destiny Aberle
SIC—2095; *Coffee roasting*
Employs—7
Sales—under $500,000
Distrib.—Local
Privately owned corporation

### COPIERS PLUS

935 West Ave. (08226)
**Phone—(609) 398-7676**
Fax—(609) 399-5509
www.dbprinting.com
Email—customerservice@dbprinting.com
Owner—Bob Matthews
SIC—2759; NAICS—323100; *Digital printing*
Employs—4
Sales—under $500,000
Distrib.—Local
Privately owned corporation

### †JOHNSON'S APPLIANCES & BEDDING

930 Asbury Ave., P.O. Box 95 (08226)
**Phone—(609) 399-1598**
Fax—(609) 398-4808
www.johnsonsappliances.net
Email—tg0521@aol.com
Pres. & Dir., Opers. & Sales—Don Johnson
SIC—5064; 5023; *Company headquarters & wholesaler of household appliances & bedding*
Employs—30; Estab.—1945
Sales—$6Mil-$10Mil
3,000 sq ft site, Distrib.—Local
Privately owned corporation

### MC SIGNS

231 West Ave. (08226)
**Phone—(609) 399-7446**
www.mcsignstudio.com
Email—signsalsbymc@gmail.com
Owner—Mark Crego
SIC—3993; *Interior & exterior signs & vinyl lettering*
Employs—10; Estab.—1980
Sales—$500,000-$1Mil (est)
Distrib.—Intl.
Privately owned corporation

### OCEAN CITY VINYL FENCE CO., INC.

719 Haven Ave. (08226)
**Phone—(609) 399-8288**
Fax—(609) 399-0558
www.oceancityfence.com
Pres.—Harry Williams
Estimator—Al McBride
SIC—3089; *Vinyl fencing & railing*
Employs—5; Estab.—1983
3,000 sq ft site, Distrib.—Regional
Privately owned corporation

### RAUHAUSER'S CANDY

721 Asbury Ave. (08226)
**Phone—(609) 399-1465**
Fax—(609) 399-5756
www.rauhausers.com
Owner—Rodney Blomdahl
SIC—2066; 3942; NAICS—339931; *Chocolate candy, tinware & stuffed animal gifts*
Employs—10; Estab.—2009
Sales—under $500,000
Distrib.—Local
Privately owned corporation

### SAMPLE MEDIA, INC.

801 Asbury St., 3rd Fl. (08226)
**Phone—(609) 399-1220**
National—(800) 356-3791
Fax—(609) 399-0416

www.ocsentinel.com
Email—customerservice@ocsentinel.com
Publisher & Editor—David Nahan
Adv. Mgr.—Robert Elder
Classified Mgr.—Mary Jane Weissenberg
SIC—2711; 2741; *Community newspaper & tourist-vacation based publication publishing; Brand name—Ocean City Sentinel; Cape May Star & Wave; Sure Guide; Sentinel of Somers Point; Linwood and Northfield*
Employs—35; Estab.—1880
Distrib.—National
Privately owned corporation

### SHRIVER'S SALT WATER TAFFY & FUDGE

9th St. & Boardwalk, P.O. Box 899 (08226)
**Phone—(609) 399-0100**
National—(877) 668-2339
Fax—(609) 398-2075
www.shrivers.com
Email—info@shrivers.com
Pres.—Meryl Vangelov
V-P.—Virginia G. Berwick
V-P.—Blue Vangelov
GM—Holly Kisby
Bookkeeper—Kathy Simth
SIC—2064; NAICS—311300; *Saltwater taffy, fudge, macaroons, jellies, nuts, chocolates, novelty candy & gift items; Brand name—Coal Candy; Gold Candy*
Employs—45; Estab.—1898
Distrib.—National
Privately owned sub-S corp.

### STEEL'S FUDGE, INC.

1000 Boardwalk (08226)
**Phone—(609) 398-2383**
Fax—(609) 345-1870
www.steelsfudge.com
Email—info@steelsfudge.com
GM—Mimi Steel
SIC—2064; NAICS—311300; *Fudge, taffy, peanut brittle & caramel popcorn*
Employs—10; Estab.—1990
Sales—under $500,000
Distrib.—National
Privately owned corporation
AKA: George Steel
Parent co.—Steel's Fudge, Inc., Atlantic City, NJ
Phone—(609) 345-4051
See Parent Co. Section for full profile.

## Ocean Grove

(Monmouth—N.E.)

### FRANKLEN SHEET METAL CO., INC.

122 S. Main St. (07756)
**Phone—(732) 988-0808**
National—(800) 273-6073
Fax—(732) 774-4285
www.franklensheetmetal.com
Email—franklen@verizon.net
Owner & Pres.—Steven Smith
SIC—3444; 3449; *Roof coping sheet metal fabrication & stainless steel products, including ducts, back splashes, countertops & hoods & commercial HVAC services*
Employs—12; Estab.—1982
Sales—$2Mil-$2.5Mil
6,000 sq ft site, Distrib.—Regional
Privately owned sub-S corp.

### GENGARO STONE, LLC

90 S. Main St. (07756)
**Phone—(732) 776-6000**
Fax—(732) 776-6660
Email—gsstone1@optimum.net
Pres.—Sam Gengaro

## Ocean Grove—(cont.)

SIC—2542; 3281; NAICS—
327991; *Solid-surface
countertops, including marble &
granite*
Employs—12; Estab.—2002
Sales—under $500,000
Distrib.—Local
Limited Liability Company

### HOFFMAN EXTRUSIONS, INC.

103 1/2 Mount Tabor Way, P.O.
Box 397 (07756-0397)
**Phone—(732) 774-2728**
Fax—(732) 774-1819
Pres.—Carl Hoffman
SIC—3354; NAICS—331316;
*Aluminum & brass extrusions*
Employs—2; Estab.—1991
Sales—under $500,000
Distrib.—National
Privately owned corporation

NEW ENTRY
### MARCIA'S MELODIES

61 Pilgrim Pathway, Unit 3 (07756)
**Phone—(732) 988-3191**
Email—marciahendron@gmail.com
Pres.—Marcia Hendron
SIC—2741; *Sheet music
publishing*
Employs—4; Estab.—1994
Sales—under $500,000
Distrib.—National
Sole ownership

## Ocean View

(Cape May—S.E.)

### ACTION SUPPLY, INC.

1413 Stagecoach Rd. (08230)
**Phone—(609) 390-0663**
National—(888) 390-6453
Fax—(609) 390-2491
www.actionsupplyco.com
Email—support@
actionsupplyco.com
Pres.—Tom Tower
Sales Mgr.—George Smith
SIC—3273; 5032; NAICS—
327320; *Corporate headquarters
& manufacturer of ready-mixed
concrete & distributor of masonry
supplies*
Employs—50; Estab.—1985
Sales—$500,000-$1Mil
Distrib.—Regional
Privately owned corporation

### KELTEX IMPRINTED APPAREL, INC.

428-A Woodbine Oceanview Rd.
(08230)
**Phone—(609) 624-3252**
Fax—(609) 624-0318
www.keltexapparel.com
Email—ckelly@keltexapparel.com
Pres.—Christopher Kelly
Treas., Hum. Res. Mgr.—Robyn
Kelly
SIC—2396; 2395; *Textile screen
printing, embroidery, signs,
banners & imprinted promotional
items*
Employs—25; Estab.—1988
16,000 sq ft site, Distrib.—National
Privately owned sub-S corp.

### MERLINO MARBLE & GRANITE, INC.

92 Route 50 (08230)
**Phone—(609) 624-9500**
Fax—(609) 624-9555
www.merlinomarble.com
Email—tim@merlinomarble.com
Pres.—Timothy Merlino

SIC—3281; 2542; *Natural stone &
solid-surface countertops,
including marble, granite,
limestone & quartz-based solid-
surface materials*
Employs—2; Estab.—2007
Sales—$1Mil
Distrib.—Local
Privately owned corporation

### SUN EMBROIDERY SCREEN PRINTING CO.

12 Route 50, P.O. Box 349 (08230)
**Phone—(609) 624-1231**
www.sunembroideryscreenprinting
.com
Email—sun-embroidery@
comcast.net
Owner—Jennifer DeRosa
SIC—2396; 2395; *Textile screen
printing & embroidery, including
polo shirts*
Employs—2; Estab.—2002
Sales—under $500,000 (est)
Distrib.—National

## Oceanport

(Monmouth—N.E.)

### COMMVAULT SYSTEMS, INC.

2 Crescent Pl., P.O. Box 900
(07757)
**Phone—(732) 870-4000**
Fax—(732) 870-4525
www.commvault.com
Pres., CEO—N. Robert Hammer
Sr. V-P., CFO—Brian Carolan
Ex. V-P., COO—Alan G. Bunte
V-P., CAO—Gary Merrill
Sr. V-P., Worldwide Sales—Ron
Miller
Sr. V-P., Mktg.—David West
SIC—7372; *Data & information
management software
development; Brand name—
Simpana®*
Employs—800; Estab.—1998
Company-wide Emp.: 1,268
134,000 sq ft site,
Publicly owned corporation

### GROUP THERMO, INC. (H Q)

137 S. Pemberton Ave. (07757)
**Phone—(908) 757-8955**
Fax—(888) 746-3557
www.ergomax.com
Email—info@ergomax.com
Pres.—Adam Duch
SIC—3443; *Corporate
headquarters; heat exchangers
for on-demand water heating
(mfg. subcontracted)*
Employs—4; Estab.—1992
Sales—$500,000-$1Mil (est)
Distrib.—National
Privately owned corporation

### HYTEK INDUSTRIES CORP.

215 Comanche Dr., P.O. Box 56
(07757)
**Phone—(732) 229-5730**
Fax—(732) 870-2325
www.hytekind.com
Email—info@hytekind.com
Pres., Hum. Res. & IT Mgr.—Joan
Sigmond
Off. Mgr.—Lori Petrone
SIC—2869; *Fire-resistant
hydraulic fluids*
Employs—5; Estab.—1980
Sales—under $500,000
Distrib.—Intl.
Privately owned corporation

### ROSANO TRUCKING, INC.

26 Maple Ave. (07757)
**Phone—(732) 542-5009**
Fax—(732) 542-5014
Email—rti1@comcast.net
Owner & GM—Frank Rosano

SIC—1442; NAICS—327991;
*Sand & gravel processing*
Employs—1; Estab.—1981
Sales—$1Mil-$2.5Mil
Distrib.—Local
Privately owned corporation

### ROY PRESS PRINTERS

57 Bridgewaters Dr., Apt. 17
(07757)
**Phone—(732) 922-9460**
Fax—(732) 922-6860
www.roypressprinters.com
Email—roypressprinters@
verizon.net
Owner—Ralph Lawrence
Off. & Sales Mgr.—Lynne Groves
SIC—2759; NAICS—323100;
*Commercial printing*
Employs—3; Estab.—1886
Sales—under $500,000
6,000 sq ft site, Distrib.—Local
Privately owned sub-S corp.

## Oceanville

(Atlantic—S.E.)

### MODERN BOAT WORKS, INC.

P.O. Box 456 (08231)
**Phone—(609) 241-8916**
National—(800) 666-8433
Fax—(609) 241-8892
www.tidewaterworkshop.com
Email—customers@
tidewaterworkshop.com
Pres., CEO—Peter Caporilli
Off. Mgr.—Sarah Caporilli
SIC—2511; *Cedar outdoor
furniture*
Employs—10; Estab.—1991
15,000 sq ft site, Distrib.—National
Privately owned corporation
DBA: Tidewater Workshop

## Ogdensburg

(Sussex—N.W.)

### I & E CO.

150 Main St. (07439)
**Phone—(973) 579-0009**
Fax—(973) 823-0613
www.iekiosk.com
Pres.—Joseph Trobert
IT & Mktg. Mgr.—Mark Iwanski
Pur. Agt.—Bruce Lewczuk
SIC—3571; *Touchscreen kiosks*
Employs—12; Estab.—1977
Distrib.—National
Privately owned sub-S corp.

### QUANTUM PHARMACEUTICALS, INC. (H Q)

P.O. Box 244 (07439)
**Phone—(877) 873-3762**
Fax—(973) 827-4899
www.usderm.com
Email—msteele@usptg.com
Pres. & Mng. Member—Mark
Steele
SIC—2834; NAICS—325412;
*Corporate headquarters;
pharmaceutical preparations
(mfg. subcontracted)*
Employs—7
Sales—$2.5Mil-$5Mil (est)
Distrib.—Intl.
Privately owned corporation

## Old Bridge

(Middlesex—N.E.)

### BLONDER TONGUE LABORATORIES, INC.

1 Jake Brown Rd., P.O. Box 1000
(08857)
**Phone—(732) 679-4000**
National—(800) 523-6049
Fax—(732) 679-4353
www.blondertongue.com
Email—info@blondertongue.com

CEO—James Luksch
Pres.—Robert J. Palle
Sr. V-P., CFO & Hum. Res. Mgr.—
Eric Skolnik
Ex. V-P.—Emily Nikoo
V-P., Mfg.—Al Horvath
V-P., Engrg.—Nez Nikoo
Dir., Sales & Serv. Comms.—
Lynne Russo
SIC—3663; NAICS—334220;
*Corporate headquarters &
electronic equipment; Brand
name—Blonder Tongue
Laboratories, Inc.; R.L. Drake
Holdings, LLC*
Employs—150; Estab.—1950
Sales—$25Mil-$30Mil
300,000 sq ft site, Distrib.—Intl.
Publicly owned corporation

### BOB'S SIGNS CO.

1918 Englishtown Rd., P.O. Box 15
(08857)
**Phone—(732) 521-4554**
Fax—(732) 521-0798
www.bobssigns.us
Email—bobsign732@aol.com
Owner—Robert Miller
Shop Foreman—Tom Saccoccio
SIC—3993; *Interior & exterior
signs*
Employs—3; Estab.—1976
Sales—under $500,000
Distrib.—Regional
Sole ownership

### BRIGHT SIGNS, LLC

2626 County Road 516 (08857)
**Phone—(732) 679-7440**
Fax—(732) 679-7441
Owner—Ho Yung Yun
SIC—3993; 3089; *Magnetic &
commercial signs & vinyl
lettering*
Employs—2; Estab.—2001
Sales—under $500,000 (est)
Distrib.—Local
Sole ownership

### FI COMPANIES

3150 Bordentown Ave. (08857)
**Phone—(732) 727-8100**
National—(800) 803-4462
Fax—(732) 727-1881
www.ficompanies.com
Email—sales@ficompanies.com
Pres., CEO—Scott Forman
V-P., Fin.—Ronald Sherry
Mktg. Mgr.—Amy Fonzi
IT Mgr.—Phil Cicone
Hum. Res. Mgr.—Kristie Abrantes
Accts. Rec. Supv.—Anita James
Coordinator—Erin Maloney
SIC—2541; 2542; 2431; NAICS—
321900; *Store fixtures, displays
& cabinets, including installation*
Employs—50; Estab.—1984
39,000 sq ft site, Distrib.—National
Sole ownership
AKA: Forman Industries

### FORTE PALLET, INC.

3 Water Works Rd. (08857)
**Phone—(732) 727-3879**
Email—pallet387@aol.com
Owner & Pres.—Tony Forte
SIC—2448; NAICS—321920;
*Wooden pallets & skids*
Employs—3; Estab.—1974
Sales—$500,000-$1Mil
22,000 sq ft site, Distrib.—Local
Privately owned corporation

### MADISON INDUSTRIES, INC.

554 Waterworks Rd. (08857)
**Phone—(732) 727-2225**
Fax—(732) 727-2653
www.oldbridgechem.com
Email—info@oldbridgechem.com
Pres.—Bruce Bzura
Ex. V-P.—Joel Bzura
V-P., Mfg.—Wayne Jensen
Cont.—Richard Koski
Sales Mgr.—Justin Bzura

GEOGRAPHICAL

## Old Bridge—(cont.)

Hum. Res. Mgr.—Laurie Bzura
SIC—2819; 3295; *Zinc-based chemicals*
Employs—75; Estab.—1962
Sales—$25Mil–$35Mil
Distrib.—Intl.
Privately owned corporation
Also see: Old Bridge Chemical, Inc., same loc.

**MIDHATTAN WOODWORKING**

3130 Bordentown Ave. (08857)
**Phone—(732) 727-3020**
Fax—(732) 727-0201
www.midhattan.com
Email—egreco@midhattan.com
Ptnr.—George Greco
Ptnr.—Ed Greco
SIC—2431; 2434; NAICS—337110; *Architectural millwork, including cabinets*
Employs—45; Estab.—1932
Distrib.—Regional
Privately owned partnership

**MONTEATH MOULDING**

3150 Bordentown Ave. (08857)
Mail addr: P.O. Box 757, South Amboy (08879)
**Phone—(732) 727-4000**
National—(800) 922-1029
Fax—(732) 721-1752
www.monteath.com
Email—monteath@att.net
Pres.—Steve Wilson
Secy-Treas.—Barbara Wilson
SIC—2426; *Hardwood mouldings, lumber & millwork*
Employs—20; Estab.—1988
Distrib.—Regional
Privately owned corporation

**NIFTY PRODUCTS**

4 Jocama Blvd. (08857)
Mail addr: P.O. Box 161, Marlboro (07746)
**Phone—(732) 591-1140**
National—(800) 631-2172
Fax—(732) 591-8477
www.niftypack.com
Email—sales@niftypack.com
Pres.—Norman Ferber
V-P., Mktg.—Marcy Thomson
Cont.—Audrey Tick
SIC—2672; 3423; NAICS—322222; *Shipping room tape guns, tape & stretch film*
Employs—25; Estab.—1975
Distrib.—National
Privately owned corporation

**OLD BRIDGE CHEMICAL, INC.**

554 Waterworks Rd. (08857)
**Phone—(732) 727-2225**
Fax—(732) 727-2653
www.oldbridgechem.com
Email—info@oldbridgechem.com
Pres.—Bruce Bzura
Ex. V-P.—Joel Bzura
V-P., Mfg.—Wayne Jensen
Cont.—Richard Koski
Sales Mgr.—Justin Bzura
IT Mgr.—Kevin Hildreth
Hum. Res. Mgr.—Jill Bzura
R & D Mgr.—Stephen Wolenuk
SIC—2819; *Copper sulfate & carbonate & basic copper sulfate*
Employs—100; Estab.—1962
Distrib.—Intl.
Privately owned corporation
Also see: Madison Industries, Inc., same loc.

**PAZERA CABINETS DOOR**

Div. of Pazera Assocs., Inc.
3160 Bordentown Ave. (08857)
**Phone—(732) 727-1600**
Fax—(732) 721-4248
Ptnr.—Paul Pazera

SIC—2434; NAICS—337110; *Wooden cabinet doors & drawer fronts*
Employs—5; Estab.—2000
Sales—under $500,000 (est)
Distrib.—Local
Privately owned corporation
Parent co.—Pazera Assocs., Inc., Calverton, NY
Phone—(631) 727-2258
See Parent Co. Section for full profile.

**PRIMARY SYSTEMS, INC.**

30 State Route 18, Ste. 1 (08857-1420)
**Phone—(732) 679-2200**
　　　　(732) 679-4747
Fax—(732) 254-4040
www.primarysys.com
Email—experts@primarysys.com
Pres.—Eric Alter
V-P., Sales & Mktg. & Dir., Hum. Res. & IT—Scott M. Alter
Special Proj. Coord.—Virginia Newman
SIC—3821; NAICS—339111; *Automation control & information systems*
Employs—15; Estab.—1989
Sales—$1Mil–$2.5Mil
Distrib.—National
Privately owned corporation

**STAVOLA OLD BRIDGE MATERIALS**

85 Waterworks Rd. (08857)
Mail addr: P.O. Box 482, Red Bank (07701)
**Phone—(732) 721-6900**
Fax—(732) 637-1044
www.stavola.com
Opers. Mgr.—Nick Cox
SIC—2951; NAICS—324121; *Asphalt*
Employs—30; Estab.—1957
Sales—$1Mil–$2.5Mil (est)
Distrib.—Local
Privately owned corporation

NEW ENTRY
**SUBURBAN CAPS, INC.**

899 State Route 18 (08857)
**Phone—(732) 251-4383**
www.subcaps.com
Principal—Scott Kidd
SIC—3713; 3089; *Truck caps & accessories*
Employs—2
Sales—under $500,000 (est)

**SUPERIOR SIGNAL COMPANY LLC**

178 W. Greystone Rd. (08857)
Mail addr: P.O. Box 96, Spotswood (08884-0096)
**Phone—(732) 251-0800**
National—(800) 945-8378
Fax—(732) 251-9442
www.superiorsignal.com
Email—info@superiorsignal.com
Pres.—James A. Kovacs
Dir., Mktg.—Helen Kovacs
Prod. Admn.—Rita Hussey
SIC—3829; *Ultrasonic leak detectors & smoke generators; Brand name—Superior Smoke®; AccuTrak®; Sport Smoke*
Employs—20; Estab.—1954
Sales—$2.5Mil–$5Mil
Distrib.—National
Limited Liability Company

**TRI-STATE GLASS & MIRROR, INC.**

11-A Jocama Blvd. (08857)
**Phone—(732) 591-5545**
Fax—(732) 591-5596
Ptnr.—Michael Panebianco
Ptnr.—Roseann Panebianco
SIC—3231; NAICS—327215; *Glass mirrors & shower doors*
Employs—3; Estab.—1993
Sales—under $500,000
Distrib.—Local
Privately owned corporation

**YONKERS PLYWOOD MFG.**

3130 Bordentown Ave., P.O. Box 152 (08857)
**Phone—(732) 727-1200**
Fax—(732) 727-0201
Email—info@yonkersplywood.com
Pres.—Edmund Greco
SIC—2431; 2435; NAICS—321211; *Plywood doors & panels*
Employs—25
Sales—$2.5Mil–$5Mil (est)
Distrib.—National
Privately owned corporation

## Old Tappan

(Bergen—N.E.)

**ABC DIGITAL ELECTRONICS, INC.**

44 Country Squire Rd. (07675)
**Phone—(201) 666-6888**
Email—richcurran@verizon.net
Pres.—C. H. Wu
COO—Benjamin Cheng
GM—Richard Curran
SIC—3825; 3829; NAICS—334500; *Production line electrical/electronic test equipment*
Employs—3; Estab.—1973
Sales—under $1Mil
5,000 sq ft site, Distrib.—Intl.
Privately owned corporation
AKA: Automation Dynamics

**DRY ICE CORP. (H Q)**

189 Central Ave. (07675)
**Phone—(201) 767-3200**
Fax—(201) 767-6554
www.dryicecorp.com
Email—sales@dryicecorp.com
Pres., CEO—Arthur Ramsdell, Jr.
V-P.—Roger Hawkes
Cont., Hum. Res. & IT Mgr.—Marita Viray
Dir., Sales & Mktg.—Pat Walsh
SIC—2813; NAICS—325120; *Corporate headquarters; industrial, propane & compressed gases & dry ice*
Employs—15; Estab.—1965
Sales—$5Mil–$10Mil (est)
Distrib.—Regional
Privately owned corporation
AKA: American Compressed Gases

**EULER INDUSTRIES, INC.**

464 Old Tappan Rd. (07675)
**Phone—(201) 666-9523**
Fax—(201) 666-9523
Owner & Pres.—Friedrich Euler
SIC—3554; NAICS—333291; *Pulp mill tools*
Employs—5; Estab.—2000
Sales—under $500,000
Distrib.—Local
Privately owned corporation

**MITRONIX, INC.**

239 Old Tappan Rd. (07675)
**Phone—(201) 263-0063**
Fax—(201) 263-0016
www.mitronix.com
Email—sales@mitronix.com
Pres.—Jeffrey Weinstein
V-P.—Raul Arjona
Off. Mgr.—Kathie Weinstein
SIC—3643; NAICS—335129; *Custom lamp holders & light sockets*
Employs—3; Estab.—1990
Distrib.—Intl.
Privately owned sub-S corp.

**NUTRA NUTS, INC. (H Q)**

180 Old Tappan Rd. (07675)
**Phone—(201) 768-0218**
www.nutranuts.com
Email—gocorny@nutranuts.com
Pres.—Mark Porro
CFO—Michael Porro

SIC—2096; *Corporate headquarters; half-popped organic popcorn snacks (mfg. done in company-owned factory in Commerce, CA); Brand name—Grandpa Po's Originals*
Employs—3; Estab.—1998
Sales—$500,000–$1Mil
2,500 sq ft site, Distrib.—Intl.
Privately owned corporation

**PEARSON TECHNOLOGY**

Div. of Pearson Education, Inc.
200 Old Tappan Rd. (07675)
**Phone—(201) 767-5000**
National—(877) 311-0948
Fax—(201) 767-5225
www.pearsoned.com
Email—communications@pearsoned.com
Facility Mgr.—Joe Cabrerra
SIC—2731; *Educational book publishing for grades K-12*
Employs—480; Estab.—1972
Sales—$25Mil–$50Mil (est)
Distrib.—Intl.
Publicly owned corporation
Parent co.—Pearson Education, Inc., Upper Saddle River, NJ
Phone—(201) 236-7000
See Parent Co. Section for full profile.

## Oldwick

(Hunterdon—N.W.)

**A.M. BEST CO.**

1 Ambest Rd. (08858)
**Phone—(908) 439-2200**
Fax—(908) 439-3027
www.ambest.com
Email—arthur.snyder@ambest.com
Pres.—Arthur Snyder III
MIS Mgr.—Paul Tinnirello
Hum. Res. Mgr.—Sandra Czarnecki
SIC—2741; *Insurance information publishing*
Employs—500
Distrib.—Intl.

## Oradell

(Bergen—N.E.)

**A TO Z RUBBER STAMPS**

617 Oradell Ave. (07649)
**Phone—(201) 265-9595**
www.atozstamps.com
Email—atozstamps@aol.com
Manager—Linda Shaffer
SIC—3953; *Rubber stamps, seals & marking devices for the commercial, legal, medical & government sectors*
Employs—2
Sales—under $500,000 (est)

**AMERICAN FORECLOSURES, INC.**

P.O. Box 601 (07649)
**Phone—(201) 501-0200**
National—(800) 758-1236
Fax—(201) 661-2860
www.americanforeclosures.com
Email—customerservice@americanforeclosures.com
Pres.—Craig Laube
V-P.—Cynthia Ehrlich

## Oradell—(cont.)

SIC—2721; 2741; *Monthly conventional & online regional distressed pre-foreclosure & bank foreclosure real estate property magazine publishing for home buyers & real estate investors; Brand name— American Foreclosures & Auctions; www.americanforeclosures.com; www.njlispendens.com; www.nylispendens.com; www.phillylispendens.com; How to Buy & Sell Foreclosures Guide*
Employs—5; Estab.—1991
Sales—under $500,000
Distrib.—National
Privately owned corporation

**BERGEN COUNTY MAGAZINE, THE**
297 Kinderkamack Rd., Ste. 135 (07649)
**Phone—(201) 265-2286**
(201) 694-5197
Fax—(201) 265-5664
www.bcthemag.com
Email—steven@bcthemag.com
Ptnr. & Co-Publisher—Sharon Goldstein
Ptnr.—Steven Goldstein
SIC—2721; *Regional upscale magazine publishing; Brand name—BC The Mag*
Employs—10; Estab.—2001
Sales—$500,000-$1Mil
Distrib.—Local
Limited Liability Company

**EMERSON SPEED PRINTING**
379 Kinderkamack Rd. (07649)
**Phone—(201) 265-7977**
Fax—(201) 265-7397
www.emersonspeedprinting.com
Email—emersons@optonline.net
Owner & Pres.—Herb Kassab
SIC—2752; 2759; NAICS— 323100; *Commercial offset printing & graphic design of invitations, cards & promotional specialties*
Employs—4; Estab.—1982
Distrib.—National
Privately owned corporation

**HANDYGUIDE, INC.**
721 Village Rd., P.O. Box 205 (07649)
**Phone—(201) 262-9478**
www.handyguide.com
Email—info@handyguide.com
Pres.—Iris Orsini
SIC—2741; *Industrial book publishing guide*
Employs—3; Estab.—1998
Sales—under $500,000 (est)
Distrib.—Regional
Privately owned corporation

**PRODUCE NEWS, THE**
800 Kinderkamack Rd., Ste. 100 (07649)
**Phone—(201) 986-7990**
Fax—(201) 986-7996
www.theproducenews.com
Email—newsdesk@ theproducenews.com
Publisher & Editor—John Groh
Pres.—Jack Bricker
Acct. Mgr.—Sue Marcus
Adv. Mgr.—Debbie Negron
SIC—2711; *Weekly trade newspaper publishing for the fresh fruit & vegetable industry*
Employs—11; Estab.—1897
Sales—$500,000-$1Mil
Distrib.—Intl.
Privately owned corporation

**Q-T FOUNDATIONS CO., INC.**
496 Kinderkamack Rd., Ste. 107 (07649)
**Phone—(201) 986-7800**
National—(888) 937-2727
Fax—(201) 986-2920
www.qtbras.com
Email—qtsales@qtbras.com
Pres.—Lawrence Kutzin
V-P., Sales—Meryl Kutzin
Opers. Mgr.—Evan Kutzin
SIC—2342; NAICS—315200; *Women's foundation garments, bras & panties; Brand name—Q-T Intimates; La Leche League International Intimates; Creme Bralee*
Employs—20; Estab.—1945
Sales—$5Mil-$10Mil
Distrib.—National
Privately owned sub-S corp.

**R T I, INC.**
401 Hasbrouck Blvd. (07649-2263)
**Phone—(201) 261-5852**
Fax—(201) 265-1221
www.thecellularshield.com
Email—buyrti@aol.com
Owner & Pres.—Richard Tashjian
SIC—3571; 7372; 3663; NAICS— 334111; *Computers, software development & radiation shielding devices for cellular & cordless phones*
Employs—10; Estab.—1980
Sales—$5Mil-$10Mil
3,000 sq ft site, Distrib.—Intl.
Limited Liability Company
AKA: Richard Tashjian Int'l

**SALTO DECORATORS, LLC**
80-82 Kinderkamack Rd. (07649)
**Phone—(201) 261-2518**
Fax—(201) 261-2546
Email—salto8082@yahoo.com
Pres.—Walter Kruger
SIC—2512; NAICS—337121; *Upholstered furniture*
Employs—1; Estab.—1967
Sales—under $500,000
2,200 sq ft site, Distrib.—Regional
Privately owned corporation

**SCIENTIFIC INDUSTRIES, INC.**
660 Kinderkamack Rd., Ste. 203 (07649)
**Phone—(973) 473-6900**
National—(866) 473-6900
www.fulcruminc.net
Email—customerservice@ torbal.com
Prod. Mktg. Mgr.—Thomas Wright
SIC—3339; 3596; 3821; NAICS— 331419; *Pharmacy pilling counting & weighing scales & balances & precision laboratory scales & balances*
Employs—6; Estab.—2000
Sales—$1Mil-$2.5Mil
Distrib.—National
Privately owned corporation
AKA: Torbal

---

## Orange
### (Essex—N.E.)

NEW ENTRY
**ACADEMY FENCE CO., INC.**
119 N. Day St. (07050)
**Phone—(973) 674-0600**
Fax—(973) 674-0400
www.academyfence.com
Email—info@academyfence.com
Owner—Lou Cavallo
SIC—3444; 2499; *Aluminum & wooden fencing & installation & repair services*
Employs—20; Estab.—1970
Sales—$500,000-$1Mil
Distrib.—Local
Privately owned corporation

**ALBERONA IRON WORK, INC.**
452 Scotland Rd. (07050)
**Phone—(973) 674-3375**
www.alberonaironworks.com
Email—alberonaironworks@ verizon.net
Pres.—Tony Prioletti
SIC—3446; 3441; NAICS— 332323; *Ornamental ironwork & structural steel fabrication of stairs & railings*
Employs—3; Estab.—1970
Sales—under $500,000
5,000 sq ft site, Distrib.—Local
Publicly owned corporation

**ARMOR GUARD BUSINESS CENTER**
139 Main St. (07050)
**Phone—(973) 676-6900**
Fax—(973) 676-9555
Owner—Michael Whatley
SIC—2752; NAICS—323100; *Offset printing*
Employs—1; Estab.—1982
Sales—under $500,000
Distrib.—Local
Sole ownership

**BANNER CHEMICAL CORP.**
111 Hill St. (07050)
**Phone—(973) 676-2900**
Fax—(973) 676-4564
www.bannerchemical.com
Email—dave@bannerchemical.com
Pres.—David Herman
SIC—2842; 2841; 5169; NAICS— 325612; *Manufacturer & distributor of sanitary maintenance hand soaps, disinfectants, deodorants & cleaners for kitchens & laundries & ice melters, sweeping compounds, absorbents & floor finishes; Brand name—MAG Ice Melter; Morton & Cargill Rock Salt; Peladow; Grit-Go Hand Soap; Blot-Out Vomitus Absorbent; Z-Goop Sanitary Absorbent; Ban-Dis Disinfectant; Supreme Pine Oil; Lightning Degreaser; Kinder Chemical Line*
Employs—10; Estab.—1970
30,000 sq ft site, Distrib.— Regional
Privately owned sub-S corp.
AKAs: Peerless Dust Killer & Harwal Sales & Paxon Manufacturing

†**BELLEVILLE SCALE & BALANCE, LLC**
50 S. Center St. (07050)
Mail addr: P.O. Box 540, Orange (07051-0540)
**Phone—(973) 759-4487**
National—(800) 257-0555
Fax—(973) 676-7990
www.bellevillescale.com
Email—ld@bellevillescale.com
Ptnr. & Pres.—Thomas Rockhill
Ptnr. & Secy-Treas.—Pauline M. Rockhill
CFO & Qual. Assur. Mgr.—Carol Rendfrey
SIC—5046; 5084; 5087; *Distributor of industrial, truck & railroad scales & laboratory balances, including service & rentals; Brand name—Fairbanks; Cardinal; B-TEK; Sartorius; CAS; GSE/SPX; Weightronix; Doran; Ohaus; A/D*
Employs—22; Estab.—1973
Sales—$2.5Mil-$5Mil
5,000 sq ft site, Distrib.—Local
Privately owned corporation
ISO rating—17025:2005
AKA: Brandywine Scale LLC Newark Delaware

**BLEND-RITE INDUSTRIES, INC.**
585 Forest St., Unit 4 (07050)
**Phone—(973) 395-3889**
National—(877) 505-3900
Fax—(973) 395-3891
www.br-industries.com
Email—brindustries@aol.com
Pres.—Milt Westrich
Off. Mgr.—Sam Smith
Graphic Designer—Scott Steel
SIC—3824; NAICS—334514; *Water meters*
Employs—15; Estab.—1988
Distrib.—National
Privately owned corporation

**DCM INDUSTRIES LLC**
50 S. Center St., Unit 8 (07050)
Mail addr: P.O. Box 40, Little Falls (07424-0040)
**Phone—(973) 675-3200**
(973) 768-0016
Fax—(973) 675-3444
Email—dcmshine@aol.com
Owner—Dave Myers
V-P.—Mary Ellen Rohr
SIC—3599; *General machining job shop*
Employs—5; Estab.—2003
Sales—under $500,000
3,000 sq ft site, Distrib.—National
Limited Liability Company

**EAST TRADING WEST INVESTMENTS LLC**
200 S. Jefferson St. (07050)
**Phone—(973) 678-0800**
National—(800) 538-7446
Fax—(973) 674-4111
Email—americantraffic2013@ gmail.com
Owner, Pres. & CFO—M. G. Khaleeli
Shop Supv.—Richard Vieruel
SIC—3993; 3429; *Fabricated regulatory, warning, construction & wayfinding signs, supply posts & hardware for sign mounting*
Employs—6; Estab.—1914
Sales—$500,000-$1Mil
7,000 sq ft site, Distrib.—Regional
Limited Liability Company
AKA: American Traffic & Street Sign

**INDUSTRIAL RAZOR BLADE CO., INC.**
575 Nassau St. (07050)
**Phone—(973) 673-4286**
Fax—(973) 673-7165
www.industrialrazor.com
Email—sales@industrialrazor.com
Owner—Frank Florey
SIC—3421; *Custom blades & knives*
Employs—2; Estab.—1974
Sales—under $500,000 (est)
Distrib.—National
Privately owned corporation

**INSTANT PRINTING**
355 Main St. (07050)
**Phone—(973) 675-6266**
Fax—(973) 674-2342
Owner—Bharati Tolia
GM—Sam Ramirez
Sales Mgr.—Amit Tolia
SIC—2752; NAICS—323100; *Instant printing of office supplies, brochures & business & prescription forms*
Employs—4; Estab.—1992
Sales—under $500,000
1,000 sq ft site, Distrib.—National
Sole ownership

**LAGNIAPPE FOODS, INC.**
546 Mitchell St. (07050)
**Phone—(973) 674-0498**
National—(800) 524-6427
Fax—(973) 674-3381
www.lagniappefoods.com
Pres.—Thomas Dowd

GEOGRAPHICAL

## Orange—(cont.)

SIC—2092; NAICS—311712; *Crab cakes & seafood sausages*
Employs—25; Estab.—1985
Sales—$1Mil-$2.5Mil
35,000 sq ft site, Distrib.—National
Privately owned corporation

### LOCAL TALK PRINTING CLUB
26 Main St. (07050)
**Phone—(973) 678-2582**
www.localtalknews.com
Email—info@localtalknews.com
V-P., Opers.—Dhiren Shah
SIC—2759; NAICS—323100; *Commercial printing*
Employs—4; Estab.—1985
Sales—$500,000-$1Mil (est)
Distrib.—Regional
Privately owned corporation

### LYCORED CORP.
377 Crane St. *(07050)*
Mail addr: P.O. Box 759, Orange (07051)
**Phone—(877) 592-6733**
National—(800) 882-0322
Fax—(973) 882-0323
www.lycored.com
Email—info@lycored.com
CFO—Benjamin Regev
V-P., Opers.—Mohamed Aly
V-P., Mktg.—Scott Larkin
V-P., Bus. Dev.—Doug Lynch
IT Mgr.—Nadya Ramos
Acctg. & Hum. Res. Mgr.—Janine Lee
Manager—Eric Annebach
Cust. Serv. Rep.—Jennifer Swatt
SIC—2834; 2833; NAICS—325412; *Bulk, added-value nutrients & ingredients for the nutritional & dietary supplement, functional food & beverage & nutricosmetic industries*
Employs—40; Estab.—2006
Sales—$11Mil-$25Mil
Distrib.—Intl.
Privately owned corporation

### MASTER CRAFT STEEL RULE DIE
84 Bell St. (07050)
**Phone—(973) 674-7662**
Fax—(862) 233-6725
Email—jerseymastercraft@yahoo.com
Owner—Bruno Nieves
SIC—3544; *Steel rule dies for corrugated box cutting*
Employs—1
Sales—under $500,000 (est)
Distrib.—National
Limited Liability Company

### METFAB METALS, LLC
560 Freeman St. (07050)
**Phone—(973) 675-7676**
Fax—(973) 675-7446
www.metfabmetals.com
Email—info@metfabsteelworks.com
Pres.—James Murray
Estimator—Chris Di Simone
SIC—3449; 3448; 3429; NAICS—332999; *Metal curtain wall parts, wall panels & stone & masonry anchors*
Employs—18; Estab.—1986
7,500 sq ft site, Distrib.—Intl.
Limited Liability Company

### NEW JERSEY GRANITE & MARBLE CORP.
50 S. Center St., Unit 3 (07050)
**Phone—(973) 266-8952**
Fax—(973) 266-8953
www.newjerseybestgranite.com
Email—sales@njbestgranite.com
Pres.—Plauton Soreas
Off. Mgr.—Mila Reis
Off. Mgr.—Megan Pross

SIC—3281; NAICS—327991; *Granite & marble countertops*
Employs—6; Estab.—2003
Sales—under $500,000
Distrib.—Local
Privately owned corporation

### NEWARK TRADE TYPOGRAPHERS, INC.
177 Oakwood Ave. (07050)
**Phone—(973) 674-3727**
Fax—(973) 674-8752
www.newarktrade.com
Email—desktop@newarktrade.com
Pres., Sales Mgr.—Robert Wislocky
V-P.—Bob Rozman
SIC—2759; 2791; NAICS—323122; *Digital color printing, including typesetting, proofreading, laminating, mounting, binding, scanning & design of brochures & posters*
Employs—20; Estab.—1938
Sales—$1Mil-$2.5Mil
Distrib.—Local
Privately owned corporation

### PEACE MEDICAL, INC.
50 S. Center St., Ste. 11 (07050)
**Phone—(973) 672-2120**
National—(800) 537-9564
Fax—(973) 672-3404
www.peacemedical.com
Email—info@peacemedical.com
Pres.—Tim Fegan
SIC—3841; *Respiratory machines, including filtration products & monitors for the healthcare industry*
Employs—12; Estab.—1974
Sales—$1Mil-$2.5Mil
Distrib.—Intl.
Privately owned corporation

### SAVIGNANO FOODS CORP.
107 S. Jefferson St. (07050)
**Phone—(973) 673-7537**
Fax—(973) 673-8231
www.andreafoods.com
Email—sales@andreafoods.com
Ptnr. & Pres.—Michael Savignano
Accts. Rec. Mgr.—Cathy Bravo
SIC—2098; 2038; NAICS—311823; *Frozen Italian pasta*
Employs—40; Estab.—1977
Sales—$10Mil-$25Mil (est)
Distrib.—Local
Privately owned corporation
DBA: Andrea Foods

### SERRANI'S BAKERY
114 S. Essex Ave. (07050)
**Phone—(973) 678-1777**
Fax—(973) 325-0789
Owner—William Serrani
SIC—2051; NAICS—311812; *Bread*
Employs—12; Estab.—1948
Sales—$1Mil-$2.5Mil
Distrib.—Local
Privately owned corporation

### SUNSHINE METAL & SIGN, INC.
467 Maryland St. (07050)
**Phone—(973) 676-4432**
Fax—(973) 676-7392
Owner—John White
SIC—2653; NAICS—322211; *Corrugated boxes*
Employs—5; Estab.—1982
Sales—under $500,000
Distrib.—Local
Privately owned corporation

### †SUPREME ENERGY, INC.
532 Freeman St. *(07050)*
**Phone—(973) 678-1800**
National—(800) 832-7090
Fax—(973) 672-0148
www.supremeenergyinc.com
Email—info@supremeenergyinc.com
Pres.—Deborah Fineman

Dir., Sales—Ted Ballison
Dir., Fin. & IT—Manny Sevdalis
Mktg. Mgr.—Dominic Valli
Admn. Mgr.—Marian Tafuri
Bus. Dev. Mgr.—Rick Zaccari
Cust. Relationship Mgr.—Breezy Bozik
SIC—5172; *Distributor of heating oil for commercial & residential customers, including full-service HVAC installation & maintenance*
Employs—100
Distrib.—National
Privately owned corporation

### T & E INDUSTRIES, INC.
215 Watchung Ave. (07050)
**Phone—(973) 672-5454**
Fax—(973) 672-0180
www.teindustries.com
Email—sales@teindustries.com
Pres.—Edward McEntee
Bookkeeper—Tammy Perrony
SIC—3679; 3053; NAICS—339991; *Electronic components & glass-to-metal hermetic seals*
Employs—48; Estab.—1961
Sales—$5Mil-$10Mil
30,000 sq ft site, Distrib.—Intl.
Privately owned corporation

### TRYCO TOOL & MFG., INC.
363 S. Jefferson St. (07050)
**Phone—(973) 674-6867**
Fax—(973) 674-1244
www.trycotool.com
Owner—Art Melillo
Pres.—Nelson Melillo
GM—Arthur Stasiak
Bookkeeper—Terry Zaccone
SIC—3469; 3544; NAICS—333500; *Metal stampings & dies*
Employs—60; Estab.—1948
40,000 sq ft site, Distrib.—Intl.
Privately owned corporation

### UNICORP, INC.
291 Cleveland St. (07050)
Mail addr: P.O. Box 280, Orange (07051)
**Phone—(973) 674-1700**
National—(800) 526-1389
Fax—(973) 674-3803
www.unicorpinc.com
Email—sales@unicorpinc.com
Pres.—Steven Mercadante
V-P., Sales & Mktg.—George A. Recentio
Comp.—Walter Pula
Plt. Mgr.—Joe Gonzalez
Qual. Control Mgr.—Jim Fixx
SIC—3452; 3429; 3679; NAICS—332722; *Precision electronic component hardware, fasteners, standoffs & spacers, swage standoffs, male-female standoffs, male-male standoffs, captive panel hardware, insulating washers, handles, thumb screws, shoulder screws & cable ties*
Employs—40; Estab.—1971
40,000 sq ft site, Distrib.—Intl.
Privately owned sub-S corp.

### WELDALL WELDING & IRONWORKS
115-117 S. Day St. (07050)
**Phone—(973) 674-8868**
Fax—(973) 676-1260
Email—anthony5453@verizon.net
Pres.—Anthony Prioletti
SIC—3446; 3599; NAICS—332323; *Ornamental iron & steel gates, fences, railings & window guards & welding job shop*
Employs—1; Estab.—1978
Sales—under $500,000
1,200 sq ft site, Distrib.—Local
Sole ownership

## Oxford
(Warren—N.W.)

### JOST BROTHERS, INC.
295 Jost Dr. (07863)
Mail addr: P.O. Box 203, Washington (07882-0203)
**Phone—(908) 453-2266**
National—(800) 631-7640
Fax—(908) 453-4961
www.jostjewelry.com
Email—gold@jostjewelry.com
Pres.—Charlie Jost
SIC—3911; NAICS—339911; *Custom handmade gold & silver jewelry, including specialty items & repair service*
Employs—4; Estab.—1950
Sales—$100,000-$250,000
Distrib.—National
Privately owned sub-S corp.

### PHELPS MFG., LLC
567 Brass Castle Rd. (07863)
**Phone—(908) 453-2288**
Fax—(908) 453-2286
www.phelpsmanufacturing.com
Email—sales@phelpsmanufacturing.com
Pres.—Fred Phelps
SIC—3599; *Precision machining job shop*
Employs—4; Estab.—2006
Sales—under $500,000
2,000 sq ft site, Distrib.—Local
Privately owned corporation

### TILCON, INC., OXFORD QUARRY
Div. of Tilcon New York Inc.
193 Mount Pisgah Ave., P.O. Box 120 (07863)
**Phone—(908) 453-4141**
(908) 399-1191
National—(800) 789-7625
Fax—(908) 453-4265
www.tilconny.com
Email—info@tilconny.com
GM, Aggregates—Brad Carroll
Sales & Mktg. Mgr.—Bill Godfrey
Plt. Mgr.—Rusty Bonney
Scalehouse Mgr.—Jack Laros
Pub. Rels. Mgr.—Karen Edgar
SIC—1429; 2951; NAICS—212319; *Stone quarrying & asphalt*
Employs—17
Distrib.—Regional
Publicly owned corporation
Parent co.—Tilcon New York Inc., West Nyack, NY
Phone—(845) 358-4500
See Parent Co. Section for full profile.

## Palisades Park
(Bergen—N.E.)

### BETTER HOME PLASTICS CORP.
439 Commercial Ave. (07650)
**Phone—(201) 592-0370**
Fax—(201) 592-0824
Pres.—Ronald Haboush
SIC—3089; 2392; NAICS—326199; *Plastic housewares, plastic & fabric shower curtains, tablecloths & bathroom accessories*
Employs—20; Estab.—1965
Distrib.—Intl.
Privately owned corporation

### DELTA CORRUGATED PAPER PRODUCTS
199 W. Ruby Ave. (07650)
**Phone—(201) 941-1910**
Fax—(201) 941-9399
www.deltacorrugated.com
Pres.—Wally Lieb
IT Mgr.—John Polbos

## Palisades Park—(cont.)

SIC—2653; NAICS—322211;
*Corrugated paper products*
Employs—150; Estab.—1957
Sales—$25Mil-$50Mil (est)
Distrib.—Local
Privately owned corporation

**KOREA DAILY, INC.**
10 E. Brinkerhoff Ave., Ste. 2-B
(07650)
**Phone—(201) 944-8299**
Fax—(201) 944-8434
www.koreadaily.com
Pres.—Tyung Sohn
SIC—2711; *Korean newspaper
publishing*
Employs—4; Estab.—1981
Sales—under $500,000 (est)
Distrib.—National
Privately owned corporation

**MEADOW BURKE PRODUCTS**
269 Commercial Ave. (07650)
**Phone—(201) 242-8989**
National—(800) 207-7778
Fax—(201) 242-8860
www.meadowburke.com
Email—wboyle@meadowburke.com
Sales Mgr., District—Don Fowler
Opers. Mgr.—William Boyle
Cust. Serv. Rep.—Steve De Steno
SIC—3449; 3496; *Steel
reinforcing bars, wire ties &
dovetail anchor slot*
Employs—4; Estab.—1957
31,000 sq ft site, Distrib.—Local
Privately owned corporation
Parent co.—Meadow Burke
Products, Tampa, FL
Phone—(813) 248-1944
See Parent Co. Section for full profile.

**NORTH JERSEY PROSTHETICS &
ORTHOTICS**
39 Broad Ave. (07650)
**Phone—(201) 943-4448**
Fax—(201) 941-1711
Ptnr. & Pres.—Anthony Marano
Ptnr. & V-P.—Diane Marano
SIC—3842; *Orthopedic, orthotic &
prosthetic appliances, including
artificial limbs & braces*
Employs—4; Estab.—1971
Sales—$500,000-$1Mil
Distrib.—Regional
Sole ownership

**PRECIOUS METALS PROCESSING
CONSULTANTS, INC.**
430 Bergen Blvd. (07650)
**Phone—(201) 944-8053**
(201) 694-1251
Fax—(201) 944-8003
www.preciousmetals-pmpc.com
Email—info@preciousmetals-
pmpc.com
Pres.—Randy Epner
SIC—3559; *Electrolytic metal
recovery equipment for heavy &
precious metals recycling; Brand
name—Gold Bug; Ionnet;
Bombardier; Dummycell;
IonnetX*
Employs—4; Estab.—1979
Sales—$500,000-$1Mil
Distrib.—Intl.
Privately owned corporation
AKA: PMPC

**PRO PRINTING, INC.**
472 Broad Ave. (07650)
**Phone—(201) 346-0305**
Fax—(201) 346-0213
www.proprintinginc.com
Email—proprinting@verizon.net
Pres.—Heug Lee
SIC—2759; NAICS—323100;
*Commercial printing*
Employs—2; Estab.—1994
Distrib.—Local
Privately owned corporation

**SOX TROT, INC.**
373 Grand Ave. (07650)
**Phone—(201) 944-5250**
National—(800) 648-0330
Fax—(201) 944-1768
www.soxtrot.com
Email—sales@soxtrot.com
Hum. Res., Off., Opers. & Sales
Mgr.—Sandy Benedetti
Acct. Mgr.—Laura Raffiani
Off. Mgr.—Debbie Coppola
SIC—2252; *Women's & girls'
hosiery & boot socks for the
equestrian industry*
Employs—10; Estab.—1981
Sales—$500,000-$1Mil
Distrib.—National
Privately owned corporation

**TEKNICOM SALES CO.**
470 Commercial Ave. (07650)
Mail addr: P.O. Box 1056,
Maywood (07607-7056)
**Phone—(201) 327-4500**
Fax—(201) 327-4501
www.teknicomsales.com
Email—teknicom@aol.com
Pres.—Don Duthaler
SIC—3669; NAICS—334290;
*Elevator hands-free telephone &
intercom systems, including
voice location messages &
battery backup; Brand name—
ECS 300*
Employs—9; Estab.—1987
Sales—$1Mil-$2.5Mil
Distrib.—National
Privately owned corporation

## Palmyra

(Burlington—S.E.)

**BRIDGE ROTARY MACHINE CO., LLC**
614 Kennedy St., P.O. Box 45
(08065)
**Phone—(856) 829-3110**
Fax—(856) 786-8147
www.bridgeonline.com
Email—sales@bridgeonline.com
Opers. Mgr.—Nickolas Cimino
SIC—3556; NAICS—333294;
*Food processing machinery*
Employs—30; Estab.—1958
Distrib.—Intl.
Limited Liability Company
AKA: Bridge Machine

**B-TECH VALVE, LLC**
200 Cinnaminson Ave. (08065)
**Phone—(609) 321-2205**
www.b-techvalves.com
Email—sales@b-techvalves.com
Owner & Pres.—Charles G. Bauer
SIC—3491; 3492; *Variable nozzle
desuperheater valves for
process & power plants; Brand
name—LPD Desuperheater;
SPAD Desuperheater*
Employs—2; Estab.—2005
Sales—under $500,000
1,000 sq ft site, Distrib.—National
Limited Liability Company

**DEVECE & SHAFFER, INC.**
400 Legion Ave., P.O. Box 201
(08065)
**Phone—(856) 829-7282**
Fax—(856) 829-1779
www.devece.com
Email—dnsprint@aol.com
Pres.—William J. DeVece
SIC—2759; NAICS—323100;
*Commercial printing*
Employs—4; Estab.—1959
Sales—$400,000
7,000 sq ft site, Distrib.—Regional
Privately owned corporation

**HERCULES WELDING & MACHINE
CO.**
616 5th St. (08065)
**Phone—(856) 829-1820**
Fax—(856) 829-1219
Pres.—Edward Beddall
Foreman—Patrick Davies
SIC—3599; *General machining
job shop*
Employs—2; Estab.—1913
Sales—under $500,000
Distrib.—Local
Privately owned corporation

**MOZER, INC., THEODORE E.**
601 W. 4th St., P.O. Box 25
(08065)
**Phone—(856) 829-1432**
Fax—(856) 829-1865
www.theodoremozer.com
Email—info@theodoremozer.com
Pres.—Theodore E. Mozer, Jr.
Corp. V-P., GM—Thomas Mozer
Off. Mgr.—Donna Jackson
SIC—3499; *Metal fabrication*
Employs—12; Estab.—1935
Sales—$500,000-$1Mil
Distrib.—National
Privately owned corporation

**MURPHY & READ SPRING MFG. CO.**
617 W. 6th St., P.O. Box 211
(08065)
**Phone—(856) 829-6887**
National—(800) 524-0344
Fax—(856) 829-7244
www.mrspring.com
Email—sales@mrspring.com
Pres.—John Seemuller
V-P. & Opers. Mgr.—Ted
Seemuller
V-P., Engrg.—Stephen Seemuller
SIC—3495; 3496; *Wire springs &
forms, including torsion springs,
wire forms & flat forms & short-
run CNC turning & machining*
Employs—15; Estab.—1917
Sales—$1Mil-$5Mil
20,000 sq ft site, Distrib.—Intl.
Privately owned sub-S corp.
ISO rating—9001:2008

**PAMARCO GLOBAL GRAPHICS,
IMAGING DIV.**
Div. of Pamarco Technologies, Inc.
1 Roto Ave. (08065)
**Phone—(856) 829-4585**
Fax—(856) 829-0246
www.pamarcoglobal.com
Email—info@pamarcoglobal.com
Pres.—John Burgess
Plt. Mgr.—Gary White
Off. Admn.—Valorie Buttocovla
SIC—3593; NAICS—333995;
*Metal cylinders engraving*
Employs—20; Estab.—1947
Distrib.—Intl.
Privately owned corporation
Parent co.—Pamarco
Technologies, Inc., Roselle, NJ
Phone—(908) 241-1200
See Parent Co. Section for full profile.

**PHILADELPHIA SIGN CO.**
707 W. Spring Garden St. (08065)
**Phone—(856) 829-1460**
Fax—(856) 829-8549
www.philadelphiasign.com
Pres.—Bob Mehmet
Hum. Res. Mgr.—Shelly Robinson
Proj. Mgr.—Scott Corsello
Pur. Agt.—James Chapman
SIC—3993; 3089; *Signs & vinyl
lettering*
Employs—300; Estab.—1917
Distrib.—National
Privately owned corporation

## Paramus

(Bergen—N.E.)

**ACCESSORY WORKSHOP (H Q)**
16 Arcadian Ave., Ste. C-7 (07652)
**Phone—(888) 691-3047**
Fax—(201) 368-0663
www.accessoryworkshop.com
Email—info@
accessoryworkshop.com
Opers. Mgr.—Sean Mahoney
Mktg. Mgr.—Kim Hotz
SIC—3089; *Company
headquarters; faux leather
portfolio cases for tablet
computers (mfg. done in China);
Brand name—tyPad®; tyPillow;
padstand™*
Employs—10; Estab.—2010
Sales—$1Mil-$2.5Mil (est)
Distrib.—Intl.
Privately owned corporation

**ADVANCED INDUSTRIAL
TECHNOLOGY**
640 Cambridge Rd. (07652-4204)
**Phone—(201) 265-1414**
www.advantechnology.com
Email—jcw.pe@
advantechnology.com
Pres.—T. S. Wang
Dir.—Jerry Wang
SIC—3569; *Pollution control
equipment*
Employs—12; Estab.—1970
Sales—$1Mil-$5Mil
Distrib.—National
Privately owned corporation

**†B/E CONSUMABLES MANAGEMENT**
Div. of B/E Aerospace, Inc.
650 From Rd. (07652)
**Phone—(201) 265-8770**
National—(800) 631-1993
Fax—(201) 265-3765
www.beaerospace.com
Email—terry_bond@
beaerospace.com
Pres.—Robert Marchetti
Dir., Sales—Leiza Minchella
SIC—5072; *Distributor of
aerospace fasteners*
Employs—50; Estab.—1980
Distrib.—Intl.
Publicly owned corporation
Parent co.—B/E Aerospace, Inc.,
Wellington, FL
Phone—(561) 791-5000
See Parent Co. Section for full profile.

**BARRINGTON PRESS INC**
37 Spring Valley Ave. (07652)
**Phone—(201) 843-6556**
Fax—(201) 843-6262
www.barringtonpress.com
Email—info@barringtonpress.com
Pres., CEO—Paul E. Ramirez
V-P.—Linda Ramirez
GM—Sal Petrane
SIC—2759; 2752; NAICS—
323100; *Offset, digital, instant,
color & large-format color
printing, including bindery,
fulfillment, mailing services &
one-to-one marketing*
Employs—10; Estab.—1983
Sales—$1Mil-$2.5Mil
6,000 sq ft site, Distrib.—National
Privately owned corporation

**BLINDS TO GO, INC.**
101 E. State Route 4 (07652)
**Phone—(732) 321-5000**
National—(800) 254-6377
Fax—(732) 906-0808
www.blindstogo.com
Email—nudofia@blindstogo.com
CEO—Nkere Udofia
IT Mgr.—Hitesh Barot
Store Mgr.—Sheryl Antonio

GEOGRAPHICAL

## Paramus—(cont.)

SIC—2591; NAICS—337920; *Corporate headquarters & window blinds; Brand name— Blinds To Go*
Employs—15
Sales—$1Mil-$2.5Mil
Sole ownership

**BNP MEDIA, INC.**
210 E. State Route 4, Ste. 203 (07652)
**Phone—(201) 291-9001**
Fax—(201) 291-9002
www.bnpmedia.com
Email—portfolio@bnpmedia.com
Editor—Michael Reis
Off. Mgr.—Lisa Rymaniak
SIC—2721; *Periodical publishing*
Employs—5; Estab.—1989
Sales—under $500,000 (est)
Distrib.—National
Privately owned corporation
Parent co.—BNP Media, Inc., Troy, MI
Phone—(248) 362-3700
See Parent Co. Section for full profile.

**†CAMERICAN INTERNATIONAL**
45 Eisenhower Dr., Ste. 310 (07652)
**Phone—(201) 587-0101**
Fax—(201) 587-2040
www.camerican.com
Email—info@camerican.com
Pres.—Lawrence Abramson
Off. Mgr.—Sandy Axelrod
SIC—5142; 5149; *Distributor of imported packaged & frozen food products*
Employs—40; Estab.—1994
Distrib.—National
Privately owned corporation

**†COLDSTAT REFRIGERATION**
60 Eisenhower Dr. (07652-1401)
Mail addr: P.O. Box 246, Paramus (07653-0246)
**Phone—(201) 599-1200**
            (201) 655-7430
Fax—(201) 599-9676
www.coldstat.com
Email—info@coldstat.com
Owner & Pres.—Ion Sarkisian
Cont.—Larry Morgan
SIC—5078; 5046; 5087; *Wholesaler of commercial refrigeration & cooking equipment, including installation, maintenance & repairs; Brand name—Master-Bilt; Beverage-Air; Delfield; Manitowoc; True; Ice-O-Matic; Norlake; Perlick; Kolpak*
Employs—15; Estab.—1971
Distrib.—Regional
Privately owned corporation
AKA: SSSS LLC

NEW ENTRY
**COMMERCE ENTERPRISES, INC.**
61 S. Paramus Rd., Ste. 135 (07652)
**Phone—(201) 368-2100**
Fax—(201) 368-3438
www.cianj.org
Pres.—John Galandak
SIC—2721; *Magazine publishing*
Employs—12
Sales—$1Mil-$2.5Mil (est)
Distrib.—Regional
Privately owned corporation

**CURTISS-WRIGHT SURFACE TECHNOLOGIES**
Div. of Curtiss-Wright Corp.
80 Highway 4 E., Ste. 310 (07652)
**Phone—(201) 843-7800**
Fax—(201) 843-3460
www.metalimprovement.com
Email—info@metalimprovement.com

V-P., Cont. & Dir., Hum. Res.— David Rivellini
Hum. Res. Mgr.—Nancy Chippendale
SIC—3499; NAICS—332811; *Divisional headquarters & metal fabrication*
Employs—31
Nationwide: 1,200; Worldwide: 1,800
Sales—$2.5Mil-$5Mil (est)
Distrib.—National
Publicly owned corporation
Parent co.—Curtiss-Wright Corp., Parsippany, NJ
Phone—(973) 541-3700
See Parent Co. Section for full profile.

**DATA ACCESS DATAPATCH, INC.**
40 Eisenhower Dr., Ste. 101 (07652)
**Phone—(201) 843-5468**
Fax—(201) 843-9491
www.data-access.com
Email—info@data-access.com
Pres.—Mark Barbalat
GM & Hum. Res. Mgr.—Vitaly Dekhtievsky
IT Mgr.—Alex Vovk
Accts. Rec. Mgr.—Casey Dent
SIC—3679; *Computer cables*
Employs—65; Estab.—1993
Sales—$5Mil-$10Mil
Distrib.—Local
Privately owned corporation

**FANTASIA INDUSTRIES CORP.**
20 Park Pl. (07652)
**Phone—(201) 261-7070**
Fax—(201) 261-3060
www.fantasiahaircare.com
Email—fantasia@fantasiahaircare.com
CEO—Archie Bogosian
Pres. & V-P.—Paul Bogosian
V-P.—Jack Bogosian
Dir., Adv.—Toni Paldino
Cred. Mgr.—Michelle Gaiccio
Pur. Agt.—Peggy Raymond
SIC—2844; NAICS—325600; *Hair care products*
Employs—29; Estab.—1967
Sales—$500,000-$1Mil
Distrib.—Local
Privately owned corporation

**FASTSIGNS®**
407 Sette Dr. (07652)
**Phone—(201) 587-8444**
Fax—(201) 587-8889
www.fastsigns.com
Email—71@fastsigns.com
Owner—Glenn Lanzl
SIC—3993; *Interior & exterior signs*
Employs—3; Estab.—1990
Sales—under $500,000
Distrib.—Local
Limited Liability Company

**FEDEX OFFICE & PRINT CENTER**
Div. of FedEx Office & Print Services, Inc.
315 N. Route 17 (07652)
**Phone—(201) 599-0031**
National—(800) 463-3339
Fax—(201) 599-3396
www.fedex.com
Email—usa1282@fedex.com
Hum. Res. Mgr.—Denise Brathwaite
Store Mgr.—Chris Cook
Asst. Mgr.—Chris Vazquez
Consultant—Christine Spencer
SIC—2759; 2752; NAICS—323100; *Commercial, digital, business form & large-format printing*
Employs—7; Estab.—1964
Sales—under $500,000
Distrib.—Intl.
Publicly owned corporation

Parent co.—FedEx Office & Print Services, Inc., Dallas, TX
Phone—(214) 550-7000
See Parent Co. Section for full profile.

**GENERAL MACHINE & EXPERIMENTAL WORKS**
117 Gertrude Ave. (07652)
**Phone—(201) 843-9035**
Fax—(201) 843-9064
www.generalmachineandexpworks.com
Email—sales@generalmachineandexpworks.com
Pres.—Paul Oelkrug
V-P.—Regina Oelkrug
SIC—3599; *Packaging components & general machining job shop*
Employs—5; Estab.—1952
Sales—$500,000-$1Mil
4,000 sq ft site, Distrib.—National
Privately owned sub-S corp.

**GLOBE SCIENTIFIC, INC.**
610 Winters Ave. (07652)
Mail addr: P.O. Box 1625, Paramus (07653-1625)
**Phone—(201) 599-1400**
National—(800) 394-4562
Fax—(201) 599-1406
www.globescientific.com
Email—mail@globescientific.com
Pres.—Milton Diamond
V-P., Sales & Mktg.—Dara Diamond
V-P., Fin. & Pur.—Lisa Berger
V-P., Prod. Dev.—David Ackley
SIC—3821; 3089; 3231; NAICS—339111; *Laboratory plastic ware, glassware & equipment, including microscope slides, beakers, racks, test tubes & caps, cryogenic tubes, transfer pipettes, bottles & containers, rockers, centrifuges, autoclaves & ovens; Brand name—Sedi-Rate; Diamond Pipettors; CryoClear Cryogenic Vials; Uri-Pak; Diamond SeroLogic; Uniplast Serological Pipettes; DiamondWhite Microscope Slides; Perfect Smear; Diamond Perfect Mark*
Employs—45; Estab.—1982
Sales—$18Mil
40,000 sq ft site, Distrib.—Intl.
Sole ownership

**HANK'S SIGNS**
793 Jersey Pl. (07652)
**Phone—(201) 652-5979**
Fax—(201) 670-0502
Owner—Hank Emr
SIC—3993; *Interior & exterior signs*
Employs—2; Estab.—1958
Sales—under $500,000
Distrib.—Regional
Sole ownership

**ILIE'S ETERNALLY FLAWLESS**
275 E. State Route 4 (07652)
**Phone—(201) 487-1991**
Fax—(201) 487-1991
www.ilieseternallyflawless.com
Email—iliesjewelry@verizon.net
Owner—Yves Ilie
Manager—Michael Ilie
SIC—3911; *Precious metal jewelry*
Employs—2
Privately owned corporation

**INTERNATIONAL DATA GROUP**
650 From Rd., Ste. 558 (07652)
**Phone—(201) 634-2300**
Fax—(201) 634-9286
www.idg.com
Email—idgcorpcom@idg.com
Off. Mgr.—Kathy Georgiyevskaya

SIC—2721; *Trade & consumer technology magazine publishing*
Employs—5; Estab.—2003
Sales—under $500,000
Distrib.—Regional
Privately owned corporation
Parent co.—International Data Group, Boston, MA
Phone—(617) 534-1200
See Parent Co. Section for full profile.

**KIMCO PRODUCTS, LLC**
64 E. Midland Ave., Ste. 5 (07652-2934)
**Phone—(201) 265-6800**
National—(800) 930-2241
Fax—(201) 265-9350
www.booksox.com
Email—admin@booksox.com
Pres.—Dennis Grande
CFO—Brent Rance
SIC—2399; *Fabric book covers, fabric wine bottle covers, fabric tissue box covers & fabric planter/flower pot covers; Brand name—Book Sox; Wine Sox; Tissue Box Sox; Pot Sox*
Employs—20; Estab.—1992
76,000 sq ft site, Distrib.—National
Privately owned sub-S corp.

**KOCH MODULAR PROCESS SYSTEMS, LLC**
45 Eisenhower Dr., Ste. 350 (07652)
**Phone—(201) 368-2929**
Fax—(201) 368-8989
www.modularprocess.com
Pres.—George Schlowsky
Hum. Res. Mgr.—Lisa Dolugo
SIC—3559; *Preassembled modular mass transfer distillation & chemical separation systems for the chemical, pharmaceutical, biotech, food & frangance industries*
Employs—60; Estab.—1994
Distrib.—Intl.
Limited Liability Company

**KRAUSE CANDY, INC., MRS. HANNA**
89 Westview Ave. (07652)
**Phone—(201) 843-0337**
National—(888) 657-2873
Fax—(201) 291-5388
www.hannakrausecandy.com
Email—sales@hannakrausecandy.com
Pres.—Karl Krause
Secy., Hum. Res. & Off. Mgr.— Linda Menzo
SIC—2064; 2068; NAICS—311911; *Chocolate candies & assorted nuts*
Employs—17; Estab.—1959
Sales—under $500,000
Distrib.—National
Privately owned corporation

**METROPOLITAN WINDOW FASHIONS**
799 Route 17 S. (07652)
**Phone—(201) 689-6030**
National—(800) 968-6666
Fax—(201) 689-6033
www.windowfashions.com
Email—paramus@windowfashions.com
Owner—Bruce Heyman
Off. Mgr.—Nancy Kerr
SIC—2391; NAICS—314121; *Draperies, curtains & window treatments*
Employs—4; Estab.—1950
Sales—under $500,000 (est)
Distrib.—Local
Privately owned corporation

**MOVADO GROUP, INC.**
650 From Rd., 3rd Fl. (07652)
**Phone—(201) 267-8000**
Fax—(201) 267-8070
www.movadogroup.com
Chrm., Pres.—G. Grinberg

## Paramus—(cont.)

CEO—Efraim Grinberg
CFO—Sally Demarsilis
Ex. V-P., COO—Richard J. Cote
Sr. V-P., Mktg.—Mary Leach
Dir., Pur.—Lawrence Levine
SIC—3873; 5094; NAICS—
334518; *Manufacturer &
distributor of watches &
timepieces*
Employs—300; Estab.—1999
Distrib.—Intl.
Privately owned corporation

### NETWRIX CORP.

12 N. State Route 17, Ste. 104
(07652)
Mail addr: 165 Morningside Rd.,
Paramus (07652)
**Phone—(201) 490-8840**
(949) 407-5125
National—(888) 638-9749
Fax—(201) 490-8841
www.netwrix.com
Email—daniel.pershing@
netwrix.com
Pres., CEO—Michael Fimin
Mktg. Mgr.—Nick Cavalancia
Territory Mgr.—Ray Nicosia
SIC—7372; *Change reporting,
auditing & identity management
software development; Brand
name—NetWrix®*
Employs—12; Estab.—2010
Distrib.—Intl.
Privately owned corporation

### NEXT DAY SIGNS & BANNERS, INC.

300 Route 17 (07652)
**Phone—(201) 986-1960**
Fax—(201) 986-1959
Pres.—Robert Ryan
SIC—3993; *Interior & exterior vinyl
signs*
Employs—3; Estab.—1992
Sales—under $500,000
Distrib.—Local
Privately owned corporation

### NICE SYSTEMS, INC. (H Q)

461 From Rd. (07652)
**Phone—(201) 964-2600**
(201) 549-1888
Fax—(201) 964-2610
www.nice.com
Email—nice.sales@nice.com
Pres., Americas—Barak Eilam
V-P., Mktg.—Einat Weiss
V-P., Hum. Res.—Greg Meadows
SIC—3661; *Corporate
headquarters; telephones (mfg.
done in Israel)*
Employs—180
Sales—$50Mil-$100Mil (est)
Distrib.—Intl.
Publicly owned corporation

### PAGES PRINTING & GRAPHICS

300 N. Route 17 (07652)
**Phone—(201) 261-3883**
Fax—(201) 261-7162
www.pagesgraphics.com
Email—print@pagesgraphics.com
Owner—Ron Sallemi
Prodn. Mgr.—Tony Pep
SIC—2759; 2752; 2789; NAICS—
323100; *Full-service commercial,
offset, digital, full-color & instant
printing, binding, graphic
design, direct mail & marketing
services*
Employs—7; Estab.—1979
Sales—$1Mil-$2.5Mil
Distrib.—Regional
Sole ownership

### REGALE, INC., KRISTIAN

4 Forest Ave., Ste. 202 (07652)
**Phone—(201) 587-9800**
National—(877) 610-9440
Fax—(201) 587-9801
www.kristianregale.com
Email—info@kristianregale.com

V-P., Opers.—Casey Beard
SIC—2086; *Nonalcoholic
Swedish-style sparkling juice
beverages*
Employs—5; Estab.—1987
Sales—$2.6Mil-$5Mil
Distrib.—National
Privately owned corporation

### RENELL LABEL PRINT, INC.

15 Sunflower Ave. (07652)
Mail addr: P.O. Box 403, Saddle
River (07458-0403)
**Phone—(201) 652-6544**
National—(888) 736-3551
Fax—(201) 445-0050
www.renell.com
Email—support@renell.com
Pres.—W. Rene Huber
Cust. Serv. & Opers. Mgr.—Trish
Howard
SIC—2672; 2675; NAICS—
322222; *Pressure-sensitive,
paper, foil & clear labels,
including removable adhesive,
polyester film & vinyl labels,
coupons, consecutive
numbering & bar codes,
imprintable wallet-size cards,
die-cut tag & card constructions
& laminations; Brand name—EZ-
Tacks®; EZ-Strips; EZ-Boards®;
EZ-Clips; EZ-Stickers;
LintLikkers®*
Employs—8; Estab.—1967
Sales—$700,000-$1Mil
5,000 sq ft site, Distrib.—Intl.
Privately owned sub-S corp.

### SAI GLOBAL LTD.

Div. of SAI Global, Inc.
210 State Route 4 E. (07652)
**Phone—(201) 986-1131**
National—(888) 454-2688
Fax—(201) 986-0271
www.saiglobal.com
Email—uspubsales@saiglobal.com
V-P., N. America—Stuart Bowyer
Publication Specialist—Heather
Winkler
SIC—2741; *Industrial technical
standards publishing for the
engineering & legal markets &
the military*
Employs—10; Estab.—1999
Sales—$1Mil-$2.5Mil
Distrib.—Intl.
Privately owned corporation
DBA: ILI Publishing
Parent co.—SAI Global, Inc.,
Plainsboro, NJ
Phone—(609) 955-5100
See Parent Co. Section for full profile.

NEW ENTRY
### SALEM STEEL N.A., LLC (H Q)

80 Route 4 E., Ste. 168 (07652)
**Phone—(201) 843-1000**
Fax—(201) 843-1008
www.salemsteel.com
Email—info@salemsteel.com
Owner—Ronald S. Herman
SIC—3317; *Company
headquarters; steel pipe & tubes
(mfg. done overseas)*
Employs—8
Sales—$1Mil-$2.5Mil (est)
Distrib.—Intl.
Limited Liability Company

### STIEFEL CORP., GEORGE G. (H Q)

364 N. Farview Ave. (07652)
**Phone—(201) 967-0868**
Fax—(201) 967-0864
Ptnr.—George Stiefel
Ptnr.—Trude Stiefel
SIC—2499; *Corporate
headquarters; wooden picture
frames (mfg. done in Mexico)*
Employs—2; Estab.—1996
Sales—under $500,000 (est)
200 sq ft site, Distrib.—National
Privately owned corporation

### VERSA PRODUCTS CO., INC.

22 Spring Valley Rd. (07652)
**Phone—(201) 843-2400**
Fax—(201) 843-2931
www.versa-valves.com
Email—sales@versa-valves.com
Pres.—Jan L. Larsson
Cont.—Gus Badia
Sales & Mktg. Mgr.—Gerry
Gramegna
Mfg. Mgr.—Ron Morgner
Hum. Res. Mgr.—Toni Shostak
Cust. Serv. Rep.—Patty Bandy
SIC—3492; NAICS—332912;
*Pneumatic valves*
Employs—155; Estab.—1961
Distrib.—Intl.
Privately owned corporation
ISO rating—9001

---

## Park Ridge

(Bergen—N.E.)

### AVIDA, INC.

174-B Kinderkamack Rd., P.O. Box
2 (07656)
**Phone—(201) 802-0749**
www.avidasw.com
Email—info@avidasw.com
Pres.—Eric Kruegle
SIC—3663; 3861; 3699; NAICS—
334290; *Security surveillance
equipment for the protection of
dignitaries & VIPs & self-
protection for teams on
temporary assignment, including
IP video mesh nodes, wireless
intrusion sensors & video
verification & low light video &
PTZ IP cameras*
Employs—5; Estab.—1995
Sales—$1Mil-$2.5Mil
2,000 sq ft site, Distrib.—Intl.
Privately owned corporation

### BAUER PRECISION, INC.

174 Kinderkamack Rd., Ste. D
(07656)
**Phone—(201) 307-0369**
Fax—(201) 307-1284
www.bauerprecision.com
Email—bauerprecision@verizon.net
Owner & Pres.—Peter Bauer
SIC—3599; *Precision machining
job shop, including CNC milling
& turning & small hand tappers*
Employs—4; Estab.—1988
Sales—$500,000-$1Mil
2,500 sq ft site, Distrib.—National
Privately owned corporation

### FORINO KITCHEN CABINETS, INC.

33 S. Maple Ave. (07656)
**Phone—(201) 573-0990**
Fax—(201) 573-0208
www.forinocabinet.com
Email—forinocab@yahoo.com
Pres.—Charles Forino
SIC—2434; NAICS—337110;
*Custom wooden kitchen
cabinets*
Employs—8; Estab.—1965
Sales—$500,000-$1Mil
Distrib.—Local
Privately owned corporation

### RENEW GRAPHICS

16 W. Park Ave. (07656)
**Phone—(201) 802-1900**
Fax—(201) 802-1911
Owner—Mike Collins
SIC—2752; 2759; NAICS—
323100; *Lithographic &
commercial printing*
Employs—2; Estab.—1997
Sales—under $500,000
Distrib.—Local
Sole ownership

### ROYAL KNITWEAR, INC.

115 Perry St. (07656)
**Phone—(201) 391-8368**
Fax—(201) 391-8362
Pres.—Edmund Abdelhak
V-P.—Rue Abdelhak
SIC—2369; NAICS—315200;
*Children's sweaters*
Employs—10; Estab.—1957
Sales—$500,000-$1Mil
Distrib.—National
Privately owned corporation

### RUNTAK RAILS, LLC

174 Kinderkamack Rd., Ste. A
(07656)
**Phone—(201) 391-0380**
Fax—(201) 690-6484
Owner—Steve Runtak
SIC—3446; *Custom architectural
metalwork*
Employs—5; Estab.—2002
Sales—$500,000-$1Mil (est)
1,700 sq ft site, Distrib.—National
Limited Liability Company

### SCULPTURESQUE, INC.

7 Etheridge Pl. (07656)
**Phone—(201) 573-9150**
www.sculpturesqueart.com
Owner—Catherine Schmitt
SIC—3299; 3089; 3366;
*Commercial & fine art sculptures
& fiberglass plaster & bronze
castings*
Employs—1
Sales—under $500,000 (est)
Privately owned corporation

### SIGNS OF THE TIMES BY BEUTEL & SONS

81 Park Ave. (07656)
**Phone—(201) 391-8444**
www.thesignguy.biz
Email—gabeutel@yahoo.com
Owner—George Beutel
Graphic Artist—Robert Beutel
SIC—3993; 3089; *Vinyl interior &
exterior signs & lettering*
Employs—2; Estab.—1998
Sales—under $500,000
Distrib.—Local
Privately owned corporation

### SONY ELECTRONICS, INC.

1 Sony Dr. (07656)
**Phone—(201) 930-1000**
Fax—(201) 930-7202
www.sony.com
Email—sales@sony.com
Facility Mgr.—Phillip D'Anna
Sr. Pub. Rels. Mgr.—Marcy Cohen
SIC—3674; 3571; 3577; 3679;
NAICS—334413; *Consumer &
professional audio & video
equipment, computer &
peripheral products, recording
media, energy products &
semiconductors; Brand name—
Sony*
Employs—300
Sales—$100Mil-$250Mil (est)
Parent co.—Sony Electronics, Inc.,
San Diego, CA
Phone—(858) 942-2400
See Parent Co. Section for full profile.

---

## Parlin

(Middlesex—N.E.)

### ASHLAND AQUALON, INC.

Div. of Ashland, Inc.
50 S. Minnisink Ave. (08859)
**Phone—(732) 254-1234**
Fax—(732) 257-4363
www.ashland.com
Email—info@ashland.com
Plt. Mgr.—Andre Simons
Sched. Mgr.—Margaret Nemuth

GEOGRAPHICAL

## Parlin—(cont.)

SIC—2823; NAICS—325221;
*Hydroxy ethyl cellulose*
Employs—93; Estab.—1998
Distrib.—National
Publicly owned corporation
Parent co.—Ashland, Inc.,
Wilmington, DE
Phone—(302) 995-3000
See Parent Co. Section for full profile.

**CRYOGENIC EQUIPMENT & REPAIR CO., INC. (CERCO)**
3143 Bordentown Ave., Bldg. 4
(08859-1163)
**Phone—(732) 727-1555**
Fax—(732) 727-4925
www.cercoinc.com
Email—cerco13551@aol.com
Pres.—Catherine Helmer
SIC—3679; *New & refurbished cryogenic equipment, including liquid helium transfer & nitrogen lines & liquid helium adapters*
Employs—5; Estab.—1985
Sales—under $500,000
4,000 sq ft site, Distrib.—National
Privately owned corporation
AKA: CERCO

**HD MICROSYSTEMS**
250 Cheesequake Rd. (08859)
**Phone—(732) 613-2500**
National—(800) 346-5656
Fax—(732) 613-2502
www.hdmicrosystems.com
Email—hdmicrosystems@
usa.dupont.com
Prod. Mgr.—Doug Heden
Cust. Serv. Rep.—Marie Carrano
SIC—2821; NAICS—325211;
*High-performance polymers & polyimide coatings; Brand name—Pyralir ®*
Employs—30; Estab.—1997
20,000 sq ft site, Distrib.—Intl.
ISO rating—9001:2000
AKA: Hitachi Chemical

**INDUSTRIAL SUMMIT TECHNOLOGY CORP.**
250 Cheesequake Rd. (08859)
**Phone—(732) 238-2211**
Fax—(732) 238-2369
www.istusa.com
Email—infoist@istusa.com
CEO—T. Sakane
SIC—2821; NAICS—325211;
*Polyimide resins for wire coatings & polyimide resins for prepreg materials for the aero industry; Brand name—Pyre ML for Wire Coating; Skybond for Prepreg/Composite Materials*
Employs—50; Estab.—1982
50,000 sq ft site, Distrib.—Intl.
Privately owned corporation

**JOYREI ENTERPRISES, INC.**
3143 Bordentown Ave. (08859)
**Phone—(732) 727-0742**
GM—Jeff Reising
Off. Mgr.—Jim Johnson
SIC—3599; *General machining job shop*
Employs—6; Estab.—1985
Sales—$500,000-$1Mil (est)
Distrib.—Local
Privately owned corporation

**PARLIN PRECISION PRODUCTS, INC.**
999 Route 9 (08859)
**Phone—(732) 727-6111**
Fax—(732) 727-8911
www.parlinprecision.com
Email—sales@parlinprecision.com
Pres.—Lee White
Bookkeeper—Mary White

SIC—3599; *Precision machining job shop*
Employs—3; Estab.—1983
Sales—over $500,000
3,500 sq ft site, Distrib.—Regional
Privately owned corporation

---

## Parsippany
(Morris—N.W.)

**ACTAVIS, INC.**
Morris Corporate Ctr. 3, 400
Interpace Pkwy. (07054)
**Phone—(862) 261-7000**
National—(800) 432-8534
Fax—(862) 261-7001
www.actavis.com
Email—info@activis.com
Ex. Chrm. of the Board—Paul M.
Bisaro
Pres., CEO—Brenton L. Saunders
COO—Bob Stewart
CFO, Global—R. Todd Joyce
Chief Hum. Res. Officer—Karen
Ling
Chief Comms. Officer—Charles M.
Mayr
Chief Legal Officer, Global—Bob
Bailey
Ex. V-P., Comml.—Bil Meury
Ex. V-P., Comml., N. American
Generic & Intl.—David Buchen
V-P., Inv. Rels.—Lisa DeFrancesco
Ex. Dir., Corp. Comms.—Steve
Sost
SIC—2834; NAICS—325412;
*Corporate headquarters & pharmaceuticals*
Employs—600; Estab.—1983
Sales—$6Bill-$10Bil
Distrib.—Intl.
Privately owned corporation

**ALLSTATE CAN CORP.**
1 Woodhollow Rd. *(07054)*
**Phone—(973) 560-9030**
Fax—(973) 560-9217
www.allstatecan.com
Email—tincans@allstatecan.com
Pres.—Richard D. Papera
V-P., Treas.—Michael Papera
V-P., Mfg.—Ronald J. Papera
V-P., Engrg.—Louis R. Papera
Cont.—Robert M. Cucci
Dir., Creative & Mktg.—Leslie
Wing
SIC—3411; NAICS—332431;
*Decorative & custom metal containers, tins & cans for the cosmetics, food, coffee, tea, gift & stationery, automobile wax, chemcial & petroleum products & printing ink industries*
Employs—80; Estab.—1910
Sales—$25Mil
135,000 sq ft site, Distrib.—
National
Privately owned sub-S corp.

**ASSOCIATED PILE & FITTING**
Div. of Skyline Steel, LLC
8 Wood Hollow Rd., Plz. 1, P.O.
Box 5933 (07054)
**Phone—(973) 773-8400**
National—(800) 526-9047
Fax—(973) 773-8442
www.associatedpile.com
Email—apf@associatedpile.com
Manager—Matt Scerbak
Asst. Mgr.—Judith Pomo
SIC—3429; 5072; *Manufacturer & distributor of points & splicers for pipe, sheet, timber & concrete piling*
Employs—4; Estab.—1957
Sales—under $500,000
Distrib.—Intl.
Limited Liability Company
Parent co.—Skyline Steel, LLC,
Parsippany, NJ
Phone—(973) 428-6100
See Parent Co. Section for full profile.

**ATLAS COPCO NORTH AMERICA, LLC (H Q)**
7 Campus Dr., Ste. 200 (07054-4413)
**Phone—(973) 397-3400**
Fax—(973) 397-3456
www.atlascopco.com
Email—customerfinance@
us.atlascopco.com
Pres., AC Holdings USA—Jim
Levitt
V-P., Fin.—Eric Moore
Bus. Mgr., Reg.—Johan
Ehrenborg
Bus. Mgr.—Shawn McGill
SIC—3563; 3533; 3423; NAICS—
333912; *Company headquarters; industrial air & gas compressors & generators, mining, construction & oilfield equipment & power tools & supplies*
Employs—40
Worldwide: 33,000
Sales—$50Mil
Distrib.—National
Publicly owned corporation

**B & G FOODS, INC. (H Q)**
4 Gatehall Dr., Ste. 110 (07054-4522)
**Phone—(973) 401-6500**
Fax—(973) 630-6550
www.bgfoods.com
Email—contactus@bgfoods.com
Pres.—David Wenner
CFO—Robert Cantwell
Ex. V-P., Sales—Vanessa Maskal
Ex. V-P., Opers.—Bill Herbes
V-P., Hum. Res.—Andy Chosso
V-P., Qual. Control—William Wright
V-P., Dist.—Chris Bauman
Dir., IT—Steve DePaul
Dir., Fin.—Amy Chiovari
SIC—2033; 2096; 2087; 2035;
NAICS—311421; *Corporate headquarters; preserves, jams, jellies, snack foods, beans, syrup, hot pepper sauce, salad dressing, spices & processed meats; Brand name—B & G; Polaner; Maple Grove Farms; Accent; Underwood; Red Devil; Emeril; Ortega; Cream of Wheat; Vermont Maid Syrup; Grandma's Molasses; Regina Wine Vinegar; B&M Baked Beans; Trappey's; Mrs. Dash; Sugar Twin; Baker's Joy*
Employs—70
Sales—$650Mil
130,000 sq ft site, Distrib.—
National
Publicly owned corporation

**BELCO TECHNOLOGIES CORP.**
Div. of E. I. du Pont de Nemours &
Co.
9 Entin Rd. (07054)
**Phone—(973) 884-4700**
Fax—(973) 884-4775
www.belcotech.dupont.com
Email—info@dupont.com
Pres.—Kevin Gilman
V-P., Sales & Mktg.—Nick
Confuorto
V-P., Precontracts—Tom Saley
V-P., Construction & Projs.—Bill
Boska
Procurement Mgr.—Bill Scherler
SIC—3543; 3564; NAICS—
332997; *Air pollution control systems*
Employs—55; Estab.—1968
Distrib.—Intl.
Publicly owned corporation
Parent co.—E. I. du Pont de
Nemours & Co., Wilmington, DE
Phone—(302) 774-1000
See Parent Co. Section for full profile.

**†BUSINESS FURNITURE, INC.**
10 Lanidex Plz. W., Ste. 202
(07054-2720)
**Phone—(973) 503-0730**
Fax—(973) 503-1565
www.bfionline.com
Email—bziegler@bfifurniture.com
Pres., CEO—Dan Morley
Sr. V-P.—Bill Ziegler
Dir., Sales—Bryan Effron
SIC—5021; *Distributor of office furniture, including chairs, desks, cubicles & file & storage units; Brand name—Herman Miller; National; Global; Geiger; Gunlocke*
Employs—35; Estab.—1983
Sales—$25Mil
14,000 sq ft site, Distrib.—Intl.
Privately owned partnership
AKA: bfi
Parent co.—Business Furniture,
Inc., Elizabeth, NJ
Phone—(908) 355-3400
See Parent Co. Section for full profile.

**CATBRIDGE MACHINERY, LLC**
222 New Rd., Ste. 1 (07054)
**Phone—(973) 808-0029**
Fax—(973) 808-0076
www.catbridge.com
Pres.—Michael Pappas
SIC—3554; NAICS—333291;
*Paper converting machinery, including slitters, rewinders & coating machines*
Employs—40; Estab.—1999
Sales—$5Mil-$10Mil (est)
Distrib.—Intl.
Limited Liability Company

**CDS PACKAGING, LLC**
237 Vaile Rd. (07054)
Mail addr: P.O. Box 412, Mount
Tabor (07878)
**Phone—(973) 219-1496**
Email—kraftape@aol.com
Pres., CEO—David Hirdler
SIC—2653; 2759; NAICS—
322211; *Corrugated & solid fiber packaging supplies & brochure & business card printing*
Employs—2; Estab.—2000
Sales—under $500,000 (est)
Distrib.—Regional

**CELLEBRITE USA CORP.**
7 Campus Dr., Ste. 210 (07054)
**Phone—(201) 848-8552**
Fax—(201) 848-9982
www.cellebriteusa.com
CEO—Jim Grady
IT Mgr.—Shachar Melamed
Hum. Res. Mgr.—Nancy Albilia
SIC—3663; NAICS—334220;
*Mobile interceptor communications equipment*
Employs—40; Estab.—2001
Sales—$1Mil-$2.5Mil
Distrib.—National
Privately owned corporation

**CENTRAL PLASTICS CO.**
333 New Rd. (07054)
**Phone—(973) 808-0990**
Fax—(973) 808-0866
www.plasticprofiles.com
Email—plasticpro@optonline.net
Pres.—Frank Tripucka
V-P.—Michelle Tripucka
Off. Mgr.—Terry Taillon
SIC—3082; 3081; NAICS—
326121; *Plastic sheet, rod & tubing*
Employs—5; Estab.—1976
Distrib.—Intl.
Privately owned corporation

**CHEMTRADE CHEMICAL, LLC**
Div. of Chemtrade Logistics, Inc.
90 E. Halsey Rd., 3rd Fl. (07054)
**Phone—(973) 515-0900**
National—(800) 631-8050

## Parsippany—(cont.)

Fax—(973) 515-3229
www.generalchemical.com
Email—info@genchemcorp.com
Pres., CEO—William Redmond
CFO—Doug Grierson
Bus. & Mktg. Mgr.—Lisa Brownlee
SIC—2819; *Company
headquarters & industrial
chemicals, including sulfuric
acid & sodium nitrate*
Employs—140; Estab.—1983
Sales—$50Mil-$100Mil (est)
Publicly owned corporation
Parent co.—Chemtrade Logistics,
Inc.
Phone—(416) 496-5856
See Parent Co. Section for full profile.

**CROLL-REYNOLDS (H Q)**
6 Campus Dr. (07054)
**Phone—(908) 232-4200**
Fax—(908) 232-2146
www.croll.com
Email—info@croll.com
Pres.—Samuel Croll
SIC—3569; *Company
headquarters; industrial process
vacuum & air pollution control
systems*
Employs—25
Sales—$2.5Mil-$5Mil (est)
Privately owned corporation

**CRONITE CO., INC.**
120 E. Halsey Rd., P.O. Box 6330
(07054)
**Phone—(973) 887-7900**
Fax—(973) 887-0015
www.cronite.com
Email—info@cronite.com
Pres.—Robert Steffens
V-P., CFO—Thomas R. Ward
Off. Mgr.—Patty Salzesen
SIC—3555; NAICS—333293;
*Etching & engraving equipment
& supplies*
Employs—15; Estab.—1886
40,000 sq ft site, Distrib.—Intl.
Privately owned corporation
Also see: Prismacolor Corp., same
loc.

**CURTISS-WRIGHT CORP. (H Q)**
10 Waterview Blvd., 2nd Fl.
(07054)
**Phone—(973) 541-3700**
Fax—(973) 541-3699
www.curtisswright.com
Email—investor@curtisswright.com
Chrm.—Martin R. Benante
CEO—David Adams
V-P., CFO—Glenn Tynan
V-P., Gen. Counsel & Secy.—Paul
Ferdenzi
V-P., Hum. Res. & Assoc. Gen.
Counsel—Joanne Karimi
Hum. Res. Mgr.—Janine O'Rourke
Off. Mgr.—Jane Winter
SIC—3479; 3492; NAICS—
332912; *Corporate
headquarters; flow control
systems & metal treatment &
motion control products*
Employs—50
Worldwide: 7,600
Sales—$5Mil-$10Mil (est)
Publicly owned corporation

**CUSTOM SPINE, INC. (H Q)**
9 Campus Dr. (07054)
**Phone—(973) 808-0019**
Fax—(877) 770-7746
www.customspine.com
Email—info@customspine.com
CEO—Mahmoud Abdelgany
CFO—David Hess
V-P., Sales, Western Reg.—
Randal Clarke
Mktg. & Opers. Mgr.—Mark Foldy

SIC—3842; *Corporate
headquarters; spinal implants &
instruments (mfg.
subcontracted); Brand name—
ISSYS LP; Pathway AVID;
Pathway TLIF; Pathway PLIF;
Pathway ACIF; Regent ACP;
Securis*
Employs—16; Estab.—2003
Distrib.—National
Privately owned corporation

**DAIICHI SANKYO, INC. (H Q)**
2 Hilton Ct. (07054)
**Phone—(973) 944-2600**
Fax—(973) 944-2645
www.dsi.com
Email—dsipublicaffairs@dsi.com
Pres., CEO—Ken Keller
CSO—Glenn J. Gormley
V-P., Hum. Res.—Danesha Dixon
Corp. Rels. Mgr.—Kim Wix
SIC—2834; *Corporate
headquarters; pharmaceuticals
for hypertension, hyperlipidermia
& bacterial infection; Brand
name—Azor®; Benicar®;
Effient™; Evoxac®; SPRIX®;
TRIBENZOR™; Welchol®;
ZELBORAF™*
Employs—560; Estab.—2006
Sales—$250Mil-$500Mil (est)
Distrib.—Intl.

**DAX SYSTEMS, INC.**
343 New Rd., Ste. 4 (07054)
**Phone—(973) 227-8111**
National—(877) 432-9797
Fax—(973) 227-8197
www.daxsystems.com
Email—sales@daxsystems.com
Pres.—Ernie Kaminaris
SIC—3571; *Computer servers*
Employs—6; Estab.—1990
Distrib.—National
Privately owned corporation

**DIALOGIC CORP.**
Div. of Dialogic, Inc.
1515 State Route 10 E. (07054)
**Phone—(973) 967-6000**
Fax—(973) 967-6006
www.dialogic.com
Email—dialogic@dialogic.com
Hum. Res. Mgr.—Ester Zohn
Hum. Res. Coord.—Patty O'Brien
SIC—3571; NAICS—334111;
*Computers & computer parts*
Employs—120; Estab.—2006
Sales—$11Mil-$25Mil
Distrib.—Intl.
Publicly owned corporation
Parent co.—Dialogic, Inc.,
Parsippany, NJ
Phone—(800) 755-4444
See Parent Co. Section for full profile.

NEW ENTRY
**DIALOGIC, INC. (H Q)**
4 Gatehall Dr. (07054)
**Phone—(800) 755-4444**
Fax—(408) 750-9510
www.dialogic.com
Email—dialogic@dialogic.com
Pres., CEO—Kevin Cook
Ex. V-P., CFO—Bob Dennerlein
Sr. V-P., Worldwide Sales—Bill
Crank
Sr. V-P., Opers. & Prod. Dev.—
Kevin Gould
Sr. V-P., Hum. Res.—Rosanna
Sargent
SIC—3661; 3669; 3571; 3993;
*Corporate headquarters;
telecommunications equipment;
wireless communications
systems, computers & electronic
message displays*
Employs—100
Sales—$25Mil-$50Mil (est)
Publicly owned corporation

**DIGITAL PRINT SOLUTIONS, LLC**
5 Eastmans Rd. (07054)
**Phone—(973) 263-1890**
Fax—(973) 263-2054
www.us319.alphagraphics.com
Email—us319@alphagraphics.com
Owner—Joseph Yutsus
Graphic Designer—Rafael
Gutierrez
SIC—2759; NAICS—323100;
*Commercial printing*
Employs—15; Estab.—1990
Sales—$1Mil-$2.5Mil
4,500 sq ft site, Distrib.—Regional
Limited Liability Company
AKA: Alphagraphics 319

**DONRAY PRINTING**
2 Eastmans Rd. (07054)
**Phone—(973) 515-8100**
Fax—(973) 515-8102
www.donrayprinting.com
Email—ray@donrayprinting.com
Pres.—Ray Ferriola
Cont.—Bill Savastano
SIC—2396; *Textile & apparel
sublimation printing*
Employs—18; Estab.—1987
36,000 sq ft site, Distrib.—National
Privately owned corporation

**DSM PHARMACEUTICAL
PRODUCTS, INC. (H Q)**
45 Waterview Blvd. (07054)
**Phone—(973) 257-1063**
(973) 257-8500
National—(800) 526-0189
Fax—(973) 257-8600
www.dsm.com
Email—webshop.dmpna@dsm.com
Pres., CEO—Alexander Wessels
Pres. & Bus. Unit Dir., Biologics—
Karen King
Pres., Group Protection—Hugh
Welsh
Sr. V-P., Hum. Res.—Stan Veltman
V-P., Mktg. & Strategy—Paul Sidhu
Dir., Comms. & Mktg.—Guy Tiene
Bldg. Mgr.—Catherine Dooney
SIC—2833; 2048; 2844; 2836;
*Corporate headquarters; liquid &
dry vitamins, vitamin premixes,
carotenoids, LC-PUFAs,
nutraceuticals, sunscreens, feed
enzymes & probiotics*
Employs—165
Sales—$500Mil
Distrib.—Intl.
Privately owned corporation

**EARTHCOLOR**
Div. of EarthColor, Inc.
345 Walsh Dr. (07054)
**Phone—(973) 884-1300**
National—(800) 843-2285
Fax—(973) 952-8283
www.earthcolor.com
Email—cylam@earthcolor.com
Pres.—Greg Matonti
Ex. V-P.—Bruce Wexler
IT Mgr.—Bill Wallburg
SIC—2759; NAICS—323100;
*Company headquarters &
commercial printing*
Employs—300; Estab.—1922
Sales—$20Mil-$25Mil
Distrib.—National
Privately owned corporation
Parent co.—EarthColor, Inc.,
Parsippany, NJ
Phone—(973) 884-1300
See Parent Co. Section for full profile.

**EARTHCOLOR, INC.**
249 Pomeroy Rd., P.O. Box 169
(07054)
**Phone—(973) 884-1300**
National—(800) 843-2285
Fax—(973) 952-8296
www.earthcolor.com
Email—info@earthcolor.com
CEO—Robert Kashan
V-P., IT—William Chillin

V-P., Fin.—Nat Modugno
Dir., Mktg.—Karen Missud
Dir., Hum. Res.—Alan Liebeskind
SIC—2752; 2791; NAICS—
323122; *Corporate headquarters
& commercial offset printing,
electronic prepress & finishing
services*
Employs—100; Estab.—1988
Sales—$25Mil-$100Mil
243,475 sq ft site, Distrib.—
National
Privately owned partnership

**EBI**
Div. of Biomet, Inc.
399 Jefferson Rd. (07054)
**Phone—(973) 299-9300**
National—(800) 526-2579
www.biomet.com
Email—biomet@biomet.com
Pres.—Adam Johnson
Mfg. Mgr.—Roman Steciuk
Hum. Res. Mgr.—Barbara Vlatimer
Hum. Res. Generalist—Tiffany
Sanchez
SIC—3842; *Athletic knee braces*
Employs—300
Distrib.—Intl.
Privately owned corporation
AKA: Biomet Spine & Bone
Healing Technologies
Parent co.—Biomet, Inc., Warsaw,
IN
Phone—(574) 267-6639
See Parent Co. Section for full profile.

**ELECTRONIC DRIVES & CONTROLS,
INC.**
17 Eastmans Rd. (07054)
**Phone—(973) 428-0500**
Fax—(973) 428-0135
www.electronicdrives.com
Email—sales@electronicdrives.com
Pres.—Henry Dillard III
V-P.—Charles Dillard
Off. Mgr.—Naomi Dillard
SIC—3625; 3566; NAICS—
335314; *Electronic drives &
controls systems*
Employs—26; Estab.—1968
Sales—$6Mil
20,000 sq ft site, Distrib.—
Regional
Privately owned sub-S corp.

**ELECTRONIKA FOR INDUSTRY, INC.**
3599 Route 46 (07054)
Mail addr: 1 Hyler Ct., Boonton
(07005)
**Phone—(973) 575-4994**
National—(855) 334-1020
Fax—(973) 575-7994
Email—customerservice@
eficontrol.com
Pres.—Witold Tarnawski
Opers. Mgr.—Marsha Tarnawski
SIC—3625; NAICS—335314;
*Industrial controls*
Employs—9; Estab.—1989
Distrib.—National
Privately owned corporation
AKA: EFI, Inc.

NEW ENTRY
**ELEVATE HR, INC.**
1055 Parsippany Blvd., Ste. 511
(07054)
**Phone—(973) 917-3230**
Fax—(973) 917-3231
www.elevate-hr.com
Email—info@elevate-hr.com
Pres.—David M. Erickson
SIC—7372; *Human capital
management (HCM) software
development; Brand name—
Elevate®; Dynamics®*
Employs—20

**ELITE GRAPHICS, INC.**
333 Littleton Rd., Ste. 200 (07054)
**Phone—(973) 882-9769**
Fax—(973) 808-1862

GEOGRAPHICAL

## Parsippany—(cont.)

Email—egiprint@optonline.net
Pres.—John Westlake
SIC—2759; NAICS—323100;
Commercial printing
Employs—7; Estab.—1984
Distrib.—Local
Privately owned corporation

**EVONIK CORPORATION (H Q)**
299 Jefferson Rd. (07054)
**Phone—(973) 929-8000**
National—(800) 334-8772
Fax—(973) 929-8013
www.evonik.com
Email—info@evonik.com
Pres.—John Rolando
CFO—Burkhard Zoller
Media Rels. Mgr.—Mike Sheridan
SIC—2819; 2821; 3471; 2851;
NAICS—325211; Corporate
headquarters; industrial
performance materials, coatings,
fillers & specialty polymers &
color pigments
Employs—421; Estab.—2000
Sales—$25Mil–$50Mil
Distrib.—Intl.
Privately owned corporation
ISO rating—9002

**EXTREMITY MEDICAL, LLC**
300 Interpace Pkwy., Ste. 410
(07054)
**Phone—(973) 588-8980**
National—(888) 499-0079
Fax—(973) 316-9901
www.extremitymedical.com
Email—customerservice@
extremitymedical.com
Pres., CEO—James Gannoe
Accts. Specialist—Marie McNeill
SIC—3842; Orthopedic implants
Employs—20
Distrib.—Intl.
Limited Liability Company

**FAMCAM, INC.**
3 Eastmans Rd. (07054)
**Phone—(973) 319-3033**
Fax—(973) 319-3035
Email—nkoch@famcam-inc.com
Pres.—Samir Aboulhosn
Mktg. & Opers. Mgr.—Nada Koch
SIC—3599; General machining
job shop
Employs—10; Estab.—1983
Sales—$1Mil–$5Mil
18,000 sq ft site, Distrib.—Intl.
Privately owned corporation
ISO rating—AS9100C, 9001:2008
Also see: Severna Operations,
Inc., same loc.

**†FINLANDIA CHEESE, INC.**
2001 U.S. Highway 46, Ste. 303
(07054)
**Phone—(973) 316-6699**
(800) 496-3822
Fax—(973) 316-6609
www.finlandiacheese.com
Email—info@finlandiacheese.com
Pres.—Chris Franco
Cont. & Hum. Res. Mgr.—Monique
Chiarito
Dir., Mktg.—Frank Belfiore
IT Mgr.—Melissa Krupar
Cust. Serv. Rep.—Teresa
Dacunha
Cust. Serv. Rep.—Holly Plut
SIC—5143; Distributor of cheese
Employs—15; Estab.—1998
Distrib.—Intl.
Privately owned corporation

**FLUOROTHERM POLYMERS, INC.**
333 New Rd., Ste. 1 (07054)
**Phone—(973) 575-0760**
National—(877) 777-2629
Fax—(973) 575-0431
www.fluorotherm.com
Email—sales@fluorotherm.com
Pres., CEO—P. N. Shukla

Mktg. Mgr.—S. P. Shukla
SIC—3443; 3089; Immersion coil,
shell & tube corrosion resistant
heat exchangers, fluoropolymer,
PTFE, TFE, FEP, PFA, MFA,
EFTFE & ultra pure tubing &
fluoroplastic tubes & coils; Brand
name—Fluorotherm; H2
Employs—12; Estab.—1992
Sales—$1.5Mil–$2.5Mil
7,500 sq ft site, Distrib.—Intl.
Privately owned corporation

**FREEMAN PRODUCTS, INC. (H Q)**
71 Walsh Dr. (07054)
**Phone—(201) 475-8888**
National—(800) 537-3362
Fax—(201) 791-3003
www.freemanproductsworldwide.c
om
Email—sales@fpworldwide.com
Ptnr.—Vincent Cariello
Ptnr.—George Cariello
SIC—3914; 3499; NAICS—
339912; Corporate
headquarters; trophy & award
components
Employs—25; Estab.—1959
Distrib.—Intl.
Privately owned corporation
AKA: AMG Intl.

**FRONTLINE MEDICAL
COMMUNICATIONS, INC.**
7 Century Dr., Ste. 302 (07054)
**Phone—(973) 206-3434**
Fax—(973) 206-9360
www.frontlinemedcom.com
Email—sales@
frontlinemedcom.com
Chrm.—Stephen Stoneburn
Pres., CEO, Clinical Content Div.—
Marcy Holeton
CEO, Med. News Div.—Alan J.
Imhoff
Dir., Mfg. Svcs.—Mike Wendt
Dir., Hum. Res. & Opers.—Carolyn
Caccavelli
IT Mgr.—Tim Riley
SIC—2721; Corporate
headquarters & magazine
publishing
Employs—100; Estab.—2003
Sales—$5Mil–$10Mil
Distrib.—National
Privately owned corporation

**FRONTLINE MEDICAL
COMMUNICATIONS, INC.**
7 Century Dr. (07054)
**Phone—(973) 290-8200**
Fax—(973) 290-8250
www.frontlinemedcom.com
Email—aimhoff@
frontlinemedcom.com
Pres., CEO—Alan J. Imhoff
V.-P., Mktg.—Sylvia H. Reitman
SIC—2721; 2741; Monthly print &
online medical tabloid publishing
Employs—187
Sales—$10Mil–$25Mil (est)
Privately owned corporation
Parent co.—Frontline Medical
Communications, Inc.,
Parsippany, NJ
Phone—(973) 206-3434
See Parent Co. Section for full profile.

**FUTURE ELECTRONICS CORP.**
959 Route 46 E., Ste. 303,
Parsippany Pl (07054)
**Phone—(973) 299-0400**
National—(800) 445-6806
Fax—(973) 299-1377
www.futureelectronics.com
Email—eservice@
futureelectronics.com
Dir. & GM—Tom Tosco
Sales Rep.—Bruce Lettenhan
SIC—3679; Electronic
components
Employs—10; Estab.—1977
Distrib.—Local
Privately owned corporation

Parent co.—Future Electronics
Corp.
Phone—(514) 694-7710
See Parent Co. Section for full profile.

**GENESIS PHARMACEUTICAL, INC.
(H Q)**
8 Campus Dr. (07054)
**Phone—(800) 459-8663**
www.glytone-usa.com
Email—customerservice@
pfdcusa.com
CEO—Laurent-Emmanuel Siffre
CFO—Francois Viargues
V.-P., Retail Sales—Jacqueline
Flam
V.-P., Bus. Units, Dispensing &
Export—Pascal Voltzenlugel
Dir., Sales, Natl.—Sege Bouteleau
Hum. Res. Mgr.—Bud Metz
SIC—2834; NAICS—325412;
Corporate headquarters;
medicated skin cream
Employs—40
Distrib.—National
AKA: Pierre Fabre Dermo
Cosmetique, USA

**HARVEY WESTBURY CORP. (H Q)**
160 Littleton Rd., Ste. 308 (07054)
**Phone—(201) 468-7779**
Fax—(973) 794-6611
www.harveywestbury.com
Email—hwestsales@aol.com
CEO—Eugene Chiaramonte
SIC—2842; NAICS—325612;
Corporate headquarters;
automotive & marine polishes &
waxes (mfg. subcontracted)
Employs—3; Estab.—1968
Sales—under $500,000
5,000 sq ft site, Distrib.—National
Sole ownership

**†IKO INTERNATIONAL, INC.**
91 Walsh Dr. (07054)
**Phone—(973) 402-0254**
National—(800) 922-0337
Fax—(973) 402-0441
www.ikont.com
Email—eco@ikonet.co.jp
Pres.—Dan Sugihara
Sales Mgr.—John Longo
Asst. Mgr.—Shintaro Harumoto
SIC—5085; Corporate
headquarters & wholesaler of
needle roller bearings & linear
rolling guide units
Employs—10
Distrib.—Intl.
Privately owned sub-S corp.
AKA: Nippon Thompson Co. Ltd.

**INDUSTRY PUBLICATIONS, INC.**
3621 Hill Rd. (07054)
**Phone—(973) 331-9545**
Fax—(973) 331-9547
www.indoorcomfortmarketing.com
Publisher—Cynthia Hundley
V.-P., Admn.—Sue Carver
Ex. Editor—Michael SanGiovanni
Editorial Dir.—Ava Caridat
SIC—2721; Bimonthly print &
online magazine publishing
Employs—12; Estab.—1980
Sales—$1Mil–$2.5Mil (est)
Distrib.—National
Privately owned corporation

**†INTERNATIONAL PLAYTHINGS LLC**
75D Lackawanna Ave. (07054)
**Phone—(973) 316-2500**
National—(800) 631-1272
Fax—(973) 316-5883
www.intplay.com
Email—info@intplay.com
CEO—Michael Varda
SIC—5092; Wholesaler of
children's toys & games
Employs—30; Estab.—1994
Distrib.—Intl.
Limited Liability Company

**J.P. VEGGIES, INC.**
222 New Rd. (07054)
**Phone—(973) 808-1540**
Fax—(973) 882-3030
www.veggieland.com
Email—info@veggieland.com
CEO—Philip Grabow
Pres.—Jason Wilson
V.-P.—Cynthia Wilson
SIC—2099; Vegetarian food
products, including veggie
burgers, soy chicken nuggets &
patties & meatless meatballs &
sausage
Employs—38; Estab.—1994
Distrib.—National
Privately owned sub-S corp.
DBA: VeggieLand

**JHP PHARMACEUTICALS, LLC**
1 Upper Pond Rd., Bldg. D (07054-
1050)
**Phone—(973) 658-3530**
Fax—(866) 923-4547
www.jhppharma.com
Email—corporate.information@
jhppharma.com
Pres., CEO—Stuart Hinchen
Dir., Hum. Res.—Carolyn
Kaminski
Acct. Mgr., Natl.—Robert Killian
Acct. Mgr., Natl.—Peter Gargiulo
SIC—2834; NAICS—325412;
Company headquarters &
pharmaceuticals
Employs—30; Estab.—2007
Nationwide: 330
Sales—$10Mil–$25Mil
Distrib.—Intl.
Limited Liability Company

**JODHPURI, INC.**
260-A Walsh Dr. (07054)
**Phone—(973) 299-7009**
National—(877) 356-7277
Fax—(973) 299-7005
www.jodhpuri-inc.com
Email—sales@jodhpuri-inc.com
Pres., CEO—L. C. Mehta
Ex. V.-P.—Sheila Mehta
Sales Coord.—Janet Vosquez
SIC—3999; Custom & private
label home fragrance products &
accessories for upscale &
specialty stores, large retail
chains & supermarkets,
including reed diffusers,
potpourri, incense, candles, gift
sets & artificial flowers & trees
Employs—90; Estab.—1990
60,000 sq ft site, Distrib.—Intl.
Privately owned sub-S corp.
AKAs: Jodhpuri Collections, LLC &
Flora Garden, Inc

**†KENSEAL CONSTRUCTION
PRODUCTS CORP.**
799 Edwards Rd. (07054)
**Phone—(973) 287-5858**
National—(877) 849-8300
Fax—(973) 736-7772
www.kenseal.com
Email—info@kenseal.com
Cont.—Charles J. Meyers
Regional Mgr.—Scott Gallion
SIC—5169; 5198; Distributor of
sealants, concrete admixtures,
liquid pigments, epoxies &
adhesives for the construction &
masonry industries
Employs—20; Estab.—2005
Distrib.—National
Privately owned corporation
Parent co.—Kenseal Construction
Products Corp., Baltimore, MD
Phone—(410) 646-5801
See Parent Co. Section for full profile.

**†KENT INTERNATIONAL INC.**
60 E. Halsey Rd. (07054)
**Phone—(973) 434-8181**
National—(800) 451-5368
Fax—(973) 434-8189

## Parsippany—(cont.)

www.kentbicycles.com
Email—scottk@kentbicycles.com
CEO—Arnold Kamler
Pres.—Scott Kamler
Sr. V.-P.—Chris Hoover
SIC—5091; *Wholesaler of bicycles & accessories; Brand name—Kent; Thruster; WeeRide; USA Helmet; Northwoods; Giordano; BCA*
Employs—70; Estab.—1958
Sales—$205Mil
67,000 sq ft site, Distrib.—Intl.
Privately owned corporation

### LOR-TECH PLASTICS, LLC

3 Eastmans Rd., Unit 3 (07054-3702)
**Phone—(973) 503-1750**
Fax—(973) 503-1752
www.lortechplastics.com
Email—nkoch@lortechplastics.com
Pres.—Nada A. Koch
SIC—3089; *Custom plastic injection molding for the medical, aerospace, consumer products, military, automotive & electronics industries*
Employs—4; Estab.—2009
Sales—$500,000
10,000 sq ft site, Distrib.—Intl.
Limited Liability Company

### MACROSOFT, INC.

2 Sylvan Way (07054)
**Phone—(973) 889-0500**
Fax—(973) 889-0616
www.macrosoftinc.com
Email—info@macrosoftinc.com
CEO—Ronald Mueller
Pres.—Edward G. Sable
V.-P., Sales & Mktg.—John Kullman
V.-P., Tech.—G. N. Shah
Hum. Res. Mgr.—Jessica Kundilas
SIC—7372; *Software development*
Employs—120; Estab.—1993
Distrib.—National
Privately owned corporation

NEW ENTRY
### MAXIMUM MATERIAL HANDLING, LLC

750 Edwards Rd. (07054)
**Phone—(973) 227-1227**
Fax—(973) 227-2289
www.maximummh.com
Email—info@maximummh.com
Pres.—Michael Dal Bon, Jr.
Off. Mgr.—Renee Del Vecchio
SIC—3536; *Material handling equipment, including cranes, hoists & winches*
Employs—6; Estab.—2006
Sales—$1Mil-$2.5Mil (est)
Distrib.—Local
Limited Liability Company

### MEDICINES CO., THE

8 Sylvan Way (07054)
**Phone—(973) 290-6000**
National—(800) 388-1183
Fax—(973) 656-9898
www.themedicinescompany.com
Email—investor.relations@themedco.com
CEO—Clive Meanwell
Pres.—Glenn Sblendorio
CAO—William O'Connor
Sr. V.-P., Gen. Counsel—Paul M. Antinori
Comms. Specialist—Anabel Tonkovic

SIC—2834; NAICS—325412; *Company headquarters & biopharmaceuticals for acute cardiovascular & critical care patients & hospitals*
Employs—170; Estab.—1996
Sales—$101Mil-$1Bil
Distrib.—Intl.
Publicly owned corporation

### MEDTRONIC, INC.

300 Interpace Pkwy. (07054)
**Phone—(516) 222-2848**
National—(800) 221-0257
Fax—(973) 658-1011
www.medtronic.com
Email—info@medtronic.com
V.-P.—Thomas Conlin
Administrator—Karen Conlin
SIC—3845; NAICS—334500; *Implantable cardioverter defibrillators*
Employs—40; Estab.—1960
Sales—$6Mil-$10Mil
Distrib.—Local
Publicly owned corporation
Parent co.—Medtronic, Inc., Minneapolis, MN
Phone—(763) 514-4000
See Parent Co. Section for full profile.

### METEM CORP.

700 Parsippany Rd. (07054)
**Phone—(973) 887-6635**
Fax—(973) 887-1755
www.metem.com
Email—hr@metem.com
Chrm.—Duval Goldthwaite
CEO—Steven Goldthwaite
Dir., Fin.—Vincent Abate
Hum. Res. Mgr.—Elise Mundrick
SIC—3599; *Corporate headquarters & general machining job shop*
Employs—180; Estab.—1962
Sales—$20Mil
Distrib.—National
Privately owned sub-S corp.

### MICROLAB/FXR

25 Eastmans Rd. (07054)
**Phone—(973) 386-9696**
Fax—(973) 386-9191
www.microlab.fxr.com
Email—sales@microlab.fxr.com
Dir., Field Sales—Rand Skopas
Dir., Opers.—Danny Larsen
Prodn. Mgr.—Jeff Roberts
SIC—3679; *Passive wireless electronic components*
Employs—120; Estab.—1950
23,000 sq ft site, Distrib.—Intl.
Also see: Wireless Telecom Group, Inc., same loc.

### MILLENNIUM SYSTEMS INTERNATIONAL

28 Eastmans Rd. (07054)
**Phone—(973) 402-9500**
National—(888) 813-2141
Fax—(973) 402-8815
www.harms-software.com
Email—sales@harms-software.com
Founder & CEO—John Harms
V.-P., Sales—Robert Maconi
Dir., Hum. Res., IT & Opers. Mgr.—Matt Scudder
Pub. Rels. Mgr.—Matt Martinelli
Opers. Coord.—Lauren Neglia
Opers. Coord.—Alexa Raciotti
SIC—7372; *Beauty industry software development*
Employs—60; Estab.—1987
Distrib.—Intl.
Privately owned corporation
AKA: Millennium

### MOOSE MOUNTAIN MARKETING, INC. (H Q)

8 Wood Hollow Rd., Ste. 302 (07054)
**Phone—(973) 884-8900**
National—(888) 666-7388
Fax—(973) 884-8999

www.moosemountaintoys.com
Email—info@moosemountaintoys.com
Pres.—Ronald Lokos
SIC—3944; *Corporate headquarters; toys (mfg. done overseas)*
Employs—10; Estab.—1996
Sales—under $500,000
Distrib.—National
Privately owned corporation

### NOVARTIS CONSUMER HEALTH (H Q)

200 Kimball Dr. (07054)
**Phone—(973) 503-8000**
Fax—(973) 503-8450
www.us.novartis.com
Email—media.relations@novartis.com
CEO—Brian McNamara
CFO, OTC Div.—Tobias Hestler
V.-P. & Assoc. Gen. Counsel—Bryant Arron
V.-P., Hum. Res.—Anthony Webster
Gen. Counsel, OTC—Greg Tole
SIC—2834; NAICS—325412; *Company headquarters; pharmaceuticals; Brand name—Diovan; Gleevec; Lotel; Zometa; Lamisil; Neoral; Sandostatin; Lescol; Trileptal; Femara*
Employs—1000; Estab.—1996
Sales—$500Mil-$1Bil (est)
Distrib.—Intl.
Publicly owned corporation

### OHAUS CORP.

Div. of Mettler-Toledo, LLC
7 Campus Dr., Ste. 310 (07054)
**Phone—(973) 377-9000**
National—(800) 672-7722
Fax—(973) 944-7177
www.ohaus.com
Email—sales@ohaus.com
Pres.—Ted Xia
Head of Mktg.—Carl Joslyn
Sr. Mktg. Specialist—Mania Harley
SIC—3821; 3829; NAICS—339111; *Analytical & precision balances & scales for the laboratory, education, food, pharmaceutical, industrial & specialty market industries; Brand name—Ohaus; Adventurer Pro; Scout Pro; Pioneer; Ranger; Discovery; Explorer; Explorer Pro; Defender; Triple Pro; Harvard Junior; Trooper; Voyager*
Employs—100; Estab.—1907
Distrib.—Intl.
Publicly owned corporation
ISO rating—9001
Parent co.—Mettler-Toledo, LLC, Columbus, OH
Phone—(614) 438-4511
See Parent Co. Section for full profile.

### PACIRA PHARMACEUTICALS, INC. (H Q)

5 Sylvan Way (07054)
**Phone—(973) 254-3560**
www.pacira.com
Email—jessica.cho@pacira.com
Chrm., Pres. & CEO—David Stack
Sr. V.-P., CFO—James Scibetta
Sr. V.-P., Chief Comml. Officer—Taunia Markvicka
SIC—2834; *Corporate headquarters; clinical & commercial development of acute care products, including non-opioid products for postsurgical pain control; Brand name—DepoCyt(e)®; Exparel®*
Employs—52; Estab.—2007
Sales—$25Mil-$50Mil (est)
Distrib.—National
Publicly owned corporation

### PBF ENERGY PARTNERS L. P. (H Q)

1 Sylvan Way (07054-3887)
**Phone—(973) 455-7500**
www.pbfenergy.com
Email—info@pbfenergy.com
Chrm.—Thomas O'Malley
CEO—Thomas J. Nimbley
Pres.—Michael D. Gayda
CFO—Eric Young
Sr. V.-P., Gen. Counsel & Secy.—Jeffrey Dill
Ex. V.-P.—Mathew Lucey
Dir., Inv. Rels.—Colin Murray
Dir., Compensation—Wendy Ho Tai
SIC—2911; *Company headquarters; crude oil refining*
Employs—170; Estab.—2008
Company-wide: 1,300
Sales—$250Mil-$500Mil (est)
Distrib.—National
Publicly owned corporation

### PNY TECHNOLOGIES, INC.

100 Jefferson Rd. *(07054)*
**Phone—(973) 515-9700**
National—(800) 769-7079
Fax—(973) 560-5590
www.pny.com
Email—info@pny.com
Pres.—Gadi Cohen
Sr. V.-P., Bus. Dev.—John Hughes
V.-P., Sales—Anthony Gomez
Hum. Res. Mgr.—Carmen Bayman
SIC—3674; NAICS—334413; *Video & flash cards & memory chips & workstation graphics*
Employs—200; Estab.—1985
Sales—$350Mil-$400Mil
Distrib.—Intl.
Privately owned corporation

### PRINTING INDUSTRIES, LLC

1543 U.S. Highway 46 E. (07054)
**Phone—(973) 334-9775**
National—(877) 470-4225
Fax—(973) 334-3007
www.drprinting.net
Email—sendittous@drprinting.net
V.-P.—Deron Baumfeld
SIC—2759; *Commercial printing, including business cards, letterheads, business forms, brochures, booklets & postcards*
Employs—8; Estab.—1979
Sales—$500,000-$1Mil
2,200 sq ft site, Distrib.—Local
Limited Liability Company

### PRISMACOLOR CORP.

120 E. Halsey Rd., P.O. Box 6330 (07054)
**Phone—(973) 887-7900**
Fax—(973) 887-0015
www.cronite.com
Email—info@cronite.com
Pres.—Robert Steffens
GM—Milton Braff
Off. Mgr.—Patty Salvesen
SIC—2893; NAICS—325910; *Printing ink*
Employs—20; Estab.—1968
10,000 sq ft site, Distrib.—Intl.
Privately owned sub-S corp.
Also see: Cronite Co., Inc., same loc.

### RECKITT BENCKISER, INC.

399 Interpace Pkwy., P.O. Box 225 (07054)
**Phone—(973) 404-2600**
National—(800) 333-3899
Fax—(973) 404-5700
www.reckittbenckiser.com
Email—info@reckittbenckiser.com
Pres., Frenchs Food Prod.—Elliott Penner
Ex. V.-P., N. America—Rob de Groot
V.-P., Hum. Res.—Beverly Wilen
GM, Household Prod. Sales—Anthony Jenkinson

GEOGRAPHICAL

## Parsippany—(cont.)

GM, Household Prod. Mktg.—
Alexander Iacik
SIC—2035; 2087; 2844; NAICS—
311900; Corporate headquarters
& consumer cleaning, food,
home, health & personal care
products including barbecue &
hot sauces, mustard, dish
detergent, stain removers & air
fresheners
Employs—375
Sales—$1.4Bil
Distrib.—National
Publicly owned corporation

**†SAFILO USA, INC. (H Q)**
801 Jefferson Rd. (07054)
**Phone—(973) 952-2800**
Fax—(973) 560-1592
www.safilousa.com
Email—safilogallery@safilo.com
Pres., COO—Ross Brown Lee
Sr. V-P., Sales—Mark Ugenti
V-P., Acctg.—Gary Graham
V-P., Hum. Res.—Robin Kreitner
V-P., Prod. Design & Dev.—Timm
Parker
IT Mgr.—Jeff Wolf
SIC—5048; Corporate
headquarters; distributor of
eyewear
Employs—350
Privately owned corporation

**SCHAEDLER QUINZEL, INC. (H Q)**
1259 U.S. Highway 46, Ste. 4
(07054)
Mail addr: P.O. Box 280, Ringwood
(07456)
**Phone—(973) 263-4949**
Fax—(973) 506-4081
www.schaedlerprecision.com
Email—johns@
schaedlerprecision.com
Pres.—John N. Schaedler
GM—Bill Schaedler
SIC—3823; Corporate
headquarters; polymer-based
precision rulers (mfg.
subcontracted)
Employs—2
Sales—under $500,000
Distrib.—Intl.
Privately owned corporation
AKA: Schaedler Precision Rules

**SCHNEIDER ELECTRIC**
Div. of Schneider Electric USA,
Inc.
2001 Highway 46, Ste. 402
(07054)
**Phone—(973) 263-6100**
National—(888) 778-2733
Fax—(859) 817-6538
www.squared.com
Email—info@squared.com
Opers. Mgr.—Ashish Sawardekar
Consultant, Tech.—Brian Price
SIC—3679; 3699; Electrical
distribution, control & automation
equipment
Employs—30; Estab.—1904
Distrib.—Intl.
Publicly owned corporation
Parent co.—Schneider Electric
USA, Inc., Palatine, IL
Phone—(847) 397-2600
See Parent Co. Section for full profile.

**SEVERNA OPERATIONS, INC.**
3 Eastmans Rd. (07054)
**Phone—(973) 503-1600**
Fax—(973) 503-1704
www.severna.com
Email—nkoch@severna.com
Pres.—Samir Aboulhosn
Mktg. & Opers. Mgr.—Nada Koch
Mfg. Engr.—Phillip Koch

SIC—3089; 3599; Custom
precision machined parts &
fluoropolymer & molded
products
Employs—20; Estab.—1960
Sales—$5Mil-$10Mil
32,000 sq ft site, Distrib.—Intl.
Sole ownership
ISO rating—9002, AS9100C
Also see: Famcam, Inc., same loc.

**SKYLINE STEEL, LLC (H Q)**
Div. of Nucor Corp.
8 Woodhollow Rd., Ste. 102
(07054)
**Phone—(973) 428-6100**
Fax—(973) 428-8093
www.skylinesteel.com
Email—pipe@skylinesteel.com
CEO—Laurent De Mey
CFO—Judith Gorog
Sales Opers. Mgr.—Holly Dwyer
SIC—3312; Company
headquarters; structural steel
processing & fabrication, sheet
metal pilings & spiral steel
welded pipes
Employs—30; Estab.—1968
Sales—$5Mil-$10Mil (est)
Distrib.—Regional
Limited Liability Company
Parent co.—Nucor Corp.,
Charlotte, NC
Phone—(704) 366-7000
See Parent Co. Section for full profile.

**SONNEBORN, LLC**
Div. of One Equity Partners, LLC
600 Parsippany Rd., Ste. 100
(07054-3715)
**Phone—(201) 760-2940**
Fax—(201) 760-2967
www.sonneborn.com
Email—luther.jones@
sonneborn.com
CEO—Paul Raymond
CFO—James Stiff
Ex. V-P., Sales & Mktg.—Luther
Jones
Hum. Res. Mgr.—Kristine Conforti
SIC—2911; 5172; NAICS—
324110; Company headquarters
& manufacturer & wholesaler of
petroleum based products;
Brand name—SonneNatural;
Sonnecone; Lilac; SonneWarmix
Employs—12; Estab.—2005
Company-wide: 360
Sales—$450Mil-$475Mil
5,562 sq ft site, Distrib.—Intl.
Limited Liability Company
Parent co.—One Equity Partners,
LLC, New York, NY
Phone—(212) 277-1500
See Parent Co. Section for full profile.

**STEINEN MFG. CO., WM.**
29 E. Halsey Rd. (07054)
**Phone—(973) 887-6400**
National—(800) 724-3343
Fax—(973) 887-4632
www.steinen.com
Email—inquiries@steinen.com
CEO—William F. Steinen, Jr.
CFO—Tom Keenan
COO—Bill Rotenberry
SIC—3432; NAICS—332900;
Company headquarters &
industrial spray, oil burner &
misting/fogging nozzles &
accessories; Brand name—
Dyna Coin
Employs—80; Estab.—1907
Sales—$10Mil
44,000 sq ft site, Distrib.—Intl.
Privately owned corporation

**STRATEGIC PRODUCTS &
SERVICES, LLC**
300 Littleton Rd., 2nd Fl. (07054)
**Phone—(888) 777-7280**
Fax—(973) 540-1221
www.spscom.com

Chrm. of the Board, Pres. &
CEO—John Poole
V-P., Sales—Vel Johnson
V-P., Sales & Mktg.—Jim Maynard
IT Mgr.—Craig Eberle
Hum. Res. Mgr.—Andrew
Schechter
Off. Mgr.—Liz Bilaney
SIC—7373; IT & telephone
systems integration, including
design, installation & support of
converged communication
solutions & advanced IP
telephony
Employs—126; Estab.—2009
Distrib.—Intl.
Limited Liability Company

**SUMTOTAL SYSTEMS, LLC**
Div. of SumTotal Systems, Inc.
600 Parsippany Rd. (07054)
**Phone—(973) 364-0480**
National—(877) 274-4381
www.sumtotalsystems.com
Email—info@sumtotalsystems.com
CFO—Jeff Laborde
COO—Hardeep Gulati
V-P., Sales—Bill Shaheen
V-P., Mktg.—Hollo Rollo
V-P., Hum. Res.—Richard Oyen
V-P., Prod. Mgmt.—Morne Swart
IT Mgr.—Kurt Ferguson
SIC—7372; Workforce
management software
development, including time &
attendance, scheduling,
absence management, travel &
expenses & self-service
functions
Employs—200; Estab.—1996
Sales—over $1Bil
Distrib.—Intl.
Privately owned corporation
Parent co.—SumTotal Systems,
Inc., Gainesville, FL
Phone—(352) 264-2800
See Parent Co. Section for full profile.

**SUN CHEMICAL CORP.**
35 Waterview Blvd., Ste. 100
(07054)
**Phone—(973) 404-6000**
Fax—(973) 404-6001
www.sunchemical.com
Email—sunchemical@
sunchemical.com
Pres., CEO—Rudi Lenz
Pres., N. American Inks—Charles
Murray
Sr. V-P., Chief Administrative
Officer—John McKeown
Chief Proc. Officer—Edward Pruitt
CFO—Gerry Brady
Gen. Counsel & Secy.—James R.
Van Horn
V-P., Prod. Mgmt. & Publication
Ink—Dennis Sweet
SIC—2893; 2816; 2865; NAICS—
325910; Corporate headquarters
& printing inks & pigments for the
packaging, publication,
coatings, plastics, cosmetics &
industrial industries
Employs—125
Company-wide: 8,000
Sales—$25Mil-$50Mil
Distrib.—National
Publicly owned corporation

**SUN PLASTECH INC.**
1055 Parsippany Blvd., Ste. 405
(07054-1272)
**Phone—(973) 257-1999**
National—(800) 787-4348
Fax—(973) 257-1011
www.asaclean.com
Email—sales@asaclean.com
Pres.—Glenn Kornfeld
V-P.—Joseph Serell
Mktg. Mgr.—Miyuki Matsumine

SIC—2821; NAICS—325211;
Purging compound for
thermoplastic resins; Brand
name—ASACLEAN
Employs—20; Estab.—1996
Distrib.—Intl.
Privately owned corporation

**UB COMMUNICATIONS**
10 Lodge Ln. (07054)
**Phone—(973) 331-9391**
Fax—(973) 331-9393
www.ub-communications.com
Email—dursone710@aol.com
Ptnr.—David Ursone
Ptnr.—Frances Bergesen
SIC—2791; NAICS—323122;
Electronic prepress
Employs—2; Estab.—1986
Sales—under $500,000
Distrib.—National
Privately owned partnership

**UKRAINIAN NATIONAL
AFFILIATION, INC.**
2200 State Route 10, P.O. Box 280
(07054)
**Phone—(973) 292-9800**
National—(800) 253-9862
Fax—(973) 644-9510
www.svoboda-news.com
Email—svoboda@svoboda-
news.com
Editor-in-Chief—Roma Hadzewycz
IT Mgr.—Igor Piliphchuk
Administrator—Walter Honcharyk
SIC—2711; Ukrainian-language
weekly newspaper publishing
Employs—25; Estab.—1893
Sales—under $500,000
Distrib.—Intl.
Privately owned corporation
AKA: Ukrainian Weekly

**†UNIMET METAL SUPPLY CO., INC.**
150 Lackawanna Ave. (07054)
**Phone—(973) 673-5700**
National—(800) 526-4004
Fax—(973) 334-0399
www.unimetmetalsupply.com
Email—sales@
unimetmetalsupply.com
Pres.—Robert Flynn
CFO—Dennis Flynn
V-P.—Louis Nordt
SIC—5051; 3312; Corporate
headquarters & steel service
center, including steel slitting,
coil stock & sheet metal leveling
Employs—70; Estab.—1989
Company-wide: 150
95,000 sq ft site, Distrib.—Intl.
Privately owned corporation
ISO rating—9001:2008

**VALIDUS PHARMACEUTICALS, LLC**
119 Cherry Hill Rd., Ste. 310
(07054)
**Phone—(973) 265-2777**
National—(866) 982-5438
Fax—(973) 265-2770
www.validuspharma.com
Email—jhunter@
validuspharma.com
CEO—James Hunter
Pres.—Lee Rios
V-P., Sales & Mktg.—Richard Post
Opers. Mgr.—Diane Hofman
SIC—2834; NAICS—325412;
Pharmaceutical products
Employs—10; Estab.—2007
8,000 sq ft site, Distrib.—National
Limited Liability Company

**VAN DAM MACHINE CORP.**
81-B Walsh Dr. (07054)
**Phone—(973) 257-7050**
Fax—(973) 257-7398
www.vandammachine.com
Email—info@vandamusa.com
Cont., Fin. & MIS Mgr.—Kim
Filippone

## Parsippany—(cont.)

SIC—3555; NAICS—333293;
*Plastic printing machinery*
Employs—20; Estab.—1972
Sales—$500,000-$1Mil
21,000 sq ft site, Distrib.—Intl.
Privately owned corporation

**VANDERBILT INDUSTRIES**
2 Cranberry Rd. (07054)
**Phone—(973) 316-3900**
National—(800) 654-1981
Fax—(973) 334-4850
www.vanderbiltindustries.com
Pres.—Mitchell Kane
SIC—3679; 3651; 7373; 7372;
NAICS—334310; *Computer
controlled building security
systems & software*
Employs—75; Estab.—1982
Distrib.—Intl.

**WIRELESS TELECOM GROUP, INC.**
25 Eastmans Rd. *(07054)*
**Phone—(973) 386-9696**
Fax—(973) 386-9191
www.wtcom.com
Email—info@wtcom.com
Pres., CEO—Paul Genova
V.-P., Engrg.—Ron Swanson
Dir., Hum. Res.—Joanne Motta
Pur. Mgr.—Sue King
IT Mgr.—Santos Colon
Qual. Assur. Mgr.—Jack Rogalski
Maint. Mgr.—John Strauss
Cust. Serv. Rep.—Rose Nystrand
SIC—3825; NAICS—334500;
*Wireless communication test &
measurement equipment*
Employs—95; Estab.—1985
45,000 sq ft site, Distrib.—Intl.
Also see: Microlab/FXR, same loc.
DBA: Noisecom Boonton Microlab

**WOCKHARDT USA, LLC (H Q)**
20 Waterview Blvd., Ste. 3 (07054-
1271)
**Phone—(973) 257-4960**
National—(800) 346-6854
Fax—(973) 257-4961
www.wockhardtusa.com
Email—contactusa@wockhardt.com
Pres., N. Amer.—Sunil Khera
Sr. V.-P., Sales & Mktg.—Michael
Craney
Gen. Counsel—Antonia F. Giuliana
SIC—2834; NAICS—325412;
*Company headquarters; generic
pharmaceuticals*
Employs—32; Estab.—2004
Sales—$10Mil-$25Mil (est)
Distrib.—Intl.
Limited Liability Company

**YUKON GRAPHICS, INC.**
239 New Rd., Ste. B-110 (07054)
**Phone—(973) 575-5700**
Fax—(973) 357-5795
www.yukongraphics.com
Pres.—Alan Verbeke
Prod. Mgr.—Lisa Bednars
SIC—2759; NAICS—323100;
*Commercial, color & digital
printing & graphic design*
Employs—7; Estab.—1998
Sales—$1Mil-$2.5Mil
Distrib.—Local
Privately owned corporation

**ZIMMER TRABECULAR METAL
TECHNOLOGY**
Div. of Zimmer Holdings, Inc.
10 Pomeroy Rd. (07054)
**Phone—(973) 576-0032**
National—(800) 613-6131
www.zimmer.com
Email—sales@zimmer.com
Dir., Prod. Dev.—Scott Cron
GM—Ajey Atre
IT Mgr.—Scott Dekrammer
Hum. Res. Generalist—Chris
Lowman

SIC—3842; *Surgical joint
replacement implants &
products for knee, hip & acute &
chronic back pain*
Employs—50; Estab.—2005
Distrib.—National
Publicly owned corporation
Parent co.—Zimmer Holdings,
Inc., Warsaw, IN
Phone—(574) 267-6131
See Parent Co. Section for full profile.

## Passaic

(Passaic—N.E.)

**ACME ENGRAVING CO., INC.**
19-37 Delaware Ave., P.O. Box
1657 (07055)
**Phone—(973) 778-0885**
Fax—(973) 778-1790
www.acmeengraving.com
Email—customer.service@
acmeengraving.com
Pres., CEO—Roy Murat
Bus. Mgr.—Andrea Tissot-Rebner
SIC—3479; *Gravure & rotary
engraving*
Employs—5; Estab.—1962
Sales—$1Mil-$2.5Mil
35,000 sq ft site, Distrib.—National
Privately owned corporation

**ALLIANCE SIGN CO., INC.**
37 Grove St. (07055)
**Phone—(973) 458-0900**
Fax—(201) 325-8713
www.alliancesignnj.com
Email—dennis@alliancesignnj.com
Owner—Daniel Casabona
Sales Mgr.—Nigel James
SIC—3993; *Custom signs*
Employs—30; Estab.—2002
Sales—$2.5Mil-$5Mil (est)
Distrib.—Regional
Privately owned corporation

**AMERICAN POWER CORD CORP.**
217 Brook Ave., 3rd Fl. (07055)
**Phone—(973) 574-8301**
Fax—(973) 574-8302
www.americanpowercord.com
Email—shockcord@
americanpowercord.com
Pres., Fin. & MIS Mgr.—Makil
Simon
Off. & Plt. Mgr.—Levon Beharry
SIC—2298; 2241; NAICS—
313221; *Braided & knitted elastic
cordage*
Employs—5; Estab.—1994
Sales—$1Mil-$2.5Mil
5,000 sq ft site, Distrib.—Intl.
Privately owned corporation

**ARTISTIC FENCE**
757 River Dr. (07055)
**Phone—(973) 779-4540**
Fax—(973) 894-3520
www.artisticfencenj.com
Pres.—Steven Boggio
SIC—3496; 2499; *Chain link &
wooden fencing*
Employs—20; Estab.—1983
Sales—$1Mil-$5Mil
Distrib.—Local

**†ATLANTIC COAST FIBERS, LLC**
101 7th St. (07055)
**Phone—(973) 614-9600**
Fax—(973) 614-1663
www.atlanticcoastfibers.com
Email—info@
atlanticcoastfibers.com
Owner—Chris Riviello
Member, LLC—Vince Riviello
V.-P., Pur. & Sales—Fred Petrone
SIC—5093; *Wholesaler of
recycled paper & commercial,
industrial & municipal recycling*
Employs—100
Sales—$10Mil-$25Mil
100,000 sq ft site, Distrib.—Intl.
Limited Liability Company

**BARTLO PACKAGING, INC.**
61 Willet St., Bldg. Z (07055-1971)
**Phone—(973) 778-6900**
Fax—(973) 778-9375
www.bartlo.com
Email—wfurtak@bartlo.com
Pres.—Allen Bartlo
V.-P.—Walter Furtak
GM—Gale Furtak
Traf. Mgr.—Petey Soriano
SIC—2899; 3081; *Contract
chemical packaging in water-
soluble film of solids & liquids,
including tableting & blending*
Employs—40; Estab.—1971
Sales—$1Mil-$5Mil
45,000 sq ft site, Distrib.—National
Privately owned sub-S corp.
ISO rating—9001:2000

**†BENDHEIM**
61 Willett St., Bldg. PP (07055)
**Phone—(973) 471-1733**
National—(800) 221-7379
Fax—(973) 471-1640
www.bendheim.com
Email—info@bendheim.com
Pres.—Robert Jason
Dir., Mktg.—Jen Miret
SIC—5039; *Distributor of specialty
& decorative glass for architects,
contractors, designers &
homeowners, including
architectural, tempered,
laminated, etched, colored,
back-painted, patterned, art &
restoration glass; Brand name—
Restoration Glass; Lamberts
Mouth-Blown Glass; Lamberts
Channel Glass; Color Coated
Glass; EcoGlass; VintageWire
Laminated Glass; Jelly Bean
Glass; Chic Glass; Houdini
Glass; eh Oui for Bendheim
Laminated Glass Collection*
Employs—50; Estab.—1927
Distrib.—Intl.
Privately owned corporation

**BENDIX ARCHITECTURAL
PRODUCTS, INC.**
90 Dayton Ave., Ste. 34 (07055)
**Phone—(973) 473-4780**
National—(800) 526-0240
Fax—(973) 473-4785
www.bendixarchitectural.com
Email—exec@
bendixarchitectural.com
Chrm., Pres.—David Garrett
V.-P.—Jay Garrett
Cust. Serv. Rep.—Barbara Stiehl
SIC—2431; 2499; NAICS—
321900; *Decorative mouldings &
hand-carved wood products*
Employs—6; Estab.—1924
11,000 sq ft site, Distrib.—Regional
Privately owned corporation

**CASABONA SIGNS, LLC**
37 Grove St. (07055)
**Phone—(201) 325-8711**
National—(800) 297-2021
Fax—(201) 325-8713
Email—casabonasigns@aol.com
Owner—Daniel Casabona
SIC—3993; *Custom signs*
Employs—2
Sales—$1Mil-$2.5Mil
Distrib.—Regional
Limited Liability Company

**CITKOWSKI CO.**
90 Dayton Ave. (07055)
**Phone—(973) 390-5477**
Email—citkowskico@gmail.com
Pres., CEO—Mario Citkowski
SIC—2434; NAICS—337110;
*Architectural woodworking*
Employs—4; Estab.—2003
Sales—under $500,000
Distrib.—Local
Privately owned corporation

**COLOMBINO HEADWEAR, INC.**
61 Willet St. (07055)
**Phone—(973) 473-4733**
Pres.—Jerry Colombino
SIC—2353; *Straw hats*
Employs—15; Estab.—1967
Distrib.—National
Privately owned corporation

**COUNTERTOPS PLUS, INC.**
61 Willet St., Bldg. T (07055)
**Phone—(973) 365-2232**
Fax—(973) 365-0960
Pres.—Leo Sullivan
Off. Mgr.—Theresa Sullivan
Foreman—Scott Sullivan
Installer—Anthony Sullivan
SIC—2542; *Plastic laminated
countertops*
Employs—8; Estab.—1993
8,500 sq ft site, Distrib.—Local
Privately owned corporation

**CROWN PRECISION CORP.**
61 Willet St., Ste. 13 (07055-1971)
**Phone—(973) 470-0097**
Fax—(973) 470-9763
Email—crownprec@live.com
Owner & Pres.—Todd W. Evans
V.-P.—Patricia R. Evans
SIC—3599; *Precision machined
components for the electro-
optical industry*
Employs—4; Estab.—1997
Sales—over $500,000
Distrib.—Regional
Privately owned sub-S corp.

**CUSTOM COUNTERS BY PRECISION**
11-17 Linden St. (07055)
**Phone—(973) 773-0111**
Fax—(973) 773-8203
www.ccbp.net
Email—info@ccbp.net
Pres.—William Prusiensky
GM—Gary Juganuv
Bookkeeper—Diana Lipthay
SIC—2542; *Laminate, solid-
surface, engineered stone
countertops fabrication; Brand
name—DuPont; Zodiaq;
Cambria; Silestone;
Caesarstone*
Employs—30; Estab.—1988
Sales—under $5Mil
Distrib.—Local
Privately owned sub-S corp.

**CUSTOM LABELS, INC.**
61 Willet St., Bldg. J (07055)
**Phone—(973) 473-1934**
Fax—(973) 473-1509
www.customlabelsinc.com
Email—sales@customlabelsinc.com
Pres., Off. Mgr.—Abraham Rubin
SIC—2759; NAICS—323100;
*Custom label printing*
Employs—4; Estab.—1999
Sales—$500,000-$1Mil
Distrib.—Regional
Privately owned corporation

**CUSTOM WOODCRAFT CO.**
81 Park Pl. (07055)
**Phone—(973) 472-0824**
Fax—(973) 472-0824
Pres.—Israel Obando
SIC—2434; NAICS—337110;
*Custom wooden cabinets*
Employs—1; Estab.—1988
Sales—under $500,000
Distrib.—Local
Sole ownership

**DANOR SIGNS, LLC**
47 Central Ave. (07055)
**Phone—(973) 471-2897**
Fax—(973) 472-1626
Email—danorsigns@optonline.net
Pres.—Daniel Ovido

GEOGRAPHICAL

## Passaic—(cont.)

SIC—3993; Neon, interior &
exterior signs
Employs—1; Estab.—1995
Sales—under $500,000 (est)
Distrib.—Local
Limited Liability Company

### DE MEO BROTHERS., INC.

2 Brigton Ave. (07055)
**Phone—(973) 778-8100**
Fax—(973) 778-8126
Sales Mgr.—Shayna Dowek
SIC—3999; Human hair goods,
wigs, weaves & related items
Employs—9; Estab.—1908
Distrib.—Intl.
Privately owned corporation

### DIMILO INDUSTRIES

90 Dayton Ave., Ste. 38 (07055)
**Phone—(973) 955-0460**
www.dimiloindustries.net
Email—rkrauser1@gmail.com
Pres.—Richard Krauser
SIC—2393; Custom canvas bags,
including tote, garment, laundry,
duffel, golf & toiletry bags &
backpacks
Employs—12; Estab.—2007
13,000 sq ft site, Distrib.—Intl.
Limited Liability Company

### E T MFG., INC.

90 Dayton Ave., Bldg. 10-C, Ste.
89 (07055)
**Phone—(973) 777-6662**
Fax—(973) 777-8002
www.co-opline.com
Email—etmfg1@aol.com
Pres.—Michele Albo
Dir., Opers.—John Vuolo
SIC—3089; Vinyl heat sealing &
products, including contract
heat sealing & hot stamping
Employs—37; Estab.—1947
26,000 sq ft site, Distrib.—
Regional
Privately owned sub-S corp.
AKA: Ferber Plastics

### EAST COAST EMBOSSING

35 8th St., P.O. Box 1076 (07055)
**Phone—(973) 777-9830**
Fax—(973) 777-0678
Pres.—Anthony Maltese, Jr.
SIC—2261; NAICS—313311;
Textile embossing
Employs—15; Estab.—1982
20,000 sq ft site, Distrib.—National
Privately owned corporation
Also see: Sunbrite Dye Co., same
loc.

NEW ENTRY
### FAIRY TALES HAIR CARE CORP.

90-B Dayton Ave. (07055)
**Phone—(973) 473-8182**
National—(888) 244-1990
Fax—(973) 473-8185
www.fairytaleshaircare.com
Email—contact@
fairytaleshaircare.com
Owner—Risa Barash
Mktg. Mgr.—Melissa Banzaca
SIC—2844; Hair care products,
including shampoos &
conditioners
Employs—12; Estab.—1999
Sales—$1Mil-$2.5Mil
2,000 sq ft site, Distrib.—National
Privately owned corporation

### FALSTROM CO.

1 Falstrom Ct., P.O. Box 118
(07055)
**Phone—(973) 777-0013**
Fax—(973) 777-6396
www.falstromcompany.com
Chrm., Pres. & CEO—Clifford
Lindholm III
Sales Mgr.—William Caudle

IT Mgr.—Richard Siaonzecki
SIC—2542; Industrial metal
cabinets
Employs—70; Estab.—1870
Distrib.—National
Privately owned corporation

### FERGUSON FIRE & FABRICATION, INC.

Div. of Ferguson Enterprises
151 Randolph St. (07055)
**Phone—(973) 614-9292**
Fax—(973) 614-0518
www.fergusonfire.com
Email—pat.conklin@ferguson.com
Manager—Peter Braid
SIC—3498; NAICS—332996;
Metal pipe & fittings fabrication
Employs—40; Estab.—1977
70,000 sq ft site, Distrib.—
Regional
Publicly owned corporation
Parent co.—Ferguson Enterprises,
Pomona, CA
Phone—(909) 517-3085
See Parent Co. Section for full profile.

### GEIGER TOOL & MFG. CO., INC.

50 Liberty St. (07055)
**Phone—(973) 777-2136**
Fax—(973) 777-1514
www.geigertool.com
Email—info@geigertool.com
Pres., CEO—Joseph Szczesny
V-P.—James Schormann
Cont.—Debrah Heller
Bookkeeper—Elba Vasquez
SIC—3599; 3544; NAICS—
333500; Precision machining &
tool & die job shop
Employs—21; Estab.—1947
Sales—$1Mil-$2Mil
20,000 sq ft site, Distrib.—Intl.
Privately owned corporation
ISO rating—AS9100C, 9001
AKA: Liberty Precision Industries

### GLOBAL PARTNERS IN SHIELDING, INC.

90 Dayton Ave., Ste. 13 (07055)
**Phone—(973) 574-9077**
National—(877) 505-0258
Fax—(973) 574-9078
www.shieldingsystems.com
Email—sales@
shieldingsystems.com
Pres.—Donald Hener
GM & Opers. Mgr.—Mark Holder
Proj. Mgr.—Taylor Brady
SIC—3448; 3442; 3842; 3499;
NAICS—332311; Industrial EMI,
RFI & X-ray shielding doors &
enclosures
Employs—35; Estab.—1998
Sales—$4.5Mil-$8Mil
22,000 sq ft site, Distrib.—Intl.
Privately owned corporation
ISO rating—9001:2008
AKA: GPS Specialty Doors

### GLOBAL WIRE & CABLE, INC.

61 Willet St., Bldg. S (07055)
**Phone—(973) 471-1000**
Fax—(973) 471-6033
Pres.—George Szakacs
SIC—3315; Wire & cable
Employs—3; Estab.—1973
Sales—$500,000-$1Mil (est)
Distrib.—National

### GPS SPECIALTY DOORS, INC.

90 Dayton Ave., Unit 4-B (07055)
**Phone—(973) 778-6200**
Fax—(973) 778-2177
www.gps-door.com
Email—info@gps-door.com
Pres.—Fred Bolio
Engrg. Mgr.—Matt Erszkowicz
Proj. Engr.—Pete Jorgensen

SIC—2431; 3089; NAICS—
332321; Hangar, acoustic, air
plenum, reverberation chamber
& blast, anechoic & RF/EMI
shielded doors
Employs—50; Estab.—1998
Sales—$11Mil-$25Mil
Distrib.—Intl.
Privately owned corporation
AKA: Global Partners In Shielding

### GREEN TREE PACKING, INC.

65 Central Ave., P.O. Box 386
(07055)
**Phone—(973) 473-1305**
National—(800) 562-6934
Fax—(973) 473-7975
www.greentreepacking.com
Pres.—Michael Waters
Cust. Serv. Mgr.—Jim J. O'Hara
SIC—2011; 2091; NAICS—
311611; Meat processing &
packing of seafood
Employs—100; Estab.—1969
Sales—$25Mil-$50Mil (est)
Distrib.—Local
Privately owned corporation

### HESSBURG, INC., MICHALE A.

180 Autumn St. (07055)
**Phone—(973) 777-8700**
Fax—(973) 777-7715
www.hessburgusa.com
Email—rrioux@hessbergusa.com
Dir., Opers.—Rene Rioux
SIC—2241; NAICS—313221;
Textile trimmings
Employs—9; Estab.—1962
30,000 sq ft site, Distrib.—Intl.
Privately owned corporation

### INTERCHANGE EQUIPMENT, INC.

90 Dayton Ave., Ste. 200 (07055)
**Phone—(973) 473-5005**
National—(800) 822-5457
Fax—(973) 473-4485
www.interchangecorp.com
Email—sales@
interchangecorp.com
Pres.—Marc Herrmann
V-P.—Sylve Ericsson
SIC—3555; 5084; Manufacturer &
distributor of printing & drying
equipment for the textile,
graphics, industrial screen
printing & digital printing
industries
Employs—15; Estab.—1994
Sales—$5Mil
25,000 sq ft site, Distrib.—Intl.
Privately owned corporation

NEW ENTRY
### IVO DELICIOUS MEAT PRODUCTS, INC.

206 Dayton Ave. (07055)
**Phone—(973) 223-4044**
Pres.—Ivelin Naydenov
SIC—2011; 3089; Beef & pork
processing & packaging
Employs—4
Sales—$1Mil-$2.5Mil (est)

### J M J WOODWORKING, INC.

100 8th St., Bldg. 300 (07055)
**Phone—(973) 471-6449**
Fax—(973) 470-0650
www.jmjww.com
Email—info@jmjww.com
Pres.—Jack Mroz
SIC—2541; 2431; NAICS—
321900; Commercial wooden
cabinets, paneling & fixtures
Employs—6; Estab.—1996
Distrib.—Regional

### JACK GEORGES, INC.

823 Main Ave. (07055)
**Phone—(973) 777-6999**
Fax—(973) 777-6028
www.jackgeorges.com
Email—jgi@jackgeorges.com
Pres.—Jack Georges

V-P.—Frank Georges
GM—Dany Chalhoub
SIC—3171; 3161; 3172; 3199;
NAICS—316992; Leather
briefcases, totes, handbags,
planners, wallets & accessories
Employs—15; Estab.—1987
Sales—$5Mil-$10Mil
16,000 sq ft site, Distrib.—Intl.
Privately owned corporation

### JACKIE EVANS, INC.

1823 3rd St. (07055)
**Phone—(973) 471-6991**
Fax—(973) 471-1843
www.jackieevans.com
Pres. & V-P.—Mario Monaco
GM—Dora Amorim
Asst. Shpg. Mgr.—Amit Gajjar
SIC—2339; Women's clothing
Employs—50; Estab.—1973
Distrib.—National
Privately owned corporation

### JAY-BEE LAMP & SHADE CO., INC.

33 Hoover Ave. (07055)
**Phone—(973) 473-1569**
www.libertylampandshade.com
Pres., Pers. Mgr.—Robert
Schurman
SIC—3645; NAICS—335121;
Lampshades & lamps
Employs—4; Estab.—1962
Sales—$500,000-$1Mil
7,500 sq ft site, Distrib.—National
Privately owned corporation
AKA: Liberty Lamp & Shade

### JRM INDUSTRIES, INC.

1 Mattimore St. (07055)
**Phone—(973) 779-9340**
National—(800) 533-2697
Fax—(973) 779-8017
www.jrm.com
Email—info@jrm.com
Pres.—Louis S. Simon
Off. Mgr.—Myriam Oliver
Fin. Mgr.—Joann Makowka
SIC—2297; 2241; NAICS—
313230; Corporate headquarters
& ribbons, bows, garment labels,
hang tags, tapes & pressure-
sensitive labels
Employs—20; Estab.—1920
Sales—$6Mil-$10Mil
36,000 sq ft site, Distrib.—Intl.
Privately owned sub-S corp.

### K & K AUTOMOTIVE, INC.

979 Main Ave. (07055)
**Phone—(973) 777-2235**
Fax—(973) 777-4777
Email—kkautomotivenj@gmail.com
Pres., GM—Abraham Hazin
SIC—3519; Rebuilt automotive &
marine engines
Employs—6; Estab.—1969
Sales—$1Mil-$2.5Mil
Distrib.—Local
Privately owned corporation

### K D INDUSTRIES, INC.

18 Falstrom Ct. (07055)
**Phone—(973) 594-4800**
Fax—(973) 594-4700
Email—chrisd@kdindinc.com
Pres.—Chris D'Alessandro
V-P.—Glenn D'Alessandro
Pur. Agt.—Diane Cario
Bookkeeper—Carolyn Barhorst
SIC—3599; General machining
job shop
Employs—34; Estab.—1987
Sales—$1Mil-$5Mil
25,000 sq ft site, Distrib.—National
Privately owned sub-S corp.
ISO rating—9001:2008

### KINNERY METAL

11 Exchange Pl. (07055)
**Phone—(973) 473-4664**
Fax—(973) 473-4994
Email—kinerymetal@aol.com
Owner—Naresh Chaudhari

## Passaic—(cont.)

SIC—3599; *CNC machining job shop*
Employs—3; Estab.—2001
Sales—under $500,000
Distrib.—Local
Limited Liability Company

### LBU, INC.
217 Brook Ave., Ste. 6 (07055)
**Phone—(973) 773-4800**
National—(800) 678-4528
Fax—(973) 773-6005
www.lbuinc.com
Email—info@lbuinc.com
Founder & Pres.—Jeff Mayer
CFO—Jerry Cong
V-P.—Brian Seltzer
Sales Mgr.—Fred King
Opers. Mgr.—Bruce Glasser
Sales Rep.—Walter Lewis
SIC—2393; 3171; 2392; NAICS—314911; *Custom hand, cosmetic, laundry, travel, beach, canvas & holiday messenger bags & totes, backpacks, aprons, tablet & carrying cases, pillows & sleeves*
Employs—50; Estab.—1985
Distrib.—National
Privately owned corporation

### LOVELINE INDUSTRIES, INC.
90 Dayton Ave., Ste. 33 (07055-7014)
**Phone—(973) 928-3427**
Fax—(973) 928-3428
www.lovelineindustries.com
Email—lovelineind@optonline.net
Pres.—Morton Goldstein
V-P.—Daniel Goldstein
Fin. Mgr.—Adam Goldstein
SIC—2253; 2389; 2385; 3993; NAICS—315200; *Hi-visibility safety clothing, including rainwear, safety vests, flags, sweatbands, winterliners & prison clothing; Brand name—Samson Brand*
Employs—15; Estab.—1933
Sales—$500,000-$1Mil
10,000 sq ft site, Distrib.—Intl.
Privately owned corporation

### MAJESTIC INDUSTRIES, INC.
225 Passaic St. (07055)
**Phone—(973) 473-3434**
Fax—(973) 473-3825
www.majesticindustries.com
Email—joa@majesticindustries.com
Pres.—Peter Ferentinos
Administrator—Debby Schab
SIC—2599; *Hospitality seating for hospitals, casinos, restaurants & bars, including chairs & stools*
Employs—20; Estab.—1998
Sales—$2.5Mil-$5Mil (est)
Distrib.—National
Privately owned corporation

### MERCURY ADHESIVES, INC.
140 Dayton Ave. (07055)
**Phone—(973) 472-3307**
Fax—(973) 472-3309
Owner & Pres.—Joel Zeichner
Off. Mgr.—Maria Auiglar
SIC—2891; NAICS—325520; *Hot-melt adhesives*
Employs—8; Estab.—1981
Distrib.—National
Privately owned corporation

### MERCURY PLASTIC BAG CO., INC.
168 7th St. (07055)
**Phone—(973) 778-7200**
Fax—(973) 778-0549
www.mercuryplasticbag.com
Email—mercury@conversent.net
Pres.—Marvin Rosen
V-P.—Stuart Rosen
SIC—2673; *Plastic bags*
Employs—25; Estab.—1961
14,000 sq ft site, Distrib.—National
Sole ownership

### MERRY MODES 2000
61 Willet St., Ste. 2 (07055-1971)
**Phone—(973) 773-2501**
National—(800) 631-0036
Fax—(973) 773-2502
www.merrymodes2000.com
Email—sales@merrymodes2000.com
Owner—Anthony Dell'Aquila
V-P.—Mary Grace Dell'Aquila
SIC—2341; 2342; 2399; NAICS—315200; *Custom handmade bridal petticoats, bras & control slips, mattress protectors, doggie coats & dog leashes & collars; Brand name—Merry Modes*
Employs—8; Estab.—1947
Sales—$1Mil-$2.5Mil
15,000 sq ft site, Distrib.—Intl.
Privately owned corporation
Also see: Textiles By Anthony, Inc., same loc.

### MILLIMETER WAVE TECHNOLOGY
90 Dayton Ave., Ste. 6-E (07055)
**Phone—(845) 369-7808**
Fax—(978) 336-0575
www.mwt-materials.com
Email—info@mwt-materials.com
Pres.—Michael Katz
SIC—3663; NAICS—334220; *Waterproof composite microwave & millimeter wave absorber materials for wireless communication equipment, including RF consulting & engineering for EMI control*
Employs—10; Estab.—1998
Sales—under $500,000
Distrib.—Intl.
Privately owned corporation
AKA: MWT Materials

### MIRROTEK INTERNATIONAL, LLC
90 Dayton Ave., Bldg. 1-F (07055)
**Phone—(973) 472-1400**
Fax—(973) 472-5170
www.mirrotek.com
Email—info@mirrotek.com
Pres.—Joe Bezzy
MIS Mgr.—Boaz Bezzy
Off. Mgr.—Becky Bezzy
Fin. Mgr.—Avner Bezzy
SIC—3231; 2099; 3999; *Decorative & dressing mirrors, home decor, bulk food products & beverages for supermarkets, TV shopping networks, warehouse clubs & department stores; Brand name—Iron Chef Foods*
Employs—45; Estab.—1995
50,000 sq ft site, Distrib.—National
Privately owned corporation

### N.Y. TEXTILE MILLS, INC.
90 Dayton Ave., Bldg. 5-A (07055)
**Phone—(973) 777-9871**
Fax—(973) 777-9803
www.nywebbing.com
Email—john@nywebbing.com
Pres.—John Park
SIC—2241; NAICS—313221; *Narrow-woven polypropylene webbing*
Employs—7
Sales—$1Mil-$2.5Mil (est)

### NETWORK, THE
105-B Van Houten Ave., P.O. Box 5338 (07055)
**Phone—(973) 778-7222**
Fax—(973) 778-0770
www.networkpublication.com
Email—info@networkpublication.com
Publisher—Norman Shapiro
Editor—Risa Shapiro
Off. Mgr.—Helen Feinberg

SIC—2741; *Jewish community directory publishing*
Employs—5; Estab.—1990
Sales—under $500,000
Distrib.—Local
Privately owned corporation

NEW ENTRY
### NEW GRANITE & MARBLE, LLC
35 8th St., Ste. 6 (07055)
**Phone—(973) 767-6216**
Fax—(973) 778-4781
www.newgranitemarble.com
Email—info@newgranitemarble.com
Owner—Maclej Tuniewicz
SIC—3281; *Granite & marble fabrication*
Employs—2
Sales—under $500,000 (est)
Limited Liability Company

### NORTHEAST PRO-TECH, INC.
61 Willet St., Bldg. L (07055)
**Phone—(973) 777-5654**
Fax—(973) 472-5437
Pres., Hum. Res. Mgr.—Frank Dework
Prodn. Mgr.—Dennis Dework
Prodn. Mgr.—Simon Arteagh
SIC—2834; NAICS—325412; *Food additive blending*
Employs—5; Estab.—1980
Sales—$1Mil-$2.5Mil
Distrib.—Intl.
Privately owned corporation

### OLDE GRANDDAD INDUSTRIES
1 Market St. (07055)
**Phone—(201) 997-1899**
Fax—(201) 997-3800
www.classicmats.com
Email—mkostak@classicmats.com
Owner—Mike Kostak
SIC—3714; 2396; *Automotive mats, air fresheners & accessories; Brand name—Classic Car Accessories*
Employs—10; Estab.—1989
Sales—$1Mil-$2.5Mil
Distrib.—Intl.
Privately owned corporation

### PARSELLS PRINTING, INC.
280 Main Ave. (07055)
**Phone—(973) 473-2700**
Fax—(973) 473-6383
Email—mail@parsellsprinting.com
Pres.—James Parsells
V-P.—Ronald Parsells
SIC—2752; NAICS—323100; *Offset printing & binding*
Employs—5; Estab.—1976
9,000 sq ft site, Distrib.—Regional
Privately owned corporation

### PASSAIC LEATHER COAT, INC.
51 Market St. (07055)
**Phone—(973) 777-4026**
www.passaicleather.com
Email—info@passaicleather.com
Pres.—B. A. Focarino
V-P., Pers. & Sales—A. B. Focarino
SIC—2386; NAICS—315200; *Leather jackets & coats; Brand name—Passaic Leather*
Employs—5; Estab.—1936
Sales—under $500,000
4,000 sq ft site, Distrib.—Regional
Privately owned corporation

### PERILSTEIN GLASS
285 Howe Ave., P.O. Box 84 (07055)
**Phone—(973) 777-3610**
National—(800) 427-3610
Fax—(973) 777-9261
www.kossonglass.com
Pres.—David Perilstein
Sales Mgr.—Jesse Valle

SIC—3499; 3231; NAICS—327215; *Metal & glass fabrication*
Employs—30; Estab.—1971
Sales—$500,000-$1Mil
Distrib.—Regional
Privately owned corporation

### PLASTIC PLUS, INC. (H Q)
184 Willet St. (07055)
**Phone—(973) 614-0271**
Fax—(973) 767-2599
www.plasticplusinc.com
Email—sales@plasticplusinc.com
Pres.—Vijay Chokshi
V-P.—Mira V. Chokshi
Off. Mgr.—Viral V. Chokshi
SIC—3086; *Corporate headquarters; plastic plates for the foodservice & catering industries (mfg. done in India)*
Employs—3; Estab.—2005
Sales—$500,000-$1Mil (est)
Distrib.—National
Privately owned corporation

### PUEBLA FOODS, INC.
118 1st St. (07055)
**Phone—(973) 473-4494**
Fax—(973) 473-3854
Email—pueblasds@aol.com
Pres.—Felix Sanchez, Sr.
Off. Mgr.—Marta Acebedo
SIC—2099; *Tortillas*
Employs—25; Estab.—1975
Sales—$2.5Mil-$5Mil (est)
Distrib.—Regional
Privately owned corporation

### QUALCO, INC.
225 Passaic St. (07055)
**Phone—(973) 473-1222**
Fax—(973) 473-0535
Pres.—John Ferentinos
GM—Ed Solla
Qual. Control Mgr.—Paul Yager
Administrator—Debbie Schaub
SIC—2812; NAICS—325181; *Swimming pool chemicals*
Employs—30; Estab.—1986
Distrib.—Regional
Privately owned corporation

### R & R PLASTICS, INC.
62-70 Myrtle Ave. (07055)
**Phone—(973) 365-8083**
Fax—(973) 779-4353
www.rrplastics.com
Email—sergio@rrplastics.com
Pres., CFO—R. Russell Corona
Ex. V-P., Mfg.—Sergio Valente
SIC—3648; 3089; NAICS—335129; *Lighting diffusers & replacement plastics for lighting*
Employs—12; Estab.—1977
30,000 sq ft site, Distrib.—National
Privately owned sub-S corp.

### R L R FOIL STAMPING, LLC
245 4th St. (07055)
**Phone—(973) 778-9464**
Fax—(973) 778-9434
Pres.—Lawrence Vincent
V-P.—Richard Vincent
Pressman—Michael Vincent
SIC—3469; *Foil stampings*
Employs—10; Estab.—1990
Sales—$500,000-$1Mil
Distrib.—Local
Privately owned corporation

### REHTEK MACHINE CO.
135 Monroe St. (07055)
**Phone—(973) 365-2101**
Fax—(973) 365-2174
www.rehtek.com
Email—s.reh@rehtek.com
Pres., MIS Mgr.—Stephen K. Reh
V-P., Fin.—Paul Reh
Supervisor—Edwin Sanchez
Bookkeeper—Gail James

GEOGRAPHICAL

## Passaic—(cont.)

SIC—3599; *Precision machining of electronics & medical components*
Employs—10; Estab.—1990
11,000 sq ft site, Distrib.—National
Privately owned sub-S corp.
ISO rating—9001:2008

### RIVERS EDGE WOODWORKS & DESIGN

90 Dayton Ave. (07055)
**Phone—(973) 337-2288**
www.riversedgewoodworks.com
Email—info@riversedgewoodwork.com
Pres.—Gary Odendahl
SIC—2431; 2434; *Wooden cabinetry & interior millwork*
Employs—2; Estab.—2009
Sales—under $500,000
5,000 sq ft site, Distrib.—Local
Sole ownership

### ROSS, INC., A. W.

297 Monroe St. (07055)
**Phone—(973) 471-5900**
Fax—(973) 471-5926
Email—awrossinc@gmail.com
Co-Pres.—Vojtek Rys
Co-Pres.—Betty Rys
Accountant—Tatiana Glowacki
SIC—2434; 2541; NAICS—337110; *Wooden kitchen cabinets & countertops*
Employs—14; Estab.—1972
Distrib.—Local
Privately owned corporation

### SANDIK MFG., INC.

100 8th St., Bldg. 33-A (07055)
**Phone—(973) 779-0707**
Fax—(973) 779-2844
Pres.—Girish Shah
V-P., GM & MIS—Anup Shah
SIC—3599; *General machining job shop*
Employs—5; Estab.—1979
Sales—$500,000-$1Mil
4,000 sq ft site, Distrib.—Regional
Privately owned sub-S corp.

### SCHMIDT STEEL, J. G.

211 Central Ave. (07055)
**Phone—(973) 473-4822**
Fax—(973) 473-5031
Email—donna@jgschmidtsteel.com
Owner—Bob Schlaier
V-P.—Raymond Schlaier
SIC—3441; NAICS—332312; *Structural steel fabrication*
Employs—18; Estab.—1945
20,000 sq ft site, Distrib.—Regional
Privately owned corporation

### SIGNMASTERS, INC.

217 Brook Ave., 2nd Fl., Front (07055)
**Phone—(973) 614-8300**
Fax—(973) 614-1086
www.signmastersinc.com
Email—mail@signmastersinc.com
Pres.—Howard Muser
SIC—2752; 2759; NAICS—323100; *Offset printing & glass & plastic screen printing*
Employs—75; Estab.—1975
Sales—$6Mil-$10Mil
Distrib.—National
Privately owned corporation

### STERLING PRODUCTS

90 Dayton Ave., Bldg. 12-C, Ste. 77 (07055)
**Phone—(973) 471-2858**
Fax—(973) 471-2454
www.zipynet.com
Email—sterling@zipynet.com
Off. Mgr.—Judy Russell

SIC—3089; 3083; NAICS—326130; *Acrylic lampshades, acrylic sheets, marblized color acrylic sheets & acrylic diffusers*
Employs—30; Estab.—1987
Distrib.—Intl.
Privately owned corporation

### STONE SYSTEMS OF NJ

95 8th St., P.O. Box 4207 (07055)
**Phone—(973) 778-5525**
Fax—(973) 778-5515
GM—Thomas Landers
Proj. Mgr.—Lenny Ventimeglia
SIC—2541; *Countertops*
Employs—80; Estab.—1989
Distrib.—Regional
Privately owned corporation

### SUNBRITE DYE CO.

35 8th St., P.O. Box 1076 (07055)
**Phone—(973) 777-9830**
Fax—(973) 777-0678
Email—info@sunbritedyeco.com
Plt. Mgr.—Ralph Schiano
SIC—2262; 2261; NAICS—313311; *Textile finishing & dyeing*
Employs—90; Estab.—1958
Distrib.—National
Privately owned corporation
Also see: East Coast Embossing, same loc.

### TECHNICAL NAME PLATE CORP.

92 1st St. (07055)
**Phone—(973) 773-4256**
National—(800) 932-0777
Fax—(973) 773-1391
www.technicalnameplate.com
Email—dsalvatore@technical.com
Pres.—Perla Navarro
GM—Dom Salvatore
SIC—3499; 3089; NAICS—332812; *Metal, vinyl, polyester film, plastic & bar code nameplates, panels, decals, labels, identification & UID plates, scales, wiring diagrams, markers & related identification products; Brand name—LEXCALS*
Employs—20; Estab.—1966
10,000 sq ft site, Distrib.—National
Privately owned corporation
ISO rating—9001:2008, AS9100
AKA: ASAP Nameplate & Label Co.

### TEXTILES BY ANTHONY, INC.

61 Willett St., Bldg. 12, 2nd Fl. (07055)
**Phone—(973) 773-2501**
National—(800) 631-0036
Fax—(973) 773-2502
Owner & Pres.—Anthony Dell'aquila
Off. Mgr.—Mary Dell'aquila
SIC—2342; 2341; NAICS—315200; *Women's bridal petticoats, half-slips & bras*
Employs—20; Estab.—1982
14,000 sq ft site, Distrib.—Regional
Privately owned corporation
Also see: Merry Modes 2000, same loc.

### TRIPLE B FABRICATING, INC.

61 Willett St., Ste. 12 (07055)
**Phone—(973) 773-2266**
Fax—(973) 773-6607
Email—info@triplebfabricating.com
Pres.—Glenn Burriello
SIC—3441; NAICS—332312; *Structural steel fabrication*
Employs—13; Estab.—1980
6,000 sq ft site, Distrib.—Local
Privately owned corporation

### TRI-STATE BUILDING MATERIALS CO.

65 Lodi St. (07055)
**Phone—(973) 472-2377**
Fax—(973) 472-1149

www.tristatewindows.com
Email—office@tristatewindows.com
Pres.—Charles Cangialosi
Off. Mgr.—Cathleen Barbeira
SIC—3089; 3442; NAICS—332321; *Aluminum & vinyl windows & doors*
Employs—18; Estab.—1979
22,000 sq ft site, Distrib.—Regional
Privately owned corporation

### VALLE PRECISION MACHINE CO., INC.

58 Myrtle Ave. (07055)
**Phone—(973) 773-3037**
Fax—(973) 773-8120
Email—valleprecision@aol.com
Pres.—Louis Valle
Off. Mgr.—Carol Valle
SIC—3599; *Machine parts*
Employs—6; Estab.—1980
Sales—under $500,000
Distrib.—National
Privately owned corporation

### WICK IT, LLC

1 Gregory Ave. (07055)
Mail addr: P.O. Box 1, Wood Ridge (07075)
**Phone—(973) 249-2970**
National—(866) 394-2548
Fax—(866) 494-2548
www.wickit.net
Email—info@wickit.net
Owner—Joe Blythe
SIC—3999; *Candle wicks & wick clip assemblies*
Employs—7; Estab.—1998
Sales—under $500,000
Distrib.—National
Limited Liability Company

---

## Paterson

(Passaic—N.E.)

### A & F SIGN COMPANY LLC

28 E. Railway Ave. (07503)
**Phone—(973) 278-3707**
Fax—(973) 278-8337
www.afsigncompany.com
Email—afsignco@optonline.net
Sole Member—Frank Ferrucci
SIC—3993; 3089; 3499; 2499; *Architectural, illuminated, non-illuminated, aluminum, plastic, stainless steel, brass & bronze ADA signs, channel & dimensional lettering & plaques*
Employs—1; Estab.—1946
Sales—under $500,000
Distrib.—National
Limited Liability Company

### A B C CRATING & RIGGING CO.

1-21 Erie St. (07524)
Mail addr: P.O. Box 8287, Haledon (07538)
**Phone—(973) 684-0046**
Fax—(973) 684-3541
www.abccrating.com
Email—abccratingco@aol.com
Pres.—Andrew Tuohy
SIC—2449; NAICS—321920; *Wooden crates*
Employs—10; Estab.—1945
Sales—$500,000-$1Mil
Distrib.—Regional
Privately owned corporation

NEW ENTRY
### ABBA METAL WORKS, INC.

337 River St. (07524)
**Phone—(973) 684-0808**
Fax—(973) 684-0866
www.abbametalworksinc.com
Pres.—Corrado Abbattista
V-P.—Mark Abbattista

SIC—3441; 3446; 3599; *Structural steel fabrication & ornamental metalwork & welding job shop*
Employs—7; Estab.—1986
Sales—$20Mil
Distrib.—Local
Privately owned corporation

### ABBOTT INDUSTRIES

1-11 Morris St. (07501)
Mail addr: P.O. Box 5397, North Branch (08876)
**Phone—(973) 345-1116**
Fax—(973) 345-9154
www.aibottles.com
Email—abbott.industries@verizon.net
Pres.—Harold Sheck
V-P.—John Klandt
Cust. Serv. Rep.—Marie Sefchik
SIC—3085; NAICS—326160; *Plastic bottles*
Employs—3; Estab.—1972
Sales—under $500,000
19,500 sq ft site, Distrib.—Regional
Privately owned corporation

### ABCO METAL, LLC

138 3rd Ave. (07514)
**Phone—(973) 772-8160**
Fax—(973) 772-1455
www.abcocnc.com
Email—sales@abcocnc.com
Pres. & Sales Mgr.—Todd Abrams
SIC—3599; *Precision machining job shop*
Employs—25; Estab.—1940
2,000 sq ft site, Distrib.—Local
Limited Liability Company
Also see: Sonrise Metal, Inc., same loc.

### ABSOLUTE PACKAGING & SUPPLY, INC.

456 E. 22nd St. (07514)
**Phone—(973) 278-0202**
National—(800) 595-5789
Fax—(973) 278-0044
www.absolutepackaging.com
Email—anthony@absolutepackaging.com
Pres., GM—Anthony Stefanelli
SIC—2673; 3081; NAICS—326113; *Custom printed plastic & thermoformed trade show, retail shopping, drawstring, high-density t-shirt & grocery & low-density shopping bags, plastic sheeting & carton sealing tapes*
Employs—4; Estab.—1990
Sales—$2.6Mil-$5Mil
10,000 sq ft site, Distrib.—National
Privately owned corporation

### ACCURATE BOX CO., INC.

86 5th Ave. (07524)
**Phone—(973) 345-2000**
National—(800) 634-4725
Fax—(973) 345-8158
www.accuratebox.com
Email—sales@accuratebox.com
Pres., CEO—Lisa Hirsh
Cont. & Dir., Fin.—Jose Puignau
Sales & Mktg. Mgr.—Mark Schlossman
MIS Mgr.—John Dennehy
Hum. Res. Mgr.—Olga Izquierdo
SIC—2657; 2631; NAICS—322212; *Lithographic laminated folding cartons & boxes*
Employs—150; Estab.—1946
Sales—over $1Bil
325,000 sq ft site, Distrib.—National
Privately owned corporation

### ACCURATE BRONZE BEARING CO.

64 Illinois Ave. (07503)
**Phone—(973) 345-2304**
Fax—(973) 345-2305
Email—accuratebronze@msn.com
Pres., Secy.-Treas.—Roger R. Zito
MIS & Off. Mgr.—JoAnne Zito

## Paterson—(cont.)

SIC—3562; NAICS—332991; *Custom bronze bearings & machine parts*
Employs—5; Estab.—1952
Sales—$500,000-$1Mil
4,100 sq ft site, Distrib.—National
Privately owned corporation

**ACCURATE FLANNEL BAG CO., INC.**
468 Totowa Ave., Ste. 3 (07522)
**Phone—(973) 720-1800**
National—(800) 234-9200
Fax—(973) 689-6774
www.accuratebags.com
Email—service@accuratebags.com
Pres.—Fred Baron
V-P.—Elsie Lizasuain-King
SIC—2393; 2759; 2395; 2396;
  NAICS—326111; *Custom bags & pouches, including dustcovers, anti-tarnish flannels, jewelry pouches, shoe & bottle bags & printing & embroidery; Brand name—SILVERPAK® Anti-Tarnish Flannels*
Employs—125; Estab.—1915
Sales—$5Mil-$10Mil
15,000 sq ft site, Distrib.—Intl.
Privately owned sub-S corp.
AKA: Accurate Flannel Bag Co.

**ACE REPROGRAPHIC SERVICE, INC.**
74 E. 30th St. (07514)
**Phone—(973) 684-5945**
Fax—(973) 684-2775
www.acereprographic.com
Email—info@acereprographic.com
Pres.—Arthur L. Scialla
MIS Mgr.—Kurt Biroc
Fin. & Off. Mgr.—Eilene King
SIC—2759; 2752; NAICS—323100; *Blueprinting & color printing*
Employs—25; Estab.—1933
12,000 sq ft site, Distrib.—Local
Privately owned corporation

**AFINA CORP.**
40 Warren St. (07524)
**Phone—(973) 684-7650**
National—(800) 423-4496
Fax—(800) 367-4738
www.afinacorporation.com
Email—info@afinacorporation.com
Pres.—Raymond Lombardo
SIC—2431; 3231; NAICS—327215; *Bathroom cabinets & mirrors*
Employs—35; Estab.—1995
Sales—$6Mil-$10Mil
Distrib.—National
Privately owned corporation

**†AIRGAS EAST, INC.**
2 Beckwith Ave. (07503)
**Phone—(973) 742-2211**
Fax—(973) 742-0025
www.airgas.com
Email—info@airgas.com
Br. Mgr.—Pete Miteiko
SIC—5084; 5085; 5169; *Distributor of welding equipment, supplies & gases*
Employs—2; Estab.—1982
Distrib.—Local
Publicly owned corporation
Parent co.—Airgas East, Inc.,
  Salem, NH
  Phone—(603) 890-4600
  See Parent Co. Section for full profile.

**AJ TANNER LTD.**
93 Harrison St., 2nd Fl. (07501)
**Phone—(973) 523-5205**
  (973) 523-5204
Fax—(973) 523-5206
www.ajtanner.com
Email—sales@ajtanner.com
Owner—Stan Dworkin

SIC—3172; *Leather hair accessories*
Employs—20; Estab.—1910
Sales—$1Mil-$2.5Mil
Distrib.—National
Privately owned corporation

**AL & JOHN, INC.**
444 Marshall St. (07503)
**Phone—(973) 742-4990**
Fax—(973) 742-5141
www.aljohn.com
Email—aljohn@jmclum.com
Pres.—Alexander Oldja
Plt. Mgr.—John Udrija
IT Mgr.—Adam Grossman
Hum. Res. Mgr.—Maryanne Campana
SIC—2013; NAICS—311600; *Ham*
Employs—220; Estab.—1991
Sales—$50Mil-$100Mil (est)
Distrib.—National
Privately owned corporation

**ALBEN METAL PRODUCTS**
11 Iowa Ave. (07503)
**Phone—(973) 279-8891**
Fax—(973) 279-6529
Pres., Fin. & MIS Mgr.—Al Vollaro
Administrator—Laurette Vida
SIC—3469; 3599; *Metal stampings & CNC machining job shop*
Employs—4; Estab.—1968
Sales—$500,000-$1Mil
3,500 sq ft site, Distrib.—Regional
Privately owned corporation

**ALL SEASONS ICE CREAM CORP.**
15 E.12th St. (07524)
**Phone—(201) 878-6790**
Fax—(973) 684-1102
www.icecreamtropical.com
Email—icecreamtropical@hotmail.com
Mng. Ptnr. & Pres.—Freddy Perez
V-P.—Jeffrey Perez
SIC—2024; *Ice cream; Brand name—Esquimalito Tropical*
Employs—5; Estab.—2001
Sales—under $500,000
7,500 sq ft site, Distrib.—National
Sole ownership

**ALLEN LINEN SUPPLY**
407 20th Ave. (07513)
**Phone—(973) 742-6131**
Fax—(973) 742-0989
www.allenlinen.com
Email—linenguy@allenlinen.com
Pres.—Herb Allen III
Acctg. & Off. Mgr.—Wanda Vazquez
Pur. Agt.—Luis Cordero
SIC—2392; *Table linens*
Employs—50; Estab.—1998
Distrib.—National
Privately owned corporation

**†ALLIED BUILDING PRODUCTS CORP.**
27 Kentucky Ave. (07503)
**Phone—(973) 357-1600**
Fax—(973) 977-9282
www.alliedbuildingproducts.com
Email—acarten@alliedbuildingproducts.com
Br. Mgr.—Adam Carten
SIC—5033; 5169; *Distributor of building materials, including residential & commercial roofing, siding & waterproofing materials*
Employs—5; Estab.—2008
Sales—$500,000-$1Mil
Distrib.—Regional
Publicly owned corporation
Parent co.—Allied Building Products Corp., East Rutherford, NJ
  Phone—(201) 507-8400
  See Parent Co. Section for full profile.

**AMB ENTERPRISES, LLC**
25 Lake St. (07501)
**Phone—(973) 225-1070**
Fax—(973) 225-1079
www.bakertitan.com
Email—info@bakertitan.com
Pres.—Anthony Bucco
GM—Morris Giannelli
SIC—2891; NAICS—325520; *Adhesives*
Employs—25; Estab.—1972
25,000 sq ft site, Distrib.—National
Privately owned corporation

**AMERICAN COMB CORP.**
22 Kentucky Ave. (07503)
**Phone—(973) 523-6551**
www.americancomb.com
Email—sales@americancomb.com
Pres.—Frank Bachrach
Sales Mgr.—Al Cristantiello
Opers. & Plt. Mgr.—Richard Roig
Mktg. Mgr.—Daniel Bachrach
Accts. Payable Mgr.—Elaine Lehigh
SIC—3089; *Plastic combs & travel & bathroom accessories*
Employs—10; Estab.—1963
Sales—$1Mil-$5Mil
25,000 sq ft site, Distrib.—Intl.
Privately owned corporation
Also see: Bennett Plastics, Inc., same loc.

**AMERICAN FABRIC PROCESSORS**
555 E. 31st St. (07513)
Mail addr: P.O. Box 2067, Paterson (07509)
**Phone—(973) 278-0272**
Fax—(973) 278-9490
Email—mrdavjb@gmail.com
CEO—Joe Binson
Plt. Mgr.—Claudio Parraguirre
SIC—2261; NAICS—313311; *Textile dyeing & finishing*
Employs—80; Estab.—1953
Distrib.—Local
Privately owned corporation

**AMERICAN HOSE & HYDRAULICS, INC.**
700 21st Ave. (07513)
**Phone—(973) 684-3225**
Fax—(973) 684-3789
www.americanhose.net
Email—grahamp@americanhose.net
CIO—Graham Page
Sales Mgr.—Steve Mazzarella
Repair Shop Mgr.—Tony Labarez
Cylinder Shop Mgr.—Ed Descalzo
Truck Parts Mgr.—Sheila Dasilva
SIC—3714; *Corporate headquarters & truck parts*
Employs—100; Estab.—1968
50,000 sq ft site, Distrib.—Local
Privately owned corporation

**AMERIDERM LABORATORIES LTD.**
126 Pennsylvania Ave. (07503)
**Phone—(973) 279-5100**
National—(800) 455-7211
Fax—(973) 279-8720
www.ameriderm.com
Email—info@ameriderm.com
Owner & Pres.—Bernard Elefant
Sales Mgr.—Asher Elefant
SIC—2844; NAICS—325600; *Skincare products; Brand name—Ameriderm*
Employs—22; Estab.—1998
25,000 sq ft site, Distrib.—National
Privately owned corporation

**ANDARN ELECTRO SERVICE, INC.**
72 Michigan Ave. (07503)
Mail addr: P.O. Box 188, Park Station, Paterson (07543)
**Phone—(973) 523-6334**
Fax—(973) 523-3140
www.trbandarn.com
Email—andarnop1@aol.com
Pres., CFO—Raman D. Patel

SIC—3471; NAICS—332813; *Aluminum anodizing, including type 2, type 3, alodine, passivate, electroless nickel, black oxide & zinc clear*
Employs—30; Estab.—1950
Sales—$1Mil-$2.5Mil
10,000 sq ft site, Distrib.—Regional
Privately owned partnership
ISO rating—9000

**APOSTOLICO MACHINE**
144 Linwood Ave. (07502)
**Phone—(973) 790-3351**
Owner—Aniello Apostolico
SIC—3599; *Precision & general machining job shop*
Employs—1; Estab.—1989
Sales—under $500,000
Distrib.—Local
Sole ownership

**ARAB VOICE NEWSPAPER**
85-99 Hazel St. (07503)
**Phone—(973) 523-7815**
Fax—(973) 523-0315
www.arabvoice.com
Email—wrabah@arabvoice.com
Owner & Publisher—Walid Rabah
Treas.—Abed Mahmoud
SIC—2711; *Arabic newspaper publishing*
Employs—5; Estab.—1993
Sales—under $500,000
Distrib.—Regional
Privately owned corporation

**ARROW STEEL, INC.**
629 E. 19th St. (07514)
**Phone—(973) 523-1122**
National—(800) 582-0173
Fax—(973) 977-9490
www.arrowcompactor.com
Email—info@arrowcompactor.com
Pres.—Mario Ferraro
Corp. Secy.—Pamela Warren
SIC—3589; NAICS—333319; *Trash compactors*
Employs—8; Estab.—1977
Sales—$1Mil-$4Mil
Distrib.—Regional
Privately owned corporation

**ASI PLASTIC, INC.**
120 Getty Ave. (07503)
**Phone—(973) 345-7510**
Pres.—Bob Halek
V-P.—Mike Halek
SIC—3089; *Plastic fabrication*
Employs—2; Estab.—2009
Sales—$500,000-$1Mil
Distrib.—Local
Privately owned corporation

**ATLAS CONSOLIDATED MACHINE CORP.**
53 Bleeker St. (07524)
**Phone—(973) 684-5803**
Fax—(973) 684-3610
Pres.—Walter Wozney
SIC—3599; *General machining job shop*
Employs—2; Estab.—1960
Sales—under $500,000
4,000 sq ft site, Distrib.—National
Privately owned corporation

**B. L. WHITE WELDING & STEEL CO., INC.**
527 E. 33rd St. (07504)
**Phone—(973) 684-4111**
Fax—(973) 279-5040
Email—blwtco@aol.com
Pres.—Richard G. Haddad, Sr.
Off. Mgr.—Richard Haddad III
SIC—3441; *Structural steel fabrication*
Employs—3; Estab.—1950
Sales—$500,000-$1Mil
23,500 sq ft site, Distrib.—Regional
Privately owned corporation

GEOGRAPHICAL

## Paterson—(cont.)

### †BACON & GRAHAM, INC.
34 E. 25th St. (07514)
Mail addr: P.O. Box 35, Hawthorne (07507-0035)
**Phone—(973) 684-1488**
Fax—(973) 684-2021
www.baconandgraham.com
Email—sales@
baconandgraham.com
Pres.—Craig Bacon
V-P., GM—Patrick Rooney
SIC—5085; 5113; 5169; 5084;
*Wholesaler of packaging, shipping, foodservice, janitorial & maintenance supplies & packaging machinery & tools; Brand name—Shuford; Intertape; ITW; Polyair; Sigma Stretch; Pregis; Better Packages; Best Pack; FP Intl; Crown Mats; Clorox; Rubbermaid; Colgate-Palmolive; Dart; Dial; Diversey; Dixie; Sanitaire; GP; Gojo; P&G; Simple Green; SOLO*
Employs—30; Estab.—1939
Distrib.—Regional
Privately owned corporation

### BAKERS PUFF PASTRY
1 Industrial Plz. (07503)
**Phone—(973) 977-2255**
Fax—(573) 577-2253
Pres.—Anthony Cipriano
Dept. Mgr.—Orlie Parker
SIC—2053; NAICS—311813;
*Frozen bakery products*
Employs—15; Estab.—1988
Sales—$2.5Mil-$5Mil (est)
Distrib.—National
Sole ownership

### BAKER-TITAN ADHESIVES
25 Lake St. *(07501)*
**Phone—(973) 225-1070**
National—(866) 998-4826
Fax—(973) 225-1079
www.bakertitan.com
Email—info@bakertitan.com
Plt. Mgr.—Carlos Garcia
SIC—2891; NAICS—325520;
*Water-based & hot-melt adhesives*
Employs—8; Estab.—1972
40,000 sq ft site, Distrib.—National
Privately owned corporation

### BEECH WOODWORKS, INC.
9 Kentucky Ave. (07503)
**Phone—(973) 225-0111**
Fax—(973) 225-0112
Email—beechwoodworks@
verizon.net
Pres.—Tom Connor
Cabinetmaker—Vince Liaukus
SIC—2434; 2431; NAICS—
337110; *Wooden cabinets*
Employs—4; Estab.—1987
Distrib.—Local
Privately owned corporation

### BENNETT PLASTICS, INC.
22 Kentucky Ave. (07503)
**Phone—(973) 684-1501**
Fax—(973) 523-0257
www.bennettplasticsinc.com
Email—steve@
bennettplasticsinc.com
Pres.—Frank Bachrach
V-P., GM—Steven Fell
V-P.—Richard Roig
Pers. Mgr.—Elaine Lehigh
SIC—3089; *Custom plastic injection molding, including tooling, design & fabrication*
Employs—50; Estab.—1984
Sales—$1Mil-$5Mil
36,500 sq ft site, Distrib.—National
Privately owned corporation
Also see: American Comb Corp., same loc.

### BERGEN SCREEN PRINTING, INC.
255 W. Broadway (07522)
**Phone—(973) 595-1222**
Fax—(973) 595-5707
www.bergenscreen.com
Email—info@bergenscreen.com
Pres.—Uday Patel
SIC—2759; 2752; 3993; 2396;
NAICS—323113; *Screen & wide-format digital printing of POP displays, signs, banners, decals, promotional products & textiles, including UV, solvent, water-based & specialty inks & paper, plastic, fabric, metal, wood, glass & ceramic print substrates*
Employs—5; Estab.—2001
9,500 sq ft site, Distrib.—Regional
Privately owned corporation

### BERGEN SIGN CO., INC.
161 E. Railway Ave. (07503)
**Phone—(973) 742-7755**
National—(800) 289-7755
Fax—(973) 742-0598
www.bergensign.com
Email—richw@bergensign.com
Pres.—Tom Schneider
COO—Richard Walker
Proj. Mgr.—Don Lindholm
Administrator—Abigail Rott
SIC—3993; *Interior & exterior signs*
Employs—20; Estab.—1918
Distrib.—Intl.
Privately owned corporation

### BEY ELECTRONICS CORP.
39 Kentucky Ave. (07503)
**Phone—(973) 225-9494**
Fax—(973) 225-9415
www.beyelectronics.com
Email—volkern@bey-usa.com
GM & Fin. Mgr.—Rena Nuss
GM—Volker Nuss
Chief Engr. & R & D Mgr.—Joe Buccino
Shop Mgr.—Ralph Fishner
SIC—3677; 3612; NAICS—
334416; *Electronic transformers*
Employs—12; Estab.—1962
Sales—under $500,000
8,000 sq ft site, Distrib.—Intl.
Privately owned corporation

### BOGUE SYSTEMS, INC.
100 Pennsylvania Ave. (07503)
Mail addr: P.O. Box 3027, Paterson (07509)
**Phone—(973) 523-2200**
National—(800) 247-2033
Fax—(973) 278-8468
www.boguesystems.com
Email—bogueelect@aol.com
Pres.—Anthony Sabatino
V-P., GM—James J. Castellanos
V-P., Opers.—Marvin Krantzow
V-P., Engrg.—Raymond Conway
Corp. Secy.—Nancy Izcone
SIC—3594; 3612; NAICS—
333996; *Electric motor battery chargers, elevator lift uninterruptible power supplies, frequency changers & power conversion systems*
Employs—44; Estab.—1892
30,000 sq ft site, Distrib.—Intl.
Privately owned corporation
ISO rating—9001:2008

### BRENTRICK, INC.
527 E. 39th St. (07504)
**Phone—(973) 357-3579**
National—(866) 440-3579
Fax—(973) 357-3581
www.brentrick.com
Email—sales@brentrick.com
Pres.—Rick Coren
SIC—3082; NAICS—326121;
*Plastic extrusions, including table skirting clips for the display & manufacturing industries*
Employs—4; Estab.—1996
Sales—$1Mil-$2.5Mil
Distrib.—Intl.
Privately owned corporation

### †BRIDY SALES & LEASING CO., INC.
115 Madison Ave. (07524)
**Phone—(973) 345-4311**
Fax—(973) 279-0152
Email—bridysales@optonline.net
Owner—Ralph Bridy
V-P.—Dawn Bridy
SIC—5078; *Distributor of beverage dispensers & ice machines*
Employs—16; Estab.—1973
Sales—$1Mil-$2.5Mil
Distrib.—Local
Privately owned corporation

### BRIGHT MACHINERY MFG. GROUP, INC.
239 Lindbergh Pl., Bldg. 2-A (07503)
**Phone—(973) 345-7405**
Fax—(973) 718-7428
Email—sales@brightmachinery.com
Owner—Fred Gull
Logistics Mgr.—Sarah Basvi
SIC—3599; *Machined parts & general machining job shop*
Employs—2; Estab.—2008
Sales—under $500,000
Distrib.—National
Privately owned corporation

### BRISAR INDUSTRIES, INC.
150 E. 7th St. (07524)
**Phone—(973) 278-2500**
Fax—(973) 782-5570
www.brisar.com
Email—info@brisar.com
Pres.—Mark Cohen
Ex. V-P.—Adel Elsayed
SIC—2671; 3999; 3089;
*Pharmaceutical, cosmetic, R.F. & blister card packaging, shrink-wrap cartons & floor/counter displays; Brand name—3089*
Employs—45; Estab.—1971
160,000 sq ft site, Distrib.—Intl.
Privately owned corporation

### C & S MACHINERY REBUILDING CORP.
636 E. 19th St. (07514)
**Phone—(973) 742-7302**
Fax—(973) 742-4034
Pres.—Cosmo Scardino
SIC—3542; NAICS—333513;
*Rebuilt metal coating machinery*
Employs—4; Estab.—1984
Sales—under $500,000
3,000 sq ft site, Distrib.—Intl.
Privately owned corporation

### CACCIOLA IRON WORKS
65 N. 9th St. (07522)
**Phone—(973) 595-0854**
Fax—(973) 595-6712
www.cacciolairon.com
Pres.—Angelo Cacciola
Estimator—Anthony Cacciola
Welder—John Fricano
SIC—3462; NAICS—332111;
*Railings*
Employs—4; Estab.—1983
Sales—under $500,000
7,000 sq ft site, Distrib.—Regional
Privately owned corporation

### CADIE PRODUCTS CORP.
151 E. 11th St. (07524)
**Phone—(973) 278-8300**
Fax—(973) 278-0303
www.cadieproducts.com
Email—customerservice@
cadie.com
Pres.—Edwin W. Meyers
Ex. V-P.—Kenneth Meyers
Fin. & MIS Mgr.—Bob Appelbaum
SIC—2842; NAICS—325612;
*Stain removers, cleaning & cooking aids & polishing cloths; Brand name—Cadie*
Employs—50; Estab.—1939
Sales—$5Mil-$10Mil
35,000 sq ft site, Distrib.—Intl.
Privately owned corporation

### CALLEN PHOTO MOUNT CORP.
185 6th Ave., Ste. 1 (07524)
**Phone—(973) 925-2390**
Fax—(973) 925-9615
www.callencorp.com
Asst. V-P.—Dennis Callen
SIC—2679; NAICS—322200;
*Picture framing mats*
Employs—15; Estab.—1945
Distrib.—Local
Privately owned corporation

### CAPITAL OFFSET, INC.
257 10th Ave. (07524)
Mail addr: P.O. Box 357, Clifton (07015-0357)
**Phone—(973) 279-3023**
Fax—(973) 279-0105
Email—capitaloffset@aol.com
Pres.—Robert Catalino
V-P.—Ken Myers
Acct. & Sales Mgr.—Nancy Myers
SIC—2759; NAICS—323100;
*Commercial, corporate stationery, envelope, form & letterhead printing*
Employs—3; Estab.—1986
Sales—under $500,000
4,000 sq ft site, Distrib.—National
Privately owned corporation

### CAPITAL SOAP PRODUCTS, LLC
33 Branch St., P.O. Box 357 (07544)
**Phone—(973) 333-6100**
Fax—(973) 333-6166
www.capitalsoap.com
Email—info@
capitalsoapproducts.com
Pres.—A. J. Kretz
SIC—2842; 2841; NAICS—
325612; *Sweeping compounds, soaps & detergents*
Employs—22; Estab.—2005
Sales—$1Mil-$2.5Mil (est)
Distrib.—Regional
Limited Liability Company

### CARDINAL COLOR, INC.
50-56 1st Ave. *(07514)*
**Phone—(973) 684-1919**
Fax—(973) 684-0865
www.cardinalcolor.com
Email—info@cardinalcolor.com
Pres., GM & Off. Mgr.—Mark Berry
CFO—B. J. Berry
MIS Mgr.—Anthony Masciulli
Off. Mgr.—Jessica Marcano
Pur. Agt.—Anna Cacciola
SIC—2816; 2865; NAICS—
325100; *Pigment dispersions*
Employs—30; Estab.—1976
20,000 sq ft site, Distrib.—Intl.
Privately owned corporation

### CARE PLUS NJ, INC.
185 6th Ave. (07524)
Mail addr: 610 Valley Health Plz., Paramus (07652)
**Phone—(973) 553-1954**
Fax—(201) 265-0366
Email—cplaserimaging@
careplusnj.org
Manager—John Maisto
SIC—3955; NAICS—339944;
*Remanufactured inkjet cartridges*
Employs—10
Distrib.—Local
Privately owned corporation

## Paterson—(cont.)

**CARL SIGN, LLC**

1200 Madison Ave. (07503-2813)
**Phone—(973) 340-0210**
Fax—(973) 340-0209
www.carlsign.com
Email—jim@carlsign.com
Owner—Jim Reilly
SIC—3993; 3089; *Truck lettering & interior & exterior signs*
Employs—2; Estab.—1962
Sales—under $500,000
Distrib.—Local
Sole ownership

**CENTER CONTRACTING CORP.**

72 Putnam St. (07524)
**Phone—(973) 523-6400**
Manager—Ralph Pecoreli
SIC—3444; *Sheet metal fabrication*
Employs—4
Sales—under $500,000 (est)
Distrib.—Local
Privately owned corporation

**CENTURY SERVICE AFFILIATES, INC.**

22 Mercer St., Ste. 1 (07524-2430)
**Phone—(973) 742-8118**
National—(800) 486-4517
Fax—(973) 742-1133
www.carrycasesplus.com
Email—info@carrycasesplus.com
Chrm.—Steven Holland
Off. Mgr.—Alley Trofel
SIC—3999; *Carrying case interiors*
Employs—29; Estab.—1986
Sales—$1Mil-$3Mil
9,000 sq ft site, Distrib.—National
Privately owned corporation
DBA: Carry Cases Plus, Inc.

**CERALLI COMPETITION ENGINES, INC.**

395 E. 18th St. (07524)
**Phone—(973) 742-4972**
Fax—(973) 742-7272
Owner & Pres.—Bill Ceralli
SIC—3714; *Rebuilt automotive engines*
Employs—1; Estab.—1970
Sales—under $500,000
Distrib.—Regional
Privately owned corporation

**CERESIST, INC.**

176 E. 7th St. (07524)
Mail addr: P.O. Box 213, Hawthorne (07507)
**Phone—(973) 345-3231**
Fax—(973) 345-3066
www.ceresist.com
Email—info@ceresist.com
Pres.—Dino Tsapatsaris
Acctg. Mgr.—Jennifer Harris
Design Engr.—Donny Suric
SIC—3491; NAICS—332911; *Ceramic-lined valves, fittings & orifice plates*
Employs—14; Estab.—1996
40,000 sq ft site, Distrib.—Intl.
Privately owned corporation

**CHEMQUIP CORP.**

258-262 Atlantic St. (07503)
**Phone—(973) 684-3009**
Fax—(973) 684-0213
www.chemquip.us
Email—chemquip@chemquip.us
Pres.—Igor Ostrer
SIC—3589; NAICS—333319; *Chemical feed systems*
Employs—10; Estab.—1983
Sales—$1Mil-$2.5Mil
Distrib.—National
Privately owned corporation

**CHURCH VESTMENT MFG. CO., INC.**

41-43 Paterson Ave. (07522)
Mail addr: P.O. Box 2334, Paterson (07509)
**Phone—(973) 942-2833**
Fax—(973) 389-9346
Pres.—Gerard J. Siccardi, Jr.
V-P.—Michelle Siccardi
SIC—2389; *Clerical robes*
Employs—5; Estab.—1955
Sales—$500,000-$1Mil
Distrib.—Intl.
Privately owned corporation

**CLOVER STAMPING CO., INC.**

60 Spruce St. (07501)
**Phone—(973) 278-4888**
National—(800) 394-4878
Fax—(973) 278-0017
www.cloverstamping.com
Email—cloverstamping@verizon.net
Pres., Sales Mgr.—Bob Kellenberger
Off. Mgr.—M. Graham
SIC—3469; 3544; 3599; NAICS—333500; *Metal stampings & tool & die job shop for the electronics, connector, heat sink, terminal, semiconductor, hardware, picture frame, lock, window & door industries*
Employs—10; Estab.—1978
Sales—$1Mil
20,000 sq ft site, Distrib.—National
Privately owned corporation

**COLTER & PETERSON, INC.**

414 E. 16th St. (07514)
**Phone—(973) 684-0901**
National—(800) 932-0780
Fax—(973) 684-0260
www.colterpeterson.com
Email—bruce@colterpeterson.com
Pres.—Bruce Peterson
CTO—Izrail Shapiro
COO—Jeff Marr
Ex. V-P.—Eric Peterson
Ex. V-P.—Don Shields
Pur. Mgr.—Marianne Disanti
Hum. Res. Mgr.—Asya Lifshitz
SIC—3554; NAICS—333291; *Corporate headquarters & paper cutter & handling machinery; Brand name—Prism; Saber; C&P Peripheral; Microcut*
Employs—40; Estab.—1932
Sales—$10Mil
16,000 sq ft site, Distrib.—National
Privately owned corporation

**COLUMBIAN IRON WORKS, INC.**

332 Vreeland Ave. (07513)
**Phone—(973) 684-2303**
Fax—(973) 684-3509
Pres.—John Marogi
SIC—3446; NAICS—332323; *Architectural ironwork*
Employs—5; Estab.—1993
Sales—$500,000-$1Mil
Distrib.—Local
Privately owned corporation

**CORONET, INC.**

77 Wood St. (07524)
Mail addr: P.O. Box Ax, Paterson (07509)
**Phone—(973) 345-7660**
Fax—(973) 345-8705
www.coronetnj.com
Email—coronetnj@aol.com
Pres.—Ronald Osur
V-P., Sales & CFO—Russell Osur
Plt. Opers. Mgr.—Steven Klauber
SIC—3646; NAICS—335122; *Fluorescent light fixtures*
Employs—24; Estab.—1946
Sales—$6Mil-$10Mil
25,000 sq ft site, Distrib.—Regional
Privately owned sub-S corp.

**CREATING YOUR DESIGN, LLC**

45 Wood St. (07524)
**Phone—(973) 357-1080**
Fax—(973) 357-1261
www.creatingyourdesign.com
Email—info@creatingyourdesign.com
Owner—David Batiz
Prodn. Mgr.—Glenn Finch
SIC—2541; 2542; 3993; 3999; *Trade show exhibits, commercial & retail store fixtures & museum exhibits*
Employs—10; Estab.—2006
Sales—$1Mil-$2.5Mil
Distrib.—National
Limited Liability Company

**CROWN ROLL LEAF, INC.**

91 Illinois Ave. (07503)
**Phone—(973) 742-4000**
(800) 631-3831
Fax—(973) 742-0219
www.crownrollleaf.com
Email—info@crownrollleaf.com
CEO—Margaret Waitts
COO—James R. Waitts
COO & Plt. Mgr.—George Waitts
V-P., Sales & Mktg.—Robert Rubino
Pur. Mgr.—Dolores Shannon
Hum. Res. Mgr.—Dawn Scharwath
R & D Mgr.—Manuel Cueli
Qual. Assur. Mgr.—Butch Florentino
Cust. Serv. Mgr.—Kelly Samra
SIC—3497; 3443; 2499; *Corporate headquarters & hot stamping & laminating foils & holograms for anticounterfeiting & security, heat transfers, holographic diffraction patterns & pressure-sensitive films*
Employs—225; Estab.—1971
Sales—$62Mil-$65Mil
150,000 sq ft site, Distrib.—Intl.
Sole ownership

**CYGNUS, LLC**

510 E. 41st St. (07504)
**Phone—(973) 523-0668**
Fax—(973) 523-0375
www.cygnusnj.com
Email—gabriela@cygnusnj.com
Ptnr.—Gabriela Naydenov
Ptnr.—Narcis Naydenov
SIC—3672; NAICS—334412; *Contract electronic manufacturing of printed circuit boards for the telecommunications, educational, medical, communications & industrial controls industries*
Employs—50; Estab.—1979
20,000 sq ft site, Distrib.—National
Limited Liability Company
ISO rating—9001:2000

**DANIELLE DIE CUT PRODUCTS, INC.**

238 Lindbergh Pl. (07503)
**Phone—(973) 278-3000**
Fax—(973) 278-3399
www.danielladiecut.com
Email—peter@danielladiecut.com
Pres.—Danny Dibetitto
Off. Mgr.—Pauline Geraci
Proj. Mgr.—Peter Carelli
Bookkeeper—Linda Caldwell
SIC—3544; 2675; 2789; NAICS—333500; *Steel rule dies & die cutting of paper folders*
Employs—20; Estab.—1990
40,000 sq ft site, Distrib.—National
Privately owned corporation

**DANTCO MIXERS CORP.**

9 Oak St. (07501)
**Phone—(973) 278-8776**
Fax—(973) 278-1538
www.dantco.com
Email—sales@dantco.com
Pres.—Michael D'Antuono
GM—Mario Fernandez
Qual. Control Mgr.—Juan Cintron
SIC—3559; 3613; *Pharmaceutical & chemical processing equipment, including mixers, kettles & control panels*
Employs—5; Estab.—1972
Sales—$500,000-$1Mil
10,000 sq ft site, Distrib.—Intl.
Privately owned corporation

**DAVE'S ARCHITECTURAL IRON, LLC**

121 McBride Ave., Ste. C (07501)
**Phone—(973) 523-6323**
Fax—(973) 523-6324
www.davesrailingsnj.com
Email—info@davesrailingsnj.com
Owner—Davis Friessen
SIC—3446; *Ornamental iron railings & gates*
Employs—2
Sales—under $500,000 (est)
Limited Liability Company

**DE JONG IRON WORKS, INC.**

223-231 Godwin Ave. (07501)
Mail addr: P.O. Box 532, Hawthorne (07507-0532)
**Phone—(973) 684-1633**
Fax—(973) 684-2309
www.dejongiron.com
Email—john@dejongiron.com
Pres.—Edward De Jong
V-P.—Jerry De Jong
Treas., MIS Mgr.—John Sibilio
SIC—3441; 5051; NAICS—332312; *Structural steel fabrication & wholesaler of structural steel products*
Employs—9; Estab.—1908
Sales—$1Mil-$1.5Mil
7,500 sq ft site, Distrib.—Local
Privately owned corporation

**DECORATIVE IRON WORKS**

7383 Belmont Ave. (07522)
**Phone—(973) 595-8517**
Fax—(973) 627-6529
www.decorativeironworks.com
Email—info@decorativeironworks.com
Owner—Joseph Monga
Fabricator—Donald Tompson
SIC—3446; NAICS—332323; *Architectural metalwork*
Employs—5; Estab.—1952
Sales—under $500,000
Distrib.—Local
Sole ownership

**DEZA MACHINE & TOOL CO.**

938 E. 19th St. (07501)
**Phone—(973) 278-6654**
Fax—(973) 278-6654
Owner—Antiono Defabrizio
SIC—3599; *General machining job shop*
Employs—1; Estab.—1996
Sales—under $500,000
Distrib.—Local
Sole ownership

**DILLON YARN CORP. (H Q)**

53 E. 34th St. (07514)
Mail addr: P.O. Box Ae, Paterson (07509)
**Phone—(973) 684-1600**
Fax—(973) 684-0407
www.dillonyarn.com
CEO—William Cohen
Pres., COO—Mitchel Weinberger
V-P., Fin.—Michelle O'Neill
Dir., Hum. Res.—Deirdre Gallenagh
MIS Mgr.—Alex Vlassis
SIC—2281; NAICS—313111; *Corporate headquarters; yarn spinning*
Employs—45
Company-wide: 95
Sales—$5Mil-$10Mil (est)
Distrib.—Intl.
Privately owned corporation

GEOGRAPHICAL

## Paterson—(cont.)

NEW ENTRY
**DRAKE MILLS, LLC**
18 E. 5th St., Ste. B (07524)
**Phone—(973) 345-0008**
Fax—(973) 345-9494
Owner—Morton Dropkin
SIC—2515; *Mattresses*
Employs—10; Estab.—2012
Sales—$1Mil-$2.5Mil (est)
Distrib.—National
Limited Liability Company

**DRAPERY CORP. OF AMERICA, INC.**
12-16 1st Ave. (07524)
**Phone—(973) 925-1200**
National—(800) 627-3221
Fax—(973) 925-1221
mysite.verizon.net/dca.inc/
Email—dca.inc@verizon.net
Pres.—George Holiat
GM & R & D Mgr.—J. M. Loughlin
MIS & Mktg. Mgr.—Peter Jesraly
Fin. Mgr.—Laureen Karanfilian
Sys. Mgr., Database—Efrain Lopez
SIC—2391; 2591; 3089; NAICS—314121; *Draperies & shower curtains, blinds & shades; Brand name—DCA; Graber; Bali; Kirsch; Nomistar; Hunter Douglas; Blindsamerica*
Employs—5; Estab.—1957
Sales—under $500,000
6,800 sq ft site, Distrib.—Intl.
Privately owned sub-S corp.
AKA: DCA, Inc.

**E & H LAMINATING & SLITTING CO.**
138 Grand St. *(07501)*
**Phone—(973) 345-1725**
Fax—(973) 345-3224
www.ehlam.com
Email—info@ehlam.com
Pres.—Kenneth S. Annitti
V-P., Sales—Ally Afflitto
SIC—2891; NAICS—325520; *Custom laminating of adhesives, transfers & tapes for the aerospace, hi-tech, industrial, electrical & consumer industries, commercial & military OEMs, airlines & maintenance, repair &overhaul facilities*
Employs—25; Estab.—1976
Sales—$12Mil-$17Mil
21,000 sq ft site, Distrib.—Intl.
Privately owned sub-S corp.

**EFX TEX, LLC**
555 E. 31st St. (07513)
**Phone—(973) 345-7601**
Fax—(973) 345-7602
GM—Emil Innocenti
SIC—2262; NAICS—313311; *Fabric finishing*
Employs—6; Estab.—1992
Sales—$500,000-$1Mil
Distrib.—Local
Limited Liability Company

**ELECTRONIC TRANSFORMER CORP.**
460 Totowa Ave. (07522)
**Phone—(973) 942-2222**
Fax—(973) 942-9014
www.electronictransformercorp.com
Email—etc@electronictransformercorp.com
Pres.—Daniel Cezar
GM & Cont. Admn.—Cliff Markowitz
Qual. Control Mgr.—Michael Golas
Fin. Mgr.—Tania Ablascha
Contract Admn.—Frances Cezar
SIC—3677; NAICS—334416; *Transformers*
Employs—45; Estab.—1937
40,000 sq ft site, Distrib.—National
Privately owned corporation

**ELEVATOR DOORS, INC./ELEVATOR CABS, INC.**
15 Jane St. (07522)
**Phone—(973) 790-9100**
          (800) 526-5264
Fax—(973) 790-1007
www.edi-eci.com
Email—info@edi-eci.com
Pres.—Paul Pedretti
COO—Jonathon Packard
V-P.—Chris Taukus
SIC—3534; NAICS—333921; *New elevator cabs & elevator entrances, including replacement hoistway doors, cab interior remodeling & escalator skirting*
Employs—100; Estab.—1944
Sales—$10Mil-$25Mil (est)
Distrib.—National
Privately owned corporation
AKA: EDI/ECI

**ELEVATOR TECHNOLOGY CORP.**
337 Market St. (07501)
Mail addr: P.O. Box 2753, Paterson (07509)
**Phone—(973) 523-7760**
Fax—(973) 523-4075
www.elevatortechnologycorp.com
Email—eltec6@verizon.net
Pres.—Shlomo Tagjer
V-P.—Doreen Glantz
SIC—3534; NAICS—333921; *Elevator replacement parts*
Employs—5; Estab.—1979
Sales—under $500,000
3,200 sq ft site, Distrib.—National
Privately owned corporation

**EMPIRE INDUSTRIES, INC.**
40 Warren St. (07524)
**Phone—(973) 279-2050**
National—(800) 367-4738
Fax—(973) 279-8987
www.empire-industries.com
Email—info@empire-industries.com
Pres.—Jacob Goren
V-P.—Bonnie Goren
SIC—2434; 2511; NAICS—337110; *Bathroom furniture, vanities, ceramic & granite countertops & bath accessories*
Employs—32; Estab.—1976
195,000 sq ft site, Distrib.—National
Privately owned corporation

**EPOCH PRESS, INC.**
75 Wood St., Ste. B (07524)
**Phone—(973) 357-0080**
Fax—(973) 357-1188
www.epochpress.com
Email—info@epochpress.com
CFO—Paulina Werthen
SIC—2759; 2711; 2732; NAICS—323117; *Web & commercial printing*
Employs—30; Estab.—2004
Sales—$2.6Mil-$5Mil
38,000 sq ft site, Distrib.—National
Privately owned sub-S corp.

**EXCEL HOBBY BLADES CORP.**
481 Getty Ave., P.O. Box 1045 (07503)
**Phone—(973) 278-4000**
Fax—(973) 278-4343
www.excelhobbyblades.com
Email—mail@excelhobbyblades.com
Pres.—Mike Hammam
V-P.—Hany Hammam
SIC—3423; NAICS—332200; *Replaceable blade knives, blades & hand tools for general use & hobbyists*
Employs—40; Estab.—1989
Distrib.—Intl.
Privately owned corporation

**FABRICOLOR HOLDINGS, INC.**
24 1/2 Van Houten St., P.O. Box 1856 (07505)
**Phone—(973) 742-5800**
Fax—(973) 742-5801
www.farbricolorholdings.com
Email—info@fabricolorholdings.com
Pres.—Miroslav E. Muzik
SIC—2865; NAICS—325100; *Specialty organic dyes*
Employs—10; Estab.—1962
Sales—$500,000-$1Mil
Distrib.—Intl.
Privately owned corporation

**†FASTENAL CO.**
443 Madison Ave. (07524)
**Phone—(973) 278-5509**
Fax—(973) 278-9624
www.fastenal.com
Email—njpat@stores.fastenal.com
Sales Rep., Inside—Joe Bresett
SIC—5072; 5084; *Wholesaler of fasteners, safety equipment, tools & abrasives*
Employs—3; Estab.—2003
Sales—under $500,000
Distrib.—Local
Publicly owned corporation
Parent co.—Fastenal Co., Winona, MN
Phone—(507) 454-5374
See Parent Co. Section for full profile.

**FLECH PAPER PRODUCTS, INC.**
55 1st Ave. (07514)
**Phone—(973) 357-8111**
Fax—(973) 357-8108
www.flech.com
Email—info@flech.com
Founder—Joseph Kandel
SIC—2679; NAICS—322200; *Poster, display, mat & mounting boards*
Employs—20; Estab.—2007
30,000 sq ft site, Distrib.—Intl.
Privately owned corporation

**FORM, FIT & FUNCTION, LLC**
25 McLean Blvd. (07514)
**Phone—(973) 442-2290**
Fax—(973) 989-8576
www.fffdesign.com
Email—inquiry@fffdesign.com
Owner—Odilo Vazquez
SIC—3599; *Precision machining job shop*
Employs—20; Estab.—1999
Sales—$1Mil-$2.5Mil
3,484 sq ft site, Distrib.—Local
Limited Liability Company

**FORTY-NINE CORP.**
34 Waite St. (07524)
Mail addr: P.O. Box 2325, Paterson (07509-2325)
**Phone—(973) 754-0313**
Fax—(973) 754-0357
www.49corp.com
Email—sales@49corp.com
Pres.—Rhoda Temkin
V-P.—Michael Temkin
SIC—3089; *PVC laminate & vinyl safety products*
Employs—2; Estab.—1949
Sales—$500,000-$1Mil
10,000 sq ft site, Distrib.—National
Privately owned corporation

**FREEDOM FENCE & BUILDING PRODUCTS**
168 Wabash Ave. (07503)
**Phone—(973) 345-0911**
Fax—(973) 345-3111
www.freedomvinyl.com
Email—freedomvinyl@aol.com
Owner—Sal Anello
SIC—3089; *Vinyl fences, decks & railings*
Employs—5; Estab.—1992
Sales—over $1Mil
Distrib.—Regional
Privately owned corporation

**G R OFFICE PRODUCTS, INC.**
11 Kentucky Ave. (07503)
**Phone—(973) 345-2769**
Fax—(973) 345-2804
www.checkmateproducts.com
Email—groffice@aol.com
Pres.—Bernardo Guterman
SIC—3089; 2541; 2599; 3999; *Floor mats, fabric-wrapped tackboards & wall & privacy panels*
Employs—2; Estab.—1989
Sales—under $500,000
5,500 sq ft site, Distrib.—National
Privately owned sub-S corp.
AKA: Check-Mate Products

**GALICIA METAL, INC.**
573 E. 19th St. (07514)
**Phone—(973) 278-1058**
Fax—(973) 278-1058
Pres.—John Martinez
V-P.—Sally Martinez
SIC—3599; *General machining job shop*
Employs—2; Estab.—1973
Sales—under $500,000
Distrib.—Local
Sole ownership

**GARAFANO & SONS, PETER**
500 Marshall St. (07503)
**Phone—(973) 278-0350**
Fax—(973) 345-7633
www.steelfab.org
Email—pgiii@aol.com
Pres.—Peter Garafano
Sales Rep.—Dan Garafano
SIC—3312; *Steel fabrication*
Employs—20
18,000 sq ft site, Distrib.—Local
Privately owned corporation
AKA: Steel Fab

**GENERAL CARBON CORPORATION**
33 Paterson St. *(07501)*
**Phone—(973) 523-2223**
Fax—(973) 523-1494
www.generalcarbon.com
Email—sales@generalcarbon.com
Pres.—Robert Muller
SIC—3624; 3559; NAICS—335991; *Activated carbon & related filtration equipment & systems*
Employs—20; Estab.—1958
Sales—$5Mil-$10Mil
Distrib.—Intl.
Privately owned corporation
ISO rating—9001:2000

**GIANELLA BAKING CO.**
298 21st Ave. (07501)
**Phone—(973) 523-9258**
Fax—(973) 523-5857
www.gianellabakery.com
Pres.—John Imparato
SIC—2051; NAICS—311812; *Bakery products*
Employs—24; Estab.—1947
10,000 sq ft site, Distrib.—Local
Privately owned corporation

**GILOSA BINDERY, INC., JOSEPH A.**
555 20th Ave. (07504)
**Phone—(973) 279-8006**
Fax—(973) 279-8008
www.gilosabindery.com
Email—gilosabindery@verizon.net
Pres.—Bob Gilosa
SIC—2789; NAICS—323121; *Bookbinding*
Employs—20; Estab.—1918
Sales—$500,000-$1Mil
Distrib.—Local
Privately owned corporation

**GIO VALI CORP.**
463 Grand St. (07505)
**Phone—(973) 279-3032**
Fax—(973) 279-6851
www.giovalicorp.com
Email—ara@giovalicorp.com

## Paterson—(cont.)

Pres.—Ara Mesrobian
SIC—3171; NAICS—316992; *Women's leather & tapestry handbags & safety, tie down & medical straps*
Employs—8; Estab.—1993
Sales—under $500,000
7,000 sq ft site, Distrib.—Local
Privately owned corporation

**GLENRO, INC.**
39 McBride Avenue Ext. (07501)
**Phone—(973) 279-5900**
National—(888) 453-6761
Fax—(973) 279-9103
www.glenro.com
Email—info@glenro.com
Pres.—Gary Van Denend
V.-P., Engrg.—Michael Papapietro
Sr. Sales Engr.—Eric Hummel
Sales Engr.—Ketan Patel
SIC—3567; 3399; NAICS—333994; *Industrial gas & electric infrared heaters, dip coating & flatbed laminating machines, lab testing lines, custom hot & through air, dual impingement ovens & thermal oxidizers & contract laminating services; Brand name—Radround; Radplane*
Employs—20; Estab.—1958
Sales—$6Mil-$10Mil
40,000 sq ft site, Distrib.—Intl.
Privately owned corporation

**GLOBAL INGREDIENTS, INC.**
317 9th Ave. (07514)
**Phone—(973) 278-6677**
www.globalingredients.net
Email—griff@globalingredients.net
Pres.—Frank Montain
V.-P., Sales—Timothy Montain
Hum. Res. & Opers. Mgr.—Griff Jones
SIC—2099; *Food ingredient stabilizers*
Employs—5; Estab.—1992
20,000 sq ft site, Distrib.—Intl.
Privately owned corporation

**GLOBAL PACKAGING MACHINERY, INC.**
36 Peel St. *(07524)*
**Phone—(973) 279-2300**
Fax—(973) 279-2301
www.globalpackmachinery.com
Email—global@globalpackmachinery.com
Owner & Dir., Engrg.—Michael Kurdyla
SIC—3565; 3599; NAICS—333993; *Cartoning & material handling machinery & refurbished packaging machinery*
Employs—5; Estab.—1998
Sales—$1Mil-$2.5Mil
Distrib.—National
Privately owned sub-S corp.

**GOLDEN SHEETS MFG.**
239 6th Ave. (07524)
**Phone—(973) 925-2242**
Fax—(973) 925-2262
www.goldensheets.com
Email—samgoldensheets@yahoo.com
GM—Ashraf Rabi
Manager—Sam Gannon
SIC—2392; *Bed sheets*
Employs—8
Sales—$1Mil-$2.5Mil (est)
Distrib.—Local
Privately owned corporation

**GREAT FALLS METALWORKS, INC.**
301 E. 22nd St. (07514)
**Phone—(973) 523-6811**
Fax—(973) 523-6010
Email—gfmw1@msn.com
CEO—J. Palombo

Sales Mgr.—Anne Brothers
Asst. Mgr.—Karen Montano
SIC—3499; *Metal fabrication*
Employs—15; Estab.—1968
12,600 sq ft site, Distrib.—Intl.
Privately owned corporation
AKA: Equitable Service

**GREENBAUM INTERIORS**
101 Washington St. *(07505)*
**Phone—(973) 279-3000**
Fax—(973) 279-3006
www.greenbauminteriors.com
Email—susan@greenbauminteriors.com
Pres.—Joseph Greenbaum
V.-P.—Susan Greenbaum Gross
SIC—2512; 2511; 2431; NAICS—337121; *Custom upholstered & wooden furniture & cabinetry, including interior design services; Brand name—Baker; Century*
Employs—40; Estab.—1952
Sales—under $10Mil
100,000 sq ft site, Distrib.—Regional
Limited Liability Company

**GREINER & SONS, INC., L. J.**
63-69 Dan Forth Ave. (07501)
**Phone—(973) 977-9441**
Fax—(973) 278-9766
Pres.—Lothar Greiner
V.-P.—Micheal Greiner
SIC—3842; *Artificial eyes*
Employs—4; Estab.—1978
Sales—under $500,000
Distrib.—Regional
Privately owned corporation

**GRIMCO PRESSES CO.**
65 1st Ave. (07514)
**Phone—(973) 345-0660**
Fax—(973) 345-0686
www.grimcopresses.com
Email—sales@grimcopresses.com
Pres.—David Grimaldi
SIC—3594; NAICS—333996; *Hydraulic & pneumatic presses*
Employs—5
Sales—$500,000-$1Mil
Distrib.—Intl.

**GUERNSEY CREST ICE CREAM CO.**
134 19th Ave. (07513)
**Phone—(973) 742-4620**
Email—guernseycrest@gmail.com
Pres.—Joy Cornwell
V.-P.—Margaret Cornwell
Plt. Mgr.—Kevin Smith
Prodn. Mgr.—Ed Livi
SIC—2024; NAICS—311520; *Ice cream*
Employs—4; Estab.—1936
Distrib.—Local
Privately owned corporation

**HC GRAPHICS SCREEN PRINTING, INC.**
238 Lindbergh Pl., Ste. 3 (07503)
**Phone—(973) 247-0544**
Fax—(973) 247-0590
www.hcgraphics.com
Email—office@hcgraphics.com
Pres.—Thomas J. Mueller
V.-P.—Carol Mueller
Off. Mgr.—Clara Vega
Estimator—Cathy Barnett
SIC—2759; 2631; NAICS—322130; *Plastic & paper screen printing*
Employs—15; Estab.—1979
Sales—$500,000-$1Mil
Distrib.—Intl.
Privately owned corporation

**HILL MACHINE, INC.**
295 Governor St. (07501)
**Phone—(973) 684-2808**
Fax—(973) 345-4080
Email—hillmixer@aol.com
Pres.—John Poulos

SIC—3556; NAICS—333294; *Food mixers*
Employs—5; Estab.—1937
Sales—$500,000-$1Mil
14,000 sq ft site, Distrib.—National
Privately owned corporation

**HO-HO-KUS, INC.**
189-201 Lyon St. (07524)
**Phone—(973) 278-2274**
Fax—(973) 278-4805
www.hohokusinc.com
Email—sales@hohokusinc.com
Sales Mgr.—Steve Sucharski
SIC—3999; *Aerospace products*
Employs—50; Estab.—1991
Sales—$1Mil-$2.5Mil
50,000 sq ft site, Distrib.—Intl.
Privately owned corporation

**HY-TEST PACKAGING CORP.**
515 E. 41st St. (07504)
**Phone—(973) 754-7000**
Fax—(973) 754-7020
www.hy-testpackaging.com
Email—hy-test@verizon.net
Pres.—Jack Smith
V.-P., Mfg.—Ted Smith
Comp.—Jackalyn Quazza
SIC—2841; 2999; 2851; 2899; NAICS—325611; *Liquid cleaning products, fuel additives & chemical specialties packaging, including formulation & blending for the marine, automotive, janitorial, industrial & household products industries; Brand name—Hy-Test; Fletcher-Smith's; Soil-Ex; MDR; Amazon's*
Employs—9; Estab.—1989
40,000 sq ft site, Distrib.—Intl.
Privately owned corporation
AKA: Marine Development & Research
Also see: Marine Development & Research Corp., same loc.

**INDEPENDENCE PLATING CORP.**
107 Alabama Ave. (07503)
**Phone—(973) 523-1776**
Fax—(973) 279-1274
www.independenceplating.com
Email—independenceplating@gmail.com
Pres., GM—Ron Knigge
Plt. Mgr.—Al Alston
SIC—3471; NAICS—332813; *Plating, including anodizing & electroless nickel & electro plating*
Employs—10; Estab.—1950
27,000 sq ft site, Distrib.—Intl.
Privately owned sub-S corp.

**INDUSTRIAL MACHINE CORP.**
44 Lehigh Ave. (07503)
**Phone—(973) 345-1800**
Fax—(973) 345-7545
www.industrialmachinecorp.com
Email—imc94@optonline.net
Pres.—Sam Szewczyk
Off. Mgr.—Kathy Sobczak
SIC—3599; 3544; *Parts, tools & general machining job shop, including experimental rebuilding, repairing & welding*
Employs—14; Estab.—1968
Sales—$500,000-$1Mil
10,000 sq ft site, Distrib.—Regional
Privately owned corporation

**INTERFOAM FABRICATORS, INC.**
155 McBride Ave. (07501)
**Phone—(973) 633-8805**
Fax—(973) 742-8682
www.interfoam.com
Email—sales@interfoam.com
V.-P.—Rick Kohler
Dir., Mktg.—Edward Walsh

SIC—3086; NAICS—326100; *Plastic foam products*
Employs—15; Estab.—1980
Sales—under $500,000
Distrib.—Intl.
Privately owned corporation

**J & J CUSTOM METAL FABRICATORS, INC.**
85 5th Ave., Ste. 17 (07524)
Mail addr: P.O. Box 3296, Wayne (07470)
**Phone—(973) 977-9373**
Fax—(973) 881-7078
Pres.—Jeff Wells
V.-P.—John Boardnan
SIC—3499; *Metal fabrication*
Employs—3; Estab.—1984
Sales—$500,000-$1Mil
Distrib.—Regional
Privately owned corporation

**J & K INGREDIENTS, INC.**
160 E. 5th St. *(07524)*
**Phone—(973) 340-8700**
Fax—(973) 340-4994
www.jkingredients.net
Email—sales@jkingredients.net
Pres.—James K. Sausville
V.-P., Sales & Mktg.—Al Orr
V.-P., R & D—Nigel Weston
Cont.—Andy Madacsi
GM—Fred Denman
SIC—2045; 2087; 2099; *Natural bread, cake & donut mixes, egg & milk replacers, flavors, chocolate cookie dip & fudge bases, shelf life extenders & processing aids for the baking industry*
Employs—80; Estab.—1899
Sales—$40Mil
100,000 sq ft site, Distrib.—Intl.
Privately owned sub-S corp.

**J C PRINTING & ADVERTISING, INC.**
168 8th Ave. (07514)
**Phone—(973) 881-8612**
Fax—(973) 881-9406
www.jcprintinginc.com
Email—jcprinting@aol.com
Pres.—James Chappell
SIC—2759; NAICS—323100; *Commercial printing*
Employs—3; Estab.—1995
Sales—$500,000-$1Mil
Distrib.—Local
Privately owned corporation

**J.I.T. MFG., INC.**
50 Peel St. (07524)
**Phone—(973) 247-7300**
Fax—(973) 247-7304
www.jitpkg.com
Email—info@jitpkg.com
Pres.—John Norton
V.-P.—Andrew Graziano
Off. Mgr.—Patricia Graziano
SIC—2631; NAICS—322130; *Paper & paperboard packaging materials, flexo printing, die-cutting & slitting/rewinding*
Employs—14; Estab.—1989
Sales—$1Mil-$5Mil
25,000 sq ft site, Distrib.—Intl.
Privately owned sub-S corp.

**JERSEY CHEMICALS, INC.**
775 River St., P.O. Box 542 (07524)
**Phone—(973) 523-3736**
Fax—(973) 523-0513
www.jerseychemicals.com
Email—dpaulen@jerseychemicals.com
Pres.—David Paulen
SIC—2899; 3589; NAICS—333319; *Swimming pool chemicals & pool related equipment*
Employs—10; Estab.—1959
12,000 sq ft site, Distrib.—National
Privately owned corporation

GEOGRAPHICAL

## Paterson—(cont.)

**KAUFMAN IRON WORKS, INC., J.**
217 Godwin Ave. (07501)
**Phone—(718) 991-5400**
Fax—(718) 893-7168
www.kaufmaniron.com
Email—kaufiron@aol.com
Pres.—Larry Kaufman
Secy., Cont.—Joseph Kaufman
Bookkeeper—Donna Boyd
SIC—3446; NAICS—332323;
Architectural ironwork, security
gates, child safety window
guards, railings & custom
ironworks
Employs—35; Estab.—1907
42,000 sq ft site, Distrib.—Local
Privately owned sub-S corp.

**KEN-MAR MACHINE & MFG.**
477 E. 30th St. (07504)
**Phone—(973) 278-5827**
Fax—(973) 278-7658
www.ken-mar-machine.com
Email—info@ken-mar-machine.com
V.-P. & Hum. Res. Mgr.—Ken
Walder
Bookkeeper—Donna Laurice
SIC—3842; Medical implants
Employs—25; Estab.—1950
Sales—$5Mil-$10Mil (est)
Distrib.—Intl.
Privately owned corporation

**KIRKER ENTERPRISES, INC.**
55 E. 6th St. (07524)
**Phone—(973) 754-9000**
Fax—(973) 754-9696
www.kirkerent.com
Email—sales@kirkerent.com
CEO—Jeffrey S. Hersh
Pres.—Jeff Kirson
Hum. Res. Mgr.—Ivy Ho
Pur. Agt.—Patty LaPenter
SIC—2844; NAICS—325600;
Corporate headquarters &
fingernail polish
Employs—100; Estab.—1992
Sales—$30Mil-$50Mil
50,000 sq ft site, Distrib.—Intl.
Privately owned corporation

**KISMET FURNITURE, INC.**
80 George St. (07503)
**Phone—(973) 278-3117**
Fax—(973) 345-0418
Pres.—Tony Kismet
SIC—2511; Custom wooden
furniture
Employs—1; Estab.—1981
Sales—under $500,000
Distrib.—National
Privately owned corporation

**KLEIN RIBBON DESIGNS, JEFFREY**
176 E. 7th St. (07524)
**Phone—(973) 684-4671**
Fax—(973) 684-1136
Email—myownribbon@aol.com
Pres.—Jeffrey Klein
SIC—2241; NAICS—313221;
Custom imprinted ribbons
Employs—10; Estab.—1932
Distrib.—Intl.
Sole ownership

**KONTOS FOODS, INC.**
100 6th Ave., P.O. Box 628 (07544)
**Phone—(973) 278-2800**
Fax—(973) 278-7943
www.kontos.com
Email—pitachef@kontos.com
Pres.—Evris Kontos
V.-P.—Steve Kontos
Corp. Ex. Chef—Demetrios A.
Haralambatos
Opers. Mgr.—Andy Vlouhoris
Hum. Res. Mgr.—Jill Capano
Logistics Mgr.—Fred Nelson

SIC—2051; 5146; 5147; 5149;
NAICS—311812; Manufacturer
of authentic ethnic hand-
stretched flatbreads, including
pita, nan, pan plano, roti &
lavash & fillo dough & products,
including spanakopita & baklava
& distributor of Mediterranean
specialty food products; Brand
name—Kontos Flatbread;
Kontos Pocket-Less Pita®;
Alexander's Great Flatbread;
Kontos Pan Plano; Kontos Fillo
Employs—150; Estab.—1987
70,000 sq ft site, Distrib.—Intl.
Privately owned corporation

**L & M MACHINE & TOOL CO., INC.**
105 Lehigh Ave. (07503)
**Phone—(973) 523-5288**
Pres.—Manny Morone
SIC—3599; General machining
job shop
Employs—10; Estab.—1959
Sales—$500,000-$1Mil
5,000 sq ft site, Distrib.—Local
Privately owned corporation

**L M C CORP.**
23 E. 23rd St. (07514)
**Phone—(973) 279-3573**
Fax—(973) 881-0235
www.l-m-c.com
Email—contact@l-m-c.com
Pres.—Julian Legeard
V.-P., Fin. & Hum. Res. Mgr.—
Jean-Paul Dorieux
Administrator—Karen Martin
SIC—3446; NAICS—332323;
Architectural metalwork
Employs—22; Estab.—1986
11,500 sq ft site, Distrib.—National
Privately owned sub-S corp.

**LA FAVORITE INDUSTRIES, INC.**
33 Shady St. (07524)
**Phone—(973) 279-1266**
Fax—(973) 279-3447
www.lafavorite.com
Email—sales@lafavorite.com
Pres.—Thomas Mastin
V.-P.—Eric Hague
Off. Mgr.—Linda Zisa
SIC—3069; Rubber expansion
joints & parts
Employs—15; Estab.—1984
Sales—$1Mil-$2.5Mil
10,000 sq ft site, Distrib.—Intl.
Privately owned corporation

**LACOA, INC.**
34 Waite St. (07524)
**Phone—(973) 754-1000**
Fax—(973) 754-1015
www.lacoa.com
Email—hector@lacoa.com
Pres.—Hector Baralt
Off. Mgr.—Marilyn Van Putin Vink
Off. Mgr.—Peggy Brown
Fin. Mgr.—Greg Baitzel
SIC—3081; NAICS—326113;
Laminate & emboss materials,
including polyester films, vinyls,
papers, PVC, olefin & fabrics for
the belt, binding, wall covering,
looseleaf, garment, display,
applications & specialty items
industries
Employs—8; Estab.—1974
28,600 sq ft site, Distrib.—Local
Privately owned corporation

**LANCO YORK, INC.**
864 E. 25th St. (07513)
**Phone—(973) 278-7400**
Fax—(973) 278-8883
www.lancoyork.com
Email—info@lancoyork.com
CEO—Mitchell J. Leibowitz
Pres.—Mark Leibowitz
Ex. V.-P., Opers.—Denis Panza
Plt. Mgr.—Pablo Salmeron
Cust. Serv. Mgr.—Christine
Leibowitz

SIC—2653; 3085; 3089; 2657;
NAICS—322211; Primary &
secondary pharmaceutical-
grade packaging components,
including bottles, closures, caps,
metered dosage delivery
systems, folding cartons, floor,
counter & point-of-purchase
displays; Brand name—Stor-Flat
Drums; Multa-Paks; Snap-Ins
Employs—25; Estab.—1942
85,000 sq ft site, Distrib.—Intl.
Privately owned sub-S corp.

**LEVINE INDUSTRIES**
86 Levine St., South Paterson Sta.
(07503)
**Phone—(973) 742-1000**
National—(800) 922-6937
Fax—(973) 742-0588
Email—levineind@aol.com
Pres.—Jess Levine
V.-P., Sales—Ted Levine
Cont., Hum. Res. Mgr.—Ken Julien
Plt. Mgr.—Dave Roberts
Cust. Serv. Rep.—Angie Castilla
SIC—2653; NAICS—322211;
Corrugated boxes
Employs—30; Estab.—1967
Distrib.—National
Privately owned partnership

**LIBERTY ENVELOPE, INC.**
45 E. 5th St. (07524)
**Phone—(973) 546-5600**
Fax—(973) 925-9609
www.dmd-liberty.com
Email—rfq@dmd-liberty.com
CEO—Kevin Guarderas
Pres.—Ligia Guardera
Dir., Sales & Mktg.—Darwin
Guarderas
Cust. Serv. Rep.—Herman
Corrales
SIC—2759; NAICS—323100;
Commercial & envelope printing
to 6 color, including direct mail
services
Employs—40; Estab.—1985
Distrib.—National
Privately owned corporation
AKA: Direct Market Desgins

**LINDSTROM & KING CO., INC.**
108 McLean Blvd. (07514)
**Phone—(973) 279-2511**
Fax—(973) 279-9650
www.lindstromking.com
Email—sales@lindstromking.com
GM—Nick Fischer
SIC—3053; NAICS—339991;
Custom stem packing die-cut
rings & washers for faucets &
valves
Employs—4; Estab.—1939
Sales—$500,000-$1Mil
6,000 sq ft site, Distrib.—Intl.
Sole ownership

**LIPO CHEMICALS, INC.**
Div. of Vantage Oleochemicals,
Inc.
207 19th Ave. (07504)
**Phone—(973) 345-8600**
Fax—(973) 345-8365
www.lipochemicals.com
Email—salesandmarketing@
lipochemicals.com
Ex. V.-P.—Conrad Kempinska
V.-P., Global Mktg.—Nancy
Clements
Dir., Sales, N. America—Michael
Lotito

SIC—2869; 2899; Corporate
headquarters & raw material
ingredients for the personal care
industry; Brand name—Desert
Whale Jojoba Company; Lipovol
Natural Oils; Liponate Emollient
Esters; Biopolymers; Natural
Exfoliants; Lipocols; Lipomulse;
Gorgonian Extract; Lipobrite
HCA-4; Liposhield HEV Melanin;
Hylasome EG-10
Employs—30; Estab.—1962
176,418 sq ft site, Distrib.—Intl.
Privately owned sub-S corp.
ISO rating—9002
Parent co.—Vantage
Oleochemicals, Inc., Chicago, IL
Phone—(773) 376-9000
See Parent Co. Section for full profile.

**LITTLE FALLS ALLOYS, INC.**
189 Caldwell Ave. (07501)
**Phone—(973) 278-1666**
Fax—(973) 278-7345
www.littlefallsalloys.com
Email—lfawire@aol.com
Chrm. of the Board—Vincent Jim
Sacco
Pres.—Donald Fellman
V.-P.—Fred Walter
Head of Sales—Tara Cullen
SIC—3351; 3357; 3471; NAICS—
331421; Copper base, bare,
round, flat & square alloys &
electroplating; Brand name—
Silvercote
Employs—30; Estab.—1946
Sales—$5Mil-$10Mil
33,000 sq ft site, Distrib.—Intl.
Privately owned corporation
ISO rating—9001:2011

**LOTITO FOODS, INC.**
Div. of Lotito Foods, Inc./Mrs.
Mazzula Foods
510 E. 35th St. (07504)
**Phone—(973) 684-2900**
Fax—(973) 357-1759
www.lotitofoods.com
Email—info@lotitofoods.com
Plt. Mgr.—William Robles
Asst. Mgr.—Rosa Then
SIC—2022; NAICS—311513;
Grated Romano cheese
processing
Employs—10; Estab.—1957
Sales—$500,000-$1Mil
Distrib.—National
Privately owned corporation
Parent co.—Lotito Foods, Inc./Mrs.
Mazzula Foods, Edison, NJ
Phone—(732) 248-0222
See Parent Co. Section for full profile.

[NEW ENTRY]
**LOVE FARMS, LLC**
204 Albion Ave. (07502)
**Phone—(973) 942-5683**
Fax—(973) 389-0749
Owner—David Adelson
SIC—2011; 2013; Meat & sausage
processing
Employs—30
Sales—$10Mil-$25Mil (est)
Distrib.—National
Limited Liability Company

**LUTJENS CO., INC., G.**
80 George St. (07503)
**Phone—(973) 278-9639**
Fax—(973) 278-0056
www.glutjens.com
Email—gcabinet1@netscape.net
Pres.—Gary Lutjens
SIC—2434; NAICS—337110;
Wooden kitchen cabinets
Employs—2; Estab.—1983
Sales—under $500,000
Distrib.—Local
Privately owned corporation

## Paterson—(cont.)

**LUX ENTERTAINMENT, LLC**
629 E. 19th St. (07514)
**Phone—(888) 282-8425**
Fax—(973) 977-9490
www.luxoutdoor.com
Email—info@luxoutdoor.com
Owner—Andrew Vaccaro
SIC—3444; 3679; NAICS—335122; *Environmentally controlled protective media equipment enclosures*
Employs—3; Estab.—2004
Sales—under $500,000
Distrib.—Intl.
Privately owned corporation

**M & S MACHINE & TOOL CORP.**
108 Maryland Ave. *(07503)*
**Phone—(973) 345-5847**
Fax—(973) 345-0579
www.mandsmachine.com
Email—nazim@mandsmachine.com
Pres.—Nazim Sulejmanovski
V-P.—Nezaket Maksut
Shop Foreman—Al Maksut
Bookkeeper—Guldan Istrefi
SIC—3599; *General machining job shop*
Employs—20; Estab.—1983
Sales—$1Mil-$2.5Mil
10,000 sq ft site, Distrib.—Regional
Privately owned corporation

**MAJKA RAILING, INC.**
125 McBride Ave. (07501)
**Phone—(973) 247-7603**
National—(800) 956-6255
Fax—(973) 247-7605
www.majkarailing.com
Email—kia@majkarailing.com
Pres.—Mary Majka
V-P., Hum. Res. & Pur. Mgr.—Keith Majka
V-P.—Fred Majka
SIC—3446; NAICS—332323; *Aluminium railings*
Employs—10; Estab.—1974
Sales—under $1Mil
22,000 sq ft site, Distrib.—Local
Privately owned corporation

**MALWIN ELECTRONICS CORP.**
52 E. 22nd St. (07514)
**Phone—(973) 881-1500**
Fax—(973) 881-7044
www.malwin.com
Email—malwin.electronics@verizon.net
Pres.—G. Weber
GM—J. Panepinto
Pur. & Repair Mgr.—Donald Van Blarcom
SIC—3812; NAICS—334511; *Simulated flight instruments*
Employs—10; Estab.—1969
5,000 sq ft site, Distrib.—National
Privately owned corporation

**MANHATTAN SIGNS, INC.**
130 Beckwith Ave. (07503)
Mail addr: 91 Tulip Ave., Ste. Kd-1, Floral Park (11001-1962)
**Phone—(973) 278-3603**
Fax—(973) 278-5798
www.manhattansignsco.com
Email—adec@manhattansignsco.com
CEO—Anthony Decrescenzo
V-P.—Marie Martineck
SIC—3993; *Interior & exterior signs, including installation*
Employs—13; Estab.—1997
Distrib.—Regional
Privately owned sub-S corp.
AKA: Manhattan Flag & Pole

**MARINE DEVELOPMENT & RESEARCH CORP.**
515 E. 41st St. (07504)
**Phone—(973) 754-7087**
Fax—(973) 754-7020
www.mdramazon.com
Email—info@mdramazon.com
Pres.—John S. Smith
V-P., Sales & Mktg.—William O'Brien
V-P., Opers.—Ted Smith
SIC—2842; 2899; NAICS—325612; *Marine maintenance products*
Employs—9; Estab.—1967
Sales—$1Mil-$5Mil
Distrib.—Intl.
Privately owned sub-S corp.
Also see: Hy-Test Packaging Corp., same loc.

**MASTER METAL POLISHING CORP.**
57 Wood St. (07520)
**Phone—(973) 684-0119**
Fax—(973) 684-7866
www.mastermetal.com
Email—sales@mastermetal.com
Pres.—Jeffrey Almeyda
V-P.—Kevin Almeyda
Corp. Secy.—Gerardo Almeyda
SIC—3471; NAICS—332813; *Metal finishing, anodizing, passivation & chemical film*
Employs—15; Estab.—1962
Sales—$500,000-$1Mil
7,000 sq ft site, Distrib.—National
Privately owned corporation
ISO rating—9001:2000

**METAL COMPONENTS**
92 Maryland Ave. (07503)
**Phone—(973) 247-1204**
Fax—(973) 247-1207
www.metalcomponentsinc1.com
Pres.—Frank Mottola
GM—Al Schroeder
Off. Mgr.—Dee Dee Tallaksen
SIC—3599; *Precision machining job shop*
Employs—35; Estab.—1959
20,000 sq ft site, Distrib.—Local
Privately owned corporation

**MIAMI ONION ROLL CO.**
111 Berkshire Ave. (07502)
**Phone—(973) 389-2202**
National—(800) 843-7055
Fax—(973) 389-2206
www.miamionionroll.com
Pres.—Harriet Davis
Off. Mgr.—Jackie Rossi
SIC—2038; 2051; NAICS—311412; *Frozen hors d'oeuvres, bread & rolls*
Employs—30; Estab.—1985
20,000 sq ft site, Distrib.—National
Privately owned corporation

**MICRON FASTENER, INC.**
85-99 Hazel St. (07503)
**Phone—(973) 278-4100**
National—(800) 923-1022
Fax—(973) 278-4101
www.grommetmart.com
Email—info@micronamerica.com
Pres., CEO—Cilek Seker
V-P.—Billy Seker
Sales Dept. Mgr.—Ozge Kucuk
Cust. Serv. Sales Rep.—Meryem Konac
SIC—3965; NAICS—339993; *Buttons, grommets, dies, jean accessories, snaps & attaching machinery*
Employs—8; Estab.—2000
Distrib.—Intl.
Privately owned corporation

**MICROSEAL INDUSTRIES, INC.**
610 E. 36th St., P.O. Box 3054 (07509)
**Phone—(973) 523-0704**
Fax—(973) 523-2085
www.microseal.com
Email—info@microseal.com
Pres.—Michael Silverstein
Dir., Sales—Charlie Facas
Pur. Agt.—Rosemary Marshall
SIC—2295; NAICS—313320; *Coating & laminating*
Employs—30; Estab.—1989
50,000 sq ft site, Distrib.—Intl.
Sole ownership

**MICROWAVE CONSULTING CORP.**
150 Railroad Ave. (07501)
**Phone—(973) 523-6700**
Fax—(973) 523-6800
www.mccnorsal.com
Email—sales@mccnorsal.com
Pres.—Scott Warner
SIC—3679; 3676; NAICS—334415; *Microwave equipment, including directional couplers, power dividers, pin-diode control components, resistors, attenuators & electronic filters*
Employs—4; Estab.—1987
Sales—$500,000-$1Mil
Distrib.—Intl.
Privately owned corporation
DBA: MCC/Norsal

**†MIVILA CORP.**
226 Getty Ave. (07503)
**Phone—(973) 278-4148**
Fax—(973) 278-9332
www.mivila.com
Email—info@mivila.com
Pres.—Ted Laoudis
SIC—5141; *Corporate headquarters & distributor of general line groceries, serving restaurants, hotels, institutions, wholesalers & redistributors*
Employs—10; Estab.—2003
320,000 sq ft site, Distrib.—Local
Privately owned corporation
AKA: Mivila Foods

**MPT DELIVERY SYSTEMS, INC.**
Div. of Pharmachem Laboratories, Inc.
95 Prince St. (07501)
**Phone—(973) 279-4132**
Fax—(973) 279-4435
www.mpti.com
Email—sales@mpti.com
Pres.—Bob McCrimlisk
Off. Mgr.—Marian Pardi
Qual. Control Mgr.—Edwin Lopez
Maint. Mgr.—George Lee
SIC—2834; 2099; NAICS—325412; *Formulation & granulation of bulk nutriceuticals & food ingredients*
Employs—50; Estab.—1978
Sales—under $500,000
35,000 sq ft site, Distrib.—Intl.
Privately owned corporation
Parent co.—Pharmachem Laboratories, Inc., Kearny, NJ
Phone—(201) 246-1000
See Parent Co. Section for full profile.

**MR. J'S XCALIBER CORP.**
39 Dundee Ave. (07503)
**Phone—(973) 278-1611**
www.xcaliberart.com
Email—jxcal@aol.com
Ptnr.—Julian Braet
Ptnr.—Linda Braet
SIC—3993; *Interior & exterior signs*
Employs—3; Estab.—1969
Sales—under $500,000 (est)
Distrib.—Local
Privately owned partnership
AKA: Xcaliber Corp.

**MUFFINS & STUFF**
53 Jersey St. (07501)
**Phone—(973) 881-9900**
Fax—(973) 881-9292
Pres.—Mendell Neustadt
Manager—Isaac Neustadt
SIC—2051; NAICS—311812; *Gourmet bread, muffins & cookies*
Employs—10; Estab.—1996
Sales—under $500,000
Distrib.—Regional
Privately owned corporation

**NEW ERA CONVERTING MACHINERY**
235 Route 20 (07504)
Mail addr: P.O. Box 377, Hawthorne (07507-0377)
**Phone—(201) 670-4848**
Fax—(201) 670-8867
www.neweraconverting.com
Email—info@neweraconverting.com
CEO—Frank P. Lembo
Pres.—Robert Pasquale
V-P., Controls—Ray Simpson
V-P.—Paul Lembo
V-P.—Rick McCarthy
Hum. Res. & IT Mgr.—Helen Pasquale
SIC—3552; NAICS—333292; *Coating, laminating, unwinding & winding machinery*
Employs—60; Estab.—1992
48,000 sq ft site, Distrib.—Intl.
Privately owned sub-S corp.

**NEW JERSEY DIAMOND PRODUCTS CO.**
108 Kentucky Ave. (07503)
**Phone—(973) 684-0949**
National—(888) 684-4115
Fax—(973) 684-3716
www.njdp.com
Email—sales@njdp.com
Pres.—Mark Zambrano
V-P. & Sales Mgr.—James Zambrano
Off. Mgr.—Lori Santiago
SIC—3291; *Diamond cutting wheels, drills & tools*
Employs—12; Estab.—1966
5,000 sq ft site, Distrib.—National
Privately owned corporation

**NEW JERSEY FRAME & MOULDING CO.**
62 Kearney St. (07522)
Mail addr: P.O. Box 2441, Paterson (07509)
**Phone—(973) 684-6001**
National—(800) 526-5281
Fax—(973) 595-9486
Email—sales@njframe.com
Pres.—Craig Aisenman
SIC—2499; *Wooden picture frames*
Employs—6; Estab.—1954
Distrib.—National
Privately owned corporation

**NEW JERSEY HALAL MEAT PACKING**
841 Main St. (07503)
**Phone—(973) 684-3648**
Fax—(973) 684-8504
Email—bros.halal@yahoo.com
Owner—Abdul Beqiri
Manager—Qerem Beqiri
SIC—2011; *Halal meat processing & packing*
Employs—4; Estab.—1990
Sales—$1Mil-$2.5Mil
Distrib.—Local
Privately owned corporation
AKA: Brothers Quality Halal Meat

**NEW WORLD INTERNATIONAL CORP.**
59 Dover St. (07501)
**Phone—(973) 881-8100**
Fax—(973) 881-1558
Email—service@newworldintl.com
Co-Pres., CEO—Carmen Bires
Co-Pres., GM—Angelo Fiorita

GEOGRAPHICAL

## Paterson—(cont.)

SIC—2844; NAICS—325600;
*Health, beauty & personal care
products*
Employs—12; Estab.—1994
Sales—$1Mil-$2.5Mil
Distrib.—National
Privately owned corporation

**NEW YORK CORRUGATED BOX CO.,
LLC**
239 Lindberg Pl., Ste. 1 (07503)
**Phone—(973) 742-5000**
Fax—(973) 742-7666
www.nycorrugatedbox.net
Email—nycorr@aol.com
Owner—Robert Rosner
SIC—2653; 3089; NAICS—
322211; *Corrugated boxes &
packaging supplies*
Employs—5; Estab.—1941
Sales—$500,000-$1Mil
Distrib.—Regional
Limited Liability Company

**NEW YORK CORRUGATED BOX, LLC**
239 Lindbergh Pl., Ste. Ll (07503)
**Phone—(973) 742-5000**
Fax—(973) 742-7666
www.nycorrugatedbox.net
Email—nycorr@aol.com
Pres.—Robert Rosner
SIC—2653; 2657; *Corrugated &
high-end gift boxes & packaging
supplies*
Employs—3; Estab.—2002
Sales—$500,000-$1Mil
Distrib.—Regional
Limited Liability Company

**NEXTWAVE WEB, LLC**
229 Marshall St. (07503)
**Phone—(973) 742-4339**
Fax—(973) 742-5949
www.nextwaveweb.com
Email—alia@nextwaveweb.com
Ptnr.—Alia Suqi
Ptnr.—Isi Suqi
SIC—2759; NAICS—323100;
*Commercial printing*
Employs—8; Estab.—2006
Sales—$500,000-$1Mil
7,500 sq ft site, Distrib.—National
Privately owned corporation

**OKONITE CO., THE**
Div. of Okonite Co., Inc., The
102 Hilltop Rd. (07513)
Mail addr.—P.O. Box 340, Ramsey
(07446)
**Phone—(201) 825-0300**
Fax—(973) 684-7307
www.okonite.com
Email—info@okonite.com
Plt. Mgr.—Steve Nicholas
Hum. Res. Mgr.—Paulette Vita
SIC—3357; *Electric wire & power
cables*
Employs—100; Estab.—1878
Sales—$26Mil-$50Mil
300,000 sq ft site, Distrib.—Intl.
Privately owned corporation
ISO rating—9002
Parent co.—Okonite Co., Inc., The,
Ramsey, NJ
Phone—(201) 825-0300
See Parent Co. Section for full profile.

**ORTHO-DYNAMICS, INC.**
210 E. 16th St. (07524)
**Phone—(973) 742-4390**
National—(800) 275-1842
Fax—(973) 742-4556
www.orthodynamics.com
Pres.—Steve Tushingham
V.-P. & Off. Mgr.—Hector Leon
Bookkeeper—Yvonne Gonzalez
SIC—3842; *Custom orthotics &
non-prescription orthotics &
braces*
Employs—18; Estab.—1993
8,000 sq ft site, Distrib.—National
Privately owned sub-S corp.

**P & S BLIZZARD CORP.**
722 Madison Ave. (07501)
**Phone—(973) 523-1700**
Fax—(973) 523-6221
Pres.—Paul Kostovski
SIC—2499; 3089; *Wooden &
plastic fences*
Employs—2; Estab.—1978
Distrib.—Local
Privately owned corporation

**PAPER TUBE & CORE, INC.**
239 Lindbergh Pl. (07503)
**Phone—(973) 977-8823**
Fax—(973) 977-8668
www.papertubeandcore.com
Email—info@
papertubeandcore.com
Pres.—Russ Panzer
V-P.—Jeff Schindle
SIC—2655; NAICS—322214;
*Recycled/reusable paper tubes
& cores for film, paper & textiles
manufacturers & converters*
Employs—25; Estab.—1992
Sales—$1Mil-$2.5Mil
Distrib.—Intl.
Sole ownership

**PARISER INDUSTRIES, INC.**
91 Michigan Ave. (07503)
**Phone—(973) 569-9090**
National—(800) 370-7627
Fax—(973) 569-9101
www.pariserchem.com
Email—info@pariserchem.com
Co-Pres.—Andrew Pariser
Co-Pres.—Scott Pariser
Cont.—John Reilley
Div. Mgr.—Art Fatica
SIC—2843; NAICS—325613;
*Chemical cleaning compounds*
Employs—25; Estab.—1971
45,000 sq ft site, Distrib.—National
Privately owned corporation

**PARSONS CABINETRY, INC.**
80 George St. (07503)
**Phone—(973) 279-4954**
Fax—(973) 279-1966
www.parsonscabinetry.com
Email—info@parsonscabinetry.com
Pres.—Winfield Parsons
GM & Head Cabinetmaker—
Stephen Parsons
SIC—2434; NAICS—337110;
*Custom kitchen cabinets*
Employs—12; Estab.—1987
Distrib.—Local
Privately owned corporation

**PATERSON MONUMENTS CO., INC.**
317 Totowa Ave. (07502)
**Phone—(973) 942-0727**
National—(800) 675-0727
Fax—(973) 835-0394
www.patersonmonument.com
Email—info@gravestones.us
Pres.—Leslie Christopher
Off. Mgr.—Diana George
SIC—3281; NAICS—327991;
*Burial monuments & engraving*
Employs—3; Estab.—1905
Distrib.—Local
Privately owned corporation

**PATERSON PICKLE CO.**
285 4th Ave. (07514)
**Phone—(973) 523-1000**
Fax—(973) 523-2228
www.patersonpickle.com
Email—eric@patersonpickle.com
Pres.—Mark Nadel
COO—Eric Nadel
Bookkeeper—Iris Rosenberg
SIC—2035; *Pickles & pickling
cucumbers*
Employs—20; Estab.—1988
Sales—under $500,000
17,500 sq ft site, Distrib.—Regional
Privately owned sub-S corp.

**PATERSON SHEET METAL WORKS,
INC.**
320 Wabash Ave. (07503)
**Phone—(973) 345-4182**
Fax—(973) 345-3931
Email—psn320@aol.com
Pres.—Richard Basilicato
Plt. Mgr.—John Koromhas
Fabricator—Mike Teller
SIC—3444; *Sheet metal
fabrication*
Employs—4; Estab.—1950
Sales—under $500,000
Distrib.—Local
Privately owned corporation

**PECATA ENTERPRISES, INC.**
18 Market St. (07501)
**Phone—(973) 523-5866**
National—(800) 567-4451
Fax—(973) 523-5460
www.ultimatetextile.com
Email—info@ultimatetextile.com
Pres.—Roger Glickman
Opers. Mgr.—Manny Del Rio
Off. Mgr.—Stella Garzon
Cust. Serv. Rep.—Diana Smith
SIC—2399; 3993; *Table linens &
printed banners*
Employs—80
Distrib.—Intl.
Privately owned corporation
AKA: Ultimate Textile

**PERAGALLO PIPE ORGAN CO.**
306 Buffalo Ave. (07503)
**Phone—(973) 684-3414**
Fax—(973) 684-2237
www.peragallo.com
Email—john4@peragallo.com
CEO—John Peragallo
Secy-Treas.—Frank Peragallo
SIC—3931; NAICS—339992;
*Handcrafted pipe organs*
Employs—15; Estab.—1918
7,000 sq ft site, Distrib.—National

**PICKLE KING**
220 Ellison St. (07505)
Mail addr.: P.O. Box 2415, Paterson
(07509-2415)
**Phone—(973) 977-2095**
Fax—(973) 977-8423
www.pickleking.net
Email—pickleking220@aol.com
Pres., GM—Richard Nadel
V.-P.—Josh Stein
Bookkeeper—Georgianne Gallipoli
Cust. Serv. Rep.—Jennifer
Bacchas
SIC—2035; 2096; *Pickles, pickled
peppers, olives & tomatoes,
coleslaw, potato, macaroni,
cucumber, olive, artichoke, egg,
bean, beef, tuna, seafood &
pasta salads & salad dressings;
Brand name—Pickle King*
Employs—12; Estab.—1958
Sales—$1Mil-$5Mil
21,000 sq ft site, Distrib.—National
Privately owned sub-S corp.

**POLY EXPRESS, LLC**
318 McLean Blvd., Bldg. 5 (07504)
**Phone—(800) 843-7659**
Fax—(888) 310-4630
www.polyexpress.com
Email—info@polyexpress.com
Pres.—Bill Parlak
SIC—2673; 3081; 3089;
*Polyethylene bags, liners, sheets
& tubing*
Employs—15; Estab.—2001
Sales—$1Mil-$2.5Mil (est)
Distrib.—National
Limited Liability Company

**POLYTRON DEVICES, INC.**
295-303 River St. (07524)
Mail addr: P.O. Box 398, Paterson
(07544)
**Phone—(973) 345-5885**
Fax—(973) 345-1264

www.polytrondevices.com
Email—sales@polytrondevices.com
Pres.—Nancy Metzger
Sales Mgr.—Sheri Lynn
Off. Mgr.—Nancy Berger
SIC—3663; 3621; NAICS—
334220; *Power supplies*
Employs—25; Estab.—1969
Sales—$1Mil-$5Mil
15,000 sq ft site, Distrib.—Intl.
Privately owned corporation

**PRECISE MACHINE & TOOL, INC.**
369 Knickerbocker Ave. (07503)
**Phone—(201) 790-3320**
Email—fatihcivi@optonline.net
Owner, Pres., Fin., Opers. & R & D
Mgr.—Fatih Civi
SIC—3599; 3543; NAICS—
332997; *CNC machining &
prototype parts*
Employs—3; Estab.—1986
Sales—under $500,000
2,000 sq ft site, Distrib.—Regional
Privately owned corporation

**PRECISION MFG., LLC**
177 Gould Ave. (07503)
**Phone—(973) 278-6600**
Fax—(973) 278-3514
Pres., GM, Sales & Mktg. Mgr.—
George Sharpe
Supervisor—Elcy Gomez
SIC—3089; *Custom plastics,
including injection molding &
electronic printed circuit board
assembly, testing & packaging*
Employs—7; Estab.—1977
Sales—$500,000-$1Mil
15,000 sq ft site, Distrib.—
Regional
Limited Liability Company

**PRINZ WOODWORKING, INC.**
381 E. 22nd St. (07514)
**Phone—(973) 977-2345**
Fax—(973) 977-2346
Email—prinzwood@aol.com
Pres.—Leonard Prinz
SIC—2431; NAICS—321900;
*Wooden cabinets & architectural
millwork*
Employs—10; Estab.—1983
Sales—$500,000-$1Mil
Distrib.—National
Privately owned corporation

**PROEDGE**
167 Genessee Ave. (07503)
**Phone—(973) 742-3900**
National—(800) 251-6114
Fax—(973) 742-3920
www.proedgetools.com
Email—proedge@proedgetools.com
Owner—Mike Hammam
Off. Mgr.—Toshanna Scott
SIC—3423; *Hobby tools, blades &
knives*
Employs—8; Estab.—1972
Sales—$500,000-$1Mil
Distrib.—Intl.
Privately owned corporation

**PROGRESS MACHINE SHOP, INC.**
41 Kentucky Ave. (07503)
**Phone—(973) 278-4999**
Owner—Tony Markovski
Foreman—Steve Markovski
SIC—3599; *General machining
job shop*
Employs—7
Sales—$500,000-$1Mil (est)
Distrib.—Regional
Sole ownership

**QUALITY FORMULATION
LABORATORIES, INC.**
110 Pennsylvania Ave. (07503)
**Phone—(973) 977-8800**
Fax—(973) 977-8833
www.qualityformulations.com
Email—elsie@
qualityformulations.com
CEO—Mohamed Desoky

## Paterson—(cont.)

Cont.—Elsie Estrada
Plt. Mgr.—Andrew Karpati
SIC—2834; 2833; NAICS—325412; *Vitamin preparations, weight loss products, nutritional supplements & natural remedies*
Employs—50; Estab.—1980
Sales—$5Mil-$10Mil
60,000 sq ft site, Distrib.—Intl.
Privately owned corporation

### QUALITY METAL FINISHING CORP.

80 George St., 1st Fl. (07503)
**Phone—(973) 345-0963**
Fax—(973) 345-0418
www.qualitymetalfinishing.net
Email—qmfc@aol.com
Pres.—Mark Leonardis
Manager—Danielle Russo
SIC—3471; NAICS—332813; *Metal finishing*
Employs—25
Distrib.—Local
Privately owned corporation

### QUALITY REBUILDERS, INC.

969 Market St. (07513)
**Phone—(973) 523-8800**
Fax—(973) 523-0806
www.qualityrebuilders.com
Email—info@qualityrebuilders.com
Pres.—Zecky Cohen
Hum. Res. Mgr.—Adriana Pitino
SIC—3714; *Car & truck front axles*
Employs—7; Estab.—1984
Sales—$1Mil-$2.5Mil (est)
Distrib.—Local
Privately owned corporation

### QUALITY SOLID SURFACE, INC.

333 Vreeland Ave. (07513)
**Phone—(973) 357-9770**
Fax—(973) 357-9773
Email—frontdesk@qsstops.com
Owner—Offer Bok
SIC—2542; 3281; NAICS—327991; *Fabrication of solid-surface countertops*
Employs—25; Estab.—1999
Sales—$1Mil-$2.5Mil
Distrib.—Local
Privately owned corporation

### RAILROAD CONSTRUCTION COMPANY, INC. (H Q)

75-77 Grove St. (07503)
**Phone—(973) 684-0362**
Fax—(973) 684-1355
www.railroadconstruction.com
Email—info@railroadconstruction.com
Pres.—Christopher Daloisio
V-P. & Secy.—James A. Daloisio
Dir., Hum. Res.—Mary Daloisio
SIC—3441; NAICS—332312; *Corporate headquarters; heavy structural steel fabrication*
Employs—100
Sales—$10Mil-$25Mil (est)

### REBCO, INC.

1171 Madison Ave., Ste. 1 (07503-2827)
**Phone—(973) 684-0200**
National—(800) 777-0787
Fax—(973) 684-0118
www.rebcoinc.com
Email—sales@rebcoinc.com
Pres.—Tony Stolarz
Cred. Mgr.—Beverly Zambon
Sales & Mktg. Supv.—Vinny Capurso
Plt. Opers. Supv.—Regina DeLoach

SIC—3442; 3354; NAICS—332321; *Commercial aluminum entrances, doors, windows & storefront systems, including extrusions & sheets*
Employs—40; Estab.—1954
Sales—$5Mil-$10Mil (est)
100,000 sq ft site, Distrib.—Regional
Privately owned sub-S corp.

### RELIABLE ELECTRIC MOTOR REPAIR, INC.

Div. of Schulz Electric Company, The
19 California Ave. (07503)
**Phone—(973) 278-8122**
Fax—(973) 278-6520
www.reliable-motor.com
Email—annmc@reliable-motor.com
GM—Ken Maulfair
SIC—3621; 5063; *Rebuilt electric motors & distributor of new electric motors*
Employs—15; Estab.—1981
Sales—$1Mil-$2.5Mil (est)
Distrib.—National
Privately owned corporation
Parent co.—Schulz Electric Company, The, New Haven, CT
Phone—(203) 562-5811
See Parent Co. Section for full profile.

### RELIANT GROUP

318 McLean Blvd. (07504)
**Phone—(973) 977-8799**
www.lionplastics.com
Email—gerardo@groupreliance.com
Plt. Mgr.—Lewis Caczolli
Hum. Res. Mgr.—Maline Caczolli
SIC—3086; NAICS—326100; *Plastic blister packaging*
Employs—25; Estab.—1982
Distrib.—Local
Privately owned corporation

### RELIANT RIBBON & TRIMS

838 21st Ave. (07513)
**Phone—(973) 881-0404**
National—(800) 886-2697
Fax—(973) 881-0560
www.reliantribbon.com
Email—info@reliantribbon.com
Pres.—Seth Shulman
V-P., Opers.—Steve Parvin
Dir., Mktg.—Joanne Sotirhos
SIC—2241; NAICS—313221; *Decorative fabric, printed & custom packaging ribbons & bows; Brand name*
Employs—50; Estab.—1963
70,000 sq ft site, Distrib.—Intl.
Privately owned corporation

### RICO FOODS, INC.

527 E. 18th St. (07514)
**Phone—(973) 278-0589**
Fax—(973) 278-0378
www.ricofoods.com
Email—info@ricofood.com
Pres.—Emilio Hernandez
V-P., Fin.—Lazara Hernandez
SIC—2038; NAICS—311412; *Hispanic food products*
Employs—36; Estab.—1989
35,000 sq ft site, Distrib.—National
Privately owned corporation

### RIGO INDUSTRIES, INC.

50 California Ave. (07503)
**Phone—(973) 881-1780**
National—(800) 426-4788
Fax—(973) 881-0906
www.rigowall.com
Email—help@rigowall.com
Pres.—Isaac Gorovitz
Administrator—Misha Gomez
SIC—3089; *Vinyl wallpaper*
Employs—50; Estab.—1984
Distrib.—Intl.
Privately owned corporation

### ROBRO MFG., INC.

288 10th Ave. (07524)
Mail addr: P.O. Box 537, Paterson (07544-0537)
**Phone—(973) 279-7237**
Fax—(973) 279-1340
www.robromfg.com
Email—robromfg@optonline.net
Pres.—Ivan Migalko
Off. Mgr.—Luba Migalko
SIC—3599; 3499; *General machining job shop, including CNC machining, welding, prototyping, assemblies & fabrication*
Employs—12; Estab.—1970
Sales—over $800,000
16,000 sq ft site, Distrib.—National
Sole ownership

### ROCCO PRESS, INC.

171 Walnut St. (07522)
**Phone—(973) 790-4000**
Fax—(973) 790-4086
www.roccopress.com
Email—roccopress@mac.com
Owner—Lou Rocco
Pres.—Lou Rocco, Jr.
Prepress Mgr.—Ray Chef
Prod. Mgr.—Christopher Watson
SIC—2759; NAICS—323100; *Commercial printing*
Employs—10; Estab.—1937
Sales—under $500,000
Distrib.—Regional
Privately owned corporation

### ROYCE ASSOCS., L. P.

28-36 Paterson St. (07501)
**Phone—(973) 279-0400**
Fax—(973) 279-3175
www.royceintl.com
Email—info@royceintl.com
GM—Hany Daood
SIC—2865; NAICS—325100; *Solvent, basic & vat dyes for plastics, oil, pulp & paper, adhesives & textiles industries*
Employs—25; Estab.—1929
Distrib.—National
Privately owned corporation
AKA: Passaic Color & Chemicals Co.
Parent co.—Royce Assocs., L. P., East Rutherford, NJ
Phone—(201) 438-5200
See Parent Co. Section for full profile.

### SABRE DIE CUTTING CO., INC.

68 Mill St. (07501)
**Phone—(973) 357-9800**
Fax—(973) 357-9996
www.sabrediecutting.com
Email—mike@sabrediecutting.com
Pres.—Michael Culver
SIC—2675; 3089; NAICS—322200; *Die cutting of paper, paperboard, plastics & fabrics*
Employs—25
Sales—$5Mil-$10Mil (est)
Distrib.—Local
Privately owned corporation

### SAMSTUBEND, INC.

31 Maryland Ave. (07503)
**Phone—(973) 278-2555**
Fax—(973) 278-2664
www.samstubendinc.com
Email—samstubend@att.net
COO—Samuel Ajadi
Plt. Mgr.—Arnold Virula
Off. Admn.—Catherine Ajadi
SIC—3317; NAICS—332996; *Boiler tube fabrication & bending, including rolling & welding*
Employs—13; Estab.—1995
12,000 sq ft site, Distrib.—Intl.
Privately owned corporation

### SAMUELSON FURNITURE, INC.

11-13 Maryland Ave. (07503)
**Phone—(973) 333-6090**
National—(888) 289-4489
Fax—(973) 333-6086
www.samuelsonfurniture.com
Email—info@samuelsonfurniture.com
Pres.—Lawrence Chalsin
V-P.—Laurie Chalsin
Cont.—Marianne St. George
SIC—2511; 2514; 2531; 2599; NAICS—337211; *Wooden & metal residential furniture & commercial furniture for the hospitality & hotel industries*
Employs—20; Estab.—1989
Distrib.—Intl.
Privately owned corporation

### †SAVCO RESTAURANT EQUIPMENT, INC.

600 Main St. (07503)
**Phone—(973) 523-4464**
Fax—(973) 523-8028
Email—savco600@aol.com
Owner—Sam Scorpo
SIC—5046; *Distributor of new & used restaurant equipment & parts*
Employs—7
Distrib.—Local
Limited Liability Company

**NEW ENTRY**

### SCREENING BASE

245 W. Broadway (07522)
**Phone—(973) 389-7950**
Email—screenbase@aol.com
Pres.—Michael Thompson
SIC—2396; *Apparel screen printing*
Employs—2; Estab.—1992
Sales—under $500,000 (est)
1,200 sq ft site, Distrib.—Local
Sole ownership

### SEABOARD PAPER & TWINE, LLC

37 E. 6th St. (07524)
**Phone—(973) 413-8100**
Fax—(775) 288-5329
www.seaboardpaperandtwine.com
Email—bob.baretz@gmail.com
Member—Robert Baretz
SIC—2671; 2298; *Waxed paper, manila rope & twine for packaging applications*
Employs—12; Estab.—2003
42,000 sq ft site, Distrib.—Regional
Limited Liability Company

### SEALY MATTRESS CO. OF NEW JERSEY

Div. of Sealy, Inc.
697 River St. (07524)
**Phone—(973) 345-8800**
Fax—(973) 345-7124
www.sealy.com
Email—jfullum@sealy.com
Pres.—David Hertz
V-P., Fin.—Joseph Fullum
SIC—2515; *Mattresses & box springs*
Employs—260; Estab.—1935
135,000 sq ft site, Distrib.—Regional
Publicly owned corporation
Parent co.—Sealy, Inc., Trinity, NC
Phone—(336) 861-3500
See Parent Co. Section for full profile.

### SENAT POULTRY, LLC

28 Warren St. (07524)
**Phone—(973) 742-4790**
(973) 742-9316
(862) 239-1708
Fax—(973) 742-4407
www.senatpoultry.com
Email—enameatpacking@hotmail.com
Ptnr.—Ali Kucukkarca
Ptnr.—Ed Kucukkarca

GEOGRAPHICAL

## Paterson—(cont.)

Pres.—Atabey Kucukkarca
GM—Amadou Samb
Qual. Control Mgr.—Steve Smith
SIC—2015; NAICS—311612; *Poultry meat processing*
Employs—30; Estab.—1989
Sales—$11Mil-$25Mil
Distrib.—Regional
Privately owned corporation
AKA: Ena Meat Packing

### SEW ANN SEW THOMAS ENTERPRISES

153 Pearl St. (07501)
**Phone—(973) 742-2664**
Fax—(973) 742-2664
Email—daileythomasg@yahoo.com
Owner—Dailey G. Thomas, Jr.
SIC—2395; 2396; *Custom embroidery & screen printing on textiles*
Employs—2; Estab.—2005
Sales—under $500,000
Distrib.—Regional
Privately owned corporation

### SHADOW RACING & HOBBY PRODUCTS, INC.

70 1st Ave. (07514)
**Phone—(973) 684-7270**
        (973) 689-6442
Fax—(973) 279-8113
www.shadowracing.com
Email—support@shadowracing.com
Owner & Pres.—Robert DeBois
V.-P.—Jerry Grandov
SIC—3714; *Race car shocks, weight jackers & set-up tools for remote-controlled car hobbyists; Brand name—Black Magic Shocks; Shockzilla*
Employs—2; Estab.—1997
Sales—$500,000-$1Mil
Distrib.—National
Privately owned sub-S corp.

### SONRISE METAL, INC.

138 3rd Ave. (07514)
**Phone—(973) 423-4717**
Fax—(973) 423-0338
www.sonrisemetal.com
Email—info@sonrisemetal.com
Pres.—Todd Abrams
GM—Jules Pushman
Hum. Res. Mgr.—Teresa Concepcion
SIC—3444; 3599; *Precision sheet metal fabrication & machining of enclosures, cabinets, panels, brackets & racks for the electronics, semiconductor, robotic, audio & defense industries*
Employs—19; Estab.—1980
Distrib.—National
Privately owned sub-S corp.
Also see: ABCO Metal, LLC, same loc.

### STARLIGHT WINDOWS MFG., INC.

50 E. 25th St. (07514)
**Phone—(973) 278-9366**
National—(877) 877-9555
Fax—(973) 278-4648
www.starlightwindows.com
Email—info@starlitewindows.com
Pres.—Juan D. Rodriguez
Corp. Secy.—Olivia Rivera
Sales Mgr.—Angelo Cardona
SIC—3089; *Vinyl windows*
Employs—5; Estab.—1988
Distrib.—National
Privately owned corporation

### STEPHEN PLASTICS, INC., DOUGLAS

22-36 Green St. (07501)
Mail addr: P.O. Box 2775, Paterson (07509)
**Phone—(973) 523-3030**
Fax—(973) 523-0643
www.douglasstephenplastics.com
Email—annabass@douglasstephen.com
V.-P.—Douglas Graff
Pur. Mgr.—Carla Farrentino
IT Mgr.—Fernando Surraco
Hum. Res. & Pers. Mgr.—Paul Beshaw
SIC—3089; *Plastic food containers*
Employs—90; Estab.—1959
Sales—$10Mil-$25Mil
Distrib.—Intl.
Privately owned corporation

### STERLING WINDOW CO.

224 21st Ave. (07501)
**Phone—(973) 742-1900**
Fax—(973) 742-1018
Pres.—Joseph J. Baldino
SIC—3442; 3089; NAICS—332321; *Vinyl & aluminum windows*
Employs—15; Estab.—1977
Sales—$500,000-$1Mil
Distrib.—Local
Sole ownership

### STUDIO J/ARCHITECTURAL GLASS EFFECTS

215 Pennsylvania Ave. (07503)
**Phone—(973) 569-0200**
National—(888) 772-5282
Fax—(973) 569-0300
www.studiojglass.com
Email—ageglass@yahoo.com
Pres.—John Leong
V.-P.—Judy Leong
Manager—Mike Leong
SIC—3231; NAICS—327215; *Custom stained & leaded architectural decorative textured clear glass, shelving & antique mirrors, including restoration*
Employs—8; Estab.—1978
Sales—$500,000-$1Mil
6,000 sq ft site, Distrib.—National
Privately owned sub-S corp.

### SUPPLY PLUS, INC.

155 Sherman Ave. (07502)
**Phone—(973) 782-5930**
National—(800) 724-5106
Fax—(973) 782-5931
V.-P.—Samuel Neustein, Jr.
SIC—3069; 3991; NAICS—339994; *Household cleaning products, sponges & scrubbers*
Employs—35; Estab.—1992
Distrib.—National
Privately owned corporation

### †SUPPLYONE, INC.

1200 Madison Ave. (07503)
**Phone—(718) 392-7400**
Fax—(718) 361-2733
www.supplyone.com
Email—sales@supplyone.com
Pres.—Jerry Vitelli
Pur. Agt.—Paul Pianchini
SIC—5087; 5113; *Distributor of corrugated boxes & janitorial cleaning supplies, including wipers, cleaning lubricants & detergents*
Employs—60; Estab.—1982
Sales—$10Mil-$25Mil
9,000 sq ft site, Distrib.—Regional
Privately owned corporation
Parent co.—SupplyOne, Inc., Devon, PA
    Phone—(484) 582-5005
See Parent Co. Section for full profile.

### SUPREME STEEL RULE DIES, INC.

985 Madison Ave. (07501)
**Phone—(973) 345-9474**
Fax—(973) 345-5925
Email—supremedies@hotmail.com
Pres.—Federico Espinal
SIC—3544; NAICS—333500; *Flat steel rule cutting dies*
Employs—2; Estab.—1981
Sales—under $500,000
Distrib.—National
Privately owned sub-S corp.

### SWEET POTATO PIE, INC.

140 Auburn St. (07501)
**Phone—(973) 279-3405**
Fax—(973) 279-1436
Email—eramsey@classicpies.com
Pres.—Edgar Ramsey
Off. Mgr.—Ila Satterfield
SIC—2051; NAICS—311812; *Bakery products, including bread & cakes*
Employs—35; Estab.—1980
Sales—$500,000-$1Mil
Distrib.—Local
Privately owned corporation

### SYNERGY MICROWAVE CORP.

201 McLean Blvd. (07504)
**Phone—(973) 881-8800**
Fax—(973) 881-8361
www.synergymwave.com
Email—sales@synergymwave.com
Pres.—Meta Rhode
Plt. Mgr.—Ray Abernathy
SIC—3679; *Microwave components, including swtiches, couplers, OC block, demodulators, filters, mixers & frequency synthesizers*
Employs—90; Estab.—1982
Distrib.—Intl.
Privately owned corporation

### T & T CABINET WORKS, INC.

388 River St. (07524)
**Phone—(973) 279-0909**
Fax—(973) 279-0909
Pres.—Tony Cercone
SIC—2511; *Wooden & laminated furniture*
Employs—6; Estab.—1977
Sales—under $500,000
Distrib.—Regional
Privately owned corporation

### T R B ELECTRO CORP.

6 Morris St., P.O. Box 840 (07501)
**Phone—(973) 278-9014**
Fax—(973) 278-5124
Email—trbelectro@aol.com
Pres., CFO—Raman D. Patel
Secy., MIS Mgr.—Dan K. Patel
SIC—3471; NAICS—332813; *Metal plating*
Employs—35; Estab.—1985
7,000 sq ft site, Distrib.—Local
Privately owned corporation

### T. S. GATES, INC.

202 12th Ave. (07501)
**Phone—(973) 523-7323**
Fax—(973) 523-7416
www.kaufmaniron.com
Email—sales@kaufmaniron.com
Pres.—Joseph Kaufman
Off. Mgr.—Joe Apuzzo
Bookkeeper—Donna Boyd
SIC—3446; NAICS—332323; *Iron gates*
Employs—30; Estab.—1995
Distrib.—Local
Privately owned corporation
AKAs: Kaufman Mfg. Group & Kaufman Iron Works & Bedlam Architect

### TABLECLOTH CO., INC.

514 Totowa Ave. (07522)
**Phone—(973) 942-1555**
National—(800) 227-5251
Fax—(800) 377-3720
www.tablecloth.com
Email—info@tablecloth.com
Pres.—Judith Metzger
Ex. V.-P.—Michael Kramer
V.-P., Opers.—Mary Kerr
SIC—2392; *Tablecloths, napkins, runners, placemats, tableskirting, chair covers & aprons*
Employs—50; Estab.—1980
Distrib.—Intl.
Privately owned sub-S corp.

### TEC INSTALLATIONS, INC.

375 E. 22nd St. (07514)
**Phone—(973) 684-0503**
Fax—(973) 684-0710
Pres.—Scott Crance
SIC—3535; NAICS—333922; *Conveyor systems*
Employs—10; Estab.—1980
Sales—$1Mil-$5Mil
20,000 sq ft site, Distrib.—Regional
Privately owned corporation

### TECH ART, INC.

12 E. 5th St. (07524)
Mail addr: P.O. Box 1556, South Hackensack (07606)
**Phone—(201) 525-0044**
Fax—(201) 487-5524
Email—paul.mcdonald@grpackaging.com
Pres.—Gerald Pfund
V.-P.—Paul McDonald
SIC—3421; NAICS—332200; *School scissor & ruler packaging*
Employs—5; Estab.—1995
Sales—under $500,000
Distrib.—Intl.
Privately owned corporation

### TECHNICAL PROCESSING, INC.

81 Dale Ave. (07501)
**Phone—(973) 278-4950**
Fax—(973) 278-9424
www.technicalprocessing.com
Email—teproducts@outlook.net
Pres.—Paul Yankner
V.-P., Cont.—Janet Raubold
Off. Mgr.—Stacey Owens
SIC—2899; *Rubber processing preparations*
Employs—20; Estab.—1967
Distrib.—Intl.
Privately owned corporation

### TEE SHIRT GUY

507 E. 41st St. (07504)
**Phone—(973) 247-3442**
Fax—(973) 247-3442
Email—teeshirtguy1@gmail.com
Owner—Rawle McCurdie
Off. Coord.—Dominique Andrade
SIC—2396; *Apparel screen printing*
Employs—4; Estab.—2005
Sales—under $500,000
Distrib.—National
Sole ownership

### THE CLI GROUP

932 Market St. (07513)
**Phone—(973) 279-9174**
Fax—(973) 279-6916
www.thecligroup.com
Email—info@thecligroup.com
Pres.—Daren Silverstein
V.-P.—Paul Harencak
Bus. Admn. Mgr.—Susan Andresen
SIC—2295; 2759; NAICS—313320; *Textile laminating, digital printing & design for distinctive cinematic wallcoverings, murals & branded/themed graphics*
Employs—15; Estab.—1960
Sales—$5Mil-$10Mil
50,000 sq ft site, Distrib.—National
Privately owned sub-S corp.

## Paterson—(cont.)

**THERMA-TECH CORP.**
300 Dakota St. (07503)
**Phone—(973) 345-0076**
Fax—(973) 345-3228
www.therma-tech.com
Email—contactus@therma-tech.com
Owner—Ben Papka
GM—Sharon Ordaniel
SIC—3433; NAICS—333414;
*Infrared heating systems*
Employs—10; Estab.—1986
Sales—$500,000-$1Mil
7,500 sq ft site, Distrib.—Intl.
Privately owned corporation

**TRIFORM PRODUCTS, INC.**
219 Lafayette St. (07524)
**Phone—(973) 278-2042**
Fax—(973) 278-0323
Pres.—Doug Troast
Sales Mgr.—Barbara Troast
Plt. Mgr.—Dwight Troast
SIC—3469; 3479; *Powder coating
& metal stampings*
Employs—12; Estab.—1975
Sales—$1Mil-$2.5Mil (est)
Distrib.—Local
Privately owned corporation

**TRINITY PRESS, LLC**
655 Market St. (07513)
**Phone—(973) 881-0690**
Fax—(973) 881-0696
Pres.—Kevin Barnes
V-P.—Ray Mininni
Off. Mgr.—Loretta Mininni
SIC—2752; 2759; NAICS—
323100; *Offset, digital,
commercial, textile &
lithographic printing*
Employs—40; Estab.—1987
23,500 sq ft site, Distrib.—
Regional
Limited Liability Company

**TRI-STATE CRATING & PALLET CO.**
85 Fulton St. *(07501)*
**Phone—(973) 357-8293**
      (888) 845-0050
Fax—(973) 357-8296
www.tristatecrating.com
Email—sales@tristatecrating.com
Chrm.—Marc Ellison
Pres., CEO—Maria Ellison
CFO—P. Ellison
V-P., Export Rigging Div.—Lee J.
Ellison
GM—Carmelo Gonzalez
Sales Mgr.—Edward Crisafulli
Acct. Mgr.—Darren Platt
Plt. Mgr.—John Arias
SIC—2448; 2441; NAICS—
321920; *Custom wooden boxes,
crates, skids, bases & pallets,
including international crating,
heat treating & fumigation*
Employs—30; Estab.—1970
Sales—$1Mil-$5Mil
100,000 sq ft site, Distrib.—
Regional
Privately owned corporation

**UEHLING INSTRUMENT CO.**
473 Getty Ave. (07503)
**Phone—(973) 742-8710**
Fax—(973) 742-1205
www.uehling.com
Email—info@uehling.com
Pres.—Richard Pavan
Sales Mgr.—John Kievit

SIC—3821; 3826; NAICS—
339111; *Liquid level & panel
mounted gages, instrumentation
& controls, including high/low,
digital/analog alarm systems &
float, ultrasonic & pressure
switches*
Employs—20; Estab.—1896
Sales—$1Mil-$5Mil
15,000 sq ft site, Distrib.—Intl.
Privately owned corporation

†**UNITED SCRAP IRON & METAL CO.**
124 Wood St. *(07524)*
**Phone—(973) 279-1683**
Fax—(973) 279-1684
www.unitedscrapironandmetal.co
m
Email—info@
unitedscrapironandmetal.com
Manager—John Lewer
SIC—5093; 5012; *Wholesaler of
recycled metal & iron & used
cars & trucks*
Employs—15; Estab.—2004
Distrib.—Local
Privately owned corporation
AKA: UPEI

**UNIVERSAL SILKSCREEN, INC.**
17 Memorial Dr. (07505)
**Phone—(973) 221-0060**
Fax—(973) 790-7923
www.universaltees.com
Email—vinnietee@aol.com
Pres.—Vince Tartaglione
SIC—2396; *Textile screen printing*
Employs—2; Estab.—1981
Sales—under $500,000
2,000 sq ft site, Distrib.—Local
Privately owned corporation

**UNLIMITED STONE DESIGNS**
7 McLean Blvd. (07514)
**Phone—(973) 523-2224**
Fax—(973) 523-2788
www.unlimitedstonedesigns.net
Email—unlimitedstonedesigns@
aol.com
Pres.—Mike Mainolfi
Salesman—Sam Wells
SIC—3281; NAICS—327991;
*Granite, marble & slate
countertops, tabletops,
bathroom vanities & stone
fabrication*
Employs—4; Estab.—2004
Sales—$1Mil-$2.5Mil
30,000 sq ft site, Distrib.—
Regional
Privately owned corporation

†**URBAN MILLWORK & SUPPLY
CORP.**
90 2nd Ave. (07514)
**Phone—(973) 278-7072**
Fax—(973) 278-0754
www.discountdoorbergencounty.c
om
Email—stundel@yahoo.com
Pres.—Brett Stundel
SIC—5031; *Wholesaler of wooden
doors*
Employs—1; Estab.—1964
Distrib.—Local
Privately owned corporation

**VAC'S BANDAGE CO.**
163 Pennsylvania Ave. (07503)
Mail addr: P.O. Box 2582, Paterson
(07509)
**Phone—(973) 345-3355**
National—(800) 327-2395
Fax—(973) 345-8311
www.vacsbandage.com
Email—sales@vacsbandage.com
Owner—Anthony Vacca
Plt. & Sales Mgr.—Brian Joyce
SIC—2211; *Horse leg wraps*
Employs—10; Estab.—1962
Distrib.—Intl.
Privately owned corporation

†**VEOLIA ENVIRONMENTAL
SERVICES**
Div. of Veolia Environmental
Services North America Corp.
27-33 Iowa Ave. (07503)
**Phone—(973) 742-6789**
www.veoliaes.com
Email—sales@veoliaes.com
Br. Mgr.—Nydia Patino
SIC—5093; *Wholesaler of
recycled aluminum, metal,
plastic, paper & newsprint*
Publicly owned corporation
Parent co.—Veolia Environmental
Services North America Corp.,
Chicago, IL
    Phone—(312) 552-2800
See Parent Co. Section for full profile.

**VIBRATION ISOLATION CO.**
225 Grand St. (07501)
**Phone—(973) 345-8282**
Fax—(973) 345-8285
www.vibrationiso.com
Email—info@vibrationiso.com
Pres.—Doug Bennett
SIC—3625; NAICS—335314;
*Vibration isolators*
Employs—10; Estab.—1975
Sales—$500,000-$1Mil
Distrib.—National
Privately owned corporation

**VISION LIGHTING, INC.**
48 N. 2nd St. (07522)
**Phone—(973) 720-1200**
Fax—(973) 720-9470
Email—vlighting@aol.com
Pres.—Barry Mabery
V-P.—Frank Giarratana
Off. Mgr.—Fred Flyntstein
SIC—3646; 3648; NAICS—
335122; *Lighting fixtures for
sports, commercial, military,
transportation & industrial
applications; Brand name—
Advantage Tennis Court Lights;
VT Tunnel Lights; RC Sports
Lights*
Employs—10; Estab.—1995
Sales—$1Mil-$2.5Mil
Distrib.—Intl.
Privately owned corporation

**WALTED DESIGNS, INC.**
70 Spruce St., Ste. 8 (07501)
**Phone—(973) 881-1944**
Fax—(973) 881-0922
Email—walteddes@aol.com
Pres.—Bhibhishan Raghubir
V-P., Sales—Carl Dindial
SIC—2261; 2396; NAICS—
313311; *Narrow fabric printing*
Employs—2; Estab.—1972
Distrib.—National
Privately owned corporation
AKA: Supreme Ribbon

**WILKSTONE, LLC**
128 19th Ave. (07513)
**Phone—(973) 684-5100**
Fax—(973) 684-4907
www.wilkstone.com
Email—info@wilkstone.com
Pres.—David A. Wilkinson
Hum. Res. Mgr.—Sheila Romeo
SIC—3281; NAICS—327991;
*Marble*
Employs—7; Estab.—1993
Sales—$500,000-$1Mil
Distrib.—Local
Privately owned corporation

**ZENEX PRECISION PRODUCTS
CORP.**
69 George St. (07503)
**Phone—(973) 523-6910**
Fax—(973) 523-4693
www.zenexprecision.com
Email—info@zenexprecision.com
Pres.—Zenon Wrowski

SIC—3599; *Precision machining
job shop*
Employs—6; Estab.—1988
Sales—under $500,000
6,000 sq ft site, Distrib.—Local
Privately owned corporation

## Paulsboro

(Gloucester—S.W.)

**A A A PHARMACEUTICAL, INC.**
157-160 W. Jefferson St. (08066)
Mail addr: 681 Main St.,
Lumberton (08048)
**Phone—(609) 288-6060**
Fax—(609) 914-4389
www.aaapharm.com
Chrm.—Shashi Sheth
Pres.—Tejash Sheth
V-P., Mfg.—Nilesh Sheth
SIC—2834; NAICS—325412;
*Pharmaceuticals*
Employs—90; Estab.—1985
25,000 sq ft site, Distrib.—Intl.
Privately owned corporation

**ACE PALLET CORP.**
215 E. Broad St., P.O. Box 228
(08066)
**Phone—(856) 423-7277**
Fax—(856) 423-9048
www.acepalletcorp.com
Email—fourways11@aol.com
Off. Mgr.—Cynthia Unger
SIC—2448; NAICS—321920;
*Wooden pallets*
Employs—30
Distrib.—Local
Privately owned corporation

**AQUATROLS CORP. OF AMERICA**
1273 Imperial Way (08066)
**Phone—(856) 537-6003**
National—(800) 257-7797
Fax—(856) 537-6018
www.aquatrols.com
Email—info@aquatrols.com
Pres., CEO—Tracy M. Jarman
Dir., Mfg.—Paul Garvin
Dir., Tech.—Stanley Kostka
Mktg. Mgr.—Colleen Clifford
Bus. Dev. Mgr.—Robert A. Moore,
Jr.
SIC—2843; NAICS—325613;
*Agricultural chemicals*
Employs—35; Estab.—1954
50,000 sq ft site, Distrib.—Intl.
Privately owned corporation

**EXXON MOBIL CORP.**
Div. of ExxonMobil Corp.
1001 Billingsport Rd. (08066)
**Phone—(856) 224-5000**
National—(800) 243-9966
Fax—(856) 224-5030
www.exxonmobil.com
Email—info@exxonmobil.com
Opers. Mgr.—Roman Perez
Cust. Serv. Mgr.—Nancy Lafferty
SIC—2992; NAICS—324191;
*Lubricating oils & greases*
Employs—130; Estab.—1991
Distrib.—National
Publicly owned corporation
Parent co.—ExxonMobil Corp.,
Irving, TX
    Phone—(972) 444-1000
See Parent Co. Section for full profile.

**HYDRAULIC PACKING & SEAL
PRODUCTS**
1224 Forest Pkwy., P.O. Box 160
(08066)
**Phone—(856) 224-1120**
Fax—(856) 224-1119
www.hpsseals.com
Email—info@hpsseals.com
CEO—Charles Schappert
V-P.—Carolyn Schappert
IT Mgr.—Vinny Palladino

**GEOGRAPHICAL**

## Paulsboro—(cont.)

SIC—3053; NAICS—339991;
*Seals, gaskets & mechanical
packings*
Employs—50; Estab.—1988
Sales—$1Mil-$2.5Mil
Distrib.—Local
Privately owned corporation

### JOHNSON MATTHEY PHARMACEUTICAL MATERIALS

Div. of Johnson Matthey, Inc.
2003 Nolte Dr. (08066)
**Phone—(856) 384-7001**
National—(800) 444-8544
Fax—(856) 384-7276
www.jmpharma.com
Email—jmpharma@jmusa.com
Dir., Bus. Dev. & Sales & Mktg.—
Joseph Moy
Sr. Prod. Mgr.—Danielle Morelli-
Blevins
Sales & Mktg. Mgr.—Kevin
Hennessy
Hum. Res. Mgr.—Jennifer Murphy
Ex. Admn.—Lisa Waltz
SIC—2833; NAICS—325411;
*Pharmaceutical ingredients*
Employs—142; Estab.—1925
Distrib.—Intl.
Publicly owned corporation
Parent co.—Johnson Matthey, Inc.,
Wayne, PA
Phone—(610) 341-8300
See Parent Co. Section for full profile.

### †KAMAN INDUSTRIAL TECHNOLOGIES CORP.

195 Borrelli Blvd., Ste. B (08066)
**Phone—(856) 284-7400**
Fax—(856) 227-1192
www.kaman.com
Email—camp01-kit@kaman.com
Team Leader—Mark Pancoast
Cust. Serv. Rep.—Tom Bondio
Cust. Serv. Rep.—Andy
Derryberry
Cust. Serv. Rep.—Ron Cummings
SIC—5084; 5085; *Distributor of
industrial equipment & supplies*
Employs—10; Estab.—1946
Distrib.—Local
Publicly owned corporation
Parent co.—Kaman Industrial
Technologies Corp., Bloomfield,
CT
Phone—(860) 687-5000
See Parent Co. Section for full profile.

### †KAMAN INDUSTRIAL TECHNOLOGIES CORP.

195 Borelli Rd. (08066)
**Phone—(856) 227-7000**
Fax—(732) 438-1158
www.kamandirect.com
Email—nwp01-kit@kaman.com
Br. Mgr.—Robert Widen
Opers. Mgr.—Richard Guy
SIC—5084; 5085; *Wholesaler of
industrial equipment & supplies,
including gear boxes, motors &
bearings*
Employs—5; Estab.—1950
Sales—$2.5Mil-$3.5Mil
5,000 sq ft site, Distrib.—National
Publicly owned corporation
Parent co.—Kaman Industrial
Technologies Corp., Bloomfield,
CT
Phone—(860) 687-5000
See Parent Co. Section for full profile.

### †LEWIS-GOETZ & CO., INC.

1571 Grandview Ave. (08066-
1804)
**Phone—(856) 579-1421**
Fax—(856) 579-1429
www.lewis-goetz.com
Email—rbianchi@lewis-goetz.com
Opers. Mgr.—Ron Bianchi
Regulatory Mgr.—Bill Bettridge

SIC—5085; *Distributor of hoses,
couplings & related rubber
products; Brand name—
Aeroquip; Thermoid; PT; Dixon;
Goodall; Titan*
Employs—18; Estab.—1935
Sales—$10Mil-$25Mil
60,000 sq ft site, Distrib.—National
Privately owned corporation
ISO rating—9002
Parent co.—Lewis-Goetz & Co.,
Inc., Pittsburgh, PA
Phone—(412) 341-7100
See Parent Co. Section for full profile.

### MCGRORY GLASS, INC.

1400 Grandview Ave. (08066)
**Phone—(856) 579-3200**
National—(800) 220-3749
Fax—(856) 579-3232
www.mcgrory-glass.com
Email—info@mcgrory-glass.com
CEO, CFO—John McGrory
V-P., Opers.—Christopher
McGrory
V-P., MIS—Gary McGrory
Hum. Res. Mgr.—Marianne Rafter
R & D Mgr.—Michael McGrory
Engrg. Mgr.—Jerry Stoneberger
SIC—3231; 3089; NAICS—
327215; *Flat glass & plastic
fabrication*
Employs—35; Estab.—1984
30,000 sq ft site, Distrib.—National
Privately owned corporation

NEW ENTRY

### NMK RESOURCES

650 Grove Rd., Ste. 111 (08066)
Mail addr: P.O. Box 309, Thorofare
(08086-0309)
**Phone—(856) 686-4904**
Fax—(856) 686-4907
www.nmkresources.com
Email—nmk@nmkresources.com
Owner—Nabil Kassem
V-P.—Ezra Benjamin
SIC—1389; *Inspection &
laboratory testing services for the
petroleum & oil industry*
Employs—15; Estab.—2014
Sales—$250Mil-$500Mil
5,000 sq ft site, Distrib.—National
Privately owned corporation

### †NUSTAR ENERGY L. P.

7 N. Delaware St. (08066)
**Phone—(856) 224-8903**
Fax—(856) 224-8905
www.nustarenergy.com
Email—john.rutkowski@
nustarenergy.com
Terminal Mgr.—Russel Wright
Terminal Rep.—Don Piel
SIC—5172; *Distributor of gasoline,
crude oil, refined products &
specialty liquids*
Employs—6; Estab.—1978
Distrib.—National
Privately owned corporation
Parent co.—NuStar Energy L. P.,
San Antonio, TX
Phone—(210) 918-2000
See Parent Co. Section for full profile.

### OSSUR AMERICAS, INC.

1414 Metropolitan Ave. (08066)
**Phone—(856) 345-6000**
National—(800) 233-6263
Fax—(856) 848-1148
www.ossur.com
Email—info@ossur.com
Dir., Dist. Ctr.—Axel Bjornsson
SIC—3842; *Cervical collars*
Employs—100; Estab.—1947
40,000 sq ft site, Distrib.—National
Publicly owned corporation
Parent co.—Ossur Americas, Inc.,
Foothill Ranch, CA
Phone—(949) 382-3883
See Parent Co. Section for full profile.

### †OWENS & MINOR, INC.

1220 Forest Pkwy. (08066)
**Phone—(856) 423-9900**
National—(866) 423-9900
Fax—(856) 423-7891
www.owens-minor.com
Email—truitt.allcott@owens-
minor.com
Reg. V-P.—Mike Nugent
SIC—5047; *Distributor of medical
& surgical supplies*
Employs—55; Estab.—1881
Distrib.—Intl.
Publicly owned corporation
Parent co.—Owens & Minor, Inc.,
Mechanicsville, VA
Phone—(804) 723-7000
See Parent Co. Section for full profile.

### PAULSBORO REFINING CO.

Div. of PBF Energy Partners L. P.
800 Billingsport Rd. (08066)
**Phone—(856) 224-6000**
Fax—(856) 224-6681
www.pbfenergy.com
Email—info@pbfenergy.com
Comp., Fin. Mgr.—Greg Paranto
GM—Jack Eisenmann
Plt. Mgr.—Steve Krynski
MIS Mgr.—John Gold III
Hum. Res. Mgr.—Carrie Kelley
EHS Mgr.—Kevin Fetchko
Comm. Rels. Admn.—Mark Wilgus
Pur. Agt.—Wendy Michael
SIC—2911; NAICS—324110;
*Gasoline, jet fuels & lubricating
oils*
Employs—460; Estab.—1998
41,382,000 sq ft site, Distrib.—
Regional
Privately owned corporation
AKA: PBF Energy Partners L. P.
Parent co.—PBF Energy Partners
L. P., Parsippany, NJ
Phone—(973) 455-7500
See Parent Co. Section for full profile.

### †RUNNEMEDE TRUCK REFRIGERATION

320 Borelli Blvd. (08066)
**Phone—(856) 423-4400**
National—(800) 254-5064
Fax—(856) 423-2903
www.runnemede.com
Email—admin@runnemede.com
Pres.—Robert Hyndman
V-P.—Gene Hyndman
Off. Mgr.—Patricia L. Michaud
SIC—5088; 5013; *Wholesaler of
truck refrigeration & heating
units, including insulated truck
bodies & parts, refrigerated truck
& trailer repairs, trailer
inspections & refrigerated trailer
rentals; Brand name—Kidron;
Van Shield; Carrier; Eagle; Kysor;
Thermo King; ATC*
Employs—10; Estab.—1950
196,020 sq ft site, Distrib.—Intl.
Privately owned sub-S corp.

### STETSERS J.D. CANVAS PRODUCTS, INC.

644 Billings Ave. (08066)
**Phone—(856) 423-4901**
National—(800) 828-8490
Fax—(856) 423-4904
www.stetserscanvas.net
Email—stetsers@verizon.net
Pres. & V-P.—David Stetser
Opers. Mgr.—John Stetser
SIC—2394; NAICS—314912;
*Custom residential & commercial
awnings & canopies*
Employs—2; Estab.—1978
Sales—under $500,000
Distrib.—Intl.
Privately owned corporation

### WARD LAFRANCE, INC.

37 W. Broad St. (08066)
**Phone—(609) 922-8383**
Fax—(856) 224-0224

www.wardlafrance.com
Email—wardlafrance@hotmail.com
Pres.—Jon Burzichelli
SIC—3711; *Fire trucks*
Employs—5; Estab.—1981
Sales—$2.5Mil-$5Mil (est)
Distrib.—Intl.
Privately owned corporation

## Peapack

(Somerset—N.E.)

### KOMLINE-SANDERSON ENGINEERING

12 Holland Ave. (07977)
**Phone—(908) 234-1000**
(800) 225-5457
Fax—(908) 234-9487
www.komline.com
Email—info@komline.com
Pres.—Russell M. Komline
V-P., Fin., Treas. & Asst. Secy.—
Robert P. Blickens
V-P., Corp. Dev. & Mktg.—
Christopher L. Komline
Dir., Hum. Res.—Annette J.
Oswald
SIC—3589; NAICS—333319;
*Process/production filtration,
drying, wastewater treatment,
sludge processing & pollution
control equipment for municipal
wastewater & electric power
utilities & industrial clients; Brand
name—Roto-Kone; Roto-Trak;
Kompress*
Employs—100; Estab.—1946
Sales—$10Mil-$25Mil
85,000 sq ft site, Distrib.—Intl.
Privately owned corporation
ISO rating—9001

## Pedricktown

(Salem—S.W.)

### BERKOWITZ, INC., L.P., J. E.

1 Gateway Blvd., P.O. Box 427
(08067)
**Phone—(856) 456-7800**
National—(800) 257-7827
Fax—(856) 299-4344
www.jeberkowitz.com
Email—info@jeberkowitz.com
Pres.—Arthur Berkowitz
Ex. V-P., CFO—Shawn Smith
Dir., Sales—Robert Price
Dir., Opers.—Jim Carroll
Sales Mgr., Inside—Brian Larson
Plt. Mgr.—Jim Mooney
Hum. Res. Mgr.—Beverly Humenik
Cred. Mgr.—Diane Decembrino
Bus. Dev. Mgr.—Michael Z.
Nicklas
Mktg. Coord.—Darlene Hatton
Data Processor—Stephanie
Nunes
SIC—3231; NAICS—327215;
*Architectural glass fabrication of
insulating, silk-screened,
spandrel, laminated & decorative
laminated glass doors, canopies
& point-supported systems,
including high-performance
coatings & heat-soak testing;
Brand name—Invisewall;
Winduo; Fusion; Temperfect;
Enviroscreen; Envirospan; Edge*
Employs—265; Estab.—1920
200,000 sq ft site, Distrib.—
National
Privately owned partnership
ISO rating—9001:2008

### CMI-PROMEX, INC.

7 Benjamin Green Rd. (08067)
**Phone—(856) 351-1000**
National—(800) 381-5808
Fax—(856) 351-1659
www.cmi-promex.com
Email—cmipromx@cmi-
promex.com
Pres.—Wayne Ligato

## Pedricktown—(cont.)

V-P., Sales—Bob Frawley
V-P., Opers.—Richard Cavalier
Sales Mgr., Northeast—Jerry Newell
Pur. Mgr.—Betty Brown
SIC—3599; 3089; *Commercial machining, engineered thermoplastics, engineering & development of specialty railroad products, including rail & curved rail expansion joints, signal housings, rails of moveable bridges & related railroad products; Brand name—Ridex®; Prolite™*
Employs—20; Estab.—1987
Sales—$2.5Mil-$5Mil
Distrib.—National
Privately owned corporation

**CST PRODUCTS, LLC**

345 Route 130, P.O. Box 402 (08067)
**Phone—(856) 299-5339**
Fax—(856) 299-5388
www.cstpavers.com
Email—info@cstpavers.com
Manager—Eric Bischoff
SIC—3272; *Concrete pavers & retaining wall blocks; Brand name—CST VERSA-LOK®; CST MONO-CAST®*
Employs—20; Estab.—1984
Sales—$1Mil-$2.5Mil (est)
Distrib.—Regional
Limited Liability Company

**†FERRELL'S OIL SERVICE**

26 E. Mill St., P.O. Box 130 *(08067)*
**Phone—(856) 299-0500**
Fax—(856) 299-4959
Email—bshaw@ferrellsoil.com
Pres.—William Ferrell, Jr.
V-P., Secy-Treas.—Betty Shaw
SIC—5172; *Distributor of home heating oil*
Employs—2; Estab.—1960
Distrib.—Local
Privately owned corporation

**LUBRIZOL ADVANCED MATERIALS, INC.**

76 Porcupine Rd. (08067)
**Phone—(856) 351-2100**
Fax—(856) 351-2128
www.lubrizol.com
Email—corporate.media@lubrizol.com
Plt. Mgr.—Pam Watley
Hum. Res. Mgr.—Amanda Furr
Manager—John Thompson
SIC—3069; *Latex*
Employs—43; Estab.—1969
Distrib.—Intl.
Publicly owned corporation
Parent co.—Lubrizol Advanced Materials, Inc., Brecksville, OH
Phone—(216) 447-5000
See Parent Co. Section for full profile.

**NEW ENTRY**

**MASTER PRINTING, INC.**

30 Pedricktown Woodstown Rd., P.O. Box 1 (08067)
**Phone—(856) 299-8318**
Owner—Lou Master
SIC—2752; *Commercial offset printing*
Employs—4
Sales—under $500,000 (est)
Privately owned corporation

**OXYVINYLS**

Div. of OxyVinyls L. P.
P.O. Box 411 (08067)
**Phone—(856) 299-8498**
www.oxyvinyl.com
Email—info@oxyvinyl.com
Plt. Mgr.—Thomas Wutka
MIS Mgr.—Ed Gibson

Admn. Mgr.—Julia E. Bouvier
SIC—3087; NAICS—325991; *PVC resin*
Employs—40; Estab.—1999
Distrib.—National
Publicly owned corporation
Parent co.—OxyVinyls L. P., Dallas, TX
Phone—(972) 720-7488
See Parent Co. Section for full profile.

## Pemberton

(Burlington—S.E.)

**AZTECH MFG., LLC**

147 W. Hampton St. *(08068)*
**Phone—(609) 726-1212**
Fax—(609) 726-0403
www.aztechmfg.com
Email—dan@aztechmfg.com
Pres., GM—Dan Murphy
SIC—3599; *Precision machining job shop*
Employs—3; Estab.—2005
Sales—under $500,000
Distrib.—Local
Privately owned corporation

**BROWN'S ENGRAVING, LLC**

12 Fort Dix Rd. (08068)
**Phone—(609) 894-4443**
Owner—Roberta Brown
SIC—3479; *Metal engraving*
Employs—1; Estab.—2007
Sales—under $500,000
Distrib.—Regional
Limited Liability Company

**J. B. WELDING**

2 Reynolds St. (08068)
**Phone—(609) 894-9842**
Fax—(609) 894-9842
www.supermedia.com
Owner—Jerry Belsito
SIC—3441; 3599; NAICS—332312; *Structural steel fabrication & welding job shop, including ornamental iron*
Employs—1; Estab.—1985
Sales—under $500,000
Distrib.—Regional
Sole ownership

**TOTALLY T SHIRTS & MORE**

201 W. Hampton St. (08068)
**Phone—(609) 894-0011**
Fax—(609) 894-1300
www.totallytshirt.com
Email—tony.m@totallytshirt.com
Owner—Tony Miralglia
SIC—2396; 2395; 3993; *T-shirt screen printing, embroidery & signs & banners*
Employs—5
Sales—$1Mil-$2.5Mil
Privately owned corporation

## Pennington

(Mercer—N.E.)

**ALTA TECHNOLOGIES, INC.**

1545 Reed Rd., P.O. Box 100 (08534)
**Phone—(609) 538-9500**
Fax—(609) 538-9501
www.altatechinc.com
Email—info@altatechinc.com
Chrm., CFO—Percy F. Leaper
Pres., R & D Mgr.—Paul G. Snook
V-P. & Hum. Res. Mgr.—Laura M. Snook
Corp. Secy.—Mary-Alice W. Leaper
SIC—2295; 3089; NAICS—313320; *Expandable monofilament braided & fiberglass sleeving for cable harness & hose assembly*
Employs—7; Estab.—1986
Sales—$1Mil-$5Mil
12,000 sq ft site, Distrib.—Intl.
Privately owned corporation

**DIVERSATECH, INC.**

1584 Reed Rd. (08534)
**Phone—(609) 730-9668**
Fax—(609) 730-9708
www.diversatech.com
Email—diversatech@earthlink.net
Pres.—Haskel Zeloof
Off. Mgr.—Beth Deene
SIC—3444; 3599; *Sheet metal fabrication & machining job shop*
Employs—5; Estab.—1985
Sales—$500,000-$1Mil
14,000 sq ft site, Distrib.—Regional
Privately owned corporation

**HOPEWELL VALLEY VINEYARDS**

46 Yard Rd. (08534)
**Phone—(609) 737-4465**
www.hopewellvalleyvineyards.com
Email—violetta@hopewellvalleyvineyards.com
Owner—Sergio Neri
SIC—2084; *Wines*
Employs—4; Estab.—2001
Distrib.—Local
Privately owned corporation

**KOOLTRONIC, INC.**

30 Pennington-Hopewell Rd., P.O. Box 240 (08534)
**Phone—(609) 466-3400**
National—(800) 321-5665
Fax—(609) 466-1114
www.kooltronic.com
Email—sales@kooltronic.com
Chrm.—G. Freedman
CEO—A. L. Freedman
Pres.—Barry J. Freedman
Opers. Mgr.—Cheryl Bruno
Hum. Res. Mgr.—Phyllis Minelli
Bus. Dev. Mgr.—Steve Coulton
SIC—3585; NAICS—333415; *Air conditioners for electronic enclosures*
Employs—150; Estab.—1956
Sales—$10Mil-$25Mil
170,000 sq ft site, Distrib.—Intl.
Privately owned corporation

**LORNAN LITHO, INC.**

130 Route 31 N., Ste. E (08534)
**Phone—(609) 818-1198**
Fax—(609) 818-0249
www.lornan.com
Owner—William Shankoff
SIC—2759; *Commercial printing*
Employs—4; Estab.—2008
2,000 sq ft site, Distrib.—National
Privately owned corporation

**METRICON CORP.**

12 N. Main St., P.O. Box 63 (08534)
**Phone—(609) 737-1052**
Fax—(609) 737-1567
www.metricon.com
Email—info@metricon.com
Pres.—John H. Jackson
Off. Mgr.—Denise Lager
R & D Mgr.—Leonid Steingart
SIC—3829; *Film thickness measuring instruments*
Employs—7; Estab.—1980
3,500 sq ft site, Distrib.—Local
Privately owned corporation

**MOUNTAIN LION, INC.**

9 Voorhees Ct., P.O. Box 799 (08534)
**Phone—(609) 730-1665**
(609) 468-2661
Fax—(609) 730-1286
www.mtlioninc.net
Email—mtlion@me.com
Pres.—John Monteleone
SIC—2732; 2789; 3089; NAICS—323117; *Book printing, binding & packaging*
Employs—1; Estab.—1983
1,300 sq ft site, Distrib.—National
Privately owned corporation

**OCEAN POWER TECHNOLOGIES, INC.**

1590 Reed Rd. (08534)
**Phone—(609) 730-0400**
Fax—(609) 730-0404
www.oceanpowertechnologies.com
Email—info@oceanpowertech.com
Interim CEO—David Keller
CFO—Mark Featherstone
COO—David Heinz
SIC—3621; NAICS—335312; *Ocean wave power electricity converters*
Employs—29; Estab.—1994
Distrib.—Intl.
Publicly owned corporation

**PD-LD, INC.**

30-B Pennington-Hopewell Rd. (08534)
**Phone—(609) 564-7900**
Fax—(609) 564-7901
www.pd-ld.com
Email—info@pd-ld.com
CEO—Vladimir Ban
Pres.—Uri Abrams
V-P., Bus. Dev.—Robert Struthers
Dir., Sales—Thomas DeBerardine
Dir., R & D—Boris Volodin
Fin. Mgr.—Karen Reid
Dept. Mgr.—Dawn Penner
SIC—3357; *Fiber optics, laser components & laser sources*
Employs—60; Estab.—1993
15,000 sq ft site, Distrib.—Intl.
Privately owned corporation

**PENNINGTON FURNACE SUPPLY, INC.**

6 Brookside Ave. (08534)
**Phone—(609) 737-2500**
Fax—(609) 737-2502
Pres.—Mark Blackwell
SIC—3567; NAICS—333994; *Channel induction furnaces*
Employs—3; Estab.—1958
Sales—$1Mil-$2.5Mil
Distrib.—Intl.
Privately owned corporation

**PENNINGTON PRINTERS, INC.**

21 Burd St. (08534)
**Phone—(609) 737-0650**
Fax—(609) 737-8170
Email—pennprint@aol.com
Pres.—Maryann Saums
V-P.—Gerald F. Keating
SIC—2752; NAICS—323100; *Offset printing & graphic design*
Employs—2; Estab.—1981
Sales—under $500,000
Distrib.—Local
Privately owned corporation

**PULSETOR, LLC**

1580 Reed Rd., Ste. C-2 (08534)
**Phone—(609) 303-0578**
www.pulsetor.com
Email—info@pulsetor.com
Chief Technical Officer—Richard Mott
Mechanical Engr.—Jeff Thompson
SIC—3829; *Silicon drift detection devices*
Employs—5; Estab.—2003
Sales—$1Mil
Distrib.—Intl.
Limited Liability Company

**ROLL TECH INDUSTRIES**

55 Route 31 S., Ste. A (08534)
**Phone—(609) 730-9500**
National—(877) 765-5832
Fax—(609) 730-8155
www.rolltechindustries.com
Email—jking@rolltechindustries.com
Pres.—John King
Plt. Mgr.—James Hodges
Hum. Res. & Off. Mgr.—Meredith Murphy

GEOGRAPHICAL

## Pennington—(cont.)

SIC—3499; *Metal roll-formed products*
Employs—26; Estab.—1952
Sales—$6Mil-$10Mil
Distrib.—National
Privately owned corporation

**TRAP ROCK INDUSTRIES, INC., PENNINGTON QUARRY**

Div. of Trap Rock Ind., LLC
120 Route 31 S. (08534)
Mail addr.: P.O. Box 419, Kingston (08528)
Phone—**(609) 737-3200**
    (609) 252-8927
Fax—(609) 497-0135
www.traprock.com
Email—gmorgan@traprock.com
Plt. Opers. Mgr.—Frank Bray
SIC—3281; 2951; NAICS—327991; *Crushed stone & hot asphalt mix*
Employs—10; Estab.—1880
Sales—over $500,000
200,000 sq ft site, Distrib.—Regional
Privately owned corporation
Parent co.—Trap Rock Ind., LLC, Kingston, NJ
    Phone—(609) 924-0300
    See Parent Co. Section for full profile.

**U. S. A. TOLERANCE RINGS**

85 Route 31 N. (08534)
Phone—**(609) 745-5000**
National—(877) 865-7464
Fax—(609) 745-5012
www.usatolerancerings.com
Email—sales@usatolerancerings.com
Pres.—Al DeBlasio
Div. Mgr.—Joseph C. Trainer
SIC—3452; NAICS—332722; *Tolerance rings/elastic shims for relaxation of tolerances of mating round parts*
Employs—6; Estab.—1961
2,000 sq ft site, Distrib.—Intl.
Privately owned corporation

**ZYDUS PHARMACEUTICALS USA, INC.**

73 Route 31 N. (08534)
Phone—**(609) 730-1900**
Fax—(609) 730-1998
www.zydususa.com
Email—sales@zydususa.com
CEO—Joseph D. Renner
V-P., Opers.—Preshant Desai
SIC—2834; NAICS—325412; *Corporate headquarters & generic pharmaceuticals*
Employs—12
Sales—$5Mil-$10Mil (est)
Distrib.—Intl.
Privately owned corporation

## Penns Grove
(Salem—S.W.)

**†PRAXAIR, INC.**

554 Shell Rd. (08069)
Phone—**(856) 299-3500**
National—(800) 772-9247
Fax—(856) 299-2427
www.praxair.com
Email—info@praxair.com
Ex. V-P.—Paul Bilek
Plt. Mgr.—Michael Barras
Tech. Rep.—Rick Farrow
SIC—5172; 5169; *Distributor of propane & oxygen gases*
Employs—10; Estab.—1982
Distrib.—Regional
Publicly owned corporation
Parent co.—Praxair, Inc., Danbury, CT
    Phone—(203) 837-2000
    See Parent Co. Section for full profile.

## Pennsauken
(Camden—S.W.)

**3D MEDICAL MFG., INC.**

Div. of 3D Medical Manufacturing, Inc.
7145 Colonial Ln. (08109)
Phone—**(856) 486-9600**
    (856) 486-9610
Fax—(856) 486-9620
www.3dmedicalmfg.com
Email—rkarpowich@3dmedicalmfg.com
V-P., Mfg.—Anthony Jenkowski
Pur. Agt.—Eline Sangos
SIC—3599; *CNC & Swiss screw turning & milling*
Employs—60; Estab.—1999
Sales—$5Mil-$10Mil (est)
5,100 sq ft site, Distrib.—National
Privately owned corporation
Parent co.—3D Medical Manufacturing, Inc., Riviera Beach, FL
    Phone—(561) 842-7175
    See Parent Co. Section for full profile.

**ABC SIGNSYSTEMS, INC.**

7970 National Hwy., P.O. Box 622 (08110)
Phone—**(856) 665-0950**
National—(800) 752-7849
Fax—(856) 665-6315
www.abcsignsystems.com
Email—sales@abcsignsystems.com
Pres.—Stephen Trifletti
Pur. Agt.—Mike Fulforth
SIC—3993; *Interior & exterior signs*
Employs—20; Estab.—1952
Sales—$500,000-$1Mil
Distrib.—National
Privately owned corporation

**ABCO SIGNS**

7300 N. Crescent Blvd., Ste. 11 (08110)
Phone—**(856) 663-6001**
Fax—(856) 663-3816
Pres.—Howard Gaston
Off. Mgr.—Sue McGarbey
SIC—3993; *Interior & exterior signs*
Employs—2; Estab.—1962
Sales—under $500,000
Distrib.—Regional
Sole ownership

**ACRO DISPLAY**

2250-A Sherman Ave. (08110-1217)
Phone—**(856) 488-9710**
Fax—(856) 488-9719
www.eastcoastcabinetsinc.com
Email—jreccinc@aol.com
Pres.—Paul Beranato, Jr.
SIC—2431; 2434; 3083; NAICS—337110; *Millwork, wooden cabinets & laminated casework*
Employs—6; Estab.—1986
20,000 sq ft site, Distrib.—National
Privately owned sub-S corp.

**ADVANCED ABRASIVES CORP.**

7980 National Hwy. (08110)
Phone—**(856) 665-9300**
Fax—(856) 488-1815
www.advancedabrasives.com
Email—aseligman@advancedabrasives.com
Pres.—Matthew Bees
V-P.—Andy Seligman
SIC—3291; *Diamond abrasives, inluding powders & slurries*
Employs—20; Estab.—2001
Distrib.—Intl.
Privately owned corporation

**AFFORDABLE OFFSET PRINTING, INC.**

809 Hylton Rd., Ste. 11 (08110-1335)
Phone—**(856) 661-0722**
Fax—(856) 661-0922
www.affordableoffset.com
Email—prepress@affordableoffset.com
Pres.—Gary Coates
Sales Mgr.—Peter Zales
Prodn. Artist—Heather Force
SIC—2752; 2759; 2791; 5199; NAICS—323100; *Offset & digital printing, electronic prepress & graphic design & distributor of promotional products*
Employs—4; Estab.—1997
4,000 sq ft site, Distrib.—Local
Privately owned corporation

**AIRBORNE SYSTEMS NORTH AMERICA OF NEW JERSEY, INC.**

Div. of TransDigm, Inc.
5800 Magnolia Ave. (08109)
Phone—**(856) 663-1275**
Fax—(856) 663-8146
www.airborne-sys.com
Email—sales@airborne-sys.com
Sr. V-P., Cust. Bus., N. America—Elizabeth Johnson
Ex. V-P., Strategy & Tech.—J. C. Berland
Mktg. Mgr.—Ann Tock
Prod. Line Mgr.—Gary Lange
SIC—2399; 3999; *Corporate headquarters & military ram-air parachute, joint precision aerial delivery & parachutist's PHAOS, OXCON & SOLR oxygen systems; Brand name—Raider Intruder™ System; Hi Glide™ System; MT-2XX System; MT-1 Series; MC-4 System; Microfly™; Firefly™; Dragonfly™*
Employs—125; Estab.—1969
Sales—$40Mil-$50Mil
45,000 sq ft site, Distrib.—Intl.
Publicly owned corporation
ISO rating—9001
Parent co.—TransDigm, Inc., Cleveland, OH
    Phone—(216) 706-2960
    See Parent Co. Section for full profile.

**AMER-RAC, LLC**

8128 River Rd. (08110)
Phone—**(856) 488-6210**
National—(800) 411-8932
Fax—(800) 664-8309
www.amer-rac.com
Email—info@amer-rac.com
Pres.—Steve Shore
Plt. Mgr.—Bob Schmitt
SIC—3496; 3499; *Steel & aluminum truck & van ladder racks & van interior shelving & interiors*
Employs—10; Estab.—2000
15,000 sq ft site, Distrib.—National
Limited Liability Company

**†AMSAN EAGLE MAINTENANCE SUPPLY**

Div. of AmSan Florida
80 Twin Bridge Dr. (08110)
Phone—**(856) 317-9500**
National—(800) 756-9022
Fax—(856) 317-9802
www.amsan.com
Email—info@amsan.com
Br. Mgr.—Candy Chapman
Consultant—Diane Pettinelli
SIC—5087; *Distributor of janitorial supplies, including paper & chemicals*
Employs—55
Distrib.—Local
Publicly owned corporation
Parent co.—AmSan Florida, Pompano Beach, FL
    Phone—(954) 972-1700
    See Parent Co. Section for full profile.

**APOLLO EAST, INC.**

7895 Airport Hwy. (08110)
Phone—**(856) 486-1882**
National—(800) 982-2115
Fax—(856) 486-7582
www.apolloembroidery.com
Email—info@apolloembroidery.com
Pres.—Dora Ngan
Opers. Mgr.—Paulo Tang
IT Mgr. & Accts. Exec.—Jessie Li
Hum. Res. Mgr.—Lisha Leong
Sales Rep.—Carol Lee
SIC—2396; 2395; *Textile screen printing & embroidery*
Employs—20; Estab.—2005
Sales—under $500,000
Distrib.—Intl.
Privately owned corporation

**†ARETT SALES CORP.**

9285 Commerce Hwy. (08110)
Phone—**(856) 751-1224**
National—(800) 257-8220
Fax—(856) 751-0604
www.arett.com
Email—sales@arett.com
Pres.—Lindsey Chesbrough
CFO—Cathy Shappert
V-P., Mktg.—Mauri Librett
Dir., Mktg.—Noah Chesbrough
SIC—5083; *Corporate headquarters & distributor of lawn & garden equipment*
Employs—100; Estab.—1951
Company-wide: 150
Sales—$150Mil
650,000 sq ft site, Distrib.—National

NEW ENTRY

**ARG PRINTING, LLC**

1601 Sherman Ave. (08110)
Phone—**(856) 665-5644**
Fax—(856) 665-4583
Owner—Randy Gilbert
SIC—2759; *Commercial printing*
Employs—3
Sales—$1Mil-$2.5Mil
3,000 sq ft site, Distrib.—National
Limited Liability Company

**†ARIVA DISTRIBUTION, INC.**

1705 Suckle Hwy. (08110)
Phone—**(856) 488-0800**
National—(800) 257-7905
Fax—(856) 488-0718
www.arivanow.com
Email—sales@arivanow.com
V-P., GM—Ray Radomicki
SIC—5111; 5113; *Wholesaler of printing paper & packaging & shipping supplies*
Employs—50; Estab.—1958
Distrib.—Local
Privately owned corporation
Parent co.—Ariva Distribution, Inc., Covington, KY
    Phone—(859) 292-5000
    See Parent Co. Section for full profile.

**†ARMOR METALS & RECYCLING**

8300 National Hwy., Ste. 2 (08110)
Phone—**(856) 665-5715**
Fax—(856) 665-5732
www.armormetalsrecycling.com
Email—frank@armormr.com
Mng. Ptnr.—Frank Lobascio
SIC—5093; 5063; *Wholesaler of scrap metals & parts reclaimed from used electronics*
Employs—10

**BARRY CALLEBAUT USA, LLC**

1500 Suckle Hwy. (08110)
Phone—**(856) 663-2260**
National—(800) 836-2626
Fax—(856) 665-0474
www.barry-callebaut.com
Email—media@barry-callebaut.com
Site Mgr.—William Hayes
Hum. Res. Mgr.—Teri Fanz

## Pennsauken—(cont.)

SIC—2066; NAICS—311300;
*Cocoa & chocolate products*
Employs—110; Estab.—1985
Sales—$50Mil-$100Mil
Distrib.—Intl.
Publicly owned corporation
Parent co.—Barry Callebaut USA,
LLC, Chicago, IL
Phone—(312) 496-7300
See Parent Co. Section for full profile.

**BEEF INTERNATIONAL, INC.**
7010 Central Hwy. (08109)
**Phone—(856) 663-6763**
National—(800) 989-2820
Fax—(856) 663-1006
www.beefinternational.com
Email—dnaab@
beefinternational.com
Sales Mgr.—Dan Naab
Div. Mgr.—Kevin Ingraldi
IT Mgr.—Karen Gaughan
Off. Mgr.—Alicia Dirienvo
SIC—2011; NAICS—311611;
*Roast beef processing &
packing*
Employs—70; Estab.—1983
Sales—$26Mil-$50Mil
Distrib.—Intl.
Privately owned corporation

**BEVERAGE DISTRIBUTION CENTER,
INC.**
Div. of PepsiCo, Inc.
8275 Route 130 (08110)
**Phone—(856) 665-6200**
Fax—(856) 661-4510
Pres., CFO—Walt Wilkinson
V-P., Opers.—George Heinhold
Dir., Hum. Res.—June Raufer
SIC—2033; 2086; 5078; NAICS—
311421; *Corporate headquarters
& manufacturer & distributor of
private label noncarbonated &
carbonated beverages, sodas &
juices*
Employs—700; Estab.—1957
Sales—$100Mil-$250Mil (est)
Privately owned corporation
AKA: Pepsi Beverages Co.
Parent co.—PepsiCo, Inc.,
Purchase, NY
Phone—(914) 253-2000
See Parent Co. Section for full profile.

**BOOMERANG USED OFFICE
FURNITURE**
9155 River Rd. (08110)
**Phone—(856) 582-0100**
Fax—(856) 582-0104
www.boomerangofficefurniture.co
m
Pres.—Seth Deforest
Cont.—Iris Schmidt
SIC—2521; *Rebuilt wooden office
furniture*
Employs—10
Sales—$1Mil-$2.5Mil (est)
Distrib.—National
Privately owned corporation

**BUSH REFRIGERATION**
1700 Admiral Wilson Blvd. (08109)
**Phone—(856) 963-1800**
Fax—(856) 963-0770
www.bushrefrigeration.com
Email—info@bushrefrigeration.com
Pres.—Alex Bush
V-P.—Mary Ann Rakus
SIC—3585; *Refrigeration systems,
including walk-in coolers &
freezers & deli, liquor, beverage,
floral & produce display coolers*
Employs—20; Estab.—1979
Distrib.—National
Privately owned corporation

**CARPENTER & PATERSON, INC.**
3900 River Rd., P.O. Box 556
(08110)
**Phone—(856) 488-1988**
Fax—(856) 488-0824

www.carpenterandpaterson.com
Email—cpsales@
carpenterandpaterson.com
Br. Mgr.—Bob Cieslikowski
SIC—3429; *Commercial &
industrial pipe hangers &
supports*
Employs—15; Estab.—1912
Sales—$1Mil-$2.5Mil (est)
Distrib.—Regional
Privately owned corporation
Parent co.—Carpenter & Paterson,
Inc., Woburn, MA
Phone—(781) 935-7036
See Parent Co. Section for full profile.

**CETYLITE, INC.**
9051 River Rd. *(08110)*
**Phone—(856) 665-6111**
National—(800) 257-7740
Fax—(856) 665-5408
www.cetylite.com
Email—marketing@cetylite.com
Pres.—Gary Wachman
CFO—Alanna Nelson
Chief Administrative Officer—
Donna Pacifico
Dir., Opers.—Bruce Epley
SIC—2834; NAICS—325412;
*Pharmaceutical liquids, gels &
ointments, including prescription
topical anesthetics &
concentrated infection
prevention products; Brand
name—Cetacaine Topical
Anesthetic; Cetylcide Hard
Surface Disinfectant*
Employs—25; Estab.—1946
Distrib.—National
Privately owned sub-S corp.

**CHAMPION WINDOW OF
PENNSAUKEN**
Div. of Champion Window
Manufacturing & Supply Co., LLC
8400 Remington Ave., Ste. B
(08110)
**Phone—(856) 662-3400**
National—(877) 462-3400
Fax—(856) 662-7911
www.championfactorydirect.com
Email—philadelphia@
championfactorydirect.com
Div. Mgr.—Todd Morganci
Off. Mgr.—Shelly Leary
SIC—3089; *Vinyl replacement
windows & siding*
Employs—35; Estab.—2000
Sales—$2.5Mil-$5Mil (est)
Distrib.—Regional
Privately owned corporation
Parent co.—Champion Window
Manufacturing & Supply Co.,
LLC, Cincinnati, OH
Phone—(513) 346-4600
See Parent Co. Section for full profile.

**CINCHSEAL**
731 Hylton Rd. *(08110)*
**Phone—(856) 662-5162**
Fax—(856) 662-5264
www.cinchseal.com
Email—jamato@cinchseal.com
Owner—David Pitchko
V-P.—Mark Pitchko
Off. Mgr.—Jessica Amato
SIC—3053; NAICS—339991;
*Rotary shaft seals for slow
turning equipment, including
screw conveyors, ribbon
blenders & paddle mixers*
Employs—15; Estab.—1974
Sales—$5Mil-$10Mil
5,000 sq ft site, Distrib.—Intl.
Privately owned corporation

**CLINTON ENVELOPE**
9130 Pennsauken Hwy., Ste. C
(08110-1285)
**Phone—(856) 314-3636**
National—(800) 344-3640
Fax—(856) 314-0121
www.clintonenvelope.com
Email—clntprnt@erols.com

GM—Bob Donner
SIC—2677; 2759; NAICS—
322232; *Envelopes, including
plain, printed, stock & specialty
& commercial printing*
Employs—7; Estab.—1933
8,000 sq ft site, Distrib.—National
Also see: TPG Graphics, same
loc.

**COLORNET, LLC**
809 Hylton Rd., Ste. 11 (08110)
**Phone—(856) 662-0652**
Fax—(856) 662-0719
www.colornetinc.com
Email—info@colornetinc.com
Mng. Member—Elizabeth
Bollinger
Acctg. Mgr.—Heather Feliciano
Graphic Designer—Melanie Sweet
SIC—2752; 2759; NAICS—
323100; *Digital & offset full color
printing, business cards,
letterhead, envelopes, forms,
postcards, sell sheets,
brochures, presentation folders,
newsletters, booklet printing,
save the date cards, wedding
invitations & announcements*
Employs—4; Estab.—1986
5,000 sq ft site, Distrib.—Regional
Limited Liability Company

**COLORSOURCE, INC.**
7025 Central Hwy. (08109)
**Phone—(856) 488-8100**
            (856) 663-4144
National—(800) 554-9169
Fax—(856) 488-9181
www.colorsourceinc.com
Email—mellis@colorsourceinc.com
Pres.—Fred DeMarco
V-P.—Murray Ellis
SIC—2759; 2789; NAICS—
323100; *Commercial printing,
binding, fulfillment & mailing
services*
Employs—9; Estab.—1983
Sales—$1Mil-$2.5Mil
7,500 sq ft site, Distrib.—Regional
Privately owned corporation

**CONNECTOR PRODUCTS, INC.**
1300 John Tipton Blvd. (08110)
**Phone—(856) 829-9190**
Fax—(856) 829-9195
www.connectorproducts.com
Email—info@
connectorproducts.com
Pres.—Nick Polidori
Sales Mgr.—Don Janssen
Off. Mgr.—Diane Jamerson
SIC—3643; NAICS—335931;
*Electrical connector terminals*
Employs—22; Estab.—1972
Sales—$5Mil
21,000 sq ft site, Distrib.—Intl.
Privately owned corporation
ISO rating—9001

**CONTEMPORARY GRAPHIC
SOLUTIONS, INC.**
7001 N. Park Dr. (08109)
**Phone—(856) 663-7277**
National—(800) 575-4238
Fax—(856) 486-1466
www.contemporygs.com
Email—sales@
contemporygs.com
Pres.—Tim Moreton
V-P., Opers.—Bob Reilley
V-P.—Jim Moreton
IT Mgr.—Phil Panelli
SIC—2759; 2789; 2675; NAICS—
323122; *Printing, packaging,
finishing, die cutting & online
eCommerce & fulfillment,
warehousing, mail & creative
services*
Employs—196; Estab.—1986
115,315 sq ft site, Distrib.—Intl.
Privately owned corporation

**CRADEN PERIPHERALS CORP.**
7860 Airport Hwy. (08109)
**Phone—(856) 488-0700**
Fax—(856) 488-0925
www.craden.com
Email—info@craden.com
Pres.—Connell McGill
Technician—Mike Wypych
SIC—2759; NAICS—323100;
*Passport & bank passbook
printing*
Employs—30; Estab.—1983
15,000 sq ft site, Distrib.—Intl.
Privately owned corporation

**CRW GRAPHICS, INC.**
Div. of Hippographics, Inc.
9100 Pennsauken Hwy. (08110)
**Phone—(856) 662-9111**
National—(800) 820-3000
Fax—(856) 665-1789
www.crwgraphics.com
Email—service@crwgraphics.com
CEO—Harriet Weiss
Pres.—Mark Weiss
V-P., Sales & Mktg.—Will
Glassman
GM—Jon Conant
Cust. Serv. Mgr.—Rich Quigley
SIC—2759; 2791; 2752; NAICS—
323122; *Commercial offset,
digital & variable printing &
electronic prepress, including
web-to-print*
Employs—130; Estab.—1964
47,000 sq ft site, Distrib.—National
Privately owned corporation
Parent co.—Hippographics, Inc.,
Pennsauken, NJ
Phone—(856) 662-9111
See Parent Co. Section for full profile.

**DATWYLER, INC.**
9012 Pennsauken Hwy. (08110)
**Phone—(856) 663-2202**
National—(800) 874-3586
Fax—(856) 663-2636
www.datwyler.com
Email—info@datwyler.com
Site Dir.—David Clark
IT Mgr.—Angel Hernandes
Acctg. Mgr.—Steven Rayca
Hum. Res. Mgr.—Tara Roysdon
Hum. Res. Generalist—Melissa
Vogel
SIC—2671; *Rubber closures &
aluminum & plastic caps for
pharmaceutical packaging, drug
delivery & diagnostics*
Employs—300
Distrib.—Intl.
Privately owned corporation
ISO rating—9002

**DCC CORPORATION**
7250 Westfield Ave., Ste. B
(08110)
**Phone—(856) 662-7272**
Fax—(856) 662-7862
www.dcccorporation.com
Email—info@dcc-c.com
Pres.—Joseph Marshall
Administrator—Mary Bohn
SIC—3548; *Thermocouple
welders for the production of
thermocouples, data loggers &
thermocouple wire; Brand
name—HotSpot; HotSpot II;
HotSpot PLUS; HotMux*
Employs—6; Estab.—1984
Sales—$500,000-$1Mil
Distrib.—Intl.
Privately owned corporation

**DELTA PAPER CORP.**
8295 National Hwy. (08110)
**Phone—(856) 532-0333**
National—(800) 403-4049
Fax—(856) 486-0180
www.deltapaper.com
Sales Mgr.—Brett Bregman
Mfg. Mgr.—Perry Jenkins
Fin. Mgr.—Dawn Harris

GEOGRAPHICAL

## Pennsauken—(cont.)

Whse. Rep.—James Schneider
SIC—2671; *Environmentally safe
packaging, wrapping materials &
fillers; Brand name—Deltapaper*
Employs—50; Estab.—1972
Sales—$11Mil-$25Mil
55,000 sq ft site, Distrib.—
Regional
Privately owned sub-S corp.

### DELUXE PACKAGING CO.

1079 Thomas Busch Memorial
Hwy. (08110)
Mail addr: P.O. Box 4462, Cherry
Hill (08034-0679)
**Phone—(856) 486-0006**
Fax—(856) 486-9255
www.deluxepkg.com
Email—deluxeken@aol.com
Ptnr., V-P., Sales & GM—Ken
Hoffman
Ptnr.—Paul Davis
SIC—2657; 3086; 2653; NAICS—
322212; *Packaging supplies,
including folding paperboard
boxes, foam, corrugated
specialties & labels; Brand
name—Polyair; 3M*
Employs—6; Estab.—1983
Sales—$1Mil-$2.5Mil
Distrib.—National
Sole ownership

### DISC MAKERS

7905 N. Route 130 (08110)
**Phone—(856) 663-9030**
National—(800) 468-9353
Fax—(856) 661-3450
www.discmakers.com
Email—info@discmakers.com
Chrm.—Morris Ballen
Pres.—Tony Van Veen
V-P., Sales—David Olinsky
V-P., Mktg.—Steven Spaas
V-P., Hum. Res.—Sue Learn
IT Mgr.—Jacob Mandel
SIC—3652; *CD & DVD replication
& packaging*
Employs—500; Estab.—1946
115,000 sq ft site, Distrib.—
National

### DOW CHEMICAL CO., THE

1500 John Tipton Blvd. (08110)
**Phone—(856) 910-4900**
Fax—(856) 663-1198
www.dow.com
Email—info@dow.com
Off. Mgr.—Sue Fitzgerald
Site Leader—Rob Buchler
SIC—3086; NAICS—326100;
*Foam insulation*
Employs—30
Sales—$500,000-$1Mil
Distrib.—Intl.
Publicly owned corporation
Parent co.—Dow Chemical Co.,
The, Midland, MI
Phone—(989) 636-1000
See Parent Co. Section for full profile.

NEW ENTRY
### DUNN FABRICATION

8470 Remington Ave. (08110)
**Phone—(856) 486-3866**
www.dunnfab.com
Email—evand@dunnfab.com
Owner—Evan Dunn
SIC—3715; 3599; *Automotive
machining job shop*
Employs—1; Estab.—2014
Sales—under $500,000 (est)
Distrib.—Local
Limited Liability Company

### †ENFASCO

1675 Hylton Rd. *(08110-1313)*
**Phone—(856) 662-7660**
Fax—(856) 662-6172
www.enfasco.com
Email—sales@enfasco.com

Pres.—Frank Bailey
Accts. Mgr.—Jamillah Estelow
SIC—5072; *Distributor of
commercial & military specialty
fasteners; Brand name—Click
Bond; Pem; Atlas; Alcoa; Huck
Tooling; Hi Shear Tooling*
Employs—20; Estab.—1978
Sales—$10Mil
Distrib.—Intl.
Privately owned corporation
ISO rating—AS9100C
AKA: Engineered Fastener Co.

### EVERITE MACHINE PRODUCTS CO.

6995 Airport Highway Ln. (08110)
**Phone—(856) 330-6700**
Fax—(215) 426-7768
www.everite.com
Email—sales@everite.com
Pres., CFO—Bruce Mergenthal
V-P., Opers.—Carlos Suarez
Dir., Engrg.—Stan Katz
Opers. Mgr.—John Travia
Off. Mgr.—Debra Lubbers
Bus. Dev. Leader, ECG—William
Clipsham
SIC—3541; 3559; NAICS—
333512; *Electrolytic &
electrochemical grinding & cutoff
machines, including abrasive
cutoff equipment & related burr-
free machining; Brand name—
Ultracut SR8; Ultragrind UG618;
Ultragrind UG824; Ultragrind
VG1000; Ultracut AR8;
Electrolyte Formula ST;
Electrolyte Formula SN*
Employs—26; Estab.—1951
60,000 sq ft site, Distrib.—Intl.
Privately owned corporation
ISO rating—9001:2000, 13485

### EXPERT TEES

1585 Highway 73 (08110)
**Phone—(609) 828-0515**
Fax—(856) 985-7263
Email—mikeetcs@verizon.net
Owner—Mike Broome
SIC—2396; *Textile screen printing*
Employs—1; Estab.—1994
Sales—under $500,000
Distrib.—Local
Sole ownership

### †FESSENDEN HALL, INC.

1050 Sherman Ave. (08110)
**Phone—(856) 665-2210**
National—(800) 220-2233
Fax—(856) 665-6518
www.fessendenhall.com
Email—edwardbirdsall@
fessendenhall.com
Pres.—Edward Birdsall
CFO—Raymond Jungclaus
IT Mgr.—Tom Boland
Hum. Res. Mgr.—Bob Moroski
Whse. Mgr.—John Laneader
SIC—5031; *Corporate
headquarters & distributor of
plywood*
Employs—120; Estab.—1890
Company-wide: 150
7,000 sq ft site, Distrib.—Local
Privately owned corporation

### FLUIDYNE CORP.

9100 Collins Ave. (08110)
**Phone—(856) 663-1818**
Fax—(856) 662-5158
Email—fluidyne@fluidyne.net
Pres.—Bill Bloemker
Off. Mgr.—Cathy Matczak
SIC—3491; NAICS—332911;
*Industrial valves*
Employs—20; Estab.—1982
Sales—$2.5Mil-$3Mil
Distrib.—National
Privately owned corporation

### †FOODS GALORE, INC.

9246 Commerce Hwy. (08110)
**Phone—(856) 488-1112**
National—(800) 220-0123

Fax—(856) 488-0261
Email—rbraun@
foodsgaloreusa.com
Pres.—Morton Waxler
CFO—Richard Braun
V-P.—G. Scott Kindness
Treas.—Kenneth Sigman
SIC—5141; 5146; 5147; 5143;
*Wholesaler of food, dairy & meat
products, meats, fish & seafood
for grocery stores; Brand
name—Artisans Pride; 900*
Employs—90; Estab.—1986
Sales—$65Mil
42,000 sq ft site, Distrib.—
Regional
Privately owned sub-S corp.

### GARRISON PRINTING CO.

7155 Airport Hwy. (08109)
**Phone—(856) 488-1900**
Fax—(856) 488-6191
www.gogarrison.com
Email—staff@gogarrison.com
Co-Pres., CFO—Jake Garrison
Co-Pres., Opers. Mgr.—Dan
Garrison
Cont.—Kate Mathew
MIS Mgr.—Len Caromano
Off. Mgr.—Claire Gardiner
SIC—2759; NAICS—323100;
*Commercial printing*
Employs—40; Estab.—1965
Sales—$6Mil-$10Mil
22,000 sq ft site, Distrib.—Local
Privately owned corporation

### †GENERAL FLOOR, INC.

Div. of General Floor Industries
815 Hylton Rd. (08110)
**Phone—(856) 663-4750**
Fax—(856) 663-3410
www.generalfloor.com
Email—info@generalfloor.com
Manager—Rob Roark
SIC—5023; 5031; *Wholesaler of
carpet, laminate, hardwood &
vinyl flooring*
Employs—3; Estab.—1990
Distrib.—Regional
Privately owned corporation
Parent co.—General Floor
Industries, Bellmawr, NJ
Phone—(856) 931-0012
See Parent Co. Section for full profile.

### GOLDEN RULE, INC.

7150 N. Park Dr., Ste. 620 (08109)
Mail addr: 1282 Surfside Industrial
Pk., Ste. A, Myrtle Beach
(29575)
**Phone—(856) 663-3074**
Fax—(856) 486-3537
Email—goldenrulenorth@aol.com
Manager—Neil Miller
SIC—3544; NAICS—333500;
*Steel rule dies*
Employs—2; Estab.—1989
Sales—$500,000-$1Mil
Distrib.—National
Privately owned corporation
Parent co.—Golden Rule, Inc.,
Myrtle Beach, SC
Phone—(843) 232-9092
See Parent Co. Section for full profile.

### †GRABBER NORTHEAST

Div. of Grabber Construction
Products, Inc.
1125 Thomas Busch Memorial
Hwy. (08110)
**Phone—(856) 662-2525**
National—(800) 662-1144
Fax—(856) 662-4605
www.grabberman.com
Email—vanesti@grabberman.com
Br. Mgr.—Val Anesti
Opers. Mgr.—Lou Thomas

SIC—5072; 5169; *Distributor of
construction equipment &
supplies, including power tools,
adhesives & fasteners*
Employs—7; Estab.—1971
Distrib.—Regional
Privately owned corporation
Parent co.—Grabber Construction
Products, Inc., Alpine, UT
Phone—(801) 492-3880
See Parent Co. Section for full profile.

### GSC IMAGING, LLC

7150 N. Park Dr., Ste. 540 (08109)
**Phone—(856) 317-9301**
Fax—(856) 317-9302
www.gscimaging.com
Email—info@gscimaging.com
Owner & Principal—Ron Coutta
Principal—William Gallagher
Principal—Robert Sinatra
SIC—2893; NAICS—325910;
*Inkjet inks*
Employs—15; Estab.—2003
Distrib.—Intl.
Limited Liability Company

### H & H INDUSTRIAL CORP.

7612 N. Crescent Blvd. (08110-
2501)
**Phone—(856) 663-4444**
National—(800) 982-0341
Fax—(856) 663-4446
www.hhindustrial.com
Email—walt@hhindustrial.com
V-P.—Maryann Hajduk
V-P.—Walter Hajduk
Cont.—John Bandura
SIC—2542; *Electronics cabinets*
Employs—35; Estab.—1954
Sales—$6Mil-$10Mil
48,000 sq ft site, Distrib.—National
Privately owned corporation

### HAYS SHEET METAL, INC.

7070 Kaighns Ave., Bldg. B
(08109-4421)
**Phone—(856) 662-7722**
Fax—(856) 662-2665
Email—hayssheetmetal@
comcast.net
Pres.—Michael P. Hays
Manager—Dan Elwell
Bookkeeper—Nancy Dalessandro
SIC—3444; 3089; *HVAC &
fiberglass duct systems*
Employs—35; Estab.—1974
20,000 sq ft site, Distrib.—
Regional
Privately owned corporation

### †HESS CORP.

123 Derousse Ave. (08110)
Mail addr: 6901 River Rd.,
Pennsauken (08110)
**Phone—(856) 663-5111**
www.hess.com
Email—webmaster@hess.com
Terminal Supt.—Brian Clark
SIC—5172; *Distributor of
petroleum, including crude oil &
gasoline*
Employs—17
Publicly owned corporation
Parent co.—Hess Corp., New
York, NY
Phone—(212) 997-8500
See Parent Co. Section for full profile.

### HIBRETT PURATEX

7001 Westfield Ave. (08110)
**Phone—(856) 662-1717**
National—(800) 257-1780
Fax—(856) 662-0550
www.hibrettpuratex.com
Email—customerservice@
hibrettpuratex.com
Pres.—John P. J. Madden

## Pennsauken—(cont.)

SIC—2899; 2819; *Custom water treatment & industrial chemicals & cleaning products for tank washing, auto detailing & food plant & general industrial cleaning*
Employs—15; Estab.—1960
20,000 sq ft site, Distrib.—National
Privately owned sub-S corp.

**HIPPOGRAPHICS, INC. (H Q)**
9100 Pennsauken Hwy. (08110)
**Phone—(856) 662-9111**
Fax—(856) 665-1789
Email—lweiss@hippographics.com
Owner & Pres.—Larry Weiss
SIC—2759; 2791; 2761; 2789; NAICS—323122; *Corporate headquarters; business form, digital & commercial printing, prepress & binding*
Employs—3; Estab.—1964
Sales—under $500,000 (est)

**HOUSE OF GOLD, INC.**
1505 Suckle Hwy. (08110)
**Phone—(856) 665-0020**
Fax—(856) 665-6270
www.houseofgold.com
Email—contact@houseofgold.com
Pres.—Scott Solomon
SIC—2789; NAICS—323121; *Foil stamping*
Employs—18; Estab.—1969
Distrib.—Local
Privately owned corporation

**IMAGE SIGNS AND MORE, LLC**
2906 N. Centre St. (08109)
**Phone—(856) 665-1890**
Fax—(856) 665-1823
www.imagesignsandmorellc.com
Email—imagesigns57@yahoo.com
Owner—Boris Rubin
SIC—3993; *Vehicle lettering & graphics & custom signs*
Employs—2; Estab.—1993
Sales—under $500,000
Distrib.—Local
Limited Liability Company

**INNOVATIVE POWDER COATINGS, LLC**
9105 Burrough-Dover Ln. (08110)
**Phone—(856) 661-0086**
Fax—(856) 910-8903
www.ipcpowder.com
Email—ipcdave@comcast.net
Owner—David Macwilliam
GM—Tim Hyde
SIC—2851; NAICS—325510; *Custom & stock colored powder coatings*
Employs—4; Estab.—2004
Sales—$2Mil-$5Mil
Distrib.—National
Limited Liability Company

**INSERTS EAST, INC.**
7045 Central Hwy. *(08109)*
**Phone—(856) 663-8181**
Fax—(856) 663-3288
www.insertseast.com
Email—general@insertseast.com
Pres., CEO—Nick Maiale
CFO—Andrew Kavulich
SIC—2759; NAICS—323100; *Commercial printing of newspaper & direct mail circulars*
Employs—200; Estab.—1997
Sales—$50Mil
150,000 sq ft site, Distrib.—National
Privately owned sub-S corp.
AKA: G&F Graphic Services

**INTERNATIONAL PROCESS EQUIPMENT CO.**
9300 Route 130 N. (08110)
Mail addr: 9300 N. Crescent Blvd., Pennsauken (08110-1303)
**Phone—(856) 665-4007**
Fax—(856) 665-3991
www.rotormill.com
Email—rotormill@aol.com
Pres.—Ronald C. Miller
Off. Mgr.—Karen Anderson
Chief Engr.—Andreas Nesemann
SIC—3532; 3531; *Pulverizers & grinders*
Employs—20; Estab.—1984
Sales—$1Mil-$5Mil
20,000 sq ft site, Distrib.—Intl.
Privately owned corporation
AKA: IPEC

**INTERNATIONAL TOWER SUPPLY**
851 Bethel Ave. (08110)
**Phone—(856) 317-0005**
Fax—(856) 317-7151
www.internationaltowersupply.com
Email—sales@internationaltowersupply.com
Mng. Ptnr.—Michael Moskowitz
Sales Mgr.—Meg Donatucci
SIC—3663; 3679; 3499; NAICS—334220; *Wireless infrastructure components, including antenna & sector mounts, site hardware, ice bridges & cable trays & custom fabrication of steel platforms*
Employs—16; Estab.—2002
Sales—$1Mil-$2.5Mil
Distrib.—National
Privately owned corporation

**J & J SNACK FOODS CORP.**
6000 Central Hwy. (08109)
**Phone—(856) 665-9534**
National—(888) 557-6225
Fax—(856) 665-6718
www.jjsnack.com
Email—webmaster@jjsnack.com
Pres., CEO—Gerald Shreiber
CFO—Dennis G. Moore
Sr. V-P., COO—Robert M. Radano
Sr. V-P., Sales—Robert Pape
V-P., Hum. Res.—Harry Fronjian
Mktg. Mgr.—Amanda Osorio
SIC—2052; *Corporate headquarters & snack foods & beverages for the food service & retail supermarket industries; Brand name—SUPERPRETZEL®; ICEE®; LUIGI'S®; Minute Maid® Juice Bars; Fruit-A-Freeze®; Whole Fruit®; SLUSH PUPPIE®; FUNNEL CAKE FACTORY®; TIO PEPE'S®; READI-BAKE®; Mrs. GoodCookie®; Dogsters®*
Employs—850; Estab.—1971
Sales—$650Mil
Distrib.—Intl.
Publicly owned corporation

**J & M PRECISION ENTERPRISES, INC.**
8103 River Rd. (08110)
**Phone—(856) 661-9595**
Fax—(856) 661-9596
www.jmggrinding.com
Email—jmprecision@verizon.net
Pres.—Marty Moskat
Off. Admn.—Beth Moskat
SIC—3599; NAICS—332710; *Precision jig, OD & ID grinding & micro welding*
Employs—2; Estab.—1992
Sales—under $500,000
2,000 sq ft site, Distrib.—National
Privately owned corporation

**JASON STEEL CO., INC.**
1701 Hylton Rd. (08110)
**Phone—(856) 663-5010**
Fax—(856) 486-1742
www.jasteel.com

Pers. Mgr.—Lou Cullen
SIC—3312; *Steel cutting & grinding*
Employs—50; Estab.—1948
Sales—$10Mil-$25Mil (est)
Distrib.—National
Privately owned corporation

**KEYSTONE ADJUSTABLE CAP CO.**
1591 Hylton Rd., Ste. B (08110)
**Phone—(856) 663-5740**
Fax—(800) 663-5432
www.keystonecap.com
Email—afeinstein@keystonecap.com
CEO—Andrew Feinstein
CFO, Fin. & MIS Mgr.—Jay Rigberg
SIC—2676; 2679; NAICS—322291; *Sanitary disposable apparel & accessories*
Employs—80; Estab.—1925
95,000 sq ft site, Distrib.—Intl.
Privately owned corporation

**KUSHNER DRAPERIES MFG., LLC**
5305 Route 70 (08109)
Mail addr: 5305 Marlton Pike, Pennsauken (08109-4749)
**Phone—(856) 317-9696**
Fax—(856) 317-9096
www.kushnerdraperies.com
Email—kushdrape@comcast.net
Chrm., CFO & Bus. Mgr.—Carla Moore
Pres.—Arthur Kushner
SIC—2391; 2221; NAICS—314121; *Draperies & upholstery; Brand name—KIRSCH HARDWARE; HUNTER DOUGLAS SHADES; KRAVET FABRICS; PINDLER & PINDLER; DURALEE; BRIMAR TRIMS; HOUSE PARTS; CONSO*
Employs—25; Estab.—1952
Sales—$1Mil-$2.5Mil (est)
12,000 sq ft site, Distrib.—National
Limited Liability Company

**LACAS COFFEE CO.**
7950 National Hwy. (08110)
**Phone—(856) 910-8662**
National—(800) 220-1133
Fax—(856) 910-8671
www.passioninacup.com
Email—info@lacascoffee.com
V-P., CEO—Tony Chigounis
Pres.—John Vastardis
CFO & Cont.—Michael Valhos
Off. Mgr.—Barbara Sijlow
SIC—2095; NAICS—311920; *Imported & specialty roasted coffees; Brand name—Lacas Coffee; Original City Roast; Dark Note; Metroline*
Employs—12; Estab.—1921
Sales—$25Mil-$50Mil
45,000 sq ft site, Distrib.—Regional
Privately owned sub-S corp.

**LIDESTRI FOODS, INC.**
1550 John Tipton Blvd. (08110)
**Phone—(856) 662-1800**
Fax—(856) 661-3226
www.lidestrifoods.com
Email—jimr@lidestrifoods.com
GM—Dave Stoklosa
IT Mgr.—Ed Guglielmo
Hum. Res. Mgr.—Kathy Jehens
SIC—2086; NAICS—311421; *Carbonated beverages*
Employs—100; Estab.—1960
Distrib.—Intl.
Privately owned corporation
Parent co.—LiDestri Foods, Inc., Fairport, NY
Phone—(585) 377-7700
See Parent Co. Section for full profile.

**†LYON, CONKLIN & CO., INC.**
Div. of Ferguson Enterprises, Inc.
1165 Thomas Busch Memorial Hwy. (08110)
**Phone—(856) 488-0191**
National—(866) 862-1860
Fax—(856) 488-1261
www.lyonconklin.com
Email—chris.long@ferguson.com
Br. Mgr., Satellite—Chris Long
SIC—5075; *Distributor of HVAC equipment & supplies*
Employs—5; Estab.—1989
Distrib.—Regional
Publicly owned corporation
Parent co.—Ferguson Enterprises, Inc., Newport News, VA
Phone—(757) 874-7795
See Parent Co. Section for full profile.

**MACRO SENSORS**
Div. of American Sensor Technologies, Inc.
7300 Route 130 N., Bldg. 22 (08110)
Mail addr: 7300 N. Crescent Blvd., Unit 22-A, Pennsauken (08110-1541)
**Phone—(856) 662-8000**
Fax—(856) 317-1005
www.macrosensors.com
Email—sales@macrosensors.com
Sales & Mktg. Mgr.—Eileen Otto
Mfg. Mgr.—James Lang
Bus. Unit Mgr.—Michael P. Eldredge
Engr. Mgr. & Designer—Martin Grezhowiak
SIC—3679; 3829; *LVDT based position sensors & support electronics, including AC/DC linear variable displacement transformers, measurement sensors & signal conditioners*
Employs—30; Estab.—1994
Sales—$4.5Mil
22,000 sq ft site, Distrib.—Intl.
Privately owned corporation
ISO rating—9002
AKA: Howard A. Schaevitz Technologies Inc
Parent co.—American Sensor Technologies, Inc., Budd Lake, NJ
Phone—(973) 448-1901
See Parent Co. Section for full profile.

**MARSDEN, INC.**
6800 Westfield Ave. (08110)
**Phone—(856) 663-2227**
Fax—(856) 663-2137
www.marsdeninc.com
Pres., CEO—Gerard J. Lucidi
V-P.—Melissa Lucidi
Sales Mgr.—Sean Conley
SIC—3567; 3826; NAICS—333994; *Gas infrared emitters & systems; Brand name—Embedded Combustion; Zero Nox; Zero CO*
Employs—15; Estab.—1975
22,000 sq ft site, Distrib.—Intl.
Privately owned sub-S corp.
ISO rating—9001:2000

**MCCORMICKS BINDERY, INC.**
5815 Magnolia Ave. (08109)
**Phone—(856) 663-8035**
Fax—(856) 665-6638
Pres.—Dan McCormick
SIC—2789; NAICS—323121; *Bookbinding*
Employs—40; Estab.—1985
Distrib.—Regional
Privately owned corporation

**MCKELLA 280**
7025 Central Hwy. (08109)
**Phone—(856) 813-1153**
National—(800) 472-7443
Fax—(856) 813-1154
www.mckella280.com
Email—jlagrossa@mckella280.com

GEOGRAPHICAL

## Pennsauken—(cont.)

Ptnr.—Joseph C. LaGrossa
Ptnr.—Richard McGee
V.-P., Prodn.—Bill Coll
V.-P., Pkg.—Ron Etter
Cont., Hum. Res. Mgr.—Rose
  Balcavage
IT Mgr.—Adam Kirchhoff
Shpg. Mgr.—Bob Walsh
SIC—2759; 2732; NAICS—
  323117; *Commercial printing,*
  *including digital & offset printing,*
  *online print management, pre-*
  *press packaging & mailing*
  *services*
Employs—80; Estab.—1975
Sales—$11Mil
48,000 sq ft site, Distrib.—National
Privately owned corporation

### MENU FOODS, INC.

Div. of Simmons Foods, Inc.
9130 Griffith Morgan Ln. (08110)
**Phone—(856) 662-7412**
       (856) 662-5050
Fax—(856) 662-4673
www.menufoods.com
Email—sheila.campbell@
  simfoods.com
Ex. V.-P., Opers.—Steve Lindsey
Cont.—John Haney
Dir., Opers.—John Morris
Sales Mgr.—Bill McKee
Hum. Res. Mgr.—Sheila Campbell
Hum. Res. Generalist—Jennifer
  Ponticiello
SIC—2047; NAICS—311111; *Dog*
  *& cat food*
Employs—280; Estab.—1982
190,000 sq ft site, Distrib.—Intl.
Privately owned corporation
Parent co.—Simmons Foods, Inc.,
  Siloam Springs, AR
  Phone—(479) 524-8151
  See Parent Co. Section for full profile.

### MOD-TEK CONVERTING, LLC

2550 Haddonfield Rd., Ste. E
(08110)
**Phone—(856) 662-6884**
Fax—(856) 662-6885
www.modtek.net
Email—sales@modtek.net
Owner—Vicki Wilkinson
SIC—2672; *Pressure-sensitive*
  *labels*
Employs—12; Estab.—2006
Distrib.—National
Limited Liability Company

### MONARCH COLOR CORP.

7247 Browning Rd. (08109)
**Phone—(856) 662-0432**
National—(800) 899-4657
Fax—(856) 662-0130
www.monarchcolor.com
Email—order@monarchcolor.com
GM—Kevin Lockwood
SIC—2893; NAICS—325910;
  *Printing ink*
Employs—25; Estab.—1967
Distrib.—National
Privately owned corporation
Parent co.—Monarch Color Corp.,
  Charlotte, NC
  Phone—(704) 394-4626
  See Parent Co. Section for full profile.

### NAPCO CABINETS, INC.

6938 Westfield Ave. (08110)
**Phone—(856) 665-0253**
Fax—(856) 665-0253
Pres., Sales Mgr.—William Cocchi
SIC—3843; NAICS—339114;
  *Dental & doctor's office laminate*
  *cabinets*
Employs—1; Estab.—1984
1,600 sq ft site, Distrib.—National
Privately owned partnership

### NATIONAL DISPLAY GROUP, INC.

6850 River Rd. (08110)
**Phone—(856) 661-1212**
Fax—(856) 661-1233
www.nationalslatwall.com
V.-P., Opers.—Gene Gold
Off. Mgr.—Bernadette Sandone
SIC—2541; *Store displays*
Employs—25; Estab.—1993
Sales—$1Mil-$2.5Mil (est)
Distrib.—Regional
Privately owned corporation
AKA: National Display

### NAZDAR CO.

7055 Central Hwy. (08109)
**Phone—(856) 663-7878**
National—(800) 257-8226
Fax—(856) 663-9467
www.sourceoneonline.com
Email—custserv@nazdar.com
Sales Mgr.—Tom O'Neil
Fin. & Opers. Mgr.—Ray Parker
Cust. Serv. Supv.—Ron Trisel
SIC—2893; NAICS—325910;
  *Screen printing inks*
Employs—20; Estab.—1948
10,000 sq ft site, Distrib.—
  Regional
Privately owned corporation
AKA: Nazdar Source One
Parent co.—Nazdar Co., Shawnee,
  KS
  Phone—(913) 422-1888
  See Parent Co. Section for full profile.

### NOVELTY CONE CO., INC.

807 Sherman Ave. (08110)
**Phone—(856) 665-9525**
Fax—(856) 665-0216
www.noveltycone.com
Owner—Steve Marinucci
Co-Plt. Mgr.—Ronald Marinucci
Off. Mgr.—Dawn Amato
SIC—2052; *Ice cream cones*
Employs—26; Estab.—1905
Sales—$5Mil-$10Mil
Distrib.—Regional
Privately owned corporation

### †NUMAX, INC.

7251-B Browning Rd. (08109)
**Phone—(856) 910-0088**
       (845) 674-9060
National—(800) 842-4230
Fax—(856) 910-0555
www.numax.com
Email—orders@numax.com
Sales Mgr.—Gary Mullins
SIC—5072; 5051; *Distributor of*
  *construction supplies, including*
  *nails, fasteners & staples*
Employs—3; Estab.—1999
Distrib.—Local
Privately owned corporation
Parent co.—Numax, Inc., New
  Windsor, NY
  Phone—(845) 674-9060
  See Parent Co. Section for full profile.

### PACKAGING CONSULTANTS ASSOCS.

7300 N. Crescent Blvd., Unit 14
(08110)
**Phone—(856) 488-0277**
Cust. Serv. Mgr.—Lorraine
  Dischert
SIC—3565; NAICS—333993; *Film*
  *equipment packaging*
Employs—10; Estab.—1976
Distrib.—National
Privately owned corporation

### PALMYRA PANTS CO., INC.

9370 Route 130 N. (08110)
**Phone—(856) 662-0398**
Fax—(856) 662-4791
www.mfo4u.com
Pres.—Howard Eisenberg
Plt. Mgr.—Lloyd Moon

SIC—2325; 3143; NAICS—
  316213; *Men's & boys' slacks &*
  *shoes*
Employs—4; Estab.—1972
Sales—$500,000-$1Mil
6,000 sq ft site, Distrib.—Local
Privately owned corporation
AKA: Factory Outlet Mens
  Clothing

### PARK PRINTING SERVICES, INC.

7300 N. Crescent Blvd., Unit 21
(08110)
**Phone—(856) 675-1600**
Fax—(856) 675-1606
www.parkprintingco.com
Email—info@parkprintingco.com
Owner, Pres. & Pur. Agt.—Don
  Reed, Sr.
V.-P., Hum. Res.—Margaret Reed
Sales & Mktg. Mgr.—Bob Bonsall
Engrg., Opers. & R & D Mgr.—Don
  Reed, Jr.
Graphics & Prepress Mgr.—Donna
  Scioli
SIC—2759; 2791; NAICS—
  323100; *Commercial printing,*
  *electronic prepress & graphics*
Employs—12; Estab.—1936
10,000 sq ft site, Distrib.—
  Regional
Privately owned corporation

### PEEK-A-BOO TOYS

9040 Pensauken Hwy. (08110)
**Phone—(856) 317-9100**
Fax—(856) 317-9718
www.peekabootoys.com
Owner—Ari Ohnona
Off. Mgr.—Alice Kramer
SIC—3942; NAICS—339931;
  *Plush toys, including teddy*
  *bears for amusement parks &*
  *carnivals*
Employs—20; Estab.—1998
Distrib.—National
Sole ownership

### †PENNOCK CO.

7135 Colonial Ln. (08109)
**Phone—(215) 492-7900**
National—(888) 736-6625
Fax—(215) 492-7901
www.pennock.com
Email—bbillings@pennock.com
Pres.—Robert P. Billings
V.-P.—Thomas Logue
Secy-Treas.—Domenick R. Sciole
Cont. & Hum. Res. Mgr.—Craig
  Levering
Dir., IT—Daniel Stevenson
SIC—5193; *Company*
  *headquarters & wholesaler of*
  *fresh & artificial flowers & floral*
  *supplies*
Employs—60; Estab.—1882
5,000 sq ft site, Distrib.—Regional
Privately owned corporation

### PEPSI-COLA & NATIONAL BRAND BEVERAGES LTD.

Div. of Beverage Distribution
  Center, Inc.
8191 N. U.S. Route 130 (08110)
Mail addr: 8275 N. Route 130,
  Pennsauken (08110)
**Phone—(856) 665-6200**
National—(800) 737-7745
Fax—(856) 662-4836
www.pepsico.com
Email—investor@pepsico.com
Pres., COO—Bob Brockway
CFO—John Dale
Dir., Fleet—Mark Stone
Sales Mgr.—Alex Woloszczuk
IT Mgr.—Santo Bonaro
Hum. Res. Mgr.—Christine
  Goodheart
Consumer Rels. Coord.—Angela
  DeLuca

SIC—2086; NAICS—312100;
  *Bottled & canned beverages*
Employs—700
Distrib.—Local
Privately owned corporation
Parent co.—Beverage Distribution
  Center, Inc., Pennsauken, NJ
  Phone—(856) 665-6200
  See Parent Co. Section for full profile.

### PERMALITH PLASTICS, LLC

6901 N. Crescent Blvd. (08110)
**Phone—(856) 488-8000**
Fax—(856) 488-2455
www.permalith.com
Email—info@permalith.com
V.-P., Sales—Gary Brown
Cont. & Hum. Res. Mgr.—Cheryl
  Ruymen
Off. Mgr.—Nancy Manion
Cust. Serv. Rep.—Gale Tetzloff
SIC—2759; 2789; 2542; 3089;
  NAICS—323100; *Plastic litho &*
  *screen printing, laminating, die*
  *cutting, plastic fabrication &*
  *bending & assembly, including*
  *displays, literature holders,*
  *plastic posters & cards,*
  *pharmaceutical packaging &*
  *counter mats*
Employs—45; Estab.—1980
60,000 sq ft site, Distrib.—National
Limited Liability Company

### PHILADELPHIA RAPID TRANSIT

2650 Haddonfield Rd. (08110)
**Phone—(856) 488-0202**
National—(800) 847-1110
Fax—(856) 488-2333
www.phillyrapid.com
Email—hats@phillyrapid.com
Pres.—Peter Goldman
V.-P.—David Goldman
SIC—2353; *Hats*
Employs—20; Estab.—1971
Sales—$5Mil-$10Mil
34,000 sq ft site, Distrib.—Intl.
Privately owned sub-S corp.

### PREFERRED PLASTICS CORP.

6512 Park Ave. (08109)
**Phone—(856) 662-6250**
Fax—(856) 662-2950
Email—preferredplasticscorp@
  verizon.net
Co-Pres., Fin. Mgr.—Joseph Flood
SIC—3544; NAICS—333500;
  *Plastic injection molds & dies,*
  *including precision machined*
  *parts & fabrication*
Employs—6; Estab.—1988
Sales—under $500,000
5,400 sq ft site, Distrib.—Local
Privately owned corporation

### PREMIER PRESS, INC.

7120 Airport Hwy. (08109)
**Phone—(856) 665-0722**
Fax—(856) 665-9377
Estimator—Kim McGuigan
SIC—2759; NAICS—323100;
  *Commercial printing*
Employs—8; Estab.—1990
Sales—under $500,000
12,800 sq ft site, Distrib.—Local
Privately owned corporation

### PRINT COMMUNICATIONS

7040 Colonial Hwy. (08109)
**Phone—(856) 488-0345**
Fax—(856) 488-0346
www.printnmail.net
Email—ssticco@printnmail.net
Pres.—Steve Sticco
Hum. Res. Mgr.—Kathy Blades
SIC—2759; NAICS—323100;
  *Commercial & direct mail*
  *printing*
Employs—5; Estab.—1962
Sales—under $500,000
2,000 sq ft site, Distrib.—Regional
Sole ownership
AKA: Print Com

## Pennsauken—(cont.)

**†PURATOS CORP.**
945 Sherman Ave. (08110)
**Phone—(856) 661-3112**
National—(800) 654-0036
Fax—(856) 661-3123
www.puratos.us
Email—infous@puratos.com
Sales Mgr.—George Rodier
SIC—5149; *Distributor of bakery ingredients*
Employs—50; Estab.—1999
Distrib.—Local
Privately owned corporation
Parent co.—Puratos Corp., Cherry Hill, NJ
    Phone—(856) 428-4300
    See Parent Co. Section for full profile.

**QUADRIGA ART, INC.**
825 Hylton Rd. (08110)
**Phone—(856) 663-2500**
Fax—(856) 663-1432
www.quadrigaart.com
Email—mschulhof@quadrigaart.com
Dir., Opers.—Tim Merges
IT Mgr.—Joe Puglisi
SIC—2771; *Greeting cards*
Employs—75; Estab.—1944
200,000 sq ft site, Distrib.—Intl.
Privately owned corporation
Parent co.—Quadriga Art, Inc., New York, NY
    Phone—(212) 685-0751
    See Parent Co. Section for full profile.

**REBUILT PARTS CO.**
7929 River Rd. (08110)
**Phone—(856) 662-3252**
Fax—(856) 662-8731
Email—driveshafts@rpcdriveline.com
GM—Henry Matznick
Machinist—John Wilkins
SIC—3714; *Front wheel axles, drive shafts & driveline products*
Employs—15; Estab.—1968
6,500 sq ft site, Distrib.—Regional
Privately owned corporation

**†RESTAURANT DEPOT, LLC**
1050 Thomas Busch Memorial Hwy. (08110)
**Phone—(856) 488-4288**
Fax—(856) 488-8490
www.restaurantdepot.com
Email—sales@restaurantdepot.com
GM—Paul Jensen
Asst. Mgr.—Jim White
Asst. Mgr.—Tom Polkovitch
Asst. Mgr.—Robert Avallone
SIC—5141; 5046; 5023; 5021; *Wholesaler of general line groceries & restaurant supplies, including fresh, frozen & dry foods, countertop equipment, cutlery, shelving & furniture*
Employs—75; Estab.—1999
Distrib.—National
Limited Liability Company
Parent co.—Restaurant Depot, LLC, College Point, NY
    Phone—(718) 762-8700
    See Parent Co. Section for full profile.

**RHOADS METAL WORKS, INC.**
1551 John Tipton Blvd. (08110)
**Phone—(856) 486-1551**
Fax—(856) 486-1710
www.rhoadsmetalworks.com
Email—mwosak@rhoadsmw.com
Pres.—William K. Rhoads
CFO—Steve Figard
Off. Mgr.—Michele Wosak
Shop Foreman—Robert Moebius

SIC—3499; *Custom metal fabrication & HVAC contracting, including mechanical services & installation of ventilation, dust control, pneumatic & trim conveying systems & engineered equipment*
Employs—37; Estab.—1896
Sales—$5Mil-$10Mil
32,000 sq ft site, Distrib.—Regional
Privately owned corporation

**†RIVER ROAD RECYCLING INC.**
450 37th St., P.O. Box 302 *(08110)*
**Phone—(856) 661-0770**
    (856) 661-8181
Fax—(856) 661-8384
www.riverroadrecycling.com
Email—chris@philametals.com
Owner—Christopher Wang
Off. Mgr.—Christine Burgmann
Scale Operator—Anthony Fortine
SIC—5093; *Wholesaler of ferrous & nonferrous scrap metals, including light iron, HMS #1 steel, insulated copper wire, copper, aluminum, stainless steel, brass, lead & catalytic converters*
Employs—15; Estab.—2007
Sales—$5Mil
18,000 sq ft site, Distrib.—Local
Privately owned corporation
AKA: Scrap Metal Recycling & Processing

**R-KANE PRODUCTS, INC.**
8351 National Hwy. (08110)
**Phone—(856) 663-0644**
National—(800) 237-9765
Fax—(856) 662-0878
www.r-kaneproducts.com
Email—r-kane@mindspring.com
Pres.—Robert Kaskey
Cust. Serv. Rep.—Linda Shore
SIC—2023; 2833; NAICS—311500; *Nutritional dietary protein meal replacement mixes for low-calorie & very-low-calorie diets administrered in medical facilities*
Employs—15; Estab.—1974
Sales—$5Mil-$10Mil (est)
Distrib.—National
Privately owned corporation

**ROYER GROUP, INC.**
7120 Airport Hwy. (08109)
**Phone—(856) 665-6400**
National—(800) 605-7693
Fax—(856) 665-6410
www.royercomm.com
Email—royercomm@royercomm.com
Pres.—Amanda Schwartz
Cust. Serv. Rep.—Lisa Schmidt
SIC—2752; 2759; NAICS—323100; *Offset & digital printing*
Employs—20; Estab.—1999
Sales—$1Mil-$2.5Mil
Distrib.—Regional
Privately owned corporation

**S & S PRECISION**
2205 Sherman Ave. (08110-1530)
**Phone—(856) 662-0006**
Fax—(856) 662-0009
www.sandsprecisionnj.com
Email—jiggrind@aol.com
Ptnr.—Walter Smith
Ptnr.—Scott Smith
SIC—3599; *Precision grinding, boring & general machining job shop*
Employs—12; Estab.—1968
Sales—$1Mil
5,000 sq ft site, Distrib.—National
Privately owned partnership

**NEW ENTRY**
**S. E. R. DIECUTTING**
7300 N. Crescent Blvd., Unit 5 (08110)
**Phone—(856) 665-8805**
www.serdiecutting.com
Email—serdiecut@aol.com
Owner—Steven Rosa
SIC—2652; 2675; *Folding paperboard boxes & paperboard die cutting*
Employs—4
Sales—under $500,000 (est)

**SCIENCE DYNAMICS CORP.**
7150 N. Park Dr., Ste. 500 (08109)
**Phone—(856) 910-1166**
Fax—(856) 910-1811
www.scidyn.com
Pres.—Paul Burgess
SIC—3661; *Commercial call management systems, including call control & monitoring systems, calling card billing systems, video over frame relay systems & IP gateways*
Employs—12; Estab.—1925
Sales—$2.5Mil-$5Mil (est)
5,000 sq ft site, Distrib.—National
Publicly owned corporation

**SEMINOLE WIRE & CABLE CO.**
7861 Airport Hwy. *(08109)*
**Phone—(856) 324-2929**
National—(800) 346-4378
Fax—(856) 438-6875
www.seminolewire.com
Email—info@seminolewire.com
CEO—George H. Genzel
Pres.—Michael J. Genzel
Off. Mgr.—Irina Zhukova
SIC—3496; *Low voltage wire & cable*
Employs—25; Estab.—1962
Sales—$1Mil-$2.5Mil
Distrib.—Intl.
Limited Liability Company

**SIGN CREW**
1426 Union Ave. (08110)
**Phone—(856) 665-3676**
National—(866) 982-7446
Fax—(856) 662-8083
www.signcrew.com
Email—sales@signcrew.com
Pres.—Joe Crew
V.-P.—Tina Crew
Designer—Joseph Crew, Jr.
SIC—3993; *Custom signage, including light box, channel letters, sandblasted, vehicle & window graphics, lobby, cubicle & directional signs*
Employs—5; Estab.—1933
Sales—$500,000-$1Mil
7,500 sq ft site, Distrib.—National
Privately owned sub-S corp.

**SIR SPEEDY PRINTING AND MARKETING SERVICES**
5505 Route 130 N. (08110)
**Phone—(856) 488-1480**
Fax—(856) 488-9326
www.sirspeedy.com/pennsauken
Email—speedy7061@aol.com
Pres.—Francis V. Gavin, Jr.
SIC—2752; 2759; 3993; NAICS—323100; *Digital color & offset printing, signs, posters, banners & graphic design, marketing, mailing & paper shredding services*
Employs—5; Estab.—1984
Sales—over $500,000
3,000 sq ft site, Distrib.—Regional
Privately owned corporation

**SISCO MFG. CO., INC.**
7930 National Hwy. (08110)
**Phone—(856) 486-7550**
Fax—(856) 486-7551
www.siscomfg.com
Email—sisco@siscomfg.com

Principal—Paul Schulte
SIC—3585; *HVAC components, including pressure & temperature test plugs & heat pump hoses*
Employs—12
20,000 sq ft site, Distrib.—Intl.
Privately owned corporation

**SOLIDSURFACE DESIGNS, INC.**
1651 Sherman Ave. (08110)
Mail addr.—P.O. Box 5356, Delanco (08075)
**Phone—(856) 910-7720**
Fax—(856) 910-7721
www.solidsurfacedesigns.com
Email—info@solidsurfacedesigns.com
Pres.—Matthew Baiada
Administrator—Jenifer Fernandes
SIC—2541; 3281; 3444; NAICS—327991; *Solid-surface, quartz, stainless steel & granite countertops*
Employs—21; Estab.—1986
Distrib.—Regional
Privately owned corporation

**SPECTRUM NEON, INC.**
9130-B Pennsauken Hwy. (08110)
Mail addr.—P.O. Box 1475, Pennsauken (08109)
**Phone—(856) 317-9223**
Fax—(856) 317-9224
Email—spectrumne@aol.com
Pres.—Teresa Simone
SIC—3993; *Neon signs*
Employs—3; Estab.—1986
Sales—under $500,000
Distrib.—Regional
Privately owned corporation

**SUN NEON SIGN & ELECTRIC CO.**
6701-B Rudderow Ave. (08109)
**Phone—(856) 663-7667**
Fax—(856) 667-1322
Pres.—Stuart Rosner
SIC—3993; *Interior & exterior signs*
Employs—1; Estab.—1945
Sales—under $500,000
Distrib.—Local
Sole ownership

**SUPPLYONE, INC.**
1090 Thomas Busch Memorial Hwy. (08110)
**Phone—(856) 727-1010**
Fax—(856) 727-1020
www.supplyone.com
Email—sales@supplyone.com
Cont.—Jason Fuller
SIC—2653; 3086; NAICS—322211; *Corrugated boxes & foam plastic packaging*
Employs—115; Estab.—1977
130,000 sq ft site, Distrib.—Intl.
Privately owned corporation
Parent co.—SupplyOne, Inc., Devon, PA
    Phone—(484) 582-5005
    See Parent Co. Section for full profile.

**TABLOID GRAPHIC SERVICES, INC.**
7101 Westfield Ave. (08110)
**Phone—(856) 486-0410**
    (856) 486-1609
National—(877) 822-5643
Fax—(856) 486-0033
www.tabloidgraphics.com
Email—tabloidtgs@aol.com
Pres.—Steve Brosious
V.-P.—Tom Lynch
Cont.—Sandie Oliver
GM—Stephen Brosious, Jr.
Plt. Mgr.—Ken Koruba
Sales Exec., Bus. Dev.—Tom Lynch III

GEOGRAPHICAL

## Pennsauken—(cont.)

SIC—2752; 2759; NAICS—323100; *Circular heat-set & cold web printing of advertising inserts, grocery, furniture, lumber, appliance, hardware & sales flyers & direct mail products*
Employs—65; Estab.—1985
Sales—$20Mil
55,000 sq ft site, Distrib.—Regional
Privately owned sub-S corp.

**TAYLOR MADE CUSTOM CABINETRY, INC.**
7035 Central Hwy., Ste. 200 (08109)
**Phone—(856) 786-5433**
Fax—(856) 786-5435
www.tmcc-inc.com
Email—info@tmcc-inc.com
Pres.—Jay Taylor
Off. Mgr.—Cory Taylor
SIC—2434; 2511; NAICS—337110; *Custom wooden cabinetry & fine furniture*
Employs—11; Estab.—1990
Sales—$1Mil-$2.5Mil
Distrib.—Regional
Privately owned corporation

**TOP LINE CO.**
2131 Bethel Ave. (08110)
**Phone—(856) 662-6400**
Fax—(856) 662-0056
www.toplinecompany.com
Owner—Bruce MacLachlan
Cust. Serv. Rep.—Donna Bates
SIC—2542; 3281; NAICS—327991; *Laminate, acrylic, marble, granite, engineered stone & concrete countertops*
Employs—50; Estab.—1981
100,000 sq ft site, Distrib.—Regional
Privately owned corporation

**TOTH INC.**
Div. of Rosenberger Of North America, LLC
6970 Central Hwy. (08109)
**Phone—(856) 662-8700**
National—(800) 835-4773
Fax—(856) 662-7454
www.rosenberger-toth.com
Email—toth@tothtech.com
V-P.—Theodore Toth, Jr.
V-P.—Ted Toth
GM—Joel Antipuna
Sales Mgr.—Tim Toth
Qual. Control Mgr.—Tony DeSilvio
Process Engr.—Pat Brady
Bookkeeper—Debbie Toth
SIC—3679; 3599; 3053; NAICS—339991; *Precision machining & assembly of machined microwave components, including fittings, gaskets, glass-to-metal seals, bonded assemblies & connectors*
Employs—48; Estab.—1948
30,000 sq ft site, Distrib.—Intl.
Privately owned corporation
AKAs: Toth Technologies & Rosenberger-Toth
Parent co.—Rosenberger Of North America, LLC, Akron, PA
Phone—(717) 859-8900
See Parent Co. Section for full profile.

**TPG GRAPHICS**
9130 Pennsauken Hwy., Ste. C (08110-1285)
**Phone—(856) 314-0117**
Fax—(856) 314-0121
Email—clntprnt@erols.com
GM—Robert Donner
SIC—2759; NAICS—323100; *Commercial printing*
Employs—6; Estab.—1933
8,000 sq ft site, Distrib.—Regional
Also see: Clinton Envelope, same loc.

**TRANSPARENT OFFICE PRODUCTS, LLC**
2550 Haddonfield Rd. (08110)
**Phone—(856) 488-5455**
Fax—(856) 488-5411
www.transoffprod.biz
Email—sales@transoffprod.biz
GM & Opers. Mgr.—Rick Brown
Asst. Mgr.—Kyle Brown
SIC—3089; *Archival document & photo protectors; Brand name—Saf-T-Stor; Perma-Saf*
Employs—4; Estab.—2002
30,000 sq ft site, Distrib.—National
Limited Liability Company

NEW ENTRY
**†TRC**
Div. of TransAxle, LLC
1700 Sherman Ave. (08110)
**Phone—(856) 910-7979**
Fax—(856) 910-1950
www.trcreman.com
Email—contact@trcreman.com
Manager—Keith Loura
SIC—5013; *Wholesaler of automatic transmissions*
Employs—20
Distrib.—Intl.
Privately owned corporation
Parent co.—TransAxle, LLC, Cinnaminson, NJ
Phone—(856) 665-4445
See Parent Co. Section for full profile.

**TURBON GROUP**
4350 Haddonfield Rd., Ste. 300 (08109)
**Phone—(856) 665-6650**
National—(800) 282-6650
Fax—(800) 257-1619
www.turbongroup.com
Email—info@turbongroup.com
CEO—Al Deluca
Sales Support Mgr.—Melissa Pizzani
Accts. Rep.—Rich Snyder
Cust. Serv. Rep.—Marie Wrights
SIC—3861; NAICS—325992; *Laser toner cartridges*
Employs—100; Estab.—1981
Distrib.—Intl.
Privately owned corporation

**VEOLIA WATER SOLUTIONS & TECHNOLOGIES NORTH AMERICA, INC.**
Div. of Veolia Water North America
6981 N. Park Dr., Ste. 600 (08109)
**Phone—(856) 438-1776**
www.veoliawaterstna.com
V-P., Opers.—Bill O'Donnell
V-P., Comml.—Denise Johnston
GM—Genevieve Leboucher
SIC—3589; NAICS—333319; *Industrial wastewater treatment plants; Brand name—Biothane UASB; Biobed EGSB; Methane Anaerobic MBR; Sulfothane Biological H2S Scrubber*
Employs—40; Estab.—1979
Sales—$12Mil-$16Mil
30,000 sq ft site, Distrib.—Intl.
Publicly owned corporation
Parent co.—Veolia Water North America, Chicago, IL
Phone—(312) 552-2800
See Parent Co. Section for full profile.

**VICTORIAN GLASS CARVER**
5515 Toms Ave. (08109)
**Phone—(856) 662-1391**
Email—glassmugcarver@comcast.net
Pres.—Rose Mary Skalski
Designer—Edward Skalski
SIC—3231; NAICS—327215; *Victorian glass art reproductions*
Employs—2; Estab.—2003
Sales—under $500,000
Distrib.—Regional
Privately owned corporation

**WERKO MACHINE CO., INC.**
9200 Collins Ave. (08110)
**Phone—(856) 662-0669**
Fax—(856) 662-7305
www.werko.com
Email—rpm@werko.com
Pres.—Robert Mueller, Sr.
V-P., GM—Robert Mueller, Jr.
SIC—3599; *Industrial machinery*
Employs—10; Estab.—1952
12,000 sq ft site, Distrib.—Local
Privately owned corporation

**WISE TAG & LABEL CO., INC.**
1077 Thomas Busch Memorial Hwy. (08110)
**Phone—(856) 663-2400**
National—(800) 222-1327
Fax—(856) 663-8610
www.wisetaglabel.com
Email—sales@wisetaglabel.com
Pres.—Doug Ford
Sales Mgr.—Jackie Reckard
SIC—2672; *Pressure-sensitive labels*
Employs—11; Estab.—1956
Sales—$1Mil-$2.5Mil
14,000 sq ft site, Distrib.—National
Privately owned corporation

**ZIN-TECH**
Div. of DiTech Group
1416 Union Ave. (08110)
**Phone—(856) 661-0900**
Fax—(856) 661-0919
www.ditechgroup.com
Email—dtztech@ditechgroup.com
Pres.—Joe Zingaro
SIC—3544; NAICS—333500; *Steel rule dies*
Employs—20; Estab.—1992
Distrib.—Local
Privately owned corporation
Parent co.—DiTech Group, York, PA
Phone—(717) 846-6002
See Parent Co. Section for full profile.

## Pennsville
(Salem—S.W.)

NEW ENTRY
**ROCKY'S T'S**
61 N. Hook Rd. (08070)
**Phone—(856) 678-2535**
Owner—Rocky Demry
SIC—2396; *T-shirt screen printing*
Employs—1
Sales—under $500,000 (est)

**SIEGFRIED USA, LLC**
33 Industrial Park Rd. *(08070)*
**Phone—(856) 678-3601**
(877) 763-8630
Fax—(856) 678-4008
www.siegfried-usa.com
Email—rita.vaneck@siegfried-usa.com
Sr. V-P., GM—Kenneth Zrebiec
Dir., Hum. Res.—Rita Van Eck
Hum. Res. Mgr.—Peggy Schultz
SIC—2834; NAICS—325412; *Pharmaceutical substances*
Employs—186; Estab.—1928
Sales—under $150Mil
57,225 sq ft site, Distrib.—Intl.
Publicly owned corporation

## Pequannock
(Morris—N.W.)

**ALLEN CABINETS & MILLWORK, INC.**
60 Newark Pompton Tpk. (07440)
**Phone—(973) 694-0665**
Fax—(973) 694-0245
www.allencabinets.com
Email—susan.murphy@allencabinets.com
GM—John Vanderstad
Bookkeeper—Sue Murphy
SIC—2542; *Laminated countertops*
Employs—4; Estab.—1989
Distrib.—Local
Privately owned corporation

**ANELLO FENCE, LLC**
50 State Route 23 (07440-1433)
**Phone—(973) 839-4100**
(973) 692-9200
Fax—(973) 692-9202
www.anellofence.com
Email—info@anellofence.com
Pres.—Steve Anello
SIC—3089; 2499; 3444; NAICS—332618; *Vinyl, aluminum & wooden fencing; Brand name—alumi-guard; bufftech*
Employs—4
Sales—$500,000-$1Mil
Distrib.—Regional
Limited Liability Company

**REEVES INTERNATIONAL, INC.**
14 Industrial Rd. (07440)
**Phone—(973) 694-5006**
Fax—(973) 694-5213
www.reevesintl.com
Email—kfallon@reevesintl.com
Pres.—Anthony Fleischmann
CFO—Arthur Minnocci
V-P., Mktg. & Prod. Dev.—Stephanie Macejko
V-P., Comms.—Kathleen Fallon
Dir., Sales, Specialty Toy Sales—Bob LaRocca
Dir., Proc.—Jeffrey Uhrig
Sales Mgr., Natl.—Edward Dean
IT Mgr.—Lisa Raimondo
SIC—3942; 3944; 5092; NAICS—339931; *Corporate headquarters & manufacturer & distributor of toys; Brand name—Breyer Animal Creations; Tolo; WOW; Enchantmints; Red Tool Box; Marvin's Magic; Basic Concepts; Tonka*
Employs—50; Estab.—1950
Sales—$2.5Mil-$5Mil (est)
Distrib.—Intl.
Sole ownership

## Perrineville
(Monmouth—N.E.)

**RDL MARKETING GROUP, LLC**
352-A Sweetmann Ln., P.O. Box 385 (08535)
**Phone—(732) 446-0817**
Owner—Robert Levine
SIC—2741; *Catalog publishing*
Employs—5
Sales—under $500,000 (est)
Distrib.—National
Limited Liability Company

## Perth Amboy
(Middlesex—N.E.)

**1 2 3 QUICK PRINT, INC.**
297 New Brunswick Ave. (08861)
**Phone—(732) 442-1771**
Fax—(732) 442-2092
www.quick123print.com
Email—quick123print@aol.com
Pres.—Dov Ehrlich

# Perth Amboy—(cont.)

Off. Mgr.—Theresa Sickle
SIC—2759; NAICS—323100;
*Commercial printing*
Employs—4; Estab.—1989
Sales—under $500,000
2,000 sq ft site, Distrib.—Local
Privately owned corporation

## ACE SIGN CO., INC.

419 Summit Ave. (08861)
Mail addr: P.O. Box 66, Perth
Amboy (08862)
**Phone—(732) 826-3858**
Fax—(732) 826-2612
www.acesigninc.com
Email—phil@acesigninc.com
Pres.—Philip Smith
Off. Mgr.—Pat Smith
SIC—3993; *Interior & exterior
signs, channel letters & screen
printing*
Employs—9; Estab.—1926
Sales—$500,000-$1Mil
4,000 sq ft site, Distrib.—Local
Privately owned corporation

## ALL MECHANICAL SERVICES, INC.

430 High St., P.O. Box 110 (08862)
**Phone—(732) 442-8292**
Fax—(732) 442-0736
Email—allmech@earthlink.net
Pres., Hum. Res. Mgr.—Greg
Huhn
Sales Rep.—John Crowley
SIC—3561; 3621; NAICS—
333911; *Rebuilt pumps & motors*
Employs—5; Estab.—1995
Sales—under $500,000
Distrib.—Local
Privately owned corporation

## ARIAS MACHINE TOOL & DIE CO.

645 Atlantic Ave. (08861)
**Phone—(732) 442-2398**
www.ariasmachine.com
Email—ariasmachine@gmail.com
Pres.—Joseph Arias
SIC—3599; NAICS—333500;
*General machining & welding
job shop*
Employs—2; Estab.—1946
Sales—under $500,000
Distrib.—Local
Privately owned corporation

## CHEMTURA CORP.

1000 Convery Blvd. (08861)
**Phone—(732) 826-6600**
Fax—(732) 826-6619
www.chemtura.com
Email—info@chemtura.com
MIS Mgr.—Amanda Figueroa
Env. Health & Safety Mgr.—Sue
Castle
Pur. Agt.—Joe Duarte
SIC—2821; 3089; *Polyester &
polyurethane materials for
industrial & printing rolls, mining
& oil & gas machinery &
equipment, mechanical goods,
solid industrial tires & wheels,
electronic devices, processing
equipment & recreation &
consumer goods*
Employs—80; Estab.—1948
Distrib.—Intl.
Publicly owned corporation
Parent co.—Chemtura Corp.,
Philadelphia, PA
Phone—(215) 446-3911
See Parent Co. Section for full profile.

## ENGLERT, INC.

1200 Amboy Ave. (08861)
**Phone—(732) 826-8614**
National—(800) 364-5378
Fax—(732) 826-8865
www.englertinc.com
Email—info@englertinc.com
CEO—Ken Krawcheck
Pres.—Deborah Tripod
CFO—Tere Valcercel

V.-P., Pur.—Brian Englert
V.-P., Specialty Prods.—Joe
Turovac
Dir., Mktg.—Mitchell Gaber
Dir., IT—John Lyness
Dir., Engrg. & Tech. Support—Joe
Tripod
Hum. Res. Mgr.—Liliana Silverio
SIC—3444; *Corporate
headquarters & metal roof,
seamless residential gutter &
rainwater harvesting systems &
composite & commercial/
industrial wall panels; Brand
name—ULTRA-Cool™; Metal
Roofing Systems; LeafGuard;
RainPro; MicroGuard; Gutter
Tunnel; SunNet*
Employs—100; Estab.—1966
Sales—$75Mil-$100Mil
17,000 sq ft site, Distrib.—Intl.
Privately owned corporation

## EVANS MACHINE & TOOL CO.

410 Summit Ave. (08861)
**Phone—(732) 442-1144**
Fax—(732) 324-1139
Pres.—Thomas S. Geslak
V.-P.—Mike Evans
SIC—3599; *General machining
job shop*
Employs—10; Estab.—1967
Sales—$500,000-$1Mil
10,000 sq ft site, Distrib.—
Regional
Privately owned corporation

## GMI

599 State St. (08861)
**Phone—(732) 442-4572**
Fax—(732) 442-9244
www.grimesmanufacturing.com
Email—chriss@
grimesmanufacturing.com
Pres.—Christopher Grimes
V.-P.—Gary Grimes
SIC—3599; *Precision machining
job shop*
Employs—10; Estab.—1985
Sales—$500,000-$1Mil
5,000 sq ft site, Distrib.—National
Privately owned corporation

## H E K MACHINE, INC.

785 State St., Ste. 2 (08861)
**Phone—(732) 442-8672**
Fax—(732) 442-2609
www.hekmachine.com
Email—hekster@comcast.net
Pres., GM, Pur. & Sales & Mktg.
Mgr.—Mike Kurth
SIC—3599; *General machining
job shop, including short-run
CNC machining & welding*
Employs—2; Estab.—1985
Sales—under $500,000
2,500 sq ft site, Distrib.—Regional
Privately owned corporation

## ILLUSION ENGRAVED

311 Fayette St. (08861)
**Phone—(732) 442-4488**
Fax—(732) 826-0694
www.illusionengraved.com
Email—illusionengraved@
yahoo.com
Off. Mgr.—Marien Arevallo
SIC—3479; *Engraving of trophies,
plaques, bronze plaques & signs*
Employs—2; Estab.—2006
Sales—under $500,000
Distrib.—Local
Sole ownership

## INDIVIDUALIZED SHIRTS, INC.

Div. of James Co., The Tom
581 Cortland St. (08861)
**Phone—(732) 826-8400**
National—(877) 477-4478
Fax—(732) 826-0686
www.individualizedshirts.com
Email—sales@
individualizedshirts.com
Pres., CEO—Joe Blair

Dir., MIS—Nancy Procanik
Plt. Mgr.—Amos Turner
SIC—2321; 2329; NAICS—
315200; *Men's shirts*
Employs—200; Estab.—1961
27,000 sq ft site, Distrib.—Intl.
Privately owned corporation
Parent co.—James Co., The Tom,
Franklin, TN
Phone—(615) 771-1122
See Parent Co. Section for full profile.

## JASON FURNITURE & PLASTIC COVERS, INC.

334 State St. (08861)
**Phone—(732) 442-9700**
Pres.—Jason Perez
SIC—3089; *Plastic furniture
slipcovers*
Employs—2; Estab.—1994
Sales—under $500,000 (est)
Distrib.—Local
Sole ownership

## LINCOLN SIGNS & AWNINGS, INC.

895 Estate St. (08861)
**Phone—(732) 442-3151**
Fax—(732) 442-3113
www.lincolnsigns.com
Email—lincolnsign@verizon.net
Pres.—Julio Hernandez
SIC—3993; 2394; NAICS—
314912; *Interior & exterior signs
& awnings*
Employs—9; Estab.—1991
Sales—under $500,000
10,000 sq ft site, Distrib.—
Regional
Privately owned corporation

## LIONELLI

345 Florida Grove Rd. (08861)
**Phone—(732) 826-7270**
Fax—(732) 826-1705
Pres.—Claude Dinucci
Off. Mgr.—Dawn Dinucci
SIC—2079; NAICS—311200;
*Olive oil blending*
Employs—2; Estab.—1924
Sales—under $500,000
Distrib.—Local
Privately owned corporation

## †MADSEN & HOWELL, INC.

500 Market St., Ste. 1 (08861)
Mail addr: P.O. Box 391, Perth
Amboy (08862-0391)
**Phone—(732) 826-4000**
Fax—(732) 826-7651
www.madsen-howell.com
Email—sales@madsen-howell.com
Pres.—Peter Madsen
SIC—5085; 5084; 5051;
*Distributor of industrial
equipment & supplies, including
abrasives, cutting tools, gaskets,
safety products, pipe, valves &
fittings*
Employs—50; Estab.—1908
Sales—$25Mil
120,000 sq ft site, Distrib.—
Regional
Privately owned corporation
ISO rating—9002

## MAGNETIC & TRANSFORMER TECHNOLOGIES CORP.

653 Sayre Ave. (08861)
**Phone—(609) 371-1258**
www.mttcorp.us
Email—info@mttcorp.us
Pres.—Samir Fattohi
SIC—3612; *Custom energy-saving
single-phase & three-phase
transformers; Brand name—Watt
Manager®; WattMan*
Employs—5; Estab.—1992
Sales—$500,000-$1Mil
Distrib.—National
Privately owned corporation
AKA: MTT Corp.

Parent co.—Magnetic &
Transformer Technologies Corp.,
Robbinsville, NJ
Phone—(609) 371-1258
See Parent Co. Section for full profile.

## MAYAB HAPPY TACOS, INC.

450 Florida Grove Rd. (08861)
**Phone—(732) 293-0400**
Fax—(732) 293-0413
V.-P.—George Alamilla
GM—Glenda Alamilla
SIC—2099; 2096; 2032; 2033;
NAICS—311830; *Flour & corn
tortillas, white & yellow corn
tortilla chips & canned Mexican
food products*
Employs—25; Estab.—1976
Distrib.—Regional
Privately owned corporation

## MONARCH TOWEL CO., INC.

737 Cortlandt St. (08861)
**Phone—(732) 442-0442**
National—(800) 729-7623
Fax—(732) 442-0419
www.monarchrobe.com
Email—sales@cottonpalace.com
Pres.—Ashley Chadowitz
V.-P.—Myron Chadowitz
Off. Mgr.—Linda Pietreski
Cust. Serv. Rep.—Erynie Ramos
Cust. Serv. Rep.—Alana Joseph
Cust. Serv. Rep.—Susan Wortley
SIC—2384; NAICS—315200;
*Bathrobes & towels*
Employs—15; Estab.—1980
Distrib.—Intl.
Privately owned corporation

## MONOGRAM CENTER

437 Amboy Ave. (08861)
**Phone—(732) 442-1800**
Fax—(732) 442-1501
www.monogramcenter.com
Email—sales@
monogramcenter.com
Ptnr.—Bill Kramer
Ptnr.—Michael Kramer
Bookkeeper—Gabi Brun
SIC—2396; 2395; *Textile screen
printing, embroidery &
monogramming*
Employs—35; Estab.—1937
Sales—$1Mil-$5Mil
Distrib.—Local
Privately owned partnership

## MORTON SALT, INC.

920 High St. (08861)
Mail addr: P.O. Box 909, Perth
Amboy (08862)
**Phone—(732) 826-3595**
National—(800) 472-1103
Fax—(732) 826-3599
www.mortonsalt.com
Email—saltinfo@morton.com
Off. Admn.—Sharon Mohan
SIC—3089; 2819; *Salt packaging*
Employs—30; Estab.—1857
Distrib.—National
Publicly owned corporation
Parent co.—Morton Salt, Inc.,
Chicago, IL
Phone—(312) 807-2000
See Parent Co. Section for full profile.

## PERFECT REMEDY PACKAGING, INC.

224 Washington St. (08861)
**Phone—(732) 697-0055**
Email—perfectremedy@webex.net
Plt. Mgr.—Morris Malmstrom
SIC—2652; NAICS—322213; *Soft
jewelry packaging*
Employs—10; Estab.—1996
Sales—$500,000-$1Mil
Distrib.—National

## †PORTEOUS FASTENER CO., INC.

1000 Amboy Ave., Ste. 1 (08861)
**Phone—(732) 376-8420**
National—(800) 935-2902
Fax—(732) 442-1761

GEOGRAPHICAL

## Perth Amboy—(cont.)

www.porteousfastener.com
Email—perthamboy@
porteousfastener.com
Region Mgr.—Jessica Roche
SIC—5072; Distributor of
fasteners
Employs—23; Estab.—2005
Distrib.—Regional
Privately owned corporation
Parent co.—Porteous Fastener
Co., Inc., Santa Fe Springs, CA
Phone—(310) 549-9180
See Parent Co. Section for full profile.

### POWER MAGNE-TECH CORP.

653 Sayre Ave. (08861)
**Phone—(732) 826-4700**
Fax—(732) 826-4706
www.pmcorpnj.com
Email—pmc@
powermagnetech.com
Pres., GM—Leon Zelcer
V-P., Opers.—Harold Tischler
Cont.—Iris Amaya
Pur. Agt.—Avi Zaluski
SIC—2759; NAICS—335311;
Transformers
Employs—20; Estab.—1976
11,000 sq ft site, Distrib.—Intl.
Privately owned corporation

### PRINTING SHOP COPY CENTER, THE

338 State St. (08861)
**Phone—(732) 826-3575**
Fax—(732) 826-3395
Email—theprintingshop@
yahoo.com
Owner—Lucy Arevelo
Graphic Designer—Darnell
Arevelo
SIC—2759; 2752; NAICS—
323100; Commercial & digital
printing & vinyl lettering
Employs—3; Estab.—1997
Sales—under $500,000
Distrib.—Local
Sole ownership

### RECONSERVE, INC.

1250 Amboy Ave. (08861)
**Phone—(732) 826-4240**
www.reconserve.com
Email—jhawrylko@reconserve.com
Sr. V-P.—John Hawrylko
GM—Rick Brown
SIC—2048; Chicken feed
Employs—30; Estab.—1995
40,000 sq ft site, Distrib.—National
Privately owned corporation
Parent co.—ReConserve, Inc.,
Santa Monica, CA
Phone—(310) 458-1574
See Parent Co. Section for full profile.

### RIVERDALE COLOR MFG., INC.

1 Walnut St. (08861)
**Phone—(732) 376-9300**
National—(800) 221-6027
Fax—(732) 376-9394
www.riverdalecolor.com
Email—info@riverdalecolor.com
Pres.—Paul Maguire
V-P., R & D—Charles B. Irish
Secy-Treas., Opers.—George
Sherman
SIC—2865; NAICS—325100;
Liquid color & additive
dispersions for the plastic
industry
Employs—36; Estab.—1985
Sales—$6Mil-$10Mil
60,000 sq ft site, Distrib.—Intl.
Privately owned sub-S corp.

### STAND-OUT SIGNS, INC.

49 W. Pond Rd. (08861-1540)
**Phone—(732) 442-9399**
National—(800) 442-3999
Fax—(732) 442-9292
www.standoutsigns.net
Email—standoutsigns@aol.com

Pres., Off. Mgr.—Joseph
Masaruca
Prodn. Mgr.—Jacki Linaperry
SIC—3993; 3444; 2759; NAICS—
323100; Neon interior & exterior
signs, banners & awnings,
channel & raised letters, light
boxes, truck & boat lettering,
wide-format digital printing &
promotional products
Employs—3; Estab.—1992
Sales—under $500,000
Distrib.—Local
Privately owned corporation
AKA: F N A Signs

### TROPICAL CHEESE INDUSTRIES, INC.

450 Fayette St. (08861)
**Phone—(732) 442-4898**
National—(888) 874-4928
Fax—(732) 442-8227
www.tropicalcheese.com
Hum. Res. Mgr.—Nestor Sabogal
Fin. Mgr.—Michelle Farkas
Sales Coord.—Raquel Rodrigues
SIC—2022; NAICS—311513;
Cheese & cheese products
Employs—250; Estab.—1982
20,000 sq ft site, Distrib.—
Regional
Privately owned corporation

### †US FOODS, INC.

1051 Amboy Ave. (08861)
**Phone—(732) 934-3400**
National—(800) 222-1278
Fax—(732) 934-2401
www.usfoods.com
Email—info@usfoods.com
Pres., Div.—Charles Gannon
V-P., Opers.—Mike Diani
Dir., Sales—Jeff Corson
Dir., Opers.—Bill Sirchio
Dir., Mktg.—Kevin O'Leary
Dir., Hum. Res.—Linda Bonsiglio
Cust. Serv. Rep.—Sharon
Moscardino
SIC—5141; 5142; Distributor of
general line groceries, including
frozen, fresh & canned food
Employs—550; Estab.—2009
Distrib.—Local
Publicly owned corporation
Parent co.—US Foods, Inc.,
Rosemont, IL
Phone—(847) 720-8000
See Parent Co. Section for full profile.

### V & R DESIGN CO.

941 State St. (08861)
**Phone—(732) 442-9249**
Fax—(732) 442-2987
Email—vnrdesign@aol.com
Owner—Victor Carollo
SIC—3499; Metal fabrication
Employs—6; Estab.—1975
Sales—$500,000-$1Mil
Distrib.—Regional
Privately owned corporation

### V & S AMBOY GALVANIZING

Div. of Voigt & Schweitzer, LLC
1190 Amboy Ave. (08861)
**Phone—(732) 442-7555**
Fax—(732) 442-5560
www.hotdipgalvanizing.com
Email—info@hotdipgalvanizing.com
Regional GM—Robert Messler
Cust. Serv. Rep.—Anthony
Starrick
SIC—3479; Steel & iron hot dip
galvanizing
Employs—40; Estab.—1985
Distrib.—Regional
Privately owned corporation
Parent co.—Voigt & Schweitzer,
LLC, Columbus, OH
Phone—(614) 449-8281
See Parent Co. Section for full profile.

### VAN HYDRAULICS

643 Sayre Ave. (08861)
**Phone—(732) 442-5500**
National—(800) 742-0457
Fax—(732) 442-5443
www.vanhydraulics.com
Email—admin@vanhydraulics.com
GM—Steve Roberts
Hum. Res. Mgr.—Alissa Moon
SIC—3511; 3599; NAICS—
333611; Rebuilt cylinders,
pumps, motors, valves &
hammers & hydraulic
components
Employs—30; Estab.—1968
Distrib.—Regional
Privately owned corporation

### VIKING MARINE PRODUCTS, INC.

1160 State St., Ste. 17 (08861)
**Phone—(732) 826-4559**
Fax—(732) 826-5533
www.vikingfender.com
Email—vikingfender@gmail.com
Pres.—Kurt Grimsgaard
V-P.—Guy Grimsgaard
Off. Mgr.—Shari Grimsgaard
SIC—3732; Tug boat & barge
fenders, docks & piers
Employs—8; Estab.—1980
Sales—$500,000-$1Mil
Distrib.—Regional
Privately owned partnership

### VIRA MFG., INC.

1 Buckingham Ave. (08861)
**Phone—(732) 442-8472**
National—(800) 305-8472
Fax—(732) 442-8464
www.viranet.com
Email—info@viranet.com
CEO—Vic Romano
Pres.—Nick Farinola
CFO—Kevin Esposito
Sr. V-P.—Jim Konicek
Ex. V-P.—Alan Rabinowitz
V-P., Opers.—Ken Viviano
Hum. Res. Admn.—Deepa
Kewalramani
SIC—2542; 2541; NAICS—
337215; Retail store fixtures,
displays, themed environments
& kiosks, including electronics
integration; Brand name—VIRA
Employs—216; Estab.—1991
Sales—$50Mil
385,000 sq ft site, Distrib.—Intl.
Privately owned corporation

### WHITE MARINE, INC.

500 Division St. (08861)
Mail addr: P.O. Box 751, Perth
Amboy (08862)
**Phone—(732) 826-4491**
National—(800) 826-4491
Fax—(732) 826-4478
www.whitemarineinc.com
Owner—Jennifer Billand
SIC—3599; Precision machine
parts
Employs—50; Estab.—1979
Sales—$5Mil-$10Mil (est)
Distrib.—Local
Privately owned corporation

### WIKSTROM MACHINES, INC.

412 Summit Ave. (08861)
**Phone—(732) 826-4800**
Fax—(732) 324-1139
Pres.—Walter Geslak
SIC—3548; Resistance welding
machinery
Employs—10; Estab.—1952
Sales—under $500,000
Distrib.—National
Privately owned corporation

## Phillipsburg

(Warren—N.W.)

### ACCURATUS CORPORATION

35 Howard St. (08865)
**Phone—(908) 213-7070**
Fax—(908) 213-7069
www.accuratus.com
Email—info@accuratus.com
Pres.—Raymond Tsao
Mktg. Mgr.—Bruce Cunningham
Fin. Mgr.—Sherry Corcoran
Cust. Serv. Mgr.—Lorraine
Simonof
SIC—3299; 3231; 5199; NAICS—
327215; Manufacturer of
advanced technical glass &
ceramic components &
distributor of machinable glass &
light reflecting ceramic; Brand
name—MACOR; Accuflect
Employs—30; Estab.—1983
Sales—$1Mil-$5Mil
21,000 sq ft site, Distrib.—Intl.
Privately owned corporation

### ATLANTIC STATES CAST IRON PIPE CO.

Div. of McWane, Inc.
183 Sitgreaves St. (08865)
**Phone—(908) 454-1161**
National—(800) 859-1161
Fax—(908) 454-1026
www.atlanticstates.com
Email—info@atlanticstates.com
V-P., GM—Dale Schmelzle
Plt. Mgr.—Dan Fittro
Prodn. Mgr.—Jim Fairchild
IT Mgr.—Omar Radwan
Hum. Res. Mgr.—Paul Carbo
Maint. Mgr.—Bud Lambert
Safety Mgr.—Brandon Lockport
Pur. Agt.—Kelly Brey
SIC—3321; NAICS—331511;
Ductile iron sewer pipes
Employs—200; Estab.—1946
Sales—$25Mil-$50Mil (est)
Distrib.—Intl.
Privately owned corporation
Parent co.—McWane, Inc.,
Birmingham, AL
Phone—(205) 414-3100
See Parent Co. Section for full profile.

NEW ENTRY
### AUTOMATIC TRANSFER, INC.

2 Industrial Rd. (08865)
**Phone—(908) 213-2830**
www.automatictransferinc.com
Email—info@
automatictransferinc.com
Pres.—Alfred W. La Costa
SIC—3861; 2679; Sublimation
toner & heat transfer paper for
the printing industry
Employs—4; Estab.—2001
Sales—$2.5Mil
11,000 sq ft site, Distrib.—Intl.
Sole ownership

NEW ENTRY
### BAER AGGREGATES, INC.

454 River Rd. (08865)
**Phone—(908) 454-4412**
Fax—(908) 454-9370
www.baerquarry.com
Pres.—Louis Mitchele
SIC—1442; 1429; Sand, gravel &
crushed stone quarrying
Employs—5

### BERRY PLASTICS, INC.

Div. of Berry Plastics Corp.
190 Strykers Rd. (08865)
**Phone—(908) 454-0900**
Fax—(908) 454-0976
www.berryplastics.com
Email—johnmcconnell@
berryplastics.com
Hum. Res. Mgr.—Kristi Price
Maint. Mgr.—John McConnell

# Phillipsburg—(cont.)

Qual. Control Techn.—Karen Rose
SIC—3085; NAICS—326160;
　*Plastic bottles &*
　*pharmaceuticals*
Employs—100; Estab.—1969
Distrib.—National
Privately owned corporation
Parent co.—Berry Plastics Corp.,
　Evansville, IN
　Phone—(812) 424-2904
　See Parent Co. Section for full profile.

## BIHLER OF AMERICA, INC.

85 Industrial Dr. (08865)
**Phone—(908) 213-9001**
Fax—(908) 454-5394
www.bihler.com
Email—info@bihler.com
CEO—Maxine Nordmeyer
Pres.—Mathias Bihler
Dir., Technical & Engrg. & Sales
　Mgr.—Max Linder
IT Mgr.—Martin Peverly
Hum. Res. Mgr.—Luz Rivera
SIC—3469; 3544; NAICS—
　333500; *Corporate headquarters*
　*& metal stampings & tool & die*
　*job shop*
Employs—235
Sales—$25Mil-$50Mil (est)
Distrib.—National
Sole ownership

## †COOPER ELECTRIC SUPPLY CO.

225 Stockton St. (08865)
**Phone—(908) 454-8500**
Fax—(908) 454-9587
www.cooper-electric.com
Email—cooperonline@cooper-
　electric.com
Br. Mgr.—Clint Ramsberger
Administrator—Jean Sedler
Administrator—Sue Brady
SIC—5063; *Distributor of electrical*
　*equipment & supplies, including*
　*wire & cable*
Employs—5; Estab.—2004
Distrib.—National
Privately owned corporation
Parent co.—Cooper Electric
　Supply Co., Monroe, NJ
　Phone—(732) 747-2233
　See Parent Co. Section for full profile.

## CROWN ROYALE LTD.

99 Broad St., P.O. Box 5238
　(08865)
**Phone—(908) 859-1999**
National—(800) 992-5400
Fax—(908) 859-1898
www.crownroyaleltd.com
Email—crownroyale@verizon.net
Pres.—Cindy Silva
SIC—2844; NAICS—325600; *Dog*
　*shampoo*
Employs—3; Estab.—1983
Sales—under $500,000
Distrib.—Intl.
Privately owned corporation

## CUSTOM LETTERING

3031 Belvidere Rd. (08865)
**Phone—(908) 454-4140**
www.custom-lettering.net
Owner—Al Pisani
SIC—3993; *Vinyl, plastic &*
　*wooden interior & exterior signs*
Employs—1; Estab.—1975
Sales—under $500,000
Distrib.—Local
Privately owned partnership

## ENGINEERED MEDICAL SOLUTIONS CO., LLC

85 Industrial Rd., Bldg. B (08865)
**Phone—(908) 329-9123**
Fax—(908) 329-9111
www.scintillantlight.com
Email—dcoppersmith@
　emedsco.com
Pres.—Maxine Nordmeyer
IT Mgr.—Martin Pevely

Comm. & Hum. Res. Mgr.—Rachel
　Littlewood
Sales Engr.—Daniel Coppersmith
SIC—3841; *Hand-held adjustable*
　*surgical lights*
Employs—5; Estab.—2001
Sales—$500,000-$1Mil
Distrib.—Local
Limited Liability Company

## FAST WELD CO.

502 New Brunswick Ave. (08865)
**Phone—(908) 213-0155**
Fax—(908) 213-0155
Owner—Frank Shepherd
SIC—3446; NAICS—332323;
　*Architectural metalwork,*
　*including railings*
Employs—1; Estab.—1990
Sales—under $500,000
Distrib.—Local
Privately owned corporation

## FERGUSON CONTAINERS

20 Industrial Rd. (08865)
**Phone—(908) 454-9755**
Fax—(908) 454-7144
www.fergusoncontainers.com
Email—mail@
　fergusoncontainers.com
GM—Ed Reichard
SIC—2653; NAICS—322211;
　*Corrugated boxes*
Employs—18; Estab.—1958
Sales—$1Mil-$5Mil
22,000 sq ft site, Distrib.—
　Regional
Privately owned sub-S corp.

## GENERAL MACHINE KRAFT, INC.

216 Broad St. (08865)
**Phone—(908) 454-5955**
Fax—(908) 859-1588
Email—general.machine@
　verizon.net
Pres.—Eugene Cancelliera
V-P., CFO—Douglas Cancelliera
SIC—3599; *Close tolerance high*
　*production & CNC machining job*
　*shop*
Employs—10; Estab.—1997
Sales—$1Mil-$2.5Mil
3,000 sq ft site, Distrib.—Regional
Privately owned corporation

## GRAPHIC ACTION, INC.

296 S. Main St. (08865)
**Phone—(908) 213-0055**
Fax—(908) 213-0948
www.graphicactionnj.com
Email—graphicaction.prosign@
　verizon.net
Pres.—Frank Geraghty
Off. Mgr.—Amy James
SIC—2752; 2759; NAICS—
　323100; *Instant printing*
Employs—5; Estab.—1989
Sales—under $500,000
750 sq ft site, Distrib.—Local
Privately owned corporation
Also see: Pro Signs, same loc.
AKA: Pro Science

## GULBRANDSEN TECHNOLOGIES, INC.

1 Riverside Way (08865)
**Phone—(908) 238-2030**
Fax—(908) 548-9700
www.gulbrandsen.com
Email—orders@gulbrandsen.com
Plt. Mgr.—Ray Freaney
Pur. Mgr.—Bill Lombardi
Cust. Serv. Mgr.—Laura Wagner
Safety Mgr.—Bob Mikovitch
Pur. Agt.—Annette Correa
SIC—2899; *Water treatment*
　*chemicals*
Employs—175; Estab.—1984
Sales—$50Mil-$100Mil
Distrib.—Regional
Privately owned corporation

Parent co.—Gulbrandsen
　Technologies, Inc., Clinton, NJ
　Phone—(908) 735-5458
　See Parent Co. Section for full profile.

## HARMONY SAND & GRAVEL, INC.

3189 Belvidere Rd. (08865)
Mail addr.: P.O. Box 277, Belvidere
　(07823)
**Phone—(908) 475-4690**
Fax—(908) 475-5760
www.harmonysandgravel.com
Email—hgravel@epix.net
Pres.—Richard L. Hummer
Cont. & Hum. Res. Mgr.—Debbie
　Herbert
Sales Mgr.—Keith Lockard
Off. Mgr.—Paul Delorenzo
SIC—3281; NAICS—327991;
　*Sand & gravel processing*
Employs—24; Estab.—1950
Sales—$1Mil-$2.5Mil
Distrib.—Regional
Privately owned corporation

## HOYT SIGNS

2825 Belvidere Rd. (08865)
**Phone—(908) 859-3768**
Fax—(908) 213-1285
www.hoytsigns.com
Email—hoytsigns@gmail.com
Owner & Pres.—Scott Hoyt
SIC—3993; *Interior & exterior*
　*signs*
Employs—1; Estab.—1972
Sales—under $500,000
2,300 sq ft site, Distrib.—Local
Sole ownership

## INFINITT NORTH AMERICA, INC.

755 Memorial Pkwy., Ste. 304
　(08865-2748)
**Phone—(908) 387-6960**
National—(800) 387-6960
Fax—(908) 387-6965
www.infinittna.com
Email—sales@infinittna.com
Pres., CEO—David Smarro
Hum. Res. Mgr.—Peter Je
Cust. Serv. Mgr.—Christian Smith
SIC—7372; *Medical imaging*
　*visualization & management*
　*software development; Brand*
　*name—Radiology PACS; RIS;*
　*INFINITT Cardiology PACS; 3D;*
　*INFINITT Smart-NET; INFINITT*
　*Orthopedic PACS; INFINITT*
　*Mammo PACS; INFINITT Dental*
　*PACS*
Employs—45; Estab.—2000
Distrib.—Intl.
Privately owned corporation

## JERSEY STRAND & CABLE, INC.

259 Center St. *(08865)*
**Phone—(908) 213-9350**
　　　　(800) 528-3900
Fax—(908) 213-2203
www.jerseystrandandcable.com
Email—sales@
　jerseystrandandcable.com
Pres.—Al Pratt
V-P., Adv.—Diane A. Pratt
Dir., Fin.—Michelle Johnson
GM—John Pratt
Sales Mgr.—Rich Filandro
Pur. Mgr.—Jim Ellis
SIC—3357; 3679; *Custom & stock*
　*small & miniature ferrous &*
　*nonferrous metal wire rope,*
　*strand & cable*
Employs—40; Estab.—1978
Sales—$5Mil-$10Mil
Distrib.—Intl.
Privately owned corporation

## KEYSTONE PACKAGING SERVICE, INC.

555 Warren St. (08865)
**Phone—(908) 454-8567**
Fax—(908) 454-7173
Pres.—John Schoeneck
GM—Enoch Schoeneck

SIC—2673; *Plastic bags*
Employs—10; Estab.—1950
Sales—$500,000-$1Mil
Distrib.—Local
Privately owned corporation

### NEW ENTRY

## MAIL TIME, INC.

224 Stockton St. (08865)
**Phone—(908) 859-5500**
Email—accountingmt@gmail.com
Owner—Mario Sgroi
Acctg. Mgr.—John Cunningham
SIC—2759; *Commercial printing*
Employs—23; Estab.—2002
Sales—$2.5Mil-$5Mil (est)
1,200 sq ft site, Distrib.—Regional
Privately owned corporation

## MEDCONNECTION, LLC

65 Howard St. (08865)
**Phone—(908) 213-7012**
Fax—(908) 454-0416
www.medconnection.net
Email—sales@medconnection.net
Pres.—Robert K. Kolonia
Plt. Mgr.—Richard Nowosielski
Admn. & Off. Mgr.—Dorothy
　Valcich
SIC—3841; *Plastic injection-*
　*molded medical supplies,*
　*including catheters & tubing hole*
　*punching & tipping*
Employs—10; Estab.—2000
Sales—over $1Mil
Distrib.—National
Limited Liability Company
ISO rating—9001:2000
Also see: Factoryone, LLC & Micro
　Molding, Inc., same loc.

## MICRO MOLDING, INC.

65 Howard St. (08865)
**Phone—(908) 454-1225**
Fax—(908) 454-0416
www.micromoldinginc.com
Email—sales@
　micromoldinginc.com
Chrm.—Gerald Detweiler
Pres.—Robert K. Kolonia
Plt. Mgr.—Shawn McGinley
Admn. Mgr.—Dorthy Valcich
Qual. Assur. Mgr.—Mark S.
　Bachman
SIC—3089; *Plastic injection*
　*molding; Brand name—*
Employs—40; Estab.—1984
26,000 sq ft site, Distrib.—National
Privately owned sub-S corp.
ISO rating—9001:2008
Also see: Factoryone, LLC &
　MedConnection, LLC, same loc.

## MOSER JEWEL CO.

518 Route 57 (08865)
**Phone—(908) 454-1155**
Fax—(908) 454-1199
www.mosercompany.com
Email—info@mosercompany.com
CEO—Sharon Duffield
V-P., Engrg. & Sales—Alexandre
　Laroche
SIC—3728; 3812; NAICS—
　334511; *Micro-precision*
　*components, instrument parts,*
　*jewel bearings & test probes*
Employs—10; Estab.—1941
Sales—$1Mil-$2.5Mil
6,300 sq ft site, Distrib.—Intl.
Privately owned corporation
AKA: Moser Co.

## OLIVER, INC., G. J.

50 Industrial Rd. (08865)
**Phone—(908) 454-9743**
Fax—(908) 454-0927
www.gjoliver.com
Email—gjo@gjoliver.net
CEO—John Oliver
Pres.—Charles Parker
Pur. Agt.—Tom Cooper

GEOGRAPHICAL

## Phillipsburg—(cont.)

SIC—3443; 3312; 3599; *Steel fabrication & machining of pressure vessels & fluid handling systems*
Employs—75; Estab.—1970
Sales—$20Mil-$25Mil
150,000 sq ft site, Distrib.—National
Privately owned corporation

### P & R PUBLISHING CO.

1102 Marble Hill Rd., P.O. Box 817 (08865)
**Phone—(908) 454-0505**
National—(800) 631-0094
Fax—(908) 859-2390
www.prpbooks.com
Email—sales@prpbooks.com
Pres.—Bryce H. Craig
V-P. & Mktg. Mgr.—Ian Thompson
Bus. Mgr.—Robert A. Fales
Acct. Admn.—Jan Powers
SIC—2731; *Book publishing*
Employs—18; Estab.—1936
12,000 sq ft site, Distrib.—Intl.
Privately owned corporation

### PHILLIPSBURG MARBLE CO.

1 Marble Hill Rd., P.O. Box 172 (08865)
**Phone—(908) 859-3435**
Fax—(908) 859-2706
www.pburgmarble.com
Email—info@pburgmarble.com
Pres.—Robert S. Barron
Sales Mgr.—Keith Nicusanti
Plt. Opers. Mgr.—Douglas Male
Off. Mgr.—Linda Kish
SIC—3281; NAICS—327991; *Architectural marble, granite, travertine, slate & limestone fabrication for residential & commercial projects*
Employs—25; Estab.—1964
Sales—$1Mil-$2.5Mil
30,000 sq ft site, Distrib.—Local
Privately owned sub-S corp.

### PRECAST MFG. CO., LLC

Div. of Precast Concrete Sales Co.
187 Strykers Rd. (08865)
**Phone—(908) 454-2122**
Fax—(908) 454-0512
www.precastmfgco.com
Email—pmcinfo@precastmfgco.com
Plt. Mgr.—Vilma Delva
MIS Mgr.—Candy Keck
SIC—3272; *Precast concrete products*
Employs—30; Estab.—1995
Sales—$1Mil-$5Mil
12,000 sq ft site, Distrib.—Regional
Limited Liability Company
Parent co.—Precast Concrete Sales Co., Valley Cottage, NY
Phone—(845) 268-4949
See Parent Co. Section for full profile.

### PRO SIGNS

296 S. Main St. (08865)
**Phone—(908) 454-4888**
Fax—(908) 213-0948
Pres.—Frank Geraghty
SIC—3993; *Interior & exterior signs*
Employs—3; Estab.—1987
Sales—under $500,000
Distrib.—Local
Privately owned corporation
Also see: Graphic Action, Inc., same loc.

### ROTONDI & SONS, INC., S.

139 Reeder Rd. (08865)
Mail addr.: P.O. Box 1407, Summit (07902)
**Phone—(908) 475-1916**
Fax—(908) 475-1978
GM—Donald Loguidice

SIC—2874; NAICS—325312; *Compost*
Employs—10; Estab.—1972
Distrib.—Local
Privately owned corporation
Parent co.—Rotondi & Sons, Inc., S., Chatham, NJ
Phone—(973) 635-7799
See Parent Co. Section for full profile.

### RUTLER SCREEN PRINTING, INC.

169 Belview Rd. (08865)
**Phone—(908) 859-3327**
Fax—(908) 859-2138
www.rutler.com
Email—allen@rutler.com
Pres. & V-P.—Allen Shubert
Cont.—Shuana Shubert
SIC—2396; 2759; NAICS—323100; *Screen printing*
Employs—22; Estab.—1954
6,000 sq ft site, Distrib.—Local
Privately owned corporation

### S C C CONCRETE

1051 River Rd., P.O. Box 47 (08865)
**Phone—(908) 859-2172**
Fax—(908) 859-1720
Pres., GM—Richard Cornely
Treas.—Patricia Cornely
Plt. Mgr.—Francis Stine
Trans. Mgr.—Jackie Slack
SIC—3273; NAICS—327320; *Ready-mixed concrete*
Employs—13; Estab.—1976
Sales—$500,000-$1Mil
Distrib.—Local
Privately owned corporation

### STATELINE FABRICATORS, LLC

167 Bronico Way (08865)
**Phone—(908) 387-8800**
Fax—(908) 387-8077
www.statelinefabricators.com
Email—stateline1@verizon.net
Owner—Ed Esposito
Off. Admn.—Gina Silvestri
SIC—3446; 3441; *Architectural & structural metal fabrication*
Employs—35; Estab.—2003
Sales—$11Mil-$25Mil
Distrib.—Local
Limited Liability Company

### T K L SPECIALTY PIPING

175 Broad St., P.O. Box 5149 (08865)
**Phone—(908) 454-0030**
Fax—(908) 213-1575
Pres.—Thomas W. Larkin
SIC—3498; NAICS—332996; *Steel pipe & adaptor nipples*
Employs—7; Estab.—1990
Sales—$500,000-$1Mil
7,000 sq ft site, Distrib.—Local
Sole ownership

### TREASURE HUNT

1223 S. Main St. (08865)
**Phone—(908) 454-0880**
Fax—(908) 859-5152
www.treasurehuntads.com
Owner—David Sisco, Jr.
SIC—2711; *Weekly classified newspaper publishing*
Employs—5; Estab.—1982
Sales—under $500,000 (est)
Distrib.—Local
Sole ownership

## Pilesgrove

(Gloucester—S.W.)

### PIERSON CONSTRUCTION CO., INC., R. E. (H Q)

426 Swedesboro Rd. (08098)
**Phone—(856) 769-8244**
Fax—(856) 769-5629
www.repierson.com
Email—info@repierson.com
V-P.—Robert Baccala
Cont.—Cherri Coles

Hum. Res. Mgr.—Donna Brady
SIC—2951; 3273; NAICS—324121; *Corporate headquarters; asphalt paving compounds & ready-mixed concrete*
Employs—50; Estab.—1980
Sales—$1Mil-$2.5Mil (est)
Privately owned corporation

## Pine Beach

(Ocean—S.E.)

### CASTLE WOODCRAFT ASSOCS.

161 Route 9, P.O. Box 426 (08741)
**Phone—(732) 349-1519**
Fax—(732) 244-3574
www.castlewoodcraft.com
Email—castlewoodcraft@verizon.net
Ptnr.—Ernest Guenzburger
Ptnr.—Gerhard Frenz
SIC—2434; 2521; 2542; 3083; NAICS—337110; *Kitchen & office wooden & plastic laminate cabinets*
Employs—15; Estab.—1946
8,000 sq ft site, Distrib.—Local
Privately owned partnership

## Pine Brook

(Morris—N.W.)

### ADHESIVE FILMS, INC.

4 Barnet Rd., P.O. Box 651 (07058)
**Phone—(973) 882-4944**
National—(888) 523-3456
Fax—(973) 882-2817
www.adhesivefilms.com
Email—info@adhesivefilms.com
Pres., CEO—John K. Farr II
CFO—Brian F. Stauff
V-P., COO—Michael Carbonare, Jr.
SIC—3081; NAICS—326113; *Thermoplastic adhesive film in roll form with or without peel away liners for bonding fabric, foam, foil, metal, plastic & wood*
Employs—18; Estab.—1997
Sales—$5Mil-$10Mil
40,000 sq ft site, Distrib.—Intl.
Privately owned sub-S corp.

### BELL-MARK SALES CO., INC.

331 Changebridge Rd., P.O. Box 2007 (07058)
**Phone—(973) 882-0202**
Fax—(973) 808-4616
www.bell-mark.com
Email—info@bell-mark.com
Pres.—John Marozzi
CFO—James Pontrella, Jr.
V-P., Sales & Mktg.—Thomas Pugh
Dir., Sales—Robert Batesko
Dir., Mktg. & IT Mgr.—Douglas C. Buch
Fin. Mgr.—Donna Rossi
SIC—3555; NAICS—333293; *Code-dating & in-line printing equipment*
Employs—30; Estab.—1959
40,000 sq ft site, Distrib.—Intl.
Privately owned corporation

### CAMBRIDGE SILVERSMITHS LTD. (H Q)

30 Hook Mountain Rd., P.O. Box 625 (07058)
**Phone—(973) 227-4400**
National—(800) 890-3366
www.cambridgesilversmiths.com
Email—charlied@camsil.com
Pres.—Roger Freeman
CFO—Mike Honig
Hum. Res. Mgr.—Charlie DePietro

SIC—3914; *Company headquarters; stainless steel flatware (mfg. done overseas)*
Employs—90; Estab.—1992
Sales—$10Mil-$25Mil (est)
Distrib.—National
Privately owned corporation

### CANVAS 4 LIFE, INC.

30 Chapin Rd., P.O. Box 216 (07058)
**Phone—(973) 276-3200**
National—(888) 407-6277
www.canvas4life.com
Email—info@canvas4life.com
CMO & COO—Cheryl Stoyle
SIC—2759; NAICS—323113; *Digital inkjet printing on canvas; Brand name—Canvas4Life; Canvas4Life.com; Art4Life; Art4Life.com*
Employs—8; Estab.—2009
Sales—$2.5Mil-$5Mil
Distrib.—National
Privately owned corporation

NEW ENTRY
### CARDINAL INTERNATIONAL, INC.

43 Route 46 E., Ste. 709, P.O. Box 897 (07058)
**Phone—(973) 628-0900**
Fax—(973) 633-5555
www.cardinalglass.com
Email—cardinalsales@arc-intl.com
Pres.—Bryan O'Rourke
SIC—3231; *Glass drinkware, dinnerware, flatware & table accessories for the foodservice industry*
Employs—10
Sales—$1Mil-$2.5Mil (est)
Distrib.—National
Privately owned corporation

### CHIRAL PHOTONICS, INC.

26 Chapin Rd., Unit 1104, P.O. Box 694 (07058)
**Phone—(973) 732-0030**
Fax—(973) 732-0031
www.chiralphotonics.com
Email—gweiner@chiralphotonics.com
Pres.—Dan Neugroschl
V-P.—Gary Weiner
SIC—3357; 3674; 3827; *Ultra high-density optical I/O solutions for photonic integration chip & photonic super computer makers & photonic IC packaging services & specialized coupling fibers & fiber arrays*
Employs—20; Estab.—1999
15,000 sq ft site, Distrib.—Intl.
Privately owned corporation

### CHRISTINE VALMY INC.

285 Changebridge Rd., Ste. 1 (07058)
**Phone—(973) 575-1050**
National—(800) 526-5057
Fax—(973) 575-1355
www.christinevalmy.com
Email—info@christinevalmy.com
Pres.—Peter DeHaydu
CFO—David Bickel
V-P.—Marina DeHaydu
Off. Mgr.—Monica Espinoza
SIC—2844; NAICS—325600; *Natural skin care products*
Employs—60; Estab.—1965
30,000 sq ft site, Distrib.—Intl.
Privately owned corporation
AKA: Christine Valmy International, Inc.

### COMPUNITE COMPUTERS, INC.

39 U.S. Highway 46, Ste. 803, P.O. Box 3 (07058)
**Phone—(973) 227-6008**
Fax—(973) 227-6608
www.compunite.com
Email—sales@compunite.com
Owner & Pres.—Steve Ferman

# Pine Brook—(cont.)

SIC—7373; *Computer network systems integration, including LANs & WANs & IT support services*
Employs—15; Estab.—1988
Distrib.—National
Privately owned corporation

**DICAR, INC.**
10 Bloomfield Ave., P.O. Box 643 (07058)
**Phone—(973) 575-1174**
National—(800) 323-4227
Fax—(973) 575-1455
www.dicar.com
Email—dicar@dicar.com
Pres.—Steve Warl
V-P., Cont.—Thomas Curcio
Hum. Res. Mgr.—Loretta Resz
Safety Mgr.—Ira Sanders
Tech. Mgr.—Raymond So
Pur. Agt.—Jim Johnson
SIC—3599; *Corporate headquarters & replacement die cutting machinery parts & cutting die supplies; Brand name— EquaMount; Equalizer; DuraBlue; TapItOn; CT Die Supplies; AirDicar*
Employs—150; Estab.—1969
Distrib.—Intl.
Privately owned corporation

**DICAR, INC.**
5 Bader Rd. (07058)
**Phone—(973) 575-4220**
Fax—(973) 575-8122
www.dicar.com
Email—dicar@dicar.com
Manager—Guillermo Pacheco
Administrator—Marisel Soto
SIC—2822; *Synthetic rubber*
Employs—72
Sales—$25Mil-$50Mil (est)
Distrib.—Intl.
Privately owned corporation
Parent co.—Dicar, Inc., Pine Brook, NJ
Phone—(973) 575-1174
See Parent Co. Section for full profile.

**DIOPSYS, INC.**
16 Chapin Rd., Ste. 912, P.O. Box 672 *(07058)*
**Phone—(973) 244-0622**
Fax—(973) 244-0670
www.diopsys.com
Email—info@diopsys.com
Pres., CEO—Joseph Fontanetta
V-P., Fin. & Hum. Res.—Scott Kahn
V-P., Clinical Doc.—Peter Derr
V-P., Bus. Dev. & Clinical Affs.— Matt Emmer
V-P., Engrg.—Laurie Cox
Dir., Insurance—Diane Fulton
Dir., Research—Alberto Gonzalez
SIC—3841; 3829; *Visual evoked potential (VEP) vision testing & medical devices; Brand name— Enfant Pediatric VEP Vision Testing System; Diopsys NOVA-VEP Vision Testing Systems*
Employs—22; Estab.—1998
Distrib.—National
Privately owned corporation

**FISNAR, INC.**
19-C Chapin Rd. Ste. 307 (07058)
**Phone—(973) 646-5044**
Fax—(201) 794-7034
www.fisnar.com
Email—info@fisnar.com
Pres.—Vladimir Siroky
Prod. Engr.—Shailesh Lad
SIC—3559; *Adhesive dispensing equipment*
Employs—40; Estab.—1986
Sales—$5Mil-$10Mil (est)
Distrib.—Intl.
Privately owned corporation

**FORD ATLANTIC FASTENER CO., INC.**
341 Changebridge Rd., P.O. Box 733 (07058)
**Phone—(973) 882-1191**
Fax—(973) 882-3884
www.fordatlantic.com
Email—eduncza@fordatlantic.com
Pres.—Anthony Innamarato
V-P., Sales—Ed Duncza
V-P., Opers.—Glenn Ehrhardt
Sales Mgr.—David Karlsruher
Off. Mgr.—Joann Dura
SIC—3452; 3429; 3451; 3469; NAICS—339993; *Standard & custom fastners, metal stampings, extrusions, castings, forgings, screw machine & cold-headed parts, injection moldings & assemblies*
Employs—40; Estab.—1982
35,000 sq ft site, Distrib.—Intl.
Privately owned corporation

**FORMSLINK SYSTEMS, INC.**
14 Hilldale Rd., P. O. Box 101 (07058)
**Phone—(973) 808-8820**
Fax—(973) 808-8829
www.formslinksystems.com
Email—formslinksystems@gmail.com
Co-Pres.—Chun Yan Lai
Co-Pres.—Patrick Lai
SIC—2759; *Commercial, large-format, laser & digital printing*
Employs—4; Estab.—1995
Sales—under $500,000
Distrib.—Local
Privately owned corporation

**FORTITUDE HEALTH**
101 U.S. Highway 46 (07058)
**Phone—(973) 396-8480**
Email—fortitudehealth@gmail.com
Pres.—Mike Marenick
Dir., Mktg.—Matt Hammer
SIC—2844; NAICS—325600; *Egg-based toiletries, including skin care lotions & shampoos; Brand name—Dermasolve*
Employs—6; Estab.—1997
Sales—under $500,000
Distrib.—Intl.
Privately owned corporation

**FRISCH PLASTICS CORP.**
81 Windsor Dr. (07058)
**Phone—(973) 685-5936**
Fax—(973) 685-5939
www.frischplastics.com
Email—sales@frischplastics.com
Pres.—Ruth Lefkowitz
Manager—Eve Lefkowitz
Manager—Roberet Lefkowitz
SIC—3089; *Plastic injection molding*
Employs—20; Estab.—1929
Distrib.—Intl.
Privately owned corporation

**†HKK CHAIN CORP. OF AMERICA**
9 Riverside Dr., P.O. Box 604 (07058)
**Phone—(973) 575-7860**
National—(800) 631-1056
Fax—(973) 575-7250
www.hkkchain.com
Email—sales@hkkchain.com
Pres., COO—Ted Kawamoto
Opers. Mgr.—John Hambright
SIC—5085; *Corporate headquarters & wholesaler of standard, roller & stainless & corrosion-resistant transmission & conveyor chains & attachments*
Employs—20
Distrib.—Intl.
Privately owned corporation

**II-VI ADVANCED MATERIALS**
Div. of II-VI Incorporated
20 Chapin Rd., Ste. 1007, P.O. Box 840 (07058)
**Phone—(973) 227-1551**
Fax—(973) 227-8658
www.iiviwbg.com
Email—wbgsales@ii-vi.com
GM—Tom Anderson
Bus. Dev. & Technical Sales Mgr.—Andy Souzis
Opers. Mgr.—Tom Wessel
Hum. Res. Mgr.—Christy Wright
SIC—3674; *Silicon carbide wafers*
Employs—40; Estab.—2001
Sales—$10Mil-$25Mil
30,000 sq ft site, Distrib.—Intl.
Publicly owned corporation
Parent co.—II-VI Incorporated, Saxonburg, PA
Phone—(724) 352-4455
See Parent Co. Section for full profile.

**†INTERNATIONAL BEAUTY PRODUCTS**
26 Chapin Rd., Ste. 1108, P.O. Box 708 (07058)
**Phone—(973) 575-6400**
Fax—(973) 575-6486
www.brushlove.com
Email—info@brushlove.com
Pres.—Henry Cho
SIC—5122; *Distributor of beauty salon products, including hair care & cosmetic products*
Employs—11

**LAGNIAPPE HEALTH ACQUISITION CO.**
Div. of Robertson Piper Software Group, Inc.
34 Maple Ave., Ste. 102, P.O. Box 727 (07058)
**Phone—(973) 256-7633**
National—(800) 835-6787
www.rxlps.com
Email—sales@rxlps.com
Qual. Assur. Analyst—Joe Pinto
SIC—7372; *Pharmacy management software development*
Employs—47; Estab.—2011
18,000 sq ft site,
Limited Liability Company
Parent co.—Robertson Piper Software Group, Inc., Chatham, NJ
Phone—(973) 435-3640
See Parent Co. Section for full profile.

**†M C MACHINERY SYSTEMS, INC.**
Div. of M C Machinery Systems, Inc., Mitsubishi E D M/Laser Div.
16 Chapin Rd., P.O. Box 405 (07058)
**Phone—(973) 244-1501**
www.mitsubishi-world.com
Email—sales@mcmachinery.com
V-P.—Nick Giannotte
SIC—5084; *Wholesaler of industrial machinery*
Employs—9; Estab.—1980
Sales—$500,000-$1Mil
5,000 sq ft site, Distrib.—Intl.
Privately owned corporation
AKA: Mitsubishi World
Parent co.—M C Machinery Systems, Inc., Mitsubishi E D M/Laser Div., Wood Dale, IL
Phone—(630) 860-4210
See Parent Co. Section for full profile.

**†MARUKA U.S.A., INC.**
45 Route 46 E., Ste. 610, P.O. Box 747 (07058)
**Phone—(973) 487-3800**
National—(800) 631-0426
Fax—(973) 487-2147
www.marukausa.com
Email—dabe@marukausa.com
Pres.—Gary Lowery
Ex. V-P.—Yosuke Yasuda
Corp. Admn. Mgr.—Doug Abe

IT Mgr.—Kazuhiko Koike
Acctg. Mgr.—Yutaka Kitajima
SIC—5084; 5085; *Corporate headquarters & distributor of CNC metal cutting machinery & parts & plastic injection molding machinery; Brand name—Toyo; Chiyoda; Hwacheon; FCS; Nakamura Tome; Feeler; Fanuc Robodrill; Kiwa; Yasda*
Employs—35; Estab.—1990
9,200 sq ft site, Distrib.—National
Publicly owned corporation

**†OLLA BEAUTY SUPPLY, INC.**
10 New Maple Ave., Unit 301-A, P.O. Box 898 (07058)
**Phone—(973) 575-5260**
(877) 940-9160
Fax—(973) 575-5219
Email—mchromey@ultradst.com
V-P.—May Chroney
Sales Mgr.—Joe Roberts
SIC—5122; *Distributor of ethnic hair care & beauty care products*
Employs—100
Distrib.—Intl.
Privately owned corporation
AKA: Ultra/Standard Distributor

**P C R TECHNOLOGIES, INC.**
26 Chapin Rd., Unit 1111 (07058)
**Phone—(973) 882-0017**
Fax—(973) 882-0113
www.pcrtechnologies.com
Email—sales@pcrtechnologies.com
Pres.—Mark Vanzini
V-P. & Qual. Control Mgr.—Peter Lemma
SIC—3599; 3089; 3471; 3479; NAICS—334412; *High-speed CNC machining of metals & plastics, including adhesive pre-forms, microwave housing machining, solder bonding & heatsink fabrication & metal finishing, marking, hardware & assembly*
Employs—9; Estab.—1987
Sales—$1.4Mil
7,000 sq ft site, Distrib.—National
Privately owned sub-S corp.
ISO rating—9001:2008

**PARKER HANNIFIN CORP.**
Div. of Parker Hannifin Corporation
45 Route 46 E., Unit 602, P.O. Box 778 (07058)
**Phone—(973) 575-4844**
National—(800) 482-8258
Fax—(973) 575-4011
www.parker.com
Email—ppfinfo@parker.com
Application Engr.—Jamari Davis
SIC—3492; 3561; NAICS—332912; *PTFE & stainless steel miniature solenoid valves & pumps for the biomedical market*
Employs—50; Estab.—1972
12,000 sq ft site, Distrib.—Intl.
Publicly owned corporation
Parent co.—Parker Hannifin Corporation, Cleveland, OH
Phone—(216) 896-3000
See Parent Co. Section for full profile.

**†SINGLE SOURCE TECHNOLOGIES**
Div. of Makino, Inc.
30 Chapin Rd., Ste. 1208, P.O. Box 655 (07058)
**Phone—(973) 227-6601**
National—(800) 336-7283
Fax—(973) 227-6605
www.edmsave.com
Email—edmsave@edmsave.com
Pres.—Nick Casbar
Sales Mgr., Natl.—Gerry Zolynski

GEOGRAPHICAL

## Pine Brook—(cont.)

SIC—5063; *Company headquarters & wholesaler of EDM machinery & supplies; Brand name—VersaCut (H,Z,Brass) EDM Wire; OKI EDM Wire; Bedra EDM Wire; Mann + Hummel Filters; Dynamic Filters; Ionoplus Oil; Poco EDM Graphite; VersaTech Wear Parts; Versa Graph Graphite*
Employs—10; Estab.—1974
Distrib.—National
Limited Liability Company
Parent co.—Makino, Inc., Mason, OH
   Phone—(513) 573-7200
   See Parent Co. Section for full profile.

### STAR LEDGER

Div. of Newark Morning Ledger Co.
26 Riverside Dr. (07058)
**Phone—(973) 882-6120**
www.nj.com/starledger
Email—sports@starledger.com
Maint. Mgr.—Joe Maker
Maint. Mgr.—Paul Gattuso
SIC—2711; *Newspaper publishing*
Employs—450; Estab.—1980
Sales—$50Mil-$100Mil
Distrib.—Local
Privately owned corporation
Parent co.—Newark Morning Ledger Co., Newark, NJ
   Phone—(973) 392-4141
   See Parent Co. Section for full profile.

### VOLTA BELTING TECHNOLOGY

11 Chapin Rd. *(07058)*
**Phone—(973) 276-7905**
Fax—(973) 276-7908
www.voltabelting.com
Email—sales@voltabelting.com
GM—Zvika Avidan
Cust. Serv. Rep.—Joanne Shapiro
SIC—3089; *Plastic conveyor belts*
Employs—15; Estab.—2004
Sales—$500,000-$1Mil
Distrib.—Intl.
Privately owned corporation

### WARREN MFG. CORP.

23 Bloomfield Ave. (07058)
**Phone—(973) 227-4220**
Fax—(973) 227-0072
Pres.—Frank Petrus
SIC—3599; *Precision machining job shop*
Employs—3
Sales—under $500,000 (est)
Privately owned corporation

### †WESTPORT CORP.

331 Changebridge Rd., P.O. Box 2002 (07058)
**Phone—(973) 575-0110**
Fax—(973) 575-8197
www.mundiwestport.com
CEO—Richard Florin
Pres.—Kevin Ross
V-P., CFO—Anthony J. Brain
V-P., COO—Robert Lombardi
V-P.—John Florin
V-P.—Jane Langendorff
SIC—5136; 5137; *Distributor of leather & synthetic wallets & handbags; Brand name—Mundi; Lilly Waters; Stella & Max; Kenneth Cole; Sag Harbor; Joseph Abboud; Fuzzy Nation; Timberland; J-Fold; Jessica McClintock; Andrew Marc; Greg Norman; Steve Madden; Kooba*
Employs—120; Estab.—1969
Sales—$125Mil
160,000 sq ft site, Distrib.—National
Privately owned corporation
DBA: Mundi Westport Group

## Pine Hill

(Camden—S.W.)

### ARTCRAFT SIGN STUDIO, INC.

738 W. Branch Ave. (08021)
**Phone—(856) 783-8008**
Fax—(856) 783-8598
www.artcraftsigns.com
Email—info@artcraftsigns.com
Pres., CFO, MIS Mgr.—Arthur Elkins
V-P.—Len Elkins
SIC—3993; 2399; 2759; NAICS—323100; *Dimensional, sandblasted, carved, interior & exterior signs, CNC routing, banners, truck lettering & digital printing*
Employs—5; Estab.—1989
Sales—under $500,000
3,800 sq ft site, Distrib.—National
Privately owned sub-S corp.

### PINE HILL MACHINE SHOP & WELDING

44 W. 3rd Ave. (08021)
**Phone—(856) 783-9842**
Ptnr.—Lisa Schaefer
Ptnr.—Joel Schaefer
SIC—3599; *General machining & welding job shop*
Employs—2; Estab.—1985
Sales—under $500,000
Distrib.—Local
Sole ownership

### PINE HILL PRINTING, INC.

200 Erial Rd. (08021)
**Phone—(856) 346-2915**
Fax—(856) 783-6633
www.pinehillprinting.com
Email—phprint1@comcast.net
Pres.—Edie McKusker
Hum. Res. Mgr.—Susan Scott
Dept. Mgr.—Sandy Bates
SIC—2759; NAICS—323100; *Commercial printing*
Employs—12; Estab.—1985
Sales—$500,000-$1Mil
Distrib.—Local
Privately owned corporation

---

## Piscataway

(Middlesex—N.E.)

### †AARON & CO.

30 Turner Pl. (08854)
Mail addr: P.O. Box 8310, Piscataway (08855-8004)
**Phone—(732) 752-8200**
National—(800) 227-6677
Fax—(732) 752-8221
www.aaronco.com
Email—bportnoy@aaronco.com
Pres.—Barry Portnoy
CFO—Anthony Conte
COO—Richard Laudino
CIO—Frank Laudino
V-P., Sales & Mktg.—Kevin Manning
V-P., Opers.—Anthony Panko
V-P., HVAC—John Provenzano
Hum. Res. Mgr.—Margie Mish
SIC—5074; *Wholesaler of plumbing & HVAC supplies*
Employs—100; Estab.—1998
Sales—over $70Mil
Distrib.—National
Privately owned corporation

### ABOUT OUR TOWN, INC.

2 Lakeview Ave., Ste. 312 (08854)
**Phone—(732) 968-1615**
Fax—(732) 968-2205
www.aboutourtown.com
Email—sales@aboutourtown.com
Owner—Ron Chilson
Editor—Claire Pyecroft

SIC—2711; *Newspaper publishing*
Employs—8; Estab.—1998
Sales—under $500,000
Distrib.—Local
Privately owned corporation

### AGILEX FLAVORS & FRAGRANCES, INC.

Div. of MidOcean Partners
140 Centennial Ave. (08854)
**Phone—(732) 393-7300**
National—(800) 542-7662
Fax—(732) 393-7379
www.agilexfragrances.com
Email—mail@agilexfragrances.com
Pres. & CEO, Fragrance Div.—Raymond Hughes
Sr. V-P., Sales—Tony Trinco
Sr. V-P., Fin. & Opers.—Kevin Gilbert
Sr. V-P., Creative Svcs.—Natalie Hinden Kuhles
V-P., Mktg.—Sharon Maes
Dir., Fragrance Dev.—Heather Adams
SIC—2844; 2899; NAICS—325600; *Corporate headquarters & fragrance oils*
Employs—150; Estab.—1987
Sales—$50Mil-$75Mil
60,000 sq ft site, Distrib.—Intl.
Privately owned corporation
Parent co.—MidOcean Partners, New York, NY
   Phone—(212) 497-1400
   See Parent Co. Section for full profile.

### †AIRGAS EAST, INC.

490 Stelton Rd. (08854)
**Phone—(732) 752-4500**
   (800) 355-2132
Fax—(732) 752-6445
www.airgas.com
Email—info@airgas.com
Administrator—Terry Dalessio
SIC—5084; 5169; *Wholesaler of welding supplies & industrial gases*
Employs—40; Estab.—1986
Distrib.—National
Publicly owned corporation
Parent co.—Airgas East, Inc., Salem, NH
   Phone—(603) 890-4600
   See Parent Co. Section for full profile.

### ALL AMERICAN POLY CORP.

40 Turner Pl. (08854)
Mail addr: P.O. Box 10148, New Brunswick (08906)
**Phone—(732) 752-3200**
National—(800) 526-3551
Fax—(732) 752-5570
www.allampoly.com
Email—info@allampoly.com
Pres.—Jack G. Klein
CFO—Joseph Weingarten
Sr. V-P., Sales—Joseph Friedman
V-P., Sales—Ben Klein
V-P.—Neil Koenig
GM—Bob MacDougall
Qual. Control Mgr.—Joe Angeline
SIC—2673; 3089; *Corporate headquarters & polyethylene products, including flexible packaging & plastic & shrinkable poly bags/wraps*
Employs—242; Estab.—1981
Sales—$75Mil
145,000 sq ft site, Distrib.—National
Privately owned corporation

**NEW ENTRY**
### AMERICAN HOME MFG., LLC

4 Corporate Pl. (08854)
**Phone—(732) 465-1530**
Fax—(732) 465-1540
Manager—Rick Bruch
SIC—2392; *Pillows & bean bags*
Employs—20
Sales—$2.5Mil-$5Mil (est)
Limited Liability Company

**NEW ENTRY**
### AMNEAL PHARMACEUTICALS, LLC

47 Colonial Dr. (08854)
**Phone—(732) 645-3030**
www.amneal.com
Email—businessdevelopment@amneal.com
Hum. Res. Mgr.—Martine Maignen
Off. Mgr.—Puja Jani
SIC—2834; *Pharmaceuticals*
Employs—25
Sales—$10Mil-$25Mil (est)
Distrib.—Intl.
Limited Liability Company
Parent co.—Amneal Pharmaceuticals, LLC, Bridgewater, NJ
   Phone—(908) 947-3120
   See Parent Co. Section for full profile.

### ARD STEEL WORKS CO.

2 Lakeview Ave., Ste. 201 (08854)
**Phone—(732) 926-9800**
Fax—(732) 926-9801
Email—ardsteelworks@aol.com
Owner—Kathryn Davisson
Foreman—Allen Davis
SIC—3441; *Structural steel fabrication*
Employs—10; Estab.—1999
Sales—$1Mil-$2.5Mil
Distrib.—Regional
Privately owned corporation

### AS AMERICA, INC. (H Q)

Div. of Sun Capital Partners, Inc.
1 Centennial Ave., P.O. Box 6820 (08855)
**Phone—(732) 980-3000**
National—(800) 442-1902
www.americanstandard-us.com
Pres., CEO—Jay Gould
CFO—Steve Delarge
COO—Kevin Oak
Sr. V-P., Gen. Counsel—Maria Chiclana
Hum. Res. Mgr.—Lisa Escuaduro
SIC—3429; *Corporate headquarters; hardware & faucets*
Employs—240
Sales—$10Mil-$25Mil (est)
Privately owned corporation
DBA: American Standard Brands
Parent co.—Sun Capital Partners, Inc., Boca Raton, FL
   Phone—(561) 394-0550
   See Parent Co. Section for full profile.

### ATLANTIC DETROIT DIESEL-ALLISON, LLC

Div. of Stewart & Stevenson Power Products, LLC- ADDA Div.
169 Old New Brunswick Rd. *(08854)*
**Phone—(732) 752-7100**
National—(800) 823-2332
Fax—(732) 752-8380
www.atlanticdda.com
Email—r.mangs@ssss.com
Off. Admn.—Elaine Loss

**REAL-TIME** Access to Industrial Leads!

EZSelect®.com

## Piscataway—(cont.)

**Warranty Admn.**—Justine Heaton
SIC—3519; 3714; *Rebuilt diesel engines & transmission equipment*
Employs—50; Estab.—1988
Distrib.—Local
Limited Liability Company
Parent co.—Stewart & Stevenson Power Products, LLC- ADDA Div., Lodi, NJ
Phone—(201) 489-5800
See Parent Co. Section for full profile.

**B & R INDUSTRIES, INC.**
196 12th St. (08854)
**Phone—(732) 752-3022**
Email—bandrind@ix.netcom.com
Pres.—Fred Bellscheidt
Off. Mgr.—Michelle Siwiec
SIC—3365; NAICS—331524; *Aluminum castings*
Employs—30; Estab.—1967
Sales—$1Mil-$5Mil
15,000 sq ft site, Distrib.—National
Privately owned corporation

**BCC (U.S.A.) INC.**
143 Ethel Rd. W. (08854)
**Phone—(732) 572-5450**
          (800) 272-1361
Fax—(732) 572-6698
www.bccusainc.com
Email—bccusainc@gmail.com
Dir. & GM—Marquis Yeh
Asst. Sales Mgr.—J. C. Liang
SIC—3568; NAICS—333613; *Split pillow block bearing housings, bearing adapters, spherical roller bearings & cycloidal speed reducers; Brand name—FSQ; BCC*
Employs—10; Estab.—1978
Sales—$5Mil-$10Mil
15,000 sq ft site, Distrib.—National
Sole ownership

**NEW ENTRY**
**BEAUTY-FILL, LLC**
170 Circle Dr. N. (08854)
**Phone—(732) 802-8200**
Fax—(732) 802-8201
Ptnr.—Gregory Harmon
SIC—3089; *Beauty care products packaging*
Employs—30
Sales—$2.5Mil-$5Mil (est)
Limited Liability Company

**BENTLEY MFG., INC.**
41 Ethel Rd. (08854)
**Phone—(732) 572-5933**
Fax—(732) 572-3144
Pres.—Victor Braha
GM—Robert Hoppeler
Prod. Mgr.—Dan Skarda
SIC—2676; NAICS—322291; *Diapers & baby wipes*
Employs—12; Estab.—1992
Distrib.—National
Privately owned corporation

**†BIO-OX INTERNATIONAL, INC.**
140 Ethel Rd. W., Ste. U (08854)
**Phone—(732) 650-9779**
National—(866) 246-6943
Fax—(866) 246-0556
www.bio-ox.com
Email—sales@bio-ox.com
Owner—Steven Schneider
Sales Rep.—Todd Lel
SIC—5169; *Distributor of cleaning compounds*
Employs—10; Estab.—2001
Sales—under $500,000
Distrib.—Local
Privately owned corporation

**BLACKSTRATUS**
1551 S. Washington Ave., Ste. 401 (08854)
**Phone—(732) 393-6000**
National—(866) 525-5666
Fax—(732) 393-6025
www.blackstratus.com
Email—info@blackstratus.com
Pres., CEO—Dale Cline
Ex. V.P., Worldwide Field Opers.—Frank Pinello
V.P., Tech.—Dave Steidle
SIC—7372; *Security information management software*
Employs—70; Estab.—1999
Distrib.—Intl.
Privately owned corporation

**†CAL-CHLOR CORP.**
141 Baekeland Ave. (08854)
**Phone—(732) 271-3500**
Fax—(732) 271-3599
www.cal-chlor.com
Email—info@cal-chlor.com
Plt. Mgr.—Mike Scelsa
Off. Mgr.—Janet Rocha
Asst. Plt. Mgr.—Chris Dugan
SIC—5169; *Distributor of dry calcium chloride & potassium chloride*
Employs—25; Estab.—1982
Distrib.—Regional
Privately owned corporation
Parent co.—Cal-Chlor Corp., Lafayette, LA
Phone—(337) 264-1449
See Parent Co. Section for full profile.

**†CENTRAL FORKLIFT, INC.**
415 Bell St. (08854)
**Phone—(732) 805-9494**
Fax—(732) 805-9496
www.centralforkliftnj.com
Email—cflrs11@gmail.com
Pres., GM—Robert Salimbene
V.-P.—Dallas Smith
SIC—5084; *Distributor of new & used forklifts & forklift batteries & tires, including installation, repair, rental & training; Brand name—HYSTER FORKLIFTS*
Employs—7; Estab.—1987
Sales—$1Mil-$2.5Mil
6,500 sq ft site, Distrib.—Local
Privately owned corporation

**CHANEL, INC.**
876 Centennial Ave. (08854)
**Phone—(732) 885-5500**
Fax—(732) 980-2058
www.chanel.com
Sr. V.-P., Opers.—Jose Monsanto
Ex. Dir., Plng. & Tech. & IT Mgr.—Tony Caruso
Dir., Hum. Res.—Steven Corbin
Hum. Res. Mgr.—Mary Borquist
Asst. Hum. Res. Mgr.—Melissa Ehrman
Hum. Res. Admn.—Donna Hart
SIC—2844; NAICS—325600; *Perfumes & cosmetics*
Employs—500
Sales—$25Mil-$100Mil
Parent co.—Chanel, Inc., New York, NY
Phone—(212) 688-5055
See Parent Co. Section for full profile.

**CLASSIC PRINTERS & CONVERTERS**
140 Ethel Rd. W., Ste. K (08854)
**Phone—(732) 985-1100**
National—(888) 891-8273
Fax—(732) 985-1560
www.tapesandlabels.com
Email—classic@tapesandlabels.com
Pres., CEO—Sat Khurana
CFO—Rajesh Mehta
V.-P., Sales & Mktg.—George Walsh
V.-P.—Raj Khurana

MIS & Opers. Mgr.—Pranay Khurana
Off. Admn.—Anna George
SIC—2671; 2672; 3081; 5084; NAICS—323111; *Manufacturer of custom printed & plain pressure-sensitive, gummed paper, high-temperature & silicone tapes, die-cut double coated foams & films, poly liners, stretch films & wrappers & shipping supplies & distributor of industrial machinery; Brand name—3M Worldwide; Glo-Vision Reflective Barrier Tape; Globrite Safety Tapes; Intertape Polymers; AChem Industries; Shurtape Technologies; Gascogne Paper; QSPAC*
Employs—9; Estab.—1985
Sales—$2.75Mil
10,000 sq ft site, Distrib.—National
Privately owned sub-S corp.

**CLEM'S ORNAMENTAL IRON WORKS, INC.**
110 11th St. (08854)
**Phone—(732) 968-7200**
Fax—(732) 968-0105
www.clemsironworks.com
Email—cciron@aol.com
Chrm., Pres.—Clement Carfaro III
SIC—3446; NAICS—332323; *Architectural & ornamental metalwork*
Employs—70; Estab.—1956
50,000 sq ft site, Distrib.—Intl.
Sole ownership

**DAQ ELECTRONICS, LLC**
262 Old New Brunswick Rd., Ste. B (08854-3756)
**Phone—(732) 981-0050**
Fax—(732) 981-0058
www.daq.net
Email—info@daq.net
V.-P., Sales & Mktg.—James W. Recchia
Comms. Mgr.—Dave Bellina
SIC—3669; 3663; NAICS—334290; *Telemetering & security equipment*
Employs—28; Estab.—2012
Sales—$5Mil-$10Mil
30,000 sq ft site, Distrib.—Intl.
Privately owned corporation

**DYNAMIC METALS, INC.**
1713 S. 2nd St. (08854)
**Phone—(908) 769-5111**
Fax—(908) 769-5057
www.dynamicmetals.com
Email—mwright@dynamicmetals.com
Pres.—Michael Wright
Plt. Mgr.—Don Parish
Fin., Hum. Res. & IT Mgr.—Dan Walsh
SIC—3499; *Metal fabrication*
Employs—60; Estab.—1980
Sales—$11Mil-$25Mil
Distrib.—National
Privately owned corporation

**EASTAR PLASTICS, INC.**
250 Circle Dr. N. (08854)
**Phone—(732) 564-1899**
Fax—(732) 627-0066
www.spectrumplans.com
GM—Ben Tran
Cust. Serv. Rep.—Kaily Psai
SIC—2673; *Plastic bags*
Employs—20; Estab.—2002
Distrib.—National
Privately owned corporation
AKA: IPS

**ELVIPHARMA, LLC**
60 Ethel Rd. W. (08854)
**Phone—(732) 433-5591**
www.elvipharmausa.com
Email—sales@elvipharmausa.com
CEO—Yovanny Garcia

Hum. Res. & IT Mgr.—Ashish Patel
SIC—3089; *Contract pharmaceutical packaging services*
Employs—10; Estab.—2013
Sales—$1Mil-$2.5Mil
9,800 sq ft site, Distrib.—Local
Limited Liability Company

**ENZON PHARMACEUTICALS, INC.**
20 Kingsbridge Rd. (08854)
**Phone—(732) 980-4500**
www.enzon.com
Email—investor@enzon.com
Ex. V.P., Hum. Res., CEO & COO—George Hubbard
Ex. V.P., R & D—Ivan Horak
Sr. Dir., IT—Philip Hoekstra
SIC—2834; 2836; NAICS—325412; *Biopharmaceuticals, including therapeutics for the treatment of patients with cancer & related life-threatening diseases*
Employs—35
Distrib.—National

**EPIC MANAGEMENT, INC. (H Q)**
136 11th St., Ste. 1 (08854-1571)
**Phone—(732) 752-6100**
Fax—(732) 752-9106
www.epicbuilds.com
Email—jlizotte@epicbuilds.com
CEO—Robert Epifano, Jr.
Pres.—John Epifano
Sr. V.-P.—Joel G. Lizotte
IT Mgr.—Miguel Alayon
SIC—2431; NAICS—321900; *Corporate headquarters; millwork & construction services*
Employs—50; Estab.—1971
Sales—$100Mil
Privately owned corporation
AKAs: Epic Millwork & Epic Interiors

**ERICSSON, INC.**
1 Ericsson Dr. (08854)
**Phone—(732) 699-2000**
www.ericsson.com
Email—media.relations@ericsson.com
Sr. Prod. Mgr.—Zach Gilstein
Sr. Hum. Res. Assoc.—Diane Yannetelli
SIC—7372; *Software-defined networking (SDN) software development for telecom operators & content providers*
Employs—2000; Estab.—1984
Publicly owned corporation
Parent co.—Ericsson, Inc., Plano, TX
Phone—(972) 583-0000
See Parent Co. Section for full profile.

**EXHIBIT CO., INC., THE**
239 Old New Brunswick Rd. (08854)
**Phone—(732) 465-1070**
Fax—(732) 465-1071
www.exhibitcompanyinc.com
Email—info@exhibitcompanyinc.com
Pres.—Frank Geraci
V.-P.—Guy Geraci
V.-P.—Rich Realbuto
Creative Dir.—Nancy Gallo
Off. Mgr.—Heather Lettieri

GEOGRAPHICAL

## Piscataway—(cont.)

SIC—3993; 2541; 2542; NAICS—337215; *Custom & portable trade show exhibits & displays, including inventory & logistics management, design & graphic production services, banners, stands & custom shipping crates, storage & signs; Brand name—LaarhovenDesign; Nimlok; ExpoStar; Prezenta; Expogo; Orbus; IMAX; Downing Displays; Sector; Exponents; Optima; Moss; Entasi; Exhibitline; XRLine; EZ-Up International; Lumaline; FLEX-display; EZ Truss; Radius*
Employs—25; Estab.—1967
70,000 sq ft site, Distrib.—Intl.
Privately owned corporation

**†FERRARO FOODS, INC.**
287 S. Randolphville Rd. (08854)
**Phone—(732) 424-3400**
Fax—(732) 424-3401
www.ferrarofoods.com
Email—sales@ferrarofoods.com
Pres.—Michael Giammarino
V-P.—Dean Barcelona
Hum. Res. Mgr.—Deborah Comine
SIC—5141; *Corporate headquarters & distributor of general line groceries, including fresh, frozen, canned, precooked & packaged foods*
Employs—34; Estab.—1975
Distrib.—Regional
Privately owned corporation

**NEW ENTRY**
**FIRST IMPRESSION PRINTING, INC.**
178-D 10th St. (08854)
**Phone—(732) 529-5450**
Pres.—Greg Thorogood
SIC—2759; *Commercial printing*
Employs—3; Estab.—2007
Sales—under $500,000
1,400 sq ft site, Distrib.—Regional
Sole ownership

**FLAVOR SOLUTIONS, INC.**
120 New England Ave. (08854)
**Phone—(732) 354-1931**
Fax—(732) 445-6145
www.flavorsolutionsinc.com
Email—customerservice@flavorsolutionsinc.com
Owner & Pres.—William A. May
V-P.—Michael May
Cust. Serv. Mgr.—Millie Fernandez
SIC—2087; *Natural & artificial food flavors, including beverage, chocolate & meat flavors*
Employs—12; Estab.—2000
Sales—$7Mil-$8Mil
Distrib.—National
Privately owned corporation

**GARDEN STATE ENGRAVING**
126 Perrine Ave. (08854)
**Phone—(732) 463-0060**
(732) 357-6489
Fax—(732) 463-9319
www.gardenstateengraving.webs.com
Email—gardenstateengraving@verizon.net
Owner, Fin. & MIS Mgr.—Linda S. Backovsky
SIC—3479; *Engraved interior, exterior, desk & wall signs, plaques, trophies & industrial panel tags*
Employs—1; Estab.—1972
Sales—under $500,000
Distrib.—Regional
Sole ownership

**GE HEALTHCARE LIFESCIENCES**
Div. of GE Healthcare
800 Centennial Ave., P.O. Box 1327 (08855)
**Phone—(732) 457-8000**
National—(800) 526-3593
Fax—(732) 457-0557
www.gehealthcare.com
Email—cs-us@ge.com
GM, Comml. Americas—Eric Roman
Plt. Mgr.—Jim Donahue
Hum. Res. Mgr.—Jessie DeLorenzo
SIC—3821; 3826; NAICS—339111; *Biotechnology testing equipment*
Employs—1000
Sales—$100Mil-$250Mil (est)
Distrib.—Intl.
Publicly owned corporation
Parent co.—GE Healthcare, Waukesha, WI
Phone—(262) 544-3011
See Parent Co. Section for full profile.

**GORGIAS PRESS**
954 River Rd., P.O. Box 6939 (08854)
**Phone—(732) 885-8900**
Fax—(732) 885-8908
www.gorgiaspress.com
Email—orders@gorgiaspress.com
Pres.—George A. Kiraz
V-P.—Christine Kiraz
Client Serv. Coord.—Joan Shields
SIC—2731; *Academic book publishing*
Employs—15; Estab.—2001
Sales—under $500,000
Distrib.—Intl.
Privately owned corporation

**GRAPHIC PACKAGING INTERNATIONAL, INC.**
Div. of Graphic Packaging Holding Company
4100 New Brunswick Ave. (08854)
**Phone—(732) 424-2100**
Fax—(732) 424-0950
www.graphicpkg.com
Email—sales@graphicpackaging.com
Hum. Res. Mgr.—Chris Moeder
SIC—2657; NAICS—322212; *Folding cartons*
Employs—200; Estab.—1966
100,000 sq ft site, Distrib.—Intl.
Publicly owned corporation
Parent co.—Graphic Packaging Holding Company, Atlanta, GA
Phone—(770) 240-7200
See Parent Co. Section for full profile.

**GRAPHIC PRESENTATION SYSTEMS, INC.**
262 Old New Brunswick Rd., Ste. F (08854)
**Phone—(732) 981-1120**
Fax—(732) 981-1540
www.gpsinj.com
Email—kkeizer@gpsinj.com
Pres., Treas.—Kevin J. Keizer
Off. Mgr.—Katherine Keizer
SIC—3993; 2541; *Trade show displays*
Employs—15; Estab.—1982
Sales—$1Mil-$2.5Mil
Distrib.—National
Privately owned corporation

**NEW ENTRY**
**HEALTH & NATURAL BEAUTY USA**
140-W Ethel Rd. W. (08854)
**Phone—(848) 202-9089**
National—(844) 346-2872
Fax—(732) 601-6723
www.hnbusa.com
Email—products@hnbusa.com
Pres.—Sayed Ibrahim

SIC—2844; *Skin & hair care products*
Employs—4
Sales—$1Mil-$2.5Mil (est)

**HERBAKRAFT, INC.**
121 Ethel Rd. W., Ste. 6 (08854)
**Phone—(732) 463-1000**
National—(855) 999-4372
Fax—(732) 463-3336
www.herbkraft.com
Email—info@herbkraft.com
Pres.—Nisha Khanijow
Admn. Mgr.—Nancy Guliano
SIC—2833; 2023; *Vitamins, minerals, dietary supplements & fibers, herbal extracts, nutraceuticals & spices*
Employs—15; Estab.—2004
Distrib.—Intl.
Privately owned corporation

**†HOFFMAN EQUIPMENT, INC.**
300 S. Randolphville Rd. (08854)
**Phone—(732) 752-3600**
National—(800) 446-3362
Fax—(732) 968-8371
www.hoffmanequip.com
Email—export@hoffmanequip.com
Pres., CEO—Timothy Watters
CFO & Hum. Res. Mgr.—Eric Shumaker
Sr. V-P., Sales & Mktg.—Mike Anderson
Acct. Mgr.—Bryan Bloyd
Cred. Mgr.—Simone Hines
Parts Mgr.—Kathy Gould
Rental Mgr.—Janine Labor
SIC—5082; *Corporate headquarters & wholesaler of heavy construction equipment*
Employs—50
3,000 sq ft site, Distrib.—Local
Privately owned corporation
AKA: Hoffman Equipment & Rentals

**†HOSE SHOP, INC., THE**
100 New England Ave., Ste. 2 (08854)
**Phone—(732) 562-1000**
Fax—(732) 562-9222
www.hoseshopinc.com
Email—tpeterson@hoseshopinc.com
Owner & GM—Thomas Peterson
Accts. Rec. Mgr.—Jeanne Peterson
Manager—Ryan Peterson
SIC—5051; 5085; *Wholesaler of hydraulic & industrial hose & related products*
Employs—13; Estab.—1975
Sales—$4.1Mil
20,000 sq ft site, Distrib.—National
Privately owned corporation

**HUMANSCALE CORP.**
Div. of Humanscale Corporation
220 Circle Dr. N. (08854)
**Phone—(732) 537-2944**
National—(800) 400-0625
Fax—(732) 356-4146
www.humanscale.com
Email—info@humanscale.com
Sr. V-P., Mktg.—Chris Gibson
SIC—3577; 2522; NAICS—337214; *Sustainable, high-performance ergonomic products, including seating, keyboard supports, monitor arms & task lighting for the workplace*
Employs—200; Estab.—1982
Distrib.—Intl.
Privately owned corporation
Parent co.—Humanscale Corporation, New York, NY
Phone—(212) 725-4749
See Parent Co. Section for full profile.

**†HUNTER WALTON & CO., INC.**
120 Circle Dr. N. (08854)
**Phone—(732) 805-0808**
Fax—(732) 805-0282

www.hunterwalton.com
Email—sales@hunterwalton.com
CEO—Peter Love
Pres.—Glenn Grimshaw, Sr.
V-P., Sales—Gary Behie
SIC—5143; *Distributor of dairy products, including cheese, butter, milk powders, margarine & shortenings; Brand name—Perfection*
Employs—10; Estab.—1827
Sales—$19Mil
700 sq ft site, Distrib.—National
Privately owned corporation

**I T O X, LLC**
15 Corporate Pl. S., Ste. 201 (08854)
**Phone—(732) 390-2815**
Fax—(732) 390-2817
www.itox.com
Email—sales@itox.com
Ex. Sales Mgr.—Nancie Frank
Cust. Serv. Mgr.—Leo Martin
SIC—3571; NAICS—334111; *Computers & motherboards*
Employs—25; Estab.—1987
Sales—$15Mil-$20Mil
1,000 sq ft site, Distrib.—National
Limited Liability Company

**INNOPHARMA, INC.**
10 Knightsbridge Rd. (08854)
**Phone—(732) 885-2939**
Fax—(732) 885-1248
www.innopharmainc.com
Email—info@innopharmainc.com
Pres., CEO—Navneet Puri
CFO—John Deighan
Dir., Hum. Res. & Administrator—Cherill Alofoje
SIC—2834; *Sterile generic injectable & ophthalmic pharmaceuticals*
Employs—50; Estab.—2005
Sales—$10Mil-$25Mil
Distrib.—Intl.
Privately owned corporation

**KENYON & SONS, INC., WILLIAM**
90 Ethel Rd. W. (08854)
**Phone—(732) 985-8980**
National—(800) 371-5010
Fax—(732) 985-1980
www.williamkenyon.com
Email—mike@williamkenyon.com
COO—Mike Wheaton
Sales & Tech. Mgr.—Dewitt Oliver
Accountant—Rose Graff
SIC—2298; *Rope*
Employs—35; Estab.—1982
Distrib.—National

**KRAMER INDUSTRIES, INC.**
140 Ethel Rd. W., Ste. U (08854)
**Phone—(732) 650-9599**
National—(888) 515-9443
Fax—(732) 650-0556
www.kramerindustriesonline.com
Email—sales@kramerindustriesonline.com
Sales Mgr.—Steve Schneider
Off. Mgr.—Todd Leonardis
Cust. Serv. Rep.—Allie Sestito
SIC—3599; *Industrial machinery*
Employs—10; Estab.—1987
Sales—$1Mil-$5Mil
Distrib.—Intl.
Privately owned corporation

**LEE LINEAR**
727 South Ave. (08854)
**Phone—(732) 752-5200**
(732) 752-5201
National—(800) 221-0811
Fax—(732) 968-7080
www.leelinear.com
Email—leelinear@linearmotion.com
Pres.—Glen Michalske

© Copyright 2015 Manufacturers' News, Inc.

D375

## Piscataway—(cont.)

SIC—3568; 3599; NAICS—
333613; *Linear motion products,
including linear shafting,
bearings & guides, shaft
supports, slide tables, carriage
locks, ball screws, cross roller
guides & custom machining;
Brand name—60 Plus Precision
Shafting; Lee Roller Bearing
Pillow Blocks; LEE LINEAR; SBC*
Employs—45; Estab.—1967
Sales—$5Mil-$10Mil
42,000 sq ft site, Distrib.—Intl.
Limited Liability Company

### L'OREAL U S A, INC.
81 New England Ave. (08854)
**Phone—(732) 562-5000**
       (732) 562-5130
Fax—(732) 562-5108
www.lorealusa.com
Email—media@us.loreal.com
Dir., Engrg.—Tom Zollo
Sr. Prod. Mgr.—Andrew Lewis
Hum. Res. Mgr.—Diana Amaya
SIC—2844; NAICS—325600;
  *Cosmetics & skincare products*
Employs—500
Sales—$100Mil-$250Mil
Distrib.—Intl.
Publicly owned corporation
Parent co.—L'Oreal U S A, Inc.,
  New York, NY
  Phone—(212) 818-1500
  See Parent Co. Section for full profile.

### †MABEY INC.
Div. of Mabey, Inc.
218 N. Randolphville Rd. (08854)
**Phone—(732) 752-6600**
Fax—(866) 422-3264
www.mabey.com
Email—info@mabey.com
Depot Mgr.—Aaron Lee
SIC—5051; 5039; 5082;
  *Distributor of structural steel
  components & composite
  matting for construction
  applications, including bridge
  support systems, trench boxes &
  framing systems*
Employs—13; Estab.—1997
Distrib.—Regional
Privately owned corporation
Parent co.—Mabey, Inc., Elkridge,
  MD
  Phone—(410) 379-2800
  See Parent Co. Section for full profile.

### MACELROY CO., INC., J. C.
91 Ethel Rd. W. (08854)
Mail addr: P.O. Box 850,
  Piscataway (08855)
**Phone—(732) 572-7100**
National—(800) 622-3576
Fax—(732) 572-7112
www.macelroy.com
Email—info@macelroy.com
Pres.—Scott J. Spota
SIC—3312; 3444; NAICS—
  332722; *Custom steel, stainless
  steel, aluminum & fiberglass
  fabrication of marine hardware,
  fenders, mooring devices,
  fasteners, security bollards,
  cleats & specialty castings*
Employs—30; Estab.—1932
80,000 sq ft site, Distrib.—Intl.
Sole ownership
AKA: Steel Technologies Corp.

### MARS INTERNATIONAL, INC.
60 Kingsbridge Rd. (08854)
**Phone—(908) 233-0044**
Fax—(908) 233-2227
www.marsint.com
Email—sales@marsint.com
CEO—Charles Engelstein
Pres.—Geoffrey Engelstein
V-P., Sales & Mktg.—Arthur Garcia
Sales & Mktg. Mgr.—Lauren
  DeNoma

MIS Mgr.—Steve Crystal
Fin. Mgr.—Fred Knopp
Logistics Mgr.—Cathie Moran
SIC—3679; *Electronic component
  assemblies*
Employs—50; Estab.—1964
Sales—over $30Mil
25,000 sq ft site, Distrib.—Intl.
Privately owned corporation
ISO rating—9001:2008

### MILLSON PRECISION MACHINING
145 11th St. (08854)
**Phone—(732) 424-1700**
Fax—(732) 424-0808
Email—millsoninc@optimum.net
Pres.—Bryan Miller
Shop Foreman—Steven Smith
SIC—3599; *Precision machining
  job shop*
Employs—3; Estab.—1992
8,000 sq ft site, Distrib.—National
Privately owned sub-S corp.

### MMC STEEL RULE DIES
864 New Brunswick Ave. (08854)
**Phone—(973) 760-3286**
Fax—(908) 757-3028
Owner—Marcello Cabrera
SIC—3544; NAICS—333500;
  *Steel rule dies*
Employs—1; Estab.—2002
Sales—under $500,000
Distrib.—Local
Sole ownership

mnileads.com
*Looking for Quality Sales Leads
on the Internet? Look no Further!*

### MONTROSE MOLDERS CORP.
25 Howard St. *(08854)*
**Phone—(908) 754-3030**
Fax—(732) 529-4236
www.montrosemolders.com
Email—bwilson@
  montrosemolders.com
CEO—William H. Wilson
CFO—Beth Halvonik
V-P., Opers.—Brendan Wilson
Sales Mgr.—Todd Nicolay
Prodn. Mgr.—Eric Rivers
Qual. Control Mgr.—Bill Roche
Matls. Mgr.—Andrew Wilson
Assembly Mgr.—Orlando Espana
Tool Room Mgr.—Andy Arway
Chief Engr.—Gary Shapiro
SIC—3089; *Plastic moldings*
Employs—163; Estab.—1973
Company-wide: 250
Sales—$25Mil-$30Mil
135,000 sq ft site, Distrib.—
  National
Privately owned corporation

### MUNIRE FURNITURE, INC.
91 New England Ave. (08854)
**Phone—(732) 339-6070**
National—(866) 468-6473
Fax—(732) 339-6071
www.munirefurniture.com
Email—info@munirefurniture.com
Pres.—Munire Hussain
Dir., Opers.—Lavina Dsouza
IT Mgr.—Anthony Politz
Hum. Res. Mgr.—Zoe Rogers
SIC—2511; *Custom wooden
  furniture*
Employs—75; Estab.—2002
Distrib.—National
Privately owned corporation

### PARAVISTA, INC., IMAGING & PRINTING
1055 Centennial Ave. (08854)
**Phone—(732) 752-1222**
Fax—(732) 752-2939
www.paravistainc.com
Email—alviral@paravistainc.com
Pres.—Michael Spallucci
V-P.—James Connell
V-P.—Mark Spallucci
SIC—2759; NAICS—323100;
  *Commercial printing*
Employs—25; Estab.—1956
16,000 sq ft site, Distrib.—
  Regional
Privately owned corporation

### PARKWAY PLASTICS, INC.
561 Stelton Rd. (08854)
**Phone—(732) 752-3636**
National—(800) 985-5370
Fax—(732) 752-4097
www.parkwayjars.com/shop
Email—sales@parkwayjars.com
Pres.—Edward Rowan
Secy-Treas., Hum. Res. & IT
  Mgr.—Kirstin Rowan Kelly
Dir., Sales—Ned Rowan
SIC—3089; *Plastic jars, closures,
  mold making & printing*
Employs—46; Estab.—1954
72,000 sq ft site, Distrib.—Intl.
Privately owned corporation

### PBL ASSAY SCIENCE
131 Ethel Rd. W., Ste. 6 (08854)
**Phone—(732) 777-9123**
www.pblassaysci.com
Email—info@pblassaysci.com
Chrm., CEO—Robert Pestka
Pres.—Timothy Doris
V-P., Science & Strategic
  Alliances—William Clark
Dir., Prod. & R & D—Thomas
  Lavoie
Dir., Bus. Dev.—Stephen Parent
SIC—2836; NAICS—325414; *Cell-
  based assay & immunoassay
  products, including interferons &
  cytokines, monoclonal &
  polyclonal antibodies, antibody
  characterization, PK & biomarker
  strategy & Ligand binding;
  Brand name—InterferonSource;
  VeriPlex; VeriKine; iLite;
  InterferonForce*
Employs—35; Estab.—1990
Distrib.—Intl.
Privately owned corporation
AKAs: PBL Biomedical Labs &
  PBL InterferonSource

### PEE WEE MOLDING CORP.
240 Circle Dr. N. (08854)
**Phone—(732) 469-0200**
Fax—(732) 469-1070
www.peeweemolding.com
Email—info@peeweemolding.com
GM—Feivel Reifman
Hum. Res. & Off. Mgr.—Chana
  Weissman
Bookkeeper—Eva Litkey
SIC—3089; *Plastic injection
  molding*
Employs—40; Estab.—1965
Sales—$11Mil-$25Mil
40,000 sq ft site, Distrib.—Intl.
Privately owned corporation

### PEPSI BEVERAGES COMPANY
2200 New Brunswick Ave. (08854)
**Phone—(732) 424-3000**
www.pepsico.com
Email—info@pepsico.com
Plt. Mgr.—Duen Pagan
Hum. Res. Mgr.—Alex Pollen
SIC—2086; NAICS—312100;
  *Carbonated beverages*
Employs—275; Estab.—1971
Distrib.—Local
Publicly owned corporation

Parent co.—Pepsi Beverages
  Company, Somers, NY
  Phone—(914) 767-6000
  See Parent Co. Section for full profile.

### PLASTIC MONOFIL CO. LTD.
25 Howard St. (08854)
**Phone—(732) 629-7701**
Fax—(732) 529-4236
www.plasticmonofil.com
Email—info@plasticmonofil.com
Ptnr.—Mike Sweeny
Ptnr.—Bill Wilson
Proj. & Sales Mgr.—Maria
  Caraballo-Vasquez
Hum. Res. & Off. Mgr.—Virginia
  Wilson
Fin. Mgr.—Beth Halvonik
SIC—3089; *Plastic injection
  molding*
Employs—20; Estab.—1971
Sales—$1Mil-$3Mil
45,700 sq ft site, Distrib.—Intl.
Privately owned corporation

### PRIME PACK, LLC
262 Old New Brunswick Rd., Ste.
  N (08854)
**Phone—(732) 253-7734**
Fax—(732) 253-7733
www.primepharmausa.com
Email—primepharmaceuticals@
  gmail.com
Dir., Qual. Control—Lakshmi
  Nagarajan
SIC—2834; *Contract
  manufacturing of dietary
  supplements & nutraceuticals,
  including antioxidants,
  multivitamins, botanicals &
  amino acids*
Employs—10; Estab.—2010
Sales—$5Mil-$10Mil (est)
10,000 sq ft site, Distrib.—National
Limited Liability Company

### PROMO GRAPHICS, INC.
24 Howard St. (08854)
**Phone—(732) 629-7300**
Fax—(732) 629-7298
www.promographics.com
Email—pgiprint@aol.com
Pres.—Debra Rossello
Sales Mgr.—Ann Fisher
Off. Mgr.—Diane Wibber
SIC—2396; *Custom textile &
  graphic substrate screen
  printing*
Employs—7; Estab.—1985
Sales—under $500,000
2,200 sq ft site, Distrib.—National
Privately owned corporation

### QUALITY SHEET METAL & WELDING
23 Clawson St. (08854)
**Phone—(732) 752-6300**
Fax—(732) 752-2266
www.qsm-w.com
Sys. Opers. Mgr.—David Doll
Fin. Mgr.—Margaret Ber
SIC—3444; 3599; *Sheet metal
  fabrication & welding job shop*
Employs—13; Estab.—1997
Sales—$1Mil-$2.5Mil
Distrib.—Regional
Privately owned corporation

### †R. E. MICHEL CO., INC.
262 Old New Brunswick Rd.
  (08854)
**Phone—(732) 465-9700**
Fax—(732) 465-9777
www.remichel.com
Email—customerservice@
  remichel.com
Br. Mgr.—Ivan Childres
SIC—5075; 5078; *Distributor of
  heating, air conditioning &
  refrigeration equipment &
  supplies*
Employs—6; Estab.—2004
Distrib.—Local
Privately owned corporation

GEOGRAPHICAL

## Piscataway—(cont.)

Parent co.—R. E. Michel Co., Inc.,
Glen Burnie, MD
Phone—(410) 760-4000
See Parent Co. Section for full profile.

### RESEARCH & EDUCATION ASSN.

Div. of Courier Corp.
61 Ethel Rd. W. (08854)
**Phone—(732) 819-8880**
National—(800) 822-0830
Fax—(732) 819-8808
www.rea.com
Email—info@rea.com
Cust. Serv. Rep.—Mariela Colon
Cust. Serv. Rep.—Navis
Balcharan
SIC—2731; 2741; *Educational
materials publishing, including
test preparation books, study
solutions manuals & software for
colleges, universities & high
schools*
Employs—20; Estab.—1959
Distrib.—National
Publicly owned corporation
AKA: REA
Parent co.—Courier Corp., North
Chelmsford, MA
Phone—(978) 251-6000
See Parent Co. Section for full profile.

### REVENT, INC.

100 Ethel Rd. W. *(08854)*
**Phone—(732) 777-9433**
National—(800) 822-9642
Fax—(732) 777-1187
www.revent.com
Email—info@revent.com
Chrm.—Tor Bolin
CEO—Daniel Lago
Pres., Intl.—Per Junesand
Comp., Hum. Res. & MIS Mgr.—
Lana Bildey
Sales Mgr., Natl.—Terry Flanagan
Sales Mgr.—Kristie Peckham
Sales Admn.—Angela Chen
Serv. Admn.—Shela Walls
Pur. Agt.—Michael Rekuc
SIC—3556; NAICS—333294;
*Commercial electric & gas
ovens; Brand name—Revent*
Employs—35; Estab.—1992
Sales—$20Mil
50,000 sq ft site, Distrib.—Intl.
Privately owned corporation

### ROBERTET FLAVORS, INC.

10 Colonial Dr. (08854)
Mail addr.: P.O. Box 6840,
Piscataway (08855-6840)
**Phone—(732) 981-8300**
Fax—(732) 981-1717
www.robertet.com
Email—robertetflavors@
robertetusa.com
Pres., COO—Robert Weinstein
V.-P., Sales & Mktg.—John Simons
Dir., Mktg. Comms.—David
Wasnak
Hum. Res. Mgr.—Marie Saracino
SIC—2087; NAICS—311900;
*Food flavoring liquids, including
dry-blended crystalized flavors*
Employs—156; Estab.—1850
110,000 sq ft site, Distrib.—Intl.
Privately owned corporation

### †ROMA FOOD ENTERPRISES, INC.

Div. of Vistar Corp.
1 Roma Blvd. (08854)
**Phone—(732) 463-7662**
National—(800) 463-7662
Fax—(732) 271-9543
www.romafood.com
Email—marcnaparstek@
vistarvsa.com
Pres.—Jim Palazzo
Dir., Mktg. Dev.—Tony DiCarlo

SIC—5141; 5142; 5143; 5147;
*Distributor of Italian & Italian-
American food products,
including cheese, meats, pasta
& salads*
Employs—100; Estab.—1988
Distrib.—National
Privately owned corporation
Parent co.—Vistar Corp.,
Centennial, CO
Phone—(303) 662-7100
See Parent Co. Section for full profile.

### S.S. WHITE TECHNOLOGIES, INC.

151 Old New Brunswick Rd.
(08854)
**Phone—(732) 474-1700**
National—(800) 779-4483
Fax—(732) 752-8315
www.sswhite.net
Email—support@sswhite.net
Pres., CEO—Rahul Shukla
V.-P., Sales & Mktg.—Brian Poloto
Dir., Fin. & Sys.—Rajen Shukla
Coordinator—Leticia Spicer
SIC—3568; 3842; NAICS—
333613; *Flexible shafts for
surgical tools, automobiles &
aircraft*
Employs—180; Estab.—1844
Sales—$26Mil-$50Mil
90,000 sq ft site, Distrib.—Intl.
Privately owned corporation
AKA: Shukla Medical

### SCHWAN COSMETICS U.S.A., INC.

21 Gordon Rd. (08854)
**Phone—(732) 777-6800**
Fax—(732) 777-6898
www.schwancosmeticsusa.com
Pres.—Paul Plut
Pur. Agt.—Marianne MacVeagh
Accts. Rep.—Liz Donahue
SIC—2844; NAICS—325600;
*Cosmetics*
Employs—95; Estab.—1995
26,000 sq ft site, Distrib.—National
Privately owned corporation
ISO rating—9002

### SECOND IMPRESSIONS, LLC

149 Stelton Rd. (08854)
**Phone—(732) 752-7171**
Fax—(732) 752-7009
www.2ndimpressions.com
Email—printpros@optonline.net
Owner—Ken Steiner
Creative Dir.—John Hewett
SIC—2759; NAICS—323100;
*Commercial printing*
Employs—3; Estab.—1983
Sales—under $500,000
Distrib.—Local
Sole ownership

### SHANGHAI FREEMEN AMERICAS, LLC (H Q)

377 Hoes Ln., Ste. 240 (08854)
**Phone—(732) 981-1288**
Fax—(732) 981-0302
www.shanghaifreemen.com
Email—info@shanghaifreemen.com
Pres.—Hanks Li
SIC—2833; 2819; NAICS—
325411; *Company headquarters;
nutritional products,
pharmaceutical excipients, food
ingredients & industrial
chemicals (mfg. done in China)*
Employs—9; Estab.—2003
Distrib.—National
Limited Liability Company

### SIEMENS HEARING INSTRUMENTS, INC.

Div. of Siemens Corporation
10 Constitution Ave., P.O. Box
1397 (08855)
**Phone—(732) 562-6600**
National—(800) 766-4500
Fax—(732) 562-6683
www.siemens-hearing.com
Email—email.us@siemens.com

Acting CEO & V.-P., Global CRM—
Scott Davis
CFO—Tony Mannucia
V.-P., Opers.—Greg Oden
V.-P., Mktg.—Alina Urdaneta
V.-P., Audiology & Compliance—
Thomas Powers
V.-P., Cust. Care—Pamela L.
Burton
V.-P., Bus. Dev.—Ronald Gleitman
Sr. Proc. Mgr.—Donna Seminara
Audiology Mgr.—Pam Dorn
SIC—3842; *Divisional
headquarters & hearing aids*
Employs—450; Estab.—1985
Sales—$50Mil-$100Mil
Distrib.—Regional
Publicly owned corporation
Parent co.—Siemens Corporation,
New York, NY
Phone—(212) 258-4000
See Parent Co. Section for full profile.

### SIGN-A-RAMA

1633 Stelton Rd. *(08854)*
**Phone—(732) 819-8844**
Fax—(732) 819-8242
www.yoursignco.com
Email—sales@yoursignco.com
Owner & Mng. Member—Matthew
Rabinowitz
Shop Mgr.—Debbie Gelormine
SIC—3993; *Interior & exterior
signs*
Employs—6; Estab.—1988
3,100 sq ft site, Distrib.—National
Privately owned corporation

### SIR SPEEDY PRINTING AND MARKETING SERVICES

1032 Stelton Rd. (08854)
**Phone—(732) 981-9011**
Fax—(732) 981-1121
www.sirspeedy.com/piscataway
Email—sirspeedy7068@
optonline.net
Pres., Fin. & GM—Mark Yanofsky
Store Mgr.—Tony Anghelone
Fin. Mgr.—Barbara Yanofsky
Graphic Designer & Typesetter—
Theresa Cario
SIC—2759; 2752; 2791; 3993;
NAICS—323100; *High-speed
full-color digital & offset printing,
graphic design & typesetting of
banners, signs, forms &
stationery*
Employs—4; Estab.—1982
Sales—under $500,000
1,250 sq ft site, Distrib.—Regional
Privately owned corporation

### SOZIO, INC.

51 Ethel Rd. W. (08854)
**Phone—(732) 572-5600**
Fax—(732) 572-0944
www.jesozio.com
Email—fbraud@jesozio.com
Cont., Pur.—Tara Devita
Cont.—Annette Peixoto
GM—Frederic Braud
Mktg. Mgr.—Michael Nina
Cust. Serv. Mgr.—Elaine
Smallwood
Qual. Control Mgr.—Janine
Brzezinski
Brief Mgr.—Irene Campanelli
Lab Mgr.—Dominique Bouley
Plt. Mgr.—John Duffy
SIC—2844; NAICS—325600;
*Fragrances for the perfume,
personal care, home fragrance &
household industries*
Employs—50; Estab.—1956
Sales—$20Mil-$25Mil
Distrib.—National
Privately owned corporation

### SPEED PRO IMAGING OF PISCATAWAY

56 Ethel Rd. W., Ste. 14 (08854-
6111)
**Phone—(732) 662-9860**
www.speedpronj.com
Email—info@speedpronj.com
Owner—R. Scott Schoner
SIC—2759; 3993; 2542; *Large-
format digital printing & banners,
vehicle & events graphics &
tradeshow displays; Brand
name—3M; Avery; Oracal*
Employs—3
Sales—under $500,000

### SPEM CORP.

403 Bell St. (08854)
**Phone—(732) 356-3366**
Fax—(732) 356-5922
www.spem.com
Email—spemcorp@aol.com
Pres.—Satish Patel
Cont.—Nina Patel
Plt. Mgr.—Suman Patel
SIC—3679; *Contract
manufacturing of electronic
products, including
electromechanical, thru-hole &
SMD technology*
Employs—9; Estab.—1992
Sales—$3Mil-$5Mil
8,000 sq ft site, Distrib.—National
Privately owned corporation

### STAR CREATION, INC. (H Q)

1506 Stelton Rd. (08854)
**Phone—(732) 819-7070**
Fax—(732) 819-9603
Pres., Hum. Res. Mgr.—Kavita
Khandelwal
IT & Opers. Mgr.—Mayur
Khandelwal
SIC—3911; *Corporate
headquarters; gemstone jewelry
(mfg. done in Thailand & India)*
Employs—5; Estab.—2000
Sales—$11Mil-$25Mil
10,000 sq ft site, Distrib.—Intl.
Privately owned corporation
AKAs: 9-5 Silver House &
Sumangal Jewelers

### STELTON CABINET & SUPPLY

1358 Stelton Rd. (08854)
**Phone—(732) 985-1035**
Fax—(732) 985-1968
www.steltoncabinet.com
Owner—Robert Aiello
Shop Mgr.—Anthony Aiello
Designer—Cathy Aiello
SIC—2434; 2541; NAICS—
337110; *Wooden cabinets &
countertops*
Employs—7; Estab.—1945
Sales—under $500,000
Distrib.—Local
Privately owned corporation

### †STRUCTURED MATERIALS INDUSTRIES, INC.

201 Circle Dr. N., Unit 102-103
(08854)
**Phone—(732) 302-9274**
Fax—(732) 302-9275
www.structuredmaterials.com
Email—sales@
structuredmaterials.com
Pres., CEO—Gary Tompa
Sr. Engr.—Gary Provost

# Piscataway—(cont.)

SIC—5084; 5099; *Distributor of MOCVD, PECVD, CVD & ALD systems & components for manufacturing & researching thin films of oxides, nitrides, carbides, graphene, chalcogenides, superconductors, TCOs, nanowires & related materials; Brand name—SpinCVD; GaNomite; ZnOmite*
Employs—15; Estab.—1992
Sales—$5Mil
7,500 sq ft site, Distrib.—Intl.
Privately owned corporation

[NEW ENTRY]

## SWISSRAY INTERNATIONAL, INC. (H Q)

31 Gordon Rd. (08854)
**Phone—(908) 353-0971**
National—(800) 903-5543
Fax—(908) 353-1237
www.swissray.com
Email—info@swissray.com
Chrm.—Alex Rosenzweig
V-P., Mktg.—Jill Wacher
SIC—3844; *Corporate headquarters; digital x-ray equipment (mfg. done in Switzerland)*
Employs—15
Sales—$2.5Mil-$5Mil (est)

## T & P MACHINE SHOP

600 Prospect Ave. (08854)
**Phone—(732) 424-9141**
Fax—(732) 752-8985
Pres.—Tony Pasquale
Off. Mgr.—Michael Pasquale
SIC—3599; 3312; *Steel machined parts & machine shop*
Employs—3; Estab.—1988
Sales—under $500,000
Distrib.—Local
Privately owned corporation

## TINGLEY RUBBER CORP.

1551 S. Washington Ave., Ste. 403 (08854-6700)
**Phone—(908) 757-7474**
Fax—(866) 757-9239
www.tingleyrubber.com
Email—njenkins@tingleyrubber.com
Chrm. of the Board—William B. McCollum
Pres., COO—Michael Zedalis
V-P., Sales—Louis Moya
Cont.—Timothy Henner
Mktg. Mgr.—James Towey
Hum. Res. Mgr.—Nancy C. Jenkins
Supply Chain Mgr.—Shawn Smith
Qual. Assur. Mgr.—Richard Hower
Cust. Serv. Supv.—Kathryn Baker
SIC—3021; NAICS—316211; *Waterproof protective footwear & clothing*
Employs—35; Estab.—1896
Sales—$2.5Mil-$5Mil (est)
Distrib.—Intl.
Privately owned sub-S corp.

## TRANE, INC. (H Q)

Div. of Ingersoll-Rand Co. Ltd.
1 Centennial Ave., P.O. Box 6820 (08855)
**Phone—(732) 652-7100**
National—(800) 872-6381
Fax—(732) 980-3340
www.trane.com
Email—info@trane.com
V-P., Compliance & Deputy Gen. Counsel—Allan Tananbaum
Facilities Mgr.—John Ward

SIC—3585; 3714; *Corporate headquarters; automotive & building heating & cooling equipment & supplies & vehicle controls*
Employs—400; Estab.—1929
Sales—$8.6Bil
140,400 sq ft site, Distrib.—Intl.
Publicly owned corporation
Parent co.—Ingersoll-Rand Co. Ltd., Davidson, NC
Phone—(704) 655-4000
See Parent Co. Section for full profile.

## TRANSACTION PUBLISHERS, INC.

10 Corporate Pl. S., Ste. 102 (08854)
**Phone—(732) 445-2280**
National—(888) 999-6778
Fax—(732) 445-2782
www.transactionpub.com
Email—trans@transactionpub.com
Pres.—Mary E. Curtis
Mktg. Mgr.—Mindy Waizer
IT Mgr.—Jeffrey Stetz
Acctg. & Hum. Res. Mgr.—Michael Celletto
Order Dept. Mgr.—Nancy Conine
Dist. Ctr. Mgr.—Frank Dixon
SIC—2731; 2741; *Social science book, eBook, series & serial publishing*
Employs—25; Estab.—1962
Sales—$1Mil-$2.5Mil
Distrib.—Intl.
Privately owned corporation

## †UNICHEM INDUSTRIES, INC.

1 Bayberry Close (08854)
**Phone—(732) 463-8442**
Fax—(732) 463-9343
Email—unichemusa@gmail.com
Pres.—Kishore Sanghvi
SIC—5093; 5169; *Wholesaler of ferrous & nonferrous scrap metals & chemicals*
Employs—2; Estab.—1990
1,000 sq ft site, Distrib.—Intl.
Privately owned sub-S corp.

## VIKOLYA CORP.

140 Ethel Rd. W., Unit J (08854)
**Phone—(732) 529-5540**
Fax—(732) 529-5541
www.vikolya.com
Email—obahet@aol.com
Owner—Mike Bahet
Hum. Res. Mgr.—Olga Bahet
Manager—Victoria Kuzmenkov
SIC—3999; *Jewelry boxes, stands & organizers*
Employs—6; Estab.—2005
Sales—under $500,000
Distrib.—National
Privately owned corporation

## WESTON MACHINE

161 11th St. (08854)
**Phone—(732) 752-2711**
Fax—(732) 752-0858
www.westonmachine.com
Email—charlie@westonmachine.com
Owner—Charlie Weston
SIC—3714; 3599; *Automotive machining job shop*
Employs—1; Estab.—1991
Sales—under $500,000
Distrib.—National
Sole ownership

## Y.C. CABLE EAST, INC.

240 Circle Dr. N. (08854)
**Phone—(732) 868-0800**
Fax—(732) 868-0810
www.yccable.com
Email—sales@yceast.com
Pres.—James Hsu
Opers. Mgr., OEM—Marlene Li

SIC—3679; *Custom & medical cable assemblies, including computer & networking cables & accessories & consumer electronics & portable speakers*
Employs—30; Estab.—1995
30,000 sq ft site, Distrib.—Intl.
Privately owned corporation

[NEW ENTRY]

## ZIEGLER CHEMICAL & MINERAL CORP.

600 Prospect Ave. (08854)
**Phone—(732) 752-4111**
Fax—(732) 752-9477
www.zieglerchemical.com
Email—info@zieglerchemical.com
Pres., Hum. Res. Mgr.—Chip Ziegler
SIC—2951; NAICS—324121; *Corporate headquarters & asphalt products*
Employs—15; Estab.—1944
Distrib.—National
Privately owned corporation

## ZIEGLER CHEMICAL & MINERAL CORP.

600 Prospect Ave., Bldg. A (08854)
**Phone—(732) 752-4111**
Fax—(732) 752-9477
www.zieglerchemical.com
Email—info@zieglerchemical.com
Sales Mgr., Asphalt—James A. Febo
Plt. Mgr.—Paul Gorman
SIC—2951; NAICS—324121; *Specialty asphalt products & cutbacks for the roofing, industrial, printing & paving industries*
Employs—25; Estab.—1944
Distrib.—Intl.
Privately owned corporation
Parent co.—Ziegler Chemical & Mineral Corp., Piscataway, NJ
Phone—(732) 752-4111
See Parent Co. Section for full profile.

## ZK SOFTWARE (H Q)

201 Circle Dr. N., Ste. 116 (08854)
**Phone—(732) 412-6007**
Fax—(732) 412-6008
www.zktechnology.com
Email—sales@zktechnology.com
CEO—Jaimin Shah
V-P., Sales—Larry Reed
Dir., Mktg.—Louisa Martinez
SIC—3577; *Company headquarters; facial & fingerprint biometric & RFID reader devices for access control & time & attendance applications (mfg. done in China)*
Employs—25; Estab.—2009
Sales—$5Mil-$10Mil (est)

# Pitman

(Gloucester—S.W.)

## COMET TOOL CO., INC.

651 Lambs Rd. (08071)
**Phone—(856) 256-1070**
Fax—(856) 256-1005
www.comettool.com
Email—sales@comettool.com
Pres.—Frank Maatje
Hum. Res. Mgr. & Off. Coord.—Jodi Spadel
SIC—3544; 3089; NAICS—333500; *Plastic injection molds & plastic molded products for the medical, pharmaceutical & foodservice industries*
Employs—80; Estab.—1973
Sales—$5Mil-$10Mil
73,000 sq ft site, Distrib.—National
Privately owned corporation

## CROSS MEDICAL SPECIALTIES, INC.

450 Andbro Dr., Unit 7 (08071)
**Phone—(856) 589-3288**
National—(800) 302-7677
Fax—(856) 589-3642
www.crossmsi.com
Email—sales@crossmsi.com
Pres.—Rita Lopes
SIC—3841; *Rebuilt medical equipment & instruments*
Employs—15; Estab.—1999
Sales—$2.5Mil-$5Mil (est)
Distrib.—Regional
Privately owned corporation

## FAZZIO & SONS, INC., FRANK J.

458 Elwood Ave. (08071)
**Phone—(856) 589-3760**
Fax—(856) 589-2655
www.fazzioconcrete.com
Email—info@fazzioconcrete.com
Pres.—Richard Fazzio
Off. Mgr.—Renee Fazzio
Accts. Rec. Mgr.—Brenna Fazzio
SIC—3273; NAICS—327320; *Ready-mixed concrete*
Employs—30; Estab.—1956
Distrib.—Local
Privately owned corporation
AKA: High Standard Construction

## GRAY CONTRACT ASSEMBLY

102 Columbia Ave. (08071)
**Phone—(856) 589-3263**
Fax—(856) 589-3263
Owner—William Gray
SIC—3679; 3672; *Cable assemblies & printed circuit boards*
Employs—4; Estab.—1996
Sales—under $500,000
1,000 sq ft site, Distrib.—Intl.
Privately owned corporation

## KANE WOOD FUEL, LLC

512 Cedar Ave. (08071)
**Phone—(856) 589-3292**
Fax—(856) 589-7791
Ptnr.—Frank Kane
Ptnr.—Marguerite Kane
SIC—2411; NAICS—113310; *Wood logging*
Employs—2; Estab.—1982
Sales—under $500,000
Distrib.—Local
Limited Liability Company

## REVIEW PRINTING, INC.

53-55 E. Holly Ave. (08071)
**Phone—(856) 589-7200**
Fax—(856) 589-7443
Email—reviewprinting@comcast.net
Pres.—Mark Petersen
V-P.—Douglas Petersen
SIC—2759; NAICS—323100; *Commercial printing*
Employs—4; Estab.—1898
Sales—under $500,000
Distrib.—Local

## RONALD-MARK ASSOCS., INC.

150 N. Summit Ave., P.O. Box 355 (08071)
**Phone—(856) 582-6766**
Fax—(856) 582-1920
www.ronaldmark.com
Email—aleone@ronaldmark.com
GM—Lawrence Wolfe
Engr.—Alfio Leone
SIC—3599; *Precision plastic size reduction & sizing of raw materials for the thermoplastic & thermoset industries*
Employs—26; Estab.—1974
51,500 sq ft site, Distrib.—Intl.
Privately owned corporation
Parent co.—Ronald-Mark Assocs., Inc., Hillside, NJ
Phone—(908) 558-0011
See Parent Co. Section for full profile.

**GEOGRAPHICAL**

## Pitman—(cont.)

**SHERIDAN OPTICAL CO., INC.**
108 Clinton Ave. (08071)
**Phone—(856) 582-0963**
Fax—(856) 582-1970
Pres.—Edward F. Sheridan
SIC—3851; NAICS—339100;
*Eyeglass lenses*
Employs—20; Estab.—1992
Sales—$2.5Mil-$5Mil (est)
Distrib.—Local
Privately owned corporation

## Pittsgrove

(Salem—)

**B & J SIGN SERVICE**
971 Landis Ave. (08318)
**Phone—(856) 455-3636**
        (609) 247-9991
Fax—(856) 451-0192
Email—bjsigns@comcast.net
Owner & Pres.—Warren Jillson
SIC—3993; *Boat & truck lettering*
Employs—1; Estab.—1961
Sales—under $500,000
3,000 sq ft site, Distrib.—Local
Sole ownership

**COLE BROS. MARBLE & GRANITE**
892 Parvins Mill Rd. (08318)
**Phone—(856) 455-7989**
Fax—(856) 455-6268
www.colebrothersgranite.com
Email—info@
    colebrothersgranite.com
Pres.—Ruth Cole
Manager—Ben Cole
SIC—3281; NAICS—327991;
*Marble & granite kitchen
countertops & bathroom vanities*
Employs—6; Estab.—1980
Sales—under $500,000
Distrib.—Regional
Privately owned corporation

**PHOENIX GLASS, LLC**
615 Alvine Rd. *(08318)*
**Phone—(856) 692-0100**
Fax—(856) 696-5155
www.pxglass.com
Email—rohrmanf@pxglass.com
V-P.—Frank Rohrman
Dir., Admn. Svcs.—Sonia Bottaro
SIC—3221; NAICS—327213;
*Glass vials & decorating
services*
Employs—70; Estab.—1999
Sales—$10Mil-$25Mil
30,000 sq ft site, Distrib.—Intl.
Privately owned corporation
ISO rating—9001:2008

**SHAFER BROS. TRAILERS**
38 Martin Ave. (08318)
**Phone—(856) 358-3483**
Fax—(856) 358-7533
Owner—Richard Shafer
SIC—3715; NAICS—336212;
*Flatbed & tri-axle trailers*
Employs—4
Sales—$500,000-$1Mil (est)

**U. S. CAST**
321 Willow Grove Rd. (08318)
Mail addr: P.O. Box 444, Vineland
    (08362-0444)
**Phone—(856) 347-2342**
Fax—(856) 347-2343
www.uscast.net
Email—sales@uscast.net
COO—Mike Bilello
CTO—John Bare
Sales Mgr.—Paul Barron
SIC—3082; NAICS—326121; *Cast
acrylic tubes & rods*
Employs—11; Estab.—1954
Sales—$1Mil-$2.5Mil
30,000 sq ft site, Distrib.—Intl.
Privately owned corporation

## Pittstown

(Hunterdon—N.W.)

**BEST BILLIARDS**
393 Pittstown Rd. (08867)
**Phone—(908) 730-0933**
www.thebestbilliards.com
Email—chuck@thebestbilliards.com
Owner & Sole Proprietor—Charles
Jacobi
SIC—3949; NAICS—339920;
*Custom pool, shuffleboard &
game tables & custom bars*
Employs—1; Estab.—1986
Sales—under $500,000
3,000 sq ft site, Distrib.—Regional
Sole ownership

**CROP PRODUCTION SERVICES,
INC.**
127 Perryville Rd. (08867)
**Phone—(908) 735-5545**
National—(888) 828-5545
Fax—(908) 735-6231
www.cropproductionservices.com
Email—info@agriumretail.com
Plt. Mgr.—Nick Hamm
Admn. Coord.—Greg Simon
SIC—2873; NAICS—325311;
*Chemical fertilizers*
Employs—5; Estab.—1930
Distrib.—Local
Publicly owned corporation
Parent co.—Crop Production
Services, Inc., Loveland, CO
Phone—(970) 685-3300
See Parent Co. Section for full profile.

**EXXCEL WELDING CORP.**
14 Brookhill Rd. (08867)
**Phone—(908) 735-0000**
Owner—Castor Rosocha
SIC—3599; *Welding job shop*
Employs—1
Sales—under $500,000 (est)

## Plainfield

(Union—N.E.)

**AMERICAN CODING & MARKING INK
CO.**
1220 North Ave. (07062)
**Phone—(908) 756-0373**
National—(800) 913-9837
Fax—(908) 756-0570
www.americancoding.com
Email—customer@
    americancoding.com
Pres.—Thomas S. Sweet
Cust. Serv. Rep.—Erica Sweet
SIC—2893; NAICS—325910;
*Coding & marking inks*
Employs—8; Estab.—1971
Sales—$1Mil-$5Mil
7,500 sq ft site, Distrib.—National
Privately owned corporation

**BLACK UNIVERSITIES SUPPLY
SHOP, THE**
410 Leland Ave. (07062)
**Phone—(908) 754-8088**
National—(800) 967-2877
Fax—(908) 754-7925
www.thebusshop.com
Email—bus_shop@comcast.net
Pres., CEO—Rubye Hickerson
CFO—Ernestine Cash

SIC—2339; 2329; 2395; 2396;
NAICS—315200; *Customized
clothing, apparel & accessories,
including screen printing &
embroidery of traditionally Black
colleges & universities, Greek
fraternities & sororities, Masonic,
Christian & Negro Baseball
League*
Employs—4; Estab.—1992
Sales—under $500,000
1,500 sq ft site, Distrib.—Intl.
Privately owned corporation
AKA: B.U.S. Shop, The

**C C & D CAPITAL CONTRACTING &
DESIGN, INC.**
640 North Ave. (07060)
Mail addr: P.O. Box 1333,
    Plainfield (07061)
**Phone—(908) 561-8411**
Fax—(908) 753-2979
Pres.—Don Finley
V-P., GM—Mark McQuillan
Off. Mgr.—Michele Reese
SIC—2541; 2542; 3993; *Point-of-
purchase displays & custom
store fixtures*
Employs—45; Estab.—1979
Sales—$6Mil-$10Mil
50,000 sq ft site, Distrib.—Intl.
Privately owned corporation

**COMMERCIAL REPROGRAPHICS,
INC.**
111 Roosevelt Ave. (07060)
**Phone—(908) 755-7070**
Fax—(908) 757-3013
Email—gregruffa@aol.com
Pres.—Gregory Ruffa
SIC—2759; NAICS—323100;
*Commercial printing; Brand
name—The Art of Wood Type*®
Employs—6; Estab.—1951
Sales—$500,000-$1Mil
Distrib.—Regional
Sole ownership

**†COOPER ELECTRIC SUPPLY CO.**
412 W. 2nd St. (07060)
**Phone—(908) 756-4090**
Fax—(908) 756-6803
www.cooper-electric.com
Email—cooperonline@cooper-
    electric.com
Br. Mgr.—Bob Gaydos
SIC—5063; *Distributor of electrical
equipment & supplies, including
connectors, wires & sockets*
Employs—9
Sales—under $500,000
Distrib.—Local
Privately owned corporation
Parent co.—Cooper Electric
Supply Co., Monroe, NJ
Phone—(732) 747-2233
See Parent Co. Section for full profile.

**DEK-TRON INTERNATIONAL CORP.**
244 E. 3rd St. (07060)
**Phone—(908) 226-1777**
Fax—(908) 226-4973
www.dektroncorp.com
Email—info@dektroncorp.com
GM & Test Engr.—Mark Tsvet
SIC—3829; *Materials testing
instruments for the paper,
plastics, textile, leather, copper
wire & cable & fiber-optic
industries*
Employs—25; Estab.—1995
Distrib.—Intl.
Privately owned corporation

**DISCO ALUMINUM**
518 South Ave. (07060-1926)
**Phone—(908) 754-2699**
        (908) 917-2430
Fax—(908) 754-4534
Email—mvillane@msn.com
Ptnr.—William Villane
Ptnr.—Michael Villane

SIC—3442; 3444; 3211; NAICS—
332439; *Custom window & door
screens, patio covers,
retractable aluminum awnings,
security storm doors & glass &
plexi storm panels; Brand
name—SilverLine by Anderson*
Employs—2; Estab.—1982
Sales—under $500,000
5,000 sq ft site, Distrib.—Regional
Privately owned partnership

**DUCTWORKS, INC.**
434 W. Front St. (07060)
Mail addr: P.O. Box 7031,
    Watchung (07069)
**Phone—(908) 754-8190**
Fax—(908) 754-5773
Email—ductworks@gmail.com
GM & Hum. Res. Mgr.—Dianne
Rocco
SIC—3444; *Sheet metal
ductwork, including spiral &
rectangular ductwork*
Employs—10; Estab.—1986
Sales—$1Mil-$2.5Mil
10,000 sq ft site, Distrib.—Local
Privately owned corporation

**F & C PROFESSIONAL ALUMINUM
RAILINGS**
1149 W. Front St. (07063)
**Phone—(908) 753-8886**
National—(877) 257-2457
Fax—(908) 753-8448
www.fcprofessional.com
Email—info@fcprofessional.com
Mng. Ptnr.—Segundo Flores
SIC—3441; NAICS—332312;
*Aluminum railings*
Employs—25; Estab.—2002
Sales—under $500,000
Distrib.—Local
Privately owned corporation

**FLECK KNITWEAR CO., INC.**
400 Leland Ave. (07062)
**Phone—(908) 754-8888**
Fax—(908) 754-8890
Email—fleckknit@aol.com
Pres., Mfg. Mgr.—Peter Fleck
SIC—2396; 2329; 2339; 2392;
NAICS—315200; *Knit blankets,
afghans, sweaters, children's,
women's & men's sportswear,
dress shirts & pants & specialty
fabrics*
Employs—15; Estab.—1959
Sales—$1Mil-$5Mil
Distrib.—National
Privately owned corporation

**HY-TECH METAL WORKS, INC.**
1252 South Ave. (07062)
**Phone—(908) 757-6754**
Fax—(908) 757-0014
Email—hytechmetalworks@
    verizon.net
Pres.—Julius Nagy
SIC—3599; *General machining
job shop*
Employs—2
Sales—under $500,000
Distrib.—National

**INJECTRON CORP.**
1000 S. 2nd St., P.O. Box 3012
    (07063)
**Phone—(908) 753-1990**
Fax—(908) 753-8537
www.injectron.com
Email—sales@injectron.com
Pres.—Louis M. Pollak
V-P., Mfg.—Eric Neuman
Cont.—Barry Eifert
Hum. Res. Mgr.—Janeth Vidarte
Shpg. Mgr.—Hugo Douglas
SIC—3089; *Plastic injection
molding*
Employs—100; Estab.—1959
Distrib.—National
Privately owned corporation

## Plainfield—(cont.)

**NEUMANN SHEET METAL, INC.**
759 North Ave. (07062)
**Phone—(908) 756-0415**
Fax—(908) 756-1613
www.nsmisheetmetal.com
Manager—George Kelly
SIC—3444; 3599; *Sheet metal fabrication & high definition plasma cutting*
Employs—4; Estab.—1911
Sales—$1Mil
Distrib.—Local
Privately owned corporation

**NEW INDUSTRIAL FOAM CORP.**
1355 W. Front St., P.O. Box 3120 (07063)
**Phone—(908) 561-4010**
Fax—(908) 561-4022
www.newindustrialfoam.com
Email—info@ newindustrialfoam.com
V-P.—Michael Weisman
SIC—3086; NAICS—326100; *Custom & specialty polyurethane, polyethylene & expanded polystyrene foam for fire retardant, mil-spec, anti-static, acoustical, insulation & filter applications, including band saw & die cutting services; Brand name—Ethafoam*
Employs—20; Estab.—1960
Sales—$1Mil-$5Mil
Distrib.—National
Privately owned corporation

**NEW JERSEY HARDWOODS, INC.**
1340 W. Front St. (07063)
**Phone—(908) 754-0990**
Fax—(908) 754-8612
www.newjerseyhardwoods.com
Pres.—O. Herttua
Off. Mgr.—Paula Herttua
Manager—Steve Herttua
SIC—2431; NAICS—321900; *Architectural millwork*
Employs—20; Estab.—1981
30,000 sq ft site, Distrib.—Regional
Privately owned sub-S corp.

**O.K. TOOL CORP.**
1233 North Ave. (07062)
**Phone—(908) 561-9920**
Pres.—Eric Kiesel
SIC—3599; *General machining job shop*
Employs—6; Estab.—1975
Sales—$500,000-$1Mil
Distrib.—Local

**PAPP IRON WORKS, INC.**
950 S. 2nd St., P.O. Box 3149 (07063)
**Phone—(908) 731-1000**
Fax—(908) 757-3567
www.pappironworks.com
Email—estimating@ pappironworks.com
Pres.—Allan Papp
Cont.—Richard Dreher
Chief Estimator—Eric Nawrotzki
SIC—3446; NAICS—332323; *Iron rails, stairways & structural steel*
Employs—50; Estab.—1948
Sales—$5Mil-$10Mil (est)
40,000 sq ft site, Distrib.—Local
Privately owned sub-S corp.

**PLAINFIELD WELDERS**
1130 North Ave. (07062)
**Phone—(908) 755-6263**
Fax—(908) 561-4969
Pres.—Gerry Ventriglia
SIC—3599; *Welding job shop*
Employs—2; Estab.—1959
Sales—under $500,000
Distrib.—Regional
Privately owned corporation

**RAK FOAM SALES, INC.**
1355 W. Front St., P.O. Box 3248 (07063)
**Phone—(908) 668-1122**
Pres.—Robert Kussner
SIC—3069; *Foam & sponge rubber*
Employs—8; Estab.—1999
Sales—under $500,000
Distrib.—National
Privately owned corporation

**REINCO, INC.**
520 North Ave. (07060)
Mail addr: P.O. Box 512, Plainfield (07061)
**Phone—(908) 755-0921**
National—(800) 526-7687
Fax—(908) 755-6379
www.reinco.com
Email—sales@reinco.com
Pres.—Erich W. Reinecker
V-P., Opers.—George F. Braun III
SIC—3524; *Power mulchers for landscape construction & erosion control*
Employs—11; Estab.—1958
Sales—$2Mil
20,000 sq ft site, Distrib.—Intl.
Privately owned corporation

**REX BEDDING & SLEEP PRODUCTS**
300 W. 4th St. (07060)
Mail addr: P.O. Box 3220, Plainfield (07063)
**Phone—(908) 668-0220**
National—(800) 223-9523
Fax—(908) 668-4870
www.rexbedding.com
Email—rexbedding@aol.com
Pres., Sales Mgr.—Jose Furman
SIC—2515; *Mattresses & box springs*
Employs—35; Estab.—1986
60,000 sq ft site, Distrib.—Local
Privately owned corporation

**RUEDI KUHNS WOOD SHOP**
509 Berckman St. (07062)
**Phone—(908) 755-6947**
Fax—(908) 755-1203
Pres.—Rudy Kuhn
SIC—2434; NAICS—337110; *Wooden kitchen cabinets*
Employs—1; Estab.—1984
Sales—under $500,000
Distrib.—Regional
Sole ownership

**S & B PALLET CO.**
1348 S. 2nd St. (07063)
**Phone—(908) 756-3606**
Fax—(908) 756-9653
www.sbpallet.com
Email—sales@sbpallet.com
Pres.—Steve Mazza
Hum. Res. & Off. Mgr.—Julia Schmitt
SIC—2448; NAICS—321920; *Wooden pallets*
Employs—60; Estab.—1998
Distrib.—Intl.
Privately owned corporation

**†UNITED SUPPLY CO., INC.**
457 W. End Ave. (07060)
**Phone—(908) 757-3232**
Fax—(908) 226-8388
www.kitchenandbathworks.com
Email—fredt@uscoinc.com
CEO—Steve Kantor
Pres.—Lynn Campagna
GM—Fred Tamberelli
IT Mgr.—Jack So
Hum. Res. Mgr.—Sue Stockinger
Showroom Mgr.—Aaron Cacchione
SIC—5075; *Corporate headquarters & distributor of HVAC systems & accessories*
Employs—20; Estab.—1912
Distrib.—Local
Privately owned corporation
AKA: Kitchen & BathWorks

---

## Plainsboro
(Middlesex—N.E.)

**BRISTOL-MYERS SQUIBB COMPANY**
777 Scudders Mill Rd. (08536)
Mail addr: P.O. Box 4500, Princeton (08543-4500)
**Phone—(609) 897-2000**
(609) 252-4000
National—(800) 332-2056
www.bms.com
Email—customer.relations@ bms.com
Dir., Adv. Res.—Karen Best
Dir., Bus. Comm.—Laura Hortas
Assoc. Adv. Res. Mgr.—Jennifer Green
SIC—2834; NAICS—325412; *Biopharmaceuticals; Brand name—ABILIFY® (aripiprazole); ATRIPLA® (efavirenz/ emtricitabine/tenofovir disoproxil fumarate); BARACLUDE® (entecavir); ERBITUX® (cetuximab); IXEMPRA® (ixabepilone); KOMBIGLYZE™ XR (saxagliptin & metformin HCl extended-release)*
Employs—1550; Estab.—1887
Distrib.—Intl.
Publicly owned corporation
Parent co.—Bristol-Myers Squibb Company, New York, NY
Phone—(212) 546-4000
See Parent Co. Section for full profile.

**FIRMENICH, INC.**
250 Plainsboro Rd. (08536)
Mail addr: P.O. Box 5880, Princeton (08543-5880)
**Phone—(609) 452-1000**
Fax—(609) 520-9780
www.firmenich.com
Email—wendy.bruzzese@ firmenich.com
Pres., N. Amer.—David Shipman
V-P., Admn. & Fin.—Douglas Lucht
V-P., Hum. Res.—Raymond Collins
Hum. Res. Proj. Mgr.—Wendy Bruzzese
SIC—2087; 2869; NAICS—311900; *Corporate headquarters & flavors & fragrances*
Employs—800; Estab.—1895
Sales—$25Mil-$100Mil
Distrib.—Intl.
Privately owned corporation

**INTEGRA LIFESCIENCES CORP.**
311 Enterprise Dr. (08536)
**Phone—(609) 275-0500**
National—(800) 997-4868
Fax—(609) 275-3684
www.integralife.com
Email—custsvcnj@integralife.com
Ex. Chrm.—Stuart M. Essig
Pres., CEO & Dir.—Peter Arduini
Corp. V-P. & Pres., Instruments— Debbi Leonetti
Corp. V-P. & Pres., Extremity Reconstruction—Robert D. Paltridge
Pres., Intl. & Corp. V-P.—Dan Reyvers
Corp. V-P. & Pres., Neurosurgery— Robert T. Davis, Jr.
Corp. V-P. & Pres., Global Spine & Orthobiotics & Head of Strategic Dev.—Brian Larkin
Pres., U.S. Spine—Kirt Stephenson
Ex. V-P., Admn. & Fin. & CFO— John B. Henneman III
Chief Scientific Officer—Simon J. Archibald
CIO—Robert Perrett
Corp. V-P., Global Opers. & Supply Chain—John Mooradian
Sr. V-P., Global Opers.—James Oti
Sr. V-P., Admn., Gen. Counsel & Secy.—Richard D. Gorelick
Sr. V-P., Corp. Dev.—Maria Platsis
Corp. V-P., Admn., Gen. Counsel & Secy.—Judith E. O'Grady
Sr. V-P., Global Supply Chain— John Bostjancic
Corp. V-P., Global Qual. Assur.— Joseph Vinhais
V-P., Treas.—Nora Brennan
V-P., Corp. Cont.—Jerry Corbin
V-P., GM, Extremity Reconstruction—William Weber
Dir., Corp. Comms.—Gianna Sabella
SIC—3842; *Corporate headquarters & artificial skin; Brand name—Vitaphore*
Employs—400
Publicly owned corporation

**INTEGRA LIFESCIENCES CORP.**
105 Morgan Ln. (08536)
**Phone—(609) 275-2700**
National—(800) 997-4868
Fax—(609) 750-4277
www.integralife.com
Email—custsvcnj@integra-ls.com
Dir., Sales Opers.—Scott Lewkowitz
Dir., Sales Training—Jenny Lapushner
SIC—3842; *Artificial skin & medical kits*
Employs—1200; Estab.—1998
Distrib.—Intl.
Publicly owned corporation
Parent co.—Integra LifeSciences Corp., Plainsboro, NJ
Phone—(609) 275-0500
See Parent Co. Section for full profile.

**INTELLISPHERE, LLC**
666 Plainsboro Rd., Ste. 300 (08536)
**Phone—(609) 716-7777**
Fax—(609) 716-4747
www.pharmacytimes.com
Email—info@mdng.com
CEO—Michael J. Hennessy
Hum. Res. Mgr.—Deborah Cropanese
Proj. Mgr.—Megan O'Connell
SIC—2721; *Healthcare magazine publishing*
Employs—80; Estab.—1998
Sales—$1Mil-$2.5Mil
Distrib.—Regional
Limited Liability Company

**NOVO NORDISK, INC. (H Q)**
800 Scudders Mill Rd. (08536)
**Phone—(609) 987-5800**
Fax—(609) 987-0462
www.novonordisk-us.com
Email—kiau@novonordisk.com
Pres.—Jesper Hoilland
Chief Global Medical Officer—Alan C. Moses
V-P., Gen. Counsel—Curt Ottmans
V-P., Sales, Natl. Diabetes—Andy Ajello
V-P., Strategic Bus. Opers.—Phil Fornecker
V-P., Brand Mktg., Diabetes— Camille Lee
V-P., Fin. & IT—Karsten Munk Knudsen
V-P., Hum. Res.—Jeff Frazier
V-P., Biopharmaceuticals—Edward Williams
Dir., Prod. Comms.—Amber Morley
Dir., Media Rels.—Ken Inchausti
SIC—2834; NAICS—325412; *Corporate headquarters; insulin & therapeutic proteins*
Employs—1000
Sales—over $4Bil
Publicly owned corporation

**GEOGRAPHICAL**

## Plainsboro—(cont.)

**SAI GLOBAL, INC.**
101 Morgan Ln., Ste. 301 (08536)
Phone—(609) 955-5100
Fax—(609) 924-9207
www.saiglobal.com/compliance
Email—info.americas@
saiglobal.com
Pres.—Tim Whipple
Mktg. Mgr.—Michael Orrick
IT Mgr.—Mark Taylor
Hum. Res. Mgr.—Pam Kohen
SIC—7372; *Corporate headquarters & compliance training courses software development*
Employs—75; Estab.—1998
Distrib.—Intl.
Publicly owned corporation

## Pleasantville

(Atlantic—S.E.)

**†ABC SUPPLY CO., INC., BRADCO DIV.**
Div. of ABC Supply Co., Inc.
725 W. Delilah Rd. (08232)
Phone—(609) 484-9100
Fax—(609) 484-0977
www.bradcosupply.com
Email—info@bradcosupply.com
Sales Mgr.—Mark Morrison
Asst. Sales Mgr.—Jason Cairns
SIC—5033; 5031; *Distributor of residential & commercial roofing, windows, vinyl siding & lumber*
Employs—13; Estab.—1991
Distrib.—Local
Privately owned corporation
Parent co.—ABC Supply Co., Inc., Beloit, WI
Phone—(608) 362-7777
See Parent Co. Section for full profile.

**ALLEN SIGNS**
600 Martin Luther King Ave. (08232)
Phone—(609) 645-9268
Email—allensigns@juno.com
Owner—Jose Allen
SIC—3993; *Interior & exterior signs*
Employs—1; Estab.—1977
Sales—under $500,000
Distrib.—Regional
Sole ownership

**ATLANTIC CITY WEEKLY, L. P.**
Div. of Review Publishing L. P.
Bayport 1, 8025 Black Horse Pike, Ste. 3 (08232)
Phone—(609) 646-4848
Fax—(609) 646-7338
www.acweekly.com
Email—info@acweekly.com
Publisher—Lew Steiner
Coordinator—Kathy Disprow
SIC—2711; *Newspaper publishing*
Employs—20; Estab.—2000
Distrib.—Local
Limited Liability Partnership
Parent co.—Review Publishing L. P., Philadelphia, PA
Phone—(215) 563-7400
See Parent Co. Section for full profile.

**BERGES TRENTON AWNING CO., INC.**
12 W. Washington Ave. (08232)
Phone—(609) 641-7861
National—(855) 692-9646
Fax—(609) 641-3332
www.bergestrentonawning.com
Email—bta1927@gmail.com
Pres.—Richard Berges

SIC—2394; NAICS—314912; *Canvas awnings*
Employs—7; Estab.—1927
Sales—$500,000-$1Mil
Distrib.—Local
Privately owned corporation

**†BILLOWS ELECTRIC SUPPLY CO., INC.**
301 N. New Rd. (08232)
Phone—(609) 345-6154
Fax—(609) 345-1418
www.billows.com
Email—johnd@billows.com
Br. Mgr.—John Dittess
SIC—5063; *Distributor of electrical equipment, light bulbs & fuses*
Employs—30; Estab.—1997
Distrib.—National
Privately owned corporation
Parent co.—Billows Electric Supply Co., Inc., Philadelphia, PA
Phone—(215) 332-9700
See Parent Co. Section for full profile.

**BONGIOVANNI CUSTOM CABINET & FURNITURE, LLC, MARIO**
7 E. Pleasant Ave. (08232-2562)
Phone—(609) 646-8488
Owner—Mario Bongiovanni
SIC—2431; NAICS—321900; *Millwork*
Employs—2; Estab.—1979
Sales—under $500,000 (est)
Distrib.—Local
Limited Liability Company

**†COLONIAL ELECTRIC SUPPLY CO., THE**
701 W. Delilah Rd. (08232)
Phone—(609) 645-8110
Fax—(609) 645-2270
www.colonialelectric.com
Email—info@colonialelectric.com
Br. Mgr.—Walt Brunetti
Mktg. Mgr.—Daniel S. Finlay
SIC—5063; *Distributor of electrical equipment & supplies, including lighting, wire & cable*
Employs—10; Estab.—2005
Distrib.—Regional
Privately owned corporation
Parent co.—Colonial Electric Supply Co., The, King of Prussia, PA
Phone—(610) 312-8100
See Parent Co. Section for full profile.

**CUSTOM EMBROIDERY**
73 E. New Jersey Ave., P.O. Box 1489 (08232)
Phone—(609) 383-9292
National—(800) 632-1089
Fax—(609) 383-1769
www.cndsales.com
Email—cdsales@comcast.net
Owner—Catherine Carbor
Off. Mgr.—Dave Carver
Manager—David Shoemaker
Embroiderer—Deneane Carver
SIC—2395; 2396; *Embroidery & textile screen printing*
Employs—12; Estab.—1994
Sales—$500,000-$1Mil
Distrib.—Local
Sole ownership
AKA: C & D Sales

**DEMARIO DESIGN & SCREEN PRINTING**
619 Church St. (08232)
Phone—(609) 645-7319
Fax—(609) 645-7664
www.demariodesign.com
Email—sales@demariodesign.com
Pres.—Richard Pitts
V-P.—Cindy Pitts

SIC—2396; 2395; *Apparel screen printing & embroidery of promotional & marketing materials*
Employs—10; Estab.—1981
Distrib.—National
Privately owned corporation

**†GRANT SUPPLY CO., INC.**
755 W. Delilah Rd. (08232)
Phone—(609) 641-1114
National—(800) 866-0158
www.grantsupply.com
Email—timo@grantsupply.com
Br. Mgr.—Tim O'Connell
Asst. Br. Mgr.—Tim Dilliplane
Whse. Mgr.—Warren White
SIC—5074; *Distributor of plumbing supplies*
Employs—15; Estab.—1988
Distrib.—Local
Privately owned corporation
Parent co.—Grant Supply Co., Inc., North Brunswick, NJ
Phone—(732) 545-1018
See Parent Co. Section for full profile.

**GREEN'S FRESH FRUIT SALAD, INC.**
125 Shadeland Ave., P.O. Box 244 (08232)
Phone—(609) 641-5455
Fax—(609) 641-5795
Pres.—Frances Green
Manager—Richard Green
SIC—2099; *Potato, pasta, fruit, lettuce, chicken & crab salad & coleslaw*
Employs—4; Estab.—1992
Sales—under $500,000
Distrib.—Local
Privately owned corporation
AKA: Salad Chef

**HAYES MINDISH, INC.**
1401 N. Main St. (08232)
Phone—(609) 641-9880
Fax—(609) 272-9222
Email—mike@hmprinting.com
Pres.—Sally Hayes
V-P.—Mike Mindish
Manager—Lawrence Hayes
SIC—2759; NAICS—323100; *Commercial printing*
Employs—3; Estab.—1993
Sales—under $500,000
Distrib.—Local
Privately owned corporation

**HI LAND PRINTERS**
121 S. Main St. (08232)
Phone—(609) 646-6319
Fax—(609) 646-4690
Email—hilandprinters@verizon.net
Owner—John McDowell
Graphic Artist—Bryan McDowell
SIC—2759; NAICS—323100; *Commercial printing*
Employs—2; Estab.—1972
Sales—under $500,000
Distrib.—Local
Sole ownership

**JENKINS PLUMBING & HEATING**
103 S. Franklin, P.O. Box 509 (08232)
Phone—(609) 641-6262
Fax—(609) 646-4687
Pres.—Jeffery C. Jenkins
Corp. Secy.—Amy Scalfaro
SIC—3444; *Sheet metal fabrication & HVAC contracting, including duct work, plumbing & heating*
Employs—20; Estab.—1957
20,000 sq ft site, Distrib.—Local
Privately owned corporation

**JOTI KITCHENS**
413 S. Main St. (08232)
Phone—(609) 383-1350
Fax—(609) 383-1016
Owner—Joe Staines, Jr.

SIC—2434; 2431; NAICS—337110; *Wooden & laminate cabinets*
Employs—3; Estab.—1981
Sales—under $500,000
1,500 sq ft site, Distrib.—Local
Privately owned corporation

**KIKER SHEET METAL CORP.**
6 S. New Rd., P.O. Box 1487 (08232)
Phone—(609) 641-4890
Fax—(609) 484-0270
www.kikerduct.com
Pres.—Brian Kiker
SIC—3444; *Sheet metal fabrication*
Employs—12; Estab.—1930
Distrib.—Local
Privately owned corporation

NEW ENTRY
**KRAMER SHY & ASSOCS.**
21 W. Delilah Rd. (08232)
Phone—(609) 646-2063
Fax—(609) 646-1519
Owner—Charles L. Kramer
Hum. Res. Mgr.—Sally Jordan
Sales Mgr.—Mel Ostrow
SIC—2731; *Book publishing for advertising applications*
Employs—5; Estab.—1985
Sales—$1Mil-$2.5Mil
1,200 sq ft site, Distrib.—National
Privately owned corporation

**MAINLAND PLATE GLASS CO., INC.**
53 E. West Jersey Ave. (08232)
Phone—(609) 641-6553
Fax—(609) 641-9236
www.mainlandplateglass.com
Pres.—Richard Bozzelli
Hum. Res. Mgr.—Joan Bozzelli
SIC—2431; 3231; NAICS—327215; *Architectural glass doors, windows, tabletops & storefronts*
Employs—10; Estab.—1966
Distrib.—Local
Privately owned corporation

**†MARJAM SUPPLY CO.**
615 W. Delilah Rd. (08232)
Phone—(609) 407-1234
Fax—(609) 858-7402
www.marjam.com
Email—carmen@marjam.com
Br. Mgr.—Steve Rios
Sales Rep.—Brandon Munson
SIC—5031; 5198; 5033; 5072; *Wholesaler of building materials, paint supplies & hardware, including vinyl & rubber flooring, adhesives, insulation, drywall, windows, lumber, paint, rollers, sandpaper, fasteners & screws*
Employs—15; Estab.—2002
Sales—$1Mil-$2.5Mil
Distrib.—Intl.
Privately owned corporation
Parent co.—MarJam Supply Co., Farmingdale, NY
Phone—(631) 249-4900
See Parent Co. Section for full profile.

**PETER LUMBER CO.**
300 E. Washington Ave., P.O. Box 32 (08232)
Phone—(609) 641-9000
Fax—(609) 641-8292
www.peterlumber.com
Email—mclane@peterlumber.com
Pres.—Hugh M. Peter
Treas. & Cont., Hum. Res.—McLane Peter
GM—Tom Snavley
Sales Mgr.—Keith Givens
Manager—Keith Anderson

## Pleasantville—(cont.)

SIC—2431; 2421; NAICS—321900; *Millwork & hardwood lumber processing*
Employs—40; Estab.—1932
Sales—$1Mil-$2.5Mil
Distrib.—Regional
Privately owned corporation

**SEABOARD INSTRUMENT CO., INC.**
4 N. 1st St. (08232)
**Phone—(609) 641-5300**
Fax—(609) 641-7786
Pres., Opers. Mgr.—Thomas J. Higbee, Sr.
SIC—3824; 3829; NAICS—334514; *Vibrating reed tachometers & frequency meters*
Employs—6; Estab.—1950
Sales—under $500,000
8,000 sq ft site, Distrib.—Intl.
Privately owned corporation

[NEW ENTRY]
**SOUTH JERSEY PUBLISHING CO.**
1000 W. Washington Ave. (08232)
**Phone—(609) 272-7000**
Fax—(609) 272-7413
www.pressofac.com
Email—hrdept@pressofac.com
Publisher—Mark L. Blum
Hum. Res. Mgr.—Danielle Daly
SIC—2711; *Newspaper publishing*
Employs—165; Estab.—2013
Sales—$5Mil-$10Mil (est)
Distrib.—Local
Publicly owned corporation
AKA: Tressos Atlantic City, The
Also see: World Media Enterprises, Inc., same loc.

†**TRI-COUNTY BUILDING SUPPLIES, INC.**
1001 Doughty Rd. (08232)
**Phone—(609) 646-0950**
Fax—(609) 383-3226
www.tcbsi.com
Pres.—Stephen Gross
Cont.—Bob Watts
GM—Pat Finnerty
SIC—5031; 5033; *Corporate headquarters & distributor of building supplies, including lumber, roofing, insulation & vinyl siding*
Employs—30; Estab.—1968
Sales—under $500,000
Distrib.—Local
Privately owned corporation

**WORLD MEDIA ENTERPRISES, INC.**
Div. of Omaha World-Herald Co.
1000 W. Washington Ave. (08232)
**Phone—(609) 272-7000**
Fax—(609) 272-7413
www.pressofatlanticcity.com
Email—hrdept@pressofac.com
Publisher—Mark L. Blum
Ex. Editor—Chris Worrell
Digital Adv. Mgr.—Jay Blankenship
Adv. Mgr.—Dave Caywood
Hum. Res. Mgr.—Danielle Daly
Fin. Mgr.—Ellen Wolcott
Circ. Mgr.—John Celestino
Cred. Mgr.—Howard Wilson
SIC—2711; *Newspaper publishing*
Employs—150; Estab.—1985
40,000 sq ft site, Distrib.—Regional
Privately owned corporation
AKA: Press Of Atlantic City, The
Also see: South Jersey Publishing Co., same loc.
Parent co.—Omaha World-Herald Co., Omaha, NE
Phone—(402) 444-1000
See Parent Co. Section for full profile.

## Pluckemin

(Somerset—N.E.)

**FRANK'S CABINET SHOP, INC.**
1992 Burnt Mills Rd., P.O. Box 78 (07978)
**Phone—(908) 658-4396**
Fax—(908) 658-9112
www.frankscabinetshop.com
Email—john@frankscabinetshop.com
Ptnr.—John Darrow
Ptnr.—Douglas Bloom
SIC—2431; 2541; NAICS—321900; *Wooden cabinets & entertainment centers*
Employs—7; Estab.—1972
Sales—$500,000-$1Mil
Distrib.—Local
Privately owned corporation
AKA: GBD Cabinet Shop, LLC

## Point Pleasant

(Ocean—S.E.)

**ALL POINTS PRINTING & GRAPHICS**
831 Arnold Ave. (08742)
**Phone—(732) 892-6670**
Fax—(732) 892-6646
Email—allpointsprint@gmail.com
Owner—Jim McClure
Bookkeeper—Liz McClure
SIC—2759; NAICS—323100; *Color, instant & wide-format printing & custom graphics of business cards, postcards & brochures*
Employs—5; Estab.—1972
Sales—under $500,000
Distrib.—Local
Privately owned corporation

**ATLAS RECORDING MACHINES CORP.**
2140 Bridge Ave. (08742)
**Phone—(732) 295-3663**
Fax—(732) 899-8306
Pres.—Anthony Hopcroft
SIC—3545; 3544; NAICS—333500; *Punches & carbide drilling tools*
Employs—5; Estab.—1978
Sales—$500,000-$1Mil (est)
Distrib.—National
Privately owned corporation

**BROADWAY SIGNS, INC.**
1029 Ocean Rd. (08742)
**Phone—(732) 892-6334**
Fax—(732) 714-0726
Pres.—Joe Mulani
SIC—3993; *Interior & exterior vinyl signs*
Employs—2; Estab.—1985
Sales—under $500,000
Distrib.—Local
Sole ownership

**EAGLE ENGINEERING & AUTOMATION, INC.**
2111 Herbertsville Rd., P.O. Box 924 (08742)
**Phone—(732) 899-2292**
Fax—(732) 899-5067
www.walker-eagle.com
Pres.—Maura Ryan
Dir., Opers.—Robert Ryan
R & D Mgr.—Jason Tiedermann
Fin. Mgr.—Maureen Akersten
SIC—3625; 3621; NAICS—335314; *Electric motor controls*
Employs—11; Estab.—1987
8,000 sq ft site, Distrib.—National
Privately owned corporation

**FINEST ENTERPRISES, INC.**
2107 Herbertsville Rd. (08742)
**Phone—(732) 892-1121**
Fax—(732) 899-3404
Pres.—Jim Horne

SIC—2434; 2431; NAICS—337110; *Wooden kitchen cabinets, millwork & stairs*
Employs—1; Estab.—1972
Sales—under $500,000
Distrib.—Local
Privately owned corporation

**S & S CUSTOM COVERS LLC**
2034 Bridge Ave. (08742)
**Phone—(732) 903-7518**
Fax—(732) 903-7519
Email—canvas2@comcast.net
Owner & Pres.—Walter Skola
SIC—2394; NAICS—314912; *Boat covers*
Employs—2; Estab.—1976
Sales—under $500,000
Distrib.—Local
Limited Liability Company

**SIGNS BY RAYMOND**
626 Route 88 (08742)
**Phone—(732) 840-7793**
Fax—(732) 840-7793
Owner—Raymond Lamonica
SIC—3993; *Interior & exterior signs*
Employs—1; Estab.—1968
Sales—under $500,000
Distrib.—Local
Sole ownership

**SPECIAL-T-GRAPHICS OF NEW JERSEY, LLC**
3105 Bridge Ave. (08742)
**Phone—(732) 899-7240**
Email—specialtgraphics@verizon.net
Pres.—Sheryl Burke
SIC—2396; *Textile screen printing, including t-shirts, caps & jackets for companies, events & fundraisers*
Employs—1; Estab.—1982
Sales—under $500,000
Distrib.—Local
Privately owned sub-S corp.

**TROPICAL EXPRESSIONS, INC.**
2127 Bridge Ave. (08742)
**Phone—(732) 899-1733**
Fax—(732) 899-4876
www.tropicalexpressions.com
Pres.—Jack McGuire
GM—Irene Cernero
SIC—2499; *Artificial trees*
Employs—5; Estab.—1989
6,000 sq ft site, Distrib.—Intl.
Privately owned sub-S corp.

## Point Pleasant Beach

(Ocean—S.E.)

**C & D PRINTING CO.**
118 Broadway (08742)
**Phone—(732) 892-8044**
Fax—(732) 892-6199
Email—cdprint@verizon.net
Owner—Brenda Nasce
SIC—2752; 2791; NAICS—323122; *Offset printing, typesetting & bookbinding*
Employs—2; Estab.—1964
Sales—under $500,000
Distrib.—Local
Sole ownership

**COLIE SAILMAKERS, INC.**
1649 Bay Ave. (08742)
**Phone—(732) 892-4344**
National—(800) 481-4349
Fax—(732) 899-8965
www.coliesails.com
Email—dev@coliesails.com
Manager—Alex Shayfer
SIC—2394; NAICS—314912; *Boat covers*
Employs—4; Estab.—1976
Sales—under $500,000
Distrib.—Intl.
Privately owned corporation

**ELMENDORF OFFICE SUPPLY , INC.**
3201 Bridge Ave., Ste. 1 (08742)
**Phone—(732) 295-8700**
Fax—(732) 295-8709
Email—gre3161@aol.com
Pres.—Laurie Sairhurst
SIC—3579; *Rebuilt typewriters & office equipment*
Employs—2; Estab.—1960
Sales—under $500,000
Distrib.—Local
Privately owned corporation

†**FISHERMANS DOCK CO-OP**
57 Channel Dr., P.O. Box 1314 (08742)
**Phone—(732) 899-1872**
Fax—(732) 899-3294
Email—coop.dock@verizon.net
Pres.—John Cole
Off. Mgr.—Alice Johnson
SIC—5146; *Wholesaler of seafood, including fish*
Employs—10; Estab.—1953
Distrib.—Regional
Privately owned corporation

**MCBRIDE AWNING CO.**
304 Richmond Ave. (08742)
**Phone—(732) 892-6256**
www.mcbrideawnings.com
Ptnr.—Jon McBride
Ptnr.—Cary McBride
Ptnr.—Brian McBride
SIC—2394; NAICS—314912; *Canvas awnings*
Employs—3; Estab.—1992
Sales—under $500,000
Distrib.—Local
Privately owned corporation

**NAUTICAL CANVAS DESIGNS**
506 Elizabeth Ave. (08742)
**Phone—(732) 892-7677**
Fax—(732) 892-7677
Member—Michael Meseroll
SIC—2394; NAICS—314912; *Canvas boat covers*
Employs—2; Estab.—1972
Sales—under $500,000
Distrib.—Local
Limited Liability Company

**OCEAN STAR, THE**
421 River Ave. (08742)
**Phone—(732) 899-7606**
Fax—(732) 899-9778
www.starnewsgroup.com
Email—info@theoceanstar.com
Publisher—James Manser
GM—Alison Manser Ertl
SIC—2711; *Newspaper publishers*
Employs—40; Estab.—1960
Sales—$1Mil-$2.5Mil (est)
Distrib.—Local
Privately owned corporation
AKAs: Coast Star, The & Star News Group, The

**PARK SALES**
P.O. Box 586 (08742)
**Phone—(732) 899-0684**
Owner—Dennis Vitkauskis
SIC—3944; *Boardwalk games*
Employs—1; Estab.—1990
Sales—under $500,000
Distrib.—Regional
Sole ownership

**STYLES MFG. CO., INC., A. E.**
416 Richmond Ave., P.O. Box 1306 (08742)
**Phone—(732) 899-0872**
Fax—(732) 899-6932
www.stylesmfg.com
Email—information@stylesmfg.com
Pres.—John Criscuolo

GEOGRAPHICAL

## Point Pleasant Beach—(cont.)

SIC—2841; 2999; 5046; 5169; *Manufacturer of car wash detergents & waxes & distributor of car wash equipment & related supplies; Brand name— Glazon™; Foamex*
Employs—15; Estab.—1932
Sales—$1Mil-$2.5Mil
Distrib.—National
Privately owned corporation

## Point Pleasant Boro
### (Ocean—S.E.)

**COLORCRAFT, INC.**
1506 Beaver Dam Rd. (08742)
**Phone—(732) 892-6639**
National—(800) 499-6639
Fax—(732) 892-5570
www.colorcraft.net
Email—colorcraft@verizon.net
Owner & Pres.—Leonard W. Thomas
SIC—3993; *Banners, signs, decals & posters*
Employs—4; Estab.—1985
Sales—under $500,000
2,000 sq ft site, Distrib.—National
Privately owned corporation

**CROFT TOOL, INC.**
2144 Bridge Ave. (08742)
**Phone—(732) 899-4885**
Fax—(732) 899-8306
Owner—Anthony Hopcroft
SIC—3546; NAICS—333991; *Power-driven hand tools*
Employs—5; Estab.—1980
Sales—$1Mil-$2.5Mil (est)
Distrib.—National
Privately owned corporation

**EMBROIDERY TECHNOLOGIES, INC.**
737 Howe St. (08742)
**Phone—(732) 295-1300**
Fax—(732) 295-1348
Pres.—Richard Poulos
SIC—2395; *Textile embroidery*
Employs—1; Estab.—1996
Sales—under $500,000
4,000 sq ft site, Distrib.—National
Privately owned corporation

**FORSBERG'S BOAT WORKS, INC.**
1692 W. End Dr. (08742)
**Phone—(732) 892-4246**
Fax—(732) 892-9401
Pres.—Nils Forsberg
Foreman—Tommy Forsberg
Foreman—Karl Forsberg
SIC—3732; *Boats*
Employs—4; Estab.—1946
Sales—under $500,000
3,528 sq ft site, Distrib.—Local
Privately owned corporation

**GARDEN STATE CANVAS PRODUCTS CO.**
1671 Beaver Dam Rd. (08742)
**Phone—(732) 892-7021**
Owner—David Toth
SIC—2394; NAICS—314912; *Canvas boat covers*
Employs—3; Estab.—1967
Sales—under $500,000
Distrib.—Local
Sole ownership

**SOVEREIGN TECHNOLOGY CORPORATION**
2200 River Rd., Unit A (08742-2297)
**Phone—(732) 298-8104**
(908) 675-6038
Fax—(732) 298-8104
www.sovtechcorp.com
Email—marketing@ sovtechcorp.com
Pres., CEO—William Robinson

CFO—Maria Robinson
Dir., Software Engrg.—Rich Solomon
Mktg. Mgr.—Tom Barnes
SIC—7372; *Real-time asset & personnel management software development for the transportation, medical, industrial industries & the government & military; Brand name—Sovereign PalTrack; SAM; AirTrack; Computer Track; PalTrack Software; ExitWatch; YardCheck; MarineCheck; ExecTrack*
Employs—15; Estab.—1995
Distrib.—National
Privately owned sub-S corp.

## Pomona
### (Atlantic—S.E.)

**ARGO CORP.**
Richard Stockton College, Ste. 202 (08240)
**Phone—(609) 652-4560**
Fax—(609) 748-5565
Email—argo@loki.stockton.edu
Publisher—Dan Grote
Editor—Emily Heerema
SIC—2711; *Newspaper publishing*
Employs—15; Estab.—1971
Sales—$1Mil-$2.5Mil
Distrib.—Local
Privately owned corporation

## Pompton Lakes
### (Passaic—N.E.)

**A M A CENTERLESS GRINDING, INC.**
88-C Cannonball Rd., P.O. Box 14 (07442)
**Phone—(973) 835-2919**
National—(800) 261-2919
Fax—(973) 835-7885
www.amacenterlessgrinding.com
Email—amaharry@optonline.net
Pres.—John Memmelaar
GM—Harry Fivehouse
SIC—3599; *Centerless grinding*
Employs—6; Estab.—1976
Sales—$1Mil-$5Mil
Distrib.—Regional
Privately owned corporation

**A WALSH IMAGING, INC.**
55 Cannonball Rd. (07442)
**Phone—(973) 616-7100**
National—(888) 235-9729
Fax—(973) 616-7191
www.awalshimaging.com
Email—main@awalshimaging.com
Pres.—Patrick Walsh
V-P., Secy.—Thomas D. Walsh
V-P., Treas., Hum. Res. & IT Mgr.—Tony Iurato
SIC—3844; NAICS—334517; *X-ray machines, digital equipment & supplies*
Employs—30; Estab.—1987
13,000 sq ft site, Distrib.—Regional
Privately owned sub-S corp.

**ALADEN ATHLETIC WEAR, LLC**
53 Cannonball Rd. (07442)
**Phone—(973) 838-2425**
Fax—(973) 838-3336
Email—aladenaw@gmail.com
Pres.—Estela Arco
SIC—2389; 2391; NAICS—315200; *Custom handmade athletic wear & uniforms for schools, professional sports teams & businesses, including varsity jackets, t-shirts, sweatshirts & draperies*
Employs—3; Estab.—1995
Sales—$500,000-$1Mil
5,000 sq ft site, Distrib.—National
Limited Liability Company

**B & L PRECISION GRINDING CORP.**
7-B Ivy St. (07442)
**Phone—(973) 839-4141**
Fax—(973) 839-4760
Email—blgrinding@verizon.net
Pres.—Lonnie Petersen
Machining Mgr.—Daniel Ambro
SIC—3599; *Centerless grinding*
Employs—2; Estab.—1986
Sales—under $500,000
1,200 sq ft site, Distrib.—National
Privately owned corporation

| NEW ENTRY |

**BALCIS SCREEN PRINTING**
219 Wanaque Ave. (07442)
**Phone—(973) 835-9948**
Fax—(973) 835-9968
Owner—Martin Balbuana
SIC—2396; 2759; *T-shirt & promotional item screen printing, including cups, pens & bags*
Employs—4
Sales—$500,000-$1Mil (est)

**COMPUTRS, INC.**
294 Wanaque Ave. (07442)
**Phone—(973) 248-9500**
Fax—(973) 248-3350
www.computrsinc.com
Email—ken@computrsinc.com
Pres.—Ken Freedman
IT Consultant—Jesse Ginder
SIC—7373; *Computer network systems integration, including LANs & WANs*
Employs—4; Estab.—1987
Sales—under $500,000
Distrib.—Local
Privately owned sub-S corp.

**GILBY'S SCREEN PRINT**
615 Ringwood Ave. (07442)
**Phone—(973) 835-5729**
Fax—(973) 835-2941
www.gilbys.com
Email—pat@gilbys.com
Owner—Patrick Smith
SIC—2396; *T-shirt screen printing*
Employs—4; Estab.—1967
Distrib.—Local
Privately owned corporation

**H2M BEVERAGES**
223 Wanaque Ave. (07442)
**Phone—(973) 831-2010**
www.h2mbeverages.com
CEO—Charles Musumeci
Dir., Promotions—Mary Byrne
SIC—2086; *Nonalcoholic beverages, including energy drinks, fruit-flavored teas & vitamin waters; Brand name— Liquid Lightning Energy Drink; Herbal Mist; 989 On Demand*
Employs—17
Sales—$5Mil-$10Mil (est)

**KAY MACHINE CO.**
130 Cannonball Rd. (07442)
**Phone—(973) 839-4404**
Fax—(973) 546-7376
Pres., Hum. Res. Mgr.—George Kaiser
SIC—3552; NAICS—333292; *Textile machinery rollers*
Employs—1; Estab.—1958
Sales—under $500,000
Distrib.—Local
Privately owned corporation

**†PBM SUPPLY CO., INC.**
88 Cannonball Rd., P.O. Box 351 (07442)
**Phone—(973) 839-0050**
Fax—(973) 839-4886
Email—pbmsupply@verizon.net
Pres.—Robert Fox

SIC—5063; 5085; 5084; *Distributor of power transmission products, including sheaves, v-belts, reducers, clutches, shafting, shaft collars, bearings & housed units, material handling, conveyor belting, pulleys, idlers & returns & conveyor belt vulcanizing on-site*
Employs—3; Estab.—1975
Distrib.—Regional
Privately owned corporation

**PRIME TIME TOYS, LLC**
P.O. Box 256 (07442-0256)
**Phone—(973) 839-5711**
Fax—(973) 839-5811
www.primetimetoys.com
Email—primetimetoys@att.net
V-P., Opers. & Manager—Mark Milano
SIC—3944; *Water & flying toys & games; Brand name—Max Liquidator; Splash Bombs; Hydro Blaster*
Employs—2; Estab.—1995
Sales—$500,000-$1Mil
Distrib.—National
Limited Liability Company

**SOLAR PRODUCTS, INC.**
228 Wanaque Ave. (07442)
**Phone—(973) 835-6581**
Fax—(973) 835-7856
www.solarproducts.com
Email—info@solarproducts.com
Pres.—Mike Sirotnak
Acct. Mgr.—Susan Robertson
Plt. Mgr.—Tim Robertson
SIC—3567; NAICS—333994; *Industrial heating units*
Employs—30; Estab.—1956
Distrib.—Intl.
Privately owned corporation

**TANDEM GRAPHICS, INC.**
207 Wanaque Ave. (07442)
**Phone—(973) 513-9779**
National—(888) 982-6336
Fax—(845) 426-2272
www.tandemgraphics.net
Email—info@tandemgraphics.net
Pres.—Michael Nass
Prodn. Mgr.—Keith Daulton
Off. Mgr.—Jessica Dahl
SIC—2759; 2752; 2791; 2789; NAICS—323122; *Banners & posters, including digital color & large-format printing, electronic prepress, scanning, finishing & mounting*
Employs—6; Estab.—1990
3,000 sq ft site, Distrib.—Local
Privately owned sub-S corp.

**VANSCO, INC.**
138-B Cannonball Rd. (07442)
**Phone—(973) 835-8423**
Fax—(973) 835-8765
www.vanscoequipment.com
Email—sales@ vanscoequipment.com
Pres.—Everett Van Steenberghe
GM—Thomas Faber
SIC—3542; NAICS—333513; *Hot stamping equipment*
Employs—2; Estab.—1972
Sales—under $500,000
4,000 sq ft site, Distrib.—National

## Pompton Plains
### (Morris—N.W.)

**AMMARK CORP.**
230 W. Parkway, Ste. 12 (07444-1060)
**Phone—(973) 616-2555**
National—(800) 937-0426
Fax—(973) 616-0246
www.ammarkcorp.com
Email—sales@ammarkcorp.com
Pres.—John T. Ford
V-P.—Veronica Ford

## Pompton Plains— (cont.)

SIC—3822; NAICS—334512; *Electric & nonelectric hydronic valves & controls*
Employs—4; Estab.—1966
Sales—$1Mil-$2.5Mil
Distrib.—Intl.
Privately owned corporation

**ANALYTICAL SALES & SERVICES, INC.**
237 W. Parkway, Ste. 1 (07444)
**Phone—(973) 616-0700**
National—(800) 899-4752
Fax—(973) 616-0133
www.analytical-sales.com
Email—info@analytical-sales.com
Pres.—David A. Isom
V-P., Sales—Rosanne G. Isom
SIC—3821; 3823; 5049; 5075; NAICS—339111; *Manufacturer & distributor of laboratory supplies & heating instrumentation; Brand name—HotSLEEVE; ColdSLEEVE; PowerSELECTOR; MultiSLEEVE; FlexChrom; AgileSLEEVE; Mighty Mats*
Employs—11; Estab.—1988
Sales—$4.5Mil
15,000 sq ft site, Distrib.—Intl.
Privately owned sub-S corp.
AKA: Analytical Sales and Products

**CAREER PRESS, INC.**
220 W. Parkway, Unit 12 (07444)
**Phone—(201) 848-0310**
Fax—(201) 848-1727
www.careerpress.com
Email—sales@careerpress.com
Pres.—Ron Fry
Dir., Sales & Mktg. Mgr.—Laurie Kelly-Pye
Off. Mgr.—Karen Roy
SIC—2731; *Book publishing*
Employs—20; Estab.—2009
Sales—$500,000-$1Mil
Distrib.—Intl.
Privately owned corporation
AKA: New Page Books

**EDWARDS COILS CORP.**
Div. of Aqua Systems, Inc.
101 Alexander Ave., Unit 6 (07444)
**Phone—(973) 835-2815**
Fax—(973) 835-2805
www.edwardscoils.com
Email—mmorabit@edwards-eng.com
Plt. Mgr.—Mark Morabito
SIC—3443; *Water-to-refrigerant heat exchangers & single & double-vented enhanced tube*
Employs—9; Estab.—1947
Sales—$1Mil-$2.5Mil
35,000 sq ft site, Distrib.—Intl.
Privately owned sub-S corp.
Parent co.—Aqua Systems, Inc., Hampton Falls, NH
Phone—(603) 778-8796
See Parent Co. Section for full profile.

**EDWARDS HYDRONIC PARTS, LLC**
101 Alexander Ave. (07444)
Mail addr.: P.O. Box 4403, Wayne (07474)
**Phone—(973) 835-7754**
Fax—(973) 835-7884
www.edwardshydronics.com
Owner & Off. Mgr.—Sam Ozdemir
SIC—3433; NAICS—333414; *Boiler parts, circulating pumps, zone valves & hydrostats*
Employs—5; Estab.—1978
Sales—$500,000-$1Mil
Distrib.—National
Privately owned corporation

**GLOBAL BUSINESS DIMENSIONS INC.**
220 W. Parkway, Ste. 8 (07444-1048)
**Phone—(973) 831-5866**
Fax—(973) 831-0867
www.globalbd.com
Email—sales@globalbd.com
Pres., CEO—Sanjay Prasad
Dir., Hum. Res.—Sarika Singh
Opers. Mgr.—Angela Hansen
Fin. Mgr.—Raju Philip
Manager—Sam Prasad
SIC—3571; 7372; 5045; NAICS—334111; *Manufacturer & distributor of personal computers, software & IT related & consumer electronics products, including maintenance, creating & installation of mobile applications; Brand name—Atlas; Intel; HP; Sony; Apple; Cisco; Seagate; Lenovo; Toshiba; Fujitsu; WD; Canon; APC; Samsung; Kingston; 3M; Nikon; Dell; Microsoft; NEC; Viewsonic; Logitec; Epson; Sandisk; Acer; Panasonic; LG; Sharp; Dlink*
Employs—25; Estab.—1994
20,000 sq ft site, Distrib.—Intl.
Privately owned corporation
ISO rating—9001:2008

**GRAPHICS PLUS CORP.**
210 W. Parkway, Ste. 7 (07444-1045)
**Phone—(973) 835-3744**
Fax—(973) 835-3942
www.graphicsplusrepro.com
Email—info@graphicsplusrepro.com
Pres.—John Prentzel
Off. Mgr.—Christian Darby
Prod. Mgr.—Anthony Joyner
SIC—2752; 2796; 2791; NAICS—323122; *Offset printing, color separations & typesetting*
Employs—5
Sales—$500,000-$1Mil (est)
Distrib.—Local
AKA: Graphics Plus Reproduction Center, Inc.

**JAN FENCE CO., INC.**
4 Industrial Rd. (07444)
**Phone—(973) 694-4055**
National—(866) 586-9968
Fax—(973) 872-8049
www.janfence.com
Email—ashley@janfence.com
Pres.—Robert Corrao
Opers. Mgr.—Marissa Leonessa
SIC—3496; 2499; 3272; 3469; *Custom industrial, residential & security aluminum, vinyl, wood & chain-link fencing, including repair & installation & mailboxes, custom gates, fountains & birdhouses; Brand name—ActiveYards; Active Yards*
Employs—15; Estab.—1955
Sales—$500,000-$1Mil
Distrib.—Regional
Privately owned corporation

**KRAFT POWER CORP.**
241 W. Parkway (07444)
**Phone—(973) 835-9800**
(800) 221-3284
Fax—(973) 835-5246
www.kraftpower.com
Email—njinfo@kraftpower.com
V-P.—Chris Stemper
Parts Mgr.—John Ferrari
Serv. Mgr.—Lou Zwernemann
OEM Mgr. & Sales Dealer—Gary Callahan

SIC—3621; 3519; 5064; 5084; *Manufacturer of combined heat & power systems & distributor of power generation systems, power transmission systems, generators, engines, parts & accessories; Brand name—GE Gas Engines; Waukesha Engine; Kohler Generators; Deutz; FW Murphy; MAN Gas Engines; KES CHP Packages; Transfluid; Heinzmann; Lister-Petter; Gill Instruments; Dresser Rand-Guascor; Arrow Engine; Hamilton Jet*
Employs—30; Estab.—1965
Sales—$2.5Mil-$5Mil
35,000 sq ft site, Distrib.—Regional
Privately owned corporation
Parent co.—Kraft Power Corp., Woburn, MA
Phone—(781) 938-9100
See Parent Co. Section for full profile.

**MEDALLION INTERNATIONAL, INC.**
233 W. Parkway (07444)
**Phone—(973) 616-3401**
Fax—(973) 616-3405
V-P.—Paula Boudjouk
Cust. Serv. Rep.—Barbara Marano
SIC—2087; 2844; NAICS—311900; *Flavors & fragrances*
Employs—15; Estab.—1982
Distrib.—Intl.
Privately owned corporation

**†METAL ASSOCIATES, INC.**
230 W. Parkway, Unit 3-2 (07444)
**Phone—(973) 835-8480**
(800) 838-1978
Fax—(973) 835-7981
www.metalassociates.com
Email—metals@rcn.com
Pres.—Charles Bareijsza
Sales Mgr.—Matt Heinz
Sales Dept. Mgr.—Steve Martiak
Sales Admn.—Judy Woodruff
SIC—5051; *Distributor of brass, copper, stainless steel & waveguide tubes*
Employs—10; Estab.—1990
Sales—$3.5Mil
5,500 sq ft site, Distrib.—Intl.
Privately owned sub-S corp.

**MORRIS INDUSTRIES, INC.**
777 Route 23, P.O. Box 278 (07444)
**Phone—(973) 835-6600**
National—(800) 835-0777
Fax—(973) 835-1245
www.morrispipe.com
Email—info@morrispipe.com
CEO—Alvin Nochenson
Pres.—Robert Nochenson
V-P.—Mike Stern
Fin., Hum. Res. & MIS Mgr.—Frank Matullo
SIC—3317; NAICS—331210; *Steel pipe products, including water well supplies & environmental products*
Employs—38; Estab.—1958
100,000 sq ft site, Distrib.—Intl.
Privately owned sub-S corp.

**PHT AEROSPACE, LLC**
230 West Pkwy., Ste. 2 (07444)
**Phone—(973) 831-1230**
Fax—(973) 831-1234
www.phtaerospace.com
Email—sales@phtaerospace.com
Dir., Opers.—Joseph Wall
Pur. Mgr.—Iris Castello
SIC—3728; 3621; *Electric motors & components for aerospace applications*
Employs—30; Estab.—2009
Distrib.—Intl.
Limited Liability Company

**STRONG MAN BUILDING PRODUCTS CORP.**
240 W. Parkway (07444)
**Phone—(973) 831-1555**
National—(800) 950-6999
Fax—(973) 831-1525
www.strongman.com
Email—sales@strongman.com
Pres.—Jay Kinder
Treas.—Elaine Kinder
GM—Robert Giannetti
SIC—3089; *Plastic tarpaulins & netting*
Employs—8; Estab.—1973
Sales—under $500,000
Distrib.—National
Privately owned corporation

**TRI-COMP, INC.**
230 West Pkwy., Unit 14 (07444)
**Phone—(973) 835-1110**
Fax—(973) 835-5015
www.tricomp.com
V-P.—Thomas Lospinoso
SIC—3053; 3082; NAICS—339991; *Plastic & magnetic gaskets*
Employs—100; Estab.—1955
Distrib.—Intl.
Privately owned corporation

**†WAYNE ELECTRICAL SUPPLY CO.**
255 W. Parkway (07444)
**Phone—(973) 839-6500**
Fax—(973) 839-2017
www.wayneelectricalsupply.com
Email—mark@wayneelectrical.com
CEO—Ryan Schmitt
Pres.—Mark Dwoskin
SIC—5063; *Distributor of electrical supplies, including wires, switches & panels*
Employs—15; Estab.—1975
Sales—$500,000-$1Mil
Distrib.—Regional
Privately owned corporation

**WIZARD PRINTING CORP.**
29 Evans Pl., Ste. 82 (07444)
**Phone—(973) 835-8048**
Fax—(973) 835-9216
www.wizardprinting.com
Email—customerservice@wizardprinting.com
Pres.—Neil Keough
MIS Mgr.—Michelle Mertrud
Bookkeeper—Stacy Zerbach
SIC—2759; NAICS—323100; *Commercial printing*
Employs—9; Estab.—1983
Sales—$500,000-$1Mil
3,000 sq ft site, Distrib.—Regional
Sole ownership

**ZAXCOM, INC.**
230 West Pkwy., Unit 9 (07444)
**Phone—(973) 835-5000**
Fax—(973) 835-6633
www.zaxcom.com
Email—info@zaxcom.com
Pres.—Glenn Sanders
Sales & Mktg. Mgr.—Colleen Goodsir
Off. & Opers. Mgr.—Lisa Apriceno
SIC—3651; NAICS—334310; *Professional audio gear for the television & film industries*
Employs—10; Estab.—1986
Sales—$1Mil-$3Mil
6,200 sq ft site, Distrib.—Intl.
Sole ownership

## Port Elizabeth
(Cumberland—S.W.)

**WHIBCO OF NEW JERSEY**
Div. of Whibco, Inc.
377 Port Cumberland Rd., P.O. Box 456 (08348)
**Phone—(856) 825-5200**
National—(800) 257-7006
Fax—(856) 825-4743

**GEOGRAPHICAL**

## Port Elizabeth—(cont.)

www.whibco.com
Email—sales@whibco.com
Plt. Mgr.—Jim Workman
Hum. Res. Mgr.—Rich Bertonazzi
Foreman—John Hughes
Scale Operator—Lisa Collins
SIC—3281; NAICS—327991;
*Industrial sand & construction
aggregate processing*
Employs—30; Estab.—1841
Distrib.—Regional
Privately owned corporation
Parent co.—Whibco, Inc.,
Bridgeton, NJ
Phone—(856) 455-9200
See Parent Co. Section for full profile.

## Port Monmouth

(Monmouth—N.E.)

### BOY ON A DOLPHIN CORP.

308 State Route 36 (07758)
**Phone—(732) 495-2200**
www.boyonadolphin1.com
Email—boyonadolphin1@aol.com
Owner—Harry Karatzia
SIC—2395; 2396; *Embroidery &
screen printing; Brand name—
Nike; Adidas; Fruit of the Loom;
Hanes; Jerzees*
Employs—2; Estab.—1993
2,000 sq ft site, Distrib.—Local
Privately owned corporation

## Port Murray

(Warren—N.W.)

### BOREALIS COMPOUNDS, INC.

176 Thomas Rd. (07865)
**Phone—(908) 850-6200**
National—(800) 407-6225
Fax—(908) 850-1236
www.borealiscompoundsinc.com
Email—peter.nielsen@
borealisgroup.com
Pres., Mfg. Mgr.—Kenneth
Wiecoreck
Cont.—Siegfried Wengler
Sales & Mktg. Mgr.—Peter Nielsen
Operation Mgr.—Richard Jones
Hum. Res. Mgr.—Kim Vervaet
Supply Chain Mgr.—Marco
Rodriguez
HSE & Qual. Mgr.—William
Wallace
Hum. Res. Generalist—Nancy
Hahn
SIC—2821; NAICS—325211;
*Polymer compounding; Brand
name—Borstar; Casico; Borcell;
Visico; Ambicat; Supercure;
SuperTR; Superclean;
Supersmooth*
Employs—116; Estab.—1997
Distrib.—Intl.
Privately owned corporation
ISO rating—9001:2000

### BUSINESS TRAVEL EXECUTIVE MAGAZINE

262 Rockport Rd. (07865)
**Phone—(908) 979-1974**
www.askbte.com
Owner—Gerald Allison
GM—Michelle Cameron
Off. Mgr.—Mary Lee DaFarrari
SIC—2721; *Monthly managed
business travel magazine
publishing*
Employs—5; Estab.—1986
Sales—under $500,000
Distrib.—National
Sole ownership

### FLEXCO MICROWAVE, INC.

17 Karville Rd., P.O. Box 115
(07865)
**Phone—(908) 835-1720**
Fax—(908) 835-0002

www.flexcomw.com
Email—sales@flexcomw.com
Pres., R & D Mgr.—William T. Pote
Sales & Mktg. Mgr.—Dan Beene
Pur. Mgr.—Ed Johnson
MIS Mgr.—Brian Barends
Fin. Mgr.—Mike Elko
Engr.—Bill Bright
SIC—3643; 3678; NAICS—
335931; *Electronic cable &
connectors*
Employs—40; Estab.—1970
18,000 sq ft site, Distrib.—Intl.
ISO rating—9001:2000
AKA: Andrex Systems

### RICKLYN CO., INC.

460 Route 57 (07865)
**Phone—(908) 689-6770**
Fax—(908) 689-5117
Pres., GM—Kevin J. Wauck
SIC—3444; *Sheet metal
fabrication*
Employs—6; Estab.—1963
11,000 sq ft site, Distrib.—Regional
Privately owned corporation

## Port Norris

(Cumberland—S.W.)

### BERRY & SONS, INC., MILLER

Robbinstown Rd., P.O. Box 174
(08349)
**Phone—(856) 785-1420**
Fax—(856) 785-2638
Pres.—Dean Berry
V-P.—Barbara Moore
Supervisor—Keith Moore
SIC—2515; *Burial casket
mattresses*
Employs—10; Estab.—1967
Distrib.—National
Privately owned sub-S corp.

### BIVALVE PACKING CO., INC.

6957 Miller Ave., P.O. Box 336
(08349)
**Phone—(856) 785-0270**
National—(800) 524-2833
Fax—(856) 785-1406
Email—eastpointoyster@aol.com
Pres., GM—Steve Fleetwood
Corp. Secy.—Wendy Chillari
SIC—2092; 2091; NAICS—
311712; *Oyster packaging*
Employs—25; Estab.—1946
Distrib.—National
Privately owned corporation

### RICCI BROTHERS SAND COMPANY, INC.

2099 Dragston Rd., P.O. Box 664
(08349)
**Phone—(856) 785-0166**
  **(888) 807-4224**
Fax—(856) 785-2136
www.riccisand.com
Email—info@riccisand.com
Owner—Sam Ricci, Sr.
GM & Hum. Res. Mgr.—Sam
Ricci, Jr.
SIC—1446; *High-purity sands &
gravels for water filtration, well &
environmental drilling, soil
remediation & industrial
applications, including floor &
flooring, epoxy, grout filler,
asphalt & seal coatings*
Employs—35; Estab.—1958
Sales—$4.8Mil
Distrib.—National
Privately owned corporation

**NEW ENTRY**

### SURFSIDE PRODUCTS, INC.

1733 Main St., P.O. Box 692
(08349)
**Phone—(856) 785-2115**
Fax—(856) 785-0975
Pres.—Peter LaMonica

SIC—2092; NAICS—311999;
*Frozen clams & shell shucking*
Employs—100
Sales—$10Mil-$25Mil (est)
Distrib.—National
Sole ownership

## Port Reading

(Middlesex—N.E.)

### A & D INDUSTRIAL & MARINE REPAIR

900 Port Reading Ave., Ste. B-2
(07064)
**Phone—(732) 541-1481**
Fax—(732) 541-4621
Email—arepairinc@aol.com
Pres.—Doug Alexander
V-P.—Alexander Papandrikos
SIC—3599; 3499; 3561; NAICS—
333911; *Machine shop,
including rebuilt industrial
pumps & metal fabrication*
Employs—12; Estab.—1986
Sales—$1Mil-$2.5Mil
Distrib.—Regional
Privately owned corporation

### ACME MFG. & COATING CO.

900 Port Reading Ave., P.O. Box
70 (07064)
**Phone—(732) 541-2800**
Fax—(732) 541-2828
Pres.—Richard Morrone
SIC—3479; *Powder coating of
architectural metalwork & signs*
Employs—5; Estab.—1987
Sales—under $500,000
Distrib.—Local
Privately owned partnership

### ALLIED OLD ENGLISH, INC.

100 Markley St. (07064)
**Phone—(732) 636-2060**
National—(800) 225-0122
Fax—(732) 636-2538
www.alliedoldenglish.com
Email—info@alliedoldenglish.com
Owner—Fred Ross
Shpg. & Whse. Mgr.—Mike Golden
Cust. Serv. Mgr.—Dennis Spicacci
Webmaster—Gregory S. Ross
SIC—2033; 2035; 2099; NAICS—
311421; *Jams, jellies &
preserves, barbecue sauces,
syrups & salad dressings; Brand
name—Saucy Susan; Sorrell
Ridge®; DAI DAY®; Mee Tu®; AH
SO®*
Employs—45; Estab.—1958
Sales—$10Mil-$25Mil (est)
Distrib.—National
Privately owned corporation

### OLIVER MFG. SUPPLY CO.

730 Port Reading Ave., P.O. Box
274 (07064-0274)
**Phone—(732) 634-8100**
Fax—(732) 636-5525
Pres.—L. Escandon
SIC—3271; NAICS—327331;
*Concrete building block*
Employs—14; Estab.—1938
Sales—$1Mil-$5Mil
Distrib.—Local
Privately owned corporation

### PYRAMID POLY BAGS, INC.

600 Markley St. (07064)
**Phone—(718) 499-1212**
Fax—(732) 596-1308
www.abalinesupply.com
Pres.—Chaya Jeremias
SIC—2656; 3089; NAICS—
322215; *Paper & plastic
tableware*
Employs—20; Estab.—1975
Sales—$2.5Mil-$5Mil (est)
Distrib.—Regional
AKA: Abaline Supply

### USG CORP., PORT READING PLT.

Div. of USG Corp.
300 Markley St. (07064)
**Phone—(732) 636-7900**
Fax—(732) 636-6097
www.usg.com
Email—info@usg.com
Plt. Mgr.—James Wilson
Hum. Res. Mgr.—Renee Jaqueth
Off. Mgr.—Mitch Koff
SIC—2891; NAICS—325520;
*Joint compounds*
Employs—100; Estab.—1902
Sales—$26Mil-$50Mil
Distrib.—National
Publicly owned corporation
Parent co.—USG Corp., Chicago,
IL
  Phone—(312) 436-4000
  See Parent Co. Section for full profile.

## Port Republic

(Atlantic—S.E.)

### ANDERSON MONOGRAMS

245 Fox Landing Rd., P.O. Box 163
(08241)
**Phone—(609) 652-5552**
Fax—(609) 652-2668
Owner—Bruce Anderson
SIC—2395; *Shirt & jacket
monogramming*
Employs—1; Estab.—1985
Sales—under $500,000
Distrib.—Local
Sole ownership

## Princeton

(Mercer—N.E.)

### ABBOTT POINT OF CARE

Div. of Abbott Laboratories
400 College Rd. E. (08540)
**Phone—(609) 454-9000**
Fax—(609) 419-9370
www.abbott.com
Email—info@abbott.com
Div. V-P., R & D—Michael P. Zelin
Facility Mgr.—Randy Reader
IT Mgr.—Mike Taylor
Hum. Res. Mgr.—Lisa Siko
SIC—3841; 3826; NAICS—
334516; *Hand-held portable
digital blood sample analyzers
for critical medical diagnostic &
data management; Brand
name—i-STAT® 1*
Employs—350; Estab.—1987
Distrib.—Intl.
Publicly owned corporation
Parent co.—Abbott Laboratories,
Abbott Park, IL
  Phone—(847) 937-6100
  See Parent Co. Section for full profile.

### ALK TECHNOLOGIES, INC.

Div. of Trimble Navigation Ltd.
457 N. Harrison St. (08540)
**Phone—(609) 683-0220**
National—(800) 377-6453
Fax—(609) 252-8166
www.alk.com
Email—salesinfo@alk.com
CTO—Mike Bodden
Sr. V-P., Opers.—Mark Hornung
V-P., Bus. Dev.—Dan Titus
Mktg. Mgr.—Kate Ashton
Hum. Res. Mgr.—Mark Stuart
Geographic Info. Sys. Specialist—
Craig Fiander
GIS Analyst—Craig Graham
SIC—7372; *Transportation &
logistics software development;
Brand name—CoPilot®; PC
MILER®*
Employs—125; Estab.—1979
Distrib.—Intl.
Publicly owned corporation

## Princeton—(cont.)

Parent co.—Trimble Navigation
Ltd., Sunnyvale, CA
Phone—(408) 481-8000
See Parent Co. Section for full profile.

**ALTECH STAR, INC.**
4365 U.S. Highway 1, Ste. 205
(08540-5785)
Phone—(609) 520-9000
Fax—(609) 520-9005
Email—sales@altechstar.com
Dir., Opers.—Jeya Lell
SIC—7372; Web-enterprise
software development for on-site
& offshore applications
Employs—35
Sales—$2.4Mil
2,000 sq ft site, Distrib.—Intl.
Privately owned corporation

**ALTINA'S CUSTOM INTERIORS**
Princeton Shopping Ctr., 301 N.
Harrison (08540)
Phone—(609) 924-3367
Fax—(609) 924-7439
Email—altinasinterior@aol.com
Owner—Altina Noel
SIC—2391; NAICS—314121;
Curtains & draperies
Employs—2; Estab.—1986
Sales—under $500,000
Distrib.—Local
Sole ownership

**AMREP CORPORATION (H Q)**
300 Alexander Pk., Ste. 204
(08540)
Phone—(609) 716-8200
Fax—(609) 716-8255
www.amrepcorp.com
V-P., CFO—Peter Pizza
V-P., Gen. Counsel & Secy.—
Christopher V. Vitale
SIC—2759; NAICS—323100;
Corporate headquarters; label &
direct mail printing & magazine
circulation
Employs—6; Estab.—1961
Sales—$500,000-$1Mil (est)

NEW ENTRY
**AVANTE INTERNATIONAL
TECHNOLOGY, INC.**
70 Washington Rd. (08540)
Phone—(609) 799-8896
Fax—(609) 799-9308
www.avantetech.com
Email—avantetech@
avantetech.com
Pres.—Kevin Chung
SIC—3579; 3679; Voting
equipment & RFID monitoring
equipment
Employs—20; Estab.—1995
Sales—$2.5Mil-$5Mil (est)
Distrib.—Intl.
Privately owned corporation
Also see: Amerasia International
Technology, Inc., same loc.

**BUSINESS TODAY**
48 University Pl. (08540)
Phone—(609) 258-1111
Fax—(609) 258-1222
www.businesstoday.org
Email—bt@businesstoday.org
Pres., Hum. Res. Mgr.—Jonathan
Hastings
V-P.—Amira Pollack
Fin. Mgr.—Carolyn Klein
SIC—2741; 2721; College student
magazine publishing
Employs—30; Estab.—1968
Distrib.—National
Privately owned corporation
AKA: Foundation For Student
Communication

**COLONIAL PRINTERS**
266 Witherspoon St. (08542)
Mail addr: 84 Castleton Rd.,
Princeton (08540)
Phone—(609) 921-1350
Fax—(609) 921-3688
www.colonialprinters.biz
Email—colonial_printers@
comcast.net
Pres.—Tom Burke
Press Supv.—Dana Nini
Pressman—Robert Morris
SIC—2752; NAICS—323100;
Offset printing
Employs—3; Estab.—1984
Sales—under $500,000
Distrib.—Local
Privately owned corporation

**COVANCE, INC. (H Q)**
210 Carnegie Ctr. (08540)
Phone—(609) 452-8550
Fax—(609) 452-9375
www.covance.com
Email—info@covance.com
Chrm., CEO—Joseph L. Herring
Sr. V-P., CIO—William Klitgaard
V-P., CFO—Allison Cornell
V-P., Hum. Res.—Lisa Uthgenannt
SIC—2834; NAICS—325412;
Corporate headquarters;
pharmaceutical development
Employs—600; Estab.—1987
Worldwide: 10,000
Sales—over $1Bil
Publicly owned corporation

**CSONKA CIGAR REQUISITES, INC.
(H Q)**
407 Blue Spring Rd. (08540)
Phone—(609) 514-2766
National—(800) 276-6522
Fax—(609) 514-7329
www.csonka/promo.com
Email—mchunko@csonka.com
Pres., CEO—Michael Chunko
SIC—3993; 3999; Corporate
headquarters; custom
promotional products, including
air purification systems, travel
humidors, flashlights, laser
pointers, lighters, games & gifts
(mfg. subcontracted)
Employs—40; Estab.—1990
Sales—$1Mil-$2.5Mil
Distrib.—Intl.
Privately owned corporation
AKA: Csonka Worldwide

**DAILY PRINCETONIAN PUBLISHING
CO., INC.**
48 University Pl. (08544)
Mail addr: P.O. Box 469, Princeton
(08542-0469)
Phone—(609) 375-8553
www.dailyprincetonian.com
Email—business@
dailyprincetonian.com
Editor-in-Chief—Marcelo
Rochabrun
Dir., Adv., Natl.—Kevin Tang
Dir., Adv.—Zoe Zhang
Bus. Mgr.—Nicholas Hu
SIC—2711; Newspaper
publishing
Employs—30; Estab.—1876
Distrib.—Local
Privately owned corporation

**DATARAM CORP.**
777 Alexander Rd. (08540)
Mail addr: P.O. Box 7528,
Princeton (08543)
Phone—(609) 799-0071
National—(800) 328-2726
Fax—(609) 799-6096
www.dataram.com
Email—webmaster@dataram.com
Pres.—John Freeman
V-P., Mfg.—Bruce Magath
V-P., Fin.—Marker Pelker

SIC—3577; NAICS—334119;
Corporate headquarters &
computer memory cards
Employs—50; Estab.—1967
Sales—under $500,000
Distrib.—National
Publicly owned corporation

**DERMA SCIENCES, INC. (H Q)**
214 Carnegie Ctr., Ste. 300
(08540)
Phone—(609) 514-4744
National—(800) 825-4325
Fax—(609) 514-8554
www.dermasciences.com
Email—info@dermasciences.com
Chrm. & CEO—Edward J. Quilty
Group Pres., Traditional Wound
Care—Robert C. Cole
Group Pres., Advanced Wound
Care—Barry Wolfenson
Ex. V-P., CFO—John E. Yetter
V-P., Hum. Res.—MaryJean
Thomaier
Dir., Corp. Mktg.—Beth Joy-
Dougherty
SIC—2844; NAICS—325600;
Corporate headquarters;
advanced & traditional wound
care items for tissue
regeneration; Brand name—
MEDIHONEY®; AMNIOEXCEL®;
BIOGUARD®; XTRASORB®;
ALGICELL® Ag; TCC-EZ®;
Derma Gran™ Ointments
Employs—45; Estab.—1984
Sales—$73Mil
12,000 sq ft site, Distrib.—Intl.
Publicly owned corporation
ISO rating—9001:2008

**DIVERSITYINC MEDIA LLC**
342 Nassau St. (08540)
Phone—(973) 494-0500
www.diversityinc.com
Email—shenry@diversityinc.com
CEO—Lucas J. Visconti
COO—Carolynn Johnson
Sr. V-P. & Ex. Editor—Barbara
Frankel
SIC—2721; Monthly diversity
management/consulting
magazine publishing; Brand
name—DiversityInc; DiversityInc
Magazine; DiversityInc Best
Practices; DiversityInc
Recruitment Network;
DiversityInc Top 50
Employs—20; Estab.—1996
Distrib.—National
Limited Liability Company

**DR. REDDY'S LABORATORIES, INC.
(H Q)**
107 College Rd. E. (08540)
Phone—(609) 375-9900
(908) 203-4900
Fax—(908) 203-4996
www.drreddys.com
Email—gwhalen@drreddys.com
Sr. Dir.—Jerry Whalen
Co-Chrm.—K. Anji Reddy
Co-Chrm., CEO—G. V. Prasad
SIC—2834; Corporate
headquarters; prescription
pharmaceuticals
Employs—50
Sales—$25Mil-$50Mil (est)
Publicly owned corporation

**EDUCATIONAL TESTING SERVICE**
660 Rosedale Rd. (08541)
Phone—(609) 921-9000
National—(800) 323-7155
Fax—(609) 734-5410
www.ets.org
Email—etsinfo@ets.org
Pres.—Walter MacDonald
Sr. V-P., R & D & CMO—Ida
Lawrence
Sr. V-P., Growth, Mktg. &
Strategy—Scott Nelson
Dir., Comm.—Tom Ewing

GM, IT, Infrastructure Svcs.—
Donald Vernam
SIC—2741; Academic test
publishing
Employs—2500
Company-wide: 3,000
Sales—$100Mil-$250Mil (est)
Distrib.—Local

**ESYSTEMS, INC.**
4390 U.S. Highway 1, Ste. 301
(08540)
Phone—(609) 945-7437
Fax—(609) 537-0070
www.esysc.com
Email—info@esysc.com
Pres.—Ashish Mukherji
V-P.—Rajesh Behl
Bus. Dev. Mgr.—Samrat Barari
SIC—7373; Computer network
systems integration, including
enterprise application
integration, LANs & data
migration & custom
programming & website
development services
Employs—50; Estab.—2011
7,000 sq ft site, Distrib.—Intl.
Privately owned corporation

**EVEX GLOBAL**
857 State Rd. (08540)
Phone—(408) 907-2994
(609) 252-9192
Fax—(609) 228-4028
www.evexglobal.com
Email—sales@evexglobal.com
Pres.—Claudio Tarquinio
SIC—3821; 3826; 7372; Scientific
instrumentation for
nanotechnology, tabletop SEM
for experienced & entry-level
electron microscopists & 3D
analytical software development
Employs—15; Estab.—1990
Sales—$101Mil-$1Bil
Distrib.—Intl.
Limited Liability Company
AKA: Evex Analytical

**FEDEX OFFICE & PRINT CENTER**
Div. of FedEx Office & Print
Services, Inc.
Highway 1 & 731 Nassau (08540)
Phone—(609) 799-2863
National—(800) 254-6567
Fax—(609) 799-4568
www.fedex.com
Email—usa1216@fedex.com
Br. Mgr.—John Schwartz
SIC—2752; NAICS—323100;
Instant printing
Employs—18; Estab.—2003
Distrib.—Intl.
Publicly owned corporation
Parent co.—FedEx Office & Print
Services, Inc., Dallas, TX
Phone—(214) 550-7000
See Parent Co. Section for full profile.

**GALLUS BIOPHARMACEUTICALS
NEW JERSEY, LLC**
Div. of Gallus BioPharmaceuticals,
LLC
201 College Rd. E. (08540)
Phone—(609) 919-3300
(609) 919-3390
www.gallusbiopharma.com
Email—info@gallusbiopharma.com
Pres., CEO—Mark R. Bamforth
CFO—Steve Kasok
Sr. V-P., Bus. Dev.—Robert Broeze
Cont. & Sr. Dir.—Todd Tobiasz
Sr. Dir., Opers.—Jeff Strand
SIC—2834; NAICS—325412;
Contract manufacturing of
pharmaceuticals
Employs—90; Estab.—1999
Sales—$1Mil-$2.5Mil
Distrib.—Local
Privately owned corporation

GEOGRAPHICAL

# Princeton—(cont.)

Parent co.—Gallus
BioPharmaceuticals, LLC, St.
Louis, MO
Phone—(314) 426-5000
See Parent Co. Section for full profile.

**HEARTLAND PAYMENT SYSTEMS, INC. (H Q)**

90 Nassau St., 2nd Fl. (08542)
**Phone—(609) 683-3831**
National—(888) 798-3131
Fax—(609) 683-3815
www.heartlandpaymentsystems.com
Email—info@
heartlandpaymentsystems.com
CEO—Robert O. Carr
CAO—Joe White
Dir., Fin. Plng. & Sys.—Robert
Taratuski
SIC—3578; *Corporate
headquarters; electronic cash
systems with smart card & off-
line magnetic stripe card
applications*
Employs—25; Estab.—1995
Sales—$5Mil-$10Mil (est)
Distrib.—National
Privately owned corporation

**INPHOT, INC.**

3490 W. Route 1 (08540)
**Phone—(609) 750-0992**
Fax—(609) 750-0993
Email—krlinga@yahoo.com
Pres.—Krishna Linga
SIC—3661; *Telecommunication
equipment components*
Employs—3; Estab.—1998
Sales—under $500,000
Distrib.—Local
Privately owned corporation

**JACOBUS PHARMACEUTICAL CO., INC.**

37 Cleveland Ln. *(08540-5290)*
Mail addr: P.O. Box 5290,
Princeton (08543-5290)
**Phone—(609) 921-7447**
Fax—(609) 799-1176
Email—LRJacobus@aol.com
Ptnr.—David Jacobus
Ptnr.—Laura Jacobus
Site Mgr.—Rich Pursell
SIC—2834; NAICS—325412;
*Corporate headquarters;
prescription pharmaceuticals;
Brand name—Dapsone USP 100
mg; Dapsone USP 25 mg;
PASER Delayed Release
Aminosalicylic Acid*
Employs—52; Estab.—1977
Sales—$10Mil-$25Mil
Distrib.—Intl.
Privately owned corporation

**JACOBUS PHARMACEUTICAL CO., INC.**

P.O. Box 5290 (08540)
**Phone—(609) 799-8221**
Email—laura.jacobus@jacobus-
pharmaceutical.com
Owner—Laura Jacobus
SIC—2834; *Prescription
pharmaceuticals; Brand name—
Dapsone USP 100 mg; Dapsone
USP 25 mg; PASER Delayed
Release Aminosalicylic Acid*
Employs—45; Estab.—1980
Sales—$25Mil-$50Mil
Distrib.—Intl.
Privately owned corporation
Parent co.—Jacobus
Pharmaceutical Co., Inc.,
Princeton, NJ
Phone—(609) 921-7447
See Parent Co. Section for full profile.

**KAVAYAH SOLUTIONS, INC.**

5 Independence Way, Ste. 360
(08540)
**Phone—(609) 919-9797**
Fax—(609) 919-9679
www.kavayahsolutions.com
Email—info@kavayahsolutions.com
Pres.—Vivek Casula
SIC—7373; *Computer network
systems integration, including
LANs & WANs & custom
programming & IT consulting
services*
Employs—18
Distrib.—Intl.
Privately owned corporation

**KOAMTAC, INC.**

116 Village Blvd., Ste. 305 (08540)
**Phone—(609) 256-4700**
Fax—(609) 228-4373
www.koamtac.com
Email—info@koamtac.com
Pres.—Hanjin Lee
SIC—3577; *Programmable
wireless data exchanging bar
code & card readers*
Employs—10
Sales—$2.5Mil-$5Mil (est)
Distrib.—Regional
Privately owned corporation

**KREMERS URBAN
PHARMACEUTICALS, INC. (H Q)**

902 Carnegie Ctr., Ste. 360
(08540)
**Phone—(609) 936-5940**
Fax—(609) 275-5352
www.kremersurban.com
Email—frank.stiefel@ucb.com
Pres., CEO—George Stevenson
V-P., CFO—Mary Ellen Champion
Chief Comml. Officer—Frank
Stiefel
V-P., R & D—Xiu Xiu Cheng
V-P., Qual. Assur., Control &
Regulatory Affs.—Susan Witham
SIC—2834; *Corporate
headquarters; specialty generic
pharmaceuticals; Brand name—
Monoket; Unierex; Mono-Gesic;
Univasc; Colyte; Verelan;
Cortifoam; Proctofoam*
Employs—14
Sales—$5Mil-$10Mil (est)
Distrib.—Intl.

**LEARNING ALLY**

20 Roszel Rd. (08540)
**Phone—(609) 452-0606**
National—(800) 221-4792
Fax—(609) 520-7990
www.learningally.org
Email—custserv@learningally.org
Pres., CEO—Andrew Friedman
Chief Prodn. & Tech. Officer—
Peter Beran
CDO—Connie Murphy
Ex. V-P.—Jim Halliday
V-P., Revenue Opers.—Jeffrey
Klein
V-P., Hum. Res.—Patricia Wilus
SIC—3652; *Company
headquarters & audio book
production for readers with
disabilities*
Employs—100; Estab.—1948
Sales—$10Mil-$25Mil
Distrib.—National

**LIEF GROUP, INC., PHILIP**

371 Sayre Dr. (08540)
**Phone—(609) 430-1000**
www.plg.us.com
Pres.—Philip Lief
Off. Mgr.—Mary Fidil
SIC—2731; *Book publishing*
Employs—4; Estab.—1996
Distrib.—National
Privately owned corporation

**LIGHTSCAPE MATERIALS, INC.**

Div. of Dow Chemical Co., The
201 Washington Rd. (08540)
**Phone—(609) 734-2227**
 (609) 734-2224
Fax—(609) 734-2249
www.dowelectronicmaterials.com
Email—jcpoinsett@dow.com
Comml. Dir., Phosphor Matls.—
Gerard Frederickson
Dir., R & D, Phosphors—Yongchi
Tian
Off. Mgr.—Jennifer Poinsett
Prod. Dev. Mgr.—Alan Thomas
SIC—2865; *Novel phosphors for
the LED lighting industry*
Employs—15; Estab.—2009
Distrib.—Intl.
Publicly owned corporation
Parent co.—Dow Chemical Co.,
The, Midland, MI
Phone—(989) 636-1000
See Parent Co. Section for full profile.

**LINGRAPHICARE AMERICA, INC.**

103 Carnegie Ctr., Ste. 204
(08540)
**Phone—(609) 275-1300**
National—(888) 274-2742
Fax—(609) 275-1311
www.aphasia.com
Email—info@lingraphica.com
CEO—Andrew Gomory
Hum. Res. Mgr.—Lynn Buschman
Off. Admn.—Larissa Cyran
SIC—3679; *Electronic interface
communication devices for
aphasia patients*
Employs—25; Estab.—1990
Distrib.—National
Privately owned corporation
AKA: Lingraphica

**LUCY'S RAVIOLI KITCHEN &
MARKET**

830 State Rd. (08540)
**Phone—(609) 924-3623**
National—(888) 728-4654
Fax—(609) 279-9118
www.lucystogo.com
Email—info@lucystogo.com
Pres.—Caron Wendell
Asst. Mgr.—Gwen Comollo
Bookkeeper—Louise Taback
SIC—2099; *Ravioli & pasta*
Employs—8; Estab.—1991
Sales—$500,000-$1Mil
Distrib.—Regional
Privately owned corporation

**M M T C, INC.**

12 Roszel Rd., Ste. A-203 (08540)
**Phone—(609) 520-9699**
Fax—(609) 520-9859
www.mmtc.net
Email—fred@mmtc.com
Pres.—Fred Sterzer
SIC—3631; NAICS—335221;
*Microwave equipment
engineering*
Employs—3; Estab.—1988
Sales—$500,000-$1Mil
Distrib.—Intl.

**MAYFAIR TECHNOLOGY, LLC**

66 Witherspoon St. (08542)
**Phone—(609) 802-1262**
Fax—(609) 784-7889
www.pendotech.com
Email—request@pendotech.com
Member & GM—James Furey
Off. Mgr.—April Hagadorn
Tech. Mgr.—Dennis Annarelli
SIC—3829; 3679; *Single-use
pressure sensors*
Employs—10; Estab.—2001
Sales—$1Mil-$2.5Mil (est)
Distrib.—Intl.
Limited Liability Company
DBA: PendoTECH

**METAL POWDER INDUSTRIES
FEDERATION**

105 College Rd. E. (08540)
**Phone—(609) 452-7700**
Fax—(609) 987-8523
www.mpif.org
Email—info@mpif.org
CEO & Ex. Dir.—C. James
Trombino
V-P., Admn. & Fin.—Jill Regan
V-P., Indl. Rels.—James R. Dale
Registrar—Judy Wuensch
SIC—2721; 2741; *Trade magazine
publishing for the metal powder
producing & consuming
industries & trade association*
Employs—14; Estab.—1944
Sales—$1Mil-$2.5Mil
Distrib.—Intl.

**MIKROS SYSTEMS CORP.**

707 Alexander Rd. (08540)
**Phone—(609) 987-1513**
Fax—(609) 987-8114
www.mikrossystems.com
Pres.—Thomas Meaney
V-P., Engrg.—Walter Bristow
SIC—3663; NAICS—334220;
*Wireless communication systems*
Employs—25; Estab.—1977
Distrib.—Intl.

**MOOFWD, INC.**

103 Carnegie Ctr., Ste. 209
(08540)
**Phone—(855) 266-6393**
Fax—(732) 422-6445
www.moofwd.com
Email—info@moofwd.com
Founder & Chrm.—Sunil Mehta
COO—Suresh Menon
Dir., Bus. Dev.—Thomas Szwech
Dir., Bus. Dev.—Tom Cibelli
SIC—7372; *Mobile application
software development*
Employs—10; Estab.—2009
Distrib.—Intl.
Privately owned corporation

**MULTIFORCE SYSTEMS CORP.**

101 Wall St. *(08540)*
**Phone—(609) 683-4242**
Fax—(609) 683-4835
www.fuelforce.com
Email—sales@fuelforce.com
V-P., Sales—Keith Griesinger
Prodn. Mgr.—David Seminara
SIC—3672; 3823; 3824; 7372;
NAICS—334412; *Automated fuel
management systems that
authorize & control the
dispensing of fuel to fleet
vehicles for federal, state & local
governments, transit authorities,
the Armed Forces, utility
companies & construction &
trucking facilities; Brand name—
FuelForce; FuelServe;
FuelServe.net; Exacta; WAVE*
Employs—19; Estab.—1990
Sales—$5Mil
4,500 sq ft site, Distrib.—National
Privately owned corporation
AKA: J B Electronics

**NELSON GLASS & ALUMINUM CO., INC.**

45 Spring St. (08542)
**Phone—(609) 924-2880**
Fax—(609) 924-6496
Pres.—Roberta Nelson
Off. Mgr.—Alice Kent
SIC—3231; NAICS—327215;
*Commercial & residential glass
products, including shower
doors & enclosures, mirrors &
tabletops & installation services*
Employs—10; Estab.—1949
Sales—$500,000-$1Mil
Distrib.—Local
Privately owned corporation

# Princeton—(cont.)

**NEOSTRATA COMPANY, INC. (H Q)**
307 College Rd. E. (08540)
**Phone—(609) 520-0715**
National—(800) 628-9904
Fax—(609) 520-0849
www.neostrata.com
Email—custsvc@neostrata.com
CEO—Mark D. Steele
V.-P., Sales & Mktg.—Kathy Dwyer
V.-P., Opers.—Hany Salama
V.-P., Consumer & Technical Affs.—
  Barbara Green
V.-P., Fin.—Dennis Reilly
SIC—2844; NAICS—325600;
  *Corporate headquarters; skin
  care products (mfg.
  subcontracted); Brand name—
  NeoStrata; Exuviance;
  Coverblend; Psorent*
Employs—60; Estab.—1988
Sales—$25Mil-$50Mil
Distrib.—Intl.
Sole ownership

**NEW JERSEY JOURNAL OF
PHARMACY**
760 Alexander Rd. (08540)
**Phone—(609) 275-4246**
Fax—(609) 275-4066
www.njpharmacist.org
Email—njpha@njpharma.org
Publisher—Maria Leibfried
SIC—2721; *Pharmacy journal
  publishing*
Employs—4
Distrib.—National

**NIKSUN, INC.**
100 Nassau Park Blvd., 3rd Fl.
  (08540)
**Phone—(609) 936-9999**
National—(888) 504-3336
Fax—(609) 419-4260
www.niksun.com
CEO—Parag Pruthi
Hum. Res. Mgr.—Niti Sahni
SIC—7372; *Network monitoring
  software development; Brand
  name—NetDetector®; NetVCR²;
  NetOmni™*
Employs—100
Distrib.—Intl.
Privately owned corporation

**†NRG ENERGY, INC. (H Q)**
211 Carnegie Ctr. (08540)
**Phone—(609) 524-4500**
National—(800) 241-4674
Fax—(609) 524-4501
www.nrgenergy.com
Email—karen.cleeve@
  nrgenergy.com
Pres., CEO—David Crane
Ex. V.-P., Chief Operating Officer—
  Mauricio Gutierrez
CAO—Denise Wilson
CFO—Kirk Andrews
Sr. V.-P.—Bob Henry
Dir., IT—Stan Gorlick
SIC—5084; *Corporate
  headquarters; diverse energy
  provider, including steam,
  nuclear, wind & conventional
  electricity power plants &
  distributor of gas & diesel engine
  parts*
Employs—340
Sales—over $2Mil

NEW ENTRY
**OAVCO LTD., LLC**
103 Carnegie Ctr. (08540)
**Phone—(609) 454-5340**
National—(855) 525-4227
Fax—(609) 545-5394
www.oavco.com
Email—info@ovaco.com
Member—Mark Stuart

SIC—3728; *Aircraft bearings*
Employs—20; Estab.—2011
Sales—$2.6Mil-$5Mil
30,000 sq ft site, Distrib.—Intl.
Limited Liability Company
AKA: Oavco Bearings

**PENETONE CORP. (H Q)**
1000 Herrontown Rd., Ste. 2
  (08540-7716)
**Phone—(609) 921-0501**
Fax—(609) 924-4308
www.west-penetone.com
Email—solutions@penetone.com
Pres.—Elwood Phares
SIC—2819; 2842; NAICS—
  325612; *Corporate
  headquarters; cleaning
  compounds & cleaners for the
  petrochemical, pulp & paper,
  printing, military, aerospace,
  supermarkets & food processing
  industries; Brand name—
  Citrikleen; Wedac; Penkleen;
  Penblitz; Penpower; Penair;
  Pensolv*
Employs—3; Estab.—1865
Sales—$1Mil-$2.5Mil (est)
Distrib.—Intl.
Sole ownership
ISO rating—9001:2008

**PEQUOD COMMUNICATIONS, INC.**
743 Alexander Rd., Ste. 15
  (08540)
**Phone—(609) 951-0300**
Fax—(609) 951-0352
www.pequod.com
Email—slee@pequod.com
Pres.—Jim Robertson
V.-P.—Andre Liu
Cont.—Robin Klain
Dir., Opers.—Shaun Lee
SIC—2752; NAICS—323100;
  *Instant printing*
Employs—20; Estab.—1987
10,000 sq ft site, Distrib.—National
Privately owned corporation

**†PRINCETON COMPUTER SUPPORT,
INC.**
3490 U.S. Highway 1, Ste. 15-E
  (08540-5920)
**Phone—(609) 520-0770**
Fax—(609) 520-0774
www.pcsi-usa.com
Email—sales@pcsi-usa.com
Pres.—Kathleen Sneedse
V.-P.—Jonathan Sneedse
SIC—5045; *Distributor of IT
  network servers & hardware
  peripherals, including monitors,
  cabling, information technology
  products & phone systems;
  Brand name—Lenovo; IBM;
  Watchguard; Sonicwall;
  Microsoft; GFI; Panosonic;
  Cisco; Symantec*
Employs—7; Estab.—1985
Sales—$1.2Mil
1,500 sq ft site, Distrib.—Regional
Privately owned corporation
AKA: PCSI

**PRINCETON PACKET, INC.**
300 Witherspoon St., P.O. Box 350
  (08542)
**Phone—(609) 924-3244**
Fax—(609) 921-2714
www.centraljersey.com
Email—feedback@
  centraljersey.com
Pres.—Jim Kilgore
CFO—Margaret Gerke
Dir., Adv.—Jim DeFillipo
Dir., IT & Prepress—Jack Francis
Dir., Hum. Res.—Ali Haider
Dir., Circ.—Michele Nesbihal
GM—Bradley Koltz

SIC—2711; *Newspaper
  publishing*
Employs—131; Estab.—1980
Sales—$1Mil-$5Mil
Distrib.—Regional
Privately owned corporation
AKA: Packet Media Group

**PRINCETON PAYMENT SOLUTIONS**
501 Forrestal Rd., Ste. 324
  (08540)
Mail addr.—116 Village Blvd., Ste.
  320, Princeton (08540)
**Phone—(609) 919-0700**
www.prinpay.com
CEO—Kevin M. McGuire
Dir.—Marilee Thompson
Mktg. Mgr.—Stephanie Levine
SIC—7372; *Credit card payment
  processing & encryption
  software development; Brand
  name—CardConnect;
  CardSecure*
Employs—20; Estab.—2004
Sales—$1Mil-$2.5Mil
Distrib.—Intl.
Limited Liability Company
AKA: PPS

**PRINCETON PRINTER**
150 Nassau St. (08542)
**Phone—(609) 924-4630**
Fax—(609) 683-9653
www.princetonprinter.com
Email—info@princetonprinter.com
CEO—Bill Howard
Principal—Cecelia Howard
Manager—Sherene Parks
SIC—2752; 2759; 2789; 3993;
  NAICS—323100; *Digital, instant
  & large-format color printing &
  binding of engineering
  blueprints, legal documents,
  thesis & related documents &
  vinyl signs & banners*
Employs—6; Estab.—1984
1,800 sq ft site, Distrib.—Local
Privately owned sub-S corp.

**PRINCETON UNIVERSITY PRESS**
41 William St. (08540)
**Phone—(609) 258-4900**
National—(800) 777-4726
Fax—(609) 258-6305
www.press.princeton.edu
Email—webmaster@
  press.princeton.edu
Dir.—Peter Dougherty
Sales Mgr.—Timothy Wilkins
Mktg. Mgr.—Adam Fortgang
IT Mgr.—Michael Volk
Hum. Res. Mgr.—Carol Swoboda
SIC—2731; *Manuscript & book
  publishing*
Employs—85; Estab.—1905
Sales—$20Mil-$25Mil
Distrib.—Intl.
Privately owned corporation

**RANBAXY, INC. (H Q)**
600 College Rd. E., Ste. 2100
  (08540)
**Phone—(609) 720-9200**
        (609) 720-8033
Fax—(609) 720-1155
www.ranbaxy.com
Email—info.unitedstates@
  ranbaxy.com
V.-P., Hum. Res.—Bernard
  Brothman
V.-P., Comm. & Govt. Affs.—
  Charles Caprariello
SIC—2834; *Corporate
  headquarters; pharmaceuticals;
  Brand name—Cefactor*
Employs—65; Estab.—1994
Company-wide: 650
Sales—$25Mil-$50Mil (est)
Distrib.—National
Privately owned corporation

**RIPEN INTERACTIVE, LLC**
117 Rockingham Row (08540)
**Phone—(609) 520-8820**
Fax—(609) 520-8810
www.ri.pn
Email—contact@ri.pn
Owner—Michael Tudor
SIC—7373; *Computer network
  system integration, including
  LANs & WANs*
Employs—30; Estab.—2003
1,000 sq ft site, Distrib.—National
Limited Liability Company
AKA: Ripen eCommerce

**ROCKWOOD HOLDINGS, INC. (H Q)**
100 Overlook Ctr., 1st Fl. (08540)
**Phone—(609) 514-0300**
Fax—(609) 514-8720
www.rocksp.com
Email—rzatta@rocksp.com
Chrm.—Seifi Ghasemi
CEO & CFO—Robert J. Zatta
V.-P., Comm. & Inv. Rels.—Nahla
  Azmy
Dir., Hum. Res.—Donna Abrunzo
SIC—2899; 3674; 3087; 3672;
  NAICS—334413; *Corporate
  headquarters; specialty
  chemicals for the pool & spa,
  printed circuit board & inorganic
  wood treatment industries,
  silicon wafers, thermoplastic
  compounds, alloys, Bentonite
  clay & thickening agents*
Employs—35; Estab.—2002
Sales—$10Mil-$25Mil (est)
6,000 sq ft site,
Publicly owned corporation
AKA: Rockwood Specialties

**SANDOZ, INC. (H Q)**
Div. of Novartis Pharmaceuticals
  Corp.
506 Carnegie Ctr., Ste. 400
  (08540-6243)
**Phone—(609) 627-8500**
National—(866) 262-3753
Fax—(609) 627-8684
www.us.sandoz.com
Email—sandra.collins@sandoz.com
Pres., U.S.A. & Head of N.A.—
  Peter Goldschmidt
CFO—James Mastakas
V.-P. & Reg. Head of Tech.
  Opers.—Jesus Corchero
V.-P., Hum. Res.—Rossana Gray
SIC—2834; NAICS—325412;
  *Corporate headquarters;
  pharmaceuticals*
Employs—200
Sales—$100Mil-$250Mil (est)
Distrib.—Local
Publicly owned corporation
Parent co.—Novartis
  Pharmaceuticals Corp., East
  Hanover, NJ
  Phone—(862) 778-8300
See Parent Co. Section for full profile.

**SARNOFF CORP.**
Div. of SRI International
201 Washington Rd. (08540)
**Phone—(609) 734-2000**
Fax—(609) 734-2040
www.sri.com
Email—bd@sri.com
Corp. Comm. Mgr.—Lou Ann
  Hodges
SIC—7373; NAICS—541512;
  *Electronic, biomedical,
  information technology, ICs,
  lasers, imagers, drug discovery,
  video for security, surveillance &
  entertainment, high-performance
  networking & wireless
  communications*
Employs—430; Estab.—1942
Distrib.—Intl.
Privately owned corporation

GEOGRAPHICAL

## Princeton—(cont.)

Parent co.—SRI International,
Menlo Park, CA
Phone—(650) 859-2000
See Parent Co. Section for full profile.

**SAWHNEY SYSTEMS, INC.**

777 Alexander Rd., Ste. 204
(08540)
**Phone—(609) 987-5000**
Fax—(609) 987-1212
www.sawhney.com
Email—info@sawhney.com
CEO—Jai Sawhney
Sales Mgr.—Robert Fourman
Off. Mgr.—Helen Austerlitz
Tech. Mgr.—Avi Zlatin
SIC—7372; Personal financial
planning software development;
Brand name—ExecPlan;
ExecPlan Express; TaxMode;
PlanMode
Employs—10; Estab.—1976
Distrib.—Intl.
Privately owned corporation

**SEIBEL GROUP, INC., THE**

741 Alexander Rd. (08540)
**Phone—(609) 799-3279**
Fax—(609) 987-0185
www.seibelgroup.com
Email—info@seibelgroup.com
Pres.—Kenneth Seibel
V.-P., Sales—Chris Chiachetti
Off. Mgr.—Debra Cronin
Off. Mgr.—Linda Deanglo
SIC—2759; 2752; NAICS—
323100; Commercial & digital
printing
Employs—11; Estab.—1974
10,000 sq ft site, Distrib.—National
Privately owned corporation
DBA: Easy Graphics Inc.

**SIGHTLOGIX, INC.**

745 Alexander Rd., Ste. 5 & 6
(08540)
**Phone—(609) 951-0008**
Fax—(609) 951-0024
www.sightlogix.com
Email—sales@sightlogix.com
Founder, Pres. & CEO—John
Romanowich
Chrm.—James Hahn
V.-P., Sales—Frank DeFina
V.-P., Admn. & Fin. & Hum. Res.
Mgr.—Gary Singer
Dir., Mktg.—Eric Heller
Dir., Intl.—Ivan Arrieta
IT Mgr.—Paul Yeh
SIC—3663; Thermal outdoor
video analytics cameras
Employs—23; Estab.—2004
Distrib.—Intl.
Privately owned corporation

**SOLIGENIX, INC.**

29 Emmons Dr., Ste. C-10 (08540)
**Phone—(609) 538-8200**
Fax—(609) 452-6467
www.soligenix.com
Email—info@soligenix.com
Pres., CEO—Christopher J.
Schaber
Sr. V.-P., CFO—Joe Wareusz
Sr. V.-P., CSO—Robert W. Brey
SIC—2834; Biopharmaceuticals &
vaccines; Brand name—orBec®
Employs—20; Estab.—2008
Sales—$10Mil-$25Mil (est)
Distrib.—Intl.

**ST ROBOTICS**

103 Carnagie Ctr., Ste. 300
(08540)
**Phone—(609) 584-7522**
www.strobotics.com
Email—sales@strobotics.com
Owner—David Sands
V.-P.—Mathew Monforte

SIC—3569; Industrial equipment
handling robots
Employs—5; Estab.—1983
Sales—under $500,000
Distrib.—Intl.
Privately owned corporation

**TBC PARTNERS, LLC**

743 Alexander Rd., Ste. 15
(08540-6328)
**Phone—(855) 937-6466**
www.mimomonitors.com
Email—info@mimomonitors.com
Pres., CEO—David Anderson
SIC—3577; Company
headquarters & miniature
touchscreen computer monitors
(mfg. done in South Korea);
Brand name—Mimo Monitors
Employs—15
Sales—$2.5Mil-$5Mil
Distrib.—Intl.
Limited Liability Company

**THERAPEDIC INTERNATIONAL, INC.
(H Q)**

103 College Rd. E., 2nd Fl.
(08540)
**Phone—(609) 720-0700**
National—(800) 314-4433
Fax—(609) 720-0797
www.therapedic.com
Email—info@therapedic.com
CEO—Gerry Borreggine
Off. Mgr.—Sharon Friedman
SIC—2515; Corporate
headquarters; mattresses (mfg.
subcontracted); Brand name—
Therapedic Sleep Products;
Pure Touch; Memory Touch
Employs—4; Estab.—2005
Distrib.—Intl.
Privately owned corporation

**THOMAS SWEET CHOCOLATES,
INC.**

29 Palmer Sq. W. (08542)
**Phone—(609) 924-7222**
Fax—(609) 683-7563
www.thomassweet.com
Email—thomassweet@verizon.net
Pres.—Marco Cucchi
Region Mgr.—Joanne Brown
Store Mgr.—Kimberly Oliver
SIC—2064; 2066; NAICS—
311300; Chocolate candy
Employs—6; Estab.—1980
Sales—under $500,000
Distrib.—Local
Privately owned corporation

**TOMORROW'S HEIRLOOMS
HANDCRAFTED GEMSTONE
JEWELRY**

2 Chambers St. (08542)
**Phone—(609) 921-9440**
www.tomorrowsheirloomsnj.com
Ptnr.—John Miller
Ptnr.—Margret Miller
SIC—3911; NAICS—339911;
Handcrafted gemstone jewelry
Employs—2; Estab.—1983
Sales—under $500,000
Distrib.—National
Privately owned partnership

**TYCO (H Q)**

9 Roszel Rd. (08540)
**Phone—(609) 720-4200**
National—(800) 320-2350
Fax—(609) 720-4208
www.tyco.com
Email—info@tyco.com
CEO—George Oliver
Ex. V.-P., CFO—Arun Nayar
COO—Brian McDonald
Sr. V.-P., CIO—John Repko
Sr. V.-P., Chief Proc. Officer—Vivek
Kamath
Ex. V.-P., Gen. Counsel—Judith
Reinsdorf
Ex. V.-P., Hum. Res.—Larry
Costello

V.-P., Global Comms.—Steve
Wasdick
Comms. Mgr.—Jaqueline Davis
SIC—3669; 3829; 3569; NAICS—
335921; Company headquarters;
security & fire protection systems
for new & existing facilities,
including intrusion, movement,
fire, smoke & flooding integrated
systems & fire detectors &
sprinklers, emergency
communications & nurse call
systems; Brand name—Scott
Safety; Visonic; Ansul; DSC;
Sensormatic; Simplex; Grinnell;
Wormald; Chemguard; TruVue;
Kantech; American Dynamics;
Hygood; Pyro-Chem; Software
House; Elpas; Bentel Security;
SprinkCAD; DBE
Employs—350
Sales—$10.5Bil
Distrib.—Intl.
Publicly owned corporation

**UTC AEROSPACE SYSTEMS-ISR
SYSTEMS (SENSORS UNLIMITED,
INC.)**

Div. of UTC Aerospace Systems,
ISR & Propeller Systems
330 Carter Rd., Ste. 100 (08540-
5914)
**Phone—(609) 520-0610**
Fax—(609) 333-8000
www.utcaerospacesystems.com
Email—communications@
utas.utc.com
Dir., Sales & Mktg.—Robert
Struthers
SIC—3674; NAICS—334413;
Infrared sensors & cameras
Employs—48; Estab.—1991
Sales—$20Mil-$30Mil
35,000 sq ft site, Distrib.—Intl.
Publicly owned corporation
ISO rating—9001
Parent co.—UTC Aerospace
Systems, ISR & Propeller
Systems, Westford, MA
Phone—(978) 303-6700
See Parent Co. Section for full profile.

**WIENER PUBLISHERS, INC.,
MARKUS**

231 Nassau St. (08542)
**Phone—(609) 921-1141**
Fax—(609) 921-1140
www.markuswiener.com
Email—publisher@
markuswiener.com
Pres.—Markus Wiener
SIC—2731; 2721; World history &
culture academic & trade book &
journal publishing, including
Caribbean, African, Latin
American & Middle-Eastern
history & culture
Employs—4
Sales—under $500,000 (est)

[NEW ENTRY]
**WORKERS' DISABILITY INCOME
SYSTEM, INC.**

56 Primrose Cir. (08540)
**Phone—(732) 274-0600**
Fax—(732) 647-1120
www.workerscompresources.com
Email—editor@
workerscompresources.com
Owner—John F. Burton, Jr.
SIC—2741; Newsletter publishing
Employs—5; Estab.—1974
Sales—under $500,000
200 sq ft site, Distrib.—National
Privately owned corporation

## Princeton Junction

(Mercer—N.E.)

**ALPHION CORP.**

196 Princeton Hightstown Rd.,
Bldg. 1-A, 2nd Fl. (08550-1672)
**Phone—(609) 936-9001**
Fax—(609) 936-9002
www.alphion.com
Email—info@alphion.com
Chrm., Pres. & CEO—Bharat P.
Dave
COO—Boris Stefanov
V.-P., Bus. Plng.—Chris Peterson
SIC—3663; 3669; NAICS—
334220; GPON-based optical
network access products for the
distribution of multiple-play
voice, high-speed data & video
services & back haul for wireless
networks; Brand name—
Alphion®
Employs—20; Estab.—2000
Sales—$10Mil-$25Mil
Distrib.—Intl.
Privately owned corporation

**AMERASIA INTERNATIONAL
TECHNOLOGY, INC.**

70 Washington Rd. (08550)
**Phone—(609) 799-9388**
Fax—(609) 799-9308
www.aitechnology.com
Email—ait@aitechnology.com
Pres., CEO—Kevin Chung
Ex. V.-P.—Cynthia Chu
Cont.—Mark Wells
Safety Mgr.—Michael Caracciolo
Qual. Assur. Mgr.—Richard
Carlson
SIC—2891; NAICS—325520;
Adhesives & epoxies for the
microelectronic industry,
including thermal management
films, greases & gels &
conductive & non-conductive
films & pastes for die-attach,
substrate, wafer lamination, LED,
semiconductor & computer
components; Brand name—
COOL-SILVER; COOL-BOND;
COOL-GELFILM; COOL-
GAPFILL; PRIMA-BOND
Employs—40; Estab.—1981
Sales—$10Mil-$25Mil
54,000 sq ft site, Distrib.—Intl.
Privately owned corporation
ISO rating—9001:2008
DBA: AI Technology, Inc.
Also see: Avante International
Technology, Inc., same loc.

**BIOMETALLICS, INC.**

37 Station Dr. (08550)
Mail addr.—P.O. Box 2251,
Princeton (08543)
**Phone—(609) 275-0133**
National—(800) 999-1961
Fax—(609) 275-9485
www.microplate.com
Email—info@microplate.com
Pres.—Christa Kuehn
V.-P., Fin. Mgr.—Karen Pieta
MIS Mgr.—J. Perry
Off. Mgr.—V. Cheng
SIC—3841; 3826; NAICS—
334516; Diagnostic veterinary
test kits & microplate analysis
software development
Employs—12; Estab.—1984
Sales—$500,000-$1Mil
10,000 sq ft site, Distrib.—Intl.
Privately owned corporation

**FUNNIBONZ, LLC**

3 Lake View Ct. (08550)
**Phone—(877) 300-2669**
Fax—(609) 845-1806
www.funnibonz.com
Email—info@funnibonz.com
Pres., CEO—James H. Barbour III
Gen. Counsel—Ryan Marrone

## Princeton Junction— (cont.)

SIC—2033; 2035; 2034; *Barbecue sauces, marinades, relishes & dry rubs; Brand name— FunniBonz Original Barbeque Sauce; FunniBonz Spicy Barbeque Sauce; FunniBonz Fiery Chipotle Barbeque Sauce; FunniBonz Sweet & Tangy Mustard Barbeque Sauce*
Employs—5; Estab.—2008
Sales—$1Mil-$2.5Mil
Distrib.—Intl.
Limited Liability Company

**LUCID TECHNOLOGIES, LLC**
231 Clarksville Rd. (08550)
**Phone—(609) 277-4138**
www.lucidcom.com
Email—info@lucidcom.com
Mng. Member—Bharath Khambadkone
Acct. Mgr.—Sanjay Kumar
SIC—7373; *Computer network systems integration*
Employs—13; Estab.—2012
Limited Liability Company

**MED A-Z.NET, LLC**
37 Station Dr., Ste. 1-E (08550)
**Phone—(609) 716-6991**
National—(888) 633-2972
Fax—(609) 228-6341
www.medaz.net
Email—sales@medaz.net
CIO—Vasu S. Iyengar
V-P., Sales—Steve Popple
SIC—7372; *Healthcare software development*
Employs—9; Estab.—1997
Sales—$500,000-$1Mil
Distrib.—National
Limited Liability Company

**MISTRAS GROUP, INC.**
195 Clarksville Rd. (08550)
**Phone—(609) 585-5588**
          (609) 716-4100
          (609) 716-4150
Fax—(609) 716-0706
www.mistrasgroup.com
Email—sales@mistrasgroup.com
Chrm., CEO—Sotirios Vahaviolos
Ex. V-P.—Mark Carlos
V-P., Opers.—Michael Farahani
V-P., PDM Prods. & Svcs.— Michael Burch
Mktg. Mgr.—Nestor S. Makarigakis
MIS Mgr.—Pam Grigas
Mktg. Svcs. Mgr.—Katie Monte
Qual. Assur. Mgr.—Norman Sondheim
Cust. Serv. Mgr.—Donald Potts
SIC—3829; 3679; NAICS— 334515; *Nondestructive ultrasonic & acoustic testing equipment & engineering services; Brand name— VibraMetrics; Physical Acoustics*
Employs—150; Estab.—1978
Company-wide: 3,500
Distrib.—Intl.
Publicly owned corporation
ISO rating—9001:2000

**R-SQUARED SERVICES & SOLUTIONS, INC.**
12 Dean Ct. (08550)
**Phone—(866) 522-8558**
Fax—(609) 778-4295
www.r2ss.com
Email—info@r2ss.com
CEO—Michael D. Bell
Hum. Res. & Off. Mgr.—Aimee Capaldi
SIC—7372; *Compliance software development for the life sciences industry*
Employs—70; Estab.—2004
6,000 sq ft site, Distrib.—Intl.
Privately owned corporation

## SCHLUMBERGER-PRINCETON TECHNOLOGY CENTER

Div. of Schlumberger Ltd.
20 Wallace Rd. (08550)
**Phone—(609) 799-1000**
Fax—(609) 897-8506
www.slb.com
Email—ptccustserv@slb.com
Pers. Mgr.—Henrietta Ayewoh
Env., Health & Safety Specialist— Sherre Wallace
SIC—3671; NAICS—334411; *Ceramic & glass photomultiplier tubes*
Employs—40; Estab.—1960
Sales—$5Mil-$10Mil (est)
50,000 sq ft site, Distrib.—National
Publicly owned corporation
Parent co.—Schlumberger Ltd., Houston, TX
    Phone—(713) 513-2000
    See Parent Co. Section for full profile.

**SEW MANY GIFTS, INC.**
6 Cranston Ct. (08550)
**Phone—(609) 275-4532**
www.sewmanygifts.com
Email—eva@sewmanygifts.com
Pres.—Eva Tootleman
SIC—2395; *Textile embroidery & monogramming*
Employs—1; Estab.—2001
Sales—under $500,000
Distrib.—Local
Sole ownership

**SIMX CORP.**
196 Princeton-Hightstown Rd., Bldg. 2-A (08550)
**Phone—(609) 750-9345**
Fax—(609) 750-9349
www.simx.com
Email—support@simx.com
Pres.—Vladimir Bernstein
Dir.—Andrei Afanassenkov
SIC—7372; *Data extraction & conversion software development & custom application development & consulting services*
Employs—6; Estab.—1993
Sales—$500,000-$1Mil
Distrib.—Intl.
Privately owned corporation

**SOUTH MILL DESIGN, LLC**
131 S. Mill Rd. (08550)
**Phone—(877) 466-0273**
Fax—(877) 466-0273
www.phubby.com
Email—info@phubby.com
Co-Founder—Ted Ross
SIC—2389; *Textile cellphone accessories, including wristband carrying pouches; Brand name—Phubby™*
Employs—3; Estab.—2007
Sales—under $500,000
2,000 sq ft site, Distrib.—Intl.
Limited Liability Company

## Prospect Park

(Passaic—N.E.)

**ENVELOPES & PRINTED PRODUCTS, INC.**
135 Fairview Ave. (07508)
**Phone—(973) 942-1232**
Fax—(973) 942-5626
www.envelopesandprintedproducts.com
Email—envelopro@aol.com
Pres., CEO—William F. Higgins

SIC—2759; 3497; NAICS— 323100; *Envelope & business card printing, foil stamping & embossing*
Employs—10; Estab.—1978
Sales—$1Mil
6,000 sq ft site, Distrib.—National
Privately owned corporation
Also see: SourceCodes & Displays, Inc., same loc.

**IMAGINE CORP., THE**
320 N. 6th St. (07508)
**Phone—(973) 942-2888**
Fax—(973) 942-2988
www.theimaginecorp.com
Email—cs@theimaginecorp.com
Cust. Serv. Mgr.—Julie Ann Karr
SIC—3089; *Plastic products*
Employs—15; Estab.—1998
21,000 sq ft site, Distrib.—National
Limited Liability Company
AKA: Imagine America, LLC

**SOURCECODES & DISPLAYS, INC.**
135 Fairview Ave. (07508)
**Phone—(973) 942-1965**
Fax—(973) 942-5626
www.specialtyprinting.com
Email—envelopro@aol.com
Pres., CEO—William F. Higgins
SIC—2759; NAICS—323100; *Display box & letterhead commercial printing*
Employs—5; Estab.—1999
Sales—$500,000-$1Mil (est)
Distrib.—National
Privately owned corporation
Also see: Envelopes & Printed Products, Inc., same loc.

## Quakertown

(Hunterdon—N.W.)

**OASIS STUDIOS, LLC**
244 Quakertown Rd., P.O. Box 306 (08868)
**Phone—(908) 735-5089**
www.oasisstudiosnj.com
Email—oasisstudios@erols.com
Ptnr.—Joe Muller
Ptnr.—Kim Muller
SIC—2396; 2395; *Textile screen printing, embroidery & graphic design*
Employs—2; Estab.—1985
Sales—under $500,000
Distrib.—Local
Limited Liability Company

## Rahway

(Union—N.E.)

**A&M INDUSTRIAL, INC.**
37 W. Cherry St., P.O. Box 1044 (07065)
**Phone—(732) 574-1111**
National—(800) 864-2660
Fax—(732) 574-2081
www.am-ind.com
Email—sales@am-ind.com
Pres.—Arnold Young
Ex. V-P.—David Young
Ex. Dir., Bus. Dev.—Kevin Rosenthal
Dir., Opers.—Tom Richards

SIC—3491; NAICS—333111; *Corporate headquarters & industrial equipment, including actuated & high-purity valves, gaskets, fittings, boiler controls, industrial hoses & hose assemblies, v-belts, metallic, coated & composite piping & steam system components; Brand name—Ridgid; Apollo; Velan; Gestra ; Ashcroft; MSA; North Safety; 3M; Iscar*
Employs—100; Estab.—1954
Sales—$10Mil-$25Mil
100,000 sq ft site, Distrib.— Regional
Privately owned corporation

**A-1 BUSINESS SERVICE**
P.O. Box 83 (07065)
**Phone—(732) 910-6995**
Fax—(732) 680-0999
Pres.—William Mendelson
V-P. & Off. Mgr.—Nina Zammit
SIC—2759; NAICS—323100; *Commercial printing*
Employs—2; Estab.—1960
Sales—under $500,000
Distrib.—Regional
Privately owned corporation

**A-AFFORDABLE SIGN.COM**
1053 Madison Hill Rd. (07065)
**Phone—(732) 287-0446**
www.a-affordablesign.com
Email—info@a-affordablesign.com
GM—Jim Miggioze
SIC—3993; 3089; *Custom signs & vinyl lettering*
Employs—12; Estab.—1987
Distrib.—Local
Privately owned corporation

**AIRTEC, INC.**
17 W. Scott Ave., P.O. Box 1181 (07065)
**Phone—(732) 382-3700**
Fax—(732) 388-0084
Email—airtecunique@aol.com
Pres.—Joseph M. Niemczyk, Sr.
Treas.—Claire J. Niemczyk
Dir., Sales—Joseph S. Niemczyk, Jr.
GM—Frank Tremmel
SIC—3444; *Sheet metal fabrication, machining & laser cutting*
Employs—9; Estab.—1960
Sales—over $1Mil
40,000 sq ft site, Distrib.—Local
Privately owned sub-S corp.
Also see: Unique Metal Products Co., Inc., same loc.

**AMERICAN PLASTIC CO.**
2137 Highway 1 (07065)
**Phone—(732) 388-1601**
Owner—Stephen Korstein
SIC—3993; 3089; *Plastic sign letters & numbers*
Employs—3; Estab.—1958
Sales—under $500,000
Distrib.—National

**API FOILS, INC.**
329 New Brunswick Ave. (07065)
**Phone—(732) 382-6800**
Fax—(732) 382-8760
www.apigroup.com
Email—marketing@api-foils.com
Pres.—Brad Mueller
V-P., Sales & Mktg.—Bob Witte
Plt. Mgr.—Ralph Acanfora
Hum. Res. Mgr.—Laura Lipinski
SIC—2759; NAICS—323100; *Hot stamping foil*
Employs—85; Estab.—1963
Sales—$50Mil-$100Mil
260,000 sq ft site, Distrib.—Intl.
Publicly owned corporation

GEOGRAPHICAL

## Rahway—(cont.)

**ARTISTIC PRODUCTS, LLC**
1905 Elizabeth Ave. (07065)
**Phone—(732) 382-4141**
Fax—(732) 382-2471
Email—artisticbias@comcast.net
Pres.—Daniel Berg
SIC—2299; *Lampshade components & textile pleating*
Employs—60; Estab.—1938
Sales—$26Mil-$50Mil
Distrib.—National
Limited Liability Company

**†ASSOCIATED PLASTICS, INC.**
179 E. Inman Ave. (07065)
**Phone—(732) 574-2800**
Fax—(732) 574-2807
www.associatedplasticsinc.com
Email—info@ associatedplasticsinc.com
Pres.—Richard W. Fisher
SIC—5162; 5085; NAICS— 326199; *Distributor of plastic pull straps, twist & cable ties & grade level & underground enclosures*
Employs—3
Distrib.—Local
Privately owned corporation

**ASTRO TOOL & MACHINE CO., INC.**
810 Martin St. (07065)
**Phone—(732) 382-2450**
          (732) 382-2402
Fax—(732) 382-6394
www.astrotoolco.com
Email—astro@astrotoolco.com
Pres., R & D Mgr.—Gary Price
Fin. Mgr.—Rose Feliciano
SIC—3541; 3452; NAICS— 333512; *Precision machine tools, including CNC grinding & waterjet cutting services*
Employs—25; Estab.—1965
15,000 sq ft site, Distrib.—Intl.
Privately owned sub-S corp.

**ATLANTIC AIR ENTERPRISES**
856 Elston St. *(07065)*
**Phone—(732) 381-4000**
          (732) 381-4016
          (800) 899-4279
Fax—(732) 499-0122
www.atlanticairent.com
Email—contactus@ atlanticairent.com
Pres., GM & Supv.—Darin Severino
Cont.—Tina Cottingham
SIC—3444; *HVAC ducts*
Employs—15; Estab.—1941
Sales—$1Mil-$5Mil
11,400 sq ft site, Distrib.—Local
Privately owned corporation

**BABINEC SHEET METAL WORKS, INC., JOSEPH**
774 Martin St. (07065)
**Phone—(732) 388-6600**
Fax—(732) 382-2018
www.babinecmetal.com
Email—jason.bab@verizon.net
CEO—Joseph T. Babinec
Pres.—Jason Babinec
Hum. Res. Mgr.—Marilene Aldes
SIC—3444; 3499; *Metal fabrication of store fixtures & point-of-purchase displays*
Employs—50; Estab.—1956
42,000 sq ft site, Distrib.—National
Privately owned corporation

**BANDA ORIENTAL, INC.**
777 W. Grand Ave. (07065-3420)
**Phone—(732) 388-8383**
www.bandaoriental.net
Email—bandaori@gmail.com
Publisher & Editor—Julia Moreira

SIC—2711; *Monthly newspaper publishing*
Employs—5
Sales—under $500,000
Privately owned corporation

**CMD MEDIA**
P.O. Box 1061 (07065)
**Phone—(732) 574-1200**
www.njtoday.net
Email—sales@njtoday.net
Publisher—Lisa McCormick
Editor—Peter Rendell
SIC—2741; *Newspaper publishing; Brand name— NJToday.Net*
Employs—14; Estab.—1822
Sales—$500,000-$1Mil
Distrib.—Local
Privately owned corporation

**D P J SIGNS**
245 E. Inman Ave. (07065)
**Phone—(732) 499-8600**
Fax—(732) 499-8623
Email—dpj@aol.com
Pres.—Derrick Dehoyo
SIC—3993; *Interior & exterior signs*
Employs—4; Estab.—1998
Distrib.—National
Privately owned corporation

**DASON STAINLESS PRODUCTS CO.**
1773 Elizabeth Ave. (07065)
**Phone—(732) 382-7272**
National—(800) 526-4346
Fax—(732) 382-7145
www.dasonstainless.com
Email—sales@dasonstainless.com
Pres.—William Thompson
Off. Mgr.—Rose Cummings
SIC—3432; NAICS—332900; *Stainless steel pipe fittings*
Employs—9; Estab.—1959
Sales—$1Mil-$2.5Mil
Distrib.—National
Privately owned corporation

**DRAPKIN PRINTING CO.**
1850 Elizabeth Ave., Ste. 1 (07065)
**Phone—(732) 381-2228**
Fax—(732) 396-3999
www.drapkinprinting.com
Email—drapco1@aol.com
Owner—Owen Drapkin
Off. Mgr.—Helene Drapkin
SIC—2759; NAICS—323100; *Commercial printing*
Employs—3; Estab.—1936
Sales—under $500,000
2,400 sq ft site, Distrib.—National
Limited Liability Company

**ELECTRONIC MARINE SYSTEMS**
800 Ferndale Pl. (07065)
**Phone—(732) 382-4344**
Fax—(732) 388-5111
www.emsmarcon.com
Email—emsmarcon@aol.com
Pres., GM—Thomas J. Priola
V-P., Opers.—Nic Depalma
Corp. Secy. & Off. Mgr.—Joyce Kopacz
Pur. Mgr.—Jeanne Priola
SIC—3571; NAICS—334111; *Control, monitoring & tank gaging systems for ships; Brand name—emsmarcon*
Employs—25; Estab.—1979
15,000 sq ft site, Distrib.—Intl.
Privately owned corporation
ISO rating—9002

**†ELECTRUM, INC.**
827 Martin St. *(07065)*
**Phone—(732) 396-1616**
          (800) 622-1192
Fax—(732) 396-9390
www.electruminc.com
Email—mdouglas@ electruminc.com
Pres.—Jack Douglas

V-P.—John Silva
Sales Mgr., Regional—John Atcachunas
Sales Mgr., Regional—Dan Trump
Off. Mgr.—Donna Helm
Fin. Mgr.—Don Savage
SIC—5093; *Wholesaler of eco- friendly recycled solder & precious metals from reclaimed materials from the electronic manufacturing industry*
Employs—15; Estab.—1976
Sales—$9.4Mil
20,000 sq ft site, Distrib.—Intl.
Privately owned corporation

**†ELIXENS AMERICA, INC.**
1443 Pinewood St. (07065)
**Phone—(732) 388-3555**
Fax—(732) 388-3565
www.elixensamerica.com
Email—aroman@ elixensamerica.com
Pres.—Adam Roman
SIC—5199; 5149; *Distributor of organic essential oils, herbs, spices, vegetable oils, aromatic raw chemicals, balsams & gums*
Employs—3; Estab.—1997
5,000 sq ft site, Distrib.—National
Privately owned corporation

**EXTRA OFFICE, INC.**
580 Leesville Ave. (07065)
**Phone—(732) 381-9773**
Fax—(732) 381-9753
www.extraoffice.net
Email—kmacdonald@extraoffice.net
Pres.—Louis Prince, Jr.
Mktg. Mgr.—Carrie McDonald
SIC—2521; 2522; NAICS— 337211; *Metal & wooden office furniture*
Employs—12; Estab.—1985
Sales—under $500,000
Distrib.—Regional
Privately owned corporation

**EXTREME CONCEPTS, LLC**
75 E. Cherry St., Ste. 9-B (07065)
**Phone—(732) 381-5100**
Fax—(732) 381-5101
Email—info@xtreme-concept.com
Ptnr. & Member—Joe Esses
Prod. Mgr.—Joe Rowley
SIC—2396; *Apparel screen printing*
Employs—10; Estab.—2007
Sales—$1Mil-$2.5Mil
Distrib.—National
Limited Liability Company

**FORTUNE RIVERSIDE AUTO PARTS, INC.**
Div. of Fortune Plastic & Metal, Inc.
900 Leesville Ave., P.O. Box 1589 (07065)
**Phone—(732) 381-3355**
Fax—(732) 381-7919
www.fortunegroup.net
Email—simonwong@ fortunegroup.net
V-P.—Simon Wong
Operating Supv.—Nicholas Lui
SIC—3341; *Scrap metal recycling*
Employs—50; Estab.—2006
Distrib.—Local
Privately owned corporation
AKA: Fortune Riverside Scrap
Parent co.—Fortune Plastic & Metal, Inc., Jersey City, NJ
Phone—(201) 333-3339
See Parent Co. Section for full profile.

**GENERAL ELECTRONIC ENTERPRISES, INC.**
132 W. Main St. (07065)
**Phone—(732) 381-1144**
Fax—(732) 388-9614
www.genelectronic.com
Email—info@genelectronic.com
Pres.—William Piegari
Admn. Mgr.—Arlene Giglio

SIC—3822; 3679; *Perimeter electric & hydronic heating control systems; Brand name— PACE Perimeter Electric Heat Control Systems; PACE Perimeter Hydronic Heat Control Systems*
Employs—12; Estab.—1977
Sales—$500,000-$1Mil
5,000 sq ft site, Distrib.—National
Privately owned corporation

**GRIGNARD CO.**
505 Capobianco Plz. (07065)
**Phone—(732) 340-1111**
Fax—(732) 340-0111
www.grignard.com
Email—etienne@grignard.com
Mng. Ptnr.—Kelly Akre
Pres., R & D Mgr.—Emile Grignard
Sales Mgr.—Etienne Grignard
Accts. Coord.—Elizabeth Wile
SIC—2992; 2842; NAICS— 324191; *Lubricating oils, greases, cleaners & chemicals*
Employs—25; Estab.—2001
Sales—$1Mil-$5Mil
Distrib.—Intl.
Privately owned corporation

**GUEST PACKAGING, LLC**
Div. of Sysco Guest Supply
414 E. Inman Ave. (07065)
**Phone—(732) 382-7270**
National—(800) 221-1457
Fax—(732) 382-0321
www.guestsupply.com
Email—eservice@guestsupply.com
V-P., Mfg.—Bob Stegman
V-P., Opers.—Gene Biber
Cont.—Dan Berry
Hum. Res. Admn.—Ellen Polvere
SIC—2844; NAICS—325600; *Personal care amenities, including skin & hair OTC & cosmetic products for the lodging & hospitality supply industries*
Employs—200; Estab.—1991
Distrib.—Intl.
Limited Liability Company
AKA: Guest Packaging
Parent co.—Sysco Guest Supply, Monmouth Junction, NJ
Phone—(609) 514-9696
See Parent Co. Section for full profile.

**HARRISON ELECTRO MECHANICAL CORP.**
1607 Coach St. (07065)
**Phone—(732) 382-6008**
Fax—(732) 388-9614
www.harrisonelectro.com
Email—info@harrisonelectro.com
Pres. & Sys. Engr.—William A. Piegari
Admn. & Fin. Mgr.—Arlene Giglio
SIC—3822; 3679; NAICS— 334512; *HVAC DDC control systems & commercial control panels; Brand name—PACE System; WebCTRL; Automated Logic*
Employs—13; Estab.—1983
Sales—$1Mil-$5Mil
10,000 sq ft site, Distrib.— Regional
Privately owned corporation

**HONE-A-MATIC TOOL & CUTTER CO.**
187 Wescott Dr. (07065)
**Phone—(732) 382-6000**
Fax—(732) 382-9732
www.honeamatic.com
Email—sales@honeamatic.com
Chrm.—Anthony R. La Mastra
Pres.—Robert La Mastra
SIC—3599; *Tooling job shop*
Employs—2; Estab.—1960
8,000 sq ft site, Distrib.—Local
Privately owned corporation

## Rahway—(cont.)

**INMAN MOLD & MFG. CO.**
815 Martin St., P.O. Box 1143 (07065)
**Phone—(732) 381-6229**
Fax—(732) 574-3604
www.inmanmolding.com
Email—sales@inmanmolding.com
Pres.—Glen Barlics
V-P.—Mark Barlics
SIC—3089; 3069; *Short & long-run plastic injection molding, including mold making, prototypes, hot stamping, silicone rubber molding, assembly & packaging*
Employs—7; Estab.—1971
17,000 sq ft site, Distrib.—National
Privately owned corporation
AKA: Barlics Mfg.

**INSTRUMENTATION TECHNOLOGY SYSTEMS, INC.**
205 E. Inman Ave. (07065)
**Phone—(732) 388-0866**
Fax—(732) 388-9690
Email—salesor@msn.com
Co-Pres., Fin. Mgr.—Anna Sadowska
Co-Pres.—Donald Lewand
SIC—3625; NAICS—335314; *Water treatment plant control systems*
Employs—6; Estab.—1980
3,500 sq ft site, Distrib.—Regional
Privately owned sub-S corp.
AKA: ITS

**J S TOOL, LLC**
187 Wescott Dr., Ste. D (07065-4706)
**Phone—(732) 815-1382**
Fax—(732) 815-0396
www.js-tool.com
Email—sales@js-tool.com
Pres.—John Skurzynski
SIC—3544; 3599; 3543; NAICS—333500; *Tool & die job shop, including fixtures, jigs, prototypes & precision machining*
Employs—2; Estab.—1986
Sales—under $500,000
Distrib.—National
Limited Liability Company

**JASON METAL PRODUCTS CORP.**
1072 Randolph Ave. (07065)
**Phone—(732) 396-1132**
Fax—(732) 396-1712
www.jasonmetalproducts.com
Email—jasonmetalprod@aol.com
Pres.—Richard Jaszyn
V-P.—Chris Jaszyn
Off. Mgr.—Linda Jaszyn
SIC—3444; *Sheet metal fabrication*
Employs—4; Estab.—1978
Sales—under $500,000
14,500 sq ft site, Distrib.—Local
Privately owned corporation

**JONART METALS, LLC**
710 New Brunswick Ave., P.O. Box 333 (07065)
**Phone—(732) 382-0300**
Fax—(732) 382-0303
www.jonartmetals.com
Email—info@jonartmetals.com
Owner—Garry Capaldo
SIC—3911; 3479; *Handcrafted gold, palladium & platinum wedding bands & engraving services*
Employs—4; Estab.—2010
Sales—$500,000
3,200 sq ft site, Distrib.—National
Limited Liability Company

**KAUFMAN STAIRS, INC.**
150 E. Inman Ave. (07065)
**Phone—(732) 388-9870**
Fax—(732) 388-8072
www.kaufmanstairs.com
Email—bob@kaufmanstairs.com
Pres., Plt. Mgr.—Alan Kaufman
V-P.—Barbara R. Simon
Sales Rep.—Mark Fiedler
SIC—2431; NAICS—321900; *Residential wooden stairs & banisters*
Employs—75; Estab.—1956
Distrib.—Regional
Privately owned corporation

**L M AIR TECHNOLOGY, INC.**
1467 Pinewood St. (07065)
**Phone—(732) 381-8200**
National—(866) 381-8200
Fax—(732) 381-4091
www.lmairtech.com
Email—sales@lmairtech.com
Pres.—Peter Daniele
V-P.—Ravi Shah
V-P.—Myron Szewczuk
SIC—3564; 3821; NAICS—339111; *Hardwall & softwall cleanrooms & lab equipment, including acid resistant polypropylene fume hoods & casework & modular & softwall air filtration units*
Employs—40; Estab.—1964
Sales—$1Mil-$5Mil
86,000 sq ft site, Distrib.—National
Privately owned sub-S corp.

**LC ENGINEERS, INC.**
1471 Pinewood St. (07065)
**Phone—(732) 340-9190**
Fax—(732) 340-9194
www.lcengineers.com
Email—lcengineers@lcengineers.com
Pres. & IT Mgr.—Suresh Kapoor
Estimator—Valeri Tomashau
SIC—3679; *Contract commercial electronic, production & electromechanical assemblies, including through hole & mixed load printed circuit boards, control panels, wiring harnesses, molded, RF & thermocouple cable/conduit, box builds & prototypes*
Employs—10; Estab.—2000
Sales—$1Mil-$2.5Mil
5,000 sq ft site, Distrib.—National
Privately owned sub-S corp.
ISO rating—9001:2008, AS9100

**LIEBERFARB, INC.**
2100 Felver Ct. (07065)
**Phone—(973) 676-9090**
Fax—(973) 676-9488
www.lieberfarb.com
Email—service@lieberfarb.com
Pres.—Mark Schonwetter
Off. Mgr.—Christine Soussa
SIC—3961; NAICS—339900; *Costume jewelry*
Employs—80
Sales—$500,000-$1Mil
Distrib.—Regional
Privately owned corporation

**LINCOLN MARBLE WORKS**
785 Martin St., P.O. Box 111 (07065)
**Phone—(732) 381-9098**
Fax—(732) 499-0192
Manager—John Szabo
SIC—3281; NAICS—327991; *Marble & granite countertops*
Employs—3; Estab.—1926
Distrib.—Local
Privately owned corporation

**LINDEN MOLD & TOOL CORP.**
155 Wescott Dr., P.O. Box C (07065)
**Phone—(732) 381-1411**
Fax—(732) 381-8770
www.lindenmold.com
Email—info@lindenmold.com
Pres.—Vincent Illuzzi
Bookkeeper—Debbie Perrotta
SIC—3544; NAICS—333500; *Plastic injection molds*
Employs—43; Estab.—1975
14,000 sq ft site, Distrib.—Intl.
Privately owned corporation

**MERCK & CO., INC.**
126 E. Lincoln Ave., P.O. Box 2000 (07065)
**Phone—(732) 594-4000**
National—(800) 672-6372
www.merck.com
Email—mrl_president@merck.com
Pres., Research Laboratories & Ex. V-P.—Peter S. Kim
Dir., Facilities Mgmt.—Paula Alston
Qual. Control Mgr.—Michael Stockl
Proj. Coord.—Gail Alston
SIC—2834; NAICS—325412; *Pharmaceuticals*
Employs—4200; Estab.—1891
Sales—over $100Mil
Distrib.—Intl.
Publicly owned corporation
Parent co.—Merck & Co., Inc., Whitehouse Station, NJ
Phone—(908) 423-1000
See Parent Co. Section for full profile.

**MR. B OFFSET PRINTING, INC.**
1850 Elizabeth Ave., Ste. B (07065)
**Phone—(732) 396-3990**
Fax—(732) 396-3999
www.mrbprinting.com
Email—mrbprinting@comcast.net
Pres.—Thomas Bayone
V-P.—Anthony Bayone
SIC—2752; 2759; NAICS—323100; *Offset & commercial printing*
Employs—2; Estab.—1979
Sales—under $500,000
3,800 sq ft site, Distrib.—Local
Privately owned corporation

**NANDVARIK SYSTEMS**
190 Lewis St. (07065)
**Phone—(732) 306-9999**
www.nandvarik.com
Email—info@nandvarik.com
COO—R. Nandvarik
SIC—7372; *Sales & marketing software development for small businesses; Brand name—NZip Sales Package; NProfile Marketing Robot*
Employs—3
Sales—under $1Mil
Distrib.—Intl.
Sole ownership

**NOVELL ENTERPRISES, INC.**
2100 Felver Ct. (07065)
**Phone—(732) 428-8300**
Fax—(732) 428-8301
www.novelldesignstudio.com
Email—sales@novelldesignstudio.com
Pres.—Victor Novogrodsky
V-P., MIS & R & D—Bruce Pucciarello
Cont., Fin. & Hum. Res. Mgr.—Dominick Venditto
IT Mgr.—Frank Rand
Off. Mgr.—Olga Leveque
SIC—3911; NAICS—339911; *Precious metal jewelry*
Employs—70; Estab.—1948
12,500 sq ft site, Distrib.—Intl.
Privately owned corporation
AKA: Wright & Lato

**OMEGA HEAT TRANSFER CO., INC.**
329 New Brunswick Ave. (07065)
**Phone—(732) 340-0023**
National—(888) 663-4224
Fax—(732) 340-0025
www.omegahtc.com
Email—steven@omegahtc.com
Pres.—Steven Simon
GM—Richie Ginelli
Pur. Mgr.—Denise Papprinno
SIC—2672; 2759; NAICS—322222; *Heat transfer labels & silkscreening*
Employs—10; Estab.—1996
Sales—$500,000-$1Mil
Distrib.—National
Privately owned corporation

**P. J. SCREENING & EMBROIDERY**
689 Jaques Ave. (07065)
**Phone—(732) 382-5183**
Fax—(732) 382-7948
www.pjscreening.com
Email—pjscreening@verizon.net
Pres.—Angela Guden
SIC—2396; 2395; *Textile screen printing & embroidery*
Employs—2; Estab.—2004
Sales—under $500,000
2,000 sq ft site, Distrib.—Local
Limited Liability Company

**PIECE OF CAKE GOURMET ICE CREAM, INC.**
62 W. Inman Ave. (07065)
**Phone—(732) 382-0281**
Fax—(732) 340-0858
www.pocicecream.com
Email—freezerjim@aol.com
Pres.—James A. Biniaris
SIC—2024; 2051; NAICS—311520; *Gourmet ice cream novelties, ice cream, sorbet, Italian ice & gelato & imported & domestic cakes*
Employs—8; Estab.—1993
Sales—$500,000-$1Mil
3,000 sq ft site, Distrib.—Local
Privately owned sub-S corp.

**PIKE & CO., INC., E. W.**
2149 Price St. (07065)
**Phone—(732) 396-0002**
Fax—(732) 396-9401
www.ewpike.net
Email—ewpike@comcast.net
Pres.—Emil Sudzina
SIC—3827; 3579; *Illuminated magnifying instruments & envelope & label moisteners*
Employs—2; Estab.—1920
Sales—under $500,000
Distrib.—Intl.
Privately owned corporation

**POLMAR IRON WORK, INC.**
673 New Brunswick Ave. (07065)
**Phone—(732) 882-0900**
Fax—(732) 882-0904
www.polmariron.com
Email—marekw@polmariron.com
Pres.—Marek Wresilo
Corp. Secy.—Martha Sztuc
Estimator—Paul Demich
SIC—3446; NAICS—332323; *Ornamental ironwork*
Employs—11; Estab.—1999
Sales—$1Mil-$2.5Mil
Distrib.—Regional
Privately owned corporation

**PREMAC, INC.**
P.O. Box 9 (07065)
**Phone—(732) 381-7550**
Pres.—Eric Schenker
V-P.—Fred Schenker
SIC—3491; 3599; NAICS—332911; *Jet pump control valves & general machining job shop*
Employs—15; Estab.—1945
Sales—under $500,000
Distrib.—National
Privately owned corporation

GEOGRAPHICAL

## Rahway—(cont.)

**PUNCH PRODUCTS U. S. A., INC.**
2131 Felver Ct. (07065)
**Phone—(732) 574-1900**
National—(800) 422-2780
Fax—(732) 574-0500
www.vision1usa.com
Email—info@vision1usa.com
Pres.—Michael Fishman
V.-P.—Mark Weissman
Hum. Res. Mgr.—Michael Calcagno
Cust. Rels. Mgr.—Mario Estrada
Cust. Rels. Rep.—Evelyn Shore
SIC—3089; 3312; *Plastic & steel promotional travel, drink & desk coffee mugs*
Employs—40; Estab.—1989
Sales—$1Mil-$5Mil
Distrib.—National
Privately owned corporation

**R&R COSMETICS, LLC**
1140 Randolph Ave. (07065)
**Phone—(732) 340-1000**
National—(800) 786-9360
Fax—(732) 340-1030
www.rubeerinju.com
Email—rubeerinju@aol.com
Ptnr.—Musthafa Kamal
Ptnr.—Eranhikkal Hanif
SIC—2844; *Skin & hair care products*
Employs—15; Estab.—2001
40,000 sq ft site, Distrib.—Intl.
Limited Liability Company

**†RAHWAY ELECTRIC SUPPLY, INC.**
Div. of US Electrical Services, Inc.
1684 Essex St. (07065)
**Phone—(732) 381-6060**
Fax—(732) 381-2519
www.rahwayelectric.com
Email—sales@rahwayelectric.com
Br. Mgr.—Clara Garcia
SIC—5063; 5051; *Distributor of electrical supplies, including bulbs, switches, wire & pipes*
Employs—10; Estab.—1979
Distrib.—Local
Privately owned corporation
Parent co.—US Electrical Services, Inc., Hartford, CT
Phone—(860) 522-3232
See Parent Co. Section for full profile.

**RAHWAY STEEL, INC.**
625 Leesville Ave., P.O. Box 276 (07065)
**Phone—(732) 388-5300**
Fax—(732) 396-0061
Pres.—Antonio Vasquez
Off. Mgr.—Ken Steinagle
SIC—3312; *Steel fabrication*
Employs—3; Estab.—1986
Sales—under $500,000
Distrib.—Local
Privately owned corporation

**ROSS CO., INC., FRANK B.**
970 New Brunswick Ave., Ste. H (07065-3814)
**Phone—(732) 669-0810**
Fax—(732) 669-0814
www.frankbross.com
Email—techinfo@rosswaxes.com
Pres.—Larry Powell
V.-P.—Carmen Mangan
SIC—2064; 3843; 2899; NAICS—339114; *Natural & synthetic waxes, including candle, candy & dental waxes*
Employs—5; Estab.—1902
Sales—$1Mil-$2.5Mil
13,000 sq ft site, Distrib.—Intl.
Privately owned sub-S corp.

**NEW ENTRY**
**ROYAL LACE CO., INC.**
902 E. Hazelwood Ave. (07065)
**Phone—(718) 495-9327**
Fax—(718) 495-2009

Email—emgee495@hotmail.com
Pres.—Moises Guttman
SIC—2258; 2259; 5131; *Manufacturer of knitted lace & wholesaler of lace fabrics*
Employs—25; Estab.—1980
Distrib.—National
Privately owned corporation

**†RSR ELECTRONICS, INC.**
900 Hart St. (07065)
**Phone—(732) 381-8777**
Fax—(732) 381-1572
www.elexp.com
Email—electron@elexp.com
Pres.—Eli Rosenbaum
Ex. V.-P.—Ajit Gulati
SIC—5063; 5065; *Distributor of electrical & electronic supplies, components, test equipment & tools*
Employs—47; Estab.—1977
89,000 sq ft site, Distrib.—Intl.
Privately owned sub-S corp.
AKA: Electronix Express

**RUDY'S & VITOR'S V. A. S. CO., INC.**
521 W. Hazelwood Ave., P.O. Box 1544 (07065)
**Phone—(732) 388-0334**
Fax—(732) 388-0059
Pres.—Vitor Soares
Corp. Secy.—Katherine Soares
SIC—3694; NAICS—336322; *Rebuilt alternators & starters*
Employs—8; Estab.—1985
Sales—$500,000-$1Mil
Distrib.—Regional
Privately owned corporation

**S D I TECHNOLOGIES, INC.**
1299 Main St. (07065)
**Phone—(877) 895-8324**
National—(800) 333-3092
Fax—(732) 574-2634
www.sdidirect.com
Email—customerservice@sdidirect.com
CEO—Ezra Ashkenazi
Hum. Res. Mgr.—Geraldine Zamorsky
Cred. Mgr.—Linda Druhot
Pur. Agt.—Edward Nehmad
SIC—3651; NAICS—334310; *Home audio devices*
Employs—70; Estab.—1998
Sales—$500,000-$1Mil
Distrib.—Regional
Privately owned corporation
AKA: Tech 2 Go

**SIGN EFFECTZ**
800 New Brunswick Ave., Ste. 7 (07065-3847)
**Phone—(732) 388-7446**
www.njsign.com
Email—signeffectz@gmail.com
Owner & Pres.—Brian Snyder
SIC—3993; 2759; 2396; NAICS—323100; *Signs, banners, decal printing, apparel screen printing & truck lettering*
Employs—1; Estab.—1997
Sales—under $500,000
Distrib.—National
Sole ownership

**SUNRISE PHARMACEUTICAL, INC.**
665 E. Lincoln Ave. (07065)
**Phone—(732) 382-6085**
Fax—(732) 382-6880
www.sunrisepharma.com
Email—info@sunrisepharma.com
CEO—Utpal Patel
Pres.—Jay Patel
V.-P., Bus. Dev. & Sales—Himanshu Brahmbhatt
SIC—2834; NAICS—325412; *Prescription & over-the-counter pharmaceutical products in oral solid dosage form*
Employs—45
35,000 sq ft site, Distrib.—National
Privately owned corporation

**SWIM 'N PLAY, INC.**
313 Regina Ave. (07065)
**Phone—(732) 574-1500**
National—(800) 631-3483
Fax—(732) 574-1551
www.swimnplay.com
Email—info@swimnplay.com
Pres.—Ray Ventrice
V.-P.—Roger Kappe
Fin. Mgr.—Milton Davies
SIC—3949; NAICS—339920; *Aboveground swimming pools & accesories*
Employs—35; Estab.—1974
Sales—$1Mil-$2.5Mil
250,000 sq ft site, Distrib.—National
Privately owned corporation

**THERMO-GRAPHICS, INC.**
915 E. Hazelwood Ave. (07065)
**Phone—(732) 669-0252**
Fax—(732) 669-0250
Email—thermogrfx@aol.com
Pres.—Seth Batzer
Manager—James Talmadge
SIC—2759; NAICS—323100; *Commercial printing*
Employs—4; Estab.—1990
Sales—$500,000-$1Mil
5,000 sq ft site, Distrib.—Local
Privately owned corporation

**TREND MACHINE, INC.**
793 Martin St., P.O. Box 218 (07065)
**Phone—(732) 382-4170**
Fax—(732) 382-4030
www.trendmachineinc.com
Email—tmachine@verizon.net
Pres.—Bill Joseph
Machinist—John Solis
SIC—3599; NAICS—332710; *Packaging machinery parts, machined metric components & special rollers with rubber coating, including manual & CNC machining & welding*
Employs—3; Estab.—1967
Sales—under $500,000
Distrib.—National
Privately owned corporation

**UNIQUE METAL PRODUCTS CO., INC.**
17 W. Scott Ave., P.O. Box 1181 (07065)
**Phone—(732) 388-1888**
Fax—(732) 388-0084
Email—airtecunique@aol.com
Pres.—Joseph S. Niemczyk
V.-P.—Joseph M. Niemczyk
SIC—3499; 3599; *Metal products, fabrication, laser cutting & CNC machining job shop*
Employs—16; Estab.—1958
Sales—$2Mil-$3Mil
40,000 sq ft site, Distrib.—National
Privately owned sub-S corp.
Also see: Airtec, Inc., same loc.

**VITALE SIGNS**
2204 Elizabeth Ave. (07065)
**Phone—(732) 388-8401**
Fax—(732) 388-0908
www.vitalesigns.com
Email—joe@vitalesigns.com
Pres.—Joe Vitale
Off. Mgr.—Fran Smith
SIC—3993; *Interior & exterior signs, truck lettering, banners, illuminated signs & letters & design, fabrication & installation*
Employs—5; Estab.—1950
Sales—over $500,000
Distrib.—Regional
Privately owned corporation

**WEST HUDSON INDUSTRIES**
1687 Saint Georges Ave. (07065-2001)
**Phone—(732) 381-6800**
(732) 574-1095
Fax—(732) 381-0004
www.njtrophy.com
Email—sales@njtrophy.com
Pres.—Les Moshinsky
SIC—3499; 3089; *Metal & plastic engraving & laminating of recognition & corporate awards, bronze plaques, badges, signs & promotional products*
Employs—4; Estab.—1948
Sales—under $500,000
3,800 sq ft site, Distrib.—National
Privately owned sub-S corp.

**WYTECH INDUSTRIES, INC.**
960 E. Hazelwood Ave. (07065)
**Phone—(732) 396-3900**
Fax—(732) 396-4943
www.wytech.com
Email—info@wytech.com
CEO—Anthony J. Casalino
Pres.—Michael Casalino
V.-P., Sales & Mktg.—Paul H. Dowd
Plt. Mgr.—Nick Frodelly
Hum. Res. Mgr.—Anna Kazimierski
SIC—3496; 3315; 3316; 3089; NAICS—332618; *Grinding, straightening, cutting, forming & heat treating of fine wire & tubing components for medical devices, including mandrels, stylets, core wires & PTFE coated hypotubes*
Employs—105; Estab.—1975
Sales—$10Mil-$12Mil
Distrib.—Intl.
Privately owned corporation
ISO rating—9001:2008

## Ramsey
(Bergen—N.E.)

**ACHILLES PROSTHETICS & ORTHOTICS, LLC**
503 N. Franklin Tpke., Ste. 12 (07446)
**Phone—(201) 785-9944**
Fax—(201) 785-9945
www.achillesnj.com
Pres.—Peter R. Buffington
SIC—3842; *Custom braces, prosthetics & orthotics*
Employs—3
Sales—$500,000-$1Mil (est)

**ADVANCED TECHNOLOGY CORP.**
79 N. Franklin Tpke., Ste. 103 (07446)
**Phone—(201) 934-7127**
Fax—(201) 236-1891
www.vetstar.com
Email—sales@vetstar.com
Pres.—Joseph Bove
SIC—7372; *Software development for the veterinary industry; Brand name—Vetstar®*
Employs—7; Estab.—1984
Privately owned corporation

**AERO TEC LABORATORIES, INC.**
45 Spear Rd. (07446)
**Phone—(201) 825-1400**
National—(800) 526-5330
Fax—(201) 825-1962
www.atlinc.com
Email—atl@atlinc.com
Pres.—Peter Regna
V.-P., Sales—David Dack
V.-P., R & D—Richard Clark

## Ramsey—(cont.)

SIC—3069; *Flexible fuel tanks & containment systems; Brand name—Petro-Flex; Chem-Flex; Aqua-Flex*
Employs—55; Estab.—1969
Sales—$10Mil-$25Mil (est)
70,000 sq ft site, Distrib.—Intl.
Privately owned corporation

**†AMD SPECIAL OIL, LLC**
90 N. Franklin Tpke. (07446)
**Phone—(201) 327-0642**
Fax—(201) 327-1814
www.amdoilsales.com
Email—info@amdoilsales.com
Pres.—Donald Griego
Cont., GM—David Triglia
Off. Mgr.—Beverley Mergl
SIC—5149; *Distributor of edible oils*
Employs—7; Estab.—1997
Sales—under $500,000
Distrib.—Intl.
Limited Liability Company
AKA: AMD Oil Sales, LLC

**APOGEE SOUND INTERNATIONAL, LLC**
50 Spring St. (07446)
**Phone—(201) 995-2001**
National—(800) 999-2809
Fax—(201) 934-1006
www.apogee-sound.com
Email—info@apogee-sound.com
V.-P., Accts., Natl.—David Chambers
Corp. Cont.—Rich Schmedel
MIS Mgr.—Gerry Daley
Hum. Res. Mgr.—Ileen Stoffer
Mktg. Comms. Mgr.—Anna Pansini
SIC—3651; NAICS—334310; *Amplifiers, speakers & processors; Brand name—Apogee Sound International*
Employs—75; Estab.—1990
Sales—$3Mil
Distrib.—Intl.
Also see: Bogen Communications, Inc., same loc.

**AURORAE (H Q)**
46 N. Central Ave. (07446)
**Phone—(551) 579-4003**
www.auroraeyoga.com
Email—dennis@auroraeyoga.com
Pres., CEO—Dennis Ingui
V.-P.—Valerie Ingui
SIC—3949; 3999; NAICS—339920; *Company headquarters; yoga mats, accessories, clothing & bags & candles (mfg. subcontracted); Brand name—AURORAE*
Employs—2; Estab.—2007
Sales—$1Mil-$5Mil
Distrib.—National
Limited Liability Company

**AYDIN JEWELRY, INC.**
885 Route 17 S. (07446)
**Phone—(201) 818-1002**
National—(800) 783-8549
Fax—(201) 818-1006
www.aydinjewelry.com
Pres.—Rick Aydin
GM—Pierre Aydin
SIC—3911; NAICS—339911; *Precious metal jewelry*
Employs—2; Estab.—1989
Sales—under $500,000 (est)
Distrib.—National
Limited Liability Company

**BOGEN COMMUNICATIONS, INC.**
50 Spring St., Ste. 1 (07446-1131)
**Phone—(201) 934-8500**
National—(800) 999-2809
Fax—(201) 934-9832
www.bogen.com
Email—info@bogen.com
Pres.—Michael Fleischer

V.-P., Fin. & CFO—Maureen A. Flotard
Sr. V.-P., Sales—Dave Chambers
V.-P., Sales, Natl. Accts.—Thomas Bisanti
V.-P., Opers.—Robert Dixon
V.-P., IT—Gerry Daley
Hum. Res. Mgr.—Eileen Stoffer
Mktg. Comms. Mgr.—Anna Pansini
Cust. Serv. Mgr.—Laura DiBartolo
SIC—3663; NAICS—334220; *Telecommunications peripherals & sound processing equipment; Brand name—Apogee Sound International; Bogen; NEAR*
Employs—85; Estab.—1932
Sales—$50Mil
70,000 sq ft site, Distrib.—Intl.
Privately owned corporation
Also see: Apogee Sound International, LLC, same loc.

**BORST CABINET CO.**
15 Schierloh Ct. (07446)
**Phone—(201) 825-4220**
Fax—(201) 825-0001
www.borstcabinetco.com
Email—borstkit@aol.com
Owner, Pres. & Sales Mgr.—David J. Borst
Corp. Secy.—Yvonne Borst
SIC—2434; 2431; 2541; 2499; NAICS—337110; *Custom & semi-custom stock kitchen & bathroom cabinets, countertops, entertainment centers & outdoor kitchens; Brand name—New River Cabinetry; Atlantis Outdoor Kitchens; Bertch; Aristokraft; Ultracraft; Custom Wood Products; Debut; Legacy*
Employs—3; Estab.—1956
Sales—under $500,000
2,000 sq ft site, Distrib.—Regional
Privately owned sub-S corp.

**CAPINTEC, INC.**
6 Arrow Rd., Ste. 101 (07446-1254)
**Phone—(201) 825-9500**
National—(800) 631-3826
Fax—(201) 825-1336
www.capintec.com
Email—getinfo@capintec.com
CEO—John Viscovic
CFO—Ralph Monaco
V.-P., Sales—Roy Eve
SIC—3845; 3841; NAICS—334500; *Corporate headquarters & radiation measuring & monitoring instruments*
Employs—26; Estab.—1964
Sales—$15Mil
Distrib.—Intl.
Privately owned corporation

**COMPORT CONSULTING CORP.**
78 Orchard St. (07446)
**Phone—(201) 236-0505**
Fax—(201) 236-1335
www.comport.com
Email—info@comport.com
Pres. & IT Mgr.—Jack Margossian
Hum. Res. Mgr.—Nancy Tizza
SIC—7373; *Computer network system integration, including LANs & WANs & IT consulting services*
Employs—20; Estab.—1992
15,000 sq ft site, Distrib.—National
Privately owned corporation

**COMPTIME PRINT & COPY CENTER**
385 N. Franklin Tpke., Ste. 6 (07446)
**Phone—(201) 760-2400**
Fax—(201) 760-9140
www.comptime.net
Email—order@comptime.net
Pres.—Christopher Tausch
Prodn. Coord.—Orlando Callegari

SIC—2759; *Commercial printing*
Employs—4
Sales—$500,000-$1Mil (est)
Distrib.—Local
Privately owned corporation

**COPERION CORP.**
Div. of Hillenbrand, Inc.
663 E. Crescent Ave. (07446)
**Phone—(201) 327-6300**
Fax—(201) 825-6460
www.coperion.com
Email—info@coperion.com
V.-P., CFO—Thomas Hummel
V.-P., Opers.—Bob Dimarino
V.-P., Cust. Serv. & Opers.—Rich Taylor
Pur. Mgr.—Robert Bolger
Hum. Res. Mgr.—Jennifer Grinthal
SIC—3082; 3559; NAICS—326121; *Corporate headquarters & plastic & human & pet food extrusions, chemical energetics & rebuilt extrusion equipment & gearboxes*
Employs—110; Estab.—1959
Sales—$100Mil
Distrib.—National
Publicly owned corporation
Parent co.—Hillenbrand, Inc., Batesville, IN
Phone—(812) 934-7000
See Parent Co. Section for full profile.

**DTROVISION, LLC**
535 E. Crescent Ave., Ste. 1 (07446)
**Phone—(201) 488-3232**
Fax—(201) 621-6118
www.purelinkav.com
Email—info@purelinkav.com
Pres.—Minsoo Park
Off. Mgr.—Kevin Kane
Mktg. Coord.—Christine Park
SIC—3651; 3577; NAICS—334310; *Professional & consumer digital A/V & PC connectivity components, including DVI/HDMI switching, conversion & distribution & fiber-optic cable equipment for long-distance HDTV extensions*
Employs—15; Estab.—2001
Sales—under $500,000
Distrib.—National
Limited Liability Company

**ELECTROMECH, INC.**
624 Swan St. (07446)
**Phone—(201) 934-3456**
Fax—(201) 934-3488
www.electromechinc.com
Email—sales@electromechinc.com
V.-P., Engrg.—Solomon Ezra
SIC—3612; NAICS—335311; *Transformers & power supplies*
Employs—25; Estab.—1979
Sales—$1Mil-$5Mil
25,000 sq ft site, Distrib.—Intl.
Privately owned sub-S corp.

**ELI JEWELS, INC.**
14 Wyckoff Ave. (07446)
**Phone—(201) 291-4200**
Fax—(201) 291-4205
www.elijewels.com
Email—info@elijewels.com
Pres.—Simon Makhlouf
Hum. Res. Mgr. & Cust. Serv. Rep.—Rachel Rosenblatt
SIC—3911; NAICS—339911; *Precious metal jewelry*
Employs—4; Estab.—2002
Sales—$500,000-$1Mil (est)
Distrib.—National
Privately owned corporation

**FEDEX OFFICE & PRINT CENTER**
Div. of FedEx Office & Print Services, Inc.
559 N. Franklin Tpke. (07446)
**Phone—(201) 818-1623**
National—(800) 463-3339
Fax—(201) 818-1625

www.fedex.com
Email—usa2053@fedex.com
Br. Mgr.—Harvey Tircio
Ctr. Specialist—Michael Cavanugh
SIC—2759; NAICS—323100; *Commercial printing*
Employs—3; Estab.—2007
Sales—under $500,000 (est)
Distrib.—Local
Publicly owned corporation
Parent co.—FedEx Office & Print Services, Inc., Dallas, TX
Phone—(214) 550-7000
See Parent Co. Section for full profile.

**†FERGUSON ENTERPRISES, INC.**
16 Arrow Rd. (07446)
**Phone—(201) 236-3111**
Fax—(201) 236-1991
www.ferguson.com
Email—joseph.proctor@ferguson.com
Br. Mgr.—Josh Reiter
Br. Mgr.—Vicki Reczkowski
Opers. Mgr.—Karen Hampton
Counter Sales Rep.—Richard Aquino
SIC—5074; *Wholesaler of plumbing pipes & valves*
Employs—15; Estab.—1953
Sales—$2.6Mil-$5Mil
Distrib.—Intl.
Publicly owned corporation
Parent co.—Ferguson Enterprises, Inc., Newport News, VA
Phone—(757) 874-7795
See Parent Co. Section for full profile.

**GLATT AIR TECHNIQUES, INC.**
20 Spear Rd. (07446)
**Phone—(201) 825-8700**
Fax—(201) 818-5580
www.glatt.com
Email—info@glattair.com
Ex. V.-P., Sales—John Carey
Ex. V.-P., Engrg. & Eqpt. Div.—Stephen Sirabian
GM & Hum. Res. Mgr.—Leah Jungrind
Administrator—Lori Sandell
SIC—3559; *Pharmaceutical processing machinery*
Employs—140; Estab.—1973
Distrib.—National
Privately owned corporation

**HIGH SPEED VIDEO**
19 Spear Rd., Ste. 104 (07446)
**Phone—(201) 327-6801**
Fax—(201) 327-6807
www.hsvideo.net
CEO—Michael Maresca
Pres.—Jim Cantalini
SIC—7372; *Enterprise-grade video communications & desktop-telepresence software development*
Employs—8; Estab.—2005
Privately owned corporation

**†INDEXING TECHNOLOGIES, INC.**
37 Orchard St. (07446)
**Phone—(201) 934-6333**
Fax—(201) 934-6488
www.indexingtechnologies.com
Email—info@indexingtechnologies.com
Pres.—Mike Bickham
Manager—Leigh Bickham
Bookkeeper—Donna Rockfeller
SIC—5084; 5085; *Wholesaler of machine tools, including turrets, spindles & parts; Brand name—SAUTER; Colombo Filippetti; Exact; LCM; Rotomors; ITI Tooling; EWS*
Employs—10; Estab.—1994
2,200 sq ft site, Distrib.—National
Privately owned corporation

GEOGRAPHICAL

## Ramsey—(cont.)

**KONICA MINOLTA BUSINESS SOLUTIONS U. S. A., INC. (H Q)**
100 Williams Dr. (07446)
**Phone—(201) 825-4000**
Fax—(201) 825-7567
www.kmbs.konicaminolta.us
Email—kharris@
kmbs.konicaminolta.us
Chrm., CEO—Toshimitsu 'Tom' Taiko
Pres., COO—Rick Taylor
CFO—John Thielke
Sr. V.-P., Mktg.—Kevin Kern
Sr. V.-P., Bus. Intelligence Svcs.—
Sam Errigo
V.-P., Sales, Dealer—Alan Nielsen
V.-P., Hum. Res.—Don Warwick
V.-P., Bus. Intelligence Serv., Prod. Plng. & Sols.—Gavin Jordan-Smith
Dir., Hum. Res.—Rod McVeigh
Corp. Comms. Mgr.—Karen Harris
SIC—3861; Corporate headquarters; production print systems, digital presses, multifunctional products & managed print & IT services; Brand name—Konica Minolta; bizhub; bizhub MarketPlace; KIP; bizhub SECURE; eCopy; Dispatcher Phoenix; NSi AutoStore; Prism DocSystem; PRISM GroupPoint; PageScope Mobile; bizhub vCare
Employs—400
Sales—$100Mil-$250Mil
Distrib.—Intl.
Publicly owned corporation

**LIQUID SOLIDS SEPARATION CORP.**
25 Arrow Rd. (07446)
**Phone—(201) 236-4833**
Fax—(201) 236-2004
www.leemlssfiltration.com
Email—info@leemlssfiltration.com
Pres.—David Painter
V.-P., Sales—Chris Tedeschi
SIC—3589; NAICS—333319; Industrial filtration equipment
Employs—35; Estab.—1987
Sales—$5Mil-$10Mil
30,000 sq ft site, Distrib.—National
Privately owned corporation
DBA: LEEM/LSS Filtration

**†MODEL ELECTRONICS, INC.**
615 E. Crescent Ave. (07446)
**Phone—(201) 961-6200**
National—(800) 433-9657
Fax—(201) 961-6282
www.modelelectronics.com
Email—lstevens@
modelelectronics.com
V.-P.—Thomas Churchill
GM—Rocco Guglielmello
Hum. Res. Mgr.—Melissa Harrison
SIC—5013; 5065; Distributor of OEM automotive electronics, instrumentation & radio & aftermarket automotive electronics, radios, navigation systems, speedometers & accessories, including repair & maintenance
Employs—55; Estab.—1992
Distrib.—National
Privately owned corporation

**OKONITE CO., INC., THE (H Q)**
102 Hilltop Rd., P.O. Box 340
(07446)
**Phone—(201) 825-0300**
Fax—(201) 825-9026
www.okonite.com
Email—info@okonite.com
Chrm., CEO—V. A. Viggiano
Pres., COO—Alfred Coppola
CFO—Dave Sokira
V.-P., Sales & Mktg.—Bruce Sellers
V.-P., Mfg.—John Silver
Dir., Adv.—Robert Seltsam
MIS Mgr.—Bill Blowers
SIC—3357; Corporate headquarters; electric cables; Brand name—Okoguard; CLX; Okonite
Employs—100; Estab.—1878
Sales—$10Mil-$25Mil
70,000 sq ft site, Distrib.—Intl.
Privately owned corporation
ISO rating—9001

**PEAPODZ, LLC**
79 S. Central Ave. (07446)
**Phone—(201) 362-8883**
www.peapodz101.com
Email—peapodz101@yahoo.com
Owner—Shelley Doherty
SIC—3842; Cold therapy ice packs
Employs—1; Estab.—2006
Sales—under $500,000
Distrib.—Intl.
Limited Liability Company

**RODMAN PUBLISHING CORP.**
70 Hilltop Rd., 3rd Fl. (07446)
**Phone—(201) 825-2552**
Fax—(201) 825-0553
www.rodmanpublishing.com
Email—info@rodpub.com
Publisher—Matthew Carey
Publisher—Howard Revitch
Asst. Publisher—Mark Weeks
Mng. Editor—Michael Barbella
Editor & Dir., Editorial—Tom Branna
Editor—Chris Delporte
Hum. Res. Mgr.—Mike Del Purgatorio
SIC—2721; Magazine publishing; Brand name—Medical Product Outsourcing; Beauty Packaging; Coatings World; Contract Pharma; Happi; Ink World; Label & Narrow Web; Nonwovens Industry; Nutraceuticals World; Orthopedic Design & Technology
Employs—50; Estab.—1957
Distrib.—Intl.
Privately owned corporation

**†TAURUS INTERNATIONAL, INC.**
275 N. Franklin Tpke., Ste. 3
(07446)
**Phone—(201) 825-2420**
Fax—(201) 825-1437
www.taurusinternational.com
Owner—William Coleman
Sales Mgr.—William Crable
Off. Mgr.—Marlene Espinal
SIC—5051; Distributor of forgings, castings & precision metal components for automotive, truck, bus, recreational vehicle & equipment OEMs
Employs—12; Estab.—1981
Distrib.—Intl.
Privately owned corporation

**TROPHY KING OF RAMSEY**
Div. of Trophy King, Inc., The
503 N. Franklin Tpke., Unit 13
(07446)
**Phone—(201) 760-6488**
Fax—(201) 760-6498
www.trophyking.net
Email—info@trophyking.net
GM—John Paluskiewicz
Engraver—Andrew Van Valen
SIC—3479; 3499; Trophy assembly & engraving
Employs—3; Estab.—1997
Sales—under $500,000
1,500 sq ft site, Distrib.—National
Privately owned sub-S corp.
Parent co.—Trophy King, Inc., The, Teaneck, NJ
Phone—(201) 836-1482
See Parent Co. Section for full profile.

**WALDEN-MOTT CORP.**
225 N. Franklin Tpke. (07446)
**Phone—(201) 818-8630**
Fax—(201) 818-8720
www.waldenmott.com
Email—editorial@waldenmott.com
Pres.—Alfred Walden
V.-P.—Charlie Walden
SIC—2721; Trade magazine publishing
Employs—2; Estab.—1884
Sales—$500,000-$1Mil
Distrib.—Intl.
Privately owned corporation

**†WURTH INTERNATIONAL TRADING AMERICA**
91 Grant St. (07446)
**Phone—(201) 995-1111**
Fax—(201) 995-9908
www.wurth-international.us
CEO—Esther Jakob
Pur. Agt.—Heike Bortes
SIC—5169; 5072; Company headquarters & distributor of chemicals, fasteners & tools for the industrial & automotive industries
Employs—7; Estab.—1991
Sales—$1Mil-$2.5Mil
Distrib.—Intl.
Privately owned corporation

---

## Rancocas
(Burlington—S.E.)

**CONSARC CORP.**
Div. of Inductotherm Corp.
100 Indel Ave., P.O. Box 156
(08073)
**Phone—(609) 267-8000**
Fax—(609) 267-1366
www.consarc.com
Email—sales@consarc.com
Pres.—William J. Marino
Ex. V.-P.—Jai K. Narayan
Corp. Secy.—Barbara Rathgeb
IT Mgr.—Mark Mahon
Hum. Res. Mgr. & Engrg. Admn.—Pat Vogel
SIC—3567; NAICS—333994; Vacuum & controlled atmosphere melting & heating equipment for superalloys, steels, titanium & engineered ceramics
Employs—109; Estab.—1962
Distrib.—Intl.
Privately owned corporation
Parent co.—Inductotherm Corp., Rancocas, NJ
Phone—(609) 267-9000
See Parent Co. Section for full profile.

**ELECTRO-STEAM GENERATOR CORP.**
Div. of Inductotherm Corp.
50 Indel Ave., P.O. Box 438
(08073)
**Phone—(609) 288-9071**
National—(866) 617-0764
Fax—(609) 288-9078
www.electrosteam.com
Email—sales@electrosteam.com
Pres.—Bob Murnane
Sales Mgr.—Brad Weigle
Plt. Mgr.—Sal Negro
SIC—3621; NAICS—335312; Stationary & portable electric & indirect steam-to-steam steam generators, including carbon & 316L stainless steel; Brand name—Little Giant; Low Boy; V-Block
Employs—10; Estab.—1952
Sales—$1Mil-$5Mil
10,000 sq ft site, Distrib.—Intl.
Privately owned corporation
Parent co.—Inductotherm Corp., Rancocas, NJ
Phone—(609) 267-9000
See Parent Co. Section for full profile.

**INDUCTOTHERM CORP.**
10 Indel Ave., P.O. Box 157
(08073-0157)
**Phone—(609) 267-9000**
National—(800) 257-9527
Fax—(609) 267-3537
www.inductotherm.com
Email—sales@inductotherm.com
Pres.—Satyen N. Prabhu
Sr. V.-P., Sales & Serv.—Joseph T. Belsh
V.-P., Admn. & Treas.—Ted Baugh
Dir., Opers.—Rajul Patel
Hum. Res. Mgr.—Georga Smith
SIC—3567; NAICS—333994; Corporate headquarters & metal induction melting, holding, heating & induction furnaces, power supplies, charging/ preheating, melt shop computer control & automatic pouring systems
Employs—200; Estab.—1953
Sales—$25Mil-$100Mil
205,555 sq ft site, Distrib.—National
Privately owned corporation
ISO rating—9001:2000

**PEMBERTON FABRICATORS, INC.**
30 Indel Ave., P.O. Box 227
(08073)
**Phone—(609) 267-0922**
Fax—(609) 261-2546
www.pemfab.com
Email—sales@pemfab.com
Pres.—Robert Murnane
V.-P.—Randy Erb
Off. Mgr.—Cheryl Parker
SIC—3444; Sheet metal fabrication
Employs—40; Estab.—1965
30,000 sq ft site, Distrib.—Intl.
Privately owned corporation

**PV/T, INC.**
Div. of Inductotherm Corp.
100 Indel Ave., P.O. Box 156
(08073)
**Phone—(609) 267-3933**
Fax—(609) 267-1366
www.pvt-vf.com
Email—sales@pvt-vf.com
Pres., CFO—Brett Wenger
Hum. Res. Mgr.—Pat Vogel
SIC—3567; NAICS—333994; Aluminum, copper, nickel, stainless & titanium vacuum HT furnaces for investment & mastermelt castings & atomization
Employs—4; Estab.—1965
55,000 sq ft site, Distrib.—Intl.
Privately owned corporation
AKA: Consarc
Parent co.—Inductotherm Corp., Rancocas, NJ
Phone—(609) 267-9000
See Parent Co. Section for full profile.

**†RANCOCAS METALS CORP.**
Div. of Inductotherm Corp.
35 Indel Ave., P.O. Box 223
(08073)
**Phone—(609) 267-4120**
(800) 762-6382
Fax—(609) 267-5690
www.rancocasmetals.com
Email—sales@rancocasmetals.com
Pres.—Robert W. Hitchon
Sales Mgr.—Jack Dooley
SIC—5051; Metal service center, including aluminum, brass, copper, stainless steel, precision plate & circle sawing, shearing & production bar cutting
Employs—25; Estab.—1961
Sales—$13Mil-$16Mil
Distrib.—National
Privately owned corporation

## Rancocas—(cont.)

Parent co.—Inductotherm Corp.,
Rancocas, NJ
Phone—(609) 267-9000
See Parent Co. Section for full profile.

**SQN BANKING SYSTEMS, INC.**

65 Indel Ave., P.O. Box 423
(08073)
**Phone—(609) 261-5500**
National—(800) 744-7226
Fax—(609) 265-9517
www.sqnbankingsystems.com
Email—info@
sqnbankingsystems.com
Pres.—Joseph Uhland, Jr.
Dir., Sales & Mktg.—Rachel
Woodman
SIC—7372; Fraud detection
software development
Employs—30; Estab.—1983
Distrib.—Intl.
Privately owned corporation

**TELEGENIX, INC.**

Div. of Inductotherm Corp.
71 Indel Ave., P.O. Box 577
(08073)
**Phone—(609) 265-3910**
National—(800) 424-5220
Fax—(609) 265-3920
www.telegenix.com
Email—sales@telegenix.com
Pres.—Joseph Miller
Dir., New Bus. Dev. & Intl. Sales—
Sean Moroney
Acctg., Hum. Res. & Off. Mgr.—
Toni Nippins
SIC—3663; 3669; 3679; Custom &
contract voice communications
systems for air traffic control &
emergency dispatch operators;
Brand name—PROCOM
Employs—14; Estab.—1964
Sales—$1Mil-$5Mil
12,000 sq ft site, Distrib.—Intl.
Privately owned corporation
ISO rating—9001:2008
Parent co.—Inductotherm Corp.,
Rancocas, NJ
Phone—(609) 267-9000
See Parent Co. Section for full profile.

---

## Randolph

(Morris—N.W.)

**ALLIEDOP, INC.**

1 Emery Ave., Ste. 1 (07869-1387)
**Phone—(973) 328-3340**
National—(800) 848-8846
Fax—(973) 328-3342
www.alliedop.com
Email—jschenkman@alliedop.com
Pres.—Joshua Schenkman
SIC—3842; Corporate
headquarters & orthopedic,
orthotic & prosthetic appliances
Employs—8; Estab.—1968
Sales—$3.1Mil
Distrib.—Regional
Privately owned corporation

**†AMERICAN DISTRIBUTORS, INC.**

2 Emery Ave., Ste. 1 (07869-1368)
**Phone—(973) 328-1181**
Fax—(973) 328-2302
www.americandistr.com
Email—sales@americandistr.com
Pres.—David Beck
Cont.—Heather Wynne
Pur. Agt.—Krista Bustamante
SIC—5063; Corporate
headquarters & distributor of
capacitors, coils, connectors,
filters, fuses & resistors
Employs—35; Estab.—1983
Sales—$48Mil
29,000 sq ft site, Distrib.—Intl.
Privately owned corporation
ISO rating—AS9100

**AMERICAN MACHINE TOOL REPAIR**

12 Middlebury Blvd. (07869)
**Phone—(973) 927-0820**
Fax—(973) 927-3814
www.amtr1964.com
Email—amtr64@aol.com
Pres.—Alex Karoly, Jr.
V-P.—Alex Karoly, Sr.
Off. Mgr.—Kate Lynch
SIC—3545; 3599; Rebuilt
production machinery, including
grinding, large boring & hand
scraping & fitting of machine
slides
Employs—8; Estab.—1967
Distrib.—National
Privately owned corporation

**ARTISAN CONTROLS CORP.**

111 Canfield Ave., Ste. B-15-18
(07869)
**Phone—(973) 598-9400**
National—(800) 457-4950
Fax—(973) 598-9410
www.artisancontrols.com
Email—sales@artisancontrols.com
Pres.—John D. Murray
V-P., Engrg. & IT Mgr.—Larry Affelt
Sales Mgr.—Maryann Peterson
Plt. Mgr.—Jack Cooper
Pur. Mgr.—Angela Donnelly
Acctg. & Hum. Res. Mgr.—Denise
Maas
SIC—3625; NAICS—335314;
Industrial controls & timers;
Brand name—Time Capsule
Employs—30; Estab.—1965
10,000 sq ft site, Distrib.—National
Privately owned sub-S corp.

**AZZOTA CORP.**

178 Franklin Rd. (07869)
**Phone—(877) 649-2746**
Fax—(800) 299-3816
www.azzota.com
Email—info@azzota.com
GM—Geoff Darling
Manager—Roy Shao
SIC—3826; 3827; 3589; 3821;
NAICS—334516; Corporate
headquarters & laboratory &
medical equipment, including
spectrophotometers,
microscopes, water purification
systems & balances, centrifuges
& incubators (mfg. done
overseas); Brand name—Azzota;
Abbota; LabShops
Employs—10; Estab.—2007
Sales—$1Mil-$5Mil
Distrib.—Intl.
Privately owned partnership
ISO rating—9001

**CRA-Z-ART**

1578 Sussex Tpke., Bldg. 5
(07869)
**Phone—(973) 543-2037**
National—(800) 272-9278
Fax—(973) 598-3810
www.cra-z-art.com
Email—helpdesk@cra-z-art.com
CEO—Nellie Mahabir
V-P.—Vito Amato
IT Mgr.—Chris Frazier
Hum. Res. Mgr.—June Dabbea
Accts. Payable Mgr.—Sharon
Salters
SIC—3952; 3951; NAICS—
339942; Company headquarters
& arts & crafts supplies,
including crayons, markers,
chalks, colored pencils (mfg.
done in China); Brand name—
Cra-Z-Art™; Cra-Z Cookn'™; 3D
Shimmer n' Sparkle™; Softee
Dough™; Puzzle Dough™
Employs—30
Sales—$2.5Mil-$5Mil (est)
Distrib.—Intl.
Limited Liability Company

**DMR SIGN SYSTEMS**

215 State Route 10, Ste. 1-A
(07869)
**Phone—(973) 361-1829**
Fax—(973) 361-4568
www.dmrsign.com
Email—sales@dmrsign.com
Pres.—Andrew Tunkel
V-P.—Grace Tunkel
SIC—3993; Interior signs for the
healthcare industry
Employs—4; Estab.—1993
Distrib.—National
Privately owned corporation

**DOUGLAS ELECTRICAL
COMPONENTS, INC.**

5 Middlebury Blvd. (07869)
**Phone—(973) 627-8230**
Fax—(866) 206-6916
www.douglaselectrical.com
Email—info@douglaselectrical.com
Pres.—Edward Douglas
Technical Sales Mgr.—Chris
Rempel
Hum. Res. Mgr.—Kim Tucci
Accts. Rep.—Jena Bundia
SIC—3679; 3672; Hermetically
sealed electrical & fiber-optic
feedthroughs for vacuum &
pressure applications, including
wire-to-wire feedthroughs,
sealed bulkhead connectors,
custom hermetic cable
harnesses & vacuum tight wire to
connector assemblies
Employs—76; Estab.—1945
30,000 sq ft site, Distrib.—Intl.
Privately owned corporation

**DOVER SIGNS MFG. & GRAPHICS,
INC.**

1471 Sussex Tpke. (07869)
**Phone—(973) 366-2229**
Fax—(973) 366-6903
Email—dover-signs@att.net
Pres.—Nanette Holder
SIC—3993; Interior & exterior vinyl
signs
Employs—3; Estab.—1967
Sales—under $500,000
2,700 sq ft site, Distrib.—Regional
Privately owned corporation

**EDGELL COMMUNICATIONS, INC.**

4 Middlebury Blvd., Ste. 1 (07869)
**Phone—(973) 607-1300**
National—(800) 948-6189
Fax—(973) 607-1395
www.edgellcommunications.com
CEO—Gabriele Edgell
Hum. Res. Mgr.—Enrico Cundri
Accts. Rec. Mgr.—Sue Gupowski
SIC—2721; Trade magazine
publishing
Employs—60; Estab.—1987
Distrib.—National
Privately owned sub-S corp.

**FALLS PRODUCTS, INC.**

220 Franklin Rd., 1st Fl. (07869)
**Phone—(973) 537-6464**
Fax—(973) 537-1661
www.fallsproducts.com
Email—d.bur.r@verizon.net
Pres.—David Vander May
SIC—3549; NAICS—333518;
Deburring machinery
Employs—2; Estab.—1988
Sales—$500,000-$1Mil
Distrib.—Intl.
Privately owned corporation

**G T MICROWAVE, INC.**

2 Emery Ave., Ste. 2 (07869)
**Phone—(973) 361-5700**
Fax—(973) 361-5722
www.gtmicrowave.com
Email—sales@gtmicrowave.com
Pres. & Chief Engr.—George
Apsley
Corp. Secy.—Ellen Baliotis
Sales Mgr.—Jacob Levy

Qual. Control Mgr.—Claudia
Hinton
Matls. Mgr.—Penny Gronenthal
SIC—3679; Microwave
components & electrical devices
Employs—23; Estab.—1995
5,000 sq ft site, Distrib.—Intl.
Privately owned sub-S corp.
ISO rating—9001:2008

**GENERAL WIRE & STAMPING CO.,
INC.**

1 Emery Ave., Unit 3 (07869)
**Phone—(973) 366-8080**
(800) 562-0237
Fax—(973) 366-3982
www.generalwire.com
Email—sales@generalwire.com
Pres.—Kenneth J. Kelly
V-P. & Sales Engr.—Patrick Egan
Off. Mgr.—Judith Kelly
SIC—3496; 3469; Wire forms &
metal stampings
Employs—12; Estab.—1974
Sales—$1Mil-$2.5Mil
12,000 sq ft site, Distrib.—Intl.
Privately owned corporation

**GLENBROOK TECHNOLOGIES, INC.**

11 Emery Ave. (07869)
**Phone—(973) 361-8866**
National—(800) 600-8866
Fax—(973) 361-9286
www.glenbrooktech.com
Email—szweig@glenbrooktech.com
Pres.—Gil Zweig
V-P.—Claire Zweig
Sales Mgr.—Steve Zweig
Accts. Mgr.—Donna Miller
Serv. Mgr.—Yvonne Coad
SIC—3559; X-ray inspection
equipment, accessories &
supplies
Employs—18; Estab.—1983
Distrib.—Intl.
Privately owned corporation

**GRANVILLE CONCRETE PRODUCTS**

1076 Route 10 (07869)
**Phone—(973) 584-6653**
Fax—(973) 584-0320
Ptnr.—Kevin Peach
Ptnr.—Brian Peach
SIC—3272; Concrete septic tanks
Employs—5; Estab.—1958
Sales—$500,000-$1Mil
Distrib.—Local
Privately owned partnership

**GRAPHICS DEPOT, INC.**

11 Middlebury Blvd., Ste. 4
(07869)
**Phone—(973) 927-8200**
Fax—(973) 927-8253
www.graphicsdepotinc.com
Email—info@graphicsdepotinc.com
Pres.—David Bernstein
GM, Hum. Res. & IT Mgr.—Joseph
Taliercio
Cust. Serv. Mgr.—Janet Carter
SIC—2759; 2752; 2789; NAICS—
323121; Digital four & full color
offset, instant, on-demand &
wide-format printing & binding &
mailing services
Employs—16; Estab.—1992
Sales—$2Mil-$2.5Mil
10,000 sq ft site, Distrib.—
Regional
Privately owned corporation

**HAWK GRAPHICS, INC.**

1248 Sussex Tpke., Ste. C-9
(07869)
Mail addr: P.O. Box 308, Mount
Freedom (07970-0308)
**Phone—(973) 895-5569**
(973) 895-4561
Fax—(973) 895-7258
www.hawkgraphicsinc.com
Email—sales@
hawkgraphicsinc.com
Pres.—Nick Battaglino
V-P.—Dorothy C. Battaglino

GEOGRAPHICAL

## Randolph—(cont.)

V-P.—John A. Battaglino
Corp. Secy.—Tara Battaglino
SIC—2759; 2752; 2789; 3993;
NAICS—323100; *Commercial offset, digital color & high-speed instant printing, embossing, hot stamping, die cutting, binding & promotional items*
Employs—20; Estab.—1981
Sales—$1Mil-$5Mil
20,000 sq ft site, Distrib.—Regional
Privately owned corporation

**†HIGH GRADE BEVERAGE**
86 Canfield Ave. (07869)
Mail addr: P.O. Box 882, Dover (07802-0882)
**Phone—(973) 927-1400**
National—(800) 696-0849
Fax—(973) 927-0375
www.hgbev.com
Email—jbenvenuto@hgbev.com
Corp. V-P.—George Policastro
Sales Mgr.—John 'Jack' Benvenuto
Operation Mgr.—Pete Castelli
SIC—5181; 5149; *Distributor of beverages, including beer, wine, spirits & soft drinks*
Employs—100; Estab.—1978
Distrib.—Local
Privately owned corporation
Parent co.—High Grade Beverage, Monmouth Junction, NJ
Phone—(732) 821-7600
See Parent Co. Section for full profile.

**JAYGO, INC.**
7 Emery Ave. (07869)
**Phone—(908) 688-3600**
National—(888) 815-2946
Fax—(908) 688-6060
www.jaygoinc.com
Email—sales@jaygoinc.com
Pres.—Jason Hayday
V-P., Engr.—Joris Banning
SIC—3556; 3559; NAICS—333294; *Industrial process equipment, including mixers, blenders & dryers for the food, chemical, cosmetic, pharmaceutical & healthcare industries; Brand name—Dragonite; Rathmann*
Employs—11; Estab.—1971
Sales—$4Mil-$6Mil
11,200 sq ft site, Distrib.—Intl.
Privately owned corporation

**JM LIFESTYLES, LLC**
215 State Route 10, Ste. 3 (07869)
**Phone—(973) 668-5057**
Fax—(973) 695-1393
www.jmlifestyles.com
Email—michelle@jmlifestyles.com
Pres.—Michelle Radley
SIC—3272; *Decorative concrete countertops, bars, floor tiles & furnishings; Brand name—Woodform; Infinicrete; JMLifestyles; Surecrete; Cheng Design Products*
Employs—6; Estab.—2006
Sales—$500,000-$1Mil
Distrib.—Intl.
Limited Liability Company

**KARR GLASS, INC., PEGGY**
100 Washington St. (07869)
**Phone—(973) 659-1200**
National—(800) 754-8585
Fax—(973) 659-1220
www.peggykarrglass.com
Email—custserv@peggykarrglass.com
Pres.—Peggy Karr
Sr. V-P.—Tim Seitz
V-P., Opers.—George Haversang
Hum. Res., IT & Off. Mgr.—Suzanne Farese

SIC—3229; NAICS—327212; *Fused glass products*
Employs—26; Estab.—1987
60,000 sq ft site, Distrib.—Intl.
Privately owned sub-S corp.

**LANDICE, INC.**
111 Canfield Ave., Unit A-1 (07869)
**Phone—(973) 927-9010**
National—(800) 526-3423
Fax—(973) 927-0630
www.landice.com
Email—sales@landice.com
Pres.—Greg Savetierie
SIC—3949; NAICS—339920; *Treadmills & elliptical trainers for residential & commercial applications*
Employs—30; Estab.—1995
Distrib.—Intl.
Privately owned corporation

**MASTERCOOL, INC.**
1 Aspen Dr. (07869)
**Phone—(973) 252-9119**
Fax—(973) 252-2455
www.mastercool.com
Email—customerservice@mastercool.com
Graphic Artist—Stephanie Bartell
SIC—3423; 3599; *Automotive air conditioning service tools & equipment*
Employs—40; Estab.—1982
20,000 sq ft site, Distrib.—National
Privately owned corporation

**MCMILLAN ANALYSIS CORP.**
39 Meadowbrook Rd. (07869)
Mail addr: P.O. Box 1323, Morristown (07962)
**Phone—(973) 328-1674**
National—(800) 724-1817
Fax—(973) 328-1303
www.optionstrategist.com
Email—info@optionstrategist.com
Owner, Pres., Publisher & Editor—Lawrence G. McMillan
Off. Mgr.—Karen Guerra
SIC—2721; *Daily & semimonthly newsletter publishing*
Employs—4; Estab.—1990
Sales—under $500,000
Distrib.—Intl.
Privately owned sub-S corp.

**MICROELETTRICA-USA, LLC**
4 Middlebury Blvd., Ste. 12 (07869)
**Phone—(973) 598-0806**
Fax—(973) 598-0677
www.microelettrica.com
Email—msusa@microelettrica.com
CFO—Raffaele diBartolomeo
GM—Graham Paton
Prodn. Mgr.—Massimiliano Tuveri
Off. Mgr.—Vanessa Giordano
Electrical Engr.—Ryan Feeney
SIC—3679; 3676; NAICS—334415; *Electronic components for industrial & railway applications, including contactors, resistors & protection relays*
Employs—15; Estab.—2001
Distrib.—Intl.
Limited Liability Company

**MODULAR PACKAGING SYSTEMS, INC.**
6 Aspen Dr. (07869)
**Phone—(973) 970-9393**
Fax—(973) 970-9388
www.modularpackaging.com
Email—sales@modularpackaging.com
Pres.—Clifford Smith
V-P.—Brad Smith
Cont.—Russell Oathout
Asst. Cont.—Matt Fortunato
Sales Mgr., Natl.—Erik Bronander

SIC—3565; 3559; *Modular packaging equipment & systems for the pharmaceutical, cosmetic & nutraceutical industries, including unscramblers, slat & electronic fillers, induction sealing, PS labeling, bundling, cartoning, conveyors & central monitoring; Brand name—48-10 slat counter; Data Technologies ICU-2-80; Kaps-All; Marburg; Labeling Systems Inc.; Abox; Inline labeling; Safeline*
Employs—13; Estab.—1965
Sales—$5Mil-$6Mil
27,000 sq ft site, Distrib.—Intl.
Privately owned corporation

NEW ENTRY
**MOUNT FREEDOM PRINTING, LLC**
1248 Sussex Tpke. (07869)
**Phone—(973) 933-2700**
Fax—(973) 933-2701
www.mountfreedomprinting.com
Email—jobs@mountfreedomprinting.com
Owner—Robert Miller
SIC—2759; *Digital printing*
Employs—4; Estab.—2009
Sales—$500,000-$1Mil (est)
Distrib.—Intl.
Limited Liability Company

**NEWTYPE, INC.**
447 State Route 10, Ste. 14 (07869)
**Phone—(973) 361-6000**
Fax—(973) 361-6005
www.newtypeinc.com
Email—info@newtypeinc.com
CEO—JoAnn Porto
Pres.—Mark Porto
Prodn. Mgr.—Raissa Spatola
SIC—2791; NAICS—323122; *Foreign-language typesetting & translations in 130 languages*
Employs—10; Estab.—1964
2,700 sq ft site, Distrib.—National
Privately owned corporation

**NORWALT DESIGN, INC.**
961 Route 10 E., Bldg. 2-A (07869)
**Phone—(973) 927-3200**
Fax—(973) 927-2841
www.norwalt.com
Email—norwalt@norwalt.com
Br. Mgr.—Michael Seidel
SIC—3565; NAICS—333993; *Packaging machinery*
Employs—45; Estab.—1971
Sales—$5Mil-$10Mil (est)
25,000 sq ft site, Distrib.—National
Privately owned corporation

**NYMAR MFG. CO., INC.**
215 State Route 10 E. (07869-2416)
**Phone—(973) 366-7265**
Fax—(973) 366-4687
www.nymar.com
Email—info@nymar.com
Pres.—Gerald Hughes
Off. Mgr.—Lisa Delvalle
SIC—3544; NAICS—333500; *Plastic blow mold tooling*
Employs—10; Estab.—1967
Sales—$1Mil-$2.5Mil
10,000 sq ft site, Distrib.—National
Privately owned corporation

**OMEGA SHIELDING PRODUCTS, INC.**
9 Emery Ave. (07869)
**Phone—(973) 366-0080**
Fax—(973) 366-8232
www.omegashielding.com
Email—sales@omegashielding.com
Pres.—Leon Komsa
Acct. Mgr.—John Reyes
Opers. & Sales Mgr.—David Carr
MIS Mgr.—Chiung Yao Chen
Qual. Mgr.—Andy Morris

SIC—3679; *EMI & RFI electronic shielding*
Employs—9; Estab.—1983
Sales—under $5Mil
12,000 sq ft site, Distrib.—Intl.
Privately owned corporation

**RAME-HART, INC.**
5 Emery Ave., Ste. 1 (07869-1300)
**Phone—(973) 335-0560**
Fax—(973) 335-2920
www.rame-hart.com
Email—info@rame-hart.com
Pres., CEO—Ken Christiansen
V-P., CFO—Robert Olich
SIC—3826; 3559; NAICS—334516; *Egg harvesting & inoculating machines for biological vaccine manufacturers*
Employs—25; Estab.—1961
Sales—$12Mil
15,000 sq ft site, Distrib.—Intl.
Privately owned corporation
ISO rating—9001

**SCREENTEK MFG. CO., INC.**
220 Franklin Rd., Ste. B (07869-1605)
**Phone—(973) 328-2121**
Fax—(973) 328-3545
www.screentek.us
Email—screentek@yahoo.com
Co-Pres., GM—Jay Thompson
SIC—3496; 3469; *Wire & fiberglass mesh & perforated metal air, gas & oil filters, baskets & strainers*
Employs—23; Estab.—1996
Distrib.—Intl.
Privately owned corporation
ISO rating—9001

**SERVOLIFT, LLC**
35 Righter Rd. (07869)
**Phone—(973) 442-7878**
Fax—(973) 442-1874
www.servo-lift.com
Email—sales@servo-lift.com
Pres.—Marc Kaufman
Cont.—Maryann Carroll
Proj. Mgr.—Mario Mauro
Prod. Mgr.—Ron Atanesian
Tech. Admn.—Chris Albert
SIC—3559; *Pharmaceuticals handling & processing equipment*
Employs—29; Estab.—1994
Sales—$6Mil-$10Mil
7,000 sq ft site, Distrib.—Intl.
Limited Liability Company

NEW ENTRY
**STUDIO FEIFISH, LLC**
54 Ironia Rd. (07869)
**Phone—(973) 303-3287**
www.feifish.com
Owner—Wenlee Fei
SIC—3911; NAICS—339914; *Cast silver jewelry, including bracelets, earrings & necklaces*
Employs—2; Estab.—2009
Sales—under $500,000 (est)
1,000 sq ft site, Distrib.—Local
Limited Liability Company

**T J'S SPORTWIDE TROPHY & AWARDS**
236 S. Salem St. (07869)
Mail addr: P.O. Box 1450, Dover (07802-1450)
**Phone—(973) 989-8775**
National—(800) 762-0049
Fax—(973) 989-8923
www.tjsportwide.com
Email—tjsportwide@aol.com
Pres.—Joe Balzarotti

## Randolph—(cont.)

**SIC**—3499; 3993; *Awards, trophies, plaques, ribbons, medals, advertising specialties & promotional products*
Employs—10; Estab.—1973
Sales—over $1Mil
5,500 sq ft site, Distrib.—National
Privately owned corporation

### TECHNOVATIONS TECHNOLOGY REVIEWS, INC.

14 Red Barn Ln. (07869)
**Phone—(973) 537-9511**
Fax—(973) 774-7093
www.technovations-usa.com
Email—info@technovations-usa.com
Pres.—Jaidev S. Talwar
SIC—2821; *PTUF impact modifiers for polyamides & conductive polymers*
Employs—5; Estab.—1998
Sales—$2.5Mil-$5Mil (est)
Distrib.—Intl.
Privately owned corporation

### ULTRAFLEX SYSTEMS, INC. (H Q)

1578 Sussex Tpke., Ste. 400 (07869-1833)
**Phone—(973) 627-8608**
National—(800) 368-7858
Fax—(973) 627-8506
www.ultraflexx.com
Email—info@ultraflexx.com
CEO—John Schleicher
SIC—3081; 2258; 2221; 2211; NAICS—326113; *Corporate headquarters; indoor & outdoor PVC substrate & mesh woven & knit polyester & cotton sign & banner textiles, including coated fabrics (mfg. subcontracted); Brand name—BIOFlex® FL; JetFlex® FL; UltraMesh®; Strip Mesh Plus; Artex® Canvas; UltraCanvas; UltraCotton; MultiTex; TrueCanvas; Ultima Supreme; UltraPoplin; FabriTac; AquaFlex*
Employs—20; Estab.—1984
Sales—over $20Mil
Distrib.—National
Privately owned corporation

### UNETTE CORP.

1578 Sussex Tpke. (07869)
**Phone—(973) 328-6800**
Fax—(973) 584-4794
www.unette.com
Email—info@unette.com
Hum. Res. & IT Mgr.—Chris Doscher
Pur. Coord.—Hope Merkel
SIC—3082; 3089; NAICS—326121; *Graduated plastic tubes & contract packaging*
Employs—30; Estab.—1955
65,000 sq ft site, Distrib.—Intl.
Privately owned corporation

### VERSEIDAG SEEMEE US, INC. (H Q)

4 Aspen Dr. (07869)
**Phone—(973) 252-1189**
National—(800) 252-1435
Fax—(973) 252-1109
www.seemeeus.com
Email—sgriswold@seemeeus.com
Pres.—Eric Tischer
Mktg. Mgr.—Sarah Griswold
SIC—2851; NAICS—325510; *Corporate headquarters; coating & composite materials for the sign, digital & screen printing industries (mfg. done overseas)*
Employs—12; Estab.—2001
Sales—$2.5Mil-$5Mil (est)
Distrib.—Local
Privately owned corporation

### ZONE DEFENSE, INC.

4 Emery Ave. (07869)
**Phone—(973) 328-0436**
Fax—(973) 366-0682
www.zonedefenseusa.com
Pres.—George Mandas
Estimator—Tony Campanella
Administrator—Pat Bien
SIC—2431; NAICS—321900; *Architectural millwork*
Employs—10; Estab.—1990
Sales—under $500,000
Distrib.—Local
Privately owned corporation

---

## Raritan

(Somerset—N.E.)

### 47 INDUSTRIES, LLC

59 2nd Ave. (08869)
**Phone—(908) 526-8865**
www.47fad.com
Email—mike@47fad.com
Owner—Mike Palazzo
SIC—3444; 3312; *Aluminum & stainless steel fabrication*
Employs—1; Estab.—1979
Sales—under $500,000 (est)
Distrib.—Regional
Privately owned corporation

### †ARCTIC GLACIER, INC.

Div. of Arctic Glacier U.S.A., Inc.
2 Johnson Dr. (08869)
**Phone—(908) 231-0100**
www.arcticglacier.com
Email—info@arcticglacier.com
Asst. Dist. Mgr.—Mike Janner
SIC—5199; *Distributor of cubed ice*
Employs—8; Estab.—1971
Sales—under $500,000
Distrib.—Local
Privately owned corporation
Parent co.—Arctic Glacier U.S.A., Inc., West St. Paul, MN
Phone—(651) 455-0410
See Parent Co. Section for full profile.

### D S F, INC.

401 U.S. Highway 202 (08869)
**Phone—(908) 218-5153**
Fax—(908) 218-5132
Email—dsfmillwork@aol.com
Pres.—Simon DeGirolamo
Hum. Res., IT & Off. Mgr.—Janet DeGirolamo
SIC—2431; 2434; NAICS—337110; *Architectural millwork & custom cabinets*
Employs—25; Estab.—1994
Sales—$2.6Mil-$5Mil
Distrib.—Regional
Privately owned corporation

### DIVERSIPRINT, INC.

1124 U.S. Highway 202, Ste. B-16 (08869)
**Phone—(908) 685-2225**
Fax—(908) 685-7150
www.promo-coach.com
Email—bob@diversiprintinc.com
Owner & Pres.—Bob Zarelli
Bookkeeper—Randy Davis
SIC—2759; 2752; *Commercial & lithographic printing*
Employs—3; Estab.—1992
Sales—under $500,000
Distrib.—Local
Privately owned corporation

### FASTSIGNS®

105 Sherman Ave. (08869)
**Phone—(908) 231-0306**
Fax—(908) 231-0411
www.fastsigns.com/197
Email—197@fastsigns.com
Owner—Tony DiRoma
SIC—3993; *Wood & metal interior & exterior signs*
Employs—3; Estab.—1993
3,500 sq ft site, Distrib.—Regional
Limited Liability Company

### FEDEX OFFICE & PRINT CENTER

Div. of FedEx Office & Print Services, Inc.
399 Highway 28 (08869)
**Phone—(908) 575-1221**
National—(800) 463-3339
Fax—(908) 575-2772
www.fedex.com
Email—usa1215@fedex.com
Center Mgr.—Rich Simone
Team Member—Doug Smith
Team Member—Sarah Smith
SIC—2759; NAICS—323100; *Commercial printing*
Employs—6; Estab.—2004
Sales—under $500,000
Distrib.—Intl.
Publicly owned corporation
Parent co.—FedEx Office & Print Services, Inc., Dallas, TX
Phone—(214) 550-7000
See Parent Co. Section for full profile.

### JANSSEN RESEARCH & DEVELOPMENT, LLC, A DIV. OF JOHNSON & JOHNSON

Div. of Johnson & Johnson
920 U.S. Highway 202, P.O. Box 300 (08869-0602)
**Phone—(908) 704-4000**
(908) 927-5440
Fax—(908) 526-5059
www.jnjpharmarnd.com
CFO—Chris Picariello
V-P., Opers.—Stuart Magloff
SIC—2834; NAICS—325412; *Pharmaceuticals; Brand name—Tylenol; Lmodrum; Motrin; Nicotrol; Lactaid*
Employs—2000; Estab.—1978
Sales—over $100Mil
Distrib.—National
Publicly owned corporation
Parent co.—Johnson & Johnson, New Brunswick, NJ
Phone—(732) 524-0400
See Parent Co. Section for full profile.

### NIC GROUP, THE

1130 U.S. Highway 202, Ste. E-6 (08869)
**Phone—(908) 253-8106**
Fax—(908) 253-0612
www.nicg.com
Email—support@nicg.com
Pres.—Michael Skomba
Off. Mgr.—Joy Sadlo
SIC—7373; *Computer network systems integration, IT consulting, custom software development & web design services*
Employs—9; Estab.—1995
Distrib.—Regional
Sole ownership

### ORTHO-CLINICAL DIAGNOSTICS, INC. (H Q)

Div. of Carlyle Group, The
1001 U.S. Highway 202, P.O. Box 350 (08869)
**Phone—(908) 218-1300**
www.orthoclinical.com
Email—media@ocdus.jnj.com
Chrm., CEO—Martin Madaus
Chief Operating Officer—Robert Yates
CFO—Jeffrey Capello
Chief Hum. Res. Officer—Beatriz Lopez
Ex. V-P., Comml.—Alex Socarras
V-P., Worldwide Qual., Regulatory & Compliance—Jennifer Paine
Gen. Counsel—Michael Schlesinger
Head of Worldwide Comm.—Stephanie Scott
SIC—2835; 3826; NAICS—325400; *Corporate headquarters; donor screening, immunohematology, clinical chemistry & immunodiagnostics products; Brand name—ORTHO™; VITROS®*
Employs—750
Worldwide: 4,500
Sales—$250Mil-$500Mil (est)
Distrib.—Intl.
Publicly owned corporation
Parent co.—Carlyle Group, The, Washington, DC, MD
Phone—(202) 347-2626
See Parent Co. Section for full profile.

### PRINT-TECH PRODUCTS, INC.

603 1st Ave., Ste. 1-C (08869)
**Phone—(908) 231-8700**
Pres.—Allan B. Sydlo
SIC—2759; NAICS—323100; *Commercial & business form printing*
Employs—2; Estab.—1994
Sales—under $500,000 (est)
Distrib.—Local
Privately owned corporation

### SOMERSET WOOD PRODUCTS CO.

10 Johnson Dr. (08869)
**Phone—(908) 526-0030**
Fax—(908) 526-9536
www.somersetwood.net
Email—swp@somersetwood.net
Pres.—Mitch Bloch
SIC—2431; NAICS—321900; *Architectural woodwork, including custom paneling, casework, cabinetry, moldings & doors*
Employs—12; Estab.—1967
Sales—$2.5Mil-$5Mil
20,000 sq ft site, Distrib.—Regional
Privately owned corporation

NEW ENTRY
### SONSCREEN GRAPHICS, INC.

77 Tillman St. (08869)
**Phone—(908) 429-1657**
Fax—(908) 429-9480
Owner—Ed Kozic
SIC—2396; 2395; *T-shirt screen printing & embroidery*
Employs—4
Sales—$500,000-$1Mil (est)
Distrib.—Regional
Sole ownership

### UFP TECHNOLOGIES, INC.

1 Johnson Dr. (08869)
**Phone—(800) 372-3172**
www.ufpt.com
Email—info@ufpt.com
Manager—Katharine Galbraith
SIC—3086; NAICS—326100; *Foam packaging, thermoforming & foam components; Brand name—*
Employs—50; Estab.—1963
67,000 sq ft site, Distrib.—Intl.
Publicly owned corporation
ISO rating—9001
Parent co.—UFP Technologies, Inc., Georgetown, MA
Phone—(800) 372-3172
See Parent Co. Section for full profile.

---

## Red Bank

(Monmouth—N.E.)

### ALL AMERICAN PRINT & COPY CENTER

518 Highway 35 (07701)
**Phone—(732) 758-6200**
Fax—(732) 758-9686
www.allamericanprint.net
Email—aapcc@comcast.net
Owner—Ralph Cucinelli
Graphic Designer—Barbara Buccilli

GEOGRAPHICAL

## Red Bank—(cont.)

SIC—2759; 2752; 2791; NAICS—323122; *Commercial offset printing & typesetting*
Employs—2; Estab.—1980
Sales—under $500,000
Distrib.—National
Limited Liability Company

### ALPHAGRAPHICS PRINTSHOPS

Div. of AlphaGraphics Printshops Of The Future
68 White St. (07701)
**Phone—(732) 758-0095**
Fax—(732) 758-0098
www.us316.alphagraphics.com
Email—us316@alphagraphics.com
Pres.—Jac Bloomberg
Creative Dir.—Christina Mantak
Opers. Mgr.—Amy Beagan
Cust. Serv. Rep.—Brandon Carson
SIC—2759; 2752; NAICS—323122; *Offset, instant, large-format & digital color printing of banners & blueprints & creative design services*
Employs—5; Estab.—1990
Sales—$1Mil
2,400 sq ft site, Distrib.—Local
Privately owned corporation
Parent co.—AlphaGraphics Printshops Of The Future, Scottsdale, AZ
Phone—(480) 991-1636
See Parent Co. Section for full profile.

### ANCHOR CONCRETE PRODUCTS, INC. (H Q)

Div. of Oldcastle, Inc.
331 Newman Springs Rd., Bldg. 2, 3rd Fl., Ste. 236 (07701)
**Phone—(732) 292-2500**
Fax—(732) 292-2650
www.anchorcp.com
Email—info@anchorcp.com
Pres.—John O'Neill
Dir., Hum. Res.—Linda Boylan
Dir., Mktg. Comm.—Teresa Hicks
Qual. Control Mgr.—Michael O'Neill, Jr.
Payroll Mgr.—Debbie Corrado
SIC—3273; 3272; NAICS—327390; *Corporate headquarters; concrete products*
Employs—20; Estab.—1950
Company-wide: 407
Sales—$2.5Mil-$5Mil
100,000 sq ft site, Distrib.—Regional
Publicly owned corporation
Parent co.—Oldcastle, Inc., Atlanta, GA
Phone—(770) 804-3363
See Parent Co. Section for full profile.

### B & C CUSTOM WOOD HANDRAIL CORP.

131 Dr. James Parker Blvd., P.O. Box 2008 (07701)
**Phone—(732) 530-6640**
Fax—(732) 842-6258
www.bcstairshop.com
Email—bc.stairs@verizon.net
Pres.—Christopher Kalkucki
Off. Mgr.—Joyce Kalkucki
SIC—2431; NAICS—321900; *Wooden stairs & railways & wood rails with metal baluster*
Employs—6; Estab.—1983
Sales—$500,000-$1Mil
4,500 sq ft site, Distrib.—Local
Privately owned corporation

### BASIL T'S BREW PUB & ITALIAN GRILL

183 Riverside Ave. (07701)
**Phone—(732) 842-5990**
Fax—(732) 842-8675
www.basilt.com
Email—johnnybrew@basilt.com
Pres., R & D Mgr.—Victor Rallo, Jr.

GM—Bryan Grober
Fin., Hum. Res. & MIS Mgr.—Terri Levinson
Manager—Rose Rubino
SIC—2082; *Beer*
Employs—60; Estab.—1988
Distrib.—Regional
Privately owned corporation

### BRAND & OPPENHEIMER CO., INC.

188 E. Bergen Pl., Ste. 201 (07701)
**Phone—(732) 224-7400**
Fax—(732) 224-1172
www.brandandoppenheimer.com
Email—info@brandandoppenheimer.com
Pres., CEO—Daniel Pezold
Cust. Serv. Mgr.—Judy Colvin
Bus. Mgr., Specialty Fabrics—David Mackney
SIC—2399; NAICS—313311; *Corporate headquarters & textile converting*
Employs—6; Estab.—1991
Sales—$500,000-$1Mil (est)
Distrib.—National
Privately owned corporation

### COREMATRIX SYSTEMS

125 Half Mile Rd., Ste. 200 (07701)
**Phone—(732) 332-1931**
National—(877) 276-2120
www.corematrix.com
Email—info@corematrix.com
Co-Founder & Pres.—Frank McMahon
Co-Founder—Paul Nix
V-P., Mktg.—Joan Rothman
V-P., Fin. & Hum. Res.—Mary Keller
SIC—7373; *Computer network systems integration & IT services*
Employs—75; Estab.—2002
Privately owned corporation

[NEW ENTRY]
### CREATIVE PRINTING RESOURCES, LLC

17 Kimberly Ct., Apt. 121 (07701)
**Phone—(732) 842-0240**
Email—cprsue@verizon.net
Owner—Susan Kelly
SIC—2759; 2678; *Commercial printing, including brochures, direct mail & stationery*
Employs—3; Estab.—1986
Sales—under $500,000
Distrib.—National
Limited Liability Company

### DENALI CO., LLC, THE (H Q)

43 W. Front St., Ste. 11 (07701-1600)
**Phone—(732) 219-7771**
National—(800) 606-4003
Fax—(732) 219-7772
www.denalico.com
Email—info@denalico.com
Pres.—Ken Lindemann
Admn. Mgr.—Henny Copeland
SIC—2396; *Company headquarters; award ribbons*
Employs—3; Estab.—1996
Company-wide: 25
Distrib.—National
Limited Liability Company

### DIVERSIFIED GRAPHIC MACHINERY

230 Highway 35 (07701)
**Phone—(732) 933-4865**
Fax—(732) 933-1504
www.dgmna.com
Email—mdebard@dgmna.com
Pres.—Michael DeBard
V-P., Sales—Paul Peyrebrune
V-P., Opers.—Walter Sussuma
Sales Mgr., Natl.—Dan Quenzer

SIC—3555; *Cold foil systems & hot foil stamping machines for the printing industry; Brand name—DGM Foildex™ Cold Foil Application System; DGM Filmdex™ UV Cast & Cure Application Systems*
Employs—10; Estab.—2000
Distrib.—Intl.
Privately owned corporation

### DOC'S DUDS, LLC

92 Half Mile Rd. (07701)
**Phone—(732) 219-0060**
Fax—(732) 224-0750
www.docsduds.com
Email—wgreer@docsduds.com
Ptnr.—Diana E. Trusky
Ptnr.—Wayne Greer
SIC—2326; 2339; *Custom lab coats for medical, dental & healthcare professionals*
Employs—15; Estab.—2004
Sales—$6Mil-$10Mil
Distrib.—Intl.
Limited Liability Company

### F T MILLWORK

9-B Catherine St. (07701)
**Phone—(732) 741-1216**
Fax—(732) 741-0216
www.mjcustomwoodworks.com
Pres.—Frank Thomas
SIC—2431; NAICS—321900; *Wooden doors, windows & millwork*
Employs—1; Estab.—1982
Sales—under $500,000
Distrib.—Local
Privately owned corporation
AKA: Custom Woodwork

### FANTASTIC SIGNS CO.

351 Shrewsbury Ave. (07701)
**Phone—(732) 747-7763**
Fax—(732) 747-7797
Email—fanjjohn@aol.com
Pres.—John Oakley
Off. Mgr.—Aren Oakley
SIC—3993; *Interior & exterior vinyl signs*
Employs—2; Estab.—1998
Sales—under $500,000
Distrib.—Local
Privately owned corporation

### †FERGUSON ENTERPRISES, INC.

207 Cooper Rd. (07701)
**Phone—(732) 530-7200**
Fax—(732) 219-0387
www.ferguson.com
Email—thomas.mcmanus@ferguson.com
Br. Mgr.—Thomas McManus
SIC—5074; 5075; *Distributor of plumbing & HVAC equipment & supplies, including pipes, fixtures, valves, fittings, pumps & well supplies*
Employs—20; Estab.—1998
Distrib.—National
Publicly owned corporation
Parent co.—Ferguson Enterprises, Inc., Newport News, VA
Phone—(757) 874-7795
See Parent Co. Section for full profile.

### IKANOS COMMUNICATIONS, INC.

100 Schultz Dr. (07701)
**Phone—(732) 345-7500**
Fax—(866) 702-1069
www.ikanos.com
Email—info@ikanos.com
Dir., Opers.—Larry Hicks
SIC—3674; NAICS—334413; *Computer chips*
Employs—100; Estab.—2009
Sales—$6Mil-$10Mil
Distrib.—Intl.
Privately owned corporation

Parent co.—Ikanos Communications, Inc., Fremont, CA
Phone—(510) 979-0400
See Parent Co. Section for full profile.

### †KNOPF AUTOMOTIVE, LLC

93 Shrewsbury Ave., Apt. 1 (07701)
**Phone—(732) 212-0444**
Fax—(732) 212-0477
www.mmknopf.com
Email—cores@mmknopf.com
Ptnr.—Marshall Knopf
Ptnr.—Woody Knopf
Pres.—Allen Wilkie
SIC—5015; *Company headquarters & wholesaler of used automotive parts*
Employs—20; Estab.—2007
Distrib.—National
Limited Liability Company

### LOG-NET, INC.

230 Half Mile Rd., 3rd Fl. (07701)
**Phone—(732) 758-6800**
Fax—(732) 747-7497
www.log-net.com
Email—sales@log-net.com
Pres., CEO—John Motley
V-P., Sales, Worldwide—John Painter
SIC—7372; *Supply chain software development*
Employs—40; Estab.—1991
Distrib.—Intl.
Privately owned corporation

### MCGINNIS PRINTING

20 Monmouth St. (07701)
**Phone—(732) 758-0060**
Fax—(732) 758-0070
Email—mcginnisprinting@comcast.net
Owner—Dennis McGinnis
GM—Jason Smith
Off. Mgr.—Mona Soliman
SIC—2752; 2791; NAICS—323122; *Offset & instant printing & typesetting*
Employs—3; Estab.—1987
Sales—under $500,000
Distrib.—Local
Sole ownership

### MEDIA VISTA, INC.

60 Broad St., Ste. 100 (07701)
**Phone—(732) 747-8060**
Fax—(732) 747-8955
www.thoroughbreddailynews.com
Email—tbrednews@aol.com
CEO—Barry Weisbord
V-P.—Susan Finley
Cust. Serv. Rep.—Vicki Forbes
SIC—2721; *Newsletter publishing*
Employs—12; Estab.—1986
Sales—$500,000-$1Mil
Distrib.—Intl.
Privately owned corporation

### MONMOUTH JOURNAL, THE

212 Maple Ave. (07701-1731)
**Phone—(732) 747-7007**
Fax—(732) 747-5445
www.themonmouthjournal.com
Email—news@themonmouthjournal.com
Mng. Editor—Gary Chapman
GM—Susan Paviluk
SIC—2711; *Weekly newspaper publishing*
Employs—10; Estab.—2004
Distrib.—Local
Limited Liability Company

### NATCORE TECHNOLOGY, INC. (H Q)

87 Maple Ave. (07701)
**Phone—(732) 576-8800**
National—(877) 700-6282
Fax—(732) 576-8809
www.natcoresolar.com
Email—info@natcoresolar.com
Chrm., Dir.—Brien Lundin
Pres., CEO & Dir.—Charles Provini

## Red Bank—(cont.)

CFO—John Meekison
Corp. Attorney—Shauna Hartman
SIC—3674; *Corporate headquarters; photovoltaic solar panels (mfg. done in Italy & China); Brand name—AR-Box™; NanoShade™*
Employs—5; Estab.—2009
Sales—$1Mil-$2.5Mil (est)
Distrib.—National
Publicly owned corporation
AKA: Nanoshade Solar

### O. CO IMPRINTS, LLC

58 W. Bergen Pl., P.O. Box 8249 (07701)
**Phone—(732) 530-3202**
Fax—(732) 219-5043
www.ocoimprints.com
Email—oco@monmouth.com
Owner—Olivia Conklin
SIC—3993; 2396; 2395; *Screen printed & embroidered garments, promotional items & advertising specialty products*
Employs—3; Estab.—1985
Sales—under $500,000
2,000 sq ft site, Distrib.—National
Limited Liability Company

### PURCHASINGNET, INC.

125 Half Mile Rd. (07701)
Mail addr: P.O. Box 480, Lincroft (07738)
**Phone—(732) 212-1500**
Fax—(732) 212-1215
www.purchasingnet.com
Pres., CEO—Tim McEneny
Sr. V-P.—Laurene Fielder
Cont.—Eileen Durkin
Mng. Dir., Sales & Mktg.—Frank A. Davis, Jr.
Off. Mgr.—Wanda DiMarco
SIC—7372; *Software development; Brand name—Pnet*
Employs—40
Distrib.—Intl.
Privately owned corporation

### SATTERFIELD ORIGINALS

130 Bodman Pl., Apt. 2 (07701)
**Phone—(908) 902-0290**
Fax—(908) 902-0290
www.satterfieldoriginals.com
Email—pat@satterfieldoriginals.com
Owner & Pres.—Patrick Satterfield
SIC—2499; 2511; NAICS—322200; *Wooden serving trays, placemats, cheese boards & specialty gifts & refinishing of old furniture & costume furniture fabrication*
Employs—5
Sales—$500,000-$1Mil
Distrib.—National
Sole ownership

### SEALS EASTERN, INC.

134 Pearl St., P.O. Box 520 (07701)
**Phone—(732) 747-9200**
Fax—(732) 747-3647
www.sealseastern.com
Email—info@sealseastern.com
CEO & Dir., Tech.—Daniel L. Hertz, Jr.
Pres., GM, Sales & Market Dev.—Daniel L. Hertz III
Qual. Assur. Mgr.—S. Iskander
SIC—3053; NAICS—339991; *Rubber seals & gaskets for the oil & gas & diesel engine industries; Brand name—7182 Series™*
Employs—137; Estab.—1960
Sales—$18Mil
70,000 sq ft site, Distrib.—Intl.
Privately owned corporation
ISO rating—9001:2008

### TWO RIVER TIMES

75 W. Front St., Ste. 2 (07701)
**Phone—(732) 219-5788**
Fax—(732) 224-0806
www.trtnj.com
Pres.—Domenic Dipiero
COO—Donna Rovere
Editor—Michele Kuhn
Classified Mgr.—Tracey Lucas
SIC—2711; *Newspaper publishing*
Employs—9; Estab.—1992
Distrib.—Local
Privately owned corporation

### ULTRA CHEMICAL, INC.

2 Bridge Ave., Ste. 630 (07701-4605)
**Phone—(732) 224-0200**
Fax—(732) 224-0017
www.ultrachem.com
Email—info@ultrachem.com
Pres.—Arthur Lynch
Dir., Sales—Jim Lynch
Dir., Raw Matls.—Brian Lynch
Off. Mgr.—Tone Monks
Technical Mgr.—Christopher Murphy
Mktg. Coord.—Ellen Edson
SIC—2844; 2899; NAICS—325600; *Custom & specialty ingredients for the personal care & cosmetics industries; Brand name—Ultrapure; Ultracolor; Ultraol; Ultra Talc*
Employs—8; Estab.—1992
Sales—under $10Mil
Distrib.—Intl.
Privately owned corporation

### WRITE IMPRESSION, THE

549 Highway 35 (07701)
**Phone—(732) 706-3700**
Fax—(732) 706-3701
www.thewriteimpressionnj.com
Email—thewriteimpressionnj@gmail.com
Owner—Kristine Ancona
SIC—2759; 2752; 2678; NAICS—322233; *Custom invitation & stationery printing*
Employs—1; Estab.—1979
Sales—under $500,000
Distrib.—Local
Privately owned corporation

---

## Richwood

(Gloucester—S.W.)

### BLUE CHIP TECHNOLOGY

267 Richwood Rd., P.O. Box 287 (08074)
**Phone—(856) 881-3133**
Fax—(856) 881-0233
www.bluechip-technology.com
Owner—Frank J. Winters
V-P.—Gloria Winters
SIC—3599; *General machining job shop*
Employs—10; Estab.—1994
Distrib.—Local
Privately owned corporation

---

## Ridgefield

(Bergen—N.E.)

### ACME ROLLING STEEL DOOR CORP.

1099 Linden Ave., P.O. Box 33 (07657)
**Phone—(201) 943-7070**
          (800) 281-5680
Fax—(201) 943-1206
www.acmedoor.com
Email—acmersd@aol.com
Pres.—Jeff Krautman
V-P., Opers.—Joe Gazzillo
Cont.—Nora Polli
Sales Mgr.—Daria Krautman

SIC—3442; NAICS—332321; *Rolling steel service & fire doors & fire door testing*
Employs—17; Estab.—1968
Sales—$5Mil
20,000 sq ft site, Distrib.—Regional
Privately owned corporation
AKA: Acme Door Service

### APPLE EXHIBITS

730 Grand Ave., Unit 1-A (07657)
**Phone—(201) 943-2775**
National—(888) 554-0600
Fax—(201) 943-2778
www.appleexhibits.com
Email—info@appleexhibits.com
Owner—Young Park
SIC—2541; 2542; 3993; NAICS—323100; *Trade show exhibits & booths & custom displays*
Employs—10; Estab.—2004
Sales—under $500,000
Distrib.—Local
Privately owned corporation

### BEBE CHIC

530 Church St. (07657)
Mail addr: 53 Howard Park Dr., Tenafly (07670-2936)
**Phone—(201) 941-5414**
Fax—(866) 374-9422
www.bebechic.com
Email—info@bebechic.com
Pres.—Caren Karpik
SIC—2392; 2399; *Children's bedding & accessories; Brand name—Bebe Chic*
Employs—8; Estab.—2001
Sales—$1Mil-$2.5Mil (est)
Distrib.—National
Privately owned corporation

### BERGEN INSTANT PRINTING, INC.

328 Broad Ave. (07657)
**Phone—(201) 945-7303**
Fax—(201) 945-3142
Email—bip.printing@verizon.net
Pres.—Bill Ackerman
Printer—Juan Dejesun
SIC—2752; NAICS—323100; *Offset printing*
Employs—3; Estab.—1979
2,000 sq ft site, Distrib.—Local
Privately owned corporation

### BIAZZO DAIRY PRODUCTS, INC.

1145 Edgewater Ave. (07657)
**Phone—(201) 941-6800**
www.biazzo.com
Email—info@biazzo.com
Owner & V-P.—John Iapichino
SIC—2022; NAICS—311513; *Ricotta & mozzarella & fresh mozaarella cheeses*
Employs—27; Estab.—1963
116,000 sq ft site, Distrib.—National
Privately owned corporation

### BRUDERER MACHINERY, INC.

1200 Hendricks Cswy. (07657)
**Phone—(201) 941-2121**
Fax—(201) 886-2010
www.brudereramericas.com
Email—info@brudereramericas.com
Pres.—Alois J. Rupp
Corp. Secy.—Donna Koterba
SIC—3541; 3542; NAICS—333512; *Corporate headquarters & high speed stamping presses*
Employs—30; Estab.—1976
40,000 sq ft site, Distrib.—Intl.
Privately owned corporation
ISO rating—9001

### CAST CLASSICS, INC.

65 Railroad Ave. (07657)
**Phone—(201) 896-1515**
Fax—(201) 896-1539
www.castclassics.com
Email—info@castclassics.com
Pres.—David Arad

SIC—2514; *Aluminum lawn furniture*
Employs—4; Estab.—1992
Distrib.—Local
Privately owned corporation

### CIVIL SERVICE LEADER

313 Broad Ave., Ste. 203 (07657)
**Phone—(201) 941-6397**
National—(800) 281-5323
Fax—(201) 941-1803
Email—njcivilserviceleader@aol.com
Owner & Publisher—John Ferrara
SIC—2711; *Newspaper publishing*
Employs—10; Estab.—1991
Sales—under $500,000 (est)
Distrib.—Local
Privately owned corporation

### COLORITE, A TEKNI-PLEX CO.

Div. of Tekni-Plex, Inc.
101 Railroad Ave. (07657)
**Phone—(201) 941-2900**
National—(800) 631-1577
Fax—(201) 941-0602
www.tekni-plex.com
Email—coloritecustserv@tekni-plex.com
Plt. Mgr.—Ross Kisciras
Hum. Res. Mgr.—Anita D'Aversa
SIC—3087; NAICS—325991; *Divisional headquarters & PVC compounds*
Employs—200; Estab.—1952
Sales—$25Mil-$100Mil
230,000 sq ft site, Distrib.—Intl.
Privately owned corporation
ISO rating—9001:2008
Parent co.—Tekni-Plex, Inc., King of Prussia, PA
   Phone—(484) 690-1520
See Parent Co. Section for full profile.

### COMFORT CONCEPTS, INC.

501 Broad Ave., Ste. 7 (07657)
**Phone—(201) 941-6700**
National—(800) 935-2241
Fax—(201) 941-6770
www.comfortconcepts.com
Email—info@comfortconcepts.com
Ptnr.—Robert Mass
Ptnr.—Gary Mass
SIC—3842; 2399; 2392; 5199; *Manufacturer & distributor of reusable under pads, diapers, briefs, bibs, specialty clothing, towels, sheets, bedspreads, pillows, pillowcases, gowns & blankets & pet products, including pads, leashes & bedding*
Employs—16; Estab.—1990
12,000 sq ft site, Distrib.—National
Privately owned sub-S corp.

### COSMETIC ESSENCE, INC.

1135 Pleasantview Ter. W. (07657)
**Phone—(201) 941-9800**
Fax—(201) 941-6497
www.cosmeticessence.com
Email—sales@cosmeticessence.com
V-P., Opers. & GM—Jeff Munafo
Hum. Res. Mgr.—Eileen McGorty
SIC—2844; NAICS—325600; *Cosmetics*
Employs—440; Estab.—2007
Sales—$100Mil-$250Mil (est)
Distrib.—National
Publicly owned corporation
Parent co.—Cosmetic Essence, Inc., Holmdel, NJ
   Phone—(732) 888-7788
See Parent Co. Section for full profile.

### GARDEN STATE PRECISION, INC.

510 Church St. (07657)
**Phone—(201) 945-6410**
Fax—(201) 945-3695
www.gardenstateprecision.com
Email—info@gardenstateprecision.com

GEOGRAPHICAL

## Ridgefield—(cont.)

Pres.—Joseph D. Molino
Off. Mgr.—Elizabeth Mullan
SIC—3544; NAICS—333500; *Tool
& die job shop*
Employs—9; Estab.—1973
Sales—$1Mil
5,000 sq ft site, Distrib.—National
Privately owned corporation

### GENERAL DEVICES

1000 River St. (07657)
**Phone—(201) 313-7075**
Fax—(201) 313-5671
www.general-devices.com
Email—info@general-devices.com
Pres.—Curt Bashford
Dir., Engrg.—Gregory Lowe
Off. Mgr.—Lisa Tooley
SIC—3845; NAICS—334500;
*EMS information, telemedicine,
communication & documentation
systems & paramedic telemetry
equipment; Brand name—
CAREpoint Workstation; Prep-
Check Electrode Impedance
Meter; Rosetta Data Translators;
e-Bridge Telemedicine System;
e-Net Messenger*
Employs—18; Estab.—1979
Sales—$2Mil-$6Mil
7,800 sq ft site, Distrib.—National
Privately owned corporation

### GENZYME CORP., BIOSURGERY DIV.

Div. of Genzyme Corp.
1125 Pleasant View Ter. (07657)
**Phone—(201) 945-9550**
Fax—(201) 402-5322
www.genzyme.com
Email—info@genzyme.com
Sr. V.-P., Opers.—Don Woodhouse
Cont.—Ed Charles
SIC—2836; NAICS—325414;
*Biotechnology products for
biosurgery applications*
Employs—300; Estab.—1999
27,910 sq ft site, Distrib.—Intl.
Publicly owned corporation
Parent co.—Genzyme Corp.,
Cambridge, MA
Phone—(617) 252-7500
See Parent Co. Section for full profile.

### GROW CO., INC.

55 Railroad Ave. (07657)
**Phone—(201) 941-8777**
        (201) 941-6716
Fax—(201) 941-1881
www.growco.us
Email—info@growco.us
Pres.—Magda Peck
V.-P.—Massoud Arvanaghi
SIC—2834; NAICS—325412;
*Biologically & physiologically
evaluated active food
supplements; Brand name—Re-
Natured; Pro-Natured; Bio-
Grown; Bio-Growth; BioGrow*
Employs—15; Estab.—1977
Sales—$8Mil-$10Mil
40,000 sq ft site, Distrib.—Intl.
Privately owned sub-S corp.

### HOLOGRAPHIC FINISHING, INC.

501 Hendricks Cswy., P.O. Box 597
(07657)
**Phone—(201) 941-4651**
National—(866) 640-7220
Fax—(201) 941-4453
www.holographicfinishing.com
Email—holo.graphic@verizon.net
Pres.—Michael Vulcano
V.-P.—Charlie Vulcano
Secy.-Treas.—Mariann Vulcano
SIC—2759; 2675; NAICS—
323100; *Paper embossing, die
cutting, glueing, stamping &
finishing*
Employs—12; Estab.—1988
Sales—$500,000-$1Mil
6,800 sq ft site, Distrib.—Regional
Sole ownership

### INSTANT IMAGE PRINTING

649 Bergen Blvd. (07657)
**Phone—(201) 945-0020**
Fax—(201) 945-2771
Owner—Rich LeBrund
SIC—2752; NAICS—323100;
*Offset printing*
Employs—1; Estab.—1985
Sales—under $500,000 (est)
Distrib.—Local
Sole ownership

### JEWELRY TRAY & PAD CO., INC.

1150 Edgewater Ave. (07657)
**Phone—(201) 941-4300**
Fax—(201) 941-1226
www.jewelrytray.com
Email—mariag@jewelrytray.com
Pres.—Aaron Rosenberg
Cont., Hum. Res. & IT Mgr.—Shari
Rosenberg
Off. Mgr.—Maria Garcia
SIC—2542; 2541; NAICS—
316999; *Jewelry displays*
Employs—22; Estab.—1954
11,250 sq ft site, Distrib.—Local
Privately owned sub-S corp.

### LASERCAM, INC.

1039 Hoyt Ave. (07657)
**Phone—(201) 941-1262**
Fax—(201) 941-2907
www.lasercam.com
Email—sales@lasercam.com
Pres.—David Shapiro
V.-P., MIS & R & D—Karl Koether
Secy.-Treas.—Stanley Shapiro
SIC—3544; NAICS—333500;
*Corporate headquarters & steel
rule dies*
Employs—40; Estab.—1979
15,000 sq ft site, Distrib.—National
Privately owned partnership

### MONDI

Div. of Tekkote Corp.
1100 Slocum Ave. (07657)
**Phone—(201) 585-8875**
www.mondi.com
Email—sales@mondi.com
GM—Paul Ortiz
SIC—2671; NAICS—322222;
*Silicone-coated release liners for
pressure-sensitive adhesive
products*
Employs—100; Estab.—1988
Sales—$25Mil-$50Mil (est)
40,000 sq ft site,
Parent co.—Tekkote Corp., Leonia,
NJ
Phone—(201) 585-8875
See Parent Co. Section for full profile.

### MONTENA TARANTO FOODS, INC.

400 Victoria Ter. *(07657)*
**Phone—(201) 943-8484**
        (800) 809-3336
Fax—(201) 943-6037
Email—montenataranto@aol.com
Pres.—Joe Taranto
V.-P.—Wade Montena
Manager—Eddie Rodriguez
SIC—2022; NAICS—311513;
*Italian cheese & cheese
products*
Employs—60; Estab.—1994
Sales—$20Mil
Distrib.—Regional
Privately owned corporation

### MORSEMERE IRONWORKS, INC.

1085 Linden Ave. (07657)
**Phone—(201) 941-1133**
Fax—(201) 941-7745
Pres., GM, Fin., Hum. Res. & IT
Mgr.—Mark Candeletti
Plt. Mgr.—Steve Birdsall
SIC—3441; NAICS—332312;
*Structural steel fabrication*
Employs—10; Estab.—1924
Sales—$500,000-$1Mil
9,000 sq ft site, Distrib.—Local
Privately owned corporation

### NEW LIFE COLOR REPRODUCTION, INC.

610 Broad Ave. (07657)
**Phone—(201) 943-7005**
www.newlifecolor.com
Email—newlifecolorrepro@nj.rr.com
Pres.—Dragaw Zibkobic
SIC—2796; NAICS—323122;
*Color separations*
Employs—4
Sales—under $500,000 (est)
Distrib.—National
Privately owned corporation

### †PC TAN, INC.

1040 Wilt Ave. (07657)
**Phone—(201) 943-6100**
National—(800) 327-8826
Fax—(201) 943-4234
www.pctan.com
Email—info@pctan.com
Pres.—Susan Miller
CFO—Michael Rolls
V.-P., Sales—Paul Manke
V.-P., Sales—Eric Haynes
SIC—5087; 5122; 5046; 5049;
NAICS—335122; *Corporate
headquarters & distributor of
imported German engineered
tanning beds, booths, parts &
accessories, including lotions,
sprays & creams; Brand name—
Uwe; KBL; Eternal Sun; Wolff;
Cosmedico; Heraeus; Australian
Gold; California Tan; Designer
Skin; Supre; MR International;
Devoted Creations; Ed Hardy;
Playboy; Fiesta Sun; ProTan;
Norvell; EyePro*
Employs—35; Estab.—1986
Distrib.—National
Privately owned corporation

### SUNSET FLORIST, LLC

470 Bergen Blvd. (07657)
**Phone—(201) 941-5411**
National—(877) 941-5411
www.sunsetflowers.net
Pres.—Harry Khorozin
SIC—3999; *Artificial flowers*
Employs—4; Estab.—1994
Sales—under $500,000 (est)
2,000 sq ft site, Distrib.—Local
Limited Liability Company

### TOUFAYAN BAKERY, INC.

175 Railroad Ave. (07657)
**Phone—(201) 941-2000**
National—(800) 328-7482
Fax—(201) 941-7988
www.toufayan.com
Email—info@toufayan.com
Pres., Pur. Agt.—Harry Toufayan
V.-P.—Gregory Toufayan
Comp., Cred. & Off. Mgr.—Kristine
Toufayan
Sales & Mktg. Mgr.—Karen
Toufayan
Traf. Mgr.—Charlie Torosian
SIC—2051; NAICS—311812;
*Corporate headquarters & pita
bread*
Employs—20; Estab.—1926
Sales—$1Mil-$5Mil
125,000 sq ft site, Distrib.—Intl.
Privately owned corporation

### TREND PRINTING INTERNATIONAL LABEL, INC.

1183 Edgewater Ave. (07657)
**Phone—(201) 941-6611**
Fax—(201) 941-6307
www.trendlabel.org
Email—trend@trendlabel.org
Pres.—David Fishbein
V.-P., Sales—Stephen D. Fishbein
SIC—2672; 3089; NAICS—
322222; *Labels & flexible
packaging*
Employs—15; Estab.—1959
Sales—$1Mil-$2.5Mil
10,000 sq ft site, Distrib.—Intl.
Privately owned sub-S corp.

### UNION CITY FILAMENT CORP.

1039-A Hoyt Ave., P.O. Box 777
(07657)
**Phone—(201) 945-3366**
Fax—(201) 945-6634
www.ucfilament.com
Email—info@ucfilament.com
CEO—Joseph E. Celia III
Pres.—Joseph E. Celia, Jr.
Admn. Mgr.—Barbara Crowley
SIC—3679; 3671; NAICS—
334411; *Electronic components*
Employs—30; Estab.—1950
Sales—$1Mil-$5Mil
Distrib.—Regional
Sole ownership

### UNIQUE EMBROIDERY, INC.

1030 Pleasantview Ter. (07657)
**Phone—(201) 943-9191**
Pres.—Robby Moutran
SIC—2395; 2396; *Custom
embroidery & apparel & textile
screen printing*
Employs—11
Sales—$500,000-$1Mil (est)
Distrib.—Local
Privately owned corporation

NEW ENTRY

### UNITED ENVELOPE & PRINTING CO., INC.

65 Railroad Ave. (07657)
**Phone—(201) 699-5800**
National—(800) 752-4012
Fax—(201) 313-7177
www.unitedenvelope.com
Email—info@unitedenvelope.com
Pres.—Ken Bernstein
CFO—Michael Mento
Ex. V.-P.—Stuart Grover
Ex. V.-P.—Jeff Worob
V.-P., Hum. Res.—Andrea
Valentino
IT Mgr.—Micheal Turdo
SIC—2752; 2677; NAICS—
322232; *Offset & letterpress
envelope printing*
Employs—75; Estab.—1926
60,000 sq ft site, Distrib.—National
Privately owned corporation

## Ridgefield Park

(Bergen—N.E.)

### ADVERTISERS SERVICES GROUP, INC.

65 Railroad Ave. (07660)
**Phone—(201) 440-5577**
Fax—(201) 440-5134
www.advertisersservices.com
Email—advertisers@verizon.net
Pres.—E. Kelly
Creative Dir.—Laura Gaffney
GM—Richard Glynn
Off. Mgr.—Pat Kelly
Fin. Mgr.—Judy Glynn
SIC—2752; NAICS—323100;
*Offset printing*
Employs—5; Estab.—1961
Sales—under $500,000
15,000 sq ft site, Distrib.—
Regional
Privately owned corporation

### ALL GRANITE & MARBLE CORP.

1 Mount Vernon St., Ste. A (07660)
**Phone—(201) 440-6779**
Fax—(201) 440-6855
www.marble.com
Email—sales@marble.com
Pres.—Richey Jaroslaw
Sales Rep.—Boco Cantoverde
SIC—3281; 2542; NAICS—
327991; *Corporate headquarters
& marble, granite & solid-surface
countertops*
Employs—10; Estab.—1998
Sales—$500,000-$1Mil (est)
Distrib.—Local
Privately owned corporation

## Ridgefield Park—(cont.)

**ALL NU TROPHY & SCREEN PRINTING**

243 Teaneck Rd. (07660)
**Phone—(201) 807-0808**
Fax—(201) 807-0041
Owner—Alan Jones
Off. Mgr.—David Brothers
SIC—2759; 2396; 3479; NAICS—323100; *Plastic & textile screen printing & engraving*
Employs—13; Estab.—1970
Distrib.—Intl.
Sole ownership

**BERGEN FENCE, INC.**

279 Bergen Tpke. (07660)
**Phone—(201) 641-2111**
Fax—(201) 641-0799
www.bergenfence.com
Email—estimate@bergenfence.com
Sales Mgr.—John Durr
SIC—2499; 3089; *Wooden & vinyl fencing*
Employs—6; Estab.—1953
Distrib.—Local
Privately owned corporation

**CLOVER PRINTING CORP.**

77 Park St. (07660)
**Phone—(201) 641-7800**
Fax—(201) 641-1855
Pres.—Harvey Kass
SIC—2759; NAICS—323100; *Commercial printing*
Employs—9
Sales—$1Mil-$2.5Mil (est)

**CONSOLIDATED PACKAGING GROUP**

30 Bergen Tpke., P.O. Box 261 (07660)
**Phone—(201) 440-4240**
Fax—(201) 440-4840
www.conpackgroup.com
Email—grk@conpackgroup.com
Pres.—William Kaufman
Ex. V-P.—Gary R. Kaufman
V-P., Prodn.—Ben Kaufman
Plt. Mgr.—Moshe Weinberger
Off. Mgr.—Evan Greenberg
SIC—3081; NAICS—326113; *Flexible laminated roll stock for the fresh & frozen food industries; Brand name—Inno-Lok™*
Employs—100; Estab.—1978
Sales—$10Mil-$20Mil
Distrib.—Intl.
Privately owned corporation

**CUSTOM FAB PIPE SUPPLY CORP.**

1-A Mount Vernon St. (07660)
**Phone—(201) 343-3739**
Fax—(201) 440-5485
Email—walt@fireguardsprinkle.com
Pres.—Walt Steinel
Bookkeeper—Dorothy Henessey
SIC—3498; NAICS—332996; *Pipe fabrication & protection*
Employs—18; Estab.—1975
Sales—under $500,000
Distrib.—Local
Privately owned corporation

**DATA COMMUNIQUE, INC.**

65 Challenger Rd., 4th Fl. (07660)
**Phone—(201) 508-6000**
Fax—(201) 438-8429
www.datacom-usa.com
Email—dkingsley@datacom-usa.com
CEO—Richard Plotka
IT Mgr.—Faisal Fareed
Hum. Res. Mgr. & Administrator—Pinakin Jani
SIC—7372; *Content management & document workflow software development*
Employs—45; Estab.—2008
Distrib.—Intl.
Privately owned corporation

**DVTEL, INC.**

65 Challenger Rd., Ste. 2 (07660-2110)
**Phone—(201) 368-9700**
Fax—(201) 368-2615
www.dvtel.com
Email—info@dvtel.com
Pres., CEO—Yoav Stern
CTO—Ed Thompson
Dir., Mktg.—Jennifer Kang
SIC—7372; *IP-based physical security system development; Brand name—iSOC V6; Latitude NVMS; Quasar IP Smart Cameras*
Employs—40
Distrib.—Regional
Privately owned corporation

**ENGINEERED DEVICES CORP.**

25 Bergen Tpke. (07660)
**Phone—(201) 641-2880**
Fax—(201) 641-0847
www.edconline.com
Email—info@edconline.com
Pres.—Antonio Limbardo
SIC—3499; *Corporate headquarters & metal fabrication*
Employs—15; Estab.—1981
Distrib.—Regional
Privately owned corporation

**KIRKWOOD NEW YORK**

1 Teaneck Rd. (07660)
**Phone—(201) 440-0800**
Fax—(201) 440-8790
www.kirkwoodnewyork.com
Pres., Sales Mgr.—Edward Kelley
SIC—2759; NAICS—323100; *Commercial printing*
Employs—30; Estab.—1990
Sales—$1Mil-$2.5Mil
Distrib.—Local
Privately owned corporation

**KUPELIAN FOODS, INC.**

146 Bergen Tpke. (07660)
**Phone—(201) 440-8055**
Pres.—Edward Kupelian
SIC—2013; 2011; NAICS—311611; *Meat processing*
Employs—5; Estab.—1977
Sales—under $500,000
Distrib.—Regional
Privately owned corporation

**PRUDENT PUBLISHING CO. (H Q)**

65 Challenger Rd. (07660)
**Phone—(201) 641-7900**
Fax—(201) 641-1401
www.gallerycollection.com
Email—support@gallerycollection.com
Chrm.—Alan Solow
Pres.—Allen Greenwald
CMO—H. L. DeVore
IT Mgr.—Juan Carlos Pinzon
Hum. Res. Mgr.—Yuhen Abreu
SIC—2771; *Company headquarters; greeting cards*
Employs—110
Company-wide: 200
Sales—$10Mil-$25Mil (est)
Distrib.—Intl.

**SAMSUNG ELECTRONICS AMERICA, INC.**

85 Challenger Rd. (07660)
**Phone—(201) 229-4000**
New Jersey—(866) 666-3136
National—(800) 726-7864
www.samsung.com
V-P., Bus. Dev.—Thomas Rhee
SIC—3679; 3651; 3577; 3634; *Electronic components, including mobile phones, HDTVs, printer equipment & home appliances*
Employs—300; Estab.—1993
Distrib.—Local
Privately owned corporation

**SOFIELD MFG. CO., INC.**

2 Main St. (07660)
**Phone—(201) 943-1118**
Fax—(201) 943-3393
Email—sofieldmfg@nj.rr.com
Pres.—Harold Sofield
V-P.—Anthony Sofield
Tool & Die Maker—Aaron Sofield
SIC—3469; *Metal stampings*
Employs—7; Estab.—1992
Sales—under $500,000
Distrib.—Regional
Privately owned corporation

**STAR SOAP & CANDLE, LLC**

300 Industrial Ave. (07660)
**Phone—(201) 690-9090**
Fax—(201) 690-9091
www.starcandle.com
Pres.—Stanley Gurewitsch
V-P.—Sam Gurewitsch
SIC—3999; *Candles*
Employs—200; Estab.—1992
35,000 sq ft site, Distrib.—National
Limited Liability Company

**THOMSEN LITHO, INC.**

217 Railroad Ave. (07660)
**Phone—(201) 489-1133**
Pres.—Greg Thomsen
SIC—2752; 2791; NAICS—323122; *Offset printing & computerized typesetting*
Employs—3; Estab.—1954
Sales—under $500,000
Distrib.—Local
Privately owned corporation

**UNITY FUELS, LLC**

225 Industrial Ave. (07660)
**Phone—(201) 641-5000**
Fax—(212) 966-0098
www.yourwasteourfuel.com
Email—info@yourwasteourfuel.com
Mng. Ptnr.—Jeff Deweese
SIC—2899; *Biodiesel fuels from used cooking oils*
Employs—40
Sales—$10Mil-$25Mil (est)
Limited Liability Company

## Ridgewood

(Bergen—N.E.)

**BIOFUSION, INC.**

310 Godwin Ave. (07450)
**Phone—(201) 447-6241**
Fax—(201) 444-2307
www.biofusion.co
Email—info@biofusion.co
CEO—David Gubb
Off. Mgr.—Barbara Bodden
SIC—2842; *Environmentally sustainable & nontoxic medical, agricultural, military & commercial cleaning chemicals; Brand name—Clutter Cleaner; Natures Solution™; Santeen Green; Green Beast*
Employs—5; Estab.—2010
Sales—$1Mil-$5Mil
Distrib.—National
Privately owned corporation

**BOOKS ARE BACK, INC.**

296 Woodside Ave. (07450)
**Phone—(201) 447-0374**
www.booksareback.com
Pres.—Daniel L. Bauch
Accountant—Joanne Bauch
SIC—2731; *Book publishing*
Employs—3; Estab.—1997
Sales—under $500,000
500 sq ft site, Distrib.—National
Privately owned corporation

**NEW ENTRY**
**FRANKLIN LAKES OAKLAND**

Div. of North Jersey Media Group, Inc.
41 Oak St. (07450)
**Phone—(201) 612-5415**
www.northjersey.com
Email—suburbannews@northjersey.com
Editor—Gertrude Walz
SIC—2711; *Newspaper publishing*
Employs—5
Sales—under $500,000 (est)
Privately owned corporation
Parent co.—North Jersey Media Group, Inc., Woodland Park, NJ
Phone—(973) 569-7000
See Parent Co. Section for full profile.

**HERITAGE, INC.**

4 Wilsey Sq., Ste. 9 (07450)
**Phone—(201) 447-2600**
Fax—(201) 447-1414
www.adheritageinc.com
Pres.—Paul Mortola
Acct. Exec.—Matt Higgins
SIC—2759; NAICS—323100; *Commercial & promotional printing, including advertising specialties, business forms, tags & custom & stock labels*
Employs—5; Estab.—1996
Sales—$500,000-$1Mil
Distrib.—Regional
Privately owned corporation

**LEA FURS, INC. LTD.**

45 S. Broad St. (07450)
**Phone—(201) 444-5554**
www.leafur.com
Email—leafurs@aol.com
Owner & Pres.—Chris Liulakis
SIC—2371; NAICS—315200; *Fur clothing & accessories*
Employs—1; Estab.—1986
Sales—under $500,000
Distrib.—Intl.
Sole ownership

**MEMORIAL ARTS, INC.**

1172 E. Ridgewood Ave. (07450)
**Phone—(201) 652-4301**
National—(800) 894-4301
Fax—(201) 652-2215
Pres.—Suzanne Ferrie
SIC—3281; NAICS—327991; *Burial monuments*
Employs—3; Estab.—1948
Sales—under $500,000
Distrib.—National
Privately owned corporation

**NEW ENTRY**
**PRINTOLOGY**

615 Franklin Tpke., Ste. 3 (07450)
**Phone—(201) 345-4632**
www.printologyusa.com
Email—printology@mac.com
Pres.—Jon Bognar
SIC—2759; 2396; *Commercial & t-shirt screen printing & promotional printing, including bags & pens*
Employs—4
Sales—$500,000-$1Mil (est)
Privately owned corporation

**REFLEX ANALYTICAL CORPORATION**

643 Albert Pl. (07450)
Mail addr: P.O. Box 119, Ridgewood (07451)
**Phone—(201) 444-8958**
Fax—(201) 670-6737
www.reflexusa.com
Email—reflexusa@att.net
V-P., Hum. Res. & IT Mgr.—Tony Jacobini

**GEOGRAPHICAL**

## Ridgewood—(cont.)

SIC—3679; 3827; NAICS—333314; *Spectroscopy accessories & photonic components, including polished optics, infrared filters, ATR crystals, prisms, rods & hemispheres & sealed liquid & variable temperature cells*
Employs—5; Estab.—1995
Sales—$1Mil-$2.5Mil
Distrib.—Intl.
Privately owned corporation

**RIDGEWOOD MEDICAL MEDIA, LLC**
P.O. Box 802 (07450)
**Phone—(201) 670-1356**
www.pppmag.com
Ptnr.—Mitch Halvorsen
Ptnr.—Deanne Halvorsen
SIC—2721; 2741; *Monthly hospital & pharmacy print & online magazine publishing*
Employs—12; Estab.—2004
Distrib.—National
Limited Liability Company
AKAs: Pharmacy Purchasing & Products & Medical Lab Management Magazine

**RIDGEWOOD PRESS, INC.**
609 Franklin Tpke. (07450)
**Phone—(201) 670-9797**
Fax—(201) 670-9798
www.ridgewoodpress.com
Email—info@ridgewoodpress.com
Pres.—Robert Modelski
SIC—2759; NAICS—323100; *Commercial printing*
Employs—10; Estab.—1978
Sales—$500,000-$1Mil
Distrib.—National
Privately owned corporation

**STRONGWALL INDUSTRIES, INC.**
107 Chestnut St. (07450)
**Phone—(201) 445-4633**
National—(800) 535-0668
Fax—(201) 447-2317
www.strongwall.com
Email—elizabethl@strongwall.com
Pres.—Nicole Kokoletsos
Sales Mgr., Natl.—Gene Petrone
Off. Mgr.—Elizabeth Lukaszek
SIC—2891; 3272; NAICS—325520; *Concrete restoration & protection products & systems, including mortars, overlays, membranes & wall & floor finishes*
Employs—12; Estab.—1982
8,000 sq ft site, Distrib.—Intl.
Privately owned corporation

**SUBURBAN GLASS & MIRROR, INC.**
418 S. Broad St. (07450)
**Phone—(201) 447-0440**
Fax—(201) 447-6928
www.suburbanglassandmirror.com
Email—info@suburbanglassandmirror.com
Pres.—Wayne Gangeri
V.-P.—Jeffrey Gangeri
GM—Matt Gangeri
GM—Frank Battaglia
Off. Mgr.—Christa Farrell
SIC—3231; 3211; NAICS—327215; *Glass & mirror fabrication, including replacement glass, framed & frameless shower doors & commercial storefronts*
Employs—20; Estab.—1961
Sales—$2.5Mil-$5Mil
Distrib.—Local
Privately owned corporation
Parent co.—Suburban Glass & Mirror, Inc., Closter, NJ
Phone—(201) 768-9586
See Parent Co. Section for full profile.

## Ringoes
(Hunterdon—N.W.)

**ARGUS INTERNATIONAL**
424 Route 31 N., P.O. Box 559 (08551)
**Phone—(609) 466-1677**
Fax—(609) 466-4111
www.argus-international.com
Email—mail@argus-international.com
Pres.—B. J. Costello
V.-P.—M. Costello
Plt. Mgr.—B. Lawrence
SIC—3672; 3679; NAICS—334412; *Printed circuit board manufacturing equipment*
Employs—35; Estab.—1965
25,000 sq ft site, Distrib.—Intl.
Privately owned corporation

**ATLANTIC SPRING CO.**
Div. of MW Industries, Inc.
137 Highway 202 S. *(08551)*
Mail addr: P.O. Box 650, Flemington (08822-0650)
**Phone—(908) 788-5800**
Fax—(908) 788-0511
www.mw-ind.com
Email—sales@mw-ind.com
GM—Jeff Vannatta
Engrg. & Sales Mgr.—John King
Matls. Mgr.—Christine Ruffolo
SIC—3493; 3496; NAICS—332611; *Custom metal springs, wire forms & assemblies*
Employs—80; Estab.—2000
Sales—$10Mil-$25Mil
65,000 sq ft site, Distrib.—Intl.
Privately owned corporation
ISO rating—AS9100C, 9100:2008
Parent co.—MW Industries, Inc., Rosemont, IL
Phone—(847) 349-5780
See Parent Co. Section for full profile.

**CATERING BY THE MADDALENAS, INC.**
415 Route 31 N. (08551)
**Phone—(609) 466-7510**
Fax—(609) 466-8981
www.maddalenascatering.com
Email—info@maddalenascatering.com
Pres.—Janet Maddalena
Hum. Res., IT & Off. Mgr.—Amber Hinshaw
SIC—2053; *Frozen cheesecake*
Employs—5; Estab.—1983
Sales—under $500,000
Distrib.—Local
Privately owned corporation
AKA: Maddalenas Cheesecake & Catering

**†FERGUSON ENTERPRISES, INC.**
404 Route 31 N. (08551)
**Phone—(609) 466-5445**
Fax—(609) 466-3272
www.ferguson.com
Email—graham.vidal@ferguson.com
Br. Mgr.—Graham Vidal
SIC—5074; 5075; *Distributor of plumbing & HVAC equipment & supplies, including pipes, fixtures, valves, fittings, pumps & well supplies*
Employs—9; Estab.—2000
Distrib.—Regional
Publicly owned corporation
Parent co.—Ferguson Enterprises, Inc., Newport News, VA
Phone—(757) 874-7795
See Parent Co. Section for full profile.

**FLEMINGTON INSTRUMENT CO., INC.**
55 Sandra Rd., P.O. Box 298 (08551)
**Phone—(908) 782-4229**
Fax—(908) 782-9910
www.flemingtoninstrument.com
Email—sales@flemingtoninstrument.com
Pres.—Ralph Migliaccio
SIC—3829; *Measurement & display instruments & UL panels*
Employs—40; Estab.—1977
Sales—$10Mil
Distrib.—Local
Privately owned corporation

**FOLDED STRUCTURES CO., LLC**
1142-A Old York Rd. (08551)
**Phone—(908) 237-1955**
www.foldedstructures.com
Email—info@foldedstructures.com
Pres.—Daniel Kling
SIC—7372; *Mathematical folding software development for designing self-assembling periodically folded sheet materials & three-dimensionally braided composites for laminated panels, structural beams, parabolic reflectors & efficient truss systems; Brand name—FoldStar*
Employs—3; Estab.—2003
Distrib.—National
Limited Liability Company

**H E D INTERNATIONAL, INC.**
449 Route 31, P.O. Box 246 (08551-0246)
**Phone—(609) 466-1900**
National—(800) 433-5456
Fax—(609) 466-3608
www.hed.com
Email—info@hed.com
Pres.—James Dennis
Sales Mgr.—Kathleen Kriskiwic
SIC—3567; NAICS—333994; *Furnaces & kilns*
Employs—9; Estab.—1967
20,000 sq ft site, Distrib.—Intl.
Privately owned corporation

**MEDICAL PACKAGING, INC.**
470 Route 31, P.O. Box 500 (08551)
**Phone—(609) 466-8991**
National—(800) 257-5282
Fax—(609) 466-3775
www.medpak.com
Email—orders@medpak.com
CEO—Andy Bartels
Mktg. Mgr.—Terry Mihalek
Medical Pkg. Rep.—Rachael Enslin
SIC—3559; 3089; 2653; NAICS—322211; *Pharmacy oral solids & liquid packaging machinery & materials*
Employs—20; Estab.—1971
Distrib.—Intl.
Privately owned corporation

**MUIRHEAD OF RINGOES NEW JERSEY, INC.**
43 U.S. Highway 202 (08551)
**Phone—(908) 782-7803**
www.muirheadfoods.com
Email—information@muirheadfoods.com
Pres.—Doris Simpson
MIS Mgr.—Barbara Simpson
SIC—2035; 2099; *Condiments, sauces & flavored nondairy butters; Brand name—Muirhead*
Employs—10; Estab.—1972
Sales—under $500,000
2,400 sq ft site, Distrib.—Intl.
Privately owned sub-S corp.
AKA: Muirhead Foods

**REAGENT CHEMICAL & RESEARCH, INC.**
115 U.S. Highway 202 (08551)
**Phone—(908) 284-2800**
Fax—(908) 284-2113
www.reagentchemical.com
Email—info@reagentchemical.com
Pres.—John T. Skeuse
Sr. V.-P.—Brian Skeuse
Sr. V.-P.—Richard Skeuse
Sr. V.-P.—Thomas Skeuse
SIC—2819; *Corporate headquarters & hydrochloric acid*
Employs—30; Estab.—1959
Company-wide: 475
Sales—$5Mil-$10Mil
Distrib.—National
Privately owned corporation
ISO rating—9002

**SCIENTIFIC INSTRUMENT SERVICES, INC.**
1027 Old York Rd. (08551)
**Phone—(908) 788-5550**
Fax—(908) 806-6631
www.sisweb.com
Email—us@sisweb.com
Pres.—John Manura
GM—Christopher Baker
Off. Mgr.—Anthony Dudick
Pur. Agt.—Kevin Jackson
SIC—3829; *Mass spectrometers, vacuum systems, tools & gas & liquid chromatographs for the scientific, medical & industrial industries*
Employs—30; Estab.—1978
20,000 sq ft site, Distrib.—National
Privately owned corporation
ISO rating—9000:2000

**UNIONVILLE, LLC**
9 Rocktown Rd. (08551)
**Phone—(908) 788-0400**
Fax—(908) 806-4692
www.unionvillevineyards.com
Email—uvineyard@aol.com
Mng. Ptnr.—John Hawkins
GM & Winemaker—Cameron Stark
Day Mgr.—Stacey Brody
SIC—2084; NAICS—312130; *Wines*
Employs—5; Estab.—1992
Sales—under $500,000
Distrib.—Local
Limited Liability Company

## Ringwood
(Passaic—N.E.)

**BACH TOOL PRECISION, INC.**
51 Executive Pkwy. (07456)
**Phone—(973) 962-6224**
Fax—(973) 932-6225
www.bachtoolprecision.com
Email—rbach@bachtoolprecision.com
Pres.—Richard Ebersbach
V.-P.—Jane Ebersbach
SIC—3599; *Precision machining of metal components for the aerospace, nuclear, defense & commercial industries*
Employs—5; Estab.—1992
Sales—$500,000-$1Mil (est)
Distrib.—Local
Privately owned corporation

**BAUER, INC., SUSAN R.**
427 Margaret King Ave. (07456)
**Phone—(973) 657-1590**
Fax—(973) 657-1591
Email—srbauerinc@aol.com
Pres.—Susan R. Bauer
GM & Estimator—Richard Bauer
SIC—3441; NAICS—332312; *Structural steel bridges for the road & construction industries*
Employs—5; Estab.—1983
Sales—$500,000-$1Mil
Distrib.—Regional
Privately owned sub-S corp.

**CIRCONIX TECHNOLOGIES, LLC**
Div. of Davis-Standard, LLC
29 Executive Pkwy. (07456)
**Phone—(973) 962-6160**
Fax—(973) 962-6016
www.circonix.com
Email—andre.icso@circonix.com

## Ringwood—(cont.)

Pres.—Andre Icso
Off. Mgr.—Esther Icso
Pur. Agt.—Virginia Chorny
SIC—3625; NAICS—335314; *Film & paper control systems*
Employs—10; Estab.—1990
Distrib.—Intl.
Limited Liability Company
AKA: Davis-Standard
Parent co.—Davis-Standard, LLC, Pawcatuck, CT
Phone—(860) 599-1010
See Parent Co. Section for full profile.

**COLORCHEM, INC.**
1010 Greenwood Lake (07456)
**Phone—(973) 728-7731**
Fax—(973) 728-3475
Pres., CEO—James C. Gayler
Secy., GM & Pur. Agt.—Mary Beth Alpisa
Qual. Control Mgr.—James H. Fersch
Traf. Mgr.—Timothy Alpisa
SIC—2816; NAICS—325100; *Rubber color dispersions*
Employs—10; Estab.—1988
Sales—$2.5Mil–$5Mil
Privately owned corporation

**G B INDUSTRIES II, INC.**
341 Margaret King Ave. (07456)
**Phone—(973) 728-5900**
Fax—(973) 728-1267
Email—sales@gbindustriesii.com
Pres., CFO—Gerard Barrere
V-P., MIS—John Barrere
GM—Tony Delaney
Off. Mgr.—Susan J. Ellison
SIC—3599; *Precision machining, including Swiss-type CNC turning with live tooling*
Employs—7; Estab.—1962
Sales—$1.5Mil
10,000 sq ft site, Distrib.—National
Privately owned corporation

**H P PERFORMANCE, INC.**
8 Industrial Pkwy. (07456)
**Phone—(973) 962-0800**
Fax—(973) 962-0828
Email—hpperformance@optonline.net
Pres.—Frank Patricola
SIC—3599; *General machining job shop*
Employs—6; Estab.—1979
Sales—$500,000–$1Mil
Distrib.—Regional
Privately owned sub-S corp.

**HALL MFG. CORP.**
297 Margaret King Ave. (07456)
**Phone—(973) 962-6022**
Fax—(973) 962-7652
www.hallmanufacturing.com
Email—sales@hallmanufacturing.com
V-P., Opers.—Michael Goceljak
Sales Mgr.—Andrew Provost
Opers. Mgr.—Kerry Clark
Shift Supv.—Frank El
SIC—3082; NAICS—326121; *Plastic extrusions, including profiles, tubes, hollow & vacuum extrusions, coextrusions & complex profiles*
Employs—30; Estab.—1946
Sales—$3Mil
21,600 sq ft site, Distrib.—National
Privately owned corporation

**INOPAK LTD.**
24 Executive Pkwy. (07456)
**Phone—(973) 962-1121**
Fax—(973) 962-0811
www.inopak.com
Email—inopak@warwick.net
Pres., CEO—John Polite
V-P., Sales—Nick Disarro

SIC—2841; NAICS—325611; *Liquid soap, dispensers & antimicrobials; Brand name—Press Pak; Inoderm soaps; Dermagel; Derma Cream; Dermex; Enrich*
Employs—25; Estab.—1989
Sales—$10Mil
35,000 sq ft site, Distrib.—National
Privately owned sub-S corp.

**MALIN CORP., JAMES S.**
3 Victoria Ln. (07456)
**Phone—(973) 831-9135**
www.jamesmalindentallab.com
Pres.—James Malin
Corp. Secy.—Audrey Malin
SIC—3843; NAICS—339114; *Prosthetic teeth*
Employs—3; Estab.—1979
Sales—under $500,000
Distrib.—Local
Privately owned corporation

**MEMBRANES INTERNATIONAL, INC.**
219 Margaret King Ave., P.O. Box 219 (07456)
**Phone—(973) 998-5530**
Fax—(973) 998-5529
www.membranesinternational.com
Email—customerservice@membranesinternational.com
Ptnr.—Dwight Loren
Ptnr.—Jack Loren
SIC—3589; 2821; NAICS—333319; *Ion exchange membranes for the water treatment & electrocoating industries; Brand name—AMI-7001S Anion Exchange Membrane; CMI-7000S Cation Exchange Membrane*
Employs—3; Estab.—1982
Sales—$1Mil–$2.5Mil
Distrib.—Intl.
Privately owned sub-S corp.

**PROGRESSIVE-RUESCH MACHINE CO., LLC**
21 Van Natta Dr. (07456)
**Phone—(973) 962-7700**
Fax—(973) 962-7774
www.progressivewinders.com
Email—sales@progressivewinders.com
CEO—Stephen Honczarenko
Buyer—Kate Cospa
SIC—3599; 3559; NAICS—333298; *Industrial machinery for the metal, plastic, converting & fiber optics industries, including traverse spooling winders, coil handling equipment, slitting lines & industrial tool lines*
Employs—17; Estab.—1896
28,000 sq ft site, Distrib.—Intl.
Limited Liability Company

**†PRO-PAC SERVICES, INC.**
15 Van Natta Dr. (07456)
**Phone—(973) 962-8080**
Fax—(973) 962-8010
www.propacservices.com
Email—jill.scialla@propacservices.com
Pres.—Brian Douglas
V-P.—Jill Scialla Douglas
SIC—5084; *Wholesaler of vacuum packaging machinery*
Employs—12; Estab.—1985
Sales—$1.7Mil
12,000 sq ft site, Distrib.—Intl.
Privately owned corporation

**SKYLINE GRAPHICS DESIGN**
11 Skyline Lake Dr. (07456)
**Phone—(973) 839-3329**
Fax—(973) 839-2411
www.skylinegraphicsonline.com
Email—skygraf@optonline.net
Pres.—Scott White
Bookkeeper—Karen Roughton

SIC—2752; 2759; 2396; 3993; NAICS—323122; *Offset, digital & digital full-color printing & graphic design of custom signs & banners & envelopes, screen printing & embroidery*
Employs—4; Estab.—1992
Sales—under $500,000
3,000 sq ft site, Distrib.—National
Privately owned corporation

**VAN ORDEN SAND & GRAVEL**
Div. of Stone Industries, Inc.
589 W. Brook Rd. (07456)
Mail addr.: P.O. Box 8246, Haledon (07538)
**Phone—(973) 839-0207**
Fax—(973) 839-7211
www.braenstone.com
Email—vosg@braenstone.com
Sales Rep.—Bucky Rodda
Dispatcher—Frank Sisco
SIC—3281; NAICS—327991; *Sand & gravel processing*
Employs—12; Estab.—1976
Sales—$1Mil–$2.5Mil
Distrib.—Local
Privately owned corporation
AKA: Braen Stone Industries
Parent co.—Stone Industries, Inc., Haledon, NJ
Phone—(973) 595-6250
See Parent Co. Section for full profile.

**†WENCO MACHINERY CORP.**
355 Margaret King Ave. (07456)
**Phone—(973) 657-9660**
National—(888) 439-3626
Fax—(973) 657-9661
www.wencomachinery.com
Email—sales@wencomachinery.com
Pres.—Will Schouten
V-P.—Eric Schouten
SIC—5084; *Wholesaler of metal stamping & fabricating machinery*
Employs—6; Estab.—1974
Sales—$1Mil–$2.5Mil
9,000 sq ft site, Distrib.—National
Privately owned corporation

## Rio Grande
(Cape May—S.E.)

**CAPE MAY BREWING CO.**
1288 Hornet Rd. (08242)
**Phone—(609) 849-9933**
www.capemaybrewery.com
Manager—Ryan Krill
Tasting Room Coord.—Ashley Sunstrom
SIC—2082; *Beer*
Employs—10; Estab.—2011
Distrib.—Regional
Privately owned corporation

**HANSEN AWNING CO.**
18 Church Rd. (08242)
**Phone—(609) 886-1685**
Ptnr.—Lillian McGill
Ptnr.—Patricia Reed
SIC—2394; *Canvas awnings*
Employs—2; Estab.—1920
Sales—under $500,000
Distrib.—Local
Privately owned partnership

**HAWK HAVEN VINEYARD & WINERY, LLC**
600 S. Railroad Ave. (08242)
**Phone—(609) 846-7347**
www.hawkhavenvineyard.com
Email—info@hawkhavenvineyard.com
Ptnr.—Todd Wuerker
Ptnr.—Kenna Wuerker
SIC—2084; *Wines*
Employs—20; Estab.—2009
Sales—under $500,000
Distrib.—Local
Limited Liability Company

**R & R SPECIALTIES**
126 Holly Dr. (08242)
**Phone—(609) 886-6651**
www.r-rspecialties.com
Email—rrspecialties@comcast.net
Ptnr.—Chandi Ankrum
Ptnr.—Tom Ankrum
SIC—3499; 3479; *Trophies & engraving*
Employs—2
Sales—under $500,000
Distrib.—Local
Sole ownership

**RESDEL CORP.**
Cape May County Industrial Pk. (08242)
**Phone—(609) 886-1111**
Fax—(609) 886-6329
www.resdel.com
Email—resdel@resdel.com
MIS & Opers. Mgr.—Debbie Fazen
Fin. Mgr.—Charles R. Manneila
SIC—3082; NAICS—326121; *Epoxy tubing*
Employs—20; Estab.—1989
Sales—$1Mil–$5Mil
10,000 sq ft site, Distrib.—Intl.
Privately owned corporation

**SEAWAVE CORP.**
1508 Route 47 (08242-1413)
**Phone—(609) 886-8600**
Fax—(609) 886-1879
www.capemaycountyherald.com
Email—advertise@cmcherald.com
Pres.—Arthur Hall
Editor—Al Campbell
Dir., Dev.—Preston Gibson
IT & Opers. Mgr.—Robert Kosinski
Adv. Mgr.—Karen Dickinson
Fin. Mgr.—Jan Iannucci
Media Mgr.—Steve Dunwoody
SIC—2711; 2741; NAICS—323122; *Weekly print & online newspaper & visitor's guide publishing; Brand name—Cape May County Herald; www.capemaycountyherald.com; Blast; www.dotheshore.com; Spout Off*
Employs—25; Estab.—1967
Sales—$2.5Mil–$5Mil
10,000 sq ft site, Distrib.—Local
Privately owned corporation

## River Edge
(Bergen—N.E.)

**BAD DOG T'S**
498 Kinderkamack Rd. (07661)
**Phone—(201) 599-2030**
Fax—(201) 599-0653
Owner—Frank Pugliese
SIC—2396; *Textile screen printing*
Employs—5; Estab.—1990
Sales—$1Mil–$2.5Mil
Distrib.—National

**BEST CAST**
822 Kinderkamack Rd. (07661)
**Phone—(201) 225-1750**
National—(877) 225-0700
Fax—(201) 225-1751
www.best-cast.com
Email—proto@best-cast.com
Pres.—Zsombar Antal
Cust. Rep.—Eva Csogor
SIC—3543; 3911; NAICS—332997; *High-resolution three-dimensionally printed miniature & jewelry prototypes & lost-wax precious metal casting for the jewelry industry*
Employs—15; Estab.—1997
Sales—$500,000–$1Mil
Distrib.—National
Privately owned corporation

GEOGRAPHICAL

## River Edge—(cont.)

**CHRISELLES DOLLS**
216 Hillbrook Dr. (07661)
**Phone—(201) 488-1905**
www.chriselles-dolls.com
Email—dianeking14@yahoo.com
Principal—Diane King
SIC—3942; Costumes for dolls
Employs—1; Estab.—2000
Distrib.—Regional
Sole ownership

**CRITCHLEY'S CANDIES**
812 Kinderkamack Rd. (07661)
**Phone—(201) 967-1800**
Fax—(201) 967-0022
www.critchleyschocolates.com
Owner—Steve Engleberg
SIC—2066; NAICS—311300;
Chocolates
Employs—3; Estab.—1954
Sales—$500,000-$1Mil
Distrib.—Local
Privately owned corporation

**CROWN TROPHY-RIVER EDGE, NJ**
488 Kinderkamack Rd. (07661)
**Phone—(201) 261-3933**
Fax—(201) 261-7745
www.crowntrophy.com
Email—crown.riveredge@
verizon.net
Owner—Chuck Hedbavny
Shop Mgr.—Mike Morgan
SIC—3479; 3993; 3499; Awards,
rotary & laser engraving, crystal,
acrylic, wood & bronze plaques,
medals, desk accessories,
gavels, imprinted ribbons,
banners, promotional advertising
& recognition specialties
Employs—5; Estab.—1989
4,000 sq ft site, Distrib.—Local
Privately owned sub-S corp.

**HALOCARBON PRODUCTS CORP. (H
Q)**
887 Kinderkamack Rd., 2nd Fl.
(07661)
**Phone—(201) 262-8899**
National—(800) 338-5803
Fax—(201) 262-0019
www.halocarbon.com
Email—info@halocarbon.com
CEO—Peter Murin
Dir., Sales—Ron Epstein
Sales & Mktg. Mgr.—Meg
Rubinstein
SIC—2819; Corporate
headquarters; industrial
chemicals for inhalation
anesthetics & pharmaceutical &
agricultural uses
Employs—13; Estab.—1950
Sales—$5Mil-$10Mil (est)
Distrib.—Intl.

**NEPHROS, INC.**
41 Grand Ave., Ste. 201 (07661)
**Phone—(201) 343-5202**
Fax—(201) 343-5207
www.nephros.com
Email—info@nephros.com
Chrm.—James S. Scibetta
Pres., CEO—John C. Houghton
Opers. Mgr.—Eileen Sukumar
SIC—3845; 3841; 3589; NAICS—
333319; Hemodiafiltration
systems for the end-stage renal
disease patient & dual-stage
cold sterilization water filtration
products
Employs—6; Estab.—1998
Sales—under $500,000
Distrib.—Local

**RE SYSTEMS GROUP, INC.**
1060 Main St., Ste. 200 (07661)
**Phone—(201) 883-1572**
Fax—(201) 883-1571
www.resystemsgroup.com
Email—rsg@resystemsgroup.com
Pres.—George Gramlich
V-P.—Bob McCann
V-P.—Ira Gidon
V-P.—Tom Gierut
SIC—2741; Reinsurance software
development & consulting
services; Brand name—Visual
Re; RSG RE; RSG Ceded;
Robis; RE EDI; RSG SQL;
Accrusys; STAR
Employs—5; Estab.—1983
Sales—under $500,000
Distrib.—Intl.
Privately owned corporation

## River Vale

(Bergen—N.E.)

**WET STONE GRAPHICS**
645 Greenway Pl. (07675)
**Phone—(201) 307-1531**
www.wetstonegiclee.com
Email—wetstone@optonline.net
Owner—Marc Cohen
SIC—2759; 2752; NAICS—
323100; Fine arts printing
Employs—1; Estab.—1999
Sales—under $500,000
Distrib.—National
Sole ownership

## Riverdale

(Morris—N.W.)

**A & A CONCRETE PRODUCTS, INC.**
2 S. Corporate Dr., P.O. Box 108
(07457)
**Phone—(973) 835-2239**
Fax—(973) 835-3095
Pres.—Sandra L. Alway
SIC—3272; Concrete septic
tanks, trench drains, drywells &
related products
Employs—7; Estab.—1976
6,000 sq ft site, Distrib.—Local
Privately owned corporation

**AMERICAN SEAMLESS GUTTER &
LEADER CORP.**
286 Hamburg Tpke. (07457)
**Phone—(973) 838-4505**
National—(888) 536-7246
Fax—(973) 838-5979
Pres.—Duane Reger
Sales Mgr.—William Reger
Off. Mgr.—Gail Reger
Whse. Mgr.—Bruce Rogers
SIC—3444; Seamless aluminum
gutters
Employs—7; Estab.—1977
Sales—$500,000-$1Mil
Distrib.—Intl.
Privately owned corporation

**B E R PLASTIC CORP.**
5 Curtis St., P.O. Box 2 (07457)
**Phone—(973) 839-2100**
Fax—(973) 839-7929
Pres.—Bernie Ewasko
V-P.—Robert Ringley
Plt. Mgr.—Walt Panski
SIC—3081; NAICS—326113;
Polyethylene film
Employs—25; Estab.—1965
Distrib.—Local
Privately owned corporation

**CAMFIL USA, INC.**
1 N. Corporate Dr. (07457)
**Phone—(973) 616-7300**
National—(866) 422-6345
Fax—(973) 616-7771
www.camfil.com
Email—info@camfilfarr.com
Pres.—Armando Brunetti
V-P., Sales—Kevin Wood
GM—Chad Haddad
Mktg. & Technical Matls. Mgr.—
Charles Seyffer
Fin. Mgr.—Frank Shahin
SIC—3564; NAICS—333400;
Corporate headquarters & air
filtration products & associated
hardware; Brand name—30/30;
Riga-Flo; Durafil; Glide/Pack;
Absolute; Aeropleat; Camsorb;
Megalam Panel
Employs—150; Estab.—1939
Sales—$120Mil
108,000 sq ft site, Distrib.—Intl.
Privately owned corporation
ISO rating—9001

**CARL STAHL SAVA INDUSTRIES,
INC.**
4 N. Corporate Dr., P.O. Box 30
(07457)
**Phone—(973) 835-0882**
Fax—(973) 835-0877
www.savacable.com
Email—sales@savacable.com
CEO—Zdenek A. Fremund
Pres.—Marc E. Alterman
V-P., Sales—Bruce R. Staubitz
V-P., Opers.—Jack Mass
V-P., Engrg.—Greg Soja
Mfg. Mgr.—Ron Paras
Pur. Mgr.—Jerry Picazio
Fin. Mgr.—Ralph Engelhardt
Qual. Assur. Mgr.—Thomas Moore
SIC—3496; 3429; 3469; 3451;
Corporate headquarters &
miniature & small wire rope,
terminals & fittings, wire rope
assemblies, idler pulleys, push-
pull control assemblies, material
lifting & handling equipment &
architectural cable products;
Brand name—I-SYS; X-TEND;
POSILOCK; NOKON
Employs—85; Estab.—1972
Sales—$15Mil-$20Mil
88,000 sq ft site, Distrib.—Intl.
Privately owned corporation
ISO rating—9001:2008
AKA: Sava Industries, Inc.

**CVE, INC.**
5 N. Corporate Dr. (07457)
**Phone—(201) 770-0005**
National—(800) 221-5552
Fax—(201) 770-1313
www.cveusa.com
Email—kwchang@cveusa.com
Pres.—Kyu T. Cho
Hum. Res. Mgr.—Lydia King
Shpg. Mgr.—Vanay Medina
Cust. Serv. Mgr.—Eanni Medina
SIC—3651; 3661; NAICS—
334310; Rebuilt consumer
electronics, including audio,
video & telecommunications
products
Employs—100; Estab.—1999
Sales—$25Mil-$50Mil (est)
90,000 sq ft site, Distrib.—National
Privately owned corporation

**D C METRIC TOOL, INC.**
11 Mathews Ave. (07457)
**Phone—(973) 838-7590**
Fax—(973) 838-1275
Pres.—Djordje Cakmak
SIC—3544; 2431; 3599; NAICS—
333500; Architectural millwork &
machining & tool & die job shop
Employs—2; Estab.—1983
Sales—under $500,000
1,500 sq ft site, Distrib.—Local
Privately owned corporation

**DIVERSITECH, INC.**
18 Hamburg Tpke. (07457)
**Phone—(973) 835-2900**
Fax—(973) 835-2865
www.diversitech.net
V-P.—Linda Weinacker
Off. Admn.—Sharon Papini
SIC—3599; Precision machining
job shop
Employs—28; Estab.—1967
Sales—$5Mil
28,000 sq ft site, Distrib.—Local
Privately owned corporation

**EVS METAL**
1 Kenner Ct. (07457)
**Phone—(973) 839-4432**
Fax—(973) 839-4440
www.evsmetal.com
Email—sales@evsmetal.com
Ptnr. & Pres.—Scott Berkowitz
Ptnr., V-P. & Dir., Mfg. & Sales—
Joseph Amico
Dir., Sales—Brent Frey
SIC—3444; Company
headquarters & precision sheet
metal fabrication, including
aluminum, steel & stainless steel
enclosures, chassis, brackets,
panels, weldments &
electromechanical assemblies
Employs—105; Estab.—1994
Sales—$14Mil
80,000 sq ft site, Distrib.—Intl.
Privately owned corporation
ISO rating—9001:2008

**GLASS CYCLE SYSTEMS, INC.**
5 Mathews Ave. (07457)
Mail addr: P.O. Box 816, Butler
(07405)
**Phone—(973) 838-0034**
www.glasscyclesystemsinc.com
Pres.—David Bowlby
SIC—3211; NAICS—327211;
Glass recycling
Employs—3; Estab.—1979
Sales—under $500,000
Distrib.—Local
Privately owned corporation

**HSH ASSOCS.**
51 Route 23 S. (07457)
**Phone—(973) 617-8700**
National—(800) 873-2837
Fax—(973) 617-8721
www.hsh.com
Email—info@hsh.com
V-P.—Keith Gumbinger
Off. Mgr.—Agnes Romlein
SIC—2741; Mortgage & consumer
loan financial information
publishing
Employs—7; Estab.—1980
Sales—under $500,000
Distrib.—Intl.
Privately owned corporation

**PK PRECISION MACHINING, INC.**
7 Mathews Ave. (07457)
**Phone—(973) 925-2020**
Fax—(973) 925-2010
www.pkprecision.com
Email—pkprecision70@
optimum.net
Ptnr.—Kenneth Androvich, Jr.
Ptnr.—Stephen Galik
SIC—3599; Precision machining
job shop, including electronic
hardware & fasteners
Employs—3; Estab.—1991
Sales—under $500,000
Distrib.—National
Privately owned sub-S corp.

**REDYREF CO.**
100 Kenner Ct. (07457)
**Phone—(718) 784-3690**
National—(800) 628-3603
Fax—(718) 784-3696
www.redyref.com
Email—sales@redyref.com
Pres.—William Pymm
V-P.—Edward Pymm
Cont.—Larry Reilly
SIC—3446; 3499; 3471; NAICS—
332323; Touchscreen building
directory, interactive kiosks,
internet & payphone kiosks &
phone booths & enclosures;
Brand name—Redyref
Employs—35; Estab.—1913
35,000 sq ft site, Distrib.—Intl.
Privately owned sub-S corp.

## Riverdale—(cont.)

**RIVERDALE ENVIRONMENTAL RECYCLING**
1 Riverdale Rd. (07457)
Mail addr: 20 Cotluss Rd., Ste. 10, Riverdale (07457)
**Phone—(973) 616-6654**
Fax—(973) 616-6470
www.1800topsoil.com
Email—sallyfane@rersupply.com
Pres.—Andrew Flockard
SIC—2875; 2421; 5032; *Manufacturer of mulch, compost & soil constituents from landscape waste & reground wood stumps, brush & wood chips & distributor of fill, stone & sand*
Employs—20; Estab.—2001
Sales—$5Mil-$10Mil (est)
Distrib.—Local
Privately owned corporation
AKA: RER Supply

**SIGMA-NETICS, INC.**
2 N. Corporate Dr. (07457)
**Phone—(973) 616-6900**
National—(800) 314-3894
Fax—(973) 616-6910
www.sigmanetics.com
Email—sales@sigmanetics.com
Pres.—Alan Glanzman
Sales Mgr.—Robert Hishmeh
Mfg. Mgr.—Nick Cannizzaro
Fin. Mgr.—Elise Furlin
Engrg. Mgr.—Claude Dacal
Cust. Serv. Mgr.—Carol Smith
SIC—3357; 3829; *Pressure switches & metal bellows*
Employs—30; Estab.—1969
Sales—$10Mil
27,000 sq ft site, Distrib.—Intl.
Privately owned corporation

**TILCON RIVERDALE QUARRY**
Div. of Tilcon New York Inc.
125 Hamburg Tpke. (07457)
Mail addr: 625 Mount Hope Rd., Wharton (07885-2807)
**Phone—(973) 835-0028**
Fax—(973) 839-7753
www.tilconny.com
Email—info@tilconny.com
Plt. Mgr.—Bill Conklin
SIC—3281; NAICS—327991; *Crushed stone*
Employs—50; Estab.—1995
Sales—$2.5Mil-$5Mil
Distrib.—Regional
Publicly owned corporation
AKA: Tilcon
Parent co.—Tilcon New York Inc., West Nyack, NY
Phone—(845) 358-4500
See Parent Co. Section for full profile.

## Riverside
(Burlington—S.E.)

**†ABC SUPPLY CO., INC.**
5004 Route 130 (08075)
**Phone—(856) 461-5252**
Fax—(856) 461-7198
www.abcsupply.com
Email—mgr085@abcsupply.com
Br. Mgr.—Ray Coxe
SIC—5033; 5031; *Wholesaler of roofing, siding, windows & doors*
Employs—5; Estab.—1986
Privately owned corporation
Parent co.—ABC Supply Co., Inc., Beloit, WI
Phone—(608) 362-7777
See Parent Co. Section for full profile.

**ALLISON SYSTEMS CORP.**
220 Adams St. (08075)
**Phone—(856) 461-9111**
National—(866) 461-9111
Fax—(856) 461-9373
www.allisonblades.com
Email—sales@allisonblades.com
Pres.—Eve Allison
V-P.—Bill Warner
Sales Mgr.—Evelyn Williams
Accts. Payable, Hum. Res. & Off. Mgr.—Barbara Meidt
Sys. Dev. Mgr.—Pete Small
Sales Rep.—William Murray
SIC—3555; NAICS—333293; *Precision doctor blades for gravure, flexographic, pad & specialty printing applications, including custom engineered blade holders, chambers, seals & actuating & control systems*
Employs—15; Estab.—1968
7,500 sq ft site, Distrib.—Intl.
Privately owned corporation

**C & C TOOL & MACHINE CO., LLC**
38 W. Scott St., P.O. Box 407 (08075)
**Phone—(856) 461-6090**
   (856) 764-0911
Fax—(856) 764-6106
Email—candctool@verizon.net
Pres., GM—Frank Canduci
V-P.—Nunzio Canduci
Machinist—Bob Canduci
SIC—3599; 3544; NAICS—333500; *CNC machining & tool & die job shop*
Employs—11; Estab.—1973
Sales—$1Mil-$2.5Mil
4,800 sq ft site, Distrib.—Local
Limited Liability Company

**CHERUBINI YACHTS, LLC**
51 Norman Ave. (08075)
**Phone—(856) 764-5319**
National—(888) 892-3527
Fax—(856) 764-7549
www.cherubiniyachts.com
Email—info@cherubiniyachts.com
Pres.—David Cherubini
SIC—3732; 3731; 3089; *Semi-custom mahogany, teak & fiberglass yachts, sailboats & powerboats, including restoration & repair*
Employs—5; Estab.—2004
Sales—$500,000-$1Mil (est)
Distrib.—Local
Limited Liability Company

**CINDERELLA CHEESECAKE CO., INC.**
208 N. Fairview St., P.O. Box 36 (08075)
**Phone—(856) 461-6302**
www.cinderellacheesecakecoinc.com
Email—info@cinderellacheesecakecoinc.com
Pres., Plt. Mgr.—Joseph Makin
SIC—2053; NAICS—311813; *Frozen cheesecake*
Employs—9; Estab.—1975
Sales—$500,000-$1Mil
Distrib.—Regional
Privately owned corporation

**CLEARDRAIN**
219 Saint Mihiel Dr. (08075)
Mail addr: P.O. Box 555, Willingboro (08046-0555)
**Phone—(856) 461-0091**
National—(800) 990-6163
Fax—(856) 461-0092
www.cleardrainusa.com
Email—sales@cleardrainusa.com
Mng. Dir.—Frank A. Chille, Jr.
SIC—3714; 3599; 3561; *Self-adjusting, self-cleaning, self-defrosting & self-lubricating preventative air brake maintenance systems for the bus, trucking, transportation & heavy construction industries & oil rigs; Brand name—ClearDrain System*
Employs—10; Estab.—1969
Sales—$1Mil
10,000 sq ft site, Distrib.—Intl.
Privately owned corporation

**DORALEX, INC.**
403 Saint Mihiel Dr. (08075)
**Phone—(856) 764-0694**
Pres.—Alexander Hwang
V-P.—Richard Hwang
SIC—3672; NAICS—334412; *Printed circuit boards, including circuits design*
Employs—6; Estab.—1977
Sales—$500,000-$1Mil
2,000 sq ft site, Distrib.—Regional
Privately owned corporation

**DRINK ATOAST CO., INC.**
603 Harrison St., P.O. Box 204 (08075)
**Phone—(856) 461-1000**
National—(877) 889-3499
Fax—(856) 461-5964
www.takaboost.com
Pres.—Daniel McDonough
Off. Mgr.—Kalena Mast
SIC—2087; 2037; NAICS—311411; *Beverages, syrups & concentrates*
Employs—5; Estab.—1913
Sales—$500,000-$1Mil
43,000 sq ft site, Distrib.—National
AKA: Boost Co., The

**GOOD IMPRESSIONS PRINTING, INC.**
28 Scott St., P.O. Box 409 (08075)
**Phone—(856) 461-3232**
Fax—(856) 461-3290
Email—goodiprint@aol.com
Pres.—Robert Price
Off. Mgr.—Kathy Johnson
SIC—2752; 2791; NAICS—323122; *Offset & instant printing, typesetting & binding*
Employs—10; Estab.—1972
Sales—under $500,000
10,000 sq ft site, Distrib.—Regional
Privately owned corporation

**HUN MACHINE WORKS, INC.**
51 Whittaker St., P.O. Box 189 (08075)
**Phone—(856) 461-7112**
Fax—(856) 461-8612
www.hunmachine.com
Email—sales@hunmachine.com
Pres., V-P., Opers. & MIS Mgr.—Robert Kiss
Fin. Mgr.—Jacqueline Barron
Sys. Admn.—Jeff Biesiada
SIC—3599; 3499; *Forgings, castings & machining job shop*
Employs—12; Estab.—1966
Sales—$500,000-$1Mil
5,000 sq ft site, Distrib.—National
Privately owned corporation

**M & D PRECISION CENTERLESS GRINDING, INC.**
120 Kossuth St. (08075)
**Phone—(856) 764-1616**
Fax—(856) 764-7444
Email—mdgrinding@verizon.net
Pres.—David R. Speegle
SIC—3599; *Precision centerless grinding job shop*
Employs—6; Estab.—1984
Sales—under $500,000
6,700 sq ft site, Distrib.—Regional
Privately owned sub-S corp.

NEW ENTRY
**NEXGEN PRESS CORP.**
859 Bridgeboro St. (08075)
**Phone—(609) 528-0370**
Fax—(856) 393-8312
www.nexgenpress.com
Email—clientservice@nexgenpress.com
Pres.—Judy Sodomin
SIC—2752; 2759; NAICS—323122; *Offset & digital printing*
Employs—1; Estab.—2006
Sales—under $500,000
Distrib.—Local
Privately owned corporation

**PER-FIL INDUSTRIES, INC.**
407 Adams St., P.O. Box 9 (08075)
**Phone—(856) 461-5700**
Fax—(856) 461-0741
www.per-fil.com
Email—sales@per-fil.com
Pres., CFO—Shari Becker
Dir.—Horst E. Boellmann
Pur. Mgr.—Charles Zeh
Fin. Mgr.—Charlotte D. Boellmann
Engrg. Mgr.—Stephen Miszencin
SIC—3565; NAICS—333993; *Auger filling equipment for powder, granular & paste products; Brand name—Micro-Recharger®; Micro-Filler®*
Employs—25; Estab.—1974
25,000 sq ft site, Distrib.—Intl.
Privately owned corporation

**SEA GULL LIGHTING PRODUCTS, LLC.**
Div. of Generation Brands, LLC
301 W. Washington St., P.O. Box 329 (08075)
**Phone—(856) 764-0500**
National—(800) 347-5483
Fax—(856) 461-0236
www.seagulllighting.com
Email—info@seagulllighting.com
Pres.—Matt Vooris
V-P., Fin.—Bruce Hawkins
SIC—3646; NAICS—335122; *Lighting fixtures*
Employs—600; Estab.—1919
900,000 sq ft site, Distrib.—National
Privately owned corporation
Parent co.—Generation Brands, LLC, Skokie, IL
Phone—(847) 410-4400
See Parent Co. Section for full profile.

**WOYSHNER SERVICE CO., INC.**
813 Edgewood Ave. (08075)
**Phone—(856) 461-9196**
Fax—(856) 461-9212
Owner—William Woyshner
Off. Mgr.—Marian Woyshner
SIC—3825; NAICS—334500; *Calibration volume chambers assembly*
Employs—3; Estab.—1982
Sales—under $500,000
Distrib.—National
Privately owned corporation

## Riverton
(Burlington—S.E.)

NEW ENTRY
**A & S SCREEN PRINTING, LP**
2305-B Garry Rd. (08077)
**Phone—(609) 702-0200**
   (609) 267-4830
Fax—(609) 267-5971
Owner—James Daly
Manager—Terry Cichon
SIC—2396; *T-shirt screen printing*
Employs—3
Sales—under $500,000 (est)
Distrib.—Local
Privately owned corporation

GEOGRAPHICAL

## Riverton—(cont.)

**ACCESS PRINTING, INC.**
510 N. Belleview Ave. (08077)
Mail addr: P.O. Box 346, Palmyra
(08065)
**Phone—(856) 829-1673**
Fax—(856) 829-3006
Email—accessprinting@verizon.net
Pres.—Richard Osbourne
V-P.—Alan Osbourne
SIC—2752; 2796; NAICS—
323122; *Offset & color printing &
bookbinding*
Employs—3; Estab.—1977
Sales—under $500,000
Distrib.—Local
Privately owned corporation

**AIRGAS SPECIALTY GASES**
Div. of Airgas, Inc.
600 Union Landing Rd. (08077)
**Phone—(856) 829-7878**
Fax—(856) 829-6576
www.airgas.com
Email—info@airgas.com
Plt. Mgr.—Jill Morrrison
Cust. Serv. Rep.—Diane Christ
SIC—2813; NAICS—325120;
*Specialty gases*
Employs—64; Estab.—1991
Distrib.—Intl.
Publicly owned corporation
Parent co.—Airgas, Inc., Radnor,
PA
Phone—(610) 687-5253
See Parent Co. Section for full profile.

**D E B MAINTENANCE, INC.**
1000 Union Landing Rd., P.O. Box
13 (08077)
**Phone—(856) 786-0440**
Fax—(856) 786-1993
Email—wktankman@aol.com
Pres.—Kenneth Williams
Off. Mgr.—Ed Hagas
SIC—3312; 3443; 3599; *Steel
fabrication, tanks, vessels &
weldments*
Employs—30; Estab.—1972
35,000 sq ft site, Distrib.—Local
Privately owned corporation

**E C TRONICS, INC.**
855 Industrial Hwy., Unit 5 (08077)
**Phone—(856) 829-7161**
Fax—(856) 829-6950
www.ectronics.com
Email—cwillard@ectronics.com
Pres.—Edwin L. Willard
Chief Mfg. Mgr.—Carl Behrry
Off. Mgr.—Carol Willard
Technician—Kevin Dedlin
SIC—3679; 3672; NAICS—
334412; *Electronic cables &
printed circuit boards*
Employs—15; Estab.—1989
Distrib.—Local
Privately owned corporation

**INTEGRATED LAMINATE SYSTEMS**
1301 Industrial Hwy. (08077)
**Phone—(856) 786-6500**
National—(800) 294-1333
Fax—(856) 786-8912
www.ilsdental.com
Email—sales@ilsdental.com
Pres.—Chris Sparacio
Cont.—Larry Sparacio
Hum. Res. Mgr.—Michelle
Herbster
SIC—3843; NAICS—339114;
*Plastic laminate dental cabinets*
Employs—45; Estab.—1985
Distrib.—Regional
Privately owned corporation

**LYNN MECHANICAL CONTRACTORS**
1810 Rowland St. (08077)
**Phone—(856) 829-1717**
Fax—(856) 829-1331
Machinist—Tim Hossler

SIC—3535; NAICS—333922;
*Conveyors*
Employs—10; Estab.—1959
Sales—$500,000-$1Mil
Distrib.—National
Privately owned corporation

**NATIONAL CASEIN OF NEW JERSEY**
Div. of National Casein Co.
401 Martha's Ln., P.O. Box 226
(08077)
**Phone—(856) 829-1880**
Fax—(856) 829-6063
www.nationalcasein.com
Email—sales@nationalcasein.com
Plt. Mgr.—David Lowery
SIC—2891; NAICS—325520;
*Casein, glues, resins &
adhesives; Brand name—Wood-
Stik*
Employs—8; Estab.—1925
Sales—under $500,000
Distrib.—Intl.
Privately owned sub-S corp.
Parent co.—National Casein Co.,
Chicago, IL
Phone—(773) 846-7300
See Parent Co. Section for full profile.

**PEDRICK TOOL & MACHINE CO.**
1518 Bannard St., P.O. Box 190
(08077)
**Phone—(856) 829-8900**
Fax—(856) 829-8902
www.pedrick.com
Email—info@pedrick.com
Pres.—Ralph M. Scott
SIC—3547; 3559; NAICS—
333516; *Bending machines for
pipes, tubes, solid bar stock,
extrusions, roll formed sections &
structural sections; Brand
name—PEDRICK rotary
compression bending machines*
Employs—10; Estab.—1875
20,000 sq ft site, Distrib.—Intl.
Sole ownership

**†SAMUEL ELLIOTT, INC.**
1818 Bannard St. (08077)
Mail addr: P.O. Box 81, Palmyra
(08065-0081)
**Phone—(856) 773-6000**
Fax—(856) 829-9055
Email—mary@richcap.com
Pres.—Mary Bossen
SIC—5149; *Wholesaler of organic
green tea; Brand name—Dr.
Lee's TeaForHealth®; 7100
EGCG® Organic Green Tea*
Employs—20; Estab.—1990
Distrib.—National
Privately owned corporation
AKA: TeaForHealth

**TOMKEN PLATING CO., INC.**
625 Pear St., P.O. Box 2323
(08077)
**Phone—(856) 829-0607**
Fax—(856) 829-5174
Email—tomkenplating@verizon.net
Pres.—Thomas H. Kennedy
MIS Mgr.—Robert Reader
SIC—3471; NAICS—332813;
*Hard chrome plating*
Employs—3; Estab.—1972
Sales—$500,000-$1Mil
11,000 sq ft site, Distrib.—National
Privately owned corporation

---

## Robbinsville

(Mercer—N.E.)

**A D K GRAPHICS, INC.**
325 Corporate Blvd. (08691)
**Phone—(609) 208-1080**
Fax—(609) 208-1268
www.adkgraphics.com
Email—sales@adkgraphicsinc.com
Pres.—David Griffiths

SIC—2759; NAICS—323100;
*Commercial printing*
Employs—5; Estab.—1978
Distrib.—Intl.
Privately owned corporation

**BIND-RITE ROBBINSVILLE**
Div. of Command Web Family Of
Companies
1 Applegate Dr. (08691)
Mail addr: 100 Castle Rd.,
Secaucus (07094)
**Phone—(609) 208-1917**
Fax—(609) 208-1334
www.bindrite.com
Email—info@bind-rite.com
Prodn. Mgr.—Helder Gomes
SIC—2791; 2796; NAICS—
323122; *Electronic prepress &
color separations*
Employs—85; Estab.—1991
185,000 sq ft site, Distrib.—
National
Limited Liability Company
Parent co.—Command Web
Family Of Companies, Secaucus,
NJ
Phone—(201) 863-8100
See Parent Co. Section for full profile.

**CASERTA, INC., THOMAS A.**
11 S. Gold Dr., Ste. E (08691)
**Phone—(609) 586-2807**
Fax—(609) 586-9285
www.casertainc.com
Email—info@casertainc.com
Pres.—Clifford Cicogna
GM—Chris Michael
Off. Mgr.—Donna Dolci
SIC—3053; 3069; *Rubber
washers, gaskets, tubing &
bushing*
Employs—15; Estab.—1948
Sales—$5Mil
Distrib.—Intl.
Privately owned sub-S corp.

**CCL LABEL, INC.**
Div. of CCL Industries Corp.
104 N. Gold Dr. (08691)
**Phone—(609) 586-1332**
National—(800) 586-1332
Fax—(609) 631-8137
www.ccllabel.com
Email—webmaster@cclind.com
GM & Opers. Mgr.—Jake Martin
Hum. Res. Mgr.—Dennis
Richardson
Qual. Assur. Mgr.—Abe Zwirn
Maint. Mgr.—Mike Frenzel
Cust. Serv. Rep.—Jessica Eliott
Cust. Serv. Rep.—Tracy Morris
SIC—2752; NAICS—323100;
*Cosmetic labels & shrink sleeves*
Employs—120; Estab.—1983
Sales—$18Mil-$22Mil
65,000 sq ft site, Distrib.—
Regional
Publicly owned corporation
Parent co.—CCL Industries Corp.,
Boston, MA
Phone—(508) 872-4511
See Parent Co. Section for full profile.

**EUPHONIC AUDIO, INC.**
18 Newtown Blvd. (08691)
**Phone—(888) 894-3790**
Fax—(609) 336-0002
www.eaamps.com
Email—contact@eaamps.com
Pres.—Larry Ullman
Sales Mgr.—Barry Lamb
SIC—3651; NAICS—334310;
*Bass guitar amplifiers & speaker
cabinets; Brand name—EA;
iAMP; Wizzy*
Employs—4; Estab.—1981
Distrib.—Intl.
Privately owned sub-S corp.

**†FASTENAL CO.**
1163 Route 130 (08691)
**Phone—(609) 259-4290**
Fax—(609) 259-0142

www.fastenal.com
Email—njrob@stores.fastenal.com
Br. Mgr.—William Strobel
SIC—5072; 5084; *Wholesaler of
fasteners, safety equipment,
tools & abrasives*
Employs—3; Estab.—2006
Sales—over $1Bil
6,000 sq ft site, Distrib.—Intl.
Publicly owned corporation
Parent co.—Fastenal Co., Winona,
MN
Phone—(507) 454-5374
See Parent Co. Section for full profile.

**GAFGEN CABINETMAKERS,
THOMAS P.**
5 Truman Ct. (08691)
**Phone—(609) 448-2060**
www.tpgcabs.com
Email—tpgcabs@aol.com
Owner—Thomas P. Gafgen
SIC—2434; 2522; 2541; 2542;
*Wooden & melamine residential
& office cabinets*
Employs—3; Estab.—1988
Distrib.—Local
Privately owned corporation

**GAUM, INC.**
1080 Route 130, P.O. Box 485
(08691)
**Phone—(609) 586-0132**
Fax—(609) 586-9748
www.gauminc.com
Email—mail@gauminc.com
Pres.—Robert Gaum
V-P.—Tom Weiss
Corp. Secy.—Sheryl Gaum
Plt. Mgr.—Gary Gessner
Chief Engr.—Peter Fishbein
Pur. Agt.—Bill Newman
Accountant—Julie Schlag
SIC—3599; *Custom industrial
machinery & machine parts*
Employs—50; Estab.—1946
Sales—$1Mil-$5Mil
25,000 sq ft site, Distrib.—National
Privately owned sub-S corp.
ISO rating—AS9100, 9001:2008

**JDSU**
Div. of JDS Uniphase Corp.
2 Applegate Dr. (08691)
**Phone—(609) 632-0800**
Fax—(609) 632-0850
www.jdsu.com
Email—jdsu@jdsu.com
V-P., GM—Greg Miller
V-P., Sales—Scott Magnacca
Dir., Opers.—Brian Erwin
Dir., Science & Tech.—Mike
Shemo
Hum. Res. Mgr.—Susan Herbert
SIC—2796; NAICS—323122;
*Company headquarters &
holographic plates & security
holograms*
Employs—120; Estab.—1988
132,000 sq ft site, Distrib.—Local
Publicly owned corporation
ISO rating—9001:2000
Parent co.—JDS Uniphase Corp.,
Milpitas, CA
Phone—(408) 546-5000
See Parent Co. Section for full profile.

**†LIFETIME BRANDS, INC.,
DISTRIBUTION CENTER**
Div. of Lifetime Brands, Inc.
12 Applegate Dr. (08691)
**Phone—(609) 208-1500**
Fax—(609) 208-2598
www.lifetimebrands.com
Email—postmaster@brands.com
Opers. Mgr.—John McCranor
Hum. Res. Mgr.—Lili Goncalves
Qual. Control Mgr.—Priscilla Clark
Pur. Agt.—Mary Ellen Kelly

# Robbinsville—(cont.)

SIC—5072; *Wholesaler of household cutlery, kitchen, pantry & bake ware & cutting boards; Brand name—Farberware; KitchenAid; Hoffritz*
Employs—240; Estab.—1998
Sales—over $100Mil
554,000 sq ft site, Distrib.—National
Publicly owned corporation
Parent co.—Lifetime Brands, Inc., Garden City, NY
　Phone—(516) 683-6000
　See Parent Co. Section for full profile.

## LINSEIS, INC.

109 N. Gold Dr. (08691)
**Phone—(609) 223-2070**
Fax—(609) 223-2074
www.linseis.com
Email—info@linseis.com
Pres.—Claus Linseis
GM, Hum. Res. & IT Mgr.—Mike Bissel
Bookkeeper—Elaine Ablett
SIC—3825; 3826; NAICS—334500; *Thermal & thermal conductivity analyzers & dilatometers, including TMA, TG-DSC, hall effect, thermobalance, volumetric & vapor sorption, pressure DSC, pressure TGA, heat flowmeters & differential scanning calorimeters*
Employs—6; Estab.—1978
Sales—$2.6Mil-$5Mil
Distrib.—Intl.
Privately owned corporation

## MAGNETIC & TRANSFORMER TECHNOLOGIES CORP. (H Q)

7 Tanager Ln. (08691)
**Phone—(609) 371-1258**
www.mttcorp.us
Email—info@mttcorp.us
Pres.—Samir Fattohi
SIC—3612; NAICS—334416; *Corporate headquarters; single & three-phase transformers*
Employs—5; Estab.—1992
Sales—$500,000-$1Mil
Distrib.—National
Privately owned corporation
AKA: MTT Corp.

## †MCMASTER-CARR SUPPLY CO.

200 New Canton Way (08691)
**Phone—(609) 259-8900**
Fax—(609) 689-3280
www.mcmaster.com
Email—nj.sales@mcmaster.com
Br. Mgr.—Michael Bostancic
SIC—5085; *Distributor of industrial supplies*
Employs—180
Privately owned corporation
Parent co.—McMaster-Carr Supply Co., Elmhurst, IL
　Phone—(630) 834-9600
　See Parent Co. Section for full profile.

## MCNEIL, INC.

15 Marlen Dr. (08691)
**Phone—(609) 890-7007**
National—(800) 722-5538
Fax—(609) 890-1414
www.mcneilusa.com
Email—sales@mcneilusa.com
Pres.—James Schuhl
Secy-Treas.—Jeffrey Poltrictzky
Cust. Serv. & Pur. Agt.—Joe Poltrictzky

SIC—3297; 3053; NAICS—327125; *Refractory materials & ceramic fiber gaskets; Brand name—Fiberfrax Ceramic Fibers; Plibrico Refractories; Nefalit Millboards; Pre-Krete Linings*
Employs—15; Estab.—1987
Sales—$2.5Mil-$5Mil
Distrib.—National
Privately owned corporation

## MONITOR PRODUCTS, INC.

7-A Marlen Dr. (08691)
**Phone—(609) 584-0505**
National—(800) 524-1102
Fax—(609) 584-7629
www.monitorproducts.com
Email—info@monitorproducts.com
V-P.—Koji Isayama
IT Mgr. & Accountant—Monika Nalipinski
SIC—3634; *Electric heating systems for homes; Brand name—Monitor; MWH180; GF; MHP*
Employs—6; Estab.—1984
Sales—under $500,000
Distrib.—Intl.
Privately owned corporation

## NASSAU COMMUNICATIONS, INC.

115 N. Gold Dr. (08691)
**Phone—(908) 625-8512**
Email—kenfisherjr@aol.com
Pres.—Ken Fisher
SIC—2759; 3993; NAICS—323122; *Commercial & digital printing & promotional items*
Employs—7; Estab.—1984
Sales—$1Mil-$2.5Mil
Distrib.—Regional
Privately owned sub-S corp.

## PRINCETON LABEL CO.

Div. of Paris Art Label Co., Inc.
1226 U.S. Highway 130 (08691)
**Phone—(609) 490-0800**
Fax—(609) 490-0272
www.princetonlabel.com
Email—robin@princetonlabel.com
GM—Donald J. Guli
Shop Mgr.—Ron Owen
Cust. Serv. Mgr.—Robin Bachman
Pur. Agt.—Lenore O'Brien
SIC—2672; NAICS—322222; *Pressure-sensitive labels*
Employs—28; Estab.—1988
10,000 sq ft site, Distrib.—Intl.
Privately owned corporation
Parent co.—Paris Art Label Co., Inc., Patchogue, NY
　Phone—(631) 467-2300
　See Parent Co. Section for full profile.

## R A S PROCESS EQUIPMENT

324 Meadowbrook Rd. (08691)
**Phone—(609) 371-1000**
Fax—(609) 371-1200
www.ras-inc.com
Email—sales@ras-inc.com
Dir.—John Bonacorda
Engrg. Mgr.—Jeff Polizzi
SIC—3443; *Heat exchangers, reactors & columns*
Employs—25; Estab.—1977
52,000 sq ft site, Distrib.—Intl.
Privately owned corporation

## SURFACE TECHNOLOGY, INC.

105 N. Gold Dr. (08691)
Mail addr: P.O. Box 8585, Trenton (08652)
**Phone—(609) 259-0099**
Fax—(609) 259-0077
www.surfacetechnology.com
Email—info@surfacetechnology.com
Pres.—Michael Feldstein
Off. Mgr.—Heidi Kellner

SIC—2899; *Plating chemicals & services*
Employs—20; Estab.—1973
Distrib.—Intl.
Privately owned corporation

## TRI STATE PERFECTION KNIFE GRINDING

3 S. Gold Dr. (08691)
**Phone—(609) 890-4989**
National—(800) 336-6260
Fax—(609) 890-7202
www.tristateknife.com
Email—sales@tristateknife.com
Owner—Chris Albanese
Pres.—Scott Peterson
Opers. Mgr.—Colleen Gibbas
SIC—3544; 3541; NAICS—333500; *Shear blades & brake dies sharpening*
Employs—8; Estab.—1923
Sales—$500,000-$1Mil
4,000 sq ft site, Distrib.—Regional
Privately owned corporation

## WEBTECH, INC.

108 N. Gold Dr. (08691)
**Phone—(609) 259-2800**
Fax—(609) 259-9311
www.webtech-hts.com
Email—amaynard@webtech-hts.com
Pres., CEO—Art Maynard
V-P, R & D—Robert Miller
Treas.—Stacy Evgeniadis
Plt. Mgr.—Eric Duluca
Cust. Serv. Rep.—Melissa Cypress
SIC—2759; NAICS—323100; *Heat transfer labels, MDFboard edging, metallized & wood grain foils, gravure cylinders & prepress, patterns & pigments for plastic labeling & decorating*
Employs—25; Estab.—1981
Sales—$1Mil-$5Mil
25,000 sq ft site, Distrib.—Intl.
Privately owned corporation

# Rochelle Park

(Bergen—N.E.)

## CORPORATE GRAPHIC SOLUTIONS, INC.

11 W. Passaic St. (07662)
**Phone—(201) 556-0700**
Fax—(201) 556-0666
www.corpgraphicsolutions.com
Email—sue@corpgraphicsolutions.com
CEO—Harvey Ginsberg
Off. Mgr.—Sue Cohen
SIC—2759; 5113; 5085; NAICS—323100; *Commercial printing & distributor of warehouse packaging materials, including V-board/corner board, tape, stretch films, bubble wrap, pallets & printed & unprinted stock & custom boxes & bags*
Employs—2; Estab.—2001
Distrib.—National
Limited Liability Company

## DIXO CO., INC.

158 Central Ave., P.O. Box 7038 (07662)
**Phone—(201) 845-6000**
www.dixopackaging.com
Email—info@dixopackaging.com
COO—Kenneth Schapiro
SIC—2899; 3089; *Contract chemical packaging*
Employs—20; Estab.—1926
Sales—under $500,000
12,000 sq ft site, Distrib.—National
Privately owned corporation

## FIBROLAN, INC.

350 W. Passaic St., Ste. 23 (07662)
**Phone—(201) 843-1626**
　(954) 816-6757
Fax—(201) 843-1628
www.fibrolan.com
Email—us-info@fibrolan.com
V-P., Sales—Paul Ellett
SIC—3679; *Layer 2 access switches & single channel fiber-optic media converters for broadband communications access; Brand name—Falcon; MetroStar*
Employs—40; Estab.—1996
Sales—$1Mil-$2.5Mil
Distrib.—National
Publicly owned corporation

## JMK TOOL, DIE & MFG. CO., INC.

19 W. Passaic St. (07662)
**Phone—(201) 845-4710**
Fax—(201) 845-0240
www.jmktool.com
Email—jkristofich@jmktool.com
Pres.—John Kristofich
Fin. Mgr.—Mary Kristofich
SIC—3469; 3544; NAICS—333500; *Metal stampings & tool & die job shop*
Employs—4; Estab.—1968
Sales—under $500,000
10,000 sq ft site, Distrib.—National
Privately owned corporation

## MERTON TECH, LLC

168 Central Ave. (07662-4003)
**Phone—(201) 881-0555**
Fax—(201) 881-0556
www.mertontechcnc.com
Email—info@mertontechcnc.com
Ptnr. & Pres.—Antonio Gil
Ptnr.—Mercedes Gil
Manager—Antonio Gil, Jr.
SIC—3841; 3842; *Contract manufacturing of medical instruments & implants for orthopaedic & spinal medical device companies*
Employs—6; Estab.—2001
Sales—$1Mil-$2.5Mil
Distrib.—Intl.
Limited Liability Company
ISO rating—13485:2003

## ORBCOMM, INC. (H Q)

395 W. Passaic St., Ste. 325 (07662-3016)
**Phone—(703) 433-6300**
　(800) 672-2666
Fax—(703) 433-6400
www.orbcomm.com
Email—customer.service@orbcomm.com
CEO—Marc J. Eisenberg
CFO—Robert G. Costantini
Ex. V-P., Sales & Mktg.—Patrick Shay
Ex. V-P., Opers. & Tech.—John J. Stolte, Jr.
Ex. V-P., Prod. Dev.—Craig Malone
Gen. Counsel—Christian G. LeBrun
SIC—3663; 7373; NAICS—334220; *Corporate headquarters; wireless networks & wireless remote monitoring & control systems for refrigerated & non-refrigerated applications primarily deployed on mobile assets; Brand name—ORBCOMM; StarTrak; MobileNet; GlobalTrak; SENS; Euroscan; Ameriscan*
Employs—50; Estab.—1997
Company-wide: 240
Sales—$70Mil
Distrib.—Intl.
Publicly owned corporation

GEOGRAPHICAL

## Rochelle Park—(cont.)

**REDFIELD CORP.**
336 W. Passaic St. (07662)
**Phone—(201) 845-3990**
National—(800) 678-4472
Fax—(201) 845-3993
www.redfieldcorp.com
Email—info@redfieldcorp.com
CEO—Andrew Gould
SIC—3842; Infrared coagulation systems; Brand name—IRC2100
Employs—5; Estab.—1987
Distrib.—Intl.
Privately owned sub-S corp.

**REMPAC FOAM, LLC (H Q)**
370 W. Passaic St. (07662)
**Phone—(973) 881-8880**
National—(800) 394-7885
Fax—(973) 881-9368
www.rempac.com
Email—foam@rempac.com
CEO—Marc Bushell
Pres.—Alan Bushell
COO—William W. Salomon
Cont.—Peter Pankiw
Hum. Res. Mgr.—Steve Sobel
SIC—3086; NAICS—326100; Company headquarters; foam fabrication
Employs—15
Company-wide: 150
Sales—$20Mil-$25Mil
80,000 sq ft site,
ISO rating—9002

**STARTRAK INFORMATION TECHNOLOGIES, LLC**
Div. of ORBCOMM, Inc.
395 W. Passaic St., Ste. 325 (07662)
**Phone—(703) 433-6300**
Fax—(703) 433-6400
www.startrak.com
Email—sales@startrak.com
V-P., Sales—Chris MacDonald
V-P., Hum. Res.—Michele Coniglio
GM—David Gsell
SIC—7373; NAICS—541512; Wireless GPS & remote monitoring & control systems integration for refrigerated & temperature-controlled rail transportation, shipping & logistics applications; Brand name—ReeferTrak; GenTrak; CargoWatch; GT1100; RT6000+
Employs—25; Estab.—1986
Sales—$18Mil
Distrib.—Intl.
Limited Liability Company
Parent co.—ORBCOMM, Inc., Rochelle Park, NJ
Phone—(703) 433-6300
See Parent Co. Section for full profile.

**STEELSON PACKAGING**
190 W. Passaic St. (07662)
**Phone—(201) 909-0011**
National—(800) 735-2247
Fax—(201) 909-0727
Email—mgsteelson@optonline.net
Owner—Martin Goz
Sales Rep.—Dan Perrius
Sales Rep.—Carey Ziontz
SIC—2673; Plastic bags
Employs—8; Estab.—2004
Sales—$1Mil-$2.5Mil
Distrib.—National
Limited Liability Company
AKAs: Steelson, LLC & Bags PIUS

**STERLING MEDICAL DEVICES**
17 Legion Pl. (07662)
**Phone—(201) 227-7569**
Fax—(201) 301-9169
www.sterlingmedicaldevices.com
Email—info@sterlingmedicaldevices.com
V-P., Engrg.—Bruce Swope
Sales Exec.—Erik Hilliard

SIC—7372; 3845; Medical device software development & electronics, including validation services
Employs—50; Estab.—1998
Distrib.—Intl.
Privately owned corporation

**SWIFT-TRACK, INC. (H Q)**
58 Schlosser Dr. (07662)
**Phone—(201) 226-9537**
Fax—(201) 291-0306
www.swifttrack.com
Email—bcoleman@swifttrack.com
Pres.—William Coleman
SIC—3229; NAICS—327215; Corporate headquarters; patented internal illuminated glass block installation systems (mfg. subcontracted); Brand name—Swift Track Glass Block System; Swift Track Glass Block Silicone
Employs—3; Estab.—1998
2,500 sq ft site, Distrib.—National
Privately owned corporation

## Rockaway
(Morris—N.W.)

**ABC PRINTING**
20 Wall St., Ste. C-5 (07866)
**Phone—(973) 664-1160**
Fax—(973) 664-1161
Owner—Yvonne Cook
Manager—Doug Strowbridge
SIC—2759; NAICS—323100; Offset & letterpress printing
Employs—4; Estab.—1987
Sales—under $500,000
Distrib.—Regional
Sole ownership

**ABLE GEAR & MACHINE CO.**
91 Stickle Ave. (07866)
**Phone—(973) 983-8055**
Fax—(973) 983-8750
www.ablegear.com
Email—robert@ablegear.com
Owner—Robert Hebrank
Machinist—Brian Hebrank
SIC—3599; General machining job shop, including gear cutting & thread milling
Employs—3; Estab.—1972
Sales—under $500,000
Distrib.—Regional
Sole ownership

**ACTIVU**
301 Round Hill Dr. (07866-1224)
**Phone—(973) 366-5550**
National—(888) 228-4881
Fax—(973) 625-7775
www.activu.com
Email—info@activu.com
CEO—Paul Noble
COO—Bob Hinkle
Acctg. & Hum. Res. Mgr.—Michael Westermann
Proj. Coord.—Chris Budd
Mktg. Specialist—Avery Quayle
SIC—7373; Computer systems integration, including net-centric, software-based command-&-control solutions for mission-critical environments
Employs—60; Estab.—1983
Distrib.—Intl.
Privately owned sub-S corp.
AKA: Activu Corp.

**ADMIRAL FILTER CO.**
18 Green Pond Rd., Unit 3 (07866)
**Phone—(973) 948-3252**
Fax—(973) 948-3657
www.admiralfilter.com
Email—info@admiralfilter.com
Plt. Mgr.—Bruce Kristiansen

SIC—3569; Oily water separators & filters
Employs—10; Estab.—2006
Sales—$500,000-$1Mil
60,000 sq ft site, Distrib.—Intl.
Privately owned corporation

**ADVANCED TECHNOLOGY GROUP, INC.**
101 Round Hill Dr. (07866)
**Phone—(973) 627-6955**
Fax—(973) 627-5980
www.advtechgr.com
Email—atggeneral@aol.com
Chrm., Pres.—Li Yuan Tao
V-P., Mfg. & Plt.—Eric Maier
Sales & Mktg. Mgr.—Faithann McIver
SIC—3451; 3679; NAICS—332721; Glass-to-metal hybrid electronic packages, screw machine parts, multi-metal packages & computer design components for electronic assemblies
Employs—35; Estab.—1989
18,000 sq ft site, Distrib.—Intl.
Privately owned corporation
ISO rating—9001:2000
AKA: ATG, Inc.

**ADVANTAGE BUSINESS MEDIA**
100 Enterprise Dr., Ste. 600, P.O. Box 912 (07866)
**Phone—(973) 920-7000**
National—(800) 222-0289
www.advantagebusinessmedia.com
Email—advantagecommunications@advantagemedia.com
Group Publisher—Tom Lynch
V-P., Hum. Res.—Suzanne Foulds
Mktg. Mgr.—Don Grennan
SIC—2721; Magazine publishing
Employs—150; Estab.—2004
Sales—$10Mil-$25Mil (est)
Distrib.—National
Privately owned corporation

**†AIR PURIFIERS, INC.**
1 Pine St. (07866)
**Phone—(973) 586-3988**
National—(800) 219-8772
Fax—(973) 586-3884
www.airpurifiersinc.com
Email—info@airpurifiersinc.com
Pres.—John Di Rezze
V-P.—David Di Rezze
SIC—5075; Distributor of pollution control systems, including dust collectors, HEPA housings, air filters, exhaust hose reels, extraction rails & kitchen exhausts; Brand name—Nederman; American Air Filter; Chicago Blower; Airflow Systems; Trion; Spencer Vacuum; Masterduct
Employs—12; Estab.—1982
Distrib.—Regional
Privately owned corporation

**ALLIED CONCRETE CO., INC.**
205 Franklin Ave. (07866)
**Phone—(973) 627-6150**
www.alliedconcrete.com
Email—alliedconcretesales@gmail.com
Dispatcher—John Elliot
SIC—3273; NAICS—327320; Ready-mixed concrete
Employs—18; Estab.—1955
Distrib.—Local
Privately owned corporation

**AM JET ENTERPRISES**
11 1/2 Elm St. (07866)
**Phone—(973) 627-5690**
Pres.—Andrew Chop
Off. Mgr.—Vicki Summers

SIC—3565; 3599; NAICS—333993; Filling & assembly machines
Employs—3; Estab.—1970
Sales—$1Mil-$2.5Mil
Distrib.—Local
Privately owned corporation

**APW COMPANY**
5 Astro Pl., Ste. B (07866-4053)
**Phone—(973) 627-0643**
Fax—(973) 627-6396
www.apwcompany.com
Email—sales@apwcompany.com
Owner & Pres.—Jason Kellenberger
Off. Mgr.—Lina Lee
SIC—3549; 3677; 3625; NAICS—333518; Standard & custom electromagnets & coil winding service, including hand-wound electrical coils, self-supporting coils, bobbin wound coils & hand-layer wound coils
Employs—10; Estab.—1944
Sales—$500,000-$1Mil
5,000 sq ft site, Distrib.—Intl.
Limited Liability Company

[NEW ENTRY]
**ASO SAFETY SOLUTIONS, INC.**
300 Round Hill Dr., Ste. 6 (07866)
**Phone—(973) 586-9600**
Fax—(973) 784-4994
www.asosafety.com
Email—sales-us@asosafety.com
Pres.—Helmut Friedrich
SIC—3069; Industrial rubber safety mats, edges & bumpers
Employs—3; Estab.—2008
Sales—$500,000-$1Mil (est)
Distrib.—Intl.
Privately owned corporation

**ATLANTIC INTERNATIONAL TECHNOLOGIES, INC.**
114 Beach St., Bldg. 3 (07866)
Mail addr: P.O. Box 637, Newfoundland (07435)
**Phone—(973) 625-0053**
Fax—(973) 625-1215
www.aitglass.com
Email—aitglass@msn.com
CEO—Robert Campbell
Cust. Serv. Mgr.—Al Desrosiers
SIC—3229; 2899; NAICS—327212; Silicate & optical glass & quartz tubing
Employs—20; Estab.—1999
Distrib.—Intl.
Privately owned corporation

**BAKER'S PERFECTION, INC.**
198 Green Pond Rd. (07866)
**Phone—(973) 983-0700**
Fax—(973) 983-8557
www.bakersperfection.biz
Pres.—Patrick S. Amello, Sr.
Off. Mgr.—Larissa Hungo
SIC—2051; 2052; NAICS—311812; Bread, rolls, cakes, cookies, pies & pastries
Employs—40; Estab.—1994
Sales—$5Mil-$10Mil (est)
Distrib.—Local
Privately owned corporation

**BTECH, INC.**
10 Astro Pl. (07866)
**Phone—(973) 983-1120**
Fax—(973) 983-1125
www.btechinc.com
Email—sales@email.btechinc.com
CEO—Manfred R. Laidig
Pres., COO—Thomas J. Leonard
Treas., CFO—Arlene M. Laidig
Sales Mgr., Natl.—Michael Phillips
Hum. Res. Mgr. & Ex. Admn.—Joyce Freiermuth
Chief Engr.—Edward Potempa
Pur. Agt. & Shpg. Coord.—Ed Martin

## Rockaway—(cont.)

SIC—3825; NAICS—334500; Stationary battery monitors, systems, battery test equipment & battery management services; Brand name—S5; Pit 12; S5 Data logger; CellQ
Employs—30; Estab.—1989
Sales—$8Mil-$10Mil
15,000 sq ft site, Distrib.—Intl.
Privately owned sub-S corp.
ISO rating—9001:2008

**CARSON & GEBEL RIBBON CO., INC.**
17 Green Pond Rd. (07866)
**Phone—(973) 627-4200**
National—(800) 223-8283
Fax—(973) 627-1175
www.cgribbon.com
Email—mrribbon@aol.com
Pres.—Henry Gebel
Sales & Mktg. Mgr.—Mike Kutleneous
MIS Mgr.—Jim Logan
Fin. & Hum. Res. Mgr.—Tom Rynkiewicz
R & D Mgr.—Doug Anderson
SIC—2241; NAICS—313221; Custom craft & decorative ribbons
Employs—30; Estab.—1927
Sales—$5Mil-$10Mil (est)
50,000 sq ft site, Distrib.—Intl.
Limited Liability Company

**CBT SUPPLY, INC. (H Q)**
83 Jacobs Rd. (07866)
Mail addr: P.O. Box 391, Hibernia (07842-0391)
**Phone—(973) 586-2783**
National—(800) 770-7042
Fax—(800) 770-7042
www.smartdesks.com
Email—sales@smartdesks.com
Pres., CEO—Jeffrey Korber
V.-P., Mktg.—John Kessell
Sales Mgr.—Eula Zerbst
IT Mgr.—Adam Kile
Hum. Res. Mgr.—Connie Selby
SIC—2531; Corporate headquarters; ergonomic laminate classroom desks & podiums & furniture for computer labs (mfg. subcontracted); Brand name—SMARTDESKS®
Employs—12; Estab.—2000
Sales—over $4Mil
30,030 sq ft site, Distrib.—Intl.
Privately owned corporation
DBA: SMARTdesks

**CLOVER CO., INC., F. G.**
40 Stickle Ave. (07866)
**Phone—(973) 625-1811**
Fax—(973) 627-1428
Ptnr. & Off. Mgr.—Cindy Just
Ptnr. & Foreman—Charles Murphy
Inspection Mgr.—Charles Murphy, Jr.
SIC—3541; 3559; NAICS—333512; Metal spinning & hydroforming
Employs—3; Estab.—1920
14,000 sq ft site, Distrib.—Regional
Privately owned corporation

**CNC SUPERMATIC LLC**
27 Old Beach Glen Rd. (07866)
**Phone—(973) 627-4433**
Fax—(973) 627-7464
www.supermaticnc.com
Email—info@supermaticnc.com
Pres.—Irene Kobrynowicz Hunter
Opers. Mgr.—Frank Pazdzierski

SIC—3451; 3599; NAICS—332721; Precision machined components for the heavy manufacturing, telecommunications & biomedical industries, including precision, CNC & screw machining
Employs—10; Estab.—1969
Sales—over $1Mil
10,000 sq ft site, Distrib.—National
Limited Liability Company

**COLOR OPTICS BY ARCADE, INC.**
Div. of Arcade Marketing, Inc.
40 Green Pond Rd. (07866)
**Phone—(973) 664-3100**
Fax—(973) 664-3115
www.coloroptics.com
Email—info@coloroptics.com
CEO—Joe Cicci
CFO—Richard Chamberlain
Ex. V.-P., Sales—James Pasciolla
V.-P., Mfg.—Mike Pasciolla
V.-P., Admn.—Margaret Sapinski
SIC—2759; 2657; 3993; 2542; NAICS—322212; Paperboard & visual packaging & commercial printing for the cosmetics, toiletries, beverage, entertainment, pharmaceuticals & consumer products markets, including folding cartons, POP displays, binding, folding, foil stamping & embossing
Employs—58; Estab.—1984
Sales—$14Mil
Distrib.—Regional
Privately owned corporation
Parent co.—Arcade Marketing, Inc., New York, NY
Phone—(212) 541-2600
See Parent Co. Section for full profile.

**DEERFIELD MACHINE & TOOL CO.**
23 Old Beach Glen Rd. (07866)
**Phone—(973) 625-0505**
Fax—(973) 625-0505
Owner—Jeff Coughlan
SIC—3451; NAICS—332721; Screw machine products
Employs—2; Estab.—1955
Sales—under $500,000
4,000 sq ft site, Distrib.—Local
Sole ownership

**EAST COAST SECURITY PRODUCTS**
53 Green Pond Rd., Ste. 1 (07866)
**Phone—(973) 625-3277**
Fax—(973) 586-4090
Pres.—William R. Vogt
Accts. Payable Mgr.—Joyce Vogt
SIC—3663; 3669; NAICS—334220; Security control equipment
Employs—11; Estab.—1998
Sales—$500,000-$1Mil
Distrib.—National
Privately owned corporation

**EIC INDUSTRY GROUP CORP. (H Q)**
53 Green Pond Rd., Ste. 3 (07866)
**Phone—(973) 983-1988**
Fax—(973) 983-2688
www.eicind.com
Email—support@eicind.com
Pres.—John Ni
V.-P.—Helen Ding
Sales Mgr.—John Finley
SIC—3429; 3621; 3568; 3469; NAICS—335312; Corporate headquarters; custom components & OEM parts, including blower wheels, blower housings, bushings, flanges, shafts, impellers, spacers, bearings, rollers, specialty nuts & mechanical subassemblies (mfg. done overseas)
Employs—5; Estab.—1995
Distrib.—Intl.
Privately owned corporation

**ENDOT INDUSTRIES, INC.**
60 Green Pond Rd. (07866)
**Phone—(973) 625-8500**
National—(800) 443-6368
Fax—(973) 625-4087
www.endot.com
Email—info@endot.com
Chrm.—Gary Wellmann
Pres.—Jennifer Marin
V.-P., Sales & Mktg.—Richard Kraft
SIC—3084; 3089; 3498; 3644; NAICS—326212; Corporate headquarters & HDPE plastic pipe for municipal water service & submersible water well pumps, fiber-optic conduit, electrical conduit & natural gas pipe & tubing; Brand name—EndoPure; Endocor; Enduct; EndoPoly; Endocore; EndoTrace; Golden Jet; Super Golden Jet; Geothermal; PE 2406/2708 Yellow Gas Pipe; PE4710 Gas Pipe
Employs—50; Estab.—1972
Company-wide: 90
Sales—$25Mil-$35Mil
65,000 sq ft site, Distrib.—Intl.
Privately owned sub-S corp.

**ESSEX FENCE CO.**
132 U.S. Highway 46 (07866)
**Phone—(973) 625-4122**
Fax—(973) 625-1222
www.essexfence.com
Email—sales@essexfence.com
Ptnr.—George Lenar
GM—Bill Lenar
Salesman—John Johnson
SIC—3089; 3444; 2499; 3496; NAICS—332618; PVC vinyl, ornamental aluminum, wood & chain-link fencing, custom gates, electric gate operators & installation
Employs—17; Estab.—1976
Sales—$1Mil-$2.5Mil
Distrib.—Local
Privately owned partnership

**FABER PRECISION, INC.**
198 Green Pond Rd., Unit D (07866)
**Phone—(973) 983-1844**
Fax—(973) 983-1848
www.faberprecision.com
Email—stacey@faberprecision.com
Ptnr.—Stacey Faber
Ptnr.—Kevin Faber
SIC—3484; 3489; NAICS—332994; Firearms for individual sportsmen & collectors & the firearms industry
Employs—7; Estab.—1996
Sales—$500,000-$1Mil
8,400 sq ft site, Distrib.—National
Limited Liability Company

**FABRITE METAL**
10 Stony Brook Rd. (07866)
**Phone—(973) 714-1813**
Email—fabritemetal@aol.com
Owner—Robert Gilmore
SIC—3499; 3599; Custom metal fabrication & precision welding job shop
Employs—1; Estab.—1999
Sales—under $500,000
Distrib.—Regional
Sole ownership

**†FERGUSON ENTERPRISES, INC.**
100 U.S. Highway 46 (07866)
**Phone—(973) 983-1177**
Fax—(973) 983-0721
www.ferguson.com
Email—james.cobb@ferguson.com
Sales Mgr.—James Cobb
Br. Mgr.—Courtney Getic
Sales Rep.—Kelly Doughty
Sales Rep.—Rob Palko

SIC—5074; Distributor of plumbing supplies, including pipes, valves, fittings & fixtures
Employs—13; Estab.—1989
Distrib.—Intl.
Publicly owned corporation
Parent co.—Ferguson Enterprises, Inc., Newport News, VA
Phone—(757) 874-7795
See Parent Co. Section for full profile.

**FIREFREEZE WORLDWIDE, INC. (H Q)**
272 Highway 46 (07866)
**Phone—(973) 627-0722**
Fax—(973) 627-2982
www.firefreeze.com
Email—info@firefreeze.com
Pres.—Eveline Giessler
SIC—2899; Corporate headquarters; fire suppressing & retarding agents & odor eliminators
Employs—5; Estab.—1991
Distrib.—Intl.
Sole ownership

**GLOBAL SEVEN, INC.**
198 Green Pond Rd., P.O. Box 696 (07866)
**Phone—(973) 664-1900**
Fax—(973) 664-1909
www.globalseven.com
Email—sales@global-seven.com
Pres., Hum. Res.—Jonathan Dean
SIC—2819; Cosmetic products, surfactants, esters, ethoxylated alcohols, castor oils, glycerine derivatives, emulsifiers, humectants & blended chemicals
Employs—50; Estab.—2000
100,000 sq ft site, Distrib.—Intl.
Privately owned sub-S corp.

**H & B PETROLEUM CO., INC.**
1 Wynding Way (07866)
**Phone—(973) 664-0144**
Fax—(973) 664-9811
www.habcool.com
Email—habcool318@aol.com
Pres.—Maureen C. Huber
SIC—2992; NAICS—324191; Tapping & metalworking oils, lubricants & greases; Brand name—Habcool Cutting Oils
Employs—2; Estab.—1919
Sales—$500,000-$1Mil
10,000 sq ft site, Distrib.—Intl.
Privately owned sub-S corp.

**HESTER BROS., INC.**
114 Beach St., Ste. 5 (07866-3529)
**Phone—(862) 432-5183**
Fax—(888) 589-0426
Email—hesterbrothers@gmail.com
Pres.—Michael Hester
SIC—2434; 2431; NAICS—337110; Custom residential cabinets & architectural millwork
Employs—3; Estab.—1992
Sales—under $500,000
6,800 sq ft site, Distrib.—Local
Privately owned corporation

**IHI IONBOND**
Div. of IHI Ionbond, LLC
200 Roundhill Dr. (07866)
**Phone—(973) 586-4700**
Fax—(973) 586-4729
www.ionbond.com
Email—infous@ionbond.com
Plt. Mgr.—Dave Neal
Segment Mgr., Global Medical Svcs.—Antonio Santana

GEOGRAPHICAL

## Rockaway—(cont.)

SIC—3479; *Biocompatible hard coatings for medical instruments, implants & dental coating applications; Brand name—Medthin*
Employs—25; Estab.—1980
Sales—$1Mil-$5Mil
20,440 sq ft site, Distrib.—Intl.
Limited Liability Company
ISO rating—9001:2008
Parent co.—IHI Ionbond, LLC, Madison Heights, MI
Phone—(248) 398-9100
See Parent Co. Section for full profile.

### KOP-COAT, INC.

36 Pine St. (07866)
**Phone—(973) 625-3100**
National—(800) 221-4466
Fax—(973) 625-8303
www.kop-coat.com
Email—info@kop-coat.com
Hum. Res. Mgr.—Donna Thoenig
R & D Mgr.—Frank Winkleman
SIC—2851; NAICS—325510;
*Marine & pool paints*
Employs—50; Estab.—1857
25,000 sq ft site, Distrib.—National
Publicly owned corporation
AKA: Pettit Paint
Parent co.—Kop-Coat, Inc., Pittsburgh, PA
Phone—(412) 227-2700
See Parent Co. Section for full profile.

### LIFE SYSTEMS, INC.

75 E. Main St. (07866)
**Phone—(973) 625-3716**
National—(800) 543-3001
Fax—(973) 625-2843
www.lifesystemssoftware.com
Email—lsisales@lifesystemssoftware.com
Pres.—Paul Bindell
V-P.—Avi Bindell
SIC—7372; *Electronic health record (EHR) systems software development for doctor's offices; Brand name—ChiroSuiteEHR; ChiroPadEMR; ChiroOffice; Paraphrase*
Employs—4; Estab.—1991
2,200 sq ft site, Distrib.—National
Privately owned corporation
DBA: Life Systems Software

### LINKER MACHINES

20 Pine St. (07866)
**Phone—(973) 983-0001**
Fax—(973) 983-0011
www.linkermachines.com
Email—sales@linkermachines.com
Pres.—Jean Hebrank
Sales Mgr.—Michael Hebrank
SIC—3556; NAICS—333294;
*Food processing equipment*
Employs—10; Estab.—1939
Sales—$500,000-$1Mil
5,700 sq ft site, Distrib.—Intl.
Privately owned corporation

### MACIE PUBLISHING CO.

10 Astro Pl., Ste. 100 (07866)
**Phone—(973) 983-8700**
Fax—(973) 983-1415
www.maciepublishing.com
Email—info@maciepublishing.com
Pres.—Ed Sueta
V-P.—Julie Sueta-Kaufmann
GM—Ed Sueta, Jr.
Off. Mgr.—Julie Loyd
SIC—2741; *Music publishing*
Employs—12; Estab.—1974
Sales—$1Mil-$2.5Mil
Distrib.—Intl.
Privately owned corporation

### MCNALLY INSTRUMENTS, LLC

11 Longview Rd. (07866)
**Phone—(973) 983-9153**
Fax—(973) 625-7794
www.strumstick.com
Email—info@strumstick.com
Ptnr.—Robert McNally
Ptnr.—Evelyn McNally
SIC—3931; *Strumsticks*
Employs—2; Estab.—2003
Sales—under $500,000 (est)
Distrib.—Intl.
Limited Liability Company

### MCWILLIAMS FORGE CO.

Div. of Precision Castparts Corp.
387 Franklin Ave. (07866)
**Phone—(973) 627-0200**
Fax—(973) 625-9316
www.mcwilliamsforge.com
Email—wgr_sales@wyman.com
Cont.—James Traynor
GM—Michele Starrs
Subcontracts Mgr. & Chief Estimator—Showyer Lou
Bus. Dev. Mgr.—Tobin Gibert
Bus. Unit Mgr.—Scott McWilliams
Qual. Engrg. Mgr.—Joseph Pascoe
Prod. Dev. Mgr., Tech.—Ettiene Rickels
Lab Supv.—Ashley Beattie
Chief Metallurgist—Lenny Rozenberg
SIC—3462; NAICS—332111;
*Titanium, nickel & alloy steel closed-die aircraft engine & frame forgings*
Employs—80; Estab.—1880
Sales—$100Mil
215,000 sq ft site, Distrib.—National
Publicly owned corporation
ISO rating—9001:2001
Parent co.—Precision Castparts Corp., Portland, OR
Phone—(503) 946-4800
See Parent Co. Section for full profile.

### MINUTEMAN PRESS OF DOVER

25 Pine St., Ste. 10 (07866)
**Phone—(973) 625-5800**
Fax—(973) 625-5808
www.rockaway.minutemanpress.com
Email—andymmp@minutemanpress.com
Pres., R & D Mgr.—Andy Krauser
SIC—2752; 2789; 2791; 3993;
NAICS—323121; *Offset & digital & color instant printing, binding, electronic prepress & advertising specialties*
Employs—2; Estab.—1992
Sales—under $500,000
1,200 sq ft site, Distrib.—Local
Privately owned sub-S corp.

### MORETRENCH AMERICAN CORP.

100 Stickle Ave. (07866)
**Phone—(973) 627-2100**
National—(800) 394-6673
Fax—(973) 627-3950
www.moretrench.com
Email—info@mtac.com
Pres.—Arthur B. Corwin
GM—Thomas J. Tuozzolo
IT Mgr.—Jamie Passalaqua
Hum. Res. Mgr.—Terence Reilly
Mktg. Coord.—Christopher Ponnwitz
SIC—3317; 3441; NAICS—331210; *Pipe & structural metal fabrication, including construction dewatering*
Employs—175; Estab.—1931
Distrib.—National
Privately owned corporation

### MORRIS TOOL & MACHINE CO.

80 Upper Hibernia Rd. (07866)
**Phone—(973) 983-9209**
(973) 901-3446
Fax—(973) 983-0704
www.morristool.com
Email—morristl@optonline.net
Owner & Pres.—Harry Pinand
SIC—3599; 3499; *Full-service precision CNC milling & machining of metal parts for the electronics RF industry, including housings, covers & carrier & mounting plates & horse stall cleaners & bedding shifters for the equine industry; Brand name—The Shaker*
Employs—3; Estab.—1981
Sales—under $500,000
4,000 sq ft site, Distrib.—Regional
Sole ownership

### MSP DIGITAL MARKETING

200 Forge Way (07866)
**Phone—(973) 298-8800**
National—(800) 649-3744
Fax—(973) 298-8710
www.mspdigital.com
Email—info@mspdigital.com
COO—Todd Logan
Manager—David Marfiewicz
Manager—Robert Logan
SIC—2759; 2752; NAICS—323100; *Commercial & digital printing & large-format inkjet signage, including QR codes, purls, CD/DVD duplication & laminating, mounting, mailing, fulfillment & cross media marketing services*
Employs—14; Estab.—1995
24,000 sq ft site, Distrib.—National
Limited Liability Company

### NICKEL ARTISTIC SERVICES, LLC

39 U.S. Highway 46 (07866)
**Phone—(973) 627-0390**
Fax—(973) 627-0388
www.nickelartistic.com
Email—info@nickelartistic.com
Mng. Member—Bryan Nickel
SIC—3993; 2759; *Interior & exterior signs & banners & commercial printing*
Employs—4; Estab.—2004
Sales—under $500,000 (est)
Distrib.—Local
Limited Liability Company

### †NORSTAT, INC.

300 Round Hill Dr., Ste. 4 (07866)
**Phone—(973) 586-2500**
Fax—(973) 586-1590
www.norstat.com
Email—breilly@norstat.com
CEO—Vincent M. Orrico
Pres.—Jean Reilly
V-P.—William C. Reilly
Sales Mgr., Natl.—John Orrico
Pur. Mgr.—Lillian Wallis
SIC—5063; 5072; *Master distributor of safety & automation products, including safety light curtains, safety controllers, safety relays, M8 & M12 connectors, DIN valve connectors, distribution boxes & safety, foot, IEC limit switches & pull cord switches; Brand name—HTP; Riese; Reer; Mechan; Pizzato; MP Sensor; AVAC*
Employs—15; Estab.—1963
25,000 sq ft site, Distrib.—Intl.
Privately owned sub-S corp.

### NORTH JERSEY MEDIA GROUP INC.

Div. of North Jersey Media Group, Inc.
100 Commons Way (07866)
**Phone—(973) 586-8000**
Fax—(973) 586-8128
www.northjersey.com
Email—njmg@northjersey.com
V-P., Circ. & Mfg.—Robert Konig
SIC—2711; 2741; 2759; *Daily local & community print & online newspaper publishing & commercial printing; Brand name—The Record; Herald News*
Employs—308; Estab.—1991
Sales—$10Mil-$25Mil
2,000 sq ft site, Distrib.—Regional
Privately owned corporation
Parent co.—North Jersey Media Group, Inc., Woodland Park, NJ
Phone—(973) 569-7000
See Parent Co. Section for full profile.

### NOVA PRECISION PRODUCTS, INC.

160 Franklin Ave. *(07866)*
**Phone—(973) 625-1586**
Fax—(973) 586-2434
www.novaprecisionproducts.com
Email—sales1@novaprecisionproducts.com
Pres.—Robert Suhoski
V-P.—Rhonda Carr
SIC—3599; NAICS—332710; *Precision CNC machining*
Employs—20; Estab.—1972
Sales—$1Mil-$5Mil
7,000 sq ft site, Distrib.—National
Privately owned corporation

### NOVA SPECIALTY CHEMICALS, LLC

404 E. Main St. *(07866)*
**Phone—(973) 586-2147**
Fax—(973) 215-2975
www.novaspecialties.com
Email—sales@novaspecialties.com
Owner—Syed Raza
SIC—2865; NAICS—325131; *Fluorescent yellow 131 & dyes for petroleum, plastics & leak detection; Brand name—Novasolve; Novafluor; Novaqua*
Employs—11
Sales—$5Mil-$10Mil (est)
Distrib.—Intl.
Limited Liability Company

NEW ENTRY
### NUCLEAR DIAGNOSTIC PRODUCTS, INC.

101 Round Hill Dr. (07866)
**Phone—(973) 664-9696**
Fax—(973) 664-9699
www.ndprx.com
Pres.—Wayne Wong
SIC—3829; *Radiopharmaceuticals*
Employs—12
Sales—$1Mil-$2.5Mil (est)

### NUTRA-MED PACKAGING, INC.

385 Franklin Ave., Ste. E (07866)
**Phone—(973) 625-2274**
www.nutra-med.com
Email—mahesh@nutra-med.com
Pres.—Mahesh Gupta
V-P. & Sales Mgr.—Kunal Gupta
Operation Mgr.—Jesus Hernandez
SIC—2833; 2834; NAICS—325411; *Contract packaging, including bottles & blisters for the pharmaceutical, nutritional & healthcare industries*
Employs—45; Estab.—1999
20,000 sq ft site, Distrib.—National
Privately owned corporation

### ORPHEUS LTD.

40 Woodland Ave. (07866)
**Phone—(973) 983-1400**
Fax—(973) 983-1401
Email—orpheusltd@optonline.net
Pres.—Richard Micchelli
Bookkeeper—Jane Micchelli
SIC—2844; NAICS—325600; *Fragrances*
Employs—8; Estab.—1992
8,000 sq ft site, Distrib.—Intl.
Privately owned corporation

## Rockaway—(cont.)

**PACKAGE DEVELOPMENT CO., INC.**

100 Round Hill Dr., Ste. 8 (07866)
**Phone—(973) 983-8500**
Fax—(973) 983-8666
www.pkgdev.com
Email—info@pkgdev.com
Pres.—Charles Schwester
V.-P., Sales—Rick Folbrecht
Admn. Mgr.—R. C. Burchell
Fin. & Hum. Res. Mgr.—Roberta Schwester
Off. Mgr.—Priscilla Jones
SIC—3089; 2657; *Thermoforming, contract & club packaging & folding cartons*
Employs—50; Estab.—1979
Sales—$11Mil-$13Mil
87,000 sq ft site, Distrib.—National
Privately owned corporation

**PANURGY OEM**

701 Ford Rd. (07866)
**Phone—(973) 625-4056**
Fax—(973) 625-9489
www.panurgyoem.com
Email—info@panurgyoem.com
Pres.—Rick Levinson
IT Mgr.—Robin Hughes
Hum. Res. Mgr.—Andrea McCurdy
Accts. Rec. Rep., Admn.—Ann Sisson
SIC—3679; 3571; NAICS—334111; *Contract electronics, computer hardware & wireless device assembly*
Employs—135; Estab.—1984
Sales—$50Mil-$100Mil
80,000 sq ft site, Distrib.—National
Limited Liability Company
AKA: Electronic Integration Services, L.L.C.

**PATRIOT AMERICAN SOLUTIONS, LLC**

5 Astro Pl. (07866)
**Phone—(973) 586-2717**
Fax—(973) 586-9770
Pres.—William O'Connor
V.-P., Cust. Serv.—Kevin P. Garvin
Prodn. Mgr.—Dawn Acosta
Hum. Res. & Off. Mgr.—Susan Reeve
Fin. Mgr.—Jay Marantz
Qual. Mgr.—John Banfield
Pur. Agt.—Annette Passaro
SIC—3672; NAICS—334412; *Electronic contract manufacturing*
Employs—50; Estab.—1976
30,000 sq ft site, Distrib.—National
Privately owned corporation

**PIERSON INDUSTRIES, INC.**

7 Astro Pl. (07866)
**Phone—(973) 627-7945**
Fax—(973) 627-1638
Pres.—Theodore Pierson
V.-P.—Maria Pierson
Plt. Mgr.—Rich Carle
Hum. Res. Mgr.—Fred Smith
SIC—3089; *Plastic injection molding*
Employs—65; Estab.—1975
Distrib.—Intl.
Privately owned sub-S corp.

**PLASTIFORM PACKAGING, INC.**

114 Beach St., Bldg. 6, P.O.Box 186 (07866)
**Phone—(973) 983-8900**
Fax—(973) 983-8989
www.plastiformpkg.com
Email—plaspackm@aol.com
Pres.—George Smith
V.-P.—M. Kathleen Smith
Admn. Supv.—Nicole DeRosa

SIC—3089; 2671; *Plastic packaging materials, rigid, blisters, trays, clamshells & displays*
Employs—25; Estab.—1958
20,000 sq ft site, Distrib.—National
Privately owned corporation

**POLYFIL CORP.**

74 Green Pond Rd., P.O. Box 130 (07866)
**Phone—(973) 627-4070**
Fax—(973) 627-7344
www.polyfilcorp.com
Email—soakes@polyfilcorp.com
Pres.—Gerald Fabiano
SIC—3089; *Plastic pellets*
Employs—23; Estab.—1985
Sales—$2.5Mil-$5Mil (est)
Distrib.—Intl.
Privately owned corporation

**PONTE MODEL MAKERS, TOM**

25 Pine St., Ste. 2 (07866)
**Phone—(973) 627-5906**
Fax—(973) 627-5907
www.pontemodels.com
Email—mike@pontemodels.com
Pres.—Michale F. Leone
SIC—3543; NAICS—332997; *Industrial prototypes, point-of-purchase displays, patent models & trade show exhibits, including thermoforming, fabrication, short run production & product development*
Employs—5; Estab.—1969
Sales—under $500,000
3,600 sq ft site, Distrib.—National
Privately owned corporation

**POWER HAWK TECHNOLOGIES, INC.**

300 Forge Way, Ste. 2 (07866)
**Phone—(973) 627-4646**
National—(800) 797-4295
Fax—(973) 627-4622
www.powerhawk.com
Email—ph2@powerhawk.com
Pres.—William Hickerson
V.-P.—John McCarthy
Off. Admn.—Dosha Hebron
SIC—3423; 3339; NAICS—331419; *Rescue tools & manual impact wrenches; Brand name—POWER HAWK RESCUE SYSTEM; SWENCH MANUAL IMPACT WRENCHES*
Employs—16; Estab.—2004
Sales—$500,000-$1Mil
Distrib.—Intl.
Privately owned corporation

**PRECISION PARTS UNLIMITED, INC.**

24 Patriot Crossing (07866-4826)
**Phone—(973) 659-3300**
Fax—(973) 659-3200
www.precisionpartsunlimited.com
Email—rosieppu@optonline.net
Owner & Pres.—Rose Rainone
SIC—3599; 3444; *Sheet metal fabrication & precision machine shop*
Employs—1; Estab.—1991
6,000 sq ft site, Distrib.—National
Privately owned sub-S corp.

**PURE RUBBER PRODUCTS CO., INC.**

300 Roundhill Dr., Ste. 5 (07866)
**Phone—(973) 784-3690**
Fax—(973) 784-3692
www.purerubber.com
Email—info@purerubber.com
Pres.—William T. McCrink
SIC—3061; NAICS—326291; *Precision custom molded rubber parts*
Employs—8; Estab.—1935
Sales—$1Mil-$2.5Mil
6,000 sq ft site, Distrib.—Intl.
Privately owned corporation
ISO rating—9001:2008

NEW ENTRY
**RENT-RITE LIFT TRUCK SERVICES**

73 Green Pond Rd., P.O. Box 349 (07866)
**Phone—(973) 586-4477**
Fax—(973) 586-0061
Owner—Paul Warren
SIC—3537; *Rebuilt forklifts*
Employs—10; Estab.—1983
Sales—$1Mil-$2.5Mil (est)
Distrib.—Local
Privately owned corporation

**ROYSONS CORP.**

40 Vanderhoof Ave. (07866)
**Phone—(973) 625-5570**
Fax—(973) 625-5917
www.roysons.com
Email—sales@roysons.com
CEO—Roy Ritchie, Sr.
Pres.—Roy Ritchie, Jr.
COO—Bill Reilly
Dir., Pur.—Pat Byle
Plt. Mgr.—Howard Levy
Cust. Serv. Mgr.—Danielle McCarney
SIC—3089; *Vinyl wall coverings & wallboard, shelving & pool liners, including industrial lamination, printing & digital media; Brand name—Roysons; Richwall; Dreamscape; HD Walls*
Employs—95; Estab.—1975
Distrib.—Intl.
Privately owned corporation

**SERVICE METAL FABRICATING, INC.**

10 Stickle Ave. (07866)
**Phone—(973) 625-8882**
Fax—(973) 625-0694
www.servicemetal.com
Email—info@servicemetal.com
Ptnr.—James Moretti
Ptnr.—Joseph Morretti, Jr.
Opers. Mgr.—Dave Lewin
SIC—3444; 3699; *Corporate headquarters & sheet metal fabrication & laser cutting*
Employs—85
Sales—$6Mil
Distrib.—Regional

**SIGNS FOR TODAY**

173 Upper Hibernia Rd. (07866)
**Phone—(973) 983-2530**
Fax—(973) 206-2293
www.signsfortoday.com
Email—sales@signsfortoday.com
Owner & Pres.—Bradley O'Connor
SIC—3993; *Carved wood & electric exterior signs & channel letters, light boxes, LED retrofits & interior 3D logos & letters; Brand name—Max Brite LEDs; Gemini 3D custom Letters and Logos*
Employs—4; Estab.—1994
Sales—under $500,000
Distrib.—National
Privately owned sub-S corp.

**STAPLING MACHINE CO., LLC**

41 Pine St. (07866)
**Phone—(973) 627-4400**
National—(800) 432-5909
Fax—(973) 627-5355
www.smcllc.com
Email—sales@smcllc.com
Pres., Fin. Mgr.—Douglas Halkenhauser
Chief Engr., Electrical—Michael Bell
SIC—3599; *Machine parts*
Employs—5; Estab.—1904
Sales—$1Mil-$5Mil
8,000 sq ft site, Distrib.—Intl.
Limited Liability Company
AKA: Stapling Machine Distribution

**STILES ENTERPRISES, INC.**

114 Beach St., P.O. Box 92 (07866)
**Phone—(973) 625-9660**
National—(800) 325-4232
Fax—(973) 625-9346
www.stilesenterprises.com
Email—info@stilesenterprises.com
Pres.—Richard Stiles
CFO—Nancy Stiles
SIC—3565; 3052; 5084; 5085; NAICS—326220; *Manufacturer & distributor of packaging machine parts & belting for the major pharmaceutical, cosmetic, food & contract packaging companies, including custom & plastic modular belting, machine replacement parts, drive & conveyor belts*
Employs—15; Estab.—1934
9,000 sq ft site, Distrib.—Intl.
Privately owned corporation

**TATA CHEMICALS NORTH AMERICA, INC. (H Q)**

100 Enterprise Dr., 7th Fl. (07866-2116)
**Phone—(973) 599-5500**
National—(800) 819-8568
Fax—(973) 599-0121
www.tatachemicals.com
Email—info-us@tatachemicals.com
Pres.—De Lyle Bloomquist
V.-P., Sales & Mktg.—Zsig Schneider
V.-P., Fin.—Ruston Bayles
V.-P., Gen. Counsel—Scott Ellis
V.-P., Mng. Dir.—Martin Keighley
Dir., Hum. Res.—John Christian
SIC—2812; NAICS—325181; *Corporate headquarters; soda ash*
Employs—38
10,000 sq ft site, Distrib.—Intl.
Publicly owned corporation

**TECH SUPPORT, INC.**

23 Pawnee Ave. (07866)
**Phone—(973) 627-8870**
Fax—(973) 627-8699
www.techsupportinc.com
Email—info@techsupportinc.com
Pres.—Charlie Calabrese
Opers. Mgr.—Amanda Rivette
SIC—7373; NAICS—541512; *Telephone call center computer integrated systems*
Employs—11; Estab.—1991
Distrib.—Intl.
Privately owned corporation

**THERMO COTE, INC.**

198 Green Pond Rd., Ste. 5 (07866-1219)
**Phone—(973) 464-3575**
Fax—(973) 664-1909
www.thermocote.com
Email—sales@thermocote.com
Pres.—Jennifer Cordero
SIC—2821; NAICS—325211; *Chemical hot melt strippable coatings; Brand name—Thermo Cote Strippable Coatings; Super X Cleaner & Degreaser*
Employs—10; Estab.—1962
Sales—$5Mil-$10Mil
Distrib.—Intl.
Privately owned sub-S corp.

**†TITANIUM INDUSTRIES, INC.**

18 Green Pond Rd. (07866)
**Phone—(973) 983-1185**
Fax—(973) 983-8015
www.titanium.com
Email—info@titanium.com
Pres., COO—Brett Paddock
CFO—Joe Ferment
V.-P., Sales & Mktg.—C. Jeffrey Wise
Sales & Mktg. Mgr., Reg.—Dan DiNapoli

GEOGRAPHICAL

## Rockaway—(cont.)

SIC—5051; *Corporate headquarters & wholesaler of titanium specialty products*
Employs—50; Estab.—2001
Distrib.—Intl.
Privately owned sub-S corp.

**TOLAN MACHINERY CO., INC./ TOLAN POLISHING CORP.**

164 Franklin Ave., P.O. Box 695 (07866)
**Phone—(973) 983-7212**
National—(800) 626-7465
Fax—(973) 983-7217
www.tolanmachinery.com
Email—looper1943@yahoo.com
Pres.—John Tolpa
V.-P., S. Reg.—David A. Toops
Off. Mgr.—Christina Nieves
Chief Engr.—William Egginghouser
Engr.—Himanshu Patel
SIC—3443; 3471; NAICS—332813; *Stainless steel & nickel alloy pressure & storage vessels, reactors, weldments & proprietary finishes of stainless, aluminum, red metals, steel sheet, plate angle & bar & metal polishing*
Employs—45; Estab.—1945
Sales—$5Mil-$10Mil
60,000 sq ft site, Distrib.—Intl.
Privately owned sub-S corp.

**TULENKO ENTERPRISES, LLC**

176 Franklin Ave. (07866)
**Phone—(973) 453-6699**
National—(800) 750-2527
Fax—(973) 453-6700
www.blast-master.com
Email—blast-master@msn.com
Owner, Fin. & R & D Mgr.—Eric A. Tulenko
SIC—3599; 3471; 3479; NAICS—332813; *Structural & architectural metal sandblasting & painting job shop; Brand name—ProScreen*
Employs—9; Estab.—1990
Sales—under $500,000
7,400 sq ft site, Distrib.—Regional
Limited Liability Company
DBA: BLAST-MASTER Sandblasting & Painting

**VINTAGE VIBE LTD.**

114 Beach St., Bldg. 5, Ground Fl. (07866-66)
**Phone—(973) 989-2178**
www.vintagevibe.com
Email—orders@vintagevibe.com
Owner—Chris Carroll
SIC—3931; *Piano parts for vintage electric pianos; Brand name—Vintage Vibe; Vibanet*
Employs—8
Sales—$500,000-$1Mil
6,500 sq ft site, Distrib.—Intl.
Limited Liability Company

**WARNER CHILCOTT**

Div. of Actavis, Inc.
100 Enterprise Dr., Ste. 280 (07866)
**Phone—(973) 442-3200**
(855) 892-8766
National—(800) 521-8813
www.actavis.com
Email—info@activis.com
CEO—Brent Saunders
Ex. V.-P., CFO—Paul Herendeen
SIC—2834; NAICS—325412; *Specialty prescription pharmaceuticals for women's healthcare & dermatology*
Employs—100; Estab.—1997
Distrib.—Intl.
Privately owned corporation

Parent co.—Actavis, Inc., Parsippany, NJ
Phone—(862) 261-7000
See Parent Co. Section for full profile.

**WELDON ASPHALT CO.**

Div. of Weldon Materials, Inc.
311 W. Main St. (07866)
**Phone—(973) 627-7500**
Fax—(973) 627-5387
www.weldonmat.com
Email—sales@weldonmat.com
GM—Todd Phillips
Dispatcher—Bob Apgar
SIC—2951; NAICS—324121; *Asphalt paving compounds*
Employs—8; Estab.—1997
Sales—$500,000-$1Mil
Distrib.—Local
Privately owned corporation
Parent co.—Weldon Materials, Inc., Westfield, NJ
Phone—(908) 233-4444
See Parent Co. Section for full profile.

**WIDE BAND SYSTEMS, INC.**

389 Franklin Ave. (07866)
**Phone—(973) 586-6500**
Fax—(973) 627-9190
www.widebandsystems.com
Email—marketing@ widebandsystems.com
Pres.—Frank Padula
SIC—3663; *Military communication systems, including digital frequency discriminators, instantaneous frequency measurement receiver systems, fast switching synthesizers & superheterodyne modules*
Employs—15; Estab.—1992
Sales—$2.5Mil-$5Mil (est)
10,000 sq ft site, Distrib.—Intl.
Privately owned corporation

## Rockleigh

(Bergen—N.E.)

**CARLEE CORP.**

28 Piermont Rd. (07647)
**Phone—(201) 768-6800**
National—(800) 822-7533
Fax—(201) 768-7614
www.carlee.com
Email—sales@carlee.com
Pres.—Bruce A. Burgermaster
Cont.—Frank Sarayli
Opers. Mgr.—Reggie Gencer
SIC—2297; NAICS—313230; *Polyester batting, fiberfill, high-loft nonwovens, filter media & mattress components for apparel, bedding, crafts, insulation, military & packaging applications*
Employs—40; Estab.—1951
Sales—$5Mil-$10Mil
50,000 sq ft site, Distrib.—Regional
Privately owned sub-S corp.

**CRESTRON ELECTRONICS, INC.**

15 Volvo Dr. (07647)
**Phone—(201) 767-3400**
National—(800) 237-2041
Fax—(201) 767-1904
www.crestron.com
Email—glauria@crestron.com
Ex. V.-P.—Randy Klein
Dir., Mktg.—Ben Bruno
Comms. Mgr.—Jeff Singer

SIC—3823; 3625; NAICS—334513; *Control systems, multimedia distribution equipment & supplies & whole-house audio & lighting controls; Brand name—Isys; Isys i/O; QuickMedia; MediaManager; RoomView; SystemBuilder; XPanel; VTPro-e; DualTouch Technology; e-Control2; Cresnet; Cameo; CresCAT; SmarTouch*
Employs—3000; Estab.—1902
50,000 sq ft site, Distrib.—Intl.
Privately owned corporation

**KDF REPROGRAPHICS, INC.**

10 Volvo Dr. (07647)
**Phone—(201) 784-9991**
National—(888) 533-2667
Fax—(201) 784-9955
www.kdf-comp.com
Email—steve@kdf-comp.com
Pres.—Steven Hoey
SIC—2759; NAICS—323100; *Blueprinting*
Employs—20; Estab.—1992
Sales—$500,000-$1Mil
Distrib.—Local
Privately owned corporation

**ROYAL SOVEREIGN INTERNATIONAL, INC.**

2 Volvo Dr. (07647)
**Phone—(201) 750-1020**
National—(800) 397-1025
Fax—(201) 750-1022
www.royalsovereign.com
Email—marketing@ royalsovereign.com
Chrm.—T. K. Lim
IT Mgr.—Harold Kim
SIC—3559; 3579; *Desktop & wide-format lamination & supplies, appliances & office products equipment*
Employs—40; Estab.—1993
Distrib.—Intl.
Privately owned corporation

**TAKASAGO INTERNATIONAL CORP.**

4 Volvo Dr., P.O. Box 932 (07647)
**Phone—(201) 767-9001**
National—(800) 883-9001
Fax—(201) 784-7277
www.takasago.com
Email—finechemicals@ takasagousa.com
Pres.—Hasiya Fujiwara
V.-P. & GM, Flavor Div.—Brian Buck
V.-P.—Bill Bushman
Cont.—Vee Ferrara
Dir., IT—Menno Poutsma
Plt. Mgr.—Dana Drevitson
Hum. Res. Mgr.—Donna Mattis
SIC—2087; NAICS—311900; *Corporate headquarters & candle fragrances*
Employs—100; Estab.—1920
Sales—$100Mil-$250Mil (est)
150,000 sq ft site, Distrib.—Intl.
Privately owned corporation

**TRUE WORLD GROUP, LLC (H Q)**

24 Link Dr. (07647)
**Phone—(201) 750-0024**
Fax—(201) 750-0025
www.trueworldgroup.com
Email—info@trueworldfoods.com
CFO—Tom Ino
Cont.—Ikue Saito
Hum. Res. Mgr.—Mike Korutio
SIC—3732; 2092; 2091; NAICS—311712; *Company headquarters; fiberglass boats & seafood processing*
Employs—10; Estab.—1995
Sales—$1Mil-$2.5Mil (est)
6,000 sq ft site, Distrib.—National
Privately owned corporation
AKA: True World Foods

## Rocky Hill

(Somerset—N.E.)

**SHEDD DESIGNS, LLC, JOHN**

200 Washington St., P.O. Box 276 (08553)
**Phone—(609) 924-6394**
Fax—(609) 924-8969
www.johnshedd.net
Email—jdshedd@verizon.net
Owner—John Shedd
SIC—3269; NAICS—327112; *Ceramic vases, dinnerware, bowls, barware, platters, trays, candlesticks, housewares, tiles & artwork*
Employs—2; Estab.—1979
Sales—under $500,000
Distrib.—Regional
Limited Liability Company
AKA: J S Studios

## Roebling

(Burlington—S.E.)

**CLARK COOPER DIV.**

Div. of Magnatrol Valve Corp.
941 Hamilton Ave. (08554)
**Phone—(856) 829-4580**
Fax—(856) 829-7303
www.clarkcooper.com
Email—info@magnatrol.com
GM—Dave Decara
Sales Mgr.—Lucy Podheiser
Design Engr.—Serge Bochnovich
SIC—3492; NAICS—332911; *Standard, custom-engineered & high-pressure solenoid valves; Brand name—Magnatrol; Clark-Cooper*
Employs—19; Estab.—1960
Sales—$2.5Mil
7,000 sq ft site, Distrib.—Intl.
Privately owned corporation
ISO rating—9001:2008
Parent co.—Magnatrol Valve Corp., Hawthorne, NJ
Phone—(973) 427-4341
See Parent Co. Section for full profile.

## Roosevelt

(Monmouth—N.E.)

**ACTION PACKAGING AUTOMATION, INC.**

15 Oscar Dr., P.O. Box 190 (08555)
**Phone—(609) 448-9210**
National—(800) 241-2724
Fax—(609) 448-8116
www.apaiusa.com
Email—sales@apaiusa.com
Sales Mgr.—John Wojnicki
Mktg. Mgr. & Sales Asst.—Robin Carroll
SIC—3565; 3569; NAICS—333993; *Packaging machinery, including automatic & semiautomatic heat seal & staple header card applicators, horizontal & vertical F/F/S stand-up & pillow pouch machines, bag open & fill & impulse & band sealers with or without vacuum & gas flush; Brand name—Autocard; Autopouch; Flat-Pak; Econopouch*
Employs—12; Estab.—1975
Sales—$2Mil
Distrib.—Intl.
Privately owned corporation

**DIAMOND MACHINE CO., INC.**

30 N. Valley Rd., P.O. Box 420 (08555)
**Phone—(609) 490-8940**
Fax—(609) 490-8944
Email—dmcinc@dmcinc.net
Pres.—George Pall

## Roosevelt—(cont.)

Treas.—Ilona Pall
SIC—3599; *General machining job shop*
Employs—4; Estab.—1994
4,800 sq ft site, Distrib.—Local
Privately owned corporation

### ICY COOLS, INC.

15 Oscar Dr., P.O. Box 686 (08555)
**Phone—(609) 448-0172**
Fax—(609) 448-8116
www.icycools.com
Email—sales@icycools.com
CEO—Paul Wojnicki
Bus. Opers. Mgr.—Liling Su
Bookkeeper—Pat Smola
SIC—3089; 2819; *Reusable hot/ cold mats for the healthcare, food & beverage & shipping industries & OEM promotional products for consumers; Brand name—Icy Cools®; IceAid; Neowrap*
Employs—10; Estab.—1996
Sales—$500,000-$1Mil
Distrib.—National
Privately owned corporation

## Roseland

(Essex—N.E.)

### ABSCO, INC.

101 Eisenhower Pkwy., Ste. 402 (07068)
**Phone—(973) 635-9040**
Fax—(973) 635-9878
www.advbiomat.com
Pres., CEO—Peter Carr
V-P.—Matt Kulik
SIC—3841; 3842; *Proprietary bone cement, cement mixing & delivery systems & external fixation devices for orthopaedic device manufacturers, orthopaedic surgeons & neurosurgeons, radiologists & interventional radiologists; Brand name—Plexis; Concert*
Employs—3; Estab.—1994
19,151 sq ft site, Distrib.—National
Privately owned corporation
ISO rating—13485

### AMANO MCGANN

Div. of Amano USA Holdings, Inc.
140 Harrison Ave. (07068)
**Phone—(973) 618-4050**
Fax—(973) 618-4051
www.amanomcgann.com
GM—Jim Newcomer
IT Mgr.—Mermon Lewis
Administrator—Cristine Charles
SIC—3559; *Pay stations & computer software for the automobile parking industry*
Employs—15; Estab.—1982
Sales—$2.5Mil-$5Mil (est)
Distrib.—Regional
Publicly owned corporation
Parent co.—Amano USA Holdings, Inc., Roseland, NJ
Phone—(973) 403-1900
See Parent Co. Section for full profile.

### AMANO USA HOLDINGS, INC.

140 Harrison Ave. (07068)
**Phone—(973) 403-1900**
National—(800) 526-2559
Fax—(973) 364-1091
www.amano.com
Email—info@amano.com
Pres., CEO—Masamiki Konno
Dir., Hum. Res.—Pat Pearson
Global Sys. Mgr.—Hiro Araseki
SIC—3579; *Corporate headquarters & time clocks, time, attendance & parking control systems & building access control products; Brand name—Amano McGann; Amano Pioneer Eclipse; Amano Cincinnati*
Employs—60; Estab.—1990
Company-wide: 500
Sales—$125Mil
30,000 sq ft site, Distrib.—Intl.
Publicly owned corporation

### †ANNIN FLAGMAKERS

105 Eisenhower Pkwy., Ste. 203 (07068-1640)
**Phone—(973) 228-9400**
National—(800) 825-3524
Fax—(973) 228-4905
www.annin.com
Email—productinfo@annin.com
Pres.—Carter Beard
Ex. V-P., Fin. & CFO—Ken Baum
Sr. V-P., Mktg.—Mary Repke
Ex. V-P.—Sandra Van Lieu
V-P., Sales, Comml.—Robert Caggiano
V-P., Opers.—Richard Caramagna
Dir., Retail Sales—Joseph Brennan
Mktg. Mgr.—Dale M. Coots
Dir., Cust. Rels. & Mktg.—Carolyn Albanese
SIC—5131; 5099; *Company headquarters & wholesaler of patriotic decorations, including custom indoor & outdoor flags, banners & flagpoles; Brand name—Nyl-Glo; Tough-Tex; Colonial Nyl-Glo; Signature; Anco-Dyed; Bulldog; Reliance; Republic*
Employs—65; Estab.—1847
Sales—$10Mil-$25Mil
Distrib.—National
Privately owned corporation

### ASHLAND, INC., INTERNATIONAL SPECIALTY PRODUCTS (H Q)

Div. of Ashland, Inc.
56 Livingston Ave., Ste. 400 (07068)
**Phone—(973) 533-5400**
Fax—(973) 533-5780
www.ashland.com
Email—info@ashland.com
Pres.—Luis Fernandez-Moreno
V-P., Innovation & Tech.—Osama Musa
Pur. Mgr.—Jeff Mason
SIC—2821; 2891; 2869; 2833; NAICS—325998; *Divisional headquarters; agricultural chemicals, nutritional supplements & polymers & organic chemical ingredients for personal care products*
Employs—170
Sales—$100Mil-$250Mil
75,000 sq ft site, Distrib.—Intl.
Privately owned corporation
Parent co.—Ashland, Inc., Covington, KY
Phone—(859) 815-3333
See Parent Co. Section for full profile.

### AUTOMATIC DATA PROCESSING, INC. (H Q)

1 ADP Blvd. (07068)
**Phone—(973) 974-5000**
National—(800) 524-7024
Fax—(973) 974-3302
www.adp.com
Email—publicrelations@adp.com
Pres., CEO—Carlos Rodriguez
Corp. V-P., CFO—Jan Siegmund
V-P., Hum. Res., Shared Svcs.—Peggy Jude
V-P., Inv. Rels.—Elena S. Charles
SIC—2752; NAICS—323100; *Corporate headquarters; offset & laser payroll check printing*
Employs—3000; Estab.—1949
Sales—$7.8Bil
Publicly owned corporation

### BARRETT PAVING MATERIALS, INC. (H Q)

3 Becker Farm Rd., Ste. 307 (07068)
**Phone—(973) 533-1001**
Fax—(973) 533-1020
www.barrettpaving.com
Email—bpmicorp@barrettpaving.com
Pres.—Robert Doucet
CFO—Fred Shelton
Corp. Cont.—Chris Winter
SIC—2951; 3273; 1442; NAICS—324121; *Corporate headquarters; asphalt paving compounds, ready-mixed concrete & sand & gravel processing*
Employs—15; Estab.—1854
Sales—$500,000-$1Mil (est)
Privately owned corporation

### BOBST NORTH AMERICA, INC.

146 Harrison Ave. (07068)
**Phone—(973) 226-8000**
Fax—(973) 226-8625
www.bobst.com
Pres.—Robert Pordon
CFO—Peter Ligotti
Hum. Res. Mgr.—Patricia Tracey
SIC—2672; *Paper, paperboard & cardboard die-cutting for the packaging industry*
Employs—115
Sales—$25Mil-$50Mil (est)

### †EASTERN MARKETING CORP.

24 Eisenhower Pkwy. (07068)
**Phone—(973) 403-8900**
National—(800) 966-8300
Fax—(973) 403-9814
www.easternmarketingcorp.com
Email—info@easternmarketingcorp.com
Pres.—Martin Friedman
SIC—5064; *Distributor of luxury kitchen appliances, outdoor gas grills, under counter refrigerators, gas & electric ranges, range hoods, garbage disposers, dishwashers & stone hearth pizza ovens; Brand name—Marvel; Lynx; Bertazzoni; VentAHood; AGA; Waste King; WoodStone; Premier; American Range; XO Ventilation*
Employs—25; Estab.—1986
Sales—over $50Mil
5,000 sq ft site, Distrib.—Regional
Privately owned corporation

### PAR CODE SYMBOLOGY, INC.

119 Harrison Ave., P.O. Box 87 (07068)
**Phone—(973) 618-0550**
National—(800) 524-0599
Fax—(973) 618-9901
www.parcode.com
Email—sales@parcode.com
Pres.—David Aranowitz
Dir., Sales—Frank Palmer
Sales Mgr.—Jason Aranowitz
Off. Mgr.—Krys Olsiewicz
SIC—2752; NAICS—323100; *Bar code labels for warehouse location identification, security, asset control, inventory control, LOGMARS & UPC applications*
Employs—20; Estab.—1981
Sales—$1Mil-$2.5Mil
10,000 sq ft site, Distrib.—National
Privately owned corporation

### PORTABLE CONTAINER SERVICES

101 Eisenhower Pkwy., Ste. 300 (07068)
**Phone—(973) 515-4721**
(866) 472-6256
Fax—(973) 515-4760
www.portablecontainerservices.com
Email—info@portablecontainerservices.com
GM, Sales—Christopher Gramcko
SIC—3443; *Steel storage & cargo containers*
Employs—3; Estab.—2002
Sales—$1Mil-$2.5Mil
Distrib.—Intl.
Privately owned corporation

### WELDON ASPHALT CO.

Div. of Weldon Materials, Inc.
1 Eisenhower Pkwy. (07068)
**Phone—(973) 228-7473**
Fax—(973) 226-4264
www.weldonmat.com
Email—sales@weldonmat.com
Plt. Mgr.—Ed Smith
SIC—2951; NAICS—324121; *Asphalt paving compounds*
Employs—3; Estab.—1950
Sales—under $500,000 (est)
Distrib.—Local
Privately owned corporation
Parent co.—Weldon Materials, Inc., Westfield, NJ
Phone—(908) 233-4444
See Parent Co. Section for full profile.

## Roselle

(Union—N.E.)

### A G MACHINE & TOOL CO.

147 E. 1st Ave. (07203)
**Phone—(908) 241-3205**
Fax—(908) 241-0518
Email—gaiello@agmachine.com
Pres.—Gregory Aiello
SIC—3599; *Precision machining job shop*
Employs—5; Estab.—1980
Distrib.—National
Privately owned corporation

### A J IMAGES, INC.

259 E. 1st Ave. (07203)
**Phone—(908) 241-6900**
Fax—(908) 241-2526
www.ajimages.com
Email—production@ajimages.com
Pres.—Janet Greebel
V-P.—Arnold Greebel
2nd V-P.—Aharon Greebel
Dir., Fin.—Steven Greebel
SIC—2759; NAICS—323100; *Commercial multi-color printing, including annual reports, direct mail, sell sheets & booklets*
Employs—23; Estab.—1967
Sales—$4Mil-$6Mil
13,200 sq ft site, Distrib.—National
Privately owned corporation

### ADVANCED CUTTING SERVICES, LLC

169 E. Highland Pkwy. (07203)
**Phone—(908) 241-5332**
National—(877) 493-7628
www.acswaterjet.com
Email—bob@acswaterjet.com
Owner, Pres. & Mng. Member—Bob Balchunas
SIC—3446; 3599; NAICS—332323; *Ecofriendly waterjet cutting & metal art fabrication, including ferrous & nonferrous metals, glass, plastics, stone & CNC controlled waterjet machining*
Employs—5; Estab.—1999
Sales—$500,000-$1Mil
3,000 sq ft site, Distrib.—Intl.
Limited Liability Company
AKA: ACS Waterjet

GEOGRAPHICAL

## Roselle—(cont.)

**AEROACOUSTIC CORP., THE**
169 E. Highland Pkwy. (07203)
**Phone—(908) 241-8600**
National—(800) 842-2376
Fax—(908) 241-8818
www.aeroacoustic.com
Email—aero@aeroacoustic.com
Pres.—Margherita Kallinger
Sales Mgr.—Jeff Mortensen
Plt. Mgr.—John LaMantia
Fin. Mgr.—Thomas Fishetti
SIC—3446; NAICS—332323; *Corporate headquarters & noise abatement equipment & assembly*
Employs—55; Estab.—1990
Sales—$5Mil-$10Mil
Distrib.—National
Privately owned corporation

**†ALLISTER BUSINESS SYSTEMS, INC.**
Div. of Kyocera Document Solutions America, Inc.
205 E. 1st Ave. (07203)
Mail addr: P.O. Box 6459, Freehold (07728)
**Phone—(732) 972-8400**
Fax—(732) 972-1469
www.allister.com
Email—dho@allister.com
Pres.—David Offenberg
Cont.—Charles Astuto
SIC—5044; 5045; 5065; *Distributor of office equipment, including copiers, digital printers & fax machines; Brand name— Kyocera Mita; Sharp; Hewlett Packard*
Employs—30; Estab.—1989
Sales—$5Mil
Distrib.—Local
Publicly owned corporation
Parent co.—Kyocera Document Solutions America, Inc., Fairfield, NJ
Phone—(973) 808-8444
See Parent Co. Section for full profile.

**AMERICAN ENVELOPE & PRINTING CO.**
212 Columbus Ave. (07203)
**Phone—(908) 241-9900**
www.americanenvelope.com
Email—info@americanenvelope.com
Owner & Pres.—Edward Nodelman
V.-P., Opers.—Jeff Yates
SIC—2677; 2759; 2752; NAICS—322232; *Envelopes & commercial printing of letterheads, business cards, fliers, postcards, signs, banners & carbonless forms; Brand name—Printmaster*
Employs—5; Estab.—1957
4,400 sq ft site, Distrib.—National
Privately owned corporation

**BINDGRAPHICS CO., INC.**
490 W. 1st Ave. (07203)
**Phone—(908) 245-1110**
Fax—(908) 245-0159
Email—bindgraphics@msn.com
Pres.—Eugene Trunzo
SIC—2789; NAICS—323121; *Pamphlet & folder binding*
Employs—20; Estab.—1975
40,000 sq ft site, Distrib.—National
Privately owned corporation
Also see: Pharma Press., Inc., same loc.

**BODYCOTE**
Div. of Bodycote Thermal Processing, Inc.
304 Cox St. (07203)
**Phone—(908) 245-0717**
National—(800) 942-3345
Fax—(908) 245-6255

www.bodycote.com
Email—robert.lobell@bodycote.com
Sales Mgr.—Paul Goins
Div. Mgr.—Bob Lobell
Cust. Serv. Mgr.—Joy Jones
Qual. Assur. Mgr.—Mikhail Gershkovich
Maint. Mgr.—Bob Carbonaro
SIC—3398; NAICS—332811; *Metal heat treating*
Employs—26; Estab.—1942
25,000 sq ft site, Distrib.—National
Privately owned corporation
Parent co.—Bodycote Thermal Processing, Inc., Dallas, TX
Phone—(214) 904-2420
See Parent Co. Section for full profile.

**COMMERCE FINANCIAL PRINTERS**
305 Cox St. (07203)
**Phone—(908) 241-9880**
National—(800) 866-1547
Fax—(908) 241-5653
Sales & Mktg. Mgr.—Kris Haskins
SIC—2759; NAICS—323100; *Financial printing*
Employs—25; Estab.—1989
Sales—$2.5Mil-$5Mil (est)
Distrib.—Intl.
Privately owned corporation

**DESIGN LINE, INC.**
283 Cox St. (07203)
**Phone—(908) 241-1911**
National—(800) 316-3400
Fax—(908) 241-0239
www.designlinefurniture.com
Email—info@designlinefurniture.com
Pres., Fin. & MIS Mgr.—Bob Hansen
SIC—2521; NAICS—337211; *Wood laminated office furniture*
Employs—6; Estab.—1961
18,000 sq ft site, Distrib.—Regional
Privately owned corporation

**EASTERN SHEET METAL & PLATE WORKS, INC.**
169 E. Highland Pkwy. (07203)
**Phone—(908) 241-6766**
Fax—(908) 241-9718
www.esmpw.com
Sales Mgr.—John Sorber
SIC—3499; *Sheet metal fabrication*
Employs—30; Estab.—1973
12,000 sq ft site, Distrib.—Intl.
Privately owned corporation

**FEDERAL MINING & MFG. CO.**
288 E. 12th Ave. (07203)
**Phone—(908) 241-9355**
National—(800) 526-4063
Fax—(908) 241-4151
www.federalmining.com
Email—rshabka@federalmining.com
Pres.—Reda Shabka
SIC—2842; NAICS—325612; *Printing & graphic arts cleaning compounds & solvents; Brand name—Fedron; Fedratone; Persolve*
Employs—5; Estab.—1935
Sales—under $500,000
3,000 sq ft site, Distrib.—National
Privately owned corporation

**FEDEX OFFICE COMMERCIAL PRESS**
Div. of FedEx Office & Print Services, Inc.
450 W. 1st Ave., P.O. Box 379 (07203)
**Phone—(908) 245-4400**
National—(866) 366-1609
Fax—(908) 245-1139
www.fedex.com
Email—gordon.eitel@fedex.com
GM, Comml. Print—Scott Porter
Sr. Opers. Mgr.—Gordon Eitel

SIC—2752; NAICS—323100; *Commercial printing*
Employs—80; Estab.—1970
Distrib.—Regional
Publicly owned corporation
AKA: FedEx Office & Print Services, Inc.
Parent co.—FedEx Office & Print Services, Inc., Dallas, TX
Phone—(214) 550-7000
See Parent Co. Section for full profile.

**FORMIA MARBLE & STONE, INC.**
219 E. 11th Ave. (07203)
**Phone—(908) 259-0606**
Fax—(908) 259-1474
Email—formiamarbleandstone@gmail.com
Pres.—Filippo Berta
Off. Mgr.—Melissa Zamor
Estimator—Nelson Del Villar
SIC—3281; NAICS—327991; *Marble, granite, limestone & onyx fabrication, including countertops*
Employs—7; Estab.—1985
Sales—$500,000-$1Mil (est)
Distrib.—Local
Privately owned corporation

**HARD ROCK MARBLE & GRANITE, INC.**
1101 Chestnut St. (07203)
**Phone—(908) 620-9150**
Fax—(908) 620-9155
Email—hardrock.marble@gmail.com
CEO—N. Ruby Renjen
Pres.—Jit Renjen
SIC—3281; 3231; 2499; 3089; NAICS—327991; *Custom marble & granite fabrication of countertops & hand-carved fireplace surrounds & vanity tops & laser etching of images on stone, glass, wood & acrylic; Brand name—Caesarstone; Silestone; Zodiaq; Cambria; Corian; Avonite; Samsung; Icestone*
Employs—12; Estab.—1996
16,200 sq ft site, Distrib.—Regional
Privately owned sub-S corp.

**†HARVEY INDUSTRIES, INC., SID**
159 E. 1st Ave. (07203)
**Phone—(908) 245-8688**
Fax—(908) 245-0552
www.sidharvey.com
Email—store049@sidharvey.com
Br. Mgr.—Don Kucza
SIC—5075; *Wholesaler of HVAC equipment*
Employs—5; Estab.—2005
Distrib.—Local
Privately owned corporation
Parent co.—Harvey Industries, Inc., Sid, Garden City, NY
Phone—(516) 745-9200
See Parent Co. Section for full profile.

**HIGHLAND METAL PRODUCTS, INC.**
153 E. Highland Pkwy. (07203)
**Phone—(908) 245-4848**
Fax—(908) 245-0232
Pres., Fin. & Sales Mgr.—Ivan Clark
Hum. Res. & IT Mgr.—Milt Migueis
SIC—3469; *Metal stampings*
Employs—10; Estab.—1947
Sales—$500,000-$1Mil
Distrib.—National
Privately owned corporation

**HUDSON MFG. CO.**
640 W. 1st Ave. (07203)
**Phone—(908) 241-3880**
Fax—(908) 241-5220
www.hudsonpunch.com
Email—sales@hudsonpunch.com
Pres.—Albert C. Maglio
Dir., Opers.—Ravi Vidyarthi
Off. Mgr.—Stephanie Darrow

SIC—3544; 3451; NAICS—332721; *Punches, die buttons & perforators*
Employs—3; Estab.—1940
Sales—$500,000-$1Mil
7,500 sq ft site, Distrib.—National
Privately owned corporation

**KRAFTWARE CORP.**
270 Cox St. (07203)
**Phone—(908) 259-8883**
National—(800) 221-1728
Fax—(908) 259-8885
www.kraftwarecorp.com
Email—sylvia@k-ware.com
Pres., CEO—Randy Grant
Ex. V.-P., Opers. & Pur.—Rip Grant
Off. Mgr.—Sylvia Matthews
SIC—3444; 3081; 3499; *Stainless steel, polyester film & metal barware, including ice buckets, fishnet placemats & wastebaskets*
Employs—22; Estab.—1944
30,000 sq ft site, Distrib.—Intl.
Privately owned corporation

**LAST CHANCE REBUILT CORP.**
340 W. 1st Ave. (07203)
**Phone—(908) 245-4421**
Owner—Navneep Singh
SIC—3714; *Rebuilt automotive parts*
Employs—5; Estab.—1993
Distrib.—Local
Privately owned corporation

**LINCOLN MOLD & DIE CORP.**
225 E. 1st Ave. (07203)
Mail addr: 2 Tillou Ct., South Orange (07079)
**Phone—(908) 241-3344**
Fax—(908) 241-4893
www.lmold.com
Email—sales@lmold.com
Pres.—Edward Drozd
V.-P.—Vincent Comitini
SIC—3544; NAICS—333500; *Plastic injection molds & tool & die job shop*
Employs—50; Estab.—1952
Sales—$5Mil-$10Mil (est)
Distrib.—Intl.
Privately owned corporation

**MECHANITRON CORP.**
310 W. 1st Ave. (07203)
**Phone—(908) 620-1001**
Fax—(908) 620-0300
www.mechanitron.com
Email—info@mechanitron.com
Pres.—Dave Newman
SIC—3599; *Thread grinding & general machining job shop*
Employs—3; Estab.—1956
Sales—under $500,000
5,000 sq ft site, Distrib.—National
Privately owned corporation

**MOKES STEEL, INC.**
280 Cox St. (07203)
**Phone—(908) 241-5344**
National—(800) 223-0276
Fax—(908) 241-4433
Email—mokessteel@verizon.net
Pres.—Albie Mokes
Opers. Mgr.—Albert J. Mokes III
Shpg. Mgr.—Mike Lauer
SIC—3312; *Steel cutting & slitting*
Employs—5; Estab.—1972
Distrib.—National
Privately owned sub-S corp.

**OCCUPATIONAL CENTER, THE**
301 Cox St. (07203)
**Phone—(908) 241-7200**
Fax—(908) 241-2025
www.occupationalcenter.org
Email—center@ocunj.com
Pres., CEO—Michele Ford
V.-P., Opers.—Steve Teitelbaum
IT Mgr. & Data Processing Coord.—Jipsy Pear
Hum. Res. Mgr.—Lynn Boyko

## Roselle—(cont.)

Payroll Admn.—Terry Vuralek
SIC—3089; *Contract packaging & assembly*
Employs—350; Estab.—1959
Sales—$2Mil
75,000 sq ft site, Distrib.—National
Privately owned corporation

**NEW ENTRY**
**OIL TANK SERVICES**
505 E. 1st Ave. *(07203)*
**Phone—(908) 241-5011**
Fax—(908) 241-5155
www.oiltankservices.com
Email—oiltank05@yahoo.com
Owner—Robby Schiff
SIC—1311; 1321; *Oil & gas exploration*
Employs—2
Distrib.—Local
Privately owned corporation

**PAMARCO TECHNOLOGIES, INC.**
235 E. 11th Ave. (07203)
**Phone—(908) 241-1200**
National—(800) 533-5396
Fax—(908) 241-4237
www.pamarcoglobal.com
Email—info@pamarcoglobal.com
Pres.—Terry Ford
CFO—Kim Parada
V-P., Sales, Natl.—John Rastetter
Hum. Res. Mgr.—Angela Grieco
SIC—3555; NAICS—333293; *Corporate headquarters & printing press rollers*
Employs—30; Estab.—1946
Distrib.—Intl.
Privately owned corporation
AKA: Pamarco Global Graphics

**PAR SHEET METAL, INC.**
220 W. 1st Ave., Ste. 2 (07203-1102)
**Phone—(908) 241-2477**
Fax—(908) 298-1266
www.nascopar.com
Email—nascopar@aol.com
Pres.—Anthony Costa
V-P.—Matthew Duffy
SIC—3444; *Sheet metal fabrication & HVAC ducts*
Employs—20; Estab.—1976
Sales—$2.5Mil-$5Mil
Distrib.—Regional
Privately owned corporation
AKA: Nasco, Inc.

**PEOPLEVISION, INC.**
311 E. 1st Ave., Bldg. A (07203)
**Phone—(973) 509-2056**
www.peoplevisionfx.com
Pres.—Wayne Sullivant
SIC—3993; 3089; *Plastic museum exhibits*
Employs—5; Estab.—1991
Sales—$500,000-$1Mil
Distrib.—Intl.
Privately owned corporation

**NEW ENTRY**
**PHARMA PRESS, INC.**
490 W. 1st Ave. (07203)
**Phone—(908) 241-4110**
Fax—(973) 376-3376
Email—pharmapress@gmail.com
Pres.—Michael Roth
Hum. Res. Mgr.—Gino Trunzo
SIC—2759; *Commercial printing*
Employs—4; Estab.—2004
Sales—$500,000-$1Mil (est)
Distrib.—Intl.
Privately owned corporation
Also see: Bindgraphics Co., Inc., same loc.

**QUALITURN CORP.**
205 Columbus Ave. (07203)
**Phone—(908) 241-4909**
Fax—(908) 241-3321
Pres.—Heinz Teska

V-P.—Mike Teska
SIC—3599; *Precision machine parts*
Employs—3; Estab.—1976
Sales—under $500,000
Distrib.—National
Privately owned corporation

**RADIANT THERMAL PRODUCTS CO.**
640 W. 1st Ave. (07203)
**Phone—(908) 241-7700**
Fax—(908) 241-7557
Email—almaglio@att.net
Pres.—Albert C. Maglio
Off. Mgr.—Stephanie Darrow
SIC—3823; 3641; NAICS—334513; *Laboratory industrial process electrodes & electric lamps*
Employs—30; Estab.—1956
Distrib.—Intl.
Privately owned corporation

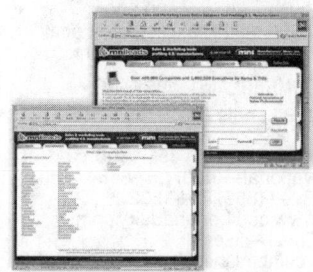

**mnileads.com**
*Looking for Quality Sales Leads on the Internet? Look no Further!*

*Discover HOT new prospects in need of your products or services!*

*The MOST in-depth information available on U.S. manufacturers, WHEN you need it, day or night.*

**STAMPLUS MFG., INC.**
654 W. 1st Ave. (07203)
**Phone—(908) 241-8844**
Fax—(908) 241-6634
www.stamplusmanufacturing.com
Email—stamplusmfg@gmail.com
Hum. Res. & Sales Mgr.—Maureen Marhon
Plt. Mgr.—Mirek Batka
Qual. Control Mgr.—Mohit Kadakia
SIC—3411; NAICS—332431; *Metal cans & covers*
Employs—21; Estab.—1990
Distrib.—National
Privately owned corporation

**STEVENSON & SMITH, INC.**
450 W. 1st Ave. (07203)
**Phone—(908) 862-4211**
Fax—(908) 862-6840
Pres.—Peter Stevenson
Off. Mgr.—Pat Bozza
SIC—2759; NAICS—323100; *Commercial printing*
Employs—7; Estab.—1983
Sales—under $500,000
Distrib.—Regional
Privately owned corporation

**VERSATILE WELDING GROUP, LLC**
340 Cox St. *(07203)*
**Phone—(908) 298-8900**
   (877) 939-5348
Fax—(908) 298-9550
www.versatile-us.com
Email—jimd@versatile-us.com
Pres.—Jim Druckenmiller

SIC—3443; 3441; 3599; NAICS—332312; *Stainless, structural & plate steel & aluminum fabrication & welding job shop, including MIG, TIG, stick & resistance welding & custom generator exhaust, railings, tanks & frames*
Employs—4; Estab.—1986
Sales—$500,000-$1Mil
3,500 sq ft site, Distrib.—Regional
Limited Liability Company

**VICTORY BOX CORP.**
645 W. 1st Ave. (07203)
**Phone—(908) 245-5100**
Fax—(908) 245-5670
Email—victorybox@skyweb.net
Pres.—Alex Landy
Off. Mgr.—Kathy Gibbons
SIC—2653; NAICS—322211; *Corrugated boxes*
Employs—135; Estab.—1989
Sales—$25Mil-$50Mil (est)
Distrib.—Local
Privately owned corporation

**VITA-PURE, INC.**
410 W. 1st Ave. (07203)
**Phone—(908) 245-1212**
Fax—(908) 245-1999
Pres.—Achyut Sahasra
Sales & Mktg. Mgr.—Charlotte Pipper
Hum. Res. Mgr.—Jacki Schaufer
SIC—2833; 2099; NAICS—325411; *Vitamins & dietary supplements*
Employs—25; Estab.—1986
Sales—$500,000-$1Mil
Distrib.—Intl.
Privately owned corporation

## Roselle Park
(Union—N.E.)

**ACCURATE MACHINE & TOOL CO.**
135 W. Clay Ave., P.O. Box 187 (07204)
**Phone—(908) 245-5545**
Fax—(908) 245-5560
Pres.—Jerry Tiehl
SIC—3544; NAICS—333500; *Tool & die job shop*
Employs—5; Estab.—1955
Sales—under $500,000
Distrib.—National
Privately owned corporation

**AYR GRAPHICS & PRINTING, INC.**
320 Chestnut St. (07204)
**Phone—(908) 241-8118**
Fax—(908) 241-7590
www.proayr.com
Email—john@proayr.com
Pres.—Carl Gamba
V-P.—John A. Gamba
SIC—2396; 2759; 2752; 3993; NAICS—323122; *Offset, color & digital printing & screen printing of corporate promotions & apparel for graphic communications & marketing projects*
Employs—8; Estab.—1980
Distrib.—Regional
Privately owned corporation
DBA: Profoma Ayr Graphics & Printing

**CASA DI TREVI**
534 W. Westfield Ave. (07204)
**Phone—(908) 259-9000**
Fax—(908) 259-9040
www.casaditrevi.com
Email—info@casaditrevi.com
Pres. & V-P.—Michael Aiello
Off. Mgr.—Erica Aiello
SIC—2098; NAICS—311823; *Gourmet pasta*
Employs—6; Estab.—1994
Distrib.—Local
Privately owned corporation

**CLIMAX BREWING CO., INC.**
112 Valley Rd. (07204)
**Phone—(908) 620-9585**
Fax—(908) 241-2295
www.climaxbrewing.com
Email—climaxbrew@aol.com
Owner & Pres.—David Hoffmann
SIC—2082; *Beer; Brand name—Climax Brewing; ESB-IPA-Nut Brown Ale; Hoffmann Lager Beers-Helles; Oktoberfest; Doppelbock*
Employs—2; Estab.—1995
Sales—under $500,000
2,500 sq ft site, Distrib.—Regional
Privately owned corporation

**CROSSFIELD PRODUCTS CORP.**
Div. of Crossfield Products Corp
140 Valley Rd. (07204)
**Phone—(908) 245-2800**
Fax—(908) 245-0659
www.crossfieldproducts.com
Email—bradw@cpcmail.net
Dir., Sales, East, Dex-O-Tex—Ed Frick
Dir., Sales, East, Miracote—George Reedy
SIC—2891; 2821; NAICS—325520; *Seamless flooring & wall coating systems, including epoxies, polymeric, cementitious, acrylics, urethanes, ESD, conductive, underlayments, waterproofing membranes, promenade/roof decking, parking deck surfacing, MVE & marine deck coatings; Brand name—Dex-O-Tex; Miracote; Decor-Flor*
Employs—45; Estab.—1938
45,000 sq ft site, Distrib.—Intl.
Privately owned corporation
Parent co.—Crossfield Products Corp, Rancho Dominguez, CA
Phone—(310) 886-9100
See Parent Co. Section for full profile.

**CUSUMANO PERMA-RAIL CO.**
213 W. Westfield Ave. (07204)
**Phone—(908) 245-9281**
Fax—(908) 245-7696
www.cusumanorailings.com
Email—cusumanorailings@verizon.net
Pres.—Jeffrey Cusumano
Plt. Mgr.—Vincent Cusumano
Off. Mgr.—Sheila Roman
SIC—3446; NAICS—332323; *Iron & aluminum railings & window guards*
Employs—15; Estab.—1962
5,000 sq ft site, Distrib.—Local
Privately owned corporation

**DELICIOUS FRESH PIEROGI, INC.**
594 Chestnut St. (07204)
**Phone—(908) 245-0550**
Fax—(908) 245-8868
www.freshpierogi.com
Email—deliciousfreshpierogi@yahoo.com
Owner & Pres.—Richard Jackiewicz
Off. Mgr.—Candy Pollock
SIC—2099; *Pierogis*
Employs—20; Estab.—1991
5,000 sq ft site, Distrib.—Regional
Privately owned corporation

**EXTRUDERS INTERNATIONAL, INC.**
181 W. Clay Ave. (07204)
**Phone—(908) 241-7750**
Fax—(908) 241-1513
Pres.—Stanley Dickerson
SIC—3599; *Machine parts*
Employs—2; Estab.—1977
Sales—under $500,000 (est)
Distrib.—Local
Privately owned corporation

GEOGRAPHICAL

## Roselle Park—(cont.)

**†GARDEN STATE TILE DISTRIBUTORS, INC.**
472 E. Westfield Ave. (07204)
**Phone—(908) 241-4900**
Fax—(908) 241-5044
www.gstile.com
Email—apetrosky@gstile.com
Br. & Opers. Mgr.—Anna Petrosky
SIC—5032; *Distributor of wall & floor tiles*
Employs—10; Estab.—1957
Sales—under $500,000
Distrib.—Local
Privately owned corporation
Parent co.—Garden State Tile
Distributors, Inc., Farmingdale, NJ
Phone—(732) 938-6675
See Parent Co. Section for full profile.

**HEXACON ELECTRIC CO.**
161 W. Clay Ave. (07204)
**Phone—(908) 245-6200**
National—(888) 439-2266
Fax—(908) 245-6176
www.hexaconelectric.com
Email—sales@hexaconelectric.com
Pres.—Kathi Johnson
V-P., Mfg.—Arthur Schwaiger
Sales Mgr.—Cilia Nino
Matls. Mgr.—Alex Schwaiger
Cust. Serv. & Sales Admn.—
Rashonda Aiken
SIC—3423; *Soldering & branding irons & soldering tips & accessories*
Employs—35; Estab.—1932
Sales—$2.5Mil-$5Mil
50,000 sq ft site, Distrib.—Intl.

**†KELLY, INC., MYLES F.**
210 W. Westfield Ave. (07204)
**Phone—(908) 245-7296**
Fax—(908) 241-3441
www.mylesfkelly.com
Email—jkellymfk@aol.com
GM—Michael Oroake
Sales Rep.—Louis Rivera
SIC—5033; 5031; *Distributor of residential & commercial roofing products, windows & doors*
Employs—9; Estab.—1932
Distrib.—Local
Privately owned corporation
Parent co.—Kelly, Inc., Myles F.,
Harrison, NJ
Phone—(973) 481-0600
See Parent Co. Section for full profile.

**MONTE PRINTING & GRAPHICS**
225 E. Clay Ave., P.O. Box 293 (07204)
**Phone—(908) 241-6600**
Fax—(908) 298-1404
Email—monteprint@aol.com
Pres.—Philip A. Montalto
Off. Mgr.—Cathy Crane
SIC—2759; NAICS—323100; *Color digital offset printing & graphic design*
Employs—6; Estab.—1979
1,850 sq ft site, Distrib.—Local
Privately owned sub-S corp.

**ROSELLE TOOL & DIE CO.**
135 W. Clay Ave., P.O. Box 103 (07204)
**Phone—(908) 245-3133**
Fax—(908) 245-4988
Email—tooldie@akc.com
Pres.—George Kaminski
Designer—Don Zentz
SIC—3544; NAICS—333500; *Tool & die job shop*
Employs—6; Estab.—1951
Sales—under $500,000
2,700 sq ft site, Distrib.—Local
Privately owned corporation

---

**NEW ENTRY**
**TOO MANY STARS**
134 E. Westfield Ave. (07204)
**Phone—(908) 445-8852**
www.toomanystars.com
Email—toomanystars1@gmail.com
Owner—Kristine Iraheta
SIC—2396; *Apparel screen printing*
Employs—3
Sales—under $500,000 (est)
Distrib.—National
Privately owned corporation

**WHEATON CO., R. W.**
215 W. Clay Ave., P.O. Box 4017 (07204)
**Phone—(908) 241-4955**
Fax—(908) 241-4561
www.rwwheaton.com
Email—ckern@rwwheaton.com
Owner & Pres.—Christopher Kern
GM—Rolla W. Wheaton III
SIC—3324; 3599; NAICS—331512; *Sand & investment castings & general machining job shop*
Employs—10; Estab.—1916
Sales—$3Mil-$4Mil
Distrib.—National
Privately owned sub-S corp.

**WOWTRIM**
178 W. Westfield Ave. (07204)
**Phone—(732) 340-0766**
National—(888) 440-0766
Fax—(732) 810-0365
www.wowtrim.com
Email—anna@wowtrim.com
Pres.—Felix Dubinsky
Off. Mgr.—Justina Drobuzyte
SIC—2431; NAICS—321900; *Wooden automotive interior trim*
Employs—22; Estab.—1999
Sales—$1Mil-$2.5Mil
18,000 sq ft site, Distrib.—National
Privately owned corporation

---

## Rosemont
### (Hunterdon—N.W.)

**†BENCHMARK**
Cane Farm, Bldg. 7, P.O. Box 214 (08556)
**Phone—(609) 397-1131**
Fax—(609) 397-1159
www.benchmarkcatalog.com
Email—ask@
benchmarkcatalog.com
Owner—Mair La Touche
Dir., Exhibition Installation—David
La Touche
Opers. Mgr., Catalog—Ginger
Nanni
SIC—5085; *Distributor of brass display & museum exhibition supplies, including mounts & tools; Brand name—Benchmark Butterfly Bookmount*
Employs—3; Estab.—1980
Sales—under $500,000
Distrib.—Intl.
Sole ownership

**BROWN TOOL & MACHINE CO., INC.**
Rosemont Raven Rock Rd., P.O.
Box 142 (08556)
**Phone—(609) 397-1751**
Fax—(609) 397-6969
www.btmco.com
Email—abbtm@verizon.net
Pres.—Alan Brown
SIC—3543; 3599; 2431; NAICS—332997; *Industrial & medical prototypes & architectural hardware & precision grinding, CNC milling & turning of short production runs*
Employs—2; Estab.—1987
Sales—under $500,000
3,000 sq ft site, Distrib.—Intl.
Privately owned corporation

---

**FREDERIKS MACHINE & TOOL, INC.**
99 Kingwood Stockton Rd., P.O.
Box 247 (08556)
**Phone—(609) 397-4991**
Fax—(609) 609-4939
www.fmtcompany.com
Email—fmtpeter@comcast.net
Pres.—Peter Frederiks
SIC—3089; 3599; *Hydraulic fittings & general machining job shop*
Employs—5; Estab.—1979
Sales—$500,000-$1Mil
14,000 sq ft site, Distrib.—National
Privately owned sub-S corp.

---

## Rosenhayn
### (Cumberland—S.W.)

**A & J CANVAS CO., INC.**
Maple Spruce St., P.O. Box 30 (08352)
**Phone—(856) 451-5606**
Fax—(856) 451-6678
Pres.—Larry Abraham
Off. Mgr.—Terry Ridgeway
SIC—2394; NAICS—314912; *Canvas truck covers*
Employs—3; Estab.—1979
Sales—under $500,000
4,500 sq ft site, Distrib.—Local
Privately owned sub-S corp.

**†CUMBERLAND DAIRY, INC.**
899 Landis Ave., P.O. Box 308 (08352)
**Phone—(856) 451-1300**
National—(800) 257-8484
Fax—(856) 451-1332
www.cumberlanddairy.com
Email—sales@
cumberlanddairy.com
Pres.—Carmine Catalana IV
CFO—John Cowan
V-P., Sales—David Catalana
SIC—5143; 5149; *Corporate headquarters & distributor of dairy products, including fluid milk & nondairy creamer & ice cream mix*
Employs—55; Estab.—1932
Company-wide: 120
Distrib.—National
Privately owned corporation

**F & S PRODUCE CO., INC.**
913 Bridgeton Ave., P.O. Box 489 (08352)
**Phone—(856) 453-0316**
National—(800) 886-3316
Fax—(856) 453-0494
www.freshcutproduce.com
Email—webmaster@
freshcutproduce.com
CEO—Salvatore Pipitone, Jr.
CFO—Lori Maddalena
V-P., Mfg.—Tom Butler
V-P., Opers.—Sam Pipitone III
Dir., IT—Ken Pugh
Dir., Tech. Svcs.—Doug Nicoll
Plt. Mgr.—Curtis Lee
Cust. Serv. Supv.—Michele
Barnstead
SIC—2034; 2099; 3089; *Fruit & vegetable processing & packaging; Brand name— Garden Pure; Garden Highway; Duane Reade; Hannaford Bros.; Mott's; Mann's Packing; Trader Joe's*
Employs—600; Estab.—1997
Sales—$50Mil-$100Mil
125,000 sq ft site, Distrib.—
Regional
Privately owned corporation

**QIS, INC.**
778 Vineland Ave., P.O. Box 517 (08352)
**Phone—(856) 455-3736**
Fax—(856) 455-3894
Pres.—Diane R. Lodge

---

SIC—3229; *Glass vials*
Employs—20; Estab.—1996
Sales—$2.5Mil-$5Mil (est)
Distrib.—Local
Privately owned corporation

**QUARK ENTERPRISES, INC.**
320 Morton Ave. (08352)
Mail addr:—P.O. Box 2396, Vineland (08362)
**Phone—(856) 455-0376**
National—(800) 955-0376
Fax—(856) 455-3373
www.quarkglass.com
Email—sales@quarkglass.com
Pres.—Doug Riley
V-P.—Susan Burt
Corp. Secy.—Pearl Riley
Sales Mgr.—Bill Guilday
Cred. Mgr.—Eleanor Weiss
SIC—3229; NAICS—327212; *Scientific glassware*
Employs—18; Estab.—1983
15,000 sq ft site, Distrib.—National
Privately owned corporation

---

## Roxbury Township
### (Morris—N.W.)

**DELTA COOLING TOWERS, INC.**
185 U.S. Highway 206 (07836)
**Phone—(973) 586-2201**
Fax—(973) 586-2243
www.deltacooling.com
Email—info@deltacooling.com
Pres.—John Flaherty
SIC—3443; *Cooling towers & air strippers; Brand name—Pioneer; Paragon; Premier; TM Series*
Employs—9; Estab.—1971
Sales—$1Mil-$2.5Mil
60,000 sq ft site, Distrib.—National
Privately owned corporation

---

## Rumson
### (Monmouth—N.E.)

**EUROTEK, INC.**
Carlton Street 61, Unit 2 (07760)
**Phone—(732) 224-1300**
Fax—(732) 224-1325
www.eurotek.com
Email—sales@eurotek.com
Pres.—Jack Ross
SIC—3841; 3826; NAICS—334516; *Medical & scientific equipment*
Employs—5; Estab.—1989
Sales—$2.6Mil-$5Mil
Distrib.—Intl.
Privately owned corporation

**NELSON PRESS**
111 E. River Rd. (07760)
**Phone—(732) 747-0330**
Fax—(732) 530-8567
www.nelsonpress.net
Email—scott@nelsonpress.net
Pres.—Scott Thompsen
Fin., MIS, Opers. & R & D Mgr.—
Sid Shapiro
SIC—2759; NAICS—323100; *Commercial printing*
Employs—5; Estab.—1900
Sales—under $500,000
5,000 sq ft site, Distrib.—National
Privately owned corporation

---

## Runnemede
### (Camden—S.W.)

**AG PETERS & SON, INC.**
1025 N. Black Horse Pike (08078)
**Phone—(856) 931-7476**
Fax—(856) 931-0382
www.agpetersfuneralsupplies.com
Email—info@
agpetersfuneralsupplies.com
Pres.—Diane Lansberry
IT Mgr.—Michael Lansberry

## Runnemede—(cont.)

Hum. Res. & Off. Mgr.—Jill
  Kershew
SIC—2339; 3999; *Burial dresses
  & funeral supplies*
Employs—7; Estab.—1931
Sales—$1Mil-$2.5Mil
Distrib.—Local
Privately owned sub-S corp.

### CAPITAL GASKET & RUBBER CORP.

325 E. Clements Bridge Rd.
  (08078-1404)
Mail addr.: P.O. Box 141, Glendora
  (08029)
**Phone—(856) 939-3670**
National—(866) 859-1631
Fax—(856) 939-3675
www.capitalgasket.com
Email—info@capitalgasket.com
V-P.—Dennis Iocono
Sales Mgr., Inside—Scott
  McDowell
SIC—3053; 3069; NAICS—
  339991; *Nonmetallic & die cut
  gaskets & rubber products;
  Brand name—JM Clipper*
Employs—5; Estab.—1986
Sales—under $500,000
3,000 sq ft site, Distrib.—Regional
Privately owned corporation

NEW ENTRY

### COLOUR GRAPHICS

521 Irish Hill Rd. (08078)
**Phone—(856) 939-5599**
Fax—(856) 939-0385
www.njprintandweb.com
Email—info@njprintandweb.com
Owner—Lawrence McCaffrey
SIC—2759; *Commercial printing &
  graphic design services*
Employs—1
Sales—under $500,000 (est)
Distrib.—Local
Privately owned corporation

### DANIEL'S CUSTOM DRAPERIES, INC.

620 W. Clements Bridge Rd.
  (08078)
**Phone—(856) 939-2212**
www.danielsdrapes.com
Email—terdan@comcast.net
Pres.—Daniel Scavette
SIC—2391; NAICS—314121;
  *Draperies, blinds & shades*
Employs—3; Estab.—1950
Sales—under $500,000
2,300 sq ft site, Distrib.—Local
Privately owned sub-S corp.

### DELUXE ITALIAN BAKERY, INC.

680 E. Clements Bridge Rd.
  (08078)
**Phone—(856) 939-5000**
Fax—(856) 939-0675
www.deluxeitalian.com
Sales Mgr.—Darek Shelby
SIC—2051; NAICS—311812;
  *Bread & pastries*
Employs—100; Estab.—1949
Distrib.—Intl.
Privately owned corporation

### RUOFF & SONS, INC.

1030 Rose Ave., P.O. Box 320
  (08078)
**Phone—(856) 931-2064**
Fax—(856) 931-0539
www.ruoffandsons.com
Email—ruoffandsons@comcast.net
Pres.—Steve Ruoff
Sales Mgr.—Albert F. Ruoff, Jr.
Hum. Res. & Off. Mgr.—Sue
  Kraszewski
SIC—3599; *Metal machine parts*
Employs—25; Estab.—1951
27,000 sq ft site, Distrib.—National
Privately owned corporation

### SILVERTOP ASSOCS., INC.

600 E. Clements Bridge Rd.
  (08078)
**Phone—(856) 939-9599**
National—(800) 217-2782
Fax—(856) 939-5990
www.rastaimposta.com
Email—orders@rastaimposta.com
Pres.—Robert Berman
SIC—2389; *Halloween costumes
  for men, women & children*
Employs—48; Estab.—1992
Sales—$5Mil-$10Mil (est)
Distrib.—Intl.
Privately owned corporation
AKA: Rasta Imposta

---

## Rutherford

(Bergen—N.E.)

### ARCHITECTURAL WINDOW MFG.

359 Veterans Blvd. (07070)
**Phone—(201) 939-2200**
Fax—(201) 939-2201
www.architecturalwindow.com
Email—sales@
  architecturalwindow.com
V-P., Sales—Ken Thompson
V-P.—Michael A. Laino
SIC—3442; 3089; *Aluminum &
  polyurethane windows*
Employs—25
Privately owned corporation

### AXS-ONE, INC.

301 Route 17, Ste. 11 (07070)
**Phone—(201) 935-3400**
Fax—(201) 935-6355
www.axsone.com
Email—hr@axsone.com
Pres., CEO—William Lyons
CFO—Susan Conner
Hum. Res. Mgr.—Christa Flannery
SIC—7372; *Email archiving
  software development; Brand
  name—AXS-One Central; AXS-
  Link for SAP; AXS-Link for
  Desktop*
Employs—150; Estab.—1977
Distrib.—Intl.
Privately owned corporation

### COLUMBIA FILTERS, INC.

255 Highland Cross (07070)
**Phone—(201) 438-3883**
Fax—(201) 438-0816
www.columbiafiltersusa.com
Email—mail@columbiafilters.com
Pres.—Nick Pizzone
SIC—3564; NAICS—333400; *Air
  conditioning filters*
Employs—10; Estab.—1976
Sales—$1Mil-$2.5Mil (est)
Distrib.—Regional
Privately owned corporation

### DAIRY DELIGHT, LLC

1 Industrial Dr. (07070)
**Phone—(201) 939-7878**
Fax—(201) 939-2888
www.normansdairy.com
Email—office@normansdairy.com
Owner—Victor Ostreicher
CFO—Shulan Ostreicher
Plt. Mgr.—Marti Kairey
Off. Mgr.—Lilach Sophar
SIC—2026; 2022; NAICS—
  311513; *Israeli dairy products*
Employs—15; Estab.—2004
Sales—$5Mil-$10Mil (est)
Distrib.—National
Sole ownership
AKA: Norman's Dairy Delight

### DELFORM, LLC

225 Highland Cross, Ste. 6
  (07070-2595)
**Phone—(201) 438-3915**
Fax—(201) 438-3917
www.delformstudios.com
Email—tracey@delformstudios.com
Ptnr. & Member—Tracey Stakelin

SIC—2511; 2514; 2519; 2599;
  NAICS—337125; *Residential &
  commercial metal & wood
  furniture, lighting fixtures &
  accessories*
Employs—5; Estab.—2001
Sales—$500,000-$1Mil
Distrib.—National
Privately owned partnership

### EAGLE FLO PUMPS, INC.

306 Orient Way (07070)
**Phone—(201) 438-8595**
Fax—(201) 438-8551
www.eagleflopump.com
Email—request@eagleflopump.com
Pres.—Joseph Hamadeh
Engr.—James Hamadeh
Accountant—Wafa Balbaki
Accountant—Faye Wolf
SIC—3561; 3491; NAICS—
  333911; *Industrial pumps &
  valves*
Employs—4; Estab.—1984
Sales—under $500,000
4,000 sq ft site, Distrib.—Intl.
Privately owned corporation

### JORY ENGRAVERS, INC.

23 W. Erie Ave. (07070)
**Phone—(201) 939-1546**
Fax—(201) 939-2952
GM—Gary Gagliardi
SIC—3479; 2396; 3499; *Metal
  engraving, screen printing, metal
  fabrication & ID plates*
Employs—3; Estab.—1963
Sales—under $500,000
Distrib.—National
Privately owned corporation

### MON FAR PRESS PRINTING

13 Franklin Pl. (07070)
**Phone—(212) 431-6245**
Owner & Pres.—Ging Wong
SIC—2752; 2759; NAICS—
  323100; *Offset & letterpress
  printing*
Employs—1; Estab.—2008
Distrib.—Local
Privately owned corporation
AKA: NY Enterprise

### SGS NORTH AMERICA, INC. (H Q)

201 Route 17 N. (07070)
**Phone—(201) 508-3000**
Fax—(201) 508-3039
www.us.sgs.com
Email—inquiries@sgs.com
CEO—Jeffrey McDonald
CFO—Michael Briganti
V-P., Hum. Res.—Kevin Clark
SIC—1389; *Corporate
  headquarters; oil & gas field
  services, including casing
  services*
Employs—125; Estab.—1878
Privately owned corporation

### SOUTH BERGENITE

Div. of North Jersey Media Group,
  Inc.
9 Lincoln Ave. (07070)
**Phone—(201) 933-1166**
Fax—(201) 933-5496
www.northjersey.com
Email—southbergenite@
  northjersey.com
Mng. Editor—Meghan Trant
Editor—Jaimie Winters
Copy Editor—Jeff Gruber
SIC—2711; 2791; NAICS—
  323122; *Newspaper publishing*
Employs—5; Estab.—1927
Sales—under $500,000
Distrib.—Local
Privately owned corporation
Parent co.—North Jersey Media
  Group, Inc., Woodland Park, NJ
Phone—(973) 569-7000
See Parent Co. Section for full profile.

### THORAMET SURGICAL PRODUCTS, INC.

301 Route 17-N, Ste. 800 (07070)
**Phone—(973) 399-7792**
National—(800) 984-9458
Fax—(973) 372-1091
www.thoramet.net
Email—pscranton@thoramet.net
CEO—Peter J. Scranton
SIC—3841; *Surgical instruments*
Employs—2; Estab.—2000
Sales—under $500,000 (est)
Distrib.—National
Privately owned corporation

---

## Saddle Brook

(Bergen—N.E.)

### 21ST CENTURY FINISHING, INC.

280 N. Midland Ave., Ste. 414
  (07663-5721)
**Phone—(201) 797-0212**
Fax—(201) 797-0181
www.21finishing.com
Email—karen@21finishing.com
Pres.—Karen DeMaio
V-P., Sales—Cunny Calandriello
V-P., Opers.—James Ramirez
SIC—2789; NAICS—323121; *Foil
  stamping, die cutting,
  embossing, gluing & hologram
  applications, including full-
  service spot & UV coatings*
Employs—19; Estab.—1990
Sales—$3.5Mil
40,000 sq ft site, Distrib.—Local
Privately owned corporation

### A A A STAMP & SEAL MFG. CO.

361 N. Midland Ave. (07663)
**Phone—(201) 796-1500**
www.aaastamp.com
Email—sales@aaastamp.com
Owner—Robert Goldman
SIC—3953; 3993; NAICS—
  339943; *Rubber stamps &
  engraved plastic signs*
Employs—4; Estab.—1968
Sales—under $500,000
Distrib.—National
Privately owned corporation

### A A GRAPHICS, INC.

431 N. Midland Ave., Unit C
  (07663)
**Phone—(201) 398-0710**
Fax—(201) 398-0925
www.aagraphicsnj.com
Email—info@aagraphicsnj.com
Pres.—Anthony Acocella
Prepress Mgr.—Rob Acocella
SIC—2752; NAICS—323100;
  *Offset printing*
Employs—4; Estab.—1994
Sales—under $500,000
Distrib.—Local
Privately owned corporation

### AARUBCO RUBBER CO.

259 2nd St., P.O. Box 8028
  (07663)
**Phone—(973) 772-8177**
National—(800) 821-2651
Fax—(973) 772-4902
www.aarubcorubber.com
Email—aarubco@
  aarubcorubber.com
Pres.—Steve Wharton
Prodn. Mgr.—Galo Macias
Prod. Dev. Mgr.—Pat Kelly
SIC—3052; NAICS—326220;
  *Rubber & rubber covered belts,
  rolls, rollers & molding*
Employs—35; Estab.—1967
Sales—over $5Mil
35,000 sq ft site, Distrib.—National
Privately owned corporation

GEOGRAPHICAL

## Saddle Brook—(cont.)

**†ACME INTERNATIONAL ENTERPRISES, INC.**
Div. of Patriarch Partners, LLC
400 Lyster Ave. (07663-5910)
**Phone—(973) 416-0400**
Fax—(973) 416-0499
www.acme-usa.com
Email—custserv@acme-usa.com
CEO—Fred Reffsin
Sr. V.-P., Prod. Dev.—Michael Romanko
Cont.—Gene Chiarmonte
Dir., IT—Joe Acosta
Dir., Pur.—Allison Hill
Dir., Admn. & Hum. Res. Mgr.—Marie Rispoli
Sales Coord. Mgr.—Phyllis Capote
Cust. Serv. Mgr.—Alex Revello
SIC—5199; *Distributor of kitchen & household tools, gadgets & accessories; Brand name—Tools & Gadgets*
Employs—65; Estab.—1920
Sales—$15Mil-$20Mil
Distrib.—Intl.
Privately owned corporation
Parent co.—Patriarch Partners, LLC, New York, NY
Phone—(212) 825-0550
See Parent Co. Section for full profile.

**ALPAK DISPLAY GROUP**
Div. of Island Container Corp.
575 N. Midland Ave. (07663)
**Phone—(201) 797-1411**
National—(866) 443-4775
Fax—(201) 797-1449
www.alpak.com
Email—info@alpak.com
V.-P., POP Sales—Jason Taub
SIC—2542; 2653; 2759; 3993; NAICS—322211; *Corrugated point-of-purchase displays, storage & file boxes, custom printed packaging, mounting, die-cutting, co-packing & fulfillment services*
Employs—30; Estab.—1955
Sales—$2Mil-$5Mil
170,000 sq ft site, Distrib.—National
Limited Liability Company
Parent co.—Island Container Corp., Wyandanch, NY
Phone—(631) 253-4400
See Parent Co. Section for full profile.

**†AMERICAN FENCE CO.**
326 U.S. Highway 46 (07663)
**Phone—(973) 546-4373**
Fax—(973) 546-8110
www.youramericanfence.com
Email—americanfenceco@verizon.net
Owner—Piero Mosca
SIC—5031; 5039; *Wholesaler of wooden, metal, aluminum ornamental & PVC fencing & accessories*
Employs—10; Estab.—1979
Sales—under $500,000
15,000 sq ft site, Distrib.—Local
Limited Liability Company

**ARROW FASTENER CO., LLC**
Div. of Masco Corp.
271 Mayhill St. (07663)
**Phone—(201) 843-6900**
National—(800) 776-2228
Fax—(201) 843-3911
www.arrowfastener.com
Email—sales@arrowfastener.com
Pres., CEO—Gary DuBoff
V.-P., IT—Ajay Kamble
Dir., Mktg.—Bill Sokol
SIC—3452; 2891; NAICS—332722; *Staplers, staples, glue guns, glues, rivet tools, nailers & nails; Brand name—Arrow; PowerShot; Electromatic*
Employs—650; Estab.—1929
250,000 sq ft site, Distrib.—Intl.
Publicly owned corporation
Parent co.—Masco Corp., Taylor, MI
Phone—(313) 274-7400
See Parent Co. Section for full profile.

**BEACON CONVERTERS, INC.**
280 Midland Ave., P.O. Box 8208 (07663)
**Phone—(201) 797-2600**
Fax—(201) 797-3015
www.beaconconverters.com
Email—info@beaconconverters.com
Pres., CEO—Jackie Daly-Johnson
V.-P. & Dir., Sales & Mktg.—Kathleen Daly Mascolo
Cont.—Megan Downing
Dir., IT & Mktg. Projs.—Terri Shank
Technical Dir.—Alison Tyler
Optimization & Prod. Dev. Mgr.—Marie Tkacik
Plt. Supt.—Ken Moyer
SIC—2673; *Sterilization packaging, including peelable & non-peelable pouches, pouches-on-a-roll, rollstock, header, flat & square bags & die-cut insert cards for the medical device & pharmaceutical industries*
Employs—70; Estab.—1947
Sales—$5Mil-$10Mil
23,000 sq ft site, Distrib.—Intl.
Privately owned corporation

**BLUE GAUNTLET FENCING GEAR, INC.**
280 N. Midland Ave., Bldg. W (07663)
**Phone—(201) 797-3332**
Fax—(201) 797-9190
www.blue-gauntlet.com
Email—fencing@blue-gauntlet.com
Pres.—Jing X. Chen
Cust. Serv. Mgr.—Vicky Chen
SIC—3949; NAICS—339920; *Fencing sport equipment*
Employs—15; Estab.—1998
Sales—$1Mil-$2.5Mil (est)
Distrib.—Local
Privately owned corporation

**CARMEL FURNITURE, INC.**
404 N. Midland Ave. (07663)
**Phone—(201) 796-0099**
Fax—(201) 796-0478
www.carmelfurniture.com
Email—info@carmelfurniture.com
Owner—Gideon Reiss
SIC—2521; *Wooden office furniture*
Employs—15
Sales—$1Mil-$2.5Mil (est)
Distrib.—Regional
Privately owned corporation

**CARPENTER & PATERSON, INC.**
369 Jefferson St. (07663)
**Phone—(973) 772-1800**
National—(800) 255-3623
Fax—(973) 772-8333
www.carpenterandpaterson.com
Email—sbsales@carpenterandpaterson.com
Br. Mgr.—Thomas Browne
SIC—3494; 3429; 3499; NAICS—332900; *Metal pipe hangers, supports, struts & hardware, including engineering; Brand name—Witch Pipe Hangers*
Employs—35; Estab.—1912
Sales—$5Mil-$10Mil
Distrib.—National
Privately owned corporation

Parent co.—Carpenter & Paterson, Inc., Woburn, MA
Phone—(781) 935-7036
See Parent Co. Section for full profile.

**CHEMAID LABORATORIES, INC.**
100 Mayhill St. (07663)
**Phone—(201) 843-3300**
Fax—(201) 843-5579
www.chemaidlabs.com
Email—customerservice@chemaidlabs.com
Pres.—Mark Reiner
SIC—2844; NAICS—325600; *Skin & hair care products*
Employs—150
Sales—$50Mil-$100Mil (est)
Distrib.—Regional
Privately owned corporation

**CIRCULITE, INC.**
250 Pehle Ave., Ste. 403 (07663)
Mail addr: 500 Frank W. Burr Blvd., Ste. 40, Teaneck (07666)
**Phone—(201) 543-2430**
Fax—(201) 543-2015
www.circulite.net
Email—information@circulite.net
Pres., CEO—Paul Southworth
V.-P., Mktg.—Gail Farnan
Hum. Res. & Off. Mgr.—Trisha Wright
SIC—3842; *Implantable blood pumps & cardiovascular devices for chronic heart patients*
Employs—20; Estab.—2004
Sales—$2.5Mil-$5Mil
Distrib.—Intl.
Privately owned corporation

**CLARK PRINTING CO.**
441 Market St. (07663)
**Phone—(201) 845-4888**
Fax—(201) 845-5888
www.clarkprinting.com
Pres., GM—Richard Lisa
Off. Mgr.—Cecelia Bentrice
SIC—2759; 2677; NAICS—322232; *Commercial & newsletter printing & envelopes*
Employs—18; Estab.—2001
Distrib.—Regional
Privately owned corporation

**DANA CLASSIC FRAGRANCES, INC. (H Q)**
Div. of Patriarch Partners, LLC
400 Lyster Ave. (07663)
**Phone—(201) 881-8550**
National—(800) 822-8547
Fax—(201) 881-8569
www.danabeauty.com
Email—customerservice@danaclassics.com
IT Mgr.—Joe Acosta
Hum. Res. Mgr.—Marie Rispoli
SIC—2844; NAICS—325600; *Corporate headquarters; fragrances (mfg. done overseas)*
Employs—10
Sales—$2.5Mil-$5Mil (est)
Distrib.—Intl.
Privately owned corporation
Parent co.—Patriarch Partners, LLC, New York, NY
Phone—(212) 825-0550
See Parent Co. Section for full profile.

NEW ENTRY
**ELITE HOME PRODUCTS**
95 Mayhill St., Ste. 3 (07663)
**Phone—(201) 880-8292**
Fax—(201) 845-4155
www.elitehomeproduct.com
Email—tlester@elitehomeproductsinc.com
V.-P.—Scott Perretz
SIC—2392; *Bed linens, including blankets & fine sheets*
Employs—50
Sales—$5Mil-$10Mil (est)

**†ENTERPRISE CORRUGATED CONTAINER, LLC**
Div. of Island Container Corp.
575 N. Midland Ave., P.O. Box 857 (07663)
**Phone—(201) 797-7200**
Fax—(201) 797-0139
www.theboxcompany.com
Email—info@theboxcompany.com
Sales Mgr.—James Breit
Cust. Serv. Rep.—Kathy Young
SIC—5113; *Distributor of corrugated boxes*
Employs—40; Estab.—1948
Sales—$25Mil
120,000 sq ft site, Distrib.—Regional
Limited Liability Company
Parent co.—Island Container Corp., Wyandanch, NY
Phone—(631) 253-4400
See Parent Co. Section for full profile.

**FAIRFIELD STAMPING CO.**
374 Midland Ave., P.O. Box 8322 (07663)
**Phone—(201) 791-9888**
Fax—(201) 791-0294
Email—standarstamping@aol.com
Co-Pres.—Steve Orkenyi
Co-Pres.—Arlene Orkenyi
SIC—3499; *Metal stampings*
Employs—9; Estab.—1994
Sales—$500,000-$1Mil (est)
Distrib.—National
Privately owned corporation

**FASTPULSE TECHNOLOGY, INC.**
220 Midland Ave. (07663)
**Phone—(973) 478-5757**
(973) 478-6306
National—(800) 449-3278
Fax—(973) 478-6115
www.fastpulse.com
Email—sales@fastpulse.com
Chrm., Pres.—Robert Goldstein
V.-P., Cont.—Marion Goldstein
GM—Mark Percevault
SIC—3827; 3699; NAICS—333314; *Electro-optical instruments for lasers, including laser pulse pickers, Q-switches, electronic drivers & Faraday effect magneto-optic isolators; Brand name—Lasermetrics*
Employs—15; Estab.—1965
Sales—$2Mil
5,000 sq ft site, Distrib.—Intl.
Privately owned sub-S corp.
AKA: Lasermetrics Division

**FRIEND SKOLER & CO., INC. (H Q)**
160 Pehle Ave., Ste. 303 (07663)
**Phone—(201) 712-0075**
Fax—(201) 712-1525
www.friendskoler.com
Email—mail@friendskoler.com
CFO & Dir., Portfolio Mgmt.—Gregory P. Sullivan
Mng. Dir.—Alexander A. Friend
Mng. Dir.—Steven F. Skoler
Dir.—Cheryl Moss
SIC—6719; 3089; *Holding company headquarters & private equity firm; plastic injection molding of pizza dough trays & plastic containers*
Employs—10; Estab.—1998

**FUNS TRUCK'N & MOBILITY**
255 Route 46 W. (07663)
**Phone—(973) 546-1900**
National—(800) 354-5005
Fax—(973) 546-1706
www.ftmobility.com
Email—npodence@ftmobility.com
Pres.—Allen Ackerman
Hum. Res. Mgr.—Nicole Pondence
Administrator—Alli Chizen

## Saddle Brook—(cont.)

SIC—3713; NAICS—336211;
  *Handicapped van conversions*
Employs—7; Estab.—1976
Sales—$1Mil-$2.5Mil
5,000 sq ft site, Distrib.—Intl.
Privately owned corporation

**GILT EDGE FOLDING BOXES, INC.**
P.O. Box 544 (07663)
**Phone—(201) 843-1450**
Fax—(201) 843-1450
Email—giltedgefb@hotmail.com
Pres.—Barbara Kotcher
GM & Fin. Mgr.—Robert Kardash
MIS Mgr.—Marilyn Chambers
SIC—2657; NAICS—322212;
  *Folding paperboard boxes*
Employs—10; Estab.—1959
Sales—$1Mil-$2Mil
34,000 sq ft site, Distrib.—Local
Privately owned corporation

**HEAD MASTERS, INC.**
263 Route 46 W. (07663)
**Phone—(201) 843-6666**
Fax—(201) 712-0989
www.headmasterinc.com
Email—info@headmasterinc.com
Pres.—Leon Touloughian
GM—Karl Touloughian
SIC—3599; *General machining
  job shop*
Employs—8; Estab.—1983
Sales—$500,000-$1Mil
Distrib.—Local
Privately owned corporation

**KAY WINDOW FASHIONS, INC.**
271 2nd St. (07663)
**Phone—(862) 591-1555**
Fax—(862) 591-1557
Email—kaywindow@optonline.net
Ptnr.—Sol Kleinstein
Ptnr.—Jeffrey Kleinstein
SIC—2391; 2591; 5023; NAICS—
  314121; *Manufacturer &
  distributor of draperies, bedding,
  cornices, Roman, balloon &
  Austrian shades, pillows &
  valances; Brand name—Levelor;
  Hunter Douglas; Kravet; Duralee;
  Norbar; Robert Allen;
  Ashbourne; Michael Textile; RM
  CoCo; Pindler & Pindler*
Employs—12; Estab.—1965
Distrib.—National
Privately owned sub-S corp.

**LEVY & RAPPEL, INC.**
339 10th St. (07663)
**Phone—(973) 478-6511**
National—(800) 564-5389
Fax—(973) 478-1760
www.levyandrappel.com
Email—info@levyandrappel.com
Pres.—David Kramer
GM—Pat Miller
SIC—3842; *Custom foot orthotics,
  ankle/foot orthotics & diabetic
  shoes & inserts*
Employs—22; Estab.—1930
Sales—$2.3Mil
5,500 sq ft site, Distrib.—Intl.
Privately owned sub-S corp.

**†M & M WHOLESALE**
66 Market St. (07663)
**Phone—(201) 368-0770**
National—(888) 604-0004
Fax—(201) 368-0774
Email—mikepapaiya@yahoo.com
Owner—Hema Papaiya
GM—Mukesh Papaiya
SIC—5194; *Wholesaler of tobacco
  products*
Employs—13; Estab.—1988
Sales—$500,000-$1Mil
Distrib.—Regional
Privately owned corporation

**MALT PRODUCTS CORP.**
88 Market St., P.O. Box 898
  (07663)
**Phone—(201) 845-4420**
National—(800) 526-0180
Fax—(201) 845-0028
www.maltproducts.com
Email—info@maltproducts.com
Pres.—Ronald Targan
V.-P.—Joe Hickenbottom
SIC—2083; NAICS—311213;
  *Corporate headquarters &
  bakery malt*
Employs—20; Estab.—1957
Sales—$5Mil-$10Mil
Distrib.—Intl.
Privately owned corporation

**MEESE ORBITRON DUNNE CO.**
535 N. Midland Ave. (07663)
**Phone—(201) 796-4667**
National—(800) 829-4535
Fax—(201) 796-5820
www.modroto.com
Email—customerservice@
  modroto.com
Plt. Mgr.—Patrick Barry
SIC—3089; *Plastic rotational
  molding & material handling
  containers*
Employs—12; Estab.—1931
25,000 sq ft site, Distrib.—National
Privately owned corporation
Parent co.—Meese Orbitron
  Dunne Co., Ashtabula, OH
  Phone—(440) 998-1202
  See Parent Co. Section for full profile.

**MIDLAND SCREEN PRINTING, INC.**
280 N. Midland Ave., Bldg. H
  (07663)
**Phone—(201) 703-0066**
Fax—(201) 703-8238
Email—midt@earthlink.net
Pres.—Robert Witrak
SIC—2396; *Textile screen printing*
Employs—15; Estab.—1970
Sales—$1Mil-$2.5Mil
Distrib.—National
Privately owned corporation

**MONA LISA COSMETICS, INC.**
280 N. Midland Ave., Ste. 520
  (07663)
**Phone—(201) 791-5644**
Fax—(201) 791-8139
Owner—Angel Mahdani
SIC—2844; *Cosmetics, including
  lip gloss & mascara*
Employs—20; Estab.—1987
Sales—under $500,000
Distrib.—National
Privately owned corporation

**MONSTER COATINGS, INC.**
306-A Capitol St. (07663)
**Phone—(973) 983-7662**
National—(888) 395-1978
Fax—(973) 794-5441
Email—monstercoatings@aol.com
Pres.—Denise Tomahatsch
Proj. Mgr.—Laszlo R. Keszthelyi
SIC—3479; 3086; 2821; *Seamless
  industrial, decorative &
  waterproofing floor & wall
  coatings, polyurethane spray
  foam insulation & terrazzo repair*
Employs—4; Estab.—2002
Sales—$1Mil-$2.5Mil
Distrib.—Regional
Privately owned corporation

**NOURISON INDUSTRIES (H Q)**
5 Sampson St. (07663)
**Phone—(201) 368-6900**
National—(800) 223-1110
Fax—(201) 368-0739
www.nourison.com
Email—info@nourison.com
Pres.—Alex Peykar
V.-P. & IT Mgr.—Andrew Peykar
Hum. Res. Mgr.—Diane
  Gabbanelli

SIC—2512; 2392; 2391; 2273;
  NAICS—337121; *Company
  headquarters; upholstered
  furniture, pillows, tapestries &
  traditional, transitional &
  contemporary area rugs for the
  residential, commercial &
  hospitality markets (mfg. done
  overseas)*
Employs—240; Estab.—1990
Sales—$500,000-$1Mil
Distrib.—Intl.
Privately owned corporation

**PARADIGM PACKAGING, LLC (H Q)**
141 N. 5th St. (07663)
**Phone—(201) 507-0900**
Fax—(201) 291-3840
www.paradigmpackaging.com
Email—mbauer@
  paradigmpackaging.com
Chrm. of the Board—Robert
  Donnahoo
Cont.—Dave Schulthies
Dir., Hum. Res.—Michele Bauer
SIC—3085; 3089; NAICS—
  326160; *Company headquarters;
  plastic containers*
Employs—100; Estab.—1972
Sales—$10Mil-$25Mil (est)
Distrib.—National
Limited Liability Company

**PATERSON PACKAGING**
269 Wilson St. (07663)
**Phone—(201) 398-9693**
Fax—(201) 398-9694
www.patpac.net
Email—patersonpack@aol.com
Owner & Pres.—Kenneth Manley
SIC—3081; 3082; 3089; 3231;
  NAICS—326113; *Flexible
  packaging, including BOPP,
  OPP, CPP, PET, rotogravure
  printed, printed & metallized film,
  shrink sleeves, labels & stand-up
  pouches, glass bottles & caps,
  mesh header bags & rigid
  plastic containers, including
  plastic thermoforming*
Employs—3; Estab.—2002
Sales—under $1.5Mil
Distrib.—National
Sole ownership

**PEOPLES EDUCATION, INC.**
299 Market St., P.O. Box 513
  (07663)
**Phone—(201) 712-0090**
National—(800) 822-1080
Fax—(201) 712-0045
www.peopleseducation.com
Email—vkiely@peoplesed.com
CEO—Ronald Berg
Ex. V.-P., CFO—Michael L.
  DeMarco
V.-P., Sales & Mktg.—Victoria Kiely
Hum. Res. Mgr.—Rejoe Joy
Cust. Serv. Mgr.—Barbara Dexter
SIC—2731; *Publisher of print &
  electronic K-12 educational
  materials, including test
  preparation instructional
  materials & college prep
  materials; Brand name—
  MeasureUp; Focused
  Instruction; StepUp to Success;
  Intervention Tool Kit*
Employs—80
Sales—$5Mil-$10Mil (est)

**PHOTOTHROW, INC.**
280 N. Midland Ave., Bldg. J-1
  (07663)
**Phone—(855) 645-4438**
National—(800) 524-0914
Fax—(201) 300-6358
www.photothrow.com
Email—andy@photothrow.com
Pres.—Andy Concilio
Off. Mgr.—Silvia Morales

SIC—2259; *Customer art-based
  blankets, pillows & sweaters*
Employs—3; Estab.—2000
Sales—$500,000-$1Mil
12,000 sq ft site, Distrib.—Intl.
Privately owned sub-S corp.
AKA: Sublimation Mall

**PRECIOUS COSMETICS CORP.**
296 Midland Ave. (07663)
Mail addr: 40 Meta Ln., Lodi
  (07644-3807)
**Phone—(973) 478-4633**
Fax—(973) 478-4670
www.preciouscosmetics.com
Email—sami052@aol.com
Pres.—Sami Mikhail
Dir., Sales—Sanaa Mikhail
SIC—2844; NAICS—325600; *Skin
  care creams & lotions, hair care
  shampoos & conditioners &
  color cosmetics; Brand name—
  Signature Club A; Suki Natural
  Pure; Lucky Chick ; Natpure
  Labs ; Vitamin Power ; CFN
  Distributors*
Employs—20; Estab.—1996
25,000 sq ft site, Distrib.—National
Sole ownership

**PRIME INGREDIENTS, INC.**
280 N. Midland Ave., Bldg. U
  (07663)
**Phone—(201) 791-6655**
National—(888) 791-6655
Fax—(201) 791-4244
www.primeingredients.com
Email—info@primeingredients.com
Pres.—James Walsh
V.-P.—Christopher Walsh
Prodn. Mgr.—Tim Walsh
Off. Mgr.—Brian Walsh
Cust. Serv. Rep.—Geri Taylor
SIC—2087; NAICS—311900;
  *Food coloring & flavoring*
Employs—15; Estab.—1989
Sales—$500,000-$1Mil
17,000 sq ft site, Distrib.—Intl.
Privately owned corporation

**PROIMAGE APPAREL, LLC**
280 N. Midland Ave., Bldg. H
  (07663)
Mail addr: 1360 Clifton Ave., Ste.
  378, Clifton (07012)
**Phone—(201) 773-9292**
Fax—(201) 773-9291
www.proimageapparel.com
Email—contact@
  proimageapparel.com
Pres.—Michael Miller
SIC—2395; *Embroidery*
Employs—6; Estab.—1964
Sales—under $500,000
Distrib.—National
Sole ownership

**SALERNO'S KITCHEN CABINETS,
INC.**
599 N. Midland Ave. (07663)
**Phone—(201) 794-1990**
Fax—(201) 794-6992
www.salernoskitchens.com
Email—info@salernoskitchens.com
Pres.—Luciano Salerno
Cont.—Maria Vilardi
SIC—2434; NAICS—337110;
  *Custom wooden kitchen
  cabinets & related cabinetry*
Employs—15; Estab.—1961
15,000 sq ft site, Distrib.—
  Regional
Privately owned sub-S corp.

**SEALED AIR CORP.**
301 Mayhill St. (07663)
**Phone—(201) 712-7000**
  (201) 712-7153
Fax—(201) 712-7070
www.sealedair.com
Email—investor.relations@
  sealedair.com
Sales Mgr., Reg.—Matthew
  Venezia

GEOGRAPHICAL

## Saddle Brook—(cont.)

IT Mgr.—Omar Mina
Hum. Res. Mgr.—Sonia Aponte
Matls. Mgr.—Margie Dorazio
SIC—3089; 3086; NAICS—
326100; *Food packaging
containers, bubble wrap &
mailers*
Employs—200; Estab.—1967
Distrib.—Intl.
Publicly owned corporation
Parent co.—Sealed Air Corp.,
Elmwood Park, NJ
Phone—(201) 791-7600
See Parent Co. Section for full profile.

**TE WIRE & CABLE, LLC**
Div. of Marmon Group, LLC, The
107 5th St. (07663)
**Phone—(201) 845-9400**
National—(888) 483-9473
Fax—(201) 291-1190
www.tewire.com
Email—sales@tewire.com
V.-P., Sales & Mktg.—Pat Durkin
V.-P., Mfg.—Pat Arnone
Dir., Tech.—Magda Clavijo
GM—Patrick Scott
Sales Mgr., Inside—Joanne Ward
Prod. Mktg. Mgr.—Vlad Fedorchak
Hum. Res. Mgr.—Lynn Manley
Cust. Serv. Rep.—Maria Alexakis
SIC—3357; *Wire & cable,
including thermocouple
extension cable, copper
instrument & control cable,
autoclave & composite
temperature sensors & heat treat
survey wire*
Employs—100; Estab.—1941
Sales—$30Mil-$50Mil
Distrib.—Intl.
Privately owned corporation
ISO rating—9001, 17025
Parent co.—Marmon Group, LLC,
The, Chicago, IL
Phone—(312) 372-9500
See Parent Co. Section for full profile.

**TINGUE, BROWN & CO. (H Q)**
535 N. Midland Ave. (07663-5521)
**Phone—(201) 796-4490**
(201) 796-5233
National—(800) 829-3864
Fax—(201) 796-5820
www.tingue.com
Email—dkoebel@tingue.com
Pres., CEO—David Tingue
CFO—John Hurst
Dir., Opers.—Dan Koebel
Pur. Mgr.—Maritza Torres
SIC—2394; 2399; 3582; NAICS—
314912; *Company headquarters;
laundry bags & machine roller
felts & plastic rotational molding;
Brand name—Poly-Trux;
Tingu'on Names; ChemGuard*
Employs—20; Estab.—1902
300,000 sq ft site, Distrib.—Intl.
Privately owned corporation

**†TRICORBRAUN**
Div. of TricorBraun, Inc.
250 Pehle Ave., Ste. 100 (07663)
**Phone—(201) 556-4800**
Fax—(201) 556-4888
www.tricorbraun.com
Email—info@tricorbraun.com
Br. & Sales Mgr.—Scott Danheiser
Logistics & Opers. Mgr.—Lee
Kimble
Cust. Serv. Rep.—Jeff Walker
SIC—5085; 5113; *Distributor of
plastic & glass bottles &
containers, plastic caps & plastic
& metal closures*
Employs—70; Estab.—1920
Sales—$15Mil-$25Mil
Distrib.—Intl.
Privately owned corporation
AKA: Winetak

Parent co.—TricorBraun, Inc.,
Plymouth Meeting, PA
Phone—(484) 534-5900
See Parent Co. Section for full profile.

**UNILUX, INC.**
59 5th St. (07663)
**Phone—(201) 712-1266**
National—(800) 522-0801
Fax—(201) 712-1366
www.unilux.com
Email—unilux@unilux.com
Pres.—Michael Simonis
V.-P., Engrg.—Matthew Runo
V.-P., Software Dev.—Chris
Kapsalis
Mktg. Mgr.—Jamie Lynn Coulter
SIC—3648; NAICS—335129;
*Strobe lights for surface
inspection in the steel, paper,
converting & printing industries
& film & video production lights
for TV commercials & feature
films*
Employs—45; Estab.—1962
20,000 sq ft site, Distrib.—Intl.
Privately owned corporation

**WESTLOCK CONTROLS CORP.**
Div. of Tyco
280 N. Midland Ave., Ste. 258
(07663)
**Phone—(201) 794-7650**
Fax—(201) 794-0913
www.westlockcontrols.com
Email—westlockinfo@
westlockcontrols.com
Cont.—Pete Mooney
GM—Leo Minervini
Sales Mgr., North American—Bill
Tatum
Sales Mgr., Inside—Lee Bradley
Plt. Mgr.—Dave Bennett
Matls. & Pur. Mgr.—Joel Wittkamp
Engrg. Mgr., Sustaining—Rhonda
Frey
Engrg. Mgr., NPD—Adam Buga
EHS Mgr.—Al Kerstner
SIC—3829; *Industrial valve
monitors & controls*
Employs—100; Estab.—1987
Distrib.—Intl.
Publicly owned corporation
Parent co.—Tyco, Princeton, NJ
Phone—(609) 720-4200
See Parent Co. Section for full profile.

**WISCO PROMO & UNIFORM, INC.**
160 Route 46 E. (07663)
**Phone—(973) 767-2022**
National—(888) 654-3335
Fax—(888) 368-3401
www.wiscopnu.com
Email—info@wiscopnu.com
Pres.—Anthony Park
Designer—Julie Kim
SIC—2395; 2396; 2759;
*Embroidery & screen printing*
Employs—4; Estab.—2001
Sales—$1Mil-$2.5Mil
7,000 sq ft site, Distrib.—National
Privately owned corporation

## Saddle River
(Bergen—N.E.)

**AMERTAC, INC.**
1 Route 17 S., Saddle River
Executive Center (07458)
**Phone—(201) 825-0388**
Fax—(201) 825-3511
www.amertac.com
Email—questions@amertac.com
COO—Sal Mirra
IT Mgr.—Ralph Angelo
Hum. Res. Mgr.—Karen Payton
Engrg. Mgr.—Grady Schenck

SIC—3399; 3089; *Decorative
metal & plastic wall plates &
night, halogen, cabinet &
fluorescent lights for residential
applications*
Employs—50; Estab.—1937
150,000 sq ft site, Distrib.—Intl.
Privately owned corporation

**CLEVE SHIRTMAKERS, INC. (H Q)**
P.O. Box 678 (07458)
**Phone—(201) 825-6122**
www.cleveshirt.com
Email—sales@cleveshirt.com
Pres.—David Stich
SIC—2321; 2329; 2325;
*Corporate headquarters; men's
shirts, shorts & casual pants
(mfg. subcontracted)*
Employs—5
Sales—under $500,000
Privately owned corporation

NEW ENTRY
**KAYSTAR PUBLISHING**
5 Harvey Ln. (07458)
**Phone—(201) 825-2736**
Owner—Kathleen Dow
SIC—2731; *Book publishing*
Employs—1; Estab.—2008
Sales—under $500,000
Distrib.—Local
Privately owned corporation

**MORE COPY PRINTING SERVICE**
358 State Route 17 (07458)
**Phone—(201) 327-1106**
Owner—Felix Gomez
SIC—2752; *Instant printing*
Employs—1
Sales—under $500,000 (est)
Privately owned corporation

**RED LETTER PRESS, INC.**
16 Deerhorn Trl. (07458)
**Phone—(201) 818-8951**
Fax—(201) 270-5115
www.red-letterpress.com
Email—info@red-letterpress.com
Owner—Jack Kreismer
SIC—2732; *Humor & trivia gift
book publishing*
Employs—3; Estab.—1980
Sales—under $500,000 (est)
Distrib.—National
Privately owned corporation

## Salem
(Salem—S.W.)

**ARDAGH GROUP**
Div. of Anchor Glass Container
Corp.
83 Griffith St. (08079)
**Phone—(856) 935-4000**
Fax—(856) 935-8889
www.ardaghgroup.com
Email—salesgroup@
anchorglass.com
GM—Gary Shears
Hum. Res. Mgr.—Morris
Pamepinto
Qual. Control Mgr.—Russ Hunter
SIC—3221; NAICS—327213;
*Glass containers*
Employs—312; Estab.—1958
Sales—$50Mil-$100Mil (est)
Distrib.—National
Privately owned corporation
Parent co.—Anchor Glass
Container Corp., Tampa, FL
Phone—(813) 884-0000
See Parent Co. Section for full profile.

**HAWK PRECISION, INC.**
849 Hawks Bridge Rd. (08079)
**Phone—(856) 299-2800**
www.hawkbullets.com
Email—info@hawkbullets.com
Owner & Pres.—Andy Hill

SIC—3483; NAICS—332993;
*Hunting bullets*
Employs—2; Estab.—1987
Sales—under $500,000
Distrib.—Intl.
Sole ownership

**MANNINGTON MILLS, INC.**
75 Mannington Mills Rd., P.O. Box
30 (08079)
**Phone—(856) 935-3000**
National—(800) 356-6787
Fax—(856) 339-6124
www.mannington.com
Email—service@mannington.com
Chrm. of the Board—Keith
Campbell
Pres., CEO—Russell Grizzle
Pres., Residential Bus.—Kim Holm
Sr. V.-P., Residential Mktg.—Ed
Duncan
Dir., Corp. Comms.—Betsy
Amoroso
SIC—3996; 2426; 2273; 3253;
NAICS—326192; *Corporate
headquarters & residential &
commercial resilient sheet, vinyl,
laminate, hardwood & porcelain
tile flooring, commercial
carpeting & rubber; Brand
name—Mannington; Burke;
Amtico*
Employs—600; Estab.—1915
Sales—$100Mil-$250Mil (est)
Distrib.—Intl.
Privately owned corporation
ISO rating—9001

**NEWS OF CUMBERLAND COUNTY,
THE**
Div. of Staten Island Publications,
Inc.
93 5th St. (08079)
**Phone—(856) 451-1000**
Fax—(856) 451-7214
www.southjerseymedia.com
Email—jowens@
southjerseymedia.com
Pres.—Joe Owens
Adv. Mgr.—Ceil Smith
SIC—2711; *Newspaper
publishing*
Employs—15; Estab.—1907
Sales—under $500,000
Distrib.—Local
Privately owned corporation
Parent co.—Staten Island
Publications, Inc., Staten Island,
NY
Phone—(718) 981-1234
See Parent Co. Section for full profile.

**PRINTERS OF SALEM COUNTY, LLC**
38 Market St. (08079)
**Phone—(856) 935-5032**
Fax—(856) 935-5036
Ptnr.—Jeff Weeks
Ptnr.—Eric Pankonk
Bookkeeper—Darlene Richardson
SIC—2759; 2791; NAICS—
323122; *Commercial printing &
electronic prepress*
Employs—3; Estab.—2004
Sales—under $500,000
Distrib.—Local
Limited Liability Company

**SOUTH JERSEY TIMES**
Div. of Staten Island Publications,
Inc.
93 5th St. (08079)
**Phone—(856) 935-1500**
Fax—(856) 935-8161
www.nj.com
Email—awoolfolk@
southjerseymedia.com
Publisher—Joseph Owens
Mng. Editor—Bill Gallo
Adv. Mgr.—Alfred Woolfolk
Off. Mgr.—Sharon Moore

## Salem—(cont.)

SIC—2711; *Daily print & online newspaper publishing*
Employs—15; Estab.—1969
Sales—$500,000-$1Mil (est)
Distrib.—Local
Privately owned corporation
AKA: South Jersey Media
Parent co.—Staten Island Publications, Inc., Staten Island, NY
Phone—(718) 981-1234
See Parent Co. Section for full profile.

---

## Sayreville
(Middlesex—N.E.)

### ALZO INTERNATIONAL, INC.
650 Jernee Mill Rd. (08872)
**Phone—(732) 254-1901**
Fax—(732) 254-4423
www.alzointernational.com
Email—carolyn.zofchak@ mail.alzointernational.com
Pres.—Albert Zofchak
V.-P., Admn. & Hum. Res. Mgr.— Carolyn Zofchak
Plt. Mgr.—Peter Sibilski
Cust. Serv. Rep.—Lisa Cesare
SIC—2844; NAICS—325600; *Toiletries & cosmetics*
Employs—25; Estab.—1974
Distrib.—Intl.
Privately owned corporation

[NEW ENTRY]
### AROMATIC INNOVATIONS
600 Hartle St. (08872)
**Phone—(732) 967-6346**
Fax—(732) 390-9502
www.aromaticinnovations.com
Email—info@ aromaticinnovations.com
Owner—Golam Bhuiyan
SIC—2844; 2899; 3999; *Fragrances, including perfumes, personal & body care products, incense, body oils, candles & essential oils*
Employs—2; Estab.—2012
Sales—$500,000-$1Mil (est)
Distrib.—Local
Privately owned corporation

### CANFIELD TECHNOLOGIES/BOW ELECTRONIC SOLDER
Div. of Kaydon Corp.
1 S. Crossman Rd. (08872)
**Phone—(732) 316-2100**
National—(800) 526-4577
Fax—(732) 316-2177
www.solders.com
Email—csynosky@kaydon.com
Cont.—Vito LiLoia
Sales Mgr.—Christina M. Synosky
Opers. Mgr.—Frank Liszka
SIC—3341; 2899; *Solder alloys & fluxes for industrial, plumbing, electronic, automotive, stained glass & OEM applications;* Brand name—*EnviroSafe; Watersafe; Evergleem; BLF; Silverflo; FloSafe Lead-Free Solders*
Employs—45; Estab.—1844
80,000 sq ft site, Distrib.—National
Publicly owned corporation
ISO rating—9001:2000
Parent co.—Kaydon Corp., Ann Arbor, MI
Phone—(734) 747-7025
See Parent Co. Section for full profile.

### CHEMO DYNAMICS, INC.
3 Crossman Rd. S. (08872)
**Phone—(732) 721-4700**
Fax—(732) 721-6835
www.chemodynamics.com
Email—office@ chemodynamics.com
Pres.—Subir Chakraborty

V.-P.—S. Narasimha Bharathi
SIC—2869; 2833; NAICS— 325411; *Fine, specialty, active pharmaceutical & intermediate chemicals, including boronic & amino acids, peptides, steroids & chiral molecules & contract research & process development services*
Employs—12; Estab.—1965
Sales—$2.5Mil-$5Mil
16,000 sq ft site, Distrib.—Intl.
Sole ownership

### COAST TO COAST LEATHER & VINYL, INC.
1 Crossman Rd. S. (08872)
**Phone—(732) 525-8877**
National—(800) 354-4401
Fax—(732) 525-2726
www.coast2coastleather.com
Email—info@ coast2coastleather.com
Co-Pres.—Michael Ross
Co-Pres.—Pam Ross
Cust. Serv. Rep.—Tiffany Hernandez
SIC—3199; 3089; NAICS— 316999; *Leather & vinyl for the automotive, furniture & aircraft industries*
Employs—10; Estab.—1985
Sales—under $500,000
Distrib.—Regional
Privately owned corporation

### EAST COAST CUSTOM
242 Main St. (08872)
**Phone—(732) 390-8238**
Fax—(732) 390-1651
Pres.—Mark Tesca
Manager—Pat Tripod
SIC—2395; 2396; *Textile embroidery & screen printing*
Employs—5; Estab.—1983
Sales—under $500,000
4,000 sq ft site, Distrib.—National
Limited Liability Company

### †FASTENAL CO.
500 Hartle St., Ste. D (08872)
**Phone—(732) 254-1117**
Fax—(732) 254-1715
www.fastenal.com
Email—njeas@stores.fastenal.com
Manager—Dan Divine
SIC—5072; 5169; *Wholesaler of industrial fasteners, tools & construction adhesives*
Employs—2; Estab.—1966
Distrib.—Local
Publicly owned corporation
Parent co.—Fastenal Co., Winona, MN
Phone—(507) 454-5374
See Parent Co. Section for full profile.

### GERDAU US, INC., SAYREVILLE
Div. of Gerdau Ameristeel US, Inc.
N. Crossman Rd., P.O. Box 249 (08872)
**Phone—(732) 721-6600**
National—(800) 721-8047
Fax—(732) 316-5262
www.gerdauameristeel.com
Email—mark.quiring@gerdau.com
V.-P., GM—Mark Quiring
Hum. Res. Mgr.—Sarita Patel
Maint. Mgr.—Tom Messner
SIC—3312; *Steel concrete reinforcement bars*
Employs—200; Estab.—1973
Distrib.—National
Publicly owned corporation
Parent co.—Gerdau Ameristeel US, Inc., Tampa, FL
Phone—(813) 286-8383
See Parent Co. Section for full profile.

### HARMAC REBAR & STEEL CORP.
301 Hartle St. (08872)
**Phone—(732) 651-7822**
National—(800) 294-4702
Fax—(732) 967-0483

www.ahharris.com
Email—info@ahharris.com
Plt. Mgr.—Larry Kuzma
Off. Mgr.—Ellie Rodriguez
SIC—3441; 3449; 3312; NAICS— 332312; *Steel rebar fabrication*
Employs—15; Estab.—1959
Distrib.—Regional
Privately owned corporation
Parent co.—HarMac Rebar & Steel Corp., Fryeburg, ME
Phone—(207) 935-3531
See Parent Co. Section for full profile.

### †INDUSTRIAL WELDING SUPPLY, INC.
4 Val St. *(08872)*
**Phone—(732) 721-1150**
National—(800) 339-1150
Fax—(732) 721-8076
www.weldingsupplynj.com
Email—indweldsup@aol.com
Pres.—Jim Cusick
V.-P.—Scott Cusick
Secy.-Treas.—Linda Cusick
SIC—5084; 5169; *Corporate headquarters & distributor of welding equipment & supplies, including welders, tanks & gases*
Employs—21; Estab.—1947
Privately owned corporation

### INTEGRITY IRON WORKS INC.
33 Brookside Ave., P.O. Box 129 (08872)
**Phone—(732) 254-2200**
(732) 718-6227
Fax—(732) 254-0931
www.integrityironworksnj.com
Email—integrityironworks@ hotmail.com
Owner—James Zagata
Sales Mgr.—Zack Zagata
Off. Mgr.—Donna Zagata
SIC—3312; *Steel fabrication*
Employs—9; Estab.—2003
8,000 sq ft site, Distrib.—Regional
Privately owned corporation

### JERSEY COOPERAGE CO.
20 River Rd. (08872)
**Phone—(732) 254-1765**
Fax—(732) 382-6713
Email—jerseycooperage@aol.com
GM, Fin. & MIS Mgr.—Michael Foglia
SIC—3312; *Steel reconditioning*
Employs—19; Estab.—1982
Sales—$1Mil-$5Mil
8,000 sq ft site, Distrib.—Intl.
Privately owned corporation

### KELKEN-GOLD, INC.
550 Hartle St., Ste. C (08872- 2771)
**Phone—(732) 416-6730**
Fax—(732) 416-3733
www.kelken.com
Email—sales@kelken.com
Pres.—Ken Ginsky
SIC—3452; 3429; 5072; 5085; *Manufacturer & distributor of anchoring systems, including chemical adhesive, epoxy & mechanical/wedge anchors, hook & anchor bolts & concrete repair & adhesive systems;* Brand name—*Keligrout; Keligrout 101; Adhesive Technology Systems; ATC*
Employs—4; Estab.—1983
Sales—$1Mil-$2.5Mil
Distrib.—Regional
Privately owned corporation
AKA: Kelken Construction Systems

### LCI GRAPHICS, INC.
2400 Main Street Ext., Ste. 8 *(08872)*
**Phone—(973) 893-2913**
Fax—(888) 852-9639
www.lcigraphics.com
Email—info@lcigraphics.com
Pres.—Daniel Seratelli

V.-P.—Daniel J. Seratelli, Jr.
SIC—2752; 2759; 2789; NAICS— 323121; *Commercial offset, web-to-print, digital color, high-speed & instant printing of business cards, sell sheets, full-color envelopes, letterheads, pads & mailing labels & fulfillment, binding & mailing services*
Employs—8; Estab.—1987
Sales—$2Mil
5,200 sq ft site, Distrib.—Regional
Privately owned corporation

### PREMIER PRINTING SOLUTIONS
508 Raritan St. (08872)
**Phone—(732) 525-0740**
Fax—(732) 525-2855
www.premierprintonline.com
Email—ed@premierprintonline.com
Ptnr. & V.-P., Opers.—Edward Ciak
Ptnr.—Carol A. Ciak
SIC—2759; 2396; NAICS— 323100; *Commercial printing & silkscreen printing of signs & clothing*
Employs—3; Estab.—1977
Sales—under $500,000
1,400 sq ft site, Distrib.—Local
Limited Liability Company

### SABERT CORP.
2288 Main Street Ext. (08872)
**Phone—(732) 721-5544**
National—(800) 722-3781
Fax—(732) 721-8443
www.sabert.com
Email—sabert@sabert.com
Pres.—Albert Salama
Hum. Res. Mgr.—Heather Daley
Payroll Admn.—Donna Assenza
SIC—3089; *Corporate headquarters & plastic trays*
Employs—150; Estab.—1983
200,000 sq ft site, Distrib.—Intl.
Privately owned corporation

### STEIMLING & SON, INC.-MACHINIST
7 Nickel Ave. (08872)
Mail addr: P.O. Box 283, Sayreville (08871)
**Phone—(732) 613-1550**
Fax—(732) 390-3317
Email—steimlingson@hotmail.com
Pres.—Linda Steimling
GM—Rich Norris
SIC—3599; *General machining job shop for large turning, boring & moderate fabrication, including 92 inch swing, 62 feet cc & CNC lathes & shafts & shaft repairs*
Employs—10; Estab.—1979
Sales—$1Mil-$2.5Mil
Distrib.—National
Privately owned sub-S corp.

### STEINER PAPER CORP.
4000 Borden Town Ave. (08872)
Mail addr: 72 Lone Star Ln., Manalapan (07726-3878)
**Phone—(732) 651-6009**
Fax—(732) 651-2773
www.steinerpaper.com
Email—steinerpaper@aol.com
Pres., CFO—Jeff Nichols
V.-P.—Mark Nichols
SIC—2679; NAICS—322200; *Paper art & archival supplies, including watercolor paper, acetate, polyester film, glassine & archival grade synthetic fiber;* Brand name—*SUN RAY; SUN SMOOTH; SUN ROUGH; WATERCOLOR PAPER*
Employs—10; Estab.—1907
Sales—$1Mil-$2.5Mil
30,000 sq ft site, Distrib.—Intl.
Privately owned corporation

GEOGRAPHICAL

## Sayreville—(cont.)

**VERTICAL PHARMACEUTICALS, INC. (H Q)**
2500 Main St., Ste. 6 (08872)
**Phone—(732) 721-0070**
Fax—(732) 721-3430
www.verticalpharma.com
Pres.—Steven Squashic
Sr. Opers. & Sales Mgr.—Mirtha Acevedo
Hum. Res. Mgr.—Pam Chiappone
SIC—2834; NAICS—325412; Corporate headquarters; pharmaceuticals (mfg. subcontracted)
Employs—10; Estab.—2003
Sales—$5Mil-$10Mil (est)
Distrib.—National
Privately owned corporation

## Scotch Plains

(Union—N.E.)

**ANDERSON PUBLISHING LTD.**
180 Glenside Ave. (07076)
**Phone—(908) 301-1995**
Fax—(908) 301-1997
www.appliedradiology.com
Email—info@appliedradiology.com
Publisher—Kieran Anderson
Pres.—O. Oliver Anderson
V-P., Opers.—Brenda Anderson
Editor-in-Chief—Stuart Mirvis
Art Dir. & Prod. Mgr.—Barbara Shopiro
SIC—2721; 2741; Print & online medical imaging journal & newsletter publishing for radiology professionals; Brand name—Applied Radiology; WebMedED; The Journal of Cardiovascular Imaging & Therapeutics
Employs—5; Estab.—1991
Distrib.—National
Privately owned corporation

**ANDRUS SCREEN PRINTING, LLC**
1915 Church Ave. (07076)
**Phone—(908) 322-4299**
Fax—(908) 322-4955
Pres., GM & Sales Mgr.—Jules Andrus
SIC—3555; NAICS—333293; Photo screens
Employs—1; Estab.—1960
Sales—under $500,000
4,000 sq ft site, Distrib.—National
Sole ownership

**ART D'MENSIONS, INC.**
1998 Scotch Plains Route 22 (07076)
**Phone—(908) 322-8488**
Fax—(908) 322-8589
www.908-322-8488.com
Email—9083228488@comcast.net
Pres.—Bernice Mattos
Plt. Mgr.—J. C. Mattos
SIC—3993; Interior & exterior signs
Employs—2; Estab.—1982
Sales—under $500,000
Distrib.—Local
Privately owned corporation

**BECU MANUFACTURING CO., INC.**
2347 Beryllium Rd. (07076)
**Phone—(908) 233-3343**
Fax—(908) 233-4182
www.becumfg.com
Email—sales@becumfg.com
Pres.—Stephan Hoeckele
GM—George Clayton

SIC—3469; 3471; 3599; Precision metal stampings, including electroplating, electroless nickel plating, assembly, wire EDM & heat treating
Employs—24; Estab.—1944
Sales—$2Mil-$5Mil
22,000 sq ft site, Distrib.—Intl.
Privately owned corporation
ISO rating—9001:2008

**†BLAKE INDUSTRIES, INC.**
660 Jerusalem Rd. (07076)
**Phone—(908) 233-7240**
Fax—(908) 233-1354
Email—blake4xray@att.net
Pres.—Dave Rognlie
V-P.—Heidi Rognlie
SIC—5049; Distributor of scientific instruments
Employs—10; Estab.—1960
Sales—$500,000-$1Mil
Distrib.—Intl.
Privately owned corporation

**CHEMLIME N. J., INC. (H Q)**
2350 South Ave. (07076)
**Phone—(908) 389-1006**
National—(800) 445-4638
Fax—(908) 389-1008
www.chemline.net
Email—chemlime@aol.com
Pres.—Daniel Fitzpatrick
Cont.—Thomas Fitzpatrick
V-P.—John Fitzpatrick
SIC—3281; NAICS—327991; Corporate headquarters; industrial lime slurry processing
Employs—20; Estab.—1995
Sales—$1Mil-$2.5Mil (est)
2,000 sq ft site, Distrib.—Regional
Privately owned corporation

**CUSTOM WOODWORKING**
813 Jerusalem Rd. (07076)
**Phone—(908) 232-9525**
Fax—(908) 232-9525
Owner & Pres.—Joseph Louis Difrancesco
SIC—2431; NAICS—321900; Wooden cabinets & millwork
Employs—2; Estab.—1980
Sales—under $500,000
Distrib.—Local
Sole ownership

**FLORENCE RAVIOLI CO.**
391 Park Ave. (07076)
**Phone—(908) 322-7222**
Fax—(908) 322-7222
www.ravioli.com
Email—webmaster@scotchplains.com
Owner—Cynthia Losanno
Dept. Mgr.—Ralph Losanno
SIC—2098; NAICS—311823; Ravioli
Employs—2; Estab.—1943
Sales—under $500,000
Distrib.—Local
Sole ownership

**GLEICHER MFG. CORP.**
851 Jerusalem Rd. (07076)
**Phone—(908) 233-2211**
National—(800) 233-2211
Fax—(908) 233-2292
www.gleicher.com
Email—sales@gleicher.com
Pres.—C. Gleicher
V-P.—Douglas Sanderson
Opers. Mgr.—Grant Cowell
SIC—2675; NAICS—322200; Adhesive tape die cutting, laminating & slitting
Employs—30; Estab.—1940
22,000 sq ft site, Distrib.—Intl.
Privately owned corporation
ISO rating—9002

**HOBBY BLADE SPECIALTY, INC.**
725 Jerusalem Rd. (07076)
**Phone—(908) 317-9306**
Fax—(908) 317-6892

Email—miketorres@verizon.net
Pres.—Mike Torres
V-P.—Ada Falcon
SIC—3599; 3421; NAICS—332200; Hunting knife blade grinding & industrial cutting tools
Employs—3; Estab.—1991
Sales—under $500,000
Distrib.—National
Privately owned corporation

**L & B PRINTING**
2590 U.S. Highway 22 (07076)
**Phone—(908) 232-7770**
　　　(908) 482-0474
Fax—(908) 232-8756
www.lbprintinginc.com
Email—lance@lbprintinginc.com
Ptnr.—Lance Booth, Sr.
Ptnr.—Betsy Booth
Sales Mgr.—Kristy Ball
Prodn. Mgr.—David Ball
SIC—2759; 2791; NAICS—323122; Commercial printing & typesetting
Employs—6; Estab.—1974
Sales—$500,000-$1Mil
6,000 sq ft site, Distrib.—Regional
Privately owned corporation

**PARKER3D**
1325 Terrill Rd. (07076)
**Phone—(908) 322-5552**
National—(800) 526-3672
Fax—(908) 322-4818
www.parker3d.com
Email—info@parker3d.com
Pres.—Richard Parker
V-P.—John Carter
SIC—3993; 2452; Custom interactive & traditional holiday displays
Employs—100; Estab.—1997
Sales—$20Mil
200,000 sq ft site, Distrib.—Intl.
Privately owned corporation

**†REBUTH METAL SERVICES**
2262 Stocker Ln., P.O. Box 488 (07076)
**Phone—(908) 889-6400**
Fax—(908) 889-6400
Email—mjrebuth@verizon.net
Owner—Michael J. Rebuth
SIC—5051; Wholesaler of steel & aluminum
Employs—10; Estab.—2004
Sales—under $500,000
Distrib.—Regional
Sole ownership

**SHOOTING STAR, INC.**
2500 Plainfield Ave. (07076)
**Phone—(908) 789-2500**
Fax—(908) 789-3356
www.shootingstargames.com
Pres.—Fred Andreae, Sr.
V-P. & Off. Mgr.—Fred Andreae, Jr.
SIC—3944; Shooting gallery gun & water games
Employs—2; Estab.—1986
Sales—under $500,000
3,000 sq ft site, Distrib.—Intl.
Privately owned corporation

**SIDELINE SPORTS**
2566 Plainfield Ave. (07076)
**Phone—(908) 322-9334**
Fax—(908) 322-6935
Owner—Imelda McEvoy
Off. Mgr.—Janice Miller
SIC—2396; 2395; Apparel screen printing & embroidery
Employs—2; Estab.—1991
Sales—under $500,000 (est)
Distrib.—Local
Sole ownership

**SYNTHETIC SURFACES INC.**
P.O. Box 241 (07076)
**Phone—(908) 233-6803**
Fax—(908) 233-6844
www.nordot.com
Email—info@nordot.com

Pres.—Norris Legue
SIC—2891; NAICS—325520; Commercial adhesives for the outdoor installation of synthetic turf & related surfaces in variable & sometimes harsh weather conditions; Brand name—NORDOT®
Employs—6; Estab.—1972
Sales—$500,000-$1Mil
Distrib.—Intl.
Privately owned corporation

**TECHNIMOLD, INC.**
715 Jerusalem Rd. (07076)
**Phone—(908) 232-8331**
Fax—(908) 232-5753
Email—tmp715@aol.com
Pres., CFO, MIS Mgr.—William McNamara
SIC—3089; Plastic injection molding
Employs—20; Estab.—1980
Sales—$1Mil-$5Mil
10,000 sq ft site, Distrib.—National
Privately owned corporation

## Sea Girt

(Monmouth—N.E.)

**RADAIRE DISTRIBUTORS, INC.**
1318 Segart Ave. (08750)
**Phone—(732) 282-1144**
National—(800) 367-0094
Fax—(732) 282-1145
Pres.—Eric Bomenblit
Mechanic—Ken White
SIC—3714; Automotive transmissions & rebuilt radiators
Employs—8; Estab.—1985
Sales—under $500,000
Distrib.—National
Privately owned corporation

**SELICK & BIRD THERMIDAIRE**
2180 Village Rd., P.O. Box 108 (08750)
**Phone—(732) 449-0017**
Fax—(732) 449-0273
www.thermidairesteamtraps.com
Email—larryselick@yahoo.com
Owner & Pres.—Lawrence Selick
SIC—3491; 3432; NAICS—332911; Steam traps & industrial supplies
Employs—2; Estab.—1958
Sales—under $500,000
2,500 sq ft site, Distrib.—Intl.
Sole ownership

## Sea Isle City

(Cape May—S.E.)

**†HERITAGE SURF & SPORT, INC.**
3700 Landis Ave. (08243)
**Phone—(609) 263-3033**
Fax—(609) 263-9696
www.heritagesurf.com
Email—bhsurf@comcast.net
Pres.—Barbara Heritage
Off. Mgr.—Brian Heritage
SIC—5091; 5136; 5137; Distributor of surfboards & sportswear
Employs—9; Estab.—1962
Distrib.—Regional
Privately owned corporation

**SEA ISLE ICE CO., INC.**
230 42nd St. (08243)
**Phone—(609) 263-8794**
National—(800) 244-8748
Fax—(609) 263-7775
www.seaisleice.com
Email—getice@seaisleice.com
Pres.—Joe Romano, Jr.
V-P.—Sue Ann Romano

## Sea Isle City—(cont.)

SIC—2097; NAICS—312113; *Ice; Brand name—Sea Isle Ice*
Employs—12; Estab.—1965
Sales—$2Mil
50,000 sq ft site, Distrib.—Local
Privately owned sub-S corp.

---

## Seabrook

(Cumberland—S.W.)

### CLEMENT PAPPAS & COMPANY, INC.

1045 Parsonage Rd. (08302)
Mail addr: 1 Collins Dr., Ste. 200, Carneys Point (08069-3640)
**Phone—(856) 455-1001**
National—(800) 257-7019
Fax—(856) 455-0580
www.clementpappas.com
Email—customerservice@ clementpappas.com
Plt. Mgr.—Adam Olds
Hum. Res. Mgr.—Russ Brandon
SIC—2033; 2086; NAICS— 311421; *Bottled & canned fruit juice & cranberry sauce; Brand name—Ruby Kist; Grown Right; 3-C; Delsea Farms*
Employs—210; Estab.—1942
Sales—$6Mil-$10Mil
500,000 sq ft site, Distrib.— National
Privately owned corporation
Parent co.—Clement Pappas & Company, Inc., Carneys Point, NJ
Phone—(856) 455-1000
See Parent Co. Section for full profile.

### SEABROOK BROS. & SONS, INC.

85 Finley Rd., P.O. Box 5103 (08302)
**Phone—(856) 455-8080**
Fax—(856) 455-9282
www.seabrookfarms.com
Email—seabrook@ seabrookfarms.com
Pres.—James Seabrook, Jr.
V-P., Sales & Sales Mgr.—Brian Seabrook
Cont.—Barbara Wiler
MIS Mgr.—Peter Seabrook
SIC—2037; NAICS—311411; *Frozen vegetables & packaging; Brand name—Seabrook Farms*
Employs—300; Estab.—1978
Sales—$112Mil
214,000 sq ft site, Distrib.— National
Privately owned sub-S corp.

---

## Secaucus

(Hudson—N.E.)

### †ACCREDITED LOCK SUPPLY

1161 Paterson Plank Rd. (07094-2715)
Mail addr: P.O. Box 1442, Secaucus (07096-1442)
**Phone—(201) 865-5015**
National—(800) 652-2835
Fax—(201) 865-5031
www.acclock.com
Email—sales@acclock.com
CEO—Ron Weaver
Pres.—Pamela Weaver
GM—Charles Weaver
Asst. GM—William Weaver
Sales Mgr.—Eric Hagee
Mktg. Mgr.—Norman Koller
Education Coord.—Ryan Weaver
SIC—5072; 5063; 5065; *Distributor of locks, door & decorative hardware, safes & access control systems*
Employs—45; Estab.—1974
75,000 sq ft site, Distrib.—Intl.
Privately owned corporation

### BML BLACKBIRD THEATRICAL SERVICES, INC.

1 Aquarium Dr. (07094)
**Phone—(201) 617-8900**
Fax—(201) 617-8908
www.bmlblackbird.com
Email—mail@bmlblackbird.com
CEO—Elliot Krowe
V-P., Sales—Shelly Diamond
Prodn. Mgr.—Bobby Deluca
Bus., Hum. Res. & Mktg. Mgr.— Julie Pincus
Mktg. Mgr.—Cathy Krowe
IT Mgr.—Miguel Sarpink
SIC—3648; NAICS—335129; *Staging, lighting, audio, rigging & video equipment for the events & entertainment industry*
Employs—80; Estab.—2006
48,000 sq ft site, Distrib.—Intl.
Privately owned corporation
AKA: 4 & 20

### COMMAND WEB FAMILY OF COMPANIES

100 Castle Rd. (07094)
Mail addr: P.O. Box 2399, Secaucus (07096)
**Phone—(201) 863-8100**
Fax—(201) 863-5443
www.commandweb.com
Email—info@commandweb.com
Pres.—Andrew Merson
Ex. V-P.—Steven Merson
Dir., Hum. Res.—Alexandra Llano
SIC—2759; NAICS—323100; *Company headquarters & commercial printing*
Employs—125; Estab.—1971
Sales—$10Mil-$20Mil
100,000 sq ft site, Distrib.— National
Privately owned sub-S corp.

### CREATIONS BY STEFANO, INC.

1261 Paterson Plank Rd. (07094)
**Phone—(201) 863-5806**
Fax—(201) 863-3803
www.stefanojewelry.com
Email—info@ creationsbystefano.com
Pres.—Stefano Simone
SIC—3915; *Jewelry*
Employs—2; Estab.—1973
Sales—under $500,000
Distrib.—Local
Privately owned corporation

### DELTA GALIL USA, INC.

1 Harmon Plz., 5th Fl. (07094)
**Phone—(201) 902-0055**
Fax—(201) 902-0070
www.deltagalil.com
Email—delta.us@deltagalil.com
CEO—Tim Regan
Sr. V-P., Hum. Res.—Robin Costa
V-P., Fin.—Stephen Mastropietro
Dir., Hum. Res.—Jason Suttile
SIC—2341; 2342; NAICS— 315200; *Corporate headquarters & lingerie*
Employs—100; Estab.—1979
Sales—$5Mil-$10Mil (est)
Distrib.—National
Publicly owned corporation

### FASTSIGNS®

255 State Route 3 (07094-3857)
**Phone—(201) 902-8640**
Fax—(201) 902-8645
www.fastsigns.com/153
Email—153@fastsigns.com
Pres.—Elizabeth Selbach
V-P.—Rose Conklin
GM—Joseph McGroarty

SIC—3993; 2759; 2541; 2542; *Yard, interior & exterior signs, banners, POP displays, window lettering, vehicle graphics, posters & full-color digital printing*
Employs—7; Estab.—1992
2,400 sq ft site, Distrib.—Local
Privately owned sub-S corp.

### FUJIKURA GRAPHICS

700 Penhorn Ave., Unit 2 (07094)
**Phone—(201) 420-5040**
National—(800) 628-0697
Fax—(201) 420-8978
www.fujikuragraphics.com
Email—marketing@picgraphics.com
Owner—Koichi Kanai
Cust. Serv. Rep.—Carolyn Harts
SIC—3069; *Rubber printing press blanket converting*
Employs—20; Estab.—1998
Sales—$500,000-$1Mil
Distrib.—Intl.
Privately owned corporation

### GENERAL GLASS INTERNATIONAL

101 Venture Way (07094)
**Phone—(201) 553-1850**
National—(800) 431-2042
Fax—(201) 553-1851
www.generalglass.com
Email—sales@generalglass.com
Pres., CEO—David Balik
V-P., Fin. & GM—Ron Vance
V-P., Sales & Mktg.—Richard Balik
SIC—3231; NAICS—327215; *Company headquarters & glass cutting*
Employs—137
Sales—$10Mil-$25Mil (est)

### GOYA FOODS, INC.

650 New County Rd. (07094)
**Phone—(201) 865-3470**
www.goya.com
Email—info@goya.com
GM—Benjamin Spenickie
SIC—2034; 2032; 2035; *Dry beans, sauces, mixes & seasonings*
Employs—60
Distrib.—Intl.
Privately owned corporation
Parent co.—Goya Foods, Inc., Secaucus, NJ
Phone—(201) 348-4900
See Parent Co. Section for full profile.

### GOYA FOODS, INC. (H Q)

100 Seaview Dr. (07094)
**Phone—(201) 348-4900**
Fax—(201) 348-6609
www.goya.com
Email—info@goya.com
Pres.—Robert Unanue
Sr. V-P.—Joseph Perez
Ex. V-P.—Peter J. Unanue
V-P., Sales & Mktg.—Conrad O. Colon
V-P., Sales—Luis Tejada
V-P., MIS—Dave Kinkela
Dir., Hum. Res.—Tony Rico
Dir., Fin.—Miguel Lugo
Dir., Pub. Rels.—Rafael Toro
SIC—2032; 2035; *Corporate headquarters; canned & packed beans, sauces, mixes & seasonings*
Employs—350; Estab.—1936
Worldwide: 3,500
Sales—$100Mil-$250Mil (est)
240,000 sq ft site, Distrib.—Intl.
Privately owned corporation

### GV FLOORS

701 Penhorn Ave., Ste. 6 (07094)
**Phone—(201) 558-7889**
Fax—(201) 558-7990
www.gvfloors.com
Email—sales@gvfloors.com
Owner—John Chen
Logistics Mgr.—Johanna Park

SIC—2426; *Hardwood flooring*
Employs—5; Estab.—2005
Sales—under $500,000 (est)
Distrib.—Local
Privately owned corporation

### HARTZ MOUNTAIN CORP., THE

400 Plaza Dr. (07094)
**Phone—(201) 271-4800**
National—(800) 275-1414
Fax—(201) 271-0068
www.hartz.com
Email—consumeraffairs@hartz.com
Div. V-P., Mktg.—Adam Coacher
Div. V-P.—Stephen Odierna
Div. V-P.—Kimberly Cassar-Crosson
Dir., Regulatory & Scientific Affs.— Georgette Wilson
Integrated Mktg. Mgr.—Jennifer Dombkowski
SIC—2834; 2047; 3199; 3999; NAICS—311119; *Corporate headquarters & animal health care products, including flea & tick sprays, vitamins, collars & biscuit treats; Brand name— Hartz; Wardley*
Employs—250; Estab.—1932
Sales—$50Mil-$100Mil
Distrib.—National
Privately owned corporation

### INFINITE VISIONS, LLC

40 Enterprise Ave. N. (07094)
**Phone—(201) 866-6946**
Fax—(201) 864-3926
Owner—Mark Summers
Opers. Mgr.—Ron Schneider
SIC—2396; *Textile screen printing*
Employs—100; Estab.—1982
Sales—$6Mil-$10Mil
Distrib.—National
Limited Liability Company

### JERSEY JOURNAL, THE

1 Harmon Plz., Ste. 1010 (07094)
**Phone—(201) 653-1000**
Fax—(201) 468-5100
www.thejerseyjournal.com
Email—denise.copeland@ jjournal.com
Publisher—Ken Whitfield
Editor—Margaret Schmidt
Dir., Opers.—Denise Copeland
Dir., Mktg.—Sharon Ambliss
SIC—2711; *Newspaper publishing*
Employs—100; Estab.—1867
Sales—$2.5Mil-$5Mil (est)
Distrib.—Local
Privately owned corporation

### †JUMP APPAREL

350 Secaucus Rd. (07094)
**Phone—(201) 558-9191**
Fax—(201) 558-9898
www.jumpapparel.com
Email—sales@jumpapparel.com
Manager—Michael Giaella
SIC—5137; *Distributor of women's clothing; Brand name—Marina; Helen Blake; Tianna B.; Scooter Tops; Jump Girl*
Employs—100
Distrib.—Local
Privately owned corporation
Parent co.—Jump Apparel, New York, NY
Phone—(212) 869-3300
See Parent Co. Section for full profile.

### LITTLEGIFTS, INC. (H Q)

600 Meadowlands Pkwy., Ste. 131 (07094)
**Phone—(212) 868-2559**
National—(800) 560-0985
Fax—(212) 208-2905
www.littlegifts.com
Email—sales@littlegifts.com
CEO—Rishi Gupta
Sales Rep.—Tom Reno

GEOGRAPHICAL

## Secaucus—(cont.)

SIC—3999; 3089; *Corporate headquarters; pet-themed gift items, including key chains, luggage tags, animal-themed bookmarks, charms, home decor items & plastic drinkware (mfg. done in China)*
Employs—12; Estab.—2007
Sales—$1Mil-$2.5Mil (est)
3,000 sq ft site, Distrib.—Intl.
Privately owned corporation
AKA: Safety Glow

**MASTER CUTLERY, INC.**
700 Penhorn Ave. (07094)
**Phone—(201) 271-7600**
National—(888) 271-7229
Fax—(201) 271-7666
www.mastercutlery.com
Email—sales@mastercutlery.com
Pres.—Victor Lee
IT Mgr.—Jodi Rose
Hum. Res. Mgr.—Kristy Hudson
SIC—3421; NAICS—332200; *Cutlery*
Employs—40; Estab.—1995
Sales—$26Mil-$50Mil
Distrib.—Intl.
Privately owned corporation

**†MIDWEST MEDICAL SUPPLY COMPANY, LLC**
Div. of Midwest Medical Supply Co., LLC
200 Seaview Dr. (07094)
**Phone—(201) 223-4602**
Fax—(201) 223-4607
www.mmseast.com
Email—general@mmsmedical.com
GM—Kevin McDonald
SIC—5047; *Distributor of surgical & medical supplies*
Employs—11
Distrib.—Local
Privately owned corporation
AKA: MMS - A Medical Supply Company
Parent co.—Midwest Medical Supply Co., LLC, Earth City, MO
Phone—(314) 291-2900
See Parent Co. Section for full profile.

**MINUTEMAN PRESS INTERNATIONAL, INC.**
1247 Patterson Plank Rd. (07094)
**Phone—(201) 866-0186**
Fax—(201) 223-9040
www.secaucus.minutemanpress.com
Email—sec@minutemanpress.com
Co-Pres.—Tom Goldgraber
Co-Pres.—Tal Goldgraber
SIC—2759; 2752; 2791; NAICS—323100; *Offset printing & computerized typesetting*
Employs—5; Estab.—1986
Sales—under $500,000
3,000 sq ft site, Distrib.—Local
Privately owned corporation

**†NEW YORK PRODUCE, INC.**
125 Seaview Dr. (07094)
**Phone—(201) 223-0909**
Fax—(201) 223-9944
www.newyorkproduceinc.com
Email—nyp0703@aol.com
Off. Mgr.—Ari Sanemeterio
Buyer—Julio Garcia
SIC—5148; *Distributor of produce*
Employs—90; Estab.—1984
65,000 sq ft site,
Privately owned corporation
Parent co.—New York Produce, Inc., Bronx, NY
Phone—(718) 585-1041
See Parent Co. Section for full profile.

**NORTH STAR TRAVEL MEDIA, LLC (H Q)**
Div. of Wicks Group Of Cos., LLC, The
100 Lighting Way, 2nd Fl. (07094)
**Phone—(201) 902-2000**
National—(800) 742-7076
Fax—(201) 902-2037
www.northstartravelmedia.com
Email—ncleenput@ntmllc.com
CEO—Tom Kemp
Publisher, Conventions & Meetings—Bernie Shrayer
Custom Publisher, Conventions & Meetings—Leslie Krautheim
V-P., IT—Rich Mastropietro
Editor-In-Chief, Travel Weekly—Arnie Weissman
Mng. Editor, Travel Weekly—Kimberly Scholz
Mng. Editor, Travel Weekly—Rebecca Tobin
Dir., Hum. Res.—Jessica Vessell
SIC—2721; *Company headquarters; travel magazine publishing*
Employs—100; Estab.—1982
Sales—$5Mil-$10Mil (est)
Distrib.—National
Limited Liability Company
Parent co.—Wicks Group Of Cos., LLC, The, New York, NY
Phone—(212) 838-2100
See Parent Co. Section for full profile.

NEW ENTRY
**PLASTIC PLUS GROUP, LLC**
600 Meadowlands Pkwy. (07094)
**Phone—(201) 561-0404**
Fax—(718) 972-1129
www.plasticplusgroup.com
Email—info@plasticplusgroup.com
Member—Joe Waltham
SIC—2671; 2673; *Flexible packaging laminate rollstock & poly bags for the snack foods, fresh produce, fruits & nuts, baked goods, coffee, lawn/garden, frozen foods, candy, pet food & care, meats/poultry & pharmaceutical markets*
Employs—70
Sales—$60Mil
Limited Liability Company

**PRG LIGHT, INC.**
Div. of Production Resource Group, LLC
915 Secaucus Ave. (07094)
**Phone—(201) 758-4000**
Fax—(201) 758-4312
www.prg.com
Email—info@prg.com
Sr. V-P.—Jim Lehner
Sales Mgr.—Scott Nestel
Proj. Mgr.—Robin Lee
SIC—3648; NAICS—335129; *Theatrical lighting equipment*
Employs—100
130,000 sq ft site, Distrib.—National
Limited Liability Company
Parent co.—Production Resource Group, LLC, New Windsor, NY
Phone—(845) 567-5700
See Parent Co. Section for full profile.

NEW ENTRY
**PROFORM ACOUSTIC SURFACES LLC**
307 Julianne Ter. (07094)
Mail addr: P.O. Box 1363, Secaucus (07094)
**Phone—(201) 553-9614**
Fax—(201) 553-0193
www.proformacoustic.com
Email—info@proformacoustic.com
Mng. Ptnr.—Anna Porcelli
Mng. Ptnr.—Ed Becker
SIC—3089; *PVC extrusions for fabricated upholstered acoustic & tack panel systems*
Employs—5
Sales—$500,000-$1Mil (est)
Limited Liability Company

**R. R. DONNELLEY & SONS CO.**
215 County Ave. (07094)
**Phone—(201) 271-1000**
Fax—(201) 271-2060
www.rrd.com
Email—info@rrd.com
V-P.—Keith Convery
Hum. Res. Mgr.—Richard Lelonde
SIC—2732; NAICS—323117; *Book printing*
Employs—400; Estab.—1907
Sales—$50Mil-$100Mil
Distrib.—National
Publicly owned corporation
Parent co.—R. R. Donnelley & Sons Co., Chicago, IL
Phone—(312) 326-8000
See Parent Co. Section for full profile.

**ROSE BRAND, INC.**
4 Emerson Ln. (07094)
Mail addr: P.O. Box 1536, Secaucus (07096-1536)
**Phone—(201) 809-1730**
National—(800) 223-1624
Fax—(201) 809-1851
www.rosebrand.com
Email—sales@rosebrand.com
Pres.—George Jacobstein
Ex. V-P.—Joshua Jacobstein
V-P., Sales & Mktg.—Peter Finder
V-P., Sales—Roger Claman
V-P., E-Commerce—Louis Peter
GM—Robert P. Bertrand
Opers. Mgr.—Victoria Williamson
SIC—2391; 2591; 2399; 3999; NAICS—314121; *Curtains, draperies, backdrops, fabrics & stage hardware for theaters, film & video production, houses of worship, schools & events*
Employs—197; Estab.—1929
Sales—$10Mil-$25Mil (est)
120,000 sq ft site, Distrib.—Intl.
Privately owned corporation

**†ROYCE LEATHER**
501 Penhorn Ave., Ste. 9 (07094)
**Phone—(201) 330-7720**
Fax—(201) 330-7660
www.royceleathergifts.com
Email—billy@royceleathergifts.com
Owner—Kathy Bauer
Dir., Mktg.—Billy Bauer
SIC—5099; 5199; *Distributor of leather luggage, briefcases, personal accessories & desk accessories, including wallets, eyeglass cases, desk blotters, wastebaskets & coasters; Brand name—The Royce Collection*
Employs—14; Estab.—1974
Sales—$5Mil
Distrib.—Intl.
Privately owned corporation

**SARKLI REPECHAGE LTD.**
300 Castle Rd. (07094)
**Phone—(201) 549-4200**
National—(800) 248-7546
Fax—(201) 549-4240
www.repechage.com
Email—cservice@repechage.com
Pres.—Lydia Sarfati
COO—David Sarfati
V-P.—Shiri Sarfati
IT Mgr.—Robert Yagley
Hum. Res. Mgr.—Theresa Zazzera
SIC—2844; NAICS—325600; *Cosmetics & skin care products; Brand name—Repechage; Kanshi; Hair Spa Hydra Amino*
Employs—60; Estab.—1980
Sales—$11Mil-$25Mil
Distrib.—Intl.
Privately owned corporation

**SECAUCUS HOME NEWS**
766 Irving Pl. (07094)
Mail addr: P.O. Box 1100, Secaucus (07096)
**Phone—(201) 867-2071**
Fax—(201) 865-3806
www.secaucushomenews.com
Email—editor@secacushomenews.com
Owner—Gretchen Henkel
SIC—2711; *Newspaper publishing*
Employs—5; Estab.—1910
Distrib.—Local
Sole ownership

**SEKISUI AMERICA CORP. (H Q)**
333 Meadowlands Pkwy., 4th Fl. (07094)
**Phone—(201) 423-7960**
Fax—(201) 423-7979
www.sekisui-corp.com
Email—info@seksui-corp.com
CFO—Akira Morimoto
V-P.—Takuji Nakayama
Treas.—Takuji Oka
SIC—2819; 2869; 3086; NAICS—326100; *Corporate headquarters; industrial chemicals*
Employs—10; Estab.—1983
Company-wide: 1,100
Sales—$2.5Mil-$5Mil (est)
Distrib.—Intl.
Publicly owned corporation

**TOSCANA CHEESE CO., INC.**
575 Windsor Dr. (07094)
**Phone—(201) 617-1500**
Fax—(201) 617-5700
www.toscanacheese.com
Pres.—Victor J. Paparazzo
Cont.—Baseer Siddiqui
Dir., Qual. Assur.—Eric Selice
Off. Mgr.—Gina Camato
SIC—2022; NAICS—311513; *European-style cheeses; Brand name—Toscana*
Employs—100; Estab.—1993
43,000 sq ft site, Distrib.—Local
Privately owned corporation

**WILENTA FEED, INC.**
46 Henry St. (07094)
**Phone—(201) 863-3035**
(201) 325-0044
Fax—(201) 863-2705
www.wilenta.com
Pres.—Peter Wilenta
IT Mgr.—Michael Wilenta
Hum. Res. Mgr.—Elene Costan
SIC—2048; *Animal feed from recycled bakery by-products*
Employs—10; Estab.—1973
Sales—$1Mil-$2.5Mil
Distrib.—Regional
Privately owned corporation

---

## Sewaren

(Middlesex—N.E.)

**AUTOMATED MEDICAL PRODUCTS CO.**
440 Cliff Rd. (07077)
Mail addr: P.O. Box 2508, Edison (08818-2508)
**Phone—(732) 602-7717**
Fax—(732) 602-7706
www.ironintern.com
Email—sales@ironintern.com
CEO—Jerry M. Brown
Pres.—Janice E. Brown
Cust. Serv. Mgr.—Dawn Mandico

## Sewaren—(cont.)

SIC—3841; *Fine stainless steel single arm & double-arm surgical instruments for open, laparoscopic, general abdominal & liver transplant surgery; Brand name—The Iron Intern®; Stieber Rib Grip Kit*
Employs—8; Estab.—1970
Sales—$1Mil-$2.5Mil
Distrib.—Intl.
Privately owned corporation
ISO rating—9001, 13485

### PSEG POWER

749 Cliff Rd. (07077)
**Phone—(732) 750-2062**
 (732) 750-2002
National—(800) 496-7734
www.pseg.com
Off. Mgr.—Carmen Esteves
Engr.—Richard Lohmann
SIC—3511; 3561; NAICS—333611; *Gas & steam turbines, electric turbines, generators & motors & large pumps, including gas turbine overhaul*
Employs—80; Estab.—1976
Sales—$10Mil-$25Mil (est)
Distrib.—Regional
Privately owned corporation
AKAs: C M S & Public Service Electric & Gas Co.

---

## Sewell

(Gloucester—S.W.)

### ACTIVE CONTROLS, LLC

597 Mantua Blvd. (08080)
**Phone—(856) 669-0940**
National—(800) 324-1527
Fax—(856) 494-4221
www.activecontrols.com
Email—info@activecontrols.com
CEO—Mike Flowers
SIC—3842; *Power wheelchair controls, components & accessories*
Employs—7; Estab.—2011
Sales—$1Mil-$2.5Mil
Distrib.—Intl.
Limited Liability Company
AKA: Mobility Parts & Service

### BURGER & SON, INC., EDWIN R.

732 Main St., P.O. Box 184 (08080)
**Phone—(856) 468-2300**
www.burgerfence.com
Email—burgerfence@aol.com
Pres.—Edwin R. Burger
Off. & Sales Mgr.—Mike Laguori
SIC—2499; 3089; *Wood, chain-link, vinyl, aluminum, steel & stainless steel fencing*
Employs—30; Estab.—1953
Distrib.—Regional
Privately owned corporation

### COPERION K-TRON PITMAN, INC.

Div. of Hillenbrand, Inc.
590 Woodbury Glassboro Rd. (08080)
**Phone—(856) 589-0500**
Fax—(856) 582-7968
www.coperionktron.com
Email—info@ktron.com
CFO, GM—Robert E. Wisniewski
V-P., Global Mktg.—Robert Barnett
Dir., Sales—John Winski
Dir., WW Qual.—Jirina Ramescu
Mktg. Mgr.—Nora Ashmen
Bus. Dev. Mgr., Chemicals & Plastics—Jaime Gomez
Bus. Dev. Mgr., Food & Pharmaceutical—Sharon Nowak
SIC—3535; *Corporate headquarters & feeding & pneumatic conveying components & systems for the food, pharmaceutical, chemical & plastics industries; Brand name—Coperion; Bulk Solids Pump Feeders; Aerolock*
Employs—100; Estab.—1964
Sales—$100Mil
90,000 sq ft site, Distrib.—Intl.
Publicly owned corporation
ISO rating—9001
Parent co.—Hillenbrand, Inc., Batesville, IN
Phone—(812) 934-7000
See Parent Co. Section for full profile.

### CREATIVE COMPETITIONS, INC.

406 Ganttown Rd. (08080)
**Phone—(856) 256-2797**
Fax—(856) 256-2798
www.odysseyofthemind.com
Email—info@odysseyofthemind.com
Dir.—Samuel W. Micklus
Asst. Dir.—Jennifer Beale
SIC—2731; *Educational book publishing*
Employs—10; Estab.—1978
Sales—$500,000-$1Mil (est)
Distrib.—Intl.
Privately owned corporation

### †DELAWARE VALLEY WHOLESALE FLORIST, INC.

520 Mantua Blvd. *(08080)*
**Phone—(856) 468-7000**
National—(800) 676-1212
Fax—(856) 464-2753
www.dvflora.com
Chrm.—John R. Wilkins
CEO—Jack Chidester
CFO—Gene Owens
Ex. V-P.—Robert M. Wilkins
V-P., Sales—John Richards
Mktg. Mgr.—Karen Urbanek
IT Mgr.—John Markhorst
Hum. Res. Mgr.—Michele Berman
SIC—5193; 5148; 5145; 5149; *Corporate headquarters & wholesaler of fresh flowers, floral supplies, fresh fruit & gourmet snacks & beverages*
Employs—50; Estab.—1959
Sales—$26Mil-$50Mil
Distrib.—Local
Privately owned corporation
AKA: Delaware Valley Floral Group

### DELPHI ENGINEERING & CONTRACTING, INC.

131 Blackwood Barnsboro Rd. (08080)
**Phone—(856) 228-5700**
National—(800) 220-4101
Fax—(856) 228-9354
www.delphiengineering.com
Email—dec76@aol.com
Pres.—Nick Pjatikin
SIC—3398; NAICS—332811; *Heat treating, including stress relieving, refractory dryout & on-site preheating for petrochemical refineries, power generating plants, fabricators & the construction industry*
Employs—8; Estab.—1976
Distrib.—National
Privately owned corporation

[NEW ENTRY]
### EAST COAST STEEL, INC.

317 Salina Rd. (08080)
**Phone—(856) 582-6776**
Fax—(856) 582-0288
www.eastcoaststeel.net
Email—esl@eastcoaststeel.com
Owner—Jim Matthews

SIC—3599; 3499; *CNC & welding machining job shop*
Employs—20
Sales—$2.5Mil-$5Mil (est)

### HUTCHINSON CABINETS, LLC

244 Bark Bridge Rd. (08080)
**Phone—(856) 468-5500**
Fax—(856) 468-4857
www.hutchinsoncabinets.com
Email—admin@hutchinsoncabinets.com
V-P.—George Hutchinson
Off. Admn.—Henrietta Hutchinson
SIC—2431; 2499; 2541; 2542; NAICS—321900; *Wooden & plastic laminate cabinets for hospitals, banks, schools, tenant/office fit outs & assisted living facilities, including reception desks, architectural paneling, store fixtures, countertops, wood mouldings & finishing*
Employs—25; Estab.—1976
32,000 sq ft site, Distrib.—Regional
Limited Liability Company

### IMPRESSIONS UNLIMITED PRINTING CO., LLC

638 Delsea Dr., P.O. Box 386 (08080)
**Phone—(856) 256-0200**
Fax—(856) 256-0005
www.iuprint.com
Email—iuprint@yahoo.com
Owner—Joe Layton
Bus. Mgr.—Kathy Layton
SIC—2752; 2759; *Commercial offset printing, including letterheads, envelopes, business cards, labels, postcards, brochures, carbonless forms, invitations & color & instant printing & blueprinting*
Employs—2; Estab.—2007
Sales—under $500,000
Distrib.—Local
Limited Liability Company

### INTERNATIONAL ROLL FORMS, INC.

8 International Ave. (08080)
Mail addr: P.O. Box 5426, Deptford (08096)
**Phone—(856) 228-7333**
 (856) 228-7100
Fax—(856) 228-3126
www.internationalrollforms.com
Email—jimv@irf-inc.com
Pres.—Jack Vosbikian
Ex. V-P.—Thomas J. Vosbikian
V-P.—Jim Vosbikian
SIC—3499; *Corporate headquarters & custom roll forming, metal stamping, tools & dies*
Employs—12; Estab.—1970
Sales—$10Mil-$25Mil
65,000 sq ft site, Distrib.—Intl.
Privately owned corporation

### J & J MARINE

1596 Hurffville Rd. (08096)
**Phone—(856) 228-4744**
Fax—(856) 228-8993
www.jjmarineperformance.com
Pres.—Jim Clauss
Opers. Mgr.—Jeff Clauss
SIC—3544; 3599; NAICS—333500; *Tool & die & machining job shop*
Employs—38; Estab.—1987
Sales—$500,000-$1Mil
Distrib.—Regional
Privately owned corporation

### JANNETTI, INC., ANTHONY J.

200 E. Holly Ave. (08080)
Mail addr: P.O. Box 56, Pitman (08071-0056)
**Phone—(856) 256-2300**
Fax—(856) 589-7463
www.ajj.com

Email—contact@ajj.com
Owner—Anthony Jannetti
Bookkeeper—Alicia Fortney
SIC—2721; *Scholarly nursing journal publishing*
Employs—70; Estab.—1998
16,000 sq ft site, Distrib.—Intl.
Privately owned corporation
AKA: Jannetti Publications

### KRAEMER GUNITE, INC.

137 Blackwood Barnsboro Rd. (08080)
Mail addr: P.O. Box 305, Pitman (08071)
**Phone—(856) 227-8097**
Fax—(856) 227-5126
www.kraemergunite.com
Pres.—Robert Kraemer, Jr.
SIC—3297; *Custom cast refractories, including ceramic fiber blankets, hard firebrick & mortars, insulating firebrick & refractory anchors & fasteners*
Employs—20; Estab.—1974
Distrib.—National
Privately owned corporation

### K-TRON ELECTRONICS

Div. of Coperion K-Tron Pitman, Inc.
590 Woodbury Glassboro Rd. (08080)
**Phone—(856) 232-2300**
 (856) 589-0500
Fax—(856) 232-7275
www.ktronelectronics.com
Email—kkressley@ktron.com
GM—Keith E. Kressley
Qual. Assur. Mgr.—Vicki Hart
Matls. Mgr.—Shelly Rice
Bus. Dev. Mgr.—Dale Roberts
SIC—3672; NAICS—334412; *Electronic contract manufacturing, including printed circuit board assembly, box builds, functional testing, RoHS & full-service turnkey processes*
Employs—35; Estab.—1987
Sales—under $10Mil
12,000 sq ft site, Distrib.—Regional
Publicly owned corporation
ISO rating—9001:2008
Parent co.—Coperion K-Tron Pitman, Inc., Sewell, NJ
Phone—(856) 589-0500
See Parent Co. Section for full profile.

### KURTH & SON, INC., EDWARD

220 Blackwood Barnsboro Rd. (08080)
**Phone—(856) 227-8811**
National—(800) 552-8853
Fax—(856) 227-9394
www.edkurthsons.com
Email—kurth@edkurthsons.com
Pres.—Andrew Kurth
Secy-Treas.—Robert Kurth
Engrg. Mgr.—Kathleen L. Stetter
SIC—3312; *Steel fabrication*
Employs—30; Estab.—1978
7,200 sq ft site, Distrib.—Local
Privately owned corporation

### NEW AGE FASTENING SYSTEMS, INC.

11 Enterprise Ct. (08080)
**Phone—(856) 218-8301**
National—(888) 889-3833
Fax—(856) 218-8305
www.newagestudwelding.com
Email—craig@newagestudwelding.com
Ptnr.—Stephen Swartz, Jr.
Opers. Mgr.—Mike Marczely
Hum. Res. Mgr.—Craig Van Hoorn
Off. Mgr.—Karrie Kindermann
Off. Admn.—Kim Harris

GEOGRAPHICAL

## Sewell—(cont.)

SIC—3548; 3291; *Stud welding equipment & blasting abrasives*
Employs—20; Estab.—1996
Distrib.—Intl.
Privately owned partnership

### OMEGA TOOL DIE

8 International Ave. (08080)
Mail addr: P.O. Box 5426, Deptford (08096)
**Phone—(856) 232-1015**
Fax—(856) 232-1305
Email—omegatool1@aol.com
Pres.—Jack Vosbikian
Manager—Bill Jones
SIC—3544; NAICS—333500; *Tool & die job shop*
Employs—8; Estab.—1999
Sales—$500,000-$1Mil (est)
Distrib.—Local
Privately owned corporation

### PROOF PRODUCTIONS, INC.

599 Mantua Blvd. (08080)
**Phone—(856) 442-0700**
Fax—(856) 442-0701
www.proofproductionsinc.com
Email—info@proofproductionsinc.com
Owner & Pres.—Steve McEntee
Off. Mgr.—Melanie Whelan
SIC—3499; 2434; NAICS—337110; *Scenic wood & metal products, including rack equipment cases, speaker cabinets, laminate-covered products, enclosures, desks & custom brackets for live theater, events & museums*
Employs—20; Estab.—2002
Sales—$500,000-$1Mil
26,000 sq ft site, Distrib.—National
Privately owned corporation

## Shamong

(Burlington—S.E.)

### HARRY SHAW MODEL MAKER INC.

401 Stokes Rd. (08088)
**Phone—(609) 268-0647**
Fax—(609) 268-8796
www.harryshawmodel.com
Email—info@hsmodel.com
Pres.—John Kerby
Secy-Treas.—Bill Jackman
Bookkeeper & Admn. Asst.—Karen Dahl
SIC—3543; NAICS—332997; *Industrial prototypes*
Employs—11; Estab.—1952
Sales—$500,000-$1Mil
Distrib.—National
Privately owned corporation

### J S DESIGNS

321 Oakshade Rd. (08088)
**Phone—(609) 268-3018**
Fax—(609) 268-5924
Owner, Fin. & MIS Mgr.—Jeff Spikol
SIC—2395; *Embroidery*
Employs—2; Estab.—1993
Sales—under $500,000
Distrib.—Local
Sole ownership

### SHAMONG MFG. CO., INC.

33 Bunker Hill Rd. (08088)
**Phone—(609) 654-2549**
Fax—(609) 953-0217
www.shamongmfg.com
Email—info@shamongmfg.com
Pres.—Don Autio
SIC—3444; *Sheet metal fabrication*
Employs—35; Estab.—1964
20,000 sq ft site, Distrib.—Intl.
Privately owned corporation

## Ship Bottom

(Ocean—S.E.)

### †PALERMO SUPPLY

Div. of Ferguson Enterprises, Inc.
1819 Central Ave. (08008)
**Phone—(609) 494-0343**
Fax—(609) 494-0186
www.ferguson.com
Email—bill.pugh@ferguson.com
Br. Mgr.—Bill Pugh
SIC—5074; *Distributor of industrial plumbing supplies, including pipes, fixtures, valves & fittings*
Employs—5; Estab.—2003
Distrib.—Local
Publicly owned corporation
Parent co.—Ferguson Enterprises, Inc., Newport News, VA
Phone—(757) 874-7795
See Parent Co. Section for full profile.

### REM SERVICES

310 W. 6th St. (08008)
**Phone—(609) 494-7760**
Email—remsvc@comcast.net
Owner—Robert Mattner
SIC—3499; 3993; 3469; 3479; NAICS—323119; *Name tags, trophies, small signs & campaign buttons & badge hot stamping & metal engraving*
Employs—1; Estab.—1981
Sales—under $500,000
Distrib.—National
Sole ownership

## Short Hills

(Essex—N.E.)

### BLAUSTEIN, INC., M.

516 Millburn Ave. (07078)
**Phone—(973) 379-1080**
Fax—(973) 376-6550
www.mblausteinfurs.com
Email—lloydperkel@mblausteinfurs.com
Chrm.—Jules Blaustein
Pres.—Lloyd Perkel
SIC—2371; 2339; NAICS—315200; *Women's & men's fur coats & outerwear*
Employs—10; Estab.—1913
Sales—$1Mil-$2.5Mil
Distrib.—Local
Privately owned corporation

### DUN & BRADSTREET CORP., THE

103 John F. Kennedy Pkwy. (07078-2708)
**Phone—(973) 921-5500**
National—(800) 234-3867
Fax—(866) 736-5413
www.dnb.com
Email—custserv@dnb.com
Pres., CEO & Dir.—Bob Carrigan
CFO—Richard Veldran
CMO—Rishi Dave
Chief Sales Officer—Mark Geneste
Chief Operating Officer—Josh Peirez
Chief Legal Officer—Chris A. Hill
Chief People Officer—John Reid-Dodick
SIC—2741; *Corporate headquarters & credit, investment analysis & rating report electronic publishing*
Employs—425
Sales—$25Mil-$50Mil
Publicly owned corporation

NEW ENTRY

### TIGHE PUBLISHING SERVICES, INC.

788 Morris Tpke., Ste. 100 (07078)
**Phone—(973) 379-7770**
www.tighepub.com
Email—info@tighepub.com
GM—Kevin Tighe

SIC—2731; *K-12 textbook publishing*
Employs—8
Sales—$500,000-$1Mil (est)
Privately owned corporation
Parent co.—Tighe Publishing Services, Inc., Chicago, IL
Phone—(773) 281-9100
See Parent Co. Section for full profile.

## Shrewsbury

(Monmouth—N.E.)

### ACCUCOLOR, LLC

771 Shrewsbury Ave., Ste. B (07702)
**Phone—(732) 741-4594**
Fax—(732) 741-5434
www.jammprinting.com
Email—jammprinting.sh@verizon.net
Owner—Robert LaBella
SIC—2791; NAICS—323122; *Company headquarters & electronic prepress & graphic design*
Employs—2; Estab.—1994
Sales—under $500,000 (est)
Distrib.—Regional
DBA: Jamm Printing

### ANGEL MEDICAL SYSTEMS, INC.

1163 Shrewsbury Ave., Ste. E (07702)
**Phone—(732) 542-5551**
National—(800) 763-5099
Fax—(732) 542-5560
www.angel-med.com
Email—info@angel-med.com
CEO—David Fischell
Dir., Clinical & Comms.—Marcia Makoviecki
SIC—3842; *Implantable cardiac monitors & alert systems in Phase II clinical trials*
Employs—50
Sales—$10Mil-$25Mil (est)

### BEDROCK GRANITE, INC.

803 Shrewsbury Ave. (07702)
**Phone—(732) 741-0010**
Fax—(732) 985-4351
www.bedrockgranite.net
Pres.—Joe Iacono
SIC—3281; NAICS—327991; *Marble & granite countertops*
Employs—6; Estab.—1987
Sales—$500,000-$1Mil (est)
Distrib.—Regional
Privately owned corporation

### BILLS, INC., JAMES W.

167 Newman Springs Rd., Ste. E (07702)
**Phone—(732) 212-1009**
(732) 489-6124
Fax—(732) 212-1052
www.jwbills.com
Email—info@jwbills.com
Pres.—James W. Bills
Corp. Secy.—Grace Bills
SIC—3444; *Architectural sheet metal fabrication*
Employs—2; Estab.—1994
Sales—$500,000-$1Mil
Distrib.—Local
Privately owned corporation

### BUILDERS ARCHITECTURAL MILLWORK

159 Newman Springs Rd. E. (07702)
**Phone—(732) 450-0056**
Fax—(732) 450-0057
www.bamillwork.com
Pres.—Anita DelPesce
Manager—Jim Daniel

SIC—2431; NAICS—321900; *Architectural millwork, including wooden interior & exterior doors & balustrade systems*
Employs—3; Estab.—2006
Sales—$1Mil-$2.5Mil
Distrib.—Local
Privately owned corporation

### CATELLI BROS. VEAL & LAMB, INC.

776 Broad St. (07702)
**Phone—(732) 741-3687**
Fax—(732) 741-3002
www.catellibrothers.com
Email—ecook@catellibrothers.com
GM & Off. Mgr.—Edward Cook
SIC—2011; NAICS—311611; *Veal & lamb processing*
Employs—22; Estab.—1946
Distrib.—National
Parent co.—Catelli Bros. Veal & Lamb, Inc., Collingswood, NJ
Phone—(856) 869-9293
See Parent Co. Section for full profile.

NEW ENTRY

### CHARTER FINANCIAL PUBLISHING NETWORK, INC.

499 Broad St. (07702)
**Phone—(732) 450-8866**
Fax—(732) 450-8877
www.fa-mag.com
Email—cstroller@fa-mag.com
CEO—Charlie Stroller
Cont.—Lori Chadwick
Circ. Mgr.—Susanna Marra
SIC—2721; *Magazine publishing for the financial sector; Brand name—Financial Advisor Magazine*
Employs—30
Sales—$2.5Mil-$5Mil (est)

### LAROSA BAKERY, INC.

79 Neuman Springs Rd. E. (07702)
**Phone—(732) 842-4324**
National—(800) 527-6722
Fax—(732) 842-8029
www.ecannoli.com
Pres.—Salvatore LaRosa, Jr.
V-P., Prodn.—Peter LaRosa
Off. Mgr.—Elizabeth Celauro
Sales Rep., Natl.—George Delaney
SIC—2052; 2051; NAICS—311812; *Italian butter cookies, biscotti, cannoli & cream*
Employs—25; Estab.—1990
Distrib.—National
Privately owned corporation

### MECHANICAL INGENUITY CORP.

61 Riordan Pl. (07702)
**Phone—(732) 842-8889**
Fax—(732) 842-9454
www.mechanicalingenuity.com
Email—info@mechanicalingenuity.com
CEO—Peter Manning
V-P., Engrg. & CFO—Howard Beckerman
Mfg. Mgr.—Dereck Jones
SIC—3823; NAICS—334513; *Control & monitoring systems, including refrigerant pressure controls, sump pump controls, high water alarms & DC/DC converters; Brand name—Prevac; Floodfree*
Employs—15; Estab.—1987
Sales—$2.5Mil-$5Mil
6,000 sq ft site, Distrib.—Intl.
Privately owned sub-S corp.

### METALLIX REFINING, INC.

59 Avenue At The Common, Ste. 201 (07702-4559)
**Phone—(732) 936-0050**
National—(800) 327-7938
Fax—(732) 936-0029
www.metallixrefining.com
Email—sales@metallixrefining.com

## Shrewsbury—(cont.)

CEO—Eric Leiner
Dir., Comml. Relationships—Maria Piastre
Asst. Mktg. Mgr.—Michelle Leiner
SIC—3339; NAICS—331419; *Corporate headquarters & precious metals refining & recycling, including gold, silver, platinum, palladium & rhodium; Brand name—Metallix Direct Gold LLC; Metallix 100% Recycled Gold*
Employs—75; Estab.—1968
Sales—$50Mil-$100Mil
Distrib.—Intl.
Sole ownership
ISO rating—9001:2008

### OMEGA GRAPHICS

661 Broad St., Ste. 3 (07702)
**Phone—(732) 530-4441**
Fax—(732) 530-4440
www.heyomega.com
Email—doug@heyomega.com
Owner & Pres.—Douglas Godfrey
SIC—2752; 2791; NAICS—323122; *Instant printing & digital layout & design*
Employs—4; Estab.—1997
Sales—over $500,000
2,000 sq ft site, Distrib.—Local
Privately owned corporation

### QUIKIE PRINT & COPY SHOPS

703 Broad St. (07702)
**Phone—(732) 933-1010**
Fax—(732) 933-1011
www.quikieprint.com
Email—qpdigital@quikieprint.com
Pres.—Francine Goldstein
Corp. Secy.—Gerald Goldstein
Manager—Allen Dougherty
SIC—2752; 2759; NAICS—323100; *Company headquarters & digital & instant printing*
Employs—5; Estab.—1980
Sales—$500,000-$1Mil
Distrib.—Regional
Privately owned corporation

### SILBERSTEIN, INC., M.

428 Broad St. (07702)
**Phone—(732) 741-1762**
Fax—(732) 741-5741
www.msilberstein.com
Email—sales@msilberstein.com
Co-Pres.—M. Silberstein
Co-Pres.—Howard Silberstein
Fin. Mgr.—Rhonda Gale
SIC—2391; 2221; NAICS—314121; *Draperies, upholstery, office furniture & computer tables*
Employs—7; Estab.—1920
Sales—under $500,000
6,000 sq ft site, Distrib.—Local
Privately owned corporation

### VERTICAL SOURCE, INC. (H Q)

812 Broad St. (07702)
**Phone—(732) 530-5330**
National—(866) 785-3343
Fax—(732) 530-5558
www.verticalsource.com
Email—info@verticalapearl.com
Pres.—Christopher Neary
Cont., Hum. Res. & IT Mgr.—Charles Moran
SIC—2329; 2339; NAICS—315200; *Corporate headquarters; fleece jackets (mfg. done overseas)*
Employs—6; Estab.—2003
Sales—$1Mil-$2.5Mil
Distrib.—Intl.
Privately owned corporation

## Sicklerville

(Camden—S.W.)

### ELECTRONIC SUBASSEMBLIES, INC.

1541 New Brooklyn Rd. (08081-3294)
**Phone—(856) 629-2492**
Fax—(856) 629-2493
www.esielectronics.com
Email—esielectronics@aol.com
V-P., GM—James J. Cunningham
Prodn. Mgr.—Michael J. Iannotti
Pur. Mgr.—Angela White
SIC—3679; *Cable, wire harness, electro & mechanical assemblies*
Employs—30; Estab.—1989
Sales—$1Mil
5,000 sq ft site, Distrib.—Regional
Privately owned sub-S corp.
AKA: ESI Electronics

### ERIAL CONCRETE, INC.

965 Hickstown Rd. (08081)
Mail addr: P.O. Box 309, Blackwood (08012)
**Phone—(856) 784-8884**
Fax—(856) 627-1979
www.erialconcrete.com
Pres.—Steve Romanowski
V-P., Cont. & Maint. Mgr.—Tom Magliano
Hum. Res., IT & MIS Mgr.—Louann Boccaleri
Dispatcher—Victor McConnell
SIC—3273; NAICS—327320; *Ready-mixed concrete*
Employs—15; Estab.—1979
Distrib.—Local
Privately owned corporation
AKA: Lower County Recycle

### MODERN GRAPHICS

547 Cross Keys Rd., Ste. B (08081)
**Phone—(856) 728-6300**
www.moderngraphics.us
Email—bill@moderngraphics.us
Owner—William Glendening II
SIC—2396; 2395; *Custom screen printing & embroidery*
Employs—1; Estab.—1995
Sales—under $500,000
1,500 sq ft site, Distrib.—Regional
Sole ownership

### †PRO-MOTION INDUSTRIES, LLC

102 Allied Pkwy. (08081)
**Phone—(856) 809-0040**
Fax—(856) 809-0041
www.pro-motion.ws
Email—rob@pro-motion.ws
Owner—Kelly Cone
Pres.—Rob Hodgson
SIC—5084; *Wholesaler of labeling equipment & contract labeling & decorating services*
Employs—12; Estab.—1994
Sales—over $3Mil
35,000 sq ft site, Distrib.—National
Limited Liability Company

### WASTEQUIP

Div. of Wastequip, Inc.
1031 Hickstown Rd. (08081)
**Phone—(856) 784-5500**
National—(800) 220-2228
Fax—(856) 346-9118
www.wastequip.com
Email—sales@wastequip.com
Pres.—Joe Futcher
Sales Mgr., Inside—Kirk Warren
Sales & Tech. Mgr.—Steve Sansalone
Hum. Res. Mgr.—Lisa Elliott
SIC—3639; NAICS—335200; *Waste-handling equipment*
Employs—100; Estab.—1973
Distrib.—National
Privately owned corporation

Parent co.—Wastequip, Inc., Charlotte, NC
Phone—(704) 366-7140
See Parent Co. Section for full profile.

## Skillman

(Somerset—N.E.)

### BIOTILLION, LLC

30 Vreeland Dr., Ste. 7 (08558)
**Phone—(609) 454-3523**
Fax—(609) 228-4433
www.biotillion.com
Email—info@biotillion.com
Owner—Hanan Davidowitz
SIC—3826; *RFID vial reading systems for biotechnology, pharmaceutical & healthcare laboratories*
Employs—3; Estab.—2009
Sales—$500,000-$1Mil (est)
2,000 sq ft site, Distrib.—Intl.
Limited Liability Company

### BLESSINGWHITE, INC.

23 Orchard Rd. (08558)
**Phone—(908) 904-1000**
National—(888) 294-3577
Fax—(908) 904-1774
www.blessingwhite.com
Email—info@bwinc.com
CEO—Chris Rice
Scheduling Mgr., Network—Fran Colavita
Client Svcs. Mgr.—Sonia Palko
SIC—8742; NAICS—541600; *Employee leadership training global consultants*
Employs—60; Estab.—1973
Distrib.—Regional
Privately owned corporation

### JOHNSON & JOHNSON CONSUMER COMPANIES, INC. (H Q)

Div. of Johnson & Johnson
199 Grandview Rd. (08558)
**Phone—(908) 874-1000**
      (908) 874-1838
Fax—(908) 874-1121
www.jnj.com
Email—info@jnj.com
Chrm., Co. Group—Roberto Marques
Pres.—Sharon D'Gastino
Dir., Internal Comms.—Iris Grossman
Dir., Qual. Assur.—Walter Joppy
Dir., R & D—George Strack
SIC—2834; 2844; 3991; NAICS—325412; *Corporate headquarters; baby, skin, hair, oral & topical care products & nutritionals*
Employs—1100
Sales—$67Bil
Distrib.—Intl.
Publicly owned corporation
Parent co.—Johnson & Johnson, New Brunswick, NJ
Phone—(732) 524-0400
See Parent Co. Section for full profile.

### SCULPTURE HOUSE, INC.

405 Skillman Rd., P.O. Box 69 (08558)
**Phone—(609) 466-2986**
Fax—(609) 466-2450
www.sculpturehouse.com
Email—customerrelations@sculpturehouse.com
Pres., CEO—Bruner Barrie
Opers. Mgr.—Sandy Little
SIC—3952; *Corporate headquarters & clay products*
Employs—11; Estab.—1918
Sales—$3Mil
40,000 sq ft site, Distrib.—Intl.
Privately owned corporation

### THE SNACK FACTORY, LLC.

Div. of Snyder's-Lance, Inc.
11 Tamarack Cir. (08558)
Mail addr: P.O. Box 3562, Princeton (08543-3562)
**Phone—(609) 683-5400**
Fax—(609) 683-9595
www.pretzelcrisps.com
Email—info@pretzelcrisps.com
Sales Serv. Coord.—Patricia Smith
SIC—2052; 2096; NAICS—311919; *Flat spreadable pretzel crackers; Brand name—PRETZEL CRISPS®*
Employs—10; Estab.—1977
Distrib.—Intl.
Publicly owned corporation
Parent co.—Snyder's-Lance, Inc., Charlotte, NC
Phone—(704) 554-1421
See Parent Co. Section for full profile.

## Somerdale

(Camden—S.W.)

### ACCURATE MOLD, INC.

900 Chestnut Ave. (08083)
**Phone—(856) 784-8484**
Email—accmold@comcast.net
Opers. Mgr.—Gary McCloskey
SIC—3544; NAICS—333500; *Injection molds for the plastics industry*
Employs—8; Estab.—1998
16,000 sq ft site, Distrib.—Local
Privately owned corporation

### BISAGA, INC.

212 Ashland Ave. (08083)
**Phone—(856) 784-7966**
Fax—(856) 784-7974
www.techniqueprecision.com
Email—robert@techniqueprecision.com
Pres.—Robert E. Bisaga
Off. Mgr.—Carol Zvanya
SIC—3599; *General machining job shop for the aerospace, military, fiber optics, drag racing & commercial industries*
Employs—11; Estab.—1980
Sales—$1Mil-$2.5Mil
16,000 sq ft site, Distrib.—National
Privately owned corporation
DBA: Technique Precision Co.

### FIORE SKYLIGHTS, INC.

Div. of Pepco Mfg. Co.
210 E. Evergreen Ave., P.O. Box 160 (08083)
**Phone—(856) 346-0118**
Fax—(856) 346-9332
www.fioreskylights.com
Email—richard@fioreskylights.com
Pres., Div.—Richard L. Materio
Cont.—Elaine Materio
SIC—3444; 3231; NAICS—327215; *Commercial & residential structural & unit skylights, canopies & fire & smoke hatches, including replacement & stained glass domes, bus shelters, equipment screens, guardrails, platforms & steel & aluminum fabrication; Brand name—Bohem Skylights*
Employs—15; Estab.—1991
Sales—$2Mil
Distrib.—National
Privately owned corporation
Parent co.—Pepco Mfg. Co., Somerdale, NJ
Phone—(856) 783-3700
See Parent Co. Section for full profile.

### FLYING FISH BREWING CO.

900 Kennedy Blvd. (08083)
**Phone—(856) 504-3442**
www.flyingfish.com
Pres.—Gene Muller
Prodn. Mgr.—John Clark
Accountant—Bryson Sundberg

GEOGRAPHICAL

## Somerdale—(cont.)

SIC—2082; *Beer; Brand name—Flying Fish*
Employs—30; Estab.—1996
15,000 sq ft site, Distrib.—Local
Privately owned corporation

### LANDSMAN CUSTOM PICTURE FRAMING

600 S. White Horse Pike (08083)
**Phone—(856) 784-2145**
Fax—(856) 784-0334
www.landsmanframing.com
Email—landsman401@gmail.com
Ptnr.—Howard Landsman
Off. Mgr.—Debbie Rexon
SIC—2499; *Wooden picture frames, including framing design & installation*
Employs—5; Estab.—1957
15,000 sq ft site, Distrib.—Regional
Sole ownership
AKA: Landsman's, The

### LIBRARY AUTOMATION TECHNOLOGIES

2 E. Atlantic Ave. (08083)
**Phone—(856) 566-4121**
Fax—(856) 346-9099
www.latcorp.com
Email—valb@latcorp.com
CEO—Oleg Boyarsky
CFO, COO & Opers. Mgr.—Val Boyarsky
SIC—3569; 7372; 3993; *Library patron self-check-in & self-checkout RFID systems, including optical media kiosks for CDs, DVDs, games & Blu-Rays & self-service material circulation, intra-facility wayfinding systems, software design, mobile apps & digital signage; Brand name—FlashScan; IMM; allCIRC; MAX; MAXine; LAT; LEAP; CUBE; qAdverts; LAT-MAP; STENA; SIP-ROUTER; L-Guide; LAT-OPAC*
Employs—15; Estab.—2001
Sales—$1Mil-$2.5Mil
6,000 sq ft site, Distrib.—National
Privately owned sub-S corp.

### LINTHICUM SAILMAKERS, INC.

607 Grace St. (08083)
**Phone—(856) 783-4288**
Fax—(856) 783-0428
www.linthicumsailmakers.com
Email—brad@linthicumsailmakers.com
Pres.—Bradford Linthicum
SIC—2394; NAICS—314912; *Sails & canvas items, upholstery & rigging*
Employs—2; Estab.—1974
Sales—under $500,000
2,800 sq ft site, Distrib.—Regional
Privately owned corporation

### PEPCO MFG. CO.

210 E. Evergreen Ave., P.O. Box 160 (08083)
**Phone—(856) 783-3700**
Fax—(856) 783-8098
www.pepcosheetmetal.com
Email—info@pepcosheetmetal.com
CEO—John Kennedy
Pres.—Frank A. Reiss
CFO—Beverly Winter
COO—Edward Miller
V-P.—Richard Materio
SIC—3499; 3444; *Company headquarters & telecommunication & computer metal enclosures & accessories & precision sheet metal fabrication of commercial skylights & solar frames*
Employs—80; Estab.—1960
Sales—$5Mil-$10Mil
Distrib.—National
Privately owned corporation
ISO rating—9001:2008

### S & S PRINTING

610 S. White Horse Pike (08083)
**Phone—(856) 784-2718**
National—(877) 774-6860
Fax—(856) 783-7653
www.ssprintingonline.com
Pres.—Carol Staines
Secy-Treas.—William Staines
SIC—2761; NAICS—323116; *Business forms printing*
Employs—2; Estab.—1985
Sales—$500,000-$1Mil
Distrib.—Regional
Privately owned corporation

### SANDOVAL GRAPHICS & PRINTING

9 Minnetonka Rd. (08083)
**Phone—(856) 435-7320**
Fax—(856) 435-7507
www.sandovalgraphics.com
Email—printing@sandovalgraphics.com
Mng. Ptnr.—Tony Sandoval
Ptnr.—Chris Sandoval
Pres.—Gilbert Sandoval
SIC—2759; 2752; 2395; 3993; NAICS—323100; *Commercial, offset & digital printing, large-format signs & posters, vinyl cut graphics & signs, custom apparel, embroidery, silk screening, heat press & image setting of film positives & negatives*
Employs—6; Estab.—1967
Sales—under $500,000
6,000 sq ft site, Distrib.—National
Limited Liability Partnership

### SIGN-A-RAMA

34 S. White Horse Pike (08083)
**Phone—(856) 627-5352**
Fax—(856) 627-5407
www.signarama-somerdale.com
Email—info@signarama-somerdale.com
Owner—Jennifer Gray
SIC—3993; 3089; *Interior, exterior & illuminated signs, banners, LEDs, monuments, vehicle & window graphics & trade show exhibits*
Employs—4; Estab.—1996
Sales—$500,000-$1Mil
1,400 sq ft site, Distrib.—Local
Limited Liability Company

### UTILITY INDUSTRIES, INC.

500 Springdale Rd., Ste. K-1 (08083)
**Phone—(856) 435-6969**
Fax—(856) 435-1302
www.utilityindustries.com
Email—utilityindustries@msn.com
Bus. Mgr.—John Wile
SIC—3443; *Conduit cable pulling devices*
Employs—6; Estab.—1965
Sales—$500,000-$1Mil
4,000 sq ft site, Distrib.—National
Privately owned corporation

## Somers Point

(Atlantic—S.E.)

### LNS INDUSTRIES, INC.

P.O. Box 98 (08244)
**Phone—(609) 927-6656**
Fax—(609) 927-6656
www.gttws.com
Email—sales@gttws.com
Pres.—Lisa Fasola
V-P.—Rick Fasola
SIC—3089; *Water-saving plastic toilet plumbing fittings*
Employs—5; Estab.—1998
Sales—under $500,000
3,000 sq ft site, Distrib.—National
Privately owned sub-S corp.

### UNIQUE LIGHTING, LLC

555 7th St. (08244)
**Phone—(609) 926-8966**
www.uniquelightingonline.com
Email—uniquelighting.jim@gmail.com
Owner—James Fox
SIC—3641; 3646; NAICS—335110; *Low-voltage light bulbs & decorative restaurant/bar lighting*
Employs—1; Estab.—1985
Sales—under $500,000
375 sq ft site, Distrib.—National
Limited Liability Company

### UNIVERSAL TAPE CO. (H Q)

110 W. New Jersey Ave. (08244)
**Phone—(609) 653-3191**
Fax—(609) 653-3184
www.universaltape.com
Email—sales@universaltape.com
Pres.—Mario Curcio
Sr. V-P., Global Sales—Bob Semet
Opers. Mgr.—Micahel Campbell
SIC—2672; NAICS—322222; *Company headquarters; double-coated adhesive tapes*
Employs—45; Estab.—1963
60,000 sq ft site, Distrib.—Intl.
Sole ownership

## Somerset

(Somerset—N.E.)

### ADVANCED FOOD SYSTEMS, INC.

21 Roosevelt Ave. (08873)
**Phone—(732) 873-6776**
Fax—(732) 873-4177
www.afsnj.com
Email—info@afsnj.com
Pres.—Yongkeun Joh
V-P.—Sun P. Joh
Hum. Res. Mgr.—Rita O'Neill
Compliance Specialist—Richelle Goldilla
SIC—2099; *Custom & specialty food ingredient systems for meat & poultry products, frozen foods, sauces & marinades; Brand name—ReadiCream®; Sealtite®; Chef-Ready®; SeasonRite®; Actobind®; Actogel®; Actoloid®*
Employs—35; Estab.—1982
Sales—$5Mil-$10Mil
72,000 sq ft site, Distrib.—National
Privately owned corporation

### AEON INDUSTRIES, INC.

76 Veronica Ave. (08873)
**Phone—(732) 246-3224**
  (908) 770-1972
Fax—(732) 828-4884
Email—aeonlabels@aol.com
Acct. & Sales Mgr.—Ken Blum
SIC—2672; 2759; NAICS—322222; *Thermal-sensitive labels & primary, industrial & commercial use tags & forms & specialty printing*
Employs—15; Estab.—1982
Sales—$1Mil-$5Mil
30,000 sq ft site, Distrib.—Intl.
Privately owned corporation

### AEROSOURCE, INC.

Div. of SAFRAN USA, Inc.
390 Campus Dr. (08873)
**Phone—(732) 469-9300**
Fax—(732) 469-8010
www.aerosourceinc.com
Email—rrist@aerosourceinc.com
V-P., GM—Robert A. Rist
Dir., Opers.—Ron Grant
Dir., Admn. & Fin.—Darryl J. Russo
Dir., Technical Svcs.—Kevin Pruett
Cust. Serv. Rep.—Tom Williams
SIC—3728; 3724; 3621; *DC10, KC10, MD10, MD11 & KC-390 air-driven generators, DC10, KC10, MD10 & MD11 voltage regulator assemblies, Ram air turbines (RAT), ice detectors & actuators*
Employs—42; Estab.—1987
39,000 sq ft site, Distrib.—Intl.
Privately owned corporation
Parent co.—SAFRAN USA, Inc., Arlington, VA
  Phone—(703) 351-9898
See Parent Co. Section for full profile.

### AKORN, INC.

72 Veronica Ave. (08873)
**Phone—(732) 846-8066**
Fax—(732) 846-7952
www.akorn.com
Email—customer.service@akorn.com
V-P., Opers.—Michael Stehn
Hum. Res. Admn.—Jennifer Ksiazak
SIC—2834; NAICS—325412; *Pharmaceuticals*
Employs—102; Estab.—1990
Distrib.—National
Publicly owned corporation
Parent co.—Akorn, Inc., Lake Forest, IL
  Phone—(847) 279-6100
See Parent Co. Section for full profile.

### ALLIEDOP

Div. of AlliedOP, Inc.
1527 Route 27 (08873)
Mail addr: 1 Emery Ave., Ste. 1, Randolph (07869)
**Phone—(732) 545-2885**
Fax—(732) 545-0153
www.alliedop.com
Email—cgmedical@aol.com
Ex. V-P.—Howard Brand
SIC—3842; *Orthotic & prosthetic appliances & products*
Employs—2; Estab.—1985
Sales—under $600,000
1,800 sq ft site, Distrib.—Local
Privately owned corporation
Parent co.—AlliedOP, Inc., Randolph, NJ
  Phone—(973) 328-3340
See Parent Co. Section for full profile.

### ALPS TECHNOLOGIES, INC.

500 Memorial Dr., Ste. 1 (08873)
**Phone—(732) 764-0777**
National—(800) 817-8763
Fax—(732) 764-0610
www.alpstech.com
Email—sales@alpstech.com
Pres.—Robert Wagner
Dir., Opers.—Peter Quense
Sales Mgr., Territory—John T. Quense
SIC—2542; 3281; *Solid-surface & granite countertops*
Employs—25; Estab.—1989
Distrib.—Regional
Privately owned sub-S corp.

### AMERICAN FIBERTEK, INC.

120 Belmont Dr. (08873-1204)
**Phone—(732) 302-0660**
Fax—(732) 302-0667
www.americanfibertek.com
Email—sales@americanfibertek.com
Pres.—Jack Fernandes
V-P., Sales—Raymond J. Sooley
V-P., Mktg.—Ed Davis
Cont., Hum. Res. & Mfg. Mgr.—Vince Tavormina
V-P., Prod. Dev.—Jim McLaughlin
V-P., Engrg.—Jack Koscinski
Accts. Rep.—Ruthann Losardo

## Somerset—(cont.)

SIC—3357; 3679; 3669; NAICS—334290; *Fiber-optic security system components & IP based video security (CCTV) systems*
Employs—70; Estab.—1984
21,000 sq ft site, Distrib.—Intl.
Privately owned corporation

**AMERIDIA**
20 Worlds Fair Dr., Ste. F (08873)
**Phone—(732) 805-4001**
Fax—(732) 805-4008
V.-P.—Daniel H. Bar
SIC—3569; *Industrial electrodialysis modules assembly*
Employs—4
5,000 sq ft site, Distrib.—Intl.
Privately owned corporation

**APICORE US, LLC**
49 Napoleon Ct. (08873-9800)
**Phone—(732) 748-8882**
Fax—(732) 748-8929
www.apicore.com
Email—support@apicore.com
Pres., CEO—Ravishanker Kovi
Hum. Res. Generalist—Alaina Plytynski
SIC—2834; NAICS—325412; *Active pharmaceutical ingredients*
Employs—45; Estab.—2003
Sales—$10Mil-$20Mil
Distrib.—Intl.
Limited Liability Company

**†APPLIED INDUSTRIAL TECHNOLOGIES, INC.**
24-C Worlds Fair Dr. (08873)
**Phone—(732) 356-0522**
Fax—(732) 356-0588
www.applied.com
Email—sc0176@applied.com
GM—Glenn Casey
Sr. Ctr. & Br. Mgr.—Vic Sufalko
SIC—5084; 5085; *Wholesaler of industrial equipment & supplies*
Employs—5
Distrib.—Local
Publicly owned corporation
Parent co.—Applied Industrial Technologies, Inc., Cleveland, OH
Phone—(216) 426-4000
See Parent Co. Section for full profile.

**ASCENTTA, INC.**
370 Campus Drive, Ste. 105 (08873)
**Phone—(732) 868-1766**
www.ascentta.com
Email—sales@ascentta.com
Dir. & Cust. Serv. Mgr.—Jennifer Ke
SIC—3679; *Fiber-optic isolator, circulator & coupler components*
Employs—7; Estab.—2003
Distrib.—Intl.
Privately owned corporation

**ASPIRE PHARMACEUTICALS, INC.**
41 Veronica Ave. (08873)
**Phone—(732) 447-1444**
Fax—(732) 447-1441
www.aspire-pharma.com
Email—sales@aspire-pharma.com
Pres.—Madhav Pai
Pur. Agt.—John Pusateri
SIC—2833; *Contract manufacturing of soft gelatin & nutritional supplements*
Employs—90
Sales—$25Mil-$50Mil (est)
Distrib.—Intl.
Privately owned corporation

**AUDIOCODES, INC.**
27 Worlds Fair Dr., 1st Fl. (08873)
**Phone—(732) 469-0880**
National—(800) 648-3647
Fax—(732) 469-2298

www.audiocodes.com
Email—info@audiocodes.com
V.-P., Call Recording Prod.—Ron Romanchik
Dir., Sales—Jerry Makowski
IT Mgr.—Daniel Gan
SIC—3672; NAICS—334412; *Corporate headquarters & recording, logging & telephone printed circuit boards for the communications industry*
Employs—80; Estab.—1991
Sales—$5Mil-$10Mil
Distrib.—Intl.
Privately owned corporation

**BASF FUEL CELL, INC.**
Div. of BASF Corporation
39 Veronica Ave. (08873)
**Phone—(732) 545-5100**
Fax—(732) 545-5170
www.basf-fuelcell.com
Email—info@basf.com
V.-P., Dir., Sales—Emory Decastro
Off. Admn. & Hum. Res. Support—Tamara Pakela
SIC—3624; NAICS—335991; *Membrane electrode assemblies, low-temperature & high-temperature gas diffusion electrodes & layers & catalysts for fuel cells*
Employs—45; Estab.—2006
Sales—$11Mil-$25Mil
40,000 sq ft site, Distrib.—Intl.
Publicly owned corporation
Parent co.—BASF Corporation, Florham Park, NJ
Phone—(973) 245-6000
See Parent Co. Section for full profile.

**BAUER GEAR MOTOR, LLC**
Div. of Altra Industrial Motion, Inc.
31 Schoolhouse Rd. (08873)
**Phone—(732) 469-8770**
Fax—(732) 469-8773
www.bauergears.com
Email—info.us@bauergears.com
Opers. Mgr.—Steven Blazek
Off. Mgr.—Jeanine Piselli
SIC—3621; *Electric gear motors*
Employs—12; Estab.—1973
Sales—$1Mil-$5.5Mil
Distrib.—Intl.
Publicly owned corporation
Parent co.—Altra Industrial Motion, Inc., Braintree, MA
Phone—(781) 917-0600
See Parent Co. Section for full profile.

**BERNAFON, LLC**
2501 Cottontail Ln. *(08873)*
Mail addr: P.O. Box 6706, Somerset (08875-6706)
**Phone—(732) 560-9996**
          (888) 941-4203
Fax—(732) 560-4877
www.bernafon-us.com
Email—info@bernafon-us.com
Pres.—Joe Lugara
V.-P., Major Acct. Sales—Tony Sulsona
Dir., IT—Lars Anderson
Dir., Hum. Res.—Andrea Maeder
Mktg. Mgr.—Benson Jung
SIC—3842; *Acrylic hearing aids*
Employs—20; Estab.—1945
Sales—$2.5Mil-$5Mil
Distrib.—National
Limited Liability Company

**BETAR, INC.**
100 Randolph Rd., Ste. 4 (08873)
**Phone—(908) 359-4200**
Fax—(908) 359-1010
www.betar.net
Email—betar@betar.net
Pres.—John M. Lohse
Off. Mgr.—Linda Stine
Shop Supv.—Marian Puzio

SIC—3599; *General machining job shop, including machining, gun drilling, honing, surface grinding, machine repair & machine building*
Employs—17; Estab.—1968
Sales—$1Mil-$5Mil
24,000 sq ft site, Distrib.—National
Privately owned sub-S corp.

**BEUMER CORPORATION**
800 Apgar Dr. (08873)
**Phone—(732) 893-2800**
Fax—(732) 805-0475
www.beumergroup.com
Email—ka.si@beumer.com
Pres., CEO—Thomas Dahlstein
COO—Ray Haggar
CSO—John Sarinick
V.-P., Corp. Dev. & CMO—Tony Barr
V.-P., Hum. Res.—Cathy Potter
Dir., Sales—Lance Anderson
Mktg. Mgr.—Katie Sisco
SIC—3535; 3569; *Conveying, loading, palletizing & packaging equipment, airport baggage handling equipment & sortation & distribution systems; Brand name—BEUMER; Crisplant; Glidepath*
Employs—175; Estab.—1977
Sales—$120Mil
105,420 sq ft site, Distrib.—Intl.
Privately owned corporation

**BLUENOG CORP.**
285 Davidson Ave., Ste. 306 (08873)
**Phone—(732) 584-2340**
Fax—(732) 457-8949
www.bluenog.com
CEO—Sastry Taravai
Hum. Res. Mgr.—Michele Ebright
SIC—7373; *Computer network system integration, including LANs & WANs*
Employs—13
Distrib.—Intl.
Privately owned corporation

**BREWER ASSOCS.**
400 Apgar Dr., Unit G (08873)
**Phone—(732) 564-9070**
Fax—(732) 564-9075
www.brewerassociates.com
Email—general@brewerassociates.com
Pres.—Thomas Flack
V.-P.—Anthony Vinhal
Fin. Mgr.—Laura Cherry
SIC—3829; 3952; *Engineering, architectural, sign making equipment & supplies; Brand name—Xerox; Kip; Oce; Gorbor; 3M; HP; Azon*
Employs—25; Estab.—1961
Sales—$7Mil
12,000 sq ft site, Distrib.—Regional
Sole ownership

**CARTERET DIE CASTING CORP.**
74 Veronica Ave., P.O. Box 5610 (08875)
**Phone—(732) 246-0070**
Fax—(732) 246-0196
www.carteretdiecasting.com
Email—info@carteretdiecasting.com
Pres.—John W. Burk
V.-P., Sales—John M. Mudrak
SIC—3364; 3363; NAICS—331522; *Zinc & aluminum die castings*
Employs—28; Estab.—1960
Sales—over $4Mil
21,200 sq ft site, Distrib.—Intl.
Privately owned corporation
ISO rating—9001:2008

**CATALENT PHARMA SOLUTIONS, INC. (H Q)**
Div. of Blackstone Group L. P., The
14 Schoolhouse Rd. (08873)
**Phone—(732) 537-6200**
Fax—(732) 537-6480
www.catalent.com
Email—info@catalent.com
Pres., CEO—John Chiminski
Sr. V.-P., CFO—Matthew M. Walsh
Sr. V.-P., Hum. Res.—Lance Miyamoto
Sr. V.-P., Global Qual. & Regulatory Affs.—Sharon Johnson
Sr. V.-P., Bus. Transformation—Roy Satchell
V.-P., Global Mktg. & Strategy—Elliott Berger
V.-P., Corp. Dev. & Strategy & Inv. Rels. Officer—Cornell Stamoran
V.-P., Global Bus. Dev.—Michael J. Valazza
SIC—2834; 2657; 3089; NAICS—325412; *Corporate headquarters; pharmaceuticals, nutrients, respiratory & eye care solutions, injectable drugs & folding paperboard boxes*
Employs—377; Estab.—2007
Worldwide: 9,000
Sales—$100Mil-$250Mil (est)
265,000 sq ft site, Distrib.—Intl.
Publicly owned corporation
Parent co.—Blackstone Group L. P., The, New York, NY
Phone—(212) 583-5000
See Parent Co. Section for full profile.

**†CAVAGNA NORTH AMERICA, INC.**
50 Napoleon Ct. (08873)
**Phone—(732) 469-2100**
Fax—(732) 469-3344
www.cavagnagroup.com
Email—info@cavagna.com
Pres.—Richard Darche
V.-P., Sales & Mktg.—Dave Ellis
Dir., Opers.—Frank Marusiak
Fin. Opers. Mgr.—Nishant Patel
Cust. Serv. Rep.—Walter Sammartano
SIC—5085; 5084; *Distributor of compressed propane, medical & scientific gas storage & control equipment, including high-pressure valves & regulators & fittings; Brand name—Cavagna*
Employs—25; Estab.—1990
Distrib.—Intl.
Privately owned corporation
ISO rating—9001

**COMPOSECURE, LLC**
500 Memorial Dr. (08873)
**Phone—(908) 518-0500**
Fax—(908) 518-0569
www.composecure.com
Email—mlogan@composecure.com
V.-P., CEO & GM—Michele Logan
CTO—John H. Herslow
Proj. Mgr.—Carolyn Pisani
Acct. Admn.—Sue Prohaska
SIC—3089; 3087; NAICS—325991; *Material science/forensics security identification products, including ID cards, holographic foil prelaminates & long-life & e-passport biopage materials*
Employs—125; Estab.—2000
7,500 sq ft site, Distrib.—Intl.
Limited Liability Company

**CONTA-CLIP, INC.**
400 Apgar Dr., Ste. D, P.O. Box 6510 (08873)
**Phone—(732) 564-0705**
Fax—(732) 564-0706
www.contaclipinc.com
Email—info@contaclip.com
Pres.—Rudolph Abraham

GEOGRAPHICAL

## Somerset—(cont.)

SIC—3679; *Electronic terminal blocks*
Employs—6; Estab.—1998
Sales—$1Mil-$2.5Mil
Distrib.—Local
Privately owned corporation

**COZZOLI MACHINE CO.**

50 Schoolhouse Rd. (08873)
**Phone—(732) 564-0400**
Fax—(732) 564-0444
www.cozzoli.com
Email—sales@cozzoli.com
Pres.—Joan Rooney
Cont.—Bill Brown
Dir., Sales & Mktg.—Jeff Ringel
Technical Dir.—Morris Bekerman
Dir., Qual. Assur.—Dragutin Stoicovici
Mktg. Mgr.—Suzy Arrasate
Hum. Res. Mgr.—Patricia Bellafronte
Sales & Mktg. Coord.—Nancy Barros
SIC—3565; NAICS—333993; *Packaging machinery*
Employs—100; Estab.—1919
Sales—$10Mil-$25Mil
100,000 sq ft site, Distrib.—Intl.
Privately owned corporation

**CPI PACKAGING, INC.**

Div. of Sealed Air Corp.
50 Jiffy Rd. (08873)
**Phone—(732) 431-3500**
National—(800) 888-1064
Fax—(732) 462-3648
www.cpipkg.com
Email—sales@cpipkg.com
Pres.—Rodney Pennington
Sales Mgr., Natl.—Doug Bush
Hum. Res. Mgr.—Martyna Reszka
SIC—3086; NAICS—326100; *Corporate headquarters & plastic foam packaging materials*
Employs—125; Estab.—1998
Sales—$2.5Mil-$5Mil
Distrib.—Regional
Privately owned corporation
Parent co.—Sealed Air Corp., Elmwood Park, NJ
Phone—(201) 791-7600
See Parent Co. Section for full profile.

**CUSTOM ESSENCE, INC.**

53 Veronica Ave. (08873)
**Phone—(732) 249-6405**
Fax—(732) 249-8528
www.customessence.com
Email—ppatel@customessence.com
Pres.—Felix Buccellato
Cont. & Hum. Res. Mgr.—Kishor Bhagat
Bus. Dev. & IT Mgr.—Prashun Patel
SIC—2844; NAICS—325600; *Fragrance oils & flavors*
Employs—25; Estab.—1981
30,000 sq ft site, Distrib.—National
Privately owned corporation

**DAVAGEN PHARMACEUTICALS, LLC**

68 Veronica Ave., Ste. 1, 2 & 10 (08873-3464)
**Phone—(732) 249-6363**
    (908) 642-4220
www.davagen.com
Email—elivshits@davagen.com
Pres.—David Humbert
V.-P., CTAO—Eugene Livshits
Prod. Mgr.—Bipin Patel
Svcs. Mgr., Analytical—Helen Livshits
Qual. Assur. Mgr.—Oleg Voronov

SIC—2834; NAICS—325412; *NBE, custom & generic liquid pharmaceuticals for infants & seniors, including product development for finished pharmaceuticals for retail pharmacies; Brand name—Walgreens; CVS*
Employs—21; Estab.—1987
Sales—$2Mil-$4Mil
15,000 sq ft site, Distrib.—Intl.
Limited Liability Company

**DAVIS-STANDARD, LLC**

220 Davidson Ave., Ste. 401 (08873)
**Phone—(908) 722-6000**
Fax—(908) 722-6444
www.davis-standard.com
Email—info@davis-standard.com
V.-P., Blown Film—Rick Keller
V.-P., Cast Film—Steve Post
V.-P., Extrusion Coating—Frank Orsini
Dir., Opers.—Michael Fegan
Prod. Mgr., Blow Molding—Mark Panaro
SIC—3559; 3599; 3569; *Converting & extrusion systems for extrusion & liquid coating, cast & blown film, blow molding, pelletizing & winding, including aftermarket parts & service; Brand name—dsX flex-pack™; dsX s-stretch™; Egan*
Employs—130; Estab.—1986
Sales—$10Mil-$25Mil
100,000 sq ft site, Distrib.—Intl.
Limited Liability Company
Parent co.—Davis-Standard, LLC, Pawcatuck, CT
Phone—(860) 599-1010
See Parent Co. Section for full profile.

**EC2 SOFTWARE SOLUTIONS**

400 Apgar Dr., Ste. I (08873)
**Phone—(732) 356-0070**
National—(800) 851-0025
Fax—(732) 356-8746
www.ec2software.com
CEO—Scott Nelson
SIC—7372; *Nuclear medicine & radiopharmacy management software development; Brand name—BioPointe®*
Employs—50
Distrib.—Intl.
Privately owned corporation

**EKORNES, INC. (H Q)**

615 Pierce St. (08873)
**Phone—(732) 302-0097**
National—(888) 329-2632
Fax—(732) 868-0613
www.ekornes.com
Email—office@ekornes.com
Pres.—Peter Bjerregaard
Cont.—Nils Tore Lande
IT Mgr.—Jihad Beaino
Hum. Res. Mgr.—John Kane
SIC—2511; 2515; *Corporate headquarters; ergonomic furniture for the home, including recliners, sofas, loveseats, accessories & mattresses (mfg. done overseas); Brand name—Stressless® Recliners; Stressless® Sofas; Ekrones® Collection Sofas*
Employs—43; Estab.—1985
Sales—$50Mil-$100Mil
Distrib.—National
Privately owned corporation

**†ELECTRIC FORKLIFT REPAIR CORP.**

837 Somerset St., P.O. Box 1126 (08875)
**Phone—(732) 249-7757**
Fax—(732) 249-7068
www.theforkliftpeople.com
Email—forkliftpeople@msn.com
Co-Pres., CEO—Raul Pretto
Co-Pres. & V.-P.—Mavi Pretto
Opers. Mgr.—Phillip Pretto

SIC—5084; *Distributor of electric & propane forklifts & diesel & aerial equipment sales, rental & service; Brand name—Tailift; Carer and UN Industrial Trucks*
Employs—15; Estab.—1987
Sales—$1.5Mil
12,500 sq ft site, Distrib.—National
Privately owned corporation

**†ELECTRONIC MEASUREMENT LABORATORIES, INC.**

668 Easton Ave. (08873)
**Phone—(732) 846-4029**
National—(800) 452-6822
Fax—(732) 828-4912
www.bestingasdetection.com
Email—sales@emlinc.com
Owner—Richard J. Pleconis
Opers. Mgr.—R. J. Pleconis
Off. Admn.—Denise Russo
SIC—5084; 5043; 5063; *Distributor of industrial gas detectors, flue gas analyzers & fall safety, PPE & related safety products*
Employs—4; Estab.—1980
Distrib.—National
Privately owned sub-S corp.

**EMMCO DEVELOPMENT CORP.**

243 Belmont Dr. (08873)
**Phone—(732) 469-6464**
Fax—(732) 469-9180
Pres.—Patrick Ryan
SIC—3562; NAICS—332991; *Sub-miniature ball bearings*
Employs—25; Estab.—2006
Sales—under $500,000
Distrib.—National
Privately owned corporation

**EPIC MILLWORK**

Div. of Epic Management, Inc.
1022 Hamilton St., Ste. G (08873)
**Phone—(732) 296-0273**
Fax—(732) 296-4800
www.epicbuilds.com
Email—vbiviano@epicbuilds.com
GM—Ray Fareri
Proj. Mgr.—Vincent Biviano
SIC—2431; NAICS—321900; *Millwork*
Employs—15; Estab.—2000
Distrib.—Local
Privately owned corporation
Parent co.—Epic Management, Inc., Piscataway, NJ
Phone—(732) 752-6100
See Parent Co. Section for full profile.

**EQUIPMENT ERECTORS, INC.**

110 Garden St. (08873)
**Phone—(732) 846-1212**
Fax—(732) 843-0833
www.equipmenterectors.com
Pres.—George Anderson
V.-P., Sales—Robert Anderson
SIC—3535; NAICS—333922; *Conveyors*
Employs—43; Estab.—1972
Sales—$5Mil-$10Mil
30,000 sq ft site, Distrib.—Intl.
Privately owned corporation

**EXP, INC.**

285 Davidson Ave. (08873)
**Phone—(732) 626-3700**
www.exphazox.com
Pres.—Sreedhar Velicheti
SIC—7372; *Environment, health & safety (QEHS), governance, risk & compliance management software development; Brand name—Expertise By Experience®*
Employs—3; Estab.—1912
800,000 sq ft site, Distrib.—Intl.
Privately owned corporation

**FALCON INDUSTRIES, INC.**

371 Campus Dr. (08873)
**Phone—(732) 563-9889**
Fax—(732) 563-0899

www.falcon-industries.com
Email—zmichalski@falcon-industries.com
Pres.—Zig Michalski
V.-P.—James Harabedian
SIC—3444; *Sheet metal fabrication*
Employs—55; Estab.—1998
43,000 sq ft site, Distrib.—Local
Privately owned corporation

**FERRERO U.S.A., INC.**

600 Cottontail Ln. (08873)
**Phone—(732) 764-9300**
Fax—(732) 764-2700
www.ferrerousa.com
CEO—Bernard Kreilmann
SIC—2066; NAICS—311300; *Chocolate products*
Employs—200; Estab.—1994
Sales—$26Mil-$50Mil
Distrib.—Intl.
Privately owned corporation

**FRANKLIN STAMP & SIGN CO.**

543 Somerset St., Ste. 1 (08873)
**Phone—(732) 846-9235**
Fax—(732) 846-9712
www.franklinstampandsign.com
Email—franklinstamp@aol.com
Co-Pres.—Harry Weber, Jr.
Co-Pres.—Eleanor Weber
V.-P.—Harry Weber
SIC—3953; 3993; 3499; 3479; NAICS—339943; *Rubber stamps, vinyl, plastic, color & magnetic signs, banners, plaques, trophies, awards, auto & window lettering, custom graphics, seals, name badges & laser engraving on glass, acrylic, wood, leather & marble*
Employs—3; Estab.—1983
Sales—under $500,000
4,000 sq ft site, Distrib.—National
Privately owned corporation

**G.J. CHEMICAL CO., INC.**

40 Veronica Ave. *(08873)*
**Phone—(973) 589-1450**
Fax—(732) 249-0082
www.gjchemical.com
Email—marketing@gjchemical.com
Pres.—Diana Colonna
V.-P., Sales—Tim Fenstemaker
Cont.—Wendell Wenger
SIC—2869; 2819; *Corporate headquarters & industrial & reagent chemicals*
Employs—30; Estab.—1974
Sales—$10Mil-$25Mil
90,000 sq ft site, Distrib.—Regional
Privately owned corporation
ISO rating—9001:2008

**†GAFFNEY-KROESE SUPPLY CORP.**

50 Randolph Rd. (08873)
Mail addr: P.O. Box 6814, Somerset (08875)
**Phone—(732) 885-9000**
Fax—(732) 885-9555
www.gaffney-kroese.com
Email—info@gaffneykroese.com
Pres.—Christopher Kroese
V.-P.—John S. 'Jack' Kroese III
Cont.—Robert Jouas
SIC—5084; 5085; 5063; *Corporate headquarters & distributor of industrial equipment & supplies, including electrical & instrumentation materials, oilfield & pump equipment, AC & DC motors & safety equipment*
Employs—75; Estab.—1931
Distrib.—National
Privately owned corporation

**GO FOTON**

28 Worlds Fair Dr. (08873)
**Phone—(732) 469-9650**
Fax—(732) 469-9654
www.gofoton.com

## Somerset—(cont.)

Email—information@gofoton.com
Pres.—Simin Cai
Hum. Res. & Off. Mgr.—Carol
  Johnson
Network Admn.—Joseph Stehley
SIC—3229; NAICS—327212;
  *Fiber-optic lenses & components*
Employs—25; Estab.—1980
Sales—$1Mil-$2.5Mil
Distrib.—Intl.
Privately owned corporation

**GREN MACHINERY CO.**

70 School House Rd. (08873)
**Phone—(732) 356-5118**
National—(866) 462-4736
Fax—(732) 649-3184
www.gren.com
Email—grenauto@grenauto.com
CEO—Gianfei Han
SIC—3714; *Automotive brake
  pads, rotors & shoes*
Employs—7; Estab.—2001
Sales—$1Mil-$2.5Mil (est)
Distrib.—National
Privately owned corporation

**HILLMAN GRAPHIC PRODUCTS**

P.O. Box 5233 (08875)
**Phone—(201) 487-6900**
         (201) 289-0186
Fax—(732) 659-6170
www.hillmangraphicproducts.com
Email—mshillman@comcast.net
Owner—Marty Hillman
SIC—2752, 2759, 3993; NAICS—
  323100; *Commercial offset &
  digital printing, ad specialties &
  promotion & menu designs for
  the restaurant industry; Brand
  name—Menus Unlimited*
Employs—4; Estab.—1994
Sales—under $500,000
Distrib.—Local
Sole ownership

**†HISCO, INC.**

55 Veronica Ave. (08873)
**Phone—(732) 745-2828**
National—(800) 526-8308
Fax—(732) 745-2820
www.hiscoinc.com
Email—gsmith@hiscoinc.com
Br. Mgr.—Greg Smith
Cust. Serv. Rep.—Karen Magaw
SIC—5169; *Distributor of industrial
  chemicals, including adhesives
  & sealants*
Employs—10; Estab.—1993
Distrib.—Local
Privately owned corporation
Parent co.—Hisco, Inc., Houston,
  TX
  Phone—(713) 934-1600
  See Parent Co. Section for full profile.

**HOUSE FOODS AMERICA CORP.**

801 Randolph Rd. (08873)
**Phone—(732) 537-9500**
Fax—(732) 537-0500
www.house-foods.com
Email—info@house-foods.com
GM—Ryan Ogawa
Pur. Agt.—Monika Lund
SIC—2099; *Tofu*
Employs—60; Estab.—2006
Distrib.—Regional
Privately owned corporation
Parent co.—House Foods America
  Corp., Garden Grove, CA
  Phone—(714) 901-4350
  See Parent Co. Section for full profile.

**HYDRATIGHT OPERATIONS**

Div. of Actuant Corp.
12 Worlds Fair Dr., Ste. A (08873-
1348)
**Phone—(732) 271-4100**
National—(800) 981-9062
Fax—(732) 271-4150
www.hydratight.com
Email—cranford@hydratight.com

IT Mgr.—Wes Harris
Hum. Res. Mgr.—Brian Hayes
Off. Mgr.—Paulette Weiss
Team Leader—Bob Boychuk
Billing Specialist—Tami Podgorski
SIC—3545, 3544; *Custom
  hydraulic & electronic torque,
  tension & machining products*
Employs—21; Estab.—2010
Sales—$1Mil-$5Mil
3,000 sq ft site, Distrib.—Intl.
Publicly owned corporation
Parent co.—Actuant Corp.,
  Menomonee Falls, WI
  Phone—(262) 293-1500
  See Parent Co. Section for full profile.

**IMAGE SYSTEMS FOR BUSINESS**

22 Worlds Fair Dr., Ste. E (08873)
**Phone—(732) 302-1500**
National—(800) 329-1500
Fax—(732) 302-1673
www.imagesysgroup.com
Email—service@
  imagesysgroup.com
Pres.—Arthur Schwartz
Cont., Hum. Res. Mgr.—Mary
  Ellen Leszek
IT Mgr.—Dave Nardone
Administrator—Amanda
  Tomaszsski
Dispatcher—Maggie Koski
SIC—3999; *Rebuilt fax copiers &
  faxes*
Employs—30; Estab.—1987
Sales—$500,000-$1Mil
Distrib.—Regional
Privately owned corporation

**†INDUSTRIAL COMBUSTION
ASSOCIATES INC.**

20 Worlds Fair Dr., Ste. C (08873-
1362)
**Phone—(732) 271-0300**
         (800) 994-6164
Fax—(732) 271-3900
www.icanj.com
Email—icanancy@verizon.net
Pres., Inside Sales—Nancy Peles-
  Hufnagel
V-P. & Sales Engr.—John
  Vanderhoof
Parts Dept. Mgr.—Donald
  Hufnagel
Sales Professional—Robert
  Buxton
Sr. Serv. Techn.—David Trimmer
Serv. Techn.—John Dvoracek
Technical Consultant—Robert
  Peles
SIC—5074; *Distributor of industrial
  & commercial heating
  equipment; Brand name—
  Patterson-Kelley Corp.; Industrial
  Combustion Inc.; Gasmaster;
  Green Boiler Tech.; WILO
  Pumps; LBG Inc.; Heat-Timer
  Corp.; Miro Pipe Stands;
  Security Chimneys International;
  DeDietrich Boilers; Rockmills
  Boilers; boiler room*
Employs—11; Estab.—1954
Sales—$4Mil
5,500 sq ft site, Distrib.—National
Privately owned corporation

**INTELLIGRATED**

Div. of Intelligrated, Inc.
265 Davidson Ave., Ste. 219
(08873)
**Phone—(732) 302-2590**
Fax—(732) 357-1800
www.intelligrated.com
Email—info@intelligrated.com
V-P., Opers., Eastern Reg.—Eric
  Palotas
Acct. Exec., Pub. Rels.—Dan
  Gauss

SIC—3535, 3569, 3559, 7372;
  NAICS—333922; *Conveyors,
  sortation, automated storage &
  retrieval, light-directed picking &
  voice picking systems, robotics
  & warehouse control & business
  intelligence software
  development & warehouse
  management services; Brand
  name—Alvey Robotics; Alvey
  Palletizers; RTS order fulfillment
  systems; Datria voice systems;
  GoalPost LMS; WCSPlus; Vision
  WMS; Accuglide; Zoneflex;
  IntelliSort; IntelliQ; IntelliStar;
  Bushman; Mathews; Cleco;
  Crisplant; Davco*
Employs—34; Estab.—2001
Distrib.—Regional
Privately owned corporation
Parent co.—Intelligrated, Inc.,
  Mason, OH
  Phone—(513) 701-7300
  See Parent Co. Section for full profile.

**IQE RF, LLC**

265 Davidson Ave., Ste. 141
(08873)
**Phone—(732) 271-5990**
Fax—(732) 412-9325
www.iqep.com
Email—sales@iqep.com
GM—Alex Ceruzzi
Sales Mgr.—Anna Monteiro
Hum. Res. Mgr.—Joan Thomas
SIC—3674; NAICS—334413;
  *Semiconductor wafer products
  for wireless & optoelectronic
  components*
Employs—68; Estab.—2006
Distrib.—Intl.
Limited Liability Company

**ITW THIELEX**

Div. of Illinois Tool Works, Inc.
95 Commerce Dr. (08873)
**Phone—(732) 873-5500**
         (866) 489-2468
New Jersey—(800) 800-4857
National—(800) 829-2942
Fax—(732) 873-0015
www.itwecps.com
Email—info@itw.com
GM—Henry Swain
Hum. Res. Mgr.—Janet Pillard
Cust. Serv. Mgr.—Donna Ferrara
SIC—3089; *Plastic electronics
  tubes*
Employs—60; Estab.—1948
Distrib.—Local
Publicly owned corporation
Parent co.—Illinois Tool Works,
  Inc., Glenview, IL
  Phone—(847) 724-7500
  See Parent Co. Section for full profile.

**IVOCLAR VIVADENT MFG., INC.**

500 Memorial Dr. (08873)
**Phone—(732) 563-4755**
Fax—(732) 563-1120
www.ivoclarvivadent.com
IT Mgr.—Rich Mccann
Hum. Res. Mgr.—Laura Ritchie
Proj. Mgr.—Lou Alcuri
SIC—3843; NAICS—339114;
  *Dental products*
Employs—120; Estab.—1970
27,000 sq ft site, Distrib.—Intl.
Privately owned corporation

**JERSEY METALWORKS, LLC**

1022 Hamilton St., Ste. A (08873)
**Phone—(732) 565-1313**
Fax—(732) 565-1315
Email—bg102@aol.com
Pres.—Ray Ferrari
SIC—3559, 3599; NAICS—
  333298; *Custom machinery*
Employs—4; Estab.—2007
Sales—$500,000-$1Mil
Distrib.—Local
Privately owned corporation

**KRAUS & NAIMER, INC.**

760 New Brunswick Rd. (08873)
**Phone—(732) 560-1240**
National—(800) 526-3966
Fax—(732) 560-8823
www.krausnaimer.com
Email—salesusa@krausnaimer.com
Pres.—Joachim L. Naimer
V-P.—Ray Parello
Cont.—Brian McNicholas
SIC—3613; NAICS—335313;
  *Corporate headquarters &
  electric switches; Brand name—
  Kraus & Naimer*
Employs—40; Estab.—1958
Sales—$10Mil-$15Mil
Distrib.—National
Privately owned corporation

**LABVANTAGE SOLUTIONS, INC.**

265 Davidson Ave. (08873)
**Phone—(908) 707-4100**
Fax—(732) 560-0121
www.labvantage.com
Pres.—Peter Bailey
Hum. Res. Mgr.—Neelash
  Mirajkumar
SIC—7372; *Laboratory
  information management
  software development*
Employs—50; Estab.—1997
Distrib.—Intl.
Privately owned corporation

**LAKE SMALL ENGINE REPAIR, LLC**

283 Cedar Grove Ln. (08873)
**Phone—(732) 873-9047**
Fax—(732) 873-3395
www.lakesmallengine.com
Email—lakesmallenginerepair@
  verizon.net
Owner—Patti Lake
SIC—3519; *Rebuilt small engines*
Employs—2; Estab.—2003
Sales—$500,000-$1Mil
Distrib.—Local
Limited Liability Company

**LIGHT AGE, INC.**

500 Apgar Dr., Ste. 1 (08873)
**Phone—(732) 563-0600**
Fax—(732) 563-1571
www.lightage.com
Email—sales@lightage.com
CEO—Donald F. Heller
Pres.—John C. Walling
Dir., Sales Opers.—Lucy Kratovil
Dir., Mktg.—George Georgitsis
Dir., Compliance & Regulatory—
  Betsy Reddington
Acctg. & Hum. Res. Mgr.—Helene
  Kaplan
SIC—3826; NAICS—334516;
  *Lasers*
Employs—50; Estab.—1985
Sales—$9Mil-$12Mil
40,000 sq ft site, Distrib.—Intl.
Privately owned corporation

**LOGAN INSTRUMENTS CORP.**

19 Schoolhouse Rd., Ste. C
(08873)
**Phone—(732) 302-9888**
Fax—(732) 302-9898
www.loganinstruments.com
Email—logan@superlink.net
Pres.—Luke Lee
MIS Mgr.—Jensen Lee
Fin. & Off. Mgr.—Wenni Lee
SIC—3826; NAICS—334516;
  *Pharmaceutical testing
  instruments*
Employs—12; Estab.—1991
Sales—$1Mil-$5Mil
8,000 sq ft site, Distrib.—Intl.
Privately owned corporation

NEW ENTRY

**LUMETA CORPORATION**

300 Atrium Dr., Ste. 302 (08873)
**Phone—(732) 357-3500**
Fax—(732) 564-0731
www.lumeta.com

**GEOGRAPHICAL**

## Somerset—(cont.)

Email—info@lumeta.com
CEO—Pat Donnellan
CFO—Kathy Kinnamon
V.-P., Mktg.—Melody Iffland
SIC—7372; *SaaS software development*
Employs—25; Estab.—2000
Distrib.—Intl.
Privately owned corporation

**MARIANO PRESS CO.**

14 Veronica Ave. (08873)
**Phone—(732) 247-6828**
Fax—(732) 214-1383
www.marianopress.com
Email—info@marianopress.com
Ptnr.—Joseph Mariano
Ptnr. & Asst. Prodn. Mgr.—Jeremy Mariano
SIC—2752; 2759; NAICS—323100; *Offset & letterpress printing*
Employs—15; Estab.—1946
8,400 sq ft site, Distrib.—Local
Privately owned partnership
Also see: Mercury Printing, Inc., same loc.

**MARMO ENTERPRISES, INC.**

468 Elizabeth Ave. (08873)
**Phone—(908) 486-4421**
Fax—(732) 649-3072
www.marmoenterprises.net
Email—drmarmo@marmoenterprises.net
Pres.—Matthew Partsinevelos
SIC—3281; 2542; NAICS—327991; *Marble, granite, limestone, slate, onyx, soapstone, quartz, cultured quartz & resin-impregnated natural quartz countertops; Brand name—Zodiaq; Silestone; Caesarstone; Hanstone; Cambria; Granite; Marble; Limestone; Onyx; Slate*
Employs—2; Estab.—1992
Sales—over $1Mil
4,000 sq ft site, Distrib.—National
Privately owned corporation

**MATRIX CONTROLS CO., INC.**

330 Elizabeth Ave. (08873)
**Phone—(732) 469-5551**
National—(800) 722-6839
Fax—(732) 469-7299
www.matrixcontrols.net
Email—craig.lindemann@matrixcontrols.net
Pres.—Brad Lindemann
V.-P., Sales & Mktg. & Sales Mgr.—Craig Lindemann
IT Mgr.—Abid Rasul
SIC—3829; 3824; NAICS—334514; *Production tracking, monitoring & scheduling, preventive maintenance, machine diagnostics, warehousing, business intelligence & automated production scheduling control systems*
Employs—14; Estab.—1950
Sales—$1Mil-$2.5Mil
4,500 sq ft site, Distrib.—Intl.
Privately owned corporation

**MEDA PHARMACEUTICALS, INC. (H Q)**

265 Davidson Ave. (08873-4120)
**Phone—(732) 564-2200**
Fax—(732) 564-2226
www.meda.us
Email—info@meda.us
Pres.—Maria Carell
CFO—Jeff Hostler
Chief Medical Officer—Nancy Ruiz
Sr. V.-P., Market Access & Opers.—Al Triunfo
V.-P., GM—Jeff Cohen
V.-P., Sales—Joseph Evans
V.-P., Mfg.—Dennis Fuge
V.-P., Mktg.—Keeshia Muhammad
V.-P., Analytical & Scientific Intelligence—Alexander D'Addio
V.-P., Corp. Dev.—Bryan Roecklein
Legal Mgr.—Pat Jennings
SIC—2834; NAICS—325412; *Corporate headquarters; prescription pharmaceuticals for allergies, respiratory ailments, cough/cold, central nervous system disorders & pediatric conditions*
Employs—85; Estab.—2001
Sales—$275Mil
Distrib.—Intl.
Privately owned corporation

**MEGAWATT MACHINE SERVICES, LLC**

417 Elizabeth Ave. (08873)
**Phone—(732) 805-4000**
National—(800) 732-0180
Fax—(732) 805-4020
www.megawattmachine.com
Email—sales@megawattmachine.com
Owner—Pauline Balogh
Proj. Mgr.—Andy Balogh
SIC—3491; 3599; NAICS—332710; *Machining of severe service control valve trim parts & rebuilt OEM valves & replacement parts for turbine, feed-water & boiler applications, including reverse engineering, hard surfacing & field machining*
Employs—30; Estab.—2000
50,000 sq ft site, Distrib.—Intl.
Limited Liability Company

**MERCURY PRINTING, INC.**

14 Veronica Ave. (08873)
**Phone—(732) 247-6828**
Fax—(732) 214-1383
www.mpiusa.com
Email—jan.vreeland@mpiusa.com
Opers. Mgr.—Jan T. Vreeland
Administrator—Tony Gallo
SIC—2752; 2761; NAICS—323116; *Clinical drug study labels & case report form printing for the pharmaceutical & biotech industries*
Employs—9; Estab.—1959
Sales—$600,000
9,000 sq ft site, Distrib.—National
Privately owned corporation
Also see: Mariano Press Co., same loc.
AKA: Mariano Press

**MICRO**

140 Belmont Dr. (08873)
**Phone—(732) 302-0800**
Fax—(732) 302-0436
www.micro-co.com
Email—sales@micro-co.com
Chrm.—Frank J. Semcer, Sr.
Pres.—Brian Semcer
V.-P., Sales & Mktg.—Carl Savage
Dir., Sales—Frank J. Semcer, Jr.
Dir., Hum. Res.—Tania Reivich
Dir., Matls.—Mario Cappuccio
Dir., Engrg.—Tom Vacca
Bus. Dev. Mgr.—Randy Palmer
Mktg. Coord.—Jim Jock
SIC—3845; 3841; 3469; NAICS—334500; *Complete medical devices & components, including fabricated tube assemblies, insert & injection molding, metal stampings, MIM/CIM, laser capabilities & clean room assembly*
Employs—350; Estab.—1945
Sales—$80Mil
100,000 sq ft site, Distrib.—Intl.
Privately owned corporation
ISO rating—13485, 14001, 9001

**NEW WORLD STAINLESS, LLC**

100 Randolph Rd., Ste. 5 (08873)
**Phone—(732) 412-7170**
Fax—(732) 412-7139
www.newworldstainless.com
Email—jz@nwstube.com
Pres., CEO—Joe Zielinski
Dir.—Mike Muskal
SIC—3498; *Precision welded small diameter stainless steel & nickel alloy tubing*
Employs—45; Estab.—2009
55,000 sq ft site, Distrib.—National
Limited Liability Company

**NJBIZ**

Div. of Journal Multimedia
220 Davidson Ave., Ste. 302 (08873)
**Phone—(732) 246-7677**
Fax—(732) 846-0421
www.njbiz.com
Email—info@njbiz.com
Publisher—Tom Curtin
SIC—2721; *Weekly business journal publishing*
Employs—30; Estab.—1987
Distrib.—Regional
Privately owned corporation
Parent co.—Journal Multimedia, Harrisburg, PA
Phone—(717) 236-4300
See Parent Co. Section for full profile.

**NOSTRUM PHARMACEUTICALS, LLC (H Q)**

1370 Hamilton St. (08873)
**Phone—(732) 543-2440**
Fax—(732) 246-7215
www.nostrumpharma.com
Email—info@nostrumpharma.com
CEO—Ronnie Toddywala
Pres.—Nirmal Mulye
V.-P., Pur. & Sales—Shelly Kaplan
Gen. Counsel—Carlton Asher
SIC—2834; NAICS—325412; *Company headquarters; generic drugs*
Employs—42; Estab.—1995
Sales—$10Mil-$25Mil (est)
Distrib.—Local
Limited Liability Company

**NOVEL LABORATORIES, INC.**

400 Campus Dr. (08873)
**Phone—(908) 603-6000**
Fax—(908) 603-6006
www.novellabs.net
Email—info@novellabs.net
Pres., CEO—Veerappan Subramanian
V.-P., Sales & Mktg.—Kevin Anderson
Gen. Counsel—Anu Radha Subramanian
Dir., Acctg. & Fin.—Arshad Kagalwalla
Dir., Prod. Dev.—James Garegnani
SIC—2834; NAICS—325412; *Pharmaceuticals*
Employs—200; Estab.—2006
Distrib.—National
Privately owned corporation

**OFS FITEL, LLC, SPECIALTY PHOTONICS DIV.**

Div. of OFS Fitel, LLC
25 Schoolhouse Rd. (08873)
**Phone—(732) 748-7400**
Fax—(732) 748-7440
www.ofsoptics.com
Email—ofs@ofsoptics.com
Manager—Joann Coyne
SIC—3357; 3229; *Specialty fiber-optic cables & fiber laser components, including unique telecommunications & nontelecommunications cables*
Employs—45; Estab.—2001
Sales—$10Mil-$25Mil (est)
Distrib.—Intl.
Limited Liability Company
Parent co.—OFS Fitel, LLC, Norcross, GA
Phone—(770) 798-2000
See Parent Co. Section for full profile.

**†OGURA INDUSTRIAL CORP.**

100 Randolph Rd., 2nd Fl. (08873)
Mail addr: P.O. Box 5790, Somerset (08875-5790)
**Phone—(732) 271-7361**
Fax—(732) 271-7580
www.ogura-clutch.com
Email—info@ogura-clutch.com
Pres.—Frank Flemming
Sales Mgr., Regional—Fred Cacace
Opers. Mgr.—R. Kiefer
SIC—5013; *Corporate headquarters & wholesaler of automotive, mobile & industrial clutches, brakes & air pumps; Brand name—OGURA*
Employs—15; Estab.—1938
Company-wide: 30
Distrib.—Intl.
Privately owned corporation
ISO rating—TS16949

**ORION PRECISION INDUSTRIES, INC.**

8 Veronica Ave. (08873)
**Phone—(732) 247-9704**
Fax—(732) 828-8878
www.orionprecision.com
Email—sales@orionprecision.com
Pres.—John Sztankovits
V.-P. & Sales Mgr.—Jim Press
Off. Mgr.—Victoria Sztankovits
SIC—3451; NAICS—332721; *Precision Swiss screw machine products*
Employs—45; Estab.—1978
15,000 sq ft site, Distrib.—National
Privately owned corporation
ISO rating—9001:2008

**OTICON, INC.**

580 Howard Ave. (08873)
Mail addr: P.O. Box 6724, Somerset (08875)
**Phone—(732) 560-1220**
National—(800) 526-3921
Fax—(732) 560-0029
www.oticonusa.com
Email—mcn@oticonusa.com
Pres.—Peer Lauritsen
CFO—Bob Buchas
V.-P., Prodn.—Tom Falvey
Dir., MIS—Lars Anderson
Dir., Hum. Res.—Andrea Maeder
SIC—3842; *Corporate headquarters & hearing aids*
Employs—460; Estab.—1904
Sales—$81Mil
40,000 sq ft site, Distrib.—Local
Privately owned corporation

**P & R FASTENERS, INC.**

325 Pierce St. (08873)
**Phone—(732) 302-3600**
Fax—(732) 302-3636
www.prfasteners.com
Email—specials@prfasteners.com
Pres.—Benjamin Margulies
GM—Philip C. Vesuvio
Opers. Mgr.—Ed Bially
Pur. Mgr.—Brian Margulies
MIS Mgr.—Ron Chomsky
Fin. & Hum. Res. Mgr.—Doug Joyce
Qual. Assur. Mgr.—Janet Hoffman
Qual. Control Mgr.—Bill Kartner
SIC—3452; NAICS—332722; *Nuts, bolts & fasteners*
Employs—60; Estab.—1969
101,000 sq ft site, Distrib.—Intl.
Sole ownership
ISO rating—QS9000, 9002

**PACON MFG., CORP.**

400 Pierce St. (08873)
**Phone—(732) 764-9070**
Fax—(732) 764-9080
www.paconmfg.com
Email—sales@paconmfg.com
Pres.—Michael Shannon
V.-P. & Hum. Res. Mgr.—Lawrence Shannon

## Somerset—(cont.)

V-P.—Michael D. Scaduto
Fin. & Off. Mgr.—Lorraine Detlefsen
Cust. Serv. Rep.—Dawn Gorman
SIC—3842; 2299; 3089; *Nonwoven disposable medical towels, drapes, dressings & water activated wipes, consumer products & custom packaging*
Employs—200; Estab.—1951
Sales—$11Mil-$25Mil
167,000 sq ft site, Distrib.—Intl.
Privately owned sub-S corp.

**PERMABOND, LLC (H Q)**
223 Churchill Ave. (08873)
**Phone—(732) 868-1372**
National—(800) 714-0170
Fax—(800) 334-3219
www.permabond.com
Email—info.americas@permabond.com
Off. Mgr.—Linda Casale
SIC—2891; 2821; 3089; *Company headquarters; engineering adhesives & sealants, including anaerobics, cyanoacrylates, epoxies, modified epoxies, MS polymers, polyurethane, UVs & structural acrylics (mfg. done in Italy)*
Employs—6; Estab.—2005
Distrib.—Intl.
Limited Liability Company
ISO rating—9001:2008

**PHILIPS LIGHTING NORTH AMERICA**
Div. of Philips Lifeline
200 Franklin Square Dr. (08873)
**Phone—(732) 563-3000**
          (732) 563-3207
National—(800) 555-0050
Fax—(732) 563-3525
www.philips.com
Email—rico.scardelletti@philips.com
Pres., Philips Lighting N. America—Bruno Biasiotta
CFO—Raoul Gatzen
V-P., Mktg., Lighting N.A.—Ted Simpson
V-P., Hum. Res.—Cathy Cubberly
GM, Light Sources & Electronics—Ed Crawford
Internal Comms. Mgr.—Rico Scardelletti
SIC—3641; 3645; 3646; 3625; NAICS—335110; *Company headquarters & light sources, electronics & professional lighting systems, including light bulbs, ballasts, lamps, luminaires & controls; Brand name—Philips*
Employs—300; Estab.—1891
Sales—over $500Mil
Distrib.—Intl.
Publicly owned corporation
Parent co.—Philips Lifeline, Framingham, MA
Phone—(508) 988-1000
See Parent Co. Section for full profile.

**PHILIPS RESPIRONICS**
200 Franklin Square Dr. (08873)
**Phone—(732) 563-3400**
National—(800) 722-9377
Fax—(973) 581-6063
www.philips.com
Email—support.contracts@philips.com
Pres.—Frans van Houten
Ex. V-P.—Jim Andrew
SIC—3841; *Inhalers, inhaler components & nebulizers for asthma control therapy*
Employs—50
Sales—$11Mil-$25Mil
Distrib.—Intl.
Privately owned corporation
AKA: Philips Healthcare

Parent co.—Philips Respironics, Murrysville, PA
Phone—(724) 387-5200
See Parent Co. Section for full profile.

**PIM BRANDS, LLC**
Div. of Promotion In Motion Cos., Inc., The
500 Pierce St. (08873)
**Phone—(732) 560-8300**
Fax—(732) 537-0066
www.promotioninmotion.com
Email—mail@promotioninmotion.com
V-P., Mfg.—Jose Sepulveda
Dir., Hum. Res.—Susan O'Donnell
Dir., Engrg.—Kevin Walsh
SIC—2064; 2066; NAICS—311300; *Licensed, proprietary & private label brand candies & fruit snacks*
Employs—200
Sales—$50Mil-$100Mil (est)
Distrib.—National
Privately owned corporation
Parent co.—Promotion In Motion Cos., Inc., The, Allendale, NJ
Phone—(201) 784-5800
See Parent Co. Section for full profile.

**POWER CONTAINER CORP.**
33 Schoolhouse Rd. (08873)
**Phone—(732) 560-3655**
Fax—(732) 560-0119
www.powercontainer.com
Email—info@powercontainer.com
Pres.—Olivier Vertaud
Acctg. Mgr.—Edward Marra
SIC—3089; *Environmentally-friendly mono-film PET aerosol & nonaerosol continuous dispensing systems*
Employs—32; Estab.—2005
Distrib.—Intl.
Privately owned corporation

**†PRECISION FASTENERS, INC.**
24 Worlds Fair Dr., Ste. D (08873)
**Phone—(732) 627-0032**
National—(800) 447-2077
Fax—(732) 627-8424
www.precisionfastenersinc.com
Email—billm@precisionfastenersinc.com
V-P., CEO—Bill Miicke
SIC—5072; 5013; *Distributor of fasteners for the automotive industry*
Employs—6; Estab.—2007
Distrib.—National
Privately owned corporation

**QUALITY SOFTWARE SYSTEMS, INC.**
80 Cottontail Ln., Ste. 105 (08873)
**Phone—(732) 805-0400**
National—(800) 338-4420
Fax—(732) 805-0401
www.qssi-wms.com
Email—info@qssi-wms.com
Pres.—Edward Troianello
Dir., Dev.—Bob Banczak
Prod. Mgr.—Robert King
SIC—7372; 7373; NAICS—541512; *Warehouse & transportation management software development, including RF, bar coding, RFID, warehouse & resource optimization, slotting & labor tracking*
Employs—40; Estab.—1985
Sales—$11Mil-$25Mil
Distrib.—Intl.
Privately owned corporation
AKA: QSSI

**R & R PRINTING & COPY CENTER**
1075 Easton Ave. (08873)
**Phone—(732) 249-9450**
Fax—(732) 249-5662
www.randrprinting.com
Email—email@randrprinting.com
Owner—Bob Sepe

Prodn. Mgr.—Maria Sepe
SIC—2752; NAICS—323100; *Instant & offset printing*
Employs—5; Estab.—1981
Sales—under $500,000
Distrib.—Local
Privately owned corporation

**RARITAN COMPUTER, INC.**
400 Cottontail Ln. (08873)
**Phone—(732) 764-8886**
National—(800) 724-8090
Fax—(732) 764-8887
www.raritan.com
Email—sales@raritan.com
Chrm., CEO—Ching-I Hsu
Sr. Mktg. Mgr.—Nicole Espasa
Sr. Prod. Mgr.—Richard Dominach
Hum. Res. Mgr.—Nicole Tyburski
SIC—7372; 3571; 3679; *Data center infrastructure management & energy management software development, intelligent rack power distribution units & KVM-over-IP switches*
Employs—150; Estab.—1993
Sales—$50Mil-$100Mil
Distrib.—National
Privately owned corporation

**RASI LABORATORIES, INC.**
20 Roosevelt Ave. (08873)
**Phone—(732) 873-8500**
Fax—(732) 873-8571
www.rasilabs.com
Email—rasilabs@yahoo.com
Pres.—Ramakrishna Gogineni
Opers. Mgr.—Suneetha Gogineni
Off. Mgr.—Heather Rovira
SIC—2834; NAICS—325412; *Vitamins & health supplements*
Employs—45; Estab.—1984
Sales—$15Mil
63,000 sq ft site, Distrib.—National
Privately owned sub-S corp.

**RED SQUARE FOODS, INC.**
62 Berry St. (08873)
**Phone—(732) 846-0190**
Fax—(732) 846-2198
www.redsquarefoods.com
Email—redsquarefoods@aol.com
Pres.—Boris Rappaport
GM & Sales Mgr.—Yury Muzykoesky
SIC—2011; 2013; 5147; NAICS—311611; *Manufacturer & distributor of deli meat products, including sausage & ravioli, blintzes, pierogies & chicken liver pate*
Employs—15; Estab.—1996
Distrib.—National
Privately owned sub-S corp.

**ROTOR CLIP COMPANY, INC.**
187 Davidson Ave. (08873)
**Phone—(732) 469-7333**
Fax—(732) 469-7898
www.rotorclip.com
Email—sales@rotorclip.com
Ptnr.—Jonathan Slass
Ptnr.—Craig Slass
Dir., Sales—Sara Mallo
Dir., Mktg.—Joe Cappello
GM—Jon Coiro
SIC—3429; 3495; *Tapered section, constant section & spiral retaining rings, hose clamps, wave springs & installation tools; Brand name—Rotor Clip; Truarc; IRR; Waldes Truarc; Rotor Clamp; TruWave; Rol-Pak; Segnor*
Employs—240; Estab.—1957
Sales—$45Mil-$50Mil
238,000 sq ft site, Distrib.—Intl.
Sole ownership
ISO rating—9001, AS9100, TS16949

**RUST-OLEUM CORP., ZINSSER BRANDS**
Div. of Rust-Oleum Corp.
173 Belmont Dr. (08873)
**Phone—(732) 469-8100**
Fax—(732) 563-9774
www.rustoleum.com
Email—bullseye@zinsser.com
Pres., Consumer Div.—Ed Voorhees
Dir., Media & Pub. Rels.—Susan White
Comm. Supv.—Katie Sikorski
SIC—2851; NAICS—325510; *Primers, sealers, waterproofers, water repellent sealers & cleaners & specialty coatings; Brand name—Bulls Eye; Bulls Eye 1-2-3; B-I-N; OKON; Cover Stain; DIF Wallpaper Remover; JOMAX; Watertite; Perma-White*
Employs—135; Estab.—1849
100,000 sq ft site, Distrib.—Intl.
Publicly owned corporation
Parent co.—Rust-Oleum Corp., Vernon Hills, IL
Phone—(847) 367-7700
See Parent Co. Section for full profile.

**SATURN OVERHEAD EQUIPMENT, LLC**
100 Apgar Dr. (08873)
**Phone—(732) 560-7210**
National—(800) 631-4473
Fax—(732) 560-7216
www.saturnoe.com
Pres.—Steve Gordon
SIC—3537; *Material handling equipment*
Employs—20; Estab.—1973
15,000 sq ft site, Distrib.—Intl.
Privately owned corporation

**†SHI INTERNATIONAL CORP.**
290 Davidson Ave. *(08873)*
**Phone—(732) 477-6479**
          (888) 764-8888
Fax—(732) 868-5844
www.shi.com
Email—michael_haluska@shi.com
Chrm., CEO—Leo Koguan
Sales Mgr.—Frank Dilusto
Facilities Mgr.—Steve Alt
Mktg. Mgr.—Janet Valvano
Hum. Res. Mgr.—Michael Haluska
Accts. Rec. Mgr.—Kerry Geisler
Hum. Res. Admn. Specialist—Kaitlyn Leopold
SIC—5045; *Wholesaler of computer hardware & software*
Employs—1100; Estab.—1989
Distrib.—National
Privately owned corporation
AKA: SHI

**SITA CORP.**
347 Elizabeth Ave., Ste. 200 (08873)
**Phone—(732) 906-7806**
Fax—(908) 756-7482
www.sitacorp.com
Email—info@sitacorp.com
Pres., CEO—Ramgopal Reddy
SIC—7373; *Computer network systems integration & value-added software reseller*
Employs—30; Estab.—1993
Distrib.—Intl.
Privately owned corporation

**SONNTAG GRAPHICS, ERIC**
93 John E. Busch Ave. (08873)
**Phone—(732) 828-5200**
Fax—(732) 247-2899
Email—ericjsonntag@yahoo.com
Owner—Eric J. Sonntag
Off. Mgr.—Loretta Sonntag

GEOGRAPHICAL

## Somerset—(cont.)

SIC—3993; *Interior & exterior signs, including logo design & hand & vehicle lettering*
Employs—2; Estab.—1975
Sales—under $500,000
Distrib.—Regional
Sole ownership

### SPC SORBENT PRODUCTS CO., INC.

Div. of Brady Worldwide, Inc.
645 Howard Ave. (08873)
**Phone—(732) 302-0080**
National—(800) 333-7672
Fax—(732) 302-0969
www.sorbentproducts.com
Email—info@sorbentproducts.com
Plt. Mgr.—Nazim Mansuri
Mfg. Mgr.—Pamela Draw
Hum. Res. Mgr.—Emes Nastrapo
Pur. Agt.—Mark Hess
SIC—2297; NAICS—313230;
*Sorbent nonwoven pads*
Employs—60; Estab.—1977
Distrib.—Intl.
Publicly owned corporation
Parent co.—Brady Worldwide, Inc.,
Milwaukee, WI
Phone—(414) 358-6600
See Parent Co. Section for full profile.

### STUART STEEL PROTECTION CORP.

411 Elizabeth Ave. (08873)
Mail addr.: P.O. Box 476, South Bound Brook (08880)
**Phone—(732) 469-5544**
Fax—(732) 469-9270
www.stuartsteel.com
Email—info@stuartsteel.com
Pres.—Gordon Stuart
Sales Mgr., Natl.—Dennis Carenza
Sales Mgr.—Theresa Petroski
Off. Mgr.—Neil Melville
SIC—3471; 2899; NAICS—332813; *Corrosion control anodes & related corrosion control products*
Employs—20; Estab.—1952
Sales—$500,000-$1Mil
7,500 sq ft site, Distrib.—Intl.
Privately owned corporation

### STULL TECHNOLOGIES, INC.

17 Veronica Ave. (08873)
**Phone—(732) 873-5000**
Fax—(732) 873-7131
www.stulltech.com
Email—jwstull@stulltech.com
Chrm., Pres.—Gene Stull
V.-P., Corp. Svcs.—Gene Stull II
Sr. Dir., Admn. & Mktg.—Jason Stull
Sr. Dir., Sales Engrg.—Jameson Stull
IT Mgr.—Mike Weitzman
Hum. Res. Mgr.—Barbara Hughes
SIC—3089; *Plastic closures & bottle caps*
Employs—130; Estab.—1947
Sales—$20Mil-$30Mil
183,000 sq ft site, Distrib.—Intl.
Privately owned corporation

### TABATCHNICK FINE FOODS, INC.

1230 Hamilton St., P.O. Box 356 (08873)
**Phone—(732) 247-6668**
Fax—(732) 247-6555
www.tabatchnick.com
Email—ben@tabatchnick.com
Pres.—Ben Tabatchnick
Cust. Serv. Rep.—Priscilla Blue
SIC—2038; NAICS—311412;
*Frozen soups*
Employs—35; Estab.—1905
Sales—$500,000-$1Mil
22,000 sq ft site, Distrib.—National
Privately owned corporation

### TAKARA BELMONT U. S. A., INC.

101 Belmont Dr. (08873)
**Phone—(732) 469-5000**
National—(800) 223-1192
Fax—(732) 469-2145
www.takarabelmont.com
Email—info@takarabelmont.com
Pres.—Karataka Yashikawa
COO—Kent Iwasaki
V.-P., Sales & Mktg., Beauty Div.—Kendrick Wong
Dir., Hum. Res.—Rachel De la Pena
SIC—2599; 3843; NAICS—339114; *Corporate headquarters & beauty, spa & dental equipment*
Employs—80; Estab.—1956
Sales—$70Mil
Distrib.—National
Privately owned corporation

### TERUMO MEDICAL CORP. (H Q)

2101 Cottontail Ln. (08873)
**Phone—(732) 302-4900**
National—(800) 283-7866
Fax—(732) 302-3093
www.terumomedical.com
Email—info@terumomedical.com
Pres., CEO—H. Arase
CFO—John Pinto
CIO—Rick Larrieu
Sr. V.-P., GM—James Rushworth
V.-P., Hum. Res.—Jeff Dobbs
Sr. Mktg. Comm. Mgr.—Rosemarie Mendes
Mktg. Mgr.—Gary Clifton
Prod. Mgr.—Chad Harshman-Smith
SIC—3841; *Corporate headquarters; blood collection devices, syringes & intravenous catheters*
Employs—120
Sales—$10Mil-$25Mil (est)
Distrib.—Intl.

### TOMER LABORATORIES

350 Campus Dr. (08873)
**Phone—(732) 560-1885**
National—(800) 563-9964
Fax—(732) 560-9321
www.tomerlabs.com
Email—tomer@tomerlabs.com
Pres.—Onkar Tomer
SIC—2023; 2833; NAICS—325411; *Dietary supplements*
Employs—3; Estab.—1999
17,000 sq ft site, Distrib.—National

### †TRI VANTAGE, LLC

16 Worlds Fair Dr. (08873)
**Phone—(732) 868-8400**
National—(800) 786-7602
Fax—(732) 563-4400
www.trivantage.com
Email—sales@trivantage.com
Br. Mgr.—John Caporaso
Cust. Serv. Rep.—Cristen Melton
SIC—5131; *Distributor of industrial & marine fabrics*
Employs—20
Distrib.—National
Privately owned corporation
Parent co.—Tri Vantage, LLC, Cleveland, OH
Phone—(216) 696-2820
See Parent Co. Section for full profile.

### TRODAT USA

48 Hellar Pk. (08873)
**Phone—(732) 529-8500**
National—(800) 876-3281
Fax—(732) 562-9515
www.trodatusa.com
Email—sales@trodat.net
V.-P., Sales—Chris Boyle
Hum. Res. Mgr.—Karyn Migut
Whse. Mgr.—Shawn Chunn
Pur. Agt.—Sharon Adams
SIC—3953; 2893; NAICS—339943; *Self-inking marking devices, notaryseals & printing inks*
Employs—42; Estab.—2007
86,000 sq ft site, Distrib.—Intl.
Privately owned corporation

### U.S. SEAL MFG.

Div. of John Crane, Inc.
400 Apgar Dr., Ste. A (08873)
**Phone—(732) 667-1100**
National—(800) 243-5489
Fax—(877) 849-7325
www.ussealmfg.com
Email—usseal@ussealmfg.com
GM—Shelby Scott
SIC—3053; *Mechanical pump seals, including centrifugal, turbine, rotary, jet & swimming pool pump seals*
Employs—10; Estab.—1961
Distrib.—Intl.
Publicly owned corporation
Parent co.—John Crane, Inc., Morton Grove, IL
Phone—(847) 967-2400
See Parent Co. Section for full profile.

### UNITED PLASTICS GROUP, INC.

30 Commerce Dr. (08873)
**Phone—(732) 873-1848**
www.theupg.com
Pres.—Chihming Wong
SIC—3089; *Precision plastic products*
Employs—35; Estab.—1998
Distrib.—Local
Privately owned corporation

### †UNIVERSAL PRESERV-A-CHEM, INC.

60 Jiffy Rd. (08873)
**Phone—(732) 568-1266**
Fax—(732) 568-1299
www.upichem.com
Email—info@upichem.com
Chrm.—Herbert Ravitz
Pres.—Dan Ravitz
Opers. Mgr.—Don Martel
Hum. Res. Mgr.—Martha Soiser
Cust. Serv. Mgr.—Steve Piekarski
SIC—5169; *Distributor of chemicals, fine chemicals, surfactants & preservatives for the cosmetic, food & pharmaceutical industries*
Employs—25; Estab.—1967
Sales—$25Mil
125,000 sq ft site, Distrib.—National
Privately owned corporation

### VEECO INSTRUMENTS, INC.

Div. of Veeco Instruments Inc.
145 Belmont Dr. (08873)
**Phone—(732) 560-5300**
Fax—(732) 560-5301
www.veeco.com
Email—sales@veeco.com
Sr. V.-P., GM—Jim Jenson
V.-P., Mktg.—Sudhakar Raman
Sr. Ex. Admn.—Joanne Weathers
SIC—3559; *Metal organic chemical vapor deposition systems for high volume LED manufacturing*
Employs—115
Distrib.—Intl.
Publicly owned corporation
Parent co.—Veeco Instruments Inc., Plainview, NY
Phone—(516) 677-0200
See Parent Co. Section for full profile.

### WALTHER ELECTRIC CORP., F.

12 Worlds Fair Dr., Ste. F (08873)
**Phone—(732) 537-9201**
National—(800) 925-8437
Fax—(732) 537-9209
www.waltherelectric.com
Email—customerservice@waltherelectric.com
GM—Ray Stark
Sales Mgr., Inside—Ray Simpsons
Hum. Res. Mgr.—Priti Pujara
SIC—3643; 3621; NAICS—335931; *Electrical plug & receptacle devices & portable power distribution units, including pin & sleeve & multi-pin rectangular connectors*
Employs—10; Estab.—1992
15,000 sq ft site, Distrib.—Intl.
Privately owned corporation

---

## Somerville

(Somerset—N.E.)

### ADVANCED INDUSTRIAL CONTROLS CORP.

10 County Line Rd., Ste. 30 (08876)
**Phone—(908) 725-7575**
Fax—(908) 725-2020
Email—aic@net-lynx.com
Pres.—Douglas K. Morrison
SIC—3613; NAICS—335313; *Industrial control systems, including design & fabrication of electrical & pneumatic control systems*
Employs—6; Estab.—1988
Sales—$2Mil
4,500 sq ft site, Distrib.—National
Privately owned corporation

### ALLOY WELDING CO., INC.

6-A Culnen Dr. (08876)
**Phone—(908) 218-1551**
Fax—(908) 218-1502
www.alloyweldingco.com
Pres.—Leonard F. Schaffenberger
Admn. Mgr.—Mara Sage
SIC—3441; 3312; NAICS—332312; *Structural steel & steel fabrication*
Employs—10; Estab.—1946
Distrib.—Regional
Privately owned corporation

### †AXIS, INC.

210 Meister Ave. (08876)
**Phone—(908) 429-0090**
Fax—(908) 429-4109
www.axisnj.com
Email—sales@axisnj.com
Sales Mgr.—Gary Eliasson
Cust. Serv. Rep.—Sandy Wolse
SIC—5065; 5084; 5085; *Distributor of electronic industrial automation & control equipment & supplies, including motors, drives, bar code scanners, sensors & enclosures*
Employs—22; Estab.—1994
Distrib.—Regional
Privately owned corporation
AKA: Axis Industrial Automation

### BOTHERS WOODWORKING, INC., A. R.

236 Dukes Pkwy., P.O. Box 127 (08876)
**Phone—(908) 725-2891**
Fax—(908) 707-1062
www.botherswoodworking.com
Email—pork@botherswoodworking.com
Pres., CFO—Charles Bothers
V.-P.—Evelyn Bothers
SIC—2434; NAICS—337110; *Wooden kitchen cabinets*
Employs—10; Estab.—1946
20,000 sq ft site, Distrib.—Regional
Privately owned corporation

### BUTENSKY SERVICES CO., INC.

3380 Route 22, P.O. Box 5020 (08876)
**Phone—(908) 707-0912**
Fax—(908) 707-9822
www.butenskyservices.com
Email—bscmechanical@butenskyservices.com
Pres.—Bryan Butensky
Accts. Mgr.—Troy Thoden

## Somerville—(cont.)

Opers. Mgr.—Brian Kredatus
SIC—3599; 3559; 3585; 3569;
NAICS—332710; *Rebuilt &
refurbished electromechanical
equipment & machinery for the
retail, industrial, institutional,
medical, commercial &
hospitality industries, including
electrical, mechanical, hydraulic,
pneumatic & refrigeration related
equipment*
Employs—50; Estab.—1987
Distrib.—Regional
Privately owned corporation

**CENTURY TUBE CORP.**
22 Tannery Rd. (08876)
**Phone—(908) 534-2001**
Fax—(908) 534-4030
www.centurytube.net
Email—centtube@aol.com
Pres.—Dominick DeAngelo
Treas.—Nick DeAngelo
Sales Rep.—David Barone
SIC—3312; 3317; NAICS—
331210; *Stainless steel tubing*
Employs—60; Estab.—1987
50,000 sq ft site, Distrib.—Local
Privately owned corporation

**CHOICE CABINETRY, LLC**
61 5th St. (08876)
**Phone—(908) 707-8801**
Fax—(908) 707-8810
www.choicecabinetry.com
Owner—Avner Shmuel
Hum. Res. Mgr.—Roberta Tagger
SIC—2434; 2542; *Wooden,
melamine & thermofoil kitchen
cabinets*
Employs—50
Sales—$2.5Mil–$5Mil (est)
Distrib.—National
Limited Liability Company

**COLORON PLASTICS CORP.**
169 Meister Ave., Front (08876)
**Phone—(908) 685-1210**
Fax—(908) 722-3632
Pres.—Ken Kirchner
SIC—3089; *Plastic pellets*
Employs—6
Distrib.—Regional
Privately owned corporation

**CONOLOG CORP.**
5 Columbia Rd. (08876)
**Phone—(908) 722-8081**
National—(800) 526-3984
Fax—(908) 722-5461
www.conolog.com
Email—conolog@conolog.com
CEO—Michael Horn
SIC—3669; 3663; NAICS—
334290; *Telemetering &
teleprotection communication
equipment & components for the
military*
Employs—12; Estab.—1968
6,600 sq ft site, Distrib.—Intl.
Privately owned corporation
Also see: Iniven, A Div. Of Conolog
Corp., same loc.

**COURIER NEWS**
Div. of Gannett Co., Inc.
92 E. Main St., Ste. 202 (08876-
2319)
**Phone—(908) 722-8800**
Fax—(908) 243-6651
www.mycentraljersey.com
Email—pgrzella@
mycentraljersey.com
Editor & GM—Paul Grzella
SIC—2711; *Weekly print & online
newspaper publishing*
Employs—51; Estab.—1884
Distrib.—Local
Publicly owned corporation

Parent co.—Gannett Co., Inc.,
McLean, VA
Phone—(703) 854-6000
See Parent Co. Section for full profile.

**COVER CO., INC., THE**
19 Readington Rd. (08876)
**Phone—(908) 707-1122**
Fax—(908) 707-1575
www.coverlon.com
Email—customerservice@pegasus-
products.com
Pres.—Frank Patel
SIC—2394; NAICS—314912;
*Sewn fabric & polypropylene
mesh webbing swimming pool
covers; Brand name—
Coverlon™*
Employs—25; Estab.—1990
Sales—$500,000–$1Mil
Distrib.—Intl.
Privately owned corporation
Also see: Pegasus Products, Inc.,
same loc.

**CUSTOM MOLDERS GROUP**
160 Meister Ave., Ste. 1 (08876)
**Phone—(908) 218-7997**
Fax—(908) 218-9521
www.custommolders.com
Email—joecaro@
custommolders.com
Pres.—Joseph L. Caro
IT Mgr.—Joe Repmann
Hum. Res. Mgr.—Glenn Loh
Cust. Serv. Rep.—Kate Mitchell
SIC—3089; *Plastic injection
molding*
Employs—50; Estab.—1998
60,000 sq ft site, Distrib.—Local
Privately owned corporation
AKA: CMG

**ETHICON, INC.**
Div. of Johnson & Johnson
737 U.S. Highway 22 W., P.O. Box
151 (08876)
**Phone—(908) 218-0707**
　　　(908) 218-2553
Fax—(908) 218-3011
www.ethiconinc.com
Email—info@ethiconinc.com
Pres., Wound Mgmt.—Daniel
Wildman
V-P., MD & D Global Biologics
Qual.—Christiana Bielinski
Group Dir. Mgr.—Jefferey
Hammond
Comms. Mgr.—Kristin Wallace
SIC—3842; *Corporate
headquarters & surgical sutures*
Employs—1300
Worldwide: 8,500
Sales—over $100Mil
Distrib.—Intl.
Publicly owned corporation
ISO rating—9001
Parent co.—Johnson & Johnson,
New Brunswick, NJ
Phone—(732) 524-0400
See Parent Co. Section for full profile.

**G & B MACHINE, INC.**
35 N. Middaugh St., Ste. 2-B
(08876-1827)
**Phone—(908) 722-7940**
Fax—(908) 722-2215
www.gbmachineinc.com
Email—sales@gbmachineinc.com
Pres.—Gary Boccadutre
SIC—3599; *CNC machining job
shop*
Employs—6; Estab.—1979
Sales—$500,000–$1Mil
Distrib.—National
Privately owned corporation

**GARRETT CLOCKS**
35 N. Middaugh St., Unit 3-C
(08876)
**Phone—(908) 231-9231**
National—(877) 514-9442
Fax—(908) 231-9238
www.officeclocks.com

Email—garrett@officeclocks.com
Owner & Founder—Garrett Moore
Off. Mgr.—Liz Marquez
SIC—3873; *World, time zone &
international clock assembly*
Employs—4; Estab.—2012
Sales—under $500,000
Distrib.—Intl.
Privately owned corporation

**†GERBER METAL SUPPLY CO.**
2 Boundary Rd. (08876)
**Phone—(908) 823-9150**
Fax—(908) 823-9160
www.gerbermetal.com
Email—pmorison@
gerbermetal.com
CEO—Glenn Gerber
Pres.—Charles Calabrese
Ex. V-P.—Peter Morison
Plt. Mgr.—Brian Quigley
SIC—5051; *Steel service center,
including sheets & cut to size
blanks*
Employs—46; Estab.—1963
Sales—$24Mil–$30Mil
55,000 sq ft site, Distrib.—
Regional
Privately owned sub-S corp.

**GLENTECH, INC.**
46 4th St. (08876)
**Phone—(908) 685-2205**
Fax—(908) 685-1626
Email—glentech1@verizon.net
Pres.—Scott Gordon
V-P.—James Gordon
SIC—3429; 3533; NAICS—
333132; *Pipeline strainers &
marine hardware*
Employs—15; Estab.—1985
Sales—$1Mil–$5Mil
9,000 sq ft site, Distrib.—Intl.
Privately owned corporation

**HAHN'S WOODWORKING CO., INC.**
181 Meister Ave. (08876)
**Phone—(908) 722-2742**
Fax—(908) 722-2736
www.hahnswoodworking.com
Email—sales@
hahnswoodworking.com
Pres.—Scott Hahn
SIC—2431; NAICS—321900;
*Wooden garage, carriage house
& matching entry doors*
Employs—15; Estab.—1984
Sales—$10Mil
20,000 sq ft site, Distrib.—Intl.
Privately owned corporation

**HAMON CORP.**
58 E. Main St., P.O. Box 1500
(08876)
**Phone—(908) 685-4000**
Fax—(908) 333-2152
www.hamonusa.com
Email—info.hcorp@hamonusa.com
CEO—William P. Dillon
Ex. V-P., Gen. Counsel—Robert
Recio
Dir., Acctg. & Fin.—P. Nathan
Rolfe
Dir., Hum. Res.—Margherita C.
Mozer
SIC—3443; 3564; NAICS—
333400; *Corporate headquarters
& heat transfer equipment,
including ESPs, fabric filters, wet
& dry FGD, combustion turbine
heat recovery steam generators
& waste heat boilers, heat
exchangers & fire heaters, gas
coolers & economizers*
Employs—100
Sales—$10Mil–$25Mil
Distrib.—Intl.
Privately owned corporation

**HOME NEWS TRIBUNE**
Div. of Gannett Co., Inc.
92 E. Main St. (08876)
**Phone—(908) 722-8800**
Fax—(732) 565-7207

www.mycentraljersey.com
Email—hntmetro@
mycentraljersey.com
Editor & GM—Paul Grzella
SIC—2711; *Newspaper
publishing*
Employs—60; Estab.—1989
Distrib.—Local
Publicly owned corporation
Parent co.—Gannett Co., Inc.,
McLean, VA
Phone—(703) 854-6000
See Parent Co. Section for full profile.

**†HOUSER WELDING SUPPLY CO., INC.**
12-14 E. Main St. (08876)
Mail addr: P.O. Box 6307,
Bridgewater (08807)
**Phone—(908) 526-7777**
Fax—(908) 526-7779
www.houserweldingsupply.com
Email—houserweldingsupply@
yahoo.com
Pres.—David Houser
Manager—Charles F. Harding
SIC—5084; 5085; *Wholesaler of
welding equipment, supplies &
gases, including industrial,
medical & laboratory gases &
safety equipment*
Employs—5; Estab.—1921
Distrib.—Local
Privately owned sub-S corp.

**INIVEN, A DIV. OF CONOLOG CORP.**
5 Columbia Rd. (08876)
**Phone—(908) 722-8081**
National—(800) 526-3984
Fax—(908) 722-5461
www.iniven.com
Email—iniven@iniven.com
CEO—Micheal Horn
Pres.—Marc Benou
Cont.—Bill Clark
SIC—3669; 3663; 3661; NAICS—
334290; *Teleprotection, telemetry
& multiplexing equipment*
Employs—12; Estab.—1968
16,000 sq ft site, Distrib.—Intl.
Also see: Conolog Corp., same
loc.

**INTERNATIONAL SHEET METAL & PLATE MFG., INC.**
112 Veterans Memorial Dr. E., P.O.
Box 5 (08876)
**Phone—(908) 722-6614**
Fax—(908) 722-4039
www.internationalsheetmetal.com
Pres.—John Novak
V-P.—Andrew Novak
Plt. Mgr.—James Gasden
Off. Mgr.—Michelle Novak
SIC—3444; *Sheet metal
fabrication*
Employs—23; Estab.—1977
Distrib.—National
Privately owned corporation

**J & M AIR, INC.**
189 S. Bridge St. (08876)
**Phone—(908) 707-4040**
National—(800) 437-3670
Fax—(908) 707-0447
www.kitchenhoods.com
Email—jamie.jmair@gmail.com
Pres.—Michael Favreau
V-P.—Jamie Favreau
Prodn. Mgr.—Eric Brescia
SIC—2514; 3444; 3499; 3599;
*Custom galvanized & stainless
steel kitchen items, including
commercial exhaust hoods,
shelving, cabinets, tables &
countertops & installation,
welding & repair services; Brand
name—J&M Air Inc; CaptiveAire*
Employs—12; Estab.—1991
Sales—$1.5Mil
7,800 sq ft site, Distrib.—Regional
Privately owned corporation

**GEOGRAPHICAL**

# Somerville—(cont.)

**NEW ENTRY**

**JESPER OFFICE, LLC**
745 Route 202/206 S., Ste. 300
(08876)
**Phone—(908) 218-4200**
Fax—(908) 218-9984
www.jesperoffice.com
Email—info@jesperoffice.com
Owner—Joern Skarregaard
SIC—2522; *Modular office
furniture*
Employs—20
Sales—$2.5Mil-$5Mil (est)
Distrib.—Intl.
Limited Liability Company

**KEY-PAK MACHINES BY LUCIANO
PACKAGING TECHNOLOGIES, INC**
29 County Line Rd. (08876)
**Phone—(908) 722-3222**
Fax—(908) 722-5005
www.lucianopackaging.com
Email—lluciano@
lucianopackaging.com
Pres., MIS Mgr.—Larry Luciano
Bookkeeper—Mariane Tuma
SIC—3565; 3596; NAICS—
333993; *Custom form, fill & seal
machinery, including packaging
design, integration solutions &
machinery rebuilds & upgrades*
Employs—10; Estab.—1991
8,500 sq ft site, Distrib.—Intl.
Privately owned corporation
AKA: Meadow Fox, LLC

**KOMPAC TECHNOLOGIES, LLC**
7 Commerce St., Ste. 1 (08876)
**Phone—(908) 534-8411**
National—(800) 541-5702
Fax—(908) 534-8412
www.kompactech.com
Email—info@kompactech.com
Pres.—Thomas Hayes
Cust. Serv. Specialist—Leigh
Brown
SIC—3555; NAICS—333293; *UV
& aqueous coating & curing,
automatic dampening & ink
fountain systems for the graphic
arts industry*
Employs—25; Estab.—1980
Sales—$1Mil-$2.5Mil
Distrib.—Intl.
Limited Liability Company

**LEGEND MACHINE & GRINDING,
LLC**
36 S. Adamsville Rd. (08876)
**Phone—(908) 685-1100**
Fax—(908) 685-1144
www.legendmachine.com
Email—sales@legendmachine.com
GM—Eric Butler
SIC—3599; *General machining &
grinding job shop*
Employs—15; Estab.—2003
Sales—$1Mil-$2.5Mil
Distrib.—National
Limited Liability Company

**PEGASUS PRODUCTS, INC.**
19 Readington Rd. (08876)
**Phone—(908) 707-1122**
Fax—(908) 707-1575
www.pegasus-products.com
Email—customerservice@pegasus-
products.com
Pres.—Frank Patel
Fin. & Off. Mgr.—Sandra Wolkwitz
Engr.—Greg Sandow
SIC—3081; 3949; NAICS—
326113; *Swimming pool & tank
liners*
Employs—30; Estab.—1982
Sales—$5Mil
50,000 sq ft site, Distrib.—Intl.
Privately owned corporation
Also see: Cover Co., Inc., The,
same loc.

**PERSONALIZED PARAPHERNALIA**
22 Division St. (08876)
**Phone—(908) 526-0602**
Fax—(908) 231-1480
Email—laasje@aol.com
Owner & Pres.—Laura Wolfe
Manager—Ashley Muentnich
SIC—2395; 2396; *Embroidery &
screen printing*
Employs—3; Estab.—1984
Sales—under $500,000
1,200 sq ft site, Distrib.—Local
Sole ownership

**PHOENIX CHEMICAL, INC.**
60 4th St. (08876)
**Phone—(908) 707-0232**
Fax—(908) 707-0186
www.phoenix-chem.com
Email—jimperante@phoenix-
chem.com
Pres.—John Imperante
Cust. Serv. Rep.—Ann Nicoloro
SIC—2869; 2843; NAICS—
325613; *Cosmetics chemicals,
including emulsifiers &
surfactants; Brand name—
Catemol; Dicopamine; Giovarez;
Neopro; Pecogel; Pecorez;
Pecosil; Pelemol*
Employs—17; Estab.—1982
Sales—$5Mil-$10Mil (est)
Distrib.—Intl.
Privately owned corporation

**PIT BULL TIRE LOCK CORP.**
205 W. Main St., 4th Fl. (08876-
2834)
**Phone—(888) 304-5625**
Fax—(908) 575-8811
www.tirelock.com
Email—pitbull@tirelock.com
Pres.—Cory Marchison
Off. Mgr.—Doreen Gossage
Specialist—Cecibel Jaramillo
SIC—3429; *Tire & wheel locks for
parking enforcement officers &
personal anti-theft security*
Employs—5; Estab.—1997
Sales—under $500,000
Distrib.—Intl.
Limited Liability Company

**POLYCEL STRUCTURAL FOAM, INC.**
68 County Line Rd. (08876)
**Phone—(908) 722-5254**
Fax—(908) 722-7457
www.polycel.com
Email—info@polycel.com
Dir., Sales & Mktg.—Michael
Sheroke
Dir., Opers.—Ayman Sawaged
Qual. Mgr.—Anna Colio
SIC—3089; *Structural foam &
injection molding*
Employs—34; Estab.—2002
150,000 sq ft site, Distrib.—
National
Sole ownership

**PRECISION GRAPHICS, INC.**
21 County Line Rd. (08876)
**Phone—(908) 707-8880**
Fax—(908) 707-8884
www.precisiongraphics.us
Pres.—Marybeth Weissman
Plt. Mgr.—Scott Zimmerman
Hum. Res. Mgr.—Diana Schneider
Qual. Assur. Mgr.—Joseph Racz
SIC—3672; NAICS—334412;
*Printed circuit boards, including
thru-hole, SM & micro BFA
assemblies, design & testing for
commercial, industrial & military-
specification applications*
Employs—48; Estab.—1971
25,000 sq ft site, Distrib.—National
Privately owned corporation

**REBTEX, INC.**
40 Industrial Pkwy. (08876)
**Phone—(908) 722-3549**
Fax—(908) 722-8150

www.rebtex.com
Email—info@rebtex.com
Pres., Plt. Mgr.—Robert Brandell
V-P.—Thomas Brandell
SIC—2262; NAICS—313311;
*Textile finishing*
Employs—50
Distrib.—Intl.
Privately owned corporation

**NEW ENTRY**

†**RIDES4U, INC.**
221 Evans Way, Ste. E (08876)
**Phone—(908) 526-8009**
Fax—(908) 526-4535
www.rides4u.com
Email—bill@rides4u.com
Owner—Len Soled
SIC—5087; 5063; *Distributor of
amusement equipment & LED
lightings*
Employs—5; Estab.—1994
Sales—under $500,000
Distrib.—Intl.
Privately owned corporation

**ROAN PRINTING, INC.**
4 E. Main St. (08876)
**Phone—(908) 526-5990**
Fax—(908) 526-4958
www.mmprinting.com
Email—customerservice@
mmprinting.com
Pres.—Sherman Feuer
V-P.—Carole Feuer
SIC—2752; NAICS—323100;
*Commercial offset printing*
Employs—6; Estab.—1979
3,500 sq ft site, Distrib.—Regional
Privately owned sub-S corp.
AKA: Minuteman Press

†**RYAN HERCO FLOW SOLUTIONS
CORP.**
50 Tannery Rd., Reading Industrial
Ctr., Bldg. 3 (08876)
**Phone—(908) 534-6111**
National—(800) 407-3726
Fax—(908) 534-5287
www.rhfs.com
Email—jmatonis@rhfs.com
Dist. Sales Mgr.—John Matonis
SIC—5162; *Distributor of plastic
products*
Employs—25; Estab.—1980
Sales—$10Mil-$15Mil
25,000 sq ft site, Distrib.—Intl.
Privately owned corporation
Parent co.—Ryan Herco Flow
Solutions Corp., Burbank, CA
Phone—(818) 841-1141
See Parent Co. Section for full profile.

**SAASHR**
Div. of Kronos, Inc.
3040 U.S. Highway 22, Ste. 200
(08876)
**Phone—(908) 722-9952**
Fax—(908) 722-2153
www.saashr.com
Email—info@saashr.com
Dir., Prod. Mgmt.—Chad
Brennaman
Bus. Dev. Mgr.—Alexandra Alvarez
SIC—7372; *Workforce
management SaaS software
development*
Employs—50
Distrib.—National
Publicly owned corporation
Parent co.—Kronos, Inc.,
Chelmsford, MA
Phone—(978) 250-9800
See Parent Co. Section for full profile.

**NEW ENTRY**

**SAVOY EXTRAORDINARY SNACK,
LLC**
35 N. Middaugh St. (08876)
**Phone—(908) 252-9800**
National—(800) 655-5985
Fax—(908) 252-9804
www.savoysnacks.com

Email—info@savoysnacks.com
Owner—Robert Valero
Plt. Mgr.—Ken Winberg
SIC—2064; 2034; *Snack foods,
including seeds, nuts, trail mixes
& dried fruit*
Employs—4; Estab.—1993
Sales—$1Mil-$2.5Mil (est)
12,000 sq ft site, Distrib.—National
Limited Liability Company

**SCIENTIFIC MATERIALS CORP.**
30 Vail Ter., P.O. Box 5298 (08876)
**Phone—(908) 218-0010**
(908) 347-9234
Fax—(908) 203-0339
www.tackymatsusa.com
Email—scientificmc@gmail.com
Pres.—Noris Batra
V-P.—Ashok Batra
V-P.—Rajiv Batra
SIC—2821; 3089; NAICS—
325211; *Contamination control
polymeric reusable & washable
tacky mats for clean rooms &
related clean room-type
conditions for hospitals & the
electronics, pharmaceutical,
food & aerospace industries;
Brand name—KLEAN TACK*
Employs—5; Estab.—1982
Sales—$2.5Mil-$5Mil
Distrib.—Intl.
Privately owned corporation

**SPECIFIED TECHNOLOGIES INC.**
210 Evans Way (08876)
**Phone—(908) 526-8000**
(800) 992-1180
Fax—(908) 526-9623
www.stifirestop.com
Email—sales@stifirestop.com
Pres.—Charbel Tagher
Sr. Ex. V-P., Opers.—Gabe
Dimarino
V-P., Sales & Mktg.—Raymond
Bruno
V-P., Fin.—Phil Pfau
Dir., Sales—Jeff Wexler
IT Mgr.—Bob Stortz
Hum. Res. Mgr.—Diana Rosario
Mktg. Comms. Mgr.—Danielle De
Gerolamo
Accts. Payable Rep.—Frank Kim
SIC—2899; *Firestop products,
including pathways &
intumescent materials; Brand
name—SpecSeal; EZ Path;
PENSIL*
Employs—60; Estab.—1990
Sales—$20Mil-$30Mil
35,000 sq ft site, Distrib.—Intl.
Privately owned corporation

**SYMBOLOGY ENTERPRISES, INC.**
185 Industrial Pkwy., Ste. H
(08876)
**Phone—(908) 725-1699**
National—(888) 484-4424
Fax—(908) 725-2093
www.printer-specials.com
Email—sales@symbology.net
V-P.—Tom McInerney
Dir., Opers. & Hum. Res. Mgr.—
Andrew Dolson
IT Mgr.—Steve Dewar
SIC—3577; 2672; NAICS—
322222; *Bar coding equipment,
including bar code & specialty
label printers, direct thermal &
thermal transfer labels & thermal
transfer ribbons*
Employs—8; Estab.—1991
Distrib.—National
Privately owned corporation

**TAYLOR FORGE STAINLESS, INC.**
22 Readington Rd., P.O. Box 610
(08876)
**Phone—(908) 722-1313**
National—(800) 223-1068
Fax—(908) 722-2943
www.taylorforgestainless.com

## Somerville—(cont.)

Email—j.hernandez@
taylorforgestainless.com
Pres.—Mike Kearney
Pur. Rep.—Josefine Hernandez
SIC—3494; NAICS—332900;
Stainless steel pipe fittings
Employs—100; Estab.—1999
Distrib.—Intl.
Privately owned corporation

## †TAYLOR OIL CO., INC.

77 2nd St., P.O. Box 974 (08876)
Phone—(908) 725-7737
National—(800) 352-4969
Fax—(908) 725-7746
www.tayloroilco.com
Email—fbloom@tayloroilco.com
Pres.—Rick Workman
Sales Mgr.—Frank Bloom
Opers. Mgr.—Eric Hoffman
SIC—5172; Corporate
headquarters & distributor of
petroleum products, including
gasoline, diesel fuel & lubricants
Employs—20; Estab.—1976
Distrib.—Regional
Privately owned corporation

## TEKNI-PLEX, INC.

201 Industrial Pkwy. (08876)
Phone—(908) 722-4800
Fax—(908) 722-4967
www.tekni-plex.com
Email—info@tekni-plex.com
Plt. Mgr.—John Kratins
IT Mgr.—Mike Potoczak
Hum. Res. Mgr.—Maggie Jara
Cust. Serv. Rep.—Lisa Markey
SIC—3086; Foam trays; Brand
name—Tekn-Films; DOLCO
Employs—100; Estab.—1962
Sales—$50Mil-$100Mil
430,000 sq ft site, Distrib.—Intl.
Privately owned corporation
ISO rating—9001:2000
Parent co.—Tekni-Plex, Inc., King
of Prussia, PA
Phone—(484) 690-1520
See Parent Co. Section for full profile.

## TOWNE TECHNOLOGIES, INC.

6-10 Bell Ave., P.O. Box 460
(08876)
Phone—(908) 722-9500
Fax—(908) 722-8394
www.townetech.com
Pres., R & D Mgr.—Hercharan S.
Dhillon
Sales Engr.—Sal LoSardo
SIC—3861; 3479; Chemically-
etched metal parts, photo plates
& masks
Employs—16; Estab.—1993
43,000 sq ft site, Distrib.—Intl.
Privately owned corporation

## TRUCKFORM, INC.

50 James St. (08876)
Phone—(908) 526-5443
Fax—(908) 526-9202
Pres.—Jules Tishler
SIC—3441; NAICS—332312;
Structural steel fabrication
Employs—4; Estab.—2002
Sales—$500,000-$1Mil (est)
Distrib.—Regional
Privately owned corporation

## UNIVERSAL BUSINESS SYSTEMS, INC.

185 Industrial Pkwy., Ste. J
(08876)
Phone—(908) 725-8899
Fax—(908) 725-1341
www.ubsys.com
Email—chris@ubsys.com
Pres.—Christofer Raffo
V-P., Opers.—Ed R. Raffo
Sales Mgr.—Mike Lindstedt

SIC—7372; ERP software for
business, financial, sales force
automation & supply chain
management
Employs—25; Estab.—1969
Distrib.—National
Privately owned sub-S corp.

## WHITEHOUSE MACHINE, LLC

3585 U.S. Highway 22 E. (08876)
Phone—(908) 534-4722
Fax—(908) 534-9662
Email—wmmco@earthlink.net
Pres.—Matthew Kessel
V-P.—Mark Kessel
SIC—3599; General machining
job shop, including CNC milling,
turning, repair work & CAD
drawings
Employs—2; Estab.—1966
4,000 sq ft site, Distrib.—Local
Privately owned sub-S corp.

## ZEUS SCIENTIFIC, INC.

200 Evans Way (08876)
Mail addr: P.O. Box 38, Raritan
(08869)
Phone—(908) 526-3744
National—(800) 286-2111
Fax—(908) 526-2058
www.zeusscientific.com
Email—info@zeusscientific.com
Pres.—Scott J. Tourville
Mktg. Mgr.—Jim Vingara
MIS Mgr.—Julius Torres
Hum. Res. Mgr.—Mary Pollock
Fin. Mgr.—Dan Moll
SIC—2833; NAICS—325411;
Diagnostic reagents & test kits
Employs—75
Distrib.—Intl.
Privately owned corporation

---

# South Amboy

(Middlesex—N.E.)

## ACE MOUNTING CO., INC.

11 Cross Ave. (08879)
Phone—(732) 721-6200
Fax—(732) 721-5005
www.acemount.com
Email—sales@acemount.com
Pres.—Albert Chiang
GM—Cindy Chiang
SIC—3069; Standard & custom-
designed vibration control
products for emergency standby
& prime power generator sets,
marine, yacht, racing boat & ferry
engines, nuclear power plant
equipment & industrial
machinery
Employs—3; Estab.—1986
Sales—under $500,000
12,000 sq ft site, Distrib.—Intl.
Privately owned corporation

## ALL STATE PLASTICS, INC.

237 Raritan St. (08879)
Phone—(732) 721-4024
National—(800) 732-3254
Fax—(732) 727-4182
www.allstateplastics.com
Email—ptfe1@optonline.net
Pres.—John R. Vaccaro
SIC—3083; NAICS—326130;
Fluoropolymer rods & tubes
Employs—35; Estab.—1970
40,000 sq ft site, Distrib.—Intl.
Privately owned sub-S corp.

## ARCHIE'S BOAT TOPS, LLC

1800 Route 35 (08879)
Phone—(732) 721-7566
Fax—(732) 721-7566
Pres.—Stanley Szeszko
V-P.—Tom Szeszko
SIC—2394; NAICS—314912;
Canvas boat tops & products
Employs—2; Estab.—1958
Sales—under $500,000
Distrib.—Local
Privately owned corporation

## CAPITOL PAVERS & RETAINING WALL, INC.

90 Main St., P.O. Box 3249
(08879)
Phone—(732) 727-5460
National—(800) 254-5098
Fax—(732) 727-8714
www.capitolconcrete.com
Email—info@capitolconcrete.com
Pres.—Norman Grossman
Dir., Mktg.—Thomas London
SIC—3272; Interlocking concrete
pavers & retaining walls; Brand
name—DiamondCrete
Employs—60; Estab.—1925
Sales—$5Mil-$10Mil
Distrib.—Regional
Privately owned corporation

## COPYSHOP OFFICE SUPPLY & REPRO CENTER

921 U.S. Highway 9 (08879)
Phone—(732) 721-5700
Fax—(732) 721-9441
www.copyshopdirect.com
Email—copyshopdirect@aol.com
Owner—Scott Restiano, Jr.
SIC—2759; 2752; 3993; NAICS—
323100; Full-service, digital &
large-format printing of signs,
banners, blueprints, business
cards, letterheads, envelopes,
stationery, postcards, brochures,
newsletters, event signage & ad
journals
Employs—3; Estab.—1977
Sales—$500,000-$1Mil
6,000 sq ft site, Distrib.—National
Limited Liability Company

## DUCTS SHEET METAL, LLC

6200 Main St. (08879)
Phone—(732) 727-8781
www.statewideconditioninginc.com
Owner—Mike Bruce
SIC—3444; Sheet metal ductwork
Employs—8; Estab.—1983
Sales—$500,000-$1Mil
8,000 sq ft site, Distrib.—Regional
Privately owned sub-S corp.

## EGGERS SAILS, INC., JOHN

7076 Route 35 (08879)
Phone—(732) 721-4667
Fax—(732) 721-4668
www.johneggers.com
CEO—John Eggers
Pres.—Ines Eggers
SIC—2394; 3546; NAICS—
314912; Sails & riggers
Employs—3; Estab.—1975
Sales—under $500,000
5,000 sq ft site, Distrib.—Local
Privately owned corporation

## METALINE PRODUCTS CO., INC.

101 N. Feltus St. & 241 Raritan St.
(08879)
Phone—(732) 721-1373
National—(877) 696-6267
Fax—(732) 727-0272
www.metalineproducts.com
Email—sales@
metalineproducts.com
Chrm. & CEO—August J. Zilincar
III
Pres.—August J. Zilincar IV
V-P., Prodn.—Mukesh Barbaria
Comp.—Kathy Jasontek
Sales Mgr., Natl.—Amanda
Gavarny
Acct. Mgr., Natl.—Frank Male, Jr.
Prodn. Mgr.—Joseph Kelly
SIC—2542; 3499; 2514; 3993;
Custom metal point-of-purchase
displays, furniture & modular
storage products; Brand name—
Mobos
Employs—35; Estab.—1923
65,000 sq ft site, Distrib.—Intl.
Privately owned sub-S corp.

## MORGAN PRINTING SERVICE, INC.

333 S. Pine Ave. (08879)
Phone—(732) 721-2959
Fax—(732) 721-5610
www.morganprintingnj.com
Email—morganpsi@optonline.net
CEO & GM—Bob Dein
Off. Mgr.—Tracy White
SIC—2759; 2752; NAICS—
323100; Color offset, digital,
instant & wide format printing,
including brochures, postcards,
business cards, letterheads,
envelopes, banners & flyers
Employs—10; Estab.—1982
7,000 sq ft site, Distrib.—National
Privately owned corporation

## R & R PRINTING CO.

107 S. Stevens Ave., P.O. Box
3204 (08879)
Phone—(732) 727-6036
Fax—(732) 727-0048
Email—rrprintingco@optonline.net
Owner—Kenneth Sumski
SIC—2752; 2791; NAICS—
323122; Offset printing,
typesetting & die cutting
Employs—1; Estab.—1968
Sales—under $500,000
Distrib.—Regional
Sole ownership

## RARITAN PRINTING PLUS FLAGS & BANNERS, INC.

109 N. Feltus St. (08879)
Mail addr: 425 Augusta St., South
Amboy (08879)
Phone—(732) 721-2121
National—(888) 283-9902
Fax—(732) 727-7876
www.raritanflag.com
Email—6joanne@raritanflag.com
Pres.—Joanne Corridon
SIC—2399; 3089; 3648; 3444;
Stock & custom U.S. outdoor &
indoor, parade, historic, state,
territory, international, Armed
Forces, religious, civilian service
& firefighter flags, banners &
related accessories, including
flag cases, poles, lighting &
decorations; Brand name—
Annin Flags; Eder Flags;
Flagsource; Valley Forge; Flag
Zone
Employs—2; Estab.—1939
Sales—under $500,000
Distrib.—National
Privately owned corporation

---

# South Bound Brook

(Somerset—N.E.)

## TRI-TECH TOOL & DESIGN CO., INC.

30 Cherry St. (08880)
Phone—(732) 469-5433
Fax—(732) 469-1595
www.tritechtool.com
Email—art@tritechtool.com
Pres.—Art Weber
V-P., Mfg.—Jason Weber
Off. Mgr.—Alexander Kelly
SIC—3089; Plastic injection
molding
Employs—25; Estab.—1980
9,500 sq ft site, Distrib.—National
Privately owned corporation

---

# South Hackensack

(Bergen—N.E.)

## A-1 TABLECLOTH CO.

450 Huyler St., Ste. 102 (07606)
Phone—(201) 727-8987
National—(800) 727-8987
Fax—(201) 727-8988
www.a1tablecloth.com
Email—a1@a1tablecloth.com
Manager—Oren Fox

GEOGRAPHICAL

## South Hackensack— (cont.)

SIC—2392; *Tablecloths, chair covers, skirts, drapes & napkins*
Employs—100; Estab.—1989
Distrib.—Intl.
Privately owned corporation

**ADCOMM, INC.**

89 Leuning St., 1st Fl. (07606)
**Phone—(201) 342-6349**
Fax—(201) 342-3339
www.cciproducts.com
Email—sales@cciproducts.com
Pres.—Allen Cohen
IT Mgr.—Joe Chen
SIC—3651; 3663; NAICS—334310; *Amplifiers for telecommunications*
Employs—100; Estab.—1996
30,000 sq ft site, Distrib.—Regional
Privately owned corporation

**ALAN SCHATZBERG & ASSOC., INC.**

45 Ruta Ct. (07606)
**Phone—(201) 440-8855**
Fax—(201) 440-8856
www.alanschatzberg.com
Email—alan@alanschatzberg.com
Pres., GM—Alan Schatzberg
SIC—2391; 2512; 2519; 5023; NAICS—314121; *Manufacturer & distributor of custom window coverings & upholstered furniture exclusively for interior designers & architects, including motorized shades & draperies, decorative hardware & custom bedding & accessories; Brand name*
Employs—12; Estab.—1997
Sales—over $500,000
7,200 sq ft site, Distrib.—Regional
Privately owned sub-S corp.

**ALPRO, INC.**

50 Romanelli Ave. (07606)
**Phone—(201) 342-4498**
Fax—(201) 342-4503
Email—alliedprocoad@msn.com
Pres.—Girish Desai
SIC—2834; *Pharmaceutical tablet film coatings*
Employs—7; Estab.—2001
10,000 sq ft site, Distrib.—National
Privately owned corporation

**AVIONIX CORP.**

35 Ruta Ct. (07606-1709)
**Phone—(201) 343-1550**
Fax—(201) 343-0499
www.avionixcorp.com
Email—avionix.corp@verizon.net
Pres.—Carmelo Scordo
V-P.—Frank Scordo
Opers. Mgr.—Kyle MacDonald
SIC—3728; 3812; NAICS—334511; *Flight instruments & electromechanical assemblies*
Employs—15; Estab.—1987
Sales—$1Mil-$5Mil
21,000 sq ft site, Distrib.—Intl.
Privately owned corporation
ISO rating—AS9100C, 9001:2008

**BIND-RITE SERVICES, INC.**

16 Horizon Blvd. (07606)
**Phone—(201) 440-5585**
Fax—(201) 440-7973
www.bindrite.net
Email—rickd@bindrite.net
Pres.—Elliot Ward
Cont.—Maria Ward
SIC—2789; NAICS—323121; *Bookbinding*
Employs—125; Estab.—1987
Distrib.—Local
Privately owned corporation

**BRABENDER® INSTRUMENTS, C. W.**

50 E. Wesley St., P.O. Box 2127 (07606)
**Phone—(201) 343-8425**
Fax—(201) 343-0608
www.cwbrabender.com
Email—cwbi@cwbrabender.com
Pres.—Richard F. Thoma
V-P., Sales & Mktg.—Kevin Van Allen
Mktg. Mgr.—Mike DiNatale
SIC—3829; 3559; *Industrial laboratory testing instruments & small-scale production equipment; Brand name—Intelli-Torque PLasti-Corder®; ATR Plasti-Corder®; Lab Station Plasti-Corder®; Prep-Center®; Prep-Mill® Two Roll Mill; Prep-Mixer®; Visco-Corder®; Elatest®; Auto-Grader®*
Employs—30; Estab.—1923
Distrib.—National
Privately owned corporation

**C L N DESIGNS, LLC**

P.O. Box 1822 (07606-0422)
**Phone—(201) 939-2120**
(201) 694-4206
Fax—(201) 939-1949
Email—jparente@clnsigns.com
Ex. V-P.—John Parente
Off. Mgr.—Susi Schwartz
SIC—3993; 2394; 3444; NAICS—314912; *ADA & safety interior & exterior signs, large-format banners, vehicle graphics, custom awnings & canopies, including logos & letters*
Employs—8; Estab.—1982
16,200 sq ft site, Distrib.—National
Limited Liability Company

**CALORIC COLOR CO., INC.**

176 Saddle River Rd., Bldg. A (07606)
**Phone—(973) 471-4748**
Fax—(973) 471-4748
Email—caloriccolorco@gmail.com
GM—June Anton
MIS Mgr.—S. Redfern
Off. Mgr.—Barbara Brown
R & D Mgr.—Vinnie Larrea
SIC—2893; NAICS—325910; *Fluoropolymer striping ink & naphtha dispersed pigments*
Employs—9; Estab.—1965
10,000 sq ft site, Distrib.—Intl.
Privately owned corporation

**CASE MEDICAL, INC.**

19 Empire Blvd. (07606)
**Phone—(201) 313-1999**
National—(888) 227-2273
Fax—(201) 373-9090
www.casemed.com
Email—info@casemed.com
CEO—Marcia A. Frieze
Corp. Secy.—Allan S. Frieze
Dir., Qual. Assur. & Control—Tania Lupu
IT Mgr.—Shashi Borade
R & D Mgr.—Ron Amster
Cust. Serv. Supv.—Natasha Queeley
SIC—3841; 2899; 7372; *Medical sterilization trays & cases & surgical instrument cleaning solutions & instrument tracking software development*
Employs—60; Estab.—1992
Sales—$1Mil-$5Mil
27,000 sq ft site, Distrib.—Intl.
Privately owned corporation

**CLEMENTS INDUSTRIES, INC.**

50 Ruta Ct. (07606)
**Phone—(201) 440-5500**
National—(800) 222-5540
Fax—(201) 440-1455
www.tach-it.com
Email—sales@tach-it.com
Pres.—Alan Clements

V-P.—Steven Clements
Hum. Res. Mgr.—Arlene Peconio
SIC—3565; NAICS—333993; *Manual & semiautomatic twist-tie machines, tape & label dispensers, bag & carton sealers, fasteners & tagging systems for the packaging industry*
Employs—12; Estab.—1963
Sales—$1Mil-$2.5Mil
Distrib.—National
Privately owned corporation

**CRYSTAL WORLD, INC.**

Div. of True World Group, LLC
89 Leuning St., Ste. A-2 (07606)
**Phone—(201) 488-0909**
National—(800) 445-4251
Fax—(201) 488-7447
www.crystalworld.com
Email—specialmarkets@crystalworld.com
Pres.—Toshi Ogawa
CFO—Kikuko Klawitter
V-P., Sales—Nicholas Mulargia
SIC—3231; NAICS—327215; *Crystal figurines & awards; Brand name—Crystal World; Crystal Optics*
Employs—24; Estab.—1983
Sales—$1Mil-$5Mil
14,600 sq ft site, Distrib.—National
Privately owned corporation
Parent co.—True World Group, LLC, Rockleigh, NJ
Phone—(201) 750-0024
See Parent Co. Section for full profile.

**DAZIAN FABRICS, LLC**

18 Central Blvd. (07606)
**Phone—(201) 549-1000**
National—(877) 232-9426
Fax—(201) 549-1055
www.dazian.com
Email—info@dazian.com
Chrm.—Milt Wolfson
Pres.—Jon Weingarten
CFO & COO—Chris Diaz
Dir., Sales—Steven Eisler
Dir., Mktg.—Karen M. Loftus
SIC—2299; 3646; 2759; 2399; *Textiles, fabricated items & LED scenic elements for the film, event, exhibit, retail & hospitality industries, including custom sewing, printing & decor rental services; Brand name—PD Cloth®; Trapeze Plus®; Trapeze® ES*
Employs—40; Estab.—1842
Sales—$10Mil
27,000 sq ft site, Distrib.—Intl.
Limited Liability Company

**ESSENTIAL DENTAL SYSTEMS, INC.**

89 Leuning St., Ste. 2 (07606)
**Phone—(201) 487-9090**
National—(800) 223-5394
Fax—(201) 487-5120
www.edsdental.com
Email—info@edsdental.com
Pres.—Barry Lee Musikant
CFO & COO—Joel Burstein
Ex. V-P.—Allan S. Deutsch
Dir., Opers.—Gary Cofrancesco
Dir., Comm. & Media—Dave Lage
SIC—3843; NAICS—339114; *Dental & endodontic instruments; Brand name—Flexi-Flow; Ti-Core; Flexi-Flange; Flexi-Post; SafeSiders; Endo-Express; Flexi-Overdenture; EZ-Change; Glove N' Care; Scrub'n Glove; EZ-Fill; EZ Fit; EDS Ultrasonic Tips*
Employs—40; Estab.—1981
Sales—$5Mil-$10Mil
15,785 sq ft site, Distrib.—Intl.
Privately owned corporation

**†FASTBOLT CORP.**

200 Louis St. (07606-1714)
**Phone—(201) 440-9100**
National—(888) 800-1392
Fax—(201) 440-9432
www.fastboltcorp.com
Email—info@fastboltcorp.com
Pres.—Albert Zaukas
CFO—John Holowko
V-P., Sales—Glenn Zaukas
V-P., Opers.—Edmund Zaukas
V-P., Bus. Dev.—Andrew Zaukas
SIC—5072; *Corporate headquarters & distributor of fasteners, including screws, nuts & bolts; Brand name—Panduit; Essentra; Avdel; Acument; Pem; Thomas & Betts; 3M; APM Hexseal; EMKA; Oetiker; RAF; Rotor Clip; Unicorp; AVDEL; AVK; Avibank; POP; IForm; Camcar; Disc-Lock; Heyco*
Employs—50; Estab.—1974
Sales—$45Mil
48,000 sq ft site, Distrib.—National
Privately owned sub-S corp.
ISO rating—9001:2000, AS9100C

**FRATELLI BERETTA U.S.A., INC.**

210 Green St. *(07606)*
**Phone—(201) 343-5161**
National—(800) 899-4332
Fax—(201) 343-5102
www.fratelliberettausa.com
Email—info@fratelliberettausa.com
Pres.—Lorenzo Beretta
V-P.—Elsie I. Steinlin
Accts. Rec. Mgr.—Yvonne Llanos
SIC—2013; NAICS—311600; *Corporate headquarters & Italian salami & prepared meat products*
Employs—23; Estab.—1997
33,000 sq ft site, Distrib.—Intl.
Privately owned corporation

**G-WAY MICROWAVE**

38 Leuning St. (07606)
**Phone—(201) 343-6388**
Fax—(201) 343-6390
www.gwaymicrowave.com
Email—margaret_argento@gwaymicrowave.com
Pres.—Greg David
Dir., Fin.—Margaret Argento
SIC—3669; NAICS—334290; *Cellular communication tower components*
Employs—19; Estab.—1997
Distrib.—Intl.
Privately owned corporation
ISO rating—9001:2008

**J & J ENGRAVING**

45 Worth St. (07606)
**Phone—(201) 342-0798**
Fax—(201) 342-4621
Email—jjengravingco@aol.com
Owner—Joseph Polifronio, Jr.
SIC—3479; 2759; 3089; NAICS—323100; *Plastic & metal engraving & screen printing*
Employs—1; Estab.—1997
Sales—under $500,000
1,000 sq ft site, Distrib.—Local
Sole ownership

**J D M WOODWORKING & CABINETRY**

226 Huyler St. (07606)
**Phone—(201) 646-1480**
Fax—(201) 646-1595
www.jdmwoodworking.com
Email—info@jdmwoodworking.com
Owner—John Moumdjian
SIC—2434; NAICS—337110; *Wooden cabinets*
Employs—1; Estab.—1980
Sales—under $500,000
Distrib.—National
Sole ownership

## South Hackensack— (cont.)

**J. JOSEPHSON, INC.**
35 Horizon Blvd. (07606)
**Phone—(201) 440-7000**
Fax—(201) 440-5495
www.jjosephson.com
Email—kvogt@jjosephson.com
Pres.—Mark Goodman
Dir., Sales—Miles Glidden
Dir., Opers.—Jeff Dugan
Dir., Hum. Res.—Kim Vogt
Dir., Fin.—Christina Bosco
Dir., Design—Jessica Reissig
Mktg. Mgr.—Diane Baker
Cust. Serv. Mgr.—Cheryl Vesey
Adjustments Coord.—Jane
  Richardson
SIC—3089; NAICS—322222;
  *Contract wall coverings; Brand
  name—Symphony; Vycon;
  Genon; Bolta; Tower*
Employs—150; Estab.—1965
Distrib.—Intl.
Privately owned corporation

**LA FORGE DE STYLE**
57 Romanelli Ave. (07606)
**Phone—(201) 488-1955**
Fax—(201) 488-1315
www.laforgedestyle.com
Email—nvmw@hotmail.com
Pres.—Patricia Gore
Fin. & MIS Mgr.—Susan Bazalo
Off. Mgr.—Minnette Evans
SIC—3446; NAICS—332323;
  *Ornamental metalwork*
Employs—5; Estab.—1998
Sales—under $500,000
2,800 sq ft site, Distrib.—Local
Privately owned corporation

**LRM PACKAGING, INC.**
41 James St. (07606)
**Phone—(201) 342-2530**
Fax—(201) 342-4351
www.lrmpackaging.com
Email—info@lrmpackaging.com
Pres.—John Natali, Jr.
Consultant—John Natali, Sr.
SIC—2656; NAICS—322215;
  *Food & specialty products
  contract packaging*
Employs—50; Estab.—1988
55,000 sq ft site, Distrib.—Local
Privately owned sub-S corp.

**M H OPTICAL SUPPLIES, INC.**
128 Leuning St. (07606)
**Phone—(201) 489-1110**
National—(800) 445-3090
Fax—(800) 235-3050
www.mhoptical.com
Email—customerservice@
  pelicanoptical.com
Pres.—Mitchell Hirsch
Prodn. Mgr.—Andy Paul
SIC—3827; NAICS—333314;
  *Corporate headquarters &
  optical lenses*
Employs—25; Estab.—1940
Sales—$1Mil-$2.5Mil (est)
Distrib.—National
Privately owned corporation

**MARINE ELECTRIC SYSTEMS, INC.**
80 Wesley St. (07606)
**Phone—(201) 531-8600**
Fax—(201) 531-8606
www.marineelectricsystems.com
Email—sales@
  marineelectricsystems.com
Pres.—H. Epstein
V-P., Sales—Caroline Coniglio

SIC—3823; 3629; NAICS—
  334513; *Electronic measurement
  systems, alarm, monitoring &
  control systems & battery
  chargers*
Employs—20; Estab.—1972
Sales—$5Mil-$10Mil
Distrib.—Intl.
Privately owned sub-S corp.

**MASTERCRAFTS**
152 Louis St. (07606)
**Phone—(201) 641-6555**
Owner—Robert J. Smith
Foreman—Paul Dripchak
SIC—2434; NAICS—337110;
  *Wooden cabinets*
Employs—4; Estab.—1971
Sales—under $500,000
Distrib.—Local
Sole ownership

**NAPOLEON/LYNX**
25 Empire Blvd. (07606)
**Phone—(973) 278-5588**
National—(800) 234-5969
Fax—(973) 742-9832
www.lynx-nsw.com
Email—info@lynx-nsw.com
GM—Max Godoy
SIC—3699; *Overhead door
  openers*
Employs—10; Estab.—1990
Sales—$1Mil-$5Mil
231 sq ft site, Distrib.—Intl.
Publicly owned corporation
Parent co.—Napoleon/Lynx,
  Archbold, OH
  Phone—(419) 445-1010
  See Parent Co. Section for full profile.

**NATUREX INC.**
375 Huyler St. (07606-1532)
**Phone—(201) 440-5000**
Fax—(201) 342-8000
www.naturex.com
Email—naturex.us@naturex.com
CFO—Gaetan Sourceau
V-P., U.S.—Stephane Ducroux
Dir., Sales, Cosmetic & Personal
  Care Ingredients—Natasha
  Gottie
SIC—2844; NAICS—325600;
  *Corporate headquarters &
  natural specialty ingredients,
  including botanical extracts for
  the food & beverage, nutrition,
  health & personal care
  industries; Brand name—
  Svetol®; PowerGrape®; Lifenol®;
  Cyracos®; Cereboost®*
Employs—170; Estab.—1997
Worldwide: 1,200
Sales—$140Mil
175,000 sq ft site, Distrib.—Intl.
Publicly owned corporation

**NEO PRINTING CO., INC.**
24 E. Wesley St. (07606)
**Phone—(201) 489-5050**
Fax—(201) 487-1555
Email—theprintgroup@optonline.net
Pres.—Michael Destefan
SIC—2752; NAICS—323100;
  *Offset printing*
Employs—10
Sales—$1Mil-$2.5Mil (est)
Distrib.—Local
Privately owned corporation
Also see: The Print Group, Inc.,
  same loc.
AKA: Print Group, The

**NJ LABEL**
30 Wesley St., Unit 7 (07606)
**Phone—(201) 833-9200**
National—(800) 325-2235
Fax—(201) 833-4263
www.njlabel.com
Owner—Steven Haedrich
Opers. Mgr.—Janice Schneider
Cust. Serv. Rep.—Sonya Nash

SIC—2754; NAICS—323111;
  *Label printing*
Employs—12; Estab.—1993
17,000 sq ft site, Distrib.—National
Privately owned corporation

**NOFIRE TECHNOLOGIES, INC.**
5 James St. (07606)
**Phone—(201) 818-1616**
Fax—(201) 818-8775
www.nofire.com
Email—nofire@nofire.net
Chrm.—Sam Oolie
Pres., CEO—Sam Gottfried
Off. Mgr.—Helene Rosen
SIC—2899; *Fire retardant
  coatings*
Employs—9; Estab.—1995
10,000 sq ft site, Distrib.—Intl.
Privately owned corporation

**NU PRODUCTS SEASONINGS CO.**
74 Louis Ct. (07606)
**Phone—(201) 440-0065**
National—(800) 836-7692
Fax—(201) 440-0096
www.nuproductsseasoning.com
Email—tim@nu-spice.com
Pres.—Henry Goldstein
Plt. Mgr.—Tim Richards
Hum. Res. & Off. Mgr.—Celia
  Hester
R & D Mgr.—Richard Lingelbach
Mktg. Coord.—Jessica Goldstein
SIC—2099; *Food seasonings*
Employs—48; Estab.—1946
Sales—$11Mil-$25Mil
14,000 sq ft site, Distrib.—National
Privately owned corporation

**PAINTING, INC.**
60 Luening St. (07606)
**Phone—(201) 489-6565**
Fax—(201) 489-5029
CEO & Fin., Hum. Res. & IT
  Mgr.—Lee M. Bronster
Pres.—Wilson Richardson
SIC—3479; 2759; NAICS—
  323100; *Metal painting & screen
  printing*
Employs—14; Estab.—1993
5,000 sq ft site, Distrib.—Regional
Privately owned sub-S corp.

**PHARMACHEM LABORATORIES, INC.**
130 Wesley St. (07606)
Mail addr: 265 Harrison Ave.,
  Kearny (07032)
**Phone—(201) 343-3611**
National—(800) 526-0609
Fax—(201) 343-5807
www.pharmachemlabs.com
Email—sales@
  pharmachemlabs.com
Plt. Mgr.—Mahesh Desai
SIC—2833; NAICS—325411;
  *Vitamins*
Employs—50; Estab.—1995
Sales—$10Mil-$25Mil (est)
Distrib.—Intl.
Privately owned corporation
Parent co.—Pharmachem
  Laboratories, Inc., Kearny, NJ
  Phone—(201) 246-1000
  See Parent Co. Section for full profile.

**PRINT GROUP, INC., THE**
24 E. Wesley St. (07606)
**Phone—(201) 487-4400**
Fax—(201) 487-1555
www.theprintgroupnj.com
Email—theprintgroup@optonline.net
Ptnr.—Martin Bender
Ptnr.—Michael Destefan
SIC—2759; 2752; 3993; NAICS—
  323100; *Digital & offset
  commercial printing &
  promotional items*
Employs—15; Estab.—1981
Distrib.—Regional
Privately owned corporation
Also see: Neo Printing Co., Inc.,
  same loc.

**SALON INTERIORS**
62 Leuning St. (07606)
**Phone—(201) 488-7888**
National—(800) 642-4205
Fax—(201) 488-0058
www.saloninteriors.com
Email—info@saloninteriors.com
Pres.—Walter Siegordner
CFO—Marilyn Murphy
Opers. Mgr.—Barbara Delph
Sr. Designer—Milton Santos
SIC—2511; 2431; *Wooden
  furniture*
Employs—20; Estab.—1979
Sales—$1Mil-$5Mil
30,000 sq ft site, Distrib.—Local
Privately owned corporation

**SCHMIDT MFG. CO., F. P.**
143 Leuning St. (07606)
**Phone—(201) 343-4241**
Fax—(201) 343-0372
Email—fpsmfg@aol.com
Owner & Pres.—Robert Schmidt
Off. Mgr.—Frances Schult
SIC—3451; NAICS—332721;
  *Screw machine products*
Employs—10; Estab.—1947
Sales—$1Mil
20,000 sq ft site, Distrib.—National
Limited Liability Company

**TENSION ENVELOPE CORP.**
Div. of Tension Corporation
19 Wesley St. *(07606)*
**Phone—(201) 487-1880**
Fax—(201) 498-0341
www.tension.com
Email—info@tensionenvelope.com
GM—Toby Reed
Prodn. Mgr.—John Patrick
Plt. Engr.—Walter Winuk
SIC—2677; NAICS—322232;
  *Envelopes*
Employs—175; Estab.—1883
140,000 sq ft site, Distrib.—
  National
Privately owned corporation
Parent co.—Tension Corporation,
  Kansas City, MO
  Phone—(816) 471-3800
  See Parent Co. Section for full profile.

**TERZANO CABINETRY, INC.**
111 Leuning St., Unit G (07606-
  1308)
**Phone—(201) 373-9500**
Fax—(201) 373-9510
www.terzanocabinetry.com
Email—info@terzanocabinetry.com
Owner & Pres.—Joe Terzano
SIC—2434; 2431; 2511; 2599;
  NAICS—337110; *Custom-
  designed handmade cabinetry &
  furniture*
Employs—8; Estab.—1994
Sales—$500,000-$1Mil
16,900 sq ft site, Distrib.—Local
Privately owned sub-S corp.

**TRADE THERMOGRAPHERS, INC.**
65 Worth St. (07606)
**Phone—(201) 489-2060**
Fax—(201) 489-6680
Email—tradethermo@optonline.net
Off. Mgr.—Lisa Margarito
SIC—2759; NAICS—323100;
  *Thermographic, commercial &
  digital printing*
Employs—9
Sales—$500,000-$1Mil
5,000 sq ft site, Distrib.—Local
Sole ownership

**†TRANSAXLE CORP.**
Div. of TransAxle, LLC
540 Huyler St. (07606)
**Phone—(201) 440-1911**
National—(800) 345-1911
Fax—(201) 440-4261
www.transaxle.com
Email—info@transaxle.com
GM—Ralph Guavagno

## South Hackensack—(cont.)

SIC—5013; *Distributor of transmission parts*
Employs—12; Estab.—1985
Sales—$2.5Mil-$5Mil
Distrib.—Intl.
Privately owned corporation
Parent co.—TransAxle, LLC, Cinnaminson, NJ
Phone—(856) 665-4445
See Parent Co. Section for full profile.

### WELTER & KREUTZ PRINTING CO.

51 Worth St., P.O. Box 1834 (07606)
**Phone—(201) 489-9098**
Fax—(201) 489-2125
www.wkprint.com
Email—mail@wkprint.com
Pres.—Robert W. Kreutz
V.-P.—Barry R. Kreutz
SIC—2759; 3993; NAICS—323100; *Commercial printing, promotional materials & electronic templates for wall & table cutouts*
Employs—6; Estab.—1973
7,400 sq ft site, Distrib.—Regional
Privately owned corporation

---

## South Orange

(Essex—N.E.)

### FRP CORP.

15 Hoskier Rd. (07079)
Mail addr: P.O. Box 72, Millburn (07041)
**Phone—(973) 763-5496**
           (973) 985-1425
Fax—(973) 763-6840
www.frpcorp.com
Email—frpcorp@aol.com
Pres.—Alan M. Tarnow
SIC—3089; 3644; *Custom molded fiberglass protection systems for third hot rail with indoor & outdoor switch boxes, including hand lay-up & compression & injection molding & pultrusion*
Employs—11; Estab.—1964
Sales—$1Mil-$2.5Mil
Distrib.—National
Privately owned sub-S corp.

### G & R GRAPHICS, INC.

303 Irvington Ave. (07079)
Mail addr: P.O. Box 7095, West Orange (07052)
**Phone—(973) 313-2200**
Fax—(973) 313-2211
www.grgraphicsinc.com
Email—gnrstamp@aol.com
Pres.—Robert Gomez
V.-P.—Robert Lewis
SIC—3953; 3479; NAICS—339943; *Rubber stamps, embossing seals, signs, nameplates, badges, labels, award plaques & engraving; Brand name—Trodat Daters; Ideal Stampes MMC; Tropar; x-stampers*
Employs—5; Estab.—1970
Sales—under $500,000
5,000 sq ft site, Distrib.—National
Privately owned corporation

### JEFFERSON PROSTHETICS & ORTHOTICS

120 Prospect St. (07079)
**Phone—(973) 762-0780**
Fax—(973) 762-1480
Email—jeffersonprosthetics@yahoo.com
Pres.—Simon Chang

SIC—3842; *Prosthetics & orthotics*
Employs—4; Estab.—1987
Sales—under $500,000
Distrib.—National
Privately owned corporation

### MEMBRANE STRUCTURE SOLUTIONS, INC.

340 N. Wyoming Ave. (07079)
Mail addr: P.O. Box 6170, West Orange (07052-9170)
**Phone—(908) 520-0112**
Fax—(908) 520-0116
www.membranestructuresinc.com
Email—waldemar@goes.com
Pres.—Waldemar Ptaszek
SIC—2394; 2295; NAICS—314912; *Coated fabric, tensile, frame & air supported structures*
Employs—40; Estab.—1998
Sales—$2.5Mil-$5Mil
Distrib.—Regional
Sole ownership

### MYERS GROUP, LLC, THE

74 Blanchard Rd. (07079)
Mail addr: P.O. Box 1162, Maplewood (07040)
**Phone—(973) 761-6414**
Fax—(973) 763-6664
www.newworldleather.com
Email—jmyers@grpusa.com
Owner & Member—Jay H. Myers
SIC—3111; *Leather tanning, converting & brokering*
Employs—8; Estab.—2000
3,880 sq ft site, Distrib.—Intl.
Limited Liability Company

### PROJECT SIGN

282 Irvington Rd. (07079)
**Phone—(973) 763-1959**
www.project-sign.com
Email—la@project-sign.com
Pres., MIS Mgr.—Larry Aufiero
SIC—3993; *Interior & exterior signs*
Employs—3; Estab.—1986
Sales—under $500,000
2,000 sq ft site, Distrib.—National
Privately owned corporation

### VOORHEIS INDUSTRIES, INC.

369 Thornden St. (07079)
Mail addr: P.O. Box 1442, West Caldwell (07007-1442)
**Phone—(973) 227-2446**
Fax—(973) 227-3972
www.voorheis.com
Email—info@voorheis.com
Co-Pres.—Steve Pozner
Co-Pres.—Marc Pozner
GM—Robert Pozner
SIC—3433; NAICS—333414; *Oil heat exchangers, burners, valve trains & weldments; Brand name—Transfilm Heater*
Employs—4; Estab.—1959
Sales—under $500,000
8,000 sq ft site, Distrib.—National
Privately owned corporation

---

## South Plainfield

(Middlesex—N.E.)

### A & A CO., INC.

2700 S. Clinton Ave. (07080)
**Phone—(908) 561-2378**
National—(800) 561-9278
Fax—(908) 561-4201
www.thermalspray.com
Email—info@thermalspray.com
Pres.—R. Stewart Brunhouse, Jr.
V.-P., Opers. & Sales—Richard S. Brunhouse
Acctg. & Off. Mgr.—Maggie Ayoub
Technical Mgr.—Riken Patel

SIC—3479; *Metal, ceramic, cermet & hard face thermal spray & nano thermal spray coatings, including grinding, lapping & machining; Brand name—Microcoat; Ceramipak; Wirewear; Resistwear*
Employs—19; Estab.—1944
22,000 sq ft site, Distrib.—National
Privately owned corporation

### ACCELERATED CNC, LLC

2500 S. Clinton Ave., Ste. A (07080)
**Phone—(908) 561-8875**
Fax—(908) 561-8897
Email—info@acceleratedcnc.com
Pres.—John Kologe
V.-P.—Bill Ehling
SIC—3599; *CNC machining job shop*
Employs—6; Estab.—2005
Sales—$1.9Mil
6,400 sq ft site,
Limited Liability Company

### AIR LIQUIDE AMERICA SPECIALTY GASES, LLC

2330 Hamilton Blvd. (07080)
**Phone—(908) 754-7700**
           (713) 624-8000
National—(888) 570-9141
Fax—(908) 754-7303
www.airliquide.com
Email—info@airliquide.com
Plt. Mgr.—Tim Dall
SIC—2813; NAICS—325120; *Industrial gases*
Employs—13; Estab.—2007
Distrib.—Intl.
Privately owned corporation
Parent co.—Air Liquide America Specialty Gases, LLC, Plumsteadville, PA
Phone—(215) 766-8860
See Parent Co. Section for full profile.

### AKA, INC.

1324 New Market Ave. (07080)
**Phone—(908) 753-8112**
Fax—(908) 668-0902
www.akaincorporated.com
Email—customercare@akaincorporated.com
Pres.—Michael Allocco
Manager—Lynne Yates
SIC—2396; 2395; 3993; 3499; *Screen printing & embroidery, exterior & magnetic signs, vinyl decals, plaques, wide-format posters & banners*
Employs—6; Estab.—1989
Sales—$500,000-$1Mil
Distrib.—Local
Privately owned corporation

### ALL ACTION ARCHITECTURAL METAL & GLASS

146 Sylvania Pl., Ste. G (07080)
**Phone—(732) 738-6655**
Fax—(732) 738-6658
www.allactionglass.com
Email—contactus@allactionglass.com
Owner—John Quinones
SIC—3446; NAICS—332323; *Architectural metalwork*
Employs—20; Estab.—1999
Sales—$6Mil-$10Mil
Distrib.—National
Privately owned corporation

### AMERICAN PANEL TEC

1640 New Market Ave., Bldg. 1-A (07080)
**Phone—(732) 968-0555**
Fax—(732) 968-4777
www.americanpaneltec.com
Email—sales@americanpaneltec.com
Pres.—John Lanzilotta

SIC—3448; NAICS—332311; *Light gage steel building panels & roof trusses*
Employs—40; Estab.—1989
90,000 sq ft site, Distrib.—Regional
Privately owned sub-S corp.
AKA: Marino Building Systems

### AMERIFAST CORP.

104 Sylvania Pl. (07080)
**Phone—(908) 754-8989**
Fax—(908) 668-1959
Email—amerifast@gmail.com
Pres.—Jim Peightel
SIC—3452; NAICS—332722; *Fasteners*
Employs—9; Estab.—1980
Sales—$2Mil-$5Mil
24,000 sq ft site, Distrib.—National
Privately owned corporation

### AMES ADVANCED MATERIAL

Div. of Ferro Corp.
3900 S. Clinton Ave. (07080)
**Phone—(908) 561-1100**
Fax—(908) 668-7896
www.ferro.com
Email—info@ferro.com
Hum. Res. Mgr.—Jennifer Quandt
SIC—3399; *Precious metal powders*
Employs—200; Estab.—2001
Distrib.—Intl.
Publicly owned corporation
ISO rating—9001
Parent co.—Ferro Corp., Mayfield Heights, OH
Phone—(216) 875-5600
See Parent Co. Section for full profile.

### ANGELO'S ICE CO., INC.

100 Sylvania Pl. (07080)
**Phone—(908) 754-4091**
Fax—(908) 754-4091
Pres.—Angelo Del Beni, Jr.
SIC—2097; NAICS—312113; *Ice cube processing*
Employs—1; Estab.—1979
Sales—under $500,000
Distrib.—Local
Privately owned corporation

### API TECHNOLOGIES CORP.

120 Corporate Blvd. (07080)
**Phone—(908) 546-3900**
National—(855) 294-3800
Fax—(908) 546-3901
www.apitech.com
Email—info@apitech.com
Dir., Opers.—Peter Paulson
Bus. Area Mgr.—Henry Gold
Creative Serv. Mgr.—Andrew Dicecco
Sales Specialist—Mike Arnone
SIC—3572; 7372; NAICS—334112; *Remote device administration products for service providers, equipment manufacturers, government & military agencies & corporations to remotely manage, monitor & secure critical voice & data networks*
Employs—20; Estab.—1983
Distrib.—Intl.
Publicly owned corporation
Parent co.—API Technologies Corp., Orlando, FL
Phone—(855) 294-3800
See Parent Co. Section for full profile.

### APPLIED OPTRONICS

Div. of Candela Corp.
111 Corporate Blvd., Bldg. J (07080)
**Phone—(908) 753-6300**
Fax—(908) 753-4041
www.applied-optronics.com
Email—sales@applied-optronics.com
GM—Victor Yantovsky

## South Plainfield— (cont.)

SIC—3674; NAICS—334413;
*Laser diodes*
Employs—15; Estab.—1990
12,000 sq ft site, Distrib.—Intl.
Privately owned corporation
Parent co.—Candela Corp.,
Wayland, MA
Phone—(508) 358-7400
See Parent Co. Section for full profile.

### ARCHCON TECHNOLOGY

5000 Hadley Rd. (07080)
**Phone—(908) 757-8817**
Fax—(908) 769-4288
Email—akumar@multiplexinc.com
V-P., Sales—Arun Kumar
IT Mgr.—Phil Bachmann
IT Mgr.—Tim Bachmann
SIC—3674; NAICS—334413;
*Photonics*
Employs—150; Estab.—1998
226,000 sq ft site, Distrib.—Intl.
Privately owned corporation
ISO rating—9001

### †ARDOM BEARING GROUP

3377 S. Clinton Ave., Unit 15
(07080-1303)
**Phone—(908) 755-3000**
Fax—(908) 755-3010
www.ardombearing.webs.com
Email—ardombearing@hotmail.com
GM—Mark A. Commesso
SIC—5085; *Distributor of
bearings, motors, reducers,
belts, sprockets, chains,
sheaves, lubes, speed
controllers, pump packings,
grease guns, fittings, couplings,
gears & shafts; Brand name—
SKF; MRC; Fafnir; Torrington;
FAG; ZKL; Lincoln; Baldor WEG;
GE; Martin; Belray; Timken Shell;
Crown; Permatex; Parker;
Rexnord; Goodyear; Dixon;
Dodge; FMS; C/R; Browning;
Consolidated; Boston;
SealMaster*
Employs—2; Estab.—1960
Sales—$1Mil-$5Mil
1,500 sq ft site, Distrib.—National
Publicly owned corporation
Parent co.—Ardom Bearing Group,
Lakewood, NJ
Phone—(732) 370-2310
See Parent Co. Section for full profile.

### ARM-R-LITE DOOR MFG. CO., INC.

2700 Hamilton Blvd. (07080)
**Phone—(908) 754-2600**
National—(800) 554-5816
Fax—(908) 754-6522
www.arm-r-lite.com
Email—info@arm-r-lite.com
Pres.—Wilma M. Dourney
V-P.—Shannon McGrady
SIC—3442; 3325; 3231; NAICS—
332321; *Residential &
commercial aluminum, steel,
glass & fiberglass overhead
sectional & garage doors; Brand
name—Electra; Titan; Arm-R-
Therm; Custom Cl; H-16
Insulator; Arm-R-Lon*
Employs—20; Estab.—1958
35,000 sq ft site, Distrib.—Intl.
Privately owned corporation

### ASCENT AROMATICS, INC.

120 Case Dr. (07080)
**Phone—(908) 755-0120**
Fax—(908) 755-0465
www.ascentaromaticsinc.com
Email—sales@
ascentaromaticsinc.com
Pres.—John Pascale
Cust. Serv. Mgr.—Ginny Butrico

SIC—2844; NAICS—325600;
*Fragrance products for use in
toiletries, air freshening
products, perfumes, household
cleaning products & industrial
use*
Employs—16; Estab.—2007
Sales—$500,000-$1Mil
19,000 sq ft site, Distrib.—Intl.
Privately owned corporation

### †ATLANTIC COAST CONTAINER BROKERAGE & SALES, INC.

906 Oak Tree Rd., Ste. P (07080-
5133)
**Phone—(908) 755-2898**
(732) 809-2549
National—(888) 935-1720
Fax—(908) 755-2731
www.accbs.com
Email—lillian@accbs.com
Pres.—Lillian Skov-Nissen
SIC—5088; 5085; *Wholesaler of
new & used ISO cargo & freight
containers*
Employs—3; Estab.—1997
Distrib.—National
Privately owned sub-S corp.
Parent co.—Atlantic Coast
Container Brokerage & Sales,
Inc., Irmo, SC
Phone—(803) 749-6061
See Parent Co. Section for full profile.

### ATLAS WELDERS & FABRICATORS CORP.

2505 S. Clinton Ave. (07080)
**Phone—(908) 561-1144**
Fax—(908) 561-9205
Email—atlas@atlasweld77.com
Pres.—Ronald Eodice
Plt. Mgr.—David Eodice
SIC—3599; *Welding job shop*
Employs—3; Estab.—1977
Distrib.—Regional
Privately owned corporation

### ATOMIC TROPHIES, INC.

201 Shevchenko Ave. (07080)
**Phone—(732) 424-7930**
National—(800) 242-4267
Fax—(732) 424-7931
www.atomictrophy.com
Email—atomic373@aol.com
Pres.—Vijay Sha
Prodn. Mgr.—Raj Rana
SIC—3499; 3479; *Trophy &
plaque assembly, engraving &
corporate awards*
Employs—4; Estab.—1966
Sales—$500,000-$1Mil
15,000 sq ft site, Distrib.—
Regional
Privately owned corporation

### †AZCO STEEL CO.

Div. of Bushwick Metals, LLC
1641 New Market Ave. (07080)
**Phone—(908) 754-8700**
(800) 221-7781
Fax—(908) 754-8728
www.azcosteel.com
Email—dmaslin@
marmonkeystone.com
Pres.—David Maslin
SIC—5051; *Wholesaler of steel*
Employs—30; Estab.—1942
Sales—$350Mil
350,000 sq ft site, Distrib.—
National
Privately owned corporation
AKA: Bushwick Metals
Parent co.—Bushwick Metals,
LLC, Bridgeport, CT
Phone—(203) 576-1800
See Parent Co. Section for full profile.

### †BARCLAY BRAND FERDON

2401 S. Clinton Ave., P.O. Box 341
(07080)
**Phone—(908) 561-2100**
Fax—(908) 561-0302
www.bbfyale.com
Email—salesinfo@bbfyale.com

Dir., Mktg.—Catherine Kenvin
SIC—5084; *Distributor of material
handling & warehouse
equipment, including forklifts,
narrow aisle reach trucks & order
pickers, rough terrain trucks,
scissor lifts & racking systems;
Brand name—Yale; Hoist; JLG;
Genie; Taylor-Dunn; Mariotti;
Sellick*
Employs—50; Estab.—1996
Distrib.—Regional
Privately owned sub-S corp.

### BCS MACHINE & MFG. CORP.

3575 Kennedy Rd. (07080)
**Phone—(908) 561-1656**
Fax—(908) 753-2076
www.supremesilkscreen.com
Email—contactus@
supremesilkscreen.com
Pres.—Sal Capparelli
V-P.—Frank Capparelli, Jr.
Treas.—Cyndi Bolesta
SIC—3599; 2395; 2396; 3993;
*CNC & general machining job
shop, including precision sheet
metal punching & forming, textile
embroidery & screen printing,
vinyl vehicle lettering, banners &
promotional products*
Employs—10; Estab.—1964
Sales—over $500,000
8,200 sq ft site, Distrib.—National
Privately owned corporation
AKA: Supreme Silk Screen &
Embroidery Co.

### BEATRICE HOME FASHIONS, INC.

151 Helen St., P.O. Box 86 (07080)
**Phone—(908) 561-7370**
Fax—(908) 757-9629
Email—bhfashions@aol.com
Pres.—Sam Gindi
SIC—2391; 2392; NAICS—
314121; *Bedspreads &
draperies*
Employs—30; Estab.—1998
Sales—under $500,000
Distrib.—Intl.
Privately owned corporation

### BENCHMARK SCIENTIFIC, INC.

116 Corporate Blvd. (07080)
Mail addr: P.O. Box 709, Edison
(08818)
**Phone—(908) 222-1712**
Fax—(908) 222-1864
www.benchmarkscientific.com
Email—info@
benchmarkscientific.com
Pres.—Walter Demsia
Opers. Mgr.—Irina Fridman
Mktg. Mgr.—Tony Demsia
SIC—3821; *Laboratory equipment
& supplies, including sterilization
& temperature control
equipment, centrifuges, shakers
& autoclaves laboratory
glassware & agarose products*
Employs—10; Estab.—2006
Sales—$1Mil-$2.5Mil (est)
Distrib.—Intl.
Privately owned corporation

### BIOACTIVE RESOURCES, LLC

138 Sylvania Pl. (07080)
**Phone—(908) 561-3114**
Fax—(908) 561-3115
www.bioactiveresources.com
Email—info@
bioactiveresources.com
CEO—Divya Desai
Pres.—Mayur Desai

SIC—2833; 2099; NAICS—
311942; *Custom botanical
powders, extracts, nutritional
ingredients & nutraceuticals for
vitamin, flavor & beverage
manufacturers, snacks, pet food,
cosmetics, functional foods,
sport & energy drinks & weight
loss product manufacturing
companies*
Employs—25; Estab.—2004
Sales—$4Mil
15,000 sq ft site, Distrib.—Intl.
Limited Liability Company

### BRACO MFG. CO. & MAGIC SAFETY PRODUCTS, INC.

4301-B New Brunswick Ave., Ste. 2
(07080)
**Phone—(732) 968-0008**
National—(800) 719-9800
Fax—(732) 752-4914
www.bracomanufacturing.com
Email—info@
bracomanufacturing.com
Ptnr.—Jack Braha
Ptnr.—Elliott Braha
Pres.—Mike Adinolfi
Accts. Rep.—Kewal Patel
SIC—2676; 2842; NAICS—
322291; *Disposable baby
diapers & safety cleaning
products; Brand name—Pure
Sight & Fog-Be-Gone Safety
Products; Diapees Diapers*
Employs—50; Estab.—1985
60,000 sq ft site, Distrib.—Intl.
Privately owned sub-S corp.

### †BRENNTAG SPECIALTIES, INC.

Div. of Brenntag North America,
Inc.
1000 Coolidge St. *(07080)*
**Phone—(908) 561-6100**
(800) 732-0562
Fax—(800) 543-1484
www.brenntagspecialties.com
Email—specialties@brenntag.com
Pres.—Steve Brauer
Ex. V-P.—Ted Hubbard
V-P., Sales—Rich Stewart
Dir., Hum. Res.—Brad Owens
Dir., Reg. Affs.—Frank McGonigle
MIS Mgr.—Bill Webb
Mktg. Svcs. Mgr.—Rick Cathcart
SIC—5198; *Divisional
headquarters & wholesaler of
fine ingredients & raw materials
for the cosmetics,
pharmaceuticals, food &
beverage, ceramics, building
products, plastics, composites,
printing inks & paints & coatings
industries*
Employs—50
Distrib.—Intl.
Privately owned corporation
ISO rating—ISO 9001:2008
Parent co.—Brenntag North
America, Inc., Reading, PA
Phone—(610) 926-6100
See Parent Co. Section for full profile.

### CAMPBELL SOUP SUPPLY CO.

Div. of Campbell Soup Co.
3500 S. Clinton Ave. (07080)
**Phone—(908) 561-1660**
Fax—(908) 561-2421
www.campbellsoup.com
Email—info@campbellsoup.com
Qual. Assur. Mgr.—Anita Solomon
SIC—2087; 2099; NAICS—
311900; *Food flavorings & spices*
Employs—30; Estab.—1960
Sales—$10Mil-$25Mil
Distrib.—Intl.
Publicly owned corporation
Parent co.—Campbell Soup Co.,
Camden, NJ
Phone—(856) 342-4800
See Parent Co. Section for full profile.

GEOGRAPHICAL

## South Plainfield— (cont.)

**CANAM STEEL CORP.**
14 Harmich Rd. *(07080)*
**Phone—(908) 561-3484**
(800) 526-7518
Fax—(908) 561-6772
www.canam-construction.com
Email—carmelina.lentine@
canam.ws
V.-P. & GM, Opers., U.S.—Tim Day
Cont. & Hum. Res. Mgr.—
Carmelina Lentine
Opers. Mgr.—Michael Polesky
SIC—3312; 3441; NAICS—
332312; *Steel decks*
Employs—50; Estab.—2010
200,000 sq ft site, Distrib.—
Regional
Privately owned corporation
Parent co.—Canam Steel Corp.,
Point Of Rocks, MD
Phone—(301) 874-5141
See Parent Co. Section for full profile.

**CAST TECHNOLOGY, INC.**
161 West St. (07080)
**Phone—(908) 753-5155**
Fax—(908) 753-5055
www.castechnology.com
Email—casttech1@comcast.net
Pres.—Kenneth Shilay
Machinist—Nick Talmo
SIC—3519; 5085; *Rebuilt engines
& distributor of bearings,
gaskets, liner & overhaul kits &
chassis parts*
Employs—7; Estab.—1978
Sales—$500,000-$1Mil
Distrib.—National
Privately owned corporation

**CENTURY CONVEYOR SERVICE, INC.**
4301 S. Clinton Ave. (07080)
**Phone—(908) 205-0625**
National—(800) 422-0224
Fax—(908) 205-8740
www.centuryconveyor.com
Email—sales@
centuryconveyor.com
Pres.—Ron Ferrara
V.-P.—J. D. Rush
Serv. & Repair Mgr.—Nick
Tarquinio
SIC—3535; 3537; 3444; 3448;
NAICS—333922; *Conveyors,
material handling equipment,
mezzanines, racks & in-plant
offices; Brand name—Hytrol
Conveyors; Wildeck Mezzanines;
Speed Rack Pallet Racking;
Triboro Shelving*
Employs—28; Estab.—1981
Sales—over $10Mil
15,000 sq ft site, Distrib.—National
Privately owned corporation

**CHATHAM BRASS, LLC**
1253 New Market Ave., Unit D
(07080)
**Phone—(908) 668-0500**
National—(800) 526-7553
Fax—(908) 668-0507
www.chathambrass.com
Email—gene@chathambrass.com
Pres.—Gene Adamusik
SIC—3432; NAICS—332900;
*Showerheads & plumbing
fixtures*
Employs—5; Estab.—1956
10,000 sq ft site, Distrib.—National
Limited Liability Company

**CLASS TOOL CO.**
2500 S. Clinton Ave., P.O. Box 286
(07080)
**Phone—(908) 561-6633**
Owner & Pres.—John Nagy

SIC—3599; *Machining job shop*
Employs—1; Estab.—1970
Sales—$50,000
2,200 sq ft site, Distrib.—Local
Sole ownership

**CLASSIC SIGNS**
3651 S. Clinton (07080)
**Phone—(908) 668-8248**
Fax—(908) 668-8119
Owner—John Mazzeo
SIC—3993; *Neon & vinyl interior &
exterior signs*
Employs—2; Estab.—1981
Sales—under $500,000
Distrib.—Local
Sole ownership

**CNC ASSOCIATES**
101 Kentile Rd. (07080)
**Phone—(718) 416-3853**
Fax—(718) 416-4077
www.cncassociates.com
Email—info@cncassociates.com
Pres.—Nathan Indig
Dispatcher—Carlo Avina
SIC—2434; 2541; NAICS—
337110; *Wooden cabinets &
countertops*
Employs—95; Estab.—1993
Distrib.—Regional
Limited Liability Company

**COLOR TECHNIQUES, INC.**
260 Ryan St. (07080)
**Phone—(908) 412-9292**
Fax—(908) 412-9339
www.color-techniques.com
Pres.—Jennifer Bolitsky
Off. Mgr.—Kelly Snell
SIC—2816; NAICS—325100;
*Cosmetic pigments*
Employs—7; Estab.—1990
Distrib.—Intl.
Privately owned corporation

**COLORFUL STORY BOOKS, INC.**
2 Hollywood Ct. (07080)
**Phone—(908) 561-3333**
National—(800) 526-7547
Fax—(908) 561-3810
www.colorfulstorybooks.com
Email—jackb@
colorfulstorybooks.com
Pres., Estimator—John Blewitt
Bookkeeper—Fran Giordano
SIC—2789; NAICS—323121;
*Bookbinding*
Employs—50; Estab.—1974
35,000 sq ft site, Distrib.—Local
Privately owned corporation

NEW ENTRY
**CONTEMPORARY BRIDE MAGAZINE**
153 Geary Dr. (07080)
**Phone—(908) 756-0123**
Fax—(908) 756-0030
www.contemporarybride.com
Email—sales@
contemporarybride.com
Publisher—Gary Paris
Editor, Travel—Guy Preston
SIC—2721; *Magazine publishing*
Employs—5; Estab.—1995
Sales—under $500,000
Distrib.—Regional
Privately owned corporation
AKA: North East Publishing

**CREATIVE INDUSTRIES**
1409 Astor St., P.O. Box 313
(07080)
**Phone—(908) 561-5600**
Fax—(908) 561-7081
Pres.—Arthur Kopacz
SIC—3089; 3599; *Plastic injection
molds & machining job shop*
Employs—14; Estab.—1970
Distrib.—National
Privately owned corporation

**CULTECH, INC.**
3500 Hatley Rd. (07080)
**Phone—(732) 225-2722**
Fax—(732) 225-4138
www.cultech.com
COO—Olivier Brigaud
Hum. Res. Mgr.—Susan Reeves
Hum. Res. Generalist—Michelle
Ronquillo
SIC—2657; NAICS—322212;
*Folding paperboard boxes;
Brand name—Chanel; L'Oreal;
Victoria Secret; Parlux; Calvin
Klein; Shiseido*
Employs—100; Estab.—1957
62,250 sq ft site, Distrib.—National
Privately owned corporation

**DREAM ON ME INDUSTRIES, INC.**
125 Helen St. (07080)
**Phone—(908) 791-0555**
www.dreamonme.com
Email—info@dreamonme.com
Pres.—Mark Severe
GM—Frank Franko
Manager—Chrissy Vales
SIC—2515; 5021; 5199;
*Manufacturer of baby mattresses
& wholesaler of baby furniture &
accessories, including gifts,
cribs, walkers & strollers*
Employs—40; Estab.—2012
Distrib.—Intl.
Privately owned corporation

**DYNAMIC DECISIONS, INC.**
2709 Hamilton Blvd. (07080)
**Phone—(908) 755-5000**
National—(800) 869-9888
Fax—(908) 755-9428
www.ddicomputer.com
Email—sales@ddicomputer.com
Pres.—Alan Fan
SIC—3571; NAICS—334111;
*Computer systems, including
servers, workstations &
notebooks*
Employs—5; Estab.—1983
Distrib.—Regional
Privately owned corporation

**EDISON FOAM PROCESSING CORP.**
Div. of Leggett & Platt, Inc.
157 Helen St. (07080)
**Phone—(732) 225-2440**
National—(800) 437-6474
Fax—(732) 225-9696
Br. Mgr.—Tom Vera
SIC—2273; NAICS—314110;
*Carpet padding*
Employs—100; Estab.—1991
Distrib.—Regional
Publicly owned corporation
AKA: Leggett & Platt
Parent co.—Leggett & Platt, Inc.,
Carthage, MO
Phone—(417) 358-8131
See Parent Co. Section for full profile.

**ELITE TOOL, INC.**
1640 New Market Ave., P.O. Box
853 (07080)
**Phone—(732) 424-1126**
Fax—(732) 424-1262
www.elitetoolinc.com
Email—elitetool@verizon.net
Owner & Pres.—Stan Kravetsky
SIC—3599; *Precision machining
job shop*
Employs—3; Estab.—1994
Sales—under $500,000
4,000 sq ft site, Distrib.—Local
Privately owned corporation

**ENGO CO.**
128 Case Dr. *(07080)*
**Phone—(908) 754-6600**
Fax—(908) 754-6605
www.engoshelving.com
Email—engo5@comcast.net
Pres., Sales Mgr.—Robert J. Engo
V.-P.—Kevin Feng
Bookkeeper—Terri Farsaris

SIC—2541; 2542; *Store fixtures*
Employs—35; Estab.—1959
Sales—$5.5Mil
60,000 sq ft site, Distrib.—
Regional
Privately owned sub-S corp.

**EVERLASTING VALVE CO.**
108 Somogyi Ct. (07080)
**Phone—(908) 769-0700**
Fax—(908) 769-8697
www.everlastingvalveusa.com
Email—info@
everlastingvalveusa.com
Pres.—Richard G. Base
V.-P., Engrg.—Jim Wilson
Gen. Sales Mgr.—David Jenkins
Sales Coord.—Donald E.
Richardson
SIC—3494; 3491; NAICS—
332911; *Boiler blowdown valves;
Brand name—Everlasting*
Employs—30; Estab.—1906
Sales—$14Mil
30,000 sq ft site, Distrib.—Intl.
Privately owned corporation
ISO rating—9001:2008

**EXACTAL TOOL & DIE LTD., INC.**
3586 Kennedy Rd. (07080)
**Phone—(908) 561-1177**
Pres.—Scott Kaese
SIC—3544; NAICS—333500; *Tool
& die job shop*
Employs—1; Estab.—1968
Sales—under $500,000
Distrib.—Local
Privately owned corporation

**†FEDERAL METALS & ALLOYS**
4216 S. Clinton Ave. (07080)
**Phone—(908) 756-0900**
Fax—(908) 756-9201
www.fedmetal.com
V.-P.—Mark Scoda
Pur. Agt.—Robert Konya
SIC—5093; *Wholesaler of
nonferrous, nickel alloys &
precious metals*
Employs—18; Estab.—1971
Sales—$1Mil-$5Mil
80,000 sq ft site, Distrib.—Local
Privately owned corporation

**FLAVOR DYNAMICS, INC.**
640 Montrose Ave. (07080)
**Phone—(908) 822-8855**
National—(888) 271-8424
Fax—(908) 822-8547
www.flavordynamics.com
Email—customercare@
flavordynamics.com
Pres.—Dolf DeRovira, Sr.
V.-P.—Marilyn DeRovira
Dir., Sales—Colleen Roberts
Plt. Mgr.—Ken Warren
Pur. Mgr.—Kristy Callari
Off. Mgr.—Marybeth Curtis
Qual. Control Mgr.—Dolf
DeRovira, Jr.
SIC—2087; NAICS—311900;
*Flavoring extracts; Brand
name—Jazzy Java; Challenge
Us Dynamic Flavor Profile
Method; Mele Kalikimocha; Chef
Assist; Technosystems;
Jamaican MeCrazy Coffee fl;
Jamaican Me Nuts Coffee fl;
Flavorcoat; Fondations; Tru
Roux; Mole Cannoli*
Employs—25; Estab.—1989
Sales—$5Mil-$7Mil
29,000 sq ft site, Distrib.—Intl.
Privately owned corporation

**FRIERI A MACHINE TOOL CO., INC.**
1112 Belmont Ave. (07080)
**Phone—(908) 753-7555**
Fax—(908) 753-6762
Email—afrierimachine@erols.com
Pres.—Andrew Frieri

## South Plainfield—(cont.)

SIC—3599; *General machining job shop*
Employs—6; Estab.—1974
Sales—$500,000-$1Mil
14,000 sq ft site, Distrib.—Local
Privately owned corporation

## G & W LABORATORIES INC.

111 Coolidge St. *(07080)*
**Phone—(908) 753-2000**
National—(800) 922-1038
Fax—(908) 753-5174
www.gwlabs.com
Email—sales@gwlabs.com
Chrm. & CEO—Ronald Greenblatt
Pres.—Kurt Orlofski
Sr. V-P., Chief Comml. Officer—Aaron Greenblatt
CFO—Glenn Vraniak
Chief Operating Officer—Roberto Darienzo
Chief Scientific Officer—Eric Mittleberg
V-P., Gen. Counsel—Stephen Greene
SIC—2834; NAICS—325412; *Pharmaceuticals; Brand name—*
Employs—350; Estab.—1919
133,500 sq ft site, Distrib.—Intl.
Privately owned corporation

## GALAXY CIRCUITS, INC.

100 Somogyi Ct. (07080)
**Phone—(908) 822-1400**
Fax—(908) 822-0200
Pres.—Navin Patel
SIC—3672; NAICS—334412; *Printed circuit boards*
Employs—10; Estab.—1987
Sales—$1Mil-$2.5Mil (est)
Distrib.—National
Privately owned corporation

## GE HEALTHCARE

900 Durham Ave. (07080)
**Phone—(908) 757-0500**
Fax—(908) 757-7518
www.gehealthcare.com
Email—info@gehealthcare.com
Qual. Control Mgr.—Bob Rogers
Site Leader—Simon Steingart
SIC—2834; NAICS—325412; *Pharmaceuticals*
Employs—17; Estab.—1972
Sales—$10Mil-$25Mil (est)
Distrib.—Regional
Publicly owned corporation
Parent co.—GE Healthcare, Waukesha, WI
Phone—(262) 544-3011
See Parent Co. Section for full profile.

## GLOPAK CORP.

132 Case Dr. (07080)
**Phone—(908) 753-8735**
Fax—(908) 753-8739
www.glopak.com
Email—cmartin@glopak.com
CEO—Cydnee Martin
V-P.—Harold Martin, Jr.
GM—Robert MacDougall
SIC—3081; *Plastic trash liners & sheeting*
Employs—35; Estab.—1966
Sales—$6Mil-$8Mil
80,000 sq ft site, Distrib.—National
Privately owned sub-S corp.

## GODFORCE TACTICAL, INC.

2614-B S. Clinton Ave. (07080)
**Phone—(908) 561-2021**
Fax—(908) 668-7716
Email—info@godforcetactical.com
Pres.—Leland C. Stanford
V-P.—Dawn Klinger

SIC—3484; 3949; NAICS—332994; *Paintball guns*
Employs—2; Estab.—1964
Sales—under $500,000 (est)
Distrib.—Intl.
Also see: Leland Ltd., Inc., same loc.

## GOLDEN WEST PAPER CONVERTING

121 Helen St. (07080)
**Phone—(908) 412-8889**
Fax—(908) 769-8860
www.goldenwestpaper.com
Email—dhooi@goldenwestpaper.com
Pres.—David Hooi
GM—Steve Smith
SIC—2679; NAICS—322200; *Paper converting*
Employs—30; Estab.—1998
Sales—$500,000-$1Mil
Distrib.—Local
Privately owned corporation

NEW ENTRY
## GREETINGTAP, LLC

832 Spicer Ave. (07080)
**Phone—(347) 731-4263**
Fax—(212) 380-1364
www.tapformessage.com
Email—sales@tapformessage.com
Owner—Kadeer Beg
SIC—2771; 3679; NAICS—323110; *Personalizable video greeting cards, stickers & hang tags with embedded NFC chips for the retail industry*
Employs—6; Estab.—2012
Sales—$500,000-$1Mil (est)
Distrib.—Intl.
Limited Liability Company
AKA: Tap For Message

## GULTON, INC.

116 Corporate Blvd., Ste. A (07080)
**Phone—(908) 791-4622**
National—(800) 356-0399
Fax—(908) 791-4627
www.gulton.com
Email—printheads@gulton.com
Pres.—Om Srivastava
V-P., Hum. Res. & IT Mgr.—Tom Michalski
Cust. Serv. Mgr.—Vivianna Alvarez
SIC—3555; NAICS—333293; *Barcode & lottery ticket thermal printing heads*
Employs—20; Estab.—2002
Sales—$500,000-$1Mil
13,000 sq ft site, Distrib.—National
Privately owned sub-S corp.

## HANSSEM CORP.

155 Helen St. (07080)
**Phone—(908) 754-4949**
www.hanssemamerica.com
Email—hsales@hanssemamerica.com
Hum. Res. Mgr.—Joochan Lee
SIC—2434; 2542; *Wooden & laminate kitchen & bathroom cabinets*
Employs—100
Sales—$5Mil-$10Mil (est)
Distrib.—Local
Privately owned corporation

## HARRIS STRUCTURAL STEEL CO., INC.

1640 New Market Ave. (07080)
**Phone—(732) 752-6070**
Fax—(732) 752-1158
Pres.—Thomas Harris, Jr.
V-P., Fin.—Marvin Strauss
GM & Sales Mgr.—Alan Davisson
Hum. Res. Mgr.—Mary Ellen Wilson
Engrg. Mgr.—William Butrico
Compensation Mgr.—Diane Mozdzierz

SIC—3312; *Steel fabrication*
Employs—70; Estab.—1910
210,000 sq ft site, Distrib.—Regional
Privately owned corporation

## HUMMEL CROTON, INC.

10 Harmich Rd. (07080)
**Phone—(908) 754-1800**
Fax—(908) 754-1815
www.hummelcroton.com
Email—sales@hummelcroton.com
Pres.—Bernard F. Schoen, Jr.
Sales Mgr.—Gail Mulligan
Sales Rep.—Eileen Gryszel
SIC—2819; *Industrial chemicals*
Employs—20; Estab.—1913
Sales—$5Mil-$10Mil
Distrib.—Intl.
Sole ownership

## ITRAN PRECISION RUBBER

375 Metuchen Rd., P.O. Box 98 (07080)
**Phone—(908) 754-8100**
Fax—(908) 754-0032
www.itranrubber.com
Email—sales@itran.net
Pres.—Richard Dougherty
V-P., Sales—Ted Lewis
SIC—3069; 3061; NAICS—326291; *Custom molded rubber products*
Employs—30; Estab.—1967
45,000 sq ft site, Distrib.—Regional
Sole ownership
ISO rating—9001:2008

## †J & H BERGE, INC.

4111 S. Clinton Ave. (07080)
**Phone—(908) 561-1234**
Fax—(908) 561-3002
www.jhberge.com
Email—sales@labmart.com
Pres.—Steven N. Krupp
V-P., Sales & Mktg.—Robert Gardner
Mktg. Coord.—Roger Liang
Accountant—Kim Colquhoun
SIC—5049; *Distributor of laboratory supplies & equipment*
Employs—17; Estab.—1850
Sales—$500,000-$1Mil
Distrib.—National
Privately owned corporation

## JERSEY TANK FABRICATORS, INC.

1271 New Market Ave. (07080)
Mail addr: P.O. Box 257, Cream Ridge (08514)
**Phone—(908) 561-2865**
Fax—(908) 561-1427
www.jerseytank.com
Email—sales@jerseytank.com
Pres.—Eric Turinsky
Opers. & Proj. Mgr.—Alan Graziano
Bookkeeper—Stacy Nownes
SIC—3441; NAICS—332312; *Structural metal fabrication*
Employs—30; Estab.—1983
Distrib.—Regional
Privately owned corporation

## †JESCO, INC.

118 Saint Nicholas Ave. (07080)
**Phone—(908) 821-1400**
Fax—(908) 821-1418
www.jesco.us
Founder & Chrm.—Lou Robustelli
Pres.—Jon Robustelli
Sales Mgr.—Anthony Falzarano
Cred. Mgr.—Bonnie Sheridan
SIC—5084; 5082; *Corporate headquarters & distributor of new & used industrial, construction & forestry equipment*
Employs—50; Estab.—1972
Distrib.—Local
Privately owned corporation

## K & A INDUSTRIES, INC.

51 Cragwood Rd., Ste. 204 (07080)
**Phone—(908) 226-7000**
National—(800) 688-9202
Fax—(908) 226-7007
www.kaindustries.com
Email—contact@kaindustries.com
Pres.—George Keelty
V-P., Opers.—Leon Deane
V-P., Fin.—Robert Aitkens
Off. Mgr.—Janet Blaes
Acct. Exec.—Allison Brown
SIC—3089; 7372; 7373; NAICS—541512; *Identification badges, identity management software & physical security systems integration*
Employs—8; Estab.—1991
Distrib.—Intl.
Privately owned sub-S corp.

## †K. S. I. TRADING CORP.

100 Wade Ave., Ste. A (07080)
**Phone—(908) 668-1380**
Fax—(908) 754-4224
www.ksiautoparts.com
Email—wayne@ksiautoparts.com
Owner—Wayne Jan
V-P., Hum. Res.—James White
Dir., IT—Charlie Tuan
SIC—5013; *Corporate headquarters & wholesaler of automotive parts*
Employs—75; Estab.—2001
Distrib.—Local
Privately owned corporation

## KEYSTONE PLASTICS, INC.

3451 S. Clinton Ave. *(07080)*
**Phone—(908) 561-1300**
        (800) 635-5238
Fax—(908) 561-5189
www.kpbrush.com
Email—jackaroe1954@yahoo.com
Pres., CFO—Marvin Naftal
V-P.—Michael Naftal
Cont.—L. Diane Seremi
Sales Mgr.—Jack Moran
SIC—3991; NAICS—339994; *Streetsweeper broom units & broom bristles*
Employs—70; Estab.—1945
62,000 sq ft site, Distrib.—Intl.
Privately owned sub-S corp.

## KOBO PRODUCTS, INC.

3474 S. Clinton Ave. (07080)
**Phone—(908) 757-0033**
Fax—(908) 757-0905
www.koboproducts.com
Email—info@koboproducts.com
Pres.—David Schlossman
Dir., Hum. Res.—Sandi Tortorella
Acct. Mgr.—Maryann Liska
SIC—2819; 2869; *Organic & inorganic cosmetic chemicals*
Employs—90; Estab.—1987
Distrib.—Intl.
Privately owned corporation

## LEHIGH UTILITY ASSOCS., INC.

1300 New Market Ave., P.O. Box 398 (07080)
**Phone—(908) 561-5252**
Fax—(908) 668-7959
Pres.—William A. Butrico
Plt. Mgr.—Frank J. Butrico
Bookkeeper—Jayne Duffy
SIC—3441; NAICS—332312; *Aluminum & steel highway sign structures*
Employs—15; Estab.—1965
Sales—under $500,000
35,000 sq ft site, Distrib.—Regional
Privately owned corporation

## LELAND LTD., INC.

2614 S. Clinton Ave., P.O. Box 466 (07080)
**Phone—(908) 561-2000**
National—(800) 984-9793

GEOGRAPHICAL

## South Plainfield—(cont.)

Fax—(908) 668-7716
www.lelandltd.com
Email—sales@leland.com
Pres., CFO—Leland C. Stanford
Asst. V.-P., Opers.—Dawn Klinger
SIC—3443; *Gas cylinders*
Employs—7; Estab.—1964
10,000 sq ft site, Distrib.—Intl.
Privately owned corporation
Also see: Godforce Tactical, Inc.,
   same loc.

### †LIFTEC, INC.
124 Sylvania Pl. (07080)
**Phone—(908) 769-0034**
National—(800) 872-4924
Fax—(908) 769-5669
www.liftec.com
Email—liftecsales@liftec.com
Pres.—Stephen Panek
CFO—Maria Sylvester
Ex. V.-P.—Tom Sylvester, Jr.
GM—Rick Mattioli
SIC—5084; 5012; *Distributor of
   industrial forklift equipment &
   material handling equipment,
   including pallet jacks, floor care
   equipment & personnel vehicles;
   Brand name—Nissan; Linde;
   Hyundai; Karcher; Flexi;
   Absolute EZ Lift / BRAVI*
Employs—50; Estab.—1976
Sales—$10Mil
28,800 sq ft site, Distrib.—Local
Privately owned sub-S corp.

### LINEAAQUA, LLC
2216 Hamilton Blvd. (07080)
**Phone—(908) 226-1199**
National—(866) 536-0593
Fax—(908) 226-1195
www.lineaaqua.net
Email—info@lineaaqua.net
Pres.—Walter Mitsel
SIC—3432; NAICS—332900;
   *Bathroom fixtures*
Employs—20; Estab.—2001
Sales—$500,000-$1Mil
Distrib.—National
Limited Liability Company

### LONZA, INC.
70 Tyler Pl. (07080)
**Phone—(908) 561-5200**
Fax—(201) 378-5194
www.lonza.com
Email—lonzapc.arch@lonza.com
Mktg. Mgr., Global—Suellen
   Bennett
SIC—2869; 2833; NAICS—
   325411; *Cosmetics ingredients,
   including biotechnological active
   ingredients, rheology modifiers,
   delivery systems, proteins,
   botanicals, preservatives &
   natural actives*
Employs—39; Estab.—1984
Sales—$10Mil-$25Mil
Distrib.—Intl.
Publicly owned corporation
AKA: Lonza Personal Care
Parent co.—Lonza, Inc., Allendale,
   NJ
   Phone—(201) 316-9200
   See Parent Co. Section for full profile.

### M & M INTERNATIONAL
3619 Kennedy Rd., Ste. A (07080)
**Phone—(908) 412-8300**
Fax—(908) 412-8310
www.mmtubing.com
Email—sales@mmtubing.com
Owner—Min Lim
SIC—3317; *Small diameter
   stainless steel tubing for the
   medical, industrial & aerospace
   industries*
Employs—10
Sales—$2.5Mil-$5Mil (est)
Distrib.—Local
Privately owned corporation

### MARDEE CO., INC.
242 Saint Nicholas Ave. (07080)
**Phone—(908) 753-4343**
Fax—(908) 753-2319
www.mardee.com
Email—info@mardee.com
Pres.—Mariano D. Santis
SIC—3652; *DVD & CD replication
   & duplication*
Employs—10; Estab.—1993
Distrib.—National
Privately owned corporation

### MICRODATA INSTRUMENT, INC.
1207 Hogan Dr. (07080)
**Phone—(908) 222-1717**
www.microdatamdi.com
Email—info@microdatamdi.com
GM—George Cai
SIC—3826; NAICS—334516;
   *Laboratory instruments,
   including microinjectors &
   microforges*
Employs—5; Estab.—1997
Sales—$500,000-$1Mil (est)
Distrib.—Local
Privately owned corporation

### MID STATE BINDERY
148 Sylvania Pl. (07080)
**Phone—(908) 755-9388**
Fax—(908) 756-6027
Owner—Steve Stout
SIC—2789; NAICS—323121;
   *Bookbinding*
Employs—2; Estab.—1990
Sales—under $500,000 (est)
Distrib.—Local
Sole ownership

### MMP, INC.
3470 S. Clinton Ave. *(07080)*
**Phone—(908) 561-4435**
Fax—(908) 561-4780
www.mmpinc.com
Email—inquiry@mmpinc.com
Pres.—Michel Mercier
V.-P.—Clotilde Aufaure
Accountant—AnnMarie Mallozzi
SIC—2844; NAICS—325600;
   *Cosmetic ingredients*
Employs—10; Estab.—1983
Sales—$2.5Mil-$5Mil
Distrib.—Intl.
Privately owned corporation

### MRP, LLC
1640 New Market Ave. (07080)
**Phone—(732) 968-6061**
Fax—(732) 968-5675
Pres.—David Floyd
Hum. Res. Mgr.—Mary O'Neill
Hum. Res. Admn.—Judy Smith
SIC—3441; NAICS—332312;
   *Structural steel fabrication*
Employs—30; Estab.—1999
Sales—$5Mil-$10Mil (est)
Distrib.—Local
Limited Liability Company

### MULTIPACKAGING SOLUTIONS
901 Durham Ave. (07080)
**Phone—(908) 757-6000**
Fax—(908) 757-6464
www.multipkg.com
Sr. V.-P., Healthcare Group—
   Shawn Smith
V.-P., Mfg.—Ron Crisafulli
Dir., Mktg.—Steven Linde
Hum. Res. Mgr.—Sharon
   Wojtkiewicz
Administrator—Vicki Nurgoll
SIC—2657; NAICS—322212;
   *Folding paperboard boxes*
Employs—210; Estab.—2005
100,000 sq ft site, Distrib.—
   National
Privately owned corporation

### NEW JERSEY EPOCH TIMES
Div. of Epoch Times International,
   Inc.
50 Cragwood Rd. (07080)
**Phone—(908) 548-8380**
Fax—(732) 907-1029
www.epochtimes.com
Email—nj@epochtimes.com
Sales Mgr.—Doris Yit
Off. Mgr.—Kelly Kwok
SIC—2711; *Chinese language
   newspaper publishing*
Employs—10; Estab.—2001
Sales—under $500,000 (est)
Distrib.—Intl.
Privately owned corporation
Parent co.—Epoch Times
   International, Inc., New York, NY
   Phone—(212) 239-2808
   See Parent Co. Section for full profile.

### OMG ELECTRONIC CHEMICALS, LLC
Div. of OM Group, Inc.
400 Corporate Ct., Ste. A (07080)
**Phone—(908) 222-5800**
National—(800) 536-1959
Fax—(908) 222-5885
www.omgi.com
Email—info@omgi.com
GM—Joseph Simeone
Admn. Supv.—Lucia Dubas
SIC—2899; *Specialty chemicals*
Employs—50
Distrib.—Intl.
Publicly owned corporation
ISO rating—9001
Parent co.—OM Group, Inc.,
   Cleveland, OH
   Phone—(216) 781-0083
   See Parent Co. Section for full profile.

### PETRA SYSTEM
1 Cragwood Rd., Ste. 303 (07080)
**Phone—(908) 462-5200**
Fax—(908) 755-0369
www.petrasystem.com
Email—info@petrasystem.com
Pres.—Steve Rhoades
V.-P., Bus. Dev. & Sales—Mike
   Feeley
V.-P., Prod. Mktg.—Khalid Rustom
V.-P., Hum. Res.—John Warren
Dir., IT—Sanjeev Malhotra
Mktg. Rep.—Michael Levi
SIC—3674; *Utility-grade smart-
   grid interactive solar energy
   collection systems for installation
   on utility poles; Brand name—
   SunWave™*
Employs—70; Estab.—2006
Distrib.—Intl.
Privately owned corporation

### PFINGST & CO., INC.
105 Snyder Rd., P.O. Box 377
   (07080)
**Phone—(908) 561-6400**
Fax—(908) 561-3213
www.pfingstco.com
Email—customerservice@
   pfingstco.com
Pres.—Karl Pfingst
Secy.-Treas.—Richard Pfingst
SIC—3546; 3843; 5099; 5049;
   NAICS—333991; *Manufacturer
   & distributor of precision tools &
   products, including flexible shaft
   machines & accessories, burs,
   silicone polishers & wood
   carving bits & steel instruments
   for jewelry manufacturers,
   dentistry, artists & hobbyists*
Employs—10; Estab.—1905
Sales—$1Mil-$5Mil
15,000 sq ft site, Distrib.—Intl.
Privately owned corporation

### POLYMER DYNAMIX, LLC
238 Saint Nicholas Ave. (07080)
**Phone—(908) 668-0300**
Fax—(908) 791-9991
www.polymerdynamix.com
Pres.—Viggy Mehta
SIC—3087; NAICS—325991;
   *Plastic resin compounding*
Employs—7; Estab.—2005
Sales—$1Mil-$2.5Mil (est)
Distrib.—Intl.
Limited Liability Company

### PRESSCRETE CO., INC., THE
128 Oak Tree Ave. (07080)
**Phone—(908) 757-8600**
Fax—(908) 757-8613
www.presscrete.net
Email—presscrete@aol.com
Pres.—Brian Fox
Off. Mgr.—Jennifer Fox
Site Supv.—Greg Fox
SIC—1389; *Compaction, pressure
   grouting, load testing &
   mudjacking & installation of
   drilled mini, cased & helical
   piles, tiebacks & rock anchors*
Employs—24; Estab.—1943
Sales—$1Mil-$2Mil
Distrib.—Regional
Privately owned corporation

### PROLONG PHARMACEUTICALS
300 Corporate Ct., Ste. B (07080)
**Phone—(908) 444-4660**
Fax—(908) 444-4661
www.prolongpharmaceuticals.com
Email—info@prolongpharma.com
Founder, CEO & Chief Science
   Officer—Abraham Abuchowski
Pres.—Glenn Kazo
V.-P., Clinical—Hemant Misra
V.-P., Quality—Richard Prince
V.-P.—Andrew Burger
SIC—2834; *Biopharmaceuticals
   for the treatment of anemia
   resulting from an oxygen
   deficiency; Brand name—
   Sanguinate™*
Employs—50; Estab.—2009
Sales—$25Mil-$50Mil (est)
24,000 sq ft site,
Privately owned corporation

### PRYSMIAN POWER CABLES & SYSTEMS, LLC
5 Hollywood Ct. (07080)
**Phone—(908) 791-2828**
Fax—(908) 791-0048
www.prysmianusa.com
Email—energy.cables.na@
   prysmian.com
Dir.—Tony Tremonte
SIC—3357; *High voltage &
   submarine cable systems*
Employs—15; Estab.—2000
Sales—$2.5Mil-$5Mil (est)
Distrib.—Local
Limited Liability Company

### PTC THERAPEUTICS, INC.
100 Corporate Ct. (07080)
**Phone—(908) 222-7000**
Fax—(908) 222-7231
www.ptcbio.com
Email—info@ptcbio.com
Co-Founder—Allan Jacobson
CEO—Stuart W. Peltz
Sr. V.-P., Corp. Dev.—Claudia
   Hirawat
Sr. V.-P., Drug Discovery—John
   Babiak
Sr. V.-P., Drug Discovery—Mark E.
   Boulding
SIC—2834; *Biopharmaceutical
   drug candidates in Phase I & II
   clinical trials*
Employs—180; Estab.—2000
Sales—$100Mil-$250Mil (est)
Distrib.—Local
Privately owned corporation

## South Plainfield— (cont.)

**PURACAP PHARMACEUTICAL, LLC**
1001 Durham Ave. (07080)
**Phone—(908) 941-5456**
Fax—(908) 941-5457
www.puracap.com
Email—info@puracap.com
Founder & CEO—Dahai Guo
V.-P., Sales & Mktg., OTC Prods.—
Sean Weeks
Sr. Dir., Brand Mktg. & Strategic
Plng.—Elise Klein
Hum. Res. Mgr.—Gopika Desai
Administrator—Lee Xu
SIC—2834; *Over-the-counter,
prescription brand & prescription
generic pharmaceuticals*
Employs—50; Estab.—2008
Sales—$6Mil-$10Mil
12,000 sq ft site, Distrib.—Intl.
Limited Liability Company

**QUALIS PACKAGING**
550 Hadley Rd. (07080)
**Phone—(908) 753-7300**
Fax—(908) 753-7532
Dir. & Hum. Res. Mgr.—Pamela
Peunaccio
SIC—3089; *Sampling products
flexible plastic packaging, tubes,
theroforms, vials, small bottles &
flow packs for the cosmetics,
fragrance, personal care & OTC
industries*
Employs—70; Estab.—1987
105,000 sq ft site, Distrib.—Intl.
Privately owned corporation

**QUALITY COSMETICS MFG.**
4455 S. Clinton Ave. (07080)
**Phone—(908) 755-9588**
Fax—(908) 755-3298
www.qualitycosmetics.com
Email—info@qualitycosmetics.com
Owner—Richard Persaud
Fin. Mgr.—Anthony Persaud
Cust. Serv. Rep.—Christina
Persaud
SIC—2844; NAICS—325600;
*Cosmetics*
Employs—40; Estab.—1984
33,000 sq ft site, Distrib.—Local
Privately owned corporation

**R & D CIRCUITS**
3601 S. Clinton Ave. (07080-1322)
**Phone—(732) 549-4554**
Fax—(732) 549-1388
www.rdcircuits.com
Email—sales@rdcircuits.com
Pres.—Jim Russell
Sales Mgr.—Tom Bresnan
Engrg. Mgr.—Tom Smith
Engrg. Mgr.—Karen Stillie
SIC—3672; NAICS—334412;
*Company headquarters &
printed circuit boards*
Employs—125; Estab.—1967
Sales—$20Mil
23,000 sq ft site, Distrib.—Intl.
Privately owned corporation
ISO rating—9001:2008

**R TAPE CORPORATION**
6 Ingersoll Rd. (07080-1306)
**Phone—(908) 753-5570**
National—(800) 440-1250
Fax—(908) 753-5014
www.rtape.com
Email—sales@rtape.com
Pres., CEO—Paul Charapata
CFO—Tom Kennedy
Cont.—Tim Riener
Sales Mgr., Inside—Laurie Richard
Hum. Res. Mgr.—Kristy Ninemin
Export Mgr.—Wendy Miller

SIC—2672; 3081; NAICS—
322222; *Corporate headquarters
& application tapes & premasks
for the sign, screen printing &
digital printing markets,
including decorative vinyl films,
overlaminates, print media, paint
masks & related auxiliary graphic
arts products; Brand name—
VinylEfx; Conform; Aplitape;
Eclypse Overlaminates;
ProGrade Paintmask; Pallet
Protek*
Employs—160; Estab.—1982
76,000 sq ft site, Distrib.—Intl.
Privately owned corporation

**RADIANT COMMUNICATIONS CORP.**
5001 Hadley Rd., P.O. Box 867
(07080)
**Phone—(908) 757-7444**
National—(800) 969-3427
Fax—(908) 757-8666
www.rccfiber.com
Email—sales@rccfiber.com
Pres.—Thomas Lewis
Cont. & IT Mgr.—David Mandell
Cust. Serv. Rep.—Kim Barrios
SIC—3679; 3669; NAICS—
334290; *IP media & fiber-optic
communications products,
components & systems for video,
audio, data, SDI, high definition,
telephone, L-band & cable
broadband applications*
Employs—60; Estab.—1985
Distrib.—National
Privately owned corporation

**RADIANT SYSTEMS, INC.**
107 Corporate Blvd., Ste. B
(07080-2482)
**Phone—(908) 668-1080**
Fax—(908) 668-1081
www.radiantinfo.com
Email—vkoduru@radiants.com
Pres.—Venu Myneni
V.-P.—Vinod Koduru
Dir., Hum. Res.—Ajaya Kapoor
Sr. Bus. Dev. Mgr.—Sam Sharma
IT Mgr.—Narsing Konduru
Payroll Mgr.—Chris Chin
Hum. Res. Coord.—Ingrid Tolliver
SIC—7373; NAICS—541512;
*Computer systems integration &
consulting; Brand name—
RADIANT Info*
Employs—365; Estab.—1995
Company-wide: 700
Sales—$50Mil
Distrib.—Intl.
Privately owned corporation
AKA: Radiant Consulting

**RELIANCE GLOBAL SERVICES, INC.**
50 Cragwood Rd., Ste. 100
(07080)
**Phone—(908) 769-1271**
Fax—(908) 769-1272
www.relianceglobal.com
Email—palvai@relianceglobal.com
Pres.—Reddy Palvai
Hum. Res. Mgr.—Vinutha Satish
SIC—7373; NAICS—541512;
*Computer integrated systems for
enterprise resource planning &
data warehousing applications*
Employs—40; Estab.—1998
Sales—$6Mil-$10Mil
Distrib.—Intl.
Privately owned corporation

**†RM METALS**
50 Cragwood Rd. (07080)
**Phone—(908) 222-1500**
Fax—(908) 222-1665
www.rm-metals.com
Email—rmmetals@gmail.com
V.-P.—Snehal 'Sam' Desai

SIC—5051; *Distributor of primary
& secondary stainless steel, coils
& sheets*
Employs—5; Estab.—1986
Distrib.—National
Sole ownership

**ROBALO ENTERPRISES**
104 New Era Dr. (07080)
**Phone—(908) 753-1075**
Fax—(908) 753-3913
www.robaloenterprise.com
Email—al505@aol.com
Owner—Albert Dilello
SIC—3089; 3999; *Contract
packaging & assembly*
Employs—45; Estab.—1984
Distrib.—National
Privately owned corporation

**RONPAK, INC.**
4301 New Brunswick Ave. (07080)
**Phone—(732) 968-8000**
Fax—(732) 968-1357
www.ronpak.com
Email—csevi@ronpak.com
Pres.—Ronald Sedley
COO—David Morris
V.-P., Sales—Chris Sevi
V.-P., Pur.—Robert Fedor
Cont. & Treas.—Bob Bowers
Acctg. & Hum. Res. Mgr.—
Susanne Opacity
Maint. Mgr.—James Spaanstria
SIC—2674; NAICS—322224;
*Corporate headquarters & paper
bags & wraps*
Employs—150; Estab.—1948
200,000 sq ft site, Distrib.—
National
Privately owned sub-S corp.

**†SAFETY-KLEEN SYSTEMS, INC.**
116 Skyline Dr. (07080)
**Phone—(908) 791-9600**
Fax—(908) 791-9620
www.safety-kleen.com
Email—info@safety-kleen.com
Manager—Thomas Colligan
Br. Admn.—Crystal Lane
Sr. Admn.—Shakee Harris
SIC—5084; 5169; *Distributor of
used industrial parts cleaning
equipment & recycled oils &
solvents*
Employs—100; Estab.—1993
Distrib.—Regional
Privately owned corporation
Parent co.—Safety-Kleen
Systems, Inc., Richardson, TX
Phone—(972) 265-2000
See Parent Co. Section for full profile.

**SEIBERT MACHINE & TOOL, INC.**
4405 S. Clinton Ave. (07080)
**Phone—(908) 754-0774**
Fax—(908) 754-0881
www.seibertmachine.com
Email—gseibert@
seibertmachine.com
Pres.—George G. Seibert
SIC—3599; 3544; NAICS—
333500; *General machining &
tool & die job shop*
Employs—3; Estab.—1995
Sales—under $500,000
6,000 sq ft site, Distrib.—Local
Privately owned corporation

**SENSIENT COSMETIC &
PHARMACEUTICAL
TECHNOLOGIES**
Div. of Sensient Technologies
Corp.
107 Wade Ave. (07080)
**Phone—(908) 757-4500**
National—(800) 543-4524
Fax—(908) 757-3170
www.sensient-tech.com
Email—
corporate.communications@
sensient-tech.com
Dir., Opers.—Anthony Toto
Qual. Assur. Mgr.—Lamita Ray

Manager—Kurt Burmeister
Pur. Agt.—Chung Hwong
Sales Rep.—Debbie Keys
SIC—2865; 2869; 2816; NAICS—
325100; *Cosmetic colorants &
specialty ingredients; Brand
name—UNIPURE*
Employs—60; Estab.—1997
Distrib.—Intl.
Publicly owned corporation
Parent co.—Sensient
Technologies Corp., Milwaukee,
WI
Phone—(414) 271-6755
See Parent Co. Section for full profile.

**SOUTH PLAINFIELD OBSERVER**
1110 Hamilton Blvd., Ste. 1-B
(07080)
**Phone—(908) 668-0010**
Fax—(908) 668-8819
www.spobserver.com
Email—spobserver@comcast.net
Pres., Publisher & Editor—Nancy
Grennier
SIC—2791; NAICS—323122;
*Newspaper electronic prepress*
Employs—6; Estab.—1997
Sales—$500,000-$1Mil
Distrib.—Local
Privately owned corporation

**SUPPORT SYSTEMS SPECIALTIES,
INC.**
25 Ridge Rd., P.O. Box 269
(07080)
**Phone—(908) 510-4349**
Fax—(908) 754-1081
www.support-sys.com
Email—josephbelardo@yahoo.com
Owner—Joseph Belardo
Dept. Admn.—Mary Belardo
SIC—3499; *Custom metal
fabrication*
Employs—13; Estab.—1994
Sales—over $2Mil
45,000 sq ft site, Distrib.—
Regional
Sole ownership

**TEVCO ENTERPRISES, INC.**
Div. of Kirker Enterprises, Inc.
110 Pomponio Ave. (07080)
**Phone—(908) 754-7306**
**(973) 754-9000**
Fax—(908) 756-0934
www.tevco.com
Email—sales@tevco.com
CFO—Sharon Muzeni
Plt. Mgr.—Nelson Owen
SIC—2844; NAICS—325600; *Nail
polish; Brand name—Durlin*
Employs—35; Estab.—1957
Distrib.—Intl.
Privately owned corporation
Parent co.—Kirker Enterprises,
Inc., Paterson, NJ
Phone—(973) 754-9000
See Parent Co. Section for full profile.

**TOYO INK AMERICA**
4301 New Brunswick Ave., Ste. A
(07080)
**Phone—(732) 752-5660**
National—(888) 855-0033
Fax—(732) 752-5944
www.toyoink.com
Plt. Mgr.—Karel Choteborsky
Off. Mgr.—Daizey Oqendo
Lab Mgr.—Jay Bosco
SIC—2893; NAICS—325910;
*Flexographic & rotogravure inks*
Employs—15; Estab.—1997
Distrib.—National
Privately owned corporation
Parent co.—Toyo Ink America,
Moorpark, CA
Phone—(805) 378-0033
See Parent Co. Section for full profile.

**TUMI, INC. (H Q)**
1001 Durham Ave. (07080)
**Phone—(908) 756-4400**
National—(800) 322-8864

GEOGRAPHICAL

## South Plainfield— (cont.)

Fax—(908) 756-5878
www.tumi.com
Email—info@tumi.com
Pres., CEO—Jerome Griffith
CFO—Mike Mardy
V.-P., IT—Jim Walsh
V.-P., Hum. Res.—Sharon Margulies
Cont.—Kaho Tong
SIC—3161; 3172; 3199; NAICS—316991; *Corporate headquarters; luggage & travel & business lifestyle accessories*
Employs—150; Estab.—1975
Sales—$10Mil-$25Mil
Distrib.—Intl.

### †UER METALS, INC.

235 Saint Nicholas Ave., P.O. Box 407 (07080)
**Phone—(908) 561-5800**
National—(800) 242-5966
Fax—(908) 561-1429
www.uermetals.com
Email—dfarley@uermetals.com
Off. Admn.—Marge Reedy
Sales Rep.—Ginny Kramer
SIC—5051; *Steel service center*
Employs—25; Estab.—1962
Distrib.—Regional
Privately owned corporation

### VALID USA, INC.

800 Montrose Ave. (07080)
**Phone—(908) 668-0999**
www.validusa.com
Email—info@validusa.com
V.-P.—Mike Mutrie
SIC—3089; *Plastic credit cards*
Employs—200; Estab.—1984
65,000 sq ft site, Distrib.—Intl.
Publicly owned corporation
Parent co.—Valid USA, Inc., Lisle, IL
Phone—(630) 852-5600
See Parent Co. Section for full profile.

### VAN NICK PALLET, INC.

104 Snyder Rd. (07080)
**Phone—(908) 753-1800**
Fax—(908) 753-1850
Email—jenduca2@aol.com
Pres.—Robert Ducalo
SIC—2448; NAICS—321920; *Wooden pallets*
Employs—15; Estab.—1999
Sales—over $1Mil
Distrib.—Local
Privately owned corporation

### VANGUARD RESEARCH INDUSTRIES

239 Saint Nicholas Ave. (07080)
**Phone—(908) 753-2770**
Fax—(908) 753-6540
www.vanguardholdings.com
Email—pcosta@vanguardholdings.com
Chrm.—Harry Sica
Pres.—Peter Costa
V.-P.—Nick Stanford
Prod. Mgr.—Horace Thompson
Pur. Agt.—Bonnie Robertson
SIC—3471; NAICS—332813; *Metal electroplating*
Employs—24; Estab.—1972
Sales—$10Mil-$12.5Mil
35,000 sq ft site, Distrib.—National
Privately owned corporation
ISO rating—9000

### VENTION MEDICAL

6 Century Rd. (07080)
**Phone—(908) 561-0717**
Fax—(908) 561-7314
www.vention.com
Email—info@medtech-grp.com
Pres.—Dan Croteau

SIC—3089; 3841; *Injection molded medical devices*
Employs—140; Estab.—1979
Sales—$25Mil
50,000 sq ft site, Distrib.—Intl.
Privately owned corporation

### VISUAL ARCHITECTURAL DESIGNS, INC.

15 Harmich Rd. (07080)
**Phone—(908) 754-3000**
Fax—(908) 755-7794
www.va-designs.com
Email—sarac@va-designs.com
Pres.—Sara Chrysanthopoulos
Proj. Mgr.—Frank Nieves
SIC—2431; 2434; 2541; NAICS—337110; *Architectural millwork, store fixtures & cabinets*
Employs—20; Estab.—1991
58,000 sq ft site, Distrib.—Regional
Privately owned corporation

### WAINER FINEST COMMUNICATIONS, INC.

4041-G Hadley Rd., Ste. 101 (07080)
**Phone—(908) 769-1160**
Fax—(908) 769-1171
www.wholefoodsmagazine.com
Pres.—Howard Wainer
Cont.—James Ciuffreda
SIC—2721; *Trade magazine publishing*
Employs—12; Estab.—1984
Sales—$500,000-$1Mil
Distrib.—National
Privately owned corporation

### WARE INDUSTRIES, INC.

400 Metuchen Rd. (07080)
**Phone—(908) 757-9000**
National—(800) 627-4661
Fax—(908) 753-8786
www.marinoware.com
Email—sales@marinoware.com
Vice Chairwoman—Ottavia McLaughlin
Pres.—Chip Gardner
CFO—Lori Hagedorn
Cont.—Kimberly Hampton
Dir., Acctg. & Fin.—Carol Cimusz
Dir., Hum. Res.—Linda Peccoralo
Dir., Corp. Matls. & Inventory—Brian McCulligh
Dir., Credit—Jane Donnellon
SIC—3499; *Corporate headquarters & steel framing products*
Employs—350; Estab.—1993
Distrib.—National
Privately owned corporation
DBA: Marinoware

---

## South River

### (Middlesex—N.E.)

### †ABINGTON RELDAN METALS, LLC

396-402 Whitehead Ave. (08882)
**Phone—(732) 238-8550**
National—(800) 764-9222
Fax—(732) 238-8555
www.armetals.com
Email—sales@armetals.com
GM—Kathleen Whitaker
Sales Admn.—Gloria Santiago
SIC—5093; *Wholesaler of precious metal scrap*
Employs—9
Distrib.—Intl.
Limited Liability Company
Parent co.—Abington Reldan Metals, LLC, Fairless Hills, PA
Phone—(267) 316-2000
See Parent Co. Section for full profile.

### AHLE CO., INC., J. M.

Div. of MORO Corp.
190 William St., Ste. 2-D (08882)
**Phone—(732) 238-1700**
Fax—(732) 238-9663
www.jmahle.com

Email—jahle@jmahle.com
Pres.—John Ahle
V.-P.—Ron Perlman
Opers. Mgr.—Doug Ahle
SIC—3449; 5039; *Rebar fabrication & distributor of construction materials, including expansion joints, sealants, waterstops & wire mesh*
Employs—29; Estab.—1980
Distrib.—Regional
Privately owned corporation
Parent co.—MORO Corp., Wayne, PA
Phone—(484) 367-0300
See Parent Co. Section for full profile.

### ALLTITE GASKET CO. INC.

323 William St. *(08882)*
**Phone—(732) 254-2154**
Fax—(732) 254-7150
www.alltitegasket.com
Email—sales@alltitegasket.com
Pres.—Ronald A. Dreger
V.-P.—John H. Graney
SIC—3053; NAICS—339991; *Industrial metal, metal clad & composition sheet gaskets for heat exchangers, compressors, condensers, pumps, valves & general industrial applications*
Employs—9; Estab.—1968
Sales—$750,000-$1Mil
5,000 sq ft site, Distrib.—Intl.
Privately owned corporation

### CIFELLI & SONS, INC.

38 Obert St., P.O. Box 538 (08882)
**Phone—(732) 238-0090**
Fax—(732) 238-0093
Pres.—Anthony J. Cifelli
Bookkeeper—Carol Kelly
SIC—2013; NAICS—311600; *Italian sausage*
Employs—15; Estab.—1974
Sales—$1Mil-$2.5Mil
Distrib.—Local
Privately owned corporation
AKA: Cifelli & Sons Italian Sausage

### CTI MOTOR DRIVES, INC.

105 Jackson St. (08882)
**Phone—(732) 613-8390**
Fax—(732) 613-8394
www.ctimotordrives.com
Email—ctimotordrives@hotmail.com
Pres.—John Micheli
V.-P.—Mike Beck
SIC—3625; NAICS—334412; *Electronic control systems for the medical & commercial industries*
Employs—18; Estab.—2000
Sales—$1Mil-$2.5Mil
6,000 sq ft site, Distrib.—National
Privately owned sub-S corp.

### DA-GREEN ELECTRONICS, INC.

37 Main St., P.O. Box 486 (08882)
**Phone—(732) 254-2735**
National—(800) 343-2677
Fax—(732) 254-9172
www.dgecorp.com
Email—info@dgecorp.com
Pres.—Barry Greenberg
V.-P.—Marc Gable
Cont.—Alan B. Kane
SIC—3678; NAICS—334417; *Electronic, electrical & military connectors*
Employs—33; Estab.—1973
Sales—$2.5Mil-$5Mil
37,000 sq ft site, Distrib.—Intl.
Privately owned corporation

### ENVIROCHEM, INC.

425 Whitehead Ave. (08882)
**Phone—(732) 238-6700**
National—(800) 526-6042
Fax—(732) 238-5590
www.envirochem-usa.com
Email—sales@envirochem-usa.com
Pres.—Deborah Gildersleeve
V.-P.—Sidney Fleisher

SIC—2842; NAICS—325612; *Institutional detergents*
Employs—50; Estab.—1975
Sales—$11Mil-$25Mil
100,000 sq ft site, Distrib.—Intl.
Privately owned corporation
Also see: Mfrs. Aid, Inc., same loc.

### MAPEI CORP.

Off White Head Ave., P.O. Box 105 (08882)
**Phone—(732) 254-8001**
National—(888) 876-2734
Fax—(732) 254-9103
www.mapei.com
Email—sales@mapei.com
Unit Mgr.—Lou Genzlinger
SIC—3255; 2899; 2891; NAICS—327124; *Mortar, grout & adhesives*
Employs—25; Estab.—1955
Distrib.—Intl.
Privately owned corporation
AKA: MAPEI New Jersey
Parent co.—MAPEI Corp., Deerfield Beach, FL
Phone—(954) 246-8888
See Parent Co. Section for full profile.

### MFRS. AID, INC.

425 Whitehead Ave. (08882)
**Phone—(732) 613-6555**
Fax—(732) 238-5590
www.envirochem-usa.com
Email—info@envirochem-usa.com
Pres.—Deborah Gildersleeve
V.-P.—Sidney Fleisher
SIC—3089; *Contract packaging*
Employs—10; Estab.—1975
100,000 sq ft site, Distrib.—National
Privately owned corporation
Also see: Envirochem, Inc., same loc.

### MILLWOOD, INC.

7 Brick Plant Rd., Ste. C (08882)
**Phone—(732) 967-8818**
Fax—(732) 967-8839
www.millwoodinc.com
Email—info@millwoodinc.com
Plt. Mgr.—Paul Eichmann
SIC—2448; *Wooden pallets*
Employs—70
Sales—$5Mil-$10Mil (est)
Distrib.—Intl.
Privately owned corporation
Parent co.—Millwood, Inc., Vienna, OH
Phone—(330) 393-4400
See Parent Co. Section for full profile.

### P K M PANEL SYSTEMS CORP.

43 Ferry St., P.O. Box 272 (08882)
**Phone—(732) 238-6760**
Fax—(732) 238-4095
Email—pkmpanelsystems@comcast.net
Pres.—Wallace Toto
Manager—Mike Ehlig
SIC—3613; NAICS—335313; *Control panels*
Employs—15; Estab.—1971
8,000 sq ft site, Distrib.—Intl.
Privately owned corporation

### PARK ROOFING & SHEET METAL CO., INC.

427 Whitehead Ave., Ste. 1 (08882)
**Phone—(732) 257-4570**
Fax—(732) 257-4714
Email—garypark@aol.com
Pres.—Craig Meltzer
Bookkeeper—Maggie Korona
SIC—3444; *Sheet metal fabrication & metal roofing*
Employs—5; Estab.—1957
Sales—$3.4Mil
11,000 sq ft site, Distrib.—Regional
Privately owned corporation

## South River—(cont.)

**ROBERT TECHNOLOGIES, INC.**
37 Main St. (08882)
**Phone—(732) 254-6389**
Fax—(732) 254-1493
www.roberttechinc.com
Email—emichels@
  roberttechinc.com
Pres.—Barry Greenberg
SIC—3643; *Electrical connectors
  for military, industrial &
  commercial markets, including
  mil-spec & quick-release solder,
  crimp & subminiature connectors*
Employs—30

**SLIKER MACHINE WERKES, LLC**
2 Maple St., P.O. Box 53 (08882)
**Phone—(732) 238-0331**
Fax—(732) 238-8359
www.slikermachine.com
Email—info@slikermachine.com
Pres.—Barbara Sliker
SIC—3599; *Precision machining
  job shop*
Employs—2; Estab.—1965
Sales—under $500,000
Distrib.—Local
Limited Liability Company

**SOUTH RIVER IRON WORKS, LLC**
132 William St. (08882)
**Phone—(732) 257-1347**
Fax—(732) 257-1432
Owner—Robert Peterson
Plt. Mgr.—Ronnie Peterson
SIC—3441; NAICS—332312;
  *Structural steel fabrication*
Employs—2; Estab.—1972
Sales—under $500,000 (est)
Distrib.—Local
Privately owned corporation

**SPORTSTAR**
19 Thomas St. (08882)
**Phone—(732) 254-9214**
Fax—(732) 432-0306
GM—Mike Shannon
Off. Mgr.—Tom Ozio
SIC—3949; NAICS—339920;
  *Sports uniforms*
Employs—4; Estab.—1996
Sales—$500,000-$1Mil
Distrib.—National
Privately owned corporation

**†STRAUSS DISCOUNT AUTO**
7-C Brick Plant Rd. (08882)
**Phone—(732) 390-9000**
Fax—(732) 651-3114
www.straussauto.com
Email—customerservice@
  straussauto.com
Pres., COO—Joe Catalano
Dir., Fin.—Paul Dawson
Benefits, Hum. Res. & Payroll
  Mgr.—Joanne Heppel
SIC—5013; *Company
  headquarters & distributor of
  automotive parts*
Employs—150
Privately owned corporation

**T D T SCREEN DESIGN & PRINTING,
INC.**
79 Whitehead Ave. (08882)
**Phone—(732) 777-1377**
National—(800) 838-3343
Fax—(732) 777-1707
Email—tdtedge@verizon.net
Pres.—Geoffrey Di Agostino
Off. Mgr.—Chris Worrell
Graphic Designer—Sean Urie
SIC—2396; *Textile screen printing*
Employs—5; Estab.—1995
Sales—$500,000-$1Mil
5,000 sq ft site, Distrib.—Local
Privately owned corporation

**WESTWOOD PRODUCTS, INC.**
330 William St., P.O. Box 610
  (08882)
**Phone—(732) 651-7700**
National—(800) 442-1630
Fax—(732) 651-7798
www.westwoodproducts.com
Email—email@
  westwoodproducts.com
Pres.—Pat DiNicola
SIC—3822; NAICS—334512; *Oil
  burner igniters & filters,
  combustion analyzers, burner
  motor couplings & heating oil
  additives*
Employs—35; Estab.—1965
Sales—$1Mil-$5Mil
24,000 sq ft site, Distrib.—National
Privately owned corporation

---

## Southampton
### (Burlington—S.E.)

**ACME/LINGO FLAGPOLES**
1865 Route 206 (08088)
**Phone—(609) 801-1897**
National—(800) 260-1897
Fax—(609) 801-1900
www.acmelingo.com
Email—info@acmelingo.com
Pres.—Jeff Lingo
SIC—3446; 3499; NAICS—
  332323; *Tubular metal products,
  custom tapered poles, lightning
  masts & antenna products*
Employs—9; Estab.—1897
18,000 sq ft site, Distrib.—Intl.
Privately owned corporation

**ALPHA 1 STUDIO, INC.**
3 Linda Ln., Ste. A (08088)
**Phone—(609) 859-2200**
National—(800) 794-2116
Fax—(609) 859-4010
www.signstudio.com
Pres., Fin., MIS & R & D Mgr.—
  Ray E. Witthauer
Art Dir.—Patti Ellis
Prodn. Mgr., Art—Lorelei Fisher
SIC—3993; 2541; *Interior &
  exterior sandblasted, wooden,
  aluminum & plastic donor
  recognition signs & displays*
Employs—6; Estab.—1979
6,100 sq ft site, Distrib.—Regional
Privately owned corporation

**J K A SPECIALTIES MFG., INC.**
157 Eayrestown Rd. (08088)
**Phone—(609) 859-2090**
National—(800) 227-3749
Fax—(609) 859-3896
www.jkaspecialties.com
Email—studio157@aol.com
Pres.—James Young
V-P.—Kimberly Brown
SIC—3965; 3993; NAICS—
  339993; *Printing of buttons, vinyl
  decals, posters, key chains,
  banners & coffee cups for
  advertising*
Employs—5; Estab.—1971
Sales—under $500,000
5,000 sq ft site, Distrib.—Intl.
Privately owned sub-S corp.

**K G M PRECISION CORP.**
1875 Route 206 (08088)
**Phone—(609) 801-0210**
Fax—(609) 801-0211
Pres.—Kenneth Mikle
V-P.—Devon Mikle
SIC—3599; *Precision machining
  job shop*
Employs—8; Estab.—1987
Distrib.—Intl.
Privately owned corporation

**L & L REDI-MIX, INC.**
1939 U.S. Highway 206 (08088)
**Phone—(800) 696-2271**
Fax—(609) 859-1209

www.llredimix.com
Email—jeff@llredimix.com
Pres.—Lin Gerber
V-P., Sales—Lin Gerber, Jr.
V-P., Opers.—Lee Gerber
V-P., Qual. Assur.—Larry Gerber
Sales Mgr.—Bob Howard
Opers. Mgr.—Jeff Lucas
SIC—3273; NAICS—327320;
  *Ready-mixed concrete*
Employs—85; Estab.—1969
Distrib.—Local
Privately owned corporation

**MEDFORD SPEED & MACHINE, INC.**
132 Red Lion Rd. (08088)
**Phone—(609) 801-0808**
Fax—(609) 801-0894
Email—medfordspeed@
  comcast.net
Pres.—Gerald Glenn
SIC—3519; *Rebuilt engines*
Employs—2; Estab.—1965
Sales—under $500,000
Distrib.—Local
Privately owned corporation

**SAU-SEA SWIMMING POOL PAINTS
AND REPAIR PRODUCTS**
1855 Route 206 (08088)
Mail addr: P.O. Box 1419, Medford
  (08055)
**Phone—(609) 859-8500**
National—(800) 472-8732
Fax—(609) 859-1500
www.sausea.com
Email—sales@sausea.com
COO—Ed Hunter
Sales Mgr.—Steve Hunter
Off. Admn.—Merrill B. Hunter
SIC—2851; 2821; NAICS—
  325510; *Eco-friendly rubber-
  base, epoxy & vinyl swimming
  pool paints & repair products for
  concrete, plaster, gunite &
  fiberglass pools*
Employs—9; Estab.—1978
Distrib.—National

**TRIPLE D ENTERPRISES, INC.**
135 Eayrestown Rd. (08088)
**Phone—(609) 859-3000**
Fax—(609) 859-4408
www.triplednj.com
Email—sales@triplednj.com
Pres.—Douglas Melegari
Off. Mgr.—Ira Feingold
Whse. Mgr.—Dennis Lang
SIC—3531; *Underground
  horizontal directional drilling,
  compaction boring & vibratory
  plowing tools; Brand name—
  ROTO-BORE*
Employs—8; Estab.—1993
Sales—$1Mil-$2.5Mil
Distrib.—Intl.
Privately owned corporation

**WOOD PRODUCTS, INC.**
34 Allentown Rd. (08088)
**Phone—(609) 859-0303**
Pres.—John W. Taylor
SIC—2431; NAICS—321900;
  *Circular & straight run stairs &
  railings*
Employs—5; Estab.—1975
Sales—$500,000-$1Mil
3,500 sq ft site, Distrib.—Local
Privately owned corporation

---

## Sparta
### (Sussex—N.W.)

**ADVANCED PRECISION, INC.**
15 Wilson Dr. (07871)
**Phone—(973) 383-2296**
National—(800) 788-9473
Fax—(973) 383-3774
www.advancedprecision.com
Email—info@
  advancedprecision.com
Pres.—Vincent Fay

SIC—3599; *Precision wire EDM
  job shop*
Employs—20; Estab.—1987
12,500 sq ft site, Distrib.—National
Privately owned corporation
ISO rating—9001:2000

**ALLIED METRICS SEALS &
FASTENERS, INC.**
2 Wilson Dr., Ste. 4 (07871)
**Phone—(973) 383-2487**
National—(800) 633-0125
Fax—(973) 383-3329
www.alliedmetrics.com
Email—sales@alliedmetrics.com
Owner—William Westerman, Sr.
GM & Opers. Mgr.—William
  Westerman, Jr.
Sales Mgr.—Sean Sosa
SIC—3053; *Hydraulic, pneumatic
  & oil seals, o-rings & gaskets*
Employs—9; Estab.—1996
Sales—$1Mil-$2.5Mil
5,000 sq ft site, Distrib.—Intl.
Privately owned corporation

**ALTAFLO**
23 Wilson Dr. *(07871)*
**Phone—(973) 300-3344**
Fax—(973) 300-3345
www.altaflo.com
Email—sales@altaflo.com
Ptnr.—Mary Hyde
Ptnr.—Donald C. Bishop
SIC—3082; 3084; NAICS—
  326121; *Fluoropolymer &
  fluoroplastic extrusions, tubing,
  profiles & pipe, including PTFE,
  FEP, EFEP, PFA, LP PFA, MFA,
  THV & PVDF; Brand name—
  ALTAFLUOR®; ALTAPAK;
  ALTATHERM; ALTAPURE;
  ALTAMED*
Employs—16; Estab.—2006
20,000 sq ft site, Distrib.—Intl.
Limited Liability Company

**APPLIED MICROPHONE
TECHNOLOGY**
104 Hillside Rd. (07871)
**Phone—(973) 729-9333**
www.appliedmicrophone.com
Email—info@
  appliedmicrophone.com
Owner—Martin Taglione
Shop Mgr.—John Fire
SIC—3651; NAICS—334310;
  *Microphones*
Employs—5; Estab.—1994
Sales—$1Mil-$2.5Mil (est)
Distrib.—Intl.
Sole ownership
AKA: AMT

**B & W PLASTICS, INC.**
20 Wilson Dr. (07871)
**Phone—(973) 383-0020**
Fax—(973) 579-5304
Email—sales@bwplastics.com
Pres., CEO, R & D Mgr.—William
  Post
Ex. V-P., Secy-Treas.—Louise Post
V-P., Prod. Dev. & Sales—Christina
  Post Gibbins
V-P. & Plt. Mgr.—William R. Post
SIC—3089; 3081; *Thermoformed
  clamshells, blister skins, point-
  of-purchase displays &
  electronic handling trays*
Employs—5; Estab.—1984
10,000 sq ft site, Distrib.—National
Privately owned corporation

**CAMAC INDUSTRIES**
18 Gail Ct. (07871)
**Phone—(973) 300-5575**
Fax—(973) 300-5576
www.camacindustries.com
Email—camacind@yahoo.com
Pres., Opers. Mgr.—Peter
  Gennaro
V-P.—Cynthia Gennaro

GEOGRAPHICAL

## Sparta—(cont.)

SIC—3561; 3544; 3443; NAICS—333911; *Industrial pumps, filters & heat exchangers; Brand name—Clydesdale Pumps & Filters*
Employs—5; Estab.—1947
Sales—$500,000-$1Mil
12,900 sq ft site, Distrib.—Intl.
Privately owned corporation

**CDS CORP.**
27 Wilson Dr., Unit C (07871)
**Phone—(973) 300-0090**
Fax—(973) 300-0061
www.cdsindexers.com
Email—info@cdsindexers.com
Pres.—Robert Zarbua
Prod. Mgr.—Steven Gough
Cust. Serv. Rep.—Lisa Gie
Cust. Serv. Rep.—Randi Dierling
SIC—3545; *Cam actuated mechanical drives & machinery for the conversion & control of motion*
Employs—25; Estab.—1999
Distrib.—Intl.
Privately owned corporation

**CHROMATIC CONTROL, LLC (H Q)**
63 Fox Trail Rd., P.O. Box 374 (07871)
**Phone—(973) 944-3996**
Fax—(973) 581-8468
www.dyn-optics.com
Email—info@dyn-optics.com
Owner—Steve Rotyliano
SIC—3823; *Company headquarters; electro-optical instrumentation for thermal sensing, thin film deposition & industrial coating applications (mfg. subcontracted)*
Employs—2; Estab.—1970
Sales—under $500,000
Distrib.—Intl.
Limited Liability Company
AKA: Dyn-Optics

**CLINICAL IMAGE RETRIEVAL, INC.**
376 Lafayette Rd., Ste. 202, P.O. Box 899 (07871)
**Phone—(973) 862-6151**
National—(888) 482-2362
Fax—(973) 862-6451
www.gaitrite.com
Email—sales@gaitrite.com
Pres.—Douglas D. Haas
Off. Mgr.—Karen Toepper
SIC—3845; NAICS—334500; *Electromedical portable walkway systems for temporospatial gait analysis; Brand name—GAITRite Electronic Walkway System*
Employs—4; Estab.—2004
Sales—$1Mil-$2.5Mil
Distrib.—Intl.
Limited Liability Company

**COLLINEAR MACHINE & DESIGN**
7 Wilson Dr. (07871)
**Phone—(973) 300-1681**
Fax—(973) 300-1683
www.collinearmachine.com
Pres.—John Sangiacomo
Off. Mgr.—Michelle Smith
SIC—3599; *Precision machining job shop*
Employs—9; Estab.—1989
Sales—$500,000-$1Mil
Distrib.—Local
Privately owned corporation

**†CORMAN BAG CO.**
7 Evergreen Pl. (07871)
**Phone—(973) 729-2816**
Fax—(973) 729-2818
www.cormanbag.com
Email—john@cormanbag.com
Manager—John Walsh

SIC—5113; *Wholesaler of packaging materials*
Employs—1; Estab.—1910
Sales—$1Mil-$2.5Mil
144 sq ft site, Distrib.—Intl.
Privately owned corporation
Parent co.—Corman Bag Co., Chelsea, MA
Phone—(617) 884-7600
See Parent Co. Section for full profile.

**ELITE PRINTING SERVICE**
30 Heritage Dr. (07871)
**Phone—(973) 729-0366**
Fax—(973) 729-4267
Email—eliteps@ptd.net
Pres.—Alison Marcinkowski
SIC—2759; NAICS—323100; *Commercial printing*
Employs—1; Estab.—1994
Sales—under $500,000
Distrib.—Local
Privately owned sub-S corp.

**ERNST CO., INC., JOHN C.**
21 Gail Ct. (07871)
**Phone—(973) 940-1600**
National—(888) 943-5000
Fax—(973) 940-1620
www.johnernst.com
Email—sales@johnernst.com
Pres.—James Wolfe
SIC—3829; 3823; 3824; 3494; NAICS—334513; *Sight glasses & windows, liquid level gages, flowmeters, ejectors, eductors & sight flow, gage glass & tank indicators*
Employs—17; Estab.—1969
Sales—over $7Mil
15,000 sq ft site, Distrib.—National
Privately owned corporation

**FLAMINGO BAY, INC.**
10 Seneca Trl. (07871)
**Phone—(973) 726-8882**
Fax—(973) 726-8883
Pres.—Bruce Miller
V-P.—Mary Ann Duhan
SIC—2899; 2819; *Fragrance & detergent compounds*
Employs—20; Estab.—1990
Sales—$5Mil-$10Mil (est)
Distrib.—National

**GRINNELL CONCRETE PAVINGSTONES, INC.**
482 Houses Corner Rd. (07871)
**Phone—(973) 383-9300**
Fax—(973) 383-3224
www.grinnellpavers.com
Email—info@grinnellpavers.com
Ptnr.—Jason N. Cofrancesco
Ptnr.—Jarrod C. Cofrancesco
SIC—3272; *Interlocking concrete paving stones, segmental retaining wall systems & wet-cast concrete products*
Employs—45; Estab.—1986
Distrib.—Regional
Privately owned corporation

**H & H SHEET METAL & MACHINING**
30 White Lake Rd. (07871)
**Phone—(973) 383-6880**
Fax—(973) 383-6650
www.hhsmm.com
Email—sales@hhsmm.com
Pres., CFO—Frederick Hohmann
Manager—Eric Hohmann
Manager—David Hohmann
Bookkeeper—Marie Hohmann
SIC—3444; 3599; *Sheet metal fabrication & CNC machining of chassis, panels, brackets & machined parts*
Employs—9; Estab.—1977
Sales—$2Mil-$5Mil
15,000 sq ft site, Distrib.—National
Privately owned sub-S corp.

**H I D SYSTEMS, INC.**
27 Brookfield Dr. (07871)
Mail addr: 520 Lafayette Rd., Rte. 15, Sparta (07871)
**Phone—(973) 383-8535**
Fax—(973) 383-1606
www.hid.com
Email—sales@hiduv.com
Co-Pres.—Shannon Lesko
Co-Pres.—Bill Lesko
SIC—3677; 3679; NAICS—334416; *Transformers & electric power supplies*
Employs—10; Estab.—1981
Sales—$3Mil
5,000 sq ft site, Distrib.—Intl.
Privately owned corporation
AKA: HID Ultraviolet

**ISTEC CORP.**
5 Park Lake Rd., Ste. 6 (07871)
**Phone—(973) 383-9888**
Fax—(973) 383-9088
www.istec-corp.com
Email—sales@istec-corp.com
Pres.—Peter Johnson
V-P.—Ed Bullis
Opers. Mgr.—Justin Johnson
SIC—3823; 3822; NAICS—334513; *Flow & BTU meters & control valves*
Employs—6; Estab.—1978
Sales—$1Mil-$2.5Mil
10,000 sq ft site, Distrib.—Intl.
Privately owned corporation

**KAISTAR RESEARCH & DEVELOPMENT, LLC**
15 Wilson Dr. (07871)
**Phone—(973) 362-1487**
Fax—(973) 362-0120
www.krdnet.com
Email—contact@krdnet.com
Pres.—Igor Kapchenko
Secy., Bookkeeper—Tanya Kapchenko
SIC—3356; 3671; NAICS—331491; *High-purity metals, special purpose & custom alloys, electron beam refined & evaporation materials & sputtering targets*
Employs—4; Estab.—2002
Sales—$500,000-$1Mil
Distrib.—Intl.
Limited Liability Company

**†LANTEK CORPORATION**
29 Brookfield Dr. (07871)
**Phone—(973) 579-8100**
Fax—(973) 579-8180
www.lantekcorp.com
Email—lantek@lantekcorp.com
GM—Frank Cervino
Opers. Mgr.—Rachel Zidek
SIC—5065; *Distributor of electronic components, connectors & military hardware, including hard-to-find & obsolete components*
Employs—20; Estab.—1994
8,300 sq ft site, Distrib.—Intl.
Privately owned corporation

**LEHIGH CEMENT CO.**
Div. of Lehigh Hanson, Inc.
66 Demarest Rd. (07871)
**Phone—(973) 579-2111**
National—(800) 962-5490
Fax—(973) 579-5069
www.lehighcement.com
Email—info@lehighcement.com
Plt. Mgr.—William Trautz
Cust. Serv. Rep.—Maryann Nied
Cust. Serv. Rep.—Susan Allen
SIC—2891; NAICS—325520; *Colored cement*
Employs—11; Estab.—1980
Sales—$1Mil-$2.5Mil
Distrib.—Regional
Publicly owned corporation

Parent co.—Lehigh Hanson, Inc., Irving, TX
Phone—(972) 653-5500
See Parent Co. Section for full profile.

**MEGA MEDIA CONCEPTS LTD.**
286 Houses Corner Rd. (07871)
**Phone—(973) 919-5661**
www.megamediaconcepts.com
Email—amy@megamediaconcepts.com
Pres.—Amy Pink
SIC—2759; 3993; *Large-format digital eco-friendly printing of signs, wall coverings & murals, vehicle wraps, vinyl banners & fleet graphics*
Employs—4; Estab.—2000
Sales—$500,000-$1Mil
Distrib.—National
Privately owned corporation

**NATURE'S CHOICE CORP.**
482 Houses Corner Rd. (07871)
**Phone—(201) 333-5244**
National—(800) 637-4140
Fax—(201) 333-4135
Pres.—Nicholas Vene
Ex. V-P.—Matthew Vastano
Hum. Res. Mgr.—Carmen Rodriguez
SIC—2875; NAICS—325314; *Corporate headquarters & soil, compost & mulch*
Employs—3; Estab.—1991
AKA: Reliable Wood Products

**OTHER ORTHODONTIC CO., INC.**
22 Gail Ct. (07871)
**Phone—(973) 383-8662**
Fax—(973) 383-3269
Email—toocinc@aol.com
Pres.—Jon Bergeron
V-P.—Paul Jovanovski
Off. Mgr.—Nancy Nish
SIC—2434; 2431; 5047; NAICS—337110; *Manufacturer of commercial wooden cabinets & wholesaler of orthodontic equipment & supplies*
Employs—9; Estab.—1984
Sales—$1Mil-$2.5Mil
Distrib.—National
Privately owned corporation
AKA: TOOC

**PIONEER PACKAGING**
31 Wilson Dr. (07871)
**Phone—(973) 300-9300**
Fax—(973) 330-0903
www.pioneerink.com
Email—info@pioneerink.com
Pres.—Mark J. Clark
Ex. V-P., Sales—Deb Taylor
GM—Ryan Brown
Off. Admn.—Linda Attanasio
SIC—2675; 2657; 2759; *Printed & die-cut consumer product packaging, including folding chipboard boxes & four-color graphics for cosmetics, pharmaceuticals & foods*
Employs—30; Estab.—2001
Sales—$10Mil-$25Mil (est)
Distrib.—Local
Privately owned corporation

**PRINTING CENTER, INC., THE**
1 White Lake Rd. (07871)
**Phone—(973) 383-6362**
Fax—(973) 383-2672
www.printcenter.com
Email—info@printcenter.com
Pres., CEO—Vincent Perrella, Jr.
Secy-Treas.—Jeanne Perrella
GM—Donna Fern
Sales Mgr.—Bill Locascio
IT Mgr.—Mike Whitaker
Off. Mgr.—Nancy Rushton
Press Mgr.—Steve Guido

## Sparta—(cont.)

**SIC**—2752; 2791; **NAICS**—323122; *Offset printing & typesetting*
Employs—25; Estab.—1976
Distrib.—Local
Privately owned corporation

**RB & A, INC.**
350 Sparta Ave., Bldg. C (07871)
**Phone—(973) 726-0830**
National—(800) 232-9899
Fax—(973) 726-8243
www.rbainc.com
Email—rod@rbainc.com
Pres.—Rod Borden
SIC—2542; 2541; 3496; *Point-of-purchase, acrylic, stock & wood displays & wire racks*
Employs—5; Estab.—1976
Sales—$500,000-$1Mil
Distrib.—Intl.
Privately owned corporation
AKA: Rod Borden & Assocs., Inc.

**RISE-N-SHINE, LLC (H Q)**
17 Woodport Rd., Ste. 1-E (07871)
**Phone—(973) 729-4141**
Fax—(973) 726-6002
www.wakeupontime.com
Founder—Cathy Beggan
SIC—2833; *Company headquarters; energy supplement tablets (mfg. subcontracted); Brand name—Wake Up On Time; Stay Up All Day; Wrinkle Remedy; Go Away Gray; Light'n Up; Stress Free; Don't Forget; Sleep Tight All Night*
Employs—10; Estab.—2006
Sales—$500,000-$1Mil
Distrib.—Intl.
Limited Liability Company

**RUBBER FAB TECHNOLOGIES GROUP**
26 Brookfield Dr. (07871)
**Phone—(973) 579-2959**
National—(866) 442-2959
Fax—(973) 579-7275
www.rubberfab.com
Email—sales@rubberfab.com
CEO—Robert Dupont, Sr.
Pres.—Patrick Parisi
CFO—Daniel Licini
Dir., Mktg. & Network Admn.—Laura Schnitzer
Sales Mgr., Natl.—Ed Kotarski
Hum. Res., IT & Off. Mgr.—Joyce Sobczak
Matls. Mgr.—Kellie Cash
SIC—3053; 3069; NAICS—339991; *Elastomeric hygienic seals, sanitary gaskets, hose assemblies & valve, pump & filler machine components for the biopharmaceutical, food, dairy, beverage, industrial & semiconductor industries*
Employs—50; Estab.—1994
30,000 sq ft site, Distrib.—Intl.
Privately owned corporation

**SPARTA SAND & GRAVEL CO., INC.**
33 Demarest Rd. (07871)
**Phone—(973) 383-4651**
Fax—(973) 383-0229
Email—spartaredimix@spartaredimix.com
Opers. Mgr.—Steve Russalesi
Opers. Mgr.—Dale Meyer
SIC—3273; NAICS—327320; *Ready-mixed concrete*
Employs—20; Estab.—1957
Distrib.—Regional
Privately owned corporation
AKA: Sparta Ready Mix

**TECHFLEX**
29 Brookfield Dr. (07871)
**Phone—(973) 300-9242**
National—(800) 323-5140

Fax—(973) 300-9409
www.techflex.com
Email—sbotarelli@techflex.com
Pres.—William Dermody III
Sales Mgr.—Steve Botarelli
SIC—3679; *Advanced braided sleeving & related products for the wire, cable & hose management & protection in deep space exploration satellites, undersea robotics, high-end race cars & computer network cable management installations*
Employs—25; Estab.—1969
60,000 sq ft site, Distrib.—Intl.
Privately owned corporation

**THERMOPLASTIC BIOLOGIC, LLC**
26 Brookfield Dr., Ste. C (07871-3212)
**Phone—(973) 383-2834**
Fax—(973) 383-4161
www.thermoplasticbiologic.com
Email—sales@tblplastics.com
Mng. Ptnr.—P. Robert DuPont, Jr.
SIC—3089; *Medical & scientific plastic tubing; Brand name—Pharm-A-Line; DairyFlow; Fluor-A-Pure; Envir-A-line*
Employs—15; Estab.—2003
Sales—$1Mil-$2.5Mil
10,000 sq ft site, Distrib.—Intl.
Limited Liability Company
AKA: TBL Plastics

**TRACE ENVIRONMENTAL SYSTEMS, INC.**
7 Park Lake Rd., Unit 9 (07871)
**Phone—(973) 383-3550**
www.traceenv.com
Email—support@traceenv.com
CEO—David Martin
Off. Mgr.—Pat Bayerlein
SIC—3826; NAICS—334516; *Air quality monitors*
Employs—5; Estab.—1996
Sales—under $500,000
Distrib.—Regional
Privately owned corporation

**TRI-COR FLEXIBLE PACKAGING, INC.**
27 Brookfield Dr. (07871)
**Phone—(973) 940-1500**
National—(866) 940-2247
Fax—(973) 940-1501
www.tri-cor.com
Email—sales@tri-cor.com
Pres.—Guy Zimmermann
SIC—2673; 3081; *Flexible polyethylene packaging for the food, dairy, beverage, bakery, produce, automotive, rubber, foam, furniture, masonry, chemical, ice, frozen food & medical industries, including films, printed pallet covers & stand-up pouches*
Employs—20; Estab.—2001
Distrib.—National
Sole ownership

---

## Spotswood

(Middlesex—N.E.)

**B P MACHINE CO., INC.**
10 American Way (08884)
**Phone—(732) 251-0449**
Fax—(732) 251-0440
www.bpmachineco.com
Email—bpmach@aol.com
Pres.—Robert Provell
SIC—3599; *General machining job shop*
Employs—5; Estab.—1988
Sales—under $500,000
Distrib.—Intl.
Privately owned sub-S corp.

**COBRA POWER SYSTEMS, INC.**
8 America Way (08884)
**Phone—(908) 486-1800**
National—(877) 214-1002
Fax—(908) 486-1826
www.cobra-power.com
Email—info@cobra-power.com
Owner—Doug Cohen
SIC—3621; NAICS—335312; *Power generation trailer, control & network packages*
Employs—7; Estab.—2003
Sales—$1Mil-$2.5Mil (est)
Distrib.—National
Privately owned corporation

**DISPLAY SALES, INC.**
P.O. Box 115 (08884)
**Phone—(732) 251-8981**
Fax—(732) 251-2318
Email—richnasca@aol.com
Pres.—Richard Nasca
SIC—2541; 3496; *Display fixtures & wire racks*
Employs—20; Estab.—1975
Distrib.—National
Privately owned sub-S corp.

**DIVERSIFIED MACHINE, LLC**
15 American Way, Ste. 12 (08884)
**Phone—(732) 251-6600**
Fax—(732) 651-6363
Email—diverisifiedmachinellc@yahoo.com
Pres.—Greg Kopitskie
SIC—3599; *General machining job shop*
Employs—1; Estab.—2007
Sales—under $500,000
Distrib.—Regional
Limited Liability Company

**INTERNATIONAL PAPER CO.**
140 Summerhill Rd. (08884)
**Phone—(732) 251-2000**
Fax—(732) 251-7044
www.internationalpaper.com
Email—info@ipaper.com
GM—Peggy Giulano
Hum. Res. Mgr.—Ilene Shemchuk
SIC—2653; NAICS—322211; *Corrugated boxes*
Employs—130; Estab.—1927
Distrib.—National
Publicly owned corporation
Parent co.—International Paper Co., Memphis, TN
Phone—(901) 419-9000
See Parent Co. Section for full profile.

**SCHWEITZER-MAUDUIT INTERNATIONAL, INC.**
Div. of Schweitzer-Mauduit International
85 Main St. (08884)
**Phone—(732) 723-6100**
Fax—(732) 251-3814
www.swmintl.com
Email—products@swm-us.com
Mill Mgr.—Greg Benedict
Hum. Res. Mgr.—John DeLuca
SIC—2621; NAICS—322100; *Cigarette paper products*
Employs—140; Estab.—1908
2,178,000 sq ft site, Distrib.—Intl.
Privately owned corporation
ISO rating—9001
AKA: SWM International
Parent co.—Schweitzer-Mauduit International, Alpharetta, GA
Phone—(770) 569-4200
See Parent Co. Section for full profile.

---

## Spring Lake

(Monmouth—N.E.)

**BROMLEY SMITH PUBLISHERS**
1014 Wall Rd., Ste. G-3, P.O. Box 312 (07762)
**Phone—(732) 449-9288**
(732) 449-8313
Fax—(732) 449-1033

www.bromleysmithpublishers.com
Email—jimsmith@bromleysmithpublishers.com
Ptnr. & Pres.—Jim Smith
Ptnr.—Susan Bromley Smith
SIC—2731; *Insurance textbook publishing for prelicensing & continuing education training*
Employs—2; Estab.—1986
Sales—under $500,000
Distrib.—National
Sole ownership

**†EDDIE KANE STEEL PRODUCTS, INC. (H Q)**
P.O. Box 133 (07762)
**Phone—(732) 974-3339**
National—(866) 974-5263
Fax—(732) 974-5677
www.eddiekanesteel.com
Email—info@eddiekanesteel.com
Pres.—Augustine Kane
SIC—5051; 3443; 3599; *Corporate headquarters; steel service center & steel plate flame cutting, blanchard grinding, shearing, bending & fabrication*
Employs—11; Estab.—2005
Privately owned corporation

**INITIAL IMPACT**
516 Warren Ave. (07762)
**Phone—(732) 449-4922**
Fax—(732) 449-0579
www.initialimpactembroidery.com
Pres.—Donna Szakats
V-P.—Dale Szakats
Off. Mgr.—Tammy Gregg
SIC—2396; 2395; *Promotional screen printing & embroidery, including corporate apparel & t-shirts, awards, drinkware & office writing instruments & stationery*
Employs—3; Estab.—1984
Sales—under $500,000
Distrib.—National
Privately owned corporation

**SCIVANTA MEDICAL CORP. (H Q)**
215 Morris Ave. (07762)
**Phone—(732) 282-1055**
Fax—(732) 282-1621
www.scivanta.com
Email—tgifford@scivanta.com
CEO—David R. LaVance
Ex. V-P., CFO—Tom Gifford
SIC—3845; *Corporate headquarters; minimally invasive cardiac monitoring devices (mfg. subcontracted)*
Employs—2
Sales—under $500,000 (est)
Distrib.—National
Privately owned corporation

---

## Springfield

(Union—N.E.)

**ACME MODEL ENGINEERING CO.**
115 Victory Rd. (07081)
**Phone—(973) 379-4193**
Fax—(973) 379-4932
www.utmfg.com
Email—utm@utmfg.com
CEO—Dorothy Principe
COO—Robin McElwee
Head of Qual.—Laura Tumblety
SIC—3444; 3089; *Aluminum battery holders*
Employs—30; Estab.—1945
1,200 sq ft site, Distrib.—Intl.
Privately owned corporation
ISO rating—9001:2008
Also see: Universal Tools & Mfg. Co., same loc.

**ALEXY, INC.**
401 Morris Ave. (07081)
**Phone—(973) 467-0030**
Fax—(973) 467-4389
Email—budgetprintnj@aol.com
Pres.—Marilyn Alexy
V-P.—Cathy Alexy

GEOGRAPHICAL

# Springfield—(cont.)

SIC—2752; NAICS—323100;
  *Offset printing*
Employs—3; Estab.—1989
Sales—under $500,000
Distrib.—Local
Privately owned corporation

**NEW ENTRY**

## ARTISAN DIGITAL, INC.

21 Fadem Rd., Unit 1 (07081)
**Phone—(973) 379-2788**
Fax—(973) 379-2882
www.artisandigital.com
Email—jobs@artisandigital.com
Owner—Kevin Hunt
SIC—2759; 3993; *Commercial
  printing & interior & exterior signs
  & graphic design services*
Employs—8; Estab.—2002
Sales—$1Mil-$5Mil
Distrib.—National
Privately owned corporation

## ATLAS MARBLE & GRANITE

44 Fadem Rd. (07081)
**Phone—(973) 491-5454**
Fax—(973) 491-2654
www.newjerseystone.com
Email—elizabeth@
  newjerseystone.com
Ptnr.—Marco Duran
Ptnr.—Elizabeth Gmyrek
SIC—3281; NAICS—327991;
  *Granite countertops*
Employs—15; Estab.—2002
Sales—$3Mil-$5Mil
Distrib.—Local
Limited Liability Company

## AZTEC SOFTWARE ASSOC., INC.

51 Commerce St., 2nd Fl. (07081)
**Phone—(973) 258-0011**
National—(800) 273-0033
Fax—(973) 258-0010
www.aztecsoftware.com
Email—sales@aztecsoftware.com
CEO—Jonathan Blitt
Pres.—Phyllis Schwartz
COO—Michael Kheyfets
Dir., Mktg.—Adrian Fajnor
Sr. Acct. Mgr.—Raeann Sereno
SIC—7372; *Basic skills
  remediation, academic, GED,
  skill building, occupational &
  ready for work software
  development for the adult,
  correctional, special &
  alternative education, workforce
  & post-secondary sectors, the
  Job Corps & 8-12 schools*
Employs—13; Estab.—1983
Distrib.—Intl.
Privately owned corporation

## B & M GRINDING CO.

50 Brown Ave. *(07081)*
**Phone—(973) 564-7648**
Fax—(973) 564-5298
www.bandmgrinding.com
Email—fred10658@yahoo.com
Ptnr.—Fred Grosso
Pres.—Joseph Fazio
SIC—3599; *Internal & external
  metal grinding*
Employs—2; Estab.—1975
Sales—$350,000-$500,000
3,600 sq ft site, Distrib.—Local
Privately owned partnership

## BARWORTH MICRO VALVE, INC.

673 Morris Tpke. (07081)
**Phone—(973) 376-4883**
Fax—(973) 376-5041
www.barworthinc.net
Email—barworthinc@yahoo.com
Pres.—Robert Swatsworth
Corp. Secy.—John Swatsworth

SIC—3491; NAICS—332911;
  *Industrial gas valves*
Employs—6; Estab.—1954
3,000 sq ft site, Distrib.—National
Privately owned corporation

## BEHRMAN HOUSE, INC.

11 Edison Pl. (07081)
**Phone—(973) 379-7200**
National—(800) 221-2755
Fax—(973) 379-7280
www.behrmanhouse.com
Email—customersupport@
  behrmanhouse.com
Pres.—David Behrman
IT Mgr.—Andy Shannon
Mktg. Coord.—Lauren Budd
SIC—2731; *Educational book
  publishing*
Employs—15; Estab.—1921
Sales—$500,000-$1Mil
Distrib.—Intl.
Privately owned corporation

## †BELAIR INSTRUMENT CO., INC.

36 Commerce St., P.O. Box 619
  (07081-0619)
**Phone—(973) 912-8900**
National—(800) 783-9424
Fax—(973) 232-0077
www.belairinc.com
Email—trevorm@belairinc.com
Pres.—David Patterson
Cont., Hum. Res. Mgr.—Jeanne
  Statile
Dir., Sales—Barry Patterson
SIC—5049; 5169; *Wholesaler of
  laboratory equipment & supplies
  for MOHS surgery, including
  cryostats, linistain, slides,
  specimen holders & chemicals;
  Brand name—Avantik Biogroup
  Division of Belair Instrument Co.
  Inc.; Avantik QS11; Avantik
  QS11UV*
Employs—32; Estab.—1984
Distrib.—National
Privately owned corporation

## BIGELOW COMPONENTS CORP.

74 Diamond Rd. (07081)
**Phone—(973) 467-1200**
Fax—(973) 467-9397
www.bigelowcomponents.com
Email—info@
  bigelowcomponents.com
Owner & Pres.—C. Brett Harman
Plt. Mgr.—George Kaschack
Qual. Mgr.—Charles Leone
Matls. Mgr.—Julian Medina
SIC—3469; 3599; NAICS—
  332710; *Precision miniature
  cold-headed & stamped metal
  parts*
Employs—20; Estab.—1957
Sales—$2.6Mil-$5Mil
Distrib.—National
Privately owned corporation
ISO rating—9001:2008

## BONNEY-VEHSLAGE TOOL CO.

3 Dundar Rd. (07081)
**Phone—(973) 589-6975**
Fax—(973) 589-0038
www.bvtoolco.com
Email—sales@bvtoolco.com
Pres.—Ramsey Vehslage
V-P.—Joseph R. Krehel
Shpg. Mgr.—Robert Krehel
SIC—3579; *Metal ticket punchers*
Employs—5; Estab.—1906
Varies: 5-9
5,000 sq ft site, Distrib.—Intl.
Privately owned corporation

## CG AUTOMATION SOLUTIONS USA

60 Fadem Rd. (07081)
**Phone—(973) 379-7400**
Fax—(973) 379-2138
www.cgautomationusa.com
Email—asolus.sales@cgglobal.com
Pres.—Normand N. Lavoie
Cont.—Carolyn Bruno
Dir., Opers.—Robert Kingsland

Dir., Fin.—Onelio Ramirez
Dir., Engrg.—Marcus Sternberg
Application Engrg. Mgr.—Stephen
  Burrowbridge
Hum. Res. Admn.—Debbie
  Machacek
SIC—3823; 3825; NAICS—
  334513; *Supervisory control &
  data acquisition equipment &
  systems*
Employs—55; Estab.—1975
Sales—$20Mil-$25Mil
Distrib.—Intl.
Publicly owned corporation
ISO rating—9001:2008

## †CHISWICK ELECTRIC CO., INC.

40 Brown Ave. (07081)
**Phone—(973) 824-9600**
National—(888) 648-3855
Fax—(973) 824-7740
www.chiswickelectric.com
Email—charlie@
  chiswickelectric.com
V-P.—Charlie Chiswick
SIC—5063; *Distributor of new AC
  & DC electric motors,
  transformers, inverters, starters,
  soft starts & DC motor controls,
  including full-service motor,
  pump & generator repair &
  industrial panel building; Brand
  name—ABB; Acme; AC Tech;
  Baldor; Bardac; Brook
  Crompton; Eaton; Elektrim; ERC;
  Emerson; EXM; FPT; Fuji; G.E.;
  Hitachi; Lafert; Leeson; Lenze;
  Lincoln; Marathon; Motortronics;
  Teco; Techtop; U.S. Electric; Weg*
Employs—15; Estab.—1928
19,000 sq ft site, Distrib.—Intl.
Privately owned corporation

## CINCINNATI THERMAL SPRAY EAST

Div. of Cincinnati Thermal Spray,
  Inc.
80 Fadem Rd. (07081)
**Phone—(973) 379-0003**
Fax—(973) 379-4066
www.cts-inc.net
Email—sales@cintithermal.com
GM—Scot Crabtree
SIC—3561; 3479; 3491; NAICS—
  333911; *Industrial pump & valve
  components & metal, ceramic &
  carbide coatings for wear &
  corrosion resistance*
Employs—28; Estab.—1979
18,000 sq ft site, Distrib.—National
Privately owned corporation
Parent co.—Cincinnati Thermal
  Spray, Inc., Cincinnati, OH
  Phone—(513) 793-0670
See Parent Co. Section for full profile.

## CORNELL MACHINE CO., THE

45 Brown Ave. (07081)
**Phone—(973) 379-6860**
Fax—(973) 379-6854
www.cornellmachine.com
Email—info@cornellmachine.com
Pres.—Martin C. Huska
Secy-Treas.—Alan J. Huska
SIC—3559; *Mechanical vacuum
  deaerators, defoamers &
  degassers; Brand name—
  Versator*
Employs—10; Estab.—1945
Distrib.—Intl.
Privately owned corporation

## †DRG INTERNATIONAL, INC.

841 Mountain Ave. *(07081)*
**Phone—(973) 564-7555**
National—(800) 321-1167
Fax—(973) 564-7556
www.drg-international.com
Email—corp@drg-international.com
Pres., CEO—Cyril E. Geacintov
SIC—5047; *Distributor of
  diagnostic kits*
Employs—25; Estab.—1970
Distrib.—Intl.
Privately owned corporation

## ELECTROID CO.

45 Fadem Rd. (07081)
**Phone—(973) 467-8100**
National—(800) 242-7184
Fax—(973) 467-2606
www.electroid.com
Email—sales@electroid.com
Pres.—Stephen Etter
Prodn. Mgr.—Robert DiTucci
Off. Mgr.—Kathie Horsch
Bus. Unit Mgr.—Stephen J.
  DiGerolamo
Strategic Sourcing Mgr.—Chuck
  Gray
Engrg. Mgr.—Ciro Giammanco
Qual. Assur. Mgr.—Marc Messina
SIC—3714; 3568; NAICS—
  333613; *Custom electromagnetic
  clutches, brakes & solenoids &
  fuel tank inerting systems*
Employs—90; Estab.—1949
Sales—$25Mil-$50Mil
56,000 sq ft site, Distrib.—Intl.
Privately owned corporation
Also see: Valcor Engineering
  Corp., 2 Lawrence Rd. loc.

## ELECTROMOTIVE, INC.

55 Brown Ave. (07081)
**Phone—(973) 564-8809**
Fax—(973) 564-5066
Email—elecinc@aol.com
Pres.—Thomas Barta
Corp. Secy.—Sandy Barta
SIC—3679; *Electrical solenoids*
Employs—10; Estab.—1969
5,400 sq ft site, Distrib.—National
Privately owned corporation

## ELKAY PRODUCTS CO., INC.

35 Brown Ave., P.O. Box 149
  (07081)
**Phone—(973) 376-7550**
National—(800) 631-7351
Fax—(973) 912-0418
www.elkayprod.com
Email—elkayprod@aol.com
Pres.—Steven Piller
Off. Mgr.—Tina Popovici
SIC—2399; 5084; 5085;
  *Manufacturer of quilted van pads
  & distributor of hand & appliance
  trucks & material handling
  products*
Employs—10; Estab.—1929
Sales—over $1Mil
25,000 sq ft site, Distrib.—National
Privately owned corporation

## EMTEC, INC.

11 Diamond Rd. (07081)
**Phone—(973) 376-4242**
National—(800) 800-8805
Fax—(973) 376-8846
www.emtecinc.com
Email—info@emtecinc.com
Chrm., Pres. & CEO—Dinesh R.
  Desai
Chief Delivery & Strategy Officer &
  Dir.—Sunil Misra
V-P., Opers.—David Micales
V-P., Mktg.—Rich Winkleman
SIC—7373; *Corporate
  headquarters & computer
  network systems integration & IT
  services, including application,
  consulting, infrastructure & cloud
  services*
Employs—65; Estab.—1964
40,000 sq ft site,
Publicly owned corporation

## EZ SOCKETS, INC.

5 Cornell Pkwy. *(07081)*
**Phone—(973) 376-5605**
  (800) 631-7833
Fax—(973) 376-7130
www.ezsockets.com
Email—ezsockets@juno.com
Pres., CFO—Edward Werner
Ex. V-P.—Mildred Werner
Comp.—Faina Goldman
Pur. Mgr.—P. Yutz

# Springfield—(cont.)

SIC—3452; NAICS—332722;
*Standard & special alloy &
stainless steel socket screw
products, including dowel pins,
pull dowels, hex keys & sets,
square head set screws & RoHs
compliant zinc plated/baked
socket caps; Brand name—YFS;
FKE; MFL*
Employs—25; Estab.—1978
Sales—$5Mil
30,000 sq ft site, Distrib.—Intl.
Privately owned corporation

## F & L MACHINERY & DESIGN, INC.

48 Commerce St. (07081)
**Phone—(973) 218-6216**
Fax—(973) 218-6975
www.fandlmachinery.com
Email—design@
fandlmachinery.com
Pres.—Fred Villaverde
Chief Engr.—Fred Villaverde, Jr.
Pur. Agt.—Edward G. Ulrich
SIC—3565; NAICS—333993;
*Packaging machinery*
Employs—9; Estab.—1992
14,000 sq ft site, Distrib.—National
Privately owned corporation

## FEDEX OFFICE & PRINT CENTER

Div. of FedEx Office & Print
Services, Inc.
55 U.S. Highway 22 E. (07081)
**Phone—(973) 376-3966**
Fax—(973) 376-4211
www.fedex.com
Email—usa1232@fedex.com
Center Mgr.—Gentry Robinson
Lead Consultant—Kendall
Johnson
Lead Consultant—Sytuana
Williams
Consultant—Raul Ramos
SIC—2752; NAICS—323100;
*Commercial & instant printing*
Employs—5; Estab.—1990
Sales—$500,000-$1Mil
Distrib.—Local
Publicly owned corporation
Parent co.—FedEx Office & Print
Services, Inc., Dallas, TX
Phone—(214) 550-7000
See Parent Co. Section for full profile.

## FOAM PACK INDUSTRIES DIV. OF PATIS, INC.

72 Fadem Rd. (07081)
**Phone—(973) 376-3700**
Fax—(973) 467-9850
www.foampackindustries.com
Email—foampack@verizon.net
Pres. & V-P.—David Goodstein
V-P., GM—Mitchell Goodstein
SIC—3086; NAICS—326100;
*Packaging EPS foam*
Employs—12; Estab.—1943
Sales—$1Mil-$2.5Mil
21,000 sq ft site, Distrib.—
Regional
Privately owned corporation

## G. COTTER ENTERPRISES, INC.

48 Brown Ave. *(07081)*
**Phone—(973) 376-5840**
Fax—(973) 376-5937
www.gcotter.com
Email—sales@gcotter.com
Pres.—Jerry Cotter
GM—Jerry Hub
Manager—Ron Toth
SIC—3599; *Micro & laser micro
welding job shop, including
CNC machining &
nondestructive testing*
Employs—13; Estab.—1972
Sales—$2.2Mil
8,000 sq ft site, Distrib.—National
Privately owned sub-S corp.
ISO rating—9000

## HUDSON ROBOTICS, INC.

10 Stern Ave. (07081)
**Phone—(973) 376-7400**
Fax—(973) 376-8265
www.hudsonrobotics.com
Email—info@hudsonrobotics.com
Pres.—Philip Farrelly
Off. Mgr.—Debbie Peterson
Serv. Mgr.—John Celecki
SIC—3569; 3823; 7372; NAICS—
334513; *Life science research
laboratory robots & scheduling
software development; Brand
name—PlateCrane; LabLinx;
Micro10; SOLO; RapidPick;
RapidWash; RapidHit; PA 1000
Print & Apply*
Employs—10; Estab.—1983
Sales—$3Mil-$5Mil
12,000 sq ft site, Distrib.—Intl.
Privately owned corporation

## JURY VERDICT REVIEW PUBLICATIONS

45 Springfield Ave. (07081)
**Phone—(973) 376-9002**
Fax—(973) 376-1775
www.zarins.com
Email—meredith@zarins.com
Publisher—Jed Zarin
Secy.-Treas.—Ellen Loren
Mktg. Mgr.—Gary Zarin
SIC—2721; *Magazine publishing*
Employs—8; Estab.—1980
Sales—$500,000-$1Mil
Distrib.—National
Privately owned corporation

## KRUG INDUSTRIES INC.

65 Brown Ave. (07081)
Mail addr: 74 Old Clinton Rd.,
Flemington (08822)
**Phone—(973) 467-1040**
Fax—(973) 467-1040
www.escomatickrug.com
Email—krugindustries@
earthlink.net
Pres.—Leslie Krug
SIC—3451; NAICS—332721;
*Screw machine products,
including collets, bearings &
treads*
Employs—2; Estab.—1971
Sales—under $500,000
800 sq ft site, Distrib.—National
Sole ownership

## †M & N BOYCHUK STONE CO., INC.

360 U.S. Highway 22, P.O. Box 133
(07081)
**Phone—(973) 376-1333**
Fax—(973) 376-4767
Email—boychukstone@yahoo.com
Pres.—Marshall Maudsley
Hum. Res. Mgr.—Nicole
Carscadden
SIC—5032; *Distributor of natural
stone, flagstone & veneers for
fireplaces, outdoor grills &
driveways*
Employs—5; Estab.—1948
Sales—under $500,000
Distrib.—Local
Privately owned corporation

## MADISON LINE, THE

40 Commerce St. (07081)
**Phone—(973) 379-1108**
Fax—(973) 379-8373
www.madisonlinecatalog.com
Email—mmartin@madisonid.com
Pres., CEO—Sheamus O'Brien
SIC—3993; 5199; *Manufacturer &
distributor of promotional
products for ASI customers*
Employs—10; Estab.—1991
Sales—$500,000-$1Mil
Distrib.—Local
Privately owned corporation

## NARVA KITCHENS & CLOSETS, INC.

101 Victory Rd. (07081)
**Phone—(718) 735-7722**
Fax—(973) 218-1202
www.icutwood.com
Email—narvakitchens@gmail.com
Pres.—Alex Morozov
SIC—2434; *Wooden kitchen
cabinets*
Employs—5; Estab.—2000
Sales—under $500,000
30,000 sq ft site, Distrib.—Local
Privately owned corporation
AKAs: Narva Kitchens & Closets &
ICUTWOOD

## †NEW JERSEY SEMICONDUCTOR PRODUCTS, INC.

20 Stern Ave. *(07081)*
**Phone—(973) 376-2922**
        (212) 227-6005
Fax—(973) 376-8960
www.njsemi.com
Email—sales@njsemi.com
Pres.—Robert Hildebrandt
V-P.—Ron Hildebrandt
Fin. Mgr.—Karen Pear
Qual. Control Mgr.—Jake Eager
Maint. Mgr.—Dave Hildebrandt
SIC—5065; *Distributor of
semiconductor products,
including diodes, transistors,
integrated circuits, rectifiers,
bridges, SCR, triacs, MOVs &
silicon & germanium diodes;
Brand name—APD; Fairchild;
Freescale; GPD; Littlefuse; IR;
Isocom; Linear Systems;
Microsemi; Motorola; National;
NewJerseySemi; Philips; NXP;
OnSemi; Semicoa; Sensitron;
Semikron; Semtech; Siliconix;
SSDI; STMIcro; Vishay; VMI*
Employs—60; Estab.—1967
Sales—$5Mil-$10Mil
32,000 sq ft site, Distrib.—Intl.
Privately owned partnership

## NEWARK BRUSH COMPANY

1 Silver Ct. (07081)
**Phone—(973) 376-1000**
National—(800) 552-7874
Fax—(973) 376-9888
www.newarkbrush.com
Pres.—Jeremy Glick
Ex. V-P.—Brian O'Leary
Cont.—Ramon Matti
Sales Rep.—Matt Stewart
SIC—3991; NAICS—339994;
*Industrial brushes & sweeper
brooms; Brand name—Danline;
Big Red*
Employs—22; Estab.—1894
55,000 sq ft site, Distrib.—Intl.
Privately owned corporation
ISO rating—9001:2008

## NEWARK DENTAL PEMCO

35 Stern Ave., P.O. Box 249
(07081)
**Phone—(973) 564-9622**
National—(800) 526-4170
Fax—(973) 564-9725
www.newarkdentalpemco.com
Email—ndc@newarkdental-
pemco.com
Owner—Lawrence Balfour
Sales Rep.—Nicole Sabastiano
SIC—3843; NAICS—339114;
*Dental cabinets*
Employs—55; Estab.—1940
Distrib.—National
Privately owned corporation

## O'BRIEN CO., INC., J.

40 Commerce St. (07081)
**Phone—(973) 379-8844**
www.jobrien.com
Email—customerservice@
jobrien.com
Pres., CEO—Sharmay O'Brien
Acctg. Mgr.—Wes Winters

SIC—3499; 3999; 5045; 5112;
*Manufacturer of lanyards, badge
reels & security identification
products & distributor of ID card
printers & ink ribbons*
Employs—20; Estab.—1984
Sales—$1Mil-$3.5Mil
Distrib.—Intl.
Privately owned corporation

## PRIDE PRODUCTS DISTRIBUTORS, LLC

673 Morris Ave., Ste. 2 (07081)
**Phone—(973) 564-6300**
Fax—(973) 564-6222
www.pride-products.com
Email—sales@pride-products.com
Pres., CEO—Andrew Nadel
Client Svcs. Mgr.—Jessie Alberto
Client Serv. Mgr.—Alyssa
Marchitto
SIC—3993; 2759; NAICS—
323100; *Promotional product
printing*
Employs—7; Estab.—1997
Sales—$1Mil-$2.5Mil
Distrib.—National
Limited Liability Company

## PRINT MEDIA

232 Morris Ave. (07081)
**Phone—(973) 467-0007**
Fax—(973) 467-5807
www.printmedia.com
Email—info@printmedianj.com
Owner—Robert Walleck
Client Serv. Rep.—Steven
Hilsenrath
SIC—2759; NAICS—323119;
*Commercial printing*
Employs—6; Estab.—2003
Sales—$500,000-$1Mil (est)
Distrib.—Local
Privately owned corporation

## PRINT TECH LTD.

49 Fadem Rd. (07081)
**Phone—(908) 232-2287**
Fax—(908) 518-7760
www.print-tech.com
Email—sales@print-tech.com
Ptnr.—Russell Evans
Ptnr.—Gary Alessio
SIC—2759; 3993; NAICS—
323100; *Company headquarters
& digital printing & signage,
including personalized
marketing, direct mail &
fulfillment; Brand name—
PrintFLEX*
Employs—35; Estab.—1978
35,000 sq ft site, Distrib.—National
Limited Liability Company

## RENARD COMMUNICATIONS, INC.

197 Mountain Ave. (07081)
**Phone—(973) 912-8550**
Fax—(973) 912-8599
www.diversitycareers.com
Email—circulation@
diversitycareers.com
Owner—Roberta Renard
Editor—Kate Colborn
Circ. Mgr.—Marcia Siegendorf
SIC—2721; *Magazine publishing*
Employs—8
Sales—$500,000-$1Mil
Distrib.—National
Privately owned corporation
AKAs: Diversity Careers & Renard
Communications

## RING CONTAINER TECHNOLOGIES

Div. of Ring Container
Technologies, Inc.
50 Fadem Rd., Ste. 1 (07081)
**Phone—(973) 258-0707**
www.ringcontainer.com
Email—questions@
ringcontainer.com
Plt. Mgr.—David Fredkin
Off. Mgr.—Mildred Lacosta

GEOGRAPHICAL

## Springfield—(cont.)

SIC—3089; *Plastic containers*
Employs—19; Estab.—1989
Distrib.—Local
Privately owned corporation
Parent co.—Ring Container
Technologies, Inc., Oakland, TN
Phone—(901) 465-6333
See Parent Co. Section for full profile.

### SELECT SERVICES

500 Morris Ave., Ste. 116 (07081-1020)
**Phone—(973) 467-8860**
National—(800) 856-8232
Fax—(973) 467-8994
www.ssprintmail.com
Email—sales@ssprintmail.com
Owner—David Hunter
SIC—2759; 3993; *Printing, direct mail service, promotional products & design*
Employs—5; Estab.—2004
Sales—under $500,000
Distrib.—National
Privately owned corporation

### SPRINGFIELD METAL PRODUCTS CO.

8 Commerce St. (07081)
**Phone—(973) 379-4600**
Fax—(973) 379-7314
Pres.—John D. Sommer
V-P., Secy.—Irene Powell
V-P., Treas.—Lori Perine
Off. Mgr.—Linda Sommer
SIC—3499; *Metal fabrication*
Employs—10; Estab.—1931
Sales—$500,000-$1Mil
6,000 sq ft site, Distrib.—National
Privately owned corporation

### STECK, INC., PAUL C.

25 Brown Ave. (07081)
**Phone—(973) 376-1830**
Fax—(973) 376-9433
www.paulcsteck.com
Email—paulcsteck@aol.com
Pres.—Emily S. Wantz
GM—Susan Wantz
Accts. Payable Mgr.—Michele Evans
SIC—3444; 3599; *Custom precision sheet metal fabrication & machining*
Employs—8; Estab.—1947
Sales—under $500,000
15,000 sq ft site, Distrib.—Intl.
Privately owned corporation

### TALBOT ASSOCS., INC.

11 Cleveland Pl. (07081)
**Phone—(973) 376-9570**
National—(800) 376-9570
Fax—(973) 376-7617
www.metalbot.com
Email—sales@metalbot.com
CEO—Jeffrey Talbot
Pres.—Duncan Talbot
SIC—3365; NAICS—331524; *Steel & aluminum castings*
Employs—14; Estab.—1947
Sales—$50Mil-$100Mil
Distrib.—Regional
Privately owned corporation

### TRICO POLY SYSTEMS, LLC

60 Brown Ave. *(07081)*
**Phone—(973) 376-7770**
Fax—(973) 376-7779
www.tricopoly.com
Email—tricopoly@verizon.net
Ptnr.—Kenneth J. Plis
Ptnr.—Shawn Alexander

SIC—3559; *Polyurethane & epoxy processing machinery, including slinger degassers, continuous MOCA melters, melting metering systems, heated trunks & vacuum equipment*
Employs—10; Estab.—2005
Sales—$1Mil-$2.5Mil
13,000 sq ft site, Distrib.—Intl.
Limited Liability Company

### TRU-FORM COSMETICS, INC.

50 Springfield Ave. (07081)
**Phone—(973) 564-9111**
National—(800) 234-9437
Fax—(973) 564-5226
Email—truformnail@aol.com
Owner—Diane Nguyen
SIC—2844; NAICS—325600; *Beauty & cosmetic products*
Employs—5
Sales—$1Mil-$2.5Mil (est)
Distrib.—Local
Privately owned corporation

### UNITED WINDOW & DOOR MFG.

24-36 Fadem Rd. (07081)
**Phone—(973) 912-0600**
National—(800) 848-4550
Fax—(973) 912-8866
www.unitedwindowmfg.com
Email—lcuccio@unitedwindowmfg.com
CFO—Gary DeNoia
V-P., Sales—Gregg Proscia
Dir., Sales & Mktg.—John D'Elena
Dir., IT—Chrisovalantis Katsaros
Principal—Howard Rose
Principal—Nick Derrico
Prodn. Mgr.—Nestor Nogueira
Hum. Res. Mgr.—Leigh Cuccio
Cust. Serv. Mgr.—Ron Glick
SIC—3089; *Vinyl windows & doors*
Employs—250; Estab.—1988
Sales—$30Mil-$35Mil
125,000 sq ft site, Distrib.—Regional
Privately owned partnership
ISO rating—9000

### UNIVERSAL TOOLS & MFG. CO.

115 Victory Rd. (07081)
**Phone—(973) 379-4193**
Fax—(973) 379-4932
www.utmfg.com
Email—utm@utmfg.com
Owner, Pres. & CEO—Dorothy Principe
COO—Robin McElwee
SIC—3544; 3469; 3429; NAICS—333514; *Tooling & precision deep drawn metal stamping of battery packs & decorative latches, locks, hinges & corners for menu holders, including dies, prototypes, short & long-run productions & JIT program*
Employs—30; Estab.—1945
Sales—$3Mil
14,000 sq ft site, Distrib.—National
Privately owned sub-S corp.
ISO rating—9001:2008
Also see: Acme Model Engineering Co., same loc.
AKA: Atco Products

### VALCOR ENGINEERING CORP.

2 Lawrence Rd. (07081)
**Phone—(973) 467-8400**
Fax—(973) 467-8382
www.valcor.com
Email—scientific@valcor.com
Pres.—Frank Tartaglia
V-P., Bus. & Prod. Dev.—Tom Tervolino
MIS & IT Mgr.—Luis Lazo
Mktg. Admn.—Jennifer Eckert

SIC—3492; NAICS—332912; *Solenoid valves & pumps*
Employs—240; Estab.—1951
Sales—$25Mil-$50Mil (est)
100,000 sq ft site, Distrib.—Intl.
Privately owned corporation
Also see: Electroid Co., 45 Fadem Rd. loc.

### VASWANI, INC.

18 Bernadette Ct. (07081)
**Phone—(973) 376-4425**
Fax—(973) 376-7040
www.vaswaniinc.com
Email—info@vaswaniinc.com
CEO—Vinay Vaswani
Pres.—Ishwar Vaswani
Hum. Res. Mgr.—Nora Monga
SIC—2521; NAICS—337211; *Contract wooden office furniture*
Employs—35; Estab.—2000
Sales—$1Mil-$2.5Mil
Distrib.—Intl.
Privately owned corporation

### VRP LU-MAX MFG. CO., INC.

44 Brown Ave. (07081)
**Phone—(973) 379-5877**
Fax—(973) 379-3876
Email—vrplumax@yahoo.com
Pres., R & D Mgr.—Paul Rodzak
SIC—3599; 3312; *Sheet metal welding, wire forming & structural fabrication*
Employs—1; Estab.—1972
Sales—under $500,000
6,000 sq ft site, Distrib.—Local
Limited Liability Company

### WPI COMMUNICATION, INC.

55 Morris Ave., Ste. 312 (07081)
**Phone—(973) 467-8700**
National—(800) 323-4995
Fax—(973) 467-0368
www.wpicommunications.com
Email—info@wpicommunications.com
Publisher—Steve Klinghoffer
Off. Mgr.—Sara Migot
SIC—2741; *Newsletter publishing*
Employs—15; Estab.—1988
Distrib.—National
Sole ownership

---

## Stanhope
### (Sussex—N.W.)

### ALL AMERICAN CRAFTS PUBLISHING, INC.

7 Waterloo Rd. (07874)
**Phone—(973) 347-6900**
Fax—(973) 347-6909
www.allamericancrafts.com
Email—bcohen@allamericancrafts.com
CEO, Publisher—Darren Cohen
Art Dir.—Kelly Albertson
Accts. Payable & Hum. Res. Mgr.—Susie Horner
Adv. Coord.—Sandy Moncelsi
Head of Adv.—Brett Cohen
SIC—2721; *Crafts magazine publishing*
Employs—40; Estab.—1985
Sales—$2.5Mil-$5Mil (est)
Distrib.—National
Sole ownership

### INTERNATIONAL FOAM PRODUCTS, INC.

P.O. Box 545 (07874)
**Phone—(201) 909-0950**
Fax—(201) 781-6152
www.internationalfoam.com
Email—mail@kemwove.com
Cont., Plt. Mgr.—Kathy Ferris

SIC—3089; *Textile & fiberfill laminating for the apparel, lingerie, medical, footwear, ski/outerwear, luggage, furniture, bedding, automotive, marine & insulation industries*
Employs—8; Estab.—2000
Distrib.—Local
Privately owned corporation
AKA: Kem-Wove, Inc.
Parent co.—International Foam Products, Inc., Charlotte, NC
Phone—(704) 588-0080
See Parent Co. Section for full profile.

### ISOLATEK INTERNATIONAL (H Q)

41 Furnace St. (07874)
**Phone—(973) 347-1200**
National—(800) 631-9600
Fax—(973) 347-9170
www.isolatek.com
Email—sales@isolatek.com
Pres., CEO—Giovanni C. Pacheco
CFO—Thomas Gallagher
V-P., Sales & Mktg.—Kurt C. Neff
Prod. Mktg. Mgr.—Linda Sikel
SIC—3296; 3479; NAICS—327993; *Company headquarters; spray applied fire resistive materials (SFRMs), intumescent thin film coatings, rigid board & thermal insulation, acoustical treatment & mineral wool fiber for the commercial, petrochemical & tunnel markets; Brand name—CAFCO; ISOLATEK; PMF / FIBERWEAR*
Employs—100; Estab.—1875
Distrib.—Intl.
Privately owned corporation

### KUEHN BEVEL, INC.

10 Furnace St. (07874)
**Phone—(973) 584-8282**
National—(800) 862-3835
Fax—(973) 527-4843
www.kuehnbevel.com
Email—alichia.pourreza@kuehnbevel.com
Pres.—Ray Kuehn
V-P., Sales & Mktg.—Alichia Pourreza
V-P., Opers.—Shawn Kuehn
SIC—2431; NAICS—321900; *Decorative edge products for laminate countertops*
Employs—10; Estab.—1991
Sales—$1Mil-$5Mil
17,000 sq ft site, Distrib.—National
Privately owned sub-S corp.

### NAVITEND

23 U.S. Highway 206 (07874)
**Phone—(973) 448-0070**
Fax—(973) 448-0264
www.navitend.com
Email—info@navitend.com
Pres.—Frank Ableson
Sales Mgr.—Barry McGuire
SIC—7373; NAICS—541512; *Bar coding & inventory & field service management & scheduling computer integrated systems*
Employs—10; Estab.—2002
Distrib.—Local
Privately owned corporation

### NEW YORK FOLDING BOX CO.

20 Continental Dr. (07874)
**Phone—(973) 347-6932**
Fax—(973) 347-2303
www.nyfoldingbox.com
Email—sales@nyfoldingbox.com
Ptnr.—Ken Kaplan
Ptnr.—Greg Kaplan
Fin., IT & Off. Mgr.—Mike Fiscella
SIC—2657; NAICS—322212; *Folding boxes*
Employs—14; Estab.—1918
100,000 sq ft site, Distrib.—National
Privately owned corporation

## Stanhope—(cont.)

**NEW ENTRY**

**PANEL COMPONENTS & SYSTEMS, INC.**
149 Main St. (07874)
**Phone—(973) 448-9400**
Fax—(973) 448-1674
www.pc-s.com
Owner—Tanja Lewit
SIC—3679; *Electrical components, including transformers, analog meters & transducers*
Employs—10
Sales—$1Mil-$2.5Mil (est)
Distrib.—Intl.

**SAXTON FALLS SAND & GRAVEL, INC.**
Waterloo Valley Rd., P.O. Box 576 (07874)
**Phone—(908) 852-0120**
Fax—(973) 440-4082
www.saxtonfalls.com
Email—rich@saxtonfalls.com
Pres.—Richard Schindelar
SIC—1442; 1429; 1479; NAICS—212321; *Sand & gravel processing, including concrete & mason sand, construction aggregates, stone, topsoil, specialty sand, retention basin soil mix & top dressing*
Employs—10; Estab.—1960
11,000 sq ft site, Distrib.—Regional
Privately owned sub-S corp.

**UNIGRAPHIC GUILD, INC.**
10 Route 206 (07874)
**Phone—(973) 219-2348**
Email—colorasap@gmail.com
Pres.—Paul Washuta
Prodn. Mgr.—Ellen Chandler
Prodn. Supv.—Judy Kent
Administrator—Terre Gallo
SIC—2759; 2752; 2789; NAICS—323100; *Commercial, color & digital printing for digital labels, print to web, QR coding, magnet postcards, intelligent mail, lamination, packaging & fulfillment services; Brand name—Uniprint; Unicard; Unibind; UniMail*
Employs—16; Estab.—1958
5,000 sq ft site, Distrib.—National
Privately owned corporation

**WAGNER INDUSTRIES, INC.**
51 Sparta Rd. (07874)
**Phone—(973) 347-0800**
Fax—(973) 347-0885
www.wagner-industries.com
Email—windust300@aol.com
Pres.—William Wagner
Off. Mgr.—Sue Gerndt
SIC—3554; NAICS—333291; *Paper converting equipment that unwinds, rewinds, slits, sheets, accumulates, edge guides, controls, laminates, coats, traverse winds & custom designed machinery & ancillary components*
Employs—11; Estab.—1985
Sales—$1Mil-$5Mil
10,000 sq ft site, Distrib.—Intl.
Privately owned sub-S corp.

## Stewartsville

(Warren—N.W.)

**LINDE GAS NORTH AMERICA, LLC**
Div. of Linde North America, Inc.
1 Greenwich St., Ste. 200 (08886-2020)
**Phone—(800) 755-9277**
Fax—(330) 392-5549
www.lindeus.com
Email—sales.lg.us@linde.com

Acct. Mgr.—Clarence Gaten
Head of Cust. Serv.—Bob White
Head of Natl. Scheduling Ctr.—Mike Armstrong
SIC—2813; *Industrial & specialty gases; Brand name—Cryoline; Ecovar; Spectra; Lifegas; REBOX*
Employs—250; Estab.—1915
30,000 sq ft site, Distrib.—Intl.
Publicly owned corporation
Parent co.—Linde North America, Inc., New Providence, NJ
Phone—(908) 464-8100
See Parent Co. Section for full profile.

**T & M PALLET CO., INC.**
116 Edison Rd. (08886)
**Phone—(908) 454-3042**
Fax—(908) 454-5959
Email—tmpallet@verizon.net
V-P.—Steve Tigar
SIC—2448; NAICS—321920; *Wooden pallets, shipping crates & boxes*
Employs—20; Estab.—1987
Sales—$1Mil-$5Mil
15,000 sq ft site, Distrib.—Regional
Privately owned corporation

**WARREN MATERIALS**
Div. of Haines & Kibblehouse, Inc.
703 Route 57 (08886)
Mail addr.—P.O. Box 196, Skippack (19474)
**Phone—(908) 859-3333**
Fax—(908) 859-3336
www.hkgroup.com
Email—hr@hkgroup.com
COO—James T. Haines
Sales Rep.—Robert Hummer
SIC—2951; 3272; NAICS—324121; *Asphalt paving compounds & bituminous concrete*
Employs—23; Estab.—1953
Sales—$500,000-$1Mil (est)
Distrib.—Regional
Privately owned corporation
Parent co.—Haines & Kibblehouse, Inc., Skippack, PA
Phone—(610) 584-8500
See Parent Co. Section for full profile.

## Stillwater

(Sussex—N.W.)

**CASTNER'S SAWMILL**
935 Fairview Lake Rd., P.O. Box 13 (07875)
**Phone—(973) 383-5661**
Fax—(973) 579-6067
Owner—Rodney Castner
SIC—2421; *Dimensional lumber*
Employs—2; Estab.—1947
Sales—under $500,000
Distrib.—Local
Privately owned corporation

**†R.P. MACHINE, LLC**
906 Stillwater Rd., P.O. Box 144 (07875)
**Phone—(973) 383-8994**
National—(800) 838-6570
Fax—(973) 300-5627
www.shoprpmachine.com
Email—info@rpmach.com
Owner—Randall Pobutkiewicz
Mng. Dir.—Lisa Labbee

SIC—5084; 5085; *Distributor of new & used sheet metal fabrication machinery & sheet metal equipment, supplies, parts & service; Brand name—Engel; Roper Whitney; Lockformer; Flagler; Rams; DuroDyne; Roto-Die; Dreis & Krump; Tennsmith; Scotchman; Iowa Precision; Piranha; Norlok; Genie; Modern Mfg.; Doran*
Employs—6; Estab.—1997
Distrib.—National
Limited Liability Company

## Stirling

(Morris—N.W.)

**EDSTON MFG. CO., INC.**
321 Warren Ave. (07980)
**Phone—(908) 647-0116**
Fax—(908) 647-0901
Email—edstonmfg@comcast.net
Pres., CFO—Paul Zuzozk
SIC—3599; *General machining job shop*
Employs—2; Estab.—1946
Sales—$1Mil-$2.5Mil
4,000 sq ft site, Distrib.—National
Sole ownership
Also see: P M Z Tool, Inc., same loc.

**ENGINEERED PLASTIC PRODUCTS, INC.**
269 Mercer St., P.O. Box 196 (07980)
**Phone—(908) 647-3500**
        (800) 304-3774
Fax—(908) 647-1868
www.engineeredplastic.com
Email—eppi@engineeredplastic.com
Pres. & Sales Mgr.—Christopher Ratti
Bookkeeper—April Babo
SIC—3089; *Custom thermoplastic vacuum forming & fabrication of plastic products*
Employs—20; Estab.—1958
Sales—$1Mil-$5Mil
27,000 sq ft site, Distrib.—National
Privately owned corporation

**FIBERGUIDE INDUSTRIES, INC.**
Div. of Halma Holdings, Inc.
1 Bay St. (07980)
**Phone—(908) 647-6601**
National—(877) 490-7803
Fax—(908) 647-8464
www.fiberguide.com
Email—info@fiberguide.com
Pres., CEO—Patricia Seniw
Cont.—Donna Passal
SIC—3229; NAICS—327212; *Corporate headquarters & optical fibers & assemblies & photonics packaging; Brand name—Superguide; Anhydroguide; Solarguide*
Employs—25; Estab.—1977
13,500 sq ft site, Distrib.—Intl.
Publicly owned corporation
ISO rating—9001:2008
Parent co.—Halma Holdings, Inc., Cincinnati, OH
Phone—(513) 772-5501
See Parent Co. Section for full profile.

**INTERTEK LABORATORIES, INC.**
340 Union St. (07980)
**Phone—(908) 903-1800**
www.interteklabsinc.com
Email—interteklabs@verizon.net
Pres., GM, Bus. & Fin. Mgr.—Mary Labella
SIC—3825; 3699; NAICS—334500; *Automatic test equipment & electronic assembly*
Employs—15; Estab.—1984
11,000 sq ft site, Distrib.—National
Privately owned corporation

**ISOLANTITE MFG. CO., INC.**
337 Warren Ave. (07980)
**Phone—(908) 647-3333**
Fax—(908) 580-0936
www.isolantite.com
Email—isolantite@isolantitemfg.com
Pres.—George W. Lumpe
Sales Mgr.—Mary Lou Hall
Fin. Mgr.—Patti Testa
Engr.—Julie Tatum
SIC—3264; NAICS—327113; *Ceramic insulators*
Employs—23; Estab.—1947
Sales—$1Mil-$5Mil
25,000 sq ft site, Distrib.—Intl.
Privately owned corporation

**M & M WELDING & STEEL FABRICATING**
344 Essex St., P.O. Box 168 (07980)
**Phone—(908) 647-6060**
Fax—(908) 647-6330
Email—mariemasek@aol.com
Pres.—Al Masek
V-P.—Marie Masek
SIC—3446; 3599; NAICS—332323; *Architectural metalwork & general machining job shop*
Employs—2; Estab.—1976
Sales—under $500,000
Distrib.—Local
Privately owned corporation

**P M Z TOOL, INC.**
321 Warren Ave. (07980)
**Phone—(908) 647-2125**
Email—pmztoolinc@comcast.net
Pres.—Paul Zuzozk
SIC—3544; NAICS—333500; *Tool & die job shop*
Employs—6; Estab.—1988
Distrib.—National
Privately owned corporation
Also see: Edston Mfg. Co., Inc., same loc.

**THERMOPLASTIC PROCESSES**
Div. of Thermoplastic Processes, Inc.
1268 Valley Rd., P.O. Box 124 (07980)
**Phone—(888) 554-6400**
Fax—(800) 874-3291
www.thermoplasticprocesses.com
Email—tpisales@excelon.com
Hum. Res. Mgr.—Debbie Adkins
Bills Rep.—Michelle Izagire
SIC—3082; NAICS—326121; *Plastic tubing*
Employs—120; Estab.—1955
Distrib.—Intl.
Privately owned corporation
Parent co.—Thermoplastic Processes, Inc., Georgetown, DE
Phone—(302) 855-0139
See Parent Co. Section for full profile.

## Stockholm

(Sussex—N.W.)

**PUL-A PUMP CORP.**
29 Paradise Trl., P.O. Box 155 (07460)
**Phone—(973) 697-2008**
Fax—(973) 697-5989
www.pulapump.com
Email—postmaster@pulapump.com
Pres., CEO—Robert A. Wilbert
V-P.—Jeanne Wilbert
SIC—3561; NAICS—333911; *Water pump hoists, pullers & pushers*
Employs—2; Estab.—1991
Sales—under $500,000
Distrib.—Intl.
Privately owned corporation

GEOGRAPHICAL

## Stockton
(Hunterdon—N.W.)

NEW ENTRY
**CUSTOM COOLING SERVICES, LLC**
99 Kingwood Stockton Rd., P.O. Box 457 (08559)
**Phone—(609) 397-4448**
Fax—(609) 397-4224
www.customcoolingservices.com
Email—info@
customcoolingservices.com
Owner—Paul Steffanelli
SIC—3444; *Sheet metal fabrication, including HVAC ductwork*
Employs—5
Sales—$500,000-$1Mil (est)
Distrib.—Local
Limited Liability Company

**LUCID LIGHTING, LLC**
811 Rosemont Ringoes Rd. (08559)
**Phone—(609) 649-0596**
Fax—(609) 657-6929
www.lucidlighting.com
Email—info@lucidlighting.com
Pres.—Robert Wallace
SIC—3646; NAICS—335122; *Residential & commercial lighting fixtures*
Employs—1; Estab.—1986
Sales—under $500,000
1,000 sq ft site, Distrib.—National
Limited Liability Company

**MAPLE LEATHER CO.**
14 Raven Rock Rd., P.O. Box 319 (08559)
**Phone—(609) 397-1199**
National—(800) 826-1199
www.mapleleather.com
Email—info@mapleleather.com
Pres.—Seymour Mondshein
Dir., Mktg.—Lisa Martin
SIC—3171; NAICS—316992; *Leather, fabric & nylon handbags, purses & backpacks accessories*
Employs—3; Estab.—1974
Sales—under $500,000
3,600 sq ft site, Distrib.—National
Privately owned corporation
AKA: Great Bags

**SUNFLOWER GLASS STUDIO**
877 Sergeantsville Rd. (08559)
**Phone—(609) 397-1535**
Fax—(609) 397-0660
www.sunflowerglassstudio.com
Email—caldwell877@comcast.net
Owner—Karen Caldwell
GM—Geoffrey Caldwell
SIC—3231; NAICS—327215; *Stained glass windows & beveled glass designs*
Employs—6; Estab.—1978
Sales—$500,000-$1Mil
Distrib.—Regional
Sole ownership

## Stratford
(Camden—S.W.)

**BUSINESS POWER, INC.**
39 Hunt Ave., Ste. C (08084)
**Phone—(856) 783-7390**
Fax—(856) 783-7290
www.businesspower.com
Email—sales@businesspower.com
Pres., CEO—Ken Baysal
SIC—7372; *Business management software development & web design services*
Employs—9; Estab.—2005
Distrib.—National
Privately owned corporation

**SOUTH JERSEY SOFT PRETZEL, INC.**
912 N. White Horse Pike, Ste. A (08084)
**Phone—(856) 435-5055**
Fax—(856) 627-2810
www.southjerseypretzel.com
Email—info@
southjerseypretzel.com
Pres.—George W. Dudley
Manager—Rich Dudley
Manager—Christine Dudley
Sales Assoc.—Ryan Dapper
SIC—2052; *Pretzels*
Employs—6; Estab.—1970
Distrib.—Local
Privately owned corporation

## Succasunna
(Morris—N.W.)

**AD-VENTURE GRAPHICS, INC.**
46 Main St. (07876)
**Phone—(973) 927-0951**
Fax—(973) 927-0432
Email—ad-venture@optonline.net
Pres.—Ray Vanderhoof
V-P., R & D—Diane Vanderhoof
SIC—3993; *Interior & exterior signs, exhibits & decals*
Employs—3; Estab.—1989
Sales—under $500,000
3,000 sq ft site, Distrib.—Local
Privately owned corporation

**BIRD TOY MAN**
197 S. Hillside Ave. (07876)
**Phone—(973) 584-0756**
www.birdtoyman.com
Email—info@birdtoyman.com
Owner—Henry E. Pedynowski
SIC—2499; 3089; 3199; 3499; NAICS—316999; *Wooden, plastic, acrylic, leather & metal pet bird toys, swings, cups, ladders, shower perches & play gyms for small birds & parrots; Brand name—Paradise Toys; Bizzy Bird Toys; Braun Brushes; Fun-Max Toys; Cage & Queen Toys; Sweet Feet & Beak; Zoo-Max T; LR Bird Toys*
Employs—1; Estab.—1989
Sales—under $500,000
Distrib.—National
Sole ownership

**CLARK'S HALLMARK SHOP**
275 State Route 10 E., Ste. 31 (07876)
**Phone—(973) 584-5119**
Fax—(973) 584-3758
GM—Alfred Clark
SIC—2759; NAICS—323100; *Invitation card imprinting*
Employs—8; Estab.—1997
Sales—$1Mil-$2.5Mil (est)
Distrib.—Local
Privately owned corporation

**GENERAL FILTER CORP.**
14 Constitution Ave. (07876)
Mail addr: P.O. Box 155, Ironia (07845)
**Phone—(973) 584-9220**
Fax—(973) 584-3499
www.generalfiltrationcorp.com
Pres., CEO—Richard Warren
SIC—2393; 2834; NAICS—314911; *Pharmaceutical filter bags*
Employs—4; Estab.—1997
2,000 sq ft site, Distrib.—Local
Privately owned corporation

**HOLLAND MANUFACTURING COMPANY, INC.**
15 Main St., P.O. Box 404 (07876)
**Phone—(973) 584-8141**
Fax—(973) 584-6233
www.hollandmfg.com
Email—hr@hollandmfg.com
Chrm., CEO—Jack Holland
Pres., COO—Sam Vodoor
Dir., Sales—Ray Hajek
Dir., Pur.—Chase Holland
Plt. Mgr.—Todd Holland
Hum. Res. Mgr.—Edelina Zajac
SIC—2672; NAICS—322222; *Corporate headquarters & packaging tapes & laminated & coated papers*
Employs—94; Estab.—1958
Distrib.—Intl.
Privately owned sub-S corp.

**HONOUR OF YOUR PRESENCE**
19 State Route 10 E., Ste. 14 (07876)
**Phone—(973) 927-6262**
National—(866) 669-9555
www.honourofyourpresence.com
Email—info@
honourofyourpresence.com
Ptnr.—Cherese Rambaldi
SIC—2759; *Invitation printing & design*
Employs—2; Estab.—2008
Sales—under $500,000
Distrib.—National
Privately owned partnership

**†KUIKEN BROTHERS COMPANY, INC.**
31 State Route 10 E. (07876)
**Phone—(973) 584-2444**
Fax—(973) 252-2443
www.kuikenbrothers.com
Email—info@kuikenbrothers.com
Store Mgr.—Marc Gattuso
SIC—5031; 5033; 5072; *Distributor of residential & commercial building materials, including lumber, moulding, windows, doors, decking, drywall, insulation, metal studs, hollow metal doors, frames & architectural hardware*
Employs—25; Estab.—2006
Distrib.—Local
Privately owned sub-S corp.
Parent co.—Kuiken Brothers Company, Inc., Fair Lawn, NJ
Phone—(201) 796-2082
See Parent Co. Section for full profile.

**MONOGRAM MADNESS**
50 Main St. (07876)
**Phone—(973) 927-5278**
Fax—(973) 927-2084
Email—monogrammadness@verizon.net
Owner—Peggy Kiefer
SIC—2395; 2396; *Embroidery & screen printing*
Employs—2; Estab.—1990
Sales—under $500,000
Distrib.—Local
Sole ownership

**RAME-HART INSTRUMENT CO., LLC**
19 Route 10 E., Ste. 11 (07876)
**Phone—(973) 448-0305**
www.ramehart.com
Principal—Carl Clegg
SIC—3827; NAICS—333314; *Goniometers*
Employs—5; Estab.—1961
Distrib.—Intl.
Limited Liability Company

**SMITH & SON, INC., R. P.**
Main St., P.O. Box 209 (07876)
**Phone—(973) 584-4063**
Email—rpsmithblock@aol.com
Pres.—Robert Smith
Bookkeeper—Sue Smith
SIC—3271; NAICS—327331; *Concrete block*
Employs—6; Estab.—1928
Distrib.—Regional
Privately owned corporation

## Summit
(Union—N.E.)

**A & J TOOL SPECIALTIES, INC.**
235 Morris Ave. (07901)
**Phone—(908) 277-0550**
Fax—(908) 277-6094
Pres.—Aldo Curiale
Secy-Treas.—Irene Curiale
Buyer—Nick Curiale
SIC—3423; *Cutting tools*
Employs—3; Estab.—1985
Sales—under $500,000
Distrib.—Local
Privately owned corporation
Also see: Summit Millwork & Supply, Inc., same loc.

**†AMERICAN ESTATES WINES, INC.**
19 Hillside Ave. (07901)
**Phone—(908) 273-5060**
Fax—(908) 273-5068
www.eamericanestates.com
Email—wines@
eamericanestates.com
Pres.—George Galey
SIC—5182; *Distributor of wines*
Employs—7; Estab.—2001
Distrib.—Intl.
Privately owned corporation

**CELGENE CORP.**
86 Morris Ave. (07901)
**Phone—(908) 673-9000**
Fax—(908) 673-9001
www.celgene.com
Email—information@celgene.com
Chrm. of the Board & CEO—Robert J. Hugin
Sr. V-P., CFO—Jacqualyn Fouse
COO—Perry Karsen
Sr. V-P., Hum. Res., Global—Philippe Van Holle
Ex. Dir., Corp. Svcs.—Vince Barilla
SIC—2834; NAICS—325412; *Corporate headquarters & biopharmaceuticals for treatment of cancer & inflammatory diseases*
Employs—800; Estab.—1986
Sales—$250Mil-$500Mil (est)
400,000 sq ft site, Distrib.—Intl.
Publicly owned corporation

**ENVIRONMOLDS, LLC**
18 Bank St., Ste. 1 (07901-3659)
**Phone—(908) 273-5401**
National—(866) 278-6653
Fax—(908) 273-9256
www.artmolds.biz
Email—info@artmolds.com
Owner—Ed McCormick
SIC—3999; *Molding & casting kits for fine art, hobby & craft applications*
Employs—10
Sales—$1Mil-$2.5Mil
Limited Liability Company
AKA: ArtMolds

**HOSOKAWA MICRON POWDER SYSTEMS**
10 Chatham Rd. (07901)
**Phone—(908) 273-6360**
Fax—(908) 273-7432
www.hmicronpowder.com
Email—info@hmicronpowder.com
V-P.—Rob Voorhees
IT Mgr.—Chris Tkachuk
Hum. Res. Mgr.—Deborah Scott
SIC—3826; 3559; *Company headquarters & powder processing equipment*
Employs—50; Estab.—1923
Sales—$11Mil-$25Mil
Distrib.—Intl.
Privately owned corporation

## Summit—(cont.)

### MARKOV PROCESSES INTERNATIONAL, LLC
25 Deforest Ave., Ste. 102 (07901-2140)
**Phone—(908) 608-1558**
Fax—(908) 608-1601
www.markovprocesses.com
Email—sales@markovprocesses.com
Chrm.—Michael Markov
CEO—Ran Fuchs
CFO—Patrick McKiernan
Hum. Res. & Off. Admn.—Mary Palmer
SIC—7372; *Financial research & reporting software development; Brand name—Stylus Pro*
Employs—36; Estab.—1992
Distrib.—Intl.
Privately owned corporation
AKA: MPI

### †MUENZ ENGINEERED SALES CO.
21 Chatham Rd. (07901)
Mail addr: P.O. Box 309, Summit (07902-0309)
**Phone—(908) 273-6755**
Fax—(908) 273-4855
www.muenz-engineeredsales.com
Email—info@muenz-engineeredsales.com
CEO—Jeff O'Sullivan
V-P.—Fred S. Brower
Sales Mgr.—Paul Dunn
SIC—5084; 5072; 5172; *Distributor of abrasives, cutting & power tools, machine accessories, coolants & lubricants; Brand name—3M; Seco; Dynabrade; Radiac; Milacron; Sumitomo; Ingersoll; Kyocera; Niagara; Standard Abrasives; Data Flute; YMW; YG1; Maford; Lenox; OSG*
Employs—16
Sales—$8Mil
Distrib.—Regional
Privately owned corporation
AKA: MESCO

### NATALE'S SUMMIT BAKERY
185 Broad St. (07901)
**Phone—(908) 277-2074**
Fax—(908) 277-0960
www.natalesbakery.com
Email—info@natalesbakery.com
Ptnr.—Eddie Natale
Ptnr.—Salvatore Natale
Ptnr.—Bernie Mahon
SIC—2051; 2052; NAICS—311812; *Bakery products, including breads, cakes, cookies, tarts, pies & pastries*
Employs—50; Estab.—1938
Distrib.—Local
Privately owned corporation

### REUNION GIFTS
20 Lowell Ave. (07901)
**Phone—(877) 873-8646**
www.reuniongifts.com
Email—admin@reuniongifts.com
Owner—Jerome Hairston
SIC—2396; *Apparel screen printing, including t-shirts, polo shirts, barbecue aprons & hats*
Employs—2; Estab.—1985
Sales—under $500,000
Distrib.—National
Privately owned corporation

### STESSL & NEUGEBAUER, INC.
9 Industrial Pl. (07901)
**Phone—(908) 277-3340**
Fax—(908) 277-0833
Email—eric@stesslandneugebauer.com
Pres.—Eric Stessl
Off. Mgr.—Toni-Anne De Falco
SIC—2391; NAICS—314121; *Custom upholstery & window treatments*
Employs—13; Estab.—1973
Distrib.—National
Privately owned corporation

### SUMMIT MILLWORK & SUPPLY, INC.
235 Morris Ave. (07901)
Mail addr: P.O. Box 373, Summit (07902-0373)
**Phone—(908) 277-0039**
Fax—(908) 277-6094
www.summitmillworkandsupply.com
Email—summitmillwork@gmail.com
Pres.—Nick Curiale
Secy-Treas.—Irene Curiale
SIC—2431; NAICS—321900; *Architectural moulding & millwork*
Employs—5; Estab.—1975
Sales—$500,000-$1Mil
5,000 sq ft site, Distrib.—Regional
Privately owned corporation
Also see: A & J Tool Specialties, Inc., same loc.

### TRACY'S STAINED GLASS STUDIO
11 New Providence Ave. (07901)
**Phone—(908) 273-8040**
www.tracysstainedglass.com
Email—scott@tracysstainedglass.com
Pres.—Judi Tracy
V-P.—Scott Tracy
SIC—3231; 3211; NAICS—327215; *Custom stained, leaded & beveled glass windows & hand-blown restoration glass*
Employs—3; Estab.—1972
Sales—under $500,000
3,200 sq ft site, Distrib.—Regional
Privately owned sub-S corp.

## Surf City
(Ocean—S.E.)

### SANDPAPER NEWSPAPER
1816 Long Beach Blvd. (08008)
**Phone—(609) 494-5900**
Fax—(609) 494-1437
www.thesandpaper.net
Email—production@thesandpaper.net
Pres.—Curt Travers
Off. Mgr.—Lee Little
SIC—2711; 2731; *Newspaper & book publishing*
Employs—30; Estab.—1975
Sales—$1Mil-$2.5Mil
Distrib.—Local
Privately owned corporation
AKA: Jersey Shore News Magazine

## Sussex
(Sussex—N.W.)

### ABACUS SYSTEMS, INC.
10 County Road 639 (07461)
**Phone—(973) 875-9900**
Fax—(866) 496-3099
www.abacussystems.us
Email—sales@abacussystems.us
Pres.—David Dipietro
SIC—7372; *Computer software development*
Employs—3; Estab.—1976
Distrib.—Intl.
Privately owned corporation

### AUTO GRAPHIX
56 Edsel Dr. (07461)
**Phone—(973) 492-1300**
www.njtrucklettering.com
Owner—Mike Paul
SIC—3993; *Interior & exterior signs & truck lettering*
Employs—1; Estab.—1989
Distrib.—Local
Sole ownership

### BONO SIGNS & DESIGNS, LLC
1 Beamer Rd. (07461)
**Phone—(973) 875-5488**
Fax—(973) 875-5488
Email—bonobear@ptd.net
Owner—Larry Bono
SIC—3993; *Interior & exterior signs*
Employs—1; Estab.—1986
Sales—under $500,000 (est)
Distrib.—Local
Sole ownership

### ECONO-PAK
1 Wiebel Plz. (07461)
**Phone—(973) 875-0990**
Fax—(973) 875-0726
www.econo-pak.com
Bookkeeper & Hum. Res. Mgr.—Vicky Ingrassellino
SIC—3089; *Contract packaging services & packaging products for the food, cosmetic & pharmaceutical industries*
Employs—200; Estab.—1998
100,000 sq ft site, Distrib.—Regional
Privately owned corporation
AKA: North American Packaging, LLC

### HIGH POINT PRECISION PRODUCTS
1 1st St. (07461)
**Phone—(973) 875-6229**
Fax—(973) 875-1116
www.highpointprecision.com
Email—mark@highpointprecision.com
Pres.—Charles Stipo
Prodn. Mgr.—Terry O'Brien
Hum. Res. Mgr.—Maureen O'Connor
SIC—3451; NAICS—332721; *Swiss screw machine products*
Employs—20; Estab.—1971
5,000 sq ft site, Distrib.—National
Privately owned corporation

### QUALECON MACHINE
235 Stateline Rd. (07461)
Mail addr: P.O. Box 532, Unionville (10988)
**Phone—(973) 875-4144**
www.kenrobertson.tv
Email—qualecon@embarqmail.com
Owner—Ken Robertson
SIC—3543; NAICS—332997; *Industrial prototypes*
Employs—1; Estab.—1971
Sales—under $500,000
2,000 sq ft site, Distrib.—Local
Sole ownership

### R.S. PHILLIPS STEEL, LLC
128 Lake Pochung Rd. (07461)
**Phone—(973) 827-6464**
Fax—(973) 827-2323
www.rsphillipssteel.com
Email—markv@rsphillipssteel.com
Ptnr.—Neil Phillips
Ptnr.—Scott Phillips
GM—Joe Thomas
Bus. Mgr.—Mark Vanderwerf
SIC—3499; 3444; *Steel & aluminum fabrication & erection*
Employs—23; Estab.—1940
5,000 sq ft site, Distrib.—Local
Limited Liability Company

### SUSSEX MEAT PACKING, INC.
205 Route 23 (07461)
**Phone—(973) 875-5641**
Fax—(973) 875-1333
www.sussexmeatpacking.com
Email—sussexmeathsd9@earthlink.net
Pres.—Henry Vandenakker
SIC—2011; NAICS—311611; *Meat processing & packing*
Employs—8; Estab.—1995
Sales—under $500,000
Distrib.—Local
Privately owned corporation

### TEK MOLDING, LLC
1440 County Route 565 (07461)
Mail addr: P.O. Box 735, Vernon (07462)
**Phone—(973) 702-0450**
Fax—(973) 702-0448
www.tekmolding.com
Email—tekmolding@warwick.net
Pres.—Tim Kenney, Sr.
Plt. Mgr.—Tim Kenney, Jr.
SIC—3069; 3089; *Custom natural & synthetic rubber & polymer molded products*
Employs—2; Estab.—2007
Sales—$1Mil-$2.5Mil
Distrib.—Intl.
Limited Liability Company

### TRI-STATE FENCES & SUPPLY, INC.
806 Route 23 (07461)
**Phone—(973) 875-3213**
Fax—(973) 702-8586
www.tristatecedarfence.com
Email—tristatefence@hotmail.com
Pres.—Allen Brands
V-P.—Cheryl-Jean Brands
SIC—2421; 2491; NAICS—321114; *Wooden fencing*
Employs—3; Estab.—1992
Sales—$500,000-$1Mil
Distrib.—Regional
Privately owned corporation

## Swedesboro
(Gloucester—S.W.)

### AMERICAN BIONOSTICA, INC.
510 Heron Dr., Ste. 203 (08085)
**Phone—(856) 467-7070**
Fax—(856) 467-7071
www.americanbionostica.com
Email—info@americanbionostica.com
Pres.—Rick Thompson
SIC—2835; 3841; NAICS—325400; *Rapid immunochromatographic tests for a broad range of substances & agents critical to the health of crops, animals & humans*
Employs—10; Estab.—2000
Distrib.—Intl.
Privately owned sub-S corp.

### ARYZTA/LA BREA BAKERY
Div. of Aryzta La Brea Bakery, Inc.
11 Technology Dr. (08085)
**Phone—(856) 417-8100**
Fax—(856) 417-8136
www.aryzta.com
Email—info@aryzta.com
GM—Tom Bent
Hum. Res. Mgr.—Janelle Reid Bailey
Maint. Mgr.—Jon Tenbroeck
SIC—2051; 2052; *Bakery products, including breads, cakes, cookies, muffins & pastries*
Employs—600; Estab.—1988
Sales—$50Mil-$100Mil
Distrib.—Intl.
Publicly owned corporation
Parent co.—Aryzta La Brea Bakery, Inc., Van Nuys, CA
Phone—(818) 742-4242
See Parent Co. Section for full profile.

### †ASSET RECOVERY SPECIALISTS, INC.
3 Killdeer Ct., Ste. 303 (08085-1753)
**Phone—(856) 467-9822**
National—(866) 467-9822
Fax—(856) 467-9844
www.equipmentrecovery.com
Email—jgonnella@equipmentrecovery.com
Br. Mgr.—Joe Gonnella

GEOGRAPHICAL

# Swedesboro—(cont.)

SIC—5045; 5044; *Wholesaler of used computers, computer peripherals & office copiers*
Employs—7; Estab.—2005
Distrib.—Intl.
Privately owned corporation
AKA: ARS East
Parent co.—Asset Recovery Specialists, Inc., San Diego, CA
Phone—(858) 277-7555
See Parent Co. Section for full profile.

## BAKERCORP.

50 Gilchris Dr. (08085)
**Phone—(856) 467-2677**
Fax—(856) 467-1171
www.bakercorp.com
Email—info@bakertanks.com
V.-P., Div.—Jon Heslin
SIC—3443; *Fiberglass & plastic liquid containment tanks*
Employs—19; Estab.—1942
Sales—$1Mil-$2.5Mil (est)
Distrib.—Regional
Privately owned corporation
Parent co.—BakerCorp., Seal Beach, CA
Phone—(562) 430-6262
See Parent Co. Section for full profile.

## CENTRAL INK CORP.

2085 Center Square Rd., Unit A (08085)
**Phone—(856) 467-5562**
Fax—(856) 467-5598
www.cicink.com
Email—info@cicink.com
Lab & Plt. Mgr.—Bruce Gill
Off. Mgr.—Tom Racite
SIC—2893; *Printing ink*
Employs—8
Distrib.—National
Privately owned corporation
Parent co.—Central Ink Corp., West Chicago, IL
Phone—(630) 231-6500
See Parent Co. Section for full profile.

## COBRA PRODUCTS, INC.

Div. of Masco Corp.
1 Warner Ct. (08085)
**Phone—(856) 241-7700**
National—(800) 835-2200
Fax—(856) 241-1699
www.cobraus.com
Email—info@cobraus.com
Cont.—Dick Hogan
Hum. Res. Mgr.—Caryn Pron
Cust. Serv. Rep.—Mary Jones
SIC—3423; *Drain-cleaning tools*
Employs—200; Estab.—2002
Sales—$50Mil-$60Mil
50,000 sq ft site, Distrib.—Intl.
Publicly owned corporation
Parent co.—Masco Corp., Taylor, MI
Phone—(313) 274-7400
See Parent Co. Section for full profile.

## DESIGN ASSISTANCE CORP.

3 Killdeer Ct., Ste. 301, P.O. Box 215 (08085)
**Phone—(856) 241-9500**
National—(800) 662-5877
Fax—(856) 241-9545
www.dacworldwide.com
Email—sales@dacworldwide.com
Pres.—Glenn Woerner
Cont.—Kelly Daroshefski
Prodn. Mgr.—John Clements
Pur. Mgr.—Mary Woerner
SIC—3999; *Training devices for mechanical, electrical, instrumentation, fluid power & HVAC skills, including industrial maintenance; Brand name— Synenergy; P.A. Hilton Ltd.; Pignat (France)*
Employs—25; Estab.—1980
Sales—$5.5Mil
30,000 sq ft site, Distrib.—Intl.
Privately owned corporation

## DIVERSIFIED INDUSTRIES, INC.

121 High Hill Rd. (08085)
**Phone—(856) 662-1981**
National—(800) 440-6008
Fax—(856) 662-5708
www.diversifiedindustries.com
Email—sales@ diversifiedindustries.com
Pres.—Bruce Castor
COO—Craig Keane
V.-P.—Jeffrey Caster
Hum. Res. Mgr.—Lori McKeage
Sales & Mktg. Coord.—Giovanna Carchidi
SIC—3086; 3069; NAICS— 326100; *Plastic foam & rubber fabrication*
Employs—65; Estab.—1982
Sales—$10Mil-$25Mil
100,000 sq ft site, Distrib.— National
Privately owned corporation
DBA: Diversified Foam Products, Inc.

## ETHYLENE ATLANTIC CORP.

136 Church St., P.O. Box 430 (08085)
**Phone—(856) 467-0010**
National—(800) 220-1269
Fax—(856) 467-0610
www.ethyleneatlantic.com
Email—sales@ethyleneatlantic.com
Pres.—Michael Johnston
V.-P., Sales—James A. Monaghan
Hum. Res. Mgr.—Barbara Johnston
Qual. Assur. Mgr.—Bruce Lantz
SIC—3089; 3499; *Plastic & metal fabrication*
Employs—20; Estab.—1960
Sales—$1Mil-$5Mil
9,000 sq ft site, Distrib.—Intl.
Privately owned corporation

## †GEXPRO

522 Pedricktown Rd. (08085)
**Phone—(856) 241-4700**
Fax—(856) 467-6908
www.gexpro.com
Email—automation@gexpro.com
Opers. Mgr.—Matt Brickner
SIC—5063; *Wholesaler of electrical & lighting supplies, including wire, cable & lighting fixtures*
Employs—22; Estab.—1908
Distrib.—Intl.
Privately owned corporation
Parent co.—Gexpro, Shelton, CT
Phone—(203) 925-2400
See Parent Co. Section for full profile.

## GINSEY INDUSTRIES, INC.

2078 Center Square Rd. (08085)
**Phone—(856) 933-1300**
National—(800) 257-7844
Fax—(856) 933-2342
www.ginsey.com
Email—service@ginsey.com
Pres., CEO—Herb Briggs
V.-P., CFO—George Valletti
Cont.—John Salvucci
Hum. Res. Mgr.—Kim Moreno
SIC—3089; 3086; NAICS— 326100; *Decorative kitchen & bathroom products*
Employs—100; Estab.—1978
125,000 sq ft site, Distrib.—Intl.
Privately owned corporation
AKA: Ginsey Home Solutions

## HEINKEL FILTERING SYSTEMS, INC.

520 Sharptown Rd. (08085)
**Phone—(856) 467-3399**
Fax—(856) 467-1010
www.heinkelusa.com
Email—info@heinkelusa.com
Pres.—Alan Ferraro
Cont. & Hum. Res. Mgr.— Josephine Hubbs

SIC—3821; 3569; NAICS— 339111; *Centrifuges, dryers, mixers, filtration & separation equipment & drying equipment technology for the pharmaceutical & chemical industries*
Employs—10; Estab.—1977
20,000 sq ft site, Distrib.—Intl.
Privately owned corporation

## HERITAGE BAG CO., INC.

Div. of Heritage Bag Co.
2321 High Hill Rd. (08085)
**Phone—(856) 467-2247**
National—(800) 227-2247
Fax—(856) 467-5591
www.heritage-bag.com
Email—randy.holmes@heritage-bag.com
V.-P., Sales—Ted Wells
Plt. Mgr.—Gary Pennington
SIC—2673; *Plastic bags; Brand name—Accufit; BioTuf*
Employs—150; Estab.—1998
Sales—$10Mil-$25Mil (est)
Distrib.—Intl.
Privately owned corporation
Parent co.—Heritage Bag Co., Carrollton, TX
Phone—(972) 241-5525
See Parent Co. Section for full profile.

## JOHN CRANE, INC.

301 Berkeley Dr. (08085)
**Phone—(856) 241-3507**
National—(800) 888-9582
Fax—(856) 241-3531
www.johncrane.com
Email—broot@johncrane.com
Plt. Mgr.—Pedro Vlasques
Buyer—Rachel Palumbo
SIC—3061; 3053; NAICS— 326291; *Mechanical seals for rotating equipment*
Employs—100
28,000 sq ft site, Distrib.—National
Publicly owned corporation
Parent co.—John Crane, Inc., Morton Grove, IL
Phone—(847) 967-2400
See Parent Co. Section for full profile.

## KERSHAW INSTRUMENTATION, LLC

517 Auburn Ave., P.O. Box 163 (08085)
**Phone—(856) 467-5482**
Fax—(856) 467-5482
www.kershawinst.com
Email—dean@kershawinst.com
Pres.—Dean Kershaw
Off. Mgr.—Lori Kershaw
SIC—3829; *Ink testing equipment*
Employs—5; Estab.—1991
Sales—$500,000-$1Mil (est)
1,000 sq ft site, Distrib.—Intl.
Privately owned corporation

## L & L KILN MFG. CO., INC.

505 Sharptown Rd. (08085)
**Phone—(856) 294-0077**
Fax—(856) 294-0070
www.hotkilns.com
Email—sales@hotkilns.com
Pres.—Stephen J. Lewicki
SIC—3567; NAICS—333994; *Ceramic kilns for potters, schools, universities & industrial applications; Brand name— Easy-Fire; Dyna-Glow; Jupiter; DaVinci; Dyna-Trol*
Employs—15; Estab.—1995
Sales—$1Mil-$5Mil
26,000 sq ft site, Distrib.—Intl.
Privately owned sub-S corp.

## MATTHIAS PAPER CORP.

301 Arlington Blvd., P.O. Box 130 (08085)
**Phone—(856) 467-6970**
National—(800) 523-7633
Fax—(856) 467-6991
www.matthiaspaper.com

Email—jmatthiasjr@ matthiaspaper.com
Pres.—John Matthias, Jr.
Ex. V.-P.—Warren G. Storck
V.-P., Fin.—Mark Sekel
Opers. Mgr.—Mike Balessandro
SIC—2679; NAICS—322200; *Corporate headquarters & paper converting*
Employs—30; Estab.—1904
50,000 sq ft site, Distrib.—National
Privately owned sub-S corp.

## †MCKESSON MEDICAL-SURGICAL

1130 Commerce Blvd. (08085)
**Phone—(856) 241-1709**
Fax—(856) 241-1654
www.mckesson.com
Email—mms.webmail@ mckesson.com
Dist. Mgr.—Dan Castro
Hum. Res. Mgr.—Michele Arnold
SIC—5047; *Distributor of medical supplies*
Employs—140; Estab.—1910
Distrib.—Regional
Publicly owned corporation
Parent co.—McKesson Medical-Surgical, Richmond, VA
Phone—(804) 264-7500
See Parent Co. Section for full profile.

## MULTI-PLASTICS, INC.

210 Commodore Dr. (08085)
**Phone—(856) 241-9014**
National—(800) 848-6982
Fax—(856) 241-1904
www.multi-plastics.com
Email—orders@multi-plastics.com
Mktg. Mgr., Natl.—Mark Hess
Supervisor—Christopher Parsio
SIC—3081; NAICS—326113; *Thin gage plastic film & sheet converting for the envelope, carton, label & printing industries*
Employs—50; Estab.—1979
Distrib.—Regional
Privately owned corporation
Parent co.—Multi-Plastics, Inc., Lewis Center, OH
Phone—(740) 548-4894
See Parent Co. Section for full profile.

## NIEHOFF ENDEX NORTH AMERICA, INC.

1 Mallard Ct. (08085)
**Phone—(856) 467-4884**
Fax—(856) 467-0584
www.niehoff-usa.com
Email—l.lent@niehoffendex.com
Pres.—Robert Wild
GM—Rolf Wurmbach
Pur. Mgr.—John Poplaski
Hum. Res. Mgr.—Eric Forstrom
Engrg. Mgr.—Fernando Pereira
Sales Admn.—Lisa Lent
SIC—3549; NAICS—333518; *Nonferrous wire processing machinery*
Employs—35; Estab.—1951
Sales—$6Mil-$10Mil
50,000 sq ft site, Distrib.—Intl.

## READY PAC

Div. of Ready Pac Produce, Inc.
101 Arlington Blvd. (08085)
**Phone—(856) 241-0900**
Fax—(856) 241-0020
www.readypac.com
Email—info@readypac.com
Dir., Facilities—Mike Morphew
Dir., IT—Phil Cook
SIC—2099; 3089; *Packaged fruits & salads*
Employs—300; Estab.—1977
Distrib.—National
Privately owned corporation
Parent co.—Ready Pac Produce, Inc., Irwindale, CA
Phone—(626) 856-8686
See Parent Co. Section for full profile.

## Swedesboro—(cont.)

### †ROMA OF MID-ATLANTIC
Div. of Vistar Corp.
301 Heron Dr. (08085)
**Phone—(856) 467-8100**
National—(800) 289-5516
Fax—(856) 467-7000
www.romafood.com
Email—info@romafood.com
Pres.—Ken Wineland
Sales Mgr.—Robert Donovan
Cust. Serv. Mgr.—Kim Thomas
Merchandising Mgr.—Amy
  Scheffler
SIC—5141; 5146; *Distributor of
  Italian & Italian-American food,
  including pasta, fish, meats,
  canned & packaged goods*
Employs—100
Sales—under $500,000
Distrib.—National
Privately owned corporation
Parent co.—Vistar Corp.,
  Centennial, CO
  Phone—(303) 662-7100
  See Parent Co. Section for full profile.

### SAVITA NATURALS LTD.
617 Heron Dr. (08085)
**Phone—(856) 467-4949**
Fax—(856) 467-5736
www.savitanaturals.com
Email—info@savitanaturals.com
Pres.—Richard Trout
Off. Mgr.—Mike Trout
Off. Mgr.—Joe Roy
SIC—2066; NAICS—311300;
  *Cocoa butter*
Employs—20; Estab.—1997
Sales—$2.6Mil-$5Mil
Distrib.—Local
Privately owned sub-S corp.

### SUPERIOR MARINE CANVAS CORP.
75 Belfiore Dr. (08085)
**Phone—(856) 241-1724**
www.superiorcanvas.com
Email—breed@superiorcanvas.com
Owner—Brian Reed
SIC—2394; NAICS—314912;
  *Marine canvas*
Employs—5; Estab.—1998
Sales—under $500,000 (est)
Distrib.—Local
Privately owned corporation

### TEAM INDUSTRIAL SERVICES
4 Killdeer Ct., Ste. 300 (08085)
**Phone—(610) 859-7800**
Fax—(610) 859-8944
www.teamindustrialservices.com
Email—philadelphiatcm@
  teaminc.com
Br. Mgr.—Matthew Keen
Opers. Mgr.—Ray Walls
Off. Mgr.—Irene Martin
SIC—3398; *Metal heat treating &
  NDE/NDT inspections & testing*
Employs—45
Sales—$5Mil-$10Mil (est)
Privately owned corporation
Parent co.—Team Industrial
  Services, Sugar Land, TX
  Phone—(281) 331-6154
  See Parent Co. Section for full profile.

### THOMAS SCIENTIFIC, INC. (H Q)
1654 High Hill Rd., Interstate 295,
  P.O. Box 99 (08085)
**Phone—(856) 467-2000**
National—(800) 345-2100
Fax—(856) 467-7647
www.thomassci.com
Email—cdk@ahthomas.com
Chrm.—Robert Patterson
Pres.—Richard Drew
V-P.—Gerald Wesner
Cont.—Craig Kingery
Hum. Res. Mgr.—John Nooney
SIC—2899; 3829; *Corporate
  headquarters; water, soil & air
  testing kits & lab supplies &
  reagents*
Employs—82; Estab.—1900
Sales—$25Mil-$50Mil (est)
Distrib.—National

### †THYSSENKRUPP MATERIALS NA COPPER & BRASS SALES DIV.
Div. of ThyssenKrupp Materials
  NA, Inc.
800 Arlington Blvd., Ste. C (08085)
**Phone—(610) 586-1800**
National—(800) 926-2600
Fax—(610) 586-0232
www.copperandbrass.com
Email—info@thyssenkrupp.com
Sales Mgr.—Robert Davis
SIC—5051; *Metal service center*
Employs—40; Estab.—1931
50,000 sq ft site, Distrib.—Intl.
Privately owned corporation
ISO rating—9001:2000
Parent co.—ThyssenKrupp
  Materials NA, Inc., Southfield, MI
  Phone—(248) 233-5600
  See Parent Co. Section for full profile.

### U. S. DROP FORGE CORP.
Highway 551, P.O. Box 131
  (08085)
**Phone—(856) 467-0500**
Fax—(856) 467-4598
Pres.—Joe Pro
Plt. Mgr.—Bill Yarger
SIC—3462; NAICS—332111;
  *Steel & iron forgings*
Employs—35; Estab.—1931
Distrib.—National
Privately owned corporation

### WAGONHOUSE WINERY, LLC
1401 State Highway 45 *(08085)*
**Phone—(609) 780-8019**
Fax—(856) 294-9814
www.wagonhousewinery.com
Email—info@
  wagonhousewinery.com
Ptnr.—Dan Brown
Ptnr.—Heather Brown
SIC—2084; *Sweet & dry red &
  white wines; Brand name—
  Wagonhouse Winery; Three Boys
  Brand*
Employs—2; Estab.—2004
Sales—under $500,000
3,000 sq ft site, Distrib.—Local
Limited Liability Company

### ZODIAC ARRESTING SYSTEMS AMERICA - LOGAN
Div. of Zodiac Aerospace, Inc.
2239 High Hill Rd. (08085)
**Phone—(856) 241-8620**
Fax—(856) 241-8621
www.emasmax.com
Email—emasmax@
  zodiacaerospace.com
Pres.—G. Kent Thompson
CFO—Nicholas M. Gallogly
V-P., Sales & Mktg.—Kevin Quan
Dir., Creative Mktg.—Stan
  Koczkodaj
SIC—3728; *Military & commercial
  aircraft arresting systems,
  including engineered material
  arresting systems for airport
  runway ends to safely decelerate
  aircraft; Brand name—
  EMASMAX*
Employs—120
Sales—$70Mil-$80Mil
Distrib.—Intl.
Privately owned corporation
ISO rating—9001:2008,
  14001:2004
AKA: Engineered Arresting
  Systems Corporation
DBA: ZAS
Parent co.—Zodiac Aerospace,
  Inc., Huntington Beach, CA
  Phone—(714) 934-0000
  See Parent Co. Section for full profile.

## Tabernacle
(Burlington—S.E.)

### COLONIAL CHEMICAL
78 Carranza Rd. (08088)
**Phone—(609) 268-1200**
National—(888) 268-1209
Fax—(609) 268-2117
www.colonial-chemical.com
Email—sales@colonial-
  chemical.com
Opers. Mgr.—Tim Gallagher
SIC—2899; *Custom chemical
  blending, packaging &
  distribution of inorganic
  chemicals, mineral acids, bases,
  oxidizers, urea & battery
  electrolyte*
Employs—50; Estab.—1970
Distrib.—National
Privately owned corporation
AKA: ESS Group

### PRECISION SIGN WORKS, LLC
82 Richter Rd. (08088)
**Phone—(609) 702-9700**
Fax—(609) 702-9702
www.precisionsignworksllc.com
Email—vic@wraptheearth.com
Owner—Victor Gorin
SIC—3993; 2759; 2396; *Exterior,
  carved, site & yard signs,
  banners, wraps, fleet graphics,
  letter routering, wide-format &
  canvas printing, boat lettering,
  wall murals, plaques & awards &
  apparel screen printing; Brand
  name—3M; Avery; Orocal*
Employs—3; Estab.—2001
Sales—$200,000
2,000 sq ft site, Distrib.—National
Limited Liability Company
AKA: Precision Screen Printing

### †WATER RESOURCES NEW JERSEY, LLC
1609 Route 206, P.O. Box 2172
  (08088)
**Phone—(609) 268-7965**
National—(888) 268-7965
Fax—(609) 268-7975
www.waterresourcesnj.com
Email—waternj@hotmail.com
Owner—S. Cocco
Pres.—Craig Cocco
Off. Mgr.—Sue Moran
Serv. Mgr.—Chris Cooco
SIC—5084; *Distributor of water
  treatment equipment for
  residential & commercial
  applications*
Employs—6; Estab.—1998
Sales—$1Mil-$2.5Mil
Distrib.—Regional
Limited Liability Company

## Teaneck
(Bergen—N.E.)

### AETREX WORLDWIDE, INC.
414 Alfred Ave. (07666-5756)
**Phone—(201) 833-2700**
National—(800) 526-2739
Fax—(201) 833-1485
www.aetrex.com
Email—info@aetrex.com
Chrm.—Richard Schwartz
CEO—Larry Schwartz
Pres.—Evan Schwartz
Dir., Mktg.—Robert DeRosa
IT Mgr.—Larry Jones
Hum. Res. Mgr.—Rosemary
  Finizio
SIC—3842; *Footwear, orthotics,
  foot health aids & related
  products; Brand name—
  Foot.com; iStep; Apex; Aetrex;
  Ambulator; Lynco; Essence;
  Gramercy*
Employs—140; Estab.—1946
70,000 sq ft site, Distrib.—Intl.
Privately owned sub-S corp.

### BUDGET PRINT
426 Cedar Ln. (07666)
**Phone—(201) 692-1412**
Fax—(201) 692-0468
www.budgetprintc.com
Email—debbie1101@aol.com
Owner & Graphic Design Mgr.—
  Debbie Passaretti
SIC—2752; 2759; NAICS—
  323100; *Offset, full color, large-
  format, instant & digital printing,
  including business cards,
  brochures, flyers, logo design &
  lamination*
Employs—2; Estab.—1984
Sales—under $500,000
1,000 sq ft site, Distrib.—Local
Limited Liability Company

### COGNIZANT TECHNOLOGY SOLUTIONS
500 Frank W. Burr Blvd. (07666)
**Phone—(201) 801-0233**
Fax—(201) 801-0243
www.cognizant.com
Email—inquiry@cognizant.com
Vice Chrm.—Lakshmi Narayanan
CEO—Francisco D'Souza
Pres.—Gordon Coburn
CFO—Karen McLaughlin
Group Chief Exec., Opers. &
  Tech.—Chandra Sekaran
Group Chief Exec., Industries &
  Markets—Rajeev Mehta
Sr. V-P., Gen. Counsel & Secy.—
  Steven Schwartz
Ex. V-P., Mktg. & Strategy—
  Malcolm Frank
Dir., IT—Ramesh Lakshminarayan
SIC—7372; *Company
  headquarters & marketing &
  business intelligence software
  development*
Employs—250; Estab.—1994
Worldwide: 145,200
Distrib.—Intl.
Publicly owned corporation

### COHEN PRINTING & INVITATION
500 Cedar Ln. (07666)
**Phone—(201) 287-0343**
www.cohenprinting.com
Email—alephbet@verizon.net
Owner—Ruth Cohen
SIC—3555; NAICS—323122;
  *Electronic prepress printing*
Employs—5
Sales—under $500,000 (est)
Distrib.—Intl.
Limited Liability Company

### CONTINENTAL SEASONING, INC.
Div. of Newly Weds Foods, Inc.
1700 Palisade Ave., P.O. Box 629
  (07666)
**Phone—(201) 837-6111**
National—(800) 631-1564
Fax—(201) 837-9248
www.continentalseasoning.com
Email—info@
  continentalseasoning.com
V-P., GM—Edward Levine
SIC—2099; *Food seasoning &
  spices*
Employs—32; Estab.—1965
Distrib.—National
Privately owned corporation
Parent co.—Newly Weds Foods,
  Inc., Chicago, IL
  Phone—(773) 489-7000
  See Parent Co. Section for full profile.

GEOGRAPHICAL

## Teaneck—(cont.)

**COTE-L INDUSTRIES, INC.**
1542 Jefferson St. (07666)
**Phone—(201) 836-0733**
Fax—(201) 836-5220
www.cotelind.com
Email—cfine@cotelind.com
CEO—Avi Aviner
Pres.—Cy Fine
Shpg. Mgr.—Miriam Fine
SIC—2821; 3993; 3669; 3679;
NAICS—325510; *Safety,
polyurethane, epoxy,
waterproofing, fire-resistant &
slip-resistant coatings for bus &
railcar floors, truck beds, ship
decks, steps, platforms &
handicap ramps & detectable
warning systems for the blind &
visually impaired; Brand name—
DURABAK™; CEASEFIRE™;
SAFTI-TRAX™; DrenchCote™*
Employs—6; Estab.—1991
Sales—$1Mil-$2.5Mil
4,150 sq ft site, Distrib.—Intl.
Privately owned sub-S corp.

**†DIAGNOSTIX PLUS, INC.**
197 Cedar Ln., Ste. 1 (07666-
4300)
**Phone—(201) 530-5505**
Fax—(201) 608-4556
www.diagplus.com
Email—info@diagplus.com
Founder, Pres. & CEO—Don
Bogutski
Mng. Dir.—Wayne Webster
Sales Mgr., Latin America &
Spain—Sonia Andreola
Export Mgr.—Diana Upton
Hum. Res. Mgr. & Administrator—
Jasmin Elsamra
SIC—5047; 3845;
*Remanufactured nuclear
medicine imaging equipment &
distributor of pre-owned nuclear
medicine & nuclear cardiology
imaging cameras, accessory
items & ancillary services,
including PET, SPECT & planar
cameras & cardiac stress test
systems; Brand name—ADAC;
Biodex; Capintec; CTI;
DIGIRAD; Philips Picker;
SOPHA; Technicare*
Employs—6; Estab.—1983
Distrib.—Intl.
Privately owned corporation

**ELLKAY, LLC**
259 Seddle Ln., 3rd Fl. (07666)
**Phone—(201) 791-0606**
Fax—(201) 791-0605
www.ellkay.com
Email—support@ellkay.com
Pres.—Kamao Patel
Off. Mgr.—Caroline Ayestas
Prod. Mgr.—Shreya Patel
SIC—7372; *Software
development*
Employs—11; Estab.—1988
Distrib.—Intl.
Privately owned corporation

**EVANS CHEMETICS LP (H Q)**
500 Frank W. Burr Blvd., 4th Fl.,
Glenpointe Center West (07666-
6802)
**Phone—(201) 992-3100**
Fax—(201) 992-3101
www.evans-chemetics.com
Email—info@evans-chemetics.com
CEO—Jelle Westra
CFO—Anthony Moschetti
Sales Mgr.—Virginia Slowik

SIC—2869; *Company
headquarters; organic sulfur
chemicals*
Employs—4
Sales—$35Mil
Distrib.—Intl.
Privately owned partnership
ISO rating—9001

**GALLERY MONOGRAMS**
360 Sherman Ave. (07666)
**Phone—(201) 569-0189**
Fax—(201) 569-0189
Owner—Devorah Goldberg
Manager—Mary Gold
Engr.—Burton S. Goldberg
SIC—2395; *Textile embroidery*
Employs—5; Estab.—1990
Sales—under $500,000
Distrib.—Local
Sole ownership

**INFOLYNX, INC.**
500 Frank W. Burr Blvd., Ste. 14
(07666)
**Phone—(201) 569-9085**
Fax—(201) 569-6991
www.infolynxeft.com
Email—support@infolynxeft.com
Pres.—Raymond Zoltowski
CIO—John Powers
SIC—7372; *Financial transaction
data software development*
Employs—5
Distrib.—National
Privately owned corporation

**INNER SPACES LIGHTING AND
DESIGN, LLC**
98 Copley Ave. (07666)
**Phone—(201) 692-0702**
www.innerspaceslighting.com
Email—sush54@optonline.net
GM—Scott Usher
SIC—3543; 3645; NAICS—
332997; *Custom LED & halogen
lighting fixtures & illuminated
panels, including elevator call
laterns & edge-lighted water
panels*
Employs—2; Estab.—1996
Sales—under $500,000
Distrib.—National
Limited Liability Company

**INTERSTATE SHOWCASE & STORE
FIXTURE CO.**
P.O. Box 941 (07666)
**Phone—(201) 467-4522**
Fax—(201) 928-0052
www.interstateshowcase.com
Email—showcase@
interstateshowcase.com
Pres., Sales & Mktg. Mgr.—Leon
Miller
SIC—2541; 2431; NAICS—
321900; *Wooden store fixtures &
millwork for pharmacies &
jewelry stores*
Employs—1; Estab.—1938
Sales—$500,000-$1Mil
Distrib.—Regional
Privately owned corporation

**J K PRINTING**
310 Edgewood Ave. (07666)
**Phone—(201) 833-8181**
Owner—Joseph Korn
SIC—2759; 2396; *Commercial
printing & apparel screen
printing*
Employs—2; Estab.—1980
Distrib.—Intl.
Privately owned corporation

**JOHNSON COPY CENTER, INC.,
ROBERT**
1438 Queen Anne Rd. (07666)
**Phone—(201) 833-8997**
Fax—(201) 833-8997
Owner—Robert Johnson

SIC—2752; NAICS—323100;
*Instant & offset printing*
Employs—1; Estab.—1977
Sales—under $500,000
Distrib.—National
Privately owned corporation

**K G DESIGNS, INC.**
581 Ogden Ave. (07666)
**Phone—(201) 692-1852**
Fax—(201) 692-1854
Pres.—Kenneth Goldman
SIC—2323; 2387; *Men's & boys'
neckware & belts*
Employs—40; Estab.—1987
Distrib.—National
Privately owned corporation

**KAY, INC., SCOTT**
780 Palisape Ave. (07666)
**Phone—(201) 287-0100**
National—(800) 487-2724
Fax—(201) 287-1617
www.scottkay.com
Email—info@scottkay.com
Pres.—Scott Kay
CFO—Jeff Simon
Cont. & Hum. Res. Mgr.—Elaine
Ye
IT Mgr.—David Ma
SIC—3911; NAICS—339911;
*Precious metal jewelry*
Employs—40; Estab.—2000
Distrib.—National
Privately owned corporation

**KUMON PUBLISHING NORTH
AMERICA, INC.**
300 W. Frank Burr Blvd., Ste. 6
(07666)
**Phone—(201) 836-2105**
Fax—(201) 836-1559
www.kumonbooks.com
Email—books@kumon.com
Pres.—Noriaki Usui
Assoc. Editor—Natalie Ledu
Sales & Mktg. Mgr.—Ivana
Rodriguez Valenti
SIC—2731; *Children's
educational workbook
publishing*
Employs—5; Estab.—2004
Sales—$500,000-$1Mil
Distrib.—Intl.
Privately owned corporation

**MAJESTIC SIGNS**
951 Teaneck Rd. (07666)
**Phone—(201) 837-8104**
Fax—(201) 837-8105
www.majesticsigns.net
Email—robert@majesticsigns.net
Owner—Robert Hamburg
Graphic Designer—Barbara
Switzer
SIC—3993; *Interior & exterior
neon, vinyl & plastic signs*
Employs—2; Estab.—2004
Sales—under $500,000
Distrib.—Local
Sole ownership

**MOTEK INDUSTRIES, LLC**
250 Park Ave. (07666)
**Phone—(201) 836-4167**
Fax—(201) 221-8577
www.motekindustries.com
Email—ruth@motekindustries.com
Pres.—Ruth Hacohen
Cust. Serv. Rep.—Beth Cabrera
SIC—3679; *Contract electronic
manufacturing for high-end OEM
manufacturers*
Employs—12; Estab.—2003
Sales—$500,000-$1Mil
Distrib.—Intl.
Limited Liability Company

**NESS TECHNOLOGIES, INC.**
300 Frank W. Burr Blvd. (07666)
**Phone—(201) 488-7222**
Fax—(201) 488-5040
www.ness.com
Dir., Mktg.—Douglas Mow

SIC—7372; *Life science &
pharmaceuticals software
development*
Employs—50; Estab.—2003
Sales—$1Mil-$2.5Mil
Distrib.—Intl.
Privately owned corporation

**OCTAL CORPORATION**
125 Galway Pl., Ste. B (07666)
**Phone—(201) 862-1010**
Fax—(201) 862-9100
www.octalcorporation.com
Email—mail@octalcorporation.com
Pres.—Dani Bar-David
V-P., Bus. Dev. & Sales—Chad
Vroman
Opers. Mgr.—Zvi Davidzon
Supply Chain Mgr.—Danille Nir
SIC—3711; 3714; 3795; 3429;
*Upgrade, retrofit & conversion
kits, components & parts for
military tracked & wheeled
vehicles & tanks, including
bellows, elbows, brackets,
cages, clamps, couplings,
exhaust pipes, oil canisters,
manifolds, fuel hoses & fuel
pump kits; Brand name—Delco
Remy; BorgWarner*
Employs—20; Estab.—1991
Sales—under $500Mil
20,000 sq ft site, Distrib.—Local
Privately owned corporation
ISO rating—9001:2008

**PHIBRO ANIMAL HEALTH CORP.**
300 Frank W. Burr Blvd., Stn. 21,
Glenpointe Center East, 3rd Fl.
(07666)
**Phone—(201) 329-7300**
National—(800) 220-4371
Fax—(201) 329-7399
www.pahc.com
Email—inquiry@pahc.com
Chrm.—Jack Bendheim
CEO—Gerald Carlson
CIO—Gary Fling
CFO—Richard Johnson
Sr. V-P., Hum. Res.—Dan Welch
V-P., Pur.—Milton Hamburger
Dir., Sales, Natl. Specialty
Chemicals—Mark Chamberlin
Dir., Opers.—Shari Seidman
Global Dir., R & D, Ethanol
Performance Sols.—Dennis
Bayrock
Tech. Mgr., Specialty Chemicals—
Michael Pollock
SIC—2048; 2819; *Corporate
headquarters & animal feed,
chemicals, vitamins & antibiotics*
Employs—100
Sales—$10Mil-$25Mil
47,000 sq ft site, Distrib.—Intl.
Privately owned corporation

**PHIBRO-TECH, INC.**
Div. of Phibro Animal Health Corp.
300 Frank W. Burr Blvd., Ste. 21,
Glenpointe Center East, 3rd Fl.
*(07666-6712)*
**Phone—(201) 329-7300**
(800) 357-6840
Fax—(201) 329-7035
www.phibro-tech.com
Email—phibro-tech@pahc.com
Pres. & Sales Mgr.—Dwight Glover
Sr. V-P., Hum. Res.—Daniel Welch
Cust. Serv. Mgr.—Laurie Lanham
SIC—3351; 2899; NAICS—
331421; *Corporate headquarters
& copper chemicals*
Employs—70; Estab.—1946
Sales—$10Mil-$25Mil
Distrib.—Intl.
Privately owned corporation
Parent co.—Phibro Animal Health
Corp., Teaneck, NJ
Phone—(201) 329-7300
See Parent Co. Section for full profile.

## Teaneck—(cont.)

**PICKLE-LICIOUS**
384 Cedar Ln. (07666)
**Phone—(201) 833-0100**
Fax—(201) 457-0501
www.picklelicious.com
Email—picklelicioussh@aol.com
Owner—Robyn Samra
SIC—2035; *Gourmet pickles*
Employs—2; Estab.—1989
Sales—under $500,000
Distrib.—Local
Privately owned corporation

**PRIMEPAK COMPANY**
133 Cedar Ln., Ste. 104 (07666)
**Phone—(201) 836-5060**
Fax—(201) 836-3275
www.primepakcompany.com
Email—info@primepak.com
CFO—Mike Heilferty
V-P., Sales—Bill Heilferty
V-P., Opers.—Christopher Poppe
V-P.—Jeanne Budka
SIC—2673; 3081; NAICS—
326199; *Plastic bags, including
high & low density, plain, printed,
degradable, stretch, shrink film,
re-closable, wicketed, t-shirt,
retail & restaurant take-out bags
& box liners & pallet covers*
Employs—34; Estab.—1973
Sales—$30Mil-$35Mil
Distrib.—National
Limited Liability Company

**†STRONG WEAR, LLC**
191 The Plaza Ave. (07666)
**Phone—(201) 837-7830**
Fax—(201) 837-1373
www.strongweargarment.com
Email—strongweargarment@
yahoo.com
Owner—Gilbert Ortiz
SIC—5136; 5137; *Distributor of
work & school uniforms &
sporting-casual wear for
individuals, small businesses,
school districts & commercial
customers, including embroidery
& screen printing*
Employs—3; Estab.—1967
Sales—over $500,000
9,000 sq ft site, Distrib.—National
Limited Liability Company

**STUDIO L CONTRACTING, LLC**
1401 Palisade Ave. (07666)
**Phone—(201) 837-1650**
Fax—(201) 786-9217
www.studiolonline.com
Email—info@studiolonline.com
Owner—David Lehmann
Off. Mgr.—Florence Wright
SIC—2431; 2511; 2521; 2434;
*Architectural millwork & custom
wooden furniture & cabinets*
Employs—6; Estab.—2006
Sales—$500,000-$1Mil
Distrib.—Regional
Limited Liability Company

**TROPHY KING, INC., THE**
309 Queen Anne Rd. (07666)
**Phone—(201) 836-1482**
National—(800) 718-5464
Fax—(201) 836-6763
www.trophyking.net
Email—awards@trophyking.net
Pres.—James Walsh
Prodn. Mgr.—Terrence Crotty
Manager—Bobby Schuvert
Engraver—Kevin Johnson
SIC—3499; 3479; *Corporate
headquarters & trophy assembly
& engraving*
Employs—6; Estab.—1958
4,000 sq ft site, Distrib.—Intl.
Privately owned corporation

**NEW ENTRY**
**UNITED MOTOR PARTS, INC.**
1130 Teaneck Rd. (07666)
**Phone—(201) 837-6760**
Fax—(201) 837-1925
www.unitedmotorparts.com
Owner—Alan Gladstein
SIC—3599; 3714; *General
machining job shop for the
automotive industry, including
automotive parts*
Employs—20; Estab.—1950
Sales—$2.5Mil-$5Mil (est)
Distrib.—Local
Privately owned corporation

---

## Tenafly
### (Bergen—N.E.)

**ALL AMERICAN METAL
FABRICATORS**
34 Harold St. (07670)
**Phone—(201) 567-2898**
Fax—(201) 567-4661
GM—Robert Leopold
SIC—3499; 3444; 3599; 3441;
NAICS—332312; *Steel/metal
fabrication, including steel stairs,
handrails, steel beams, columns,
flitch plates, brake metalwork &
welding*
Employs—6; Estab.—1995
Sales—under $1Mil
Distrib.—Local

**ALPEX WHEEL CO.**
29 Atwood Ave., P.O. Box 357
(07670-0357)
**Phone—(201) 871-1700**
Fax—(201) 871-1521
www.newmanwheel.com
Email—newman@
newmanwheel.com
MIS Mgr.—Attilo Tomasi
SIC—3291; *Abrasive wheel
dressers & grinding wheels*
Employs—4; Estab.—1993
Sales—under $500,000
10,000 sq ft site, Distrib.—
Regional
Privately owned corporation

**MATHEMATICS LEAGUE, INC.**
17 Lancaster Rd., P.O. Box 17
(07670)
**Phone—(201) 568-6328**
Fax—(201) 816-0125
www.mathleague.com
Email—comments@
mathleague.com
Pres.—Daniel R. Flegler
SIC—2731; *Mathematics textbook
publishing*
Employs—3; Estab.—1977
Sales—$500,000-$1Mil
Distrib.—Intl.
Privately owned corporation
AKA: Math League Press

**†SUPPLY SOURCE**
64 Oak Ave. (07670)
**Phone—(201) 735-0232**
        (201) 735-0233
National—(800) 288-3330
Fax—(206) 202-3455
www.repeatotype.com
Email—supplysource@gmail.com
Pres.—Fred Keen
CFO—Whitney Keen
SIC—5085; 5112; *Distributor of
office reprographic supplies,
including inkjet & laser
cartridges, bulk inkjet, digital
duplicator & mimeograph inks,
stencils & masters & stencil
correction fluids; Brand name—
Repeat-O-Type; Hewlett Packard*
Employs—2; Estab.—1931
Sales—$5Mil
Distrib.—Intl.
Limited Liability Company

**TIMESHARING TODAY, INC.**
140 County Rd., Ste. 114 (07670)
**Phone—(201) 871-4304**
Fax—(201) 871-4305
www.tstoday.com
Email—staff@tstoday.com
V-P.—Shep Altshuler
Editor—Ray Jacobs
Subscription Mgr.—Janet Monte
SIC—2721; 2741; *Bimonthly print
& online recreational timeshare
owners' informational magazine
publishing; Brand name—
TimeSharing Today*
Employs—5; Estab.—1991
Sales—under $500,000 (est)
Distrib.—Intl.
Privately owned corporation

---

## Tennent
### (Monmouth—N.E.)

**AER-X-DUST CORP.**
P.O. Box 93 (07763)
**Phone—(732) 946-9462**
Fax—(732) 946-3332
www.axdsic.com
Pres.—Guy D. Cusumano
SIC—3564; NAICS—333400;
*Landfill biogas skid systems,
including multistage centrifugal
blowers & exhausters & control
systems; Brand name—AXD;
Purgest; CNG; LNG; CCNG;
DLNG*
Employs—5; Estab.—1976
Sales—$500,000-$1Mil
Distrib.—National
Privately owned corporation

**REED & PERRINE SALES, INC.**
396 Main St., P.O. Box 100 (07763)
**Phone—(732) 446-6363**
Fax—(732) 446-1344
Email—ginny@reedandperrine.com
Pres.—Ginny Bulkowski
V-P.—Bob Bulkowski
Off. Mgr.—Tammy Smith
Pur. Agt.—Greg Mendina
SIC—2875; NAICS—325314;
*Fertilizer blending*
Employs—25; Estab.—1917
Sales—over $15Mil
12,000 sq ft site, Distrib.—
Regional
Privately owned corporation

---

## Teterboro
### (Bergen—N.E.)

**BERGEN AUTO UPHOLSTERY**
375 North St., Ste. U (07608)
**Phone—(201) 457-9100**
National—(800) 732-8750
Fax—(201) 457-9103
www.bergenseat.com
Email—bergenauto@aol.com
Owner—Nancy Citti
Sales Mgr.—Carol Griffenkranz
SIC—2531; *Bus seat upholstery*
Employs—15; Estab.—1937
Distrib.—National
Privately owned sub-S corp.

**CONSOLIDATED INSTRUMENT,
AVIONICS & RADIO SALES &
SERVICE**
510 Industrial Ave. (07608)
**Phone—(201) 288-1189**
Fax—(201) 288-8006
www.consolidatedinstrument.com
Email—sales@
consolidatedinstrument.com
Pres.—Eric Johannessen
V-P. & MIS Mgr.—Mark
Johannessen
Accountant—Elaine Otte
SIC—3728; *Repair of aircraft
instruments, avionics &
accessories, including
tachometers, altimeters, course
indicators, flight directors,
gyroscopes & radios; Brand
name—Aerotach; Hamilton
Compass*
Employs—15; Estab.—1946
5,000 sq ft site, Distrib.—Intl.
Privately owned corporation
AKA: Consolidated Instrument Co.

**CROLL-REYNOLDS**
90 Hollister Rd. (07608)
**Phone—(201) 288-9282**
www.croll.com
Email—info@croll.com
Br. Mgr.—A. Patel
SIC—3561; *Steam ejectors for
industrial process vacuum
systems*
Employs—4
Sales—$500,000-$1Mil (est)
Privately owned corporation
Parent co.—Croll-Reynolds,
Parsippany, NJ
Phone—(908) 232-4200
See Parent Co. Section for full profile.

**FOOD & BEVERAGE, INC.**
100 Hollister Rd., Unit 5 (07608)
**Phone—(201) 288-8881**
National—(866) 726-6543
Fax—(201) 288-8857
www.chriscookies.com
Email—manishwd@me.com
Ptnr.—Chris Gargiulo
Ptnr.—Manish Wadia
Ex. V-P., Hum. Res. & IT Mgr.—
Betty Osmanoglu
Dir., Sales & Mktg.—Meghna
Kashyap
Cust. Serv. Rep.—Fred Reich
Cust. Serv. Rep.—Martha Meza
SIC—2052; 2051; *Cookies,
brownies & pastries*
Employs—65; Estab.—2006
Sales—$11Mil-$25Mil
Distrib.—Regional
Privately owned corporation
AKA: Chris's Cookies

**FOOD INGREDIENT SOLUTIONS,
LLC**
10 Malcolm Ave., Unit 1 (07608)
**Phone—(201) 440-4377**
Fax—(201) 440-4211
www.foodcolor.com
Email—orders@foodcolor.com
CTO—Marilea Romabiles
SIC—2087; *Natural food colors*
Employs—9; Estab.—2001
Distrib.—Intl.
Limited Liability Company

**GALVES AUTO PRICE LIST, INC.**
430 Industrial Ave., Ste. 3 (07608)
**Phone—(201) 393-0051**
Fax—(201) 393-0508
www.galves.com
Email—info@galves.com
Off. Mgr.—Paul Rad
SIC—2731; *Auto price list book
publishing*
Employs—10; Estab.—1997
Sales—$500,000-$1Mil (est)
Distrib.—National
Privately owned corporation

**GOLDEN PLASTICS, INC.**
510-A Industrial Ave. (07608)
**Phone—(201) 393-9833**
Fax—(201) 393-9831
Email—henry@goldenplastics.com
Pres., CFO—Henry Kim
MIS Mgr.—Joon Kim
SIC—2673; 3089; *Plastic bags &
contract packaging*
Employs—8; Estab.—1981
Sales—$500,000-$1Mil
5,500 sq ft site, Distrib.—Local
Privately owned corporation

GEOGRAPHICAL

## Teterboro—(cont.)

**H & U, INC.**
375 North St., Ste. O (07608-1200)
**Phone—(201) 530-1100**
Fax—(201) 530-1101
www.sunnoodle.com
Email—info@sunnoodle.com
Dir., Comms.—Shawn Kim
GM—Kenshiro Uki
Sales Mgr.—George Kao
SIC—2098; *Japanese ramen noodles; Brand name—Sun Noodle*
Employs—16; Estab.—2012
Sales—$1Mil-$2.5Mil
10,000 sq ft site, Distrib.—National
Limited Liability Company
Parent co.—H & U, Inc., Honolulu, HI
Phone—(808) 841-5808
See Parent Co. Section for full profile.

**INTERFASHION COSMETICS CORP.**
32 Henry St. (07608)
**Phone—(201) 288-5858**
Fax—(201) 288-9466
www.ifcosmetics.com
Email—info@ifcosmetics.com
Pres.—James Chang
Off. Mgr.—Kelly White
SIC—2844; NAICS—325600; *Cosmetics*
Employs—45; Estab.—2001
Distrib.—Intl.
Privately owned corporation

**KNICK-KNACK, INC.**
20 Henry St. (07608)
**Phone—(201) 727-9339**
National—(877) 276-4683
Fax—(201) 727-9704
www.bluepointe.com
Email—scott_bluepointe@yahoo.com
Pres., Div.—Scott Banks
Dir., Opers.—Mohammed Sadiq
Shpg. Mgr.—Floren Flores
SIC—2339; 2329; NAICS—315200; *Women's, men's & adolescents' sportswear*
Employs—20; Estab.—1992
Sales—$1Mil-$2.5Mil
30,000 sq ft site, Distrib.—National
Privately owned corporation

**MICROFOLD, INC.**
375 North St., Unit C (07608)
**Phone—(201) 641-5052**
Fax—(201) 641-5054
www.microfoldinc.com
CEO—Paul Perna
Pres.—Debi Perna
SIC—2679; 2789; 2675; *Paper product folding, hole punching, computerized cutting, shrink wrapping, spot gluing, wafer sealing & in-line micro perfing*
Employs—10; Estab.—1996
Distrib.—National
Privately owned corporation

**†MOTION INDUSTRIES, INC.**
600 Hollister Rd. (07608)
**Phone—(201) 288-8111**
National—(800) 526-9328
Fax—(201) 288-8879
www.motionindustries.com
Email—john.kondel@motion-ind.com
Br. Mgr.—John Kondel
Opers. Mgr.—Deb Thomas
SIC—5085; *Distributor of industrial maintenance, repair & operation (MRO) parts including bearings, power transmission, electrical & indl. automation, material handling, hydraulic & pneumatic components, hydraulic & indl. hose & safety/ indl. supplies; Brand name—Altra; Baldor; Eaton; Emerson Industrial Automation; Gates; Lovejoy; Martin; Nexen; NSK; NTN; Rexnord; Schaeffler Group; SEW Eurodrive; SKF; SMC; Sumitomo; THK; Thomson; Timken; Tsubaki; US Motors; Vacon; Webster*
Employs—9
Distrib.—National
Privately owned corporation
Parent co.—Motion Industries, Inc., Birmingham, AL
Phone—(205) 951-1154
See Parent Co. Section for full profile.

**NORTHERN ARCHITECTURAL SYSTEMS**
111 Central Ave. (07608)
**Phone—(201) 943-6400**
Fax—(201) 943-1282
www.northernarchitecturalsystems.com
Email—info@northernarchitecturalsystems.com
Pres.—Robert Pecorella
V.-P., Bus. Dev.—Mike Richard
Dir., Pur.—Grace Piccini
Dir., Design Engrg.—Christopher Vogt
SIC—3442; NAICS—332321; *Corporate headquarters & aluminum windows, doors, window & curtain walls & storefronts for new & replacement mid-rise & high-rise construction; Brand name—Northern Architectural Systems*
Employs—149; Estab.—1956
Sales—$30Mil
127,000 sq ft site, Distrib.—Intl.
Privately owned corporation

**PANTINA COSMETICS, INC.**
30 Henry St. (07608)
**Phone—(201) 288-7767**
(201) 288-9477
National—(877) 680-9939
Fax—(201) 288-9466
www.pantina.com
Email—info@pantina.com
Founder & Hum. Res. Mgr.—Wendy Chang
Proj. Mgr.—Serin Kim
Acct. Exec.—James Chang
SIC—2844; NAICS—325600; *Cosmetics & skin care products*
Employs—20; Estab.—1992
Distrib.—Intl.
Sole ownership

**SPRING TIME BEDDING CORP.**
25 Central Ave. (07608)
Mail addr: P.O. Box 4157, South Hackensack (07606)
**Phone—(973) 473-5400**
Fax—(973) 473-0400
www.springtimebedding.com
Email—sales@springtimebedding.com
Pres.—Moshe Jakobovits
Plt. Mgr.—Moses Rosenberg
Plt. Mgr.—Isaac Jakobovits
SIC—2515; *Mattresses*
Employs—8; Estab.—2002
Sales—$1Mil-$2.5Mil (est)
20,000 sq ft site, Distrib.—Local
Privately owned corporation

**SUPERIOR PRINTING INK CO., INC.**
100 North St. (07608)
**Phone—(201) 478-5600**
Fax—(201) 478-5650
www.superiorink.com
Email—info@superiorink.com
Chrm., Pres. & CEO—Jeffrey Simons
CFO—Harold Rubin
COO—James La Rocca
Ex. V.-P.—Stanley Hittman
Corp. Cont.—Peter Nunez
Dir., Mfg. Svcs.—Dan Shevkun
Dir., Corp. Pur.—Judith Zuckerman
Dir., Hum. Res.—Robert Volante
Cred. Mgr.—Ken Hurkala
SIC—2893; NAICS—325910; *Corporate headquarters & lithographic, gravure, flexographic, gloss & metallic printing ink & coatings; Brand name—Biolocity; Elite; Evolution*
Employs—300; Estab.—1918
Sales—$50Mil-$100Mil
Distrib.—National
Privately owned corporation
ISO rating—9001:2008

**SWIFT CO., INC., JOHN S.**
375 North St., Unit N (07608)
**Phone—(201) 678-3232**
Fax—(201) 678-3001
www.johnswiftprint.com
GM—Doug Wilhelm
SIC—2759; *Commercial printing, including letterheads, business cards, brochures, magazines & phonebooks*
Employs—10; Estab.—2008
5,400 sq ft site, Distrib.—National
Privately owned corporation
Parent co.—Swift Co., Inc., John S., Buffalo Grove, IL
Phone—(847) 465-3300
See Parent Co. Section for full profile.

**†SWIFT ELECTRICAL SUPPLY CO., INC.**
100 Hollister Rd. (07608)
**Phone—(201) 462-0900**
Fax—(201) 462-0130
www.swiftelectrical.com
Email—webmaster@swiftelectrical.com
Pres.—August Sodora, Jr.
CFO—Irwin Turk
V.-P., Opers.—Bob Cueman
IT Mgr.—Keith Garrett
SIC—5063; *Corporate headquarters & distributor of electrical & lighting equipment & supplies*
Employs—56; Estab.—1943
Distrib.—Regional
Privately owned corporation

**SYMRISE, INC.**
300 North St. (07608)
**Phone—(201) 288-3200**
National—(800) 422-1559
Fax—(201) 462-2200
www.symrise.com
Email—info@symrise.com
CEO—Heinz-Jurgen Bertram
V.-P., Hum. Res.—Margaret Castello
V.-P., Supply Chain, Flavors Div., N.A.—Larry Garrow
Dir., Hum. Res., Flavors Div., N.A.—Lynn Maloney
SIC—2087; 2844; 2099; NAICS—311900; *Corporate headquarters & food flavorings & extracts & fragrances*
Employs—350; Estab.—2003
Company-wide: 4,900
Sales—$200Mil
Distrib.—Intl.
Privately owned corporation

**TRUCK PARTS SPECIALISTS**
Div. of Illinois Tool Works, Inc.
150 Central Ave. (07608)
**Phone—(201) 288-9333**
National—(800) 631-0980
Fax—(201) 288-0121
www.truckparts-specialists.com
GM—Rich Toskonka
Sales Mgr.—Fred Paul
SIC—3714; *Rebuilt transmissions*
Employs—12; Estab.—1946
Sales—under $500,000
Distrib.—National
Publicly owned corporation
Parent co.—Illinois Tool Works, Inc., Glenview, IL
Phone—(847) 724-7500
See Parent Co. Section for full profile.

**WORTMANN MACHINE WORKS, INC., E.**
50 Hollister Rd., P.O. Box 1657 (07608)
**Phone—(201) 288-1654**
Fax—(201) 288-5242
Email—wortmannmachine@aol.com
GM & Sales Mgr.—Brett Rogers
Qual. Control Mgr.—George Rogers
Bookkeeper—Nancy Cambria
SIC—3599; *Fabrication & general machining job shop*
Employs—10; Estab.—1943
Sales—$500,000-$1Mil
15,000 sq ft site, Distrib.—Local
Privately owned corporation

---

## Thorofare
(Gloucester—S.W.)

**AKERS BIOSCIENCES, INC.**
201 Grove Rd. (08086)
**Phone—(856) 848-8698**
Fax—(856) 848-0269
www.akersbiosciences.com
Email—info@akersbiosciences.com
Ex. Chrm. of the Board—Raymond F. Akers, Jr.
Ex. V.-P., Sales & Mktg.—Edwin Hendrick
V.-P., Sales & Mktg., Intl.—Nicolas Daurel
V.-P., Mktg.—Patrice Laterra McMorrow
V.-P., Fin.—Gary Rauch
Dir., Corp. & Legal Affs.—George Awad
SIC—2835; NAICS—325400; *Medical diagnostic products; Brand name—PIFA® Heparin/ PF4; PIFA® PLUSS PF4 Rapid Assays; BreathScan® Disposable Breath Alcohol Detectors; METRON™*
Employs—26; Estab.—1989
Sales—$2Mil
10,800 sq ft site, Distrib.—Intl.
Publicly owned corporation

**†ARAMSCO**
1480 Grandview Ave., P.O. Box 29 (08086)
**Phone—(856) 686-7700**
National—(800) 767-6933
Fax—(856) 848-0802
www.aramsco.com
Email—info@aramsco.com
Pres.—Rich Salerno
V.-P., Opers.—Ray Delvecchio
V.-P., Fin.—Curt Massey
Sales Mgr.—Peter Curran
Mktg. Mgr.—Janet Andrews
Hum. Res. Mgr.—Mary Ellen McKenna
SIC—5169; 5084; 5085; *Company headquarters & distributor of asbestos, lead, mold & hazardous materials abatement chemicals & industrial safety equipment & emergency preparedness supplies*
Employs—65; Estab.—1965
Distrib.—National
Privately owned sub-S corp.

**BOYLE TOOL & DIE CO., INC.**
135 Crown Point Rd. (08086)
**Phone—(856) 853-1818**
Fax—(856) 848-2418
www.boyletool.com
Email—info@boyletool.com

## Thorofare—(cont.)

Pres.—Thomas J. Boyle
Off. Mgr.—Briana Morton
Engr.—Steve Boyle
SIC—3544; 3469; NAICS—
333500; Metal stampings & tool
& die job shop
Employs—9; Estab.—1974
Sales—$500,000-$1Mil
Distrib.—Local

### †CANUSO, INC., LOUIS P.

401 Crown Point Rd., P.O. Box 501
(08086)
Phone—(856) 845-2700
Fax—(856) 845-8831
www.lpcanuso.com
Email—info@lpcanuso.com
Owner—Joseph Canuso
V-P.—Gerald Canuso
Bookkeeper—Mary Talalaj
SIC—5051; 5074; Wholesaler of
pipe, valves, fittings & industrial
piping components
Employs—65; Estab.—1965
Distrib.—Regional
Privately owned corporation

NEW ENTRY

### CHECKPOINT SYSTEMS, INC. (H Q)

101 Wolf Dr., P.O. Box 188 (08086)
Phone—(856) 848-1800
National—(800) 257-5540
Fax—(215) 568-2286
www.checkpointsystems.com
Pres., Shrink Mgmt. Sols.—
Farrokh Abadi
Pres., Merchandise Visibility,
Apparel Lab—Per Levin
Group Pres.—James Wrigley
V-P., CIO—Salvatore Dona
V-P., Global Hum. Res. Opers.—
Carol Roy
SIC—3669; NAICS—334290;
Corporate headquarters;
advanced shrink management &
retail security software & security
system parts for apparel labeling
& merchandise visibility
applications; Brand name—
Checkpoint; Alpha; OAT;
CheckPro; Check-Net; METO;
EVOLVE; Hard Tag @ Source;
Keepers; SpiderWrap; 3 Alarm
SpiderWrap; CableLok; Nano
Gate; ToteLok
Employs—200; Estab.—1969
Worldwide: 5,800
Sales—$25Mil-$50Mil (est)
Distrib.—Intl.
Privately owned corporation

### COLACE CO., LLC, THOMAS

Div. of Lipman
800 Grove Rd. (08086)
Phone—(856) 384-4980
National—(800) 875-1379
Fax—(856) 384-8120
Pres., CEO—Thomas Colace, Jr.
Treas.—Vincent Colace II
Hum. Res. Rep.—Tina Slinn
SIC—3089; Fresh tomato
packaging
Employs—120; Estab.—1954
60,000 sq ft site, Distrib.—
Regional
Parent co.—Lipman, Immokalee,
FL
Phone—(239) 657-4421
See Parent Co. Section for full profile.

### †CUSTOM PAK, INC.

Div. of Lipman
800 Grove Rd. (08086)
Phone—(856) 384-4980
www.custompakwest.com
Email—donm@custompak.net
GM & Plt. Mgr.—Don Martin

SIC—5148; Wholesaler of
produce
Employs—300; Estab.—1994
Distrib.—Regional
Privately owned corporation
AKA: Thomas Collace Co.
Parent co.—Lipman, Immokalee,
FL
Phone—(239) 657-4421
See Parent Co. Section for full profile.

### DGB BEARING & TECHNOLOGY

Div. of EnPro Industries, Inc.
700 Mid Atlantic Pkwy., P.O. Box
189 (08086)
Phone—(856) 848-3200
Fax—(856) 848-4552
www.ggbearings.com
Email—gbsales@
garlockbearings.com
Pres.—Ken Walker
V-P., Opers.—Marvin Riley
V-P., Bus. & Mktg.—Joseph Fults
Dir., Hum. Res.—Carolyn James
Plt. Mgr.—Susan Sweeney
Matls. Mgr.—Edwin Davis
Proj. Coord.—Cheryl Kelly
Sales Rep.—Irma Fennal
SIC—3562; NAICS—332991;
Bearings
Employs—250
132,000 sq ft site, Distrib.—Intl.
Publicly owned corporation
Parent co.—EnPro Industries, Inc.,
Charlotte, NC
Phone—(704) 731-1500
See Parent Co. Section for full profile.

### DUFFY, INC., ANDREW B.

322 Crown Point Rd., P.O. Box 569
(08086)
Phone—(856) 845-4900
National—(877) 223-8339
Fax—(856) 845-3921
www.abduffy.com
Email—info@abduffy.com
Pres.—Brian Duffy
Opers. Mgr.—William H. Harle
Off. Mgr.—Sherri Veicock
SIC—3499; 3599; Stainless steel,
steel, titanium, aluminum & alloy
plate sheet, pipe & structural
welding, forming & fabrication &
pressure vessels
Employs—15; Estab.—1951
Sales—$1Mil-$5Mil
15,000 sq ft site, Distrib.—National
Privately owned corporation

### †HART INDUSTRIES, INC.

135 Crown Rd. (08086)
Phone—(856) 686-1455
National—(800) 381-1418
Fax—(856) 686-1457
www.hose.com
Email—info@hartindustries.net
GM—Steve Shera
Shpg. & Rec. Mgr.—David Neal
SIC—5085; 5162; Wholesaler of
rubber & plastic hose & tubing
Employs—5; Estab.—1990
5,000 sq ft site, Distrib.—National
Privately owned corporation
Parent co.—Hart Industries, Inc.,
Middletown, OH
Phone—(513) 422-3639
See Parent Co. Section for full profile.

### INTERNATIONAL PAPER CO.

33 Phoenix Dr. (08086)
Phone—(856) 853-7000
National—(800) 569-3500
Fax—(856) 853-8057
www.internationalpaper.com
Email—sales@ipaper.com
Cont.—Richard Scott
GM—Jim Mooney

SIC—2653; 3565; NAICS—
322211; Corrugated boxes &
point-of-purchase displays &
packaging
Employs—175; Estab.—1990
400,000 sq ft site, Distrib.—
National
Publicly owned corporation
Parent co.—International Paper
Co., Memphis, TN
Phone—(901) 419-9000
See Parent Co. Section for full profile.

### MATTEO & SONS, INC., JAMES

1692 Crown Point Rd. (08086)
Phone—(856) 845-0398
Fax—(856) 845-2331
www.matteo-iron.com
Email—davespade@gmail.com
Pres.—Frank Matteo
Opers. Mgr.—Jim Matteo
SIC—3341; Scrap metal
Employs—7; Estab.—1939
Sales—under $500,000
Distrib.—Local
Privately owned corporation

### SHARED SYSTEMS TECHNOLOGY, INC.

Div. of Structural Group, Inc.
127 Salem Ave. (08086)
Mail addr.: P.O. Box 408, Sewell
(08080)
Phone—(856) 218-7900
National—(877) 701-5236
Fax—(856) 218-8410
www.sstinc.net
Email—sales@sstinc.net
Pres.—Eric Swyers
SIC—3272; Concrete coatings
Employs—20; Estab.—1993
10,000 sq ft site, Distrib.—National
Privately owned corporation
Parent co.—Structural Group, Inc.,
Hanover, MD
Phone—(410) 850-7000
See Parent Co. Section for full profile.

### SLACK, INC.

6900 Grove Rd. (08086)
Phone—(856) 848-1000
Fax—(856) 848-6091
www.slackinc.com
Email—klind@slackinc.com
Pres.—Peter Slack
Sr. V-P.—Denise Mealey
IT Mgr.—Linda Baker
Hum. Res. Mgr.—Robin Dellolio
SIC—2731; 2721; Medical book,
magazine & journal publishing
Employs—255; Estab.—1959
Distrib.—National
Privately owned corporation
AKA: Wyanoke Group, The

### TROEMNER, LLC, HENRY

201 Wolf Dr., P.O. Box 87 (08086)
Phone—(856) 686-1600
National—(800) 249-5554
Fax—(856) 686-1601
www.troemner.com
Email—troemner@troemner.com
Pres.—Wilbert Abele
V-P., Sales & Mktg.—Amy Evans
V-P., Opers.—Steve Butler
V-P.—Robert Scheu
Hum. Res. Mgr.—Allyson Lynch
Prod. Mgr.—Brian Ramey
Pur. Agt.—Joseph Hutchinson
SIC—3821; 3829; NAICS—
339111; Precision weights,
laboratory equipment &
calibration services
Employs—100; Estab.—1840
Sales—$10Mil-$15Mil
47,000 sq ft site, Distrib.—Intl.
Privately owned sub-S corp.
ISO rating—9001

### WATSON ASSOCS., INC.

800 Grove Rd. (08086)
Phone—(856) 845-8800
Fax—(856) 845-8894
Email—watsonassocinc@aol.com

Pres.—Edward Schafer
SIC—3496; 3565; NAICS—
333993; Conveyor belts &
packaging equipment
Employs—2; Estab.—1963
Sales—under $500,000
5,000 sq ft site, Distrib.—Intl.
Privately owned corporation

## Three Bridges

(Hunterdon—N.W.)

### EMERGENCY TRANSFER CONTROLS, INC.

251 Nuthatch Ct. (08887)
Phone—(908) 782-1794
Fax—(908) 782-0794
www.etccontrols.com
Email—joeragland@
etccontrols.com
V-P.—Joseph Ragland
Bookkeeper—Maria Carrillo
SIC—3625; Industrial controllers
for automatic transfer switches
(ATS), breaker pair schemes &
main-tie-main transfer schemes
in low & medium-voltage
switchgear applications
Employs—2; Estab.—2003
Sales—under $500,000
Distrib.—Intl.
Privately owned corporation

## Tinton Falls

(Monmouth—N.E.)

### BIOLOGICAL CONTROLS, INC.

749 Hope Rd., Ste. A (07724-
1433)
Phone—(732) 389-8922
National—(800) 224-9768
Fax—(732) 389-8821
www.biologicalcontrols.com
Email—sales@
biologicalcontrols.com
Pres.—Gary Messina
Off. Mgr.—Brenda Caswell
SIC—3365; 3841; 3564; NAICS—
331524; Hospital infection
control equipment & police
evidence property room air
quality control equipment; Brand
name—AirMATION; Microcon;
ACCUSTAT
Employs—5; Estab.—1973
Sales—$3Mil-$4Mil
Distrib.—Intl.
Privately owned sub-S corp.

### CONSOLIDATED MATERIAL CONVERTERS, INC.

74 Squankum Rd. (07724)
Phone—(732) 389-5973
Fax—(732) 389-9696
Email—cutting45@verizon.net
Pres.—Neal Marty
SIC—2621; 3081; NAICS—
326113; Paper & plastic slitting,
sheeting & trimming
Employs—20; Estab.—1946
Sales—$500,000-$1Mil
40,000 sq ft site, Distrib.—Local
Privately owned corporation

### CURVON CORP.

34 Apple St. (07724)
Phone—(732) 747-3832
National—(800) 631-2236
Fax—(732) 747-5491
www.curvon.com
Email—curvoncorp@aol.com
Pres.—Blake Banta
SIC—2399; Horse clothing
Employs—12; Estab.—1891
Sales—under $500,000
Distrib.—National
Privately owned corporation

GEOGRAPHICAL

## Tinton Falls—(cont.)

**E&M GOLD BEEKEEPERS, LLC**
113 Hope Rd. (07724)
Phone—(732) 542-6528
www.emgoldbeekeepers.com
Ptnr.—Mary Kosenski
Ptnr.—Ed Kosenski
SIC—2099; 2841; 2844; 3999; All-natural honey & honey & beeswax-based products, including soaps, lip balms & candles
Employs—2; Estab.—2001
Sales—under $500,000
Distrib.—National
Limited Liability Company
AKA: E&M Wedding Favors

**EAST COAST PANELBOARD, INC.**
101 Tornillo Way (07712)
Phone—(732) 739-6400
Fax—(732) 739-6482
www.ecpowersystems.com
Pres.—Salvatore Rinaldi III
V-P.—Mary Rinaldi
Treas., Hum. Res. & IT Mgr.—Maria Rahner
SIC—3613; 3625; NAICS—335313; Electrical controls, switchboards & panels
Employs—24; Estab.—1983
130,000 sq ft site, Distrib.—National
Privately owned corporation
AKA: East Coast Power Systems

**EATON FILTRATION, LLC**
Div. of Eaton Corp.
44 Apple St. (07724)
Phone—(732) 767-4200
National—(800) 859-9212
Fax—(952) 906-3706
www.eaton.com
Email—filtrationorders@eaton.com
Pres.—Rick Jacobs
Sales Mgr.—Cory Gray
Pur. Agt.—John Hanson
SIC—3569; Filtration systems
Employs—100; Estab.—1968
Distrib.—Intl.
Publicly owned corporation
Parent co.—Eaton Corp., Cleveland, OH
Phone—(216) 523-5000
See Parent Co. Section for full profile.

**ELITE STONE IMPORTERS, LLC**
45 Park Rd. (07724)
Phone—(732) 542-7900
Fax—(730) 440-4625
www.elitestoneimporters.com
Email—info@elitestoneimporters.com
Cust. Serv. Mgr.—Laurie Escalante
SIC—3281; Stone products, including countertops & vanities
Employs—8; Estab.—2010
Distrib.—Local
Limited Liability Company

**EPS CORPORATION**
78 Apple St. (07724)
Phone—(732) 747-8277
National—(800) 237-4277
Fax—(732) 530-4726
www.epscorp.com
Email—eps@epscorp.com
Chrm., CEO—Francesco A. Musorrafiti
Vice Chrm., Pres. & CIO—Antoinette M. Musorrafiti
Pres., EPS Field Serv.—Charles F. White
Sr. V-P., Gen. Counsel & CCO—John E. Gagliano
Sr. V-P., Admn. & Fin. & CFO—Susan M. Moran
V-P., Admn.—Kelley Meritzis

SIC—7373; NAICS—541512; Computer integrated systems, including the AN/PRC-112 survivable radio for the U.S. Army; Brand name—AN/PRC 112; EPS 10 Hovercraft; EPS 2.2 Hovercraft
Employs—52; Estab.—1983
Sales—$70Mil-$100Mil
1,200 sq ft site, Distrib.—Intl.
Privately owned corporation
AKA: EPS

**GRIMMER & SONS, INC., C. W.**
75 Gilbert St. W. (07701)
Phone—(732) 741-2189
Fax—(732) 741-6210
Email—grimmersteel@verizon.net
Pres.—William D. Grimmer
V-P.—Skip Hallowell
SIC—3312; Steel fabrication
Employs—6; Estab.—1927
Sales—$500,000-$1Mil
Distrib.—Local
Privately owned corporation

**GROUP C MEDIA, INC.**
44 Apple St., Ste. 3 (07724)
Phone—(732) 842-7433
National—(800) 524-0337
Fax—(732) 758-6634
www.groupc.com
Email—luann@groupc.com
Co-Pres.—Susan Coene
Co-Pres.—Ted Coene
Prodn. Mgr.—LuAnn Rathemacher
SIC—2721; 2741; Monthly print & online informational trade magazine publishing for facility management professionals
Employs—20; Estab.—1980
Distrib.—Intl.
Privately owned corporation

**HATTERAS, INC.**
56 Park Rd. (07724)
Phone—(732) 223-9888
National—(800) 695-0719
Fax—(732) 223-1232
www.hatteras-press.com
Email—print@hatteras-press.com
Pres.—Charles Duerr
CFO—Nicole Nichols
V-P., Opers.—Tom Imfeld
Pur. Mgr.—Joe Fiorvanti
IT Mgr.—Vince Gathmann
Hum. Res. Mgr.—Christine Duggan
Qual. Control Mgr.—Al Natale
SIC—2752; NAICS—323100; Offset & digital printing, fulfillment & mailing service
Employs—250; Estab.—1983
50,000 sq ft site, Distrib.—National
Privately owned sub-S corp.

**ICE KING & COLD STORAGE, INC.**
4045 Route 33 W. (07753)
Mail addr: 144 Shark River Rd., Tinton Falls (07753)
Phone—(732) 922-0852
National—(800) 848-0272
Fax—(732) 922-3445
www.icekingandcoldstorage.com
Email—ikcs@aol.com
Pres.—Adrienne Lomangino
Opers. Mgr.—Fred Lomangino
Bookkeeper—Rosemary Welsh
Dispatcher—Jim Thomas
SIC—2097; NAICS—312113; Ice cube processing & cold storage
Employs—10; Estab.—1990
Distrib.—Regional
Privately owned sub-S corp.

**JSM CO.**
1052 Wayside Rd. (07712)
Phone—(732) 695-9577
Fax—(732) 695-9578
www.jerseyspeedskiffs.com/jsm_cut-off.htm
Email—jsmcompany@verizon.net
Owner—David Paraskevas

SIC—3599; 3499; Precision automatic cut-off sawing, general machine work, metal fabrication & welding
Employs—5; Estab.—1980
Sales—under $1Mil
Distrib.—National
Sole ownership

**POLARIS PLATE HEAT EXCHANGERS**
106 Apple St., Ste. 106 (07724-2670)
Phone—(732) 345-7188
Fax—(732) 345-7166
www.polarisphe.com
Email—sales@polarisphe.com
Owner—Steve Weintraub
Sales Engr.—Rhona Weintraub
SIC—3443; Plate heat exchangers
Employs—4
Sales—$500,000-$1Mil
Privately owned corporation

**POWERTRONIC, INC.**
3092 Shafto Rd., Unit 7 (07753)
Phone—(732) 643-1500
www.powertronic.com
Email—david@powertronic.com
Pres.—David Emery
SIC—3625; Industrial control panels for commercial & industrial businesses
Employs—4
Sales—$500,000-$1Mil (est)
Distrib.—National
Privately owned corporation

**PRECISION SHOWER DOORS, INC.**
359 Essex Rd. (07753)
Phone—(732) 389-8175
National—(800) 648-7384
Fax—(732) 389-8179
www.precisionshowerdoors.com
Email—sales@precisionshowerdoors.com
Pres.—Tom Basile
V-P., Prodn. & Plt. Mgr.—Bob Petillo
SIC—3231; NAICS—327215; Frameless glass shower enclosures & glass fabrication
Employs—13; Estab.—1984
40,000 sq ft site, Distrib.—Regional
Privately owned sub-S corp.

**RANGER INDUSTRIES, INC.**
15 Park Rd. (07724)
Phone—(732) 389-1101
National—(800) 244-2211
Fax—(732) 389-1102
www.rangerink.com
Email—info@rangerink.com
Dir., Sales—Alain Avrillon
GM—Justin Russo
Cust. Serv. Rep.—Diane Spiak
SIC—2893; 3953; NAICS—325910; Ink, pads & embossing powders
Employs—62; Estab.—1929
Sales—$11Mil-$25Mil
57,000 sq ft site, Distrib.—Intl.
Privately owned corporation

**RED BANK CABINET CO.**
548 Shrewsbury Ave. (07701)
Phone—(732) 741-8080
Fax—(732) 741-2246
www.redbankcabinets.com
Email—rbc@redbankcabinets.com
Pres., R & D Mgr.—Kenneth Asmar
MIS, Opers. & Pers. Mgr.—Christine Asmar
Off. Mgr.—Jennifer Soberg

SIC—2434; 2541; NAICS—337110; Custom & semi-custom cabinets & exhibit showcases & residential, commercial, institutional & museum display casework
Employs—10; Estab.—1966
4,900 sq ft site, Distrib.—Local
Limited Liability Company

**STAVOLA CONTRACTING CO., INC.**
175 Drift Rd. (07724)
Mail addr: P.O. Box 482, Red Bank (07701)
Phone—(732) 542-2328
Fax—(732) 389-6083
www.stavola.com
Email—information@stavola.com
Pres.—Joseph Stavola
Corp. Secy.—James Stavola, Jr.
Sales Mgr.—Tony Monsalud
IT Mgr.—Jim Bean
Hum. Res. Mgr.—Dominique Goode
Off. Mgr.—Karen Dunn
SIC—2951; NAICS—324121; Corporate headquarters & asphalt paving compounds
Employs—60
Sales—$2.5Mil-$5Mil (est)
Distrib.—Local
Privately owned corporation

## Titusville
(Mercer—N.E.)

**BLAUTH MILLWORK**
57 Pleasant Valley Rd. (08560)
Phone—(609) 737-9502
Fax—(609) 737-1952
Pres.—Gerard L. Blauth
SIC—2431; NAICS—321900; Architectural millwork
Employs—1; Estab.—1983
Sales—under $500,000
8,000 sq ft site, Distrib.—Local
Privately owned corporation

**GUERARD CO., J. D.**
43 Old Washington Crossing Rd. (08560)
Phone—(609) 737-8892
Fax—(609) 737-3832
Email—mail4jg@horizon.net
Owner—John Guerard
SIC—3599; Precision machining job shop
Employs—1; Estab.—1971
Sales—under $500,000
Distrib.—Intl.
Sole ownership

**JANSSEN PHARMACEUTICALS, INC.**
Div. of Johnson & Johnson
1125 Trenton-Harbourton Rd., P.O. Box 200 (08560)
Phone—(908) 218-6000
National—(800) 682-6532
www.janssenpharmaceuticalsinc.com
Dir., Sales, Natl. Cardiology—Judith Wicklum
SIC—2834; NAICS—325412; Pharmaceuticals
Employs—2000; Estab.—1993
Sales—over $100Mil
Distrib.—Intl.
Publicly owned corporation
Parent co.—Johnson & Johnson, New Brunswick, NJ
Phone—(732) 524-0400
See Parent Co. Section for full profile.

## Toms River
(Ocean—S.E.)

**†ALABASTER SUPPLY, INC.**
2317 South St. (08753)
Phone—(732) 330-9242
National—(877) 896-9340
Fax—(877) 896-9340
shop.alabastersupply.com

## Toms River—(cont.)

Email—sales@alabastersupply.com
Pres.—Steven Pereira
SIC—5075; *Wholesaler of replacement heating parts for oil & gas burners, oil nozzles, AAMA water test kits & B-25 water nozzles, electrodes, igniters, flame rods, liquid level electrodes & feed-throughs; Brand name—Crown Engineering Corp; Monarch Nozzles; Wayne Combustion Systems; Westwood Products; U.S. Ignition; Auburn Igniters*
Employs—2; Estab.—2000
Sales—under $50,000
Distrib.—National
Privately owned sub-S corp.

### ALL AMERICAN POWDER COATING

2002 Route 9 (08755)
**Phone—(732) 349-7001**
Fax—(732) 349-7079
www.aapowdercoating.com
Email—aapowdercoating@gmail.com
Pres.—Robyn Ciccone
Manager—John Ciccone, Jr.
SIC—3471; 3479; NAICS—332812; *Blasting & powder coating*
Employs—4; Estab.—2004
Distrib.—Regional
Privately owned corporation
Also see: Ciccone Custom Railing & Manufacturing, Inc., same loc.

### †ALLIED BUILDING PRODUCTS CORP.

320 W. Water St. (08753)
**Phone—(732) 341-4767**
Fax—(732) 341-4787
www.alliedbuilding.com
Email—sales@alliedbuilding.com
Br. Mgr.—Gary Finn
SIC—5033; 5031; *Distributor of building materials & supplies, including roofing, siding, windows & doors*
Employs—10; Estab.—2006
Distrib.—National
Publicly owned corporation
Parent co.—Allied Building Products Corp., East Rutherford, NJ
Phone—(201) 507-8400
See Parent Co. Section for full profile.

### ALLIED OP

810 Hooper Ave. (08753)
**Phone—(732) 341-9191**
Fax—(732) 341-9222
www.alliedop.com
Pres.—Joshua Schenkman
Orthotist—Richard Tall
SIC—3842; *Prosthetics & orthotics*
Employs—3; Estab.—1994
1,600 sq ft site, Distrib.—Regional
Privately owned corporation

### ALL-STAR PRO TROPHY

1012 Cox Cro Rd., Ste. 10 (08755)
**Phone—(732) 364-1188**
Fax—(732) 364-1392
www.allstarprotrophies.com
Email—allstartrophynj@gmail.com
Owner—Maryanna Forman
SIC—3479; *Trophy engraving*
Employs—1; Estab.—1997
Sales—under $500,000
Distrib.—Local
Sole ownership

NEW ENTRY
### AMORY A & E CAMPIAN DENTAL ART, INC.

803 Main St., Ste. 2 (08753)
**Phone—(732) 240-0323**
Fax—(732) 240-5055
Owner—Daniel Campian
SIC—3843; *Dental prosthetics*
Employs—4
Sales—$500,000-$1Mil (est)
Distrib.—Regional
Sole ownership

### ANUCO, INC.

911 Charles Dr., P.O. Box 5016 (08753)
**Phone—(973) 887-9465**
National—(800) 842-2896
Fax—(973) 887-2157
www.anuco.com
Email—orders@anuco.com
Owner & GM—Robert Nugent, Jr.
Asst. Mgr.—John Myers
SIC—2759; 3497; NAICS—323100; *Commercial printing & foil stamping*
Employs—15; Estab.—1980
Sales—$1Mil-$2.5Mil
Distrib.—Regional
Privately owned corporation

### ATLANTIC PROTECTIVE POUCHES

1545 Route 37 W., Unit 6 (08755)
Mail addr: P.O. Box 1191, Toms River (08754-1191)
**Phone—(732) 240-3871**
National—(800) 405-3871
www.atlanticprotectivepouches.com
Email—app1191@aol.com
Pres., GM—Walter Haine
V-P.—Lorraine R. Haine
SIC—3081; 3082; *Polyester film enclosures, pouches & sleeves for collectibles, archives, exhibits, presentations & conservation*
Employs—4; Estab.—1987
Sales—under $500,000
3,000 sq ft site, Distrib.—Intl.
Privately owned corporation

### BANQUET SERVICES INTERNATIONAL

2214 Route 37 E. (08753)
**Phone—(732) 270-1188**
National—(888) 774-6808
Fax—(732) 270-9121
www.banquetservicesintl.com
Email—publishers557@aol.com
Pres.—Bob Hansen
Off. Mgr.—Rose Hansen
SIC—2759; NAICS—323100; *Commercial printing*
Employs—5; Estab.—1976
7,500 sq ft site, Distrib.—National
Sole ownership

### †BAY TREASURE SEAFOOD, LLC

2002 Lakewood Rd., Unit 4 (08755)
Mail addr: 2002 Route 9, Unit 4, Toms River (08755-1214)
**Phone—(732) 240-3474**
Fax—(732) 240-3475
Email—baytreasure@gmail.com
Member—Stephen Miller
Sales Rep.—Tony Cunha
SIC—5146; *Distributor of seafood*
Employs—10; Estab.—2006
Sales—$500,000-$1Mil
Distrib.—National
Limited Liability Company

### CENTRAL PRINTING & TYPESETTING

1501 Route 37 E. (08753)
**Phone—(732) 929-0011**
Fax—(732) 506-6341
www.centralprinting.net
Email—cprintr@aol.com
Pres.—Linda L. Adams
Prod. Mgr.—Todd Adams
SIC—2752; 2791; NAICS—323122; *Offset printing & typesetting*
Employs—3; Estab.—1985
Sales—under $500,000
Distrib.—Regional
Privately owned corporation

NEW ENTRY
### CERAMCOR, LLC

1026 Samantha Way (08753)
**Phone—(732) 929-2833**
Fax—(732) 612-1150
www.ceramcor.com
Email—rich@ceramcor.com
Owner—Richard Bergstrom
SIC—3269; *Ceramic cookware*
Employs—2; Estab.—2007
Sales—under $500,000 (est)
300 sq ft site, Distrib.—Intl.
Limited Liability Company

### CHURCH & CO.

2121 Whitesville Rd. (08755)
**Phone—(732) 363-4949**
Fax—(732) 370-4593
www.churchco.com
Email—churchco@comcast.net
Owner—David Hopkinson
SIC—3911; NAICS—339911; *Precious metal jewelry*
Employs—6; Estab.—1922
Distrib.—Regional
Privately owned corporation

### CICCONE CUSTOM RAILING & MANUFACTURING, INC.

2002 Route 9 (08755)
**Phone—(732) 349-7071**
Fax—(732) 349-7079
www.cicconerailing.com
Email—customrailing@gmail.com
Pres.—Robyn Ciccone
SIC—3446; 3444; 3499; NAICS—332323; *All-welded custom ornamental aluminum, steel & wrought iron railings, fencing, gates, columns & custom, standard & spiral stairs for exterior & interior application in commercial & private settings*
Employs—10; Estab.—1996
Sales—$1Mil-$2.5Mil
Distrib.—Regional
Privately owned corporation
Also see: All American Powder Coating, same loc.

### CIRCUITS SALES

104 Alissa Dr. (08753)
**Phone—(732) 255-1325**
Email—pcbcircuitsales@aol.com
Owner—Thomas Solosky
SIC—3672; NAICS—334412; *Printed circuit boards, including custom cable & wire assemblies, fabrication, nameplates, membrane switches & labels*
Employs—1; Estab.—1993
Distrib.—Regional
Sole ownership
ISO rating—9001:2008

### CLAYTON BLOCK CO., INC.

194 Chestnut St. (08753)
Mail addr: P.O. Box 3015, Lakewood (08701)
**Phone—(732) 349-3700**
National—(800) 662-3044
Fax—(732) 751-7630
www.claytonco.com
Email—kroe@claytonco.com
Br. Mgr.—Matthew Dingus
Asst. Mgr.—Lisa Welsh
SIC—3273; 3271; 3272; NAICS—327320; *Concrete masonry units, building supplies, bagged portland cement, lime & mortar, block retaining walls & fences & pavers*
Employs—20; Estab.—1945
Sales—$1Mil-$2.5Mil
Distrib.—Local
Privately owned corporation
Parent co.—Clayton Block Co., Inc., Neptune, NJ
Phone—(732) 751-7600
See Parent Co. Section for full profile.

### COPY SHOP, THE

20 E. Water St. (08753)
**Phone—(732) 286-2200**
Fax—(732) 286-0012
Email—tritr3@aol.com
Owner—Bob Livolsi
SIC—2759; 2752; NAICS—323100; *Instant & blueprinting*
Employs—5
Sales—$1Mil-$2.5Mil

### CREATIONS BY JEFFREY, INC.

1522 Route 37 E. (08753)
**Phone—(732) 506-0051**
Fax—(732) 606-4878
www.creationsbyjeffrey.com
Email—estimator@creationsbyjeffrey.com
Pres.—Jeffrey Jones
SIC—2434; NAICS—337110; *Wooden kitchen cabinets*
Employs—18; Estab.—1984
Distrib.—Regional
Privately owned corporation

### DIABETIC & ATHLETIC FOOT CENTER, LLC, CEDARWOOD PLZ.

226 Route 37 (08753)
**Phone—(732) 281-3134**
**(855) 348-4968**
Fax—(732) 281-3137
www.diabeticfootcenter.net
Owner—Dan Dalsey
SIC—3842; NAICS—339113; *Orthotics & prosthetics appliances*
Employs—10
Sales—$1Mil-$2.5Mil (est)
Limited Liability Company

### DOVER VINYL PRODUCTS

1746 Route 9 (08755)
**Phone—(732) 244-1444**
Fax—(732) 341-1465
www.dovervinyl.com
Email—sales@dovervinyl.com
Pres.—Kathleen M. Stern
SIC—2394; NAICS—314912; *Sewn vinyl pool liners*
Employs—23; Estab.—1980
Sales—$1Mil-$2.5Mil (est)
Distrib.—Regional
Privately owned corporation

### DR FIBERGLASS

2027 Route 37 E. (08753)
**Phone—(732) 929-8448**
Fax—(732) 929-9260
www.drfiberglass.com
Email—drfiberglass@netzero.net
Pres.—Daniel Brown
SIC—3089; *Fiberglass decks & fabrication*
Employs—3; Estab.—1990
Sales—under $500,000
1,500 sq ft site, Distrib.—Regional
Privately owned corporation

### ENGLAND ORTHOPEDICS, INC.

1002 Commons Way (08755)
**Phone—(732) 286-4444**
Fax—(732) 286-4445
Pres.—Frank Scarnati
SIC—3842; *Orthopedic, orthotic & prosthetic devices*
Employs—4; Estab.—1974
Sales—$500,000-$1Mil (est)
Distrib.—Local
Privately owned corporation

### ENGRAVING SERVICES OF NEW JERSEY

804 Columbia Rd. (08753)
**Phone—(732) 341-0170**
Owner—Richard Corbo
SIC—3479; *Metal engraving*
Employs—4; Estab.—1980
Sales—under $500,000
Distrib.—Local
Sole ownership

GEOGRAPHICAL

## Toms River—(cont.)

### FRANLEY PRODUCTS, INC.
89 Riverwood Dr., Ste. 4 (08755)
**Phone—(732) 244-1496**
CEO—Michael Mullen
Shop Foreman—Pete Mollis
SIC—2434; *Custom wooden cabinets*
Employs—2; Estab.—1965
Sales—under $500,000
Distrib.—Local
Privately owned corporation

### GIRTAIN SIGN CO.
1765 Route 9 (08755)
**Phone—(732) 349-8499**
National—(800) 834-8499
Fax—(732) 505-3673
www.girtainsigns.com
Email—girtsigns@aol.com
Ptnr.—Andy Girtain
Off. Mgr.—Lori Girtain
SIC—3993; *Interior & exterior signs*
Employs—20; Estab.—1938
5,000 sq ft site, Distrib.—Regional
Privately owned partnership

### HEYCO PRODUCTS, INC.
1800 Industrial Way N. (08755)
Mail addr: P.O. Box 517, Toms River (08754)
**Phone—(732) 286-4336**
National—(800) 526-4182
Fax—(732) 244-8843
www.heyco.com
Email—sales@heyco.com
Pres.—Bill Jemison, Jr.
V.-P., Admn. & Dir., Hum. Res.—Colleen Faulknor
Dir., Sales & Mktg.—Michael Jemison
Pur. Mgr.—Ray Berardi
IT Mgr.—Jerry Dolec
Qual. Assur. Mgr.—Pat Sardoni
SIC—3089; 3469; *Plastic electrical parts, metal stampings & nonmetallic conduit, tubing & fittings*
Employs—150; Estab.—1989
110,000 sq ft site, Distrib.—Intl.
Privately owned sub-S corp.

### INSULITE, INC.
1890 Church Rd. (08753)
**Phone—(732) 255-1700**
National—(800) 624-3857
Fax—(732) 255-1700
www.doublethepane.com
Email—doublethepane@gmail.com
Pres.—B. Albert Horn
SIC—3231; NAICS—327215; *Insulating glass*
Employs—16; Estab.—1960
Sales—$2.5Mil-$5Mil (est)
Distrib.—Local
Privately owned corporation

### JERSEY COVER CORP.
1746 Lakewood Rd. (08755)
**Phone—(732) 286-6300**
Fax—(732) 341-1465
www.jerseycover.com
Email—info@jerseycover.com
Pres.—Kathleen Stern
GM—Robert M. Stern
Bookkeeper—Kathryn Ferraro
SIC—3089; *Swimming pool safety covers; Brand name—Aqua Brella Safety Pool Covers*
Employs—10; Estab.—1991
10,000 sq ft site, Distrib.—Regional
Privately owned sub-S corp.

### KITCHEN KING, INC.
1561 Route 9 (08755)
**Phone—(732) 341-9660**
National—(800) 956-5464
Fax—(732) 341-3445
Pres.—Terry Barth
SIC—3281; 2542; NAICS—327991; *Quartz, granite & laminate countertops*
Employs—20; Estab.—1970
Sales—under $500,000
Distrib.—Regional
Privately owned corporation

### †L & W SUPPLY CORP.
1351 Route 37 W. (08755)
**Phone—(732) 341-3737**
Fax—(732) 341-4687
www.lwsupply.com
Email—lwwebmaster@lwsupply.com
Br. Mgr.—Bob Jordan
SIC—5082; *Distributor of building materials & contracting equipment*
Employs—20; Estab.—1977
Sales—$1Mil-$2.5Mil
Distrib.—Intl.
Publicly owned corporation
DBA: Building Specialties
Parent co.—L & W Supply Corp., Chicago, IL
Phone—(312) 436-4000
See Parent Co. Section for full profile.

### LANE SIGNS
34 Central Ave. (08753)
**Phone—(732) 349-1904**
Fax—(732) 505-6391
GM—John Lane
SIC—3993; *Vinyl signs*
Employs—1; Estab.—1950
Distrib.—Local

### LAURSEN SHEET METAL
69 Flint Rd. (08757)
Mail addr: P.O. Box 276, Beachwood (08722)
**Phone—(732) 349-2821**
Fax—(732) 505-1236
Email—laursen@verizon.net
Owner—Ken Laursen
SIC—3444; *Sheet metal fabrication*
Employs—15
Distrib.—Local

### LETTERMEN, INC., THE
1565 Route 37 W. (08755)
**Phone—(732) 608-0669**
Fax—(732) 608-0697
www.thelettermeninc.com
Email—thelettermeninc@aol.com
Pres.—Rose Dixon
Manager—Cathae Setaro
SIC—2396; 2395; *Imprinted sportswear screen printing, embroidery & sewing, including t-shirts, sweatshirts, uniforms, warm-ups, jackets & hats & custom varsity jacket chenille lettering & emblems*
Employs—8; Estab.—1971
Sales—$500,000-$1Mil
2,700 sq ft site, Distrib.—Regional
Privately owned corporation

### MAXFLIGHT CORP.
1 Executive Dr. (08755)
**Phone—(732) 281-2007**
Fax—(732) 281-2009
www.maxflight.com
Email—info@maxflight.com
CEO—Frank McClintic
V.-P.—Brian McClintic
Fin. & Hum. Res. Mgr.—Louis Calao
Pur. Agt.—Bill Francovitch
SIC—3599; 3699; *Amusement rides & simulators; Brand name—MaxFlight*
Employs—20; Estab.—1994
30,000 sq ft site, Distrib.—Intl.
Privately owned corporation

### MEC TECH, INC.
2200 Industrial Way S. (08755)
**Phone—(732) 505-0308**
Fax—(732) 505-2151
www.mectech.com
Email—rkulkaski@mectech.com
Pres.—Richard Kulkaski
Hum. Res. Coord.—Barbara Latka
SIC—3089; 3674; NAICS—334413; *Plastic injection molding & semiconductor parts*
Employs—30; Estab.—1986
Distrib.—Intl.
Privately owned corporation

### NOSOTROS, NEWS
P.O. Box 1337 (08754)
**Phone—(732) 845-1911**
www.nosotrosnj.com
Email—news@nosotrosnj.com
Owner—Gigi Aragon
SIC—2711; *Newspaper publishing*
Employs—1; Estab.—2002
Sales—under $500,000 (est)
Distrib.—Local
Sole ownership

### PARK STEEL & IRON CO.
82 Iron St. (08753)
**Phone—(732) 349-2400**
Fax—(732) 776-8494
Email—parksteel1@verizon.net
Plt. Mgr.—Robert Kramer
SIC—3441; 3312; NAICS—332312; *Structural steel fabrication*
Employs—2; Estab.—1918
Sales—under $500,000
Distrib.—Local
Privately owned corporation
Parent co.—Park Steel & Iron Co., Neptune City, NJ
Phone—(732) 775-7500
See Parent Co. Section for full profile.

### PEARLE VISION, INC.
Div. of Luxottica Retail North America, Inc.
1278 Hooper Ave. (08753)
**Phone—(732) 505-0533**
Fax—(732) 505-6572
www.pearlevision.com
Email—contactus@pearlevision.com
GM & Sales Mgr.—Ed Santos
Technician—Lauren Sypniewski
Optician—Jim Marcantonio
SIC—3851; NAICS—339100; *Eyeglasses*
Employs—20; Estab.—1990
Sales—$500,000-$1Mil
Distrib.—Local
Publicly owned corporation
Parent co.—Luxottica Retail North America, Inc., Mason, OH
Phone—(513) 765-6000
See Parent Co. Section for full profile.

### PERMA PURE, LLC
Div. of Halma Holdings, Inc.
8 Executive Dr. (08755)
**Phone—(732) 244-0010**
National—(800) 337-3762
Fax—(732) 244-8140
www.permapure.com
Email—info@permapure.com
Pres.—Richard Curran
V.-P., Fin. & IT Mgr.—Allan Klimusko
Acctg. & Hum. Res. Mgr.—Stacy Estelle
Cust. Serv. Mgr.—Carol Medaglia
Accts. Payable Specialist—Denise O'Hara
Cust. Serv. Rep.—Karen Kennedy
SIC—3821; 3829; NAICS—339111; *Laboratory & environmental gas analyzing systems*
Employs—56; Estab.—1972
25,000 sq ft site, Distrib.—Intl.
Publicly owned corporation
Parent co.—Halma Holdings, Inc., Cincinnati, OH
Phone—(513) 772-5501
See Parent Co. Section for full profile.

[NEW ENTRY]

### PERRULLI'S CUSTOM MEATS
1889 Route 9, Ste. 45 (08755)
**Phone—(732) 244-0470**
Owner—Dave Perrulli
SIC—2013; *Italian sausages*
Employs—2
Sales—$500,000-$1Mil (est)

### PRESSTO GRAPHICS, INC.
467 Lakehurst Rd., P.O. Box 467 (08755)
**Phone—(732) 286-9300**
Fax—(732) 286-9030
www.presstographics.com
Email—presstographics@comcast.net
Pres.—William Debernardis
Off. Mgr.—Bill Debernardis
SIC—2796; 2759; NAICS—323122; *Commercial offset & digital printing & graphic design*
Employs—8; Estab.—1984
Sales—$500,000-$1Mil
Distrib.—Local
Privately owned corporation

### PROGRESSIVE DIMENSIONS, INC.
44 Flint Rd. (08757)
**Phone—(732) 244-0109**
Fax—(732) 244-0702
www.pdtops.com
Email—info@pdtops.com
Pres.—Ed Cassidy
SIC—3281; 3089; NAICS—327991; *Granite, solid-surface & laminate countertop fabrication*
Employs—10
Sales—$500,000-$1Mil (est)
Distrib.—Local
Privately owned corporation

### RUBBER STAMP MAN, LLC
1236 Route 166, Ste. 140 (08753)
**Phone—(732) 557-0275**
www.rubberstampman.com
Email—sales@rubberstampman.com
GM—Robert Pyott
SIC—3953; *Custom rubber stamps*
Employs—3; Estab.—1998
Sales—under $500,000
1,000 sq ft site, Distrib.—Intl.
Limited Liability Company

### SDL STUDIO, LLC
1591 Route 37 W., Ste. E-4 (08755)
**Phone—(732) 473-0800**
Fax—(732) 473-0850
www.sdlcoating.com
Email—lou@sdlcoating.com
Pres.—Louis Russo
Sales & Mktg. Mgr.—Danielle Russo
SIC—3479; *Commercial, industrial & military powder & spray coating job shop*
Employs—2; Estab.—1998
Sales—under $500,000
5,000 sq ft site, Distrib.—Local
Limited Liability Company
DBA: SDL Coating

### SHELTER COVE EMBROIDERY CO.
1333 Bay Ave. (08753)
**Phone—(732) 506-7700**
National—(800) 506-7232
Fax—(732) 506-6779
www.sheltercoveemb.com
Email—info@sheltercoveemb.com
Owner—Peggi Gamba
SIC—2396; 2395; *T-shirt screen printing & embroidery*
Employs—3; Estab.—1997
Sales—under $500,000
2,000 sq ft site, Distrib.—Regional
Sole ownership

## Toms River—(cont.)

### SHORE PRECISION MFG., INC.
1000 Industrial Way N., Unit D (08755)
Phone—(732) 914-0949
Fax—(732) 914-0566
www.shoreprecisionmfg.com
Email—sales@shorepre.com
Pres.—Wayne Cornwell
Bookkeeper & Off. Mgr.—Melanie Saner
SIC—3599; Precision machining job shop
Employs—8; Estab.—1994
4,000 sq ft site, Distrib.—National
Privately owned corporation

### SHORE SIGN & BANNER
1214 Route 37 E. (08753)
Phone—(732) 270-6020
www.ashoresign.net
Email—philw@ashoresign.net
Owner—Phillip Wagner
SIC—3993; Signs, including neon & electric signs & vinyl banners
Employs—2; Estab.—2004
Sales—under $500,000
Distrib.—Local
Limited Liability Company
AKA: Philee, LLC

### SHOWCASE PUBLICATIONS, INC.
90 Irons St. (08753)
Phone—(732) 349-7775
National—(800) 392-6979
Fax—(732) 349-9020
www.autoshopper.com
Email—info@autoshopper.com
Pres.—Bob Draper
V.-P.—Bob Halucha
Corp. Secy.—Donald F. Halucha
SIC—2741; Corporate headquarters & targeted weekly photo shoppers guide publishing; Brand name—Auto Shopper; Boat Shopper; Truck Shopper; RV Shopper; Home Shopper; Bargain Shopper
Employs—50; Estab.—1977
Sales—$500,000-$1Mil
Distrib.—Local
Privately owned corporation

### SIGN CONCEPTS
33 Broad St. (08753)
Phone—(732) 341-7624
Email—wrmsigns@aol.com
Owner—Walter Myers
SIC—3993; Handcrafted, vinyl, non-vinyl & painted signs
Employs—1; Estab.—1980
Sales—under $500,000
Distrib.—Local
Sole ownership

### SLP SPECIALTY VEHICLES, INC.
1501 Industrial Way N. (08755)
Phone—(732) 240-3696
Fax—(732) 341-6084
www.slpcars.com
Pres.—Ed Hamburger
Pur. Agt.—Cathy Sheers
SIC—3711; 3713; 3519; 3714; Supercharged specialty vehicles, high horsepower cars, trucks & SUVs & related components for high-performance automotive enthusiasts
Employs—12; Estab.—1990
33,000 sq ft site, Distrib.—Intl.
Privately owned corporation

### TARGETED TECHNOLOGIES, LLC
1735 Hooper Ave., Ste. 2 (08753)
Phone—(732) 255-9005
Fax—(732) 255-5863
www.targtech.com
Email—sales@targtech.com
Ptnr.—Michael Schlachter
Ptnr.—Brian Owens
Admn. Mgr.—Donna Giblin
SIC—7373; Computer network system integration, including LANs & WANs & IT services
Employs—7; Estab.—1998
Distrib.—Regional
Limited Liability Company

### TECHNIDYNE CORP.
2190 Route 9, Ste. 9 (08755-0970)
Phone—(732) 363-1055
National—(800) 654-8073
Fax—(732) 901-0307
www.technivet.com
Email—sales@technivet.com
Pres.—Frank Jehn
SIC—3842; Veterinary scales & transport & lift tables
Employs—3; Estab.—1984
Sales—$500,000-$1Mil
Distrib.—Local
Privately owned corporation

### TIM'S AUTOMOTIVE MACHINE SHOP
1760 Highway 37 E. (08753)
Phone—(732) 573-0600
Owner—Timothy Hall
SIC—3714; 3599; Automotive machining job shop
Employs—1; Estab.—2000
Sales—under $500,000
Distrib.—Local
Sole ownership

### TLC SIGN & BANNER, INC.
188 Walnut St. (08753)
Phone—(732) 244-4225
National—(800) 201-8485
Fax—(732) 244-3699
www.tlcbanner.com
Email—tsnover@tlcbanner.com
Owner—Tim Snover
SIC—3993; 2399; Interior & exterior signs & banners
Employs—17; Estab.—1993
Sales—$2Mil
7,500 sq ft site, Distrib.—National
Privately owned corporation

### TOMS RIVER SHEET METAL CO.
400 Corporate Cir. (08755)
Phone—(732) 244-2880
National—(800) 400-2882
Fax—(732) 244-2889
Email—info@trhac.com
Salesman—Mike Beaulieu
SIC—3444; Sheet metal fabrication & HVAC
Employs—23; Estab.—1966
Sales—$2.5Mil-$5Mil (est)
Distrib.—Local
Privately owned corporation

### TRI PHASE TOOL CO.
2345 Route 9, Ste. 10 (08755)
Phone—(732) 370-4737
Fax—(732) 370-4758
Email—triphase80@msn.com
Owner & GM—Robert J. Fischer
SIC—3599; General machining job shop, including CNC machining, production, prototypes, fabrication, welding & assembly
Employs—3; Estab.—1982
Sales—under $500,000
1,500 sq ft site, Distrib.—Regional
Limited Liability Company

### WOODSHOP, INC., THE
58 Flint Rd. (08757)
Phone—(732) 349-8006
Fax—(732) 349-2708
www.thewoodshopinc.com
Email—thewoodshopinc@aol.com
Pres.—Thomas Fantaccione
Foreman—John Lang
SIC—2431; NAICS—321900; Millwork
Employs—3; Estab.—1987
Sales—under $500,000
Distrib.—National
Privately owned corporation

## Totowa
(Passaic—N.E.)

### ACCURATE DOOR & HARDWARE, INC.
10 W. End Rd. (07512)
Mail addr: P.O. Box 539, Totowa (07511)
Phone—(973) 812-2266
Fax—(973) 812-2215
www.accurate-door.com
Email—rich@accurate-door.com
Pres.—Richard Cornetto, Sr.
Pers. & Plt. Mgr.—Richard Cornetto, Jr.
Hum. Res. Mgr.—Karen Gafney
SIC—3442; 3429; NAICS—332321; Steel doors & hardware
Employs—20; Estab.—1987
Distrib.—Local
Privately owned corporation

### ADVANCED BIOTECH, INC.
10 Taft Rd. (07512)
Phone—(973) 339-6242
(973) 357-0577
Fax—(973) 357-0644
www.adv-bio.com
Email—aisernia@adv-bio.com
CEO—Robert DeSimone
Pres.—Augustin Isernia
CFO—James Mulligan
Qual. Control Mgr.—Sidney Arfa
Acct. Exec.—Diana Robinson
SIC—2087; NAICS—311900; Flavorings, extracts, natural aromatics, pyrazines, isolates & sulfur compounds
Employs—60; Estab.—1994
65,000 sq ft site, Distrib.—Intl.
Privately owned corporation
AKA: Centrome, Inc.

### ALLIANCE DESIGN, INC.
434 Union Blvd. (07512)
Phone—(973) 904-1900
Fax—(973) 904-9666
www.alliancedesign.com
Email—design@alliancedesign.com
Pres.—William Ng
Sr. Art Dir.—Susan Kluhspies
Cust. Serv. Mgr.—Jackie Bird
Proj. Coord.—Ann Fisher
Graphic Designer—Debra Faust
SIC—2791; NAICS—323122; Commercial electronic prepress & graphic design
Employs—12; Estab.—1993
Sales—$500,000-$1Mil
Distrib.—Regional
Privately owned corporation

### †ALLIED BUILDING PRODUCTS CORP.
595 Union Blvd. (07512)
Phone—(973) 790-5500
National—(800) 281-6674
Fax—(973) 790-9071
www.alliedbuilding.com
Email—sales@alliedbuilding.com
Br. Mgr.—Robert Gall
SIC—5033; 5031; Distributor of building materials & supplies, including roofing, siding, windows & doors
Employs—10; Estab.—1961
Distrib.—Local
Publicly owned corporation
AKA: Norge Building Supply
Parent co.—Allied Building Products Corp., East Rutherford, NJ
Phone—(201) 507-8400
See Parent Co. Section for full profile.

### ALPHA T'S, INC.
380 Totowa Rd., 2nd Fl. (07512)
Phone—(973) 956-7243
Fax—(973) 956-7243
www.alpha-t-shirts.com
Email—info@alpha-t-shirts.com
Pres.—Sal Mancini
SIC—2396; 2395; Textile screen printing, embroidery & promotional items
Employs—2; Estab.—1991
Sales—under $500,000
Distrib.—Local
Privately owned corporation

### AMBIX LABORATORIES
55 W. End Rd. (07512)
Phone—(973) 890-9002
National—(800) 719-9373
Fax—(973) 890-9778
www.ambixlabs.com
Email—ambixlab@aol.com
Pres.—Alvin Goren
V.-P. & Dir., Opers.—Elkin Serna
V.-P. & Dir., Mktg.—Michael Chanin
SIC—2844; 2833; 2834; NAICS—325412; Contract manufacturing of skin, hair & personal care products & liquid nutritional, herbal supplements & protein liquids; Brand name—Cosmecol; Protoganic
Employs—23; Estab.—1967
Sales—$8Mil
35,000 sq ft site, Distrib.—Intl.
Privately owned corporation

### AMERICAN TUBE & PAPER
Div. of American Paper Products
80 Furler St. (07512)
Mail addr: P.O. Box 68, Totowa (07511)
Phone—(973) 256-3600
Fax—(973) 785-3341
www.AmericanPaperProducts.com
Email—sales@americanpaperproducts.com
Off. Mgr.—Lisa Pandorf
SIC—2655; NAICS—322214; Paper tubes
Employs—30; Estab.—1920
45,000 sq ft site, Distrib.—Intl.
Privately owned corporation
Parent co.—American Paper Products, Kulpsville, PA
Phone—(215) 362-8582
See Parent Co. Section for full profile.

### AMISH DAIRY PRODUCTS, LLC
41 Vreeland Ave., Ste. 101 (07512)
Phone—(973) 256-7676
www.amishcountryfarms.com
Email—ken@acforganics.com
Mng. Member—Kenneth Tensen
SIC—2022; 2021; Dairy products, including cheese & butter
Employs—7; Estab.—1996
Sales—$2.5Mil-$5Mil (est)
Distrib.—Local
Limited Liability Company
AKA: ACF Organics, LLC

### ANTONOVICH FURS, INC.
125 Route 46 W. (07512)
Phone—(973) 785-0077
National—(800) 919-3877
Fax—(973) 785-7776
www.antonovichfurs.com
Email—dantonovich@gmail.com
Pres.—Daniel Antonovich
SIC—2371; NAICS—315200; Fur & leather coats
Employs—15; Estab.—1960
Distrib.—Regional
Privately owned corporation

### APB-DYNASONICS, INC.
20 W. End Rd. (07512)
Phone—(973) 785-1101
Fax—(973) 785-1105
www.apb-dynasonics.com
Email—info@apb-dynasonics.com
GM—Peter Patel
Prod. Mgr.—Luis DeJesus

GEOGRAPHICAL

## Totowa—(cont.)

SIC—3651; *High-performance analog mixing consoles for live concert & public performance applications; Brand name—Spectra; ProRack™; MixSwitch™*
Employs—9
Sales—$1Mil-$2.5Mil (est)
Privately owned corporation

### APOLLO FLAGS LLC
594 Union Blvd. *(07512)*
**Phone—(973) 256-8362**
National—(800) 458-8362
Fax—(973) 256-1049
www.apolloflags.com
Email—apolloflags@optonline.net
Ptnr.—Albert Potenzone
Ptnr.—Debbie Potenzone
SIC—2399; 3499; 3444; 3089; *Custom, U.S., military, state, parade, POW, MIA & national flags & accessories; Brand name—ANNIN & CO.; EDER FLAG MFG.; TWO GROUP; CUSTOM D...COR*
Employs—4; Estab.—2014
Sales—$1Mil
1,000 sq ft site, Distrib.—National
Limited Liability Company

### BALLET MAKERS, INC. (H Q)
1 Campus Rd. (07512)
**Phone—(973) 595-9000**
National—(800) 533-1887
Fax—(973) 595-9120
www.capeziodance.com
Email—epotts@balletmakers.com
CEO—Anthony Giacoio, Jr.
CEO—Marc Terlizzi
Corp. Sales & Serv. Mgr., Internet—Joel Susini
IT Mgr.—Ruth Swanson
Hum. Res. Mgr.—Lisa Eagan
SIC—3149; 2339; *Corporate headquarters; dance & dance-related footwear & apparel; Brand name—Capezio*
Employs—100; Estab.—1887
Sales—$10Mil-$25Mil
Distrib.—Intl.
Privately owned sub-S corp.

### BONDED INSULATION PRODUCTS
657 Union Blvd. (07512)
**Phone—(973) 256-2120**
National—(866) 360-0100
Fax—(973) 256-1895
www.bondedwindows.com
Email—sales@bondedwindows.com
Pres.—Harvey S. Goodman
SIC—3442; 3089; 2591; NAICS—332321; *Storm doors, vinyl all-welded replacement & new construction & storm windows, casings, sills, French doors & porch enclosures & in-between the glass mini blinds; Brand name—TrustGard; WeatherWeld; WeatherMaster; Nordic; Endura; Advantage; Craft; Newport; Endurance Storm Doors*
Employs—25; Estab.—1944
Sales—$1Mil-$5Mil
55,000 sq ft site, Distrib.—Regional
Privately owned sub-S corp.

### CANARE CORP. OF AMERICA
45 Commerce Way, Unit C (07512)
**Phone—(973) 837-0070**
Fax—(973) 837-0080
www.canare.com
Email—canare@canare.com
CEO—Kazuo Urata
V-P., Sales—Paul Ketting
SIC—3679; *Cables, connectors & fiber-optic links*
Employs—30; Estab.—1983
Distrib.—Intl.
Privately owned corporation

### CATHOLIC BOOK PUBLISHING CORP.
77 W. End Rd. (07512)
**Phone—(973) 890-2400**
Fax—(973) 890-2410
www.catholicbookpublishing.com
Email—info@catholicbookpublishing.com
Pres.—Robert Cavalero
SIC—2731; *Book publishing*
Employs—30; Estab.—1995
Sales—$1Mil-$2.5Mil (est)
Distrib.—Intl.
Privately owned corporation

### CORBION CARAVAN
Div. of Corbion
100 Adams Dr. *(07512)*
**Phone—(973) 256-8886**
(800) 526-5261
Fax—(973) 256-5789
www.corbion.com
Email—bakery@corbion.com
V-P., Pricing—Joseph Solimini
Dir., Plt.—Aamir Mausoof
Hum. Res. Mgr.—Elwood 'Woody' Lichack
SIC—2087; 2099; NAICS—311822; *Baking ingredients & mixes*
Employs—160; Estab.—2006
175,000 sq ft site, Distrib.—National
Publicly owned corporation
Parent co.—Corbion, Lenexa, KS
Phone—(913) 890-5500
See Parent Co. Section for full profile.

### CUSTOM INDEX, INC.
8 Vreeland Ave. (07512)
**Phone—(973) 890-2414**
National—(800) 291-3865
Fax—(973) 890-4117
www.customindex.com
Email—sales@customindex.com
CEO—Nafees Rahman
V-P., GM—Larry Hansen
Regional Mgr.—Owen Fishman
SIC—2675; NAICS—322200; *Corporate headquarters & index tabs & folders*
Employs—145; Estab.—1981
Sales—$15Mil-$20Mil
54,000 sq ft site, Distrib.—Local
Privately owned corporation
AKA: C. I. Filing Systems

### DERICKS SHEET METAL WORKS CO., INC.
631 Union Blvd. (07512)
**Phone—(973) 256-1818**
Fax—(973) 256-2209
Owner & GM—Keith Dericks
Treas.—Paul Dericks
SIC—3444; *Sheet metal fabrication*
Employs—22
Sales—$2.5Mil-$5Mil (est)

### ECI TECHNOLOGY, INC.
60 Gordon Dr. (07512)
**Phone—(973) 890-1114**
Fax—(973) 890-1118
www.ecitechnology.com
Email—info@ecitechnology.com
Pres., CEO—Marianna Rabinovitch
V-P.—Peter Bratin
Opers. Mgr.—Lyor Kogan
Ad Mgr.—Dan Rabinovitch
Hum. Res. Mgr.—Heather Del Plato

SIC—3826; NAICS—334516; *Chemical management systems & analyzers for the semiconductor, solar & LED production industries; Brand name—Quali-Line; QualiSurf; Quali-Fill; SurfaceScan; QualiLab*
Employs—85; Estab.—1987
Distrib.—Intl.
Privately owned corporation
ISO rating—9001:2008

### FELCO PRODUCTS, LLC
18 Furler St. (07512)
**Phone—(973) 890-7979**
Fax—(973) 890-4898
www.felcoproducts.com
Pres.—Joe Geronimo
SIC—3714; *Automotive parts, accessories & filters*
Employs—5; Estab.—2005
Distrib.—Intl.
Privately owned corporation

### GRANDVIEW PRINTING CO., INC.
33 W. End Rd. (07512)
**Phone—(973) 890-0006**
Fax—(973) 890-8837
Email—grandviewptg@aol.com
Pres.—Lewis DeMarco
V-P.—Jeff DeMarco
SIC—2752; 2759; 2771; NAICS—323100; *Commercial offset printing of greeting cards, catalogs, promotional literature, mailers, postcards, packaging, newsletters & posters*
Employs—8; Estab.—1974
Sales—$2Mil
12,000 sq ft site, Distrib.—Regional
Privately owned sub-S corp.

### INTEGRATED BUSINESS SYSTEMS, INC.
999 Riverview Dr., Ste. 280 *(07512)*
**Phone—(973) 575-4950**
Fax—(973) 575-4953
www.ibsre.com
Email—sales@ibsre.com
Pres.—Michael Mullin
V-P., Opers.—Dawn Bernstel
SIC—7372; NAICS—541512; *Property management & accounting software development; Brand name—HP; Dell; Microsoft; SonicWALL; Symantec; Cisco; Blackberry*
Employs—25; Estab.—1987
Distrib.—Regional
Privately owned corporation
AKA: IBS

### KNICKERBOCKER MACHINE SHOP, INC.
611 Union Blvd. (07512)
**Phone—(973) 256-1616**
National—(800) 631-8372
Fax—(800) 432-9277
www.alloystainless.com
Email—sales@alloystainless.com
Pres.—John Simonelli
SIC—3432; NAICS—332900; *Stainless steel pipe fittings*
Employs—70; Estab.—1944
Distrib.—Intl.
Privately owned corporation
AKAs: Knickerbocker * Alloy Stainless Products

### LIGHTNING PRESS, INC.
140 Furler St. (07512)
**Phone—(973) 890-4422**
Fax—(973) 890-4414
www.lightning-press.com
Pres.—Ron Balinski
V-P.—Diana Balinski
Off. Mgr.—Paul Balinski
Designer—Debby Graham

SIC—2732; NAICS—323117; *Book printing*
Employs—12; Estab.—1975
Sales—$500,000-$1Mil
6,500 sq ft site, Distrib.—National
Privately owned corporation

### MEDIN CORP.
11 Jackson Rd. (07512)
**Phone—(973) 779-2400**
Fax—(973) 779-2463
www.medin.com
Email—info@medin.com
Pres.—Jay Schainholz
COO—Mark DiSilvestro
V-P., Bus. Dev. & Mktg.—Charlie Phillips
V-P., Fin.—Brian Kwan
Mfg. Mgr.—Dan Wrocklage
Supply Chain Mgr.—Sumont Das
SIC—3444; *Corporate headquarters & precision sheet metal fabrication of medical sterilization trays, containers & related products*
Employs—108; Estab.—1966
108,000 sq ft site, Distrib.—Intl.
Privately owned sub-S corp.
ISO rating—9001:2000, 13485:2003
AKAs: Steralon & SourceOne

### MORENG METAL PRODUCTS
100 W. End Rd. (07512)
Mail addr: P.O. Box 185, Totowa (07511)
**Phone—(973) 256-2001**
Fax—(973) 256-1803
www.morengmetal.com
Pres.—James R. Moreng
Off. Mgr.—Heather Moreng
Cust. Serv. Rep.—Jill Russak
SIC—3499; *Metal products*
Employs—100; Estab.—1902
80,000 sq ft site, Distrib.—National
Privately owned corporation

### OMEGA PACKAGING CORP.
55 Kings Rd. (07512)
**Phone—(973) 890-9505**
Fax—(973) 890-9646
www.omegapackaging.com
Email—sales@omegapackaging.com
Pres.—Larry Kalb
V-P.—William Prosser
Hum. Res. Mgr.—Laverne Kalb
SIC—2844; NAICS—325600; *Creams, lotions & shampoos*
Employs—50; Estab.—1990
40,000 sq ft site, Distrib.—Local
Privately owned corporation

### P. F. LABORATORIES, INC.
Div. of Purdue Pharma L. P.
700 Union Blvd. (07512)
**Phone—(973) 256-3100**
National—(888) 726-7535
www.purduepharma.com
Email—info@purduepharma.com
Dir., Hum. Res.—Morolake Esi
SIC—2834; NAICS—325412; *Pharmaceuticals*
Employs—125; Estab.—1967
Distrib.—Intl.
Privately owned corporation
Parent co.—Purdue Pharma L. P., Stamford, CT
Phone—(203) 588-8000
See Parent Co. Section for full profile.

### PHOENIX DOWN CORP.
85 US Highway 46 *(07512)*
**Phone—(973) 812-8100**
(800) 255-3696
Fax—(973) 812-9077
www.phoenixdown.com
Email—phod@phoenixdown.com
Pres., CEO—John Facatselis
CFO & CTO—Mary Kelly

## Totowa—(cont.)

SIC—2392; *Pillows & comforters*
Employs—100; Estab.—1989
Sales—$60Mil
180,000 sq ft site, Distrib.—Intl.
Privately owned sub-S corp.

### PRECISION CUSTOM COATINGS, LLC

200 Maltese Dr. (07512)
**Phone—(973) 890-3873**
Fax—(973) 785-8180
www.pcc-usa.com
Email—info@pcc-usa.com
Chrm.—Peter Longo
Pres.—Scott Tesser
CFO—Rich Noble
V-P., Domestic Sales—Carl Cimno
Dir., Hum. Res.—Debra Agostinelli
Opers. Mgr.—Mohamed Kovangji
SIC—2295; 2297; 2299; NAICS—313320; *Nonwoven fabrics, coated & laminated fabrics*
Employs—275; Estab.—1987
Sales—$50Mil-$100Mil
Distrib.—Intl.
Limited Liability Company

### †PROTAMEEN CHEMICALS, INC.

375 Minnisink Rd. (07512)
Mail addr: P.O. Box 166, Totowa (07511-0166)
**Phone—(973) 256-4374**
Fax—(973) 256-6764
www.protameen.com
Email—info@protameen.com
Pres.—Emanuel Balsamides, Sr.
V-P., Mktg. & Intl. Sales—Emanuel Balsamides, Jr.
V-P., Sales—Thomas Balsamides
V-P., Opers.—Alexis Balsamides
Dir., Opers.—Lance Tkacs
Dir., Technical—Tom Velten
Sales Mgr., Domestic—John Carola
Qual. Mgr.—Carla Garnett
SIC—5169; *Distributor of chemicals & personal care polymers*
Employs—30; Estab.—1969
30,000 sq ft site, Distrib.—Intl.
Privately owned corporation

### RELIANCE ELECTRONICS, INC.

20 W. End Rd. (07512)
**Phone—(973) 237-0400**
Fax—(973) 237-0401
www.reliancenj.com
Email—peter@pnconline.com
Pres.—Peter Patel
Hum. Res., IT & Off. Mgr.—Mamta Narkhede
SIC—3672; NAICS—334412; *Printed circuit boards*
Employs—30; Estab.—2009
Sales—$2.5Mil-$5Mil (est)
Distrib.—Local
Privately owned corporation

### SANDVIK PROCESS SYSTEMS, LLC

Div. of Sandvik, Inc.
21 Campus Rd. (07512)
**Phone—(973) 790-1600**
Fax—(973) 790-9247
www.processsystems.sandvik.com
Email—spsusa.info@sandvik.com
Pres.—Robert Stivale
Cont.—Richard Podmokly
GM & Plt. Mgr.—Craig Bartsch
Facility Mgr.—Bill Achtau
Mktg. Mgr.—Rodrigo Sagastegui
Hum. Res. Admn.—Bonnie Schneider
SIC—3535; NAICS—333922; *Conveyor systems*
Employs—30; Estab.—1977
40,000 sq ft site, Distrib.—Intl.
Publicly owned corporation
ISO rating—9001
Parent co.—Sandvik, Inc., Fair Lawn, NJ
Phone—(201) 794-5000
See Parent Co. Section for full profile.

### SCHIFF FOOD PRODUCTS CO., INC.

994 Riverview Dr. (07512)
**Phone—(973) 237-1990**
Fax—(973) 237-1999
www.schifffood.com
Email—sales@schifffood.com
Pres.—David Deutscher
Chief Administrative Officer—Joseph Krausz
Hum. Res. Mgr.—Danny Ross
SIC—2099; *Spices, seeds & herbs processing & blending*
Employs—25; Estab.—1949
Sales—$2.5Mil-$5Mil (est)
200,000 sq ft site, Distrib.—Intl.
Privately owned corporation

### SK CUSTOM CREATIONS, INC.

50 Furler St. (07512)
**Phone—(973) 754-9261**
Fax—(973) 754-9267
www.skcustomcreations.com
Email—info@skccinc.com
Opers. Mgr.—Ivan Acapana
Off. Mgr.—Michael Quintanilla
SIC—2511; *Wooden furniture*
Employs—50; Estab.—2003
Sales—$2.5Mil-$5Mil (est)
Distrib.—Regional
Privately owned corporation

### SPIRAL BINDING CO., INC.

1 Maltese Dr. (07512)
Mail addr: P.O. Box 286, Totowa (07511-0286)
**Phone—(973) 256-0666**
National—(800) 631-3572
Fax—(973) 256-5981
www.spiralbinding.com
Email—info@spiralbinding.com
Pres.—Robert Roth
CFO—Bob D'Alessio
V-P., Strategic Accts.—Ann Marie Boggio
V-P.—Stephan Roth
V-P.—Matt Roth
Dir., Opers.—Richard Christmas
Integrated Mktg. Mgr.—Michael Bossard
Hum. Res. Mgr.—Doris Dytchel
SIC—3559; *Corporate headquarters & binding, laminating & finishing equipment & supplies; Brand name—Spiral Binding; James Burn International; James Burn USA; JBUSA; Foliant*
Employs—150; Estab.—1932
Distrib.—National
Privately owned corporation
AKA: Spiral James Burn

### STAR STAINLESS SCREW CO., INC. (H Q)

30 W. End Rd. *(07512)*
**Phone—(973) 256-2300**
Fax—(973) 256-2423
Pres.—Bruce Wheeler
CFO—Thomas A. Guigliano
GM & Pur. Mgr.—Bill Fivehouse
IT Mgr.—Susan Denicola
SIC—3452; NAICS—332722; *Corporate headquarters; screws*
Employs—100; Estab.—1950
Sales—$200Mil
Distrib.—National
Privately owned corporation

### TEXAS CANVAS CO.

266 Union Blvd. (07512)
**Phone—(973) 278-3802**
Fax—(973) 278-0092
www.texascanvas.com
Email—peterv@texascanvas.com
Pres.—Peter Vasquez
SIC—2394; NAICS—314912; *Canvas truck & boat covers & awnings*
Employs—10; Estab.—1952
Sales—$500,000-$1Mil
9,000 sq ft site, Distrib.—Local
Privately owned corporation

### TILCON TOTOWA ASPHALT

Div. of Tilcon New York Inc.
859 Riverview Dr. (07512)
**Phone—(973) 256-8300**
National—(800) 789-7625
Fax—(973) 256-7819
www.tilconny.com
Email—info@tilconny.com
Plt. Mgr.—Nick Esposito
SIC—2951; NAICS—324121; *Asphalt paving compounds*
Employs—5
Sales—$1Mil-$5Mil
Distrib.—Local
Publicly owned corporation
AKA: Tilcon New York Asphalt Constructions
Parent co.—Tilcon New York Inc., West Nyack, NY
Phone—(845) 358-4500
See Parent Co. Section for full profile.

### TOTOWA PRECISION TOOLING, INC.

500 Riverview Dr. (07512)
**Phone—(973) 256-2283**
Fax—(973) 256-6890
www.totowaprecision.com
Email—george@totowaprecision.com
Pres.—George Bondarenko
SIC—3841; 3544; NAICS—333500; *Medical instruments & CNC machining, wire EDM, tooling, fixturing, jig grinding & precision machining job shop*
Employs—9; Estab.—1985
Sales—$1Mil-$5Mil
5,000 sq ft site, Distrib.—National
Privately owned sub-S corp.

### TRI-CITY PRINT & COPY CENTER

155 Union Blvd. (07512)
**Phone—(973) 706-5854**
www.tricityprint.com
Email—customerservice@tricityprint.com
Pres.—G. Elia
Treas.—R. Elia
SIC—2752; 2791; NAICS—323122; *Offset printing, copying, typesetting & graphic design*
Employs—2; Estab.—1970
Sales—under $500,000
Distrib.—National
Privately owned sub-S corp.
AKA: GE Printing Inc.

### VECTRACOR, INC.

785 Totowa Rd., Ste. 100 (07512)
**Phone—(973) 904-0444**
www.vectracor.com
Email—bschreck@vectracor.com
Pres., CEO—Brad S. Schreck
SIC—3845; *Patented cardiology equipment, including cardiac monitor/ECG machines to detect ECG changes suggestive of an acute myocardial infarction in real time; Brand name—VectraplexECG System; VectraplexAMI; CEB*
Employs—8; Estab.—2009
Distrib.—Intl.
Privately owned corporation

### VERSABAR CORP.

100 Maltese Dr. (07512)
**Phone—(973) 279-8400**
National—(800) 228-3772
Fax—(973) 942-8282
www.versabar.com
Email—versaquote@gmail.com
Chrm., Pres.—William E. Taylor
CFO, Treas. & Fin. Mgr.—Sara Taylor
GM & Off. Mgr.—Joanne Eckmann
SIC—3499; *Metal framing systems*
Employs—12; Estab.—1945
22,000 sq ft site, Distrib.—National
Privately owned corporation

### VIBRA SCREW, INC.

755 Union Blvd. (07512)
Mail addr: P.O. Box 229, Totowa (07511)
**Phone—(973) 256-7410**
Fax—(973) 256-2114
www.vibrascrew.com
Email—info@vibrascrew.com
Pres.—Eugene R. Wahl
V-P.—Richard Wahl
Treas.—Ellen Skibiak
Sales Mgr., Regional—Doug Holzherr
SIC—3537; *Bulk material handling equipment; Brand name—Bin Activator; Bin Discharger; AccuFeed; VersiFeeder; Live Bins; Live Bottom Bins; FlexiFeeder; HD-2 Screw Feeder; HD Metering Conveyor; Vibra Blender; Weightotaler; Volumetric Belt Feeder*
Employs—50; Estab.—1955
Sales—$5Mil-$10Mil
50,000 sq ft site, Distrib.—Intl.
Privately owned corporation

### VISKAL PRINTING, LLC

40 Commerce Way, Unit E (07512)
**Phone—(973) 812-6600**
Fax—(973) 812-6601
www.alphagraphics.com/us543
Email—us543@alphagraphics.com
Pres.—Krishnan Thampi
Cust. Serv. Rep.—Delfin Sumcad
SIC—2759; 2752; NAICS—323100; *Brochure, stationery, newsletter & business printing*
Employs—7; Estab.—2001
Sales—under $500,000
Distrib.—Regional
Limited Liability Company
DBA: AlphaGraphics

### VITAL SIGNS, A CAREFUSION CO.

Div. of CareFusion Corp.
20 Campus Rd. (07512)
**Phone—(973) 956-5300**
     (973) 790-1330
National—(800) 932-0760
Fax—(973) 956-5436
www.carefusion.com
Email—customerservice@carefusion.com
Corp. Cont.—Daria Hennessey
IT Mgr.—Alfred Pfeiffer
Hum. Res. Mgr.—Todd Forno
Benefits Mgr.—Sharon Gill
SIC—3842; *Divisional headquarters & anesthesia, respiratory & critical care equipment*
Employs—300; Estab.—1972
Sales—$240Mil
Distrib.—Intl.
Publicly owned corporation
Parent co.—CareFusion Corp., San Diego, CA
Phone—(858) 617-2000
See Parent Co. Section for full profile.

## Towaco

(Morris—N.W.)

### AME CORPORATION

33 Jacksonville Rd., Ste. 2 (07082)
**Phone—(800) 951-0071**
www.amecorporation.com
Email—sales@amecorporation.com
New Bus. Dev. Mgr.—Clara O'Boyle

GEOGRAPHICAL

## Towaco—(cont.)

SIC—3069; 3089; 3499; *Custom rubber components, including rubber bonded-to-plastic & rubber bonded-to-metal, standard switch seals, toggles, push buttons, rotaries, self sealing fasteners, lock washers, screws & bushings*
Employs—10; Estab.—1977
Sales—$5Mil
Distrib.—Intl.
Privately owned sub-S corp.
ISO rating—9001:2008

### DELMHORST INSTRUMENT CO.

51 Indian Ln. E. (07082)
Phone—(973) 334-2557
Fax—(973) 334-2657
www.delmhorst.com
Email—info@delmhorst.com
Pres., CEO—Thomas Laurenzi
V-P., Sales & Mktg.—Paul A. Laurenzi
V-P., Opers.—John Laurenzi
SIC—3829; 3523; *Hand-held moisture testing instruments for the building trades & agriculture industries*
Employs—24; Estab.—1960
Sales—$1Mil-$5Mil
15,000 sq ft site, Distrib.—Intl.
Privately owned corporation

### DIVERSIFIED HEAT TRANSFER, INC.

439 Main Rd., Route 202 (07082)
Phone—(718) 386-6666
National—(800) 221-1522
Fax—(718) 386-7809
www.dhtnet.com
Email—dht@dhtnet.com
Pres.—Kenneth Kaplan
CFO—Eno Lelaj
Ex. V-P.—Norman R. Goldberg
V-P., Sales, Natl.—Jim Colwell
V-P., Engrg. & Sales—Thomas J. Francullo
V-P., HVAC—Jake Goldberg
SIC—3433; 3443; NAICS—333414; *Water heaters, tankless & HVAC coils & heat exchangers & indirect water heaters & tube bundles; Brand name—GEA ECOFLEX; ARISTON; BOSCH*
Employs—65; Estab.—1942
Sales—$10Mil
60,000 sq ft site, Distrib.—Intl.
Privately owned corporation

### DROM FRAGRANCES INTERNATIONAL, INC.

5 Jacksonville Rd. (07082)
Phone—(973) 316-8400
Fax—(973) 316-9039
www.drom.com
Email—info@drom.com
V-P., Mktg.—Robert Stapf
V-P.—Andrew O'Shea
SIC—2844; NAICS—325600; *Fragrances*
Employs—38; Estab.—1978
Sales—$50Mil-$100Mil
20,000 sq ft site, Distrib.—Intl.
Privately owned corporation

### †MULTIPOWER INTERNATIONAL, INC.

7 Woodshire Ter., P.O. Box 197 (07082)
Phone—(973) 727-0327
Fax—(973) 331-7242
www.multipowerinternational.com
Email—info@multipowerinternational.com
Pres.—Qiang Ge
IT Mgr.—Benjamin Ge
SIC—5088; *Wholesaler of narrow & standard gage steam locomotives & parts*
Employs—7; Estab.—1995
Sales—$1Mil
3,000 sq ft site, Distrib.—Intl.
Privately owned corporation

### NU-GRAPHICS II, INC.

84 Stonybrook Rd., P.O. Box 65 (07082)
Phone—(973) 299-0066
(973) 713-5533
Fax—(973) 299-0615
Email—jpmatisak@yahoo.com
Pres.—Jerome Matisak
SIC—2752; NAICS—323100; *Graphic art prepress & digital printing*
Employs—2; Estab.—1978
8,000 sq ft site, Distrib.—Local
Privately owned corporation

### Q GLASS CO., INC.

624 Main Rd. (07082)
Phone—(973) 335-5191
(800) 619-0069
Fax—(973) 335-2057
www.qglass.com
Email—dan@qglass.com
Pres.—Daniel J. Dotterweich III
Off. Mgr.—Crystal Fucito
SIC—3221; NAICS—327215; *Custom & standard quartz laboratory & scientific glassware & vials, including repair*
Employs—6; Estab.—1946
Sales—over $1Mil
10,000 sq ft site, Distrib.—National
Privately owned corporation

### SEA BREEZE FRUIT FLAVORS, INC.

441 Route 202 (07082)
Phone—(973) 334-7777
National—(800) 732-2733
Fax—(973) 334-2617
www.seabreezesyrups.com
Email—info@seabreezesyrups.com
Pres.—Steven Sanders
Hum. Res. & Proj. Mgr.—Josh Sanders
SIC—2087; NAICS—311900; *Syrups*
Employs—50; Estab.—1925
Sales—$10Mil
Distrib.—Regional
Privately owned sub-S corp.

### TELEDYNAMICS, LLC

45 Indian Ln. E., Ste. 1 (07082)
Phone—(973) 248-3360
National—(800) 335-3379
Fax—(973) 248-3361
www.teledynamics-llc.com
Email—info@teledynamics-llc.com
Pres., CFO—Eric J. Witt
Dir., Serv.—Brian Witt
Prodn. Mgr.—Pam Klackowski
Off. Mgr.—Maria C. Gomez
SIC—3535; NAICS—333922; *Conveyors & conveying equipment*
Employs—20; Estab.—1995
18,000 sq ft site, Distrib.—Intl.
Limited Liability Company
Also see: Imagebound, LLC, same loc.

### TROY HILLS MFG., INC.

2 Como Ct., P.O. Box 98 (07082)
Phone—(973) 263-1885
Fax—(973) 263-8084
www.troyhillsmfg.com
Email—info@troyhillsmfg.com
Pres.—Leif W. Melgaard
Off. Mgr.—Jeffery Melgaard
SIC—3585; *Ice cream freezer lids*
Employs—6; Estab.—1992
18,000 sq ft site, Distrib.—Intl.
Privately owned corporation

### UHLMANN PACKAGING SYSTEMS

44 Indian Ln. E. (07082)
Phone—(973) 402-8855
Fax—(973) 402-2144
www.uhlmannpackaging.com
Email—mhaid@uhlmann-usa.com
Pres.—Andy Stobbe
Mng. Dir., CSS—Markus Haid

SIC—3565; NAICS—333993; *Packaging machinery*
Employs—75; Estab.—1983
Sales—$1Mil-$45Mil
50,000 sq ft site, Distrib.—Local
Privately owned corporation

## Trenton

(Mercer—N.E.)

### A R J CUSTOM FABRICATION, INC.

151 Taylor St. (08638)
Phone—(609) 695-6227
Fax—(609) 695-6136
www.arjcustomfabrications.com
Email—aj9033@aol.com
Pres.—Anthony Jones
MIS Mgr.—Regina Zimmer
SIC—3312; *Stainless steel fabrication*
Employs—10; Estab.—1986
Sales—$1.5Mil
20,000 sq ft site, Distrib.—Intl.
Privately owned corporation

### A R M NATIONAL FOODS, INC.

1546 Lamberton Rd. (08611)
Phone—(609) 394-0431
Fax—(609) 396-7809
Email—armtrenton@aol.com
Pres.—Armando Rienzi
GM—Richard Wood
Off. Mgr.—Angela Rienzi
SIC—2011; NAICS—311611; *Meat processing & packing*
Employs—16; Estab.—1980
Sales—$500,000-$1Mil
Distrib.—Local
Privately owned corporation

### †ABC SUPPLY CO., INC., BRADCO DIV.

Div. of ABC Supply Co., Inc.
301 Brunswick Ave. (08618)
Phone—(609) 393-7000
Fax—(609) 393-2180
www.abcsupply.com
Email—abcinfo@abcsupply.com
Br. Mgr.—Richard Mattson
SIC—5031; 5033; *Distributor of building materials, including lumber, siding, windows & asphalt, wood & clay shingles*
Employs—10; Estab.—1987
Distrib.—Regional
Privately owned corporation
Parent co.—ABC Supply Co., Inc., Beloit, WI
  Phone—(608) 362-7777
  See Parent Co. Section for full profile.

NEW ENTRY
### ACINO PRODUCTS, LLC

9-B S. Gold Dr. (08691)
Phone—(609) 695-4300
Fax—(609) 662-1897
Member—Ravi Deshpande
SIC—2834; *Pharmaceuticals*
Employs—10
Sales—$5Mil-$10Mil (est)
Limited Liability Company

### AFRICA WORLD PRESS, INC.

541 W. Ingham Ave., Ste. B (08638)
Mail addr: P.O. Box 1892, Trenton (08607)
Phone—(609) 695-3200
Fax—(609) 695-6466
www.africaworldpressbooks.com
Email—awprsp@verizon.net
Pres., Publisher—Kassahun Checole
Off. Mgr.—Senait Checole
SIC—2731; *Book publishing*
Employs—9; Estab.—1983
6,000 sq ft site, Distrib.—Intl.
Privately owned corporation
AKA: Red Sea Press, Inc., The

### ALPHA AUTOMATION, INC.

127 Walters Ave. (08638)
Phone—(609) 882-0366
Fax—(609) 882-0382
www.alpha-automation.com
Email—info@alpha-automation.com
Pres., Bus. Mgr.—Paul Bamburak
SIC—3822; NAICS—334512; *Industrial controls testing equipment*
Employs—3; Estab.—1986
Sales—$500,000-$1Mil
Distrib.—Intl.
Privately owned corporation

### ANA DESIGN CORP.

1 Ott St. (08638)
Phone—(609) 394-0300
Fax—(609) 394-5030
www.anadesigncorp.com
Email—sales@anadesigncorp.com
Pres., R & D Mgr.—Lauren Polito
Fin. & MIS Mgr.—Thomas Agzigian
Shpg. Mgr.—Marisol Gonzalez
Sales Rep.—Nicole Hamilton
SIC—3999; *Candles*
Employs—6; Estab.—1994
Sales—under $500,000
11,000 sq ft site, Distrib.—Intl.
Privately owned corporation

### ANDREA AROMATICS, INC.

150 Enterprise Ave. (08638)
Mail addr: P.O. Box 3091, Princeton (08543-3091)
Phone—(609) 695-7710
Fax—(609) 392-8914
www.andreaaromatics.com
Email—orders@andreaaromatics.com
Pres.—Richard D'Andrea
V-P.—Michael D'Andrea
Treas.—Janine Riggs
SIC—2844; NAICS—325600; *Fragrances, deodorants, odorants, reodorants & essential oils*
Employs—20; Estab.—1980
Sales—$6Mil
21,000 sq ft site, Distrib.—Intl.
Privately owned corporation

### AREA AUTO RACING NEWS, INC.

2829 S. Broad St. (08610)
Mail addr: P.O. Box 8547, Trenton (08650)
Phone—(609) 888-3618
Fax—(609) 888-2538
www.aarn.com
Email—info@aarn.com
Publisher & Editor—Lenny H. Sammons
Photo Editor—Carol Ann Kington
Asst. Editor—Earl Krause
Asst. Editor—Steve Barrick
Dir., Adv.—Tim Hogue
Adv. Mgr.—Danny Sammons
Circ. Mgr.—Denise Dubois
SIC—2711; *Weekly racing newspaper publishing*
Employs—8; Estab.—1963
Sales—over $1Mil
Distrib.—National
Privately owned corporation

### ARTIST ABOVE THE REST

4490 Nottingham Way (08690)
Phone—(609) 433-4554
(609) 586-7247
www.artistabovetherest.com
Email—john@artistabovetherest.com
Owner—John Brennan
SIC—2396; 2759; NAICS—323100; *Decals, textile & plastic screen printing*
Employs—1; Estab.—1972
Sales—under $500,000
Distrib.—Local
Sole ownership

## Trenton—(cont.)

**†ATLAS BRONZE**
445 Bunting Ave. (08611)
**Phone—(609) 599-1402**
National—(800) 478-0887
Fax—(609) 599-1424
www.atlasbronze.com
Email—tom@atlasbronze.com
Owner & Pres.—Tom Smith
SIC—5051; *Distributor of nonferrous metals, including copper, brass & bronze wrought & cast alloys; Brand name— Spadone; Metaline*
Employs—25; Estab.—1998
Sales—$12Mil
13,000 sq ft site, Distrib.—Intl.
Privately owned sub-S corp.
ISO rating—MIL-I-45208A
AKA: Maranatha Now Inc.

**AZTEC GRAPHICS, INC.**
420 Whitehead Rd. (08619)
**Phone—(609) 587-1000**
Fax—(609) 587-9117
www.aztecgraphics.com
Email—info@aztecgraphics.com
Pres.—Ronald Balerno
Prodn. Mgr.—R. Malik
Off. Mgr.—Erin McGoldrick
SIC—2396; 2395; 3993; *Screenprinted & embroidered sportswear, promotional items, banners, signs & vinyl cut vehicle marking*
Employs—15; Estab.—1978
10,000 sq ft site, Distrib.—National
Privately owned sub-S corp.

**BARTLEY CRUCIBLE REFRACTORIES**
15 Muirhead Ave., P.O. Box 5464 (08638)
**Phone—(609) 393-0066**
Fax—(609) 393-1866
Email—crucible@aol.com
Owner—Dan Mischel
Engr.—Brian Mischel
SIC—3297; NAICS—327125; *Crucibles*
Employs—20; Estab.—1905
Sales—$2.5Mil–$5Mil (est)
Distrib.—National
Sole ownership

**BENTON GRAPHICS, INC.**
3 Industrial Dr. (08619)
**Phone—(609) 587-4000**
National—(800) 223-0093
Fax—(609) 587-9890
www.bentongraphics.com
Email—info@bentongraphics.com
Owner—Mary A. Benton
CEO—Michael A. Valachovic
V-P.—Margaret Benton/Linico
SIC—3555; NAICS—333293; *White & blue carbon steel, stainless steel & ultimeter microloy steel doctor blades for the flexo & gravure printing industry; Brand name— Ultimeter; Flipcheck; Bonded Blades*
Employs—28; Estab.—1977
22,000 sq ft site, Distrib.—Intl.
Privately owned corporation

**†BILLOWS ELECTRIC SUPPLY CO., INC.**
1719 Nottingham Way (08619)
**Phone—(609) 890-2822**
Fax—(609) 890-7017
www.billows.com
Email—paulg@billows.com
Br. Mgr.—Paul Greig
SIC—5063; *Distributor of electrical supplies*
Employs—12; Estab.—1997
Distrib.—Local
Privately owned corporation

Parent co.—Billows Electric Supply Co., Inc., Philadelphia, PA
Phone—(215) 332-9700
See Parent Co. Section for full profile.

**BILL'S PRINTING SERVICE, INC.**
2829 S. Broad St. (08610)
**Phone—(609) 888-1841**
Fax—(609) 888-4424
www.billsprinting.com
Pres.—Bill Mason
SIC—2759; 2791; NAICS— 323122; *Commercial printing & typesetting*
Employs—6; Estab.—1981
Sales—$500,000-$1Mil (est)
Distrib.—Regional
Privately owned corporation

**BOEHM PORCELAIN, LLC**
25 Princess Diana Dr. (08638)
**Phone—(609) 656-2200**
(609) 656-2201
Fax—(561) 828-2646
www.boehmporcelain.com
Email—info@boehmporcelain.com
Pres., CEO—George Parker
Gallery Mgr.—Cindy Wiltsey
SIC—3269; NAICS—327112; *Porcelain sculptures of birds, animals & flowers, wall art & pitchers, including specialty casting; Brand name—Boehm Porcelain; Boehm China*
Employs—20; Estab.—1950
Sales—$1Mil-$5Mil
15,000 sq ft site, Distrib.—Intl.
Limited Liability Company
AKAs: E.M. Boehm & Boehm Galleries

**BOLT WELDING & IRON WORKS**
78 Wall St. (08609)
**Phone—(609) 393-3993**
Fax—(609) 393-9903
Email—chiltey1@verizon.net
Owner—Christopher Hiltey
SIC—3446; NAICS—332323; *Architectural welding*
Employs—5; Estab.—1979
Sales—under $500,000
Distrib.—Regional
Sole ownership

**BWAY CORPORATION**
6 Litho Rd. (08638)
**Phone—(732) 997-4050**
Fax—(732) 997-4055
www.bwaycorp.com
Email—sales@bwaycorp.com
Plt. Mgr.—Mike Hutchison
Opers. Mgr.—Rich Shenowski
Shpg. Mgr.—Dave Heupel
Foreman—Lois Partite
Hum. Res. Rep.—Bill Radcliffe
SIC—2752; 3479; NAICS— 323100; *Lithographic printing & metal coating*
Employs—100; Estab.—1964
Sales—$10Mil-$25Mil (est)
Distrib.—Intl.
Publicly owned corporation
AKA: Trenton Metal Decorating
Parent co.—BWAY Corporation, Atlanta, GA
Phone—(770) 645-4800
See Parent Co. Section for full profile.

**†CAPITAL STEEL SERVICE, LLC**
82 Stokes Ave. (08638)
**Phone—(609) 882-6983**
Fax—(609) 882-7458
www.capitalsteelservice.com
Email—info@ capitalsteelservice.com
CEO—Allen Hickman, Sr.
Pres.—Robert V. Hickman
Opers. Mgr.—Darryl Kepler
Off. Mgr.—Maryann S. Pazdan
Acct. Supv.—Elaine Portocarrero

SIC—5051; 3441; 3446; 3498; NAICS—332312; *Metal service center & structural & ornamental steel, aluminum & pipe fabrication of machine bases, sound wall columns & custom railings, including shearing, burning & sawing*
Employs—27; Estab.—1991
Sales—$4.36Mil
5,000 sq ft site, Distrib.—Local
Limited Liability Company

**CAPITOL COPY SERVICE**
116 W. State St. (08608)
**Phone—(609) 989-8776**
Fax—(609) 989-9570
www.capitol-copy.com
Email—copy@capitol-copy.com
Pres.—Raymond Sziber
SIC—2759; 2752; NAICS— 323100; *Commercial, instant & digital printing*
Employs—7; Estab.—1980
Sales—$1Mil-$2.5Mil
Distrib.—Local
Privately owned corporation

**CAPITOL FIRE PROTECTION CO., INC.**
56 N. Logan Ave. (08609)
Mail addr.—P.O. Box 3922, Trenton (08629-0922)
**Phone—(609) 393-3936**
Fax—(609) 396-2485
Email—capitolfire@gmail.com
Pres.—Charles S. Parkerson
V-P.—John R. Poland
SIC—3569; *Automatic fire sprinkler systems & backflow preventers*
Employs—8; Estab.—1952
Sales—$1.3Mil
6,000 sq ft site, Distrib.—Local
Privately owned corporation

**CAPITOL STEEL PRODUCTS, INC.**
82 Stokes Ave., P.O. Box 5063 (08638)
**Phone—(609) 538-9313**
Fax—(609) 538-9315
Email—capitolsteel@ capitolsteel.com
Pres. & Fin. Mgr.—Alan Jenkins
V-P.—Craig Yemola
Prodn. Mgr.—Dave Fisher
Estimator—Bernard Jenkins
SIC—3441; NAICS—332312; *Structural steel fabrication*
Employs—12; Estab.—2002
15,600 sq ft site, Distrib.—Local
Privately owned corporation

**CARFARO, INC.**
2075 E. State Street Ext. (08619)
**Phone—(609) 890-6600**
Fax—(609) 890-7522
www.carfaro.com
Email—info@carfaro.com
Pres.—Joseph Carfaro
Sales Mgr., Natl.—Robert Blackman
IT Mgr.—Charles Tilton
Hum. Res. Mgr.—Nicole Sprague
SIC—3446; NAICS—332323; *Custom & prefabricated aluminum railings & fencing for resorts, hotels, multifamily & residential communities*
Employs—50; Estab.—1994
Distrib.—Intl.
Privately owned corporation

**CASE PORK ROLL CO., INC.**
644 Washington St. (08611)
Mail addr.—P.O. Box 33019, Trenton (08629-3019)
**Phone—(609) 396-8171**
National—(800) 839-7675
Fax—(609) 394-4444
Email—caseporkroll@comcast.net
Pres., GM—Tom Grieb
V-P. & Dir., HAACP—Andrew C. Grieb

V-P.—Tom Dolan
Cont.—Joseph Montefusco
Plt. Mgr.—Joseph DeBronzo
SIC—2013; NAICS—311600; *Pork rolls; Brand name—Case; Kohler; Magnolia; Thumans; Foodtown; Cloverdel; Shop-Rite*
Employs—25; Estab.—1870
Sales—$5Mil-$10Mil
Distrib.—Regional
Privately owned sub-S corp.

**CHENEY FLASHING CO., LLC**
623 Prospect St. (08618)
Mail addr.—P.O. Box 818, Trenton (08605)
**Phone—(609) 394-8175**
National—(800) 322-2873
Fax—(609) 394-8891
www.cheneyflashing.com
Email—info@cheneyflashing.com
Pres.—Richard Levine
Hum. Res. & Off. Mgr.—Cynthia M. Carlson
Asst. Off. Mgr.—Joanna Korab
SIC—3499; *Metal roofing & waterproofing systems*
Employs—15; Estab.—1928
Distrib.—Intl.
Limited Liability Company

**CMF LIMITED, INC.**
599 Ingham Ave., P.O. Box 5989 (08638)
**Phone—(609) 695-3600**
Fax—(609) 695-3763
www.cmflimited.com
Email—kschultz@cmflimited.com
Owner & Fin. Mgr.—Jerry Donahue
V-P.—Keith Schultz
SIC—3479; 3471; NAICS— 332813; *Full-service paint finishing, including powder, high-performance, marine & mil-spec coatings*
Employs—25; Estab.—1998
58,000 sq ft site, Distrib.— Regional
Privately owned sub-S corp.

**COCCO ENTERPRISES, INC.**
Div. of Level Four Orthotics & Prosthetics, Inc.
333 Chambers St. (08609)
**Phone—(609) 393-5939**
Fax—(609) 393-5924
www.cocco-ent.com
Email—cminelli@cocco-ent.com
V-P.—Cynthia Minelli
Admn. Mgr.—Lauren Campitelli
SIC—3842; *Orthotic & prosthetic devices*
Employs—15; Estab.—1950
Sales—$1Mil-$5Mil
2,500 sq ft site, Distrib.—Regional
Privately owned corporation
Parent co.—Level Four Orthotics & Prosthetics, Inc., Winston-Salem, NC
Phone—(336) 397-2165
See Parent Co. Section for full profile.

**COMPASS DISPLAY & PROMOTION CO., INC.**
1659 Calhoun St. (08638)
**Phone—(609) 695-5300**
National—(800) 726-0020
Fax—(609) 695-9788
www.compassdisplayinc.com
Email—jcarugati@ compassdisplayinc.com
CEO—Joseph Carugati
Pres., Mktg. Mgr.—Jeffrey Carugati
V-P.—Thomas Carugati
Off. Mgr.—Pat Wiley
SIC—2541; *Store floor tile displays*
Employs—58; Estab.—1969
Distrib.—Local
Privately owned corporation

GEOGRAPHICAL

## Trenton—(cont.)

**CREST ULTRASONICS CORP.**
10 Grumman Ave., P.O. Box 7266 (08628)
**Phone—(609) 883-4000**
National—(800) 992-7378
Fax—(609) 883-6452
www.crest-ultrasonics.com
Email—mvitarelli@crest-ultrasonics.com
Pres.—Michael Goodson
Cont.—Michele Vitarelli
Sales Mgr., Inside—James Jaworski
Sales Mgr., Chemical—Charles Kaczorek
Lab Mgr.—Sean Joyce
SIC—3699; *Corporate headquarters & ultrasonic cleaning equipment, including tanks, transducers, generators, ceramics, tabletop units & chemicals*
Employs—50; Estab.—1961
Sales—$25Mil
50,000 sq ft site, Distrib.—Intl.
Privately owned corporation
ISO rating—9001:2000

**CYBIS PORCELAINS STUDIO & GALLERY**
200 Elizabeth Ave., Ste. 200 (08610)
**Phone—(609) 392-6074**
www.cybisporcelain.info
Email—info@cybisporcelain.com
Pres.—Joseph Chorlton
Manager—Teresa R. Chorlton
SIC—3269; NAICS—327112; *Porcelain sculptures*
Employs—45; Estab.—1939
Distrib.—Intl.

**CYTOTHERM**
110 Sewell Ave. (08610)
**Phone—(609) 396-1456**
National—(800) 747-9699
Fax—(609) 396-9395
www.cytotherm.com
Email—serve@cytotherm.com
Pres.—Roman Kuzyk
GM—Dennis Edwards
Administrator—Yuliya Tsebriy
SIC—3845; 3088; NAICS—326191; *Digitally-controlled dry & conventional sterile water-thawing baths for the medical industry*
Employs—6; Estab.—1970
Sales—$500,000-$1Mil
2,000 sq ft site, Distrib.—Intl.
Privately owned corporation

**D & D TRAILERS, INC.**
100 Lexington Ave. (08618)
**Phone—(609) 771-0001**
National—(800) 533-0442
Fax—(609) 771-4479
www.ddtrailers.com
Email—deandetrailers@comcast.net
Pres.—G. D. Reside
Off. Mgr.—Sue Ralph
SIC—3537; *Utility trailers; Brand name—Deande*
Employs—6; Estab.—1977
10,000 sq ft site, Distrib.—Local
Privately owned sub-S corp.

**D & S CASTINGS, INC.**
300 Whitehead Rd. (08619)
**Phone—(609) 689-0100**
Fax—(609) 689-0075
Email—manny@dandscasting.com
Pres.—Deoki Sharma
GM—Manny Sharma
Sales Mgr.—Deven Sharma
SIC—3325; NAICS—331513; *Metal castings*
Employs—5; Estab.—1989
Sales—$1Mil-$2.5Mil
Distrib.—Regional
Privately owned corporation

**DELAWARE VALLEY BINDERY, INC.**
18 Graphics Dr. (08628)
**Phone—(609) 771-1550**
Fax—(609) 771-9696
www.dvbindery.com
Email—sales@dvbindery.com
Pres.—Joseph Rigby
Corp. Secy.—Ann Rigby
Dir., Mktg.—Karen Morrell
Sales Mgr.—Howard Borochaner
Off. Mgr.—Nancy Rodgers
SIC—2789; NAICS—323121; *Perfect & mechanical binding, saddle stitching, film laminating, miniature folding, tipping, gluing application & fulfillment*
Employs—30; Estab.—1954
Sales—under $500,000
43,000 sq ft site, Distrib.—National
Privately owned corporation

**DELAWARE VALLEY BOX & LUMBER CO.**
2651 E. State St. Ext. (08619)
**Phone—(609) 890-2900**
Fax—(609) 890-8241
www.delvalbox.com
Email—marketing@delvalbox.com
Pres.—Charles C. Gould
SIC—2441; NAICS—321920; *Company headquarters & wooden shipping boxes & crates*
Employs—12; Estab.—1975
Sales—$3Mil-$6Mil
20,000 sq ft site, Distrib.—Regional
Privately owned corporation

NEW ENTRY
**†EDDIE KANE STEEL PRODUCTS, INC.**
450 Southard St. (08638)
**Phone—(609) 392-1161**
Fax—(609) 392-1164
www.eddiekanesteel.com
Email—info@eddiekanesteel.com
Sales Rep.—Joe Kane
Sales Rep.—Jim Kobren
SIC—5051; *Steel service center*
Employs—10
Privately owned corporation
Parent co.—Eddie Kane Steel Products, Inc., Spring Lake, NJ
Phone—(732) 974-3339
See Parent Co. Section for full profile.

**ELECTRICAL MOTOR REPAIR CO.**
809 E. State St. (08609)
Mail addr: P.O. Box 3787, Trenton (08629-0787)
**Phone—(609) 392-6149**
National—(800) 555-6880
Fax—(609) 392-7079
www.elevatormotor.com
Email—joe@elevatormotor.com
Pres.—Paul Doran
V-P.—Joe Castiglione
Off. Mgr.—John Wassum
SIC—3621; 3568; NAICS—335312; *Couplings for elevator hoist motors & rebuilt & retrofitted elevator hoist, hydraulic pump & door motors, MG sets & gearboxes, including elevator field service*
Employs—30; Estab.—1922
Sales—$2.5Mil-$5Mil
Distrib.—Intl.
Privately owned corporation

**EWING GLASS CO.**
1354 Parkside Ave. (08638)
**Phone—(609) 882-1818**
National—(888) 882-9696
Fax—(609) 882-7339
www.ewingglassandmirror.com

Email—paul-224@comcast.net
Pres.—Steve McClenney
Off. Mgr.—Paul J. Bernhard, Jr.
SIC—3231; NAICS—327215; *Glass fabrication & installation*
Employs—7; Estab.—1975
Sales—$1Mil-$2.5Mil (est)
2,800 sq ft site, Distrib.—Local
Privately owned corporation

**†FALLPROOF SYSTEMS LLC**
61 2nd Ave. *(08619)*
**Phone—(609) 325-5555**
National—(800) 452-0222
Fax—(609) 584-8882
www.fallproof.com
Email—solutions@fallproof.com
Ptnr.—W. Burke Sinclair
Ptnr.—Mark Shadek
SIC—5084; *Distributor of fall protection equipment & supplies, including anchors, harnesses, safety netting & confined space equipment*
Employs—10; Estab.—1998
Sales—$2.5Mil-$5Mil
3,000 sq ft site, Distrib.—National
Limited Liability Company

**FARMER CO., ARTHUR E.**
47 Frazier St. (08618)
Mail addr: P.O. Box 1785, Trenton (08607)
**Phone—(609) 392-8722**
Fax—(609) 392-6744
Owner—Edward C. Farmer
GM—David Gervasio
SIC—3599; *General machining job shop*
Employs—2; Estab.—1928
Sales—under $500,000
Distrib.—Intl.
Sole ownership

**†FASTENAL CO.**
1875 N. Olden Ave. (08638)
**Phone—(609) 530-0456**
Fax—(609) 530-0458
www.fastenal.com
Email—njtre@stores.fastenal.com
Store Mgr.—Chris Varlaro
SIC—5072; 5084; 5085; *Wholesaler of fasteners, safety equipment, tools & abrasives*
Employs—4; Estab.—1968
Distrib.—Local
Publicly owned corporation
Parent co.—Fastenal Co., Winona, MN
Phone—(507) 454-5374
See Parent Co. Section for full profile.

**FIREHAWK INDUSTRIES, LLC**
309 N. Willow St. (08618)
**Phone—(609) 393-0007**
Fax—(609) 393-4448
www.firehawkindustries.com
Email—info@firehawkindustries.com
Pres.—Cary Wische
SIC—3589; NAICS—333319; *High-pressure cleaning equipment, including steam cleaners & gun kits; Brand name—Fluid Heat*
Employs—3; Estab.—2000
Sales—$500,000-$1Mil
12,000 sq ft site, Distrib.—Intl.
Limited Liability Company

**FUTURE SIGNS**
19 Bowhill Ave. (08610)
**Phone—(609) 695-6263**
Fax—(609) 695-2253
www.futuresigns.net
Email—futuresigns800@aol.com
Pres.—Rich Rutzler
MIS Mgr.—Lenny Obrzut
Fin. Mgr.—Kim Arena
Printer—Jenny Bringus

SIC—3993; *Electric & nonelectric signs*
Employs—5; Estab.—1989
Sales—under $500,000
8,000 sq ft site, Distrib.—Local
Privately owned corporation

**†GRIFFITH ELECTRIC SUPPLY CO., INC.**
5 2nd St. (08611)
**Phone—(609) 695-6121**
Fax—(609) 695-3217
www.griffithelec.com
Email—info@griffithelec.com
Pres.—William Goodwin
V-P., Sales & Mktg.—Ronald A. Lim
V-P., Opers. & Whse. Mgr.—Crystal Simmons
V-P., Pur.—Ron Kaccmarek
Dir., Admn.—Sue Adams
SIC—5063; *Corporate headquarters & wholesaler of electric supplies, including electrical switches, boxes, panels, breakers & generators & lighting*
Employs—50; Estab.—1938
Distrib.—Local
Privately owned corporation

**HALBERD MATCH CORP.**
1230 Parkway Ave., Ste. 306 (08628)
**Phone—(609) 882-7000**
Fax—(609) 882-7000
www.halberdmatch.com
Email—julia@halberdmatch.com
CEO—Michael Shutt
CDO—Julia Freedman
IT Mgr.—George Pereira
SIC—7372; *Advanced image recognition & acquisition software development & custom application integration services; Brand name—ACADEMIX*
Employs—6
Sales—$500,000-$1Mil
Distrib.—National
Privately owned corporation

**HAMILTON TRANSIT CORPORATE CENTER**
572 Whitehead Rd. (08619)
**Phone—(609) 587-1188**
Fax—(609) 587-3463
Email—pmp@pmpcomposites.com
GM—Pete Horvath
Plt. Mgr.—Larry Simmons
Bookkeeper—Nicole Horvath
SIC—3089; *Molded fiberglass products*
Employs—10
Sales—$1Mil-$2.5Mil
105,000 sq ft site, Distrib.—National
Privately owned corporation
Also see: Pahco Machine, Inc., same loc.
AKA: PMP Composites Corp.

**HARRISON HOSE & TUBING, INC.**
2705 Kuser Rd. (08691)
Mail addr: P.O. Box 9386, Trenton (08650-1386)
**Phone—(609) 631-8804**
(866) 333-3350
Fax—(609) 631-8796
www.harrisonhose.com
Email—sales@harrisonhose.com
GM—James Logue
Sales Mgr.—Mike Lyon

# Trenton—(cont.)

SIC—3052; 3069; 3082; NAICS—326220; *High-end rubber & plastic flexible hose & tubing for the distributor & OEM markets, including nylon, PVC, polyethylene, polyurethane, polypropylene, PTFE, FEP, PFA, silicone, EPDM, neoprene, nitrile, viton & pure gum*
Employs—21; Estab.—1997
Sales—$2.5Mil-$5Mil
22,000 sq ft site, Distrib.—National
Privately owned corporation
ISO rating—9001

## HARRISON MACHINE & TOOL, INC.
21 Lexington Ave. (08618)
**Phone—(609) 883-0800**
Fax—(609) 883-1177
www.harrison-machine.com
Pres.—Steve Harrison
V-P., Secy-Treas.—Marie Harrison
Foreman—Steve Adams
SIC—3599; *Precision machining job shop*
Employs—7; Estab.—1990
Sales—$1Mil-$2.5Mil
Distrib.—Local
Privately owned corporation

## †HARVEY INDUSTRIES, INC., SID
1684 5th St. (08638)
**Phone—(609) 882-1766**
Fax—(609) 882-4621
www.sidharvey.com
Email—4037@sidharvey.com
Sales Mgr.—Lew Benchoff
Manager—Mark Safko
SIC—5075; *Distributor of HVAC equipment*
Employs—8; Estab.—1970
Distrib.—National
Privately owned corporation
Parent co.—Harvey Industries, Inc., Sid, Garden City, NY
Phone—(516) 745-9200
See Parent Co. Section for full profile.

## HIBBERT GROUP
400 Pennington Ave. (08638)
Mail addr: P.O. Box 8116, Trenton (08650)
**Phone—(609) 394-7500**
Fax—(609) 656-1862
www.hibbertgroup.com
CEO—Tim Moonan
Hum. Res. Mgr.—Lori Pigott
SIC—2752; NAICS—323100; *Offset, market & letterpress printing, fulfillment & direct mail*
Employs—100; Estab.—1883
Distrib.—Intl.
Privately owned corporation

## HOMASOTE CO.
932 Lower Ferry Rd., P.O. Box 7240 (08628)
**Phone—(609) 883-3300**
National—(800) 257-9491
Fax—(609) 406-9263
www.homasote.com
Email—sales@homasote.com
Chrm., CEO—Warren L. Flicker
CFO—Ron Fasano
V-P., Opers.—Peter Tindall
Corp. Secy.—Jennifer D. Bartkovich
Dir., Sales & Mktg.—Greg O'Driscoll
Sales Opers. Mgr.—Christine Lemonick
MIS Mgr.—Richard Mangan

SIC—2631; NAICS—322130; *Recycled fiberboard products, including exterior vertical sheathing, floor underlayment, sound control, roof decking, concrete forming & expansion joint & thermal insulation for residential & commercial buildings & industrial packaging; Brand name—Pakline; 440 Soundbarrier; Homex*
Employs—105; Estab.—1909
Sales—$21Mil
550,000 sq ft site, Distrib.—Intl.
Publicly owned corporation

## HOME RUBBER CO.
31 Wolverton Ave. (08611)
Mail addr: P.O. Box 878, Trenton (08605-0878)
**Phone—(609) 394-1176**
National—(800) 257-9441
Fax—(609) 396-1985
www.homerubber.com
Email—info@homerubber.com
Pres.—Richard Balka
Cont.—Stacey Hepner
Pur. Mgr.—Chris Vaccarella
SIC—3061; 3052; NAICS—326291; *Mechanical rubber products & uncured specification rubber for molding & extruding applications*
Employs—47; Estab.—1881
65,000 sq ft site, Distrib.—Intl.
Privately owned sub-S corp.

## HUTCHINSON INDUSTRIES, INC.
460 Southard St. (08638)
**Phone—(609) 394-1010**
Fax—(609) 394-2031
www.hutchinsoninc.com
Email—sales@hutchinsoninc.com
Pres.—Olivier Marsaly
CFO—John Koblos
Dir., Sales & Mktg.—David Kritzell
IT Mgr.—Rob Geoghan
Hum. Res. & Safety Mgr.—Barbara Keeny
SIC—3069; 3444; 3714; *Corporate headquarters & rubber & aluminum fabrication of wheels & mobility components for the military, security, fire & rescue, public transit, off-the-road & off-road recreation vehicle industries*
Employs—165
Sales—$40Mil
Distrib.—Intl.

## ITALIAN PEOPLES BAKERY, INC.
307 Hudson St. (08611)
**Phone—(609) 396-9869**
Fax—(609) 394-3801
www.bakeryfresh.com
Email—ipb@bakeryfresh.com
Pres.—Carmen Guagliardo
V-P.—Patrick Gachetti
Prodn. Mgr.—Patrick Gervasio
Opers. Mgr.—Joel Harris
Bookkeeper—Rashelle Alexander
SIC—2051; 2053; NAICS—311812; *Bread, rolls, pastries & cakes*
Employs—80; Estab.—1978
13,500 sq ft site, Distrib.—Regional
Privately owned corporation
AKA: Peoples Bakery, Inc.

## JERSEY PRECAST CORPORATION
853 Nottingham Way (08638)
**Phone—(609) 689-3700**
Fax—(609) 689-3797
www.jerseyprecast.com
Email—mail@jerseyprecast.com
Chrm., Pres.—Mohamed Amir Ulislam
Prodn. Mgr.—Paul Dentel
Hum. Res. Mgr.—Aamir Hashmi
Qual. Control Mgr.—Ray Chavez

SIC—3272; *Corporate headquarters & precast & prestressed products, including piles, pile caps, bridge beams, slabs & barriers*
Employs—130; Estab.—1980
Sales—$10Mil-$15Mil
70,000 sq ft site, Distrib.—Regional
Privately owned sub-S corp.

## KAYLINE PROCESSING, INC.
31 Coates St. (08611)
**Phone—(609) 695-1440**
National—(800) 367-5546
Fax—(609) 989-1094
www.kayline.com
Email—sales@kayline.com
V-P., R & D & Sales—Harley Hoffman
Plt. Mgr.—Edwin Lieb
Qual. Control Mgr.—Ron Evans
Chief Engr.—Peter Burns
Pur. Agt.—Thomas Spinner
SIC—3081; 3089; NAICS—326113; *Vinyl printing, laminating & embossing & custom & stock vinyl covering materials*
Employs—30; Estab.—1954
70,000 sq ft site, Distrib.—Intl.
Privately owned corporation

## KNF NEUBERGER, INC.
2 Black Forest Rd. (08691)
**Phone—(609) 890-8600**
www.knf.com
Cont.—Gary Frank
Mfg. Mgr.—Juergen Strauss
Mktg. Mgr.—Mark Kinzy
Pur. Mgr.—Monica Heidenhofer
SIC—3594; 3563; NAICS—333996; *Industrial pumps & compressors; Brand name—KNF; Laboport; KNF Pumps*
Employs—105; Estab.—1977
39,000 sq ft site, Distrib.—National
Privately owned corporation
ISO rating—9001

## KPMC, INC.
113 Walters Ave. (08638)
**Phone—(609) 538-1100**
Fax—(609) 538-0510
Pres.—Don Hoven
Machinist—Bill Ford
SIC—3599; *General machining job shop*
Employs—15; Estab.—1987
Sales—$3Mil-$5Mil
10,000 sq ft site, Distrib.—Intl.
Privately owned corporation

## LEGISLATIVE INDEX OF NEW JERSEY
172 W. State St. (08608)
**Phone—(609) 393-2291**
National—(800) 468-6389
Fax—(609) 393-1990
www.govnet.com
Email—info@govnet.com
Owner, Hum. Res. & IT Mgr.—Craig Leach
SIC—2741; NAICS—323119; *State of New Jersey legislation guide publishing & printing*
Employs—3; Estab.—1913
Sales—under $500,000
Distrib.—Local
Sole ownership

## LENAPE PRODUCTS, INC.
600 Plum St. (08638)
**Phone—(609) 394-5376**
Fax—(609) 394-0929
www.plumstreetpottery.com
Email—info@lenapebath.com
Pres.—Stephen M. Bielawski

SIC—3261; NAICS—327111; *Corporate headquarters & porcelain toothbrush holders, switchplates, cabinet hardware & bathroom accessories*
Employs—5; Estab.—1920
Distrib.—Regional
Privately owned corporation
AKA: Lenape Porcelain Products

## LIBERTY PRINTING, INC.
1111 Chestnut Ave. (08611)
**Phone—(609) 396-5995**
Fax—(609) 393-7261
Email—libprtinc@aol.com
Pres.—George Demeter
GM—Mark Goodman
SIC—2752; 2791; NAICS—323122; *Offset & instant printing & typesetting*
Employs—3; Estab.—1986
Sales—under $500,000
3,000 sq ft site, Distrib.—Local
Privately owned sub-S corp.

## LOCKWOOD'S ELECTRIC MOTOR SERVICE, INC.
2239 Nottingham Way (08619)
**Phone—(609) 587-2333**
      (800) 453-3018
Fax—(609) 587-5018
www.lockwoodselectricmotor.com
Email—contactus@lockwoodselectricmotor.com
Pres.—Richard L. Dey
Sales Mgr.—Tony Sparano
SIC—3621; *Rebuilt electric motors*
Employs—35
Sales—$5Mil-$10Mil (est)

## LOEFFLER'S GOURMET
482 Whitehead Rd. (08619)
**Phone—(609) 695-5068**
Fax—(609) 586-2146
www.loefflersmeats.com
Email—loefflers@optonline.net
Pres.—Robert Trofimowicz
SIC—2013; NAICS—311600; *Luncheon meat processing & packaging*
Employs—10; Estab.—1976
Sales—$500,000-$1Mil
Distrib.—Local
Privately owned corporation

NEW ENTRY
## LOMBARDO MUSIC PUBLICATIONS
37 Pintinalli Dr. (08619)
**Phone—(609) 586-9245**
Fax—(609) 631-0465
www.lombardomusic.com
Email—lmp@lombardomusic.com
Owner—Harry Lombardozzi
SIC—2741; *Sheet music publishing*
Employs—2
Sales—under $500,000 (est)

## LUCILLE MAUD CORP.
513 N. Olden Ave. (08638)
**Phone—(609) 393-7555**
Fax—(609) 393-1140
www.lucillemaud.com
Email—information@lucillemaud.com
Pres.—Louis Muirhead
V-P., Opers.—Todd Ricker
GM—Anthony Jackson
MIS Mgr.—William Justice
SIC—7373; 5045; 5112; NAICS—541512; *Computer systems integration & distributor of computer hardware, software, peripherals & office supplies; Brand name—Cisco; Compaq; IBM; Hewlett-Packard; Nortel; Verio; Xerox; Microsoft; Intel; Lexmark; ViewSonic; NEC*
Employs—8; Estab.—1985
15,000 sq ft site, Distrib.—National
Privately owned corporation

GEOGRAPHICAL

## Trenton—(cont.)

### MARBLE & GRANITE FABRICATORS
950 Pennsylvania Ave. (08638)
**Phone—(609) 392-2792**
Fax—(609) 392-2793
www.marble-fabricators.com
Email—mgfco@yahoo.com
Owner—Andrew Podlesny
Hum. Res. & IT Mgr.—Trish Buckley
SIC—3281; *Granite & marble countertops*
Employs—8; Estab.—1996
Sales—$500,000-$1Mil (est)
Distrib.—Regional
Privately owned sub-S corp.

### MARSHALL INDUSTRIAL TECHNOLOGIES
529 S. Clinton Ave. (08611)
**Phone—(609) 394-7153**
Fax—(609) 989-7794
www.marshallindtech.com
Email—marketing@marshallindtech.com
Pres.—John Mako
V-P.—Richard Osenlund
V-P.—Rocco Carnevale
SIC—3599; 3499; *Welding, metal fabrication & machining, including turning, milling, boring, broaching, replacement & spare parts machining, fabricated components, piping systems & vessel & skid fabrication*
Employs—150; Estab.—1951
Sales—$10Mil-$25Mil
35,000 sq ft site, Distrib.—Regional
Privately owned corporation

### MARSHALL, INC., G. E.
810 S. Broad St. (08611)
**Phone—(609) 392-2464**
Fax—(609) 392-0661
Pres.—Kimberly Adler
SIC—2394; NAICS—314912; *Canvas awnings*
Employs—5; Estab.—1936
Sales—under $500,000
Distrib.—Local
Privately owned corporation

### †MERCER GROUP INTERNATIONAL, INC.
1519 Calhoun St., P.O. Box 5626 (08638)
**Phone—(609) 393-4834**
Fax—(609) 394-6019
www.mercergroup.com
Email—info@mercergroup.com
Pres.—Mario Mazza
Cont.—Ken Barker
Sales Mgr.—Tino Cantaffa
Sales Mgr.—Rich Lodgek
Whse. Mgr.—Brian Getta
SIC—5093; *Wholesaler of recycled concrete, asphalt, wood, plastic, paper & cardboard*
Employs—40; Estab.—1995
Distrib.—National

### MERCER MACHINE & TOOL PRODUCTS
332 Darcy Ave. (08629)
**Phone—(609) 587-1106**
Fax—(609) 587-1239
Pres.—Tom Erni
SIC—3599; 3544; NAICS—333500; *General machining & tool & die job shop*
Employs—5; Estab.—1994
Sales—$500,000-$1Mil
Distrib.—Regional
Privately owned corporation

### MERCER OCCUPATIONAL TRAINING
600 New York Ave. (08638)
**Phone—(609) 393-2483**
Fax—(609) 396-3599
www.arcmercer.org

Ex. Dir.—Steven Cook
Dir., Prog. & Opers. Mgr.—Joseph Gleason
Hum. Res. Mgr.—Iris Alvarez
SIC—3999; *Contract assembly*
Employs—150; Estab.—1950
Sales—$1Mil-$2.5Mil
16,000 sq ft site, Distrib.—Local
Privately owned corporation

### †METAL STOCK
471 Southard St. (08638)
Mail addr: P.O. Box 1145, Trenton (08606)
**Phone—(609) 394-1129**
Fax—(609) 394-5028
Pres.—Morris Mann
SIC—5051; *Distributor of steel sheets*
Employs—15; Estab.—1937
Sales—$2.5Mil-$5Mil
Distrib.—Local
Privately owned corporation

### MOLDED FIBERGLASS PRODUCTS
3 Industry Ct. (08638)
**Phone—(609) 538-8822**
Pres.—Ken Sutter
Fabricator—Eric Sutter
SIC—3089; *Fiberglass products fabrication*
Employs—3; Estab.—1992
Sales—under $500,000
Distrib.—National
Privately owned corporation

### †MOTION INDUSTRIES, INC.
9A S. Gold Dr. (08691)
**Phone—(609) 588-0555**
National—(800) 526-9328
Fax—(609) 588-0220
www.motionindustries.com
Email—john.velit@motion-ind.com
Br. Mgr.—John Velit
SIC—5085; *Distributor of industrial maintenance, repair & operation (MRO) parts including bearings, power transmission, electrical & indl. automation, material handling, hydraulic & pneumatic components, hydraulic & indl. hose & safety/indl. supplies; Brand name—Altra; Baldor; Eaton; Emerson Industrial Automation; Gates; Lovejoy; Martin; Nexen; NSK; NTN; Rexnord; Schaeffler Group; SEW Eurodrive; SKF; SMC; Sumitomo; THK; Thomson; Timken; Tsubaki; US Motors; Vacon; Webster*
Employs—18
Distrib.—National
Privately owned corporation
Parent co.—Motion Industries, Inc., Birmingham, AL
Phone—(205) 951-1154
See Parent Co. Section for full profile.

### MR. B. FENCE CO.
325 Stokes Ave. (08638)
**Phone—(609) 882-1896**
www.mrbfenceco.com
Pres.—Rob Barbiero
SIC—3089; 2499; *PVC & wooden fence panels & installation services*
Employs—10; Estab.—1996
Sales—$500,000-$1Mil
Distrib.—National
Privately owned corporation

### NATIONAL CERAMIC CO., INC.
500 Southard St. (08638)
**Phone—(609) 394-5373**
Fax—(609) 989-4847
www.nationalceramic.com
Email—sales@nationalceramic.com
Pres.—V. Thomas Colletti
Plt. Mgr.—Richard Miller
Off. Mgr.—Marie Borders

SIC—3264; NAICS—327113; *Ceramic electrical insulators*
Employs—9; Estab.—1906
31,000 sq ft site, Distrib.—Intl.
Privately owned corporation
Also see: X-Pando Products, Inc., same loc.

### NAVINTA, LLC
1499 Lower Ferry Rd. (08618)
**Phone—(609) 883-1135**
Fax—(609) 883-1137
Pres.—Jayshree Patel
Acctg. Mgr.—Manish Parmar
SIC—2833; NAICS—325411; *Herb & drug grading, grinding & milling*
Employs—14; Estab.—2003
Distrib.—Intl.
Limited Liability Company

### NEW JERSEY BUSINESS & INDUSTRY ASSN. (H Q)
10 W. Lafayette St. (08608)
**Phone—(609) 393-7707**
Fax—(609) 695-0442
www.njbia.org
Email—info@njbia.org
Pres.—Michele N. Siekerka
Sr. V-P., Govt. Affs.—Melanie Willoughby
V-P., Admn. & Treas.—Julia Stoller
V-P., Mktg.—Michele Glassburg
V-P., Health & Legal Affs.—Christine Stearns
V-P., Energy, Env. & Fed. Affs.—Sara Bluhm
Asst. V-P., Comm.—Steve Wilson
SIC—2721; *Company headquarters; monthly association magazine publishing; Brand name—NJBIA Employee Benefits Report*
Employs—35; Estab.—1910
Sales—$2.5Mil-$5Mil (est)
Distrib.—Regional
Privately owned corporation

### NEW JERSEY BUSINESS SYSTEMS, INC.
7-C Marlen Dr. (08691)
**Phone—(609) 587-5500**
Fax—(609) 587-6660
www.njbs.com
Email—sales@njbs.com
V-P.—Michael Bolling
Off. Mgr.—Cheryl Walsh
Bookkeeper—Laurie McAlister
SIC—7373; NAICS—541512; *LAN & wireless computer integrated systems & cable services*
Employs—20; Estab.—1968
Sales—$7Mil
Distrib.—Local
Privately owned corporation

### OMAHA STANDARD
572 Whitehead Rd. (08619)
Mail addr: P.O. Box 5757, Trenton (08638)
**Phone—(609) 588-5400**
Fax—(609) 588-4104
www.palfinger.com
Email—r.schwab@palfinger.com
V-P., Operation—Danny Anthony
Hum. Res. & Off. Mgr.—Debbie Lieggi
Accts. Payable Mgr.—Robin Schwab
SIC—3713; NAICS—336211; *Truck bodies for the waste, recycling & construction industries*
Employs—50; Estab.—1978
36,000 sq ft site, Distrib.—National

### ORTHO SAFE SYSTEMS INTERNATIONAL, INC. (H Q)
P.O. Box 9435 (08650)
**Phone—(609) 587-3859**
Fax—(609) 587-7609
www.orthosafe.com
Email—info@orthosafe.com
Pres.—Winfried Kraft

SIC—2399; *Corporate headquarters; wheelchair & occupant restraint systems (mfg. done in Taiwan)*
Employs—5
Sales—$500,000-$1Mil (est)
Distrib.—Intl.
Privately owned corporation

### PACKAGING UNLIMITED, INC.
17 Chelten Way, Bldg. A (08638)
Mail addr: P.O. Box 796, Newtown (18940)
**Phone—(609) 394-9400**
Fax—(609) 394-9445
www.pkgunlimited.com
Email—sales@pkgunlimited.com
Pres.—Frank Corrado
SIC—2653; 2759; 3086; NAICS—322211; *Printed corrugated boxes & foam supplies for packaging applications*
Employs—3; Estab.—1986
Sales—$500,000-$1Mil (est)
Distrib.—Local
Privately owned corporation

### PAHCO MACHINE, INC.
572 Whitehead Rd., Ste. 101 (08619)
**Phone—(609) 587-1188**
Fax—(609) 587-3463
Email—nicole@pmpcomposites.com
GM—Pete Horvath
Bookkeeper—Nicole Horvath
SIC—3544; 3599; NAICS—333500; *Tool & die & general machining job shop*
Employs—3; Estab.—1958
20,000 sq ft site, Distrib.—National
Privately owned corporation
Also see: Hamilton Transit Corporate Center, same loc.

### PARK AVENUE PRINTING, LLC
2001 S. Broad St. (08610)
**Phone—(609) 989-8022**
Fax—(609) 393-7544
Email—smadola@aol.com
Pres.—Steven Madola
Printer—James Madola
Printer—Tom Madola
SIC—2752; 2791; NAICS—323122; *Offset printing & typesetting*
Employs—6; Estab.—1985
Sales—$500,000-$1Mil
Distrib.—Local
Limited Liability Company

### †PENN SUPPLY, INC.
618 E. State St. (08609)
**Phone—(609) 394-1151**
Fax—(609) 394-9011
www.pennsupplynj.com
Email—sales@pennsupplynj.com
Owner—Ronald Vernon
Off. Mgr.—Diane Yonkowski
SIC—5074; 5075; *Wholesaler of plumbing & heating equipment; Brand name—Toto; American Standard; Grohe; Weil-McLain; Crown; Taco; Zoeller; Century; Gerber; Noritz; MiFab; Swanstone; Rheem; Elkay; Sloan; Delta; Jacuzzi*
Employs—10; Estab.—1982
Distrib.—Local
Privately owned sub-S corp.

### PERFORMANCE INDUSTRIES, INC.
51 Tucker St. (08618)
**Phone—(609) 392-1450**
Fax—(609) 392-2466
Pres.—Stuart Azarchi
GM—Gabe Johnson
SIC—2851; NAICS—325510; *Paint products*
Employs—20; Estab.—1946
Distrib.—Regional
Privately owned corporation

## Trenton—(cont.)

**PIERCE ROBERTS RUBBER CO., INC.**
1450 Heath Ave., P.O. Box 5007 (08638)
**Phone—(609) 394-5245**
Fax—(609) 394-0709
www.pierceroberts.com
Email—info@pierceroberts.com
Pres.—Denise Hoffman
COO—Christopher Weber
SIC—3069; *Custom molded rubber products*
Employs—20; Estab.—1911
40,000 sq ft site, Distrib.—Intl.
Privately owned corporation
ISO rating—9001:2008

**PORTFIRIO ITALIAN FOOD, INC.**
320 Anderson St. (08611)
**Phone—(609) 393-4116**
Fax—(609) 392-1773
www.portfirios.com
Pres.—John Portfirio
Treas.—Robert Calabro
Prodn. Mgr.—Joe Calabro
Manager—Anthony Calabro
SIC—2099; *Fresh pasta*
Employs—5; Estab.—1964
Sales—under $500,000
2,000 sq ft site, Distrib.—Local
Privately owned corporation

**POWER MAGNETICS, INC.**
377 Reservoir St. *(08618)*
**Phone—(609) 695-1170**
         (800) 747-0845
Fax—(609) 695-5907
www.powermagneticsinc.com
Email—sales@powermagneticsinc.com
Pres.—Carl Bannwart
Sales Mgr., Natl.—David Leis
New Bus. Dev. Mgr.—Mike Smith
SIC—3612; NAICS—335311; *Transformers, reactors & inductors*
Employs—26; Estab.—1968
Sales—$2Mil-$10Mil
15,000 sq ft site, Distrib.—Intl.
Privately owned corporation
ISO rating—9000:2008

**POWTEK POWDER COATING, INC.**
233 Dickinson St. (08638)
**Phone—(609) 394-6700**
Fax—(609) 394-0630
Email—powteksm@yahoo.com
Pres.—Fred Martucci
SIC—3479; *Metal powder coating*
Employs—6; Estab.—1997
Sales—under $500,000
Distrib.—Local
Privately owned corporation

**PRECISION TOOL & ENGINEERING, INC.**
123 Florence Ave. (08618)
**Phone—(609) 882-9223**
Fax—(609) 882-9223
Pres.—Tom Harter
SIC—3599; *Precision machining job shop*
Employs—1; Estab.—1988
Sales—under $500,000 (est)
Distrib.—Local
Privately owned corporation

**PRESTIGE ASSOCS., INC.**
39 Mead St. (08638)
Mail addr: P.O. Box 3873, Trenton (08629)
**Phone—(609) 393-1509**
Fax—(609) 393-9211
Email—prestassoc@aol.com
Pres.—Robert McGurie
Facility Mgr.—Donald Robins
Off. Mgr.—Jodie Harmon
Off. Mgr.—Sherry Sullivan

SIC—2675; NAICS—322200; *Paper & paperboard die cutting & assembly*
Employs—7; Estab.—1993
45,000 sq ft site, Distrib.—Regional
Privately owned corporation

**PRINCETON INSTRUMENTS**
Div. of Roper Industries, Inc.
3660 Quakerbridge Rd. (08619)
**Phone—(609) 587-9797**
National—(877) 474-2286
Fax—(609) 587-1970
www.princetoninstruments.com
Email—info@princetoninstruments.com
Pres.—William Asher
Hum. Res. Mgr.—Donna Chisick
SIC—3826; 3829; 3827; NAICS—334516; *High-performance CCD, ICCD, EMCCD & InGaAs cameras, spectrometers, spectrographs, imaging systems & optics & coatings solutions for the scientific research, industrial imaging & OEM communities*
Employs—60; Estab.—1981
Sales—$50Mil-$60Mil
Distrib.—Intl.
Publicly owned corporation
ISO rating—9001
AKAs: PI/Acton & Princeton Instruments/Acton
Parent co.—Roper Industries, Inc., Sarasota, FL
Phone—(941) 556-2601
See Parent Co. Section for full profile.

**PRINCETON MICROWAVE TECHNOLOGY**
5 Nami Ln. (08619)
**Phone—(609) 586-8140**
         (609) 610-1133
Fax—(609) 586-1231
www.princetonmicrowave.com
Email—sales@princetonmicrowave.com
Co-Pres.—Amarjit Kaur
Co-Pres.—Amarjit Bharj
V-P.—Sarjit S. Bharj
Prod. Mgr.—Inder Singh
SIC—3679; *Microwave components*
Employs—13; Estab.—1993
Sales—$2Mil-$3.5Mil
6,800 sq ft site, Distrib.—Regional
Privately owned corporation

**PROCESS RESEARCH PRODUCTS**
1013 Whitehead Road Ext. (08638)
**Phone—(609) 882-0400**
Fax—(609) 882-9608
www.processresearch.com
Email—sales@processresearch.com
V-P., Admn. & Fin.—Phyliss Joan
SIC—2842; 2819; NAICS—325612; *Metalworking fluids, lapping compounds & liquid cleaners*
Employs—20; Estab.—1958
40,000 sq ft site, Distrib.—Intl.
Privately owned corporation

**QUANTEM CORP.**
1457 Lower Ferry Rd. (08618)
**Phone—(609) 883-9191**
Fax—(609) 883-9879
www.quantemcorp.com
Email—info@quantemcorp.com
CEO—Chris Bromberg
GM—John Brienza
Off. Mgr.—Linda Tyler
SIC—3825; 3829; NAICS—334500; *Thermostats & temperature controls*
Employs—20; Estab.—1975
15,000 sq ft site, Distrib.—Local

**†R & R MARKETING, LLC**
2900 E. State Street Ext. (08619)
**Phone—(609) 587-6103**
National—(800) 222-1260

Fax—(609) 587-2770
www.rrmarketing.com
Email—dlowenstein@rrmarketing.com
GM—Jerry DeAngelo
Sales Mgr.—Dennis Resnick
Sales Admn.—Victoria Rudolph
SIC—5182; *Distributor of wine & liquors*
Employs—100; Estab.—1988
Distrib.—Regional
Limited Liability Company
Parent co.—R & R Marketing, LLC, West Caldwell, NJ
Phone—(973) 228-5100
See Parent Co. Section for full profile.

**RALPH CLAYTON & SONS**
Div. of Clayton Block Co., Inc.
1144 New York Ave. (08638)
Mail addr: P.O. Box 3015, Lakewood (08701)
**Phone—(609) 695-0767**
National—(800) 662-3044
Fax—(609) 695-5495
www.claytonco.com
Email—kroe@claytonco.com
Dir., Qual. Control, Concrete—Matthew Savona
Area Sales Rep.—David Dobbins
SIC—3273; NAICS—327320; *Ready-mixed concrete*
Employs—15; Estab.—1954
Sales—$2.5Mil-$5Mil (est)
Distrib.—Local
Privately owned corporation
Parent co.—Clayton Block Co., Inc., Neptune, NJ
Phone—(732) 751-7600
See Parent Co. Section for full profile.

**REES SCIENTIFIC CORP.**
1007 Whitehead Road Ext. (08638)
**Phone—(609) 530-1055**
National—(800) 327-3141
Fax—(609) 530-1854
www.reesscientific.com
Email—sales@reesscientific.com
Pres., CEO—Rees Thomas
V-P.—Michael Mothersbaugh
SIC—3823; NAICS—334513; *Environmental monitoring, integrated access control & automated watering solutions for validation, automatic reporting & wireless & hardwired sensors*
Employs—125; Estab.—1982
24,000 sq ft site, Distrib.—Intl.
Privately owned corporation

**RICHARDSON CO., J. B.**
1603 N. Olden Ave. (08638)
**Phone—(609) 695-7474**
Email—jbrjoe@gmail.com
Pres.—Joe Quinn
SIC—3273; NAICS—327320; *Ready-mixed concrete*
Employs—2; Estab.—1856
Sales—under $500,000
Distrib.—Local
Sole ownership

**RIVER HORSE**
2 Graphics Dr. (08628)
**Phone—(609) 883-0890**
Fax—(609) 882-0468
www.riverhorse.com
Email—info@riverhorse.com
Chrm., Pres.—Glenn Bernabeo
Admn. Mgr.—Sarah Cifelli
SIC—2082; *Malt liquor & beer*
Employs—20; Estab.—1997
Sales—under $500,000
Distrib.—Regional
Privately owned corporation

**ROBODYSSEY SYSTEMS, LLC**
20 Quimby Ave. (08610)
**Phone—(609) 585-8535**
Fax—(609) 585-8535
www.robodyssey.com
Email—info@robodyssey.com
Pres.—David Peins

V-P.—Brian Patton
SIC—3679; 2731; *Educational systems for teaching practical math & science skills, including autonomous robot kits, robotic sensors, programmable imbedded controllers & motor drivers & practical classroom manuals publishing for imbedded controllers; Brand name—BasicX and Robotics-The Art of Making Machines Think; Robodyssey Systems ESRA Robot; Robodyssey Systems Mouse Robot*
Employs—2; Estab.—2000
Sales—under $500,000
Distrib.—Intl.
Limited Liability Company

**ROGERS PRINTING CENTER**
11 Lexington Ave. (08618)
**Phone—(609) 883-3238**
Fax—(609) 538-0454
Email—rogerprint@aol.com
Pres.—Roger G. Chupik
SIC—2752; 2759; NAICS—323100; *Digital, offset & letterpress printing*
Employs—1; Estab.—1982
Sales—under $500,000
1,900 sq ft site, Distrib.—Regional
Sole ownership

**†RUMSEY ELECTRIC CO.**
311 N. Clinton Ave. (08638)
**Phone—(609) 989-9400**
Fax—(609) 989-9378
www.rumsey.com
Email—fpypcznski@rumsey.com
Regional Mgr.—Frank Pypcznski
SIC—5063; *Distributor of electrical supplies, including switches, wires & electric boards*
Employs—15; Estab.—1997
Distrib.—National
Privately owned corporation
Parent co.—Rumsey Electric Co., Conshohocken, PA
Phone—(610) 832-9000
See Parent Co. Section for full profile.

**S & P METAL FINISHING CORP.**
185 Oakland St. (08618)
Mail addr: P.O. Box 554, Trenton (08604)
**Phone—(609) 393-4833**
Fax—(609) 393-8090
www.mechanicalgalvanizing.com
Email—allservice@comcast.net
Pres.—Suresh Patel
V-P.—Praful Patel
Plt. Mgr.—Ramesh Kanja
Opers. Mgr.—Lukas Perez
SIC—3471; NAICS—332813; *Mechanical zinc, cadmium & tin plating & galvanizing, including conversion coatings*
Employs—6; Estab.—1970
8,000 sq ft site, Distrib.—Regional
Privately owned sub-S corp.

**SIEMENS ENERGY, INC.**
840 Nottingham Way (08638)
**Phone—(609) 890-5000**
Fax—(609) 890-9180
www.usa.siemens.com/energy
Email—support.energy@siemens.com
V-P.—Ken Win
Plt. Mgr.—Steve Bjorkman
SIC—3511; NAICS—333611; *Industrial turbines & compressors, packaging & testing*
Employs—200; Estab.—1901
Distrib.—Intl.
Publicly owned corporation
Parent co.—Siemens Energy, Inc., Orlando, FL
Phone—(407) 736-2000
See Parent Co. Section for full profile.

GEOGRAPHICAL

# Trenton—(cont.)

**†SIMS METAL MANAGEMENT**
1511 Calhoun St. (08638)
**Phone—(609) 396-0880**
Fax—(609) 396-0044
www.simsmm.com
Email—info@us.sims-group.com
GM—Juan Mezza
SIC—5093; 5065; *Wholesaler of recycled steel & parts reclaimed from used electronics*
Employs—15
Distrib.—Intl.
Privately owned corporation
Parent co.—Sims Metal Management, New York, NY
Phone—(212) 604-0710
See Parent Co. Section for full profile.

**STANLEY ACCESS TECHNOLOGIES, LLC**
17 Marlen Dr., Ste. C (08691)
**Phone—(609) 890-0877**
National—(800) 722-2377
Fax—(609) 890-1574
www.stanleyaccesstechnologies.com
Email—s-sat-satinfo@sbdinc.com
Br. Mgr.—Joe Marino
Serv. Dispatch Supv.—John Kaviner
SIC—3442; 3679; 3669; NAICS—332321; *Power-operated security & fire doors, sensors & entry control systems*
Employs—30; Estab.—1908
Distrib.—Intl.
Limited Liability Company
Parent co.—Stanley Access Technologies, LLC, Farmington, CT
Phone—(860) 677-2861
See Parent Co. Section for full profile.

**STONE TECH FABRICATION**
930 New York Ave. (08638)
**Phone—(609) 984-8818**
National—(888) 786-6319
Fax—(609) 392-5849
www.stonetechmarble.com
Pres.—Danny Vogia
SIC—3281; NAICS—327991; *Marble & granite products*
Employs—10; Estab.—1985
Sales—$500,000-$1Mil (est)
Distrib.—Intl.
Privately owned corporation

**SUBURBAN FENCE CO.**
532 Mulberry St. (08638)
**Phone—(609) 452-2630**
Fax—(609) 695-4035
Owner—Jelman S. Solomon
SIC—2499; 3446; *Wooden & steel fencing & installation services*
Employs—20; Estab.—1991
Sales—$500,000-$1Mil
Distrib.—Local
Privately owned corporation

**SWITLIK PARACHUTE CO., INC.**
1325 E. State St. (08609)
Mail addr: P.O. Box 1328, Trenton (08607-1328)
**Phone—(609) 587-3300**
Fax—(609) 586-6647
www.switlik.com
Email—info@switlik.com
Pres.—Stanley Switlik II
V-P., CFO & Dir., Hum. Res.—Michael C. Dilts
V-P., Mfg.—William C. Weber
Dir., Sales—Anthony Florio
SIC—3069; 2399; *Life rafts, aviation life vests, flight suits, life preservers & coveralls; Brand name—Switlik; Survival Technologies*
Employs—115; Estab.—1920
91,000 sq ft site, Distrib.—Intl.
Privately owned corporation
ISO rating—9001:2008

**TEKTITE INDUSTRIES, INC.**
309 N. Clinton Ave. (08638)
**Phone—(609) 656-0600**
National—(800) 540-2814
Fax—(609) 656-0063
www.tek-tite.com
Email—sales@tek-tite.com
Pres.—Scott Mele
Cust. Serv. Mgr.—Marge Powers
SIC—3648; 3645; 3646; NAICS—335129; *LED flashlights & replacement bulbs, strobe lights & specialty portable lighting; Brand name—Tektite; Tekna*
Employs—9; Estab.—1990
Sales—over $1Mil
10,000 sq ft site, Distrib.—Intl.
Privately owned corporation

**TERRACYCLE, INC.**
121 New York Ave. (08638)
**Phone—(609) 393-4252**
National—(866) 967-6766
Fax—(609) 393-4259
www.terracycle.net
Email—customersupport@terracycle.net
CEO—Tom Szaky
Cust. Serv. Rep.—Crystal Wright
SIC—3089; 2394; NAICS—325314; *Cut & sewn duffel bags, bike pouches, backpacks & totes from recycled drink pouches, chip bags & energy bar wrappers*
Employs—25; Estab.—2003
Distrib.—Intl.
Privately owned corporation

**TIMES OF TRENTON**
Div. of Staten Island Publications, Inc.
413 River View Plz. (08611)
**Phone—(609) 989-5454**
National—(800) 693-3548
Fax—(609) 989-5739
www.nj.com/times
Email—news@njtimes.com
Publisher & Editor—Sheila Gallagher-Montone
Editor, Bus. & Metro—Tony Hagen
Adv. Serv. Mgr.—Jason Matis
SIC—2711; *Conventional & online newspaper publishing*
Employs—350; Estab.—1883
Distrib.—Local
Privately owned corporation
Parent co.—Staten Island Publications, Inc., Staten Island, NY
Phone—(718) 981-1234
See Parent Co. Section for full profile.

**TITAN RACK & SHELVING, LLC**
101 Muirhead Ave. (08695)
Mail addr: 203 Easton Ave., New Brunswick (08901)
**Phone—(732) 249-0887**
Fax—(732) 249-3155
www.titanrackandshelving.com
Email—trsllc@optonline.net
CEO, CFO & Gen. Counsel—Scott Miller
COO—Gregg Miller
Off. Mgr.—Kristin Tauscher
SIC—2542; *Metal racks & shelving*
Employs—8; Estab.—2003
Sales—$1Mil-$2.5Mil
100,000 sq ft site, Distrib.—Regional
Limited Liability Company

**TRANE CO.**
Div. of Trane Commercial Systems
2231 E. State St. (08619)
**Phone—(609) 587-3400**
Fax—(609) 588-4208
www.trane.com
Email—press@trane.com
V-P., Plt.—Andy Stevenson
Hum. Res. Leader—Diane Notta
Plt. Fin. Leader—Theresa Tamburro
SIC—3585; *Commercial air conditioners & furnaces*
Employs—715
Sales—$200Mil
425,000 sq ft site, Distrib.—Intl.
Publicly owned corporation
Parent co.—Trane Commercial Systems, La Crosse, WI
Phone—(608) 787-2000
See Parent Co. Section for full profile.

**TREASURY PRINTING SERVICES**
101 Carroll St., P.O. Box 30 (08625)
**Phone—(609) 292-5133**
Fax—(609) 777-1881
CEO, Chief Printing & Reprographics—Douglas N. Krieger
SIC—2759; 2752; NAICS—323100; *Government printing for the State of New Jersey executive & legislative branches, including booklets, brochures, forms, envelopes, flyers, posters, tickets, letterheads, newsletters & business cards*
Employs—30; Estab.—1965
25,000 sq ft site, Distrib.—Local
Privately owned corporation

**TRENT CORP., THE**
1384 Yardville Hamilton Square Rd., P.O. Box 2650 (08690)
**Phone—(609) 587-7515**
Fax—(609) 586-9710
www.trentbox.com
Email—trentboxmfgco@aol.com
Pres.—Carl Angelini
GM—Lawrence Angelini
Cust. Serv. Mgr.—David Swanhart
SIC—2653; NAICS—322211; *Corrugated & bulk boxes*
Employs—20; Estab.—1959
Sales—$2.5Mil-$5Mil
45,000 sq ft site, Distrib.—Intl.
Sole ownership

**TRENTON CORRUGATED PRODUCTS, INC.**
17 Cheltan Way (08638)
**Phone—(609) 695-0808**
Fax—(609) 695-7530
www.trentoncorrugated.com
Email—sales@trentoncorrugated.com
Pres., GM—Brad Pecoraro
Sales Mgr.—Cathy Dillon
IT Mgr.—Mike Keller
SIC—2653; NAICS—322211; *Corrugated boxes*
Employs—40; Estab.—1969
Distrib.—Local
Privately owned corporation

**TRENTON HALAL PACKING CO.**
610 Roebling Ave. (08611)
**Phone—(609) 394-0331**
Fax—(609) 396-8142
Pres.—Mohammad Malik
GM—Rizwan Malik
Plt. Mgr.—Joseph Avedissian
Supervisor—Ibrahim Bah
SIC—2011; NAICS—311611; *Beef processing & packing*
Employs—10; Estab.—1994
Sales—$2.5Mil-$5Mil (est)
20,000 sq ft site, Distrib.—Regional
Privately owned corporation

**TRENTON PRINTING, LLC**
1150 Southard St., Ste. 2 (08638)
**Phone—(609) 695-6485**
Fax—(609) 695-8897
www.trentonprinting.com
Email—mail@trentonprinting.com
Pres.—David Nugent
Acctg. Mgr.—Chris Mushinsky

SIC—2752; NAICS—323100; *Graphic design, offset printing & mailing services*
Employs—12; Estab.—1929
72,000 sq ft site, Distrib.—Regional
Limited Liability Company

**TRENTON SHEET METAL**
30 Adam Ave. (08618)
Mail addr: P.O. Box 1121, Trenton (08606)
**Phone—(609) 695-6328**
Fax—(609) 695-1929
www.trentonsheetmetal.com
GM—Robert Somogyi
Off. Mgr.—Kathie Meyers
Pur. Agt.—Judith Luchenbach
SIC—3444; *Sheet metal fabrication*
Employs—25; Estab.—1919
Sales—under $500,000
Distrib.—Local
Privately owned corporation

**TRENTON STEAK CO.**
539 Chestnut Ave. (08611)
**Phone—(609) 695-6776**
Fax—(609) 695-4919
Owner—Armando Rienzi
Plt. Mgr.—Mike Wood
SIC—2011; NAICS—311611; *Meat packing*
Employs—5; Estab.—1987
Sales—$1Mil-$2.5Mil (est)
Distrib.—Regional
Privately owned corporation

**TRENTONIAN, THE**
Div. of Digital First Media
600 Perry St. (08618)
Mail addr: P.O. Box 231, Trenton (08602)
**Phone—(609) 989-7800**
Fax—(609) 393-6072
www.trentonian.com
Email—questions@trentonian.com
Publisher—Bill Murray
Art Dir.—Anne Bench
Circ. Mgr.—Phil Metz
SIC—2711; *Daily print & online newspaper publishing*
Employs—100; Estab.—1947
Sales—under $500,000
Distrib.—Local
Publicly owned corporation
Parent co.—Digital First Media, Fairless Hills, PA
Phone—(215) 504-4200
See Parent Co. Section for full profile.

**TRENTYPO, INC.**
304 Stokes Ave. (08638)
**Phone—(609) 883-2198**
Fax—(609) 883-2428
www.trentypo.com
Email—trentypo@aol.com
Pres.—Peter Simon
Prodn. Mgr.—Peter Simon II
SIC—2759; 2791; NAICS—323122; *Color printing & computerized typesetting*
Employs—8; Estab.—1960
Sales—$1Mil-$2.5Mil
Distrib.—Regional
Privately owned corporation
Also see: 312 Stokes Ave. loc.

**TRENTYPO, INC.**
312 Stokes Ave., P.O. Box 304 (08638)
**Phone—(609) 883-5971**
Fax—(609) 883-9104
Bindery Mgr.—Rich Yoder
SIC—2789; NAICS—323121; *Bookbinding & print finishing for the graphic arts industry*
Employs—5; Estab.—1976
Sales—under $500,000
5,000 sq ft site, Distrib.—Local
Privately owned sub-S corp.
Also see: 304 Stokes Ave. loc.

## Trenton—(cont.)

### TRI-STEEL FABRICATORS, INC.
501 Prospect St. (08618)
Mail addr: P.O. Box 5756, Trenton (08638)
**Phone—(609) 392-8660**
Fax—(609) 392-7626
Email—t3steelfab@aol.com
Pres.—James Werosta
Bookkeeper—Erna Werosta
SIC—3312; *Steel fabrication & erection*
Employs—18; Estab.—1972
50,000 sq ft site, Distrib.—Local
Privately owned corporation

### TROPHIES UNLIMITED
122 Fernwood Ave. (08610-4322)
**Phone—(609) 298-3544**
www.trophiesunlimited.com
Email—sales@trophiesunlimited.com
Owner—Dennis Hanft
SIC—3479; *Metal engraving*
Employs—1; Estab.—1979
Sales—under $500,000
Distrib.—Local
Sole ownership

### UNGARINI IRON WORKS, LLC
56 N. Logan Ave. (08609)
**Phone—(609) 392-0540**
Fax—(800) 285-3523
Email—kdungarinibb@gmail.com
Owner—Kris Jackaki
Estimator—Leo Morales
SIC—3446; 3441; NAICS—332323; *Ornamental ironwork & structural steel fabrication*
Employs—10; Estab.—1946
Sales—under $500,000
Distrib.—Local
Limited Liability Company

### UNION RUBBER, INC.
232 Allen St. (08618)
Mail addr: P.O. Box 1040, Trenton (08606-1040)
**Phone—(609) 396-9328**
National—(800) 334-8219
Fax—(609) 396-3587
www.papercement.com
Email—besttest@sprynet.com
Pres.—Bob Irving
Plt. Mgr.—Mike Mikulitz
Cust. Serv. Rep.—Richard Keller
SIC—2891; NAICS—325520; *Glue & rubber cement; Brand name—Best-Test; Bestine Solvent; Best Klean; Paper Pal*
Employs—8; Estab.—1919
Sales—$2.5Mil-$5Mil (est)
15,000 sq ft site, Distrib.—National
Privately owned corporation

### †VINCH RECYCLING, INC.
1607 N. Olden Ave., P.O. Box 55300 (08638)
**Phone—(609) 393-0200**
Fax—(609) 883-9380
www.jvinchandsonsinc.com
Pres.—Joseph Vinch
V-P.—Gary Vinch
Off. Mgr.—Rose Vinch
SIC—5093; *Wholesaler of recycled concrete, asphalt, wood waste & pallets*
Employs—8; Estab.—1997
Distrib.—Local
Privately owned corporation

### †W. W. GRAINGER, INC.
1585 N. Olden Ave. (08638)
**Phone—(609) 394-2620**
Fax—(609) 695-3667
www.grainger.com
Email—info@grainger.com
Br. Mgr.—Patricia James

SIC—5084; 5085; *Distributor of industrial equipment & supplies*
Employs—10; Estab.—1945
Distrib.—National
Privately owned corporation
Parent co.—W. W. Grainger, Inc., Lake Forest, IL
Phone—(847) 535-1000
See Parent Co. Section for full profile.

### WILBUR SHEET METAL, INC.
27 Ward Ave., P.O. Box 3681 (08609)
**Phone—(609) 393-5952**
Fax—(609) 393-5954
Pres.—Richard Tolocka
SIC—3444; *Sheet metal fabrication*
Employs—15; Estab.—1953
Sales—$1Mil-$2.5Mil (est)
Distrib.—Regional

### WILLARD BROS. LUMBER
300 Basin Rd. (08619)
**Phone—(609) 890-1990**
National—(800) 320-6519
Fax—(609) 586-9249
www.willardbrothers.net
Email—info@willardbrothers.net
Owner—Glen Willard
GM—Brian Millen
SIC—2421; *Dimensional & kiln-dried hardwood lumber*
Employs—10; Estab.—1979
Distrib.—Regional
Limited Liability Company

### WORLD'S FINEST, INC.
267 Hamilton Ave. (08609)
**Phone—(609) 394-8001**
Fax—(609) 394-5665
www.doworldsfinest.com
Email—wfinc267@verizion.net
Pres.—Pat Turner
SIC—2395; 2396; *Textile embroidery & silkscreening*
Employs—3; Estab.—1985
Sales—$500,000-$1Mil
Distrib.—National
Privately owned corporation

### X-PANDO PRODUCTS, INC.
500 Southard St. *(08638)*
**Phone—(609) 394-0150**
Fax—(609) 989-4847
www.xpando.com
Email—sales@xpando.com
Pres.—Lee Colletti
Off. Mgr.—Scott Hess
SIC—2891; NAICS—325520; *Pipe joint sealant compounds, tile & tub cements & sealants for cement lined pipes & metal/ceramic to glass; Brand name—X-Pando Pipe Joint Compound; X-Pando Special No. 2; X-Pandotite; X-Pandotite Special Glass Formula*
Employs—2; Estab.—1986
Sales—under $500,000
Distrib.—Intl.
Privately owned sub-S corp.
Also see: National Ceramic Co., Inc., same loc.

### NEW ENTRY
### YUME ENTERPRISES, LLC
1800 E. State St., Ste. 158 (08609)
**Phone—(609) 588-8903**
Fax—(609) 588-8758
www.perfectsnaque.com
Email—info@perfectsnaque.com
Founder & COO—Brian Allen
Pres.—Cricket Allen
SIC—2099; 2068; *Ready-to-eat gluten-free snacks, including whole sprouted lentils, quinoa & nuts; Brand name—The Perfect Snaque*
Employs—10; Estab.—2011
Sales—$1Mil
11,000 sq ft site, Distrib.—Intl.
Limited Liability Company

### ZIENOWICZ SIGNS
202 E. Canal St. (08609)
**Phone—(609) 393-4068**
Email—zsigns@verizon.net
Owner—George Zienowicz
Proj. Mgr.—Suzanne Dinger
SIC—3993; *Interior & exterior signs*
Employs—3; Estab.—1987
Sales—under $500,000
Distrib.—Local
Sole ownership

### ZYTRON CONTROL PRODUCTS, INC.
20 Lexington Ave. (08618)
**Phone—(609) 771-0101**
Fax—(609) 771-0020
www.zytron.com
Email—inquiry@zytron.com
Pres., Fin., MIS & R & D Mgr.—John Wilkinson
Sales Mgr.—Robert Tucker
Prodn. Mgr.—Jonathan Wilkinson
Off. Mgr.—Patricia Schoenemann
Material Control Mgr.—George Sare
SIC—3822; 3829; NAICS—334512; *Temperature & process controls & sensors*
Employs—25; Estab.—1985
Sales—$1Mil-$5Mil
9,500 sq ft site, Distrib.—National
Privately owned sub-S corp.

## Tuckahoe
### (Cape May—S.E.)

### OCEAN ROCKETS, INC.
5 Mosquito Landing Rd. (08250)
**Phone—(609) 628-4445**
Fax—(609) 628-4535
www.oceanrockets.com
Email—sales@oceanrockets.com
Owner—John Yank
SIC—3732; *Commercial speedboats*
Employs—30; Estab.—1991
Sales—$1Mil-$2.5Mil
Distrib.—Intl.
Sole ownership

### TUCKAHOE SAND & GRAVEL, INC.
Route 610 & Sharp Rd. (08250)
Mail addr: P.O. Box 991, Pleasantville (08232)
**Phone—(609) 861-2082**
National—(800) 922-7263
Fax—(609) 861-3671
www.tuckahoesand-gravel.com
Email—info@tuckahoesand-gravel.com
Pres.—James Johnston, Jr.
GM—Jim Johnston III
Sales Mgr.—Ron Carusi
Opers. Mgr.—Paul Castellini
Dispatcher—Barbara Evanchik
SIC—3281; NAICS—327991; *Sand & gravel processing*
Employs—15; Estab.—1948
Distrib.—Regional
Privately owned corporation

### YANK MARINE, INC.
Mosquito Landing Rd., P.O. Box 569 (08250)
**Phone—(609) 628-2928**
Fax—(609) 628-2628
www.yankmarine.com
Email—info@yankmarine.com
Pres.—John C. Yank III
Mng. Member—Bette Jean Yank
Accts. Rec. & Hum. Res. Mgr.—Kellie Hartman
SIC—3732; *Corporate headquarters & boats*
Employs—50; Estab.—1969
Sales—$1Mil-$2.5Mil
Distrib.—Regional
Privately owned corporation

## Tuckerton
### (Ocean—S.E.)

### BETHEL BINDERY, INC.
1500 Route 539 (08087)
**Phone—(609) 296-5043**
Fax—(609) 296-9483
www.bethelbindery.com
Email—books@bethelbindery.com
Owner & Pres.—Tom Giger
V-P.—Velma Giger
SIC—2789; 2752; NAICS—323121; *Thesis, genealogy, journal, CD & legal bookbinding, including restoration of Bibles & antique books, instant printing & CD to book & book to CD converting*
Employs—6; Estab.—1979
Sales—under $500,000
Distrib.—Intl.

### CUSTOM CREATIONS BY M. D.
52 Ishmael Rd. (08087)
**Phone—(609) 294-1321**
Fax—(609) 294-1311
Email—ccbymd@yahoo.com
Pres.—Mark Duym
Bus. & Fin. Mgr.—Lucille Duym
SIC—2434; NAICS—337110; *Kitchen cabinets & countertops*
Employs—5; Estab.—1987
Sales—under $500,000
3,000 sq ft site, Distrib.—National
Sole ownership

### GORDON'S MARINE SERVICE
454 S. Green St. (08087)
**Phone—(609) 296-5817**
Email—gordofordo@msn.com
Owner—Gordon Ford
SIC—3732; *Rebuilt boats*
Employs—1; Estab.—1991
Sales—under $500,000 (est)
Distrib.—Local
Privately owned corporation

### NEW ENTRY
### JETTY LIFE, LLC
1435 Route 539, Unit A-6 (08087)
**Phone—(609) 296-2411**
National—(800) 900-6435
www.jettylife.com
Email—info@jettylife.com
CEO—Jeremy Defilippis
CMO—Cory Higgins
SIC—2396; *T-shirt screen printing*
Employs—5; Estab.—2003
Sales—$500,000-$1Mil (est)
3,000 sq ft site, Distrib.—Intl.
Limited Liability Company

### TOOKER SIGN SERVICE
1439 Route 539, P.O. Box 1129 (08087)
**Phone—(609) 296-1000**
Fax—(609) 296-0324
Email—tookersigns@aol.com
Owner—Jeff Tooker
SIC—3993; 3089; *Plastic, metal, electric, nonelectric, painted, sandblasted & hand-carved interior & exterior signs, boat lettering & vehicle wraps*
Employs—1; Estab.—1964
Sales—under $500,000
Distrib.—Regional
Limited Liability Company
AKA: Willow Graphics

## Turnersville
### (Camden—S.W.)

### NEW ENTRY
### AMECHI FENCE
5950 Route 42 (08012)
**Phone—(856) 227-6691**
www.amechifenceco.com
Email—info@amechifenceco.com
Owner—Al Amechi

GEOGRAPHICAL

## Turnersville—(cont.)

SIC—2499; *Cedar wood fences*
Employs—10
Sales—$1Mil-$2.5Mil (est)
Distrib.—Local
Sole ownership

### AQUA CLEAR TACKLE

P.O. Box 8454 (08012)
**Phone—(609) 861-1088**
Fax—(609) 861-1088
www.aquacleartackle.com
Email—info@aquacleartackle.com
Ptnr., Pres. & Sales & Mktg. Mgr.—
  Mike Hanson
Off. Mgr.—Deborah Hanson
SIC—3949; NAICS—339920;
  *Fishing tackles & rigs*
Employs—3; Estab.—1978
Sales—under $500,000
700 sq ft site, Distrib.—Regional
Privately owned sub-S corp.

### C. J.'S TOOL MFG., INC.

620 Route 168 (08012)
**Phone—(856) 227-7342**
Fax—(856) 227-4122
Pres.—Charles Corbett
V-P.—John Sander
SIC—3599; *General machining
  job shop*
Employs—7; Estab.—1979
Sales—under $500,000
Distrib.—Local
Privately owned corporation
AKA: Steering Systems, Inc.

### GLASSBLOWERS.COM, INC.

P.O. Box 8089 (08012-8089)
**Phone—(856) 232-7898**
Fax—(856) 232-7669
www.glassblowers.com
Email—thomas@glassblowers.com
Owner—Thomas Cachaza
SIC—3231; NAICS—327215;
  *Scientific glassware*
Employs—1; Estab.—1990
Sales—under $500,000
2,000 sq ft site, Distrib.—Intl.
Sole ownership

### GRAPHIC IMPRESSIONS PRINTING CO.

4391 Route 42 (08012)
**Phone—(856) 728-2266**
Fax—(856) 728-1455
Sales Rep.—Dennis Neill
Typesetter—Anthoney Rocca
SIC—2761; 2759; NAICS—
  323116; *Commercial & business
  form printing*
Employs—8; Estab.—1980
Sales—$500,000-$1Mil
Distrib.—National
Privately owned corporation

### STONE GALAXY

4120 Blackhorse Pike (08012)
**Phone—(856) 219-3450**
National—(800) 680-2429
Fax—(888) 780-1169
www.stonegalaxy.com
Email—contact@stonegalaxy.com
Mng. Ptnr.—Rey Sroka
SIC—3281; *Stone fabrication,
  including countertops, vanities &
  fireplaces*
Employs—2; Estab.—2007
Distrib.—Local
Privately owned corporation
AKA: R & T Stone

---

## Union

(Union—N.E.)

### ACUPOWDER INTERNATIONAL, LLC

901 Lehigh Ave. (07083)
**Phone—(908) 851-4500**
Fax—(908) 851-4597
www.acupowder.com
Email—acupowder@
  acupowder.com

Tech. Serv. Mgr.—Ken Watson
SIC—3399; *Nonferrous metal
  powders*
Employs—75; Estab.—1916
Sales—$500,000-$1Mil
100,000 sq ft site, Distrib.—Intl.
Limited Liability Company

### ALFRED & WILLIAM, INC.

P.O. Box 364 (07083)
**Phone—(908) 686-3000**
Fax—(908) 686-3005
Pres.—Douglas V. Suckow
SIC—3493; NAICS—332611;
  *Steel machine springs*
Employs—7; Estab.—1942
Sales—$500,000-$1Mil
9,000 sq ft site, Distrib.—National
Privately owned corporation

### ALL TOOL COMPANY, INC.

899 Rahway Ave. (07083)
**Phone—(908) 687-3636**
Fax—(908) 687-4514
Email—alltoolco@aol.com
Pres.—John A. Vinciguerra
GM—Scott S. Daniels
IT, MIS, Pur. & Sales Mgr.—
  Dominick Rose
SIC—3599; *Precision machining
  job shop; Brand name—Rotadex*
Employs—13; Estab.—1939
Sales—$1Mil-$2.5Mil
15,000 sq ft site, Distrib.—
  Regional
Privately owned sub-S corp.

### ALLARY CORP. (H Q)

2204 Morris Ave., Ste. 209 (07083)
**Phone—(908) 851-0077**
Fax—(908) 851-9229
www.allarycorp.com
Email—allary@allarycorp.com
Pres.—Alan Sorrell
SIC—3965; *Corporate
  headquarters; sewing notions &
  kits (mfg. done in China)*
Employs—14
Sales—$1Mil-$2.5Mil (est)

NEW ENTRY

### AMERICA SEMICONDUCTOR, LLC

2810 Morris Ave., Ste. 204 (07083)
**Phone—(908) 810-7364**
National—(859) 899-0926
Fax—(908) 810-5334
www.americasemi.com
Email—dschroeder@
  americasemi.com
Manager—Don Schroeder
SIC—3674; *Semiconductors*
Employs—10
Sales—$2.5Mil-$5Mil (est)
Limited Liability Company

### AMERICAN BRASS & CRYSTAL, INC.

835 Lehigh Ave. (07083)
**Phone—(908) 688-8611**
National—(877) 465-5617
Fax—(908) 688-8615
www.abclighting.net
Email—abclights@gmail.com
Pres.—Ross Kirsh
V-P.—Lori Kirsh
SIC—3645; NAICS—335121; *Cast
  & crystal chandeliers*
Employs—32; Estab.—1992
Distrib.—National
Privately owned corporation

### †AMERICAN HANGER & FIXTURE CORP.

687 Lehigh Ave. (07083)
**Phone—(908) 687-1776**
Fax—(908) 687-1770
www.americanhanger.com
Email—sales@
  americanhanger.com
Pres.—Phillip Steinhardt
Hum. Res. Mgr.—Brenda Ramos

SIC—5046; *Distributor of garment
  hangers, clothing store &
  manufacturers supplies &
  fixtures*
Employs—6
Distrib.—Intl.
Privately owned corporation
AKA: HMG Sales Corp.

### AMERICAN PRODUCTS CO., INC.

Div. of Picut Manufacturing
  Company, Inc.
610 Rahway Ave. (07083)
**Phone—(908) 687-4100**
Fax—(908) 687-0037
www.amerprod.com
Email—sales@amerprod.com
Pres.—Chris Walsh
Sales Mgr.—Thea Lloyd
Matls. & Pur. Mgr.—Mike Rubin
SIC—3599; *Corporate
  headquarters & precision
  machining & assembly*
Employs—78; Estab.—1955
Sales—$13Mil
80,000 sq ft site, Distrib.—Intl.
Privately owned corporation
ISO rating—9001:2000
Parent co.—Picut Manufacturing
  Company, Inc., Warren, NJ
  Phone—(908) 754-1333
  See Parent Co. Section for full profile.

### ANISHA ENTERPRISES, INC.

2165 Morris Ave. (07083)
**Phone—(908) 964-3380**
Fax—(908) 964-9103
www.axiamprinting.com
Email—print@axiamprinting.com
Pres.—P. J. Jhawar
Ex. V-P. & Off. Mgr.—Dan
  Maheshwari
V-P., Publisher—P. Jhawar
SIC—2752; NAICS—323100;
  *Instant printing, bindery, mailing
  & fulfillment*
Employs—6; Estab.—1985
5,000 sq ft site, Distrib.—Local
Privately owned sub-S corp.
DBA: Axiam Printing

### ARMORPOXY, INC.

805 Lehigh Ave. (07083)
**Phone—(908) 810-9613**
National—(888) 755-7361
Fax—(908) 810-9612
www.armorpoxy.com
Email—info@armorpoxy.com
Pres.—Michael Logan
SIC—2851; *Commercial grade
  epoxy coatings & shot blasting,
  concrete surface prep, diamond
  floor grinding, adhesive &
  coating removal & floor leveling
  services; Brand name—
  Armorpoxy; Prep-Crete*
Employs—18
Sales—$5Mil-$10Mil
Privately owned corporation

### B & G INTERNATIONAL, INC.

1085 Morris Ave. (07083)
**Phone—(973) 824-0334**
Fax—(973) 824-2221
www.bgintr.com
Pres., CEO—Chet Kolton
Ex. V-P., CFO—Michael Normam
Plt. Mgr.—Jake Strassburger
Acctg. Mgr.—Josephine Andrade
SIC—3089; 3663; NAICS—
  334220; *Printed & die-cut plastic
  tags & hangers for retail
  merchandise, including RFID-
  integrated media for case, pallet
  & item identification*
Employs—30; Estab.—1983
Sales—$15Mil-$18Mil
45,000 sq ft site, Distrib.—Intl.
Privately owned corporation
AKA: B & G Plastics

### BEVERAGE MEDIA GROUP, INC.

2444 Morris Ave., Ste. 318 (07083)
**Phone—(908) 964-5060**
Fax—(908) 964-1472
www.bevnetwork.com
Email—awolters@bevmedia.com
Off. Mgr.—Angel Wolters
SIC—2721; *Trade journal
  publishing*
Employs—2; Estab.—1949
Sales—under $500,000
Distrib.—Local
Privately owned corporation
Parent co.—Beverage Media
  Group, Inc., New York, NY
  Phone—(212) 571-3232
  See Parent Co. Section for full profile.

### BILCAR SIGNS

2131 Morris Ave. (07083)
**Phone—(908) 687-3777**
Fax—(908) 687-1442
www.bilcarsigns.com
Email—bilcar2131@aol.com
Co-Pres.—Carlo Filipelli
Co-Pres.—Rosemarie Filipelli
SIC—3993; *Interior & exterior
  signs*
Employs—2; Estab.—1956
Sales—under $500,000
1,200 sq ft site, Distrib.—Local
Privately owned corporation

### CANARY CLOSETS & CABINETRY

697 Rahway Ave. (07083)
**Phone—(908) 851-2894**
Fax—(908) 851-2895
www.canaryclosetsandcabinetry.c
  om
Email—john@canarycc.com
Owner—John Canary
Prodn. Mgr.—Steve Siebert
Bookkeeper—Karol Weiland
SIC—3089; *Closet organization
  products*
Employs—15; Estab.—2001
Sales—$2Mil-$2.5Mil
9,600 sq ft site, Distrib.—Local
Sole ownership

### †CAP BARBELL, INC.

625 Rahway Ave. (07083)
**Phone—(908) 624-1133**
Fax—(908) 624-0603
www.capbarbell.com
Email—isabelt@capbarbell.com
Owner—Isabel Tseng
Traf. Coord.—Stuart Ramirez
SIC—5091; *Distributor of exercise
  equipment, including weight
  sets, dumbbells, hand grips &
  upright bicycles*
Employs—23; Estab.—1994
Distrib.—Local
Privately owned corporation

### CCSI GROUP, THE

1351 Morris Ave., P.O. Box 3554
  (07083)
**Phone—(908) 686-6464**
Fax—(908) 686-1986
www.ccsigroup.com
Email—info@ccsigroup.com
Owner—Doug Rotoly
Manager—Dave King
SIC—7373; NAICS—541512;
  *Business infrastructure
  computer integrated systems*
Employs—10; Estab.—1998
Sales—$500,000-$1Mil
Distrib.—Local
Privately owned corporation

### CE DE CANDY, INC.

1091 Lousons Rd. (07083)
**Phone—(908) 964-0660**
Fax—(908) 964-0911
www.smarties.com
Email—cede@smarties.com
Chrm.—Edward Dee
Pres.—Jonathan Dee
V-P., Sales & Mktg.—Eric Ostrow
V-P., Opers.—Sarah Dee

## Union—(cont.)

Cont.—Tina Moyer
IT Mgr.—Rick Depinto
Hum. Res. Mgr.—Jessica Dee
Qual. Assur. Mgr.—Jennifer
Goldberg
Cust. Serv. Rep.—Michele Arcaro
SIC—2064; NAICS—311300;
Dextrose candy tablets & novelty
candies; Brand name—Smarties
Employs—125; Estab.—1949
Sales—$35Mil
100,000 sq ft site, Distrib.—
National
Privately owned corporation
AKA: Smarties Candy Co.

**CORONATION SHEET METAL CO.,
INC.**
2198 Stanley Ter. (07083)
**Phone—(908) 686-0930**
Fax—(908) 686-1534
www.coronationsheetmetal.com
Email—info@
coronationsheetmetal.com
Pres.—Joe Cafiero
V-P. & Plt. Mgr.—Stephen Cafiero
Off. Mgr.—Helen Albright
SIC—3444; Sheet metal
fabrication
Employs—15; Estab.—1946
Sales—$500,000-$1Mil
10,000 sq ft site, Distrib.—
Regional

**CRETER, INC., PHILIP**
20 Monroe St. (07083)
**Phone—(908) 686-2910**
Fax—(908) 687-1853
Email—philipcreter@gmail.com
Pres.—Doris Logan
V-P.—Bruce Logan
SIC—3599; Precision & CNC
machining job shop
Employs—4; Estab.—1941
Sales—$500,000-$1Mil (est)
Distrib.—National
Privately owned corporation

**D & D TECHNOLOGY, INC.**
254 Elmwood Ave., P.O. Box 3636
(07083)
**Phone—(908) 688-5154**
Fax—(908) 688-5184
www.ddtechinc.com
Email—info@ddtechinc.com
Pres.—Edward G. Varga, Jr.
SIC—3089; Plastic parts
Employs—8; Estab.—1989
Sales—$500,000-$1Mil
Distrib.—National
Privately owned corporation

**DEEP FOODS, INC.**
1090 Springfield Rd. (07083)
**Phone—(908) 810-7500**
National—(800) 468-6499
Fax—(908) 810-8482
www.deepfoods.com
Email—deepimports@yahoo.com
Pres., CFO—Arvind Amin
GM & MIS Mgr.—Archie Amin
Hum. Res. Mgr.—Pravin Amin
Hum. Res. Generalist—Jackie
Henning
SIC—2099; Indian foods &
flavorings
Employs—290; Estab.—1977
Sales—under $500,000
120,000 sq ft site, Distrib.—Intl.
Privately owned corporation

**DESIGN A SIGN, INC.**
745 Lehigh Ave., Ste. 3 (07083)
**Phone—(908) 656-0822**
(908) 889-9146
Fax—(908) 964-8407
www.njdesignasign.com
Email—designasigninc@
comcast.net
Owner & Pres.—William T.
Meehan, Jr.

SIC—3993; Development, neon,
carved gold leaf & LED signs,
truck, car & channel lettering,
light boxes & awnings
Employs—1; Estab.—1995
Sales—under $500,000
2,400 sq ft site, Distrib.—Regional
Privately owned corporation

**DORAN, LLC**
599 Green Ln. (07083)
**Phone—(908) 289-9200**
Fax—(908) 289-9202
Plt. Mgr.—Randolph Wojcik
SIC—3312; 3599; Steel fabrication
& precision machining job shop
Employs—5; Estab.—1996
Distrib.—National
Limited Liability Company

**†DUNPHEY-SMITH CO.**
30 Progress St. (07083)
**Phone—(908) 687-6292**
National—(800) 458-4328
Fax—(908) 687-8675
www.dunpheysmith.com
Email—tom@dunpheysmith.com
V-P.—Thomas McCreesh, Jr.
GM & IT Mgr.—Jeffrey Clayton
SIC—5075; Distributor of heating
& air conditioning equipment;
Brand name—TEMPSTAR; HEIL;
Honeywell; Hart and Cooley;
Southwark Metal; Field Controls;
Bramec; Samsung/Quietside;
Fantech; CMC Howell;
Diversitech; Duro Dyne; Malco;
Ameri-Flow Registers; Polyken;
Airtec; Mueller; Grayflex
Employs—12; Estab.—1919
32,000 sq ft site, Distrib.—Local
Sole ownership

**DURA TAPE INTERNATIONAL**
2816 Morris Ave., Ste. 21 (07083)
**Phone—(908) 687-8273**
National—(800) 249-1357
www.duratape.com
Email—sales@duratape.com
Pres., Fin. & R & D Mgr.—Lee
Goldman
SIC—2891; 3999; NAICS—
325520; Water-activated &
fiberglass mesh joint tape, metal
flex corner & wallboard tapes,
taping tools & perforated drywall
joint paper; Brand name—Wet-
N-Stick; Grabber; DAP;
WallSpan; Rad's Screen Fixer
Employs—11; Estab.—1953
11,000 sq ft site, Distrib.—Intl.
Limited Liability Company

**DUREX, INC.**
5 Stahuber Ave. (07083)
**Phone—(908) 688-0800**
Fax—(908) 688-0718
www.durexinc.com
Email—info@durexinc.com
Pres., CEO—Robert Denholtz
V-P. & Engrg. Mgr.—Frank Helbig
Cont.—Sherry Fackenberg
Dir., Opers.—Bill Rochelle
IT Mgr.—Kim Smethers
Hum. Res. Mgr.—Linda
Willoughby
Qual. Mgr.—Bill Jensen
SIC—3469; 3544; NAICS—
333500; Metal stampings, sheet
metal fabrication, powder
coating & tool & die job shop
Employs—150; Estab.—1946
Sales—$15Mil-$20Mil
140,000 sq ft site, Distrib.—Intl.
Privately owned corporation
Also see: Sternvent, same loc.
AKA: Creative Surveying

**DYNA-LITE, INC.**
1050 Commerce Ave. (07083)
**Phone—(908) 687-8800**
National—(800) 722-6638
Fax—(908) 686-6682
www.dynalite.com

Email—flash@dynalite.com
Pres., GM—Peter Poremba
Sales Mgr.—Jim Morton
Pur. Mgr.—Orlando Delacruz
Serv. Mgr.—John Prazeres
SIC—3861; Photographic lighting
equipment
Employs—18; Estab.—1970
Sales—$2.6Mil-$5Mil
10,000 sq ft site, Distrib.—Local
Privately owned corporation

**ECHO MOLDING, INC.**
911 Springfield Rd. (07083)
**Phone—(908) 688-0099**
Fax—(908) 688-0529
www.echomolding.com
Email—info@echomolding.com
Pres.—Dieter Hekler
Off. Mgr.—Kim Power
SIC—3089; Custom injection
molded plastic products
Employs—40; Estab.—1975
30,000 sq ft site, Distrib.—National
Privately owned corporation

**†EMILIANI ENTERPRISES**
600 Green Ln. (07083)
**Phone—(908) 964-6340**
(800) 624-0405
Fax—(908) 558-9234
www.emiliani.com
Email—info@emiliani.com
CEO—Don Emiliani
Pres., COO—Carl Galasso
Ex. V-P., Corp. Strategy—Andre
Chiavelli
V-P., IT—Lisa Cascadden
Hum. Res. Mgr.—Laura Lamera
SIC—5122; Distributor of beauty
care products, including
cosmetics & hair
Employs—200; Estab.—1999
Distrib.—Regional
Privately owned corporation

**EUREKA SPRING CO.**
999 Rahway Ave. (07083)
Mail addr: P.O. Box 5067, Newark
(07105)
**Phone—(973) 589-4960**
Fax—(973) 589-0103
www.eurekaspringco.com
Email—contactus@
eurekaspringco.com
Pres.—Douglas Suckow
V-P.—Elizabeth Suckow
SIC—3493; NAICS—332611; Coil
& flat metal springs
Employs—20; Estab.—1908
10,000 sq ft site, Distrib.—Intl.
Privately owned corporation

**EXTRACTS & INGREDIENTS LTD.,
DIV. OF MORRE-TEC INDUSTRIES,
INC.**
Div. of MORRE-TEC Industries,
Inc.
1 Gary Rd. (07083)
**Phone—(908) 688-9009**
Fax—(908) 688-9005
www.morretec.com
Email—sales@morretec.com
Pres.—Leonard Glass
Mng. Dir.—David Fondots
Mktg. Coord.—Melissa Bevilaque
SIC—2833; 2899; 2099; 2834;
Botanical extracts, nutritive oils,
certified organic products &
special excipients & additives for
personal care & the cosmetic,
nutritional supplement & food
industries
Employs—5; Estab.—1987
Company-wide: 25
Distrib.—Intl.
ISO rating—9001:2008
Parent co.—MORRE-TEC
Industries, Inc., Union, NJ
Phone—(908) 688-9009
See Parent Co. Section for full profile.

**FASTSIGNS®**
2290 Route 22 E. (07083)
**Phone—(908) 810-1400**
Fax—(908) 810-1221
www.fastsigns.com/24
Email—24@fastsigns.com
Pres., Fin. & R & D Mgr.—Mark
Favaloro
MIS Mgr.—Eugene Dogans
SIC—3993; Interior & exterior
neon & vinyl signs
Employs—20; Estab.—1990
Sales—under $500,000
1,600 sq ft site, Distrib.—Regional
Privately owned corporation

**FLOW-TURN, INC.**
1050 Commerce Ave., Ste. 1
(07083-5087)
**Phone—(908) 687-3225**
Fax—(908) 687-1715
www.flow-turn.com
Email—sales@flow-turn.com
Pres.—Hermann Miedel
GM—Dan Otero
SIC—3535; NAICS—333922; Belt
curve conveyors
Employs—19; Estab.—1981
Sales—$3Mil
36,000 sq ft site, Distrib.—National
Privately owned sub-S corp.

**FOREMOST MFG. CO., INC.**
941 Ball Ave. (07083)
**Phone—(908) 687-4646**
Fax—(908) 687-8821
www.foremost-mfg.com
Pres., CEO—Herb S. Schiller
Fin. Mgr.—Mike Moritz
SIC—3444; Aluminum lighting
reflectors
Employs—150; Estab.—1960
42,000 sq ft site, Distrib.—National
Privately owned corporation

**GAISER'S EUROPEAN STYLE
PROVISIONS, INC.**
2019 Morris Ave. (07083)
**Phone—(908) 686-3421**
Fax—(908) 686-7131
Email—gaisers@verizon.net
Pres.—Boris Vadrar
Sales Mgr.—Liliya Tabachnik
Opers. Mgr.—Igor Deneseko
SIC—2011; NAICS—311611; Meat
processing & packing
Employs—10; Estab.—1995
Distrib.—Local
Privately owned corporation

**GAVAN GRAHAM ELECTRICAL
PRODUCTS**
751 Rahway Ave. (07083)
**Phone—(908) 729-9000**
Fax—(908) 729-9001
www.gavangraham.com
Email—ncummerson@
gavangraham.com
Pres.—Norm Cummerson
SIC—3312; Stainless steel
enclosures, switch & panel
boards
Employs—30; Estab.—1945
Distrib.—Local
Privately owned corporation

**GOLDSTEIN SETTING CO INC /TA
DANMAR JEWELERS**
2464 Morris Ave. (07083)
**Phone—(908) 964-1034**
Fax—(908) 964-1254
Email—jammdan@aol.com
Pres.—Joseph Goldstein
V-P.—Myrna Goldstein
SIC—3911; NAICS—339911;
Gemstone & diamond setting
Employs—5; Estab.—1972
Sales—under $700,000
15,000 sq ft site, Distrib.—Local
Publicly owned corporation

GEOGRAPHICAL

© Copyright 2015 Manufacturers' News, Inc.    † Indicates wholesaler / distributor.

## Union—(cont.)

NEW ENTRY
**HAMMER TOO, LLC**
2576-B U.S. Highway 22 E. (07083)
**Phone—(908) 688-5601**
Fax—(908) 686-6005
www.cartridgeworld.com
Email—cartridgeworldunion@gmail.com
Mng. Member—Alexander Martello
SIC—3861; *Remanufactured toner cartridges*
Employs—4
Sales—$1Mil-$2.5Mil (est)
Distrib.—Intl.
Limited Liability Company
AKA: Cartridge World Of Union

**HATHAWAY PLASTICS, INC.**
911 Springfield Rd. (07083)
**Phone—(908) 688-9494**
Fax—(908) 688-9411
Email—info@hathawayplastics.com
Pres.—Robert Daniel
SIC—3089; 2542; 3993; NAICS—337215; *Plastic molded point-of-purchase displays*
Employs—3; Estab.—1972
Distrib.—National
Privately owned corporation

**HILLSIDE SPINNING & STAMPING CO., INC.**
1060 Commerce Ave. (07083)
**Phone—(908) 964-3080**
Fax—(908) 964-3082
Admn. Mgr.—George Thomas
SIC—3469; *Metal stampings*
Employs—20; Estab.—1947
30,000 sq ft site, Distrib.—National
Privately owned corporation

**HUMMEL DISTRIBUTING CORP.**
850 Springfield Rd., P.O. Box 3199 (07083)
**Phone—(908) 688-5300**
Fax—(908) 688-6020
www.hummelprintmail.com
Email—hummeltrnt@aol.com
Co-Pres., Hum. Res. Mgr.—John Hummel
Co-Pres.—Lorraine Hummel
IT Mgr.—Art Levin
Off. Mgr.—Tina Palmarozzo
Supervisor—Jennie Helbig
SIC—2752; 2791; NAICS—323122; *Offset printing & typesetting*
Employs—35; Estab.—1884
Distrib.—National
Privately owned corporation

**HUTCHINSON CO., WILLIAM T.**
453 Lehigh Ave. (07083)
**Phone—(908) 688-0533**
National—(800) 544-7934
Fax—(908) 688-8296
www.hssblanks.com
Email—sales@hssblanks.com
Pres.—Dean Roth
GM—Jim Bond
Off. Mgr.—Jen Tarabokia
SIC—3545; *Drill & reamer blanks, punches, core rods, gage pins, cutting tools & shop supplies*
Employs—12; Estab.—1927
Sales—$1Mil-$5Mil
7,000 sq ft site, Distrib.—Intl.
Privately owned sub-S corp.

**INDUSTRIAL FERGUSON FOUNDRY**
2365 Route 22 W., P.O. Box 531 (07083)
**Phone—(908) 686-8888**
Fax—(908) 686-8891
www.industrialferguson.com
Email—sally@industrialferguson.com
Pres.—Ken Karpovich
V.-P.—Sally Lim

SIC—3363; 3366; 3339; NAICS—331521; *Copper, brass, bronze & aluminum castings*
Employs—15; Estab.—1963
Sales—$2.5Mil
25,000 sq ft site, Distrib.—Intl.
Privately owned sub-S corp.

**INFINITY DESIGN & PRINTING**
1358 Burnet Ave. (07083)
**Phone—(908) 206-8844**
www.infinitydesign.com
Email—colorprinting@aol.com
Owner—Pierre Filsaime
SIC—2759; 2791; NAICS—323122; *Commercial printing & graphic design*
Employs—5; Estab.—2003
Sales—under $500,000
Distrib.—National
Sole ownership

**INSTRU-MET CORP.**
931 Lehigh Ave. (07083)
**Phone—(908) 851-0700**
Fax—(908) 686-1688
www.instrumet.com
Email—sales@instrumet.com
Pres.—Paul Metzger
V.-P.—Ward Ruoff
Off. Coord.—Maria Silva
Machinist—Bob Ski
SIC—3829; *Tensile strength testing machines*
Employs—8; Estab.—1974
Sales—$1Mil-$2.5Mil
Distrib.—National
Privately owned corporation

**INTERNATIONAL PAINT, LLC**
2270 Morris Ave. (07083)
**Phone—(908) 686-1300**
Fax—(908) 686-8545
www.yachtpaint.com
Email—interluxtechnicalservice@yachtpaint.com
Plt. Mgr.—Michael Del Mauro
Pur. Agt.—Colleen Ordner
SIC—2851; NAICS—325510; *Paints; Brand name—Interlux; Awlgrip; International*
Employs—100; Estab.—1909
140,000 sq ft site, Distrib.—Intl.
Limited Liability Company
ISO rating—9001:2000
Parent co.—International Paint, LLC, Houston, TX
Phone—(713) 682-1711
See Parent Co. Section for full profile.

**JAY BEE OIL & GAS, INC.**
1720 U.S. Highway 22 E. (07083)
**Phone—(908) 686-1493**
Fax—(908) 688-4380
Pres.—Randy Broda
SIC—1382; *Oil & gas exploration*
Employs—3; Estab.—1996
Sales—under $500,000
Distrib.—Local
Privately owned corporation

**JEDCO ADHESIVES CO., DIV. OF MORRE-TEC INDUSTRIES, INC.**
Div. of MORRE-TEC Industries, Inc.
1 Gary Rd. (07083)
**Phone—(908) 688-9009**
Fax—(908) 688-9005
www.morretec.com
Email—sales@morretec.com
Pres.—Leonard Glass
GM—Aaron Kopstick
Plt. Mgr.—John Tierney
Mktg. Coord.—Melissa Bevilaque
SIC—2891; NAICS—325520; *Solvent & water-based adhesives; Brand name—JedBond*
Employs—25; Estab.—1992
Sales—$1Mil-$2.5Mil
Distrib.—National
Privately owned sub-S corp.
ISO rating—9001:2008

Parent co.—MORRE-TEC Industries, Inc., Union, NJ
Phone—(908) 688-9009
See Parent Co. Section for full profile.

**KALUSTYAN CORP.**
855 Rahway Ave. (07083)
**Phone—(908) 688-6111**
National—(800) 441-2133
Fax—(908) 688-4415
www.kalustyan.com
Email—kerri@kalustyan.com
CEO—Errol Karakash
V.-P., Opers.—Fernando Porras
Sales Mgr., Natl.—Kerri Goad
Cust. Serv. Rep., Inside Sales—Nancy Guzman
Cust. Serv. Rep., Inside Sales—Joyell Goad
SIC—2099; *Cooking spices*
Employs—65; Estab.—1948
110,000 sq ft site, Distrib.—Intl.
Privately owned corporation

**KENTUCKY CABINET CORP.**
Div. of Gold & Reiss Corp.
601 Lehigh Ave. (07083)
**Phone—(347) 452-5797**
Fax—(908) 349-2255
Plt. Mgr.—Peter Drake
SIC—2434; NAICS—337110; *Custom wooden cabinets*
Employs—25; Estab.—2005
Sales—$1Mil-$2.5Mil (est)
Distrib.—Regional
Privately owned corporation
Parent co.—Gold & Reiss Corp., Brooklyn, NY
Phone—(718) 680-2600
See Parent Co. Section for full profile.

**LINCOLN ELECTRIC PRODUCTS CO., INC.**
947 Lehigh Ave. (07083)
**Phone—(908) 688-2900**
National—(800) 526-4407
Fax—(908) 688-8549
www.leproduct.com
Email—info@lincolnelectricproduct.com
CEO—Bruce Leff
V.-P.—Matt Leff
Prodn. Mgr.—Ed Jahn
IT Mgr.—Jay Patel
Estimator—Tony Restivo
Estimator—Gemma Bilis
SIC—3613; NAICS—335313; *Electrical control panels & switchgears*
Employs—30; Estab.—1949
50,000 sq ft site, Distrib.—Regional
Privately owned corporation

**LIONI LATTICINI, INC.**
555 Lehigh Ave. (07083)
**Phone—(908) 686-6061**
Fax—(908) 686-3449
www.lionimozzarella.com
Email—info@lionimozzarella.com
V.-P.—Salvatore Salzarulo
Dir., Sales & Mktg.—Lori Church
Plt. Opers. Mgr.—Ray Stevanovic
Pers. Mgr.—Teresa Salzarulo
Off. Mgr.—Andrea Salzarulo
SIC—2022; NAICS—311513; *Mozzarella cheese; Brand name—Lioni Latticini*
Employs—30; Estab.—1980
Distrib.—National
Privately owned corporation

†**MACK BORING & PARTS CO.**
2365 U.S. Highway 22 W., P.O. Box 3116 (07083)
**Phone—(908) 964-0700**
National—(800) 622-5364
Fax—(908) 964-8475
www.mackboring.com
Email—info@mackboring.com
Chrm.—Ned McGovern
Pres.—Steve McGovern
COO—Patrick McGovern
Mktg. Mgr.—Steve Gribbin

IT Mgr.—Joe Vita
Hum. Res. Mgr.—Louis Massa
SIC—5084; *Company headquarters & full service distributor of marine & industrial diesel engines, generators & transmissions, application guidance, parts, service & training services; Brand name—Yanmar; Mitsubishi; Isuzu; Scania; Steyr; Global Power Products; Aquadrive; ZF*
Employs—55; Estab.—1921
Sales—$11Mil-$30Mil
Distrib.—National
Privately owned corporation

**MAJOR PRINTING CO., INC.**
934 Savitt Pl., P.O. Box 1356 (07083)
**Phone—(908) 686-7296**
Fax—(908) 686-9229
www.majorprinting.com
Email—email@majorprinting.com
Owner & Pres.—Joseph Stampone
SIC—2752; 2791; NAICS—323122; *Offset printing & typesetting*
Employs—2; Estab.—1954
Sales—under $500,000
6,000 sq ft site, Distrib.—Regional
Privately owned sub-S corp.

**MARVIC CORP./A.J.D. STONE**
2450 Iorio St. (07083)
**Phone—(908) 686-4340**
Fax—(908) 686-9085
www.countertopsofnj.com
Email—marviccorp@yahoo.com
Pres., Marvic Corp.—Alfred J. D'Alessandro
Secy-Treas.—Vittoria D'Alessandro
IT Mgr.—Ivan Marinov
Off. Mgr.—Mildred Carbone
Bookkeeper—Francis Stanzione
SIC—2542; 3281; 2541; 3272; NAICS—327991; *Granite, quartz, solid-surface, concrete, exotic wood & laminate countertops*
Employs—100; Estab.—1961
Sales—$12Mil
45,000 sq ft site, Distrib.—Local
Privately owned corporation

**MERRILL CORP.**
649 Rahway Ave. (07083)
**Phone—(908) 688-5757**
Fax—(908) 688-2695
www.merrillcorp.com
Email—newark-dms@merrillcorp.com
Opers. Mgr.—Tom MacDonald
SIC—2759; NAICS—323100; *Financial printing*
Employs—100; Estab.—1980
Distrib.—Intl.
Publicly owned corporation
Parent co.—Merrill Corp., St. Paul, MN
Phone—(651) 646-4501
See Parent Co. Section for full profile.

**MIELE IRON WORKS, INC.**
2340 Route 22 E. (07083)
**Phone—(908) 686-0943**
www.mieleironworks.com
Email—mielesteel@aol.com
Pres.—Raphael Miele
Fin. Mgr.—Linda Miele
SIC—3442; NAICS—332321; *Steel cellar doors & railings*
Employs—2; Estab.—1936
Sales—under $500,000
Distrib.—Local
Privately owned corporation

**MORRE-TEC INDUSTRIES, INC.**
1 Gary Rd. (07083)
**Phone—(908) 688-9009**
Fax—(908) 688-9005
www.morretec.com

## Union—(cont.)

Email—sales@morretec.com
Pres.—Leonard Glass
GM—Aaron Kopstick
Plt. Mgr.—John Tierney
Import & Export Mgr.—Frimma Messer
SIC—2819; 2899; *Corporate headquarters & bromine compounds & chemical preparations & specialty chemicals*
Employs—25; Estab.—1987
25,000 sq ft site, Distrib.—Intl.
Privately owned sub-S corp.
ISO rating—9001:2008

**MULBERRY METAL PRODUCTS, INC.**
2199 Stanley Ter. (07083)
**Phone—(908) 688-8850**
Fax—(908) 688-7294
www.mulberrymetal.com
Email—info@mulberrymetal.com
CFO—Patricia Lynch
Ex. V.-P.—Richard E. Mueller
V.-P., Mktg.—Kristina I. Horn
V.-P., Pur.—Bruce W. Burck
Sales Mgr., Natl.—Robert H. Walker
Cred. Mgr.—Karen Raymond
SIC—3699; 3499; 3089; 3312; *Metal & plastic wallplates & weatherproof, steel outlet box covers & conduit bodies*
Employs—100; Estab.—1926
Sales—$25Mil
127,000 sq ft site, Distrib.—National
Privately owned corporation

**NEDCO CONVEYOR TECHNOLOGY CO.**
967 Lehigh Ave. *(07083)*
**Phone—(908) 964-9400**
National—(888) 286-3326
Fax—(908) 964-9411
www.nedcoconveyor.com
Email—nedconvey@aol.com
Pres.—Curtis Tarlton
Secy-Treas.—Theresa Tarlton
GM—Hector Perez
SIC—3535; NAICS—333922; *Conveyors & bucket elevators; Brand name—NEDCO; ULTRA-LIFT; ZEPHER*
Employs—40; Estab.—1960
Sales—$5Mil-$10Mil
22,000 sq ft site, Distrib.—National
Privately owned sub-S corp.

**NOVEL BOX CO. LTD.**
825 Lehigh Ave. (07083)
Mail addr: 659 Berriman St., Brooklyn (11208)
**Phone—(908) 686-7772**
National—(800) 965-9192
Fax—(908) 686-7774
www.novelbox.com
Email—moishe1@novelbox.com
Owner & Pres.—Moishe Sternhill
SIC—2657; 2674; 3993; 5113; NAICS—322212; *Manufacturer & distributor of jewelry, gemstone & pen boxes, displays, pouches & packaging*
Employs—50; Estab.—1948
Sales—$10Mil-$25Mil
Distrib.—National
Limited Liability Company

**OERTEL ORTHOPEDICS, INC.**
Div. of Modern Limb & Brace Co.
2095 U.S. Highway 22 W. (07083)
**Phone—(908) 688-1818**
Fax—(908) 688-6616
Email—oertelorthopedics@optimum.net
Off. Mgr.—N. Oertel

SIC—3842; *Artificial limbs & braces*
Employs—6; Estab.—1967
Sales—$500,000-$1Mil
3,000 sq ft site, Distrib.—Local
Privately owned corporation
Parent co.—Modern Limb & Brace Co., Watchung, NJ
Phone—(908) 757-2702
See Parent Co. Section for full profile.

**OKAI CORP.**
687 Lehigh Ave., Ste. 3 (07083)
**Phone—(908) 687-4443**
(800) 223-0025
Fax—(908) 687-8714
www.okai.com
Email—sales@okai.com
Pres.—Mary Orella
V.-P.—Michael McCoy
SIC—2899; *Solders*
Employs—6; Estab.—1981
Distrib.—Intl.
Privately owned corporation

**OLINER FIBRE CO., INC.**
2391 Vauxhall Rd., P.O. Box 308 (07083)
**Phone—(908) 688-5800**
National—(800) 654-6373
Fax—(908) 688-5853
www.oliner.com
Email—info@oliner.com
Pres.—Andrew Oliner
Prodn. Mgr.—Daisy Rodriguez
SIC—3082; 3089; NAICS—326121; *Plastic extrusions & fiberboard cutting*
Employs—22; Estab.—1910
40,000 sq ft site, Distrib.—Intl.
Privately owned corporation

**PAIGE ELECTRIC CO. L. P.**
1160 Springfield Rd., P.O. Box 368 *(07083)*
**Phone—(908) 687-7810**
(800) 327-2443
Fax—(908) 687-8860
www.paigecable.com
Email—info@paigeelectric.com
Pres.—Louis Grotta
Ex. V.-P.—Henry J. Coffey
V.-P., Pur.—Marty Fox
V.-P., Fin.—Bill Watkins
SIC—3679; *Company headquarters & electronic & electrical wire & cable & cable assemblies*
Employs—40; Estab.—1958
Sales—$175Mil
Distrib.—Intl.
Limited Liability Partnership
ISO rating—9001:2008

**PATEL PRINTING PLUS CORP.**
1036 Commerce Ave. (07083)
**Phone—(908) 964-6422**
National—(800) 801-7746
Fax—(908) 964-7949
www.patelprintingplus.com
Email—patel3plus@aol.com
Pres.—J. C. Patel
V.-P. & Manager—Sharon Patel
Cust. Serv. Rep.—Jennifer Fernandez
SIC—2759; NAICS—323100; *Commercial printing, graphic design & mailing services*
Employs—10; Estab.—1976
Sales—$500,000-$1Mil
5,600 sq ft site, Distrib.—National
Privately owned corporation

**†PHILIPS LUMINARIES NA**
Div. of Philips Lighting North America
2345 Vauxhall Rd., P.O. Box 129 (07083)
**Phone—(908) 964-7000**
National—(800) 334-2212
Fax—(908) 687-3611
www.stonco.com
Email—jim.lewis@philips.com
Dir., Supply Group—James Lewis

Sr. Mktg. Mgr.—Barret Gorman
Acct. Mgr., Recruitment—Laurie Boss
SIC—5063; *Wholesaler of commercial & industrial lighting fixtures, including floodlights, surface-mounted fixtures, lampholders, lighting controls & mounting accessories*
Employs—35; Estab.—1948
195,000 sq ft site, Distrib.—National
Publicly owned corporation
AKAs: Stonco Lighting * Crescent Lighting * Exceline
Parent co.—Philips Lighting North America, Somerset, NJ
Phone—(732) 563-3000
See Parent Co. Section for full profile.

**†PLYWOOD & DOOR MFRS. CORP. (H Q)**
1435 Morris Ave., 3rd Fl., P.O. Box 1212 (07083)
**Phone—(908) 687-7890**
Fax—(908) 687-5750
www.pdusa.com
Email—info@pdusa.com
Pres.—Juhani Haikala
Cont.—Ken Walsh
Sales Mgr.—Jack Petronick
Import Mgr.—Karina Tiainen
SIC—5031; *Corporate headquarters; wholesaler of imported hardwood, birch & plywood*
Employs—7; Estab.—1980
Distrib.—National
Privately owned corporation

**PRENTCO CO.**
952 Koehl Ave. (07083)
**Phone—(908) 687-9518**
Fax—(908) 687-0611
www.prentco.com
Email—c.steinberg@prentco.com
Owner—Chris Steinberg
Pres.—Ronald Steinberg
SIC—3544; NAICS—333500; *Investment casting molds & tools*
Employs—9; Estab.—1953
Sales—$500,000-$1Mil
Distrib.—National
Privately owned corporation

**PROMO ADVERTISING**
1174 Chestnut St. (07083)
**Phone—(908) 810-8888**
Fax—(908) 810-0440
www.tshirtportal.com
Email—service@promo88.com
Pres.—Sharon Zhang
SIC—2396; 2395; *Apparel screen printing & embroidery*
Employs—5; Estab.—1996
Sales—under $500,000
Distrib.—Intl.
Privately owned corporation

**†QUALITY SEALS, INC.**
2444 Morris Ave., Ste. 201 (07083-5726)
**Phone—(908) 206-0410**
National—(800) 346-7464
Fax—(908) 206-0420
www.qualityseals.com
Email—sales@qualityseals.com
GM—Steve Patterson
Pur. Mgr.—Patti Rooth
SIC—5085; 5162; *Distributor of rubber & plastic products, including tubing, molded rubber, packing & seals*
Employs—3; Estab.—1978
Sales—$2.6Mil-$5Mil
Distrib.—Intl.
Privately owned corporation
ISO rating—9001:2008

**QUICKLY PRINTING, INC.**
1965 Morris Ave. (07083)
**Phone—(908) 687-6000**
Fax—(908) 687-6006

Email—qpteam@quicklyprinting.com
Pres.—Larry Kovacs
GM—Jack Reyes
SIC—2752; 2759; 2761; NAICS—323116; *Instant printing, including business & post cards, letterheads, envelopes, brochures, carbonless forms, flyers & graphic & logo design*
Employs—6; Estab.—1995
Sales—$500,000-$1Mil
Distrib.—Local
Privately owned corporation

**R M F ASSOCS., INC.**
202 Carolyn Rd. (07083)
**Phone—(908) 687-9355**
V.-P.—Michael Rodgers
Treas.—L. J. Martin
Chief of Security—Thomas Swift
SIC—3499; 3469; *Fabricated metal choke & chamber brushes & fiber-optic products*
Employs—140; Estab.—1968
35,000 sq ft site, Distrib.—National
Privately owned corporation

**RAYMOND OF NJ, LLC**
1000 Brighton St. (07083)
**Phone—(908) 624-9570**
(800) 800-2024
Fax—(908) 624-9553
www.raymond-nj.com
Email—info@raymond-nj.com
Owner—Cliff Sneyers
Hum. Res. Mgr.—Tina Cipreian
Payroll Mgr.—Lynn Monschker
SIC—3537; *Lift trucks & replacement parts*
Employs—135; Estab.—1977
Sales—$10Mil-$25Mil
Distrib.—Local
Limited Liability Company

**RESISTANCE WELDING SOLUTIONS, INC.**
1090 Lousons Rd. *(07083)*
**Phone—(908) 964-9100**
(800) 223-0909
Fax—(908) 964-4492
www.lors.com
Email—sales@lors.com
CEO—Gregory W. Labelle
Pres.—Edmundo Narvaez
Cont.—Lynn-Anne Kocon
Fin. Mgr.—Marilyn Cascarelli
SIC—3548; 3549; 3699; 3589; NAICS—333518; *Resistance welding equipment, including electrodes, holders, fixtures, tooling & accessories, ferrous wire benders & mesh welders; Brand name—LORS*
Employs—20; Estab.—1960
Sales—$2Mil-$5Mil
20,000 sq ft site, Distrib.—Intl.
Privately owned sub-S corp.
DBA: LORS Machinery

**ROCKWOOD CORP. / SPEEDWELL TARGETS**
410 Clermont Ter., Ste. D (07083)
**Phone—(908) 355-8600**
National—(800) 243-8274
Fax—(908) 355-1414
www.speedwelltargets.com
Email—sales@speedwelltargets.com
Pres.—Michael Panos
SIC—3949; NAICS—339920; *Qualification, military, NRA competition, IPSC, IDPA & law enforcement paper, cardboard & steel shooting targets*
Employs—4; Estab.—1984
Distrib.—National
Privately owned corporation
AKA: Speedwell

GEOGRAPHICAL

## Union—(cont.)

**RUMMEL INDUSTRIES, INC.**
697 Rahway Ave., P.O. Box 1326 (07083)
**Phone—(908) 688-6600**
National—(800) 526-4549
Fax—(908) 686-4612
www.rummelindustries.com
Email—sales@rummelindustries.com
Pres.—Peter Rummel
V-P. & Off. Mgr.—Walter Rummel
Sales Mgr.—George Leslie
Acctg. Mgr.—Michael Rummel
Prod. Mgr.—Sam Marcantonio
SIC—3089; 3499; *Corporate headquarters & plastic & metal fabrication*
Employs—18; Estab.—1928
27,000 sq ft site, Distrib.—National
Privately owned sub-S corp.

**S S ART & ENGRAVING CORP.**
1023 Commerce Ave. (07083)
**Phone—(908) 686-5536**
Fax—(908) 686-4933
www.ssstudios.com
Email—sales@ssstudios.com
Pres., Fin. & Sales Mgr.—Robert Burslem
V-P.—Deborah Burslem
SIC—2791; NAICS—323122; *Electronic prepress for the packaging industry*
Employs—15; Estab.—1921
Sales—$1Mil-$5Mil
15,000 sq ft site, Distrib.—Intl.
Privately owned sub-S corp.
AKA: SS Studios

**SATEC, INC. (H Q)**
10 Milltown Ct. *(07083)*
**Phone—(908) 686-9510**
Fax—(908) 686-9520
www.satec-global.com
Email—satec@oksatec.com
Pres.—Edwin Hoinowski
V-P., Sales—Juan Diaz
Cont., Opers. Mgr.—Richard Galasso
Comms. & Mktg. Mgr.—Esli J. Latorre
SIC—3825; NAICS—334500; *Corporate headquarters; power meters, power quality & fault recording analysis equipment for measurement, monitoring & control applicatoins (mfg. done overseas)*
Employs—16; Estab.—1997
15,000 sq ft site, Distrib.—National
Privately owned corporation

**SATURN TOOL & DIE, INC.**
1064 Commerce Ave. (07083)
**Phone—(908) 964-0504**
Fax—(732) 523-2520
Email—saturntool@gmail.com
Pres.—Robert Wilson
SIC—3599; 3544; NAICS—333500; *CNC machining & tool & die job shop, including small lot production & stamping*
Employs—3; Estab.—1994
Sales—under $500,000
2,000 sq ft site, Distrib.—Intl.
Privately owned sub-S corp.

**SCHAEFER, INC., ERNEST**
731 Lehigh Ave. *(07083)*
**Phone—(908) 964-1280**
Fax—(908) 964-6787
www.ernestschaeferinc.com
Email—eschaeferinc@aol.com
Pres.—Ernest Schaefer III
MIS Mgr.—Robyn Miller
R & D Mgr.—Eric Schaefer
Manager—Jim Brown

SIC—3555; NAICS—333293; *Zinc & brass type for hot foil stamping & bookbinding supplies; Brand name—Kwikprint Stamping Machines; Holliston Materials; Davey Binders Board*
Employs—6; Estab.—1922
Sales—under $1Mil
10,000 sq ft site, Distrib.—National
Privately owned corporation

**SCHOTT BROS., INC.**
735 Rahway Ave. (07083)
**Phone—(908) 527-0011**
National—(800) 631-5407
Fax—(908) 527-6185
www.schottnyc.com
Email—schottnyc@schottnyc.com
CEO—Steve Colin
Pres.—Roslyn Schott
CFO—Jason Schott
V-P., Sales—Don King
SIC—2386; 2329; 2339; NAICS—315200; *Outerwear & sportswear; Brand name—Schott NYC; Perfecto by Schott*
Employs—120; Estab.—1913
Sales—$5Mil-$15Mil
58,000 sq ft site, Distrib.—Intl.
Privately owned sub-S corp.

**SHAFFER PRODUCTS, INC.**
20 Milltown Rd., P.O. Box 427 (07083)
**Phone—(908) 206-1980**
National—(800) 992-5684
Fax—(908) 206-1975
www.shafferproducts.com
Email—sales@shafferproducts.com
Pres.—James K. Shahidi
Sales Mgr.—Paul Silverthorne
Off. Mgr.—Gail Hirst
SIC—2393; NAICS—314911; *Woven & conductive filters for separating solids from air or liquid stream, including fluid bed dryer, jet milling product collection & transfer bags, centrifuge liners/bags & plate & frame filter press cloths; Brand name—Non-leak; dual lock; ultra-lock*
Employs—25; Estab.—1945
Sales—$2.5Mil-$5Mil
Distrib.—Intl.
Privately owned sub-S corp.
Also see: Summit Filter Corporation, same loc.

**SIEMENS INDUSTRY, INC., WATER TECHNOLOGIES**
Div. of Evoqua Water Technologies
2 Milltown Ct. (07083)
**Phone—(908) 851-2277**
National—(866) 926-8420
Fax—(908) 851-6906
www.evoqua.com
Email—customerservice@evoqua.com
Area Mgr.—Mark Kelly
Plt. Mgr.—William Ronayne
SIC—3589; NAICS—333319; *Water purification & anti-corrosion equipment*
Employs—100; Estab.—1985
Distrib.—Intl.
Publicly owned corporation
Parent co.—Evoqua Water Technologies, Alpharetta, GA
Phone—(978) 614-7111
See Parent Co. Section for full profile.

**STERNVENT**
5 Stahuber Ave. (07083)
**Phone—(908) 688-0807**
National—(800) 383-3878
Fax—(908) 688-0718
www.sternvent.com
Email—info@sternvent.com
Pres.—Robert Denholtz
Prod. & Sales Mgr.—Peter Levitt

SIC—3564; NAICS—333400; *Dust collection systems used for industrial & school operations that produce wood, metal & chemical dusts; Brand name—Vibraclean; Dust Switch; Sternpulse*
Employs—20; Estab.—1952
Sales—$1Mil-$5Mil
35,000 sq ft site, Distrib.—Intl.
Privately owned corporation
Also see: Durex, Inc., same loc.

**SUMMIT FILTER CORPORATION**
20 Milltown Rd., P.O. Box 427 (07083)
**Phone—(908) 687-3500**
National—(800) 321-4850
Fax—(908) 687-4202
www.summitfilter.com
Email—sales@summitfilter.com
Pres.—James K. Shahidi
V-P., Opers.—Lois Gloss
Dir., Sales & Mktg.—Cathy Maher
SIC—3564; NAICS—333400; *Industrial fabric filter, pleated, centrifuge & fluid bed dryer bags & cages for separation of solids from air & liquid streams; Brand name—SRC; MaxClad II; Unipore; PermaShield; Dual Shield; Detect-A-Glow*
Employs—30; Estab.—1945
Sales—$5Mil
25,000 sq ft site, Distrib.—Intl.
Privately owned sub-S corp.
Also see: Shaffer Products, Inc., same loc.

**SUMMIT STEEL CORP.**
1435 Morris Ave. (07083-3302)
**Phone—(908) 688-8817**
Fax—(908) 688-8843
Email—summitsteel@comcast.net
Pres., Secy.—Lila Lulinski
Ex. V-P.—Ira Lulinski
Opers. Mgr.—Pearla Lulinski
Proj. Mgr.—Thomas J. Hayes
SIC—3441; NAICS—332312; *Structural steel & ornamental iron fabrication*
Employs—10; Estab.—1988
Distrib.—Local
Privately owned corporation

**TESSLER & WEISS, INC.**
2389 Vauxhall Rd., P.O. Box 3414 (07083)
**Phone—(908) 686-0513**
Fax—(908) 686-9165
www.camelogbridal.com
Email—custsvc@tesslerweiss.com
Pres.—Mark Tessler
Prod. Mgr.—Paul Cavallaro
Cust. Serv. Rep.—Fran Alercio
SIC—3915; *Jewelry findings*
Employs—155; Estab.—1958
Distrib.—National
Privately owned corporation

**THERMO PLASTICS TECHNOLOGIES, INC.**
1119 Morris Ave. (07083)
**Phone—(908) 687-4833**
Fax—(908) 687-5829
Email—thmoplastic@aol.com
Pres.—Tino Quint
SIC—3089; *Plastic products for the cosmetics industry*
Employs—48
Sales—$1Mil-$3Mil
30,000 sq ft site, Distrib.—Local
Privately owned corporation

**TURBOBRAZE CORP.**
687 Lehigh Ave., P.O. Box 897 (07083)
**Phone—(908) 687-1030**
National—(800) 526-4932
Fax—(908) 687-2786
www.turbobraze.com
Email—sales@turbobraze.com
Pres.—Mary Orella

V-P., MIS & R & D—Michael McCoy
Custom Svcs. Mgr.—Jim Blackwood
SIC—2899; *Brazing paste & flux*
Employs—8; Estab.—1974
Sales—$1Mil-$5Mil
25,000 sq ft site, Distrib.—Intl.
Privately owned sub-S corp.

**VALCONN ELECTRONICS, INC.**
909 Rahway Ave. (07083)
**Phone—(908) 687-1600**
Fax—(908) 687-8599
www.valconn.com
Pres.—Joel Cohn
SIC—3679; *Custom cable assemblies & electronic components*
Employs—20
Sales—$2.5Mil-$5Mil (est)
Distrib.—Local
Privately owned corporation

**VULCAN TOOL CO., INC.**
1080-C Garden State Rd. (07083)
**Phone—(908) 686-0550**
Fax—(908) 686-8522
www.vulcantool.com
Email—sales@vulcantool.com
Pres.—Anton Heldmann
V-P.—Richard Heldmann
SIC—3728; *Aerospace components*
Employs—20; Estab.—1992
15,000 sq ft site, Distrib.—National
Privately owned corporation

**WORRALL COMMUNITY NEWSPAPERS, INC.**
1291 Stuyvesant Ave., P.O. Box 1596 (07083)
**Phone—(908) 686-7700**
Fax—(908) 686-4169
www.unionnewsdaily.com
Email—class@thelocalsource.com
Publisher—David Worrall
V-P., Opers.—Peter Worrall
V-P., Acctg. & Hum. Res. Mgr.—Nancy Worrall
V-P., Editorial—Raymond Worrall
SIC—2711; *Weekly print & online newspaper publishing*
Employs—50
Distrib.—Local
Privately owned corporation

**XO ATHLETIC CO.**
911 Springfield Rd. (07083)
**Phone—(908) 964-1242**
Fax—(908) 964-1248
www.xoathletic.com
CEO—Michael T. Landi
Dir., Opers.—Catherine Gallagher
SIC—3949; *Athletic protection products, including mouthguards, vests & cups; Brand name—XO Heartshield™*
Employs—10
Sales—under $500,000
Distrib.—Intl.
Privately owned corporation

**ZETA PRODUCTS, INC.**
1060 Garden State Rd. (07083)
**Phone—(908) 688-0440**
National—(800) 688-0221
Fax—(908) 688-9335
www.zetaproducts.com
Email—info@zetaproducts.com
Pres.—Michael Naso
Secy., Off. Mgr.—Theresa Somma
Sales Rep.—Edward Darnsteadt
SIC—3861; *Film cartridges & microfilm storage items*
Employs—4; Estab.—1977
15,000 sq ft site, Distrib.—Intl.
Privately owned corporation

**ZIEZER TOOL CO., INC.**
960 Koehl Ave. (07083)
**Phone—(908) 686-1332**
Fax—(906) 686-9106
Pres.—Ron Ziezer

## Union—(cont.)

SIC—3599; *Precision machine parts*
Employs—3; Estab.—1984
Sales—under $500,000 (est)
Distrib.—Regional

---

## Union Beach
(Monmouth—N.E.)

**SIGN MAKER**
1005 Union Ave. (07735)
**Phone—(732) 739-4800**
Fax—(732) 739-1004
Owner—Nancy McCarthy
SIC—3993; *Interior & exterior vinyl, paper, plexiglass & magnetic signs & lettering*
Employs—1; Estab.—1999
Sales—under $500,000
Distrib.—Local
Sole ownership

---

## Union City
(Hudson—N.E.)

**AMERICAN METAL FAB & WELDING**
706 7th St. (07087)
**Phone—(201) 295-8888**
Email—fab706@yahoo.com
GM—Maher Gazawneh
SIC—3444; 3599; *Custom sheet metal fabrication & welding job shop*
Employs—2; Estab.—1999
2,000 sq ft site, Distrib.—Local
Sole ownership

**APPETITO PROVISIONS CO., INC.**
609 10th St., P.O. Box 8098 (07087)
**Phone—(201) 864-3410**
www.appetitosausage.com
Email—appetito@verizon.net
Pres.—Michael Tota
SIC—2013; NAICS—311600; *Sausage processing*
Employs—25; Estab.—1966
35,000 sq ft site, Distrib.—Regional
Privately owned sub-S corp.

**BHAMRA CHAIN MFG. CO.**
1020 Springfield Rd. (07087)
**Phone—(908) 686-4555**
Fax—(908) 686-4556
www.bhamrachain.com
Email—bhamracorp@aol.com
Ptnr. & Pres.—Ajit Bhamra
Ptnr.—Varmeet Bhamra
SIC—3911; NAICS—339911; *Precious & base metal chains for the jewelry industry*
Employs—3; Estab.—1980
Sales—under $1Mil
5,000 sq ft site, Distrib.—National
Privately owned corporation

NEW ENTRY
**C GRAPHICS STUDIO**
410 32nd St. (07087)
**Phone—(201) 866-0592**
Fax—(201) 866-2233
Email—cgrafix1@optonline.net
Ptnr.—Tony Castillo
SIC—2759; *Commercial printing & graphic design services*
Employs—4
Sales—$500,000-$1Mil (est)

**CUNY & GUERBER, INC.**
2100 Kerrigan Ave., P.O. Box 1192 (07087)
**Phone—(201) 617-5800**
Fax—(201) 617-5557
www.cuny.biz
Email—sales@cuny.biz
Pres.—David B. Matthews, Jr.
V-P.—Raymond E. Cuny
V-P.—Steve W. Matthews

Acctg. & Hum. Res. Mgr.—Phyllis C. Peare
SIC—7373; 5084; 5065; 5063; *Industrial automation systems integration & distributor of electronic & electrical equipment & supplies*
Employs—35; Estab.—1924
Distrib.—Regional
Privately owned corporation

**EASTERN EMBLEM MFG. CORP.**
509 18th St., P.O. Box 828 (07087)
**Phone—(201) 867-3159**
National—(800) 344-5112
Fax—(201) 867-7248
www.easternemblem.com
Email—info@easternemblem.com
Pres.—Sheldon Lefkowitz
Off. Mgr.—Kathy Craig
SIC—2395; *Embroidery & metal & print logos*
Employs—5; Estab.—1960
Distrib.—Intl.
Privately owned corporation

**HAMILTON EMBROIDERY, INC.**
907-909 21st St. (07087)
**Phone—(201) 867-4084**
Fax—(201) 867-2066
www.hamiltonembroidery.com
Email—fblaso@cs.com
Pres.—Frank Blaso
SIC—2397; 2395; NAICS—313222; *Schiffli machine embroideries & trims*
Employs—7; Estab.—1952
Sales—$1Mil-$5Mil
40,000 sq ft site, Distrib.—Intl.
Privately owned sub-S corp.

**IMAGERY EMBROIDERY CORPORATION**
2907-2911 Jeannette St. (07087)
**Phone—(201) 343-9333**
Fax—(201) 343-9202
www.imagerycorp.com
Email—info@imagerycorp.com
Pres.—Eddison S. Cruz
SIC—2395; 2396; *Machined & digitized embroidery, monogramming, screen & direct-to-garment printing, packaging & artwork & fulfillment services*
Employs—10; Estab.—1982
Sales—$750,000-$1Mil
5,500 sq ft site, Distrib.—National
Privately owned corporation

**JARCO U. S. CASTING CORP.**
109 45th St. (07087)
**Phone—(201) 271-0003**
Fax—(201) 271-0009
www.jarcousa.com
Email—info@jarcousa.com
Pres.—Mario A. Herrera
Ex. V-P.—Felix L. Disla
Fin. Mgr.—Major Disla
SIC—3993; 3499; *Cast metal emblems & advertising specialties*
Employs—35; Estab.—1949
13,000 sq ft site, Distrib.—Intl.
Privately owned corporation

**JEWELRY ARTS MFG., INC.**
1701 Summit Ave. (07087)
**Phone—(201) 864-5188**
Fax—(201) 864-5411
www.jarts.com
Pres.—Alberto Tapia
Manager—Alina Valencia
SIC—3911; NAICS—339911; *Precious metal jewelry*
Employs—50; Estab.—1987
Sales—$1Mil-$2.5Mil
Distrib.—Intl.
Privately owned corporation

†**K & J SCRAP METAL, INC.**
609 25th St. (07087)
**Phone—(201) 348-3368**
Pres.—Kevin Istok

SIC—5093; *Wholesaler of scrap metals*
Employs—3; Estab.—1990
Distrib.—Local
Privately owned corporation

**LEON PRINTING**
1421 New York Ave. (07087)
**Phone—(201) 867-3206**
Owner—Lewis Leon
Pressman—Gilbert Gonzales
Off. Mgr.—Vivian Gonzalez
SIC—2759; NAICS—323100; *Commercial printing*
Employs—3; Estab.—1963
Sales—under $500,000
Distrib.—Local
Sole ownership

**LIBERTY BRAND PASTRIES & FOODS**
2409 Central Ave. (07087)
**Phone—(201) 863-3350**
Fax—(201) 863-3351
Owner & Pres.—Maria Scrchis
SIC—2051; NAICS—311812; *Bakery products, including pastries, cookies & strudels*
Employs—1; Estab.—1985
Sales—under $500,000
Distrib.—Local
Sole ownership

**LICINI BROS. PROVISIONS, INC.**
907 West St. (07087)
**Phone—(201) 865-1130**
Fax—(201) 866-5258
Pres.—Danny Licini
Manager—Gio Licini
SIC—2013; NAICS—311600; *Fresh & dried sausages*
Employs—10; Estab.—1971
Sales—under $500,000
Distrib.—Local
Privately owned corporation

**LOS GALLEGUITOS**
147 48th St. (07087)
**Phone—(201) 865-7232**
Fax—(201) 865-4658
www.losgalleguitos.com
Email—flt21@aol.com
Owner—Francisco Torres
SIC—2013; NAICS—311600; *Spanish sausage processing & packing*
Employs—10; Estab.—1979
Distrib.—Regional
Privately owned sub-S corp.

**NOBLEWORKS, INC.**
500 Patterson Plank Rd. (07087)
Mail addr: P.O. Box 1275, Hoboken (07030-1275)
**Phone—(201) 420-0095**
National—(800) 346-6253
Fax—(201) 420-0679
www.nobleworkscards.com
Email—info@nobleworksinc.com
Pres.—Ron Kanfi
Off. Mgr.—Lori Cogan
SIC—2771; *Greeting cards*
Employs—2; Estab.—1986
Sales—under $500,000
2,500 sq ft site, Distrib.—Intl.
Privately owned corporation

**NORTH JERSEY PAPER BOX CORP.**
132 32nd St., P.O. Box 700 (07087)
**Phone—(201) 348-4233**
Fax—(201) 348-4288
www.capitolbox.com
Owner—Ed Maleh
Opers. Mgr.—Harvey Goch
SIC—2671; *Rigid paper boxes*
Employs—20; Estab.—2005
Distrib.—Local
Privately owned corporation

**PLEATING PLUS LTD.**
527 40th St. (07087)
**Phone—(201) 863-2991**
Pres.—Ernest Vega

SIC—2395; *Contract pleating & tucking*
Employs—5; Estab.—1989
Sales—under $500,000 (est)
Distrib.—Regional

**REDWALLET CONNECTION, LLC**
907 21st St. (07087)
**Phone—(201) 223-2644**
National—(800) 316-5119
Fax—(201) 223-1055
www.redwalletconnection.com
Email—redwalletinc@aol.com
Pres., CEO—Linda C. Lafferty
SIC—2675; NAICS—322200; *Pressboard, file, classification, presentation, patent & trademark folders, portfolios & expanding file envelopes & open pockets*
Employs—50; Estab.—1992
28,000 sq ft site, Distrib.—Intl.
Limited Liability Company

**SUMMIT TOOL CO., INC.**
719 23rd St. (07087)
**Phone—(201) 867-8600**
Fax—(201) 867-2111
Pres.—Paul Cairoli
SIC—3544; 3599; NAICS—333500; *Machining job shop*
Employs—3; Estab.—1949
Sales—under $500,000
5,000 sq ft site, Distrib.—Regional
Privately owned corporation

**TANNER ASSOCS.**
600 Palisade Ave. (07087)
**Phone—(201) 865-4500**
Fax—(201) 865-7776
Owner, Fin. & GM—Irving Tanner
SIC—2392; 2221; 2211; NAICS—313210; *Cotton & nylon cloth dry cleaning & ironing pads, covers & supplies & cotton & nylon cloths for pressing machines*
Employs—3; Estab.—1950
Sales—under $500,000
5,000 sq ft site, Distrib.—National
Privately owned partnership

**U.S.A. DISTRIBUTORS, INC.**
3711 Hudson Ave. (07087)
**Phone—(201) 348-1959**
Fax—(201) 348-3385
www.elespecial.com
Email—aibarria@elespecial.com
Pres.—Antonio Ibarria
Dir.—Jose Sibaja
Sales Mgr.—Anthony Ibarria
Regional Mgr.—John Ibarria
Group Mgr.—Carmen Asmat
SIC—2711; 2721; *Newspaper & magazine publishing*
Employs—100; Estab.—1995
Distrib.—Regional
Privately owned corporation
AKAs: El Especial & El Especialito & Personalidades

**UNION CITY MIRROR & TABLE CO.**
129 34th St. (07087)
**Phone—(201) 867-1827**
Fax—(201) 867-2552
www.unioncitymirrortable.com
Email—chopper@unioncitymirrortable.com
Pres., R & D Mgr.—Thomas Russo
COO, R & D Mgr.—Gene Russo
SIC—2511; 2599; 3231; 2499; NAICS—327215; *French Provincial wooden & occasional furniture & accessories, including tables, consoles, mirrors, living rooms, bedrooms, dining rooms & capo-di-monte lamps*
Employs—6; Estab.—1921
75,000 sq ft site, Distrib.—Intl.
Privately owned sub-S corp.

GEOGRAPHICAL

## Union City—(cont.)

**UNITED STATES BUSINESS CARD CO.**
540 39th St., Ste. 33 (07087)
**Phone—(201) 863-8776**
(212) 586-5911
National—(888) 959-9828
www.usbcards.net
Email—usbcards@earthlink.net
Owner—Richard Meneely
SIC—2759; *Letterpress, business card, invitation, hang tag & short run printing*
Employs—1; Estab.—2000
Sales—$40,000
750 sq ft site, Distrib.—Intl.
Sole ownership
AKA: All Cards Man

## Upper Montclair

(Essex—N.E.)

**N J SPORT ACTION**
5 Riverview Dr. W. (07043)
**Phone—(973) 783-9236**
Fax—(973) 783-9236
www.njsportaction.net
Email—njsportaction@aol.com
Owner—W. L. 'Bill' Allen, Jr.
SIC—2711; 2721; *Newspaper & magazine publishing*
Employs—10; Estab.—1983
Sales—$500,000-$1Mil
Distrib.—Regional
Sole ownership

## Upper Saddle River

(Bergen—N.E.)

**AMERICAN INSTITUTE OF FOOD DISTRIBUTION, INC.**
10 Mountain View Rd., Ste. S-125 (07458)
**Phone—(201) 791-5570**
Fax—(201) 791-5222
www.foodinstitute.com
Email—info@foodinstitute.com
Pres.—Brian Todd
V.-P., CFO—Cathie Sloam
Editor—Virginia Harte
Off. Mgr.—April Brendl
SIC—2721; *Food industry periodical publishing*
Employs—13; Estab.—1928
Distrib.—Intl.
Privately owned corporation
AKA: Food Institute, The

**AMFINE CHEMICAL CORP.**
10 Mountainview Rd., Ste. N-215 (07458-1936)
**Phone—(201) 818-0159**
Fax—(201) 818-0259
www.amfine.com
Email—sales@amfine.com
Ex. V.-P.—Takeyuki Mototani
V.-P., Global Sales & Mktg.—Peter Goman
V.-P., Opers.—M. Jay Kolaya
Tech. Mktg. Mgr.—Manabu Ishii
SIC—2869; *Corporate headquarters & plastic additives; Brand name—ADK Stabilizers; Adeka Additives; Adeka Cizer*
Employs—9; Estab.—1994
5,000 sq ft site, Distrib.—Intl.
Privately owned partnership
ISO rating—9000

**ATLANTIC EQUIPMENT ENGINEERS, INC.**
24 Industrial Ave., P.O. Box 181 (07458)
**Phone—(201) 828-9400**
National—(800) 486-2436
Fax—(201) 387-0291
www.micronmetals.com
Email—info@micronmetals.com
Pres., GM, Fin. & MIS Mgr.—Alan Kessler
V.-P., Opers.—Barry Kessler
Off. & Sales Mgr.—Mike Gerald
Cust. Serv. Supv.—Kelly Stephenson
SIC—3399; NAICS—331492; *High purity metal powders & compounds*
Employs—12; Estab.—1963
Sales—$1Mil-$5Mil
12,000 sq ft site, Distrib.—Intl.
Privately owned corporation
Also see: VAR-LAC-OID Chemical Co., Inc., same loc.

**BCT-NY/NJ**
11 Industrial Ave. (07458)
**Phone—(201) 236-0088**
Fax—(201) 236-9010
Email—cs@bct-nynj.com
Pres., GM—Douglas Negrin
Ex. V.-P.—Susan Negrin
Plt. Mgr.—Elisha Phillips
SIC—2752; 2754; 3953; NAICS—323111; *Rubber stamps & offset printing of business cards & stationery, letterheads & announcements*
Employs—10; Estab.—2005
Sales—$1Mil-$2.5Mil
Distrib.—National
Privately owned corporation

**DIHCO, INC.**
612 E. Crescent Ave. *(07458)*
**Phone—(201) 327-0518**
Fax—(201) 327-8759
Email—DIHCO-INC@hotmail.com
Pres.—Peter Diamantes
V.-P.—Gary Berberian
Bookkeeper—Nancy Gudelski
SIC—3599; *General machining job shop*
Employs—4; Estab.—1976
Sales—under $500,000
4,000 sq ft site, Distrib.—Local
Privately owned corporation

**HOFMANN TOOL & DIE CORP.**
356 Route 17 N. (07458)
**Phone—(201) 327-0226**
Fax—(201) 825-1634
Email—hofmann.tool@worldnet.att.net
Pres.—Charlie S. Franco
SIC—3544; NAICS—333500; *Tool & die job shop*
Employs—6; Estab.—1967
Sales—under $500,000
5,000 sq ft site, Distrib.—Local
Privately owned corporation

**ONKYO USA CORP. (H Q)**
18 Park Way (07458)
**Phone—(201) 785-2600**
National—(800) 229-1687
Fax—(201) 785-2650
www.onkyousa.com
Email—mkatsman@onkyousa.com
Pres.—Hiroshi Izutani
Acctg. Mgr.—Mila Katsman
Cred. Mgr.—Mathew Attanasio
SIC—3651; NAICS—334310; *Corporate headquarters; home theater systems, amplifiers & speakers (mfg. done overseas)*
Employs—40
Sales—$10Mil-$25Mil (est)
Distrib.—Intl.

**PEARSON EDUCATION, INC.**
1 Lake St. (07458)
**Phone—(201) 236-7000**
National—(800) 745-8489
www.pearsoned.com
Email—communications@pearsoned.com
CEO—Marjorie Scardino
Ex. V.-P., CFO & COO—George Warner
Sr. V.-P., Comm.—Wendy Spiegel
Ex. V.-P., Opers.—John LaVacca
Ex. V.-P., Hum. Res.—Angela Schwers
SIC—2731; 2721; 2741; *Corporate headquarters & educational book, materials, literature & periodical publishing*
Employs—2500; Estab.—1996
Sales—$100Mil-$250Mil (est)
Distrib.—Intl.
Publicly owned corporation

**PENTEK, INC.**
1 Park Way, 2nd Fl. (07458)
**Phone—(201) 818-5900**
Fax—(201) 818-5904
www.pentek.com
Email—sales@pentek.com
Pres.—Dan Shamah
V.-P.—Rodger Hosking
Dir., Engrg.—Paul Mesibov
Mktg. Mgr.—Gina Peter
Hum. Res. Mgr.—Kerry Campbell
SIC—3825; NAICS—334500; *Digital signal processing, software radio & data acquisition systems & boards*
Employs—55; Estab.—1989
Sales—$10Mil-$25Mil
Distrib.—Intl.
Privately owned corporation

**SHERWIN-WILLIAMS CO., THE, WOODCARE PRODUCTS DIV. (H Q)**
Div. of Sherwin-Williams Co., The
10 Mountainview Rd. (07458)
**Phone—(201) 818-7500**
www.sherwin.com
Email—info@sherwin.com
V.-P., Mktg.—Janet Krakow
Dir., Mktg.—Jacquelyn Ferrara
Dir., Tech.—George Mayerhauser
SIC—2851; NAICS—325510; *Divisional headquarters; wood finishes; Brand name—Minwax®*
Employs—60
Sales—$10Mil-$25Mil (est)
Distrib.—National
Publicly owned corporation
Parent co.—Sherwin-Williams Co., The, Cleveland, OH
Phone—(216) 566-2000
See Parent Co. Section for full profile.

**SONNTEK, INC.**
125 Pleasant Ave. (07458)
**Phone—(201) 236-9300**
Fax—(201) 236-2277
www.sonntek.com
Email—sonntek@aol.com
Pres.—David Keller
SIC—3826; NAICS—334516; *Chromatographic research instruments*
Employs—7; Estab.—1983
Sales—$1Mil-$2.5Mil
5,000 sq ft site, Distrib.—Intl.
Privately owned corporation

**TRIANGLE MFG.**
116 Pleasant Ave. (07458)
**Phone—(201) 825-1212**
Fax—(201) 825-2742
www.trianglemfg.com
Email—mail@trianglemfg.com
Pres.—Dax Strohmeyer
Fin. & MIS Mgr.—Nicholas Aselta
Hum. Res. Mgr.—Ann McGinley
Maint. Mgr.—Scott Van Deweert
Sales Exec.—Robert Imhoff
SIC—3841; *Medical devices, including implants & surgical powered & nonpowered instrumentation*
Employs—165; Estab.—1955
50,000 sq ft site, Distrib.—National
Privately owned corporation

**VAR-LAC-OID CHEMICAL CO., INC.**
24 Industrial Ave., P.O. Box 181 (07458)
**Phone—(201) 236-8800**
Fax—(201) 387-0291
www.cesium-chloride.com
Email—info@cesium-chloride.com
Pres.—Alan Kessler
Cust. Serv. Rep.—Kelly Stephenson
SIC—2819; *Cesium chloride*
Employs—15; Estab.—1923
Sales—$500,000-$1Mil
Distrib.—Regional
Privately owned corporation
Also see: Atlantic Equipment Engineers, Div. Of Micron Metals, same loc.

## Ventnor City

(Atlantic—S.E.)

**DELAWARE FOOD MARKET**
6506 Ventnor Ave. (08406)
**Phone—(609) 822-0222**
Owner—William Deluca
SIC—2011; NAICS—311611; *Meat packing & processing*
Employs—7; Estab.—1947
Sales—$2.5Mil-$5Mil (est)
Distrib.—Local
Privately owned corporation

**HARRIS KENYA GEM CO., TOM**
6504 Ventnor Ave. (08406)
**Phone—(609) 823-3315**
Fax—(609) 822-2992
www.kenyagemco.com
Email—kenyagemco@aol.com
Owner—Tom Harris
SIC—3911; *Precious metal, gold & diamond jewelry*
Employs—2; Estab.—1948
Sales—under $500,000
1,500 sq ft site, Distrib.—Local
Sole ownership

**JAGIELKY'S HOME MADE CANDY**
5115 Ventnor Ave. (08406)
**Phone—(609) 823-6501**
Fax—(609) 487-9736
www.jagielkyscandy.com
Pres.—Michael Carr
Sales Mgr.—Ann Carr
SIC—2064; NAICS—311300; *Candy & assorted chocolates*
Employs—7; Estab.—1972
Sales—under $500,000
3,500 sq ft site, Distrib.—Regional
Privately owned corporation

**VENTNOR PRINT SHOP CO.**
128 N. Wyoming Ave., P.O. Box 2174 (08406)
**Phone—(609) 822-2974**
Fax—(609) 822-2974
Pres.—Richard Juliano
Pressman—Joe Juliano
SIC—2759; NAICS—323100; *Commercial printing*
Employs—2; Estab.—1941
Sales—under $500,000
Distrib.—Local
Privately owned corporation

## Vernon

(Sussex—N.W.)

**CONGRUENT MACHINING CO., INC.**
107 Maple Grange Rd., P.O. Box 888 *(07462)*
**Phone—(973) 764-6767**
Fax—(973) 875-8327
www.congruentmachine.com
Email—info@congruentmachine.com
Pres.—Jerry Caiafa
SIC—3451; NAICS—332721; *Screw machine products*
Employs—5; Estab.—1980
Sales—under $500,000
Distrib.—Intl.
Privately owned corporation

**EASCO SHOWER DOORS CO.**
Div. of Lenape Products, Inc.
3 Industrial Dr. (07462)
**Phone—(973) 209-4141**
National—(800) 974-6937
Fax—(973) 209-7621

## Vernon—(cont.)

www.easco-shower.com
Email—sales@easco-shower.com
Dir., Engrg. & Opers.—Vincent
Bottaro
Cust. Serv. Mgr.—Ken Spreen
SIC—3231; 3442; NAICS—
327215; *Glass & aluminum
shower doors & tub enclosures*
Employs—28; Estab.—1980
15,000 sq ft site, Distrib.—
Regional
Privately owned corporation
AKA: Plum Street Pottery
Parent co.—Lenape Products, Inc.,
Trenton, NJ
Phone—(609) 394-5376
See Parent Co. Section for full profile.

### INDEMAX, INC.

1 Industrial Dr. (07462)
**Phone—(973) 209-2424**
National—(800) 345-7185
Fax—(973) 209-2644
www.indemax.com
Email—service@indemax.com
Chrm.—A. Infurna
Pres.—R. Infurna
Secy-Treas., CFO—P. Infurna
SIC—3599; *Glue machine parts*
Employs—18; Estab.—1978
Sales—over $3Mil
10,000 sq ft site, Distrib.—Intl.
Privately owned corporation

### METALFAB, INC.

11 Prices Switch Rd., P.O. Box 9
(07462)
**Phone—(973) 764-2000**
National—(800) 764-2999
Fax—(973) 764-0272
www.metalfabinc.com
Email—sales@metalfabinc.com
COO—Mike Randazzo
V-P., Sales & Mktg.—Dan Higgins
Engrg. Mgr.—Mike McMahon
SIC—3523; 3535; 3569; 3443;
NAICS—333922; *Large plate
steel fabrication & dry bulk
material handling systems &
equipment, including bin
activators, vibrating bins,
volumetric & gravimetric screw
feeders, bulk bag unloaders,
blenders & flexible screw &
vibrating tube conveyors; Brand
name—Better Weigh™
Gravimetric Feeders; Convey-
All™ Conveyors; Posibin™
Vibrating Bins; MetaTech™
Volumetric Feeders*
Employs—30; Estab.—1977
30,000 sq ft site, Distrib.—Intl.
Privately owned sub-S corp.

### T E O FABRICATIONS, INC.

95 Maple Grange Rd., P.O. Box
232 (07462)
**Phone—(973) 764-5500**
Fax—(973) 764-5510
www.teopro.com
Email—teopro@warwick.net
Pres.—Robert Hearn
SIC—3711; 3714; *Race cars &
components*
Employs—6; Estab.—1987
Sales—$5Mil-$10Mil (est)
Distrib.—Regional
Privately owned corporation

### THERMAFREEZE PRODUCTS CORP.
(H Q)

107 Maple Grange Rd. (07462)
**Phone—(877) 777-8397**
National—(877) 676-7696
Fax—(732) 676-7697
www.thermafreezecorp.com
Email—support@thermafreeze.com
Pres.—Sahin Atlas
Manager—Truman Ellis

SIC—3842; 3089; *Corporate
headquarters; reusable ice
packs for medical applications &
food preservation*
Employs—3; Estab.—2008
Sales—under $500,000
Distrib.—National

### V G CONTROLS, INC.

11 Butternut Dr. (07462)
**Phone—(973) 764-6500**
National—(800) 524-6994
Fax—(973) 764-6603
www.vgcontrols.com
Email—vginfo@vgcontrols.com
Pres.—V. Gelman
V-P.—Helen Gelman
Hum. Res. Mgr.—Elaina Bubnove
SIC—3679; *Electronic systems*
Employs—10; Estab.—1982
Sales—$1Mil-$2.5Mil
Distrib.—Intl.
Privately owned corporation

---

## Verona

### (Essex—N.E.)

### CAMECO, INC.

100 Pine St. *(07044)*
**Phone—(973) 239-2700**
Fax—(973) 239-5392
www.camecoinc.com
Email—info@camecoinc.com
Manager—Bill Schneider
SIC—2011; NAICS—311611; *Meat
processing*
Employs—130; Estab.—1946
20,000 sq ft site, Distrib.—National
Privately owned corporation

### CHAVEZ JEWELRY, MARIE

642 Bloomfield Ave. (07044)
**Phone—(973) 337-8551**
www.mariechavez.com
Email—comments@
mariechavez.com
Owner—Marie Chavez
SIC—3911; *Precious metal
jewelry, including gold & silver
jewelry*
Employs—5
Sales—$500,000-$1Mil (est)
Distrib.—National
Privately owned corporation

### FERRANTE PRESS, INC.

516 Bloomfield Ave. (07044)
**Phone—(973) 239-4344**
Fax—(973) 239-4806
Email—ferrantepress@yahoo.com
GM—Vincent Ferrante
Printer—David Adams
SIC—2759; 2791; NAICS—
323122; *Offset & letterpress
printing, typesetting & graphic
design*
Employs—3; Estab.—1926
Sales—under $500,000
Distrib.—Regional
Privately owned corporation

### HEALTHCARE MARKETERS
EXCHANGE

104 Park Ave. (07044)
**Phone—(973) 744-9505**
www.hmexchange.com
Email—editorial@hmexchange.com
Owner—Nancy Leonard
SIC—2741; *Monthly newsletter for
the healthcare market*
Employs—1
Sales—under $500,000 (est)

### RELIANCE GRAPHICS, INC.

80 Pompton Ave., Ste. 1 (07044)
**Phone—(973) 239-5411**
www.relianceballots.com
Pres.—Robert Fetterly
SIC—2759; *Election ballot printing*
Employs—3; Estab.—1980
Distrib.—Local
Privately owned corporation

### SERAFINO PRINTING CO., INC.

516 Bloomfield Ave. (07044)
**Phone—(973) 857-3450**
Fax—(973) 239-4806
Email—serafinoprintinginc@
yahoo.com
Pres.—Cathy Horling
Manager—Vincent Ferrante
Pressman—Charlie Nixon
SIC—2752; 2759; NAICS—
323129; *Offset & letterpress
printing*
Employs—3; Estab.—1933
Sales—$500,000-$1Mil
Distrib.—Regional
Privately owned corporation

### SUBITO MUSIC CORPORATION

60 Depot St. (07044)
**Phone—(973) 857-3440**
Fax—(973) 857-3442
www.subitomusic.com
Email—mail@subitomusic.com
Owner & GM—Stephen
Culbertson
Off. Mgr.—Lee Kotsambas
Cust. Serv. Mgr.—Patricia
Kotsambas
Shpg. Mgr.—David Smith
SIC—2741; 2791; NAICS—
323122; *Sheet music printing &
typesetting*
Employs—10; Estab.—1980
Sales—under $500,000
3,000 sq ft site, Distrib.—Intl.
Privately owned corporation

---

## Villas

### (Cape May—S.E.)

### SHOPPE CAPE MAY COUNTY
SHOPPERS GUIDE

2503 Bayshore Rd. (08251)
**Phone—(609) 886-4112**
www.shoppenews.com
Email—sales@shoppenews.com
Pres., Publisher—Otto Jensch
Off., Sales & Mktg. Mgr.—Jeannie
Nagle
SIC—2741; NAICS—323122;
*Weekly print & online shopper &
vacation guide publishing;
Brand name—The Shoppe;
Sand Dollar Vacation Guide*
Employs—8; Estab.—1998
Sales—under $500,000
Distrib.—Local
Privately owned corporation

---

## Vincentown

### (Burlington—S.E.)

### GALLANT LABORATORIES, INC.

142 Stockes Rd. (08088)
**Phone—(609) 268-0953**
Fax—(609) 654-4146
Pres.—Gary Gallant
SIC—2844; NAICS—325600;
*Cosmetics*
Employs—3
Sales—$1Mil-$2.5Mil (est)
Distrib.—Local
Privately owned corporation

### GENIE HOUSE, INC.

139 Red Lion Rd., P.O. Box 2478
(08088)
**Phone—(609) 859-0600**
National—(800) 634-3643
Fax—(609) 859-0565
www.geniehouse.com
Email—geniehouse@
geniehouse.com
Pres.—Lloyd Williams, Jr.
V-P.—Deborah Williams

SIC—3645; 3646; NAICS—
335121; *Residential &
commercial lighting fixtures*
Employs—22; Estab.—1967
Sales—$1Mil-$5Mil
9,500 sq ft site, Distrib.—National
Privately owned corporation

### MEDFORD CEDAR PRODUCTS, INC.

59 Old Red Lion Rd. (08088)
**Phone—(609) 859-1400**
Fax—(609) 859-2778
www.medfordcedar.com
Email—sales@medfordcedar.com
Pres.—Albin E. Scheibner
Off. Mgr.—Charlene Scheibner
SIC—2452; 5032; NAICS—
321992; *Manufacturer of cedar
garden structures, including
pergolas & distributor of cedar &
composite products, including
dimension lumber, decking,
siding & shingles*
Employs—7; Estab.—1987
Sales—$1Mil-$2.5Mil
Distrib.—Regional
Privately owned corporation

### RCC FABRICATORS, INC.

Div. of Railroad Construction
Company, Inc.
2035 Highway 206 (08088)
**Phone—(609) 859-9350**
Fax—(609) 859-9355
www.rccfabricators.com
Email—info@rccfabricators.com
Pres.—Alfonso Daloisio
V-P.—William Waskiewicz
SIC—3312; *Heavy steel
fabrication*
Employs—25; Estab.—2001
Distrib.—Regional
Privately owned corporation
Parent co.—Railroad Construction
Company, Inc., Paterson, NJ
Phone—(973) 684-0362
See Parent Co. Section for full profile.

### †SAFETY-KLEEN SYSTEMS, INC.

123 Red Lion Rd. (08088)
**Phone—(609) 859-2049**
Fax—(609) 859-1740
www.safety-kleen.com
Email—info@safety-kleen.com
Manager—Keith Wilson
SIC—5093; *Wholesaler of
recycled oils & solvents*
Employs—25
Distrib.—National
Privately owned corporation
Parent co.—Safety-Kleen
Systems, Inc., Richardson, TX
Phone—(972) 265-2000
See Parent Co. Section for full profile.

### WARD SAND & MATERIALS

Div. of James D. Morrissey, Inc.
223 Sooy Place Rd. (08088)
**Phone—(609) 859-2860**
Fax—(609) 859-4294
www.jdm-inc.com
Plt. Mgr.—Bob Catapianco
Scalemaster—Robert Rambo
SIC—1442; *Surface mining of
sand*
Employs—10
Sales—under $500,000
Privately owned corporation
Parent co.—James D. Morrissey,
Inc., Philadelphia, PA
Phone—(215) 333-8000
See Parent Co. Section for full profile.

---

## Vineland

### (Cumberland—S.W.)

### A M K GLASS, INC.

2880 Industrial Way (08360)
**Phone—(856) 692-1488**
National—(800) 407-4527
Fax—(856) 691-5084
www.amkglass.com
Email—sales@amkglass.com

GEOGRAPHICAL

## Vineland—(cont.)

Pres.—Kristine Kousmine
V-P., Sales & Acct. Mgr.—Michael Kousmine
V-P., Mfg.—Marc Kousmine
SIC—3231; NAICS—327215; *Laboratory glassware*
Employs—25; Estab.—1975
Sales—$500,000-$1Mil
10,000 sq ft site, Distrib.—Intl.
Privately owned corporation

### ACE GLASS, INC.

1430 N. West Blvd. (08360)
Mail addr: P.O. Box 688, Vineland (08362)
**Phone—(856) 692-3333**
National—(800) 223-4524
Fax—(800) 543-6752
www.aceglass.com
Email—sales@aceglass.com
Pres., CEO—Richard Kramme
V-P., IT—Jeff Kramme
SIC—3229; 3821; NAICS—327212; *Scientific glassware & laboratory equipment*
Employs—80; Estab.—1936
Distrib.—Intl.
Privately owned corporation

### ADVANCED SAFETY PRODUCTS, INC.

37 S. Valley Ave. (08360)
**Phone—(856) 691-1700**
National—(877) 882-4747
Fax—(856) 494-7893
www.cleangripcleaner.com
Email—info@cleangripcleaner.com
Pres.—Michael Schimmel
SIC—2842; 3069; NAICS—325612; *Bathtub & floor cleaning chemicals & bathtub, permanent & rubber mats; Brand name—CleanGrip Non Slip Cleaner*
Employs—5; Estab.—1993
Sales—$1Mil-$2.5Mil
Distrib.—Intl.
Privately owned sub-S corp.

### AGC ACQUISITION, LLC

3740 N. West Blvd. (08360)
**Phone—(856) 692-4435**
National—(800) 845-0026
Fax—(856) 692-5357
www.andrews-glass.com
Email—mail@andrews-glass.com
V-P., Fin. & Treas.—Peggy McMahon
V-P., Engrg.—Wayne Downs
Dir., Bus. Dev.—Carl Carelli
Cust. Serv. & Hum. Res. Mgr.—Rebecca Puff
SIC—3231; NAICS—327215; *Precision laboratory & industrial glass & quartz products, including precision bore tubing, latex dipping molds, laser components, PID lamps, pressure reaction vessels, filtration & distillation systems & custom engineered & OEM parts; Brand name—Lab Crest; Robu*
Employs—40; Estab.—1992
30,000 sq ft site, Distrib.—Intl.
Privately owned sub-S corp.
ISO rating—9001:2008
AKA: Andrews Glass Co.

### †AIRGAS EAST, INC.

1750 Gallagher Dr. (08360)
**Phone—(856) 692-7734**
National—(866) 718-0685
Fax—(856) 692-1904
www.airgas.com
Email—info@airgas.com
Accts. Mgr.—Joe Gernaloff
Br. Mgr.—Nick Derienzo
SIC—5084; 5085; *Wholesaler of welding equipment & supplies, including gases*
Employs—4; Estab.—1985
Sales—$1Mil-$2.5Mil
Distrib.—Local
Publicly owned corporation
Parent co.—Airgas East, Inc., Salem, NH
Phone—(603) 890-4600
See Parent Co. Section for full profile.

### ALLIED SPECIALTY FOODS, INC.

313 Hickory Pl. (08360)
**Phone—(856) 507-1100**
National—(800) 247-3354
Fax—(856) 507-0540
www.alliedsteaks.com
Email—info@alliedsteaks.com
Pres.—Paul Litten
V-P., Fin.—Darren Buseman
Off. Mgr.—Debby Dunn
SIC—2011; NAICS—311611; *Meat processing & packing*
Employs—80; Estab.—1953
35,000 sq ft site, Distrib.—Intl.
Privately owned corporation

### AL'S HOME MADE CANDIES

1133 Fairmount Ave. (08360)
**Phone—(856) 691-4536**
Pres.—Cathy Sterling
SIC—2064; NAICS—311300; *Candy*
Employs—1; Estab.—1912
Sales—under $500,000
Distrib.—Local
Sole ownership

### †AMERICAN TIME RECORDER

Div. of Time Systems International, Inc.
2661 Brunetta Dr. (08360)
**Phone—(856) 691-7976**
National—(800) 664-7976
Fax—(856) 692-8121
www.amertime.com
Email—support@amertime.com
Sales & Serv. Mgr.—Bryan Presgraves
SIC—5044; 5099; *Distributor of computerized time clocks, biometric hand punch & finger reading systems, proximity badges, bar code & magnetic stripe systems, time cards, ribbons & time card & badge racks; Brand name—Acroprint Time Recorders; Amano Time Recorders; Lathem Time Recorders; Simplex Time Recorders; Widmer Time Stamps; RapidPrint Time Stamp; Icon Time Systems*
Employs—1; Estab.—1967
Sales—under $500,000
Distrib.—National
Privately owned corporation
Parent co.—Time Systems International, Inc., Englewood, NJ
Phone—(973) 472-2202
See Parent Co. Section for full profile.

### ASSEM-PAK, INC.

1649 Castpa Pl. (08360)
**Phone—(856) 692-3355**
Fax—(856) 692-3480
www.assempak.com
Email—dbayer@assempak.com
Pres.—Don Bayer
Cont.—Jack Matty, Jr.
SIC—3826; NAICS—334516; *Analytical instruments for the pharmaceutical industry*
Employs—140; Estab.—2000
40,000 sq ft site, Distrib.—Intl.
Privately owned corporation

### ATCO RUBBER PRODUCTS, INC.

1480 N. West Blvd. (08360)
**Phone—(856) 794-3393**
National—(800) 877-3828
Fax—(856) 794-3397
www.atcoflex.com
Email—info@atcoflex.com
Plt. Mgr.—George Raroha
SIC—3069; *Flexible ducts for residential & commercial heating, ventilating & air conditioning systems*
Employs—50; Estab.—1957
Distrib.—National
Privately owned corporation
Parent co.—ATCO Rubber Products, Inc., Fort Worth, TX
Phone—(817) 595-2894
See Parent Co. Section for full profile.

### †ATLANTIC TIME SYSTEMS

112 N. 8th St. (08360)
Mail addr: P.O. Box 589, Minotola (08341-0589)
**Phone—(856) 692-9594**
National—(800) 669-9590
Fax—(856) 691-7655
www.shop.atlantictimesystems.com
Email—sales@atlantictimesystems.com
Pres., CEO—Norton D. Fern
SIC—5044; *Distributor of PC-based & Internet based time & labor management systems & conventional time clocks & payroll recorders; Brand name—Acroprint; Amano Cincinnati; Isgus; Lathem; Midwest Time; Rapidprint; Time America; Widmer Time Recorder*
Employs—3; Estab.—1984
2,700 sq ft site, Distrib.—Intl.
Privately owned sub-S corp.

### AUNT KITTY'S FOODS, INC.

Div. of Hanover Foods Corp.
270 N. Mill Rd. (08360)
**Phone—(856) 691-2100**
Fax—(856) 696-1295
www.auntkittys.com
Email—janicem@auntkittys.com
Cont.—Richard Kebler
Plt. Mgr.—Randy Horowitz
Prodn. Mgr.—Pete Mazola
Qual. Control Mgr.—Cletus Beckel
Hum. Res. Admn.—Janice Mistretta
SIC—2032; *Canned soup, ravioli, stew & chili*
Employs—130; Estab.—1940
260,000 sq ft site, Distrib.—Intl.
Privately owned corporation
Parent co.—Hanover Foods Corp., Hanover, PA
Phone—(717) 632-6000
See Parent Co. Section for full profile.

### †AUTOPART INTERNATIONAL, INC.

1773 Pine Ave., Unit A (08360)
**Phone—(856) 405-0346**
National—(800) 242-5700
www.autopartintl.com
Email—info@autopartintl.com
Br. Mgr.—Dana Kidd
SIC—5013; *Wholesaler of aftermarket automotive parts*
Employs—10; Estab.—2008
Distrib.—Local
Publicly owned corporation
Parent co.—Autopart International, Inc., Norton, MA
Phone—(781) 784-1111
See Parent Co. Section for full profile.

### BABBITT MFG. CO., INC.

719 E. Park Ave. (08360)
**Phone—(856) 692-3245**
Fax—(856) 692-4403
www.babbitmfg.com
Pres.—Brian Gavigan
V-P.—Steven Gavigan
SIC—3444; *Sheet metal fabrication*
Employs—10; Estab.—1950
Sales—$500,000-$1Mil
Distrib.—Local
Privately owned corporation

### BELLCO GLASS, INC.

340 Edrudo Rd. (08360)
Mail addr: P.O. Box 869, Vineland (08362-0869)
**Phone—(856) 691-1075**
National—(800) 257-7043
Fax—(856) 691-3247
www.bellcoglass.com
Email—cservice@bellcoglass.com
Pres.—Steven J. Harker
CFO & COO—Aaron Sackstein
IT Mgr.—Rob Jannone
SIC—3821; 3221; 3231; NAICS—339111; *Biological glassware & equipment*
Employs—77; Estab.—1936
Sales—$12Mil
100,000 sq ft site, Distrib.—National
Sole ownership

### BIERIG BROS., INC.

3539 Reilly Ct. (08360)
Mail addr: P.O. Box 357, Vineland (08362)
**Phone—(856) 691-9765**
Fax—(856) 692-7869
www.bierigbrothers.com
Email—biebros@aol.com
V-P.—Jacob Bierig
IT & Qual. Assur. Mgr.—Alan Bierig
Hum. Res. Mgr.—David Bierig
Maint. Mgr.—Daniel Bierig
Process Mgr.—Michael Bierig
Bookkeeper—Betty Buglio
SIC—2011; NAICS—311611; *Meat processing & packing*
Employs—30; Estab.—1955
Distrib.—Regional
Privately owned corporation

### BORRELLI STEEL FABRICATORS, LLC

2800 Industrial Way (08360)
**Phone—(856) 690-8850**
Fax—(856) 690-8851
www.borrellisteel.com
Email—vborrelli@borrellisteel.com
Pres.—Vincent J. Borrelli
Cont.—Patty Lipschultz
Opers. Mgr.—Jay Pride
Hum. Res., IT & Off. Mgr.—Julann Borrelli
SIC—3441; 3446; NAICS—332312; *Structural steel fabrication & ironwork*
Employs—25; Estab.—1992
10,500 sq ft site, Distrib.—Regional
Limited Liability Company
DBA: Borrelli Construction

### BOSTON TECHNOLOGIES, INC.

610 E. Landis Ave. (08360)
**Phone—(856) 692-4958**
Fax—(856) 691-8160
www.bostontech.com
Email—info@bostontech.com
Pres.—David E. Boston
GM—John Garavento
Off. Mgr.—Beth Boston
SIC—7372; *Behavioral healthcare software development*
Employs—5; Estab.—1983
Sales—$500,000-$1Mil
Distrib.—National
Privately owned corporation

### BRIDOR USA

Div. of Bridor, Inc.
2260 Industrial Way (08360)
**Phone—(800) 361-1450**
(856) 691-8000
Fax—(856) 691-8814
www.bridor.com
Qual. Control Mgr.—Sergio Perez

## Vineland—(cont.)

SIC—2051; NAICS—311812;
*Bakery products, including
breads, croissants & pastries*
Employs—20; Estab.—2005
Sales—$2.5Mil-$5Mil (est)
Distrib.—Intl.
Privately owned corporation
Parent co.—Bridor, Inc.
Phone—(450) 641-1265
See Parent Co. Section for full profile.

### BUZZ-BEE CABINETRY CO.

589 N. East Ave. (08360)
**Phone—(856) 691-5474**
Fax—(856) 691-5474
Owner—Paul Buzby
SIC—2434; 3083; NAICS—
337110; *Wooden cabinets &
laminating*
Employs—1; Estab.—1988
Sales—under $500,000
Distrib.—Local
Sole ownership

### C D S SHEET METAL, INC.

1200 S. West Blvd., Ste. E (08360)
**Phone—(856) 794-5080**
Fax—(856) 794-5081
Pres.—Nick Emioholtz
Shop Foreman—Chris Matter
SIC—3444; *Sheet metal
fabrication*
Employs—3; Estab.—1990
Sales—under $500,000 (est)
Distrib.—Local
Privately owned corporation

### CERVINIS, INC.

3656 N. Mill Rd. (08360)
**Phone—(856) 691-1744**
National—(800) 488-6057
Fax—(856) 691-5331
www.cervinis.com
Email—info@cervinis.com
Pres.—Dan Cervinis
Hum. Res. Mgr.—Judy Coulter
Sales Rep.—Jim Frye
SIC—3089; 2396; *Fiberglass
automotive products*
Employs—65; Estab.—1989
Sales—$5Mil-$10Mil (est)
Distrib.—Intl.
Privately owned corporation
AKA: Cervinis Auto Designs

### CHEMGLASS, INC.

3800 N. Mill Rd. (08360)
**Phone—(856) 696-0014**
National—(800) 843-1794
Fax—(856) 696-9102
www.chemglass.com
Email—customer-service@
chemglass.com
CEO—Walter Surdam
Pres.—Steve Ware
V-P.—David Surdam
Cont.—Susan Toulson
Dir., Hum. Res.—Jacki Eilenberg
Tech. Svcs. Mgr.—Howard
Hayman
SIC—3231; 3229; NAICS—
327215; *Scientific glassware &
related products*
Employs—200; Estab.—1946
125,000 sq ft site, Distrib.—Intl.
Privately owned sub-S corp.

### †COLONIAL ELECTRIC SUPPLY CO., THE

64 W. Landis Ave. (08360)
**Phone—(856) 462-6300**
Fax—(856) 794-9890
www.colonialelectric.com
Email—michael.farside@
colonialelectric.com
Br. Mgr.—Mike Farside
SIC—5063; *Distributor of electrical
equipment & supplies, including
lighting, wire & cable*
Employs—6; Estab.—2006
Distrib.—Local
Privately owned corporation

Parent co.—Colonial Electric
Supply Co., The, King of Prussia,
PA
Phone—(610) 312-8100
See Parent Co. Section for full profile.

### COMPASS WIRE CLOTH, INC.

1942 N. Mill Rd. (08360)
**Phone—(856) 853-7616**
National—(800) 257-5241
Fax—(856) 853-1387
www.compasswire.com
Email—sales@compasswire.com
Pres.—Michael McGrath
GM—Christopher Toppi
Hum. Res. Mgr.—Eileen Duffy
Accts. Rep.—Angela Maddox
SIC—3357; *Vibratory hooked,
pretension, aggregate, fabric,
vinyl & metal edged screens,
wear parts & related products for
OEM equipment & architectural,
decorative & specialty products*
Employs—48; Estab.—1982
30,000 sq ft site, Distrib.—National
Privately owned corporation
ISO rating—9001:2000

### COMTEC SYSTEMS, INC.

2658 N. West Blvd. (08360)
**Phone—(856) 691-5111**
National—(800) 622-5532
Fax—(856) 696-4666
www.comtecusa.net
Email—solutions@comtecusa.net
Owner—Michael Vertolli
SIC—7373; *Computer &
telephone system integration*
Employs—35; Estab.—1991
Distrib.—Intl.
Privately owned corporation

### CONTE'S PASTA CO., INC.

310 Wheat Rd. (08360)
**Phone—(856) 697-3400**
National—(800) 211-6607
Fax—(856) 697-1757
www.contespasta.com
Email—contespasta@comcast.net
Pres.—Mauro 'Mike' Conte
V-P., Opers.—Judy A. Sabella
Prod. Mgr.—Ronald L. Walters, Jr.
Prod. Mgr.—Claudio Conte
SIC—2098; 2051; NAICS—
311823; *Frozen regular & gluten-
free pizzas, prebaked pizza
shells, pasta, pierogies,
microwave meals, sauces, garlic
bread & knishes*
Employs—35; Estab.—1988
29,000 sq ft site, Distrib.—Intl.
Privately owned corporation

### CROWN CLOTHING CO., INC.

609 Paul St. (08360)
**Phone—(856) 691-0343**
Fax—(856) 691-1771
Email—crowncloco@aol.com
Pres.—Marsha Levin
Plt. Mgr.—Russel Carder
Hum. Res. Mgr.—Wanda Ludlum
SIC—2311; NAICS—315200;
*Military uniforms*
Employs—160; Estab.—1940
30,000 sq ft site, Distrib.—National
Privately owned sub-S corp.

### CUMBERLAND MARBLE & MONUMENT, INC.

2858 S. West Blvd. (08360)
**Phone—(856) 691-3334**
Fax—(856) 691-5997
Email—kim.presgraves@
comcast.net
Pres.—Paul Presgraves, Jr.
V-P.—Dennis Presgraves
Corp. Secy.—Kim Presgraves
Treas.—Paul Presgraves III
SIC—3281; NAICS—327991;
*Graveyard monuments*
Employs—4; Estab.—1990
Sales—under $500,000
Distrib.—Regional
Privately owned corporation

### CUMBERLAND VACUUM PRODUCTS

720 S. West Blvd. (08360)
**Phone—(856) 691-9155**
Fax—(856) 692-8114
www.cumberlandvacuum.com
Email—info@
cumberlandvacuum.com
Pres.—Lloyd Ronchetti
Sales Mgr.—Michael Selby
SIC—2992; NAICS—324191;
*Vacuum pump lubricants*
Employs—5; Estab.—1981
Sales—$1Mil
15,000 sq ft site, Distrib.—Intl.
Privately owned sub-S corp.

### CUSTOM CABLE CRAFTERS, INC.

1830 Gallagher Dr., Ste. 103
(08360)
**Phone—(856) 696-3151**
Fax—(856) 696-5987
www.customcablecrafters.com
Email—cable.man@comcast.net
Pres., CEO—Robert A. Nestor
Fin. Mgr.—Monica Nestor
Manager—Ryan Fitzgerald
SIC—3679; *Cable assemblies*
Employs—10; Estab.—1991
5,000 sq ft site, Distrib.—National
Privately owned corporation

### CUSTOM GRAPHICS, INC.

71 W. Landis Ave. (08360)
**Phone—(856) 691-7858**
Fax—(856) 691-0190
www.customgraphics71.com
Email—office@
customgraphics71.com
Pres.—Jim McMahon
Secy-Treas.—Russ Hall
Off. Mgr.—Mike Arkainno
Cust. Serv. Rep.—Susan Pritchard
SIC—2396; *Textile screen printing*
Employs—19; Estab.—1997
Distrib.—Local
Privately owned corporation

### D ELECTRIC MOTORS, INC.

94 W. Sherman Ave. (08360)
Mail addr: P.O. Box 2367, Vineland
(08362)
**Phone—(856) 696-5959**
Fax—(856) 692-2505
www.delectricmotors.com
Email—devind@
delectricmotors.com
Pres., CFO—Anthony Desiere
V-P., MIS—Daryl Desiere
Secy-Treas., Hum. Res. & IT
Mgr.—Devin Desiere
Off. Mgr.—Jackie Desiere
SIC—3621; NAICS—335312;
*Rebuilt electric motors*
Employs—15; Estab.—1978
35,000 sq ft site, Distrib.—
Regional
Privately owned corporation

### DAILY JOURNAL, THE

Div. of Gannett Co., Inc.
891 E. Oak Rd. (08360)
**Phone—(856) 691-5000**
Fax—(856) 563-5282
www.thedailyjournal.com
Email—djlocalnews@
thedailyjournal.com
Dir., Adv.—Joseph Calchi
Dist. Mgr.—Les Olson
Prepress Mgr.—Sean Friel
SIC—2711; *Newspaper
publishing*
Employs—100; Estab.—1875
Distrib.—Local
Publicly owned corporation
Parent co.—Gannett Co., Inc.,
McLean, VA
Phone—(703) 854-6000
See Parent Co. Section for full profile.

### DDM STEEL CONSTRUCTION

3659 N. Delsea Dr. (08360)
**Phone—(856) 794-9400**
Fax—(856) 794-9500

www.ddm-steel.com
Email—rich@ddmservicesinc.com
Pres.—Rich Meckenfuss
Estimator—Jim O'Connor
Estimator—John Dill, Jr.
SIC—3441; 3499; NAICS—
332312; *Structural steel & metal
fabrication*
Employs—3; Estab.—2010
Company-wide: 10
Sales—$1Mil
Distrib.—Regional
Privately owned corporation

### DECORATION DESIGN SOLUTIONS

1299 W. Forest Grove Rd. (08360)
**Phone—(856) 589-1250**
Fax—(856) 696-0907
Pres.—Steve Wargo
Fin. & Hum. Res. Mgr.—Lisa
Marcasciano
SIC—2759; NAICS—323100;
*Plastic tube screen printing*
Employs—50; Estab.—1967
Distrib.—Intl.
Privately owned corporation

### DEROSSI & SON CO.

411 S. 6th St. (08360)
Mail addr: P.O. Box 1324, Vineland
(08362)
**Phone—(856) 691-0061**
Fax—(856) 691-5342
www.derossi-son.com
Email—gov@derossi-son.com
Pres.—D. Derossi
Dir., Hum. Res. & Pers.—Debbie
Pepper
Bookkeeper—Betty Maurone
SIC—2311; NAICS—315200;
*Military uniforms*
Employs—200; Estab.—1928
Sales—$6Mil-$10Mil
Distrib.—National
Privately owned sub-S corp.

### DESIGNS BY JAMES

892 N. Delsea Dr. (08360)
**Phone—(856) 692-1316**
www.designsbyjames.com
Email—info@designsbyjames.com
Pres.—James Crescenzo
Signmaker—Rocky Vasquez
SIC—2396; 3993; 2395; 2761;
NAICS—323116; *Interior &
exterior signs, screen printing &
embroidery, advertising
specialties & business stationery*
Employs—3
Sales—under $500,000
1,600 sq ft site, Distrib.—Regional

### DUN-RITE SAND & GRAVEL CO., INC.

3765 Mays Landing Rd. (08361)
**Phone—(856) 825-9900**
www.dunritesand.com
Email—rpusloski@dunritesand.com
Sales Mgr.—Ronald S. Pusloski
Site Mgr.—Tony Pizzo
Opers. Mgr.—Stephen M. Mayo
Hum. Res., IT & Proj. Mgr.—
Charles Pinotti
Dispatcher—Charles Lathrop
SIC—1442; 1429; *Sand, gravel &
crushed stone quarrying*
Employs—18
Distrib.—Regional
Privately owned corporation
Parent co.—Dun-Rite Sand &
Gravel Co., Inc., Vineland, NJ
Phone—(856) 692-2520
See Parent Co. Section for full profile.

### DUN-RITE SAND & GRAVEL CO., INC. (H Q)

573 E. Grant Ave. (08360)
**Phone—(856) 692-2520**
Fax—(856) 692-1105
www.dunritesand.com
Email—rpusloski@dunritesand.com
Pres.—Peter Galetto
Off. Mgr.—Fay Platania

GEOGRAPHICAL

## Vineland—(cont.)

SIC—1442; 1429; *Corporate headquarters; sand, gravel & crushed stone quarrying*
Employs—30; Estab.—1963
Distrib.—Regional
Privately owned corporation

**DUTRA SHEET METAL CO.**
1940 S. West Blvd., Ste. E (08360)
**Phone—(856) 692-8058**
Fax—(856) 692-4472
www.dutrasheetmetal.com
Email—dutrasheetmetal@comcast.net
Owner & Fin. Mgr.—D'lee Dutra
CFO—Margaret Dutra
GM—Dan Dutra
SIC—3444; *Sheet metal fabrication*
Employs—11; Estab.—1961
Sales—under $500,000
6,000 sq ft site, Distrib.—Local
Sole ownership

**EATEM FOODS COMPANY**
1829 Gallagher Dr. (08360)
**Phone—(856) 692-1663**
National—(800) 683-2836
Fax—(856) 692-0847
www.eatemfoods.com
Email—sales@eatemfoods.com
Pres., CEO—Ron Savelli
MIS Mgr.—Debbi Green
Hum. Res. Mgr.—Patti Adamson
Plt. Engr.—Chris Burrows
SIC—2034; *Concentrated organic & kosher soup & seasoning bases & savory flavor systems; Brand name—Eatem*
Employs—65; Estab.—1983
Sales—$40Mil-$45Mil
55,200 sq ft site, Distrib.—Intl.
Privately owned corporation

**ECOTEC, INC.**
1944 E. Elmer Rd. (08361)
**Phone—(856) 205-9283**
National—(866) 326-7321
Fax—(856) 205-0884
www.ecotec-inc.com
Email—info@ecotec-inc.com
Pres., R & D Mgr.—Larry Mitchell
Secy., MIS Mgr.—Jana Platanella
Fin. Mgr.—Don Wagner
SIC—3589; NAICS—333319; *Ecologically sensitive water treatment equipment, including humidifier pretreatment systems & physical water treatment devices; Brand name—ECOTEC Physical Water Conditioners; ECOTEC PWC/Nano Humidifier Pre-treatment*
Employs—6; Estab.—1989
Sales—$2Mil
5,200 sq ft site, Distrib.—Intl.
Privately owned corporation

**EVEY ENGINEERING CO., LLC**
158 Weymouth Rd. (08360)
**Phone—(856) 692-6705**
www.eveyvacuumservice.com
Email—sales@eveyvacuumservice.com
Pres.—Donald Callahan
SIC—3563; NAICS—333912; *Rebuilt vacuum pumps, blowers & systems*
Employs—2; Estab.—1963
40,000 sq ft site, Distrib.—National
Privately owned corporation

**EVR SCREEN PRINTING**
217 W. Peach St., Ste. 2 (08360)
**Phone—(856) 794-8118**
Fax—(856) 457-7479
www.evrscreenprinting.com
Owner—Ehren Vonreuter

SIC—2396; *Textile screen printing*
Employs—2; Estab.—1994
Sales—under $500,000 (est)
40,000 sq ft site, Distrib.—Local
Privately owned corporation

**FINNERAN ASSOCS., J. G.**
3600 Reilly Ct. (08360)
**Phone—(856) 696-3605**
National—(800) 552-3696
Fax—(856) 696-9002
www.jgfinneran.com
Email—info@jgfinneran.com
CEO—Jerry Finneran
Pres.—Jo Finneran
Sr. V-P.—Sandy F. Hitchner
V-P., Global Sales & Mktg.—Janet F. Cohen
Sales & Mktg. Mgr., Domestic—Dawn C. Nelson
Prodn. Mgr.—Damon Hitchner
Pur. Mgr.—Steve McKishen
Hum. Res. Mgr.—Michelle Zenchuk
Engrg. & R & D Mgr.—Randy Eccles
Qual. Assur. Mgr.—Sharon Bruno
SIC—3229; 3221; NAICS—327212; *Company headquarters & laboratory glass, vials & accessories*
Employs—95; Estab.—1977
Sales—$10Mil-$25Mil
30,000 sq ft site, Distrib.—National
Privately owned corporation
ISO rating—9001:2008

**FNS CUSTOM WINDOW TREATMENT**
2954 N. West Blvd. (08360)
**Phone—(856) 696-4070**
Email—fandscustomwindows@gmail.com
Ptnr.—Sandy Cerione
Ptnr.—Frank Cerione
SIC—2391; 2591; NAICS—314121; *Custom draperies, blinds & shutters, including design, fabrication & installation*
Employs—3; Estab.—2005
Sales—under $500,000
Distrib.—Local
Sole ownership

**GARDEN STATE HIGHWAY PRODUCTS, INC.**
1740 E. Oak Rd. (08361)
**Phone—(856) 692-7572**
National—(800) 338-5685
Fax—(856) 692-6797
www.gardenstatehwy.com
Email—sales@gardenstatehwy.com
Pres.—Sharon Green
V-P.—Robert Green
Treas.—Margaret Eiselman
Sales Mgr.—Frank Kates
Prodn. Mgr.—Joe McCracken
Mktg. Mgr.—Dawn Kutner
Svcs. Mgr.—Scott Clark
Svcs. Mgr.—Howie Raines
SIC—3993; 5085; *Manufacturer of traffic, street, specialty & overhead signs & distributor of traffic safety products, including installation & certification*
Employs—48; Estab.—1987
26,000 sq ft site, Distrib.—National
Privately owned sub-S corp.

**GENERAL MILLS PROGRESSO**
Div. of General Mills, Inc.
500 W. Elmer Rd. (08360)
**Phone—(856) 691-1565**
National—(800) 200-9377
Fax—(856) 794-1574
www.progressosoup.com
Email—corporate.response@genmills.com
Plt. Mgr.—Becky Crane
Opers. Mgr.—Jon Spear
Hum. Res. Mgr.—Heather Cole
Engr. Mgr.—Curt Howard
Cust. Serv. Mgr.—Adrian Walker
Fin. Mgr.—Kim West

SIC—2033; 2032; NAICS—311421; *Canned soups & meals; Brand name—Progresso; Hamburger Helper*
Employs—475; Estab.—1948
Sales—$25Mil-$100Mil
565,400 sq ft site, Distrib.—National
Publicly owned corporation
AKA: General Mills/Progresso Quality Foods
Parent co.—General Mills, Inc., Minneapolis, MN
Phone—(763) 764-7600
See Parent Co. Section for full profile.

**GERRESHEIMER GLASS, INC.**
91 W. Forest Grove Rd. (08360)
**Phone—(856) 507-5600**
Fax—(856) 794-2162
www.gerresheimer.com
Email—info@gerresheimer.com
Cont.—Bill Miskelly
Mfg. Mgr.—William Luzzo
Plt. Opers. Mgr.—Sean Fitzpatrick
IT Mgr.—George Rears
Acctg. Mgr.—William Miskelly
Hum. Res. Mgr.—Pam Shapiro
Qual. Assur. Mgr.—Stacey Picerno
SIC—3221; 3841; NAICS—327213; *Glass vials & pharmaceutical, biotech, ophthalmic, diagnostic & medical packaging solutions*
Employs—180; Estab.—1949
Sales—$50Mil-$100Mil
Distrib.—Intl.
Privately owned corporation
Parent co.—Gerresheimer Glass, Inc., Vineland, NJ
Phone—(856) 692-3600
See Parent Co. Section for full profile.

**GERRESHEIMER GLASS, INC.**
537 Crystal Ave. *(08360)*
**Phone—(856) 692-3600**
National—(800) 257-7045
Fax—(856) 794-5593
www.gerresheimer.com
Email—info-tubing-us@gerresheimer.com
CFO—Chris Bouffard
Ex. V-P., Tubular Glass Tubing—John McDermott
V-P., Hum. Res.—Susan Kinnon
SIC—3231; 3229; NAICS—327215; *Corporate headquarters & blown glassware, including vials, bottles & labware for pharmaceutical, science, food & cosmetic applications; Brand name—Kimax*
Employs—260; Estab.—1901
Sales—$225Mil
1,400,000 sq ft site, Distrib.—Intl.
Privately owned corporation
ISO rating—9002

**GILLESPIE, INC., PAUL J.**
2565 Brunetta Dr. (08360)
**Phone—(856) 839-0891**
Fax—(856) 839-0893
www.pjgillespieinc.com
Email—paulgillespie@comcast.net
Pres.—Donna Ruberti
Off. Mgr.—Laura Sikking
SIC—3272; *Precast concrete products*
Employs—15; Estab.—1983
Distrib.—Regional
Privately owned corporation

**GLASS DYNAMICS, LLC**
2662 Hance Bridge Rd. (08361)
**Phone—(856) 205-1530**
Fax—(856) 507-1471
www.glassdynamicsllc.com
Email—sales@glassdynamicsllc.com
CEO & Head of Opers.—Kimberlie Lawson
Pres.—Sharon Studstill

SIC—3231; 3221; 3646; 3229; *Custom & precision glass fabrication of industrial lighting fixtures, optical glass components, glass bottles, vials, architectural glass dividers & decorative elements*
Employs—9; Estab.—2005
Sales—$1Mil-$2.5Mil
10,000 sq ft site, Distrib.—National
Limited Liability Company

**GLASTRON, INC.**
Div. of Restek Corp.
510 N. West Blvd. (08360)
Mail addr: P.O. Box 687, Vineland (08362-0687)
**Phone—(856) 692-0500**
National—(877) 692-0501
Fax—(856) 692-0340
www.glastroninc.com
Email—sales@glastroninc.com
Pres.—Bryan Wolcott
Sr. V-P., Opers.—Ed Rohland
Hum. Res. Mgr.—Lillian Fuentes
Fin. Mgr.—Kathy Turner
Pur. Agt.—Sherry Schwenger
SIC—3221; 3229; 3231; NAICS—327213; *Corporate headquarters & specialty graduated laboratory & OEM glassware, including close tolerance seals, specialty coil wrapping, ultrasonic milling, flat, step, centerless & taper grinding & precision drilling*
Employs—65; Estab.—1969
Sales—$5Mil-$10Mil
Distrib.—National
Privately owned corporation
ISO rating—9001:2000
Parent co.—Restek Corp., Bellefonte, PA
Phone—(814) 353-1300
See Parent Co. Section for full profile.

NEW ENTRY
**GNC VENTURE GROUP, INC.**
1639 Percy Ln. (08361)
**Phone—(856) 690-1999**
Fax—(856) 690-1610
www.gncventuregroup.net
Email—gncventuregroup@aol.com
Owner—Jerry Covella
SIC—2721; *Magazine publishing*
Employs—4
Sales—under $500,000 (est)

**GORGO PALLET CO.**
646 S. Delsea Dr. (08360)
**Phone—(856) 692-0303**
www.gorgopallet.com
Email—sales@gorgopallet.com
Pres.—Nick Biagi
SIC—2448; NAICS—321920; *Wooden pallets*
Employs—30
Sales—$2.5Mil-$5Mil (est)
Distrib.—Regional

**GRAPHICOLOR CORP.**
3490 N. Mill Rd. (08360)
**Phone—(856) 691-2507**
National—(800) 552-2507
Fax—(856) 696-3229
www.graphicolorcorp.com
Email—info@graphicolorcorp.com
Pres., Fin., MIS & R & D Mgr.—Robert W. Stenger, Jr.
SIC—2759; NAICS—323100; *Commercial printing*
Employs—20; Estab.—1919
Sales—$2Mil-$2.5Mil
10,000 sq ft site, Distrib.—National
Privately owned corporation

**H.P. MACHINE SHOP, INC.**
415 Oxford St. (08360-2780)
**Phone—(856) 692-1192**
Fax—(856) 692-1445
www.hp-machine.com
Email—sales@hp-machine.com
Pres.—John Petyan

## Vineland—(cont.)

SIC—3599; *Machining of plastics, stainless steel & super alloy component parts, including turned & milled parts for the defense, laboratory & water treatment industries*
Employs—9; Estab.—1966
7,000 sq ft site, Distrib.—National
Privately owned sub-S corp.

### HESS GLASS PRODUCTS
601 N. Orchard Rd. (08360)
**Phone—(856) 691-1432**
Fax—(856) 692-8202
Email—ladyofglass87@yahoo.com
Owner & Pres.—Doris Danna
SIC—3229; 3231; NAICS—327212; *Hospital, laboratory & pharmaceutical glassware*
Employs—1; Estab.—1943
2,600 sq ft site, Distrib.—Local
Sole ownership

### HOWE'S STANDARD PUBLISHING CO., INC.
1980 S. West Blvd. (08360)
**Phone—(856) 691-2000**
Fax—(856) 692-4399
www.standard-publishing.com
Email—info@standard-publishing.com
Pres.—Barry Opromollo
Hum. Res. Mgr.—Nancy Halter
SIC—2752; 2721; 2732; NAICS—323117; *Commercial printing*
Employs—30; Estab.—1892
20,000 sq ft site, Distrib.—National
Privately owned corporation
AKA: Standard Publishing

### INTERNATIONAL GLASS WORK, INC.
723 E. Park Ave., P.O. Box 1015 (08360)
**Phone—(856) 691-5628**
Fax—(856) 691-7410
Owner—Louis Pomales
SIC—3221; NAICS—327215; *Scientific glass test tubes & flasks*
Employs—1; Estab.—1991
Distrib.—Local
Sole ownership

### J.D. MACHINE PARTS, INC.
158 W. Weymouth Rd. (08360)
Mail addr: P.O. Box 639, Newfield (08344-0639)
**Phone—(856) 691-8430**
Fax—(856) 692-9444
www.jdmachineparts.com
Email—sales@jdmachineparts.com
Pres.—Joseph Di Mento
GM—K. Dan Ferus
SIC—3599; *Custom CNC machine parts & fabrication, including electric motor service & repair*
Employs—18; Estab.—1983
26,000 sq ft site, Distrib.—Local
Privately owned sub-S corp.

### JOFFE LUMBER & SUPPLY, INC.
18 Burns Ave. (08360)
Mail addr: P.O. Box 2309, Vineland (08362)
**Phone—(856) 825-9550**
National—(800) 922-0711
Fax—(856) 327-0798
CEO—Sol G. Joffe
Pres.—Michael Bergen
V-P.—Steve Wolf
Off. Mgr.—Connie Scapellato
SIC—2431; 3089; 3442; NAICS—332321; *Wooden & vinyl windows, steel & interior doors, wooden stairs & architectural millwork*
Employs—50; Estab.—1933
125,000 sq ft site, Distrib.—Regional
Privately owned sub-S corp.

### KENNEDY CONCRETE
Div. of Action Supply, Inc.
1969 S. East Ave. (08360)
**Phone—(856) 692-8650**
Fax—(856) 692-6677
www.kennedyconcretenj.com
Email—kennco@icehouse.net
GM—Richard Jacobs
SIC—3273; NAICS—327320; *Ready-mixed concrete*
Employs—30; Estab.—1997
Distrib.—Local
Privately owned corporation
Parent co.—Action Supply, Inc., Ocean View, NJ
Phone—(609) 390-0663
See Parent Co. Section for full profile.

**NEW ENTRY**

### KMS PRINTING & GRAPHICS, INC.
401 N. Brookfield St. (08361)
**Phone—(856) 205-0200**
Fax—(856) 205-0200
Pres.—Kathryn M. Stanger
SIC—2759; *Commercial printing*
Employs—1
Sales—under $500,000 (est)
Distrib.—Local
Privately owned corporation

### LATTIMER USA
3603 N. Mill Rd. (08360)
**Phone—(856) 691-2203**
National—(800) 257-7061
Fax—(856) 691-5509
www.lattimermachining.com
Email—sales@lattimermachining.com
Pres., GM—Steve Abernathy
CFO—Walt Martin
V-P., Sales—Paul Ney
Engrg. Mgr.—Dan McNaul
SIC—3599; *Precision CNC milling & turning, assembly, welding, engineering & turnkey project management services*
Employs—36; Estab.—1977
20,000 sq ft site, Distrib.—Intl.
Privately owned corporation

**NEW ENTRY**

### LAWALL & SON, INC., HARRY J.
3071 E. Chestnut Ave., Ste. C-9 (08361)
**Phone—(856) 691-7764**
Fax—(856) 691-7147
www.lawall.com
Manager—Harry Lawall
SIC—3842; *Orthotics & prosthetics*
Employs—7
Sales—$1Mil-$2.5Mil (est)
Privately owned corporation

### LEAK DETECTION ASSOCIATES, INC.
3003 N. Mill Rd. (08360-1523)
**Phone—(856) 405-6636**
(856) 405-6289
Fax—(856) 213-6124
www.heliumleak.com
Email—jeff@heliumleak.com
CEO—Darrell Morrow
Pres.—Jeff Morrow-Lucas
SIC—3569; *Turnkey helium leak detectors & systems & helium leak-testing services for the pharmaceutical & food industries; Brand name—SIMS 1284+; SIMS 1282+*
Employs—4; Estab.—1993
Sales—$500,000-$1Mil
12,000 sq ft site, Distrib.—Intl.
Privately owned sub-S corp.
AKA: LDA

### LIMPERT BROS., INC.
202 N. West Blvd. (08360)
Mail addr: P.O. Box 1480, Vineland (08362)
**Phone—(856) 691-1353**
National—(800) 691-1353

Fax—(856) 794-8968
www.limpertbrothers.com
Chrm., Pres.—Pearl Giordano
Secy., Off. Mgr.—Ruth Dawson
Pur. Agt.—Jeanna Whittick
SIC—2024; 2064; NAICS—311520; *Ice cream, frozen desserts, bakery fillings & toppings*
Employs—20; Estab.—1897
Distrib.—National
Privately owned corporation

### MARCACCI MEATS, INC.
1853 Vine Rd. (08361)
**Phone—(856) 691-4848**
Fax—(856) 691-2294
Pres.—Mehmet Silpagar
Bookkeeper—Lisa Baldosaro
SIC—2011; NAICS—311611; *Meat packing & processing*
Employs—6; Estab.—1950
Sales—$500,000-$1Mil
Distrib.—Local
Privately owned corporation

### MARTIN, INC., H. S.
1149 Southeast Blvd. (08360)
Mail addr: P.O. Box 661, Vineland (08362-0661)
**Phone—(856) 692-8700**
National—(800) 755-2924
Fax—(856) 692-3805
www.hsmartin.com
Email—info@hsmartin.com
Pres.—Nontas Kontes
V-P.—John L. Treires
Secy-Treas., GM—James E. Kontes
SIC—3231; NAICS—327215; *Laboratory glass, reactors, distillation systems, flasks, condensers, columns, bell jars, column packing, laboratory glassware, glass blowing, OEM products & custom manufacturing; Brand name—Glas Col; Huber; Julabo; Arrow Mixers; Welch Vacuum Products*
Employs—20; Estab.—1934
Sales—$2Mil
17,500 sq ft site, Distrib.—Intl.
Privately owned corporation

### N D S TECHNOLOGIES, INC.
891 E. Oak Rd. (08360)
**Phone—(856) 691-0330**
National—(800) 637-0377
Fax—(856) 696-3533
www.ndsglass.com
Email—nneill@ndsglass.com
Pres., R & D Mgr.—Norman A. Neill
CFO, Hum. Res. & MIS Mgr.—Robert Degrazia
Mktg. Mgr.—Matt Hemple
Off. Mgr.—Josie Neill
Prodn. Planner—Margaret Mays
SIC—3229; NAICS—327212; *Laboratory, filtration & specialty glassware, including chromatography columns, developing tanks, sprayers & mobile phase reservoirs*
Employs—40; Estab.—1990
8,000 sq ft site, Distrib.—Intl.
Privately owned corporation

### N. B. & SONS, LLC
402 E. Wheat Rd. (08360)
**Phone—(856) 692-6191**
Fax—(856) 692-0299
www.nbandsons.com
Email—annettewalters@nbandsons.com
Pres.—Maria Berezin
Off. Mgr.—Annette Berezin Walters
Prod. Mgr.—Nikolai Berezin

SIC—3599; *Precision machined parts, including nozzles & related accessories for the injection blow molding industry*
Employs—6; Estab.—1984
Sales—$400,000
2,400 sq ft site, Distrib.—Intl.
Limited Liability Company

### OMNI BAKING CO.
2621 Freddy Ln. (08360)
**Phone—(856) 205-1485**
Fax—(856) 205-1735
www.omnibaking.com
Hum. Res. Mgr.—Elenore Mesiano
SIC—2051; NAICS—311812; *Contract baking of frozen Italian rolls*
Employs—250; Estab.—1996
150,000 sq ft site, Distrib.—National
Privately owned partnership

### PAFA TRAINING CENTER, INC.
1301 W. Forest Grove Rd., Bldg. 3-C (08360)
**Phone—(856) 696-1414**
(856) 696-1661
Fax—(856) 691-6560
www.pafacom.org
Email—pafa@comcast.net
Pres., CEO, COO—Michelle Vernamonti
SIC—3999; *Contract assembly*
Employs—70; Estab.—1994
Sales—$5Mil-$10Mil
Distrib.—Local
Privately owned corporation

### PARRISH SIGN CO., INC.
2242 S. Delsea Dr. (08360)
**Phone—(856) 696-4040**
National—(800) 321-7118
Fax—(856) 692-0606
www.parrishsign.com
Email—sales@parrishsign.com
Pres.—Charles Parrish
GM—Craig Parrish
Cust. Serv. Rep.—Tricia Solomon
SIC—3993; 2759; 2396; 3089; NAICS—323100; *Full color, digitally printed, lighted, real estate & contractor signs, banners & plastic, metal, foam & channel letters & neon & LED truck lettering*
Employs—9; Estab.—1959
Sales—$500,000-$1Mil
30,000 sq ft site, Distrib.—National
Privately owned corporation

### PHILCORR, LLC
2317 Almond Rd. (08360)
**Phone—(856) 205-0557**
Fax—(856) 205-0539
Email—philcorr@philcorr.com
Cont.—Mark Thuer
GM & Plt. Mgr.—Ken Mello
IT Mgr.—Christina Narbut
Hum. Res. Mgr.—Brenda McDermott
Cust. Serv. & Shpg. Mgr.—Craig Clauser
Acctg. Rep.—Anne Prickette
SIC—2679; NAICS—322200; *Corrugated sheets*
Employs—70; Estab.—1995
75,000 sq ft site, Distrib.—Regional
Limited Liability Company

### PHOENIX BUSINESS FORMS, INC.
2231 N. East Blvd. (08360)
**Phone—(856) 691-2266**
Fax—(856) 691-1532
www.phoenixforms.com
Email—phnxfrms@comcast.net
Pres.—Joanne Buckalew
Acct. Exec.—Brenda Carpani

**GEOGRAPHICAL**

## Vineland—(cont.)

SIC—2759; 2791; NAICS—
323122; *Commercial printing,
typesetting, promotional
products & selective gifts
programs*
Employs—5; Estab.—1992
Sales—$500,000-$1Mil
5,500 sq ft site, Distrib.—Regional
Privately owned corporation

**PIERSON MATERIALS CORP., R. E.**
Div. of Pierson Construction Co.,
Inc., R. E.
184 W. Sherman Ave. (08360)
**Phone—(856) 696-2901**
Fax—(856) 696-0185
www.repiersongroup.com
Email—info@repdemo.com
Plt. Mgr.—Geoff Warren, Jr.
Dispatcher—Tammy Barton
SIC—3273; NAICS—327320;
*Ready-mixed concrete*
Employs—10; Estab.—2004
Distrib.—Local
Privately owned corporation
Parent co.—Pierson Construction
Co., Inc., R. E., Pilesgrove, NJ
Phone—(856) 769-8244
See Parent Co. Section for full profile.

**PRECISION ELECTRONIC GLASS,
INC.**
1013 Hendee Rd. *(08360-3295)*
**Phone—(856) 691-2234**
(800) 982-4734
Fax—(856) 691-3090
www.pegglass.com
Email—info@pegglass.com
Pres.—Philip M. Rossi
Cont.—Albert Karwowski
Dir., Sales—Ron Mazzuca
R & D Mgr.—Vince Giacomelli
Prodn. Control Mgr.—Max Kirsch
Qual. Mgr.—Robert Wilhelm
Engr.—Steve Farside
SIC—3231; NAICS—327215;
*Precision custom glass & quartz
components; Brand name—Best
Bore*
Employs—75; Estab.—1962
Sales—$8Mil
53,000 sq ft site, Distrib.—Intl.
Privately owned sub-S corp.
ISO rating—9001:2008
AKA: PEG

**PYROTECHNIC INDUSTRIES, INC.**
Div. of Pyrotecnico
1640 Garden Rd. (08360)
**Phone—(856) 697-1023**
Fax—(856) 697-9557
www.vinelandfireworks.com
Email—mbriggs@pyrotecnico.com
Off. Mgr.—Raquel Flowers
SIC—2892; NAICS—325920;
*Fireworks*
Employs—6; Estab.—1910
Sales—$500,000-$1Mil
Distrib.—National
Privately owned corporation
DBA: Pyrotecnico
Parent co.—Pyrotecnico, New
Castle, PA
Phone—(724) 652-9555
See Parent Co. Section for full profile.

**QUALITY PRINTING**
1181 E. Landis Ave., Ste. 3
(08360)
**Phone—(856) 691-7577**
Fax—(856) 691-8164
www.qualityprintingnj.com
Email—info@qualityprintingnj.com
Ptnr.—Jerry Dondero
Ptnr.—Philip DeRosa

SIC—2759; 3993; NAICS—
323100; *Printing, advertising
specialty products & wearables,
signs, banners & logo design*
Employs—2; Estab.—1975
Sales—under $500,000
1,000 sq ft site, Distrib.—National
Privately owned partnership

**RADCO ENTERPRISES, INC.**
734 Oxford St. (08360)
**Phone—(856) 691-3125**
Email—rvl99@yahoo.com
Pres.—Ralph Laragione
SIC—3599; *General machining
job shop*
Employs—1; Estab.—1977
Sales—under $500,000
Distrib.—Local
Sole ownership

**RAZ PERFORMANCE MACHINE**
247 Harding Hwy. (08360)
**Phone—(856) 697-4275**
Fax—(856) 697-4090
www.razperformance.com
Email—rayscan1@comcast.net
Ptnr.—Raymond Zieger
SIC—3714; 3599; *Rebuilt
automotive motors & machining
job shop*
Employs—2; Estab.—2004
Sales—under $500,000
Distrib.—Local
Sole ownership

**RFC CONTAINER CO.**
2066 S. East Ave. (08360)
**Phone—(856) 692-0404**
Fax—(856) 692-2085
www.rfccontainer.com
Email—boxes@rfccontainer.com
Pres.—Mario Russo
V.-P.—Thomas Russo
SIC—2653; NAICS—322211; *Wax-
treated corrugated multicolor &
display work containers &
cardboard boxes*
Employs—65; Estab.—1976
100,000 sq ft site, Distrib.—
National
Privately owned sub-S corp.

**RICH PRODUCTS**
Div. of Rich Products Corp.
1910 Gallagher Dr. (08360)
**Phone—(856) 696-5600**
National—(800) 654-9731
Fax—(716) 634-4222
www.rich.com
Email—mlinnehan@rich.com
Cont.—MaryJo Nailor
GM & Plt. Mgr.—Adebisi Campbell
Plt. Mgr.—Anthony Battle
Hum. Res. Mgr.—Margaret
Linnehan
Qual. Assur. Mgr.—Judy Perry
SIC—2038; NAICS—311412;
*Frozen Italian meatballs; Brand
name—Battistoni*
Employs—110; Estab.—1966
110,000 sq ft site, Distrib.—Intl.
Privately owned corporation
Parent co.—Rich Products Corp.,
Buffalo, NY
Phone—(716) 878-8000
See Parent Co. Section for full profile.

**RICHLAND GLASS CO., INC.**
1640 S. West Blvd. (08360)
**Phone—(856) 691-1697**
National—(800) 755-3937
Fax—(856) 691-4525
www.richlandglass.com
Email—sales@richlandglass.com
Pres., GM—Jack Carson
Sales Mgr.—Bart Norbury
Sales Mgr.—Jennifer Dolson
Off. Mgr.—Kim Guinan
Cust. Serv. Mgr.—Tina Parent

SIC—3231; 3221; NAICS—
327215; *Custom & standard
glass products, including glass
cutting components, tubular
glass vials & bore glass tubing
for the electronic, lighting,
industrial, cosmetic, scientific &
diagnostic industries*
Employs—100; Estab.—1960
100,000 sq ft site, Distrib.—Intl.
Privately owned sub-S corp.

**RUDCO PRODUCTS, INC.**
114 E. Oak Rd. (08360)
Mail addr:. P.O. Box 705, Vineland
(08362-0705)
**Phone—(856) 691-0800**
National—(800) 828-2234
Fax—(856) 696-0084
www.rudco.com
Email—sales@rudco.com
Pres.—Bob Rudolph
V.-P., Sales—Mike Avis
V.-P.—Mark Rudolph
Cont. & Off. Mgr.—Joseph
Traviello
Hum. Res. Mgr.—Debbie Berns
SIC—3312; *Corporate
headquarters & hot-rolled steel
containers*
Employs—60; Estab.—1976
Sales—$10Mil-$25Mil
150,000 sq ft site, Distrib.—
National
Sole ownership

**R-WAY TOOLING & METAL WORKS**
224 S. Lincoln Ave. (08361)
**Phone—(856) 692-2218**
Fax—(856) 692-5952
www.rwaytooling.com
Email—office@rwaytooling.com
Cont.—Scott Sikora
SIC—3599; 3499; *Steel fabrication
& general machining job shop*
Employs—8; Estab.—1987
Sales—under $500,000
Distrib.—Local
Limited Liability Company

**SEREN I.P.S., INC.**
1670 Gallagher Dr. (08360)
**Phone—(856) 205-1131**
Fax—(856) 205-1141
www.serenips.com
Email—info@serenips.com
Pres.—Lawrence Hooper
Sales & Mktg. Mgr.—Mike Lagarde
Prodn. Mgr.—Carl Keller
Opers. Mgr.—Ed Dunn
Acctg. & Hum. Res. Mgr.—
Kathleen Coe
Cust. Serv. Mgr.—Tom Bouillon
SIC—3621; NAICS—335312;
*Radio frequency power supplies*
Employs—45; Estab.—1992
Distrib.—Intl.
Privately owned corporation

**SIEMENS INDUSTRY, INC., WATER
TECHNOLOGIES**
Div. of Evoqua Water Technologies
1901 W. Garden Rd. (08360)
**Phone—(856) 507-9000**
Fax—(856) 507-9343
www.siemens.com/water
Email—information.water@
siemens.com
V.-P., GM—Guy Chadwell
Hum. Res. Mgr.—Tracy Moore
SIC—3589; NAICS—333319;
*Water treatment equipment*
Employs—180; Estab.—1997
Sales—$25Mil-$100Mil
Distrib.—Local
Publicly owned corporation
Parent co.—Evoqua Water
Technologies, Alpharetta, GA
Phone—(978) 614-7111
See Parent Co. Section for full profile.

**SIR SPEEDY PRINTING**
22 W. Landis Ave., Ste. Q (08360)
**Phone—(856) 691-0741**
National—(888) 696-3089
Fax—(856) 691-4655
www.sirspeedy.com/vineland
Email—sirspeedyvineland@
gmail.com
GM & Cust. Serv. Mgr.—Allison
Trovarelli
SIC—2759; 2752; NAICS—
323121; *Instant, commercial,
high-speed color & instant,
large-format & poster printing,
binding, graphic artwork &
mailing, shredding, promotional
& marketing services*
Employs—9; Estab.—1980
Sales—$500,000-$1Mil
3,000 sq ft site, Distrib.—National
Sole ownership

**SMITH STEEL RULE DIE, MICHAEL**
2479 S. Main Rd. (08360)
**Phone—(856) 692-5510**
Fax—(856) 692-8152
Owner—Michael Smith
SIC—3544; NAICS—333500;
*Steel rule dies*
Employs—1; Estab.—1968
Sales—under $500,000
Distrib.—Regional
Sole ownership

**SMITH'S CONCRETE PRODUCTS**
3504 S. West Blvd. (08360)
**Phone—(856) 696-3102**
www.smithsconcreteproducts.com
Owner, Sales & Mktg. Mgr.—
Richard S. Smith
SIC—3272; *Concrete stepping
stones*
Employs—1; Estab.—1983
Sales—under $50,000
Distrib.—Local
Sole ownership

**SOUTH JERSEY ICE & COLD
STORAGE LLC**
544 E. Pear St. (08360)
**Phone—(856) 692-3990**
Fax—(856) 692-3992
Email—vineland-ice@verizon.net
Member—Mark DiMeo
SIC—2097; NAICS—312113;
*Block ice, bagged ice & cold
storage*
Employs—6; Estab.—1998
Sales—$500,000-$1Mil
50,000 sq ft site, Distrib.—Local
Limited Liability Company

**SOUTH JERSEY PRECISION TOOL &
MOLD, INC.**
4375 S. Lincoln Ave. (08361-7757)
**Phone—(856) 327-0500**
Fax—(856) 327-9442
www.southjerseyprecision.com
Email—sales@
southjerseyprecision.com
Pres.—Victor Rone
GM & Plt. Mgr.—Wayne Reeves
Off. Mgr.—Bernadette Bundy
SIC—3544; NAICS—333500;
*Plastic injection molds*
Employs—16; Estab.—1992
Sales—$500,000-$1Mil
9,000 sq ft site, Distrib.—National
Privately owned sub-S corp.

**†SOUTH JERSEY WELDING SUPPLY
CO.**
94 W. Forest Grove Rd. (08360)
**Phone—(856) 691-9659**
Fax—(856) 696-1007
www.sjwelding.com
Email—sales@sjwelding.com
Owner—Robert Thorton, Jr.

## Vineland—(cont.)

SIC—5084; 5085; 5169;
*Distributor of welding equipment & supplies, including gases*
Employs—15; Estab.—1951
Distrib.—Local
Sole ownership
Parent co.—South Jersey Welding Supply Co., Maple Shade, NJ
Phone—(856) 778-4440
See Parent Co. Section for full profile.

**†SOUTH JERSEY WIPING CLOTH**

314 Rosewood Ave. (08360)
Mail addr: P.O. Box 929, Vineland (08362-0929)
**Phone—(856) 696-0129**
National—(800) 335-7247
Fax—(856) 696-5052
Email—sjwipingcloths@comcast.net
Owner—Dennis Koons
SIC—5199; *Distributor of wiping cloths*
Employs—1; Estab.—1976
Sales—under $500,000
Distrib.—Local
Privately owned corporation

**SOUTHERN NEW JERSEY STEEL, INC**

2591 N. East Blvd. (08360)
**Phone—(856) 696-1612**
Fax—(856) 696-9508
www.snjs.org
Email—steel@snjs.org
Pres.—Hugh McCaffrey
Secy-Treas.—Sue Dods
Hum. Res. & Risk Mgr.—Tracey Atkinson
Pur. Agt.—Tom Maccarone
SIC—3441; NAICS—332312;
*Structural steel fabrication*
Employs—35; Estab.—1991
Sales—$13Mil
24,000 sq ft site, Distrib.—Regional
Privately owned corporation

**TJK MACHINE, LLC**

870 E. Elmer Rd. (08360)
**Phone—(856) 691-7811**
Fax—(856) 691-7255
Email—tjkmachine@comcast.net
Owner—Nancy Parkin
SIC—3599; *General machining job shop*
Employs—4; Estab.—2003
Sales—under $500,000
Distrib.—Intl.
Limited Liability Company

**TOWNSEND FARMS, INC.**

3501 S. East Blvd. (08360)
**Phone—(856) 825-5240**
Fax—(856) 825-8789
www.townsendfarms.com
Email—marilyn@townsendfarms.com
Opers. Mgr.—David Rodigan
SIC—2037; 3089; *Individually quick-frozen berry processing & packaging*
Employs—100; Estab.—1906
Sales—$11Mil-$25Mil
Distrib.—Regional
Privately owned corporation
Parent co.—Townsend Farms, Inc., Fairview, OR
Phone—(503) 666-1780
See Parent Co. Section for full profile.

**TRANSWEB, LLC**

1473 W. Forest Grove Rd. (08360)
**Phone—(856) 205-1313**
Fax—(856) 205-1333
V.-P.—Kumar Ogale
Pur. Agt.—Anisa Tull
SIC—2297; NAICS—313230;
*Nonwoven filter materials*
Employs—50; Estab.—1997
Sales—$10Mil-$25Mil (est)
Distrib.—Intl.
Limited Liability Company

**TUCKAHOE MFG.**

327 Tuckahoe Rd. (08360)
**Phone—(856) 696-4100**
National—(800) 220-3368
Fax—(877) 253-3908
Owner—John Tombleson
SIC—3089; *Vinyl strip doors & strip material*
Employs—6; Estab.—1988
Sales—under $500,000
1,940 sq ft site, Distrib.—National
Privately owned corporation

**†UNITED ELECTRIC SUPPLY CO.**

1150 W. Garden Rd. (08360)
**Phone—(856) 691-6668**
National—(800) 322-8196
Fax—(856) 691-6699
www.unitedelectric.com
Email—jpetka@unitedelectric.com
Br. Mgr.—Jim Petka
SIC—5063; *Wholesaler of electrical supplies, including switches, wire & cable*
Employs—7
Distrib.—Regional
Privately owned corporation
Parent co.—United Electric Supply Co., New Castle, DE
Phone—(800) 322-3374
See Parent Co. Section for full profile.

**UNIVERSAL MOLD & TOOL, INC.**

1200 S. West Blvd., Bldg. 4 (08360)
**Phone—(856) 563-0488**
www.universalmoldandtool.com
Ptnr., GM, Hum. Res., IT & Plt. Mgr.—David Rainear
Ptnr.—Mike Mitros
SIC—3544; NAICS—333500;
*Molds & tooling*
Employs—18; Estab.—1999
Distrib.—Intl.
Privately owned corporation

**URBAN SIGN & CRANE, INC.**

527 E. Chestnut Ave., P.O. Box 640 (08360)
**Phone—(856) 691-8388**
Fax—(856) 692-8688
www.urbansigncompany.com
Email—sdavis@urbansigncompany.com
Pres.—Seth Davis
Bookkeeper—Taryn Wisneski
SIC—3993; *Interior & exterior signs*
Employs—12; Estab.—2003
30,000 sq ft site, Distrib.—Local
Privately owned corporation

**V M GLASS CO.**

3231 N. Mill Rd. (08360)
**Phone—(856) 794-9333**
(856) 794-3479
National—(800) 400-6625
Fax—(856) 794-9695
www.vmglass.com
Email—vmglass1@aol.com
Pres., Sales Mgr.—Michael Greico
Fin. & Off. Mgr.—Debbie S. Herrera
SIC—3231; NAICS—327215;
*Scientific glassware*
Employs—9; Estab.—1987
Sales—$500,000-$1Mil
5,700 sq ft site, Distrib.—Intl.
Privately owned corporation

**VERTOL MACHINE**

15 Burns Ave. (08360)
**Phone—(856) 327-2489**
Fax—(856) 327-2504
Owner—James Vertolli
SIC—3599; *General machining of custom & contract industrial products*
Employs—1; Estab.—1975
Sales—under $500,000
Distrib.—Regional
Sole ownership

**VINELAND PACKAGING CORP.**

3602 N. Mill Rd. (08360)
**Phone—(856) 794-3300**
Fax—(856) 794-2668
www.vpcbox.com
Email—service@vpcbox.com
Pres.—Joe D'alessandro
Sales Mgr.—Michael D'alessandro
SIC—2653; NAICS—322211;
*Corrugated & solid fiber packaging cartons, partitions, inserts, pads & liners & bakery circles, including rotary & flatbed die cutting, in-line printing & gluing*
Employs—35; Estab.—1994
Distrib.—Regional
Privately owned sub-S corp.

**VINELAND SYRUP, INC.**

723 Southeast Blvd. (08360)
Mail addr: P.O. Box 1326, Vineland (08362-1326)
**Phone—(856) 691-5772**
National—(800) 642-9124
Fax—(856) 691-0359
www.vinelandsyrup.com
Email—info@vinelandsyrup.com
Pres.—Mel Kornbluh
GM & Plt. Mgr.—David Myers
Off. Mgr.—Traci Mayhew
Bookkeeper—Brenda Montana
SIC—2087; NAICS—311900;
*Soda syrups*
Employs—35; Estab.—1963
Sales—$2.6Mil-$5Mil
Distrib.—Regional
Privately owned corporation

**†WEINSTEIN SUPPLY CO.**

Div. of Hajoca Corp.
4019 S. Main Rd. (08360)
**Phone—(856) 825-1460**
Fax—(856) 825-4410
www.hajoca.com
Email—prf413@hajoca.com
Dir., Hum. Res.—Mary Melson
Br. Mgr.—Joe Breslin
Sales Rep., Inside—Dan Stellwag
Sales Rep., Inside—Mark Love
SIC—5074; *Wholesaler of plumbing & heating equipment & supplies; Brand name—Mainline; Luxart; Moen; Bradford White; Allied Air; Aker; Gerber; Kohler; Sterling; Viega; Wardflex; TracPipe; Myers*
Employs—4; Estab.—1975
Sales—$3Mil-$5Mil
12,000 sq ft site, Distrib.—Local
Privately owned corporation
Parent co.—Hajoca Corp., Ardmore, PA
Phone—(610) 649-1430
See Parent Co. Section for full profile.

**WILMAD-LABGLASS**

Div. of SP Industries, Inc.
1172 N. West Blvd. (08360)
Mail addr: P.O. Box 610, Vineland (08362)
**Phone—(856) 691-3200**
National—(800) 220-5171
Fax—(856) 691-6206
www.wilmad-labglass.com
Email—cs@wilmad-labglass.com
Dir., Sales & Mktg.—Doug Grady
Dir., Opers.—Don Power
Dir., Engrg.—Dave Cross
Prod. Mgr.—Miao Wang
SIC—3229; 3231; 3821; NAICS—327212; *Divisional headquarters & precision engineered scientific & laboratory glassware & equipment, including NMR & EPR sample tubes & accessories, condensers, adapters, flasks & filtration systems; Brand name—Wilmad; LabGlass; Benchmark; IKA; Caframo; Julabo; Corning; Glas-Col; Welch; Gardner/Denver*
Employs—133; Estab.—1951
60,000 sq ft site, Distrib.—Intl.
Privately owned corporation
ISO rating—9001:2008
AKA: SP Industries, Wilmad-LabGlass Div.
Parent co.—SP Industries, Inc., Warminster, PA
Phone—(215) 672-7800
See Parent Co. Section for full profile.

**†ZUCCA, INC., L. J.**

760 S. Delsea Dr., P.O. Box 1447 (08362)
**Phone—(856) 692-7425**
National—(800) 552-2639
Fax—(856) 696-7112
www.ljzucca.com
Pres.—Louis Zucca, Jr.
V.-P.—Tom Zucca
Treas.—Scott Zucca
SIC—5194; *Corporate headquarters & wholesaler of cigars & cigarettes*
Employs—70; Estab.—1947
Privately owned corporation

## Voorhees

(Camden—S.W.)

**A B JERSEY TRAILER CORP.**

100 Kresson Gibbsboro Rd. (08043)
**Phone—(856) 784-7766**
Fax—(856) 784-7768
Secy-Treas.—Christine Barnabie
SIC—3715; NAICS—336212;
*Flatbed trailers*
Employs—1; Estab.—1968
Distrib.—Local
Sole ownership

**AMERICAN WATER WORKS CO., INC. (H Q)**

1025 Laurel Oak Rd. (08043)
**Phone—(856) 346-8200**
Fax—(856) 309-4890
www.amwater.com
Email—maureen.duffy@amwater.com
Pres., CEO—Susan Story
Sr. V.-P., CFO—Linda Sullivan
V.-P., Ext. Comms.—Maureen Duffy
Dir., Bus. Dev.—David Marino
Dir., Comms. & Ext. Affs.—Peter A. Eschbach
SIC—3589; NAICS—333319;
*Corporate headquarters; wastewater treatment equipment & services*
Employs—300; Estab.—1886
Statewide: 1,600; Company-wide: 7,000
Sales—$50Mil-$100Mil (est)
Distrib.—National
Publicly owned corporation

**BEAUTICRAFT SLIPCOVER CO.**

9 Wynnewood Dr. (08043)
**Phone—(215) 625-7979**
Email—jdav1943@yahoo.com
Owner & V.-P.—S. Davidson
SIC—3089; *Plastic & fabric slipcovers & window treatments*
Employs—8; Estab.—1955
Sales—$500,000-$1Mil
2,500 sq ft site, Distrib.—Local
Sole ownership
AKA: Phillips Ostroff

GEOGRAPHICAL

## Voorhees—(cont.)

**BIOAIR SOLUTIONS, LLC**
110 Kresson-Gibbsboro Rd., Ste. 303 (08043)
**Phone—(856) 258-6969**
Fax—(856) 258-6975
www.bioairsolutions.com
Email—info@bioairsolutions.com
Owner—Louis D. Leroux
Sales Mgr.—Christopher West
SIC—3564; *Biological odor control filter systems; Brand name—ecofilter™; ecopure™; ecocarb™*
Employs—35; Estab.—2008
Sales—$500,000-$1Mil
Distrib.—Intl.
Limited Liability Company

**BRIDGEVIEW INDUSTRIAL FINISHERS, INC.**
241 Terrace Blvd. *(08043)*
**Phone—(856) 768-3624**
Fax—(856) 768-2218
www.bvfinishers.com
Email—sales@bvfinishers.com
Pres.—Nancy Wood
V-P.—Ron Wood
Off. Mgr.—Donna Brady
SIC—3471; 3479; NAICS—332813; *Metal finishing, powder coating & silk screening*
Employs—9; Estab.—1963
Sales—$500,000-$1Mil
12,000 sq ft site, Distrib.—Local
Privately owned corporation

**DELCREST SIGN CO., INC.**
1202 Haddonfield-Berlin Rd., Ste. 1 (08043)
**Phone—(856) 768-5552**
Fax—(856) 767-3257
www.delcrestsign.com
Email—sales@delcrestsign.com
Owner—Willy Johnson
SIC—3993; 3089; *Vinyl & neon signs*
Employs—4; Estab.—1978
Distrib.—National
Privately owned corporation

NEW ENTRY
**FORMS PLUS MORE, LLC**
6 Harwood Dr. (08043)
**Phone—(856) 753-8886**
Fax—(856) 753-8788
www.formsplusmorenj.com
Email—sarah@formsplusmorenj.com
Owner—Susan Love
Opers. Mgr.—Sarah Love
SIC—2759; *Commercial printing & graphic services & promotional item screen printing, including mugs & pens*
Employs—4; Estab.—1994
Sales—under $500,000
Distrib.—Local
Limited Liability Company

**†HANGER PROSTHETICS & ORTHOTICS**
Div. of Hanger, Inc.
201 White Horse Rd. E. (08043)
**Phone—(856) 309-0709**
Fax—(856) 309-2499
www.hanger.com
Email—info@hanger.com
Br. Mgr.—Dennise Dehaven
Off. Admn.—Marga Engler
SIC—5047; *Distributor of prosthetics & orthopedic braces & supports*
Employs—3; Estab.—2000
Distrib.—National
Publicly owned corporation
Parent co.—Hanger, Inc., Austin, TX
Phone—(512) 777-3800
See Parent Co. Section for full profile.

**INTERSTATE SALES NEW OF JERSEY, LLC**
1226 Haddonfield-Berlin Rd., Unit C-2 (08043)
Mail addr: P.O. Box 822, Cherry Hill (08003-0822)
**Phone—(856) 433-8692**
(609) 320-3410
Fax—(856) 433-8991
www.issnj.net
Email—info@issnj.net
Ptnr. & Pres.—Steven Osder
Ptnr.—Nancy Denenberg
SIC—2035; 2034; 2099; *Private label seasonings, spices, mustards, oils & vinegars for food manufacturers, foodservice distributors & retailers; Brand name—Colby Farms*
Employs—10; Estab.—1993
Sales—$2.5Mil-$5Mil
10,000 sq ft site, Distrib.—Regional
Limited Liability Company
AKA: Colby Farms

**LINK BURNS MFG. CO., INC.**
253 American Way (08043)
**Phone—(856) 429-6844**
Fax—(856) 429-3734
www.linkburns.com
Email—linkburns@aol.com
Pres.—Dan Zoltowski
GM—Bob Knorr
SIC—3444; *Sheet metal fabrication*
Employs—20; Estab.—1956
Sales—$500,000-$1Mil
23,000 sq ft site, Distrib.—National
Privately owned corporation

**MITCHELL, INC., DAVID**
210 Park Dr. (08043)
**Phone—(856) 429-2610**
Fax—(856) 429-8058
V-P.—Ken Bond
SIC—2015; *Poultry processing*
Employs—15; Estab.—1979
Sales—$2.6Mil-$5Mil
Distrib.—Local
Privately owned corporation

**MOBILE POWER INTERNATIONAL, LLC**
1010 Old Egg Harbor Rd. (08043)
**Phone—(856) 784-3195**
Fax—(856) 784-3196
www.mobilepowerintl.com
Email—sales@mobilepowerintl.com
Owner—Anthony F. Amorosia
Dir., Pur. & Sales Mgr.—Andy Brazier
SIC—3674; 3621; 3589; 3561; *Contract manufacturing & metal fabrication of mobile solar-powered generators, water purification systems & agricultural water pumping systems*
Employs—12; Estab.—2008
Sales—$2Mil-$5Mil
85,000 sq ft site, Distrib.—Intl.
Limited Liability Company

**MOMMA'S HOME MADE, LLC**
1225 Haddonfield Berlin Rd., Southgate Plz., Ste. 2 (08043)
**Phone—(856) 753-3250**
www.mommashomemade.com
Email—daisysmith1942@gmail.com
Ptnr.—Daisy Smith
Ptnr.—Jaconda Bell
SIC—2033; 2099; *Gourmet, 50% less sugar added & no sugar/no butter applesauce, apple carrot cake in-a-jar, apple garlic hot wing sauce & sweet potato syrup; Brand name—Momma's Home Made*
Employs—2; Estab.—2013
Sales—$500,000-$1Mil
1,200 sq ft site, Distrib.—Regional
Limited Liability Company

**ORTHOLOGIX, LLC**
2301 E. Evesham Rd., Ste. 303 (08043)
**Phone—(856) 651-1510**
Fax—(215) 244-4114
www.orthologix.com
Principal—Eileen Levis
SIC—3842; *Orthotics & prosthetics*
Employs—25
Sales—$5Mil-$10Mil (est)
Distrib.—Regional
Limited Liability Company

**PENN JERSEY PRESS**
P.O. Box 1103 (08043)
**Phone—(856) 627-2200**
Fax—(856) 258-4533
www.pennjerseypress.com
Email—rick622@comcast.net
Pres.—Rick Fichter
SIC—2759; NAICS—323100; *Commercial printing*
Employs—1; Estab.—1976
Sales—under $500,000
4,500 sq ft site, Distrib.—National
Privately owned corporation

**PRODUCTIVE INDUSTRIAL FINISHING**
103 American Way (08043)
**Phone—(856) 427-9646**
www.productiveplastics.com
Pres.—Hal Gilham
Off. Mgr.—Richard Kot
SIC—3471; 3479; NAICS—332813; *Metal finishing, powder coating & painting*
Employs—7; Estab.—1991
Sales—$500,000-$1Mil
Distrib.—Regional
Privately owned corporation

**†SERVICE LAMP CORP.**
112 Route 73 (08043)
Mail addr: P.O. Box 249, Marlton (08053)
**Phone—(856) 768-0404**
Fax—(856) 768-8270
www.servicelamp.com
Email—info@servicelamp.com
Owner—Mark Kushner
SIC—5063; *Distributor of commercial, industrial & residential lighting fixtures, ballasts & lamps; Brand name—Philips; General Electric; Sylvania*
Employs—12
Distrib.—National
Privately owned corporation

**STEWART BUSINESS FORMS, INC.**
28 Redstone Ridge, P.O. Box 715 (08043)
**Phone—(856) 768-2011**
National—(800) 922-6668
Fax—(856) 768-2033
Email—stewartbf@verizon.net
Pres., CFO—Gail Stewart
V-P.—James Stewart
SIC—2761; 2759; NAICS—323116; *Business forms & printing*
Employs—2; Estab.—1984
Sales—under $500,000
Distrib.—Regional
Privately owned corporation

**TUCKER INTERNATIONAL, LLC**
200 W. Somerdale Rd., Ste. B (08043)
**Phone—(856) 216-1333**
Fax—(856) 216-0334
www.phlatball.com
Email—info@phlatball.com
Pres.—Michael J. Goldman
IT & Assoc. Prod. Mgr.—Lisa Hartshorne
Hum. Res. Mgr. & Bookkeeper—Maureen Goldman
Prod. Mgr.—Doren Peterson

SIC—3944; *Children's toys & games*
Employs—5; Estab.—2001
Sales—$1Mil-$2.5Mil
Distrib.—National
Privately owned corporation

---

## Waldwick
(Bergen—N.E.)

**AVENUE PRINTING CO.**
143 Franklin Tpke. (07463)
**Phone—(201) 652-2035**
www.avenueprinting.com
Email—avenueprinting@optonline.net
Owner—Ruth Amarante
SIC—2759; 2752; 2791; 2789; NAICS—323122; *Commercial offset spot & digital full-color printing & copy service, in-house design & binding, ad journals, forms, newsletters, business cards, labels & social invitations; Brand name—Carlson Craft; Birchcraft; Royal Imprints; Business Cards Tomorrow; Label Works; McPhearsons*
Employs—3; Estab.—1955
Sales—under $500,000
2,000 sq ft site, Distrib.—National
Privately owned partnership

**CORBETT INDUSTRIES, INC.**
39 Hewson Ave., Ste. B, P.O. Box 212 (07463)
**Phone—(201) 445-6311**
National—(800) 442-4028
Fax—(201) 445-6316
www.corbettind.com
Email—info@corbettind.com
Pres., Engrg. Mgr.—Richard J. Geier
Dir., Field Svcs.—William Carman
GM, Fin., Off. & Sales Mgr.—Justin Krouse
Off. Mgr.—Kathy Degelman
SIC—3433; 3567; NAICS—333414; *Industrial heating equipment, ovens & furnaces*
Employs—15; Estab.—1951
10,000 sq ft site, Distrib.—National
Privately owned corporation

**DESIGN PRODUCTION, INC.**
9 Industrial Pk. (07463)
**Phone—(201) 447-5656**
Fax—(201) 447-5858
www.dpdisplay.com
Pres.—Thomas Murphy
SIC—3993; 2542; *Point-of-purchase displays*
Employs—25; Estab.—1958
Distrib.—Local
Privately owned corporation

**E M ORTHODONTIC LABS, INC.**
6 Lafayette Pl., P.O. Box 112 (07463)
**Phone—(201) 652-4411**
Fax—(201) 652-6369
Email—emolab@prodigy.net
Pres.—Paul Macz
SIC—3843; NAICS—339114; *Orthodontic retainers*
Employs—7; Estab.—1980
Sales—under $500,000
1,000 sq ft site, Distrib.—National
Privately owned corporation

**FALCON STAINLESS & ALLOYS CORP.**
39 Hewson Ave., Ste. A (07463-1832)
**Phone—(201) 670-8300**
National—(800) 631-0728
Fax—(201) 670-0033
www.falcon-metals.com
Email—query@falcon-metals.com
V-P.—Paul Chignola

## Waldwick—(cont.)

**SIC**—3312; 3325; **NAICS**—331513; *Stainless steel & alloys & open die forgings*
**Employs**—8; **Estab.**—1959
**Sales**—$5Mil
6,000 sq ft site, **Distrib.**—National
Privately owned corporation

### HOUSECHEM, A DIV. OF MENSHEN PACKAGING U.S.A., INC.

25 Industrial Park *(07463-1514)*
**Phone**—**(201) 445-8808**
Fax—(201) 445-2810
www.housechem.com
Email—info@housechem.com
V.-P., Opers. & Sales—Rogelio Ayala
Hum. Res. & Off. Mgr.—Nicole Attardo
Asst. Sales & Mktg. Mgr.—Joann Alfano
Sales Admn.—Maria A. Ayala
**SIC**—2842; **NAICS**—325612; *Lavatory care & air freshening products for the retail & janitorial markets, including toilet bowl cleaners, urinal blocks & screens, solid gels & scented oils; Brand name—Duette*
**Employs**—60; **Estab.**—1990
**Sales**—$5Mil-$10Mil
75,000 sq ft site, **Distrib.**—Intl.
Privately owned corporation
Also see: Menshen Packaging USA, Inc., 21 Industrial Pk.

### KOELLMANN GEAR CORP.

8 Industrial Pk. (07463)
**Phone**—**(201) 447-0200**
Fax—(201) 447-6595
www.koellmanngear.com
Email—info@koellmann.com
Pres.—Michael Rasovic
Sales Rep.—Christofer Cunningham
**SIC**—3462; **NAICS**—332111; *Gear reducers*
**Employs**—15; **Estab.**—1974
**Distrib.**—Intl.
Privately owned corporation

### MENSHEN PACKAGING U.S.A., INC.

21 Industrial Park *(07463-1512)*
**Phone**—**(201) 445-7436**
Fax—(201) 445-3473
www.menshenusa.com
Email—info@menshenusa.com
V.-P., Opers. & Sales—Rogelio Ayala
Sales Mgr.—Lee Fantone
Hum. Res. & Off. Mgr.—Nicole Attardo
Cust. Serv. Mgr.—Cathie Granatell
Sales Admn.—Maria A. Ayala
**SIC**—3089; 2842; *Custom plastic injection molding & contract manufacturing of toilet bowl cleaners & air fresheners*
**Employs**—78; **Estab.**—1976
**Sales**—$5Mil-$10Mil
75,000 sq ft site, **Distrib.**—Intl.
Privately owned corporation
**ISO rating**—14001, 9001
Also see: Housechem, A Division Of Menshen Packaging USA, Inc., 25 Industrial Pk.

### MIDLAN CORP.

3 Bohnert Pl. (07463)
**Phone**—**(201) 445-4405**
National—(800) 845-4405
Fax—(201) 445-3770
www.midlancorp.com
Pres., GM—Jacob Van Dyke
**SIC**—3555; **NAICS**—333293; *Printing press ink dryers*
**Employs**—10; **Estab.**—1995
**Sales**—$500,000-$1Mil (est)
**Distrib.**—National
Privately owned corporation

### MOSSTYPE CORP.

150 Franklin Tpke. (07463)
**Phone**—**(201) 444-8000**
Fax—(201) 444-0095
www.mosstype.com
Email—mosstype@mosstype.com
GM—Edgar Coscolluela
Off. Mgr.—Lorraine Fiore
**SIC**—3555; **NAICS**—333293; *Flexographic equipment & supplies; Brand name—D-Mount; Mounter-proofer; Aeromount; Sealedge; Platekote; Transmount Carriers*
**Employs**—20
**Sales**—$2Mil-$5Mil
**Distrib.**—Intl.
Sole ownership

### NEXCORE TECHNOLOGY, INC.

150 Hopper Ave. (07463)
**Phone**—**(201) 968-9400**
National—(877) 639-2673
Fax—(201) 968-0597
www.nexcoretech.com
Pres.—Milton Frank
IT Mgr.—Brian Goetz
Hum. Res. Mgr.—Linda Lahowchic
Cust. Serv. Coord.—Jeanine Scheuermann
Pur. Agt.—Janet Dellacasa
**SIC**—3845; **NAICS**—334500; *Endoscopic light sources, fluid monitoring & hydrothermal ablation systems & energy generators*
**Employs**—35; **Estab.**—1999
30,000 sq ft site, **Distrib.**—Local
Privately owned corporation
**ISO rating**—9001:2000

### PURPLE PEBBLE, LLC (H Q)

58 Grand Ave. (07463)
**Phone**—**(201) 444-7439**
Fax—(201) 652-2871
www.purplepebble.com
Email—sales@purplepebble.com
Owner—Heather D. Vaul
**SIC**—2399; 2392; *Company headquarters; dog leashes, bedding, walking aids & stuffed toys (mfg. subcontracted)*
**Employs**—1; **Estab.**—2003
**Sales**—under $500,000 (est)
**Distrib.**—National
Limited Liability Company

### †ROCKET BUILDING SUPPLY CO., INC.

13 Hewson Ave. (07463)
**Phone**—**(201) 652-8884**
Fax—(201) 652-1744
Email—rbs8884@aol.com
Pres.—Ron Durante
Opers. Mgr.—Bruce Ash
Off. Mgr.—Pearl Pope
**SIC**—5032; *Distributor of building supplies, including brick, concrete block, pavers, bluestone, wall stone, sheetrock, drainage materials, sand & 5/8 inch crushed stone; Brand name—Hanover Pavers*
**Employs**—5; **Estab.**—1968
65,340 sq ft site, **Distrib.**—Local
Privately owned sub-S corp.

### †STAUFF CORP.

7 William Demarest Pl. (07463)
**Phone**—**(201) 444-7800**
Fax—(201) 444-7852
www.stauffusa.com
Pres.—Peter Anderton
IT Mgr.—Nick Monfredi
Hum. Res. Mgr.—Mike Digeronimo
**SIC**—5085; 5072; *Corporate headquarters & wholesaler of clamps & connectors*
**Employs**—25; **Estab.**—1987
**Distrib.**—Intl.
Privately owned corporation

### SUPERIOR TRADEMARK, INC.

45 Zazzetti St., P.O. Box 35 (07463)
**Phone**—**(201) 652-1900**
National—(800) 964-0748
Fax—(201) 447-8867
www.superiortrademark.com
Email—leslie@superiortrademark.com
Pres.—Gordon McIntire
Off. Mgr.—Leslie Becher
**SIC**—3479; 2752; **NAICS**—323100; *Heat transfer labels, identification tags, firefighter accountability & command systems, engraving & signs; Brand name—Supamark; Dashboard Commander*
**Employs**—10; **Estab.**—1929
**Sales**—$1Mil-$2.5Mil
6,000 sq ft site, **Distrib.**—Intl.
Privately owned corporation
**AKAs**: Samson Sign & American Trademark Co.

### WALDWICK PRINTING CO.

1 Harrison Ave. (07463)
**Phone**—**(201) 652-5848**
Fax—(201) 652-3120
www.waldwickprinting.com
Email—print@waldwickprinting.com
Owner—William Cook
Pressman—Bill Cook, Jr.
**SIC**—2759; **NAICS**—323100; *Commercial printing*
**Employs**—4; **Estab.**—1954
**Sales**—under $500,000
**Distrib.**—Local
Sole ownership

## Wall

(Monmouth—N.E.)

### AMERICAN PLUS PRINTERS, INC.

2604 Atlantic Ave. (07719)
**Phone**—**(732) 528-2170**
Fax—(732) 528-2174
www.americanplus.net
Email—americanplus@mac.com
Pres.—Dianne Strohmenger
Prodn. Mgr.—Jim Heffernan
Off. Mgr.—Pat Keefe
**SIC**—2752; 2791; **NAICS**—323122; *Offset printing & electronic prepress*
**Employs**—12; **Estab.**—2002
**Distrib.**—Regional
Privately owned corporation

### ATHLETES IMAGE, INC.

1865 State Route 35 (07719-3561)
**Phone**—**(732) 974-1600**
Fax—(732) 449-7971
www.tshirtteam.com
Email—xwear@aol.com
Pres.—Richard Markus
Manager—Doug Culbert
Sales Rep.—Ken Long
**SIC**—2395; *Textile embroidery*
**Employs**—13; **Estab.**—1979
**Sales**—$500,000-$1Mil
2,300 sq ft site, **Distrib.**—Regional
Privately owned corporation

### BEL RAY CO., LLC

1201 Bowman Ave. (07719)
Mail addr: P.O. Box 526, Farmingdale (07727-0526)
**Phone**—**(732) 938-2421**
   (732) 378-4075
Fax—(732) 938-4232
www.belray.com
Email—customerservice@belray.com
Pres.—Bryan Yourdon
Mktg. Mgr.—Kristine DeSario

**SIC**—2992; **NAICS**—324191; *Lubricating oils for the aerospace, automotive, energy, food, marine, military, mining, motorcyle, OEM, steel, textile & powersports industries; Brand name—Bel-Ray; Total Performance Lubricants*
**Employs**—100; **Estab.**—1946
**Distrib.**—National
Publicly owned corporation

### BIO-KEY INTERNATIONAL, INC. (H Q)

3349 Highway 138, Bldg. A, Ste.E (07719)
**Phone**—**(732) 359-1100**
National—(866) 846-2594
Fax—(732) 359-1101
www.bio-key.com
Email—information@bio-key.com
Pres., CEO—Michael W. DePasquale
Mktg. Mgr.—Scott Mahnken
Hum. Res. Mgr.—Cecilia Welch
**SIC**—7372; *Corporate headquarters; fingerprint-based biometric identification software development for public safety & commercial applications*
**Employs**—10; **Estab.**—2003
**Sales**—$500,000-$1Mil
**Distrib.**—Intl.
Publicly owned corporation

### COATES INTERNATIONAL LTD.

2100 Highway 34 & Ridgewood Rd. (07719)
**Phone**—**(732) 449-7717**
Fax—(732) 449-0764
www.coatesengine.com
Email—info@coatesengine.com
Pres., CEO—George J. Coates
CFO & Dir.—Barry Kaye
V.-P., Secy.—Gregory Coates
Dir.—Richard Evans
Dir.—Frank Adipetro
Dir.—Mike Suchar
Hum. Res. Mgr.—Bernadette Coates
Fin. Mgr.—Shirley Naidel
Comm. Mgr.—Alicia Fenn
**SIC**—3519; 3592; 3612; 3694; **NAICS**—336311; *Spherical rotary valve system for internal combustion engines & motorcycles & industrial generators*
**Employs**—14; **Estab.**—1987
**Sales**—$3Mil-$5Mil
30,000 sq ft site, **Distrib.**—Intl.
Publicly owned corporation
Also see: Coates Precision Engineering Ltd., same loc.

### COATES PRECISION ENGINEERING LTD.

2100 Highway 34 & Ridgewood Rd. (07719)
**Phone**—**(732) 449-7717**
Fax—(732) 449-0764
www.coatesengine.com
Email—info@coatesengine.com
Pres.—George Coates
**SIC**—3714; *Automotive engines, including industrial engines*
**Employs**—15; **Estab.**—1988
**Sales**—$2Mil-$10Mil
304,920 sq ft site, **Distrib.**—Intl.
Privately owned corporation
Also see: Coates International Ltd., same loc.

### DEITZ CO., INC.

1750 Highway 34, P.O. Box 1108 (07719)
**Phone**—**(732) 681-0200**
Fax—(732) 681-8468
www.deitzco.com
Email—contact-pharmafill@deitzco.com
Pres.—John Deitz
V.-P.—Charles Deitz
V.-P.—James Deitz

GEOGRAPHICAL

## Wall—(cont.)

SIC—3565; NAICS—333993; *Pharmaceutical & vitamin bottle filling equipment, including tablet counters, cotton & desiccant inserters, turntables, conveyers, cappers, labelers, sealers, banders & heat tunnels; Brand name—Pharmafill; Eyemark Controls*
Employs—18; Estab.—1948
12,000 sq ft site, Distrib.—Intl.
Privately owned corporation

### †DOOR JOCKEY, INC.

915 18th Ave. (07719)
**Phone—(732) 942-6099**
(732) 245-0227
Fax—(732) 942-6033
Email—ken@doorjockey.com
Pres.—Ken Karmazyn
COO—Peter Karmazyn
SIC—5031; *Distributor of pedestrian automatic commercial doors, door operating equipment & related supplies, including installation & service*
Employs—3; Estab.—2008
Sales—$1Mil
2,800 sq ft site, Distrib.—National
Privately owned sub-S corp.
AKA: Jersey Door Control, Inc./ Bulldog Associates

### †EARLE ASPHALT COMPANY

1800 Route 34, Bldg. 2, Ste. 205 (07719)
Mail addr.—P.O. Box 556, Farmingdale (07727-0556)
**Phone—(732) 308-1113**
Fax—(732) 462-9626
www.earleco.com
Email—info@earleco.com
Pres.—Walter R. Earle II
V-P.—Thomas J. Earle
Hum. Res. Mgr.—Darlene Rasmussen
SIC—5032; *Company headquarters & distributor of asphalt*
Employs—25; Estab.—1968
Distrib.—National
Limited Liability Company

### FIRE HOOKS UNLIMITED

1827 Old Mill Rd. (07719)
**Phone—(732) 280-7737**
Fax—(732) 280-7792
www.firehooksunlimited.net
Email—hydraram@aol.com
CEO, R & D Mgr.—Bob Farrell
Pres.—Mary Farrell
SIC—3546; 3569; 3423; NAICS—333991; *Firefighting tools & equipment*
Employs—18; Estab.—1980
20,000 sq ft site, Distrib.—National
Privately owned corporation

### KEMPTON WOOD PRODUCTS, LLC

2800 Ridgewood Rd. (07719)
**Phone—(732) 449-8673**
www.kemptonshed.com
Email—info@kemptonshed.com
Manager—Kevin Kempton
SIC—2452; 2541; 2542; NAICS—321992; *Wooden & vinyl storage buildings, pool bars & cabanas*
Employs—6; Estab.—1984
Distrib.—Regional
Limited Liability Company

### MACLEARIE

917 18th Ave. (07719)
**Phone—(732) 974-8878**
Fax—(732) 681-2775
www.ibcplus.com
Email—orders@ibcplus.com
Owner—Jim McCleary

SIC—2759; 2761; NAICS—323116; *Business card & form printing*
Employs—5; Estab.—1987
Sales—$500,000-$1Mil
Distrib.—Local
Sole ownership

### MINUTEMAN PRESS

1818 Highway 35 (07719)
**Phone—(732) 449-1760**
Fax—(732) 449-0841
www.minutemanpress.com
Pres.—Chris Maguire
SIC—2752; NAICS—323100; *Offset printing*
Employs—5; Estab.—1976
Distrib.—Local
Privately owned corporation

### PLASTI-CLAD METAL PRODUCTS

2601 Ridgewood Rd. (07719)
Mail addr.—P.O. Box 440, Allenwood (08720)
**Phone—(732) 449-2665**
National—(800) 328-9473
Fax—(732) 449-4483
www.plasti-clad.com
Email—sales@plasti-clad.com
Pres.—Mark Matthews
SIC—3315; *Plastic coated steel wire*
Employs—10; Estab.—1952
Sales—$1Mil-$5Mil
20,000 sq ft site, Distrib.—Intl.
Privately owned corporation

### RFM PRINTING, INC.

1715 Highway 34, P.O. Box 1430 (07719)
**Phone—(732) 938-4400**
Fax—(732) 751-2601
www.rfmprinting.com
Email—print@rfmprinting.com
Pres.—Robert McKenna
Prodn. Mgr.—Mike Surowiec
Acctg. Mgr.—Dawn Pyskaty
SIC—2752; NAICS—323100; *Coldset web offset printing*
Employs—25; Estab.—1998
Sales—$1Mil-$2.5Mil
Distrib.—Local
Privately owned corporation

---

## Wall Township

(Monmouth—N.E.)

### AIR CRUISERS, LLC

1747 State Route 34 (07727)
**Phone—(732) 681-3527**
Fax—(732) 681-9163
www.aircruisers.com
Email—aircruisers@zodiacaerospace.com
Pres.—John O'Donnell
CFO—John Melone
V-P., Mfg.—Neil Cavaleri
V-P., IT—Robert Schalhoub
V-P., Hum. Res.—Scott Ernst
V-P., Supply Chain—Dan Kline
Plt. Mgr.—Paul Patterson
SIC—3089; *Company headquarters & inflatable survival equipment*
Employs—250; Estab.—1935
Sales—$25Mil-$50Mil
Distrib.—Intl.
Privately owned corporation
DBA: Zodiac Aerospace Evacuation Systems America

### †ALLIED BUILDING PRODUCTS CORP.

2065 State Route 34 (07719)
**Phone—(732) 449-3355**
Fax—(732) 449-0342
www.alliedbuilding.com
Email—sales@alliedbuilding.com
Br. Mgr.—Gary Finn

SIC—5033; 5031; *Distributor of building materials & supplies, including roofing, siding, windows & doors*
Employs—5
Distrib.—Intl.
Publicly owned corporation
Parent co.—Allied Building Products Corp., East Rutherford, NJ
Phone—(201) 507-8400
See Parent Co. Section for full profile.

### †ATLANTIC WINDOW & DOOR, INC.

1608 Dubac Rd. (07719-3771)
**Phone—(732) 793-2452**
Fax—(732) 793-2944
www.exteriorsbyatlantic.com
Email—atlanticwindoor@aol.com
Pres.—Mark Daly
GM—Bill Keller
SIC—5031; 5033; *Distributor of home improvement products, including roofing, siding, windows, doors, kitchen cabinets, hurricane shutters & installation*
Employs—5; Estab.—1964
Distrib.—Local
Privately owned corporation

### GARDEN STATE PRECAST, INC.

1630 Wyckoff Rd. (07719)
Mail addr.—P.O. Box 702, Farmingdale (07727)
**Phone—(732) 938-4436**
National—(800) 501-9522
Fax—(732) 938-7096
www.gardenstateprecast.com
Email—komalley@gardenstateprecast.com
Pres.—Kirby O'Malley
V-P.—Daniel P. Morris
Corp. Secy.—Gene O'Malley
SIC—3272; *Precast concrete products*
Employs—75; Estab.—1999
Distrib.—Regional
Privately owned sub-S corp.

### GORE & ASSOCS., INC., W. L.

1746 State Route 34 N. (07727)
**Phone—(732) 681-7070**
Fax—(732) 681-1623
www.gore.com
Email—info@gore.com
IT & MIS Mgr.—Andy Marotta
Hum. Res. Mgr.—Lori Lamastra
Fin. Mgr.—Tami Le Compte
SIC—3841; *Disposable medical devices*
Employs—160; Estab.—1960
60,000 sq ft site, Distrib.—Intl.
Privately owned corporation
Parent co.—Gore & Assocs., Inc., W. L., Newark, DE
Phone—(302) 738-4880
See Parent Co. Section for full profile.

### KAVON FILTER PRODUCTS CO., INC.

5022 Industrial Rd., P.O. Box 1166 (07719)
**Phone—(732) 938-3135**
Fax—(732) 938-7540
www.kavonfilter.com
Email—kavonfilter@optonline.net
V-P., Sales & Mktg.—Douglas Von Bulow
V-P. & Plt. Mgr.—Michael J. Cavanaugh
V-P. & Shpg. Mgr.—Francis L. Cavanaugh, Jr.
GM—Linda Von Bulow
SIC—2674; 5085; NAICS—322224; *Manufacturer & distributor of industrial filter paper & cloth & custom filters for fluid bed dryers, centrifuge & dust bags, liners, rotary drum vacuum & filter press cloth & packs for presses*
Employs—20; Estab.—1962
11,100 sq ft site, Distrib.—Intl.
Privately owned sub-S corp.

### †NUTLEY HEATING & COOLING SUPPLY CO.

Div. of Nutley Heating & Cooling Supply Co., Inc.
5016 Industrial Rd. (07727)
**Phone—(732) 919-1933**
Fax—(732) 919-7455
www.nutleysupply.com
Email—craigsoden@nutleysupply.com
Manager—Craig Soden
SIC—5074; *Distributor of HVAC equipment, boilers, radiators, industrial burners & accessories*
Employs—6; Estab.—1947
Distrib.—Regional
Privately owned corporation
Parent co.—Nutley Heating & Cooling Supply Co., Inc., Clifton, NJ
Phone—(973) 470-8844
See Parent Co. Section for full profile.

### OPDYKE AWNING, INC.

2036 State Route 35 (07719)
**Phone—(732) 449-5940**
Fax—(732) 974-2108
www.opdykeawning.com
Email—info@opdykeawning.com
Pres.—James Opdyke
GM—Michele Forsberg
SIC—2394; NAICS—314912; *Residential & commercial awnings & canopies & canvas products*
Employs—18; Estab.—1914
Sales—$500,000-$1Mil
20,000 sq ft site, Distrib.—National
Privately owned corporation

---

## Wallington

(Bergen—N.E.)

### AEROSPACE MANUFACTURING CORPORATION

80 Van Winkle Ave., P.O. Box 3398 (07057)
**Phone—(973) 472-9888**
(973) 472-2300
National—(800) 916-9886
Fax—(973) 472-4120
www.aero-space.us
Email—aerospace@aero-space.us
Pres.—Al Shafa
Mktg. Mgr.—Vivian Chastan
Off. Mgr.—Mary Decicco
Pur. Agt.—Lester Paszkowski
SIC—3452; NAICS—332722; *Fasteners for the aerospace industry*
Employs—26; Estab.—1986
Sales—$2.6Mil-$5Mil
35,000 sq ft site, Distrib.—Regional
Privately owned corporation
ISO rating—9001

### ART PUBLISHING GROUP, THE

480 Main Ave., Unit 4 (07057)
**Phone—(201) 842-8500**
National—(800) 760-3058
Fax—(201) 842-8546
www.theartpublishinggroup.com
Email—contact@theartpublishinggroup.com
Pres.—John Bridgewater
SIC—2741; *Fine art printing, including motivational, religious & ethnic posters, decorative wall decor & photographic prints*
Employs—10; Estab.—1972
Sales—$500,000-$1Mil
Distrib.—Intl.
Limited Liability Company

### BRENNER METAL PRODUCTS CORP.

16 Main Ave., P.O. Box 16 (07057)
**Phone—(973) 778-2466**
Fax—(973) 778-8780
www.brennermetal.com
Email—brennermet@aol.com

## Wallington—(cont.)

Pres.—Christine Brenner
Off. Mgr.—June Abbott
SIC—2599; *Military hospital beds & cabinets*
Employs—30; Estab.—1968
Sales—$500,000-$1Mil
40,000 sq ft site, Distrib.—National
Privately owned sub-S corp.

### C & K PRINTING CO., INC.

203 Paterson Ave., Ste. 1 (07057)
**Phone—(973) 473-0739**
Pres.—Gatnerek Truck
SIC—2759; NAICS—323100;
*Commercial printing*
Employs—1; Estab.—1976
Sales—under $500,000
Distrib.—Local
Sole ownership

### FARMLAND DAIRIES

Div. of Borden Dairy Co.
520 Main Ave., P.O. Box 3340
(07057)
**Phone—(973) 777-2500**
National—(800) 631-7739
Fax—(201) 249-3810
www.bordendairy.com
Email—info@bordendairy.com
GM—Ronald Gaidusek
IT Mgr.—Michael Humphreys
Hum. Res. Mgr.—Kara Weist
Prodn. Supv.—Kevin Schuttack
Payroll Supv.—Lynne Carloni
SIC—2026; NAICS—311500; *Milk*
Employs—350; Estab.—1914
Sales—$101Mil-$1Bil
Distrib.—National
Publicly owned corporation
Parent co.—Borden Dairy Co.,
Dallas, TX
Phone—(214) 526-1687
See Parent Co. Section for full profile.

### HYGLOSS PRODUCTS, INC.

45 Hathaway St. (07057)
**Phone—(973) 458-1700**
National—(800) 444-9456
Fax—(973) 458-1745
www.hygloss.com
Email—info@hygloss.com
Pres.—Moshe Neurath
Sales Mgr.—Mordy Schiller
SIC—2679; 2678; 3952; 3999;
*Arts & crafts products for teachers, parents & retailers, including specialty paper, paper craft products & classroom supplies*
Employs—30; Estab.—1985
Sales—$1Mil-$5Mil
20,000 sq ft site, Distrib.—Intl.
Privately owned sub-S corp.

### INFO SYSTEM

345 Main Ave. (07057)
**Phone—(973) 777-4448**
Fax—(973) 777-4405
Email—abecadlo@cs.com
Owner—Wojciech Marchel
Hum. Res. Mgr.—Andy Pelczynski
SIC—2711; 2732; *Newspaper publishing & booklet printing*
Employs—10; Estab.—1992
Sales—$500,000-$1Mil
2,400 sq ft site, Distrib.—Regional
Limited Liability Company

### METRO CANDY APPLE CORP.

203 Paterson Ave., Ste. 1 (07057)
**Phone—(973) 772-0837**
Fax—(973) 772-0914
www.metrocandyapple.com
Email—metrocandyapple@
gmail.com
Owner—Ellen Coughlin
SIC—2064; NAICS—311300;
*Candy apples*
Employs—4; Estab.—1969
Sales—under $500,000
Distrib.—Local
Privately owned corporation

### PARK PLUS, INC.

480 Main Ave., Ste. 1 (07057)
Mail addr: 31 Ironhorse Rd.,
Oakland (07436)
**Phone—(973) 574-8020**
National—(800) 966-5509
Fax—(973) 574-8030
www.parkplusinc.com
Email—info@parkplusinc.com
CEO—Ronald Astrup
Dir.—Ryan Astrup
SIC—3829; 3679; *Valet parking equipment & high density & automated parking systems;
Brand name—AutoPark;
SpaceMaker; Car Stacker; Lift Sliding System; Park Plus*
Employs—9; Estab.—1969
Sales—$500,000-$1Mil
Distrib.—Intl.
Privately owned corporation

### PROMOTION WORKS

45 Wadsworth St. (07057)
**Phone—(201) 842-1107**
Fax—(201) 842-1302
Email—sales@worksnj.com
Pres.—John Cherup
Off. Mgr.—Scott Lugg
Off. Mgr.—Donna Poulasboria
SIC—2395; *Embroidery*
Employs—10; Estab.—1990
3,000 sq ft site, Distrib.—Regional
Privately owned corporation

### RS RUBBER CORP.

55 Paterson Ave., P.O. Box 3400
(07057-3400)
**Phone—(973) 777-2200**
Fax—(973) 777-7175
www.rsrubber.com
Email—rsrubber@aol.com
GM—Bob Busch
SIC—3052; 3053; 5085; NAICS—
326220; *Manufacturer & distributor of industrial rubber products, including sheet rubber, gaskets, hoses & belting;
Brand name—Garlock; Klinger/
Thermoseal/WL Gore; Bilt Rite;
Eaton; Dixon; Clipper; Leader;
Flexitallic; Parker; Blue Max;
Task Line; Flexhaust*
Employs—10; Estab.—1988
Sales—$1Mil-$5Mil
Distrib.—National
Privately owned corporation

### SHERWIN-WILLIAMS CO., THE

6 Currie Ave. (07057)
**Phone—(201) 933-3800**
Fax—(201) 933-3810
www.sherwin-williams.com
Email—info@sherwin.com
Br. Mgr.—Edward Squier
SIC—2851; NAICS—325510;
*Paint, pigments, product finishes & color blending*
Employs—13; Estab.—1866
10,000 sq ft site, Distrib.—National
Publicly owned corporation
Parent co.—Sherwin-Williams Co.,
The, Cleveland, OH
Phone—(216) 566-2000
See Parent Co. Section for full profile.

### †STANLEY FOAM RUBBER CORP.

14 Orchard St. *(07057)*
**Phone—(973) 778-1660**
Fax—(973) 778-9014
www.stanleyfoam.com
Email—stanleyfoam@yahoo.com
Pres.—Burt Alkes
V-P.—JoAnn Alkes
SIC—5199; *Distributor of polyurethane foam, upholstery supplies & vinyl*
Employs—7; Estab.—1950
7,200 sq ft site, Distrib.—National
Privately owned corporation

### TRIANGLE INK CO., INC.

53-57 Van Dyke St. (07057)
**Phone—(201) 935-2777**
National—(800) 524-1592
Fax—(201) 935-5961
www.triangleink.com
Email—info@triangleink.com
Co-CEO & Dir., Sales—Kevin J.
Sweeney
Co-CEO & Dir., Lab—Robert M.
Smith
SIC—2893; 2899; NAICS—
325910; *Screen printing inks & supplies; Brand name—Phoenix White; Tri-Etch*
Employs—11; Estab.—1979
Sales—$1Mil-$5Mil
Distrib.—Intl.
Privately owned corporation

---

## Wanaque

### (Passaic—N.E.)

### PRINTING IMAGES

546 Ringwood Ave. (07465)
**Phone—(973) 839-9500**
Fax—(973) 839-2417
Email—printingimages@
optonline.net
Owner—Peter Kramer
Off. Mgr.—Eileen Kramer
SIC—2752; NAICS—323100;
*Instant & offset printing*
Employs—3; Estab.—1995
Sales—under $500,000
Distrib.—Local
Sole ownership

---

## Wantage

### (Sussex—N.W.)

### KUIKEN BROTHERS COMPANY, INC.

175 Route 23 (07461)
**Phone—(973) 875-5106**
Fax—(973) 875-0810
www.kuikenbrothers.com
Email—info@kuikenbrothers.com
Location Mgr.—Ken Hynnes
Sales Rep.—Bill Oekley
SIC—2421; 2431; NAICS—
321900; *Lumber, hardware, windows & building supplies*
Employs—15; Estab.—1912
Sales—$500,000-$1Mil
Distrib.—Regional
Privately owned sub-S corp.
Parent co.—Kuiken Brothers
Company, Inc., Fair Lawn, NJ
Phone—(201) 796-2082
See Parent Co. Section for full profile.

### SUSSEX INNOVATIONS, LLC

137 Libertyville Rd. (07461)
**Phone—(917) 699-9489**
Email—robynmartinez1@aol.com
CEO—Raj Sinha
Pres.—Robyn Martinez
V-P., Mktg.—Nelson Martinez
SIC—2033; *Food products, including jellies & salsa*
Employs—3; Estab.—2009
Sales—under $500,000
Distrib.—Local
Limited Liability Company

### TIMPLEX CORP.

1370 State Route 23 (07461)
**Phone—(973) 875-5500**
Fax—(973) 875-6732
www.timplex.com
Email—timplex@embarqmail.com
Pres.—Ron Slate
GM & Sales Mgr.—Douglas J.
Slate
Off. Mgr.—Lynn Meyer

SIC—2439; 3312; NAICS—
321200; *Wooden trusses & light gage, cold formed steel trusses, including solid sawn & LVL timber systems*
Employs—16; Estab.—1969
15,000 sq ft site, Distrib.—
Regional
Privately owned corporation

### WARD & SONS, INC., J. B.

1434 Route 565 (07461)
**Phone—(973) 827-4600**
Fax—(973) 827-8119
www.jbward.com
Email—sales@jbward.com
Pres.—Ed Boscia
SIC—3991; NAICS—339994;
*Industrial brushes*
Employs—4; Estab.—1855
Sales—$1Mil
5,000 sq ft site, Distrib.—Intl.
Privately owned corporation

---

## Waretown

### (Ocean—S.E.)

### CLAYTON BLOCK CO., INC.

Route 9 (08758)
Mail addr: P.O. Box 3015,
Lakewood (08701)
**Phone—(609) 693-3000**
National—(800) 585-6403
Fax—(732) 751-7630
www.claytonco.com
Email—kroe@claytonco.com
IT Mgr.—Scott Milne
Head of Dept.—Craig MacFarlane
Sales Rep.—Brian Tart
SIC—3271; 3272; NAICS—
327331; *Concrete masonry units, building supplies, bagged portland cement, lime & mortar, block retaining walls & fences & pavers*
Employs—20; Estab.—1985
Sales—$1Mil-$2.5Mil
Distrib.—Local
Privately owned corporation
Parent co.—Clayton Block Co.,
Inc., Neptune, NJ
Phone—(732) 751-7600
See Parent Co. Section for full profile.

### R WELDING

97 Main St. (08758)
**Phone—(609) 971-6017**
Owner—Risden Russell
SIC—3567; 3599; NAICS—
333994; *Commercial & industrial desiccate dehumidifier component parts & welding job shop*
Employs—2; Estab.—1990
Sales—under $500,000
Distrib.—Local
Sole ownership

---

## Warren

### (Somerset—N.E.)

### 21ST CENTURY OPTICAL

5 Powder Horn Dr. (07059)
**Phone—(973) 379-2020**
National—(800) 526-4942
Fax—(973) 379-2131
Email—sgoptical@aol.com
GM—Ed Glassheim
SIC—3231; 3089; NAICS—
327215; *Glass, plastic & polycarbonate fabrication*
Employs—10; Estab.—1981
Sales—under $500,000
4,500 sq ft site, Distrib.—Regional
Privately owned sub-S corp.

### A MAT CONTROL TECHNOLOGIES, LLC

70 Mount Bethel Rd. (07059)
**Phone—(908) 756-1699**
Pres.—Jens Waale

GEOGRAPHICAL

## Warren—(cont.)

SIC—3829; *Programmable smokehouse process controllers; Brand name—Minimat; Rokomat*
Employs—2; Estab.—1992
Sales—under $500,000
Distrib.—Intl.
Limited Liability Company

**ANADIGICS, INC.**
141 Mount Bethel Rd. (07059)
**Phone—(908) 668-5000**
Fax—(908) 412-5942
www.anadigics.com
Email—info@anadigics.com
Plt. Mgr.—Henry Ostrowski
Hum. Res. Mgr.—Betsy Madura
Maint. Techn.—Scott Capps
SIC—3674; NAICS—334413; *Radio frequency integrated circuits*
Employs—550; Estab.—1985
Sales—$80Mil-$100Mil
Distrib.—Intl.
Publicly owned corporation
ISO rating—9001

**ASSOCIATED ANVIL IRON WORKS**
38 Patterson Ave. (07059)
**Phone—(908) 647-0290**
        (908) 803-1492
Fax—(908) 647-0920
Email—aaiwinc@gmail.com
Pres.—Raymond Di Giambattista
GM—Matt Di Giambattista
SIC—3441; NAICS—332312; *Structural steel fabrication*
Employs—2; Estab.—1946
Sales—under $500,000
2,000 sq ft site, Distrib.—Local

**ASTROLAB, INC.**
4 Powderhorn Dr. (07059)
**Phone—(732) 560-3800**
Fax—(732) 560-9570
www.astrolab.com
Email—sales@astrolab.com
GM—Stephen J. Toma
Sales Mgr.—Mary Ceres
Sales Rep.—Cristal Wilson
SIC—3679; *Microwave components*
Employs—46; Estab.—1962
22,500 sq ft site, Distrib.—Intl.
Privately owned corporation

**BALLARD COLLECTION, INC.**
221 Stirling Rd., Ste. E & F (07059)
**Phone—(908) 604-0082**
Fax—(908) 931-9222
www.karenleeballard.com
Owner & CEO—Karen L. Engemann
SIC—2392; *Tablecloths*
Employs—7; Estab.—1995
Sales—$500,000-$1Mil
Distrib.—Regional
Privately owned corporation

**BEVELED EDGE**
51 Mount Bethel Rd. (07059)
**Phone—(908) 754-6772**
Fax—(908) 754-3255
www.bevelededgewarren.com
Owner—Scott Andrus
SIC—2499; *Picture frames*
Employs—2; Estab.—1989
Sales—under $500,000
Distrib.—Local
Sole ownership

**C S L WATER QUALITY, INC.**
156 Mount Bethel Rd., P.O. Box 4246 (07059)
**Phone—(908) 647-1400**
Fax—(908) 647-1080
www.cslwater.com
Email—info@cslwater.com
Pres.—John V. Truglio
V-P.—Gary Thorp

SIC—2899; 3589; NAICS—333319; *Water treatment chemicals, filters, feed equipment & testing*
Employs—7; Estab.—1930
Distrib.—Regional
Privately owned corporation
AKA: C S L Water Treatment

**CHATHAM CONTAINER DISPLAY CORP.**
6 Northridge Way (07059-5332)
Mail addr.: P.O. Box 7351, Watchung (07069-0795)
**Phone—(800) 266-4848**
Email—chatmdsply@aol.com
Pres.—James Irvine
Ex. V-P.—Scott B. Irvine
V-P., Sales—Molly M. Irvine
Secy-Treas.—Carol S. Irvine
SIC—2541; 3089; *Point-of-purchase displays & packaging materials, including corrugated, folding stock & wire, fabricated & molded plastics & foams for the garden center & foodservice industries; Brand name—CHATHAM Carry-Out Trays*
Employs—4; Estab.—1964
Sales—under $500,000
1,600 sq ft site, Distrib.—National
Privately owned corporation

**CHROMIS FIBEROPTICS, INC.**
6 Powderhorn Dr. (07059)
**Phone—(732) 764-0900**
Fax—(732) 764-0933
www.chromisfiber.com
Email—info@chromisfiber.com
CEO—Whitney White
Off. Mgr.—David Corsini
SIC—3357; 3089; *Perfluorinated plastic optical fibers for data communications*
Employs—10; Estab.—2003
Distrib.—Intl.
Privately owned corporation

**DEALAMAN ENTERPRISES, INC.**
214 Mountain View Rd. (07059)
Mail addr.: 218 Mountain View Rd., Warren (07059-5099)
**Phone—(908) 755-1780**
Fax—(908) 604-8030
www.dealamanenterprises.com
Email—dealamanenterprises@gmail.com
Pres.—George Dealaman
V-P.—Bruce Dealaman
Off. Mgr.—Janet Abeles
SIC—2011; NAICS—311611; *Pork processing for wholesale & retail customers, including suckling pigs & roasting pigs*
Employs—16; Estab.—1969
Distrib.—Regional
Privately owned corporation

**ELGEE MFG. CO.**
225 Stirling Rd. (07059)
**Phone—(908) 647-4100**
National—(800) 742-0400
Fax—(908) 647-4242
www.elgee.com
Email—sales@elgee.com
Pres.—Stephen Heinle
Off. Mgr.—Debbie Isselin
Assembling Mgr.—Will Winton
SIC—3589; NAICS—333319; *Industrial power vacuums & sweepers*
Employs—6; Estab.—1959
Sales—$500,000-$1Mil
10,000 sq ft site, Distrib.—Regional
Privately owned corporation

**ESSILOR LABORATORIES**
Div. of Essilor Of America, Inc.
5 Powderhorn Dr. (07059)
**Phone—(732) 563-9884**
National—(877) 265-9884
www.essilorusa.com
Email—info@essilorusa.com

GM—Debra Case
Off. Mgr.—Diana O'Neal
Cust. Serv. Rep.—Jesse Griffith
SIC—3851; NAICS—339100; *Eyeglass lenses*
Employs—14; Estab.—2002
Distrib.—Regional
Publicly owned corporation
Parent co.—Essilor Of America, Inc., Dallas, TX
Phone—(214) 496-4000
See Parent Co. Section for full profile.

**GARAN ELECTRONICS, INC.**
223 Stirling Rd., Unit C (07059)
**Phone—(908) 484-7100**
Fax—(908) 484-7099
www.garanelec.com
Email—garanelec@optonline.net
Mng. Ptnr.—Robert Mills
GM—Richard Mills
SIC—3089; 3679; *Plastic electronic hardware, including bobbins, spools, shells, washers, stand offs, terminal boards, bushings, spacers, headers, cases, core tubes & coil forms for the electronics industry*
Employs—10; Estab.—1957
6,000 sq ft site, Distrib.—Intl.
Limited Liability Company

**GRAPHIC IMAGERY, INC.**
122 Mount Bethel Rd., Ste. 2 (07059)
**Phone—(908) 755-2882**
National—(800) 774-6863
Fax—(908) 755-2077
www.graphicimagery.com
Email—imagery@graphicimagery.com
Pres.—Linda Maher
Proj. Coord.—Jessica Foerst
SIC—2759; 2752; NAICS—323100; *Commercial offset, digital & web printing, graphic design, direct mail services & interactive media*
Employs—10; Estab.—1988
10,000 sq ft site, Distrib.—National
Privately owned corporation
AKA: 1800printme.com

**G-U TEK, INC.**
266 King George Rd., Ste. B-2 (07059)
**Phone—(908) 626-0012**
Fax—(908) 626-0066
www.gutekinc.com
Email—info@gutekinc.com
Pres.—Anthony Solazzo
SIC—3841; *Medical devices*
Employs—5; Estab.—2002
Sales—$500,000-$1Mil
Distrib.—National
Privately owned corporation

**MAGNUM TECHNOLOGIES, INC.**
95 Mount Bethel Rd. (07059)
**Phone—(908) 546-7950**
Fax—(908) 546-7951
www.magnumt.com
Email—info@magnumt.com
Pres.—Raj Subramanian
Hum. Res. Mgr.—Sree Kotala
Fin. Mgr.—Chaya Rajaram
SIC—7372; *Enterprise content managment & planning & supply chain management software development & IT consulting for the financial services, retail, distribution, healthcare, pharmaceutical, insurance & manufacturing markets*
Employs—60; Estab.—2000
Distrib.—Intl.
Privately owned corporation
AKA: Magnum

**MONOSOL RX, LLC (H Q)**
30 Technology Dr. (07059)
**Phone—(908) 941-1900**
www.monosolrx.com

Email—dbarber@monosolrx.com
Pres., CEO—Mark Schobel
Pres., COO—Keith J. Kendall
Sr. V-P., R & D—Eric Dadey
V-P., Hum. Res.—Theresa Wood
V-P., Fin.—Robert Arnold
V-P., Bus. Dev.—Daniel Barber
SIC—2834; *Company headquarters; film-based pharmaceuticals; Brand name—PharmFilm® Technology; Zuplenz®; Suboxone®*
Employs—15; Estab.—2000
Sales—$5Mil-$10Mil (est)
Limited Liability Company

**PICUT MANUFACTURING COMPANY, INC.**
140 Mount Bethel Rd. (07059-5147)
**Phone—(908) 754-1333**
Fax—(908) 754-3280
www.picut.com
Email—sales@picut.com
Pres.—Frederick Picut
CFO—Ray Mattes
V-P.—Richard Picut
V-P.—Russell Picut
Cont.—Cheryl Lloyd
GM—Dan Scagliozzi
Hum. Res. Mgr.—Chris Hardgrove
SIC—3599; *Corporate headquarters & general machining job shop*
Employs—98
Sales—$15Mil-$18Mil
50,000 sq ft site, Distrib.—Regional
Privately owned sub-S corp.

**STR8UP BEVERAGES, LLC**
16 Mount Bethel Rd., Ste. 260 (07059)
**Phone—(908) 451-1393**
www.fyxxwater.com
Email—mitch@fyxxwater.com
Owner—Mitch Rappel
SIC—2086; *Caffeine-infused water bottling*
Employs—15; Estab.—2007
Sales—$5Mil
Distrib.—Intl.
Limited Liability Company

**SUPERIOR CUSTOM KITCHENS, LLC**
126 Mount Bethel Rd. (07059)
**Phone—(908) 753-6005**
Fax—(908) 753-6906
www.superiorcustomkitchens.com
Email—supkit@optonline.net
Ptnr.—Joe Borin
Ptnr.—Jack Barna
Draftsman—Christine Whitehead
SIC—2434; 2521; NAICS—337110; *Custom & semi-custom cabinets for full or partial kitchens, bathrooms, bars & offices & remodeling services; Brand name—Woodmode; Brookhaven; Superior Custom Cabinets*
Employs—10; Estab.—1961
Sales—$2.5Mil-$5Mil
Distrib.—Local
Privately owned partnership

**TRIDENT IONIC, INC.**
19 Olsen Dr. (07059)
**Phone—(908) 647-4329**
www.tridentionic.com
Email—tfitzgerald@tridentionic.com
Pres.—Carol Fitzgerald
GM—Tom Fitzgerald
SIC—3589; NAICS—333319; *Water treatment systems*
Employs—2; Estab.—1996
Sales—under $500,000
Distrib.—Intl.
Privately owned corporation

**VANTAGE TOOL & MFG.**
223 Stirling Rd. (07059)
**Phone—(908) 647-1010**
Fax—(908) 647-4242

## Warren—(cont.)

Email—vantage@elgee.com
Pres.—Stephen Heinle
Secy. & Off. Mgr.—Debbie Isselin
SIC—3544; NAICS—333500; *Tool & die job shop, including general machine work, welding, sheet metal fabrication & vacuum sweepers for factory floors & parking lots*
Employs—3; Estab.—1984
Sales—$500,000-$1Mil
5,000 sq ft site, Distrib.—Regional
Privately owned sub-S corp.

## Washington

(Warren—N.W.)

### ABILITIES OF NORTHWEST JERSEY, INC.

264 Route 31 N., P.O. Box 251 *(07882)*
**Phone—(908) 689-1118**
Fax—(908) 689-6363
www.abilitiesnw.com
Email—info@abilitiesnw.com
CEO—Cindy Wildermuth
CFO—Michael Nicholson
CDO—Sue Zukoski
SIC—3089; 3999; 2395; 2396; *Contract packaging/fulfillment, including shrink wrapping, box assembly, production, labeling, heat sealing, collating, blister packing, screen printing, embroidery & electronic recycling*
Employs—300; Estab.—1974
Sales—$5Mil
Distrib.—Regional
Privately owned corporation

### ALL SPORTS STADIUM, LLC

297 Route 31 S. (07882)
**Phone—(908) 689-0411**
Fax—(908) 689-4701
www.allsportsstadium.com
Email—1allsports@comcast.net
Pres.—Armin Kososki
GM—Linda Parente
Manager—Lisa Swick
Sales Assoc.—Rob Kososki
SIC—2396; 2395; *Textile screen printing & embroidery & sporting goods equipment*
Employs—7; Estab.—1989
1,200 sq ft site, Distrib.—National
Limited Liability Company

**NEW ENTRY**
### ARCHITECTURAL CABINETRY

51 Willow St. (07882)
**Phone—(908) 689-1600**
Fax—(908) 689-1603
www.archcabmill.com
Email—info@archcabmill.com
Owner—Cheryl Fortner
SIC—2434; 2431; *Custom wooden architectural cabinets & millwork*
Employs—5; Estab.—2013
Sales—$500,000-$1Mil
7,000 sq ft site, Distrib.—Regional
Privately owned corporation

### BASF CORP.

Div. of BASF Corporation
2 Pleasant View Ave. (07882)
**Phone—(908) 689-7540**
National—(800) 542-3020
Fax—(908) 689-7708
www.basf.com
Email—info@basf.com
Security Supv.—Bruce Bluhm
SIC—2843; NAICS—325613; *Surfactants*
Employs—70; Estab.—1957
Sales—$500,000-$1Mil
Distrib.—Intl.
Publicly owned corporation

Parent co.—BASF Corporation, Florham Park, NJ
Phone—(973) 245-6000
See Parent Co. Section for full profile.

### CANDLE ARTISANS, INC.

253 E. Washington Ave., P.O. Box 190 (07882)
**Phone—(908) 689-2000**
National—(800) 422-6357
Fax—(908) 689-2387
www.candleartisans.com
Email—sales@candleartisans.com
Pres.—Robert D. Rumfield
Off. Mgr.—Kathy White
SIC—3999; *Paraffin wax candles*
Employs—20; Estab.—1962
Distrib.—Intl.
Privately owned sub-S corp.

**NEW ENTRY**
### CAPRA CUSTOM CABINETRY & MILLWORK, LLC

259 E. Washington Ave. (07882)
**Phone—(908) 797-9848**
www.capracustom.com
Owner—John Capra
SIC—2434; 2521; 2431; *Custom residential & commercial casework & millwork*
Employs—2; Estab.—2000
Sales—under $500,000 (est)
Distrib.—Regional
Limited Liability Company

### CUSTOM WOOD CREATIONS, INC.

51 Willow St. (07882)
**Phone—(908) 835-8999**
Fax—(908) 835-8666
Pres.—Ejlat Fuer
SIC—2431; NAICS—321900; *Millwork*
Employs—2; Estab.—1998
Sales—under $500,000 (est)
Distrib.—Local
Privately owned corporation

### †FRANKLIN FARMS EAST, INC.

111 W. Washington Ave. (07882)
Mail addr.: P.O. Box 164, Asbury (08802)
**Phone—(908) 835-0016**
Fax—(908) 835-0760
www.franklinfarmseast.com
Email—simpson@franklinfarmseast.com
Pres.—Donald L. Riggs
V-P, Opers.—Adrienne Riggs
Off. Mgr.—Cathy Pineno
SIC—5149; *Wholesaler of nonfat dry milks & whey powder*
Employs—14; Estab.—1993
Distrib.—National
Privately owned corporation

### GOOD IMPRESSIONS, INC.

325 W. Washington Ave. (07882)
**Phone—(908) 689-3071**
Fax—(908) 689-7369
www.good-impressions.com
Email—gooddeals@good-impressions.com
Pres.—Marion Kennedy
Acct. Mgr.—Bonnie Groff
SIC—2752; 2791; NAICS—323122; *Offset printing & typesetting*
Employs—10; Estab.—1977
Sales—$500,000-$1Mil
Distrib.—Local
Privately owned corporation

### H A Z LABORATORIES

39 Hartmans Corner Rd. (07882)
**Phone—(908) 453-3300**
Fax—(908) 453-3310
www.hazlabs.com
Email—info@hazlabs.com
Pres.—Henry Zajac

SIC—3625; 3679; NAICS—335314; *Industrial controls*
Employs—15; Estab.—1978
Sales—$500,000-$1Mil
10,000 sq ft site, Distrib.—Intl.
Privately owned corporation

### HERBALIST & ALCHEMIST, INC.

51 S. Wandling Ave. (07882)
**Phone—(908) 689-9020**
National—(800) 611-8235
Fax—(908) 689-9071
www.herbalist-alchemist.com
Email—herbalist@nac.net
CEO—Beth Lambert
Pres.—David Winston
Administrative Mgr.—Cara-lin Whelan
SIC—2833; NAICS—325411; *Bottled herbal extracts*
Employs—15; Estab.—1982
Distrib.—National
Privately owned sub-S corp.

**NEW ENTRY**
### MYSTIC TIMBER, LLC

95 Youmans Ave. (07882)
**Phone—(908) 223-7878**
Fax—(908) 689-0388
www.mystictimber.com
Email—info@mystictimber.com
Principal—Bruce Jorgensen
SIC—3999; *Wooden smoking accessories, including smoking wands & dabbers*
Employs—4; Estab.—2007
Sales—under $500,000
500 sq ft site, Distrib.—Intl.
Limited Liability Company

### RDO INDUCTION LLC

2170 State Route 57 W. (07882-3523)
**Phone—(908) 835-7222**
Fax—(908) 835-7272
www.rdoinduction.com
Email—info@rdoinduction.com
CEO & Principal—Robert Okner
SIC—3567; 3569; *Induction heating, melting & casting equipment*
Employs—4; Estab.—1989
Sales—$1Mil-$5Mil
9,000 sq ft site, Distrib.—Intl.
Limited Liability Company

### REXAM HEALTHCARE PACKAGING, INC.

Div. of Rexam, Inc.
14-B Brass Castle Rd. (07882)
**Phone—(908) 689-1660**
Fax—(908) 689-4955
www.rexam.com
Email—info@rexam.com
Plt. Mgr.—Anzideo Ranalli
Hum. Res. Mgr. & Plt. Accountant—Donna Smith
SIC—3085; *Disposable plastic pharmaceutical bottles*
Employs—50; Estab.—2007
Sales—$5Mil-$10Mil (est)
Distrib.—Regional
Publicly owned corporation
Parent co.—Rexam, Inc., Charlotte, NC
Phone—(704) 551-1500
See Parent Co. Section for full profile.

### WITTE CO., INC., THE

507 Route 31 S., P.O. Box 47 (07882)
**Phone—(908) 689-6500**
National—(866) 265-4071
Fax—(908) 537-6806
www.witte.com
Email—info@witte.com
Pres.—Richard Witte
V-P.—Tyson Witte

SIC—3559; 3556; NAICS—333294; *Continuous drying, cooling & separating equipment; Brand name—Witte*
Employs—40; Estab.—1938
Sales—$7Mil-$9Mil
48,000 sq ft site, Distrib.—Intl.
Privately owned sub-S corp.

### WORLD APOSTOLATE OF FATIMA USA

674 Mountain View Rd., P.O. Box 976 (07882)
**Phone—(908) 689-1701**
National—(866) 513-1917
Fax—(908) 689-0721
www.wasusa.org
Email—service@bluearmy.com
Ex. Dir.—David Carollo
Shrine Coord.—Judy Ritchie
Bookkeeper—Crystal Gild
SIC—2721; *Quarterly magazine publishing*
Employs—10; Estab.—1947
Sales—$500,000-$1Mil (est)
Distrib.—National
Privately owned corporation
AKA: Blue Army of Our Lady of Fatima

## Watchung

(Union—N.E.)

### DEBLYN SCREEN PRINTERS

717 Mountain Blvd. (07069)
**Phone—(908) 756-8459**
www.deblyn.com
Email—dabuhot@deblyn.com
Ptnr.—Debra Buhot
Ptnr.—Linda Carter
SIC—2396; 2395; *Textile screen printing & embroidery, including digitizing*
Employs—2; Estab.—1981
Sales—under $500,000
Distrib.—National
Privately owned partnership

### L & Z TOOL & ENGINEERING, INC.

1691 U.S. Highway 22 *(07069)*
**Phone—(908) 322-2220**
Fax—(908) 322-3758
www.lztool.com
Email—webmaster@lztool.com
Pres., CEO, CFO—Thomas LaMarca
Sr. V-P.—T. J. LaMarca
V-P.—Lance LaMarca
Dir., Mktg.—Frank Cooper
Prodn. Mgr.—Chris Ammon
Off. Mgr.—Judy Schulein
Chief Engr.—Bobby Wolff
Sales Engr.—Peter Russoniello
SIC—3544; NAICS—333500; *Injection molding tools*
Employs—35; Estab.—1952
Sales—$1Mil-$5Mil
20,000 sq ft site, Distrib.—Regional
Privately owned corporation

### MODERN LIMB & BRACE CO.

916 Somerset St. (07069)
**Phone—(908) 757-2702**
Fax—(908) 757-0744
www.modernlimbandbrace.com
Email—modernlimb@optimum.net
Owner, Pres. & CFO—Horst Oertel
SIC—3842; *Company headquarters & prosthetics & orthotics*
Employs—6; Estab.—1967
Sales—$500,000-$1Mil
3,000 sq ft site, Distrib.—Local
Privately owned corporation

### SWEET SUCCESS

14 Ellison Rd. (07069)
**Phone—(908) 561-2997**
www.sweetsuccessgiftbaskets.com
Email—sales@sweetsuccessgiftbaskets.com

GEOGRAPHICAL

## Watchung—(cont.)

Pres.—Stella Testa
SIC—3999; *All-occasion, fruit & gourmet, corporate, holiday & seasonal, thank you, get-well, new-baby & sympathy gift baskets*
Employs—2; Estab.—2002
Sales—under $500,000
Distrib.—Regional
Limited Liability Company

### TINA'S WINDOW DECORATING

968 Somerset St. (07069)
**Phone—(908) 668-0066**
Fax—(908) 668-0066
www.tinaswindowsdecorating.com
Email—tinaswindowsdecorating@gmail.com
Owner—Tina Caruso
SIC—2591; NAICS—337920; *Window treatments*
Employs—2; Estab.—1987
Sales—under $500,000
Distrib.—Intl.
Sole ownership

### WELDON ASPHALT CO.

Div. of Weldon Materials, Inc.
1 New Providence Rd. (07060)
Mail addr: 141 Central Ave., Westfield (07090)
**Phone—(908) 233-9440**
National—(888) 322-2231
Fax—(908) 322-4198
www.weldonmat.com
Email—sales@weldonmat.com
GM—Robbie Roberts
SIC—1429; 2951; 3273; NAICS—324121; *Crushed aggregates, hot-mixed asphalt & ready-mixed concrete for homeowners & professional contractors*
Employs—75; Estab.—1908
Distrib.—Local
Privately owned corporation
Parent co.—Weldon Materials, Inc., Westfield, NJ
Phone—(908) 233-4444
See Parent Co. Section for full profile.

## Waterford Works

(Camden—S.W.)

### BERLIN NEON SIGN, INC.

326 Old White Horse Pike (08089)
**Phone—(856) 767-0525**
Fax—(856) 767-2130
Pres.—Tim Manna
SIC—3993; 3446; 2499; *Neon signs & flagpoles*
Employs—2; Estab.—1944
Distrib.—Local

### †MACAULEY, INC., JAMES R.

1 Industrial Dr., P.O. Box 704 (08089)
**Phone—(856) 767-3474**
　　　　(800) 854-2296
Fax—(856) 767-7423
Email—macauleyplastic@aol.com
Pres.—George MacAuley
SIC—5162; 5085; *Wholesaler of plastic pails & plastic cans*
Employs—2; Estab.—1984
Sales—under $2Mil
10,000 sq ft site, Distrib.—Regional
Privately owned corporation

### †MCJUNKIN RED MAN CORPORATION

Div. of MRC Global, Inc.
305 Center Ave. (08089)
**Phone—(856) 753-7690**
Fax—(856) 767-0256
www.mrcpvf.com
Email—tim.fish@mrcpvf.com
Br. Mgr.—Tim Fish
Whse. Mgr.—Mark Hermsen

SIC—5084; 5085; *Distributor of oilfield equipment, including natural gas fittings & piping*
Employs—4; Estab.—1932
Sales—over $1Bil
Distrib.—National
Publicly owned corporation
Parent co.—MRC Global, Inc., Houston, TX
Phone—(713) 655-1005
See Parent Co. Section for full profile.

## Wayne

(Passaic—N.E.)

### ALTECH ABRASIVES SERVICES

130 Ryerson Ave., Ste. 103 (07470)
**Phone—(973) 305-1922**
Fax—(973) 305-8667
Owner & Pres.—Kemper Smith
SIC—3541; NAICS—333512; *Metal cutting*
Employs—1; Estab.—1991
Sales—under $500,000
Distrib.—Local
Sole ownership

### AMERICAN SCREEN PRINTING

272 Kent Ave. (07470-7226)
**Phone—(973) 471-0206**
Fax—(973) 471-0941
www.amrcnscreen.com
Email—amrcnscreen@aol.com
Pres.—Howard Bischoff
SIC—2396; 3993; *Textile screen printing & signs*
Employs—1; Estab.—2003
Sales—$500,000-$1Mil
Distrib.—Regional

### AMERICAN WOODCARVING, LLC

1123 State Route 23, Ste. 6 (07470)
**Phone—(973) 835-8510**
Fax—(973) 835-8638
www.woodensigns.com
Email—mike@woodensigns.com
Pres.—Mike Holst
SIC—3993; 2394; *Signs, displays & awnings & custom routing services*
Employs—7; Estab.—1986
Sales—under $1Mil
Distrib.—National
Limited Liability Company

### ART GRAPHIC IMPRESSIONS

1044 State Route 23, Ste. 101 (07470)
**Phone—(973) 696-2800**
www.artgraphicimpressions.com
Email—wberkenbush@agiprint.net
Pres.—William Berkenbush
SIC—2759; NAICS—323100; *Commercial printing*
Employs—10; Estab.—1972
Sales—$1.5Mil-$2Mil
1,000 sq ft site, Distrib.—National
Privately owned corporation

### BEL-ART PRODUCTS, INC.

Div. of Maddak Inc.
661 State Route 23 (07470)
**Phone—(973) 694-0500**
　　　　(973) 628-8600
National—(800) 423-5278
Fax—(973) 694-7199
www.belart.com
Email—info@belart.com
COO—Brad Mahood
Asst. V-P., Opers.—Bob Schaal
Hum. Res. Mgr.—Lucie Zembruski

SIC—3821; 3479; NAICS—332710; *Corporate headquarters & laboratory products, including beakers, bottles, clamps & holders, cylinders, desiccators, dry ice makers, fume hoods, funnels, pipettor & test tube racks, siphons & pumps & safety supplies; Brand name—Chromage; Clavies; Ellipso-Spoon; Ergopet; Fluo-Kem; Frigimat; Fritware; Holdfast; Lab-Aire; Mico-Mill; Odo-Clave; Poxygrid; Scienceware; Secador; Spinbar; Sterilware; Techni-Dome; Vikem; Magic Touch; Hot Hand*
Employs—85; Estab.—1948
Sales—$10Mil-$25Mil
50,000 sq ft site, Distrib.—National
Privately owned corporation
Parent co.—Maddak Inc., Wayne, NJ
Phone—(973) 628-7600
See Parent Co. Section for full profile.

### BONLAND INDUSTRIES, INC.

50 Newark Pompton Tpke. (07470)
Mail addr: P.O. Box 200, Wayne (07474)
**Phone—(973) 694-3211**
Fax—(973) 628-1120
www.bonlandhvac.com
Email—bboniface@bonlandhvac.com
CEO—William Boniface
Pres.—Andrew Boniface
Admn. Mgr.—Laurie Hughes
Hum. Res. Mgr.—Holly Reger
SIC—3444; *Corporate headquarters & sheet metal fabrication*
Employs—50; Estab.—1957
Company-wide: 200
Sales—$41Mil
40,000 sq ft site, Distrib.—Local
Privately owned corporation

### BORO SAWMILL & TIMBER CO., INC.

139 Ryerson Ave. (07470)
**Phone—(973) 832-4607**
Fax—(973) 832-4615
www.borosawmill.com
Email—info@borosawmill.com
Pres.—Gregory Sussek
V-P., Pur. & Sales—Jack Sussek
Opers. Mgr.—Bob Sago, Sr.
SIC—2421; 2426; 2431; 5031; *Manufacturer & wholesaler of construction timber & lumber products for crane mats, float stages & custom & architectural millwork*
Employs—11; Estab.—1925
Distrib.—National
Privately owned corporation

### †BP LUBRICANTS USA, INC.

Div. of BP America, Inc.
1500 Valley Rd. (07470)
**Phone—(973) 633-2200**
National—(800) 462-0835
Fax—(973) 633-5305
www.bpusa.com
Email—info@bpusa.com
Pres.—Marcia Brand
CFO—David Duggan
V-P., Sales, N. America—Mike Munroe
V-P., Mktg.—Desmond Johnson
V-P., Hum. Res.—Marianne Geuss
SIC—5172; *Corporate headquarters & distributor of synthetic lubricants for automotive service providers & retailers & degreasers, lubes & transmission fluids for the boating, motorcycle, racing & snowmobile industries*
Employs—250
Publicly owned corporation

Parent co.—BP America, Inc., Houston, TX
Phone—(281) 366-2000
See Parent Co. Section for full profile.

### BUTLER SIGN COMPANY

582 Fairfield Rd. (07470)
**Phone—(973) 633-5757**
National—(800) 287-4461
Fax—(973) 633-7449
www.butlersignco.com
Pres.—John J. Janis, Jr.
Off. Mgr.—Vicki Barrella
Bus. Admn.—Edward DeZuzio
SIC—3993; *ADA, architectural, changeable letter, digital, dimensional, display, electric, electronic, electronic moving message, illuminated, LED, metal, neon, plastic & sandblasted interior & exterior signs*
Employs—19; Estab.—1979
Sales—$5Mil
6,800 sq ft site, Distrib.—Regional
Privately owned sub-S corp.

### CALED INDUSTRIES, INC.

26 Hanes Dr. (07470)
**Phone—(973) 696-7575**
National—(800) 652-2533
Fax—(973) 696-4290
www.caledclean.com
Email—jbelluscio@caledclean.com
Pres., GM—Jack Belluscio
Opers. Mgr.—Steve Hoh
SIC—2899; *Chemical blending; Brand name—Caled Chemical; Hypur*
Employs—20; Estab.—1960
Sales—$5Mil-$10Mil
40,000 sq ft site, Distrib.—Intl.
Privately owned corporation

### CARDINAL COMPONENTS, INC.

145 U.S. Highway 46 W., Wayne Interchange I (07470-6812)
**Phone—(973) 785-1333**
Fax—(973) 785-0053
www.cardinalxtal.com
Email—sales@cardinalxtal.com
Pres.—Carl E. Fabend
COO—James Magos
SIC—3679; 3691; 3692; *Standard & custom quartz crystals, oscillators, TCXO, VCXO, field instantly programmable oscillators, real time clocks, solid-state batteries & thin film rechargeable smart solid-state batteries (SSB); Brand name—FIPO; Field Industry Programmable Oscillator; TCXO; VCXO*
Employs—15; Estab.—1986
Sales—$10Mil-$12Mil
Distrib.—Intl.
Privately owned corporation
ISO rating—9001:2008

### CARTRIDGE WORLD OF WAYNE, LLC

1055 Hamburg Tpke. (07470)
**Phone—(973) 696-2880**
Fax—(973) 696-2855
www.cartridgeworld.com/usa/usa88/
Email—cartridgeworldwayne@gmail.com
Owner—Rosemarie Peluso
SIC—3955; 5044; 5112; *Eco-friendly remanufactured printer cartridges & distributor of office equipment & supplies*
Employs—4; Estab.—2005
Sales—$500,000-$1Mil
2,000 sq ft site, Distrib.—National
Limited Liability Company

### CHIPP II

7 Spring Hill Cir. (07470)
**Phone—(212) 687-0850**
www.chipp2.com
Email—jwinston@chipp2.com

## Wayne—(cont.)

Pres.—Janet Winston
SIC—2323; 2253; *Men's neckties, women's scarves & blazer pocket badges*
Employs—2; Estab.—1980
Sales—under $500,000
Distrib.—National
Privately owned corporation

**†COBALT MEDICAL SUPPLY, INC.**
4 Haul Rd. (07470)
Mail addr: P.O. Box 367, Pequannock (07440-0367)
**Phone—(973) 305-0730**
          (888) 350-3790
Fax—(201) 465-3041
www.cobaltmed.com
Email—sales@cobaltmed.com
Opers. Mgr.—Tamar Rees
SIC—5047; *Distributor of medical equipment & supplies, including bandages & cotton balls*
Employs—15; Estab.—1989
Distrib.—Regional
Privately owned corporation

**CREATIVE INDUSTRIAL KITCHENS**
8 Leo Pl. (07470)
**Phone—(973) 633-0420**
Fax—(973) 633-7022
Owner—Tom Walsh
SIC—3589; NAICS—333319; *Stainless steel food service equipment*
Employs—20; Estab.—1987
Sales—$2.5Mil-$5Mil (est)
10,000 sq ft site, Distrib.—Regional

**DERMA-SAFE CO., LLC**
32 Juniper Rd. (07470)
**Phone—(973) 839-6383**
Fax—(973) 839-6383
www.lakebottomblanket.com
Owner—Paul Grosjean
SIC—3423; 3425; *American-made folding utility knives, survival saws & aquatic weed control products*
Employs—2; Estab.—1979
Sales—under $500,000
1,000 sq ft site, Distrib.—Intl.
Limited Liability Company

**DESIGN ACCENTS, LLC**
1330 Hamburg Tpke. (07470)
**Phone—(201) 660-2446**
Fax—(609) 228-5551
www.designaccentsllc.com
Email—info@designaccentsllc.com
Member—Aman Kakar
SIC—2392; *Designer pillows & throws*
Employs—4; Estab.—2007
Sales—$1.5Mil
Distrib.—Intl.
Limited Liability Company

**DI FERRARO, INC.**
28 Burgess Pl. (07470)
**Phone—(973) 694-7200**
Fax—(973) 694-4313
www.totowaconcrete.com
Email—mferrarojr@aol.com
Co-Pres.—Mario Ferraro, Jr.
Co-Pres.—Anna Ferraro
V-P.—Mario Ferraro, Sr.
Plt. Mgr.—Jim Mundy
SIC—3272; *Precast concrete products & burial vaults*
Employs—25; Estab.—1971
Distrib.—National
Privately owned sub-S corp.

**DONNELLY INDUSTRIES, INC.**
557 Route 23 S. (07470)
**Phone—(973) 672-1800**
Fax—(973) 677-1824
www.donnellyconstruction.com
Email—cpowers@donnellyind.com
Pres., CEO—Rod Donnelly

CFO & Hum. Res. Mgr.—Drew Struss
COO—Chris Powers
V-P., Special Projs.—Frank Leone
SIC—2431; NAICS—321900; *Commercial millwork for architects, national retailers, shopping center landlords, country clubs, hospitals, medical facilities, schools, churches & pharmacies*
Employs—90; Estab.—1977
Distrib.—Local
Privately owned corporation

**ECCO HIGH FREQUENCY**
2360 Hamburg Tpke. (07470)
**Phone—(973) 248-3366**
Fax—(973) 248-3304
www.glowtestertechnologies.com
Email—resullivan@glowtestertechnologies.com
Pres.—Richard E. Sullivan
SIC—3567; NAICS—333994; *Induction heating & melting equipment, including jewelry & dental casting machines; Brand name—EccoCast; ECM1; M69; G4; G5; Glowtester*
Employs—8; Estab.—1937
Sales—$1Mil-$5Mil
15,000 sq ft site, Distrib.—Intl.
Privately owned corporation

**ELEVATOR PRODUCTS CORP.**
Div. of Schindler Elevator Corp.
100 Dermarest Dr. (07470)
Mail addr: P.O. Box 999, Wayne (07474)
**Phone—(973) 341-8000**
National—(877) 225-5372
Fax—(973) 341-8080
www.epco.us
Email—hibba.saati@epco.us
Mfg. Mgr.—Eudoro Perez
Mktg. Mgr.—Hibba Saati
Pur. Mgr.—Angel Perez
Hum. Res. Admn.—Geri Barom
SIC—3534; NAICS—333921; *Elevator components*
Employs—85; Estab.—1953
53,000 sq ft site, Distrib.—Intl.
Privately owned corporation
Parent co.—Schindler Elevator Corp., Morristown, NJ
Phone—(973) 397-6500
See Parent Co. Section for full profile.

**EXHIBITCRAFT, INC.**
22 Riverview Dr., Ste. 103 (07470)
**Phone—(973) 686-9393**
Fax—(973) 686-9593
www.exhibitcraftnj.com
Email—sales@exhibitcraftnj.com
Pres.—Scott Walode
SIC—2541; 2542; 3993; *Customized trade show exhibits, show services, corporate interiors, social media marketing & promotional items; Brand name—Abex; Classic; Interlok; TigerMark; Armstrong; Optima; Moss; Orbus; TigerLite*
Employs—15; Estab.—1995
Sales—$2.5Mil-$5Mil
36,000 sq ft site, Distrib.—Local
Privately owned corporation

**EXPRESS GRAPHICS**
17 Dupont Ter. (07470)
Mail addr: P.O. Box 4091, Wayne (07474)
**Phone—(973) 696-3165**
Fax—(973) 696-3175
www.expressgraphicsnj.com
Email—kurt@expressgraphic.com
Owner—Kurt Gough
SIC—2759; *Commercial printing*
Employs—3; Estab.—1998
Sales—under $500,000
Distrib.—Local
Sole ownership

**FIDELITY INDUSTRIES, INC.**
559 R.R. 23 S. (07470)
Mail addr: P.O. Box 218, Wayne (07474)
**Phone—(973) 696-9120**
Fax—(973) 696-4123
www.fidelitywall.com
Email—info@fidelitywall.com
V-P. & Hum. Res. Mgr.—Samuel Brook
IT Mgr.—Laibel Karp
SIC—2679; NAICS—322200; *Vinyl-backed wall coverings*
Employs—50; Estab.—1977
300,000 sq ft site, Distrib.—National
Privately owned corporation

**FILTREX, INC.**
450 Hamburg Tpke. (07470)
Mail addr: P.O. Box 2273, Wayne (07474)
**Phone—(973) 595-0400**
Fax—(973) 595-6506
Email—filtrex1@aol.com
Pres.—Kenneth A. Bergstrom
Secy.-Treas.—Lucrecia A. Kobierowski
Pur. Mgr.—Mike Tardy
Acctg. Mgr.—Mary Ellen Micola
SIC—3589; NAICS—333319; *Swimming pool filters*
Employs—8; Estab.—1974
Sales—$500,000-$1Mil
Distrib.—Intl.
Privately owned corporation

**FIN-TEK OZONE**
6 Leo Pl. (07470)
**Phone—(973) 628-2988**
          (973) 988-1081
Fax—(973) 628-2989
www.fin-tek.com
Email—mary@fin-tek.com
Pres., Fin., MIS & R & D Mgr.—Donald Finnegan
V-P.—Mary Finnegan
Dir., Sales Dev.—Mickey Walsh
SIC—3589; 3621; NAICS—333319; *Water purifying ozone generators & monitors*
Employs—10; Estab.—1987
Sales—$1Mil-$5Mil
3,000 sq ft site, Distrib.—Intl.
Privately owned sub-S corp.

**FUJI FILM MEDICAL SYSTEMS U.S.A., INC.**
10 Highpoint Dr. (07470-7431)
**Phone—(973) 633-5600**
National—(800) 385-4666
Fax—(973) 633-8818
www.fujinonendoscopy.com
Email—g5info@fujinon.com
Pres.—Keiichi Nagata
V-P., Opers.—Kurt Cannon
IT Mgr.—Dom Bastello
Hum. Res. Mgr.—Maria Uram
Corp. Comms. Mgr.—Lucia Pintauro
Qual. Control Mgr.—John Brzezinski
SIC—3845; NAICS—334500; *Corporate headquarters & endoscopic equipment (mfg. done in Japan)*
Employs—65; Estab.—1974
Sales—$10Mil-$25Mil (est)
Distrib.—Intl.
Publicly owned corporation

**GAF**
1361 Alps Rd. (07470)
**Phone—(973) 628-3000**
          (800) 766-3411
National—(800) 365-7353
www.gaf.com
Email—commercialsales@gaf.com
Pres., CEO—Bob Tafaro
Sr. V-P., CFO—John Rebele
Hum. Res. Mgr.—Becky Petraska
Mktg. Comms. Mgr.—Alyssa Hall

SIC—2952; NAICS—324122; *Company headquarters & commercial & residential roofing systems, ventilation & accessories; Brand name—Timberline Shingles; Cobra Ridge Vents*
Employs—400; Estab.—1886
Sales—under $3Bil
125,000 sq ft site, Distrib.—Intl.
Privately owned corporation

**†GILL ASSOCS. IDENTIFICATION SYSTEMS, LLC**
2025 Hamburg Tpke., Ste. M (07470-6250)
**Phone—(973) 835-5456**
National—(800) 334-4128
Fax—(973) 835-3235
www.identificationusa.com
Email—dave@identificationusa.com
Owner & Member—Dave Gill
SIC—5043; *Distributor of photo identification card printers & systems, including badge reels & holders, lanyards, proximity cards & repair; Brand name—Polaroid; Evolis; Zebra; Fargo; Datacard; Magic Card*
Employs—6; Estab.—1979
Sales—$1.2Mil
1,500 sq ft site, Distrib.—National
Limited Liability Company

**GRAPHIC CONCEPTS/REPRODUCTION, INC.**
111 Butternut Dr. (07470)
**Phone—(973) 706-6400**
Fax—(973) 706-6414
www.graphicconcepts.com
Email—sales@graphicconcepts.com
Pres., GM—Linda Gaba
SIC—2752; NAICS—323100; *Offset & digital printing*
Employs—4; Estab.—1977
5,000 sq ft site, Distrib.—National
Privately owned corporation

**HAIER AMERICA TRADING, LLC (HQ)**
1800 Valley Rd. (07470)
**Phone—(973) 617-1800**
National—(800) 461-8890
www.haieramerica.com
Email—productinfo@haieramerica.com
Pres.—Shariff Kan
Sr. Corp. Comm. Mgr.—James Lies
SIC—3663; 3629; NAICS—334220; *Company headquarters; appliances & electronics*
Employs—100; Estab.—1998
Sales—over $500Mil
Distrib.—National
Limited Liability Company

**HAYDON CORP.**
415 Hamberg Tpke., Bldg. D (07470)
**Phone—(973) 904-0800**
National—(800) 242-9366
Fax—(973) 904-0016
www.2haydon.com
Pres.—Doug Hillman
V-P.—Robert Gerber
Engrg. & Maint. Mgr.—Pat Mullen
Fin. Mgr.—Raj Komdar
SIC—3442; 3449; NAICS—332321; *Metal struts & baseboards*
Employs—65
120,000 sq ft site, Distrib.—Local
Privately owned corporation

**HERO'S SALUTE AWARDS CO.**
1875 State Route 23 (07470)
**Phone—(973) 696-5085**
National—(888) 457-8080
Fax—(973) 696-9114
www.heros-salute.com
Email—orders@heros-salute.com
Pres.—Robert Terry
V-P.—Troy Terry

GEOGRAPHICAL

## Wayne—(cont.)

GM—Monica Luyster
Fin. Mgr.—Margaret Terry
SIC—3479; 3993; 2399;
*Awards, trophies, signs,
banners, flags & engraving*
Employs—10; Estab.—1972
Sales—$1Mil-$2.5Mil
4,000 sq ft site, Distrib.—National
Privately owned sub-S corp.

### HINCHMAN & SON, INC., HERBERT J.

26 Pike Dr. (07470)
**Phone—(973) 942-2063**
Fax—(973) 942-9319
www.hinchcrete.com
Pres.—Donald Hinchman
Off. Mgr.—Karen Hinchman
Bookkeeper—Jill Whitney
SIC—3273; NAICS—327320;
*Ready-mixed concrete*
Employs—17; Estab.—1928
3,500 sq ft site, Distrib.—Local
Limited Liability Company

### IMAGE MAKERS PRINTING, COPY & SIGN CENTER

1581 State Route 23 (07470-7508)
**Phone—(973) 633-1771**
Fax—(973) 628-8238
www.imagemakersprinting.com
Email—image.makers.printing@
gmail.com
Pres.—Gino Nuzzo
Manager—Michael Coss
Graphic Artist—Julia Calabrese
SIC—2752; 2759; 3993; 2789;
NAICS—323100; *High-speed
color printing, blueprinting &
signs, including in-house design
& bindery work*
Employs—5; Estab.—1984
Sales—$500,000-$1Mil
1,500 sq ft site, Distrib.—Local
Privately owned corporation

### INTERMARKET TECHNOLOGY, INC.

92 Newark Pompton Tpke. (07470)
**Phone—(973) 872-9090**
Fax—(973) 872-9010
www.intmarktech.com
Email—customerservice@
intmarktech.com
Pres., Hum. Res. & IT Mgr.—Scott
Gardner
Cont.—Steven Smith
Dir., Sales—Patty Boyle
Bookkeeper—Nina Dellorto
SIC—2542; *Point-of-purchase
fixtures*
Employs—40; Estab.—1995
45,000 sq ft site, Distrib.—National
Privately owned corporation

### KROWNE METAL CORP.

100 Haul Rd. (07470)
**Phone—(973) 305-3300**
National—(800) 631-0442
Fax—(973) 872-1129
www.krowne.com
Email—customerservice@
krowne.com
Ex. V-P.—Roger Forman
Ex. V-P.—Frank Bastante
SIC—3444; 3499; *Stainless steel
bar & restaurant equipment,
including foodservice faucets*
Employs—44; Estab.—1957
Distrib.—National
Privately owned corporation

### LEIF J. OSTBERG, INC. (H Q)

401 Hamburg Tpke., Ste. 305
(07470)
**Phone—(973) 956-6990**
Fax—(973) 956-6991
www.ljoinc.com
Email—ljo@ljoinc.com
Pres.—Jim Kimberlin

SIC—3143; 3144; 3149; 3142;
*Corporate headquarters; men's,
women's & children's footwear,
including casual, sports, hiking
& work footwear & slippers (mfg.
done in China & Vietnam)*
Employs—20; Estab.—1986
Sales—$500,000-$1Mil
Distrib.—Intl.
Privately owned corporation

### MADDAK INC.

Div. of SP Industries, Inc.
661 State Route 23 (07470)
**Phone—(973) 628-7600**
National—(800) 443-4926
www.maddak.com
Email—custservice@maddak.com
COO—Brad Mahood
Ex. V-P.—Mary Seto
Dir., MIS—Israel Engle
Dir., Prod. Dev.—Kathleen Hanek
Mktg. Mgr.—Susan Tulanowski
Hum. Res. Mgr.—Lucie Zembruski
Cust. Serv. Rep.—Cathy Jacovelli
SIC—3842; *Corporate
headquarters & home healthcare
products for seniors, people with
disabilities & people recovering
from injuries & illnesses; Brand
name—Ableware*
Employs—100; Estab.—1971
Sales—$10Mil-$25Mil (est)
50,000 sq ft site, Distrib.—Intl.
Privately owned corporation
Parent co.—SP Industries, Inc.,
Warminster, PA
Phone—(215) 672-7800
See Parent Co. Section for full profile.

### MANE USA, INC.

60 Demarest Dr. (07470)
**Phone—(973) 633-5533**
Fax—(973) 633-5538
www.mane.com
Email—requests@mane.com
Pres., CEO—Jean M. Mane
V-P., Consumer Goods & CFO—
Tathiana Remick
V-P., Opers.—Larry Deraney
V-P., MIS—Chris Chludzinski
V-P., Hum. Res.—Deborah
Knighton
Dir., Qual. Assur.—Dianne Dolan
Dir., Supply Chain—Todd Greene
SIC—2844; 2869; NAICS—
325600; *Corporate headquarters
& fragrance ingredients,
fragrances & flavors*
Employs—138; Estab.—1981
Sales—$25Mil-$50Mil
60,000 sq ft site, Distrib.—Intl.
Privately owned corporation

### MANIFOLD PRINTERS, INC.

189 Berdan Ave., Ste. 456 (07470)
**Phone—(973) 345-5900**
Fax—(973) 709-0260
Email—printrs4@aol.com
Pres.—Oscar Cone
SIC—2752; NAICS—323100;
*Lithographic printing*
Employs—20; Estab.—2005
Sales—under $500,000
22,000 sq ft site, Distrib.—Local
Privately owned corporation

### MAQUET CARDIOVASCULAR, LLC

45 Barbour Pond Dr. (07470)
**Phone—(973) 709-7000**
National—(800) 225-3238
Fax—(973) 860-0983
www.maquet.com
Email—info@maquet-inc.com
Pres., CEO—Peter Hinchliffe
Pres., Cardiopulmonary & CEO—
Wolfgang Rencken
CFO—Gerhard Mayer
Ex. V-P., Global Sales & Mktg.—
John Saavedra
V-P., Mktg.—Brad Cilley
MIS Mgr.—Richard Tartini
Hum. Res. Mgr.—Beverly Walker

SIC—3842; *Company
headquarters & surgical vascular
grafts*
Employs—500; Estab.—1964
Sales—$25Mil-$100Mil
280,000 sq ft site, Distrib.—Intl.
Limited Liability Company
ISO rating—9001

### MARTIN SPROCKET & GEAR, INC.

7 Highpoint Dr. (07470)
**Phone—(973) 633-5700**
Fax—(973) 633-7196
www.martinsprocket.com
Email—rbongiorno@
martinsprocket.com
Dist. Mgr.—Rick Bongiorno
SIC—3599; *General machining
job shop*
Employs—6; Estab.—1951
Sales—under $500,000
Distrib.—Regional
Privately owned corporation
Parent co.—Martin Sprocket &
Gear, Inc., Arlington, TX
Phone—(817) 258-3000
See Parent Co. Section for full profile.

### MAYER/BERKSHIRE CORP. (H Q)

25 Edison Rd., P.O. Box 244
(07474)
**Phone—(973) 696-6200**
National—(800) 245-6789
Fax—(973) 696-6203
www.eberkshire.com
Email—customerservice@
eberkshire.com
CEO—Chester Mayer
Ex. V-P.—Michael Mayer
V-P.—Robert Mayer
Off. Mgr.—Doris Martin
SIC—2252; *Corporate
headquarters; hosiery, including
socks, stockings, pantyhose,
knee-highs & leggings; Brand
name—Berkshire Hosiery*
Employs—50; Estab.—1945
Sales—$2.5Mil-$5Mil (est)
Distrib.—National
Privately owned corporation

### METRO PACKAGING & IMAGING, INC.

5 Haul Rd. (07470)
**Phone—(973) 709-9100**
Fax—(973) 709-9477
www.metro-pi.com
Email—info@metro-pi.com
Chrm., CEO—Manuel Detorres
Pres.—Armand Detorres
V-P., Prod.—George Fantry
Ex. Mgr., Prepress—Eric Detorres
IT Mgr.—Leo McLaughlin
Hum. Res. Mgr.—Alicia Detorres
SIC—2759; NAICS—323100;
*Folding carton printing, including
digital imaging, die cutting,
folding & gluing*
Employs—110; Estab.—1964
95,000 sq ft site, Distrib.—Intl.
Privately owned corporation

### NORTH JERSEY METAL FABRICATORS, INC.

130 Ryerson Ave., Ste. 107
(07470)
**Phone—(973) 305-9830**
Fax—(973) 305-9832
Email—njmfab@optonline.net
Pres.—Bill Ecker
Off. Mgr.—Robert Ecker
Bus. Foreman—Richard Ecker
SIC—3449; 3444; 3441; 3231;
NAICS—332999; *Metal,
aluminum, stainless steel & glass
fabrication of railings*
Employs—7; Estab.—1979
Distrib.—Regional
Privately owned corporation

### PASSAIC COUNTY WELDERS, INC.

100 Parish Dr. (07470)
**Phone—(973) 696-1200**
Fax—(973) 696-1411

www.pcwfab.com
Email—robert@pcwfab.com
V-P.—Robert Grimbilas
V-P.—Peter Grimbilas
Hum. Res. & Off. Mgr.—Teresa
Katonka
Proj. Coord.—Tom Smith
SIC—3312; 3441; 3499; 3599;
NAICS—332312; *Welding &
structural steel, steel, sheet
metal & architectural fabrication
of weldments, tanks, cones &
hoppers, including heavy plate
fabrication, large forming &
rolling & sandblasting*
Employs—38; Estab.—1948
Sales—$7.2Mil
29,000 sq ft site, Distrib.—
Regional
Privately owned sub-S corp.

### PASSAIC RUBBER CO., INC.

45 Demarest Dr. (07470)
Mail addr: P.O. Box 505, Wayne
(07474-0505)
**Phone—(973) 696-9500**
Fax—(973) 696-0686
www.passaic.com
Email—answers@passaic.com
Chrm., COO—Jeff Leach
Pres., CEO—J. D. Mathey
V-P., Opers.—James Leach
Plt. Mgr.—Glenn Kuras
Off. Mgr.—Susan Bender
SIC—3069; 3052; 3061; NAICS—
326220; *Private label & contract
rubber coated fabrics, sleeves,
belting & roof membranes,
rubber covered rollers &
calendered rubber, including
slitting, converting, molding &
rubber lining metal parts*
Employs—35; Estab.—1919
Sales—over $10Mil
70,000 sq ft site, Distrib.—Intl.
Privately owned partnership

### PATRIOT PICKLE

20 Edison Dr. (07470)
**Phone—(973) 709-9487**
National—(866) 345-5845
Fax—(973) 709-9608
www.patriotpickle.com
Email—ajmackey@
patriotpickle.com
Pres.—Bill McEntee
Off. Mgr.—Amanda Mackey
SIC—2035; *Pickles*
Employs—50; Estab.—1997
Sales—$5Mil-$10Mil
Distrib.—Local
Privately owned corporation

### PIERMOUNT IRONWORKS, INC.

129 Old Turnpike Rd. (07470)
**Phone—(973) 837-1750**
Fax—(973) 837-1752
www.piermount.com
Pres.—David Finucane
Opers. Mgr.—Pat Kelly, Jr.
Off. Mgr.—Linda Kelly
SIC—3441; NAICS—332312;
*Structural steel fabrication &
erection*
Employs—15; Estab.—1996
Distrib.—Local
Privately owned corporation

### POCHET OF AMERICA, INC.

415 Hamburg Tpke., Ste. 2
(07470-2104)
**Phone—(973) 942-4923**
Fax—(973) 942-5364
Email—mlakshmi@pochet.fr
Pres.—Borislav Zivkovic
Cont.—Maha Sambamurthy
Dir., Sales—Olivier Trevidic
Dir., Indl. Opers.—Jonathan Clark

## Wayne—(cont.)

SIC—2759; 3231; NAICS—
327215; *Corporate headquarters
& perfume bottle screen printing*
Employs—100; Estab.—1983
Sales—$40Mil
73,000 sq ft site, Distrib.—Intl.
Privately owned corporation

**POLYMERIC RESOURCES
CORPORATION, INC.**

55 Haul Rd. (07470)
**Phone—(973) 694-4141**
National—(800) 626-7050
Fax—(973) 694-3549
www.nylene.com
Email—info@nylene.com
Pres.—Sol Schlesinger
V.-P., Plt. Opers.—Moses Friedman
SIC—2821; 3087; NAICS—
325991; *Corporate headquarters
& plastic resin compounds &
nylon specialties; Brand name—
Nylene*
Employs—50; Estab.—1978
Sales—$50Mil-$100Mil
230,000 sq ft site, Distrib.—Intl.
Privately owned corporation
ISO rating—QS9000
AKA: PRC Custom Resins

**PRO LINE MFG. CO., LLC**

186 Parish Dr. (07470)
**Phone—(973) 692-9696**
National—(800) 334-4612
Fax—(973) 692-0999
www.prolineboots.com
Email—toplineus@aol.com
V.-P.—T. S. Kim
V.-P.—Bob Hollenberg
Dir., Prod. Dev.—Juno Yoon
Acctg. Mgr.—Jenny Kang
Sales & Mktg. Team Leader—
Ellen Campbell
SIC—3021; NAICS—339920;
*Fishing, hunting & rubber boots
& waders; Brand name—Pro
Line; Winchester; Duck
Commander; Buck Commander;
Team Realtree Baby Shoes; Girls
With Guns*
Employs—40; Estab.—1975
Sales—$20Mil-$25Mil
Distrib.—Intl.
Privately owned corporation

**REED-LANE, INC.**

359 Newark Pompton Tpke.
(07470)
**Phone—(973) 709-1090**
National—(877) 290-1090
Fax—(973) 709-1091
www.reedlane.com
Email—info@reedlane.com
Pres.—Patricia Elvin
CFO—Carmine Sodora
Cont.—Chris Preta
IT Mgr.—Joe Estrada
Hum. Res. Mgr.—Nelly Petrasek
SIC—3089; 2899; 3999; NAICS—
334418; *Contract assembly &
packaging for the
pharmaceutical industry*
Employs—175; Estab.—1959
Distrib.—National
Privately owned corporation

**REEVES INTERNATIONAL, INC.**

34 Owens Dr. (07470)
**Phone—(973) 956-9555**
National—(800) 444-4775
Fax—(973) 956-0077
www.breyerhorses.com
Email—breyerwebstore@
reevesintl.com
Prodn. Mgr.—Bill Rausch
Whse. Mgr.—Frank Casamento
Cust. Serv. Mgr.—Tom Garrison
Hum. Res. Admn.—Diane Wheeler

SIC—3944; 3089; *Model horses*
Employs—100; Estab.—1978
Sales—$10Mil-$25Mil (est)
Distrib.—Intl.
Privately owned corporation
Parent co.—Reeves International,
Inc., Pequannock, NJ
Phone—(973) 694-5006
See Parent Co. Section for full profile.

**RIDGID PAPER TUBE CORP.**

10 Owens Dr. (07470-2341)
**Phone—(973) 942-7000**
(888) 278-7029
Fax—(973) 942-1675
www.ridgidpapertube.com
Email—michael@
ridgidpapertube.com
Pres.—Thomas Horsburgh
V.-P., Hum. Res. & CFO—Michael
Horsburgh, Jr.
V.-P., Sales & Mktg.—Michael
Horsburgh
Off. Mgr.—Josephine Horsburgh
SIC—2655; NAICS—322214;
*Mailing & shipping tubes,
converter & tape & label cores,
display poles, concrete forms,
paper test cylinders, collection
containers, round packaging,
straight cylinder lab grade white
paper containers with lids*
Employs—30; Estab.—1950
Sales—$1Mil-$5Mil
34,000 sq ft site, Distrib.—National
Privately owned corporation

**ROBYN PACKAGING CO., INC.**

31 Augusta Dr. (07470)
**Phone—(973) 696-2059**
Fax—(973) 694-7238
www.robynpackaging.com
Email—robynpkg@gmail.com
Pres.—George DeAngelo
V.-P., Mfg.—George Flowers
Sales Mgr.—Harry Brown
Plt. Mgr.—Robert Maka
SIC—3089; *Plastic bags & labels*
Employs—40; Estab.—1974
Sales—$5Mil-$10Mil
35,000 sq ft site, Distrib.—
Regional
Privately owned corporation

**ROYAL ADHESIVE, INC.**

Div. of Royal Adhesives &
Sealants, LLC
48 Burgess Pl. (07470)
**Phone—(973) 694-0845**
Fax—(973) 694-5678
www.royaladhesives.com
Email—karl.huelsenbeck@
rascp.com
Pres.—Victoria Corbo
V.-P., Opers.—Karl Huelsenbeck
SIC—2891; 2851; NAICS—
325520; *Industrial adhesives,
coatings & specialty products*
Employs—30; Estab.—1946
22,500 sq ft site, Distrib.—Intl.
Privately owned corporation
ISO rating—9000:2000
Parent co.—Royal Adhesives &
Sealants, LLC, South Bend, IN
Phone—(574) 246-5000
See Parent Co. Section for full profile.

**SAINT-GOBAIN PERFORMANCE
PLASTICS**

150 Dey Rd. (07470)
**Phone—(973) 696-4700**
Fax—(973) 696-4056
www.plastics.saint-gobain.com
Email—sgppl.marketing@saint-
gobain.com
Sales Mgr., Global—William O.
Textoris
Plt. Mgr.—Rene Sarmiento
Hum. Res. Mgr.—MaryLou
DeSimone
Prod. Mgr., Films—Dierdre Zammit
Cust. Serv. Mgr.—Barbara Surace
Literature Coord.—Joan Kirby

SIC—3081; 3562; NAICS—
326113; *Plastic film &
maintenance-free bearings*
Employs—250
Sales—$50Mil-$100Mil
Distrib.—Intl.
Publicly owned corporation
ISO rating—AS9100C, TS16949,
9001, 14001
Parent co.—Saint-Gobain
Performance Plastics, Aurora,
OH
Phone—(216) 245-0529
See Parent Co. Section for full profile.

**SCHELD ASSOCS., INC.**

37 Pleasantview Dr. (07470)
**Phone—(973) 694-0637**
Pres.—John Scheld
Off. Mgr.—Carla Scheld
SIC—3089; *Specialty polymers
for mechanical seals, toys &
prototypes*
Employs—3; Estab.—1982
Sales—under $500,000 (est)
Distrib.—National

**SCREENS, INC.**

130 Ryerson Ave., Ste. 219
(07470)
**Phone—(973) 633-8558**
Pres.—Robert Vorndran
SIC—3442; *Aluminum window
screens*
Employs—4; Estab.—1990
Distrib.—National
Privately owned corporation

**SELLERS & JOSEPHSON, LLC**

559 Route 23 (07470)
**Phone—(201) 567-1353**
Fax—(201) 567-8179
www.sjwallcovering.com
Email—service@sjwallcovering.com
Pres., CEO—Shmuel Brook
SIC—2679; 3069; NAICS—
322200; *Wallcoverings*
Employs—49; Estab.—2010
100,000 sq ft site, Distrib.—
National
Privately owned corporation

**SUNBELT CORP.**

63 Atwood Pl. (07470)
**Phone—(803) 329-9787**
National—(800) 768-9787
Fax—(803) 329-3350
www.sunbeltcolors.com
Email—sunbelt@sunbeltcolors.com
Bus. Dev. Mgr.—Ken Mackinnon
Technical Mgr.—George Cherry
EHS & Qual. Control Mgr.—Larry
D. French, Jr.
SIC—2865; 2899; NAICS—
325100; *Solvent dyes, water-
based dyes, powder dyes, liquid
dyes, acid & liquid dyes, textile
dyes & specialty chemicals;
Brand name—Morfast®;
Navipol®; Navipon; Navalene;
Morplas®; Navinon®; Navilan®*
Employs—4; Estab.—1987
Distrib.—National
Privately owned corporation
Parent co.—Sunbelt Corp., Rock
Hill, SC
Phone—(803) 329-9787
See Parent Co. Section for full profile.

**SWANSON ASSOCS.**

P.O. Box 151 (07470)
**Phone—(973) 984-5930**
Email—swansonfireball@
yahoo.com
Owner—Kent Swanson
SIC—3694; 3699; *Model airplane
glow plugs & igniters for
scientific instruments; Brand
name—Fireball Glow Plugs*
Employs—2; Estab.—1948
Sales—under $500,000
500 sq ft site, Distrib.—Intl.
Sole ownership

**TOPLINE PRODUCTS CO., INC.**

155 Route 46 W., 2nd Fl. (07470)
**Phone—(973) 785-1600**
Fax—(973) 785-8866
www.topline-usa.com
Email—mail@topline-usa.com
Pres.—Charles Chang
Cont.—Horng Yang
SIC—2844; NAICS—325600;
*Corporate headquarters &
cosmetics*
Employs—35
Sales—$10Mil-$25Mil (est)
Distrib.—National
Privately owned corporation
ISO rating—9000

**TORNQVIST**

29 Hanes Dr. (07470)
**Phone—(973) 686-5999**
Fax—(973) 686-5995
www.tqfab.com
Email—info@tqfab.com
Off. Mgr.—Adam Mosciszko
SIC—3499; 3599; *Metal
fabrication, laser cutting &
welding job shop*
Employs—22; Estab.—1872
Sales—$1Mil-$5Mil
27,500 sq ft site, Distrib.—Regional
Privately owned sub-S corp.

**UNIVERSAL METALCRAFT, INC.**

24 Burgess Pl. (07470)
**Phone—(973) 345-3284**
Fax—(973) 345-7648
www.umcraft.com
Email—eric@umcraft.com
Pres.—Eric Wenstrom
Manager—Marc Wenstrom
SIC—3599; *General & precision
machining job shop, including
cutting, grinding, turning, milling,
drilling & wire EDM*
Employs—25; Estab.—1974
Sales—$2.6Mil-$5Mil
12,000 sq ft site, Distrib.—National
Sole ownership

**US SIGN & LIGHTING SERVICE, LLC**

105 Dorsa Ave. (07470)
**Phone—(973) 305-8900**
Fax—(973) 305-8901
www.ussignservice.com
Email—sales@ussignservice.com
GM—John Kelley
SIC—3993; *Interior & exterior
signs*
Employs—7
Sales—$500,000-$1Mil (est)
Limited Liability Company

**VERACITI, INC.**

1044 Route 23, Ste. 102 (07470)
**Phone—(973) 887-8660**
Fax—(973) 947-7575
www.veraciti.com
Email—support@veraciti.com
Pres. & IT Mgr.—Frank Altieri
Sales Rep.—Chris Fitzpatrick
Dispatcher—Carlos Gambina
SIC—7373; NAICS—541512;
*Computer network & wireless
security integrated systems &
online backup & managed
services*
Employs—7; Estab.—2000
Distrib.—National
Privately owned corporation

**VISION RESEARCH, INC.**

Div. of AMETEK, Inc.
100 Dey Rd. (07470)
**Phone—(973) 696-4500**
National—(866) 450-7426
Fax—(973) 696-0560
www.visionresearch.com
Email—phantom@
visionresearch.com
V.-P., Bus. Unit & GM—Jay
Stepleton
Dir., Mktg.—Rick Robinson
E-Mktg. Mgr.—Randy Feldman

GEOGRAPHICAL

# Enjoy *real-time* access to the *freshest*
# New Jersey industrial info at EZSelect®.com

## Learn how an EZSelect.com subscription to our industrial information databases can empower you today!

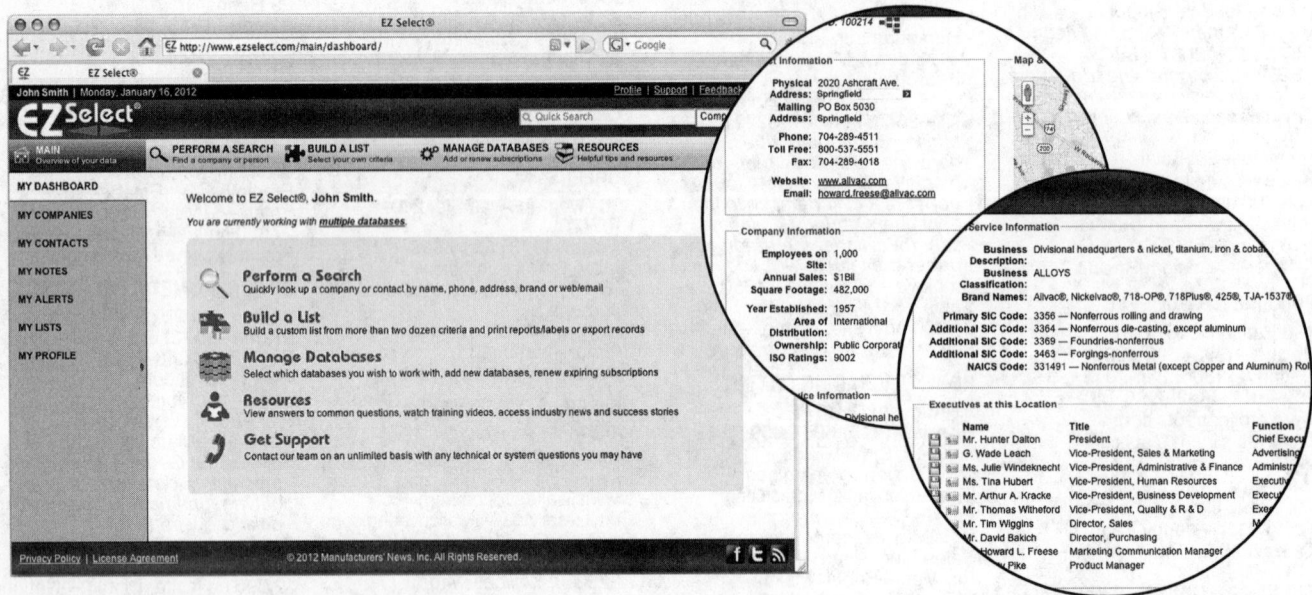

## Powerful online search & contact management tools!

Manufacturers' News, Inc. is proud to introduce **EZSelect.com**; our revolutionary and powerful new search and contact management software for your industrial database subscription.

If you liked our EZ-Select CD-ROMs, then get ready; **EZSelect.com** has been completely redesigned and enhanced from the ground up. And there's nothing to install on your computer! EZ Select.com is entirely WEB BASED so you can access your database subscription from any computer and ALWAYS work with our freshest data in real time!

Here are some of the ways you can use this powerful business tool:

- Identify your best prospects by location, industry, and size.
- Get instant counts, build and save lists of companies and contacts.
- Export leads to CRM softare or for mailing and telemarketing.
- Locate execs by name or title and sync with your address book.
- Add notes, connect through social networking and much more!

## NEW JERSEY

| EZSelect.com subscription | # of Firms | Annual Price |
|---|---|---|
| Full Version | 10,183 | $642 |
| 20+ employees | 4,118 | $472 |
| Basic Version | 10,183 | $225 |

Prices subject to change

**The Full & 20+ version of EZ Select** includes advanced features including the ability to export profiles, print address labels, print summary and detail reports, and browse all profiles.

**The Basic version of EZ Select** can sort, print 1 profile at a time & no export.

# Visit **EZSelect.com** for more information on this and other databases!

## Wayne—(cont.)

SIC—3861; *Corporate headquarters & high-speed cameras & motion analysis systems; Brand name—Phantom; Miro*
Employs—100; Estab.—1992
Company-wide: 195
Sales—$50Mil-$100Mil
Distrib.—Intl.
Publicly owned corporation
Parent co.—AMETEK, Inc., Berwyn, PA
Phone—(610) 647-2121
See Parent Co. Section for full profile.

**WAYNE MEAT CORP.**
2234 Hamburg Tpke. (07470)
**Phone—(973) 835-0211**
Opers. Mgr.—Marty Powers
Manager—Micheal Powers
SIC—2011; NAICS—311611; *Meat processing & packing*
Employs—5; Estab.—1979
Sales—under $500,000
Distrib.—Local
Privately owned corporation

## Weehawken

(Hudson—N.E.)

**ARECIA'S CREATIONS**
3704 Park Ave. (07086)
**Phone—(201) 864-7388**
Fax—(201) 864-7388
Owner—Arecia Hernandez
Sales Mgr.—Margarita Leon
SIC—2335; NAICS—315200; *Wedding, sweet sixteen & communion dresses*
Employs—2; Estab.—1984
Sales—under $500,000
Distrib.—Local
Sole ownership

**E F DESIGN LTD.**
600 Harbor Blvd., Unit 1022 (07086)
**Phone—(201) 319-9075**
(201) 601-7990
Fax—(201) 319-9076
www.demika.com
Email—info@demika.com
Chrm.—Robert Fuhrman
Pres.—Esther Fuhrman
Off. Mgr.—Natalie Vasilyeva
SIC—3961; NAICS—339900; *Patented jewelry accessories, including self-locking clasps & earring backs in 14-K gold; Brand name—ClickSecure; Demika*
Employs—4; Estab.—1987
Sales—over $10Mil
Distrib.—Intl.
Privately owned corporation

**HANOVER DIRECT, INC. (H Q)**
1500 Harbor Blvd., 1st Fl. (07086)
**Phone—(201) 863-7300**
Fax—(201) 272-3465
www.hanoverdirect.com
Email—information@hanoverdirect.com
Pres., CEO—Don Kelley
CIO—Lander Bravo
Mktg. Mgr.—Maria Liguiri
IT Mgr.—Jesus M. Garcia
SIC—2392; *Corporate headquarters; home furnishings*
Employs—50
Sales—$25Mil-$50Mil
Distrib.—Intl.

**MICROS RETAIL SYSTEMS, INC.**
1500 Harbor Blvd., Ste. 2 (07086-6768)
**Phone—(201) 866-1000**
Fax—(201) 866-8282
www.microsnyc.com
Email—lubodar@microsnyc.com
Pres.—Lubodar Olesnycky

Dir., Sales, NY State—Todd Smith
Dir., Sales, NJ—Tom Zerrenner
SIC—7372; 3577; *Point-of-sale software development & hardware, including installation & professional services*
Employs—108; Estab.—1986
Sales—$17Mil-$20Mil
18,500 sq ft site, Distrib.—Regional
Privately owned sub-S corp.

**SWATCH GROUP (U.S.), INC. (H Q)**
1200 Harbor Blvd., 7th Fl. (07086)
**Phone—(201) 271-1400**
National—(877) 839-5223
Fax—(201) 558-5042
www.swatchgroup.com
Email—info@swatchgroup.com
Pres.—Caroline Faivet
V.-P., IT—Steve Bolcar
Hum. Res. & Payroll Mgr.—Sue Horn
SIC—3699; 3679; *Corporate headquarters; pulsed laser/sources & electronic component micro-crystals & watches*
Employs—125
Sales—$25Mil-$50Mil (est)

**WOOD SHED, INC., THE**
4500 Park Ave. (07086)
**Phone—(201) 866-7949**
Fax—(201) 866-5719
www.woodshedwoodworking.com
Pres.—Roland Arlt
Foreman—Mike Fiorenza
SIC—2511; 2434; 2431; *Wooden furniture, bookcases & kitchen cabinets*
Employs—3; Estab.—1971
Sales—under $500,000
Distrib.—Local
Privately owned corporation

## Wenonah

(Gloucester—S.W.)

**ALETE PRINTING, LLC**
722 Dartmouth Ct., P.O. Box 371 (08090)
**Phone—(856) 468-3536**
Fax—(856) 468-8283
www.aleteprinting.net
Email—aleteprint@verizon.net
V.-P., CEO—John Koskinen
Pres.—Patricia Ann Koskinen
SIC—2759; 2761; 2395; 2396; *Commercial & variable data printing of brochures, business & continuous custom forms, catalogs & promotional products & screen printing & embroidery of apparel & team uniforms*
Employs—4; Estab.—2000
Sales—$500,000-$1Mil
Distrib.—National
Limited Liability Company

**COTTERMAN, INC.**
100 Hayes Ave., P.O. Box 278 (08090)
**Phone—(856) 464-6820**
(856) 577-0245
Fax—(856) 464-6930
www.cottermaninc.com
Email—welders@cottermancorp.com
Pres.—William Thomas
Off. & Proj. Mgr.—Kate Parkin
Qual. Control Mgr.—John Raffaghello
Lead Mechanic—Jeffrey Griner
SIC—3599; 3498; *High-pressure piping & industrial welding job shop*
Employs—20; Estab.—1999
Distrib.—Local
Privately owned corporation

**TRANSITION METALS TECHNOLOGY**
314 N. West Ave. (08090)
**Phone—(856) 468-6747**
Fax—(856) 464-1835
www.metalsminerals.com
Email—archie@metalsminerals.com
Pres., CEO—Edward L. Payer
Plt. Mgr.—Robert Klinger
SIC—1231; NAICS—212113; *Anthracite coal mining, including production steel mill fluxes, bagged anthracite coal & magnetite ore for heavy media*
Employs—39; Estab.—1963
Sales—$6Mil-$10Mil
Distrib.—Intl.
Limited Liability Company

## West Berlin

(Camden—S.W.)

**ADAPTER TECHNOLOGIES, INC.**
154 Cooper Rd., Unit 1303 (08091)
**Phone—(856) 767-3930**
Pres., Plt. Mgr.—John Miller
SIC—3699; *Electronic connectors & assemblies*
Employs—6; Estab.—1994
Sales—under $500,000
Distrib.—National
Privately owned corporation

**ASCALON STUDIOS, INC.**
430 Cooper Rd. (08091)
**Phone—(856) 768-3779**
National—(888) 280-5656
Fax—(856) 768-3902
www.ascalonstudios.com
Email—info@ascalonstudios.com
Pres., Hum. Res. Mgr.—David Ascalon
V.-P.—Ronit Ascalon
SIC—3231; 3259; NAICS—327215; *Sculptures, memorials, monuments, stained glass windows, architectural glass art, specialty furniture & donor recognition project*
Employs—10; Estab.—1982
5,000 sq ft site, Distrib.—National
Privately owned sub-S corp.

**ATI AUDIO**
154 Cooper Road S-902 (08091)
Mail addr.: P.O. Box 1530, Voorhees (08043-7530)
**Phone—(856) 719-9900**
Fax—(856) 719-9903
www.atiaudio.com
Email—sales@daysequerra.com
Pres.—David Day
V.-P.—Sheryl Murphy
Off. Mgr.—Cynthia Henderson
SIC—3663; NAICS—334220; *Broadcast audio equipment; Brand name—ATI; ATI Digital Audio; MatchMaker; NanoAmp; MicroAmp; Encore; Ultimike*
Employs—12; Estab.—1979
3,500 sq ft site, Distrib.—Intl.
Privately owned corporation

**B-TRON CORP.**
154 Cooper Rd., Ste. 1203 (08091)
**Phone—(856) 719-8485**
Fax—(856) 719-8373
www.b-tron.com
Email—btronclare@aol.com
Pres., Fin. & GM—Walter Kiss
Secy., MIS Mgr.—Clare A. Buniak
SIC—3663; NAICS—334220; *CCTV & access control power supplies*
Employs—4; Estab.—1998
Sales—under $500,000
Distrib.—Intl.
Privately owned corporation

**COLORTEC PRINTING & MAILING LLC**
424 Kelley Dr., Ste. A (08091-9285)
**Phone—(856) 767-0108**
Fax—(856) 767-1975
www.colorteconline.com
Email—wfarlow@colorteconline.com
Ptnr.—Lori Burroughs
Ptnr.—Liz Farlow
Ptnr.—Wayne Farlow
SIC—2759; 2752; NAICS—323100; *Commercial, offset, digital & direct mail printing & mailing services for direct mail advertising materials, including graphic design, presorting & addressing*
Employs—5; Estab.—1984
Sales—under $500,000
4,000 sq ft site, Distrib.—Regional
Limited Liability Company

**COMPEX CORP.**
439 Commerce Ln., Ste. 1 (08091)
**Phone—(856) 335-2277**
Fax—(856) 335-7223
www.compexcorp.com
Email—sales@compexcorp.com
Pres.—David Gordon
Opers. Mgr.—Andrew Gordon
Fin. & MIS Mgr.—John Weaver
Qual. Control Mgr.—James Polite
SIC—3679; *Electronic components*
Employs—45; Estab.—1976
16,000 sq ft site, Distrib.—Intl.
Sole ownership

**CONCEPT GROUP, INC.**
380 Cooper Rd. *(08091)*
**Phone—(856) 767-5506**
Fax—(856) 768-3981
www.conceptgroupinc.com
Email—applications@conceptgroupinc.com
Pres.—Aarne Ried
Cont.—Richard Riabko
GM—William E. Thomas
SIC—3599; 3479; *Precision vacuum brazing & CNC machining & glass-to-metal seals; Brand name—Insulon Technology™*
Employs—16; Estab.—1971
Sales—$5Mil-$8Mil
13,000 sq ft site, Distrib.—Intl.
Privately owned corporation
ISO rating—AS9100

**CONTINENTAL CAST STONE EAST**
Div. of Continental Cast Stone Mfg., Inc.
400 Cooper Rd. (08091)
**Phone—(856) 753-4000**
Fax—(856) 753-8700
www.caststone.net
Email—sales@caststone.net
Pres.—Bill Russell
Plt. Mgr.—Robert Criteli
Bookkeeper—Judy Stanley
SIC—3272; *Architectural cast stone*
Employs—50; Estab.—1996
30,000 sq ft site, Distrib.—Regional
Privately owned sub-S corp.
Parent co.—Continental Cast Stone Mfg., Inc., Shawnee, KS
Phone—(913) 422-7575
See Parent Co. Section for full profile.

**DUCA PRINTING CO., INC.**
247 Haddon Ave. (08091)
**Phone—(856) 767-2242**
Fax—(856) 768-5985
Email—vduca@aol.com
Pres.—Vincent Duca
Corp. Secy.—Louise Duca

GEOGRAPHICAL

## West Berlin—(cont.)

SIC—2752; 2791; NAICS—
323122; *Offset printing &
typesetting*
Employs—4; Estab.—1975
Sales—under $500,000
3,200 sq ft site, Distrib.—National
Privately owned corporation

### DYNASIL CORP. OF AMERICA

385 Cooper Rd. (08091)
**Phone—(856) 767-4600**
Fax—(856) 767-6813
www.dynasilfusedsilica.com
Email—info@dynasilfusedsilica.com
V.-P., Sales & Mktg. & GM—Bruce
Leonetti
Sales Mgr., Inside—Michael A.
Orlando, Jr.
SIC—3211; 3827; NAICS—
327211; *Precision fused silica &
quartz optical blanks & optical
components; Brand name—
Dynasil®*
Employs—16; Estab.—1960
Sales—$2.6Mil-$5Mil
16,000 sq ft site, Distrib.—Intl.
Publicly owned corporation
AKA: Dynasil Fused Silica
Parent co.—Dynasil Corp. Of
America, Watertown, MA
Phone—(617) 668-6855
See Parent Co. Section for full profile.

### EAST COAST PLASTICS, INC.

427 Commerce Ln., Ste. 7 (08091)
**Phone—(856) 768-8700**
Fax—(856) 768-8282
www.eastcoastplasticsonline.com
Email—eastcoastplastics@
verizon.net
Pres., CFO—David Lorenz
MIS & Sales Mgr.—Frank Hibler
SIC—3089; *Plastic injection
molding for consumer & medical
products*
Employs—14; Estab.—1994
9,000 sq ft site, Distrib.—National
Privately owned sub-S corp.

### ES INDUSTRIES

701 S. Route 73 (08091)
**Phone—(856) 753-8400**
National—(800) 356-6140
Fax—(856) 753-8484
www.esind.com
Email—info@esind.com
Pres., Sales Mgr.—David Kohler
V.-P., Dir., Tech.—Matthew
Przybyciel
Off. Mgr.—Sandra Huff
Administrator—Jessie Kay
SIC—3826; NAICS—334516;
*Laboratory chromatographic
instruments*
Employs—9; Estab.—1962
Sales—$500,000-$1Mil
15,000 sq ft site, Distrib.—Intl.
Privately owned sub-S corp.

### FOODLINE PIPING PRODUCTS CO.

225 Edgewood Ave. (08091)
**Phone—(856) 767-1177**
Fax—(856) 768-1560
www.foodlinepp.com
Email—sales@foodlinepp.com
Pres.—Daniel Diadul
Plt. Mgr.—James Kohler
Off. Mgr.—Maria Forbes
SIC—3556; NAICS—333294;
*Aluminum piping & tank UV
systems for food processing;
Brand name—Foodline*
Employs—7; Estab.—1971
Distrib.—Intl.
Privately owned corporation

### GALAXY TRANSFORMER & MAGNETICS, LLC

386 Cooper Rd. (08091)
Mail addr: P.O. Box 27, Atco
(08004-0027)
**Phone—(856) 753-4546**
www.galaxytransformers.com
Email—willcurry@
galaxytransformers.com
Owner—James Curry
GM—Ken Burns
Off. Mgr.—Will Curry
SIC—3612; NAICS—335311;
*Electrical & high frequency
transformers*
Employs—12; Estab.—1998
Distrib.—Intl.
Limited Liability Company

### †GARDEN STATE TILE DISTRIBUTORS, INC.

790 S. Route 73 (08091)
**Phone—(856) 753-0300**
Fax—(856) 753-1835
www.gstile.com
Email—nscanlan@gstile.com
GM—Nancy Scanlan
Off. Mgr.—Mike Hubert
SIC—5032; *Distributor of ceramic
floor tile*
Employs—15; Estab.—1957
Sales—$1Mil-$5Mil
Distrib.—Regional
Privately owned corporation
Parent co.—Garden State Tile
Distributors, Inc., Farmingdale,
NJ
Phone—(732) 938-6675
See Parent Co. Section for full profile.

### GENERAL SIGN CO., INC.

105 Chestnut Ave. (08091)
**Phone—(856) 753-3535**
Fax—(856) 753-3737
www.generalsignnj.com
Email—neongeneral@aol.com
Pres.—Steve Brocco
Prodn. Mgr.—David Smith
SIC—3993; *Interior & exterior
signs*
Employs—6; Estab.—1975
Sales—$500,000-$1Mil
Distrib.—Local
Privately owned corporation

### HORIZON LABEL, LLC

1049 Industrial Dr. (08091)
**Phone—(856) 767-0777**
National—(877) 407-4704
Fax—(856) 767-4334
www.horizonlabel.com
Email—sales@horizonlabel.com
Pres.—Paul Falkowski
GM—Ron Davis
SIC—2672; NAICS—322222;
*Pressure-sensitive labels*
Employs—7; Estab.—1999
12,000 sq ft site, Distrib.—National
Limited Liability Company
Also see: Taunton Graphics, Inc.,
same loc.

### HUGGINS ALUMINUM PRODUCTS

576 N. Route 73 (08091)
**Phone—(856) 767-0506**
Fax—(856) 753-1110
www.hugginsawnings.com
Email—hugginsawnings@
verizon.net
Ptnr.—George E. Metzler
Ptnr.—Susanna C. Metzler
Ptnr.—Michael Metzler

SIC—3444; 2394; NAICS—
314912; *Screen & fully insulated
enclosures, aluminum & fabric
stationary & retractable awnings
& carports; Brand name—
Aristocrat Retractable Fabric
Awnings*
Employs—3; Estab.—1961
Sales—under $500,000
6,250 sq ft site, Distrib.—Regional
Privately owned partnership
DBA: Huggins Awnings & Patio
Rooms

### †INTERSTATE BATTERY SYSTEM OF AMERICA, INC.

408 Commerce Ln. (08091)
**Phone—(856) 767-3903**
National—(800) 541-8419
Fax—(856) 753-8222
www.interstatebatteries.com
Email—ib4686mg@ibsa.com
GM—Robert Marshall
SIC—5063; 5013; *Wholesaler of
batteries, including cash register,
cordless tool, emergency
lighting & automotive batteries*
Employs—8
Sales—under $500,000
Distrib.—Regional
Privately owned corporation
Parent co.—Interstate Battery
System Of America, Inc., Dallas,
TX
Phone—(972) 991-1444
See Parent Co. Section for full profile.

### J M J PROFILE, INC.

154 Copper Rd., Unit 1303
(08091)
**Phone—(856) 767-3930**
National—(888) 273-4565
Fax—(856) 767-3931
www.jmjprofile.com
Email—sales@jmjprofile.com
Pres.—Joseph Colachi
SIC—3089; *Plastic fabrication*
Employs—12; Estab.—1995
Sales—$1Mil-$2.5Mil (est)
Distrib.—Regional
Privately owned corporation

### KESSLER STEEL RULE DIE, INC.

1004 Industrial Dr., Ste. 10 (08091)
**Phone—(856) 278-3802**
        (856) 767-0231
Fax—(856) 767-0232
Email—kesslerdie@verizon.net
Pres.—Dennis Kessler
SIC—3544; NAICS—333500;
*Steel rule dies*
Employs—6; Estab.—1992
Sales—$500,000-$1Mil
2,000 sq ft site, Distrib.—Regional
Privately owned sub-S corp.

### LIGHTING PREVENTION SYSTEMS, INC.

154 Cooper Rd., Unit 1201, P.O.
Box 353 (08091)
**Phone—(856) 767-7806**
National—(888) 667-8745
Fax—(856) 767-7547
www.lpsnet.com
Email—info@lpsnet.com
Pres.—Ian Fawthrop
V.-P.—Jessica Jones
Off. Mgr.—Debbie Minniti
Manager—Patricia McLaughlin
SIC—3643; NAICS—335931;
*Lightning protection products,
grounding systems & surge
protection; Brand name—Erico;
Eritech; Critec; Independent
Protection Company; ALS
Dissipation Air Terminals*
Employs—10; Estab.—1995
Sales—$2Mil
5,000 sq ft site, Distrib.—Intl.
Privately owned corporation

### LIGHTNING PREVENTION SYSTEMS, INC.

154 Cooper Rd., Ste. 1201 (08091)
**Phone—(856) 767-7209**
Fax—(856) 767-7547
www.lpsnet.com
Email—info@lpsnet.com
CEO—Patricia McLaughlin
Pres.—Ian Fawthrop
V.-P.—Jessica Jones
SIC—3643; NAICS—335931;
*Lightning protection equipment
for commercial, industrial &
residential structures, including
design & installation*
Employs—10; Estab.—1997
10,000 sq ft site, Distrib.—National
Privately owned corporation

### M C CUSTOM SHEET METAL FABRICATION, INC.

215-E Old Egg Harbor Rd., Ste. E
(08091-1653)
**Phone—(856) 767-9509**
Fax—(856) 767-3826
Email—mccustom1@yahoo.com
Pres.—Michael Franchi
Off. Mgr.—Marissa Pigliacellia
SIC—3444; *Custom stock fittings
for HVAC ducts & trunk ducts*
Employs—7; Estab.—1982
Sales—$900,000
4,000 sq ft site, Distrib.—Regional
Privately owned sub-S corp.

### MAXTEX, INC.

159 N. Cooper Rd. (08091)
Mail addr: P.O. Box 294, Berlin
(08009)
**Phone—(856) 767-7960**
National—(800) 201-0548
Fax—(856) 768-1959
www.maxtex.com
Email—nickm@maxtex.com
Pres.—Nick Macaroni
Bookkeeper—Debbie Macaroni
SIC—2396; *Textile screen printing*
Employs—5; Estab.—1981
11,000 sq ft site, Distrib.—National
Privately owned corporation
DBA: Max Graphics

### MEDPLAST GROUP

Div. of MedPlast, Inc.
225 Old Egg Harbor Rd. *(08091)*
**Phone—(856) 753-7600**
Fax—(856) 768-1445
www.medplastgroup.com
Email—dcain@medplastgroup.com
Cont.—Sandra Hall
GM—William Eggimann
Hum. Res. Mgr.—Kelly Sullivan
Engrg. Mgr.—Doug Cain
SIC—3089; *Plastic injection
molding*
Employs—180; Estab.—1959
Sales—$25Mil-$50Mil
60,000 sq ft site, Distrib.—National
Privately owned corporation
ISO rating—13485
Parent co.—MedPlast, Inc.,
Tempe, AZ
Phone—(480) 968-6653
See Parent Co. Section for full profile.

### NOVAFLEX INDUSTRIES, INC.

Div. of Flexmaster Canada Ltd.
1024 Industrial Dr. (08091)
**Phone—(856) 768-2275**
National—(800) 225-0215
Fax—(856) 768-2385
www.novaflex.com
Email—jmccool@novaflex.com
Br. Mgr.—Jerome McCool
SIC—3052; NAICS—326220;
*Industrial duct hoses*
Employs—10; Estab.—1975
Sales—under $500,000
Distrib.—National
Privately owned corporation

## West Berlin—(cont.)

Parent co.—Flexmaster Canada Ltd.
Phone—(905) 731-9411
See Parent Co. Section for full profile.

**OUT ISLAND SPORT YACHTS, INC.**
107 Edgewood Ave. (08091)
**Phone—(609) 861-4000**
www.outislandsportyachts.com
Email—outislandboatworks@yahoo.com
Pres.—Scott Jastrzembski
SIC—3732; 3089; 5088; *Manufacturer of custom-built fiberglass boats, including boat painting & gel coat repair & distributor of new & used marine parts; Brand name—outisland yachts; silverhawk boats; east coast skiffs*
Employs—6; Estab.—2000
Sales—$2.5Mil
37,000 sq ft site, Distrib.—Intl.
Privately owned corporation

**PACKAGING GRAPHICS, INC.**
435 Commerce Ln., P.O. Box 160 (08091)
**Phone—(856) 767-9000**
Fax—(856) 767-2759
www.packaginggraphics.com
Email—sales@packaginggraphics.com
Pres.—Eileen Koff
SIC—2796; NAICS—323122; *Printing plates*
Employs—20; Estab.—1966
Sales—$1Mil-$2.5Mil
Distrib.—National
Privately owned corporation

**PHOENIX TOOL & MACHINE, INC.**
1044 Industrial Dr., Unit 5 (08091)
**Phone—(856) 753-5565**
Fax—(856) 753-9755
Pres.—John Dusak
Off. Mgr.—Pat Dusak
SIC—3599; *General machining job shop*
Employs—6; Estab.—1997
Sales—$500,000-$1Mil (est)
Distrib.—Local
Privately owned corporation

**PRECISION ROLLERS, INC.**
155 Cooper Rd. (08091)
**Phone—(856) 768-7696**
Fax—(856) 768-7696
Pres.—Louis Marquez
SIC—3599; *General machining job shop*
Employs—2; Estab.—1987
Sales—under $500,000 (est)
Distrib.—Local
Sole ownership

**PRECISION SPECIALISTS MACHINE, LLC**
1004 Industrial Dr., Ste. 5 (08091)
**Phone—(856) 768-5990**
Fax—(856) 768-6394
www.psm-llc.com
Email—sales@psm-llc.com
Pres., CEO—Richard Bottoni
V-P., CFO—Terry Bottoni
Qual. Mgr.—Allison Bottoni
SIC—3599; *CNC machining, assembly & finishing job shop*
Employs—12; Estab.—1982
Sales—$1Mil-$2.5Mil
10,000 sq ft site, Distrib.—National
Limited Liability Company
ISO rating—AS9100C, 9001:2008

**PRINCETON TEC**
110 Collings Ave. (08091)
**Phone—(609) 298-9331**
Fax—(609) 298-9601
www.princetec.com
Email—contact@princetec.com
Dir., Pur.—Mark Buehler

SIC—3089; *Plastic parts, including precision tooling, custom injection molding & mold making job shop*
Employs—8; Estab.—1976
30,500 sq ft site, Distrib.—Intl.
Privately owned corporation
Parent co.—Princeton Tec, Bordentown, NJ
Phone—(609) 298-9331
See Parent Co. Section for full profile.

**PRINTING PLUS OF SOUTH JERSEY**
406 N. Route 73 (08091)
**Phone—(856) 767-3232**
Fax—(856) 767-3976
www.printingplussj.com
Email—printingplus.sj@verizon.net
Ptnr.—Robert Behnke
Ptnr.—Karen Behnke
SIC—2759; 2752; NAICS—323100; *Instant, digital & small-format & large-format color printing*
Employs—7; Estab.—1982
Sales—$500,000-$1Mil
Distrib.—Local
Privately owned corporation

**PRO-FIT PROSTHETIC & ORTHOTIC, LLC**
215 Edgewood Ave. *(08091)*
**Phone—(856) 809-9910**
　　　　　(800) 996-7380
Fax—(856) 809-9945
www.profitlab.net
Email—pro.fit@comcast.net
Owner—Tom Dalsey
Off. Mgr.—Elaine Harmon
Hum. Res. Specialist—Sonya Spisak
SIC—3842; *Comprehensive prosthetics & orthotics*
Employs—27; Estab.—2000
Sales—$500,000-$1Mil
Distrib.—Local
Limited Liability Company

**RESINTECH, INC.**
160 Cooper Rd. *(08091)*
**Phone—(856) 768-9600**
Fax—(856) 768-9601
www.resintech.com
Email—ixresin@resintech.com
Pres.—Michael Gottlieb
V-P.—Jeffrey Gottlieb
Dir., Mktg.—Chuck Durbin
IT Mgr.—Sterling Jaynes
Hum. Res. Mgr.—Patricia Ruggeri
SIC—2899; *Water purification chemicals*
Employs—60; Estab.—1986
Sales—$25Mil-$50Mil (est)
Distrib.—Intl.
Privately owned corporation

**SPARTAN AIR PURIFICATION**
150 Cooper Rd., Ste. E-14 (08091)
**Phone—(856) 768-2929**
National—(800) 972-3557
Fax—(856) 768-3350
www.spartanair.com
Email—danspartan@comcast.net
Owner—Dan Fitzpatrick
Off. Mgr.—Denise Bees
SIC—3564; NAICS—333400; *Air purification systems*
Employs—3; Estab.—1987
Sales—under $500,000
Distrib.—Regional
Privately owned corporation

**SUNHILLO CORP.**
444 Kelly Dr. (08091)
**Phone—(856) 767-7676**
Fax—(856) 767-9557
www.sunhillo.com
Email—sales@sunhillo.com
Pres.—David Whitman
V-P.—Robert Walczak
Hum. Res. Mgr.—Lyle Steffens

SIC—7373; NAICS—541512; *Legacy platform data transport & data communications gateway integrated systems*
Employs—40; Estab.—1980
Distrib.—Intl.
Privately owned corporation

**TAUNTON GRAPHICS, INC.**
1049 Industrial Dr. (08091)
**Phone—(856) 719-8084**
Fax—(856) 719-8086
www.horizonlabel.com
Email—paul@horizonlabel.com
Pres.—Paul Falkowski
SIC—2759; NAICS—323100; *Label printing & graphic design*
Employs—7; Estab.—1981
Sales—$3Mil-$5Mil
10,000 sq ft site, Distrib.—Regional
Privately owned corporation
Also see: Horizon Label, LLC, same loc.

**TECHNITOOL, INC.**
1028 Industrial Dr. (08091)
**Phone—(856) 768-2707**
Fax—(856) 768-2807
www.technitool.com
Email—info@technitool.com
Pres.—Sal Russomanno
V-P., Secy.—Pete Welding
SIC—3089; *Plastic injection molding*
Employs—11; Estab.—1975
Sales—$1Mil-$10Mil
20,000 sq ft site, Distrib.—National
Privately owned corporation

**TECHNOBOX, INC.**
154 Cooper Rd., Ste. 901 (08091)
**Phone—(856) 809-2306**
Fax—(856) 809-2601
www.technobox.com
Pres.—Joseph Norris
Bookkeeper—Lorraine Opdam
SIC—3672; 3679; *Printed circuit cards & boards & design services*
Employs—8; Estab.—2001
Sales—under $500,000
Distrib.—Intl.
Privately owned corporation

**TELECOM ASSISTANCE GROUP, INC.**
150 Cooper Rd., Ste. F-15 (08091)
**Phone—(856) 753-8585**
Fax—(856) 768-7645
www.tagcords.com
Email—marketing@tagcords.com
V-P.—Murray Kaplan
GM—John Humes
Off. Mgr.—Marie Scott
SIC—3661; *Telecommunications testing equipment & testing & patch cords*
Employs—30; Estab.—1989
5,400 sq ft site, Distrib.—National
Privately owned corporation

**THOSANI, INC.**
150 Cooper Rd., Ste. E-12 (08091)
**Phone—(856) 753-9000**
Fax—(856) 753-0267
www.thosaniinc.com
Email—thosaniinc@verizon.net
Pres., Treas.—Jitendra Thosani
Secy., Pur. Agt.—Bhanu Thosani
Bus. Dev. Mgr.—Raj Sam
SIC—3679; *Wire harness & cable assemblies*
Employs—5; Estab.—1979
Sales—$500,000-$1Mil
3,900 sq ft site, Distrib.—Local
Privately owned corporation

**THWING-ALBERT INSTRUMENT COMPANY**
14 W. Collings Ave. (08091)
**Phone—(856) 767-1000**
Fax—(856) 767-2615
www.thwingalbert.com

Email—info@thwingalbert.com
Pres.—Joseph W. Raab
Ex. V-P.—Scott M. Raab
V-P., Sales & Mktg.—Steve Berg
Mktg. Mgr.—Brenda Fisher
Off. Mgr.—Eva McCarthy
Serv. Mgr.—Nancy Sudan
SIC—3829; NAICS—334515; *Testing equipment to measure physical properties of paper, paperboard, tissue paper, flexible packaging, plastic film, nonwovens & textiles; Brand name—ProTear; ProGage; Vantage; JDC*
Employs—50; Estab.—1899
Sales—$5Mil-$10Mil
26,000 sq ft site, Distrib.—Intl.
Privately owned corporation

**TICO MFG., INC.**
1044 Industrial Dr., Unit 9 (08091)
**Phone—(856) 767-8430**
Fax—(856) 767-8431
www.ticomanufacturing.com
Email—roger@ticomanufacturing.com
Pres.—Roger Sobradl
Hum. Res. Mgr.—Jessica Garcia
Off. Mgr.—Kevin Rink
SIC—3452; 3495; 3679; 3479; *Military, commercial & industrial fasteners, machined components & related hardware for fighter jets, unmanned drones, missile systems, military vessels & combat vehicles, including electronic spacers, springs, cable & metal heat treating*
Employs—9; Estab.—1995
Sales—$6Mil-$10Mil
Distrib.—Intl.
Privately owned corporation

**TOOL SHOP, INC.**
335 Chestnut Ave., P.O. Box 36 (08091)
**Phone—(856) 767-8077**
Fax—(856) 767-8103
www.toolshopinc.com
Email—shop97@aol.com
Pres.—Paul Bruninghaus
Plt. Mgr.—Stan Misiak
Off. Mgr.—Martha Bruninghaus
SIC—3541; 3545; NAICS—333512; *Screw machine cutting tools, including wire EDM & small quantity contract machining & laser tool marking*
Employs—9; Estab.—1969
Sales—$1Mil-$2Mil
4,000 sq ft site, Distrib.—National
Privately owned sub-S corp.

**TOWNSEND PRESS, INC.**
439 Kelley Dr. (08091)
**Phone—(856) 753-0554**
National—(800) 772-6410
Fax—(856) 753-0649
www.townsendpress.com
Ptnr. & CFO—Judith Nadell
Ptnr.—John Langan
GM—George Henry
Off. Mgr.—Emily Donovan
Cust. Serv. Rep.—Liz Cocco
Cust. Serv. Rep.—Shiela Akers
SIC—2731; *Book publishing*
Employs—6; Estab.—1991
Sales—under $500,000 (est)
Distrib.—National
Privately owned corporation

**TRIPLE-T CUTTING TOOLS, INC.**
135 Edgewood Ave. (08091)
**Phone—(856) 768-0800**
Fax—(856) 768-3773
www.triple-t.com
Email—steve.thomas@triple-t.com
Pres.—Steve Thomas
V-P., Treas.—Michael Thomas
Qual. Mgr.—Donna Gauntt

GEOGRAPHICAL

## West Berlin—(cont.)

SIC—3541; 3559; NAICS—333512; *Cutting tools for the metal & plastic cutting & optical industries, including carbide end mills & optical cutters*
Employs—14; Estab.—1995
Sales—$3Mil-$3.5Mil
13,800 sq ft site, Distrib.—Intl.
Privately owned sub-S corp.

### UNIVERSAL WINDOWS, LLC

407 Bloomfield Dr. (08091)
**Phone—(856) 719-0020**
National—(800) 275-8490
Fax—(856) 719-0028
www.universalwindowsllc.com
Email—info@
universalwindowsllc.com
Pres.—Joseph Battaglia, Sr.
Expeditor—Bill Van Orsdell
SIC—3089; *Vinyl windows & patio doors*
Employs—20; Estab.—1979
25,000 sq ft site, Distrib.—Regional
Privately owned corporation

## West Caldwell

(Essex—N.E.)

### ALFA WASSERMANN, INC.

4 Henderson Dr. (07006)
**Phone—(973) 882-8630**
National—(800) 220-4488
Fax—(973) 276-0383
www.alfawassermannus.com
Email—sales@awst.com
CEO—Ira Nordlicht
SIC—3841; *Medical laboratory instruments*
Employs—100
Sales—$10Mil-$25Mil (est)
60,000 sq ft site, Distrib.—Intl.

### ATLANTIC ZEISER, INC.

15 Patton Dr. (07006)
**Phone—(973) 228-0800**
National—(800) 750-3706
Fax—(973) 228-9064
www.atlanticzeiser.com
Email—sales@
atlanticzeiserusa.com
Pres., CEO—Thomas Coco
CFO, Cont.—Mike Raimondo
Dir., Cust. Svcs.—Kyle Severson
Sales Mgr., Natl.—Dave Belan
SIC—3555; NAICS—333293; *High resolution drop-on-demand inkjet printing systems, verification cameras, magnetic encoding, RFID & chip programming systems, mechanical numbering & bar code machines & late stage printing units for the packaging industry; Brand name—OMEGA; DELTA; GAMMA; Cardline; Cardline Versa; DIGILINE; Magmaster; Persoline; SMARTCURE; VERICAM*
Employs—40; Estab.—1952
Sales—over $10Mil
40,000 sq ft site, Distrib.—Intl.
Privately owned corporation

### CONNELL INDUSTRIES, INC.

13 Fairfield Ave. *(07006-7603)*
**Phone—(877) 926-6635**
Fax—(305) 675-2612
www.connell-ind.com
Email—vincent.digangi@connell-ind.com
Pres.—Vincent DiGangi

SIC—3569; 3625; 3564; 3829; NAICS—335314; *Industrial automation systems & equipment for the industrial & manufacturing industries, including controls, air recycling systems, hot fill testing equipment & movable bridge control systems; Brand name—Technoplan Engineering*
Employs—5; Estab.—1996
Sales—$500,000-$1Mil
Distrib.—National
Privately owned sub-S corp.

### CORPORATE COMMUNICATIONS GROUP, THE

14 Henderson Dr. (07006)
**Phone—(973) 808-0009**
Fax—(973) 808-9740
www.corpcomm.com
Email—jepinkin@corpcomm.com
Pres.—Lois Pinkin
V-P., Bus. Dev.—Jeff Pinkin
V-P., Printing—Rick Walsh
Opers. Mgr.—Jeffrey Lawshe
IT Mgr.—Don Giacobe
Hum. Res. Mgr.—Barbara Cadmus
Maint. Mgr.—John Mundy
SIC—2759; 2752; NAICS—323100; *Digital & offset printing, including wafer-sealed brochures & postcards*
Employs—180; Estab.—1964
Distrib.—National
Privately owned corporation
AKA: CCG Marketing Solutions

NEW ENTRY
### CROSSFIRE PUBLICATIONS

551 Bloomfield Ave., Apt. C-14 (07006-7548)
**Phone—(973) 403-1633**
Fax—(973) 403-1633
www.crossfirepublications.com
Email—gregrusso@verizon.net
V-P.—Rita Cristello
Principal—Gregory Russo
SIC—2731; 2791; *Music book publishing & electronic prepress*
Employs—5; Estab.—1995
Sales—under $500,000
Distrib.—Intl.
Sole ownership

### CTC INTERNATIONAL, INC.

11 York Ave. (07006)
Mail addr.: P.O. Box 1137, West Caldwell (07007)
**Phone—(973) 228-2300**
Fax—(973) 228-7076
www.ctcint.com
Email—info@ctcint.com
Pres.—Erwin Herbert
V-P., Sales—Rich Herbert
V-P., Mfg.—Ed Caprario
Chief Engr.—Frank Donovan
Technical Sales Engr.—Rob Keuhlen
SIC—3559; 3569; *Automation equipment, including lap & butt splicers, unwind & rewind stands, web accumulators, turret rewinders, splice tables & unwind tension compensators*
Employs—25; Estab.—1961
40,000 sq ft site, Distrib.—Intl.
Sole ownership

### DIAMOND CASE CO.

45 Fairfield Pl. (07006)
**Phone—(973) 227-8707**
Fax—(973) 227-8707
Email—diamondcaseco@yahoo.com
Pres.—Frank Johnston
GM—Tom Sorenson
SIC—3161; NAICS—316991; *Luggage*
Employs—12; Estab.—1932
Sales—$1Mil-$2.5Mil
Distrib.—Intl.
Privately owned corporation

### DIRECT PRINTING IMPRESSIONS

33 Fairfield Pl. (07006)
**Phone—(973) 227-6111**
Fax—(973) 227-6655
www.dpiprints.com
Email—rich@dpiprints.com
V-P., Sales—Richard Luggiero
Opers. Mgr.—Ray Luggiero
Off. Mgr.—Maria Lojo
SIC—2759; 2789; NAICS—323100; *Commercial & digital printing & mailing, fulfillment, film laminating & finishing services*
Employs—25; Estab.—1990
Sales—$2.5Mil-$5Mil
27,000 sq ft site, Distrib.—National
Privately owned sub-S corp.

### E. GREENE OF NORTH CAROLINA, INC.

P.O. Box 1017 (07007)
**Phone—(973) 838-5200**
National—(877) 838-5250
Fax—(973) 838-5210
www.egreene.com
Email—customerservice@egreene.com
GM—Jed Firestone
Off. Mgr.—Susan Wayne
SIC—2759; 2677; NAICS—322232; *Financial printing of security envelopes & safe deposit box vault supplies; Brand name—Fitzall Caution Signals; Smead Products*
Employs—30; Estab.—1927
Distrib.—Intl.
Privately owned corporation
DBAs: E Greene of NC & egnc

### ESSEX RISE

4 Fairfield Crescent (07006)
**Phone—(973) 575-7483**
Fax—(973) 575-0576
www.essexrise.com
Email—sbohanon@essexrise.com
CEO—C. Wampler
GM—Shawn Bohanon
SIC—3537; *Material handling systems, including conveyors & hydraulic lifts*
Employs—10; Estab.—1992
15,000 sq ft site, Distrib.—Intl.
Privately owned corporation
Also see: Richards Industries Co., same loc.

### FANCORT INDUSTRIES, INC.

31 Fairfield Pl. (07006)
**Phone—(973) 575-0610**
National—(888) 326-2678
Fax—(973) 575-9234
www.fancort.com
Email—sales@fancort.com
Pres., CEO & MIS Mgr.—Ronald J. Corey
V-P.—Robert Antonelli
SIC—3679; 3544; NAICS—333500; *Electronic production racks & fixtures for printed circuit board assembly & handling, including printed circuit board depaneling, hot bar & robotic soldering, robotic screw fastening & pneumatic & servo presses*
Employs—20; Estab.—1972
Sales—$1Mil-$2.5Mil
12,000 sq ft site, Distrib.—Intl.
Privately owned corporation

### †FOX ELECTRIC SUPPLY CO., INC.

Div. of Electrical Wholesalers, Inc.
1 Dodge Dr. (07006)
**Phone—(973) 227-4151**
Fax—(973) 227-8455
www.foxelectricsupply.com
Email—sales@
foxelectricsupply.com
Pres.—Bruce Fox

SIC—5063; *Wholesaler of electrical supplies, including bulbs, switches & conduit*
Employs—30
Distrib.—National
Privately owned corporation
Parent co.—Electrical Wholesalers, Inc., Hartford, CT
Phone—(860) 522-3232
See Parent Co. Section for full profile.

### GARDEN STATE NUTRITIONALS, LLC

8 Henderson Dr. (07006)
**Phone—(973) 575-9200**
National—(800) 526-9095
Fax—(973) 575-6782
www.gardenstatenutritionals.com
Email—info@
gardenstatenutritional.com
CEO—Keith Frankel
COO—David Illingworth
Ex. V-P.—Rick Handel
V-P., Prod. Dev.—Terry Coyle
SIC—2834; 2833; 2844; NAICS—325412; *Dietary supplements, including tablets, capsules, powders, liquids & cosmetics*
Employs—400; Estab.—1998
Sales—over $150Mil
Distrib.—Intl.
Limited Liability Company
Also see: Vitaquest International, LLC, same loc.

### IMPACT INSTRUMENTATION, INC.

27 Fairfield Pl. (07006)
Mail addr.: P.O. Box 508, Caldwell (07007-0508)
**Phone—(973) 882-1212**
National—(800) 969-0750
Fax—(973) 882-4993
www.impactii.com
Email—sales@impactii.com
Pres.—L. Sherman
Chief Clinical & Technology Officer—George Beck
V-P., Sales & Serv.—Dave DeSantis
V-P., Bus. Dev. & Mktg.—Dennis Mattessich
Corp. Secy.—M. L. Chettum
Comp.—Rod Zbikowski
Sales & Mktg. Mgr. & Coord.—Anthony Altamore
Fin. Mgr.—Mel Chettum
SIC—3841; *Portable ventilators, automatic resuscitators, portable suction equipment & mounting systems; Brand name—Uni-Vent®; EMV+®; Eagle™; EagleII™; AEV®; Ultra-Lite®; Vac-Pak®; Vac-PakII®; SMEED™; Sorensen®; Porta-Wall™; EMLAB; CCLAW*
Employs—165; Estab.—1977
Sales—$15Mil
62,000 sq ft site, Distrib.—Intl.
Privately owned corporation
ISO rating—13485:2003

### JJ PRODUCTS, INC.

133 Mountain Ave. (07006)
**Phone—(973) 228-3460**
National—(800) 654-2356
Fax—(973) 226-5304
www.jjproducts.net
Email—customerservice@
jjproducts.net
Pres.—Jim Bocchini
SIC—3714; *Automobile arm rests & accessories*
Employs—3; Estab.—1985
Sales—under $500,000
2,000 sq ft site, Distrib.—National
Privately owned corporation

### JRE INCORPORATED

22 Fairfield Pl. (07006)
**Phone—(973) 808-0055**
Fax—(973) 808-7196
www.jreinc.com
Email—sales@jreinc.com
Pres.—James Tuscano

## West Caldwell—(cont.)

V-P., Fin.—Theresa A. Tuscano
SIC—3672; 3679; NAICS—
334412; *Printed circuit board
assemblies, including SMT,
BGA, thru-hole, turnkey,
mechanical & wire harness
assemblies & lead free solder*
Employs—35; Estab.—1985
18,000 sq ft site, Distrib.—Local
Privately owned corporation
ISO rating—9001:2000

### LTS LOHMANN THERAPY SYSTEMS CORP.

21 Henderson Dr. (07006)
**Phone—(973) 244-2026**
National—(800) 587-1872
Fax—(973) 396-5327
www.LtsLohmann.com
Email—casey.sharp@lts-corp.com
Pres.—Joachim Franke
CFO—Jennifer Everett
V-P.—Casey Sharp
Acctg. Mgr. & Buyer—Gerri
Chambers
SIC—2834; 2836; NAICS—
325412; *Contract manufacturing
of drug delivery systems,
including transdermal, oral film &
adhesive laminate intermediates*
Employs—300; Estab.—1992
Distrib.—Intl.
Privately owned corporation

### LUMENARC, INC.

37 Fairfield Pl. (07006)
**Phone—(973) 227-8048**
National—(800) 876-3486
Fax—(973) 227-3942
Email—rbhalla@lumenarc.com
Pres.—Harminder Bhalla
V-P.—Ranbir S. Bhalla
GM—Martin Apryasz
Sales Mgr.—Judy Madera
SIC—3641; 3646; 5063; NAICS—
335110; *Manufacturer of high-
intensity discharge light bulbs &
distributor of lighting products,
including light bulbs, ballasts &
lighting fixtures for industrial &
commercial applications; Brand
name—USA/LONG LIFE
BRAND*
Employs—12; Estab.—1983
25,000 sq ft site, Distrib.—Intl.
Privately owned sub-S corp.

### †MARCHESINI PACKAGING MACHINERY

43 Fairfield Pl. (07006)
**Phone—(973) 575-7445**
Fax—(973) 575-4051
www.marchesinusa.com
Email—info@marchesinusa.com
GM—Anna Marie Bellina
SIC—5084; 5085; 5113;
*Wholesaler of packaging
machinery & supplies*
Employs—18; Estab.—1992
Sales—$1Mil-$2.5Mil
23,000 sq ft site, Distrib.—National
Privately owned corporation

### MASI ELECTRONICS, DON

25 Walden Pl. *(07006)*
**Phone—(973) 618-6288**
Email—dmedon@verizon.net
Owner—Don Masi
SIC—3679; 3669; NAICS—
334290; *Security systems,
including intercoms, system
integraters, public address &
CCTV systems & monitoring*
Employs—5; Estab.—1972
Sales—under $500,000
Distrib.—Regional
Sole ownership
DBA: DME Security & Electronics

### MERRIMAC INDUSTRIES, INC.

Div. of Crane Co.
41 Fairfield Pl. (07006)
**Phone—(973) 575-1300**
Fax—(973) 882-5981
www.merrimacind.com
Email—sales@merrimacind.com
V-P., COO—Reynold K. Green
V-P., CTO—James Logothetis
V-P., Opers.—Bob Harring
V-P., Hum. Res.—Adriana Mazza
V-P., Engrg.—Chris Connelly
V-P., R & D—Brian Dornan
Dir., Bus. Dev.—Paul Skolnick
Facility Mgr.—Edward
Stelmaszczyk
SIC—3679; *Electronic
components; Brand name—
Multi-Mix ®*
Employs—120; Estab.—1954
70,000 sq ft site, Distrib.—Intl.
Publicly owned corporation
ISO rating—9001
Parent co.—Crane Co., Stamford,
CT
Phone—(203) 363-7300
See Parent Co. Section for full profile.

### MICROGEN, INC.

33 Clinton Rd., Ste. 102 (07006)
**Phone—(973) 575-9025**
Fax—(973) 575-9075
www.microgeninc.com
Email—info@microgeninc.com
Pres.—Robert G. Prince
V-P.—Hillary Prince
SIC—2842; NAICS—325612;
*Antimicrobial spray, wipe,
concentrate & super concentrate
disinfectants & disinfectant
cleaners for household, office &
retail applications, water
damage & the transportation,
hospitality & manufacturing
industries; Brand name—
DISNFX-125 a.k.a. D-125; Public
Places Spray Disinfectant; CCX-
151 Super Concentrated
Disinfectant; Public Places Wipe
Disinfectant*
Employs—3; Estab.—1987
1,273 sq ft site, Distrib.—National
Privately owned sub-S corp.

### †MONARCH ELECTRIC CO., INC.

Div. of Electrical Wholesalers, Inc.
1 Dodge Dr. (07006)
**Phone—(973) 227-4151**
Fax—(973) 227-8455
www.monarchelectric.com
Email—jrivera@usesi.com
Pres.—Greg Griswald
SIC—5063; *Wholesaler of
electrical supplies*
Employs—150; Estab.—1990
Distrib.—Local
Privately owned corporation
Parent co.—Electrical
Wholesalers, Inc., Hartford, CT
Phone—(860) 522-3232
See Parent Co. Section for full profile.

### NRESEARCH, INC.

267 Fairfield Ave. *(07006)*
**Phone—(973) 808-8811**
National—(800) 424-7853
Fax—(973) 808-0086
www.nresearch.com
Email—sales@nresearch.com
Pres.—Akos Sule
Prodn. Mgr.—Attila Kiss
SIC—3492; 3494; NAICS—
332912; *Miniature solenoid-
operated PTFE isolation &
single, dual & synchronous
switching pinch valves, inert
fittings & connectors; Brand
name—NResearch® Inc.*
Employs—23; Estab.—1977
Sales—$3Mil-$4Mil
24,000 sq ft site, Distrib.—Intl.
Sole ownership

### ORIGINAL BAGEL & BIALY CO.

2 Fairfield Crescent (07006)
**Phone—(973) 227-5777**
Fax—(973) 227-5767
www.originalbagel.com
Email—bruce@originalbagel.com
Chrm., CEO—Bruce Levenbrook
Pres., Secy.—Dave Harris
V-P., Opers.—Bill Lasek
V-P., Fin.—Garrett Levenbrook
Sales Mgr., Natl.—Terry Martin
Logistics Mgr.—Bill Anzenberger
SIC—2051; NAICS—311812;
*Bagels for foodservice, prisons,
supermarkets, military, colleges,
public schools, universities &
convenience stores; Brand
name—Original Bagel*
Employs—39; Estab.—1995
Sales—$11Mil-$18Mil
35,000 sq ft site, Distrib.—National
Privately owned corporation

### O'SULLIVAN COMMUNICATIONS

1 Fairfield Crescent (07006)
**Phone—(973) 227-5112**
Fax—(973) 830-1830
www.oneworldonestop.com
Email—info@oneworldonestop.com
Dir., Bus. Dev.—Dawn Bruno
Hum. Res. Mgr.—Dana Vickers
SIC—2752; *Commercial
lithographic printing & project
management, graphic design, IT,
copywriting, editing, translation,
proofreading & logistics services*
Employs—65; Estab.—2006
Sales—$5Mil-$10Mil (est)
Distrib.—Intl.
Privately owned corporation

### PELLA WINDOWS & DOORS

Div. of Pella Corp.
4 Dedrick Pl. (07006)
**Phone—(973) 575-0200**
Fax—(973) 882-5747
www.westcaldwell.pella.com
Email—dkobza@njpella.com
Pres.—David Sidman
Sr. V-P.—Alan Wechsler
V-P., Opers.—Jack Goldman
SIC—2431; 3089; NAICS—
321900; *Wood, wood-clad &
vinyl windows & doors*
Employs—170; Estab.—1953
Distrib.—Regional
Privately owned corporation
Parent co.—Pella Corp., Pella, IA
Phone—(641) 621-1000
See Parent Co. Section for full profile.

### POTDEVIN MACHINE CO.

26 Fairfield Pl. (07006)
Mail addr: P.O. Box 1409, West
Caldwell (07007-1409)
**Phone—(201) 288-1941**
Fax—(201) 288-3770
www.potdevin.com
Email—sales@potdevin.com
Pres.—Robert S. Potdevin
Sales Mgr.—Jimmy Byrnes
SIC—3554; NAICS—333291;
*Gluing equipment*
Employs—15; Estab.—1893
25,000 sq ft site, Distrib.—Intl.
Privately owned corporation

### NEW ENTRY
### PRIVATE JOURNEY MAGAZINE, THE

1120 Bloomfield Ave., Ste. 107
(07006)
**Phone—(973) 244-0301**
www.privatejourneymagazine.com
Email—gstampone@
theprivatejourneymagazine.com
Founder—James Kerwin
SIC—2721; *Magazine publishing*
Employs—20
Sales—$1Mil-$2.5Mil (est)
Privately owned corporation

### †R & R MARKETING, LLC

Div. of Charmer Sunbelt Group,
The
10 Patton Dr. (07006)
**Phone—(973) 228-5100**
National—(800) 222-1260
Fax—(973) 403-8679
www.rrmarketing.com
Email—dsiegel@rrmarketing.com
Pres.—Jon Maslin
V-P., Opers.—Doug Siegel
V-P., Fin.—Dennis M. Portsmore
SIC—5182; *Company
headquarters & distributor of
wine & liquors*
Employs—200; Estab.—1933
167,000 sq ft site, Distrib.—
Regional
Privately owned corporation
Parent co.—Charmer Sunbelt
Group, The, New York, NY
Phone—(212) 699-7000
See Parent Co. Section for full profile.

### R. R. DONNELLEY & SONS CO.

5 Henderson Dr. (07006)
**Phone—(973) 882-7000**
Fax—(973) 882-9543
www.rrd.com
Email—info@rrd.com
Dir., Hum. Res.—Liz Greenberg
GM—Russell Radil
IT Mgr.—David Nunn
Prodn. Comm. Ctr. Mgr.—Phillip
Clark
SIC—2759; NAICS—323100;
*Direct mail printing & fulfillment
for custom & personalized
marketing communications*
Employs—242; Estab.—2006
145,000 sq ft site, Distrib.—
National
Publicly owned corporation
Parent co.—R. R. Donnelley &
Sons Co., Chicago, IL
Phone—(312) 326-8000
See Parent Co. Section for full profile.

### R.J. PRINTING, INC.

5 Dodd Rd. (07006)
**Phone—(973) 226-9509**
Fax—(973) 226-9507
Email—printshackwc@aol.com
Pres.—Ron Culmone
V-P.—Janet Culmone
SIC—2759; NAICS—323100;
*Commercial printing*
Employs—2; Estab.—1986
Sales—under $500,000
1,200 sq ft site, Distrib.—Local
Privately owned corporation
AKA: Print Shack

### RICHARDS INDUSTRIES CO.

4 Fairfield Crescent (07006)
**Phone—(973) 575-7480**
Fax—(973) 575-6783
www.rifab.com
Email—info@rifab.com
GM—Chuck Wampler
Off. & Pur. Mgr.—Pat Spina
MIS Mgr.—Shawn Bohanon
MIS Mgr.—John Horrigan
Fin. Mgr.—Jackie Wampler
SIC—3312; *Steel fabrication*
Employs—20; Estab.—1956
25,000 sq ft site, Distrib.—Intl.
Privately owned corporation
Also see: Essex Rise, same loc.

### SELCO MFG. CORP.

3 Fairfield Crescent (07006)
**Phone—(973) 244-1177**
Fax—(973) 244-9292
www.selcomfg.com
Email—mmathis@selcomfg.com
Pres.—Travis Hutchinson
V-P.—Peter Hutchinson
Fin. & MIS Mgr.—Bill Manzini
Off. Mgr.—Muffy Mathis

GEOGRAPHICAL

## West Caldwell—(cont.)

SIC—3499; *Fabricated products for the infrastructure market, including machining & assembly; Brand name—Hope Electrical Products Co., Inc.*
Employs—55; Estab.—1970
Sales—$10Mil-$15Mil
46,000 sq ft site, Distrib.—National
Privately owned corporation
ISO rating—9001:2008

### SLOAN & CO., INC.

38 Fairfield Pl. (07006)
**Phone—(973) 227-3555**
National—(800) 242-7095
Fax—(973) 227-8731
www.sloanandcompany.com
Email—info@sloanandcompany.com
Pres.—Scott Casabona
V.-P., Sales—Carmen Santillo
Fin. Mgr.—Bill Pezzano
Sales Rep.—Bill Boyan
SIC—2431; 3296; NAICS—327993; *Architectural millwork & acoustical ceilings & walls & carpeting*
Employs—25; Estab.—1964
Distrib.—Local
Privately owned corporation

### †TOOL-KRIB SUPPLY CO. (H Q)

787 Passaic Ave., P.O. Box 6064 (07006)
**Phone—(973) 808-4550**
Fax—(973) 808-4544
www.toolkrib.com
Email—sales@toolkrib.com
GM—Bob Nichols
Opers. Mgr.—Todd Yelyn
SIC—5084; *Company headquarters; wholesaler of cutting tools*
Employs—11; Estab.—1938
Distrib.—National
Privately owned corporation

### VITAQUEST INTERNATIONAL, LLC

8 Henderson Dr. (07006)
**Phone—(973) 575-9200**
National—(800) 526-9095
Fax—(973) 276-7111
www.vitaquest.com
GM—Allen Pagliuco
SIC—2833; NAICS—325411; *Vitamins*
Employs—600; Estab.—1998
Distrib.—National
Limited Liability Company
Also see: Garden State Nutritionals, LLC, same loc.

## West Cape May
### (Cape May—S.E.)

### CAPE MAY STAR & WAVE

600 Park Blvd., Ste. 28 (08204)
**Phone—(609) 884-3466**
Fax—(609) 884-2893
www.starandwave.com
Email—cmstarwave@comcast.net
Mng. Editor—Jack Fichter
Bus. Officer—Rosanne Borgo
SIC—2711; *Newspaper publishing*
Employs—3; Estab.—1854
Sales—under $500,000
800 sq ft site, Distrib.—Local
Privately owned corporation

## West Collingswood Heights
### (Camden—S.W.)

### AMERICAN ASPHALT CO., INC.

116 Main St. (08059)
**Phone—(856) 456-2899**
Fax—(856) 456-4398

www.americanasphaltcompany.com
Email—bobbrown@americanasphaltcompany.com
Pres., CEO—Robert M. Brown
COO—Joseph R. Ford
V.-P., Sales & Mktg.—Dave Sulkin
V.-P., Construction—Robert Moncrief
Cont.—Karen Ioven
Dir., Mktg.—Maryann Busler
SIC—2951; NAICS—324121; *Corporate headquarters & asphalt paving materials & compounds for general contractors, homebuilders, municipalities & commercial clients & asphalt paving contracting, including road construction & underground utilities; Brand name—EZ Street Cold Asphalt*
Employs—50; Estab.—1903
Company-wide: 100
Sales—$15Mil-$20Mil
5,000 sq ft site, Distrib.—Regional
Privately owned corporation

## West Creek
### (Ocean—S.E.)

### CLAYTON & SONS, RALPH

125 Cox Crossing Rd. (08092)
Mail addr: P.O. Box 3015, Lakewood (08701)
**Phone—(609) 597-2233**
National—(800) 662-3044
Fax—(732) 751-7630
www.claytononline.com
Email—kroe@claytonco.com
Plt. Mgr. & Dispatcher—John Pietrow
Hum. Res. Mgr.—Wayne Tart
Batchman—Mike Wroble
SIC—3271; 3273; NAICS—327331; *Concrete block & ready-mixed concrete*
Employs—15; Estab.—1974
Sales—under $500,000
Distrib.—Regional
Privately owned corporation
Parent co.—Clayton & Sons, Ralph, Neptune, NJ
Phone—(732) 751-7600
See Parent Co. Section for full profile.

### CUSTOMSHOTS

189 Silver Lake Dr. (08092)
**Phone—(609) 296-1811**
(609) 709-2999
www.customshots.com
Email—diane@customshots.com
Owner & Sales Mgr.—Diane Hillman
SIC—2771; *Custom photographic greeting cards, including birthday, anniversary, graduation, holiday, note, thank you, invitations & announcements printing & graphic design; Brand name—CustomShots*
Employs—1; Estab.—1999
Sales—under $500,000
325 sq ft site, Distrib.—Intl.
Sole ownership

### HANDMADE FURNITURE CO.

612 Main St. (08092)
**Phone—(609) 597-2708**
Fax—(609) 978-0636
www.handmadefurniture.com
Email—handmadefurniture@aol.com
Owner—Cathy Woodward
GM—Rich Woodward
Opers. Mgr.—Lester Smiejan
SIC—2434; 2511; NAICS—337110; *Wooden cabinets & furniture*
Employs—17; Estab.—1972
Sales—$1Mil-$2.5Mil
Distrib.—National
Privately owned corporation

## HOMESTEAD FENCE CONTRACTORS, LLC

637 Main St. (08092)
**Phone—(609) 296-1829**
Fax—(609) 597-0090
www.homesteadfence.com
Email—info@homesteadfence.com
Pres.—Nathan Foote
Bookkeeper—Joan Peterson
SIC—2499; 3089; 2452; NAICS—321992; *Wooden & PVC fences & prefabricated buildings*
Employs—14; Estab.—1973
Sales—$500,000-$1Mil
Distrib.—Local
Limited Liability Company

### PURVES MARINE WORKS

197 Main St. (08092)
**Phone—(609) 296-1263**
Fax—(609) 296-1263
Email—cmpurves@msn.com
Co-Pres.—Chester Purves
Co-Pres.—Mary Purves
SIC—3599; *General machining job shop*
Employs—2; Estab.—1999
Sales—under $500,000
Distrib.—Regional
Sole ownership

### VALARO'S SCREEN PRINTING

50 Mayetta Landing Rd. (08092)
**Phone—(609) 597-7075**
Fax—(609) 597-7075
Owner—David Valaro
SIC—2396; *Textile screen printing*
Employs—1; Estab.—1980
Sales—under $500,000
Distrib.—Local
Sole ownership

## West Deptford
### (Gloucester—S.W.)

### ART GUILD, INC.

300 Wolf Dr. (08086)
**Phone—(856) 853-7500**
Fax—(856) 853-0916
www.artguildinc.com
Email—info@artguildinc.com
Pres.—Doug Zegel
Proj. Mgr.—Rich Clark
Proj. Mgr.—Desiree Williams
Pur. Agt.—Brian Moore
SIC—2541; 2542; 3993; *Corporate headquarters & trade show displays & exhibits*
Employs—210; Estab.—1956
Sales—$5Mil-$10Mil
250,000 sq ft site, Distrib.—Intl.
Privately owned corporation

### AUTOMATIC PLATING, INC.

3410 Jessup Rd., P.O. Box 54 (08086)
**Phone—(856) 845-7323**
Fax—(856) 848-8639
Pres.—Ralph Dreyfuss
SIC—3471; NAICS—332813; *Metal finishing*
Employs—10; Estab.—1969
Sales—$500,000-$1Mil
Distrib.—Regional
Privately owned corporation

### BOSTIK, INC.

2000 Nolte Dr. (08066)
**Phone—(856) 848-8669**
Fax—(856) 848-1646
www.bostik-us.com
Email—josephweirich@bostik-us.com
Plt. Mgr.—Joe Harris
Qual. Mgr.—Paul Dollard, Sr.
Shift Supv.—Joe Foy
Planner—Paul Dollard, Jr.

SIC—2891; 2899; 2951; NAICS—325520; *Carpet & vinyl adhesives, tile grouts, mortars & mastics*
Employs—20; Estab.—1950
Sales—$5Mil-$10Mil (est)
Distrib.—Intl.
Privately owned corporation
Parent co.—Bostik, Inc., Wauwatosa, WI
Phone—(414) 774-2250
See Parent Co. Section for full profile.

### BUMPER SPECIALTIES, INC.

1607 Imperial Way (08066)
**Phone—(856) 251-9993**
(856) 345-7650
National—(800) 541-2500
Fax—(856) 345-7690
www.bumperspecialties.com
Email—bumperinfo@bumperspecialties.com
Pres.—Leon Braunstein
Cont.—Robert Steers
Sales Mgr.—Gregg Wattenmaker
Mktg. Mgr.—Mason Richards
Administrator—Peggy Magee
SIC—3089; *Polyurethane self adhesive bumpers*
Employs—77; Estab.—1990
88,000 sq ft site, Distrib.—Intl.
Privately owned corporation

### CENTO FINE FOODS

100 Cento Blvd. (08086)
**Phone—(856) 853-5445**
Fax—(856) 853-2843
www.cento.com
Email—info@cento.com
Manager—Anthony Varretta
SIC—2033; 2098; 2051; 2052; *Italian food products, including canned tomatoes, pastas, breads & confectionery products*
Employs—10; Estab.—1985
Distrib.—National
Privately owned corporation

### †COOPER ELECTRIC SUPPLY CO.

1251 Metropolitan Ave. (08066)
**Phone—(856) 853-9922**
Fax—(856) 853-9581
www.cooper-electric.com
Email—kate.bell@cooper-electric.com
Lighting Mgr.—Kate Bell
SIC—5063; *Distributor of electrical equipment & supplies, including connectors, wires & sockets*
Employs—7
Distrib.—Local
Privately owned corporation
Parent co.—Cooper Electric Supply Co., Monroe, NJ
Phone—(732) 747-2233
See Parent Co. Section for full profile.

### FORT NASSAU GRAPHICS

1757 Imperial Way (08066)
**Phone—(856) 853-2800**
Fax—(856) 853-2879
www.fortnassaugraphics.net
Email—bfrancis@fortnassaugraphics.com
Pres.—Paul F. Cipolone
V.-P.—Brian Francis
Secy-Treas.—Jenai Cipolone
Estimator—Tom Benson
SIC—2752; NAICS—323100; *Offset printing*
Employs—40; Estab.—1979
19,200 sq ft site, Distrib.—National
Privately owned corporation

### IPAK, INC

301 Grove Rd. (08086-2214)
**Phone—(856) 486-0066**
National—(800) 355-1354
Fax—(856) 486-3557
www.ipak.com
Email—kprimak@ipak.com
Mng. Ptnr.—Sheryl Schreiber
Pres.—Karen Primak
COO—Christa Groeller

## West Deptford—(cont.)

SIC—3089; 2759; NAICS—323100; *Contract printing & packaging*
Employs—90; Estab.—1993
Sales—$10Mil-$25Mil (est)
Distrib.—National
Privately owned corporation

**JOHNSON MATTHEY, INC.**
2001 Nolte Dr. (08066)
**Phone—(856) 384-7000**
Fax—(856) 384-7217
www.matthey.com
Email—group.info@matthey.com
Dir., Fin.—Mike Bell
GM, Chemicals & Refining—Robert Bullen-Smith
GM, Catalysis & Chiral Technologies—Gerard Compagnoni
Opers. Mgr.—Elba Lizardi
IT Mgr.—Roger Swinburn
Hum. Res. Mgr.—John DiCarlo
Hum. Res. Generalist—Gloria Kim
SIC—2819; *Autocatalysts, heavy-duty diesel catalysts & pollution control systems for fuel cells, chemical processes, fine chemicals, chemical catalysts, active pharmaceutical ingredients & the marketing, refining & fabrication of precious metals*
Employs—280; Estab.—1817
Sales—over $1Bil
280,000 sq ft site, Distrib.—Intl.
Publicly owned corporation
ISO rating—9001:14001
Parent co.—Johnson Matthey, Inc., Wayne, PA
Phone—(610) 341-8300
See Parent Co. Section for full profile.

**LAMATEK, INC.**
1226 Forest Pkwy. (08066)
**Phone—(856) 599-6000**
National—(800) 526-2835
Fax—(856) 599-6010
www.lamatek.com
Email—lbasara@lamatek.com
Pres.—G. Robert Carlson
Dir., Sales & Mktg.—Laura Basara
Sr. Acct. Mgr.—Janine Clauss
IT Mgr.—Shawn Newman
Hum. Res. Mgr.—Monique Woods
Qual. Mgr.—Terri Chicosky
SIC—3053; NAICS—339991; *Foam & sponge rubber tapes & adhesive-backed gaskets*
Employs—40; Estab.—1983
50,000 sq ft site, Distrib.—Intl.
Privately owned corporation

**MID STATES SPIRAL, INC.**
Div. of S S M Industries, Inc.
1425 Grandview Ave. (08066)
**Phone—(215) 744-2846**
www.ssmi.biz
CEO—Bob Seiden
Sales Rep.—Bob Johnson
SIC—3444; *Sheet metal fabrication & ducts*
Employs—3
Parent co.—S S M Industries, Inc., Pittsburgh, PA
Phone—(412) 777-5100
See Parent Co. Section for full profile.

**PRECISION ORTHOTIC LAB INTERNATIONAL**
1595 Imperial Way (08066)
Mail addr: P.O. Box 85, Thorofare (08086)
**Phone—(856) 848-6226**
National—(800) 336-6302
Fax—(856) 848-7944
www.precisionorthotic.com
Email—aaron@precisionorthotic.com
Pres.—Aaron Adams
Manager—Dawn Smith

SIC—3842; *Orthopedic foot appliances*
Employs—18; Estab.—1977
3,000 sq ft site, Distrib.—Intl.
Privately owned corporation

**R J GRAPHICS, INC.**
206 Crown Point Rd., P.O. Box 293 (08086)
**Phone—(856) 848-1986**
Fax—(856) 848-5040
www.rjgraphicsprinting.com
Email—rjgisales@comcast.net
Pres.—Rita L. Iannelli
Prodn. Mgr.—Christine Iannelli
Prodn. Mgr.—Robert Iannelli, Jr.
Benefits Admn.—Donna Dickson
Estimator—Debbie Prinz
SIC—2752; NAICS—323100; *Offset printing*
Employs—30; Estab.—1971
Sales—under $500,000
Distrib.—Regional
Privately owned corporation

**SOLVAY SPECIALTY POLYMERS USA, INC.**
10 Leonard Ln. (08086)
**Phone—(856) 853-8119**
National—(800) 554-2874
Fax—(856) 853-6405
www.solvaysolexis.com
Email—solvaysolexisinfo@solvay.com
Pres.—Laird McBeth
Cont.—James Ford
Sales Mgr.—Robert Grinwis
Plt. Mgr.—Geoffrey Pass
Hum. Res. Mgr.—Charles Jones
SIC—2821; NAICS—325211; *Corporate headquarters & fluoropolymers; Brand name—Halar; Algoflon*
Employs—150; Estab.—1985
Company-wide: 229
400,000 sq ft site, Distrib.—National
Privately owned corporation
ISO rating—9002

**SSM INDUSTRIES, INC.**
Div. of S S M Industries, Inc.
1425 Grandview Ave. (08066)
**Phone—(856) 345-2525**
Fax—(856) 345-2520
www.ssmi.biz
Email—rschnell@ssmi.biz
GM—Ron Schnell
SIC—3444; *Sheet metal fabrication*
Employs—30; Estab.—1991
Distrib.—Local
Privately owned corporation
Parent co.—S S M Industries, Inc., Pittsburgh, PA
Phone—(412) 777-5100
See Parent Co. Section for full profile.

**SYMA SYSTEMS, INC.**
Div. of Art Guild, Inc.
300 Wolf Dr. (08086)
**Phone—(856) 686-4190**
　　　(856) 853-7500
Fax—(856) 686-4191
www.artguildinc.com
Email—shyams@artguildinc.com
V.-P., Sales & Mktg.—Stanley R. Hyams
Acct. Mgr.—Dianne Sartini
SIC—2541; 2542; *Custom trade show & museum exhibits & showcases, including modular temporary & permanent museum construction & rental exhibits; Brand name—Syma System; Syma Molto; Syma 408; Syma Orbit; Syma Rondo; Syma 20; Syma Deco*
Employs—100; Estab.—1939
Company-wide: 150
Sales—$1Mil-$5Mil
385,000 sq ft site, Distrib.—Intl.
Privately owned corporation

Parent co.—Art Guild, Inc., West Deptford, NJ
Phone—(856) 853-7500
See Parent Co. Section for full profile.

**†VALLEY NATIONAL GASES, WV LLC**
Div. of Matheson Tri-Gas, Inc.
201 Crown Point Rd. (08086)
**Phone—(856) 848-7321**
Fax—(856) 848-4272
www.mathesontrigas.com
Email—webmaster@vngas.com
GM—Wendy Hughes
Sales Rep.—Neil Stokes
SIC—5084; 5085; 5169; *Distributor of welding supplies, including gases*
Employs—10; Estab.—1980
Distrib.—Regional
Privately owned corporation
Parent co.—Matheson Tri-Gas, Inc., Independence, OH
Phone—(216) 573-9909
See Parent Co. Section for full profile.

## West Long Branch
### (Monmouth—N.E.)

**ART'S EMBROIDERY, LLC**
175 Monmouth Rd. (07764)
**Phone—(732) 870-1155**
Fax—(732) 222-0297
www.artsembroideryllc.com
Email—artsemb@aol.com
Ptnr.—Ina Kraucis
Ptnr.—Art Kraucis
SIC—2395; 2396; *Embroidery, screen printing & sports lettering*
Employs—4; Estab.—1989
Sales—under $500,000
Distrib.—Regional
Limited Liability Company

**BORO PRINTING, INC.**
813 Broadway (07764)
**Phone—(732) 229-1899**
Fax—(732) 222-6809
www.boroprinting.com
Email—info@boroprinting.com
Pres.—Gary Delatush
GM—Todd Delatush
SIC—2759; 2791; NAICS—323122; *Offset, digital color & large-format printing & typesetting*
Employs—5; Estab.—1977
Sales—under $500,000
5,000 sq ft site, Distrib.—Local
Privately owned corporation

**COMFORT REVOLUTION (H Q)**
187 Route 36, Ste. 205 (07764)
Mail addr: P.O. Box 1290, Eatontown (07724)
**Phone—(732) 272-9111**
Fax—(732) 870-8600
www.comfortrevolution.com
Email—info@comfortrevolution.com
Founder & CEO—Michael Fux
Sr. V.-P., CFO—Thomas Bruno
Sales Mgr.—Victoria Bae
SIC—2515; 2392; *Company headquarters; foam mattresses, mattress toppers & pillows*
Employs—20; Estab.—2007
Sales—$2.5Mil-$5Mil (est)
Distrib.—National
Privately owned corporation

**FORMAX PRINTERS**
200 Wall St. (07764)
**Phone—(732) 229-5063**
Fax—(732) 229-2089
Off. Mgr.—Michael Moratis
Manager—Linda Schwart
SIC—2752; NAICS—323100; *Instant printing*
Employs—3; Estab.—1978
Sales—under $500,000
Distrib.—Local
Sole ownership

**INNOCOR, INC. (H Q)**
187 State Route 36, Ste. 101 (07764-1343)
**Phone—(732) 263-0800**
National—(888) 999-0499
Fax—(732) 263-0900
www.sleepinnovations.com
Email—customerservice@sleepinnovations.com
CEO—Michael C. Thompson
CFO—Bob Thompson
CIO—Malek Shamoun
Ex. V.-P., Sales, Retail—Mark Wooters
Ex. V.-P., Mfg.—Stephen Setzer
Ex. V.-P., Channel Mktg.—Lisa Thorstenson
Ex. V.-P., Bus. & Prod. Dev.—Michael Loomis
V.-P., Hum. Res.—Katherine Sems
SIC—2515; 3086; 2392; *Corporate headquarters; polyurethane & memory foam pillows, mattresses & related comfort products*
Employs—70; Estab.—1996
Sales—$40Mil
Distrib.—Intl.
Publicly owned corporation

**KLOSE ASSOCS., INC.**
804 Broadway (07764)
**Phone—(732) 229-8950**
Fax—(732) 229-8955
www.kloseassociates.com
Email—raymond@kloseassociates.com
Pres., CEO, CFO—Raymond G. Klose
SIC—2541; 2542; *Trade show exhibit booths & displays; Brand name—Popart; Kolors; Premier Portable Architecture; Komponents KolorSTAND*
Employs—15; Estab.—1983
Sales—$2Mil-$3Mil
50,000 sq ft site, Distrib.—Intl.
Privately owned sub-S corp.

**REDI PACKAGING, INC.**
265 Highway 36, Ste. 109 (07764)
**Phone—(732) 544-1480**
www.redipackaging.com
Email—mail@redipackaging.com
Pres.—Cyndi Hogan
Off. & Sales Mgr.—Marybeth Spann
SIC—3081; 3082; 3083; 2673; NAICS—326113; *Polyethylene & polypropylene products, including bags, tubing & sheeting*
Employs—12; Estab.—1977
Sales—$1Mil-$2.5Mil
Distrib.—National
Privately owned corporation

**SIERRA PACKAGING, INC.**
60 State Route 36, Ste. C (07764)
**Phone—(732) 571-2900**
Fax—(732) 571-2930
Email—pdorato@sierra-packaging.com
Owner & Pres.—Paul S. Charpentier
Sales Mgr.—Paul Dorato
SIC—2673; *Plastic bags & liners*
Employs—5; Estab.—1990
Distrib.—Regional
Privately owned corporation

**SYSTEMS DESIGN TECHNOLOGY**
P.O. Box 547 (07764)
**Phone—(732) 571-4547**
Fax—(732) 229-0031
Email—ltisound@gmail.com
Pres.—Felix 'Phil' Foggia

GEOGRAPHICAL

## West Long Branch—(cont.)

SIC—3651; NAICS—334310; *Sound, video & communications systems; Brand name—Audio-Technica; QSC Audio; Peavey AA; DBX Professional; Listen Technology; Avlex Microphones; Superlux Microphones; MiPro Wireless Microphones; Klein Electronics ( Black-Box Radio)*
Employs—1; Estab.—2000
Distrib.—Local
Limited Liability Company

---

## West Milford
(Passaic—N.E.)

**†AWISCO WEST MILFORD, LLC**
Div. of AWISCO New York Corp.
26 Industrial Rd. (07480-4600)
**Phone—(973) 728-9008**
Fax—(973) 728-8172
www.awisco.com
Email—sales@awisco.net
Br. Mgr.—Andrew Cullen
SIC—5085; 5084; 5169; *Distributor of welding, industrial & safety supplies & compressed gases; Brand name—Miller Electric; Thermadyne; Linde; Metabo; Scotchman; John Tillman; ESAB; Hougen*
Employs—8
Distrib.—Regional
Privately owned corporation
Parent co.—AWISCO New York Corp., Maspeth, NY
Phone—(718) 786-7788
See Parent Co. Section for full profile.

**BEL-TECH STAMPING, INC.**
26 Industrial Rd., Ste. A (07480)
**Phone—(973) 728-8229**
Pres.—Steve Baun
SIC—3469; *Metal stampings*
Employs—7; Estab.—1995
Sales—under $500,000
Distrib.—National
Privately owned corporation

**FISCHER LASER MARKING, INC.**
384 Otterhole Rd. (07480)
**Phone—(973) 616-4696**
Fax—(973) 616-4706
Email—fischerlaser@optimum.net
Owner & Pres.—Sharon Fischer
SIC—3479; 3599; *Laser engraving & laser marking job shop*
Employs—4; Estab.—1996
Sales—under $500,000
3,000 sq ft site, Distrib.—National
Privately owned corporation

**INSTRUMENTATION DESIGN & SERVICE CO.**
256 Bearfort Rd. (07480)
**Phone—(973) 728-3748**
Fax—(973) 728-2124
Pres.—Jerry Oselador
SIC—3613; *Instrument panels*
Employs—2; Estab.—1983
Sales—under $500,000
Distrib.—Local
Sole ownership

**INTERNATIONAL CONVERTING MACHINERY, INC.**
45 Camelot Dr. (07480)
**Phone—(973) 728-2600**
Fax—(973) 728-9107
Pres., Sales & Mktg. Mgr.—Ted Gusek, Sr.
SIC—3554; NAICS—333291; *Converting machinery*
Employs—2; Estab.—1994
Sales—under $500,000
6,500 sq ft site, Distrib.—Intl.
Privately owned corporation

**JARCO INDUSTRIES, INC.**
1803 Union Valley Rd. (07480)
**Phone—(973) 728-5012**
Fax—(973) 728-0268
www.jarcoindustriesinc.com
Email—jarcoinc@verizon.net
Pres.—Steve Jarvis
SIC—3599; *Precision machining job shop*
Employs—5; Estab.—1987
Sales—$500,000-$1Mil
Distrib.—Regional
Privately owned sub-S corp.

**SELLING PRECISION, INC.**
264 Marshall Hill Rd. *(07480)*
**Phone—(973) 728-1214**
(800) 676-2417
Fax—(973) 728-9386
www.sellingprecision.com
Email—sales@sellingprecision.com
Pres.—William Calcagno
V-P.—Kenneth H. Calcagno
Bookkeeper—Margaret Bush
SIC—3499; *Hydraulic manifolds*
Employs—26; Estab.—1971
Sales—$1Mil-$5Mil
10,000 sq ft site, Distrib.—National
Privately owned corporation

**SIMPLE SOLUTIONS DISTRIBUTION, LLC (H Q)**
6 Jacobs Rd. (07480)
**Phone—(973) 846-7817**
National—(866) 667-8465
Fax—(973) 858-0219
www.industrialodorcontrol.com
Email—sales@industrialodorcontrol.com
Ptnr. & Mktg. Mgr.—Andrew McGibbon
Ptnr.—Eileen Pagano
SIC—3569; 2819; *Company headquarters; odor control activated carbon filters for residential & industrial wastewater systems (mfg. subcontracted); Brand name—Wolverine Brand Carbon Filters*
Employs—2; Estab.—2003
Sales—under $500,000
Distrib.—Intl.
Limited Liability Company

**SYMCON, INC.**
47 Cedar Ln. (07480)
**Phone—(201) 967-7378**
Fax—(973) 728-8680
Email—symcon@optonline.net
Pres.—Stella Scilingo
V-P., GM—Michael Scilingo
SIC—3613; 3679; 3625; 3629; NAICS—335313; *Electromechanical assemblies*
Employs—6; Estab.—1970
Sales—under $500,000
Distrib.—National
Privately owned corporation

---

## West New York
(Hudson—N.E.)

**CAMBIO NEWSPAPER**
604 56th St. (07093)
Mail addr: P.O. Box 4681, Union City (07087)
**Phone—(201) 902-0811**
Fax—(201) 865-4303
www.cambionewspaper.com
Email—cambionewspaper@yahoo.com
Dir.—Yamile Camacho
SIC—2711; *Newspaper publishing*
Employs—14; Estab.—2005
Sales—$500,000-$1Mil
Distrib.—Local
Privately owned corporation

NEW ENTRY
**†E-Z EDGE, INC.**
6119 Adams St. (07093)
**Phone—(201) 295-1171**
National—(800) 232-4470
www.e-zedge.com
Email—order@e-zedge.com
Owner—Michael Maffei
SIC—5046; *Distributor of food processing equipment & supplies, including knives, blades, plates, injector needles & packaging inserts*
Employs—4
Distrib.—Intl.
Privately owned corporation

**HILL CROSS CO., INC.**
543 56th St., P.O. Box 60 (07093)
**Phone—(201) 864-3393**
Fax—(201) 864-5448
www.hillcross.com
Email—hlcrs@verizon.net
Pres., CFO—Christopher C. Hammer
V-P., Quality—Donald Rosegren
Off. Mgr.—Jane Schroeck
SIC—3471; NAICS—332813; *Electroplating*
Employs—8; Estab.—1946
Sales—under $500,000
18,000 sq ft site, Distrib.—Intl.
Privately owned sub-S corp.

**I & F SCALLOP THREAD CO., INC.**
6002 Adams St. (07093)
**Phone—(201) 868-6550**
Pres.—Michael Iann
SIC—2299; *Scallop cutting*
Employs—1; Estab.—1947
Sales—under $500,000
Distrib.—Local
Privately owned corporation

**IMPERIAL DRUG & SPICE CORP.**
5620 Kennedy Blvd. W. (07093)
Mail addr: P.O. Box 8624, Woodcliff Lake (07677-8624)
**Phone—(201) 348-1551**
Fax—(201) 348-1552
www.imperialdrug.com
Email—info@imperialdrug.com
Pres.—Victoria Weingartner
Opers. Mgr.—Jim Weingartner
SIC—2023; 2844; *Latino/Hispanic health & beauty care products, including dietary supplements, cod liver oils & hair & skin oils & cream*
Employs—5; Estab.—1988
Sales—$500,000-$1Mil
10,000 sq ft site, Distrib.—Intl.
Privately owned corporation

**J & S FINISHING, INC.**
443 62nd St. (07093)
**Phone—(201) 854-0338**
Fax—(201) 854-0420
www.jandsuniforms.com
Email—jands@aol.com
Pres.—Pedro Calvo
Corp. Secy.—Maria Calvo
SIC—2395; 2389; *Embroidery & school uniforms*
Employs—15; Estab.—1987
Sales—under $500,000
4,000 sq ft site, Distrib.—Local
Privately owned corporation

**†JOSMO SHOES, INC.**
601 59th St. (07093)
**Phone—(201) 617-1477**
National—(800) 572-5353
Fax—(201) 617-1470
www.josmo.com
Email—info@josmo.com
Owner—Sam Esquenazi
GM—James Perez

SIC—5139; *Wholesaler of children's shoes; Brand name—Laura Ashley; Joseph Allen*
Employs—100; Estab.—1980
Sales—$11Mil-$25Mil
Distrib.—Local
Privately owned corporation

**LA DOMINICA**
635 56th St. (07093)
**Phone—(201) 348-4294**
Fax—(201) 348-4299
Pres.—Venancia Dominguez
SIC—2034; *Plantain chips*
Employs—10; Estab.—1984
Distrib.—Local
Privately owned corporation

**LAMAR DIAMOND JEWELRY CORP.**
5600 John F. Kennedy Blvd., Ste. 109 (07093)
**Phone—(201) 863-8683**
Fax—(201) 863-8684
Pres.—Lisette George
SIC—3911; NAICS—339911; *Precious metal jewelry*
Employs—2; Estab.—1970
Sales—$1Mil-$2.5Mil
Distrib.—National
Privately owned corporation

**LEE ELECTRIC, INC.**
309-11 51st St., P.O. Box 238 (07093)
**Phone—(201) 866-3656**
National—(800) 433-3417
Fax—(201) 866-0735
www.leeelectric.com
Email—staff@leeelectric.com
Pres., GM—Andrew Abramowitz
Bookkeeper—Mark Abramowitz
SIC—3669; NAICS—334290; *Electric locks*
Employs—5; Estab.—1951
Sales—under $500,000
10,000 sq ft site, Distrib.—National
Privately owned corporation

**MANOLUCCI DESIGNS**
220 61st St., Ste. 2-D (07093)
**Phone—(201) 861-2259**
Fax—(201) 861-2284
www.manolucci.com
Email—clientservices@manolucci.com
Pres.—Chris Vartanian
Dir.—Christina Campagnoli
SIC—3171; NAICS—316992; *Leather handbags*
Employs—3; Estab.—1983
Sales—under $500,000
Distrib.—Regional
Privately owned corporation

**MASHAL SIGNS CO., INC.**
568 55th St. (07093)
**Phone—(201) 348-8500**
Fax—(201) 348-8804
Email—mashalsign@aol.com
Owner & CEO—Alai Mashal
SIC—3993; *Custom signs & awnings*
Employs—6; Estab.—1996
Sales—$500,000-$1Mil
Distrib.—Local
Privately owned corporation

**MICHAEL'S COMMERCIAL SIGNS**
629 62nd St., Ste. 31 (07093)
**Phone—(201) 868-7166**
Fax—(201) 868-1972
Email—michaelssigns@verizon.net
Mng. Ptnr. & Pres.—Ruben Gonzalez
SIC—3993; 2759; NAICS—323100; *Interior & exterior signs, bus & truck lettering & wraps, striping & labels*
Employs—4; Estab.—1981
Sales—under $500,000
3,500 sq ft site, Distrib.—Regional
Limited Liability Company

## West New York—(cont.)

**†MUNDO ESOTERICO DIST INC**
6207 Madison St. (07093)
**Phone—(201) 766-4084**
(201) 868-3997
Fax—(201) 766-4084
www.mundoesotericonj.com
Email—sales@
mundoesotericonj.com
GM—Beder Marina
SIC—5199; 5192; *Wholesaler of
religious goods, including
books, perfumes, sprays &
candles*
Employs—1; Estab.—2005
Privately owned corporation

**NU-STYLE EMBROIDERY & BUTTON
CO., INC.**
5212 Polk St. (07093)
**Phone—(201) 864-1808**
Fax—(201) 867-3481
Email—newstylelace@gmail.com
Pres.—Jay Rosner
SIC—3965; 2387; 2258; 2395;
NAICS—339993; *Apparel
buttons, belts, neckties, lace &
embroidery*
Employs—5; Estab.—1990
Sales—under $500,000
Distrib.—Local
Limited Liability Company
Also see: Nu-Style Embroidery &
Trimming, same loc.

**NU-STYLE EMBROIDERY &
TRIMMING**
5212 Polk St. (07093)
**Phone—(201) 864-1808**
Email—nustylelace@gmail.com
Pres.—Sam Rosner
SIC—2395; 3965; NAICS—
339993; *Embroidery & lace
covered buttons & belts*
Employs—2; Estab.—1987
Sales—under $500,000
Distrib.—National
Privately owned corporation
Also see: Nu-Style Embroidery &
Button Co., Inc., same loc.

**PRIAMO DESIGNS LTD.**
6614 Broadway (07093)
**Phone—(201) 861-8808**
Fax—(201) 861-0170
Email—priamo@aol.com
Pres.—Priamo Espaillat
SIC—2341; NAICS—315200;
*Women's lingerie*
Employs—5; Estab.—1981
Sales—under $500,000
Distrib.—Local
Privately owned corporation

**PROMEKO, INC.**
543 59th St. (07093)
**Phone—(201) 861-6446**
Fax—(201) 861-5245
www.promekoinc.com
Email—promekoinc@aol.com
Pres.—Edalio Rondon
SIC—2844; NAICS—325600;
*Health & beauty aids*
Employs—7; Estab.—1977
15,000 sq ft site, Distrib.—National
Privately owned partnership

**RAZA-DESIGNS, INC.**
220 61st St., Ste. 2-C (07093)
**Phone—(201) 430-8590**
(917) 586-1146
National—(800) 715-2195
Fax—(201) 443-1205
www.razadesigns.com
Email—bevluch@gmail.com
Pres.—Beverly Luchfeld

SIC—2335; 2339; 2389; NAICS—
315200; *Hostess & formal
gowns, loungewear & robes,
theatrical costumes, caftans,
peignoir sets & zip hoodies*
Employs—2; Estab.—1994
Sales—$500,000-$1Mil
1,200 sq ft site, Distrib.—Intl.
Privately owned corporation

**ROYAL PRINTING SERVICE**
441 51st St. (07093)
**Phone—(201) 863-3131**
Fax—(201) 867-4437
Pres.—Ralph Passante, Sr.
SIC—2752; NAICS—323100;
*Offset printing*
Employs—40; Estab.—1932
Sales—$11Mil-$25Mil
Distrib.—Regional
Privately owned corporation

**SEW IN STYLE, INC.**
220 61st St. (07093)
**Phone—(201) 868-8568**
Fax—(201) 868-8736
Email—sewinstyleco@aol.com
Pres.—Angel Hernando
SIC—2369; NAICS—315200;
*Children's sportswear*
Employs—5; Estab.—2000
Sales—$500,000-$1Mil
Distrib.—Local
Privately owned corporation

**SWISSTEX CO.**
220 61st St., 2nd Fl. (07093)
**Phone—(201) 861-8000**
Fax—(201) 861-8001
Owner—Robert Wolfe
SIC—2339; *Women's clothing*
Employs—20; Estab.—1934
10,000 sq ft site, Distrib.—National
Sole ownership

**WEBER & DOEBRICH, INC.**
119 61st St. (07093)
**Phone—(201) 867-1540**
Fax—(201) 854-5564
Email—wedoembroidery@
gmail.com
Pres.—Jane Zellweger
SIC—2395; 2397; NAICS—
313222; *Embroidery*
Employs—3; Estab.—1979
Sales—under $500,000
Distrib.—National
Privately owned corporation

**WINDOW SUPPLY CORP.**
5410 Kennedy Blvd. (07093)
**Phone—(201) 392-1213**
Fax—(201) 392-1840
www.windowworldsupply.com
Pres.—Enildo Diaz
SIC—3442; NAICS—332321;
*Aluminum windows*
Employs—1; Estab.—1996
Sales—under $500,000 (est)
Distrib.—Local
Privately owned corporation

---

## West Orange
(Essex—N.E.)

**A & F ELECTROPLATING, INC.**
106 Ashland Ave. (07052)
**Phone—(973) 736-4344**
Email—afplating@aol.com
Pres.—Frank Chabala
V.-P.—Barry Chabala
SIC—3471; NAICS—332813;
*Electroplating*
Employs—2; Estab.—1968
Sales—under $500,000
Distrib.—National
Privately owned corporation

**†A-ABLE FENCE BUILDERS**
28 Lakeside Ave. (07052)
**Phone—(973) 325-1900**
Fax—(973) 325-2292
Email—aablefence@aol.com

Owner—William Byrne
GM—Ted Kinsella
SIC—5031; 5039; *Wholesaler &
installer of wooden & metal
fences; Brand name—DoorKing;
Jerith; Westmoreland II; Delgard*
Employs—10; Estab.—1971
Sales—$1Mil-$5Mil
Distrib.—Local
Privately owned corporation

**ALL SIGNS DIRECT, LLC**
38 Washington St. (07052)
**Phone—(973) 736-7446**
National—(888) 904-7446
Fax—(973) 736-9477
www.allsignsdirect.com
Email—info@allsignsdirect.com
Pres.—Rick Iannuzzelli
SIC—3993; *Interior & exterior
signs*
Employs—7; Estab.—1977
Sales—$500,000-$1Mil (est)
Distrib.—Intl.
Limited Liability Company

**†AWISCO CORP.**
Div. of AWISCO New York Corp.
24 Lakeside Ave. (07052)
**Phone—(973) 736-0200**
National—(800) 834-1925
Fax—(973) 736-7541
www.awisco.com
Email—sales@awisco.net
Br. Mgr.—Abel Marriott
SIC—5084; 5085; 5169;
*Wholesaler of welding
equipment, industrial & safety
supplies & compressed gases;
Brand name—Miller Electric;
Hobart Brothers; Thermadyne;
ESAB; Lincoln; Direct Wire and
Cable; United Abrasives;
Metabo Tool; Linde Gases;
Hougen Mfg; John Tillman;
Capital Safety; North Safety;
MSA*
Employs—6; Estab.—2007
Sales—$1Mil-$2.5Mil
2,500 sq ft site, Distrib.—Regional
Privately owned corporation
Parent co.—AWISCO New York
Corp., Maspeth, NY
Phone—(718) 786-7788
See Parent Co. Section for full profile.

**BILDISCO DOOR MFG., INC.**
21 Central Ave. (07052)
**Phone—(973) 673-2400**
Fax—(973) 673-2236
www.bildisco.com
Email—bildiscomfg@comcast.net
Pres.—Bruno Valente
Pur. Agt.—Susan Hetli
SIC—2431; 3442; 5072; NAICS—
332321; *Manufacturer of
wooden & metal doors &
distributor of architectural door
hardware for institutional &
commercial buildings & facilities
& apartment buildings &
complexes*
Employs—11; Estab.—1981
Sales—$500,000-$1Mil
Distrib.—Regional
Privately owned corporation

**COZZOLINO FURNITURE DESIGN,
INC.**
20 Standish Ave. (07052)
**Phone—(973) 731-9292**
Fax—(973) 731-0190
www.cozzolino.com
Email—info@cozzolino.com
Owner & Dir.—Steven Cozzolino
Cont.—Linda Duckworth
SIC—2431; NAICS—321900;
*Custom architectural millwork*
Employs—23; Estab.—1978
Sales—$1Mil-$2.5Mil
Distrib.—Regional
Privately owned corporation

**D & M PRINTING, INC.**
46 Watson Ave. (07052)
**Phone—(973) 731-1300**
Fax—(973) 731-4013
Email—dnmprtg@verizon.net
Pres.—Michael Napolitano
V.-P.—Donald Covert
Pressman—Michael Perrini
SIC—2759; NAICS—323119;
*Commercial printing*
Employs—5; Estab.—1980
Sales—under $500,000
Distrib.—Local
Privately owned corporation

**ETTA CONTROLS, INC.**
31 Belgrade Ter. (07052)
**Phone—(973) 731-6552**
(973) 723-5758
Fax—(973) 731-6578
Email—ettacontrols@aol.com
Pres.—Paul Rametta
SIC—3613; 3561; 3556; 7373;
NAICS—335313; *Control panels,
system integrators, pumps,
pump controls & bakery
equipment for small, medium &
large bakeries*
Employs—6; Estab.—1986
2,000 sq ft site, Distrib.—National
Privately owned corporation

**FABULOUS INTERIORS**
470 Prospect Ave., Ste. 105
(07052)
**Phone—(973) 736-1200**
(973) 673-2220
Fax—(973) 736-3017
www.fabulouswallcoverings.com
Email—sales@
fabulouswallcoverings.com
Mng. Ptnr.—Jeffrey Fischman
Ptnr.—Anne Fischman
SIC—2679; 2591; 2391; NAICS—
337920; *Wall coverings &
converted paper products,
including borders, window
shades, shadings, window
treatments, upholstery, fabrics,
curtains & draperies*
Employs—2; Estab.—2013
Sales—$1Mil
Distrib.—National
Limited Liability Company

**HANGER PROSTHETICS &
ORTHOTICS, INC.**
Div. of Hanger, Inc.
59 Main St., Ste. 111 (07052)
**Phone—(973) 736-0628**
Fax—(973) 736-1640
www.hanger.com
Email—info@hanger.com
Clinic Mgr.—Jenny Adase
SIC—3842; *Prosthetic &
orthopedic appliances*
Employs—12; Estab.—1949
Sales—$1Mil-$2.5Mil
5,000 sq ft site, Distrib.—Regional
Publicly owned corporation
Parent co.—Hanger, Inc., Austin,
TX
Phone—(512) 777-3800
See Parent Co. Section for full profile.

**NATIONAL COMMUNICATION, INC.**
69 Washington St. (07052)
**Phone—(973) 325-3151**
Fax—(973) 325-2690
www.trynci.net
Email—ncisales@trynci.com
Pres., Hum. Res. Mgr.—Andrew
Brooke
Pur. Mgr.—Larry Doctor
SIC—3679; *Cable assemblies*
Employs—17; Estab.—1988
Distrib.—Intl.
Privately owned corporation

**NEXT STEP ORTHOPEDICS, INC.**
331 Main St. (07052)
**Phone—(973) 736-2244**
Fax—(973) 736-2227

GEOGRAPHICAL

## West Orange—(cont.)

www.nextsteportho.com
Email—brendat@nextsteportho.com
Ptnr.—Michael Moschella
Ptnr.—Paul Duffy
Off. Mgr.—Brenda Tappins
SIC—3842; *Orthopedic, orthotic & prosthetic appliances*
Employs—4; Estab.—2002
Sales—$1Mil-$2.5Mil
2,200 sq ft site, Distrib.—Local
Privately owned sub-S corp.

**PACKAGING MACHINERY & EQUIPMENT CO.**
181 Watson Ave. (07052)
**Phone—(973) 325-2418**
Fax—(973) 325-6937
Email—packmach@aol.com
Corp. Secy.—Mary E. Cameron
GM—James Clark
SIC—3565; NAICS—333993; *Packaging machinery*
Employs—5; Estab.—1972
Sales—$500,000-$1Mil
Distrib.—Intl.
Privately owned corporation

**†PIONEER BEARING CORP.**
623 Eagle Rock Ave., Ste. 135 (07052-2948)
**Phone—(973) 325-9095**
National—(800) 989-9126
Fax—(973) 325-9159
www.pioneerbearing.com
Email—pbc@comcast.net
Pres.—Kenneth Abeles
SIC—5085; *Distributor of commercial & industrial miniature, precision, inch & metric series bearings; Brand name—NMB; NHBB; Timken; SKF; Torrington; Barden; MPB; RMB; EZO; IJK; FAFNIR; SMT; FAG; RBC*
Employs—1; Estab.—1990
Sales—under $500,000
500 sq ft site, Distrib.—National
Privately owned sub-S corp.

**PLATE CRAFT, INC.**
172-174 Main St. (07052)
**Phone—(973) 736-4404**
Pres.—Dominick Calabrese, Jr.
V-P.—Theresa Calabrese
SIC—2796; NAICS—323122; *Printing plates*
Employs—3; Estab.—1968
Sales—under $500,000
Distrib.—Regional
Privately owned corporation

**PROGRESSIVE PRINTING CORP.**
24 Park Ave. (07052)
**Phone—(973) 736-5800**
Fax—(973) 736-1985
Pres.—Andrea Risoli
Corp. Secy.—Michael Risoli
SIC—2759; NAICS—323100; *Commercial printing & graphic design*
Employs—4; Estab.—1982
Sales—under $500,000
Distrib.—Local
Privately owned corporation

**REEL PARTS CO.**
10 Park Ave. (07052)
**Phone—(973) 731-9559**
Fax—(973) 731-8889
www.valleydie.com
Email—reelinfo@reel-parts.com
Pres.—John Dyer
Hum. Res. Mgr.—Kay Dyer
SIC—3569; 3499; *Corrugated, PVC, masonite & wooden reels, cores, plugs & tubes*
Employs—6; Estab.—1960
Sales—$500,000-$1Mil (est)
Distrib.—Regional
Privately owned sub-S corp.
Also see: Valley Die-Cutting Co., Inc., same loc.

**SIGNRIGHT, INC.**
76 Ashland Ave. (07052)
**Phone—(973) 731-8882**
Fax—(973) 731-6248
www.sign-right.com
Email—al@sign-right.com
Ptnr.—Stephen Hanley
SIC—3993; *Interior & exterior signs*
Employs—8; Estab.—1995
Sales—under $500,000
Distrib.—Regional
Privately owned sub-S corp.

**SURE MARK LABELS, INC.**
4 Flynn Ter., P.O. Box 501 (07052)
**Phone—(973) 768-4859**
Email—jv.politan@verizon.net
Pres.—James V. Politan
SIC—2759; NAICS—323100; *Printed labels*
Employs—5; Estab.—1972
10,000 sq ft site, Distrib.—Local
Privately owned corporation

**VALLEY DIE-CUTTING CO., INC.**
10 Park Ave. (07052)
**Phone—(973) 731-8884**
Fax—(973) 731-8889
www.valleydie.com
Email—customerservice@valleydie.com
Pres.—John Dyer
CFO & Hum. Res. Mgr.—Kaye Dyer
Opers. Mgr.—Harold Lohse
Prod. Mgr.—Chris Hernandez
SIC—2675; NAICS—322200; *Die-cutting, embossing & foil stamping*
Employs—50; Estab.—1955
Distrib.—Regional
Privately owned corporation
Also see: Reel Parts Co., same loc.

**XPRESA LABELS CORP.**
681 Eagle Rock Ave. (07052)
**Phone—(973) 669-8444**
National—(877) 637-7500
Fax—(877) 637-7500
www.xpresadesigns.com
Email—sales@xpresalabels.com
Pres.—Tamer Ozaydin
Off. Mgr.—Joe Spano
SIC—2395; *Labels, including woven, adhesive woven, clothing/garment, flag, hang tags, badge & patch embroidery*
Employs—10; Estab.—2001
Sales—$500,000-$1Mil
Distrib.—Intl.
AKA: Xpresa Woven Label Designs

**†YECIES, INC., HERMAN W.**
11 Roosevelt Ave., P.O. Box 6186 (07052)
**Phone—(973) 736-7362**
National—(800) 255-6998
Fax—(973) 731-6146
www.hermanwyecies.com
Email—jyecies@aol.com
Pres.—Roberta Yecies
Sales Engr.—Gary Mega
Acctg. Exec.—Clara Crockett
SIC—5084; 5085; *Wholesaler of industrial equipment & supplies, including precision instruments, carbide, high speed & cobalt cutting tools, abrasives, adhesives & band saw blades; Brand name—Walter-Valenite; L. S. Starrett Co; OSG; Lenox; MorseCutting Tools; Yale Sales; General Tools; Cooper Tools; Brown & Sharpe; 3M; United Abrasives; All American Drill Bushing; SPI; Danaher; Fastcut; Grobet; ToolMex*
Employs—3; Estab.—1927
Sales—$1Mil
2,500 sq ft site, Distrib.—National
Privately owned corporation
AKA: NJ Engineering & Supply

## West Paterson

(Passaic—N.E.)

**FSR, INC.**
244 Bergen Blvd. (07424)
**Phone—(973) 785-4347**
National—(800) 332-3771
Fax—(973) 785-3318
www.fsrinc.com
Email—sales@fsrinc.com
Chrm.—William Fitzsimmons
Pres.—Jan Sandri
CFO—Frank Van Morrelgem
Sales Mgr.—Paul Fitzsimmons
Mktg. Mgr.—Donnell Johnson
IT Mgr.—Walter Gould
Admn. Serv. & Hum. Res. Mgr.—Lynne Faye
SIC—3651; 3669; 3679; NAICS—334310; *Signal management & infrastructure systems & equipment for the audio/video, datacom, education, hospitality, government & religious markets*
Employs—80; Estab.—1981
30,000 sq ft site, Distrib.—Intl.
Privately owned corporation

**O & C DIE CUTTERS & FINISHERS**
16 Andrews Dr. (07424)
**Phone—(973) 890-7778**
Fax—(973) 890-4659
Email—odit@ocdiecutters.com
Pres.—Odit Ramnarian
SIC—2675; 3469; NAICS—322200; *Die cutting, foil stamping & mounting*
Employs—20; Estab.—1993
Sales—$2.6Mil-$5Mil
Distrib.—Local
Privately owned corporation

**QUALIPAC AMERICA CORP.**
Div. of Pochet Of America, Inc.
1 Garret Mountain Plz., 5th Fl. (07424)
**Phone—(973) 389-7730**
Fax—(973) 389-7732
www.qualipac.fr
Email—gtirico@puchet.fr
Pres.—Eric Vanin
Sr. Proj. Engr.—Kristen Mollet
Sales Coord.—Karen Malcolm
Hum. Res. Coord.—Brenda Tolota
SIC—3085; NAICS—326160; *Plastic bottles & cosmetic packaging*
Employs—15; Estab.—1996
Distrib.—Intl.
Privately owned corporation
Parent co.—Pochet Of America, Inc., Wayne, NJ
  Phone—(973) 942-4923
  See Parent Co. Section for full profile.

**TOMCEL MACHINE, INC.**
86 Lackawanna Ave. (07424)
**Phone—(973) 256-8257**
Pres.—Rick Foy
SIC—3599; *General machining job shop*
Employs—2; Estab.—1992
Sales—under $500,000
Distrib.—Local
Privately owned sub-S corp.

## West Trenton

(Mercer—N.E.)

**NEUROTRON MEDICAL**
800 Silvia St. (08628)
**Phone—(609) 896-3444**
National—(800) 367-1238
Fax—(609) 896-2798
www.neumedinc.com
Email—info@neumedinc.com
Owner—Jack Guldalian
SIC—3841; 3845; *Diagnostic & electrotherapy medical equipment*
Employs—10; Estab.—1989
Sales—$1Mil-$5Mil
Distrib.—National
Privately owned corporation
DBA: Neu Med, Inc.

**RBC BEARINGS, INC.**
400 Sullivan Way (08628)
**Phone—(609) 882-5050**
Fax—(609) 882-5533
www.rbcbearings.com
Email—info@rbcbearings.com
Plt. Mgr.—Deval Glover
SIC—3562; NAICS—332991; *Standard & custom engineered bearings for industrial, aerospace & defense applications; Brand name—Nice Ball Bearings; RBC Bearings*
Employs—125; Estab.—1919
100,000 sq ft site, Distrib.—Intl.
Publicly owned corporation
ISO rating—9001:2000, AS9100C
Parent co.—RBC Bearings, Inc., Oxford, CT
  Phone—(203) 267-7001
  See Parent Co. Section for full profile.

**T A C TECHNICAL INSTRUMENT CORP.**
21 W. Piper Ave., Trenton-Mercer Airport (08628)
**Phone—(609) 882-2894**
Fax—(609) 882-3147
www.tactictest.com
Email—tactictest@aol.com
Pres.—Frederick Beck
Plt. Mgr.—Howard Hunter
Off. Mgr.—Ruth Kontura
SIC—3829; *Ultrasonic inspection machinery*
Employs—15; Estab.—1962
Sales—$1Mil-$5Mil
9,000 sq ft site, Distrib.—Intl.
Privately owned corporation

## Westampton

(Burlington—S.E.)

**EATON CORP., ELECTRICAL DIV.**
96 Stemmers Ln. (08060)
**Phone—(609) 835-4230**
National—(800) 326-5750
Fax—(609) 835-4777
www.eatonelectrical.com
Email—customer@eaton.com
Plt. Mgr.—Nick Kluf
Inventory Control & Prodn. Mgr.—Ben Miller
SIC—3613; NAICS—335313; *Electrical panel boards*
Employs—15; Estab.—2001
Sales—$2.5Mil-$5Mil (est)
Distrib.—National
Publicly owned corporation
Parent co.—Eaton Corp., Electrical Div., Raleigh, NC
  Phone—(919) 870-3000
  See Parent Co. Section for full profile.

## Westampton—(cont.)

**MITCHELL'S WOODWORKING, LLC**
780 Jacksonville Mount Holly Rd.
(08060)
**Phone—(609) 261-7500**
www.mitchellswoodworking.com
Email—gordon@
mitchellswoodworking.com
Owner—Gordon Mitchell
SIC—2434; 2431; NAICS—
337110; *Custom cabinets &
millwork, including bookcases,
wall units & desks for offices &
kitchens*
Employs—3; Estab.—1990
Sales—under $500,000
4,600 sq ft site, Distrib.—Local
Limited Liability Company

**PARIS BUSINESS PRODUCTS, INC.**
800 Highland Dr. (08060)
**Phone—(609) 265-9200**
National—(800) 523-6454
Fax—(609) 261-4853
www.pariscorp.com
Email—info@pariscorp.com
Pres.—Gerard Toscani
IT Mgr.—Daryll Dickinson
Hum. Res. Mgr.—Jill Blanco
Accts. Payable Rep.—Charlotte
Miller
SIC—2679; NAICS—322200;
*Paper converting*
Employs—81; Estab.—1964
Sales—$60Mil-$65Mil
120,000 sq ft site, Distrib.—
National
Privately owned corporation

**SIR SPEEDY**
897 Rancocas Rd. (08060)
**Phone—(609) 267-1232**
Fax—(609) 267-8289
www.sirspeedy.com
Email—speedy7113@verizon.net
GM—Joseph Barlam
SIC—2759; 3993; NAICS—
323100; *Offset printing, including
color, instant, white digital
imaging, large-format &
advertising specialties & mailing
services*
Employs—4; Estab.—1987
Sales—under $500,000
Distrib.—Regional
Limited Liability Company

**TRAVALLIANCE MEDIA, LLC**
593 Rancocas Rd. (08060)
**Phone—(856) 505-1400**
National—(877) 727-0035
Fax—(856) 727-0136
www.travalliancemedia.com
Pres., CEO—Mark Murphy
V-P., Sales—Kerry Dolan
Dir., Mktg.—Courtney Love
Cust. Serv. Rep.—Victoria
Benecke
Accountant—Janette Braggs
SIC—2721; *Travel agent
magazine publishing*
Employs—50; Estab.—2002
Distrib.—National
Limited Liability Company
AKA: Travel Tribe, LLC

**†XPEDX LLC A VERITIV COMPANY**
Div. of Veritiv Corp.
1200 Highland Dr., Ste. 1-B
(08060-5118)
**Phone—(609) 518-9700**
National—(800) 257-9013
Fax—(877) 898-7508
www.xpedx.com
Email—terence.sheehy@
veritivcorp.com
GM—Terence M. Sheehy
Sales Mgr., Facility Sols.—
Thomas Dougherty
Sales Mgr., Packaging—Mark
Basilii

Sales Mgr., Printing Papers—
Michael Burns
Admn. & Facility Mgr.—Carson
Cooper
Cust. Serv. Mgr.—Jeffrey Marrow
Logistics Mgr.—John Afflerbach
SIC—5111; 5113; *Distributor of
printing & writing paper,
packaging, graphics & facility
supplies; Brand name—
Hammermill; SAPPI; New Page;
Appleton; MeadWestvaco;
Springhill; Georgia Pacific;
Wausau; Neenah; Mohawk;
Glatfelter; Fasson*
Employs—98; Estab.—1898
142,000 sq ft site, Distrib.—
Regional
Publicly owned corporation
Parent co.—Veritiv Corp.,
Loveland, OH
Phone—(513) 965-2900
See Parent Co. Section for full profile.

---

## Westfield
### (Union—N.E.)

**AJ PRINTING SOLUTIONS, LLC**
781 Hyslip Ave. (07090)
**Phone—(908) 202-0974**
    (908) 372-4863
Fax—(908) 543-1119
www.sites.google.com/site/
ajprintingsolutionsllc
Email—aandjprinting@gmail.com
Owner—Gary Wasserman
SIC—2759; 2752; *Flexographic &
offset printing of packaging
components for the generic &
cosmetics industries, including
folding cartons, packaging
inserts & pressure-sensitive
labels*
Employs—1; Estab.—2008
Sales—under $500,000
Distrib.—National
Limited Liability Company

**ALFA PRODUCTION SYSTEMS**
522 Boulevard (07090)
**Phone—(908) 654-0255**
www.alfasystems.biz
Email—alfaworks@aol.com
V-P., Sales—Charles Holhea
Dir., Engrg.—Steve Williams
SIC—3569; *Automation machinery*
Employs—19; Estab.—1984
Sales—$1Mil-$2.5Mil
Distrib.—Intl.
Privately owned corporation

NEW ENTRY
**ATLANTIC BEACH SOAP CO.**
231 North Ave. W., Ste. 2 (07090)
**Phone—(908) 272-7595**
www.atlanticbeachsoapco.com
Email—atlanticbeachsoap@
verizon.net
Owner—Shaun Blackie
SIC—2841; *Handcrafted soaps,
including olive oil & shea butter-
based soaps*
Employs—2; Estab.—2002
Sales—$1Mil-$2.5Mil (est)
Distrib.—Local
Limited Liability Company

**BRASS SHOP, INC.**
611 Central Ave. (07090)
**Phone—(908) 232-2161**
Fax—(908) 232-6634
Email—frankielamps@comcast.net
Pres.—Frank Giannone
Off. Mgr.—Margaret Giannone
SIC—3446; 3471; NAICS—
332323; *Rebuilt brass lighting,
lamp restoration & polishing*
Employs—2; Estab.—1980
Sales—under $500,000
Distrib.—Local
Privately owned corporation

**BRUMMER'S HANDMADE
CHOCOLATES**
125 E. Broad St. (07090)
**Phone—(908) 232-1904**
Owner—George Brummer
SIC—2066; NAICS—311300;
*Handmade chocolate candy*
Employs—3; Estab.—1989
Sales—under $500,000
Distrib.—Local
Sole ownership

**FALCON PRINTING CO.**
613 Central Ave. (07090)
**Phone—(908) 232-1991**
Fax—(908) 232-8466
Email—falconqg@aol.com
Ptnr.—Anthony Archambault
SIC—2759; 2796; 2791; NAICS—
323122; *Commercial printing,
typesetting & color separations*
Employs—4; Estab.—1983
Sales—under $1.5Mil
Distrib.—Regional
Publicly owned corporation

**HANDLER MFG. CO., INC.**
612 North Ave. E. (07090)
Mail addr: P.O. Box 520, Westfield
(07091)
**Phone—(908) 233-7796**
Fax—(908) 233-7340
www.handlermfg.com
Email—info@handlermfg.com
CEO—William A. Lehman
Pres.—Rick La Duca
Secy-Treas.—L. Lehman
Cont.—Sandra Hanrahan
SIC—3843; NAICS—339114;
*Dentists' metal processing
equipment & industrial dust
collectors; Brand name—Red
Wing*
Employs—40; Estab.—1920
34,000 sq ft site, Distrib.—Intl.
Privately owned sub-S corp.

**SIGN TECH**
Div. of Print Tech Ltd.
361 South Ave. E. (07090)
**Phone—(908) 232-2287**
Fax—(908) 654-4847
www.print-tech.com
Email—sales@print-tech.com
GM—Gary Alessio
Manager—Steve Fucito
SIC—3993; *Interior & exterior
signs; Brand name—PrintFLEX*
Employs—30; Estab.—1987
Sales—under $500,000
Distrib.—Regional
Limited Liability Company
Parent co.—Print Tech Ltd.,
Springfield, NJ
Phone—(908) 232-2287
See Parent Co. Section for full profile.

**SIR SPEEDY WESTFIELD**
516 North Ave. E. (07090)
**Phone—(908) 232-1001**
Fax—(908) 232-5922
www.sirspeedywestfield.com
Email—print@
sirspeedywestfield.com
Owner & V-P., MIS—Barbara
Murphy
Pres., CFO—James T. Murphy
SIC—2759; *Digital printing &
graphic design, mailing &
marketing services*
Employs—5; Estab.—1992
Sales—under $500,000
2,000 sq ft site, Distrib.—Local
Privately owned corporation

**W B C INDUSTRIES, INC.**
625 Central Ave. (07090)
**Phone—(908) 789-1234**
National—(800) 818-2932
Fax—(908) 232-5219
www.wbcindustries.com
Email—sales@wbcindustries.com
Pres.—Scott Viglianti

SIC—3452; NAICS—332722;
*Hook & loop fastening systems*
Employs—20; Estab.—1963
20,000 sq ft site, Distrib.—National
Privately owned corporation

**WATCHUNG COMMUNICATIONS,
INC.**
251 North Ave. W. (07090)
Mail addr: P.O. Box 250, Westfield
(07091-0250)
**Phone—(908) 232-4407**
Fax—(908) 232-0473
www.goleader.com
Email—editor@goleader.com
Publisher—Horace Corbin
Editor—Paul Peyton
Bus. Mgr.—Rob Connelly
SIC—2711; *Weekly print & online
newspaper publishing; Brand
name—Westfield Leader; Scotch
Plains-Fanwood Times*
Employs—9; Estab.—1890
Sales—under $1Mil
Distrib.—Regional
Privately owned corporation
AKA: The Westfield Leader/Scotch
Plains-Fanwood Times

**WELDON MATERIALS, INC. (H Q)**
141 Central Ave. (07090)
**Phone—(908) 233-4444**
Fax—(908) 233-4215
www.weldonmat.com
Email—billw@weldonmat.com
Pres., Cont.—Richard Weldon
V-P.—William Weldon
Hum. Res. Mgr.—Eileen Mooney
SIC—3273; 2951; NAICS—
327320; *Corporate
headquarters; ready-mixed
concrete, aggregates & asphalt
paving compounds*
Employs—30; Estab.—1892
Sales—$5Mil-$10Mil
Distrib.—Local
Privately owned corporation

---

## Westmont
### (Camden—S.W.)

**SEVERINO PASTA MFG. CO.**
110 Haddon Ave. (08108)
**Phone—(856) 854-7666**
Fax—(856) 854-6098
www.severinopasta.com
Email—pseverino@
severinopasta.com
Owner—Joseph Severino
GM—Louis Severino
Off. Mgr.—Carla Severino
Bookkeeper—Patty Snyder
SIC—2098; NAICS—311823;
*Pasta*
Employs—22; Estab.—1971
Sales—$500,000-$1Mil
Distrib.—Regional
Sole ownership

---

## Westville
### (Gloucester—S.W.)

**ARTEX KNITTING MILLS, INC.**
300 Harvard Ave., P.O. Box 183
(08093)
**Phone—(856) 456-2800**
Fax—(856) 456-4111
www.artexknit.com
Email—sales@artexknit.com
Pres.—Arthur Pottash
V-P., Pur.—Bernie Gerbarg
Plt. Mgr.—Gary Rothschild
Administrator—Christine
McGovern
SIC—2253; *Knit scarves & caps*
Employs—90; Estab.—1926
80,000 sq ft site, Distrib.—Intl.
Privately owned corporation

GEOGRAPHICAL

## Westville—(cont.)

### BARCUS CO., INC., EDGAR C.
Route 45 & Park Ave., P.O. Box 128 (08093)
**Phone—(856) 456-0204**
Fax—(856) 456-5970
www.barcusdie.com
Pres.—Leo Laskowski
V-P.—Edgar Barcus
V-P.—Harry Laskowski
SIC—3544; NAICS—333500; Steel rule dies
Employs—17; Estab.—1950
3,800 sq ft site, Distrib.—National
Privately owned sub-S corp.

### COLONIAL SEAL CO.
1114 Crown Point Rd. (08093)
**Phone—(856) 432-0012**
National—(800) 564-2201
Fax—(856) 845-0660
www.colonialseal.com
Email—sales@colonialseal.com
Pres.—Stephen A. Maloney
Sales Mgr.—Katrina Mackey
Opers. Mgr.—Shannon Dolan
SIC—3053; 3061; 3069; NAICS—339991; Oil, rotary shaft, custom metal cased, hydraulic & lathe cut seals & rubber molded parts, bushings & gaskets; Brand name—Garlock; JM Clipper; Chicago Rawhide; Stemco; SKF; National; Timken; Parker; Hallite
Employs—6; Estab.—1994
Sales—$1.5Mil
10,000 sq ft site, Distrib.—Intl.
Privately owned sub-S corp.
ISO rating—9001

### CORNELL & CO., INC.
224 Cornell Ln. (08093)
Mail addr: P.O. Box 807, Woodbury (08096)
**Phone—(856) 742-1900**
Fax—(856) 742-8186
www.cornellcraneandsteel.com
Pres.—Delor Cornell
Corp. Secy.—Kate Flaherty
IT Mgr.—Gary Schmidt
Gen. Admn.—Betty O'Donnell
SIC—3312; Steel fabrication, erection & equipment services
Employs—40; Estab.—1955
Sales—$50Mil-$100Mil
Distrib.—Regional
Privately owned corporation

### DAVE'S SWIFT PRINT
P.O. Box 313 (08093)
**Phone—(856) 853-8528**
Fax—(856) 853-8268
www.noproblemprinter.com
Email—question@ noproblemprinter.com
Owner—Dave Kuncas
Pres.—Teresa Kuncas
SIC—2752; NAICS—323100; Instant printing
Employs—5; Estab.—1989
Sales—under $500,000
Distrib.—Local
Privately owned corporation

### HYDRO-MECHANICAL SYSTEMS, INC.
1030 Delsea Dr., P.O. Box 87 (08093)
**Phone—(856) 848-8888**
Fax—(856) 848-6071
www.hydromechanical.com
Email—projects@ hydropartsandmechanical.com
Pres.—Howard Rosenbloom
Accts. Rec. Mgr.—Anita Carney
Proj. Mgr.—Stephen Rosenbloom

SIC—3621; 3694; NAICS—335312; Hydrostatic motors & electric & diesel engines & hydraulic, electric & diesel starting systems for gas turbines & custom mechanical power transmission systems
Employs—17; Estab.—1971
Sales—$2.6Mil-$5Mil
Distrib.—Intl.
Privately owned corporation

### INTELCO OF DELAWARE VALLEY
250 Harvard Ave., P.O. Box 9 (08093)
**Phone—(856) 456-6755**
National—(800) 989-8677
Fax—(856) 456-9422
www.intelcousa.com
Email—accounting@intelcousa.com
Pres.—Mike Wells
V-P.—Grant Wells
Cont., Hum. Res. & Off. Mgr.— Cindy Elias
Sales Mgr.—Bill Harker
SIC—2541; 2542; 3281; NAICS—327991; Company headquarters & solid-surface, plastic laminated, wooden & granite countertops
Employs—120; Estab.—1987
Sales—$5Mil-$10Mil
Distrib.—Local
Privately owned corporation

### J. JEB PRODUCTS, LLC
10 Cutler Ave., P.O. Box 40 (08093)
**Phone—(856) 845-4455**
Fax—(856) 845-3127
www.jjebproducts.com
Email—info@jjebproducts.com
Pres.—Jack Sukala
V-P.—Evelyn Sukala
SIC—3643; 3678; NAICS—335931; 120 volt connectors for engine pre-heaters & mobile appliances
Employs—2; Estab.—1960
Distrib.—Intl.
Limited Liability Company

### KB ACRYLICS, INC.
Div. of KB Design Group, Inc.
I-295 Industrial Ctr., Bldg. B, Box 47 (08093)
**Phone—(856) 589-3110**
www.kbdesigngroupinc.com
Email—info@kbdesigngroupinc.com
Pres.—Ben Bonaccorso
SIC—3089; Acrylic fabrication & machining, oven bending & vacuum compression forming
Employs—5; Estab.—1995
Sales—$750,000-$1Mil
20,000 sq ft site, Distrib.—National
Privately owned corporation
Parent co.—KB Design Group, Inc., Pitman, NJ
Phone—(856) 589-3110
See Parent Co. Section for full profile.

### KIVA PRINTING & GRAPHICS
50 Cutler Ave. (08093)
Mail addr: P.O. Box 246, Thorofare (08086)
**Phone—(877) 777-5482**
Fax—(877) 777-7311
www.kivagroup.org
Email—sales@kivafresh.org
Pres., GM—Tyler Wilson
Printing Consultant—Tonya Swales
SIC—2759; 2752; NAICS—323100; Offset & commercial printing
Employs—12; Estab.—1986
Sales—under $500,000
Distrib.—Local
Privately owned corporation

### ROBESSA ENTERPRISES, INC.
1030 Delsea Dr., P.O. Box 72 (08093)
**Phone—(856) 251-0055**
Fax—(856) 853-9281
www.robessa.com
Email—info@robessa.com
Owner—William Green
GM—Mike Walter
IT Mgr.—Steve Labelle
SIC—2653; 3089; 3999; Corrugated boxes & contract packaging & product assembly
Employs—10
30,000 sq ft site, Distrib.—Local
Privately owned corporation
AKA: Rogers Containers

### THERMAL-CHEK, INC.
912 Broadway (08093)
**Phone—(856) 742-1200**
National—(800) 742-1201
Fax—(856) 742-1199
Pres.—Joseph Heaton, Sr.
V-P.—Joseph Heaton, Jr.
SIC—3089; Vinyl windows
Employs—20; Estab.—1967
Sales—$1Mil-$5Mil
55,000 sq ft site, Distrib.—Local

### UGO DI LULLO & SONS
1004 Edgewater Ave., P.O. Box 126 (08093)
**Phone—(856) 456-3700**
Fax—(856) 456-7161
Email—ugodilullo1@verizon.net
Owner—Ugo Di Lullo
Off. Mgr.—Michelle Mattei
SIC—2032; Soups, gravy, broth, spaghetti & canned meatball sauces, corned beef hash & beef stew
Employs—9; Estab.—1939
15,000 sq ft site, Distrib.—Intl.
Sole ownership

---

## Westwood
### (Bergen—N.E.)

### ALPINE CORP.
42 Bergenline Ave. (07675)
**Phone—(201) 666-0959**
Fax—(201) 666-2569
V-P.—Thomas Wanner
GM—Jeno Peter
GM—John Francer
SIC—3728; Aerospace components
Employs—10; Estab.—1971
Distrib.—National
Privately owned corporation
AKA: Alpine Machine & Tool Corp.

### AMERICAN MACHINE SPECIALTIES, INC.
51 Bergenline Ave. (07675)
**Phone—(201) 664-2100**
Fax—(201) 664-2291
www.americanmachinespecialties. com
Email—amscony@aol.com
Pres.—Norman Illian
V-P.—Dan Doran
Off. Mgr.—Ann Marie DeQuattro
SIC—3599; General machining job shop
Employs—10; Estab.—1990
Sales—$500,000-$1Mil
Distrib.—Local
Privately owned corporation

NEW ENTRY
### ASIAMERICA INGREDIENTS, INC.
245 Old Hook Rd., Ste. 3 (07675)
**Phone—(201) 497-5993**
Fax—(201) 497-5994
www.asiamericaingredients.com
Email—info@ asiamericaingredients.com
Owner—Mark Zhang

SIC—2833; 2023; 2844; 2099; Ingredients blending for the nutraceutical & dietary supplement, food, pharmaceutical, beverage, cosmetic, pet food & personal care industries
Employs—4
Sales—$1Mil-$2.5Mil (est)

### ATLANTIC SCREENPRINTING
339 Fairview Ave. (07675-2163)
**Phone—(201) 383-0995**
Fax—(201) 383-0997
www.atlanticscreen.com
Email—info@atlanticscreen.net
Pres., Sales Mgr.—Ken Kristofick
V-P. & Manager—Jeff Kristofick
SIC—2396; Textile screen printing
Employs—4; Estab.—1989
Sales—$500,000-$1Mil
6,000 sq ft site, Distrib.—National

### †AVERY FILTER CO., INC.
99 Kinderkamack Rd., Ste. 209 (07675-3020)
**Phone—(201) 666-9664**
Fax—(201) 666-3802
www.averyfilter.com
Email—ken@averyfilter.com
Pres.—Quentin Avery
V-P., Sales & Engr.—Ken Lindgren
Off. Mgr.—Marlene Vangeles
SIC—5084; 5085; Distributor of filter paper, filter press cloths, pressure leaf filter bags, fabricated cloth filters, used & reconditioned filter presses, membrane filter presses & pressure leaf filters; Brand name—Avery Filter; Ahlstrom Filter Paper
Employs—4; Estab.—1965
Sales—$1.5Mil
2,500 sq ft site, Distrib.—Intl.
Privately owned sub-S corp.

### CEA INSTRUMENT, INC.
160 Tillman St. (07675)
**Phone—(201) 967-5660**
National—(888) 893-9640
Fax—(201) 967-8450
www.ceainstr.com
Email—ceainstr@aol.com
V-P., Sales & Mktg.—Steven Adelman
SIC—3823; NAICS—334513; Portable & wall-mounted hazardous & toxic gas detection instruments
Employs—4; Estab.—1972
Sales—$1Mil-$2.5Mil
Distrib.—Intl.
Privately owned corporation

### CH TECHNOLOGIES, INC.
263 Center Ave., Ste. 2 (07675-1738)
**Phone—(201) 666-2335**
National—(800) 468-6943
Fax—(201) 666-8611
www.chtechusa.com
Email—sales@chtechusa.com
Pres. & Chief Scientist—Rudolph J. Jaeger
COO—Bridget Corbett Jaeger
CFO—Janet Squilanti
SIC—3841; Medical research inhalation exposure systems & animal restraint tubes; Brand name—Wholesale Distributors-Palas GmBH
Employs—3; Estab.—1994
Sales—$500,000-$1Mil
Distrib.—Intl.
Privately owned sub-S corp.

### COMPLETE PLASTIC DISTRIBUTORS, INC.
778 Carver Ave. (07675)
**Phone—(201) 666-8600**
Fax—(201) 666-8010
www.completeplasticsnj.com
Email—cpdplastic@aol.com

## Westwood—(cont.)

**Owner**—Andy Kestenbaum
SIC—3089; 5162; *Plastic fabrication & distributor of plastic sheet, rod & tubing*
Employs—5; Estab.—1973
Sales—under $500,000
Distrib.—Regional
Privately owned corporation
Also see: Frame & Print, same loc.

### CONRAD'S CONFECTIONERY, INC.

107 Westwood Ave. (07675)
**Phone—(201) 664-2895**
www.conradscandy.com
Email—contactus@ conradscandy.com
Owner—J. J. Krachtus
SIC—2066; 2024; *Chocolates & ice cream*
Employs—8; Estab.—1928
Sales—$2.5Mil-$5Mil
Distrib.—National
Privately owned corporation

### DARKSTAR WOODWORKING

123 Woodland Ave. (07675)
**Phone—(201) 248-1575**
Fax—(201) 358-9169
www.darkstarwoodworking.com
Email—ron@ darkstarwoodworking.com
Owner—Ronald Maxon
SIC—2434; *Wooden household cabinets*
Employs—1; Estab.—2000
Sales—under $500,000
Distrib.—Local
Sole ownership

### EAGLE BUTTON CO., INC.

700-76 Broadway (07675)
**Phone—(201) 652-4063**
Fax—(201) 652-2003
www.eaglebutton.com
Email—buttons@eaglebutton.com
Pres.—Arthur Simon
Cont.—Marvin Swartz
IT Mgr.—Kevin Casey
SIC—3965; NAICS—339993; *Designer buttons for apparel*
Employs—25; Estab.—1926
Distrib.—Intl.
Privately owned corporation

### FRAME & PRINT

778 Carver Ave. (07675)
**Phone—(201) 358-0404**
Fax—(201) 666-8010
Pres., GM—Andy Kestenbaum
SIC—2499; 3499; *Wooden & metal picture frames & custom picture framing*
Employs—5; Estab.—1985
Sales—under $500,000
Distrib.—Local
Privately owned corporation
Also see: Complete Plastic Distributors, Inc., same loc.

### HOBOKEN HEARTH PRODUCTS, LLC

46 Bi-State Plz. (07675)
**Phone—(551) 206-3350**
Fax—(201) 722-0840
www.modfyres.com
Email—gary@modfyres.com
Mng. Member—Gary P. Vanderbeck
SIC—3429; *Andirons*
Employs—3
Limited Liability Company

### KURT VERSEN INC

Div. of Hubbell Lighting, Inc.
10 Charles St. (07675)
**Phone—(201) 664-8200**
Fax—(201) 664-4801
www.kurtversen.com
Email—contact@kurtversen.com
V-P., Opers. & Sales—Nancy Stathes
IT Mgr.—Angela Rafferty

Hum. Res. Mgr.—Sandra Lechich
Cust. Serv. Rep.—Diane Muse
SIC—3646; NAICS—335122; *Commercial lighting fixtures*
Employs—130; Estab.—1957
Distrib.—Regional
Publicly owned corporation
Parent co.—Hubbell Lighting, Inc., Greenville, SC
Phone—(864) 678-1000
See Parent Co. Section for full profile.

### LANMAN & KEMP-BARCLAY & CO., INC.

25 Woodland Ave., P.O. Box 421 (07675)
**Phone—(201) 666-4990**
National—(800) 848-5047
Fax—(201) 666-5836
www.lanman-and-kemp.com
Email—sales@lanman-and-kemp.com
Pres.—George Miller
GM—Daisy Villegas
Prodn. Mgr.—Gary Nickich
SIC—2844; 2841; NAICS—325611; *Colognes, hair tonics & soaps*
Employs—15; Estab.—1808
Sales—$1Mil-$2.5Mil
20,000 sq ft site, Distrib.—Regional
Privately owned corporation

### MAGESTIC SYSTEMS, INC.

205 Fairview Ave. (07675)
**Phone—(201) 263-0090**
Fax—(201) 263-0091
www.magestic.com
Email—sales@magestic.com
Dir., Bus. Dev.—Massimiliano Moruzzi
Sales & Mktg. Prog. Mgr.—Dylan MacLean
SIC—7372; *Nesting software development for CNC cutting, CNC punching, laser projection applications, automated fiber placement (AFP), automated tape laying (ATL), CAD/CAM, composite & sheet metal manufacturing, assembly, kitting & part sorting*
Employs—15; Estab.—1991
Distrib.—Intl.
Privately owned corporation

### NORWOLF TOOL WORKS, INC.

6 Sullivan St. (07675)
**Phone—(201) 666-6655**
National—(888) 667-9653
Fax—(201) 666-7611
www.norwolf.com
Email—norwolfmls@aol.com
Pres.—Steve Spirer
Shop Mgr.—John Lam
SIC—3423; *Hand tools, hydraulic wrenches, stud removers & sockets*
Employs—5; Estab.—1995
Sales—$1Mil-$2.5Mil
6,000 sq ft site, Distrib.—Intl.
Privately owned corporation

### †OBERG & LINDQUIST CORP.

671 Broadway (07675)
**Phone—(201) 664-1300**
Fax—(201) 664-8974
www.obergandlindquist.com
Email—bill@obergandlindquist.com
Pres.—John Oberg
Sales Mgr.—Bill Volz
Off. Mgr.—Michelle Skura
Sales Rep.—James Boreniuf

SIC—5064; 5049; 5087; 5046; *Distributor of industrial, residential, commercial & professional kitchen appliances, including cooking ranges, refrigeration, coffee & beverage systems, dishwashers, disposals, compactors & outdoor grills*
Employs—50; Estab.—1947
Sales—$10Mil
Distrib.—Regional
Privately owned corporation

### REVELATION TECHNOLOGIES, INC.

99 Kinderkamack Rd., Ste. 109 (07675)
**Phone—(201) 594-1422**
National—(800) 262-4747
Fax—(201) 722-9815
www.revelation.com
Email—info@revelation.com
Pres.—Michael Ruane
Dir., Accts.—Dee Trahey
Cust. Serv. Mgr.—Victoria Luttino
SIC—7372; *Software development & office automation*
Employs—17; Estab.—1982
7,000 sq ft site, Distrib.—Intl.
Privately owned corporation

### TONI EMBROIDERY CO.

475 Broadway (07675)
**Phone—(201) 664-6909**
Fax—(201) 664-1203
Email—toniemb@aol.com
Owner—Tom Cornicelli
Manager—Toni Thom
SIC—2395; *Embroidery*
Employs—5; Estab.—1978
Sales—under $500,000 (est)
Distrib.—Regional
Privately owned corporation

---

## Wharton

### (Morris—N.W.)

### APPLIED RESOURCE CORP.

105 W. Dewey Ave., Ste. 311 (07885)
**Phone—(973) 328-3882**
Fax—(973) 328-3885
www.appliedresource.com
Email—mark@appliedresource.com
Pres.—Mark Colello
GM—Paul Potts
SIC—3613; 3679; NAICS—335313; *Aerospace components & switches, including precision machining & electromechanical assemblies*
Employs—22; Estab.—1972
13,000 sq ft site, Distrib.—National
Privately owned corporation

### BERKSHIRE MACHINE, INC.

390 Route 15 S. (07885)
**Phone—(973) 366-7710**
Fax—(973) 366-5468
Pres.—Gerald Munsterer
Machinist—Andy Chernati
SIC—3599; *General machining job shop*
Employs—2; Estab.—1961
Sales—$500,000-$1Mil
5,000 sq ft site, Distrib.—Local
Privately owned corporation

### BOLTTECH MANNINGS, INC.

321 Richard Mine Rd., Ste. 300 (07885)
**Phone—(973) 537-1576**
National—(800) 447-4473
Fax—(973) 537-1581
www.bolttechmannings.com
Email—sales@ bolttechmannings.com
Sales & Mktg. Mgr.—Scott Herland
Opers. Mgr.—Jay Romeo

SIC—3398; NAICS—332811; *Heat treating, induction, hydraulic bolting & resistance products & services*
Employs—20; Estab.—1989
Sales—$20Mil
50,000 sq ft site, Distrib.—Intl.
Privately owned corporation
Parent co.—Bolttech Mannings, Inc., North Versailles, PA
Phone—(724) 872-4873
See Parent Co. Section for full profile.

### CONVERTECH, INC.

353 Richard Mine Rd. (07885)
**Phone—(973) 328-1850**
www.convertech.com
Email—info@convertech.com
Pres.—Larry Taitel
SIC—3593; 3492; NAICS—333995; *Pneumatic airshafts & printing press components*
Employs—50; Estab.—1978
38,000 sq ft site, Distrib.—Intl.
Privately owned sub-S corp.

### DEFINED PRO MACHINING, LLC

105 W. Dewey Ave., Ste. 205 (07885-1642)
**Phone—(973) 941-2430**
Fax—(973) 891-1039
www.definedpro.com
Email—hf@definedpro.com
Owner & Mng. Member—Henrietta Fidler
SIC—3599; *CNC machining job shop, including CNC turning & milling*
Employs—5; Estab.—2009
Sales—under $500,000
Distrib.—National
Limited Liability Company

### DIMENSIONAL MERCHANDISING, INC.

86 N. Main St. (07885)
**Phone—(973) 328-1600**
Fax—(973) 328-6241
www.dminj.com
Email—info@dminj.com
Pres.—Douglas A. Sylva
Dir., Engrg. & Facilities—Tim Boehm
Dir., Mfg.—Robert C. Taylor
Dir., IT & Operating Sys.—James P. Campisi
Dir., Bus. Process—Catherine Anne Jones
Dir., R & D—Geraldine C. Molina
Dir., Qual.—John Moyer
GM—Elaine J. Balady
Ex. Sales Admn.—Kim Ferris
SIC—2833; 2834; 2844; *Contract manufacturing & packaging of health & beauty aids, toiletries, cosmetics, OTC & nutraceuticals, including filling & turnkey processes*
Employs—85; Estab.—1973
Sales—$30Mil-$40Mil
275,000 sq ft site, Distrib.—Intl.
Privately owned sub-S corp.
DBA: DMI Personal Care

### EMBROIDER THIS CO.

7 Duck Point Trl. (07885)
**Phone—(973) 663-5551**
Fax—(973) 337-2257
www.embroiderthis.net
Email—debbie@embroiderthis.net
Owner—Donna Sanderson
SIC—2395; 2396; *Embroidery, screen printing & heat transfers*
Employs—3; Estab.—1994
Sales—under $500,000
Distrib.—National
Sole ownership

### GAS DRYING, INC.

355 W. Dewey Ave., P.O. Box 504 (07885)
**Phone—(973) 361-2212**
Fax—(973) 361-4215
www.gasdrying.com

GEOGRAPHICAL

## Wharton—(cont.)

Email—gasdrying@nac.net
Pres.—Gary Behrens
SIC—3567; NAICS—333994;
*Industrial compressed air & gas dryers*
Employs—15; Estab.—1957
20,000 sq ft site, Distrib.—Intl.
Privately owned corporation

NEW ENTRY
**JACK DOHENY COMPANIES, INC.**
15 Taylor Rd., Ste. 1 (07885)
**Phone—(973) 659-0061**
Fax—(973) 659-0080
www.dohenysupplies.com
Email—tyrose@
dohenycompanies.com
GM—Ty Rose
SIC—3713; NAICS—336399;
*Pump trucks, vacuum trucks & sewer cleaning equipment*
Employs—40
Sales—$5Mil-$10Mil (est)
Distrib.—National
Privately owned corporation
Parent co.—Jack Doheny
Companies, Inc., Northville, MI
Phone—(248) 349-0904
See Parent Co. Section for full profile.

†**LONGO ELECTRICAL-MECHANICAL**
1 Harry Shupe Blvd. (07885)
**Phone—(973) 537-0400**
Fax—(973) 537-0404
www.elongo.com
Email—info@elongo.com
Owner—Joseph J. Longo
V.-P., Sales—Dominic Diclementi
V.-P., Engrg.—Andy Fuls
Dir., Mktg.—Peter Sonderburg
Cust. Serv. Rep.—Sue Urban
SIC—5063; 5084; *Wholesaler of motors, pumps, switchgears, fans, transformers, air compressors & wind & solar power generation equipment, including service*
Employs—100; Estab.—1945
Sales—$20Mil
Distrib.—Regional
Sole ownership
ISO rating—9001

**MACHINE CORP., E. B.**
320 Richard Mine Rd. (07885)
**Phone—(973) 442-7729**
Fax—(973) 328-4961
Pres.—Emil Boller
SIC—3544; 3599; NAICS—
333500; *Mold, grinding, tool, die & CNC machining job shop*
Employs—3; Estab.—1996
Sales—under $500,000
Distrib.—Local
Privately owned corporation

**MARTIN TOOL CO., INC.**
60 Route 15 S. (07885)
**Phone—(973) 361-9212**
Fax—(973) 361-8711
Pres., Hum. Res. Mgr.—Louis
Martin
Sys. Mgr.—Oscar Nieves
SIC—3841; *Medical devices*
Employs—12; Estab.—1981
Sales—$1Mil-$2.5Mil
Distrib.—Local
Privately owned corporation

**METRO FLAG CO.**
Div. of National Flag & Display Co.,
Inc.
353 Richard Mine Rd., Unit 100
(07885-1800)
**Phone—(973) 366-1776**
(212) 462-4000
Fax—(973) 366-0956
Email—sales@metroflag.com
Ex. V.-P.—Donald Bornstein

SIC—2399; *Custom flags & banners; Brand name—Metro*
Employs—27; Estab.—1921
Sales—$2Mil
23,500 sq ft site, Distrib.—Intl.
Privately owned corporation
Parent co.—National Flag &
Display Co., Inc., New York, NY
Phone—(212) 462-4000
See Parent Co. Section for full profile.

**NOWAK, INC.**
17 Robert St., Ste. B-5 (07885)
**Phone—(973) 366-7208**
Fax—(973) 366-8445
Email—nowakinc@aol.com
Pres., CEO—Mark Nowak
Off. Mgr.—Lori Michalski
SIC—3599; *Precision machining job shop, including CNC milling & turning*
Employs—15; Estab.—1977
Sales—$1.7Mil
5,200 sq ft site, Distrib.—Regional
Privately owned corporation

**OBJECT DESIGN, INC.**
105 W. Dewey Ave., Bldg. C, Unit 5
(07885)
**Phone—(973) 442-5790**
Fax—(973) 442-5793
www.amsproduct.com
Email—info@amsproduct.com
Pres.—Amy Kim
SIC—2393; 2399; NAICS—
314911; *Commercial laundry bags & industrial washer nets*
Employs—8; Estab.—1998
Sales—$500,000-$1Mil
Distrib.—National
Privately owned corporation
AKA: AMS Products, LLC

**ODYSSEY SPECIALTY VEHICLES**
317 Richard Mine Rd. (07885)
**Phone—(973) 328-2667**
National—(800) 535-9441
Fax—(973) 328-2639
www.odysseysv.com
Email—sales@odysseyauto.com
CEO—Daniel Huang
CFO—Jaspal Singh
Chief Operating Officer—Paul
Evans
SIC—3711; 3714; 3715; *First response EMS, Fire Chief & command units, specialty law enforcement & commercial vehicles based on sport utility vehicles, van, trucks, light rescues, trailers & related specialty chassis; Brand name—Odyssey Specialty Vehicles*
Employs—30; Estab.—1979
20,000 sq ft site, Distrib.—Intl.
Limited Liability Company
AKA: EchoStream Motor Group,
LLC

**PANELCRAFT, INC.**
105 W. Dewey Ave., Bldg. C, Unit
16 (07885)
**Phone—(973) 895-2700**
Fax—(866) 451-1928
www.panelcraftusa.com
Email—sales@panelcraftusa.com
Pres.—Frank Brown
Qual. Assur. Mgr.—Tom Brown
SIC—3728; *Aircraft instrument panels*
Employs—10; Estab.—2003
Sales—$500,000-$1Mil
Distrib.—National
Privately owned sub-S corp.

**PHOENIX INDUSTRIES, LLC**
105 W. Dewey Ave., P.O. Box 416
*(07885)*
**Phone—(973) 366-4199**
Fax—(973) 366-5288
www.phoenixpkgind.com
Email—vnorcia@
phoenixpkgind.com
Pres., GM—Vincent Norcia

Sales Mgr.—Brent Norcia
Off. Mgr.—Judy Morris
SIC—2673; 3081; NAICS—
326113; *Polyethylene bags, sheeting & shrink & stretch films*
Employs—5; Estab.—1972
Sales—$2Mil-$3Mil
Distrib.—National
Limited Liability Company

**PRECISION WELDING**
845 Berkshire Valley Rd. (07885)
**Phone—(973) 366-7316**
Fax—(973) 695-1308
www.precweld.com
Email—jimweld@aol.com
Owner—Jim Stanlick
SIC—3499; 3599; *Metal fabrication & welding job shop*
Employs—7; Estab.—1978
Sales—$500,000-$1Mil
7,000 sq ft site, Distrib.—Regional
Sole ownership

**SAFE-STRAP CO.**
105 W. Dewey Ave., Bldg. D, Ste.
410 (07885)
**Phone—(973) 442-4623**
National—(800) 356-7796
Fax—(973) 442-8195
www.safestrap.com
Email—info@safestrap.com
Pres.—Paul Giampavolo
Mktg. Mgr.—Renee Kenney
SIC—2399; 3089; *Shopping cart seat belts, shop-along child carriers, shopping cart safe & infant seats & baby changing stations*
Employs—55; Estab.—1983
Distrib.—National
Privately owned corporation

**SPECIAL OPTICS MANUFACTURE & DESIGN, INC.**
315 Richard Mine Rd. (07885)
**Phone—(973) 366-7289**
Fax—(973) 366-7407
www.specialoptics.com
Email—sales@specialoptics.com
Cont.—Tom Young
GM—Steven Morales
SIC—3851; NAICS—339100;
*Laser optic lenses*
Employs—18; Estab.—1990
Sales—$1Mil-$5Mil
13,000 sq ft site, Distrib.—
Regional
Privately owned corporation

**SUNSET PRINTING AND ENGRAVING**
10 Kice Ave. (07885)
**Phone—(973) 537-9600**
National—(800) 978-6738
Fax—(973) 537-9601
www.sunsetcorpid.com
Email—sales@sunsetcorpid.com
Pres.—Mitchel Wainer
V.-P.—Robert Wainer
Sales Mgr.—Deron Wainer
Manager—Jared Wainer
SIC—2759; 2752; 2754; NAICS—
323111; *Commercial offset & on demand printing, including fulfillment, mailing services, engraving & foil stamping*
Employs—42; Estab.—1945
Sales—$5Mil-$10Mil
Distrib.—Intl.
Privately owned corporation

**TILCON NEW YORK, INC.**
Div. of Tilcon New York Inc.
625 Mount Hope Rd. (07885)
**Phone—(973) 366-7741**
National—(800) 789-7625
Fax—(973) 366-8501
www.tilconny.com
Email—info@tilconny.com
Pres., Div.—Sean O'Sullivan
V.-P., Fin.—Guy Corulli
GM, Sales—Josh Benson
GM, Asphalt Plts.—Scott Laudone

GM, Aggregates—Brad Carroll
Hum. Res. Mgr.—Anne Poltorak
Pub. Rels. Mgr.—Karen Edgar
Contract Admn.—Wendy Arias
SIC—2951; NAICS—324121;
*Asphalt paving compounds*
Employs—500
Sales—$10Mil-$25Mil
Distrib.—Local
Publicly owned corporation
Parent co.—Tilcon New York Inc.,
West Nyack, NY
Phone—(845) 358-4500
See Parent Co. Section for full profile.

**TOP SHOPS, LLC**
361 W. Dewey Ave., Ste. 8 (07885)
**Phone—(973) 442-0050**
Fax—(973) 442-0056
www.topshopsnj.com
Email—topshops@optonline.net
Owner—Reggie Matthews
Fabricator—Nick Ianetti
SIC—3281; 2542; *Granite & solid-surface countertops*
Employs—3; Estab.—2005
Sales—under $500,000
Distrib.—Local
Limited Liability Company

NEW ENTRY
**TRIANGLE AUTOMATIC, INC.**
105 W. Dewey Ave., Ste. 305
(07885)
**Phone—(973) 625-3830**
Fax—(973) 625-7649
Manager—Viggy Rosa
SIC—3599; *General machining job shop*
Employs—3
Sales—under $500,000 (est)
Distrib.—Intl.
Privately owned corporation

**TURUL BOOKBINDERY, INC.**
60 Route 15 S. (07885)
**Phone—(973) 361-2810**
Fax—(973) 361-6762
www.thebookbindery.com
Email—turul1@aol.com
Pres.—Margit P. Rahill
Secy.-Treas.—Michael Rahill
MIS & Opers. Mgr.—Michael L.
Rahill
SIC—2789; 2675; NAICS—
323121; *Custom books & boxes, bookbinding, including gold stamping & die cutting, hard & soft cover binding, leather work, restoration of rare books, record & ledger books & maps; Brand name—U-Bind it*
Employs—5; Estab.—1932
Sales—under $500,000
3,500 sq ft site, Distrib.—Intl.
Privately owned corporation

**WHITLOCK PACKAGING CORP.**
92 N. Main St. (07885)
**Phone—(973) 361-9794**
Fax—(973) 361-2202
www.whitlockpkg.com
Email—info@whitlockpkg.com
Cont.—Mary Clyburn
GM—John Piekarski
SIC—2033; 2086; NAICS—
311421; *Noncarbonated beverages & fruit juice*
Employs—200
Distrib.—National
Privately owned corporation
Parent co.—Whitlock Packaging
Corp., Tulsa, OK
Phone—(918) 524-4029
See Parent Co. Section for full profile.

## Whippany

(Morris—N.W.)

**3M CO.**
140 Algonquin Pkwy. (07981)
**Phone—(973) 884-2500**
National—(800) 346-5676
Fax—(908) 884-0392
www.3m.com
Email—info@3m.com
Plt. Supv.—Vic Ison
Proc. Coord.—Charmaine
Puntasecca
Hum. Res. Rep.—Roxanne
Williams
SIC—3291; 3544; NAICS—
333500; *Diamond grinding
wheels, tools & routers*
Employs—50; Estab.—1952
Distrib.—National
Publicly owned corporation
Parent co.—3M Co., St. Paul, MN
Phone—(651) 733-1110
See Parent Co. Section for full profile.

**AIR GROUP, LLC**
1 Prince Rd. (07981)
**Phone—(973) 887-5099**
National—(800) 545-1020
Fax—(973) 887-2218
www.airgroupllc.com
Email—info@airgroupllc.com
Pres.—John A. Conforti
Hum. Res. Mgr.—Mary Ellen
Conforti
SIC—3444; *Custom commercial
HVAC sheet metal ductwork
fabrication & commercial &
residential HVAC system
installation services*
Employs—187; Estab.—1965
Distrib.—Local
Limited Liability Company

**APHENA PHARMA SOLUTIONS-NJ,
INC.**
125 Algonquin Pkwy. *(07981)*
**Phone—(973) 887-4440**
Fax—(973) 887-9098
www.aphenapharma.com
Email—sales@aphenapharma.com
Pres., CEO—Kevin Kerchner
V-P., Sales & Mktg.—Eric Allen
V-P., Solid Dose Div.—Bob Scott
V-P., Semi-Solid Liquid Div.—
George Galgano
SIC—3089; *Pharmaceutical
packaging*
Employs—160
Sales—$50Mil-$100Mil
Distrib.—Intl.
Privately owned corporation

**BAYER HEALTHCARE
PHARMACEUTICALS (H Q)**
Div. of Bayer MaterialScience, LLC
100 Bayer Blvd. (07981)
**Phone—(862) 404-3000**
National—(888) 842-2937
www.pharma.bayer.com
Email—marcy.funk@bayer.com
V-P., Growth & Innovation—Barton
Warner
V-P., GM, Womens Healthcare—
Paul Bedard
Assoc. Dir., Pub. Rels.—Marcy
Funk
SIC—2834; NAICS—325412;
*Divisional headquarters;
pharmaceuticals*
Employs—500
Sales—$250Mil-$500Mil (est)
Publicly owned corporation
Parent co.—Bayer
MaterialScience, LLC, Pittsburgh,
PA
Phone—(412) 777-2000
See Parent Co. Section for full profile.

**BAYER HEALTHCARE, CONSUMER
CARE DIV.**
Div. of Bayer Healthcare
100 Bayer Blvd., P.O. Box 915
(07962-1910)
**Phone—(862) 404-3000**
National—(800) 331-4536
www.bayercare.com
Email—sales@bayerus.com
Pres.—Erica Mann
V-P., Hum. Res.—Sean Kolb-Hunt
Pub. Rels. Coord.—Alexandra
Borschik
SIC—2834; NAICS—325412;
*Pharmaceuticals & vitamins*
Employs—2500; Estab.—1994
Sales—over $1Bil (est)
Privately owned corporation
Parent co.—Bayer Healthcare,
Warrendale, PA
Phone—(412) 767-2400
See Parent Co. Section for full profile.

**BREEZE-EASTERN CORP.**
35 Melanie Ln. (07981)
**Phone—(973) 602-1001**
National—(800) 929-1919
Fax—(973) 739-9334
www.breeze-eastern.com
Email—marketing@breeze-
eastern.com
Pres.—Brad Peterson
V-P., Opers.—Rodger Hahneman
V-P., IT—Robert Radicchi
V-P., Cust. Care—Mike Koons
SIC—3728; 3536; NAICS—
333923; *Aerospace rescue
hoists & winches, cargo hooks,
weapons handling equipment &
motion control systems for the
aerospace, defense &
commercial industries*
Employs—200; Estab.—1926
188,000 sq ft site, Distrib.—Intl.
Privately owned corporation

**CAMBRIDGE SHEET METAL, INC.**
14 Troy Hills Rd., Ste. 6 (07981)
**Phone—(973) 386-0788**
Fax—(973) 386-0828
Email—jimsal@csmnj.com
Owner, Pres. & GM—Jim
Salvatoriello
SIC—3444; *Sheet metal
fabrication*
Employs—10; Estab.—1991
Sales—under $3Mil
12,000 sq ft site, Distrib.—Local
Privately owned corporation

**DOSCH KING EMULSIONS, INC.**
16 Troy Hills Rd. (07981)
**Phone—(973) 887-0145**
National—(800) 222-3209
Fax—(973) 887-4942
Email—doschkingco@optimum.net
Pres., Sales Mgr.—David King
Plt. Mgr.—Peter King
SIC—2951; NAICS—324121;
*Asphalt emulsion*
Employs—40; Estab.—1926
Sales—$1Mil-$2.5Mil
Distrib.—Regional
Privately owned corporation

**†EQUIPMENT SOLUTIONS CORP.**
622 State Route 10, Ste. 20
(07981)
**Phone—(973) 887-9277**
Fax—(973) 887-4807
www.equipsol.com
Email—bret@equipsol.com
Pres., GM—Bret Schwerdt
Off. Mgr.—Ermi Rossi
SIC—5044; 5046; *Distributor of
mailing, packaging & bindery
equipment & office products,
including paper shredders,
collators, paper folders, drills,
booklet makers, cutters, inkjet
addressing, wafer sealers, shrink
wrap & digital finishing; Brand
name—Morgana; DUPLO;
MBM; Secap; Propack;
Baumfolder; Streamfeeder;
Beseler; Formax*
Employs—4; Estab.—1991
Sales—$2Mil
Distrib.—Regional
Privately owned corporation

**†FASTENAL CO.**
53 S. Jefferson Rd., Ste. K (07981)
**Phone—(973) 428-3300**
Fax—(973) 428-3199
www.fastenal.com
Email—njwhp@stores.fastenal.com
Br. Mgr.—Jason Smith
Sales Rep., Outside—Alex
Thompson
SIC—5072; 5084; 5085;
*Wholesaler of fasteners, safety
equipment, tools & abrasives*
Employs—3; Estab.—2003
Distrib.—Local
Publicly owned corporation
Parent co.—Fastenal Co., Winona,
MN
Phone—(507) 454-5374
See Parent Co. Section for full profile.

**GEL CONCEPTS, LLC**
30 Leslie Ct. (07981)
**Phone—(973) 884-8995**
Fax—(973) 884-1331
www.natragel.com
Email—info@gelconcepts.com
Pres., CEO—Lawrence Kersen
Off. Mgr.—Roxanne Coll
SIC—2833; NAICS—325411;
*Hydrogel polymers for plastic
surgery, dermatology & spa
applications*
Employs—25; Estab.—2001
Distrib.—Intl.
Limited Liability Company
Also see: Poly-Gel, LLC, same loc.

**HALO PHARMACEUTICAL, INC.**
30 N. Jefferson Rd. (07981)
**Phone—(973) 428-4000**
Fax—(973) 428-4063
www.halopharma.com
Email—info@halopharma.com
Pres., CEO—Clive V. Bennett
Chief Scientific Officer—George
Bobotas
V-P., Mfg.—Glenn Herring
V-P., Fin.—Mark Stier
V-P., Prod. Dev.—Abdel A. Fawzy
V-P., Qual. Assur.—Phyllis
Lambridis
Dir., Hum. Res.—Kristin Berkinsky
Compliance Mgr.—Frank Adair
Hum. Res. Admn.—Kim Kozas
SIC—2834; *Contract
manufacturing of
pharmaceuticals*
Employs—200
Sales—$100Mil-$250Mil (est)
167,000 sq ft site, Distrib.—Intl.
Privately owned corporation

**KRATOS-CTI**
Div. of Kratos-New England
9 Whippany Rd., Bldg. A-1 (07981)
**Phone—(973) 884-2580**
Fax—(973) 887-6245
www.kratosepd.com
Email—kratoscti@
kratosdefense.com
Dir., Qual. Control—Art Alexander
GM—Ed Weatherwax
Sales & Mktg. Mgr.—Bob Badami
IT Mgr.—Allen Cob
SIC—3679; 3931; NAICS—
339992; *Oscillators &
synthesizers*
Employs—70; Estab.—1973
Sales—$15Mil-$30Mil
24,000 sq ft site, Distrib.—Local
Publicly owned corporation
Parent co.—Kratos-New England,
Woburn, MA
Phone—(781) 729-9450
See Parent Co. Section for full profile.

**†M. O. INDUSTRIES, INC.**
9 Whippany Rd., Bldg. B1-2
(07981-1530)
**Phone—(973) 386-9228**
Fax—(973) 428-0221
www.moindustries.com
Email—sales@moindustries.com
Pres.—Alex Maier
SIC—5047; *Distributor of
pharmaceutical handling
equipment*
Employs—6; Estab.—1979
Sales—$2.6Mil-$5Mil
5,000 sq ft site, Distrib.—National
Privately owned corporation

**MARK/TRECE, INC.**
160 Algonquin Pkwy. (07981)
**Phone—(973) 884-1005**
Fax—(973) 884-2938
www.marktrece.com
Email—njsales@marktrece.com
GM—Paul Rachanow
Hum. Res. & Off. Mgr.—Bonnie
Novotny
SIC—2796; 3544; NAICS—
323122; *Corrugated &
flexographic printing plates &
steel rule dies*
Employs—30; Estab.—1964
Sales—under $500,000
Distrib.—National
Privately owned corporation
Parent co.—Mark/Trece, Inc.,
Joppa, MD
Phone—(410) 879-0060
See Parent Co. Section for full profile.

**†MASDA CORP.**
22 Troy Rd., P.O. Box D (07981)
**Phone—(973) 386-1100**
National—(800) 221-1425
Fax—(973) 884-8963
Email—darchdw@masdacorp.com
GM—Dan Darche
Asst. Mgr.—Joseph M. Darche
SIC—5074; 5031; *Distributor of
fireplaces, kitchen cabinets,
pellet & wood stoves, venting
products & outdoor gas grills;
Brand name—IHP Fireplaces &
Stoves; Firemagic Gas
Barbeques; Real Fyre Gas Logs;
Securitychimneys; Elkay Kitchen
Cabinets; Osburn Woodstoves*
Employs—8; Estab.—1945
Sales—$5Mil-$10Mil
Distrib.—Regional
Privately owned corporation

**MORRIS SIGN CO.**
30 Troy Rd. (07981)
**Phone—(973) 386-1755**
Fax—(973) 386-5878
www.morrissign.com
Email—morrissign@aol.com
Pres.—Michael Hoehn
V-P.—Chris Hoehn
Manager—Maureen Hoehn
SIC—3993; *Interior & exterior
signs*
Employs—9; Estab.—1993
8,000 sq ft site, Distrib.—Local
Limited Liability Company

**NEW JERSEY JEWISH NEWS**
901 Route 10 (07981)
**Phone—(973) 887-3900**
Fax—(973) 887-4152
www.njjewishnews.com
Email—info@njjewishnews.com
COO, GM—Rick Keslenbaum

GEOGRAPHICAL

## Whippany—(cont.)

Off. Mgr.—Beryll Grinberg Kaplan
Classified Supv.—Lauri Geers
SIC—2711; 2741; NAICS—
323119; *Weekly, biweekly &
monthly print & online Jewish
newspaper publishing*
Employs—30; Estab.—1948
Sales—$1Mil-$2.5Mil
Distrib.—Regional
Privately owned corporation

### ONE SOURCE COMMUNICATIONS, INC.

9 Whippany Rd., Bldg. C-4 (07981-1530)
Phone—(973) 463-0250
Fax—(973) 463-0254
Email—lbrown@1sourceusa.com
Pres.—Tom Coultas
CFO—Wayne Coultas
Off. Mgr.—Lisa Brown
SIC—2759; NAICS—323100;
*Commercial printing*
Employs—12; Estab.—1985
Distrib.—Local
Privately owned corporation

### POLY-GEL, LLC

30 Leslie Ct. (07981)
Phone—(973) 884-3300
National—(866) 628-7243
Fax—(973) 884-1331
www.polygel.com
Email—tim@polygel.com
Pres.—Larry Kersen
V-P., Sales & Mktg.—Peter Bickel
Cont.—Tim Lemin
SIC—2833; 2844; NAICS—
325411; *Medical, orthopedic &
skin care gelatin products;
Brand name—PolyGel;
GelSmart; HealixCare; NatraGel*
Employs—50
Distrib.—Intl.
Privately owned corporation
Also see: Gel Concepts, LLC,
same loc.

### POWER DYNAMICS, INC.

145 Algonquin Pkwy. (07981)
Phone—(973) 560-0019
Fax—(973) 560-0076
www.powerdynamics.com
Email—customerservice@
powerdynamics.com
CEO—James Papianni
Pres., Mktg. Mgr.—Frank Petrillo
V-P.—Janice Christofferson
Matls., Opers. & Pur. Mgr.—
Michael Meehan
Engrg. Mgr.—Paul Battista
SIC—3699; *Electrical equipment,
including IEC connectors, EMI/
RFI filters, pins, sleeves & power
cords*
Employs—178; Estab.—1979
21,000 sq ft site, Distrib.—Intl.
Privately owned corporation
ISO rating—9002

### STEPHEN GOULD CORPORATION

35 S. Jefferson Rd. (07981)
Phone—(973) 428-1510
(973) 428-1500
Fax—(973) 428-9634
www.stephengould.com
Email—j.sales@stephengould.com
Pres., CEO—Michael Golden
Ex. V-P.—John Golden
V-P.—Peter Van Slyke
Dir., Legal Affs.—Patricia Curran
Sales Mgr.—Aaron Salko
Hum. Res. Mgr.—Robin Freid
Steinberg

SIC—2671; 2653; 3089; 5113;
NAICS—322211; *Corporate
headquarters & packaging
materials, including cartons &
industrial packaging, corrugated
boxes, foam & plastic, flexible
paper, packaging systems &
point-of-purchase displays &
distributor of packaging
materials*
Employs—110; Estab.—1939
Varies: 100-150
Sales—$550Mil
20,000 sq ft site, Distrib.—Intl.
Privately owned corporation
ISO rating—9001

### †SUBURBAN PROPANE PARTNERS, L.P. (H Q)

240 Route 10 W., P.O. Box 206
(07981-0206)
Phone—(973) 887-5300
Fax—(973) 515-5994
www.suburbanpropane.com
Email—sales@
suburbanpropane.com
CEO—Michael Dunn
CFO—Michael Stivala
CAO—Michael A. Kuglin
V-P., Operational Support &
Analysis—Mark Wienberg
Sr. V-P., Admn.—Michael Keating
V-P., Gen. Counsel—Paul E. Abel
Dir., IS—Dale Amabile
SIC—5172; *Company
headquarters; distributor of
propane gas*
Employs—300
Distrib.—National
Publicly owned corporation

### THOMPSON MATERIALS CORP.

15 Leslie Ct. (07981)
Phone—(973) 386-1400
Fax—(973) 386-1405
Email—thompsonmaterials@
gmail.com
GM—Ed Ries
Prodn. Supv.—Richard Wasky
Sales Rep.—Phil Karp
Sales Rep.—Dave Santangelo
SIC—3312; *Steel rebar*
Employs—30; Estab.—1970
Sales—$500,000-$1Mil
Distrib.—Local
Privately owned corporation

### WHIPPANY ACTUATION SYSTEM

Div. of GE Aviation Systems, LLC
110 Algonquin Pkwy. (07981)
Phone—(973) 428-9898
Fax—(973) 428-8532
www.ge.com
Email—gemediarelations@ge.com
Accts. Payable Supv.—Mary
Hubert
SIC—3764; *Aerospace parts*
Employs—225
128,000 sq ft site, Distrib.—Intl.
Publicly owned corporation
Parent co.—GE Aviation Systems,
LLC, Cincinnati, OH
Phone—(513) 243-2000
See Parent Co. Section for full profile.

## Whitehouse

(Hunterdon—N.W.)

### AMERICAN DISPLAY

291 Route 22 E, Bldg. 8, P.O. Box
244 (08888)
Phone—(908) 534-2700
(908) 391-0523
National—(888) 534-7446
Fax—(908) 534-6966
www.americandisplayusa.com
Email—americandisplay@aol.com
Pres.—Keith La Rue
Prodn. Mgr.—James Gudzinas
Off. Mgr.—Donna Merola
Proj. Mgr.—Anita Thompson
Installation Mgr.—Sean Neil

SIC—3993; *ADA, Braille,
corporate wall, office & cubicle,
exterior site, LED illuminated &
nonilluminated signs & letters,
including corporate logo design*
Employs—9; Estab.—1977
Sales—$1Mil-$1.5Mil
7,200 sq ft site, Distrib.—Intl.
Privately owned sub-S corp.
DBA: Larue Manufacturing
Corporation

### DALLAS GROUP OF AMERICA, INC., THE (H Q)

374 Route 22, P.O. Box 489
(08888)
Phone—(908) 534-7800
National—(800) 367-4188
Fax—(908) 534-0084
www.dallasgrp.com
Email—info@dallasgrp.com
Pres.—Robert H. Dallas II
V-P., Sales & Mktg.—Jay Munson
IT Mgr.—Pat Dalvenzio
Hum. Res. Mgr.—Diane Tracy
SIC—2819; *Corporate
headquarters; ammonium
chloride & synthetic magnesium
silicate; Brand name—Magnesol*
Employs—20; Estab.—1988
Company-wide: 130
Sales—$40Mil-$50Mil
Distrib.—Intl.
Privately owned corporation

### DAY TOOL & MFG., INC.

6 Carman Ln., P.O. Box 466
*(08888)*
Phone—(908) 439-3800
Fax—(908) 439-3955
www.daytool.com
Email—juddcallahan@daytool.com
Pres.—John J. Callahan III
Off. Mgr.—Ruthann Strauch
SIC—3544; 3599; 3559; NAICS—
333500; *Custom machines,
precision tooling, stamping dies
& machined parts for the
aerospace, biotech, medical,
pharmaceutical, packaging,
electronic & semiconductor
industries & the military*
Employs—19; Estab.—1962
Sales—under $6Mil
24,000 sq ft site, Distrib.—Intl.
Privately owned corporation
ISO rating—AS9100C, 9001:2008

### EAGLE EYEWEAR, INC. (H Q)

P.O. Box 486 (08888)
Phone—(908) 236-9300
Fax—(908) 236-9301
www.eagleeyewear.com
Email—sales@eagleeyewear.com
Pres.—William Marfuggi
Dir., Opers.—Cristina Marfuggi
SIC—3851; NAICS—339100;
*Corporate headquarters;
eyeglass frames (mfg. done
overseas)*
Employs—2; Estab.—1989
Sales—under $500,000 (est)
Distrib.—Intl.
Limited Liability Company

### HAYNES CORP.

6 Carman Ln., P.O. Box 467
(08888)
Phone—(908) 439-4600
Fax—(908) 439-4621
www.haynes-corp.com
Email—sales@haynes-corp.com
Pres.—Steve Haynes
Sr. Sys. Engr.—Steve Smith
SIC—3569; *Custom automation
machinery for the electronic,
food, medical, plastic,
packaging & converting
industries*
Employs—7
Sales—$500,000-$1Mil
5,000 sq ft site, Distrib.—Intl.
Privately owned corporation

### HOWMAN ELECTRONICS

Route 22 E., Salem Industrial Pk.
(08888)
Mail addr: 291 U.S. Highway 22,
Ste. 40, Lebanon (08833-5072)
Phone—(908) 534-2247
Fax—(908) 534-9357
www.howmaneng.com
Email—sales@howmaneng.com
Owner & Pres.—Salvatore
Treppiccione
V-P. & Dir., Engrg.—David Ward
GM—Robert J. Sikora
SIC—3625; NAICS—335314;
*Industrial controls*
Employs—15; Estab.—1987
Sales—$2.5Mil
6,000 sq ft site, Distrib.—National
Privately owned corporation
DBA: Howman Engineering

### READINGTON FARMS, INC.

Div. of Wakefern Food Corp.
12 Mill Rd., P.O. Box 164 (08888)
Phone—(908) 534-2121
National—(800) 426-1707
Fax—(908) 534-4377
Plt. Mgr.—Doug McDowell
Admn. & Hum. Res. Mgr.—Lori
Snyder
SIC—2026; NAICS—311500; *Milk;
Brand name—Shop Rite; Price
Rite; Durling Farms*
Employs—200; Estab.—1888
Sales—$50Mil-$100Mil
Distrib.—Regional
Privately owned corporation
Parent co.—Wakefern Food Corp.,
Keasbey, NJ
Phone—(732) 906-5932
See Parent Co. Section for full profile.

### WALTRON, BULL & ROBERTS, LLC

50 Tannery Rd., P.O. Box 70
(08888)
Phone—(908) 534-5100
National—(800) 242-7353
Fax—(908) 534-5546
www.waltron.net
Email—waltron@waltron.net
Chrm.—John M. Walsh III
Pres., CEO, CFO & COO—
Jonathan C. Guy
Prod. & Sales Mgr.—Joseph
Schultheis
Pur. Mgr.—Gary Peckman
Cust. Serv. Rep.—Felicia Rosocha
SIC—3826; NAICS—334516;
*Analytical instruments for ultra
pure water applications*
Employs—12; Estab.—1903
Sales—$2.6Mil-$5Mil
14,200 sq ft site, Distrib.—Intl.
Limited Liability Company
AKA: Waltron

## Whitehouse Station

(Hunterdon—N.W.)

### †AMARR GARAGE DOORS

12 Coddington Rd. (08889)
Phone—(908) 534-4112
Fax—(908) 534-5713
www.amarr.com
Email—marketing@amarr.com
Matls. Mgr.—Victor Vergalito
Serv. Mgr.—Tamara Young
SIC—5031; NAICS—332321;
*Distributor of steel garage doors*
Employs—50; Estab.—2004
Distrib.—Intl.
Privately owned corporation
Parent co.—Amarr Garage Doors,
Winston-Salem, NC
Phone—(336) 744-5100
See Parent Co. Section for full profile.

### D & M PRINTERS

43 School Rd. (08889)
Phone—(908) 534-4101
Owner—Liz Dembeski

## Whitehouse Station— (cont.)

SIC—2759; 2752; NAICS— 323100; *Commercial offset printing*
Employs—1; Estab.—1977
Sales—under $500,000
Distrib.—Local
Sole ownership

**DBM OF AMERICA, INC.**
295 U.S. Highway 22 E., Ste. 104 (08889)
**Phone—(908) 534-1665**
Fax—(908) 534-1244
www.dbma.com
Email—info@dbma.com
Pres.—David Weston
Off. Mgr.—Judy Houck
SIC—7373; *Computer network system integration, including LANs & WANs*
Employs—3; Estab.—1985
Distrib.—Regional
Privately owned corporation

**EXPERIMENTAL MACHINE & TOOL**
114 Pulaski Rd. (08889)
**Phone—(908) 534-4725**
Fax—(908) 534-1688
Pres.—John Nieliwodski
GM—Stan Nieliwodski
SIC—3599; *General machining job shop*
Employs—4; Estab.—1950
Sales—$500,000-$1Mil (est)
Distrib.—Regional

**FIBER OPTIC SYSTEMS, INC.**
P.O. Box 62 (08889)
**Phone—(908) 534-5500**
National—(800) 809-3674
www.fosi.com
Email—info@fosi.com
Pres.—Cyr A. Ryan
SIC—2542; 3993; *Fiber-optic displays, exhibits & advertising specialties*
Employs—6; Estab.—1970
8,000 sq ft site, Distrib.—Intl.
Privately owned corporation

**FIMBEL ARCHITECTURAL DOOR SPECIALTIES**
8 Coddington Rd. (08889)
Mail addr: P.O. Box 96, Whitehouse (08888-0096)
**Phone—(908) 534-1732**
Fax—(908) 534-9259
www.fimbelads.com
Email—sales@fimbelads.com
Pres., Cont.—Edward Fimbel III
V-P.—Jeff Deal
Engrg. & Pur. Mgr.—Joe Tarrant
IT Mgr.—Mike Donatelli
Cust. Serv. Rep.—Judy Hendershot
Cust. Serv. Rep.—Mary Emilut
SIC—3442; 2431; NAICS— 332321; *Vinyl, composite, metal, fiberglass, aluminum & wooden architectural, commercial, carriage house, specialty & residential overhead garage doors & millwork; Brand name— Euro-Dor; Iso-Dor; Roaring Twenties; Early American; Presidential Series; American Legends; AC-50 Aluminum; Dur-A-Guard; Thermo-Cycle*
Employs—50; Estab.—1924
Sales—$7Mil-$10Mil
90,000 sq ft site, Distrib.—Intl.
Limited Liability Company

**GALOSSI GLASS DESIGN, INC.**
12 Van Pelt Dr. (08889-3902)
**Phone—(908) 232-2111**
(908) 303-2886
Fax—(908) 691-2496
www.galossiglassdesign.com
Email—glassman587@aol.com

Pres.—Alfredo Galossi
SIC—3231; NAICS—327215; *Stained glass shower doors*
Employs—2; Estab.—1982
Sales—$500,000-$1Mil
Distrib.—National
Privately owned corporation

**HUNTERDON ORNAMENTAL CONCRETE, INC.**
440 Highway 22 (08889)
**Phone—(908) 534-4556**
Email—grasso440@comcast.net
Pres.—Steve Grasso
V-P.—Gladys Grasso
SIC—3272; *Precast concrete products*
Employs—2; Estab.—1975
Sales—under $500,000
Distrib.—Local
Privately owned corporation

**MERCK & CO., INC. (H Q)**
1 Merck Dr., P.O. Box 100 (08889)
**Phone—(908) 423-1000**
National—(800) 444-2080
Fax—(908) 735-1253
www.merck.com
Email—kyra_lindemann@ merck.com
Chrm. & CEO—Kenneth C. Frazier
Pres., Global Human Health & Ex. V-P.—Adam H. Schechter
Pres., Mfg. Div. & Ex. V-P.—William A. Deese
Pres., Merck Consumer Care & Ex. V-P.—Bridgette P. Heller
Pres., Merck Animal Health & Ex. V-P.—Richard R. DeLuca, Jr.
Pres., Merck Research Labs & Ex. V-P.—Roger Perlmutter
Ex. V-P., CFO—Robert M. Davis
Ex. V-P., CIO—Clark Golestani
Ex. V-P., Chief Medical Officer— Michael Rosenblatt
Ex. V-P., Chief Strategy Officer— Cuong Viet Do
Ex. V-P., Chief Compliance & Ethics Officer—Michael J. Holston
Sr. V-P., U.S. Reg.—James Mackey
Sr. V-P., Inv. Rels.—Joseph Romanelli
Ex. V-P., Gen. Counsel—Bruce N. Kuhlik
Ex. V-P., Hum. Res.—Mirian M. Graddick-Weir
Ex. Dir., MMD Global Comms.— Kyra Lindemann
SIC—2834; NAICS—325412; *Corporate headquarters; pharmaceuticals*
Employs—2000; Estab.—1891
Worldwide: 80,000
Sales—$47Bil
Distrib.—National
Publicly owned corporation

**MINALEX CORP.**
25 Coddington Rd., P.O. Box 247 (08889)
**Phone—(908) 534-4044**
Fax—(908) 534-6788
www.minalex.com
Email—sales@minalex.com
Pres.—James Casey
V-P.—Jim Kowalski
Opers. Mgr.—Christopher Casey
Info. Sys. Mgr.—Thomas Kelly
Engr.—Michael Casey
SIC—3354; NAICS—331316; *Aluminum extrusions*
Employs—35; Estab.—1965
Sales—$10Mil
25,000 sq ft site, Distrib.—Intl.
Privately owned corporation
ISO rating—9001:2000

**VIANINI PIPE, INC.**
39 County Line Rd. (08889)
Mail addr: P.O. Box 678, Somerville (08876)
**Phone—(908) 534-4021**
Fax—(908) 534-5011
www.vianinipipe.com
Email—carl@vianinipipe.com
Pres.—Alex Narcise
V-P.—Carl Leonhard
Sales Mgr., RCP Div.—Herman Jamnick
Sales Mgr., PCCP Div.—Kevin Brown
Plt. Mgr.—Jere Burd
Hum. Res., IT & Off. Mgr.— Rhonda Woolf
Trade Mgr.—Vickie Rosevelt
SIC—3272; 3498; NAICS— 332996; *Prestress, jacking & reinforced concrete pipe*
Employs—100; Estab.—1968
Distrib.—Local
Privately owned corporation

---

## Whiting
(Ocean—S.E.)

**BIG EYE LAMP, INC.**
870 Route 530, Ste. 2 (08759)
**Phone—(732) 557-9400**
Fax—(732) 557-9111
www.bigeyelamp.com
Email—infobigeye@aol.com
Pres.—William J. O'Hara
V-P.—Patrick O'Hara
IT Mgr.—Ryan O'Hara
SIC—3648; NAICS—335129; *High intensity magnifying lamps*
Employs—6; Estab.—1981
5,500 sq ft site, Distrib.—Intl.
Privately owned corporation

**JARAHIAN MILLWORK, INC.**
870 Route 530, Ste. 4 (08759)
**Phone—(732) 240-5151**
Pres.—Harold Jarahian
Off. Mgr.—Kristin M. McLaughlin
SIC—2431; NAICS—321900; *Millwork*
Employs—3; Estab.—1978
Sales—under $500,000
Distrib.—Local
Privately owned corporation

**VILLAGE OPTICIANS**
550 Route 530 (08759)
**Phone—(732) 350-1900**
Fax—(732) 350-0093
www.villageopticians.com
Email—bobaronb@msn.com
Owner & Optician—Joel C. Wolf
SIC—3827; NAICS—333314; *Optical lens grinding*
Employs—4; Estab.—1991
Sales—under $500,000
Distrib.—Local
Sole ownership

---

## Wildwood
(Cape May—S.E.)

**ABS SIGN CO., INC.**
3008 Park Blvd. (08260)
**Phone—(609) 522-6833**
Fax—(609) 522-0680
www.absneon.com
Email—abssign@aol.com
Pres.—Randy Hentges
Graphic Designer—Alex Figueroa
Bookkeeper—Carol Hentges
SIC—3993; *Interior & exterior signs*
Employs—6; Estab.—1964
Sales—$500,000-$1Mil
Distrib.—Local
Privately owned sub-S corp.

**†BILLOWS ELECTRIC SUPPLY CO., INC.**
3901 New Jersey Ave. (08260)
**Phone—(609) 522-7736**
Fax—(609) 729-1188
www.billows.com
Email—sgittle@billows.com
Manager—Fran Dwestefano
SIC—5063; *Distributor of electrical supplies, including fixtures & panels; Brand name—Cutler-Hammer*
Employs—5; Estab.—1950
2,000 sq ft site, Distrib.—Local
Privately owned corporation
Parent co.—Billows Electric Supply Co., Inc., Philadelphia, PA
Phone—(215) 332-9700
See Parent Co. Section for full profile.

**CUSTOM CABINETS BY JIM BUCKO, INC.**
135 W. Burk Ave. (08260)
**Phone—(609) 889-7666**
Fax—(609) 522-0366
www.jimbucko.com
Email—jbucko@comcast.net
Pres.—James Bucko
Off. Mgr.—Linda Black
SIC—2434; 2541; NAICS— 337110; *Wooden kitchen cabinets, display cases & fixtures*
Employs—6; Estab.—1980
Sales—$500,000-$1Mil
Distrib.—Local
Privately owned corporation

**†GROVE SUPPLY, INC.**
3801 Park Blvd. (08260)
**Phone—(609) 522-1449**
Fax—(609) 522-3107
www.grovesupplyinc.com
Email—info@grovesupplyinc.com
Br. Mgr.—Bud Fox
SIC—5074; 5075; *Wholesaler of HVAC & plumbing equipment & supplies, including pumps & valves*
Employs—5; Estab.—2003
Distrib.—Local
Privately owned corporation
Parent co.—Grove Supply, Inc., Warminster, PA
Phone—(215) 672-8666
See Parent Co. Section for full profile.

**HARRIS MINIATURE GOLF COURSES, INC.**
141 W. Burk Ave. (08260)
**Phone—(609) 522-4200**
National—(888) 294-6530
Fax—(609) 729-0100
www.harrisminigolf.com
Email—info@harrisminigolf.com
Pres.—Richard Lahey
CFO—Sue Waters
COO—Glenn F. Lynn
V-P.—Patrick Boylan
SIC—3949; NAICS—339920; *Miniature golf course construction*
Employs—15; Estab.—1979
10,000 sq ft site, Distrib.—National
Privately owned corporation

**†JOHNSON'S APPLIANCES & BEDDING**
2510 New York Ave. (08260)
**Phone—(609) 522-1421**
Fax—(609) 522-1436
www.johnsonsappliances.net
Email—tg0521@aol.com
GM—Jerry Stroh
SIC—5064; 5023; *Wholesaler of household appliances & bedding*
Employs—3; Estab.—1947
Sales—under $500,000
5,000 sq ft site, Distrib.—Local
Privately owned corporation

GEOGRAPHICAL

## Wildwood—(cont.)

Parent co.—Johnson's Appliances & Bedding, Ocean City, NJ
Phone—(609) 399-1598
See Parent Co. Section for full profile.

### LAURA'S FUDGE, INC.

357 E. Wildwood Ave., P.O. Box 871 (08260)
**Phone—(609) 729-1555**
National—(800) 452-8727
Fax—(609) 522-9013
www.laurasfudge.com
Email—laura@laurasfudge.com
Pres., COO, Secy. & Opers. Mgr.—Lori Bradshaw Roach
MIS & Prodn. Mgr.—David Roach
SIC—2064; 2052; NAICS—311300; Fudge, candy, macaroon cookies, confections, chocolate covered fruit, candy apples & chocolate covered bacon
Employs—12; Estab.—1926
Sales—$500,000-$1Mil
2,700 sq ft site, Distrib.—Local
Privately owned corporation

### †SEASHORE SUPPLY OF WILDWOOD

306 Wildwood Ave. (08260)
**Phone—(609) 522-1491**
Fax—(609) 522-6456
www.teamace.com
Email—teamace@comcast.net
Br. Mgr.—Mark Tilsner
Sales Rep.—Chris Gallagher
SIC—5074; 5075; 5085; 5063; Distributor of plumbing, HVAC & electrical supplies for general contractors
Employs—3; Estab.—1919
Sales—under $500,000
Distrib.—Local
Privately owned corporation

### SUN BY THE SEA

224 W. 23rd Ave., P.O. Box 2101 (08260)
**Phone—(609) 522-2721**
Fax—(609) 522-2721
www.sunbythesea.com
Email—thesunbythesea@gmail.com
Pres.—Dorothy Kulisek
SIC—2711; Newspaper publishing
Employs—2; Estab.—2004
Sales—under $500,000
Distrib.—Local
Privately owned corporation

## Wildwood Crest

(Cape May—S.E.)

### LEADER PRINTERS

5914 New Jersey Ave. (08260)
**Phone—(609) 729-0161**
Fax—(609) 523-0464
www.leaderprinters.com
Email—support@leaderprinters.com
Pres.—Dennis Hall
SIC—2752; 2759; 2791; NAICS—323122; Offset printing & typesetting
Employs—6; Estab.—1974
3,300 sq ft site, Distrib.—Regional
Privately owned corporation

### SANDPIPER EMBROIDERY, INC.

5905 New Jersey Ave. (08260)
**Phone—(609) 522-4560**
Fax—(609) 523-8535
www.sandpiperembroidery.com
Email—sandpiperembroidery@comcast.net
Owner—Virginia Fineberg

SIC—2395; 3999; 2284; 2281; Embroidery products, designs & supplies for the commercial & home embroidery industries
Employs—3; Estab.—1982
Sales—under $500,000 (est)
Distrib.—National
Privately owned corporation

## Williamstown

(Gloucester—S.W.)

### ADVANCED WELDING SERVICE, INC.

300 Thomas Ave., Ste. 701-1 (08094)
**Phone—(856) 875-2500**
Fax—(856) 875-2700
Pres.—Michael Hammond
SIC—3599; 3499; Welding & fabrication job shop
Employs—8; Estab.—2010
Sales—$500,000-$1Mil
Distrib.—Local
Privately owned corporation

### BLACK CAR NEWS

420 Inverness Rd. (08094)
**Phone—(856) 262-2368**
National—(800) 723-9119
www.blackcarnews.com
Email—michele@blackcarnews.com
Manager—Michele Norton
SIC—2711; Newsletter publishing for the car & livery markets
Employs—1; Estab.—2006
Sales—under $500,000 (est)
Distrib.—Regional
Privately owned corporation
Parent co.—Black Car News, Cherry Hill, NJ
Phone—(856) 751-0656
See Parent Co. Section for full profile.

### COSMIC CUSTOM SCREEN PRINTING, LLC

1629 N. Black Horse Pike (08094)
**Phone—(856) 629-8337**
www.craigscosmic.com
Pres.—Jessica Craig
SIC—2396; Textile screen printing
Employs—2; Estab.—1987
Sales—under $500,000
Distrib.—National
Privately owned corporation

### C-SPORTS

2045 S. Black Horse Pike (08094)
**Phone—(856) 875-5680**
Fax—(856) 875-4636
Email—c-sports@hotmail.com
Owner—Mark Cannon
SIC—2395; 2396; Textile screen printing & embroidery
Employs—2; Estab.—1997
Sales—under $500,000
Distrib.—Local
Sole ownership

### D. F. ENTERPRISE, LLC

3254 S. Black Horse Pike (08094)
**Phone—(856) 875-1777**
Fax—(856) 875-1734
Email—dfenterprisellc@comcast.net
Owner & Pres.—Scott Richardson
V-P.—Barbara Fuhrer
SIC—3479; 3471; 3599; NAICS—332813; Industrial metal coatings, hard chrome, ultra bright, mid-phosphorus electroless nickel plating & micro laser welding
Employs—2; Estab.—1992
Sales—under $500,000
Distrib.—Regional
Limited Liability Company

### DODSON VAULT CO., E.

P.O. Box 966 (08094)
**Phone—(856) 728-7660**
Owner—Ed Dodson

SIC—3272; Concrete burial vaults
Employs—2; Estab.—1986
Sales—under $500,000 (est)
Distrib.—Local
Sole ownership

### DONALDSON CO., INC., R. J.

1287 Glassboro Rd. (08094)
**Phone—(856) 629-2737**
Fax—(856) 629-1956
www.donaldsonwire.com
Email—donaldsonco@verizon.net
Pres.—Douglas Donaldson
V-P.—Scott Donaldson
Corp. Secy.—JoAnn Kirk
SIC—3496; Wire mesh partitions & infill panels & window guards
Employs—8; Estab.—1972
Sales—$500,000-$1Mil
15,000 sq ft site, Distrib.—National
Privately owned sub-S corp.

### F P DEVELOPMENTS, INC.

402 S. Main St. (08094)
**Phone—(856) 875-7100**
Fax—(856) 875-6717
www.fpdevelopments.com
Email—sales@fpdevelopments.com
Pres.—Fred Pfleger
GM, Hum. Res., IT & MIS Mgr.—David R. Pfleger
Fin. Mgr.—Ginny B. Pfleger
Engrg. Mgr.—Brian Rodilosso
Machine Shop Mgr.—Greg Emmons
Pur. Agt.—Lisa Myers
SIC—3565; NAICS—333993; Pharmaceuticals & industrial packaging machinery & hospital automation equipment
Employs—32; Estab.—1994
Sales—$1Mil-$5Mil
24,000 sq ft site, Distrib.—Intl.
Privately owned corporation

### GAMBARDELLA RACING & PERFORMANCE, INC.

1999 S. Black Horse Pike (08094)
**Phone—(856) 728-1869**
Fax—(856) 728-9099
www.gambardellaracing.com
Email—tony@gambardellaracing.com
Pres., Shop Mgr.—Tony Gambardella
SIC—3711; Race car bodies & components
Employs—3; Estab.—1983
Sales—under $500,000
Distrib.—National
Privately owned corporation

### GECKO GRAPHICS, INC.

128 Berlin Cross Keys Rd. (08094)
**Phone—(856) 740-9042**
Fax—(856) 740-9043
www.geckographicsinc.com
Email—info@geckographicsinc.com
Pres.—Alice Gorney
SIC—3089; 2759; 2499; 3199; Laser engraving on acrylic, plastics, paper, wood, cardboard, leather & textiles
Employs—3; Estab.—1995
Sales—under $500,000
Distrib.—Local
Privately owned corporation

### GRAPHIC IMAGE

1401 N. Black Horse Pike, Ste. A (08094)
**Phone—(856) 262-8900**
National—(800) 232-5550
Fax—(856) 262-8950
www.graphicimage.com
Email—jim@graphicimagetees.com
Owner—Jim McGhee
SIC—2759; 2395; Commercial printing, t-shirt screen printing & digital embroidery
Employs—8
Sales—$1Mil-$2.5Mil (est)
Distrib.—Intl.
Privately owned corporation

### HAMMONTON MOLD CO., INC.

4171 S. Black Horse Pike (08094)
**Phone—(856) 728-9112**
www.hammontonmold.com
Email—steve@hammontonmold.com
Pres.—Steve Domazet
V-P.—Ivan Domazet
Off. Mgr.—Kristen Domazet
SIC—3544; NAICS—333500; Injection blow molds & stretch blow molds for the plastic bottle industry
Employs—16; Estab.—1986
Sales—$1Mil-$2.5Mil
Distrib.—National
Privately owned corporation

### †HOFFMAN EQUIPMENT, INC.

2610 S. Black Horse Pike (08094)
**Phone—(856) 875-0036**
National—(800) 463-3626
Fax—(856) 875-0058
www.hoffmanequip.com
Email—jeff.pauls@hoffmanequip.com
Opers. Mgr.—Jeff Pauls
SIC—5082; Distributor of construction cranes
Employs—5; Estab.—1922
Sales—$5Mil-$10Mil
25,000 sq ft site, Distrib.—Local
Privately owned corporation
Parent co.—Hoffman Equipment, Inc., Piscataway, NJ
Phone—(732) 752-3600
See Parent Co. Section for full profile.

### MONROE TOOL & DIE, INC.

197 Sharp Rd. (08094)
**Phone—(856) 629-5164**
Fax—(856) 875-8868
Email—monroetooldie@yahoo.com
Pres., CFO—Steven Kennedy
MIS Mgr.—Holly Kennedy
SIC—3544; 3469; NAICS—333500; Metal stampings & tool & die job shop
Employs—8; Estab.—1964
Sales—$1Mil-$5Mil
6,000 sq ft site, Distrib.—National
Privately owned corporation

### MSD PRECISION

300 Thomas Ave., Bldg. 6 (08094)
**Phone—(856) 262-8142**
Fax—(856) 262-9508
Email—msdprecision@verizon.net
Owner—Mark Dejong
SIC—3599; Precision machining job shop
Employs—3; Estab.—1991
Sales—under $500,000
Distrib.—Local
Sole ownership

### O K TOOL & DIE CO.

603 Bluebell Rd. (08094)
**Phone—(856) 629-5757**
Fax—(856) 629-1028
Pres.—Kenneth Ostapovich
V-P.—Judith Ostapovich
SIC—3089; 3544; NAICS—333500; Plastic products & tool & die job shop
Employs—15; Estab.—1962
Sales—$500,000-$1Mil
10,000 sq ft site, Distrib.—National
Privately owned sub-S corp.

### OLDCASTLE PRECAST, INC.

1920 12th St. (08094)
**Phone—(609) 561-3400**
National—(800) 642-3755
Fax—(609) 561-5786
www.oldcastleprecast.com
Email—info@oldcastleprecast.com
Plt. Mgr.—Dennis Stevenson
Opers. Mgr.—George Hand II

## Williamstown—(cont.)

SIC—3272; *Concrete pipes*
Employs—20; Estab.—1936
Sales—$2.6Mil-$5Mil
Distrib.—Regional
Publicly owned corporation
Parent co.—Oldcastle Precast,
  Inc., Auburn, WA
  Phone—(253) 833-2777
  See Parent Co. Section for full profile.

### †PIERSON MATERIALS, INC., R. E.

Div. of Pierson Construction Co.,
  Inc., R. E.
151 Industrial Dr. (08094)
Mail addr: P.O. Box 704,
  Bridgeport (08014)
**Phone—(856) 740-2400**
Fax—(856) 740-4200
www.repiersongroup.com
Email—info@repdemo.com
Asst. Treas.—Joe Huffner
GM—Brian Hart
SIC—5032; *Distributor of ready-
  mixed concrete*
Employs—10; Estab.—2002
Distrib.—Local
Privately owned corporation
Parent co.—Pierson Construction
  Co., Inc., R. E., Pilesgrove, NJ
  Phone—(856) 769-8244
  See Parent Co. Section for full profile.

### PIRAMAL GLASS USA, INC.

918 E. Malaga Rd. (08094)
**Phone—(856) 728-9300**
Fax—(856) 696-2301
www.piramal.com
Email—info@piramal.com
IT Mgr.—Brad Reckhart
Hum. Res. Mgr.—Dean Harding
SIC—3221; NAICS—327213;
  *Glass containers for
  pharmaceutical & cosmetic
  products packaging*
Employs—90; Estab.—1907
Sales—under $500,000
Distrib.—Intl.
Privately owned corporation

### PRECISION BALL SPECIALTIES, INC.

1451 Glassboro Rd. (08094)
**Phone—(856) 881-5646**
National—(888) 929-0863
Fax—(856) 881-5789
www.precisionballspecialties.com
Email—carols@
  precisionballspecialties.com
Off. & Sales Mgr.—Carol Symanski
SIC—3544; 3562; *Ball bearing
  cages*
Employs—3; Estab.—1982
Distrib.—National
Privately owned sub-S corp.

### PRECISION METALCRAFTERS, INC.

17 Filbert St. (08094)
**Phone—(856) 629-1020**
Fax—(856) 875-8658
www.precision-metalcrafters.com
Email—precisionmetalcrafters@
  yahoo.com
Ptnr.—Frank Falconi
Ptnr.—Louise Falconi
Off. Mgr.—Joanna Buehler
SIC—3444; *Sheet metal
  fabrication*
Employs—10; Estab.—1968
Sales—$1Mil-$5Mil
35,000 sq ft site, Distrib.—National
Privately owned corporation

### QEI CORP.

1 Airport Dr., P.O. Box 805 (08094)
**Phone—(856) 728-2020**
National—(800) 334-9154
Fax—(856) 629-1751
www.qei-broadcast.com
Email—qeisales@qei-
  broadcast.com
Pres.—Jay Osselburn
V-P., Mfg.—Eric Harvey

V-P., Opers.—Edwin Etschman
SIC—3663; NAICS—334220;
  *Analog radio broadcasting
  transmitters, monitors &
  equipment & STL & RF
  amplifiers for scientific &
  industrial applications*
Employs—10; Estab.—1971
Distrib.—Intl.
Privately owned corporation

### R & T CUSTOM CABINETS

1311 Herbert Blvd. (08094)
**Phone—(856) 728-1979**
Owner—Richard Digirolamo
SIC—2434; 2541; NAICS—
  337110; *Wood & laminate kitchen
  cabinets & store fixtures*
Employs—2; Estab.—1982
Sales—under $500,000
Distrib.—Local
Sole ownership

### R F VII, INC.

1041 Glassboro Rd., Bldg. 6
  (08094)
**Phone—(856) 875-2121**
Fax—(856) 875-2119
www.rfvii.com
Email—rfvii@yahoo.com
Pres., Treas.—Kelly Barber
V-P., Sales—Steven Barber
SIC—3825; *Radio frequency
  plasma generators, tuners,
  modules & match boxes for the
  RF vacuum & ICP industries*
Employs—13; Estab.—1993
Sales—$500,000-$1Mil
5,000 sq ft site, Distrib.—National
Privately owned corporation

### SOUTH STATE, INC.

Div. of South State Materials, LLC
1340 Glassboro Rd. (08094)
**Phone—(856) 881-6030**
Fax—(856) 881-6031
www.southstateinc.com
Email—info@southstateinc.com
GM—Jay Heim
Foreman—John Johnson
SIC—2951; *Asphalt paving
  compounds*
Employs—15; Estab.—1977
Distrib.—Local
Privately owned corporation
Parent co.—South State Materials,
  LLC, Bridgeton, NJ
  Phone—(856) 451-5300
  See Parent Co. Section for full profile.

### TUBE CRAFT OF AMERICA

667 Lebanon Ave. (08094)
**Phone—(856) 629-5626**
Fax—(856) 728-1304
www.tubecraftflange.com
Email—sff-sales@verizon.net
Pres.—Alexandra Taniewski
V-P., GM, Bookkeeper &
  Typesetter—Iwan Taniewski
Off. Mgr.—Diane Marino
SIC—3312; *Steel pipe flanges*
Employs—4; Estab.—1972
Sales—under $500,000
15,000 sq ft site, Distrib.—National
Privately owned corporation

### UNIVERSITY FASHIONS

1888 Winslow Rd., Bldg. B (08094)
**Phone—(856) 228-1615**
Fax—(856) 367-2252
www.universityfashions.com
Email—sales@
  universityfashions.com
Owner & Pres.—Ulysses James
Sales Rep.—Zach James
SIC—2396; 2395; *Textile screen
  printing & embroidery, including
  t-shirts, duffel bags, backpacks,
  knit caps & towels*
Employs—7; Estab.—1993
Sales—under $500,000
Distrib.—National
Privately owned corporation

### VECTOR PRECISION MACHINING, INC.

1558 Janvier Rd. (08094)
**Phone—(856) 740-5131**
Fax—(856) 740-5132
Email—vector_machining_inc@
  yahoo.com
Pres.—Pawel Les
SIC—3599; *Precision machining
  job shop*
Employs—5; Estab.—2002
Sales—under $500,000
5,000 sq ft site, Distrib.—Regional
Privately owned corporation

### VFI FABRICATORS, INC.

300 Thomas Ave., Bldg. 1, Ste.
  101 (08094)
**Phone—(856) 629-8786**
Fax—(856) 629-0463
www.vfifab.com
Email—afabricojr@vfifab.com
Pres.—Alfred E. Fabrico
Off. Mgr.—Barbara Vella
SIC—3444; *Sheet metal
  fabrication*
Employs—30; Estab.—1980
Sales—$500,000-$1Mil
Distrib.—National
Privately owned corporation

### VIOLET PACKING

Div. of B & G Foods, Inc.
123 Railroad Ave. (08094)
**Phone—(856) 629-7428**
Fax—(856) 629-6340
www.bgfoods.com
Email—sales@bgfoods.com
Br. Mgr.—Darrell Cran
Off. Mgr.—Belinda Leech
SIC—2035; *Crushed tomatoes,
  pizza, spaghetti & marinara
  sauces*
Employs—17; Estab.—2010
Distrib.—National
Publicly owned corporation
Parent co.—B & G Foods, Inc.,
  Parsippany, NJ
  Phone—(973) 401-6500
  See Parent Co. Section for full profile.

### WASTEQUIP, INC.

460 New Brooklyn Rd. (08094)
**Phone—(856) 629-9222**
National—(800) 220-2248
Fax—(856) 629-3604
www.wastequip.com
Email—sales@wastequip.com
Plt. Mgr.—Fred Straub
SIC—3411; 3412; NAICS—
  332431; *Steel waste containers*
Employs—75; Estab.—1977
60,000 sq ft site, Distrib.—
  Regional
Privately owned corporation
Parent co.—Wastequip, Inc.,
  Charlotte, NC
  Phone—(704) 366-7140
  See Parent Co. Section for full profile.

### WOOD WORKS

1111 N. Black Horse Pike (08094)
**Phone—(856) 728-4520**
Fax—(856) 875-1428
www.thewoodworks-nj.com
Email—sales@thewoodworks-
  nj.com
Mng. Ptnr.—Carol Bartling
GM—Jim O'Donnell
Sales Mgr.—Jeff Adams
SIC—2434; 2431; 2511; NAICS—
  337110; *Wooden cabinets &
  bookcases*
Employs—6; Estab.—1984
Sales—$500,000-$1Mil (est)
Distrib.—Local
Privately owned corporation

### ZERO TOLERANCE MACHINE

1650 Glassboro Rd. (08094)
**Phone—(856) 881-9072**
Fax—(856) 881-9002
Email—k_homeyer@msn.com

Ptnr.—Kenneth Homeyer
Ptnr.—John Buhrman
SIC—3599; *Military & aircraft
  machine parts*
Employs—2; Estab.—1999
Sales—under $500,000
Distrib.—Regional
Privately owned partnership

## Willingboro

(Burlington—S.E.)

### BURLINGTON COUNTY TIMES, INC.

Div. of Calkins Media, Inc.
4284 Route 130 (08046)
**Phone—(609) 871-8000**
Fax—(215) 269-0490
www.burlingtoncountytimes.com
Email—sellis@calkins.com
Dir., Strategy—Stanley M. Ellis
GM—Steve Todd
SIC—2711; NAICS—323119;
  *Weekly print & online newspaper
  publishing*
Employs—110; Estab.—1958
Distrib.—Local
Privately owned corporation
Parent co.—Calkins Media, Inc.,
  Levittown, PA
  Phone—(215) 949-4000
  See Parent Co. Section for full profile.

### COUNTERFIT

1 Ironside Ct. (08046)
**Phone—(609) 871-8888**
Fax—(609) 871-8889
Pres.—Steve Daiagi
SIC—3281; NAICS—327991;
  *Marble & granite countertops*
Employs—14; Estab.—1997
Sales—$1Mil-$2.5Mil (est)
Distrib.—Regional
Privately owned corporation

### GARVEY PRECISION MACHINE, INC.

19 Ironside Ct. (08046)
**Phone—(609) 835-4900**
Fax—(609) 835-4905
www.garveyprecisionmachine.com
Email—adavis@
  garveyprecisionmachine.com
Pres.—Joseph Corr
V-P.—Alexis Davis
SIC—3599; *Precision machining
  job shop*
Employs—22; Estab.—1953
25,000 sq ft site, Distrib.—National
Privately owned corporation

### MAXTER CORP. (H Q)

51 Edgemont Ln. (08046)
**Phone—(609) 877-9700**
Fax—(609) 877-9712
www.maxteronline.com
Email—info@maxteronline.com
Pres.—John Mughal
Mktg. Mgr.—Paul Ouko
SIC—3841; *Corporate
  headquarters; surgical
  instruments, including
  instruments for general,
  endoscopic & laparoscopic
  surgery (mfg. done in Germany)*
Employs—4
Sales—$500,000-$1Mil (est)
Distrib.—Local
Privately owned corporation

### QUALITY BAKERY PRODUCTS OF NEW JERSEY, INC.

Div. of Hearthside Food Solutions,
  LLC
24 Ironside Ct. (08046)
Mail addr: 1809 Underwood Blvd.,
  Delran (08075-1232)
**Phone—(609) 871-7393**
  (630) 967-3600
Fax—(609) 871-4853
GM—Nate Mariano

GEOGRAPHICAL

## Willingboro—(cont.)

SIC—2051; NAICS—311812; *Breadcrumbs*
Employs—30
Distrib.—Local
Privately owned corporation
Parent co.—Hearthside Food Solutions, LLC, Downers Grove, IL
Phone—(630) 967-3600
See Parent Co. Section for full profile.

**SPORTS PARADISE**
4230 Route 130 (08046)
**Phone—(609) 877-1826**
Fax—(609) 877-1203
www.sportsparadise.net
Email—willingboro@ sportsparadise.net
Pres.—Fred Streiber
V-P.—Craig Streiber
Off. Mgr.—Dena Sauer
Manager—Greg Smith
Manager—Howard Stern
SIC—2395; 2396; *Team sports uniform embroidery & screen printing for high school coaches, athletic directors & team coordinators*
Employs—5; Estab.—1975
Sales—$1Mil-$2.5Mil
Distrib.—Local
Privately owned corporation

## Windsor
### (Mercer—N.E.)

**ABCO PRINTING CO.**
92 N. Main St. (08561)
**Phone—(609) 259-4900**
Fax—(609) 259-4901
www.abcoprinting-nj.com
Email—info@abcoprinting-nj.com
Pres.—Russ Pareti
V-P., Prodn.—Bob Taylor
SIC—2759; NAICS—323100; *Commercial printing*
Employs—12; Estab.—1949
20,000 sq ft site, Distrib.—Regional
Limited Liability Company

**CENTRAL MILLWORK OF NEW JERSEY**
92 N. Main St., Bldg. 11, P.O. Box 447 (08561)
**Phone—(609) 448-7700**
Fax—(609) 448-2882
www.centralmillworknj.com
Email—kevin@ centralmillworknj.com
Owner, Pres. & GM—Kevin Coyle
SIC—2499; 2434; NAICS—337110; *Architectural woodwork & cabinets; Brand name—Corian; Meganite; Formica; Wilsonart; Nevamar*
Employs—7; Estab.—1990
Sales—$500,000-$1Mil
6,000 sq ft site, Distrib.—Local
Privately owned corporation

**INNOLUTIONS, INC.**
92 N. Main St., P.O. Box 384 (08561)
**Phone—(609) 490-9799**
Fax—(609) 490-9788
www.innoinc.com
Email—info@innoinc.com
Pres.—Manny Patel
V-P.—Pat Patel
Software Engr. Mgr.—Mike Friedman
SIC—3625; 3555; NAICS—335314; *Electronic printing press controls*
Employs—9; Estab.—1991
Sales—$1Mil-$2.5Mil
Distrib.—Intl.
Privately owned corporation

**MAIN STREET AWARDS, INC.**
55 N. Main St., P.O. Box 323 (08561)
**Phone—(609) 448-6324**
Fax—(609) 448-6484
www.mainstreetawards.com
Email—mainstreetbk@aol.com
Ptnr.—Carol Whitehouse
Ptnr.—Betsy Kerlin
SIC—3479; *Recognition awards, trophies, plaques & corporate awards engraving*
Employs—2; Estab.—1985
Sales—under $500,000
Distrib.—Local
Privately owned sub-S corp.

**†PINE ENVIRONMENTAL SERVICES, LLC**
92 N. Main St., Bldg. 20 (08561)
Mail addr: P.O. Box 943, Hightstown (08520)
**Phone—(609) 371-9663**
National—(800) 301-9663
Fax—(609) 371-1663
www.pine-environmental.com
Email—pine-nj@pine-environmental.com
Ptnr.—Angelo Pinheiro
Ptnr.—Roger Pinheiro
Sales Rep. & Mgr.—Kim Dasilva
SIC—5087; *Company headquarters & distributor of environmental monitoring equipment & sampling & safety supplies*
Employs—60; Estab.—1995
Distrib.—National
Limited Liability Company

**PYROMETER INSTRUMENT CO., INC.**
92 N. Main St., Bldg. 18-D, P.O. Box 479 (08561)
**Phone—(609) 443-5522**
National—(800) 468-7976
Fax—(609) 443-5590
www.pyrometer.com
Email—sales@pyrometer.com
CEO—David Crozier
Pres., Sales Mgr.—Judd Parrish
Dir., Engrg.—Alexander Dmitriyev
SIC—3829; *Precision infrared thermometers with automatic emissivity correction & thermocouple pyrometers; Brand name—Pyrolaser; Pyrofiber; Optitherm III; MicroTherm*
Employs—6; Estab.—1928
Sales—$1Mil-$2Mil
15,000 sq ft site, Distrib.—National
Privately owned corporation

**SILVER BRUSH LTD.**
92 N. Main St., Bldg. 18-E, P.O. Box 414 (08561)
**Phone—(609) 443-4900**
Fax—(609) 443-4888
www.silverbrush.com
Email—info@silverbrush.com
Pres.—Deirdra Silver
SIC—3991; NAICS—339994; *Brushes for arts & crafts & beauty salon applications*
Employs—5; Estab.—1987
Sales—$500,000-$1Mil (est)
Distrib.—Regional
Privately owned corporation

**SOPHISTICATED CHOCOLATES MFG., INC.**
92 N. Main St. (08561)
**Phone—(609) 443-4747**
Fax—(609) 443-8762
www.dbchocolate.com
Email—admin@dbchocolate.com
Pres., CFO—Robert P. Hicks
V-P.—Dave Hicks
Plt. Mgr.—Christine O'Brian
MIS Mgr.—Bradley Hicks

SIC—2064; NAICS—311300; *Chocolates; Brand name—David Bradley Chocolatier*
Employs—15; Estab.—1982
Sales—$500,000-$1Mil
6,800 sq ft site, Distrib.—Local
Privately owned sub-S corp.
DBA: David Bradley Chocolatier

**SPEC STEEL RULE DIES, INC.**
92 N. Main St., Bldg. 1-B, P.O. Box 33 (08561)
**Phone—(609) 443-9200**
Fax—(609) 443-9230
Pres., R & D Mgr.—John Nagy
Corp. Secy.—Alice Orchard
Fin. Mgr.—Peter Palladino
SIC—3544; 2796; NAICS—323122; *Steel rule dies & rubber printing plates*
Employs—24; Estab.—1981
7,000 sq ft site, Distrib.—Regional
Privately owned corporation

## Winslow
### (Camden—S.W.)

**AMERICAN FLUX & METALS CORP.**
352 E. Fleming Pike, P.O. Box 74 (08095)
**Phone—(609) 561-7500**
Fax—(609) 561-3724
www.americanflux.net
Email—rodw@americanflux.net
GM—Rod Werner
GM—Jerry Fields
Prod. Supv.—Robert Martin
SIC—2899; *Molybdenum & EFR flux processing*
Employs—26; Estab.—1994
22,000 sq ft site, Distrib.—Intl.
Privately owned partnership

**†BINDER MACHINERY CO., INC.**
201 N. Route 73 (08095)
Mail addr: P.O. Box 259, Cedar Brook (08018)
**Phone—(856) 767-5900**
Fax—(856) 768-5643
www.bindermachinery.com
Pres.—Alan Binder
Serv. Mgr.—Jim Riley
SIC—5082; *Distributor of heavy construction equipment*
Employs—20; Estab.—1959
Distrib.—Regional
Privately owned corporation

## Wood Ridge
### (Bergen—N.E.)

**ACADEMIA FURNITURE INDUSTRIES**
4 Passaic St. (07075)
Mail addr: 74 Passaic St., Wood Ridge (07075)
**Phone—(973) 472-0100**
Fax—(973) 472-8444
www.academiafurniture.com
Pres.—Shabsi Goldman
Asst. Cont.—Yoni Liani
SIC—2531; *Wooden & steel classroom & computer lab furniture*
Employs—25; Estab.—2004
Sales—$5Mil-$10Mil (est)
Distrib.—Intl.
Privately owned corporation

**CERTECH, INC.**
1 Park Pl. W. (07075)
**Phone—(201) 939-7400**
Fax—(201) 939-2037
www.mtccertech.com
Email—evan.reed@morganplc.com
Pres.—John Stang
V-P., GM—Nicholas Korenowski
GM—Lawrence Bodden
Sales Mgr.—Evan Reed
Hum. Res. Mgr.—Frances Villaman

SIC—3264; NAICS—327113; *Corporate headquarters & industrial ceramics*
Employs—220
Sales—$10Mil-$25Mil
Distrib.—Intl.
Publicly owned corporation
ISO rating—AS9100

**CONTINENTAL CAP CO.**
64 Passaic St. (07075)
**Phone—(973) 778-2628**
Fax—(973) 778-2583
www.concapusa.com
Owner—Tina Hsu
SIC—2395; *Apparel embroidery*
Employs—5; Estab.—1996
Sales—under $500,000 (est)

**IMS PET INDUSTRIES**
34 Passaic St. (07075)
**Phone—(973) 249-0026**
National—(800) 394-4467
Fax—(973) 249-0081
www.imspet.com
Email—info@imspet.com
Pres.—Sam Blachorsky
Accts. Mgr.—Karen Krotoski
Administrator—Camille Rotonells
SIC—2047; NAICS—311111; *Pet food ingredients & pet treats*
Employs—40; Estab.—1992
Sales—$10Mil-$25Mil (est)
Distrib.—National
Privately owned corporation

**SKYLINE WINDOWS, LLC**
210 Park Pl. E. (07075)
**Phone—(201) 531-9600**
Fax—(201) 896-4166
www.skylinewindows.com
Email—info@skylinewindows.com
Plt. Mgr.—Karl L. Zeyher
SIC—3442; NAICS—332321; *Heavy commercial architectural aluminum tilt & turn, casement & double hung windows & doors, including design & installation*
Employs—83; Estab.—1996
43,000 sq ft site, Distrib.—Local
Limited Liability Company
Parent co.—Skyline Windows, LLC, Bronx, NY
Phone—(212) 491-3000
See Parent Co. Section for full profile.

**STARFIRE LIGHTING, INC.**
7 Donna Dr. (07075)
**Phone—(201) 438-9540**
National—(800) 443-8823
Fax—(201) 438-9541
www.starfirelighting.com
Email—info@starfirelighting.com
Pres., Fin. & GM—Zachary Gomes
V-P., R & D—Craig Newman
Sales Mgr.—Jack Mashel
Fin. Mgr.—Tante Rivera
SIC—3646; 3645; NAICS—335122; *Commercial & residential linear & recessed lighting fixtures & chandeliers; Brand name—Xenflex; TechTrac; Tubelights; Tru-Lux; Starfield; Starpoint; VersaLux*
Employs—55; Estab.—1981
Sales—$8Mil-$10Mil
50,000 sq ft site, Distrib.—National
Privately owned corporation

**TECH-PAK, INC.**
Div. of President Container Group
100 Blum, P.O. Box 51 (07075)
**Phone—(201) 935-3800**
Fax—(201) 935-1008
www.pcg.com
Email—info@pcg.com
Sr. Design Engr.—Ed Garcia
SIC—2653; 2542; NAICS—322211; *Corrugated store displays*
Employs—40; Estab.—2001
Sales—$500,000-$1Mil
Distrib.—Regional
Privately owned corporation

## Wood Ridge—(cont.)

Parent co.—President Container Group, Moonachie, NJ
Phone—(201) 933-7500
See Parent Co. Section for full profile.

## Woodbine
(Cape May—S.E.)

**CANVAS LADY, THE**
19 Killdeer Hill Rd. (08270)
**Phone—(609) 628-3257**
Fax—(609) 628-3257
www.thecanvasladynj.com
Email—thecanvaslady@comcast.net
Owner—Eva White
SIC—2394; *Canvas boat covers*
Employs—2; Estab.—2005
Sales—under $500,000 (est)
Distrib.—Local
Privately owned corporation

**G & J SOLUTIONS, INC.**
419 Madison Ave. (08270)
**Phone—(609) 861-9838**
National—(800) 688-7845
Fax—(609) 861-9840
www.billscanvasshop.com
Email—info@billscanvasshop.com
Pres., GM & Pur. Agt.—John Di Pompeo
V-P. & Hum. Res. Mgr.—Grace T. Di Pompeo
SIC—2394; NAICS—314912; *Fabric awnings*
Employs—15; Estab.—1975
7,800 sq ft site, Distrib.—Regional
Privately owned corporation
DBA: Bill's Canvas Shop

**†HANSON AGGREGATES BETTER MATERIALS CORP.**
Div. of Lehigh Hanson, Inc.
1401 Route 610 (08270)
**Phone—(856) 447-4294**
National—(800) 732-0068
Fax—(609) 861-2234
www.lehighhanson.com
Email—info@lehighcement.com
Plt. Mgr.—Al Lorenzo
Sales Admn.—Charlotte DiPasquale
SIC—5032; *Distributor of commercial sand & gravel*
Employs—12; Estab.—1967
Distrib.—Local
Publicly owned corporation
Parent co.—Lehigh Hanson, Inc., Irving, TX
Phone—(972) 653-5500
See Parent Co. Section for full profile.

## Woodbridge
(Middlesex—N.E.)

**A. HANTMAN INC**
309 Michaels Ct. (07095)
**Phone—(212) 239-1358**
(732) 407-7499
Fax—(732) 634-0383
Email—ohantman@aol.com
Pres.—Charlotte Hantman
Dir., Tech.—Peter Giannopoulos
SIC—2371; NAICS—315200; *Fur trimmings & accessories*
Employs—7; Estab.—1947
Sales—$250,000-$350,000
Distrib.—Intl.
Sole ownership

**ALAN CHEMICAL CORP., INC.**
843 Rahway Ave., Ste. 400 (07095-3649)
**Phone—(732) 855-6828**
National—(888) 252-6246
Fax—(732) 855-6829
www.alanchem.com
Email—sales@alanchem.com
Pres.—Alan Braxton

Off. Mgr.—Maria Appolito
SIC—2899; *Cleaning chemicals*
Employs—6; Estab.—1986
Sales—under $500,000
Distrib.—Regional
Privately owned corporation

**NEW ENTRY**
**AMBOY GROUP**
1 Amboy Ave. (07095)
**Phone—(732) 510-5600**
National—(800) 431-6365
Fax—(732) 510-5601
www.tommymoloneys.com
Email—info@tommymoloneys.com
Pres.—William Colbert
SIC—2011; *Packaged Irish meat & breakfast gift baskets*
Employs—15; Estab.—2000
Distrib.—Local
Privately owned corporation

**ANTONIO'S PASTA**
545 U.S. Highway 9 N. (07095)
**Phone—(732) 442-1640**
National—(888) 268-6646
Fax—(732) 442-4033
www.antoniospasta.com
Email—sales@antoniospasta.com
Pres.—Barbara Winant
Off. Mgr.—Sandra Winant
Sales Rep.—Steven Winant
SIC—2098; NAICS—311823; *Filled & fresh pasta*
Employs—6; Estab.—1974
Sales—$1Mil-$2.5Mil
Distrib.—Regional
Privately owned sub-S corp.

**CAMO SOFTWARE**
1 Woodbridge Ctr., Ste. 319 (07095)
**Phone—(732) 726-9200**
Fax—(973) 556-1229
www.camo.com
Email—usaadmn@camo.com
Accts. Mgr.—John Chartier
Off. Admn.—Elina Rapoport
SIC—7372; *Multivariate analysis software development*
Employs—4; Estab.—1984
Distrib.—Local
Privately owned corporation

**NEW ENTRY**
**E*PRO, INC.**
1000 U.S. Highway 9 N., Ste. 303 (07095)
**Phone—(732) 283-0499**
Fax—(732) 283-0489
www.eprocorp.com
Email—sales@epro-tech.com
Pres.—Sadeesh Venugopal
Opers. Mgr.—Christa Dibenedetto
SIC—7373; *Computer network system integration, including LANs & WANs, custom software development & IT consulting services*
Employs—12; Estab.—1999
Distrib.—Intl.
Privately owned corporation

**NEW ENTRY**
**FIBRENETICS, INC.**
2 Cutters Dock Rd. (07095)
**Phone—(732) 636-5670**
Fax—(732) 636-6624
www.fibglass.com
Email—info@fibglass.com
Owner—Herbert Segars
SIC—3089; 3498; NAICS—332996; *Fiberglass tanks & metal pipe fabrication*
Employs—10; Estab.—1970
Sales—under $500,000
2,000 sq ft site, Distrib.—Regional
Privately owned corporation

**HESS CORP.**
1 Hess Plz. (07095)
**Phone—(732) 750-6000**
Fax—(732) 750-6708
www.hessenergy.com
Email—webmaster@hess.com
Pres., Mktg. & Refining—F. Borden Walker
CIO—Jeff Steinhorn
V-P., Hum. Res.—David Goodes
Dir., Mktg. & Research, Comms.—Lorrie Hecker
Coordinator—Judy Giordano
SIC—2911; NAICS—324110; *Petroleum refining*
Employs—925
Sales—over $1Bil
Distrib.—Local
Publicly owned corporation
Parent co.—Hess Corp., New York, NY
Phone—(212) 997-8500
See Parent Co. Section for full profile.

**INTELLIGENT SECURITY SYSTEMS**
1480 U.S. Highway 9 N., Ste. 202 (07095)
**Phone—(732) 855-1111**
Fax—(732) 855-1175
www.isscctv.com
Email—info@isscctv.com
CFO—Boris Kalk
COO—Aluisio Figueiredo
IT Mgr.—Eugene Beytenbrod
Off. Mgr.—Mari Robert
SIC—7372; 3663; *Analytic software development & security surveillance & control systems for networked digital video & audio recording, video image pattern processing & digital data transmission*
Employs—180; Estab.—1996
4,606 sq ft site, Distrib.—Intl.
Privately owned corporation

**†KESSLER INDUSTRIES, INC.**
500 Green St. (07095)
**Phone—(973) 684-2130**
National—(800) 526-5104
Fax—(973) 684-0180
www.ksdusa.com
Email—hr@ksdusa.com
Pres.—Neil Kessler
V-P., GM—Tim Hagan
V-P., Opers.—John Streppone
V-P., Fin.—Douglas Goudsward
SIC—5051; *Distributor of steel & PVC pipe, copper tubing, PEX tubing, fittings & accessories & plumbing ware; Brand name—American Standard; Bradford White; Delta; Pex pipe and fittings; Copper pipe and fittings; Steel pipe; Insinkerator*
Employs—65; Estab.—1951
Sales—over $120Mil
1,000,000 sq ft site, Distrib.—National
Privately owned sub-S corp.
AKA: Kessler Sales & Distribution

**MAN DIESEL & TURBO**
2 Amboy Ave., Bldg. 2 (07095)
**Phone—(732) 582-8200**
Fax—(732) 582-0032
www.mandieselturbo.us.com
Email—primeserv-nyc@mandieselturbo.com
GM—Angel Colon Perez
Expense Admn.—Zoy Muja
SIC—3511; 3599; *Divisional headquarters & rebuilt rotating turbine equipment & general machining job shop*
Employs—22; Estab.—2008
Sales—$5Mil-$10Mil (est)
42,000 sq ft site,

**MAUSER USA LLC**
14 Convery Blvd. (07095)
**Phone—(732) 634-6000**
Fax—(732) 634-2927

www.mausergroup.com
Email—info.us@mausergroup.com
Plt. Mgr.—Dennis Mullin
Plt. Supt.—Giovanni Balsano
SIC—3412; NAICS—332439; *Steel drums*
Employs—100; Estab.—1950
Sales—$20Mil-$35Mil
120,000 sq ft site, Distrib.—Intl.
Publicly owned corporation
ISO rating—9001
Parent co.—MAUSER USA LLC, East Brunswick, NJ
Phone—(732) 353-7000
See Parent Co. Section for full profile.

**PHIL'S SIGN SHOP**
55 Cutters Dock Rd. (07095)
**Phone—(732) 726-1555**
Fax—(732) 726-1555
www.philssignshop.com
Email—philssign1@gmail.com
Owner—Peter Starlin
SIC—3993; *Wooden, plastic & aluminum interior, exterior, truck & boat signs & vinyl & painted lettering*
Employs—2; Estab.—1972
Sales—under $500,000
400 sq ft site, Distrib.—Regional
Sole ownership

**STONE MOUNTAIN PRINTING**
74 Main St., Ste. 1 (07095)
**Phone—(732) 634-4444**
Fax—(732) 634-4415
www.smprinting.com
Email—steve@smprinting.com
Pres.—Steve Steinberg
Secy-Treas.—Hank Steinberg
Cust. Serv. Rep.—Anna Lopez
SIC—2759; 3993; 3089; NAICS—323100; *Commercial & digital printing, graphic design, signage, promotional gifts & packaging supplies*
Employs—8; Estab.—1985
Sales—$1Mil
7,000 sq ft site, Distrib.—Local
Privately owned corporation

**WOODBRIDGE MACHINE & TOOL CO., INC.**
259 Bergen St. (07095)
**Phone—(732) 634-0179**
Fax—(732) 602-0922
Pres.—Steve Sepa
SIC—3599; *Precision machining job shop*
Employs—7; Estab.—1947
Sales—under $500,000
Distrib.—Regional
Privately owned corporation

**WOODBRIDGE MONUMENT FACTORY, INC.**
10 Main St., Ste. K (07095)
**Phone—(732) 634-1521**
National—(800) 729-0582
Fax—(732) 750-0120
www.sprungmonuments.com
Email—info@sprungmonuments.com
Pres.—Adam Sprung
Supervisor—John Lange
SIC—3281; NAICS—327991; *Burial monument engraving*
Employs—6
Sales—$500,000-$1Mil (est)
Distrib.—Regional
Privately owned corporation
AKA: Sprung Monument Corp.

**WOODBRIDGE PRINTING CENTER**
1201 U.S. Highway 9 S. (07095)
**Phone—(732) 855-1996**
Fax—(732) 855-7645
www.woodbridgeprintingcenter.com
Email—njprinter@aol.com
Owner & Pres.—Frank Racz
Fin. Mgr.—Anna Racz

GEOGRAPHICAL

## Woodbridge—(cont.)

SIC—2752; 2759; NAICS—
323122; Offset & digital printing
Employs—7; Estab.—1977
Sales—$500,000-$1Mil
15,000 sq ft site, Distrib.—
Regional
Sole ownership

---

## Woodbury
(Gloucester—S.W.)

### BELLIA BUSINESS PRODUCTS & SERVICES, INC.

1047 N. Broad St. (08096)
Phone—(856) 845-2234
Fax—(856) 845-1180
www.bellia.net
Email—retail@bellia.net
Pres.—Thomas Bellia
Sales Mgr.—Andrew Bellia
Prodn. Mgr.—Sal Bellia
Hum. Res. Mgr.—Fran Bellia
SIC—2789; 2759; NAICS—
323121; Spiral & GBC binding &
commercial printing
Employs—30; Estab.—1983
Sales—$1Mil-$2.5Mil (est)
6,000 sq ft site, Distrib.—Local
Privately owned corporation
AKA: Bellia Enterprises

NEW ENTRY

### DOMICO UPHOLSTERY CO.

1337 Delsea Dr. (08096)
Phone—(856) 853-8181
Fax—(856) 853-8029
www.domicointeriors.com
Owner—Dennis Domico
SIC—2599; Wooden upholstered
furniture for the restaurant
industry
Employs—4; Estab.—1985
Sales—$500,000-$1Mil
2,500 sq ft site, Distrib.—Intl.
Privately owned corporation

### †DORNISCH ENTERPRISES, INC.

112 Cromwell Ct. (08096)
Phone—(856) 863-1225
National—(800) 593-2893
Fax—(856) 863-1208
www.worldwidesafebrokers.com
Email—info@
worldwidesafebrokers.com
Pres.—Edward C. Dornisch
V-P., CFO—Mildred A. Dornisch
SIC—5044; Distributor of
commercial & residential safes &
insulated filing systems; Brand
name—A & B Safe; Fire King;
Meilink; Mutual; Sentry; National
Safe; Hayman; Keystone
Employs—3; Estab.—1996
Distrib.—Intl.
Privately owned corporation
AKA: World Wide Safe Brokers

### FERRETT PRINTING, INC.

468 Warwick Rd. (08096)
Phone—(856) 686-4896
Fax—(856) 686-4834
www.ferrettprinting.com
Email—ferrettprinting@verizon.net
Owner—Nicholas Ferrett
SIC—2759; NAICS—323100;
Commercial printing
Employs—1; Estab.—2001
Sales—under $500,000
Distrib.—National
Privately owned corporation

### GARIEL SCREEN PRINTING

729 Mantua Pike (08096)
Phone—(856) 848-3240
National—(800) 442-7435
Fax—(856) 384-8549
www.gariel.com
Email—info@gariel.com
Owner—Gary Lizzi

Hum. Res., IT & Opers. Mgr.—
Margie Lizzi
SIC—2396; 2395; T-shirt screen
printing & embroidery
Employs—7; Estab.—1978
Sales—under $500,000
Distrib.—National
Sole ownership

### HENRY CORP., E. P.

201 Park Ave., P.O. Box 615
(08096)
Phone—(856) 845-6200
National—(800) 444-3679
Fax—(856) 845-0023
www.ephenry.com
Email—info@ephenry.com
CEO—James C. Henry III
Pres.—Eric Long
Ex. V-P., Sales & Mktg.—Leonard
Valentino
V-P., Fin.—James Nash
Dir., Mktg.—Marianne Anzaldo
SIC—3272; Corporate
headquarters & architectural
concrete products, including
pavers & cast stone pavers,
permeable paving systems,
retaining walls, profile &
standard concrete masonry units
& cast veneer stone; Brand
name—Cast Veneer Stone;
Coventry Pavers; Coventry Wall
Systems; DevonStone Cast
Stone Pavers; Eco Paver;
SilkStone Pavers Walls;
BishopStone; GloucesterStone;
Highland Wall
Employs—150; Estab.—1903
Distrib.—Regional
Privately owned sub-S corp.

### K B CUSTOM INTERIORS

10-B Greenwood Ave. (08096)
Phone—(856) 845-9112
Fax—(856) 845-9118
Gen. Ptnr.—Kurt Lobach
Ptnr.—Bill Haynes
SIC—2431; NAICS—321900;
Architectural millwork
Employs—2; Estab.—1987
Sales—under $500,000
Distrib.—Regional
Privately owned partnership

### MONOGRAM SHOPPE

5 S. Broad St. (08096)
Phone—(856) 845-9299
Email—monogramshoppe@
yahoo.com
Ptnr.—Dottie McQuade
Ptnr.—Dottie Lange
SIC—2395; Apparel
monogramming
Employs—2; Estab.—1984
Sales—under $500,000
Distrib.—Local
Privately owned corporation

### MORRIS GRAPHICS, INC.

660 N. Broad St. (08096)
Phone—(856) 845-4980
Fax—(856) 853-5787
www.morrisgraphics.com
Pres.—Jeff Morris
V-P.—Theresa Morris
Acct. Exec.—Mike Morris
SIC—2759; 2752; NAICS—
323100; Short-run digital & long
run offset printing, including
mailing lists & direct mail
processing
Employs—5; Estab.—1981
Sales—$500,000-$1Mil
9,000 sq ft site, Distrib.—National
Privately owned sub-S corp.

### NEW ROSE, INC.

1500 Almonesson Rd., Ste. 8
(08096)
Phone—(856) 812-0509
www.embroidme-deptford.com
Pres.—Rosemary Jones

SIC—2395; 2396; 2759;
Embroidery & apparel, garment,
textile & promotional item scrennn
printing
Employs—3; Estab.—2005
Sales—under $500,000 (est)
1,000 sq ft site, Distrib.—Local
Privately owned corporation
DBA: EmbroidMe

### ONE TWO THREE, INC.

537 Mantua Ave., Ste. B, P.O. Box
123 (08096)
Phone—(856) 251-1238
National—(800) 276-1232
Fax—(856) 251-1540
www.easyas1-2-3.com
Email—orders@easyas1-2-3.com
Pres.—Randall Rigley
Art Dir.—Angela Latini
Prodn. Mgr.—Bob Malloy
SIC—2759; NAICS—323100;
Commercial printing
Employs—15; Estab.—1992
3,000 sq ft site, Distrib.—National
Privately owned corporation

### SIR SPEEDY PRINTING CENTERS

39 S. Broad St. (08096)
Phone—(856) 251-0220
Fax—(856) 251-1329
www.sirspeedy.com/woodbury
Email—inbox@sirspeedywdby.com
Pres.—Michael Kelly
V-P.—Patricia Kelly
Prod. Mgr.—Mike Kelly, Jr.
SIC—2759; NAICS—323100;
Instant & digital printing
Employs—5; Estab.—1996
2,000 sq ft site, Distrib.—Local
Limited Liability Company
AKA: Kelly Graphics, LLC

### SOUTH JERSEY TIMES

309 S. Broad St., P.O. Box 639
(08096)
Phone—(856) 845-3300
Fax—(856) 384-8729
www.nj.com
Email—trutledge@
southjerseymedia.com
Publisher & Ex. Editor—Joseph P.
Owens
Dir., Hum. Res.—Tina Rutledge
MIS Mgr.—Ed Murray
Cred. Mgr.—Ellen Moore
SIC—2711; Newspaper printing;
Brand name—South Jersey
Times
Employs—125; Estab.—1897
18,000 sq ft site, Distrib.—Local
Privately owned corporation

### SPECIALTY CASTINGS, INC.

42 Curtis Ave. (08096)
Phone—(856) 845-3105
Pres., CFO, MIS Mgr.—John
Cowgill
Fin. & Off. Mgr.—Daniel Cowgill
SIC—3089; Polyurethane roller
castings
Employs—7
Sales—$500,000-$1Mil
4,800 sq ft site, Distrib.—Intl.

### WILLIAM B. SNELBAKER & SON

Div. of White Valley Memorials
43 Cooper St. (08096)
Phone—(856) 845-0634
Fax—(856) 384-0073
www.monumentsofdistinction.com
GM—Treva Oster
SIC—3281; Stone monuments
Employs—1; Estab.—1985
Distrib.—Local
Sole ownership
Parent co.—White Valley
Memorials, Berlin, NJ
Phone—(856) 767-3030
See Parent Co. Section for full profile.

## Woodbury Heights
(Gloucester—S.W.)

### CHAMBERS SHEET METAL, BILL

371 N. Glassboro Rd., P.O. Box
172 (08097)
Phone—(856) 848-4774
Fax—(856) 845-5166
Owner—Bill Chambers
Off. Mgr.—Ann Chambers
SIC—3444; Sheet metal
fabrication
Employs—3; Estab.—1971
Sales—under $500,000
Distrib.—Local
Sole ownership

### CONCORD TRUSS CO.

692 S. Evergreen Ave. (08097)
Phone—(856) 845-3848
Fax—(856) 845-0831
www.concordtruss.com
Email—contact@concordtruss.com
Pres., CFO—Richard Phalines
V-P.—John Gligor
Hum. Res. Coord.—Mary Stewart
SIC—2439; NAICS—321200;
Wooden trusses
Employs—60; Estab.—1977
Sales—$11Mil-$25Mil
40,000 sq ft site, Distrib.—
Regional
Privately owned corporation

### ELLENBY TECHNOLOGIES, INC.

412 Grandview Ave. (08097)
Phone—(856) 848-2020
Fax—(856) 848-7080
www.ellenbytech.com
Email—bobdobbins212@
ellenbytech.com
CEO—Bob Dobbins
Dir., Mktg.—Otto Lohse
MIS Mgr.—Scott Barnes
SIC—3679; 3829; 3581; NAICS—
333311; Contract electronic
manufacturing of vending
electronics, including electronic
controllers & smart safes,
reverse engineering, control
board & LED lighting
assemblies, subassemblies &
retrofit kits; Brand name—
CashTrak Electronic Safes
Employs—53; Estab.—1989
Sales—$5Mil-$10Mil
50,000 sq ft site, Distrib.—Intl.
Privately owned sub-S corp.

### EXCEL COLOR GRAPHICS, INC.

207 W. Jersey Ave. (08097)
Phone—(856) 848-3345
Fax—(856) 848-3233
Email—excelcolor207@cs.com
Pres.—Jean Paul Bonnette
V-P.—Warren Sipple
Sales Mgr.—Linda Bonnette
SIC—2752; 2791; NAICS—
323122; Offset, instant &
commercial printing &
typesetting
Employs—5; Estab.—1988
Sales—$500,000-$1Mil
Distrib.—Local
Privately owned corporation

### SIGN BOY, LLC

370 N. Glassboro Rd. (08097)
Phone—(856) 384-2937
Fax—(856) 384-2881
www.signboyusa.com
Email—signboy@signboyusa.com
Pres.—Scott Phillip
SIC—3993; Interior & exterior
signs
Employs—1; Estab.—1990
16,000 sq ft site, Distrib.—National
Privately owned corporation

## Woodcliff Lake
### (Bergen—N.E.)

**BMW OF NORTH AMERICA, LLC (H Q)**
300 Chestnut Ridge Rd. (07677)
Mail addr: P.O. Box 1227, Westwood (07675-1227)
**Phone—(201) 307-4000**
National—(800) 526-0818
Fax—(201) 307-4095
www.bmwgroupna.com
Email—customerrelations@bmwusa.com
Chrm., CEO—Ludwig Willisch
Ex. V-P., Opers.—J. Chris Koenders
Ex. V-P., Cust. Rels. & Sales Channel Dev.—Peter Miles
V-P., Mktg.—Trudy Hardy
SIC—3711; 3713; 3751; NAICS—336211; *Company headquarters; automobiles, passenger cars, light trucks & motorcycles*
Employs—1000; Estab.—1975
Sales—$99Bil
Distrib.—National
Privately owned corporation

**CAST, INC. (H Q)**
11 Stonewall Ct. (07677)
**Phone—(201) 391-8300**
Fax—(201) 391-8694
www.cast-inc.com
Email—info@cast-inc.com
Pres.—Hal Barbour
COO—Nikos Zervas
Sr. V-P.—Bill Finch
V-P., Sales—Meredith Lucky
V-P., IP & Opers.—Newton Abdalla
SIC—7372; *Corporate headquarters; semiconductor software development for electronic systems designers (mfg. done at a company-owned facility in Boston, MA); Brand name—CAST™*
Employs—50; Estab.—1993
Privately owned corporation

**EISAI, INC. (H Q)**
100 Tice Blvd. (07677)
**Phone—(201) 692-1100**
National—(888) 992-8747
Fax—(201) 692-1804
www.eisai.com
Email—neriman_botas@eisai.com
Chrm. & CEO—Yuji Matsue
Pres., COO—Shaji Procida
Pres., Bus. Dev.—Alex Scott
Sr. V-P., Hum. Res.—Neriman Botas
SIC—2834; NAICS—325412; *Corporate headquarters; pharmaceuticals*
Employs—800
Sales—$1Mil-$5Mil
Publicly owned corporation

**I.D. SYSTEMS, INC.**
123 Tice Blvd., Ste. 101 (07677-7671)
**Phone—(201) 996-9000**
National—(866) 410-0152
Fax—(201) 996-9144
www.id-systems.com
Email—info@id-systems.com
Chrm., Pres. & CEO—Kenneth S. Ehrman
CFO—Ned Mavrommatis
COO—Norm Ellis
CTO—Michael L. Ehrman
Ex. V-P., Opers.—Curt Lloyd
Ex. V-P., Mktg. & Prod. Dev.—Todd Felker
SIC—7373; 7372; 3669; NAICS—541512; *Wireless systems integration & software development for tracking, managing & monitoring enterprise assets, including industrial vehicles, airport ground support & handling equipment & transportation assets; Brand name—Vehicle Asset Communicator; PowerFleet; PowerBox; AvRamp; SafeNav; RentalFleet; VeriWise; didBox*
Employs—100; Estab.—1993
Distrib.—Intl.
Publicly owned corporation

**OPPENHEIM PLASTICS CO., INC.**
90 Broadway (07677)
Mail addr: P.O. Box 310, Saddle River (07458-0310)
**Phone—(201) 391-3811**
Fax—(201) 391-4811
www.oppenheimplastics.com
Email—sales@oppenheimplastics.com
Pres.—Florence Oppenheim
SIC—3089; *Plastic injection molded rigid boxes & containers*
Employs—30; Estab.—1950
Sales—$2.5Mil-$5Mil
Distrib.—Intl.
Privately owned corporation

**PAR PHARMACEUTICAL COS., INC.**
300 Tice Blvd. (07677)
**Phone—(201) 802-4000**
Fax—(201) 802-4600
www.parpharm.com
Email—steve.montalto@parpharm.com
CEO—Paul Campanelli
Pres.—Thomas Haughey
Ex. V-P., CFO—Michael A. Tropiano
Sr. V-P., Hum. Res.—Steve Montalto
SIC—2834; NAICS—325412; *Corporate headquarters & pharmaceuticals; Brand name—Megace ES; Nascobal*
Employs—125; Estab.—1978
Company-wide: 650
Sales—$750Mil-$1Bil
Distrib.—National
Publicly owned corporation

**STRATIVA PHARMACEUTICALS (H Q)**
Div. of Par Pharmaceutical Cos., Inc.
300 Tice Blvd. (07677)
**Phone—(201) 802-4000**
www.strativapharma.com
Pres.—Paul Campanelli
V-P., Sales—Rick Painter
V-P., Mktg.—John Ameres
Sr. Dir., Alliance Mgmt.—Rob Campanelli
SIC—2834; *Company headquarters; pharmaceuticals; Brand name—Megace®; Nascobat®*
Employs—150; Estab.—2007
Sales—$50Mil-$100Mil (est)
Publicly owned corporation
Parent co.—Par Pharmaceutical Cos., Inc., Woodcliff Lake, NJ
Phone—(201) 802-4000
See Parent Co. Section for full profile.

**SYNCSORT, INC.**
50 Tice Blvd., Ste. 250 (07677)
**Phone—(201) 930-9700**
www.syncsort.com
Email—info@syncsort.com
CEO—Lonnie Jaffe
SIC—7372; *Downloadable data integration & data protection software development*
Employs—10; Estab.—1968
Privately owned corporation

## Woodland Park
### (Union—N.E.)

**ACE METAL KRAFT CO., INC.**
815 McBride Ave. (07424)
**Phone—(973) 278-6605**
Fax—(973) 278-5894
www.acemetalkraft.com
Email—gert@acemetalkraft.com
Pres.—Richard Zega
V-P.—John Lamanna
Administrator—Gert Bouchard
SIC—3499; *Precision metal fabrication*
Employs—9; Estab.—1959
6,400 sq ft site, Distrib.—Regional
Privately owned sub-S corp.

**ACME PLASTICS, INC.**
222 Browertown Rd., P.O. Box 806 (07424)
**Phone—(973) 256-6666**
National—(800) 234-1991
Fax—(973) 256-4107
www.acmeplastics.com
Email—salesnj@acmeplastics.com
Pres.—Lawrence Levinson
V-P., Sales—Rick Levinson
Acct. Mgr.—Steven McGinnis
SIC—3089; *Corporate headquarters & plastic products*
Employs—100; Estab.—1979
Sales—$10Mil-$25Mil
Distrib.—National
Privately owned corporation

**BMB FASTENERS, INC.**
86 Lackawanna Ave., Ste. 208 (07424-3803)
Mail addr: 230 Route 206, Ste. 404, Flanders (07836)
**Phone—(973) 256-4010**
National—(800) 635-9227
Fax—(973) 256-0032
www.bmbfasteners.com
Email—sales@bmbfasteners.com
Owner & Pres.—Larry Malone
V-P., Opers.—Jay Minichino
SIC—3451; 3423; 3545; 3965; NAICS—332721; *Screws, fasteners, bolts, nuts & washers; Brand name—Micro Plastic; StayFast; EZ Lok; Amaton; Raf; Ideal Fasteners; Superior Washer; Hindley; Alcoa; Tridair; Kato; Lamatech*
Employs—over 8; Estab.—1976
Sales—over $1.5Mil
6,600 sq ft site, Distrib.—National
Privately owned sub-S corp.
ISO rating—9001:2000

**BROMILOW'S CHOCOLATES, INC.**
350 Rifle Camp Rd. (07424)
**Phone—(973) 684-1496**
Fax—(973) 345-0564
www.bromilow.com
Email—sweetspot@bromilow.com
Pres., CEO—Thomas Stewart
Secy.-Treas.—Ida Stewart
SIC—2064; 2066; NAICS—311300; *Homemade chocolates*
Employs—12; Estab.—1957
Distrib.—Local
Privately owned sub-S corp.

**CENTURY BATHWORKS, INC.**
250 Lackawanna Ave. (07424-2962)
**Phone—(973) 785-4290**
(800) 524-2578
Fax—(973) 785-0777
www.centurybathworks.com
Email—info@centurybathworks.com
Pres.—Michael MacMillan
Sales Mgr., Natl.—John Spazante
SIC—3231; NAICS—327215; *Framed & frameless glass shower & tub door enclosures & standard & custom size medicine cabinets with or without electric option; Brand name—Glasstec; Brassline; Elite; Centec; Select; Lucette; Crest; Caprice; Century Bathworks Inc.*
Employs—125; Estab.—1946
Sales—$23Mil
100,000 sq ft site, Distrib.—National
Privately owned corporation
Also see: Screens & Fabricated Metals Corp., 1265 McBride Ave.

**COMMUNITY NEWSPAPERS & MAGAZINES OF NORTH JERSEY MEDIA GROUP**
Div. of North Jersey Media Group, Inc.
1 Garret Mountain Plz., P.O. Box 471 (07424)
**Phone—(973) 569-7000**
Fax—(973) 569-7268
www.northjersey.com
Email—njmg@northjersey.com
V-P., Publisher—Janice Friedman
V-P., Publisher—Michael Lawson
Pres.—Stephen Borg
V-P., Prodn.—Glenn Garvie
Dir., Dist.—Doug Seiferling
Dir., Creative Svcs.—John Flynn
SIC—2711; 2721; 2741; *Daily print & online newspaper & monthly print & online magazine publishing*
Employs—132
Sales—$10Mil-$25Mil
Distrib.—Local
Privately owned corporation
Parent co.—North Jersey Media Group, Inc., Woodland Park, NJ
Phone—(973) 569-7000
See Parent Co. Section for full profile.

**CYTEC INDUSTRIES, INC. (H Q)**
5 Garret Mountain Plz. (07424-3317)
**Phone—(973) 357-3100**
National—(800) 652-6013
Fax—(973) 357-3058
www.cytec.com
Email—custinfo@cytec.com
Chrm., Pres. & CEO—Shane D. Fleming
Pres., Engineered Matls.—William Wood
Pres., Specialty Chemicals—Michael Rodossich
V-P., CFO—Daniel G. Darazsdi
V-P., Gen. Counsel & Secy.—Roy Smith
V-P., Hum. Res.—Regina Charles
V-P., Bus. & Corp. Dev.—William N. Avrin
SIC—2899; *Corporate headquarters; specialty chemicals & materials*
Employs—499
Sales—$3.2Bil
Publicly owned corporation

**ELLIOTT GLASS CO., INC.**
192 Lackawanna Ave., Ste. 103 (07424-2995)
**Phone—(973) 256-8098**
Fax—(973) 256-5339
www.elliottglass.com
Email—elliottglassco@verizon.net
Manager—Kevin Elliott
SIC—3231; 3211; NAICS—327215; *Glass fabrication*
Employs—6; Estab.—1964
Sales—under $1Mil
400 sq ft site, Distrib.—Regional
Privately owned corporation

GEOGRAPHICAL

## Woodland Park—(cont.)

**†FUSECO, INC.**
Div. of Fuseco Inc.
86 Lackawanna Ave., Ste. 240
 (07424-3804)
**Phone—(973) 894-3727**
National—(888) 840-3873
Fax—(973) 894-3731
www.fuseco.com
Email—fnj@fuseco.com
Br. Mgr.—Bill Engel
SIC—5063; *Distributor of fuses,
 fuse blocks & distribution blocks;
 Brand name—Busmann; Ferraz;
 Marathon; Littelfuse; GE; S&C;
 Mersen*
Employs—5; Estab.—1978
Sales—$500,000-$1Mil
4,500 sq ft site, Distrib.—National
Privately owned corporation
Parent co.—Fuseco Inc., Dallas,
 TX
 Phone—(214) 357-6676
 See Parent Co. Section for full profile.

**GOURMET FOODS, INC.**
25 Andrews Dr. (07424)
**Phone—(973) 237-1776**
Fax—(973) 237-1788
www.gourmetfoodsinc.com
Email—gourmetfoodsinc@
 gourmetfoodsinc.com
Pres.—Alfred Fuchs
Hum. Res. & IT Mgr.—Nibia
 Perdomo
Off. Mgr.—Rose Wallace
SIC—2099; 2092; NAICS—
 311712; *Gourmet canapes,
 vegetables, sushi & seafood*
Employs—50; Estab.—1991
Sales—$5Mil-$10Mil (est)
Distrib.—Regional
Privately owned corporation
Parent co.—Gourmet Foods, Inc.,
 Rancho Dominguez, CA
 Phone—(310) 632-3300
 See Parent Co. Section for full profile.

**KERN PRINTERS & STATIONERS**
86 Lackawanna Ave., Unit 105
 (07424)
**Phone—(201) 226-0270**
Fax—(201) 226-0271
www.kernservices.net
Email—office@officekern.com
Pres.—Thomas Mandel
GM—James Best
SIC—2752; 2759; NAICS—
 323100; *Offset & digital printing
 & graphic design & direct mail
 services*
Employs—5; Estab.—1948
Sales—$500,000-$1Mil
Distrib.—Local
Privately owned corporation

**NEW JERSEY METER CO.**
1 Hazel St. (07424)
**Phone—(973) 345-6200**
Fax—(973) 279-5958
www.njmeter.com
Email—info@njmeter.com
Pres.—Anthony Abbate
Off. Mgr. & Bookkeeper—Elaine
 Valvano
SIC—3569; 3443; *Dry air
 separators & condensate drains*
Employs—5; Estab.—1985
Sales—$500,000-$1Mil
Distrib.—Intl.
Privately owned corporation

**NORTH JERSEY MEDIA GROUP, INC.**
1 Garret Mountain Plz., P.O. Box
 471 (07424)
**Phone—(973) 569-7000**
Fax—(973) 569-7268
www.northjersey.com
Email—njmg@northjersey.com
Chrm. of the Board—Malcolm A.
 Borg
Pres.—Stephen A. Borg
CFO—Thomas G. Heffernan
V-P., Gen. Counsel—Jennifer A.
 Borg
V-P., Editor—Martin Gottlieb
V-P., Circ. & Mfg.—Robert Konig
V-P., Hum. Res.—Susan Beard
V-P., Internet Tech.—Yuri Demidov
Dir., Sales, Corp. & Natl.—Richard
 Colandrea
Dir., Mktg.—Maggie Grande
SIC—2711; 2721; 2741; 2759;
 NAICS—323100; *Corporate
 headquarters & daily & weekly
 newspaper publishing &
 magazine & specialty
 publication publishing &
 commercial printing; Brand
 name—The Record; Herald
 News; NorthJersey.com; (201)
 Magazine; Bergen.com;
 BergenCounty.com*
Employs—425; Estab.—1895
Sales—over $175Mil
Distrib.—Regional
Privately owned corporation

**PREMIER COMPACTION SYSTEMS**
264 Lackawanna Ave. *(07424)*
**Phone—(201) 819-9564**
 (800) 877-7475
 (973) 305-6646
National—(800) 872-7448
Fax—(973) 305-8424
www.pcs-green.com
Email—john@pfmgreen.com
Pres.—Robert Frustaci
V-P.—Bruce Klarberg
Application Engr.—John Frustaci
SIC—3589; NAICS—333319;
 *Refuse compactors &
 containers, recycling & chute
 sanitizing systems, hopper doors
 & trash sorters; Brand name—
 Hico-Hivolex; Chutes
 International; American Chute*
Employs—25; Estab.—1993
Sales—$7Mil
30,000 sq ft site, Distrib.—National
Privately owned corporation

**RECORD, THE**
Div. of North Jersey Media Group,
 Inc.
1 Garret Mountain Plz., P.O. Box
 471 (07424)
**Phone—(973) 569-7770**
National—(888) 473-2673
Fax—(201) 457-2520
www.northjersey.com
Email—newsroom@northjersey.com
IT Mgr.—Greg Hoffman
Hum. Res. Mgr.—Marisol Jaquez
Asst. Editorial Mgr.—Douglas
 Clancy
SIC—2711; *Daily newspaper
 publishing*
Employs—200; Estab.—1999
Sales—over $1Bil
Distrib.—Regional
Privately owned corporation
AKA: North Jersey Media Group
Parent co.—North Jersey Media
 Group, Inc., Woodland Park, NJ
 Phone—(973) 569-7000
 See Parent Co. Section for full profile.

**†SCALES INDUSTRIAL
 TECHNOLOGIES, INC OF NJ**
Div. of Scales Industrial
 Technologies, Inc.
185 Lackawanna Ave. (07424)
**Phone—(973) 890-1010**
Fax—(973) 890-7343
www.scalesindtech.com
Email—rhohn@scalesair.com
GM—Rich Hohn
Sales Mgr.—Jim Osmun
Serv. Mgr.—Bob Lamanna
SIC—5084; *Distributor of air & gas
 compressors, parts & service;
 Brand name—Gardner-Denver;
 Quincy; Kobelco; Cameron;
 Hankison; Parker*
Employs—45; Estab.—1966
Distrib.—National
Privately owned corporation
Parent co.—Scales Industrial
 Technologies, Inc., Carle Place,
 NY
 Phone—(516) 248-9096
 See Parent Co. Section for full profile.

**SCREENS & FABRICATED METALS
 CORP.**
1265 McBride Ave., P.O. Box 647
 (07424)
**Phone—(973) 785-1414**
National—(800) 850-7140
Fax—(973) 785-0378
www.windowscreens.com
Email—sfabricate@aol.com
Pres.—Mike McMillan
V-P.—Phil Bochune
Bookkeeper—Michelle Cryan
SIC—3442; 3499; 3543; NAICS—
 332321; *Screen & storm doors,
 security screens, window
 guards, storm panels, porch
 enclosures, screening supplies,
 child guards & screens & metal
 fabrication, tool, die, welding &
 prototype work*
Employs—50; Estab.—1950
Sales—$1Mil-$2.5Mil
35,000 sq ft site, Distrib.—Intl.
Privately owned sub-S corp.
Also see: Century Bathworks, Inc.,
 250 Lackawanna Ave.

**WAYNETODAY**
Div. of North Jersey Media Group,
 Inc.
1 Garret Mountain Plz., P.O. Box
 471 (07424)
**Phone—(973) 569-7393**
Fax—(973) 569-7377
www.northjersey.com
Email—today@northjersey.com
Publisher—Mike Lawson
Editor—Christa Limone
SIC—2741; *Weekly northern New
 Jersey newsletter publishing*
Employs—5
Sales—under $500,000
Distrib.—Local
Privately owned corporation
Parent co.—North Jersey Media
 Group, Inc., Woodland Park, NJ
 Phone—(973) 569-7000
 See Parent Co. Section for full profile.

## Woodstown
(Salem—S.W.)

**PERKINS CO., INC., P. W.**
221 Commissioners Pike (08098)
**Phone—(856) 769-3525**
Fax—(856) 769-2177
www.decarbite.com
Email—pwpco@mindspring.com
Pres.—Darlene A. Perkins
Plt. Mgr.—Charles B. Perkins
SIC—2835; NAICS—325400;
 *Research laboratory reagents,
 including granular CO2
 absorbent; Brand name—
 Decarbite*
Employs—4; Estab.—1970
Sales—under $500,000
Distrib.—National
Privately owned corporation
ISO rating—9001:2008

**SOUTH JERSEY FARMERS
 EXCHANGE, INC.**
101 East Ave. (08098)
**Phone—(856) 769-0062**
Fax—(856) 769-0343
Email—sjfe@mindspring.com
Pres.—Lee Williams
SIC—2875; NAICS—325314;
 *Fertilizer blending*
Employs—6; Estab.—1903
Distrib.—Local
Privately owned corporation

**WOODSTOWN ICE & COAL CO.**
50 E. Grant St., P.O. Box 285
 (08098)
**Phone—(856) 769-0069**
Fax—(856) 769-0071
www.woodstownice-coal.com
Email—wicossr@magpage.com
Owner—Doug Macaluso
Bookkeeper—Kathy Aders
SIC—2048; *Livestock feed*
Employs—7; Estab.—1975
Sales—$1Mil-$2.5Mil
Distrib.—Local
Privately owned corporation

## Woolwich Township
(Gloucester—S.W.)

**DAMASK'S CANDIES, INC.**
2255 Highway 322 (08085)
**Phone—(856) 467-1661**
Fax—(856) 467-1661
Owner—Douglas Damask
Bookkeeper—Sharon Damask
SIC—2064; NAICS—311300;
 *Candy*
Employs—5; Estab.—1915
Sales—under $500,000
Distrib.—Local
Sole ownership

**GARMAR INDUSTRIES, INC.**
1625 Route 322, P.O. Box 460
 (08085)
**Phone—(856) 241-9700**
National—(800) 856-9663
Fax—(856) 241-2810
www.garmarlumber.com
Email—garmarlumber@
 earthlink.net
V-P.—Jerry Bernard
MIS Mgr.—Aimee Morton
Fin. Mgr.—Howard Bernard
SIC—2421; 2435; 2436; NAICS—
 321211; *Dimensional lumber,
 crating stock, plywood, pallet
 lumber & collated nails*
Employs—33; Estab.—1972
Distrib.—National
Privately owned corporation

**GRASSO FOODS, INC.**
2111 Kings Hwy., P.O. Box 127
 (08085)
**Phone—(856) 467-2222**
Fax—(856) 467-5474
Pres.—Janet Schumann
Hum. Res. Mgr.—Lily Williams
Bookkeeper—Melody Lloyd
SIC—2037; NAICS—311411;
 *Frozen bell peppers*
Employs—150; Estab.—1974
Distrib.—Local
Privately owned corporation

**THE NEW TOWN PRESS**
421 Stone Meeting House Rd.
 (08085)
**Phone—(856) 467-3113**
Fax—(856) 467-3364
www.newtownpress.com
Email—editor@newtownpress.com
Owner, Publisher, Fin. & MIS
 Mgr.—Karen E. Viereck
SIC—2711; NAICS—323122;
 *Monthly newspaper publishing*
Employs—1; Estab.—1971
Sales—under $500,000
Distrib.—Local
Privately owned sub-S corp.

## Wrightstown
(Burlington—S.E.)

**MARANATHA CERAMIC TILE & MARBLE, INC.**
253 Cookstown New Egypt Rd. (08562)
**Phone—(609) 758-1168**
Fax—(609) 758-1633
www.maranathastairs.com
Email—info@maranathastairs.com
Ptnr. & Pres.—Thomas Raab
Ptnr. & Treas.—Patricia Raab
SIC—2431; 3499; NAICS—321900; *Manufacturer & distributor of custom wooden interior & metal interior & exterior spiral stairs, railings, circulars, balusters, panels & flares, custom dovetailed kitchen & bathroom cabinetry & furniture; Brand name—Kountry Kraft; Jim Bishop Cabinets; House of Forgings; Enkeboll; Oak Pointe Stair Systems; Old World Millworks; Stair Parts Direct; Woodmark*
Employs—20; Estab.—1983
Distrib.—Regional
Privately owned corporation
DBA: Maranatha Wood Stairs

**SPECIALTY FABRICATORS, LLC**
118 Meany Rd. (08562)
**Phone—(609) 758-6995**
Fax—(609) 758-8130
www.specialtyfabricators.com
Email—specfab@specialtyfabricators.com
Pres.—Edward Symbouras
V-P.—Patricia Symbouras
Hum. Res. & Off. Mgr.—Vicki Anderson
Mfg. Sys. Mgr.—Al Reasoner
Sales Coord.—Susan Cooke
SIC—2542; 2541; *Refrigerated & heated grocery displays & showcases*
Employs—25; Estab.—1994
21,000 sq ft site, Distrib.—National
Limited Liability Company

## Wyckoff
(Bergen—N.E.)

**ALLIEDOP, INC.**
579 Goffle Rd. (07481)
Mail addr.: 1 Emery Ave., Ste. 1, Randolph (07869-1387)
**Phone—(201) 444-7750**
Fax—(201) 612-1323
www.alliedop.com
Email—jschenkman@alliedop.com
Practitioner—Michael Rebarber
SIC—3842; *Orthopedic braces & prosthesis*
Employs—5; Estab.—1981
Sales—$1Mil-$2.5Mil
Distrib.—Local
Privately owned corporation
Parent co.—AlliedOP, Inc., Randolph, NJ
Phone—(973) 328-3340
See Parent Co. Section for full profile.

**BUDD BUILT IN VACUUM CLEANERS**
445 W. Main St. (07481)
**Phone—(201) 891-3010**
Fax—(201) 891-7901
www.buddvac.com
Email—sales@buddvac.com
Pres.—William Schwartz
SIC—3589; 3635; NAICS—333319; *Industrial & household central vacuum cleaners*
Employs—25; Estab.—1965
Sales—$500,000-$1Mil
Distrib.—Local
Privately owned corporation

**CORDES PRINTING, INC.**
460 Braen Ave. (07481)
**Phone—(201) 652-7272**
Fax—(201) 652-1495
www.cordesprinting.com
Email—mark@cordesprinting.com
Pres.—Mark Cordes
SIC—2759; NAICS—323100; *Commercial printing*
Employs—7; Estab.—1975
Sales—$500,000-$1Mil
Distrib.—Regional
Privately owned corporation

**DAF PRODUCTS, INC.**
420 Braen Ave. (07481)
**Phone—(201) 251-1222**
National—(800) 228-9837
Fax—(201) 251-1221
www.dafproducts.com
Pres.—Thomas Palmer
Sales Coord.—Jourdan Jones
SIC—2295; NAICS—313320; *Laminated fabrics for tents, banners & awnings*
Employs—20; Estab.—1999
Distrib.—Intl.
Privately owned corporation

**D'LITE PRODUCTS, INC.**
540 Ravine Ct. (07481)
**Phone—(201) 444-0822**
Fax—(201) 689-0708
www.dlitemagic.com
Email—sales@dlitemagic.com
Pres.—Bill Hennessy
SIC—3944; NAICS—334413; *Magic & novelty products*
Employs—10; Estab.—1996
Distrib.—Intl.
Privately owned corporation

**†DYNACLEAR PACKAGING / PRO PACK, INC.**
500 W. Main St. (07481)
**Phone—(201) 337-1001**
Fax—(201) 337-5001
www.shrinkfilm.com
Email—info@shrinkfilm.com
Chrm., CEO—Peter Quercia
SIC—5084; 5162; *Full-service distributor of custom & standard packaging equipment & supplies, including shrink & stretch wrappers, form, fill & seal machinery, case sealers & packaging films; Brand name—Dynaclear films; Dynaseal packaging machinery; DaVinci packaging machinery; Dynawrap packaging machinery; Vulcan Shrink tunnel systems; Wrapid stretch wrapping machines; Razorpack carton sealers; Dynastrap strapping machinery*
Employs—12; Estab.—1992
25,000 sq ft site, Distrib.—Intl.
Privately owned corporation

**ETHICAL ALTERNATIVE PRODUCTS, LLC**
525 Cedar Hill Ave. (07481)
**Phone—(201) 251-7771**
National—(800) 861-0492
Fax—(201) 612-6921
www.ethicalalternativeproducts.com
Email—info@ethicalalternativeproducts.com
Ptnr.—Gerald Bruno
Ptnr.—Monica McGarry
SIC—2834; 2833; *Company headquarters & pharmaceuticals & dietary supplements (mfg. subcontracted); Brand name—OmniFlex; ThioGel; ThioGel L; Tendonex*
Employs—5; Estab.—2005
Sales—under $500,000
Distrib.—National
Limited Liability Company

**FARRIER SPORTING GOODS, INC.**
Godwin & Crescent Aves. (07481)
**Phone—(201) 891-9520**
Fax—(201) 891-6608
www.farriersportinggoods.com
Email—farriersports@aol.com
Pres.—Charles Coleman
SIC—2396; 2395; 3479; *Sports & athletic equipment, footwear, apparel & screen printing*
Employs—4; Estab.—1971
Sales—under $500,000
Distrib.—Local
Privately owned corporation

**HEALTHTOOLS, LLC (H Q)**
681 Lawlins Rd., Unit 70 (07481)
**Phone—(201) 465-4381**
www.eatsmartproducts.com
Email—sales@eatsmartproducts.com
Member—William T. Geronimo
Dir., Pub. Rels.—Maria Geronimo
Mktg. Mgr.—Joe Origoni
SIC—3634; *Company headquarters; kitchen & bathroom digital weighing scales (mfg. done in China); Brand name—EatSmart Nutrition Scale™; EatSmart Precision Pro Digital Kitchen Scale™; EatSmart Digital Bathroom Scale™*
Employs—3; Estab.—2005
Sales—$1Mil-$2.5Mil
Distrib.—National
Limited Liability Company
AKA: EatSmart Products

**MAIN & SONS, INC., ROBERT A.**
555 Goffle Rd., P.O. Box 159 (07481)
**Phone—(201) 447-3700**
Fax—(201) 447-0302
www.ramsco-inc.com
Email—info@ramsco-inc.com
Pres., CFO & V-P., Opers.—William Main
V-P., Adv.—Georgette Hermann
V-P., Hum. Res. & IT Mgr.—Tim Denbleyker
SIC—3965; 3496; NAICS—339993; *Pins & pointed wire products, including micro perforating rolls*
Employs—13; Estab.—1954
28,000 sq ft site, Distrib.—Intl.
Privately owned corporation

**RADIATION SYSTEMS, INC.**
455 W. Main St. (07481)
**Phone—(201) 891-7515**
Fax—(201) 891-4407
www.radiationsystems.com
Email—info@radiationsystems.com
Pres., Sales Mgr.—Richard Ver Hage
GM—J. William Van Dyke, Jr.
Off. Mgr.—Glenn Ver Hage
Off. Mgr.—Heidi Ver Hage
SIC—3567; 3312; NAICS—333994; *Infrared ovens systems & stainless steel fabrication*
Employs—7; Estab.—1973
Sales—$500,000-$1Mil
10,000 sq ft site, Distrib.—National
Privately owned corporation

**RAO CONTRACT SALES, INC.**
392 Atwood Pl. (07481)
**Phone—(201) 652-1500**
National—(800) 445-7065
Fax—(973) 279-6448
www.rao.com
Email—info@rao.com
Pres., Treas.—Brian Bergman
IT Mgr.—Seth Bergman
Hum. Res. & Off. Mgr.—Alison Ehrlich

SIC—2499; *Preframed artwork, mirrors, bulletin boards & safety mirrors for the hospitality industry & government*
Employs—8; Estab.—1974
Sales—$500,000-$1Mil (est)
Distrib.—National
Privately owned corporation

**RETE BIOMEDICAL COMMUNICATIONS CORP.**
191 Godwin Ave., Ste. 1 (07481)
**Phone—(201) 891-8205**
(201) 753-2962
Fax—(201) 891-8206
www.retebiomed.com
Email—gutkin@retebiomed.com
Pres.—Stephen W. Gutkin
SIC—2721; *Medical communications & pharmaceutical marketing journal publishing*
Employs—1; Estab.—1992
Sales—under $1Mil
750 sq ft site, Distrib.—Intl.
Privately owned sub-S corp.

**RIDGEWOOD AWNING CO., INC.**
445 W. Main St., Ste. 6 (07481)
**Phone—(201) 847-0909**
Fax—(201) 847-0990
www.ridgewoodawning.com
Email—awnings@optonline.net
Pres.—Richard Ackerman
V-P.—Peter Ackerman
SIC—2394; NAICS—314912; *Canvas awnings*
Employs—12; Estab.—1934
Sales—$500,000-$1Mil
Distrib.—Regional
Privately owned corporation

**SIR SPEEDY PRINTING**
405 Goffle Rd. (07481)
**Phone—(201) 444-0234**
Fax—(201) 444-6170
www.sirspeedy.com/wyckoff
Email—sirspeedy01@optimum.net
Pres.—Gregg Miller
SIC—2759; NAICS—323100; *Commercial & instant printing, bindery & graphics*
Employs—7; Estab.—1974
5,400 sq ft site, Distrib.—Local
Privately owned corporation

**SUMMIT INTERNATIONAL FILTRATION SYSTEMS**
500 W. Main St., Ste. 10 (07481)
**Phone—(201) 847-2370**
Fax—(201) 847-2371
www.summitfiltration.com
Email—sales@summitfiltration.com
Pres.—Charles Cole III
V-P., Sales—Rick Koontz
SIC—3569; *Filtration equipment for separation of solids from liquids*
Employs—6; Estab.—1959
Distrib.—Regional
Privately owned corporation

**TRAP-ZAP ENVIRONMENTAL SYSTEMS, INC.**
255 Braen Ave. (07481)
**Phone—(201) 251-9970**
National—(800) 282-8727
Fax—(201) 251-0903
www.trapzap.com
Email—zsiguencia@trapzap.com
Pres.—Robert Belle
Off. Mgr.—Drenda Brown
Dispatcher—Donna Schmitt
SIC—3089; 2842; NAICS—325612; *Biodegradable restaurant grease trap cleaning compounds & dispensers*
Employs—20; Estab.—1988
Sales—$500,000-$1Mil
Distrib.—Local
Privately owned corporation

**GEOGRAPHICAL**

## Wyckoff—(cont.)

**U.S. LASER CORP.**

825 Windham Ct. N., Ste. 2
(07481-3470)
**Phone—(201) 848-9200**
Fax—(201) 848-9006
www.uslasercorp.com
Email—sales@uslasercorp.com
Pres., CFO—Robert Regna
V-P., R & D—Carl Miller
Dir., Bus. Dev.—Eric Fink
SIC—3699; *10-watt to 2500-watt*
*YAG, fiber & Vanadate lasers &*
*industrial laser systems for laser*
*marking, engraving, cutting,*
*welding, resistor trimming,*
*photovoltaic scribing, micro*
*machining & laser cladding*
*systems*
Employs—17; Estab.—1979
Sales—$3Mil-$5Mil
20,000 sq ft site, Distrib.—Intl.
Privately owned corporation

**VAN GROUW WELDING &**
**FABRICATING**

430 W. Main St. *(07481)*
**Phone—(201) 891-4199**
Fax—(201) 847-0132
Email—vangrouw001@optonline.net
Owner—Ken Vandenberg
SIC—3312; *Steel fabrication*
Employs—4; Estab.—2002
Sales—$500,000-$1Mil
Distrib.—Local
Privately owned corporation

**VICTORY IRON WORKS, INC.**

780 Mountain Ave. (07481)
**Phone—(973) 427-4498**
Fax—(201) 848-7875
Pres.—Teresa Edson
Sales Mgr.—Michael Edson
Bus. Mgr.—Jane Schinke
SIC—3312; *Steel fabrication*
Employs—6; Estab.—1929
Sales—$1Mil-$2.5Mil
Distrib.—Local
Privately owned corporation

---

## Yardville

(Mercer—N.E.)

**STONITE COIL CORP.**

476 Route 156, P.O. Box 11036
(08620)
**Phone—(609) 585-6600**
Fax—(609) 585-6603
www.stonitecoil.com
Email—sales@stonitecoil.com
Pres.—William Engel
V-P.—Scott Root
Pur. Mgr.—Allyson Desante
Off. Mgr.—Sandra Merritt
Engr. Mgr., Electrical—Hank
DelGatto
Engr. Mgr., Mechanical—Al
Montagna
SIC—3677; 3621; NAICS—
334416; *Electronic coils*
Employs—25; Estab.—1950
9,000 sq ft site, Distrib.—Intl.
Privately owned corporation

# Reach Industrial Buyers Over the Internet!

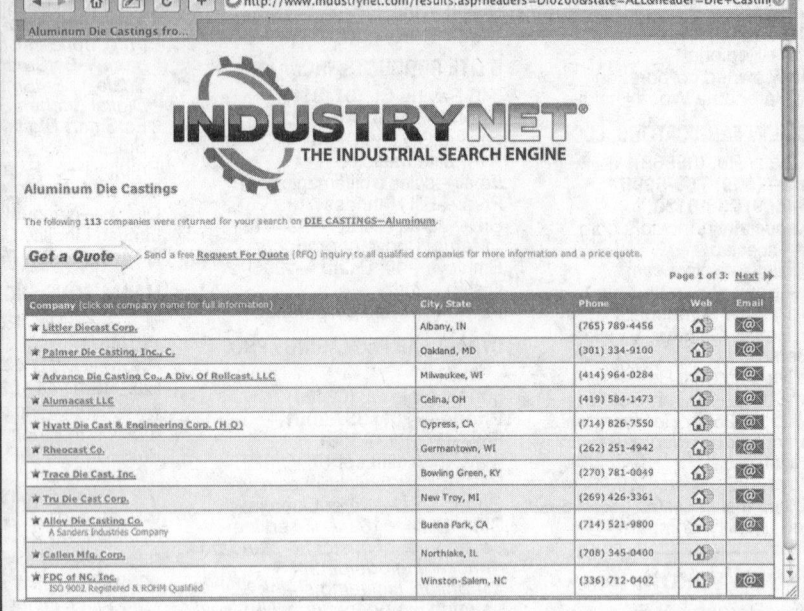

# mni's Industrial Search Engine

Allows decision makers to shop for products & industrial services among the 430,000 companies in MNI's database of U.S. manufacturers & suppliers. This is the guide to *"who makes it," "who does it,"* and *"who supplies it!"*

## Absolutely free to users!
## No registration, hassle or obligation!

# IndustryNet.com

# ALPHABETICAL INDEX OF MANUFACTURING & WHOLESALER S.I.C. CODES
### S.I.C. codes for wholesale operations are in the 50XX and 51XX series.

## A

| | |
|---|---|
| 3291 | Abrasive products |
| 2891 | Adhesives & sealants |
| 2879 | Agricultural chemicals, nec |
| 3721 | Aircraft |
| 3724 | Aircraft engines & engine parts |
| 3728 | Aircraft parts & equipment |
| 2812 | Alkalies & chlorine |
| 3363 | Aluminum die castings |
| 3354 | Aluminum extruded products |
| 3355 | Aluminum rolling & drawing |
| 3353 | Aluminum sheet, plate & foil |
| 3334 | Aluminum—primary |
| 3483 | Ammunition, except for small arms |
| 3826 | Analytical instruments |
| 1231 | Anthracite mining |
| 2389 | Apparel & accessories, nec |
| 3639 | Appliances—household, nec |
| 3446 | Architectural metal work |
| 3292 | Asbestos products |
| 2952 | Asphalt felts & coatings |
| 2951 | Asphalt paving mixtures & blocks |
| 3651 | Audio & video equipment—household |
| 5012 | Automobiles & other motor vehicles |
| 2396 | Automotive & apparel trimmings |
| 3465 | Automotive stampings |

## B

| | |
|---|---|
| 2673 | Bags: plastics, laminated & coated |
| 2674 | Bags: uncoated paper & multiwall |
| 2393 | Bags—textile |
| 2053 | Bakery products—frozen, except bread |
| 3412 | Barrels, drums & pails—metal |
| 3692 | Batteries—primary, dry & wet |
| 3691 | Batteries—storage |
| 3562 | Bearings—ball & roller |
| 5181 | Beer & ale |
| 2063 | Beet sugar |
| 2387 | Belts—apparel |
| 2836 | Biological products, except diagnostic |
| 1221 | Bituminous coal & lignite—surface |
| 1222 | Bituminous coal—underground |
| 2782 | Blankbooks & looseleaf binders |
| 3312 | Blast furnaces & steel mills |
| 2331 | Blouses & shirts—women's & misses' |
| 3564 | Blowers & fans |
| 3732 | Boat building & repairing |
| 3452 | Bolts, nuts, rivets & washers |
| 2732 | Book printing |
| 2731 | Book publishing |
| 2789 | Bookbinding & related work, nec |
| 5192 | Books, periodicals & newspapers |
| 2086 | Bottled & canned soft drinks |
| 2653 | Boxes—corrugated & solid fiber |
| 2657 | Boxes—folding paperboard |
| 2652 | Boxes—setup paperboard |
| 2342 | Bras, girdles & allied garments |
| 2051 | Bread, cake & related products |
| 3251 | Brick & structural clay tile |
| 5032 | Brick, stone & related construction materials |
| 1622 | Bridge, tunnel & elevated highway construction |
| 2211 | Broadwoven fabric mills, cotton |
| 2221 | Broadwoven fabric mills, manmade |
| 2231 | Broadwoven fabric mills, wool |
| 3991 | Brooms & brushes |
| 3995 | Burial caskets |
| 2761 | Business forms—manifold |
| 2021 | Butter—creamery |

## C

| | |
|---|---|
| 3578 | Calculating & accounting equipment |
| 2064 | Candy & other confectionery products |
| 2062 | Cane sugar refining |
| 2091 | Canned & cured fish & seafoods |
| 2033 | Canned fruits & vegetables |
| 2032 | Canned specialties |
| 3411 | Cans—metal |
| 2394 | Canvas & related products |
| 3624 | Carbon & graphite products |
| 2895 | Carbon black |
| 3955 | Carbon paper & inked ribbons |
| 3592 | Carburetors, pistons, rings & valves |
| 1751 | Carpentry work |
| 2273 | Carpets & rugs |
| 2823 | Cellulosic manmade fibers |

| | |
|---|---|
| 3241 | Cement, hydraulic |
| 3253 | Ceramic wall & floor tile |
| 2043 | Cereal breakfast foods |
| 2022 | Cheese, natural & processed |
| 1479 | Chemical & fertilizer mining, nec |
| 2899 | Chemical preparations, nec |
| 5169 | Chemicals & allied products, nec |
| 2819 | Chemicals—industrial inorganic, nec |
| 2869 | Chemicals—industrial organic, nec |
| 2131 | Chewing & smoking tobacco |
| 2067 | Chewing gum |
| 2066 | Chocolate & cocoa products |
| 2111 | Cigarettes |
| 2121 | Cigars |
| 1459 | Clay & related minerals, nec |
| 3255 | Clay refractories |
| 2329 | Clothing—men's & boys', nec |
| 2326 | Clothing—men's & boys', work |
| 5052 | Coal & other minerals & ores |
| 1241 | Coal mining services |
| 2295 | Coated fabrics, not rubberized |
| 2095 | Coffee—roasted |
| 3316 | Cold finishing of steel shapes |
| 5046 | Commercial equipment, nec |
| 3669 | Communications equipment, nec |
| 3563 | Compressors—air & gas |
| 7373 | Computer integrated systems design |
| 3577 | Computer peripheral equipment |
| 3572 | Computer storage devices |
| 3575 | Computer terminals |
| 5045 | Computers, peripherals & software |
| 3271 | Concrete block & brick |
| 3272 | Concrete products |
| 1771 | Concrete work |
| 3273 | Concrete—ready-mixed |
| 5145 | Confectionery |
| 5082 | Construction & mining machinery & equipment |
| 3531 | Construction machinery |
| 5039 | Construction materials, nec |
| 1442 | Construction sand & gravel |
| 2679 | Converted paper products, nec |
| 3535 | Conveyors & conveying equipment |
| 2052 | Cookies & crackers |
| 3631 | Cooking equipment—household |
| 3366 | Copper foundries |
| 1021 | Copper ores |
| 3351 | Copper rolling & drawing |
| 3331 | Copper—primary |
| 2298 | Cordage & twine |
| 2074 | Cottonseed oil mills |
| 3466 | Crowns & closures |
| 1311 | Crude petroleum & natural gas |
| 1423 | Crushed & broken granite |
| 1422 | Crushed & broken limestone |
| 1429 | Crushed & broken stone, nec |
| 3643 | Current-carrying wiring devices |
| 2391 | Curtains & draperies |
| 3087 | Custom compound purchased resins |
| 3281 | Cut stone & stone products |
| 3421 | Cutlery |
| 2865 | Cyclic crudes & intermediates |

## D

| | |
|---|---|
| 5143 | Dairy products, except dried or canned |
| 2034 | Dehydrated fruits, vegetables & soups |
| 3843 | Dental equipment & supplies |
| 2835 | Diagnostic substances |
| 2675 | Die-cut paper & board |
| 3544 | Dies, tools, jigs & fixtures—special |
| 1411 | Dimension stone |
| 2047 | Dog & cat food |
| 3942 | Dolls & stuffed toys |
| 3442 | Doors, sash & trim—metal |
| 2591 | Drapery hardware & blinds & shades |
| 2361 | Dresses & blouses—girl's & children's |
| 2335 | Dresses—women's, juniors' & misses' |
| 1381 | Drilling oil & gas wells |
| 5122 | Drugs, proprietaries & sundries |
| 2023 | Dry, condensed, evaporated products |
| 5099 | Durable goods, nec |

## E

| | |
|---|---|
| 3634 | Electric housewares & fans |
| 5063 | Electrical apparatus & wiring supplies |
| 5064 | Electrical appliances, TV & radios |

| | |
|---|---|
| 3699 | Electrical equipment & supplies, nec |
| 3629 | Electrical industrial apparatus, nec |
| 1731 | Electrical work |
| 3825 | Electricity measuring instruments |
| 3845 | Electromedical equipment |
| 3313 | Electrometallurgical products |
| 3671 | Electron tubes |
| 3675 | Electronic capacitors |
| 3677 | Electronic coils & transformers |
| 3679 | Electronic components, nec |
| 3571 | Electronic computers |
| 3678 | Electronic connectors |
| 5065 | Electronic parts & equipment, nec |
| 3676 | Electronic resistors |
| 3534 | Elevators & moving stairways |
| 3694 | Engine electrical equipment |
| 3519 | Engines—internal combustion, nec |
| 2677 | Envelopes |
| 3822 | Environmental controls |
| 1794 | Excavation work |
| 2892 | Explosives |

## F

| | |
|---|---|
| 2297 | Fabrics—nonwoven |
| 5083 | Farm & garden machinery & equipment |
| 3523 | Farm machinery & equipment |
| 5159 | Farm products, raw materials, nec |
| 5191 | Farm supplies |
| 3965 | Fasteners, buttons, needles & pins |
| 2077 | Fats & oils—animal & marine |
| 2079 | Fats & oils—edible, nec |
| 2048 | Feeds—prepared |
| 1061 | Ferroalloy ores, except vanadium |
| 2875 | Fertilizers, mixing only |
| 2655 | Fiber cans, drums & similar products |
| 2261 | Finishing plants, cotton |
| 2262 | Finishing plants, manmade |
| 2269 | Finishing plants, nec |
| 5146 | Fish & seafoods |
| 2092 | Fish—fresh or frozen prepared |
| 2087 | Flavoring extracts & syrups |
| 3996 | Floor coverings—hard surface |
| 1752 | Floor laying & floor work |
| 2041 | Flour & other grain mill products |
| 2045 | Flour mixes & doughs—prepared |
| 5193 | Flower, nursery stock & florists' supplies |
| 3824 | Fluid meters & counting devices |
| 3593 | Fluid power cylinders & actuators |
| 3594 | Fluid power pumps & motors |
| 3492 | Fluid power valves & hose fittings |
| 2099 | Food preparations, nec |
| 3556 | Food products machinery |
| 5139 | Footwear |
| 3131 | Footwear cut stock |
| 3149 | Footwear, except rubber, nec |
| 3143 | Footwear—men's, except athletic |
| 3021 | Footwear—rubber & plastic |
| 3144 | Footwear—women's, except athletic |
| 3462 | Forgings—iron & steel |
| 3463 | Forgings—nonferrous |
| 3365 | Foundries—aluminum |
| 3321 | Foundries—gray & ductile iron |
| 3322 | Foundries—malleable iron |
| 3369 | Foundries—nonferrous, nec |
| 3325 | Foundries—steel |
| 3324 | Foundries—steel investment |
| 5148 | Fresh fruits & vegetables |
| 2038 | Frozen specialties |
| 2037 | Fruits & vegetables, frozen |
| 2371 | Fur goods |
| 3567 | Furnaces & ovens—industrial |
| 2392 | Furnishings—house |
| 5021 | Furniture |
| 2599 | Furniture & fixtures, nec |
| 2519 | Furniture—household, nec |
| 2514 | Furniture—metal household |
| 2531 | Furniture—public building & related |
| 2512 | Furniture—upholstered household |
| 2511 | Furniture—wood household |

## G

| | |
|---|---|
| 3944 | Games, toys & children's vehicles |
| 2813 | Gases—industrial |
| 3053 | Gaskets, packing & sealing devices |
| 1793 | Glass & glazing work |

2676 Sanitary paper products
2013 Sausages & other prepared meat products
3425 Saw blades & handsaws
2421 Sawmills & planing mills, general
2429 Sawmills—special product, nec
3596 Scales & balances, except laboratory
2397 Schiffli machine embroideries
5093 Scrap & waste materials
3451 Screw machine products
3812 Search & navigation equipment
3341 Secondary nonferrous metals
3674 Semiconductors & related devices
3263 Semivitreous table & kitchenware
5087 Service establishment equipment
3589 Service industry machinery, nec
3444 Sheet metal work
3731 Ship building & repairing
2321 Shirts—men's & boys'
3993 Signs & advertising specialties
1044 Silver ores
3914 Silverware & plated ware
1521 Single-family housing construction
3142 Slippers—house
3484 Small arms
3482 Small arms ammunition
2841 Soap & other detergents
2436 Softwood veneer & plywood
2075 Soybean oil mills
3764 Space propulsion units & parts
3769 Space vehicle equipment, nec
1799 Special trade contractors, nec
3566 Speed changers, drives & gears
3949 Sporting & athletic goods, nec
5091 Sporting & recreational goods & supplies
3493 Springs—steel, except wire
5112 Stationery & office supplies
2678 Stationery products
3317 Steel pipe & tubes
3315 Steel wire & related products
3259 Structural clay products, nec
3441 Structural metal—fabricated
1791 Structural steel erection
2439 Structural wood members, nec
2061 Sugar—raw cane
2311 Suits & coats—men's & boys'
2337 Suits & coats—women's & misses'
2843 Surface active agents
3841 Surgical & medical instruments
3842 Surgical appliances & supplies
3613 Switchgear & switchboard apparatus

## T

3795 Tanks & tank components
3661 Telephone & telegraph apparatus
1743 Terrazzo, tile, marble, mosaic work
2299 Textile goods, nec
3552 Textile machinery
2399 Textile products—fabricated, nec
2284 Thread mills
2282 Throwing & winding mills
2296 Tire cord & fabrics
3011 Tires & inner tubes
5014 Tires & tubes
5194 Tobacco & tobacco products
2141 Tobacco stemming & redrying
2844 Toilet preparations
3423 Tools—hand & edge
5092 Toys & hobby goods & supplies
3612 Transformers
5088 Transportation equipment & supplies
3799 Transportation equipment, nec
3792 Travel trailers & campers
2325 Trousers & slacks—men's & boys'
3713 Truck & bus bodies
3715 Truck trailers
3537 Trucks & tractors—industrial
3511 Turbines & turbine generator sets
2517 TV & radio cabinets—wood
2791 Typesetting

## U

2322 Underwear & nightwear—men's & boys'
2341 Underwear—women's & children's
1094 Uranium-radium-vanadium ores

## V

3635 Vacuum cleaners—household
3494 Valves & pipe fittings

3491 Valves—industrial
2076 Vegetable oil mills
3581 Vending machines—automatic
3262 Vitreous china table & kitchenware

## W

5075 Warm air heating & air conditioning
3873 Watches, clocks, watchcases & parts
1781 Water well drilling
1623 Water, sewer & utility lines
2385 Waterproof outerwear
2257 Weft knit fabric mills
3548 Welding apparatus
2046 Wet corn milling
5182 Wine & distilled alcoholic beverages
2084 Wines, brandy, & brandy spirits
3496 Wire products—misc. fabricated
3495 Wire springs
3644 Wiring devices—non-current carrying
5137 Women's, children's & infants' clothing
2449 Wood containers, nec
2491 Wood preserving
2499 Wood products, nec
2493 Wood products—reconstituted
3553 Woodworking machinery
1795 Wrecking & demolition work

## X

3844 X-ray apparatus & tubes

## Y

2281 Yarn spinning mills

ALPHA INDEX OF S.I.C. CODES

**S.I.C. codes for wholesale operations are in the 50XX and 51XX series.**

# Industry Database Subscriptions at EZSelect.com

**EZSelect.com** is online database software offering real-time access to the freshest info! **mni** databases give you the flexibility to find new leads the way **YOU need them!** Select a database and target new customers or suppliers by industry! **For additional industries, call 800-221-2172 or visit EZSelect.com.**

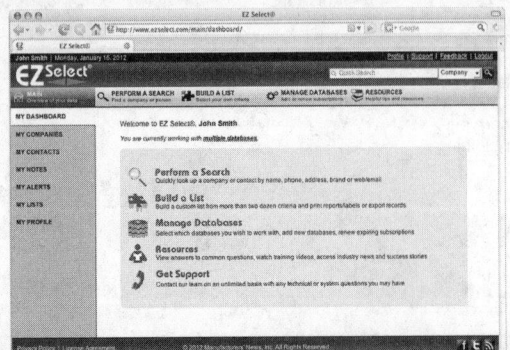

Learn how an EZSelect.com subscription to our industrial information databases can empower you today!

## NATIONAL DATABASES BY INDUSTRY @ EZSelect.com subscription*

| SIC | Industry Description | EZSelect.com Full Subscription | EZSelect.com 20+ Emp. Subscription | EZSelect.com Basic Subscription |
|---|---|---|---|---|
| 20 | Food and Kindred Products | $1,340 | $856 | $469 |
| 27 | Printing and Publishing | $2,080 | $845 | $728 |
| 28 | Chemicals & Allied Products | $1,048 | $676 | $367 |
| 30 | Rubber & Misc. Plastic Products | $1,054 | $749 | $369 |
| 34 | Fabricated Metal Products | $1,946 | $1,080 | $681 |
| 35 | Industrial & Comm. Machinery & Computer Equipment | $2,457 | $1,178 | $860 |
| 36 | Electronic & Other Electric Equip. | $1,079 | $734 | $378 |
| 50 | Wholesale Trade (durable) | $2,152 | $1,040 | $753 |
| 51 | Wholesale Trade (non-durable) | $956 | $614 | $335 |
| 73 | Software Systems & Design | $494 | $369 | $173 |

Visit **EZSelect.com** for these and other U.S. industrial databases

 **Manufacturers' News, Inc.**
Directories & Databases since 1912

1633 Central St., Evanston, IL 60201 • 888-752-5200

© Copyright 2015 Manufacturers' News, Inc.


# S.I.C. SECTION

This section indexes the state's manufacturers, processors, wholesalers and distributors according to Standard Industrial Classifications (S.I.C.). Developed by the U.S. Government, this system assigns each industrial process a four-digit number. Codes used are from the most recent manual published by the U.S. Government Office of Management & Budget. Refer to individual profiles for equivalent North American Industrial Classification System (NAICS) designations.

Companies are identified in alphabetical order within each of these four-digit classifications. Each entry contains the company name, address, telephone number, a company contact, employee count at this location and a partial description of the business. A ⋆ indicates a new entry added for this edition.

## 12 COAL MINING

### 1231 Anthracite mining

Transition Metals Technology, 314 N. West Ave., Wenonah 08090
Pres., CEO—Edward L. Payer, 39 emp., *Anthracite coal mining, including production* ........... (856) 468-6747

## 13 OIL & GAS EXTRACTION

### 1311 Crude petroleum & natural gas

Hess Corp., 2800 U.S. Highway 1, North Brunswick 08902
Manager—Roman Ozhogan, 35 emp., *Oil & gas exploration & production* ........... (732) 940-3705
Majka & Sons Fuel Service, Joseph A., 568 Paulison Ave., Clifton 07011
Pres., GM—Scott Majka, 15 emp., *Oil production* ........... (973) 777-8484
Oil Tank Services, 505 E. 1st Ave., Roselle 07203
⋆ Owner—Robby Schiff, 2 emp., *Oil & gas exploration* ........... (908) 241-5011
VGS Group, Inc., 197 State Route 18, Ste. 235, East Brunswick 08816
⋆ Founder & Chrm.—Siva Coramutta, 23 emp., *Oil & gas production* ........... (732) 887-5912

### 1321 Natural gas liquids

Oil Tank Services, 505 E. 1st Ave., Roselle 07203
⋆ Owner—Robby Schiff, 2 emp., *Oil & gas exploration* ........... (908) 241-5011

### 1382 Oil & gas exploration services

Hess Corp., 2800 U.S. Highway 1, North Brunswick 08902
Manager—Roman Ozhogan, 35 emp., *Oil & gas exploration & production* ........... (732) 940-3705
Jay Bee Oil & Gas, Inc., 1720 U.S. Highway 22 E., Union 07083
Pres.—Randy Broda, 3 emp., *Oil & gas exploration* ........... (908) 686-1493
Woodruff Energy, Inc., 73 Water St., P.O. Box 777, Bridgeton 08302
Pres.—Robert Woodruff, Jr., 50 emp., *Oil & natural gas exploration services* ........... (856) 455-1111

### 1389 Oil & gas field services, nec

Camin Cargo Control, Inc. (H Q), 230 Marion Ave., Linden 07036
Pres.—Carlos Camin, 60 emp., *Corporate headquarters; oilfield services* ........... (908) 523-0616
NMK Resources, 650 Grove Rd., Ste. 111, Paulsboro 08066
⋆ Owner—Nabil Kassem, 15 emp., *Inspection & laboratory testing services* ........... (856) 686-4904
Presscrete Co., Inc., The, 128 Oak Tree Ave., South Plainfield 07080
Pres.—Brian Fox, 24 emp., *Compaction, pressure grouting, load* ........... (908) 757-8600
SGS North America, Inc. (H Q), 201 Route 17 N., Rutherford 07070
CEO—Jeffrey McDonald, 125 emp., *Corporate headquarters; oil & gas field* ........... (201) 508-3000

## 14 NONMETALLIC MINERALS, EXCEPT FUELS

### 1411 Dimension stone

Braen Stone, 217 Limecrest Rd., Lafayette 07848
Off. Mgr.—Pam Kronyak, 12 emp., *Aggregate quarrying* ........... (973) 383-7100
Ozer International, LLC, 145 Manchester Pl., Newark 07104
Pres.—Sualp Yurteri, 25 emp., *Manufacturer of granite & marble kitchen* ........... (973) 497-5656

### 1423 Crushed & broken granite

Eastern Concrete Materials, Inc., 3620 Route 23 N., Hamburg 07419
V-P.—David Besaw, 20 emp., *Crushed stone & granite quarrying* ........... (973) 827-7625

### 1429 Crushed & broken stone, nec

Baer Aggregates, Inc., 454 River Rd., Phillipsburg 08865
⋆ Pres.—Louis Mitchele, 5 emp., *Sand, gravel & crushed stone quarrying* ........... (908) 454-4412
Dun-Rite Sand & Gravel Co., Inc., 3765 Mays Landing Rd., Vineland 08361
Sales Mgr.—Ronald S. Pusloski, 18 emp., *Sand, gravel & crushed stone quarrying* ........... (856) 825-9900
Dun-Rite Sand & Gravel Co., Inc. (H Q), 573 E. Grant Ave., Vineland 08360
Pres.—Peter Galetto, 30 emp., *Corporate headquarters; sand, gravel* ........... (856) 692-2520
Eastern Concrete Materials, Inc., 1 Railroad Ave., Glen Gardner 08826
Plt. & Sr. Proj. Mgr.—Mike Guida, 15 emp., *Crushed granite stone* ........... (908) 537-2135
Eastern Concrete Materials, Inc., 3620 Route 23 N., Hamburg 07419
V-P.—David Besaw, 20 emp., *Crushed stone & granite quarrying* ........... (973) 827-7625
Estes Co., Inc., Clifford W., 182 Fairfield Rd., Ste. 8, Fairfield 07004
Chrm.—Douglas Estes, 6 emp., *Corporate headquarters & aquarium gravel* ........... (973) 575-4400
Mount Construction Co., Inc. (H Q), 427 S. White Horse Pike, P.O. Box 619, Berlin 08009
Pres., CEO—Dave Smith, 13 emp., *Corporate headquarters; bituminous* ........... (856) 768-8493
S & Y Natural Stone, LLC, 1000 Main Ave., Clifton 07011
⋆ Owner—Mehmet Caymaz, 4 emp., *Broken marble quarrying* ........... (862) 200-5156
Saxton Falls Sand & Gravel, Inc., Waterloo Valley Rd., P.O. Box 576, Stanhope 07874
Pres.—Richard Schindelar, 10 emp., *Sand & gravel processing, including* ........... (908) 852-0120
Stavola Construction Materials, Inc., 810 Thompson Ave., Bound Brook 08805
Corp. Secy.—Helen Stokes, 50 emp., *Construction stone aggregates & asphalt* ........... (732) 356-7100
Tilcon, Inc., Oxford Quarry, 193 Mount Pisgah Ave., P.O. Box 120, Oxford 07863
GM, Aggregates—Brad Carroll, 17 emp., *Stone quarrying & asphalt* ........... (908) 453-4141
Weldon Asphalt Co., 1 New Providence Rd., Watchung 07060
GM—Robbie Roberts, 75 emp., *Crushed aggregates, hot-mixed asphalt* ........... (908) 233-9440

### 1442 Construction sand & gravel

Ace Crete Products, Inc., 250 Hickory Ln., Bayville 08721
Pres.—Martin E. Tanzer, 12 emp., *Manufacturer & distributor of industrial* ........... (732) 269-1400
Baer Aggregates, Inc., 454 River Rd., Phillipsburg 08865
⋆ Pres.—Louis Mitchele, 5 emp., *Sand, gravel & crushed stone quarrying* ........... (908) 454-4412
Barrett Paving Materials, Inc. (H Q), 3 Becker Farm Rd., Ste. 307, Roseland 07068
Pres.—Robert Doucet, 15 emp., *Corporate headquarters; asphalt paving* ........... (973) 533-1001
Buck Mining & Materials, Inc., P.O. Box 1386, Hightstown 08520
Owner—Maureen Stone, 5 emp., *Sand & gravel processing & dirt mining* ........... (732) 446-9336
Cape Mining & Recycling, LLC, 560 Goshen Rd., P.O. Box 246, Cape May Court House 08210
⋆ Owner—Phil Heun, Jr., 20 emp., *Stone recycling & sand & gravel processing* ........... (609) 465-3277
Dun-Rite Sand & Gravel Co., Inc., 3765 Mays Landing Rd., Vineland 08361
Sales Mgr.—Ronald S. Pusloski, 18 emp., *Sand, gravel & crushed stone quarrying* ........... (856) 825-9900
Dun-Rite Sand & Gravel Co., Inc. (H Q), 573 E. Grant Ave., Vineland 08360
Pres.—Peter Galetto, 30 emp., *Corporate headquarters; sand, gravel* ........... (856) 692-2520
Hanson Aggregate BMC, 1101 Railroad Ave., Newport 08345
Sales Mgr.—Dave Hergert, 25 emp., *Sand & gravel processing* ........... (856) 447-4294
Hanson Aggregates North America, 311 Unexpected Rd., Buena 08310
Plt. Mgr.—Frank Berghos, 4 emp., *Sand & gravel processing* ........... (856) 697-1616
Ole Hansen & Son, Inc. (H Q), 523 S. Leipzig Ave., P.O. Box 1020, Cologne 08213
Chrm.—Roger B. Hansen, 50 emp., *Corporate headquarters; sand & gravel* ........... (609) 965-3700
Ole Hansen & Sons, Inc., 100 Old Port Republic Rd., Absecon 08205
Supervisor—Chris Patterson, 4 emp., *Sand & gravel mining* ........... (609) 652-5666
Rosano Trucking, Inc., 26 Maple Ave., Oceanport 07757
Owner & GM—Frank Rosano, 1 emp., *Sand & gravel processing* ........... (732) 542-5009
Saxton Falls Sand & Gravel, Inc., Waterloo Valley Rd., P.O. Box 576, Stanhope 07874
Pres.—Richard Schindelar, 10 emp., *Sand & gravel processing, including* ........... (908) 852-0120
Ward Sand & Materials, 223 Sooy Place Rd., Vincentown 08088
Plt. Mgr.—Bob Catapianco, 10 emp., *Surface mining of sand* ........... (609) 859-2860
WHIBCO, Inc. (H Q), 87 E. Commerce St., Bridgeton 08302
Pres.—Wade R. Sjogren, 30 emp., *Corporate headquarters; sand & gravel* ........... (856) 455-9200

### 1446 Industrial sand

Estes Co., Inc., Clifford W., 182 Fairfield Rd., Ste. 8, Fairfield 07004
Chrm.—Douglas Estes, 6 emp., *Corporate headquarters & aquarium gravel* ........... (973) 575-4400
Inversand Co., 226 N. Atlantic Ave., P.O. Box 650, Clayton 08312
Pres.—Tom Carrocino, 50 emp., *Manganese greensand for municipal &* ........... (856) 881-2345
Ricci Brothers Sand Company, Inc., 2099 Dragston Rd., P.O. Box 664, Port Norris 08349
Owner—Sam Ricci, Sr., 35 emp., *High-purity sands & gravels for water* ........... (856) 785-0166
U.S. Silica Co., 9035 Noble St., P.O. Box 254, Mauricetown 08329
Plt. Mgr.—Justo Lucena, 50 emp., *Industrial silica sand* ........... (856) 785-0720

### 1459 Clay & related minerals, nec

American Beryllia, Inc., 16 1st Ave., Haskell 07420
CEO—Nussy Brauner, 25 emp., *Beryllium oxide ceramic parts, including* ........... (973) 248-8080

### 1479 Chemical & fertilizer mining, nec

Saxton Falls Sand & Gravel, Inc., Waterloo Valley Rd., P.O. Box 576, Stanhope 07874
Pres.—Richard Schindelar, 10 emp., *Sand & gravel processing, including* ........... (908) 852-0120

### 1499 Miscellaneous nonmetallic minerals, except fuels

Buck Mining & Materials, Inc., P.O. Box 1386, Hightstown 08520
Owner—Maureen Stone, 5 emp., *Sand & gravel processing & dirt mining* ........... (732) 446-9336
Schundler Co., Inc., 150 Whitman Ave., Edison 08817
Admn. & Sales Mgr.—Vikki Warman, 30 emp., *Perlite & vermiculite aggregates &* ........... (732) 287-2244
Wantage Stone, LLC, 80 State Route 23, Hamburg 07419
Cont.—Christina Fama, 6 emp., *Dolomite dimension quarrying* ........... (973) 702-7866

## 20 FOOD AND KINDRED PRODUCTS

### 2011 Meat packing plants

814 Americas, 814 2nd Ave., Elizabeth 07202
GM—Michael Patracuolla, 22 emp., *Meat packing & processing* ........... (908) 354-2674
A R M National Foods, Inc., 1546 Lamberton Rd., Trenton 08611
Pres.—Armando Rienzi, 16 emp., *Meat processing & packing* ........... (609) 394-0431
A. Gimenez Trading, LLC, 5 Wegmann Way, Oak Ridge 07438
Mng. Member—Melissa Laserna, 8 emp., *Beef, pork, sausage & chicken processing* ........... (973) 697-2240
Allied Specialty Foods, Inc., 313 Hickory Pl., Vineland 08360
Pres.—Paul Litten, 80 emp., *Meat processing & packing* ........... (856) 507-1100
Amboy Group, 1 Amboy Ave., Woodbridge 07095
⋆ Pres.—William Colbert, 15 emp., *Packaged Irish meat & breakfast gift* ........... (732) 510-5600
American Halal Slaughter House, 270 Raymond Blvd., Newark 07105
Pres.—Omar Mady, 17 emp., *Halal meat processing & packing for* ........... (973) 817-8444
Basha USA, LLC, 390 Broadway, Bayonne 07002
⋆ Owner—M. Merget, 4 emp., *Meat processing* ........... (201) 339-9770
Beef International, Inc., 7010 Central Hwy., Pennsauken 08109
Sales Mgr.—Dan Naab, 70 emp., *Roast beef processing & packing* ........... (856) 663-6763
Bergen Wholesale Meats Corp., 154 Hackensack Ave., Hackensack 07601
⋆ Owner—Ernest W. Hanabergh III, 10 emp., *Meat processing* ........... (201) 342-2138
Best Provision Co., Inc., 144 Avon Ave., Newark 07108
CEO—Len Karp, 100 emp., *Beef & deli meat processing & packing* ........... (973) 242-5000
Bierig Bros., Inc., 3539 Reilly Ct., Vineland 08360
V-P.—Jacob Bierig, 30 emp., *Meat processing & packing* ........... (856) 691-9765
Bringhurst Bros., Inc., 38 W. Taunton Rd., Berlin 08009
Pres.—Ralph Bringhurst, Jr., 20 emp., *Bacon, kielbasa, bologna, scrapple,* ........... (856) 767-0110
Brown & Co., C. W., 161 Kings Hwy., Mount Royal 08061
Pres.—Robert Botto, 6 emp., *Meat processing* ........... (856) 423-3700
Buona Vita, Inc., 1 S. Industrial Blvd., Bridgeton 08302
Pres.—Paul InFranco, 100 emp., *Italian beef braciola, meatballs, meatloaf* ........... (856) 453-7972
Burger Maker, Inc., 666 16th St., Carlstadt 07072
Pres.—David Schweid, 200 emp., *Gourmet hamburger patties for foodservice* ........... (201) 939-4747
Cameco, Inc., 100 Pine St., Verona 07044
Manager—Bill Schneider, 130 emp., *Meat processing* ........... (973) 239-2700
Catelli Bros. Veal & Lamb, Inc., 50 Ferry Ave., Collingswood 08103
Pres.—Anthony Catelli, 225 emp., *Corporate headquarters & veal & lamb* ........... (856) 869-9293
Catelli Bros. Veal & Lamb, Inc., 776 Broad St., Shrewsbury 07702
GM & Off. Mgr.—Edward Cook, 22 emp., *Veal & lamb processing* ........... (732) 741-3687

F2 © Copyright 2015 Manufacturers' News, Inc. S.I.C. SECTION

Dealaman Enterprises, Inc., 214 Mountain View Rd., Warren 07059
Pres.—George Dealaman, 16 emp., *Pork processing for wholesale & retail* ........ (908) 755-1780
Delaware Food Market, 6506 Ventnor Ave., Ventnor City 08406
Owner—William Deluca, 7 emp., *Meat packing & processing* ........ (609) 822-0222
Foote's Slaughter House, 28 Swedesboro Rd., Monroeville 08343
Owner—Gerald B. Thomas, 1 emp., *Meat processing* ........ (856) 358-8550
Gaiser's European Style Provisions, Inc., 2019 Morris Ave., Union 07083
Pres.—Boris Vadrar, 10 emp., *Meat processing & packing* ........ (908) 686-3421
Golden Platter Foods, Inc., 37 Tompkins Point Rd., Newark 07114
V-P.—Scott Bennett, 40 emp., *Poultry & meat processing* ........ (973) 242-0290
Great American Veal Co., Inc., 50 Avenue L, Ste. 5, Newark 07105
Pres.—Zarko Grgas, 50 emp., *Meat processing, including veal rib* ........ (973) 589-6363
Green Tree Packing, Inc., 65 Central Ave., P.O. Box 386, Passaic 07055
Pres.—Michael Waters, 100 emp., *Meat processing & packing of seafood* ........ (973) 473-1305
Ivo Delicious Meat Products, Inc., 206 Dayton Ave., Passaic 07055
★ Pres.—Ivelin Naydenov, 4 emp., *Beef & pork processing & packaging* ........ (973) 223-4044
Kleemeyer & Merkel, Inc., 68 Britten Rd., P.O. Box 204, Green Village 07935
Pres., GM—Tim Nugent, 15 emp., *Pork, beef, lamb, goat & veal processing* ........ (973) 377-0875
Kupelian Foods, Inc., 146 Bergen Tpke., Ridgefield Park 07660
Pres.—Edward Kupelian, 5 emp., *Meat processing* ........ (201) 440-8055
Lipari's Sausage, Inc., 220 6th Ave., Hawthorne 07506
V-P., CEO & COO—Joe Manganella, 25 emp., *Meat & sausage processing, cutting* ........ (973) 304-0137
Love Farms, LLC, 204 Albion Ave., Paterson 07502
★ Owner—David Adelson, 30 emp., *Meat & sausage processing* ........ (973) 942-5683
Magnolia Beef Co., LLC, 1070 Magnolia Ave., Elizabeth 07201
Pres.—Alan Simberloff, 25 emp., *Meat & poultry processing* ........ (908) 352-9412
Marcacci Meats, Inc., 1853 Vine Rd., Vineland 08361
Pres.—Mehmet Silpagar, 6 emp., *Meat packing & processing* ........ (856) 691-4848
Mayabeque Products Corp., 7424 Bergenline Ave., Ste. 1, North Bergen 07047
★ Pres.—Andre Idavoy, 7 emp., *Meat processing* ........ (201) 869-0531
Megas Yeeros, LLC, 165 Chubb Ave., Lyndhurst 07071
★ Pres., GM—Nikos Stergiou, 20 emp., *Lamb, beef, pork & chicken gyros meat* ........ (212) 777-6342
New Jersey Halal Meat Packing, 841 Main St., Paterson 07503
Owner—Abdul Beqiri, 4 emp., *Halal meat processing & packing* ........ (973) 684-3648
Real Kosher LLC, 146 Christie St., Newark 07105
Dir., Mktg.—Jerry Abramson, 20 emp., *Kosher fresh meats, sausages & provisions* ........ (973) 690-5394
Red Square Foods, Inc., 62 Berry St., Somerset 08873
Pres.—Boris Rappaport, 15 emp., *Manufacturer & distributor of deli* ........ (732) 846-0190
Rexell Foods Corp., 120 Orchard St., Newark 07102
Off. Mgr.—Violet Engalla, 6 emp., *Meat processing* ........ (973) 741-0404
RobDav Distributors, Inc., 1251 Yardville Allentown Rd., Allentown 08501
Pres.—Robby Goldstein, 10 emp., *Beef & pork processing* ........ (609) 259-6335
Streit & Son Co., Inc., Carl, 703 Atkins Ave., Neptune 07753
Pres.—Jim Robinson, 5 emp., *Meat, poultry & pork processing* ........ (732) 775-0803
Sussex Meat Packing, Inc., 205 Route 23, Sussex 07461
Pres.—Henry Vandenakker, 8 emp., *Meat processing & packing* ........ (973) 875-5641
Thumann, Inc., 670 Dell Rd., Carlstadt 07072
GM—Bob Burke, Sr., 210 emp., *Meat processing & packing* ........ (201) 935-3636
Trenton Halal Packing Co., 610 Roebling Ave., Trenton 08611
Pres.—Mohammad Malik, 10 emp., *Beef processing & packing* ........ (609) 394-0331
Trenton Steak Co., 539 Chestnut Ave., Trenton 08611
Owner—Armando Rienzi, 5 emp., *Meat packing* ........ (609) 695-6776
Unity Brand Halal Products, 94 Orange St., Newark 07102
Owner & Pres.—Akbar Salam, 6 emp., *Meat processing* ........ (973) 624-4847
Wayne Meat Corp., 2234 Hamburg Tpke., Wayne 07470
Opers. Mgr.—Marty Powers, 5 emp., *Meat processing & packing* ........ (973) 835-0211

## 2013 Sausages & other prepared meat products

A. Gimenez Trading, LLC, 5 Wegmann Way, Oak Ridge 07438
Mng. Member—Melissa Laserna, 8 emp., *Beef, pork, sausage & chicken processing* ........ (973) 697-2240
Abeles & Heymann Kosher Products, 739 Ramsey Ave., Hillside 07205
Pres., CEO—Micha Rakaby, 25 emp., *Kosher deli foods & packaging* ........ (908) 206-8886
Al & John, Inc., 444 Marshall St., Paterson 07503
Pres.—Alexander Oldja, 220 emp., *Ham* ........ (973) 742-4990
Appetito Provisions Co., Inc., 609 10th St., P.O. Box 8098, Union City 07087
Pres.—Michael Tota, 25 emp., *Sausage processing* ........ (201) 864-3410
Applegate Farms (H Q), 750 Route 202 S., Ste. 300, Bridgewater 08807
Founder & CEO—Stephen McDonnell, 50 emp., *Company headquarters; natural & organic* .. (866) 587-5858
Bringhurst Bros., Inc., 38 W. Taunton Rd., Berlin 08009
Pres.—Ralph Bringhurst, Jr., 20 emp., *Bacon, kielbasa, bologna, scrapple,* ........ (856) 767-0110
Carnegie Deli, Inc., 605 Washington Ave., Carlstadt 07072
Pres., GM—James Jorgenson, 14 emp., *Deli products* ........ (201) 507-5557
Case Pork Roll Co., Inc., 644 Washington St., Trenton 08611
Pres., GM—Tom Grieb, 25 emp., *Pork rolls* ........ (609) 396-8171
Cifelli & Sons, Inc., 38 Obert St., P.O. Box 538, South River 08882
Pres.—Anthony J. Cifelli, 15 emp., *Italian sausage* ........ (732) 238-0090
Corte Provisions, 574 Ferry St., Newark 07105
Opers. Mgr.—Rui Serra, 14 emp., *Sausage processing* ........ (973) 712-0970
Dutch's Meats, Inc., 30 Morse Ave., Ewing 08638
Pres.—Dominic Granaldi, Jr., 10 emp., *Meat processing, including ground beef* ........ (609) 882-6650
Fratelli Beretta U.S.A., Inc., 210 Green St., South Hackensack 07606
Pres.—Lorenzo Beretta, 23 emp., *Corporate headquarters & Italian salami* ........ (201) 343-5161
Globe Packaging Co., Inc., 368 Paterson Plank Rd., Carlstadt 07072
Pres.—Issy Bank, 11 emp., *Plastic, collagen, fibrous, cellulose* ........ (201) 939-3335
Great American Veal Co., Inc., 50 Avenue L, Ste. 5, Newark 07105
Pres.—Zarko Grgas, 50 emp., *Meat processing, including veal rib* ........ (973) 589-6363
Groezinger Provision, Inc., 1200 7th Ave., Neptune 07753
Pres.—Laurie Cummins, 20 emp., *Gourmet pates, mousses, terrines &* ........ (732) 775-3220
JMA Sausage And Meat Company, Inc., 205 Stuyvesant Ave., Ste. 211, Lyndhurst 07071
Pres.—Joe Aragona, Jr., 5 emp., *Italian sausage, breakfast sausage,* ........ (201) 636-2022
Kupelian Foods, Inc., 146 Bergen Tpke., Ridgefield Park 07660
Pres.—Edward Kupelian, 5 emp., *Meat processing* ........ (201) 440-8055
Licini Bros. Provisions, Inc., 907 West St., Union City 07087
Pres.—Danny Licini, 10 emp., *Fresh & dried sausages* ........ (201) 865-1130
Loeffler's Gourmet, 482 Whitehead Rd., Trenton 08619
Pres.—Robert Trofimowicz, 10 emp., *Luncheon meat processing & packaging* ........ (609) 695-5068
Lopes Co., 304 Walnut St., Newark 07105
Pres.—Hermino Lopes, 4 emp., *Sausage* ........ (973) 344-3063
Los Galleguitos, 147 48th St., Union City 07087
Owner—Francisco Torres, 10 emp., *Spanish sausage processing & packing* ........ (201) 865-7232
Love Farms, LLC, 204 Albion Ave., Paterson 07502
★ Owner—David Adelson, 30 emp., *Meat & sausage processing* ........ (973) 942-5683
Marathon Enterprises, Inc. (H Q), 9 Smith St., Englewood 07631
Owner—Nikki Rosen, 60 emp., *Corporate headquarters; hot dogs* ........ (201) 935-3330
Martin's Specialty Sausage Co., 150 Harmony Rd., Mickleton 08056
Pres.—Martin Guinta, 30 emp., *Sausage* ........ (856) 423-4000
Nitta Casings Inc., 141 Southside Ave., Bridgewater 08807
Pres., CEO—Rod Moore, 192 emp., *Edible collagen sausage casings & collagen* ........ (908) 218-4400
Perrulli's Custom Meats, 1889 Route 9, Ste. 45, Toms River 08755
★ Owner—Dave Perrulli, 2 emp., *Italian sausages* ........ (732) 244-0470
Premio Foods, Inc., 50 Utter Ave., Hawthorne 07506
Pres.—Mark Cinque, 100 emp., *Sausages* ........ (973) 427-1106
PRG Packing Corp. (H Q), 2071 Lemoine Ave., Fort Lee 07024
Owner—Guillermo Gonzalez, 125 emp., *Corporate headquarters; smoked meat* ........ (201) 242-5500
Pulaski Meat Products Co., 123 N. Wood Ave., Linden 07036
Pres.—Ron Pulaski, 20 emp., *Prepared meat products* ........ (908) 925-5380
Real Kosher LLC, 146 Christie St., Newark 07105
Dir., Mktg.—Jerry Abramson, 20 emp., *Kosher fresh meats, sausages & provisions* ........ (973) 690-5394
Red Square Foods, Inc., 62 Berry St., Somerset 08873
Pres.—Boris Rappaport, 15 emp., *Manufacturer & distributor of deli* ........ (732) 846-0190
Seabra Group (H Q), 574 Ferry St., Newark 07105
Pres.—Antonio Seabra, 26 emp., *Company headquarters; sausage processing* ........ (973) 491-0399
Wagner Provisions Co., Inc., 54 E. Broad St., P.O. Box 169, Gibbstown 08027
Pres., GM—Herb Wagner, 10 emp., *Meat snack products* ........ (856) 423-1630

## 2015 Poultry slaughtering & processing

A. Gimenez Trading, LLC, 5 Wegmann Way, Oak Ridge 07438
Mng. Member—Melissa Laserna, 8 emp., *Beef, pork, sausage & chicken processing* ........ (973) 697-2240
B & B Poultry Co., Inc., Almond Rd., P.O. Box 307, Norma 08347
Pres.—Mark Fisher, 150 emp., *Poultry processing* ........ (856) 692-8893
Best Provision Co., Inc., 144 Avon Ave., Newark 07108
CEO—Len Karp, 100 emp., *Beef & deli meat processing & packing* ........ (973) 242-5000
Deb-El Food Products, LLC, 2 Papetti Plz., P.O. Box 876, Elizabeth 07206
Pres.—Elliot Gibber, 75 emp., *Dried eggs* ........ (908) 351-0330
Golden Platter Foods, Inc., 37 Tompkins Point Rd., Newark 07114
V-P.—Scott Bennett, 40 emp., *Poultry & meat processing* ........ (973) 242-0290
Great American Veal Co., Inc., 50 Avenue L, Ste. 5, Newark 07105
Pres.—Zarko Grgas, 50 emp., *Meat processing, including veal rib* ........ (973) 589-6363
Hinck's Turkey Farm, Inc., 3930 Belmar Blvd., Neptune 07753
Pres.—Robert L. Longo, 9 emp., *Turkey processing* ........ (732) 681-0508
I S E Farms, Inc., 110 Goodspring Rd., P.O. Box 567, Broadway 08808
Site Mgr.—Orlando Santiago Cruz, 85 emp., *Egg processing* ........ (908) 454-4148
Magnolia Beef Co., LLC, 1070 Magnolia Ave., Elizabeth 07201
Pres.—Alan Simberloff, 25 emp., *Meat & poultry processing* ........ (908) 352-9412
Megas Yeeros, LLC, 165 Chubb Ave., Lyndhurst 07071
★ Pres., GM—Nikos Stergiou, 20 emp., *Lamb, beef, pork & chicken gyros meat* ........ (212) 777-6342
Michael Foods, Inc., 847 North Ave., Elizabeth 07201
Dir., Hum. Res.—Jack Novak, 75 emp., *Egg products* ........ (908) 282-7140
Mitchell, Inc., David, 210 Park Dr., Voorhees 08043
V-P.—Ken Bond, 15 emp., *Poultry processing* ........ (856) 429-2610
New York Poultry Co., Inc., 3351 Tremley Point Rd., Linden 07036
Pres.—John Nasary, 15 emp., *Poultry processing* ........ (908) 523-1600
Papetti's Hygrade Egg Products, Inc., 877 North Ave. E., Elizabeth 07201
Acctg. Mgr.—Sanjeev Lund, 7 emp., *Chicken egg processing* ........ (908) 282-7140
Puglisi Egg Farms, Inc., 75 Easy St., Howell 07731
Pres.—John Puglisi, 40 emp., *Egg production & processing* ........ (732) 938-2373
San Miguel Live Poultry, LLC, 499 Orange St., Newark 07107
★ Manager—Alex Montalbo, 3 emp., *Poultry processing* ........ (973) 482-1007
Senat Poultry, LLC, 28 Warren St., Paterson 07524
Ptnr.—Ali Kucukkarca, 30 emp., *Poultry meat processing* ........ (973) 742-4790
Streit & Son Co., Inc., Carl, 703 Atkins Ave., Neptune 07753
Pres.—Jim Robinson, 5 emp., *Meat, poultry & pork processing* ........ (732) 775-0803

## 2021 Butter—creamery

Amish Dairy Products, LLC, 41 Vreeland Ave., Ste. 101, Totowa 07512
Mng. Member—Kenneth Tensen, 7 emp., *Dairy products, including cheese &* ........ (973) 256-7676

## 2022 Cheese, natural & processed

Amish Dairy Products, LLC, 41 Vreeland Ave., Ste. 101, Totowa 07512
Mng. Member—Kenneth Tensen, 7 emp., *Dairy products, including cheese &* ........ (973) 256-7676
Anderson International Foods, Inc., 95 Burma Rd., Jersey City 07305
Pres.—Bridgitte Mizrahi, 30 emp., *Cheese* ........ (516) 747-2210
Antonio Mozzarella Factory, Inc., 631 Frelinghuysen Ave., Newark 07114
Pres.—Tom Tugliese, 22 emp., *Mozzarella cheese* ........ (973) 353-9411
Arthur Schuman, Inc., 40 New Dutch Ln., Fairfield 07004
Pres.—Neal Schuman, 85 emp., *Corporate headquarters & wedges, grated* ........ (973) 227-0030
Biazzo Dairy Products, Inc., 1145 Edgewater Ave., Ridgefield 07657
Owner & V-P.—John Iapichino, 27 emp., *Ricotta & mozzarella & fresh mozaarella* ........ (201) 941-6800
Capital Foods, Inc., 1701 E. Elizabeth Ave., Linden 07036
Pres.—Joseph Falcone, 22 emp., *Ricotta cheese* ........ (908) 587-9050
Cognati Cheese Co., Inc., 205 Moonachie Rd., 2nd Fl., Moonachie 07074
Pres.—Alain Voss, 45 emp., *Cheese* ........ (201) 807-9100
Colonna Brothers, Inc., 4102 Bergen Tpke., P.O. Box 808, North Bergen 07047
Pres.—Peter Colonna, 100 emp., *Private label & branded grated & shredded* ........ (201) 864-1115
Dairy Delight, LLC, 1 Industrial Dr., Rutherford 07070
Owner—Victor Ostreicher, 15 emp., *Israeli dairy products* ........ (201) 939-7878
J.V.M. Sales, Inc., 3401-A Tremley Point Rd., Linden 07036
Pres., CEO—Marybeth Tomasino, 70 emp., *Cheese* ........ (908) 862-4866
John Wm. Macy CheeseSticks, Inc., 80 Kipp Ave., Elmwood Park 07407
Pres., Hum. Res.—John Macy, 60 emp., *Gourmet breadsticks, dessert twists* ........ (201) 791-8036
Lebanon Cheese Co., Inc., 3 Railroad Ave., P.O. Box 63, Lebanon 08833
Pres.—Joe Lotito, 5 emp., *Ricotta cheese* ........ (908) 236-2611
Lioni Latticini, Inc., 555 Lehigh Ave., Union 07083
V-P.—Salvatore Salzarulo, 30 emp., *Mozzarella cheese* ........ (908) 686-6061
Losurdo Foods, Inc., 20 Owens Rd., Hackensack 07601
Founder—Michael Losurdo, 100 emp., *Corporate headquarters & dairy products* ........ (201) 343-6680
Lotito Foods, Inc., 510 E. 35th St., Paterson 07504
Plt. Mgr.—William Robles, 10 emp., *Grated Romano cheese processing* ........ (973) 684-2900
Lotito Foods, Inc./Mrs. Mazzula Foods, 240 Carter Dr., Edison 08817
Pres.—Christopher Lotito, 200 emp., *Corporate headquarters & cheese & sun-dried* ........ (732) 248-0222
Montena Taranto Foods, Inc., 400 Victoria Ter., Ridgefield 07657
Pres.—Joe Taranto, 60 emp., *Italian cheese & cheese products* ........ (201) 943-8484
Sankar Assocs., Inc., 14 Empire Blvd., Moonachie 07074
Pres.—Burton Kreindel, 30 emp., *Contract cheese packaging for the dairy* ........ (201) 994-1700

Tipico Products, Inc., 490 Oberlin Ave. S., Lakewood 08701
GM—Bob Castellano, 150 emp., *Processed cheese*.......... (732) 942-8820
Toscana Cheese Co., Inc., 575 Windsor Dr., Secaucus 07094
Pres.—Victor J. Paparazzo, 100 emp., *European-style cheeses*.......... (201) 617-1500
Tropical Cheese Industries, Inc., 450 Fayette St., Perth Amboy 08861
Hum. Res. Mgr.—Nestor Sabogal, 250 emp., *Cheese & cheese products*.......... (732) 442-4898
Vitamia & Sons, 206 Harrison Ave., Lodi 07644
Pres.—Anthony Vitamia, 12 emp., *Ravioli, pasta, sauces, bread, cheese*.......... (973) 546-1140

## 2023 Dry, condensed, evaporated products

AkPharma, Inc., 6840 Old Egg Harbor Rd., Egg Harbor Township 08234
★ Owner—Alan Kligerman, 5 emp., *Dietary supplements*.......... (609) 645-5100
American Casein Co., Inc., 109 Elbow Ln., Burlington 08016
CEO—Adam Cabot, 50 emp., *Powdered protein ingredients for nutritional*.......... (609) 387-3130
Asiamerica Ingredients, Inc., 245 Old Hook Rd., Ste. 3, Westwood 07675
★ Owner—Mark Zhang, 4 emp., *Ingredients blending for the nutraceutical*.......... (201) 497-5993
CCA Industries, Inc. (H Q), 200 Murray Hill Pkwy., East Rutherford 07073
Pres., CEO—Richard Kornhauser, 135 emp., *Corporate headquarters; topical & OTC*.......... (201) 935-3232
Clofine Dairy & Food Products, Inc., 1407 New Rd., P.O. Box 335, Linwood 08221
Chrm.—Larry Clofine, 17 emp., *Manufacturer & distributor of dried*.......... (609) 653-1000
Cumberland Dairy, Inc., 80 Edward Ave., Bridgeton 08302
V-P., Opers.—Frank Catalana, 65 emp., *Milk & ice cream mixes*.......... (856) 451-1300
DNE Nutraceuticals, Inc., 700 Central Ave., Farmingdale 07719
★ V-P.—Paul Kugielsky, 50 emp., *Contract manufacturing of dietary supplements*.......... (732) 806-9538
HerbaKraft, Inc., 121 Ethel Rd. W., Ste. 6, Piscataway 08854
Pres.—Nisha Khanijow, 15 emp., *Vitamins, minerals, dietary supplements*.......... (732) 463-1000
Imperial Drug & Spice Corp., 5620 Kennedy Blvd. W., West New York 07093
Pres.—Victoria Weingartner, 5 emp., *Latino/Hispanic health & beauty care*.......... (201) 348-1551
Inergetics, Inc., 550 Broad St., 12th Fl., Newark 07102
Opers. Mgr.—Sherman Fan, 10 emp., *Nutritional drink mixes for cancer*.......... (908) 604-2500
Losurdo Foods, Inc., 20 Owens Rd., Hackensack 07601
Founder—Michael Losurdo, 100 emp., *Corporate headquarters & dairy products*.......... (201) 343-6680
MYOS Corp. (H Q), 45 Horsehill Rd., Ste. 106, Cedar Knolls 07927
★ Pres.—Peter Levy, 10 emp., *Corporate headquarters; bionutritional*.......... (973) 509-0444
R-Kane Products, Inc., 8351 National Hwy., Pennsauken 08110
Pres.—Robert Kaskey, 15 emp., *Nutritional dietary protein meal replacement*.......... (856) 663-0644
Tomer Laboratories, 350 Campus Dr., Somerset 08873
Pres.—Onkar Tomer, 3 emp., *Dietary supplements*.......... (732) 560-1885
Tuscan Dairy, Inc., 117 Cumberland Blvd., Burlington 08016
Plt. Mgr.—Eric Bayer, 200 emp., *Dairy products*.......... (609) 499-2600

## 2024 Ice cream & frozen desserts

Alice Corp., 815 Fairview Ave., Unit 9-A, Fairview 07022
Pres.—Yoshi Yuyama, 10 emp., *Japanese mochi ice cream*.......... (201) 943-5877
All Seasons Ice Cream Corp., 15 E.12th St., Paterson 07524
Mng. Ptnr. & Pres.—Freddy Perez, 5 emp., *Ice cream*.......... (201) 878-6790
Applegate Farm Homemade Ice Cream, Inc., 616 Grove St., Montclair 07043
Pres., CEO—Jason Street, 15 emp., *Ice cream*.......... (973) 744-5900
Arctic Ice Cream, 22 Arctic Pkwy., Ewing 08638
Pres.—Thomas Green, 10 emp., *Ice cream*.......... (609) 393-4264
Bindi North America, Inc., 507 Main St., Belleville 07109
Pur. Mgr.—Trish Bortone, 50 emp., *Frozen desserts*.......... (973) 751-1754
Bindi North America, Inc. (H Q), 630 Belleville Tpke., Kearny 07032
Pres., CEO—Attilio Bindi, 40 emp., *Corporate headquarters; frozen desserts*.......... (973) 812-8118
Clyde's Ices & Ice Cream, Inc., 48 Gaston Ave., Garfield 07026
Pres.—Tim Devens, 8 emp., *Ice cream & frozen desserts*.......... (973) 546-2760
Conrad's Confectionery, Inc., 107 Westwood Ave., Westwood 07675
Owner—J. J. Krachtus, 8 emp., *Chocolates & ice cream*.......... (201) 664-2895
Dairyland Ice Cream, 487 Chancellor Ave., Irvington 07111
Pres.—Arthur Anastasia, 20 emp., *Ice cream*.......... (973) 923-7625
Guernsey Crest Ice Cream Co., 134 19th Ave., Paterson 07513
Pres.—Joy Cornwell, 4 emp., *Ice cream*.......... (973) 742-4620
Halo Farm, Inc., 970 Spruce St., Lawrenceville 08648
Pres.—Jerry Reilly, 20 emp., *Ice cream, milk & fruit drinks*.......... (609) 695-3311
Johanna Foods, Inc., 20 Johanna Farms Rd., P.O. Box 272, Flemington 08822
Pres.—Robert Facchina, 580 emp., *Corporate headquarters & fruit juices*.......... (908) 788-2200
Kwality Foods, LLC, 1734 Oak Tree Rd., Edison 08820
Member—Kanti Parekh, 5 emp., *All-natural handmade ethnic flavored*.......... (732) 906-1941
Leo's Famous Yum Yum, 7 Tomlinson Mill Rd., Ste. 5, Medford 08055
CEO—Rick Cirelli, 7 emp., *Ice cream & frozen desserts*.......... (856) 797-8771
Limpert Bros., Inc., 202 N. West Blvd., Vineland 08360
Chrm., Pres.—Pearl Giordano, 20 emp., *Ice cream, frozen desserts, bakery*.......... (856) 691-1353
Maglione's Italian Ices, 111 Madison St., Iselin 08830
Ptnr. & GM—Michael Maglione, 12 emp., *Italian ices*.......... (732) 283-0705
Manischewitz Co., The (H Q), 80 Avenue K, Newark 07105
Pres.—Mark Weinstein, 65 emp., *Company headquarters; kosher cookies*.......... (201) 553-1100
Mister Cookie Face, LLC, 1989 Rutgers University Blvd., Lakewood 08701
Plt. Controller—Suzanne Crovo, 100 emp., *Private label contract manufacturing*.......... (732) 370-5533
Mr. Green Tea Ice Cream Co., 25 Church St., Unit 104, Keyport 07735
★ CEO—Richard Emanuel, 21 emp., *Ice cream*.......... (732) 446-9800
Nasto's Ice Cream Co., Inc., 236 Jefferson St., Newark 07105
Pres., CEO—Frank Nasto III, 19 emp., *Ice cream*.......... (973) 589-3333
Piece Of Cake Gourmet Ice Cream, Inc., 62 W. Inman Ave., Rahway 07065
Pres.—James A. Biniaris, 8 emp., *Gourmet ice cream novelties, ice cream*.......... (732) 382-0281
RW Delights, Inc., 50 Division Ave., Ste. 44, Millington 07946
Pres., CEO—Roxanne Kam, 4 emp., *Frozen souffles*.......... (718) 683-1038
Tofutti Brands, Inc., 50 Jackson Dr., Cranford 07016
Pres., CEO—David Mintz, 15 emp., *Kosher soy-based ice cream, dessert*.......... (908) 272-2400
Unilever North America, 700 Sylvan Ave., Englewood Cliffs 07632
Pres., N. America—Kees Kruythoff, 1900 emp., *Company headquarters & food & personal*... (201) 567-8000
Water Ice Factory, Inc., 15 Evergreen Rd., Chatham 08084
★ Owner—Ralph Skidmore, 5 emp., *Frozen ice cream desserts*.......... (856) 627-6831

## 2026 Milk—fluid

Clofine Dairy & Food Products, Inc., 1407 New Rd., P.O. Box 335, Linwood 08221
Chrm.—Larry Clofine, 17 emp., *Manufacturer & distributor of dried*.......... (609) 653-1000
Cumberland Dairy, Inc., 80 Edward Ave., Bridgeton 08302
V-P., Opers.—Frank Catalana, 65 emp., *Milk & ice cream mixes*.......... (856) 451-1300
Dairy Delight, LLC, 1 Industrial Dr., Rutherford 07070
Owner—Victor Ostreicher, 15 emp., *Israeli dairy products*.......... (201) 939-7878
Farmland Dairies, 520 Main Ave., P.O. Box 3340, Wallington 07057
GM—Ronald Gaidusek, 350 emp., *Milk*.......... (973) 777-2500
Halo Farm, Inc., 970 Spruce St., Lawrenceville 08648
Pres.—Jerry Reilly, 20 emp., *Ice cream, milk & fruit drinks*.......... (609) 695-3311
Readington Farms, Inc., 12 Mill Rd., P.O. Box 164, Whitehouse 08888
Plt. Mgr.—Doug McDowell, 200 emp., *Milk*.......... (908) 534-2121
Tuscan Dairy, Inc., 117 Cumberland Blvd., Burlington 08016
Plt. Mgr.—Eric Bayer, 200 emp., *Dairy products*.......... (609) 499-2600
Valley Shepherd Creamery, 50 Fairmount Rd., Long Valley 07853
Owner—Eran Wajswol, 6 emp., *Cheeses*.......... (908) 876-3200

## 2032 Canned specialties

Aunt Kitty's Foods, Inc., 270 N. Mill Rd., Vineland 08360
Cont.—Richard Kebler, 130 emp., *Canned soup, ravioli, stew & chili*.......... (856) 691-2100
Campbell Soup Co. (H Q), 1 Campbell Pl., Camden 08103
Chrm.—Paul Charron, 1200 emp., *Company headquarters; canned soups,*.......... (856) 342-4800
General Mills Progresso, 500 W. Elmer Rd., Vineland 08360
Plt. Mgr.—Becky Crane, 475 emp., *Canned soups & meals*.......... (856) 691-1565
Goya Foods, Inc., 650 New County Rd., Secaucus 07094
GM—Benjamin Spenickie, 60 emp., *Dry beans, sauces, mixes & seasonings*.......... (201) 865-3470
Goya Foods, Inc. (H Q), 100 Seaview Dr., Secaucus 07094
Pres.—Robert Unanue, 350 emp., *Corporate headquarters; canned & packed*.......... (201) 348-4900
Mayab Happy Tacos, Inc., 450 Florida Grove Rd., Perth Amboy 08861
V-P.—George Alamilla, 25 emp., *Flour & corn tortillas, white & yellow*.......... (732) 293-0400
Nestle Healthcare Nutrition, Inc. (H Q), 12 Vreeland Rd., 2nd Fl., P.O. Box 697, Florham Park 07932
Reg. Bus. Head, N. America—David Yates, 400 emp., *Corporate headquarters; baby food &* (973) 593-7500
Ugo Di Lullo & Sons, 1004 Edgewater Ave., P.O. Box 126, Westville 08093
Owner—Ugo Di Lullo, 9 emp., *Soups, gravy, broth, spaghetti & canned*.......... (856) 456-3700

## 2033 Canned fruits & vegetables

Allied Old English, Inc., 100 Markley St., Port Reading 07064
Owner—Fred Ross, 45 emp., *Jams, jellies & preserves, barbecue*.......... (732) 636-2060
B & G Foods, Inc. (H Q), 4 Gatehall Dr., Ste. 110, Parsippany 07054
Pres.—David Wenner, 70 emp., *Corporate headquarters; preserves,*.......... (973) 401-6500
Beverage Distribution Center, Inc., 8275 Route 130, Pennsauken 08110
Pres., CFO—Walt Wilkinson, 700 emp., *Corporate headquarters & manufacturer*.......... (856) 665-6200
C & E Canners, Inc., 1249 Mays Landing Rd., P.O. Box 229, Hammonton 08037
Pres.—Robert Cappuccio, 26 emp., *Canned cranberry sauce, ketchup, lemon*.......... (609) 561-1078
Campbell Soup Co. (H Q), 1 Campbell Pl., Camden 08103
Chrm.—Paul Charron, 1200 emp., *Company headquarters; canned soups,*.......... (856) 342-4800
Cento Fine Foods, 100 Cento Blvd., West Deptford 08086
Manager—Anthony Varretta, 10 emp., *Italian food products, including canned*.......... (856) 853-5445
Chelten House Products, Inc., 607 Heron Dr., P.O. Box 434, Bridgeport 08014
CEO—Steve Dabrow, 150 emp., *Organic & natural sauces, dressings*.......... (856) 467-1600
Clement Pappas & Company, Inc., 1045 Parsonage Rd., Seabrook 08302
Plt. Mgr.—Adam Olds, 210 emp., *Bottled & canned fruit juice & cranberry*.......... (856) 455-1001
Clement Pappas & Company, Inc. (H Q), 1 Collins Dr., Ste. 200, Carneys Point 08069
CEO—Mark McNeil, 125 emp., *Corporate headquarters; bottled & canned*.......... (856) 455-1000
Dr Pepper Snapple Group, Inc., 1200 Milik St., Carteret 07008
Plt. Mgr.—Saul Cruz, 200 emp., *Juices*.......... (732) 969-1600
FunniBonz, LLC, 3 Lake View Ct., Princeton Junction 08550
Pres., CEO—James H. Barbour III, 5 emp., *Barbecue sauces, marinades, relishes*.......... (877) 300-2669
General Mills Progresso, 500 W. Elmer Rd., Vineland 08360
Plt. Mgr.—Becky Crane, 475 emp., *Canned soups & meals*.......... (856) 691-1565
Gregory Packaging, Inc., 247 Rome St., P.O. Box 5188, Newark 07105
Pres.—Ed Gregory, 49 emp., *Juice packaging*.......... (973) 465-1113
Johanna Foods, Inc., 20 Johanna Farms Rd., P.O. Box 272, Flemington 08822
Pres.—Robert Facchina, 580 emp., *Corporate headquarters & fruit juices*.......... (908) 788-2200
Manischewitz Co., The (H Q), 80 Avenue K, Newark 07105
Pres.—Mark Weinstein, 65 emp., *Company headquarters; kosher cookies*.......... (201) 553-1100
Mayab Happy Tacos, Inc., 450 Florida Grove Rd., Perth Amboy 08861
V-P.—George Alamilla, 25 emp., *Flour & corn tortillas, white & yellow*.......... (732) 293-0400
Miel Patisserie, LLC, 1990 Route 70 E., Ste. 14, Cherry Hill 08003
Owner—Gelareh Nouri, 12 emp., *Fresh pastries, specialty & wedding*.......... (856) 424-6435
Momma's Home Made, LLC, 1225 Haddonfield Berlin Rd., Southgate Plz., Ste. 2, Voorhees 08043
Ptnr.—Daisy Smith, 2 emp., *Gourmet, 50% less sugar added & no*.......... (856) 753-3250
Ocean Spray Cranberries, Inc., 104 E. Park St., Bordentown 08505
Cont.—Mike Brumfield, 250 emp., *Cranberry juice*.......... (609) 298-0905
Pinnacle Foods Group, LLC (H Q), 121 Woodcrest Rd., Cherry Hill 08003
CEO—Bob Gamgort, 220 emp., *Company headquarters; branded frozen*.......... (856) 969-7100
Roselli's Food Specialties, Inc., L. E., 155 Church Rd., Medford 08055
Pres.—Laura Roselli, 12 emp., *Frozen pasta products & pasta sauces*.......... (609) 654-4816
Sunny Delight Beverages Co., 10 Corn Rd., Dayton 08810
Plt. Mgr.—Donald Ruddy, 130 emp., *Juice bottling*.......... (732) 329-2391
Sunny Slope Farms, 400 Greenwich Rd., Bridgeton 08302
Pres.—Al Caggiano, 15 emp., *Apples & peaches processing*.......... (856) 451-0022
Sussex Innovations, LLC, 137 Libertyville Rd., Wantage 07461
CEO—Raj Sinha, 3 emp., *Food products, including jellies &*.......... (917) 699-9489
Vitamia & Sons, 206 Harrison Ave., Lodi 07644
Pres.—Anthony Vitamia, 12 emp., *Ravioli, pasta, sauces, bread, cheese*.......... (973) 546-1140
Walden Farms, Inc., 1209 W. Saint Georges Ave., Linden 07036
Pres., CFO—Mitchell Berko, 20 emp., *Salad dressings, condiments, syrups*.......... (908) 925-9494
Wayne County Foods, Inc., 360 Coit St., Irvington 07111
Pres.—Peter Nemeth, 30 emp., *Private label fruit blend, grape &*.......... (973) 399-0101
Whitlock Packaging Corp., 92 N. Main St., Wharton 07885
Cont.—Mary Clyburn, 200 emp., *Noncarbonated beverages & fruit juice*.......... (973) 361-9794

## 2034 Dehydrated fruits, vegetables & soups

American Custom Drying Co., 109 Elbow Ln., Burlington 08016
CEO—Adam Cabot, 70 emp., *Contract & toll processing, including*.......... (609) 387-3933
Bunge North America, Inc., 125 Sanford Ave., Kearny 07032
Sales Mgr., Inside—C. C. Petford, 65 emp., *Spices, shortenings, oils, margarines*.......... (201) 467-0200
Comarco Products, 501 Jackson St., Camden 08104
Pres.—Tom Hoversen, 35 emp., *Vegetable processing*.......... (856) 342-7557
Eatem Foods Company, 1829 Gallagher Dr., Vineland 08360
Pres., CEO—Ron Savelli, 65 emp., *Concentrated organic & kosher soup*.......... (856) 692-1663
F & S Produce Co., Inc., 913 Bridgeton Ave., P.O. Box 489, Rosenhayn 08352
CEO—Salvatore Pipitone, Jr., 600 emp., *Fruit & vegetable processing & packaging*.......... (856) 453-0316
FunniBonz, LLC, 3 Lake View Ct., Princeton Junction 08550
Pres., CEO—James H. Barbour III, 5 emp., *Barbecue sauces, marinades, relishes*.......... (877) 300-2669
Goya Foods, Inc., 650 New County Rd., Secaucus 07094
GM—Benjamin Spenickie, 60 emp., *Dry beans, sauces, mixes & seasonings*.......... (201) 865-3470
Hain Celestial Group, Inc., The, 50 Knickerbocker Rd., Moonachie 07074
Plt. Mgr.—Yoses Brecher, 100 emp., *Vegetable chips*.......... (201) 935-4500



★ Indicates new listing this edition.

International Foodsource, LLC, 52 Richboynton Rd., Dover 07801
Pres.—David Lipson, 120 emp., *Dried fruits, nuts & gourmet food products* ........ (973) 361-7044
Interstate Sales New of Jersey, LLC, 1226 Haddonfield-Berlin Rd., Unit C-2, Voorhees 08043
Ptnr. & Pres.—Steven Osder, 10 emp., *Private label seasonings, spices, mustards* ........ (856) 433-8692
La Dominica, 635 56th St., West New York 07093
Pres.—Venancia Dominguez, 10 emp., *Plantain chips* ........ (201) 348-4294
Lotito Foods, Inc./Mrs. Mazzula Foods, 240 Carter Dr., Edison 08817
Pres.—Christopher Lotito, 200 emp., *Corporate headquarters & cheese & sun-dried* ........ (732) 248-0222
M. A. R. Kit, Inc., 1095 Cinnaminson Ave., Cinnaminson 08077
Pres., GM—Michael Georgetti, 18 emp., *Italian pasta, sauces, soups & prepared* ........ (856) 829-5992
R.A.B. Food Group, LLC, 80 Avenue K, Newark 07105
Plt. Mgr.—Randall Copeland, 200 emp., *Kosher cookies, noodles, dry soup mix* ........ (201) 553-1100
RC Fine Foods, Inc., 139 Stryker Ln., Hillsborough 08844
Pres.—Susan Goldman, 70 emp., *Soup, sauce, gravy, salad dressing* ........ (908) 359-5500
Savoy Extraordinary Snack, LLC, 35 N. Middaugh St., Somerville 08876
★ Owner—Robert Valero, 4 emp., *Snack foods, including seeds, nuts,* ........ (908) 252-9800
Star Snacks, LLC, 105 Harbor Dr., Jersey City 07305
Mng. Ptnr.—Mendel Brachfeld, 200 emp., *Nuts & dried fruit* ........ (201) 200-9820
Westco Fruit & Nut Products Co., Inc., 93-97 Coit St., Irvington 07111
Pres., Hum. Res. Mgr.—Rivka F. Moradi, 3 emp., *Nuts, dried fruit & candy* ........ (973) 373-1866
Woodstock Farms Mfg., 96 Executive Ave., Edison 08817
Hum. Res. Mgr.—Virginia Johnson, 120 emp., *Organic, kosher & natural nuts, seeds* ........ (732) 650-9905

## 2035 Pickles, sauces & salad dressings

Allied Old English, Inc., 100 Markley St., Port Reading 07064
Owner—Fred Ross, 45 emp., *Jams, jellies & preserves, barbecue* ........ (732) 636-2060
B & G Foods, Inc. (H Q), 4 Gatehall Dr., Ste. 110, Parsippany 07054
Pres.—David Wenner, 70 emp., *Corporate headquarters; preserves,* ........ (973) 401-6500
Ba-Tampte Pickle Products, Inc., 2660 Main Rd., Franklinville 08322
★ Owner—Howard Silberstein, 12 emp., *Pickles* ........ (856) 697-9815
C & E Canners, Inc., 1249 Mays Landing Rd., P.O. Box 229, Hammonton 08037
Pres.—Robert Cappuccio, 26 emp., *Canned cranberry sauce, ketchup, lemon* ........ (609) 561-1078
Chelten House Products, Inc., 607 Heron Dr., P.O. Box 434, Bridgeport 08014
CEO—Steve Dabrow, 150 emp., *Organic & natural sauces, dressings* ........ (856) 467-1600
Dee & L, LLC, 67 Lefante Way, P.O. Box 3431, Bayonne 07002
Dir., Opers.—Larry Kahn, 20 emp., *Mayonnaises, salad dressings & fruit* ........ (201) 858-0131
FunniBonz, LLC, 3 Lake View Ct., Princeton Junction 08550
Pres., CEO—James H. Barbour III, 5 emp., *Barbecue sauces, marinades, relishes* ........ (877) 300-2669
Goya Foods, Inc., 650 New County Rd., Secaucus 07094
GM—Benjamin Spenickie, 60 emp., *Dry beans, sauces, mixes & seasonings* ........ (201) 865-3470
Goya Foods, Inc. (H Q), 100 Seaview Dr., Secaucus 07094
Pres.—Robert Unanue, 350 emp., *Corporate headquarters; canned & packed* ........ (201) 348-4900
Great Garlic Foods, Inc., 709 5th Ave., Bradley Beach 07720
Pres.—Joe Desantis, Jr., 10 emp., *Garlic & pesto sauce & spreads* ........ (732) 775-3311
Hengstenberg GmbH, 90 Pershing Pl., Cresskill 07626
★ Owner—Steffen Hengstenberg, 4 emp., *Pickles* ........ (201) 568-6596
Interstate Sales New of Jersey, LLC, 1226 Haddonfield-Berlin Rd., Unit C-2, Voorhees 08043
Ptnr. & Pres.—Steven Osder, 10 emp., *Private label seasonings, spices, mustards* ........ (856) 433-8692
Kaplan & Zubrin, Inc., 2nd & Kaighn Ave., Camden 08103
Pres.—Ronald Kaplan, 30 emp., *Pickles* ........ (856) 964-1083
L & D's Sapore Ravioli & Cheese, Inc., 429-B Lincoln Blvd., Middlesex 08846
Mng. Ptnr.—Anthony Florano, 15 emp., *Handmade fresh & frozen Italian ravioli* ........ (732) 563-9190
M. A. R. Kit, Inc., 1095 Cinnaminson Ave., Cinnaminson 08077
Pres., GM—Michael Georgetti, 18 emp., *Italian pasta, sauces, soups & prepared* ........ (856) 829-5992
Muirhead Of Ringoes New Jersey, Inc., 43 U.S. Highway 202, Ringoes 08551
Pres.—Doris Simpson, 10 emp., *Condiments, sauces & flavored nondairy* ........ (908) 782-7803
Oasis Foods Co., 635 Ramsey Ave., P.O. Box 697, Hillside 07205
Pres., CEO—William Gillingham, 150 emp., *Vegetable oils, salad dressings, sauces* ........ (908) 964-0477
Paterson Pickle Co., 285 4th Ave., Paterson 07514
Pres.—Mark Nadel, 20 emp., *Pickles & pickling cucumbers* ........ (973) 523-1000
Patriot Pickle, 20 Edison Dr., Wayne 07470
Pres.—Bill McEntee, 50 emp., *Pickles* ........ (973) 709-9487
Pickle King, 220 Ellison St., Paterson 07505
Pres., GM—Richard Nadel, 12 emp., *Pickles, pickled peppers, olives &* ........ (973) 977-2095
Pickle-Licious, 384 Cedar Ln., Teaneck 07666
Owner—Robyn Samra, 2 emp., *Gourmet pickles* ........ (201) 833-0100
RC Fine Foods, Inc., 139 Stryker Ln., Hillsborough 08844
Pres.—Susan Goldman, 70 emp., *Soup, sauce, gravy, salad dressing* ........ (908) 359-5500
Reckitt Benckiser, Inc., 399 Interpace Pkwy., P.O. Box 225, Parsippany 07054
Pres., Frenchs Food Prod.—Elliott Penner, 375 emp., *Corporate headquarters & consumer cleaning* (973) 404-2600
Silver Palate Kitchens, Inc., 211 Knickerbocker Rd., P.O. Box 512, Cresskill 07626
Pres.—Peter Harris, 10 emp., *Pasta & cooking sauces, condiments,* ........ (201) 568-0110
Unilever North America, 700 Sylvan Ave., Englewood Cliffs 07632
Pres., N. America—Kees Kruythoff, 1900 emp., *Company headquarters & food & personal* ... (201) 567-8000
Violet Packing, 123 Railroad Ave., Williamstown 08094
Br. Mgr.—Darrell Cran, 17 emp., *Crushed tomatoes, pizza, spaghetti* ........ (856) 629-7428
Walden Farms, Inc., 1209 W. Saint Georges Ave., Linden 07036
Pres., CFO—Mitchell Berko, 20 emp., *Salad dressings, condiments, syrups* ........ (908) 925-9494

## 2037 Fruits & vegetables, frozen

Dewy Meadow Foods, Inc., 1018 Rector Rd., Bridgewater 08807
Pres.—Randolph Krogoll, 20 emp., *Frozen meat pies & bakery products* ........ (908) 218-5655
Drink Atoast Co., Inc., 603 Harrison St., P.O. Box 204, Riverside 08075
Pres.—Daniel McDonough, 5 emp., *Beverages, syrups & concentrates* ........ (856) 461-1000
Grasso Foods, Inc., 2111 Kings Hwy., P.O. Box 127, Woolwich Township 08085
Pres.—Janet Schumann, 150 emp., *Frozen bell peppers* ........ (856) 467-2222
Seabrook Bros. & Sons, Inc., 85 Finley Rd., P.O. Box 5103, Seabrook 08302
Pres.—James Seabrook, Jr., 300 emp., *Frozen vegetables & packaging* ........ (856) 455-8080
Townsend Farms, Inc., 3501 S. East Blvd., Vineland 08360
Opers. Mgr.—David Rodigan, 100 emp., *Individually quick-frozen berry processing* ........ (856) 825-5240

## 2038 Frozen specialties

Bylada Foods, LLC, 140 W. Commercial Ave., Moonachie 07074
GM—Eric Silverman, 35 emp., *Miniature pizza bagels* ........ (201) 933-7474
Caesar's Pasta, 1001 Lower Landing Rd., Ste. 311, Blackwood 08012
Pres.—Michael Lodato, 50 emp., *Frozen pasta meals, including meat,* ........ (856) 227-2585
Classic Cake Co., The, 480 Evesham Rd., Cherry Hill 08003
Owner—Barry Krachman, 70 emp., *Cakes, cookies, pastries, pies, artisan* ........ (856) 751-5448
Dewy Meadow Foods, Inc., 1018 Rector Rd., Bridgewater 08807
Pres.—Randolph Krogoll, 20 emp., *Frozen meat pies & bakery products* ........ (908) 218-5655
Fillo Factory, Inc., 10 Fairway Ct., Northvale 07647
CEO—Ron Rexroth, 150 emp., *Private label fillo doughs, organic* ........ (201) 439-1036
Gourmet Kitchen, Inc., 1238 State Route 33, Neptune 07753
CEO—Raymond Walsh, 80 emp., *Manufacturer & distributor of frozen* ........ (732) 775-5222
Kellogg Co., 322 S. Egg Harbor Rd., Hammonton 08037
Hum. Res. Mgr.—Monica Raker, 120 emp., *Frozen waffles* ........ (609) 567-2300
Ko-Fro Foods, Inc., 23 Mileed Way, Avenel 07001
CEO—Calvin Mendelsohn, 10 emp., *Frozen pizza & lasagna* ........ (732) 499-8282
M & G Food, Inc., 1295 Main Ave., Clifton 07011
Pres.—Michael Dutch, 6 emp., *Homemade fresh & frozen pierogies* ........ (973) 340-0340
McCain Foods USA, Inc., 11 Gregg St., Lodi 07644
Hum. Res. Mgr.—Barbara German, 120 emp., *Frozen pizza* ........ (201) 368-0600
Miami Onion Roll Co., 111 Berkshire Ave., Paterson 07502
Pres.—Harriet Davis, 30 emp., *Frozen hors d'oeuvres, bread & rolls* ........ (973) 389-2202
Mitsui Foods, Inc., 35 Maple St., Norwood 07648
Pres., CEO—Tom Osada, 60 emp., *Manufacturer of frozen pasta products* ........ (201) 750-0500
North Jersey Ravioli Co., 65 Pacific Ave., Garfield 07026
Pres.—Anthony Apolito, 2 emp., *Ravioli* ........ (973) 772-5050
Old Fashioned Kitchen, Inc., 1045 Towbin Ave., Lakewood 08701
Pres.—Jay Conzen, 85 emp., *Frozen foods* ........ (732) 364-4100
Pinnacle Foods Group, LLC (H Q), 121 Woodcrest Rd., Cherry Hill 08003
CEO—Bob Gamgort, 220 emp., *Company headquarters; branded frozen* ........ (856) 969-7100
Rich Products, 1910 Gallagher Dr., Vineland 08360
Cont.—MaryJo Nailor, 110 emp., *Frozen Italian meatballs* ........ (856) 696-5600
Rico Foods, Inc., 527 E. 18th St., Paterson 07514
Pres.—Emilio Hernandez, 36 emp., *Hispanic food products* ........ (973) 278-0589
Roselli's Food Specialties, Inc., L. E., 155 Church Rd., Medford 08055
Pres.—Laura Roselli, 12 emp., *Frozen pasta products & pasta sauces* ........ (609) 654-4816
San Marco Ravioli, Inc., 38 Davey St., Bloomfield 07003
Pres.—Eugene Siciliano, 14 emp., *Frozen pasta* ........ (973) 748-4545
Savignano Foods Corp., 107 S. Jefferson St., Orange 07050
Ptnr. & Pres.—Michael Savignano, 40 emp., *Frozen Italian pasta* ........ (973) 673-7537
Star Ravioli Mfg. Co., Inc., 2 Anderson Ave., Moonachie 07074
Pres., CFO—Laurence Piretra, 12 emp., *Fresh & frozen gourmet Italian ravioli* ........ (201) 933-6427
Tabatchnick Fine Foods, Inc., 1230 Hamilton St., P.O. Box 356, Somerset 08873
Pres.—Ben Tabatchnick, 35 emp., *Frozen soups* ........ (732) 247-6668
Tovli, Inc., 49 Hunter St., Newark 07114
Pres.—Abraham Osterichner, 25 emp., *Specialty frozen food products* ........ (718) 417-6677
Ungar's Food Products, Inc., 9 Boumar Pl., Elmwood Park 07407
Pres.—Peter Praeger, 45 emp., *Frozen kosher food products, including* ........ (201) 703-1300

## 2041 Flour & other grain mill products

Bay State Milling Co., 404 Getty Ave., Clifton 07011
Sales Mgr.—Vince Malara, 60 emp., *Flour & animal feed milling* ........ (973) 772-1000
Green & Sons, Inc., Jonathan, 48 Squankum-Yellowbrook Rd., Howell 07731
CEO—Barry Green, 30 emp., *Grass seeds, fertilizers & turf chemicals* ........ (732) 938-7007
Panera Bread Co., LLC, 5 E. Evans St., Fairfield 07004
GM—Vince Chiappetta, 80 emp., *Bread dough* ........ (973) 276-0250
Tatz Industries, Inc., William, 11 Railroad Pl., Belleville 07109
Pres.—William Tatz, 5 emp., *Custom blended bakery products, including* ........ (973) 751-0720

## 2043 Cereal breakfast foods

MYOS Corp. (H Q), 45 Horsehill Rd., Ste. 106, Cedar Knolls 07927
★ Pres.—Peter Levy, 10 emp., *Corporate headquarters; bionutritional* ........ (973) 509-0444

## 2045 Flour mixes & doughs—prepared

Fairfield Gourmet Food Corp., 11 Cliffside Dr., Cedar Grove 07009
Pres., CEO—Ari Margulies, 100 emp., *Corporate headquarters & frozen cookie* ........ (973) 227-2800
Fillo Factory, Inc., 10 Fairway Ct., Northvale 07647
CEO—Ron Rexroth, 150 emp., *Private label fillo doughs, organic* ........ (201) 439-1036
J & J Snack Foods Corp., 361 Benigno Blvd., Ste. A, Bellmawr 08031
★ Manager—Bob Cranmer, 150 emp., *Frozen pretzel dough* ........ (856) 933-3597
J & K Ingredients, Inc., 160 E. 5th St., Paterson 07524
Pres.—James K. Sausville, 80 emp., *Natural bread, cake & donut mixes,* ........ (973) 340-8700
Jimmy's Cookies, LLC, 18-01 River Rd., Fair Lawn 07410
Pres.—Michael Pisani, 60 emp., *Gourmet cookies & cookie dough* ........ (201) 797-8900
Losurdo Foods, Inc., 20 Owens Rd., Hackensack 07601
Founder—Michael Losurdo, 100 emp., *Corporate headquarters & dairy products* ........ (201) 343-6680
Pinnacle Foods Group, LLC (H Q), 121 Woodcrest Rd., Cherry Hill 08003
CEO—Bob Gamgort, 220 emp., *Company headquarters; branded frozen* ........ (856) 969-7100
Puratos Corp., 1941 Old Cuthbert Rd., Cherry Hill 08034
Pres., U.S.—Frederic Duvauchelle, 100 emp., *Corporate headquarters & bread, bagel* ........ (856) 428-4300

## 2046 Wet corn milling

Ingredion Incorporated (H Q), 10 Finderne Ave., Ste. C, Bridgewater 08807
Global Dir., Innovation & Mktg. Excellence—Jill Schimmel, 250 emp., *Divisional headquarters;* (908) 685-5555

## 2047 Dog & cat food

Bravo Packing, 59 N. Gothwood Ave., Carneys Point 08069
Owner—Joe Merola, 5 emp., *Natural pet food & treats* ........ (856) 299-1044
Daybrook Holdings, Inc. (H Q), 161 Madison Ave., 2nd Fl., Morristown 07960
Pres., CEO—Gregory F. Holt, 6 emp., *Corporate headquarters; fish meal &* ........ (973) 538-6766
Dr. Harvey's Healthy Formulations Inc., 25 W. Highland Ave., Atlantic Highlands 07716
Owner—Harvey Cohen, 6 emp., *Health foods for companion pets* ........ (732) 787-2400
Fat Murray's Doggy Treats, 3 Deer Hill Dr., P.O. Box 32, Montville 07045
Owner—Ronda Fliss, 3 emp., *Gourmet baked dog treats* ........ (973) 299-2968
Hartz Mountain Corp., The, 400 Plaza Dr., Secaucus 07094
Div. V-P., Mktg.—Adam Coacher, 250 emp., *Corporate headquarters & animal health* ........ (201) 271-4800
IMS Pet Industries, 34 Passaic St., Wood Ridge 07075
Pres.—Sam Blachorsky, 40 emp., *Pet food ingredients & pet treats* ........ (973) 249-0026
Innovation Concepts, Inc. (H Q), 870 Warwick Tpke., Hewitt 07421
Pres.—Robert Tolve, 5 emp., *Corporate headquarters; dog treats* ........ (973) 853-5300
Loving Pets Corp., 110 Melrich Rd., Ste. 1, Cranbury 08512
Owner—Eric Abbey, 20 emp., *Natural pet treats & accessories, including* ........ (609) 655-3700
Menu Foods, Inc., 9130 Griffith Morgan Ln., Pennsauken 08110
Ex. V-P., Opers.—Steve Lindsey, 280 emp., *Dog & cat food* ........ (856) 662-7412

## 2048 Feeds—prepared

Abba Products Corp., 1301 Central Ave., Hillside 07205
Pres., GM—Mike Abbate, 100 emp., *Bird feed* ........ (908) 353-0669
Bay State Milling Co., 404 Getty Ave., Clifton 07011
Sales Mgr.—Vince Malara, 60 emp., *Flour & animal feed milling* ........ (973) 772-1000
Daybrook Holdings, Inc. (H Q), 161 Madison Ave., 2nd Fl., Morristown 07960
Pres., CEO—Gregory F. Holt, 6 emp., *Corporate headquarters; fish meal &* ........ (973) 538-6766

DSM Pharmaceutical Products, Inc. (H Q), 45 Waterview Blvd., Parsippany 07054
Pres., CEO—Alexander Wessels, 165 emp., *Corporate headquarters; liquid & dry* ........ (973) 257-1063
Epicore Networks U.S.A., Inc., 4 Lina Ln., Eastampton 08060
CEO—Bill Long, 7 emp., *Specialty feeds for adult shrimp &* ........ (609) 267-9118
Mid Jersey Pet Supply, 296 Pershing Ave., Carteret 07008
Pres.—Ed Rutkowski, 5 emp., *Frozen fish food* ........ (732) 541-2807
Phibro Animal Health Corp., 300 Frank W. Burr Blvd., Stn. 21, Glenpointe Center East, 3rd Fl., Teaneck 07666
Chrm.—Jack Bendheim, 100 emp., *Corporate headquarters & animal feed* ........ (201) 329-7300
R World Enterprises, 197 Congress St., Jersey City 07307
Ptnr.—Marian Pacailler, 3 emp., *Birdseeds* ........ (201) 795-2428
ReConserve, Inc., 1250 Amboy Ave., Perth Amboy 08861
Sr. V-P.—John Hawrylko, 30 emp., *Chicken feed* ........ (732) 826-4240
Research Diets, Inc., 20 Jules Ln., New Brunswick 08901
Pres.—E. Ulman, 50 emp., *Laboratory animal feed* ........ (732) 247-2390
Wilenta Feed, Inc., 46 Henry St., Secaucus 07094
Pres.—Peter Wilenta, 10 emp., *Animal feed from recycled bakery by-products* ........ (201) 863-3035
Woodstown Ice & Coal Co., 50 E. Grant St., P.O. Box 285, Woodstown 08098
Owner—Doug Macaluso, 7 emp., *Livestock feed* ........ (856) 769-0069

## 2051 Bread, cake & related products

A & A Soft Pretzel Co., 1100 N. 32nd St., Camden 08105
Pres.—Nicholas Panara, 2 emp., *Soft pretzels* ........ (856) 338-0208
AHB Foods International, 823 E. Gate Dr., Unit 3, Mount Laurel 08054
Pres.—Jay Roseman, 30 emp., *Artisan baked goods & breads* ........ (856) 642-9955
Americas Bakery, 32-50 Buffington St., P.O. Box 5099, Irvington 07111
Ptnr.—Tony Vicente, 55 emp., *Bread rolls* ........ (973) 372-0700
Anthony & Sons Italian Bakery, 20 Luger Rd., Denville 07834
GM—Phillip Dattolo, 55 emp., *Fresh artisan breads & sandwich rolls* ........ (973) 625-2323
Antique Bakery & Pizzeria, Inc., 122 Willow Ave., Hoboken 07030
Pres.—Ivan Rodriguez, 6 emp., *Italian bread* ........ (201) 714-9323
Aryzta/La Brea Bakery, 11 Technology Dr., Swedesboro 08085
GM—Tom Bent, 600 emp., *Bakery products, including breads,* ........ (856) 417-8100
Automatic Rolls Of New Jersey, Inc., 1 Gourmet Ln., Edison 08837
GM & Plt. Mgr.—Wayne Chandler, 75 emp., *Hamburger buns* ........ (732) 549-2243
Bakers Bounty, 7 Maple Ave., Linden 07036
Owner—Gerry LaPrete, 7 emp., *Baked goods, including cakes & pies* ........ (908) 587-1602
Baker's Perfection, Inc., 198 Green Pond Rd., Rockaway 07866
Pres.—Patrick S. Amello, Sr., 40 emp., *Bread, rolls, cakes, cookies, pies* ........ (973) 983-0700
Bakery, The, 99 N. Washington Ave., Bergenfield 07621
Owner—Brian Driscoll, 10 emp., *Bakery products, including cakes, bread* ........ (201) 384-1456
Balthazar Bakery, 214 S. Dean St., Englewood 07631
Owner—Keith McNally, 60 emp., *Bakery products* ........ (201) 503-9717
Bella Palermo Pastry Shop, Inc., 619 Elizabeth Ave., Elizabeth 07206
Pres.—Joe Oliver, 10 emp., *Custom wedding, birthday & Italian* ........ (908) 354-8610
Bread & Bagels, 1600 Church Rd., Cherry Hill 08002
Owner—Heechul Bang, 4 emp., *Bread & bagels* ........ (856) 667-2333
Bridor USA, 2260 Industrial Way, Vineland 08360
Qual. Control Mgr.—Sertgio Perez, 20 emp., *Bakery products, including breads,* ........ (856) 691-8000
Brother's Quality Bakery, 365 Kearny Ave., Kearny 07032
Chrm.—Michael Gencarelli, 20 emp., *Bread, muffins, pastries & cakes* ........ (201) 991-4364
Brothers Quality Bakery Of Allwood, 70 Market St., Clifton 07012
Co-Pres.—Michael Gencorelli, 15 emp., *Bakery products* ........ (973) 473-1467
Cacia's Bakery, 1010 S. Black Horse Pike, Blackwood 08012
Owner—Raymond Cacia, 4 emp., *Bread* ........ (856) 228-5986
Cake Specialty, Inc., 255 Goffle Rd., Hawthorne 07506
Secy-Treas.—Mike Despirto, 9 emp., *Cakes, cookies & baked goods* ........ (973) 238-0500
Calandra's Italian & French Bakery, 204 1st Ave. W., Newark 07107
Pres.—Luciano Calandra, 60 emp., *Italian & French baked goods, including* ........ (973) 484-5598
Cento Fine Foods, 100 Cento Blvd., West Deptford 08086
Manager—Anthony Varretta, 10 emp., *Italian food products, including canned* ........ (856) 853-5445
Certified Bakery, Inc., 20 Universal Pl., Carlstadt 07072
Pres.—Sam Grunfeld, 75 emp., *Breads & rolls* ........ (201) 635-9245
Classic Cake Co., The, 480 Evesham Rd., Cherry Hill 08003
Owner—Barry Krachman, 70 emp., *Cakes, cookies, pastries, pies, artisan* ........ (856) 751-5448
Columbus Bakery, Inc., 197 Bloomfield Ave., Bloomfield 07003
Pres.—Jack Gambino, 9 emp., *Bakery products* ........ (973) 429-1697
Conte's Pasta Co., Inc., 310 Wheat Rd., Vineland 08360
Pres.—Mauro 'Mike' Conte, 35 emp., *Frozen regular & gluten-free pizzas* ........ (856) 697-3400
D & C Bagel Boys, Inc., 1055-C Highway 34, Matawan 07747
Pres.—David Glasser, 11 emp., *Bagels* ........ (732) 566-4523
Del Buono Baking Co., 319 Black Horse Pike, Haddon Heights 08035
Pres.—Tom Witman, 25 emp., *Bakery products* ........ (856) 546-9585
Deluxe Italian Bakery, Inc., 680 E. Clements Bridge Rd., Runnemede 08078
Sales Mgr.—Darek Shelby, 100 emp., *Bread & pastries* ........ (856) 939-5000
Ecce Panis, 3-B Brick Plant Rd., East Brunswick 08816
Plt. Mgr.—Mike Vallen, 150 emp., *Bread* ........ (732) 254-1770
Elegant Desserts, 275 Warren St., Lyndhurst 07071
Owner—John Mazur, 20 emp., *Cakes, pastries & tortes* ........ (201) 933-0770
Fairfield Gourmet Food Corp., 11 Cliffside Dr., Cedar Grove 07009
Pres., CEO—Ari Margulies, 100 emp., *Corporate headquarters & frozen cookie* ........ (973) 227-2800
Farinhas Bakery, Inc., 301 Harrison Ave., Harrison 07029
Manager—Clara Estrada, 18 emp., *Bread & doughnuts* ........ (973) 482-5640
Food & Beverage, Inc., 100 Hollister Rd., Unit 5, Teterboro 07608
Ptnr.—Chris Gargiulo, 65 emp., *Cookies, brownies & pastries* ........ (201) 288-8881
Formica Bros. Bakery, 2310 Arctic Ave., Atlantic City 08401
Owner—Frank Formica, 35 emp., *Breads, cookies & cakes* ........ (609) 348-8934
Fragale's Baking Co., 68-74 Gaston Ave., Garfield 07026
Owner—Andrew Fragale, 12 emp., *Bakery products* ........ (973) 546-0327
Gelbstein Bakery, 415 Clifton Ave., Lakewood 08701
Owner—Louie Friedman, 20 emp., *Bread* ........ (732) 363-3636
Gianella Baking Co., 298 21st Ave., Paterson 07501
Pres.—John Imparato, 24 emp., *Bakery products* ........ (973) 523-9258
Ginsburg Bakery, Inc., 300 N. Tennessee Ave., Atlantic City 08401
CEO—John V. Mulloy, Sr., 180 emp., *Fresh & frozen bread, bagels & rolls* ........ (609) 345-2265
Gourmet Dessert Outlet, LLC, 851 Van Houten Ave., Clifton 07013
Owner—Ezzat Tadros, 6 emp., *Gourmet bakery products, including* ........ (973) 815-1111
Guttenplan's Frozen Dough Specialists, Inc., 100 Highway 36, Middletown 07748
Pres.—Abraham Littenberg, 90 emp., *Frozen dough* ........ (732) 495-9480
Hudson Bread, 5601-5711 Tonnelle Ave., North Bergen 07047
Pres.—Mariusz Kolodziej, 90 emp., *Artisan bread* ........ (201) 422-7900
International Delights Bakery Co., 230 Brighton Rd., Clifton 07012
Pres.—Spiro Sayegh, 50 emp., *Bakery products* ........ (973) 928-5582
Italian Peoples Bakery, Inc., 307 Hudson St., Trenton 08611
Pres.—Carmen Guagliardo, 80 emp., *Bread, rolls, pastries & cakes* ........ (609) 396-9869
James Candy Company, 1519 Boardwalk, Atlantic City 08401
Pres.—Frank J. Glaser, 100 emp., *Salt water taffy, cream mints, macaroons* ........ (609) 344-1519
Jersey Shore CPL, Inc., 301-C Commerce Dr., Freehold 07728
Supervisor—Gary Chlenber, 60 emp., *Doughnuts* ........ (732) 308-9990
Joey's Fine Foods, Inc., 135 Manchester Pl., Newark 07104
Pres.—Joseph Aihini, 60 emp., *Cakes, cookies & pastries* ........ (973) 482-1400
John Wm. Macy CheeseSticks, Inc., 80 Kipp Ave., Elmwood Park 07407
Pres., Hum. Res.—John Macy, 60 emp., *Gourmet breadsticks, dessert twists* ........ (201) 791-8036
Kashmir Crown Bakery, 710 W. Linden Ave., Linden 07036
Owner—Z. Ahmed, 60 emp., *Bakery products* ........ (908) 474-1470
Kashmir Crown Baking, LLC, 1030 W. Linden Ave., Linden 07036
★ Pres.—Sajjad Ahmed, 70 emp., *Bakery products, including breads,* ........ (908) 474-0970
Kontos Foods, Inc., 100 6th Ave., P.O. Box 628, Paterson 07544
Pres.—Evris Kontos, 150 emp., *Manufacturer of authentic ethnic hand-stretch* ........ (973) 278-2800
La Esperanza Baking, 148 W. Forest Ave., Englewood 07631
Owner—Elena Queiruga, 40 emp., *Hispanic, American & Italian bread* ........ (201) 871-1934
LaRosa Bakery, Inc., 79 Neuman Springs Rd. E., Shrewsbury 07702
Pres.—Salvatore LaRosa, Jr., 25 emp., *Italian butter cookies, biscotti, cannoli* ........ (732) 842-4324
Liberty Brand Pastries & Foods, 2409 Central Ave., Union City 07087
Owner & Pres.—Maria Scrchis, 1 emp., *Bakery products, including pastries* ........ (201) 863-3350
Lithuanian Bakery, Inc., T. J., 131 Inslee Pl., Elizabeth 07206
Owner & Pres.—John Backiel, 80 emp., *Bakery products* ........ (908) 354-0970
Mara's Gourmet Cheesecake, 281 Speedwell Ave., Morristown 07960
Pres.—Glenn Magley, 4 emp., *Cakes & pies* ........ (973) 682-9200
Mendoker's Quality Bakery, Inc., 34 W. Railroad Ave., Jamesburg 08831
Pres.—Edward Mendoker, 50 emp., *Bakery & deli products* ........ (732) 521-0056
Miami Onion Roll Co., 111 Berkshire Ave., Paterson 07502
Pres.—Harriet Davis, 30 emp., *Frozen hors d'oeuvres, bread & rolls* ........ (973) 389-2202
Miel Patisserie, LLC, 1990 Route 70 E., Ste. 14, Cherry Hill 08003
Owner—Gelareh Nouri, 12 emp., *Fresh pastries, specialty & wedding* ........ (856) 424-6435
Mother's Kitchen, Inc., 499 Veterans Dr., Burlington 08016
Plt. Mgr.—Scott Stone, 220 emp., *Cheesecake & cakes* ........ (609) 589-3033
Muffins & Stuff, 53 Jersey St., Paterson 07501
Pres.—Mendell Neustadt, 10 emp., *Gourmet bread, muffins & cookies* ........ (973) 881-9900
Natale's Summit Bakery, 185 Broad St., Summit 07901
Ptnr.—Eddie Natale, 50 emp., *Bakery products, including breads,* ........ (908) 277-2074
Nicolos Italian Bakery & Deli, Inc., 6 Baldwin St., Montclair 07042
Pres.—Nicolos Zecchino, Sr., 9 emp., *Bakery products, including bread &* ........ (973) 746-1398
Omni Baking Co., 2621 Freddy Ln., Vineland 08360
Hum. Res. Mgr.—Elenore Mesiano, 250 emp., *Contract baking of frozen Italian rolls* ........ (856) 205-1485
Original Bagel & Bialy Co., 2 Fairfield Crescent, West Caldwell 07006
Chrm., CEO—Bruce Levenbrook, 39 emp., *Bagels for foodservice, prisons, supermarkets* .... (973) 227-5777
Orlando Bakery, 236 Harrison Ave., Lodi 07644
Salesperson—Daniel Cartel, 15 emp., *Bakery products* ........ (973) 772-8883
Orthodox Baking Co., Inc., 555 Cortlandt St., Belleville 07109
Pres.—Michael Oberlander, 10 emp., *Gluten-free cakes, cookies & brownies* ........ (973) 844-9393
Paramount Bakeries, Inc., 61 Davenport Ave., Newark 07107
Pres.—Shraga Zabludovsky, 50 emp., *Baked goods* ........ (973) 482-6638
Piece Of Cake Gourmet Ice Cream, Inc., 62 W. Inman Ave., Rahway 07065
Pres.—James A. Biniaris, 8 emp., *Gourmet ice cream novelties, ice cream* ........ (732) 382-0281
Plaza 70 Bagels, 65 Highway 70 E., Marlton 08053
Pres.—Tony Naimoli, 2 emp., *Bagels* ........ (856) 983-5151
Pride Gourmet Bakers, Inc., 450 Getty Ave., Clifton 07011
Owner & Pres.—Jose Cavan, 50 emp., *Cakes, pastries & cookies* ........ (973) 340-3200
Prince Donut Co., Inc., 2345 E. Linden Ave., Linden 07036
GM—Fernando Inahuazo, 50 emp., *Bakery products* ........ (908) 925-2262
Quality Bakery Products Of New Jersey, Inc., 24 Ironside Ct., Willingboro 08046
GM—Nate Mariano, 30 emp., *Breadcrumbs* ........ (609) 871-7393
R. P. Baking Co., 840 Jersey St., Harrison 07029
Plt. Mgr.—Angel Santos, 400 emp., *Bread & bakery products* ........ (973) 483-3374
Ronic, Inc., 173 Ray St., Garfield 07026
Pres., Hum. Res. & IT Mgr.—Nick Aiello, 8 emp., *Bakery products, including breads,* ........ (973) 772-2217
Royal Baking Co., 8 Empire Blvd., Moonachie 07074
Owner & Pres.—Jack Dipiazza, 80 emp., *Bakery products, including bread &* ........ (201) 296-0888
Santos Bakery, 123 Hudson St., Newark 07103
Owner—Ablio Santos, 12 emp., *Bakery products* ........ (973) 732-7200
Scala Pastry, 1896 U.S. Highway 130, North Brunswick 08902
Owner—Paul Scala, 5 emp., *Fresh bakery products, including bread* ........ (732) 398-9808
Schripps European Bread, Inc., 5410 Tonnelle Ave., North Bergen 07047
Pres., CFO, MIS Mgr.—Dan Marcus, 40 emp., *European bread, rolls & pretzels* ........ (201) 867-0909
Serrani's Bakery, 114 S. Essex Ave., Orange 07050
Owner—William Serrani, 12 emp., *Bread* ........ (973) 678-1777
Sweet Potato Pie, Inc., 140 Auburn St., Paterson 07501
Pres.—Edgar Ramsey, 35 emp., *Bakery products, including bread &* ........ (973) 279-3405
Tatz Industries, Inc., William, 11 Railroad Pl., Belleville 07109
Pres.—William Tatz, 5 emp., *Custom blended bakery products, including* ........ (973) 751-0720
Teixeira's Bakery, 113-129 Kossuth St., P.O. Box 5550, Newark 07105
CEO—Manuel Teixeira, 280 emp., *Bakery products* ........ (973) 589-8875
Terrigno's Bakery, 632 N. Pearl St., Bridgeton 08302
Owner—Cosmo Terrigno, 15 emp., *Bread & cakes* ........ (856) 451-6368
Tofutti Brands, Inc., 50 Jackson Dr., Cranford 07016
Pres., CEO—David Mintz, 15 emp., *Kosher soy-based ice cream, dessert* ........ (908) 272-2400
Toufayan Bakery, Inc., 175 Railroad Ave., Ridgefield 07657
Pres., Pur. Agt.—Harry Toufayan, 20 emp., *Corporate headquarters & pita bread* ........ (201) 941-2000
Uptown Bakeries/J & J Snack Foods, 300 Eagle Ct., P.O. Box 257, Bridgeport 08014
V-P., GM—Tom Hunter, 250 emp., *Bakery products* ........ (856) 467-9552
Vieira's Bakery, 34-48 Avenue K, Newark 07105
Pres.—Carlos Vieira, 70 emp., *Portuguese bread* ........ (973) 589-7719
Vieiras Bakery, Inc., 34 Avenue K, Ste. 48, Newark 07105
Owner—Carlos Vieira, 10 emp., *Fresh & frozen Portuguese breads* ........ (973) 465-1212
Vitamia & Sons, 206 Harrison Ave., Lodi 07644
Pres.—Anthony Vitamia, 12 emp., *Ravioli, pasta, sauces, bread, cheese* ........ (973) 546-1140
Zaiya, Inc., 185 Kenneth St., Hackensack 07601
Pres.—Yoko Sano, 20 emp., *Bread* ........ (201) 343-3988

**★ Indicates new listing this edition.**

Zinicola Baking Co., 127 King St., Nutley 07110
Pres.—George Zinicola, 11 emp., *Italian bread & rolls* (973) 667-1306

## 2052 Cookies & crackers

Aryzta/La Brea Bakery, 11 Technology Dr., Swedesboro 08085
GM—Tom Bent, 600 emp., *Bakery products, including breads,* (856) 417-8100

Baker's Perfection, Inc., 198 Green Pond Rd., Rockaway 07866
Pres.—Patrick S. Amello, Sr., 40 emp., *Bread, rolls, cakes, cookies, pies* (973) 983-0700

Cake Specialty, Inc., 255 Goffle Rd., Hawthorne 07506
Secy-Treas.—Mike Despirto, 9 emp., *Cakes, cookies & baked goods* (973) 238-0500

Cento Fine Foods, 100 Cento Blvd., West Deptford 08086
Manager—Anthony Varretta, 10 emp., *Italian food products, including canned* (856) 853-5445

Classic Cake Co., The, 480 Evesham Rd., Cherry Hill 08003
Owner—Barry Krachman, 70 emp., *Cakes, cookies, pastries, pies, artisan* (856) 751-5448

Continental Cookies, Inc., 185 S. Newman St., Hackensack 07601
Pres., Fin. & MIS Mgr.—Stefan Gavosto, 15 emp., *Cookies* (201) 498-1966

Direct Sales & Services, 141 Lanza Ave., Bldg. 8, Garfield 07026
Pres.—David Caine, 25 emp., *Cookies & crackers* (973) 340-4480

Food & Beverage, Inc., 100 Hollister Rd., Unit 5, Teterboro 07608
Ptnr.—Chris Gargiulo, 65 emp., *Cookies, brownies & pastries* (201) 288-8881

Formica Bros. Bakery, 2310 Arctic Ave., Atlantic City 08401
Owner—Frank Formica, 35 emp., *Breads, cookies & cakes* (609) 348-8934

Gourmet Dessert Outlet, LLC, 851 Van Houten Ave., Clifton 07013
Owner—Ezzat Tadros, 6 emp., *Gourmet bakery products, including* (973) 815-1111

J & J Snack Foods Corp., 6000 Central Hwy., Pennsauken 08109
Pres., CEO—Gerald Shreiber, 850 emp., *Corporate headquarters & snack foods* (856) 665-9534

James Candy Company, 1519 Boardwalk, Atlantic City 08401
Pres.—Frank J. Glaser, 100 emp., *Salt water taffy, cream mints, macaroons* (609) 344-1519

Jimmy's Cookies, LLC, 18-01 River Rd., Fair Lawn 07410
Pres.—Michael Pisani, 60 emp., *Gourmet cookies & cookie dough* (201) 797-8900

Joey's Fine Foods, Inc., 135 Manchester Pl., Newark 07104
Pres.—Joseph Aihini, 60 emp., *Cakes, cookies & pastries* (973) 482-1400

John Wm. Macy CheeseSticks, Inc., 80 Kipp Ave., Elmwood Park 07407
Pres., Hum. Res.—John Macy, 60 emp., *Gourmet breadsticks, dessert twists* (201) 791-8036

Kashmir Crown Baking, LLC, 1030 W. Linden Ave., Linden 07036
★ Pres.—Sajjad Ahmed, 70 emp., *Bakery products, including breads,* (908) 474-0970

LaRosa Bakery, Inc., 79 Neuman Springs Rd. E., Shrewsbury 07702
Pres.—Salvatore LaRosa, Jr., 25 emp., *Italian butter cookies, biscotti, cannoli* (732) 842-4324

Laura's Fudge, Inc., 357 E. Wildwood Ave., P.O. Box 871, Wildwood 08260
Pres., COO, Secy. & Opers. Mgr.—Lori Bradshaw Roach, 12 emp., *Fudge, candy, macaroon cookies, confections* (609) 729-1555

Lee Sims Chocolates, 743 Bergen Ave., Jersey City 07306
Pres., CEO—Nicholas Vlahakis, 8 emp., *Assorted chocolate candy, mixed nuts* (201) 433-1308

Manischewitz Co., The (H Q), 80 Avenue K, Newark 07105
Pres.—Mark Weinstein, 65 emp., *Company headquarters; kosher cookies* (201) 553-1100

Mondelez International, Inc., 22-11 State Route 208, Fair Lawn 07410
Cont.—Jared Goldberg, 500 emp., *Cookies & crackers* (201) 794-4000

Natale's Summit Bakery, 185 Broad St., Summit 07901
Ptnr.—Eddie Natale, 50 emp., *Bakery products, including breads,* (908) 277-2074

Novelty Cone Co., Inc., 807 Sherman Ave., Pennsauken 08110
Owner—Steve Marinucci, 26 emp., *Ice cream cones* (856) 665-9525

Orthodox Baking Co., Inc., 555 Cortlandt St., Belleville 07109
Pres.—Michael Oberlander, 10 emp., *Gluten-free cakes, cookies & brownies* (973) 844-9393

Pride Gourmet Bakers, Inc., 450 Getty Ave., Clifton 07011
Owner & Pres.—Jose Cavan, 50 emp., *Cakes, pastries & cookies* (973) 340-3200

R.A.B. Food Group, LLC, 80 Avenue K, Newark 07105
Plt. Mgr.—Randall Copeland, 200 emp., *Kosher cookies, noodles, dry soup mix* (201) 553-1100

Schripps European Bread, Inc., 5410 Tonnelle Ave., North Bergen 07047
Pres., CFO, MIS Mgr.—Dan Marcus, 40 emp., *European bread, rolls & pretzels* (201) 867-0909

South Jersey Soft Pretzel, Inc., 912 N. White Horse Pike, Ste. A, Stratford 08084
Pres.—George W. Dudley, 6 emp., *Pretzels* (856) 435-5055

The Snack Factory, LLC., 11 Tamarack Cir., Skillman 08558
Sales Serv. Coord.—Patricia Smith, 10 emp., *Flat spreadable pretzel crackers* (609) 683-5400

Tofutti Brands, Inc., 50 Jackson Dr., Cranford 07016
Pres., CEO—David Mintz, 15 emp., *Kosher soy-based ice cream, dessert* (908) 272-2400

Tripician Macaroons, 640 White Horse Pike, Absecon 08201
Ptnr.—Mark Sabino, 6 emp., *Macaroons* (609) 645-1546

## 2053 Bakery products—frozen, except bread

Bakers Puff Pastry, 1 Industrial Plz., Paterson 07503
Pres.—Anthony Cipriano, 15 emp., *Frozen bakery products* (973) 977-2255

Catering By The Maddalenas, Inc., 415 Route 31 N., Ringoes 08551
Pres.—Janet Maddalena, 5 emp., *Frozen cheesecake* (609) 466-7510

Cinderella Cheesecake Co., Inc., 208 N. Fairview St., P.O. Box 36, Riverside 08075
Pres., Plt. Mgr.—Joseph Makin, 9 emp., *Frozen cheesecake* (856) 461-6302

Dewy Meadow Foods, Inc., 1018 Rector Rd., Bridgewater 08807
Pres.—Randolph Krogoll, 20 emp., *Frozen meat pies & bakery products* (908) 218-5655

Italian Peoples Bakery, Inc., 307 Hudson St., Trenton 08611
Pres.—Carmen Guagliardo, 80 emp., *Bread, rolls, pastries & cakes* (609) 396-9869

Mini Frost Foods Corp., 1237 Belmont Ave., Haledon 07508
Pres.—Katherine Kelly, 15 emp., *Frozen fruit-filled pastries* (973) 427-4258

Taste It Presents, Inc., 200 Sumner Ave., Kenilworth 07033
Pres.—John Alair, 50 emp., *Frozen desserts* (908) 241-9191

## 2064 Candy & other confectionery products

Al's Home Made Candies, 1133 Fairmount Ave., Vineland 08360
Pres.—Cathy Sterling, 1 emp., *Candy* (856) 691-4536

Ashton Food Machinery Co., Inc., P.O. Box 60, Montville 07045
Pres., Fin. & R & D Mgr.—Lawrence Oberman, 10 emp., *Peanut processing machinery, blanchers* (973) 521-7603

Astor Chocolate Corp., 651 New Hampshire Ave., Lakewood 08701
Chrm.—David Grunhut, 150 emp., *Gourmet Belgian chocolates & specialty* (732) 901-1001

Au'Some Inc. (H Q), 2031 Highway 130, Ste. E., Bldg. A, Monmouth Junction 08852
CEO—David Tsu, 10 emp., *Corporate headquarters; candy & fruit* (732) 951-8818

Bayard's Chocolate Co., Inc., 2325 Marlton Pike West, Cherry Hill 08002
Pres.—Frank Glaser, 15 emp., *Candy* (856) 663-2565

Birnn Chocolates, Inc., 314 Cleveland Ave., Highland Park 08904
Pres.—John Cunnell, 4 emp., *Chocolate confectionery* (732) 545-4400

Bromilow's Chocolates, Inc., 350 Rifle Camp Rd., Woodland Park 07424
Pres., CEO—Thomas Stewart, 12 emp., *Homemade chocolates* (973) 684-1496

Capco Enterprises, Inc., 34 DeForest Ave., Ste. 3, East Hanover 07936
Pres.—Carole Lapone, 13 emp., *Roasted & sundae flavored Jordan almonds* (973) 884-0044

Ce De Candy, Inc., 1091 Lousons Rd., Union 07083
Chrm.—Edward Dee, 125 emp., *Dextrose candy tablets & novelty candies* (908) 964-0660

Chilton Laboratories, 299-B Fairfield Ave., Fairfield 07004
Pres.—Steven Heydt, 10 emp., *Caffeinated candy* (973) 575-1990

Chocolate Belles, 249 Chamber Bridge Rd., Brick 08723
Owner—Ann Shortt, 2 emp., *Chocolate bunnies candy* (732) 920-2266

CNS Confectionery Products, LLC, 33 Hook Rd., Bayonne 07002
Pres., Opers. Mgr.—Eva Deutsch, 12 emp., *Bulk sweetened, toasted & desiccated* (201) 823-1400

Confection Collection, 6754 Route 9, Howell 07731
Owner—Sarah Cywiak, 3 emp., *Chocolates, nuts, dried fruit, candy* (732) 905-3039

Criterion Chocolates, Inc., 125 Lewis St., Eatontown 07724
V-P., GM—Ronald Boyadjian, 15 emp., *Chocolate candy* (732) 542-7847

Damask's Candies, Inc., 2255 Highway 322, Woolwich Township 08085
Owner—Douglas Damask, 5 emp., *Candy* (856) 467-1661

Duffys Delicious Candies Co., Inc., 29 N. Broadway, Gloucester City 08030
Owner—Barbara Hall, 10 emp., *Candy* (856) 456-2955

Giambri's Quality Sweets, 26 Brand Ave., Clementon 08021
Pres.—David Giambri, 10 emp., *Candy* (856) 783-1099

Healthy Food Brands, LLC, 122 Quentin Ave., New Brunswick 08901
GM—Joe Eckstein, 105 emp., *Candy & confectionery packaging* (212) 444-9909

Hillside Candy Co., 35 Hillside Ave., Hillside 07205
Owner—Ted Cohen, 37 emp., *Organic, sugar & sugar-free candy* (973) 926-2300

J. Emanuel Chocolatier, 461-B Main St., Chester 07930
Pres.—Alfred Michael Canzano, 5 emp., *Artisan chocolate products, including* (908) 955-7591

Jagielky's Home Made Candy, 5115 Ventnor Ave., Ventnor City 08406
Pres.—Michael Carr, 7 emp., *Candy & assorted chocolates* (609) 823-6501

James Candy Company, 1519 Boardwalk, Atlantic City 08401
Pres.—Frank J. Glaser, 100 emp., *Salt water taffy, cream mints, macaroons* (609) 344-1519

Kings Candy Co., Inc., 55 Bank St., P.O. Box 264, Elmwood Park 07407
Pres.—Louis Lapone, 15 emp., *Candy* (201) 791-4444

Krause Candy, Inc., Mrs. Hanna, 89 Westview Ave., Paramus 07652
Pres.—Karl Krause, 17 emp., *Chocolate candies & assorted nuts* (201) 843-0337

Laura's Fudge, Inc., 357 E. Wildwood Ave., P.O. Box 871, Wildwood 08260
Pres., COO, Secy. & Opers. Mgr.—Lori Bradshaw Roach, 12 emp., *Fudge, candy, macaroon cookies, confections* (609) 729-1555

Limpert Bros., Inc., 202 N. West Blvd., Vineland 08360
Chrm., Pres.—Pearl Giordano, 20 emp., *Ice cream, frozen desserts, bakery* (856) 691-1353

Lucille's Own Made Candy Co., 156 E. Route 72, Manahawkin 08050
Ptnr.—Janice M. Eismann, 10 emp., *Chocolate candy* (609) 597-7300

Manhattan Chocolates Co., 186 E. 22nd St., Bayonne 07002
GM—Michael Herzod, 50 emp., *Chocolates & candies* (201) 339-6886

Mars Chocolate North America, 800 High St., Hackettstown 07840
Hum. Res. Bus. Ptnr.—Nicholas Miele, 1480 emp., *Divisional headquarters & candy* (908) 852-1000

Metro Candy Apple Corp., 203 Paterson Ave., Ste. 1, Wallington 07057
Owner—Ellen Coughlin, 4 emp., *Candy apples* (973) 772-0837

Morinaga America, Inc., 400 Kelby St., 14th Fl., Fort Lee 07024
Br. Mgr.—Keita Morinaga, 3 emp., *Japanese candy* (201) 947-0408

Nuts.Com, 125 Moen St., Cranford 07016
Pres.—Jeff Braverman, 40 emp., *Nut roasting & dried fruits & candies* (908) 523-0333

Old Monmouth Peanut Brittle Co., 627 Park Ave., Freehold 07728
Pres.—Hal Gunther, 4 emp., *Peanut brittle* (732) 462-1311

Paulaur Corp., 105 Melrich Rd., Cranbury 08512
V-P., CFO—Mitchell Stefaniak, 100 emp., *Contract blended food ingredients for* (609) 395-8844

PIM Brands, LLC, 500 Pierce St., Somerset 08873
V-P., Mfg.—Jose Sepulveda, 200 emp., *Licensed, proprietary & private label* (732) 560-8300

Promotion In Motion Cos., Inc., The (H Q), 25 Commerce Dr., Allendale 07401
Pres., CEO—Michael Rosenberg, 40 emp., *Corporate headquarters; candy & fruit* (201) 784-5800

Puratos Corp., 1941 Old Cuthbert Rd., Cherry Hill 08034
Pres., U.S.—Frederic Duvauchelle, 100 emp., *Corporate headquarters & bread, bagel* (856) 428-4300

Ross Co., Inc., Frank B., 970 New Brunswick Ave., Ste. H, Rahway 07065
Pres.—Larry Powell, 5 emp., *Natural & synthetic waxes, including* (732) 669-0810

Savoy Extraordinary Snack, LLC, 35 N. Middaugh St., Somerville 08876
★ Owner—Robert Valero, 4 emp., *Snack foods, including seeds, nuts,* (908) 252-9800

Shriver's Salt Water Taffy & Fudge, 9th St. & Boardwalk, P.O. Box 899, Ocean City 08226
Pres.—Meryl Vangelov, 45 emp., *Saltwater taffy, fudge, macaroons,* (609) 399-0100

Sophisticated Chocolates Mfg., Inc., 92 N. Main St., Windsor 08561
Pres., CFO—Robert P. Hicks, 15 emp., *Chocolates* (609) 443-4747

Steel's Fudge, Inc., 1928 E. Riverside Dr., Atlantic City 08401
Opers. Mgr.—Andy Stipa, 40 emp., *Fudge candy* (609) 345-4051

Steel's Fudge, Inc., 1000 Boardwalk, Ocean City 08226
GM—Mimi Steel, 10 emp., *Fudge, taffy, peanut brittle & caramel* (609) 398-2383

Steel's Fudge, Inc (H Q), 2719 Boardwalk, Atlantic City 08401
Pres.—George Steel, 3 emp., *Corporate headquarters; fudge & salt* (609) 345-4051

Thomas Sweet Chocolates, Inc., 29 Palmer Sq. W., Princeton 08542
Pres.—Marco Cucchi, 6 emp., *Chocolate candy* (609) 924-7222

Van Holten's Homemade Candy, Inc., 1893 Route 88, Brick 08724
★ Owner—Bob Meyer, 4 emp., *Chocolates & fudge* (732) 840-0888

Westco Fruit & Nut Products Co., Inc., 93-97 Coit St., Irvington 07111
Pres., Hum. Res. Mgr.—Rivka F. Moradi, 3 emp., *Nuts, dried fruit & candy* (973) 373-1866

## 2066 Chocolate & cocoa products

American Instants, Inc., 117 Bartley Flanders Rd., P.O. Box 817, Flanders 07836
CEO—Christopher Roche, 60 emp., *Instant beverages, including cappuccino* (973) 584-8811

Astor Chocolate Corp., 651 New Hampshire Ave., Lakewood 08701
Chrm.—David Grunhut, 150 emp., *Gourmet Belgian chocolates & specialty* (732) 901-1001

Barry Callebaut USA, LLC, 1500 Suckle Hwy., Pennsauken 08110
Site Mgr.—William Hayes, 110 emp., *Cocoa & chocolate products* (856) 663-2260

Bergen Marzipan & Chocolate, 205 S. Washington Ave., Bergenfield 07621
Pres.—Eddie Serpin, 3 emp., *Chocolate & marzipan candies* (201) 385-8343

Birnn Chocolates, Inc., 314 Cleveland Ave., Highland Park 08904
Pres.—John Cunnell, 4 emp., *Chocolate confectionery* (732) 545-4400

Bromilow's Chocolates, Inc., 350 Rifle Camp Rd., Woodland Park 07424
Pres., CEO—Thomas Stewart, 12 emp., *Homemade chocolates* (973) 684-1496

Brummer's Handmade Chocolates, 125 E. Broad St., Westfield 07090
Owner—George Brummer, 3 emp., *Handmade chocolate candy* (908) 232-1904

Classic Cake Co., The, 480 Evesham Rd., Cherry Hill 08003
Owner—Barry Krachman, 70 emp., *Cakes, cookies, pastries, pies, artisan* (856) 751-5448

Cocoa Processing Corp., 650 Ramsey Ave., Hillside 07205
V-P.—Michael Mecca, 10 emp., *Cocoa & sugar processing* (201) 792-5866

Conrad's Confectionery, Inc., 107 Westwood Ave., Westwood 07675
Owner—J. J. Krachtus, 8 emp., *Chocolates & ice cream* (201) 664-2895

Critchley's Candies, 812 Kinderkamack Rd., River Edge 07661
Owner—Steve Engleberg, 3 emp., *Chocolates* (201) 967-1800

© Copyright 2015 Manufacturers' News, Inc.


Criterion Chocolates, Inc., 125 Lewis St., Eatontown 07724
V-P., GM—Ronald Boyadjian, 15 emp., *Chocolate candy* ........ (732) 542-7847
Enjou Chocolate, Inc., 8 Dehart St., Morristown 07960
Pres.—Wendy Taffet, 10 emp., *Chocolate candy* ........ (973) 993-9090
Ferrero U.S.A., Inc., 600 Cottontail Ln., Somerset 08873
CEO—Bernard Kreilmann, 200 emp., *Chocolate products* ........ (732) 764-9300
Genevieve'S, Inc., 174 Ray St., Garfield 07026
Pres.—David Dzwilewski, 7 emp., *Chocolate candy* ........ (973) 772-8816
J. Emanuel Chocolatier, 461-B Main St., Chester 07930
Pres.—Alfred Michael Canzano, 5 emp., *Artisan chocolate products, including* ........ (908) 955-7591
James Candy Company, 1519 Boardwalk, Atlantic City 08401
Pres.—Frank J. Glaser, 100 emp., *Salt water taffy, cream mints, macaroons* ........ (609) 344-1519
Krause's Homemade Candy Co., 50 Bergen Blvd., Fairview 07022
Ptnr.—Nicole Cinquegrana, 15 emp., *Chocolate candy* ........ (201) 943-4790
Lee Sims Chocolates, 743 Bergen Ave., Jersey City 07306
Pres., CEO—Nicholas Vlahakis, 8 emp., *Assorted chocolate candy, mixed nuts* ........ (201) 433-1308
Mecca & Sons Trucking Corp. (H Q), 580 Luis Munoz Marin Blvd., Jersey City 07310
Pres.—Helen Mecca, 30 emp., *Corporate headquarters; cocoa & sugar* ........ (201) 792-5866
Nouveautes, Inc., 70 Clinton Rd., Fairfield 07004
Pres.—David Little, 15 emp., *Chocolate products* ........ (973) 882-8850
PIM Brands, LLC, 500 Pierce St., Somerset 08873
V-P., Mfg.—Jose Sepulveda, 200 emp., *Licensed, proprietary & private label* ........ (732) 560-8300
Promotion In Motion Cos., Inc., The (H Q), 25 Commerce Dr., Allendale 07401
Pres., CEO—Michael Rosenberg, 40 emp., *Corporate headquarters; candy & fruit* ........ (201) 784-5800
Puratos Corp., 1941 Old Cuthbert Rd., Cherry Hill 08034
Pres., U.S.—Frederic Duvauchelle, 100 emp., *Corporate headquarters & bread, bagel* ........ (856) 428-4300
Rauhauser's Candy, 721 Asbury Ave., Ocean City 08226
Owner—Rodney Blomdahl, 10 emp., *Chocolate candy, tinware & stuffed* ........ (609) 399-1465
Richards Chocolates Co., Inc., Al, 851 Broadway, Bayonne 07002
Pres.—Fred Stancampiano, 10 emp., *Chocolate candy* ........ (201) 436-0915
Savita Naturals Ltd., 617 Heron Dr., Swedesboro 08085
Pres.—Richard Trout, 20 emp., *Cocoa butter* ........ (856) 467-4949
Thomas Sweet Chocolates, Inc., 29 Palmer Sq. W., Princeton 08542
Pres.—Marco Cucchi, 6 emp., *Chocolate candy* ........ (609) 924-7222
Varda International Corp., 41 S. Spring St., Elizabeth 07201
Pres.—Varda Shamban, 3 emp., *Chocolates* ........ (908) 354-9090
Yoo-Hoo Chocolate Beverage Corp., 600 Commercial Ave., Carlstadt 07072
Plt. Mgr.—William Pedoto, 64 emp., *Noncarbonated chocolate beverages* ........ (201) 933-0070

## 2067 Chewing gum

GumRunners, LLC, 333 Washington St., P.O. Box 392, Jersey City 07303
Co-Founder—Laurence Molloy, 4 emp., *Caffeinated & noncaffeinated chewing* ........ (201) 678-9300

## 2068 Nuts & seeds—salted & roasted

Capco Enterprises, Inc., 34 DeForest Ave., Ste. 3, East Hanover 07936
Pres.—Carole Lapone, 13 emp., *Roasted & sundae flavored Jordan almonds* ........ (973) 884-0044
Gel Spice Co., Inc., 48 Hook Rd., P.O. Box 285, Bayonne 07002
Pres.—Andre Engel, 225 emp., *Spices, seasonings, seeds, extracts* ........ (201) 339-0700
International Foodsource, LLC, 52 Richboynton Rd., Dover 07801
Pres.—David Lipson, 120 emp., *Dried fruits, nuts & gourmet food products* ........ (973) 361-7044
Krause Candy, Inc., Mrs. Hanna, 89 Westview Ave., Paramus 07652
Pres.—Karl Krause, 17 emp., *Chocolate candies & assorted nuts* ........ (201) 843-0337
Lee Sims Chocolates, 743 Bergen Ave., Jersey City 07306
Pres., CEO—Nicholas Vlahakis, 8 emp., *Assorted chocolate candy, mixed nuts* ........ (201) 433-1308
Nuts.Com, 125 Moen St., Cranford 07016
Pres.—Jeff Braverman, 40 emp., *Nut roasting & dried fruits & candies* ........ (908) 523-0333
Nutsco, Inc., 1115 S. 2nd St., Camden 08103
Owner & Pres.—Francisco Assis, 12 emp., *Cashew processing* ........ (856) 966-6400
Star Snacks, LLC, 105 Harbor Dr., Jersey City 07305
Mng. Ptnr.—Mendel Brachfeld, 200 emp., *Nuts & dried fruit* ........ (201) 200-9820
Westco Fruit & Nut Products Co., Inc., 93-97 Coit St., Irvington 07111
Pres., Hum. Res. Mgr.—Rivka F. Moradi, 3 emp., *Nuts, dried fruit & candy* ........ (973) 373-1866
Woodstock Farms Mfg., 96 Executive Ave., Edison 08817
Hum. Res. Mgr.—Virginia Johnson, 120 emp., *Organic, kosher & natural nuts, seeds* ........ (732) 650-9905
Yume Enterprises, LLC, 1800 E. State St., Ste. 158, Trenton 08609
★ Founder & COO—Brian Allen, 10 emp., *Ready-to-eat gluten-free snacks, including* ........ (609) 588-8903

## 2075 Soybean oil mills

National Lecithin, Inc. (H Q), 93 Spring St., Ste. 303, Newton 07860
Pres.—Patricia Bruno, 2 emp., *Corporate headquarters; soybean lecithin* ........ (973) 940-8920

## 2079 Fats & oils—edible, nec

A Taste Of Olive, LLC, 106 Kings Hwy. E., Ste. A, Haddonfield 08033
Manager—Fabio Auguadro, 10 emp., *Olive oils & vinegars* ........ (856) 795-0043
Aarhus United USA, Inc., 131 Marsh St., Newark 07114
CFO—Peter Maulbeck, 80 emp., *Edible oils* ........ (973) 344-1300
Lionelli, 345 Florida Grove Rd., Perth Amboy 08861
Pres.—Claude Dinucci, 2 emp., *Olive oil blending* ........ (732) 826-7270
Oasis Foods Co., 635 Ramsey Ave., P.O. Box 697, Hillside 07205
Pres., CEO—William Gillingham, 150 emp., *Vegetable oils, salad dressings, sauces* ........ (908) 964-0477
Supreme Oil Co., Inc., 80 S. Dean St., Englewood 07631
Pres.—Seymour Unterman, 150 emp., *Edible vegetable oil* ........ (201) 567-3177

## 2082 Malt beverages

Anheuser-Busch Cos., Inc., 200 U.S. Highway 1 & 9, Newark 07114
Hum. Res. Mgr.—Fran Justin, 500 emp., *Malt beverages* ........ (973) 645-7700
Basil T's Brew Pub & Italian Grill, 183 Riverside Ave., Red Bank 07701
Pres., R & D Mgr.—Victor Rallo, Jr., 60 emp., *Beer* ........ (732) 842-5990
Cape May Brewing Co., 1288 Hornet Rd., Rio Grande 08242
Manager—Ryan Krill, 10 emp., *Beer* ........ (609) 849-9933
Climax Brewing Co., Inc., 112 Valley Rd., Roselle Park 07204
Owner & Pres.—David Hoffmann, 2 emp., *Beer* ........ (908) 620-9585
Cricket Hill Brewing Co., Inc., 24 Kulick Rd., Fairfield 07004
Pres.—Rick Reed, 3 emp., *Microbrewery of lagers & ales* ........ (973) 276-9415
Flying Fish Brewing Co., 900 Kennedy Blvd., Somerdale 08083
Pres.—Gene Muller, 30 emp., *Beer* ........ (856) 504-3442
High Point Brewing Co., Inc., 22 Park Pl., Butler 07405
Pres.—Greg Zaccardi, 3 emp., *Beer* ........ (973) 838-7400
Malt Products Corp., 121 E. Hunter Ave., Maywood 07607
Plt. Mgr.—Chuck Stewart, 16 emp., *Malt extracts* ........ (201) 845-9106
New Jersey Beer Co., LLC, 4201 Tonnelle Ave., North Bergen 07047
Manager—Kevin Napoli, 5 emp., *Beer* ........ (201) 758-8342
River Horse, 2 Graphics Dr., Trenton 08628
Chrm., Pres.—Glenn Bernabeo, 20 emp., *Malt liquor & beer* ........ (609) 883-0890
Tun Tavern Restaurant & Brewery, 2 Convention Blvd., Atlantic City 08401
Pres.—Montgomery Dahm, 30 emp., *Beer* ........ (609) 347-7800

## 2083 Malt

Malt Products Corp., 88 Market St., P.O. Box 898, Saddle Brook 07663
Pres.—Ronald Targan, 20 emp., *Corporate headquarters & bakery malt* ........ (201) 845-4420

## 2084 Wines, brandy, & brandy spirits

Alba Vineyard, 269 Route 627, Milford 08848
Owner & Pres.—Thomas Sharko, 4 emp., *Wines* ........ (908) 995-7800
Amalthea Cellars Farm Winery, 209 Vineyard Rd., Atco 08004
Owner—Louis Caracciolo, 2 emp., *Handcrafted red & white wines* ........ (856) 768-8585
Balic Winery, Inc., 6623 Harding Hwy., Mays Landing 08330
Pres.—Bojan Balic, 4 emp., *Wines* ........ (609) 625-2166
Bellview Winery, 150 Atlantic St., Landisville 08326
Pres.—Jim Quarella, 6 emp., *Dry & sweet red & white wines* ........ (856) 697-7172
Bloomfield Wines, Inc., 339 Broad St., Bloomfield 07003
Manager—Kurt Pato, 4 emp., *Wines* ........ (973) 743-2020
CAVA Winery & Vineyard, Inc., 3619 State Route 94, Hamburg 07419
CEO—Anthony Riccio, 30 emp., *Wines* ........ (973) 823-9463
Cream Ridge Winery, 145 Route 539 S., P.O. Box 98, Cream Ridge 08514
Owner—Thomas R. Amabile, 8 emp., *Wines* ........ (609) 259-9797
Four Sisters Winery, 783 County Road 519, Belvidere 07823
Pres. & Event Planner—Robert Matarazzo, 9 emp., *Wines* ........ (908) 475-3671
Grape Escape, The, 12 Stults Rd., Ste. 101, Dayton 08810
Pres.—Edward Ventura, 10 emp., *Wines* ........ (609) 409-9463
Hawk Haven Vineyard & Winery, LLC, 600 S. Railroad Ave., Rio Grande 08242
Ptnr.—Todd Wuerker, 20 emp., *Wines* ........ (609) 846-7347
Heritage Vineyards of Richwood, LLC, 480 Mullica Hill Rd., Mullica Hill 08062
Ptnr.—William H. Heritage, 15 emp., *Wines* ........ (856) 589-4474
Hopewell Valley Vineyards, 46 Yard Rd., Pennington 08534
Owner—Sergio Neri, 4 emp., *Wines* ........ (609) 737-4465
Monroeville Vineyard & Winery, LLC, 314 Richwood Rd., Monroeville 08343
★ GM—Debra Basile, 4 emp., *Wines* ........ (856) 521-0523
Natali Vineyards, LLC, 221 N. Delsea Dr., Cape May Court House 08210
Pres.—Alfred Natali, 6 emp., *Wine* ........ (609) 465-0075
Oasis Foods Co., 635 Ramsey Ave., P.O. Box 697, Hillside 07205
Pres., CEO—William Gillingham, 150 emp., *Vegetable oils, salad dressings, sauces* ........ (908) 964-0477
Plagido's Winery, 570 N. 1st Rd., Hammonton 08037
Owner—Ollie Tomasello, 3 emp., *Wines* ........ (609) 567-4633
Renault Winery, 72 N. Bremen Ave., Egg Harbor City 08215
Owner—Joseph Milza, 150 emp., *Wines* ........ (609) 965-2111
Rex Wine Vinegar Co., 828-830 Raymond Blvd., Newark 07105
Pres.—Vincent Carlesimo, 8 emp., *Cooking wines & vinegars* ........ (973) 589-6911
Royal Wine Corp., 63 Lefante Way, Bayonne 07002
Pres., CEO—David Herzog, 150 emp., *Corporate headquarters & wine* ........ (718) 534-0200
Sharrott Winery, LLC, 370 S. Egg Harbor Rd., Blue Anchor 08037
Pres.—Larry Sharrott, 10 emp., *Red & white wines* ........ (609) 567-9463
Tomasello Winery, Inc., 225 White Horse Pike, Hammonton 08037
Chrm., Pres., CFO—Charles J. Tomasello, Sr., 8 emp., *Wines* ........ (609) 561-0567
Unionville, LLC, 9 Rocktown Rd., Ringoes 08551
Mng. Ptnr.—John Hawkins, 5 emp., *Wines* ........ (908) 788-0400
W J R B, Inc., 711 Town Bank Rd., Cape May 08204
Pres.—Toby Craig, 5 emp., *Wines* ........ (609) 884-1169
Wagonhouse Winery, LLC, 1401 State Highway 45, Swedesboro 08085
Ptnr.—Dan Brown, 2 emp., *Sweet & dry red & white wines* ........ (609) 780-8019
Westfall Winery, LLC, 141 Clove Rd., Montague 07827
Ptnr.—Loren Mortimer, 4 emp., *Company headquarters & wines* ........ (973) 293-3428

## 2085 Liquors—distilled & blended

Black Prince Distillery, Inc., 691 Clifton Ave., Clifton 07011
V-P., Opers.—Richard Noone, 30 emp., *Distilled liquors* ........ (973) 365-2050
Grant & Sons, Inc., William, 130 Fieldcrest Ave., Edison 08837
IT Mgr.—Ray Focht, 70 emp., *Distilled & blended liquors* ........ (732) 225-9000
Jersey Artisan Distilling, 32 Pier Ln. W., Bldg. C, Fairfield 07004
Owner—Krista Haley, 2 emp., *Distilled spirits* ........ (973) 521-7623
Laird & Co., Inc., 1 Laird Rd., Eatontown 07724
Pres.—Larrie Laird, 40 emp., *Corporate headquarters & manufacturer* ........ (732) 542-0312

## 2086 Bottled & canned soft drinks

American Instants, Inc., 117 Bartley Flanders Rd., P.O. Box 817, Flanders 07836
CEO—Christopher Roche, 60 emp., *Instant beverages, including cappuccino* .... (973) 584-8811
Beverage Distribution Center, Inc., 8275 Route 130, Pennsauken 08110
Pres., CFO—Walt Wilkinson, 700 emp., *Corporate headquarters & manufacturer* ........ (856) 665-6200
Clement Pappas & Company, Inc., 1045 Parsonage Rd., Seabrook 08302
Plt. Mgr.—Adam Olds, 210 emp., *Bottled & canned fruit juice & cranberry* ........ (856) 455-1001
Clement Pappas & Company, Inc. (H Q), 1 Collins Dr., Ste. 200, Carneys Point 08069
CEO—Mark McNeil, 125 emp., *Corporate headquarters; bottled & canned* ........ (856) 455-1000
Crystal Beverage Corp., 174 Sanford Ave., P.O. Box 393, Kearny 07032
Pres., Plt. Mgr.—John Apolinario, 13 emp., *Soft drinks* ........ (201) 991-2342
Dee & L, LLC, 67 Lefante Way, P.O. Box 3431, Bayonne 07002
Dir., Opers.—Larry Kahn, 20 emp., *Mayonnaises, salad dressings & fruit* ........ (201) 858-0131
H2m Beverages, 223 Wanaque Ave., POMPTON LAKES 07442
CEO—Charles Musumeci, 17 emp., *Nonalcoholic beverages, including energy* .. (973) 831-2010
Hillside Bottling Corp., 1 Evans Terminal, Hillside 07205
Plt. Mgr.—Frank Zurawel, 10 emp., *Soft drinks* ........ (908) 353-6773
LiDestri Foods, Inc., 1550 John Tipton Blvd., Pennsauken 08110
GM—Dave Stoklosa, 100 emp., *Carbonated beverages* ........ (856) 662-1800
Maplewood Beverage Packers, LLC, 45 Camptown Rd., Maplewood 07040
GM—Nick DiMirio, 175 emp., *Beverage bottling* ........ (973) 416-4582
Nestle Waters North America, Inc., 111 Thomas McGovern Dr., Jersey City 07305
Factory Mgr.—Djenane Fleurentin, 13 emp., *Bottled water* ........ (201) 451-4000
Pepsi Beverages Company, 2200 New Brunswick Ave., Piscataway 08854
Plt. Mgr.—Duen Pagan, 275 emp., *Carbonated beverages* ........ (732) 424-3000
Pepsi-Cola & National Brand Beverages Ltd., 8191 N. U.S. Route 130, Pennsauken 08110
Pres., COO—Bob Brockway, 700 emp., *Bottled & canned beverages* ........ (856) 665-6200
Regale, Inc., Kristian, 4 Forest Ave., Ste. 202, Paramus 07652
V-P., Opers.—Casey Beard, 5 emp., *Nonalcoholic Swedish-style sparkling* ........ (201) 587-9800
Str8up Beverages, LLC, 16 Mount Bethel Rd., Ste. 260, Warren 07059
Owner—Mitch Rappel, 15 emp., *Caffeine-infused water bottling* ........ (908) 451-1393

S.I.C.

**★ Indicates new listing this edition.**

Union Beverage Packers, LLC, 600 N. Union Ave., Hillside 07205
CEO—Yaron Gohar, 190 emp., *Beverage bottling* .......... (908) 206-9111
Water Shoppe, Inc., The, 112 N. 3rd St., 2nd Fl., Camden 08102
Pres.—Carol Alexander, 4 emp., *Bottled water* .......... (856) 964-4500
Whitlock Packaging Corp., 92 N. Main St., Wharton 07885
Cont.—Mary Clyburn, 200 emp., *Noncarbonated beverages & fruit juice* .......... (973) 361-9794
Yoo-Hoo Chocolate Beverage Corp., 600 Commercial Ave., Carlstadt 07072
Plt. Mgr.—William Pedoto, 64 emp., *Noncarbonated chocolate beverages* .......... (201) 933-0070

## 2087 Flavoring extracts & syrups

Adron, Inc., 94 Fanny Rd., P.O. Box 270, Boonton 07005
Ex. Pres.—Robert L. Anaducci, 30 emp., *Food flavorings* .......... (973) 334-1600
Advanced Biotech, Inc., 10 Taft Rd., Totowa 07512
CEO—Robert DeSimone, 60 emp., *Flavorings, extracts, natural aromatics* .......... (973) 339-6242
Allen Flavors, Inc., 23 Progress St., Edison 08820
Pres.—Joseph Allen, 150 emp., *Custom beverage pre-mixes & bases,* .......... (908) 561-5995
B & G Foods, Inc. (H Q), 4 Gatehall Dr., Ste. 110, Parsippany 07054
Pres.—David Wenner, 70 emp., *Corporate headquarters; preserves,* .......... (973) 401-6500
C B Food, Inc., 1 Madison St., Bldg. B, East Rutherford 07073
Pres., Sales Mgr.—Milton Becker, 5 emp., *Drink mixes* .......... (973) 773-9224
Campbell Soup Supply Co., 3500 S. Clinton Ave., South Plainfield 07080
Qual. Assur. Mgr.—Anita Solomon, 30 emp., *Food flavorings & spices* .......... (908) 561-1660
Citromax USA, 444 Washington Ave., Carlstadt 07072
Pres.—Vivian Glueck, 35 emp., *Citrus processing, including natural* .......... (201) 933-8405
Colgate-Palmolive Co., 400 Elbow Ln., Burlington 08016
Cont.—Angelie George, 30 emp., *Fragrances & flavors* .......... (609) 239-2000
Corbion Caravan, 100 Adams Dr., Totowa 07512
V-P., Pricing—Joseph Solimini, 160 emp., *Baking ingredients & mixes* .......... (973) 256-8886
Drink Atoast Co., Inc., 603 Harrison St., P.O. Box 204, Riverside 08075
Pres.—Daniel McDonough, 5 emp., *Beverages, syrups & concentrates* .......... (856) 461-1000
Elan Chemical Company, Inc., 268 Doremus Ave., Newark 07105
Pres., CEO—Jocelyn Kapp-Manship, 60 emp., *Food flavorings & fragrance ingredients* .......... (973) 344-8014
Firmenich, Inc., 250 Plainsboro Rd., Plainsboro 08536
Pres., N. Amer.—David Shipman, 800 emp., *Corporate headquarters & flavors &* .......... (609) 452-1000
Flaroma, Inc., 96 Fanny Rd., P.O. Box 325, Mountain Lakes 07046
Pres.—Bob Amaducci, 30 emp., *Food flavorings* .......... (973) 316-8185
Flavor & Fragrance Specialties, Inc. (H Q), 3 Industrial Ave., Mahwah 07430
Pres.—Michael Bloom, 50 emp., *Corporate headquarters; food flavorings* .......... (201) 825-2025
Flavor Dynamics, Inc., 640 Montrose Ave., South Plainfield 07080
Pres.—Dolf DeRovira, Sr., 25 emp., *Flavoring extracts* .......... (908) 822-8855
Flavor Solutions, Inc., 120 New England Ave., Piscataway 08854
Owner & Pres.—William A. May, 12 emp., *Natural & artificial food flavors,* .......... (732) 354-1931
Flavors Materials International, Inc., 10-D Englehard Ave., Avenel 07001
Pres.—Paul Ahn, 25 emp., *Food flavorings* .......... (732) 499-9700
Food Ingredient Solutions, LLC, 10 Malcolm Ave., Unit 1, Teterboro 07608
CTO—Marilea Romabiles, 9 emp., *Natural food colors* .......... (201) 440-4377
Foote & Jenks Corp., 1420 Crestmont Ave., Camden 08103
Pres.—Michael Baskin, 20 emp., *Food flavorings & fragrances* .......... (856) 966-0700
Frutarom USA, Inc., 9500 Railroad Ave., North Bergen 07047
Plt. Mgr.—Gary Bath, 125 emp., *Flavorings, flavoring extracts, pharma/nutrac* .......... (201) 861-9500
Gel Spice Co., Inc., 48 Hook Rd., P.O. Box 285, Bayonne 07002
Pres.—Andre Engel, 225 emp., *Spices, seasonings, seeds, extracts* .......... (201) 339-0700
Givaudan Flavors Corp., 245 Merry Ln., East Hanover 07936
Hum. Res. Generalist—Tracey Mara, 200 emp., *Flavors & flavoring materials* .......... (973) 386-9800
Hagelin Flavor Technologies, 200 Meister Ave., Branchburg 08876
Pres.—Craig Hagelin, 65 emp., *Company headquarters & flavors for* .......... (908) 707-4400
IFC Products, Inc., 568 E. Elizabeth Ave., P.O. Box 2175, Linden 07036
Pres.—Joseph Christiano, 4 emp., *Flavorings, extracts, essential oils* .......... (908) 587-1221
IFC Solutions, 1601 E. Linden Ave., Linden 07036
Pres.—David J. Dukes, 22 emp., *Food color concentrates, food-grade* .......... (908) 862-8810
Intarome Fragrance & Flavor Corp., 370 Chestnut St., Norwood 07648
Pres., CEO—Daniel G. Funsch, 53 emp., *Fragrances & flavors* .......... (201) 767-8700
International Flavors & Fragrances, Inc., 150 Docks Corner Rd., Dayton 08810
Hum. Res. Bus. Ptnr., Flavors & Fragrances—Rebecca Force, 300 emp., *Flavoring & fragrances*. (732) 329-4600
International Flavors & Fragrances, Inc., 600 Highway 36, Hazlet 07730
Plt. Mgr.—David Smith, 250 emp., *Flavors & fragrances* .......... (732) 264-4500
J & K Ingredients, Inc., 160 E. 5th St., Paterson 07524
Pres.—James K. Sausville, 80 emp., *Natural bread, cake & donut mixes,* .......... (973) 340-8700
Kerry Ingredients, 26 Minneakoning Rd., Flemington 08822
Plt. Mgr.—Jason Kehn, 48 emp., *Seasonings* .......... (908) 782-4919
Kerry Ingredients & Flavors, 160 Terminal Ave., Clark 07066
Cont.—Angel Albanese, 135 emp., *Flavorings & natural products* .......... (732) 882-0202
Mafco Worldwide Corp., 300 Jefferson St., Camden 08104
Sr. V-P., Gen. Counsel—Thomas Molchan, 150 emp., *Corporate headquarters & tobacco flavors* (856) 964-8840
Medallion International, Inc., 233 W. Parkway, Pompton Plains 07444
V-P.—Paula Boudjouk, 15 emp., *Flavors & fragrances* .......... (973) 616-3401
Natural Flavors, Inc., 268 Doremus Ave., Newark 07105
Pres.—Herb Stein, 25 emp., *Natural flavorings* .......... (973) 589-1230
Premier Specialties, Inc., 236 Blackford Ave., Middlesex 08846
Pres., Hum. Res. Mgr.—Roger Rich, 21 emp., *Fragrances & flavors* .......... (732) 469-6615
Prime Ingredients, Inc., 280 N. Midland Ave., Bldg. U, Saddle Brook 07663
Pres.—James Walsh, 15 emp., *Food coloring & flavoring* .......... (201) 791-6655
RC Fine Foods, Inc., 139 Stryker Ln., Hillsborough 08844
Pres.—Susan Goldman, 70 emp., *Soup, sauce, gravy, salad dressing* .......... (908) 359-5500
Reckitt Benckiser, Inc., 399 Interpace Pkwy., P.O. Box 225, Parsippany 07054
Pres., Frenchs Food Prod.—Elliott Penner, 375 emp., *Corporate headquarters & consumer cleaning* (973) 404-2600
Robertet Flavors, Inc., 10 Colonial Dr., Piscataway 08854
Pres., COO—Robert Weinstein, 156 emp., *Food flavoring liquids, including dry-blended* .......... (732) 981-8300
Sea Breeze Fruit Flavors, Inc., 441 Route 202, Towaco 07082
Pres.—Steven Sanders, 50 emp., *Syrups* .......... (973) 334-7777
Sentrex Ingredients, LLC, 350 Cantor Ave., Linden 07036
Member—Arthur Gurerrera, 5 emp., *Extracts, concentrates, essences &* .......... (908) 862-4440
Spectra Colors Corp., 25 Rizzolo Rd., Kearny 07032
Pres., Mktg. Mgr.—Luis B. Marrero, 30 emp., *Colorants & dyes for the ink, food,* .......... (201) 997-0606
Spray-Tek, Inc., 344 Cedar Ave., Middlesex 08846
Mng. Ptnr., Pres. & CEO—David A. Brand, 40 emp., *Corporate headquarters & food flavorings* . (732) 469-0050
Summit Hill Flavors, 253 Lackland Dr. W., Middlesex 08846
Pres.—Robert Delin, 30 emp., *Savory natural & organic food flavors* .......... (732) 805-0335
Supreme Mfg. Co., Inc., 5 Connerty Ct., East Brunswick 08816
Pres.—Cliff Krause, 34 emp., *Granita, frozen drinks mix, fruit juice* .......... (732) 254-0087
Symrise, Inc., 300 North St., Teterboro 07608
CEO—Heinz-Jurgen Bertram, 350 emp., *Corporate headquarters & food flavorings* .......... (201) 288-3200
Takasago International Corp., 4 Volvo Dr., P.O. Box 932, Rockleigh 07647
Pres.—Hasiya Fujiwara, 100 emp., *Corporate headquarters & candle fragrances* .......... (201) 767-9001
Vineland Syrup, Inc., 723 Southeast Blvd., Vineland 08360
Pres.—Mel Kornbluh, 35 emp., *Soda syrups* .......... (856) 691-5772
Walden Farms, Inc., 1209 W. Saint Georges Ave., Linden 07036
Pres., CFO—Mitchell Berko, 20 emp., *Salad dressings, condiments, syrups* .......... (908) 925-9494
Whittle & Mutch, Inc., 712 Fellowship Rd., Mount Laurel 08054
Pres.—John C. Mutch, Jr., 14 emp., *Flavoring extracts* .......... (856) 235-1165

## 2091 Canned & cured fish & seafoods

Bivalve Packing Co., Inc., 6957 Miller Ave., P.O. Box 336, Port Norris 08349
Pres., GM—Steve Fleetwood, 25 emp., *Oyster packaging* .......... (856) 785-0270
Green Tree Packing, Inc., 65 Central Ave., P.O. Box 386, Passaic 07055
Pres.—Michael Waters, 100 emp., *Meat processing & packing of seafood* .......... (973) 473-1305
Snow'S, 994 Ocean Dr., Cape May 08204
V-P., GM—Steve Veltman, 90 emp., *Canned clams, clam chowder, broths* .......... (609) 884-0440
True World Group, LLC (H Q), 24 Link Dr., Rockleigh 07647
CFO—Tom Ino, 10 emp., *Company headquarters; fiberglass boats* .......... (201) 750-0024

## 2092 Fish—fresh or frozen prepared

Bivalve Packing Co., Inc., 6957 Miller Ave., P.O. Box 336, Port Norris 08349
Pres., GM—Steve Fleetwood, 25 emp., *Oyster packaging* .......... (856) 785-0270
Certified Clam Corp., 190 Bay Ave., P.O. Box 383, Highlands 07732
Pres.—Kathy Armstrong, 12 emp., *Fresh clam processing* .......... (732) 872-6650
Cuisine Innovations, LLC, 1920 Swarthmore Ave., Ste. 1, Lakewood 08701
Ptnr.—Paul Bensabat, 75 emp., *Seafood processing* .......... (732) 730-9310
Gourmet Foods, Inc., 25 Andrews Dr., Woodland Park 07424
Pres.—Alfred Fuchs, 50 emp., *Gourmet canapes, vegetables, sushi* .......... (973) 237-1776
Lagniappe Foods, Inc., 546 Mitchell St., Orange 07050
Pres.—Thomas Dowd, 25 emp., *Crab cakes & seafood sausages* .......... (973) 674-0498
Lamonica Fine Foods, 48 Gorton Rd., P.O. Box 309, Millville 08332
Pres.—Danny LaVecchia, 200 emp., *Wild caught clam products, including* .......... (856) 825-8111
LM Foods, LLC, 100 Raskulinecz Rd., Carteret 07008
Pres.—Mark Olivito, 90 emp., *Surimi seafood products* .......... (732) 855-9500
Lund's Fisheries Co., 997 Ocean Dr., P.O. Box 830, Cape May 08204
Pres.—Jeffrey Reichle, 200 emp., *Company headquarters & fish processing* .......... (609) 884-7600
Moveable Feast, Inc., 99 Grand St., Ste. 8, Moonachie 07074
Owner—Alain Quirin, 5 emp., *Smoked fish, including salmon, trout* .......... (201) 939-4500
Off The Hook Seafood, LLC, 126-A Greenwood Ave., Midland Park 07432
Ptnr.—John Sclafani, 4 emp., *Seafood processing for hotels, stadiums* .......... (201) 444-8895
Pinnacle Foods Group, LLC (H Q), 121 Woodcrest Rd., Cherry Hill 08003
CEO—Bob Gamgort, 220 emp., *Company headquarters; branded frozen* .......... (856) 969-7100
Ruggiero Seafood, Inc., 474 Wilson Ave., P.O. Box 5369, Newark 07105
Pres.—Rocco Ruggiero, 50 emp., *Frozen seafood, including calamari,* .......... (973) 589-0524
Surfside Products, Inc., 1733 Main St., P.O. Box 692, Port Norris 08349
★ Pres.—Peter LaMonica, 100 emp., *Frozen clams & shell shucking* .......... (856) 785-2115
Sweet Water Seafood Corp., 369 Washington Ave., Carlstadt 07072
Pres.—Joseph Niece, 5 emp., *Fish processing* .......... (201) 939-6622
True World Group, LLC (H Q), 24 Link Dr., Rockleigh 07647
CFO—Tom Ino, 10 emp., *Company headquarters; fiberglass boats* .......... (201) 750-0024

## 2095 Coffee—roasted

American Instants, Inc., 117 Bartley Flanders Rd., P.O. Box 817, Flanders 07836
CEO—Christopher Roche, 60 emp., *Instant beverages, including cappuccino* .... (973) 584-8811
Caffe Borbone USA, 19 Commerce Rd., Ste. G, Fairfield 07004
Pres.—Antonio Amato, 8 emp., *Espresso coffee packing & distributor* .......... (973) 227-7799
Coffee Assocs., Inc., 178 Old River Rd., P.O. Box 240, Edgewater 07020
Pres.—William Callas, 40 emp., *Coffee roasting & packing* .......... (201) 945-1060
Coffee Co., LLC, The, 928 Boardwalk, Ocean City 08226
Owner—Joan Williamson, 7 emp., *Coffee roasting* .......... (609) 399-5533
Corim Industries, 1112 Industrial Pkwy., Brick 08724
Pres.—Sam Teren, 20 emp., *Coffee roasting & packing* .......... (732) 840-1670
Greene Bros. Specialty Coffee Roasters, Inc., 313 High St., Hackettstown 07840
Pres.—David Greene, 12 emp., *Coffee roasting* .......... (908) 979-0022
Jersey Shore Coffee Roasters, LLC, 64 Thompson Ave., Ste. B, Leonardo 07737
Manager—Greg Martinez, 4 emp., *Coffee roasting* .......... (732) 291-0505
Kobrick Coffee Co., Inc., 693 Luis Marin Blvd., Jersey City 07310
Pres.—Steve Kobrick, 30 emp., *Coffee roasting* .......... (201) 656-6313
La Sierra Coffee Roasters, LLC, 42 Bartley Rd., Flanders 07836
Owner—Jorge Henao, 7 emp., *Coffee roasting & packaging* .......... (973) 927-9595
Lacas Coffee Co., 7950 National Hwy., Pennsauken 08110
V-P., CEO—Tony Chigounis, 12 emp., *Imported & specialty roasted coffees* .......... (856) 910-8662
Melitta U. S. A., 1401 Berlin Rd., Cherry Hill 08034
Plt. Mgr.—Vinny Tagliaferro, 50 emp., *Coffee roasting & packing* .......... (856) 428-7202
Nestle' USA, Inc., Beverage Div., 61 Jerseyville Ave., Freehold 07728
Plt. Mgr.—Joe Rechtiene, 315 emp., *Coffee & tea blending* .......... (732) 462-1300
Pan American Coffee Co., LLC, 500 16th St., Hoboken 07030
Pres.—Roy Montes, 40 emp., *Coffee roasting* .......... (201) 963-2329
Tata Global Beverages (H Q), 155 Chestnut Ridge Rd., 2nd Fl., Montvale 07645
CFO—Tom Corcoran, 50 emp., *Company headquarters; coffee roasting* .......... (201) 571-0300
W.B. Law & Son, Inc., 280 Wilson Ave., Unit B, Newark 07105
Owner—David M. Mendez, 38 emp., *Coffee & coffee related products* .......... (973) 344-2270

## 2096 Potato chips & similar snacks

B & G Foods, Inc. (H Q), 4 Gatehall Dr., Ste. 110, Parsippany 07054
Pres.—David Wenner, 70 emp., *Corporate headquarters; preserves,* .......... (973) 401-6500
Federal Pretzel Baking Co., 300 Eagle Ct., P.O. Box 257, Bridgeport 08014
GM—Tom Hunter, 20 emp., *Soft pretzels* .......... (215) 467-0505
Golden Fluff, Inc., 118 Monmouth Ave., Lakewood 08701
Pres.—Ephraim Schwinder, 9 emp., *Popcorn* .......... (732) 367-5448
Leng-D'Or USA, Inc., 50 W. Ferris St., East Brunswick 08816
Dir., Plt.—Ricardo Mendoza, 15 emp., *Potato pellet snacks, tortilla & corn* .......... (732) 254-4300
Mayab Happy Tacos, Inc., 450 Florida Grove Rd., Perth Amboy 08861
V-P.—George Alamilla, 25 emp., *Flour & corn tortillas, white & yellow* .......... (732) 293-0400
Nutra Nuts, Inc. (H Q), 180 Old Tappan Rd., Old Tappan 07675
Pres.—Mark Porro, 3 emp., *Corporate headquarters; half-popped* .......... (201) 768-0218
Nutrition North America, 10 Saddle Rd., Cedar Knolls 07927
Cust. Serv. Rep.—Tajah Muhammad, 26 emp., *Metabolic nutritional drink formulas* .......... (973) 734-0023
Pickle King, 220 Ellison St., Paterson 07505
Pres., GM—Richard Nadel, 12 emp., *Pickles, pickled peppers, olives &* .......... (973) 977-2095

© Copyright 2015 Manufacturers' News, Inc.



The Snack Factory, LLC., 11 Tamarack Cir., Skillman 08558
Sales Serv. Coord.—Patricia Smith, 10 emp., Flat spreadable pretzel crackers ........ (609) 683-5400

## 2097 Ice—manufactured

Angelo's Ice Co., Inc., 100 Sylvania Pl., South Plainfield 07080
Pres.—Angelo Del Beni, Jr., 1 emp., Ice cube processing ........ (908) 754-4091
Artic Ice Mfg. & Dry Ice Co., 158 Semel Ave., Garfield 07026
Ptnr.—John Minichetti, 5 emp., Dry & block ice & ice cubes ........ (201) 370-3141
Ice King & Cold Storage, Inc., 4045 Route 33 W., Tinton Falls 07753
Pres.—Adrienne Lomangino, 10 emp., Ice cube processing & cold storage ........ (732) 922-0852
Sea Isle Ice Co., Inc., 230 42nd St., Sea Isle City 08243
Pres.—Joe Romano, Jr., 12 emp., Ice ........ (609) 263-8794
South Jersey Ice & Cold Storage LLC, 544 E. Pear St., Vineland 08360
Member—Mark DiMeo, 6 emp., Block ice, bagged ice & cold storage ........ (856) 692-3990

## 2098 Macaroni & spaghetti

Antonio's Pasta, 545 U.S. Highway 9 N., Woodbridge 07095
Pres.—Barbara Winant, 6 emp., Filled & fresh pasta ........ (732) 442-1640
Bruno The King Of Ravioli Co., 174 Union St., Hackensack 07601
★ Pres.—Glen Rassam, 3 emp., Pasta products ........ (201) 646-0505
Caesar's Pasta, 1001 Lower Landing Rd., Ste. 311, Blackwood 08012
Pres.—Michael Lodato, 50 emp., Frozen pasta meals, including meat, ........ (856) 227-2585
Campbell Soup Co. (H Q), 1 Campbell Pl., Camden 08103
Chrm.—Paul Charron, 1200 emp., Company headquarters; canned soups, ........ (856) 342-4800
Casa Di Trevi, 534 W. Westfield Ave., Roselle Park 07204
Pres. & V-P.—Michael Aiello, 6 emp., Gourmet pasta ........ (908) 259-9000
Cento Fine Foods, 100 Cento Blvd., West Deptford 08086
Manager—Anthony Varretta, 10 emp., Italian food products, including canned ........ (856) 853-5445
Conte's Pasta Co., Inc., 310 Wheat Rd., Vineland 08360
Pres.—Mauro 'Mike' Conte, 35 emp., Frozen regular & gluten-free pizzas ........ (856) 697-3400
DiPietro Foods, Inc., 1701 Springfield Ave., Maplewood 07040
Pres.—Lucy DiPietro Manzella, 3 emp., Uncooked pasta ........ (973) 762-4077
D'Orazio Foods, Inc., 960 Creek Rd., Bellmawr 08031
Pres.—Anthony D'Orazio, 100 emp., Frozen pasta ........ (856) 931-1900
Florence Ravioli Co., 391 Park Ave., Scotch Plains 07076
Owner—Cynthia Losanno, 2 emp., Ravioli ........ (908) 322-7222
H & U, Inc., 375 North St., Ste. O, Teterboro 07608
Dir., Comms.—Shawn Kim, 16 emp., Japanese ramen noodles ........ (201) 530-1100
L & D's Sapore Ravioli & Cheese, Inc., 429-B Lincoln Blvd., Middlesex 08846
Mng. Ptnr.—Anthony Florano, 15 emp., Handmade fresh & frozen Italian ravioli ........ (732) 563-9190
M. A. R. Kit, Inc., 1095 Cinnaminson Ave., Cinnaminson 08077
Pres., GM—Michael Georgetti, 18 emp., Italian pasta, sauces, soups & prepared ........ (856) 829-5992
Mitsui Foods, Inc., 35 Maple St., Norwood 07648
Pres., CEO—Tom Osada, 60 emp., Manufacturer of frozen pasta products ........ (201) 750-0500
Mr. Pasta, 159 Ridge Rd., North Arlington 07031
Owner & GM—Silvano Masiero, 5 emp., Pasta ........ (201) 991-5959
Raffetto's Corp., 62 W. Commercial Ave., Moonachie 07074
Pres.—Richard Raffetto, 15 emp., Fresh macaroni, spaghetti & fettuccini ........ (201) 372-1222
Rosa-Ly Pirogi, 256 Madison Ave., Irvington 07111
Owner—Gregory Baran, 1 emp., Pasta products ........ (973) 371-0650
Roselli's Food Specialties, Inc., L. E., 155 Church Rd., Medford 08055
Pres.—Laura Roselli, 12 emp., Frozen pasta products & pasta sauces ........ (609) 654-4816
Savignano Foods Corp., 107 S. Jefferson St., Orange 07050
Ptnr. & Pres.—Michael Savignano, 40 emp., Frozen Italian pasta ........ (973) 673-7537
Severino Pasta Mfg. Co., 110 Haddon Ave., Westmont 08108
Owner—Joseph Severino, 22 emp., Pasta ........ (856) 854-7666
Star Ravioli Mfg. Co., Inc., 2 Anderson Ave., Moonachie 07074
Pres., CFO—Laurence Piretra, 12 emp., Fresh & frozen gourmet Italian ravioli ........ (201) 933-6427
Vitamia & Sons, 206 Harrison Ave., Lodi 07644
Pres.—Anthony Vitamia, 12 emp., Ravioli, pasta, sauces, bread, cheese ........ (973) 546-1140
Zeregas Sons, Inc., A., 20-01 Broadway, P.O. Box 241, Fair Lawn 07410
Pres., GM—John B. Vermylen, 150 emp., Corporate headquarters & pasta ........ (201) 797-1400

## 2099 Food preparations, nec

A Taste Of Olive, LLC, 106 Kings Hwy. E., Ste. A, Haddonfield 08033
Manager—Fabio Auguadro, 10 emp., Olive oils & vinegars ........ (856) 795-0043
Abraham's Natural Foods, 9 Long Branch Ave., P.O. Box 89, Long Branch 07740
Owner—Louis Fellman, 5 emp., Hummus dip ........ (732) 229-5799
Advanced Food Systems, Inc., 21 Roosevelt Ave., Somerset 08873
Pres.—Yongkeun Joh, 35 emp., Custom & specialty food ingredient ........ (732) 873-6776
Allied Old English, Inc., 100 Markley St., Port Reading 07064
Owner—Fred Ross, 45 emp., Jams, jellies & preserves, barbecue ........ (732) 636-2060
American Instants, Inc., 117 Bartley Flanders Rd., P.O. Box 817, Flanders 07836
CEO—Christopher Roche, 60 emp., Instant beverages, including cappuccino ........ (973) 584-8811
Arthur Schuman, Inc., 40 New Dutch Ln., Fairfield 07004
Pres.—Neal Schuman, 85 emp., Corporate headquarters & wedges, grated ........ (973) 227-0030
Asiamerica Ingredients, Inc., 245 Old Hook Rd., Ste. 3, Westwood 07675
★ Owner—Mark Zhang, 4 emp., Ingredients blending for the nutraceutical ........ (201) 497-5993
Bioactive Resources, LLC, 138 Sylvania Pl., South Plainfield 07080
CEO—Divya Desai, 25 emp., Custom botanical powders, extracts, ........ (908) 561-3114
Brand Aromatics, Inc., 1600 Oak St., P.O. Box 3033, Lakewood 08701
Pres.—Karl E. Brand, 40 emp., Concentrated savory flavoring ingredients ........ (732) 363-8080
Campbell Soup Supply Co., 3500 S. Clinton Ave., South Plainfield 07080
Qual. Assur. Mgr.—Anita Solomon, 30 emp., Food flavorings & spices ........ (908) 561-1660
Carrington Co., LLC (H Q), 7 Reuten Dr., Closter 07624
CEO—Debbie Shandel, 10 emp., Company headquarters; 100% organic, ........ (800) 505-9546
Carrington Tea, LLC, 7 Reuten Dr., P.O. Box 102, Closter 07624
CEO—David Eben, 8 emp., Tea ........ (201) 261-5517
Clement Pappas & Company, Inc. (H Q), 1 Collins Dr., Ste. 200, Carneys Point 08069
CEO—Mark McNeil, 125 emp., Corporate headquarters; bottled & canned ........ (856) 455-1000
Colonna Brothers, Inc., 4102 Bergen Tpke., P.O. Box 808, North Bergen 07047
Pres.—Peter Colonna, 100 emp., Private label & branded grated & shredded ........ (201) 864-1115
ConAgra Food Ingredients, 6 Santa Fe Way, Cranbury 08512
GM—Joanna Holmes, 90 emp., Spices ........ (609) 409-6200
Continental Seasoning, Inc., 1700 Palisade Ave., P.O. Box 629, Teaneck 07666
V-P., GM—Edward Levine, 32 emp., Food seasoning & spices ........ (201) 837-6111
Corbion Caravan, 100 Adams Dr., Totowa 07512
V-P., Pricing—Joseph Solimini, 160 emp., Baking ingredients & mixes ........ (973) 256-8886
Deep Foods, Inc., 1090 Springfield Rd., Union 07083
Pres., CFO—Arvind Amin, 290 emp., Indian foods & flavorings ........ (908) 810-7500
Delicious Fresh Pierogi, Inc., 594 Chestnut St., Roselle Park 07204
Owner & Pres.—Richard Jackiewicz, 20 emp., Pierogis ........ (908) 245-0550

E&M Gold Beekeepers, LLC, 113 Hope Rd., Tinton Falls 07724
Ptnr.—Mary Kosenski, 2 emp., All-natural honey & honey & beeswax-based ........ (732) 542-6528
Eastern Tea Corp., 1 Engelhard Dr., Monroe Township 08831
Pres.—Paul Barbakoff, 50 emp., Tea ........ (609) 860-1100
Extracts & Ingredients Ltd., Div. Of MORRE-TEC Industries, Inc., 1 Gary Rd., Union 07083
Pres.—Leonard Glass, 5 emp., Botanical extracts, nutritive oils, ........ (908) 688-9009
F & S Produce Co., Inc., 913 Bridgeton Ave., P.O. Box 489, Rosenhayn 08352
CEO—Salvatore Pipitone, Jr., 600 emp., Fruit & vegetable processing & packaging ........ (856) 453-0316
Farbest-Tallman Foods Corp. (H Q), 160 Summit Ave., Ste. 200, Montvale 07645
Pres.—Daniel M. Meloro, 17 emp., Corporate headquarters; food blending ........ (201) 573-4900
Fillo Factory, Inc., 10 Fairway Ct., Northvale 07647
CEO—Ron Rexroth, 150 emp., Private label fillo doughs, organic ........ (201) 439-1036
Flavor Development Corp., 388 Chestnut St., Norwood 07648
Pres.—Joseph Staffieri, 12 emp., Flavors ........ (201) 784-8188
Gel Spice Co., Inc., 48 Hook Rd., P.O. Box 285, Bayonne 07002
Pres.—Andre Engel, 225 emp., Spices, seasonings, seeds, extracts ........ (201) 339-0700
Global Ingredients, Inc., 317 9th Ave., Paterson 07514
Pres.—Frank Montain, 5 emp., Food ingredient stabilizers ........ (973) 278-6677
Gourmet Foods, Inc., 25 Andrews Dr., Woodland Park 07424
Pres.—Alfred Fuchs, 50 emp., Gourmet canapes, vegetables, sushi ........ (973) 237-1776
Gourmet Kitchen, Inc., 1238 State Route 33, Neptune 07753
CEO—Raymond Walsh, 80 emp., Manufacturer & distributor of frozen ........ (732) 775-5222
Green's Fresh Fruit Salad, Inc., 125 Shadeland Ave., P.O. Box 244, Pleasantville 08232
Pres.—Frances Green, 4 emp., Potato, pasta, fruit, lettuce, chicken ........ (609) 641-5455
Harris Tea Co., 344 New Albany Rd., Moorestown 08057
Sr. V-P.—Robert Hackel, 80 emp., Company headquarters & tea, tea bags ........ (856) 793-0290
Hilltop Honey, LLC, 15 Hill St., North Caldwell 07006
Pres.—Joseph Lelinho, 3 emp., Honey, beeswax, pollen, propolis, hand ........ (201) 953-0198
House Foods America Corp., 801 Randolph Rd., Somerset 08873
GM—Ryan Ogawa, 60 emp., Tofu ........ (732) 537-9500
Importers Service Corp., 65 Brunswick Ave., Edison 08817
Pres.—Eric Berliner, 40 emp., Food ingredients ........ (732) 248-1946
International Coconut Corp., 225 W. Grand St., Elizabeth 07202
Pres.—Richard Kesselhaut, 5 emp., Sweetened coconut ........ (908) 289-1555
International Foodsource, LLC, 52 Richboynton Rd., Dover 07801
Pres.—David Lipson, 120 emp., Dried fruits, nuts & gourmet food products ........ (973) 361-7044
Interstate Sales New of Jersey, LLC, 1226 Haddonfield-Berlin Rd., Unit C-2, Voorhees 08043
Ptnr. & Pres.—Steven Osder, 10 emp., Private label seasonings, spices, mustards ........ (856) 433-8692
J & K Ingredients, Inc., 160 E. 5th St., Paterson 07524
Pres.—James K. Sausville, 80 emp., Natural bread, cake & donut mixes, ........ (973) 340-8700
J.P. Veggies, Inc., 222 New Rd., Parsippany 07054
CEO—Philip Grabow, 38 emp., Vegetarian food products, including ........ (973) 808-1540
Kalustyan Corp., 855 Rahway Ave., Union 07083
CEO—Errol Karakash, 65 emp., Cooking spices ........ (908) 688-6111
Lorenzo Food Group, Inc., 196 Coolidge Ave., Englewood 07631
★ Owner—John Lorenzo, 5 emp., Fresh sandwiches, salads & dessert ........ (201) 868-9088
Lucy's Ravioli Kitchen & Market, 830 State Rd., Princeton 08540
Pres.—Caron Wendell, 8 emp., Ravioli & pasta ........ (609) 924-3623
Manischewitz Co., The (H Q), 80 Avenue K, Newark 07105
Pres.—Mark Weinstein, 65 emp., Company headquarters; kosher cookies ........ (201) 553-1100
Mayab Happy Tacos, Inc., 450 Florida Grove Rd., Perth Amboy 08861
V-P.—George Alamilla, 25 emp., Flour & corn tortillas, white & yellow ........ (732) 293-0400
Mincing Overseas Spice Co., 10 Tower Rd., Bldg. KN, Dayton 08810
Pres.—M. Ruparelia, 30 emp., Bulk spices ........ (732) 355-9944
Mirrotek International, LLC, 90 Dayton Ave., Bldg. 1-F, Passaic 07055
Pres.—Joe Bezzy, 45 emp., Decorative & dressing mirrors, home ........ (973) 472-1400
Momma's Home Made, LLC, 1225 Haddonfield Berlin Rd., Southgate Plz., Ste. 2, Voorhees 08043
Ptnr.—Daisy Smith, 2 emp., Gourmet, 50% less sugar added & no ........ (856) 753-3250
MPT Delivery Systems, Inc., 95 Prince St., Paterson 07501
Pres.—Bob McCrimlisk, 50 emp., Formulation & granulation of bulk nutriceutic ........ (973) 279-4132
Muirhead Of Ringoes New Jersey, Inc., 43 U.S. Highway 202, Ringoes 08551
Pres.—Doris Simpson, 10 emp., Condiments, sauces & flavored nondairy ........ (908) 782-7803
MYOS Corp. (H Q), 45 Horsehill Rd., Ste. 106, Cedar Knolls 07927
★ Pres.—Peter Levy, 10 emp., Corporate headquarters; bionutritional ........ (973) 509-0444
Nestle' USA, Inc., Beverage Div., 61 Jerseyville Ave., Freehold 07728
Plt. Mgr.—Joe Rechtiene, 315 emp., Coffee & tea blending ........ (732) 462-1300
New Crushed Toast Corp., 625 Pennsylvania Ave., Linden 07036
Ptnr. & Pres.—Carlito Perez, 8 emp., 50-lb. bags- 2,000-lb bags of breadcrumbs ........ (908) 925-2920
Nu Products Seasonings Co., 74 Louis Ct., South Hackensack 07606
Pres.—Henry Goldstein, 48 emp., Food seasonings ........ (201) 440-0065
Nutrition North America, 10 Saddle Rd., Cedar Knolls 07927
Cust. Serv. Rep.—Tajah Muhammad, 26 emp., Metabolic nutritional drink formulas ........ (973) 734-0023
Oasis Foods Co., 635 Ramsey Ave., P.O. Box 697, Hillside 07205
Pres., CEO—William Gillingham, 150 emp., Vegetable oils, salad dressings, sauces ........ (908) 964-0477
Oriental Aromatics, Inc., 21 Spielman Rd., Fairfield 07004
Pres., CEO—Dharmil Bodani, 25 emp., Fragrances & flavors ........ (973) 227-0400
Panzarotti Tarantini Pizza, Inc., 2060 Springdale Rd., Ste. 300, Cherry Hill 08003
CEO—Leo Tarantini, 12 emp., Pizza puffs ........ (856) 489-0026
Paulaur Corp., 105 Melrich Rd., Cranbury 08512
V-P., CFO—Mitchell Stefaniak, 100 emp., Contract blended food ingredients for ........ (609) 395-8844
Portfirio Italian Food, Inc., 320 Anderson St., Trenton 08611
Pres.—John Portfirio, 5 emp., Fresh pasta ........ (609) 393-4116
Puebla Foods, Inc., 118 1st St., Passaic 07055
Pres.—Felix Sanchez, Sr., 25 emp., Tortillas ........ (973) 473-4494
Puratos Corp., 1941 Old Cuthbert Rd., Cherry Hill 08034
Pres., U.S.—Frederic Duvauchelle, 100 emp., Corporate headquarters & bread, bagel ........ (856) 428-4300
R.A.B. Food Group, LLC, 80 Avenue K, Newark 07105
Plt. Mgr.—Randall Copeland, 200 emp., Kosher cookies, noodles, dry soup mix ........ (201) 553-1100
RC Fine Foods, Inc., 139 Stryker Ln., Hillsborough 08844
Pres.—Susan Goldman, 70 emp., Soup, sauce, gravy, salad dressing ........ (908) 359-5500
Ready Pac, 101 Arlington Blvd., Swedesboro 08085
Dir., Facilities—Mike Morphew, 300 emp., Packaged fruits & salads ........ (856) 241-0900
Ready Pac Produce, Inc., 700 Railroad Ave., P.O. Box 6, Florence 08518
Cont.—Bernard Ganski, 550 emp., Packaged salads ........ (609) 499-1900
Reeves Enterprises, Inc., 571 Central Ave., New Providence 07974
Pres.—Edward Reeves, 7 emp., Tea blending & packaging ........ (908) 665-9511
Rex Wine Vinegar Co., 828-830 Raymond Blvd., Newark 07105
Pres.—Vincent Carlesimo, 8 emp., Cooking wines & vinegars ........ (973) 589-6911
Savoury Systems International, Inc., 230 Industrial Pkwy., Ste. C, P.O. Box 5487, Branchburg 08876
Pres.—David Adams, 18 emp., Yeast, organic yeast & seafood extracts ........ (908) 526-2524
Schiff Food Products Co., Inc., 994 Riverview Dr., Totowa 07512
Pres.—David Deutscher, 25 emp., Spices, seeds & herbs processing & ........ (973) 237-1990



★ Indicates new listing this edition.

Sentrex Ingredients, LLC, 350 Cantor Ave., Linden 07036
Member—Arthur Gurerrera, 5 emp., *Extracts, concentrates, essences &* .......... (908) 862-4440
Sheri's Cookery, Inc., 33 Delancy St., Newark 07105
CEO—Murray Forman, 20 emp., *Mixed potato, macaroni & pasta salads* .......... (973) 589-2060
Silver Palate Kitchens, Inc., 211 Knickerbocker Rd., P.O. Box 512, Cresskill 07626
Pres.—Peter Harris, 10 emp., *Pasta & cooking sauces, condiments,* .......... (201) 568-0110
Spice Co., 6-C Terminal Way, Avenel 07001
Ptnr.—Andy Barna, 70 emp., *Spices* .......... (732) 499-9070
Springdale Farm Market, Inc., 1638 Springdale Rd., Cherry Hill 08003
Pres.—Mary A. Jarvis, 45 emp., *Fruit & vegetable processing* .......... (856) 424-8674
Stepan Co., 100 W. Hunter Ave., Maywood 07607
V-P., Specialty Prods.—Robert Peacock, 95 emp., *Food products chemicals, oils & emulsifiers* (201) 845-3030
Sterling Food Flavorings, LLC, 182 Ridge Rd., Ste. G, Dayton 08810
Ex. Dir.—Vitas Roman, 10 emp., *Savory food flavors, seasonings, HVP* .......... (732) 438-1620
Summit Hill Flavors, 253 Lackland Dr. W., Middlesex 08846
Pres.—Robert Delin, 30 emp., *Savory natural & organic food flavors* .......... (732) 805-0335
Symrise, Inc., 300 North St., Teterboro 07608
CEO—Heinz-Jurgen Bertram, 350 emp., *Corporate headquarters & food flavorings* .......... (201) 288-3200
Ungar's Food Products, Inc., 9 Boumar Pl., Elmwood Park 07407
Pres.—Peter Praeger, 45 emp., *Frozen kosher food products, including* .......... (201) 703-1300
Unilever North America, 700 Sylvan Ave., Englewood Cliffs 07632
Pres., N. America—Kees Kruythoff, 1900 emp., *Company headquarters & food & personal* ... (201) 567-8000
Vita-Pure, Inc., 410 W. 1st Ave., Roselle 07203
Pres.—Achyut Sahasra, 25 emp., *Vitamins & dietary supplements* .......... (908) 245-1212
Viva Mexican Restaurant, 117 Broad St., Unit 1, Flemington 08822
Owner—Filiberto Arias, 10 emp., *Frozen Mexican entrees* .......... (908) 788-0744
WhiteWave Foods Co., 70 Rosenhayn Ave., Bridgeton 08302
Plt. Mgr.—John Bodrog, 100 emp., *Soy milk* .......... (856) 459-3890
Yume Enterprises, LLC, 1800 E. State St., Ste. 158, Trenton 08609
★ Founder & COO—Brian Allen, 10 emp., *Ready-to-eat gluten-free snacks, including* .......... (609) 588-8903
Zina's Salads, Inc., 11 Great Meadow Ln., East Hanover 07936
Pres., R & D Mgr.—Igor Shaknovich, 24 emp., *Prepared salads* .......... (973) 428-0660

## 21 TOBACCO PRODUCTS

### 2111 Cigarettes

Eonsmoke, LLC (H Q), 1500 Main Ave., Ste. 2, Clifton 07011
CFO—Gregory Grishayev, 7 emp., *Company headquarters; electronic cigarettes* .......... (800) 616-3711
Mafco Worldwide Corp., 300 Jefferson St., Camden 08104
Sr. V-P., Gen. Counsel—Thomas Molchan, 150 emp., *Corporate headquarters & tobacco flavors* (856) 964-8840
Sherman, Inc. (H Q), Nat, 2200 Fletcher Ave., Fort Lee 07024
Pres., CEO—Joel Sherman, 20 emp., *Corporate headquarters; cigars, cigarettes* .......... (201) 735-9000

### 2121 Cigars

Sherman, Inc. (H Q), Nat, 2200 Fletcher Ave., Fort Lee 07024
Pres., CEO—Joel Sherman, 20 emp., *Corporate headquarters; cigars, cigarettes* .......... (201) 735-9000

### 2131 Chewing & smoking tobacco

Sherman, Inc. (H Q), Nat, 2200 Fletcher Ave., Fort Lee 07024
Pres., CEO—Joel Sherman, 20 emp., *Corporate headquarters; cigars, cigarettes* .......... (201) 735-9000

## 22 TEXTILE MILL PRODUCTS

### 2211 Broadwoven fabric mills, cotton

Absecon Mills, Inc., 901 W. Aloe St., P.O. Box 672, Cologne 08213
Pres., CEO—Randolph S. Taylor, 200 emp., *Upholstery, ballistics & composite* .......... (609) 965-5373
De Leo Textiles (H Q), 53 Dwight Pl., Fairfield 07004
CEO & CFO—Craig E. De Leo, 10 emp., *Company headquarters; automotive, upholstery* ..... (973) 439-6801
Har-Tru Sports, 1715 Oak St., Ste. 1, Lakewood 08701
Dir., Sales—Tracy Lynch, 30 emp., *Netting products & knitted industrial* .......... (434) 295-6167
In-Pak Services, Inc., 474 Getty Ave., Clifton 07011
Pres.—Brian Billes, 20 emp., *Cotton-cloth binder slip covers* .......... (973) 595-5250
Jacquard Fabrics Co., Inc., 1965 Swarthmore Ave., Lakewood 08701
Owner & Pres.—Leonard Gliner, 40 emp., *Upholstery fabrics* .......... (732) 905-4545
Lawrence Custom Drapery Shop, 323 4th St., Ewing 08638
Pres.—Charlie Cullen, 20 emp., *Custom draperies, window treatments* .......... (609) 695-3877
Stanbee Co., Inc., 70 Broad St., P.O. Box 436, Carlstadt 07072
Pres.—Michael Berkson, 40 emp., *Thermoplastic counter & boxtoe materials* .......... (201) 933-9666
Stanek Netting, Inc., 111 Orange St., Bloomfield 07003
Pres.—Jeremy Stanek, 5 emp., *Industrial & athletic raschel knitted* .......... (973) 680-1616
Tanner Assocs., 600 Palisade Ave., Union City 07087
Owner, Fin. & GM—Irving Tanner, 3 emp., *Cotton & nylon cloth dry cleaning &* .......... (201) 865-4500
Ultraflex Systems, Inc. (H Q), 1578 Sussex Tpke., Ste. 400, Randolph 07869
CEO—John Schleicher, 20 emp., *Corporate headquarters; indoor & outdoor* .......... (973) 627-8608
Vac's Bandage Co., 163 Pennsylvania Ave., Paterson 07503
Owner—Anthony Vacca, 10 emp., *Horse leg wraps* .......... (973) 345-3355

### 2221 Broadwoven fabric mills, manmade

A. Smith & Son, Inc., 300 W. Broad St., Ste. A, Burlington 08016
Pres.—John R. Smith, 7 emp., *Nylon, canvas & textile products, bags* .......... (609) 747-0800
Avon Fabrics, Inc., 484 Lincoln Blvd., Middlesex 08846
Owner—D. J. Jain, 3 emp., *Woven, embroidered & novelty silk fabrics* .......... (732) 764-9700
De Leo Textiles (H Q), 53 Dwight Pl., Fairfield 07004
CEO & CFO—Craig E. De Leo, 10 emp., *Company headquarters; automotive, upholstery* ..... (973) 439-6801
Eastern Silk Mills, Inc., 212 Catherine St., Elizabeth 07201
Pres., Hum. Res. Mgr.—Chong Kim, 30 emp., *Silk dyeing, printing & finishing* .......... (908) 355-6700
Fablok Mills, Inc., 140 Spring St., Murray Hill 07974
Pres.—Alex Fisher, 45 emp., *Nylon, polyester & polypropylene knitted* .......... (908) 464-1950
Kushner Draperies Mfg., LLC, 5305 Route 70, Pennsauken 08109
Chrm., CFO & Bus. Mgr.—Carla Moore, 25 emp., *Draperies & upholstery* .......... (856) 317-9696
Lawrence Custom Drapery Shop, 323 4th St., Ewing 08638
Pres.—Charlie Cullen, 20 emp., *Custom draperies, window treatments* .......... (609) 695-3877
Pegasus Home Fashions, Inc., 107 Trumbull St., Bldg. G-1, P.O. Box 9030, Elizabeth 07206
GM—Carmine Spinella, 70 emp., *Pillows, comforters, blankets, quilts* .......... (908) 965-1919
Silberstein, Inc., M., 428 Broad St., Shrewsbury 07702
Co-Pres.—M. Silberstein, 7 emp., *Draperies, upholstery, office furniture* .......... (732) 741-1762
Tanner Assocs., 600 Palisade Ave., Union City 07087
Owner, Fin. & GM—Irving Tanner, 3 emp., *Cotton & nylon cloth dry cleaning &* .......... (201) 865-4500
Ultraflex Systems, Inc. (H Q), 1578 Sussex Tpke., Ste. 400, Randolph 07869
CEO—John Schleicher, 20 emp., *Corporate headquarters; indoor & outdoor* .......... (973) 627-8608
Wearbest Sil-Tex Mills, Ltd., 325 Midland Ave., P.O. Box 589, Garfield 07026
Pres.—Irwin Gasner, 90 emp., *Indoor & outdoor woven jacquard fabrics* .......... (973) 340-8844

### 2231 Broadwoven fabric mills, wool

Water-Jel Technologies, 50 Broad St., Carlstadt 07072
CFO—John McAndris, 80 emp., *Sterile burn dressings, fire blankets* .......... (201) 507-8300

### 2241 Narrow fabric mills

A. Smith & Son, Inc., 300 W. Broad St., Ste. A, Burlington 08016
Pres.—John R. Smith, 7 emp., *Nylon, canvas & textile products, bags* .......... (609) 747-0800
AISCO, 35 Mileed Way, P.O. Box 30, Avenel 07001
Pres.—Susan Gronbeck, 15 emp., *Lifting & securing webbing products* .......... (732) 574-3233
All Lace Processing Corp., 1109 Grand Ave., Unit 4, North Bergen 07047
Pres.—Key Gaetano, 15 emp., *Lace cutting & separating* .......... (201) 867-8795
American Power Cord Corp., 217 Brook Ave., 3rd Fl., Passaic 07055
Pres., Fin. & MIS Mgr.—Makil Simon, 5 emp., *Braided & knitted elastic cordage* .......... (973) 574-8301
Ardwyn Binding Products Co., 681 Main St., Bldg. 7, Belleville 07109
Ptnr. & Sales Mgr.—Kathy Naegele, 65 emp., *Bindings, trimmings, twist cord braids* .......... (973) 751-4002
Avon Fabrics, Inc., 484 Lincoln Blvd., Middlesex 08846
Owner—D. J. Jain, 3 emp., *Woven, embroidered & novelty silk fabrics* .......... (732) 764-9700
Carson & Gebel Ribbon Co., Inc., 17 Green Pond Rd., Rockaway 07866
Pres.—Henry Gebel, 30 emp., *Custom craft & decorative ribbons* .......... (973) 627-4200
Cottage Lace & Ribbon Co., 21 TFH Plaza Union & 3rd Ave., Neptune 07753
Pres.—Shahid Waseem, 2 emp., *Manufacturer of wired ribbons & distributor* .......... (732) 776-9353
Hessburg, Inc., Michale A., 180 Autumn St., Passaic 07055
Dir., Opers.—Rene Rioux, 9 emp., *Textile trimmings* .......... (973) 777-8700
JRM Industries, Inc., 1 Mattimore St., Passaic 07055
Pres.—Louis S. Simon, 20 emp., *Corporate headquarters & ribbons, bows* .......... (973) 779-9340
Klein Ribbon Designs, Jeffrey, 176 E. 7th St., Paterson 07524
Pres.—Jeffrey Klein, 10 emp., *Custom imprinted ribbons* .......... (973) 684-4671
Mactex, LLC, 489-A Getty Ave., Clifton 07011
Owner—Rory McNamara, 12 emp., *Tubular woven fabrics* .......... (973) 340-3131
Modern International Corp., 145 Cliffwood Ave., Cliffwood 07721
Pres., GM—Daniel Stern, 20 emp., *Wire, steel & plastic strapping, packaging* .......... (732) 696-9100
N.Y. Textile Mills, Inc., 90 Dayton Ave., Bldg. 5-A, Passaic 07055
Pres.—John Park, 7 emp., *Narrow-woven polypropylene webbing* .......... (973) 777-9871
Offray Specialty Narrow Fabrics, Inc. (H Q), 4 Essex Ave., Ste. 403, Bernardsville 07924
Pres., CEO—Denise A. Offray, 9 emp., *Corporate headquarters; specialty high-perfor* .......... (908) 879-3636
Paris Lace, 1500 Main Ave., Clifton 07011
Pres., Plt. Mgr.—Joseph Dickinson, 50 emp., *Lace* .......... (973) 478-9035
Reliant Ribbon & Trims, 838 21st Ave., Paterson 07513
Pres.—Seth Shulman, 50 emp., *Decorative fabric, printed & custom* .......... (973) 881-0404
R-Pac International Corp., 69 Kingsland Ave., Marino Plz. 1, Clifton 07014
Plt. Mgr.—Daniel Rodriguez, 6 emp., *Woven textile labels* .......... (973) 916-1600
Snapco Mfg. Corp., 140 Central Ave., Hillside 07205
Chrm., Pres., CFO & R & D Mgr.—Jeffrey G. Spitz, 25 emp., *Snap, fastener tape, eyelets, grommets* (973) 282-0300
The Star Group, 80-A Industrial Rd., Lodi 07644
Pres.—Michael Friedman, 10 emp., *Woven & fabric labels, hang tags &* .......... (973) 778-8600

### 2251 Hosiery—women's, except socks

Gordon Mills Mfg., Inc. (H Q), 68 Sherwood Dr., Morristown 07960
Pres.—Bernard Factor, 3 emp., *Corporate headquarters; manufacturer* .......... (973) 359-1080

### 2252 Hosiery

Mayer/Berkshire Corp. (H Q), 25 Edison Rd., P.O. Box 244, Wayne 07474
CEO—Chester Mayer, 50 emp., *Corporate headquarters; hosiery, including* .......... (973) 696-6200
Sox Trot, Inc., 373 Grand Ave., Palisades Park 07650
Hum. Res., Off., Opers. & Sales Mgr.—Sandy Benedetti, 10 emp., *Women's & girls' hosiery* . (201) 944-5250
Standard Merchandising Co. (H Q), 1125 Wright Ave., Camden 08103
Pres., CFO—Jeff Tarnoff, 50 emp., *Company headquarters; men's & women's* .......... (856) 964-9700

### 2253 Knit outerwear mills

Artex Knitting Mills, Inc., 300 Harvard Ave., P.O. Box 183, Westville 08093
Pres.—Arthur Pottash, 90 emp., *Knit scarves & caps* .......... (856) 456-2800
Bear Hands Ltd., 38 Main St., Little Ferry 07643
Owner—Jeffrey Golden, 5 emp., *Fleece hats, mittens & scarves* .......... (201) 807-9898
Chipp II, 7 Spring Hill Cir., Wayne 07470
Pres.—Janet Winston, 2 emp., *Men's neckties, women's scarves & blazer* .......... (212) 687-0850
Loveline Industries, Inc., 90 Dayton Ave., Ste. 33, Passaic 07055
Pres.—Morton Goldstein, 15 emp., *Hi-visibility safety clothing, including* .......... (973) 928-3427
Team U. S. A., 200 Badger Ave., Newark 07108
Pres.—Shiv Thapar, 20 emp., *Team sports uniforms* .......... (973) 596-2800
Triumph Knitting, Inc., 18-20 Di Carolis Ct., Hackensack 07601
Pres.—Steve Gerber, 19 emp., *Industrial & polyester fabrics, apparel* .......... (201) 646-0022

### 2254 Knit underwear mills

Carter Co., The William, 17 The Promenade, Edgewater 07020
Owner—William Carter, 8 emp., *Children's shirts & under clothing* .......... (201) 313-1783
Triumph Knitting, Inc., 18-20 Di Carolis Ct., Hackensack 07601
Pres.—Steve Gerber, 19 emp., *Industrial & polyester fabrics, apparel* .......... (201) 646-0022

### 2257 Weft knit fabric mills

Markbilt Technical Fabrics Corp., 1875 McCarter Hwy., Newark 07104
Pres.—Mark Woltin, 100 emp., *Stretch knit, 3D & upholstery fabrics* .......... (973) 482-6400
Meadows Knitting Corp., 1875 McCarter Hwy., Newark 07104
V-P.—Marty Sohn, 100 emp., *Knit textile products* .......... (973) 482-6400
Triumph Knitting, Inc., 18-20 Di Carolis Ct., Hackensack 07601
Pres.—Steve Gerber, 19 emp., *Industrial & polyester fabrics, apparel* .......... (201) 646-0022

### 2258 Lace & warp knit fabric mills

International Veiling Corp., 244 Hazel St., 2nd Fl., Clifton 07011
V-P.—David Wiley, 49 emp., *Lace & net dyeing & finishing* .......... (973) 772-3100
Jason Mills, LLC, 440 S. Main St., Milltown 08850
Pres.—Michael Lavroff, 5 emp., *Knitted mesh fabrics for the military* .......... (732) 651-7200
Nu-Style Embroidery & Button Co., Inc., 5212 Polk St., West New York 07093
Pres.—Jay Rosner, 5 emp., *Apparel buttons, belts, neckties, lace* .......... (201) 864-1808
Royal Lace Co., Inc., 902 E. Hazelwood Ave., Rahway 07065
★ Pres.—Moises Guttman, 25 emp., *Manufacturer of knitted lace & wholesaler* .......... (718) 495-9327
Team U. S. A., 200 Badger Ave., Newark 07108
Pres.—Shiv Thapar, 20 emp., *Team sports uniforms* .......... (973) 596-2800

Ultraflex Systems, Inc. (H Q), 1578 Sussex Tpke., Ste. 400, Randolph 07869
CEO—John Schleicher, 20 emp., Corporate headquarters; indoor & outdoor ........................ (973) 627-8608

## 2259 Knitting mills, nec

Ansell Healthcare Products, LLC (H Q), 111 Wood Ave. S., Ste. 210, Iselin 08830
Chrm.—Glenn Barnes, 200 emp., Company headquarters; industrial work ........................ (732) 345-5400
Bear Hands Ltd., 38 Main St., Little Ferry 07643
Owner—Jeffrey Golden, 5 emp., Fleece hats, mittens & scarves ........................ (201) 807-9898
Fablok Mills, Inc., 140 Spring St., Murray Hill 07974
Pres.—Alex Fisher, 45 emp., Nylon, polyester & polypropylene knitted ........................ (908) 464-1950
Photothrow, Inc., 280 N. Midland Ave., Bldg. J-1, Saddle Brook 07663
Pres.—Andy Concilio, 3 emp., Customer art-based blankets, pillows ........................ (855) 645-4438
Royal Lace Co., Inc., 902 E. Hazelwood Ave., Rahway 07065
★ Pres.—Moises Guttman, 25 emp., Manufacturer of knitted lace & wholesaler ........................ (718) 495-9327
Triumph Knitting, Inc., 18-20 Di Carolis Ct., Hackensack 07601
Pres.—Steve Gerber, 19 emp., Industrial & polyester fabrics, apparel ........................ (201) 646-0022

## 2261 Finishing plants, cotton

American Fabric Processors, 555 E. 31st St., Paterson 07513
CEO—Joe Binson, 80 emp., Textile dyeing & finishing ........................ (973) 278-0272
Davol, Inc., 1822 Underwood Blvd., Delran 08075
Plt. Mgr.—Jose Nunez, 13 emp., Medical textiles ........................ (856) 764-8158
Diversitex, Inc. (H Q), 376 Hollywood Ave., Ste. 203, Fairfield 07004
Pres.—William C. Summers, 16 emp., Corporate headquarters; cotton fabric ........................ (973) 808-4566
E & W Textile Processors, Inc., 293 Morrissee Ave., Haledon 07508
Pres., Cont.—Joseph Pizzoli, 30 emp., Textile dyeing ........................ (973) 942-8718
East Coast Embossing, 35 8th St., P.O. Box 1076, Passaic 07055
Pres.—Anthony Maltese, Jr., 15 emp., Textile embossing ........................ (973) 777-9830
Martin Corp., 171 N. Pearl St., Bridgeton 08302
Pres., Treas.—Will Martin, 16 emp., Dyers & finishers ........................ (856) 451-0900
Paul Dyeing Co., 626 Orange St., Newark 07107
Pres.—Laurie Braun, 17 emp., Dyeing of fashion apparel, table linens ........................ (973) 484-1121
Safer Holding Corp., 1875 McCarter Hwy., Newark 07104
Pres., CEO—Albert Safer, 150 emp., Corporate headquarters & textile dyeing ........................ (973) 482-6400
Sunbrite Dye Co., 35 8th St., P.O. Box 1076, Passaic 07055
Plt. Mgr.—Ralph Schiano, 90 emp., Textile finishing & dyeing ........................ (973) 777-9830
Walted Designs, Inc., 70 Spruce St., Ste. 8, Paterson 07501
Pres.—Bhibhishan Raghubir, 2 emp., Narrow fabric printing ........................ (973) 881-1944

## 2262 Finishing plants, manmade

EFX Tex, LLC, 555 E. 31st St., Paterson 07513
GM—Emil Innocenti, 6 emp., Fabric finishing ........................ (973) 345-7601
Paul Dyeing Co., 626 Orange St., Newark 07107
Pres.—Laurie Braun, 17 emp., Dyeing of fashion apparel, table linens ........................ (973) 484-1121
Rebtex, Inc., 40 Industrial Pkwy., Somerville 08876
Pres., Plt. Mgr.—Robert Brandell, 50 emp., Textile finishing ........................ (908) 722-3549
Safer Holding Corp., 1875 McCarter Hwy., Newark 07104
Pres., CEO—Albert Safer, 150 emp., Corporate headquarters & textile dyeing ........................ (973) 482-6400
Sunbrite Dye Co., 35 8th St., P.O. Box 1076, Passaic 07055
Plt. Mgr.—Ralph Schiano, 90 emp., Textile finishing & dyeing ........................ (973) 777-9830

## 2269 Finishing plants, nec

Allied Bias Products Corp., 430 Communipaw Ave., Ste. 3, Jersey City 07304
Pres.—Leonard Staloff, 12 emp., Textile converting, slitting & cutting ........................ (201) 432-6050
Dye Into Print, Inc., 167 Fornelius Ave., Clifton 07013
Pres.—Mathew Lederman, 62 emp., Wide-format dye sublimation textile ........................ (973) 772-8019
Tex Print USA, LLC, 20-21 Wagaraw Rd., Bldg. 37, Fair Lawn 07410
★ CEO—Edward Margarucci, Sr., 20 emp., Textile dye sublimation & heat transfer ........................ (201) 773-6531
Textile Creations, Inc. (H Q), 8-B S. Gold Dr., Hamilton 08691
Pres.—Jim Hankin, 10 emp., Corporate headquarters; cotton textile ........................ (609) 631-4433

## 2273 Carpets & rugs

Couristan, Inc., 2 Executive Dr., Ste. 400, Fort Lee 07024
Pres.—Ronald J. Couri, 50 emp., Residential & commercial carpets, including ........................ (201) 585-8500
Edison Foam Processing Corp., 157 Helen St., South Plainfield 07080
Br. Mgr.—Tom Vera, 100 emp., Carpet padding ........................ (732) 225-2440
Innovative Carpets, 45 Legion Dr., Cresskill 07626
Owner—Robert Couri, 7 emp., Carpets & rugs ........................ (201) 894-1008
Loominaries Handweaving, 23 Big Spring Rd., Califon 07830
Owner—Patricia Lukas, 1 emp., Custom & production rag rugs ........................ (908) 832-6652
Mannington Mills, Inc., 75 Mannington Mills Rd., P.O. Box 30, Salem 08079
Chrm. of the Board—Keith Campbell, 600 emp., Corporate headquarters & residential ........................ (856) 935-3000
Michaelian & Kohlberg (H Q), 100 Hoffman Pl., Hillside 07205
Owner & Designer—Teddy Sumner, 4 emp., Company headquarters; hand-knotted ........................ (908) 522-1004
Newark Auto Top Co., Inc., 23 Centerway, East Orange 07017
Pres.—Ben Hershkowitz, 20 emp., Custom replacement carpets for cars ........................ (973) 677-9935
Nourison Industries (H Q), 5 Sampson St., Saddle Brook 07663
Pres.—Alex Peykar, 240 emp., Company headquarters; upholstered furniture ........................ (201) 368-6900

## 2281 Yarn spinning mills

Brawer Bros., Inc. (H Q), 375 Diamond Bridge Ave., P.O. Box 640, Hawthorne 07506
CEO—Skip Smith, 8 emp., Corporate headquarters; yarn ........................ (973) 238-1800
Dillon Yarn Corp. (H Q), 53 E. 34th St., Paterson 07514
CEO—William Cohen, 45 emp., Corporate headquarters; yarn spinning ........................ (973) 684-1600
Middleburg Yarn Processing Co., Inc. (H Q), 375 Diamond Bridge Ave., P.O. Box 640, Hawthorne 07507
CEO—Skip Smith, 12 emp., Corporate headquarters; yarn processing ........................ (973) 238-1800
Multi-Tex Products Corp., 54 2nd Ave., Kearny 07032
Pres.—Michaelene Dwulet, 8 emp., Metallic yarns, including braiding ........................ (201) 991-7262
Orchard Yarn & Thread Co., Inc., 135 Kero Rd., Carlstadt 07072
CEO—David Blumenthal, 70 emp., Corporate headquarters & wool yarn ........................ (201) 804-3999
Sandpiper Embroidery, Inc., 5905 New Jersey Ave., Wildwood Crest 08260
Owner—Virginia Fineberg, 3 emp., Embroidery products, designs & supplies ........................ (609) 522-4560

## 2282 Throwing & winding mills

Ashfar Enterprises, Inc. (H Q), 200 Metro Plex Dr., Ste. 275, Edison 08817
Pres.—Farooq Sattar, 9 emp., Corporate headquarters; polyester & ........................ (848) 202-1581

## 2284 Thread mills

Advance Fiber Technologies, 344 Lodi St., Hackensack 07601
Pres.—Peter Phillips, 50 emp., Industrial sewing & fiberglass threads ........................ (201) 488-2700
Creations By Mariola, 18 Riveredge Dr., Fairfield 07004
Owner—Mariola Dlugosh, 1 emp., Contract sewing ........................ (973) 808-9109
Dollfus Mieg Co., Inc., 10 Basin Dr., Ste. 130, Kearny 07032
CEO—Joseph McCabe, 25 emp., Needlework & embroidery threads & fabrics ........................ (973) 589-0606
Sandpiper Embroidery, Inc., 5905 New Jersey Ave., Wildwood Crest 08260
Owner—Virginia Fineberg, 3 emp., Embroidery products, designs & supplies ........................ (609) 522-4560

## 2295 Coated fabrics, not rubberized

, 101 West St., Hillsdale 07642
Pres.—Clifford Hart, 2 emp., Textile converting of printed vinyl ........................ (201) 666-8585
Alpha Assocs., Inc., 145 Lehigh Ave., Lakewood 08701
Chrm., CEO—A. Louis Avallone, 100 emp., Coated & impregnated high-temperature ........................ (732) 730-1800
Alta Technologies, Inc., 1545 Reed Rd., P.O. Box 100, Pennington 08534
Chrm., CFO—Percy F. Leaper, 7 emp., Expandable monofilament braided & fiberglass ........................ (609) 538-9500
DAF Products, Inc., 420 Braen Ave., Wyckoff 07481
Pres.—Thomas Palmer, 20 emp., Laminated fabrics for tents, banners ........................ (201) 251-1222
Membrane Structure Solutions, Inc., 340 N. Wyoming Ave., South Orange 07079
Pres.—Waldemar Ptaszek, 40 emp., Coated fabric, tensile, frame & air ........................ (908) 520-0112
Microseal Industries, Inc., 610 E. 36th St., P.O. Box 3054, Paterson 07509
Pres.—Michael Silverstein, 30 emp., Coating & laminating ........................ (973) 523-0704
Precision Custom Coatings, LLC, 200 Maltese Dr., Totowa 07512
Chrm.—Peter Longo, 275 emp., Nonwoven fabrics, coated & laminated ........................ (973) 890-3873
Satesa Corp., 154 W. Forest Ave., Englewood 07631
Pres.—Randy Loew, 4 emp., Laminating, coating & converting of ........................ (201) 871-8989
Sommers Plastic Products, Inc., 31 Styertowne Rd., Clifton 07012
Chrm.—Edward Schecter, 20 emp., Plastic & vinyl fabrics, including ........................ (973) 777-7888
The CLI Group, 932 Market St., Paterson 07513
Pres.—Daren Silverstein, 15 emp., Textile laminating, digital printing ........................ (973) 279-9174

## 2297 Fabrics—nonwoven

Avanti, 2650 U.S. Highway 130., Ste. I, Cranbury 08512
Engr.—Rajiv Toprani, 4 emp., Polypropylene & polyethylene spundbond ........................ (609) 655-5333
Carlee Corp., 28 Piermont Rd., Rockleigh 07647
Pres.—Bruce A. Burgermaster, 40 emp., Polyester batting, fiberfill, high-loft ........................ (201) 768-6800
Fablok Mills, Inc., 140 Spring St., Murray Hill 07974
Pres.—Alex Fisher, 45 emp., Nylon, polyester & polypropylene knitted ........................ (908) 464-1950
JRM Industries, Inc., 1 Mattimore St., Passaic 07055
Pres.—Louis S. Simon, 20 emp., Corporate headquarters & ribbons, bows ........................ (973) 779-9340
Precision Custom Coatings, LLC, 200 Maltese Dr., Totowa 07512
Chrm.—Peter Longo, 275 emp., Nonwoven fabrics, coated & laminated ........................ (973) 890-3873
SPC Sorbent Products Co., Inc., 645 Howard Ave., Somerset 08873
Plt. Mgr.—Nazim Mansuri, 60 emp., Sorbent nonwoven pads ........................ (732) 302-0080
TransWeb, LLC, 1473 W. Forest Grove Rd., Vineland 08360
V-P.—Kumar Ogale, 50 emp., Nonwoven filter materials ........................ (856) 205-1313

## 2298 Cordage & twine

American Power Cord Corp., 217 Brook Ave., 3rd Fl., Passaic 07055
Pres., Fin. & MIS Mgr.—Makil Simon, 5 emp., Braided & knitted elastic cordage ........................ (973) 574-8301
Brown & Perkins, Inc., 1193 Route 535, P.O. Box 412, Cranbury 08512
Pres.—E. T. Comly, 16 emp., Manufacturer & distributor of wire ........................ (609) 655-1150
Doran Sling & Assembly Corp., 1285 Central Ave., Hillside 07205
CEO—Barry Lemberg, 24 emp., Wire rope, chain, nylon & wire rope ........................ (908) 351-7800
Egg Harbor Rope Products, Inc., 5105 White Horse Pike, P.O. Box 294, Egg Harbor City 08215
Pres.—Fred Good, 3 emp., Nylon rope & anchor & dock line for ........................ (609) 965-2435
Kenyon & Sons, Inc., William, 90 Ethel Rd. W., Piscataway 08854
COO—Mike Wheaton, 35 emp., Rope ........................ (732) 985-8980
Kinedyne Corp. (H Q), 151 Industrial Pkwy., Branchburg 08876
Pres.—James M. Klausmann, 20 emp., Corporate headquarters; cargo control ........................ (908) 231-1800
Seaboard Paper & Twine, LLC, 37 E. 6th St., Paterson 07524
Member—Robert Baretz, 12 emp., Waxed paper, manila rope & twine for ........................ (973) 413-8100
U. S. Wire & Cable, Inc., 33 Queen St., Newark 07114
Pres.—David Rauch, 100 emp., Wire, cables, cords & accessories ........................ (973) 824-5529

## 2299 Textile goods, nec

, 101 West St., Hillsdale 07642
Pres.—Clifford Hart, 2 emp., Textile converting of printed vinyl ........................ (201) 666-8585
American Waste & Textile, LLC, 73 Vesey St., Newark 07105
Ptnr., CEO & MIS Mgr.—Jeffrey Belfer, 10 emp., Wiping cloths, industrial work gloves ........................ (973) 589-6252
Artistic Products, LLC, 1905 Elizabeth Ave., Rahway 07065
Pres.—Daniel Berg, 60 emp., Lampshade components & textile pleating ........................ (732) 382-4141
Associated Fabrics Corp., 15-01 Pollitt Dr., Ste. 7, Fair Lawn 07410
Pres.—Martin Markowitz, 6 emp., Fabric converting & distributor of ........................ (800) 232-4077
Caltex Industries, Inc., 1301 W. Elizabeth Ave., Ste. E-1, Linden 07036
Pres.—Arnold Gottfried, 20 emp., Wiping cloths from recycled apparel ........................ (973) 273-1707
Central Shippee, Inc., 46 Star Lake Rd., Bloomingdale 07403
Pres.—Eric Hubner, 30 emp., Manufacturer of custom woven decorative ........................ (973) 838-1616
Chasen & Sons, Inc., M., 117 S. 20th St., Irvington 07111
GM—David Schachman, 15 emp., Mattress components, including filling ........................ (973) 374-8956
Chasen & Sons, Inc., M., 123 S. 20th St., Irvington 07111
Pres., CEO—Alan Schachman, 20 emp., Corporate headquarters & mattress filling ........................ (973) 589-8700
Dazian Fabrics, LLC, 18 Central Blvd., South Hackensack 07606
Chrm.—Milt Wolfson, 40 emp., Textiles, fabricated items & LED scenic ........................ (201) 549-1000
I & F Scallop Thread Co., Inc., 6002 Adams St., West New York 07093
Pres.—Michael Iann, 1 emp., Scallop cutting ........................ (201) 868-6550
ITW Professional Brands, 1295 Towbin Ave., Lakewood 08701
Cont.—Michael Mont'Etna, 300 emp., Disposable wiping products for the ........................ (732) 363-9281
Pacon Mfg., Corp., 400 Pierce St., Somerset 08873
Pres.—Michael Shannon, 200 emp., Nonwoven disposable medical towels, ........................ (732) 764-9070
Precision Custom Coatings, LLC, 200 Maltese Dr., Totowa 07512
Chrm.—Peter Longo, 275 emp., Nonwoven fabrics, coated & laminated ........................ (973) 890-3873

# 23 APPAREL & OTHER TEXTILE PRODUCTS

## 2311 Suits & coats—men's & boys'

Bethel Industries, Inc., 3423 John F. Kennedy Blvd., Jersey City 07307
Pres.—Sun Kim, 110 emp., Women's jackets & men's & women's military ........................ (201) 656-8222
Crown Clothing Co., Inc., 609 Paul St., Vineland 08360
Pres.—Marsha Levin, 160 emp., Military uniforms ........................ (856) 691-0343
DeRossi & Son Co., 411 S. 6th St., Vineland 08360
Pres.—D. Derossi, 200 emp., Military uniforms ........................ (856) 691-0061
Fabian Couture Group International, 205 Chubb Ave., Ste. 1, Lyndhurst 07071
Pres.—Allan Weiss, 35 emp., Men's tuxedos, shirts & ties ........................ (201) 460-7776

S.I.C.

★ Indicates new listing this edition.

Hope Uniform Co., Inc., 4 Columbia St., P.O. Box 224, Columbia 07832
Pres.—Paul Lantz, 16 emp., *Police & firemen's uniforms* ........ (908) 496-4899
Tony Jones Apparel, Inc., 300-1 Route 17 S., Unit C, Lodi 07644
Pres.—John Yi, 7 emp., *Men's apparel* ........ (973) 773-6200
Universal Uniform, 1015 Broad St., P.O. Box 637, Newark 07102
Pres.—Paul Marchese, 13 emp., *Police & firemen uniforms* ........ (973) 622-5700

## 2321 Shirts—men's & boys'

Carter Co., The William, 17 The Promenade, Edgewater 07020
Owner—William Carter, 8 emp., *Children's shirts & under clothing* ........ (201) 313-1783
Cleve Shirtmakers, Inc. (H Q), P.O. Box 678, Saddle River 07458
Pres.—David Stich, 5 emp., *Corporate headquarters; men's shirts* ........ (201) 825-6122
Fabian Couture Group International, 205 Chubb Ave., Ste. 1, Lyndhurst 07071
Pres.—Allan Weiss, 35 emp., *Men's tuxedos, shirts & ties* ........ (201) 460-7776
Gambert Shirts, LLC, L., 61 Freeman St., 5th Fl., Newark 07105
Owner & Pres.—Lorraine Gambert, 90 emp., *Custom & private label ready-to-wear* ........ (973) 344-3440
Individualized Shirts, Inc., 581 Cortland St., Perth Amboy 08861
Pres., CEO—Joe Blair, 200 emp., *Men's shirts* ........ (732) 826-8400
Jade Eastern Trading, Inc., 245 Moonachie Rd., Moonachie 07074
Pres.—J. R. Lee, 15 emp., *Men's polo, dress, denim & woven shirts* ........ (201) 440-8500
Merc USA, Inc., 41 Newman St., Hackensack 07601
Pres.—Jahan Astaneha, 10 emp., *Men's shirts & trousers* ........ (201) 489-3527
Omavi Clothing Co. (H Q), 701-703 McCarter Hwy., Ste. 102, Newark 07102
Pres.—Hakim Stevens, 5 emp., *Company headquarters; men's clothing* ........ (973) 642-2000
R. B.'s Rubber Stamp, Inc., 551 W. Side Ave., Jersey City 07304
Pres.—Leila Bahadur, 2 emp., *Rubber stamps, marking devices, signs* ........ (201) 547-9955
Skip Gambert & Assocs., Inc., 436 Ferry St., Ste. 2, Newark 07105
Pres.—David Gambert, Jr., 140 emp., *Custom shirts for men* ........ (973) 344-3373
Tony Jones Apparel, Inc., 300-1 Route 17 S., Unit C, Lodi 07644
Pres.—John Yi, 7 emp., *Men's apparel* ........ (973) 773-6200
Venus Knitting Mills, Inc., 140 Spring St., Bldg. 1, New Providence 07974
Pres.—Bob Fermach, 20 emp., *Sporting goods* ........ (908) 464-2400

## 2323 Neckwear—men's & boys'

Chipp II, 7 Spring Hill Cir., Wayne 07470
Pres.—Janet Winston, 2 emp., *Men's neckties, women's scarves & blazer* ........ (212) 687-0850
Fabian Couture Group International, 205 Chubb Ave., Ste. 1, Lyndhurst 07071
Pres.—Allan Weiss, 35 emp., *Men's tuxedos, shirts & ties* ........ (201) 460-7776
Goodman & Co., Inc., Bob, 2 Steward Ln., Englishtown 07726
Pres.—Bob Goodman, 4 emp., *Men's neckwear & cufflinks* ........ (732) 446-0252
K G Designs, Inc., 581 Ogden Ave., Teaneck 07666
Pres.—Kenneth Goldman, 40 emp., *Men's & boys' neckware & belts* ........ (201) 692-1852
Stewart, Inc., Robert, 120 Little St., Belleville 07109
Chrm.—George Goldman, 15 emp., *Men's & boys' neckwear* ........ (973) 751-5151

## 2325 Trousers & slacks—men's & boys'

Cleve Shirtmakers, Inc. (H Q), P.O. Box 678, Saddle River 07458
Pres.—David Stich, 5 emp., *Corporate headquarters; men's shirts* ........ (201) 825-6122
LT Apparel Group, 301 Herrod Blvd., P.O. Box 1001, Dayton 08810
CEO—Morris Scotton, 100 emp., *Children's clothing, including boys'* ........ (732) 438-5500
Merc USA, Inc., 41 Newman St., Hackensack 07601
Pres.—Jahan Astaneha, 10 emp., *Men's shirts & trousers* ........ (201) 489-3527
Palmyra Pants Co., Inc., 9370 Route 130 N., Pennsauken 08110
Pres.—Howard Eisenberg, 4 emp., *Men's & boys' slacks & shoes* ........ (856) 662-0398

## 2326 Clothing—men's & boys', work

A-1 Uniforms, Inc., 721 Broadway, Camden 08103
Pres.—Ralph Ishack, 3 emp., *Manufacturer & wholesaler of custom* ........ (856) 963-7680
Alpine Trading Co., Inc., 400 Overpeck Pl., Englewood 07631
Pres.—Jacob Arden, 40 emp., *Police, security, airline & corrections* ........ (201) 871-6111
Asia Trading, 390 Nye Ave., Irvington 07111
Pres.—Meir Frei, 20 emp., *Manufacturer & distributor of security* ........ (973) 577-1300
Bestwork Industries For The Blind, Inc., 1940 Almay Ave., Ste. 200, Cherry Hill 08003
Pres.—Belinda Moore, 100 emp., *Fabric safety vests, work aprons, tool* ........ (856) 939-5220
Doc's Duds, LLC, 92 Half Mile Rd., Red Bank 07701
Ptnr.—Diana E. Trusky, 15 emp., *Custom lab coats for medical, dental* ........ (732) 219-0060
Happy Chef Uniforms, Inc., 22 Park Pl., Butler 07405
Ex. V-P.—Howard Curtin, 40 emp., *Manufacturer & distributor of restaurant* ........ (973) 492-2525
Oakwood Uniform & Equipment Co., 400 E. Main St., Maple Shade 08052
Pres.—Sally Corson, 15 emp., *Police, firefighter, postal & public* ........ (856) 779-7680
Red The Uniform Tailor, Inc., 475 Oberlin Ave. S., Lakewood 08701
CEO—Patricia Klein, 60 emp., *Corporate headquarters & men's & women's* ........ (848) 299-0100
Shelton, LLC, Todd, 450 Murray Hill Pkwy., Ste. C-2, East Rutherford 07073
Owner—Todd Shelton, 6 emp., *Men's casual clothing, including pants* ........ (551) 655-4106

## 2329 Clothing—men's & boys', nec

Alfred's Sport Shop, 32 Main St., Madison 07940
GM—Chuck Bleakley, 6 emp., *Baseball, softball & lacrosse equipment* ........ (973) 377-0051
Ameri-Tex, Inc., 461 Frelinghuysen Ave., Newark 07114
Pres.—Greg Opiola, 8 emp., *Knit goods, including sweaters, scarves* ........ (973) 286-0102
Black Universities Supply Shop, The, 410 Leland Ave., Plainfield 07062
Pres., CEO—Rubye Hickerson, 4 emp., *Customized clothing, apparel & accessories* ........ (908) 754-8088
Bright Ideas USA, LLC, 890 Morris Ave., Lakewood 08701
Mng. Member & GM—Deena Leiman, 4 emp., *Company headquarters & safety & nighttime* . (732) 886-8865
Campus Classics, 3206 Route 38, P.O. Box 757, Mount Laurel 08054
GM—Gerald Duncan, 2 emp., *Silk screening & computerized embroidery* ........ (856) 234-7474
Capco Sportswear Inc. (H Q), 100 W. Commercial Ave., Moonachie 07074
GM—Wally Richards, 10 emp., *Corporate headquarters; stock blank* ........ (201) 939-9228
Central Mills, Inc., 473 Ridge Rd., Dayton 08810
Owner—Maurice Shalom, 200 emp., *Men's & women's sportswear* ........ (732) 329-2009
Cleve Shirtmakers, Inc. (H Q), P.O. Box 678, Saddle River 07458
Pres.—David Stich, 5 emp., *Corporate headquarters; men's shirts* ........ (201) 825-6122
Ermenegildo Zegna Corp. (H Q), 100 W. Forest Ave., Ste. A, Englewood 07631
Pres.—Robert Aldrich, 50 emp., *Corporate headquarters; men's clothing* ........ (201) 816-0921
Fleck Knitwear Co., Inc., 400 Leland Ave., Plainfield 07062
Pres., Mfg. Mgr.—Peter Fleck, 15 emp., *Knit blankets, afghans, sweaters, children's* ........ (908) 754-8888
Folsom Corp. (H Q), 43 McKee Dr., Ste. 1, P.O. Box 6660, Mahwah 07430
Pres., CEO—Robert Feldscott, 20 emp., *Corporate headquarters; sport fishing* ........ (201) 529-3550
Gold Attachments Sewing Supply, Inc., 7051 Kennedy Blvd., North Bergen 07047
Pres.—Elsayed Elsamra, 3 emp., *Men's & women's clothing* ........ (201) 854-0320
Individualized Shirts, Inc., 581 Cortland St., Perth Amboy 08861
Pres., CEO—Joe Blair, 200 emp., *Men's shirts* ........ (732) 826-8400

Kerry Wilkens, Inc., 780 State Route 36, Belford 07718
Pres., Store Mgr.—Kerry Wilkens, 7 emp., *Canvas tarpaulins, custom sandbox covers* ........ (732) 787-0070
Knick-Knack, Inc., 20 Henry St., Teterboro 07608
Pres., Div.—Scott Banks, 20 emp., *Women's, men's & adolescents' sportswear* ........ (201) 727-9339
Link Theory, 165 Polito Ave., Lyndhurst 07071
Hum. Res. Mgr.—Emma Morgan, 100 emp., *Men's & women's clothing* ........ (201) 728-5700
Military Equipment Corp. Of America (H Q), P.O. Box 181, Mantoloking 08738
Pres.—Robert C. Mehlin, Sr., 2 emp., *Corporate headquarters; military nylon* ........ (908) 769-1000
Omavi Clothing Co. (H Q), 701-703 McCarter Hwy., Ste. 102, Newark 07102
Pres.—Hakim Stevens, 5 emp., *Company headquarters; men's clothing* ........ (973) 642-2000
Onwards, Inc. (H Q), 10 Connor Dr., Manalapan 07726
Pres.—Yang-Sup Cha, 3 emp., *Corporate headquarters; men's, women's* ........ (732) 309-7348
Red The Uniform Tailor, Inc., 475 Oberlin Ave. S., Lakewood 08701
CEO—Patricia Klein, 60 emp., *Corporate headquarters & men's & women's* ........ (848) 299-0100
Schott Bros., Inc., 735 Rahway Ave., Union 07083
CEO—Steve Colin, 120 emp., *Outerwear & sportswear* ........ (908) 527-0011
Team U. S. A., 200 Badger Ave., Newark 07108
Pres.—Shiv Thapar, 20 emp., *Team sports uniforms* ........ (973) 596-2800
Unicor Federal Prison Industries, Inc., 5835 Doughboy Loop, P.O. Box 38, Fort Dix 08640
Factory Mgr., Recycling—Jeff Eobstell, 600 emp., *Institutional & law enforcement clothing* .... (609) 723-1100
Venus Knitting Mills, Inc., 140 Spring St., Bldg. 1, New Providence 07974
Pres.—Bob Fermach, 20 emp., *Sporting goods* ........ (908) 464-2400
Vertical Source, Inc. (H Q), 812 Broad St., Shrewsbury 07702
Pres.—Christopher Neary, 6 emp., *Corporate headquarters; fleece jackets* ........ (732) 530-5330

## 2331 Blouses & shirts—women's & misses'

Carter Co., The William, 17 The Promenade, Edgewater 07020
Owner—William Carter, 8 emp., *Children's shirts & under clothing* ........ (201) 313-1783
Gambert Shirts, LLC, L., 61 Freeman St., 5th Fl., Newark 07105
Owner & Pres.—Lorraine Gambert, 90 emp., *Custom & private label ready-to-wear* ........ (973) 344-3440
Krazy Kat Sportswear, LLC, 100 Triangle Blvd., Carlstadt 07072
CEO—Bansi Laknani, 60 emp., *Women's woven blouses, dresses, skirts* ........ (201) 438-3399
Lilo Maternity, LLC, 1526 Laguna Ln., Lakewood 08701
Owner—Neal Benedek, 6 emp., *Maternity clothing, including t-shirts* ........ (732) 370-5456
R. B.'s Rubber Stamp, Inc., 551 W. Side Ave., Jersey City 07304
Pres.—Leila Bahadur, 2 emp., *Rubber stamps, marking devices, signs* ........ (201) 547-9955
Red The Uniform Tailor, Inc., 475 Oberlin Ave. S., Lakewood 08701
CEO—Patricia Klein, 60 emp., *Corporate headquarters & men's & women's* ........ (848) 299-0100
Silkhouse International, Inc., 28 Garden Pl., Ste. 128, Edgewater 07020
Pres.—Michael Liu, 5 emp., *Women's clothing* ........ (201) 945-4569

## 2335 Dresses—women's, juniors' & misses'

Arecia's Creations, 3704 Park Ave., Weehawken 07086
Owner—Arecia Hernandez, 2 emp., *Wedding, sweet sixteen & communion* ........ (201) 864-7388
Miller, LLC, Sally (H Q), 30 N. Main St., Milltown 08850
Member—Sally Miller, 13 emp., *Company headquarters; preteen & teen* ........ (732) 729-4840
RAZA-Designs, Inc., 220 61st St., Ste. 2-C, West New York 07093
Pres.—Beverly Luchfeld, 2 emp., *Hostess & formal gowns, loungewear* ........ (201) 430-8590
Silkhouse International, Inc., 28 Garden Pl., Ste. 128, Edgewater 07020
Pres.—Michael Liu, 5 emp., *Women's clothing* ........ (201) 945-4569

## 2337 Suits & coats—women's & misses'

Asia Trading, 390 Nye Ave., Irvington 07111
Pres.—Meir Frei, 20 emp., *Manufacturer & distributor of security* ........ (973) 577-1300
Bethel Industries, Inc., 3423 John F. Kennedy Blvd., Jersey City 07307
Pres.—Sun Kim, 110 emp., *Women's jackets & men's & women's military* ........ (201) 656-8222
Lilo Maternity, LLC, 1526 Laguna Ln., Lakewood 08701
Owner—Neal Benedek, 6 emp., *Maternity clothing, including t-shirts* ........ (732) 370-5456
Oakwood Uniform & Equipment Co., 400 E. Main St., Maple Shade 08052
Pres.—Sally Corson, 15 emp., *Police, firefighter, postal & public* ........ (856) 779-7680
Red The Uniform Tailor, Inc., 475 Oberlin Ave. S., Lakewood 08701
CEO—Patricia Klein, 60 emp., *Corporate headquarters & men's & women's* ........ (848) 299-0100
Silkhouse International, Inc., 28 Garden Pl., Ste. 128, Edgewater 07020
Pres.—Michael Liu, 5 emp., *Women's clothing* ........ (201) 945-4569
Unicor Federal Prison Industries, Inc., 5835 Doughboy Loop, P.O. Box 38, Fort Dix 08640
Factory Mgr., Recycling—Jeff Eobstell, 600 emp., *Institutional & law enforcement clothing* .... (609) 723-1100

## 2339 Outerwear—women's & misses', nec

A-1 Uniforms, Inc., 721 Broadway, Camden 08103
Pres.—Ralph Ishack, 3 emp., *Manufacturer & wholesaler of custom* ........ (856) 963-7680
AG Peters & Son, Inc., 1025 N. Black Horse Pike, Runnemede 08078
Pres.—Diane Lansberry, 7 emp., *Burial dresses & funeral supplies* ........ (856) 931-7476
Alfred's Sport Shop, 32 Main St., Madison 07940
GM—Chuck Bleakley, 6 emp., *Baseball, softball & lacrosse equipment* ........ (973) 377-0051
Alpine Trading Co., Inc., 400 Overpeck Pl., Englewood 07631
Pres.—Jacob Arden, 40 emp., *Police, security, airline & corrections* ........ (201) 871-6111
Ambassador Uniform Group, Inc., 289 Highway 33 E., Manalapan 07726
Pres.—Allan Behm, 8 emp., *Manufacturer & wholesaler of service* ........ (732) 792-1111
Ameri-Tex, Inc., 461 Frelinghuysen Ave., Newark 07114
Pres.—Greg Opiola, 8 emp., *Knit goods, including sweaters, scarves* ........ (973) 286-0102
Attitudes In Dressing, Inc., 107 Trumbull St., Bldg. B-8, Elizabeth 07206
CEO—Michael Rubin, 14 emp., *Women's & girls' clothing* ........ (908) 354-7218
Bal Togs Industries, 6605-09 Smith Ave., North Bergen 07047
Pres.—Bruce Kopelman, 100 emp., *Dance & exercise clothing* ........ (201) 866-0201
Ballet Makers, Inc. (H Q), 1 Campus Rd., Totowa 07512
CEO—Anthony Giacoio, Jr., 100 emp., *Corporate headquarters; dance & dance-related* ........ (973) 595-9000
Black Universities Supply Shop, The, 410 Leland Ave., Plainfield 07062
Pres., CEO—Rubye Hickerson, 4 emp., *Customized clothing, apparel & accessories* ........ (908) 754-8088
Blaustein, Inc., M., 516 Millburn Ave., Short Hills 07078
Chrm.—Jules Blaustein, 10 emp., *Women's & men's fur coats & outerwear* ........ (973) 379-1080
Bright Ideas USA, LLC, 890 Morris Ave., Lakewood 08701
Mng. Member & GM—Deena Leiman, 4 emp., *Company headquarters & safety & nighttime* . (732) 886-8865
Calvaruso Clothing, G. & F., 345 Palisade Ave., Cliffside Park 07010
Owner—Frank Calvaruso, 2 emp., *Custom made women's clothing & alterations* ........ (201) 945-7118
Central Mills, Inc., 473 Ridge Rd., Dayton 08810
Owner—Maurice Shalom, 200 emp., *Men's & women's sportswear* ........ (732) 329-2009
CS Apparel, Inc. (H Q), 3910 Park Ave., Ste. 2, Edison 08820
Owner—Gopal Karnani, 5 emp., *Corporate headquarters; women's casual* ........ (732) 906-9666
Doc's Duds, LLC, 92 Half Mile Rd., Red Bank 07701
Ptnr.—Diana E. Trusky, 15 emp., *Custom lab coats for medical, dental* ........ (732) 219-0060
Fleck Knitwear Co., Inc., 400 Leland Ave., Plainfield 07062
Pres., Mfg. Mgr.—Peter Fleck, 15 emp., *Knit blankets, afghans, sweaters, children's* ........ (908) 754-8888

Folsom Corp. (H Q), 43 McKee Dr., Ste. 1, P.O. Box 6660, Mahwah 07430
Pres., CEO—Robert Feldscott, 20 emp., *Corporate headquarters; sport fishing* .................... (201) 529-3550
Gold Attachments Sewing Supply, Inc., 7051 Kennedy Blvd., North Bergen 07047
Pres.—Elsayed Elsamra, 3 emp., *Men's & women's clothing* .................... (201) 854-0320
Happy Chef Uniforms, Inc., 22 Park Pl., Butler 07405
Ex. V-P.—Howard Curtin, 40 emp., *Manufacturer & distributor of restaurant* .................... (973) 492-2525
Jackie Evans, Inc., 1823 3rd St., Passaic 07055
Pres. & V-P.—Mario Monaco, 50 emp., *Women's clothing* .................... (973) 471-6991
Kerry Wilkens, Inc., 780 State Route 36, Belford 07718
Pres., Store Mgr.—Kerry Wilkens, 7 emp., *Canvas tarpaulins, custom sandbox covers* .................... (732) 787-0070
Knick-Knack, Inc., 20 Henry St., Teterboro 07608
Pres., Div.—Scott Banks, 20 emp., *Women's, men's & adolescents' sportswear* .................... (201) 727-9339
Krazy Kat Sportswear, LLC, 100 Triangle Blvd., Carlstadt 07072
CEO—Bansi Laknani, 60 emp., *Women's woven blouses, dresses, skirts* .................... (201) 438-3399
Link Theory, 165 Polito Ave., Lyndhurst 07071
Hum. Res. Mgr.—Emma Morgan, 100 emp., *Men's & women's clothing* .................... (201) 728-5700
LT Apparel Group, 301 Herrod Blvd., P.O. Box 1001, Dayton 08810
CEO—Morris Scotton, 100 emp., *Children's clothing, including boys'* .................... (732) 438-5500
M&S Canada Corp., 8 Arosa Hill, Lakewood 08701
Pres.—Malkie Mosokowitz, 3 emp., *Women's & girl's sportswear* .................... (732) 901-6636
Metropolitan Mfg., Inc., 450 Murray Hill Pkwy., East Rutherford 07073
★ Pres.—Tony Terrigno, 60 emp., *Women's clothing, including blouses* .................... (201) 933-8111
Military Equipment Corp. Of America (H Q), P.O. Box 181, Mantoloking 08738
Pres.—Robert C. Mehlin, Sr., 2 emp., *Corporate headquarters; military nylon* .................... (908) 769-1000
Mizrak, 288 Livingston Ave., 1st Fl., Lyndhurst 07071
Pres.—Yalcin Mizrak, 2 emp., *Women's & children's sportswear* .................... (973) 622-0328
Onwards, Inc. (H Q), 10 Connor Dr., Manalapan 07726
Pres.—Yang-Sup Cha, 3 emp., *Corporate headquarters; men's, women's* .................... (732) 309-7348
RAZA-Designs, Inc., 220 61st St., Ste. 2-C, West New York 07093
Pres.—Beverly Luchfeld, 2 emp., *Hostess & formal gowns, loungewear* .................... (201) 430-8590
RMI Hoobing, 460 Veterans Dr., Burlington 08016
Pres.—Alan Wallace, 10 emp., *Women's sportswear* .................... (609) 387-1999
Schott Bros., Inc., 735 Rahway Ave., Union 07083
CEO—Steve Colin, 120 emp., *Outerwear & sportswear* .................... (908) 527-0011
Silkhouse International, Inc., 28 Garden Pl., Ste. 128, Edgewater 07020
Pres.—Michael Liu, 5 emp., *Women's clothing* .................... (201) 945-4569
Sno Skins, Inc. (H Q), 11 Melanie Ln., Ste. 3, East Hanover 07936
Pres.—Steve Weiss, 6 emp., *Corporate headquarters; women's sportswear* .................... (973) 884-8801
Swisstex Co., 220 61st St., 2nd Fl., West New York 07093
Owner—Robert Wolfe, 20 emp., *Women's clothing* .................... (201) 861-8000
Team U. S. A., 200 Badger Ave., Newark 07108
Pres.—Shiv Thapar, 20 emp., *Team sports uniforms* .................... (973) 596-2800
Vertical Source, Inc. (H Q), 812 Broad St., Shrewsbury 07702
Pres.—Christopher Neary, 6 emp., *Corporate headquarters; fleece jackets* .................... (732) 530-5330
Wacoal America, Inc., 1 Wacoal Plz., Lyndhurst 07071
Plt. Mgr.—Ismael Vicens, 200 emp., *Intimate apparel* .................... (201) 933-8400
Zaralo, LLC, 1 Cape May St., Harrison 07029
Owner—David Lomita, 28 emp., *Women's clothing* .................... (862) 902-5220

## 2341 Underwear—women's & children's

Delta Galil USA, Inc., 1 Harmon Plz., 5th Fl., Secaucus 07094
CEO—Tim Regan, 100 emp., *Corporate headquarters & lingerie* .................... (201) 902-0055
Dolce Vita Intimates, LLC (H Q), 1000 1st St., Harrison 07029
Ptnr.—Jack Thekkekara, 30 emp., *Corporate headquarters; women's nightgowns* .................... (973) 482-8400
Maidenform Brands, Inc., 485 U.S. Highway 1 S., Bldg. F, Iselin 08830
Sr. V-P. & Mng. Dir., Intl.—Patricia J. Royak, 225 emp., *Lingerie* .................... (732) 621-2500
Merry Modes 2000, 61 Willet St., Ste. 2, Passaic 07055
Owner—Anthony Dell'Aquila, 8 emp., *Custom handmade bridal petticoats,* .................... (973) 773-2501
National Mill Industry, Inc. (H Q), 22 Jackson Dr., Cranford 07016
Pres.—Victor Shacalo, 40 emp., *Corporate headquarters; lingerie (mfg.* .................... (908) 862-8400
Priamo Designs Ltd., 6614 Broadway, West New York 07093
Pres.—Priamo Espaillat, 5 emp., *Women's lingerie* .................... (201) 861-8808
Textiles By Anthony, Inc., 61 Willett St., Bldg. 12, 2nd Fl., Passaic 07055
Owner & Pres.—Anthony Dell'aquila, 20 emp., *Women's bridal petticoats, half-slips* .................... (973) 773-2501
Wacoal America, Inc., 1 Wacoal Plz., Lyndhurst 07071
Plt. Mgr.—Ismael Vicens, 200 emp., *Intimate apparel* .................... (201) 933-8400

## 2342 Bras, girdles & allied garments

Delta Galil USA, Inc., 1 Harmon Plz., 5th Fl., Secaucus 07094
CEO—Tim Regan, 100 emp., *Corporate headquarters & lingerie* .................... (201) 902-0055
Dolce Vita Intimates, LLC (H Q), 1000 1st St., Harrison 07029
Ptnr.—Jack Thekkekara, 30 emp., *Corporate headquarters; women's nightgowns* .................... (973) 482-8400
Maidenform Brands, Inc., 485 U.S. Highway 1 S., Bldg. F, Iselin 08830
Sr. V-P. & Mng. Dir., Intl.—Patricia J. Royak, 225 emp., *Lingerie* .................... (732) 621-2500
Merry Modes 2000, 61 Willet St., Ste. 2, Passaic 07055
Owner—Anthony Dell'Aquila, 8 emp., *Custom handmade bridal petticoats,* .................... (973) 773-2501
Q-T Foundations Co., Inc., 496 Kinderkamack Rd., Ste. 107, Oradell 07649
Pres.—Lawrence Kutzin, 20 emp., *Women's foundation garments, bras &* .................... (201) 986-7800
Textiles By Anthony, Inc., 61 Willett St., Bldg. 12, 2nd Fl., Passaic 07055
Owner & Pres.—Anthony Dell'aquila, 20 emp., *Women's bridal petticoats, half-slips* .................... (973) 773-2501
Wacoal America, Inc., 1 Wacoal Plz., Lyndhurst 07071
Plt. Mgr.—Ismael Vicens, 200 emp., *Intimate apparel* .................... (201) 933-8400

## 2353 Hats, caps & millinery

Alboum Hat Co., Inc., W., 1439 Springfield Ave., Irvington 07111
Pres.—W. Alboum, 20 emp., *Hats & caps* .................... (973) 371-9100
Baik Kwang Corp., 601 Commercial Ave., P.O. Box 7072, Carlstadt 07072
Pres.—Sung Y. Park, 10 emp., *Skiing hats & baseball caps* .................... (201) 507-9985
Bear Hands Ltd., 38 Main St., Little Ferry 07643
Owner—Jeffrey Golden, 5 emp., *Fleece hats, mittens & scarves* .................... (201) 807-9898
Capco Sportswear Inc. (H Q), 100 W. Commercial Ave., Moonachie 07074
GM—Wally Richards, 10 emp., *Corporate headquarters; stock blank* .................... (201) 939-9228
Castellane Mfg. Co., 1405 Cantillion Blvd., P.O. Box 921, Mays Landing 08330
Pres.—Nicholas Castellane, 15 emp., *Uniform hats* .................... (609) 625-3427
Colombino Headwear, Inc., 61 Willet St., Passaic 07055
Pres.—Jerry Colombino, 15 emp., *Straw hats* .................... (973) 473-4733
Gibson Designs, Inc., Kathy, 1416 Willow Ave., Hoboken 07030
Pres.—Ruth Wiener, 20 emp., *Bridal veils & accessories* .................... (201) 420-0088
Headwear Creations, Inc., 200 Wright St., Newark 07114
Pres.—Ruben Spitz, 45 emp., *Casual hats & caps for men & women* .................... (973) 622-1144
Kathy Jeanne, Inc., 7 Industrial Rd., Fairfield 07004
Pres.—Jeanne Gerish, 9 emp., *Hats* .................... (973) 575-9898

NES Enterprises, Inc., 513 Washington Ave., Carlstadt 07072
CEO—Sheldon Salkovitch, 9 emp., *Men's hat linings* .................... (201) 964-1400
Philadelphia Rapid Transit, 2650 Haddonfield Rd., Pennsauken 08110
Pres.—Peter Goldman, 20 emp., *Hats* .................... (856) 488-0202
Serratelli Hat Co., Inc., 418-26 Central Ave., P.O. Box 7069, Newark 07107
Pres.—Dean Serratelli, 49 emp., *Cowboy hats* .................... (973) 623-4133
Unionwear/New Jersey Headwear Corp., 305 3rd Ave. W., Ste. 5, Newark 07107
Pres.—Mitchell Cahn, 50 emp., *Custom embroidered, screenprinted &* .................... (973) 497-0102

## 2361 Dresses & blouses—girl's & children's

Carter Co., The William, 17 The Promenade, Edgewater 07020
Owner—William Carter, 8 emp., *Children's shirts & under clothing* .................... (201) 313-1783
Metropolitan Mfg., Inc., 450 Murray Hill Pkwy., East Rutherford 07073
★ Pres.—Tony Terrigno, 60 emp., *Women's clothing, including blouses* .................... (201) 933-8111
Miller, LLC, Sally (H Q), 30 N. Main St., Milltown 08850
Member—Sally Miller, 13 emp., *Company headquarters; preteen & teen* .................... (732) 729-4840

## 2369 Outerwear—girl's & children's, nec

8 To 20 Partners, LLC, 5 Paddock St., Avenel 07001
Pres.—Saul Tawil, 150 emp., *Children's clothing* .................... (732) 855-1400
Celebrity International, Inc. (H Q), 51 Saw Mill Pond Rd., Edison 08817
Pres.—Eli Matalon, 50 emp., *Corporate headquarters; children's* .................... (732) 476-2999
Children's Apparel Network Ltd., 77 S. 1st St., Elizabeth 07206
Pres.—Nathan Shalom, 18 emp., *Baby clothing* .................... (908) 351-4477
Kerry Wilkens, Inc., 780 State Route 36, Belford 07718
Pres., Store Mgr.—Kerry Wilkens, 7 emp., *Canvas tarpaulins, custom sandbox covers* .................... (732) 787-0070
M&S Canada Corp., 8 Arosa Hill, Lakewood 08701
Pres.—Malkie Mosokowitz, 3 emp., *Women's & girl's sportswear* .................... (732) 901-6636
Mizrak, 288 Livingston Ave., 1st Fl., Lyndhurst 07071
Pres.—Yalcin Mizrak, 2 emp., *Women's & children's sportswear* .................... (973) 622-0328
Nano's, LLC, 22 Park Pl., P.O. Box 41, Butler 07405
Ptnr.—Patricia Pienkowska, 2 emp., *Children's clothing* .................... (973) 616-1515
Royal Knitwear, Inc., 115 Perry St., Park Ridge 07656
Pres.—Edmund Abdelhak, 10 emp., *Children's sweaters* .................... (201) 391-8368
Sew In Style, Inc., 220 61st St., West New York 07093
Pres.—Angel Hernando, 5 emp., *Children's sportswear* .................... (201) 868-8568

## 2371 Fur goods

A. Hantman Inc, 309 Michaels Ct., Woodbridge 07095
Pres.—Charlotte Hantman, 7 emp., *Fur trimmings & accessories* .................... (212) 239-1358
American Fur Felt, LLC, 53 Rome St., Newark 07105
Pres.—Lucilio Pereira, 11 emp., *Fur felt cutting* .................... (973) 344-3026
Antonovich Furs, Inc., 125 Route 46 W., Totowa 07512
Pres.—Daniel Antonovich, 15 emp., *Fur & leather coats* .................... (973) 785-0077
Blaustein, Inc., M., 516 Millburn Ave., Short Hills 07078
Chrm.—Jules Blaustein, 10 emp., *Women's & men's fur coats & outerwear* .................... (973) 379-1080
Lea Furs, Inc. Ltd., 45 S. Broad St., Ridgewood 07450
Owner & Pres.—Chris Liulakis, 1 emp., *Fur clothing & accessories* .................... (201) 444-5554

## 2381 Gloves—fabric dress & work

Ansell Healthcare Products, LLC (H Q), 111 Wood Ave. S., Ste. 210, Iselin 08830
Chrm.—Glenn Barnes, 200 emp., *Company headquarters; industrial work* .................... (732) 345-5400

## 2384 Robes & dressing gowns

Dolce Vita Intimates, LLC (H Q), 1000 1st St., Harrison 07029
Ptnr.—Jack Thekkekara, 30 emp., *Corporate headquarters; women's nightgowns* .................... (973) 482-8400
Monarch Towel Co., Inc., 737 Cortlandt St., Perth Amboy 08861
Pres.—Ashley Chadowitz, 15 emp., *Bathrobes & towels* .................... (732) 442-0442

## 2385 Waterproof outerwear

Loveline Industries, Inc., 90 Dayton Ave., Ste. 33, Passaic 07055
Pres.—Morton Goldstein, 15 emp., *Hi-visibility safety clothing, including* .................... (973) 928-3427

## 2386 Leather & sheep-lined clothing

Cockpit USA, Inc., 725 New Point Rd., Elizabeth 07201
Br. Mgr.—Andrew Baljeet, 12 emp., *Men's & women's leather jackets* .................... (908) 558-9704
Passaic Leather Coat, Inc., 51 Market St., Passaic 07055
Pres.—B. A. Focarino, 5 emp., *Leather jackets & coats* .................... (973) 777-4026
Prime Fur & Leather, Inc., 2931 Industrial Ave., Fairview 07022
Pres.—Brian S. Han, 10 emp., *Men's & women's leather jackets* .................... (201) 941-9600
Schott Bros., Inc., 735 Rahway Ave., Union 07083
CEO—Steve Colin, 120 emp., *Outerwear & sportswear* .................... (908) 527-0011
Serratelli Hat Co., Inc., 418-26 Central Ave., P.O. Box 7069, Newark 07107
Pres.—Dean Serratelli, 49 emp., *Cowboy hats* .................... (973) 623-4133
Unik International, Inc., 40 Triangle Blvd., Carlstadt 07072
Pres.—Akmal Khilji, 22 emp., *Leather clothing* .................... (201) 531-1777

## 2387 Belts—apparel

K G Designs, Inc., 581 Ogden Ave., Teaneck 07666
Pres.—Kenneth Goldman, 40 emp., *Men's & boys' neckware & belts* .................... (201) 692-1852
Nu-Style Embroidery & Button Co., Inc., 5212 Polk St., West New York 07093
Pres.—Jay Rosner, 5 emp., *Apparel buttons, belts, neckties, lace* .................... (201) 864-1808

## 2389 Apparel & accessories, nec

Aladen Athletic Wear, LLC, 53 Cannonball Rd., Pompton Lakes 07442
Pres.—Estela Arco, 3 emp., *Custom handmade athletic wear & uniforms* .................... (973) 838-2425
Ambassador Uniform Group, Inc., 289 Highway 33 E., Manalapan 07726
Pres.—Allan Behm, 8 emp., *Manufacturer & wholesaler of service* .................... (732) 792-1111
Bear Hands Ltd., 38 Main St., Little Ferry 07643
Owner—Jeffrey Golden, 5 emp., *Fleece hats, mittens & scarves* .................... (201) 807-9898
Church Vestment Mfg. Co., Inc., 41-43 Paterson Ave., Paterson 07522
Pres.—Gerard J. Siccardi, Jr., 5 emp., *Clerical robes* .................... (973) 942-2833
Costume Gallery, 4451 Route 130 S., Burlington 08016
Pres.—Linda Bradbury, 120 emp., *Dance recital costumes* .................... (609) 386-6601
Creative Costume Co., 61 Wilk Rd., Edison 08837
Ptnr.—Susan Handler, 2 emp., *Costumes* .................... (212) 564-5552
Daly's Custom Racing Apparel, P.O. Box 355, Berlin 08009
CEO—Ryan Daly, 3 emp., *Horse racing apparel, including jockey* .................... (856) 768-6411
Empire Designs, Inc., 7 Main St., Englishtown 07726
Pres.—Kathleen T. Bien, 1 emp., *Embroidery, screen printing, promotional* .................... (732) 446-6447
Gaiser, Inc., Robert F., 292 Main St., P.O. Box 807, Butler 07405
Pres.—Stephen Gaiser, 18 emp., *Clerical vestments* .................... (973) 838-0696

S.I.C.

★ Indicates new listing this edition.

Harbor Linen, LLC (H Q), 2 Foster Ave., Gibbsboro 08026
Chrm.—Earl Waxman, 100 emp., *Company headquarters; manufacturer* (856) 435-2000
Harbro Church Arts, Inc., 231 Herbert Ave., P.O. Box 776, Closter 07624
Pres.—Robert J. Harrison, 3 emp., *Washable judicial robes for men & women* (201) 768-5500
Honeywell International, Inc. (H Q), 101 Columbia Rd., Morristown 07962
Chrm., CEO—David M. Cote, 1500 emp., *Corporate headquarters; control & energy* (973) 455-2000
J & S Finishing, Inc., 443 62nd St., West New York 07093
Pres.—Pedro Calvo, 15 emp., *Embroidery & school uniforms* (201) 854-0338
Jade Apparel, Inc., 133 Kossuth St., Newark 07105
Pres.—Teddy Maroulis, 400 emp., *Contract manufacturing for the apparel* (973) 522-1003
Krazy Kat Sportswear, LLC, 100 Triangle Blvd., Carlstadt 07072
CEO—Bansi Laknani, 60 emp., *Women's woven blouses, dresses, skirts* (201) 438-3399
Loveline Industries, Inc., 90 Dayton Ave., Ste. 33, Passaic 07055
Pres.—Morton Goldstein, 15 emp., *Hi-visibility safety clothing, including* (973) 928-3427
Malhame Vestment, 239 Route 206, Branchville 07826
★ GM—James Pecoy, 12 emp., *Religious garments* (973) 948-8401
NurseJoe.Com, 11 Plainfield Ave., Metuchen 08840
★ Owner—Jose Mancheno, 2 emp., *Men's & women's medical scrubs for* (848) 250-9900
Peach Boutique, The, 1139 E. Jersey St., Ste. 319, Elizabeth 07201
Pres., GM & Hum. Res. Mgr.—Roslyn Rearden, 6 emp., *Clerical & choir robes & embroidery* (908) 351-0739
RAZA-Designs, Inc., 220 61st St., Ste. 2-C, West New York 07093
Pres.—Beverly Luchfeld, 2 emp., *Hostess & formal gowns, loungewear* (201) 430-8590
Silvertop Assocs., Inc., 600 E. Clements Bridge Rd., Runnemede 08078
Pres.—Robert Berman, 48 emp., *Halloween costumes for men, women &* (856) 939-9599
Sipp Silk, 216 Hedgeman Rd., Moorestown 08057
Ptnr.—George Sipp, 2 emp., *Jockey uniforms, silks, blinkers, helmet* (856) 234-6224
Some's World-Wide Uniforms, 314 Main St., Hackensack 07601
CEO—Andrea Some, 30 emp., *Governmental uniforms & accessories* (201) 843-1199
South Mill Design, LLC, 131 S. Mill Rd., Princeton Junction 08550
Co-Founder—Ted Ross, 3 emp., *Textile cellphone accessories, including* (877) 466-0273
Standard Merchandising Co. (H Q), 1125 Wright Ave., Camden 08103
Pres., CFO—Jeff Tarnoff, 50 emp., *Company headquarters; men's & women's* (856) 964-9700
Trim & Tassels, LLC (H Q), 204 Passaic Ave., Unit 3, Fairfield 07004
Owner—Pradeep Jalan, 3 emp., *Company headquarters; graduation caps* (973) 808-1566
Tronex International, Inc., 300 International Dr., Mount Olive 07828
Pres., CEO—Donald L. Chu, 69 emp., *Advanced medical, hospital health &* (973) 335-2888
United Sport Apparel, 20 Gloria Ln., Fairfield 07004
V-P.—Karen Morgan, 45 emp., *Athletic jackets* (973) 575-7840
Vantage Apparel, 100 Vantage Dr., Avenel 07001
Pres.—Ira Neaman, 500 emp., *Logo & identity apparel* (732) 340-3000

## 2391 Curtains & draperies

Ackerson Drapery & Decorating Services, Inc., 500 James St., Ste. 14, Lakewood 08701
Pres., CFO—Ronni Leddy, 8 emp., *Theatrical stage curtains & window* (732) 905-4433
Aladen Athletic Wear, LLC, 53 Cannonball Rd., Pompton Lakes 07442
Pres.—Estela Arco, 3 emp., *Custom handmade athletic wear & uniforms* (973) 838-2425
Alan Schatzberg & Assoc., Inc., 45 Ruta Ct., South Hackensack 07606
Pres., GM—Alan Schatzberg, 12 emp., *Manufacturer & distributor of custom* (201) 440-8855
Altina's Custom Interiors, Princeton Shopping Ctr., 301 N. Harrison, Princeton 08540
Owner—Altina Noel, 2 emp., *Curtains & draperies* (609) 924-3367
Atlantic City Shade Shop, Inc., 500 Tilton Rd., P.O. Box 217, Northfield 08225
Owner, MIS Mgr. & Chief Engr.—Howard Markman, 16 emp., *Manufacturer & distributor of pleated* (609) 641-8700
Bai Lar Interior Services, Inc., 554 New Brunswick Ave., Fords 08863
Pres.—James E. Quinn, 5 emp., *Manufacturer & distributor of commercial* (732) 738-0350
Baum Draperies, 666 Passaic Ave., Nutley 07110
Ptnr.—Robert Baum, 5 emp., *Draperies & curtains* (973) 661-1841
Beatrice Home Fashions, Inc., 151 Helen St., P.O. Box 86, South Plainfield 07080
Pres.—Sam Gindi, 30 emp., *Bedspreads & draperies* (908) 561-7370
Beltor Mfg. Corp., 50 Union Ave., Ste. 12, Berlin 08009
Pres. & V-P.—Derek Torok, 6 emp., *Cubicle curtains & curtain tracks* (856) 768-5570
Best Drapery & Blind Mfg. Co., 1 Kresson Rd., Cherry Hill 08034
Pres.—James Logan, 2 emp., *Custom draperies* (856) 429-2242
Bloomfield Drapery Co., Inc., 948 Paterson Ave., East Rutherford 07073
Pres.—Steve Gold, 15 emp., *Manufacturer & distributor of theatrical* (973) 777-3566
Crown Custom Cleaners, 27 E. Kings Hwy., Audubon 08106
Owner—Bruce Yun, 2 emp., *Custom draperies & textile household* (856) 310-0710
Custom Decorators Workroom, 415 E. Main St., Denville 07834
Ptnr.—Walter Kunzel, Jr., 5 emp., *Custom furniture & draperies* (973) 625-0516
Daniel's Custom Draperies, Inc., 620 W. Clements Bridge Rd., Runnemede 08078
Pres.—Daniel Scavette, 3 emp., *Draperies, blinds & shades* (856) 939-2212
Don's Drapery Mfg. Co., 145 Heckel St., Belleville 07109
Pres.—Joyce Dolan, 16 emp., *Draperies, blinds & window treatments* (973) 751-1544
Drapery & More, Inc., 2321 Kennedy Blvd., Ste. 2401-B-1, North Bergen 07047
Pres.—Ally Espana, 9 emp., *Custom window treatments, including* (201) 271-9661
Drapery Corp. Of America, Inc., 12-16 1st Ave., Paterson 07524
Pres.—George Holiat, 5 emp., *Draperies & shower curtains, blinds* (973) 925-1200
Fabulous Interiors, 470 Prospect Ave., Ste. 105, West Orange 07052
Mng. Ptnr.—Jeffrey Fischman, 2 emp., *Wall coverings & converted paper products* (973) 736-1200
FNS Custom Window Treatment, 2954 N. West Blvd., Vineland 08360
Ptnr.—Sandy Cerione, 3 emp., *Custom draperies, blinds & shutters* (856) 696-4070
Frank's Upholstery & Draperies, 49 S. Boulevard Ave., Maple Shade 08052
Owner—Frank Troso, 5 emp., *Upholstered furniture & draperies* (856) 779-8585
Hansen Co., Inc., Joseph C., 629 Grove St., Ste. 26, Jersey City 07310
Pres.—Barney Simon, 3 emp., *Manufacturer of stage & theater draperies* (201) 222-1677
Hospi-Tel Mfg. Co., Inc., 545 N. Arlington Ave., East Orange 07017
Pres.—David Freedland, 80 emp., *Shower & cubicle curtains & mattress* (973) 678-7100
Interior Art & Design, Inc., 59 Oak St., Hackensack 07601
★ Owner—Ori Katzin, 20 emp., *Custom window coverings, including* (201) 488-8855
Ka-Lor Cubicle & Supply Co., Inc., P.O. Box 804, Fair Lawn 07410
Pres.—Dennis Brett, 21 emp., *Hospital & institutional cubicle, shower* (201) 891-8077
Kay Window Fashions, Inc., 271 2nd St., Saddle Brook 07663
Ptnr.—Sol Kleinstein, 12 emp., *Manufacturer & distributor of draperies* (862) 591-1555
Kushner Draperies Mfg., LLC, 5305 Route 70, Pennsauken 08109
Chrm., CFO & Bus. Mgr.—Carla Moore, 25 emp., *Draperies & upholstery* (856) 317-9696
Lawrence Custom Drapery Shop, 323 4th St., Ewing 08638
Pres.—Charlie Cullen, 20 emp., *Custom draperies, window treatments* (609) 695-3877
Master Drapery Workroom, Inc., 220 N. 14th St., Kenilworth 07033
Pres., Sales Mgr.—Phil Ricca, 4 emp., *Draperies* (908) 272-4404
McKnight Drapery Services, 126 Majestic S., Lincroft 07738
Owner—Gail McKnight, 1 emp., *Draperies* (732) 741-3655
Metropolitan Window Fashions, 799 Route 17 S., Paramus 07652
Owner—Bruce Heyman, 4 emp., *Draperies, curtains & window treatments* (201) 689-6030
Milltex Mfg. Co., 1101 Industrial Pkwy., Brick 08724
Pres.—Martin Metzger, Sr., 8 emp., *Comforters, draperies, window treatments* (732) 840-3021
North Jersey Window Treatments, LLC, 164 South St., Hackensack 07601
Pres.—Martin Gutman, 12 emp., *Draperies & window treatments* (201) 487-2121
Nourison Industries (H Q), 5 Sampson St., Saddle Brook 07663
Pres.—Alex Peykar, 240 emp., *Company headquarters; upholstered furniture* (201) 368-6900
Precision Blinds Products, Inc., 637 Boulevard, Kenilworth 07033
Pres.—Robert Schreiber, 3 emp., *Window treatments, flooring & wall* (908) 245-7766
Rose Brand, Inc., 4 Emerson Ln., Secaucus 07094
Pres.—George Jacobstein, 197 emp., *Curtains, draperies, backdrops, fabrics* (201) 809-1730
Silberstein, Inc., M., 428 Broad St., Shrewsbury 07702
Co-Pres.—M. Silberstein, 7 emp., *Draperies, upholstery, office furniture* (732) 741-1762
Stessl & Neugebauer, Inc., 9 Industrial Pl., Summit 07901
Pres.—Eric Stessl, 13 emp., *Custom upholstery & window treatments* (908) 277-3340
Stich N' Sew Centre, 123 E County Line Rd., Lakewood 08701
★ Owner—Beth Fisher, 40 emp., *Custom window treatments, including* (732) 363-2220
Superior Drapery Co. & Harbor Linen Co, 2 Foster Ave., Gibbsboro 08026
Drapery Div. Mgr.—Paul J. Lieberman, 50 emp., *Custom window treaments & bedding for ...* (856) 435-2000
Unicor Federal Prison Industries, Inc., 5835 Doughboy Loop, P.O. Box 38, Fort Dix 08640
Factory Mgr., Recycling—Jeff Eobstell, 600 emp., *Institutional & law enforcement clothing* (609) 723-1100
Weiss & Sons, Inc., I., 815 Fairview Ave., Ste. 10, Fairview 07022
Pres.—David Rosenberg, 33 emp., *Theatrical draperies & rigging equipment* (201) 402-6500
Windowscapes, 5 Winay Ter., Long Valley 07853
★ Owner—Kathy Sheola, 1 emp., *Draperies* (908) 850-0678

## 2392 Furnishings—house

A-1 Tablecloth Co., 450 Huyler St., Ste. 102, South Hackensack 07606
Manager—Oren Fox, 100 emp., *Tablecloths, chair covers, skirts,* (201) 727-8987
Allen Linen Supply, 407 20th Ave., Paterson 07513
Pres.—Herb Allen III, 50 emp., *Table linens* (973) 742-6131
AMD Fine Linens, LLC, 18 W. Forest Ave., Englewood 07631
Owner—Gianni Romagnolo, 7 emp., *Bed linens* (201) 568-5255
American Home Mfg., LLC, 4 Corporate Pl., Piscataway 08854
★ Manager—Rick Bruch, 20 emp., *Pillows & bean bags* (732) 465-1530
Avanti Linens, Inc., 234 Moonachie Rd., Moonachie 07074
Chrm.—Arthur Tauber, 165 emp., *Embellished & bordered towels & kitchen* (201) 641-7766
Avon Fabrics, Inc., 484 Lincoln Blvd., Middlesex 08846
Owner—D. J. Jain, 3 emp., *Woven, embroidered & novelty silk fabrics* (732) 764-9700
Ballard Collection, Inc., 221 Stirling Rd., Ste. E & F, Warren 07059
Owner & CEO—Karen L. Engemann, 7 emp., *Tablecloths* (908) 604-0082
Bananafish, 250 Passaic St., Newark 07104
Owner—Steven Betesh, 30 emp., *Infant bedding* (212) 686-4666
Beatrice Home Fashions, Inc., 151 Helen St., P.O. Box 86, South Plainfield 07080
Pres.—Sam Gindi, 30 emp., *Bedspreads & draperies* (908) 561-7370
Bebe Chic, 530 Church St., Ridgefield 07657
Pres.—Caren Karpik, 8 emp., *Children's bedding & accessories* (201) 941-5414
Bedding Industries Of America, 1375 Jersey Ave., North Brunswick 08902
Pres.—Stuart Carlitz, 100 emp., *Mattresses* (732) 628-0800
Better Home Plastics Corp., 439 Commercial Ave., Palisades Park 07650
Pres.—Ronald Haboush, 20 emp., *Plastic housewares, plastic & fabric* (201) 592-0370
Capco Sportswear Inc. (H Q), 100 W. Commercial Ave., Moonachie 07074
GM—Wally Richards, 10 emp., *Corporate headquarters; stock blank* (201) 939-9228
Chiromatic, Inc., 1375 Jersey Ave., North Brunswick 08902
Pres.—Debbie Carlitz, 2 emp., *Firm & pressure relieving visco-elastic* (800) 526-5116
Closet Butler, 3 Spielman Rd., Fairfield 07004
Pres.—John Doyle, 10 emp., *Wooden closets & storage systems* (973) 729-9222
Comfort Concepts, Inc., 501 Broad Ave., Ste. 7, Ridgefield 07657
Ptnr.—Robert Mass, 16 emp., *Manufacturer & distributor of reusable* (201) 941-6700
Comfort Revolution (H Q), 187 Route 36, Ste. 205, West Long Branch 07764
Founder & CEO—Michael Fux, 20 emp., *Company headquarters; foam mattresses* (732) 272-9111
Costa Marine Canvas & Enclosures, LLC, 1324 Moss Mill Rd., Egg Harbor City 08215
Owner—Donna Costa, 15 emp., *Canvas boat covers, cushions, enclosures* (609) 965-1538
Crown Custom Cleaners, 27 E. Kings Hwy., Audubon 08106
Owner—Bruce Yun, 2 emp., *Custom draperies & textile household* (856) 310-0710
Design Accents, LLC, 1330 Hamburg Tpke., Wayne 07470
Member—Aman Kakar, 4 emp., *Designer pillows & throws* (201) 660-2446
Elite Home Products, 95 Mayhill St., Ste. 3, Saddle Brook 07663
★ V-P.—Scott Perretz, 50 emp., *Bed linens, including blankets & fine* (201) 880-8292
Fleck Knitwear Co., Inc., 400 Leland Ave., Plainfield 07062
Pres., Mfg. Mgr.—Peter Fleck, 15 emp., *Knit blankets, afghans, sweaters, children's* (908) 754-8888
Franco Mfg. Co., Inc. (H Q), 555 Prospect St., Metuchen 08840
Pres.—Louis D. Franco, 100 emp., *Corporate headquarters; textile towels* (732) 494-0500
Golden Sheets Mfg., 239 6th Ave., Paterson 07524
GM—Ashraf Rabi, 8 emp., *Bed sheets* (973) 925-2242
Hanover Direct, Inc. (H Q), 1500 Harbor Blvd., 1st Fl., Weehawken 07086
Pres., CEO—Don Kelley, 50 emp., *Corporate headquarters; home furnishings* (201) 863-7300
Harbor Linen, LLC (H Q), 2 Foster Ave., Gibbsboro 08026
Chrm.—Earl Waxman, 100 emp., *Company headquarters; manufacturer* (856) 435-2000
Hedaya Home Fashions, Inc., 1111 Jefferson Ave., Elizabeth 07201
Pres.—Nathan Hedaya, 40 emp., *Aprons, towels, oven mitts, place mats* (908) 352-0808
Hospi-Tel Mfg. Co., Inc., 545 N. Arlington Ave., East Orange 07017
Pres.—David Freedland, 80 emp., *Shower & cubicle curtains & mattress* (973) 678-7100
Innocor, Inc. (H Q), 187 State Route 36, Ste. 101, West Long Branch 07764
CEO—Michael C. Thompson, 70 emp., *Corporate headquarters; polyurethane* (732) 263-0800
Ka-Lor Cubicle & Supply Co., Inc., P.O. Box 804, Fair Lawn 07410
Pres.—Dennis Brett, 21 emp., *Hospital & institutional cubicle, shower* (201) 891-8077
LBU, Inc., 217 Brook Ave., Ste. 6, Passaic 07055
Founder & Pres.—Jeff Mayer, 50 emp., *Custom hand, cosmetic, laundry, travel* (973) 773-4800
Logo Knits, Inc., 42-A Cindy Ln., Ocean 07712
Pres.—Paul Van Anda, 12 emp., *Knitted blankets & embroidery* (732) 382-6961
Milltex Mfg. Co., 1101 Industrial Pkwy., Brick 08724
Pres.—Martin Metzger, Sr., 8 emp., *Comforters, draperies, window treatments* (732) 840-3021
Nourison Industries (H Q), 5 Sampson St., Saddle Brook 07663
Pres.—Alex Peykar, 240 emp., *Company headquarters; upholstered furniture* (201) 368-6900
Phoenix Down Corp., 85 US Highway 46, Totowa 07512
Pres., CEO—John Facatselis, 100 emp., *Pillows & comforters* (973) 812-8100
Purple Pebble, LLC (H Q), 58 Grand Ave., Waldwick 07463
Owner—Heather D. Vaul, 1 emp., *Company headquarters; dog leashes,* (201) 444-7439
Quickie Mfg. Corp. (H Q), 1150 Taylors Ln., P.O. Box 156, Cinnaminson 08077
Ex. V-P., Engrg.—Jace Weaver, 70 emp., *Corporate headquarters; cleaning products* (856) 829-7900
Sleepable Sofas Ltd., 6 Empire Blvd., Moonachie 07074
Pres., CEO—Darren DeMatteo, 65 emp., *Company headquarters & custom upholstered* (973) 546-4502

Something Different Linen, Inc., 167 Fornelius Ave., Clifton 07013
Co-Pres.—Mitchell Smith, 65 emp., *Tablecloths* .......... (973) 772-8019
Superior Drapery Co. & Harbor Linen Co, 2 Foster Ave., Gibbsboro 08026
Drapery Div. Mgr.—Paul J. Lieberman, 50 emp., *Custom window treaments & bedding for ...* (856) 435-2000
Tablecloth Co., Inc., 514 Totowa Ave., Paterson 07522
Pres.—Judith Metzger, 50 emp., *Tablecloths, napkins, runners, placemats* .......... (973) 942-1555
Tanner Assocs., 600 Palisade Ave., Union City 07087
Owner, Fin. & GM—Irving Tanner, 3 emp., *Cotton & nylon cloth dry cleaning &* .......... (201) 865-4500
Tiffanees Toys, Inc., 601 Nassau St., Ste. 593, North Brunswick 08902
Pres.—Mirta D'Amaro, 13 emp., *Stuffed toys, pet beds, pillow cushions* .......... (732) 828-6333
Unicor Federal Prison Industries, Inc., 5835 Doughboy Loop, P.O. Box 38, Fort Dix 08640
Factory Mgr., Recycling—Jeff Eobstell, 600 emp., *Institutional & law enforcement clothing* .... (609) 723-1100

## 2393 Bags—textile

A. Smith & Son, Inc., 300 W. Broad St., Ste. A, Burlington 08016
Pres.—John R. Smith, 7 emp., *Nylon, canvas & textile products, bags* .......... (609) 747-0800
Accurate Flannel Bag Co., Inc., 468 Totowa Ave., Ste. 3, Paterson 07522
Pres.—Fred Baron, 125 emp., *Custom bags & pouches, including dustcovers* .......... (973) 720-1800
Bestwork Industries For The Blind, Inc., 1940 Almay Ave., Ste. 200, Cherry Hill 08003
Pres.—Belinda Moore, 100 emp., *Fabric safety vests, work aprons, tool* .......... (856) 939-5220
DiMilo Industries, 90 Dayton Ave., Ste. 38, Passaic 07055
Pres.—Richard Krauser, 12 emp., *Custom canvas bags, including tote,* .......... (973) 955-0460
General Filter Corp., 14 Constitution Ave., Succasunna 07876
Pres., CEO—Richard Warren, 4 emp., *Pharmaceutical filter bags* .......... (973) 584-9220
Halsted Corp., 78 Halladay St., Jersey City 07304
Pres.—Michael J. Murphy, 35 emp., *Manufacturer & distributor of industrial* .......... (201) 433-3323
LBU, Inc., 217 Brook Ave., Ste. 6, Passaic 07055
Founder & Pres.—Jeff Mayer, 50 emp., *Custom hand, cosmetic, laundry, travel* .......... (973) 773-4800
MP Technologies, LLC (H Q), 345 Claremont Ave., Ste. 26, Montclair 07042
Chrm.—John Mahdessian, 15 emp., *Company headquarters; pocket stain* .......... (646) 366-1155
Object Design, Inc., 105 W. Dewey Ave., Bldg. C, Unit 5, Wharton 07885
Pres.—Amy Kim, 8 emp., *Commercial laundry bags & industrial* .......... (973) 442-5790
Shaffer Products, Inc., 20 Milltown Rd., P.O. Box 427, Union 07083
Pres.—James K. Shahidi, 25 emp., *Woven & conductive filters for separating* .......... (908) 206-1980
Wheelchair Gear, 126 Cindy Dr., Egg Harbor Township 08234
Owner & Hum. Res. Mgr.—Leslie Snyder, 2 emp., *Wheelchair convenience accessories,* ...... (609) 653-6787

## 2394 Canvas & related products

(MASAco) Michael Anthony Sign & Awning, Inc., 21 Randolph Ave., Avenel 07001
Pres.—Michael Bradley, 35 emp., *Electric signs, including storefront* .......... (732) 453-6120
A & J Canvas Co., Inc., Maple Spruce St., P.O. Box 30, Rosenhayn 08352
Pres.—Larry Abraham, 3 emp., *Canvas truck covers* .......... (856) 451-5606
A. Smith & Son, Inc., 300 W. Broad St., Ste. A, Burlington 08016
Pres.—John R. Smith, 7 emp., *Nylon, canvas & textile products, bags* .......... (609) 747-0800
ACS Canvas & Awnings, 83 Union St., Medford 08055
Owner—Alan C. Schwarzwalder, 2 emp., *Residential & commercial awnings, canopies* .......... (609) 953-9700
Air World, Inc., 126 Christie Ave., Mahwah 07430
Pres.—Sam Oh, 20 emp., *Cloth covers for apparel cleaning presses* .......... (201) 831-0700
American Woodcarving, LLC, 1123 State Route 23, Ste. 6, Wayne 07470
Pres.—Mike Holst, 7 emp., *Signs, displays & awnings & custom* .......... (973) 835-8510
Archie's Boat Tops, LLC, 1800 Route 35, South Amboy 08879
Pres.—Stanley Szeszko, 2 emp., *Canvas boat tops & products* .......... (732) 721-7566
Artisan Awning Co., 17 Jefferson St., P.O. Box 387, Newton 07860
Owner—Randall R. De Groat, 2 emp., *Custom canvas awnings & canopies* .......... (973) 383-5608
Awning Concepts & Design, Inc., 916 Route 33, Freehold 07728
Pres.—Mark Pedersen, 8 emp., *Awnings* .......... (732) 462-1131
Awning Shoppe, The, 190 Highway 36, Keansburg 07734
Ptnr.—Tom McCarthy, 8 emp., *Canopies, awnings & outdoor canvas* .......... (732) 787-4246
Batten The Hatches, 70 State Route 181, Lake Hopatcong 07849
Owner—Maria Pappas, 2 emp., *Canvas boat covers* .......... (973) 663-1910
Bay Shore Canvas, 310 Firehouse Rd., Brick 08723
Owner—Joe Cannella, 1 emp., *Boating canvas* .......... (732) 477-8520
Beachwood Canvas Works, LLC, 39 Lake Ave., P.O. Box 137, Island Heights 08732
Pres. & Bookkeeper—Dan Janquitto, 10 emp., *Canvas products* .......... (732) 929-3168
Beaton Sails, Inc., 72 Beaton Rd., Brick 08723
Pres.—Mark Beaton, 2 emp., *Canvas sails* .......... (732) 920-6638
Berges Trenton Awning Co., Inc., 12 W. Washington Ave., Pleasantville 08232
Pres.—Richard Berges, 7 emp., *Canvas awnings* .......... (609) 641-7861
Blacher Canvas Products, Inc., 604 Bound Brook Rd., Dunellen 08812
Pres.—George Rodoussakis, 7 emp., *Canvas awnings* .......... (732) 968-3666
Brown's Awning Co., 628 West Ave., Ocean City 08226
Pres.—Christina Russick, 7 emp., *Canvas awnings* .......... (609) 398-6262
C L N Designs, LLC, P.O. Box 1822, South Hackensack 07606
Ex. V-P.—John Parente, 8 emp., *ADA & safety interior & exterior signs* .......... (201) 939-2120
CAD SIGNS, 169 Lodi St., Hackensack 07601
Pres.—Alex Galiano, 30 emp., *Signs, banners, vinyl letters & graphics* .......... (201) 267-0457
Canvas Lady, The, 19 Killdeer Hill Rd., Woodbine 08270
Owner—Eva White, 2 emp., *Canvas boat covers* .......... (609) 628-3257
Canvas Shop Of Avon, Inc., 504 Main St., Avon by the Sea 07717
Pres.—R. Glovich, 6 emp., *Canvas boat covers & awnings* .......... (732) 988-5775
Capitol City Aluminum Products, 407 Rutgers Ave., Hamilton 08619
Pres.—Louis Battaglia, 5 emp., *Canvas & aluminum awnings & entries* .......... (609) 587-3653
Colie Sailmakers, Inc., 1649 Bay Ave., Point Pleasant Beach 08742
Manager—Alex Shayfer, 4 emp., *Boat covers* .......... (732) 892-4344
Costa Marine Canvas & Enclosures, LLC, 1324 Moss Mill Rd., Egg Harbor City 08215
Owner—Donna Costa, 15 emp., *Canvas boat covers, cushions, enclosures* .......... (609) 965-1538
Cover Co., Inc., The, 19 Readington Rd., Somerville 08876
Pres.—Frank Patel, 25 emp., *Sewn fabric & polypropylene mesh webbing* .......... (908) 707-1122
Custom Designers, LLC, 80 Greenwood Ave., Ste. 14, Midland Park 07432
Owner—Harry E. Parker, 4 emp., *Custom canvas boat covers, car & boat* .......... (201) 652-5219
Deroche Canvas, Inc., 283 County Road 519, Belvidere 07823
Pres.—Dan C. Deroche, 2 emp., *Industrial truck tarps* .......... (908) 475-2266
Dover Vinyl Products, 1746 Route 9, Toms River 08755
Pres.—Kathleen M. Stern, 23 emp., *Sewn vinyl pool liners* .......... (732) 244-1444
DSM Enterprises, Inc., 132 Lewis St., Unit B-5, Eatontown 07724
Pres.—Mark Donahue, 6 emp., *Acrylic, vinyl & canvas awnings* .......... (732) 380-9779
Eggers Sails, Inc., John, 7076 Route 35, South Amboy 08879
CEO—John Eggers, 3 emp., *Sails & riggers* .......... (732) 721-4667
Fiber-Lite Mfg. Co., Inc., 1152 Greenpond Rd., Newfoundland 07435
Owner—Joe Taranto, 5 emp., *Custom canvas awnings & canopies* .......... (973) 208-1300
Fisher & Sons, Inc., Harold F., 200 Ash St., Delanco 08075
Pres., CFO—Frank Fisher, 2 emp., *Canvas products* .......... (856) 461-2883
Fisher Canvas Products, Inc., 415 Saint Mary St., Burlington 08016
Pres., Fin., MIS & R & D Mgr.—Frederick Fisher, 7 emp., *Canvas boat covers & bags, awnings,* (609) 239-2733
G & J Solutions, Inc., 419 Madison Ave., Woodbine 08270
Pres., GM & Pur. Agt.—John Di Pompeo, 15 emp., *Fabric awnings* .......... (609) 861-9838
Galleria Enterprises, Inc., 300-3 State Route 17 S., Ste. E, Lodi 07644
Ptnr. & CEO—Joe Simeone, 7 emp., *Folding & stick umbrellas & canvas* .......... (646) 416-6683
Garden State Canvas Products Co., 1671 Beaver Dam Rd., Point Pleasant Boro 08742
Owner—David Toth, 3 emp., *Canvas boat covers* .......... (732) 892-7021
Gioia Sails Inc., 1951 Rutgers University Blvd., Lakewood 08701
Owner & Sales Mgr.—Don Gioia, 30 emp., *Corporate headquarters & canvas products* ........ (732) 901-6770
GTM Signs, Inc., 1298 Hurffville Rd., Deptford 08096
Ptnr.—Karl Baker, 8 emp., *Signs & canvas & standing seam awnings* .......... (856) 227-2333
Hansen Awning Co., 18 Church Rd., Rio Grande 08242
Ptnr.—Lillian McGill, 2 emp., *Canvas awnings* .......... (609) 886-1685
Hudson Awning & Sign Co., Inc., 27 Cottage St., Bayonne 07002
Pres.—Edward Burak, 35 emp., *Lightweight fabric & membrane structures* .......... (201) 339-7171
Huggins Aluminum Products, 576 N. Route 73, West Berlin 08091
Ptnr.—George E. Metzler, 3 emp., *Screen & fully insulated enclosures* .......... (856) 767-0506
J & L Boat Canvas, 190 Drum Point Rd., Brick 08723
★ Owner—John Ribaudo, 1 emp., *Boat canvas & awnings* .......... (732) 262-1535
Jim's Signs, 1400 Rahway Ave., Ste. 3, Avenel 07001
Owner & Pres.—Jim Petrocy, 10 emp., *Plastic & reflective safety, ADA, room* .......... (732) 381-8700
Kendall Mfg. Co., Inc., 1366 Chews Landing Rd., Clementon 08021
Owner—James W. Strater, 3 emp., *Vinyl & wooden windows & doors & retractable* .......... (856) 227-2132
Kerry Wilkens, Inc., 780 State Route 36, Belford 07718
Pres., Store Mgr.—Kerry Wilkens, 7 emp., *Canvas tarpaulins, custom sandbox covers* .......... (732) 787-0070
Kraftwork Custom Design, 1837 S. Broad St., Hamilton 08610
Owner—Michael K. Sylvester, 4 emp., *Dimensional, carved, gold, neon, channel* .......... (609) 848-0578
Laggren's, LLC, P.O. Box 7173, Monroe Township 08831
Pres.—David Lasser, 10 emp., *Canvas awnings, window shades, blinds* .......... (609) 235-9883
Lincoln Signs & Awnings, Inc., 895 Estate St., Perth Amboy 08861
Pres.—Julio Hernandez, 9 emp., *Interior & exterior signs & awnings* .......... (732) 442-3151
Linthicum Sailmakers, Inc., 607 Grace St., Somerdale 08083
Pres.—Bradford Linthicum, 2 emp., *Sails & canvas items, upholstery &* .......... (856) 783-4288
Lippincott Marine, 74 Norman Ave., Delran 08075
Owner—Howard Lippincott, 2 emp., *Canvas marine products* .......... (856) 764-8282
Lloyd's Of Millville, Inc., 208 S. Wade Blvd., Millville 08332
Pres., Fin. & R & D Mgr.—Ben Lloyd, Jr., 3 emp., *Canvas goods, sewing & retractable* .......... (856) 825-0345
Main Attractions, Inc., 85 Newfield Ave., Edison 08837
Pres.—Rocky Sconda, 35 emp., *Canvas products* .......... (732) 225-3500
Marshall, Inc., G. E., 810 S. Broad St., Trenton 08611
Pres.—Kimberly Adler, 5 emp., *Canvas awnings* .......... (609) 392-2464
McBride Awning Co., 304 Richmond Ave., Point Pleasant Beach 08742
Ptnr.—Jon McBride, 3 emp., *Canvas awnings* .......... (732) 892-6256
Meadowlands Signs, 58 State Route 17, Hasbrouck Heights 07604
★ Owner—Jose Fuentes, 4 emp., *Interior & exterior signs & canvas* .......... (201) 426-0420
Membrane Structure Solutions, Inc., 340 N. Wyoming Ave., South Orange 07079
Pres.—Waldemar Ptaszek, 40 emp., *Coated fabric, tensile, frame & air* .......... (908) 520-0112
Monmouth & Ocean County Awning Co., 508 Main St., Asbury Park 07712
Owner—Douglas Maxwell, 6 emp., *Canvas awnings* .......... (732) 775-4881
Moorhouse Sailmakers, Inc., 52 Stacy Haines Rd., Lumberton 08048
Owner—John MacCausland, 3 emp., *Boat sails* .......... (609) 654-7819
MPT Industries, 85 Franklin Rd., Hamilton Bus. Park, Ste. 6-B, Dover 07801
Owner & Pres.—Michael Trueba, Jr., 7 emp., *Automotive covers & lubricants* .......... (973) 989-9220
Nautical Canvas Designs, 506 Elizabeth Ave., Point Pleasant Beach 08742
Member—Michael Meseroll, 2 emp., *Canvas boat covers* .......... (732) 892-7677
North Sails New Jersey, 2422 Highway 34, Manasquan 08736
Owner & Pres.—Henry Bossett, 3 emp., *Polyester, aramid fiber, carbon, canvas* .......... (732) 528-8899
Opdyke Awning, Inc., 2036 State Route 35, Wall Township 07719
Pres.—James Opdyke, 18 emp., *Residential & commercial awnings &* .......... (732) 449-5940
Rainmen U. S. A., Inc., 10 Maple St., Norwood 07648
Owner—Jeff Nanus, 200 emp., *Umbrellas, canvas bags & accessories* .......... (201) 784-3244
Ridgewood Awning Co., Inc., 445 W. Main St., Ste. 6, Wyckoff 07481
Pres.—Richard Ackerman, 12 emp., *Canvas awnings* .......... (201) 847-0909
Ries Co., Inc., R. E., 107 Lake Ave., Brielle 08730
Pres.—Raymond E. Ries, 4 emp., *Canvas boat covers & commercial upholstery* .......... (732) 892-1842
S & S Custom Covers LLC, 2034 Bridge Ave., Point Pleasant 08742
Owner & Pres.—Walter Skola, 2 emp., *Boat covers* .......... (732) 903-7518
Sailworks At 43, 43 Norman Ave., Delran 08075
Owner, Pres. & GM—Burt Geiges, 1 emp., *Boat sails* .......... (856) 764-0888
Shore Awning Co., Inc., 556 Industrial Way W., Eatontown 07724
Pres., CEO—Michael McClellan, 10 emp., *Canvas awnings* .......... (732) 578-1882
Signs By Lynn, 329 Kearny Ave., Ste. A, Kearny 07032
Owner—Lynn Oelz, 3 emp., *Commercial, residential, ADA & architectural* .......... (201) 998-4273
Signs Of 2000, 421 Broad St., Clifton 07011
GM—Ray Salem, 10 emp., *Interior & exterior signs & awnings* .......... (973) 253-1333
Stetsers J.D. Canvas Products, Inc., 644 Billings Ave., Paulsboro 08066
Pres. & V-P.—David Stetser, 2 emp., *Custom residential & commercial awnings* .......... (856) 423-4901
Superior Marine Canvas Corp., 75 Belfiore Dr., Swedesboro 08085
Owner—Brian Reed, 5 emp., *Marine canvas* .......... (856) 241-1724
TerraCycle, Inc., 121 New York Ave., Trenton 08638
CEO—Tom Szaky, 25 emp., *Cut & sewn duffel bags, bike pouches* .......... (609) 393-4252
Texas Canvas Co., 266 Union Blvd., Totowa 07512
Pres.—Peter Vasquez, 10 emp., *Canvas truck & boat covers & awnings* .......... (973) 278-3802
Tingue, Brown & Co. (H Q), 535 N. Midland Ave., Saddle Brook 07663
Pres., CEO—David Tingue, 20 emp., *Company headquarters; laundry bags* .......... (201) 796-4490
Vannote Custom Canvas, 1904 Grand Central Ave., Lavallette 08735
Owner—Thomas Vannote, 1 emp., *Marine canvas* .......... (732) 830-6555
Weathercraft Mfg. Co., 13 Emerson Plz. E., Emerson 07630
Pres.—Salvatore Gebbia, 15 emp., *Aluminum awnings & enclosures, retractable* .......... (201) 262-0055

## 2395 Pleating & stitching

A A Patchworks, Inc. (H Q), 311 Mechanic St., Boonton 07005
Pres.—Frank Wagenhoffer, 8 emp., *Corporate headquarters; embroidered* .......... (973) 810-2121
A2Z Emblems, LLC, 125 W. Route 130 N., Ste. C, Burlington 08016
Owner—Annette Zelauskas, 4 emp., *Apparel & garment screen printing &* .......... (609) 239-9800
A-Aaabacus Printing & Promotional Specialties Of Metuchen, 243 Amboy Ave., Metuchen 08840
Owner—Sam H. Van Chama, 2 emp., *Commercial printing, binding & graphic* .......... (732) 767-9204
Abilitees Unlimited, Inc., 23 Adams St., Metuchen 08840
Owner & Pres.—Helen Lenihan, 8 emp., *Textile embroidery & screen & offset* .......... (732) 494-1513
Abilities Of Northwest Jersey, Inc., 264 Route 31 N., P.O. Box 251, Washington 07882
CEO—Cindy Wildermuth, 300 emp., *Contract packaging/fulfillment, including* .......... (908) 689-1118

S.I.C.

Accent Apparel LLC, 405 Atlantic City Blvd., Beachwood 08722
Owner—Kevin McMahon, 3 emp., *Embroidery, screen printing & direct-to-garme* (732) 341-7576
Accurate Flannel Bag Co., Inc., 468 Totowa Ave., Ste. 3, Paterson 07522
Pres.—Fred Baron, 125 emp., *Custom bags & pouches, including dustcovers* (973) 720-1800
Ace Screen Printing, LLC, 24 High St. W., Glassboro 08028
★ Owner—Adam Szyfman, 4 emp., *T-shirt screen printing & embroidery* (856) 881-1188
Active Imprints, 4266 U.S. Highway 1, Monmouth Junction 08852
Pres.—Duane Watlington, 9 emp., *Custom imprinted promotional products* (732) 329-2613
Adpro Imprints, Inc., 3411 Rose Ave., Ocean 07712
Pres.—Peter L. Demaree, Jr., 5 emp., *Textile screen printing, embroidery* (732) 493-8555
ADV Promos & More, LLC, 12 Baltusrol St., Hamilton Square 08690
Owner—Andrea M. Anepete, 1 emp., *Custom printed promotional products* (609) 587-7500
AKA, Inc., 1324 New Market Ave., South Plainfield 07080
Pres.—Michael Allocco, 6 emp., *Screen printing & embroidery, exterior* (908) 753-8112
Alete Printing, LLC, 722 Dartmouth Ct., P.O. Box 371, Wenonah 08090
V-P., CEO—John Koskinen, 4 emp., *Commercial & variable data printing* (856) 468-3536
All Sports Stadium, LLC, 297 Route 31 S., Washington 07882
Pres.—Armin Kososki, 7 emp., *Textile screen printing & embroidery* (908) 689-0411
All-Star Pro & Sport Store, 642 State Route 35 N., Neptune 07753
Owner—Joe Storzieri, 2 emp., *Trophies, plaques & textile embroidery* (732) 774-3444
Alpha T'S, Inc., 380 Totowa Rd., 2nd Fl., Totowa 07512
Pres.—Sal Mancini, 2 emp., *Textile screen printing, embroidery* (973) 956-7243
Anderson Monograms, 245 Fox Landing Rd., P.O. Box 163, Port Republic 08241
Owner—Bruce Anderson, 1 emp., *Shirt & jacket monogramming* (609) 652-5552
Apollo East, Inc., 7895 Airport Hwy., Pennsauken 08110
Pres.—Dora Ngan, 20 emp., *Textile screen printing & embroidery* (856) 486-1882
Apparel Zone, Inc., 165 Amboy Rd., Ste. 505, Morganville 07751
Pres.—Todd Berman, 5 emp., *Apparel embroidery & screen printing* (732) 441-7780
Aristocrat Embroidery Corp., 7014 Jackson St., Guttenberg 07093
Pres.—Craig Goldman, 5 emp., *Embroidery* (201) 869-9126
Ariston Multimedia, LLC, 94 Valley Rd., Clifton 07013
★ Owner—Bernard Williams, 4 emp., *Commercial printing, t-shirt screen* (973) 553-2727
Art Graphics, 54 Delsea Dr. N., Glassboro 08028
Ptnr.—Art Dorn, 3 emp., *Textile screen printing, embroidery* (856) 881-5029
Art's Embroidery, LLC, 175 Monmouth Rd., West Long Branch 07764
Ptnr.—Ina Kraucis, 4 emp., *Embroidery, screen printing & sports* (732) 870-1155
Athletes Image, Inc., 1865 State Route 35, Wall 07719
Pres.—Richard Markus, 13 emp., *Textile embroidery* (732) 974-1600
Athletic Imprinters, Inc., 775 Ashbourne Ave., Lindenwold 08021
Owner, Pres. & CEO—Dennis Tallman, 2 emp., *Embroidery & heat press, tackle twill* (856) 346-4545
Aztec Graphics, Inc., 420 Whitehead Rd., Trenton 08619
Pres.—Ronald Balerno, 15 emp., *Screenprinted & embroidered sportswear* (609) 587-1000
Bailey's Printing, Inc., 191 Throckmorton St., Freehold 07728
Pres.—Randy Bailey, 2 emp., *Commerical & screen printing & custom* (732) 462-8010
BCS Machine & Mfg. Corp., 3575 Kennedy Rd., South Plainfield 07080
Pres.—Sal Capparelli, 10 emp., *CNC & general machining job shop, including* (908) 561-1656
Black Universities Supply Shop, The, 410 Leland Ave., Plainfield 07062
Pres., CEO—Rubye Hickerson, 4 emp., *Customized clothing, apparel & accessories* (908) 754-8088
Blue Streak Screen Printing Co., 33 E. Railroad Ave., Monroe Township 08831
Pres.—James Craparotta, 3 emp., *Textile screen printing & custom embroidery* (732) 656-0400
Bon-Jour Group, LLC, 1100 Blanch Ave., Norwood 07648
Owner & Pres.—Michael Tchertchian, 17 emp., *Embroidery & screen printing of promotional* (201) 646-1070
Boy On A Dolphin Corp., 308 State Route 36, Port Monmouth 07758
Owner—Harry Karatzia, 2 emp., *Embroidery & screen printing* (732) 495-2200
C & P Embroidery, LLC, 6602 Smith Ave., North Bergen 07047
Pres., Fin. & MIS Mgr.—Ivonne Heguy, 5 emp., *Military emblems* (201) 854-0388
Capco Sportswear Inc. (H Q), 100 W. Commercial Ave., Moonachie 07074
GM—Wally Richards, 10 emp., *Corporate headquarters; stock blank* (201) 939-9228
CDK Industry, LLC, 900 Haddonfield Rd., Cherry Hill 08002
Pres., GM—James Walford, 3 emp., *Horse racing equipment & embroidery* (856) 488-5456
Class Act Embroidery, 86 N. Beverwyck Rd., Ste. A, Lake Hiawatha 07034
Owner—Kathy Breslow, 5 emp., *Textile screen printing & embroidery* (973) 394-0045
Cobyco, Inc., 65 Wilson Ave., Manalapan 07726
Pres.—Elana Keinan, 2 emp., *Embroidery* (732) 446-4448
Color Screen Pros, 100 Verona Ave., Newark 07104
Owner—Oscar Cano, 8 emp., *Apparel & promotional item screen printing* (973) 268-5080
Colorcraft Sign Co., 400 Magnolia St., Beverly 08010
Owner—Steve Molnar, 8 emp., *Full-color graphics, vinyl, vehicle* (609) 386-1115
Concept Printing, Inc., 160 Woodbine St., Ste. 2, Bergenfield 07621
Pres.—Kerry Monahan-Gaughan, 6 emp., *Offset & screen printing, embroidery* (201) 387-6000
Continental Cap Co., 64 Passaic St., Wood Ridge 07075
Owner—Tina Hsu, 5 emp., *Apparel embroidery* (973) 778-2628
Cox Merchandising, LLC, Fred, 34 Radburn Rd., Glen Rock 07452
CEO—Fred Cox, 2 emp., *Embroidery* (201) 310-0740
Craftmaster Printing, Inc., 2024 Corlies Ave., Neptune 07753
Pres.—Curtis Baumgartner, 4 emp., *Corporate headquarters & single-color* (732) 775-0011
Creative Embroidery Corp., 305 3rd Ave. W., Ste. 3, Newark 07107
★ Pres.—Steve Diamond, 20 emp., *Custom apparel screen printing & embroidery* (973) 497-5700
Creative Screen Design, 531 Route 68, P.O. Box 369, Columbus 08022
Owner—Cathy Cox, 2 emp., *Textile screen printing, embroidery* (609) 424-3334
C-Sports, 2045 S. Black Horse Pike, Williamstown 08094
Owner—Mark Cannon, 2 emp., *Textile screen printing & embroidery* (856) 875-5680
Custom Embroidery, 73 E. New Jersey Ave., P.O. Box 1489, Pleasantville 08232
Owner—Catherine Carbor, 12 emp., *Embroidery & textile screen printing* (609) 383-9292
D and S Designs, P.O. Box 1707, Bridgeton 08302
Owner—Sandra L. Rodriguez, 2 emp., *Custom screen printing & embroidery* (856) 451-0954
Deblyn Screen Printers, 717 Mountain Blvd., Watchung 07069
Ptnr.—Debra Buhot, 2 emp., *Textile screen printing & embroidery* (908) 756-8459
DeMario Design & Screen Printing, 619 Church St., Pleasantville 08232
Pres.—Richard Pitts, 10 emp., *Apparel screen printing & embroidery* (609) 645-7319
Design-N-Stitch, Inc., 194 Atlantic St., Hackensack 07601
Ptnr. & Pres.—John Fitzpatrick, 8 emp., *Screen printing & embroidery of t-shirts* (201) 488-1314
Designs By James, 892 N. Delsea Dr., Vineland 08360
Pres.—James Crescenzo, 3 emp., *Interior & exterior signs, screen printing* (856) 692-1316
Dezine Line, Inc., 1104 Route 46 E., Ledgewood 07852
Pres.—Steve Mattero, 6 emp., *Textile screen printing & embroidery* (973) 989-1009
Dolly Screen Printing, Inc., 1-19 Elm St., Freehold 07728
Pres.—Mike Dolly, 9 emp., *Textile screen printing & embroidery* (732) 294-8979
Dr. T-Shirt, 221 Parker Ave., Manasquan 08736
Pres.—Robert Giaquinto, 3 emp., *T-shirt screen printing & embroidery* (732) 223-3866
Eagle Embroidery & Graphix, 587 White Horse Pike, Hammonton 08037
Owner—Phyllis Mazzeo, 1 emp., *Textile screen printing & custom embroidery* (609) 561-1457

East Coast Custom, 242 Main St., Sayreville 08872
Pres.—Mark Tesca, 5 emp., *Textile embroidery & screen printing* (732) 390-8238
Eastern Emblem Mfg. Corp., 509 18th St., P.O. Box 828, Union City 07087
Pres.—Sheldon Lefkowitz, 5 emp., *Embroidery & metal & print logos* (201) 867-3159
Easy Prints, Inc., 172 Main St., Metuchen 08840
★ Owner—Darren Swan, 5 emp., *T-shirt screen printing & embroidery* (848) 229-2410
Elmwood Industries, 8 Paul Kohner Pl., Elmwood Park 07407
Supervisor—Diane Zirpoli, 2 emp., *Apparel screen printing & embroidery* (201) 703-1220
Embroider This Co., 7 Duck Point Trl., Wharton 07885
Owner—Donna Sanderson, 3 emp., *Embroidery, screen printing & heat* (973) 663-5551
Embroidery By Cozy, Inc., 695 Passaic Ave., Nutley 07110
Pres.—Ralph Savastano, 15 emp., *Embroidery* (973) 661-9781
Embroidery Concept & Design, LLC, 201 Pond Ave., Middlesex 08846
Pres., CEO—Wahid Sattar, 15 emp., *Embroidery* (732) 926-9400
Embroidery Technologies, Inc., 737 Howe St., Point Pleasant Boro 08742
Pres.—Richard Poulos, 1 emp., *Textile embroidery* (732) 295-1300
Embroidme, 215 U.S. Highway 22, Green Brook 08812
Owner—Joann Karnila, 3 emp., *Textile embroidery* (732) 752-1871
Empire Designs, Inc., 7 Main St., Englishtown 07726
Pres.—Kathleen T. Bien, 1 emp., *Embroidery, screen printing, promotional* (732) 446-6447
Engraver's Bench & Greek Unique, Inc., 1212 Raymond Blvd., Newark 07102
Owner & Pres.—Willie J. Williams, 3 emp., *Metal, wood, plastic & glass engraving* (973) 297-1810
ERL Embroidery & Screen Printing, 8 Evergreen Dr., Lincoln Park 07035
CEO—Michael Hackett, 2 emp., *Textile embroidery & screen printing* (973) 633-7428
Excel Silk Screening, 2320 Old York Rd., Bordentown 08505
Pres.—Brian Noble, 1 emp., *Apparel screen printing & embroidery* (609) 499-4990
Falls Screen Printing, Inc., 25 Amity St., Little Falls 07424
Pres.—Jay Brady, 4 emp., *Textile screen printing & embroidery* (973) 812-0555
Family Screen Printing, Inc., 104 W. Browning Rd., Bellmawr 08031
Pres.—Bob Armstrong, 6 emp., *Apparel screen printing & embroidery* (856) 933-2780
Fancy Threads, 31 Railroad Pl., Hopewell 08525
Owner—Debbie Varbasse, 1 emp., *Embroidery & textile screen printing* (609) 466-0050
Faraj, Inc., 422 Cliff St., Fairview 07022
Pres.—Zackary Faraj, 80 emp., *100% domestic mass-produced fabric* (201) 313-4480
Farrier Sporting Goods, Inc., Godwin & Crescent Aves., Wyckoff 07481
Pres.—Charles Coleman, 4 emp., *Sports & athletic equipment, footwear* (201) 891-9520
Finesse & Lucas, 40 Chestnut St., Ste. 14, Lakewood 08701
Pres.—Luz A. Fredes, 2 emp., *Embroidery & screen printing* (732) 367-0839
First Impressions Screen Printing, 1703 State Route 27, Edison 08817
Owner—Bill Miers, 2 emp., *Textile screen printing & embroidery* (732) 777-7872
Gallery Monograms, 360 Sherman Ave., Teaneck 07666
Owner—Devorah Goldberg, 5 emp., *Textile embroidery* (201) 569-0189
Garden State Embroidery, 1879 Old Cuthbert Rd., Unit 10, Cherry Hill 08034
Owner—Dave Bewick, 5 emp., *Embroidery* (856) 616-9490
Gariel Screen Printing, 729 Mantua Pike, Woodbury 08096
Owner—Gary Lizzi, 7 emp., *T-shirt screen printing & embroidery* (856) 848-3240
Gem Sports, 36-10 Broadway, Fair Lawn 07410
Pres.—Michael Cebulski, 4 emp., *Textile screen printing & embroidery* (201) 791-1776
Gough Engraving & Advertising Specialties, 1745 N. Olden Avenue Ext., Ewing 08638
Owner—Kathleen Gough, 4 emp., *Brass & plastic engraving, award plaques* (609) 882-8700
Graphic Image, 1401 N. Black Horse Pike, Ste. A, Williamstown 08094
Owner—Jim McGhee, 8 emp., *Commercial printing, t-shirt screen* (856) 262-8900
Hamilton Embroidery, Inc., 907-909 21st St., Union City 07087
Pres.—Frank Blaso, 7 emp., *Schiffli machine embroideries & trims* (201) 867-4084
House Printing, LLC, 311 Kearny Ave., Kearny 07032
★ Owner—Juan Calva, 1 emp., *T-shirt screen printing & embroidery* (201) 772-5988
Image Screen Printing, Inc., 532 Lincoln Blvd., Middlesex 08846
Pres., CFO—Gary Mangee, 8 emp., *Textile screen printing & embroidery* (732) 560-1817
Imagery Embroidery Corporation, 2907-2911 Jeannette St., Union City 07087
Pres.—Eddison S. Cruz, 10 emp., *Machined & digitized embroidery, monogramming* (201) 343-9333
In Stitches Embroidery, Inc., 1020 Campus Dr., Morganville 07751
Pres.—Harry Harkavy, 10 emp., *Custom embroidery* (732) 460-2660
Initial Impact, 516 Warren Ave., Spring Lake 07762
Pres.—Donna Szakats, 3 emp., *Promotional screen printing & embroidery* (732) 449-4922
J & G Enterprises, Inc., 182 High St., Nutley 07110
Principal & Manager—John Mancini, 1 emp., *Custom apparel embroidery & screen* (973) 667-7673
J & S Finishing, Inc., 443 62nd St., West New York 07093
Pres.—Pedro Calvo, 15 emp., *Embroidery & school uniforms* (201) 854-0338
J S Designs, 321 Oakshade Rd., Shamong 08088
Owner, Fin. & MIS Mgr.—Jeff Spikol, 2 emp., *Embroidery* (609) 268-3018
J. R.'s Screen Printing, 1930 Greenwood Lake Tpke., P.O. Box 561, Hewitt 07421
Owner, Hum. Res. & IT Mgr.—John Reape, Jr., 2 emp., *Textile screen printing & embroidery.* (973) 728-7802
JABS Personal Stitch, Inc., 1120 Raritan Rd., Clark 07066
Ptnr.—Joseph Arancio, 2 emp., *Textile screen printing & embroidery* (732) 396-9699
Jill's Thrill, Inc., 18 Hardley Dr., Cranbury 08512
Pres.—John Wiegand, 2 emp., *Apparel screen printing & embroidery* (609) 395-9900
K & C Fund Raising & Promotions, 101 S. Delsea Dr., Clayton 08312
Ptnr. & Hum. Res. Mgr.—Kathleen Cromley, 3 emp., *Embroidery* (856) 881-6019
Keltex Imprinted Apparel, Inc., 428-A Woodbine Oceanview Rd., Ocean View 08230
Pres.—Christopher Kelly, 25 emp., *Textile screen printing, embroidery* (609) 624-3252
KMBA Fashions, Inc., 272 Elmwood Ave., Bldg. 3, East Orange 07018
Pres.—William Cotton, Jr., 6 emp., *Screen printing & embroidery of men's* (973) 789-1652
Kraftwork Custom Design, 1837 S. Broad St., Hamilton 08610
Owner—Michael K. Sylvester, 4 emp., *Dimensional, carved, gold, neon, channel* (609) 848-0578
Landsman Uniforms, Inc., 4450 Black Horse Pike, Ste. 3958, Mays Landing 08330
★ Owner—Janet Smith, 15 emp., *Custom embroidery* (609) 909-1000
Lettermen, Inc., The, 1565 Route 37 W., Toms River 08755
Pres.—Rose Dixon, 8 emp., *Imprinted sportswear screen printing* (732) 608-0669
Life A Stitch, 37 Jackson Ave., Carteret 07008
★ Owner—Ray Malivuk, 2 emp., *Embroidery, t-shirt screen printing* (732) 969-0232
Li'l Inspirations, LLC, P.O. Box 5754, Hillsborough 08844
Pres.—Sandra Kircher, 2 emp., *Custom embroidery of personalized wedding* (908) 369-5840
Logo Knits, Inc., 42-A Cindy Ln., Ocean 07712
Pres.—Paul Van Anda, 12 emp., *Knitted blankets & embroidery* (732) 382-6961
M&R Designs & Promotions, 21 Stone Oak Ln., Oak Ridge 07438
Owner—Doreen Scott, 4 emp., *Promotional products screen printing* (908) 928-9400
Mark Sports, 9 E. 31st St., Bayonne 07002
★ Owner—Dominick Landante, 2 emp., *T-shirt screen printing & embroidery* (201) 437-9900
Mayos Sportswear, Inc., 1 Hollywood Ave., Bldg. 2-D, Ho-Ho-Kus 07423
Pres.—Bob Mainenti, 6 emp., *Textile screen printing & embroidery* (201) 652-8570
MJ Corporate Sales, Inc., 109 W. Park Dr., Unit B, Mount Laurel 08054
★ Owner—John Dikmak, 25 emp., *Apparel screen printing & embroidery* (856) 778-0055

MJG Screen Printing & Embroidery, 24 Commerce Rd., Ste. K, Fairfield 07004
Owner—Michael Garamella, 4 emp., T-shirt screen printing & embroidery (973) 575-8877
Modern Graphics, 547 Cross Keys Rd., Ste. B, Sicklerville 08081
Owner—William Glendening II, 1 emp., Custom screen printing & embroidery (856) 728-6300
Monogram Center, 437 Amboy Ave., Perth Amboy 08861
Ptnr.—Bill Kramer, 35 emp., Textile screen printing, embroidery (732) 442-1800
Monogram Madness, 50 Main St., Succasunna 07876
Owner—Peggy Kiefer, 2 emp., Embroidery & screen printing (973) 927-5278
Monogram Shoppe, 5 S. Broad St., Woodbury 08096
Ptnr.—Dottie McQuade, 2 emp., Apparel monogramming (856) 845-9299
Murray's Uniforms, Inc., 312 Main St., Bradley Beach 07720
Pres.—Andrew Bartlett, 3 emp., Textile screen printing & embroidery (732) 774-2671
New Jersey Logowear, 100 McKinley Ave., Ste. 6, Manahawkin 08050
★ Ptnr.—Keith Anderson, 7 emp., Promotional item, apparel & textile (609) 597-9400
New Rose, Inc., 1500 Almonesson Rd., Ste. 8, Woodbury 08096
Pres.—Rosemary Jones, 3 emp., Embroidery & apparel, garment, textile (856) 812-0509
Newton Printing & Embroidery, 75 Main St., Franklin 07416
Owner—Frank Newton, 10 emp., Promotional & corporate branding products (973) 827-2006
Newton Trophy & Sport Center, 1-3 Milk St., Bldg. 3, Branchville 07826
Pres.—Linda Moran, 5 emp., Textile screen printing, embroidery (973) 948-0613
Norco, Inc., 237 South Ave., P.O. Box 186, Garwood 07027
Pres.—Michael Rosenberg, 15 emp., Lapel pins, dog tags, giant magnetic (908) 789-1550
Nu-Style Embroidery & Button Co., Inc., 5212 Polk St., West New York 07093
Pres.—Jay Rosner, 5 emp., Apparel buttons, belts, neckties, lace (201) 864-1808
Nu-Style Embroidery & Trimming, 5212 Polk St., West New York 07093
Pres.—Sam Rosner, 2 emp., Embroidery & lace covered buttons & (201) 864-1808
O. Co Imprints, LLC, 58 W. Bergen Pl., P.O. Box 8249, Red Bank 07701
Owner—Olivia Conklin, 3 emp., Screen printed & embroidered garments (732) 530-3202
Oasis Studios, LLC, 244 Quakertown Rd., P.O. Box 306, Quakertown 08868
Ptnr.—Joe Muller, 2 emp., Textile screen printing, embroidery (908) 735-5089
P. J. Screening & Embroidery, 689 Jaques Ave., Rahway 07065
Pres.—Angela Guden, 2 emp., Textile screen printing & embroidery (732) 382-5183
Peach Boutique, The, 1139 E. Jersey St., Ste. 319, Elizabeth 07201
Pres., GM & Hum. Res. Mgr.—Roslyn Rearden, 6 emp., Clerical & choir robes & embroidery (908) 351-0739
Personalized Paraphernalia, 22 Division St., Somerville 08876
Owner & Pres.—Laura Wolfe, 3 emp., Embroidery & screen printing (908) 526-0602
Pleating Plus Ltd., 527 40th St., Union City 07087
Pres.—Ernest Vega, 5 emp., Contract pleating & tucking (201) 863-2991
Pro Image Promotions, Inc., 489 U.S. Highway 46, Kenvil 07847
Pres.—Brian Hewitt, 4 emp., Promotional textile screen printing (973) 252-8000
Professional Images, LLC, 17 E. Linden Ave., Englewood 07631
Owner—Steve Nicholson, 1 emp., Screen printing & embroidery of promotional (201) 569-4251
ProImage Apparel, LLC, 280 N. Midland Ave., Bldg. H, Saddle Brook 07663
Pres.—Michael Miller, 6 emp., Embroidery (201) 773-9292
Promo Advertising, 1174 Chestnut St., Union 07083
Pres.—Sharon Zhang, 5 emp., Apparel screen printing & embroidery (908) 810-8888
Promotion Works, 45 Wadsworth St., Wallington 07057
Pres.—John Cherup, 10 emp., Embroidery (201) 842-1107
Pyramid Imprints, 28 N. Washington Ave., Bergenfield 07621
Owner—Eleanor Garcia, 2 emp., Commercial screen printing, textile (201) 384-0336
R & R Graphics, Inc., 1724 Route 70 E., Unit B, Cherry Hill 08003
V-P.—Richard Risse, 25 emp., Textile embroidery (856) 751-7671
R K E Athletic Lettering, 1901 State Route 71, Ste. 1-C, Belmar 07719
Owner—Ted Maciejewski, 6 emp., Textile embroidery (732) 280-1111
RKM Enterprises, Inc., 177 Mercer St., Hightstown 08520
Pres.—Dave Babcock, 4 emp., Textile screen printing & embroidery (609) 448-7539
Sandoval Graphics & Printing, 9 Minnetonka Rd., Somerdale 08083
Mng. Ptnr.—Tony Sandoval, 6 emp., Commercial, offset & digital printing (856) 435-7320
Sandpiper Embroidery, Inc., 5905 New Jersey Ave., Wildwood Crest 08260
Owner—Virginia Fineberg, 3 emp., Embroidery products, designs & supplies (609) 522-4560
Satesa Corp., 154 W. Forest Ave., Englewood 07631
Pres.—Randy Loew, 4 emp., Laminating, coating & converting of (201) 871-8989
Schreyer Embroidery Co., Inc., 50 Industrial Ave., Fairview 07022
Pres.—Christine Martin, 4 emp., Embroidery (201) 943-6221
Screen Creations Plus, 8 Hillside Ave., Newton 07860
Owner—Dawn Alvarez, 2 emp., Textile screen printing & embroidery (973) 579-5015
Semel's Embroidery & Screen Printing, Inc., 1078 U.S. Highway 46, Clifton 07013
Chrm.—Charlotte Semel, 25 emp., Contract vintage chain-stitch embroidery (973) 473-3959
Sequins City, 1302 13th St., North Bergen 07047
★ Pres.—Raymond Hill, 6 emp., Fabric & textile embroidery (201) 348-8111
Service Apex, 564-A Union Ave., Bridgewater 08807
★ Pres.—Ken Griggs, 10 emp., Commercial printing, t-shirt screen (732) 560-2222
Sew Ann Sew Thomas Enterprises, 153 Pearl St., Paterson 07501
Owner—Dailey G. Thomas, Jr., 2 emp., Custom embroidery & screen printing (973) 742-2664
Sew Many Gifts, Inc., 6 Cranston Ct., Princeton Junction 08550
Pres.—Eva Tootleman, 1 emp., Textile embroidery & monogramming (609) 275-4532
Shangri La Farm, LLC, 1055 Maxim Southard Rd., Howell 07731
Owner—Elaine Taylor, 1 emp., Embroidery (732) 901-8777
Shelter Cove Embroidery Co., 1333 Bay Ave., Toms River 08753
Owner—Peggi Gamba, 3 emp., T-shirt screen printing & embroidery (732) 506-7700
Sideline Sports, 2566 Plainfield Ave., Scotch Plains 07076
Owner—Imelda McEvoy, 2 emp., Apparel screen printing & embroidery (908) 322-9334
Signarama, 655 S. White Horse Pike, Hammonton 08037
Owner—Richard Matteo, 3 emp., Illuminated & non-illuminated full-color (609) 878-3375
Smith Enterprises, 8-A Deptford Rd., Glassboro 08028
Owner—Damian Smith, 4 emp., Apparel screen printing & embroidery (215) 416-9881
Smitteez Sportswear, 224 Main St., P.O. Box 274, Keansburg 07734
Owner—James Smith, 4 emp., Apparel & athletic uniform screen printing (732) 787-5500
Sonscreen Graphics, Inc., 77 Tillman St., Raritan 08869
★ Owner—Ed Kozic, 4 emp., T-shirt screen printing & embroidery (908) 429-1657
Southern Ocean Marine Sportswear, 79 S. Main St., Ste. 2, Barnegat 08005
Owner—Sherry Haferbier, 4 emp., Manufacturer of embroidered & screen-printed (609) 698-8868
Sparkle Embroidery Monograms, 550 Bridgeton Pike, Ste. 12, Mantua 08051
Owner—Teri Warming, 5 emp., Apparel embroidery, monogramming & (856) 468-0304
Special T'S, 12 Kings Ct., Flemington 08822
Pres.—Ryan Amato, 15 emp., Custom & contract screen printing & (908) 806-8337
Sports Paradise, 4230 Route 130, Willingboro 08046
Pres.—Fred Streiber, 5 emp., Team sports uniform embroidery & screen (609) 877-1826
Sports Time, 40 Oak St., Norwood 07648
Pres.—Evan Baumgarten, 6 emp., Textile screen printing & embroidery (201) 768-1101
Star Embroidery Corp., 305 3rd Ave. W., Newark 07107
Owner, GM, Hum. Res. & IT Mgr.—Dean Gannet, 20 emp., Embroidery (973) 481-4300
Steve's Screen Printing, 660 Mitchell Ln., Martinsville 08836
Owner—Stephen Niederle, 1 emp., Textile, metal, plastic & wood screen (732) 469-7670
Stitch-It-Up Embroidery, 151 Fisher Rd., Mahwah 07430
★ Principal—Christine D. Domizio, 1 emp., Custom embroidery & apparel screen (201) 512-9881
Stylus Custom Apparel, Inc., 729 E. Elizabeth Ave., Linden 07036
Pres.—Domenic Muscillo, 4 emp., Custom embroidery & apparel screen (908) 587-0800
Sun Embroidery Screen Printing Co., 12 Route 50, P.O. Box 349, Ocean View 08230
Owner—Jennifer DeRosa, 2 emp., Textile screen printing & embroidery (609) 624-1231
Sun Tee, LLC, 25 Amity St., Ste. 1, Little Falls 07424
Pres.—Mark Babin, 11 emp., Screen printing & embroidery (973) 812-0349
Tone Embroidery, Inc., 333 Bergen Blvd., Fairview 07022
Pres.—Haim Sasson, 15 emp., Custom embroidery (201) 943-1082
Toni Embroidery Co., 475 Broadway, Westwood 07675
Owner—Tom Cornicelli, 5 emp., Embroidery (201) 664-6909
Totally T Shirts & More, 201 W. Hampton St., Pemberton 08068
Owner—Tony Miralglia, 5 emp., T-shirt screen printing, embroidery (609) 894-0011
Trenton Joe's Embroidery, 4 Scotch Rd., Ewing 08628
Owner—Joseph Chiarello, 7 emp., Embroidery, screen printing & promotional (609) 538-9450
Unionwear/New Jersey Headwear Corp., 305 3rd Ave. W., Ste. 5, Newark 07107
Pres.—Mitchell Cahn, 50 emp., Custom embroidered, screenprinted & (973) 497-0102
Unique Embroidery, Inc., 1030 Pleasantview Ter., Ridgefield 07657
Pres.—Robby Moutran, 11 emp., Custom embroidery & apparel & textile (201) 943-9191
UniServ Advertising, Inc., 37 State Route 35 N., Neptune 07753
Pres.—Glen Suchecki, 11 emp., Apparel & promotional item screen printing (732) 774-1010
University Apparel, Inc., 2501 Mount Holly Rd., Ste. 262, Burlington 08016
Pres.—Jerry Hamm, 2 emp., Fraternal embroidery & lettering, Masonic (609) 871-3601
University Fashions, 1888 Winslow Rd., Bldg. B, Williamstown 08094
Owner & Pres.—Ulysses James, 7 emp., Textile screen printing & embroidery (856) 228-1615
Weber & Doebrich, Inc., 119 61st St., West New York 07093
Pres.—Jane Zellweger, 3 emp., Embroidery (201) 867-1540
What A Tee 2, Inc., 82 Sussex St., Hackensack 07601
Pres.—Harry Poulas, 10 emp., T-shirt screen printing & embroidery (201) 457-0060
William Usdan & Sons LLC, 140 Little St., Belleville 07109
Pres.—Simon Markman, 5 emp., Paper & fabric converting & distributor (973) 844-9988
Wisco Promo & Uniform, Inc., 160 Route 46 E., Saddle Brook 07663
Pres.—Anthony Park, 4 emp., Embroidery & screen printing (973) 767-2022
World's Finest, Inc., 267 Hamilton Ave., Trenton 08609
Pres.—Pat Turner, 3 emp., Textile embroidery & silkscreening (609) 394-8001
Wostbrock Embroidery, Inc., 11 Paterson Ave., Midland Park 07432
Pres.—Henry Wostbrock, 4 emp., Embroidery (201) 445-3074
Xpresa Labels Corp., 681 Eagle Rock Ave., West Orange 07052
Pres.—Tamer Ozaydin, 10 emp., Labels, including woven, adhesive woven (973) 669-8444
Yippee Printing & Marketing, 115 River Rd., Bldg. 10, Edgewater 07020
Manager—Shawn Spellbring, 4 emp., Screen, offset & digital printing & (201) 313-1900
Zeek's Tees, 515 Highway 36, Belford 07718
Owner—Frank Zechman, 6 emp., Textile embroidery, screen & digital (732) 291-2700

## 2396 Automotive & apparel trimmings

A & S Screen Printing, LP, 2305-B Garry Rd., Riverton 08077
★ Owner—James Daly, 3 emp., T-shirt screen printing (609) 267-4830
A A Patchworks, Inc. (H Q), 311 Mechanic St., Boonton 07005
Pres.—Frank Wagenhoffer, 8 emp., Corporate headquarters; embroidered (973) 810-2121
A.B. Tees Screen Printing, LLC, 7 Sherman Ave., 3rd Fl., Jersey City 07307
Pres.—Anthony Blunda, Jr., 4 emp., Custom & contract textile screen printing (201) 239-0022
A.C. Printed Sportswear, Inc., 1319 Memorial Ave., Atlantic City 08401
Pres.—Edward Dinick Antonia, 2 emp., T-shirt screen printing (609) 344-5057
A-1 Advanced Marking Technologies, LLC, 1420 Route 53, P.O. Box 485, Mount Tabor 07878
Pres., Off. & Plt. Mgr.—Cynthia Hopping, 12 emp., Hot stamping, screen printing & pad (973) 627-0155
A2Z Emblems, LLC, 125 W. Route 130 N., Ste. C, Burlington 08016
Owner—Annette Zelauskas, 4 emp., Apparel & garment screen printing & (609) 239-9800
A-Aaabacus Printing & Promotional Specialties Of Metuchen, 243 Amboy Ave., Metuchen 08840
Owner—Sam H. Van Chama, 2 emp., Commercial printing, binding & graphic (732) 767-9204
Abilitees Unlimited, Inc., 23 Adams St., Metuchen 08840
Owner & Pres.—Helen Lenihan, 8 emp., Textile embroidery & screen & offset (732) 494-1513
Abilities Of Northwest Jersey, Inc., 264 Route 31 N., P.O. Box 251, Washington 07882
CEO—Cindy Wildermuth, 300 emp., Contract packaging/fulfillment, including (908) 689-1118
Accent Apparel LLC, 405 Atlantic City Blvd., Beachwood 08722
Owner—Kevin McMahon, 3 emp., Embroidery, screen printing & direct-to-garme (732) 341-7576
Accurate Flannel Bag Co., Inc., 468 Totowa Ave., Ste. 3, Paterson 07522
Pres.—Fred Baron, 125 emp., Custom bags & pouches, including dustcovers (973) 720-1800
Ace Screen Printing, LLC, 24 High St. W., Glassboro 08028
★ Owner—Adam Szyfman, 4 emp., T-shirt screen printing & embroidery (856) 881-1188
Action Screen Printing, 151 Main St., Franklin 07416
Ptnr.—Wayne Carney, 4 emp., Textile screen & pad printing (973) 209-2491
Active Imprints, 4266 U.S. Highway 1, Monmouth Junction 08852
Pres.—Duane Watlington, 9 emp., Custom imprinted promotional products (732) 329-2613
Adpro Imprints, Inc., 3411 Rose Ave., Ocean 07712
Pres.—Peter L. Demaree, Jr., 5 emp., Textile screen printing, embroidery (732) 493-8555
ADV Promos & More, LLC, 12 Baltusrol St., Hamilton Square 08690
Owner—Andrea M. Anepete, 1 emp., Custom printed promotional products (609) 587-7500
AKA, Inc., 1324 New Market Ave., South Plainfield 07080
Pres.—Michael Allocco, 6 emp., Screen printing & embroidery, exterior (908) 753-8112
Alete Printing, LLC, 722 Dartmouth Ct., P.O. Box 371, Wenonah 08090
V-P., CEO—John Koskinen, 4 emp., Commercial & variable data printing (856) 468-3536
Alfred's Sport Shop, 32 Main St., Madison 07940
GM—Chuck Bleakley, 6 emp., Baseball, softball & lacrosse equipment (973) 377-0051
All Nu Trophy & Screen Printing, 243 Teaneck Rd., Ridgefield Park 07660
Owner—Alan Jones, 13 emp., Plastic & textile screen printing & (201) 807-0808
All Sports Stadium, LLC, 297 Route 31 S., Washington 07882
Pres.—Armin Kososki, 7 emp., Textile screen printing & embroidery (908) 689-0411
Alpha T'S, Inc., 380 Totowa Rd., 2nd Fl., Totowa 07512
Pres.—Sal Mancini, 2 emp., Textile screen printing, embroidery (973) 956-7243
American Images, LLC, 1910 Fairfax Ave., Cherry Hill 08003
Pres.—Wayne Baw, 4 emp., Textile screen printing (856) 424-3944
American Screen Printing, 272 Kent Ave., Wayne 07470
Pres.—Howard Bischoff, 1 emp., Textile screen printing & signs (973) 471-0206
American Youth Enterprises, Inc., 120 Marlin Ln., P.O. Box 653, Mays Landing 08330
Pres.—David Hagan, 8 emp., Promotional products screen printing (609) 909-1900
Apollo East, Inc., 7895 Airport Hwy., Pennsauken 08110
Pres.—Dora Ngan, 20 emp., Textile screen printing & embroidery (856) 486-1882
Apparel Group America, Inc., 250 Belmont Ave., Haledon 07508
Pres.—Vincent Musarra, 120 emp., Apparel screen printing & packaging (973) 942-6800

S.I.C.

Apparel Zone, Inc., 165 Amboy Rd., Ste. 505, Morganville 07751
Pres.—Todd Berman, 5 emp., *Apparel embroidery & screen printing* (732) 441-7780
Art Graphics, 54 Delsea Dr. N., Glassboro 08028
Ptnr.—Art Dorn, 3 emp., *Textile screen printing, embroidery* (856) 881-5029
Artist Above The Rest, 4490 Nottingham Way, Trenton 08690
Owner—John Brennan, 1 emp., *Decals, textile & plastic screen printing* (609) 586-7247
Art's Embroidery, LLC, 175 Monmouth Rd., West Long Branch 07764
Ptnr.—Ina Kraucis, 4 emp., *Embroidery, screen printing & sports* (732) 870-1155
Atlantic Screenprinting, 339 Fairview Ave., Westwood 07675
Pres., Sales Mgr.—Ken Kristofick, 4 emp., *Textile screen printing* (201) 383-0995
Ayr Graphics & Printing, Inc., 320 Chestnut St., Roselle Park 07204
Pres.—Carl Gamba, 8 emp., *Offset, color & digital printing &* (908) 241-8118
Aztec Graphics, Inc., 420 Whitehead Rd., Trenton 08619
Pres.—Ronald Balerno, 15 emp., *Screenprinted & embroidered sportswear* (609) 587-1000
Bad Dog T'S, 498 Kinderkamack Rd., River Edge 07661
Owner—Frank Pugliese, 5 emp., *Textile screen printing* (201) 599-2030
Bailey's Printing, Inc., 191 Throckmorton St., Freehold 07728
Pres.—Randy Bailey, 2 emp., *Commerical & screen printing & custom* (732) 462-8010
Balcis Screen Printing, 219 Wanaque Ave., Pompton Lakes 07442
★ Owner—Martin Balbuana, 4 emp., *T-shirt & promotional item screen printing* (973) 835-9948
Bantle's Banners & Signs, 213 Clements Bridge Rd., Barrington 08007
Owner—Janice Bantle, 3 emp., *Street, door, window & magnetic vehicle* (856) 546-1112
BCS Machine & Mfg. Corp., 3575 Kennedy Rd., South Plainfield 07080
Pres.—Sal Capparelli, 10 emp., *CNC & general machining job shop, including* (908) 561-1656
Bergen Screen Printing, Inc., 255 W. Broadway, Paterson 07522
Pres.—Uday Patel, 5 emp., *Screen & wide-format digital printing* (973) 595-1222
Black Universities Supply Shop, The, 410 Leland Ave., Plainfield 07062
Pres., CEO—Rubye Hickerson, 4 emp., *Customized clothing, apparel & accessories* (908) 754-8088
Blue Streak Screen Printing Co., 33 E. Railroad Ave., Monroe Township 08831
Pres.—James Craparotta, 3 emp., *Textile screen printing & custom embroidery* (732) 656-0400
Bon-Jour Group, LLC, 1100 Blanch Ave., Norwood 07648
Owner & Pres.—Michael Tchertchian, 17 emp., *Embroidery & screen printing of promotional* (201) 646-1070
Boy On A Dolphin Corp., 308 State Route 36, Port Monmouth 07758
Owner—Harry Karatzia, 2 emp., *Embroidery & screen printing* (732) 495-2200
Branded Screen Printing, LLC, 45 Warren St., P.O. Box 687, Chester 07930
Pres.—Chris Smith, 5 emp., *Textile screen printing* (908) 879-7411
Brown & Co., Inc., Bill, 275 Whitehead Rd., Hamilton 08619
★ Off. Mgr.—Ken Bruce, 2 emp., *T-shirt & textile & promotional item* (609) 396-9191
Camden Printworks, 1621 S. Broadway, Camden 08104
GM—Adam Woods, 8 emp., *Custom t-shirt & sweatshirt screen* (856) 365-1424
Cameo Novelty & Pen, 400 Hillside Ave., Hillside 07205
Pres.—Sol Oberlander, 20 emp., *Promotional product screen printing* (973) 923-1600
Campus Coordinates, 1711 Ginesi Dr., Ste. 1, Freehold 07728
GM—Kevin Drake, 8 emp., *Textile screen printing* (732) 866-6060
Carol's Creations, LLC, 112 Kipling Rd., Cherry Hill 08003
★ Owner—Carol Decuzzi, 2 emp., *Custom & one-off apparel & textile* (856) 428-0621
Cervinis, Inc., 3656 N. Mill Rd., Vineland 08360
Pres.—Dan Cervinis, 65 emp., *Fiberglass automotive products* (856) 691-1744
Clarici Digital, 88 Youngs Rd., Mercerville 08619
Owner & Pres.—Gene Clarici, Jr., 25 emp., *Screenprinted graphics, digital printing* (609) 587-7204
Class Act Embroidery, 86 N. Beverwyck Rd., Ste. A, Lake Hiawatha 07034
Owner—Kathy Breslow, 5 emp., *Textile screen printing & embroidery* (973) 394-0045
Color Flo Graphics Corp., 10 Dell Glen Ave., Ste. 1, Lodi 07644
Owner & GM—Peter Young, 15 emp., *Textile screen printing* (201) 525-0105
Color Screen Pros, 100 Verona Ave., Newark 07104
Owner—Oscar Cano, 8 emp., *Apparel & promotional item screen printing* (973) 268-5080
Colorcraft Sign Co., 400 Magnolia St., Beverly 08010
Owner—Steve Molnar, 8 emp., *Full-color graphics, vinyl, vehicle* (609) 386-1115
Comp24, LLC, 190 Jony Dr., Carlstadt 07072
★ Dir., Opers.—Paul Rosenblit, 28 emp., *Company headquarters & textile screen* (201) 716-5200
Concept Printing, Inc., 160 Woodbine St., Ste. 2, Bergenfield 07621
Pres.—Kerry Monahan-Gaughan, 6 emp., *Offset & screen printing, embroidery* (201) 387-6000
Cosmic Custom Screen Printing, LLC, 1629 N. Black Horse Pike, Williamstown 08094
Pres.—Jessica Craig, 2 emp., *Textile screen printing* (856) 629-8337
Craftmaster Printing, Inc., 2024 Corlies Ave., Neptune 07753
Pres.—Curtis Baumgartner, 4 emp., *Corporate headquarters & single-color* (732) 775-0011
Creative Embroidery Corp., 305 3rd Ave. W., Ste. 3, Newark 07107
★ Pres.—Steve Diamond, 20 emp., *Custom apparel screen printing & embroidery* (973) 497-5700
Creative Screen Design, 531 Route 68, P.O. Box 369, Columbus 08022
Owner—Cathy Cox, 2 emp., *Textile screen printing, embroidery* (609) 424-3334
C-Sports, 2045 S. Black Horse Pike, Williamstown 08094
Owner—Mark Cannon, 2 emp., *Textile screen printing & embroidery* (856) 875-5680
Custom Embroidery, 73 E. New Jersey Ave., P.O. Box 1489, Pleasantville 08232
Owner—Catherine Carbor, 12 emp., *Embroidery & textile screen printing* (609) 383-9292
Custom Graphics, Inc., 71 W. Landis Ave., Vineland 08360
Pres.—Jim McMahon, 19 emp., *Textile screen printing* (856) 691-7858
D and S Designs, P.O. Box 1707, Bridgeton 08302
Owner—Sandra L. Rodriguez, 2 emp., *Custom screen printing & embroidery* (856) 451-0954
Dead End Screen Prints, Inc., 266 Lewis St., North Plainfield 07060
Pres.—Rudy Basso, 3 emp., *T-shirt, hat, sweatshirt, jacket &* (908) 754-4552
Deblyn Screen Printers, 717 Mountain Blvd., Watchung 07069
Ptnr.—Debra Buhot, 2 emp., *Textile screen printing & embroidery* (908) 756-8459
DeMario Design & Screen Printing, 619 Church St., Pleasantville 08232
Pres.—Richard Pitts, 10 emp., *Apparel screen printing & embroidery* (609) 645-7319
Denali Co., LLC, The (H Q), 43 W. Front St., Ste. 11, Red Bank 07701
Pres.—Ken Lindemann, 3 emp., *Company headquarters; award ribbons* (732) 219-7771
Dependabilities Screen Printing, 632 Hulses Corner Rd., Howell 07731
Owner—Don Green, 4 emp., *T-shirt & school uniform screen printing* (732) 886-0800
Designer T'S, 1165 Marlkress Rd., Ste. F, Cherry Hill 08003
Owner—James Kelly, 40 emp., *T-shirt screen printing* (856) 751-4545
Design-N-Stitch, Inc., 194 Atlantic St., Hackensack 07601
Ptnr. & Pres.—John Fitzpatrick, 8 emp., *Screen printing & embroidery of t-shirts* (201) 488-1314
Designs By James, 892 N. Delsea Dr., Vineland 08360
Pres.—James Crescenzo, 3 emp., *Interior & exterior signs, screen printing* (856) 692-1316
Dezine Line, Inc., 1104 Route 46 E., Ledgewood 07852
Pres.—Steve Mattero, 6 emp., *Textile screen printing & embroidery* (973) 989-1009
Direct Development, LLC, 1338 State Route 36, Hazlet 07730
★ Owner—Vinod Gopal, 8 emp., *Commercial, promotional & apparel screen* (732) 739-8890
Dolly Screen Printing, Inc., 1-19 Elm St., Freehold 07728
Pres.—Mike Dolly, 9 emp., *Textile screen printing & embroidery* (732) 294-8979
Donray Printing, 2 Eastmans Rd., Parsippany 07054
Pres.—Ray Ferriola, 18 emp., *Textile & apparel sublimation printing* (973) 515-8100
Dot Graphix, Inc., 79 S. Main St., Ste. 13, Barnegat 08005
★ Pres.—Joe Lopes, 10 emp., *T-shirt screen printing* (609) 660-0087
Dr. T-Shirt, 221 Parker Ave., Manasquan 08736
Pres.—Robert Giaquinto, 3 emp., *T-shirt screen printing & embroidery* (732) 223-3866
Eagle Embroidery & Graphix, 587 White Horse Pike, Hammonton 08037
Owner—Phyllis Mazzeo, 1 emp., *Textile screen printing & custom embroidery* (609) 561-1457
East Coast Custom, 242 Main St., Sayreville 08872
Pres.—Mark Tesca, 5 emp., *Textile embroidery & screen printing* (732) 390-8238
Easy Prints, Inc., 172 Main St., Metuchen 08840
★ Owner—Darren Swan, 5 emp., *T-shirt screen printing & embroidery* (848) 229-2410
Elmwood Industries, 8 Paul Kohner Pl., Elmwood Park 07407
Supervisor—Diane Zirpoli, 2 emp., *Apparel screen printing & embroidery* (201) 703-1220
Embroider This Co., 7 Duck Point Trl., Wharton 07885
Owner—Donna Sanderson, 3 emp., *Embroidery, screen printing & heat* (973) 663-5551
Empire Designs, Inc., 7 Main St., Englishtown 07726
Pres.—Kathleen T. Bien, 1 emp., *Embroidery, screen printing, promotional* (732) 446-6447
Engraver's Bench & Greek Unique, Inc., 1212 Raymond Blvd., Newark 07102
Owner & Pres.—Willie J. Williams, 3 emp., *Metal, wood, plastic & glass engraving* (973) 297-1810
ERL Embroidery & Screen Printing, 8 Evergreen Dr., Lincoln Park 07035
CEO—Michael Hackett, 2 emp., *Textile embroidery & screen printing* (973) 633-7428
EVR Screen Printing, 217 W. Peach St., Ste. 2, Vineland 08360
Owner—Ehren Vonreuter, 2 emp., *Textile screen printing* (856) 794-8118
Excel Silk Screening, 2320 Old York Rd., Bordentown 08505
Pres.—Brian Noble, 1 emp., *Apparel screen printing & embroidery* (609) 499-4990
Expert Tees, 1585 Highway 73, Pennsauken 08110
Owner—Mike Broome, 1 emp., *Textile screen printing* (609) 828-0515
Extreme Concepts, LLC, 75 E. Cherry St., Ste. 9-B, Rahway 07065
Ptnr. & Member—Joe Esses, 10 emp., *Apparel screen printing* (732) 381-5100
Falls Screen Printing, Inc., 25 Amity St., Little Falls 07424
Pres.—Jay Brady, 4 emp., *Textile screen printing & embroidery* (973) 812-0555
Family Screen Printing, Inc., 104 W. Browning Rd., Bellmawr 08031
Pres.—Bob Armstrong, 6 emp., *Apparel screen printing & embroidery* (856) 933-2780
Fancy Threads, 31 Railroad Pl., Hopewell 08525
Owner—Debbie Varbasse, 1 emp., *Embroidery & textile screen printing* (609) 466-0050
Farrier Sporting Goods, Inc., Godwin & Crescent Aves., Wyckoff 07481
Pres.—Charles Coleman, 4 emp., *Sports & athletic equipment, footwear* (201) 891-9520
Finesse & Lucas, 40 Chestnut St., Ste. 14, Lakewood 08701
Pres.—Luz A. Fredes, 2 emp., *Embroidery & screen printing* (732) 367-0839
First Impressions Screen Printing, 1703 State Route 27, Edison 08817
Owner—Bill Miers, 2 emp., *Textile screen printing & embroidery* (732) 777-7872
Fleck Knitwear Co., Inc., 400 Leland Ave., Plainfield 07062
Pres., Mfg. Mgr.—Peter Fleck, 15 emp., *Knit blankets, afghans, sweaters, children's* (908) 754-8888
Flying Fish Studio, 130 Park Blvd., Cape May 08204
Owner—Sue Lotozo, 4 emp., *Textile screen printing* (609) 884-2760
Flying T-Shirts, 217 1st Ave., Cape May Court House 08210
Owner—Edward Donnelly, 2 emp., *T-shirt screen printing* (609) 463-0397
G & M Printwear, 549 S. Broadway St., Gloucester City 08030
Owner—Robert Dill, 5 emp., *Textile screen printing* (856) 742-5551
Galaxy Glass & Stone, 277 Fairfield Rd., P.O. Box 10154, Fairfield 07004
Pres., CEO—Eugene M. Negrin, 35 emp., *Custom & decorative architectural glass* (973) 575-3440
Gariel Screen Printing, 729 Mantua Pike, Woodbury 08096
Owner—Gary Lizzi, 7 emp., *T-shirt screen printing & embroidery* (856) 848-3240
Gem Sports, 36-10 Broadway, Fair Lawn 07410
Pres.—Michael Cebulski, 4 emp., *Textile screen printing & embroidery* (201) 791-1776
Gilby's Screen Print, 615 Ringwood Ave., Pompton Lakes 07442
Owner—Patrick Smith, 4 emp., *T-shirt screen printing* (973) 835-5729
Gough Engraving & Advertising Specialties, 1745 N. Olden Avenue Ext., Ewing 08638
Owner—Kathleen Gough, 4 emp., *Brass & plastic engraving, award plaques* (609) 882-8700
Harmony Printing, 504 Aldrich Rd., Ste. 22, Howell 07731
Owner & CEO—Bill Blake, 4 emp., *Promotional item & apparel, garment* (732) 987-9040
Hollie Studios, 200-C Valentine, P.O. Box 530, Hackettstown 07840
Owner—John Mandick, 4 emp., *Textile screen printing* (908) 852-7263
House Printing, LLC, 311 Kearny Ave., Kearny 07032
★ Owner—Juan Calva, 1 emp., *T-shirt screen printing & embroidery* (201) 772-5988
Image Screen Printing, Inc., 532 Lincoln Blvd., Middlesex 08846
Pres., CFO—Gary Mangee, 8 emp., *Textile screen printing & embroidery* (732) 560-1817
Imagepoint Screen Printing, 69 Water St., Newton 07860
Owner & Pres.—John Fernicola, 12 emp., *Custom imprinted apparel* (908) 684-1768
Imagery Embroidery Corporation, 2907-2911 Jeannette St., Union City 07087
Pres.—Eddison S. Cruz, 10 emp., *Machined & digitized embroidery, monogramming* (201) 343-9333
Imprint Specialties, Inc., 601 New Broadway, Brooklawn 08030
Pres.—Francis Ferry, 5 emp., *Commercial screen printing & awards* (856) 456-2999
Imprintz Custom Printed Graphics, Inc., Garfield & Decatur Sts., P.O. Box 315, Beverly 08010
Pres.—Leah Arter, 4 emp., *Screen printing* (609) 386-5673
Infinite Print, 225 New York Ave., Jersey City 07307
Owner—Robert Pracht, 1 emp., *Textile screen printing* (862) 668-3094
Infinite Visions, LLC, 40 Enterprise Ave. N., Secaucus 07094
Owner—Mark Summers, 100 emp., *Textile screen printing* (201) 866-6946
Initial Impact, 516 Warren Ave., Spring Lake 07762
Pres.—Donna Szakats, 3 emp., *Promotional screen printing & embroidery* (732) 449-4922
InnerWorkings, Inc., 7 Joanna Ct., Ste. H, East Brunswick 08816
Br. Mgr.—Sam Wilk, 30 emp., *Screen printing of promotional items* (732) 651-8822
J & G Enterprises, Inc., 182 High St., Nutley 07110
Principal & Manager—John Mancini, 1 emp., *Custom apparel embroidery & screen* (973) 667-7673
J K Printing, 310 Edgewood Ave., Teaneck 07666
Owner—Joseph Korn, 2 emp., *Commercial printing & apparel screen* (201) 833-8181
J. R.'s Screen Printing, 1930 Greenwood Lake Tpke., P.O. Box 561, Hewitt 07421
Owner, Hum. Res. & IT Mgr.—John Reape, Jr., 2 emp., *Textile screen printing & embroidery.* (973) 728-7802
JABS Personal Stitch, Inc., 1120 Raritan Rd., Clark 07066
Ptnr.—Joseph Arancio, 2 emp., *Textile screen printing & embroidery* (732) 396-9699
Jetty Life, LLC, 1435 Route 539, Unit A-6, Tuckerton 08087
★ CEO—Jeremy Defilippis, 5 emp., *T-shirt screen printing* (609) 296-2411
Jill's Thrill, Inc., 18 Hardley Dr., Cranbury 08512
Pres.—John Wiegand, 2 emp., *Apparel screen printing & embroidery* (609) 395-9900
Jory Engravers, Inc., 23 W. Erie Ave., Rutherford 07070
GM—Gary Gagliardi, 3 emp., *Metal engraving, screen printing, metal* (201) 939-1546
Keltex Imprinted Apparel, Inc., 428-A Woodbine Oceanview Rd., Ocean View 08230
Pres.—Christopher Kelly, 25 emp., *Textile screen printing, embroidery* (609) 624-3252
KMBA Fashions, Inc., 272 Elmwood Ave., Bldg. 3, East Orange 07018
Pres.—William Cotton, Jr., 6 emp., *Screen printing & embroidery of men's* (973) 789-1652
Kraftwork Custom Design, 1837 S. Broad St., Hamilton 08610
Owner—Michael K. Sylvester, 4 emp., *Dimensional, carved, gold, neon, channel* (609) 848-0578

Lettermen, Inc., The, 1565 Route 37 W., Toms River 08755
Pres.—Rose Dixon, 8 emp., *Imprinted sportswear screen printing* ... (732) 608-0669

Life A Stitch, 37 Jackson Ave., Carteret 08008
★ Owner—Ray Malivuk, 2 emp., *Embroidery, t-shirt screen printing* ... (732) 969-0232

M&R Designs & Promotions, 21 Stone Oak Ln., Oak Ridge 07438
Owner—Doreen Scott, 4 emp., *Promotional products screen printing* ... (908) 928-9400

Margola Corp., 232 S. Van Brunt St., Englewood 07631
Owner—Neil Chalfin, 6 emp., *Manufacturer & distributor of rhinestones* ... (201) 816-9500

Mark Sports, 9 E. 31st St., Bayonne 07002
★ Owner—Dominick Landante, 2 emp., *T-shirt screen printing & embroidery* ... (201) 437-9900

Marmus, Inc., 51 E. Front St., Keyport 07735
Pres.—Terry Musson, 1 emp., *Textile screen, commercial, digital* ... (732) 264-3681

Maxtex, Inc., 159 N. Cooper Rd., West Berlin 08091
Pres.—Nick Macaroni, 5 emp., *Textile screen printing* ... (856) 767-7960

Mayos Sportswear, Inc., 1 Hollywood Ave., Bldg. 2-D, Ho-Ho-Kus 07423
Pres.—Bob Mainenti, 6 emp., *Textile screen printing & embroidery* ... (201) 652-8570

Metro Printing & Promotions, LLC, 311 Mechanic St., Boonton 07005
Owner—Steve Rotella, 6 emp., *T-shirt screen & offset printing* ... (973) 316-1600

Midland Screen Printing, Inc., 280 N. Midland Ave., Bldg. H, Saddle Brook 07663
Pres.—Robert Witrak, 15 emp., *Textile screen printing* ... (201) 703-0066

Minuteman Press, Inc./Windsor Graphics, 2100 Nottingham Way, Hamilton 08619
Owner—Anthony Loffredo, 4 emp., *Offset, screen & digital color printing* ... (609) 586-3838

MJ Corporate Sales, Inc., 109 W. Park Dr., Unit B, Mount Laurel 08054
★ Owner—John Dikmak, 25 emp., *Apparel screen printing & embroidery* ... (856) 778-0055

MJG Screen Printing & Embroidery, 24 Commerce Rd., Ste. K, Fairfield 07004
Owner—Michael Garamella, 4 emp., *T-shirt screen printing & embroidery* ... (973) 575-8877

Modern Graphics, 547 Cross Keys Rd., Ste. B, Sicklerville 08081
Owner—William Glendening II, 1 emp., *Custom screen printing & embroidery* ... (856) 728-6300

Monogram Center, 437 Amboy Ave., Perth Amboy 08861
Ptnr.—Bill Kramer, 35 emp., *Textile screen printing, embroidery* ... (732) 442-1800

Monogram Madness, 50 Main St., Succasunna 07876
Owner—Peggy Kiefer, 2 emp., *Embroidery & screen printing* ... (973) 927-5278

MPT Industries, 85 Franklin Rd., Hamilton Bus. Park, Ste. 6-B, Dover 07801
Owner & Pres.—Michael Trueba, Jr., 7 emp., *Automotive covers & lubricants* ... (973) 989-9220

Murray's Uniforms, Inc., 312 Main St., Bradley Beach 07720
Pres.—Andrew Bartlett, 3 emp., *Textile screen printing & embroidery* ... (732) 774-2671

Na-Vet Printing Co., 506 Elizabeth Ave., Elizabeth 07206
Pres.—Larry Franchini, 4 emp., *Commercial, digital & color printing* ... (908) 353-4441

New Jersey Logowear, 100 McKinley Ave., Ste. 6, Manahawkin 08050
★ Ptnr.—Keith Anderson, 7 emp., *Promotional item, apparel & textile* ... (609) 597-9400

New Rose, Inc., 1500 Almonesson Rd., Ste. 8, Woodbury 08096
Pres.—Rosemary Jones, 3 emp., *Embroidery & apparel, garment, textile* ... (856) 812-0509

Newton Printing & Embroidery, 75 Main St., Franklin 07416
Owner—Frank Newton, 10 emp., *Promotional & corporate branding products* ... (973) 827-2006

Norgus Silk Screen Co., 58 Sylvan Ave., Clifton 07011
Owner & Pres.—Sanjay Thakker, 8 emp., *Screen, cylindrical, digital & large-format* ... (973) 365-0600

Northwest Essex Community Healthcare Network, Inc., 83 Walnut St., Montclair 07042
GM & Prod. Mgr.—William Delorenzo, 125 emp., *Contract assembly, packaging & screen* ... (973) 744-7733

O. Co Imprints, LLC, 58 W. Bergen Pl., P.O. Box 8249, Red Bank 07701
Owner—Olivia Conklin, 3 emp., *Screen printed & embroidered garments* ... (732) 530-3202

Oasis Studios, LLC, 244 Quakertown Rd., P.O. Box 306, Quakertown 08868
Ptnr.—Joe Muller, 2 emp., *Textile screen printing, embroidery* ... (908) 735-5089

Odd-It-Tees, 405 S. Main St., Forked River 08731
Owner—William Austin, 4 emp., *Textile screen printing* ... (609) 693-8337

Old Hights Print Shop, Inc., 133 S. Main St., Hightstown 08520
Pres.—Cathy M. Simmons, 3 emp., *Commercial, digital & screen printing* ... (609) 443-4700

Olde Granddad Industries, 1 Market St., Passaic 07055
Owner—Mike Kostak, 10 emp., *Automotive mats, air fresheners & accessories* ... (201) 997-1899

One Stop Printing, LLC, 135 Kearny Ave., Ste. B, Kearny 07032
Owner—Darwin Yamuca, 2 emp., *Commercial printing, t-shirt screen* ... (201) 991-3320

P. J. Screening & Embroidery, 689 Jaques Ave., Rahway 07065
Pres.—Angela Guden, 2 emp., *Textile screen printing & embroidery* ... (732) 382-5183

Parrish Sign Co., Inc., 2242 S. Delsea Dr., Vineland 08360
Pres.—Charles Parrish, 9 emp., *Full color, digitally printed, lighted* ... (856) 696-4040

Personalized Paraphernalia, 128 Division St., Somerville 08876
Owner & Pres.—Laura Wolfe, 3 emp., *Embroidery & screen printing* ... (908) 526-0602

Photo Art Stencil & Sign Corp., 701 17th Ave., P.O. Box 127, Lake Como 07719
Pres.—Frederick J. Tanis, 2 emp., *Industrial & yard signs & screen printing* ... (732) 681-7300

Precision Sign Works, LLC, 82 Richter Rd., Tabernacle 08088
Owner—Victor Gorin, 3 emp., *Exterior, carved, site & yard signs* ... (609) 702-9700

Premier Printing Solutions, 508 Raritan St., Sayreville 08872
Ptnr. & V-P., Opers.—Edward Ciak, 3 emp., *Commercial printing & silkscreen printing* ... (732) 525-0740

Printmasters, 1108 Goffle Rd., Hawthorne 07506
Pres.—Paula Cornett, 4 emp., *Business printing, graphics & design* ... (973) 427-6598

Printology, 615 Franklin Tpke., Ste. 3, Ridgewood 07450
★ Pres.—Jon Bognar, 4 emp., *Commercial & t-shirt screen printing* ... (201) 345-4632

Pro Image Promotions, Inc., 489 U.S. Highway 46, Kenvil 07847
Pres.—Brian Hewitt, 4 emp., *Promotional textile screen printing* ... (973) 252-8000

Professional Images, LLC, 17 E. Linden Ave., Englewood 07631
Owner—Steve Nicholson, 1 emp., *Screen printing & embroidery of promotional* ... (201) 569-4251

Proforma Spectrum Graphics, 373 Route 46 W., Bldg. D, Ste. 130, Fairfield 07004
Pres.—John Vento, 20 emp., *Company headquarters & business form* ... (973) 882-8666

Promo Advertising, 1174 Chestnut St., Union 07083
Pres.—Sharon Zhang, 5 emp., *Apparel screen printing & embroidery* ... (908) 810-8888

Promo Graphics, Inc., 24 Howard St., Piscataway 08854
Pres.—Debra Rossello, 7 emp., *Custom textile & graphic substrate* ... (732) 629-7300

Promotions & Unicorns Too, Inc., 71 W.Main St., Ste. 102, Freehold 07728
Pres.—Robert Einhorn, 5 emp., *Promotional item, apparel, garment* ... (732) 308-3444

Pyramid Imprints, 28 N. Washington Ave., Bergenfield 07621
Owner—Eleanor Garcia, 2 emp., *Commercial screen printing, textile* ... (201) 384-0336

R & D Promotions, Ltd., 164 Van Liew Ave., Milltown 08850
★ Owner—Rick Dadika, 3 emp., *T-shirt screen printing* ... (732) 828-7408

Red Diamond Co., Inc., 368 Cortlandt St., Belleville 07109
Pres.—Marc Tartaglia, 5 emp., *Textile screen printing* ... (973) 759-2700

Reunion Gifts, 20 Lowell Ave., Summit 07901
Owner—Jerome Hairston, 2 emp., *Apparel screen printing, including* ... (877) 873-8646

RKM Enterprises, Inc., 177 Mercer St., Hightstown 08520
Pres.—Dave Babcock, 4 emp., *Textile screen printing & embroidery* ... (609) 448-7539

Rocky's T'S, 61 N. Hook Rd., Pennsville 08070
★ Owner—Rocky Demry, 1 emp., *T-shirt screen printing* ... (856) 678-2535

Rutler Screen Printing, Inc., 169 Belview Rd., Phillipsburg 08865
Pres. & V-P.—Allen Shubert, 22 emp., *Screen printing* ... (908) 859-3327

S & P Tees, 14 Frederick St., Hackensack 07601
Owner & Pres.—Paul Tortorici, 1 emp., *Textile screen printing* ... (201) 996-1411

S & W Custom Screen Printing, 147 Main St., Hackettstown 07840
Pres., GM—Justin Weiss, 5 emp., *T-shirt screen printing* ... (908) 852-4808

Screen Creations Plus, 8 Hillside Ave., Newton 07860
Owner—Dawn Alvarez, 2 emp., *Textile screen printing & embroidery* ... (973) 579-5015

Screen Play, Inc., 1275 Bloomfield Ave., Ste. 5, Fairfield 07004
Pres.—Stephen Wacker, 4 emp., *T-shirt screen printing* ... (973) 227-9014

Screen Reproductions Co., Inc., 850 Washington Ave., Carlstadt 07072
Pres., Fin., GM & R & D Mgr.—Larry Wiessenburg, 20 emp., *Vinyl wallpaper screen printing.* (201) 935-0830

Screen Tech Of New Jersey, Inc., 1800 W. Blancke St., Linden 07036
Pres.—Bob Barron, 30 emp., *Glass silk screening* ... (908) 862-8000

Screening Base, 245 W. Broadway, Paterson 07522
★ Pres.—Michael Thompson, 2 emp., *Apparel screen printing* ... (973) 389-7950

Semel's Embroidery & Screen Printing, Inc., 1078 U.S. Highway 46, Clifton 07013
Chrm.—Charlotte Semel, 25 emp., *Contract vintage chain-stitch embroidery* ... (973) 473-3959

Service Apex, 564-A Union Ave., Bridgewater 08807
★ Pres.—Ken Griggs, 10 emp., *Commercial printing, t-shirt screen* ... (732) 560-2222

Sew Ann Sew Thomas Enterprises, 153 Pearl St., Paterson 07501
Owner—Dailey G. Thomas, Jr., 2 emp., *Custom embroidery & screen printing* ... (973) 742-2664

Shelter Cove Embroidery Co., 1333 Bay Ave., Toms River 08753
Owner—Peggi Gamba, 3 emp., *T-shirt screen printing & embroidery* ... (732) 506-7700

Showcase Graphics, LLC, 33 E. Main St., Ste. 4, Moorestown 08057
Owner—Debra Marsdale, 3 emp., *Commercial & digital printing of packaging* ... (856) 722-5400

Sideline Sports, 2566 Plainfield Ave., Scotch Plains 07076
Owner—Imelda McEvoy, 2 emp., *Apparel screen printing & embroidery* ... (908) 322-9334

Sign Effectz, 800 New Brunswick Ave., Ste. 7, Rahway 07065
Owner & Pres.—Brian Snyder, 1 emp., *Signs, banners, decal printing, apparel* ... (732) 388-7446

Signarama, 655 S. White Horse Pike, Hammonton 08037
Owner—Richard Matteo, 3 emp., *Illuminated & non-illuminated full-color* ... (609) 878-3375

Signs & Lines Printing, 242 Gibbsboro Rd., Lindenwold 08021
Owner, Hum. Res. & IT Mgr.—Dan Krug, 2 emp., *Vinyl letter signs & textile screen* ... (856) 784-0400

Sir Speedy Printing Center, 122 Ridge Rd., Lyndhurst 07071
Dir.—Tom Penisch, 5 emp., *Full-color digital, traditional offset* ... (201) 896-2727

Skyline Graphics Design, 11 Skyline Lake Dr., Ringwood 07456
Pres.—Scott White, 4 emp., *Offset, digital & digital full-color* ... (973) 839-3329

Smith Enterprises, 8-A Deptford Rd., Glassboro 08028
Owner—Damian Smith, 4 emp., *Apparel screen printing & embroidery* ... (215) 416-9881

Smitteez Sportswear, 224 Main St., P.O. Box 274, Keansburg 07734
Owner—James Smith, 4 emp., *Apparel & athletic uniform screen printing* ... (732) 787-5500

Sonscreen Graphics, Inc., 77 Tillman St., Raritan 08869
★ Owner—Ed Kozic, 4 emp., *T-shirt screen printing & embroidery* ... (908) 429-1657

South Jersey Custom Screen Printing, 481 W. Route 38, Maple Shade 08052
Owner—Stan Jay, 2 emp., *Custom screen printing* ... (856) 482-1500

South Jersey Graphics, 203 W. Merchant St., Audubon 08106
Ptnr.—James Fleming, 5 emp., *T-shirt screen printing* ... (856) 546-0464

Southern Ocean Marine Sportswear, 79 S. Main St., Ste. 2, Barnegat 08005
Owner—Sherry Haferbier, 4 emp., *Manufacturer of embroidered & screen-printed* ... (609) 698-8868

Sparkle Embroidery Monograms, 550 Bridgeton Pike, Ste. 12, Mantua 08051
Owner—Teri Warming, 5 emp., *Apparel embroidery, monogramming &* ... (856) 468-0304

Special T'S, 12 Kings Ct., Flemington 08822
Pres.—Ryan Amato, 15 emp., *Custom & contract screen printing &* ... (908) 806-8337

Special-T-Graphics Of New Jersey, LLC, 3105 Bridge Ave., Point Pleasant 08742
Pres.—Sheryl Burke, 1 emp., *Textile screen printing, including* ... (732) 899-7240

Spoo, Inc., 225 NY Ave., Ste. 1, Jersey City 07307
Pres.—Chris Norelli, 1 emp., *Screen printing* ... (201) 420-0075

Sports Paradise, 4230 Route 130, Willingboro 08046
Pres.—Fred Streiber, 5 emp., *Team sports uniform embroidery & screen* ... (609) 877-1826

Sports Time, 40 Oak St., Norwood 07648
Pres.—Evan Baumgarten, 6 emp., *Textile screen printing & embroidery* ... (201) 768-1101

Stefan Enterprises, Inc., 141 Lanza Ave., Bldg. 16-E, Garfield 07026
Pres.—Stefan Missbrenner, 20 emp., *Textile printing* ... (973) 253-6005

Stelair Design Corp., 570 Broadway, Long Branch 07740
Pres.—Howard Steel, 1 emp., *Textile screen printing* ... (732) 571-3391

Steve's Screen Printing, 660 Mitchell Ln., Martinsville 08836
Owner—Stephen Niederle, 1 emp., *Textile, metal, plastic & wood screen* ... (732) 469-7670

Stitch-It-Up Embroidery, 151 Fisher Rd., Mahwah 07430
★ Principal—Christine D. Domizio, 1 emp., *Custom embroidery & apparel screen* ... (201) 512-9881

Stone Graphics Co., Inc., 5020 Industrial Rd., Farmingdale 07727
Pres.—Raymond C. Stone, 6 emp., *Screen printing, large-format digital* ... (732) 919-1111

Stylus Custom Apparel, Inc., 729 E. Elizabeth Ave., Linden 07036
Pres.—Domenic Muscillo, 4 emp., *Custom embroidery & apparel screen* ... (908) 587-0800

Sun Embroidery Screen Printing Co., 12 Route 50, P.O. Box 349, Ocean View 08230
Owner—Jennifer DeRosa, 2 emp., *Textile screen printing & embroidery* ... (609) 624-1231

Sun Tee, LLC, 25 Amity St., Ste. 1, Little Falls 07424
Pres.—Mark Babin, 11 emp., *Screen printing & embroidery* ... (973) 812-0349

Suzie Mac Specialties, Inc., 12-B Connery Ct., East Brunswick 08816
Pres.—Suzanne MacDougall, 9 emp., *Custom & screenprinted photoluminescent* ... (732) 238-3500

Swift Print Solutions, LLC, 405 Front St., Belvidere 07823
Owner—Linda Swift, 4 emp., *Commercial, screen & instant printing* ... (908) 475-1374

T D T Screen Design & Printing, Inc., 79 Whitehead Ave., South River 08882
Pres.—Geoffrey Di Agostino, 5 emp., *Textile screen printing* ... (732) 777-1377

Tee Shirt Guy, 507 E. 41st St., Paterson 07504
Owner—Rawle McCurdie, 4 emp., *Apparel screen printing* ... (973) 247-3442

Tees To Please Screen Printing, 15 Minneakoing Dr., P.O. Box 542, Flemington 08822
Owner—Greg Legacki, 10 emp., *T-shirt screen printing* ... (908) 788-5508

Too Many Stars, 134 E. Westfield Ave., Roselle Park 07204
★ Owner—Kristine Iraheta, 3 emp., *Apparel screen printing* ... (908) 445-8852

Totally T Shirts & More, 201 W. Hampton St., Pemberton 08068
Owner—Tony Miraglia, 5 emp., *T-shirt screen printing, embroidery* ... (609) 894-0011

Town Line Trophies, 2 Amberfield Dr., Delran 08075
Ptnr. & Off. Mgr.—Nancy Hagmaier, 3 emp., *Trophies, plaques, bronze castings,* ... (856) 461-0540

Trenton Joe's Embroidery, 4 Scotch Rd., Ewing 08628
Owner—Joseph Chiarello, 7 emp., *Embroidery, screen printing & promotional* ... (609) 538-9450

T-Rific Tees, LLC, 100 N. 12th St., Ste. 2, Kenilworth 07033
Pres.—Victor Herman, 12 emp., *Custom silk screen printing* ... (908) 272-5140

Unionwear/New Jersey Headwear Corp., 305 3rd Ave. W., Ste. 5, Newark 07107
Pres.—Mitchell Cahn, 50 emp., *Custom embroidered, screenprinted &* ... (973) 497-0102

Unique Embroidery, Inc., 1030 Pleasantview Ter., Ridgefield 07657
Pres.—Robby Moutran, 11 emp., *Custom embroidery & apparel & textile* ... (201) 943-9191

Unique Screen Printing Corp., Inc., 1016 McKinley St., Linden 07036
Pres.—Jose Grajeda, 30 emp., *Textile screen printing & novelties* ... (908) 925-3773

UniServ Advertising, Inc., 37 State Route 35 N., Neptune 07753
Pres.—Glen Suchecki, 11 emp., *Apparel & promotional item screen printing* ........ (732) 774-1010
Universal Silkscreen, Inc., 17 Memorial Dr., Paterson 07505
Pres.—Vince Tartaglione, 2 emp., *Textile screen printing* ........ (973) 221-0060
University Apparel, Inc., 2501 Mount Holly Rd., Ste. 262, Burlington 08016
Pres.—Jerry Hamm, 2 emp., *Fraternal embroidery & lettering, Masonic* ........ (609) 871-3601
University Fashions, 1888 Winslow Rd., Bldg. B, Williamstown 08094
Owner & Pres.—Ulysses James, 7 emp., *Textile screen printing & embroidery* ........ (856) 228-1615
Vacord Screen Printing, 1621 S. Broadway, Camden 08104
★ Owner—Stuart Brent, 2 emp., *Textile screen printing, including* ........ (888) 787-4587
Valaro's Screen Printing, 50 Mayetta Landing Rd., West Creek 08092
Owner—David Valaro, 1 emp., *Textile screen printing* ........ (609) 597-7075
Vernon Display Graphics, 145 Commerce Rd., Carlstadt 07072
Cont.—Todd Smith, 34 emp., *Screen printing & grand-format digital* ........ (201) 935-7117
Wagner Foto Screen Process, 4 Mark Rd., Kenilworth 07033
Pres.—Bob Masucci, 2 emp., *Screen printing of clothing* ........ (908) 624-0800
Walted Designs, Inc., 70 Spruce St., Ste. 8, Paterson 07501
Pres.—Bhibhishan Raghubir, 2 emp., *Narrow fabric printing* ........ (973) 881-1944
Walter's Signs, 159 W. White Horse Pike, Berlin 08009
Owner—Walter Schmitz, 2 emp., *Interior & exterior signs, commercial* ........ (856) 210-6324
What A Tee 2, Inc., 82 Sussex St., Hackensack 07601
Pres.—Harry Poulas, 10 emp., *T-shirt screen printing & embroidery* ........ (201) 457-0060
Wisco Promo & Uniform, Inc., 160 Route 46 E., Saddle Brook 07663
Pres.—Anthony Park, 4 emp., *Embroidery & screen printing* ........ (973) 767-2022
Work 'N' Wear Store, 73 Market St., Morristown 07960
Owner—Bob Hellreisel, 2 emp., *Textile screen printing* ........ (973) 267-2373
Works, The, 17 Claremont Rd., Bernardsville 07924
Owner—Bob Ditrani, 1 emp., *T-shirt screen printing* ........ (908) 766-7744
World's Finest, Inc., 267 Hamilton Ave., Trenton 08609
Pres.—Pat Turner, 3 emp., *Textile embroidery & silkscreening* ........ (609) 394-8001
Yesterwear Productions, Inc., 705 Smithville Rd., Lumberton 08048
Pres.—Cary Chasky, 50 emp., *T-shirt screen printing* ........ (609) 567-2544
Yippee Printing & Marketing, 115 River Rd., Bldg. 10, Edgewater 07020
Manager—Shawn Spellbring, 4 emp., *Screen, offset & digital printing &* ........ (201) 313-1900
Your Tops, Inc., 101 S. 21st St., Kenilworth 07033
Pres.—Gary Wiese, 2 emp., *Screen printing* ........ (908) 272-0011
Zeek's Tees, 515 Highway 36, Belford 07718
Owner—Frank Zechman, 6 emp., *Textile embroidery, screen & digital* ........ (732) 291-2700
Zone Two, Inc., 245 Hickory Ln., Bayville 08721
Pres.—Rick Gettis, 11 emp., *Textile screen printing* ........ (732) 237-0767

## 2397 Schiffli machine embroideries

Dearbrook Fabrics, Inc., 430 Walker St., P.O. Box 338, Fairview 07022
Pres.—Edward Parseghian, 10 emp., *Schiffli machine embroidery* ........ (201) 945-4141
Hamilton Embroidery, Inc., 907-909 21st St., Union City 07087
Pres.—Frank Blaso, 7 emp., *Schiffli machine embroideries & trims* ........ (201) 867-4084
Weber & Doebrich, Inc., 119 61st St., West New York 07093
Pres.—Jane Zellweger, 3 emp., *Embroidery* ........ (201) 867-1540

## 2399 Textile products—fabricated, nec

A & R Sewing Co., Inc., 451 Communipaw Ave., Jersey City 07304
Pres.—Jerry Ragoobir, 12 emp., *Contract sewing* ........ (201) 332-0622
Acadia Scenic, Inc., 130 Bay St., Jersey City 07302
Pres.—David Lawson, 25 emp., *Theatrical scenery buildings* ........ (201) 653-8889
Airborne Systems North America Of New Jersey, Inc., 5800 Magnolia Ave., Pennsauken 08109
Sr. V-P., Cust. Bus., N. America—Elizabeth Johnson, 125 emp., *Corporate headquarters & military ram-air* (856) 663-1275
American Fur Felt, LLC, 53 Rome St., Newark 07105
Pres.—Lucilio Pereira, 11 emp., *Fur felt cutting* ........ (973) 344-3026
Apollo Flags LLC, 594 Union Blvd., Totowa 07512
Ptnr.—Albert Potenzone, 4 emp., *Custom, U.S., military, state, parade* ........ (973) 256-8362
Apparel Distribution, Inc., 45 Saw Mill Pond Rd., Edison 08817
V-P.—Robert Shaw, 75 emp., *Apparel label sewing, pick ticket,* ........ (732) 287-1110
Artcraft Sign Studio, Inc., 738 W. Branch Ave., Pine Hill 08021
Pres., CFO, MIS Mgr.—Arthur Elkins, 5 emp., *Dimensional, sandblasted, carved, interior* ...... (856) 783-8008
Astro Sign Co., 230 E. High St., Route 322, Glassboro 08028
Pres.—Christopher Painter, 16 emp., *Signs, vehicle lettering, banners,* ........ (856) 881-4300
Atlas Auto Trim, Inc., 81 Highway 1, Edison 08817
Pres.—Sanford Dubin, 6 emp., *Automotive seat covers* ........ (732) 985-6800
Aura Badge Co., 264 Clayton Ave., Monroeville 08343
Owner & IT Mgr.—Phil Barbaro, 70 emp., *Promotional & identification products* ........ (856) 881-9026
Avanti Linens, Inc., 234 Moonachie Rd., Moonachie 07074
Chrm.—Arthur Tauber, 165 emp., *Embellished & bordered towels & kitchen* ........ (201) 641-7766
Bebe Chic, 530 Church St., Ridgefield 07657
Pres.—Caren Karpik, 8 emp., *Children's bedding & accessories* ........ (201) 941-5414
Brand & Oppenheimer Co., Inc., 188 E. Bergen Pl., Ste. 201, Red Bank 07701
Pres., CEO—Daniel Pezold, 6 emp., *Corporate headquarters & textile converting* ........ (732) 224-7400
Central Shippee, Inc., 46 Star Lake Rd., Bloomingdale 07403
Pres.—Eric Hubner, 30 emp., *Manufacturer of custom woven decorative* ........ (973) 838-1616
City Glass Co., 282 Broadway, P.O. Box 178, Bayonne 07002
Pres.—Allan McCleod, 50 emp., *Architectural metals, glass & custom* ........ (201) 436-8400
Clothes Horse, Inc., 2200 Wallace Blvd., Ste. A, Cinnaminson 08077
Pres., Fin. & MIS Mgr.—Katrina L. Coldren, 13 emp., *Horse blankets & saddle cloths* ........ (856) 829-8460
Comfort Concepts, Inc., 501 Broad Ave., Ste. 7, Ridgefield 07657
Ptnr.—Robert Mass, 16 emp., *Manufacturer & distributor of reusable* ........ (201) 941-6700
Curvon Corp., 34 Apple St., Tinton Falls 07724
Pres.—Blake Banta, 12 emp., *Horse clothing* ........ (732) 747-3832
Custom Converters, Inc., 115 Naylon Ave., Livingston 07039
Pres.—Mark Krause, 10 emp., *Paper, plastic film, aluminum foil* ........ (973) 994-9000
Dazian Fabrics, LLC, 18 Central Blvd., South Hackensack 07606
Chrm.—Milt Wolfson, 40 emp., *Textiles, fabricated items & LED scenic* ........ (201) 549-1000
Dye Into Print, Inc., 167 Fornelius Ave., Clifton 07013
Pres.—Mathew Lederman, 62 emp., *Wide-format dye sublimation textile* ........ (973) 772-8019
Eastern Sign Co., 3011 Ocean Heights Ave., Ste. B, Egg Harbor Township 08234
Ptnr.—Michael Franklin, 5 emp., *Interior & exterior signs & banners* ........ (609) 927-0885
Elkay Products Co., Inc., 35 Brown Ave., P.O. Box 149, Springfield 07081
Pres.—Steven Piller, 10 emp., *Manufacturer of quilted van pads &* ........ (973) 376-7550
Exacta Industries, Inc., 20 John F. Kennedy Dr. N., Bloomfield 07003
Pres.—Ory Giberstein, 50 emp., *Contract textile cutting* ........ (973) 259-0104
Globe Packaging Co., Inc., 368 Paterson Plank Rd., Carlstadt 07072
Pres.—Issy Bank, 11 emp., *Plastic, collagen, fibrous, cellulose* ........ (201) 939-3335
Golden Rule Creations, 250 Terrace Rd., Franklin Lakes 07417
★ Owner—Fred Schiker, 4 emp., *Custom emblems & patches* ........ (201) 337-4050
Griffin Care, LLC, 80 Manheim Ave., Bridgeton 08302
CEO—Mark Naim, 80 emp., *Absorbent disposable incontinence products* ........ (856) 455-6870
Hedaya Home Fashions, Inc., 1111 Jefferson Ave., Elizabeth 07201
Pres.—Nathan Hedaya, 40 emp., *Aprons, towels, oven mitts, place mats* ........ (908) 352-0808
Hero's Salute Awards Co., 1875 State Route 23, Wayne 07470
Pres.—Robert Terry, 10 emp., *Awards, trophies, signs, banners, flags* ........ (973) 696-5085
Industrial Filters Co., Inc., 9 Industrial Rd., Fairfield 07004
Pres.—Steven Donker, 7 emp., *Industrial water filters* ........ (973) 575-0533
Kimco Products, LLC, 64 E. Midland Ave., Ste. 5, Paramus 07652
Pres.—Dennis Grande, 20 emp., *Fabric book covers, fabric wine bottle* ........ (201) 265-6800
Kinedyne Corp. (H Q), 151 Industrial Pkwy., Branchburg 08876
Pres.—James M. Klausmann, 20 emp., *Corporate headquarters; cargo control* ........ (908) 231-1800
Laggren's, LLC, P.O. Box 7173, Monroe Township 08831
Pres.—David Lasser, 10 emp., *Canvas awnings, window shades, blinds* ........ (609) 235-9883
Margola Corp., 232 S. Van Brunt St., Englewood 07631
Owner—Neil Chalfin, 6 emp., *Manufacturer & distributor of rhinestones* ........ (201) 816-9500
Merry Modes 2000, 61 Willet St., Ste. 2, Passaic 07055
Owner—Anthony Dell'Aquila, 8 emp., *Custom handmade bridal petticoats,* ........ (973) 773-2501
Metro Flag Co., 353 Richard Mine Rd., Unit 100, Wharton 07885
Ex. V-P.—Donald Bornstein, 27 emp., *Custom flags & banners* ........ (973) 366-1776
Newton Trophy & Sport Center, 1-3 Milk St., Bldg. 3, Branchville 07826
Pres.—Linda Moran, 5 emp., *Textile screen printing, embroidery* ........ (973) 948-0613
North Sails New Jersey, 2422 Highway 34, Manasquan 08736
Owner & Pres.—Henry Bossett, 3 emp., *Polyester, aramid fiber, carbon, canvas* ........ (732) 528-8899
Object Design, Inc., 105 W. Dewey Ave., Bldg. C, Unit 5, Wharton 07885
Pres.—Amy Kim, 8 emp., *Commercial laundry bags & industrial* ........ (973) 442-5790
Ortho Safe Systems International, Inc. (H Q), P.O. Box 9435, Trenton 08650
Pres.—Winfried Kraft, 5 emp., *Corporate headquarters; wheelchair* ........ (609) 587-3859
Pecata Enterprises, Inc., 18 Market St., Paterson 07501
Pres.—Roger Glickman, 80 emp., *Table linens & printed banners* ........ (973) 523-5866
Prismatix Decal, Inc., 324 Railroad Ave., Hackensack 07601
Pres., CEO—Miriam Salomon, 10 emp., *Decals, emblems, trophies & engraving* ........ (201) 525-2800
Purple Pebble, LLC (H Q), 58 Grand Ave., Waldwick 07463
Owner—Heather D. Vaul, 1 emp., *Company headquarters; dog leashes,* ........ (201) 444-7439
Raritan Printing Plus Flags & Banners, Inc., 109 N. Feltus St., South Amboy 08879
Pres.—Joanne Corridon, 2 emp., *Stock & custom U.S. outdoor & indoor* ........ (732) 721-2121
Rose Brand, Inc., 4 Emerson Ln., Secaucus 07094
Pres.—George Jacobstein, 197 emp., *Curtains, draperies, backdrops, fabrics* ........ (201) 809-1730
Safe-Strap Co., 105 W. Dewey Ave., Bldg. D, Ste. 410, Wharton 07885
Pres.—Paul Giampavolo, 55 emp., *Shopping cart seat belts, shop-along* ........ (973) 442-4623
Satesa Corp., 154 W. Forest Ave., Englewood 07631
Pres.—Randy Loew, 4 emp., *Laminating, coating & converting of* ........ (201) 871-8989
Screen-Trans Development Corp., 100 Grand St., Moonachie 07074
Pres.—Robert DeVries, 25 emp., *Fabric banners, including textile screen* ........ (201) 933-7800
Spar-Tex Co., Inc., 200 Lehigh Ave., Lakewood 08701
Owner—Charles Sparacino, 100 emp., *Contract sewing of home textiles &* ........ (732) 367-4400
Steelstran Industries, Inc., 35 Mileed Way, P.O. Box 30, Avenel 07001
CEO—Peter Gronbeck, 5 emp., *Corporate headquarters & rope & wooden* ........ (732) 574-0700
Switlik Parachute Co., Inc., 1325 E. State St., Trenton 08609
Pres.—Stanley Switlik II, 115 emp., *Life rafts, aviation life vests, flight* ........ (609) 587-3300
Tiffanees Toys, Inc., 601 Nassau St., Ste. 593, North Brunswick 08902
Pres.—Mirta D'Amaro, 13 emp., *Stuffed toys, pet beds, pillow cushions* ........ (732) 828-6333
Tingue, Brown & Co. (H Q), 535 N. Midland Ave., Saddle Brook 07663
Pres., CEO—David Tingue, 20 emp., *Company headquarters; laundry bags* ........ (201) 796-4490
TLC Sign & Banner, Inc., 188 Walnut St., Toms River 08753
Owner—Tim Snover, 17 emp., *Interior & exterior signs & banners* ........ (732) 244-4225
Union Hill Corp. (H Q), 34 Water St., Englishtown 07726
CEO—Mike Conforth, 4 emp., *Corporate headquarters; horse tack,* ........ (732) 786-9422

# 24 LUMBER & WOOD PRODUCTS

## 2411 Logging

Kane Wood Fuel, LLC, 512 Cedar Ave., Pitman 08071
Ptnr.—Frank Kane, 2 emp., *Wood logging* ........ (856) 589-3292
MAUSER USA LLC, 35 Cotters Ln., Ste. C, East Brunswick 08816
Pres., CEO—Jeff Simmonds, 80 emp., *Company headquarters & plastic containers* ........ (732) 353-7000
Mountain Top Logging, LLC, P.O. Box 324, Lebanon 08833
Pres.—Matthew Good, 1 emp., *Logging* ........ (908) 413-2982

## 2421 Sawmills & planing mills, general

Ackley's Sawmill, 98 W. Deerfield Rd., Bridgeton 08302
Ptnr.—Kenneth B. Ackley, 2 emp., *Lumber processing* ........ (856) 451-3704
Agincourt Fine Wood, 212 E. Mountain Rd., Hillsborough 08844
Owner—Francis Martin, 3 emp., *Lumber processing & millwork* ........ (908) 874-4737
Bayway Lumber, 43 Porete Ave., North Arlington 07031
Pres. & V-P.—Todd Anderson, 8 emp., *Lumber processing* ........ (201) 991-4200
Boro Sawmill & Timber Co., Inc., 139 Ryerson Ave., Wayne 07470
Pres.—Gregory Sussek, 11 emp., *Manufacturer & wholesaler of construction* ........ (973) 832-4607
Britton Industries, Inc., 227 Bakers Basin Rd., P.O. Box 6499, Lawrenceville 08648
Pres.—James Britton, 80 emp., *Bulk organic triple ground root & color* ........ (609) 588-8225
Castner's Sawmill, 935 Fairview Lake Rd., P.O. Box 13, Stillwater 07875
Owner—Rodney Castner, 2 emp., *Dimensional lumber* ........ (973) 383-5661
Cutler Bros. Box & Lumber Co., 711 W. Prospect Ave., P.O. Box 217, Fairview 07022
Owner—Gregory Cutler, 30 emp., *Pallets, skids, boxes & lumber* ........ (201) 943-2535
Delmont Sawmill, 4416 Route 47, Delmont 08314
Owner—Peter Boyce, 2 emp., *Lumber processing* ........ (856) 785-1018
Dreyer's Lumber & Hardware, Inc., 348 Elberon Blvd., Oakhurst 07755
★ Owner—Walter Dreyer, 4 emp., *Lumber processing & millwork & distributor* ........ (732) 531-0220
Edgewater Building Supply, Inc., 704 Woodlane Rd., Beverly 08010
Pres.—Paul Witkowski, 3 emp., *Lumber processing & custom millwork* ........ (609) 387-0136
Empire Lumber & Millwork Co., 377 Frelinghuysen Ave., Newark 07114
Chrm.—Ira Kent, 35 emp., *Architectural millwork, dimension lumber* ........ (973) 242-2700
Garmar Industries, Inc., 1625 Route 322, P.O. Box 460, Woolwich Township 08085
V-P.—Jerry Bernard, 33 emp., *Dimensional lumber, crating stock,* ........ (856) 241-9700
Jefferson Lumber & Millwork Corp., 298 Espanong Rd., Lake Hopatcong 07849
Pres.—Mary Lytle, 15 emp., *Lumber processing & millwork* ........ (973) 663-3100
Kuiken Brothers Company, Inc., 6-02 Fair Lawn Ave., P.O. Box 1040, Fair Lawn 07410
Pres.—Douglas Kuiken, 31 emp., *Corporate headquarters & lumber processing* ........ (201) 796-2082
Kuiken Brothers Company, Inc., 175 Route 23, Wantage 07461
Location Mgr.—Ken Hynnes, 15 emp., *Lumber, hardware, windows & building* ........ (973) 875-5106
Peter Lumber Co., 300 E. Washington Ave., P.O. Box 32, Pleasantville 08232
Pres.—Hugh M. Peter, 40 emp., *Millwork & hardwood lumber processing* ........ (609) 641-9000

© Copyright 2015 Manufacturers' News, Inc.


PJ Murphy Forest Products Corp. (H Q), 150 River Rd., Bldg. L, Ste. 1, P.O. Box 300, Montville 07045
Pres.—Fred Faehner, 5 emp., *Corporate headquarters; sanitized animal* ... (973) 316-0800
ProBuild Co., LLC, 817 Eastgate Dr., Ste. 101, Mount Laurel 08054
Area V-P.—Rob Gaites, 50 emp., *Lumber processing* ... (856) 505-1100
Riephoff Sawmill, Inc., 763 Route 524, Allentown 08501
Pres.—John Falconio, 20 emp., *Lumber processing & crane mats, dunnage* ... (609) 259-7265
Riverdale Environmental Recycling, 1 Riverdale Rd., Riverdale 07457
Pres.—Andrew Flockard, 20 emp., *Manufacturer of mulch, compost & soil* ... (973) 616-6654
Royal Lumber & Millwork Co., Inc., 455 Schuyler Ave., P.O. Box 443, Kearny 07032
V-P.—Arthur Rogoff, 5 emp., *Millwork & lumber processing* ... (201) 991-8550
Sawdust Depot, 1 Boumar Pl., Elmwood Park 07407
Pres.—Vincent Ippolito, 8 emp., *Sawdust & wood shavings* ... (201) 703-8400
Schairer Bros., 254 S. Bremen Ave., Egg Harbor City 08215
Ptnr.—Paul Schairer, 8 emp., *Lumber processing & sawmilling* ... (609) 965-0996
Tri-State Fences & Supply, Inc., 806 Route 23, Sussex 07461
Pres.—Allen Brands, 3 emp., *Wooden fencing* ... (973) 875-3213
Willard Bros. Lumber, 300 Basin Rd., Trenton 08619
Owner—Glen Willard, 10 emp., *Dimensional & kiln-dried hardwood lumber* ... (609) 890-1990
Woodhaven Lumber & Millwork, Inc., 200 James St., P.O. Box 870, Lakewood 08701
Pres.—Alan Robinson, 152 emp., *Millwork, including decks, railings* ... (732) 901-0030

## 2426 Hardwood dimension & flooring mills

Boards & Beams Co., LLC, 1275 Bloomfield Ave., Ste. 92, Fairfield 07004
Owner—Steve Djurasek, 10 emp., *Western red cedar & primed pine mouldings* ... (973) 299-6100
Boro Sawmill & Timber Co., Inc., 139 Ryerson Ave., Wayne 07470
Pres.—Gregory Sussek, 11 emp., *Manufacturer & wholesaler of construction* ... (973) 832-4607
Dubin Bros. Lumber Co., Inc., 710 Newton Ave., P.O. Box 85, Oaklyn 08107
Pres.—Richard Dubin, 5 emp., *Dimensional lumber* ... (856) 854-4675
GV Floors, 701 Penhorn Ave., Ste. 6, Secaucus 07094
Owner—John Chen, 5 emp., *Hardwood flooring* ... (201) 558-7889
Log Power, Inc., 646 Route 524, P.O. Box 597, Allentown 08501
Pres.—Robert Hooper, 15 emp., *Hardwood floors, including long & wide* ... (609) 259-9709
Mannington Mills, Inc., 75 Mannington Mills Rd., P.O. Box 30, Salem 08079
Chrm. of the Board—Keith Campbell, 600 emp., *Corporate headquarters & residential* ... (856) 935-3000
Monteath Moulding, 3150 Bordentown Ave., Old Bridge 08857
Pres.—Steve Wilson, 20 emp., *Hardwood mouldings, lumber & millwork* ... (732) 727-4000
Rex Lumber Co., 1 Station St., P.O. Box 1776, Englishtown 07726
Owner & Opers. Mgr.—Ben Forester, 85 emp., *FSC certified custom tropical & domestic* ... (732) 446-4200
Wood & Laminates, Inc., 102 Route 46 E., Lodi 07644
Pres.—Gabriel Salazar, 20 emp., *Custom bars & interiors for homes,* ... (973) 773-7475
Woodwork & More, LLC, 24 W. Gorman Ave., Collingswood 08108
Owner—Edward Satkowski, 1 emp., *Woodworking, including millwork, railing* ... (856) 986-3140

## 2431 Millwork

Acro Display, 2250-A Sherman Ave., Pennsauken 08110
Pres.—Paul Beranato, Jr., 6 emp., *Millwork, wooden cabinets & laminated* ... (856) 488-9710
Afina Corp., 40 Warren St., Paterson 07524
Pres.—Raymond Lombardo, 35 emp., *Bathroom cabinets & mirrors* ... (973) 684-7650
Agincourt Fine Wood, 212 E. Mountain Rd., Hillsborough 08844
Owner—Francis Martin, 3 emp., *Lumber processing & millwork* ... (908) 874-4737
Agresti Construction Co., Inc., 356 Glenwood Ave., East Orange 07017
Pres.—James Agresti, 12 emp., *Architectural millwork & custom cabinetry* ... (201) 825-8500
Alex's Custom Kitchens, LLC, 824 Paterson Ave., East Rutherford 07073
Owner—Louie Alexander Eliades, 1 emp., *Custom wooden kitchen cabinets, vanities* ... (201) 933-9359
Alliance Woodwork Corp., 19 Ogden Ct., P.O. Box 684, Middletown 07748
Pres.—Jean Brandel, 6 emp., *Architectural woodwork & moulding* ... (732) 671-6884
Alvaro Stairs, LLC, 4201 Tonnelle Ave., Ste. 12, North Bergen 07047
★ Principal—Enrique Bernar, 5 emp., *Wooden stairs* ... (201) 864-6754
American Mica Corp., 1015 Pennsylvania Ave., Linden 07036
Pres.—Ray Bailey, 3 emp., *Architectural millwork* ... (908) 587-5237
American Stair & Rail Artisans, LLC, 687 Prospect St., Ste. 420, Lakewood 08701
Owner—Renee Brown, 15 emp., *Interior stairs, rails & replacement* ... (732) 363-3734
Architectural Cabinetry, 51 Willow St., Washington 07882
★ Owner—Cheryl Fortner, 5 emp., *Custom wooden architectural cabinets* ... (908) 689-1600
Architectural Woodworking Assocs., LLC, 4 7th St., Frenchtown 08825
Ptnr.—John Gehman, 6 emp., *Architectural millwork & wooden cabinets* ... (908) 996-7866
Artcraft Cabinets Woodworking, 165 Broad Ave., Fairview 07022
Owner—Hans Kraenclein, 2 emp., *Architectural woodwork* ... (201) 943-6090
Artistic Doors & Windows, 10 S. Inman Ave., Avenel 07001
Pres.—Enrico Autovino, 45 emp., *Custom hardwood doors & windows & high-end* ... (732) 726-9400
Atlas Woodwork, 212 Wright St., Newark 07114
Pres.—Antonio Martins, 10 emp., *Wooden kitchen cabinets & commercial* ... (973) 621-9595
Atlas Woodworking, Inc., 15 Naugle St., Closter 07624
Pres.—Kenneth J. Ewald, 15 emp., *Architectural woodworking* ... (201) 784-1949
B & B Millwork, 333 Monroe Ave., Kenilworth 07033
Owner—Mel Krause, 20 emp., *Wooden doors & mouldings* ... (973) 249-0300
B & C Custom Wood Handrail Corp., 131 Dr. James Parker Blvd., P.O. Box 2008, Red Bank 07701
Pres.—Christopher Kalkucki, 6 emp., *Wooden stairs & railways & wood rails* ... (732) 530-6640
Beech Woodworks, Inc., 9 Kentucky Ave., Paterson 07503
Pres.—Tom Connor, 4 emp., *Wooden cabinets* ... (973) 225-0111
Bell Arte Woodworking, Inc., 10 W. Mravlag Pl., Elizabeth 07201
Pres.—Giusette Chillemi, 12 emp., *Wooden store fixtures & cabinets &* ... (908) 355-1199
Bendix Architectural Products, Inc., 90 Dayton Ave., Ste. 34, Passaic 07055
Chrm., Pres.—David Garrett, 6 emp., *Decorative mouldings & hand-carved* ... (973) 473-4780
Bennett Cabinets, Inc., 1251 Highway 1, Edison 08837
Pres.—Michael Bennett, 6 emp., *Custom wooden kitchen cabinets & architectura* ... (732) 548-1616
Bildisco Door Mfg., Inc., 21 Central Ave., West Orange 07052
Pres.—Bruno Valente, 11 emp., *Manufacturer of wooden & metal doors* ... (973) 673-2400
Black Millwork & Center Lumber Co., 220 W. Crescent Ave., Allendale 07401
Pres.—Michael Rottenberg, 10 emp., *Millwork* ... (201) 934-0100
Blauth Millwork, 57 Pleasant Valley Rd., Titusville 08560
Pres.—Gerard L. Blauth, 1 emp., *Architectural millwork* ... (609) 737-9502
Boards & Beams Co., LLC, 1275 Bloomfield Ave., Ste. 92, Fairfield 07004
Owner—Steve Djurasek, 10 emp., *Western red cedar & primed pine mouldings* ... (973) 299-6100
Bongiovanni Custom Cabinet & Furniture, LLC, Mario, 7 E. Pleasant Ave., Pleasantville 08232
Owner—Mario Bongiovanni, 2 emp., *Millwork* ... (609) 646-8488
Boro Sawmill & Timber Co., Inc., 139 Ryerson Ave., Wayne 07470
Pres.—Gregory Sussek, 11 emp., *Manufacturer & wholesaler of construction* ... (973) 832-4607
Borst Cabinet Co., 15 Schierloh Ct., Ramsey 07446
Owner, Pres. & Sales Mgr.—David J. Borst, 3 emp., *Custom & semi-custom stock kitchen* ... (201) 825-4220
Bossen Architectural Millwork, Inc., 1818 Bannard St., Cinnaminson 08077
Pres.—Joseph H. Bossen, 30 emp., *Architectural millwork & hardwood radius* ... (856) 786-1100
Brown Tool & Machine Co., Inc., Rosemont Raven Rock Rd., P.O. Box 142, Rosemont 08556
Pres.—Alan Brown, 2 emp., *Industrial & medical prototypes & architectur* ... (609) 397-1751
Builders Architectural Millwork, 159 Newman Springs Rd. E., Shrewsbury 07702
Pres.—Anita DelPesce, 3 emp., *Architectural millwork, including wooden* ... (732) 450-0056
Cabinet-Tronics, Inc., 100 Birmingham Rd., P.O. Box 198, Birmingham 08011
Pres.—Michael Lockwood, 15 emp., *Commercial grade millwork & casework* ... (609) 267-2625
Capra Custom Cabinetry & Millwork, LLC, 259 E. Washington Ave., Washington 07882
★ Owner—John Capra, 2 emp., *Custom residential & commercial casework* ... (908) 797-9848
Classic Coves, P.O. Box 266, Garwood 07027
Pres.—Mark Wellnitz, 2 emp., *Indirect & accent cove lighting for* ... (908) 344-1776
Cobb's Mill, LLC, 146 Cobbs Mill Rd., Bridgeton 08302
Treas.—Williams Cobb, 2 emp., *Millwork* ... (856) 451-0671
Collingswood Architectural Millwork, Inc., 715 Taylor Ave., Collingswood 08107
Pres.—Robert Engelke, 17 emp., *Millwork, cabinets & countertops* ... (856) 854-0440
Costas Architectural Woodworking, 248 Montgomery St., Bloomfield 07003
Ptnr.—Oscar Costa, 8 emp., *Custom residential & commercial kitchen* ... (973) 429-7004
Cozzolino Furniture Design, Inc., 20 Standish Ave., West Orange 07052
Owner & Dir.—Steven Cozzolino, 23 emp., *Custom architectural millwork* ... (973) 731-9292
Creative Innovations, Inc., 20-21 Wagaraw Rd., Ste. 31-B, Fair Lawn 07410
Pres.—Joseph Batavia, 8 emp., *Wooden kitchen & bath cabinets & millwork* ... (973) 636-9060
Creative Wood Products, Inc., 370 Whiteville Rd., Jackson 08527
Pres.—George Tomaszewicz, 8 emp., *Millwork* ... (732) 370-0051
Custom Interiors, Inc., 47 W. Grand Ave., Montvale 07645
Pres.—Keith D. Wright, 2 emp., *Wooden cabinets & custom woodworking* ... (201) 573-9702
Custom Wood Creations, Inc., 51 Willow St., Washington 07882
Pres.—Ejlat Fuer, 2 emp., *Millwork* ... (908) 835-8999
Custom Wood, LLC, 400 Goldman Dr., Cream Ridge 08514
Off. Mgr.—Lisa Zucatti, 4 emp., *Kitchen & bathroom cabinets & granite* ... (609) 758-8288
Custom Woodworking, 813 Jerusalem Rd., Scotch Plains 07076
Owner & Pres.—Joseph Louis Difrancesco, 2 emp., *Wooden cabinets & millwork* ... (908) 232-9525
CWI Architectural Millwork, LLC, 8 Deptford Rd., Dept. D, Glassboro 08028
Member—David N. Ganor, 7 emp., *Architectural millwork* ... (856) 307-7900
D & D Millwork Co., Inc., 10-12 N. 7th St., Belleville 07109
Pres.—Bernard D'Avella, 5 emp., *Wooden & plastic laminate cabinets,* ... (973) 759-6336
D C Metric Tool, Inc., 11 Mathews Ave., Riverdale 07457
Pres.—Djordje Cakmak, 2 emp., *Architectural millwork & machining* ... (973) 838-7590
D S F, Inc., 401 U.S. Highway 202, Raritan 08869
Pres.—Simon DeGirolamo, 25 emp., *Architectural millwork & custom cabinets* ... (908) 218-5153
DCI Metro, Inc., 1 Maple St., Unit 1, East Rutherford 07073
Pres.—William Mihatov, 28 emp., *Wood & metal doors & frames & hardware* ... (201) 340-4329
Design Of Tomorrow, Inc., 24 Sherwood Ln., Fairfield 07004
Pres., GM—David Roitburg, 15 emp., *Casework & millwork for schools & laboratorie* ... (973) 227-5676
Designers Kitchens, Inc., 250 Faraday Ave., Jackson 08527
Pres.—Edwin Rivera, 15 emp., *Architectural woodwork & wooden cabinets* ... (732) 370-5500
DiNaso Building Supplies, 133 Ocean Ave., Lakewood 08701
Br. Mgr.—Billy Epp, 50 emp., *Prime trim wooden doors & windows* ... (732) 886-6666
Distinctive Wood Work, Inc., 70 Stacy Haines Rd., Ste. D, Lumberton 08048
Owner—Jim Cherubino, 3 emp., *Custom residential & commercial millwork* ... (609) 714-8505
Distinctive Woodworking, 703 Van Rossum Ave., Unit 1, Beverly 08010
Owner—Robert Hoffman, 10 emp., *Wooden & metal stairs* ... (609) 877-8122
Diversified Millwork, Inc., 420 N. 2nd Rd., Unit C, Hammonton 08037
Pres.—Don McFaul, 10 emp., *Wooden, plastic laminate & solid-surface* ... (609) 270-7385
DMD Stairs & Rails, LLC, 370 Whitesville Rd., Ste. 8, Jackson 08527
Pres.—Douglas Diani, 20 emp., *Wooden & metal stairs & railings* ... (732) 901-0102
Donnelly Industries, Inc., 557 Route 23 S., Wayne 07470
Pres., CEO—Rod Donnelly, 90 emp., *Commercial millwork for architects,* ... (973) 672-1800
Downtown Interiors, LLC, 629 Grove St., 8th Fl., Jersey City 07310
Pres.—Hertzel Abraham, 12 emp., *Custom cabinets* ... (201) 798-4728
Dreyer's Lumber & Hardware, Inc., 348 Elberon Blvd., Oakhurst 07755
★ Owner—Walter Dreyer, 4 emp., *Lumber processing & millwork & distributor* ... (732) 531-0220
Dubell Lumber Co., 102 S. Route 73, Cedar Brook 08018
Hum. Res. Mgr.—Pam Clow, 16 emp., *Architectural millwork* ... (609) 567-2467
Eastern Millwork, Inc., 18 Chapel Ave., Jersey City 07305
Pres.—Andrew Campbell, 60 emp., *Commercial wooden cabinets, stairs* ... (201) 451-9510
Edgewater Building Supply, Inc., 704 Woodlane Rd., Beverly 08010
Pres.—Paul Witkowski, 3 emp., *Lumber processing & custom millwork* ... (609) 387-0136
Empire Lumber & Millwork Co., 377 Frelinghuysen Ave., Newark 07114
Chrm.—Ira Kent, 35 emp., *Architectural millwork, dimension lumber* ... (973) 242-2700
Epic Management, Inc. (H Q), 136 11th St., Ste. 1, Piscataway 08854
CEO—Robert Epifano, Jr., 50 emp., *Corporate headquarters; millwork &* ... (732) 752-6100
Epic Millwork, 1022 Hamilton St., Ste. G, Somerset 08873
GM—Ray Fareri, 15 emp., *Millwork* ... (732) 296-0273
Eppley Building & Design, Inc., 220-B Goffle Rd., Hawthorne 07506
Pres.—Paul Eppley, 35 emp., *Custom cabinets & architectural millwork* ... (973) 636-9499
Excel Die Corp., 19 Grant St., Linden 07036
Pres.—Hanna Krysa, 4 emp., *Metal stamping, millwork & tool & die* ... (908) 587-2606
F T Millwork, 9-B Catherine St., Red Bank 07701
Pres.—Frank Thomas, 1 emp., *Wooden doors, windows & millwork* ... (732) 741-1216
Fi Companies, 3150 Bordentown Ave., Old Bridge 08857
Pres., CEO—Scott Forman, 50 emp., *Store fixtures, displays & cabinets* ... (732) 727-8100
Fimbel Architectural Door Specialties, 8 Coddington Rd., Whitehouse Station 08889
Pres., Cont.—Edward Fimbel III, 50 emp., *Vinyl, composite, metal, fiberglass* ... (908) 534-1732
Finest Enterprises, Inc., 2107 Herbertsville Rd., Point Pleasant 08742
Pres.—Jim Horne, 1 emp., *Wooden kitchen cabinets, millwork &* ... (732) 892-1121
Foley-Waite Assocs., Inc., 225 Belleville Ave., P.O. Box 164, Bloomfield 07003
Chrm. & V-P.—Kathryn W. Schackner, 9 emp., *Architectural millwork* ... (973) 743-0700
Foremost Wood Products, 191 Vineyard Rd., Edison 08817
Pres.—John Autovino, 5 emp., *Wooden products, including doors &* ... (718) 447-5836
Frank's Cabinet Shop, Inc., 1992 Burnt Mills Rd., P.O. Box 78, Pluckemin 07978
Ptnr.—John Darrow, 7 emp., *Wooden cabinets & entertainment centers* ... (908) 658-4396
G & G Stairs, 2559 U.S. Highway 9, Howell 07731
Pres.—Sean Coffey, 2 emp., *Wooden stairs & railings* ... (732) 905-3083
Garden State Woodworking Co., 344 Hoover Ave., Bloomfield 07003
Pres.—John Falk, 3 emp., *Millwork* ... (973) 748-2661
Garfield Cabinets & Millwork, Inc., 22 Garfield Ave., Garfield 07026
Pres.—James DeVito, Jr., 2 emp., *Wooden cabinets & millwork* ... (973) 340-0507
Glen Rock Stair Corp., 551 Commerce St., Franklin Lakes 07417
Pres.—Nick Veenstra, 25 emp., *Wooden stairs* ... (201) 337-9595
GPS Specialty Doors, Inc., 90 Dayton Ave., Unit 4-B, Passaic 07055
Pres.—Fred Bolio, 50 emp., *Hangar, acoustic, air plenum, reverberation* ... (973) 778-6200

S.I.C.

★ **Indicates new listing this edition.**

Greenbaum Interiors, 101 Washington St., Paterson 07505
Pres.—Joseph Greenbaum, 40 emp., *Custom upholstered & wooden furniture* ........ (973) 279-3000

Greenbrook Stairs, Inc., 14 Dayton St., Bernardsville 07924
Pres.—Keith Fitting, 8 emp., *Wooden stairs & railings* ........ (908) 221-9145

GT Millwork, LLC, 2180 Hedding Rd., Columbus 08022
Ptnr.—Gary Teyhen, 6 emp., *Residential & commercial woodworking* ........ (609) 291-9222

H2L, LLC, 4201 Tonnelle Ave., Ste. 2, North Bergen 07047
Off. Mgr.—Michelle Bastiar, 9 emp., *Commercial & residential wooden millwork* ........ (201) 864-0060

Hahn's Woodworking Co., Inc., 181 Meister Ave., Somerville 08876
Pres.—Scott Hahn, 15 emp., *Wooden garage, carriage house & matching* ........ (908) 722-2742

Hansen's Cabinet Shop, Inc., 42 Park Ave., Madison 07940
Pres.—A. Hansen, 4 emp., *Custom wooden & plastic laminated cabinets* ........ (973) 377-2444

Hester Bros., Inc., 114 Beach St., Ste. 5, Rockaway 07866
Pres.—Michael Hester, 3 emp., *Custom residential cabinets & architectural* ........ (862) 432-5183

Hutchinson Cabinets, LLC, 244 Bark Bridge Rd., Sewell 08080
V-P.—George Hutchinson, 25 emp., *Wooden & plastic laminate cabinets* ........ (856) 468-5500

Iacovelli Stairs, Inc., 707 Challenger Way, Forked River 08731
Pres.—Joseph Iacovelli, 10 emp., *Wooden stairs & railings* ........ (609) 693-3476

Interstate Showcase & Store Fixture Co., P.O. Box 941, Teaneck 07666
Pres., Sales & Mktg. Mgr.—Leon Miller, 1 emp., *Wooden store fixtures & millwork for* ........ (201) 467-4522

J M J Woodworking, Inc., 100 8th St., Bldg. 300, Passaic 07055
Pres.—Jack Mroz, 6 emp., *Commercial wooden cabinets, paneling* ........ (973) 471-6449

Jafco Industries, LLC, 136 Lincoln Blvd., Middlesex 08846
Pres.—Abe Werczberger, 20 emp., *Architectural millwork & plastic laminate* ........ (732) 356-1502

Jantek Industries, LLC, 230 Route 70, Medford 08055
CEO—Keith Kailian, 40 emp., *Windows, doors & related products for* ........ (609) 654-1030

Jarahian Millwork, Inc., 870 Route 530, Ste. 4, Whiting 08759
Pres.—Harold Jarahian, 3 emp., *Millwork* ........ (732) 240-5151

Jefferson Lumber & Millwork Corp., 298 Espanong Rd., Lake Hopatcong 07849
Pres.—Mary Lytle, 15 emp., *Lumber processing & millwork* ........ (973) 663-3100

JM Custom Design Millwork, 101 Hobart St., Hackensack 07601
Owner—Joseph Marrella, 2 emp., *Custom millwork, including wooden doors* ........ (201) 487-8990

Joffe Lumber & Supply, Inc., 18 Burns Ave., Vineland 08360
CEO—Sol G. Joffe, 50 emp., *Wooden & vinyl windows, steel & interior* ........ (856) 825-9550

Jorgensen-Carr Ltd., 50 Dey St., 4th Fl., Jersey City 07306
Pres.—Mike Jorgenson, 5 emp., *Furniture & architectural woodworking* ........ (201) 792-2278

Joti Kitchens, 413 S. Main St., Pleasantville 08232
Owner—Joe Staines, Jr., 3 emp., *Wooden & laminate cabinets* ........ (609) 383-1350

K B Custom Interiors, 10-B Greenwood Ave., Woodbury 08096
Gen. Ptnr.—Kurt Lobach, 2 emp., *Architectural millwork* ........ (856) 845-9112

K W, Inc., 1536 Lower Ferry Rd., Ewing 08618
Pres.—Kurt Watson, 3 emp., *Commercial casework, architectural* ........ (609) 882-6363

Kaufman Stairs, Inc., 150 E. Inman Ave., Rahway 07065
Pres., Plt. Mgr.—Alan Kaufman, 75 emp., *Residential wooden stairs & banisters* ........ (732) 388-9870

Kendall Mfg. Co., Inc., 1366 Chews Landing Rd., Clementon 08021
Owner—James W. Strater, 3 emp., *Vinyl & wooden windows & doors & retractable* ........ (856) 227-2132

Kuehn Bevel, Inc., 10 Furnace St., Stanhope 07874
Pres.—Ray Kuehn, 10 emp., *Decorative edge products for laminate* ........ (973) 584-8282

Kuiken Brothers Company, Inc., 175 Route 23, Wantage 07461
Location Mgr.—Ken Hynnes, 15 emp., *Lumber, hardware, windows & building* ........ (973) 875-5106

Lardieri's Custom Woodworking, Inc., 1830 Swarthmore Ave., Ste. 6, Lakewood 08701
Co-Pres., Off. Mgr.—Robert Lardieri, Sr., 6 emp., *Custom wooden kitchen cabinets, entertainment* (732) 905-6334

Lauderdale Millwork, Inc., 77 Industrial Rd., Berkeley Heights 07922
Owner & Pres.—John Lauderdale, 4 emp., *Wooden cabinets, doors, mouldings &* ........ (908) 508-9550

Lee's Woodworking, Inc., 726 Walling Ave., Belmar 07719
Owner—Bill Lee, 2 emp., *Custom, residential & commercial furniture* ........ (732) 681-1002

Leiz Custom Woodwork, David, 2301 E. Edgar Rd., Bldg. 5-A, Linden 07036
Owner & Pres.—David Leiz, 4 emp., *Wooden kitchen, built-in & entertainment* ........ (908) 486-1533

Longo's Cabinet Shop, 101 Monroe St., Garfield 07026
Owner—Tom Esposito, 1 emp., *Wooden & laminate cabinets* ........ (973) 472-3567

Mainland Plate Glass Co., Inc., 53 E. West Jersey Ave., Pleasantville 08232
Pres.—Richard Bozzelli, 10 emp., *Architectural glass doors, windows,* ........ (609) 641-6553

Mango Custom Cabinets, Inc., 216 W. Stiger St., Hackettstown 07840
Owner—Richard Mango, 20 emp., *Architectural millwork, including custom* ........ (908) 813-3077

Manhattan Door Corp., 109 Kero Rd., Carlstadt 07072
Owner—Michael Sklar, 40 emp., *Custom flush wooden doors* ........ (718) 963-1111

Maranatha Ceramic Tile & Marble, Inc., 253 Cookstown New Egypt Rd., Wrightstown 08562
Ptnr. & Pres.—Thomas Raab, 20 emp., *Manufacturer & distributor of custom* ........ (609) 758-1168

Master Craftsman, LLC, 417 N. Grove St., Bldg. 2, Unit D, Berlin 08009
Pres.—Patt Plungis, 3 emp., *Architectural millwork* ........ (856) 768-8088

Midhattan Woodworking, 3130 Bordentown Ave., Old Bridge 08857
Ptnr.—George Greco, 45 emp., *Architectural millwork, including cabinets* ........ (732) 727-3020

Miller Fabricators, 1135 Mount Ephraim Ave., Camden 08103
Owner, Pres. & CEO—Aaron Miller, 10 emp., *Laminated countertops & custom cabinetry* ........ (856) 541-9499

Mitchell's Woodworking, LLC, 780 Jacksonville Mount Holly Rd., Westampton 08060
Owner—Gordon Mitchell, 3 emp., *Custom cabinets & millwork, including* ........ (609) 261-7500

Mountain Millwork, 14 Clifton Ave. S., Lakewood 08701
Manager—Nathan Joseph, 3 emp., *Architectural millwork & wooden kitchen* ........ (732) 901-9400

Mountain Millwork, Inc., 1014 Route 9, Bayville 08721
Ptnr.—Edward Pryce, 7 emp., *Architectural woodwork* ........ (732) 606-1701

New Century Wood Products, 131 Lincoln Blvd., Middlesex 08846
★ Owner—David Lomonte, 10 emp., *Millwork & casework* ........ (732) 271-2557

New Jersey Hardwoods, Inc., 1340 W. Front St., Plainfield 07063
Pres.—O. Herttua, 20 emp., *Architectural millwork* ........ (908) 754-0990

Osborn's Mill, 149 Yellowbrook Rd., Farmingdale 07727
GM—Mark Piccolo, 6 emp., *Architectural millwork* ........ (732) 751-0889

Other Orthodontic Co., Inc., 22 Gail Ct., Sparta 07871
Pres.—Jon Bergeron, 9 emp., *Manufacturer of commercial wooden cabinets* ........ (973) 383-8662

Paramount Fixture Corp., 175 Mount Pleasant Ave., Newark 07104
Owner & Pres.—Stephen Porcelli, 35 emp., *Custom wooden & metal store fixtures* ........ (973) 485-1585

Pella Windows & Doors, 4 Dedrick Pl., West Caldwell 07006
Pres.—David Sidman, 170 emp., *Wood, wood-clad & vinyl windows & doors* ........ (973) 575-0200

Peter Lumber Co., 300 E. Washington Ave., P.O. Box 32, Pleasantville 08232
Pres.—Hugh M. Peter, 40 emp., *Millwork & hardwood lumber processing* ........ (609) 641-9000

Poandl Brothers Woodworking, Inc., 20 N. 7th Ave., P.O. Box 4015, Long Branch 07740
Pres.—William Poandl, 4 emp., *Architectural millwork, including solid* ........ (732) 229-8585

Pompton Millwork, Inc., 1458 Ringwood Ave., Haskell 07420
Pres.—William Kealy, 2 emp., *Millwork & wooden products* ........ (973) 835-0585

Precision Cabinets, 410 E. Freehold Rd., Freehold 07728
Owner—Robert Blatchley, 3 emp., *Wooden kitchen & office cabinets* ........ (732) 462-3342

Prestige Millwork, LLC, 152 U.S. Highway 206, Bldg. 17-A, Hillsborough 08844
Owner, Pres. & Sales Mgr.—Dan Bugasch, 25 emp., *Architectural woodwork & casework* ........ (908) 526-5100

Price Millwork, 305 Dennis Dr., Absecon 08201
Owner—Gary Price, 1 emp., *Millwork* ........ (609) 652-0123

Prinz Woodworking, Inc., 381 E. 22nd St., Paterson 07514
Pres.—Leonard Prinz, 10 emp., *Wooden cabinets & architectural millwork* ........ (973) 977-2345

Props, Displays & Interiors, Inc., 45 Glenwood Pl., East Orange 07017
Pres., GM—Stephen Sebbane, 10 emp., *Retail displays, cabinets & woodworking* ........ (862) 704-6463

R & R Stairs, Inc., 131 Wood Ave., Middlesex 08846
Pres.—Rich Kaminski, 20 emp., *Interior wooden & ornamental metal* ........ (732) 752-9400

Ramsay Cabinetmakers, Inc., David, 310 Mill St., Moorestown 08057
Pres.—David Ramsay III, 8 emp., *High-end custom cabinetry, furniture* ........ (856) 234-7776

Randall Mfg. Co., Inc., 200 Sylvan Ave., Newark 07104
Pres.—Cary Tinfow, 22 emp., *Metal & wood building products* ........ (973) 484-7600

Rex Lumber Co., 1 Station St., P.O. Box 1776, Englishtown 07726
Owner & Opers. Mgr.—Ben Forester, 85 emp., *FSC certified custom tropical & domestic* ........ (732) 446-4200

Rhodes & Rhodes Millwork Co., Inc., 3011 Ocean Heights Ave., Unit A, Egg Harbor Township 08234
Pres.—Scott Rhodes, 4 emp., *Millwork* ........ (609) 653-3180

Ridge Doors, 335 New Rd., P.O. Box 180, Monmouth Junction 08852
Pres., GM—Marcelle Bouvier, 5 emp., *Custom wooden garage doors & replacement* ........ (732) 329-2311

Rivers Edge Woodworks & Design, 90 Dayton Ave., Passaic 07055
Pres.—Gary Odendahl, 2 emp., *Wooden cabinetry & interior millwork* ........ (973) 337-2288

Royal Lumber & Millwork Co., Inc., 455 Schuyler Ave., P.O. Box 443, Kearny 07032
V-P.—Arthur Rogoff, 5 emp., *Millwork & lumber processing* ........ (201) 991-8550

RSL, Inc., 3049 Fernwood Ave., Egg Harbor Township 08234
Plt. Mgr.—Steven Nixon, Sr., 20 emp., *Wooden & door inserts* ........ (609) 645-9770

Salon Interiors, 62 Leuning St., South Hackensack 07606
Pres.—Walter Siegordner, 20 emp., *Wooden furniture* ........ (201) 488-7888

SandKamp Woodworks, LLC, 430 Communipaw Ave., Jersey City 07304
Owner & Pres.—Anthony Sandkamp, 3 emp., *Wooden kitchen & custom built-in cabinets* ........ (201) 200-0101

Sawitz Store Fixture, Inc., 130 Grand St., Carlstadt 07072
Pres.—Daniel Sawitz, 28 emp., *Wooden, laminate & solid-surface store* ........ (201) 842-9444

Sherman & Son, Inc., W. F., 84 Broad St., Manasquan 08736
Pres.—Donald F. Sherman, Jr., 10 emp., *Wooden furniture & architectural millwork* ........ (732) 223-1505

Sloan & Co., Inc., 38 Fairfield Pl., West Caldwell 07006
Pres.—Scott Casabona, 25 emp., *Architectural millwork & acoustical* ........ (973) 227-3555

Somerset Wood Products Co., 10 Johnson Dr., Raritan 08869
Pres.—Mitch Bloch, 12 emp., *Architectural woodwork, including custom* ........ (908) 526-0030

South Jersey Lumbermans, Inc., 6268 Holly St., Mays Landing 08330
Pres., GM—Stephen Pinkos, 3 emp., *Wooden boat & deck components & millwork* ........ (609) 965-1411

Specialty Stair & Rail, LLC, 1717 State Route 34 Cliff St., Bldg. 8, P.O. Box 642, Farmingdale 07727
Ptnr.—Stacy Bloodgood, Jr., 7 emp., *Wooden stairs & railings* ........ (732) 359-8174

Stevens Cabinet & Millwork, 776 Frenchtown Rd., Milford 08848
Owner—Paul Stevens, 3 emp., *Wooden kitchen & office cabinets &* ........ (908) 996-6290

Studio L Contracting, LLC, 1401 Palisade Ave., Teaneck 07666
Owner—David Lehmann, 6 emp., *Architectural millwork & custom wooden* ........ (201) 837-1650

Summit Millwork & Supply, Inc., 235 Morris Ave., Summit 07901
Pres.—Nick Curiale, 5 emp., *Architectural moulding & millwork* ........ (908) 277-0039

Tea & Elle Woodworks, LLC, 5004 Industrial Rd., Farmingdale 07727
Owner—Todd Gleason, 7 emp., *CNC components & parts* ........ (732) 938-9660

Terzano Cabinetry, Inc., 111 Leuning St., Unit G, South Hackensack 07606
Owner & Pres.—Joe Terzano, 8 emp., *Custom-designed handmade cabinetry* ........ (201) 373-9500

Trade Images, 701 S. Harding Hwy., Buena 08310
Pres.—David Bird, 25 emp., *Architectural millwork & custom cabinetry* ........ (856) 697-2700

Vanco Millwork, Inc., 18 Microlab Rd., Livingston 07039
CEO—Lyn Vanadia, 8 emp., *Custom cabinetry, millwork & architectural* ........ (973) 992-3061

V-Custom Millwork, Inc., 1480 Highway 22, P.O. Box 6842, Bridgewater 08807
Pres.—Susan Schumer, 10 emp., *Millwork, including wall & stair wainscoting* ........ (732) 469-9600

Versatile Distributors, Inc., 80 Industrial Rd., Lodi 07644
Pres.—Joel Cuccio, 55 emp., *Vinyl windows, entry & storm doors* ........ (973) 779-1400

Visual Architectural Designs, Inc., 15 Harmich Rd., South Plainfield 07080
Pres.—Sara Chrysanthopoulos, 20 emp., *Architectural millwork, store fixtures* ........ (908) 754-3000

West Hudson Millwork, Inc., 60 Arlington Ave., Kearny 07032
Pres.—Jonathan David Giordano, 2 emp., *Wooden & laminated cabinets, furniture* ........ (201) 991-7191

Wood & Laminates, Inc., 102 Route 46 E., Lodi 07644
Pres.—Gabriel Salazar, 20 emp., *Custom bars & interiors for homes,* ........ (973) 773-7475

Wood Artisans, Inc., 49 Oak St., Norwood 07648
Pres.—Harland Reese, 2 emp., *Wooden cabinets & millwork* ........ (201) 768-1663

Wood Products, Inc., 34 Allentown Rd., Southampton 08088
Pres.—John W. Taylor, 5 emp., *Circular & straight run stairs & railings* ........ (609) 859-0303

Wood Shed, Inc., The, 4500 Park Ave., Weehawken 07086
Pres.—Roland Arlt, 3 emp., *Wooden furniture, bookcases & kitchen* ........ (201) 866-7949

Wood Works, 1111 N. Black Horse Pike, Williamstown 08094
Mng. Ptnr.—Carol Bartling, 6 emp., *Wooden cabinets & bookcases* ........ (856) 728-4520

Woodchucker, Inc., The, 42 Bridgeton-Fairton Rd., P.O. Box 380, Fairton 08320
Pres.—Karen Love Millul, 4 emp., *Commercial & residential woodworking* ........ (856) 575-0200

Woodhaven Lumber & Millwork, Inc., 200 James St., P.O. Box 870, Lakewood 08701
Pres.—Alan Robinson, 152 emp., *Millwork, including decks, railings* ........ (732) 901-0030

Woodhut, LLC, 339 Fairfield Rd., Freehold 07728
★ Member—Merrill Hassell, 10 emp., *Wooden doors & windows* ........ (732) 414-6440

Woodshop, Inc., The, 58 Flint Rd., Toms River 08757
Pres.—Thomas Fantaccione, 3 emp., *Millwork* ........ (732) 349-8006

Woodtec, Inc., 300 Stiger St., Hackettstown 07840
Pres.—John Marra, 7 emp., *Millwork* ........ (908) 979-0180

Woodwork & More, LLC, 24 W. Gorman Ave., Collingswood 08108
Owner—Edward Satkowski, 1 emp., *Woodworking, including millwork, railing* ........ (856) 986-3140

Wowtrim, 178 W. Westfield Ave., Roselle Park 07204
Pres.—Felix Dubinsky, 22 emp., *Wooden automotive interior trim* ........ (732) 340-0766

Yonkers Plywood Mfg., 3130 Bordentown Ave., P.O. Box 152, Old Bridge 08857
Pres.—Edmund Greco, 25 emp., *Plywood doors & panels* ........ (732) 727-1200

Zone Defense, Inc., 4 Emery Ave., Randolph 07869
Pres.—George Mandas, 10 emp., *Architectural millwork* ........ (973) 328-0436

## 2434 Kitchen cabinets—wood

Acro Display, 2250-A Sherman Ave., Pennsauken 08110
Pres.—Paul Beranato, Jr., 6 emp., *Millwork, wooden cabinets & laminated* ........ (856) 488-9710

Advanced Cabinets, 654 4th St., Newark 07107
Owner—Pompeo Leone, 2 emp., *Wooden kitchen cabinets* ........ (973) 481-3441

Alex's Custom Kitchens, LLC, 824 Paterson Ave., East Rutherford 07073
Owner—Louie Alexander Eliades, 1 emp., *Custom wooden kitchen cabinets, vanities* ........ (201) 933-9359

Architectural Cabinetry, 51 Willow St., Washington 07882
★ Owner—Cheryl Fortner, 5 emp., *Custom wooden architectural cabinets* ........ (908) 689-1600

Architectural Woodworking Assocs., LLC, 4 7th St., Frenchtown 08825
Ptnr.—John Gehman, 6 emp., *Architectural millwork & wooden cabinets* ........ (908) 996-7866

Artisan Kitchen Studio, LLC, 26 Cokesbury Rd., P.O. Box 151, Lebanon 08833
Pres.—Richard Butler, 2 emp., *Wooden & laminate cabinets & custom* ........ (908) 236-7233
Atlas Woodwork, 212 Wright St., Newark 07114
Pres.—Antonio Martins, 10 emp., *Wooden kitchen cabinets & commercial* ........ (973) 621-9595
Beech Woodworks, Inc., 9 Kentucky Ave., Paterson 07503
Pres.—Tom Connor, 4 emp., *Wooden cabinets* ........ (973) 225-0111
Bell Arte Woodworking, Inc., 10 W. Mravlag Pl., Elizabeth 07201
Pres.—Giusette Chillemi, 12 emp., *Wooden store fixtures & cabinets &* ........ (908) 355-1199
Bennett Cabinets, Inc., 1251 Highway 1, Edison 08837
Pres.—Michael Bennett, 6 emp., *Custom wooden kitchen cabinets & architectura* ........ (732) 548-1616
Borst Cabinet Co., 15 Schierloh Ct., Ramsey 07446
Owner, Pres. & Sales Mgr.—David J. Borst, 3 emp., *Custom & semi-custom stock kitchen* .... (201) 825-4220
Bothers Woodworking, Inc., A. R., 236 Dukes Pkwy., P.O. Box 127, Somerville 08876
Pres., CFO—Charles Bothers, 10 emp., *Wooden kitchen cabinets* ........ (908) 725-2891
Bozzone Custom Woodwork, Inc., 77 N. Beverwyck Rd., Lake Hiawatha 07034
Pres.—Lou Bozzone, 4 emp., *Wooden & laminate cabinets* ........ (973) 334-5598
Britton Cabinets, 199 Westwood Ave., Long Branch 07740
Owner & Pres.—Tim Britton, 10 emp., *Wooden kitchen cabinets* ........ (732) 222-2232
Buzz-Bee Cabinetry Co., 589 N. East Ave., Vineland 08360
Owner—Paul Buzby, 1 emp., *Wooden cabinets & laminating* ........ (856) 691-5474
Cabinet Works Corp., 511 W. Kings Hwy., Mount Ephraim 08059
Pres.—Frank Cavallaro, 3 emp., *Wooden & laminate cabinets & architectural* ........ (856) 931-7289
Capra Custom Cabinetry & Millwork, LLC, 259 E. Washington Ave., Washington 07882
★ Owner—John Capra, 2 emp., *Custom residential & commercial casework* ........ (908) 797-9848
Castle Woodcraft Assocs., 161 Route 9, P.O. Box 426, Pine Beach 08741
Ptnr.—Ernest Guenzburger, 15 emp., *Kitchen & office wooden & plastic laminate* ........ (732) 349-1519
Central Millwork Of New Jersey, 92 N. Main St., Bldg. 11, P.O. Box 447, Windsor 08561
Owner, Pres. & GM—Kevin Coyle, 7 emp., *Architectural woodwork & cabinets* ........ (609) 448-7700
Choice Cabinetry, LLC, 61 5th St., Somerville 08876
Owner—Avner Shmuel, 50 emp., *Wooden, melamine & thermofoil kitchen* ........ (908) 707-8801
Citkowski Co., 90 Dayton Ave., Passaic 07055
Pres., CEO—Mario Citkowski, 4 emp., *Architectural woodworking* ........ (973) 390-5477
CNC Associates, 101 Kentile Rd., South Plainfield 07080
Pres.—Nathan Indig, 95 emp., *Wooden cabinets & countertops* ........ (718) 416-3853
Codfish Park Design, LLC, 39 Commerce St., Chatham 07928
Chief Cabinet Officer—Tyler Merson, 2 emp., *Residential wooden cabinets & furniture* ........ (646) 298-4050
Colfax Cabinet Co., Inc., 86 Ackerman Ave., Clifton 07011
Pres.—Martin Lovy, 15 emp., *Custom wooden kitchen cabinets* ........ (973) 546-5422
Collingswood Architectural Millwork, Inc., 715 Taylor Ave., Collingswood 08107
Pres.—Robert Engelke, 17 emp., *Millwork, cabinets & countertops* ........ (856) 854-0440
Corporate Woodworking, Inc., 368 Passaic Ave., P.O. Box 10362, Fairfield 07004
Pres.—Dan Andersen, 15 emp., *Wooden & laminated cabinets* ........ (973) 227-2211
Costas Architectural Woodworking, 248 Montgomery St., Bloomfield 07003
Ptnr.—Oscar Costa, 8 emp., *Custom residential & commercial kitchen* ........ (973) 429-7004
Creations By Jeffrey, Inc., 1522 Route 37 E., Toms River 08753
Pres.—Jeffrey Jones, 18 emp., *Wooden kitchen cabinets* ........ (732) 506-0051
Creative Cabinet Designs, Inc., 301 Main St., Boonton 07005
Pres.—Manuel Silva, 10 emp., *Wooden kitchen & bathroom cabinets* ........ (973) 402-5886
Creative Innovations, Inc., 20-21 Wagaraw Rd., Ste. 31-B, Fair Lawn 07410
Pres.—Joseph Batavia, 8 emp., *Wooden kitchen & bath cabinets & millwork* ........ (973) 636-9060
Custom Cabinets By Jim Bucko, Inc., 135 W. Burk Ave., Wildwood 08260
Pres.—James Bucko, 6 emp., *Wooden kitchen cabinets, display cases* ........ (609) 889-7666
Custom Creations By M. D., 52 Ishmael Rd., Tuckerton 08087
Pres.—Mark Duym, 5 emp., *Kitchen cabinets & countertops* ........ (609) 294-1321
Custom Interiors, Inc., 47 W. Grand Ave., Montvale 07645
Pres.—Keith D. Wright, 2 emp., *Wooden cabinets & custom woodworking* ........ (201) 573-9702
Custom Wood Furniture, Inc., 37 E. Clinton St., P.O. Box 3034, Newton 07860
Pres.—John Kweselait, 15 emp., *Wooden & laminated cabinets* ........ (973) 579-4880
Custom Wood, LLC, 400 Goldman Dr., Cream Ridge 08514
Off. Mgr.—Lisa Zucatti, 4 emp., *Kitchen & bathroom cabinets & granite* ........ (609) 758-8288
Custom Woodcraft Co., 81 Park Pl., Passaic 07055
Pres.—Israel Obando, 1 emp., *Custom wooden cabinets* ........ (973) 472-0824
D S F, Inc., 401 U.S. Highway 202, Raritan 08869
Pres.—Simon DeGirolamo, 25 emp., *Architectural millwork & custom cabinets* ........ (908) 218-5153
Darkstar Woodworking, 123 Woodland Ave., Westwood 07675
Owner—Ronald Maxon, 1 emp., *Wooden household cabinets* ........ (201) 248-1575
Designers Kitchens, Inc., 250 Faraday Ave., Jackson 08527
Pres.—Edwin Rivera, 15 emp., *Architectural woodwork & wooden cabinets* ........ (732) 370-5500
Diversified Millwork, Inc., 420 N. 2nd Rd., Unit C, Hammonton 08037
Pres.—Don McFaul, 10 emp., *Wooden, plastic laminate & solid-surface* ........ (609) 270-7385
East Coast Counter Tops, Inc., 166 Main St., P.O. Box 645, Lakewood 08701
Pres.—Ofer Malhi, 10 emp., *Wooden countertops & cabinets* ........ (732) 363-7734
Eastern Millwork, Inc., 18 Chapel Ave., Jersey City 07305
Pres.—Andrew Campbell, 60 emp., *Commercial wooden cabinets, stairs* ........ (201) 451-9510
Empire Industries, Inc., 40 Warren St., Paterson 07524
Pres.—Jacob Goren, 32 emp., *Bathroom furniture, vanities, ceramic* ........ (973) 279-2050
Eppley Building & Design, Inc., 220-B Goffle Rd., Hawthorne 07506
Pres.—Paul Eppley, 35 emp., *Custom cabinets & architectural millwork* ........ (973) 636-9499
Feldman Assocs., Inc., F. L., 811 Memorial Dr., Asbury Park 07712
Pres.—Frank Feldman, 8 emp., *Wooden cabinets & furniture* ........ (732) 776-8544
Finest Enterprises, Inc., 2107 Herbertsville Rd., Point Pleasant 08742
Pres.—Jim Horne, 1 emp., *Wooden kitchen cabinets, millwork &* ........ (732) 892-1121
Forino Kitchen Cabinets, Inc., 33 S. Maple Ave., Park Ridge 07656
Pres.—Charles Forino, 8 emp., *Custom wooden kitchen cabinets* ........ (201) 573-0990
Franley Products, Inc., 89 Riverwood Dr., Ste. 4, Toms River 08755
CEO—Michael Mullen, 2 emp., *Custom wooden cabinets* ........ (732) 244-1496
Gafgen Cabinetmakers, Thomas P., 5 Truman Ct., Robbinsville 08691
Owner—Thomas P. Gafgen, 3 emp., *Wooden & melamine residential & office* ........ (609) 448-2060
Garfield Cabinets & Millwork, Inc., 22 Garfield Ave., Garfield 07026
Pres.—James DeVito, Jr., 2 emp., *Wooden cabinets & millwork* ........ (973) 340-0507
Handmade Furniture Co., 612 Main St., West Creek 08092
Owner—Cathy Woodward, 17 emp., *Wooden cabinets & furniture* ........ (609) 597-2708
Hansen's Cabinet Shop, Inc., 42 Park Ave., Madison 07940
Pres.—A. Hansen, 4 emp., *Custom wooden & plastic laminated cabinets* ........ (973) 377-2444
Hanssem Corp., 155 Helen St., South Plainfield 07080
Hum. Res. Mgr.—Joochan Lee, 100 emp., *Wooden & laminate kitchen & bathroom* ........ (908) 754-4949
Hester Bros., Inc., 114 Beach St., Ste. 5, Rockaway 07866
Pres.—Michael Hester, 3 emp., *Custom residential cabinets & architectural* ........ (862) 432-5183
J D M Woodworking & Cabinetry, 226 Huyler St., South Hackensack 07606
Owner—John Moumdjian, 1 emp., *Wooden cabinets* ........ (201) 646-1480
Joti Kitchens, 413 S. Main St., Pleasantville 08232
Owner—Joe Staines, Jr., 3 emp., *Wooden & laminate cabinets* ........ (609) 383-1350

KBM Kitchen & Bath, 75 Harrison St., Little Falls 07424
Pres.—Boris Karpovski, 8 emp., *Kitchen & bathroom cabinets* ........ (973) 890-4900
Kentucky Cabinet Corp., 601 Lehigh Ave., Union 07083
Plt. Mgr.—Peter Drake, 25 emp., *Custom wooden cabinets* ........ (347) 452-5797
Kitchen Kraftsman, The, 343 State Route 34, Matawan 07747
Owner—Jimmy Kuck, 2 emp., *Custom & semicustom wooden kitchen* ........ (732) 583-3321
Kobolak & Son, Inc., 1818 Bannard St., Cinnaminson 08077
Pres.—Erno Kobolak, 30 emp., *Custom cabinetry* ........ (856) 829-6106
Laminate Creations, LLC, 1235 Hurffville Rd., Deptford 08096
Member—James Martucci, 6 emp., *Wooden & laminate kitchen cabinets,* ........ (856) 232-8323
Laminetics, Inc., 1263 River Ave., Lakewood 08701
Pres.—Robert Kicak, 3 emp., *Wooden & laminated countertops & cabinets* ........ (732) 367-1116
Lawler Woodwork, LLC, 938 Lakewood Farmingdale Rd., Howell 07731
Owner—John Lawler, 10 emp., *Commercial & residential wooden cabinets* ........ (732) 942-7204
Lee's Woodworking, Inc., 726 Walling Ave., Belmar 07719
Owner—Bill Lee, 2 emp., *Custom, residential & commercial furniture* ........ (732) 681-1002
Leiz Custom Woodwork, David, 2301 E. Edgar Rd., Bldg. 5-A, Linden 07036
Owner & Pres.—David Leiz, 4 emp., *Wooden kitchen, built-in & entertainment* ........ (908) 486-1533
Longo's Cabinet Shop, 101 Monroe St., Garfield 07026
Owner—Tom Esposito, 1 emp., *Wooden & laminate cabinets* ........ (973) 472-3567
Lutjens Co., Inc., G., 80 George St., Paterson 07503
Pres.—Gary Lutjens, 2 emp., *Wooden kitchen cabinets* ........ (973) 278-9639
Mango Custom Cabinets, Inc., 216 W. Stiger St., Hackettstown 07840
Owner—Richard Mango, 20 emp., *Architectural millwork, including custom* ........ (908) 813-3077
Mastercrafts, 152 Louis St., South Hackensack 07606
Owner—Robert J. Smith, 4 emp., *Wooden cabinets* ........ (201) 641-6555
Miceli Cabinet Corp., 128 Madison Ave., Englewood 07631
Pres.—Joseph Schabes, 2 emp., *Wooden cabinets* ........ (201) 933-4004
Midhattan Woodworking, 3130 Bordentown Ave., Old Bridge 08857
Ptnr.—George Greco, 45 emp., *Architectural millwork, including cabinets* ........ (732) 727-3020
Miller Fabricators, 1135 Mount Ephraim Ave., Camden 08103
Owner, Pres. & CEO—Aaron Miller, 10 emp., *Laminated countertops & custom cabinetry* ........ (856) 541-9499
Millner Kitchens, Inc., 200-B Whitehead Rd., Ste. 108, Hamilton 08619
Pres.—John Millner, 8 emp., *Wooden kitchen cabinets* ........ (609) 890-7300
Mitchell's Woodworking, LLC, 780 Jacksonville Mount Holly Rd., Westampton 08060
Owner—Gordon Mitchell, 3 emp., *Custom cabinets & millwork, including* ........ (609) 261-7500
Miter Box, LLC, 4-21 Banta Pl., Ste. B, Fair Lawn 07410
Owner—Frank Inserra, 7 emp., *Wooden cabinets* ........ (201) 773-6209
Mountain Millwork, 14 Clifton Ave. S., Lakewood 08701
Manager—Nathan Joseph, 3 emp., *Architectural millwork & wooden kitchen* ........ (732) 901-9400
Mr. Paul's Custom Cabinets, 2416 Highway 35, Manasquan 08736
Pres.—Paul Waltsak, 3 emp., *Wooden kitchen & bath cabinets* ........ (732) 528-9427
Narva Kitchens & Closets, Inc., 101 Victory Rd., Springfield 07081
Pres.—Alex Morozov, 5 emp., *Wooden kitchen cabinets* ........ (718) 735-7722
New Century Wood Products, 131 Lincoln Blvd., Middlesex 08846
★ Owner—David Lomonte, 10 emp., *Millwork & casework* ........ (732) 271-2557
On The Level Counter Top, Inc., 825 Brook Rd., Lakewood 08701
★ Pres.—Vito G. Paratore, 1 emp., *Wooden kitchen cabinets & formica countertops* ........ (732) 370-4186
Other Orthodontic Co., Inc., 22 Gail Ct., Sparta 07871
Pres.—Jon Bergeron, 9 emp., *Manufacturer of commercial wooden cabinets* ........ (973) 383-8662
Parsons Cabinetry, Inc., 80 George St., Paterson 07503
Pres.—Winfield Parsons, 12 emp., *Custom kitchen cabinets* ........ (973) 279-4954
Pazera Cabinets Door, 3160 Bordentown Ave., Old Bridge 08857
Ptnr.—Paul Pazera, 5 emp., *Wooden cabinet doors & drawer fronts* ........ (732) 727-1600
Precision Cabinets, 410 E. Freehold Rd., Freehold 07728
Owner—Robert Blatchley, 3 emp., *Wooden kitchen & office cabinets* ........ (732) 462-3342
Proof Productions, Inc., 599 Mantua Blvd., Sewell 08080
Owner & Pres.—Steve McEntee, 20 emp., *Scenic wood & metal products, including* ........ (856) 442-0700
R & T Custom Cabinets, 1131 Herbert Blvd., Williamstown 08094
Owner—Richard Digirolamo, 2 emp., *Wood & laminate kitchen cabinets &* ........ (856) 728-1979
Red Bank Cabinet Co., 548 Shrewsbury Ave., Tinton Falls 07701
Pres., R & D Mgr.—Kenneth Asmar, 10 emp., *Custom & semi-custom cabinets & exhibit* ........ (732) 741-8080
Rivers Edge Woodworks & Design, 90 Dayton Ave., Passaic 07055
Pres.—Gary Odendahl, 2 emp., *Wooden cabinetry & interior millwork* ........ (973) 337-2288
Ross, Inc., A. W., 297 Monroe St., Passaic 07055
Co-Pres.—Vojtek Rys, 14 emp., *Wooden kitchen cabinets & countertops* ........ (973) 471-5900
Royal Cabinet Co., Inc., 152 U.S. Highway 206, Unit 14-D, Hillsborough 08844
Pres.—Paul Y. McDonald, 30 emp., *Wooden, laminated & commercial kitchen* ........ (908) 203-8000
Ruedi Kuhns Wood Shop, 509 Berckman St., Plainfield 07062
Pres.—Rudy Kuhn, 1 emp., *Wooden kitchen cabinets* ........ (908) 755-6947
Salerno's Kitchen Cabinets, Inc., 599 N. Midland Ave., Saddle Brook 07663
Pres.—Luciano Salerno, 15 emp., *Custom wooden kitchen cabinets & related* ........ (201) 794-1990
Sam's Custom Woodworking, 14 Dunham Ln., Mount Holly 08060
Owner—Samuel Sortino, 1 emp., *Wooden cabinets* ........ (609) 267-4962
SandKamp Woodworks, LLC, 430 Communipaw Ave., Jersey City 07304
Owner & Pres.—Anthony Sandkamp, 3 emp., *Wooden kitchen & custom built-in cabinets* ........ (201) 200-0101
Shearman Cabinets, Inc., 195 N. Munn Ave., East Orange 07017
Pres.—Thomas Shearman, 5 emp., *Wooden cabinets* ........ (973) 677-0071
Shekia Group, LLC, The, 1130 King Georges Post Rd., Edison 08837
Owner—Henry Linn, 15 emp., *Wooden kitchen cabinets* ........ (732) 372-7668
Stelton Cabinet & Supply, 1358 Stelton Rd., Piscataway 08854
Owner—Robert Aiello, 7 emp., *Wooden cabinets & countertops* ........ (732) 985-1035
Stevens Cabinet & Millwork, 776 Frenchtown Rd., Milford 08848
Owner—Paul Stevens, 3 emp., *Wooden kitchen & office cabinets &* ........ (908) 996-6290
Studio L Contracting, LLC, 1401 Palisade Ave., Teaneck 07666
Owner—David Lehmann, 6 emp., *Architectural millwork & custom wooden* ........ (201) 837-1650
Superior Custom Kitchens, LLC, 126 Mount Bethel Rd., Warren 07059
Ptnr.—Joe Borin, 10 emp., *Custom & semi-custom cabinets for full* ........ (908) 753-6005
T J Mfg., Inc., Allaire Airport, Bldg. 25, P.O. Box 2361, Farmingdale 07727
Pres.—Tom Goski, 1 emp., *Wooden kitchen & bathroom cabinets* ........ (732) 938-7325
Taylor Made Cabinets, 516 E. Bay Ave., Manahawkin 08050
Ptnr. & Plt. Mgr.—Dave Taylor, 15 emp., *Wooden & laminate cabinets* ........ (609) 978-6900
Taylor Made Custom Cabinetry, Inc., 7035 Central Hwy., Ste. 200, Pennsauken 08109
Pres.—Jay Taylor, 11 emp., *Custom wooden cabinetry & fine furniture* ........ (856) 786-5433
Terzano Cabinetry, Inc., 111 Leuning St., Unit G, South Hackensack 07606
Owner & Pres.—Joe Terzano, 8 emp., *Custom-designed handmade cabinetry* ........ (201) 373-9500
Trade Images, 701 S. Harding Hwy., Buena 08310
Pres.—David Bird, 25 emp., *Architectural millwork & custom cabinetry* ........ (856) 697-2700
Urvesh Granite (USA), Inc., 1777 Route 130 S., North Brunswick 08902
Pres.—Bharat Patel, 8 emp., *Granite countertops & wooden kitchen* ........ (201) 369-3934
Vanco Millwork, Inc., 18 Microlab Rd., Livingston 07039
CEO—Lyn Vanadia, 8 emp., *Custom cabinetry, millwork & architectural* ........ (973) 992-3061



★ Indicates new listing this edition.

Visual Architectural Designs, Inc., 15 Harmich Rd., South Plainfield 07080
Pres.—Sara Chrysanthopoulos, 20 emp., *Architectural millwork, store fixtures* (908) 754-3000
Will's Custom Displays & Woodwork, 1202 E. Elizabeth Ave., Linden 07036
Owner—Will Alicea, 1 emp., *Wooden cabinets, displays & store fixtures* (908) 925-0008
Wood Artisans, Inc., 49 Oak St., Norwood 07648
Pres.—Harland Reese, 2 emp., *Wooden cabinets & millwork* (201) 768-1663
Wood Shed, Inc., The, 4500 Park Ave., Weehawken 07086
Pres.—Roland Arlt, 3 emp., *Wooden furniture, bookcases & kitchen* (201) 866-7949
Wood Shop, 24 Water St., Englishtown 07726
Owner—Bruce Evano, 1 emp., *Wooden kitchen cabinets* (732) 446-3377
Wood Works, 1111 N. Black Horse Pike, Williamstown 08094
Mng. Ptnr.—Carol Bartling, 6 emp., *Wooden cabinets & bookcases* (856) 728-4520
Wood-O-Rama, Inc., 100 67th St., Closter 07624
Pres.—Carlos Caronedo, 2 emp., *Custom wooden kitchen cabinets & counters* (201) 768-1180
Woodwork 4 U, LLC, 205 Frelinghuysen Ave., Newark 07114
Pres.—Michal Jenicek, 5 emp., *Wooden kitchen cabinets & showcases* (973) 643-3044

## 2435 Hardwood veneer & plywood

Garmar Industries, Inc., 1625 Route 322, P.O. Box 460, Woolwich Township 08085
V-P.—Jerry Bernard, 33 emp., *Dimensional lumber, crating stock,* (856) 241-9700
UFP Berlin, LLC, 159 Jackson Rd., Berlin 08009
GM—David Goldman, 60 emp., *Wooden roof trusses & wall panels* (856) 767-0043
Yonkers Plywood Mfg., 3130 Bordentown Ave., P.O. Box 152, Old Bridge 08857
Pres.—Edmund Greco, 25 emp., *Plywood doors & panels* (732) 727-1200

## 2436 Softwood veneer & plywood

Garmar Industries, Inc., 1625 Route 322, P.O. Box 460, Woolwich Township 08085
V-P.—Jerry Bernard, 33 emp., *Dimensional lumber, crating stock,* (856) 241-9700
UFP Berlin, LLC, 159 Jackson Rd., Berlin 08009
GM—David Goldman, 60 emp., *Wooden roof trusses & wall panels* (856) 767-0043

## 2439 Structural wood members, nec

Concord Truss Co., 692 S. Evergreen Ave., Woodbury Heights 08097
Pres., CFO—Richard Phalines, 60 emp., *Wooden trusses* (856) 845-3848
ProBuild Co., LLC, 210 Williamstown Rd., Berlin 08009
Plt. Mgr.—Russ Gervasi, 30 emp., *Wooden roof & floor trusses* (856) 767-3153
Timplex Corp., 1370 State Route 23, Wantage 07461
Pres.—Ron Slate, 16 emp., *Wooden trusses & light gage, cold formed* (973) 875-5500
UFP Berlin, LLC, 159 Jackson Rd., Berlin 08009
GM—David Goldman, 60 emp., *Wooden roof trusses & wall panels* (856) 767-0043

## 2441 Nailed wood boxes & shook

C & D Cases, Inc., 407 River Rd., Unit 9, Clifton 07014
Pres.—Coy Frisbee, 4 emp., *Travel, sample & musical instrument* (973) 473-4800
Cases By Source, Inc., 215 Island Rd., Mahwah 07430
V-P.—Matthew Adler, 25 emp., *Aluminum, plastic & wood SKB, ATA,* (201) 831-0005
Delaware Valley Box & Lumber Co., 2651 E. State St. Ext., Trenton 08619
Pres.—Charles C. Gould, 12 emp., *Company headquarters & wooden shipping* (609) 890-2900
Tri-State Crating & Pallet Co., 85 Fulton St., Paterson 07501
Chrm.—Marc Ellison, 30 emp., *Custom wooden boxes, crates, skids,* (973) 357-8293
Vandereems Mfg. Co., Inc., 40 Schoon Ave., Hawthorne 07506
Pres.—John Vandereems, 6 emp., *Wooden crates, boxes & custom pallets* (973) 427-2355

## 2448 Pallets & skids—wood

Ace Pallet Corp., 215 E. Broad St., P.O. Box 228, Paulsboro 08066
Off. Mgr.—Cynthia Unger, 30 emp., *Wooden pallets* (856) 423-7277
ATCO Pallet Co., 1000 Creek Rd., P.O. Box 5115, Delanco 08075
Pres. & Dir., Opers. & Sales—David Hajduk, 28 emp., *Company headquarters & wooden* (856) 461-8141
Avenel Pallet Co., Inc., Foot Of S. 2nd St., P.O. Box 276, Dunellen 08812
Pres.—Vincent Colonna, 11 emp., *Wooden pallets* (732) 752-0500
Baxter Co., Inc., E. L., 70 S. 7th Ave., P.O. Box 277, Long Branch 07740
CEO—Elwood Baxter, 14 emp., *Packaging, shipping & handling supplies* (732) 229-8219
Budget Pallet, Inc., 3225 Dell Ave., North Bergen 07047
Pres.—Ernest Parodi, 15 emp., *Wooden pallets* (201) 330-2800
Coyote Pallet Co., 13 Oradell Rd., Hewitt 07421
Owner—Donald Coyote, 3 emp., *Wooden pallets* (973) 853-7266
Cutler Bros. Box & Lumber Co., 711 W. Prospect Ave., P.O. Box 217, Fairview 07022
Owner—Gregory Cutler, 30 emp., *Pallets, skids, boxes & lumber* (201) 943-2535
D & H Pallets, LLC, 45 Verona Ave., Newark 07104
★ Owner—Ramon Munoz, 6 emp., *Wooden pallets* (973) 481-2981
Delisa Pallet Corp., 91-97 Blanchard St., Newark 07105
Pres.—John Delisa, 15 emp., *New, used & reconditioned wooden pallets* (973) 344-8600
Eagle Pallet, 108 S. Wade Blvd., Millville 08332
Pres.—Ken Giaccio, 15 emp., *New, recycled, re-manufactured, custom* (856) 765-9444
Electronic Power Designs, Inc., 132 Union Ave., Bloomingdale 07403
Pres.—Gregory J. Brown, 15 emp., *Gaseous piping skids & industrial control* (973) 838-7055
Extreme Pallet, 301-317 Astor St., Newark 07114
Pres.—Eddie Sanchez, 3 emp., *Wooden pallets* (973) 596-1400
Extreme Pallet, Inc., 315 Astor St., Newark 07114
Pres.—Eddie Sanchez, 11 emp., *ISPM 15 certified custom wooden pallets* (973) 286-1717
F & R Pallets, Inc., 1929 S. 4th St., Camden 08104
Pres.—Ronald Abate, 45 emp., *Wooden pallets* (856) 964-8516
Forte Pallet, Inc., 3 Water Works Rd., Old Bridge 08857
Owner & Pres.—Tony Forte, 3 emp., *Wooden pallets & skids* (732) 727-3879
General Pallet, LLC, 97 River Rd., Flemington 08822
Ptnr.—Donald W. Baldwin, 7 emp., *New & reconditioned wooden, plastic* (908) 238-1000
Gorgo Pallet Co., 646 S. Delsea Dr., Vineland 08360
Pres.—Nick Biagi, 30 emp., *Wooden pallets* (856) 692-0303
IFCO Systems, 320 Dulty's Ln., P.O. Box 1333, Burlington 08016
GM—Taylor Thomas, 79 emp., *Wooden pallets* (609) 386-5200
ISCO, 1 Commerce Dr., Bldg. 3, Barrington 08007
Manager—Aaron Snethen, 50 emp., *Wooden pallets* (856) 672-9182
JUST Nation, LLC, 359 Central Ave., Newark 07103
★ Owner—S. Crespo, 4 emp., *Wooden pallets* (973) 485-5878
Love Pallet Company, LLC., 460 Mundet Pl., P.O. Box 774, Hillside 07205
Ptnr.—Brenda Cardoza, 16 emp., *Wooden pallets* (908) 964-3385
Millwood, Inc., 7 Brick Plant Rd., Ste. C, South River 08882
Plt. Mgr.—Paul Eichmann, 70 emp., *Wooden pallets* (732) 967-8818
Northeast Pallet Recycling, LLC, 133 Yellowbrook Rd., Farmingdale 07727
Pres.—Nicolas Martinez, 10 emp., *Recycled wooden pallets* (732) 751-1919
Notie Corp., 177-A Route 526, Allentown 08501
Plt. Mgr.—Mike Weatherholtz, 5 emp., *Wooden pallets* (609) 259-3477
Pedestal Pallet Co., 777 N. Avenue Ext., P.O. Box 450, Dunellen 08812
Owner—John Ruotulo, 15 emp., *Wooden pallets & skids* (732) 968-7488
Poor Boy Pallet, LLC, 45 Finley Rd., Bridgeton 08302
Member—Dennis Macklin, 20 emp., *Wooden pallets* (856) 451-3771
S & B Pallet Co., 1348 S. 2nd St., Plainfield 07063
Pres.—Steve Mazza, 60 emp., *Wooden pallets* (908) 756-3606
Select Enterprises, Inc., 71 Executive Ave., Edison 08817
Pres.—Tom Lordi, 6 emp., *Wooden pallets* (732) 287-8622
T & M Pallet Co., Inc., 116 Edison Rd., Stewartsville 08886
V-P.—Steve Tigar, 20 emp., *Wooden pallets, shipping crates & boxes* (908) 454-3042
Tri-State Crating & Pallet Co., 85 Fulton St., Paterson 07501
Chrm.—Marc Ellison, 30 emp., *Custom wooden boxes, crates, skids,* (973) 357-8293
Van Nick Pallet, Inc., 104 Snyder Rd., South Plainfield 07080
Pres.—Robert Ducalo, 15 emp., *Wooden pallets* (908) 753-1800
Vandereems Mfg. Co., Inc., 40 Schoon Ave., Hawthorne 07506
Pres.—John Vandereems, 6 emp., *Wooden crates, boxes & custom pallets* (973) 427-2355
Warren Pallet Co., Inc., 601 County Road 627, Bloomsbury 08804
Pres.—Donald Tigar, Sr., 18 emp., *Custom, new & reconditioned wooden* (908) 995-7172

## 2449 Wood containers, nec

A B C Crating & Rigging Co., 1-21 Erie St., Paterson 07524
Pres.—Andrew Tuohy, 10 emp., *Wooden crates* (973) 684-0046
Baxter Co., Inc., E. L., 70 S. 7th Ave., P.O. Box 277, Long Branch 07740
CEO—Elwood Baxter, 14 emp., *Packaging, shipping & handling supplies* (732) 229-8219
Delaware Valley Box & Lumber Co., 14 Austin Ave., Glendora 08029
Opers. Mgr.—Chris Gould, 20 emp., *Corrugated boxes & wooden crates* (856) 939-1900
Jan Packaging, Inc., 100 Harrison St., Dover 07801
Pres.—Karl Malavarca, 80 emp., *Wooden shipping crates for export packing* (973) 361-7200
MAUSER USA LLC, 35 Cotters Ln., Ste. C, East Brunswick 08816
Pres., CEO—Jeff Simmonds, 80 emp., *Company headquarters & plastic containers* (732) 353-7000
Vandereems Mfg. Co., Inc., 40 Schoon Ave., Hawthorne 07506
Pres.—John Vandereems, 6 emp., *Wooden crates, boxes & custom pallets* (973) 427-2355

## 2451 Mobile homes

Casework Design, 10 County Line Rd., Ste 26, Branchburg 08876
Owner—Michael Rowden, 3 emp., *Store & commercial fixtures, business* (908) 722-7401

## 2452 Prefabricated wood buildings

Craft Line Cabinet Corp., 10 Walnut St., Clifton 07013
Owner—Gam Danziger, 10 emp., *Laminated cabinets* (973) 777-8808
Homestead Fence Contractors, LLC, 637 Main St., West Creek 08092
Pres.—Nathan Foote, 14 emp., *Wooden & PVC fences & prefabricated* (609) 296-1829
Kempton Wood Products, LLC, 2800 Ridgewood Rd., Wall 07719
Manager—Kevin Kempton, 6 emp., *Wooden & vinyl storage buildings, pool* (732) 449-8673
Laracca Mfg., Inc., 395 Little Falls Rd., Cedar Grove 07009
Pres.—Anthony Laracca, 20 emp., *Wooden storage sheds* (973) 571-1452
Medford Cedar Products, Inc., 59 Old Red Lion Rd., Vincentown 08088
Pres.—Albin E. Scheibner, 7 emp., *Manufacturer of cedar garden structures* (609) 859-1400
Mr. Fence, 3468 U.S. Highway 9, Ste. 2, Freehold 07728
Owner—Dan Caporellie, 8 emp., *Vinyl, aluminum, wood & chain-link* (732) 303-1614
NMN Closet, Inc., 40 Veterans Blvd., Carlstadt 07072
Pres.—Norman Holtz, 40 emp., *Shelving products for closets, home* (201) 964-9600
Parker3d, 1325 Terrill Rd., Scotch Plains 07076
Pres.—Richard Parker, 100 emp., *Custom interactive & traditional holiday* (908) 322-5552

## 2491 Wood preserving

Cox Industries, 1517 Route 38 W., P.O. Box 507, Hainesport 08036
Plt. Mgr.—Phil Taylor, 10 emp., *Wood preservation* (609) 267-4700
Tri-State Fences & Supply, Inc., 806 Route 23, Sussex 07461
Pres.—Allen Brands, 3 emp., *Wooden fencing* (973) 875-3213

## 2493 Wood products—reconstituted

California Closets, 4 Gardner Rd., Ste. 5, Fairfield 07004
Ptnr.—Marty Ginsberg, 50 emp., *Melamine & MDF closets & related custom* (973) 882-3800

## 2499 Wood products, nec

A & F Sign Company LLC, 28 E. Railway Ave., Paterson 07503
Sole Member—Frank Ferrucci, 1 emp., *Architectural, illuminated, non-illuminated* (973) 278-3707
A. L. Don, 1 Dock St., Matawan 07747
CEO—Peter Gronbeck, 8 emp., *Wooden & synthetic pilot & debarkation* (732) 574-1441
Abate Fence, Inc., 3619 Route 23, Hamburg 07419
Pres.—Dominick Rotolo, 5 emp., *Wooden, wire, aluminum & PVC fences* (973) 827-4167
Academy Fence Co., Inc., 119 N. Day St., Orange 07050
★ Owner—Lou Cavallo, 20 emp., *Aluminum & wooden fencing & installation* (973) 674-0600
Acadia Scenic, Inc., 130 Bay St., Jersey City 07302
Pres.—David Lawson, 25 emp., *Theatrical scenery buildings* (201) 653-8889
Accent Fence, Inc., 1450 Bremen Ave., P.O. Box 656, Egg Harbor City 08215
Pres.—Greg Carnasale, 20 emp., *Wooden, metal & vinyl fences & ornamental* (609) 965-6400
Alenco Fence & Supply Corp., 167 Route 70, Bldg. B, Medford 08055
Owner—Chris Murphy, 10 emp., *Wooden, aluminum, chain-link & vinyl* (609) 654-6060
Alex's Custom Kitchens, LLC, 824 Paterson Ave., East Rutherford 07073
Owner—Louie Alexander Eliades, 1 emp., *Custom wooden kitchen cabinets, vanities* (201) 933-9359
All Quality Fence, 1266 Route 46, P.O. Box 85, Ledgewood 07852
Owner—John Johnson, 6 emp., *Aluminum, red & white cedar, chain-link* (973) 927-0722
All-Star Pro & Sport Store, 642 State Route 35 N., Neptune 07753
Owner—Joe Storzieri, 2 emp., *Trophies, plaques & textile embroidery* (732) 774-3444
All-State Fence, Inc., 1389 Highway 9 N., Howell 07731
Pres.—Scott Skrable, 10 emp., *Corporate headquarters & wooden fences* (732) 431-4944
All-State Fence, Inc., 1389 Route 9 N., Howell 07731
Pres.—Scott Skrable, 8 emp., *Residential & commercial chain-link* (732) 431-4944
Amechi Fence, 5950 Route 42, Turnersville 08012
★ Owner—Al Amechi, 10 emp., *Cedar wood fences* (856) 227-6691
Anello Fence, LLC, 50 State Route 23, Pequannock 07440
Pres.—Steve Anello, 4 emp., *Vinyl, aluminum & wooden fencing* (973) 839-4100
Arthur Schuman, Inc., 40 New Dutch Ln., Fairfield 07004
Pres.—Neal Schuman, 85 emp., *Corporate headquarters & wedges, grated* (973) 227-0030
Artistic Doors & Windows, 10 S. Inman Ave., Avenel 07001
Pres.—Enrico Autovino, 45 emp., *Custom hardwood doors & windows & high-end* (732) 726-9400
Artistic Fence, 757 River Dr., Passaic 07055
Pres.—Steven Boggio, 20 emp., *Chain link & wooden fencing* (973) 779-4540
B&D Marketing, Inc., 1879 Old Cuthbert Rd., Ste. 21, Cherry Hill 08034
Pres.—Marlene Epworth, 5 emp., *Custom donor recognition wall displays* (856) 354-2004

Bendix Architectural Products, Inc., 90 Dayton Ave., Ste. 34, Passaic 07055
Chrm., Pres.—David Garrett, 6 emp., *Decorative mouldings & hand-carved* .......... (973) 473-4780
Bergen Fence, Inc., 279 Bergen Tpke., Ridgefield Park 07660
Sales Mgr.—John Durr, 6 emp., *Wooden & vinyl fencing* .......... (201) 641-2111
Berlin Neon Sign, Inc., 326 Old White Horse Pike, Waterford Works 08089
Pres.—Tim Manna, 2 emp., *Neon signs & flagpoles* .......... (856) 767-0525
Beta Craft, Inc., 2682 Route 130, P.O. Box 536, Cranbury 08512
Pres.—Arthur Hasselbach, 2 emp., *Pinewood derby kits & supplies & orchid* .......... (609) 655-1940
Beveled Edge, 51 Mount Bethel Rd., Warren 07059
Owner—Scott Andrus, 2 emp., *Picture frames* .......... (908) 754-6772
Bird Toy Man, 197 S. Hillside Ave., Succasunna 07876
Owner—Henry E. Pedynowski, 1 emp., *Wooden, plastic, acrylic, leather &* .......... (973) 584-0756
Blue Anchor Fence, LLC, 314 Arrowood Ave., Hammonton 08037
Pres.—Raymond Reyes, 6 emp., *Wooden fences* .......... (609) 561-1874
Bond Parade Floats Displays, Inc., 111 Clifton Blvd., Clifton 07011
Pres.—Robert DeVito, 20 emp., *Parade floats* .......... (973) 778-3333
Borst Cabinet Co., 15 Schierloh Ct., Ramsey 07446
Owner, Pres. & Sales Mgr.—David J. Borst, 3 emp., *Custom & semi-custom stock kitchen* .... (201) 825-4220
Bossen Architectural Millwork, Inc., 1818 Bannard St., Cinnaminson 08077
Pres.—Joseph H. Bossen, 30 emp., *Architectural millwork & hardwood radius* .......... (856) 786-1100
Burger & Son, Inc., Edwin R., 732 Main St., P.O. Box 184, Sewell 08080
Pres.—Edwin R. Burger, 30 emp., *Wood, chain-link, vinyl, aluminum,* .......... (856) 468-2300
Central Millwork Of New Jersey, 92 N. Main St., Bldg. 11, P.O. Box 447, Windsor 08561
Owner, Pres. & GM—Kevin Coyle, 7 emp., *Architectural woodwork & cabinets* .......... (609) 448-7700
Crown Roll Leaf, Inc., 91 Illinois Ave., Paterson 07503
CEO—Margaret Waitts, 225 emp., *Corporate headquarters & hot stamping* .......... (973) 742-4000
Custom Products Mfg., Inc., 430 Sand Shore Rd., Ste. 4 & 5, Hackettstown 07840
Pres.—Haywood Huntley, 15 emp., *Museum gift items* .......... (908) 852-2078
Cutting Board Co., 291 Highway 22, Lebanon 08833
Ptnr. & Reg. Mgr.—Anthony Pizzelanti, 3 emp., *Standard, custom, glass, plastic &* .......... (908) 725-0187
Delta Fence Co., 541 Spring St., Elizabeth 07201
Owner—Carlos Milanes, 4 emp., *Wooden, vinyl & chain link fences* .......... (908) 355-9066
DiPasquale Fence Co., 196 Route 9 N., Englishtown 07726
Plt. Mgr.—Henry DiPasquale, 12 emp., *Ornamental aluminum, wooden, PVC &* .......... (732) 536-0660
Eastern Millwork, Inc., 18 Chapel Ave., Jersey City 07305
Pres.—Andrew Campbell, 60 emp., *Commercial wooden cabinets, stairs* .......... (201) 451-9510
Emerson Fence, Inc., 10 Lincoln Blvd., P.O. Box 306, Emerson 07630
Pres.—Robert Skrable, Jr., 20 emp., *Manufacturer & distributor of custom* .......... (201) 265-5150
Essex Coatings, LLC, 135 Essex Ave. E., Avenel 07001
Off. Mgr.—Liz Flott, 10 emp., *Wood composite panel UV coating service* .......... (732) 855-9400
Essex Fence Co., 132 U.S. Highway 46, Rockaway 07866
Ptnr.—George Lenar, 17 emp., *PVC vinyl, ornamental aluminum, wood* .......... (973) 625-4122
Federal Bronze Casting Industries, 9 Backus St., Newark 07105
Pres.—Doug Reichard, 42 emp., *Brass, bronze & aluminum castings &* .......... (973) 589-7575
Fence Max, 6514 Black Horse Pike, Egg Harbor Township 08234
Owner & GM—Mark Amechi, 20 emp., *Commercial, residential & industrial* .......... (609) 646-2430
Fences By Taylor, Inc., 1246 Highway 33, Howell 07731
Pres.—Paul Taylor, 20 emp., *Wooden fences* .......... (732) 349-8626
Frame & Print, 778 Carver Ave., Westwood 07675
Pres., GM—Andy Kestenbaum, 5 emp., *Wooden & metal picture frames & custom* .......... (201) 358-0404
Garden State Foliage, LLC, 600 Central Ave., Farmingdale 07727
Ptnr.—Neil M. Roth, 20 emp., *Christmas decorations, dried foliage* .......... (732) 751-0075
Gecko Graphics, Inc., 128 Berlin Cross Keys Rd., Williamstown 08094
Pres.—Alice Gorney, 3 emp., *Laser engraving on acrylic, plastics* .......... (856) 740-9042
Gianetto Wood Carvings, Vincent, 617 Delanco Rd., Beverly 08010
Owner—Vincent Gianetto III, 1 emp., *Wood carvings* .......... (609) 877-6233
Guardian Fence Co., Inc., 180 Wright St., P.O. Box 2009, Newark 07114
Pres.—Nancy Maccarelli, 20 emp., *Chain-link, wooden & vinyl fencing* .......... (973) 824-1850
Haddon Fence Co., Inc., 1460 Route 38, Hainesport 08036
Pres.—Roger Miller, 6 emp., *Wooden fencing* .......... (609) 261-1286
Hard Rock Marble & Granite, Inc., 1101 Chestnut St., Roselle 07203
CEO—N. Ruby Renjen, 12 emp., *Custom marble & granite fabrication* .......... (908) 620-9150
Helricks Picture Framing, Inc., 158 W. Clinton St., Ste. G, Dover 07801
Pres.—Peter Harris, 10 emp., *Picture frames* .......... (973) 361-1301
Homestead Fence Contractors, LLC, 637 Main St., West Creek 08092
Pres.—Nathan Foote, 14 emp., *Wooden & PVC fences & prefabricated* .......... (609) 296-1829
Huber Corp., J.M. (H Q), 499 Thornall St., 8th Fl., Edison 08837
Pres., CEO—Michael Marberry, 65 emp., *Corporate headquarters; hydrocolloids* .......... (732) 549-8600
Hutchinson Cabinets, LLC, 244 Bark Bridge Rd., Sewell 08080
V-P.—George Hutchinson, 25 emp., *Wooden & plastic laminate cabinets* .......... (856) 468-5500
Ill-Eagle Enterprises Ltd., 385 Main St., Little Falls 07424
Pres.—Darryl Sage, 44 emp., *Trophies, awards & picture frames* .......... (973) 237-1111
Imprint Specialties, Inc., 601 New Broadway, Brooklawn 08030
Pres.—Francis Ferry, 5 emp., *Commercial screen printing & awards* .......... (856) 456-2999
Ironbound Trophy Center, 289 Lafayette St., Ste. A, Newark 07105
Owner—Christine Naia, 3 emp., *Trophies & plaques & acrylics, corporate* .......... (973) 344-3872
Jan Fence Co., Inc., 4 Industrial Rd., Pompton Plains 07444
Pres.—Robert Corrao, 15 emp., *Custom industrial, residential & security* .......... (973) 694-4055
Jantek Industries, LLC, 230 Route 70, Medford 08055
CEO—Keith Kailian, 40 emp., *Windows, doors & related products for* .......... (609) 654-1030
JM Custom Design Millwork, 101 Hobart St., Hackensack 07601
Owner—Joseph Marrella, 2 emp., *Custom millwork, including wooden doors* .......... (201) 487-8990
L & M Art Gallery, LLC, 126 Elmora Ave., Elizabeth 07202
Pres.—Michael Sirotkin, 3 emp., *Wooden & metal picture frames* .......... (908) 351-2633
Landsman Custom Picture Framing, 600 S. White Horse Pike, Somerdale 08083
Ptnr.—Howard Landsman, 5 emp., *Wooden picture frames, including framing* .......... (856) 784-2145
Lardieri's Custom Woodworking, Inc., 1830 Swarthmore Ave., Ste. 6, Lakewood 08701
Co-Pres., Off. Mgr.—Robert Lardieri, Sr., 6 emp., *Custom wooden kitchen cabinets, entertainment* (732) 905-6334
Larson-Juhl, LLC, 165 Clinton Rd., Caldwell 07006
Off. Mgr.—Nina Rivera, 30 emp., *Wooden picture frames* .......... (973) 439-1801
Legacy Stairs & Millwork, Inc., 1000 Airport Rd., Ste. 104, Lakewood 08701
Owner—Stephen Hasse, 6 emp., *Custom wooden, steel & aluminum conventional* .......... (732) 905-7705
Modelsmith International, Inc., 66 Willow Ave., 2nd Fl., Hoboken 07030
Pres.—Karol Popek, 5 emp., *Steel, wood & acrylic fabrication,* .......... (201) 714-9519
MP Technologies, LLC (H Q), 345 Claremont Ave., Ste. 26, Montclair 07042
Chrm.—John Mahdessian, 15 emp., *Company headquarters; pocket stain* .......... (646) 366-1155
Mr. B. Fence Co., 325 Stokes Ave., Trenton 08638
Pres.—Rob Barbiero, 10 emp., *PVC & wooden fence panels & installation* .......... (609) 882-1896
Mr. Fence, 3468 U.S. Highway 9, Ste. 2, Freehold 07728
Owner—Dan Caporellie, 8 emp., *Vinyl, aluminum, wood & chain-link* .......... (732) 303-1614
Murphy Fence Co., Inc., 507 Seashore Rd., Cape May 08204
CEO—Amy Litton, 25 emp., *Wooden, PVC & aluminum fencing & PVC* .......... (609) 886-1635
New Jersey Frame & Moulding Co., 62 Kearney St., Paterson 07522
Pres.—Craig Aisenman, 6 emp., *Wooden picture frames* .......... (973) 684-6001
New York Blackboard of NJ, Inc., 83 U.S. Highway 22, Hillside 07205
Pres.—Henry Ruggiero, 6 emp., *Markerboards, chalkboards, bulletin* .......... (973) 926-1600
Nicholas Designs, R., 41 Portland Ave., Bergenfield 07621
Owner & GM—Robert Stephan, 1 emp., *Wooden picture frames* .......... (201) 385-8713
Officemate International Corp., 90 Newfield Ave., Edison 08837
Cont.—Roger Ko, 100 emp., *Office supplies* .......... (732) 225-7422
P & S Blizzard Corp., 722 Madison Ave., Paterson 07501
Pres.—Paul Kostovski, 2 emp., *Wooden & plastic fences* .......... (973) 523-1700
Picture-It, Inc., 1703 State Route 27, Edison 08817
Pres.—Roy Taetzsch, 5 emp., *Acrylic, crystal, glass & wooden awards* .......... (732) 819-0420
Pompton Millwork, Inc., 1458 Ringwood Ave., Haskell 07420
Pres.—William Kealy, 2 emp., *Millwork & wooden products* .......... (973) 835-0585
Post To Post, LLC, 2545 Fire Rd., Ste. 1, Egg Harbor Township 08234
★ Principal—Richard Sonsini, 7 emp., *Architectural metalwork & wooden &* .......... (609) 646-9300
Prestige Millwork, LLC, 152 U.S. Highway 206, Bldg. 17-A, Hillsborough 08844
Owner, Pres. & Sales Mgr.—Dan Bugasch, 25 emp., *Architectural woodwork & casework* ..... (908) 526-5100
RaGar Co., Inc., 2106 Kings Hwy., Asbury Park 07712
★ Pres., CEO—Lisa Raimondo, 5 emp., *Wooden & leather jewelry boxes* .......... (732) 493-1416
RAO Contract Sales, Inc., 392 Atwood Pl., Wyckoff 07481
Pres., Treas.—Brian Bergman, 8 emp., *Preframed artwork, mirrors, bulletin* .......... (201) 652-1500
Rex Lumber Co., 1 Station St., P.O. Box 1776, Englishtown 07726
Owner & Opers. Mgr.—Ben Forester, 85 emp., *FSC certified custom tropical & domestic* ...... (732) 446-4200
Riephoff Sawmill, Inc., 763 Route 524, Allentown 08501
Pres.—John Falconio, 20 emp., *Lumber processing & crane mats, dunnage* .......... (609) 259-7265
Satterfield Originals, 130 Bodman Pl., Apt. 2, Red Bank 07701
Owner & Pres.—Patrick Satterfield, 5 emp., *Wooden serving trays, placemats, cheese* .......... (908) 902-0290
Shurts Frames & Molding, Don, 294 Lanes Mill Rd., Howell 07731
Owner—Don Shurts, 2 emp., *Wooden picture frames & mouldings* .......... (732) 363-1323
Signs & Graphix, 433 Bloomfield Ave., Caldwell 07006
Owner—Eric Sterru, 1 emp., *Big format interior, exterior & job* .......... (973) 226-8392
Sky Frame & Art, Inc., 28 Evans Terminal, Hillside 07205
Pres.—Robert Benrimon, 20 emp., *Corporate headquarters & custom picture* .......... (908) 354-5656
South Jersey Lumbermans, Inc., 6268 Holly St., Mays Landing 08330
Pres., GM—Stephen Pinkos, 3 emp., *Wooden boat & deck components & millwork* .......... (609) 965-1411
Steelstran Industries, Inc., 35 Mileed Way, P.O. Box 30, Avenel 07001
CEO—Peter Gronbeck, 5 emp., *Corporate headquarters & rope & wooden* .......... (732) 574-0700
Stiefel Corp., George G. (H Q), 364 N. Farview Ave., Paramus 07652
Ptnr.—George Stiefel, 2 emp., *Corporate headquarters; wooden picture* .......... (201) 967-0868
Suburban Fence Co., 532 Mulberry St., Trenton 08638
Owner—Jelman S. Solomon, 20 emp., *Wooden & steel fencing & installation* .......... (609) 452-2630
Taylor Fence Co., 1246 Route 33, Farmingdale 07727
Owner—Paul Crooks, 50 emp., *Wooden, chain-link & aluminum fencing* .......... (732) 747-5498
Todd Architectural Models, 54 Mountainview Rd., P.O. Box 1002, Chatham 07928
Pres.—Douglas Pitney, 7 emp., *Wooden, plastic & metal architectural* .......... (973) 507-4072
Tropar Mfg. Co., Inc., 5 Vreeland Rd., Florham Park 07932
Pres.—Peter E. Ilaria, 60 emp., *Corporate headquarters & plaques, clocks* .......... (973) 822-2400
Tropical Expressions, Inc., 2127 Bridge Ave., Point Pleasant 08742
Pres.—Jack McGuire, 5 emp., *Artificial trees* .......... (732) 899-1733
Union City Mirror & Table Co., 129 34th St., Union City 07087
Pres., R & D Mgr.—Thomas Russo, 6 emp., *French Provincial wooden & occasional* .......... (201) 867-1827
W & E Baum, Inc., 89 Bannard St., Freehold 07728
CEO—Maurice Zagha, 25 emp., *Wooden, marble, metal, acrylic, glass* .......... (732) 866-1881
Walpole Woodworkers, Inc., 540 Tabor Rd., Morris Plains 07950
GM—Barry Stegenga, 12 emp., *Wooden fences* .......... (973) 539-3555
Wine Products, Inc., 2416 Highway 35, Ste. B, Manasquan 08736
Pres.—John Kuntz, 2 emp., *Wooden & metal wine racks* .......... (732) 528-5222
Woodchucker, Inc., The, 42 Bridgeton-Fairton Rd., P.O. Box 380, Fairton 08320
Pres.—Karen Love Millul, 4 emp., *Commercial & residential woodworking* .......... (856) 575-0200
Woodhaven Lumber & Millwork, Inc., 200 James St., P.O. Box 870, Lakewood 08701
Pres.—Alan Robinson, 152 emp., *Millwork, including decks, railings* .......... (732) 901-0030
Woodline Works Corp., 625 Jersey Ave., New Brunswick 08901
Owner, GM & Hum. Res. Mgr.—Song Wu, 30 emp., *Unfinished pine wood crafts* .......... (732) 828-9100
Woodwork & More, LLC, 24 W. Gorman Ave., Collingswood 08108
Owner—Edward Satkowski, 1 emp., *Woodworking, including millwork, railing* .......... (856) 986-3140

## 25 FURNITURE & FIXTURES

### 2511 Furniture—wood household

Barlow Tyrie, Inc., 1263 Glen Ave., Ste. 230, Moorestown 08057
Ex. V-P.—C. W. Hessler, 8 emp., *High-end residential & commercial outdoor* .......... (856) 273-7878
Berg Furniture U. S. A., Inc., 120 E. Gloucester Pike, Barrington 08007
V-P.—Almog Lieber, 90 emp., *Juvenile furniture* .......... (856) 310-0511
Codfish Park Design, LLC, 39 Commerce St., Chatham 07928
Chief Cabinet Officer—Tyler Merson, 2 emp., *Residential wooden cabinets & furniture* .......... (646) 298-4050
Creative Furniture, Inc. (H Q), 240 Mill Rd., Edison 08817
★ Owner—Leonid Kitovsky, 10 emp., *Corporate headquarters; household furniture* .......... (732) 248-0255
Czar, Inc., 51 Montgomery St., Belleville 07109
Pres., Pers. Mgr.—Aza Gershkovich, 11 emp., *Wooden furniture* .......... (973) 278-4002
Danan Design Corp., 599 Franklin Ave., Franklin Lakes 07417
Pres.—Ralph Jaffe, 2 emp., *Wooden & plastic laminate furniture* .......... (201) 891-5342
Delform, LLC, 225 Highland Cross, Ste. 6, Rutherford 07070
Ptnr. & Member—Tracey Stakelin, 5 emp., *Residential & commercial metal & wood* .......... (201) 438-3915
DeSaussure Equipment Co., Inc., 23 W. Howcroft Rd., Maywood 07607
CEO—William Desaussure, 40 emp., *Wooden, laminated & folded banquet* .......... (201) 845-4242
Designs In Wood, 209 Williams Ave., Barrington 08007
Owner, Plt. & Sales Mgr.—Richard Feldstein, 1 emp., *Hardwood furniture* .......... (856) 546-8338
Desiron, 820 Colfax Ave., Kenilworth 07033
Pres.—Frank Carsaro, 10 emp., *Residential wooden & metal furniture* .......... (908) 241-7776
Dornan, Inc., 333 Cedarcroft Dr., Brick 08724
Pres.—Rita Dornan, 2 emp., *Brass & pewter miniature castings &* .......... (732) 295-4491
Ekornes, Inc. (H Q), 615 Pierce St., Somerset 08873
Pres.—Peter Bjerregaard, 43 emp., *Corporate headquarters; ergonomic furniture* .......... (732) 302-0097
Empire Industries, Inc., 40 Warren St., Paterson 07524
Pres.—Jacob Goren, 32 emp., *Bathroom furniture, vanities, ceramic* .......... (973) 279-2050
Feldman Assocs., Inc., F. L., 811 Memorial Dr., Asbury Park 07712
Pres.—Frank Feldman, 8 emp., *Wooden cabinets & furniture* .......... (732) 776-8544
Furniture Mill, Inc., The, 1536 Lower Ferry Rd., Ewing 08628
Owner—Barb Conover, 4 emp., *Furniture refinishing* .......... (609) 771-0274
Greenbaum Interiors, 101 Washington St., Paterson 07505
Pres.—Joseph Greenbaum, 40 emp., *Custom upholstered & wooden furniture* .......... (973) 279-3000

S.I.C.

★ **Indicates new listing this edition.**

Handmade Furniture Co., 612 Main St., West Creek 08092
Owner—Cathy Woodward, 17 emp., *Wooden cabinets & furniture* ........ (609) 597-2708
Jenkins, Inc., Brad, 291 Mount Kemble Ave., Morristown 07960
Pres. & Principal—Brad Jenkins, 4 emp., *Architectural & interior design, including* ........ (973) 331-1995
Jorgensen-Carr Ltd., 50 Dey St., 4th Fl., Jersey City 07306
Pres.—Mike Jorgenson, 5 emp., *Furniture & architectural woodworking* ........ (201) 792-2278
Keator Bilt Custom Cabinets, 805 2nd Ave., Asbury Park 07712
Owner—Andrew Keator, 3 emp., *Wooden & laminate cabinets* ........ (732) 776-5133
Kismet Furniture, Inc., 80 George St., Paterson 07503
Pres.—Tony Kismet, 1 emp., *Custom wooden furniture* ........ (973) 278-3117
Lee's Woodworking, Inc., 726 Walling Ave., Belmar 07719
Owner—Bill Lee, 2 emp., *Custom, residential & commercial furniture* ........ (732) 681-1002
Modern Boat Works, Inc., P.O. Box 456, Oceanville 08231
Pres., CEO—Peter Caporilli, 10 emp., *Cedar outdoor furniture* ........ (609) 241-8916
Munire Furniture, Inc., 91 New England Ave., Piscataway 08854
Pres.—Munire Hussain, 75 emp., *Custom wooden furniture* ........ (732) 339-6070
Panline USA, Inc., 251 Union St., Northvale 07647
Pres.—Fred Keeler, 66 emp., *Juvenile toys, including bathtub play* ........ (201) 750-8010
Ramsay Cabinetmakers, Inc., David, 310 Mill St., Moorestown 08057
Pres.—David Ramsay III, 8 emp., *High-end custom cabinetry, furniture* ........ (856) 234-7776
Saco & Birnbaum Fine Woodworking, 71 Glenwood Pl., East Orange 07017
Owner—Danny Birnbaum, 4 emp., *Residential & commercial wooden furniture* ........ (973) 675-8999
Salon Interiors, 62 Leuning St., South Hackensack 07606
Pres.—Walter Siegordner, 20 emp., *Wooden furniture* ........ (201) 488-7888
Samuelson Furniture, Inc., 11-13 Maryland Ave., Paterson 07503
Pres.—Lawrence Chalsin, 20 emp., *Wooden & metal residential furniture* ........ (973) 333-6090
SandKamp Woodworks, LLC, 430 Communipaw Ave., Jersey City 07304
Owner & Pres.—Anthony Sandkamp, 3 emp., *Wooden kitchen & custom built-in cabinets* ........ (201) 200-0101
Satterfield Originals, 130 Bodman Pl., Apt. 2, Red Bank 07701
Owner & Pres.—Patrick Satterfield, 5 emp., *Wooden serving trays, placemats, cheese* ........ (908) 902-0290
Sherman & Son, Inc., W. F., 84 Broad St., Manasquan 08736
Pres.—Donald F. Sherman, Jr., 10 emp., *Wooden furniture & architectural millwork* ........ (732) 223-1505
SK Custom Creations, Inc., 50 Furler St., Totowa 07512
Opers. Mgr.—Ivan Acapana, 50 emp., *Wooden furniture* ........ (973) 754-9261
Studio L Contracting, LLC, 1401 Palisade Ave., Teaneck 07666
Owner—David Lehmann, 6 emp., *Architectural millwork & custom wooden* ........ (201) 837-1650
T & T Cabinet Works, Inc., 388 River St., Paterson 07524
Pres.—Tony Cercone, 6 emp., *Wooden & laminated furniture* ........ (973) 279-0909
Taylor Made Custom Cabinetry, Inc., 7035 Central Hwy., Ste. 200, Pennsauken 08109
Pres.—Jay Taylor, 11 emp., *Custom wooden cabinetry & fine furniture* ........ (856) 786-5433
Tea & Elle Woodworks, LLC, 5004 Industrial Rd., Farmingdale 07727
Owner—Todd Gleason, 7 emp., *CNC components & parts* ........ (732) 938-9660
Terzano Cabinetry, Inc., 111 Leuning St., Unit G, South Hackensack 07606
Owner & Pres.—Joe Terzano, 8 emp., *Custom-designed handmade cabinetry* ........ (201) 373-9500
Union City Mirror & Table Co., 129 34th St., Union City 07087
Pres., R & D Mgr.—Thomas Russo, 6 emp., *French Provincial wooden & occasional* ........ (201) 867-1827
West Hudson Millwork, Inc., 60 Arlington Ave., Kearny 07032
Pres.—Jonathan David Giordano, 2 emp., *Wooden & laminated cabinets, furniture* ........ (201) 991-7191
Wood Shed, Inc., The, 4500 Park Ave., Weehawken 07086
Pres.—Roland Arlt, 3 emp., *Wooden furniture, bookcases & kitchen* ........ (201) 866-7949
Wood Works, 1111 N. Black Horse Pike, Williamstown 08094
Mng. Ptnr.—Carol Bartling, 6 emp., *Wooden cabinets & bookcases* ........ (856) 728-4520

## 2512 Furniture—upholstered household

Alan Schatzberg & Assoc., Inc., 45 Ruta Ct., South Hackensack 07606
Pres., GM—Alan Schatzberg, 12 emp., *Manufacturer & distributor of custom* ........ (201) 440-8855
Creative Furniture, Inc. (H Q), 240 Mill Rd., Edison 08817
★ Owner—Leonid Kitovsky, 10 emp., *Corporate headquarters; household furniture* ........ (732) 248-0255
Frank's Upholstery & Draperies, 49 S. Boulevard Ave., Maple Shade 08052
Owner—Frank Troso, 5 emp., *Upholstered furniture & draperies* ........ (856) 779-8585
Greenbaum Interiors, 101 Washington St., Paterson 07505
Pres.—Joseph Greenbaum, 40 emp., *Custom upholstered & wooden furniture* ........ (973) 279-3000
Masters Interiors, Inc., 1500 Main Ave., Clifton 07011
Owner—Kevin Costello, 30 emp., *Upholstered wooden furniture, sofas* ........ (973) 253-0784
Nourison Industries (H Q), 5 Sampson St., Saddle Brook 07663
Pres.—Alex Peykar, 240 emp., *Company headquarters; upholstered furniture* ........ (201) 368-6900
Salto Decorators, LLC, 80-82 Kinderkamack Rd., Oradell 07649
Pres.—Walter Kruger, 1 emp., *Upholstered furniture* ........ (201) 261-2518
Sleepable Sofas Ltd., 6 Empire Blvd., Moonachie 07074
Pres., CEO—Darren DeMatteo, 65 emp., *Company headquarters & custom upholstered* ........ (973) 546-4502

## 2514 Furniture—metal household

Aram, Inc., Michael, 2102 83rd St., North Bergen 07047
Pres.—Michael Wolohojis, 7 emp., *Hand-crafted metal tableware, hardware* ........ (201) 758-2551
Cast Classics, Inc., 65 Railroad Ave., Ridgefield 07657
Pres.—David Arad, 4 emp., *Aluminum lawn furniture* ........ (201) 896-1515
Creative Furniture, Inc. (H Q), 240 Mill Rd., Edison 08817
★ Owner—Leonid Kitovsky, 10 emp., *Corporate headquarters; household furniture* ........ (732) 248-0255
Delform, LLC, 225 Highland Cross, Ste. 6, Rutherford 07070
Ptnr. & Member—Tracey Stakelin, 5 emp., *Residential & commercial metal & wood* ........ (201) 438-3915
Desiron, 820 Colfax Ave., Kenilworth 07033
Pres.—Frank Carsaro, 10 emp., *Residential wooden & metal furniture* ........ (908) 241-7776
J & M Air, Inc., 189 S. Bridge St., Somerville 08876
Pres.—Michael Favreau, 12 emp., *Custom galvanized & stainless steel* ........ (908) 707-4040
Jenkins, Inc., Brad, 291 Mount Kemble Ave., Morristown 07960
Pres. & Principal—Brad Jenkins, 4 emp., *Architectural & interior design, including* ........ (973) 331-1995
Knickerbocker Bed Co., 770 Commercial Ave., Carlstadt 07072
Pres.—Milton Polevoy, 30 emp., *Metal bed frames* ........ (201) 933-3100
Metaline Products Co., Inc., 101 N. Feltus St. & 241 Raritan St., South Amboy 08879
Chrm. & CEO—August J. Zilincar III, 35 emp., *Custom metal point-of-purchase displays* ........ (732) 721-1373
Missry Assocs., Inc., 100 S. Washington Ave., Dunellen 08812
Pres.—Edward Missry, 200 emp., *Home & garden decorative accessories* ........ (732) 752-7500
Samuelson Furniture, Inc., 11-13 Maryland Ave., Paterson 07503
Pres.—Lawrence Chalsin, 20 emp., *Wooden & metal residential furniture* ........ (973) 333-6090

## 2515 Mattresses & bedsprings

Bedding Industries Of America, 1375 Jersey Ave., North Brunswick 08902
Pres.—Stuart Carlitz, 100 emp., *Mattresses* ........ (732) 628-0800
Berry & Sons, Inc., Miller, Robbinstown Rd., P.O. Box 174, Port Norris 08349
Pres.—Dean Berry, 10 emp., *Burial casket mattresses* ........ (856) 785-1420
Chiromatic, Inc., 1375 Jersey Ave., North Brunswick 08902
Pres.—Debbie Carlitz, 2 emp., *Firm & pressure relieving visco-elastic* ........ (800) 526-5116
Comfort Revolution (H Q), 187 Route 36, Ste. 205, West Long Branch 07764
Founder & CEO—Michael Fux, 20 emp., *Company headquarters; foam mattresses* ........ (732) 272-9111
Drake Mills, LLC, 18 E. 5th St., Ste. B, Paterson 07524
★ Owner—Morton Dropkin, 10 emp., *Mattresses* ........ (973) 345-0008
Dream On Me Industries, Inc., 125 Helen St., South Plainfield 07080
Pres.—Mark Severe, 40 emp., *Manufacturer of baby mattresses & wholesaler* ........ (908) 791-0555
Ekornes, Inc. (H Q), 615 Pierce St., Somerset 08873
Pres.—Peter Bjerregaard, 43 emp., *Corporate headquarters; ergonomic furniture* ........ (732) 302-0097
Gerson Industries, Inc., 20-21 Wagaraw Rd., Bldg. 37, P.O. Box 12, Fair Lawn 07410
Pres.—Louis Goldfond, 14 emp., *Mattresses & box springs* ........ (973) 423-6100
Innocor, Inc. (H Q), 187 State Route 36, Ste. 101, West Long Branch 07764
CEO—Michael C. Thompson, 70 emp., *Corporate headquarters; polyurethane* ........ (732) 263-0800
M & R Diamond Quilting Co., Inc., 35 South Ave., Fanwood 07023
Pres., Fin. & MIS Mgr.—Ron Shovlin, 10 emp., *Mattresses & box springs* ........ (908) 322-4178
Masters Interiors, Inc., 1500 Main Ave., Clifton 07011
Owner—Kevin Costello, 30 emp., *Upholstered wooden furniture, sofas* ........ (973) 253-0784
New England Bedding Transport, 102 3rd Ave., Kearny 07032
Pres., Hum. Res. & IT Mgr.—Douglas Daly, 8 emp., *Mattresses* ........ (201) 997-2337
Orange Mattress, 77 Central Ave., Clark 07066
Manager—Mindy Segal, 15 emp., *Mattresses & box springs* ........ (973) 761-1100
Rex Bedding & Sleep Products, 300 W. 4th St., Plainfield 07060
Pres., Sales Mgr.—Jose Furman, 35 emp., *Mattresses & box springs* ........ (908) 668-0220
Sealy Mattress Co. Of New Jersey, 697 River St., Paterson 07524
Pres.—David Hertz, 260 emp., *Mattresses & box springs* ........ (973) 345-8800
Spring Time Bedding Corp., 25 Central Ave., Teterboro 07608
Pres.—Moshe Jakobovits, 8 emp., *Mattresses* ........ (973) 473-5400
Therapedic International, Inc. (H Q), 103 College Rd. E., 2nd Fl., Princeton 08540
CEO—Gerry Borreggine, 4 emp., *Corporate headquarters; mattresses* ........ (609) 720-0700
White Lotus Home, 431 Raritan Ave., Highland Park 08904
Pres.—Marlon Pando, 20 emp., *Natural & organic mattresses & bedding* ........ (732) 828-2111

## 2517 TV & radio cabinets—wood

Showtech, Inc., 40 Entin Rd., Clifton 07014
Owner—Dan Zazzali, 7 emp., *Wooden audio & video cabinets* ........ (973) 249-6336

## 2519 Furniture—household, nec

Alan Schatzberg & Assoc., Inc., 45 Ruta Ct., South Hackensack 07606
Pres., GM—Alan Schatzberg, 12 emp., *Manufacturer & distributor of custom* ........ (201) 440-8855
Custom Decorators Workroom, 415 E. Main St., Denville 07834
Ptnr.—Walter Kunzel, Jr., 5 emp., *Custom furniture & draperies* ........ (973) 625-0516
Delform, LLC, 225 Highland Cross, Ste. 6, Rutherford 07070
Ptnr. & Member—Tracey Stakelin, 5 emp., *Residential & commercial metal & wood* ........ (201) 438-3915
Missry Assocs., Inc., 100 S. Washington Ave., Dunellen 08812
Pres.—Edward Missry, 200 emp., *Home & garden decorative accessories* ........ (732) 752-7500

## 2521 Office furniture—wood

Arnold Furniture Mfrs., Inc., 400 Coit St., Irvington 07111
Pres.—Julius Arnold, 23 emp., *Corporate headquarters & conference* ........ (973) 399-0505
Arnold Kolax Furniture, Inc., 146 Coit St., Irvington 07111
Pres.—Eric Arnold, 12 emp., *Fine wooden library & office furniture* ........ (973) 375-3344
Arnold Reception Desks, Inc., 120 Coit St., Irvington 07111
Pres.—William Kolax, 27 emp., *Reception desks, workstations & courtroom* ........ (973) 375-8101
Atlas Desk & Office Equipment Corp., 185-193 Central Ave., 2nd Fl., Newark 07103
Pres.—Mark Parra, 12 emp., *Office furniture & equipment* ........ (973) 242-8989
BIF New York, Inc., 465 Barell Ave., Carlstadt 07072
Pres.—Tommy Lee, 10 emp., *Office furniture, including chairs,* ........ (201) 933-7777
Boomerang Used Office Furniture, 9155 River Rd., Pennsauken 08110
Pres.—Seth Deforest, 10 emp., *Rebuilt wooden office furniture* ........ (856) 582-0100
Capra Custom Cabinetry & Millwork, LLC, 259 E. Washington Ave., Washington 07882
★ Owner—John Capra, 2 emp., *Custom residential & commercial casework* ........ (908) 797-9848
Carmel Furniture, Inc., 404 N. Midland Ave., Saddle Brook 07663
Owner—Gideon Reiss, 15 emp., *Wooden office furniture* ........ (201) 796-0099
Casey's Executive Interiors, 152 Route 22 W., P.O. Box 7070, Green Brook 08812
Ptnr.—Casey Chung, 10 emp., *Wooden & metal office furniture* ........ (732) 968-3236
Castle Woodcraft Assocs., 161 Route 9, P.O. Box 426, Pine Beach 08741
Ptnr.—Ernest Guenzburger, 15 emp., *Kitchen & office wooden & plastic laminate* ........ (732) 349-1519
Contemporary Wall Systems, Inc., 50 Williams Pkwy., Ste. F, P.O. Box 356, East Hanover 07936
Pres.—Robert Behringer, 10 emp., *Modular wall systems for commercial* ........ (973) 884-0474
Dauphin North America, 100 Fulton St., Boonton 07005
CEO—Nick Bayvel, 75 emp., *Office chairs* ........ (973) 263-1100
Design Line, Inc., 283 Cox St., Roselle 07203
Pres., Fin. & MIS Mgr.—Bob Hansen, 6 emp., *Wood laminated office furniture* ........ (908) 241-1911
Design Of Tomorrow, Inc., 24 Sherwood Ln., Fairfield 07004
Pres., GM—David Roitburg, 15 emp., *Casework & millwork for schools & laboratorie* ........ (973) 227-5676
Distinctive Wood Work, Inc., 70 Stacy Haines Rd., Ste. D, Lumberton 08048
Owner—Jim Cherubino, 3 emp., *Custom residential & commercial millwork* ........ (609) 714-8505
Extra Office, Inc., 580 Leesville Ave., Rahway 07065
Pres.—Louis Prince, Jr., 12 emp., *Metal & wooden office furniture* ........ (732) 381-9773
Ge-Ro Desk Co., 334 N. 5th St., Newark 07107
Owner—Rolf J. Hoppe, 9 emp., *Wooden office furniture* ........ (973) 485-0505
Global - The Total Office (H Q), 17 W. Stow Rd., P.O. Box 562, Marlton 08053
Pres.—Jon Abraham, 175 emp., *Company headquarters; metal, plastic* ........ (856) 596-3390
Hoppe Co., Inc., R. J., 340 N. 5th St., Newark 07107
Pres.—Rolf B. Hoppe, Jr., 10 emp., *Wooden office furniture, specialty* ........ (973) 485-5665
K W, Inc., 1536 Lower Ferry Rd., Ewing 08618
Pres.—Kurt Watson, 3 emp., *Commercial casework, architectural* ........ (609) 882-6363
Keator Bilt Custom Cabinets, 805 2nd Ave., Asbury Park 07712
Owner—Andrew Keator, 3 emp., *Wooden & laminate cabinets* ........ (732) 776-5133
Studio L Contracting, LLC, 1401 Palisade Ave., Teaneck 07666
Owner—David Lehmann, 6 emp., *Architectural millwork & custom wooden* ........ (201) 837-1650
Superior Custom Kitchens, LLC, 126 Mount Bethel Rd., Warren 07059
Ptnr.—Joe Borin, 10 emp., *Custom & semi-custom cabinets for full* ........ (908) 753-6005
Vaswani, Inc., 18 Bernadette Ct., Springfield 07081
CEO—Vinay Vaswani, 35 emp., *Contract wooden office furniture* ........ (973) 376-4425

## 2522 Office furniture, except wood

Arnold Desks, Inc., 1409 Chestnut Ave., P.O. Box 842, Hillside 07205
Steel Mgr.—Matt Stoffers, 18 emp., *Contemporary & traditional case goods* ........ (908) 686-5656
Arnold Furniture Mfrs., Inc., 400 Coit St., Irvington 07111
Pres.—Julius Arnold, 23 emp., *Corporate headquarters & conference* ........ (973) 399-0505
BIF New York, Inc., 465 Barell Ave., Carlstadt 07072
Pres.—Tommy Lee, 10 emp., *Office furniture, including chairs,* ........ (201) 933-7777

Casey's Executive Interiors, 152 Route 22 W., P.O. Box 7070, Green Brook 08812
Ptnr.—Casey Chung, 10 emp., *Wooden & metal office furniture* ........ (732) 968-3236
Concord Products Co., Inc., 251 Benigno Blvd., Bellmawr 08031
Pres.—Larry Anthonsen, 55 emp., *Office furniture* ........ (856) 933-3000
Contemporary Wall Systems, Inc., 50 Williams Pkwy., Ste. F, P.O. Box 356, East Hanover 07936
Pres.—Robert Behringer, 10 emp., *Modular wall systems for commercial* ........ (973) 884-0474
Extra Office, Inc., 580 Leesville Ave., Rahway 07065
Pres.—Louis Prince, Jr., 12 emp., *Metal & wooden office furniture* ........ (732) 381-9773
Gafgen Cabinetmakers, Thomas P., 5 Truman Ct., Robbinsville 08691
Owner—Thomas P. Gafgen, 3 emp., *Wooden & melamine residential & office* ........ (609) 448-2060
Global - The Total Office (H Q), 17 W. Stow Rd., P.O. Box 562, Marlton 08053
Pres.—Jon Abraham, 175 emp., *Company headquarters; metal, plastic* ........ (856) 596-3390
Gordon International, Inc., 6 Paragon Way, Freehold 07728
★ Pres.—Peter Spaldaning, 11 emp., *Office furniture* ........ (732) 431-3361
Humanscale Corp., 220 Circle Dr. N., Piscataway 08854
Sr. V-P., Mktg.—Chris Gibson, 200 emp., *Sustainable, high-performance ergonomic* ........ (732) 537-2944
Jesper Office, LLC, 745 Route 202/206 S., Ste. 300, Somerville 08876
★ Owner—Joern Skarregaard, 20 emp., *Modular office furniture* ........ (908) 218-4200
LaCour, Inc., 36 Kulick Rd., Fairfield 07004
Pres.—Paul M. LaCour, 20 emp., *Composite trading & industrial desks* ........ (973) 227-4755
Stylex, 740 Coopertown Rd., P.O. Box 5038, Delanco 08075
Pres.—John Golden, 150 emp., *Seating office furniture* ........ (856) 461-5600

## 2531 Furniture—public building & related

Academia Furniture Industries, 4 Passaic St., Wood Ridge 07075
Pres.—Shabsi Goldman, 25 emp., *Wooden & steel classroom & computer* ........ (973) 472-0100
Arnold Kolax Furniture, Inc., 146 Coit St., Irvington 07111
Pres.—Eric Arnold, 12 emp., *Fine wooden library & office furniture* ........ (973) 375-3344
Bergen Auto Upholstery, 375 North St., Ste. U, Teterboro 07608
Owner—Nancy Citti, 15 emp., *Bus seat upholstery* ........ (201) 457-9100
Blickman, Inc., 500 U.S. Highway 46, Clifton 07011
Pres.—Rob Freedman, 85 emp., *Stainless steel & chrome hospital furniture* ........ (973) 330-0557
C C S Stone, 9-11 Caesar Pl., Moonachie 07074
Pres.—Don Mitnick, 25 emp., *Marble, granite, slate & limestone* ........ (201) 933-1515
CBT Supply, Inc. (H Q), 83 Jacobs Rd., Rockaway 07866
Pres., CEO—Jeffrey Korber, 12 emp., *Corporate headquarters; ergonomic laminate* ........ (973) 586-2783
Deitz & Sons, Inc., M., 490 Hillside Ave., Hillside 07205
Pres.—Ken Deitz, 15 emp., *Wooden restaurant chairs & barstools* ........ (908) 686-8800
Design Of Tomorrow, Inc., 24 Sherwood Ln., Fairfield 07004
Pres., GM—David Roitburg, 15 emp., *Casework & millwork for schools & laboratorie* ........ (973) 227-5676
Distinctive Wood Work, Inc., 70 Stacy Haines Rd., Ste. D, Lumberton 08048
Owner—Jim Cherubino, 3 emp., *Custom residential & commercial millwork* ........ (609) 714-8505
Early Childhood Resources, LLC, 2165 Center Square Rd., Logan Township 08085
Pres.—Mitchell Lynn, 6 emp., *Stackable school chairs, wooden children's* ........ (856) 638-1170
Global - The Total Office (H Q), 17 W. Stow Rd., P.O. Box 562, Marlton 08053
Pres.—Jon Abraham, 175 emp., *Company headquarters; metal, plastic* ........ (856) 596-3390
Hausmann Industries, Inc., 130 Union St., Northvale 07647
CEO—David Hausmann, 100 emp., *American-made healthcare products,* ........ (201) 767-0255
Infanti Brand Chair & Stools, 1153 W. Elizabeth Ave., Linden 07036
V-P., Sales & Mktg.—Jack Douglass, 10 emp., *Stacking aluminum banquet chairs, barstools.* (718) 447-5632
Infinite Manufacturing Group, Inc., 171 Coit St., Irvington 07111
Founder & CEO—Bernard Alloysius, 20 emp., *Indoor & outdoor architectural signage* ........ (973) 649-9950
Samuelson Furniture, Inc., 11-13 Maryland Ave., Paterson 07503
Pres.—Lawrence Chalsin, 20 emp., *Wooden & metal residential furniture* ........ (973) 333-6090
Top Line Seating, Inc., 540 S. 31st St., Kenilworth 07033
CEO—Carl Friedrich, 15 emp., *Bar stools & chairs for the casino* ........ (908) 241-9051
Tower Systems, Inc.- Atlantic Towers & St. Croix Marine Products, 235 Hickory Ln., P.O. Box D, Bayville 08721
Pres.—Steve Tull, 7 emp., *Fabricated aluminum boat accessories* ........ (732) 237-8800
Tri-State Leather, Inc., 504 4th Ave., Elizabeth 07202
Cont.—Walter Ramirez, 14 emp., *Automotive seats* ........ (908) 275-3310
Union County Seating & Supply Co., Inc., 121 N. Michigan Ave., Ste. E, Kenilworth 07033
Owner & Pres.—Bruce Bussell, 26 emp., *New & remanufactured transit & coach* ........ (908) 241-4949

## 2541 Partitions & fixtures—wood

10-31, Inc., 2 W. Crisman Rd., Columbia 07832
Pres.—William Stender, 24 emp., *Custom wooden, plastic & glass artwork* ........ (908) 496-4946
Agresti Construction Co., Inc., 356 Glenwood Ave., East Orange 07017
Pres.—James Agresti, 12 emp., *Architectural millwork & custom cabinetry* ........ (201) 825-8500
Algar-The Display Connection Inc., 131 W. Commercial Ave., Moonachie 07074
Pres.—Deian Urso, 65 emp., *Point-of-purchase displays* ........ (201) 438-1000
Alpha 1 Studio, Inc., 3 Linda Ln., Ste. A, Southampton 08088
Pres., Fin., MIS & R & D Mgr.—Ray E. Witthauer, 6 emp., *Interior & exterior sandblasted, wooden* . (609) 859-2200
Alternative Air & Store Fixtures, 3-C Mary Way, Hainesport 08036
Ptnr.—James Lunstead, 6 emp., *Refrigerated & dry custom & standard* ........ (609) 261-5870
Apple Exhibits, 730 Grand Ave., Unit 1-A, Ridgefield 07657
Owner—Young Park, 10 emp., *Trade show exhibits & booths & custom* ........ (201) 943-2775
Art Guild, Inc., 300 Wolf Dr., West Deptford 08086
Pres.—Doug Zegel, 210 emp., *Corporate headquarters & trade show* ........ (856) 853-7500
Atlas Woodwork, 212 Wright St., Newark 07114
Pres.—Antonio Martins, 10 emp., *Wooden kitchen cabinets & commercial* ........ (973) 621-9595
Bell Arte Woodworking, Inc., 10 W. Mravlag Pl., Elizabeth 07201
Pres.—Giusette Chillemi, 12 emp., *Wooden store fixtures & cabinets &* ........ (908) 355-1199
Blanc Industries, Inc., 88 King St., Dover 07801
Pres.—Didier Blanc, 60 emp., *Corporate headquarters & point-of-purchase* ........ (973) 678-1200
Borst Cabinet Co., 15 Schierloh Ct., Ramsey 07446
Owner, Pres. & Sales Mgr.—David J. Borst, 3 emp., *Custom & semi-custom stock kitchen* .... (201) 825-4220
C C & D Capital Contracting & Design, Inc., 640 North Ave., Plainfield 07060
Pres.—Don Finley, 45 emp., *Point-of-purchase displays & custom* ........ (908) 561-8411
California Closet Co., 2666 U.S. Highway 130, Cranbury 08512
Pres.—Dan Nili, 15 emp., *Wooden closets* ........ (609) 655-1899
Casework Design, 10 County Line Rd., Ste 26, Branchburg 08876
Owner—Michael Rowden, 3 emp., *Store & commercial fixtures, business* ........ (908) 722-7401
CDI Group, Inc., 1135 W. Elizabeth Ave., Linden 07036
CEO—Jordan Ruddy, 20 emp., *Manufacturer of custom modular trade* ........ (908) 862-1493
Chatham Container Display Corp., 6 Northridge Way, Warren 07059
Pres.—James Irvine, 4 emp., *Point-of-purchase displays & packaging* ........ (800) 266-4848
Choice Signs, 3407 Rose Ave., Ste. 3, Ocean 07712
V-P., Opers.—Daniel Kowalski, 3 emp., *ADA braille, vinyl & magnetic interior* ........ (732) 493-1644
City Diecutting, Inc., 1 Cory Rd., Ste. C, Morristown 07960
Pres.—Eric DeVos, 18 emp., *Semi-gloss, water resistant, black* ........ (973) 270-0370
Closettech, 203 Woodward Rd., Englishtown 07726
Owner—Joe Adelfio, 20 emp., *Wooden & plastic laminate custom closet* ........ (732) 792-0088
CNC Associates, 101 Kentile Rd., South Plainfield 07080
Pres.—Nathan Indig, 95 emp., *Wooden cabinets & countertops* ........ (718) 416-3853
Commerce Sign Solutions, LLC, 540 Cranbury Rd., Ste. 334, East Brunswick 08816
Owner—Linda Harrington, 1 emp., *ADA & architectural signs, banners,* ........ (732) 238-7000
Compass Display & Promotion Co., Inc., 1659 Calhoun St., Trenton 08638
CEO—Joseph Carugati, 58 emp., *Store floor tile displays* ........ (609) 695-5300
Creating Your Design, LLC, 45 Wood St., Paterson 07524
Owner—David Batiz, 10 emp., *Trade show exhibits, commercial & retail* ........ (973) 357-1080
Creative Design Plus, 1634 E. Elizabeth Ave., Linden 07036
GM—Ping Larrabee, 8 emp., *Commercial printing, advertising specialties* ........ (732) 287-3336
Cross Country Box Co., Inc., 2-8 Central Ave., East Orange 07018
Pres.—Dan Goldman, 9 emp., *Rigid paperboard boxes, folding cartons* ........ (973) 673-8349
Custom Cabinets By Jim Bucko, Inc., 135 W. Burk Ave., Wildwood 08260
Pres.—James Bucko, 6 emp., *Wooden kitchen cabinets, display cases* ........ (609) 889-7666
D & D Millwork Co., Inc., 10-12 N. 7th St., Belleville 07109
Pres.—Bernard D'Avella, 5 emp., *Wooden & plastic laminate cabinets,* ........ (973) 759-6336
Datascan Graphics, Inc., 55 Madison Ave., Ste. 400, Morristown 07960
★ Pres.—Roy House, 25 emp., *Point-of-purchase displays* ........ (973) 543-4800
Design Display Group, Inc., 105 Amor Ave., Carlstadt 07072
Pres., CEO—Andrew Freedman, 150 emp., *Custom point-of-purchase displays &* ........ (201) 438-6000
Detail Model & Machine, 61 Woodstown Rd., Mullica Hill 08062
Owner—David Rose, 4 emp., *Training & trade show models & trade* ........ (856) 223-0184
Dimensional Communications Inc., 1595 MacArthur Blvd., Mahwah 07430
Pres.—Douglas Fixell, 70 emp., *Trade show displays & booths* ........ (201) 767-1500
Direct Cabinet Sales, 265 Central Ave., Clark 07066
Off. Mgr.—Antonio Koutsouzos, 8 emp., *Custom wooden & wire closets & shelves* ........ (732) 382-8080
Display Sales, Inc., P.O. Box 115, Spotswood 08884
Pres.—Richard Nasca, 20 emp., *Display fixtures & wire racks* ........ (732) 251-8981
Diversified Fixture, Inc., 1930 Swarthmore Ave., Lakewood 08701
Pres., CEO—Jerry Vitillo, 10 emp., *Wood & plastic store fixtures, medical* ........ (732) 886-0600
East Coast Counter Tops, Inc., 166 Main St., P.O. Box 645, Lakewood 08701
Pres.—Ofer Malhi, 10 emp., *Wooden countertops & cabinets* ........ (732) 363-7734
Engo Co., 128 Case Dr., South Plainfield 07080
Pres., Sales Mgr.—Robert J. Engo, 35 emp., *Store fixtures* ........ (908) 754-6600
Excelsior Metal Products, LLC, 151 State Route 33, Ste. 201, Manalapan 07726
Mng. Ptnr.—Jordan Cayne, 13 emp., *Contract manufacturing of electronic* ........ (732) 651-9914
Exhibit Co., Inc., The, 239 Old New Brunswick Rd., Piscataway 08854
Pres.—Frank Geraci, 25 emp., *Custom & portable trade show exhibits* ........ (732) 465-1070
ExhibitCraft, Inc., 22 Riverview Dr., Ste. 103, Wayne 07470
Pres.—Scott Walode, 15 emp., *Customized trade show exhibits, show* ........ (973) 686-9393
FASTSIGNS®, 255 State Route 3, Secaucus 07094
Pres.—Elizabeth Selbach, 7 emp., *Yard, interior & exterior signs, banners* ........ (201) 902-8640
Fi Companies, 3150 Bordentown Ave., Old Bridge 08857
Pres., CEO—Scott Forman, 50 emp., *Store fixtures, displays & cabinets* ........ (732) 727-8100
Frank's Cabinet Shop, Inc., 1992 Burnt Mills Rd., P.O. Box 78, Pluckemin 07978
Ptnr.—John Darrow, 7 emp., *Wooden cabinets & entertainment centers* ........ (908) 658-4396
G & M Custom Formica Work, 120 Francis St., Bldg. C, Keyport 07735
Ptnr.—George Macchia, 3 emp., *Plastic laminated countertops* ........ (732) 888-0360
G R Office Products, Inc., 11 Kentucky Ave., Paterson 07503
Pres.—Bernardo Guterman, 2 emp., *Floor mats, fabric-wrapped tackboards* ........ (973) 345-2769
Gafgen Cabinetmakers, Thomas P., 5 Truman Ct., Robbinsville 08691
Owner—Thomas P. Gafgen, 3 emp., *Wooden & melamine residential & office* ........ (609) 448-2060
Gotham Group, The, 202 W. Parkway Dr., Ste. 2, Egg Harbor Township 08234
Pres.—Qiang Wang, 16 emp., *Large-format digital displays, specialty* ........ (609) 645-2211
Grand Displays, Inc., 12 Empire Blvd., Moonachie 07074
Pres.—Susan Ostreicher, 60 emp., *Paper die cutting & displays* ........ (201) 994-1500
Graphic Presentation Systems, Inc., 262 Old New Brunswick Rd., Ste. F, Piscataway 08854
Pres., Treas.—Kevin J. Keizer, 15 emp., *Trade show displays* ........ (732) 981-1120
H2L, LLC, 4201 Tonnelle Ave., Ste. 2, North Bergen 07047
Off. Mgr.—Michelle Bastiar, 9 emp., *Commercial & residential wooden millwork* ........ (201) 864-0060
Henschel-Steinau, Inc., 50 Commerce Dr., Allendale 07401
Pres.—Gary Forman, 40 emp., *Point-of-purchase displays* ........ (201) 760-4100
Hutchinson Cabinets, LLC, 244 Bark Bridge Rd., Sewell 08080
V-P.—George Hutchinson, 25 emp., *Wooden & plastic laminate cabinets* ........ (856) 468-5500
Impact Displays Group, LLC, 310 13th St., Carlstadt 07072
★ CEO—Gill Horowitz, 32 emp., *Point-of-purchase displays* ........ (212) 842-1800
Impact Unlimited, Inc., 250 Ridge Rd., P.O. Box 558, Dayton 08810
Chrm.—Richard Nelson, 150 emp., *Trade show exhibit, event & meeting* ........ (732) 274-2000
Imperial Design, 729 Charles St., Gloucester City 08030
Owner—Derek Cohen, 3 emp., *Wooden countertops* ........ (856) 742-8480
Intelco Of Delaware Valley, 250 Harvard Ave., P.O. Box 9, Westville 08093
Pres.—Mike Wells, 120 emp., *Company headquarters & solid-surface* ........ (856) 456-6755
Interstate Showcase & Store Fixture Co., P.O. Box 941, Teaneck 07666
Pres., Sales & Mktg. Mgr.—Leon Miller, 1 emp., *Wooden store fixtures & millwork for* ........ (201) 467-4522
J M J Woodworking, Inc., 100 8th St., Bldg. 300, Passaic 07055
Pres.—Jack Mroz, 6 emp., *Commercial wooden cabinets, paneling* ........ (973) 471-6449
Jewelry Tray & Pad Co., Inc., 1150 Edgewater Ave., Ridgefield 07657
Pres.—Aaron Rosenberg, 22 emp., *Jewelry displays* ........ (201) 941-4300
K W, Inc., 1536 Lower Ferry Rd., Ewing 08618
Pres.—Kurt Watson, 3 emp., *Commercial casework, architectural* ........ (609) 882-6363
Kempton Wood Products, LLC, 2800 Ridgewood Rd., Wall 07719
Manager—Kevin Kempton, 6 emp., *Wooden & vinyl storage buildings, pool* ........ (732) 449-8673
Klose Assocs., Inc., 804 Broadway, West Long Branch 07764
Pres., CEO, CFO—Raymond G. Klose, 15 emp., *Trade show exhibit booths & displays* ........ (732) 229-8950
Laurel Mfrs., Inc., 620 Cooper St., P.O. Box 5306, Delanco 08075
Pres.—Dan Iosca, 40 emp., *Wooden & metal store fixtures* ........ (856) 461-6600
Lawler Woodwork, LLC, 938 Lakewood Farmingdale Rd., Howell 07731
Owner—John Lawler, 10 emp., *Commercial & residential wooden cabinets* ........ (732) 942-7204
Lynch Exhibits, 7 Campus Dr., Burlington 08016
Pres.—Michael Carrozza, 110 emp., *Trade show displays* ........ (609) 387-1600
Mango Custom Cabinets, Inc., 216 W. Stiger St., Hackettstown 07840
Owner—Richard Mango, 20 emp., *Architectural millwork, including custom* ........ (908) 813-3077
Marvic Corp./A.J.D. Stone, 2450 Iorio St., Union 07083
Pres., Marvic Corp.—Alfred J. D'Alessandro, 100 emp., *Granite, quartz, solid-surface, concrete* (908) 686-4340
Meridian Surfaces, 677 Ramapo Valley Rd., Oakland 07436
Owner—Dan Lazzara, 2 emp., *Countertops* ........ (201) 337-7888
Modern Equipment Co., Inc., 19 Ann St., Bordentown 08505
Owner—David Dunigan, 24 emp., *Wooden & metal commercial cabinets* ........ (609) 298-2100
Modern Showcase, Inc., 610 Commercial Ave., Carlstadt 07072
Pres.—John Kang, 10 emp., *Metal & wooden store fixtures* ........ (201) 935-2929

S.I.C.

★ Indicates new listing this edition.

MPM Display, Inc., 74 Woolsey St., Irvington 07111
Pres., Plt. Opers. Mgr.—Michael Bertko, 10 emp., *Point-of-purchase displays* (973) 374-3477
National Display Group, Inc., 6850 River Rd., Pennsauken 08110
V-P., Opers.—Gene Gold, 25 emp., *Store displays* (856) 661-1212
Ostlund, Inc., Cal, 555 N. Michigan Ave., Kenilworth 07033
Pres., CEO—Cal Ostlund, Jr., 50 emp., *Trade show exhibits* (908) 688-4466
Paramount Fixture Corp., 175 Mount Pleasant Ave., Newark 07104
Owner & Pres.—Stephen Porcelli, 35 emp., *Custom wooden & metal store fixtures* (973) 485-1585
Parkway Wire Frame Co., Inc., 249 Astor St., Newark 07114
Pres.—Mark Hoglund, 9 emp., *Window displays* (973) 242-5220
Porta-Display, Inc., 790 Bloomfield Ave., Ste. B-2, Clifton 07012
Pres.—George Kruse, 2 emp., *Convention exhibits* (973) 574-0057
Preferred Display, Inc., 310 Brighton Rd., Clifton 07012
Pres.—Robert Rousseau, 250 emp., *Corporate headquarters & plastic, aluminum* (973) 405-5137
R & T Custom Cabinets, 1311 Herbert Blvd., Williamstown 08094
Owner—Richard Digirolamo, 2 emp., *Wood & laminate kitchen cabinets &* (856) 728-1979
Rand Diversified, 3 Ethel Rd., Ste. 301, Edison 08817
Chrm.—Jack Wuensch, 40 emp., *Company headquarters & point-of-purchase* (732) 287-2525
RB & A, Inc., 350 Sparta Ave., Bldg. C, Sparta 07871
Pres.—Rod Borden, 5 emp., *Point-of-purchase, acrylic, stock &* (973) 726-0830
Red Bank Cabinet Co., 548 Shrewsbury Ave., Tinton Falls 07701
Pres., R & D Mgr.—Kenneth Asmar, 10 emp., *Custom & semi-custom cabinets & exhibit* (732) 741-8080
Regal-Pinnacle Mfg., Inc., 220 Route 70, Ste. A, Medford 08055
Pres.—Peter C. Palko, 75 emp., *Wooden & metal display fixtures & refrigerate* (609) 714-2330
Reliance Plastic & Chemical Corp., 38-27 Wilson St., P.O. Box 395, Fair Lawn 07410
★ Pres.—Fred Levine, 10 emp., *Flexible down drains for erosion control* (201) 797-8014
Rich's Kitchens, Inc., 309 Hamburg Tpke., Butler 07405
Pres.—Richard Palinski, 4 emp., *Plastic laminated countertops* (973) 838-4026
Ross, Inc., A. W., 297 Monroe St., Passaic 07055
Co-Pres.—Vojtek Rys, 14 emp., *Wooden kitchen cabinets & countertops* (973) 471-5900
S M Counter Tops, LLC, 432 Boston Ave., Egg Harbor Township 08234
Pres.—Stephen Morin, 1 emp., *Plastic laminated countertops* (609) 926-9301
Sawitz Store Fixture, Inc., 130 Grand St., Carlstadt 07072
Pres.—Daniel Sawitz, 28 emp., *Wooden, laminate & solid-surface store* (201) 842-9444
Shelving Depot, Inc., 419 W. Elizabeth Ave., Linden 07036
Pres.—Richard Kurland, 12 emp., *Shelving, store fixtures, metal, wooden* (908) 474-8000
SolidSurface Designs, Inc., 1651 Sherman Ave., Pennsauken 08110
Pres.—Matthew Baiada, 21 emp., *Solid-surface, quartz, stainless steel* (856) 910-7720
Specialty Fabricators, LLC, 118 Meany Rd., Wrightstown 08562
Pres.—Edward Symbouras, 25 emp., *Refrigerated & heated grocery displays* (609) 758-6995
Speedpro Imaging, 52 E. Centre St., Ste. 3-B, Nutley 07110
Pres.—Doug Nixon, 4 emp., *Large-format graphic printing, including* (973) 542-8384
Stelton Cabinet & Supply, 1358 Stelton Rd., Piscataway 08854
Owner—Robert Aiello, 7 emp., *Wooden cabinets & countertops* (732) 985-1035
Stevens Cabinet & Millwork, 776 Frenchtown Rd., Milford 08848
Owner—Paul Stevens, 3 emp., *Wooden kitchen & office cabinets &* (908) 996-6290
Stone Systems Of NJ, 95 8th St., P.O. Box 4207, Passaic 07055
GM—Thomas Landers, 80 emp., *Countertops* (973) 778-5525
SYMA Systems, Inc., 300 Wolf Dr., West Deptford 08086
V-P., Sales & Mktg.—Stanley R. Hyams, 100 emp., *Custom trade show & museum exhibits* (856) 686-4190
Tea & Elle Woodworks, LLC, 5004 Industrial Rd., Farmingdale 07727
Owner—Todd Gleason, 7 emp., *CNC components & parts* (732) 938-9660
TimBar Corp., 15-01 Pollitt Dr., Unit 9, Fair Lawn 07410
Proj. Mgr.—Stasi Hinz, 12 emp., *Point-of-purchase displays, corrugated* (201) 568-7300
Trans World Marketing Corp., 360 Murray Hill Pkwy., East Rutherford 07073
CEO—James Cavaluzzi, 300 emp., *In-store retail displays, fixtures,* (201) 935-5565
Unified Resources In Display, Inc./Display Pro Manufacturing, 40 Boright Ave., Kenilworth 07033
Pres., GM—Dennis Polvere, 20 emp., *Point-of-purchase displays, assembly* (908) 272-1112
Vermont Store Fixture Corporation, 265 Greenwood Ave., Midland Park 07432
GM—Joseph Motisi, 9 emp., *Wooden store fixtures* (201) 652-3401
Vira Mfg., Inc., 1 Buckingham Ave., Perth Amboy 08861
CEO—Vic Romano, 216 emp., *Retail store fixtures, displays, themed* (732) 442-8472
Visual Architectural Designs, Inc., 15 Harmich Rd., South Plainfield 07080
Pres.—Sara Chrysanthopoulos, 20 emp., *Architectural millwork, store fixtures* (908) 754-3000
Visual Graphic Systems, Inc., 330 Washington Ave., Carlstadt 07072
Chrm.—Don Healy, 155 emp., *Custom eco-friendly interior & exterior* (201) 528-2700
Wagner Rack, Inc., 2 Broad St., Clifton 07013
Pres.—Ronald Wagner, 14 emp., *Wooden magazine, book & retail display* (973) 278-6966
Will's Custom Displays & Woodwork, 1202 E. Elizabeth Ave., Linden 07036
Owner—Will Alicea, 1 emp., *Wooden cabinets, displays & store fixtures* (908) 925-0008
Wood & Laminates, Inc., 102 Route 46 E., Lodi 07644
Pres.—Gabriel Salazar, 20 emp., *Custom bars & interiors for homes,* (973) 773-7475
Wood-O-Rama, Inc., 100 67th St., Closter 07624
Pres.—Carlos Caronedo, 2 emp., *Custom wooden kitchen cabinets & counters* (201) 768-1180
Woodwork 4 U, LLC, 205 Frelinghuysen Ave., Newark 07114
Pres.—Michal Jenicek, 5 emp., *Wooden kitchen cabinets & showcases* (973) 643-3044
Zaller Studios, Inc., 265 Watsessing Ave., Bloomfield 07003
Pres.—Gabriel Pereira, 6 emp., *Point-of-purchase displays & vinyl,* (973) 743-5175

## 2542 Partitions & fixtures, except wood

10-31, Inc., 2 W. Crisman Rd., Columbia 07832
Pres.—William Stender, 24 emp., *Custom wooden, plastic & glass artwork* (908) 496-4946
Accent Kitchen & Bath Center & Countertops, 510 Englishtown Rd., Monroe 08831
Off. Mgr.—Christopher John, 3 emp., *Plastic laminate & high-density board* (732) 786-1001
ACD Custom Granite, Inc., 1304 Roller Rd., Ocean 07712
Pres.—Cynthia Schomaker, 13 emp., *Natural & engineered stone fabrication* (732) 695-2400
All Granite & Marble Corp., 1 Mount Vernon St., Ste. A, Ridgefield Park 07660
Pres.—Richey Jaroslaw, 10 emp., *Corporate headquarters & marble, granite* (201) 440-6779
Allen Cabinets & Millwork, Inc., 60 Newark Pompton Tpk., Pequannock 07440
GM—John Vanderstad, 4 emp., *Laminated countertops* (973) 694-0665
Alpak Display Group, 575 N. Midland Ave., Saddle Brook 07663
V-P., POP Sales—Jason Taub, 30 emp., *Corrugated point-of-purchase displays* (201) 797-1411
ALPS Technologies, Inc., 500 Memorial Dr., Ste. 1, Somerset 08873
Pres.—Robert Wagner, 25 emp., *Solid-surface & granite countertops* (732) 764-0777
Alternative Air & Store Fixtures, 3-C Mary Way, Hainesport 08036
Ptnr.—James Lunstead, 6 emp., *Refrigerated & dry custom & standard* (609) 261-5870
ALU, Inc., 240 Anderson Ave., Moonachie 07074
CFO & COO—Daniele Cincotti, 15 emp., *Aluminum store display fixtures* (201) 617-2000
American Van Equipment, Inc., 149 Lehigh Ave., Lakewood 08701
Pres.—Charles Richter, 95 emp., *Aluminum, steel & hot dipped galvanized* (800) 526-4743
AMKO Displays, LLC (H Q), 4 Barrett Ave., Moonachie 07074
Pres.—Douglas Lim, 3 emp., *Company headquarters; display cases* (201) 460-7199
Apple Exhibits, 730 Grand Ave., Unit 1-A, Ridgefield 07657
Owner—Young Park, 10 emp., *Trade show exhibits & booths & custom* (201) 943-2775
Architectural Acrylics, 5 Rockhill Rd., Ste. 3, Cherry Hill 08003
Owner—Scott Springman, 10 emp., *Acrylic store fixtures* (856) 751-2411
Archive Designs, Inc., 238 Emmet St., Newark 07114
Pres.—John Olaya, 5 emp., *Large steel document storage systems* (973) 242-6400
Art Guild, Inc., 300 Wolf Dr., West Deptford 08086
Pres.—Doug Zegel, 210 emp., *Corporate headquarters & trade show* (856) 853-7500
Artisan Kitchen Studio, LLC, 26 Cokesbury Rd., P.O. Box 151, Lebanon 08833
Pres.—Richard Butler, 2 emp., *Wooden & laminate cabinets & custom* (908) 236-7233
Better Plastics, Inc., 1 Mallory Ave., Jersey City 07305
Pres.—Debra Fiore, 10 emp., *Plastic laminated solid surface countertops* (201) 332-6777
Blanc Display Group, The, 88 King St., Ste. 1, Dover 07801
Pres.—Didier Blanc, 100 emp., *Custom point-of-purchase displays,* (973) 537-0090
Blanc Industries, Inc., 88 King St., Dover 07801
Pres.—Didier Blanc, 60 emp., *Corporate headquarters & point-of-purchase* (973) 678-1200
Bozzone Custom Woodwork, Inc., 77 N. Beverwyck Rd., Lake Hiawatha 07034
Pres.—Lou Bozzone, 4 emp., *Wooden & laminate cabinets* (973) 334-5598
C C & D Capital Contracting & Design, Inc., 640 North Ave., Plainfield 07060
Pres.—Don Finley, 45 emp., *Point-of-purchase displays & custom* (908) 561-8411
Cabinet Works Corp., 511 W. Kings Hwy., Mount Ephraim 08059
Pres.—Frank Cavallaro, 3 emp., *Wooden & laminate cabinets & architectural* (856) 931-7289
California Closets, 4 Gardner Rd., Ste. 5, Fairfield 07004
Ptnr.—Marty Ginsberg, 50 emp., *Melamine & MDF closets & related custom* (973) 882-3800
Casework Design, 10 County Line Rd., Ste 26, Branchburg 08876
Owner—Michael Rowden, 3 emp., *Store & commercial fixtures, business* (908) 722-7401
Castle Woodcraft Assocs., 161 Route 9, P.O. Box 426, Pine Beach 08741
Ptnr.—Ernest Guenzburger, 15 emp., *Kitchen & office wooden & plastic laminate* (732) 349-1519
Choice Cabinetry, LLC, 61 5th St., Somerville 08876
Owner—Avner Shmuel, 50 emp., *Wooden, melamine & thermofoil kitchen* (908) 707-8801
City Diecutting, Inc., 1 Cory Rd., Ste. C, Morristown 07960
Pres.—Eric DeVos, 18 emp., *Semi-gloss, water resistant, black* (973) 270-0370
Clip Strip Corp., 343 S. River St., Hackensack 07601
Pres.—Edward D. Spitaletta, 6 emp., *Point-of-purchase merchandise & store* (201) 342-9155
Closettech, 203 Woodward Rd., Englishtown 07726
Owner—Joe Adelfio, 20 emp., *Wooden & plastic laminate custom closet* (732) 792-0088
Color Optics By Arcade, Inc., 40 Green Pond Rd., Rockaway 07866
CEO—Joe Cicci, 58 emp., *Paperboard & visual packaging & commercial* (973) 664-3100
Coloredge, 190 Jony Dr., Carlstadt 07072
Dir.—Tony Chester, 50 emp., *Large-format printing & visual displays* (201) 716-5200
Commerce Sign Solutions, LLC, 540 Cranbury Rd., Ste. 334, East Brunswick 08816
Owner—Linda Harrington, 1 emp., *ADA & architectural signs, banners,* (732) 238-7000
Corporate Woodworking, Inc., 368 Passaic Ave., P.O. Box 10362, Fairfield 07004
Pres.—Dan Andersen, 15 emp., *Wooden & laminated cabinets* (973) 227-2211
Countertops Plus, Inc., 61 Willet St., Bldg. T, Passaic 07055
Pres.—Leo Sullivan, 8 emp., *Plastic laminated countertops* (973) 365-2232
Creating Your Design, LLC, 45 Wood St., Paterson 07524
Owner—David Batiz, 10 emp., *Trade show exhibits, commercial & retail* (973) 357-1080
Creative Design Plus, 1634 E. Elizabeth Ave., Linden 07036
GM—Ping Larrabee, 8 emp., *Commercial printing, advertising specialties* (732) 287-3336
Custom Counters By Precision, 11-17 Linden St., Passaic 07055
Pres.—William Prusiensky, 30 emp., *Laminate, solid-surface, engineered* (973) 773-0111
Custom Wood Furniture, Inc., 37 E. Clinton St., P.O. Box 3034, Newton 07860
Pres.—John Kweselait, 15 emp., *Wooden & laminated cabinets* (973) 579-4880
D & D Millwork Co., Inc., 10-12 N. 7th St., Belleville 07109
Pres.—Bernard D'Avella, 5 emp., *Wooden & plastic laminate cabinets,* (973) 759-6336
Da Vinci Displays, LLC, 123 Taft Dr., Brick 08724
CEO—Donna Tietjen, 2 emp., *Plastic displays & fixtures for retail* (732) 730-3001
Datascan Graphics, Inc., 55 Madison Ave., Ste. 400, Morristown 07960
★ Pres.—Roy House, 25 emp., *Point-of-purchase displays* (973) 543-4800
Design Display Group, Inc., 105 Amor Ave., Carlstadt 07072
Pres., CEO—Andrew Freedman, 150 emp., *Custom point-of-purchase displays &* (201) 438-6000
Design Production, Inc., 9 Industrial Pk., Waldwick 07463
Pres.—Thomas Murphy, 25 emp., *Point-of-purchase displays* (201) 447-5656
Detail Model & Machine, 61 Woodstown Rd., Mullica Hill 08062
Owner—David Rose, 4 emp., *Training & trade show models & trade* (856) 223-0184
Dimensional Communications Inc., 1595 MacArthur Blvd., Mahwah 07430
Pres.—Douglas Fixell, 70 emp., *Trade show displays & booths* (201) 767-1500
Direct Cabinet Sales, 265 Central Ave., Clark 07066
Off. Mgr.—Antonio Koutsouzos, 8 emp., *Custom wooden & wire closets & shelves* (732) 382-8080
Diversified Fixture, Inc., 1930 Swarthmore Ave., Lakewood 08701
Pres., CEO—Jerry Vitillo, 10 emp., *Wood & plastic store fixtures, medical* (732) 886-0600
Diversified Millwork, Inc., 420 N. 2nd Rd., Unit C, Hammonton 08037
Pres.—Don McFaul, 10 emp., *Wooden, plastic laminate & solid-surface* (609) 270-7385
Engo Co., 128 Case Dr., South Plainfield 07080
Pres., Sales Mgr.—Robert J. Engo, 35 emp., *Store fixtures* (908) 754-6600
Excelsior Metal Products, LLC, 151 State Route 33, Ste. 201, Manalapan 07726
Mng. Ptnr.—Jordan Cayne, 13 emp., *Contract manufacturing of electronic* (732) 651-9914
Exhibit Co., Inc., The, 239 Old New Brunswick Rd., Piscataway 08854
Pres.—Frank Geraci, 25 emp., *Custom & portable trade show exhibits* (732) 465-1070
ExhibitCraft, Inc., 22 Riverview Dr., Ste. 103, Wayne 07470
Pres.—Scott Walode, 15 emp., *Customized trade show exhibits, show* (973) 686-9393
Falstrom Co., 1 Falstrom Ct., P.O. Box 118, Passaic 07055
Chrm., Pres. & CEO—Clifford Lindholm III, 70 emp., *Industrial metal cabinets* (973) 777-0013
FASTSIGNS®, 255 State Route 3, Secaucus 07094
Pres.—Elizabeth Selbach, 7 emp., *Yard, interior & exterior signs, banners* (201) 902-8640
Fi Companies, 3150 Bordentown Ave., Old Bridge 08857
Pres., CEO—Scott Forman, 50 emp., *Store fixtures, displays & cabinets* (732) 727-8100
Fiber Optic Systems, Inc., P.O. Box 62, Whitehouse Station 08889
Pres.—Cyr A. Ryan, 6 emp., *Fiber-optic displays, exhibits & advertising* (908) 534-5500
Frazier Industrial Co., 91 Fairview Ave., P.O. Box F, Long Valley 07853
CEO—William Mascharka, 100 emp., *Company headquarters & structural steel* (908) 876-3001
G & M Custom Formica Work, 120 Francis St., Bldg. C, Keyport 07735
Ptnr.—George Macchia, 3 emp., *Plastic laminated countertops* (732) 888-0360
Gafgen Cabinetmakers, Thomas P., 5 Truman Ct., Robbinsville 08691
Owner—Thomas P. Gafgen, 3 emp., *Wooden & melamine residential & office* (609) 448-2060
GAW Associates, Inc., 670 Deer Rd., Unit A, Cherry Hill 08034
Pres.—Kathleen Gaw-Betz, 10 emp., *Electronic cabinets/racks, custom cable* (856) 608-1428
Gengaro Stone, LLC, 90 S. Main St., Ocean Grove 07756
Pres.—Sam Gengaro, 12 emp., *Solid-surface countertops, including* (732) 776-6000
Gotham Group, The, 202 W. Parkway Dr., Ste. 2, Egg Harbor Township 08234
Pres.—Qiang Wang, 16 emp., *Large-format digital displays, specialty* (609) 645-2211

Grand Displays, Inc., 12 Empire Blvd., Moonachie 07074
Pres.—Susan Ostreicher, 60 emp., *Paper die cutting & displays* ........ (201) 994-1500
H & H Industrial Corp., 7612 N. Crescent Blvd., Pennsauken 08110
V-P.—Maryann Hajduk, 35 emp., *Electronics cabinets* ........ (856) 663-4444
H2L, LLC, 4201 Tonnelle Ave., Ste. 2, North Bergen 07047
Off. Mgr.—Michelle Bastiar, 9 emp., *Commercial & residential wooden millwork* ........ (201) 864-0060
Handy Store Fixtures, Inc., 337 Sherman Ave., Newark 07114
Pres.—Paul Kurland, 100 emp., *Steel shelving* ........ (973) 242-1600
Hansen's Cabinet Shop, Inc., 42 Park Ave., Madison 07940
Pres.—A. Hansen, 4 emp., *Custom wooden & plastic laminated cabinets* ........ (973) 377-2444
Hanssem Corp., 155 Helen St., South Plainfield 07080
Hum. Res. Mgr.—Joochan Lee, 100 emp., *Wooden & laminate kitchen & bathroom* ........ (908) 754-4949
Hathaway Plastics, Inc., 911 Springfield Rd., Union 07083
Pres.—Robert Daniel, 3 emp., *Plastic molded point-of-purchase displays* ........ (908) 688-9494
Holtec International (H Q), 555 Lincoln Dr. W., Ste. 1, Marlton 08053
Pres., CEO—Kris Singh, 170 emp., *Company headquarters; steel fabrication* ........ (856) 797-0900
Hudson Display Corp., 831 Frelinghuysen Ave., Newark 07114
Pres.—Maggie Marin, 4 emp., *Plastic display fixtures* ........ (973) 623-8255
Hutchinson Cabinets, LLC, 244 Bark Bridge Rd., Sewell 08080
V-P.—George Hutchinson, 25 emp., *Wooden & plastic laminate cabinets* ........ (856) 468-5500
Impact Displays Group, LLC, 310 13th St., Carlstadt 07072
★ CEO—Gill Horowitz, 32 emp., *Point-of-purchase displays* ........ (212) 842-1800
Infinite Manufacturing Group, Inc., 171 Coit St., Irvington 07111
Founder & CEO—Bernard Alloysius, 20 emp., *Indoor & outdoor architectural signage* ........ (973) 649-9950
Intelco Of Delaware Valley, 250 Harvard Ave., P.O. Box 9, Westville 08093
Pres.—Mike Wells, 120 emp., *Company headquarters & solid-surface* ........ (856) 456-6755
Intermarket Technology, Inc., 92 Newark Pompton Tpke., Wayne 07470
Pres., Hum. Res. & IT Mgr.—Scott Gardner, 40 emp., *Point-of-purchase fixtures* ........ (973) 872-9090
Jafco Industries, LLC, 136 Lincoln Blvd., Middlesex 08846
Pres.—Abe Werczberger, 20 emp., *Architectural millwork & plastic laminate* ........ (732) 356-1502
JED Display, LLC, 55 Arlington Ave., Kearny 07032
Owner, Cont. & Manager—James B. Howell, Jr., 5 emp., *Point-of-purchase displays & specialty* . (201) 340-2329
Jewelry Tray & Pad Co., Inc., 1150 Edgewater Ave., Ridgefield 07657
Pres.—Aaron Rosenberg, 22 emp., *Jewelry displays* ........ (201) 941-4300
Kempton Wood Products, LLC, 2800 Ridgewood Rd., Wall 07719
Manager—Kevin Kempton, 6 emp., *Wooden & vinyl storage buildings, pool* ........ (732) 449-8673
Kitchen King, Inc., 1561 Route 9, Toms River 08755
Pres.—Terry Barth, 20 emp., *Quartz, granite & laminate countertops* ........ (732) 341-9660
Klose Assocs., Inc., 804 Broadway, West Long Branch 07764
Pres., CEO, CFO—Raymond G. Klose, 15 emp., *Trade show exhibit booths & displays* ........ (732) 229-8950
Kubik Maltbie, Inc., 7000 Commerce Pkwy., Ste. C, Mount Laurel 08054
Pres.—Charles M. Maltbie, Jr., 40 emp., *Glass & metal museum showcases & displays* ........ (856) 234-0052
Laminate Creations, LLC, 1235 Hurffville Rd., Deptford 08096
Member—James Martucci, 6 emp., *Wooden & laminate kitchen cabinets,* ........ (856) 232-8323
Laminetics, Inc., 1263 River Ave., Lakewood 08701
Pres.—Robert Kicak, 3 emp., *Wooden & laminated countertops & cabinets* ........ (732) 367-1116
Laurel Mfrs., Inc., 620 Cooper St., P.O. Box 5306, Delanco 08075
Pres.—Dan Iosca, 40 emp., *Wooden & metal store fixtures* ........ (856) 461-6600
Longo's Cabinet Shop, 101 Monroe St., Garfield 07026
Owner—Tom Esposito, 1 emp., *Wooden & laminate cabinets* ........ (973) 472-3567
Marmo Enterprises, Inc., 468 Elizabeth Ave., Somerset 08873
Pres.—Matthew Partsinevelos, 2 emp., *Marble, granite, limestone, slate,* ........ (908) 486-4421
Marvic Corp./A.J.D. Stone, 2450 Iorio St., Union 07083
Pres., Marvic Corp.—Alfred J. D'Alessandro, 100 emp., *Granite, quartz, solid-surface, concrete* . (908) 686-4340
Merlino Marble & Granite, Inc., 92 Route 50, Ocean View 08230
Pres.—Timothy Merlino, 2 emp., *Natural stone & solid-surface countertops* ........ (609) 624-9500
Metaline Products Co., Inc., 101 N. Feltus St. & 241 Raritan St., South Amboy 08879
Chrm. & CEO—August J. Zilincar III, 35 emp., *Custom metal point-of-purchase displays* ........ (732) 721-1373
Miller Fabricators, 1135 Mount Ephraim Ave., Camden 08103
Owner, Pres. & CEO—Aaron Miller, 10 emp., *Laminated countertops & custom cabinetry* ........ (856) 541-9499
Modern Equipment Co., Inc., 19 Ann St., Bordentown 08505
Owner—David Dunigan, 24 emp., *Wooden & metal commercial cabinets* ........ (609) 298-2100
Modern Showcase, Inc., 610 Commercial Ave., Carlstadt 07072
Pres.—John Kang, 10 emp., *Metal & wooden store fixtures* ........ (201) 935-2929
NEMA Associates, Inc., 57 Bruen St., Newark 07105
Pres., CEO—Juan Carlos Lopez, 14 emp., *Full-service digital, large-format,* ........ (973) 274-0052
Nomadic Display, 4-6 Just Rd., Fairfield 07004
Sales Mgr.—Michael Hurley, 10 emp., *Portable & modular display systems* ........ (862) 210-8120
Nulab Furniture Corp., 11 Federal Rd., Monroe Township 08831
CEO—Fran Ditringo, 20 emp., *Laboratory furniture* ........ (732) 792-0050
On The Level Counter Top, Inc., 825 Brook Rd., Lakewood 08701
★ Pres.—Vito G. Paratore, 1 emp., *Wooden kitchen cabinets & formica countertops* ........ (732) 370-4186
Ostlund, Inc., Cal, 555 N. Michigan Ave., Kenilworth 07033
Pres., CEO—Cal Ostlund, Jr., 50 emp., *Trade show exhibits* ........ (908) 688-4466
Paramount Fixture Corp., 175 Mount Pleasant Ave., Newark 07104
Owner & Pres.—Stephen Porcelli, 35 emp., *Custom wooden & metal store fixtures* ........ (973) 485-1585
Permalith Plastics, LLC, 6901 N. Crescent Blvd., Pennsauken 08110
V-P., Sales—Gary Brown, 45 emp., *Plastic litho & screen printing, laminating* ........ (856) 488-8000
Porta-Display, Inc., 790 Bloomfield Ave., Ste. B-2, Clifton 07012
Pres.—George Kruse, 2 emp., *Convention exhibits* ........ (973) 574-0057
Preferred Display, Inc., 310 Brighton Rd., Clifton 07012
Pres.—Robert Rousseau, 250 emp., *Corporate headquarters & plastic, aluminum* ........ (973) 405-5137
Presentation Solutions, Inc., 432 Clearstream Rd., Jackson 08527
Pres.—Margo Sweeney, 4 emp., *Trade show exhibits* ........ (732) 961-1960
Quality Solid Surface, Inc., 333 Vreeland Ave., Paterson 07513
Owner—Offer Bok, 25 emp., *Fabrication of solid-surface countertops* ........ (973) 357-9770
Rand Diversified, 3 Ethel Rd., Ste. 301, Edison 08817
Chrm.—Jack Wuensch, 40 emp., *Company headquarters & point-of-purchase* ........ (732) 287-2525
RB & A, Inc., 350 Sparta Ave., Bldg. C, Sparta 07871
Pres.—Rod Borden, 5 emp., *Point-of-purchase, acrylic, stock &* ........ (973) 726-0830
Red Feather Marketing Group, 332 Main St., Madison 07940
Ptnr.—Steve Becker, 7 emp., *Advertising specialties, including* ........ (973) 966-1399
Regal-Pinnacle Mfg., Inc., 220 Route 70, Ste. A, Medford 08055
Pres.—Peter C. Palko, 75 emp., *Wooden & metal display fixtures & refrigerate* ........ (609) 714-2330
Rock-Tenn Co., 15 Garner Rd., Fairfield 07004
Off. Mgr.—Ashley Shiminsky, 40 emp., *Paperboard & corrugated display prototypes* ........ (973) 594-6000
Royal Cabinet Co., Inc., 152 U.S. Highway 206, Unit 14-D, Hillsborough 08844
Pres.—Paul Y. McDonald, 30 emp., *Wooden, laminated & commercial kitchen* ........ (908) 203-8000
Sama Plastics Corp., 20 Sand Park Rd., Cedar Grove 07009
Pres.—Mark Wolfberg, 45 emp., *Acrylic & wood display fixture & point-of-pur* ........ (973) 239-7200
Sawitz Store Fixture, Inc., 130 Grand St., Carlstadt 07072
Pres.—Daniel Sawitz, 28 emp., *Wooden, laminate & solid-surface store* ........ (201) 842-9444

Shelving Depot, Inc., 419 W. Elizabeth Ave., Linden 07036
Pres.—Richard Kurland, 12 emp., *Shelving, store fixtures, metal, wooden* ........ (908) 474-8000
Sign-A-Rama, 1459 Highway 38, P.O. Box 360, Hainesport 08036
Owner—Gary Kuffer, 4 emp., *Interior & exterior, ADA & project* ........ (609) 702-1444
Sophisticated Storage Solutions, LLC, 7-W Chimney Rock Rd., Bridgewater 08807
Owner—Jacki Melchior, 7 emp., *Customized laminate closets, storage* ........ (732) 356-4200
South Jersey Metal, Inc., 1651 Hurffville Rd., Route 41, P.O. Box 5148, Deptford 08096
Pres.—Joseph Wagner, 20 emp., *Commercial stainless steel kitchen* ........ (856) 228-0642
SpaceNow! Corporation, 234 Emmet St., Newark 07114
Pres., R & D Mgr.—Bernard Morcheles, 5 emp., *High density mobile filing & storage* ........ (973) 504-8585
Spark Wire Products Co., Inc., 158 River Rd., Clifton 07014
Pres.—Paul Fessak, 5 emp., *Wire display racks* ........ (973) 773-6945
Spaulding Fabricators Inc., 1136 Industrial Pkwy., Brick 08724
Pres.—Stephen Spaulding, 21 emp., *Solid-surface, granite & engineered* ........ (732) 840-4433
Specialty Fabricators, LLC, 118 Meany Rd., Wrightstown 08562
Pres.—Edward Symbouras, 25 emp., *Refrigerated & heated grocery displays* ........ (609) 758-6995
Speed Pro Imaging Of Piscataway, 56 Ethel Rd. W., Ste. 14, Piscataway 08854
Owner—R. Scott Schoner, 3 emp., *Large-format digital printing & banners* ........ (732) 662-9860
Speedpro Imaging, 52 E. Centre St., Ste. 3-B, Nutley 07110
Pres.—Doug Nixon, 4 emp., *Large-format graphic printing, including* ........ (973) 542-8384
Stone Surfaces, Inc., 890 Paterson Plank Rd., East Rutherford 07073
Pres.—Michael Sakosits, 30 emp., *Solid surface & stone countertops* ........ (201) 935-8803
Strive Group, LLC, The, 160 Chubb Ave., Ste. 101, Lyndhurst 07071
Owner—Jeff Schuoski, 9 emp., *Point-of-purchase displays* ........ (973) 893-1300
SYMA Systems, Inc., 300 Wolf Dr., West Deptford 08086
V-P., Sales & Mktg.—Stanley R. Hyams, 100 emp., *Custom trade show & museum exhibits* ... (856) 686-4190
Taylor Made Cabinets, 516 E. Bay Ave., Manahawkin 08050
Ptnr. & Plt. Mgr.—Dave Taylor, 15 emp., *Wooden & laminate cabinets* ........ (609) 978-6900
Tech-Pak, Inc., 100 Blum, P.O. Box 51, Wood Ridge 07075
Sr. Design Engr.—Ed Garcia, 40 emp., *Corrugated store displays* ........ (201) 935-3800
Testrite Instrument Co., 216 S. Newman St., Hackensack 07601
Pres.—Larry Rubin, 120 emp., *Telescopic aluminum tube educational* ........ (201) 543-0240
Titan Rack & Shelving, LLC, 101 Muirhead Ave., Trenton 08695
CEO, CFO & Gen. Counsel—Scott Miller, 8 emp., *Metal racks & shelving* ........ (732) 249-0887
Top Line Co., 2131 Bethel Ave., Pennsauken 08110
Owner—Bruce MacLachlan, 50 emp., *Laminate, acrylic, marble, granite,* ........ (856) 662-6400
Top Shops, LLC, 361 W. Dewey Ave., Ste. 8, Wharton 07885
Owner—Reggie Matthews, 3 emp., *Granite & solid-surface countertops* ........ (973) 442-0050
Trans World Marketing Corp., 360 Murray Hill Pkwy., East Rutherford 07073
CEO—James Cavaluzzi, 300 emp., *In-store retail displays, fixtures,* ........ (201) 935-5565
Trinity Mfg., LLC, 60 Leonard St., Metuchen 08840
Ptnr.—Randy Riley, 10 emp., *Plastic thermoformed displays for retail* ........ (732) 549-2866
Unified Resources In Display, Inc./Display Pro Manufacturing, 40 Boright Ave., Kenilworth 07033
Pres., GM—Dennis Polvere, 20 emp., *Point-of-purchase displays, assembly* ........ (908) 272-1112
United Hospital Supply Corp., 4422 Route 130 S., Burlington 08016
Pres.—Matthew Lyons, 85 emp., *Medical, laboratory, bank, security* ........ (609) 387-7580
Vira Mfg., Inc., 1 Buckingham Ave., Perth Amboy 08861
CEO—Vic Romano, 216 emp., *Retail store fixtures, displays, themed* ........ (732) 442-8472
Visual Graphic Systems, Inc., 330 Washington Ave., Carlstadt 07072
Chrm.—Don Healy, 155 emp., *Custom eco-friendly interior & exterior* ........ (201) 528-2700
Zaller Studios, Inc., 265 Watsessing Ave., Bloomfield 07003
Pres.—Gabriel Pereira, 6 emp., *Point-of-purchase displays & vinyl,* ........ (973) 743-5175

## 2591 Drapery hardware & blinds & shades

Ackerson Drapery & Decorating Services, Inc., 500 James St., Ste. 14, Lakewood 08701
Pres., CFO—Ronni Leddy, 8 emp., *Theatrical stage curtains & window* ........ (732) 905-4433
Art's Windows, Inc., 199 Ocean Ave., Lakewood 08701
Pres.—Art Engel, 9 emp., *Window treatments* ........ (732) 367-1770
Atlantic City Shade Shop, Inc., 500 Tilton Rd., P.O. Box 217, Northfield 08225
Owner, MIS Mgr. & Chief Engr.—Howard Markman, 16 emp., *Manufacturer & distributor of pleated* (609) 641-8700
Bai Lar Interior Services, Inc., 554 New Brunswick Ave., Fords 08863
Pres.—James E. Quinn, 5 emp., *Manufacturer & distributor of commercial* ........ (732) 738-0350
Beltor Mfg. Corp., 50 Union Ave., Ste. 12, Berlin 08009
Pres. & V-P.—Derek Torok, 6 emp., *Cubicle curtains & curtain tracks* ........ (856) 768-5570
Blinds To Go, Inc., 1800 Cedar Bridge Ave., Lakewood 08701
Plt. Mgr.—Alfredo Fuentes, 150 emp., *Vertical & venetian window blinds &* ........ (732) 901-2001
Blinds To Go, Inc., 101 E. State Route 4, Paramus 07652
CEO—Nkere Udofia, 15 emp., *Corporate headquarters & window blinds* ........ (732) 321-5000
Bloomfield Drapery Co., Inc., 948 Paterson Ave., East Rutherford 07073
Pres.—Steve Gold, 15 emp., *Manufacturer & distributor of theatrical* ........ (973) 777-3566
Bonded Insulation Products, 657 Union Blvd., Totowa 07512
Pres.—Harvey S. Goodman, 25 emp., *Storm doors, vinyl all-welded replacement* ........ (973) 256-2120
C & M Shade Corp., 53 Dwight Pl., Fairfield 07004
Pres.—Allen Francus, 13 emp., *Manufacturer & distributor of motorized* ........ (201) 807-1200
Capitol City Aluminum Products, 407 Rutgers Ave., Hamilton 08619
Pres.—Louis Battaglia, 5 emp., *Canvas & aluminum awnings & entries* ........ (609) 587-3653
Custom Window Treatments By Wayne Lubin, 1029 U.S. Highway 9, Howell 07731
Owner—Wayne Lubin, 5 emp., *Custom window treatments for commercial* ........ (732) 462-4961
Drapery & More, Inc., 2321 Kennedy Blvd., Ste. 2401-B-1, North Bergen 07047
Pres.—Ally Espana, 9 emp., *Custom window treatments, including* ........ (201) 271-9661
Drapery Corp. Of America, Inc., 12-16 1st Ave., Paterson 07524
Pres.—George Holiat, 5 emp., *Draperies & shower curtains, blinds* ........ (973) 925-1200
Fabulous Interiors, 470 Prospect Ave., Ste. 105, West Orange 07052
Mng. Ptnr.—Jeffrey Fischman, 2 emp., *Wall coverings & converted paper products* ........ (973) 736-1200
FNS Custom Window Treatment, 2954 N. West Blvd., Vineland 08360
Ptnr.—Sandy Cerione, 3 emp., *Custom draperies, blinds & shutters* ........ (856) 696-4070
Friedland & Bros., Inc., Ralph, 17 Industrial Dr., Keyport 07735
Pres.—Ely Tawil, 30 emp., *Window shades* ........ (732) 290-9800
Griffith Shade Co., 308 Washington Ave., Ste. 1, Nutley 07110
Pres. & Shop Mgr.—John K. Griffith, 4 emp., *Venetian & vertical blinds, cellular* ........ (973) 667-1474
Hudson & Bergen Co., 350 Belleville Tpk., Kearny 07032
Pres., CFO—Steven C. Boyd, 4 emp., *Venetian blinds & window shades* ........ (201) 991-4900
Kay Window Fashions, Inc., 271 2nd St., Saddle Brook 07663
Ptnr.—Sol Kleinstein, 12 emp., *Manufacturer & distributor of draperies* ........ (862) 591-1555
Laggren's, LLC, P.O. Box 7173, Monroe Township 08831
Pres.—David Lasser, 10 emp., *Canvas awnings, window shades, blinds* ........ (609) 235-9883
Lawrence Custom Drapery Shop, 323 4th St., Ewing 08638
Pres.—Charlie Cullen, 20 emp., *Custom draperies, window treatments* ........ (609) 695-3877
North Jersey Window Treatments, LLC, 164 South St., Hackensack 07601
Pres.—Martin Gutman, 12 emp., *Draperies & window treatments* ........ (201) 487-2121
Power Shade Co., Inc., 112 Paris Ave., Northvale 07647
Pres.—Greg Powers, 10 emp., *Window blinds & shades* ........ (201) 767-3727

S.I.C.

Precision Blinds Products, Inc., 637 Boulevard, Kenilworth 07033
Pres.—Robert Schreiber, 3 emp., *Window treatments, flooring & wall* .......... (908) 245-7766
Rose Brand, Inc., 4 Emerson Ln., Secaucus 07094
Pres.—George Jacobstein, 197 emp., *Curtains, draperies, backdrops, fabrics* .......... (201) 809-1730
Spotless Shade, LLC, 1217 U.S. Highway 1, Edison 08837
Owner & GM—Scott Fitzgerald, 5 emp., *Venetian & vertical blinds & window* .......... (732) 548-1711
Tina's Window Decorating, 968 Somerset St., Watchung 07069
Owner—Tina Caruso, 2 emp., *Window treatments* .......... (908) 668-0066
Window Covering Concepts, 29 Bella Rd., Lumberton 08048
★ Owner—Damien Latini, 1 emp., *Custom draperies* .......... (609) 261-1181
Window Creations By Emmy Ltd., 103 Summerset St., Garfield 07026
★ Pres.—Otto Eisenberger, 4 emp., *Window treatments* .......... (718) 965-3844

## 2599 Furniture & fixtures, nec

Brenner Metal Products Corp., 16 Main Ave., P.O. Box 16, Wallington 07057
Pres.—Christine Brenner, 30 emp., *Military hospital beds & cabinets* .......... (973) 778-2466
Deitz & Sons, Inc., M., 490 Hillside Ave., Hillside 07205
Pres.—Ken Deitz, 15 emp., *Wooden restaurant chairs & barstools* .......... (908) 686-8800
Delform, LLC, 225 Highland Cross, Ste. 6, Rutherford 07070
Ptnr. & Member—Tracey Stakelin, 5 emp., *Residential & commercial metal & wood* .......... (201) 438-3915
Distinctive Wood Work, Inc., 70 Stacy Haines Rd., Ste. D, Lumberton 08048
Owner—Jim Cherubino, 3 emp., *Custom residential & commercial millwork* .......... (609) 714-8505
Domico Upholstery Co., 1337 Delsea Dr., Woodbury 08096
★ Owner—Dennis Domico, 4 emp., *Wooden upholstered furniture for the* .......... (856) 853-8181
Drake Corp., 154 Tices Ln., East Brunswick 08816
Pres.—Ralph Drake, 8 emp., *Polymer-composite hotel furniture,* .......... (732) 254-1530
G R Office Products, Inc., 11 Kentucky Ave., Paterson 07503
Pres.—Bernardo Guterman, 2 emp., *Floor mats, fabric-wrapped tackboards* .......... (973) 345-2769
Gar Products, 170 Lehigh Ave., Lakewood 08701
Owner—Jay Garfunkle, 140 emp., *Commercial, hospitality, outdoor &* .......... (732) 364-2100
GAW Associates, Inc., 670 Deer Rd., Unit A, Cherry Hill 08034
Pres.—Kathleen Gaw-Betz, 10 emp., *Electronic cabinets/racks, custom cable* .......... (856) 608-1428
Global - The Total Office (H Q), 17 W. Stow Rd., P.O. Box 562, Marlton 08053
Pres.—Jon Abraham, 175 emp., *Company headquarters; metal, plastic* .......... (856) 596-3390
Hausmann Industries, Inc., 130 Union St., Northvale 07647
CEO—David Hausmann, 100 emp., *American-made healthcare products,* .......... (201) 767-0255
Infanti Brand Chair & Stools, 1153 W. Elizabeth Ave., Linden 07036
V-P., Sales & Mktg.—Jack Douglass, 10 emp., *Stacking aluminum banquet chairs, barstools.* (718) 447-5632
Infinite Manufacturing Group, Inc., 171 Coit St., Irvington 07111
Founder & CEO—Bernard Alloysius, 20 emp., *Indoor & outdoor architectural signage* .......... (973) 649-9950
Jenkins, Inc., Brad, 291 Mount Kemble Ave., Morristown 07960
Pres. & Principal—Brad Jenkins, 4 emp., *Architectural & interior design, including* .......... (973) 331-1995
Laminate Creations, LLC, 1235 Hurffville Rd., Deptford 08096
Member—James Martucci, 6 emp., *Wooden & laminate kitchen cabinets,* .......... (856) 232-8323
Majestic Industries, Inc., 225 Passaic St., Passaic 07055
Pres.—Peter Ferentinos, 20 emp., *Hospitality seating for hospitals,* .......... (973) 473-3434
Marlo Mfg. Co., Inc., 301 Division St., Boonton 07005
Ex. V-P.—Paul Peruccio, 50 emp., *Stainless steel restaurant equipment* .......... (973) 423-0226
MossFauset Woodworking, 49 Harrison St., 13th Fl., Hoboken 07030
Owner—Kelly Fauset, 3 emp., *Handcrafted custom high-end residential* .......... (201) 714-9797
Samuelson Furniture, Inc., 11-13 Maryland Ave., Paterson 07503
Pres.—Lawrence Chalsin, 20 emp., *Wooden & metal residential furniture* .......... (973) 333-6090
Sawitz Store Fixture, Inc., 130 Grand St., Carlstadt 07072
Pres.—Daniel Sawitz, 28 emp., *Wooden, laminate & solid-surface store* .......... (201) 842-9444
Stryker Corp., 2 Pearl Ct., Allendale 07401
IT Mgr.—James Anastasio, 180 emp., *Orthopaedic beds for spinal cord patients* .......... (201) 760-8000
Takara Belmont U. S. A., Inc., 101 Belmont Dr., Somerset 08873
Pres.—Karataka Yashikawa, 80 emp., *Corporate headquarters & beauty, spa* .......... (732) 469-5000
Terzano Cabinetry, Inc., 111 Leuning St., Unit G, South Hackensack 07606
Owner & Pres.—Joe Terzano, 8 emp., *Custom-designed handmade cabinetry* .......... (201) 373-9500
Top Line Seating, Inc., 540 S. 31st St., Kenilworth 07033
CEO—Carl Friedrich, 15 emp., *Bar stools & chairs for the casino* .......... (908) 241-9051
Union City Mirror & Table Co., 129 34th St., Union City 07087
Pres., R & D Mgr.—Thomas Russo, 6 emp., *French Provincial wooden & occasional* .......... (201) 867-1827

# 26 PAPER & ALLIED PRODUCTS

## 2611 Pulp mills

All American Recycling Corp., 2 Hope St., Jersey City 07307
Pres.—Vincent M. Ponte, 137 emp., *Paper & plastic recycling, including* .......... (201) 656-3363
Campbell Converting Corp., 703 Van Rossum Ave., Unit 2, Beverly 08010
Owner & Pres.—C. Norman Campbell, 8 emp., *Paper converting & wide-format printing* .......... (609) 835-2720
Newark Group, Inc., The, 60 Lockwood St., Newark 07105
V-P., GM—Charles M. Stone, 40 emp., *Recycled paper* .......... (973) 465-3900

## 2621 Paper mills

American Waste & Textile, LLC, 73 Vesey St., Newark 07105
Ptnr., CEO & MIS Mgr.—Jeffrey Belfer, 10 emp., *Wiping cloths, industrial work gloves* .......... (973) 589-6252
Consolidated Material Converters, Inc., 74 Squankum Rd., Tinton Falls 07724
Pres.—Neal Marty, 20 emp., *Paper & plastic slitting, sheeting* .......... (732) 389-5973
LPS Industries, Inc., 10 Caesar Pl., Moonachie 07074
CEO—Madeleine Robinson, 225 emp., *Paperboard boxes & tubes, paper & foil* .......... (201) 438-3515
Omni W.C., Inc., 166 National Rd., Edison 08817
Pres., Fin. & GM—Gary Tumminello, 18 emp., *Paper & vinyl wall coverings* .......... (732) 248-0999
Raybold Mfg., Inc., Disposable Products Div., 102 S. 8th St., Millville 08332
Pres.—Bill Riland, 10 emp., *Disposable paper slippers* .......... (856) 327-7733
Schweitzer-Mauduit International, Inc., 85 Main St., Spotswood 08884
Mill Mgr.—Greg Benedict, 140 emp., *Cigarette paper products* .......... (732) 723-6100
Soundview Paper Co., 1 Market St., Elmwood Park 07407
CEO—George Wurtz, 580 emp., *Company headquarters & eco-friendly* .......... (201) 796-4000
Yerg Accounting Supplies, 85 Washington Ave., Belleville 07109
Pres.—Kathleen Yerg Marmo, 3 emp., *Columnar accounting pads & analysis* .......... (973) 759-4041

## 2631 Paperboard mills

Accurate Box Co., Inc., 86 5th Ave., Paterson 07524
Pres., CEO—Lisa Hirsh, 150 emp., *Lithographic laminated folding cartons* .......... (973) 345-2000
HC Graphics Screen Printing, Inc., 238 Lindbergh Pl., Ste. 3, Paterson 07503
Pres.—Thomas J. Mueller, 15 emp., *Plastic & paper screen printing* .......... (973) 247-0544
Homasote Co., 932 Lower Ferry Rd., P.O. Box 7240, Trenton 08628
Chrm., CEO—Warren L. Flicker, 105 emp., *Recycled fiberboard products, including* .......... (609) 883-3300
J.I.T. Mfg., Inc., 50 Peel St., Paterson 07524
Pres.—John Norton, 14 emp., *Paper & paperboard packaging materials* .......... (973) 247-7300

## 2652 Boxes—setup paperboard

Allstate Paper Box Co., Inc., 223 Raymond Blvd., Newark 07105
Pres.—Matt Elias, 70 emp., *Set-up paperboard, folding & vinyl* .......... (973) 589-2600
Capitol Box Corp., 1300 6th St., North Bergen 07047
Pres.—Edward Maleh, 26 emp., *Rigid set-up paper board boxes* .......... (201) 867-6018
Century Packaging, Inc., 42 Edgeboro Rd., East Brunswick 08816
Pres., CFO—Tom Picciolo, Jr., 40 emp., *Paper boxes* .......... (732) 249-6600
Cross Country Box Co., Inc., 2-8 Central Ave., East Orange 07018
Pres.—Dan Goldman, 9 emp., *Rigid paperboard boxes, folding cartons* .......... (973) 673-8349
Elite Packaging Corp., 40 Cotters Ln., Ste. E, East Brunswick 08816
Owner & Pres.—Mario Magali, 100 emp., *Contract packaging & hand assembly* .......... (732) 651-9955
LPS Industries, Inc., 10 Caesar Pl., Moonachie 07074
CEO—Madeleine Robinson, 225 emp., *Paperboard boxes & tubes, paper & foil* .......... (201) 438-3515
McLean Packaging Corp., 1504 Glen Ave., Moorestown 08057
Pres.—Joseph Fenkel, 80 emp., *Corporate headquarters & paper set-up* .......... (856) 359-2600
Paperboard Products Co., 21 Shafer Pl., Hackensack 07601
Pres.—Jonathan Marks, 22 emp., *Paperboard containers & boxes* .......... (201) 440-1600
Perfect Remedy Packaging, Inc., 224 Washington St., Perth Amboy 08861
Plt. Mgr.—Morris Malmstrom, 10 emp., *Soft jewelry packaging* .......... (732) 697-0055
S. E. R. Diecutting, 7300 N. Crescent Blvd., Unit 5, Pennsauken 08110
★ Owner—Steven Rosa, 4 emp., *Folding paperboard boxes & paperboard* .......... (856) 665-8805
Shure-Pak Corp., 1500 N. 10th St., P.O. Box 105, Millville 08332
Pres.—Aaron Sheppard, 4 emp., *Paperboard folding cartons* .......... (856) 825-0808
Source Packaging, Inc., 215 Island Rd., Mahwah 07430
Pres.—Allen Adler, 20 emp., *Presentation & protective packaging* .......... (201) 831-0005
Specialty Paper Box Co., 14 Highland Dr., North Caldwell 07006
Pres.—Harry Engel III, 4 emp., *Setup, corrugated & plastic boxes* .......... (973) 396-8556
United States Box Corp., 1296 McCarter Hwy., Newark 07104
Pres.—Alan Kossoff, 65 emp., *Folding & setup paperboard boxes* .......... (973) 481-2000

## 2653 Boxes—corrugated & solid fiber

Albert Paper Products Co., 464 Coit St., Irvington 07111
Pres.—Richard M. Kenah, 25 emp., *Corrugated & paperboard boxes, including* .......... (973) 373-0330
Alpak Display Group, 575 N. Midland Ave., Saddle Brook 07663
V-P., POP Sales—Jason Taub, 30 emp., *Corrugated point-of-purchase displays* .......... (201) 797-1411
Balsco Corrugated Box & Display, LLC, 160 Union Ave., East Rutherford 07073
Pres.—Vincent Scolaro, 5 emp., *Corrugated boxes & displays* .......... (973) 546-0500
Baxter Co., Inc., E. L., 70 S. 7th Ave., P.O. Box 277, Long Branch 07740
CEO—Elwood Baxter, 14 emp., *Packaging, shipping & handling supplies* .......... (732) 229-8219
Beisler Weidmann Co., Inc., 233 Cortlandt St., Belleville 07109
Pres.—Warren Beisler, 12 emp., *Corrugated boxes* .......... (973) 759-5020
Bell Container Corp., 615 Ferry St., P.O. Box 5728, Newark 07105
Pres.—Arnold Kaplan, 175 emp., *Corrugated boxes & containers* .......... (973) 344-4400
CDS Packaging, LLC, 237 Vaile Rd., Parsippany 07054
Pres., CEO—David Hirdler, 2 emp., *Corrugated & solid fiber packaging* .......... (973) 219-1496
Creoh U. S. A., 910 E. County Line Rd., Ste. 202-A, Lakewood 08701
Pres., CEO—Joe Zicherman, 5 emp., *Corrugated boxes* .......... (718) 821-0570
Custom Liners, Inc., 1555 Ruth Rd., Ste. 7, North Brunswick 08902
Owner—John Boag, 4 emp., *Corrugated liners & partitions for* .......... (201) 569-1889
Delaware Valley Box & Lumber Co., 14 Austin Ave., Glendora 08029
Opers. Mgr.—Chris Gould, 20 emp., *Corrugated boxes & wooden crates* .......... (856) 939-1900
Delta Corrugated Paper Products, 199 W. Ruby Ave., Palisades Park 07650
Pres.—Wally Lieb, 150 emp., *Corrugated paper products* .......... (201) 941-1910
Deluxe Packaging Co., 1079 Thomas Busch Memorial Hwy., Pennsauken 08110
Ptnr., V-P., Sales & GM—Ken Hoffman, 6 emp., *Packaging supplies, including folding* .......... (856) 486-0006
Easy Pak Services Of New Jersey, 6 Nicholas Ct., P.O. Box 676, Dayton 08810
Pres.—Victor Veston, 28 emp., *Cardboard & plastic packaging materials* .......... (732) 274-2428
E-Z Do, Inc., 40 Executive Ave., Edison 08817
Pres., CEO—Mark S. Densen, 150 emp., *Houseware products, including bath,* .......... (732) 287-8111
Ferguson Containers, 20 Industrial Rd., Phillipsburg 08865
GM—Ed Reichard, 18 emp., *Corrugated boxes* .......... (908) 454-9755
G & S Feldman, Inc., P.O. Box 1136, Oakhurst 07755
Pres., Sales Mgr.—Kenny Feldman, 12 emp., *Corrugated boxes* .......... (732) 918-8838
Georgia Pacific, Inc., 623 Riegelsville Rd., Milford 08848
GM—David Bailey, 68 emp., *Corrugated paper sheets* .......... (908) 995-2228
Gloucester City Box Works, LLC, 775 Charles St., Gloucester City 08030
Pres.—Kathy White, 9 emp., *Contract packaging* .......... (856) 456-9032
Graph Corr, LLC, 4 Corn Rd., Dayton 08810
Cont.—John Daly, 26 emp., *Litho laminated sheets & finished cartons* .......... (732) 355-0088
International Paper Co., 100 E. Gloucester Pike, Barrington 08007
Cont.—William Zorzanello, 140 emp., *Corrugated boxes* .......... (856) 546-7000
International Paper Co., 370 Benigno Blvd., Bellmawr 08031
Mfg. Mgr.—Steven Forlano, 84 emp., *Corrugated boxes* .......... (856) 931-8000
International Paper Co., 101 Ford Ave., Milltown 08850
GM—Rob Marquis, 40 emp., *Corrugated boxes* .......... (732) 828-1700
International Paper Co., 140 Summerhill Rd., Spotswood 08884
GM—Peggy Giulano, 130 emp., *Corrugated boxes* .......... (732) 251-2000
International Paper Co., 33 Phoenix Dr., Thorofare 08086
Cont.—Richard Scott, 175 emp., *Corrugated boxes & point-of-purchase* .......... (856) 853-7000
Interstate Container Brunswick, LLC, 501 Finnegan Ln., North Brunswick 08902
Opers. Mgr.—Dave McQade, 300 emp., *Corrugated boxes, die cuts & displays* .......... (732) 821-8100
Kampack, Inc., 100 Frontage Rd., Newark 07114
CEO—Karen Mehiel, 125 emp., *Corporate headquarters & corrugated* .......... (973) 589-7400
Lanco York, Inc., 864 E. 25th St., Paterson 07513
CEO—Mitchell J. Leibowitz, 25 emp., *Primary & secondary pharmaceutical-grade* .......... (973) 278-7400
Levine Industries, 86 Levine St., South Paterson Sta., Paterson 07503
Pres.—Jess Levine, 30 emp., *Corrugated boxes* .......... (973) 742-1000
Levine Packaging Supply Corp., 400 U.S. Highway 46 E., Fairfield 07004
V-P.—L. Levine, 20 emp., *Manufacturer of corrugated boxes &* .......... (973) 575-3383
MAUSER USA LLC, 35 Cotters Ln., Ste. C, East Brunswick 08816
Pres., CEO—Jeff Simmonds, 80 emp., *Company headquarters & plastic containers* .......... (732) 353-7000
Medical Packaging, Inc., 470 Route 31, P.O. Box 500, Ringoes 08551
CEO—Andy Bartels, 20 emp., *Pharmacy oral solids & liquid packaging* .......... (609) 466-8991
National Packaging Corp., 14 Campus Dr., Kearny 07032
Pres.—Martin Schlesinger, 25 emp., *Corrugated cartons & packaging materials* .......... (973) 344-0100
New York Corrugated Box Co., LLC, 239 Lindberg Pl., Ste. 1, Paterson 07503
Owner—Robert Rosner, 5 emp., *Corrugated boxes & packaging supplies* .......... (973) 742-5000
New York Corrugated Box, LLC, 239 Lindbergh Pl., Ste. LI, Paterson 07503
Pres.—Robert Rosner, 3 emp., *Corrugated & high-end gift boxes &* .......... (973) 742-5000

Packaging Corp. Of America, Cranbury Creative Design Center, 8 E. Stow Rd., Ste. 100, Marlton 08053
GM, Packaging Engrg. & Design Ctr. Mgr.—Paul Freeman, 10 emp., Corrugated boxes & displays. (856) 596-5020
Packaging Unlimited, Inc., 17 Chelten Way, Bldg. A, Trenton 08638
Pres.—Frank Corrado, 3 emp., Printed corrugated boxes & foam supplies (609) 394-9400
Paige Packaging, 1 Paul Kohner Pl., Elmwood Park 07407
Owner—Allan Levine, 35 emp., Corrugated boxes (973) 483-0505
President Container Group, 200 W. Commercial Ave., Moonachie 07074
Pres.—Marvin Grossbard, 100 emp., Company headquarters & corrugated paperboard (201) 933-7500
Progress Display, Inc., 39 Progress St., Edison 08820
Ptnr.—Doug Forrestal, 10 emp., Corrugated paperboard displays (908) 757-6650
Raritan Packaging Industries, Inc., 570 Jersey Ave., New Brunswick 08901
CEO, CFO—Sandy Newman, 2 emp., Corrugated boxes, packaging supplies (732) 246-7200
Rectico, Inc., 12 Gloria Ln., Unit 1, Fairfield 07004
Pres.—Scott Sandler, 10 emp., Crating, corrugated boxes & contract (973) 575-0009
RFC Container Co., 2066 S. East Ave., Vineland 08360
Pres.—Mario Russo, 65 emp., Wax-treated corrugated multicolor & (856) 692-0404
Robessa Enterprises, Inc., 1030 Delsea Dr., P.O. Box 72, Westville 08093
Owner—William Green, 10 emp., Corrugated boxes & contract packaging (856) 251-0055
Rock-Tenn Co., 1 Corn Rd., P.O. Box 440, Dayton 08810
GM—Bob O'Connell, 120 emp., Corrugated boxes (732) 274-2500
Rock-Tenn Co., 2013 McCarter Hwy., Newark 07104
Pres.—Steven Grossman, 200 emp., Corrugated cardboard packaging & point-of-sal (973) 268-4938
RTS Packaging, LLC, 869 State Highway 12, Frenchtown 08825
GM—Greg Lawrence, 62 emp., Fiberboard box partitions (908) 782-0505
Signode Packaging Group, 151 Fabyan Pl., Newark 07112
Prodn. Mgr.—Jorge Jarrin, 35 emp., Fiberboard & corrugated packaging materials (800) 235-4066
Specialty Paper Box Co., 14 Highland Dr., North Caldwell 07006
Pres.—Harry Engel III, 4 emp., Setup, corrugated & plastic boxes (973) 396-8556
State Container Corp., 111 W. Commercial Ave., Moonachie 07074
GM—Carmine Barresi, 60 emp., Corrugated boxes & containers (201) 933-5200
Stephen Gould Corporation, 35 S. Jefferson Rd., Whippany 07981
Pres., CEO—Michael Golden, 110 emp., Corporate headquarters & packaging (973) 428-1510
Sunshine Metal & Sign, Inc., 467 Maryland St., Orange 07050
Owner—John White, 5 emp., Corrugated boxes (973) 676-4432
SupplyOne, Inc., 1090 Thomas Busch Memorial Hwy., Pennsauken 08110
Cont.—Jason Fuller, 115 emp., Corrugated boxes & foam plastic packaging (856) 727-1010
Sutherland Packaging, Inc., 254 Brighton Ave., P.O. Box 1429, Andover 07821
Pres.—Thomas W. Sutherland, 65 emp., Corrugated boxes & displays (973) 786-5141
Taurus Display Corp., 1249 Glen Ave., Moorestown 08057
Pres.—Thomas Petroni, 25 emp., Corrugated displays (856) 793-3500
Tech-Pak, Inc., 100 Blum, P.O. Box 51, Wood Ridge 07075
Sr. Design Engr.—Ed Garcia, 40 emp., Corrugated store displays (201) 935-3800
TimBar Corp., 15-01 Pollitt Dr., Unit 9, Fair Lawn 07410
Proj. Mgr.—Stasi Hinz, 12 emp., Point-of-purchase displays, corrugated (201) 568-7300
Trent Corp., The, 1384 Yardville Hamilton Square Rd., P.O. Box 2650, Trenton 08690
Pres.—Carl Angelini, 20 emp., Corrugated & bulk boxes (609) 587-7515
Trenton Corrugated Products, Inc., 17 Cheltan Way, Trenton 08638
Pres., GM—Brad Pecoraro, 40 emp., Corrugated boxes (609) 695-0808
U.S. ProPack, Inc., 341 Fairfield Rd., Freehold 07728
Pres.—Stephen Miller, 10 emp., Industrial & promotional packaging (732) 294-4500
Victory Box Corp., 645 W. 1st Ave., Roselle 07203
Pres.—Alex Landy, 135 emp., Corrugated boxes (908) 245-5100
Vineland Packaging Corp., 3602 N. Mill Rd., Vineland 08360
Pres.—Joe D'alessandro, 35 emp., Corrugated & solid fiber packaging (856) 794-3300
Woodland Mfg. Co., Inc., 1936 E. State St., Hamilton 08619
Pres., Prodn. Mgr.—L. A. Marcinkus, Jr., 13 emp., Corrugated boxes (609) 587-4180

## 2655 Fiber cans, drums & similar products

A P S Supply Co., 711 Cooper St., Beverly 08010
Pres.—Stan Lewis, 17 emp., Fiber expansions (609) 877-7900
American Tube & Paper, 80 Furler St., Totowa 07512
Off. Mgr.—Lisa Pandorf, 30 emp., Paper tubes (973) 256-3600
Enviro-Pak, Inc., 125 National Rd., Edison 08817
Pres.—Edward Fitzpatrick, 25 emp., Fiber drums (732) 248-1600
Greif, Inc., 200 Rike Dr., Millstone Township 08535
Plt. Supv.—William Guttridge, 35 emp., Fibre drums (609) 448-5300
Kearny Steel Container Corp., 401 South St., Newark 07105
Pres.—Michael Verzaleno, 75 emp., Reconditioned & new steel, fiber & (973) 589-2070
LPS Industries, Inc., 10 Caesar Pl., Moonachie 07074
CEO—Madeleine Robinson, 225 emp., Paperboard boxes & tubes, paper & foil (201) 438-3515
Paper Tube & Core, Inc., 239 Lindbergh Pl., Paterson 07503
Pres.—Russ Panzer, 25 emp., Recycled/reusable paper tubes & cores (973) 977-8823
Patrick J. Kelly Drums, Inc., 1810 River Ave., Camden 08105
Owner & Pres.—Patrick J. Kelly, 49 emp., New & reconditioned industrial steel (856) 963-1795
Ridgid Paper Tube Corp., 10 Owens Dr., Wayne 07470
Pres.—Thomas Horsburgh, 30 emp., Mailing & shipping tubes, converter (973) 942-7000
Signode Packaging Group, 151 Fabyan Pl., Newark 07112
Prodn. Mgr.—Jorge Jarrin, 35 emp., Fiberboard & corrugated packaging materials (800) 235-4066
Sonoco Products Co., 5 Stults Rd., Dayton 08810
Plt. Mgr.—Russ Dean, 60 emp., Fiber cans (609) 655-0300
Tunnel Barrel & Drum Co., Inc., 85 Triangle Blvd., Carlstadt 07072
Pres.—Anthony Urcioli, 20 emp., Reconditioned fiber & plastic drums (201) 933-1444

## 2656 Sanitary food containers

LRM Packaging, Inc., 41 James St., South Hackensack 07606
Pres.—John Natali, Jr., 50 emp., Food & specialty products contract (201) 342-2530
Pyramid Poly Bags, Inc., 600 Markley St., Port Reading 07064
Pres.—Chaya Jeremias, 20 emp., Paper & plastic tableware (718) 499-1212

## 2657 Boxes—folding paperboard

Accurate Box Co., Inc., 86 5th Ave., Paterson 07524
Pres., CEO—Lisa Hirsh, 150 emp., Lithographic laminated folding cartons (973) 345-2000
Allstate Paper Box Co., Inc., 223 Raymond Blvd., Newark 07105
Pres.—Matt Elias, 70 emp., Set-up paperboard, folding & vinyl (973) 589-2600
Bielen Graphic Arts, R. J., 6 Jules Ln., New Brunswick 08901
Pres.—Robert J. Bielen, 11 emp., Laser die cutting & gold stamping of (732) 545-3501
Catalent Pharma Solutions, Inc. (H Q), 14 Schoolhouse Rd., Somerset 08873
Pres., CEO—John Chiminski, 377 emp., Corporate headquarters; pharmaceuticals (732) 537-6200
Century Packaging, Inc., 42 Edgeboro Rd., East Brunswick 08816
Pres., CFO—Tom Picciolo, Jr., 40 emp., Paper boxes (732) 249-6600
Coastal Packaging, 48 Sellers St., Kearny 07032
Pres.—Morris Lefkowitz, 16 emp., Folding boxes (201) 955-4414
Color Optics By Arcade, Inc., 40 Green Pond Rd., Rockaway 07866
CEO—Joe Cicci, 58 emp., Paperboard & visual packaging & commercial (973) 664-3100
Concord Paper Mfg., Inc., 375 Sylvan Ave., Ste. 23, Englewood Cliffs 07632
Dir., Sales & Mktg.—Donna Parker, 4 emp., Shipping boxes & folding cartons, printing (201) 567-2529
Cross Country Box Co., Inc., 2-8 Central Ave., East Orange 07018
Pres.—Dan Goldman, 9 emp., Rigid paperboard boxes, folding cartons (973) 673-8349
Cultech, Inc., 3500 Hatley Rd., South Plainfield 07080
COO—Olivier Brigaud, 100 emp., Folding paperboard boxes (732) 225-2722
Deluxe Packaging Co., 1079 Thomas Busch Memorial Hwy., Pennsauken 08110
Ptnr., V-P., Sales & GM—Ken Hoffman, 6 emp., Packaging supplies, including folding (856) 486-0006
Four Star Reproduction, Inc., 52 Paterson Ave., Ste. 2, Newton 07860
Pres.—Charles Cioppa, 35 emp., Commercial offset & digital printing (862) 268-8200
Gilt Edge Folding Boxes, Inc., P.O. Box 544, Saddle Brook 07663
Pres.—Barbara Kotcher, 10 emp., Folding paperboard boxes (201) 843-1450
Graphic Packaging International, Inc., 4100 New Brunswick Ave., Piscataway 08854
Hum. Res. Mgr.—Chris Moeder, 200 emp., Folding cartons (732) 424-2100
Keystone Folding Box Co., Inc., 367 Verona Ave., Newark 07104
Pres.—Wade E. Hartman, 65 emp., Folding paperboard boxes & child resistant (973) 483-1054
Lanco York, Inc., 864 E. 25th St., Paterson 07513
CEO—Mitchell J. Leibowitz, 25 emp., Primary & secondary pharmaceutical-grade (973) 278-7400
Mondo International, Inc., 464 Coit St., P.O. Box 894, Irvington 07111
Pres.—Robert Raimondo, 10 emp., Paperboard products, including cartons (973) 256-6123
MultiPackaging Solutions, 901 Durham Ave., South Plainfield 07080
Sr. V-P., Healthcare Group—Shawn Smith, 210 emp., Folding paperboard boxes (908) 757-6000
New York Corrugated Box, LLC, 239 Lindbergh Pl., Ste. LI, Paterson 07503
Pres.—Robert Rosner, 3 emp., Corrugated & high-end gift boxes & (973) 742-5000
New York Folding Box Co., 20 Continental Dr., Stanhope 07874
Ptnr.—Ken Kaplan, 14 emp., Folding boxes (973) 347-6932
Novel Box Co. Ltd., 825 Lehigh Ave., Union 07083
Owner & Pres.—Moishe Sternhill, 50 emp., Manufacturer & distributor of jewelry (908) 686-7772
Package Development Co., Inc., 100 Round Hill Dr., Ste. 8, Rockaway 07866
Pres.—Charles Schwester, 50 emp., Thermoforming, contract & club packaging (973) 983-8500
Pin Point Container Corp., 669 Tanyard Rd., Deptford 08096
Pres.—Bruce Baelz, 6 emp., Folding paperboard boxes, packaging (856) 848-2115
Pioneer Packaging, 31 Wilson Dr., Sparta 07871
Pres.—Mark J. Clark, 30 emp., Printed & die-cut consumer product (973) 300-9300
Ruffino Packaging, Inc., 63 Green St., Hackensack 07601
Pres.—Joseph Ruffino, 18 emp., Folding cartons, including blisters (201) 487-1260
Shure-Pak Corp., 1500 N. 10th St., P.O. Box 105, Millville 08332
Pres.—Aaron Sheppard, 4 emp., Paperboard folding cartons (856) 825-0808
Unifoil Corp., 12 Vanil Rd. E., Fairfield 07004
Sales Rep.—Brian Leverock, 3 emp., Metallized & holographic film laminated (973) 244-9900
United States Box Corp., 1296 McCarter Hwy., Newark 07104
Pres.—Alan Kossoff, 65 emp., Folding & setup paperboard boxes (973) 481-2000
Vanguard Packaging, Inc., 620 Ramsey Ave., Hillside 07205
Pres.—Michael Wische, 3 emp., Custom packaging materials, including (973) 391-9200

## 2671 Paper coated & laminated, packaging

Brisar Industries, Inc., 150 E. 7th St., Paterson 07524
Pres.—Mark Cohen, 45 emp., Pharmaceutical, cosmetic, R.F. & blister (973) 278-2500
Chambord Prints, Inc., 38 Jackson St., Hoboken 07030
Pres.—Dennis Shah, 12 emp., Hand-printed wallpaper (201) 795-2007
Classic Printers & Converters, 140 Ethel Rd. W., Ste. K, Piscataway 08854
Pres., CEO—Sat Khurana, 9 emp., Manufacturer of custom printed & plain (732) 985-1100
Datwyler, Inc., 9012 Pennsauken Hwy., Pennsauken 08110
Site Dir.—David Clark, 300 emp., Rubber closures & aluminum & plastic (856) 663-2202
Delta Paper Corp., 8295 National Hwy., Pennsauken 08110
Sales Mgr.—Brett Bregman, 50 emp., Environmentally safe packaging, wrapping (856) 532-0333
Ever-Ready Media Packaging, P.O. Box 40, Haworth 07641
Pres.—Marshall Weingarden, 5 emp., Contract media packaging, including (973) 566-9333
Label Graphics Mfg., Inc., 175 Paterson Ave., Little Falls 07424
Pres.—Thomas Silvano, 50 emp., Corporate headquarters & pressure-sensitive (973) 890-5665
Mondi, 1100 Slocum Ave., Ridgefield 07657
GM—Paul Ortiz, 100 emp., Silicone-coated release liners for (201) 585-8875
North Jersey Paper Box Corp., 132 32nd St., P.O. Box 700, Union City 07087
Owner—Ed Maleh, 20 emp., Rigid paper boxes (201) 348-4233
Plastic Plus Group, LLC, 600 Meadowlands Pkwy., Secaucus 07094
★ Member—Joe Waltham, 70 emp., Flexible packaging laminate rollstock (201) 561-0404
Plastiform Packaging, Inc., 114 Beach St., Bldg. 6, P.O.Box 186, Rockaway 07866
Pres.—George Smith, 25 emp., Plastic packaging materials, rigid, (973) 983-8900
Power Bag & Film, LLC, 189 W. Valley Brook Rd., Califon 07830
Manager—Trevor Power, 3 emp., Polyethlene & polypropylene monolayer (908) 832-6648
Ringel Bros., Inc., 7 W. Shelton Ter., P.O. Box 727, Hillside 07205
Pres.—Doug Eppel, 14 emp., Paper converting (908) 688-9222
Seaboard Paper & Twine, LLC, 37 E. 6th St., Paterson 07524
Member—Robert Baretz, 12 emp., Waxed paper, manila rope & twine for (973) 413-8100
Stephen Gould Corporation, 35 S. Jefferson Rd., Whippany 07981
Pres., CEO—Michael Golden, 110 emp., Corporate headquarters & packaging (973) 428-1510
TCP Reliable, Inc., 551 Raritan Center Pkwy., Edison 08837
Pres., CEO—Maurice Barakat, 50 emp., Temperature control packaging (732) 346-9200
Tekkote Corp., 580 Willow Tree Rd., Leonia 07605
Dir., Fin.—Ron Saia, 90 emp., Corporate headquarters & silicone-coated (201) 585-8875
Tri-Seal, 112 Church St., Flemington 08822
Plt. Controller—Sue Franson, 120 emp., Flexible packaging & cap liners (908) 782-4000

## 2672 Paper coated & laminated

Aeon Industries, Inc., 76 Veronica Ave., Somerset 08873
Acct. & Sales Mgr.—Ken Blum, 15 emp., Thermal-sensitive labels & primary, (732) 246-3224
Almetek Industries, Inc., 2 Joy Dr., Hackettstown 07840
CEO—Lori McMahon, 75 emp., Metal & polyethelene safety signs, (908) 850-9700
American Biltrite, Inc., 105 Whittendale Dr., Moorestown 08057
V-P., GM—Michel Merky, 100 emp., Pressure-sensitive tape, including (856) 778-0700
Beau Label LLC, 385 Hillside Ave., Hillside 07205
Pres.—Vincent J. Melapioni, 80 emp., Pressure-sensitive labels (973) 318-7800
BOBST North America, Inc., 146 Harrison Ave., Roseland 07068
Pres.—Robert Pordon, 115 emp., Paper, paperboard & cardboard die-cutting (973) 226-8000
Butler Printing & Laminating, 250 Hamburg Tpke., P.O. Box 836, Butler 07405
Pres.—James Berezny, 55 emp., Vinyl wall covering, printing & laminating (973) 838-8550
Capital Label & Affixing Co., 1100 Taylors Ln., Unit 5, Cinnaminson 08077
Pres.—Frank Cooper, 4 emp., Pressure-sensitive labels (856) 786-1700

CCL Label TubeDec, 92 Ark Rd., Lumberton 08048
CEO—Joseph T. Sanski, 320 emp., *Pressure-sensitive labels* ............ (609) 953-5050
CCL Label, Inc., 120 Stockton St., Hightstown 08520
V-P., Sales, North America—Robert Ryckman, 100 emp., *Pharmaceutical & consumer product pressure-se*. (609) 443-3700
Certified Labeling Solutions, 51 Old Camplain Rd., Hillsborough 08844
Pres.—Joseph F. Braun, 30 emp., *Pressure-sensitive labels* ............ (908) 704-9997
Chesapeake Pharmaceutical & Healthcare Packaging, 6 Commerce Rd., Fairfield 07004
GM—Jim Struhar, 105 emp., *Label, insert & outsert printing for* ............ (973) 808-8000
Classic Printers & Converters, 140 Ethel Rd. W., Ste. K, Piscataway 08854
Pres., CEO—Sat Khurana, 9 emp., *Manufacturer of custom printed & plain* ............ (732) 985-1100
Decker Tape Products, Inc., 2 Stewart Pl., Fairfield 07004
Pres.—Jack Decker, 90 emp., *Adhesive tapes* ............ (973) 227-5350
Diversified Display Products, LLC, 777 Ramsey Ave., P.O. Box 913, Hillside 07205
Owner—David Rosen, 24 emp., *Coated paper products* ............ (908) 686-2200
Holland Manufacturing Company, Inc., 15 Main St., P.O. Box 404, Succasunna 07876
Chrm., CEO—Jack Holland, 94 emp., *Corporate headquarters & packaging* ............ (973) 584-8141
Horizon Label, LLC, 1049 Industrial Dr., West Berlin 08091
Pres.—Paul Falkowski, 7 emp., *Pressure-sensitive labels* ............ (856) 767-0777
Innovative Labeling, Inc., 12 Gloria Ln., Ste. 4, Fairfield 07004
Pres.—Cheryl Ziemba, 4 emp., *Indoor & outdoor nameplates & labels* ............ (973) 227-4800
J F I Printing, Inc., 357 Cortlandt St., Belleville 07109
Pres.—Joseph Iannone, 4 emp., *Pressure-sensitive adhesive labels* ............ (973) 759-3444
Johnson & Mayer, Inc., 58 Hobart St., Hackensack 07601
Pres.—Mitchell Perdue, 20 emp., *Decals* ............ (201) 646-1717
L V Adhesive, Inc., 341 Michele Pl., Carlstadt 07072
Pres., CEO—Linda Owen, 50 emp., *Pressure-sensitive adhesive papers* ............ (212) 925-2600
Label Graphics Mfg., 315 Fairfield Rd., Unit 1, Fairfield 07004
V-P. & Off. Mgr.—Denise Silvano, 10 emp., *Pressure-sensitive labels & flexible* ............ (973) 890-5665
Lamart Corp., 16 Richmond St., Clifton 07011
Pres.—Steve Hirsh, 80 emp., *Paper coating & laminating* ............ (973) 772-6262
Lamitech, Inc., 322 Half-Acre Rd., Cranbury 08512
GM—Adam Reiser, 25 emp., *Paper & vinyl lamination* ............ (609) 860-8037
Luminer Converting Group, Inc., 1925 Swarthmore Ave., Ste. 5, Lakewood 08701
Pres., Hum. Res. & IT Mgr.—Thomas Spina, 25 emp., *Corporate headquarters & pressure-sensitive* (732) 886-6557
Main Tape Co., Inc., 1 Capital Dr., Ste. 101, Cranbury 08512
Pres.—Karen Olson, 150 emp., *Pressure sensitive tapes & films* ............ (609) 395-1704
Maintape, Inc., 1 Capital Dr., Ste. 101, Bldg. 1, Cranbury 08512
Pres.—Karen Olsen, 100 emp., *Manufacturer & distributor of adhesive-backed* ............ (609) 395-1704
Metro Tag & Label, Inc., 25 E. Spring Valley Ave., Ste. 200, Maywood 07607
Pres.—Phil Glassman, 3 emp., *Commercial offset & digital printing* ............ (201) 845-4747
Mod-Tek Converting, LLC, 2550 Haddonfield Rd., Ste. E, Pennsauken 08110
Owner—Vicki Wilkinson, 12 emp., *Pressure-sensitive labels* ............ (856) 662-6884
Motif Industries, Inc., 8 Commerce Rd., Fairfield 07004
Pres.—Al Elkay, 28 emp., *Ophthalmic products, including lens* ............ (973) 575-1800
Nifty Products, 4 Jocama Blvd., Old Bridge 08857
Pres.—Norman Ferber, 25 emp., *Shipping room tape guns, tape & stretch* ............ (732) 591-1140
Nitto Denko America Automotive, Inc., 1990 Rutgers Blvd., Lakewood 08701
Dir., Opers.—Eric G. Pike, 100 emp., *Pressure-sensitive tapes & foam rubber* ............ (732) 901-7905
Omega Heat Transfer Co., Inc., 329 New Brunswick Ave., Rahway 07065
Pres.—Steven Simon, 10 emp., *Heat transfer labels & silkscreening* ............ (732) 340-0023
Princeton Label Co., 1226 U.S. Highway 130, Robbinsville 08691
GM—Donald J. Guli, 28 emp., *Pressure-sensitive labels* ............ (609) 490-0800
R Tape Corporation, 6 Ingersoll Rd., South Plainfield 07080
Pres., CEO—Paul Charapata, 160 emp., *Corporate headquarters & application* ............ (908) 753-5570
Renell Label Print, Inc., 15 Sunflower Ave., Paramus 07652
Pres.—W. Rene Huber, 8 emp., *Pressure-sensitive, paper, foil & clear* ............ (201) 652-6544
Rush Index Tabs, Inc., 60 Willow St., East Rutherford 07073
Pres.—Jay A. Cohen, 40 emp., *Plastic coated index tabs & dividers* ............ (201) 531-1555
Scientific Labeling Systems, Inc., 339 6th Ave. W., Newark 07107
Pres.—Richard D. Powers, 7 emp., *Pressure-sensitive labels* ............ (973) 722-8229
Symbology Enterprises, Inc., 185 Industrial Pkwy., Ste. H, Somerville 08876
V-P.—Tom McInerney, 8 emp., *Bar coding equipment, including bar* ............ (908) 725-1699
Trek, Inc., 43 Cranmer Rd., P.O. Box 275, Bayville 08721
Pres.—Jack Dynarski, 4 emp., *Short-run digital printed labels, including* ............ (732) 269-6300
Trend Printing International Label, Inc., 1183 Edgewater Ave., Ridgefield 07657
Pres.—David Fishbein, 15 emp., *Labels & flexible packaging* ............ (201) 941-6611
Tri-State Tape & Label Co., Inc., 351 Railroad Ave., P.O. Box 377, Beverly 08010
Pres.—David F. Wimer, 7 emp., *Flexible packaging, digital, offset* ............ (800) 682-7892
Universal Tape Co. (H Q), 110 W. New Jersey Ave., Somers Point 08244
Pres.—Mario Curcio, 45 emp., *Company headquarters; double-coated* ............ (609) 653-3191
Wise Tag & Label Co., Inc., 1077 Thomas Busch Memorial Hwy., Pennsauken 08110
Pres.—Doug Ford, 11 emp., *Pressure-sensitive labels* ............ (856) 663-2400
Yellow Stone Distributing Co., 50 Kulick Rd., Fairfield 07004
Pres.—Yimin Shiuey, 15 emp., *Pressure-sensitive labels* ............ (973) 808-8188

## 2673 Bags: plastics, laminated & coated

A N S Plastics Corp., 625 Jersey Ave., Ste. 11, New Brunswick 08901
V-P.—Ramy Samuel, 18 emp., *Plastic & HDPE shopping, custom printed* ............ (732) 247-2776
A-1 Plastics, 136 Tichenor St., Newark 07105
Pers. Mgr.—Sam Rosenburg, 40 emp., *Plastic bags* ............ (973) 344-4441
Absolute Packaging & Supply, Inc., 456 E. 22nd St., Paterson 07514
Pres., GM—Anthony Stefanelli, 4 emp., *Custom printed plastic & thermoformed* ............ (973) 278-0202
All American Poly Corp., 40 Turner Pl., Piscataway 08854
Pres.—Jack G. Klein, 242 emp., *Corporate headquarters & polyethylene* ............ (732) 752-3200
Alpha Industries Corp. (H Q), P.O. Box 808, Lyndhurst 07071
CEO—Alfred Teo, 20 emp., *Corporate headquarters; plastic bags* ............ (201) 933-6000
Beacon Converters, Inc., 280 Midland Ave., P.O. Box 8208, Saddle Brook 07663
Pres., CEO—Jackie Daly-Johnson, 70 emp., *Sterilization packaging, including* ............ (201) 797-2600
Beta Plastics Corp., 120 Amor Ave., Carlstadt 07072
Plt. Mgr.—Roland Teo, 100 emp., *Plastic bags* ............ (201) 933-1400
Broadway Industries, 1 S. Middlesex Ave., Monroe 08831
Pres.—Albert S. Kohn, 22 emp., *Plastic upholstery & mattress covers* ............ (609) 662-3970
Central Poly Corp., 2400 Bedle Pl., Linden 07036
Pres.—Andrew Hoffer, 10 emp., *Plastic bags* ............ (908) 862-7570
Champion Plastics Corp., 220 Clifton Blvd., Clifton 07011
GM—John Callaghan, 140 emp., *Polyethelene bags, liners, films, sheeting* ............ (973) 777-9400
D C Plastic Products, 12 E. 2nd St., P.O. Box 353, Bayonne 07002
Pres.—David Moskovits, 15 emp., *Plastic garbage bags* ............ (201) 339-0111
Dana Poly Inc., 1301 W. Elizabeth Ave., Linden 07036
CEO—Mendy Rosner, 40 emp., *Plastic & polyethylene bags* ............ (908) 474-0600
Eastar Plastics, Inc., 250 Circle Dr. N., Piscataway 08854
GM—Ben Tran, 20 emp., *Plastic bags* ............ (732) 564-1899
Encore Poly Corp., 240 W. Passaic St., Ste. 7, Maywood 07607
Plt. & Sales Mgr.—Sandy Stevens, 10 emp., *Polybags* ............ (201) 845-4510
E-Z Do, Inc., 40 Executive Ave., Edison 08817
Pres., CEO—Mark S. Densen, 150 emp., *Houseware products, including bath,* ............ (732) 287-8111
Fine Wrap Industry, Inc., 123 Town Square Pl., Jersey City 07310
Pres.—Bob Jones, 10 emp., *Flexible plastic food product bags* ............ (732) 960-9602
Gemini Plastic Films Corp., 535 Midland Ave., P.O. Box 360, Garfield 07026
CEO—Andrew Del Presto, 40 emp., *Plastic bags & films* ............ (973) 340-0700
Globe Packaging Co., Inc., 368 Paterson Plank Rd., Carlstadt 07072
Pres.—Issy Bank, 11 emp., *Plastic, collagen, fibrous, cellulose* ............ (201) 939-3335
Golden Plastics, Inc., 510-A Industrial Ave., Teterboro 07608
Pres., CFO—Henry Kim, 8 emp., *Plastic bags & contract packaging* ............ (201) 393-9833
Halsted Corp., 78 Halladay St., Jersey City 07304
Pres.—Michael J. Murphy, 35 emp., *Manufacturer & distributor of industrial* ............ (201) 433-3323
Heritage Bag Co., Inc., 2321 High Hill Rd., Swedesboro 08085
V-P., Sales—Ted Wells, 150 emp., *Plastic bags* ............ (856) 467-2247
Inteplast Group Ltd. (H Q), 9 Peach Tree Hill Rd., Livingston 07039
Founder & Pres.—John Young, 237 emp., *Company headquarters; BOPP, stretch* ............ (973) 994-8000
Keystone Packaging Service, Inc., 555 Warren St., Phillipsburg 08865
Pres.—John Schoeneck, 10 emp., *Plastic bags* ............ (908) 454-8567
KNF Flexpak Corporation., 44 Howell St., Jersey City 07306
GM—Paul Bellantonio, 40 emp., *Plastic bag extrusions* ............ (201) 656-4012
Lally-Pak, Inc., 1209 Central Ave., Hillside 07205
Pres.—Henry Herbst, 55 emp., *Plastic bags* ............ (908) 353-3344
LPS Industries, Inc., 10 Caesar Pl., Moonachie 07074
CEO—Madeleine Robinson, 225 emp., *Paperboard boxes & tubes, paper & foil* ............ (201) 438-3515
Mercury Plastic Bag Co., Inc., 168 7th St., Passaic 07055
Pres.—Marvin Rosen, 25 emp., *Plastic bags* ............ (973) 778-7200
Nexus Plastics, Inc., 1 Loretto Ave., Hawthorne 07506
Pres., CEO—Marwan Sholakh, 90 emp., *Corporate headquarters & poly packaging* ............ (973) 427-3311
NYP Corp., 805 E. Grand St., Elizabeth 07201
Pres. & V-P., Sales—Gerald P. Labelle, 50 emp., *Corporate headquarters & polyester,* ............ (908) 351-6550
Omega Plastics Corp., Page & Schuyler Ave., Bldg. 3, P.O. Box 808, Lyndhurst 07071
Pres.—Ed Miller, 50 emp., *Divisional headquarters & plastic bags* ............ (201) 933-5353
Phoenix Industries, LLC, 105 W. Dewey Ave., P.O. Box 416, Wharton 07885
Pres., GM—Vincent Norcia, 5 emp., *Polyethylene bags, sheeting & shrink* ............ (973) 366-4199
Plastic Plus Group, LLC, 600 Meadowlands Pkwy., Secaucus 07094
★ Member—Joe Waltham, 70 emp., *Flexible packaging laminate rollstock* ............ (201) 561-0404
Poly Express, LLC, 318 McLean Blvd., Bldg. 5, Paterson 07504
Pres.—Bill Parlak, 15 emp., *Polyethylene bags, liners, sheets &* ............ (800) 843-7659
Polyair North East, 495 Meadow Ln., Carlstadt 07072
Sales Mgr.—Jim Brennan, 60 emp., *Packaging materials, including bubble* ............ (201) 804-1700
Power Bag & Film, LLC, 189 W. Valley Brook Rd., Califon 07830
Manager—Trevor Power, 3 emp., *Polyethlene & polypropylene monolayer* ............ (908) 832-6648
Primepak Company, 133 Cedar Ln., Ste. 104, Teaneck 07666
CFO—Mike Heilferty, 34 emp., *Plastic bags, including high & low* ............ (201) 836-5060
Redi Packaging, Inc., 265 Highway 36, Ste. 109, West Long Branch 07764
Pres.—Cyndi Hogan, 12 emp., *Polyethylene & polypropylene products* ............ (732) 544-1480
Rutan Poly Industries, Inc., 39 Siding Pl., Mahwah 07430
Pres.—Arnold Tanowitz, 32 emp., *Plastic bags, films, tubing & sheeting* ............ (201) 529-1474
Shiprite Packaging, Inc., 161 Woodbine St., Bergenfield 07621
Pres., GM—Mayer Schlisser, 2 emp., *Plastic bags* ............ (201) 385-4747
Sierra Packaging, Inc., 60 State Route 36, Ste. C, West Long Branch 07764
Owner & Pres.—Paul S. Charpentier, 5 emp., *Plastic bags & liners* ............ (732) 571-2900
Southeastern Plastics Corp., 15 Home News Row, New Brunswick 08901
GM—Greg Gallo, 57 emp., *Plastic garment & laundry bags* ............ (732) 846-8500
Steelson Packaging, 190 W. Passaic St., Rochelle Park 07662
Owner—Martin Goz, 8 emp., *Plastic bags* ............ (201) 909-0011
Tee Pee Packaging Corp., 85 Harrison St., Dover 07801
Pres.—Charles Deehan, 40 emp., *Plastic bags* ............ (973) 328-6500
Top Notch Plastics, 217 Bradwick Way, Marlboro 07746
Owner—Ted Green, 25 emp., *Plastic bags* ............ (732) 946-0049
Tri-Cor Flexible Packaging, Inc., 27 Brookfield Dr., Sparta 07871
Pres.—Guy Zimmermann, 20 emp., *Flexible polyethylene packaging for* ............ (973) 940-1500
X-L Plastics, Inc., 220 Clifton Blvd., Clifton 07011
Pres.—Melvin Fischman, 50 emp., *Plastic bags* ............ (973) 777-1888

## 2674 Bags: uncoated paper & multiwall

Allstate Paper Box Co., Inc., 223 Raymond Blvd., Newark 07105
Pres.—Matt Elias, 70 emp., *Set-up paperboard, folding & vinyl* ............ (973) 589-2600
Duro Bag Mfg. Co., 750 Dowd Ave., Elizabeth 07201
GM & Plt. Mgr.—Mike Davidson, 275 emp., *Paper bags* ............ (908) 351-2400
Kavon Filter Products Co., Inc., 5022 Industrial Rd., P.O. Box 1166, Wall Township 07719
V-P., Sales & Mktg.—Douglas Von Bulow, 20 emp., *Manufacturer & distributor of industrial* ... (732) 938-3135
Novel Box Co. Ltd., 825 Lehigh Ave., Union 07083
Owner & Pres.—Moishe Sternhill, 50 emp., *Manufacturer & distributor of jewelry* ............ (908) 686-7772
Ronpak, Inc., 4301 New Brunswick Ave., South Plainfield 07080
Pres.—Ronald Sedley, 150 emp., *Corporate headquarters & paper bags* ............ (732) 968-8000

## 2675 Die-cut paper & board

Arch Crown, Inc., 460 Hillside Ave., Ste. 1, Hillside 07205
CEO—Norman Liebman, 32 emp., *Tags & labels, including die cutting* ............ (973) 731-6300
Berry Business Procedure Co., 6 Park St., P.O. Box 845, Cranford 07016
Pres.—David M. Cheek, 4 emp., *Commercial & business form printing* ............ (908) 272-6464
Bielen Graphic Arts, R. J., 6 Jules Ln., New Brunswick 08901
Pres.—Robert J. Bielen, 11 emp., *Laser die cutting & gold stamping of* ............ (732) 545-3501
Contemporary Graphic Solutions, Inc., 7001 N. Park Dr., Pennsauken 08109
Pres.—Tim Moreton, 196 emp., *Printing, packaging, finishing, die* ............ (856) 663-7277
Custom Index, Inc., 8 Vreeland Ave., Totowa 07512
CEO—Nafees Rahman, 145 emp., *Corporate headquarters & index tabs* ............ (973) 890-2414
Danielle Die Cut Products, Inc., 238 Lindbergh Pl., Paterson 07503
Pres.—Danny Dibetitto, 20 emp., *Steel rule dies & die cutting of paper* ............ (973) 278-3000
Davis Paper Dimensions, Inc., 400 Benigno Blvd., Bellmawr 08031
Pres.—Betty Davis, 16 emp., *Die cutting, embossing, foil stampings* ............ (856) 931-6040
Dynamic Die Cutting & Finishings, 104-110 South St., Newark 07114
Pres.—Emilio Esteva, 10 emp., *Paper die cutting* ............ (973) 589-8338
Gleicher Mfg. Corp., 851 Jerusalem Rd., Scotch Plains 07076
Pres.—C. Gleicher, 30 emp., *Adhesive tape die cutting, laminating* ............ (908) 233-2211
Grand Displays, Inc., 12 Empire Blvd., Moonachie 07074
Pres.—Susan Ostreicher, 60 emp., *Paper die cutting & displays* ............ (201) 994-1500
Holographic Finishing, Inc., 501 Hendricks Cswy., P.O. Box 597, Ridgefield 07657
Pres.—Michael Vulcano, 12 emp., *Paper embossing, die cutting, glueing* ............ (201) 941-4651

Meadowbrook Inventions, Inc., 260 Mine Brook Rd., P.O. Box 960, Bernardsville 07924
Pres.—Harold Sutton, 42 emp., Polyester, metal & heat fusible fiber .......... (908) 766-0606
Microfold, Inc., 375 North St., Unit C, Teterboro 07608
CEO—Paul Perna, 10 emp., Paper product folding, hole punching .......... (201) 641-5052
Minuteman Press, 1 Trenton Ave., Clifton 07011
Principal—Joseph Mulligan, 18 emp., Offset & digital printing, promotional .......... (973) 894-1500
Nal-Pak Paper Specialties, LLC, 18 Monterey Ln., Englishtown 07726
Pres.—Murray Kaplan, 5 emp., Clear poly film & waxed paper die cutting .......... (732) 462-5196
New York Sample Card Co., Inc., 812 Jersey Ave., 3rd Fl., Jersey City 07310
Pres., MIS Mgr.—Kenneth Ehrlich, 25 emp., Sample cards & books, including color .......... (201) 526-9040
O & C Die Cutters & Finishers, 16 Andrews Dr., West Paterson 07424
Pres.—Odit Ramnarian, 20 emp., Die cutting, foil stamping & mounting .......... (973) 890-7778
Perfect Finishing, Inc., 40 Webro Rd., Clifton 07012
Co-Pres.—Bruce Flaim, 50 emp., Corporate headquarters & paper die .......... (973) 472-7400
Peterson Steel Rule Die Corp., 35 Broad St., Carlstadt 07072
Pres.—Leonard Esposito, 10 emp., Steel rule dies, die cutting & finishing .......... (201) 935-6180
Pioneer Packaging, 31 Wilson Dr., Sparta 07871
Pres.—Mark J. Clark, 30 emp., Printed & die-cut consumer product .......... (973) 300-9300
Postalogic, LLC, 64 Outwater Ln., Ste. 1, Garfield 07026
Pres.—Brian Parker, 40 emp., Binding & finishing services for the .......... (973) 546-1400
Prestige Assocs., Inc., 39 Mead St., Trenton 08638
Pres.—Robert McGurie, 7 emp., Paper & paperboard die cutting & assembly .......... (609) 393-1509
Quick Cut Stamping & Embossing, Inc., 815 E. Main St., Maple Shade 08052
Pres.—Holly Zahradnick, 10 emp., Die cutting, foil stamping & embossing .......... (856) 321-0050
Raybold Mfg., Inc., 102 S. 8th St., Millville 08332
Pres.—William Riland, 9 emp., Screen printing of glass bottles & .......... (856) 327-7733
Redwallet Connection, LLC, 907 21st St., Union City 07087
Pres., CEO—Linda C. Lafferty, 50 emp., Pressboard, file, classification, presentatio .......... (201) 223-2644
Renell Label Print, Inc., 15 Sunflower Ave., Paramus 07652
Pres.—W. Rene Huber, 8 emp., Pressure-sensitive, paper, foil & clear .......... (201) 652-6544
Rush Index Tabs, Inc., 60 Willow St., East Rutherford 07073
Pres.—Jay A. Cohen, 40 emp., Plastic coated index tabs & dividers .......... (201) 531-1555
S. E. R. Diecutting, 7300 N. Crescent Blvd., Unit 5, Pennsauken 08110
★ Owner—Steven Rosa, 4 emp., Folding paperboard boxes & paperboard .......... (856) 665-8805
Sabre Die Cutting Co., Inc., 68 Mill St., Paterson 07501
Pres.—Michael Culver, 25 emp., Die cutting of paper, paperboard, plastics .......... (973) 357-9800
Turul Bookbindery, Inc., 60 Route 15 S., Wharton 07885
Pres.—Margit P. Rahill, 5 emp., Custom books & boxes, bookbinding, .......... (973) 361-2810
US Magic Box, Inc., 221 McArthur Ave., Garfield 07026
Pres.—Sam Omar, 62 emp., Die & laser cutting & printing for .......... (973) 772-2070
V M C Die Cutting Corp., 357 Cortlandt St., Belleville 07109
Pres.—Vincenza Reczynski, 4 emp., Die cutting, embossing, foil stamping .......... (973) 450-4655
Valenta & Sons, Inc., Jerry, 40 Schoon Ave., Hawthorne 07506
Pres.—Jerry Valenta, 6 emp., Jacquard card cutting .......... (973) 423-2220
Valley Die-Cutting Co., Inc., 10 Park Ave., West Orange 07052
Pres.—John Dyer, 50 emp., Die-cutting, embossing & foil stamping .......... (973) 731-8884
Web-Cote Industries, Inc., 141 Wheatsworth Rd., P.O. Box 120, Hamburg 07419
Pres.—James Cowen, 20 emp., Paper label tapes .......... (973) 827-2299

## 2676 Sanitary paper products

American Hygiene Industries, LLC, 60 Page Rd., Clifton 07012
Pres.—Chris Fuhrmann, 25 emp., Wet wipes for baby, disinfecting, antibacteri .......... (973) 928-6533
Bentley Mfg., Inc., 41 Ethel Rd., Piscataway 08854
Pres.—Victor Braha, 12 emp., Diapers & baby wipes .......... (732) 572-5933
Braco Mfg. Co. & Magic Safety Products, Inc., 4301-B New Brunswick Ave., Ste. 2, South Plainfield 07080
Ptnr.—Jack Braha, 50 emp., Disposable baby diapers & safety cleaning .......... (732) 968-0008
Keystone Adjustable Cap Co., 1591 Hylton Rd., Ste. B, Pennsauken 08110
CEO—Andrew Feinstein, 80 emp., Sanitary disposable apparel & accessories .......... (856) 663-5740

## 2677 Envelopes

ADM Corp., 100 Lincoln Blvd., Middlesex 08846
Chrm., CEO—Mary Mota, 150 emp., Pressure-sensitive envelopes .......... (732) 469-0900
Allied Envelope Co., Inc., 33 Commerce Rd., Carlstadt 07072
Pres.—James Royer, 50 emp., Full-service direct mail & commercial .......... (201) 440-2000
American Envelope & Printing Co., 212 Columbus Ave., Roselle 07203
Owner & Pres.—Edward Nodelman, 5 emp., Envelopes & commercial printing of .......... (908) 241-9900
Cenveo, Inc., 25 Linden Ave. E., Jersey City 07305
Plt. Mgr.—Vito Mazza, 96 emp., Envelope printing .......... (201) 434-2100
Clark Printing Co., 441 Market St., Saddle Brook 07663
Pres., GM—Richard Lisa, 18 emp., Commercial & newsletter printing & .......... (201) 845-4888
Clinton Envelope, 9130 Pennsauken Hwy., Ste. C, Pennsauken 08110
GM—Bob Donner, 7 emp., Envelopes, including plain, printed .......... (856) 314-3636
E. Greene Of North Carolina, Inc., P.O. Box 1017, West Caldwell 07007
GM—Jed Firestone, 30 emp., Financial printing of security envelopes .......... (973) 838-5200
Reliable Envelope & Graphics, Inc., 85 Main Ave., Elmwood Park 07407
Chrm.—Gene Murphy, 25 emp., Custom & standard envelopes, including .......... (201) 794-7756
Tension Envelope Corp., 19 Wesley St., South Hackensack 07606
GM—Toby Reed, 175 emp., Envelopes .......... (201) 487-1880
United Envelope & Printing Co., Inc., 65 Railroad Ave., Ridgefield 07657
★ Pres.—Ken Bernstein, 75 emp., Offset & letterpress envelope printing .......... (201) 699-5800

## 2678 Stationery products

Creative Printing Resources, LLC, 17 Kimberly Ct., Apt. 121, Red Bank 07701
★ Owner—Susan Kelly, 3 emp., Commercial printing, including brochures .......... (732) 842-0240
Hygloss Products, Inc., 45 Hathaway St., Wallington 07057
Pres.—Moshe Neurath, 30 emp., Arts & crafts products for teachers .......... (973) 458-1700
Precise Continental, 1 Cape May St., Harrison 07029
Pres.—Jim Donnelly, 38 emp., Company headquarters & engraved stationery .......... (973) 350-0330
Write Impression, The, 549 Highway 35, Red Bank 07701
Owner—Kristine Ancona, 1 emp., Custom invitation & stationery printing .......... (732) 706-3700

## 2679 Converted paper products, nec

Allied Group, Inc., 5 Coldhill Rd., Bldg. 19, P.O. Box 209, Mendham 07945
Pres.—Ed Thomas, 24 emp., Coalescing filters, mist eliminators .......... (973) 543-5404
Automatic Transfer, Inc., 2 Industrial Rd., Phillipsburg 08865
★ Pres.—Alfred W. La Costa, 4 emp., Sublimation toner & heat transfer paper .......... (908) 213-2830
Callen Photo Mount Corp., 185 6th Ave., Ste. 1, Paterson 07524
Asst. V-P.—Dennis Callen, 15 emp., Picture framing mats .......... (973) 925-2390
Campbell Converting Corp., 703 Van Rossum Ave., Unit 2, Beverly 08010
Owner & Pres.—C. Norman Campbell, 8 emp., Paper converting & wide-format printing .......... (609) 835-2720
Custom Converters, Inc., 115 Naylon Ave., Livingston 07039
Pres.—Mark Krause, 10 emp., Paper, plastic film, aluminum foil .......... (973) 994-9000
Dikeman Laminating Corp., 181 Sargeant Ave., Clifton 07013
Pres.—Jeff Snyder, 36 emp., Corporate headquarters & UV coating .......... (973) 473-5696
Fabulous Interiors, 470 Prospect Ave., Ste. 105, West Orange 07052
Mng. Ptnr.—Jeffrey Fischman, 2 emp., Wall coverings & converted paper products .......... (973) 736-1200
Fidelity Industries, Inc., 559 R.R. 23 S., Wayne 07470
V-P. & Hum. Res. Mgr.—Samuel Brook, 50 emp., Vinyl-backed wall coverings .......... (973) 696-9120
Flech Paper Products, Inc., 55 1st Ave., Paterson 07514
Founder—Joseph Kandel, 20 emp., Poster, display, mat & mounting boards .......... (973) 357-8111
Georgia Pacific, Inc., 623 Riegelsville Rd., Milford 08848
GM—David Bailey, 68 emp., Corrugated paper sheets .......... (908) 995-2228
Golden West Paper Converting, 121 Helen St., South Plainfield 07080
Pres.—David Hooi, 30 emp., Paper converting .......... (908) 412-8889
Hygloss Products, Inc., 45 Hathaway St., Wallington 07057
Pres.—Moshe Neurath, 30 emp., Arts & crafts products for teachers .......... (973) 458-1700
Keystone Adjustable Cap Co., 1591 Hylton Rd., Ste. B, Pennsauken 08110
CEO—Andrew Feinstein, 80 emp., Sanitary disposable apparel & accessories .......... (856) 663-5740
Laminated Industries, Inc., 2000 Brunswick Ave., Linden 07036
Pres.—Mendel Schwimmer, 40 emp., Paper converting .......... (908) 862-5995
Lizard Label, Inc., 10-E Commerce Rd., Fairfield 07004
Pres.—Joseph Winter, 10 emp., Digitally printed pressure-sensitive .......... (973) 808-0098
Matthias Paper Corp., 301 Arlington Blvd., P.O. Box 130, Swedesboro 08085
Pres.—John Matthias, Jr., 30 emp., Corporate headquarters & paper converting .......... (856) 467-6970
Microfold, Inc., 375 North St., Unit C, Teterboro 07608
CEO—Paul Perna, 10 emp., Paper product folding, hole punching .......... (201) 641-5052
Newark Group, Inc., The (H Q), 20 Jackson Dr., Cranford 07016
Pres., CEO—Frank Papa, 60 emp., Corporate headquarters; paper converting .......... (908) 276-4000
Newco, Inc., 1 Hicks Ave., Newton 07860
Pres.—James Berezny, 62 emp., Vinyl wall coverings .......... (973) 383-7777
Norpak Corp., 70 Blanchard St., Newark 07105
V-P., GM—James G. Coraci, 60 emp., Paper converting .......... (973) 589-4200
Nosaj Disposables, Inc., 3 Security Dr., Ste. 312, P.O. Box 355, Cranbury 08512
Pres.—Stanley Slosberg, 20 emp., Disposable paper products, safety equipment .......... (800) 631-3809
Papertec, Inc., 141 Lanza Ave., Bldg. 29, Garfield 07026
Pres., CFO, Sales Mgr.—Ted Bielen, 15 emp., Paper & film converting, including .......... (862) 591-1100
Paris Business Products, Inc., 800 Highland Dr., Westampton 08060
Pres.—Gerard Toscani, 81 emp., Paper converting .......... (609) 265-9200
Philcorr, LLC, 2317 Almond Rd., Vineland 08360
Cont.—Mark Thuer, 70 emp., Corrugated sheets .......... (856) 205-0557
Quality Paper Converters Of New Jersey, Inc., 673 S. 21st St., Irvington 07111
Pres.—John Cumming, 20 emp., Paper converting .......... (973) 399-1200
Ringel Bros., Inc., 7 W. Shelton Ter., P.O. Box 727, Hillside 07205
Pres.—Doug Eppel, 14 emp., Paper converting .......... (908) 688-9222
Rockline Industries, Inc., 1 Kramer Dr., P.O. Box 189, Montville 07045
Plt. Mgr.—Chris Bruno, 160 emp., Coffee filters .......... (973) 257-9346
Roosevelt Paper Co., 1 Roosevelt Dr., Mount Laurel 08054
Chrm., CEO—Ted Kosloff, 132 emp., Company headquarters & printing paper .......... (856) 303-4100
Sellers & Josephson, LLC, 559 Route 23, Wayne 07470
Pres., CEO—Shmuel Brook, 49 emp., Wallcoverings .......... (201) 567-1353
Steiner Paper Corp., 4000 Borden Town Ave., Sayreville 08872
Pres., CFO—Jeff Nichols, 10 emp., Paper art & archival supplies, including .......... (732) 651-6009
U.S. Pulp & Paper Corp., 1930 Marlton Pike E., Ste. N-73, Cherry Hill 08003
Pres.—Arnold Cohen, 20 emp., Paper converting & distributor of packaging .......... (856) 489-3500
United Label Corp., 65 Chambers St., Newark 07105
V-P., Sales—John T. O'Connor, 10 emp., Pressure-sensitive paper labels .......... (973) 589-6500
William Usdan & Sons LLC, 140 Little St., Belleville 07109
Pres.—Simon Markman, 5 emp., Paper & fabric converting & distributor .......... (973) 844-9988

# 27 PRINTING & PUBLISHING

## 2711 Newspapers

24 Horas-Portuguese Daily Newspaper, 68 Madison St., Newark 07105
Pres.—Victor Alves, 10 emp., Newspaper publishing .......... (973) 817-7400
About Our Town, Inc., 2 Lakeview Ave., Ste. 312, Piscataway 08854
Owner—Ron Chilson, 8 emp., Newspaper publishing .......... (732) 968-1615
Advocate Publishing Corp., 171 Clifton Ave., P.O. Box 9500, Newark 07104
Assoc. Publisher & Editor—Deacon Al Frank, 5 emp., Print & online newspaper, magazine, .. (973) 497-4200
African Telecom, Inc., 463 N. Arlington Ave., Ste. 17, East Orange 07017
Pres., Publisher—Chika Onyeani, 5 emp., Weekly Africa-themed print & online .......... (973) 675-9919
America OGGI, 475 Walnut St., Norwood 07648
Pres., Editor—Andrea Mantineo, 40 emp., Daily print & online Italian language .......... (201) 358-6697
Arab Voice Newspaper, 85-99 Hazel St., Paterson 07503
Owner & Publisher—Walid Rabah, 5 emp., Arabic newspaper publishing .......... (973) 523-7815
Area Auto Racing News, Inc., 2829 S. Broad St., Trenton 08610
Publisher & Editor—Lenny H. Sammons, 8 emp., Weekly racing newspaper publishing .......... (609) 888-3618
Argo Corp., Richard Stockton College, Ste. 202, Pomona 08240
Publisher—Dan Grote, 15 emp., Newspaper publishing .......... (609) 652-4560
Arts Weekly, Inc., 52 Sindle Ave., P.O. Box 1140, Little Falls 07424
Publisher—Chris Farinas, 10 emp., Weekly newspaper publishing .......... (973) 812-6766
Asbury Park Press, 3600 Highway 66, Neptune 07753
GM, Adv., Retail—Regan Apo, 500 emp., Newspaper publishing .......... (732) 922-6000
Asbury Park Press, Inc. (H Q), 3600 Highway 66, P.O. Box 1550, Neptune 07754
Pres., Publisher—Thomas M. Donovan, 450 emp., Corporate headquarters; newspaper printing (732) 922-6000
Atlantic City Weekly, L. P., Bayport 1, 8025 Black Horse Pike, Ste. 3, Pleasantville 08232
Publisher—Lew Steiner, 20 emp., Newspaper publishing .......... (609) 646-4848
Banda Oriental, Inc., 777 W. Grand Ave., Rahway 07065
Publisher & Editor—Julia Moreira, 5 emp., Monthly newspaper publishing .......... (732) 388-8383
Bayonne Community News, 170 Broadway, Bayonne 07002
Pres.—Lucha Malato, 9 emp., Newspaper publishing .......... (201) 437-2460
Beacon Publishing Co., Inc., 775 Valley Rd., Clifton 07013
Editor & GM—Richard A. Sokerka, 7 emp., Local Catholic newspaper publishing .......... (973) 279-8845
Black Car News, 714 Crestbrook Ave., Cherry Hill 08003
Publisher—Neil Weiss, 2 emp., Company headquarters & newsletter publishing .......... (856) 751-0656
Black Car News, 420 Inverness Rd., Williamstown 08094
Manager—Michele Norton, 1 emp., Newsletter publishing for the car & .......... (856) 262-2368
Brazilian Voice, 412 Chestnut St., P.O. Box 5686, Newark 07105
CEO—Roberto Leman, 5 emp., Newspaper publishing .......... (973) 491-6200
Bright Side Newspaper, 1560 Route 83, Cape May Court House 08210
★ Owner—Daniel Keen, 4 emp., Newspaper publishing .......... (609) 861-2034

S.I.C.

Broad Street Media, 53 Haddonfield Rd., Ste. 306, Cherry Hill 08002
Dir., Prodn.—Darwin Oordt, 25 emp., Newspaper publishing ... (856) 779-3800
Burlington County Times, Inc., 4284 Route 130, Willingboro 08046
Dir., Strategy—Stanley M. Ellis, 110 emp., Weekly print & online newspaper publishing ... (609) 871-8000
Cambio Newspaper, 604 56th St., West New York 07093
Dir.—Yamile Camacho, 14 emp., Newspaper publishing ... (201) 902-0811
Cape May Star & Wave, 600 Park Blvd., Ste. 28, West Cape May 08204
Mng. Editor—Jack Fichter, 3 emp., Newspaper publishing ... (609) 884-3466
Catamaran Media Co., LLC, 3120 Fire Rd., Egg Harbor Township 08234
Adv. Sales Mgr.—Bob Fertch, 20 emp., Weekly print & online newspaper publishing ... (609) 383-8994
Catamaran Media Co., LLC, 3120 Fire Rd., Egg Harbor Township 08234
Manager—James Miller, 4 emp., Newspaper printing & publishing ... (609) 266-1860
Catamaran Media Co., LLC, 507 S. Shore Rd., Marmora 08223
Publisher—Rick Travers, 50 emp., Company headquarters & newspaper publishing ... (609) 624-8900
Catholic Star Herald, 15 N. 7th St., Camden 08102
Mng. Editor—Carl Peters, 8 emp., 45 weeks per year Catholic newspaper ... (856) 583-6142
Central Record Corp., The, 32 S. Main St., Ste. A, P.O. Box 1027, Medford 08055
Publisher—Edward Condra, 30 emp., Weekly print & online newspaper publishing ... (609) 654-9221
Chinese Newsweek Corp., 32 Bridge St., Metuchen 08840
Owner—Meilun Lee, 5 emp., Weekly online newspaper publishing ... (732) 744-1000
Cindy Merckx Publications, LLC, 330 Oak Ave., Malaga 08328
Owner & Publisher—Cindy Merckx, 2 emp., Newspaper publishing ... (856) 694-1600
Civil Service Leader, 313 Broad Ave., Ste. 203, Ridgefield 07657
Owner & Publisher—John Ferrara, 10 emp., Newspaper publishing ... (201) 941-6397
Coaster, The, 1011 Main St., Asbury Park 07712
Ptnr. & Editor—Ellen Carroll, 13 emp., Newspaper publishing ... (732) 775-3010
Community News Service, LLC, 15 Princess Rd., Ste. K, Lawrenceville 08648
Co-Publisher—James Griswold, 14 emp., Community newspaper publishing ... (609) 396-1511
Community Newspapers & Magazines Of North Jersey Media Group, 1 Garret Mountain Plz., P.O. Box 471, Woodland Park 07424
V-P., Publisher—Janice Friedman, 132 emp., Daily print & online newspaper & monthly ... (973) 569-7000
Contemporary, Inc., 161 Coolidge Ave., Englewood 07631
Pres.—Anthony Cantone, 22 emp., Electronic prepress & printing ... (201) 569-3900
County Seat, LLC, 77 Hudson St., Hackensack 07601
Publisher—Gail Zisa, 6 emp., Monthly print & online newspaper publishing ... (201) 488-5795
Courier News, 92 E. Main St., Ste. 202, Somerville 08876
Editor & GM—Paul Grzella, 51 emp., Weekly print & online newspaper publishing ... (908) 722-8800
Courier-Post Newspaper, 301 Cuthbert Rd., Cherry Hill 08002
Dir., Sales & GM—Bill Janus, 200 emp., Newspaper publishing ... (856) 663-6000
Criterion Publishing Co., 87 Forrest St., P.O. Box 4278, Metuchen 08840
V-P., GM—Christopher M. Crane, 7 emp., Newspaper publishing ... (732) 548-8300
Cumberland & Salem Guide, 874 N. Pearl St., P.O. Box 735, Bridgeton 08302
Publisher—James Kinkade, 10 emp., Newspaper publishing ... (856) 451-1177
Daily Journal, The, 891 E. Oak Rd., Vineland 08360
Dir., Adv.—Joseph Calchi, 100 emp., Newspaper publishing ... (856) 691-5000
Daily Princetonian Publishing Co., Inc., 48 University Pl., Princeton 08544
Editor-in-Chief—Marcelo Rochabrun, 30 emp., Newspaper publishing ... (609) 375-8553
Dow Jones & Co., Inc., 4300 N. Route 1, Monmouth Junction 08852
Proj. Specialist—Carissa Salvatore, 1200 emp., Newspaper publishing ... (609) 520-4000
Elmer Times Co., Inc., 21 State St., Elmer 08318
Pres.—Mark Foster, 4 emp., Weekly newspaper publishing ... (856) 358-6171
Epoch Press, Inc., 75 Wood St., Ste. B, Paterson 07524
CFO—Paulina Werthen, 30 emp., Web & commercial printing ... (973) 357-0080
Evergreen Printing, 101 Haag Ave., Bellmawr 08031
V-P., Sales & Mktg.—John Dreisbach, 100 emp., Newspaper printing & publishing ... (856) 933-0222
Exit Zero Publishing, 109 Sunset Blvd., Ste. D, Cape May 08204
Pres., Publisher & Editor—Jack Wright, 4 emp., Weekly newspaper publishing ... (609) 770-8479
Filipino Express Newspaper, Inc., 2711 John F. Kennedy Blvd., Jersey City 07306
Publisher & GM—Lito Gajilan, 7 emp., Newspaper publishing ... (201) 434-1114
Forked River Gazette, Inc., 119 Voyager Rd., Manahawkin 08050
Pres., Publisher—Jennifer Grazioso, 1 emp., Newspaper publishing ... (609) 693-7490
Franklin Lakes Oakland, 41 Oak St., Ridgewood 07450
★ Editor—Gertrude Walz, 5 emp., Newspaper publishing ... (201) 612-5415
Gloucester City News, Inc., 34 S. Broadway, P.O. Box 151, Gloucester City 08030
Publisher—Albert J. Countryman, Jr., 4 emp., Newspaper publishing ... (856) 456-1199
Greater Media Newspapers, 198 Route 9 N., P.O. Box 950, Manalapan 07726
Publisher & GM—Ben Cannizzaro, 74 emp., Weekly print & online newspaper publishing ... (732) 358-5200
Gujarat Samachar, 3 State Route 27, Ste. 307, Edison 08820
Manager—Harshad Patel, 1 emp., Newspaper publishing for the Indian ... (732) 452-1755
Hammonton Gazette, Inc., 233 Bellevue Ave., P.O. Box 1228, Hammonton 08037
Pres.—Gabriel Donio, 5 emp., Newspaper publishing ... (609) 704-1939
Hammonton News & Atlantic County Newspaper Group, 115 12th St., Hammonton 08037
Ex. Editor—Nora Grasso, 3 emp., Newspaper publishing ... (609) 561-2300
Hawthorne Press, 463 Lafayette Ave., P.O. Box 1, Hawthorne 07507
Pres.—Linda C. Missonellie, 10 emp., Weekly newspaper publishing ... (973) 427-3330
Hispano Publishing, LLC, 437 Linden Ave., Elizabeth 07208
Ex. Dir.—Nelson Franco, 5 emp., Spanish newspaper publishing ... (908) 351-9390
Home News Tribune, 92 E. Main St., Somerville 08876
Editor & GM—Paul Grzella, 60 emp., Newspaper publishing ... (908) 722-8800
Hudson Reporter Assocs., LP, 1400 Washington St., P.O. Box 3069, Hoboken 07030
Co-Publisher—Lucha Malato, 25 emp., Newspaper publishing ... (201) 798-7800
Info System, 345 Main Ave., Wallington 07057
Owner—Wojciech Marchel, 10 emp., Newspaper publishing & booklet printing ... (973) 777-4448
Italian Tribune Publishing Co., 7 N. Willow St., Ste. 8-C, Montclair 07042
Publisher—A. J. Buddy Fortunato, 8 emp., Newspaper publishing ... (973) 860-0101
JB Offset Printing Corp., 475 Walnut St., Norwood 07648
Pres.—Andrea Mantineo, 9 emp., Offset newspaper printing ... (201) 664-4400
Jersey Journal, The, 1 Harmon Plz., Ste. 1010, Secaucus 07094
Publisher—Ken Whitfield, 100 emp., Newspaper publishing ... (201) 653-1000
Jersey Paw Prints, P.O. Box 26, Mays Landing 08330
Owner, Publisher & Editor—Carol Ruck, 1 emp., Newspaper publishing ... (609) 909-5100
Jimcam Publishing, Inc., 19 W. Pleasant Ave., Maywood 07607
Co-Publisher—Jim Hornes, 2 emp., Newspaper publishing & invitation printing ... (201) 843-5700
Journal Register Co., The, 32 S. Main St., Ste. A, Medford 08055
Editor—Jenn Lucas, 12 emp., Weekly print & online newspaper publishing ... (609) 654-5000
Korea Daily, Inc., 10 E. Brinkerhoff Ave., Ste. 2-B, Palisades Park 07650
Pres.—Tyung Sohn, 4 emp., Korean newspaper publishing ... (201) 944-8299
Korean Bergen News, 210 Sylvan Ave., Ste. 23, Englewood Cliffs 07632
Owner—Thomas Bae, 15 emp., Ethnic newspaper & magazine publishing ... (201) 894-9061
Lake Hopatcong News, 37 Nolans Point Park Rd., Lake Hopatcong 07849
★ Publisher & Editor-in-Chief—Karen Fucito, 1 emp., Newspaper publishing ... (973) 663-2800
Latinos Unidos De Nueva Jersey, LLC, 190 Hickory Rd., Jackson 08527
Pres.—Jorge Rod, 6 emp., Latin monthly newspaper printing & ... (732) 534-5959
Lavoz Spanish Newspapers, P.O. Box 899, Elizabeth 07207
Publisher—Daniel Garcia, 5 emp., Newspaper publishing ... (908) 352-6654
Life & Leisure, LLC, 234 Main St., Ste. 2, Lincoln Park 07035
★ Publisher & Editor—Joe Pellegrino, 8 emp., Newpaper publishing ... (973) 696-8009
Link News Inc., The, 176 Broadway, P.O. Box 120, Long Branch 07740
Owner—Patty O'Neill, 3 emp., Weekly newspaper publishing ... (732) 222-4300
Luso-Americano Co., Inc., 88 Ferry St., Newark 07105
Pres.—Tony Matinho, 16 emp., Newspaper publishing ... (973) 589-4600
Metropolitan Corporate Counsel, 1180 Wychwood Rd., Mountainside 07092
CIO & IT Mgr.—Mag Smith, 13 emp., Legal newspaper publishing ... (908) 654-4840
Micromedia Publications, Inc., 15 Union Ave., P.O. Box 521, Lakehurst 08733
Publisher—Stewart Swann, 12 emp., Newspaper publishing ... (732) 657-7344
Monmouth Journal, The, 212 Maple Ave., Red Bank 07701
Mng. Editor—Gary Chapman, 10 emp., Weekly newspaper publishing ... (732) 747-7007
N J Sport Action, 5 Riverview Dr. W., Upper Montclair 07043
Owner—W. L. 'Bill' Allen, Jr., 10 emp., Newspaper & magazine publishing ... (973) 783-9236
New Jersey Epoch Times, 50 Cragwood Rd., South Plainfield 07080
Sales Mgr.—Doris Yit, 10 emp., Chinese language newspaper publishing ... (908) 548-8380
New Jersey Herald, The, 2 Spring St., P.O. Box 10, Newton 07860
Interim Publisher & Dir., Adv. & Mktg.—Keith Flinn, 60 emp., Newspaper publishing ... (973) 383-1500
New Jersey Jewish News, 901 Route 10, Whippany 07981
COO, GM—Rick Keslenbaum, 30 emp., Weekly, biweekly & monthly print & ... (973) 887-3900
New York Daily News, 125 Theodore Conrad Dr., Jersey City 07305
Sr. Mng. Editor—Robert Moore, 600 emp., Newspaper publishing ... (201) 946-6000
Newark Morning Ledger Co., 1 Star Ledger Plz., Newark 07102
Publisher—Rich Vezza, 400 emp., Divisional headquarters & newspaper ... (973) 392-4141
News Of Cumberland County, The, 93 5th St., Salem 08079
Pres.—Joe Owens, 15 emp., Newspaper publishing ... (856) 451-1000
NJN Publishing Independent Press, Inc., 309 South St., New Providence 07974
Hum. Res. Rep.—Lindsey Gartner, 15 emp., Newspaper publishing ... (908) 464-1025
NJN Publishing, Inc. (H Q), 8 Minneakoning Rd., Flemington 08822
Publisher—Joe Gioioso, 75 emp., Corporate headquarters; newspaper publishing ... (908) 782-4747
North Jersey Media Group Inc., 100 Commons Way, Rockaway 07866
V-P., Circ. & Mfg.—Robert Konig, 308 emp., Daily local & community print & online ... (973) 586-8000
North Jersey Media Group, Inc., 181 Milburn Ave., Ste. 201, Millburn 07041
★ Editor & Manager—Harry Trumbore, 5 emp., Weekly newspaper publishing ... (973) 921-6451
North Jersey Media Group, Inc., 1 Garret Mountain Plz., P.O. Box 471, Woodland Park 07424
Chrm. of the Board—Malcolm A. Borg, 425 emp., Corporate headquarters & daily & weekly. (973) 569-7000
Nosotros, News, P.O. Box 1337, Toms River 08754
Owner—Gigi Aragon, 1 emp., Newspaper publishing ... (732) 845-1911
Ocean Star, The, 421 River Ave., Point Pleasant Beach 08742
Publisher—James Manser, 40 emp., Newspaper publishers ... (732) 899-7606
Post Eagle Newspaper, Inc., 800 Van Houten Ave., Clifton 07013
Mng. Editor—Matt Grabowski, 3 emp., Newspaper publishing ... (973) 473-5414
Princeton Packet, Inc., 300 Witherspoon St., P.O. Box 350, Princeton 08542
Pres.—Jim Kilgore, 131 emp., Newspaper publishing ... (609) 924-3244
Produce News, The, 800 Kinderkamack Rd., Ste. 100, Oradell 07649
Publisher & Editor—John Groh, 11 emp., Weekly trade newspaper publishing for ... (201) 986-7990
Record, The, 1 Garret Mountain Plz., P.O. Box 471, Woodland Park 07424
IT Mgr.—Greg Hoffman, 200 emp., Daily newspaper publishing ... (973) 569-7770
Recorder Newspaper Co., 530 E. Main St., P.O. Box 600, Chester 07930
Mng. Editor—Mike Condon, 7 emp., Weekly newspaper publishing ... (908) 766-3900
Recorder Publishing Co. (H Q), 17-19 Morristown Rd., P.O. Box 687, Bernardsville 07924
Ptnr.—Stephen W. Parker, 50 emp., Company headquarters; newspaper publishing ... (908) 766-3900
Reminder Newspaper, 2 W. Vine St., P.O. Box 1600, Millville 08332
Pres., Publisher—Darrell Kopp, 15 emp., Weekly online & printed newspaper publishing ... (856) 825-8811
Retrospect, The, 732 Haddon Ave., P.O. Box 296, Collingswood 08108
Owner—Brett Ainsworth, 6 emp., Newspaper publishing ... (856) 854-1400
Salty Dog, The, 254 Brick Blvd., Ste. 1, Brick 08723
Owner & Pres.—Art Peters, 5 emp., Biweekly print & online boating shopper ... (732) 714-8400
Sample Media, Inc., 801 Asbury St., 3rd Fl., Ocean City 08226
Publisher & Editor—David Nahan, 35 emp., Community newspaper & tourist-vacation ... (609) 399-1220
Sandpaper Newspaper, 1816 Long Beach Blvd., Surf City 08008
Pres.—Curt Travers, 30 emp., Newspaper & book publishing ... (609) 494-5900
Seawave Corp., 1508 Route 47, Rio Grande 08242
Pres.—Arthur Hall, 25 emp., Weekly print & online newspaper & visitor's ... (609) 886-8600
Secaucus Home News, 766 Irving Pl., Secaucus 07094
Owner—Gretchen Henkel, 5 emp., Newspaper publishing ... (201) 867-2071
South Bergenite, 9 Lincoln Ave., Rutherford 07070
Mng. Editor—Meghan Trant, 5 emp., Newspaper publishing ... (201) 933-1166
South Jersey Publishing Co., 1000 W. Washington Ave., Pleasantville 08232
★ Publisher—Mark L. Blum, 165 emp., Newspaper publishing ... (609) 272-7000
South Jersey Times, 93 5th St., Salem 08079
Publisher—Joseph Owens, 15 emp., Daily print & online newspaper publishing ... (856) 935-1500
South Jersey Times, 309 S. Broad St., P.O. Box 639, Woodbury 08096
Publisher & Ex. Editor—Joseph P. Owens, 125 emp., Newspaper printing ... (856) 845-3300
Star Ledger, 26 Riverside Dr., Pine Brook 07058
Maint. Mgr.—Joe Maker, 450 emp., Newspaper publishing ... (973) 882-6120
Star News Group, 13 Broad St., Manasquan 08736
Pres., Publisher—James Manser, 35 emp., Newspaper publishing ... (732) 223-0076
Sun By The Sea, 224 W. 23rd Ave., P.O. Box 2101, Wildwood 08260
Pres.—Dorothy Kulisek, 2 emp., Newspaper publishing ... (609) 522-2721
Targum Publishing Co., 126 College Ave., Ste. 431, New Brunswick 08901
Opers. Mgr.—Liz Katz, 80 emp., Daily newspaper publishing ... (732) 932-7051
The New Town Press, 421 Stone Meeting House Rd., Woolwich Township 08085
Owner, Publisher, Fin. & MIS Mgr.—Karen E. Viereck, 1 emp., Monthly newspaper publishing. (856) 467-3113
The Observer, 39 Seeley Ave., Kearny 07032
Pres.—Mary Tortoreti, 12 emp., Weekly newspaper publishing ... (201) 991-1600
Thomson Reuters Corp., 492 River Rd., Nutley 07110
★ Br. Mgr.—Jim McHugh, 15 emp., Newspaper publishing ... (973) 662-3070
Times Of Trenton, 413 River View Plz., Trenton 08611
Publisher & Editor—Sheila Gallagher-Montone, 350 emp., Conventional & online newspaper publishing (609) 989-5454
Treasure Hunt, 1223 S. Main St., Phillipsburg 08865
Owner—David Sisco, Jr., 5 emp., Weekly classified newspaper publishing ... (908) 454-0880
Trentonian, The, 600 Perry St., Trenton 08618
Publisher—Bill Murray, 100 emp., Daily print & online newspaper publishing ... (609) 989-7800
Two River Times, 75 W. Front St., Ste. 2, Red Bank 07701
Pres.—Domenic Dipiero, 9 emp., Newspaper publishing ... (732) 219-5788
U.S. 1 Publishing Co., 15 Princess Rd., Lawrenceville 08648
Publisher—Richard K. Rein, 10 emp., Newspaper publishing ... (609) 452-7000

U.S.A. Distributors, Inc., 3711 Hudson Ave., Union City 07087
Pres.—Antonio Ibarria, 100 emp., *Newspaper & magazine publishing* .................... (201) 348-1959
Ukrainian National Affiliation, Inc., 2200 State Route 10, P.O. Box 280, Parsippany 07054
Editor-in-Chief—Roma Hadzewycz, 25 emp., *Ukrainian-language weekly newspaper* ........... (973) 292-9800
Verona-Cedar Grove Times, 130 Valley Rd., Montclair 07042
Publisher—Mike Lawson, 5 emp., *Weekly print & online community newspaper* .................... (973) 233-5048
Villadom Times, The, 333 Godwin Ave., P.O. Box 96, Midland Park 07432
Ptnr. & Co-Publisher—Albert Vierheilig, 20 emp., *Newspaper publishing* .................... (201) 652-0744
Visual Impact Advertising, Inc., 9 Highland Pl., Maplewood 07040
Owner—Karen Duncan, 7 emp., *Magazine publishing, including recipes* .................... (973) 763-4900
Watchung Communications, Inc., 251 North Ave. W., Westfield 07090
Publisher—Horace Corbin, 9 emp., *Weekly print & online newspaper publishing* .................... (908) 232-4407
Webco Graphics/W.G.I. Corp., 1875 Swarthmore Ave., Lakewood 08701
Pres.—Glenn Davis, 12 emp., *Newsprint printing of newspapers, brochures* .................... (732) 370-2900
West Essex Tribune, Inc., 495 S. Livingston Ave., P.O. Box 65, Livingston 07039
Publisher—Jennifer Cone Chciuk, 10 emp., *Community newspaper publishing* .................... (973) 992-1771
World Journal, Inc., 41-A Bridge St., Metuchen 08840
Off. Mgr.—Allen Chang, 5 emp., *Newspaper publishing* .................... (732) 632-8890
World Media Enterprises, Inc., 1000 W. Washington Ave., Pleasantville 08232
Publisher—Mark L. Blum, 150 emp., *Newspaper publishing* .................... (609) 272-7000
Worrall Community Newspapers, Inc., 1291 Stuyvesant Ave., P.O. Box 1596, Union 07083
Publisher—David Worrall, 50 emp., *Weekly print & online newspaper publishing* .................... (908) 686-7700

## 2721 Periodicals

Advanstar Communications, Inc., 485 U.S. Highway 1 S., Ste. 200, Iselin 08830
★ Publisher—Mike Tracey, 50 emp., *Magazine publishing* .................... (732) 346-3000
Advantage Business Media, 100 Enterprise Dr., Ste. 600, P.O. Box 912, Rockaway 07866
Group Publisher—Tom Lynch, 150 emp., *Magazine publishing* .................... (973) 920-7000
Advocate Publishing Corp., 171 Clifton Ave., P.O. Box 9500, Newark 07104
Assoc. Publisher & Editor—Deacon Al Frank, 5 emp., *Print & online newspaper, magazine,...* (973) 497-4200
Airbrush Action, Inc., 3209 Atlantic Ave., P.O. Box 438, Allenwood 08720
Pres.—Cliff Stieglitz, 10 emp., *Magazine publishing* .................... (732) 223-7878
Alexander Publishing, Inc., 8 Depot Sq., Englewood 07631
★ Pres.—Geoffrey Steck, 4 emp., *Newsletter publishing* .................... (201) 569-5373
All American Crafts Publishing, Inc., 7 Waterloo Rd., Stanhope 07874
CEO, Publisher—Darren Cohen, 40 emp., *Crafts magazine publishing* .................... (973) 347-6900
American Foreclosures, Inc., P.O. Box 601, Oradell 07649
Pres.—Craig Laube, 5 emp., *Monthly conventional & online regional* .................... (201) 501-0200
American Institute Of Food Distribution, Inc., 10 Mountain View Rd., Ste. S-125, Upper Saddle River 07458
Pres.—Brian Todd, 13 emp., *Food industry periodical publishing* .................... (201) 791-5570
American Lawyer's Media, Inc., 238 Mulberry St., 2nd Fl., Newark 07102
Publisher & Hum. Res. Mgr.—Robert Speinbaum, 30 emp., *Law journal publishing* .................... (973) 642-0075
Anderson Publishing Ltd., 180 Glenside Ave., Scotch Plains 07076
Publisher—Kieran Anderson, 5 emp., *Print & online medical imaging journal* .................... (908) 301-1995
Art Culinaire Magazine, 40 Mills St., Morristown 07963
Pres., Publisher—Franz Mitterer, 4 emp., *Magazine publishing* .................... (973) 993-5500
Aviation International News, 214 Franklin Ave., Midland Park 07432
Pres.—Wilson Leach, 23 emp., *Company headquarters & magazine publishing* .................... (201) 444-5075
Bauer Publishing Co., 270 Sylvan Ave., Ste. 210, Englewood Cliffs 07632
CEO—Hubert Boehle, 400 emp., *Weekly cooking, health & practical* .................... (201) 569-6699
Bergen County Magazine, The, 297 Kinderkamack Rd., Ste. 135, Oradell 07649
Ptnr. & Co-Publisher—Sharon Goldstein, 10 emp., *Regional upscale magazine publishing*.... (201) 265-2286
Beverage Media Group, Inc., 2444 Morris Ave., Ste. 318, Union 07083
Off. Mgr.—Angel Wolters, 2 emp., *Trade journal publishing* .................... (908) 964-5060
BlueSpire Strategic Marketing, 110 Summit Ave., Ste. B, Montvale 07645
Pres., CEO—Kathryn Hammond, 35 emp., *Contract medical magazine publishing* .................... (201) 740-6100
BNP Media, Inc., 210 E. State Route 4, Ste. 203, Paramus 07652
Editor—Michael Reis, 5 emp., *Periodical publishing* .................... (201) 291-9001
Borton Enterprises, 178 Woodruff Rd., Bridgeton 08302
Pres.—Brad Borton, 10 emp., *Equestrian magazine publishing* .................... (856) 453-9221
Business Today, 48 University Pl., Princeton 08540
Pres., Hum. Res. Mgr.—Jonathan Hastings, 30 emp., *College student magazine publishing*.. (609) 258-1111
Business Travel Executive Magazine, 262 Rockport Rd., Port Murray 07865
Owner—Gerald Allison, 5 emp., *Monthly managed business travel magazine* .................... (908) 979-1974
Buyers Laboratory LLC, 20 Railroad Ave., Hackensack 07601
CEO—Gerry Stoia, 40 emp., *Newsletter & test report publishing* .................... (201) 488-0404
Cape Publishing, Inc., 513 Washington St., Cape May 08204
★ Owner—Bernar Haas, 5 emp., *Magazine publishing* .................... (609) 898-4500
Carstens Publications, Inc., 108 Phil Hardin Rd., Newton 07860
Pres.—Henry R. Carstens, 20 emp., *Magazine publishing* .................... (973) 383-3355
Charter Financial Publishing Network, Inc., 499 Broad St., Shrewsbury 07702
★ CEO—Charlie Stroller, 30 emp., *Magazine publishing for the financial* .................... (732) 450-8866
Children's Technology Review, 120 Main St., Flemington 08822
Pres.—Warren Buckleiter, 5 emp., *Monthly computer software periodical* .................... (908) 284-0404
Civic Research Institute, Inc., 4478 Route 27, P.O. Box 585, Kingston 08528
Pres.—Mark Peel, 3 emp., *Periodical publishing* .................... (609) 683-4450
Clifton Merchant Magazine, 1288 Main Ave., Clifton 07011
★ Owner—Tom Hawrylko, 4 emp., *Monthly magazine publishing* .................... (973) 253-4400
Columbia Marketing Corp., 221 Rutgers St., Maplewood 07040
Pres.—Alan H. Beck, 2 emp., *Tourist guides & travel map & magazine* .................... (973) 275-1700
Commerce Enterprises, Inc., 61 S. Paramus Rd., Ste. 135, Paramus 07652
★ Pres.—John Galandak, 12 emp., *Magazine publishing* .................... (201) 368-2100
Community Newspapers & Magazines Of North Jersey Media Group, 1 Garret Mountain Plz., P.O. Box 471, Woodland Park 07424
V-P., Publisher—Janice Friedman, 132 emp., *Daily print & online newspaper & monthly* .......... (973) 569-7000
Contemporary Bride Magazine, 153 Geary Dr., South Plainfield 07080
★ Publisher—Gary Paris, 5 emp., *Magazine publishing* .................... (908) 756-0123
CPMAG, LLC, 6903 Jackson St., Guttenberg 07093
★ CFO—Matt Barteluce, 3 emp., *Magazine publishing* .................... (201) 868-8585
Data Centrum Communications, Inc., 135 Chestnut Ridge Rd., 2nd Fl., Montvale 07645
★ Pres., CEO—Eric Jensen, 30 emp., *Magazine publishing* .................... (201) 391-1911
Dentistry Today, Inc., 100 Passaic Ave., Ste. 220, Fairfield 07004
★ Publisher—Paul Radcliffe, 20 emp., *Clinical news magazine publishing for* .................... (973) 882-4700
DiversityInc Media LLC, 342 Nassau St., Princeton 08540
CEO—Lucas J. Visconti, 20 emp., *Monthly diversity management/consulting* .................... (973) 494-0500
Drug Delivery Technology, LLC, 219 Changebridge Rd., Montville 07045
Pres., Publisher—Ralph Vitaro, 25 emp., *Pharmaceutical & biological delivery* .................... (973) 299-1200
Edgell Communications, Inc., 4 Middlebury Blvd., Ste. 1, Randolph 07869
CEO—Gabriele Edgell, 60 emp., *Trade magazine publishing* .................... (973) 607-1300
Friday Morning Quarterback, 1930 Marlton Pike E., Ste. F-36, Cherry Hill 08003
Pres.—Kal Rudman, 15 emp., *Radio industry magazine publishing* .................... (856) 424-9114
Frontline Medical Communications, Inc., 7 Century Dr., Parsippany 07054
Pres., CEO—Alan J. Imhoff, 187 emp., *Monthly print & online medical tabloid* .................... (973) 290-8200
Frontline Medical Communications, Inc., 7 Century Dr., Ste. 302, Parsippany 07054
Chrm.—Stephen Stoneburn, 100 emp., *Corporate headquarters & magazine publishing* ....... (973) 206-3434
GNC Venture Group, Inc., 1639 Percy Ln., Vineland 08361
★ Owner—Jerry Covella, 4 emp., *Magazine publishing* .................... (856) 690-1999
Group C Media, Inc., 44 Apple St., Ste. 3, Tinton Falls 07724
Co-Pres.—Susan Coene, 20 emp., *Monthly print & online informational* .................... (732) 842-7433
Hague Academic Press Ltd., 75 Lohs Pl., Harrington Park 07640
★ Pres.—Marsha Cohen, 2 emp., *Trade magazine publishing* .................... (201) 750-9091
Harrison Scott Publications, Inc., 5 Marine View Plz., Ste. 400, Hoboken 07030
Publisher—Andrew Albert, 25 emp., *Newsletter publishing* .................... (201) 659-1700
Health Resources Publishing LLC, P.O. Box 456, Allenwood 08720
CEO—Robert Jenkins, 5 emp., *Management news & reference information* .................... (732) 292-1100
Hi Class Living Magazine, 120 Sylvan Ave., Ste. 209, Englewood Cliffs 07632
Owner & Publisher—Michael Raviv, 4 emp., *Lifestyle magazine publishing* .................... (201) 363-0200
Hobby Publications, Inc., 83 South St., Unit 307, Freehold 07728
Pres.—David Gherman, 25 emp., *Magazine publishing* .................... (732) 536-5160
Homes & Estates Magazines, 173 Morris St., Morristown 07960
Publisher—Pete Best, 4 emp., *Real estate magazine publishing* .................... (973) 605-1877
Howe's Standard Publishing Co., Inc., 1980 S. West Blvd., Vineland 08360
Pres.—Barry Opromollo, 30 emp., *Commercial printing* .................... (856) 691-2000
Industry Publications, Inc., 3621 Hill Rd., Parsippany 07054
Publisher—Cynthia Hundley, 12 emp., *Bimonthly print & online magazine publishing* ............ (973) 331-9545
Information Today, Inc., 143 Old Marlton Pike, Medford 08055
Pres., Publisher—Thomas H. Hogan, 30 emp., *Corporate headquarters & magazine &* .......... (609) 654-6266
Intellisphere, LLC, 666 Plainsboro Rd., Ste. 300, Plainsboro 08536
CEO—Michael J. Hennessy, 80 emp., *Healthcare magazine publishing* .................... (609) 716-7777
International Data Group, 650 From Rd., Ste. 558, Paramus 07652
Off. Mgr.—Kathy Georgiyevskaya, 5 emp., *Trade & consumer technology magazine* ............. (201) 634-2300
iVillage, Inc., 900 Sylvan Ave., Englewood Cliffs 07632
Editor—Jeff Cox, 200 emp., *Magazine, journal & book publishing* .................... (212) 664-4444
Jannetti, Inc., Anthony J., 200 E. Holly Ave., Sewell 08080
Owner—Anthony Jannetti, 70 emp., *Scholarly nursing journal publishing* .................... (856) 256-2300
Jersey Shore Publications, P.O. Box 176, Bay Head 08742
Publisher & Editor—George Valente, 6 emp., *Book & magazine publishing* .................... (732) 892-1276
Jewish Voice, 73 Dana Pl., P.O. Box 8097, Englewood 07631
★ Editor—Susan Rosenbluth, 4 emp., *Magazine publishing* .................... (201) 569-2845
JOC Group, Inc., 2 Penn Plz. E., 12th Fl., Newark 07105
CEO—Gavin Carter, 120 emp., *Corporate headquarters & magazine publishing* .................... (973) 776-8660
Jostens, Inc., 86 Roseville Rd., Andover 07821
GM—Lou Esposito, 6 emp., *Periodical publishing* .................... (973) 584-5843
Journal America, 1950 Greenwood Lake Tpke., P.O. Box 459, Hewitt 07421
★ Owner—George Malmgren, 10 emp., *Journal publishing* .................... (973) 728-8355
Jury Verdict Review Publications, 45 Springfield Ave., Springfield 07081
Publisher—Jed Zarin, 8 emp., *Magazine publishing* .................... (973) 376-9002
Korean Bergen News, 210 Sylvan Ave., Ste. 23, Englewood Cliffs 07632
Owner—Thomas Bae, 15 emp., *Ethnic newspaper & magazine publishing* .................... (201) 894-9061
Lawyers Diary and Manual, 890 Mountain Ave., New Providence 07974
COO & Publisher—Ed Denne, 50 emp., *Legal information resource & lawyer* .................... (973) 642-1440
Leonard Publications, Inc., 10 W. Hanover Ave., P.O. Box 553, Mount Freedom 07970
Pres.—Pat Leonard, 2 emp., *Quarterly informational magazine publishing* .................... (973) 895-6000
Limo Digest, 3 Reeves Station Rd., Medford 08055
Assoc. Publisher—Dawn Sheldon, 10 emp., *Magazine publishing* .................... (609) 953-4900
Magazine Of Fantasy & Science Fiction, The, 105 Leonard St., Jersey City 07307
★ Publisher & Editor—Gordon Van Gelder, 4 emp., *Magazine publishing* .................... (201) 876-2551
McGraw-Hill Construction, 148 Princeton Hightstown Rd., Hightstown 08520
★ Power Source Mgr.—Andrea Kerwin, 3 emp., *Bimonthly print & online magazine publishing*.. (800) 393-6343
McMillan Analysis Corp., 39 Meadowbrook Rd., Randolph 07869
Owner, Pres., Publisher & Editor—Lawrence G. McMillan, 4 emp., *Daily & semimonthly newsletter publishing*. (973) 328-1674
Media Vista, Inc., 60 Broad St., Ste. 100, Red Bank 07701
CEO—Barry Weisbord, 12 emp., *Newsletter publishing* .................... (732) 747-8060
Metal Powder Industries Federation, 105 College Rd. E., Princeton 08540
CEO & Ex. Dir.—C. James Trombino, 14 emp., *Trade magazine publishing for the metal* ....... (609) 452-7700
Middlesex Publications, Inc., 850 Carolier Ln., North Brunswick 08902
Owner—Mark Chelton, 12 emp., *Monthly print & online parenting &* .................... (732) 435-0005
Modern Drummer Publications, Inc., 271 Route 46 W., Ste. 212, Fairfield 07004
Pres.—Isabel Spagnardi, 15 emp., *Magazine publishing* .................... (973) 239-4140
Music Trades Magazine Corp., 80 West St., P.O. Box 432, Englewood 07631
Publisher—Paul Majeski, 6 emp., *Music trade magazine publishing* .................... (201) 871-1965
N J Sport Action, 5 Riverview Dr. W., Upper Montclair 07043
Owner—W. L. 'Bill' Allen, Jr., 10 emp., *Newspaper & magazine publishing* .................... (973) 783-9236
N.V. Business Publishers Corp. (H Q), 43 Main St., P.O. Box 188, Avon by the Sea 07717
Vice Chrm., Pres.—Tom Vilardi, 5 emp., *Corporate headquarters; weekly, bi-weekly* ............ (732) 502-0500
New Jersey Business & Industry Assn. (H Q), 10 W. Lafayette St., Trenton 08608
Pres.—Michele N. Siekerka, 35 emp., *Company headquarters; monthly association* ............. (609) 393-7707
New Jersey Business Magazine, 310 Passaic Ave., Ste. 201, Fairfield 07004
Publisher—Vincent Schweikert, 10 emp., *Electronic magazine prepress printing* .................... (973) 882-5004
New Jersey Countryside Magazine, 134 S. Finley Ave., Basking Ridge 07920
Owner, Publisher & Editor—Allene Stanton Fay, 3 emp., *Bimonthly regional lifestyle magazine* (908) 221-1171
New Jersey Journal Of Pharmacy, 760 Alexander Rd., Princeton 08540
Publisher—Maria Leibfried, 4 emp., *Pharmacy journal publishing* .................... (609) 275-4246
New Jersey Media Group, 11 Melanie Ln., Unit 22-A, East Hanover 07936
Dir., Adv.—Susan Papay, 10 emp., *Monthly advertising magazine publishing* .................... (973) 434-8888
New Jersey Monthly Magazine, Inc., 55 S. Park Pl., P.O. Box 920, Morristown 07963
Pres., Publisher—Keith Tomlinson, 40 emp., *Magazine publishing* .................... (973) 539-8230
NJBIZ, 220 Davidson Ave., Ste. 302, Somerset 08873
Publisher—Tom Curtin, 30 emp., *Weekly business journal publishing* .................... (732) 246-7677
North Jersey Media Group, Inc., 1 Garret Mountain Plz., P.O. Box 471, Woodland Park 07424
Chrm. of the Board—Malcolm A. Borg, 425 emp., *Corporate headquarters & daily & weekly*. (973) 569-7000
North Star Travel Media, LLC (H Q), 100 Lighting Way, 2nd Fl., Secaucus 07094
CEO—Tom Kemp, 100 emp., *Company headquarters; travel magazine* .................... (201) 902-2000
Octagon Communications Corp., 385 Sylvan Ave., Ste. 16, Englewood Cliffs 07632
Owner & Publisher—Douglas Markhouse, 10 emp., *Magazine publishing for the aerospace*. (201) 569-5870
Ophthalmology Times, 485F U.S. Highway 1 S., Ste. 1, Iselin 08830
★ Publisher & Editor—Leo Avila, 4 emp., *Monthly magazine publishing* .................... (732) 346-3060
Pageworks, LLC, P.O. Box 892, Murray Hill 07974
Pres.—Jean Unger, 3 emp., *Children's places & events guide publishing* .................... (908) 665-0607
PaperClip Communications, Inc., 125 Paterson Ave., Little Falls 07424
Pres.—Andy McLaughlin, 20 emp., *Specialty printing & online information* .................... (973) 256-1333
Pearson Education, Inc., 1 Lake St., Upper Saddle River 07458
CEO—Marjorie Scardino, 2500 emp., *Corporate headquarters & educational* .................... (201) 236-7000

S.I.C.

PI Magazine, 4400 U.S. Highway 9, Ste. 1000, Freehold 07728
★ Publisher—Jimmie Mesis, 2 emp., *Trade magazine publishing* (732) 308-3800

Positive Publications, LLC, 65 Madison Ave., Ste. 510, Morristown 07960
COO—Susan Poeton, 21 emp., *Magazine publishing for the manufacturing* (973) 218-0310

Powers & Co., M. J., 65 Madison Ave., Ste. 220, Morristown 07960
Pres., Publisher—Michael Powers, 3 emp., *Medical newsletter publishing* (973) 898-1200

Private Journey Magazine, The, 1120 Bloomfield Ave., Ste. 107, West Caldwell 07006
★ Founder—James Kerwin, 20 emp., *Magazine publishing* (973) 244-0301

Program Dynamics, Inc., 43 Pennsylvania Ave., P.O. Box 929, Flemington 08822
Pres., GM—Stephen Barrick, 2 emp., *Automobile racing program & magazine* (908) 782-9398

Renard Commmunications, Inc., 197 Mountain Ave., Springfield 07081
Owner—Roberta Renard, 8 emp., *Magazine publishing* (973) 912-8550

Rete Biomedical Communications Corp., 191 Godwin Ave., Ste. 1, Wyckoff 07481
Pres.—Stephen W. Gutkin, 1 emp., *Medical communications & pharmaceutical* (201) 891-8205

Ridgewood Medical Media, LLC, P.O. Box 802, Ridgewood 07450
Ptnr.—Mitch Halvorsen, 12 emp., *Monthly hospital & pharmacy print &* (201) 670-1356

Rodman Publishing Corp., 70 Hilltop Rd., 3rd Fl., Ramsey 07446
Publisher—Matthew Carey, 50 emp., *Magazine publishing* (201) 825-2552

Sino Monthly New Jersey, Inc., 18 Sheppard Pl., Edison 08817
Editor-in-Chief—Ivey Lee, 5 emp., *Chinese monthly magazine publishing* (732) 650-0688

SJ Magazine, 1223 N. Church St., Moorestown 08057
Publisher & Editor—Marianne Aleardi, 7 emp., *Magazine publishing* (856) 722-9300

Slack, Inc., 6900 Grove Rd., Thorofare 08086
Pres.—Peter Slack, 255 emp., *Medical book, magazine & journal publishing* (856) 848-1000

Society Of Naval Architects & Marine Engineers, 601 Pavonia Ave., Ste. 400, Jersey City 07306
Ex. Dir.—Erik Seither, 18 emp., *Architectural & engineering journal* (201) 798-4800

Steppin Out Magazine, 21-07 Maple Ave., Fair Lawn 07410
Publisher—Jeff Trent, 5 emp., *Magazine publishing* (201) 703-0911

Tatra Eagle, Inc., 31 Madison Ave., Hasbrouck Heights 07604
Pres.—Jane Kedron, 3 emp., *Periodical publishing* (201) 288-3815

Thomas Greco Publishing Inc., 244 Chestnut St., Ste. 202, Nutley 07110
Pres., Publisher—Tom Greco, 7 emp., *Automotive trade magazine publishing* (973) 667-6922

TimeSharing Today, Inc., 140 County Rd., Ste. 114, Tenafly 07670
V-P.—Shep Altshuler, 5 emp., *Bimonthly print & online recreational* (201) 871-4304

Travalliance Media, LLC, 593 Rancocas Rd., Westampton 08060
Pres., CEO—Mark Murphy, 50 emp., *Travel agent magazine publishing* (856) 505-1400

U.S.A. Distributors, Inc., 3711 Hudson Ave., Union City 07087
Pres.—Antonio Ibarria, 100 emp., *Newspaper & magazine publishing* (201) 348-1959

Urner Barry Publications, 182 Queens Blvd., Bayville 08721
Pres., Publisher—Paul Brown, Jr., 40 emp., *Commercial, offset, envelope, business* (732) 240-5330

Vicinity Media Group, 165 Passaic Ave., Ste. 107, Fairfield 07004
Founder & CEO—David Black, 8 emp., *Magazine publishing* (973) 276-1688

Wainer Finest Communications, Inc., 4041-G Hadley Rd., Ste. 101, South Plainfield 07080
Pres.—Howard Wainer, 12 emp., *Trade magazine publishing* (908) 769-1160

Wainscot Media, 110 Summit Ave., Montvale 07645
Cont.—Agnes Salves, 50 emp., *Custom regional health & lifestyle* (201) 571-2244

Walden-Mott Corp., 225 N. Franklin Tpke., Ramsey 07446
Pres.—Alfred Walden, 2 emp., *Trade magazine publishing* (201) 818-8630

Wiener Publishers, Inc., Markus, 231 Nassau St., Princeton 08542
Pres.—Markus Wiener, 4 emp., *World history & culture academic &* (609) 921-1141

Wiley & Sons, Inc., John, 111 River St., Hoboken 07030
Pres., CEO—Stephen M. Smith, 2000 emp., *Corporate headquarters & scientific* (201) 748-6000

Williams Publications, Inc., E. W., 2125 Center Ave., Ste. 305, Fort Lee 07024
Pres.—Andy Williams, 8 emp., *Magazine publishing* (201) 592-7007

World Apostolate of Fatima USA, 674 Mountain View Rd., P.O. Box 976, Washington 07882
Ex. Dir.—David Carollo, 10 emp., *Quarterly magazine publishing* (908) 689-1701

## 2731 Book publishing

Aesthetic Press, Inc., P.O. Box 5306, North Branch 08876
Pres.—Susan Choroszewski, 3 emp., *Book, calendar & card publishing &* (908) 369-3777

Africa World Press, Inc., 541 W. Ingham Ave., Ste. B, Trenton 08638
Pres., Publisher—Kassahun Checole, 9 emp., *Book publishing* (609) 695-3200

Amphibian Press, LLC, 309 Hutchinson Ave., Haddonfield 08033
★ Owner—Margaret Westermaier, 1 emp., *Chapbook publishing* (856) 547-3022

Barricade Books, Inc., 2037 Lemoine Ave., Fort Lee 07024
Pres.—Carole Stuart, 7 emp., *Book publishing* (201) 944-7600

Behrman House, Inc., 11 Edison Pl., Springfield 07081
Pres.—David Behrman, 15 emp., *Educational book publishing* (973) 379-7200

Bongo Vista Publishing, LLC, 32 Catalpa Ave., Hackensack 07601
★ Owner—Mario Sen, 2 emp., *Book publishing* (201) 343-0252

Books Are Back, Inc., 296 Woodside Ave., Ridgewood 07450
Pres.—Daniel L. Bauch, 3 emp., *Book publishing* (201) 447-0374

Bromley Smith Publishers, 1014 Wall Rd., Ste. G-3, P.O. Box 312, Spring Lake 07762
Ptnr. & Pres.—Jim Smith, 2 emp., *Insurance textbook publishing for prelicensin* (732) 449-9288

Career Press, Inc., 220 W. Parkway, Unit 12, Pompton Plains 07444
Pres.—Ron Fry, 20 emp., *Book publishing* (201) 848-0310

Catholic Book Publishing Corp., 77 W. End Rd., Totowa 07512
Pres.—Robert Cavalero, 30 emp., *Book publishing* (973) 890-2400

Corfacts, Inc., P.O. Box 10, Morris Plains 07950
Principal—John Ford, 7 emp., *Online business-to-business directory* (973) 998-6935

Counsel Press, LLC, 517 U.S. Highway 1 S., Ste. 1160, Iselin 08830
★ Manager—Robert L. Pincu, 2 emp., *Book publishing for the law profession* (732) 750-9229

Courier Corp., 1 International Blvd., Ste. 400, Mahwah 07495
CEO—James Conway III, 5 emp., *Book publishing* (201) 934-7100

Creative Competitions, Inc., 406 Ganttown Rd., Sewell 08080
Dir.—Samuel W. Micklus, 10 emp., *Educational book publishing* (856) 256-2797

Crossfire Publications, 551 Bloomfield Ave., Apt. C-14, West Caldwell 07006
★ V-P.—Rita Cristello, 5 emp., *Music book publishing & electronic* (973) 403-1633

Enslow Publishing Group, 40 Industrial Rd., Berkeley Heights 07922
Pres.—Mark Enslow, 30 emp., *Book publishing* (908) 771-9400

Frogworks.com, LLC, 48 Sutton Rd., Lebanon 08833
Pres.—Rolf Margenau, 2 emp., *Book publishing* (908) 832-6704

Galves Auto Price List, Inc., 430 Industrial Ave., Ste. 3, Teterboro 07608
Off. Mgr.—Paul Rad, 10 emp., *Auto price list book publishing* (201) 393-0051

Gann Law Books, Inc., 1 Washington Pk., Ste. 1300, Newark 07102
Pres.—Michael Protzel, 19 emp., *Law book publishing* (973) 268-1200

Gorgias Press, 954 River Rd., P.O. Box 6939, Piscataway 08854
Pres.—George A. Kiraz, 15 emp., *Academic book publishing* (732) 885-8900

Health Resources Publishing LLC, P.O. Box 456, Allenwood 08720
CEO—Robert Jenkins, 5 emp., *Management news & reference information* (732) 292-1100

Information Today, Inc., 143 Old Marlton Pike, Medford 08055
Pres., Publisher—Thomas H. Hogan, 30 emp., *Corporate headquarters & magazine &* (609) 654-6266

iVillage, Inc., 900 Sylvan Ave., Englewood Cliffs 07632
Editor—Jeff Cox, 200 emp., *Magazine, journal & book publishing* (212) 664-4444

Jersey Shore Publications, P.O. Box 176, Bay Head 08742
Publisher & Editor—George Valente, 6 emp., *Book & magazine publishing* (732) 892-1276

Jigsaw Publishing, LLC, 8 Hemlock Ct., Butler 07405
Owner—Graham Fill, 1 emp., *Children's novelty book publishing* (973) 838-4838

Just Us Books, Inc., P.O. Box 5306, East Orange 07019
Pres., CEO—Wade Hudson, 2 emp., *Book publishing* (973) 672-7701

Kaystar Publishing, 5 Harvey Ln., Saddle River 07458
★ Owner—Kathleen Dow, 1 emp., *Book publishing* (201) 825-2736

Kids At Our House, 47 Stoneham Pl., Metuchen 08840
Ptnr.—Danny Adlerman, 2 emp., *Picture book & novel publishing* (732) 548-1779

Kovco Publishing, Inc., 230 W. Passaic St., Maywood 07607
Pres.—Frank W. Kovats, 2 emp., *Real estate textbook publishing* (201) 843-9099

Kramer Shy & Assocs., 21 W. Delilah Rd., Pleasantville 08232
★ Owner—Charles L. Kramer, 5 emp., *Book publishing for advertising applications* (609) 646-2063

Kumon Publishing North America, Inc., 300 W. Frank Burr Blvd., Ste. 6, Teaneck 07666
Pres.—Noriaki Usui, 5 emp., *Children's educational workbook publishing* (201) 836-2105

Lief Group, Inc., Philip, 371 Sayre Dr., Princeton 08540
Pres.—Philip Lief, 4 emp., *Book publishing* (609) 430-1000

Machon Beer Hatorah, Inc., 41 E. 8th St., Lakewood 08701
Pres.—Rabbi Lazar Apter, 3 emp., *Hebrew-language book publishing* (732) 364-9638

Malletech, LLC, 1107 11th Ave., Neptune 07753
CEO—Leigh H. Stevens, 15 emp., *Keyboard percussion instruments, marimbas* (732) 774-0011

Manning Publication Co., 1233 Heartwood Dr., Cherry Hill 08003
★ Ptnr.—Marjan Bace, 12 emp., *Book publishing* (856) 375-2597

Mathematics League, Inc., 17 Lancaster Rd., P.O. Box 17, Tenafly 07670
Pres.—Daniel R. Flegler, 3 emp., *Mathematics textbook publishing* (201) 568-6328

Nersesian Publishing, Roy, 10 Maryland Rd., Maplewood 07040
Principal—Roy L. Nersesian, 1 emp., *Book publishing* (973) 762-8604

New Horizon Press, Inc., 34 Church St., Liberty Corner 07938
Pres., Publisher—Joan Dunphy, 4 emp., *Book publishing* (908) 604-6311

Nylabone Products, 1 TFH Plz., 3rd & Union Ave., P.O. Box 427, Neptune City 07753
Ex. V-P.—Mark E. Johnson, 250 emp., *Pet chew toys & pet book publishing* (732) 988-8400

P & R Publishing Co., 1102 Marble Hill Rd., P.O. Box 817, Phillipsburg 08865
Pres.—Bryce H. Craig, 18 emp., *Book publishing* (908) 454-0505

Paulist Press, 997 MacArthur Blvd., Mahwah 07430
Pres.—Father Mark-David Janus, 50 emp., *Religious book publishing* (201) 825-7300

Pearson Education, Inc., 1 Lake St., Upper Saddle River 07458
CEO—Marjorie Scardino, 2500 emp., *Corporate headquarters & educational* (201) 236-7000

Pearson Technology, 200 Old Tappan Rd., Old Tappan 07675
Facility Mgr.—Joe Cabrerra, 480 emp., *Educational book publishing for grades* (201) 767-5000

Pegasus Group Publishing, 188 Route 10 W., Ste. 307, East Hanover 07936
Pres.—Bruce Warren, 10 emp., *Book publishing* (973) 884-9100

Peoples Education, Inc., 299 Market St., P.O. Box 513, Saddle Brook 07663
CEO—Ronald Berg, 80 emp., *Publisher of print & electronic K-12* (201) 712-0090

Princeton Book Co., 614 U.S. Highway 130, Ste. 1-C, Hightstown 08520
Pres.—Charles H. Woodford, 3 emp., *Dance book publishing* (609) 426-0602

Princeton University Press, 41 William St., Princeton 08540
Dir.—Peter Dougherty, 85 emp., *Manuscript & book publishing* (609) 258-4900

Research & Education Assn., 61 Ethel Rd. W., Piscataway 08854
Cust. Serv. Rep.—Mariela Colon, 20 emp., *Educational materials publishing, including* (732) 819-8880

Robodyssey Systems, LLC, 20 Quimby Ave., Trenton 08610
Pres.—David Peins, 2 emp., *Educational systems for teaching practical* (609) 585-8535

Ross & Perry, Inc., 203 Chews Landing Rd., Haddonfield 08033
★ Manager—George Ross Fisher, 3 emp., *Book publishing* (856) 429-5752

Rutgers University Press, 106 Somerset St., 3rd Fl., New Brunswick 08901
Dir., Sales & Mktg.—Elizabeth Scarpelli, 17 emp., *Nonfiction book publishing* (848) 445-7781

Sandpaper Newspaper, 1816 Long Beach Blvd., Surf City 08008
Pres.—Curt Travers, 30 emp., *Newspaper & book publishing* (609) 494-5900

Slack, Inc., 6900 Grove Rd., Thorofare 08086
Pres.—Peter Slack, 255 emp., *Medical book, magazine & journal publishing* (856) 848-1000

SQP, Inc., 3206 Route 206, P.O. Box 248, Columbus 08022
★ Pres.—Sal Quartuccio, 4 emp., *Book publishing* (609) 298-5111

Tage Publishing Service, Inc., 5 Brownstone Way, Ho-Ho-Kus 07423
Pres.—Tony Caruso, 2 emp., *Book publishing* (201) 445-3050

Tighe Publishing Services, Inc., 788 Morris Tpke., Ste. 100, Short Hills 07078
★ GM—Kevin Tighe, 8 emp., *K-12 textbook publishing* (973) 379-7770

Townsend Press, Inc., 439 Kelley Dr., West Berlin 08091
Ptnr. & CFO—Judith Nadell, 6 emp., *Book publishing* (856) 753-0554

Transaction Publishers, Inc., 10 Corporate Pl. S., Ste. 102, Piscataway 08854
Pres.—Mary E. Curtis, 25 emp., *Social science book, eBook, series* (732) 445-2280

Trilogy Publications, LLC, 560 Sylvan Ave., Ste. 1240, Englewood Cliffs 07632
Owner—Rose Reichman, 6 emp., *Children's book publishing* (201) 816-1211

Wahida Clark Publishing, LLC, 60 Evergreen Pl., Ste. 904, East Orange 07018
★ Manager—Mia Evans, 10 emp., *Book publishing* (973) 678-9982

Weidner Publishing Group, 114 Woodbine Ave., Merchantville 08109
Pres.—James Weidner, 7 emp., *Medical textbook publishing* (856) 486-1755

Whitehurst & Clark, Inc., 1200 County Road 523, Flemington 08822
Owner—Brad Seales, 15 emp., *Textbook publishing* (908) 782-2323

Wiener Publishers, Inc., Markus, 231 Nassau St., Princeton 08542
Pres.—Markus Wiener, 4 emp., *World history & culture academic &* (609) 921-1141

Wiley & Sons, Inc., John, 111 River St., Hoboken 07030
Pres., CEO—Stephen M. Smith, 2000 emp., *Corporate headquarters & scientific* (201) 748-6000

World Scientific Publishing Co., Inc., 27 Warren St., Ste. 401-402, Hackensack 07601
★ Pres.—Doreen Phua, 10 emp., *Book publishing* (201) 487-9655

## 2732 Book printing

Dawn Bible Students Assn., 199 Railroad Ave., East Rutherford 07073
Plt. Mgr.—Ken M. Fernets, 6 emp., *Book printing & typesetting* (201) 438-6421

Epoch Press, Inc., 75 Wood St., Ste. B, Paterson 07524
CFO—Paulina Werthen, 30 emp., *Web & commercial printing* (973) 357-0080

Howe's Standard Publishing Co., Inc., 1980 S. West Blvd., Vineland 08360
Pres.—Barry Opromollo, 30 emp., *Commercial printing* (856) 691-2000

Info System, 345 Main Ave., Wallington 07057
Owner—Wojciech Marchel, 10 emp., *Newspaper publishing & booklet printing* (973) 777-4448

Lightning Press, Inc., 140 Furler St., Totowa 07512
Pres.—Ron Balinski, 12 emp., *Book printing* (973) 890-4422

McKella 280, 7025 Central Hwy., Pennsauken 08109
Ptnr.—Joseph C. LaGrossa, 80 emp., *Commercial printing, including digital* (856) 813-1153

Mountain Lion, Inc., 9 Voorhees Ct., P.O. Box 799, Pennington 08534
Pres.—John Monteleone, 1 emp., *Book printing, binding & packaging* (609) 730-1665

R. R. Donnelley & Sons Co., 215 County Ave., Secaucus 07094
V-P.—Keith Convery, 400 emp., *Book printing* ..... (201) 271-1000
Red Letter Press, Inc., 16 Deerhorn Trl., Saddle River 07458
Owner—Jack Kreismer, 3 emp., *Humor & trivia gift book publishing* ..... (201) 818-8951

## 2741 Publishing—miscellaneous

A.M. Best Co., 1 Ambest Rd., Oldwick 08858
Pres.—Arthur Snyder III, 500 emp., *Insurance information publishing* ..... (908) 439-2200
Advocate Publishing Corp., 171 Clifton Ave., P.O. Box 9500, Newark 07104
Assoc. Publisher & Editor—Deacon Al Frank, 5 emp., *Print & online newspaper, magazine,...* (973) 497-4200
Aesthetic Press, Inc., P.O. Box 5306, North Branch 08876
Pres.—Susan Choroszewski, 3 emp., *Book, calendar & card publishing &* ..... (908) 369-3777
African Telecom, Inc., 463 N. Arlington Ave., Ste. 17, East Orange 07017
Pres., Publisher—Chika Onyeani, 5 emp., *Weekly Africa-themed print & online* ..... (973) 675-9919
Alexander Communications Group, Inc., 712 Main St., Ste. 187-B, Boonton 07005
Pres.—Lawrence Alexander, 11 emp., *Newsletter publishing & printing* ..... (973) 265-2300
America OGGI, 475 Walnut St., Norwood 07648
Pres., Editor—Andrea Mantineo, 40 emp., *Daily print & online Italian language* ..... (201) 358-6697
American Foreclosures, Inc., P.O. Box 601, Oradell 07649
Pres.—Craig Laube, 5 emp., *Monthly conventional & online regional* ..... (201) 501-0200
Anderson Publishing Ltd., 180 Glenside Ave., Scotch Plains 07076
Publisher—Kieran Anderson, 5 emp., *Print & online medical imaging journal* ..... (908) 301-1995
Art Publishing Group, The, 480 Main Ave., Unit 4, Wallington 07057
Pres.—John Bridgewater, 10 emp., *Fine art printing, including motivational* ..... (201) 842-8500
Baxter Corp., The, 511 Commerce St., P.O. Box 645, Franklin Lakes 07417
Pres.—George Bowen, 5 emp., *Textile patterns & machinery, loom* ..... (201) 337-1212
BlueSpire Strategic Marketing, 110 Summit Ave., Ste. B, Montvale 07645
Pres., CEO—Kathryn Hammond, 35 emp., *Contract medical magazine publishing* ..... (201) 740-6100
Business Today, 48 University Pl., Princeton 08540
Pres., Hum. Res. Mgr.—Jonathan Hastings, 30 emp., *College student magazine publishing..* (609) 258-1111
Buyers Laboratory LLC, 20 Railroad Ave., Hackensack 07601
CEO—Gerry Stoia, 40 emp., *Newsletter & test report publishing* ..... (201) 488-0404
CMD Media, P.O. Box 1061, Rahway 07065
Publisher—Lisa McCormick, 14 emp., *Newspaper publishing* ..... (732) 574-1200
Columbia Marketing Corp., 221 Rutgers St., Maplewood 07040
Pres.—Alan H. Beck, 2 emp., *Tourist guides & travel map & magazine* ..... (973) 275-1700
Community Newspapers & Magazines Of North Jersey Media Group, 1 Garret Mountain Plz., P.O. Box 471, Woodland Park 07424
V-P., Publisher—Janice Friedman, 132 emp., *Daily print & online newspaper & monthly* ..... (973) 569-7000
County Seat, LLC, 77 Hudson St., Hackensack 07601
Publisher—Gail Zisa, 6 emp., *Monthly print & online newspaper publishing* ..... (201) 488-5795
Discount Office Supply, 146 Hudson St., Hackensack 07601
Pres.—Larry Barr, 5 emp., *Pamphlet, brochure, stationery & business* ..... (201) 342-3030
Dun & Bradstreet Corp., The, 103 John F. Kennedy Pkwy., Short Hills 07078
Pres., CEO & Dir.—Bob Carrigan, 425 emp., *Corporate headquarters & credit, investment....* (973) 921-5500
Educational Testing Service, 660 Rosedale Rd., Princeton 08541
Pres.—Walter MacDonald, 2500 emp., *Academic test publishing* ..... (609) 921-9000
Franklin Electronic Publishers, Inc., 8 Terri Ln., Burlington 08016
Pres., CEO—Barry Lipsky, 30 emp., *Electronic language learning handheld* ..... (609) 386-2500
Frontline Medical Communications, Inc., 7 Century Dr., Parsippany 07054
Pres., CEO—Alan J. Imhoff, 187 emp., *Monthly print & online medical tabloid* ..... (973) 290-8200
Galaxy Of Graphics Ltd., 30 Murray Hill Pkwy., Ste. 300, East Rutherford 07073
Asst. Cont.—Stewart Fredrik, 12 emp., *Art poster & print publishing* ..... (201) 806-2100
Geographia Map Co., Inc., 75 Moore St., Hackensack 07601
Pres.—Israel Polak, 15 emp., *Publisher & distributor of maps* ..... (201) 488-4411
Group C Media, Inc., 44 Apple St., Ste. 3, Tinton Falls 07724
Co-Pres.—Susan Coene, 20 emp., *Monthly print & online informational* ..... (732) 842-7433
Handyguide, Inc., 721 Village Rd., P.O. Box 205, Oradell 07649
Pres.—Iris Orsini, 3 emp., *Industrial book publishing guide* ..... (201) 262-9478
Health Resources Publishing LLC, P.O. Box 456, Allenwood 08720
CEO—Robert Jenkins, 5 emp., *Management news & reference information* ..... (732) 292-1100
Healthcare Marketers Exchange, 104 Park Ave., Verona 07044
Owner—Nancy Leonard, 1 emp., *Monthly newsletter for the healthcare* ..... (973) 744-9505
Heritage Publishing, LLC, 620 High Bridge Rd., Colts Neck 07722
★ Co-Publisher—Nick Montalbano, 4 emp., *Home improvement guide publishing* ..... (732) 747-7770
HSH Assocs., 51 Route 23 S., Riverdale 07457
V-P.—Keith Gumbinger, 7 emp., *Mortgage & consumer loan financial* ..... (973) 617-8700
Imagination Arts Publications, 57 Thunderhead Pl., P.O. Box 103, Mahwah 07430
Owner—Judith Peck, 1 emp., *Creative art book publishing* ..... (201) 529-5105
Jersey Job Guide, Inc., 422 Morris Ave., Ste. 5, Long Branch 07740
Pres.—Mike Beson, 6 emp., *Employment advertising publishing* ..... (732) 263-9675
Journal Register Co., The, 32 S. Main St., Ste. A, Medford 08055
Editor—Jenn Lucas, 12 emp., *Weekly print & online newspaper publishing* ..... (609) 654-5000
Lawyers Diary and Manual, 890 Mountain Ave., New Providence 07974
COO & Publisher—Ed Denne, 50 emp., *Legal information resource & lawyer* ..... (973) 642-1440
Learning Links, Inc., P.O. Box 326, Cranbury 08512
★ Pres.—Russell Wagner, 12 emp., *Educational literature study guide* ..... (516) 437-9071
Legislative Index Of New Jersey, 172 W. State St., Trenton 08608
Owner, Hum. Res. & IT Mgr.—Craig Leach, 3 emp., *State of New Jersey legislation guide* .... (609) 393-2291
LexisNexis Martindale-Hubell, 121 Chanlon Rd., New Providence 07974
Dir., Sales—Greg Schraft, 500 emp., *Directory publishing* ..... (908) 464-6800
Lombardo Music Publications, 37 Pintinalli Dr., Trenton 08619
★ Owner—Harry Lombardozzi, 2 emp., *Sheet music publishing* ..... (609) 586-9245
Macie Publishing Co., 10 Astro Pl., Ste. 100, Rockaway 07866
Pres.—Ed Sueta, 12 emp., *Music publishing* ..... (973) 983-8700
Malletech, LLC, 1107 11th Ave., Neptune 07753
CEO—Leigh H. Stevens, 15 emp., *Keyboard percussion instruments, marimbas* (732) 774-0011
Marcia's Melodies, 61 Pilgrim Pathway, Unit 3, Ocean Grove 07756
★ Pres.—Marcia Hendron, 4 emp., *Sheet music publishing* ..... (732) 988-3191
McGraw-Hill Construction, 148 Princeton Hightstown Rd., Hightstown 08520
★ Power Source Mgr.—Andrea Kerwin, 3 emp., *Bimonthly print & online magazine publishing..* (800) 393-6343
Metal Powder Industries Federation, 105 College Rd. E., Princeton 08540
CEO & Ex. Dir.—C. James Trombino, 14 emp., *Trade magazine publishing for the metal* ..... (609) 452-7700
Metro Publishing Group, Inc., 626 McCarthy Dr., New Milford 07646
★ Owner—Bob Nesoff, 5 emp., *Travel guide publishing* ..... (201) 385-2000
Middlesex Publications, Inc., 850 Carolier Ln., North Brunswick 08902
Owner—Mark Chelton, 12 emp., *Monthly print & online parenting &* ..... (732) 435-0005
Network, The, 105-B Van Houten Ave., P.O. Box 5338, Passaic 07055
Publisher—Norman Shapiro, 5 emp., *Jewish community directory publishing* ..... (973) 778-7222
New Jersey Jewish News, 901 Route 10, Whippany 07981
COO, GM—Rick Keslenbaum, 30 emp., *Weekly, biweekly & monthly print &* ..... (973) 887-3900

North Jersey Media Group Inc., 100 Commons Way, Rockaway 07866
V-P., Circ. & Mfg.—Robert Konig, 308 emp., *Daily local & community print & online* ..... (973) 586-8000
North Jersey Media Group, Inc., 1 Garret Mountain Plz., P.O. Box 471, Woodland Park 07424
Chrm. of the Board—Malcolm A. Borg, 425 emp., *Corporate headquarters & daily & weekly*. (973) 569-7000
Novak Co., Tony, 185 Bayview Rd., P.O. Box 333, Newport 08345
Owner—Tony Novak, 1 emp., *Financial & tax planning guide publishing* ..... (856) 649-4171
Observer, P.O. Box 445, Hasbrouck Heights 07604
Editor—Constance Doheny, 7 emp., *Newspaper publishing* ..... (201) 288-0333
Pageworks, LLC, P.O. Box 892, Murray Hill 07974
Pres.—Jean Unger, 3 emp., *Children's places & events guide publishing* ..... (908) 665-0607
PaperClip Communications, Inc., 125 Paterson Ave., Little Falls 07424
Pres.—Andy McLaughlin, 20 emp., *Specialty printing & online information* ..... (973) 256-1333
Pearson Education, Inc., 1 Lake St., Upper Saddle River 07458
CEO—Marjorie Scardino, 2500 emp., *Corporate headquarters & educational* ..... (201) 236-7000
Physician's Weekly, 180 Mount Airy Rd., Ste. 102, Basking Ridge 07920
Pres.—Clay Romweber, 10 emp., *Medical newsletter publishing* ..... (908) 766-0402
Program Dynamics, Inc., 43 Pennsylvania Ave., P.O. Box 929, Flemington 08822
Pres., GM—Stephen Barrick, 2 emp., *Automobile racing program & magazine* ..... (908) 782-9398
R. R. Bowker, 630 Central Ave., New Providence 07974
V-P., Bus. Dev.—Angela D'Agostino, 95 emp., *Bibliographical information directory* ..... (908) 795-3500
RDL Marketing Group, LLC, 352-A Sweetmann Ln., P.O. Box 385, Perrineville 08535
Owner—Robert Levine, 5 emp., *Catalog publishing* ..... (732) 446-0817
RE Systems Group, Inc., 1060 Main St., Ste. 200, River Edge 07661
Pres.—George Gramlich, 5 emp., *Reinsurance software development &* ..... (201) 883-1572
Research & Education Assn., 61 Ethel Rd. W., Piscataway 08854
Cust. Serv. Rep.—Mariela Colon, 20 emp., *Educational materials publishing, including* ..... (732) 819-8880
Ridgewood Medical Media, LLC, P.O. Box 802, Ridgewood 07450
Ptnr.—Mitch Halvorsen, 12 emp., *Monthly hospital & pharmacy print &* ..... (201) 670-1356
Roth Studio Collection, LLC, The Judith, 3 Stone House Rd., Mendham 07945
★ Pres.—Judith Roth, 6 emp., *Calendar printing* ..... (973) 543-4455
SAI Global Ltd., 210 State Route 4 E., Paramus 07652
V-P., N. America—Stuart Bowyer, 10 emp., *Industrial technical standards publishing* ..... (201) 986-1131
Salty Dog, The, 254 Brick Blvd., Ste. 1, Brick 08723
Owner & Pres.—Art Peters, 5 emp., *Biweekly print & online boating shopper* ..... (732) 714-8400
Sample Media, Inc., 801 Asbury St., 3rd Fl., Ocean City 08226
Publisher & Editor—David Nahan, 35 emp., *Community newspaper & tourist-vacation* ..... (609) 399-1220
Seawave Corp., 1508 Route 47, Rio Grande 08242
Pres.—Arthur Hall, 25 emp., *Weekly print & online newspaper & visitor's* ..... (609) 886-8600
Seidman Productions, Inc., 254 E. Gibbsboro Rd., Ste. C, Lindenwold 08021
Pres.—Jay Seidman, 3 emp., *Monthly boxing program publishing* ..... (856) 627-1356
Shipserv, 1090 King Georges Post Rd., Edison 08837
Editor—Don Staffin, 6 emp., *International shipping & offshore drilling* ..... (215) 862-3353
Shoppe Cape May County Shoppers Guide, 2503 Bayshore Rd., Villas 08251
Pres., Publisher—Otto Jensch, 8 emp., *Weekly print & online shopper & vacation* ..... (609) 886-4112
Showcase Publications, Inc., 90 Irons St., Toms River 08753
Pres.—Bob Draper, 50 emp., *Corporate headquarters & targeted weekly* ..... (732) 349-7775
SMR Research Corp., 300 Valentine St., Hackettstown 07840
Pres.—Stuart Feldstein, 10 emp., *Research study publishing, including* ..... (908) 852-7677
Subito Music Corporation, 60 Depot St., Verona 07044
Owner & GM—Stephen Culbertson, 10 emp., *Sheet music printing & typesetting* ..... (973) 857-3440
TimeSharing Today, Inc., 140 County Rd., Ste. 114, Tenafly 07670
V-P.—Shep Altshuler, 5 emp., *Bimonthly print & online recreational* ..... (201) 871-4304
Transaction Publishers, Inc., 10 Corporate Pl. S., Ste. 102, Piscataway 08854
Pres.—Mary E. Curtis, 25 emp., *Social science book, eBook, series* ..... (732) 445-2280
University Publications, 562 Morley Ct., Belford 07718
Owner—Frank Lake, 7 emp., *Daily planner & college yearbook publishing* ..... (732) 495-9000
Verona-Cedar Grove Times, 130 Valley Rd., Montclair 07042
Publisher—Mike Lawson, 5 emp., *Weekly print & online community newspaper* ..... (973) 233-5048
Vitamin Retailer, 431 Cranbury Rd., Ste. C, East Brunswick 08816
Owner & Publisher—Daniel McSweeney, 8 emp., *Vitamin supplement magazine publishing..* (732) 432-9600
WayneToday, 1 Garret Mountain Plz., P.O. Box 471, Woodland Park 07424
Publisher—Mike Lawson, 5 emp., *Weekly northern New Jersey newsletter* ..... (973) 569-7393
Workers' Disability Income System, Inc., 56 Primrose Cir., Princeton 08540
★ Owner—John F. Burton, Jr., 5 emp., *Newsletter publishing* ..... (732) 274-0600
WPI Communication, Inc., 55 Morris Ave., Ste. 312, Springfield 07081
Publisher—Steve Klinghoffer, 15 emp., *Newsletter publishing* ..... (973) 467-8700

## 2752 Lithographic printing—commercial

A A Graphics, Inc., 431 N. Midland Ave., Unit C, Saddle Brook 07663
Pres.—Anthony Acocella, 4 emp., *Offset printing* ..... (201) 398-0710
A M Graphics Co., Inc., 68 Schraalenburgh Rd., Harrington Park 07640
Pres., Plt. Opers., Sales & Mktg. Mgr.—John Motta, 3 emp., *Offset printing & graphics* ..... (201) 767-5320
A To Z Printing & Promotions, 1455 Main Ave., Clifton 07011
Pres.—Eyad Asmar, 7 emp., *Lithographic & commercial printing* ..... (973) 916-9995
Abilitees Unlimited, Inc., 23 Adams St., Metuchen 08840
Owner & Pres.—Helen Lenihan, 8 emp., *Textile embroidery & screen & offset* ..... (732) 494-1513
ACB Reproduction, 2060 Springdale Rd., Cherry Hill 08003
Manager—Andy Bonachea, 8 emp., *Instant printing* ..... (856) 751-0360
Access Printing, Inc., 510 N. Belleview Ave., Riverton 08077
Pres.—Richard Osbourne, 3 emp., *Offset & color printing & bookbinding* ..... (856) 829-1673
Accurate Plastic Printers, LLC, 30 Colfax Ave., Clifton 07013
Pres.—Carlos Agudelo, 20 emp., *Plastic product offset & digital printing* ..... (973) 591-0180
Ace Lithographers, 22 Russo Pl., Berkeley Heights 07922
Pres.—John Cooper, 28 emp., *Commercial, offset & digital printing* ..... (908) 665-1700
Ace Reprographic Service, Inc., 74 E. 30th St., Paterson 07514
Pres.—Arthur L. Scialla, 25 emp., *Blueprinting & color printing* ..... (973) 684-5945
Ace Twill, 22 Russo Pl., Berkeley Heights 07922
Sales Rep.—George Twill, 30 emp., *Digital & offset printing* ..... (908) 665-1700
Adams Printing & Graphics, 886 N. Pearl St., Bridgeton 08302
Owner—Mary Swain, 3 emp., *Commercial offset & digital printing* ..... (856) 455-7177
Advertiser, The, 235 Blackwood Ave., P.O. Box 54, Franklinville 08322
Owner—Stanley Deininger, 1 emp., *Offset & letterpress printing* ..... (856) 694-0444
Advertisers Services Group, Inc., 65 Railroad Ave., Ridgefield Park 07660
Pres.—E. Kelly, 5 emp., *Offset printing* ..... (201) 440-5577
AELitho Group, Inc., 450 Broad St., P.O. Box 9000, Beverly 08010
Pres.—Annette Yellin, 80 emp., *Printing, including forms, business* ..... (609) 239-0700
Affordable Copies Center, 55 Halsey St., Newark 07102
Owner—Jaman Monir, 2 emp., *Instant printing & electronic prepress* ..... (973) 802-1007
Affordable Offset Printing, Inc., 809 Hylton Rd., Ste. 11, Pennsauken 08110
Pres.—Gary Coates, 4 emp., *Offset & digital printing, electronic* ..... (856) 661-0722
Ahern's Printing & Graphics, 231 Parker Ave., Manasquan 08736
Owner—Matthew Ahern, 8 emp., *Blueprinting* ..... (732) 223-1476

© Copyright 2015 Manufacturers' News, Inc.


AJ Printing Solutions, LLC, 781 Hyslip Ave., Westfield 07090
Owner—Gary Wasserman, 1 emp., *Flexographic & offset printing of packaging* ...... (908) 202-0974
Alexy, Inc., 401 Morris Ave., Springfield 07081
Pres.—Marilyn Alexy, 3 emp., *Offset printing* ...... (973) 467-0030
All American Print & Copy Center, 518 Highway 35, Red Bank 07701
Owner—Ralph Cucinelli, 2 emp., *Commercial offset printing & typesetting* ...... (732) 758-6200
Allegra Marketing Print & Mail, 533 S. Shore Rd., Marmora 08223
Owner—Nicholas Wieand, 10 emp., *Offset printing & typesetting* ...... (609) 390-1400
Allegra Print & Imaging, Inc., 12 Stults Rd., Dayton 08810
Pres.—Ellis Galimidi, 35 emp., *Offset, digital, instant & color printing* ...... (609) 771-4000
Allen Group SMC, 60 Readington Rd., Branchburg 08876
Pres.—Steven Hegna, 60 emp., *Envelope & offset printing & typesetting* ...... (908) 231-1100
Allied Envelope Co., Inc., 33 Commerce Rd., Carlstadt 07072
Pres.—James Royer, 50 emp., *Full-service direct mail & commercial* ...... (201) 440-2000
ALL-STATE LEGAL, 1 Commerce Dr., Cranford 07016
Pres., CEO—Robert H. Busch, 230 emp., *Full-color engraving & printing of* ...... (908) 272-0800
Allstate Printing Packaging, Inc., 791 Paulison Ave., Ste. 3, Clifton 07011
Owner & Pres.—Sam Zhong, 85 emp., *Commercial offset printing* ...... (973) 473-0700
Alma Offset Co., Inc., 225 Bakers Basin Rd., P.O. Box 6487, Lawrenceville 08648
Pres.—Dan Markowski, 7 emp., *Offset printing* ...... (609) 587-5480
Alpha Graphics, 95 Greenwood Ave., Midland Park 07432
Pres.—Mark Shishmanian, 7 emp., *Offset printing, graphic design & binding* ...... (201) 447-4800
AlphaGraphics, 5 N. Olney Ave., Ste. 200, Cherry Hill 08003
Owner—Dave Sanford, 19 emp., *Digital & offset printing & graphic* ...... (856) 761-8000
AlphaGraphics, 401 Jersey Ave., Ste. F, New Brunswick 08901
Pres.—H. J. Kim, 5 emp., *Offset printing* ...... (732) 247-0809
AlphaGraphics 321, 90 Saw Mill Pond Rd., Heller Industrial Pk., Edison 08817
Pres., CFO—Carl A. Venable, 4 emp., *Digital & offset printing, promotional* ...... (732) 985-6677
AlphaGraphics of Mahwah, 1 Lethbridge Plz., Route 17 N., Mahwah 07430
Pres.—John Chrisostomou, 6 emp., *Digital, direct mail & business printing* ...... (201) 327-2200
AlphaGraphics Printshops, 68 White St., Red Bank 07701
Pres.—Jac Bloomberg, 5 emp., *Offset, instant, large-format & digital* ...... (732) 758-0095
AlphaGraphics, Inc., 173 Route 206 N., Hillsborough 08844
Pres.—Thomas Hopkins, 10 emp., *Offset & digital printing* ...... (908) 281-9476
Alphagraphics, Inc., 60 Speedwell Ave., Morristown 07960
Owner—Brian Harrigan, 7 emp., *Commercial offset & instant printing* ...... (973) 984-0066
American Envelope & Printing Co., 212 Columbus Ave., Roselle 07203
Owner & Pres.—Edward Nodelman, 5 emp., *Envelopes & commercial printing of* ...... (908) 241-9900
American Graphic Systems, Inc., 39-26 Broadway, Fair Lawn 07410
Pres.—Stan Schechter, 5 emp., *Offset printing & signs* ...... (201) 796-0666
American Plus Printers, Inc., 2604 Atlantic Ave., Wall 07719
Pres.—Dianne Strohmenger, 12 emp., *Offset printing & electronic prepress* ...... (732) 528-2170
Anisha Enterprises, Inc., 2165 Morris Ave., Union 07083
Pres.—P. J. Jhawar, 6 emp., *Instant printing, bindery, mailing* ...... (908) 964-3380
Anthony Quality Printing, Mark, 187 Garibaldi Ave., Lodi 07644
Owner—Mark Anthony, 7 emp., *Offset printing* ...... (973) 815-1113
Apex Printing Services, Inc., 6 Ilene Ct., Bldg. 6, Unit 16, Hillsborough 08844
Owner & Pres.—Dave Nazarenko, 5 emp., *Offset printing* ...... (908) 281-9221
Apollo Quik Print Co., Inc., 49 Orchard St., Hackensack 07601
Pres.—Kevin Bliss, 4 emp., *Offset printing & typesetting* ...... (201) 488-1101
ARC Document Solutions, 844 Fairfield Ave., Kenilworth 07033
Dir., Sales—Jeffrey Jimenez, 40 emp., *Blueprinting, including reprographic* ...... (973) 372-5200
Arc Reprographics, Inc., 1110 New Rd., Absecon 08201
Pres.—John Curry, 7 emp., *Blueprinting & typesetting* ...... (609) 646-9324
Arista Custom Tapes, Inc., 20 Argyle Pl., North Arlington 07031
Pres.—Thoms Lefkowitz, 7 emp., *Label & tape printing* ...... (201) 997-7610
Armor Guard Business Center, 139 Main St., Orange 07050
Owner—Michael Whatley, 1 emp., *Offset printing* ...... (973) 676-6900
Arms Graphics, 169 Paris Ave., Northvale 07647
Pres.—Allan Schneider, 3 emp., *Offset & instant printing & typesetting* ...... (201) 767-6504
Ascot Tag & Label Co., Inc., 577 3rd St., Newark 07107
Pres. & V-P.—Charles DeFranza, 45 emp., *Tags, labels & commercial printing* ...... (973) 482-0900
Atlantic Printing & Graphics, LLC, 1301 W. Park Ave., Ocean 07712
Owner—Ed Lawrence, 5 emp., *Commercial & instant printing* ...... (732) 493-4222
Automatic Data Processing, Inc. (H Q), 1 ADP Blvd., Roseland 07068
Pres., CEO—Carlos Rodriguez, 3000 emp., *Corporate headquarters; offset & laser* ...... (973) 974-5000
Avenue Printing Co., 143 Franklin Tpke., Waldwick 07463
Owner—Ruth Amarante, 3 emp., *Commercial offset spot & digital full-color* ...... (201) 652-2035
Ayr Graphics & Printing, Inc., 320 Chestnut St., Roselle Park 07204
Pres.—Carl Gamba, 8 emp., *Offset, color & digital printing &* ...... (908) 241-8118
B & B Press, Inc., 24 Cokesbury Rd., Ste. 11, Lebanon 08833
Pres., GM—Mark Bistis, 6 emp., *Offset & digital printing, graphic* ...... (908) 840-4323
B & L Printing Co., Inc., 46 Old Camplain Rd., Hillsborough 08844
Pres., CFO—Gerald Harris, 4 emp., *Commercial offset, digital color, instant* ...... (908) 707-1311
B & W Printing Co., Inc., 730 Fairfield Ave., Kenilworth 07033
Sales Mgr.—Gary Butler, 5 emp., *Instant digital & commercial printing* ...... (908) 241-3060
Bannon Group, 629 Grove St., Jersey City 07310
Pres.—Michael Falcone, 3 emp., *Color, offset, direct mail & digital* ...... (201) 451-6500
Barrington Press Inc, 37 Spring Valley Ave., Paramus 07652
Pres., CEO—Paul E. Ramirez, 10 emp., *Offset, digital, instant, color & large-forma* ...... (201) 843-6556
Barton & Cooney, LLC, 300 Richards Run, Burlington 08016
Pres., COO—Patrick M. Doyle, 110 emp., *Direct mail & digital printing, variable* ...... (609) 747-9300
Bassano Printers & Lithographers, 67 Royal Ave., Hawthorne 07506
Pres., MIS Mgr.—Ronald C. Bassano, 5 emp., *Lithographic printing* ...... (973) 423-1400
BBC Printing, 4 Main St., P.O. Box 276, Branchville 07826
Owner—Duncan F. Caldwell, 4 emp., *Digital, large-format & offset printing* ...... (973) 948-7998
BCT-NY/NJ, 11 Industrial Ave., Upper Saddle River 07458
Pres., GM—Douglas Negrin, 10 emp., *Rubber stamps & offset printing of* ...... (201) 236-0088
Beacon Offset Co., Inc., 204 Russell Pl., Hackensack 07601
Pres.—Vivian Hollenbeck, 6 emp., *Offset printing* ...... (201) 488-4241
Belle Mead Printing, LLC, 42 Old Camplain Rd., Hillsborough 08844
Owner—Thomas E. Lemore, 3 emp., *Offset, digital & promotional printing* ...... (908) 595-9500
Bergen Instant Printing, Inc., 328 Broad Ave., Ridgefield 07657
Pres.—Bill Ackerman, 3 emp., *Offset printing* ...... (201) 945-7303
Bergen Screen Printing, Inc., 255 W. Broadway, Paterson 07522
Pres.—Uday Patel, 5 emp., *Screen & wide-format digital printing* ...... (973) 595-1222
Bernardsville Print Center, 21 Mine Brook Rd., Bernardsville 07924
Pres.—Richard C. Steinberg, 7 emp., *Digital instant, commercial, 1-4 color* ...... (908) 766-4073
Bethel Bindery, Inc., 1500 Route 539, Tuckerton 08087
Owner & Pres.—Tom Giger, 6 emp., *Thesis, genealogy, journal, CD & legal* ...... (609) 296-5043
Bon Venture, Inc., 34 Ironia Rd., P.O. Box 850, Flanders 07836
Pres.—Thomas Garde, 40 emp., *Offset printing* ...... (973) 584-5699
BP Graphics & Printing, 315 4th St., Lakewood 08701
Pres.—Ben Heineman, 15 emp., *Instant printing & typesetting* ...... (732) 905-9830
Budget Print, 426 Cedar Ln., Teaneck 07666
Owner & Graphic Design Mgr.—Debbie Passaretti, 2 emp., *Offset, full color, large-format, instant* (201) 692-1412
Budget Print Center, 2510 Atlantic Ave., Atlantic City 08401
Ptnr.—Ellen Fishlevich, 2 emp., *Offset printing & computerized typesetting* ...... (609) 348-4589
Budget Print Center, 332 Broad St., Bloomfield 07003
Owner—Thomas D. DeStefano, 8 emp., *Offset & digital printing* ...... (973) 743-0073
Budget Print Center, 590 Valley Rd., Montclair 07043
Owner—Dave Pradip, 3 emp., *Offset printing & typesetting* ...... (973) 744-5520
Budget Printing, LLC, 70 Westfield Ave., Clark 07066
Owner & Pres.—Robert Borg, 6 emp., *Full-color digital, offset & screen* ...... (732) 574-1330
Burlington Press, 328 High St., Burlington 08016
CEO—Richard Lewis, 7 emp., *Digital, offset & large-format printing* ...... (609) 387-0030
Burns, Inc., Joseph, 241 W. Union Ave., Bound Brook 08805
Pres., CEO—Mary McClintock, 10 emp., *Variable, digital color & black & white* ...... (732) 356-7990
Business Card Express, 8 E. Stow Rd., Ste. 140, P.O. Box 728, Marlton 08053
Pres.—John McTigue, 38 emp., *Offset printing & computerized typesetting* ...... (856) 596-3150
Butler Printing & Laminating, 250 Hamburg Tpke., P.O. Box 836, Butler 07405
Pres.—James Berezny, 55 emp., *Vinyl wall covering, printing & laminating* ...... (973) 838-8550
BWAY Corporation, 6 Litho Rd., Trenton 08638
Plt. Mgr.—Mike Hutchison, 100 emp., *Lithographic printing & metal coating* ...... (732) 997-4050
C & D Printing Co., 118 Broadway, Point Pleasant Beach 08742
Owner—Brenda Nasce, 2 emp., *Offset printing, typesetting & bookbinding* ...... (732) 892-8044
C & R Printing, Inc., 400 Gotham Pkwy., Carlstadt 07072
GM—Dave Clarizio, 10 emp., *Offset printing* ...... (201) 933-8000
Cantone Press, Inc., 161 Coolidge Ave., Englewood 07631
Owner—Joe Cantone, 10 emp., *Typesetting & offset printing* ...... (201) 569-2288
Cape Printing Express, Inc., 821 Shunpike Rd., Cape May 08204
Pres.—Richard Adelizzi, 2 emp., *Offset printing & typesetting* ...... (609) 884-8080
Capitol Copy Service, 116 W. State St., Trenton 08608
Pres.—Raymond Sziber, 7 emp., *Commercial, instant & digital printing* ...... (609) 989-8776
Castle Printing, Inc., 1501 U.S. Highway 46, Ledgewood 07852
Ptnr. & Pres.—Kevin Ebner, 9 emp., *Offset, instant, wide-format & digital* ...... (973) 584-0990
CCL Label, Inc., 104 N. Gold Dr., Robbinsville 08691
GM & Opers. Mgr.—Jake Martin, 120 emp., *Cosmetic labels & shrink sleeves* ...... (609) 586-1332
Central Printing & Typesetting, 1501 Route 37 E., Toms River 08753
Pres.—Linda L. Adams, 3 emp., *Offset printing & typesetting* ...... (732) 929-0011
Centurion Printing, 761 Lexington Ave., Kenilworth 07033
Owner—Anthony Caccavale, 4 emp., *Offset printing* ...... (908) 241-9839
Challenge Printing Co., The, 2 Bridewell Pl., Clifton 07014
Pres.—Theodore Sasso, 230 emp., *Company headquarters & labels, inserts* ...... (973) 471-4700
Colonial Printers, 266 Witherspoon St., Princeton 08542
Pres.—Tom Burke, 3 emp., *Offset printing* ...... (609) 921-1350
Colony, LLC, 852 S. Orange Ave., P.O. Box 6444, Newark 07106
Off. Mgr.—Todd Glass, 2 emp., *Offset printing* ...... (973) 375-4315
Color Screen Pros, 100 Verona Ave., Newark 07104
Owner—Oscar Cano, 8 emp., *Apparel & promotional item screen printing* ...... (973) 268-5080
Colornet, LLC, 809 Hylton Rd., Ste. 11, Pennsauken 08110
Mng. Member—Elizabeth Bollinger, 4 emp., *Digital & offset full color printing* ...... (856) 662-0652
Colortec Printing & Mailing LLC, 424 Kelley Dr., Ste. A, West Berlin 08091
Ptnr.—Lori Burroughs, 5 emp., *Commercial, offset, digital & direct* ...... (856) 767-0108
Commercial Business Forms, 240 Cedar Knolls Rd., Ste. 203, Cedar Knolls 07927
Pres.—Michael Gordon, 12 emp., *Commercial/business & color printing* ...... (973) 682-9000
Computer Share, Inc., 480 Washington Blvd., Jersey City 07310
Pres.—Bernie O'Connor, 120 emp., *Offset printing of business & financial* ...... (201) 680-5307
Concept Printing, Inc., 160 Woodbine St., Ste. 2, Bergenfield 07621
Pres.—Kerry Monahan-Gaughan, 6 emp., *Offset & screen printing, embroidery* ...... (201) 387-6000
Consortium Companies, 400 Raritan Center Pkwy., Edison 08837
Pres.—Lawrence Solomon, 22 emp., *Commercial, offset & digital printing* ...... (732) 512-1777
Content Critical LLC, 800 Central Blvd., Carlstadt 07072
CEO—Fred VanAlstyne, 203 emp., *Lithographic, wide-format & digital* ...... (201) 528-2777
Control Group, The, 500 Walnut St., Norwood 07648
Ptnr.—William Cheringal, 50 emp., *Pressure-sensitive label printing* ...... (201) 768-1900
Copy Shop, The, 20 E. Water St., Toms River 08753
Owner—Bob Livolsi, 5 emp., *Instant & blueprinting* ...... (732) 286-2200
Copyshop Office Supply & Repro Center, 921 U.S. Highway 9, South Amboy 08879
Owner—Scott Restiano, Jr., 3 emp., *Full-service, digital & large-format* ...... (732) 721-5700
Corporate Communications Group, The, 14 Henderson Dr., West Caldwell 07006
Pres.—Lois Pinkin, 180 emp., *Digital & offset printing, including* ...... (973) 808-0009
Cottrell Graphics, LLC, 1525 Prospect St., Unit 314, Lakewood 08701
Pres.—David F. Cottrell, 4 emp., *Instant printing* ...... (732) 349-7430
Counter-Fit Quick Printing, Inc., 145 Newark Ave., Belleville 07109
Pres.—Alan Nelson, 1 emp., *Offset printing & typesetting* ...... (201) 420-7926
Cox Printers, 1634 E. Elizabeth Ave., Linden 07036
Pres.—Michael Kaufman, 28 emp., *Commercial, offset & digital printing* ...... (908) 928-1010
Craftmaster Printing, Inc., 2024 Corlies Ave., Neptune 07753
Pres.—Curtis Baumgartner, 4 emp., *Corporate headquarters & single-color* ...... (732) 775-0011
Craftmaster Printing, Inc., 3 Main St., New Egypt 08533
Manager & Graphic Artist—Sherry Nepulis, 1 emp., *Instant & color printing & blueprinting* .... (609) 758-5990
Craftsmen Printers, The, 855 Bloomfield Ave., Clifton 07012
Pres.—Jaqueline Bischoff, 18 emp., *Printing of package inserts (PIs),* ...... (973) 773-8950
Creative Color Lithographers, Inc., 611 South Ave., Garwood 07027
Pres.—Chris Christopher, 18 emp., *Offset printing & typesetting* ...... (908) 789-2295
CRT International, Inc., 260 Wagner St., Middlesex 08846
V-P., Hum. Res. & IT—Carmine Tarantino, 8 emp., *Commercial & packaging printing of* ...... (973) 887-7737
CRW Graphics, Inc., 9100 Pennsauken Hwy., Pennsauken 08110
CEO—Harriet Weiss, 130 emp., *Commercial offset, digital & variable* ...... (856) 662-9111
D & I Printing Co., Inc., 23 Chestnut St., Englewood 07631
Pres.—Gus Dovi, 10 emp., *Offset printing* ...... (201) 871-3620
D & M Printers, 43 School Rd., Whitehouse Station 08889
Owner—Liz Dembeski, 1 emp., *Commercial offset printing* ...... (908) 534-4101
Dave's Swift Print, P.O. Box 313, Westville 08093
Owner—Dave Kuncas, 5 emp., *Instant printing* ...... (856) 853-8528
Deans Graphics, 16 Mill St., P.O. Box 809, Mount Holly 08060
Pres.—Stephen Deans, 5 emp., *Web & sheetfed offset printing & graphic* ...... (609) 261-8817
Deleon Printing & Supply, Inc., 311 Palisade Ave., Jersey City 07307
Pres.—Paul Deleon, 3 emp., *Commercial printing, including blueprinting* ...... (201) 798-8440
Design 446, 2411 Atlantic Ave., Ste. 4, Manasquan 08736
Owner & Hum. Res. Mgr.—Tom Vialne, 40 emp., *Offset & digital printing & typesetting* ...... (732) 223-0100

DG3 North America, Inc., 180 Pulaski St., Bayonne 07002
Ex. V-P.—Jonathan Vitale, 100 emp., Offset printing ............ (201) 946-0156
DG3 North America, Inc., 100 Burma Rd., Jersey City 07305
CFO, The CGI Group—L. J. Baillargeon, 400 emp., Offset & digital printing, including ............ (201) 793-5000
Discount Office Supply, 146 Hudson St., Hackensack 07601
Pres.—Larry Barr, 5 emp., Pamphlet, brochure, stationery & business ............ (201) 342-3030
Diversiprint, Inc., 1124 U.S. Highway 202, Ste. B-16, Raritan 08869
Owner & Pres.—Bob Zarelli, 3 emp., Commercial & lithographic printing ............ (908) 685-2225
Dogstar Digital, LLC, 429 Redmond Ave., Oakhurst 07755
Owner—Jay Armbrust, 2 emp., Full-service offset, color & digital ............ (732) 768-3699
Dohrman Printing Co., Inc., 445 Industrial Rd., Carlstadt 07072
Pres., Fin., MIS & R & D Mgr.—Kenny Bell, 6 emp., Commercial offset 1-6 color, digital ............ (201) 933-0346
Downtown Printing Center, Inc., 46 Paterson St., New Brunswick 08901
Pres.—Juan Ruiz, 14 emp., Offset printing & typesetting ............ (732) 246-7990
DPI Copies Printing & Graphics, Inc., 2070 Route 70 E., Cherry Hill 08003
Pres.—Michael Jones, 10 emp., Digital printing ............ (856) 874-1355
Duca Printing Co., Inc., 247 Haddon Ave., West Berlin 08091
Pres.—Vincent Duca, 4 emp., Offset printing & typesetting ............ (856) 767-2242
Dynamic Printing & Graphics, Inc., 250 Delawanna Ave., Clifton 07014
Pres., CEO—Lou Mascola, 7 emp., Offset printing, color separations ............ (973) 473-7177
EarthColor, Inc., 249 Pomeroy Rd., P.O. Box 169, Parsippany 07054
CEO—Robert Kashan, 100 emp., Corporate headquarters & commercial ............ (973) 884-1300
Elmwood Press, Inc., 85 Main Ave., Elmwood Park 07407
Owner & Off. Mgr.—Kimberly A. Murphy, 10 emp., Offset, digital & direct mail printing ............ (201) 794-6273
Emerson Speed Printing, 379 Kinderkamack Rd., Oradell 07649
Owner & Pres.—Herb Kassab, 4 emp., Commercial offset printing & graphic ............ (201) 265-7977
Engraved Images, Route 202 & Demun Pl., P.O. Box 966, Far Hills 07931
Owner—Heidi Gammon, 5 emp., Offset & color printing & engraving ............ (908) 234-0323
Excel Color Graphics, Inc., 207 W. Jersey Ave., Woodbury Heights 08097
Pres.—Jean Paul Bonnette, 5 emp., Offset, instant & commercial printing ............ (856) 848-3345
Express Press, 145 North Ave., Belleville 07109
Owner—Robert LaRiccia, 2 emp., Offset printing ............ (973) 751-1287
Express Printing, Inc., 209 W. Saint Georges Ave., Linden 07036
Pres.—Sam Kamdar, 4 emp., Offset printing & typesetting ............ (908) 925-6300
Express Tag & Label Co., 52 N. Main St., Marlboro 07746
Owner—Gerald Tomaselli, 4 emp., Printed labels & tags, postcards & ............ (718) 965-1400
F S T Printing, Inc., 1324 Bound Brook Rd., Middlesex 08846
Pres.—Sal Buonocore, 5 emp., Offset & instant printing & electronic ............ (732) 560-3749
Farmingdale Printing, 70 Main St., Farmingdale 07727
Pres.—Tom Trenholm, 3 emp., Offset & digital printing & electronic ............ (732) 938-2727
Fast Copy Printing Center, 81 Broad St., Keyport 07735
Owner, Fin. & MIS Mgr.—William Sacks, 4 emp., Offset & instant printing & typesetting ............ (732) 739-4646
Fast Print, LLC, 514 Main St., Fort Lee 07024
Pres.—Anthony Clemente, 2 emp., Offset printing & electronic prepress ............ (201) 944-2350
Federal Direct (H Q), 95 Main Ave., Ste. 2, Clifton 07014
CEO—Bernie Steins, 45 emp., Company headquarters; direct marketing ............ (973) 667-9800
FedEx Office & Print Center, 1160 Marlton Pike E., Cherry Hill 08034
Center Mgr.—John Shannon, 10 emp., Instant printing ............ (856) 427-0099
FedEx Office & Print Center, 212 State Route 18, East Brunswick 08816
Br. Mgr.—Andrew Takacs, 12 emp., Instant printing & vinyl banners ............ (732) 249-9222
FedEx Office & Print Center, 450 Tilton Rd., Northfield 08225
Center Mgr.—Brian Sherr, 7 emp., Instant printing ............ (609) 569-8100
FedEx Office & Print Center, 315 N. Route 17, Paramus 07652
Hum. Res. Mgr.—Denise Brathwaite, 7 emp., Commercial, digital, business form ............ (201) 599-0031
FedEx Office & Print Center, Highway 1 & 731 Nassau, Princeton 08540
Br. Mgr.—John Schwartz, 18 emp., Instant printing ............ (609) 799-2863
FedEx Office & Print Center, 55 U.S. Highway 22 E., Springfield 07081
Center Mgr.—Gentry Robinson, 5 emp., Commercial & instant printing ............ (973) 376-3966
FedEx Office Commercial Press, 450 W. 1st Ave., P.O. Box 379, Roselle 07203
GM, Comml. Print—Scott Porter, 80 emp., Commercial printing ............ (908) 245-4400
Fidelis Group, Inc., 223 Gates Rd., Unit A, Little Ferry 07643
Pres.—Lizleen Singh, 80 emp., Commercial offset printing & direct ............ (201) 641-4701
Finas Finishing, Inc., 50 Stacy Haines Rd., Lumberton 08048
Pres.—John Fina, 8 emp., Metal & plastic screen printing, industrial ............ (609) 267-4836
FLM Graphics Corp., 123 Lehigh Dr., Fairfield 07004
CEO—Frank L. Misischia, 65 emp., Commercial printing, large-format digital ............ (973) 575-9450
Formax Printers, 200 Wall St., West Long Branch 07764
Off. Mgr.—Michael Moratis, 3 emp., Instant printing ............ (732) 229-5063
Fort Nassau Graphics, 1757 Imperial Way, West Deptford 08066
Pres.—Paul F. Cipolone, 40 emp., Offset printing ............ (856) 853-2800
Four Star Reproduction, Inc., 52 Paterson Ave., Ste. 2, Newton 07860
Pres.—Charles Cioppa, 35 emp., Commercial offset & digital printing ............ (862) 268-8200
Full House Printing, Inc., 60 Newark St., Hoboken 07030
Pres.—Larry Weiss, 7 emp., Offset printing ............ (201) 798-7073
Gangi Graphics, 1669 Highway 88 W., Brick 08724
Ptnr.—John Gangi, 7 emp., Offset & digital printing & electronic ............ (732) 840-8680
Gateway Press, 984 State Route 36, Atlantic Highlands 07716
Owner—James Meyer, 3 emp., Commercial offset & instant printing ............ (732) 291-1757
Gavin Printing, Inc., 1057 Glen Rd., Fort Lee 07024
Ptnr.—Chang Shin, 2 emp., Offset printing ............ (212) 721-9009
GINN Co., 812 Jersey Ave., Jersey City 07310
Pres.—Robert Glickenhaus, 20 emp., Christmas, wedding, social, business ............ (201) 216-1660
GM Printing, 106 Pleasant Ave., Bergenfield 07621
Pres.—Greg Madison, 7 emp., Instant, commercial & large-format ............ (201) 385-2525
GMPC Printing, 1 Trenton Ave., Clifton 07011
Principal—Joseph Mulligan, 18 emp., Offset printing & typesetting ............ (973) 894-1500
Good Impressions Printing, Inc., 28 Scott St., P.O. Box 409, Riverside 08075
Pres.—Robert Price, 10 emp., Offset & instant printing, typesetting ............ (856) 461-3232
Good Impressions, Inc., 325 W. Washington Ave., Washington 07882
Pres.—Marion Kennedy, 10 emp., Offset printing & typesetting ............ (908) 689-3071
Gracis, Inc., 25 Graphic Pl., Moonachie 07074
Pres.—Robert Powell, 2 emp., Offset printing & typesetting ............ (201) 296-0700
Grandview Printing Co., Inc., 33 W. End Rd., Totowa 07512
Pres.—Lewis DeMarco, 8 emp., Commercial offset printing of greeting ............ (973) 890-0006
Graphic Action, Inc., 296 S. Main St., Phillipsburg 08865
Pres.—Frank Geraghty, 5 emp., Instant printing ............ (908) 213-0055
Graphic Center, The, P.O. Box 595, Mount Freedom 07970
Owner & CFO—Sandra Guido, 12 emp., Commercial & digital printing of booklets ............ (973) 366-6676
Graphic Concepts/Reproduction, Inc., 111 Butternut Dr., Wayne 07470
Pres., GM—Linda Gaba, 4 emp., Offset & digital printing ............ (973) 706-6400
Graphic Imagery, Inc., 122 Mount Bethel Rd., Ste. 2, Warren 07059
Pres.—Linda Maher, 10 emp., Commercial offset, digital & web printing ............ (908) 755-2882
Graphics Depot, Inc., 11 Middlebury Blvd., Ste. 4, Randolph 07869
Pres.—David Bernstein, 16 emp., Digital four & full color offset, instant ............ (973) 927-8200
Graphics Plus Corp., 210 W. Parkway, Ste. 7, Pompton Plains 07444
Pres.—John Prentzel, 5 emp., Offset printing, color separations ............ (973) 835-3744
Graphix One, LLC, 725 Lincoln Blvd., Middlesex 08846
Ptnr.—Jeff Yingling, 3 emp., Commercial, screen & offset printing ............ (732) 560-4700
Great Northern Commercial Service, Inc., 401 Greenwich St., Belvidere 07823
Pres., Off. Mgr.—Anna Quinn, 4 emp., Offset printing ............ (908) 475-8855
Greentree Printing, 9004 Lincoln Dr. W., Ste. G, Marlton 08053
Ptnr. & Pres.—Paul Barbera, 3 emp., Offset, instant & full-color printing ............ (856) 596-2330
H & S Graphics, 196 Garibaldi Ave., Ste. 3, Lodi 07644
Pres., Emeritus—John Santangelo, 8 emp., Color commercial offset printing ............ (973) 779-5880
Happle Printing Partnership, Inc., 81 Cape May Ave., P.O. Box 36, Dorothy 08317
★ Pres.—Ken Happle, 7 emp., Digital & offset printing ............ (609) 476-2929
Hatteras, Inc., 56 Park Rd., Tinton Falls 07724
Pres.—Charles Duerr, 250 emp., Offset & digital printing, fulfillment ............ (732) 223-9888
Hawk Graphics, Inc., 1248 Sussex Tpke., Ste. C-9, Randolph 07869
Pres.—Nick Battaglino, 20 emp., Commercial offset, digital color & ............ (973) 895-5569
Hawk Technologies, Inc., 3710 U.S. Highway 9 S., P.O. Box 6685, Freehold 07728
★ Pres.—Alex Sokolovski, 10 emp., Computer systems integration, including ............ (732) 577-8581
Hibbert Group, 400 Pennington Ave., Trenton 08638
CEO—Tim Moonan, 100 emp., Offset, market & letterpress printing ............ (609) 394-7500
Hillman Graphic Products, P.O. Box 5233, Somerset 08875
Owner—Marty Hillman, 4 emp., Commercial offset & digital printing ............ (201) 487-6900
Holzer & Assocs., LLC, Philip, 350 Michelle Pl., Carlstadt 07072
Owner & Chrm.—Stuart Holzer, 50 emp., Offset printing ............ (212) 691-9500
Howe's Standard Publishing Co., Inc., 1980 S. West Blvd., Vineland 08360
Pres.—Barry Opromollo, 30 emp., Commercial printing ............ (856) 691-2000
Hummel Distributing Corp., 850 Springfield Rd., P.O. Box 3199, Union 07083
Co-Pres., Hum. Res. Mgr.—John Hummel, 35 emp., Offset printing & typesetting ............ (908) 688-5300
Hygrade Business Group, Inc., 232 Entin Rd., P.O. Box 1099, Clifton 07014
Pres., CEO—Victor Albetta, 40 emp., Offset, digital & color printing of ............ (973) 249-6700
Image Makers Printing, Copy & Sign Center, 1581 State Route 23, Wayne 07470
Pres.—Gino Nuzzo, 5 emp., High-speed color printing, blueprinting ............ (973) 633-1771
Impact Printing, 762 Green St., Iselin 08830
Owner—Eugene Lucas II, 2 emp., Offset printing & typesetting ............ (732) 636-8893
Impressions Unlimited Printing Co., LLC, 638 Delsea Dr., P.O. Box 386, Sewell 08080
Owner—Joe Layton, 2 emp., Commercial offset printing, including ............ (856) 256-0200
Impressive Printing, Inc., 313 10th St., Carlstadt 07072
Pres.—Robert Egan, 2 emp., Commercial, full-color & large-format ............ (201) 933-1650
Ink Well Printers Inc., 38 S. 21st St., Kenilworth 07033
Pres.—Elizabeth Ensslin, 4 emp., Offset printing & typesetting ............ (908) 272-8090
Inkwell Corp., 1414 Elmira St., Cape May 08204
Pres.—Heide Cummings, 3 emp., Offset printing & textile screen printing ............ (609) 884-0350
Instant Image Printing, 649 Bergen Blvd., Ridgefield 07657
Owner—Rich LeBrund, 1 emp., Offset printing ............ (201) 945-0020
Instant Printing, 355 Main St., Orange 07050
Owner—Bharati Tolia, 4 emp., Instant printing of office supplies ............ (973) 675-6266
Instant Printing, Inc., 241 E. Blackwell St., Dover 07801
Pres.—Ann Medore, 4 emp., Commercial, offset & digital printing ............ (973) 366-6855
J & J Printing Co., 1023 Broadway, Bayonne 07002
Owner—Fran Tagliareni, 6 emp., Offset printing & typesetting ............ (201) 858-8895
J M J Printing & Graphics, Inc., 1403 State Route 23, Ste. 8, Butler 07405
Pres.—Debby Greenberg, 20 emp., Printing & contract packaging ............ (973) 838-3400
Jamesburg Press Madison Printing, Inc., 9 E. Railroad Ave., Jamesburg 08831
Pres.—Fred Voza, 2 emp., Offset printing & typesetting ............ (732) 521-0262
JB Offset Printing Corp., 475 Walnut St., Norwood 07648
Pres.—Andrea Mantineo, 9 emp., Offset newspaper printing ............ (201) 664-4400
Jimcam Publishing, Inc., 19 W. Pleasant Ave., Maywood 07607
Co-Publisher—Jim Hornes, 2 emp., Newspaper publishing & invitation printing ............ (201) 843-5700
Johnson Copy Center, Inc., Robert, 1438 Queen Anne Rd., Teaneck 07666
Owner—Robert Johnson, 1 emp., Instant & offset printing ............ (201) 833-8997
Jon-Da Printing Co., 234 16th St., 8th Fl., Jersey City 07310
GM—Melody Serra, 14 emp., Offset printing ............ (201) 653-6200
Kay Printing Co., 220 Entin Rd., Clifton 07014
Ptnr. & Pres.—Richard Kirschenbaum, 60 emp., Company headquarters & commercial printing (973) 330-3000
Kern Printers & Stationers, 86 Lackawanna Ave., Unit 105, Woodland Park 07424
Pres.—Thomas Mandel, 5 emp., Offset & digital printing & graphic ............ (201) 226-0270
Keskes Printing Co., 5 W. Taunton Ave., Berlin 08009
Owner—Jean Keskes, 5 emp., Offset, digital & letterpress printing ............ (856) 767-4733
Keystone Printing, Inc., 21-C E. Madison Ave., Dumont 07628
Pres.—Janice Worner, 4 emp., Digital offset printing, typesetting ............ (201) 387-7252
Kiva Printing & Graphics, 50 Cutler Ave., Westville 08093
Pres., GM—Tyler Wilson, 12 emp., Offset & commercial printing ............ (877) 777-5482
L P B Graphics, Inc., 512-514 Route 27, Iselin 08830
Pres.—Lisa Berg, 8 emp., Commercial offset printing & typesetting ............ (732) 283-4333
Lamb Printing, Inc., 700 Grand Ave., Hackettstown 07840
Pres.—Michael Lamb, 6 emp., Offset printing ............ (908) 852-5354
Langendorff Corp., 633 Grove St., Jersey City 07310
Pres.—Frank Langendorff, 6 emp., Commercial offset printing ............ (201) 659-6300
LAS Printing, 1 Trenton Ave., Clifton 07011
Pres.—Joe Conti, 10 emp., Commercial printing, electronic prepress ............ (201) 991-5362
Laser Dim Graphics & Printing, 2 Parkwood Ln., Colts Neck 07722
Pres.—James Asghar, 10 emp., Digital & offset printing ............ (732) 821-9000
Laureate Press, Inc., 1336 W. Central Ave., P.O. Box 343, Egg Harbor City 08215
Pres.—Janet Rotellini, 6 emp., Offset printing & typesetting ............ (609) 965-0447
Lavallette Printing, 301 Grand Central, Lavallette 08735
Owner—Bruno Hornung, 1 emp., Instant printing ............ (732) 793-8303
LCI Graphics, Inc., 2400 Main Street Ext., Ste. 8, Sayreville 08872
Pres.—Daniel Seratelli, 8 emp., Commercial offset, web-to-print, digital ............ (973) 893-2913
Leader Printers, 5914 New Jersey Ave., Wildwood Crest 08260
Pres.—Dennis Hall, 6 emp., Offset printing & typesetting ............ (609) 729-0161
Liberty Printing, Inc., 1111 Chestnut Ave., Trenton 08611
Pres.—George Demeter, 3 emp., Offset & instant printing & typesetting ............ (609) 396-5995
Linder & Co., Inc., 1183 W. Side Ave., Jersey City 07306
Pres.—George R. Linder, 18 emp., Commercial offset, conventional & digital ............ (201) 386-8788
Lont & OverKamp, 175 U.S. Highway 46, Fairfield 07004
CEO—Ken Lont, 50 emp., Offset, digital & direct mail printing ............ (973) 942-2243
MacFerren's Printing & Co., 3 Democrat Rd., Gibbsboro 08026
Owner—Mike Macferren, 3 emp., Lithographic & commercial printing ............ (856) 435-7066
Mackey's Print Xpress, 1107 7th Ave., Neptune 07753
Owner & Pres.—Ron Mackey, 3 emp., Single, multicolor offset & digital ............ (732) 775-1730

S.I.C.

★ **Indicates new listing this edition.**

F40 © Copyright 2015 Manufacturers' News, Inc. S.I.C. SECTION

MacLearie Printing, LLC, 917 18th Ave., Belmar 07719
Pres.—James MacLearie, 6 emp., *Offset printing & typesetting* ........ (732) 681-2772
Magic Printing Corp., 386 Avenel St., Avenel 07001
Pres.—Steven Glassman, 20 emp., *Business card & stationery printing* ........ (732) 726-0620
Major Printing Co., Inc., 934 Savitt Pl., P.O. Box 1356, Union 07083
Owner & Pres.—Joseph Stampone, 2 emp., *Offset printing & typesetting* ........ (908) 686-7296
Manifold Printers, Inc., 189 Berdan Ave., Ste. 456, Wayne 07470
Pres.—Oscar Cone, 20 emp., *Lithographic printing* ........ (973) 345-5900
Mariano Press Co., 14 Veronica Ave., Somerset 08873
Ptnr.—Joseph Mariano, 15 emp., *Offset & letterpress printing* ........ (732) 247-6828
Mark Lithography, Inc., 220 Entin Rd., Clifton 07014
Pres.—Charles Tumminello, 35 emp., *Offset printing & color separations* ........ (973) 538-5557
Market Street Printing, Inc., 122 N. 6th St., Camden 08102
Pres.—Mookie Kamerkar, 3 emp., *Commercial offset printing & typesetting* ........ (856) 964-5995
Marmus, Inc., 51 E. Front St., Keyport 07735
Pres.—Terry Musson, 1 emp., *Textile screen, commercial, digital* ........ (732) 264-3681
Master Printing Co., P.O. Box 9609, Elizabeth 07202
Pres.—Bill DePaolo, 3 emp., *Offset printing, graphics & copywriting* ........ (908) 351-1568
Master Printing, Inc., 30 Pedricktown Woodstown Rd., P.O. Box 1, Pedricktown 08067
★ Owner—Lou Master, 4 emp., *Commercial offset printing* ........ (856) 299-8318
Mastergraphx, Inc., 45 Stouts Ln., Ste. 14, P.O. Box 567, Monmouth Junction 08852
Pres.—Robert Copeland, 10 emp., *Offset printing & typesetting* ........ (732) 329-0088
McGinnis Printing, 20 Monmouth St., Red Bank 07701
Owner—Dennis McGinnis, 3 emp., *Offset & instant printing & typesetting* ........ (732) 758-0060
Mediagraphics, Inc., 25 Somerset Pl., Clifton 07012
Pres.—Marge Offutt, 12 emp., *Large-format color printing of smart* ........ (973) 777-2202
Menco Business Products, 178 Route 206 S., Hillsborough 08844
Pres.—Ozzie Mendez, 15 emp., *Offset printing, typesetting & color* ........ (908) 281-0911
Merchant Street Printer, LLC, 107 E. Atlantic Ave., Audubon 08106
Owner—Charlotte Skeggs, 4 emp., *Offset printing & advertising specialties* ........ (856) 547-1991
Mercury Printing, Inc., 14 Veronica Ave., Somerset 08873
Opers. Mgr.—Jan T. Vreeland, 9 emp., *Clinical drug study labels & case report* ........ (732) 247-6828
Metro Tag & Label, Inc., 25 E. Spring Valley Ave., Ste. 200, Maywood 07607
Pres.—Phil Glassman, 3 emp., *Commercial offset & digital printing* ........ (201) 845-4747
Minuteman Press, 35 W. White Horse Pike, Berlin 08009
Pres., Sales Mgr.—Kevin J. Humphrey, 4 emp., *Commercial & digital instant & full-color* ........ (856) 753-0055
Minuteman Press, 1 Trenton Ave., Clifton 07011
Principal—Joseph Mulligan, 18 emp., *Offset & digital printing, promotional* ........ (973) 894-1500
Minuteman Press, 349 U.S. Highway 9, Ste. 7, Englishtown 07726
Pres.—Joe Lorenz, 6 emp., *Instant printing & mailing & bindery* ........ (732) 536-8788
Minuteman Press, 35 Scotch Rd., Ewing 08628
Pres.—Ted Blumenthal, 4 emp., *Digital, offset, full color & instant* ........ (609) 883-0799
Minuteman Press, 23-51 Fair Lawn Ave., Fair Lawn 07410
Pres., CEO—Mitch Palin, 4 emp., *Full-color & instant printing & graphic* ........ (201) 791-0550
Minuteman Press, 1299 Route 38, Ste. 2, Hainesport 08036
Pres. & Cust. Serv. Rep.—Frank Bittner, 7 emp., *Offset printing & graphic design* ........ (609) 261-1024
Minuteman Press, 19 Sheridan Ave., Ho-Ho-Kus 07423
Member—Suzanne Seise, 3 emp., *Digital, offset & high-speed printing* ........ (201) 444-0236
Minuteman Press, 1818 Highway 35, Wall 07719
Pres.—Chris Maguire, 5 emp., *Offset printing* ........ (732) 449-1760
Minuteman Press Corp., 55 Commerce St., Newark 07102
Pres.—Holly Kaplansky, 4 emp., *Commercial offset & instant printing* ........ (973) 624-6907
Minuteman Press International, Inc., 1247 Patterson Plank Rd., Secaucus 07094
Co-Pres.—Tom Goldgraber, 5 emp., *Offset printing & computerized typesetting* ........ (201) 866-0186
Minuteman Press Of Dover, 25 Pine St., Ste. 10, Rockaway 07866
Pres., R & D Mgr.—Andy Krauser, 2 emp., *Offset & digital & color instant printing* ........ (973) 625-5800
Minuteman Press Of North Arlington, 75 Ridge Rd., North Arlington 07031
V.-P.—Amir Djabini, 5 emp., *Instant printing, electronic prepress* ........ (201) 991-1030
Minuteman Press, Inc., 216 Boulevard, Hasbrouck Heights 07604
Manager—Tom Colletti, 4 emp., *Offset printing & typesetting* ........ (201) 288-7787
Minuteman Press, Inc./Windsor Graphics, 2100 Nottingham Way, Hamilton 08619
Owner—Anthony Loffredo, 4 emp., *Offset, screen & digital color printing* ........ (609) 586-3838
Mon Far Press Printing, 13 Franklin Pl., Rutherford 07070
Owner & Pres.—Ging Wong, 1 emp., *Offset & letterpress printing* ........ (212) 431-6245
More Copy Printing Service, 358 State Route 17, Saddle River 07458
Owner—Felix Gomez, 1 emp., *Instant printing* ........ (201) 327-1106
Morgan Printing Service, Inc., 333 S. Pine Ave., South Amboy 08879
CEO & GM—Bob Dein, 10 emp., *Color offset, digital, instant & wide* ........ (732) 721-2959
Morris County Duplicating Corp., 1 Lafayette Ave., Morristown 07960
Pres.—Ernie D'Angelo, 30 emp., *Full-service document imaging, scanning* ........ (973) 993-8484
Morris Forms Corp., 5 Saddle Rd., Cedar Knolls 07927
Pres.—Carl Badenhausen, 5 emp., *Color, offset & digital printing of* ........ (973) 829-1200
Morris Graphics, Inc., 660 N. Broad St., Woodbury 08096
Pres.—Jeff Morris, 5 emp., *Short-run digital & long run offset* ........ (856) 845-4980
Mount Freedom Printing, P.O. Box 285, Mount Freedom 07970
Graphic Design Mgr.—Barbara Connolly, 3 emp., *Color offset printing, typesetting* ........ (908) 362-9299
Mr. B Offset Printing, Inc., 1850 Elizabeth Ave., Ste. B, Rahway 07065
Pres.—Thomas Bayone, 2 emp., *Offset & commercial printing* ........ (732) 396-3990
MSP Digital Marketing, 200 Forge Way, Rockaway 07866
COO—Todd Logan, 14 emp., *Commercial & digital printing & large-format* ........ (973) 298-8800
My Way Prints, Inc., 1376 Route 23, Butler 07405
Pres.—Myron Friedman, 3 emp., *Offset printing & typesetting* ........ (973) 492-1212
National Reprographics, Inc., 3175 Princeton Pike, Lawrenceville 08648
GM—Kathy Dotta, 2 emp., *Instant printing & blueprinting* ........ (609) 896-4100
Na-Vet Printing Co., 506 Elizabeth Ave., Elizabeth 07206
Pres.—Larry Franchini, 4 emp., *Commercial, digital & color printing* ........ (908) 353-4441
NEMA Associates, Inc., 57 Bruen St., Newark 07105
Pres., CEO—Juan Carlos Lopez, 14 emp., *Full-service digital, large-format,* ........ (973) 274-0052
Neo Printing Co., Inc., 24 E. Wesley St., South Hackensack 07606
Pres.—Michael Destefan, 10 emp., *Offset printing* ........ (201) 489-5050
New Jersey Reprographics, Inc., 110 Center St., Garwood 07027
Pres., CFO—Joseph Bizzarro, 4 emp., *Offset & digital color printing of* ........ (908) 789-1616
New Standard Printing Corp., 118 Lincoln Ave., Dover 07801
Pres.—Michael Wetzel, 5 emp., *Offset printing* ........ (973) 366-0006
New York Sample Card Co., Inc., 812 Jersey Ave., 3rd Fl., Jersey City 07310
Pres., MIS Mgr.—Kenneth Ehrlich, 25 emp., *Sample cards & books, including color* ........ (201) 526-9040
Nexgen Press Corp., 859 Bridgeboro St., Riverside 08075
★ Pres.—Judy Sodomin, 1 emp., *Offset & digital printing* ........ (609) 528-0370
Nitka Graphics, Inc., 355 E. 54th St., Elmwood Park 07407
Pres.—Hayim Nitka, 12 emp., *Annual report, newsletter, brochure* ........ (201) 797-3000
Novel Lithographers, Inc., 1 Kero Rd., Carlstadt 07072
Pres.—Martin Zarett, 10 emp., *Lithographic printing* ........ (201) 372-3900
Nu-Graphics Ii, Inc., 84 Stonybrook Rd., P.O. Box 65, Towaco 07082
Pres.—Jerome Matisak, 2 emp., *Graphic art prepress & digital printing* ........ (973) 299-0066
Office Prints, The, 30 Journal Sq., Jersey City 07306
Art Dir.—Ashley Centeno, 9 emp., *Instant printing & graphic design services* ........ (201) 222-5555
Old Hights Print Shop, Inc., 133 S. Main St., Hightstown 08520
Pres.—Cathy M. Simmons, 3 emp., *Commercial, digital & screen printing* ........ (609) 443-4700
Oliveri Printing Corporation, Carl, 316 Main St., Ste. 1, East Rutherford 07073
Owner & Pres.—Carl Oliveri, 10 emp., *Commercial offset & digital printing* ........ (201) 438-0888
Omega Graphics, 661 Broad St., Ste. 3, Shrewsbury 07702
Owner & Pres.—Douglas Godfrey, 4 emp., *Instant printing & digital layout &* ........ (732) 530-4441
One Source Solutions, 220 Encin Rd., Clifton 07014
Pres.—Roy Winters, 12 emp., *Offset printing & computerized typesetting* ........ (973) 242-4040
O'Sullivan Communications, 1 Fairfield Crescent, West Caldwell 07006
Dir., Bus. Dev.—Dawn Bruno, 65 emp., *Commercial lithographic printing &* ........ (973) 227-5112
P B A Printing, 170 Malvern St., Newark 07105
Owner—Joe Figueiredo, 4 emp., *Offset printing & typesetting* ........ (973) 817-9712
P I P Printing, 2960 Yorktowne Blvd., Brick 08723
Owner—Tim Fazio, 2 emp., *Offset printing* ........ (732) 255-1980
P I P Printing Of Livingston, 465 W. Mount Pleasant Ave., Livingston 07039
Pres.—Georgia Solofoff, 9 emp., *Commercial & instant printing* ........ (973) 533-9330
Paci Press, Inc., 25 First St., Rear Bldg., Lodi 07644
Pres.—William Lorusso, 1 emp., *Offset & letterpress printing* ........ (973) 478-6550
Pages Printing & Graphics, 300 N. Route 17, Paramus 07652
Owner—Ron Sallemi, 7 emp., *Full-service commercial, offset, digital* ........ (201) 261-3883
Pantone LLC, 590 Commerce Blvd., Carlstadt 07072
Sr. V.-P., GM—Ron Potesky, 100 emp., *Standardized color matching systems* ........ (201) 935-5500
Paper Mart, Inc., 151 Ridgedale Ave., East Hanover 07936
IT & Off. Mgr.—Joseph Kramer, 100 emp., *Offset printing* ........ (973) 884-2505
PaperClip Communications, Inc., 125 Paterson Ave., Little Falls 07424
Pres.—Andy McLaughlin, 20 emp., *Specialty printing & online information* ........ (973) 256-1333
Papson Printing Corp., 115 Hudson St., Hackensack 07601
Pres., Off. Mgr.—Chris Papson, 3 emp., *Offset printing & typesetting* ........ (201) 342-2860
Par Code Symbology, Inc., 119 Harrison Ave., P.O. Box 87, Roseland 07068
Pres.—David Aranowitz, 20 emp., *Bar code labels for warehouse location* ........ (973) 618-0550
Park Avenue Printing, LLC, 2001 S. Broad St., Trenton 08610
Pres.—Steven Madola, 6 emp., *Offset printing & typesetting* ........ (609) 989-8022
Parsells Printing, Inc., 280 Main Ave., Passaic 07055
Pres.—James Parsells, 5 emp., *Offset printing & binding* ........ (973) 473-2700
Paul-Mark Printing, 37 Stokes St., Freehold 07728
Pres.—Mark Lamhut, 5 emp., *Offset & digital printing, letterpress* ........ (732) 462-9110
PDEC, Inc., 2101 Atlantic Ave., Manasquan 08736
Pres.—Joseph Sodano, 15 emp., *Offset printing* ........ (732) 223-5995
Peacock Printing Products, Inc., 48 Woodbine St., Bergenfield 07621
Pres., CEO—Craig Langslet, 20 emp., *Commercial, instant, digital, offset* ........ (201) 385-5585
Pedeco Printing, Inc., 12 Summers Dr., Jackson 08527
Pres.—Tom Degliomini, 12 emp., *Offset & lithographic printing* ........ (732) 363-0510
Pennington Printers, Inc., 21 Burd St., Pennington 08534
Pres.—Maryann Saums, 2 emp., *Offset printing & graphic design* ........ (609) 737-0650
Pequod Communications, Inc., 743 Alexander Rd., Ste. 15, Princeton 08540
Pres.—Jim Robertson, 20 emp., *Instant printing* ........ (609) 951-0300
Perma Graphics, Inc., 25 Graphic Pl., Moonachie 07074
Pres.—Rita Caloni, 15 emp., *Offset printing* ........ (201) 814-1200
Pictorial Offset Corporation, 111 Amor Ave., Carlstadt 07072
Chairperson—Meryle Samuels, 300 emp., *Sheet-fed & web printing, including* ........ (201) 935-7100
Pinnacle Press, Inc., 41 Prospect St., Midland Park 07432
Owner—Howard Siegel, 7 emp., *Offset printing* ........ (201) 652-0500
Pirolli Printing Co., Inc., 860 W. Browning Rd., Bellmawr 08031
Pres.—Kathleen A. Pirolli, 17 emp., *Offset printing, including forms, brochures* ........ (856) 933-1285
Poggi Press, The, 1501 Adams St., P.O. Box M-668, Hoboken 07030
Pres.—Charles Poggi, 21 emp., *Commercial, offset & digital printing* ........ (201) 659-0837
Precise Printing, 748 Lincoln Blvd., Middlesex 08846
Pres.—Frank Tredici, 3 emp., *Offset printing* ........ (732) 271-8626
Precision Printing Group, LLC, 117 Jackson Rd., Berlin 08009
Pres.—Lori Colucci, 40 emp., *Prepress & offset digital printing* ........ (856) 753-7903
Premier Graphics, Inc., 500 Central Ave., Atlantic Highlands 07716
Pres.—Toni Madalone, 20 emp., *Offset printing & typesetting* ........ (732) 872-9933
Press Room, Inc., The, 100 Youngs Rd., Ste. 2, Mercerville 08619
Pres., Hum. Res. Mgr.—Ted Altomari, 8 emp., *Commercial offset, digital & instant* ........ (609) 689-3817
Presto Print & Copy, 79 S. Main St., Ste. 3, Lodi 07644
Pres.—George Nigito, 3 emp., *Offset printing* ........ (973) 777-8377
Primary Colors Graphics, 629 Grove St., 7th Fl., Jersey City 07310
Pres.—Cindy Wong, 20 emp., *Offset printing* ........ (201) 526-9300
Princeton Printer, 150 Nassau St., Princeton 08542
CEO—Bill Howard, 6 emp., *Digital, instant & large-format color* ........ (609) 924-4630
Princetonian Graphics, Inc., 45 Stouts Ln., Ste. 4, Monmouth Junction 08852
Pres.—Joseph Menig, 14 emp., *Offset & digital printing & graphic* ........ (732) 329-8282
Print Art, Inc., 6726 Delilah Rd., Egg Harbor Township 08234
Pres.—Carl Blase, 50 emp., *Custom commercial, grand format & digital* ........ (609) 645-1940
Print Group, Inc., The, 24 E. Wesley St., South Hackensack 07606
Ptnr.—Martin Bender, 15 emp., *Digital & offset commercial printing* ........ (201) 487-4400
Print Solutions, 320 S. Dean St., Englewood 07631
Pres.—Paul Vartanian, 6 emp., *Offset printing* ........ (201) 567-9622
Printers Place North, LLC, 2 Kiel Ave., Ste. 154, Kinnelon 07405
Pres.—Mary Murphy, 2 emp., *Offset printing* ........ (973) 838-3741
Printing Center, Inc., The, 1 White Lake Rd., Sparta 07871
Pres., CEO—Vincent Perrella, Jr., 25 emp., *Offset printing & typesetting* ........ (973) 383-6362
Printing Craftsman, Inc., 130 Bergen Blvd., Fairview 07022
Pres.—Kenneth Stueben, 10 emp., *Commercial, offset, digital, & lithographic* ........ (201) 943-0276
Printing Images, 546 Ringwood Ave., Wanaque 07465
Owner—Peter Kramer, 3 emp., *Instant & offset printing* ........ (973) 839-9500
Printing Plus Of South Jersey, 406 N. Route 73, West Berlin 08091
Ptnr.—Robert Behnke, 7 emp., *Instant, digital & small-format & large-forma* ........ (856) 767-3232
Printing Shop Copy Center, The, 338 State St., Perth Amboy 08861
Owner—Lucy Arevelo, 3 emp., *Commercial & digital printing & vinyl* ........ (732) 826-3575
Printing Techniques, Inc., 48 Franklin Ave., Nutley 07110
Pres.—Joseph Vitiello, Jr., 11 emp., *Commercial sheetfed, offset & digital* ........ (973) 667-2606
Printing To Go, 578 Park Ave., Freehold 07728
Owner—Cindy Ziegler, 5 emp., *Printing, including instant & large-format* ........ (732) 462-0333
Printmasters, 1108 Goffle Rd., Hawthorne 07506
Pres.—Paula Cornett, 4 emp., *Business printing, graphics & design* ........ (973) 427-6598
Professional Printing Services, 116 N. Haddon Ave., Haddonfield 08033
Owner & Pres.—Joe McElroy, 3 emp., *Instant printing* ........ (856) 429-8644

© Copyright 2015 Manufacturers' News, Inc.


Pronto Print, 1329 Hurffville Rd., Deptford 08096
Owner—Gene Duffy, 3 emp., *Offset printing* .......... (856) 232-7200
Purcell Printing Co., Robert, 244 Kamena St., Fairview 07022
Pres.—Robert Purcell, Sr., 3 emp., *Offset & commercial printing* .......... (201) 941-0375
QP2000, LLC, 827 W. Park Ave., Ocean 07712
GM—John Thompson, 5 emp., *Offset & instant printing, digital* .......... (732) 531-8860
Quality Repro Centers, Inc., 296 Route 46 E., P.O. Box 111, Elmwood Park 07407
Pres.—Joe DiGiaimo, 6 emp., *Commercial & digital color printing* .......... (201) 794-3905
Quickly Printing, Inc., 1965 Morris Ave., Union 07083
Pres.—Larry Kovacs, 6 emp., *Instant printing, including business* .......... (908) 687-6000
Quikie Print & Copy Shop, 827 W. Park, Ocean 07712
Manager—Darleen Calgon, 4 emp., *Instant printing* .......... (732) 531-8860
Quikie Print & Copy Shops, 703 Broad St., Shrewsbury 07702
Pres.—Francine Goldstein, 5 emp., *Company headquarters & digital & instant* .......... (732) 933-1010
R & R Printing & Copy Center, 1075 Easton Ave., Somerset 08873
Owner—Bob Sepe, 5 emp., *Instant & offset printing* .......... (732) 249-9450
R & R Printing Co., 107 S. Stevens Ave., P.O. Box 3204, South Amboy 08879
Owner—Kenneth Sumski, 1 emp., *Offset printing, typesetting & die* .......... (732) 727-6036
R J Graphics, Inc., 206 Crown Point Rd., P.O. Box 293, West Deptford 08086
Pres.—Rita L. Iannelli, 30 emp., *Offset printing* .......... (856) 848-1986
Ramsey Print Corp., 1000 Wall St. W., Ste. 2, Lyndhurst 07071
CFO—Jeffrey Beecher, 6 emp., *Offset printing & computerized typesetting* .......... (201) 460-1008
Rapid Print & Copy Service, 78 Summerhill Rd., East Brunswick 08816
Pres.—Roly Kapoano, 2 emp., *Offset printing & typesetting* .......... (732) 238-9056
Ray's Reproductions, Inc., 39 Bland St., Emerson 07630
Pres.—Ray Stuart, 5 emp., *Digital, offset, large-format & instant* .......... (201) 666-5650
Razor Printing, 78 Summerhill Rd., East Brunswick 08816
Owner—Michael Sciara, 2 emp., *Instant printing* .......... (732) 238-7520
Regal Printers, Inc., 707-3 Old Shore Rd., Forked River 08731
Pres.—Tom Trenholm, 4 emp., *Lithographic printing* .......... (609) 693-3533
Register Lithographers, Ltd., 1155 Bloomfield Ave., Clifton 07012
Pres.—Joe Fishman, 50 emp., *Commercial & lithographic printing* .......... (973) 916-2804
Reliable Envelope & Graphics, Inc., 85 Main Ave., Elmwood Park 07407
Chrm.—Gene Murphy, 25 emp., *Custom & standard envelopes, including* .......... (201) 794-7756
Renew Graphics, 16 W. Park Ave., Park Ridge 07656
Owner—Mike Collins, 2 emp., *Lithographic & commercial printing* .......... (201) 802-1900
Restaurant Graphics, Inc., 67 Newark Way, Maplewood 07040
Pres.—Tom Stravakis, 7 emp., *Lithographic & commercial printing* .......... (973) 763-4036
Rethink Color, a division of NRI, 3175 Princeton Pike, Lawrenceville 08648
Reg. V-P.—Frank Plum, 20 emp., *Blueprinting & digital, color, instant* .......... (609) 896-4100
RFM Printing, Inc., 1715 Highway 34, P.O. Box 1430, Wall 07719
Pres.—Robert McKenna, 25 emp., *Coldset web offset printing* .......... (732) 938-4400
Riverside Prints LLC, 11 Lawrence Cir., Middletown 07748
Pres., CEO—Howard Kirschner, 2 emp., *Large-format digital & offset printing* .......... (732) 671-8222
Roan Printing, Inc., 4 E. Main St., Somerville 08876
Pres.—Sherman Feuer, 6 emp., *Commercial offset printing* .......... (908) 526-5990
Rogers Printing Center, 11 Lexington Ave., Trenton 08618
Pres.—Roger G. Chupik, 1 emp., *Digital, offset & letterpress printing* .......... (609) 883-3238
Royal Printing Service, 441 51st St., West New York 07093
Pres.—Ralph Passante, Sr., 40 emp., *Offset printing* .......... (201) 863-3131
Royer Graphics, Inc., 101 Lincoln Dr., Laurel Springs 08021
Pres.—Tony Cannuli, 8 emp., *Offset, digital & web printing & graphic* .......... (856) 344-7935
Royer Group, Inc., 7120 Airport Hwy., Pennsauken 08109
Pres.—Amanda Schwartz, 20 emp., *Offset & digital printing* .......... (856) 665-6400
Rush Graphics, Inc., 1122 Goffle Rd., Hawthorne 07506
Pres.—Zora Agheli, 10 emp., *Electronic prepress & commercial printing* .......... (973) 427-9393
Safeguard, 1253 Springfield Ave., Ste. 258, New Providence 07974
Pres.—Anthony 'Tony' De Paola, 1 emp., *Offset printing, vinyl signs & advertising* .......... (973) 887-9500
Sanakirk, Inc., 1400 Berlin Rd., Ste. 123, Cherry Hill 08003
CEO—Kirk R. Runton, 4 emp., *Commercial, digital, small-format &* .......... (856) 429-0715
Sandoval Graphics & Printing, 9 Minnetonka Rd., Somerdale 08083
Mng. Ptnr.—Tony Sandoval, 6 emp., *Commercial, offset & digital printing* .......... (856) 435-7320
School Publications Co., Inc., 1520 Washington Ave., P.O. Box 1067, Neptune 07753
Pres.—Albert G. Kirms, 20 emp., *School newspaper, yearbook & literary* .......... (732) 988-1100
Schuyler Printing Co., Inc., 71 Kearny Ave., Kearny 07032
Pres.—Edward A. Conlon, 4 emp., *Offset printing & typesetting* .......... (201) 997-8083
Scott Graphics Printing, Inc., 690-D River Rd., New Milford 07646
Pres.—Scott McNiff, 15 emp., *Commercial, offset, textile screen* .......... (201) 262-0473
Seibel Group, Inc., The, 741 Alexander Rd., Princeton 08540
Pres.—Kenneth Seibel, 11 emp., *Commercial & digital printing* .......... (609) 799-3279
Serafino Printing Co., Inc., 516 Bloomfield Ave., Verona 07044
Pres.—Cathy Horling, 3 emp., *Offset & letterpress printing* .......... (973) 857-3450
Sheridan Communication, Inc., 1425 3rd Ave., Alpha 08865
CEO—James Sheridan, 50 emp., *Offset & 4-color printing & electonic* .......... (908) 454-0700
Showcase Graphics, LLC, 33 E. Main St., Ste. 4, Moorestown 08057
Owner—Debra Marsdale, 3 emp., *Commercial & digital printing of packaging* .......... (856) 722-5400
Signmasters, Inc., 217 Brook Ave., 2nd Fl., Front, Passaic 07055
Pres.—Howard Muser, 75 emp., *Offset printing & glass & plastic screen* .......... (973) 614-8300
Sir Speedy Printing, 22 W. Landis Ave., Ste. Q, Vineland 08360
GM & Cust. Serv. Mgr.—Allison Trovarelli, 9 emp., *Instant, commercial, high-speed color* .......... (856) 691-0741
Sir Speedy Printing And Marketing Services, 5505 Route 130 N., Pennsauken 08110
Pres.—Francis V. Gavin, Jr., 5 emp., *Digital color & offset printing, signs* .......... (856) 488-1480
Sir Speedy Printing and Marketing Services, 1032 Stelton Rd., Piscataway 08854
Pres., Fin. & GM—Mark Yanofsky, 4 emp., *High-speed full-color digital & offset* .......... (732) 981-9011
Sir Speedy Printing Center, 28 Campus Dr., Edison 08837
Owner & Pres.—Robert Chido, 7 emp., *Offset & digital printing & typesetting* .......... (732) 225-2272
Sir Speedy Printing Center, 122 Ridge Rd., Lyndhurst 07071
Dir.—Tom Penisch, 5 emp., *Full-color digital, traditional offset* .......... (201) 896-2727
Sir Speedy Printing Center, 300 S. Lenola Rd., Ste. 22, Maple Shade 08052
Pres.—Dennis Marks, 8 emp., *Offset, single, multicolor & color* .......... (856) 866-0588
Sir Speedy Printing Of East Hanover, 50 Route 10 W., East Hanover 07936
Owner—Perdipe Dave, 10 emp., *Offset printing & typesetting* .......... (973) 884-0005
Skyline Graphics Design, 11 Skyline Lake Dr., Ringwood 07456
Pres.—Scott White, 4 emp., *Offset, digital & digital full-color* .......... (973) 839-3329
Small Business Service Center, 122 E. Kings Hwy., Ste. 504, Maple Shade 08052
CEO—Sandy Testa, 20 emp., *Laser, inkjet, digital, lettershop* .......... (856) 234-8059
Spruce Run Printing, 2005 Route 31, Clinton 08809
Ptnr.—Tom Kowal, 3 emp., *Offset printing & binding of banners* .......... (908) 638-6464
Square One, Inc., 111 Gaither Dr., Ste. 104, Mount Laurel 08054
Pres.—Colin Townsend, 45 emp., *Commercial, offset & digital printing* .......... (856) 234-6999
Squiggly Productions, LLC, 164 Main St., Butler 07405
Owner—Guy Scognamiglio, 2 emp., *Offset & full-color digital printing* .......... (973) 838-7475
Standard Printing & Mail Service, 30-A Plymouth St., P.O. Box 11021, Fairfield 07004
Pres., GM—Kevin Walsh, 12 emp., *Offset & direct mail printing, electronic* .......... (973) 790-3333
Studio 042, 423 Bloomfield Ave., Montclair 07042
CEO—Scott F. Kennedy, 10 emp., *Commercial & instant printing* .......... (973) 509-7591
Stuyvesant Press, Inc., 119 Coit St., Irvington 07111
Pres., CEO—Michael Roesch, 10 emp., *Offset, commercial, digital, color* .......... (973) 399-3880
Sunset Printing And Engraving, 10 Kice Ave., Wharton 07885
Pres.—Mitchel Wainer, 42 emp., *Commercial offset & on demand printing* .......... (973) 537-9600
Superior Trademark, Inc., 45 Zazzetti St., P.O. Box 35, Waldwick 07463
Pres.—Gordon McIntire, 10 emp., *Heat transfer labels, identification* .......... (201) 652-1900
Swift Print Solutions, LLC, 405 Front St., Belvidere 07823
Owner—Linda Swift, 4 emp., *Commercial, screen & instant printing* .......... (908) 475-1374
T C Graphics, Inc., 109 South Ave. W., Cranford 07016
Pres.—Tom Carvalho, 9 emp., *Offset printing, typesetting & color* .......... (908) 276-7710
Tabloid Graphic Services, Inc., 7101 Westfield Ave., Pennsauken 08110
Pres.—Steve Brosious, 65 emp., *Circular heat-set & cold web printing* .......... (856) 486-0410
Tandem Graphics, Inc., 207 Wanaque Ave., Pompton Lakes 07442
Pres.—Michael Nass, 6 emp., *Banners & posters, including digital* .......... (973) 513-9779
Target Printing & Graphics, 9 E. Passaic St., Hackensack 07601
Pres.—Tony Flaim, 9 emp., *Offset & digital printing, signs, banners* .......... (201) 883-0200
Tech Repro, Inc., 65 Zabriskie St., Hackensack 07601
Pres.—Kevin Tremble, 10 emp., *Large-format, instant & color printing* .......... (201) 489-1333
Terminal Printing Co., 94 River St., P.O. Box 30, Hoboken 07030
Owner—John A. Bado III, 20 emp., *Offset printing & typesetting* .......... (201) 659-5924
Thewal, Inc., 12 Center St., Chatham 07928
Ptnr. & Pres.—Susan Kessel, 10 emp., *Commercial & digital printing, electronic* .......... (973) 635-1880
Thomsen Litho, Inc., 217 Railroad Ave., Ridgefield Park 07660
Pres.—Greg Thomsen, 3 emp., *Offset printing & computerized typesetting* .......... (201) 489-1133
Tomad, Inc., 129 Cincinnati Ave., Egg Harbor City 08215
Pres., Hum. Res. Mgr.—Brian Dagostino, 12 emp., *Offset printing & typesetting* .......... (609) 965-0808
Treasury Printing Services, 101 Carroll St., P.O. Box 30, Trenton 08625
CEO, Chief Printing & Reprographics—Douglas N. Krieger, 30 emp., *Government printing for the* (609) 292-5133
Trenton Printing, LLC, 1150 Southard St., Ste. 2, Trenton 08638
Pres.—David Nugent, 12 emp., *Graphic design, offset printing & mailing* .......... (609) 695-6485
Tretina Printing, Inc., 1301 State Route 36, Concord Ctr., Hazlet 07730
Pres.—Jan Tretina, Sr., 8 emp., *Commercial & offset printing & mailing* .......... (732) 264-2324
Triangle Repro Center, 222 Dutch Neck Rd., East Windsor 08520
Owner & GM—Mike Cocciolillo, 5 emp., *Large-format printing* .......... (609) 448-8161
Tri-City Print & Copy Center, 155 Union Blvd., Totowa 07512
Pres.—G. Elia, 2 emp., *Offset printing, copying, typesetting* .......... (973) 706-5854
Trinity Press, LLC, 655 Market St., Paterson 07513
Pres.—Kevin Barnes, 40 emp., *Offset, digital, commercial, textile* .......... (973) 881-0690
Tri-Plex Business Products, Inc / Graphic Solutions, 400 Morris Ave., Ste. 220, Denville 07834
Pres.—Walter Lapham, 9 emp., *Digital color, commercial, offset,* .......... (973) 627-5388
Tri-State Tape & Label Co., Inc., 351 Railroad Ave., P.O. Box 377, Beverly 08010
Pres.—David F. Wimer, 7 emp., *Flexible packaging, digital, offset* .......... (800) 682-7892
Tropp Printing Corp., 8 Woodhollow Dr., Holmdel 07733
Pres.—William Tropp, 5 emp., *Offset & color printing & electronic* .......... (212) 233-4519
Trout Printing LLC, 33 Reeves St., Millville 08332
Owner—Bo Novakowski, 5 emp., *Commercial offset printing* .......... (856) 327-8366
Trukmann's Inc., 4 Wing Dr., Cedar Knolls 07927
CEO—Paul Korman, 25 emp., *Commercial, large-format, lithographic* .......... (973) 538-7718
Unigraphic Guild, Inc., 10 Route 206, Stanhope 07874
Pres.—Paul Washuta, 16 emp., *Commercial, color & digital printing* .......... (973) 219-2348
United Envelope & Printing Co., Inc., 65 Railroad Ave., Ridgefield 07657
★ Pres.—Ken Bernstein, 75 emp., *Offset & letterpress envelope printing* .......... (201) 699-5800
Universal Graphics Co., 497 Bloomfield Ave., Bloomfield 07003
Pres.—Michael Zwier, 5 emp., *Commercial offset printing* .......... (973) 748-4009
Universal Prints, Inc., 625 Newark Ave., Jersey City 07306
Pres.—David Gabriel, 2 emp., *Commercial & instant printing* .......... (201) 656-7878
Urner Barry Publications, 182 Queens Blvd., Bayville 08721
Pres., Publisher—Paul Brown, Jr., 40 emp., *Commercial, offset, envelope, business* .......... (732) 240-5330
Verna Printing Co., Inc., 85 Washington Ave., Belleville 07109
Pres.—John Verna, 8 emp., *Offset printing* .......... (973) 751-6462
Veterano Ward Commercial Printing, 301 Bradshaw Ave., Haddonfield 08033
Owner—Frank Ward, 4 emp., *Offset printing & typesetting* .......... (856) 429-5460
Viskal Printing, LLC, 40 Commerce Way, Unit E, Totowa 07512
Pres.—Krishnan Thampi, 7 emp., *Brochure, stationery, newsletter &* .......... (973) 812-6600
Watson Graphics, Inc., 578 Kearny Ave., Kearny 07032
Pres.—Marlene Watson, 1 emp., *Offset, instant, color & thermographic* .......... (201) 955-0283
Wet Stone Graphics, 645 Greenway Pl., River Vale 07675
Owner—Marc Cohen, 1 emp., *Fine arts printing* .......... (201) 307-1531
Wheal-Grace Corp., 300 Ralph St., P.O. Box 67, Belleville 07109
Pres.—Nancy Salvini, 19 emp., *Commercial, offset & digital printing* .......... (973) 450-8100
Wiley's Lake Press, Inc., 1902 Greenwood Lake Tpke., Hewitt 07421
Pres.—Richard Wiley, 2 emp., *Offset & color printing of brochures* .......... (973) 728-9231
Woodbridge Printing Center, 1201 U.S. Highway 9 S., Woodbridge 07095
Owner & Pres.—Frank Racz, 7 emp., *Offset & digital printing* .......... (732) 855-1996
Word Center Printing, 1905 Highway 33, Ste. 10, Hamilton Square 08690
Owner, Fin., GM & MIS Mgr.—Marilyn Silverman, 4 emp., *Full-color & high-speed printing of* (609) 586-5825
Work Of Art Corp., 801 Olive Ave., Cherry Hill 08002
GM—Darren Winthrop, 3 emp., *Offset printing* .......... (856) 488-1188
Write Impression, The, 549 Highway 35, Red Bank 07701
Owner—Kristine Ancona, 1 emp., *Custom invitation & stationery printing* .......... (732) 706-3700

## 2754 Printing, gravure—commercial

Allen Group SMC, 60 Readington Rd., Branchburg 08876
Pres.—Steven Hegna, 60 emp., *Envelope & offset printing & typesetting* .......... (908) 231-1100
BCT-NY/NJ, 11 Industrial Ave., Upper Saddle River 07458
Pres., GM—Douglas Negrin, 10 emp., *Rubber stamps & offset printing of* .......... (201) 236-0088
Constant Services, Inc., 17 Commerce Rd., Fairfield 07004
Pres.—Vincent Pepe, 30 emp., *Rotogravure printing & laminating of* .......... (973) 227-2990
Control Group, The, 500 Walnut St., Norwood 07648
Ptnr.—William Cheringal, 50 emp., *Pressure-sensitive label printing* .......... (201) 768-1900
Hygrade Business Group, Inc., 232 Entin Rd., P.O. Box 1099, Clifton 07014
Pres., CEO—Victor Albetta, 40 emp., *Offset, digital & color printing of* .......... (973) 249-6700
NJ Label, 30 Wesley St., Unit 7, South Hackensack 07606
Owner—Steven Haedrich, 12 emp., *Label printing* .......... (201) 833-9200

Sunset Printing And Engraving, 10 Kice Ave., Wharton 07885
Pres.—Mitchel Wainer, 42 emp., *Commercial offset & on demand printing* (973) 537-9600

## 2759 Printing—commercial, nec

1 2 3 Quick Print, Inc., 297 New Brunswick Ave., Perth Amboy 08861
Pres.—Dov Ehrlich, 4 emp., *Commercial printing* (732) 442-1771
1 Stop Wraps, LLC, 1525 Prospect St., Ste. 602, Lakewood 08701
Owner & Pres.—Frank Mele, 4 emp., *Signs & large-format digital printing* (732) 363-7800
A D K Graphics, Inc., 325 Corporate Blvd., Robbinsville 08691
Pres.—David Griffiths, 5 emp., *Commercial printing* (609) 208-1080
A G F Printing, Inc., 92 Bogart Ave., Garfield 07026
Ptnr.—Frank Elia, 5 emp., *Commercial printing* (973) 253-8550
A J Images, Inc., 259 E. 1st Ave., Roselle 07203
Pres.—Janet Greebel, 23 emp., *Commercial multi-color printing, including* (908) 241-6900
A T Information Products, Inc., 575 Corporate Dr., Mahwah 07430
Pres.—Joseph Traut, 9 emp., *Inkjet printing & labeling systems* (201) 529-0202
A-1 Advanced Marking Technologies, LLC, 1420 Route 53, P.O. Box 485, Mount Tabor 07878
Pres., Off. & Plt. Mgr.—Cynthia Hopping, 12 emp., *Hot stamping, screen printing & pad* (973) 627-0155
A-1 Business Service, P.O. Box 83, Rahway 07065
Pres.—William Mendelson, 2 emp., *Commercial printing* (732) 910-6995
A-Aabacus Printing & Promotional Specialties Of Metuchen, 243 Amboy Ave., Metuchen 08840
Owner—Sam H. Van Chama, 2 emp., *Commercial printing, binding & graphic* (732) 767-9204
ABC Printing, 20 Wall St., Ste. C-5, Rockaway 07866
Owner—Yvonne Cook, 4 emp., *Offset & letterpress printing* (973) 664-1160
ABCO Printing Co., 92 N. Main St., Windsor 08561
Pres.—Russ Pareti, 12 emp., *Commercial printing* (609) 259-4900
Accent Apparel LLC, 405 Atlantic City Blvd., Beachwood 08722
Owner—Kevin McMahon, 3 emp., *Embroidery, screen printing & direct-to-garme* (732) 341-7576
Accurate Flannel Bag Co., Inc., 468 Totowa Ave., Ste. 3, Paterson 07522
Pres.—Fred Baron, 125 emp., *Custom bags & pouches, including dustcovers* (973) 720-1800
Accurate Plastic Printers, LLC, 30 Colfax Ave., Clifton 07013
Pres.—Carlos Agudelo, 20 emp., *Plastic product offset & digital printing* (973) 591-0180
Ace Lithographers, 22 Russo Pl., Berkeley Heights 07922
Pres.—John Cooper, 28 emp., *Commercial, offset & digital printing* (908) 665-1700
Ace Reprographic Service, Inc., 74 E. 30th St., Paterson 07514
Pres.—Arthur L. Scialla, 25 emp., *Blueprinting & color printing* (973) 684-5945
Ace Twill, 22 Russo Pl., Berkeley Heights 07922
Sales Rep.—George Twill, 30 emp., *Digital & offset printing* (908) 665-1700
Action Graphics, Inc., 600 Ryerson Rd., Ste. G, Lincoln Park 07035
Pres., CFO & Treas.—Dale E. Park, 24 emp., *Commercial printing & mailing services* (973) 633-6500
Action Office Supplies, Inc., 687 Prospect St., Ste. 480, Lakewood 08701
Pres.—Sonny Arora, 21 emp., *Commercial printing & distributor of* (732) 534-3000
Acu-Data Business Products, Inc., 1572 State Route 23, Ste. D, Butler 07405
Pres.—Gerald J. Vinci, 2 emp., *Business forms, advertising specialties* (973) 838-5678
Adams Printing & Graphics, 886 N. Pearl St., Bridgeton 08302
Owner—Mary Swain, 3 emp., *Commercial offset & digital printing* (856) 455-7177
ADV Promos & More, LLC, 12 Baltusrol St., Hamilton Square 08690
Owner—Andrea M. Anepete, 1 emp., *Custom printed promotional products* (609) 587-7500
Aeon Industries, Inc., 76 Veronica Ave., Somerset 08873
Acct. & Sales Mgr.—Ken Blum, 15 emp., *Thermal-sensitive labels & primary,* (732) 246-3224
Affordable Offset Printing, Inc., 809 Hylton Rd., Ste. 11, Pennsauken 08110
Pres.—Gary Coates, 4 emp., *Offset & digital printing, electronic* (856) 661-0722
Agfa Corp. (H Q), 611 River Dr., Elmwood Park 07407
Pres.—Peter Wilkens, 100 emp., *Corporate headquarters; digital offset* (201) 440-0111
AJ Printing Solutions, LLC, 781 Hyslip Ave., Westfield 07090
Owner—Gary Wasserman, 1 emp., *Flexographic & offset printing of packaging* (908) 202-0974
Al Quick Quality Printers, Inc., 77 Tuers Ave., Jersey City 07306
Pres.—Al Gonzalez, 3 emp., *Commercial printing* (201) 659-4003
Alcop Adhesive Label Co., 826 Perkins Ln., P.O. Box 398, Beverly 08010
Pres.—Wilmer P. Webster III, 12 emp., *Label printing* (609) 871-4400
Alete Printing, LLC, 722 Dartmouth Ct., P.O. Box 371, Wenonah 08090
V-P., CEO—John Koskinen, 4 emp., *Commercial & variable data printing* (856) 468-3536
Alex Real, LLC, 501 Prospect St., Ste. 107, Lakewood 08701
★ Pres.—Alexander Vorhand, 11 emp., *Promotional printing, including towels* (732) 730-8770
Alexander, Inc., Sandy, 200 Entin Rd., Clifton 07014
Pres., CEO—Michael Graff, 250 emp., *Corporate headquarters & commercial* (973) 470-8100
Alfred's Sport Shop, 32 Main St., Madison 07940
GM—Chuck Bleakley, 6 emp., *Baseball, softball & lacrosse equipment* (973) 377-0051
All American Graphic Arts, 763 Ramsey Ave., Hillside 07205
Owner—Ed Rodriguez, 2 emp., *Foil stamping & embossing & stationery* (908) 686-1479
All American Print & Copy Center, 518 Highway 35, Red Bank 07701
Owner—Ralph Cucinelli, 2 emp., *Commercial offset printing & typesetting* (732) 758-6200
All Nu Trophy & Screen Printing, 243 Teaneck Rd., Ridgefield Park 07660
Owner—Alan Jones, 13 emp., *Plastic & textile screen printing &* (201) 807-0808
All Points Printing & Graphics, 831 Arnold Ave., Point Pleasant 08742
Owner—Jim McClure, 5 emp., *Color, instant & wide-format printing* (732) 892-6670
All The Best Invitations, 123 W. Mount Pleasant Ave., Livingston 07039
Owner—Peter Turkell, 2 emp., *Invitation printing* (973) 992-4033
Allegra, 12 Stults Rd., Ste. 100, Dayton 08810
Pres.—Charles J. Jendrejeski, 30 emp., *60-inch digital inkjet large-format* (609) 771-4000
Allegra Marketing Print Mail, 665 State Route 27, Iselin 08830
Pres.—Alkesh Shah, 3 emp., *Digital color, instant, direct mail* (732) 404-0665
Allegra Print & Imaging, Inc., 12 Stults Rd., Dayton 08810
Pres.—Ellis Galimidi, 35 emp., *Offset, digital, instant & color printing* (609) 771-4000
Allied Envelope Co., Inc., 33 Commerce Rd., Carlstadt 07072
Pres.—James Royer, 50 emp., *Full-service direct mail & commercial* (201) 440-2000
Allied Printing & Graphics, 4 Madison Rd., Fairfield 07004
Pres.—Domenick Pascarella, 20 emp., *Commercial printing* (973) 227-0520
ALL-STATE LEGAL, 1 Commerce Dr., Cranford 07016
Pres., CEO—Robert H. Busch, 230 emp., *Full-color engraving & printing of* (908) 272-0800
Allure Visuals & Printing, 9 1st St., Lodi 07644
Manager—Joe Soleck, 2 emp., *Commercial printing, including letterheads* (201) 288-1111
All-Ways Advertising Co., 1442 Broad St., Bloomfield 07003
Pres.—Rob Lieberman, 30 emp., *Promotional product commercial printing* (973) 338-0700
Almetek Industries, Inc., 2 Joy Dr., Hackettstown 07840
CEO—Lori McMahon, 75 emp., *Metal & polyethelene safety signs,* (908) 850-9700
Alpak Display Group, 575 N. Midland Ave., Saddle Brook 07663
V-P., POP Sales—Jason Taub, 30 emp., *Corrugated point-of-purchase displays* (201) 797-1411
Alpha Processing Co. Inc., 210 Delawanna Ave., P.O. Box 936, Clifton 07014
Pres.—Richard Jenny, 50 emp., *Metal products painting, powder coating* (973) 777-1737
AlphaGraphics, 5 N. Olney Ave., Ste. 200, Cherry Hill 08003
Owner—Dave Sanford, 19 emp., *Digital & offset printing & graphic* (856) 761-8000
AlphaGraphics, 1111 U.S. Highway 22 E., Mountainside 07092
Owner & Pres.—Patrick Rotondo, 3 emp., *Digital large-format & offset printing* (908) 233-5553
AlphaGraphics, 558 Central Ave., New Providence 07974
Owner—Michael Tan, 10 emp., *Commercial printing* (908) 277-3000
AlphaGraphics 321, 90 Saw Mill Pond Rd., Heller Industrial Pk., Edison 08817
Pres., CFO—Carl A. Venable, 4 emp., *Digital & offset printing, promotional* (732) 985-6677
AlphaGraphics of Mahwah, 1 Lethbridge Plz., Route 17 N., Mahwah 07430
Pres.—John Chrisostomou, 6 emp., *Digital, direct mail & business printing* (201) 327-2200
AlphaGraphics Printshops, 68 White St., Red Bank 07701
Pres.—Jac Bloomberg, 5 emp., *Offset, instant, large-format & digital* (732) 758-0095
Alphagraphics, Inc., 60 Speedwell Ave., Morristown 07960
Owner—Brian Harrigan, 7 emp., *Commercial offset & instant printing* (973) 984-0066
American Advertising, 131 Landing Rd., Landing 07850
Pres.—Clark Wheeler, 5 emp., *Direct mail printing* (973) 398-6200
American Banknote Corp. (H Q), 2200 Fletcher Ave., Ste. 501, Fort Lee 07024
Chrm., CEO—Steven Singer, 10 emp., *Corporate headquarters; stock certificate* (201) 592-3400
American Envelope & Printing Co., 212 Columbus Ave., Roselle 07203
Owner & Pres.—Edward Nodelman, 5 emp., *Envelopes & commercial printing of* (908) 241-9900
American Youth Enterprises, Inc., 120 Marlin Ln., P.O. Box 653, Mays Landing 08330
Pres.—David Hagan, 8 emp., *Promotional products screen printing* (609) 909-1900
Amerifilm Converters, 85 Lincoln Hwy., Kearny 07032
Dir., Sales—Peter Campisi, 25 emp., *Flexographic printing* (973) 690-5900
AMREP Corporation (H Q), 300 Alexander Pk., Ste. 204, Princeton 08540
V-P., CFO—Peter Pizza, 6 emp., *Corporate headquarters; label & direct* (609) 716-8200
Anna Soiree, 2005 State Route 35, Ste. 19, Oakhurst 07755
Owner—Nicole Chambers, 2 emp., *Invitation printing* (732) 686-9570
Anuco, Inc., 911 Charles Dr., P.O. Box 5016, Toms River 08753
Owner & GM—Robert Nugent, Jr., 15 emp., *Commercial printing & foil stamping* (973) 887-9465
API Foils, Inc., 329 New Brunswick Ave., Rahway 07065
Pres.—Brad Mueller, 85 emp., *Hot stamping foil* (732) 382-6800
Apparel Distribution, Inc., 45 Saw Mill Pond Rd., Edison 08817
V-P.—Robert Shaw, 75 emp., *Apparel label sewing, pick ticket,* (732) 287-1110
Apple Printing Co., Inc., 5 Weymouth Rd., P.O. Box 574, Hammonton 08037
Pres.—Michael Crescenzo, 3 emp., *Commercial printing* (609) 561-4411
Applied Image, Inc., 800 Business Park Dr., Freehold 07728
Pres.—Allen Shanosky, 20 emp., *Large-format graphic printing & environmental* (732) 410-2444
AQL Decorating Co., Inc., 215 Bergen Blvd., Fairview 07022
Pres.—Jim Sheehan, 85 emp., *Plastic bottle screen printing* (201) 941-1610
Arch Crown, Inc., 460 Hillside Ave., Ste. 1, Hillside 07205
CEO—Norman Liebman, 32 emp., *Tags & labels, including die cutting* (973) 731-6300
Archive Print, Inc., 3203 Atlantic Ave., Allenwood 08720
Pres.—David Thiel, 1 emp., *Fine art digital giclee printing* (732) 528-5300
ARG Printing, LLC, 1601 Sherman Ave., Pennsauken 08110
★ Owner—Randy Gilbert, 3 emp., *Commercial printing* (856) 665-5644
Ariston Multimedia, LLC, 94 Valley Rd., Clifton 07013
★ Owner—Bernard Williams, 4 emp., *Commercial printing, t-shirt screen* (973) 553-2727
Art Graphic Impressions, 1044 State Route 23, Ste. 101, Wayne 07470
Pres.—William Berkenbush, 10 emp., *Commercial printing* (973) 696-2800
Art Press Printing, Inc., 124 Clements Bridge Rd., Barrington 08007
Owner & Pres.—Robert McHugh, 10 emp., *Commercial printing & typesetting* (856) 547-8953
Artcraft Sign Studio, Inc., 738 W. Branch Ave., Pine Hill 08021
Pres., CFO, MIS Mgr.—Arthur Elkins, 5 emp., *Dimensional, sandblasted, carved, interior* (856) 783-8008
Artisan Digital, Inc., 21 Fadem Rd., Unit 1, Springfield 07081
★ Owner—Kevin Hunt, 8 emp., *Commercial printing & interior & exterior* (973) 379-2788
Artist Above The Rest, 4490 Nottingham Way, Trenton 08690
Owner—John Brennan, 1 emp., *Decals, textile & plastic screen printing* (609) 586-7247
ASAP Coastal Printing and Signs, 775 N. Main St., Manahawkin 08050
Pres.—Jovi M. Flores, 5 emp., *Offset & direct mail market printing* (609) 597-7421
Ascot Tag & Label Co., Inc., 577 3rd St., Newark 07107
Pres. & V-P.—Charles DeFranza, 45 emp., *Tags, labels & commercial printing* (973) 482-0900
Associated Mailing & Printing Services, LLC, 50 Tannery Rd., Ste. 2, Branchburg 08876
Pres.—Christopher Halligan, 12 emp., *Commercial printing, mailing services* (908) 541-9700
Athens Printing Co., Inc., 95 Myer St., Hackensack 07601
★ CEO—Spyros Papathanasiou, 1 emp., *Commercial printing* (201) 342-1771
Atlantic Envelope Co., 16 Passaic Ave., Unit 7, Fairfield 07004
Pres.—Christopher Molinari, 6 emp., *Envelope printing* (973) 882-0436
Atlantic Printing & Graphics, LLC, 1301 W. Park Ave., Ocean 07712
Owner—Ed Lawrence, 5 emp., *Commercial & instant printing* (732) 493-4222
Atlantic Printing Co., 262 Circle Dr., Brick 08723
Pres.—Joseph Vrabel, 2 emp., *Commercial printing* (732) 920-2300
Avenue Printing Co., 143 Franklin Tpke., Waldwick 07463
Owner—Ruth Amarante, 3 emp., *Commercial offset spot & digital full-color* (201) 652-2035
Ayers Printing, 1413 Chestnut Ave., Hillside 07205
Pres.—James L. Ayers, 5 emp., *Commercial printing* (908) 687-2891
Ayr Graphics & Printing, Inc., 320 Chestnut St., Roselle Park 07204
Pres.—Carl Gamba, 8 emp., *Offset, color & digital printing &* (908) 241-8118
B & B Press, Inc., 24 Cokesbury Rd., Ste. 11, Lebanon 08833
Pres., GM—Mark Bistis, 6 emp., *Offset & digital printing, graphic* (908) 840-4323
B & L Printing Co., Inc., 46 Old Camplain Rd., Hillsborough 08844
Pres., CFO—Gerald Harris, 4 emp., *Commercial offset, digital color, instant* (908) 707-1311
Bailey's Printing, Inc., 191 Throckmorton St., Freehold 07728
Pres.—Randy Bailey, 2 emp., *Commerical & screen printing & custom* (732) 462-8010
Balcis Screen Printing, 219 Wanaque Ave., Pompton Lakes 07442
★ Owner—Martin Balbuana, 4 emp., *T-shirt & promotional item screen printing* (973) 835-9948
Bankers Pen, Inc., 141 Lanza Ave., Bldg. 12, Garfield 07026
★ Cust. Serv. Mgr.—Sandy Aubry, 30 emp., *Promotional item screen printing, including* (800) 499-7367
Bannon Group, 629 Grove St., Jersey City 07310
Pres.—Michael Falcone, 3 emp., *Color, offset, direct mail & digital* (201) 451-6500
Banquet Services International, 2214 Route 37 E., Toms River 08753
Pres.—Bob Hansen, 5 emp., *Commercial printing* (732) 270-1188
Bantle's Banners & Signs, 213 Clements Bridge Rd., Barrington 08007
Owner—Janice Bantle, 3 emp., *Street, door, window & magnetic vehicle* (856) 546-1112
Barrington Press Inc, 37 Spring Valley Ave., Paramus 07652
Pres., CEO—Paul E. Ramirez, 10 emp., *Offset, digital, instant, color & large-forma* (201) 843-6556
Bartlett Printing & Graphics, Inc., 4495 Route 130 S., Burlington 08016
CEO—Clifford Lewis, 3 emp., *Offset printing & typesetting* (609) 386-1525
Barton & Cooney, LLC, 300 Richards Run, Burlington 08016
Pres., COO—Patrick M. Doyle, 110 emp., *Direct mail & digital printing, variable* (609) 747-9300
BBC Printing, 4 Main St., P.O. Box 276, Branchville 07826
Owner—Duncan F. Caldwell, 4 emp., *Digital, large-format & offset printing* (973) 948-7998
Bell Signs, 3125 Woodbridge Ave., Ste. 5-C, Edison 08837
Ptnr.—Stephen Bell, 2 emp., *Sandblasted, carved & site interior* (732) 738-0010

Belle Mead Printing, LLC, 42 Old Camplain Rd., Hillsborough 08844
Owner—Thomas E. Lemore, 3 emp., Offset, digital & promotional printing ........ (908) 595-9500
Bellia Business Products & Services, Inc., 1047 N. Broad St., Woodbury 08096
Pres.—Thomas Bellia, 30 emp., Spiral & GBC binding & commercial printing ........ (856) 845-2234
Bellia Print & Copy Center, 190 William L. Dalton Dr., Glassboro 08028
Owner—Thomas Bellia, 4 emp., Commercial printing for small & large ........ (856) 582-4004
Bergen Screen Printing, Inc., 255 W. Broadway, Paterson 07522
Pres.—Uday Patel, 5 emp., Screen & wide-format digital printing ........ (973) 595-1222
Bernardsville Print Center, 21 Mine Brook Rd., Bernardsville 07924
Pres.—Richard C. Steinberg, 7 emp., Digital instant, commercial, 1-4 color ........ (908) 766-4073
Berry Business Procedure Co., 6 Park St., P.O. Box 845, Cranford 07016
Pres.—David M. Cheek, 4 emp., Commercial & business form printing ........ (908) 272-6464
Bill's Printing Service, Inc., 2829 S. Broad St., Trenton 08610
Pres.—Bill Mason, 6 emp., Commercial printing & typesetting ........ (609) 888-1841
Bistis Press, 1310 Clinton Ave., Irvington 07111
Ptnr.—Nick Bistis, 2 emp., Commercial printing & typesetting ........ (973) 373-8033
Blue Dog Graphics, 222 River St., Hackensack 07601
Pres.—Donald Perlman, 5 emp., Printing & promotional products ........ (201) 343-3343
Blue Parachute, 263 Amboy Ave., Ste. 1, Metuchen 08840
Pres.—David Friedberg, 4 emp., Commercial printing, large-format signage ........ (732) 767-1320
Bon-Jour Group, LLC, 1100 Blanch Ave., Norwood 07648
Owner & Pres.—Michael Tchertchian, 17 emp., Embroidery & screen printing of promotional (201) 646-1070
Boro Printing, Inc., 813 Broadway, West Long Branch 07764
Pres.—Gary Delatush, 5 emp., Offset, digital color & large-format ........ (732) 229-1899
Brimar Industries, Inc., 64 Outwater Ln., 3rd Fl., P.O. Box 467, Garfield 07026
Pres.—Brian Costello, 60 emp., Printed identification labels, decals ........ (973) 340-7889
Brooke Business Forms & Supplies, Inc., 50 U.S. Highway 9, Ste. 303, Morganville 07751
★ Pres.—Neil Rosen, 8 emp., Commercial printing ........ (732) 617-7550
Brown & Co., Inc., Bill, 275 Whitehead Rd., Hamilton 08619
★ Off. Mgr.—Ken Bruce, 2 emp., T-shirt & textile & promotional item ........ (609) 396-9191
Brussian Strokes Sign Co., 15-A Melanie Ln., Ste. 3-A, East Hanover 07936
Owner—David Gersham, 3 emp., Trade show, interior & exterior signs ........ (973) 515-5151
Budget Print, 426 Cedar Ln., Teaneck 07666
Owner & Graphic Design Mgr.—Debbie Passaretti, 2 emp., Offset, full color, large-format, instant (201) 692-1412
Budget Print Center, 332 Broad St., Bloomfield 07003
Owner—Thomas D. DeStefano, 8 emp., Offset & digital printing ........ (973) 743-0073
Budget Print Center, 177 S. Centre St., Ste. 200-K, Merchantville 08109
Owner—Thomas Jenkins, 3 emp., Commercial printing, marketing, graphic ........ (856) 438-6204
Budget Printing Center, 300 E.Greentree Rd., Unit 14, Marlton 08053
Owner—Bo Sidhu, 2 emp., Commercial printing, including wedding ........ (856) 596-2980
Budget Printing, LLC, 70 Westfield Ave., Clark 07066
Owner & Pres.—Robert Borg, 6 emp., Full-color digital, offset & screen ........ (732) 574-1330
Burlington Press, 328 High St., Burlington 08016
CEO—Richard Lewis, 7 emp., Digital, offset & large-format printing ........ (609) 387-0030
Business Graphics, 22 Park Pl., P.O. Box 832, Butler 07405
Owner & Pres.—Robert Femia, 1 emp., Commercial printing ........ (973) 838-9553
C & A Press, Inc., 636 State Route 18, East Brunswick 08816
Owner—Joe Kim, 3 emp., Commercial printing ........ (732) 238-1150
C & C Signs & Banners, 812 Forepeak Dr., Forked River 08731
★ Owner—Paul Colucci, 1 emp., Interior & exterior signs & vinyl lettering ........ (609) 693-4667
C & K Printing Co., Inc., 203 Paterson Ave., Ste. 1, Wallington 07057
Pres.—Gatnerek Truck, 1 emp., Commercial printing ........ (973) 473-0739
C & S Hot Stamping Co., 20 Edgewater Pl., Edgewater 07020
Owner—Carmen Marino, 5 emp., Contract commercial printing ........ (201) 840-4004
C & W Systems, 17-04 Split Rock Rd., P.O. Box 201, Fair Lawn 07410
Owner—Walter Miller, 1 emp., Commercial business form & envelope ........ (201) 791-7892
C B Printing & Graphics, Inc., 795 Susquehanna Ave., Franklin Lakes 07417
★ Owner—Craig Barbero, 5 emp., Commercial printing & graphic design ........ (201) 445-6500
C Graphics Studio, 410 32nd St., Union City 07087
★ Ptnr.—Tony Castillo, 4 emp., Commercial printing & graphic design ........ (201) 866-0592
Calandra Printing, 491 Bloomfield Ave., Caldwell 07006
Owner—Keith Calandra, 4 emp., Commercial printing ........ (973) 228-1649
Cameo Novelty & Pen, 400 Hillside Ave., Hillside 07205
Pres.—Sol Oberlander, 20 emp., Promotional product screen printing ........ (973) 923-1600
Campbell Converting Corp., 703 Van Rossum Ave., Unit 2, Beverly 08010
Owner & Pres.—C. Norman Campbell, 8 emp., Paper converting & wide-format printing ........ (609) 835-2720
Canvas 4 Life, Inc., 30 Chapin Rd., P.O. Box 216, Pine Brook 07058
CMO & COO—Cheryl Stoyle, 8 emp., Digital inkjet printing on canvas ........ (973) 276-3200
Capital Offset, Inc., 257 10th Ave., Paterson 07524
Pres.—Robert Catalino, 3 emp., Commercial, corporate stationery, envelope ........ (973) 279-3023
Capital Printing Corp., 420 South Ave., Middlesex 08846
Pres.—Nolan Russo, 120 emp., Commercial & business form printing ........ (732) 560-1515
Capitol Copy Service, 116 W. State St., Trenton 08608
Pres.—Raymond Sziber, 7 emp., Commercial, instant & digital printing ........ (609) 989-8776
Castle Printing, Inc., 1501 U.S. Highway 46, Ledgewood 07852
Ptnr. & Pres.—Kevin Ebner, 9 emp., Offset, instant, wide-format & digital ........ (973) 584-0990
Catamaran Media Co., LLC, 3120 Fire Rd., Egg Harbor Township 08234
Manager—James Miller, 4 emp., Newspaper printing & publishing ........ (609) 266-1860
CCL Label TubeDec, 92 Ark Rd., Lumberton 08048
CEO—Joseph T. Sanski, 320 emp., Pressure-sensitive labels ........ (609) 953-5050
CDS Packaging, LLC, 237 Vaile Rd., Parsippany 07054
Pres., CEO—David Hirdler, 2 emp., Corrugated & solid fiber packaging ........ (973) 219-1496
Chesapeake Pharmaceutical & Healthcare Packaging, 6 Commerce Rd., Fairfield 07004
GM—Jim Struhar, 105 emp., Label, insert & outsert printing for ........ (973) 808-8000
Cheshire Studio, Inc., 261 Main St., 2nd Fl., Ledgewood 07852
Pres.—Jack Hurdes, 2 emp., Commercial printing, advertising specialties ........ (973) 240-7360
Choice Signs, 3407 Rose Ave., Ste. 3, Ocean 07712
V-P., Opers.—Daniel Kowalski, 3 emp., ADA braille, vinyl & magnetic interior ........ (732) 493-1644
City Print Shop, Inc., 157 Sip Ave., Jersey City 07306
Owner & Pres.—Craig Olsen, 1 emp., Commercial printing ........ (201) 792-6699
Clarici Digital, 88 Youngs Rd., Mercerville 08619
Owner & Pres.—Gene Clarici, Jr., 25 emp., Screenprinted graphics, digital printing ........ (609) 587-7204
Clark Printing Co., 441 Market St., Saddle Brook 07663
Pres., GM—Richard Lisa, 18 emp., Commercial & newsletter printing & ........ (201) 845-4888
Clark's Hallmark Shop, 275 State Route 10 E., Ste. 31, Succasunna 07876
GM—Alfred Clark, 8 emp., Invitation card imprinting ........ (973) 584-5119
Clayton Press, Inc., P.O. Box 676, Asbury Park 07712
Pres.—David Roszel, 3 emp., Commercial printing ........ (732) 774-2624
Clinton Envelope, 9130 Pennsauken Hwy., Ste. C, Pennsauken 08110
GM—Bob Donner, 7 emp., Envelopes, including plain, printed ........ (856) 314-3636
Clondalkin Pharma & Healthcare, 1224 N. Church St., Moorestown 08057
Dir., Opers.—Chris Lengthorn, 177 emp., Inserts, labels & stickers printing ........ (856) 439-1700
Clover Printing Corp., 77 Park St., Ridgefield Park 07660
Pres.—Harvey Kass, 9 emp., Commercial printing ........ (201) 641-7800
CMYK Printing, Inc., 180 Coolidge Ave., Englewood 07631
CEO—Charles Ambrogio, 21 emp., Commercial printing, including brochures ........ (201) 458-1300
Color Optics By Arcade, Inc., 40 Green Pond Rd., Rockaway 07866
CEO—Joe Cicci, 58 emp., Paperboard & visual packaging & commercial ........ (973) 664-3100
Color Screen Pros, 100 Verona Ave., Newark 07104
Owner—Oscar Cano, 8 emp., Apparel & promotional item screen printing ........ (973) 268-5080
Coloredge, 190 Jony Dr., Carlstadt 07072
Dir.—Tony Chester, 50 emp., Large-format printing & visual displays ........ (201) 716-5200
Colornet, LLC, 809 Hylton Rd., Ste. 11, Pennsauken 08110
Mng. Member—Elizabeth Bollinger, 4 emp., Digital & offset full color printing ........ (856) 662-0652
ColorSource, Inc., 7025 Central Hwy., Pennsauken 08109
Pres.—Fred DeMarco, 9 emp., Commercial printing, binding, fulfillment ........ (856) 488-8100
Colortec Printing & Mailing LLC, 424 Kelley Dr., Ste. A, West Berlin 08091
Ptnr.—Lori Burroughs, 5 emp., Commercial, offset, digital & direct ........ (856) 767-0108
Colour Graphics, 521 Irish Hill Rd., Runnemede 08078
★ Owner—Lawrence McCaffrey, 1 emp., Commercial printing & graphic design ........ (856) 939-5599
Columbia Press, Inc., 12 Industrial Rd., P.O. Box 10723, Fairfield 07004
Pres.—Charles Puleo, 20 emp., Commercial printing ........ (973) 575-6535
Command Web Family Of Companies, 100 Castle Rd., Secaucus 07094
Pres.—Andrew Merson, 125 emp., Company headquarters & commercial printing ........ (201) 863-8100
Commerce Financial Printers, 305 Cox St., Roselle 07203
Sales & Mktg. Mgr.—Kris Haskins, 25 emp., Financial printing ........ (908) 241-9880
Commerce Sign Solutions, LLC, 540 Cranbury Rd., Ste. 334, East Brunswick 08816
Owner—Linda Harrington, 1 emp., ADA & architectural signs, banners, ........ (732) 238-7000
Commercial Business Forms, 240 Cedar Knolls Rd., Ste. 203, Cedar Knolls 07927
Pres.—Michael Gordon, 12 emp., Commercial/business & color printing ........ (973) 682-9000
Commercial Reprographics, Inc., 111 Roosevelt Ave., Plainfield 07060
Pres.—Gregory Ruffa, 6 emp., Commercial printing ........ (908) 755-7070
Com-Pak, Inc., 365 New Albany Rd., Moorestown 08057
CEO—Clif McDougall, 280 emp., Commercial & digital printing & binding ........ (856) 802-1900
Compass Signs, LLC, 1 Market Yard, Freehold 07728
Owner—Jeff Cherchia, 4 emp., Trade show & fleet graphics, interior ........ (732) 294-7977
Composition Printing, P.O. Box 55, Jersey City 07303
Pres., Fin. & R & D Mgr.—Allen Gradin, 6 emp., Commercial & color printing of business ........ (201) 798-0531
Comptime Print & Copy Center, 385 N. Franklin Tpke., Ste. 6, Ramsey 07446
Pres.—Christopher Tausch, 4 emp., Commercial printing ........ (201) 760-2400
Computoprint Corp., 1360 Clifton Ave., Ste. 402, Clifton 07012
Pres.—Marie Duplak, 10 emp., Commercial printing ........ (973) 574-8800
Concord Paper Mfg., Inc., 375 Sylvan Ave., Ste. 23, Englewood Cliffs 07632
Dir., Sales & Mktg.—Donna Parker, 4 emp., Shipping boxes & folding cartons, printing ........ (201) 567-2529
Connection Printing, Inc., 86 5th Ave., Hawthorne 07506
Pres.—Bob Rino, 4 emp., Commercial printing & typesetting ........ (973) 423-2004
Consortium Companies, 400 Raritan Center Pkwy., Edison 08837
Pres.—Lawrence Solomon, 22 emp., Commercial, offset & digital printing ........ (732) 512-1777
Contemporary Graphic Solutions, Inc., 7001 N. Park Dr., Pennsauken 08109
Pres.—Tim Moreton, 196 emp., Printing, packaging, finishing, die ........ (856) 663-7277
Contemporary, Inc., 161 Coolidge Ave., Englewood 07631
Pres.—Anthony Cantone, 22 emp., Electronic prepress & printing ........ (201) 569-3900
Content Critical LLC, 800 Central Blvd., Carlstadt 07072
CEO—Fred VanAlstyne, 203 emp., Lithographic, wide-format & digital ........ (201) 528-2777
Copiers Plus, 935 West Ave., Ocean City 08226
Owner—Bob Matthews, 4 emp., Digital printing ........ (609) 398-7676
Copy Shop, The, 20 E. Water St., Toms River 08753
Owner—Bob Livolsi, 5 emp., Instant & blueprinting ........ (732) 286-2200
Copy-Rite Printing, 378 N. Main St., Manahawkin 08050
Owner—Gail Moro, 4 emp., Commercial printing ........ (609) 597-9182
Copyshop Office Supply & Repro Center, 921 U.S. Highway 9, South Amboy 08879
Owner—Scott Restiano, Jr., 3 emp., Full-service, digital & large-format ........ (732) 721-5700
Corbi Printing Co., Inc., 106 W. Atlantic Ave., Audubon 08106
Pres.—Thomas Corbi, 8 emp., Commercial printing ........ (856) 547-2555
Cordes Printing, Inc., 460 Braen Ave., Wyckoff 07481
Pres.—Mark Cordes, 7 emp., Commercial printing ........ (201) 652-7272
Cornerstone Print & Imaging, LLC, 179 State Highway 31, Flemington 08822
Owner—Arthur Clarke, 6 emp., Commercial printing ........ (908) 782-7966
Corporate Communications Group, The, 14 Henderson Dr., West Caldwell 07006
Pres.—Lois Pinkin, 180 emp., Digital & offset printing, including ........ (973) 808-0009
Corporate Graphic Solutions, Inc., 11 W. Passaic St., Rochelle Park 07662
CEO—Harvey Ginsberg, 2 emp., Commercial printing & distributor of ........ (201) 556-0700
Corporate Graphics & Envelope Mfg., Inc., 29 Brook Ave., Maywood 07607
Pres.—Peter Levenson, 5 emp., Commercial envelope printing ........ (201) 880-4006
Cox Printers, 1634 E. Elizabeth Ave., Linden 07036
Pres.—Michael Kaufman, 28 emp., Commercial, offset & digital printing ........ (908) 928-1010
Craden Peripherals Corp., 7860 Airport Hwy., Pennsauken 08109
Pres.—Connell McGill, 30 emp., Passport & bank passbook printing ........ (856) 488-0700
Craftmaster Printing, Inc., 2024 Corlies Ave., Neptune 07753
Pres.—Curtis Baumgartner, 4 emp., Corporate headquarters & single-color ........ (732) 775-0011
Craftmaster Printing, Inc., 3 Main St., New Egypt 08533
Manager & Graphic Artist—Sherry Nepulis, 1 emp., Instant & color printing & blueprinting ........ (609) 758-5990
Creative Design Plus, 1634 E. Elizabeth Ave., Linden 07036
GM—Ping Larrabee, 8 emp., Commercial printing, advertising specialties ........ (732) 287-3336
Creative Print Group, Inc., The, 7905 Browning Rd., Ste. 112, Merchantville 08109
Pres.—Howard Friedman, 16 emp., Commercial printing ........ (856) 486-1700
Creative Printing Resources, LLC, 17 Kimberly Ct., Apt. 121, Red Bank 07701
★ Owner—Susan Kelly, 3 emp., Commercial printing, including brochures ........ (732) 842-0240
Crown Assocs. U. S. A., Inc., 19 Winged Foot Dr., Livingston 07039
Pres.—Linda Hart, 3 emp., Business & greeting card printing ........ (973) 785-3477
CRT International, Inc., 260 Wagner St., Middlesex 08846
V-P., Hum. Res. & IT—Carmine Tarantino, 8 emp., Commercial & packaging printing of ........ (973) 887-7737
CRW Graphics, Inc., 9100 Pennsauken Hwy., Pennsauken 08110
CEO—Harriet Weiss, 130 emp., Commercial offset, digital & variable ........ (856) 662-9111
Custom Labels, Inc., 61 Willet St., Bldg. J, Passaic 07055
Pres., Off. Mgr.—Abraham Rubin, 4 emp., Custom label printing ........ (973) 473-1934
D & M Printers, 43 School Rd., Whitehouse Station 08889
Owner—Liz Dembeski, 1 emp., Commercial offset printing ........ (908) 534-4101
D & M Printing, Inc., 46 Watson Ave., West Orange 07052
Pres.—Michael Napolitano, 5 emp., Commercial printing ........ (973) 731-1300
D and S Designs, P.O. Box 1707, Bridgeton 08302
Owner—Sandra L. Rodriguez, 2 emp., Custom screen printing & embroidery ........ (856) 451-0954
Dalfen Unlimited, 27 1/2 Lentz Ave., Newark 07105
Owner—Ed Norton, 5 emp., Commercial printing ........ (973) 344-4006

S.I.C.

Dash Industries, Inc., 639 5th St., Lakewood 08701
Owner—Alan Dirshawitz, 2 emp., *Disposable plastic bags & tablecloths* ........ (732) 364-5850
Dash Printing, Inc., 52 Woodbine St., Ste. 3, Bergenfield 07621
Owner—David Ashendorf, 3 emp., *Commercial printing, including digital* ........ (201) 338-2561
Dazian Fabrics, LLC, 18 Central Blvd., South Hackensack 07606
Chrm.—Milt Wolfson, 40 emp., *Textiles, fabricated items & LED scenic* ........ (201) 549-1000
Decoration Design Solutions, 1299 W. Forest Grove Rd., Vineland 08360
Pres.—Steve Wargo, 50 emp., *Plastic tube screen printing* ........ (856) 589-1250
Deleon Printing & Supply, Inc., 311 Palisade Ave., Jersey City 07307
Pres.—Paul Deleon, 3 emp., *Commercial printing, including blueprinting* ........ (201) 798-8440
Delgen Press, Inc., 250 Delawanna Ave., Clifton 07014
Pres.—Gregory E. Tolve, 5 emp., *Commercial printing* ........ (973) 472-2266
Delta Printing Co., 1000 Wall Street W., Lyndhurst 07071
GM—Vick Mazbanian, 8 emp., *Commercial, instant, offset & digital* ........ (201) 935-0036
Design 446, 2411 Atlantic Ave., Ste. 4, Manasquan 08736
Owner & Hum. Res. Mgr.—Tom Vialne, 40 emp., *Offset & digital printing & typesetting* ........ (732) 223-0100
DeVece & Shaffer, Inc., 400 Legion Ave., P.O. Box 201, Palmyra 08065
Pres.—William J. DeVece, 4 emp., *Commercial printing* ........ (856) 829-7282
DG3 North America, Inc., 100 Burma Rd., Jersey City 07305
CFO, The CGI Group—L. J. Baillargeon, 400 emp., *Offset & digital printing, including* ........ (201) 793-5000
Digital Color Concepts, Inc., 256 Sheffield St., Mountainside 07092
Pres.—Don Terwilliger, 80 emp., *Corporate headquarters & commercial* ........ (908) 264-0504
Digital Print Solutions, LLC, 5 Eastmans Rd., Parsippany 07054
Owner—Joseph Yutsus, 15 emp., *Commercial printing* ........ (973) 263-1890
Digital Productions, Inc., 410 Southgate Ct., Mickleton 08056
Pres.—Charles Budd, 12 emp., *Digital printing & point-of-purchase* ........ (856) 224-1111
Direct Development, LLC, 1338 State Route 36, Hazlet 07730
★ Owner—Vinod Gopal, 8 emp., *Commercial, promotional & apparel screen* ........ (732) 739-8890
Direct Printing Impressions, 33 Fairfield Pl., West Caldwell 07006
V-P., Sales—Richard Luggiero, 25 emp., *Commercial & digital printing & mailing* ........ (973) 227-6111
Discount Digital Print, LLC, 629 Grove St., 16th Fl., Jersey City 07310
★ Owner—Jim Dilworth, 8 emp., *Digital printing* ........ (201) 659-9600
Discount Office Supply, 146 Hudson St., Hackensack 07601
Pres.—Larry Barr, 5 emp., *Pamphlet, brochure, stationery & business* ........ (201) 342-3030
Diversified Impressions, Inc., 119 Coit St., Irvington 07111
Pres.—Richard Feldman, 6 emp., *Commercial printing & typesetting* ........ (973) 399-9041
Diversiprint, Inc., 1124 U.S. Highway 202, Ste. B-16, Raritan 08869
Owner & Pres.—Bob Zarelli, 3 emp., *Commercial & lithographic printing* ........ (908) 685-2225
Divine Printing, Inc., 131 Liberty St., Metuchen 08840
Pres.—David Silbiger, 15 emp., *Commercial printing* ........ (732) 632-8800
DL Printing Co., Inc., 283 Prospect Ave., Avenel 07001
Pres.—Dave Lospinoso, 5 emp., *Commercial printing* ........ (732) 750-1917
Dogstar Digital, LLC, 429 Redmond Ave., Oakhurst 07755
Owner—Jay Armbrust, 2 emp., *Full-service offset, color & digital* ........ (732) 768-3699
Dohrman Printing Co., Inc., 445 Industrial Rd., Carlstadt 07072
Pres., Fin., MIS & R & D Mgr.—Kenny Bell, 6 emp., *Commercial offset 1-6 color, digital* ........ (201) 933-0346
Dolce Bros. Printing, 29 Brook Ave., Maywood 07607
CEO—James Dolce, 35 emp., *Commercial printing* ........ (201) 843-0400
Drapkin Printing Co., 1850 Elizabeth Ave., Ste. 1, Rahway 07065
Owner—Owen Drapkin, 3 emp., *Commercial printing* ........ (732) 381-2228
Drew & Rogers, Inc., 30 Plymouth St., Fairfield 07004
Pres.—Thomas M. Rogers, 35 emp., *Commercial & business form printing* ........ (973) 575-6210
Driscoll Label Co., Inc., 19 West St., East Hanover 07936
Pres.—John Raguso, Jr., 20 emp., *Labels* ........ (973) 585-7295
DSA Graphics, LLC, 431 E. Main St., Ste. 3, Denville 07834
★ Owner—Dominic Santaite, 4 emp., *Commercial & promotional screen printing* ........ (973) 625-7760
Duffy Printing Co., 2389 Atco Ave., Atco 08004
Pres.—Alan Duffy, 5 emp., *Commercial printing* ........ (856) 768-1046
E. Greene Of North Carolina, Inc., P.O. Box 1017, West Caldwell 07007
GM—Jed Firestone, 30 emp., *Financial printing of security envelopes* ........ (973) 838-5200
Eagle Enterprises, Inc., 11 W. Ormond Ave., Cherry Hill 08002
Pres.—Paul Fisherkeller, 5 emp., *Commercial printing* ........ (856) 427-0787
EarthColor, 345 Walsh Dr., Parsippany 07054
Pres.—Greg Matonti, 300 emp., *Company headquarters & commercial printing* ........ (973) 884-1300
EarthDigital, 77 Moonachie Ave., Moonachie 07074
Pres.—Nicholas Brusco, 175 emp., *Digital printing & fulfillment & mailing* ........ (551) 497-5400
eDigital Graphics, 326 U.S. Highway 22, Ste. 12-A, Dunellen 08812
★ Owner—Elly Ezra, 10 emp., *Digital printing* ........ (732) 968-1234
Edison Lithographing Corp., 3725 Tonnelle Ave., North Bergen 07047
Pres.—George Gross, 80 emp., *Large-format printing & finishing* ........ (201) 902-9191
Elite Graphics, Inc., 333 Littleton Rd., Ste. 200, Parsippany 07054
Pres.—John Westlake, 7 emp., *Commercial printing* ........ (973) 882-9769
Elite Printing Service, 30 Heritage Dr., Sparta 07871
Pres.—Alison Marcinkowski, 1 emp., *Commercial printing* ........ (973) 729-0366
Elmwood Press, Inc., 85 Main Ave., Elmwood Park 07407
Owner & Off. Mgr.—Kimberly A. Murphy, 10 emp., *Offset, digital & direct mail printing* ........ (201) 794-6273
Emerson Speed Printing, 379 Kinderkamack Rd., Oradell 07649
Owner & Pres.—Herb Kassab, 4 emp., *Commercial offset printing & graphic* ........ (201) 265-7977
EMMC Co., 1 Nicola Pl., Belleville 07109
Pres.—Byshek Gasior, 3 emp., *General machining, fabricating & welding* ........ (973) 751-0100
Engraved Images, Route 202 & Demun Pl., P.O. Box 966, Far Hills 07931
Owner—Heidi Gammon, 5 emp., *Offset & color printing & engraving* ........ (908) 234-0323
Enterprise Press, Inc., 1 W. Forest Ave., Englewood 07631
Owner—Robert Hort, 150 emp., *Commercial printing* ........ (201) 894-0444
Entite Press, Inc., 139 Stokes Rd., Medford Lakes 08055
Pres.—William M. Frame, 1 emp., *Commercial printing* ........ (609) 714-9213
Envelopes & Printed Products, Inc., 135 Fairview Ave., Prospect Park 07508
Pres., CEO—William F. Higgins, 10 emp., *Envelope & business card printing,* ........ (973) 942-1232
Enviroprint USA, 11 Maiden Ln., Bound Brook 08805
Pres., Fin. & R & D Mgr.—Gerald F. Truppelli, 7 emp., *Eco-friendly soy-based digital & commercial* . (732) 356-5959
Epoch Press, Inc., 75 Wood St., Ste. B, Paterson 07524
CFO—Paulina Werthen, 30 emp., *Web & commercial printing* ........ (973) 357-0080
Excellent Printing & Graphics, 333 Hazel St., Clifton 07011
Owner & Hum. Res. Mgr.—Monty Abelghani, 15 emp., *Commercial printing* ........ (973) 773-6661
Express Graphics, 17 Dupont Ter., Wayne 07470
Owner—Kurt Gough, 3 emp., *Commercial printing* ........ (973) 696-3165
Express It, Inc., 61 Haddon Ave., Haddon Township 08108
Pres.—Steve Jones, 4 emp., *Commercial printing* ........ (856) 854-1888
Express Tag & Label Co., 52 N. Main St., Marlboro 07746
Owner—Gerald Tomaselli, 4 emp., *Printed labels & tags, postcards &* ........ (718) 965-1400
Extreme Digital Graphics, 7 Kingsbridge Rd., Ste. 1, Fairfield 07004
Pres.—Lynn Casile, 10 emp., *Commercial printing* ........ (973) 227-5599

F & M Expressions Unlimited, 211 Island Rd., Mahwah 07430
Pres., CEO—Frank Flanagan, 100 emp., *Heat transfer & decal printing* ........ (201) 512-3338
F I P Graphics, Inc., P.O. Box 952, Maywood 07607
Pres., GM—Larry Eisen, 5 emp., *Commercial printing & graphic design* ........ (201) 362-3194
Fairfield Litho II Corp., 123 Lehigh Dr., Fairfield 07004
Pres.—William Rakowitz, 80 emp., *Commercial printing* ........ (973) 575-7550
Falcon Printing Co., 613 Central Ave., Westfield 07090
Ptnr.—Anthony Archambault, 4 emp., *Commercial printing, typesetting &* ........ (908) 232-1991
Faraj, Inc., 422 Cliff St., Fairview 07022
Pres.—Zackary Faraj, 80 emp., *100% domestic mass-produced fabric* ........ (201) 313-4480
Farmingdale Printing, 70 Main St., Farmingdale 07727
Pres.—Tom Trenholm, 3 emp., *Offset & digital printing & electronic* ........ (732) 938-2727
FASTSIGNS®, 255 State Route 3, Secaucus 07094
Pres.—Elizabeth Selbach, 7 emp., *Yard, interior & exterior signs, banners* ........ (201) 902-8640
Federal Direct (H Q), 95 Main Ave., Ste. 2, Clifton 07014
CEO—Bernie Steins, 45 emp., *Company headquarters; direct marketing* ........ (973) 667-9800
Federal Label Systems, Inc., 385 Hillside Ave., Hillside 07205
Pres.—Paul E. Rothchild, 40 emp., *Instant redeemable coupons & extended* ........ (718) 899-6000
FedEx Office & Print Center, 1 Quality Way, Iselin 08830
Off. Mgr.—Kathleen Murray, 4 emp., *Commercial & instant printing, signs* ........ (732) 636-3580
FedEx Office & Print Center, 1211 Route 73, Mount Laurel 08054
GM & Br. Mgr.—Seth Stocking, 8 emp., *Laser printing* ........ (856) 273-5959
FedEx Office & Print Center, 315 N. Route 17, Paramus 07652
Hum. Res. Mgr.—Denise Brathwaite, 7 emp., *Commercial, digital, business form* ........ (201) 599-0031
FedEx Office & Print Center, 559 N. Franklin Tpke., Ramsey 07446
Br. Mgr.—Harvey Tircio, 3 emp., *Commercial printing* ........ (201) 818-1623
FedEx Office & Print Center, 399 Highway 28, Raritan 08869
Center Mgr.—Rich Simone, 6 emp., *Commercial printing* ........ (908) 575-1221
Ferrante Press, Inc., 516 Bloomfield Ave., Verona 07044
GM—Vincent Ferrante, 3 emp., *Offset & letterpress printing, typesetting* ........ (973) 239-4344
Ferrett Printing, Inc., 468 Warwick Rd., Woodbury 08096
Owner—Nicholas Ferrett, 1 emp., *Commercial printing* ........ (856) 686-4896
First Impression Printing, Inc., 178-D 10th St., Piscataway 08854
★ Pres.—Greg Thorogood, 3 emp., *Commercial printing* ........ (732) 529-5450
Flexo Craft Prints, Inc., 1000 1st St., Harrison 07029
Pres.—Mendel Klein, 15 emp., *Gift wrap printing, heat transfer paper* ........ (973) 482-7200
FLM Graphics Corp., 123 Lehigh Dr., Fairfield 07004
CEO—Frank L. Misischia, 65 emp., *Commercial printing, large-format digital* ........ (973) 575-9450
Forms Management Services, Inc., 162 Lodi St., Hackensack 07601
Pres.—Frank Rizzo, 5 emp., *Commercial printing* ........ (201) 336-3200
Forms Plus More, LLC, 6 Harwood Dr., Voorhees 08043
★ Owner—Susan Love, 4 emp., *Commercial printing & graphic services* ........ (856) 753-8886
Formslink Systems, Inc., 14 Hilldale Rd., P. O. Box 101, Pine Brook 07058
Co-Pres.—Chun Yan Lai, 4 emp., *Commercial, large-format, laser & digital* ........ (973) 808-8820
Four Star Reproduction, Inc., 52 Paterson Ave., Ste. 2, Newton 07860
Pres.—Charles Cioppa, 35 emp., *Commercial offset & digital printing* ........ (862) 268-8200
FrontEnd Graphics, 1951 Old Cuthbert Rd., Ste. 414, Cherry Hill 08034
Owner, Pres. & Mktg. Mgr.—Elizabeth Maul, 6 emp., *Digital direct mail printing, large* ........ (856) 547-1600
G & H Soho, Inc., 413 Market St., Elmwood Park 07407
Pres.—James K. Harris, 15 emp., *On demand digital printing & electronic* ........ (201) 216-9400
Gail's Lettering & Design, 24 Beaver Ave., Annandale 08801
Pres.—Gail Kugelman, 2 emp., *Interior & exterior signs & truck lettering* ........ (908) 735-4628
Galaxy Glass & Stone, 277 Fairfield Rd., P.O. Box 10154, Fairfield 07004
Pres., CEO—Eugene M. Negrin, 35 emp., *Custom & decorative architectural glass* ........ (973) 575-3440
Gangi Graphics, 1669 Highway 88 W., Brick 08724
Ptnr.—John Gangi, 7 emp., *Offset & digital printing & electronic* ........ (732) 840-8680
Garrison Printing Co., 7155 Airport Hwy., Pennsauken 08109
Co-Pres., CFO—Jake Garrison, 40 emp., *Commercial printing* ........ (856) 488-1900
Gateway Press, 984 State Route 36, Atlantic Highlands 07716
Owner—James Meyer, 3 emp., *Commercial offset & instant printing* ........ (732) 291-1757
Gator Communication Group, 175 Route 46 W., Fairfield 07004
Pres.—Richard Bitetti, 30 emp., *Commercial printing* ........ (973) 233-6700
Gecko Graphics, Inc., 128 Berlin Cross Keys Rd., Williamstown 08094
Pres.—Alice Gorney, 3 emp., *Laser engraving on acrylic, plastics* ........ (856) 740-9042
Gerardi Press, Inc., 3 Luger Rd., Ste. 3, P.O. Box 545, Denville 07834
Owner—Keith Gerardi, 8 emp., *Commercial printing, including brochures* ........ (973) 627-2600
Giordano, Inc., Philip A., 59 Garfield Ave., Garfield 07026
Ptnr.—Robert Giordano, 3 emp., *Commercial printing, electronic prepress* ........ (973) 546-9267
Glassboro Printing, Inc., 30 N. Academy St., Glassboro 08028
Pres.—Norman Murphy, 3 emp., *Commercial printing* ........ (856) 881-2600
Global Graphics, Inc., 1945 State Route 27, Ste. 5, Edison 08817
Pres.—Chen-Li Fang, 2 emp., *Commercial printing* ........ (732) 287-9390
Global Print Media, 421 W. County Line Rd., Lakewood 08701
Pres.—Jacob Stendig, 6 emp., *Commercial printing* ........ (732) 886-0505
Global Soft Digital Solutions, Inc., 500 Corporate Dr., Mahwah 07430
Pres.—Christopher Petro, 50 emp., *Digital & large-format printing, fleet* ........ (201) 684-0900
Glorin Printing, Inc., 258 Clifton Ave., Newark 07104
Pres., Hum. Res. & IT Mgr.—Irving Linares, 3 emp., *Commercial printing & electronic prepress* (973) 481-3233
GM Printing, 106 Pleasant Ave., Bergenfield 07621
Pres.—Greg Madison, 7 emp., *Instant, commercial & large-format* ........ (201) 385-2525
GMS Litho, Inc., 16 Passaic Ave., Fairfield 07004
Pres.—Greg Enright, 10 emp., *Commercial printing* ........ (973) 575-9400
Goffco Industries, Inc., 10 Park Pl., Bldg. 6-6, Butler 07405
Pres.—Leslie Gough, 6 emp., *Commercial printing* ........ (973) 492-0150
Grandview Printing Co., Inc., 33 W. End Rd., Totowa 07512
Pres.—Lewis DeMarco, 8 emp., *Commercial offset printing of greeting* ........ (973) 890-0006
Graphic Action, Inc., 296 S. Main St., Phillipsburg 08865
Pres.—Frank Geraghty, 5 emp., *Instant printing* ........ (908) 213-0055
Graphic Center, The, P.O. Box 595, Mount Freedom 07970
Owner & CFO—Sandra Guido, 12 emp., *Commercial & digital printing of booklets* ........ (973) 366-6676
Graphic Express Menu Co., Inc., 200 Clifton Blvd., Ste. 6, Clifton 07011
Cust. Serv. Rep.—Anissa High, 30 emp., *Menu covers* ........ (973) 685-0022
Graphic Image, 1401 N. Black Horse Pike, Ste. A, Williamstown 08094
Owner—Jim McGhee, 8 emp., *Commercial printing, t-shirt screen* ........ (856) 262-8900
Graphic Image, Inc., 445 Route 46, Hackettstown 07840
Pres.—Claudia Ehrgott, 4 emp., *Commercial printing, signs, posters* ........ (908) 852-7007
Graphic Imagery, Inc., 122 Mount Bethel Rd., Ste. 2, Warren 07059
Pres.—Linda Maher, 10 emp., *Commercial offset, digital & web printing* ........ (908) 755-2882
Graphic Impressions Printing Co., 4391 Route 42, Turnersville 08012
Sales Rep.—Dennis Neill, 8 emp., *Commercial & business form printing* ........ (856) 728-2266
Graphic Marketing Group, 7 Kingsbridge Rd., Ste. 2, Fairfield 07004
Pres.—David Greene, 2 emp., *Commercial printing & vehicle wraps* ........ (973) 276-7901

© Copyright 2015 Manufacturers' News, Inc.


Graphic Printing Co., Inc., 283 Lincoln Blvd., Middlesex 08846
Pres.—William Gazi, 2 emp., *Commercial printing* .......... (732) 627-9000
Graphic Solutions & Signs, LLC, 82 Burlews Ct., Hackensack 07601
★ Member—Felipe Alarcon, 18 emp., *Interior & exterior signs & vinyl lettering* .......... (201) 343-7446
Graphic Techniques, LLC, 10 S. West Blvd., P.O. Box 4, Newfield 08344
Pres.—Darryl Erickson, 3 emp., *Commercial printing & typesetting* .......... (856) 697-2480
Graphicolor Corp., 3490 N. Mill Rd., Vineland 08360
Pres., Fin., MIS & R & D Mgr.—Robert W. Stenger, Jr., 20 emp., *Commercial printing* .......... (856) 691-2507
Graphics Depot, Inc., 11 Middlebury Blvd., Ste. 4, Randolph 07869
Pres.—David Bernstein, 16 emp., *Digital four & full color offset, instant* .......... (973) 927-8200
Graphiry Printing, 308 Morris Ave., Elizabeth 07208
Owner—Luis Arias, 6 emp., *Commercial printing* .......... (908) 353-2223
Graphix Integrated, Inc., 971 Leonardville Rd., Atlantic Highlands 07716
Prodn. Mgr.—Alex Kreymerman, 4 emp., *Giclee printing, shadow boxes, laser* .......... (732) 872-8282
Graphix One, LLC, 725 Lincoln Blvd., Middlesex 08846
Ptnr.—Jeff Yingling, 3 emp., *Commercial, screen & offset printing* .......... (732) 560-4700
Greentree Printing, 9004 Lincoln Dr. W., Ste. G, Marlton 08053
Ptnr. & Pres.—Paul Barbera, 3 emp., *Offset, instant & full-color printing* .......... (856) 596-2330
Greenwich Graphics, LLC, 234 16th St., 8th Fl., Jersey City 07310
Owner, Pres. & MIS Mgr.—Wolfe Gluck, 8 emp., *Printing plates, computerized typesetting* .... (212) 727-1116
Gregory Press, Inc., 7 Mark Rd., Ste. A, Kenilworth 07033
Pres.—Gregory P. Loessel, 23 emp., *Commercial printing* .......... (908) 686-0030
Happle Printing Partnership, Inc., 81 Cape May Ave., P.O. Box 36, Dorothy 08317
★ Pres.—Ken Happle, 7 emp., *Digital & offset printing* .......... (609) 476-2929
Harmony Printing, 504 Aldrich Rd., Ste. 22, Howell 07731
Owner & CEO—Bill Blake, 4 emp., *Promotional item & apparel, garment* .......... (732) 987-9040
Harwill Corp., 3175 Princeton Pike, Lawrenceville 08648
Pres.—Steve Portrude, 6 emp., *Commercial & digital printing, typesetting* .......... (609) 895-1955
Hawk Graphics, Inc., 1248 Sussex Tpke., Ste. C-9, Randolph 07869
Pres.—Nick Battaglino, 20 emp., *Commercial offset, digital color &* .......... (973) 895-5569
Hayes Mindish, Inc., 1401 N. Main St., Pleasantville 08232
Pres.—Sally Hayes, 3 emp., *Commercial printing* .......... (609) 641-9880
HC Graphics Screen Printing, Inc., 238 Lindbergh Pl., Ste. 3, Paterson 07503
Pres.—Thomas J. Mueller, 15 emp., *Plastic & paper screen printing* .......... (973) 247-0544
Heritage, Inc., 4 Wilsey Sq., Ste. 9, Ridgewood 07450
Pres.—Paul Mortola, 5 emp., *Commercial & promotional printing,* .......... (201) 447-2600
Hermitage Press, Inc., 1595 5th St., Ewing 08638
Pres.—Michael Stoeckle, 21 emp., *Commercial printing* .......... (609) 882-3600
Hi Land Printers, 121 S. Main St., Pleasantville 08232
Owner—John McDowell, 2 emp., *Commercial printing* .......... (609) 646-6319
HighRoad Press, 220 Anderson Ave., Moonachie 07074
★ Owner & CEO—Hallie Satz, 45 emp., *Commercial, digital, sheet-fed & web* .......... (201) 708-6900
Hillman Graphic Products, P.O. Box 5233, Somerset 08875
Owner—Marty Hillman, 4 emp., *Commercial offset & digital printing* .......... (201) 487-6900
Hippographics, Inc. (H Q), 9100 Pennsauken Hwy., Pennsauken 08110
Owner & Pres.—Larry Weiss, 3 emp., *Corporate headquarters; business form* .......... (856) 662-9111
Holographic Finishing, Inc., 501 Hendricks Cswy., P.O. Box 597, Ridgefield 07657
Pres.—Michael Vulcano, 12 emp., *Paper embossing, die cutting, glueing* .......... (201) 941-4651
Honour Of Your Presence, 19 State Route 10 E., Ste. 14, Succasunna 07876
Ptnr.—Cherese Rambaldi, 2 emp., *Invitation printing & design* .......... (973) 927-6262
Howard, Inc., James, 1500 Main Ave., Ste. 3, Clifton 07011
Pres., CEO—Timothy James, 15 emp., *Commercial & digital printing* .......... (973) 928-1560
Hub Print & Copy Center, The, 2037 Lemoine Ave., Fort Lee 07024
Pres.—Gerard Tonner, 2 emp., *Commercial printing & binding services* .......... (201) 585-7887
Hubler & Assocs., 146 E. Holly Ave., Oaklyn 08107
Owner—Richard G. Hubler, 2 emp., *Commercial printing* .......... (856) 906-5341
Ideal-Jacobs Corp., 515 Valley St., Maplewood 07040
Pres.—Andrew C. Jacobs, 30 emp., *Commercial screen printing* .......... (973) 275-5100
Iken Media, LLC, 70 Triangle Blvd., Carlstadt 07072
★ Owner—David Eichen, 5 emp., *Commercial printing & interior & exterior* .......... (201) 372-0800
Image Makers Printing, Copy & Sign Center, 1581 State Route 23, Wayne 07470
Pres.—Gino Nuzzo, 5 emp., *High-speed color printing, blueprinting* .......... (973) 633-1771
Impressions Unlimited Printing Co., LLC, 638 Delsea Dr., P.O. Box 386, Sewell 08080
Owner—Joe Layton, 2 emp., *Commercial offset printing, including* .......... (856) 256-0200
Impressive Printing, Inc., 313 10th St., Carlstadt 07072
Pres.—Robert Egan, 2 emp., *Commercial, full-color & large-format* .......... (201) 933-1650
Imprint Specialties, Inc., 601 New Broadway, Brooklawn 08030
Pres.—Francis Ferry, 5 emp., *Commercial screen printing & awards* .......... (856) 456-2999
Industrial Labeling Systems, Inc., 50 Kulick Rd., Fairfield 07004
Pres.—Yimin Shiuey, 15 emp., *Label printing* .......... (973) 882-9688
Infinity Design & Printing, 1358 Burnet Ave., Union 07083
Owner—Pierre Filsaime, 5 emp., *Commercial printing & graphic design* .......... (908) 206-8844
InnerWorkings, Inc., 7 Joanna Ct., Ste. H, East Brunswick 08816
Br. Mgr.—Sam Wilk, 30 emp., *Screen printing of promotional items* .......... (732) 651-8822
Inserts East, Inc., 7045 Central Hwy., Pennsauken 08109
Pres., CEO—Nick Maiale, 200 emp., *Commercial printing of newspaper &* .......... (856) 663-8181
Instant Printing, Inc., 241 E. Blackwell St., Dover 07801
Pres.—Ann Medore, 4 emp., *Commercial, offset & digital printing* .......... (973) 366-6855
IPAK, Inc, 301 Grove Rd., West Deptford 08086
Mng. Ptnr.—Sheryl Schreiber, 90 emp., *Contract printing & packaging* .......... (856) 486-0066
ITW Covid Security Group, 32 Commerce Dr., Ste. 1, Cranbury 08512
Cont., IT Mgr.—Jim Violett, 67 emp., *Holographic highly secure polymer materials* .......... (609) 395-5600
J & G Enterprises, Inc., 182 High St., Nutley 07110
Principal & Manager—John Mancini, 1 emp., *Custom apparel embroidery & screen* .......... (973) 667-7673
J & J Engraving, 45 Worth St., South Hackensack 07606
Owner—Joseph Polifronio, Jr., 1 emp., *Plastic & metal engraving & screen* .......... (201) 342-0798
J & R Printing, Inc., 301 S. Main St., Cape May Court House 08210
Owner & Pres.—Jerry Gau, 1 emp., *Commercial printing* .......... (609) 465-3530
J C Printing & Advertising, Inc., 168 8th Ave., Paterson 07514
Pres.—James Chappell, 3 emp., *Commercial printing* .......... (973) 881-8612
J K Printing, 310 Edgewood Ave., Teaneck 07666
Owner—Joseph Korn, 2 emp., *Commercial printing & apparel screen* .......... (201) 833-8181
J M J Printing & Graphics, Inc., 1403 State Route 23, Ste. 8, Butler 07405
Pres.—Debby Greenberg, 20 emp., *Printing & contract packaging* .......... (973) 838-3400
JA Visual Group, 150 Commerce Rd., Unit 3, Carlstadt 07072
Pres.—Teri Uto, 20 emp., *Digital C-printing for the signage* .......... (212) 463-0545
Jamm Litho, Inc., 185 Broadway, Long Branch 07740
Owner—Robert LaBella, 9 emp., *Commercial printing* .......... (732) 870-1999
Jamm Printing, 108 W. Sylvania Ave., Neptune 07753
Owner—Robert LaBella, 7 emp., *Commercial printing & typesetting* .......... (732) 502-0110
JDS Graphics, Inc., 220 Entin Rd., Clifton 07014
Pres.—Debra Yuran, 5 emp., *Commercial printing* .......... (973) 330-3300

Jefferson Printing Service, 184 Jefferson St., Newark 07105
★ Pres.—Julio DePaula, 10 emp., *Commercial printing, signage & vehicle* .......... (973) 491-0019
JEM Print Co., 36 Atlantic St., Bridgeton 08302
Pres., CFO—Herman Evans, Jr., 4 emp., *Commercial printing & typesetting* .......... (856) 451-3885
Jersey Printing Assocs., Inc., 153 1st Ave., P.O. Box 355, Atlantic Highlands 07716
Pres.—Greg Heh, 25 emp., *Commercial printing* .......... (732) 872-9654
Jim's Signs, 1400 Rahway Ave., Ste. 3, Avenel 07001
Owner & Pres.—Jim Petrocy, 10 emp., *Plastic & reflective safety, ADA, room* .......... (732) 381-8700
JMC Design & Graphics, Inc., 144 Fairfield Rd., Fairfield 07004
Pres.—Joseph Caniano, 7 emp., *Commercial printing & graphic design* .......... (973) 276-9033
Johnson & Mayer, Inc., 58 Hobart St., Hackensack 07601
Pres.—Mitchell Perdue, 20 emp., *Decals* .......... (201) 646-1717
Johnston Letter Co., Inc., 1634 E. Elizabeth Ave., Linden 07036
Pres.—Michael Kaufman, 25 emp., *Commercial printing, including variable* .......... (908) 928-1217
K R B Printing For Business, 1165 Marlkress Rd., Ste. G, Cherry Hill 08003
Ptnr.—Kurt Barbera, 12 emp., *Commercial printing & electronic prepress* .......... (856) 751-5200
KD Envelopes & Printing, LLC, 7 Mark Rd., Kenilworth 07033
Owner—Donna Loessel, 3 emp., *Envelope printing* .......... (908) 686-1798
KDF Reprographics, Inc., 10 Volvo Dr., Rockleigh 07647
Pres.—Steven Hoey, 20 emp., *Blueprinting* .......... (201) 784-9991
Kemm Graphics, 94 Providence Blvd., Kendall Park 08824
Owner—Eric Sichel, 5 emp., *Commercial printing* .......... (732) 718-3449
Kern Printers & Stationers, 86 Lackawanna Ave., Unit 105, Woodland Park 07424
Pres.—Thomas Mandel, 5 emp., *Offset & digital printing & graphic* .......... (201) 226-0270
Keskes Printing Co., 5 W. Taunton Ave., Berlin 08009
Owner—Jean Keskes, 5 emp., *Offset, digital & letterpress printing* .......... (856) 767-4733
Kintech Printing & Direct Mail, 2400 Belmar Blvd., Ste. E-6, P.O. Box 12, Belmar 07719
★ Ptnr.—Gary Porter, 10 emp., *Commercial printing & promotional item* .......... (732) 280-6245
Kirkwood New York, 1 Teaneck Rd., Ridgefield Park 07660
Pres., Sales Mgr.—Edward Kelley, 30 emp., *Commercial printing* .......... (201) 440-0800
Kirms Printing Co., Inc., 1520 Washington Ave., P.O. Box 1067, Neptune 07753
Pres.—Albert Kirms, 20 emp., *School newspaper & leisure guide printing* .......... (732) 774-8000
Kiva Printing & Graphics, 50 Cutler Ave., Westville 08093
Pres., GM—Tyler Wilson, 12 emp., *Offset & commercial printing* .......... (877) 777-5482
KMS Printing & Graphics, Inc., 401 N. Brookfield St., Vineland 08361
★ Pres.—Kathryn M. Stanger, 1 emp., *Commercial printing* .......... (856) 205-0200
Knockout Graphics, Inc., 522 Cookman Ave., Asbury Park 07712
Pres.—Margaret Brunett, 7 emp., *Commercial printing* .......... (732) 774-3331
Koday Press, Inc., 69 Armour Pl., Dumont 07628
Pres.—Eugene Koblantz, 12 emp., *Commercial printing* .......... (201) 387-0001
Kraftape Printers, Inc., 124 Orchard St., Newark 07102
★ V-P.—Robert Hirtler, 6 emp., *Commercial printing, including sealing* .......... (973) 824-3005
L & B Printing, 2590 U.S. Highway 22, Scotch Plains 07076
Ptnr.—Lance Booth, Sr., 6 emp., *Commercial printing & typesetting* .......... (908) 232-7770
Label Graphics Mfg., Inc., 175 Paterson Ave., Little Falls 07424
Pres.—Thomas Silvano, 50 emp., *Corporate headquarters & pressure-sensitive* .......... (973) 890-5665
Label Master, Inc., 89 Dell Glen Ave., Lodi 07644
Pres.—Robert Mazzella, 10 emp., *Pressure-sensitive labels* .......... (973) 546-3110
Label Tek, Inc., 357 Cortlandt St., Ste. 4, Belleville 07109
★ CEO—Rusty Pace, 8 emp., *Commercial label printing* .......... (201) 390-3856
Langendorff Corp., 633 Grove St., Jersey City 07310
Pres.—Frank Langendorff, 6 emp., *Commercial offset printing* .......... (201) 659-6300
Laser Dim Graphics & Printing, 2 Parkwood Ln., Colts Neck 07722
Pres.—James Asghar, 10 emp., *Digital & offset printing* .......... (732) 821-9000
Latta Graphics, Inc., 180 Cool Edge Ave., Englewood 07631
Pres., Hum. Res. Mgr.—Eileen Latta, 18 emp., *Commercial printing* .......... (201) 440-4040
LCI Graphics, Inc., 2400 Main Street Ext., Ste. 8, Sayreville 08872
Pres.—Daniel Seratelli, 8 emp., *Commercial offset, web-to-print, digital* .......... (973) 893-2913
Leader Printers, 5914 New Jersey Ave., Wildwood Crest 08260
Pres.—Dennis Hall, 6 emp., *Offset printing & typesetting* .......... (609) 729-0161
Leon Printing, 1421 New York Ave., Union City 07087
Owner—Lewis Leon, 3 emp., *Commercial printing* .......... (201) 867-3206
Liberty Envelope, Inc., 45 E. 5th St., Paterson 07524
CEO—Kevin Guarderas, 40 emp., *Commercial & envelope printing to 6* .......... (973) 546-5600
Linder & Co., Inc., 1183 W. Side Ave., Jersey City 07306
Pres.—George R. Linder, 18 emp., *Commercial offset, conventional & digital* .......... (201) 386-8788
Lithotone Co., 255 Queen Ann Rd., Bogota 07603
Pres.—James Fessel, 4 emp., *Commercial printing* .......... (201) 343-3883
Litvany Printing, LLC, Steve, 1275 Bloomfield Ave., Ste. 13-R, Fairfield 07004
Pres.—Steve Litvany, 2 emp., *Commercial printing* .......... (973) 244-0144
Lizard Label, Inc., 10-E Commerce Rd., Fairfield 07004
Pres.—Joseph Winter, 10 emp., *Digitally printed pressure-sensitive* .......... (973) 808-0098
Local Talk Printing Club, 26 Main St., Orange 07050
V-P., Opers.—Dhiren Shah, 4 emp., *Commercial printing* .......... (973) 678-2582
Logotech, Inc., 18 Madison Rd., Fairfield 07004
Pres.—Leslie Gurland, 35 emp., *Pressure-sensitive labels* .......... (973) 882-9595
Lombardo Graphic Consultants, Inc., 429 Lacey Rd., Ste. 8, Forked River 08731
Pres.—Eileen M. Lombardo, 7 emp., *Commercial, business form & package* .......... (609) 693-1727
Lont & OverKamp, 175 U.S. Highway 46, Fairfield 07004
CEO—Ken Lont, 50 emp., *Offset, digital & direct mail printing* .......... (973) 942-2243
Lornan Litho, Inc., 130 Route 31 N., Ste. E, Pennington 08534
Owner—William Shankoff, 4 emp., *Commercial printing* .......... (609) 818-1198
LRP & P Graphics, 1165 Marlkress Rd., Cherry Hill 08003
Pres.—Joan Buehler, 30 emp., *Offset & digital printing & typesetting* .......... (856) 424-0158
MacFerren's Printing & Co., 3 Democrat Rd., Gibbsboro 08026
Owner—Mike Macferren, 3 emp., *Lithographic & commercial printing* .......... (856) 435-7066
Mackey's Print Xpress, 1107 7th Ave., Neptune 07753
Owner & Pres.—Ron Mackey, 3 emp., *Single, multicolor offset & digital* .......... (732) 775-1730
Maclearie, 917 18th Ave., Wall 07719
Owner—Jim McCleary, 5 emp., *Business card & form printing* .......... (732) 974-8878
Magnetic Ticket & Label Corp., 151 Cortlandt St., Belleville 07109
Plt. Mgr.—Yahya Kashani, 27 emp., *Tags & labels* .......... (973) 759-6500
Mail Time, Inc., 224 Stockton St., Phillipsburg 08865
★ Owner—Mario Sgroi, 23 emp., *Commercial printing* .......... (908) 859-5500
Main Street Graphics, Inc., 30 W. Main St., Maple Shade 08052
Pres.—Eileen Cusumano, 4 emp., *Commercial offset printing* .......... (856) 755-3523
Mantua Sign & Lighting, 550 Bridgeton Pike, Ste. 5, Mantua 08051
★ Owner—Jay Glaser, 3 emp., *Interior & exterior signs, channel* .......... (856) 415-0022
Manzi Printers, Inc., 132 Lewis St., Ste. B-2, Eatontown 07724
Owner—Mike Manzi, 3 emp., *Commercial printing* .......... (732) 542-1927
Marange Printing, Inc., 195 Cortlandt St., Belleville 07109
V-P., CEO—Angelo Autiero, 35 emp., *Commercial printing* .......... (973) 751-3600



**★ Indicates new listing this edition.**

Mariano Press Co., 14 Veronica Ave., Somerset 08873
Ptnr.—Joseph Mariano, 15 emp., *Offset & letterpress printing* .......... (732) 247-6828
Market Street Printing, Inc., 122 N. 6th St., Camden 08102
Pres.—Mookie Kamerkar, 3 emp., *Commercial offset printing & typesetting* .......... (856) 964-5995
Marmus, Inc., 51 E. Front St., Keyport 07735
Pres.—Terry Musson, 1 emp., *Textile screen, commercial, digital* .......... (732) 264-3681
Martin Printing Service, Inc., 63 Liberty St., Little Ferry 07643
Pres.—Al Martin, 3 emp., *Commercial printing* .......... (201) 440-0410
Master Business Forms Co., 195 Allwood Rd., Clifton 07012
Owner & Pres.—Art Moloughney, 50 emp., *Business forms & digital printing* .......... (973) 594-8743
Master Printing, Inc., 445 Industrial Rd., Carlstadt 07072
Pres.—John Aresta, 25 emp., *Commercial printing* .......... (201) 842-9100
McElwee & Quinn, LLC, 2070 E. Route 70, Ste. 4, Cherry Hill 08003
Pres.—Mary McElwee, 5 emp., *Financial printing* .......... (856) 229-7015
McKella 280, 7025 Central Hwy., Pennsauken 08109
Ptnr.—Joseph C. LaGrossa, 80 emp., *Commercial printing, including digital* .......... (856) 813-1153
Mediagraphics, Inc., 25 Somerset Pl., Clifton 07012
Pres.—Marge Offutt, 12 emp., *Large-format color printing of smart* .......... (973) 777-2202
Mega Media Concepts Ltd., 286 Houses Corner Rd., Sparta 07871
Pres.—Amy Pink, 4 emp., *Large-format digital eco-friendly printing* .......... (973) 919-5661
Merlin Graphics, Inc., 194 Christie Ave., Clifton 07011
Pres.—Joan Barbini, 2 emp., *Commercial, business card & letterhead* .......... (201) 795-3330
Merrill Corp., 649 Rahway Ave., Union 07083
Opers. Mgr.—Tom MacDonald, 100 emp., *Financial printing* .......... (908) 688-5757
Metro Packaging & Imaging, Inc., 5 Haul Rd., Wayne 07470
Chrm., CEO—Manuel Detorres, 110 emp., *Folding carton printing, including* .......... (973) 709-9100
Metro Printing & Promotions, LLC, 311 Mechanic St., Boonton 07005
Owner—Steve Rotella, 6 emp., *T-shirt screen & offset printing* .......... (973) 316-1600
Metro Tag & Label, Inc., 25 E. Spring Valley Ave., Ste. 200, Maywood 07607
Pres.—Phil Glassman, 3 emp., *Commercial offset & digital printing* .......... (201) 845-4747
Metro Web Corp., 5901 Tonnelle Ave., North Bergen 07047
Chrm. of the Board & Pres.—William Vogel, 65 emp., *Financial document printing for the* .......... (201) 553-0700
Michael's Commercial Signs, 629 62nd St., Ste. 31, West New York 07093
Mng. Ptnr. & Pres.—Ruben Gonzalez, 4 emp., *Interior & exterior signs, bus & truck* .......... (201) 868-7166
Mid Atlantic Graphix, Inc., 2558 Tilton Rd., Egg Harbor Township 08234
CEO—J. Riley Gunnels, 14 emp., *Commercial & digital printing & graphic* .......... (609) 569-9990
Minisink Press, Inc., 2 Water St., P.O. Box 278, Newton 07860
Pres.—Tom Delaney, Jr., 2 emp., *Commercial printing* .......... (973) 383-1350
Mint Printing & Design, 475 Westminster Pl., Lodi 07644
Ptnr.—Tom Davis, 4 emp., *Commercial printing & graphic design* .......... (973) 546-2060
Minuteman Press, 35 W. White Horse Pike, Berlin 08009
Pres., Sales Mgr.—Kevin J. Humphrey, 4 emp., *Commercial & digital instant & full-color* .......... (856) 753-0055
Minuteman Press, 2060 Springdale Rd., Ste. 700, Cherry Hill 08003
Owner—Frank J. Bittner III, 7 emp., *Commercial printing* .......... (856) 817-8400
Minuteman Press, 1 Trenton Ave., Clifton 07011
Principal—Joseph Mulligan, 18 emp., *Offset & digital printing, promotional* .......... (973) 894-1500
Minuteman Press, 35 Scotch Rd., Ewing 08628
Pres.—Ted Blumenthal, 4 emp., *Digital, offset, full color & instant* .......... (609) 883-0799
Minuteman Press, 23-51 Fair Lawn Ave., Fair Lawn 07410
Pres., CEO—Mitch Palin, 4 emp., *Full-color & instant printing & graphic* .......... (201) 791-0550
Minuteman Press, 19 Sheridan Ave., Ho-Ho-Kus 07423
Member—Suzanne Seise, 3 emp., *Digital, offset & high-speed printing* .......... (201) 444-0236
Minuteman Press, 120 Speedwell Ave., Morristown 07960
Owner—John Volpecello, Jr., 3 emp., *Commercial & instant printing* .......... (973) 539-0610
Minuteman Press Corp., 55 Commerce St., Newark 07102
Pres.—Holly Kaplansky, 4 emp., *Commercial offset & instant printing* .......... (973) 624-6907
Minuteman Press International, Inc., 1247 Patterson Plank Rd., Secaucus 07094
Co-Pres.—Tom Goldgraber, 5 emp., *Offset printing & computerized typesetting* .......... (201) 866-0186
Minuteman Press of Livingston, LLC, 47 E. Northfield Rd., Livingston 07039
Pres.—Bhuman Patel, 2 emp., *Instant printing, signs, banners &* .......... (973) 992-3136
Minuteman Press, Inc./Windsor Graphics, 2100 Nottingham Way, Hamilton 08619
Owner—Anthony Loffredo, 4 emp., *Offset, screen & digital color printing* .......... (609) 586-3838
Mira Plastics Co., Inc., 1 Mira Ave., Fredon Twp., P. O. Box 399, Newton 07860
Pres.—Anthony Miragliotta, 25 emp., *Thermoplastic injection molding, hot* .......... (973) 383-6380
MJ Corporate Sales, Inc., 109 W. Park Dr., Unit B, Mount Laurel 08054
★ Owner—John Dikmak, 25 emp., *Apparel screen printing & embroidery* .......... (856) 778-0055
MJM Impressions LLC, 20-10 Maple Ave., Bldg. 35-E, P.O. Box 2, Fair Lawn 07410
Pres.—Mitchell Kempin, 2 emp., *Commercial printing of promotional* .......... (973) 423-4999
Mon Far Press Printing, 13 Franklin Pl., Rutherford 07070
Owner & Pres.—Ging Wong, 1 emp., *Offset & letterpress printing* .......... (212) 431-6245
Monarch Art Plastics, LLC, 3838 Church Rd., Mount Laurel 08054
CEO—William Shanley, 25 emp., *Custom plastics printing & fabrication* .......... (856) 235-5151
Monte Printing & Graphics, 225 E. Clay Ave., P.O. Box 293, Roselle Park 07204
Pres.—Philip A. Montalto, 6 emp., *Color digital offset printing & graphic* .......... (908) 241-6600
Moonlight Imaging, Inc., 5 Plains Rd., Augusta 07822
V-P.—Daniel Van Demoere, 8 emp., *Commercial printing* .......... (973) 300-1001
Morgan Printing Service, Inc., 333 S. Pine Ave., South Amboy 08879
CEO & GM—Bob Dein, 10 emp., *Color offset, digital, instant & wide* .......... (732) 721-2959
Morris County Duplicating Corp., 1 Lafayette Ave., Morristown 07960
Pres.—Ernie D'Angelo, 30 emp., *Full-service document imaging, scanning* .......... (973) 993-8484
Morris Forms Corp., 5 Saddle Rd., Cedar Knolls 07927
Pres.—Carl Badenhausen, 5 emp., *Color, offset & digital printing of* .......... (973) 829-1200
Morris Graphics, Inc., 660 N. Broad St., Woodbury 08096
Pres.—Jeff Morris, 5 emp., *Short-run digital & long run offset* .......... (856) 845-4980
Mount Freedom Printing, LLC, 1248 Sussex Tpke., Randolph 07869
★ Owner—Robert Miller, 4 emp., *Digital printing* .......... (973) 933-2700
Mountain Printing Co., Inc., 27 N. Atlantic Ave., P.O. Box 608, Berlin 08009
Pres.—Rose Marie DePasquale, 30 emp., *Computer-to-plate commercial printing* .......... (856) 767-7600
Mr. B Offset Printing, Inc., 1850 Elizabeth Ave., Ste. B, Rahway 07065
Pres.—Thomas Bayone, 2 emp., *Offset & commercial printing* .......... (732) 396-3990
Mr. Printer, 466 New Brunswick Ave., Fords 08863
Owner—Gary Meyer, 2 emp., *Commercial printing* .......... (732) 738-3977
MSP Digital Marketing, 200 Forge Way, Rockaway 07866
COO—Todd Logan, 14 emp., *Commercial & digital printing & large-format* .......... (973) 298-8800
My Private Label, LLC, 112 East Ave., Ste. 5, Hackettstown 07840
★ Owner—John Salvia, 5 emp., *Custom label printing* .......... (908) 441-2375
Narciso Printing, Inc., 120-22 Malvern St., Newark 07105
Pres.—Felix Narciso, 6 emp., *Commercial printing* .......... (973) 578-2088
Nassau Communications, Inc., 115 N. Gold Dr., Robbinsville 08691
Pres.—Ken Fisher, 7 emp., *Commercial & digital printing & promotional* .......... (908) 625-8512
National Color Graphics, 1755 Williamstown Rd., Erial 08081
Owner—Jeffery Hughes, 10 emp., *Commercial printing* .......... (856) 435-6800

Na-Vet Printing Co., 506 Elizabeth Ave., Elizabeth 07206
Pres.—Larry Franchini, 4 emp., *Commercial, digital & color printing* .......... (908) 353-4441
Nelson Press, 111 E. River Rd., Rumson 07760
Pres.—Scott Thompsen, 5 emp., *Commercial printing* .......... (732) 747-0330
NEMA Associates, Inc., 57 Bruen St., Newark 07105
Pres., CEO—Juan Carlos Lopez, 14 emp., *Full-service digital, large-format,* .......... (973) 274-0052
New Jersey Logowear, 100 McKinley Ave., Ste. 6, Manahawkin 08050
★ Ptnr.—Keith Anderson, 7 emp., *Promotional item, apparel & textile* .......... (609) 597-9400
New Jersey Reprographics, Inc., 110 Center St., Garwood 07027
Pres., CFO—Joseph Bizzarro, 4 emp., *Offset & digital color printing of* .......... (908) 789-1616
New Line Printing & Technology, Inc., 1011 Route 22 E., Mountainside 07092
Pres.—John Luciano, 7 emp., *Commercial printing* .......... (973) 232-5003
New Print Shop, Inc., 558 Central Ave., New Providence 07974
Pres.—Mike Tan, 6 emp., *Commercial & medical printing* .......... (609) 392-0782
New Rose, Inc., 1500 Almonesson Rd., Ste. 8, Woodbury 08096
Pres.—Rosemary Jones, 3 emp., *Embroidery & apparel, garment, textile* .......... (856) 812-0509
Newark Industrial Spraying, Inc., 12 Amsterdam St., Newark 07105
Pres.—Richard D. Wantz, 15 emp., *Industrial powder coating, spray painting* .......... (973) 344-6855
Newark Trade Typographers, Inc., 177 Oakwood Ave., Orange 07050
Pres., Sales Mgr.—Robert Wislocky, 20 emp., *Digital color printing, including typesetting* .......... (973) 674-3727
Nexgen Press Corp., 859 Bridgeboro St., Riverside 08075
★ Pres.—Judy Sodomin, 1 emp., *Offset & digital printing* .......... (609) 528-0370
Nextwave Web, LLC, 229 Marshall St., Paterson 07503
Ptnr.—Alia Suqi, 8 emp., *Commercial printing* .......... (973) 742-4339
Nickel Artistic Services, LLC, 39 U.S. Highway 46, Rockaway 07866
Mng. Member—Bryan Nickel, 4 emp., *Interior & exterior signs & banners* .......... (973) 627-0390
Nitka Graphics, Inc., 355 E. 54th St., Elmwood Park 07407
Pres.—Hayim Nitka, 12 emp., *Annual report, newsletter, brochure* .......... (201) 797-3000
Norgus Silk Screen Co., 58 Sylvan Ave., Clifton 07011
Owner & Pres.—Sanjay Thakker, 8 emp., *Screen, cylindrical, digital & large-format* .......... (973) 365-0600
North Hudson Press, 429 Hancock Pl., Fairview 07022
★ Owner—Vincent Petrigliano, 3 emp., *Commercial printing* .......... (201) 941-2520
North Jersey Media Group Inc., 100 Commons Way, Rockaway 07866
V-P., Circ. & Mfg.—Robert Konig, 308 emp., *Daily local & community print & online* .......... (973) 586-8000
North Jersey Media Group, Inc., 1 Garret Mountain Plz., P.O. Box 471, Woodland Park 07424
Chrm. of the Board—Malcolm A. Borg, 425 emp., *Corporate headquarters & daily & weekly* . (973) 569-7000
Northwest Essex Community Healthcare Network, Inc., 83 Walnut St., Montclair 07042
GM & Prod. Mgr.—William Delorenzo, 125 emp., *Contract assembly, packaging & screen* .......... (973) 744-7733
Novatech Graphics, 54 Birch Ave., Ste. A, Little Silver 07739
Owner—David J. McCartney, 3 emp., *Full-color printed envelopes for the* .......... (732) 469-1887
Nunn & Son Custom Lettering, 10 Harding Dr., Brick 08724
Pres.—James Nunn, 1 emp., *Interior & exterior signs, banners,* .......... (732) 899-9682
Oceanic Graphic Printing USA, 105 Main St., 3rd Fl., Hackensack 07601
Pres.—David Li, 10 emp., *Commercial printing* .......... (201) 883-1816
Ocsidot, Inc., 116 South Ave., Garwood 07027
Owner—John Todisco, 15 emp., *Commercial printing* .......... (908) 789-3300
Office Depot Business Solution Div. Of New Jersey, 4 Brighton Rd., Clifton 07012
Dir., Sales—Steve Cimilluca, 150 emp., *Promotional & commercial printing &* .......... (973) 594-3000
Old Hights Print Shop, Inc., 133 S. Main St., Hightstown 08520
Pres.—Cathy M. Simmons, 3 emp., *Commercial, digital & screen printing* .......... (609) 443-4700
Oliveri Printing Corporation, Carl, 316 Main St., Ste. 1, East Rutherford 07073
Owner & Pres.—Carl Oliveri, 10 emp., *Commercial offset & digital printing* .......... (201) 438-0888
Omega Heat Transfer Co., Inc., 329 New Brunswick Ave., Rahway 07065
Pres.—Steven Simon, 10 emp., *Heat transfer labels & silkscreening* .......... (732) 340-0023
On Target Printing & Graphics, LLC, 202 Fairfield Rd., Fairfield 07004
Owner—Jeff Greulich, 5 emp., *Commercial printing & graphic design* .......... (973) 287-6222
One Source Communications, Inc., 9 Whippany Rd., Bldg. C-4, Whippany 07981
Pres.—Tom Coultas, 12 emp., *Commercial printing* .......... (973) 463-0250
One Stop Printing, LLC, 135 Kearny Ave., Ste. B, Kearny 07032
Owner—Darwin Yamuca, 2 emp., *Commercial printing, t-shirt screen* .......... (201) 991-3320
One Two Three, Inc., 537 Mantua Ave., Ste. B, P.O. Box 123, Woodbury 08096
Pres.—Randall Rigley, 15 emp., *Commercial printing* .......... (856) 251-1238
Oscar Printing Services, 549 Newark Ave., Jersey City 07306
Pres.—Oscar Fernando, 1 emp., *Commercial printing* .......... (201) 659-1588
O'Shea's Printing Services Co., Inc., 483 Main St., Hackensack 07601
Pres.—William Bracken, 3 emp., *Commercial printing & related services* .......... (201) 343-8668
Otis Graphics, Inc., 290 Grant Ave., Lyndhurst 07071
Pres.—Patricia Motisi, 5 emp., *Commercial printing* .......... (201) 438-7120
P I P Printing Of Livingston, 465 W. Mount Pleasant Ave., Livingston 07039
Pres.—Georgia Solofoff, 9 emp., *Commercial & instant printing* .......... (973) 533-9330
Packaging Unlimited, Inc., 17 Chelten Way, Bldg. A, Trenton 08638
Pres.—Frank Corrado, 3 emp., *Printed corrugated boxes & foam supplies* .......... (609) 394-9400
Pages Printing & Graphics, 300 N. Route 17, Paramus 07652
Owner—Ron Sallemi, 7 emp., *Full-service commercial, offset, digital* .......... (201) 261-3883
Painting, Inc., 60 Luening St., South Hackensack 07606
CEO & Fin., Hum. Res. & IT Mgr.—Lee M. Bronster, 14 emp., *Metal painting & screen printing* (201) 489-6565
Painton Studios, Inc., 299 U.S. Highway 22, Ste. 21, Green Brook 08812
Pres.—Lisa J. Secula, 3 emp., *4-color digital printing, signage,* .......... (732) 302-0200
Pamco Printers & Stationers, P.O. Box 567, Hopewell 08525
Owner—Vincent Mistretta, 3 emp., *Commercial printing* .......... (609) 309-5025
PaperClip Communications, Inc., 125 Paterson Ave., Little Falls 07424
Pres.—Andy McLaughlin, 20 emp., *Specialty printing & online information* .......... (973) 256-1333
Paragon Printing Shop, 600 Columbia Ave., Millville 08332
Owner—Todd Cimino, 5 emp., *Commercial printing, electronic prepress* .......... (856) 825-2497
Paravista, Inc., Imaging & Printing, 1055 Centennial Ave., Piscataway 08854
Pres.—Michael Spallucci, 25 emp., *Commercial printing* .......... (732) 752-1222
Park Printing Services, Inc., 7300 N. Crescent Blvd., Unit 21, Pennsauken 08110
Owner, Pres. & Pur. Agt.—Don Reed, Sr., 12 emp., *Commercial printing, electronic prepress* (856) 675-1600
Parkway Printing, Inc., 52 N. Main St., Ste. C-11, Marlboro 07746
Pres., Off. Mgr.—Robin Meringolo, 5 emp., *Commercial printing, computerized typesetting* ... (732) 308-0300
Parrish Sign Co., Inc., 2242 S. Delsea Dr., Vineland 08360
Pres.—Charles Parrish, 9 emp., *Full color, digitally printed, lighted* .......... (856) 696-4040
Pat Publications, 1165 Marlkress Rd., Ste. M, P.O. Box 1536, Cherry Hill 08003
V-P.—Carl Buehler, 20 emp., *Commercial printing* .......... (856) 424-0158
Patel Printing Plus Corp., 1036 Commerce Ave., Union 07083
Pres.—J. C. Patel, 10 emp., *Commercial printing, graphic design* .......... (908) 964-6422
Paul-Mark Printing, 37 Stokes St., Freehold 07728
Pres.—Mark Lamhut, 5 emp., *Offset & digital printing, letterpress* .......... (732) 462-9110
Peacock Printing Products, Inc., 48 Woodbine St., Bergenfield 07621
Pres., CEO—Craig Langslet, 20 emp., *Commercial, instant, digital, offset* .......... (201) 385-5585
Penn Jersey Press, P.O. Box 1103, Voorhees 08043
Pres.—Rick Fichter, 1 emp., *Commercial printing* .......... (856) 627-2200

Perfect Printing, Inc., 1533 Glen Ave., Moorestown 08057
Pres., GM—Joe Olivo, 50 emp., *Commercial offset & digital printing* (856) 787-1877
Permalith Plastics, LLC, 6901 N. Crescent Blvd., Pennsauken 08110
V-P., Sales—Gary Brown, 45 emp., *Plastic litho & screen printing, laminating* (856) 488-8000
Peter J. Morley LLC, 21 Village Ct., Hazlet 07730
Pres.—Pete Morley, 3 emp., *Business printing & promotional products* (732) 264-0010
Pharma Press, Inc., 490 W. 1st Ave., Roselle 07203
★ Pres.—Michael Roth, 4 emp., *Commercial printing* (908) 241-4110
Phoenix Business Forms, Inc., 2231 N. East Blvd., Vineland 08360
Pres.—Joanne Buckalew, 5 emp., *Commercial printing, typesetting, promotional* (856) 691-2266
Photo Art Stencil & Sign Corp., 701 17th Ave., P.O. Box 127, Lake Como 07719
Pres.—Frederick J. Tanis, 2 emp., *Industrial & yard signs & screen printing* (732) 681-7300
Pine Hill Printing, Inc., 200 Erial Rd., Pine Hill 08021
Pres.—Edie McKusker, 12 emp., *Commercial printing* (856) 346-2915
Pioneer Packaging, 31 Wilson Dr., Sparta 07871
Pres.—Mark J. Clark, 30 emp., *Printed & die-cut consumer product* (973) 300-9300
Plymouth Printing Co., Inc. (H Q), 450 North Ave., P.O. Box 68, Cranford 07016
CEO—H. D. Auerbach, 8 emp., *Corporate headquarters; pharmaceutical* (908) 276-8100
Pochet Of America, Inc., 415 Hamburg Tpke., Ste. 2, Wayne 07470
Pres.—Borislav Zivkovic, 100 emp., *Corporate headquarters & perfume bottle* (973) 942-4923
Poggi Press, The, 1501 Adams St., P.O. Box M-668, Hoboken 07030
Pres.—Charles Poggi, 21 emp., *Commercial, offset & digital printing* (201) 659-0837
Postcardsrus, Inc, 440 West St., Ste. 2-S, Fort Lee 07024
★ Pres.—Mark Kleinfeld, 40 emp., *Commercial printing* (201) 944-7070
Precision Sign Works, LLC, 82 Richter Rd., Tabernacle 08088
Owner—Victor Gorin, 3 emp., *Exterior, carved, site & yard signs* (609) 702-9700
Premier Press, Inc., 7120 Airport Hwy., Pennsauken 08109
Estimator—Kim McGuigan, 8 emp., *Commercial printing* (856) 665-0722
Premier Printing Solutions, 508 Raritan St., Sayreville 08872
Ptnr. & V-P., Opers.—Edward Ciak, 3 emp., *Commercial printing & silkscreen printing* (732) 525-0740
Premium Color Graphics, Inc., 651 Garden St., Carlstadt 07072
Pres.—John E. Watson, 30 emp., *Commercial printing* (973) 472-7007
Press Room, Inc., The, 100 Youngs Rd., Ste. 2, Mercerville 08619
Pres., Hum. Res. Mgr.—Ted Altomari, 8 emp., *Commercial offset, digital & instant* (609) 689-3817
Pressto Graphics, Inc., 467 Lakehurst Rd., P.O. Box 467, Toms River 08755
Pres.—William Debernardis, 8 emp., *Commercial offset & digital printing* (732) 286-9300
Pressworks, 1879 Old Cuthbert Rd., Unit 28, Cherry Hill 08034
Ptnr.—Diane Reilly, 10 emp., *Commercial printing & promotional products* (856) 427-9001
Pride Products Distributors, LLC, 673 Morris Ave., Ste. 2, Springfield 07081
Pres., CEO—Andrew Nadel, 7 emp., *Promotional product printing* (973) 564-6300
Princeton Printer, 150 Nassau St., Princeton 08542
CEO—Bill Howard, 6 emp., *Digital, instant & large-format color* (609) 924-4630
Princetonian Graphics, Inc., 45 Stouts Ln., Ste. 4, Monmouth Junction 08852
Pres.—Joseph Menig, 14 emp., *Offset & digital printing & graphic* (732) 329-8282
Print Art, Inc., 6726 Delilah Rd., Egg Harbor Township 08234
Pres.—Carl Blase, 50 emp., *Custom commercial, grand format & digital* (609) 645-1940
Print Communications, 7040 Colonial Hwy., Pennsauken 08109
Pres.—Steve Sticco, 5 emp., *Commercial & direct mail printing* (856) 488-0345
Print Group, Inc., The, 24 E. Wesley St., South Hackensack 07606
Ptnr.—Martin Bender, 15 emp., *Digital & offset commercial printing* (201) 487-4400
Print House, Inc., The, 6535 U.S. Highway 9, Howell 07731
Pres.—Leah Kovalenko, 4 emp., *Commercial printing* (732) 364-4254
Print Media, 232 Morris Ave., Springfield 07081
Owner—Robert Walleck, 6 emp., *Commercial printing* (973) 467-0007
Print Shoppe, 1077-M Highway 34, Matawan 07747
Pres.—Paul Silvergold, 15 emp., *Commercial printing* (732) 583-4343
Print Shoppe, Inc., 15 Minneakoning Rd., Ste. 305, Flemington 08822
Pres.—Denise Hayes, 9 emp., *Commercial printing* (908) 782-9213
Print Sign & Design, 1791 S. Burlington Rd., Bridgeton 08302
Pres.—Susan Lucas, 8 emp., *Commercial printing, typesetting &* (856) 451-8766
Print Tech Ltd., 49 Fadem Rd., Springfield 07081
Ptnr.—Russell Evans, 35 emp., *Company headquarters & digital printing* (908) 232-2287
Print Wrap Corp., 95 Sand Park Rd., Cedar Grove 07009
V-P.—Roger Neiman, 15 emp., *Flexographic printing* (973) 239-1144
Printech, 35 Main St., Flemington 08822
Pres.—Joseph Mastrull, 9 emp., *Commercial printing* (908) 782-9986
Printers Of Salem County, LLC, 38 Market St., Salem 08079
Ptnr.—Jeff Weeks, 3 emp., *Commercial printing & electronic prepress* (856) 935-5032
Printer's Place, Inc., The, 8 S. Fullerton Ave., Montclair 07042
Pres.—Francis Michael Lami, 6 emp., *Commercial printing* (973) 744-8889
Printflex, 1250 U.S. Highway 46, Little Falls 07424
Owner—Trish Arminio, 3 emp., *Commercial & instant printing, including* (973) 256-5900
Printing Craftsman, Inc., 130 Bergen Blvd., Fairview 07022
Pres.—Kenneth Stueben, 10 emp., *Commercial, offset, digital, & lithographic* (201) 943-0276
Printing Delite, Inc., 279 Sanford St., East Orange 07018
Pres.—Felipe Gomez, 4 emp., *Offset printing* (973) 676-3033
Printing Industries, LLC, 1543 U.S. Highway 46 E., Parsippany 07054
V-P.—Deron Baumfeld, 8 emp., *Commercial printing, including business* (973) 334-9775
Printing Plus Of South Jersey, 406 N. Route 73, West Berlin 08091
Ptnr.—Robert Behnke, 7 emp., *Instant, digital & small-format & large-forma* (856) 767-3232
Printing Shop Copy Center, The, 338 State St., Perth Amboy 08861
Owner—Lucy Arevelo, 3 emp., *Commercial & digital printing & vinyl* (732) 826-3575
Printing Techniques, Inc., 48 Franklin Ave., Nutley 07110
Pres.—Joseph Vitiello, Jr., 11 emp., *Commercial sheetfed, offset & digital* (973) 667-2606
Printmasters, 1108 Goffle Rd., Hawthorne 07506
Pres.—Paula Cornett, 4 emp., *Business printing, graphics & design* (973) 427-6598
Printology, 615 Franklin Tpke., Ste. 3, Ridgewood 07450
★ Pres.—Jon Bognar, 4 emp., *Commercial & t-shirt screen printing* (201) 345-4632
Print-Tech Products, Inc., 603 1st Ave., Ste. 1-C, Raritan 08869
Pres.—Allan B. Sydlo, 2 emp., *Commercial & business form printing* (908) 231-8700
Printworx, 2103 Whitehorse Mercerville Rd., Hamilton 08619
Owner—Carolyn D'Amico, 4 emp., *Graphic design & blueprints, including* (609) 586-3006
Prism Color Corp., 31 Twosome Dr., Ste. 1, Moorestown 08057
Co-Pres.—Edward Brown, 70 emp., *Commercial printing* (856) 234-7515
Prism Digital Communications, LLC, 1011 U.S. Highway 22, Ste. 1, Mountainside 07092
★ Ptnr. & Mng. Dir.—Brian Dewitt, 10 emp., *Commercial printing* (908) 789-7747
Pro Printing, Inc., 472 Broad Ave., Palisades Park 07650
Pres.—Heug Lee, 2 emp., *Commercial printing* (201) 346-0305
Product Identification Co., Inc., 141 Lanza Ave., Bldg. 19, Garfield 07026
Pres.—Les Weinstock, 20 emp., *Aluminum, vinyl & polyester nameplates* (973) 955-4747
Professional Images, LLC, 17 E. Linden Ave., Englewood 07631
Owner—Steve Nicholson, 1 emp., *Screen printing & embroidery of promotional* (201) 569-4251

Proforma Spectrum Graphics, 373 Route 46 W., Bldg. D, Ste. 130, Fairfield 07004
Pres.—John Vento, 20 emp., *Company headquarters & business form* (973) 882-8666
Proforma Unlimited Marketing Expressions, 36 Keswick Ave., Ewing 08638
Ptnr.—Susan Barosko, 3 emp., *Commercial printing, stationery & promotional* (609) 882-0112
Progressive Printing Corp., 24 Park Ave., West Orange 07052
Pres.—Andrea Risoli, 4 emp., *Commercial printing & graphic design* (973) 736-5800
Promotional Graphics Etc., Inc., 85 Wagaraw Rd., Hawthorne 07506
Pres.—Dianne Dopp, 10 emp., *Printed labels, including ESD static* (973) 423-3900
Promotions & Unicorns Too, Inc., 71 W.Main St., Ste. 102, Freehold 07728
Pres.—Robert Einhorn, 5 emp., *Promotional item, apparel, garment* (732) 308-3444
Pro-Screen Printing, Inc., 590 Belleville Tpke., Bldg. 24, Kearny 07032
Pres.—Dilip Lavani, 8 emp., *Plastic bottles & silk screen printing* (201) 246-7600
Purcell Printing Co., Robert, 244 Kamena St., Fairview 07022
Pres.—Robert Purcell, Sr., 3 emp., *Offset & commercial printing* (201) 941-0375
Pyramid Imprints, 28 N. Washington Ave., Bergenfield 07621
Owner—Eleanor Garcia, 2 emp., *Commercial screen printing, textile* (201) 384-0336
QP2000, LLC, 827 W. Park Ave., Ocean 07712
GM—John Thompson, 5 emp., *Offset & instant printing, digital* (732) 531-8860
Quad/Graphics, Inc., 28 Engelhard Dr., Monroe Township 08831
GM & Plt. Mgr.—George Lane, 169 emp., *Direct marketing print production* (609) 495-1200
Quality Concepts, Inc., 730 Marne Hwy., Moorestown 08057
Ptnr. & V-P., Sales & Mktg.—Michael Santori, 15 emp., *Commercial printing & promotional items* (856) 235-0909
Quality Printing, 1181 E. Landis Ave., Ste. 3, Vineland 08360
Ptnr.—Jerry Dondero, 2 emp., *Printing, advertising specialty products* (856) 691-7577
Quality Repro Centers, Inc., 296 Route 46 E., P.O. Box 111, Elmwood Park 07407
Pres.—Joe DiGiaimo, 6 emp., *Commercial & digital color printing* (201) 794-3905
Quickly Printing, Inc., 1965 Morris Ave., Union 07083
Pres.—Larry Kovacs, 6 emp., *Instant printing, including business* (908) 687-6000
Quikie Print & Copy Shops, 703 Broad St., Shrewsbury 07702
Pres.—Francine Goldstein, 5 emp., *Company headquarters & digital & instant* (732) 933-1010
R. R. Donnelley & Sons Co., 5 Henderson Dr., West Caldwell 07006
Dir., Hum. Res.—Liz Greenberg, 242 emp., *Direct mail printing & fulfillment* (973) 882-7000
R.J. Printing, Inc., 5 Dodd Rd., West Caldwell 07006
Pres.—Ron Culmone, 2 emp., *Commercial printing* (973) 226-9509
Rapid Tag & Label, Inc., 5 Fir Ct., Ste. 4, Oakland 07436
Pres.—Lester Szajna, 5 emp., *Bar code label printing* (201) 337-5551
Raritan Valley Printing Co., 7 Sheephill Cir., Branchburg 08876
Ptnr. & Pres.—Arthur E. Fritz, 3 emp., *Commercial printing, signs & banners* (908) 725-4140
Raybold Mfg., Inc., 102 S. 8th St., Millville 08332
Pres.—William Riland, 9 emp., *Screen printing of glass bottles &* (856) 327-7733
Ray's Reproductions, Inc., 39 Bland St., Emerson 07630
Pres.—Ray Stuart, 5 emp., *Digital, offset, large-format & instant* (201) 666-5650
Red Feather Marketing Group, 332 Main St., Madison 07940
Ptnr.—Steve Becker, 7 emp., *Advertising specialties, including* (973) 966-1399
Redi-Mail Direct Marketing, 107 Little Falls Rd., Fairfield 07004
GM, BDO Opers.—Jay Menna, 100 emp., *Digital printing* (973) 808-4500
Regen & Co., Inc., 20-21 Wagaraw Rd., Bldg. 32, Fair Lawn 07410
GM—Alan Regen, 5 emp., *Commercial printing, letterhead engraving* (973) 423-4236
Register Lithographers, Ltd., 1155 Bloomfield Ave., Clifton 07012
Pres.—Joe Fishman, 50 emp., *Commercial & lithographic printing* (973) 916-2804
Reliance Graphics, Inc., 80 Pompton Ave., Ste. 1, Verona 07044
Pres.—Robert Fetterly, 3 emp., *Election ballot printing* (973) 239-5411
Renew Graphics, 16 W. Park Ave., Park Ridge 07656
Owner—Mike Collins, 2 emp., *Lithographic & commercial printing* (201) 802-1900
Repromatic Printing Co., Inc., 216 Little Falls Rd., Unit 3, Cedar Grove 07009
Pres., GM—Paul Molinari, 4 emp., *Commercial printing* (973) 239-7610
Restaurant Graphics, Inc., 67 Newark Way, Maplewood 07040
Pres.—Tom Stravakis, 7 emp., *Lithographic & commercial printing* (973) 763-4036
Rethink Color, a division of NRI, 3175 Princeton Pike, Lawrenceville 08648
Reg. V-P.—Frank Plum, 20 emp., *Blueprinting & digital, color, instant* (609) 896-4100
Review Printing, Inc., 53-55 E. Holly Ave., Pitman 08071
Pres.—Mark Petersen, 4 emp., *Commercial printing* (856) 589-7200
Ridgewood Press, Inc., 609 Franklin Tpke., Ridgewood 07450
Pres.—Robert Modelski, 10 emp., *Commercial printing* (201) 670-9797
Riedel Sign Co., Inc., 15 Warren St., Little Ferry 07643
Pres.—William C. Riedel, 5 emp., *Interior & exterior signs, vehicle* (201) 641-9121
Riegel Communication Group, One Graphics Dr., P.O. Box 7430, Ewing 08628
Pres.—Kathleen Atkins, 75 emp., *Commercial printing* (609) 771-0555
Rios Engraving, 1 Maple Ave., Morristown 07960
Owner, Plt. Opers. & Sales & Mktg. Mgr.—Rolando G. Rios, 3 emp., *Custom & laser engraving* (973) 539-5749
Riverside Acquisition Group, LLC (H Q), 365 New Albany Rd., Moorestown 08057
Pres.—Cliff McDuggle, 7 emp., *Company headquarters & private investment* (856) 802-1900
Riverside Graphics, Inc., 40 Little St., Belleville 07109
★ Pres.—Paul Caprio, 10 emp., *Commercial printing & graphic design* (973) 844-1011
Riverside Prints LLC, 11 Lawrence Cir., Middletown 07748
Pres., CEO—Howard Kirschner, 2 emp., *Large-format digital & offset printing* (732) 671-8222
Rocco Press, Inc., 171 Walnut St., Paterson 07522
Owner—Lou Rocco, 10 emp., *Commercial printing* (973) 790-4000
Rogers Printing Center, 11 Lexington Ave., Trenton 08618
Pres.—Roger G. Chupik, 1 emp., *Digital, offset & letterpress printing* (609) 883-3238
Roll Flex Label Co., LLC, 199 Lee Pl., Hackensack 07601
Owner—William Zink, 7 emp., *Pressure-sensitive label printing* (201) 489-3330
Roned Printing, 6 DeForest Ave., Ste. 2, East Hanover 07936
Owner—Ronald Russo, 3 emp., *Commercial printing* (973) 386-1848
Roy Press Printers, 57 Bridgewaters Dr., Apt. 17, Oceanport 07757
Owner—Ralph Lawrence, 3 emp., *Commercial printing* (732) 922-9460
Royer Graphics, Inc., 101 Lincoln Dr., Laurel Springs 08021
Pres.—Tony Cannuli, 8 emp., *Offset, digital & web printing & graphic* (856) 344-7935
Royer Group, Inc., 7120 Airport Hwy., Pennsauken 08109
Pres.—Amanda Schwartz, 20 emp., *Offset & digital printing* (856) 665-6400
Rutler Screen Printing, Inc., 169 Belview Rd., Phillipsburg 08865
Pres. & V-P.—Allen Shubert, 22 emp., *Screen printing* (908) 859-3327
S & M Press, Inc., 169 Semel Ave., Ste. 2, Garfield 07026
Owner—Maxine Bing, 11 emp., *Commercial printing, promotional items* (973) 778-4405
S J Print Solutions, 257 Ford Rd., Howell 07731
Pres.—Adeline McGovern, 4 emp., *Commercial, digital & color printing* (732) 363-7711
Sanakirk, Inc., 1400 Berlin Rd., Ste. 123, Cherry Hill 08003
CEO—Kirk R. Runton, 4 emp., *Commercial, digital, small-format &* (856) 429-0715
Sandoval Graphics & Printing, 9 Minnetonka Rd., Somerdale 08083
Mng. Ptnr.—Tony Sandoval, 6 emp., *Commercial, offset & digital printing* (856) 435-7320
Sapphire Envelope & Graphics Co., Inc., 214 W. Davis Rd., Magnolia 08049
Pres.—Anthony Mellaca, 10 emp., *Commercial printing* (856) 782-2227

S.I.C.

F48 © Copyright 2015 Manufacturers' News, Inc. S.I.C. SECTION

Scheller Printing Co., Lewis, 2275 Old Georges Rd., New Brunswick 08902
Pres.—Lewis Scheller, 3 emp., *Commercial printing* ............ (732) 843-5050
Scott Graphics Printing, Inc., 690-D River Rd., New Milford 07646
Pres.—Scott McNiff, 15 emp., *Commercial, offset, textile screen* ............ (201) 262-0473
Second Impressions, LLC, 149 Stelton Rd., Piscataway 08854
Owner—Ken Steiner, 3 emp., *Commercial printing* ............ (732) 752-7171
Seibel Group, Inc., The, 741 Alexander Rd., Princeton 08540
Pres.—Kenneth Seibel, 11 emp., *Commercial & digital printing* ............ (609) 799-3279
Select Services, 500 Morris Ave., Ste. 116, Springfield 07081
Owner—David Hunter, 5 emp., *Printing, direct mail service, promotional* ............ (973) 467-8860
Selover Co., LLC, R. N., 17 Wolf Rd., Millville 08332
Owner & Pres.—Richard Selover, 1 emp., *Commercial printing* ............ (856) 293-9009
Serafino Printing Co., Inc., 516 Bloomfield Ave., Verona 07044
Pres.—Cathy Horling, 3 emp., *Offset & letterpress printing* ............ (973) 857-3450
Service Apex, 564-A Union Ave., Bridgewater 08807
★ Pres.—Ken Griggs, 10 emp., *Commercial printing, t-shirt screen* ............ (732) 560-2222
Service Apex, 299 U.S. Highway 22, Green Brook 08812
Owner—Ken Griggs, 6 emp., *Digital commercial printing, signs,* ............ (732) 424-1616
Sheridan Communication, Inc., 1425 3rd Ave., Alpha 08865
CEO—James Sheridan, 50 emp., *Offset & 4-color printing & electonic* ............ (908) 454-0700
Shore Point Communications, 160 Lehigh Ave., Ste. B, Lakewood 08701
Pres.—David Francis, 9 emp., *Commercial printing & direct mailing* ............ (732) 961-7936
Showcase Graphics, LLC, 33 E. Main St., Ste. 4, Moorestown 08057
Owner—Debra Marsdale, 3 emp., *Commercial & digital printing of packaging* ............ (856) 722-5400
Showcase Printing Of Iselin, 181 E. James Pl., Iselin 08830
Pres.—Vivian Hoppock, 2 emp., *Commercial printing* ............ (732) 283-0438
Shreeji Printing Corp., 55 Veterans Blvd., Carlstadt 07072
Pres.—Dilip Patel, 16 emp., *Full color printing of pressure-sensitive* ............ (201) 842-9500
Sign Effectz, 800 New Brunswick Ave., Ste. 7, Rahway 07065
Owner & Pres.—Brian Snyder, 1 emp., *Signs, banners, decal printing, apparel* ............ (732) 388-7446
Signarama, 655 S. White Horse Pike, Hammonton 08037
Owner—Richard Matteo, 3 emp., *Illuminated & non-illuminated full-color* ............ (609) 878-3375
Signarama, 349 U.S. Highway 9, Ste. 6, Manalapan 07726
Ptnr. & Pres.—Jackie Barber, 4 emp., *Full-service commercial & residential* ............ (732) 536-7575
Sign-A-Rama, 400 Fairfield Rd., Ste. 5, Fairfield 07004
Owner & Mng. Member—Eric Bleezarde, 7 emp., *Interior & exterior architectural signs* ............ (973) 227-6363
Sign-A-Rama, 1459 Highway 38, P.O. Box 360, Hainesport 08036
Owner—Gary Kuffer, 4 emp., *Interior & exterior, ADA & project* ............ (609) 702-1444
Signmasters, Inc., 217 Brook Ave., 2nd Fl., Front, Passaic 07055
Pres.—Howard Muser, 75 emp., *Offset printing & glass & plastic screen* ............ (973) 614-8300
SignPros, 1215 Black Horse Pike, Glendora 08029
Owner & Pres.—Nick Kappatos, 18 emp., *LED channel letters, illuminated sign* ............ (856) 939-1099
Signs By Tomorrow, 326 U.S. Highway 22, Ste. 8-B, Green Brook 08812
Owner—Rajesh Patel, 4 emp., *Interior & exterior, trade show, architectura* ............ (732) 424-9785
Signs Of Sense, 79 Bassett Hwy., Dover 07801
Owner & Pres.—Scott Rothbart, 3 emp., *Full-color interior & exterior signs* ............ (973) 361-0037
Sir Speedy, 897 Rancocas Rd., Westampton 08060
GM—Joseph Barlam, 4 emp., *Offset printing, including color, instant* ............ (609) 267-1232
Sir Speedy Printing, 3100 Quakerbridge Rd., Mercerville 08619
Pres.—David A. Kaplan, 9 emp., *Printing, mailing, fulfillment & marketing* ............ (609) 586-8222
Sir Speedy Printing, 897 Rancocas Rd., Mount Holly 08060
Pres.—Joseph Barlam, 2 emp., *Commercial printing & typesetting* ............ (609) 267-1232
Sir Speedy Printing, 22 W. Landis Ave., Ste. Q, Vineland 08360
GM & Cust. Serv. Mgr.—Allison Trovarelli, 9 emp., *Instant, commercial, high-speed color* ............ (856) 691-0741
Sir Speedy Printing, 405 Goffle Rd., Wyckoff 07481
Pres.—Gregg Miller, 7 emp., *Commercial & instant printing, bindery* ............ (201) 444-0234
Sir Speedy Printing And Marketing Services, 5505 Route 130 N., Pennsauken 08110
Pres.—Francis V. Gavin, Jr., 5 emp., *Digital color & offset printing, signs* ............ (856) 488-1480
Sir Speedy Printing and Marketing Services, 1032 Stelton Rd., Piscataway 08854
Pres., Fin. & GM—Mark Yanofsky, 4 emp., *High-speed full-color digital & offset* ............ (732) 981-9011
Sir Speedy Printing Center, 28 Campus Dr., Edison 08837
Owner & Pres.—Robert Chido, 7 emp., *Offset & digital printing & typesetting* ............ (732) 225-2272
Sir Speedy Printing Center, 122 Ridge Rd., Lyndhurst 07071
Dir.—Tom Penisch, 5 emp., *Full-color digital, traditional offset* ............ (201) 896-2727
Sir Speedy Printing Center, 300 S. Lenola Rd., Ste. 22, Maple Shade 08052
Pres.—Dennis Marks, 8 emp., *Offset, single, multicolor & color* ............ (856) 866-0588
Sir Speedy Printing Centers, 39 S. Broad St., Woodbury 08096
Pres.—Michael Kelly, 5 emp., *Instant & digital printing* ............ (856) 251-0220
Sir Speedy Westfield, 516 North Ave. E., Westfield 07090
Owner & V-P., MIS—Barbara Murphy, 5 emp., *Digital printing & graphic design,* ............ (908) 232-1001
Sky Printing Co., 338 Montgomery St., Jersey City 07302
Owner—Laurie Benjamin, 1 emp., *Business format digital printing* ............ (201) 433-3133
Skylands Press, 57 Trinity St., P.O. Box 809, Newton 07860
Owner—John Daly, 3 emp., *Commercial printing* ............ (973) 383-5006
Skyline Graphics Design, 11 Skyline Lake Dr., Ringwood 07456
Pres.—Scott White, 4 emp., *Offset, digital & digital full-color* ............ (973) 839-3329
Small Business Service Center, 122 E. Kings Hwy., Ste. 504, Maple Shade 08052
CEO—Sandy Testa, 20 emp., *Laser, inkjet, digital, lettershop* ............ (856) 234-8059
Smith, Inc., Roy D., 20 Foster St., P.O. Box 537, Bergenfield 07621
Owner—Roy D. Smith, 5 emp., *Commercial printing* ............ (201) 384-4163
Sommers Plastic Products, Inc., 31 Styertowne Rd., Clifton 07012
Chrm.—Edward Schecter, 20 emp., *Plastic & vinyl fabrics, including* ............ (973) 777-7888
SourceCodes & Displays, Inc., 135 Fairview Ave., Prospect Park 07508
Pres., CEO—William F. Higgins, 5 emp., *Display box & letterhead commercial* ............ (973) 942-1965
South Jersey Custom Screen Printing, 481 W. Route 38, Maple Shade 08052
Owner—Stan Jay, 2 emp., *Custom screen printing* ............ (856) 482-1500
SpectraMedia, 1634 E. Elizabeth Ave., Linden 07036
Owner—Mike Kaufman, 25 emp., *Financial printing, including finance* ............ (908) 928-1220
Speed Pro Imaging Of Piscataway, 56 Ethel Rd. W., Ste. 14, Piscataway 08854
Owner—R. Scott Schoner, 3 emp., *Large-format digital printing & banners* ............ (732) 662-9860
Speedpro Imaging, 52 E. Centre St., Ste. 3-B, Nutley 07110
Pres.—Doug Nixon, 4 emp., *Large-format graphic printing, including* ............ (973) 542-8384
Sports Information Media, Inc., 343 Millburn Ave., Ste. 208, Millburn 07041
Ptnr. & Pres.—Mark Furman, 5 emp., *Commercial printing of lineup cards* ............ (973) 564-5014
Square One, Inc., 111 Gaither Dr., Ste. 104, Mount Laurel 08054
Pres.—Colin Townsend, 45 emp., *Commercial, offset & digital printing* ............ (856) 234-6999
Squiggly Productions, LLC, 164 Main St., Butler 07405
Owner—Guy Scognamiglio, 2 emp., *Offset & full-color digital printing* ............ (973) 838-7475
Standard Printing & Mail Service, 30-A Plymouth St., P.O. Box 11021, Fairfield 07004
Pres., GM—Kevin Walsh, 12 emp., *Offset & direct mail printing, electronic* ............ (973) 790-3333
Stand-Out Signs, Inc., 49 W. Pond Rd., Perth Amboy 08861
Pres., Off. Mgr.—Joseph Masaruca, 3 emp., *Neon interior & exterior signs, banners* ............ (732) 442-9399

Staples Contract Digital Copy Services, 258 Fernwood Ave., Edison 08837
GM—Robert Zatorsky, 20 emp., *Digital color, black & white & large-format* ............ (732) 346-1377
Starnet Business Solutions, Inc., 46 Industrial Ave., Mahwah 07430
CEO—John S. Brink, 30 emp., *Digital offset & commercial printing* ............ (201) 760-2600
Stauts Printing & Graphics, 12 Maine Trl., Medford 08055
Bus. Mgr.—W. Stauts, 5 emp., *Commercial printing & typesetting* ............ (609) 654-5382
Stevenson & Smith, Inc., 450 W. 1st Ave., Roselle 07203
Pres.—Peter Stevenson, 7 emp., *Commercial printing* ............ (908) 862-4211
Stewart Business Forms, Inc., 28 Redstone Ridge, P.O. Box 715, Voorhees 08043
Pres., CFO—Gail Stewart, 2 emp., *Business forms & printing* ............ (856) 768-2011
Stobbs Printing Co., Inc., 18 Washington St., P.O. Box 91, Bloomfield 07003
Pres.—Gail Tunstead, 5 emp., *Commercial printing* ............ (973) 748-4441
Stone Graphics Co., Inc., 5020 Industrial Rd., Farmingdale 07727
Pres.—Raymond C. Stone, 6 emp., *Screen printing, large-format digital* ............ (732) 919-1111
Stone Mountain Printing, 74 Main St., Ste. 1, Woodbridge 07095
Pres.—Steve Steinberg, 8 emp., *Commercial & digital printing, graphic* ............ (732) 634-4444
Studio 042, 423 Bloomfield Ave., Montclair 07042
CEO—Scott F. Kennedy, 10 emp., *Commercial & instant printing* ............ (973) 509-7591
Stuyvesant Press, Inc., 119 Coit St., Irvington 07111
Pres., CEO—Michael Roesch, 10 emp., *Offset, commercial, digital, color* ............ (973) 399-3880
Sunset Printing And Engraving, 10 Kice Ave., Wharton 07885
Pres.—Mitchel Wainer, 42 emp., *Commercial offset & on demand printing* ............ (973) 537-9600
Sure Mark Labels, Inc., 4 Flynn Ter., P.O. Box 501, West Orange 07052
Pres.—James V. Politan, 5 emp., *Printed labels* ............ (973) 768-4859
Suzie Mac Specialties, Inc., 12-B Connery Ct., East Brunswick 08816
Pres.—Suzanne MacDougall, 9 emp., *Custom & screenprinted photoluminescent* ............ (732) 238-3500
Swift Co., Inc., John S., 375 North St., Unit N, Teterboro 07608
GM—Doug Wilhelm, 10 emp., *Commercial printing, including letterheads* ............ (201) 678-3232
Swift Print Solutions, LLC, 405 Front St., Belvidere 07823
Owner—Linda Swift, 4 emp., *Commercial, screen & instant printing* ............ (908) 475-1374
Symphony Printing, 19-21 Brook St., Belleville 07109
Pres.—Leroy Johnson, 6 emp., *Commercial printing* ............ (973) 751-5100
Tabloid Graphic Services, Inc., 7101 Westfield Ave., Pennsauken 08110
Pres.—Steve Brosious, 65 emp., *Circular heat-set & cold web printing* ............ (856) 486-0410
Tandem Graphics, Inc., 207 Wanaque Ave., Pompton Lakes 07442
Pres.—Michael Nass, 6 emp., *Banners & posters, including digital* ............ (973) 513-9779
Tangent Graphics, 151 Hobart St., Hackensack 07601
Pres.—John Wehle, 8 emp., *Commercial printing* ............ (201) 488-2840
Tanter, Inc., 151 Westfield Ave., Clark 07066
Pres.—Walter Swierc, 2 emp., *Commercial printing* ............ (732) 382-3555
Target Printing & Graphics, 9 E. Passaic St., Hackensack 07601
Pres.—Tony Flaim, 9 emp., *Offset & digital printing, signs, banners* ............ (201) 883-0200
Taunton Graphics, Inc., 1049 Industrial Dr., West Berlin 08091
Pres.—Paul Falkowski, 7 emp., *Label printing & graphic design* ............ (856) 719-8084
Tech Repro, Inc., 65 Zabriskie St., Hackensack 07601
Pres.—Kevin Tremble, 10 emp., *Large-format, instant & color printing* ............ (201) 489-1333
TEMPTIME Corp., 116 The American Rd., 2nd Fl., Morris Plains 07950
Pres.—Renaat Van den Hooff, 70 emp., *Time & temperature sensitive indicator* ............ (973) 984-6000
The CLI Group, 932 Market St., Paterson 07513
Pres.—Daren Silverstein, 15 emp., *Textile laminating, digital printing* ............ (973) 279-9174
Thermo-Graphics, Inc., 915 E. Hazelwood Ave., Rahway 07065
Pres.—Seth Batzer, 4 emp., *Commercial printing* ............ (732) 669-0252
Thewal, Inc., 12 Center St., Chatham 07928
Ptnr. & Pres.—Susan Kessel, 10 emp., *Commercial & digital printing, electronic* ............ (973) 635-1880
TPG Graphics, 9130 Pennsauken Hwy., Ste. C, Pennsauken 08110
GM—Robert Donner, 6 emp., *Commercial printing* ............ (856) 314-0117
Trade Thermographers, Inc., 65 Worth St., South Hackensack 07606
Off. Mgr.—Lisa Margarito, 9 emp., *Thermographic, commercial & digital* ............ (201) 489-2060
Treasury Printing Services, 101 Carroll St., P.O. Box 30, Trenton 08625
CEO, Chief Printing & Reprographics—Douglas N. Krieger, 30 emp., *Government printing for the* (609) 292-5133
Trek, Inc., 43 Cranmer Rd., P.O. Box 275, Bayville 08721
Pres.—Jack Dynarski, 4 emp., *Short-run digital printed labels, including* ............ (732) 269-6300
Trentypo, Inc., 304 Stokes Ave., Trenton 08638
Pres.—Peter Simon, 8 emp., *Color printing & computerized typesetting* ............ (609) 883-2198
Tretina Printing, Inc., 1301 State Route 36, Concord Ctr., Hazlet 07730
Pres.—Jan Tretina, Sr., 8 emp., *Commercial & offset printing & mailing* ............ (732) 264-2324
Trico Web, LLC, 75 Broad St., Carlstadt 07072
★ Owner—Don Juliano, 20 emp., *Commercial printing* ............ (201) 438-3860
Tri-Lon Color Graphics, Inc., 220 Anderson Ave., Moonachie 07074
Pres.—David Strickler, 35 emp., *Digital printing* ............ (201) 708-6900
Trinity Press, LLC, 655 Market St., Paterson 07513
Pres.—Kevin Barnes, 40 emp., *Offset, digital, commercial, textile* ............ (973) 881-0690
Tri-Plex Business Products, Inc / Graphic Solutions, 400 Morris Ave., Ste. 220, Denville 07834
Pres.—Walter Lapham, 9 emp., *Digital color, commercial, offset,* ............ (973) 627-5388
Tri-State Tape & Label Co., Inc., 351 Railroad Ave., P.O. Box 377, Beverly 08010
Pres.—David F. Wimer, 7 emp., *Flexible packaging, digital, offset* ............ (800) 682-7892
Tropp Printing Corp., 8 Woodhollow Dr., Holmdel 07733
Pres.—William Tropp, 5 emp., *Offset & color printing & electronic* ............ (212) 233-4519
Trout Printing LLC, 33 Reeves St., Millville 08332
Owner—Bo Novakowski, 5 emp., *Commercial offset printing* ............ (856) 327-8366
Trukmann's Inc., 4 Wing Dr., Cedar Knolls 07927
CEO—Paul Korman, 25 emp., *Commercial, large-format, lithographic* ............ (973) 538-7718
Type-O-Graphics, LLC, 222 Outwater Ln., Ste. 1, Garfield 07026
Pres.—Ruth Valdez, 5 emp., *Commercial printing & typesetting* ............ (973) 253-3333
U. S. S. Corp., 780 Frelinghuysen Ave., Newark 07114
COO—Carlos Matos, 200 emp., *Glass screen printing* ............ (973) 242-1110
Unigraphic Guild, Inc., 10 Route 206, Stanhope 07874
Pres.—Paul Washuta, 16 emp., *Commercial, color & digital printing* ............ (973) 219-2348
Unimac Graphics, LLC, 350 Michele Pl., Carlstadt 07072
Pres.—Steven Rickett, 300 emp., *Large-format, web & sheet-fed commercial* ............ (201) 372-1000
UniServ Advertising, Inc., 37 State Route 35 N., Neptune 07753
Pres.—Glen Suchecki, 11 emp., *Apparel & promotional item screen printing* ............ (732) 774-1010
United Forms Finishing, 1413 Chestnut Ave., 1st Fl., Hillside 07205
Pres., Fin. & Sales Mgr.—Liz Demkin, 20 emp., *Commercial offset & laser printing* ............ (908) 687-0494
United Label Corp., 65 Chambers St., Newark 07105
V-P., Sales—John T. O'Connor, 10 emp., *Pressure-sensitive paper labels* ............ (973) 589-6500
United States Business Card Co., 540 39th St., Ste. 33, Union City 07087
Owner—Richard Meneely, 1 emp., *Letterpress, business card, invitation* ............ (201) 863-8776
Unity Graphics & Engraving/Unity Steel Rule Die, 210 S. Van Brunt St., P.O. Box 88, Englewood 07631
Ptnr.—Diane Iamartino, 50 emp., *Rubber printing, plate engraving &* ............ (201) 569-6400

Universal Graphics Co., 497 Bloomfield Ave., Bloomfield 07003
Pres.—Michael Zwier, 5 emp., *Commercial offset printing* ........ (973) 748-4009
Universal Prints, Inc., 625 Newark Ave., Jersey City 07306
Pres.—David Gabriel, 2 emp., *Commercial & instant printing* ........ (201) 656-7878
Upper Case Printing, LLC, 752 Porchtown, Franklinville 08322
Owner—Richard Procida, 1 emp., *Commercial printing* ........ (856) 875-5000
Urner Barry Publications, 182 Queens Blvd., Bayville 08721
Pres., Publisher—Paul Brown, Jr., 40 emp., *Commercial, offset, envelope, business* ........ (732) 240-5330
US Magic Box, Inc., 221 McArthur Ave., Garfield 07026
Pres.—Sam Omar, 62 emp., *Die & laser cutting & printing for* ........ (973) 772-2070
Ventnor Print Shop Co., 128 N. Wyoming Ave., P.O. Box 2174, Ventnor City 08406
Pres.—Richard Juliano, 2 emp., *Commercial printing* ........ (609) 822-2974
Vernon Display Graphics, 145 Commerce Rd., Carlstadt 07072
Cont.—Todd Smith, 34 emp., *Screen printing & grand-format digital* ........ (201) 935-7117
Victor's Printing, 3 Perina Blvd., Cherry Hill 08003
CEO, CFO—Len Victor, 35 emp., *Commercial printing* ........ (856) 424-4600
Viskal Printing, LLC, 40 Commerce Way, Unit E, Totowa 07512
Pres.—Krishnan Thampi, 7 emp., *Brochure, stationery, newsletter &* ........ (973) 812-6600
Waldwick Printing Co., 1 Harrison Ave., Waldwick 07463
Owner—William Cook, 4 emp., *Commercial printing* ........ (201) 652-5848
Wall Street Group, Inc., 1 Edward Hart Dr., Jersey City 07305
Pres.—Phillip J. McGee, 35 emp., *Commercial printing* ........ (201) 333-4784
Walter's Signs, 159 W. White Horse Pike, Berlin 08009
Owner—Walter Schmitz, 2 emp., *Interior & exterior signs, commercial* ........ (856) 210-6324
Washington Stamp Exchange, Inc., 2 Vreeland Rd., Florham Park 07932
Pres.—Michael August, 10 emp., *Commercial printing* ........ (973) 966-0001
Watson Graphics, Inc., 578 Kearny Ave., Kearny 07032
Pres.—Marlene Watson, 1 emp., *Offset, instant, color & thermographic* ........ (201) 955-0283
Weaver Assocs. Printing Service, Inc., 945 Lincoln Ave. E., Cranford 07016
Owner & Pres.—John Weaver, 15 emp., *Commercial printing* ........ (908) 272-6224
Webco Graphics/W.G.I. Corp., 1875 Swarthmore Ave., Lakewood 08701
Pres.—Glenn Davis, 12 emp., *Newsprint printing of newspapers, brochures* ........ (732) 370-2900
Webtech, Inc., 108 N. Gold Dr., Robbinsville 08691
Pres., CEO—Art Maynard, 25 emp., *Heat transfer labels, MDFboard edging* ........ (609) 259-2800
Welter & Kreutz Printing Co., 51 Worth St., P.O. Box 1834, South Hackensack 07606
Pres.—Robert W. Kreutz, 6 emp., *Commercial printing, promotional materials* ........ (201) 489-9098
Wet Stone Graphics, 645 Greenway Pl., River Vale 07675
Owner—Marc Cohen, 1 emp., *Fine arts printing* ........ (201) 307-1531
Wheal-Grace Corp., 300 Ralph St., P.O. Box 67, Belleville 07109
Pres.—Nancy Salvini, 19 emp., *Commercial, offset & digital printing* ........ (973) 450-8100
White Eagle Printing Co., 2550 Kuser Rd., Hamilton 08691
Pres.—Eric Bielawski, 20 emp., *Commercial printing* ........ (609) 586-2032
Wholesale Print House, 1757 John F. Kennedy Blvd., Jersey City 07305
★ Owner—Omar Gordon, 3 emp., *Commercial printing , including business* ........ (201) 333-7746
Wilcox Press, 6 Main St., Hamburg 07419
Owner—Jody Palmasano, 4 emp., *Commercial printing* ........ (973) 827-7474
Wiley's Lake Press, Inc., 1902 Greenwood Lake Tpke., Hewitt 07421
Pres.—Richard Wiley, 2 emp., *Offset & color printing of brochures* ........ (973) 728-9231
Williams Berell, Inc., 612 E. Elizabeth Ave., P.O. Box 1341, Linden 07036
Pres.—Barry Boydman, 2 emp., *Commercial printing* ........ (908) 486-4952
Wisco Promo & Uniform, Inc., 160 Route 46 E., Saddle Brook 07663
Pres.—Anthony Park, 4 emp., *Embroidery & screen printing* ........ (973) 767-2022
Wizard Printing Corp., 29 Evans Pl., Ste. 82, Pompton Plains 07444
Pres.—Neil Keough, 9 emp., *Commercial printing* ........ (973) 835-8048
Woodbridge Printing Center, 1201 U.S. Highway 9 S., Woodbridge 07095
Owner & Pres.—Frank Racz, 7 emp., *Offset & digital printing* ........ (732) 855-1996
Word Center Printing, 1905 Highway 33, Ste. 10, Hamilton Square 08690
Owner, Fin., GM & MIS Mgr.—Marilyn Silverman, 4 emp., *Full-color & high-speed printing of* (609) 586-5825
Write Impression, The, 549 Highway 35, Red Bank 07701
Owner—Kristine Ancona, 1 emp., *Custom invitation & stationery printing* ........ (732) 706-3700
Yukon Graphics, Inc., 239 New Rd., Ste. B-110, Parsippany 07054
Pres.—Alan Verbeke, 7 emp., *Commercial, color & digital printing* ........ (973) 575-5700
Zeek's Tees, 515 Highway 36, Belford 07718
Owner—Frank Zechman, 6 emp., *Textile embroidery, screen & digital* ........ (732) 291-2700
Zenith Printing, 7440 Baxter Ave., Merchantville 08109
★ Owner—Mark Wintermute, 1 emp., *Commercial printing, including business* ........ (856) 662-6275

## 2761 Business forms—manifold

Acu-Data Business Products, Inc., 1572 State Route 23, Ste. D, Butler 07405
Pres.—Gerald J. Vinci, 2 emp., *Business forms, advertising specialties* ........ (973) 838-5678
Alete Printing, LLC, 722 Dartmouth Ct., P.O. Box 371, Wenonah 08090
V-P., CEO—John Koskinen, 4 emp., *Commercial & variable data printing* ........ (856) 468-3536
Berry Business Procedure Co., 6 Park St., P.O. Box 845, Cranford 07016
Pres.—David M. Cheek, 4 emp., *Commercial & business form printing* ........ (908) 272-6464
C & W Systems, 17-04 Split Rock Rd., P.O. Box 201, Fair Lawn 07410
Owner—Walter Miller, 1 emp., *Commercial business form & envelope* ........ (201) 791-7892
Capital Printing Corp., 420 South Ave., Middlesex 08846
Pres.—Nolan Russo, 120 emp., *Commercial & business form printing* ........ (732) 560-1515
Comply, Inc., 330 Dalziel Rd., Linden 07036
Off. & Sales Mgr.—Shari Klein-Katz, 10 emp., *Commercial business form printing* ........ (908) 862-6600
County Graphics Forms Management Co., 2 Stercho Rd., Linden 07036
Pres.—Robert Gaudiosi, 20 emp., *Business form printing* ........ (908) 474-9797
CRT International, Inc., 260 Wagner St., Middlesex 08846
V-P., Hum. Res. & IT—Carmine Tarantino, 8 emp., *Commercial & packaging printing of* ........ (973) 887-7737
Degree Day Systems, Inc., 33 Village Park Rd., P.O. Box 510, Cedar Grove 07009
Pres., Treas.—Thomas Saczawa, 10 emp., *Business forms & meter tickets for* ........ (973) 239-7900
Deluxe Mfg. Operations, Inc., 105 U.S. Highway 46, Mountain Lakes 07046
Plt. Mgr.—Steve Penna, 200 emp., *Check printing* ........ (973) 334-8000
Designs By James, 892 N. Delsea Dr., Vineland 08360
Pres.—James Crescenzo, 3 emp., *Interior & exterior signs, screen printing* ........ (856) 692-1316
Drew & Rogers, Inc., 30 Plymouth St., Fairfield 07004
Pres.—Thomas M. Rogers, 35 emp., *Commercial & business form printing* ........ (973) 575-6210
Federal Direct (H Q), 95 Main Ave., Ste. 2, Clifton 07014
CEO—Bernie Steins, 45 emp., *Company headquarters; direct marketing* ........ (973) 667-9800
Graphic Impressions Printing Co., 4391 Route 42, Turnersville 08012
Sales Rep.—Dennis Neill, 8 emp., *Commercial & business form printing* ........ (856) 728-2266
Hippographics, Inc. (H Q), 9100 Pennsauken Hwy., Pennsauken 08110
Owner & Pres.—Larry Weiss, 3 emp., *Corporate headquarters; business form* ........ (856) 662-9111
Hygrade Business Group, Inc., 232 Entin Rd., P.O. Box 1099, Clifton 07014
Pres., CEO—Victor Albetta, 40 emp., *Offset, digital & color printing of* ........ (973) 249-6700
J Z D, LLC, 733 Route 18, East Brunswick 08816
Pres.—David Loewenstein, 3 emp., *Business form printing* ........ (732) 257-2727
Maclearie, 917 18th Ave., Wall 07719
Owner—Jim McCleary, 5 emp., *Business card & form printing* ........ (732) 974-8878
Maggio Data Forms Printing Ltd., 171 Heller Pl., Bellmawr 08031
GM—Adolf Fiebelkorn, 35 emp., *Business form printing* ........ (856) 931-7805
Master Business Forms Co., 195 Allwood Rd., Clifton 07012
Owner & Pres.—Art Moloughney, 50 emp., *Business forms & digital printing* ........ (973) 594-8743
Mercury Printing, Inc., 14 Veronica Ave., Somerset 08873
Opers. Mgr.—Jan T. Vreeland, 9 emp., *Clinical drug study labels & case report* ........ (732) 247-6828
Morris Forms Corp., 5 Saddle Rd., Cedar Knolls 07927
Pres.—Carl Badenhausen, 5 emp., *Color, offset & digital printing of* ........ (973) 829-1200
New Jersey Business Forms Mfg. Corp., 55 W. Sheffield Ave., Englewood 07631
Pres.—David Harnett, 65 emp., *Business form printing* ........ (201) 569-4500
Proforma Spectrum Graphics, 373 Route 46 W., Bldg. D, Ste. 130, Fairfield 07004
Pres.—John Vento, 20 emp., *Company headquarters & business form* ........ (973) 882-8666
Quality Repro Centers, Inc., 296 Route 46 E., P.O. Box 111, Elmwood Park 07407
Pres.—Joe DiGiaimo, 6 emp., *Commercial & digital color printing* ........ (201) 794-3905
Quickly Printing, Inc., 1965 Morris Ave., Union 07083
Pres.—Larry Kovacs, 6 emp., *Instant printing, including business* ........ (908) 687-6000
Roelyn Litho, Inc., 687 Propect St., Unit 410, Lakewood 08701
Pres.—Vincent Praino, 8 emp., *Business form printing* ........ (732) 942-9650
S & S Printing, 610 S. White Horse Pike, Somerdale 08083
Pres.—Carol Staines, 2 emp., *Business forms printing* ........ (856) 784-2718
Sky Printing Co., 338 Montgomery St., Jersey City 07302
Owner—Laurie Benjamin, 1 emp., *Business format digital printing* ........ (201) 433-3133
Stewart Business Forms, Inc., 28 Redstone Ridge, P.O. Box 715, Voorhees 08043
Pres., CFO—Gail Stewart, 2 emp., *Business forms & printing* ........ (856) 768-2011
Tri-Plex Business Products, Inc / Graphic Solutions, 400 Morris Ave., Ste. 220, Denville 07834
Pres.—Walter Lapham, 9 emp., *Digital color, commercial, offset,* ........ (973) 627-5388

## 2771 Greeting cards

Crown Assocs. U. S. A., Inc., 19 Winged Foot Dr., Livingston 07039
Pres.—Linda Hart, 3 emp., *Business & greeting card printing* ........ (973) 785-3477
CustomShots, 189 Silver Lake Dr., West Creek 08092
Owner & Sales Mgr.—Diane Hillman, 1 emp., *Custom photographic greeting cards,* ........ (609) 296-1811
GINN Co., 812 Jersey Ave., Jersey City 07310
Pres.—Robert Glickenhaus, 20 emp., *Christmas, wedding, social, business* ........ (201) 216-1660
Grandview Printing Co., Inc., 33 W. End Rd., Totowa 07512
Pres.—Lewis DeMarco, 8 emp., *Commercial offset printing of greeting* ........ (973) 890-0006
Greetingtap, LLC, 832 Spicer Ave., South Plainfield 07080
★ Owner—Kadeer Beg, 6 emp., *Personalizable video greeting cards* ........ (347) 731-4263
Lydia's Land, LLC, P.O. Box 852, Marlton 08053
Owner—Lydia Land, 1 emp., *Handmade greeting cards* ........ (856) 983-7258
Minuteman Press Of North Arlington, 75 Ridge Rd., North Arlington 07031
V-P.—Amir Djabini, 5 emp., *Instant printing, electronic prepress* ........ (201) 991-1030
Nobleworks, Inc., 500 Patterson Plank Rd., Union City 07087
Pres.—Ron Kanfi, 2 emp., *Greeting cards* ........ (201) 420-0095
Prudent Publishing Co., 400 N. Frontage Rd., Landing 07850
Plt. Mgr.—Sharon Ruthnan, 100 emp., *Greeting cards publishing* ........ (973) 347-4554
Prudent Publishing Co. (H Q), 65 Challenger Rd., Ridgefield Park 07660
Chrm.—Alan Solow, 110 emp., *Company headquarters; greeting cards* ........ (201) 641-7900
Quadriga Art, Inc., 825 Hylton Rd., Pennsauken 08110
Dir., Opers.—Tim Merges, 75 emp., *Greeting cards* ........ (856) 663-2500

## 2782 Blankbooks & looseleaf binders

Deluxe Mfg. Operations, Inc., 105 U.S. Highway 46, Mountain Lakes 07046
Plt. Mgr.—Steve Penna, 200 emp., *Check printing* ........ (973) 334-8000
DSA Graphics, LLC, 431 E. Main St., Ste. 3, Denville 07834
★ Owner—Dominic Santaite, 4 emp., *Commercial & promotional screen printing* ........ (973) 625-7760
Infor Metal & Tooling Manufacturing Corporation, 16 Commerce Rd., Cedar Grove 07009
Pres.—Charles Insel, 10 emp., *Contract metal stamping, tool & die* ........ (973) 571-9520
Jonathan Leasing Corp., 17 Water St., Lebanon 08833
Pres.—Barry A. Reed, 3 emp., *Loose-leaf binders, index tabs, media* ........ (908) 226-3434
Myron Corp., 205 Maywood Ave., Maywood 07607
CEO—Jim Adler, 450 emp., *Imprinted personalized business gifts* ........ (201) 843-6464
New York Sample Card Co., Inc., 812 Jersey Ave., 3rd Fl., Jersey City 07310
Pres., MIS Mgr.—Kenneth Ehrlich, 25 emp., *Sample cards & books, including color* ........ (201) 526-9040

## 2789 Bookbinding & related work, nec

21st Century Finishing, Inc., 280 N. Midland Ave., Ste. 414, Saddle Brook 07663
Pres.—Karen DeMaio, 19 emp., *Foil stamping, die cutting, embossing* ........ (201) 797-0212
Abbey/Watchung, LLC, 16 N. 26th St., Kenilworth 07033
Pres. & Member—Margaret A. Beute, 5 emp., *Film, archival & vinyl laminating,* ........ (908) 241-7717
Abby Bindery, LLC, 121 Christie St., Newark 07105
Member—Jeff Maida, 30 emp., *Bookbinding* ........ (973) 690-5509
Allegra Marketing Print Mail, 665 State Route 27, Iselin 08830
Pres.—Alkesh Shah, 3 emp., *Digital color, instant, direct mail* ........ (732) 404-0665
Alpha Graphics, 95 Greenwood Ave., Midland Park 07432
Pres.—Mark Shishmanian, 7 emp., *Offset printing, graphic design & binding* ........ (201) 447-4800
Arch Crown, Inc., 460 Hillside Ave., Ste. 1, Hillside 07205
CEO—Norman Liebman, 32 emp., *Tags & labels, including die cutting* ........ (973) 731-6300
Avenue Printing Co., 143 Franklin Tpke., Waldwick 07463
Owner—Ruth Amarante, 3 emp., *Commercial offset spot & digital full-color* ........ (201) 652-2035
Bassil Bookbinding & Finishing, Inc., 2 Alsan Way, Little Ferry 07643
Pres.—Eli Bassil, 15 emp., *Bookbinding* ........ (201) 440-4925
Bellia Business Products & Services, Inc., 1047 N. Broad St., Woodbury 08096
Pres.—Thomas Bellia, 30 emp., *Spiral & GBC binding & commercial printing* ........ (856) 845-2234
Bernardsville Print Center, 21 Mine Brook Rd., Bernardsville 07924
Pres.—Richard C. Steinberg, 7 emp., *Digital instant, commercial, 1-4 color* ........ (908) 766-4073
Bethel Bindery, Inc., 1500 Route 539, Tuckerton 08087
Owner & Pres.—Tom Giger, 6 emp., *Thesis, genealogy, journal, CD & legal* ........ (609) 296-5043
Bielen Graphic Arts, R. J., 6 Jules Ln., New Brunswick 08901
Pres.—Robert J. Bielen, 11 emp., *Laser die cutting & gold stamping of* ........ (732) 545-3501
Bindgraphics Co., Inc., 490 W. 1st Ave., Roselle 07203
Pres.—Eugene Trunzo, 20 emp., *Pamphlet & folder binding* ........ (908) 245-1110
Bind-Rite Services, Inc., 16 Horizon Blvd., South Hackensack 07606
Pres.—Elliot Ward, 125 emp., *Bookbinding* ........ (201) 440-5585
Bound To Last, 144 E. 9th St., Lakewood 08701
★ Owner—Joseph Apfel, 1 emp., *Bookbinding* ........ (732) 942-0423
C W C Industries, Inc., 185 Foundry St., Newark 07105
Pres.—Stan Acroman, 10 emp., *Hot stamping foil* ........ (973) 344-1434
Colorful Story Books, Inc., 2 Hollywood Ct., South Plainfield 07080
Pres., Estimator—John Blewitt, 50 emp., *Bookbinding* ........ (908) 561-3333

ColorSource, Inc., 7025 Central Hwy., Pennsauken 08109
Pres.—Fred DeMarco, 9 emp., *Commercial printing, binding, fulfillment* (856) 488-8100
Com-Pak, Inc., 365 New Albany Rd., Moorestown 08057
CEO—Clif McDougall, 280 emp., *Commercial & digital printing & binding* (856) 802-1900
Contemporary Graphic Solutions, Inc., 7001 N. Park Dr., Pennsauken 08109
Pres.—Tim Moreton, 196 emp., *Printing, packaging, finishing, die* (856) 663-7277
Content Critical LLC, 800 Central Blvd., Carlstadt 07072
CEO—Fred VanAlstyne, 203 emp., *Lithographic, wide-format & digital* (201) 528-2777
CRT International, Inc., 260 Wagner St., Middlesex 08846
V-P., Hum. Res. & IT—Carmine Tarantino, 8 emp., *Commercial & packaging printing of* (973) 887-7737
Custom & Wasmund Bindery, 9 Sheridan Ave., Clifton 07011
Pres.—Lance Belostock, 11 emp., *Bookbinding & duplication services* (973) 815-1400
Danielle Die Cut Products, Inc., 238 Lindbergh Pl., Paterson 07503
Pres.—Danny Dibetitto, 20 emp., *Steel rule dies & die cutting of paper* (973) 278-3000
Delaware Valley Bindery, Inc., 18 Graphics Dr., Trenton 08628
Pres.—Joseph Rigby, 30 emp., *Perfect & mechanical binding, saddle* (609) 771-1550
Direct Printing Impressions, 33 Fairfield Pl., West Caldwell 07006
V-P., Sales—Richard Luggiero, 25 emp., *Commercial & digital printing & mailing* (973) 227-6111
DSA Graphics, LLC, 431 E. Main St., Ste. 3, Denville 07834
★ Owner—Dominic Santaite, 4 emp., *Commercial & promotional screen printing* (973) 625-7760
E & M Bindery, Inc., 11 Peekay Dr., Clifton 07014
Pres.—Gary Markovits, 100 emp., *Bookbinding* (973) 777-9300
Edison Lithographing Corp., 3725 Tonnelle Ave., North Bergen 07047
Pres.—George Gross, 80 emp., *Large-format printing & finishing* (201) 902-9191
Engraved Images, Route 202 & Demun Pl., P.O. Box 966, Far Hills 07931
Owner—Heidi Gammon, 5 emp., *Offset & color printing & engraving* (908) 234-0323
Everbind Marco Book Co., Inc., 60 Industrial Rd., P.O. Box 695, Lodi 07644
Pres.—Stewart Penn, 50 emp., *Bookbinding* (973) 458-0485
Federal Direct (H Q), 95 Main Ave., Ste. 2, Clifton 07014
CEO—Bernie Steins, 45 emp., *Company headquarters; direct marketing* (973) 667-9800
Flortek Corp., 39 W. 55th St., Bayonne 07002
Pres.—Warren Harris, 45 emp., *Upholstery, textile & wall covering* (201) 436-7700
Gilosa Bindery, Inc., Joseph A., 555 20th Ave., Paterson 07504
Pres.—Bob Gilosa, 20 emp., *Bookbinding* (973) 279-8006
Globe Die Cutting Products, 76 Liberty St., P.O. Box 4339, Metuchen 08840
Cont., Sales Mgr.—Joel Nagler, 110 emp., *Print finishing for the folding carton* (732) 494-7744
Glue-Fold, Inc., Div. Of Perfect Finishing, Inc., 40 Webro Rd., Clifton 07012
CFO—Isabel Garcia, 6 emp., *Gluing, including affixing, attaching* (973) 575-8400
Graphics Depot, Inc., 11 Middlebury Blvd., Ste. 4, Randolph 07869
Pres.—David Bernstein, 16 emp., *Digital four & full color offset, instant* (973) 927-8200
Greentree Printing, 9004 Lincoln Dr. W., Ste. G, Marlton 08053
Ptnr. & Pres.—Paul Barbera, 3 emp., *Offset, instant & full-color printing* (856) 596-2330
Hawk Graphics, Inc., 1248 Sussex Tpke., Ste. C-9, Randolph 07869
Pres.—Nick Battaglino, 20 emp., *Commercial offset, digital color &* (973) 895-5569
HighRoad Press, 220 Anderson Ave., Moonachie 07074
★ Owner & CEO—Hallie Satz, 45 emp., *Commercial, digital, sheet-fed & web* (201) 708-6900
Hippographics, Inc. (H Q), 9100 Pennsauken Hwy., Pennsauken 08110
Owner & Pres.—Larry Weiss, 3 emp., *Corporate headquarters; business form* (856) 662-9111
House Of Gold, Inc., 1505 Suckle Hwy., Pennsauken 08110
Pres.—Scott Solomon, 18 emp., *Foil stamping* (856) 665-0020
Hub Print & Copy Center, The, 2037 Lemoine Ave., Fort Lee 07024
Pres.—Gerard Tonner, 2 emp., *Commercial printing & binding services* (201) 585-7887
IDP Films, 24 Commerce Rd., Ste. P, Fairfield 07004
Owner—Jin Kim, 4 emp., *Foil stamping* (973) 227-1661
Image Makers Printing, Copy & Sign Center, 1581 State Route 23, Wayne 07470
Pres.—Gino Nuzzo, 5 emp., *High-speed color printing, blueprinting* (973) 633-1771
LB Book Bindery, LLC, 19 Gardner Rd., Ste. I, Fairfield 07004
Ptnr.—Frank Lozito, 15 emp., *Bookbinding* (973) 244-0442
LCI Graphics, Inc., 2400 Main Street Ext., Ste. 8, Sayreville 08872
Pres.—Daniel Seratelli, 8 emp., *Commercial offset, web-to-print, digital* (973) 893-2913
Linder & Co., Inc., 1183 W. Side Ave., Jersey City 07306
Pres.—George R. Linder, 18 emp., *Commercial offset, conventional & digital* (201) 386-8788
LoGatto Bookbinding, Inc., 390 Paterson Ave., P.O. Box 7483, East Rutherford 07073
Pres., Pur., Sales & Mktg. Mgr.—Michael Logatto, 4 emp., *Cloth & leather bookbinding* (201) 438-4344
Lont & OverKamp, 175 U.S. Highway 46, Fairfield 07004
CEO—Ken Lont, 50 emp., *Offset, digital & direct mail printing* (973) 942-2243
McCormicks Bindery, Inc., 5815 Magnolia Ave., Pennsauken 08109
Pres.—Dan McCormick, 40 emp., *Bookbinding* (856) 663-8035
Meadowlands Bindery, Inc., 146 W. Commercial Ave., Moonachie 07074
Pres.—Carmine Idone, 40 emp., *Bookbinding* (201) 935-6161
Microfold, Inc., 375 North St., Unit C, Teterboro 07608
CEO—Paul Perna, 10 emp., *Paper product folding, hole punching* (201) 641-5052
Mid State Bindery, 148 Sylvania Pl., South Plainfield 07080
Owner—Steve Stout, 2 emp., *Bookbinding* (908) 755-9388
Miniature Folding, 300 9th Ave., Hawthorne 07506
Pres.—Christopher Taliercio, Sr., 20 emp., *Miniature folding, padding, tipping* (201) 773-6477
Minuteman Press, 349 U.S. Highway 9, Ste. 7, Englishtown 07726
Pres.—Joe Lorenz, 6 emp., *Instant printing & mailing & bindery* (732) 536-8788
Minuteman Press, 19 Sheridan Ave., Ho-Ho-Kus 07423
Member—Suzanne Seise, 3 emp., *Digital, offset & high-speed printing* (201) 444-0236
Minuteman Press Of Dover, 25 Pine St., Ste. 10, Rockaway 07866
Pres., R & D Mgr.—Andy Krauser, 2 emp., *Offset & digital & color instant printing* (973) 625-5800
Minuteman Press Of North Arlington, 75 Ridge Rd., North Arlington 07031
V-P.—Amir Djabini, 5 emp., *Instant printing, electronic prepress* (201) 991-1030
Mountain Lion, Inc., 9 Voorhees Ct., P.O. Box 799, Pennington 08534
Pres.—John Monteleone, 1 emp., *Book printing, binding & packaging* (609) 730-1665
New York Sample Card Co., Inc., 812 Jersey Ave., 3rd Fl., Jersey City 07310
Pres., MIS Mgr.—Kenneth Ehrlich, 25 emp., *Sample cards & books, including color* (201) 526-9040
Northeast Bindery, Inc., 419 Trumbull St., Elizabeth 07206
Owner & Pres.—Bel Romlochan, 22 emp., *Bookbinding* (908) 436-3737
Nu E-Z Custom Bindery, LLC, 111 Essex St., Hackensack 07601
Pres.—Julia Paulucci, 40 emp., *Die cutting, gluing, wire-o-binding* (201) 488-4140
O&T-Suter Conservation, LLC, 96 Hillside Ave., Emerson 07630
Pres. & Manager—Millie Suter, 4 emp., *Hand bookbinding, including paper &* (201) 265-0262
Pages Printing & Graphics, 300 N. Route 17, Paramus 07652
Owner—Ron Sallemi, 7 emp., *Full-service commercial, offset, digital* (201) 261-3883
Paul-Mark Printing, 37 Stokes St., Freehold 07728
Pres.—Mark Lamhut, 5 emp., *Offset & digital printing, letterpress* (732) 462-9110
Perfect Finishing, Inc., 40 Webro Rd., Clifton 07012
Co-Pres.—Bruce Flaim, 50 emp., *Corporate headquarters & paper die* (973) 472-7400
Permalith Plastics, LLC, 6901 N. Crescent Blvd., Pennsauken 08110
V-P., Sales—Gary Brown, 45 emp., *Plastic litho & screen printing, laminating* (856) 488-8000
Poplar Bindery, Inc., 300 Mill St., Moorestown 08057
Pres.—Steve Heisler, 16 emp., *Print finishing & binding of pharmaceutical* (856) 727-8030
Postalogic, LLC, 64 Outwater Ln., Ste. 1, Garfield 07026
Pres.—Brian Parker, 40 emp., *Binding & finishing services for the* (973) 546-1400
Precision Printing Group, LLC, 117 Jackson Rd., Berlin 08009
Pres.—Lori Colucci, 40 emp., *Prepress & offset digital printing* (856) 753-7903
Princeton Printer, 150 Nassau St., Princeton 08542
CEO—Bill Howard, 6 emp., *Digital, instant & large-format color* (609) 924-4630
Quick Cut Stamping & Embossing, Inc., 815 E. Main St., Maple Shade 08052
Pres.—Holly Zahradnick, 10 emp., *Die cutting, foil stamping & embossing* (856) 321-0050
Reid Book Binding, D., 543 New Durham Rd., Metuchen 08840
Owner—David Reid, 2 emp., *Bookbinding* (732) 494-9589
Riverside Acquisition Group, LLC (H Q), 365 New Albany Rd., Moorestown 08057
Pres.—Cliff McDuggle, 7 emp., *Company headquarters & private investment* (856) 802-1900
Spink & Gabor, Inc., 11 Troast Ct., Clifton 07011
Pres.—Edward R. Spink, 3 emp., *Bookbinding* (973) 478-4551
Spruce Run Printing, 2005 Route 31, Clinton 08809
Ptnr.—Tom Kowal, 3 emp., *Offset printing & binding of banners* (908) 638-6464
Square One, Inc., 111 Gaither Dr., Ste. 104, Mount Laurel 08054
Pres.—Colin Townsend, 45 emp., *Commercial, offset & digital printing* (856) 234-6999
Squiggly Productions, LLC, 164 Main St., Butler 07405
Owner—Guy Scognamiglio, 2 emp., *Offset & full-color digital printing* (973) 838-7475
Tandem Graphics, Inc., 207 Wanaque Ave., Pompton Lakes 07442
Pres.—Michael Nass, 6 emp., *Banners & posters, including digital* (973) 513-9779
Tech Repro, Inc., 65 Zabriskie St., Hackensack 07601
Pres.—Kevin Tremble, 10 emp., *Large-format, instant & color printing* (201) 489-1333
Thewal, Inc., 12 Center St., Chatham 07928
Ptnr. & Pres.—Susan Kessel, 10 emp., *Commercial & digital printing, electronic* (973) 635-1880
Trentypo, Inc., 312 Stokes Ave., P.O. Box 304, Trenton 08638
Bindery Mgr.—Rich Yoder, 5 emp., *Bookbinding & print finishing for the* (609) 883-5971
Turul Bookbindery, Inc., 60 Route 15 S., Wharton 07885
Pres.—Margit P. Rahill, 5 emp., *Custom books & boxes, bookbinding,* (973) 361-2810
Unigraphic Guild, Inc., 10 Route 206, Stanhope 07874
Pres.—Paul Washuta, 16 emp., *Commercial, color & digital printing* (973) 219-2348
Unimac Graphics, LLC, 350 Michele Pl., Carlstadt 07072
Pres.—Steven Rickett, 300 emp., *Large-format, web & sheet-fed commercial* (201) 372-1000
V M C Die Cutting Corp., 357 Cortlandt St., Belleville 07109
Pres.—Vincenza Reczynski, 4 emp., *Die cutting, embossing, foil stamping* (973) 450-4655

## 2791 Typesetting

A M Graphy, 95 Myer St., Hackensack 07601
★ Ptnr.—Leandro Morales, 3 emp., *Electronic prepress* (201) 488-0360
Accucolor, LLC, 771 Shrewsbury Ave., Ste. B, Shrewsbury 07702
Owner—Robert LaBella, 2 emp., *Company headquarters & electronic prepress* (732) 741-4594
Affordable Copies Center, 55 Halsey St., Newark 07102
Owner—Jaman Monir, 2 emp., *Instant printing & electronic prepress* (973) 802-1007
Affordable Offset Printing, Inc., 809 Hylton Rd., Ste. 11, Pennsauken 08110
Pres.—Gary Coates, 4 emp., *Offset & digital printing, electronic* (856) 661-0722
Afton Publishing, LLC, P.O. Box 1399, Andover 07821
Ptnr. & Pres.—Patricia J. Cunningham, 2 emp., *Electronic prepress* (973) 579-2442
All American Print & Copy Center, 518 Highway 35, Red Bank 07701
Owner—Ralph Cucinelli, 2 emp., *Commercial offset printing & typesetting* (732) 758-6200
Allegra Marketing Print & Mail, 533 S. Shore Rd., Marmora 08223
Owner—Nicholas Wieand, 10 emp., *Offset printing & typesetting* (609) 390-1400
Allegra Marketing Print Mail, 665 State Route 27, Iselin 08830
Pres.—Alkesh Shah, 3 emp., *Digital color, instant, direct mail* (732) 404-0665
Allen Group SMC, 60 Readington Rd., Branchburg 08876
Pres.—Steven Hegna, 60 emp., *Envelope & offset printing & typesetting* (908) 231-1100
Alliance Design, Inc., 434 Union Blvd., Totowa 07512
Pres.—William Ng, 12 emp., *Commercial electronic prepress & graphic* (973) 904-1900
AlphaGraphics, 12 Stults Rd., Ste. 100, Dayton 08810
Pres.—David Kovacs, 15 emp., *Printing, digital archiving, finishing* (609) 860-9444
Alphagraphics, Inc., 60 Speedwell Ave., Morristown 07960
Owner—Brian Harrigan, 7 emp., *Commercial offset & instant printing* (973) 984-0066
American Plus Printers, Inc., 2604 Atlantic Ave., Wall 07719
Pres.—Dianne Strohmenger, 12 emp., *Offset printing & electronic prepress* (732) 528-2170
Apollo Quik Print Co., Inc., 49 Orchard St., Hackensack 07601
Pres.—Kevin Bliss, 4 emp., *Offset printing & typesetting* (201) 488-1101
Arc Reprographics, Inc., 1110 New Rd., Absecon 08201
Pres.—John Curry, 7 emp., *Blueprinting & typesetting* (609) 646-9324
Arms Graphics, 169 Paris Ave., Northvale 07647
Pres.—Allan Schneider, 3 emp., *Offset & instant printing & typesetting* (201) 767-6504
Art Press Printing, Inc., 124 Clements Bridge Rd., Barrington 08007
Owner & Pres.—Robert McHugh, 10 emp., *Commercial printing & typesetting* (856) 547-8953
Avenue Printing Co., 143 Franklin Tpke., Waldwick 07463
Owner—Ruth Amarante, 3 emp., *Commercial offset spot & digital full-color* (201) 652-2035
B & W Printing Co., Inc., 730 Fairfield Ave., Kenilworth 07033
Sales Mgr.—Gary Butler, 5 emp., *Instant digital & commercial printing* (908) 241-3060
Bartlett Printing & Graphics, Inc., 4495 Route 130 S., Burlington 08016
CEO—Clifford Lewis, 3 emp., *Offset printing & typesetting* (609) 386-1525
Bill's Printing Service, Inc., 2829 S. Broad St., Trenton 08610
Pres.—Bill Mason, 6 emp., *Commercial printing & typesetting* (609) 888-1841
Bind-Rite Robbinsville, 1 Applegate Dr., Robbinsville 08691
Prodn. Mgr.—Helder Gomes, 85 emp., *Electronic prepress & color separations* (609) 208-1917
Bistis Press, 1310 Clinton Ave., Irvington 07111
Ptnr.—Nick Bistis, 2 emp., *Commercial printing & typesetting* (973) 373-8033
Boro Printing, Inc., 813 Broadway, West Long Branch 07764
Pres.—Gary Delatush, 5 emp., *Offset, digital color & large-format* (732) 229-1899
BP Graphics & Printing, 315 4th St., Lakewood 08701
Pres.—Ben Heineman, 15 emp., *Instant printing & typesetting* (732) 905-9830
Budget Print Center, 2510 Atlantic Ave., Atlantic City 08401
Ptnr.—Ellen Fishlevich, 2 emp., *Offset printing & computerized typesetting* (609) 348-4589
Budget Print Center, 590 Valley Rd., Montclair 07043
Owner—Dave Pradip, 3 emp., *Offset printing & typesetting* (973) 744-5520
Business Card Express, 8 E. Stow Rd., Ste. 140, P.O. Box 728, Marlton 08053
Pres.—John McTigue, 38 emp., *Offset printing & computerized typesetting* (856) 596-3150
C & D Printing Co., 118 Broadway, Point Pleasant Beach 08742
Owner—Brenda Nasce, 2 emp., *Offset printing, typesetting & bookbinding* (732) 892-8044
Cantone Press, Inc., 161 Coolidge Ave., Englewood 07631
Owner—Joe Cantone, 10 emp., *Typesetting & offset printing* (201) 569-2288
Cape Printing Express, Inc., 821 Shunpike Rd., Cape May 08204
Pres.—Richard Adelizzi, 2 emp., *Offset printing & typesetting* (609) 884-8080

Central Printing & Typesetting, 1501 Route 37 E., Toms River 08753
Pres.—Linda L. Adams, 3 emp., *Offset printing & typesetting* .......... (732) 929-0011

Connection Printing, Inc., 86 5th Ave., Hawthorne 07506
Pres.—Bob Rino, 4 emp., *Commercial printing & typesetting* .......... (973) 423-2004

Counter-Fit Quick Printing, Inc., 145 Newark Ave., Belleville 07109
Pres.—Alan Nelson, 1 emp., *Offset printing & typesetting* .......... (201) 420-7926

Creative Color Lithographers, Inc., 611 South Ave., Garwood 07027
Pres.—Chris Christopher, 18 emp., *Offset printing & typesetting* .......... (908) 789-2295

Criterion Publishing Co., 87 Forrest St., P.O. Box 4278, Metuchen 08840
V-P., GM—Christopher M. Crane, 7 emp., *Newspaper publishing* .......... (732) 548-8300

Crossfire Publications, 551 Bloomfield Ave., Apt. C-14, West Caldwell 07006
★ V-P.—Rita Cristello, 5 emp., *Music book publishing & electronic* .......... (973) 403-1633

CRW Graphics, Inc., 9100 Pennsauken Hwy., Pennsauken 08110
CEO—Harriet Weiss, 130 emp., *Commercial offset, digital & variable* .......... (856) 662-9111

Dawn Bible Students Assn., 199 Railroad Ave., East Rutherford 07073
Plt. Mgr.—Ken M. Fernets, 6 emp., *Book printing & typesetting* .......... (201) 438-6421

Deans Graphics, 16 Mill St., P.O. Box 809, Mount Holly 08060
Pres.—Stephen Deans, 5 emp., *Web & sheetfed offset printing & graphic* .......... (609) 261-8817

Denni's Studio, 169 Semel Ave., Garfield 07026
Owner—Denise Blatt, 1 emp., *Electronic prepress & graphic design* .......... (973) 220-4898

Diversified Impressions, Inc., 119 Coit St., Irvington 07111
Pres.—Richard Feldman, 6 emp., *Commercial printing & typesetting* .......... (973) 399-9041

Downtown Printing Center, Inc., 46 Paterson St., New Brunswick 08901
Pres.—Juan Ruiz, 14 emp., *Offset printing & typesetting* .......... (732) 246-7990

Duca Printing Co., Inc., 247 Haddon Ave., West Berlin 08091
Pres.—Vincent Duca, 4 emp., *Offset printing & typesetting* .......... (856) 767-2242

Dynamic Printing & Graphics, Inc., 250 Delawanna Ave., Clifton 07014
Pres., CEO—Lou Mascola, 7 emp., *Offset printing, color separations* .......... (973) 473-7177

EarthColor, Inc., 249 Pomeroy Rd., P.O. Box 169, Parsippany 07054
CEO—Robert Kashan, 100 emp., *Corporate headquarters & commercial* .......... (973) 884-1300

Excel Color Graphics, Inc., 207 W. Jersey Ave., Woodbury Heights 08097
Pres.—Jean Paul Bonnette, 5 emp., *Offset, instant & commercial printing* .......... (856) 848-3345

Express Printing, Inc., 209 W. Saint Georges Ave., Linden 07036
Pres.—Sam Kamdar, 4 emp., *Offset printing & typesetting* .......... (908) 925-6300

F S T Printing, Inc., 1324 Bound Brook Rd., Middlesex 08846
Pres.—Sal Buonocore, 5 emp., *Offset & instant printing & electronic* .......... (732) 560-3749

Falcon Printing Co., 613 Central Ave., Westfield 07090
Ptnr.—Anthony Archambault, 4 emp., *Commercial printing, typesetting &* .......... (908) 232-1991

Farmingdale Printing, 70 Main St., Farmingdale 07727
Pres.—Tom Trenholm, 3 emp., *Offset & digital printing & electronic* .......... (732) 938-2727

Fast Copy Printing Center, 81 Broad St., Keyport 07735
Owner, Fin. & MIS Mgr.—William Sacks, 4 emp., *Offset & instant printing & typesetting* .......... (732) 739-4646

Fast Print, LLC, 514 Main St., Fort Lee 07024
Pres.—Anthony Clemente, 2 emp., *Offset printing & electronic prepress* .......... (201) 944-2350

Ferrante Press, Inc., 516 Bloomfield Ave., Verona 07044
GM—Vincent Ferrante, 3 emp., *Offset & letterpress printing, typesetting* .......... (973) 239-4344

Filipino Express Newspaper, Inc., 2711 John F. Kennedy Blvd., Jersey City 07306
Publisher & GM—Lito Gajilan, 7 emp., *Newspaper publishing* .......... (201) 434-1114

Four Star Reproduction, Inc., 52 Paterson Ave., Ste. 2, Newton 07860
Pres.—Charles Cioppa, 35 emp., *Commercial offset & digital printing* .......... (862) 268-8200

FrontEnd Graphics, 1951 Old Cuthbert Rd., Ste. 414, Cherry Hill 08034
Owner, Pres. & Mktg. Mgr.—Elizabeth Maul, 6 emp., *Digital direct mail printing, large* .......... (856) 547-1600

G & H Soho, Inc., 413 Market St., Elmwood Park 07407
Pres.—James K. Harris, 15 emp., *On demand digital printing & electronic* .......... (201) 216-9400

Giordano, Inc., Philip A., 59 Garfield Ave., Garfield 07026
Ptnr.—Robert Giordano, 3 emp., *Commercial printing, electronic prepress* .......... (973) 546-9267

Glorin Printing, Inc., 258 Clifton Ave., Newark 07104
Pres., Hum. Res. & IT Mgr.—Irving Linares, 3 emp., *Commercial printing & electronic prepress* (973) 481-3233

Gloucester City News, Inc., 34 S. Broadway, P.O. Box 151, Gloucester City 08030
Publisher—Albert J. Countryman, Jr., 4 emp., *Newspaper publishing* .......... (856) 456-1199

GM Printing, 106 Pleasant Ave., Bergenfield 07621
Pres.—Greg Madison, 7 emp., *Instant, commercial & large-format* .......... (201) 385-2525

GMPC Printing, 1 Trenton Ave., Clifton 07011
Principal—Joseph Mulligan, 18 emp., *Offset printing & typesetting* .......... (973) 894-1500

Good Impressions Printing, Inc., 28 Scott St., P.O. Box 409, Riverside 08075
Pres.—Robert Price, 10 emp., *Offset & instant printing, typesetting* .......... (856) 461-3232

Good Impressions, Inc., 325 W. Washington Ave., Washington 07882
Pres.—Marion Kennedy, 10 emp., *Offset printing & typesetting* .......... (908) 689-3071

Gracis, Inc., 25 Graphic Pl., Moonachie 07074
Pres.—Robert Powell, 2 emp., *Offset printing & typesetting* .......... (201) 296-0700

Graphic Techniques, LLC, 10 S. West Blvd., P.O. Box 4, Newfield 08344
Pres.—Darryl Erickson, 3 emp., *Commercial printing & typesetting* .......... (856) 697-2480

Graphics Plus Corp., 210 W. Parkway, Ste. 7, Pompton Plains 07444
Pres.—John Prentzel, 5 emp., *Offset printing, color separations* .......... (973) 835-3744

Graphictone, 360 Sylvan Ave., Ste. 4, Englewood Cliffs 07632
Pres.—Kirby Tan, 5 emp., *Electronic prepress, including print-on-deman* .......... (201) 568-2008

Greenwich Graphics, LLC, 234 16th St., 8th Fl., Jersey City 07310
Owner, Pres. & MIS Mgr.—Wolfe Gluck, 8 emp., *Printing plates, computerized typesetting* .... (212) 727-1116

Harwill Corp., 3175 Princeton Pike, Lawrenceville 08648
Pres.—Steve Portrude, 6 emp., *Commercial & digital printing, typesetting* .......... (609) 895-1955

Hippographics, Inc. (H Q), 9100 Pennsauken Hwy., Pennsauken 08110
Owner & Pres.—Larry Weiss, 3 emp., *Corporate headquarters; business form* .......... (856) 662-9111

Hummel Distributing Corp., 850 Springfield Rd., P.O. Box 3199, Union 07083
Co-Pres., Hum. Res. Mgr.—John Hummel, 35 emp., *Offset printing & typesetting* .......... (908) 688-5300

Impact Printing, 762 Green St., Iselin 08830
Owner—Eugene Lucas II, 2 emp., *Offset printing & typesetting* .......... (732) 636-8893

Imtech Graphics, Inc., 545 Dell Rd., Carlstadt 07072
Pres.—Gary Cordovano, 130 emp., *Electronic prepress, commercial printing* .......... (201) 933-8002

Infinity Design & Printing, 1358 Burnet Ave., Union 07083
Owner—Pierre Filsaime, 5 emp., *Commercial printing & graphic design* .......... (908) 206-8844

Ink Well Printers Inc., 38 S. 21st St., Kenilworth 07033
Pres.—Elizabeth Ensslin, 4 emp., *Offset printing & typesetting* .......... (908) 272-8090

J & J Printing Co., 1023 Broadway, Bayonne 07002
Owner—Fran Tagliareni, 6 emp., *Offset printing & typesetting* .......... (201) 858-8895

J K Design, Inc., 465 Amwell Rd., Hillsborough 08844
Pres.—Jerome Kaulius, 45 emp., *Computerized typesetting & color separations* .......... (908) 428-4700

Jamesburg Press Madison Printing, Inc., 9 E. Railroad Ave., Jamesburg 08831
Pres.—Fred Voza, 2 emp., *Offset printing & typesetting* .......... (732) 521-0262

Jamm Printing, 108 W. Sylvania Ave., Neptune 07753
Owner—Robert LaBella, 7 emp., *Commercial printing & typesetting* .......... (732) 502-0110

JEM Print Co., 36 Atlantic St., Bridgeton 08302
Pres., CFO—Herman Evans, Jr., 4 emp., *Commercial printing & typesetting* .......... (856) 451-3885

Jersey Paw Prints, P.O. Box 26, Mays Landing 08330
Owner, Publisher & Editor—Carol Ruck, 1 emp., *Newspaper publishing* .......... (609) 909-5100

K R B Printing For Business, 1165 Marlkress Rd., Ste. G, Cherry Hill 08003
Ptnr.—Kurt Barbera, 12 emp., *Commercial printing & electronic prepress* .......... (856) 751-5200

Keystone Printing, Inc., 21-C E. Madison Ave., Dumont 07628
Pres.—Janice Worner, 4 emp., *Digital offset printing, typesetting* .......... (201) 387-7252

L & B Printing, 2590 U.S. Highway 22, Scotch Plains 07076
Ptnr.—Lance Booth, Sr., 6 emp., *Commercial printing & typesetting* .......... (908) 232-7770

L P B Graphics, Inc., 512-514 Route 27, Iselin 08830
Pres.—Lisa Berg, 8 emp., *Commercial offset printing & typesetting* .......... (732) 283-4333

LAS Printing, 1 Trenton Ave., Clifton 07011
Pres.—Joe Conti, 10 emp., *Commercial printing, electronic prepress* .......... (201) 991-5362

Laureate Press, Inc., 1336 W. Central Ave., P.O. Box 343, Egg Harbor City 08215
Pres.—Janet Rotellini, 6 emp., *Offset printing & typesetting* .......... (609) 965-0447

Leader Printers, 5914 New Jersey Ave., Wildwood Crest 08260
Pres.—Dennis Hall, 6 emp., *Offset printing & typesetting* .......... (609) 729-0161

Liberty Printing, Inc., 1111 Chestnut Ave., Trenton 08611
Pres.—George Demeter, 3 emp., *Offset & instant printing & typesetting* .......... (609) 396-5995

Lont & OverKamp, 175 U.S. Highway 46, Fairfield 07004
CEO—Ken Lont, 50 emp., *Offset, digital & direct mail printing* .......... (973) 942-2243

LRP & P Graphics, 1165 Marlkress Rd., Cherry Hill 08003
Pres.—Joan Buehler, 30 emp., *Offset & digital printing & typesetting* .......... (856) 424-0158

MacLearie Printing, LLC, 917 18th Ave., Belmar 07719
Pres.—James MacLearie, 6 emp., *Offset printing & typesetting* .......... (732) 681-2772

Main Street Communications, 15 W. Main St., Clinton 08809
Admn. Mgr.—Craig Reuter, 3 emp., *Typesetting & graphic design* .......... (908) 735-7570

Major Printing Co., Inc., 934 Savitt Pl., P.O. Box 1356, Union 07083
Owner & Pres.—Joseph Stampone, 2 emp., *Offset printing & typesetting* .......... (908) 686-7296

Market Street Printing, Inc., 122 N. 6th St., Camden 08102
Pres.—Mookie Kamerkar, 3 emp., *Commercial offset printing & typesetting* .......... (856) 964-5995

Mastergraphx, Inc., 45 Stouts Ln., Ste. 14, P.O. Box 567, Monmouth Junction 08852
Pres.—Robert Copeland, 10 emp., *Offset printing & typesetting* .......... (732) 329-0088

McGinnis Printing, 20 Monmouth St., Red Bank 07701
Owner—Dennis McGinnis, 3 emp., *Offset & instant printing & typesetting* .......... (732) 758-0060

Menco Business Products, 178 Route 206 S., Hillsborough 08844
Pres.—Ozzie Mendez, 15 emp., *Offset printing, typesetting & color* .......... (908) 281-0911

Millennium Graphics, Inc., 35 Vanderburg Rd., Marlboro 07746
Owner—Robert Klepner, 13 emp., *Electronic prepress* .......... (732) 431-0440

Minuteman Press, 1299 Route 38, Ste. 2, Hainesport 08036
Pres. & Cust. Serv. Rep.—Frank Bittner, 7 emp., *Offset printing & graphic design* .......... (609) 261-1024

Minuteman Press International, Inc., 1247 Patterson Plank Rd., Secaucus 07094
Co-Pres.—Tom Goldgraber, 5 emp., *Offset printing & computerized typesetting* .......... (201) 866-0186

Minuteman Press Of Dover, 25 Pine St., Ste. 10, Rockaway 07866
Pres., R & D Mgr.—Andy Krauser, 2 emp., *Offset & digital & color instant printing* .......... (973) 625-5800

Minuteman Press Of North Arlington, 75 Ridge Rd., North Arlington 07031
V-P.—Amir Djabini, 5 emp., *Instant printing, electronic prepress* .......... (201) 991-1030

Minuteman Press, Inc., 216 Boulevard, Hasbrouck Heights 07604
Manager—Tom Colletti, 4 emp., *Offset printing & typesetting* .......... (201) 288-7787

Mount Freedom Printing, P.O. Box 285, Mount Freedom 07970
Graphic Design Mgr.—Barbara Connolly, 3 emp., *Color offset printing, typesetting* .......... (908) 362-9299

My Way Prints, Inc., 1376 Route 23, Butler 07405
Pres.—Myron Friedman, 3 emp., *Offset printing & typesetting* .......... (973) 492-1212

Na-Vet Printing Co., 506 Elizabeth Ave., Elizabeth 07206
Pres.—Larry Franchini, 4 emp., *Commercial, digital & color printing* .......... (908) 353-4441

New Jersey Business Magazine, 310 Passaic Ave., Ste. 201, Fairfield 07004
Publisher—Vincent Schweikert, 10 emp., *Electronic magazine prepress printing* .......... (973) 882-5004

Newark Trade Typographers, Inc., 177 Oakwood Ave., Orange 07050
Pres., Sales Mgr.—Robert Wislocky, 20 emp., *Digital color printing, including typesetting* ...... (973) 674-3727

Newtype, Inc., 447 State Route 10, Ste. 14, Randolph 07869
CEO—JoAnn Porto, 10 emp., *Foreign-language typesetting & translations* .......... (973) 361-6000

Omega Graphics, 661 Broad St., Ste. 3, Shrewsbury 07702
Owner & Pres.—Douglas Godfrey, 4 emp., *Instant printing & digital layout &* .......... (732) 530-4441

One Source Solutions, 220 Encin Rd., Clifton 07014
Pres.—Roy Winters, 12 emp., *Offset printing & computerized typesetting* .......... (973) 242-4040

P B A Printing, 170 Malvern St., Newark 07105
Owner—Joe Figueiredo, 4 emp., *Offset printing & typesetting* .......... (973) 817-9712

Painton Studios, Inc., 299 U.S. Highway 22, Ste. 21, Green Brook 08812
Pres.—Lisa J. Secula, 3 emp., *4-color digital printing, signage,* .......... (732) 302-0200

Papson Printing Corp., 115 Hudson St., Hackensack 07601
Pres., Off. Mgr.—Chris Papson, 3 emp., *Offset printing & typesetting* .......... (201) 342-2860

Paragon Printing Shop, 600 Columbia Ave., Millville 08332
Owner—Todd Cimino, 5 emp., *Commercial printing, electronic prepress* .......... (856) 825-2497

Park Avenue Printing, LLC, 2001 S. Broad St., Trenton 08610
Pres.—Steven Madola, 6 emp., *Offset printing & typesetting* .......... (609) 989-8022

Park Printing Services, Inc., 7300 N. Crescent Blvd., Unit 21, Pennsauken 08110
Owner, Pres. & Pur. Agt.—Don Reed, Sr., 12 emp., *Commercial printing, electronic prepress* (856) 675-1600

Parkway Printing, Inc., 52 N. Main St., Ste. C-11, Marlboro 07746
Pres., Off. Mgr.—Robin Meringolo, 5 emp., *Commercial printing, computerized typesetting* .... (732) 308-0300

Perfect Printing, Inc., 1533 Glen Ave., Moorestown 08057
Pres., GM—Joe Olivo, 50 emp., *Commercial offset & digital printing* .......... (856) 787-1877

Phoenix Business Forms, Inc., 2231 N. East Blvd., Vineland 08360
Pres.—Joanne Buckalew, 5 emp., *Commercial printing, typesetting, promotional* .......... (856) 691-2266

Post Eagle Newspaper, Inc., 800 Van Houten Ave., Clifton 07013
Mng. Editor—Matt Grabowski, 3 emp., *Newspaper publishing* .......... (973) 473-5414

Precision Printing Group, LLC, 117 Jackson Rd., Berlin 08009
Pres.—Lori Colucci, 40 emp., *Prepress & offset digital printing* .......... (856) 753-7903

Premier Graphics, Inc., 500 Central Ave., Atlantic Highlands 07716
Pres.—Toni Madalone, 20 emp., *Offset printing & typesetting* .......... (732) 872-9933

Press Room, Inc., The, 100 Youngs Rd., Ste. 2, Mercerville 08619
Pres., Hum. Res. Mgr.—Ted Altomari, 8 emp., *Commercial offset, digital & instant* .......... (609) 689-3817

Print Sign & Design, 1791 S. Burlington Rd., Bridgeton 08302
Pres.—Susan Lucas, 8 emp., *Commercial printing, typesetting &* .......... (856) 451-8766

Printers Of Salem County, LLC, 38 Market St., Salem 08079
Ptnr.—Jeff Weeks, 3 emp., *Commercial printing & electronic prepress* .......... (856) 935-5032

Printing Center, Inc., The, 1 White Lake Rd., Sparta 07871
Pres., CEO—Vincent Perrella, Jr., 25 emp., *Offset printing & typesetting* .......... (973) 383-6362

Printing Craftsman, Inc., 130 Bergen Blvd., Fairview 07022
Pres.—Kenneth Stueben, 10 emp., *Commercial, offset, digital, & lithographic* .......... (201) 943-0276

R & R Printing Co., 107 S. Stevens Ave., P.O. Box 3204, South Amboy 08879
Owner—Kenneth Sumski, 1 emp., *Offset printing, typesetting & die* .......... (732) 727-6036

Ramsey Print Corp., 1000 Wall St. W., Ste. 2, Lyndhurst 07071
CFO—Jeffrey Beecher, 6 emp., *Offset printing & computerized typesetting* .......... (201) 460-1008

**★ Indicates new listing this edition.**

© Copyright 2015 Manufacturers' News, Inc.


Rapid Print & Copy Service, 78 Summerhill Rd., East Brunswick 08816
Pres.—Roly Kapoano, 2 emp., *Offset printing & typesetting* ... (732) 238-9056

Restaurant Graphics, Inc., 67 Newark Way, Maplewood 07040
Pres.—Tom Stravakis, 7 emp., *Lithographic & commercial printing* ... (973) 763-4036

Riverside Prints LLC, 11 Lawrence Cir., Middletown 07748
Pres., CEO—Howard Kirschner, 2 emp., *Large-format digital & offset printing* ... (732) 671-8222

RPR Graphics, Inc., 1136 U.S. Highway 22, P.O. Box 1159, Mountainside 07092
Pres., CEO—Laura Ruocco, 20 emp., *Digital asset management, electronic* ... (908) 654-8080

Rubber Stamp Engraving, 386 Avenel St., Avenel 07001
Owner & Pres.—Steven Glassman, 15 emp., *Plastic engraving, interior & exterior* ... (732) 726-5664

Rush Graphics, Inc., 1122 Goffle Rd., Hawthorne 07506
Pres.—Zora Agheli, 10 emp., *Electronic prepress & commercial printing* ... (973) 427-9393

S S Art & Engraving Corp., 1023 Commerce Ave., Union 07083
Pres., Fin. & Sales Mgr.—Robert Burslem, 15 emp., *Electronic prepress for the packaging* ... (908) 686-5536

Schuyler Printing Co., Inc., 71 Kearny Ave., Kearny 07032
Pres.—Edward A. Conlon, 4 emp., *Offset printing & typesetting* ... (201) 997-8083

Sheridan Communication, Inc., 1425 3rd Ave., Alpha 08865
CEO—James Sheridan, 50 emp., *Offset & 4-color printing & electonic* ... (908) 454-0700

Shorewood Digital Design & Development Center, 1 Kero Rd., Carlstadt 07072
Prodn. Mgr.—Dolores Jett, 35 emp., *Electronic prepress* ... (201) 372-3900

Sir Speedy Printing, 897 Rancocas Rd., Mount Holly 08060
Pres.—Joseph Barlam, 2 emp., *Commercial printing & typesetting* ... (609) 267-1232

Sir Speedy Printing and Marketing Services, 1032 Stelton Rd., Piscataway 08854
Pres., Fin. & GM—Mark Yanofsky, 4 emp., *High-speed full-color digital & offset* ... (732) 981-9011

Sir Speedy Printing Center, 28 Campus Dr., Edison 08837
Owner & Pres.—Robert Chido, 7 emp., *Offset & digital printing & typesetting* ... (732) 225-2272

Sir Speedy Printing Of East Hanover, 50 Route 10 W., East Hanover 07936
Owner—Perdipe Dave, 10 emp., *Offset printing & typesetting* ... (973) 884-0005

South Bergenite, 9 Lincoln Ave., Rutherford 07070
Mng. Editor—Meghan Trant, 5 emp., *Newspaper publishing* ... (201) 933-1166

South Plainfield Observer, 1110 Hamilton Blvd., Ste. 1-B, South Plainfield 07080
Pres., Publisher & Editor—Nancy Grennier, 6 emp., *Newspaper electronic prepress* ... (908) 668-0010

Square One, Inc., 111 Gaither Dr., Ste. 104, Mount Laurel 08054
Pres.—Colin Townsend, 45 emp., *Commercial, offset & digital printing* ... (856) 234-6999

Squiggly Productions, LLC, 164 Main St., Butler 07405
Owner—Guy Scognamiglio, 2 emp., *Offset & full-color digital printing* ... (973) 838-7475

Standard Printing & Mail Service, 30-A Plymouth St., P.O. Box 11021, Fairfield 07004
Pres., GM—Kevin Walsh, 12 emp., *Offset & direct mail printing, electronic* ... (973) 790-3333

Stauts Printing & Graphics, 12 Maine Trl., Medford 08055
Bus. Mgr.—W. Stauts, 5 emp., *Commercial printing & typesetting* ... (609) 654-5382

Stuyvesant Press, Inc., 119 Coit St., Irvington 07111
Pres., CEO—Michael Roesch, 10 emp., *Offset, commercial, digital, color* ... (973) 399-3880

Subito Music Corporation, 60 Depot St., Verona 07044
Owner & GM—Stephen Culbertson, 10 emp., *Sheet music printing & typesetting* ... (973) 857-3440

T C Graphics, Inc., 109 South Ave. W., Cranford 07016
Pres.—Tom Carvalho, 9 emp., *Offset printing, typesetting & color* ... (908) 276-7710

Tandem Graphics, Inc., 207 Wanaque Ave., Pompton Lakes 07442
Pres.—Michael Nass, 6 emp., *Banners & posters, including digital* ... (973) 513-9779

Tech Repro, Inc., 65 Zabriskie St., Hackensack 07601
Pres.—Kevin Tremble, 10 emp., *Large-format, instant & color printing* ... (201) 489-1333

Terminal Printing Co., 94 River St., P.O. Box 30, Hoboken 07030
Owner—John A. Bado III, 20 emp., *Offset printing & typesetting* ... (201) 659-5924

Thewal, Inc., 12 Center St., Chatham 07928
Ptnr. & Pres.—Susan Kessel, 10 emp., *Commercial & digital printing, electronic* ... (973) 635-1880

Thomsen Litho, Inc., 217 Railroad Ave., Ridgefield Park 07660
Pres.—Greg Thomsen, 3 emp., *Offset printing & computerized typesetting* ... (201) 489-1133

Tomad, Inc., 129 Cincinnati Ave., Egg Harbor City 08215
Pres., Hum. Res. Mgr.—Brian Dagostino, 12 emp., *Offset printing & typesetting* ... (609) 965-0808

Trentypo, Inc., 304 Stokes Ave., Trenton 08638
Pres.—Peter Simon, 8 emp., *Color printing & computerized typesetting* ... (609) 883-2198

Tri-City Print & Copy Center, 155 Union Blvd., Totowa 07512
Pres.—G. Elia, 2 emp., *Offset printing, copying, typesetting* ... (973) 706-5854

Tropp Printing Corp., 8 Woodhollow Dr., Holmdel 07733
Pres.—William Tropp, 5 emp., *Offset & color printing & electronic* ... (212) 233-4519

Type-N-Graphic, 170 Kinnelon Rd., Ste. 12, Kinnelon 07405
V-P.—Jim Kapotes, 5 emp., *Commercial typesetting* ... (973) 838-6544

Type-O-Graphics, LLC, 222 Outwater Ln., Ste. 1, Garfield 07026
Pres.—Ruth Valdez, 5 emp., *Commercial printing & typesetting* ... (973) 253-3333

Typeworks, 228 Jefferson St., Apt. 4, Hoboken 07030
Pres.—Janice Weiss, 4 emp., *Computerized typesetting, graphic design* ... (201) 653-8380

UB Communications, 10 Lodge Ln., Parsippany 07054
Ptnr.—David Ursone, 2 emp., *Electronic prepress* ... (973) 331-9391

Veterano Ward Commercial Printing, 301 Bradshaw Ave., Haddonfield 08033
Owner—Frank Ward, 4 emp., *Offset printing & typesetting* ... (856) 429-5460

Webco Graphics/W.G.I. Corp., 1875 Swarthmore Ave., Lakewood 08701
Pres.—Glenn Davis, 12 emp., *Newsprint printing of newspapers, brochures* ... (732) 370-2900

xpedx, 261 River Rd., Clifton 07014
Br. & Div. Mgr.—John Ransone, 50 emp., *Distributor of printing paper & graphics* ... (973) 405-2300

### 2796 Platemaking services

Access Printing, Inc., 510 N. Belleview Ave., Riverton 08077
Pres.—Richard Osbourne, 3 emp., *Offset & color printing & bookbinding* ... (856) 829-1673

Action Graphics, Inc., 600 Ryerson Rd., Ste. G, Lincoln Park 07035
Pres., CFO & Treas.—Dale E. Park, 24 emp., *Commercial printing & mailing services* ... (973) 633-6500

Bartlett Printing & Graphics, Inc., 4495 Route 130 S., Burlington 08016
CEO—Clifford Lewis, 3 emp., *Offset printing & typesetting* ... (609) 386-1525

Bind-Rite Robbinsville, 1 Applegate Dr., Robbinsville 08691
Prodn. Mgr.—Helder Gomes, 85 emp., *Electronic prepress & color separations* ... (609) 208-1917

BP Graphics & Printing, 315 4th St., Lakewood 08701
Pres.—Ben Heineman, 15 emp., *Instant printing & typesetting* ... (732) 905-9830

DAA International LLC, 24 Commerce Rd., Ste. L, Fairfield 07004
Dir., Bus.—Daniel Dombrowski, 5 emp., *Polyester laser printing, metal & ink* ... (973) 575-7444

Diamond Die Cutters & Embossers, 629 Grove St., 6th Fl., Jersey City 07310
GM—Moon Mui, 15 emp., *Die cutting, metal stamping & embossing* ... (201) 876-8540

Discount Office Supply, 146 Hudson St., Hackensack 07601
Pres.—Larry Barr, 5 emp., *Pamphlet, brochure, stationery & business* ... (201) 342-3030

Dynamic Printing & Graphics, Inc., 250 Delawanna Ave., Clifton 07014
Pres., CEO—Lou Mascola, 7 emp., *Offset printing, color separations* ... (973) 473-7177

Engraver's Bench & Greek Unique, Inc., 1212 Raymond Blvd., Newark 07102
Owner & Pres.—Willie J. Williams, 3 emp., *Metal, wood, plastic & glass engraving* ... (973) 297-1810

Falcon Printing Co., 613 Central Ave., Westfield 07090
Ptnr.—Anthony Archambault, 4 emp., *Commercial printing, typesetting &* ... (908) 232-1991

Faust, Inc., Rudolph, 542 South Ave. E., Cranford 07016
Pres.—Peter Faust, 3 emp., *Engraving ink* ... (908) 507-5104

Flexi Printing Plate Co., Inc., 50 Commercial Ave., Moonachie 07074
Pres.—John Moss, 50 emp., *Printing plates, commercial printing* ... (201) 939-3600

Globe Photoengraving Co., LLC, 19 N. Washington Ave., Little Ferry 07643
V-P.—Alan Soojian, 12 emp., *Photoengraving* ... (201) 489-2300

Graphics Plus Corp., 210 W. Parkway, Ste. 7, Pompton Plains 07444
Pres.—John Prentzel, 5 emp., *Offset printing, color separations* ... (973) 835-3744

Greenwich Graphics, LLC, 234 16th St., 8th Fl., Jersey City 07310
Owner, Pres. & MIS Mgr.—Wolfe Gluck, 8 emp., *Printing plates, computerized typesetting* ... (212) 727-1116

Harwill Corp., 3175 Princeton Pike, Lawrenceville 08648
Pres.—Steve Portrude, 6 emp., *Commercial & digital printing, typesetting* ... (609) 895-1955

Inkwell Corp., 1414 Elmira St., Cape May 08204
Pres.—Heide Cummings, 3 emp., *Offset printing & textile screen printing* ... (609) 884-0350

J K Design, Inc., 465 Amwell Rd., Hillsborough 08844
Pres.—Jerome Kaulius, 45 emp., *Computerized typesetting & color separations* ... (908) 428-4700

JDSU, 2 Applegate Dr., Robbinsville 08691
V-P., GM—Greg Miller, 120 emp., *Company headquarters & holographic* ... (609) 632-0800

Mark Lithography, Inc., 220 Entin Rd., Clifton 07014
Pres.—Charles Tumminello, 35 emp., *Offset printing & color separations* ... (973) 538-5557

Mark/Trece, Inc., 160 Algonquin Pkwy., Whippany 07981
GM—Paul Rachanow, 30 emp., *Corrugated & flexographic printing* ... (973) 884-1005

Menco Business Products, 178 Route 206 S., Hillsborough 08844
Pres.—Ozzie Mendez, 15 emp., *Offset printing, typesetting & color* ... (908) 281-0911

Nash Engraving, Inc., 528 Nicholson Rd., Gloucester City 08030
Owner—M. Nash, 4 emp., *Mechanical engraving of signs, nameplates* ... (856) 456-5656

New Life Color Reproduction, Inc., 610 Broad Ave., Ridgefield 07657
Pres.—Dragaw Zibkobic, 4 emp., *Color separations* ... (201) 943-7005

Packaging Graphics, Inc., 435 Commerce Ln., P.O. Box 160, West Berlin 08091
Pres.—Eileen Koff, 20 emp., *Printing plates* ... (856) 767-9000

Plate Craft, Inc., 172-174 Main St., West Orange 07052
Pres.—Dominick Calabrese, Jr., 3 emp., *Printing plates* ... (973) 736-4404

Pressto Graphics, Inc., 467 Lakehurst Rd., P.O. Box 467, Toms River 08755
Pres.—William Debernardis, 8 emp., *Commercial offset & digital printing* ... (732) 286-9300

RPR Graphics, Inc., 1136 U.S. Highway 22, P.O. Box 1159, Mountainside 07092
Pres., CEO—Laura Ruocco, 20 emp., *Digital asset management, electronic* ... (908) 654-8080

Rush Graphics, Inc., 1122 Goffle Rd., Hawthorne 07506
Pres.—Zora Agheli, 10 emp., *Electronic prepress & commercial printing* ... (973) 427-9393

Spec Steel Rule Dies, Inc., 92 N. Main St., Bldg. 1-B, P.O. Box 33, Windsor 08561
Pres., R & D Mgr.—John Nagy, 24 emp., *Steel rule dies & rubber printing plates* ... (609) 443-9200

Standard Embossing Plate, 129 Pulaski St., Newark 07105
Ptnr. & Pres.—Chris Fleissner, 3 emp., *Leather embossing & embossing plates* ... (973) 344-6670

T C Graphics, Inc., 109 South Ave. W., Cranford 07016
Pres.—Tom Carvalho, 9 emp., *Offset printing, typesetting & color* ... (908) 276-7710

Unity Graphics & Engraving/Unity Steel Rule Die, 210 S. Van Brunt St., P.O. Box 88, Englewood 07631
Ptnr.—Diane Iamartino, 50 emp., *Rubber printing, plate engraving &* ... (201) 569-6400

## 28 CHEMICALS & ALLIED PRODUCTS

### 2812 Alkalies & chlorine

Church & Dwight Co., Inc., 800 Airport Rd., Lakewood 08701
Plt. Mgr.—Timothy O'Farrell, 200 emp., *Sodium bicarbonate* ... (732) 730-3100

Qualco, Inc., 225 Passaic St., Passaic 07055
Pres.—John Ferentinos, 30 emp., *Swimming pool chemicals* ... (973) 473-1222

TATA Chemicals North America, Inc. (H Q), 100 Enterprise Dr., 7th Fl., Rockaway 07866
Pres.—De Lyle Bloomquist, 38 emp., *Corporate headquarters; soda ash* ... (973) 599-5500

### 2813 Gases—industrial

Air Liquide America L.P., A-Line Rd., P.O. Box 155, Gibbstown 08027
Plt. Mgr.—Dan Dingman, 13 emp., *Dry ice* ... (856) 423-5220

Air Liquide America Specialty Gases, LLC, 2330 Hamilton Blvd., South Plainfield 07080
Plt. Mgr.—Tim Dall, 13 emp., *Industrial gases* ... (908) 754-7700

Airgas East, Inc., 270 Benigno Blvd., Bellmawr 08031
Sales & Mktg. Mgr.—Sue Krotzer, 30 emp., *Medical gases* ... (856) 933-0544

Airgas East, Inc., 1-D Frassetto Way, Lincoln Park 07035
Br. Mgr.—Alex Jimenez, 25 emp., *Medical gases* ... (973) 633-9666

Airgas Specialty Gases, 600 Union Landing Rd., Riverton 08077
Plt. Mgr.—Jill Morrison, 64 emp., *Specialty gases* ... (856) 829-7878

Dry Ice Corp. (H Q), 189 Central Ave., Old Tappan 07675
Pres., CEO—Arthur Ramsdell, Jr., 15 emp., *Corporate headquarters; industrial,* ... (201) 767-3200

Falcon Safety Products, Inc., 25 Imclone Dr., P.O. Box 1299, Branchburg 08876
Pres.—Phil Lapin, 60 emp., *Compressed gas computer cleaning products* ... (908) 707-4900

LifeGas, LLC, 174 Ridge Rd., Ste. A, Dayton 08810
GM—David Knight, 15 emp., *Medical compressed oxygen* ... (866) 543-3427

Linde Electronics & Specialty Gases, 80 Industrial Dr., Alpha 08865
Plt. Mgr.—Steve Earl, 100 emp., *Industrial & environmental gases* ... (908) 454-7455

Linde Gas North America, LLC, 1 Greenwich St., Ste. 200, Stewartsville 08886
Acct. Mgr.—Clarence Gaten, 250 emp., *Industrial & specialty gases* ... (800) 755-9277

Linde North America, Inc. (H Q), 575 Mountain Ave., New Providence 07974
Pres.—Patrick F. Murphy, 575 emp., *Corporate headquarters; industrial* ... (908) 464-8100

Matheson Tri-Gas, Inc., 150 Allen Rd., Ste. 302, Basking Ridge 07920
Ex. Chrm., Board of Dirs.—Bill Kroll, 75 emp., *Company headquarters & industrial gases* ... (908) 991-9200

Praxair, 515 E. Edgar Rd., Linden 07036
Opers. Mgr.—Mike Anuszeniski, 2 emp., *Welding equipment & specialty gases* ... (908) 862-7200

Praxair, Inc., Rairatan Bay, Plt. 907, 60 Crows Mill Rd., Keasbey 08832
GM—Mike Beaudrow, 8 emp., *Nitrogen & oxygen processing* ... (732) 738-4150

Welco Acetylene Corp., 321 Roanoke Ave., Newark 07105
V-P.—John Smith, 14 emp., *Acetylene gas* ... (973) 465-1043

### 2816 Pigments—inorganic

BASF Corporation, Catalysts Div., 25 Middlesex-Essex Tpke., P.O. Box 770, Iselin 08830
Dir., Hum. Res.—Krisanne Pook, 400 emp., *Divisional headquarters & environmental* ... (732) 205-5000

Breen Color Concentrates, Inc., 11 Kari Dr., Lambertville 08530
Pres.—Howard DeMonte, 60 emp., *Color concentrates* ... (609) 397-8200

Cardinal Color, Inc., 50-56 1st Ave., Paterson 07514
Pres., GM & Off. Mgr.—Mark Berry, 30 emp., *Pigment dispersions* ... (973) 684-1919

Color Techniques, Inc., 260 Ryan St., South Plainfield 07080
Pres.—Jennifer Bolitsky, 7 emp., *Cosmetic pigments* ... (908) 412-9292

Colorchem, Inc., 1010 Greenwood Lake, Ringwood 07456
Pres., CEO—James C. Gayler, 10 emp., *Rubber color dispersions* ........ (973) 728-7731
Dispersion Technology, Inc., 1885 Swarthmore Ave., Lakewood 08701
Pres.—Yogesh Parikh, 10 emp., *Pigment dispersion of silicones & silicone* ........ (732) 364-4488
K V K U. S. A., Inc., 19-A Home News Row, New Brunswick 08901
GM—Gregory McMorray, 6 emp., *Ink pigment dispersions* ........ (732) 846-2355
Kronos Worldwide, Inc., 5 Cedarbrook Dr., Ste. 2, Cranbury 08512
Co-Pres., Sales & Mktg.—H. Joseph Maas, 35 emp., *Titanium dioxide* ........ (609) 860-6200
O'Neil Color & Compounding Corp., 61 River Dr., Garfield 07026
Sales Mgr.—David Sarkisian, 38 emp., *Dry color compounding* ........ (973) 777-8999
Penn Color, Inc., 30 Kohner Pl., Elmwood Park 07407
Prodn. Mgr.—Bob Frei, 80 emp., *Plastic colorants, industrial coatings* ........ (201) 791-5100
Sensient Cosmetic & Pharmaceutical Technologies, 107 Wade Ave., South Plainfield 07080
Dir., Opers.—Anthony Toto, 60 emp., *Cosmetic colorants & specialty ingredients* ........ (908) 757-4500
Sun Chemical Corp., 35 Waterview Blvd., Ste. 100, Parsippany 07054
Pres., CEO—Rudi Lenz, 125 emp., *Corporate headquarters & printing inks* ........ (973) 404-6000

## 2819 Chemicals—industrial inorganic, nec

A. L. Wilson Chemical Co., 1050 Harrison Ave., P.O. Box 207, Kearny 07032
Pres.—Fred Schwarzmann, 20 emp., *High-performance chemical products* ........ (201) 997-3300
Ajinomoto North America, Inc. (H Q), 400 Kelby St., Ste. 18, Fort Lee 07024
Pres.—Tomoya Yoshizumi, 35 emp., *Corporate headquarters; amino acids* ........ (201) 292-3200
Aromor Flavors & Fragrances, Inc., 560 Sylvan Ave., Ste. 60, Englewood Cliffs 07632
Sales Mgr.—Carol Feldman, 2 emp., *Aroma chemicals for the fragrances* ........ (201) 503-1662
BASF Corporation, Catalysts Div., 25 Middlesex-Essex Tpke., P.O. Box 770, Iselin 08830
Dir., Hum. Res.—Krisanne Pook, 400 emp., *Divisional headquarters & environmental* ........ (732) 205-5000
Bluestar Silicones U.S.A. Corp. (H Q), 2 Tower Center Blvd., Ste. 1601, East Brunswick 08816
Pres.—Chris York, 20 emp., *Corporate headquarters; industrial* ........ (732) 227-2060
Bracco Diagnostics, Inc., 259 Prospect Plains Rd., Bldg. H, Monroe Township 08831
Pres., CEO—Vittorio Puppo, 175 emp., *Corporate headquarters & barium & radiologica* ........ (609) 514-2200
Chemetall, 675 Central Ave., New Providence 07974
Pres., CEO—Ron Felber, 100 emp., *Company headquarters & surface treatment* ........ (908) 464-6900
Chemtrade, 330 Doremus Ave., Newark 07105
Plt. Mgr.—Mathew Cusmano, 4 emp., *Aluminum sulfate* ........ (973) 589-5300
Chemtrade Chemical, LLC, 90 E. Halsey Rd., 3rd Fl., Parsippany 07054
Pres., CEO—William Redmond, 140 emp., *Company headquarters & industrial chemicals* ........ (973) 515-0900
Cooper Chemical Co., 20 Parker Rd., Long Valley 07853
Pres., MIS Mgr.—Hugo L. Kleinhans, 8 emp., *Pharmaceutical intermediate chemicals* ........ (908) 876-3231
Croda, Inc. (H Q), 300 Columbus Cir., Ste. A, Edison 08837
Pres.—Kevin Gallagher, 100 emp., *Corporate headquarters; specialty chemicals* ........ (732) 417-0800
Cyalume Specialty Products, 100 W. Main St., P.O. Box 669, Bound Brook 08805
Pres.—James G. Schleck, 28 emp., *Bulk active pharmaceutical ingredients* ........ (732) 469-7760
Dallas Group Of America, Inc., The (H Q), 374 Route 22, P.O. Box 489, Whitehouse 08888
Pres.—Robert H. Dallas II, 20 emp., *Corporate headquarters; ammonium chloride* ........ (908) 534-7800
DPT Lakewood, LLC, 1200 Paco Way, Bldg. 19, Lakewood 08701
Site Mgr.—Gene Ciolfi, 700 emp., *Pharmaceuticals, health care & chemical* ........ (732) 367-9000
Elementis Chromium, Inc. (H Q), 469 Old Trenton Rd., East Windsor 08512
Chrm.—Andrew Duff, 130 emp., *Corporate headquarters; chromium chemicals* ........ (609) 443-2000
Evonik Corporation (H Q), 299 Jefferson Rd., Parsippany 07054
Pres.—John Rolando, 421 emp., *Corporate headquarters; industrial* ........ (973) 929-8000
Fabric Chemical Corp., 61 Cornelison Ave., Jersey City 07304
Pres.—Andrew Jacobson, 9 emp., *Laboratory chemicals* ........ (201) 432-0440
Flamingo Bay, Inc., 10 Seneca Trl., Sparta 07871
Pres.—Bruce Miller, 20 emp., *Fragrance & detergent compounds* ........ (973) 726-8882
G.J. Chemical Co., Inc., 128 Doremus Ave., Newark 07105
Pres.—Diana Colonna, 25 emp., *Laboratory chemicals* ........ (973) 589-4176
G.J. Chemical Co., Inc., 40 Veronica Ave., Somerset 08873
Pres.—Diana Colonna, 30 emp., *Corporate headquarters & industrial* ........ (973) 589-1450
Global Seven, Inc., 198 Green Pond Rd., P.O. Box 696, Rockaway 07866
Pres., Hum. Res.—Jonathan Dean, 50 emp., *Cosmetic products, surfactants, esters* ........ (973) 664-1900
Halocarbon Products Corp. (H Q), 887 Kinderkamack Rd., 2nd Fl., River Edge 07661
CEO—Peter Murin, 13 emp., *Corporate headquarters; industrial* ........ (201) 262-8899
Hibrett Puratex, 7001 Westfield Ave., Pennsauken 08110
Pres.—John P. J. Madden, 15 emp., *Custom water treatment & industrial* ........ (856) 662-1717
Hummel Croton, Inc., 10 Harmich Rd., South Plainfield 07080
Pres.—Bernard F. Schoen, Jr., 20 emp., *Industrial chemicals* ........ (908) 754-1800
Icy Cools, Inc., 15 Oscar Dr., P.O. Box 686, Roosevelt 08555
CEO—Paul Wojnicki, 10 emp., *Reusable hot/cold mats for the healthcare* ........ (609) 448-0172
Ikaria, Inc. (H Q), 53 Frontage Rd., P.O. Box 9001, Hampton 08827
Chrm., CEO—Daniel Tasse, 175 emp., *Holding company headquarters; pharmaceutical* ........ (908) 238-6600
Indco, Inc., 511 Essex St., P.O. Box 109, Gloucester City 08030
Pres.—Fred Binter, 30 emp., *Contract blending of water-based chemicals* ........ (856) 456-6100
Jarchem Industries, Inc., 414 Wilson Ave., Newark 07105
V-P., Sales & Mktg.—Dennis Boyd, 50 emp., *Acetate salts, specialty branched &* ........ (973) 344-0600
Johnson Matthey, Inc., 2001 Nolte Dr., West Deptford 08066
Dir., Fin.—Mike Bell, 280 emp., *Autocatalysts, heavy-duty diesel catalysts* ........ (856) 384-7000
Joseph Oat Corp., 2500 S. Broadway, Camden 08104
Pres., Opers.—Ron Kaplan, 100 emp., *Nuclear components fabrication, including* ........ (856) 541-2900
KOBO Products, Inc., 3474 S. Clinton Ave., South Plainfield 07080
Pres.—David Schlossman, 90 emp., *Organic & inorganic cosmetic chemicals* ........ (908) 757-0033
Kuehne Co., 86 Hackensack Ave., Kearny 07032
Pres., CEO—Don Nicolai, 80 emp., *Company headquarters & bleach* ........ (973) 589-0700
Lonza, Inc., 90 Boroline Rd., Allendale 07401
Pres.—Jeanne Thoma, 161 emp., *Corporate headquarters & industrial* ........ (201) 316-9200
LyondellBasell Industries, 340 Meadow Rd., Edison 08817
Plt. Mgr.—David Schutka, 65 emp., *Chemicals* ........ (732) 777-2272
Madison Industries, Inc., 554 Waterworks Rd., Old Bridge 08857
Pres.—Bruce Bzura, 75 emp., *Zinc-based chemicals* ........ (732) 727-2225
MEL Chemicals, 500 Barbertown Point Breeze Rd., Flemington 08822
Opers. Mgr.—Gavin Edwards, 50 emp., *Zirconium chemicals* ........ (908) 782-5800
MORRE-TEC Industries, Inc., 1 Gary Rd., Union 07083
Pres.—Leonard Glass, 25 emp., *Corporate headquarters & bromine compounds* ........ (908) 688-9009
Morton Salt, Inc., 920 High St., Perth Amboy 08861
Off. Admn.—Sharon Mohan, 30 emp., *Salt packaging* ........ (732) 826-3595
Munzing, 1455 Broad St., Bloomfield 07003
V-P., Mfg. & Prod. Mgmt.—Mike Riggs, 39 emp., *Defoamers, dispersants, rheology modifiers* (973) 279-1306
Old Bridge Chemical, Inc., 554 Waterworks Rd., Old Bridge 08857
Pres.—Bruce Bzura, 100 emp., *Copper sulfate & carbonate & basic* ........ (732) 727-2225
P Q Corp., 2 Paddock St., Avenel 07001
Plt. Mgr.—Ted Freeman, 20 emp., *Silicate gels* ........ (732) 750-9040
Penetone Corp. (H Q), 1000 Herrontown Rd., Ste. 2, Princeton 08540
Pres.—Elwood Phares, 3 emp., *Corporate headquarters; cleaning compounds* ........ (609) 921-0501
Phibro Animal Health Corp., 300 Frank W. Burr Blvd., Stn. 21, Glenpointe Center East, 3rd Fl., Teaneck 07666
Chrm.—Jack Bendheim, 100 emp., *Corporate headquarters & animal feed* ........ (201) 329-7300
Plenum Scientific Research, Inc., 210 Lee Pl., Hackensack 07601
Pres., R & D Mgr.—Shajadi Parvin, 10 emp., *Biochemicals & chemical reagents* ........ (201) 489-2771
PMC Group, Inc. (H Q), 1288 Route 73, Mount Laurel 08054
Pres., COO—Debtash Chakrabarti, 35 emp., *Corporate headquarters; industrial* ........ (856) 533-1866
Process Research Products, 1013 Whitehead Road Ext., Trenton 08638
V-P., Admn. & Fin.—Phyliss Joan, 20 emp., *Metalworking fluids, lapping compounds* ........ (609) 882-0400
Reade Manufacturing Co., 2590 Ridgeway Blvd., Manchester 08759
Pres.—James Gardella, 30 emp., *Magnesium grinding* ........ (732) 657-6451
Reagent Chemical & Research, Inc., 115 U.S. Highway 202, Ringoes 08551
Pres.—John T. Skeuse, 30 emp., *Corporate headquarters & hydrochloric* ........ (908) 284-2800
Scientific Design Co., Inc., 49 Industrial Ave., Little Ferry 07643
Pres., CEO—Paul Lamb, 135 emp., *Chemical catalysts* ........ (201) 641-0500
Sekisui America Corp. (H Q), 333 Meadowlands Pkwy., 4th Fl., Secaucus 07094
CFO—Akira Morimoto, 10 emp., *Corporate headquarters; industrial* ........ (201) 423-7960
Shanghai Freemen Americas, LLC (H Q), 377 Hoes Ln., Ste. 240, Piscataway 08854
Pres.—Hanks LI, 9 emp., *Company headquarters; nutritional products* ........ (732) 981-1288
Simple Solutions Distribution, LLC (H Q), 6 Jacobs Rd., West Milford 07480
Ptnr. & Mktg. Mgr.—Andrew McGibbon, 2 emp., *Company headquarters; odor control* ........ (973) 846-7817
Solvay U. S. A., Inc., 8 Cedar Brook Dr., CN-7500, Cranbury 08512
CFO—Mark Dahlinger, 350 emp., *Corporate headquarters & industrial* ........ (609) 860-4000
Summit Chemical Specialty Products, 45 River Rd., Ste. 300, Flemington 08822
Ptnr. & CEO—Richard Rosen, 35 emp., *Aluminum compounds & industrial chemicals* ........ (908) 782-9500
Sysco Guest Supply (H Q), 4301 Highway 1, P.O. Box 902, Monmouth Junction 08852
Pres., COO—Paul T. Xenis, 140 emp., *Divisional headquarters; personal care* ........ (609) 514-9696
Tyger Scientific, Inc., 324 Stokes Ave., Ewing 08638
Chrm., CEO—Adam Yuan, 10 emp., *Organic intermediates & specialty chemicals* ........ (609) 434-0144
VAR-LAC-OID Chemical Co., Inc., 24 Industrial Ave., P.O. Box 181, Upper Saddle River 07458
Pres.—Alan Kessler, 15 emp., *Cesium chloride* ........ (201) 236-8800
W.D. Service Company, Inc., 780 Creek Rd., Bellmawr 08031
CEO—Paul A. Cuccinello, 9 emp., *Concentrated reagent grade ammonia* ........ (856) 931-6100
Water Mark Technologies, Inc., 762 State Route 15 S., Ste. 2-B, Lake Hopatcong 07849
★ Pres.—Phil Reilly, 8 emp., *Organic & inorganic chemicals for the* ........ (973) 663-3438

## 2821 Plastic materials & resins

A & C Catalysts, Inc., 1600 W. Blancke St., Linden 07036
Dir., Mktg., Consumer—John Wolfe, 35 emp., *Plastic resins* ........ (908) 474-9393
Akcros Chemicals, Inc., 500 Jersey Ave., New Brunswick 08901
Site Mgr.—George Turk, 45 emp., *PVC, oxide & coating additives* ........ (732) 247-2202
Alva-Tech, Inc., 1208 Columbus Rd., Ste. G, Burlington 08016
Pres.—Phillip Valenziano, 20 emp., *Intumescent firestop products & joint* ........ (609) 747-1133
Anti-Hydro International, Inc., 45 River Rd., Ste. 200, Flemington 08822
Dir., Opers.—Bruce Kreielsheimer, 12 emp., *Concrete admixtures, coatings, industrial* ........ (908) 284-9000
AOS Thermal Compounds, LLC, 22 Meridian Rd., Ste. 6, Eatontown 07724
Pres., CEO—John Ziemski, 12 emp., *Heat sink compounds & thermal interface* ........ (732) 389-5514
Ashland, Inc., International Specialty Products (H Q), 56 Livingston Ave., Ste. 400, Roseland 07068
Pres.—Luis Fernandez-Moreno, 170 emp., *Divisional headquarters; agricultural* ........ (973) 533-5400
Biosearch Medical Products, Inc., 35 Industrial Pkwy., Branchburg 08876
Pres., CEO & V-P.—Manfred F. Dyck, 50 emp., *Biocompatible hydrophilic polymer coatings* . (908) 722-5000
Borealis Compounds, Inc., 176 Thomas Rd., Port Murray 07865
Pres., Mfg. Mgr.—Kenneth Wiecoreck, 116 emp., *Polymer compounding* ........ (908) 850-6200
Cambridge Industries Of America Co., Inc., 7-33 Amsterdam St., Newark 07105
Pres.—Phillip Rhodes, 8 emp., *Epoxy resins & plastercicers* ........ (973) 465-0077
Cardolite Corp., 500 Doremus Ave., Newark 07105
Pres.—Anthony Stonis, 80 emp., *Epoxy resins* ........ (973) 344-5015
Chemtura Corp., 1000 Convery Blvd., Perth Amboy 08861
MIS Mgr.—Amanda Figueroa, 80 emp., *Polyester & polyurethane materials* ........ (732) 826-6600
Claude Bamberger Molding Compounds Corp., 111 Paterson Plank Rd., P.O. Box 67, Carlstadt 07072
Pres.—Claude Bamberger, 7 emp., *Manufacturer & distributor of purging* ........ (201) 933-6262
Clausen Co., The, 1055 King George Post Rd., Edison 08817
Pres., CEO—Donald J. Peck, 15 emp., *Automotive refinishing products* ........ (732) 738-1165
Commercial Products Co. U. S. A., 117 Ethel Ave., P.O. Box 504, Hawthorne 07507
Pres.—Charles Arnaldi, 5 emp., *Textile resins & softeners* ........ (973) 427-6887
COTE-L Industries, Inc., 1542 Jefferson St., Teaneck 07666
CEO—Avi Aviner, 6 emp., *Safety, polyurethane, epoxy, waterproofing* ........ (201) 836-0733
Crossfield Products Corp., 140 Valley Rd., Roselle Park 07204
Dir., Sales, East, Dex-O-Tex—Ed Frick, 45 emp., *Seamless flooring & wall coating systems* .. (908) 245-2800
CVC Thermoset Specialties, Inc., 844 N. Lenola Rd., Ste. 1, Moorestown 08057
V-P., Sales & Mktg.—Charles Zarnitz, 50 emp., *Plastic resins & monomers* ........ (856) 533-3000
Deltech Resin Co., 49 Rutherford St., Newark 07105
Prodn. Mgr.—Haresh Kothari, 20 emp., *Polyurethane dispersions, including* ........ (973) 589-0880
Endurance Net, Inc., 763-B Railroad Ave., Florence 08518
Pres.—Anita Scarperia, 15 emp., *Barrier netting for schools, parks,* ........ (609) 499-3450
Epolin, 358-364 Adams St., Newark 07105
CEO—Greg Amato, 11 emp., *Organic, infrared & absorbing dyes* ........ (973) 465-9495
Esco Optics, 1 Tideland Rd., P.O. Box 308, Oak Ridge 07438
Pres.—Lee Steneken, 33 emp., *American-made custom & standard optical* ........ (973) 697-3700
Evonik Corporation (H Q), 299 Jefferson Rd., Parsippany 07054
Pres.—John Rolando, 421 emp., *Corporate headquarters; industrial* ........ (973) 929-8000
Federal Plastics Corp., 570 South Ave. E., Ste. F-1, Cranford 07016
Pres.—Peter T. Triano, 10 emp., *Compounder & distributor of thermoplastics* ........ (908) 272-5800
Graver Technologies, LLC, 72 Lockwood St., Newark 07105
Dir., Opers. & Plt. Mgr.—Jim Sheridan, 40 emp., *Ion exchange resins & water treatment* ........ (973) 690-5290
HD MicroSystems, 250 Cheesequake Rd., Parlin 08859
Prod. Mgr.—Doug Heden, 30 emp., *High-performance polymers & polyimide* ........ (732) 613-2500
Heroflon USA Corp., Home State Road 249, Hillsborough 08844
Off. Mgr.—Jennifer Dockweiler, 4 emp., *Plastic raw materials, including PTFE* ........ (908) 829-4949
Hydromer, Inc., 35 Industrial Pkwy., Branchburg 08876
Pres., CEO—Manfred F. Dyck, 70 emp., *Hydrophilic polymer-based & hydrogel* ........ (908) 722-5000
Industrial Summit Technology Corp., 250 Cheesequake Rd., Parlin 08859
CEO—T. Sakane, 50 emp., *Polyimide resins for wire coatings* ........ (732) 238-2211
Innovative Resin Systems, Inc., 257 Wilson Ave., Newark 07105
Pres.—Pinakin Patel, 15 emp., *Custom epoxy, polyurethane & acrylic* ........ (973) 465-6887
ITW Covid Security Group, 32 Commerce Dr., Ste. 1, Cranbury 08512
Cont., IT Mgr.—Jim Violett, 67 emp., *Holographic highly secure polymer materials* ........ (609) 395-5600
Master Bond, Inc., 154 Hobart St., Hackensack 07601
Pres.—James Brenner, 20 emp., *Custom adhesives, sealants, coatings* ........ (201) 343-8983
Membranes International, Inc., 219 Margaret King Ave., P.O. Box 219, Ringwood 07456
Ptnr.—Dwight Loren, 3 emp., *Ion exchange membranes for the water* ........ (973) 998-5530

S.I.C.

★ **Indicates new listing this edition.**

Metal Management Northeast, Inc., 1 Linden Ave. E., Jersey City 07305
GM—Joe Payaso, 250 emp., *Metal recycling* ..... (201) 577-3200
Monster Coatings, Inc., 306-A Capitol St., Saddle Brook 07663
Pres.—Denise Tomahatsch, 4 emp., *Seamless industrial, decorative & waterproofi* ..... (973) 983-7662
Palmer Asphalt Co., Inc., 196 W. 5th St., P.O. Box 58, Bayonne 07002
Pres.—Van Ripps, 10 emp., *Energy saving roof coatings, cool roof* ..... (201) 339-0855
Permabond, LLC (H Q), 223 Churchill Ave., Somerset 08873
Off. Mgr.—Linda Casale, 6 emp., *Company headquarters; engineering adhesives* ..... (732) 868-1372
Phillips 66 Bayway Refinery, 1400 Park Ave., Linden 07036
Refinery Mgr.—Brian Coffman, 800 emp., *Oil refining & refined fuel & plastic* ..... (908) 523-5000
Polymeric Resources Corporation, Inc., 55 Haul Rd., Wayne 07470
Pres.—Sol Schlesinger, 50 emp., *Corporate headquarters & plastic resin* ..... (973) 694-4141
Polyurethane Specialties Co., 624 Schuyler Ave., Lyndhurst 07071
Owner—Phil Gianatasio, 30 emp., *Polyurethane processing* ..... (201) 438-2325
Polyvel, Inc., 100 9th St., Hammonton 08037
Pres.—Brian Tidwell, 20 emp., *Plastic additive concentrates* ..... (609) 567-0080
Rimtec Corp., 1702 Beverly Rd., Burlington 08016
Pres.—Takara Fujii, 100 emp., *Polyvinyl chloride pellets* ..... (609) 387-0011
ROWA Group USA, LLC, 100 9th St., Hammonton 08037
Pres.—Dave Baglia, 13 emp., *Plastic resins* ..... (609) 567-8600
Safas Corp., 2 Ackerman Ave., Clifton 07011
Pres.—Akbar Ghahary, 30 emp., *Sprayable polyester resin surfacing* ..... (973) 772-5252
Sau-Sea Swimming Pool Paints And Repair Products, 1855 Route 206, Southampton 08088
COO—Ed Hunter, 9 emp., *Eco-friendly rubber-base, epoxy & vinyl* ..... (609) 859-8500
Scientific Materials Corp., 30 Vail Ter., P.O. Box 5298, Somerville 08876
Pres.—Noris Batra, 5 emp., *Contamination control polymeric reusable* ..... (908) 218-0010
Solvay Specialty Polymers USA, Inc., 10 Leonard Ln., West Deptford 08086
Pres.—Laird McBeth, 150 emp., *Corporate headquarters & fluoropolymers* ..... (856) 853-8119
Sun Plastech Inc., 1055 Parsippany Blvd., Ste. 405, Parsippany 07054
Pres.—Glenn Kornfeld, 20 emp., *Purging compound for thermoplastic* ..... (973) 257-1999
Synray Corp., 209 N. Michigan Ave., Kenilworth 07033
Pres.—Stan Lesniewski, 30 emp., *Alkyd & acrylic resins & saturated* ..... (908) 245-2600
Technovations Technology Reviews, Inc., 14 Red Barn Ln., Randolph 07869
Pres.—Jaidev S. Talwar, 5 emp., *PTUF impact modifiers for polyamides* ..... (973) 537-9511
TEX-NET, Inc., 763-B Railroad Ave., Florence 08518
Pres.—John Scarperia, 20 emp., *Polyester, polypropylene & nylon barrier* ..... (609) 499-9111
Thermo Cote, Inc., 198 Green Pond Rd., Ste. 5, Rockaway 07866
Pres.—Jennifer Cordero, 10 emp., *Chemical hot melt strippable coatings* ..... (973) 464-3575
Thinfilms, Inc., 15 Ilene Ct., Ste. 6, Hillsborough 08844
Pres.—Arshad Mumtaz, 11 emp., *Thin film coatings* ..... (908) 359-7014
US Concrete Materials, LLC, 189 Berkley Pl., Dumont 07628
Pres.—Robert K. Bortnick, 3 emp., *Construction chemicals, cold/hot weather* ..... (201) 385-6470

## 2822 Rubber—synthetic

Cherokee Rubber Co., 5 Laurel Dr., Unit 13, Flanders 07836
Pres.—Gilbert J. Stroming II, 12 emp., *Synthetic rubber tubing & cast polyurethane* ..... (973) 584-3733
Commercial Products Co. U. S. A., 117 Ethel Ave., P.O. Box 504, Hawthorne 07507
Pres.—Charles Arnaldi, 5 emp., *Textile resins & softeners* ..... (973) 427-6887
Dicar, Inc., 5 Bader Rd., Pine Brook 07058
Manager—Guillermo Pacheco, 72 emp., *Synthetic rubber* ..... (973) 575-4220
Ja-Bar Silicone Corp., 252 Brighton Rd., P.O. Box 1249, Andover 07821
Pres.—Gilbert Jacobs, 78 emp., *Silicone rubber sheets, molded seals* ..... (973) 786-5000
Rubber & Silicone Products Co., Inc., 17 Montesano Rd., Fairfield 07004
Pres.—Jeffery Dylla, 25 emp., *Molded rubber & urethane rollers &* ..... (973) 227-2300

## 2823 Cellulosic manmade fibers

Ashland Aqualon, Inc., 50 S. Minnisink Ave., Parlin 08859
Plt. Mgr.—Andre Simons, 93 emp., *Hydroxy ethyl cellulose* ..... (732) 254-1234

## 2824 Organic fibers, noncellulosic

American Casein Co., Inc., 109 Elbow Ln., Burlington 08016
CEO—Adam Cabot, 50 emp., *Powdered protein ingredients for nutritional* ..... (609) 387-3130
Interspec, 5025 Industrial Rd., Farmingdale 07727
Owner—Richard P. Deacon, 7 emp., *Flame-retardant cubicle curtain fabrics* ..... (732) 938-4114

## 2833 Medicinals & botanicals

Ambix Laboratories, 55 W. End Rd., Totowa 07512
Pres.—Alvin Goren, 23 emp., *Contract manufacturing of skin, hair* ..... (973) 890-9002
Ashland, Inc., International Specialty Products (H Q), 56 Livingston Ave., Ste. 400, Roseland 07068
Pres.—Luis Fernandez-Moreno, 170 emp., *Divisional headquarters; agricultural* ..... (973) 533-5400
Asiamerica Ingredients, Inc., 245 Old Hook Rd., Ste. 3, Westwood 07675
★ Owner—Mark Zhang, 4 emp., *Ingredients blending for the nutraceutical* ..... (201) 497-5993
Aspire Pharmaceuticals, Inc., 41 Veronica Ave., Somerset 08873
Pres.—Madhav Pai, 90 emp., *Contract manufacturing of soft gelatin* ..... (732) 447-1444
Bioactive Resources, LLC, 138 Sylvania Pl., South Plainfield 07080
CEO—Divya Desai, 25 emp., *Custom botanical powders, extracts,* ..... (908) 561-3114
Certified Processing Corp., 184 Route 22 E., Hillside 07205
Pres.—Paul P. Iacono, 2 emp., *Caffeine refining* ..... (973) 923-5200
Chemo Dynamics, Inc., 3 Crossman Rd. S., Sayreville 08872
Pres.—Subir Chakraborty, 12 emp., *Fine, specialty, active pharmaceutical* ..... (732) 721-4700
Chilton Laboratories, 299-B Fairfield Ave., Fairfield 07004
Pres.—Steven Heydt, 10 emp., *Caffeinated candy* ..... (973) 575-1990
Dimensional Merchandising, Inc., 86 N. Main St., Wharton 07885
Pres.—Douglas A. Sylva, 85 emp., *Contract manufacturing & packaging* ..... (973) 328-1600
DNE Nutraceuticals, Inc., 700 Central Ave., Farmingdale 07719
★ V-P.—Paul Kugielsky, 50 emp., *Contract manufacturing of dietary supplements* ..... (732) 806-9538
DSM Nutritional Products, Inc., 206 Macks Island Dr., Belvidere 07823
Site Dir.—Dave Ellis, 350 emp., *Vitamins & nutritional additives* ..... (908) 475-5300
DSM Pharmaceutical Products, Inc. (H Q), 45 Waterview Blvd., Parsippany 07054
Pres., CEO—Alexander Wessels, 165 emp., *Corporate headquarters; liquid & dry* ..... (973) 257-1063
Ecuadorian Rainforest, LLC, 25 Main St., Bldg. 6, Belleville 07109
Pres.—Marlene Siegel, 15 emp., *Contract manufacturer of dietary supplements* ..... (973) 759-2002
Ethical Alternative Products, LLC, 525 Cedar Hill Ave., Wyckoff 07481
Ptnr.—Gerald Bruno, 5 emp., *Company headquarters & pharmaceuticals* ..... (201) 251-7771
Extracts & Ingredients Ltd., Div. Of MORRE-TEC Industries, Inc., 1 Gary Rd., Union 07083
Pres.—Leonard Glass, 5 emp., *Botanical extracts, nutritive oils,* ..... (908) 688-9009
Garden State Nutritionals, LLC, 8 Henderson Dr., West Caldwell 07006
CEO—Keith Frankel, 400 emp., *Dietary supplements, including tablets* ..... (973) 575-9200
Gel Concepts, LLC, 30 Leslie Ct., Whippany 07981
Pres., CEO—Lawrence Kersen, 25 emp., *Hydrogel polymers for plastic surgery* ..... (973) 884-8995
Hamilltime Enterprises, Inc., 1761 U.S. Highway 9, Howell 07731
Owner—John Hamill, 2 emp., *Contract packaging of herbal products* ..... (732) 303-5998
HerbaKraft, Inc., 121 Ethel Rd. W., Ste. 6, Piscataway 08854
Pres.—Nisha Khanijow, 15 emp., *Vitamins, minerals, dietary supplements* ..... (732) 463-1000
Herbalist & Alchemist, Inc., 51 S. Wandling Ave., Washington 07882
CEO—Beth Lambert, 15 emp., *Bottled herbal extracts* ..... (908) 689-9020
IVC Industries, Inc., 500 Halls Mill Rd., Freehold 07728
Pres., CEO—Steven Dai, 410 emp., *Corporate headquarters & pregnancy* ..... (732) 308-3000
Jamol Laboratories, Inc., 13 Ackerman Ave., P.O. Box 313, Emerson 07630
Pres.—Emil Scott Lucia, 5 emp., *OTC botanical nose drops for the treatment* ..... (201) 262-6363
Johnson Matthey Pharmaceutical Materials, 2003 Nolte Dr., Paulsboro 08066
Dir., Bus. Dev. & Sales & Mktg.—Joseph Moy, 142 emp., *Pharmaceutical ingredients* ..... (856) 384-7001
Lonza, Inc., 70 Tyler Pl., South Plainfield 07080
Mktg. Mgr., Global—Suellen Bennett, 39 emp., *Cosmetics ingredients, including biotechnolog* (908) 561-5200
LycoRed Corp., 377 Crane St., Orange 07050
CFO—Benjamin Regev, 40 emp., *Bulk, added-value nutrients & ingredients* ..... (877) 592-6733
Mushroom Wisdom, Inc., 1 Madison St., Bldg. F, East Rutherford 07073
Pres.—Mike Shirota, 13 emp., *Dietary supplements, tea, skin cream* ..... (973) 470-0010
Navinta, LLC, 1499 Lower Ferry Rd., Trenton 08618
Pres.—Jayshree Patel, 14 emp., *Herb & drug grading, grinding & milling* ..... (609) 883-1135
Nutra-Med Packaging, Inc., 385 Franklin Ave., Ste. E, Rockaway 07866
Pres.—Mahesh Gupta, 45 emp., *Contract packaging, including bottles* ..... (973) 625-2274
Nutri Pet Research, Inc./NUPRO Supplements, 227 State Route 33 E., Manalapan 07726
Pres.—Janis Gianforte-Horner, 7 emp., *Holistic pet vitamin supplements &* ..... (732) 786-8822
NVE, Inc., 15 Whitehall Rd., Andover 07821
Pres.—Robert Occhifinto, 75 emp., *Herbal supplements* ..... (973) 786-7868
Pharmachem Laboratories, Inc., 265 Harrison Ave., Kearny 07032
Pres.—Dave Holmes, 50 emp., *Corporate headquarters & nutritional* ..... (201) 246-1000
Pharmachem Laboratories, Inc., 130 Wesley St., South Hackensack 07606
Plt. Mgr.—Mahesh Desai, 50 emp., *Vitamins* ..... (201) 343-3611
Poly-Gel, LLC, 30 Leslie Ct., Whippany 07981
Pres.—Larry Kersen, 50 emp., *Medical, orthopedic & skin care gelatin* ..... (973) 884-3300
Purest Colloids, Inc., 600 Highland Dr., Ste. 602, Mount Holly 08060
Pres.—Frank S. Key, 6 emp., *Colloidal silver supplements* ..... (609) 267-2112
Quality Formulation Laboratories, Inc., 110 Pennsylvania Ave., Paterson 07503
CEO—Mohamed Desoky, 50 emp., *Vitamin preparations, weight loss products* ..... (973) 977-8800
Rise-N-Shine, LLC (H Q), 17 Woodport Rd., Ste. 1-E, Sparta 07871
Founder—Cathy Beggan, 10 emp., *Company headquarters; energy supplement* ..... (973) 729-4141
R-Kane Products, Inc., 8351 National Hwy., Pennsauken 08110
Pres.—Robert Kaskey, 15 emp., *Nutritional dietary protein meal replacement* ..... (856) 663-0644
Shanghai Freemen Americas, LLC (H Q), 377 Hoes Ln., Ste. 240, Piscataway 08854
Pres.—Hanks Ll, 9 emp., *Company headquarters; nutritional products* ..... (732) 981-1288
Solgar, Inc., 500 Willow Tree Rd., Leonia 07605
Hum. Res. Mgr.—Rose Asvala, 100 emp., *Nutritional supplements* ..... (201) 944-2311
Soma Labs, Inc., 252 Wagner St., Middlesex 08846
Pres.—John Botzolakis, 56 emp., *Private label vitamins & nutritional* ..... (732) 271-3444
SPEX CertiPrep, Inc., 203 Norcross Ave., Metuchen 08840
Chrm.—Neil Stein, 80 emp., *Organic & inorganic certified reference* ..... (732) 549-7144
Spray-Tek, Inc., 344 Cedar Ave., Middlesex 08846
Mng. Ptnr., Pres. & CEO—David A. Brand, 40 emp., *Corporate headquarters & food flavorings* (732) 469-0050
Telmark Packaging Corp., 30 Freneau Ave., Ste. 2-B, Matawan 07747
Pres.—Eric Ludwig, 8 emp., *Contract formulation, manufacturing* ..... (732) 739-9100
Thermo Fisher Scientific, 755 U.S. Highway 202, Bridgewater 08807
Site Mgr.—Thomas Campbell, 162 emp., *Bioreagants & specialty chemicals for* ..... (908) 526-1800
Toll Compaction Group, LLC, 14 Memorial Dr., Neptune 07753
Mng. Ptnr. & Pres., IT—Rod Pritchard, 46 emp., *Company headquarters & granulation,* ..... (732) 776-8225
Tomer Laboratories, 350 Campus Dr., Somerset 08873
Pres.—Onkar Tomer, 3 emp., *Dietary supplements* ..... (732) 560-1885
Triarco Industries, Inc. (H Q), 2 Brighton Rd., Ste. 404, Clifton 07012
Pres.—Rodger R. Rhode, Jr., 5 emp., *Corporate headquarters; herbal dietary* ..... (973) 942-5100
Vitamins for Life, LLC, 1806 Bellmore St., P.O. Box 853, Oakhurst 07755
Pres.—Mark Gruberg, 35 emp., *Nutritional supplements* ..... (732) 663-1559
Vita-Pure, Inc., 410 W. 1st Ave., Roselle 07203
Pres.—Achyut Sahasra, 25 emp., *Vitamins & dietary supplements* ..... (908) 245-1212
Vitaquest International, LLC, 8 Henderson Dr., West Caldwell 07006
GM—Allen Pagliuco, 600 emp., *Vitamins* ..... (973) 575-9200
Windmill Health Products, LLC, 6 Henderson Dr., Caldwell 07006
Pres.—Howard Munk, 45 emp., *Manufacturer & distributor of vitamin* ..... (973) 575-6591
Zeus Scientific, Inc., 200 Evans Way, Somerville 08876
Pres.—Scott J. Tourville, 75 emp., *Diagnostic reagents & test kits* ..... (908) 526-3744

## 2834 Pharmaceutical preparations

A A A Pharmaceutical, Inc., 157-160 W. Jefferson St., Paulsboro 08066
Chrm.—Shashi Sheth, 90 emp., *Pharmaceuticals* ..... (609) 288-6060
Acino Products, LLC, 9-B S. Gold Dr., Trenton 08691
★ Member—Ravi Deshpande, 10 emp., *Pharmaceuticals* ..... (609) 695-4300
Actavis Elizabeth, LLC, 200 Elmora Ave., Elizabeth 07202
Dir., Qual. Control—Scott Allen, 580 emp., *Generic modified-release solid & oral* ..... (908) 527-9100
Actavis, Inc., Morris Corporate Ctr. 3, 400 Interpace Pkwy., Parsippany 07054
Ex. Chrm. of the Board—Paul M. Bisaro, 600 emp., *Corporate headquarters & pharmaceuticals* (862) 261-7000
Aerie Pharmaceuticals, Inc., 135 U.S. Highway 206, Ste. 15, Bedminster 07921
CEO—Vince Anido, 20 emp., *Pharmaceutical drug candidates for* ..... (908) 470-4320
Akorn, Inc., 72 Veronica Ave., Somerset 08873
V-P., Opers.—Michael Stehn, 102 emp., *Pharmaceuticals* ..... (732) 846-8066
Akrimax Pharmaceuticals, LLC (H Q), 11 Commerce Dr., 1st Fl., Ste. 100, Cranford 07016
Pres.—Donald C. Olsen, 15 emp., *Company headquarters; specialty pharmaceutica* ..... (908) 372-0506
Alpro, Inc., 50 Romanelli Ave., South Hackensack 07606
Pres.—Girish Desai, 7 emp., *Pharmaceutical tablet film coatings* ..... (201) 342-4498
Ambix Laboratories, 55 W. End Rd., Totowa 07512
Pres.—Alvin Goren, 23 emp., *Contract manufacturing of skin, hair* ..... (973) 890-9002
Amerigen Pharmaceuticals, Inc. (H Q), 9 Polito Ave., Ste. 900, Lyndhurst 07071
Pres.—John Lowry, 20 emp., *Corporate headquarters; generic pharmaceutica* ..... (732) 993-9827
Amneal Pharmaceuticals, LLC, 400 Crossing Blvd., 3rd Fl., Bridgewater 08807
Chrm., Co-CEO—Chirag Patel, 65 emp., *Company headquarters & pharmaceuticals* ..... (908) 947-3120
Amneal Pharmaceuticals, LLC, 47 Colonial Dr., Piscataway 08854
★ Hum. Res. Mgr.—Martine Maignen, 25 emp., *Pharmaceuticals* ..... (732) 645-3030
Apicore US, LLC, 49 Napoleon Ct., Somerset 08873
Pres., CEO—Ravishanker Kovi, 45 emp., *Active pharmaceutical ingredients* ..... (732) 748-8882
Archon Vitamin Corp., 3775 Park Ave., Ste. 1, Edison 08820
Dir., Pur.—Tracy Daniels, 65 emp., *Vitamins & nutritional supplements* ..... (973) 371-1700
Baumar Industries, Inc., 29 E. Centre St., Nutley 07110
Pres., CFO—Arthur Bautis, 10 emp., *Contract chemical tablets* ..... (973) 667-5490
Bayer HealthCare Pharmaceuticals (H Q), 100 Bayer Blvd., Whippany 07981
V-P., Growth & Innovation—Barton Warner, 500 emp., *Divisional headquarters; pharmaceuticals* (862) 404-3000

Bayer Healthcare, Consumer Care Div., 100 Bayer Blvd., P.O. Box 915, Whippany 07962
  Pres.—Erica Mann, 2500 emp., *Pharmaceuticals & vitamins* .................... (862) 404-3000

Bentley Laboratories, LLC, 111 Fieldcrest Ave., Edison 08837
  CEO—Brian T. Fitzpatrick, 200 emp., *Cosmetics & pharmaceuticals* .................... (732) 512-0200

Bristol-Myers Squibb Company, 777 Scudders Mill Rd., Plainsboro 08536
  Dir., Adv. Res.—Karen Best, 1550 emp., *Biopharmaceuticals* .................... (609) 897-2000

Caldwell Consumer Health, LLC (H Q), 8 Elmer St., Ste. 1, Madison 07940
  CEO—Michael Lesser, 6 emp., *Company headquarters; personal healthcare* .................... (973) 360-1090

Cambrex Corp., 1 Meadowlands Plz., Ste. 1510, East Rutherford 07073
  Pres., CEO—Steven Klosk, 22 emp., *Corporate headquarters & active pharmaceutica* .................... (201) 804-3000

Carecam International, Inc., 10 Plog Rd., Fairfield 07004
  Co-Pres.—Mohit Jain, 65 emp., *Pharmaceuticals* .................... (973) 227-0720

Catalent Pharma Solutions, Inc. (H Q), 14 Schoolhouse Rd., Somerset 08873
  Pres., CEO—John Chiminski, 377 emp., *Corporate headquarters; pharmaceuticals* .................... (732) 537-6200

Celgene Corp., 86 Morris Ave., Summit 07901
  Chrm. of the Board & CEO—Robert J. Hugin, 800 emp., *Corporate headquarters & biopharmaceuticals* (908) 673-9000

Center For Educational Advancement, 11 Minneakoning Rd., Flemington 08822
  Pres.—Michael Skoczek, 35 emp., *Contract pharmaceutical packaging,* .................... (908) 782-1480

Central Admixture Pharmacy Services, 160 W. Forest Ave., Englewood 07631
  Br. Mgr.—Daniel Buchner, 50 emp., *Pharmaceuticals* .................... (201) 541-0080

Cetylite, Inc., 9051 River Rd., Pennsauken 08110
  Pres.—Gary Wachman, 25 emp., *Pharmaceutical liquids, gels & ointments* .................... (856) 665-6111

CMIC CMO USA Corp., 3 Cedarbrook Dr., Ste. 3, Cranbury 08512
  Ex. V-P. & Dir.—Gary Wada, 42 emp., *Pharmaceuticals* .................... (609) 395-9700

Comar, LLC, 1 Comar Pl., Buena 08310
  CEO—Michael Ruggieri, 265 emp., *Plastic pharmaceutical packaging &* .................... (856) 692-6100

Command Nutritionals, LLC, 10 Washington Ave., Ste. 1, Fairfield 07004
  Pres.—Scott Biedron, 25 emp., *Contract manufacturer of nutritional* .................... (973) 227-8210

Contract Coatings, Inc., 161 Beech St., Hackensack 07601
  Owner—Bob Patel, 15 emp., *Pharmaceuticals, including table coatings* .................... (201) 343-3131

ConvaTec, Inc., CenterPoint II, Ste. 205, 1140 Route 22 E., Bridgewater 08807
  CEO—Ken Berger, 300 emp., *Corporate headquarters & health care* .................... (732) 412-5500

Core Tech Solutions, Inc., 50 Lake Dr. E. Windsor, Hightstown 08520
  Pres.—Kirti H. Valia, 10 emp., *Pharmaceutical preparations* .................... (609) 443-1400

CorePharma, LLC, 215 Wood Ave., Middlesex 08846
  CEO—Christopher Worrell, 200 emp., *Contract generic prescription pharmaceuticals* .................... (732) 868-1090

Cornerstone Pharmaceuticals, Inc., 1 Duncan Dr., Cranbury 08512
  CEO—Robert Shorr, 15 emp., *Drug candidates in Phase II clinical* .................... (609) 409-7050

Covance, Inc. (H Q), 210 Carnegie Ctr., Princeton 08540
  Chrm., CEO—Joseph L. Herring, 600 emp., *Corporate headquarters; pharmaceutical* .................... (609) 452-8550

Cyalume Specialty Products, 100 W. Main St., P.O. Box 669, Bound Brook 08805
  Pres.—James G. Schleck, 28 emp., *Bulk active pharmaceutical ingredients* .................... (732) 469-7760

Daiichi Sankyo, Inc. (H Q), 2 Hilton Ct., Parsippany 07054
  Pres., CEO—Ken Keller, 560 emp., *Corporate headquarters; pharmaceuticals* .................... (973) 944-2600

davAgen Pharmaceuticals, LLC, 68 Veronica Ave., Ste. 1, 2 & 10, Somerset 08873
  Pres.—David Humbert, 21 emp., *NBE, custom & generic liquid pharmaceuticals* .................... (732) 249-6363

Dermarite Industries, LLC, 7777 W. Side Ave., P.O. Box 7209, North Bergen 07047
  Pres.—Naftali Minzer, 98 emp., *Skin, wound & personal care products* .................... (973) 569-9000

Dimensional Merchandising, Inc., 86 N. Main St., Wharton 07885
  Pres.—Douglas A. Sylva, 85 emp., *Contract manufacturing & packaging* .................... (973) 328-1600

DMS Laboratories, Inc., 2 Darts Mill Rd., Flemington 08822
  Pres.—Nicholas A. Gallo III, 5 emp., *Veterinary rapid test kits for canine* .................... (908) 782-3353

DPT Lakewood, LLC, 1200 Paco Way, Bldg. 19, Lakewood 08701
  Site Mgr.—Gene Ciolfi, 700 emp., *Pharmaceuticals, health care & chemical* .................... (732) 367-9000

Dr. Reddy's Laboratories, Inc. (H Q), 107 College Rd. E., Princeton 08540
  Sr. Dir.—Jerry Whalen, 50 emp., *Corporate headquarters; prescription* .................... (609) 375-9900

Eagle Nutritionals, 485 Washington Ave., Carlstadt 07072
  Owner—Marlon Durham, 45 emp., *Vitamins* .................... (201) 964-1441

Eisai, Inc. (H Q), 100 Tice Blvd., Woodcliff Lake 07677
  Chrm. & CEO—Yuji Matsue, 800 emp., *Corporate headquarters; pharmaceuticals* .................... (201) 692-1100

Eli Lilly & Co., 33 ImClone Dr., Branchburg 08876
  Assoc. V-P., Fin. Analysis & Plng.—Lori Macomber, 650 emp., *Oncology pharmaceutical drug* (908) 541-8100

Eli Lilly (H Q), 440 Route 22 E., Bridgewater 08807
  V-P., Global Qual.—Carole Beer, 350 emp., *Divisional headquarters; oncology pharmaceuti..* (908) 541-8100

Elite Pharmaceuticals, Inc., 165 Ludlow Ave., Northvale 07647
  Chrm.—Jerry Treppel, 40 emp., *Oral controlled-release pharmaceuticals* .................... (201) 750-2646

Enzon Pharmaceuticals, Inc., 20 Kingsbridge Rd., Piscataway 08854
  Ex. V-P., Hum. Res., CEO & COO—George Hubbard, 35 emp., *Biopharmaceuticals, including* (732) 980-4500

Ethical Alternative Products, LLC, 525 Cedar Hill Ave., Wyckoff 07481
  Ptnr.—Gerald Bruno, 5 emp., *Company headquarters & pharmaceuticals* .................... (201) 251-7771

Excellium Pharmaceutical, Inc., 3 Oak Rd., Ste. G, Fairfield 07004
  Pres.—Hasmukh Doshi, 35 emp., *Generic prescription pharmaceuticals* .................... (973) 276-9600

Exeltis, 1 Main St., Ste. 203, Chatham 07928
  CEO—Maria Carell, 25 emp., *Pharmaceuticals.* .................... (973) 324-0200

Extracts & Ingredients Ltd., Div. Of MORRE-TEC Industries, Inc., 1 Gary Rd., Union 07083
  Pres.—Leonard Glass, 5 emp., *Botanical extracts, nutritive oils,* .................... (908) 688-9009

Food Sciences Corporation, 821 E. Gate Dr., Mount Laurel 08054
  Pres.—Robert Schwartz, 150 emp., *Weight loss meal replacements & protein* .................... (856) 778-8080

Frinton Laboratories, Inc., 4204 Sylon Blvd., Hainesport 08036
  ★ Pres.—George Inglessis, 4 emp., *Pharmaceuticals* .................... (856) 722-7037

G & W Laboratories Inc., 111 Coolidge St., South Plainfield 07080
  Chrm. & CEO—Ronald Greenblatt, 350 emp., *Pharmaceuticals* .................... (908) 753-2000

Gallus BioPharmaceuticals New Jersey, LLC, 201 College Rd. E., Princeton 08540
  Pres., CEO—Mark R. Bamforth, 90 emp., *Contract manufacturing of pharmaceuticals* .................... (609) 919-3300

Garden State Nutritionals, LLC, 8 Henderson Dr., West Caldwell 07006
  CEO—Keith Frankel, 400 emp., *Dietary supplements, including tablets* .................... (973) 575-9200

GE Healthcare, 900 Durham Ave., South Plainfield 07080
  Qual. Control Mgr.—Bob Rogers, 17 emp., *Pharmaceuticals* .................... (908) 757-0500

Genavite, LLC, 235 Clifton Blvd., Clifton 07011
  Owner—Bharat Patel, 10 emp., *Vitamin coatings* .................... (973) 779-1532

General Filter Corp., 14 Constitution Ave., Succasunna 07876
  Pres., CEO—Richard Warren, 4 emp., *Pharmaceutical filter bags* .................... (973) 584-9220

Genesis Pharmaceutical, Inc. (H Q), 8 Campus Dr., Parsippany 07054
  CEO—Laurent-Emmanuel Siffre, 40 emp., *Corporate headquarters; medicated skin* .................... (800) 459-8663

Granulation Technology, Inc., 12 Industrial Rd., Fairfield 07004
  Pres.—Alka Nigalaye, 6 emp., *Granulation pharmaceutical processing* .................... (973) 276-0740

Grow Co., Inc., 55 Railroad Ave., Ridgefield 07657
  Pres.—Magda Peck, 15 emp., *Biologically & physiologically evaluated* .................... (201) 941-8777

Guardian Drug Co., Inc., 2 Charles Ct., Dayton 08810
  Pres.—Arvind B. Dhruv, 110 emp., *Over-the-counter pharmaceutical preparations* .................... (609) 860-2600

Halo Pharmaceutical, Inc., 30 N. Jefferson Rd., Whippany 07981
  Pres., CEO—Clive V. Bennett, 200 emp., *Contract manufacturing of pharmaceuticals* .................... (973) 428-4000

Hartz Mountain Corp., The, 400 Plaza Dr., Secaucus 07094
  Div. V-P., Mktg.—Adam Coacher, 250 emp., *Corporate headquarters & animal health* .................... (201) 271-4800

Hemispherx Biopharma, Inc., 783 Jersey Ave., New Brunswick 08901
  V-P., Opers.—Wayne Springate, 30 emp., *Pharmaceuticals* .................... (732) 249-3250

Heritage Pharmaceuticals, Inc. (H Q), 12 Christopher, Ste. 300, Eatontown 07724
  CEO—Jeffrey Glazer, 15 emp., *Corporate headquarters; generic pharmaceutica* .................... (732) 429-1000

Hovione, LLC, 40 Lake Dr., East Windsor 08520
  Hum. Res. Mgr.—Lavinia Emery, 50 emp., *Active pharmaceutical ingredients* .................... (609) 918-2600

I G I Laboratories, Inc., 105 Lincoln Ave., P.O. Box 687, Buena 08310
  Pres., CEO—Jason Grenfell-Gardner, 45 emp., *Contract manufacturing of pharmaceuticals..* (856) 697-1441

Ikaria, Inc. (H Q), 53 Frontage Rd., P.O. Box 9001, Hampton 08827
  Chrm., CEO—Daniel Tasse, 175 emp., *Holding company headquarters; pharmaceutical* .................... (908) 238-6600

Immunomedics, Inc., 300 The American Rd., Morris Plains 07950
  Pres., CEO—Cynthia L. Sullivan, 125 emp., *Humanized monoclonal antibody-based* .................... (973) 605-8200

Inergetics, Inc., 550 Broad St., 12th Fl., Newark 07102
  Opers. Mgr.—Sherman Fan, 10 emp., *Nutritional drink mixes for cancer* .................... (908) 604-2500

InnoPharma, Inc., 10 Knightsbridge Rd., Piscataway 08854
  Pres., CEO—Navneet Puri, 50 emp., *Sterile generic injectable & ophthalmic* .................... (732) 885-2939

Insmed, Inc., 10 Finderne Ave., Bridgewater 08807
  Pres.—Will Lewis, 80 emp., *Inhaled pharmaceuticals for the site-specific* .................... (908) 977-9900

Intergel Vitamin Co., 191 40th St., Irvington 07111
  Dir., Opers.—Eric Sylvester, 100 emp., *Pharmaceutical & nutritional products* .................... (973) 371-4400

Jacobus Pharmaceutical Co., Inc., 37 Cleveland Ln., Princeton 08540
  Ptnr.—David Jacobus, 52 emp., *Corporate headquarters; prescription* .................... (609) 921-7447

Jacobus Pharmaceutical Co., Inc., P.O. Box 5290, Princeton 08540
  Owner—Laura Jacobus, 45 emp., *Prescription pharmaceuticals* .................... (609) 799-8221

Jamol Laboratories, Inc., 13 Ackerman Ave., P.O. Box 313, Emerson 07630
  Pres.—Emil Scott Lucia, 5 emp., *OTC botanical nose drops for the treatment* .................... (201) 262-6363

Janssen Pharmaceuticals, Inc., 1125 Trenton-Harbourton Rd., P.O. Box 200, Titusville 08560
  Dir., Sales, Natl. Cardiology—Judith Wicklum, 2000 emp., *Pharmaceuticals* .................... (908) 218-6000

Janssen Research & Development, LLC, A Div. of Johnson & Johnson, 920 U.S. Highway 202, P.O. Box 300, Raritan 08869
  CFO—Chris Picariello, 2000 emp., *Pharmaceuticals* .................... (908) 704-4000

JHP Pharmaceuticals, LLC, 1 Upper Pond Rd., Bldg. D, Parsippany 07054
  Pres., CEO—Stuart Hinchen, 30 emp., *Company headquarters & pharmaceuticals* .................... (973) 658-3530

Johnson & Johnson (H Q), 1 Johnson & Johnson Plz., New Brunswick 08933
  Worldwide Chrm., Consumer Div.—Jesse Wu, 900 emp., *Company headquarters; surgical ..* (732) 524-0400

Johnson & Johnson Consumer Companies, Inc. (H Q), 199 Grandview Rd., Skillman 08558
  Chrm., Co. Group—Roberto Marques, 1100 emp., *Corporate headquarters; baby, skin,* .................... (908) 874-1000

Kremers Urban Pharmaceuticals, Inc. (H Q), 902 Carnegie Ctr., Ste. 360, Princeton 08540
  Pres., CEO—George Stevenson, 14 emp., *Corporate headquarters; specialty generic* .................... (609) 936-5940

Life Science Laboratories, LLC, 170 Oberlin Ave. N., Ste. 26, Lakewood 08701
  Owner—Yochanan Bulka, 10 emp., *Nutritional supplements* .................... (732) 367-1900

Life Science Labs Supplements, LLC, 170 Oberlin Ave., Lakewood 08701
  ★ Ex. V-P.—Adeena Zabrowsky, 14 emp., *Nutritional supplements* .................... (732) 367-1749

Lipo Chemicals, Inc., 1515 W. Blancke St., Linden 07036
  Cont.—Anthony Vicale, 35 emp., *Cosmetic ingredients & pharmaceutical* .................... (973) 926-0331

LTS Lohmann Therapy Systems Corp., 21 Henderson Dr., West Caldwell 07006
  Pres.—Joachim Franke, 300 emp., *Contract manufacturing of drug delivery* .................... (973) 244-2026

LycoRed Corp., 377 Crane St., Orange 07050
  CFO—Benjamin Regev, 40 emp., *Bulk, added-value nutrients & ingredients* .................... (877) 592-6733

Manhattan Drug Co., Inc., 225 Long Ave., Bldg. 15, 3rd Fl., Hillside 07205
  CEO—E. Gerald Kay, 90 emp., *Nutritional supplements & vitamin preparation* .................... (973) 926-0816

Meda Pharmaceuticals, Inc. (H Q), 265 Davidson Ave., Somerset 08873
  Pres.—Maria Carell, 85 emp., *Corporate headquarters; prescription* .................... (732) 564-2200

Medicines Co., The, 8 Sylvan Way, Parsippany 07054
  CEO—Clive Meanwell, 170 emp., *Company headquarters & biopharmaceuticals* .................... (973) 290-6000

Merck & Co., Inc., 2000 Galloping Hill Rd., Kenilworth 07033
  Ex. Dir., Global Benefits—Mary Weber, 2600 emp., *Pharmaceuticals, for allergies, skin* .................... (908) 298-4000

Merck & Co., Inc., 126 E. Lincoln Ave., P.O. Box 2000, Rahway 07065
  Pres., Research Laboratories & Ex. V-P.—Peter S. Kim, 4200 emp., *Pharmaceuticals* .................... (732) 594-4000

Merck & Co., Inc. (H Q), 1 Merck Dr., P.O. Box 100, Whitehouse Station 08889
  Chrm. & CEO—Kenneth C. Frazier, 2000 emp., *Corporate headquarters; pharmaceuticals* .................... (908) 423-1000

Merial Ltd., 631 U.S. Highway 1, North Brunswick 08902
  Opers. Mgr.—Heidi Tomenehok, 75 emp., *Pharmaceuticals* .................... (732) 729-5700

Milestone PharmTech USA, Inc., 100 Jersey Ave., Bldg. D, Box D-4, New Brunswick 08901
  CEO—Eric Zhang, 5 emp., *Chemical intermedia for the pharmaceuticals* .................... (732) 579-8201

Mitsubishi Tanabe Pharma America, Inc. (H Q), 525 Washington Blvd., Ste. 400, Jersey City 07310
  Pres.—Takashi Nagago, 75 emp., *Corporate headquarters; pharmaceutical* .................... (908) 607-1980

MonoSol Rx, LLC (H Q), 30 Technology Dr., Warren 07059
  Pres., CEO—Mark Schobel, 15 emp., *Company headquarters; film-based pharmaceutic* .................... (908) 941-1900

MPT Delivery Systems, Inc., 95 Prince St., Paterson 07501
  Pres.—Bob McCrimlisk, 50 emp., *Formulation & granulation of bulk nutriceutic* .................... (973) 279-4132

Northeast Pro-Tech, Inc., 61 Willet St., Bldg. L, Passaic 07055
  Pres., Hum. Res. Mgr.—Frank Dework, 5 emp., *Food additive blending* .................... (973) 777-5654

Nostrum Pharmaceuticals, LLC (H Q), 1370 Hamilton St., Somerset 08873
  CEO—Ronnie Toddywala, 42 emp., *Company headquarters; generic drugs* .................... (732) 543-2440

Novartis Consumer Health (H Q), 200 Kimball Dr., Parsippany 07054
  CEO—Brian McNamara, 1000 emp., *Company headquarters; pharmaceuticals* .................... (973) 503-8000

Novartis Pharmaceuticals Corp. (H Q), 1 Health Plz., East Hanover 07936
  Pres.—Christi Shaw, 4390 emp., *Corporate headquarters; pharmaceuticals* .................... (862) 778-8300

Novel Laboratories, Inc., 400 Campus Dr., Somerset 08873
  Pres., CEO—Veerappan Subramanian, 200 emp., *Pharmaceuticals* .................... (908) 603-6000

Novo Nordisk, Inc. (H Q), 800 Scudders Mill Rd., Plainsboro 08536
  Pres.—Jesper Hoilland, 1000 emp., *Corporate headquarters; insulin & therapeutic* .................... (609) 987-5800

NPS Pharmaceuticals, Inc. (H Q), 550 Hills Dr., Bedminster 07921
  CEO—Francois Nader, 200 emp., *Corporate headquarters; drug candidates* .................... (908) 450-5300

Nutra-Med Packaging, Inc., 385 Franklin Ave., Ste. E, Rockaway 07866
  Pres.—Mahesh Gupta, 45 emp., *Contract packaging, including bottles* .................... (973) 625-2274

Nutri Pet Research, Inc./NUPRO Supplements, 227 State Route 33 E., Manalapan 07726
  Pres.—Janis Gianforte-Horner, 7 emp., *Holistic pet vitamin supplements &* .................... (732) 786-8822

OHM Laboratories, Inc., 14 Terminal Rd., New Brunswick 08901
  V-P., GM—Bob Patton, 400 emp., *Pharmaceuticals* .................... (732) 514-4380

OHM Laboratories, Inc., 1385 Livingston Ave., P.O. Box 7397, North Brunswick 08902
  CFO—Manjeet Bindra, 160 emp., *Pharmaceuticals* .................... (732) 418-2235

P. F. Laboratories, Inc., 700 Union Blvd., Totowa 07512
  Dir., Hum. Res.—Morolake Esi, 125 emp., *Pharmaceuticals* .................... (973) 256-3100

Pacira Pharmaceuticals, Inc. (H Q), 5 Sylvan Way, Parsippany 07054
  Chrm., Pres. & CEO—David Stack, 52 emp., *Corporate headquarters; clinical &* .................... (973) 254-3560

S.I.C.

Par Pharmaceutical Cos., Inc., 300 Tice Blvd., Woodcliff Lake 07677
CEO—Paul Campanelli, 125 emp., *Corporate headquarters & pharmaceuticals* .......... (201) 802-4000
PediatRx, Inc. (H Q), 90 Fairmount Rd. W., P.O. Box 423, Califon 07830
Founder, Chrm. & CEO—Cameron Durrant, 2 emp., *Corporate headquarters; specialty pharmaceuti* (908) 975-0753
PharMEDium, 43 Distribution Blvd., Edison 08817
IT Mgr.—Chris Lee, 25 emp., *Sterile pharmaceutical compounding* .......... (732) 287-8655
Prime Pack, LLC, 262 Old New Brunswick Rd., Ste. N, Piscataway 08854
Dir., Qual. Control—Lakshmi Nagarajan, 10 emp., *Contract manufacturing of dietary supplements* (732) 253-7734
Prolong Pharmaceuticals, 300 Corporate Ct., Ste. B, South Plainfield 07080
Founder, CEO & Chief Science Officer—Abraham Abuchowski, 50 emp., *Biopharmaceuticals for the* . (908) 444-4660
PTC Therapeutics, Inc., 100 Corporate Ct., South Plainfield 07080
Co-Founder—Allan Jacobson, 180 emp., *Biopharmaceutical drug candidates in* .......... (908) 222-7000
PuraCap Pharmaceutical, LLC, 1001 Durham Ave., South Plainfield 07080
Founder & CEO—Dahai Guo, 50 emp., *Over-the-counter, prescription brand* .......... (908) 941-5456
Quality Formulation Laboratories, Inc., 110 Pennsylvania Ave., Paterson 07503
CEO—Mohamed Desoky, 50 emp., *Vitamin preparations, weight loss products* .......... (973) 977-8800
Quantum Pharmaceuticals, Inc. (H Q), P.O. Box 244, Ogdensburg 07439
Pres. & Mng. Member—Mark Steele, 7 emp., *Corporate headquarters; pharmaceutical* .......... (877) 873-3762
Ranbaxy, Inc. (H Q), 600 College Rd. E., Ste. 2100, Princeton 08540
V-P., Hum. Res.—Bernard Brothman, 65 emp., *Corporate headquarters; pharmaceuticals* .......... (609) 720-9200
Raritan Pharmaceuticals, Inc., 8 Joanna Ct., East Brunswick 08816
Pres.—Vin Nayak, 250 emp., *Pharmaceuticals* .......... (732) 432-8200
Rasi Laboratories, Inc., 20 Roosevelt Ave., Somerset 08873
Pres.—Ramakrishna Gogineni, 45 emp., *Vitamins & health supplements* .......... (732) 873-8500
Roche Nutley, 340 Kingsland St., Nutley 07110
V-P. & Head of Medicinal Chemistry—Karen Lackey, 1000 emp., *Pharmaceutical drug candidates* (973) 235-5000
Sabinsa Corp., 20 Lake Dr., East Windsor 08520
Chrm.—M. Majeed, 30 emp., *Corporate headquarters & phytonutrients* .......... (732) 777-1111
Sandoz, Inc. (H Q), 506 Carnegie Ctr., Ste. 400, Princeton 08540
Pres., U.S.A. & Head of N.A.—Peter Goldschmidt, 200 emp., *Corporate headquarters; pharmaceuticals* (609) 627-8500
Sanofi U. S. (H Q), 55 Corporate Dr., Bridgewater 08807
Sr. V-P., Global Svcs.—Gregory Irace, 2000 emp., *Company headquarters; pharmaceuticals* (908) 981-5000
Sciecure Pharma, Inc., 11 Deerpark Dr., Ste. 120, Monmouth Junction 08852
Pres.—Nolan Wang, 20 emp., *Generic pharmaceutical prototypes &* .......... (732) 329-8089
Shionogi, Inc. (H Q), 300 Campus Dr., Florham Park 07932
Sales Mgr., District—Byron Brown, 200 emp., *Corporate headquarters; pharmaceuticals* .......... (973) 966-6900
Siegfried USA, LLC, 33 Industrial Park Rd., Pennsville 08070
Sr. V-P., GM—Kenneth Zrebiec, 186 emp., *Pharmaceutical substances* .......... (856) 678-3601
Soligenix, Inc., 29 Emmons Dr., Ste. C-10, Princeton 08540
Pres., CEO—Christopher J. Schaber, 20 emp., *Biopharmaceuticals & vaccines* .......... (609) 538-8200
Strativa Pharmaceuticals (H Q), 300 Tice Blvd., Woodcliff Lake 07677
Pres.—Paul Campanelli, 150 emp., *Company headquarters; pharmaceuticals* .......... (201) 802-4000
Sun Pharmaceutical Industries, Inc., 270 Prospect Plains Rd., Cranbury 08512
GM—Scott Randby, 160 emp., *Pharmaceutical preparations* .......... (609) 495-2800
Sunrise Pharmaceutical, Inc., 665 E. Lincoln Ave., Rahway 07065
CEO—Utpal Patel, 45 emp., *Prescription & over-the-counter pharmaceutica* .......... (732) 382-6085
Tamir Biotechnology, Inc. (H Q), 11 Deer Park Dr., Monmouth Junction 08852
Pres., CEO—Charles Muniz, 5 emp., *Corporate headquarters; biopharmaceutical* .......... (732) 823-1003
Telmark Packaging Corp., 30 Freneau Ave., Ste. 2-B, Matawan 07747
Pres.—Eric Ludwig, 8 emp., *Contract formulation, manufacturing* .......... (732) 739-9100
Teva Pharmaceuticals U.S.A., Inc., 8-10 Gloria Ln., Fairfield 07004
Cont.—Ron Pisano, 75 emp., *Pharmaceuticals* .......... (973) 575-2775
ThromboGenics, Inc., 101 Wood Ave. S., Ste. 600, Iselin 08830
Head of N. American Opers.—Keith Stewaid, 20 emp., *Ophthalmic pharmaceutical drug candidates* (732) 590-2900
Torpac, Inc., 333 U.S. Highway 46, Fairfield 07004
Pres.—Raj Tahil, 10 emp., *Custom & large-size two-piece empty* .......... (973) 244-1125
Tris Pharma, Inc., 2033 U.S. Highway 130, Ste. D, Monmouth Junction 08852
Pres., CEO—Ketan Mehta, 300 emp., *Over-the-counter, branded & generic* .......... (732) 940-2800
TYRX, Inc., 1 Deer Park Dr., Ste. G, Monmouth Junction 08852
Dir., Mktg.—Randy Mansfield, 34 emp., *Implantable combination drug & device* .......... (732) 246-8676
Unimed International, Inc., 105 Newfield Ave., Ste. F, Edison 08837
CEO—George Faltaous, 20 emp., *All-natural antioxidant skin care &* .......... (800) 754-6211
Universal Laboratories, Inc., 3 Terminal Rd., New Brunswick 08901
Pres., CEO—Mike Rockoff, 200 emp., *Vitamin preparations & food supplements* .......... (732) 545-3130
Validus Pharmaceuticals, LLC, 119 Cherry Hill Rd., Ste. 310, Parsippany 07054
CEO—James Hunter, 10 emp., *Pharmaceutical products* .......... (973) 265-2777
Vertical Pharmaceuticals, Inc. (H Q), 2500 Main St., Ste. 6, Sayreville 08872
Pres.—Steven Squashic, 10 emp., *Corporate headquarters; pharmaceuticals* .......... (732) 721-0070
Vils Pharma, Inc., 135 Glendale Ave., Edison 08817
Co-Pres.—A. J. Upadhyay, 5 emp., *Pharmaceutical coating* .......... (732) 777-6023
Warner Chilcott, 100 Enterprise Dr., Ste. 280, Rockaway 07866
CEO—Brent Saunders, 100 emp., *Specialty prescription pharmaceuticals* .......... (973) 442-3200
Westward Pharmaceutical Corp., 2 Esterbrook Ln., Cherry Hill 08003
Cont.—George Muench, 850 emp., *Injectable pharmaceuticals* .......... (856) 424-3700
West-Ward Pharmaceutical Corp., 401 Industrial Way W., Eatontown 07724
Pres., CEO—Michael Raya, 350 emp., *Solid dose, injectible & generic pharmaceutic* .......... (732) 542-1191
Wockhardt USA, LLC (H Q), 20 Waterview Blvd., Ste. 3, Parsippany 07054
Pres., N. Amer.—Sunil Khera, 32 emp., *Company headquarters; generic pharmaceuticals* .... (973) 257-4960
Xerimis Inc., 102 Executive Dr., Moorestown 08057
CEO—Carol Sue Bernardo, 100 emp., *Custom primary & secondary clinical* .......... (856) 727-9940
Zydus Pharmaceuticals USA, Inc., 73 Route 31 N., Pennington 08534
CEO—Joseph D. Renner, 12 emp., *Corporate headquarters & generic pharmaceutic* .......... (609) 730-1900

## 2835 Diagnostic substances

3D Biotek, LLC, 1 Ilene Ct., Hillsborough 08844
CEO—Qing Liu, 3 emp., *3D in-vitro cell culture scaffolds* .......... (732) 729-6270
AIRMED Biotech, LLC, 510 Titus Rd., Lambertville 08530
Pres., CEO—Jack Kerins, 5 emp., *Saliva, blood & urine test devices* .......... (215) 378-9114
Akers Biosciences, Inc., 201 Grove Rd., Thorofare 08086
Ex. Chrm. of the Board—Raymond F. Akers, Jr., 26 emp., *Medical diagnostic products* .......... (856) 848-8698
American Bionostica, Inc., 510 Heron Dr., Ste. 203, Swedesboro 08085
Pres.—Rick Thompson, 10 emp., *Rapid immunochromatographic tests for* .......... (856) 467-7070
AP Diagnostic Laboratories, Inc., 1692 Oak Tree Rd., Ste. 17, Edison 08820
Pres.—Harshad Patel, 10 emp., *Diagnostic test kits* .......... (732) 906-7800
Bracco Diagnostics, Inc., 259 Prospect Plains Rd., Bldg. H, Monroe Township 08831
Pres., CEO—Vittorio Puppo, 175 emp., *Corporate headquarters & barium & radiologica* .......... (609) 514-2200
Cenmed Enterprises, 121 Jersey Ave., New Brunswick 08901
Sales Mgr.—Rizwan Chaudhry, 12 emp., *Manufacturer of diagnostic drug tests* .......... (732) 447-1100
Cenogenics Corp., 100 Route 520, P.O. Box 308, Morganville 07751
Pres.—Michael Katz, 15 emp., *Contract medical stool, blood, urinalysis* .......... (732) 536-6457
Church & Dwight Co., Inc., 326 Half Acre Rd., Cranbury 08512
Hum. Res. Mgr.—Maria Moke, 75 emp., *Pregnancy test kits* .......... (609) 655-6000
Diagnostic Specialties, 4 Leonard St., Metuchen 08840
Pres., MIS Mgr.—Praful Raja, 6 emp., *Medical diagnostic test kits, including* .......... (732) 549-4011
E N G Scientific, Inc., 82 Industrial St. E., Clifton 07012
Pres., CEO—Henry Eng, 5 emp., *Clinical diagnostic stains & reagents* .......... (973) 472-7200
Enterix, Inc., 236 Fernwood Ave., Edison 08837
V-P.—Robert Dachille, 24 emp., *Colorectal cancer testing kits* .......... (732) 429-1899
Euroimmun US, Inc., 1100 The American Rd., Ste. 1, Morris Plains 07950
★ Mng. Dir.—Hamid Erfanian, 13 emp., *Diagnostic test kits, including autoimmune* .......... (973) 656-1000
Hilin Life Products, Inc., 211 Warren St., Ste. 211, Newark 07103
CEO—Helen Denise, 6 emp., *Fertility management test kits* .......... (973) 648-0265
Laboratory Diagnostics Co., Inc., 100 Route 520, P.O. Box 160, Morganville 07751
Pres.—Michael Katz, 15 emp., *Medical diagnostic test kits, including* .......... (732) 536-6300
MicroSurfaces, Inc., 1 W. Forest Ave., Englewood 07631
Pres.—Athena Guo, 6 emp., *Protein microarrays* .......... (201) 408-5596
Origio, Inc., 77 Elbo Ln., Mount Laurel 08054
Ex. V-P., Mfg.—Allan Toft Jacobsen, 30 emp., *In-vitro fertilization (IVF) substances* .......... (856) 762-2000
Ortho-Clinical Diagnostics, Inc. (H Q), 1001 U.S. Highway 202, P.O. Box 350, Raritan 08869
Chrm., CEO—Martin Madaus, 750 emp., *Corporate headquarters; donor screening* .......... (908) 218-1300
Perkins Co., Inc., P. W., 221 Commissioners Pike, Woodstown 08098
Pres.—Darlene A. Perkins, 4 emp., *Research laboratory reagents, including* .......... (856) 769-3525
Pharmaseq, Inc., 11 Deerpark Dr., Ste. 104, Monmouth Junction 08852
CEO—Richard J. Morris, 5 emp., *Commercial physical research laboratory* .......... (732) 355-0100
Princeton BioMeditech Corp., 4242 U.S. Highway 1, Monmouth Junction 08852
Pres.—Jemo Kang, 70 emp., *One-step advanced rapid diagnostic* .......... (732) 274-1000
Roche Molecular Systems, Inc., 1080 U.S. Highway 202 S., Branchburg 08876
Sr. Hum. Res. Mgr.—Kristen Cohen, 500 emp., *Diagnostic & blood screening assays* .......... (908) 253-7200
Sensonics, Inc., 125 White Horse Pike, P.O. Box 112, Haddon Heights 08035
Pres., CEO—Richard Doty, 9 emp., *Corporate headquarters & quantitative* .......... (800) 547-8838
Thermo Fisher Scientific, 755 U.S. Highway 202, Bridgewater 08807
Site Mgr.—Thomas Campbell, 162 emp., *Bioreagants & specialty chemicals for* .......... (908) 526-1800
Worthington Biochemical Corp., 730 Vassar Ave., Lakewood 08701
Pres.—Von Worthington, 50 emp., *Highly purified enzymes* .......... (732) 942-1660

## 2836 Biological products, except diagnostic

Celldex Therapeutics, Inc., 53 Frontage Rd., Ste. 200, Hampton 08827
★ CEO—Anthony S. Marucci, 50 emp., *Pharmaceuticals* .......... (908) 200-7500
Collagen Matrix, Inc., 509 Commerce St., Franklin 07417
Dir., Mfg.—Greg Owens, 25 emp., *Collagen & mineral-based extracellular* .......... (201) 405-1477
Collagen Matrix, Inc., 15 Thornton Rd., Oakland 07436
Pres., CEO—Shu-Tung Li, 80 emp., *Corporate headquarters & collagen &* .......... (201) 405-1477
DSM Pharmaceutical Products, Inc. (H Q), 45 Waterview Blvd., Parsippany 07054
Pres., CEO—Alexander Wessels, 165 emp., *Corporate headquarters; liquid & dry* .......... (973) 257-1063
Enzon Pharmaceuticals, Inc., 20 Kingsbridge Rd., Piscataway 08854
Ex. V-P., Hum. Res., CEO & COO—George Hubbard, 35 emp., *Biopharmaceuticals, including* (732) 980-4500
Genzyme Corp., Biosurgery Div., 1125 Pleasant View Ter., Ridgefield 07657
Sr. V-P., Opers.—Don Woodhouse, 300 emp., *Biotechnology products for biosurgery* .......... (201) 945-9550
Ipsen Biopharmaceuticals, Inc., 106 Allen Rd., 3rd Fl., Basking Ridge 07920
Pres., N. America—Cynthia Schwalm, 40 emp., *Biopharmaceuticals for endocrine &* .......... (866) 837-2422
LTS Lohmann Therapy Systems Corp., 21 Henderson Dr., West Caldwell 07006
Pres.—Joachim Franke, 300 emp., *Contract manufacturing of drug delivery* .......... (973) 244-2026
Monmouth BioProducts, 3 Industrial Ct., Ste. 4, Freehold 07728
Owner—Sean M. Duddy, 6 emp., *Bacteria & enzymes for wastewater,* .......... (732) 863-0300
Nitta Casings Inc., 141 Southside Ave., Bridgewater 08807
Pres., CEO—Rod Moore, 192 emp., *Edible collagen sausage casings & collagen* .......... (908) 218-4400
PBL Assay Science, 131 Ethel Rd. W., Ste. 6, Piscataway 08854
Chrm., CEO—Robert Pestka, 35 emp., *Cell-based assay & immunoassay products* .......... (732) 777-9123
Princeton Separation, Inc., 100 Commerce Dr., Freehold 07728
Pres.—Paul Nix, 19 emp., *Molecular separation products for proteins* .......... (732) 431-3338
Progenitor Cell Therapy, LLC, 4 Pearl Ct., Ste. C, Allendale 07401
Pres.—Robert Preti, 60 emp., *Contract manufacturing of cell & tissue-based* .......... (201) 883-5300
Suven Life Sciences Ltd., 1100 Cornwall Rd., Monmouth Junction 08852
CEO—Venkat Jasti, 10 emp., *Pharmaceutical development carbohydrate-based* .......... (732) 274-0037
TYRX, Inc., 1 Deer Park Dr., Ste. G, Monmouth Junction 08852
Dir., Mktg.—Randy Mansfield, 34 emp., *Implantable combination drug & device* .......... (732) 246-8676
Xerimis Inc., 102 Executive Dr., Moorestown 08057
CEO—Carol Sue Bernardo, 100 emp., *Custom primary & secondary clinical* .......... (856) 727-9940

## 2841 Soap & other detergents

American Spraytech, LLC, 205 Meister Ave., Branchburg 08876
Pres.—Allen S. Lalwani, 19 emp., *Contract manufacturer of cosmetics,* .......... (908) 725-6060
Aqua Products, Inc., 2703 River Rd., P.O. Box 231, Cinnaminson 08077
Pres.—Sam Jones, Sr., 25 emp., *Laundry detergent, cleaning compounds* .......... (856) 829-8444
Arol Chemical Products Co., 649 Ferry St., Newark 07105
Pres.—Salvatore Coppola, 6 emp., *Textile washing & base maintenance* .......... (973) 344-1510
Atlantic Beach Soap Co., 231 North Ave. W., Ste. 2, Westfield 07090
★ Owner—Shaun Blackie, 2 emp., *Handcrafted soaps, including olive* .......... (908) 272-7595
Avianne Health Care Systems, 115 1st St., Lodi 07644
Pres.—Robert Siconolfi, 1 emp., *Soap* .......... (201) 288-4100
Banner Chemical Corp., 111 Hill St., Orange 07050
Pres.—David Herman, 10 emp., *Manufacturer & distributor of sanitary* .......... (973) 676-2900
Buhler Inc, 40 Whitney Rd., Mahwah 07430
Pres.—Steve Jacobson, 15 emp., *Processing equipment for the chemical* .......... (201) 847-0600
Capital Soap Products, LLC, 33 Branch St., P.O. Box 357, Paterson 07544
Pres.—A. J. Kretz, 22 emp., *Sweeping compounds, soaps & detergents* .......... (973) 333-6100
Cavalier Chemical Co., 26 Papetti Plz., Elizabeth 07206
Owner—Norman Lubin, *Laundry detergents & kitchen cleaners* .......... (908) 558-0110
Church & Dwight Co., Inc. (H Q), 500 Charles Ewing Blvd., Ewing 08628
Chrm., CEO—James Craigie, 400 emp., *Corporate headquarters; detergents,* .......... (609) 683-5900
Diamond Chemical Company, Inc., Union Ave. & DuBois St., P.O. Box 7428, East Rutherford 07073
Pres.—Harold Diamond, 200 emp., *Industrial & institutional detergents* .......... (201) 935-4300
Dynamic Blending Co., Inc., 1475 S. 6th St., Camden 08104
Pres.—Terence O'Reiley, 11 emp., *Detergents* .......... (856) 541-6626
E&M Gold Beekeepers, LLC, 113 Hope Rd., Tinton Falls 07724
Ptnr.—Mary Kosenski, 2 emp., *All-natural honey & honey & beeswax-based* .......... (732) 542-6528
Epic Industries, 1007 Jersey Ave., New Brunswick 08901
V-P.—Sam Levine, 60 emp., *Cleaners, detergents, sanitizers, deodorizers* .......... (732) 249-6867
Hy-Test Packaging Corp., 515 E. 41st St., Paterson 07504
Pres.—Jack Smith, 9 emp., *Liquid cleaning products, fuel additives* .......... (973) 754-7000
Inopak Ltd., 24 Executive Pkwy., Ringwood 07456
Pres., CEO—John Polite, 25 emp., *Liquid soap, dispensers & antimicrobials* .......... (973) 962-1121
International Products Corp., 201 Connecticut Dr., Burlington 08016
Pres.—Kathy J. Wyrofsky, 25 emp., *Precision cleaners & temporary assembly* .......... (609) 386-8770

InventeK Colloidal Cleaners, LLC (USA), 106 Gaither Dr., Mount Laurel 08054
Pres.—Yasmin Andrecola, 25 emp., Nontoxic & eco-friendly colloidal cleaning .......... (856) 206-0058
Jobe Industries, Inc. (H Q), 1600 W. Elizabeth Ave., P.O. Box 1367, Linden 07036
CEO—Sheila Reicher, 19 emp., Corporate headquarters; industrial .......... (908) 862-0400
Lanman & Kemp-Barclay & Co., Inc., 25 Woodland Ave., P.O. Box 421, Westwood 07675
Pres.—George Miller, 15 emp., Colognes, hair tonics & soaps .......... (201) 666-4990
Lerro Products, Inc., 1321 Walnut St., Camden 08103
Pres.—Dan Albanese, 20 emp., Janitorial soap & chemicals .......... (856) 203-3561
Metro-Chem, Inc., 24 Pennsylvania Ave., P.O. Box 401, Kearny 07032
Owner—Pete Potocki, 14 emp., Industrial laundry detergent .......... (973) 589-2800
Pilot Chemical Co., 267 Homestead Ave., Avenel 07001
Off. Mgr.—Kim Fletcher, 25 emp., Surfactants .......... (732) 634-6613
Polycracker, Inc., 487 Division St., Boonton 07005
Pres.—Sherylin Doyle, 3 emp., Biodegradable, environmentally safe .......... (973) 335-2828
Stanson Corp., 2 N. Hackensack Ave., Kearny 07032
Pres.—Robert Holuba, 100 emp., Powder & liquid detergents, softeners .......... (973) 344-8666
Styles Mfg. Co., Inc., A. E., 416 Richmond Ave., P.O. Box 1306, Point Pleasant Beach 08742
Pres.—John Criscuolo, 15 emp., Manufacturer of car wash detergents .......... (732) 899-0872
SWI International, Inc., 487 Division St., Boonton 07005
Pres. & Manager—Sharon Lippman, 5 emp., Detergents & degreasers .......... (973) 334-2525
Tessie's Soap Box, 65 South St., Jersey City 07307
★ Owner—Teresa Cooper, 2 emp., Laundry detergent .......... (201) 533-8337

## 2842 Polishes & sanitation goods

A. L. Wilson Chemical Co., 1050 Harrison Ave., P.O. Box 207, Kearny 07032
Pres.—Fred Schwarzmann, 20 emp., High-performance chemical products .......... (201) 997-3300
Advanced Safety Products, Inc., 37 S. Valley Ave., Vineland 08360
Pres.—Michael Schimmel, 5 emp., Bathtub & floor cleaning chemicals .......... (856) 691-1700
Aqua Products, Inc., 2703 River Rd., P.O. Box 231, Cinnaminson 08077
Pres.—Sam Jones, Sr., 25 emp., Laundry detergent, cleaning compounds .......... (856) 829-8444
Banner Chemical Corp., 111 Hill St., Orange 07050
Pres.—David Herman, 10 emp., Manufacturer & distributor of sanitary .......... (973) 676-2900
Biofusion, Inc., 310 Godwin Ave., Ridgewood 07450
CEO—David Gubb, 5 emp., Environmentally sustainable & nontoxic .......... (201) 447-6241
Braco Mfg. Co. & Magic Safety Products, Inc., 4301-B New Brunswick Ave., Ste. 2, South Plainfield 07080
Ptnr.—Jack Braha, 50 emp., Disposable baby diapers & safety cleaning .......... (732) 968-0008
Cadie Products Corp., 151 E. 11th St., Paterson 07524
Pres.—Edwin W. Meyers, 50 emp., Stain removers, cleaning & cooking .......... (973) 278-8300
Capital Soap Products, LLC, 33 Branch St., P.O. Box 357, Paterson 07544
Pres.—A. J. Kretz, 22 emp., Sweeping compounds, soaps & detergents .......... (973) 333-6100
Chemique, Inc., 315 N. Washington Ave., Moorestown 08057
Pres.—Edward Drazga, 10 emp., Kitchen & bathroom cleaners, marble .......... (856) 235-4161
Chemspa Industries, Inc., 22 Deforest Ave., East Hanover 07936
CEO—Jerome Rudy, 6 emp., Air fresheners, aromas & maintenance .......... (973) 386-1158
Earth Friendly Products, Inc., 380 Chestnut St., Norwood 07648
Pur. Mgr.—Keith Dutter, 20 emp., Cleaning compounds .......... (201) 750-7701
Edwards Creative Products, Inc., 910 Beechwood Ave., Cherry Hill 08002
Pres.—Charles S. Cohen, 10 emp., Household cleaning compounds .......... (856) 665-3200
Envirochem, Inc., 425 Whitehead Ave., South River 08882
Pres.—Deborah Gildersleeve, 50 emp., Institutional detergents .......... (732) 238-6700
Federal Mining & Mfg. Co., 288 E. 12th Ave., Roselle 07203
Pres.—Reda Shabka, 5 emp., Printing & graphic arts cleaning compounds .......... (908) 241-9355
Foster & Co., Inc., 15 Wing Dr., Cedar Knolls 07927
Pres., Fin. & MIS Mgr.—Richard Foster, 30 emp., Cleaning & polishing compounds, industrial (973) 267-4100
Global Specialty Products USA, Inc., 10 Eagle Ave., Ste. 500, Mount Holly 08060
Pres.—Theresa Wansiki, 12 emp., Environmentally safe, nonhazardous, .......... (609) 518-7577
Grignard Co., 505 Capobianco Plz., Rahway 07065
Mng. Ptnr.—Kelly Akre, 25 emp., Lubricating oils, greases, cleaners .......... (732) 340-1111
Harvey Westbury Corp. (H Q), 160 Littleton Rd., Ste. 308, Parsippany 07054
CEO—Eugene Chiaramonte, 3 emp., Corporate headquarters; automotive .......... (201) 468-7779
Hayward Industries, Inc., 620 Division St., Elizabeth 07201
Chrm.—Oscar Davis, 100 emp., Corporate headquarters & swimming pool .......... (908) 351-5400
Hood Finishing Products, Inc., 9 Factory Ln., Middlesex 08846
Pres.—Erick Kasner, 6 emp., Wood finishing & refinishing products .......... (732) 805-0088
Housechem, A Div. of Menshen Packaging U.S.A., Inc., 25 Industrial Park, Waldwick 07463
V-P., Opers. & Sales—Rogelio Ayala, 60 emp., Lavatory care & air freshening products .......... (201) 445-8808
Indco, Inc., 511 Essex St., P.O. Box 109, Gloucester City 08030
Pres.—Fred Binter, 30 emp., Contract blending of water-based chemicals .......... (856) 456-6100
International Products Corp., 201 Connecticut Dr., Burlington 08016
Pres.—Kathy J. Wyrofsky, 25 emp., Precision cleaners & temporary assembly .......... (609) 386-8770
InventeK Colloidal Cleaners, LLC (USA), 106 Gaither Dr., Mount Laurel 08054
Pres.—Yasmin Andrecola, 25 emp., Nontoxic & eco-friendly colloidal cleaning .......... (856) 206-0058
Kavango, Inc., 544 Lincoln Blvd., Middlesex 08846
Manager—Peter Rigg, 20 emp., Fragrance gels, sachets & beads & air .......... (732) 424-2430
Liquid Glass Enterprises, Inc., 93 Railroad Ave., Bergenfield 07621
Pres. & Chief Scientist—John R. Heywang, 5 emp., Liquid automotive, marine, aircraft .......... (201) 387-6755
Marine Development & Research Corp., 515 E. 41st St., Paterson 07504
Pres.—John S. Smith, 9 emp., Marine maintenance products .......... (973) 754-7087
Matchless United Co., 801 E. Linden Ave., Linden 07036
GM—Ricki Patchkiewitz, 8 emp., Polishing compounds, aqueous cleaners .......... (908) 862-7300
Menshen Packaging U.S.A., Inc., 21 Industrial Park, Waldwick 07463
V-P., Opers. & Sales—Rogelio Ayala, 78 emp., Custom plastic injection molding & .......... (201) 445-7436
Microgen, Inc., 33 Clinton Rd., Ste. 102, West Caldwell 07006
Pres.—Robert G. Prince, 3 emp., Antimicrobial spray, wipe, concentrate .......... (973) 575-9025
MP Technologies, LLC (H Q), 345 Claremont Ave., Ste. 26, Montclair 07042
Chrm.—John Mahdessian, 15 emp., Company headquarters; pocket stain .......... (646) 366-1155
Munzing, 1455 Broad St., Bloomfield 07003
V-P., Mfg. & Prod. Mgmt.—Mike Riggs, 39 emp., Defoamers, dispersants, rheology modifiers (973) 279-1306
NCH Corp., 34 Stouts Ln., P.O. Box 25, Monmouth Junction 08852
Plt. Mgr.—Julie Kormos, 12 emp., Cleaning chemicals .......... (732) 329-8111
Penetone Corp., 700 Gotham Pkwy., Ste. 2, Carlstadt 07072
V-P., GM, Fin. & Pur. Mgr.—Bruce Muretta, 27 emp., Industrial cleaning compounds .......... (201) 567-3000
Penetone Corp. (H Q), 1000 Herrontown Rd., Ste. 2, Princeton 08540
Pres.—Elwood Phares, 3 emp., Corporate headquarters; cleaning compounds .......... (609) 921-0501
Petronio Shoe Products Corp., 305 Cortlandt St., Belleville 07109
Pres.—Donald Rinaldi, 8 emp., Professional-grade cleaning, polishing .......... (973) 751-7579
Process Research Products, 1013 Whitehead Road Ext., Trenton 08638
V-P., Admn. & Fin.—Phyliss Joan, 20 emp., Metalworking fluids, lapping compounds .......... (609) 882-0400
Reckitt Benckiser, LLC, 799 U.S. Highway 206, P.O. Box 5817, Hillsborough 08844
Plt. Mgr.—Cal Smedberg, 230 emp., Household & professional cleaning supplies .......... (908) 533-2000
Swisher Hygiene Inc., 1805 Lower Rd., Linden 07036
CEO—William Pierce, 20 emp., Cleaning compounds .......... (800) 221-0806
Trap-Zap Environmental Systems, Inc., 255 Braen Ave., Wyckoff 07481
Pres.—Robert Belle, 20 emp., Biodegradable restaurant grease trap .......... (201) 251-9970
United Energy Corp., 3526 U.S. Highway 9 S., Ste. 103, Howell 07731
Chrm.—Jack Silver, 5 emp., Specialty chemicals for the oil & gas .......... (732) 994-5225

## 2843 Surface active agents

A. L. Wilson Chemical Co., 1050 Harrison Ave., P.O. Box 207, Kearny 07032
Pres.—Fred Schwarzmann, 20 emp., High-performance chemical products .......... (201) 997-3300
Aquatrols Corp. Of America, 1273 Imperial Way, Paulsboro 08066
Pres., CEO—Tracy M. Jarman, 35 emp., Agricultural chemicals .......... (856) 537-6003
Ardmore, Inc., 29 Riverside Ave., Bldg. 14, Newark 07104
Pres., CFO—Albert Sharphouse, 8 emp., Personal care product intermediate .......... (973) 481-2406
Atlas Refinery, Inc., 142 Lockwood St., Newark 07105
CEO—Steve B. Schroeder, 21 emp., Lubricants for leather & leather finishing .......... (973) 589-2002
BASF Corp., 2 Pleasant View Ave., Washington 07882
Security Supv.—Bruce Bluhm, 70 emp., Surfactants .......... (908) 689-7540
Consolidated Chemex Corp., 235 Jersey Ave., New Brunswick 08901
Pres.—Walter M. Geslak, 18 emp., Pressure washers & cleaning chemicals .......... (732) 828-7676
Grant Industries, Inc., 125 Main Ave., Elmwood Park 07407
Pres.—Michael Granatell, 85 emp., Textile chemicals & cosmetics .......... (201) 791-6700
Jarchem Industries, Inc., 414 Wilson Ave., Newark 07105
V-P., Sales & Mktg.—Dennis Boyd, 50 emp., Acetate salts, specialty branched & .......... (973) 344-0600
Munzing, 1455 Broad St., Bloomfield 07003
V-P., Mfg. & Prod. Mgmt.—Mike Riggs, 39 emp., Defoamers, dispersants, rheology modifiers (973) 279-1306
Pariser Industries, Inc., 91 Michigan Ave., Paterson 07503
Co-Pres.—Andrew Pariser, 25 emp., Chemical cleaning compounds .......... (973) 569-9090
Penetone Corp., 700 Gotham Pkwy., Ste. 2, Carlstadt 07072
V-P., GM, Fin. & Pur. Mgr.—Bruce Muretta, 27 emp., Industrial cleaning compounds .......... (201) 567-3000
Phoenix Chemical, Inc., 60 4th St., Somerville 08876
Pres.—John Imperante, 17 emp., Cosmetics chemicals, including emulsifiers .......... (908) 707-0232
Pilot Chemical Co., 267 Homestead Ave., Avenel 07001
Off. Mgr.—Kim Fletcher, 25 emp., Surfactants .......... (732) 634-6613
Shamrock Technologies, Inc., 255 Pacific St., Newark 07114
Chrm.—William B. Neuberg, 100 emp., Corporate headquarters & micronized .......... (973) 242-2999
Stepan Co., 220 4th St., Fieldsboro 08505
Hum. Res. Specialist—Stacey Santoleri, 50 emp., Surfactants .......... (609) 298-1222

## 2844 Toilet preparations

3lab, Inc. (H Q), 100 W. Sheffield Ave., Englewood 07631
Pres.—David C. Chung, 10 emp., Corporate headquarters; skin care products .......... (201) 567-9100
A. P. Deauville, LLC, 594 Jersey Ave., New Brunswick 08901
Pres., CEO—Frederick Horowitz, 35 emp., Deodorants, anti-perspirants, body .......... (732) 545-0200
ADM Tronics Unlimited, Inc., 224 Pegasus Ave., Northvale 07647
Pres.—Andre DiMino, 14 emp., Contract manufacturing of medical electronic .......... (201) 767-6040
Agilex Flavors & Fragrances, Inc., 140 Centennial Ave., Piscataway 08854
Pres. & CEO, Fragrance Div.—Raymond Hughes, 150 emp., Corporate headquarters & fragrance (732) 393-7300
Alzo International, Inc., 650 Jernee Mill Rd., Sayreville 08872
Pres.—Albert Zofchak, 25 emp., Toiletries & cosmetics .......... (732) 254-1901
Ambix Laboratories, 55 W. End Rd., Totowa 07512
Pres.—Alvin Goren, 23 emp., Contract manufacturing of skin, hair .......... (973) 890-9002
American Spraytech, LLC, 205 Meister Ave., Branchburg 08876
Pres.—Allen S. Lalwani, 19 emp., Contract manufacturer of cosmetics, .......... (908) 725-6060
Ameriderm Laboratories Ltd., 126 Pennsylvania Ave., Paterson 07503
Owner & Pres.—Bernard Elefant, 22 emp., Skincare products .......... (973) 279-5100
Andrea Aromatics, Inc., 150 Enterprise Ave., Trenton 08638
Pres.—Richard D'Andrea, 20 emp., Fragrances, deodorants, odorants, reodorants .......... (609) 695-7710
Aromatic Innovations, 600 Hartle St., Sayreville 08872
★ Owner—Golam Bhuiyan, 2 emp., Fragrances, including perfumes, personal .......... (732) 967-6346
Ascent Aromatics, Inc., 120 Case Dr., South Plainfield 07080
Pres.—John Pascale, 16 emp., Fragrance products for use in toiletries .......... (908) 755-0120
Asiamerica Ingredients, Inc., 245 Old Hook Rd., Ste. 3, Westwood 07675
★ Owner—Mark Zhang, 4 emp., Ingredients blending for the nutraceutical .......... (201) 497-5993
Atlantis Aromatics, Inc., 5047 Industrial Rd., Ste. 4, Farmingdale 07727
Pres.—Phillip Abbott, 6 emp., Fragrances .......... (732) 919-1112
Beilis Development, LLC (H Q), 20-21 Wagaraw Rd., Bldg. 31-B, Fair Lawn 07410
CTO—Kenneil Rey, 15 emp., Company headquarters; cosmetics (mfg. .......... (973) 559-5670
Bentley Laboratories, LLC, 111 Fieldcrest Ave., Edison 08837
CEO—Brian T. Fitzpatrick, 200 emp., Cosmetics & pharmaceuticals .......... (732) 512-0200
Bernard, Inc., Dennis, 142 Ely Harmony Rd., Freehold 07728
CEO—Dennis Bernard, 30 emp., Hair care products, including shampoos .......... (800) 541-5456
Biogenesis, Inc., 296 Washington Ave., Hackensack 07601
Pres.—Ann Rabbani, 10 emp., Skin care products .......... (201) 678-1992
Caldwell Consumer Health, LLC (H Q), 8 Elmer St., Ste. 1, Madison 07940
CEO—Michael Lesser, 6 emp., Company headquarters; personal healthcare .......... (973) 360-1090
Carter Solution, Inc., The Jane, 45 S. 17th St., East Orange 07018
Owner—Jane Carter, 5 emp., Hair care products, including shampoos .......... (973) 677-1008
CCA Industries, Inc. (H Q), 200 Murray Hill Pkwy., East Rutherford 07073
Pres., CEO—Richard Kornhauser, 135 emp., Corporate headquarters; topical & OTC .......... (201) 935-3232
Chanel, Inc., 876 Centennial Ave., Piscataway 08854
Sr. V-P., Opers.—Jose Monsanto, 500 emp., Perfumes & cosmetics .......... (732) 885-5500
Chemaid Laboratories, Inc., 100 Mayhill St., Saddle Brook 07663
Pres.—Mark Reiner, 150 emp., Skin & hair care products .......... (201) 843-3300
Chemspa Industries, Inc., 22 Deforest Ave., East Hanover 07936
CEO—Jerome Rudy, 6 emp., Air fresheners, aromas & maintenance .......... (973) 386-1158
Christine Valmy Inc., 285 Changebridge Rd., Ste. 1, Pine Brook 07058
Pres.—Peter DeHaydu, 60 emp., Natural skin care products .......... (973) 575-1050
Cococare Products, Inc., 85 Franklin Rd., Dover 07801
Pres., CFO—Gerald Jay Dubin, 20 emp., Health & beauty aids .......... (973) 989-8880
Colgate-Palmolive Co., 400 Elbow Ln., Burlington 08016
Cont.—Angelie George, 30 emp., Fragrances & flavors .......... (609) 239-2000
Colgate-Palmolive Co., 191 E. Hanover Ave., Morristown 07960
Dir., Plt.—Tia Pillers, 568 emp., Soft soap & deodorants .......... (973) 630-1500
Colora Henna, 217 Washington Ave., Carlstadt 07072
Pres.—Esther Benattar, 9 emp., Hair coloring preparations .......... (201) 939-0969
Continental Aromatics, 1 Thomas Rd. S., Hawthorne 07506
Owner—Ira Schneider, 30 emp., Fragrances .......... (973) 238-9300
Contract Filling, Inc., 10 Cliffside Dr., Cedar Grove 07009
Pres.—William Lizzi, 300 emp., Deodorants & perfumes contract filling .......... (973) 239-6608

S.I.C.

ConvaTec, Inc., CenterPoint II, Ste. 205, 1140 Route 22 E., Bridgewater 08807
CEO—Ken Berger, 300 emp., *Corporate headquarters & health care* ........ (732) 412-5500

Cosmetic Coatings, Inc., 219 Broad St., P.O. Box 95, Carlstadt 07072
Pres.—Richard Gottesman, 20 emp., *Nail polish* ........ (201) 438-7150

Cosmetic Essence, Inc., 50 Clearview Rd., Edison 08837
Plt. Mgr.—David Cassidy, 90 emp., *Fragrance compounds* ........ (732) 225-2031

Cosmetic Essence, Inc., 1135 Pleasantview Ter. W., Ridgefield 07657
V-P., Opers. & GM—Jeff Munafo, 440 emp., *Cosmetics* ........ (201) 941-9800

Cosmetic Essence, Inc. (H Q), 2182 Route 35 S., Holmdel 07733
Pres., CEO—Peter Martin, 350 emp., *Corporate headquarters; fragrance blending* ........ (732) 888-7788

Cosmetics & Perfume Filling & Packaging, Inc., 30 Engelhard Dr., Monroe 08831
Pres.—Devraj Vaghani, 100 emp., *Contract manufacturing & packaging* ........ (973) 680-8900

Creative Concepts Corp., 70 Oak St., Ste. 202, Norwood 07648
Pres.—Jean P. Subrenat, 5 emp., *Perfumes & fragrances* ........ (201) 750-1234

Crown Royale Ltd., 99 Broad St., P.O. Box 5238, Phillipsburg 08865
Pres.—Cindy Silva, 3 emp., *Dog shampoo* ........ (908) 859-1999

Custom Essence, Inc., 53 Veronica Ave., Somerset 08873
Pres.—Felix Buccellato, 25 emp., *Fragrance oils & flavors* ........ (732) 249-6405

Dana Classic Fragrances, Inc. (H Q), 400 Lyster Ave., Saddle Brook 07663
IT Mgr.—Joe Acosta, 10 emp., *Corporate headquarters; fragrances* ........ (201) 881-8550

Davion, Inc., 29-75 Riverside Ave., Bldg. 10, Newark 07104
Pres.—James Placa, 30 emp., *Cosmetics & baby care products* ........ (973) 485-0793

Davlyn Industries, Inc., 7 Fitzgerald Ave., Monroe Township 08831
Ex. Dir., Opers.—Tom Halligan, 180 emp., *Cosmetics & skin care products* ........ (609) 860-5100

Derma Sciences, Inc. (H Q), 214 Carnegie Ctr., Ste. 300, Princeton 08540
Chrm. & CEO—Edward J. Quilty, 45 emp., *Corporate headquarters; advanced &* ........ (609) 514-4744

Dermarite Industries, LLC, 7777 W. Side Ave., P.O. Box 7209, North Bergen 07047
Pres.—Naftali Minzer, 98 emp., *Skin, wound & personal care products* ........ (973) 569-9000

Dimensional Merchandising, Inc., 86 N. Main St., Wharton 07885
Pres.—Douglas A. Sylva, 85 emp., *Contract manufacturing & packaging* ........ (973) 328-1600

Drom Fragrances International, Inc., 5 Jacksonville Rd., Towaco 07082
V-P., Mktg.—Robert Stapf, 38 emp., *Fragrances* ........ (973) 316-8400

DSM Pharmaceutical Products, Inc. (H Q), 45 Waterview Blvd., Parsippany 07054
Pres., CEO—Alexander Wessels, 165 emp., *Corporate headquarters; liquid & dry* ........ (973) 257-1063

E&M Gold Beekeepers, LLC, 113 Hope Rd., Tinton Falls 07724
Ptnr.—Mary Kosenski, 2 emp., *All-natural honey & honey & beeswax-based* ........ (732) 542-6528

E. T. Browne Drug Company, Inc., 440 Sylvan Ave., P.O. Box 1613, Englewood Cliffs 07632
Chrm.—Arnold H. Neis, 65 emp., *Corporate headquarters & skin & hair* ........ (201) 894-9020

Elan Chemical Company, Inc., 268 Doremus Ave., Newark 07105
Pres., CEO—Jocelyn Kapp-Manship, 60 emp., *Food flavorings & fragrance ingredients* ........ (973) 344-8014

Englewood Lab, LLC, 88 W. Sheffield Ave., Englewood 07631
CEO—David Chung, 50 emp., *Contract manufacturing of skin care* ........ (201) 567-2267

Fairy Tales Hair Care Corp., 90-B Dayton Ave., Passaic 07055
★ Owner—Risa Barash, 12 emp., *Hair care products, including shampoos* ........ (973) 473-8182

Fantasia Industries Corp., 20 Park Pl., Paramus 07652
CEO—Archie Bogosian, 29 emp., *Hair care products* ........ (201) 261-7070

Fiabila, Inc., 114 Iron Mountain Rd., Mine Hill 07803
Pres.—Pierre Miasnik, 15 emp., *Nail polish* ........ (973) 659-9510

Finger Mates, Inc., 707 10th Ave., Belmar 07719
CEO—Anthony Esposito, 7 emp., *Fingernail treatment, skin care & hair* ........ (732) 681-4411

Flavor & Fragrance Specialties, Inc. (H Q), 3 Industrial Ave., Mahwah 07430
Pres.—Michael Bloom, 50 emp., *Corporate headquarters; food flavorings* ........ (201) 825-2025

Foote & Jenks Corp., 1420 Crestmont Ave., Camden 08103
Pres.—Michael Baskin, 20 emp., *Food flavorings & fragrances* ........ (856) 966-0700

Fortitude Health, 101 U.S. Highway 46, Pine Brook 07058
Pres.—Mike Marenick, 6 emp., *Egg-based toiletries, including skin* ........ (973) 396-8480

Fragrance Resources, Inc., 620 Route 3 W., Clifton 07014
Mktg. Mgr.—Michael Simpson, 5 emp., *Corporate headquarters & perfumes* ........ (973) 777-2979

Fragrance Resources, Inc., 275 Clark St., P.O. Box 110, Keyport 07735
V-P.—Larry Zakreski, 60 emp., *Fragrance compounds* ........ (732) 264-6767

French Color & Fragrance Co., 488 Grand Ave., Englewood 07631
Pres.—Peter A. French, 17 emp., *Fragrances & dyes for candles* ........ (201) 567-6883

Gallant Laboratories, Inc., 142 Stockes Rd., Vincentown 08088
Pres.—Gary Gallant, 3 emp., *Cosmetics* ........ (609) 268-0953

Garden State Nutritionals, LLC, 8 Henderson Dr., West Caldwell 07006
CEO—Keith Frankel, 400 emp., *Dietary supplements, including tablets* ........ (973) 575-9200

Givaudan Fragrances Corp., 300 Waterloo Valley Rd., Mount Olive 07828
V-P., Opers.—John Trombley, 200 emp., *Perfumes, fragrances & personal care* ........ (973) 448-6500

Global Colorants, Inc., 83 Roosevelt Ave., Belleville 07109
V-P. & Plt. Mgr.—Frank Penta, 2 emp., *Chemical cosmetic & personal care product* ........ (973) 751-2227

Grant Industries, Inc., 125 Main Ave., Elmwood Park 07407
Pres.—Michael Granatell, 85 emp., *Textile chemicals & cosmetics* ........ (201) 791-6700

Guest Packaging, LLC, 414 E. Inman Ave., Rahway 07065
V-P., Mfg.—Bob Stegman, 200 emp., *Personal care amenities, including* ........ (732) 382-7270

Hair Systems, Inc., 30 Park Ave., P.O. Box 449, Englishtown 07726
Pres., CEO—William E. Covey, Jr., 90 emp., *Hair bleaches, dyes & liquids* ........ (732) 446-2202

Health & Natural Beauty USA, 140-W Ethel Rd. W., Piscataway 08854
★ Pres.—Sayed Ibrahim, 4 emp., *Skin & hair care products* ........ (848) 202-9089

Hilltop Honey, LLC, 15 Hill St., North Caldwell 07006
Pres.—Joseph Lelinho, 3 emp., *Honey, beeswax, pollen, propolis, hand* ........ (201) 953-0198

IFC Products, Inc., 568 E. Elizabeth Ave., P.O. Box 2175, Linden 07036
Pres.—Joseph Christiano, 4 emp., *Flavorings, extracts, essential oils* ........ (908) 587-1221

Imperial DAX Co., Inc., 120 New Dutch Ln., Fairfield 07004
Pres.—David Joy, 25 emp., *Hair & skin care products, including* ........ (973) 227-6105

Imperial Drug & Spice Corp., 5620 Kennedy Blvd. W., West New York 07093
Pres.—Victoria Weingartner, 5 emp., *Latino/Hispanic health & beauty care* ........ (201) 348-1551

Innovative Cosmetics, Inc., 270 Clifton Blvd., Clifton 07011
Pres.—F. A. Park, 40 emp., *Cosmetics* ........ (973) 773-7700

Intarome Fragrance & Flavor Corp., 370 Chestnut St., Norwood 07648
Pres., CEO—Daniel G. Funsch, 53 emp., *Fragrances & flavors* ........ (201) 767-8700

Interfashion Cosmetics Corp., 32 Henry St., Teterboro 07608
Pres.—James Chang, 45 emp., *Cosmetics* ........ (201) 288-5858

International Aromatics, Inc., 200 Anderson Ave., Moonachie 07074
Pres.—Gary Gerardi, 15 emp., *Fragrances* ........ (201) 964-0900

International Flavors & Fragrances, Inc., 150 Docks Corner Rd., Dayton 08810
Hum. Res. Bus. Ptnr., Flavors & Fragrances—Rebecca Force, 300 emp., *Flavoring & fragrances.* (732) 329-4600

International Flavors & Fragrances—Inc., 600 Highway 36, Hazlet 07730
Plt. Mgr.—David Smith, 250 emp., *Flavors & fragrances* ........ (732) 264-4500

Irving Rice & Co., 161 Docks Corner Rd., Dayton 08810
Pres.—Kathleen Molyneaux, 35 emp., *Cosmetics* ........ (609) 655-6890

Johnson & Johnson Consumer Companies, Inc. (H Q), 199 Grandview Rd., Skillman 08558
Chrm., Co. Group—Roberto Marques, 1100 emp., *Corporate headquarters; baby, skin,* ........ (908) 874-1000

Kerry Ingredients & Flavors, 160 Terminal Ave., Clark 07066
Cont.—Angel Albanese, 135 emp., *Flavorings & natural products* ........ (732) 882-0202

Kirker Enterprises, Inc., 55 E. 6th St., Paterson 07524
CEO—Jeffrey S. Hersh, 100 emp., *Corporate headquarters & fingernail* ........ (973) 754-9000

Lanman & Kemp-Barclay & Co., Inc., 25 Woodland Ave., P.O. Box 421, Westwood 07675
Pres.—George Miller, 15 emp., *Colognes, hair tonics & soaps* ........ (201) 666-4990

Lasting Impression, Inc., 333 S. Dean St., Englewood 07631
Owner—Darlene Story, 15 emp., *Cosmetics* ........ (201) 871-7388

L'Oreal U S A, Inc., 222 Terminal Ave., Clark 07066
V-P., Engrg.—Serge Pepin, 400 emp., *Hair care products* ........ (732) 499-2838

L'Oreal U S A, Inc., 81 New England Ave., Piscataway 08854
Dir., Engrg.—Tom Zollo, 500 emp., *Cosmetics & skincare products* ........ (732) 562-5000

Lubrizol Advanced Materials, Inc., 1 Industrial W., Clifton 07012
Cont.—Jack Lewis, 15 emp., *Personal care & industrial organic* ........ (973) 471-1300

Mane USA, Inc., 60 Demarest Dr., Wayne 07470
Pres., CEO—Jean M. Mane, 138 emp., *Corporate headquarters & fragrance* ........ (973) 633-5533

Medallion International, Inc., 233 W. Parkway, Pompton Plains 07444
V-P.—Paula Boudjouk, 15 emp., *Flavors & fragrances* ........ (973) 616-3401

MMP, Inc., 3470 S. Clinton Ave., South Plainfield 07080
Pres.—Michel Mercier, 10 emp., *Cosmetic ingredients* ........ (908) 561-4435

Mona Lisa Cosmetics, Inc., 280 N. Midland Ave., Ste. 520, Saddle Brook 07663
Owner—Angel Mahdani, 20 emp., *Cosmetics, including lip gloss & mascara* ........ (201) 791-5644

Naturex Inc., 375 Huyler St., South Hackensack 07606
CFO—Gaetan Sourceau, 170 emp., *Corporate headquarters & natural specialty* ........ (201) 440-5000

Neostrata Company, Inc. (H Q), 307 College Rd. E., Princeton 08540
CEO—Mark D. Steele, 60 emp., *Corporate headquarters; skin care products* ........ (609) 520-0715

New World International Corp., 59 Dover St., Paterson 07501
Co-Pres., CEO—Carmen Bires, 12 emp., *Health, beauty & personal care products* ........ (973) 881-8100

Novapac Laboratories, Inc., 545 N. Arlington Ave., East Orange 07017
Owner—Gene Marc, 3 emp., *Cosmetics, including fragrances, night* ........ (973) 414-8800

Nu-World Corp., 300 Milik St., Carteret 07008
Cont.—Susan Pace, 50 emp., *Cosmetics* ........ (732) 541-6300

Omega Packaging Corp., 55 Kings Rd., Totowa 07512
Pres.—Larry Kalb, 50 emp., *Creams, lotions & shampoos* ........ (973) 890-9505

Orpheus Ltd., 40 Woodland Ave., Rockaway 07866
Pres.—Richard Micchelli, 8 emp., *Fragrances* ........ (973) 983-1400

Pantina Cosmetics, Inc., 30 Henry St., Teterboro 07608
Founder & Hum. Res. Mgr.—Wendy Chang, 20 emp., *Cosmetics & skin care products* ........ (201) 288-7767

Paramount Cosmetics, Inc., 93 Entin Rd., Ste. 4, Clifton 07014
Pres.—Sanford Salzman, 95 emp., *Contract manufacturing & private label* ........ (973) 472-2323

PhytoCeuticals, Inc., 37 Midland Ave., Elmwood Park 07407
Pres.—Mostafa Omar, 5 emp., *Skin care products* ........ (201) 791-2255

Pinnacle Cosmetics Packaging, LLC, 80 Market St., P.O. Box 733, Kenilworth 07033
Owner—Ed Halsch, 15 emp., *Perfume packaging* ........ (908) 241-7777

Poly-Gel, LLC, 30 Leslie Ct., Whippany 07981
Pres.—Larry Kersen, 50 emp., *Medical, orthopedic & skin care gelatin* ........ (973) 884-3300

Pooka, Inc., 87 Halsey St., Newark 07102
Pres.—Dawn Fitch, 3 emp., *Natural bath & body care products,* ........ (973) 954-2471

Precious Cosmetics Corp., 296 Midland Ave., Saddle Brook 07663
Pres.—Sami Mikhail, 20 emp., *Skin care creams & lotions, hair care* ........ (973) 478-4633

Premier Specialties, Inc., 236 Blackford Ave., Middlesex 08846
Pres., Hum. Res. Mgr.—Roger Rich, 21 emp., *Fragrances & flavors* ........ (732) 469-6615

Procter & Gamble Mfg. Co., 100 Essex Ave. E., Avenel 07001
Br. Mgr.—Sandy Moshier, 70 emp., *Industrial perfumes for detergents* ........ (732) 602-4500

Promeko, Inc., 543 59th St., West New York 07093
Pres.—Edalio Rondon, 7 emp., *Health & beauty aids* ........ (201) 861-6446

QRS Beauty Corp., 11 Commercial Ave., Fairview 07022
Pres.—Jang 'John' Park, 4 emp., *Nail polishes, nail lacquers, color* ........ (201) 313-0305

Quality Cosmetics Mfg., 4455 S. Clinton Ave., South Plainfield 07080
Owner—Richard Persaud, 40 emp., *Cosmetics* ........ (908) 755-9588

R&R Cosmetics, LLC, 1140 Randolph Ave., Rahway 07065
Ptnr.—Musthafa Kamal, 15 emp., *Skin & hair care products* ........ (732) 340-1000

Razac Products Co., Inc., 25 Brenner St., Newark 07108
CEO—William Dowdy, 35 emp., *Hair care products* ........ (973) 622-3700

Reckitt Benckiser, Inc., 399 Interpace Pkwy., P.O. Box 225, Parsippany 07054
Pres., Frenchs Food Prod.—Elliott Penner, 375 emp., *Corporate headquarters & consumer cleaning* (973) 404-2600

Revicci, Inc., 25 Sycamore Ter., Livingston 07039
Co-Pres.—Theresa Choi, 2 emp., *Skin care products* ........ (973) 994-1421

Reviva Labs, Inc., 705 Hopkins Rd., Haddonfield 08033
Pres.—Stephen Strassler, 32 emp., *Skin care products* ........ (856) 428-3885

Robertet-Novarome Fragrances, Inc., 400 International Dr., Mount Olive 07828
Prodn. Mgr.—Sterling Lutz, 85 emp., *Perfume & essential oils* ........ (973) 575-4550

Royale Cosmetics Corp., 4-A Jules Ln., New Brunswick 08901
Pres.—Steve Tulshi, 12 emp., *Cosmetics* ........ (732) 246-7275

Sarkli Repechage Ltd., 300 Castle Rd., Secaucus 07094
Pres.—Lydia Sarfati, 60 emp., *Cosmetics & skin care products* ........ (201) 549-4200

Schwan Cosmetics U.S.A., Inc., 21 Gordon Rd., Piscataway 08854
Pres.—Paul Plut, 99 emp., *Cosmetics* ........ (732) 777-6800

Scories, Inc., 28 Vassar Ave., P.O. Box 4223, Newark 07112
Pres.—William Hall, 15 emp., *Natural hair care products for dandruff* ........ (973) 923-1372

Shira Esthetics, Inc., 65 S. 21st St., Ste. 2, Kenilworth 07033
Pres.—Yair Nezaria, 21 emp., *Beauty, body & skin care products,* ........ (908) 497-9497

Shiseido America, Inc., 366 Princeton Hightstown Rd., East Windsor 08520
Pres., COO—Edward Houlihan, 160 emp., *Cosmetics & fragrances* ........ (609) 371-5800

Sozio, Inc., 51 Ethel Rd. W., Piscataway 08854
Cont.—Annette Peixoto, 50 emp., *Fragrances for the perfume, personal* ........ (732) 572-5600

Syence Skincare Laboratories Inc., 99 W. Mill Rd., Long Valley 07853
Owner & Dir.—Sean Campbell, 6 emp., *High-end skincare preparations, including* ........ (908) 791-0044

Symrise Purescents, 1715 Oak St., Ste. 3, Lakewood 08701
Pres.—Jack Corley, 17 emp., *Fragrance oils* ........ (732) 922-2520

Symrise, Inc., 180 Industrial Pkwy., Branchburg 08876
V-P.—Mike O'Hara, 50 emp., *Natural & synthetic fragrances* ........ (908) 429-6946

Symrise, Inc., 300 North St., Teterboro 07608
CEO—Heinz-Jurgen Bertram, 350 emp., *Corporate headquarters & food flavorings* ........ (201) 288-3200

Sysco Guest Supply (H Q), 4301 Highway 1, P.O. Box 902, Monmouth Junction 08852
Pres., COO—Paul T. Xenis, 140 emp., *Divisional headquarters; personal care* ........ (609) 514-9696

Takasago International Corp., 267 Union St., Northvale 07647
Pur. Agt.—Rich Bartilotti, 60 emp., *Fragrances* ........ (201) 767-9001

Telmark Packaging Corp., 30 Freneau Ave., Ste. 2-B, Matawan 07747
Pres.—Eric Ludwig, 8 emp., *Contract formulation, manufacturing* ........ (732) 739-9100

Tevco Enterprises, Inc., 110 Pomponio Ave., South Plainfield 07080
CFO—Sharon Muzeni, 35 emp., *Nail polish* ........ (908) 754-7306

Topline Products Co., Inc., 155 Route 46 W., 2nd Fl., Wayne 07470
Pres.—Charles Chang, 35 emp., *Corporate headquarters & cosmetics* (973) 785-1600
Tru-Form Cosmetics, Inc., 50 Springfield Ave., Springfield 07081
Owner—Diane Nguyen, 5 emp., *Beauty & cosmetic products* (973) 564-9111
Ultra Chemical, Inc., 2 Bridge Ave., Ste. 630, Red Bank 07701
Pres.—Arthur Lynch, 8 emp., *Custom & specialty ingredients for* (732) 224-0200
Ungerer & Co., 4 Bridgewater Ln., P.O. Box U, Lincoln Park 07035
Pres.—Kenneth G. Voorhees, 135 emp., *Company headquarters & fragrances &* (973) 628-0600
Unilever North America, 700 Sylvan Ave., Englewood Cliffs 07632
Pres., N. America—Kees Kruythoff, 1900 emp., *Company headquarters & food & personal* (201) 567-8000
Unimed International, Inc., 105 Newfield Ave., Ste. F, Edison 08837
CEO—George Faltaous, 20 emp., *All-natural antioxidant skin care &* (800) 754-6211
Unipack, Inc., 681 Main St., Bldg. 27, Belleville 07109
Pres.—Dinesh Patel, 10 emp., *Toiletries* (973) 450-9880
Victory International U. S. A., LLC, 75 Newfield Ave., Edison 08837
Pres.—Anil K. Monga, 10 emp., *Perfumes* (732) 417-1040
Water-Jel Technologies, 50 Broad St., Carlstadt 07072
CFO—John McAndris, 80 emp., *Sterile burn dressings, fire blankets* (201) 507-8300
Windmill Health Products, LLC, 6 Henderson Dr., Caldwell 07006
Pres.—Howard Munk, 45 emp., *Manufacturer & distributor of vitamin* (973) 575-6591
World Wide Packaging, LLC, 15 Vreeland Rd., Florham Park 07932
Chrm.—Jeffrey S. Schneider, 50 emp., *Contract manufacturing of packaging* (973) 805-6500
Y, Inc., 20-21 Wagaraw Rd., Bldg. 32, Fair Lawn 07410
Pres.—Dong Jin Yoon, 4 emp., *Manufacturer & distributor of professional* (201) 773-8425

## 2851 Paints & allied products

Advanced Protective Products, Inc., 17-12 River Rd., Fair Lawn 07410
Owner & Pres.—Tom Heiss, 12 emp., *Rust-converting paint primers* (718) 359-1315
Agate Lacquer Tri-Nat, LLC, 824 South Ave., Middlesex 08846
Owner—James Natalini, 2 emp., *Clear coat, air dry, baking & water* (732) 968-1080
ALT Global, LLC, 3 Edison Pl., Ste. 2, Fairfield 07004
Manager—Eric Fischetti, 10 emp., *Advanced cold applied liquid roofing* (973) 287-6158
American Chemical & Adhesive LLC, 410 Division St., Elizabeth 07201
Pres.—Qamar Zaman, 5 emp., *Plastic & metal coatings & flux* (908) 353-2260
Andek Corporation, 850 Glen Ave., P.O. Box 392, Moorestown 08057
Pres.—Harvey Liss, 20 emp., *High-performance coatings & sealant* (856) 786-6900
Antistatic Industries, A Div. of ADM Tronics, Inc., 224 Pegasus Ave., Northvale 07647
Pres., CEO—Andre DiMino, 15 emp., *Static dissipative products, including* (201) 767-6040
Armorpoxy, Inc., 805 Lehigh Ave., Union 07083
Pres.—Michael Logan, 18 emp., *Commercial grade epoxy coatings & shot* (908) 810-9613
Benjamin Moore & Co., 134 Lister Ave., Newark 07105
Plt. Mgr.—Ward Bubeck, 55 emp., *Commercial & industrial paints & coatings* (973) 344-1200
Benjamin Moore & Co. (H Q), 101 Paragon Dr., Montvale 07645
CEO—Mike Searles, 400 emp., *Divisional headquarters; paints & coatings* (201) 573-9600
Ceronics, Inc., 5 Dock St., P.O. Box 75, Matawan 07747
Pres.—Richard Patton, 7 emp., *High temperature ceramic coatings* (732) 566-5600
Chemique, Inc., 315 N. Washington Ave., Moorestown 08057
Pres.—Edward Drazga, 10 emp., *Kitchen & bathroom cleaners, marble* (856) 235-4161
Chris Industries, Inc., 98 Industrial Ct., Freehold 07728
Pres.—David A. Christie, 4 emp., *Water-based coatings* (732) 431-1800
Clausen Co., The, 1055 King George Post Rd., Edison 08817
Pres., CEO—Donald J. Peck, 15 emp., *Automotive refinishing products* (732) 738-1165
Colorco, Inc., 1261 W. Elizabeth Ave., Linden 07036
Pres.—Christopher Bates, 34 emp., *Custom dry color & color concentrates* (908) 862-3010
Colorflo, Inc., 1261 W. Elizabeth Ave., Linden 07036
Pres.—Harold Penson, 5 emp., *Liquid colorants & PVC dispersions* (908) 862-3010
Columbia Paint Lab, Inc., 452 Communipaw Ave., Jersey City 07304
Pres.—George Pahiakos, 17 emp., *Paints* (201) 435-4884
Dolph Co., John C., 320 New Rd., Monmouth Junction 08852
Site Mgr.—Thomas Wacker, 24 emp., *Electrical insulating varnishes & resins* (732) 329-2333
DriTac Flooring Products, LLC, 60 Webro Rd., Clifton 07012
Pres.—Yale Block, 20 emp., *Eco-friendly industrial adhesives &* (973) 614-9000
Duraamen Engineered Products, Inc., 457 Frelinghuysen Ave., Newark 07114
Pres.—Victor Pachade, 10 emp., *Epoxy & decorative concrete floor coatings* (973) 230-1301
Dux Paints, Inc., 18 Mill St., Lodi 07644
Pres.—Howard Goldstein, 10 emp., *Paints* (973) 473-2376
Elementis Specialties, Inc. (H Q), 469 Old Trenton Rd., East Windsor 08512
Pres.—Greg McClatchy, 129 emp., *Corporate headquarters; paint, adhesive* (609) 443-2000
Epoplex, 1000 E. Park Ave., P.O. Box 308, Maple Shade 08052
GM—Kent Stough, Jr., 87 emp., *Epoxy paint & adhesives* (856) 667-8399
Evonik Corporation (H Q), 299 Jefferson Rd., Parsippany 07054
Pres.—John Rolando, 421 emp., *Corporate headquarters; industrial* (973) 929-8000
Ferro Corp., 54 Kellogg Ct., Edison 08817
Site Mgr.—Mike McKinney, 30 emp., *Liquid & paste pigment, polymer additives* (732) 287-1930
Flexabar Corp., 1969 Rutgers Blvd., Lakewood 08701
CEO—Andrew Guglielmo, 21 emp., *Marine paints & coatings* (732) 901-6500
Flexdel Corp., 1969 Rutgers University Blvd., Lakewood 08701
Pres.—Richard J. Guglielmo, Jr., 20 emp., *Environmentally friendly water-resistant* (732) 901-7771
Garon Products, Inc., 256 Maxim Rd., Howell 07731
V-P., Pur. & Whse. Opers.—Michael Crowley, 4 emp., *Concrete floor repair products & concrete* (732) 828-6400
Garon Products, Inc., 2430 Route 34, Ste. B-12, Manasquan 08736
Pres.—Arthur Crowley, 15 emp., *Corporate headquarters & floor coatings* (732) 223-2500
General Plastics Corp., 55 La France Ave., Bloomfield 07003
Pres.—Robert Scher, 13 emp., *Fluoropolymer coatings & liquid & powder* (973) 748-5500
GFC Coatings & Chemicals, 18 Mill St., Lodi 07644
Pres.—Jeffrey Klein, 9 emp., *Custom industrial paints, lacquers,* (973) 272-0257
Hartin Paint & Filler Corp., 14th & Broad Sts., Carlstadt 07072
Pres.—Richard Gottesman, 20 emp., *Paints* (201) 438-3300
Hawthorne Paint Co., Inc., 66 5th Ave., Hawthorne 07506
Pres., Fin. & MIS Mgr.—Murray Greene, 9 emp., *Commercial, residential, industrial* (973) 423-2335
Hood Finishing Products, Inc., 9 Factory Ln., Middlesex 08846
Pres.—Erick Kasner, 6 emp., *Wood finishing & refinishing products* (732) 805-0088
Hy-Test Packaging Corp., 515 E. 41st St., Paterson 07504
Pres.—Jack Smith, 9 emp., *Liquid cleaning products, fuel additives* (973) 754-7000
InMat Inc., 216 U.S. Highway 206, Ste. 7, Hillsborough 08844
Pres., CEO—Harris Goldberg, 6 emp., *Specialty nanocomposite barrier coatings* (908) 874-7788
Innovative Powder Coatings, LLC, 9105 Burrough-Dover Ln., Pennsauken 08110
Owner—David Macwilliam, 4 emp., *Custom & stock colored powder coatings* (856) 661-0086
International Paint, LLC, 2270 Morris Ave., Union 07083
Plt. Mgr.—Michael Del Mauro, 100 emp., *Paints* (908) 686-1300
Jema-American, Inc., 824 South Ave., Middlesex 08846
Pres.—James Natalini, 8 emp., *Specialty coatings for the vacuum metallizing* (732) 968-5333
Kop-Coat, Inc., 36 Pine St., Rockaway 07866
Hum. Res. Mgr.—Donna Thoenig, 50 emp., *Marine & pool paints* (973) 625-3100
Landzettel & Sons, Inc., 17-12 River Rd., Fair Lawn 07410
Pres.—Walter J. Landzettel, 8 emp., *Private label oil & latex paints &* (201) 796-3506
Milspray, LLC, 845 Towbin Ave., Lakewood 08701
Pres., CEO—Brian Feser, 40 emp., *Mil-spec paint, renewable energy, corrosion* (732) 886-2223
Muralo Co., Inc., 148 E. 5th St., Bayonne 07002
Pres.—James F. Norton, 50 emp., *Corporate headquarters & paints, brushes* (201) 437-0770
National Paint Industries, 1999 Elizabeth St., North Brunswick 08902
Co-Pres.—Michael Schnurr, 45 emp., *Company headquarters & paints & coatings* (732) 821-3200
Palma, Inc., 14 Salter Pl., P.O. Box 2539, Bloomfield 07003
Bookkeeper—Lori Henle, 15 emp., *Epoxy flooring mixtures* (800) 336-7256
Pan Technology, 117 Moonachie Ave., Carlstadt 07072
Pres.—Robert Rossomando, 48 emp., *Industrial paints, color concentrates* (201) 438-7878
Penn Jersey Paint Co., Inc., 1255 McCarter Hwy., Newark 07104
Pres.—Ernest Castroaro, 4 emp., *Paints* (973) 482-5430
Performance Industries, Inc., 51 Tucker St., Trenton 08618
Pres.—Stuart Azarchi, 20 emp., *Paint products* (609) 392-1450
Plastics Consulting & Mfg. Co., 1431 Ferry Ave., Camden 08104
Pres.—Steven Schwartz, 20 emp., *Tetrafluoroethylene, flouropolymer* (856) 963-7700
R V Tech, Inc., 801 Magnolia Ave., Bldg. 3-B, Elizabeth 07201
Pres.—Mayur Shah, 5 emp., *Industrial paints, coatings & adhesives* (908) 469-8701
Rich Art Color Co., Inc., 202 Pegasus Ave., Northvale 07647
Pres.—Marc Jennings, 15 emp., *Washable & non-washable paints & decorative* (201) 767-0009
Royal Adhesive, Inc., 48 Burgess Pl., Wayne 07470
Pres.—Victoria Corbo, 30 emp., *Industrial adhesives, coatings & specialty* (973) 694-0845
Rust-Oleum Corp., 480 Frelinghuysen Ave., Newark 07114
Plt. Mgr.—Robert Nanes, 50 emp., *Specialty paint* (732) 469-8100
Rust-Oleum Corp., ZINSSER Brands, 173 Belmont Dr., Somerset 08873
Pres., Consumer Div.—Ed Voorhees, 135 emp., *Primers, sealers, waterproofers, water* (732) 469-8100
Sau-Sea Swimming Pool Paints And Repair Products, 1855 Route 206, Southampton 08088
COO—Ed Hunter, 9 emp., *Eco-friendly rubber-base, epoxy & vinyl* (609) 859-8500
Seagrave Coatings Corp., 209 N. Michigan Ave., Kenilworth 07033
Pres.—Peter Tepperman, 20 emp., *Paints & industrial coatings* (201) 933-1000
Sherwin-Williams Co., The, 6 Currie Ave., Wallington 07057
Br. Mgr.—Edward Squier, 13 emp., *Paint, pigments, product finishes &* (201) 933-3800
Sherwin-Williams Co., The, Woodcare Products Div. (H Q), 10 Mountainview Rd., Upper Saddle River 07458
V-P., Mktg.—Janet Krakow, 60 emp., *Divisional headquarters; wood finishes* (201) 818-7500
Spectrachem, 10 Dell Glen Ave., Ste. 3-A, Lodi 07644
Pres.—Zaghary Kousoulis, 10 emp., *Water-based pigment dispersions & textile* (973) 253-3553
Talon Paint Products, Inc., 1999 Elizabeth St., North Brunswick 08902
Pres.—Michael Schnurr, 45 emp., *Paints* (732) 821-3200
Target Coatings, Inc., 17-12 River Rd., Fair Lawn 07410
Pres., Plt. Mgr.—Jeff Weiss, 10 emp., *Water-based wood coatings for the furniture* (800) 752-9922
Tenax Finishing Products Co., 390 Adams St., Newark 07114
Pres., MIS Mgr.—James O'Neill, 11 emp., *Paints* (973) 589-9000
Troy Chemicals, 1 Avenue L, Newark 07105
IT Mgr.—Tregg Favoy, 100 emp., *Paint additives* (973) 589-2500
Verseidag Seemee US, Inc. (H Q), 4 Aspen Dr., Randolph 07869
Pres.—Eric Tischer, 12 emp., *Corporate headquarters; coating & composite* (973) 252-1189

## 2861 Gum & wood chemicals

L.A. Champon & Co., Inc. (H Q), 266 Broadway, Long Branch 07740
Owner—Charles Champon, 10 emp., *Corporate headquarters; cedar oil* (732) 923-0003
Narad Marketing Corporation, 200 Piaget Ave., Clifton 07011
Pres.—Narie Rekha, 10 emp., *Synthetic organic & leak detection* (973) 881-0206

## 2865 Cyclic crudes & intermediates

Adam, Gates & Co., LLC, 249 Homestead Rd., Hillsborough 08844
Member—Abdelhamid Ramadan, 10 emp., *Fine & specialty chemicals & near-infrared* (908) 829-3386
Cardinal Color, Inc., 50-56 1st Ave., Paterson 07514
Pres., GM & Off. Mgr.—Mark Berry, 30 emp., *Pigment dispersions* (973) 684-1919
Cycle Chem, Inc., 201 S. 1st St., Elizabeth 07206
Pres.—Michael Persico, 60 emp., *Recycled-content oil* (908) 355-5800
Dispersion Technology, Inc., 1885 Swarthmore Ave., Lakewood 08701
Pres.—Yogesh Parikh, 10 emp., *Pigment dispersion of silicones & silicone* (732) 364-4488
Dudley Chemical Corp., 125 Kenyon Dr., Ste. 1, Lakewood 08701
Owner—Art Foulsham, 18 emp., *Biological stains & dyes* (732) 886-3100
Epolin, 358-364 Adams St., Newark 07105
CEO—Greg Amato, 11 emp., *Organic, infrared & absorbing dyes* (973) 465-9495
Fabricolor Holdings, Inc., 24 1/2 Van Houten St., P.O. Box 1856, Paterson 07505
Pres.—Miroslav E. Muzik, 10 emp., *Specialty organic dyes* (973) 742-5800
Ferro Corp., 54 Kellogg Ct., Edison 08817
Site Mgr.—Mike McKinney, 30 emp., *Liquid & paste pigment, polymer additives* (732) 287-1930
Fine Organics Corp., 420 Kuller Rd., P.O. Box 2277, Clifton 07015
Pres., CEO & COO—Gary F. Straub, 14 emp., *Industrial chemical cleaning compounds* (973) 478-1000
Greenville Colorants (H Q), 20 Linden Ave. E., Jersey City 07305
Owner & Co-Chrm.—Ronald M. Weiss, 8 emp., *Company headquarters; industrial colorants* (201) 595-0200
Lightscape Materials, Inc., 201 Washington Rd., Princeton 08540
Comml. Dir., Phosphor Matls.—Gerard Frederickson, 15 emp., *Novel phosphors for the LED lighting* (609) 734-2227
Narad Marketing Corporation, 200 Piaget Ave., Clifton 07011
Pres.—Narie Rekha, 10 emp., *Synthetic organic & leak detection* (973) 881-0206
Nova Specialty Chemicals, LLC, 404 E. Main St., Rockaway 07866
Owner—Syed Raza, 11 emp., *Fluorescent yellow 131 & dyes for petroleum* (973) 586-2147
Penn Color, Inc., 30 Kohner Pl., Elmwood Park 07407
Prodn. Mgr.—Bob Frei, 80 emp., *Plastic colorants, industrial coatings* (201) 791-5100
Pride Solvents & Chemical Co., 211 Randolph Ave., Avenel 07001
Br. Mgr.—Gary Kalundt, 50 emp., *Industrial chemicals & solvents, including* (732) 499-0125
Rainbow Specialty Colors, Inc., 27 Utter Ave., Ste. B, Hawthorne 07506
Owner—Dayana Dill, 10 emp., *Dyes & color concentrates* (973) 304-0912
Resolv Corporation, 410 Division St., Elizabeth 07201
Plt. Mgr.—Robert Zaman, 9 emp., *Dyes & colors blending for plastics* (973) 676-5141
Riverdale Color Mfg., Inc., 1 Walnut St., Perth Amboy 08861
Pres.—Paul Maguire, 36 emp., *Liquid color & additive dispersions* (732) 376-9300
Royce Assocs., L. P., 28-36 Paterson St., Paterson 07501
GM—Hany Daood, 25 emp., *Solvent, basic & vat dyes for plastics* (973) 279-0400
Royce Assocs., L. P. (H Q), 35 Carlton Ave., East Rutherford 07073
Pres.—Jay Royce, 20 emp., *Company headquarters; textile & industrial* (201) 438-5200
Sensient Cosmetic & Pharmaceutical Technologies, 107 Wade Ave., South Plainfield 07080
Dir., Opers.—Anthony Toto, 60 emp., *Cosmetic colorants & specialty ingredients* (908) 757-4500

© Copyright 2015 Manufacturers' News, Inc.


Spectrachem, 10 Dell Glen Ave., Ste. 3-A, Lodi 07644
Pres.—Zaghary Kousoulis, 10 emp., *Water-based pigment dispersions & textile* ... (973) 253-3553

Sun Chemical Corp., 35 Waterview Blvd., Ste. 100, Parsippany 07054
Pres., CEO—Rudi Lenz, 125 emp., *Corporate headquarters & printing inks* ... (973) 404-6000

Sunbelt Corp., 63 Atwood Pl., Wayne 07470
Bus. Dev. Mgr.—Ken Mackinnon, 4 emp., *Solvent dyes, water-based dyes, powder* ... (803) 329-9787

## 2869 Chemicals—industrial organic, nec

Ajinomoto North America, Inc. (H Q), 400 Kelby St., Ste. 18, Fort Lee 07024
Pres.—Tomoya Yoshizumi, 35 emp., *Corporate headquarters; amino acids* ... (201) 292-3200

Amfine Chemical Corp., 10 Mountainview Rd., Ste. N-215, Upper Saddle River 07458
Ex. V-P.—Takeyuki Mototani, 9 emp., *Corporate headquarters & plastic additives* ... (201) 818-0159

Aromor Flavors & Fragrances, Inc., 560 Sylvan Ave., Ste. 60, Englewood Cliffs 07632
Sales Mgr.—Carol Feldman, 2 emp., *Aroma chemicals for the fragrances* ... (201) 503-1662

Ashland, Inc., International Specialty Products (H Q), 56 Livingston Ave., Ste. 400, Roseland 07068
Pres.—Luis Fernandez-Moreno, 170 emp., *Divisional headquarters; agricultural* ... (973) 533-5400

Cambrex Corp., 1 Meadowlands Plz., Ste. 1510, East Rutherford 07073
Pres., CEO—Steven Klosk, 22 emp., *Corporate headquarters & active pharmaceutica* ... (201) 804-3000

Chemo Dynamics, Inc., 3 Crossman Rd. S., Sayreville 08872
Pres.—Subir Chakraborty, 12 emp., *Fine, specialty, active pharmaceutical* ... (732) 721-4700

Chemtura Corp., Hatco Div., 1020 King George Post Rd., Fords 08863
Opers. Mgr.—Michael Goldberg, 145 emp., *Synthetic lubricants & intermediate* ... (732) 738-1000

Creation Flavors International LLC, 1 Richmond St., Ste. 3038, New Brunswick 08901
Manager—Rick Kamdem, 12 emp., *Flavors for dog & cat food formulas* ... (732) 763-8622

Croda, Inc. (H Q), 300 Columbus Cir., Ste. A, Edison 08837
Pres.—Kevin Gallagher, 100 emp., *Corporate headquarters; specialty chemicals* ... (732) 417-0800

Cyalume Specialty Products, 100 W. Main St., P.O. Box 669, Bound Brook 08805
Pres.—James G. Schleck, 28 emp., *Bulk active pharmaceutical ingredients* ... (732) 469-7760

Elementis Specialties, Inc. (H Q), 469 Old Trenton Rd., East Windsor 08512
Pres.—Greg McClatchy, 129 emp., *Corporate headquarters; paint, adhesive* ... (609) 443-2000

Epolin, 358-364 Adams St., Newark 07105
CEO—Greg Amato, 11 emp., *Organic, infrared & absorbing dyes* ... (973) 465-9495

Evans Chemetics LP (H Q), 500 Frank W. Burr Blvd., 4th Fl., Glenpointe Center West, Teaneck 07666
CEO—Jelle Westra, 4 emp., *Company headquarters; organic sulfur* ... (201) 992-3100

Firmenich, Inc., 150 Firmenich Way, Newark 07114
Dir., Chem. Mfg.—Claudio Barbosa, 185 emp., *Encapsulated flavors for the beverages* ... (973) 589-3443

Firmenich, Inc., 250 Plainsboro Rd., Plainsboro 08536
Pres., N. Amer.—David Shipman, 800 emp., *Corporate headquarters & flavors &* ... (609) 452-1000

FUJIFILM Hunt Chemicals U.S.A., Inc. (H Q), 40 Boroline Rd., Allendale 07401
Pres.—Toshiki Taguchi, 50 emp., *Corporate headquarters; specialty chemicals* ... (201) 995-2200

G.J. Chemical Co., Inc., 128 Doremus Ave., Newark 07105
Pres.—Diana Colonna, 25 emp., *Laboratory chemicals* ... (973) 589-4176

G.J. Chemical Co., Inc., 40 Veronica Ave., Somerset 08873
Pres.—Diana Colonna, 30 emp., *Corporate headquarters & industrial* ... (973) 589-1450

General Chemical Corp., 235 Snyder Ave., Berkeley Heights 07922
Dir., Opers.—Walter Kramer, 20 emp., *Industrial inorganic chemicals* ... (908) 464-1500

Givaudan Flavors Corp., 245 Merry Ln., East Hanover 07936
Hum. Res. Generalist—Tracey Mara, 200 emp., *Flavors & flavoring materials* ... (973) 386-9800

Givaudan Fragrances Corp., 300 Waterloo Valley Rd., Mount Olive 07828
V-P., Opers.—John Trombley, 200 emp., *Perfumes, fragrances & personal care* ... (973) 448-6500

GP Chemicals, Inc. (H Q), 7225 Bergenline Ave., North Bergen 07047
Pres.—Michael Politopoulos, 2 emp., *Corporate headquarters; specialty &* ... (201) 869-2200

HYCHEM Corporation, 611 Main St., Ste. B-2, Belmar 07719
Pres.—Henry Yard, 20 emp., *Surfactants, oleochemicals & esters* ... (732) 280-8803

Hytek Industries Corp., 215 Comanche Dr., P.O. Box 56, Oceanport 07757
Pres., Hum. Res. & IT Mgr.—Joan Sigmond, 5 emp., *Fire-resistant hydraulic fluids* ... (732) 229-5730

Jarchem Industries, Inc., 414 Wilson Ave., Newark 07105
V-P., Sales & Mktg.—Dennis Boyd, 50 emp., *Acetate salts, specialty branched &* ... (973) 344-0600

Kerry Ingredients & Flavors, 160 Terminal Ave., Clark 07066
Cont.—Angel Albanese, 135 emp., *Flavorings & natural products* ... (732) 882-0202

KOBO Products, Inc., 3474 S. Clinton Ave., South Plainfield 07080
Pres.—David Schlossman, 90 emp., *Organic & inorganic cosmetic chemicals* ... (908) 757-0033

Linde North America, Inc. (H Q), 575 Mountain Ave., New Providence 07974
Pres.—Patrick F. Murphy, 575 emp., *Corporate headquarters; industrial* ... (908) 464-8100

Lipo Chemicals, Inc., 1515 W. Blancke St., Linden 07036
Cont.—Anthony Vicale, 35 emp., *Cosmetic ingredients & pharmaceutical* ... (973) 926-0331

Lipo Chemicals, Inc., 207 19th Ave., Paterson 07504
Ex. V-P.—Conrad Kempinska, 30 emp., *Corporate headquarters & raw material* ... (973) 345-8600

Lonza, Inc., 70 Tyler Pl., South Plainfield 07080
Mktg. Mgr., Global—Suellen Bennett, 39 emp., *Cosmetics ingredients, including biotechnolog* (908) 561-5200

Lubrizol Advanced Materials, Inc., 1 Industrial W., Clifton 07012
Cont.—Jack Lewis, 15 emp., *Personal care & industrial organic* ... (973) 471-1300

LyondellBasell Industries, 340 Meadow Rd., Edison 08817
Plt. Mgr.—David Schutka, 65 emp., *Chemicals* ... (732) 777-2272

LyondellBasell Industries, 300 Doremus Ave., Newark 07105
Site Mgr.—Jim Hilliard, 6 emp., *Industrial ethanol products* ... (973) 578-2200

Mane USA, Inc., 60 Demarest Dr., Wayne 07470
Pres., CEO—Jean M. Mane, 138 emp., *Corporate headquarters & fragrance* ... (973) 633-5533

Narad Marketing Corporation, 200 Piaget Ave., Clifton 07011
Pres.—Narie Rekha, 10 emp., *Synthetic organic & leak detection* ... (973) 881-0206

Pflaumer Bros., 1008 Whitehead Road Ext., Ewing 08638
Pres.—Harley McNair, 15 emp., *Specialty chemicals for coatings, paints* ... (609) 883-4610

Phoenix Chemical, Inc., 60 4th St., Somerville 08876
Pres.—John Imperante, 17 emp., *Cosmetics chemicals, including emulsifiers* ... (908) 707-0232

Phoenix Resins, Inc., 602 Union Landing Rd., Cinnaminson 08077
Pres.—J. B. Currell, 4 emp., *Bio-based cleaning solvents* ... (856) 303-9245

PMC Group, Inc. (H Q), 1288 Route 73, Mount Laurel 08054
Pres., COO—Debtash Chakrabarti, 35 emp., *Corporate headquarters; industrial* ... (856) 533-1866

Pride Solvents & Chemical Co., 211 Randolph Ave., Avenel 07001
Br. Mgr.—Gary Kalundt, 50 emp., *Industrial chemicals & solvents, including* ... (732) 499-0125

Reedy International Corp., 25 E. Front St., Ste. 200, Keyport 07735
Sr. Prod. Mgr.—Theresa Healy, 12 emp., *Plastic foaming & nucleating agents* ... (732) 264-1777

Resolv Corporation, 410 Division St., Elizabeth 07201
Plt. Mgr.—Robert Zaman, 9 emp., *Dyes & colors blending for plastics* ... (973) 676-5141

Sekisui America Corp. (H Q), 333 Meadowlands Pkwy., 4th Fl., Secaucus 07094
CFO—Akira Morimoto, 10 emp., *Corporate headquarters; industrial* ... (201) 423-7960

Sensient Cosmetic & Pharmaceutical Technologies, 107 Wade Ave., South Plainfield 07080
Dir., Opers.—Anthony Toto, 60 emp., *Cosmetic colorants & specialty ingredients* ... (908) 757-4500

Shamrock Technologies, Inc., 255 Pacific St., Newark 07114
Chrm.—William B. Neuberg, 100 emp., *Corporate headquarters & micronized* ... (973) 242-2999

Solvay U. S. A., Inc., 8 Cedar Brook Dr., CN-7500, Cranbury 08512
CFO—Mark Dahlinger, 350 emp., *Corporate headquarters & industrial* ... (609) 860-4000

Stepan Co., 100 W. Hunter Ave., Maywood 07607
V-P., Specialty Prods.—Robert Peacock, 95 emp., *Food products chemicals, oils & emulsifiers* (201) 845-3030

Symrise, Inc., 180 Industrial Pkwy., Branchburg 08876
V-P.—Mike O'Hara, 50 emp., *Natural & synthetic fragrances* ... (908) 429-6946

Takasago International Corp., 267 Union St., Northvale 07647
Pur. Agt.—Rich Bartilotti, 60 emp., *Fragrances* ... (201) 767-9001

Troy Chemicals, 1 Avenue L, Newark 07105
IT Mgr.—Tregg Favoy, 100 emp., *Paint additives* ... (973) 589-2500

Tyger Scientific, Inc., 324 Stokes Ave., Ewing 08638
Chrm., CEO—Adam Yuan, 10 emp., *Organic intermediates & specialty chemicals* ... (609) 434-0144

Ungerer & Co., 4 Bridgewater Ln., P.O. Box U, Lincoln Park 07035
Pres.—Kenneth G. Voorhees, 135 emp., *Company headquarters & fragrances &* ... (973) 628-0600

Veolia ES Technical Solutions, LLC, 125 Factory Ln., Middlesex 08846
Cont.—Ray Clark, 90 emp., *Solvent recycling* ... (732) 469-5100

Water Mark Technologies, Inc., 762 State Route 15 S., Ste. 2-B, Lake Hopatcong 07849
★ Pres.—Phil Reilly, 8 emp., *Organic & inorganic chemicals for the* ... (973) 663-3438

## 2873 Nitrogenous fertilizers

Crop Production Services, Inc., 127 Perryville Rd., Pittstown 08867
Plt. Mgr.—Nick Hamm, 5 emp., *Chemical fertilizers* ... (908) 735-5545

W.D. Service Company, Inc., 780 Creek Rd., Bellmawr 08031
CEO—Paul A. Cuccinello, 9 emp., *Concentrated reagent grade ammonia* ... (856) 931-6100

## 2874 Phosphatic fertilizers

Innophos, Inc. (H Q), 259 Prospect Plains Rd., Bldg. A, Cranbury 08512
Chrm., Pres. & CEO—Randolph Gress, 106 emp., *Corporate headquarters; performance-critical* (609) 495-2495

Rotondi & Sons, Inc., S., 139 Reeder Rd., Phillipsburg 08865
GM—Donald Loguidice, 10 emp., *Compost* ... (908) 475-1916

Rotondi & Sons, Inc., S. (H Q), 3 Watchung Ave., Chatham 07928
Pres., CEO—Angelo Rotondi, 11 emp., *Corporate headquarters; compost & yard* ... (973) 635-7799

## 2875 Fertilizers, mixing only

Britton Industries, Inc., 227 Bakers Basin Rd., P.O. Box 6499, Lawrenceville 08648
Pres.—James Britton, 80 emp., *Bulk organic triple ground root & color* ... (609) 588-8225

Chamberlin & Barclay, Inc., 2 Hightstown Cranbury Station Rd., Cranbury 08512
Pres.—David Barclay, 9 emp., *Fertilizer blending* ... (609) 655-0700

Doggett Corp., The, 30 Cherry St., Lebanon 08833
Pres., CEO—Roger D. Mellick, 6 emp., *Tree & specialty fertilizers* ... (908) 236-6335

Espoma Co., 6 Espoma Rd., Millville 08332
Pres.—Serge Brunner, 25 emp., *Organic plant food* ... (856) 825-0542

Fairfield Pallet Co., Inc., 282 Rockville Rd., P.O. Box 361, Fairton 08320
Pres.—Michael Smith, 50 emp., *Mulch & wholesaler of rebuilt wooden* ... (856) 455-7999

Green & Sons, Inc., Jonathan, 48 Squankum-Yellowbrook Rd., Howell 07731
CEO—Barry Green, 30 emp., *Grass seeds, fertilizers & turf chemicals* ... (732) 938-7007

Growmark FS, LLC, 60 Lehigh Ave., P.O. Box 116, Bloomsbury 08804
Sales Mgr.—Rick Klevze, 10 emp., *Fertilizer blending* ... (908) 479-4500

Nature's Choice Corp., 40 Foul Rift Rd., Belvidere 07823
Site Mgr.—Brad Muffley, 10 emp., *Mulch compost & top soil* ... (908) 475-1804

Nature's Choice Corp., 482 Houses Corner Rd., Sparta 07871
Pres.—Nicholas Vene, 3 emp., *Corporate headquarters & soil, compost* ... (201) 333-5244

Plant Food Co., Inc., 38 Hightstown Cranbury Station Rd., Cranbury 08512
Pres.—Ted Platz, 35 emp., *Fertilizer blending* ... (609) 448-0935

Reed & Perrine Sales, Inc., 396 Main St., P.O. Box 100, Tennent 07763
Pres.—Ginny Bulkowski, 25 emp., *Fertilizer blending* ... (732) 446-6363

Riverdale Environmental Recycling, 1 Riverdale Rd., Riverdale 07457
Pres.—Andrew Flockard, 20 emp., *Manufacturer of mulch, compost & soil* ... (973) 616-6654

South Jersey Farmers Exchange, Inc., 101 East Ave., Woodstown 08098
Pres.—Lee Williams, 6 emp., *Fertilizer blending* ... (856) 769-0062

## 2879 Agricultural chemicals, nec

Green & Sons, Inc., Jonathan, 48 Squankum-Yellowbrook Rd., Howell 07731
CEO—Barry Green, 30 emp., *Grass seeds, fertilizers & turf chemicals* ... (732) 938-7007

InventeK Colloidal Cleaners, LLC (USA), 106 Gaither Dr., Mount Laurel 08054
Pres.—Yasmin Andrecola, 25 emp., *Nontoxic & eco-friendly colloidal cleaning* ... (856) 206-0058

Mitchell Products, LLC, 1205 W. Main St., Millville 08332
Member—Dave Mitchell, 6 emp., *Soil & turf conditioning chemicals* ... (856) 327-2005

PIC Corp., 1101 W. Elizabeth Ave., P.O. Box 4258, Linden 07036
Pres.—Allen Rubel, 24 emp., *Pesticides & insect & rodent control* ... (908) 862-7977

## 2891 Adhesives & sealants

Alva-Tech, Inc., 1208 Columbus Rd., Ste. G, Burlington 08016
Pres.—Phillip Valenziano, 20 emp., *Intumescent firestop products & joint* ... (609) 747-1133

AMB Enterprises, LLC, 25 Lake St., Paterson 07501
Pres.—Anthony Bucco, 25 emp., *Adhesives* ... (973) 225-1070

Amerasia International Technology, Inc., 70 Washington Rd., Princeton Junction 08550
Pres., CEO—Kevin Chung, 40 emp., *Adhesives & epoxies for the microelectronic* ... (609) 799-9388

American Adhesives & Coatings, Inc., 470 Mulberry St., Newark 07114
Pres., Hum. Res. & IT Mgr.—Joanne Hayo, 10 emp., *Adhesives & adhesive coatings* ... (973) 623-7070

Andek Corporation, 850 Glen Ave., P.O. Box 392, Moorestown 08057
Pres.—Harvey Liss, 20 emp., *High-performance coatings & sealant* ... (856) 786-6900

Anti-Hydro International, Inc., 45 River Rd., Ste. 200, Flemington 08822
Dir., Opers.—Bruce Kreielsheimer, 12 emp., *Concrete admixtures, coatings, industrial* ... (908) 284-9000

Arrow Fastener Co., LLC, 271 Mayhill St., Saddle Brook 07663
Pres., CEO—Gary DuBoff, 650 emp., *Staplers, staples, glue guns, glues* ... (201) 843-6900

Ashland, Inc., International Specialty Products (H Q), 56 Livingston Ave., Ste. 400, Roseland 07068
Pres.—Luis Fernandez-Moreno, 170 emp., *Divisional headquarters; agricultural* ... (973) 533-5400

Baker-Titan Adhesives, 25 Lake St., Paterson 07501
Plt. Mgr.—Carlos Garcia, 8 emp., *Water-based & hot-melt adhesives* ... (973) 225-1070

Bostik, Inc., 2000 Nolte Dr., West Deptford 08066
Plt. Mgr.—Joe Harris, 20 emp., *Carpet & vinyl adhesives, tile grouts* ... (856) 848-8669

Compounders, Inc., 15 Marl Rd., P.O. Box 413, Farmingdale 07727
Pres.—Harold Saunders, 6 emp., *Adhesives* ... (732) 938-5007

Crossfield Products Corp., 140 Valley Rd., Roselle Park 07204
Dir., Sales, East, Dex-O-Tex—Ed Frick, 45 emp., *Seamless flooring & wall coating systems* .. (908) 245-2800

Custom Building Products, Inc., 2115 High Hill Rd., Logan Township 08085
Plt. Mgr.—Joan Clugsten, 180 emp., *Flooring grout & mortar* ... (856) 467-9226

DriTac Flooring Products, LLC, 60 Webro Rd., Clifton 07012
Pres.—Yale Block, 20 emp., *Eco-friendly industrial adhesives &* ... (973) 614-9000

Dura Tape International, 2816 Morris Ave., Ste. 21, Union 07083
Pres., Fin. & R & D Mgr.—Lee Goldman, 11 emp., *Water-activated & fiberglass mesh joint* .... (908) 687-8273

E & H Laminating & Slitting Co., 138 Grand St., Paterson 07501
Pres.—Kenneth S. Anniti, 25 emp., *Custom laminating of adhesives, transfers* ... (973) 345-1725
FASTENation, Inc., 120 Brighton Rd., Ste. 2, Clifton 07012
Owner & CEO—Jayne Petak, 22 emp., *Manufacturer & distributor of hook-* ... (973) 591-1277
Flexcraft Industries, Inc., 390 Adams St., P.O. Box 2098, Newark 07114
Pres.—Bruce Machlader, 15 emp., *Electronic packaging sealants* ... (973) 589-3403
Garon Products, Inc., 256 Maxim Rd., Howell 07731
V-P., Pur. & Whse. Opers.—Michael Crowley, 4 emp., *Concrete floor repair products & concrete* . (732) 828-6400
Gluefast Co., Inc., 3535 State Route 66, Ste. 1, Neptune 07753
Pres.—Lester Mallet, 10 emp., *Glue & gluing equipment for the packaging* ... (732) 918-4600
Honeywell International, Inc. (H Q), 101 Columbia Rd., Morristown 07962
Chrm., CEO—David M. Cote, 1500 emp., *Corporate headquarters; control & energy* ... (973) 455-2000
Hudson Industries Corp., 271 U.S. Highway 46, Ste. F-207, Fairfield 07004
Pres.—Lee Kornbluh, 2 emp., *Corporate headquarters & animal hide* ... (973) 402-0100
Innovative Resin Systems, Inc., 257 Wilson Ave., Newark 07105
Pres.—Pinakin Patel, 15 emp., *Custom epoxy, polyurethane & acrylic* ... (973) 465-6887
Ja-Bar Silicone Corp., 252 Brighton Rd., P.O. Box 1249, Andover 07821
Pres.—Gilbert Jacobs, 78 emp., *Silicone rubber sheets, molded seals* ... (973) 786-5000
Jedco Adhesives Co., Div. Of Morre-Tec Industries, Inc., 1 Gary Rd., Union 07083
Pres.—Leonard Glass, 25 emp., *Solvent & water-based adhesives* ... (908) 688-9009
Lehigh Cement Co., 66 Demarest Rd., Sparta 07871
Plt. Mgr.—William Trautz, 11 emp., *Colored cement* ... (973) 579-2111
MAPEI Corp., Off White Head Ave., P.O. Box 105, South River 08882
Unit Mgr.—Lou Genzlinger, 25 emp., *Mortar, grout & adhesives* ... (732) 254-8001
Master Bond, Inc., 154 Hobart St., Hackensack 07601
Pres.—James Brenner, 20 emp., *Custom adhesives, sealants, coatings* ... (201) 343-8983
Mercury Adhesives, Inc., 140 Dayton Ave., Passaic 07055
Owner & Pres.—Joel Zeichner, 8 emp., *Hot-melt adhesives* ... (973) 472-3307
Mitronics Products, Inc., 239 Morristown Rd., P.O. Box 196, Gillette 07933
Pres.—Eric Bergman, 6 emp., *Electronic ceramic seals* ... (908) 647-5006
Mon-Eco Industries, Inc., 5 Joanna Ct., East Brunswick 08816
Pres.—Phil Buzzerio, 16 emp., *Adhesives & sealants* ... (732) 257-7942
National Casein Of New Jersey, 401 Martha's Ln., P.O. Box 226, Riverton 08077
Plt. Mgr.—David Lowery, 8 emp., *Casein, glues, resins & adhesives* ... (856) 829-1880
Palmetto Adhesives Co., Inc., 1785 Burlington Rd., Bridgeton 08302
Plt. Mgr.—Ray Charlton, 15 emp., *Adhesives* ... (856) 451-0405
Permabond, LLC (H Q), 223 Churchill Ave., Somerset 08873
Off. Mgr.—Linda Casale, 6 emp., *Company headquarters; engineering adhesives* ... (732) 868-1372
Petronio Shoe Products Corp., 305 Cortlandt St., Belleville 07109
Pres.—Donald Rinaldi, 8 emp., *Professional-grade cleaning, polishing* ... (973) 751-7579
PRC-DeSoto International, Inc., 823 E. Gate Dr., Unit 4, Mount Laurel 08054
Cust. Serv. Mgr.—Mary Ready, 30 emp., *Aerospace sealants & coatings blending* ... (856) 234-1600
Pro-Tapes & Specialties, 621 Route 1 S., North Brunswick 08902
Ptnr.—Barry Hart, 96 emp., *Tapes & adhesives* ... (732) 346-0900
Quality Coatings, Island Dragway Rd., P.O. Box 13, Great Meadows 07838
Owner & GM—Paul Englehart, 8 emp., *Pressure-sensitive adhesives* ... (908) 637-4556
R V Tech, Inc., 801 Magnolia Ave., Bldg. 3-B, Elizabeth 07201
Pres.—Mayur Shah, 5 emp., *Industrial paints, coatings & adhesives* ... (908) 469-8701
Royal Adhesive, Inc., 48 Burgess Pl., Wayne 07470
Pres.—Victoria Corbo, 30 emp., *Industrial adhesives, coatings & specialty* ... (973) 694-0845
Signature Marketing & Mfg., 301 Wagaraw Rd., Hawthorne 07506
Owner & Pres.—Michael Assile, 6 emp., *Manufacturer & wholesaler of adhesives* ... (973) 427-3700
Sika Corp., 995 Towbin Ave., Lakewood 08701
Off. Mgr.—Kathy Murphy, 30 emp., *Sealants, adhesives & primers* ... (973) 473-3330
Sika Corporation, 201 Polito Ave., Lyndhurst 07071
Pres., CEO—Christoph Ganz, 107 emp., *Corporate headquarters & concrete materials* ... (201) 933-8800
Solar Compounds Corp., 1201 W. Blancke St., P.O. Box 1097, Linden 07036
Ex. V-P.—Joseph Barbanel, 30 emp., *Wire, cable, flooding & filling compounds* ... (908) 862-2813
Stonhard, A Div. Of StonCor Group, 1000 E. Park Ave., P.O. Box 308, Maple Shade 08052
Pres.—David Reif, 500 emp., *Company headquarters & seamless, resilient* ... (856) 779-7500
Strongwall Industries, Inc., 107 Chestnut St., Ridgewood 07450
Pres.—Nicole Kokoletsos, 12 emp., *Concrete restoration & protection products* ... (201) 445-4633
Synthetic Surfaces Inc., P.O. Box 241, Scotch Plains 07076
Pres.—Norris Legue, 6 emp., *Commercial adhesives for the outdoor* ... (908) 233-6803
Union Rubber, Inc., 232 Allen St., Trenton 08618
Pres.—Bob Irving, 8 emp., *Glue & rubber cement* ... (609) 396-9328
US Concrete Materials, LLC, 189 Berkley Pl., Dumont 07628
Pres.—Robert K. Bortnick, 3 emp., *Construction chemicals, cold/hot weather* ... (201) 385-6470
USG Corp., Port Reading Plt., 300 Markley St., Port Reading 07064
Plt. Mgr.—James Wilson, 100 emp., *Joint compounds* ... (732) 636-7900
Utility Development Corp., 112 Naylon Ave., Livingston 07039
Pres.—Harry S. Katz, 6 emp., *Plastic foam, adhesives, polymer composite* ... (973) 994-4334
Vertellus Performance Materials, Inc., 40 Avenue A, Bayonne 07002
Dir., Bus.—Tom Pensak, 40 emp., *Coatings & adhesives* ... (201) 858-8810
X-Pando Products, Inc., 500 Southard St., Trenton 08638
Pres.—Lee Colletti, 2 emp., *Pipe joint sealant compounds, tile* ... (609) 394-0150
Zymet, Inc., 7 Great Meadow Ln., East Hanover 07936
Pres.—Karl Loh, 11 emp., *Electronic & fiber-optic adhesives,* ... (973) 428-5245

## 2892 Explosives

Cartridge Actuated Devices, Inc., 40 Old Indian Spring Rd., Andover 07821
V-P.—Ed Soohoo, 30 emp., *Pyrotechnic devices* ... (973) 347-2281
Garden State Fireworks, Inc., 383 Carlton Rd., P.O. Box 403, Millington 07946
V-P.—August Nunzio Santore, 24 emp., *Manufacturer & distributor of fireworks* ... (908) 647-1086
Pyrotechnic Industries, Inc., 1640 Garden Rd., Vineland 08360
Off. Mgr.—Raquel Flowers, 6 emp., *Fireworks* ... (856) 697-1023

## 2893 Ink—printing

ACTEGA Kelstar, Inc., 950 S. Chester Ave., Ste. B-2, Delran 08075
Pres., CEO—Mark Westwell, 85 emp., *Aqueous, UV & adhesive coatings, specialty* ... (856) 829-6300
American Coding & Marking Ink Co., 1220 North Ave., Plainfield 07062
Pres.—Thomas S. Sweet, 8 emp., *Coding & marking inks* ... (908) 756-0373
American Ink Jet Systems, Inc., 34 Chestnut St., Emerson 07630
Pres.—Stephen Saltman, 5 emp., *Manufacturer of inkjet inks, bulk ink* ... (201) 263-9177
Caloric Color Co., Inc., 176 Saddle River Rd., Bldg. A, South Hackensack 07606
GM—June Anton, 9 emp., *Fluoropolymer striping ink & naphtha* ... (973) 471-4748
Central Ink Corp., 2085 Center Square Rd., Unit A, Swedesboro 08085
Lab & Plt. Mgr.—Bruce Gill, 8 emp., *Printing ink* ... (856) 467-5562
Champion Ink Co., Inc., 2045 88th St., North Bergen 07047
Pres.—Ray Czorniewy, 3 emp., *Screen printing ink* ... (201) 868-4100
Faust, Inc., Rudolph, 542 South Ave. E., Cranford 07016
Pres.—Peter Faust, 3 emp., *Engraving ink* ... (908) 507-5104
Flint Group, 6 Corn Rd., Dayton 08810
Opers. Mgr.—Don Witt, 15 emp., *Printing ink* ... (732) 329-4627
GSC Imaging, LLC, 7150 N. Park Dr., Ste. 540, Pennsauken 08109
Owner & Principal—Ron Coutta, 15 emp., *Inkjet inks* ... (856) 317-9301
J.M. Fry Co., Inc., 124 Tices Ln., Ste. A, East Brunswick 08816
Br. Mgr.—Nick Melillo, 8 emp., *Flexographic, offset & gravure printing* ... (732) 238-1060
Monarch Color Corp., 7247 Browning Rd., Pennsauken 08109
GM—Kevin Lockwood, 25 emp., *Printing ink* ... (856) 662-0432
Nazdar Co., 7055 Central Hwy., Pennsauken 08109
Sales Mgr.—Tom O'Neil, 20 emp., *Screen printing inks* ... (856) 663-7878
Pertech Inks Corp., 140 Grand St., Carlstadt 07072
IT Mgr.—Joseph Benton, 25 emp., *Printing inks* ... (908) 354-1700
Printers' Service, Inc., 26 Blanchard St., Newark 07105
Chrm.—Richard B. Liroff, 100 emp., *Corporate headquarters & pressroom* ... (973) 589-7800
Prismacolor Corp., 120 E. Halsey Rd., P.O. Box 6330, Parsippany 07054
Pres.—Robert Steffens, 20 emp., *Printing ink* ... (973) 887-7900
Ranger Industries, Inc., 15 Park Rd., Tinton Falls 07724
Dir., Sales—Alain Avrillon, 62 emp., *Ink, pads & embossing powders* ... (732) 389-1101
Selective Coatings & Inks, Inc., 5008 Industrial Rd., Farmingdale 07727
Pres.—William Zak, 10 emp., *Printing ink* ... (732) 938-7677
Solar Color Chemical Corp., 180 River Rd., Edgewater 07020
Owner & Pres.—Randy Stasi, 1 emp., *Screen printing ink* ... (201) 945-5775
Spectra Colors Corp., 25 Rizzolo Rd., Kearny 07032
Pres., Mktg. Mgr.—Luis B. Marrero, 30 emp., *Colorants & dyes for the ink, food,* ... (201) 997-0606
Spectrachem, 10 Dell Glen Ave., Ste. 3-A, Lodi 07644
Pres.—Zaghary Kousoulis, 10 emp., *Water-based pigment dispersions & textile* ... (973) 253-3553
Sun Chemical Corp., 631 Central Ave., Carlstadt 07072
Opers. Mgr.—Paul Haig, 30 emp., *Printing ink* ... (201) 933-4500
Sun Chemical Corp., 390 Central Ave., East Rutherford 07073
Maint. Supv.—George Rodriguez, 30 emp., *Printing ink* ... (201) 438-4041
Sun Chemical Corp., 35 Waterview Blvd., Ste. 100, Parsippany 07054
Pres., CEO—Rudi Lenz, 125 emp., *Corporate headquarters & printing inks* ... (973) 404-6000
Superior Printing Ink Co., Inc., 666 E. Linwood Ave., Maple Shade 08052
Br. Mgr.—Joe Kissinger, 8 emp., *Printing inks* ... (856) 482-9066
Superior Printing Ink Co., Inc., 100 North St., Teterboro 07608
Chrm., Pres. & CEO—Jeffrey Simons, 300 emp., *Corporate headquarters & lithographic* ... (201) 478-5600
Supreme Ink Co., Inc., 65 McWhorter St., Newark 07105
Pres.—John Ahmed, 12 emp., *Printing ink* ... (973) 344-2922
Total Ink Solutions, 200 S. Newman St., Unit 4, Hackensack 07601
Pres.—Luis Uribe, 6 emp., *Plastisol, water-based, solvent-based* ... (201) 487-9600
Toyo Ink America, 4301 New Brunswick Ave., Ste. A, South Plainfield 07080
Plt. Mgr.—Karel Choteborsky, 15 emp., *Flexographic & rotogravure inks* ... (732) 752-5660
Toyo Ink America, LLC, 30 Murray Hill Pkwy., Ste. 100, East Rutherford 07073
Manager—Vito Vannetti, 8 emp., *Commercial printing inks & polymer* ... (201) 804-0616
Triangle Ink Co., Inc., 53-57 Van Dyke St., Wallington 07057
Co-CEO & Dir., Sales—Kevin J. Sweeney, 11 emp., *Screen printing inks & supplies* ... (201) 935-2777
Trodat USA, 48 Hellar Pk., Somerset 08873
V-P., Sales—Chris Boyle, 42 emp., *Self-inking marking devices, notaryseals* ... (732) 529-8500
US Ink Corp., 390 Central Ave., East Rutherford 07073
GM—Eddie Cabbell, 21 emp., *Printing ink* ... (201) 438-4041
US Ink Corp. (H Q), 631 Central Ave., Carlstadt 07072
Pres.—Michael Dodd, 65 emp., *Corporate headquarters; printing ink* ... (201) 935-8666
Uvitec Printing Ink, Inc., 14 Mill St., Lodi 07644
Pres.—George A. Dakos, 18 emp., *Ultraviolet curable printing inks &* ... (973) 778-0737
WYLD Grand Format Imaging, LLC, 1618 E. Elizabeth Ave., Linden 07036
Member—William J. DiStaso, 3 emp., *Inks for the commercial printing markets* ... (908) 587-2995

## 2899 Chemical preparations, nec

A. L. Wilson Chemical Co., 1050 Harrison Ave., P.O. Box 207, Kearny 07032
Pres.—Fred Schwarzmann, 20 emp., *High-performance chemical products* ... (201) 997-3300
ACTEGA Kelstar, Inc., 950 S. Chester Ave., Ste. B-2, Delran 08075
Pres., CEO—Mark Westwell, 85 emp., *Aqueous, UV & adhesive coatings, specialty* ... (856) 829-6300
Adam, Gates & Co., LLC, 249 Homestead Rd., Hillsborough 08844
Member—Abdelhamid Ramadan, 10 emp., *Fine & specialty chemicals & near-infrared* ... (908) 829-3386
ADM Tronics Unlimited, Inc., 224 Pegasus Ave., Northvale 07647
Pres.—Andre DiMino, 14 emp., *Contract manufacturing of medical electronic* ... (201) 767-6040
Agilex Flavors & Fragrances, Inc., 140 Centennial Ave., Piscataway 08854
Pres. & CEO, Fragrance Div.—Raymond Hughes, 150 emp., *Corporate headquarters & fragrance* (732) 393-7300
Alan Chemical Corp., Inc., 843 Rahway Ave., Ste. 400, Woodbridge 07095
Pres.—Alan Braxton, 6 emp., *Cleaning chemicals* ... (732) 855-6828
American By-Products Recyclers, LLC, 301 Roycefield Rd., Hillsborough 08844
Owner—Robert Soracco, 10 emp., *Biodiesel fuel from recycled cooking* ... (973) 267-0109
American Flux & Metals Corp., 352 E. Fleming Pike, P.O. Box 74, Winslow 08095
GM—Rod Werner, 26 emp., *Molybdenum & EFR flux processing* ... (609) 561-7500
Anhydrides & Chemicals, Inc., 7-33 Amsterdam St., Newark 07105
V-P.—Phillip Rhodes, 7 emp., *Anhydrides for curing epoxy resins,* ... (973) 465-0077
Aromatic Innovations, 600 Hartle St., Sayreville 08872
★ Owner—Golam Bhuiyan, 2 emp., *Fragrances, including perfumes, personal* ... (732) 967-6346
Ashland, Inc., 116 Summit Ave., Chatham 07928
V-P.—Sharrann Simmons, 22 emp., *Specialty chemical active ingredients* ... (973) 635-1551
Atlantic International Technologies, Inc., 114 Beach St., Bldg. 3, Rockaway 07866
CEO—Robert Campbell, 20 emp., *Silicate & optical glass & quartz tubing* ... (973) 625-0053
Bartlo Packaging, Inc., 61 Willet St., Bldg. Z, Passaic 07055
Pres.—Allen Bartlo, 40 emp., *Contract chemical packaging in water-soluble* ... (973) 778-6900
BASF Corporation (H Q), 100 Park Ave., Florham Park 07932
Chrm., CEO—Hans Engel, 1400 emp., *Corporate headquarters; industrial* ... (973) 245-6000
Bergen International, LLC, 411 Route 17 S., Ste. 100, Hasbrouck Heights 07604
Ptnr.—Dick Leahy, 30 emp., *Company headquarters & chemical foaming* ... (201) 299-4499
Boiardi Products Corp., 453 Main St., Ste. 4, Little Falls 07424
Plt. Mgr.—Peter Klotz, 7 emp., *Tile grouting material* ... (973) 256-1100
Bostik, Inc., 2000 Nolte Dr., West Deptford 08066
Plt. Mgr.—Joe Harris, 20 emp., *Carpet & vinyl adhesives, tile grouts* ... (856) 848-8669
Butler Engineering Assocs., Inc., 764 Ramsey Ave., Hillside 07205
Pres.—Chad Hetzell, 12 emp., *HVAC water treatment products* ... (908) 688-3300
C & S Scientific Corp., P.O. Box 1056, Hightstown 08520
Pres.—Jerome Sava, 10 emp., *Heating oil & diesel fuel additives* ... (609) 448-7037
C S L Water Quality, Inc., 156 Mount Bethel Rd., P.O. Box 4246, Warren 07059
Pres.—John V. Truglio, 7 emp., *Water treatment chemicals, filters,* ... (908) 647-1400
Caled Industries, Inc., 26 Hanes Dr., Wayne 07470
Pres., GM—Jack Belluscio, 20 emp., *Chemical blending* ... (973) 696-7575
Canfield Technologies/Bow Electronic Solder, 1 S. Crossman Rd., Sayreville 08872
Cont.—Vito LiLoia, 45 emp., *Solder alloys & fluxes for industrial* ... (732) 316-2100

S.I.C.

Capsugel (H Q), 412 Mount Kemble Ave., Ste. 200-C, Morristown 07960
Pres., CEO—Guido Driesen, 67 emp., *Company headquarters; hard gelatin* .......... (862) 242-1700
Cargille TAB-PRO Corp., 4 E. Frederick Pl., Cedar Knolls 07927
V-P.—Catherine Cargille, 13 emp., *Contract chemical tabletting & blending* .......... (973) 267-8888
Case Medical, Inc., 19 Empire Blvd., South Hackensack 07606
CEO—Marcia A. Frieze, 60 emp., *Medical sterilization trays & cases* .......... (201) 313-1999
Chem-Is-Try, Inc., 160-1 Liberty St., Metuchen 08840
Pres.—Praful K. Porwal, 3 emp., *Contract manufacturing of specialty* .......... (732) 372-7311
ClorDiSys Solutions, Inc., 291 Route 22 E., Salem Industrial Park 5, Lebanon 08833
Dir., Opers.—Paul Lorcheim, 25 emp., *Chlorine dioxide sterilization & decontaminat* .......... (908) 236-4100
Cogesco Water Technologies Corp., 891 Bloomfield Ave., Clifton 07012
Pres.—Gilles Reche, 4 emp., *Water treatment chemicals* .......... (973) 249-9711
Colonial Chemical, 78 Carranza Rd., Tabernacle 08088
Opers. Mgr.—Tim Gallagher, 50 emp., *Custom chemical blending, packaging* .......... (609) 268-1200
Custom Building Products, Inc., 2115 High Hill Rd., Logan Township 08085
Plt. Mgr.—Joan Clugsten, 180 emp., *Flooring grout & mortar* .......... (856) 467-9226
Cyalume Specialty Products, 100 W. Main St., P.O. Box 669, Bound Brook 08805
Pres.—James G. Schleck, 28 emp., *Bulk active pharmaceutical ingredients* .......... (732) 469-7760
Cytec Industries, Inc. (H Q), 5 Garret Mountain Plz., Woodland Park 07424
Chrm., Pres. & CEO—Shane D. Fleming, 499 emp., *Corporate headquarters; specialty chemicals* (973) 357-3100
Darling Ingredients, Inc., 825 Wilson Ave., Newark 07105
Pres.—Neil Katchen, 200 emp., *Inedible tallow* .......... (973) 465-1900
Dixo Co., Inc., 158 Central Ave., P.O. Box 7038, Rochelle Park 07662
COO—Kenneth Schapiro, 20 emp., *Contract chemical packaging* .......... (201) 845-6000
Dolph Co., John C., 320 New Rd., Monmouth Junction 08852
Site Mgr.—Thomas Wacker, 24 emp., *Electrical insulating varnishes & resins* .......... (732) 329-2333
E. I. du Pont de Nemours & Co., Chambers Works Plt., 67 Canal St., Deepwater 08023
Plt. Mgr.—Tim McDaniel, 980 emp., *Chemical additives* .......... (856) 299-5000
Elementis Specialties, Inc., 400 Claremont Ave., Jersey City 07304
Plt. Mgr.—Parkash Patel, 40 emp., *Rheological additives* .......... (201) 395-5108
Epicor, Inc., 1414 E. Linden Ave., P.O. Box 1608, Linden 07036
Pres.—R. M. Bussiculo, 20 emp., *Powdered ion-exchange resins & mixtures* .......... (908) 925-0800
Extracts & Ingredients Ltd., Div. Of MORRE-TEC Industries, Inc., 1 Gary Rd., Union 07083
Pres.—Leonard Glass, 5 emp., *Botanical extracts, nutritive oils,* .......... (908) 688-9009
Ferro Corp., Delaware River Plt., 170 U.S. Route 130 S., P.O. Box 309, Bridgeport 08014
Plt. & Supply Chain Utility Mgr.—Bob Knighton, 100 emp., *Commodity chemicals* .......... (856) 467-8216
Fine Organics Corp., 420 Kuller Rd., P.O. Box 2277, Clifton 07015
Pres., CEO & COO—Gary F. Straub, 14 emp., *Industrial chemical cleaning compounds* .......... (973) 478-1000
Firefreeze Worldwide, Inc., 429 Rockaway Valley Rd., Boonton 07005
Sales Rep., Outside—Ray Giessler, 2 emp., *Fire suppression agents* .......... (973) 394-1335
Firefreeze Worldwide, Inc. (H Q), 272 Highway 46, Rockaway 07866
Pres.—Eveline Giessler, 5 emp., *Corporate headquarters; fire suppressing* .......... (973) 627-0722
Flamingo Bay, Inc., 10 Seneca Trl., Sparta 07871
Pres.—Bruce Miller, 20 emp., *Fragrance & detergent compounds* .......... (973) 726-8882
Fluoramics, Inc., 18 Industrial Ave., Mahwah 07430
Pres.—Franklin G. Reick, 7 emp., *Industrial lubricants, engine oil additives* .......... (201) 825-8110
FUJIFILM Hunt Chemicals U.S.A., Inc. (H Q), 40 Boroline Rd., Allendale 07401
Pres.—Toshiki Taguchi, 50 emp., *Corporate headquarters; specialty chemicals* .......... (201) 995-2200
Fuller Construction Products, Inc., H.B., 59 Brunswick Ave., Edison 08817
Facility Mgr.—Michael Emery, 23 emp., *High-tech surface preparation mortar* .......... (732) 287-8330
Garon Products, Inc., 256 Maxim Rd., Howell 07731
V-P., Pur. & Whse. Opers.—Michael Crowley, 4 emp., *Concrete floor repair products & concrete* . (732) 828-6400
Garratt-Callahan Co., 306 Talmadge Rd., Edison 08817
Off. Mgr.—Tina Decicco, 5 emp., *Water treatment chemicals* .......... (732) 287-2200
GEO Specialty Chemicals, Inc., 1st & Essex St., Harrison 07029
Plt. Mgr.—Jorge Tena, 8 emp., *Chemicals* .......... (973) 484-8400
Graver Technologies, LLC, 72 Lockwood St., Newark 07105
Dir., Opers. & Plt. Mgr.—Jim Sheridan, 40 emp., *Ion exchange resins & water treatment* .......... (973) 690-5290
Gulbrandsen Technologies, Inc., 1 Riverside Way, Phillipsburg 08865
Plt. Mgr.—Ray Freaney, 175 emp., *Water treatment chemicals* .......... (908) 238-2030
Gulbrandsen Technologies, Inc. (H Q), 2 Main St., P.O. Box 5523, Clinton 08809
Founder & CEO—Donald Gulbrandsen, 12 emp., *Corporate headquarters; water treatment* .. (908) 735-5458
Hibrett Puratex, 7001 Westfield Ave., Pennsauken 08110
Pres.—John P. J. Madden, 15 emp., *Custom water treatment & industrial* .......... (856) 662-1717
Honeywell International, Inc. (H Q), 101 Columbia Rd., Morristown 07962
Chrm., CEO—David M. Cote, 1500 emp., *Corporate headquarters; control & energy* .......... (973) 455-2000
Houghton Chemical Corp., 30 Amor Ave., Carlstadt 07072
Plt. Mgr.—Roosevelt Boyd, 4 emp., *Heat transfer fluids & antifreeze* .......... (800) 777-2466
Huber Corp., J.M. (H Q), 499 Thornall St., 8th Fl., Edison 08837
Pres., CEO—Michael Marberry, 65 emp., *Corporate headquarters; hydrocolloids* .......... (732) 549-8600
HYCHEM Corporation, 611 Main St., Ste. B-2, Belmar 07719
Pres.—Henry Yard, 20 emp., *Surfactants, oleochemicals & esters* .......... (732) 280-8803
Hycrete, Inc., 462 Barell Ave., Carlstadt 07072
Pres.—Jason Tuerack, 20 emp., *Concrete waterproofing admixtures* .......... (201) 386-8110
Hy-Test Packaging Corp., 515 E. 41st St., Paterson 07504
Pres.—Jack Smith, 9 emp., *Liquid cleaning products, fuel additives* .......... (973) 754-7000
Indco, Inc., 511 Essex St., P.O. Box 109, Gloucester City 08030
Pres.—Fred Binter, 30 emp., *Contract blending of water-based chemicals* .......... (856) 456-6100
Indofine Chemical Co., Inc., 121 Stryker Ln., Hillsborough 08844
Pres.—Vigi Bezwada, 30 emp., *Organic & inorganic chemical processing* .......... (908) 359-6778
Industrial Water Technologies, Inc., 6 Village Ct., Hazlet 07730
Pres., CFO—Richard Demartino, 9 emp., *Specialty chemicals for wastewater,* .......... (732) 888-1233
INTERCAT, Inc. (H Q), 2399 Highway 34, Ste. C-1, Manasquan 08736
Corp. Cont.—Dawn Serani, 8 emp., *Corporate headquarters; fuel additives* .......... (732) 223-4644
J & J Materials, Inc., 49 Laurel Ave., P.O. Box 2128, Neptune City 07753
Pres.—Stephen J. Zschiegner, 10 emp., *Precious metal chemicals, compounds* .......... (732) 988-3300
Jersey Chemicals, Inc., 775 River St., P.O. Box 542, Paterson 07524
Pres.—David Paulen, 10 emp., *Swimming pool chemicals & pool related* .......... (973) 523-3736
Kenrich Petrochemicals, Inc., 140 E. 22nd St., P.O. Box 32, Bayonne 07002
Pres.—Salvatore J. Monte, 30 emp., *Chemical additives, including titanates* .......... (201) 823-9000
Koslow Scientific Co., 172 Walkers Ln., Englewood 07631
Pres.—Wolfgang Koslow, 30 emp., *Metal analyzing kits* .......... (201) 541-9100
L & R Mfg. Co., Inc., 577 Elm St., P.O. Box 607, Kearny 07032
Pres.—Robert J. Lazarus, 100 emp., *Manufacturer & distributor of ultrasonic* .......... (201) 991-5330
Landzettel & Sons, Inc., 17-12 River Rd., Fair Lawn 07410
Pres.—Walter J. Landzettel, 8 emp., *Private label oil & latex paints &* .......... (201) 796-3506
Lipo Chemicals, Inc., 207 19th Ave., Paterson 07504
Ex. V-P.—Conrad Kempinska, 30 emp., *Corporate headquarters & raw material* .......... (973) 345-8600
MAPEI Corp., Off White Head Ave., P.O. Box 105, South River 08882
Unit Mgr.—Lou Genzlinger, 25 emp., *Mortar, grout & adhesives* .......... (732) 254-8001
Marine Development & Research Corp., 515 E. 41st St., Paterson 07504
Pres.—John S. Smith, 9 emp., *Marine maintenance products* .......... (973) 754-7087

MORRE-TEC Industries, Inc., 1 Gary Rd., Union 07083
Pres.—Leonard Glass, 25 emp., *Corporate headquarters & bromine compounds* .......... (908) 688-9009
National Refrigerants, Inc., 661 Kenyon Ave., Bridgeton 08302
GM & Plt. Mgr.—John McDevitt, 70 emp., *Refrigerants blending & packaging* .......... (856) 455-4555
NEXT Medical Products, 45 Columbia Rd., Branchburg 08876
★ Dir., Cust. Serv.—John Buday, 6 emp., *Ultrasound scanning gels & medical* .......... (800) 458-4254
Nofire Technologies, Inc., 5 James St., South Hackensack 07606
Chrm.—Sam Oolie, 9 emp., *Fire retardant coatings* .......... (201) 818-1616
O & S Research, Inc., 1912 Bannard St., P.O. Box 221, Cinnaminson 08077
Pres.—Anderson L. McCabe, 40 emp., *Anti-glare optical coatings & glass* .......... (856) 829-2800
OKAI Corp., 687 Lehigh Ave., Ste. 3, Union 07083
Pres.—Mary Orella, 6 emp., *Solders* .......... (908) 687-4443
OMG Electronic Chemicals, LLC, 400 Corporate Ct., Ste. A, South Plainfield 07080
GM—Joseph Simeone, 50 emp., *Specialty chemicals* .......... (908) 222-5800
OPS Diagnostics, LLC, 291 U.S. Highway 22 E., Bldg. 6, Lebanon 08833
Pres.—David Burden, 3 emp., *Laboratory equipment & reagent prototyping* .......... (908) 253-3444
Orient Corp. Of America (H Q), 6 Commerce Dr., Ste. 301, Cranford 07016
Pres.—Akihiro Takahashi, 5 emp., *Corporate headquarters; chemical dyes* .......... (908) 298-0990
Oriental Aromatics, Inc., 21 Spielman Rd., Fairfield 07004
Pres., CEO—Dharmil Bodani, 25 emp., *Fragrances & flavors* .......... (973) 227-0400
Pem All Fire Extinguisher Corp., 39-A Myrtle St., P.O. Box 586, Cranford 07016
Pres.—Tom Moskaluk, 15 emp., *Fire extinguishers & suppression systems* .......... (908) 276-0211
Pharmaceutical Innovations, 897 Frelinghuysen Ave., Newark 07114
Pres.—Gilbert Buchalter, 20 emp., *Ultrasound & electromedical gels &* .......... (973) 242-2901
Phibro-Tech, Inc., 300 Frank W. Burr Blvd., Ste. 21, Glenpointe Center East, 3rd Fl., Teaneck 07666
Pres. & Sales Mgr.—Dwight Glover, 70 emp., *Corporate headquarters & copper chemicals* ... (201) 329-7300
Plenum Scientific Research, Inc., 210 Lee Pl., Hackensack 07601
Pres., R & D Mgr.—Shajadi Parvin, 10 emp., *Biochemicals & chemical reagents* .......... (201) 489-2771
Reed-Lane, Inc., 359 Newark Pompton Tpke., Wayne 07470
Pres.—Patricia Elvin, 175 emp., *Contract assembly & packaging for the* .......... (973) 709-1090
Resintech, Inc., 160 Cooper Rd., West Berlin 08091
Pres.—Michael Gottlieb, 60 emp., *Water purification chemicals* .......... (856) 768-9600
Rockwood Holdings, Inc. (H Q), 100 Overlook Ctr., 1st Fl., Princeton 08540
Chrm.—Seifi Ghasemi, 35 emp., *Corporate headquarters; specialty chemicals* .......... (609) 514-0300
Ross Co., Inc., Frank B., 970 New Brunswick Ave., Ste. H, Rahway 07065
Pres.—Larry Powell, 5 emp., *Natural & synthetic waxes, including* .......... (732) 669-0810
Siemens Industry, Inc., Water Technologies, 20 Murray Hill Pkwy., Ste. 140, East Rutherford 07073
Br. Mgr.—Michael Schweiger, 50 emp., *Water treatment & purification products* .......... (201) 531-9338
Solv-Tec, Inc., 3860 Sylon Blvd., Hainesport 08036
Pres.—Patrick O'Brien, 8 emp., *Leak repair sealant additives for automotive* .......... (609) 261-4242
Specified Technologies Inc., 210 Evans Way, Somerville 08876
Pres.—Charbel Tagher, 60 emp., *Firestop products, including pathways* .......... (908) 526-8000
Spectra Colors Corp., 25 Rizzolo Rd., Kearny 07032
Pres., Mktg. Mgr.—Luis B. Marrero, 30 emp., *Colorants & dyes for the ink, food,* .......... (201) 997-0606
Spectrum Chemical Mfg. Corp., 769 Jersey Ave., New Brunswick 08901
★ Cont.—Steve Toigo, 110 emp., *Laboratory chemicals, including steroids* .......... (732) 214-1300
Stuart Steel Protection Corp., 411 Elizabeth Ave., Somerset 08873
Pres.—Gordon Stuart, 20 emp., *Corrosion control anodes & related* .......... (732) 469-5544
Summit Chemical Specialty Products, 45 River Rd., Ste. 300, Flemington 08822
Ptnr. & CEO—Richard Rosen, 35 emp., *Aluminum compounds & industrial chemicals* .......... (908) 782-9500
Sunbelt Corp., 63 Atwood Pl., Wayne 07470
Bus. Dev. Mgr.—Ken Mackinnon, 4 emp., *Solvent dyes, water-based dyes, powder* .......... (803) 329-9787
Surface Technology, Inc., 105 N. Gold Dr., Robbinsville 08691
Pres.—Michael Feldstein, 20 emp., *Plating chemicals & services* .......... (609) 259-0099
Technical Processing, Inc., 81 Dale Ave., Paterson 07501
Pres.—Paul Yankner, 20 emp., *Rubber processing preparations* .......... (973) 278-4950
The Lifestyle Company, Inc., 6 Paragon Way, Ste. 112, Freehold 07728
Pres., CEO—Tom Seidner, 4 emp., *Plastic for contact lenses & contact* .......... (732) 303-7849
Thermo Fisher Scientific, 755 U.S. Highway 202, Bridgewater 08807
Site Mgr.—Thomas Campbell, 162 emp., *Bioreagants & specialty chemicals for* .......... (908) 526-1800
Thomas Scientific, Inc. (H Q), 1654 High Hill Rd., Interstate 295, P.O. Box 99, Swedesboro 08085
Chrm.—Robert Patterson, 82 emp., *Corporate headquarters; water, soil* .......... (856) 467-2000
Triangle Ink Co., Inc., 53-57 Van Dyke St., Wallington 07057
Co-CEO & Dir., Sales—Kevin J. Sweeney, 11 emp., *Screen printing inks & supplies* .......... (201) 935-2777
Troy Corp., 8 Vreeland Rd., Florham Park 07932
Chrm., CEO—Daryl Smith, 70 emp., *Corporate headquarters & biocides &* .......... (973) 443-4200
Turbobraze Corp., 687 Lehigh Ave., P.O. Box 897, Union 07083
Pres.—Mary Orella, 8 emp., *Brazing paste & flux* .......... (908) 687-1030
Tyger Scientific, Inc., 324 Stokes Ave., Ewing 08638
Chrm., CEO—Adam Yuan, 10 emp., *Organic intermediates & specialty chemicals* .......... (609) 434-0144
Ultra Chemical, Inc., 2 Bridge Ave., Ste. 630, Red Bank 07701
Pres.—Arthur Lynch, 8 emp., *Custom & specialty ingredients for* .......... (732) 224-0200
United Energy Corp., 3526 U.S. Highway 9 S., Ste. 103, Howell 07731
Chrm.—Jack Silver, 5 emp., *Specialty chemicals for the oil & gas* .......... (732) 994-5225
Unity Fuels, LLC, 225 Industrial Ave., Ridgefield Park 07660
Mng. Ptnr.—Jeff Deweese, 40 emp., *Biodiesel fuels from used cooking oils* .......... (201) 641-5000
US Concrete Materials, LLC, 189 Berkley Pl., Dumont 07628
Pres.—Robert K. Bortnick, 3 emp., *Construction chemicals, cold/hot weather* .......... (201) 385-6470
Vinchem, Inc., 301 Main. St., P.O. Box 639, Chatham 07928
Pres.—Vincent Ursino, 6 emp., *Chemical preparations* .......... (973) 635-4841
Voltaix, LLC (H Q), 3121 U.S. Highway 22, P.O. Box 5357, Branchburg 08876
Pres., CEO—Paul Burlingame, 95 emp., *Company headquarters; electronic chemicals* .......... (908) 231-9060
Wilpak Industries, Inc., 244 Dukes St., Kearny 07032
Pres.—Tony Sheng, 5 emp., *Inks for writing instruments & writing* .......... (201) 997-7600

## 29 PETROLEUM & COAL PRODUCTS

### 2911 Petroleum refining

Aeropres Corp., 318 Valley Rd., Hillsborough 08844
Plt. Mgr.—Gordon Sammis, 8 emp., *Liquid petroleum gas processing* .......... (908) 722-2571
Hess Corp., 1 Hess Plz., Woodbridge 07095
Pres., Mktg. & Refining—F. Borden Walker, 925 emp., *Petroleum refining* .......... (732) 750-6000
Lubriplate Lubricants Co., 129 Lockwood St., Newark 07105
Pres., CEO—Richard McCluskey, 20 emp., *Company headquarters & industrial lubricants* .... (973) 589-9150
Paulsboro Refining Co., 800 Billingsport Rd., Paulsboro 08066
Comp., Fin. Mgr.—Greg Paranto, 460 emp., *Gasoline, jet fuels & lubricating oils* .......... (856) 224-6000
PBF Energy Partners L. P. (H Q), 1 Sylvan Way, Parsippany 07054
Chrm.—Thomas O'Malley, 170 emp., *Company headquarters; crude oil refining* .......... (973) 455-7500
Power Mist Racing, LLC, 67 Stickles Pond Rd., Newton 07860
Pres.—Rick Fales, 1 emp., *Racing oils, lubricants & fuels* .......... (973) 383-1061
Sonneborn, LLC, 600 Parsippany Rd., Ste. 100, Parsippany 07054
CEO—Paul Raymond, 12 emp., *Company headquarters & manufacturer* .......... (201) 760-2940

© Copyright 2015 Manufacturers' News, Inc.


Technol Fuel Conditioners, Inc., 145 Wyckoff Rd., Ste. 300, Eatontown 07724
Owner—Odette Lichtman, 4 emp., *Fuel additives* ........ (732) 542-0111

## 2951 Asphalt paving mixtures & blocks

American Asphalt Co., Inc., 116 Main St., West Collingswood Heights 08059
Pres., CEO—Robert M. Brown, 50 emp., *Corporate headquarters & asphalt paving* ........ (856) 456-2899
American Asphalt Company, Inc., 1701 River Rd., Burlington 08016
Pres., CEO—Robert M. Brown, 10 emp., *Asphalt paving materials & compounds* ........ (856) 456-2899
Arawak Paving Company, 7503 Weymouth Rd., Hammonton 08037
Pres.—John M. Barrett, 80 emp., *Company headquarters & asphalt paving* ........ (609) 561-4100
Asphalt Paving Systems, 500 N. Egg Harbor Rd., P.O. Box 530, Hammonton 08037
Owner—Robert Caposerri, 15 emp., *Asphalt paving mixtures & blocks* ........ (609) 561-4161
Barrett Paving Materials, Inc. (H Q), 3 Becker Farm Rd., Ste. 307, Roseland 07068
Pres.—Robert Doucet, 15 emp., *Corporate headquarters; asphalt paving* ........ (973) 533-1001
Beaver Run Farms, 300 Beaver Run Rd., Lafayette 07848
GM—Tim Shotmeyer, 15 emp., *Asphalt paving compounds & crushed* ........ (973) 875-5555
Blueknight Energy Partners L. P., King & Jersey St., P.O. Box 31, Gloucester City 08030
Prod. Mgr.—Dave White, 10 emp., *Asphalt products* ........ (856) 456-6673
Bostik, Inc., 2000 Nolte Dr., West Deptford 08066
Plt. Mgr.—Joe Harris, 20 emp., *Carpet & vinyl adhesives, tile grouts* ........ (856) 848-8669
Brick-Wall Corp., 25 1st Ave., Ste. 200, Atlantic Highlands 07716
Pres.—Lawrence Hesse, 29 emp., *Corporate headquarters & asphalt paving* ........ (732) 787-0226
Brick-Wall Corp., 2215 Lacey Rd., Forked River 08731
Plt. Mgr.—Jeff Grossman, 20 emp., *Asphalt paving compounds* ........ (609) 693-6223
Colas, Inc. (H Q), 163 Madison Ave., Ste. 500, Morristown 07960
Pres.—Georges Ausseil, 10 emp., *Corporate headquarters; asphalt paving* ........ (973) 290-9082
Dosch King Emulsions, Inc., 16 Troy Hills Rd., Whippany 07981
Pres., Sales Mgr.—David King, 40 emp., *Asphalt emulsion* ........ (973) 887-0145
Flemington Bituminous Corp., 205 Pennsylvania Ave., Flemington 08822
Pres.—Richard Mannon, 6 emp., *Asphalt paving compounds* ........ (908) 782-2722
Meredith Paving Corp., 1300 Union Landing Rd., Cinnaminson 08077
Pres.—Andrew Zorn, 26 emp., *Asphalt paving compounds* ........ (856) 829-4343
Mount Construction Co., Inc. (H Q), 427 S. White Horse Pike, P.O. Box 619, Berlin 08009
Pres., CEO—Dave Smith, 13 emp., *Corporate headquarters; bituminous* ........ (856) 768-8493
National Paving Co., Inc., 148 Williamstown Rd., P.O. Box 5, Berlin 08009
GM—Bill Rambo, 9 emp., *Asphalt paving compounds* ........ (856) 767-1950
Newark Asphalt Corp., 30 Passaic St., Newark 07104
GM—Joseph Biggica, 6 emp., *Asphalt paving compounds* ........ (973) 268-3636
Owens Corning, 1249 Newark Tpke., Kearny 07032
Plt. Mgr., Asphalt—Raul Martinez, 90 emp., *Asphalt paving compounds* ........ (201) 998-5666
Pierson Construction Co., Inc., R. E. (H Q), 426 Swedesboro Rd., Pilesgrove 08098
V-P.—Robert Baccala, 50 emp., *Corporate headquarters; asphalt paving* ........ (856) 769-8244
Pierson Materials Inc., R. E., 860 Oak Grove Rd., P.O. Box 704, Bridgeport 08014
GM—Slavie Mokienko, 35 emp., *Asphalt paving materials, including* ........ (856) 467-4199
South State Materials, LLC, 202 Reeves Rd., P.O. Box 68, Bridgeton 08302
Pres.—Chester Ottinger, Jr., 65 emp., *Company headquarters & asphalt paving* ........ (856) 451-5300
South State, Inc., 1340 Glassboro Rd., Williamstown 08094
GM—Jay Heim, 15 emp., *Asphalt paving compounds* ........ (856) 881-6030
Sta-Seal, Inc., 5205 Route 130 S., Bordentown 08505
Manager—Gilbert Girard, 3 emp., *Hot mix asphalt* ........ (609) 924-0300
Stavola Construction Materials, Inc., 810 Thompson Ave., Bound Brook 08805
Corp. Secy.—Helen Stokes, 50 emp., *Construction stone aggregates & asphalt* ........ (732) 356-7100
Stavola Contracting Co., Inc., 120 Old Bergen Mill Rd., Englishtown 07726
Owner & Manager—Joe Stavola, 4 emp., *Asphalt* ........ (732) 542-2328
Stavola Contracting Co., Inc., 175 Drift Rd., Tinton Falls 07724
Pres.—Joseph Stavola, 60 emp., *Corporate headquarters & asphalt paving* ........ (732) 542-2328
Stavola Old Bridge Materials, 85 Waterworks Rd., Old Bridge 08857
Opers. Mgr.—Nick Cox, 30 emp., *Asphalt* ........ (732) 721-6900
Stone Industries, Inc., 400-402 Central Ave., Haledon 07508
Chairwoman & CEO—Janet Braen, 150 emp., *Corporate headquarters & crushed stone* ........ (973) 595-6250
Stone, Inc., A. E., 1435 Doughty Rd., Egg Harbor Township 08234
CEO—Thomas K. Ritter, 50 emp., *Corporate headquarters & asphalt paving* ........ (609) 641-2781
Tilcon New York, Inc., 625 Mount Hope Rd., Wharton 07885
Pres., Div.—Sean O'Sullivan, 500 emp., *Asphalt paving compounds* ........ (973) 366-7741
Tilcon Totowa Asphalt, 859 Riverview Dr., Totowa 07512
Plt. Mgr.—Nick Esposito, 5 emp., *Asphalt paving compounds* ........ (973) 256-8300
Tilcon, Inc., Oxford Quarry, 193 Mount Pisgah Ave., P.O. Box 120, Oxford 07863
GM, Aggregates—Brad Carroll, 17 emp., *Stone quarrying & asphalt* ........ (908) 453-4141
Trap Rock, 27 Maple Ave., Mount Holly 08060
Sales Mgr.—Michael Conti, 5 emp., *Asphalt paving compounds & concrete* ........ (609) 265-8500
Trap Rock Ind., LLC, 4415 Route 27, P.O. Box 419, Kingston 08528
Pres.—William H. Stavola, 350 emp., *Company headquarters & crushed stone* ........ (609) 924-0300
Trap Rock Industries, Foot of Crows Mill Rd., Keasbey 08832
V-P.—Wayne Bryant, 10 emp., *Asphalt paving compounds* ........ (732) 738-4222
Trap Rock Industries, Inc., Pennington Quarry, 120 Route 31 S., Pennington 08534
Plt. Opers. Mgr.—Frank Bray, 10 emp., *Crushed stone & hot asphalt mix* ........ (609) 737-3200
Walter R. Earle Corporation, 655 S. Hope Chapel Rd., Jackson 08527
V-P.—Thomas J. Earle, 35 emp., *Asphalt paving compounds* ........ (732) 657-8551
Warren Materials, 703 Route 57, Stewartsville 08886
COO—James T. Haines, 23 emp., *Asphalt paving compounds & bituminous* ........ (908) 859-3333
Weldon Asphalt Co., 1100 Harrison Ave., Kearny 07032
Plt. Mgr.—Jerome Mars, 4 emp., *Asphalt paving compounds* ........ (201) 991-3200
Weldon Asphalt Co., 311 W. Main St., Rockaway 07866
GM—Todd Phillips, 8 emp., *Asphalt paving compounds* ........ (973) 627-7500
Weldon Asphalt Co., 1 Eisenhower Pkwy., Roseland 07068
Plt. Mgr.—Ed Smith, 3 emp., *Asphalt paving compounds* ........ (973) 228-7473
Weldon Asphalt Co., 1 New Providence Rd., Watchung 07060
GM—Robbie Roberts, 75 emp., *Crushed aggregates, hot-mixed asphalt* ........ (908) 233-9440
Weldon Asphalt Corp., 2000 Marshes Dock Rd., Linden 07036
Br. Mgr.—Dominic Mileto, 4 emp., *Hot mix asphalt for driveway, parking* ........ (908) 862-0646
Weldon Materials, Inc., 181 Route 181, Lake Hopatcong 07849
V-P.—Bill Weldon, 40 emp., *Asphalt paving compounds & crushed* ........ (973) 663-1800
Weldon Materials, Inc. (H Q), 141 Central Ave., Westfield 07090
Pres., Cont.—Richard Weldon, 30 emp., *Corporate headquarters; ready-mixed* ........ (908) 233-4444
Winslow Hot Mix, LLC, 784 Piney Hollow Rd., Hammonton 08037
Opers. Mgr.—Mike Gooch, 4 emp., *Asphalt products* ........ (609) 561-2100
Young Asphalt Paving Materials, Robert, 830 Burnt Meadow Rd., Hewitt 07421
Pres.—Bill Young, 10 emp., *Asphalt paving compounds* ........ (973) 728-8133
Ziegler Chemical & Mineral Corp., 600 Prospect Ave., Piscataway 08854
★ Pres., Hum. Res. Mgr.—Chip Ziegler, 15 emp., *Corporate headquarters & asphalt products* .. (732) 752-4111

Ziegler Chemical & Mineral Corp., 600 Prospect Ave., Bldg. A, Piscataway 08854
Sales Mgr., Asphalt—James A. Febo, 25 emp., *Specialty asphalt products & cutbacks* ........ (732) 752-4111

## 2952 Asphalt felts & coatings

Barrett Co., 33 Stonehouse Rd., P.O. Box 421, Millington 07946
Pres.—Timothy Barrett, 8 emp., *High-performance roofing & waterproofing* ........ (908) 647-0100
Blueknight Energy Partners L. P., King & Jersey St., P.O. Box 31, Gloucester City 08030
Prod. Mgr.—Dave White, 10 emp., *Asphalt products* ........ (856) 456-6673
GAF, 1361 Alps Rd., Wayne 07470
Pres., CEO—Bob Tafaro, 400 emp., *Company headquarters & commercial &* ........ (973) 628-3000
Karnak Corp., 330 Central Ave., Clark 07066
Pres., Chairwoman—Sarah J. Jelin, 75 emp., *Corporate headquarters & roof coatings* ........ (732) 388-0300
Palmer Asphalt Co., Inc., 196 W. 5th St., P.O. Box 58, Bayonne 07002
Pres.—Van Ripps, 10 emp., *Energy saving roof coatings, cool roof* ........ (201) 339-0855
Titan Converting, 150 Fieldcrest Ave., Ste. A, Edison 08837
Pres.—Carl McNamara, 10 emp., *Asphalt & polyethylene-coated building* ........ (732) 225-2080
United Asphalt Co., Inc., 237 N. Grove St., Berlin 08009
Pres., GM—Mark Umosella, 20 emp., *Roofing asphalt* ........ (856) 753-9811
Winslow Hot Mix, LLC, 784 Piney Hollow Rd., Hammonton 08037
Opers. Mgr.—Mike Gooch, 4 emp., *Asphalt products* ........ (609) 561-2100

## 2992 Lubricating oils & greases

Anderol, Inc., 215 Merry Ln., East Hanover 07936
Pur. Mgr.—Linda Santos, 80 emp., *Industrial lubricants & greases* ........ (973) 887-7410
AOS Thermal Compounds, LLC, 22 Meridian Rd., Ste. 6, Eatontown 07724
Pres., CEO—John Ziemski, 12 emp., *Heat sink compounds & thermal interface* ........ (732) 389-5514
Bel Ray Co., LLC, 1201 Bowman Ave., Wall 07719
Pres.—Bryan Yourdon, 100 emp., *Lubricating oils for the aerospace,* ........ (732) 938-2421
Cargille Laboratories, 55 Commerce Rd., Cedar Grove 07009
Pres., Tech.—William J. Sacher, 22 emp., *Refractive index & sink-float standards* ........ (973) 239-6633
Chemtura Corp., Hatco Div., 1020 King George Post Rd., Fords 08863
Opers. Mgr.—Michael Goldberg, 145 emp., *Synthetic lubricants & intermediate* ........ (732) 738-1000
Clarkson & Ford Co., 30 Industrial St. W., Clifton 07012
Pres.—Frank Johnson, 10 emp., *Custom industrial lubricating, hydraulic* ........ (973) 777-0300
Cumberland Vacuum Products, 720 S. West Blvd., Vineland 08360
Pres.—Lloyd Ronchetti, 5 emp., *Vacuum pump lubricants* ........ (856) 691-9155
Exxon Mobil Corp., 1001 Billingsport Rd., Paulsboro 08066
Opers. Mgr.—Roman Perez, 130 emp., *Lubricating oils & greases* ........ (856) 224-5000
Fluoramics, Inc., 18 Industrial Ave., Mahwah 07430
Pres.—Franklin G. Reick, 7 emp., *Industrial lubricants, engine oil additives* ........ (201) 825-8110
FTI, Inc. (H Q), 8 Vreeland Rd., Florham Park 07932
V-P.—William B. Smith, 120 emp., *Corporate headquarters; gun lubricants* ........ (973) 443-4200
Gordon Terminal Service Co. Of New Jersey, Inc., 2 Hook Rd., P.O. Box 143, Bayonne 07002
V-P., GM—Thomas S. Gordon, 70 emp., *Industrial lubricants compounding* ........ (201) 437-8300
Grignard Co., 505 Capobianco Plz., Rahway 07065
Mng. Ptnr.—Kelly Akre, 25 emp., *Lubricating oils, greases, cleaners* ........ (732) 340-1111
H & B Petroleum Co., Inc., 1 Wynding Way, Rockaway 07866
Pres.—Maureen C. Huber, 2 emp., *Tapping & metalworking oils, lubricants* ........ (973) 664-0144
International Products Corp., 201 Connecticut Dr., Burlington 08016
Pres.—Kathy J. Wyrofsky, 25 emp., *Precision cleaners & temporary assembly* ........ (609) 386-8770
Lockrey Company LLC, 1280 Old York Rd., Burlington 08016
Pres.—George Eldredge, 12 emp., *Aerospace & industrial lubricants* ........ (856) 665-4794
Lubriplate Lubricants Co., 129 Lockwood St., Newark 07105
Pres., CEO—Richard McCluskey, 20 emp., *Company headquarters & industrial lubricants* .... (973) 589-9150
Magnalube, Inc., 1331 W. Edgar Rd., P.O. Box 1250, Linden 07036
Pres.—Kerby Saunders, 8 emp., *Specialty lubricants* ........ (718) 729-1000
Mil-Comm Products Co., Inc., 2 Carlton Ave., East Rutherford 07073
Pres., CEO—Gordon Furlong, 10 emp., *Extreme performance, all-synthetic,* ........ (201) 935-8561
Total Specialties USA, Inc., 5 N. Stiles St., Linden 07036
Pres.—Mark Neustead, 65 emp., *Corporate headquarters & petroleum* ........ (908) 862-9300
Unique Technologies Assocs., 42 Milled Way, Avenel 07001
Pres.—Eugene Kverel, 10 emp., *Graphite lubricants* ........ (732) 882-0777

## 2999 Petroleum & coal products, nec

Hy-Test Packaging Corp., 515 E. 41st St., Paterson 07504
Pres.—Jack Smith, 9 emp., *Liquid cleaning products, fuel additives* ........ (973) 754-7000
Phillips 66 Bayway Refinery, 1400 Park Ave., Linden 07036
Refinery Mgr.—Brian Coffman, 800 emp., *Oil refining & refined fuel & plastic* ........ (908) 523-5000
Styles Mfg. Co., Inc., A. E., 416 Richmond Ave., P.O. Box 1306, Point Pleasant Beach 08742
Pres.—John Criscuolo, 15 emp., *Manufacturer of car wash detergents* ........ (732) 899-0872

# 30 RUBBER & MISCELLANEOUS PLASTIC PRODUCTS

## 3011 Tires & inner tubes

Custom Bandag, Inc., 401 E. Linden Ave., Linden 07036
Chrm., Pres.—Fernando de Jesus, 40 emp., *Tire retreading* ........ (908) 862-2400

## 3021 Footwear—rubber & plastic

Pro Line Mfg. Co., LLC, 186 Parish Dr., Wayne 07470
V-P.—T. S. Kim, 40 emp., *Fishing, hunting & rubber boots & waders* ........ (973) 692-9696
Tingley Rubber Corp., 1551 S. Washington Ave., Ste. 403, Piscataway 08854
Chrm. of the Board—William B. McCollum, 35 emp., *Waterproof protective footwear & clothing* (908) 757-7474

## 3052 Hose & belting—rubber & plastic

Aarubco Rubber Co., 259 2nd St., P.O. Box 8028, Saddle Brook 07663
Pres.—Steve Wharton, 35 emp., *Rubber & rubber covered belts, rolls* ........ (973) 772-8177
Aflex Extrusion Technologies, Inc., 1600 Livingston Ave., North Brunswick 08902
Co-Pres.—Daryl Little, 10 emp., *Plastic extruded products, including* ........ (732) 752-0048
Armstrong Industrial Hose Products, LLC, 1400 E. State St., Hamilton 08609
Pres., CEO—Brian Logue, 14 emp., *Rubber & plastic tubing & hose* ........ (609) 989-5161
Atlantic Rubber Enterprises, 35 Union Valley Rd., Newfoundland 07435
Pres.—Phillip Corbae, 3 emp., *Hose assemblies* ........ (973) 697-5900
Belting Industries Co., Inc., 20 Boright Ave., P.O. Box 310, Kenilworth 07033
Owner—Scott Cooper, 23 emp., *Corporate headquarters & industrial* ........ (908) 272-8591
BRECOflex Co., L.L.C., 222 Industrial Way W., Eatontown 07724
Pres.—Bernie Fuellemann, 70 emp., *Polyurethane timing & woven endless* ........ (732) 460-9500
Components & Controls, Inc., 495 Washington Ave., P.O. Box 437, Carlstadt 07072
Pres., CEO—Jerry Orlando, 21 emp., *Flexible metal & TFE hoses & industrial* ........ (201) 438-9190
Couse & Bolten Co., 90 South St., Dock 5, Newark 07114
Owner, CEO & COO—Michael Nelson, 7 emp., *Manufacturer & distributor of hydraulic* ........ (973) 344-6330
Cumberland Valve, Inc., 746 Shiloh Pike, Bridgeton 08302
GM—Thomas M. Davis, 11 emp., *Hydraulic hose assemblies* ........ (856) 451-1324

DYNA-Veyor, Inc., 10 Hudson St., Newark 07103
Pres., CEO—Steve Ayre, 18 emp., *Plastic conveyor chains, belting, sprockets* ........ (973) 484-1119
Flexon Industries Corp., 1 Flexon Plz., Newark 07114
CEO—Alex Folkman, 100 emp., *Garden hoses* ........ (973) 824-5530
Forbo Siegling, LLC, 130 Coolidge Ave., Englewood 07631
Br. Mgr.—Ron Supino, 15 emp., *Conveyor belting* ........ (201) 567-6100
Harrison Hose & Tubing, Inc., 2705 Kuser Rd., Trenton 08691
GM—James Logue, 21 emp., *High-end rubber & plastic flexible* ........ (609) 631-8804
Home Rubber Co., 31 Wolverton Ave., Trenton 08611
Pres.—Richard Balka, 47 emp., *Mechanical rubber products & uncured* ........ (609) 394-1176
Industrial Rubber Co., 938-940 S. Elmora Ave., Elizabeth 07202
Pres.—Peter J. Dugett, 25 emp., *Rubber hose, hydraulic fittings, sheets* ........ (908) 351-1550
Jason Industrial Inc., 340 Kaplan Dr., P.O. Box 10004, Fairfield 07004
Pres.—Phillip Cohenca, 50 emp., *Corporate headquarters & rubber timing* ........ (973) 227-4904
Novaflex Industries, Inc., 1024 Industrial Dr., West Berlin 08091
Br. Mgr.—Jerome McCool, 10 emp., *Industrial duct hoses* ........ (856) 768-2275
Passaic Rubber Co., Inc., 45 Demarest Dr., Wayne 07470
Chrm., COO—Jeff Leach, 35 emp., *Private label & contract rubber coated* ........ (973) 696-9500
Polytech Design, Inc., 26 W. 1st St., Clifton 07011
Pres., GM—Zak Shasha, 13 emp., *Rubber & plastic timing belts* ........ (973) 340-1390
Prestige Rubber Mfg., 11 Spielman Rd., Fairfield 07004
Pres.—Steve Kelley, 7 emp., *Rubber tubing & expansion joints &* ........ (973) 227-2505
Reliance Plastic & Chemical Corp., 38-27 Wilson St., P.O. Box 395, Fair Lawn 07410
★ Pres.—Fred Levine, 10 emp., *Flexible down drains for erosion control* ........ (201) 797-8014
Rema Tip Top/North America, Inc. (H Q), 119 Rockland Ave., Northvale 07647
Pres.—Olafur Gunnarsson, 25 emp., *Corporate headquarters; rubber, epoxy* ........ (201) 768-8100
RS Rubber Corp., 55 Paterson Ave., P.O. Box 3400, Wallington 07057
GM—Bob Busch, 10 emp., *Manufacturer & distributor of industrial* ........ (973) 777-2200
Rubber Fabrication & Molding, Inc., 1100 Route 519, P.O. Box 412, Johnsonburg 07846
Pres.—Bill Washer, Sr., 5 emp., *Rubber hose & fittings* ........ (908) 852-7725
Saint-Gobain Performance Plastics, 460 Milltown Rd., Bridgewater 08807
Plt. Mgr.—Massimo Caiati, 60 emp., *Flexible fluoropolymer hoses & fittings* ........ (908) 218-8888
Saint-Gobain Performance Plastics, 460 Milltown Rd., Bridgewater 08807
Plt. Mgr.—Massimo Caiati, 60 emp., *Flexible fluoropolymer hoses & fittings* ........ (908) 218-8888
Stiles Enterprises, Inc., 114 Beach St., P.O. Box 92, Rockaway 07866
Pres.—Richard Stiles, 15 emp., *Manufacturer & distributor of packaging* ........ (973) 625-9660

## 3053 Gaskets, packing & sealing devices

Allied Metrics Seals & Fasteners, Inc., 2 Wilson Dr., Ste. 4, Sparta 07871
Owner—William Westerman, Sr., 9 emp., *Hydraulic, pneumatic & oil seals, o-rings* (973) 383-2487
Alltite Gasket Co. Inc., 323 William St., South River 08882
Pres.—Ronald A. Dreger, 9 emp., *Industrial metal, metal clad & composition* ........ (732) 254-2154
Alpine Elastomer Products, LLC, 308 Division St., Boonton 07005
Owner—David McCrink, 4 emp., *Custom molded rubber & plastic products* ........ (973) 299-0123
AMP Custom Rubber, Inc., 3 Cass St., Ste. 8, Keyport 07735
Pres., Sales Mgr.—John Petrizzo, 15 emp., *Gaskets* ........ (732) 888-2714
Arcy Mfg. Co., Inc., 575 Industrial Rd., Carlstadt 07072
Pres.—Bob Mattesky, 10 emp., *Industrial gaskets & sealing products* ........ (201) 635-1910
Aspe, Inc., 2 Daniel Rd. E., Fairfield 07004
Pres.—Nancy Dam, 20 emp., *Hermetic sealing devices* ........ (973) 808-1155
Baxter Rubber Co., 10 Spielman Rd., Fairfield 07004
Owner & Cust. Sales Rep.—Dan Lambert, 15 emp., *Manufacturer & distributor of rubber* ........ (973) 227-1956
Capital Gasket & Rubber Corp., 325 E. Clements Bridge Rd., Runnemede 08078
V-P.—Dennis Iocono, 5 emp., *Nonmetallic & die cut gaskets & rubber* ........ (856) 939-3670
Caserta, Inc., Thomas A., 11 S. Gold Dr., Ste. E, Robbinsville 08691
Pres.—Clifford Cicogna, 15 emp., *Rubber washers, gaskets, tubing & bushing* ........ (609) 586-2807
CinchSeal, 731 Hylton Rd., Pennsauken 08110
Owner—David Pitchko, 15 emp., *Rotary shaft seals for slow turning* ........ (856) 662-5162
Coast Rubber & Gasket, Inc., 1208 Columbus Rd., Ste. G, Burlington 08016
Pres., Plt. Mgr.—Vito Massa, 6 emp., *Gaskets & electrical insulators* ........ (609) 747-0110
Colonial Seal Co., 1114 Crown Point Rd., Westville 08093
Pres.—Stephen A. Maloney, 6 emp., *Oil, rotary shaft, custom metal cased* ........ (856) 432-0012
Custom Gasket Mfg., 640 E. Palisade Ave., Englewood Cliffs 07632
CEO—Eric Helf, 15 emp., *Custom molded rubber & die-cut products* ........ (201) 331-6363
DSO Fluid Handling Co., Inc., 300 McGaw Dr., Ste. 2, Edison 08837
V-P., GM, Bus. Dev. & Sales—Ed Clark, 15 emp., *Replacement parts for sanitary food* ........ (732) 225-9100
Flowserve Corp., 401 Heron Dr., P.O. Box 563, Bridgeport 08014
GM—Dave Siek, 40 emp., *Mechanical seals* ........ (856) 241-7800
Foster & Co., Inc., 15 Wing Dr., Cedar Knolls 07927
Pres., Fin. & MIS Mgr.—Richard Foster, 30 emp., *Cleaning & polishing compounds, industrial* (973) 267-4100
Frontline Industries, Inc., 990 Chancellor Ave., Irvington 07111
Pres.—Alfredo Ciotola, 15 emp., *Custom mechanical seals, flexible shaft* ........ (973) 373-7211
General Rubber Corp., 850 Washington Ave., Front, Carlstadt 07072
V-P., Sales—Kelvin Mayrina, 10 emp., *Piping & ducting expansion joints,* ........ (201) 935-1900
HK Metal Craft Mfg. Corp., 35 Industrial Rd., Lodi 07644
Chrm., Pres.—Joshua Hopp, 36 emp., *Metal washers & gaskets, spring washers* ........ (973) 471-7770
Hydraulic Packing & Seal Products, 1224 Forest Pkwy., P.O. Box 160, Paulsboro 08066
CEO—Charles Schappert, 50 emp., *Seals, gaskets & mechanical packings* ........ (856) 224-1120
Industrial Rubber Co., 938-940 S. Elmora Ave., Elizabeth 07202
Pres.—Peter J. Dugett, 25 emp., *Rubber hose, hydraulic fittings, sheets* ........ (908) 351-1550
Ja-Bar Silicone Corp., 252 Brighton Rd., P.O. Box 1249, Andover 07821
Pres.—Gilbert Jacobs, 78 emp., *Silicone rubber sheets, molded seals* ........ (973) 786-5000
John Crane, Inc., 301 Berkeley Dr., Swedesboro 08085
Plt. Mgr.—Pedro Vlasques, 100 emp., *Mechanical seals for rotating equipment* ........ (856) 241-3507
Lamatek, Inc., 1226 Forest Pkwy., West Deptford 08066
Pres.—G. Robert Carlson, 40 emp., *Foam & sponge rubber tapes & adhesive-backed* ........ (856) 599-6000
Lindstrom & King Co., Inc., 108 McLean Blvd., Paterson 07514
GM—Nick Fischer, 4 emp., *Custom stem packing die-cut rings &* ........ (973) 279-2511
McNeil, Inc., 15 Marlen Dr., Robbinsville 08691
Pres.—James Schuhl, 15 emp., *Refractory materials & ceramic fiber* ........ (609) 890-7007
Mercer Gasket & Shim, Inc., 110 Benigno Blvd., Bellmawr 08031
Chrm.—Gloria Taraborelli, 25 emp., *Gaskets, including metal, semi-metallic* ........ (856) 931-5000
Metallo Gasket Co., Inc., 16 Bethany St., New Brunswick 08901
Pres., CEO—Frederick Haleluk, 10 emp., *Gaskets, shims, washers, raschig rings* ........ (732) 545-7223
ProGasket Aerospace & Automotive, LLC, 14 Doty Rd., Haskell 07420
Pres.—Mitch Prodani, 10 emp., *Metal stampings for the aerospace &* ........ (973) 831-4533
RS Rubber Corp., 55 Paterson Ave., P.O. Box 3400, Wallington 07057
GM—Bob Busch, 10 emp., *Manufacturer & distributor of industrial* ........ (973) 777-2200
Rubber Fab Technologies Group, 26 Brookfield Dr., Sparta 07871
CEO—Robert Dupont, Sr., 50 emp., *Elastomeric hygienic seals, sanitary* ........ (973) 579-2959
S.S.P. Manufacturing, Inc., 83 Spring Ln., Hackettstown 07840
Pres., Sales Mgr.—Ray Romanick, 9 emp., *CNC lathe-cut custom plastic goods* ........ (908) 852-3125
Seals Eastern, Inc., 134 Pearl St., P.O. Box 520, Red Bank 07701
CEO & Dir., Tech.—Daniel L. Hertz, Jr., 137 emp., *Rubber seals & gaskets for the oil* ........ (732) 747-9200
Specialty Rubber, Inc., 4500 White Horse Pike, P.O. Box 483, Elwood 08217
Pres.—Richard Orosz, 5 emp., *Rubber gaskets* ........ (609) 704-2555
Sterling Seal & Supply, Inc., 1105 Green Grove Rd., Neptune 07753
Pres.—Angelo Derosa, 13 emp., *Corporate headquarters & o-rings &* ........ (732) 918-8004
T & E Industries, Inc., 215 Watchung Ave., Orange 07050
Pres.—Edward McEntee, 48 emp., *Electronic components & glass-to-metal* ........ (973) 672-5454
Toth Inc., 6970 Central Hwy., Pennsauken 08109
V-P.—Theodore Toth, Jr., 48 emp., *Precision machining & assembly of machined* ........ (856) 662-8700
Trico Hose & Gasket Corp., 700-2 Challenger Way, Lacey Business Pk., Forked River 08731
Owner—Adrian Seitz, 4 emp., *Manufacturer of rubber gaskets & seals* ........ (609) 693-5301
Tri-Comp, Inc., 230 West Pkwy., Unit 14, Pompton Plains 07444
V-P.—Thomas Lospinoso, 100 emp., *Plastic & magnetic gaskets* ........ (973) 835-1110
U.S. Seal Mfg., 400 Apgar Dr., Ste. A, Somerset 08873
GM—Shelby Scott, 10 emp., *Mechanical pump seals, including centrifugal* ........ (732) 667-1100
ZaGO Mfg. Co., Inc., 21 E. Runyon St., Newark 07114
Pres.—Harvey Rottenstrich, 24 emp., *Self-sealing fasteners, nuts, toggle* ........ (973) 643-6700

## 3061 Mechanical rubber goods

APM Hexseal Corp., 44 Honeck St., Englewood 07631
Pres.—David Morse, 40 emp., *Rubber environmental seals for the* ........ (201) 569-5700
Colonial Seal Co., 1114 Crown Point Rd., Westville 08093
Pres.—Stephen A. Maloney, 6 emp., *Oil, rotary shaft, custom metal cased* ........ (856) 432-0012
Custom Gasket Mfg., 640 E. Palisade Ave., Englewood Cliffs 07632
CEO—Eric Helf, 15 emp., *Custom molded rubber & die-cut products* ........ (201) 331-6363
Frontline Industries, Inc., 990 Chancellor Ave., Irvington 07111
Pres.—Alfredo Ciotola, 15 emp., *Custom mechanical seals, flexible shaft* ........ (973) 373-7211
Home Rubber Co., 31 Wolverton Ave., Trenton 08611
Pres.—Richard Balka, 47 emp., *Mechanical rubber products & uncured* ........ (609) 394-1176
Itran Precision Rubber, 375 Metuchen Rd., P.O. Box 98, South Plainfield 07080
Pres.—Richard Dougherty, 30 emp., *Custom molded rubber products* ........ (908) 754-8100
John Crane, Inc., 301 Berkeley Dr., Swedesboro 08085
Plt. Mgr.—Pedro Vlasques, 100 emp., *Mechanical seals for rotating equipment* ........ (856) 241-3507
JW Industries, Inc., 21 Elbo Ln., Mount Laurel 08054
V-P.—Jack Fecher, 2 emp., *Custom molded rubber parts, rubber-to-metal* ........ (856) 235-9285
Kinnarney Rubber Co., Inc., 450 Main St., P.O. Box 37, Mantua 08051
Pres.—Jim Kinnarney, 10 emp., *Molded rubber products, including masking* ........ (856) 468-1320
Mid-State Enterprises, Inc., 155 Van Winkle Rd., Hawthorne 07506
Pres., CFO—David C. Humphreys, 6 emp., *Industrial rubber bellows* ........ (973) 427-6040
Minor Rubber Co., Inc., 49 Ackerman St., Bloomfield 07003
Pres.—David Humphreys, 28 emp., *Standard, custom, molded, extruded,* ........ (973) 338-6800
Passaic Rubber Co., Inc., 45 Demarest Dr., Wayne 07470
Chrm., COO—Jeff Leach, 35 emp., *Private label & contract rubber coated* ........ (973) 696-9500
Pure Rubber Products Co., Inc., 300 Roundhill Dr., Ste. 5, Rockaway 07866
Pres.—William T. McCrink, 8 emp., *Precision custom molded rubber parts* ........ (973) 784-3690
Rubber & Silicone Products Co., Inc., 17 Montesano Rd., Fairfield 07004
Pres.—Jeffery Dylla, 25 emp., *Molded rubber & urethane rollers &* ........ (973) 227-2300

## 3069 Rubber products—fabricated, nec

Accu-Seal Rubber, Inc., 18-F Home News Row, New Brunswick 08901
Pres.—Pravin Tejani, 4 emp., *Extruded, molded & fabricated rubber* ........ (732) 246-4333
Ace Mounting Co., Inc., 11 Cross Ave., South Amboy 08879
Pres.—Albert Chiang, 3 emp., *Standard & custom-designed vibration* ........ (732) 721-6200
Advanced Safety Products, Inc., 37 S. Valley Ave., Vineland 08360
Pres.—Michael Schimmel, 5 emp., *Bathtub & floor cleaning chemicals* ........ (856) 691-1700
Aero Tec Laboratories, Inc., 45 Spear Rd., Ramsey 07446
Pres.—Peter Regna, 55 emp., *Flexible fuel tanks & containment systems* ........ (201) 825-1400
Alpha Assocs., Inc., 145 Lehigh Ave., Lakewood 08701
Chrm., CEO—A. Louis Avallone, 100 emp., *Coated & impregnated high-temperature* ........ (732) 730-1800
Alpine Elastomer Products, LLC, 308 Division St., Boonton 07005
Owner—David McCrink, 4 emp., *Custom molded rubber & plastic products* ........ (973) 299-0123
AME Corporation, 33 Jacksonville Rd., Ste. 2, Towaco 07082
New Bus. Dev. Mgr.—Clara O'Boyle, 10 emp., *Custom rubber components, including* ........ (800) 951-0071
Ames Rubber Corp., 19 Ames Blvd., Hamburg 07419
Pres., CEO—Charles Roberts, 110 emp., *Molded & non-molded rubber products* ........ (973) 827-9101
Ansell Healthcare Products, LLC (H Q), 111 Wood Ave. S., Ste. 210, Iselin 08830
Chrm.—Glenn Barnes, 200 emp., *Company headquarters; industrial work* ........ (732) 345-5400
Armstrong Industrial Hose Products, LLC, 1400 E. State St., Hamilton 08609
Pres., CEO—Brian Logue, 14 emp., *Rubber & plastic tubing & hose* ........ (609) 989-5161
ASO Safety Solutions, Inc., 300 Round Hill Dr., Ste. 6, Rockaway 07866
★ Pres.—Helmut Friedrich, 3 emp., *Industrial rubber safety mats, edges* ........ (973) 586-9600
ATCO Rubber Products, Inc., 1480 N. West Blvd., Vineland 08360
Plt. Mgr.—George Raroha, 50 emp., *Flexible ducts for residential & commercial* ........ (856) 794-3393
B Green Innovations, Inc., 750 State Route 34, Ste. 8, Matawan 07747
Pres., CEO—Jerome Mahoney, 4 emp., *100% recycled rubber-based anti-vibration* ........ (732) 696-9333
Banks Bros. Corp., 24 Federal Plz., Bloomfield 07003
Pres.—Stanley Banks, 4 emp., *Corporate headquarters & molded urethane* ........ (973) 680-4488
Baxter Rubber Co., 10 Spielman Rd., Fairfield 07004
Owner & Cust. Sales Rep.—Dan Lambert, 15 emp., *Manufacturer & distributor of rubber* ........ (973) 227-1956
Bergen Mfg. & Supply Co., Inc., 2025 85th St., North Bergen 07047
Pres.—Steven Petrone, 10 emp., *Rubber products* ........ (201) 854-3461
Capital Gasket & Rubber Corp., 325 E. Clements Bridge Rd., Runnemede 08078
V-P.—Dennis Iocono, 5 emp., *Nonmetallic & die cut gaskets & rubber* ........ (856) 939-3670
Cargille Laboratories, 55 Commerce Rd., Cedar Grove 07009
Pres., Tech.—William J. Sacher, 22 emp., *Refractive index & sink-float standards* ........ (973) 239-6633
Caserta, Inc., Thomas A., 11 S. Gold Dr., Ste. E, Robbinsville 08691
Pres.—Clifford Cicogna, 15 emp., *Rubber washers, gaskets, tubing & bushing* ........ (609) 586-2807
Colemax Group, LLC / Prima Cases, P.O. Box 103, Glen Rock 07452
Mng. Dir.—Richard Flashenberg, 6 emp., *Leather, synthetic & molded carrying* ........ (201) 489-1080
Colonial Seal Co., 1114 Crown Point Rd., Westville 08093
Pres.—Stephen A. Maloney, 6 emp., *Oil, rotary shaft, custom metal cased* ........ (856) 432-0012
Continental Roller Co., Inc., 75 Arlington Ave., Kearny 07032
Owner—Carmine Bruzzesi, 6 emp., *Printing rollers for sheetfeed & web* ........ (201) 997-7999
Custom Gasket Mfg., 640 E. Palisade Ave., Englewood Cliffs 07632
CEO—Eric Helf, 15 emp., *Custom molded rubber & die-cut products* ........ (201) 331-6363
Diversified Industries, Inc., 121 High Hill Rd., Swedesboro 08085
Pres.—Bruce Castor, 65 emp., *Plastic foam & rubber fabrication* ........ (856) 662-1981
Eastern Molding Co., Inc., 597 Main St., Belleville 07109
Pres.—Peter De Nicholas, 7 emp., *Molded rubber parts* ........ (973) 759-0220
Fujikura Graphics, 700 Penhorn Ave., Unit 2, Secaucus 07094
Owner—Koichi Kanai, 20 emp., *Rubber printing press blanket converting* ........ (201) 420-5040

Goodyear Rubber Products Corp., 1583 Livingston Ave., Ste. 4, North Brunswick 08902
Pres.—Andrew Warga, 6 emp., *Rubber & plastic hose, conveyor belting* ........ (732) 448-1111
Harrison Hose & Tubing, Inc., 2705 Kuser Rd., Trenton 08691
GM—James Logue, 21 emp., *High-end rubber & plastic flexible* ........ (609) 631-8804
Hawthorne Rubber Mfg. Corp., 35 4th Ave., P.O. Box 171, Hawthorne 07507
Chrm., Pres., CFO—Michael Morton, 30 emp., *Molded rubber parts* ........ (973) 427-3337
Henderson Aquatic, Inc., 1 White Hall, Millville 08332
Pres.—Allan Edmund, 45 emp., *Wet suits for water sports* ........ (856) 825-4771
Herring Co., Inc., D. C., 1750 Brielle Ave., Ste. B-2, Ocean 07712
Founder—Daniel C. Herring, 6 emp., *Extruded cellular rubber products* ........ (732) 695-2272
Hutchinson Industries, Inc., 460 Southard St., Trenton 08638
Pres.—Olivier Marsaly, 165 emp., *Corporate headquarters & rubber & aluminum* ........ (609) 394-1010
Inman Mold & Mfg. Co., 815 Martin St., P.O. Box 1143, Rahway 07065
Pres.—Glen Barlics, 7 emp., *Short & long-run plastic injection* ........ (732) 381-6229
Itran Precision Rubber, 375 Metuchen Rd., P.O. Box 98, South Plainfield 07080
Pres.—Richard Dougherty, 30 emp., *Custom molded rubber products* ........ (908) 754-8100
JW Industries, Inc., 21 Elbo Ln., Mount Laurel 08054
V-P.—Jack Fecher, 2 emp., *Custom molded rubber parts, rubber-to-metal* ........ (856) 235-9285
La Favorite Industries, Inc., 33 Shady St., Paterson 07524
Pres.—Thomas Mastin, 15 emp., *Rubber expansion joints & parts* ........ (973) 279-1266
Lubrizol Advanced Materials, Inc., 76 Porcupine Rd., Pedricktown 08067
Plt. Mgr.—Pam Watley, 43 emp., *Latex* ........ (856) 351-2100
Manville Rubber Products, Inc., 1009 Kennedy Blvd., Manville 08835
Pres.—Sophia Gajewski, 35 emp., *Rubber products, including molded rubber* ........ (908) 526-9111
Mercer Coating & Lining Co., Inc., 1410 E. Linden Ave., P.O. Box 1656, Linden 07036
CEO—R. Bussiculo, 12 emp., *Rubber linings, sandblasting & painting* ........ (908) 925-5000
Metropolitan Rubber Co., 135 Lawrence St., Hackensack 07601
Pres.—Jerry Simmons, 8 emp., *Industrial rubber products, including* ........ (201) 489-0909
Minor Rubber Co., Inc., 49 Ackerman St., Bloomfield 07003
Pres.—David Humphreys, 28 emp., *Standard, custom, molded, extruded,* ........ (973) 338-6800
Nestle Healthcare Nutrition, Inc. (H Q), 12 Vreeland Rd., 2nd Fl., P.O. Box 697, Florham Park 07932
Reg. Bus. Head, N. America—David Yates, 400 emp., *Corporate headquarters; baby food &* (973) 593-7500
Newark Auto Top Co., Inc., 23 Centerway, East Orange 07017
Pres.—Ben Hershkowitz, 20 emp., *Custom replacement carpets for cars* ........ (973) 677-9935
Nitto Denko America Automotive, Inc., 1990 Rutgers Blvd., Lakewood 08701
Dir., Opers.—Eric G. Pike, 100 emp., *Pressure-sensitive tapes & foam rubber* ........ (732) 901-7905
Passaic Rubber Co., Inc., 45 Demarest Dr., Wayne 07470
Chrm., COO—Jeff Leach, 35 emp., *Private label & contract rubber coated* ........ (973) 696-9500
Pierce Roberts Rubber Co., Inc., 1450 Heath Ave., P.O. Box 5007, Trenton 08638
Pres.—Denise Hoffman, 20 emp., *Custom molded rubber products* ........ (609) 394-5245
Portaseal, LLC, 1 John St., P.O. Box 1203, Morristown 07962
Pres.—Stanley D. Grabowy, 10 emp., *Weatherstripping* ........ (973) 539-0100
Prestige Rubber Mfg., 11 Spielman Rd., Fairfield 07004
Pres.—Steve Kelley, 7 emp., *Rubber tubing & expansion joints &* ........ (973) 227-2505
RAK Foam Sales, Inc., 1355 W. Front St., P.O. Box 3248, Plainfield 07063
Pres.—Robert Kussner, 8 emp., *Foam & sponge rubber* ........ (908) 668-1122
Reddaway Mfg. Co., Inc., 32 Euclid Ave., Newark 07105
CEO—William T. Walker, 14 emp., *Industrial brake linings, friction* ........ (973) 589-1410
Rema Tip Top/North America, Inc. (H Q), 119 Rockland Ave., Northvale 07647
Pres.—Olafur Gunnarsson, 25 emp., *Corporate headquarters; rubber, epoxy* ........ (201) 768-8100
Ronald-Mark Assocs., Inc., 1227 Central Ave., P.O. Box 776, Hillside 07205
Pres., CEO—Les Satz, 50 emp., *Corporate headquarters & vinyl, film* ........ (908) 558-0011
Rubber Fab Technologies Group, 26 Brookfield Dr., Sparta 07871
CEO—Robert Dupont, Sr., 50 emp., *Elastomeric hygienic seals, sanitary* ........ (973) 579-2959
RubbeRecycle, LLC, 1985 Rutgers Blvd., Lakewood 08701
Ptnr.—Robert Gestetner, 40 emp., *Recycled tire rubber mulch & curbs* ........ (732) 363-0600
Sellers & Josephson, LLC, 559 Route 23, Wayne 07470
Pres., CEO—Shmuel Brook, 49 emp., *Wallcoverings* ........ (201) 567-1353
Snapco Mfg. Corp., 140 Central Ave., Hillside 07205
Chrm., Pres., CFO & R & D Mgr.—Jeffrey G. Spitz, 25 emp., *Snap, fastener tape, eyelets, grommets* (973) 282-0300
Southland Mfg. Co., 316 Great Meadows Rd., P.O. Box 350, Hope 07844
Pres.—L. R. Trumpore, 2 emp., *Custom industrial molded rubber products* ........ (908) 459-5858
Star-Glo Industries, LLC, 2 Carlton Ave., East Rutherford 07073
Pres.—Edward Peterhoff, 90 emp., *Swiss machining & rubber molding for* ........ (201) 939-6162
Supply Plus, Inc., 155 Sherman Ave., Paterson 07502
V-P.—Samuel Neustein, Jr., 35 emp., *Household cleaning products, sponges* ........ (973) 782-5930
Suspended Aquatic Mentor, 628 South Ave., Garwood 07027
★ Manager—Daniel Cynamon, 4 emp., *Aquatic rescue tubes* ........ (973) 376-3335
Switlik Parachute Co., Inc., 1325 E. State St., Trenton 08609
Pres.—Stanley Switlik II, 115 emp., *Life rafts, aviation life vests, flight* ........ (609) 587-3300
TEK Molding, LLC, 1440 County Route 565, Sussex 07461
Pres.—Tim Kenney, Sr., 2 emp., *Custom natural & synthetic rubber &* ........ (973) 702-0450
Thermwell Products Co., Inc., 420 State Route 17, Mahwah 07430
Pres.—David B. Gerstein, 350 emp., *Weatherstripping & sealing products* ........ (201) 684-4400
Trico Hose & Gasket Corp., 700-2 Challenger Way, Lacey Business Pk., Forked River 08731
Owner—Adrian Seitz, 4 emp., *Manufacturer of rubber gaskets & seals* ........ (609) 693-5301

## 3081 Plastic film & sheet—unsupported

Abbey/Watchung, LLC, 16 N. 26th St., Kenilworth 07033
Pres. & Member—Margaret A. Beute, 5 emp., *Film, archival & vinyl laminating,* ........ (908) 241-7717
Absolute Packaging & Supply, Inc., 456 E. 22nd St., Paterson 07514
Pres., GM—Anthony Stefanelli, 4 emp., *Custom printed plastic & thermoformed* ........ (973) 278-0202
Adhesive Films, Inc., 4 Barnet Rd., P.O. Box 651, Pine Brook 07058
Pres., CEO—John K. Farr II, 18 emp., *Thermoplastic adhesive film in roll* ........ (973) 882-4944
AEP Industries Inc. (H Q), 95 Chestnut Ridge Rd., Montvale 07645
Chrm., Pres. & CEO—J. Brendan Barba, 200 emp., *Corporate headquarters; polyethylene* ... (201) 641-6600
Amcor Flexibles, Inc., 220 Shreve St., Mount Holly 08060
GM—Greg Dubler, 30 emp., *Sterilized medical packaging* ........ (609) 267-5900
Atlantic Protective Pouches, 1545 Route 37 W., Unit 6, Toms River 08755
Pres., GM—Walter Haine, 4 emp., *Polyester film enclosures, pouches* ........ (732) 240-3871
B & W Plastics, Inc., 20 Wilson Dr., Sparta 07871
Pres., CEO, R & D Mgr.—William Post, 5 emp., *Thermoformed clamshells, blister skins* ........ (973) 383-0020
B E R Plastic Corp., 5 Curtis St., P.O. Box 2, Riverdale 07457
Pres.—Bernie Ewasko, 25 emp., *Polyethylene film* ........ (973) 839-2100
Bartlo Packaging, Inc., 61 Willet St., Bldg. Z, Passaic 07055
Pres.—Allen Bartlo, 40 emp., *Contract chemical packaging in water-soluble* ........ (973) 778-6900
Baxter Co., Inc., E. L., 70 S. 7th Ave., P.O. Box 277, Long Branch 07740
CEO—Elwood Baxter, 14 emp., *Packaging, shipping & handling supplies* ........ (732) 229-8219
Central Plastics Co., 333 New Rd., Parsippany 07054
Pres.—Frank Tripucka, 5 emp., *Plastic sheet, rod & tubing* ........ (973) 808-0990
CET Films, Inc., 1650 Corporate Rd. W., Lakewood 08701
Sales Mgr.—Guy Leigh, 14 emp., *Metallized, acrylic & polycarbonate* ........ (732) 367-5511
Champion Plastics Corp., 220 Clifton Blvd., Clifton 07011
GM—John Callaghan, 140 emp., *Polyethelene bags, liners, films, sheeting* ........ (973) 777-9400
Classic Printers & Converters, 140 Ethel Rd. W., Ste. K, Piscataway 08854
Pres., CEO—Sat Khurana, 9 emp., *Manufacturer of custom printed & plain* ........ (732) 985-1100
Consolidated Material Converters, Inc., 74 Squankum Rd., Tinton Falls 07724
Pres.—Neal Marty, 20 emp., *Paper & plastic slitting, sheeting* ........ (732) 389-5973
Consolidated Packaging Group, 30 Bergen Tpke., P.O. Box 261, Ridgefield Park 07660
Pres.—William Kaufman, 100 emp., *Flexible laminated roll stock for the* ........ (201) 440-4240
Co-Planar, Inc., 88 Ford Rd, P.O. Box 1115, Denville 07834
Pres.—James Cote, 28 emp., *Metal & polyester film stampings* ........ (973) 625-3500
Croton Products, 514 Wellington St., Middlesex 08846
Owner—David Jablonski, 1 emp., *Two-ply reinforced polyethylene tarps* ........ (732) 560-9223
Custom Converters, Inc., 115 Naylon Ave., Livingston 07039
Pres.—Mark Krause, 10 emp., *Paper, plastic film, aluminum foil* ........ (973) 994-9000
DAA International LLC, 24 Commerce Rd., Ste. L, Fairfield 07004
Dir., Bus.—Daniel Dombrowski, 5 emp., *Polyester laser printing, metal & ink* ........ (973) 575-7444
Emco Industrial Plastics, Inc., 99 Commerce Rd., P.O. Box 2503, Cedar Grove 07009
Pres.—William Egner, 75 emp., *Plastic fabrication & distributor of* ........ (973) 559-5610
Endurance Net, Inc., 763-B Railroad Ave., Florence 08518
Pres.—Anita Scarperia, 15 emp., *Barrier netting for schools, parks,* ........ (609) 499-3450
Gemini Plastic Films Corp., 535 Midland Ave., P.O. Box 360, Garfield 07026
CEO—Andrew Del Presto, 40 emp., *Plastic bags & films* ........ (973) 340-0700
General Film Products, 107 Trumbull St., Bldg. R-2, Elizabeth 07206
Hum. Res. & IT Mgr. & Prodn. Coord.—Michael Eisner, 50 emp., *Film products* ........ (908) 351-0454
Globe Packaging Co., Inc., 368 Paterson Plank Rd., Carlstadt 07072
Pres.—Issy Bank, 11 emp., *Plastic, collagen, fibrous, cellulose* ........ (201) 939-3335
Glopak Corp., 132 Case Dr., South Plainfield 07080
CEO—Cydnee Martin, 35 emp., *Plastic trash liners & sheeting* ........ (908) 753-8735
Griff Decorative Films Ltd., 700 Vassar Ave., Lakewood 08701
GM—Gene Silvestro, 10 emp., *Decorative thin plastic film, including* ........ (732) 367-2166
Hillside Plastics Corp., 125 Long Ave., P.O. Box 609, Hillside 07205
Pres.—Harold Kaufman, 85 emp., *Plastic extrusions of shrink bundling* ........ (800) 837-7731
Inteplast Group Ltd. (H Q), 9 Peach Tree Hill Rd., Livingston 07039
Founder & Pres.—John Young, 237 emp., *Company headquarters; BOPP, stretch* ........ (973) 994-8000
Johns Manville, 1000 Liddle Ave., Edison 08837
Plt. Mgr.—Mark Sessler, 50 emp., *Fiberglass insulation & plastic coverings* ........ (732) 225-9190
Kappus Plastics Co., Inc., 61-65 Route 31 S., P.O. Box 151, Hampton 08827
GM—Kathleen Herbert, 50 emp., *Plastic sheeting* ........ (908) 537-2288
Kayline Processing, Inc., 31 Coates St., Trenton 08611
V-P., R & D & Sales—Harley Hoffman, 30 emp., *Vinyl printing, laminating & embossing* ........ (609) 695-1440
Kraftware Corp., 270 Cox St., Roselle 07203
Pres., CEO—Randy Grant, 22 emp., *Stainless steel, polyester film & metal* ........ (908) 259-8883
LACOA, Inc., 34 Waite St., Paterson 07524
Pres.—Hector Baralt, 8 emp., *Laminate & emboss materials, including* ........ (973) 754-1000
Laird Plastics, Inc., 135 Fieldcrest Ave., Ste. 135-F, Edison 08837
GM—J. J. Duberville, 20 emp., *Plastic see-thru, mechanical & corrosive* ........ (732) 593-2777
Main Tape Co., Inc., 1 Capital Dr., Ste. 101, Cranbury 08512
Pres.—Karen Olson, 150 emp., *Pressure sensitive tapes & films* ........ (609) 395-1704
Merlin Industries, Inc., 2904 E. State Street Ext., Hamilton 08619
Pres.—Andrew Maggion, 200 emp., *Vinyl pool covers, liners & safety* ........ (609) 807-1000
Metal FX Films, LLC, 27 Kearney St., Unit B, Bridgewater 08807
★ Ptnr.—Charles Yetka, 5 emp., *Polyester films* ........ (732) 560-1297
Multi-Plastics, Inc., 210 Commodore Dr., Swedesboro 08085
Mktg. Mgr., Natl.—Mark Hess, 50 emp., *Thin gage plastic film & sheet converting* ........ (856) 241-9014
National Shrinkwrap, 6220 U.S. Highway 9, Howell 07731
Owner & Pres.—Art Marko, 2 emp., *Shrink-wrapping machinery & film* ........ (732) 942-4554
Nexus Plastics, Inc., 1 Loretto Ave., Hawthorne 07506
Pres., CEO—Marwan Sholakh, 90 emp., *Corporate headquarters & poly packaging* ........ (973) 427-3311
Paterson Packaging, 269 Wilson St., Saddle Brook 07663
Owner & Pres.—Kenneth Manley, 3 emp., *Flexible packaging, including BOPP,* ........ (201) 398-9693
Pegasus Products, Inc., 19 Readington Rd., Somerville 08876
Pres.—Frank Patel, 30 emp., *Swimming pool & tank liners* ........ (908) 707-1122
Phoenix Industries, LLC, 105 W. Dewey Ave., P.O. Box 416, Wharton 07885
Pres., GM—Vincent Norcia, 5 emp., *Polyethylene bags, sheeting & shrink* ........ (973) 366-4199
Polinas Plastics America, Inc., 98 Scoles Ave., Clifton 07012
★ Pres.—Ron Scardina, 2 emp., *Plastic film for labels* ........ (973) 777-8950
Poly Express, LLC, 318 McLean Blvd., Bldg. 5, Paterson 07504
Pres.—Bill Parlak, 15 emp., *Polyethylene bags, liners, sheets &* ........ (800) 843-7659
Poly One Corp., 297 Ferry St., Newark 07105
Sales Mgr., Natl.—Joe Herres, 100 emp., *Plastic sheet & film* ........ (973) 522-2800
Primepak Company, 133 Cedar Ln., Ste. 104, Teaneck 07666
CFO—Mike Heilferty, 34 emp., *Plastic bags, including high & low* ........ (201) 836-5060
Primex Plastics Corp., 65 River Dr., Garfield 07026
GM & Sales Mgr.—Aaron Putnam, 100 emp., *Polystyrene sheets & rolls* ........ (973) 470-8000
R Tape Corporation, 6 Ingersoll Rd., South Plainfield 07080
Pres., CEO—Paul Charapata, 160 emp., *Corporate headquarters & application* ........ (908) 753-5570
Redi Packaging, Inc., 265 Highway 36, Ste. 109, West Long Branch 07764
Pres.—Cyndi Hogan, 12 emp., *Polyethylene & polypropylene products* ........ (732) 544-1480
Ronald-Mark Assocs., Inc., 1227 Central Ave., P.O. Box 776, Hillside 07205
Pres., CEO—Les Satz, 50 emp., *Corporate headquarters & vinyl, film* ........ (908) 558-0011
Rutan Poly Industries, Inc., 39 Siding Pl., Mahwah 07430
Pres.—Arnold Tanowitz, 32 emp., *Plastic bags, films, tubing & sheeting* ........ (201) 529-1474
Saint-Gobain Performance Plastics, 150 Dey Rd., Wayne 07470
Sales Mgr., Global—William O. Textores, 250 emp., *Plastic film & maintenance-free bearings* (973) 696-4700
Satesa Corp., 154 W. Forest Ave., Englewood 07631
Pres.—Randy Loew, 4 emp., *Laminating, coating & converting of* ........ (201) 871-8989
Sigma Plastics Group (H Q), Page & Schuyler Aves., Bldg. 5, P.O. Box 808, Lyndhurst 07071
Ex. V-P.—Alan Teo, 200 emp., *Company headquarters; plastic sheeting* ........ (201) 933-6000
Sigma Stretch Film, Page Ave., Bldg. 5 & 8, P.O. Box 808, Lyndhurst 07071
Cust. Serv. Rep.—Sabrina Protomastro, 100 emp., *Plastic stretch film* ........ (201) 507-9100
Sommers Plastic Products, Inc., 31 Styertowne Rd., Clifton 07012
Chrm.—Edward Schecter, 20 emp., *Plastic & vinyl fabrics, including* ........ (973) 777-7888
SunFlex Packagers, Inc., 2 Commerce Dr., Cranford 07016
Pres., CEO—Manoj Patel, 10 emp., *Plastic film & converting of flexible* ........ (908) 709-1500
TEX-NET, Inc., 763-B Railroad Ave., Florence 08518
Pres.—John Scarperia, 20 emp., *Polyester, polypropylene & nylon barrier* ........ (609) 499-9111
Top Notch Plastics, 217 Bradwick Way, Marlboro 07746
Owner—Ted Green, 25 emp., *Plastic bags* ........ (732) 946-0049
Tri-Cor Flexible Packaging, Inc., 27 Brookfield Dr., Sparta 07871
Pres.—Guy Zimmermann, 20 emp., *Flexible polyethylene packaging for* ........ (973) 940-1500
Ultraflex Systems, Inc. (H Q), 1578 Sussex Tpke., Ste. 400, Randolph 07869
CEO—John Schleicher, 20 emp., *Corporate headquarters; indoor & outdoor* ........ (973) 627-8608

VisiPak, a Sinclair & Rush Company, 640 Dell Rd., Ste. 1, P.O. Box 0188, Carlstadt 07072
Dir., Sales & Mktg.—Jeff Barket, 90 emp., *Plastic tube packaging containers,* ...... (800) 949-1141
X-L Plastics, Inc., 220 Clifton Blvd., Clifton 07011
Pres.—Melvin Fischman, 50 emp., *Plastic bags* ...... (973) 777-1888

## 3082 Plastic profile shapes—unsupported

A+ Products, Inc., 8 Timber Ln., Marlboro Industrial Pk., Marlboro 07746
Founder & Pres.—Mike Schreiber, 40 emp., *Corporate headquarters & custom & standard* ... (732) 866-9111
Aflex Extrusion Technologies, Inc., 1600 Livingston Ave., North Brunswick 08902
Co-Pres.—Daryl Little, 10 emp., *Plastic extruded products, including* ...... (732) 752-0048
Altaflo, 23 Wilson Dr., Sparta 07871
Ptnr.—Mary Hyde, 16 emp., *Fluoropolymer & fluoroplastic extrusions* ...... (973) 300-3344
Apco Extruders, Inc., 180 National Rd., Edison 08817
Pres.—Emmanuel Parnes, 50 emp., *Plastic extrusions* ...... (732) 287-5555
Atlantic Protective Pouches, 1545 Route 37 W., Unit 6, Toms River 08755
Pres., GM—Walter Haine, 4 emp., *Polyester film enclosures, pouches* ...... (732) 240-3871
Brentrick, Inc., 527 E. 39th St., Paterson 07504
Pres.—Rick Coren, 4 emp., *Plastic extrusions, including table* ...... (973) 357-3579
Central Plastics Co., 333 New Rd., Parsippany 07054
Pres.—Frank Tripucka, 5 emp., *Plastic sheet, rod & tubing* ...... (973) 808-0990
Cobon Plastics Corp., 90 South St., Dock 5, Newark 07114
Pres., CEO—Michael F. Nelson, 11 emp., *Plastic tubing for the medical & laboratory* ...... (973) 334-6330
Coperion Corp., 663 E. Crescent Ave., Ramsey 07446
V-P., CFO—Thomas Hummel, 110 emp., *Corporate headquarters & plastic &* ...... (201) 327-6300
Emco Industrial Plastics, Inc., 99 Commerce Rd., P.O. Box 2503, Cedar Grove 07009
Pres.—William Egner, 75 emp., *Plastic fabrication & distributor of* ...... (973) 559-5610
Fram Trak Industries, Inc., 205 Hallock Ave., Middlesex 08846
Pres., CEO—Al Santelli, Sr., 50 emp., *Custom & stock plastic extrusions &* ...... (732) 424-8400
Hall Mfg. Corp., 297 Margaret King Ave., Ringwood 07456
V-P., Opers.—Michael Goceljak, 30 emp., *Plastic extrusions, including profiles* ...... (973) 962-6022
Harrison Hose & Tubing, Inc., 2705 Kuser Rd., Trenton 08691
GM—James Logue, 21 emp., *High-end rubber & plastic flexible* ...... (609) 631-8804
Hillside Plastics Corp., 125 Long Ave., P.O. Box 609, Hillside 07205
Pres.—Harold Kaufman, 85 emp., *Plastic extrusions of shrink bundling* ...... (800) 837-7731
Hishi Plastics U. S. A., Inc., 600-F Ryerson Rd., Lincoln Park 07035
Cont., Hum. Res. Mgr. & Accountant—Maiko Kishinaka, 62 emp., *PVC heat shrinkable tubing* . (973) 633-1230
Interplast, Inc., 100 Connecticut Dr., P.O. Box 1328, Burlington 08016
Pres.—Allen Langman, 20 emp., *Corporate headquarters & PTFE, FEP,* ...... (609) 386-4990
Jabat, Inc., K., 342 Highway 22 W., Green Brook 08812
CEO—Susan McGill, 16 emp., *Plastic tubing & profiles* ...... (732) 469-8177
KNF Flexpak Corporation., 44 Howell St., Jersey City 07306
GM—Paul Bellantonio, 40 emp., *Plastic bag extrusions* ...... (201) 656-4012
Laird Plastics, Inc., 135 Fieldcrest Ave., Ste. 135-F, Edison 08837
GM—J. J. Duberville, 20 emp., *Plastic see-thru, mechanical & corrosive* ...... (732) 593-2777
Laminate Creations, LLC, 1235 Hurffville Rd., Deptford 08096
Member—James Martucci, 6 emp., *Wooden & laminate kitchen cabinets,* ...... (856) 232-8323
Oliner Fibre Co., Inc., 2391 Vauxhall Rd., P.O. Box 308, Union 07083
Pres.—Andrew Oliner, 22 emp., *Plastic extrusions & fiberboard cutting* ...... (908) 688-5800
Paterson Packaging, 269 Wilson St., Saddle Brook 07663
Owner & Pres.—Kenneth Manley, 3 emp., *Flexible packaging, including BOPP,* ...... (201) 398-9693
Patwin Plastics, Inc., 2300 E. Linden Ave., Linden 07036
Pres.—Tom Hannen, 30 emp., *Plastic extrusions* ...... (908) 486-6600
Petro Packaging Co., Inc., 16 Quine St., P.O. Box 546, Cranford 07016
Pres.—Rick Petrozziello, 35 emp., *Custom extruded CAB & PETG tubing,* ...... (908) 272-4054
Petro Plastics, 450 South Ave., P.O. Box 167, Garwood 07027
Pres.—Louis Petrozziello, 45 emp., *Plastic extrusions* ...... (908) 789-1200
Precision Escalators, 147 N. Michigan Ave., Kenilworth 07033
Pres.—Gregory Maroukian, 7 emp., *Precision urethane parts* ...... (908) 259-9017
Pro-Form Packaging, Inc., 777 North Avenue Ext., P.O. Box 4231, Dunellen 08812
Pres.—Kenneth Gibbs, 20 emp., *Custom & contract thermoformed packaging* ...... (732) 968-8123
Redi Packaging, Inc., 265 Highway 36, Ste. 109, West Long Branch 07764
Pres.—Cyndi Hogan, 12 emp., *Polyethylene & polypropylene products* ...... (732) 544-1480
Resdel Corp., Cape May County Industrial Pk., Rio Grande 08242
MIS & Opers. Mgr.—Debbie Fazen, 20 emp., *Epoxy tubing* ...... (609) 886-1111
Rotuba Extruders, Inc., 1401 S. Park Ave., Linden 07036
Pres., CEO—Adam Bell, 120 emp., *Plastic extrusions for lighting & point-of-pu* ...... (908) 486-1000
Rutan Poly Industries, Inc., 39 Siding Pl., Mahwah 07430
Pres.—Arnold Tanowitz, 32 emp., *Plastic bags, films, tubing & sheeting* ...... (201) 529-1474
Saint-Gobain Performance Plastics, 210 Harmony Rd., Mickleton 08056
Plt. Mgr.—Regan Gallo, 80 emp., *Plastic tubing* ...... (856) 423-6630
Thermoplastic Processes, 1268 Valley Rd., P.O. Box 124, Stirling 07980
Hum. Res. Mgr.—Debbie Adkins, 120 emp., *Plastic tubing* ...... (888) 554-6400
Tri-Comp, Inc., 230 West Pkwy., Unit 14, Pompton Plains 07444
V-P.—Thomas Lospinoso, 100 emp., *Plastic & magnetic gaskets* ...... (973) 835-1110
U. S. Cast, 321 Willow Grove Rd., Pittsgrove 08318
COO—Mike Bilello, 11 emp., *Cast acrylic tubes & rods* ...... (856) 347-2342
Unette Corp., 1578 Sussex Tpke., Randolph 07869
Hum. Res. & IT Mgr.—Chris Doscher, 30 emp., *Graduated plastic tubes & contract* ...... (973) 328-6800
VisiPak, a Sinclair & Rush Company, 640 Dell Rd., Ste. 1, P.O. Box 0188, Carlstadt 07072
Dir., Sales & Mktg.—Jeff Barket, 90 emp., *Plastic tube packaging containers,* ...... (800) 949-1141
Zeus Industrial Products, Inc., 134 Chubb Way, Branchburg 08876
IT Mgr.—Kevin Resinger, 200 emp., *Fluoropolymer & specialized PTFE tubing* ...... (908) 526-6500

## 3083 Laminated plastic plate & sheet

Acro Display, 2250-A Sherman Ave., Pennsauken 08110
Pres.—Paul Beranato, Jr., 6 emp., *Millwork, wooden cabinets & laminated* ...... (856) 488-9710
All State Plastics, Inc., 237 Raritan St., South Amboy 08879
Pres.—John R. Vaccaro, 35 emp., *Fluoropolymer rods & tubes* ...... (732) 721-4024
Bilfinger Water Technologies, 708 Challenger Way, Forked River 08731
Plt. Mgr.—Hank Leavitt, 25 emp., *PVC casings, fittings & ground water* ...... (609) 693-9434
Bozzone Custom Woodwork, Inc., 77 N. Beverwyck Rd., Lake Hiawatha 07034
Pres.—Lou Bozzone, 4 emp., *Wooden & laminate cabinets* ...... (973) 334-5598
Buzz-Bee Cabinetry Co., 589 N. East Ave., Vineland 08360
Owner—Paul Buzby, 1 emp., *Wooden cabinets & laminating* ...... (856) 691-5474
Cabinet Works Corp., 511 W. Kings Hwy., Mount Ephraim 08059
Pres.—Frank Cavallaro, 3 emp., *Wooden & laminate cabinets & architectural* ...... (856) 931-7289
Castle Woodcraft Assocs., 161 Route 9, P.O. Box 426, Pine Beach 08741
Ptnr.—Ernest Guenzburger, 15 emp., *Kitchen & office wooden & plastic laminate* ...... (732) 349-1519
CET Films, Inc., 1650 Corporate Rd. W., Lakewood 08701
Sales Mgr.—Guy Leigh, 14 emp., *Metallized, acrylic & polycarbonate* ...... (732) 367-5511
Corporate Woodworking, Inc., 368 Passaic Ave., P.O. Box 10362, Fairfield 07004
Pres.—Dan Andersen, 15 emp., *Wooden & laminated cabinets* ...... (973) 227-2211
Craft Line Cabinet Corp., 10 Walnut St., Clifton 07013
Owner—Gam Danziger, 10 emp., *Laminated cabinets* ...... (973) 777-8808
Custom Wood Furniture, Inc., 37 E. Clinton St., P.O. Box 3034, Newton 07860
Pres.—John Kweselait, 15 emp., *Wooden & laminated cabinets* ...... (973) 579-4880
Cutting Board Co., 291 Highway 22, Lebanon 08833
Ptnr. & Reg. Mgr.—Anthony Pizzelanti, 3 emp., *Standard, custom, glass, plastic &* ...... (908) 725-0187
Dikeman Laminating Corp., 181 Sargeant Ave., Clifton 07013
Pres.—Jeff Snyder, 36 emp., *Corporate headquarters & UV coating* ...... (973) 473-5696
Emco Industrial Plastics, Inc., 99 Commerce Rd., P.O. Box 2503, Cedar Grove 07009
Pres.—William Egner, 75 emp., *Plastic fabrication & distributor of* ...... (973) 559-5610
Glenmore Plastic Industries, Inc., 115 Newfield Ave., Edison 08837
Pres.—Harold Lebwohl, 25 emp., *Plastic laminating* ...... (718) 649-7800
Imco Reinforced Plastics, Inc., 858 N. Lenola Rd., Moorestown 08057
GM & MIS Mgr.—Henry W. Regan, 20 emp., *Fiberglass products* ...... (856) 235-7254
Jafco Industries, LLC, 136 Lincoln Blvd., Middlesex 08846
Pres.—Abe Werczberger, 20 emp., *Architectural millwork & plastic laminate* ...... (732) 356-1502
Longo's Cabinet Shop, 101 Monroe St., Garfield 07026
Owner—Tom Esposito, 1 emp., *Wooden & laminate cabinets* ...... (973) 472-3567
Plastics For Chemicals, Inc., 710 Old Shore Rd., Forked River 08731
Pres., GM—John Donovan, 5 emp., *Tetrafluoroethylene products* ...... (609) 242-9100
R & M Mfg., Inc., 20 Abeel Rd., Monroe 08831
Pres.—Tom Marvel, 25 emp., *Plastic laminate architectural casework* ...... (609) 495-8032
Redi Packaging, Inc., 265 Highway 36, Ste. 109, West Long Branch 07764
Pres.—Cyndi Hogan, 12 emp., *Polyethylene & polypropylene products* ...... (732) 544-1480
Rutan Poly Industries, Inc., 39 Siding Pl., Mahwah 07430
Pres.—Arnold Tanowitz, 32 emp., *Plastic bags, films, tubing & sheeting* ...... (201) 529-1474
Sterling Products, 90 Dayton Ave., Bldg. 12-C, Ste. 77, Passaic 07055
Off. Mgr.—Judy Russell, 30 emp., *Acrylic lampshades, acrylic sheets,* ...... (973) 471-2858
Taylor Made Cabinets, 516 E. Bay Ave., Manahawkin 08050
Ptnr. & Plt. Mgr.—Dave Taylor, 15 emp., *Wooden & laminate cabinets* ...... (609) 978-6900
Wood & Laminates, Inc., 102 Route 46 E., Lodi 07644
Pres.—Gabriel Salazar, 20 emp., *Custom bars & interiors for homes,* ...... (973) 773-7475

## 3084 Plastic pipe

Advanced Drainage Systems, Inc., 300 Progress Ct., Logan Township 08085
Plt. Accountant—Jerri Haas, 64 emp., *Corrugated plastic pipes* ...... (856) 467-4779
Altaflo, 23 Wilson Dr., Sparta 07871
Ptnr.—Mary Hyde, 16 emp., *Fluoropolymer & fluoroplastic extrusions* ...... (973) 300-3344
Bilfinger Water Technologies, 708 Challenger Way, Forked River 08731
Plt. Mgr.—Hank Leavitt, 25 emp., *PVC casings, fittings & ground water* ...... (609) 693-9434
Cutting Edge Grower Supply LLC, 5033 Industrial Rd., Farmingdale 07727
Pres.—Anthonie Barendregt, 5 emp., *PVC drip irrigation pipes* ...... (732) 905-9220
Endot Industries, Inc., 60 Green Pond Rd., Rockaway 07866
Chrm.—Gary Wellmann, 50 emp., *Corporate headquarters & HDPE plastic* ...... (973) 625-8500
Saint-Gobain Performance Plastics, 460 Milltown Rd., Bridgewater 08807
Plt. Mgr.—Massimo Caiati, 60 emp., *Flexible fluoropolymer hoses & fittings* ...... (908) 218-8888
Tri-State Pump, Inc., 5044 Industrial Rd., Ste. C, Farmingdale 07727
Co-Pres.—Mike Caringi, 10 emp., *Industrial pumps* ...... (732) 223-3222

## 3085 Plastic bottles

Abbott Industries, 1-11 Morris St., Paterson 07501
Pres.—Harold Sheck, 3 emp., *Plastic bottles* ...... (973) 345-1116
American Ink Jet Systems, Inc., 34 Chestnut St., Emerson 07630
Pres.—Stephen Saltman, 5 emp., *Manufacturer of inkjet inks, bulk ink* ...... (201) 263-9177
Berry Plastics, 34 Engelhard Dr., Monroe Township 08831
Plt. Mgr.—Bob Loftus, 300 emp., *Plastic bottles* ...... (609) 655-4600
Berry Plastics, Inc., 190 Strykers Rd., Phillipsburg 08865
Hum. Res. Mgr.—Kristi Price, 100 emp., *Plastic bottles & pharmaceuticals* ...... (908) 454-0900
Consolidated Container Co., 28-36 Slater Dr., Elizabeth 07206
Plt. Admn. & Hum. Res. Rep.—Stephanie Cruz, 42 emp., *Plastic bottles* ...... (908) 351-7919
Container Mfg., Inc., 50 Baekeland Ave., P.O. Box 428, Middlesex 08846
Pres.—David Jennings, 42 emp., *Plastic bottles* ...... (732) 563-0100
Graham Packaging Co. L. P., 600 5th St., Belvidere 07823
Plt. Mgr.—Joe Richey, 115 emp., *Plastic bottles* ...... (908) 475-2181
Lanco York, Inc., 864 E. 25th St., Paterson 07513
CEO—Mitchell J. Leibowitz, 25 emp., *Primary & secondary pharmaceutical-grade* ...... (973) 278-7400
Nestle Healthcare Nutrition, Inc. (H Q), 12 Vreeland Rd., 2nd Fl., P.O. Box 697, Florham Park 07932
Reg. Bus. Head, N. America—David Yates, 400 emp., *Corporate headquarters; baby food &* (973) 593-7500
Pace Packaging Corp., 3 Sperry Rd., Fairfield 07004
Pres.—Kenneth Regula, 48 emp., *Automatic plastic bottle unscrambling* ...... (973) 227-1040
Paradigm Packaging, LLC (H Q), 141 N. 5th St., Saddle Brook 07663
Chrm. of the Board—Robert Donnahoo, 100 emp., *Company headquarters; plastic containers* (201) 507-0900
Pro-Screen Printing, Inc., 590 Belleville Tpke., Bldg. 24, Kearny 07032
Pres.—Dilip Lavani, 8 emp., *Plastic bottles & silk screen printing* ...... (201) 246-7600
Q-Pak, Inc., 2145 McCarter Hwy., Newark 07104
Pres.—Michael Formica, 20 emp., *Plastic bottles* ...... (973) 483-4404
Qualipac America Corp., 1 Garret Mountain Plz., 5th Fl., West Paterson 07424
Pres.—Eric Vanin, 15 emp., *Plastic bottles & cosmetic packaging* ...... (973) 389-7730
Rexam Healthcare Packaging, Inc., 14-B Brass Castle Rd., Washington 07882
Plt. Mgr.—Anzideo Ranalli, 50 emp., *Disposable plastic pharmaceutical bottles* ...... (908) 689-1660
Siloa, Inc. (H Q), 2493 Lamington Rd., Ste. C, Bedminster 07921
Pres.—Mark Bellard, 3 emp., *Corporate headquarters; plastic & metal* ...... (908) 234-9040
Tri-Delta Plastics, Inc., 208 Cougar Ct., Hillsborough 08844
Pres.—Thomas Dolan, 90 emp., *Plastic bottles* ...... (908) 722-6021

## 3086 Plastic foam products

A & S Packaging & Display Corp., 120 Kero Rd., Carlstadt 07072
Pres.—Roy Andersen, 15 emp., *Foam, EPS, polystyrene, polyethylene* ...... (201) 531-1900
ABAA, Inc. (H Q), P.O. Box 26, Bernardsville 07924
Owner—Diane Zissu, 4 emp., *Corporate headquarters; plastic foam* ...... (908) 766-4900
Capital Foam Products, Inc., 75 E. Union Ave., P.O. Box 7564, East Rutherford 07073
Pres.—Bart Krupp, 45 emp., *Foam fabrication* ...... (201) 933-5277
Chiromatic, Inc., 1375 Jersey Ave., North Brunswick 08902
Pres.—Debbie Carlitz, 2 emp., *Firm & pressure relieving visco-elastic* ...... (800) 526-5116
CPI Packaging, Inc., 50 Jiffy Rd., Somerset 08873
Pres.—Rodney Pennington, 125 emp., *Corporate headquarters & plastic foam* ...... (732) 431-3500
Deluxe Packaging Co., 1079 Thomas Busch Memorial Hwy., Pennsauken 08110
Ptnr., V-P., Sales & GM—Ken Hoffman, 6 emp., *Packaging supplies, including folding* ...... (856) 486-0006
Diversified Industries, Inc., 121 High Hill Rd., Swedesboro 08085
Pres.—Bruce Castor, 65 emp., *Plastic foam & rubber fabrication* ...... (856) 662-1981
Dow Chemical Co., The, 1500 John Tipton Blvd., Pennsauken 08110
Off. Mgr.—Sue Fitzgerald, 30 emp., *Foam insulation* ...... (856) 910-4900

DV8 Enterprises, LLC, 141 W. Commercial Ave., Moonachie 07074
Pres., CEO—Michael Mozeika III, 25 emp., Reticulated polyurethane foams & flexible.......... (201) 641-4944
Ever-Ready Media Packaging, P.O. Box 40, Haworth 07641
Pres.—Marshall Weingarden, 5 emp., Contract media packaging, including.......................... (973) 566-9333
F X I, Foamex Innovations Div., 13 Manor Rd., East Rutherford 07073
Plt. Mgr.—Andrew Albanese, 80 emp., Polyurethane foam .................................... (201) 933-8540
Foam Pack Industries Div. Of Patis, Inc., 72 Fadem Rd., Springfield 07081
Pres. & V-P.—David Goodstein, 12 emp., Packaging EPS foam ............................. (973) 376-3700
Foam Rubber Fabricators, Inc., 740 Washington Ave., Ste. 1, Belleville 07109
Pres.—Arthur Lerner, 15 emp., Urethane foam fabrication ................................ (973) 751-1445
Ginsey Industries, Inc., 2078 Center Square Rd., Swedesboro 08085
Pres., CEO—Herb Briggs, 100 emp., Decorative kitchen & bathroom products.................... (856) 933-1300
Innocor, Inc. (H Q), 187 State Route 36, Ste. 101, West Long Branch 07764
CEO—Michael C. Thompson, 70 emp., Corporate headquarters; polyurethane.......................... (732) 263-0800
Inoac - Crest Foam, 100 Carol Pl., Moonachie 07074
V-P., Mfg.—Jay Patel, 75 emp., Polyurethane reticulated ester & ether.................................. (201) 807-0809
Interfoam Fabricators, Inc., 155 McBride Ave., Paterson 07501
V-P.—Rick Kohler, 15 emp., Plastic foam products .......................................... (973) 633-8805
International Cushioning Co., 240 Boundary Rd., Marlboro 07746
Pres.—Buddy Bussey, 25 emp., Company headquarters & polystyrene ................................ (732) 683-9600
Monmouth Rubber & Plastics Corp., 75 Long Branch Ave., Long Branch 07740
Pres. & Sales Mgr.—John M. Bonforte, Jr., 47 emp., Closed cell sponge rubber & plastic...... (732) 229-3444
Monster Coatings, Inc., 306-A Capitol St., Saddle Brook 07663
Pres.—Denise Tomahatsch, 4 emp., Seamless industrial, decorative & waterproofi.............. (973) 983-7662
Multi Plastics Extrusions, 30 Production Way, Avenel 07001
Plt. Mgr.—Doug Griswold, 87 emp., Plastic packaging film ................................. (732) 388-2300
New Industrial Foam Corp., 1355 W. Front St., P.O. Box 3120, Plainfield 07063
V-P.—Michael Weisman, 20 emp., Custom & specialty polyurethane, polyethylene................. (908) 561-4010
Packaging Unlimited, Inc., 17 Chelten Way, Bldg. A, Trenton 08638
Pres.—Frank Corrado, 3 emp., Printed corrugated boxes & foam supplies............................ (609) 394-9400
Plastic Plus, Inc. (H Q), 184 Willet St., Passaic 07055
Pres.—Vijay Chokshi, 3 emp., Corporate headquarters; plastic plates ................................ (973) 614-0271
Poly Molding, LLC, 96 4th Ave., Haskell 07420
Pres.—Adam Corn, 19 emp., Expanded polystyrene insulation.......................... (973) 835-7161
Princeton Case Co., Inc., 615 Sherwood Pkwy., Mountainside 07092
V-P.—Steve Parker, Jr., 21 emp., Plastic carrying cases & foam fabrication............................ (908) 687-1750
Reliant Group, 318 McLean Blvd., Paterson 07504
Plt. Mgr.—Lewis Caczolli, 25 emp., Plastic blister packaging............................................ (973) 977-8799
Rempac Foam, LLC (H Q), 370 W. Passaic St., Rochelle Park 07662
CEO—Marc Bushell, 15 emp., Company headquarters; foam fabrication................................ (973) 881-8880
Robertson Industries, 19 State Route 23, Montague 07827
Owner—Craig Robertson, 7 emp., Foam fabrication for packaging...................................... (973) 293-8666
Sealed Air Corp., 301 Mayhill St., Saddle Brook 07663
Sales Mgr., Reg.—Matthew Venezia, 200 emp., Food packaging containers, bubble wrap .... (201) 712-7000
Sealed Air Corp. (H Q), 200 Riverfront Blvd., 3rd Fl., Elmwood Park 07407
Pres., CEO—Jerome Peribere, 100 emp., Corporate headquarters; food packaging .............. (201) 791-7600
Sekisui America Corp. (H Q), 333 Meadowlands Pkwy., 4th Fl., Secaucus 07094
CFO—Akira Morimoto, 10 emp., Corporate headquarters; industrial ..................... (201) 423-7960
SupplyOne, Inc., 1090 Thomas Busch Memorial Hwy., Pennsauken 08110
Cont.—Jason Fuller, 115 emp., Corrugated boxes & foam plastic packaging ........................ (856) 727-1010
TCP Reliable, Inc., 551 Raritan Center Pkwy., Edison 08837
Pres., CEO—Maurice Barakat, 50 emp., Temperature control packaging................................ (732) 346-9200
Tekni-Plex, Inc., 201 Industrial Pkwy., Somerville 08876
Plt. Mgr.—John Kratins, 100 emp., Foam trays .................................................... (908) 722-4800
U.S. ProPack, Inc., 341 Fairfield Rd., Freehold 07728
Pres.—Stephen Miller, 10 emp., Industrial & promotional packaging .................................... (732) 294-4500
UFP Technologies, Inc., 1 Johnson Dr., Raritan 08869
Manager—Katharine Galbraith, 50 emp., Foam packaging, thermoforming & foam ................ (800) 372-3172
Utility Development Corp., 112 Naylon Ave., Livingston 07039
Pres.—Harry S. Katz, 6 emp., Plastic foam, adhesives, polymer composite......................... (973) 994-4334
WinCup, 190 Liberty St., Metuchen 08840
Plt. Mgr.—Mike Revier, 120 emp., Foam cups & containers ............................... (732) 494-1999

## 3087 Custom compound purchased resins

Colorite, A Tekni-Plex Co., 101 Railroad Ave., Ridgefield 07657
Plt. Mgr.—Ross Kisciras, 200 emp., Divisional headquarters & PVC compounds.................... (201) 941-2900
CompoSecure, LLC, 500 Memorial Dr., Somerset 08873
V-P., CEO & GM—Michele Logan, 125 emp., Material science/forensics security..................... (908) 518-0500
Compounding Engineering Solutions, Inc., 473 Highway 46 W., Clifton 07011
Pres.—Arash Kiani, 10 emp., Plastic compound materials ................................ (973) 340-4000
Faust Thermographic, Inc., 325 Cantor Ave., P.O. Box 1277, Linden 07036
Pres.—Craig Schwartzer, 8 emp., Thermographic printing powders ..................... (908) 474-0555
Formosa Plastics Corp. U.S.A. (H Q), 9 Peach Tree Hill Rd., Livingston 07039
V-P., GM, Vinyl—Dick Heinle, 265 emp., Corporate headquarters; plastic resins..................... (973) 992-2090
OxyVinyls, P.O. Box 411, Pedricktown 08067
Plt. Mgr.—Thomas Wutka, 40 emp., PVC resin ........................................................ (856) 299-8498
Polymer Dynamix, LLC, 238 Saint Nicholas Ave., South Plainfield 07080
Pres.—Viggy Mehta, 7 emp., Plastic resin compounding ...................................... (908) 668-0300
Polymeric Resources Corporation, Inc., 55 Haul Rd., Wayne 07470
Pres.—Sol Schlesinger, 50 emp., Corporate headquarters & plastic resin ............................. (973) 694-4141
Rockwood Holdings, Inc. (H Q), 100 Overlook Ctr., 1st Fl., Princeton 08540
Chrm.—Seifi Ghasemi, 35 emp., Corporate headquarters; specialty chemicals........................ (609) 514-0300

## 3088 Plastic plumbing fixtures

CytoTherm, 110 Sewell Ave., Trenton 08610
Pres.—Roman Kuzyk, 6 emp., Digitally-controlled dry & conventional................................... (609) 396-1456

## 3089 Plastic products, nec

21st Century Optical, 5 Powder Horn Dr., Warren 07059
GM—Ed Glassheim, 10 emp., Glass, plastic & polycarbonate fabrication .............................. (973) 379-2020
A & F Sign Company LLC, 28 E. Railway Ave., Paterson 07503
Sole Member—Frank Ferrucci, 1 emp., Architectural, illuminated, non-illuminated.................. (973) 278-3707
A & L Plastics Co., Inc., 2 Municipal Rd., P.O. Box 160, Newton 07860
Pres.—Michael O'Shea, 10 emp., Custom plastic extrusion, raised floor ................................ (973) 383-2221
A & S Packaging & Display Corp., 120 Kero Rd., Carlstadt 07072
Pres.—Roy Andersen, 15 emp., Foam, EPS, polystyrene, polyethylene .................................. (201) 531-1900
A. L. Don, 1 Dock St., Matawan 07747
CEO—Peter Gronbeck, 8 emp., Wooden & synthetic pilot & debarkation ............................... (732) 574-1441
A+ Products, Inc., 8 Timber Ln., Marlboro Industrial Pk., Marlboro 07746
Founder & Pres.—Mike Schreiber, 40 emp., Corporate headquarters & custom & standard ... (732) 866-9111
A-1 J D K Specialties, 1 Millstream Rd., Cream Ridge 08514
Owner—Gary Conk, Sr., 1 emp., Plastic & metal trophies, plaques &....................................... (732) 928-9495
A-Affordable Sign.Com, 1053 Madison Hill Rd., Rahway 07065
GM—Jim Miggioze, 12 emp., Custom signs & vinyl lettering.................................. (732) 287-0446
Abilities Of Northwest Jersey, Inc., 264 Route 31 N., P.O. Box 251, Washington 07882
CEO—Cindy Wildermuth, 300 emp., Contract packaging/fulfillment, including....................... (908) 689-1118
Accessory Workshop (H Q), 16 Arcadian Ave., Ste. C-7, Paramus 07652
Opers. Mgr.—Sean Mahoney, 10 emp., Company headquarters; faux leather ........................ (888) 691-3047
Ace Tool & Mfg. Co., Inc., 532 Mulberry St., Ste. 1, Newark 07114
Pres.—Charles Kolarsick, 9 emp., Plastic injection molding................................. (973) 824-0222
Acme Model Engineering Co., 115 Victory Rd., Springfield 07081
CEO—Dorothy Principe, 30 emp., Aluminum battery holders .............................. (973) 379-4193
Acme Plastics, Inc., 222 Browertown Rd., P.O. Box 806, Woodland Park 07424
Pres.—Lawrence Levinson, 100 emp., Corporate headquarters & plastic products .............. (973) 256-6666
Acrilex, Inc., 230 Culver Ave., Jersey City 07305
Pres.—Steven R. Sullivan, 50 emp., Corporate headquarters & acrylic sheet ....................... (201) 333-1500
Acupac Packaging, Inc., 55 Ramapo Valley Rd., Mahwah 07430
GM—Stephanie Hayano, 200 emp., Contract packaging............................................ (201) 529-3434
Advance Tool & Die, Inc., 1401 Bremen Ave., Egg Harbor City 08215
Pres., GM & Opers. Mgr.—Robert C. Sullivan, 2 emp., Plastic injection molds & dies & plastic (856) 854-6329
Advanced Molding Concepts, 329 Wilson Ave., Aberdeen 07747
Owner—Mike Guglielmo, 6 emp., Custom prototypes & precision machining......................... (732) 390-8366
Air Cruisers, LLC, 1747 State Route 34, Wall Township 07727
Pres.—John O'Donnell, 250 emp., Company headquarters & inflatable survival ..................... (732) 681-3527
Alenco Fence & Supply Corp., 167 Route 70, Bldg. B, Medford 08055
Owner—Chris Murphy, 10 emp., Wooden, aluminum, chain-link & vinyl ................................. (609) 654-6060
All American Poly Corp., 40 Turner Pl., Piscataway 08854
Pres.—Jack G. Klein, 242 emp., Corporate headquarters & polyethylene ................................ (732) 752-3200
All American Recycling Corp., 2 Hope St., Jersey City 07307
Pres.—Vincent M. Ponte, 137 emp., Paper & plastic recycling, including ................................ (201) 656-3363
All Poly Mfg., LLC, 200 Craig Rd., Ste. 201, Manalapan 07726
Off. Mgr.—Jennifer Thomas, 7 emp., Plastic packaging materials ........................... (732) 431-6630
All Quality Fence, 1266 Route 46, P.O. Box 85, Ledgewood 07852
Owner—John Johnson, 6 emp., Aluminum, red & white cedar, chain-link................................ (973) 927-0722
All Seasons Door & Window, Inc., 28 Edgeboro Rd., East Brunswick 08816
Pres., CFO—Steven Yu, 30 emp., Vinyl & aluminum windows ................................ (732) 238-7100
Allgrind Plastics, Inc., 6 Vliet Farm Rd., Asbury 08802
Pres., Fin. & R & D Mgr.—Bill Willoughby, 13 emp., Custom grinding, granulating, pulverizing (908) 479-4400
Alliance Vinyl Window Co., Inc., 301 Crescent Blvd., Mount Ephraim 08059
Pres., GM & Sales Mgr.—Jeff Hersh, 45 emp., Corporate headquarters & vinyl replacement . (856) 456-4954
All-Star Pro & Sport Store, 642 State Route 35 N., Neptune 07753
Owner—Joe Storzieri, 2 emp., Trophies, plaques & textile embroidery .................................. (732) 774-3444
All-State Fence, Inc., 1389 Route 9 N., Howell 07731
Pres.—Scott Skrable, 8 emp., Residential & commercial chain-link........................................ (732) 431-4944
Alpine Elastomer Products, LLC, 308 Division St., Boonton 07005
Owner—David McCrink, 4 emp., Custom molded rubber & plastic products ........................... (973) 299-0123
Alta Technologies, Inc., 1545 Reed Rd., P.O. Box 100, Pennington 08534
Chrm., CFO—Percy F. Leaper, 7 emp., Expandable monofilament braided & fiberglass........ (609) 538-9500
Amcor Rigid Plastics, 625 Sharp St., Millville 08332
Cont.—Kara Carland, 175 emp., Plastic caps & closures ....................................... (856) 327-1540
AME Corporation, 33 Jacksonville Rd., Ste. 2, Towaco 07082
New Bus. Dev. Mgr.—Clara O'Boyle, 10 emp., Custom rubber components, including........... (800) 951-0071
American Braiding & Mfg., Inc., 247 Old Tavern Rd., Howell 07731
Pres.—Gerald Bailey, 10 emp., Mechanical compression packing...................... (732) 938-6333
American Comb Corp., 22 Kentucky Ave., Paterson 07503
Pres.—Frank Bachrach, 10 emp., Plastic combs & travel & bathroom accessories................ (973) 523-6551
American Infinity Compounding Corp., 2079 Center Square Rd., Logan Township 08085
Pres.—Carlos Carreno, 17 emp., Custom compounded plastic resins..................................... (856) 467-3030
American Marking Systems, Inc., 1015 Paulison Ave., Clifton 07011
Pres.—John Collins, 30 emp., Corporate headquarters & custom office ................................. (973) 478-5600
American Plastic Co., 2137 Highway 1, Rahway 07065
Owner—Stephen Korstein, 3 emp., Plastic sign letters & numbers ....................................... (732) 388-1601
AmerTac, Inc., 1 Route 17 S., Saddle River Executive Center, Saddle River 07458
COO—Sal Mirra, 50 emp., Decorative metal & plastic wall plates ......................................... (201) 825-0388
Anello Fence, LLC, 50 State Route 23, Pequannock 07440
Pres.—Steve Anello, 4 emp., Vinyl, aluminum & wooden fencing...................... (973) 839-4100
Aphena Pharma Solutions-NJ, Inc., 125 Algonquin Pkwy., Whippany 07981
Pres., CEO—Kevin Kerchner, 160 emp., Pharmaceutical packaging ..................................... (973) 887-4440
Apollo Flags LLC, 594 Union Blvd., Totowa 07512
Ptnr.—Albert Potenzone, 4 emp., Custom, U.S., military, state, parade ................................ (973) 256-8362
Apparel Group America, Inc., 250 Belmont Ave., Haledon 07508
Pres.—Vincent Musarra, 120 emp., Apparel screen printing & packaging................................ (973) 942-6800
ARC Plasmet Corp., 4131 Bergen Tpke., North Bergen 07047
Pres.—Tony Calana, 9 emp., Plastic fabrication & machining job ........................................ (201) 867-8533
Architectural Window Mfg., 359 Veterans Blvd., Rutherford 07070
V-P., Sales—Ken Thompson, 25 emp., Aluminum & polyurethane windows.............................. (201) 939-2200
Arizona Signs & Truck Lettering, 3121 Route 73 S., Maple Shade 08052
Owner—Jeffrey Chudoff, 5 emp., Vinyl interior & exterior signs, lettering............................. (856) 482-2288
ASI Plastic, Inc., 120 Getty Ave., Paterson 07503
Pres.—Bob Halek, 2 emp., Plastic fabrication ................................................. (973) 345-7510
Assemblies Unlimited, Inc., 530 N. Michigan Ave., Kenilworth 07033
Pres.—Randy Shaw, 100 emp., Full turnkey contract packaging & fulfillment.......................... (877) 273-6259
AVCON, 1915 Swarthmore Ave., Ste. 3, Lakewood 08701
CEO—Larry Stanley, 35 emp., Structural maintenance-free thermoplastic.............................. (732) 286-9496
B & G International, Inc., 1085 Morris Ave., Union 07083
Pres., CEO—Chet Kolton, 30 emp., Printed & die-cut plastic tags & hangers ......................... (973) 824-0334
B & W Plastics, Inc., 20 Wilson Dr., Sparta 07871
Pres., CEO, R & D Mgr.—William Post, 5 emp., Thermoformed clamshells, blister skins ........ (973) 383-0020
B&D Marketing, Inc., 1879 Old Cuthbert Rd., Ste. 21, Cherry Hill 08034
Pres.—Marlene Epworth, 5 emp., Custom donor recognition wall displays ............................. (856) 354-2004
Badge Company Of New Jersey, 223 Hamden Rd., P.O. Box 100, Annandale 08801
GM—Robert Marlow, 3 emp., Manufacturer & distributor of badges .................................... (908) 735-7700
BE & K Plastics, 340 E. Broad St., Burlington 08016
★ V-P.—Bob Shimmeng, 12 emp., Plastic food containers ................................... (609) 386-3200
Beauticraft Slipcover Co., 9 Wynnewood Dr., Voorhees 08043
Owner & V-P.—S. Davidson, 8 emp., Plastic & fabric slipcovers & window ............................ (215) 625-7979
Beauty-Fill, LLC, 170 Circle Dr. N., Piscataway 08854
★ Ptnr.—Gregory Harmon, 30 emp., Beauty care products packaging.............................. (732) 802-8200
Belleville Corp., 328 Belleville Tpke., Kearny 07032
Chrm., Pres.—Alan Gildenberg, 7 emp., Vinyl windows & doors ........................... (201) 991-6222
Belmont Wholesale Fence Mfg., 112-114 Monroe St., Garfield 07026
Manager—Joe Merchant, 19 emp., Vinyl fences & fencing materials ..................................... (973) 472-5121
Bennett Plastics, Inc., 22 Kentucky Ave., Paterson 07503
Pres.—Frank Bachrach, 50 emp., Custom plastic injection molding, including......................... (973) 684-1501

Bergen Barrel & Drum Co., 43 O'Brien St., Ste. 45, Kearny 07032
Off. Mgr.—Mary Mecka, 15 emp., *Polyethylene drums* ........ (201) 998-3500
Bergen Fence, Inc., 279 Bergen Tpke., Ridgefield Park 07660
Sales Mgr.—John Durr, 6 emp., *Wooden & vinyl fencing* ........ (201) 641-2111
Berkeley Contract Packaging, LLC, 530 N. Michigan Ave., Kenilworth 07033
Pres.—Jack Concannon, 158 emp., *Company headquarters & contract packaging* ........ (908) 810-4000
Bestwork Industries For The Blind, Inc., 1940 Almay Ave., Ste. 200, Cherry Hill 08003
Pres.—Belinda Moore, 100 emp., *Fabric safety vests, work aprons, tool* ........ (856) 939-5220
Better Home Plastics Corp., 439 Commercial Ave., Palisades Park 07650
Pres.—Ronald Haboush, 20 emp., *Plastic housewares, plastic & fabric* ........ (201) 592-0370
Better Sleep Co., Inc., 100 Readington Rd., Ste. 2, Branchburg 08876
CEO—Robert Emery, 10 emp., *Vinyl bath pillows & shower caddies* ........ (908) 393-0120
Bipore, Inc., 31 Industrial Pkwy., Northvale 07647
Pres.—Durmus Koch, 50 emp., *Plastic medical devices* ........ (201) 767-1993
Bird Toy Man, 197 S. Hillside Ave., Succasunna 07876
Owner—Henry E. Pedynowski, 1 emp., *Wooden, plastic, acrylic, leather &* ........ (973) 584-0756
Bonded Insulation Products, 657 Union Blvd., Totowa 07512
Pres.—Harvey S. Goodman, 25 emp., *Storm doors, vinyl all-welded replacement* ........ (973) 256-2120
Bright Signs, LLC, 2626 County Road 516, Old Bridge 08857
Owner—Ho Yung Yun, 2 emp., *Magnetic & commercial signs & vinyl* ........ (732) 679-7440
Brisar Industries, Inc., 150 E. 7th St., Paterson 07524
Pres.—Mark Cohen, 45 emp., *Pharmaceutical, cosmetic, R.F. & blister* ........ (973) 278-2500
Broadway Industries, 1 S. Middlesex Ave., Monroe 08831
Pres.—Albert S. Kohn, 22 emp., *Plastic upholstery & mattress covers* ........ (609) 662-3970
Bumper Specialties, Inc., 1607 Imperial Way, West Deptford 08066
Pres.—Leon Braunstein, 77 emp., *Polyurethane self adhesive bumpers* ........ (856) 251-9993
Burger & Son, Inc., Edwin R., 732 Main St., P.O. Box 184, Sewell 08080
Pres.—Edwin R. Burger, 30 emp., *Wood, chain-link, vinyl, aluminum,* ........ (856) 468-2300
C & C Signs & Banners, 812 Forepeak Dr., Forked River 08731
★ Owner—Paul Colucci, 1 emp., *Interior & exterior signs & vinyl lettering* ........ (609) 693-4667
C & K Plastics, Inc., 159 Liberty St., Metuchen 08840
Pres.—Robert Carrier, 58 emp., *Plastic thermoforming, including vacuum* ........ (732) 549-0011
C T A Mfg. Corp., 263 Veterans Blvd., Carlstadt 07072
Pres.—Michael Borghard, 40 emp., *Handtools* ........ (201) 896-1000
California Closets, 4 Gardner Rd., Ste. 5, Fairfield 07004
Ptnr.—Marty Ginsberg, 50 emp., *Melamine & MDF closets & related custom* ........ (973) 882-3800
Canary Closets & Cabinetry, 697 Rahway Ave., Union 07083
Owner—John Canary, 15 emp., *Closet organization products* ........ (908) 851-2894
Carl Sign, LLC, 1200 Madison Ave., Paterson 07503
Owner—Jim Reilly, 2 emp., *Truck lettering & interior & exterior* ........ (973) 340-0210
Cary Compounds, LLC, 5 Nicholas Ct., Dayton 08810
Pres.—Charles Cary, 25 emp., *Plastic pellets* ........ (732) 274-2626
Cases By Source, Inc., 215 Island Rd., Mahwah 07430
V-P.—Matthew Adler, 25 emp., *Aluminum, plastic & wood SKB, ATA,* ........ (201) 831-0005
Catalent Pharma Solutions, Inc. (H Q), 14 Schoolhouse Rd., Somerset 08873
Pres., CEO—John Chiminski, 377 emp., *Corporate headquarters; pharmaceuticals* ........ (732) 537-6200
Center For Educational Advancement, 11 Minneakoning Rd., Flemington 08822
Pres.—Michael Skoczek, 35 emp., *Contract pharmaceutical packaging,* ........ (908) 782-1480
Center Vocational Rehabilitation, 15 Meridian Rd., Ste. 1, Eatontown 07724
CEO—Russell Anderson, 150 emp., *Contract packaging services, including* ........ (732) 544-1800
Central Art & Engineering, Inc., 500 Goldman Dr., P.O. Box 289, Cream Ridge 08514
Pres., Hum. Res. Mgr.—John Makkay, 8 emp., *Custom plastic fabrication & cutting* ........ (609) 758-5922
Cervinis, Inc., 3656 N. Mill Rd., Vineland 08360
Pres.—Dan Cervinis, 65 emp., *Fiberglass automotive products* ........ (856) 691-1744
Champion Window Of Pennsauken, 8400 Remington Ave., Ste. B, Pennsauken 08110
Div. Mgr.—Todd Morganci, 35 emp., *Vinyl replacement windows & siding* ........ (856) 662-3400
Chatham Container Display Corp., 6 Northridge Way, Warren 07059
Pres.—James Irvine, 4 emp., *Point-of-purchase displays & packaging* ........ (800) 266-4848
Chemtura Corp., 1000 Convery Blvd., Perth Amboy 08861
MIS Mgr.—Amanda Figueroa, 80 emp., *Polyester & polyurethane materials* ........ (732) 826-6600
Cherubini Yachts, LLC, 51 Norman Ave., Riverside 08075
Pres.—David Cherubini, 5 emp., *Semi-custom mahogany, teak & fiberglass* ........ (856) 764-5319
Chromis Fiberoptics, Inc., 6 Powderhorn Dr., Warren 07059
CEO—Whitney White, 10 emp., *Perfluorinated plastic optical fibers* ........ (732) 764-0900
CK Manufacturing, Inc., 8 Gardner Rd., Fairfield 07004
Pres.—Richard Cafaro, 20 emp., *Plastic injection molds & molding* ........ (973) 808-3500
Clip Strip Corp., 343 S. River St., Hackensack 07601
Pres.—Edward D. Spitaletta, 6 emp., *Point-of-purchase merchandise & store* ........ (201) 342-9155
CMI-Promex, Inc., 7 Benjamin Green Rd., Pedricktown 08067
Pres.—Wayne Ligato, 20 emp., *Commercial machining, engineered thermoplasti* ........ (856) 351-1000
Coast To Coast Leather & Vinyl, Inc., 1 Crossman Rd. S., Sayreville 08872
Co-Pres.—Michael Ross, 10 emp., *Leather & vinyl for the automotive,* ........ (732) 525-8877
Colace Co., LLC, Thomas, 800 Grove Rd., Thorofare 08086
Pres., CEO—Thomas Colace, Jr., 120 emp., *Fresh tomato packaging* ........ (856) 384-4980
Colemax Group, LLC / Prima Cases, P.O. Box 103, Glen Rock 07452
Mng. Dir.—Richard Flashenberg, 6 emp., *Leather, synthetic & molded carrying* ........ (201) 489-1080
Colorcraft Sign Co., 400 Magnolia St., Beverly 08010
Owner—Steve Molnar, 8 emp., *Full-color graphics, vinyl, vehicle* ........ (609) 386-1115
Coloron Plastics Corp., 169 Meister Ave., Front, Somerville 08876
Pres.—Ken Kirchner, 6 emp., *Plastic pellets* ........ (908) 685-1210
Comar, LLC, 1 Comar Pl., Buena 08310
CEO—Michael Ruggieri, 265 emp., *Plastic pharmaceutical packaging &* ........ (856) 692-6100
Comet Tool Co., Inc., 651 Lambs Rd., Pitman 08071
Pres.—Frank Maatje, 80 emp., *Plastic injection molds & plastic molded* ........ (856) 256-1070
Commercial Water Sports, Inc., 28 Clermont Dr., Cape May Court House 08210
Pres.—Rob Guarini, 5 emp., *Custom commercial fiberglass 31-foot* ........ (609) 624-3404
Complete Plastic Distributors, Inc., 778 Carver Ave., Westwood 07675
Owner—Andy Kestenbaum, 5 emp., *Plastic fabrication & distributor of* ........ (201) 666-8600
CompoSecure, LLC, 500 Memorial Dr., Somerset 08873
V-P., CEO & GM—Michele Logan, 125 emp., *Material science/forensics security* ........ (908) 518-0500
Congoleum Corp., 3500 Quakerbridge Rd., P.O. Box 3127, Mercerville 08619
Pres., CEO—Robert Moran, 354 emp., *Corporate headquarters & resilient* ........ (609) 584-3000
Consolidated Container Co., LLC, 4 Pleasant Hill Rd., Monroe Township 08831
Plt. Mgr.—Tom Walker, 37 emp., *Plastic containers* ........ (609) 655-0855
Corbco, Inc., 40 Canterbury Dr., Forked River 08731
Pres.—Hipolito Paul Corbacho, 3 emp., *Plastic packaging prototyping* ........ (908) 239-3279
Cosmetics & Perfume Filling & Packaging, Inc., 30 Engelhard Dr., Monroe 08831
Pres.—Devraj Vaghani, 100 emp., *Contract manufacturing & packaging* ........ (973) 680-8900
Cospack America Corp., 3856 Park Ave., Edison 08820
Pres.—Charles Hous, 20 emp., *Contract cosmetics & skincare packaging* ........ (732) 548-5858
Couse & Bolten Co., 90 South St., Dock 5, Newark 07114
Owner, CEO & COO—Michael Nelson, 7 emp., *Manufacturer & distributor of hydraulic* ........ (973) 344-6330
Creative Industries, 1409 Astor St., P.O. Box 313, South Plainfield 07080
Pres.—Arthur Kopacc, 14 emp., *Plastic injection molds & machining* ........ (908) 561-5600
Creative Patterns & Mfg., Inc., 54 Freeman St., P.O. Box 5549, Newark 07105
Co-Pres.—David Cummins, 9 emp., *Plastic fabrication* ........ (973) 589-1391
Curbell, Inc., Plastics Div., 844 N. Lenola Rd., Ste. 6, Moorestown 08057
Admn. Mgr.—Nicole Weiss, 10 emp., *Plastic fabrication* ........ (856) 778-1100
Custom Craft Plastics, 100 King Arthurs Ct., P.O. Box 6029, North Brunswick 08902
Off. Mgr.—Tracy Geraci, 100 emp., *Plastic injection molding* ........ (732) 843-3000
Custom Gasket Mfg., 640 E. Palisade Ave., Englewood Cliffs 07632
CEO—Eric Helf, 15 emp., *Custom molded rubber & die-cut products* ........ (201) 331-6363
Custom Molders Group, 160 Meister Ave., Ste. 1, Somerville 08876
Pres.—Joseph L. Caro, 50 emp., *Plastic injection molding* ........ (908) 218-7997
Cutting Board Co., 291 Highway 22, Lebanon 08833
Ptnr. & Reg. Mgr.—Anthony Pizzelanti, 3 emp., *Standard, custom, glass, plastic &* ........ (908) 725-0187
D & D Technology, Inc., 254 Elmwood Ave., P.O. Box 3636, Union 07083
Pres.—Edward G. Varga, Jr., 8 emp., *Plastic parts* ........ (908) 688-5154
Dash Industries, Inc., 639 5th St., Lakewood 08701
Owner—Alan Dirshawitz, 2 emp., *Disposable plastic bags & tablecloths* ........ (732) 364-5850
Daysol Industries, 40 Boright Ave., Kenilworth 07033
Pres.—Dennis Polvere, 25 emp., *Plastic vacuum forming, hot stamping* ........ (908) 272-5900
Delcrest Sign Co., Inc., 1202 Haddonfield-Berlin Rd., Ste. 1, Voorhees 08043
Owner—Willy Johnson, 4 emp., *Vinyl & neon signs* ........ (856) 768-5552
DiPasquale Fence Co., 196 Route 9 N., Englishtown 07726
Plt. Mgr.—Henry DiPasquale, 12 emp., *Ornamental aluminum, wooden, PVC &* ........ (732) 536-0660
Dirory Industries, Inc., 39 Progress St., Edison 08820
Pres.—Roger Robinson, 15 emp., *Contract packaging* ........ (908) 757-6650
Diversified Precision Tooling, 143 Baker St., Dover 07801
Pres.—Bob Minahan, 1 emp., *Plastic injection molding & casting* ........ (973) 361-8545
Dixo Co., Inc., 158 Central Ave., P.O. Box 7038, Rochelle Park 07662
COO—Kenneth Schapiro, 20 emp., *Contract chemical packaging* ........ (201) 845-6000
Dolphin Industries Ltd., 2141 River Rd., P.O. Box 344, Egg Harbor City 08215
Pres.—Antonio Pacheco, 9 emp., *Fiberglass swimming pools* ........ (609) 965-5188
Dor-Win Mfg. Co., 109 Midland Ave., Elmwood Park 07407
Pres.—Marco Cangialosi, 40 emp., *Vinyl windows & doors & steel & fiberglass* ........ (201) 796-4300
DPT Lakewood, LLC, 1200 Paco Way, Bldg. 19, Lakewood 08701
Site Mgr.—Gene Ciolfi, 700 emp., *Pharmaceuticals, health care & chemical* ........ (732) 367-9000
DR Fiberglass, 2027 Route 37 E., Toms River 08753
Pres.—Daniel Brown, 3 emp., *Fiberglass decks & fabrication* ........ (732) 929-8448
Drake Corp., 154 Tices Ln., East Brunswick 08816
Pres.—Ralph Drake, 8 emp., *Polymer-composite hotel furniture,* ........ (732) 254-1530
Drapery Corp. Of America, Inc., 12-16 1st Ave., Paterson 07524
Pres.—George Holiat, 5 emp., *Draperies & shower curtains, blinds* ........ (973) 925-1200
DSM Enterprises, Inc., 132 Lewis St., Unit B-5, Eatontown 07724
Pres.—Mark Donahue, 6 emp., *Acrylic, vinyl & canvas awnings* ........ (732) 380-9779
DU Technologies, Inc., 300 W. Commercial Ave., Moonachie 07074
Pres.—Marcel Branis, 25 emp., *Insulated flexible plastic ductwork* ........ (201) 729-0070
Dynaflow Engineering, 106 Egel Ave., Middlesex 08846
Pres.—Ross Block, 5 emp., *Stainless, alloy & plastic gear pumps* ........ (732) 356-9790
E & T Plastics, 824 E. Gate Dr., Ste. E, Mount Laurel 08054
Sales Mgr.—Ed Godshalk, 8 emp., *Plastic fabrication* ........ (856) 787-0900
E T Mfg., Inc., 90 Dayton Ave., Bldg. 10-C, Ste. 89, Passaic 07055
Pres.—Michele Albo, 37 emp., *Vinyl heat sealing & products, including* ........ (973) 777-6662
East Coast Plastics, Inc., 427 Commerce Ln., Ste. 7, West Berlin 08091
Pres., CFO—David Lorenz, 14 emp., *Plastic injection molding for consumer* ........ (856) 768-8700
Easter Seal Society Of New Jersey, 133 Main St., Franklin 07416
Site Mgr.—Peggy Skipp, 70 emp., *Contract packaging* ........ (973) 827-9066
Easter Seals New Jersey (H Q), 9 Terminal Rd., New Brunswick 08901
CEO—Brian Fitzgerald, 55 emp., *Company headquarters; contract assembly* ........ (732) 257-6662
Easy Pak Services Of New Jersey, 6 Nicholas Ct., P.O. Box 676, Dayton 08810
Pres.—Victor Veston, 28 emp., *Cardboard & plastic packaging materials* ........ (732) 274-2428
Echo Molding, Inc., 911 Springfield Rd., Union 07083
Pres.—Dieter Hekler, 40 emp., *Custom injection molded plastic products* ........ (908) 688-0099
Econo-PAK, 1 Wiebel Plz., Sussex 07461
Bookkeeper & Hum. Res. Mgr.—Vicky Ingrassellino, 200 emp., *Contract packaging services* (973) 875-0990
ElviPharma, LLC, 60 Ethel Rd. W., Piscataway 08854
CEO—Yovanny Garcia, 10 emp., *Contract pharmaceutical packaging services* ........ (732) 433-5591
Emerson Fence, Inc., 10 Lincoln Blvd., P.O. Box 306, Emerson 07630
Pres.—Robert Skrable, Jr., 20 emp., *Manufacturer & distributor of custom* ........ (201) 265-5150
EMI Yoshi, Inc., 1200 Jersey Ave., North Brunswick 08902
Ptnr.—Harry Meisels, 21 emp., *Premium disposable plastic servingware* ........ (732) 248-5533
Endot Industries, Inc., 60 Green Pond Rd., Rockaway 07866
Chrm.—Gary Wellmann, 50 emp., *Corporate headquarters & HDPE plastic* ........ (973) 625-8500
Engineered Plastic Products, Inc., 269 Mercer St., P.O. Box 196, Stirling 07980
Pres. & Sales Mgr.—Christopher Ratti, 20 emp., *Custom thermoplastic vacuum forming* ........ (908) 647-3500
Engineering Laboratories, Inc., 360 W. Oakland Ave., Oakland 07436
Pres.—Daniel S. Mason, 30 emp., *Plastic industrial balls, beads & small* ........ (201) 337-8116
Essex Fence Co., 132 U.S. Highway 46, Rockaway 07866
Ptnr.—George Lenar, 17 emp., *PVC vinyl, ornamental aluminum, wood* ........ (973) 625-4122
Ethylene Atlantic Corp., 136 Church St., P.O. Box 430, Swedesboro 08085
Pres.—Michael Johnston, 20 emp., *Plastic & metal fabrication* ........ (856) 467-0010
Ever-Ready Media Packaging, P.O. Box 40, Haworth 07641
Pres.—Marshall Weingarden, 5 emp., *Contract media packaging, including* ........ (973) 566-9333
Exothermic Molding, Inc., 50 Lafayette Pl., Kenilworth 07033
Pres., R & D Mgr.—Paul K. Steck, 17 emp., *Reaction injection molding, contract* ........ (908) 272-2299
E-Z Do, Inc., 40 Executive Ave., Edison 08817
Pres., CEO—Mark S. Densen, 150 emp., *Houseware products, including bath,* ........ (732) 287-8111
F & S Produce Co., Inc., 913 Bridgeton Ave., P.O. Box 489, Rosenhayn 08352
CEO—Salvatore Pipitone, Jr., 600 emp., *Fruit & vegetable processing & packaging* ........ (856) 453-0316
Federal Plastics Corp., 570 South Ave. E., Ste. F-1, Cranford 07016
Pres.—Peter T. Triano, 10 emp., *Compounder & distributor of thermoplastics* ........ (908) 272-5800
Fibrenetics, Inc., 2 Cutters Dock Rd., Woodbridge 07095
★ Owner—Herbert Segars, 10 emp., *Fiberglass tanks & metal pipe fabrication* ........ (732) 636-5670
Fitzpak, Inc., 110 Melrich Rd., Ste. 2, Cranbury 08512
Pres., CFO & Pers. Mgr.—Andrew Fitzsimmons, 37 emp., *Plastic thermoforming* ........ (609) 860-0095
Five Star Building Products, Inc., 2012 86th St., North Bergen 07047
Pres.—Daniel Politi, 15 emp., *Aluminum & vinyl doors & windows* ........ (201) 869-4181
Flex Craft Co., 814 Asbury Ave., Asbury Park 07712
Pres.—Russell Smith, 60 emp., *Plastic blow molding & injection molding* ........ (732) 502-9500
Flex Moulding, Inc., 112 Wells Ave., Jersey City 07306
GM—Al Smith, 15 emp., *Cast polyester mouldings, preformed* ........ (201) 360-3634
Flexcon Products Corp., 200 Connell Dr., Ste. 1200, Berkeley Heights 07922
Pres., GM & Plt. Mgr.—Stephen M. Beckerman, 50 emp., *Plastic storage containers* ........ (908) 871-7000

Fluorotherm Polymers, Inc., 333 New Rd., Ste. 1, Parsippany 07054
Pres., CEO—P. N. Shukla, 12 emp., *Immersion coil, shell & tube corrosion* ........ (973) 575-0760
Fordion Packaging Ltd., 185 Linden St., Hackensack 07601
Owner—Francis Harvey, 15 emp., *Plastic bags* ........ (201) 692-1344
Forem Packaging, Inc., 2-44 Cornelia St., P.O. Box 50090, Newark 07105
V-P., GM—Howard N. Slade, 18 emp., *Flexible packaging materials* ........ (973) 589-0402
Forty-Nine Corp., 34 Waite St., Paterson 07524
Pres.—Rhoda Temkin, 2 emp., *PVC laminate & vinyl safety products* ........ (973) 754-0313
Fram Trak Industries, Inc., 205 Hallock Ave., Middlesex 08846
Pres., CEO—Al Santelli, Sr., 50 emp., *Custom & stock plastic extrusions &* ........ (732) 424-8400
Frame-A-Coin Mfg., 318 Front St., Ste. 1, Belvidere 07823
Pres.—Andrew Lewis, 6 emp., *American-made high-grade plastic sleeves/hold* (973) 822-0094
Frederiks Machine & Tool, Inc., 99 Kingwood Stockton Rd., P.O. Box 247, Rosemont 08556
Pres.—Peter Frederiks, 5 emp., *Hydraulic fittings & general machining* ........ (609) 397-4991
Freedom Fence & Building Products, 168 Wabash Ave., Paterson 07503
Owner—Sal Anello, 5 emp., *Vinyl fences, decks & railings* ........ (973) 345-0911
Friend Skoler & Co., Inc. (H Q), 160 Pehle Ave., Ste. 303, Saddle Brook 07663
CFO & Dir., Portfolio Mgmt.—Gregory P. Sullivan, 10 emp., *Holding company headquarters & private* . (201) 712-0075
Frisch Plastics Corp., 81 Windsor Dr., Pine Brook 07058
Pres.—Ruth Lefkowitz, 20 emp., *Plastic injection molding* ........ (973) 685-5936
FRP Corp., 15 Hoskier Rd., South Orange 07079
Pres.—Alan M. Tarnow, 11 emp., *Custom molded fiberglass protection* ........ (973) 763-5496
G R Office Products, Inc., 11 Kentucky Ave., Paterson 07503
Pres.—Bernardo Guterman, 2 emp., *Floor mats, fabric-wrapped tackboards* ........ (973) 345-2769
Garan Electronics, Inc., 223 Stirling Rd., Unit C, Warren 07059
Mng. Ptnr.—Robert Mills, 10 emp., *Plastic electronic hardware, including* ........ (908) 484-7100
Garden State Foliage, LLC, 600 Central Ave., Farmingdale 07727
Ptnr.—Neil M. Roth, 20 emp., *Christmas decorations, dried foliage* ........ (732) 751-0075
Gecko Graphics, Inc., 128 Berlin Cross Keys Rd., Williamstown 08094
Pres.—Alice Gorney, 3 emp., *Laser engraving on acrylic, plastics* ........ (856) 740-9042
General Pallet, LLC, 97 River Rd., Flemington 08822
Ptnr.—Donald W. Baldwin, 7 emp., *New & reconditioned wooden, plastic* ........ (908) 238-1000
Generant Co., Inc., 1865 Route 23 S., P.O. Box 768, Butler 07405
V-P.—Dino D'Onofrio, 140 emp., *Pressure regulating valves & instrument* ........ (973) 838-6500
Genesis Biotechnology Group (H Q), 1000 Waterview Dr., Hamilton 08691
CEO—Eli Mordechai, 950 emp., *Company headquarters; disposable plastic* ........ (609) 786-2800
Ginsey Industries, Inc., 2078 Center Square Rd., Swedesboro 08085
Pres., CEO—Herb Briggs, 100 emp., *Decorative kitchen & bathroom products* ........ (856) 933-1300
Glitterex Corp., 7 Commerce Dr., Cranford 07016
Pres.—Babu Shetty, 44 emp., *Plastic & aluminum glitters* ........ (908) 272-9121
Globe Scientific, Inc., 610 Winters Ave., Paramus 07652
Pres.—Milton Diamond, 45 emp., *Laboratory plastic ware, glassware* ........ (201) 599-1400
GMB North America, Inc., 100 Herrod Blvd., Dayton 08810
Pres.—Ben Koo, 50 emp., *Water pumps* ........ (609) 655-2422
Golden Plastics, Inc., 510-A Industrial Ave., Teterboro 07608
Pres., CFO—Henry Kim, 8 emp., *Plastic bags & contract packaging* ........ (201) 393-9833
Goodyear Rubber Products Corp., 1583 Livingston Ave., Ste. 4, North Brunswick 08902
Pres.—Andrew Warga, 6 emp., *Rubber & plastic hose, conveyor belting* ........ (732) 448-1111
GPS Specialty Doors, Inc., 90 Dayton Ave., Unit 4-B, Passaic 07055
Pres.—Fred Bolio, 50 emp., *Hangar, acoustic, air plenum, reverberation* ........ (973) 778-6200
Graph Corr, LLC, 4 Corn Rd., Dayton 08810
Cont.—John Daly, 26 emp., *Litho laminated sheets & finished cartons* ........ (732) 355-0088
Graphic Express Menu Co., Inc., 200 Clifton Blvd., Ste. 6, Clifton 07011
Cust. Serv. Rep.—Anissa High, 30 emp., *Menu covers* ........ (973) 685-0022
Graphic Solutions & Signs, LLC, 82 Burlews Ct., Hackensack 07601
★ Member—Felipe Alarcon, 18 emp., *Interior & exterior signs & vinyl lettering* ........ (201) 343-7446
Grewe Plastics, Inc., 123 S. 15th St., Newark 07107
Dir., Sales & Mktg.—Allen Blum, 10 emp., *Plastic fabrication* ........ (973) 485-7602
Guardian Fence Co., Inc., 180 Wright St., P.O. Box 2009, Newark 07114
Pres.—Nancy Maccarelli, 20 emp., *Chain-link, wooden & vinyl fencing* ........ (973) 824-1850
Hamilton Transit Corporate Center, 572 Whitehead Rd., Trenton 08619
GM—Pete Horvath, 10 emp., *Molded fiberglass products* ........ (609) 587-1188
Hard Rock Marble & Granite, Inc., 1101 Chestnut St., Roselle 07203
CEO—N. Ruby Renjen, 12 emp., *Custom marble & granite fabrication* ........ (908) 620-9150
Hathaway Plastics, Inc., 911 Springfield Rd., Union 07083
Pres.—Robert Daniel, 3 emp., *Plastic molded point-of-purchase displays* ........ (908) 688-9494
Hays Sheet Metal, Inc., 7070 Kaighns Ave., Bldg. B, Pennsauken 08109
Pres.—Michael P. Hays, 35 emp., *HVAC & fiberglass duct systems* ........ (856) 662-7722
Heyco Products, Inc., 1800 Industrial Way N., Toms River 08755
Pres.—Bill Jemison, Jr., 150 emp., *Plastic electrical parts, metal stampings* ........ (732) 286-4336
Hoffman Precision Plastics, Inc., 548 Almonesson Rd., P.O. Box 338, Blackwood 08012
Pres.—Robert J. Hoffman, Sr., 8 emp., *Custom plastic injection molding &* ........ (856) 228-3550
Homestead Fence Contractors, LLC, 637 Main St., West Creek 08092
Pres.—Nathan Foote, 14 emp., *Wooden & PVC fences & prefabricated* ........ (609) 296-1829
Honeyware, Inc., 244 Dukes St., Kearny 07032
Chrm. & CEO—Tony Sheng, 60 emp., *Plastic injection molding, tooling* ........ (201) 997-5900
Hudson Community Enterprises, 780 Montgomery St., Jersey City 07306
Pres.—Joe Brown, 65 emp., *Contract packaging* ........ (201) 432-5959
Hyde Co., A. L., 1 Main St., P.O. Box 62, Grenloch 08032
Cont.—Dennis Palludino, 90 emp., *Extruded plastic products* ........ (856) 227-0500
Icy Cools, Inc., 15 Oscar Dr., P.O. Box 686, Roosevelt 08555
CEO—Paul Wojnicki, 10 emp., *Reusable hot/cold mats for the healthcare* ........ (609) 448-0172
Ideal Window Mfg., Inc., 100 W. 7th St., Bayonne 07002
CFO—Carlene Balance, 130 emp., *Vinyl windows & doors* ........ (201) 437-4300
Imagine Corp., The, 320 N. 6th St., Prospect Park 07508
Cust. Serv. Mgr.—Julie Ann Karr, 15 emp., *Plastic products* ........ (973) 942-2888
Imco Reinforced Plastics, Inc., 858 N. Lenola Rd., Moorestown 08057
GM & MIS Mgr.—Henry W. Regan, 20 emp., *Fiberglass products* ........ (856) 235-7254
Injection Works, Inc., 104 Gaither Dr., Mount Laurel 08054
Owner—Chris Rapacki, 25 emp., *Plastic injection molding* ........ (856) 802-6444
Injectron Corp., 1000 S. 2nd St., P.O. Box 3012, Plainfield 07063
Pres.—Louis M. Pollak, 100 emp., *Plastic injection molding* ........ (908) 753-1990
Inman Mold & Mfg. Co., 815 Martin St., P.O. Box 1143, Rahway 07065
Pres.—Glen Barlics, 7 emp., *Short & long-run plastic injection* ........ (732) 381-6229
Innovative Resin Systems, Inc., 257 Wilson Ave., Newark 07105
Pres.—Pinakin Patel, 15 emp., *Custom epoxy, polyurethane & acrylic* ........ (973) 465-6887
Intech Corp., 250 Herbert Ave., Closter 07624
Pres.—Georg Bartosch, 7 emp., *Self-lubricating plastic non-hygroscopic* ........ (201) 767-8066
Intek Plastics, Inc., 150 5th Ave., Hawthorne 07506
GM & Sales Mgr.—Joseph S. Ganguzza, 35 emp., *Custom & stock plastic profile extrusions*. (973) 427-7331
Interlink Products International, Inc., 1315 E. Elizabeth Ave., Linden 07036
Pres.—Eli Zhadanov, 10 emp., *Plastic injection molding* ........ (908) 862-8090

International Foam Products, Inc., P.O. Box 545, Stanhope 07874
Cont., Plt. Mgr.—Kathy Ferris, 8 emp., *Textile & fiberfill laminating for* ........ (201) 909-0950
Interplex NAS Inc., Beta Div., 232 Pegasus Ave., Northvale 07647
Dir., Bus. Dev.—Joe Praino, 70 emp., *Metal stampings & plastic injection* ........ (201) 367-1300
INTEX Millwork Solutions, LLC, 20 Bogden Blvd., Millville 08332
Owner—Joe Umosella, 20 emp., *Custom PVC millwork, including pergola* ........ (856) 293-4100
IPAK, Inc, 301 Grove Rd., West Deptford 08086
Mng. Ptnr.—Sheryl Schreiber, 90 emp., *Contract printing & packaging* ........ (856) 486-0066
Iron Mountain Plastics, Inc., 112 Greenwood Ave., Midland Park 07432
Pres.—Richard Ver Hage, 19 emp., *Laboratory plastics* ........ (201) 445-0063
Ironbound Trophy Center, 289 Lafayette St., Ste. A, Newark 07105
Owner—Christine Naia, 3 emp., *Trophies & plaques & acrylics, corporate* ........ (973) 344-3872
ITW Thielex, 95 Commerce Dr., Somerset 08873
GM—Henry Swain, 60 emp., *Plastic electronics tubes* ........ (732) 873-5500
Ivo Delicious Meat Products, Inc., 206 Dayton Ave., Passaic 07055
★ Pres.—Ivelin Naydenov, 4 emp., *Beef & pork processing & packaging* ........ (973) 223-4044
J & J Engraving, 45 Worth St., South Hackensack 07606
Owner—Joseph Polifronio, Jr., 1 emp., *Plastic & metal engraving & screen* ........ (201) 342-0798
J M J Printing & Graphics, Inc., 1403 State Route 23, Ste. 8, Butler 07405
Pres.—Debby Greenberg, 20 emp., *Printing & contract packaging* ........ (973) 838-3400
J M J Profile, Inc., 154 Copper Rd., Unit 1303, West Berlin 08091
Pres.—Joseph Colachi, 12 emp., *Plastic fabrication* ........ (856) 767-3930
J. Josephson, Inc., 35 Horizon Blvd., South Hackensack 07606
Pres.—Mark Goodman, 150 emp., *Contract wall coverings* ........ (201) 440-7000
James Alexander Corp., 845 State Route 94, Blairstown 07825
Pres.—Francesca Fazzolari, 100 emp., *Contract packaging, including crushable* ........ (908) 362-9266
Jason Furniture & Plastic Covers, Inc., 334 State St., Perth Amboy 08861
Pres.—Jason Perez, 2 emp., *Plastic furniture slipcovers* ........ (732) 442-9700
Jerhel Plastics, Inc. (H Q), 63 New Hook Rd., Bayonne 07002
Pres.—Leonard Mecca, 10 emp., *Corporate headquarters; plastic injection* ........ (201) 436-6662
Jersey Cover Corp., 1746 Lakewood Rd., Toms River 08755
Pres.—Kathleen Stern, 10 emp., *Swimming pool safety covers* ........ (732) 286-6300
Jersey Windows & Building Supplies, 831 Broadway, Newark 07104
Store Mgr.—Will Zapata, 2 emp., *Vinyl & aluminum windows & vinyl siding* ........ (973) 482-3614
JerseyCarts, LLC, 6 Whiskey Ln., Flemington 08822
Owner—Greg Merrigan, 1 emp., *Golf carts, vinyl banners & signs* ........ (908) 806-6400
Jewel Precision Sheet Metal Machining, Inc., 200 Commerce Rd., Cedar Grove 07009
Pres.—Ignazio Graziano, 75 emp., *Sheet metal & plastic fabrication,* ........ (973) 857-5545
Jim's Signs, 1400 Rahway Ave., Ste. 3, Avenel 07001
Owner & Pres.—Jim Petrocy, 10 emp., *Plastic & reflective safety, ADA, room* ........ (732) 381-8700
J-Mac Plastics, Inc., 40 Lafayette Pl., Kenilworth 07033
Pres.—John McNamara, 17 emp., *Plastic injection molding* ........ (908) 709-1111
Joffe Lumber & Supply, Inc., 18 Burns Ave., Vineland 08360
CEO—Sol G. Joffe, 50 emp., *Wooden & vinyl windows, steel & interior* ........ (856) 825-9550
Johns Manville, 1000 Liddle Ave., Edison 08837
Plt. Mgr.—Mark Sessler, 50 emp., *Fiberglass insulation & plastic coverings* ........ (732) 225-9190
K & A Industries, Inc., 51 Cragwood Rd., Ste. 204, South Plainfield 07080
Pres.—George Keelty, 8 emp., *Identification badges, identity management* ........ (908) 226-7000
Kappus Plastics Co., Inc., 61-65 Route 31 S., P.O. Box 151, Hampton 08827
GM—Kathleen Herbert, 50 emp., *Plastic sheeting* ........ (908) 537-2288
Kayden Mfg., Inc., 83-A Burlews Ct., Hackensack 07601
Owner & Pres.—Jeff Kayden, 5 emp., *Vinyl swimming pool liners & sheet* ........ (201) 880-9898
Kayline Processing, Inc., 31 Coates St., Trenton 08611
V-P., R & D & Sales—Harley Hoffman, 30 emp., *Vinyl printing, laminating & embossing* ........ (609) 695-1440
KB Acrylics, Inc., I-295 Industrial Ctr., Bldg. B, Box 47, Westville 08093
Pres.—Ben Bonaccorso, 5 emp., *Acrylic fabrication & machining, oven* ........ (856) 589-3110
Kearny Steel Container Corp., 401 South St., Newark 07105
Pres.—Michael Verzaleno, 75 emp., *Reconditioned & new steel, fiber &* ........ (973) 589-2070
Kendall Mfg. Co., Inc., 1366 Chews Landing Rd., Clementon 08021
Owner—James W. Strater, 3 emp., *Vinyl & wooden windows & doors & retractable* ........ (856) 227-2132
Ketec, Inc., 1256 N. Church St., Ste. A, Moorestown 08057
Pres.—George Kaltner, 14 emp., *Theft-prevention tags & detection systems* ........ (856) 778-4343
Kin Core, 70 North St., P.O. Box 485, Bloomsbury 08804
Pres.—John Haday, 2 emp., *Plastic products* ........ (908) 479-1188
Koba Corp., 60 Baekeland Ave., Middlesex 08846
Pres.—Franz Bach, 17 emp., *Plastic flower pots* ........ (732) 469-0110
Label Graphics Mfg., 315 Fairfield Rd., Unit 1, Fairfield 07004
V-P. & Off. Mgr.—Denise Silvano, 10 emp., *Pressure-sensitive labels & flexible* ........ (973) 890-5665
Laird Plastics, Inc., 135 Fieldcrest Ave., Ste. 135-F, Edison 08837
GM—J. J. Duberville, 20 emp., *Plastic see-thru, mechanical & corrosive* ........ (732) 593-2777
Lanco York, Inc., 864 E. 25th St., Paterson 07513
CEO—Mitchell J. Leibowitz, 25 emp., *Primary & secondary pharmaceutical-grade* ........ (973) 278-7400
Lawrence Mold and Tool Corp., 1412 Ohio Ave., Lawrenceville 08648
Owner—George Lesenskyj, 25 emp., *Plastic injection molding & tool &* ........ (609) 392-5422
Leco Plastics, Inc., 130 Gamewell St., Hackensack 07601
Pres.—Barry Schwartz, 9 emp., *Plastic extrusions & molding* ........ (201) 343-3330
Life Of The Party, LLC, 832 Ridgewood Ave., Ste. 4, North Brunswick 08902
Pres.—Carole Krinsky, 15 emp., *Plastic candy & craft molds* ........ (732) 828-0886
LittleGifts, Inc. (H Q), 600 Meadowlands Pkwy., Ste. 131, Secaucus 07094
CEO—Rishi Gupta, 12 emp., *Corporate headquarters; pet-themed* ........ (212) 868-2559
LMT Mercer Group, Inc., 690 Puritan Ave., Lawrence Township 08648
Pres.—Anthony Lesensky, 45 emp., *Vinyl fence, deck & railing components* ........ (609) 989-0399
LNS Industries, Inc., P.O. Box 98, Somers Point 08244
Pres.—Lisa Fasola, 5 emp., *Water-saving plastic toilet plumbing* ........ (609) 927-6656
LOR-TECH Plastics, LLC, 3 Eastmans Rd., Unit 3, Parsippany 07054
Pres.—Nada A. Koch, 4 emp., *Custom plastic injection molding for* ........ (973) 503-1750
M. S. Plastics Packaging Co., Inc., 10 Park Pl., Bldg. 2-1A-2, Butler 07405
Pres.—Al Saraisky, 15 emp., *Plastic film & bag packaging* ........ (973) 492-2400
Madan Plastics, Inc., 108 N. Union Ave., Ste. 3, Cranford 07016
GM—Michael Madan, 50 emp., *Plastic injection molding, pizza dough* ........ (908) 276-8484
Margola Corp., 232 S. Van Brunt St., Englewood 07631
Owner—Neil Chalfin, 6 emp., *Manufacturer & distributor of rhinestones* ........ (201) 816-9500
Marleen, Inc., 1101 N. 10th St., P.O. Box 70, Millville 08332
Pres.—Preston Hickman, 15 emp., *Contract packaging* ........ (856) 327-8281
Marlo Plastic Products, Inc., 289 State Route 33, Manalapan 07726
Pres., R & D Mgr.—Arthur Livingston, 40 emp., *Soft vinyl plastic products* ........ (732) 792-1984
Marlow Candy & Nut Co., 65 Honeck St., Englewood 07631
Owner—Mike Serpin, 25 emp., *Contract & private label packaging* ........ (201) 569-7606
Master Wire Mfg., Inc., 1019 Black Horse Pike, Route 322, P.O. Box 328, Hammonton 08037
Pres.—Geraldine Hefferon, 16 emp., *Chain-link & PVC fencing & ornamental* ........ (609) 567-1616
MAUSER USA LLC, 35 Cotters Ln., Ste. C, East Brunswick 08816
Pres., CEO—Jeff Simmonds, 80 emp., *Company headquarters & plastic containers* ........ (732) 353-7000

McGrory Glass, Inc., 1400 Grandview Ave., Paulsboro 08066
CEO, CFO—John McGrory, 35 emp., *Flat glass & plastic fabrication* ........ (856) 579-3200
MCT Dairies, Inc., 15 Bleeker St., Millburn 07041
Pres., CEO—Kenneth Meyers, 11 emp., *Corporate headquarters & wholesaler* ........ (973) 258-9600
Meadowbrook Inventions, Inc., 260 Mine Brook Rd., P.O. Box 960, Bernardsville 07924
Pres.—Harold Sutton, 42 emp., *Polyester, metal & heat fusible fiber* ........ (908) 766-0606
MEC TECH, Inc., 2200 Industrial Way S., Toms River 08755
Pres.—Richard Kulkaski, 30 emp., *Plastic injection molding & semiconductor* ........ (732) 505-0308
Medical Packaging, Inc., 470 Route 31, P.O. Box 500, Ringoes 08551
CEO—Andy Bartels, 20 emp., *Pharmacy oral solids & liquid packaging* ........ (609) 466-8991
MedPlast Group, 225 Old Egg Harbor Rd., West Berlin 08091
Cont.—Sandra Hall, 180 emp., *Plastic injection molding* ........ (856) 753-7600
Meese Orbitron Dunne Co., 535 N. Midland Ave., Saddle Brook 07663
Plt. Mgr.—Patrick Barry, 12 emp., *Plastic rotational molding & material* ........ (201) 796-4667
Mega Fortris Americas, Inc., 3 Chris Ct., P.O. Box 934, Dayton 08810
★ Owner—Claus Holmelund, 7 emp., *Plastic security seals & boxes for* ........ (732) 230-3015
Menshen Packaging U.S.A., Inc., 21 Industrial Park, Waldwick 07463
V-P., Opers. & Sales—Rogelio Ayala, 78 emp., *Custom plastic injection molding &* ........ (201) 445-7436
Merit Trophies & Engraving, Inc., 184 Main St., Hackensack 07601
V-P., GM—Jim Dolack, 5 emp., *Laser engraving of signs, plaques,* ........ (201) 487-5780
Merlin Industries, Inc., 2904 E. State Street Ext., Hamilton 08619
Pres.—Andrew Maggion, 200 emp., *Vinyl pool covers, liners & safety* ........ (609) 807-1000
Method Assocs., Inc., 120 Francis St., Ste. 2, Keyport 07735
Pres., Plt. Mgr.—Malcom Will, 20 emp., *Contract packaging* ........ (732) 888-0444
Metropole, Inc., 214 Clifton Blvd., Clifton 07011
Pres.—David Finlay, 10 emp., *Custom exterior terra cotta, granite* ........ (973) 473-2727
Mfrs. Aid, Inc., 425 Whitehead Ave., South River 08882
Pres.—Deborah Gildersleeve, 10 emp., *Contract packaging* ........ (732) 613-6555
Micro Molding, Inc., 65 Howard St., Phillipsburg 08865
Chrm.—Gerald Detweiler, 40 emp., *Plastic injection molding* ........ (908) 454-1225
Microcast Technologies Corp., 1611 W. Elizabeth Ave., Linden 07036
Pres.—Dean Fuschetti, 120 emp., *Metal plating, plastic injection molding* ........ (908) 523-9503
Mid-Continent Packaging Co., Inc. (H Q), 55 Jacobus Ave., 1st Fl., Kearny 07032
Pres.—Mark Epstein, 60 emp., *Corporate headquarters; chemical packaging* ........ (973) 589-3544
Miller & Sons, Inc., I. V., 15 Cindy Ln., Ocean 07712
Pres., CFO—George H. Miller, 18 emp., *Metallizing of plastic packaging components* ........ (732) 493-4040
Mira Plastics Co., Inc., 1 Mira Ave., Fredon Twp., P. O. Box 399, Newton 07860
Pres.—Anthony Miragliotta, 25 emp., *Thermoplastic injection molding, hot* ........ (973) 383-6380
Missry Assocs., Inc., 100 S. Washington Ave., Dunellen 08812
Pres.—Edward Missry, 200 emp., *Home & garden decorative accessories* ........ (732) 752-7500
Modelsmith International, Inc., 66 Willow Ave., 2nd Fl., Hoboken 07030
Pres.—Karol Popek, 5 emp., *Steel, wood & acrylic fabrication,* ........ (201) 714-9519
Modern Fence & Construction, LLC, 1527 Livingston Ave., North Brunswick 08902
Pres.—Kenneth Walewski, 3 emp., *Manufacturer & wholesaler of PVC &* ........ (732) 238-5588
Modern International Corp., 145 Cliffwood Ave., Cliffwood 07721
Pres., GM—Daniel Stern, 20 emp., *Wire, steel & plastic strapping, packaging* ........ (732) 696-9100
Molded Fiberglass Products, 3 Industry Ct., Trenton 08638
Pres.—Ken Sutter, 3 emp., *Fiberglass products fabrication* ........ (609) 538-8822
Monarch Art Plastics, LLC, 3838 Church Rd., Mount Laurel 08054
CEO—William Shanley, 25 emp., *Custom plastics printing & fabrication* ........ (856) 235-5151
Montrose Molders Corp., 25 Howard St., Piscataway 08854
CEO—William H. Wilson, 163 emp., *Plastic moldings* ........ (908) 754-3030
Morton Salt, Inc., 920 High St., Perth Amboy 08861
Off. Admn.—Sharon Mohan, 30 emp., *Salt packaging* ........ (732) 826-3595
Mountain Lion, Inc., 9 Voorhees Ct., P.O. Box 799, Pennington 08534
Pres.—John Monteleone, 1 emp., *Book printing, binding & packaging* ........ (609) 730-1665
Mr. B. Fence Co., 325 Stokes Ave., Trenton 08638
Pres.—Rob Barbiero, 10 emp., *PVC & wooden fence panels & installation* ........ (609) 882-1896
Mr. Ice Bucket, LLC, 345 Sandford St., New Brunswick 08901
Pres.—Fred Haleluk, 5 emp., *Vinyl cover ice buckets & trays* ........ (732) 545-0420
Mulberry Metal Products, Inc., 2199 Stanley Ter., Union 07083
CFO—Patricia Lynch, 100 emp., *Metal & plastic wallplates & weatherproof* ........ (908) 688-8850
Multi-Pak Packaging, 19 Spielman Rd., Fairfield 07004
Pres.—John Culligan, 100 emp., *Contract packaging of pharmaceuticals* ........ (973) 439-1182
Murphy Fence Co., Inc., 507 Seashore Rd., Cape May 08204
CEO—Amy Litton, 25 emp., *Wooden, PVC & aluminum fencing & PVC* ........ (609) 886-1635
N.J. Plastics Machining & Fabricating, Inc., 46 Liverpool Ave., P.O. Box 646, Egg Harbor City 08215
Pres.—Don Magdon, 3 emp., *Plastic products, including cup holders* ........ (609) 965-1550
Nal-Pak Paper Specialties, LLC, 18 Monterey Ln., Englishtown 07726
Pres.—Murray Kaplan, 5 emp., *Clear poly film & waxed paper die cutting* ........ (732) 462-5196
NEAC, Inc., 526 Pacific Ave., #2202, Atlantic City 08401
Pres.—Joel H. Miller, 5 emp., *Contract manufacturing of metal & plastic* ........ (908) 903-9100
Nelson Custom Case Co., 1014 State Route 173, Bloomsbury 08804
Owner—William A. Nelson III, 3 emp., *ATA style custom cases, including LED* ........ (908) 479-6902
New Brunswick Lamp Shade Co., 7 Terminal Rd., New Brunswick 08901
CEO—Paul Zankel, 20 emp., *Lampshades* ........ (732) 545-0377
New York Corrugated Box Co., LLC, 239 Lindberg Pl., Ste. 1, Paterson 07503
Owner—Robert Rosner, 5 emp., *Corrugated boxes & packaging supplies* ........ (973) 742-5000
Newark Liner & Washer, Inc., 819 Broadway, Newark 07104
Pres.—Avelina Figueroa, 28 emp., *Bottle cap liners* ........ (973) 482-5400
Newton T & M Corp., 119 Fredon Springdale Rd., Newton 07860
Pres., Plt. Mgr.—Ralph Meola, 8 emp., *Plastic injection molding & molds* ........ (973) 383-1232
Nexus Plastics, Inc., 1 Loretto Ave., Hawthorne 07506
Pres., CEO—Marwan Sholakh, 90 emp., *Corporate headquarters & poly packaging* ........ (973) 427-3311
Ninsa Vinyl Fence, LLC, 125 Lincoln St., Hammonton 08037
Owner—Greg Fondacaro, 8 emp., *Vinyl fence sections, posts, gates* ........ (609) 561-5397
North America Packaging Corp. (NAMPAC), 7 Wheeling Rd., Dayton 08810
Plt. Mgr.—Tamlin Ferguson, 140 emp., *Plastic pails & lids* ........ (732) 997-4100
Northwest Essex Community Healthcare Network, Inc., 83 Walnut St., Montclair 07042
GM & Prod. Mgr.—William Delorenzo, 125 emp., *Contract assembly, packaging & screen* ........ (973) 744-7733
Novembal U. S. A., A Tetra Pak Co., 3 Greek Ln., Edison 08817
Plt. Mgr.—John Famiglietti, 62 emp., *Plastic bottle closures (caps) for* ........ (732) 287-4949
O K Tool & Die Co., 603 Bluebell Rd., Williamstown 08094
Pres.—Kenneth Ostapovich, 15 emp., *Plastic products & tool & die job shop* ........ (856) 629-5757
Occupational Center, The, 301 Cox St., Roselle 07203
Pres., CEO—Michele Ford, 350 emp., *Contract packaging & assembly* ........ (908) 241-7200
Occupational Training Center, 215 W. White Horse Pike, Berlin 08009
Ex. Dir.—Loret McClain, 35 emp., *Contract assembly & packaging, including* ........ (856) 768-0845
Ocean City Vinyl Fence Co., Inc., 719 Haven Ave., Ocean City 08226
Pres.—Harry Williams, 5 emp., *Vinyl fencing & railing* ........ (609) 399-8288

Oliner Fibre Co., Inc., 2391 Vauxhall Rd., P.O. Box 308, Union 07083
Pres.—Andrew Oliner, 22 emp., *Plastic extrusions & fiberboard cutting* ........ (908) 688-5800
Omni W.C., Inc., 166 National Rd., Edison 08817
Pres., Fin. & GM—Gary Tumminello, 18 emp., *Paper & vinyl wall coverings* ........ (732) 248-0999
Oppenheim Plastics Co., Inc., 90 Broadway, Woodcliff Lake 07677
Pres.—Florence Oppenheim, 30 emp., *Plastic injection molded rigid boxes* ........ (201) 391-3811
Organize It All, Inc., 24 River St., Ste. 201, Bogota 07603
Pres.—James Lee, 30 emp., *Corporate headquarters & plastic housewares* ........ (201) 488-0808
Out Island Sport Yachts, Inc., 107 Edgewood Ave., West Berlin 08091
Pres.—Scott Jastrzembski, 6 emp., *Manufacturer of custom-built fiberglass* ........ (609) 861-4000
Ovadia Corp., 101 E. Main St., 2nd Fl., Little Falls 07424
V-P.—Steven Ovadia, 40 emp., *Plastic jewelry display trays* ........ (973) 256-9200
Owens Plastic Products, Inc., 393 Main St., P.O. Box 118, Cedarville 08311
Pres., CFO—Celeste Owens, 10 emp., *Transfer, compression, injection &* ........ (856) 447-3500
P & S Blizzard Corp., 722 Madison Ave., Paterson 07501
Pres.—Paul Kostovski, 2 emp., *Wooden & plastic fences* ........ (973) 523-1700
P C R Technologies, Inc., 26 Chapin Rd., Unit 1111, Pine Brook 07058
Pres.—Mark Vanzini, 9 emp., *High-speed CNC machining of metals* ........ (973) 882-0017
Package Development Co., Inc., 100 Round Hill Dr., Ste. 8, Rockaway 07866
Pres.—Charles Schwester, 50 emp., *Thermoforming, contract & club packaging* ........ (973) 983-8500
Pacon Mfg., Corp., 400 Pierce St., Somerset 08873
Pres.—Michael Shannon, 200 emp., *Nonwoven disposable medical towels,* ........ (732) 764-9070
Paradigm Packaging, LLC (H Q), 141 N. 5th St., Saddle Brook 07663
Chrm. of the Board—Robert Donnahoo, 100 emp., *Company headquarters; plastic containers* (201) 507-0900
Parkway Plastics, Inc., 561 Stelton Rd., Piscataway 08854
Pres.—Edward Rowan, 46 emp., *Plastic jars, closures, mold making* ........ (732) 752-3636
Parrish Sign Co., Inc., 2242 S. Delsea Dr., Vineland 08360
Pres.—Charles Parrish, 9 emp., *Full color, digitally printed, lighted* ........ (856) 696-4040
Paterson Packaging, 269 Wilson St., Saddle Brook 07663
Owner & Pres.—Kenneth Manley, 3 emp., *Flexible packaging, including BOPP,* ........ (201) 398-9693
Patrick J. Kelly Drums, Inc., 1810 River Ave., Camden 08105
Owner & Pres.—Patrick J. Kelly, 49 emp., *New & reconditioned industrial steel* ........ (856) 963-1795
Paul's Custom Awards & Trophy, Inc., 200 White Horse Pike, Barrington 08007
Pres.—Paul McGuigan, 8 emp., *Trophy engraving & plaques* ........ (856) 547-7777
PDQ Plastics, Inc., 7 Hook Rd., P.O. Box 1001, Bayonne 07002
Pres.—Barry Nathans, 22 emp., *Plastic pallets* ........ (201) 823-0270
Pee Wee Molding Corp., 240 Circle Dr. N., Piscataway 08854
GM—Feivel Reifman, 40 emp., *Plastic injection molding* ........ (732) 469-0200
Peerless Coatings, LLC, 220-A Goffle Rd., Hawthorne 07506
GM—Joe Hyer, 45 emp., *Metal & plastic coatings* ........ (973) 427-8771
Pella Windows & Doors, 4 Dedrick Pl., West Caldwell 07006
Pres.—David Sidman, 170 emp., *Wood, wood-clad & vinyl windows & doors* ........ (973) 575-0200
Peoplevision, Inc., 311 E. 1st Ave., Bldg. A, Roselle 07203
Pres.—Wayne Sullivant, 5 emp., *Plastic museum exhibits* ........ (973) 509-2056
Permabond, LLC (H Q), 223 Churchill Ave., Somerset 08873
Off. Mgr.—Linda Casale, 6 emp., *Company headquarters; engineering adhesives* ........ (732) 868-1372
Permalith Plastics, LLC, 6901 N. Crescent Blvd., Pennsauken 08110
V-P., Sales—Gary Brown, 45 emp., *Plastic litho & screen printing, laminating* ........ (856) 488-8000
Petro Extrusion Technologies, Inc., 490 South Ave., Garwood 07027
Pres.—Robert Petrozziello, 40 emp., *Plastic extrusions* ........ (908) 789-3338
Pharmakon Corp., 2200 Wallace Blvd., Unit C, P.O. Box 217, Cinnaminson 08077
Pres.—William H. Shaffer, Sr., 10 emp., *Tabletop pharmaceutical displays* ........ (856) 829-3161
Philadelphia Sign Co., 707 W. Spring Garden St., Palmyra 08065
Pres.—Bob Mehmet, 300 emp., *Signs & vinyl lettering* ........ (856) 829-1460
Phoenix Mfg., Inc., 1306 Brielle Ave., Ocean 07712
Pres.—Richard Sheridan, 10 emp., *PVC & aluminum railings & PVC pergolas* ........ (732) 380-1666
Picture-It, Inc., 1703 State Route 27, Edison 08817
Pres.—Roy Taetzsch, 5 emp., *Acrylic, crystal, glass & wooden awards* ........ (732) 819-0420
Pierson Industries, Inc., 7 Astro Pl., Rockaway 07866
Pres.—Theodore Pierson, 65 emp., *Plactic injection molding* ........ (973) 627-7945
Plastasonics, Inc., 5031 Industrial Rd., Farmingdale 07727
Pres.—Gary Young, 15 emp., *Headphones, handsets & headsets, including* ........ (732) 938-7694
Plastic Monofil Co. Ltd., 25 Howard St., Piscataway 08854
Ptnr.—Mike Sweeny, 20 emp., *Plastic injection molding* ........ (732) 629-7701
Plastic Services, Inc., 200 Pacific Ave., Jersey City 07304
Pres.—Jeff Turner, 20 emp., *Plastic reprocessing & wholesaler of* ........ (201) 200-1200
Plastics For Chemicals, Inc., 710 Old Shore Rd., Forked River 08731
Pres., GM—John Donovan, 5 emp., *Tetrafluoroethylene products* ........ (609) 242-9100
Plastiform Packaging, Inc., 114 Beach St., Bldg. 6, P.O.Box 186, Rockaway 07866
Pres.—George Smith, 25 emp., *Plastic packaging materials, rigid,* ........ (973) 983-8900
Plast-O-Matic Valves, Inc., 1384 Pompton Ave., Ste. 1, Cedar Grove 07009
Pres.—Tim Delorenzo, 60 emp., *Thermoplastic valves & controls for* ........ (973) 256-3000
PMC Group, Inc. (H Q), 1288 Route 73, Mount Laurel 08054
Pres., COO—Debtash Chakrabarti, 35 emp., *Corporate headquarters; industrial* ........ (856) 533-1866
Poandl Brothers Woodworking, Inc., 20 N. 7th Ave., P.O. Box 4015, Long Branch 07740
Pres.—William Poandl, 4 emp., *Architectural millwork, including solid* ........ (732) 229-8585
Poly Express, LLC, 318 McLean Blvd., Bldg. 5, Paterson 07504
Pres.—Bill Parlak, 15 emp., *Polyethylene bags, liners, sheets &* ........ (800) 843-7659
Polyair North East, 495 Meadow Ln., Carlstadt 07072
Sales Mgr.—Jim Brennan, 60 emp., *Packaging materials, including bubble* ........ (201) 804-1700
Polycel Structural Foam, Inc., 68 County Line Rd., Somerville 08876
Dir., Sales & Mktg.—Michael Sheroke, 34 emp., *Structural foam & injection molding* ........ (908) 722-5254
Polyfil Corp., 74 Green Pond Rd., P.O. Box 130, Rockaway 07866
Pres.—Gerald Fabiano, 23 emp., *Plastic pellets* ........ (973) 627-4070
Polymer Solutions International, Inc., 9 Roxbury Dr., Medford 08055
Pres.—D. Kelly, 15 emp., *Plastic material handling equipment* ........ (609) 714-2899
Polymer Technologies, Inc., 10 Clifton Blvd., Clifton 07011
Pres.—Neal Goldenberg, 70 emp., *Custom plastic & metal injection molding* ........ (973) 778-9100
POLY-Version, Inc., 49 Fisk St., Jersey City 07305
Pres., CEO—Philip Goldschmiedt, 35 emp., *Disposable plastic gloves laminated* ........ (201) 451-0600
Post To Post, LLC, 2545 Fire Rd., Ste. 1, Egg Harbor Township 08234
★ Principal—Richard Sonsini, 7 emp., *Architectural metalwork & wooden &* ........ (609) 646-9300
Power Container Corp., 33 Schoolhouse Rd., Somerset 08873
Pres.—Olivier Vertaud, 32 emp., *Environmentally-friendly mono-film* ........ (732) 560-3655
Precision Mfg., LLC, 177 Gould Ave., Paterson 07503
Pres., GM, Sales & Mktg. Mgr.—George Sharpe, 7 emp., *Custom plastics, including injection* (973) 278-6600
Precision Technology, Inc., 50 Maple St., P.O. Box 422, Norwood 07648
Pres., CEO—Ira Housman, 40 emp., *Plastic components for orthopedic body* ........ (201) 767-1600
Princeton Case Co., Inc., 615 Sherwood Pkwy., Mountainside 07092
V-P.—Steve Parker, Jr., 21 emp., *Plastic carrying cases & foam fabrication* ........ (908) 687-1750
Princeton Tec, 110 Collings Ave., West Berlin 08091
Dir., Pur.—Mark Buehler, 8 emp., *Plastic parts, including precision* ........ (609) 298-9331

Pro Plastics, Inc., 1190 Sylvan St., P.O. Box 1489, Linden 07036
Pres.—George Sievewright, 12 emp., *Manufacturer of custom plastic parts* .......... (908) 925-5555
Product Identification Co., Inc., 141 Lanza Ave., Bldg. 19, Garfield 07026
Pres.—Les Weinstock, 20 emp., *Aluminum, vinyl & polyester nameplates* .......... (973) 955-4747
Productive Plastics, Inc., 103 W. Park Dr., Mount Laurel 08054
Pres.—Hal Gilham, 60 emp., *Thermoformed plastic components including* .......... (856) 778-4300
Proform Acoustic Surfaces LLC, 307 Julianne Ter., Secaucus 07094
★ Mng. Ptnr.—Anna Porcelli, 5 emp., *PVC extrusions for fabricated upholstered* .......... (201) 553-9614
Pro-Form Packaging, Inc., 777 North Avenue Ext., P.O. Box 4231, Dunellen 08812
Pres.—Kenneth Gibbs, 20 emp., *Custom & contract thermoformed packaging* .......... (732) 968-8123
Progressive Dimensions, Inc., 44 Flint Rd., Toms River 08757
Pres.—Ed Cassidy, 10 emp., *Granite, solid-surface & laminate countertop* .......... (732) 244-0109
Punch Products U. S. A., Inc., 2131 Felver Ct., Rahway 07065
Pres.—Michael Fishman, 40 emp., *Plastic & steel promotional travel,* .......... (732) 574-1900
Pyramid Poly Bags, Inc., 600 Markley St., Port Reading 07064
Pres.—Chaya Jeremias, 20 emp., *Paper & plastic tableware* .......... (718) 499-1212
Qualis Packaging, 550 Hadley Rd., South Plainfield 07080
Dir. & Hum. Res. Mgr.—Pamela Peunaccio, 70 emp., *Sampling products flexible plastic* .......... (908) 753-7300
Quality Industries, Inc., 204 Getty Ave., Clifton 07011
Pres.—Andrew Ponikowski, 10 emp., *Fabrication & machining shop, including* .......... (973) 478-4425
Quality Packaging Specialists International, LLC, 5 Cooper St., Burlington 08016
Pres., CEO—Mike Ricketts, 250 emp., *Company headquarters & contract packaging* .......... (609) 239-0503
Quickie Mfg. Corp. (H Q), 1150 Taylors Ln., P.O. Box 156, Cinnaminson 08077
Ex. V-P., Engrg.—Jace Weaver, 70 emp., *Corporate headquarters; cleaning products* .......... (856) 829-7900
R & R Plastics, Inc., 62-70 Myrtle Ave., Passaic 07055
Pres., CFO—R. Russell Corona, 12 emp., *Lighting diffusers & replacement plastics* .......... (973) 365-8083
Railing Dynamics, Inc., 1201 N. 10th St., Millville 08332
Dir., Opers.—Wayne Batchelder, 70 emp., *Vinyl railings* .......... (856) 327-1698
Railing Dynamics, Inc. (H Q), 135 Steelmanville Rd., Egg Harbor Township 08234
Pres.—Chris Terrels, 30 emp., *Corporate headquarters; vinyl railings* .......... (609) 601-1300
Ramco Mfg. Co., Inc., 365 Carnegie Ave., Kenilworth 07033
Pres.—Kevin J. Nee, 25 emp., *Flanges, expansion & threaded pipe* .......... (908) 245-4500
Raritan Printing Plus Flags & Banners, Inc., 109 N. Feltus St., South Amboy 08879
Pres.—Joanne Corridon, 2 emp., *Stock & custom U.S. outdoor & indoor* .......... (732) 721-2121
Raritan Valley Workshop, 9 Terminal Rd., New Brunswick 08901
Plt. Mgr.—Andy Scisorek, 250 emp., *Contract packaging & assembly* .......... (732) 828-8080
Raybold Mfg., Inc., 102 S. 8th St., Millville 08332
Pres.—William Riland, 9 emp., *Screen printing of glass bottles &* .......... (856) 327-7733
Ready Pac, 101 Arlington Blvd., Swedesboro 08085
Dir., Facilities—Mike Morphew, 300 emp., *Packaged fruits & salads* .......... (856) 241-0900
Rectico, Inc., 12 Gloria Ln., Unit 1, Fairfield 07004
Pres.—Scott Sandler, 10 emp., *Crating, corrugated boxes & contract* .......... (973) 575-0009
Reed-Lane, Inc., 359 Newark Pompton Tpke., Wayne 07470
Pres.—Patricia Elvin, 175 emp., *Contract assembly & packaging for the* .......... (973) 709-1090
Reeves International, Inc., 34 Owens Dr., Wayne 07470
Prodn. Mgr.—Bill Rausch, 100 emp., *Model horses* .......... (973) 956-9555
Reiss Mfg., Inc., 75 Mount Vernon Rd., P.O. Box 310, Englishtown 07726
Pres.—Carl Reiss, 125 emp., *Corporate headquarters & plastic injection* .......... (732) 446-6100
Reliance Plastic & Chemical Corp., 38-27 Wilson St., P.O. Box 395, Fair Lawn 07410
★ Pres.—Fred Levine, 10 emp., *Flexible down drains for erosion control* .......... (201) 797-8014
Rema Tip Top/North America, Inc. (H Q), 119 Rockland Ave., Northvale 07647
Pres.—Olafur Gunnarsson, 25 emp., *Corporate headquarters; rubber, epoxy* .......... (201) 768-8100
Research & Mfg. Corp. Of America, 1130 W. Elizabeth, Linden 07036
Pres.—Charles Semah, 25 emp., *Plastic injection molding* .......... (908) 862-6744
Rigo Industries, Inc., 50 California Ave., Paterson 07503
Pres.—Isaac Gorovitz, 50 emp., *Vinyl wallpaper* .......... (973) 881-1780
Rimmel Rogers, Inc., 250 Passaic St., Newark 07104
Pres.—Manoj Doshi, 7 emp., *Contract packaging & distributor of* .......... (201) 998-4700
Ring Container Technologies, 50 Fadem Rd., Ste. 1, Springfield 07081
Plt. Mgr.—David Fredkin, 19 emp., *Plastic containers* .......... (973) 258-0707
Rios Engraving, 1 Maple Ave., Morristown 07960
Owner, Plt. Opers. & Sales & Mktg. Mgr.—Rolando G. Rios, 3 emp., *Custom & laser engraving* (973) 539-5749
Robalo Enterprises, 104 New Era Dr., South Plainfield 07080
Owner—Albert Dilello, 45 emp., *Contract packaging & assembly* .......... (908) 753-1075
Robessa Enterprises, Inc., 1030 Delsea Dr., P.O. Box 72, Westville 08093
Owner—William Green, 10 emp., *Corrugated boxes & contract packaging* .......... (856) 251-0055
Robyn Packaging Co., Inc., 31 Augusta Dr., Wayne 07470
Pres.—George DeAngelo, 40 emp., *Plastic bags & labels* .......... (973) 696-2059
Ronald-Mark Assocs., Inc., 1227 Central Ave., P.O. Box 776, Hillside 07205
Pres., CEO—Les Satz, 50 emp., *Corporate headquarters & vinyl, film* .......... (908) 558-0011
Royal Prime Window Specialist, Inc., 742 Fairfield Ave., Kenilworth 07033
Pres. & IT Mgr.—Andrew Inelli, 6 emp., *High-end vinyl replacement windows* .......... (908) 354-7600
Royal Slide Sales Co., Inc., 42 Hepworth Pl., Garfield 07026
V-P.—Lewis Neuman, 15 emp., *Home furnishings packaging bags, cosmetics* .......... (973) 777-1177
Roysons Corp., 40 Vanderhoof Ave., Rockaway 07866
CEO—Roy Ritchie, Sr., 95 emp., *Vinyl wall coverings & wallboard, shelving* .......... (973) 625-5570
Rubber Stamp Engraving, 386 Avenel St., Avenel 07001
Owner & Pres.—Steven Glassman, 15 emp., *Plastic engraving, interior & exterior* .......... (732) 726-5664
Rummel Industries, Inc., 697 Rahway Ave., P.O. Box 1326, Union 07083
Pres.—Peter Rummel, 18 emp., *Corporate headquarters & plastic &* .......... (908) 688-6600
S L M Mfg. Corp., 47 Langstaff Ave., Edison 08817
Pres.—Thomas Vajtay, 8 emp., *Transparent semi-rigid, collapsible* .......... (732) 469-7500
S.S.P. Manufacturing, Inc., 83 Spring Ln., Hackettstown 07840
Pres., Sales Mgr.—Ray Romanick, 9 emp., *CNC lathe-cut custom plastic goods* .......... (908) 852-3125
Sabert Corp., 2288 Main Street Ext., Sayreville 08872
Pres.—Albert Salama, 150 emp., *Corporate headquarters & plastic trays* .......... (732) 721-5544
Sabre Die Cutting Co., Inc., 68 Mill St., Paterson 07501
Pres.—Michael Culver, 25 emp., *Die cutting of paper, paperboard, plastics* .......... (973) 357-9800
Safe-Strap Co., 105 W. Dewey Ave., Bldg. D, Ste. 410, Wharton 07885
Pres.—Paul Giampavolo, 55 emp., *Shopping cart seat belts, shop-along* .......... (973) 442-4623
Sama Plastics Corp., 20 Sand Park Rd., Cedar Grove 07009
Pres.—Mark Wolfberg, 45 emp., *Acrylic & wood display fixture & point-of-pur* .......... (973) 239-7200
Sankar Assocs., Inc., 14 Empire Blvd., Moonachie 07074
Pres.—Burton Kreindel, 30 emp., *Contract cheese packaging for the dairy* .......... (201) 994-1700
Sap Seal Products, 52 Woodbine St., Bergenfield 07621
Pres.—Ernie Ness, 5 emp., *Lubricant-prefilled reusable threaded* .......... (201) 385-5553
Sasa Demarle, Inc., 8 Corporate Dr., Cranbury 08512
CEO—Rudy Boussemart, 12 emp., *Nonstick flexible bakeware* .......... (609) 395-0219
Scheld Assocs., Inc., 37 Pleasantview Dr., Wayne 07470
Pres.—John Scheld, 3 emp., *Specialty polymers for mechanical seals* .......... (973) 694-0637
Schutz Container Systems, Inc., 200 Aspen Hill Rd., P.O. Box 5950, North Branch 08876
Pres., CEO—Frederik Wenzel, 65 emp., *Corporate headquarters & plastic containers* .......... (908) 526-6161

Scientific Materials Corp., 30 Vail Ter., P.O. Box 5298, Somerville 08876
Pres.—Noris Batra, 5 emp., *Contamination control polymeric reusable* .......... (908) 218-0010
Sculpturesque, Inc., 7 Etheridge Pl., Park Ridge 07656
Owner—Catherine Schmitt, 1 emp., *Commercial & fine art sculptures &* .......... (201) 573-9150
Sealed Air Corp., 301 Mayhill St., Saddle Brook 07663
Sales Mgr., Reg.—Matthew Venezia, 200 emp., *Food packaging containers, bubble wrap* ... (201) 712-7000
Sealed Air Corp. (H Q), 200 Riverfront Blvd., 3rd Fl., Elmwood Park 07407
Pres., CEO—Jerome Peribere, 100 emp., *Corporate headquarters; food packaging* .......... (201) 791-7600
Severna Operations, Inc., 3 Eastmans Rd., Parsippany 07054
Pres.—Samir Aboulhosn, 20 emp., *Custom precision machined parts & fluoropolym* .......... (973) 503-1600
Sign-A-Rama, 1459 Highway 38, P.O. Box 360, Hainesport 08036
Owner—Gary Kuffer, 4 emp., *Interior & exterior, ADA & project* .......... (609) 702-1444
Sign-A-Rama, 34 S. White Horse Pike, Somerdale 08083
Owner—Jennifer Gray, 4 emp., *Interior, exterior & illuminated signs* .......... (856) 627-5352
SignPros, 1215 Black Horse Pike, Glendora 08029
Owner & Pres.—Nick Kappatos, 18 emp., *LED channel letters, illuminated sign* .......... (856) 939-1099
Signs & Graphix, 433 Bloomfield Ave., Caldwell 07006
Owner—Eric Sterru, 1 emp., *Big format interior, exterior & job* .......... (973) 226-8392
Signs By Tomorrow, 326 U.S. Highway 22, Ste. 8-B, Green Brook 08812
Owner—Rajesh Patel, 4 emp., *Interior & exterior, trade show, architectura* .......... (732) 424-9785
Signs Of Sense, 79 Bassett Hwy., Dover 07801
Owner & Pres.—Scott Rothbart, 3 emp., *Full-color interior & exterior signs* .......... (973) 361-0037
Signs Of The Times By Beutel & Sons, 81 Park Ave., Park Ridge 07656
Owner—George Beutel, 2 emp., *Vinyl interior & exterior signs & lettering* .......... (201) 391-8444
Siloa, Inc. (H Q), 2493 Lamington Rd., Ste. C, Bedminster 07921
Pres.—Mark Bellard, 3 emp., *Corporate headquarters; plastic & metal* .......... (908) 234-9040
Silver Line Building Products, LLC, 1 Silver Line Dr., P.O. Box 6029, North Brunswick 08902
V-P., Sales—Al Worthing, 3000 emp., *Company headquarters & vinyl windows* .......... (732) 435-1000
Sky Frame & Art, Inc., 28 Evans Terminal, Hillside 07205
Pres.—Robert Benrimon, 20 emp., *Corporate headquarters & custom picture* .......... (908) 354-5656
Source Packaging, Inc., 215 Island Rd., Mahwah 07430
Pres.—Allen Adler, 20 emp., *Presentation & protective packaging* .......... (201) 831-0005
Spaulding Fabricators Inc., 1136 Industrial Pkwy., Brick 08724
Pres.—Stephen Spaulding, 21 emp., *Solid-surface, granite & engineered* .......... (732) 840-4433
Specialty Castings, Inc., 42 Curtis Ave., Woodbury 08096
Pres., CFO, MIS Mgr.—John Cowgill, 7 emp., *Polyurethane roller castings* .......... (856) 845-3105
Specialty Paper Box Co., 14 Highland Dr., North Caldwell 07006
Pres.—Harry Engel III, 4 emp., *Setup, corrugated & plastic boxes* .......... (973) 396-8556
Stanbee Co., Inc., 70 Broad St., P.O. Box 436, Carlstadt 07072
Pres.—Michael Berkson, 40 emp., *Thermoplastic counter & boxtoe materials* .......... (201) 933-9666
Star-Glo Industries, LLC, 2 Carlton Ave., East Rutherford 07073
Pres.—Edward Peterhoff, 90 emp., *Swiss machining & rubber molding for* .......... (201) 939-6162
Starlight Windows Mfg., Inc., 50 E. 25th St., Paterson 07514
Pres.—Juan D. Rodriguez, 5 emp., *Vinyl windows* .......... (973) 278-9366
Stefano Fence Systems, Inc., 737 New Durham Rd., Edison 08817
★ Owner—Stephen Smith, 15 emp., *Aluminum architectural metalwork &* .......... (732) 321-5050
Stephen Gould Corporation, 35 S. Jefferson Rd., Whippany 07981
Pres., CEO—Michael Golden, 110 emp., *Corporate headquarters & packaging* .......... (973) 428-1510
Stephen Plastics, Inc., Douglas, 22-36 Green St., Paterson 07501
V-P.—Douglas Graff, 90 emp., *Plastic food containers* .......... (973) 523-3030
Sterling Products, 90 Dayton Ave., Bldg. 12-C, Ste. 77, Passaic 07055
Off. Mgr.—Judy Russell, 30 emp., *Acrylic lampshades, acrylic sheets,* .......... (973) 471-2858
Sterling Window Co., 224 21st Ave., Paterson 07501
Pres.—Joseph J. Baldino, 15 emp., *Vinyl & aluminum windows* .......... (973) 742-1900
Stone Crafters, LLC, 6084 Reega Ave., Egg Harbor Township 08234
★ Owner—Bill Millar, 15 emp., *Granite, marble & cultured quartz countertops* .......... (609) 646-0406
Stone Mountain Printing, 74 Main St., Ste. 1, Woodbridge 07095
Pres.—Steve Steinberg, 8 emp., *Commercial & digital printing, graphic* .......... (732) 634-4444
StoneShop, 670 Deer Rd., Ste. 202, Cherry Hill 08034
★ V-P.—Richard Holmes, 10 emp., *Granite, marble & engineered quartz* .......... (856) 795-8900
Strong Man Building Products Corp., 240 W. Parkway, Pompton Plains 07444
Pres.—Jay Kinder, 8 emp., *Plastic tarpaulins & netting* .......... (973) 831-1555
Stuart Mills, Inc., 25 Stillwater Rd., Newton 07860
Pres.—Stuart Mills, 6 emp., *CNC milling & turning, sheet metal* .......... (973) 579-5717
Stull Technologies, Inc., 17 Veronica Ave., Somerset 08873
Chrm., Pres.—Gene Stull, 130 emp., *Plastic closures & bottle caps* .......... (732) 873-5000
Suburban Caps, Inc., 899 State Route 18, Old Bridge 08857
★ Principal—Scott Kidd, 2 emp., *Truck caps & accessories* .......... (732) 251-4383
Survivor II, Inc., 919 Fairmount Ave., Elizabeth 07201
Ptnr.—Tony Casas, 20 emp., *Vinyl windows* .......... (908) 353-1155
Sysco Guest Supply (H Q), 4301 Highway 1, P.O. Box 902, Monmouth Junction 08852
Pres., COO—Paul T. Xenis, 140 emp., *Divisional headquarters; personal care* .......... (609) 514-9696
Tauber Co., LLC, G. G., 289 State Route 33, Ste. 12, Manalapan 07726
Pres.—Becky Livingston, 4 emp., *Vinyl badge holders, promotions & awards* .......... (301) 881-3567
Taylor Windows, Inc., 61 Central Ave., East Orange 07018
Pres., CFO—Pat Taylor, 5 emp., *Vinyl windows assembly* .......... (973) 672-3000
Technical Name Plate Corp., 92 1st St., Passaic 07055
Pres.—Perla Navarro, 20 emp., *Metal, vinyl, polyester film, plastic* .......... (973) 773-4256
Technimold, Inc., 715 Jerusalem Rd., Scotch Plains 07076
Pres., CFO, MIS Mgr.—William McNamara, 20 emp., *Plastic injection molding* .......... (908) 232-8331
Technitool, Inc., 1028 Industrial Dr., West Berlin 08091
Pres.—Sal Russomanno, 11 emp., *Plastic injection molding* .......... (856) 768-2707
TEK Molding, LLC, 1440 County Route 565, Sussex 07461
Pres.—Tim Kenney, Sr., 2 emp., *Custom natural & synthetic rubber &* .......... (973) 702-0450
Telemark CNC, LLC, 429 Rockaway Valley Rd., Bldg. 2200, Boonton 07005
Owner—William Hovey, 5 emp., *Precision Swiss CNC machining of stainless* .......... (973) 794-4857
TerraCycle, Inc., 121 New York Ave., Trenton 08638
CEO—Tom Szaky, 25 emp., *Cut & sewn duffel bags, bike pouches* .......... (609) 393-4252
The Star Group, 80-A Industrial Rd., Lodi 07644
Pres.—Michael Friedman, 10 emp., *Woven & fabric labels, hang tags &* .......... (973) 778-8600
ThermaFreeze Products Corp. (H Q), 107 Maple Grange Rd., Vernon 07462
Pres.—Sahin Atlas, 3 emp., *Corporate headquarters; reusable ice* .......... (877) 777-8397
Thermal-Chek, Inc., 912 Broadway, Westville 08093
Pres.—Joseph Heaton, Sr., 20 emp., *Vinyl windows* .......... (856) 742-1200
Thermo Plastics Technologies, Inc., 1119 Morris Ave., Union 07083
Pres.—Tino Quint, 48 emp., *Plastic products for the cosmetics* .......... (908) 687-4833
Thermoplastic Biologic, LLC, 26 Brookfield Dr., Ste. C, Sparta 07871
Mng. Ptnr.—P. Robert DuPont, Jr., 15 emp., *Medical & scientific plastic tubing* .......... (973) 383-2834
Todd Architectural Models, 54 Mountainview Rd., P.O. Box 1002, Chatham 07928
Pres.—Douglas Pitney, 7 emp., *Wooden, plastic & metal architectural* .......... (973) 507-4072
Tooker Sign Service, 1439 Route 539, P.O. Box 1129, Tuckerton 08087
Owner—Jeff Tooker, 1 emp., *Plastic, metal, electric, nonelectric* .......... (609) 296-1000

**★ Indicates new listing this edition.**

Town & Country Plastics, Inc., P.O. Box 269, Morganville 07751
Pres., Sales Mgr.—Harold Marmel, 18 emp., *Plastic pollution control & chemically* ................ (732) 780-5300
Townsend Farms, Inc., 3501 S. East Blvd., Vineland 08360
Opers. Mgr.—David Rodigan, 100 emp., *Individually quick-frozen berry processing* ............... (856) 825-5240
Transparent Office Products, LLC, 2550 Haddonfield Rd., Pennsauken 08110
GM & Opers. Mgr.—Rick Brown, 4 emp., *Archival document & photo protectors* ..................... (856) 488-5455
Trap-Zap Environmental Systems, Inc., 255 Braen Ave., Wyckoff 07481
Pres.—Robert Belle, 20 emp., *Biodegradable restaurant grease trap* ..................... (201) 251-9970
Trend Printing International Label, Inc., 1183 Edgewater Ave., Ridgefield 07657
Pres.—David Fishbein, 15 emp., *Labels & flexible packaging* ..................... (201) 941-6611
Trinity Mfg., LLC, 60 Leonard St., Metuchen 08840
Ptnr.—Randy Riley, 10 emp., *Plastic thermoformed displays for retail* ..................... (732) 549-2866
Tri-Seal, 112 Church St., Flemington 08822
Plt. Controller—Sue Franson, 120 emp., *Flexible packaging & cap liners* ..................... (908) 782-4000
Tri-State Building Materials Co., 65 Lodi St., Passaic 07055
Pres.—Charles Cangialosi, 18 emp., *Aluminum & vinyl windows & doors* ..................... (973) 472-2377
Tri-Tech Tool & Design Co., Inc., 30 Cherry St., South Bound Brook 08880
Pres.—Art Weber, 25 emp., *Plastic injection molding* ..................... (732) 469-5433
Tropar Mfg. Co., Inc., 5 Vreeland Rd., Florham Park 07932
Pres.—Peter E. Ilaria, 60 emp., *Corporate headquarters & plaques, clocks* ..................... (973) 822-2400
Tuckahoe Mfg., 327 Tuckahoe Rd., Vineland 08360
Owner—John Tombleson, 6 emp., *Vinyl strip doors & strip material* ..................... (856) 696-4100
Tunnel Barrel & Drum Co., Inc., 85 Triangle Blvd., Carlstadt 07072
Pres.—Anthony Urcioli, 20 emp., *Reconditioned fiber & plastic drums* ..................... (201) 933-1444
Tyz-All Plastics, LLC, 130 Gamewell St., Hackensack 07601
Pres.—Betty Ballin, 10 emp., *Plastic products* ..................... (201) 343-1200
Unette Corp., 1578 Sussex Tpke., Randolph 07869
Hum. Res. & IT Mgr.—Chris Doscher, 30 emp., *Graduated plastic tubes & contract* ............. (973) 328-6800
Unifoil Corp., 12 Daniel Rd., Ste. 101, Fairfield 07004
Pres., CEO—Joseph Funicelli, 105 emp., *Corporate headquarters & aluminum foil* ............... (973) 244-9900
Unit Pack Co., Inc., 7 Lewis Rd., Cedar Grove 07009
Pres.—Ernest Losser, 30 emp., *Plastic containers* ..................... (973) 239-4112
United Equipment & Fabricators, 175 Orange St., Newark 07103
Manager—Robert Ayars, 5 emp., *Custom plastic, fiberglass, stainless* ..................... (973) 242-2737
United Plastics Group, Inc., 30 Commerce Dr., Somerset 08873
Pres.—Chihming Wong, 35 emp., *Precision plastic products* ..................... (732) 873-1848
United Window & Door Mfg., 24-36 Fadem Rd., Springfield 07081
CFO—Gary DeNoia, 250 emp., *Vinyl windows & doors* ..................... (973) 912-0600
Universal Windows, LLC, 407 Bloomfield Dr., West Berlin 08091
Pres.—Joseph Battaglia, Sr., 20 emp., *Vinyl windows & patio doors* ..................... (856) 719-0020
Valid USA, Inc., 800 Montrose Ave., South Plainfield 07080
V-P.—Mike Mutrie, 200 emp., *Plastic credit cards* ..................... (908) 668-0999
Valley Plastic Molding Co., Inc., P.O. Box 30, Boonton 07005
Pres., CFO—Mike Berhman, 8 emp., *Custom compression molding & thermoset* ..................... (973) 334-2100
Van Ness Plastic Molding Co., 400 Brighton Rd., Clifton 07012
Pres.—William Van Ness, 150 emp., *Plastic injection molding* ..................... (973) 778-9500
Vention Medical, 6 Century Rd., South Plainfield 07080
Pres.—Dan Croteau, 140 emp., *Injection molded medical devices* ..................... (908) 561-0717
Viking Mold & Tool, Inc., 64 Tuckahoe Rd., Dorothy 08317
Pres.—James Sullivan, 5 emp., *Plastic injection & blow molding* ..................... (609) 476-9333
Vinylast, Inc., 1830 Swarthmore Ave., Lakewood 08701
Pres., GM—Steven J. Leary, 20 emp., *Aluminum & vinyl windows, doors, railings* ............. (732) 367-7200
VisiPak, a Sinclair & Rush Company, 640 Dell Rd., Ste. 1, P.O. Box 0188, Carlstadt 07072
Dir., Sales & Mktg.—Jeff Barket, 90 emp., *Plastic tube packaging containers,* ..................... (800) 949-1141
Visual Packaging Corp., 91 4th Ave., Haskell 07420
Pres.—Don Stackhouse, 6 emp., *Plastic boxes* ..................... (973) 835-7055
Viz Plastic Products Ltd., 210 Industrial Pkwy., Northvale 07647
Pres., Hum. Res., IT & Off. Mgr.—Dimitrios Lymberis, 5 emp., *Plastic products, including* ..... (201) 784-4442
Volta Belting Technology, 11 Chapin Rd., Pine Brook 07058
GM—Zvika Avidan, 15 emp., *Plastic conveyor belts* ..................... (973) 276-7905
Vo-Toys, Inc., 400 S. 5th St., Harrison 07029
Pres.—Arthur Hirschberg, 125 emp., *Pet accessories & products, including* ..................... (973) 484-0088
W Y Plastic Industry, Inc., 2500 Secaucus Rd., North Bergen 07047
GM—Bill Cheng, 6 emp., *Plastic products* ..................... (201) 617-8000
Waste Management, Inc., 107 Silvia St., Ewing 08628
Cont.—Tom Utermark, 120 emp., *Glass, scrap metal, plastic, paper,* ..................... (609) 587-1500
Weiss-Aug Co. Inc., 220 Merry Ln., East Hanover 07936
CEO—Dieter Weissenrieder, 200 emp., *Custom insert molding, precision metal* ..................... (973) 887-7600
West Hudson Industries, 1687 Saint Georges Ave., Rahway 07065
Pres.—Les Moshinsky, 4 emp., *Metal & plastic engraving & laminating* ..................... (732) 381-6800
Wiggins Plastics, Inc., 180 Kingsland Rd., P.O. Box 1077, Clifton 07014
Pres.—Isaac Weinberger, 65 emp., *Custom injection, compression & transfer* ..................... (973) 667-7200
Window Shapes, Inc., 225 Liberty St., Metuchen 08840
Owner & V-P.—Tom Change, 25 emp., *Vinyl architectural shaped windows,* ..................... (848) 229-2431
World Wide Packaging, LLC, 15 Vreeland Rd., Florham Park 07932
Chrm.—Jeffrey S. Schneider, 50 emp., *Contract manufacturing of packaging* ..................... (973) 805-6500
Wytech Industries, Inc., 960 E. Hazelwood Ave., Rahway 07065
CEO—Anthony J. Casalino, 105 emp., *Grinding, straightening, cutting, forming* ..................... (732) 396-3900
Xenopore Corp., 299 Wagaraw Rd., Hawthorne 07506
Pres.—Allan Douglas, 8 emp., *Plastic & glass laboratory plates &* ..................... (973) 423-2400
Yuhl Products, Inc., 15 N. 7th St., Kenilworth 07033
Pres.—Ron Yuhl, 3 emp., *Plastic injection molding, including* ..................... (908) 276-5180

## 31 LEATHER & LEATHER PRODUCTS

### 3111 Leather tanning & finishing

Myers Group, LLC, The, 74 Blanchard Rd., South Orange 07079
Owner & Member—Jay H. Myers, 8 emp., *Leather tanning, converting & brokering* ..................... (973) 761-6414

### 3142 Slippers—house

Leif J. Ostberg, Inc. (H Q), 401 Hamburg Tpke., Ste. 305, Wayne 07470
Pres.—Jim Kimberlin, 20 emp., *Corporate headquarters; men's, women's* ..................... (973) 956-6990
Raybold Mfg., Inc., Disposable Products Div., 102 S. 8th St., Millville 08332
Pres.—Bill Riland, 10 emp., *Disposable paper slippers* ..................... (856) 327-7733
S. Goldberg & Co., Inc., 3 University Plz., Ste. 400, Hackensack 07601
Pres.—Bernie Leifer, 73 emp., *Corporate headquarters & men's & women's* ..................... (201) 342-1200

### 3143 Footwear—men's, except athletic

Carlascio Inc. Orthotics, Prosthetic, Custom Shoes, 283 Grove St., Jersey City 07302
Owner—Louis Carlascio, 11 emp., *Custom handmade orthotics, prosthetics* ..................... (201) 333-8716
Carrini, Inc. (H Q), 140 Smith St., 5th Fl., Keasbey 08832
Pres.—Eli Chabot, 18 emp., *Corporate headquarters; men's, women's* ..................... (732) 650-1775
Leif J. Ostberg, Inc. (H Q), 401 Hamburg Tpke., Ste. 305, Wayne 07470
Pres.—Jim Kimberlin, 20 emp., *Corporate headquarters; men's, women's* ..................... (973) 956-6990
Palmyra Pants Co., Inc., 9370 Route 130 N., Pennsauken 08110
Pres.—Howard Eisenberg, 4 emp., *Men's & boys' slacks & shoes* ..................... (856) 662-0398

### 3144 Footwear—women's, except athletic

AeroGroup International, Inc. (H Q), 201 Meadow Rd., Edison 08817
Pres.—Jules Schneider, 120 emp., *Corporate headquarters; women's shoes* ..................... (732) 985-6900
Carlascio Inc. Orthotics, Prosthetic, Custom Shoes, 283 Grove St., Jersey City 07302
Owner—Louis Carlascio, 11 emp., *Custom handmade orthotics, prosthetics* ..................... (201) 333-8716
Carrini, Inc. (H Q), 140 Smith St., 5th Fl., Keasbey 08832
Pres.—Eli Chabot, 18 emp., *Corporate headquarters; men's, women's* ..................... (732) 650-1775
Gordon Mills Mfg., Inc. (H Q), 68 Sherwood Dr., Morristown 07960
Pres.—Bernard Factor, 3 emp., *Corporate headquarters; manufacturer* ..................... (973) 359-1080
Leif J. Ostberg, Inc. (H Q), 401 Hamburg Tpke., Ste. 305, Wayne 07470
Pres.—Jim Kimberlin, 20 emp., *Corporate headquarters; men's, women's* ..................... (973) 956-6990

### 3149 Footwear, except rubber, nec

Ballet Makers, Inc. (H Q), 1 Campus Rd., Totowa 07512
CEO—Anthony Giacoio, Jr., 100 emp., *Corporate headquarters; dance & dance-related* ....... (973) 595-9000
Carlascio Inc. Orthotics, Prosthetic, Custom Shoes, 283 Grove St., Jersey City 07302
Owner—Louis Carlascio, 11 emp., *Custom handmade orthotics, prosthetics* ..................... (201) 333-8716
Carrini, Inc. (H Q), 140 Smith St., 5th Fl., Keasbey 08832
Pres.—Eli Chabot, 18 emp., *Corporate headquarters; men's, women's* ..................... (732) 650-1775
Leif J. Ostberg, Inc. (H Q), 401 Hamburg Tpke., Ste. 305, Wayne 07470
Pres.—Jim Kimberlin, 20 emp., *Corporate headquarters; men's, women's* ..................... (973) 956-6990

### 3161 Luggage

Case-It, 1050 Valley Brook Ave., Lyndhurst 07071
Pres.—Adam Merzon, 10 emp., *Carrying cases* ..................... (201) 804-5556
Diamond Case Co., 45 Fairfield Pl., West Caldwell 07006
Pres.—Frank Johnston, 12 emp., *Luggage* ..................... (973) 227-8707
Jack Georges, Inc., 823 Main Ave., Passaic 07055
Pres.—Jack Georges, 15 emp., *Leather briefcases, totes, handbags* ..................... (973) 777-6999
TUMI, Inc. (H Q), 1001 Durham Ave., South Plainfield 07080
Pres., CEO—Jerome Griffith, 150 emp., *Corporate headquarters; luggage & travel* ............... (908) 756-4400

### 3171 Purses & handbags—women's

Gio Vali Corp., 463 Grand St., Paterson 07505
Pres.—Ara Mesrobian, 8 emp., *Women's leather & tapestry handbags* ..................... (973) 279-3032
Jack Georges, Inc., 823 Main Ave., Passaic 07055
Pres.—Jack Georges, 15 emp., *Leather briefcases, totes, handbags* ..................... (973) 777-6999
Jaclyn, Inc., 197 W. Spring Valley Ave., Ste. 1, Maywood 07607
Chrm.—Allan Ginsburg, 100 emp., *Corporate headquarters & handbags &* ..................... (201) 909-6000
LBU, Inc., 217 Brook Ave., Ste. 6, Passaic 07055
Founder & Pres.—Jeff Mayer, 50 emp., *Custom hand, cosmetic, laundry, travel* ..................... (973) 773-4800
Manolucci Designs, 220 61st St., Ste. 2-D, West New York 07093
Pres.—Chris Vartanian, 3 emp., *Leather handbags* ..................... (201) 861-2259
Maple Leather Co., 14 Raven Rock Rd., P.O. Box 319, Stockton 08559
Pres.—Seymour Mondshein, 3 emp., *Leather, fabric & nylon handbags, purses* ..................... (609) 397-1199
Miller Corp., Carol S., 98 Saddlewood Dr., Ste. A, Hillsdale 07642
★ Pres.—Carol Schepker, 4 emp., *Women's handbags* ..................... (201) 406-4578

### 3172 Leather goods—personal

AJ Tanner Ltd., 93 Harrison St., 2nd Fl., Paterson 07501
Owner—Stan Dworkin, 20 emp., *Leather hair accessories* ..................... (973) 523-5204
Browbands With Bling & Other Things, 985 Farmingdale Rd., Jackson 08527
★ Owner—Katherine Griffin, 1 emp., *Custom handcrafted leather products* ..................... (732) 740-8300
Colemax Group, LLC / Prima Cases, P.O. Box 103, Glen Rock 07452
Mng. Dir.—Richard Flashenberg, 6 emp., *Leather, synthetic & molded carrying* ..................... (201) 489-1080
Ivyskin, LLC, 282 Grand Ave., Englewood 07631
Pres.—Mike Panahi, 7 emp., *Leather cellular telephone cases* ..................... (201) 266-5555
Jack Georges, Inc., 823 Main Ave., Passaic 07055
Pres.—Jack Georges, 15 emp., *Leather briefcases, totes, handbags* ..................... (973) 777-6999
TUMI, Inc. (H Q), 1001 Durham Ave., South Plainfield 07080
Pres., CEO—Jerome Griffith, 150 emp., *Corporate headquarters; luggage & travel* ............... (908) 756-4400

### 3199 Leather goods, nec

Badge Company Of New Jersey, 223 Hamden Rd., P.O. Box 100, Annandale 08801
GM—Robert Marlow, 3 emp., *Manufacturer & distributor of badges* ..................... (908) 735-7700
Bird Toy Man, 197 S. Hillside Ave., Succasunna 07876
Owner—Henry E. Pedynowski, 1 emp., *Wooden, plastic, acrylic, leather &* ..................... (973) 584-0756
Browbands With Bling & Other Things, 985 Farmingdale Rd., Jackson 08527
★ Owner—Katherine Griffin, 1 emp., *Custom handcrafted leather products* ..................... (732) 740-8300
Coast To Coast Leather & Vinyl, Inc., 1 Crossman Rd. S., Sayreville 08872
Co-Pres.—Michael Ross, 10 emp., *Leather & vinyl for the automotive,* ..................... (732) 525-8877
Gecko Graphics, Inc., 128 Berlin Cross Keys Rd., Williamstown 08094
Pres.—Alice Gorney, 3 emp., *Laser engraving on acrylic, plastics* ..................... (856) 740-9042
Hartz Mountain Corp., The, 400 Plaza Dr., Secaucus 07094
Div. V-P., Mktg.—Adam Coacher, 250 emp., *Corporate headquarters & animal health* ........... (201) 271-4800
Jack Georges, Inc., 823 Main Ave., Passaic 07055
Pres.—Jack Georges, 15 emp., *Leather briefcases, totes, handbags* ..................... (973) 777-6999
Leather Handle Mfg. Co., 44 Dickerson St., Newark 07103
Pres.—Walter Robak, 7 emp., *Leather handles* ..................... (973) 485-2866
Pt Of Vu, LLC, 52 Edinborough Ct., Hackettstown 07840
Ptnr.—Louis Strauss, 5 emp., *Natural sea (Tilapia fish) leather* ..................... (908) 979-1360
RaGar Co., Inc., 2106 Kings Hwy., Asbury Park 07712
★ Pres., CEO—Lisa Raimondo, 5 emp., *Wooden & leather jewelry boxes* ..................... (732) 493-1416
TUMI, Inc. (H Q), 1001 Durham Ave., South Plainfield 07080
Pres., CEO—Jerome Griffith, 150 emp., *Corporate headquarters; luggage & travel* ............... (908) 756-4400
Union Hill Corp. (H Q), 34 Water St., Englishtown 07726
CEO—Mike Conforth, 4 emp., *Corporate headquarters; horse tack,* ..................... (732) 786-9422

## 32 STONE, CLAY & GLASS PRODUCTS

### 3211 Glass—flat

Brick Glass Co., 214 Midstreams Pl., Brick 08724
Owner—Louis Raccuglia, 6 emp., *Aluminum storefronts, curtain walls* ..................... (732) 899-8811
Disco Aluminum, 518 South Ave., Plainfield 07060
Ptnr.—William Villane, 2 emp., *Custom window & door screens, patio* ..................... (908) 754-2699
Dynasil Corp. Of America, 385 Cooper Rd., West Berlin 08091
V-P., Sales & Mktg. & GM—Bruce Leonetti, 16 emp., *Precision fused silica &* ..................... (856) 767-4600

Elco Glass Industries Co., Inc., 1855 Swarthmore Ave., Lakewood 08701
Pres.—E. Bavarsky, 25 emp., *Flat glass* (732) 363-6550

Elliott Glass Co., Inc., 192 Lackawanna Ave., Ste. 103, Woodland Park 07424
Manager—Kevin Elliott, 6 emp., *Glass fabrication* (973) 256-8098

Feldman Stained Glass, 401 Halladay St., Jersey City 07304
Proprietor—Larry A. Feldman, 3 emp., *Custom stained glass windows, skylights* (201) 434-2887

Glass Cycle Systems, Inc., 5 Mathews Ave., Riverdale 07457
Pres.—David Bowlby, 3 emp., *Glass recycling* (973) 838-0034

Jersey Tempered Glass, Inc., 2035 Briggs Rd., P.O. Box 205, Mount Laurel 08054
Pres.—Nicholas Concio, 30 emp., *Tempered glass, including beveled,* (856) 273-8700

Penta Glass Industries, Inc., 71 Hepworth Pl., Garfield 07026
Pres.—Jim Huddleston, 6 emp., *Glass store windows & curtain walls* (973) 478-2110

Precision Mirror & Glass, Inc., 89 Route 35 N., Eatontown 07724
Pres.—Tom Basile, 5 emp., *Frame-less tempered, laminated & etched* (732) 389-8175

RSL, Inc. (H Q), 3092 English Creek Ave., Egg Harbor Township 08234
Pres.—Ron Lewkowitz, 12 emp., *Corporate headquarters; vinyl door* (609) 484-1600

Somerset Glass Co., Inc., 2086 U.S. Highway 130, North Brunswick 08902
★ Pres.—Bill Hand, 10 emp., *Frameless shower door enclosures for* (732) 297-7444

Suburban Glass & Mirror, Inc., 231 Herbert Ave., Closter 07624
Pres.—Wayne Gangeri, 20 emp., *Corporate headquarters & glass & mirror* (201) 768-9586

Suburban Glass & Mirror, Inc., 418 S. Broad St., Ridgewood 07450
Pres.—Wayne Gangeri, 20 emp., *Glass & mirror fabrication, including* (201) 447-0440

Tracy's Stained Glass Studio, 11 New Providence Ave., Summit 07901
Pres.—Judi Tracy, 3 emp., *Custom stained, leaded & beveled glass* (908) 273-8040

## 3221 Glass containers

Andon Brush Co., Inc., 1 Merrit Ave., Little Falls 07424
Pres., GM—Robert Newell, 15 emp., *Dental, pharmaceutical, cosmetic, commercial* (973) 256-6611

Ardagh Group, 443 S. East Ave., P.O. Box 400, Bridgeton 08302
Sales Mgr., Natl.—John Orr, 350 emp., *Glass containers* (856) 455-2000

Ardagh Group, 83 Griffith St., Salem 08079
GM—Gary Shears, 312 emp., *Glass containers* (856) 935-4000

Bellco Glass, Inc., 340 Edrudo Rd., Vineland 08360
Pres.—Steven J. Harker, 77 emp., *Biological glassware & equipment* (856) 691-1075

Finneran Assocs., J. G., 3600 Reilly Ct., Vineland 08360
CEO—Jerry Finneran, 95 emp., *Company headquarters & laboratory glass* (856) 696-3605

Gerresheimer Glass, Inc., 91 W. Forest Grove Rd., Vineland 08360
Cont.—Bill Miskelly, 180 emp., *Glass vials & pharmaceutical, biotech* (856) 507-5600

Gerresheimer, Inc., 1300 Wheaton Ave., Millville 08332
V-P., Molded Glass Div., U.S.A.—Norman Angel, 230 emp., *Glass pharmaceutical & cosmetic* (856) 506-0501

Glass Dynamics, LLC, 2662 Hance Bridge Rd., Vineland 08361
CEO & Head of Opers.—Kimberlie Lawson, 9 emp., *Custom & precision glass fabrication* (856) 205-1530

Glastron, Inc., 510 N. West Blvd., Vineland 08360
Pres.—Bryan Wolcott, 65 emp., *Corporate headquarters & specialty* (856) 692-0500

International Glass Work, Inc., 723 E. Park Ave., P.O. Box 1015, Vineland 08360
Owner—Louis Pomales, 1 emp., *Scientific glass test tubes & flasks* (856) 691-5628

Phoenix Glass, LLC, 615 Alvine Rd., Pittsgrove 08318
V-P.—Frank Rohrman, 70 emp., *Glass vials & decorating services* (856) 692-0100

Piramal Glass USA, Inc., 918 E. Malaga Rd., Williamstown 08094
IT Mgr.—Brad Reckhart, 90 emp., *Glass containers for pharmaceutical* (856) 728-9300

Piramal Glass-USA, Inc. (H Q), 401 Route 73 N., Bldg. 10, Ste. 202, Lake Center Executive Pk., Marlton 08053
CEO—Niraj Tipre, 25 emp., *Corporate headquarters; glass containers* (856) 293-6400

Q Glass Co., Inc., 624 Main Rd., Towaco 07082
Pres.—Daniel J. Dotterweich III, 6 emp., *Custom & standard quartz laboratory* (973) 335-5191

Richland Glass Co., Inc., 1640 S. West Blvd., Vineland 08360
Pres., GM—Jack Carson, 100 emp., *Custom & standard glass products, including* (856) 691-1697

Technical Glass Products, Inc., 243 E. Blackwell St., Ste. B, Dover 07801
Pres.—Joseph Murray, 5 emp., *Glassware, including viscometers, thermometer* (973) 989-5500

## 3229 Glass—pressed & blown, nec

Ace Glass, Inc., 1430 N. West Blvd., Vineland 08360
Pres., CEO—Richard Kramme, 80 emp., *Scientific glassware & laboratory equipment* (856) 692-3333

Atlantic International Technologies, Inc., 114 Beach St., Bldg. 3, Rockaway 07866
CEO—Robert Campbell, 20 emp., *Silicate & optical glass & quartz tubing* (973) 625-0053

Chemglass, Inc., 3800 N. Mill Rd., Vineland 08360
CEO—Walter Surdam, 200 emp., *Scientific glassware & related products* (856) 696-0014

Database Access Systems, Inc., 60 Midvale Rd., Ste. 206, P.O. Box 126, Mountain Lakes 07046
Pres., CEO—Michael Palazzi, 4 emp., *Fiber-optic network cards & switches* (973) 335-0800

Decor, Inc., 60 Cedar Ln., Englewood 07631
Pres.—Richard Engel, 180 emp., *Glass decorating* (201) 569-1900

Durand Glass Mfg. Co., 901 S. Wade Blvd., Millville 08332
CEO—Fred Dohn, 700 emp., *Glass tableware* (856) 327-4800

Fiberguide Industries, Inc., 1 Bay St., Stirling 07980
Pres., CEO—Patricia Seniw, 25 emp., *Corporate headquarters & optical fibers* (908) 647-6601

Finneran Assocs., J. G., 3600 Reilly Ct., Vineland 08360
CEO—Jerry Finneran, 95 emp., *Company headquarters & laboratory glass* (856) 696-3605

Friedrich & Dimmock, Inc., 2127 Wheaton Ave., P.O. Box 230, Millville 08332
CEO—Joseph A. Plumbo, 45 emp., *Manufacturer of precision glass & quartz* (856) 825-0305

Gerresheimer Glass, Inc., 537 Crystal Ave., Vineland 08360
CFO—Chris Bouffard, 260 emp., *Corporate headquarters & blown glassware* (856) 692-3600

Glass Dynamics, LLC, 2662 Hance Bridge Rd., Vineland 08361
CEO & Head of Opers.—Kimberlie Lawson, 9 emp., *Custom & precision glass fabrication* (856) 205-1530

Glastron, Inc., 510 N. West Blvd., Vineland 08360
Pres.—Bryan Wolcott, 65 emp., *Corporate headquarters & specialty* (856) 692-0500

Go Foton, 28 Worlds Fair Dr., Somerset 08873
Pres.—Simin Cai, 25 emp., *Fiber-optic lenses & components* (732) 469-9650

Hess Glass Products, 601 N. Orchard Rd., Vineland 08360
Owner & Pres.—Doris Danna, 1 emp., *Hospital, laboratory & pharmaceutical* (856) 691-1432

Inrad Optics, Inc., 181 Legrand Ave., Northvale 07647
Chrm.—Jan Winston, 65 emp., *OEM custom optics, laser accessories* (201) 767-1910

Jersey Tempered Glass, Inc., 2035 Briggs Rd., P.O. Box 205, Mount Laurel 08054
Pres.—Nicholas Concio, 30 emp., *Tempered glass, including beveled,* (856) 273-8700

Karr Glass, Inc., Peggy, 100 Washington St., Randolph 07869
Pres.—Peggy Karr, 26 emp., *Fused glass products* (973) 659-1200

N D S Technologies, Inc., 891 E. Oak Rd., Vineland 08360
Pres., R & D Mgr.—Norman A. Neill, 40 emp., *Laboratory, filtration & specialty* (856) 691-0330

New Brunswick Lamp Shade Co., 7 Terminal Rd., New Brunswick 08901
CEO—Paul Zankel, 20 emp., *Lampshades* (732) 545-0377

OFS Fitel, LLC, Specialty Photonics Div., 25 Schoolhouse Rd., Somerset 08873
Manager—Joann Coyne, 45 emp., *Specialty fiber-optic cables & fiber* (732) 748-7400

QIS, Inc., 778 Vineland Ave., P.O. Box 517, Rosenhayn 08352
Pres.—Diane R. Lodge, 20 emp., *Glass vials* (856) 455-3736

Quark Enterprises, Inc., 320 Morton Ave., Rosenhayn 08352
Pres.—Doug Riley, 18 emp., *Scientific glassware* (856) 455-0376

Quest Industries, LLC, 480 Mundet Pl., Hillside 07205
CEO—Ravi Reddy, 90 emp., *Company headquarters & decorative glassware* (908) 851-9070

Solar Furnace Glass, 4 Camp Wasigan Rd., Blairstown 07825
★ Owner—Al Hough, 1 emp., *Decorative glass* (908) 362-9661

Swift-Track, Inc. (H Q), 58 Schlosser Dr., Rochelle Park 07662
Pres.—William Coleman, 3 emp., *Corporate headquarters; patented internal* (201) 226-9537

Wheaton Industries, Inc., 1501 N. 10th St., Millville 08332
Pres., CEO—Wayne L. Brinster, 300 emp., *Corporate headquarters & scientific* (856) 825-1100

Wilmad-LabGlass, 1172 N. West Blvd., Vineland 08360
Dir., Sales & Mktg.—Doug Grady, 133 emp., *Divisional headquarters & precision* (856) 691-3200

## 3231 Glass products from purchased glass

10-31, Inc., 2 W. Crisman Rd., Columbia 07832
Pres.—William Stender, 24 emp., *Custom wooden, plastic & glass artwork* (908) 496-4946

21st Century Optical, 5 Powder Horn Dr., Warren 07059
GM—Ed Glassheim, 10 emp., *Glass, plastic & polycarbonate fabrication* (973) 379-2020

A M K Glass, Inc., 2880 Industrial Way, Vineland 08360
Pres.—Kristine Kousmine, 25 emp., *Laboratory glassware* (856) 692-1488

A W Eurostile, 736 Route 35, Ocean 07712
Pres.—Andrea Wyman, 10 emp., *Manufacturer & distributor of marble* (732) 493-1883

Accuratus Corporation, 35 Howard St., Phillipsburg 08865
Pres.—Raymond Tsao, 30 emp., *Manufacturer of advanced technical* (908) 213-7070

Ad Plus, 111 Cambridge Ave., Linwood 08221
Owner—Leonard Demingo, 1 emp., *Glass fabrication* (609) 653-7007

Afina Corp., 40 Warren St., Paterson 07524
Pres.—Raymond Lombardo, 35 emp., *Bathroom cabinets & mirrors* (973) 684-7650

AGC Acquisition, LLC, 3740 N. West Blvd., Vineland 08360
V-P., Fin. & Treas.—Peggy McMahon, 40 emp., *Precision laboratory & industrial glass* (856) 692-4435

American Glass Crafters, Inc., 193 Veterans Blvd., Carlstadt 07072
Pres.—Joseph Cano, 35 emp., *Frameless shower doors* (201) 525-1116

Arm-R-Lite Door Mfg. Co., Inc., 2700 Hamilton Blvd., South Plainfield 07080
Pres.—Wilma M. Dourney, 20 emp., *Residential & commercial aluminum,* (908) 754-2600

Artique Glass Studio, 483 S. Broad St., Glen Rock 07452
Owner—Jay Demauro, 6 emp., *Stained glass fabrication* (201) 444-3500

Ascalon Studios, Inc., 430 Cooper Rd., West Berlin 08091
Pres., Hum. Res. Mgr.—David Ascalon, 10 emp., *Sculptures, memorials, monuments, stained* (856) 768-3779

B&D Marketing, Inc., 1879 Old Cuthbert Rd., Ste. 21, Cherry Hill 08034
Pres.—Marlene Epworth, 5 emp., *Custom donor recognition wall displays* (856) 354-2004

Bellco Glass, Inc., 340 Edrudo Rd., Vineland 08360
Pres.—Steven J. Harker, 77 emp., *Biological glassware & equipment* (856) 691-1075

Berkowitz, Inc., L.P., J. E., 1 Gateway Blvd., P.O. Box 427, Pedricktown 08067
Pres.—Arthur Berkowitz, 265 emp., *Architectural glass fabrication of* (856) 456-7800

Blue Star Glass, Inc., 2300 U.S. Highway 1, Bldg. 31, North Brunswick 08902
GM—MeMelida Mavric-Halkic, 15 emp., *Commercial glass tempering & fabrication* (732) 422-1272

Brick Glass Co., 214 Midstreams Pl., Brick 08724
Owner—Louis Raccuglia, 6 emp., *Aluminum storefronts, curtain walls* (732) 899-8811

Bridgeton Trophy & Engraving, 641 Landis Ave., Bridgeton 08302
Owner—Tom D'Agostino, 10 emp., *Engraved trophies, glass etching &* (856) 451-9007

Camden Glass, Inc., 111 Marlton Ave., Camden 08105
Pres.—James Keller, 8 emp., *Glass cutting, glazing, beveling &* (856) 365-0142

Cardinal International, Inc., 43 Route 46 E., Ste. 709, P.O. Box 897, Pine Brook 07058
★ Pres.—Bryan O'Rourke, 10 emp., *Glass drinkware, dinnerware, flatware* (973) 628-0900

Cargille Laboratories, 55 Commerce Rd., Cedar Grove 07009
Pres., Tech.—William J. Sacher, 22 emp., *Refractive index & sink-float standards* (973) 239-6633

Carlisle Machine Works, Inc., 412 S. Wade Blvd., Bldg. 5, P.O. Box 746, Millville 08332
Pres.—Mary Dougherty, 23 emp., *Custom fabrication & machining of industrial* (856) 825-0627

Century Bathworks, Inc., 250 Lackawanna Ave., Woodland Park 07424
Pres.—Michael MacMillan, 125 emp., *Framed & frameless glass shower & tub* (973) 785-4290

Chemglass, Inc., 3800 N. Mill Rd., Vineland 08360
CEO—Walter Surdam, 200 emp., *Scientific glassware & related products* (856) 696-0014

City Glass Co., 282 Broadway, P.O. Box 178, Bayonne 07002
Pres.—Allan McCleod, 50 emp., *Architectural metals, glass & custom* (201) 436-8400

Clifton Mirror & Glass Co., Inc., 188 Getty Ave., Clifton 07011
Cont.—Dale Calabro, 50 emp., *Glass fabrication, table tops & replacement* (973) 772-7770

Creamer Glass, LLC, 411 N. 10th St., Millville 08332
Owner & GM—Todd Miskelly, 5 emp., *Glass fabrication* (856) 327-2023

Creations In Glass, 344 Main St., Hackensack 07601
Owner—Joe Henchewski, 2 emp., *Custom stained glass windows, etched* (201) 488-0229

Crystal World, Inc., 89 Leuning St., Ste. A-2, South Hackensack 07606
Pres.—Toshi Ogawa, 24 emp., *Crystal figurines & awards* (201) 488-0909

Cutting Board Co., 291 Highway 22, Lebanon 08833
Ptnr. & Reg. Mgr.—Anthony Pizzelanti, 3 emp., *Standard, custom, glass, plastic &* (908) 725-0187

De Dietrich U. S. A., Inc. (H Q), 244 Sheffield St., Mountainside 07092
Pres.—Don Doell, 30 emp., *Corporate headquarters; glass lining* (908) 317-2585

Durand Glass Mfg. Co., 901 S. Wade Blvd., Millville 08332
CEO—Fred Dohn, 700 emp., *Glass tableware* (856) 327-4800

Easco Shower Doors Co., 3 Industrial Dr., Vernon 07462
Dir., Engrg. & Opers.—Vincent Bottaro, 28 emp., *Glass & aluminum shower doors & tub* (973) 209-4141

Eastern Glass Resources, Inc., 770 Supor Blvd., Harrison 07029
★ Owner—Phil Phisher, 30 emp., *Insulated & tempered glass & architectural* (973) 483-8411

Elliott Glass Co., Inc., 192 Lackawanna Ave., Ste. 103, Woodland Park 07424
Manager—Kevin Elliott, 6 emp., *Glass fabrication* (973) 256-8098

Ewing Glass Co., 1354 Parkside Ave., Trenton 08638
Pres.—Steve McClenney, 7 emp., *Glass fabrication & installation* (609) 882-1818

Feldman Stained Glass, 401 Halladay St., Jersey City 07304
Proprietor—Larry A. Feldman, 3 emp., *Custom stained glass windows, skylights* (201) 434-2887

Fiore Skylights, Inc., 210 E. Evergreen Ave., P.O. Box 160, Somerdale 08083
Pres., Div.—Richard L. Materio, 15 emp., *Commercial & residential structural* (856) 346-0118

Floxite Company, Inc., 31 Industrial Ave., Ste. 2, Mahwah 07430
Pres.—Bruce Pitot, 8 emp., *Cosmetic vanity, wall, travel, lighted* (201) 529-2019

Frank's Aluminum Glass & Mirrors Co., 588 Park Ave., Freehold 07728
Pres.—Anthony Santoriello, 4 emp., *Decorative mirrors* (732) 462-8141

Freehold Glass & Mirror, Inc., 38 South St., Freehold 07728
Pres.—David Gross, 6 emp., *Custom frameless & framed shower &* (732) 462-6200

Galaxy Glass & Stone, 277 Fairfield Rd., P.O. Box 10154, Fairfield 07004
Pres., CEO—Eugene M. Negrin, 35 emp., *Custom & decorative architectural glass* (973) 575-3440

Galossi Glass Design, Inc., 12 Van Pelt Dr., Whitehouse Station 08889
Pres.—Alfredo Galossi, 2 emp., *Stained glass shower doors* (908) 232-2111

General Glass International, 101 Venture Way, Secaucus 07094
Pres., CEO—David Balik, 137 emp., Company headquarters & glass cutting ........ (201) 553-1850
General Metal & Glass Co., 613 Kaighn Ave., Camden 08101
GM—Bill Tuling, 3 emp., Glass & metal windows ........ (856) 365-6323
Gerresheimer Glass, Inc., 537 Crystal Ave., Vineland 08360
CFO—Chris Bouffard, 260 emp., Corporate headquarters & blown glassware ........ (856) 692-3600
Glass Dynamics, LLC, 2662 Hance Bridge Rd., Vineland 08361
CEO & Head of Opers.—Kimberlie Lawson, 9 emp., Custom & precision glass fabrication ........ (856) 205-1530
Glassblowers.Com, Inc., P.O. Box 8089, Turnersville 08012
Owner—Thomas Cachaza, 1 emp., Scientific glassware ........ (856) 232-7898
GlassRoots, Inc., 10 Bleeker St., Newark 07102
Dir., Hum. Res.—Katie Witzig, 20 emp., Glass jewelry, beadmaking & mosaics ........ (973) 353-9555
Glaston America, Inc., 600-D Commerce Pkwy., Mount Laurel 08054
★ V-P.—Scott Steffy, 60 emp., Architectural glass fabrication, including ........ (856) 786-1200
Glastron, Inc., 510 N. West Blvd., Vineland 08360
Pres.—Bryan Wolcott, 65 emp., Corporate headquarters & specialty ........ (856) 692-0500
Globe Scientific, Inc., 610 Winters Ave., Paramus 07652
Pres.—Milton Diamond, 45 emp., Laboratory plastic ware, glassware ........ (201) 599-1400
Gorkin Glass Co., Inc., 26 Race St., North Plainfield 07060
Pres.—William Schultz, 15 emp., Glass shower doors & mirrors ........ (908) 756-0544
Hard Rock Marble & Granite, Inc., 1101 Chestnut St., Roselle 07203
CEO—N. Ruby Renjen, 12 emp., Custom marble & granite fabrication ........ (908) 620-9150
Hess Glass Products, 601 N. Orchard Rd., Vineland 08360
Owner & Pres.—Doris Danna, 1 emp., Hospital, laboratory & pharmaceutical ........ (856) 691-1432
Hiemer & Co., Edward W., 141 Wabash Ave., Clifton 07011
Pres.—Judith Van Wie, 10 emp., Fabrication & restoration of stained ........ (973) 772-5081
Hudson United Glass & Window Corp., 476 Hudson St., Hackensack 07601
Pres.—John Monacchio, 3 emp., Glass cutting & fabrication ........ (201) 440-3937
Insulite, Inc., 1890 Church Rd., Toms River 08753
Pres.—B. Albert Horn, 16 emp., Insulating glass ........ (732) 255-1700
J & R Lamb Studios, Inc., 190 Greenwood Ave., Midland Park 07432
Pres.—Donald Samick, 7 emp., Stained glass windows & restoration ........ (201) 891-8585
James Alexander Corp., 845 State Route 94, Blairstown 07825
Pres.—Francesca Fazzolari, 100 emp., Contract packaging, including crushable ........ (908) 362-9266
Jantek Industries, LLC, 230 Route 70, Medford 08055
CEO—Keith Kailian, 40 emp., Windows, doors & related products for ........ (609) 654-1030
Jersey Tempered Glass, Inc., 2035 Briggs Rd., P.O. Box 205, Mount Laurel 08054
Pres.—Nicholas Concio, 30 emp., Tempered glass, including beveled, ........ (856) 273-8700
Lager Glass Co., Inc., 1913 Heck Ave., P.O. Box 426, Neptune 07753
Pres.—Dean Lager, 8 emp., Glass fabrication ........ (732) 775-9220
Laser Xpressions, Inc., 3710 Route 9 S., 2nd Fl., Freehold 07728
★ Pres.—Aco Sokolovski, 14 emp., Laser engraving of metal plaques & ........ (732) 303-9530
Le Papillon, 120 Albany St., Ste. 300, New Brunswick 08901
Owner—Watson Warriner, 20 emp., Glass perfume vials ........ (732) 843-6116
Legacy Stairs & Millwork, Inc., 1000 Airport Rd., Ste. 104, Lakewood 08701
Owner—Stephen Hasse, 6 emp., Custom wooden, steel & aluminum conventional ........ (732) 905-7705
Mainland Plate Glass Co., Inc., 53 E. West Jersey Ave., Pleasantville 08232
Pres.—Richard Bozzelli, 10 emp., Architectural glass doors, windows, ........ (609) 641-6553
Martin, Inc., H. S., 1149 Southeast Blvd., Vineland 08360
Pres.—Nontas Kontes, 20 emp., Laboratory glass, reactors, distillation ........ (856) 692-8700
Matawan Stained Glass, 77-A Main St., Matawan 07747
Owner & Pres.—Jim Wallace, 2 emp., Stained glass ........ (732) 583-1030
McGrory Glass, Inc., 1400 Grandview Ave., Paulsboro 08066
CEO, CFO—John McGrory, 35 emp., Flat glass & plastic fabrication ........ (856) 579-3200
Mirrotek International, LLC, 90 Dayton Ave., Bldg. 1-F, Passaic 07055
Pres.—Joe Bezzy, 45 emp., Decorative & dressing mirrors, home ........ (973) 472-1400
Mullin Glass Co., Inc., 268 Main St., Butler 07405
Pres.—Gerald Mullin, Jr., 2 emp., Glass fabrication ........ (973) 838-6767
Nelson Glass & Aluminum Co., Inc., 45 Spring St., Princeton 08542
Pres.—Roberta Nelson, 10 emp., Commercial & residential glass products ........ (609) 924-2880
New Century Building Systems, Inc., 70 Sewell St., P.O. Box 775, Glassboro 08028
Pres.—Thomas Salzer, 8 emp., Aluminum windows & glass curtain walls ........ (856) 863-8036
Norman's Glass & Auto Services, Inc., 4482 Route 130 S., Burlington 08016
Pres.—John Farfalla, 10 emp., Automotive, residential & commercial ........ (609) 386-7100
North Jersey Metal Fabricators, Inc., 130 Ryerson Ave., Ste. 107, Wayne 07470
Pres.—Bill Ecker, 7 emp., Metal, aluminum, stainless steel & ........ (973) 305-9830
O & S Research, Inc., 1912 Bannard St., P.O. Box 221, Cinnaminson 08077
Pres.—Anderson L. McCabe, 40 emp., Anti-glare optical coatings & glass ........ (856) 829-2800
Oldcastle BuildingEnvelope®, 1500 Glen Ave., Moorestown 08057
Sales Mgr.—Brian Moore, 100 emp., Glass & metal fabrication ........ (866) 653-2278
Paterson Packaging, 269 Wilson St., Saddle Brook 07663
Owner & Pres.—Kenneth Manley, 3 emp., Flexible packaging, including BOPP, ........ (201) 398-9693
Penta Glass Industries, Inc., 71 Hepworth Pl., Garfield 07026
Pres.—Jim Huddleston, 6 emp., Glass store windows & curtain walls ........ (973) 478-2110
Perilstein Glass, 285 Howe Ave., P.O. Box 84, Passaic 07055
Pres.—David Perilstein, 30 emp., Metal & glass fabrication ........ (973) 777-3610
Phillips Safety Products, Inc., 123 Lincoln Blvd., Middlesex 08846
Pres.—Robert Phillips, 10 emp., Lead glass windows, glass etching, ........ (732) 356-1493
Picture-It, Inc., 1703 State Route 27, Edison 08817
Pres.—Roy Taetzsch, 5 emp., Acrylic, crystal, glass & wooden awards ........ (732) 819-0420
Pochet Of America, Inc., 415 Hamburg Tpke., Ste. 2, Wayne 07470
Pres.—Borislav Zivkovic, 100 emp., Corporate headquarters & perfume bottle ........ (973) 942-4923
Potters Industries, Inc., 600 Industrial Rd., Carlstadt 07072
Plt. Mgr.—Glenn Evers, 15 emp., Industrial glass beads ........ (201) 460-0666
Precision Electronic Glass, Inc., 1013 Hendee Rd., Vineland 08360
Pres.—Philip M. Rossi, 75 emp., Precision custom glass & quartz components ........ (856) 691-2234
Precision Mirror & Glass, Inc., 89 Route 35 N., Eatontown 07724
Pres.—Tom Basile, 5 emp., Frame-less tempered, laminated & etched ........ (732) 389-8175
Precision Shower Doors, Inc., 359 Essex Rd., Tinton Falls 07753
Pres.—Tom Basile, 13 emp., Frameless glass shower enclosures & ........ (732) 389-8175
Pride Tempered Glass Products, LLC, 2001 S. 6th St., Camden 08104
Pres.—John Galan, 10 emp., Tempered & insulated glass & mirrors ........ (856) 365-1200
Quantum Coating, Inc., 1259 N. Church St., Bldg. 1, Moorestown 08057
Pres.—D. Patriarca, 34 emp., Anti-reflective coated display panels ........ (856) 231-0706
Quest Industries, LLC, 480 Mundet Pl., Hillside 07205
CEO—Ravi Reddy, 90 emp., Company headquarters & decorative glassware ........ (908) 851-9070
Rambusch Company, 160 Cornelison Ave., Jersey City 07304
Chrm.—Martin V. Rambusch, 43 emp., Standard & custom lighting fixtures ........ (201) 333-2525
Raybold Mfg., Inc., 102 S. 8th St., Millville 08332
Pres.—William Riland, 9 emp., Screen printing of glass bottles & ........ (856) 327-7733
Richland Glass Co., Inc., 1640 S. West Blvd., Vineland 08360
Pres., GM—Jack Carson, 100 emp., Custom & standard glass products, including ........ (856) 691-1697
Rios Engraving, 1 Maple Ave., Morristown 07960
Owner, Plt. Opers. & Sales & Mktg. Mgr.—Rolando G. Rios, 3 emp., Custom & laser engraving (973) 539-5749
Royal Prime Window Specialist, Inc., 742 Fairfield Ave., Kenilworth 07033
Pres. & IT Mgr.—Andrew Inelli, 6 emp., High-end vinyl replacement windows ........ (908) 354-7600
Seagull Stained Glass, 1917 Kuehnle Ave., Atlantic City 08401
Proprietor & Ptnr.—Linda Spolitino, 2 emp., Sand carved glass ........ (609) 345-3126
Seashore Glass & Mirror, 2547 Fire Rd., Ste. 2-B, Egg Harbor Township 08234
Owner & Pres.—Joseph Pitzo, 4 emp., Heavy, frameless, framed & semi frameless ........ (609) 407-6032
Solar Furnace Glass, 4 Camp Wasigan Rd., Blairstown 07825
★ Owner—Al Hough, 1 emp., Decorative glass ........ (908) 362-9661
Somerset Glass Co., Inc., 2086 U.S. Highway 130, North Brunswick 08902
★ Pres.—Bill Hand, 10 emp., Frameless shower door enclosures for ........ (732) 297-7444
SRS, Inc., 74 Liberty St., P.O. Box 4277, Metuchen 08840
Pres.—Rich Blatman, 22 emp., Stainless steel, bronze & glass guardrails ........ (732) 548-6630
Stained Glass Design, Inc., 87 Dellglen Ave., Lodi 07644
Pres., Sales Mgr.—George Geswaldo, 3 emp., Stained glass ........ (973) 772-5070
Studio J/Architectural Glass Effects, 215 Pennsylvania Ave., Paterson 07503
Pres.—John Leong, 8 emp., Custom stained & leaded architectural ........ (973) 569-0200
Style Rite Of America, Inc., 118 Seger Ave., Clifton 07011
Ptnr.—Jaime Galorenzo, 15 emp., Framed, frameless & heavy glass shower ........ (973) 478-1100
Suburban Glass & Mirror, Inc., 231 Herbert Ave., Closter 07624
Pres.—Wayne Gangeri, 20 emp., Corporate headquarters & glass & mirror ........ (201) 768-9586
Suburban Glass & Mirror, Inc., 418 S. Broad St., Ridgewood 07450
Pres.—Wayne Gangeri, 20 emp., Glass & mirror fabrication, including ........ (201) 447-0440
Summit Group II, 333 16th St., Carlstadt 07072
Pres.—Tom Klein, 5 emp., Steel railings, ornamental iron, structural ........ (201) 460-8888
Sunflower Glass Studio, 877 Sergeantsville Rd., Stockton 08559
Owner—Karen Caldwell, 6 emp., Stained glass windows & beveled glass ........ (609) 397-1535
Technical Glass Products, Inc., 243 E. Blackwell St., Ste. B, Dover 07801
Pres.—Joseph Murray, 5 emp., Glassware, including viscometers, thermometer ........ (973) 989-5500
Thermoseal Industries, LLC, 400 Water St., Gloucester City 08030
Pres.—Richard A. Chubb, 50 emp., Glass insulating ........ (856) 456-3109
Tracy's Stained Glass Studio, 11 New Providence Ave., Summit 07901
Pres.—Judi Tracy, 3 emp., Custom stained, leaded & beveled glass ........ (908) 273-8040
Tri-State Glass & Mirror, Inc., 11-A Jocama Blvd., Old Bridge 08857
Ptnr.—Michael Panebianco, 3 emp., Glass mirrors & shower doors ........ (732) 591-5545
Triton Associated Industries, Inc., North Brewster Rd., P.O. Box 627, Buena 08310
V-P.—Wayne Edwards, 20 emp., Glass tube cutting ........ (856) 697-3050
Twin Glass Co., 6422 Black Horse Pike, Egg Harbor Township 08234
V-P.—Scott Summers, 6 emp., Glass, mirrors, storefronts, curtain ........ (609) 645-8834
Union City Mirror & Table Co., 129 34th St., Union City 07087
Pres., R & D Mgr.—Thomas Russo, 6 emp., French Provincial wooden & occasional ........ (201) 867-1827
Union County Plate Glass Co. (H Q), 1050 Elizabeth Ave., P.O. Box 9027, Elizabeth 07201
Pres.—Charles J. Komoroski, Jr., 60 emp., Company headquarters; plate glass, ........ (908) 354-0380
V M Glass Co., 3231 N. Mill Rd., Vineland 08360
Pres., Sales Mgr.—Michael Greico, 9 emp., Scientific glassware ........ (856) 794-9333
Victorian Glass Carver, 5515 Toms Ave., Pennsauken 08109
Pres.—Rose Mary Skalski, 2 emp., Victorian glass art reproductions ........ (856) 662-1391
VitroCom, Inc., 8 Morris Ave., P.O. Box 125, Mountain Lakes 07046
Plt. Mgr.—Phill Motyka, 30 emp., Fiber-optic components & technical ........ (973) 402-1443
W & E Baum, Inc., 89 Bannard St., Freehold 07728
CEO—Maurice Zagha, 25 emp., Wooden, marble, metal, acrylic, glass ........ (732) 866-1881
Wheaton Glass Warehouse, 1501 N. 10th St., Millville 08332
Pres.—Steve Drozdow, 60 emp., Glass fabrication ........ (856) 327-5228
Wilmad-LabGlass, 1172 N. West Blvd., Vineland 08360
Dir., Sales & Mktg.—Doug Grady, 133 emp., Divisional headquarters & precision ........ (856) 691-3200
Window Shapes, Inc., 225 Liberty St., Metuchen 08840
Owner & V-P.—Tom Change, 25 emp., Vinyl architectural shaped windows, ........ (848) 229-2431
Xenopore Corp., 299 Wagaraw Rd., Hawthorne 07506
Pres.—Allan Douglas, 8 emp., Plastic & glass laboratory plates & ........ (973) 423-2400

## 3241 Cement, hydraulic

Holcim U.S., 595 Morgan Blvd., Camden 08104
Plt. Mgr.—Fred Hyatt, 15 emp., Cement ........ (856) 964-2555

## 3253 Ceramic wall & floor tile

Ferro Corp., 54 Kellogg Ct., Edison 08817
Site Mgr.—Mike McKinney, 30 emp., Liquid & paste pigment, polymer additives ........ (732) 287-1930
GlassRoots, Inc., 10 Bleeker St., Newark 07102
Dir., Hum. Res.—Katie Witzig, 20 emp., Glass jewelry, beadmaking & mosaics ........ (973) 353-9555
Mannington Mills, Inc., 75 Mannington Mills Rd., P.O. Box 30, Salem 08079
Chrm. of the Board—Keith Campbell, 600 emp., Corporate headquarters & residential ........ (856) 935-3000
Vanea USA, Inc., 410 Market St., Elmwood Park 07407
V-P.—Sandro Marchi, 10 emp., Italian-style ceramic tile & kitchen ........ (201) 796-0722

## 3255 Clay refractories

Fuller Construction Products, Inc., H.B., 59 Brunswick Ave., Edison 08817
Facility Mgr.—Michael Emery, 23 emp., High-tech surface preparation mortar ........ (732) 287-8330
MAPEI Corp., Off White Head Ave., P.O. Box 105, South River 08882
Unit Mgr.—Lou Genzlinger, 25 emp., Mortar, grout & adhesives ........ (732) 254-8001
Nth Degree Products, LLC, 404 Laurel Ridge Rd., Hainesport 08036
CEO—Donald G. Lopata, 2 emp., High-temperature ceramic refractories ........ (609) 518-9447

## 3259 Structural clay products, nec

Ascalon Studios, Inc., 430 Cooper Rd., West Berlin 08091
Pres., Hum. Res. Mgr.—David Ascalon, 10 emp., Sculptures, memorials, monuments, stained (856) 768-3779
Nth Degree Products, LLC, 404 Laurel Ridge Rd., Hainesport 08036
CEO—Donald G. Lopata, 2 emp., High-temperature ceramic refractories ........ (609) 518-9447

## 3261 Plumbing fixtures—vitreous

Lenape Products, Inc., 600 Plum St., Trenton 08638
Pres.—Stephen M. Bielawski, 5 emp., Corporate headquarters & porcelain ........ (609) 394-5376
Vanea USA, Inc., 410 Market St., Elmwood Park 07407
V-P.—Sandro Marchi, 10 emp., Italian-style ceramic tile & kitchen ........ (201) 796-0722

## 3264 Porcelain electrical supplies

Advanced Cerametrics, Inc., 245 N. Main St., P.O. Box 128, Lambertville 08530
V-P., COO—Michael Hendricks, 20 emp., Advanced ceramic fibers & shapes & ........ (609) 397-2900
Ceramic Magnetics, Inc., 16 Law Dr., Fairfield 07004
Dir., Tech. & Qual. Assur. Mgr.—John Ings, 42 emp., Ferrite cores ........ (973) 227-4222
Ceramic Products, Inc., 221 Park St., Hackensack 07601
Pres.—Tony Vidaic, 8 emp., Ceramic fixtures, wear pins & insulators ........ (201) 342-8200

Certech, Inc., 1 Park Pl. W., Wood Ridge 07075
Pres.—John Stang, 220 emp., *Corporate headquarters & industrial* ........ (201) 939-7400
Crystex Composites, LLC, 125 Clifton Blvd., Clifton 07011
Pres., CEO—George Flores, 35 emp., *Machinable & moldable inorganic glass-mica* ........ (973) 779-8866
Electro Ceramic Industries, 75 Kennedy St., Hackensack 07601
Pres.—Frank Floystad, 20 emp., *Metal & ceramic seals* ........ (201) 342-2630
Fermag Technologies, 80 Executive Ave., Edison 08817
Pres.—John Perkins, 8 emp., *Magnetic powders* ........ (732) 985-7300
Isolantite Mfg. Co., Inc., 337 Warren Ave., Stirling 07980
Pres.—George W. Lumpe, 23 emp., *Ceramic insulators* ........ (908) 647-3333
National Ceramic Co., Inc., 500 Southard St., Trenton 08638
Pres.—V. Thomas Colletti, 9 emp., *Ceramic electrical insulators* ........ (609) 394-5373
Oxford Instruments Superconducting Technology, Inc., 600 Milik St., Carteret 07008
Pres.—Jeff Parrell, 212 emp., *Corporate headquarters & superconductor* ........ (732) 541-1300
Pekay Industries, Inc., Southard Ave., P.O. Box 559, Farmingdale 07727
Pres., GM—Peter Kowalenko, 12 emp., *Electronics ceramic terminals* ........ (732) 938-2722

## 3269 Pottery products, nec

Boehm Porcelain, LLC, 25 Princess Diana Dr., Trenton 08638
Pres., CEO—George Parker, 20 emp., *Porcelain sculptures of birds, animals* ........ (609) 656-2200
Ceramcor, LLC, 1026 Samantha Way, Toms River 08753
★ Owner—Richard Bergstrom, 2 emp., *Ceramic cookware* ........ (732) 929-2833
Curran Pfeiff Corp., Liddle Ave., Edison 08837
Pres., Hum. Res., Sales & Mktg. Mgr.—George Pfeiff, Jr., 11 emp., *Ceramic products, including* (732) 225-0555
Cybis Porcelains Studio & Gallery, 200 Elizabeth Ave., Ste. 200, Trenton 08610
Pres.—Joseph Chorlton, 45 emp., *Porcelain sculptures* ........ (609) 392-6074
Eigen Arts, Inc., 150 Bay St., Jersey City 07302
Pres.—Paul Brothe, 6 emp., *Ceramic dinnerware, vases, planters* ........ (201) 798-7310
Hopewell Pottery, 18 Burton Ave., Hopewell 08525
Owner—Constance McIndoe, 1 emp., *Pottery* ........ (609) 466-9048
Morgan Advanced Ceramics, Inc., 26 Madison Rd., Fairfield 07004
GM—Jerry McConvery, 30 emp., *Ceramic parts* ........ (973) 227-8877
Mottahedeh & Co., Inc., 5 Corporate Dr., Cranbury 08512
Pres.—Wendy Kvalheim, 12 emp., *Porcelain dinnerware* ........ (609) 409-1490
Our Name Is Mud, 15 Potter St., Ste. 1, Haddonfield 08033
Pres.—Kip Veasey, 1 emp., *Pottery products* ........ (856) 375-2098
Shedd Designs, LLC, John, 200 Washington St., P.O. Box 276, Rocky Hill 08553
Owner—John Shedd, 2 emp., *Ceramic vases, dinnerware, bowls, barware* ........ (609) 924-6394

## 3271 Concrete block & brick

Cambridge Pavers, Inc., Jerome Ave., P.O. Box 157, Lyndhurst 07071
Owner, Chrm., Pres. & CEO—Charles H. Gamarekian, 150 emp., *Interlocking concrete paving stones* (201) 933-5000
Clayton & Sons, Ralph, 125 Cox Crossing Rd., West Creek 08092
Plt. Mgr. & Dispatcher—John Pietrow, 15 emp., *Concrete block & ready-mixed concrete* ........ (609) 597-2233
Clayton Block Co., Inc, 2 Porete Ave., North Arlington 07031
Gen. Sales Mgr.—Joseph Scaramuzzo, 32 emp., *Concrete block & architectural precast* ........ (201) 955-6292
Clayton Block Co., Inc., 1601 18th Ave., Belmar 07719
Store Mgr.—Jerry Dooley, 15 emp., *Concrete block* ........ (732) 681-1414
Clayton Block Co., Inc., 1025 Route 1 S., Edison 08837
GM—Matt Emmert, 50 emp., *Concrete block* ........ (732) 549-1234
Clayton Block Co., Inc., 225 Throckmorton St., Freehold 07728
Off. Mgr.—Tom Boulter, 7 emp., *Concrete blocks* ........ (732) 462-1860
Clayton Block Co., Inc., 194 Chestnut St., Toms River 08753
Br. Mgr.—Matthew Dingus, 20 emp., *Concrete masonry units, building supplies* ........ (732) 349-3700
Clayton Block Co., Inc., Route 9, Waretown 08758
IT Mgr.—Scott Milne, 20 emp., *Concrete masonry units, building supplies* ........ (609) 693-3000
Eastern Concrete Materials, Inc. (H Q), 475 Market St., 3rd Fl., Elmwood Park 07407
Pres.—Mike Gentoso, 40 emp., *Corporate headquarters; ready-mixed* ........ (201) 797-7979
Oliver Mfg. Supply Co., 730 Port Reading Ave., P.O. Box 274, Port Reading 07064
Pres.—L. Escandon, 14 emp., *Concrete building block* ........ (732) 634-8100
Paverart, LLC, 2512 Egg Harbor Rd., Ste. C, Lindenwold 08021
Pres.—Mick Seroka, 5 emp., *Decorative interlocking concrete paving* ........ (856) 783-7000
Reuther Material Co., Inc., 5303 Tonnelle Ave., North Bergen 07047
V-P., Opers.—Douglas Reuther, 20 emp., *Concrete block* ........ (201) 863-3550
Smith & Son, Inc., R. P., Main St., P.O. Box 209, Succasunna 07876
Pres.—Robert Smith, 6 emp., *Concrete block* ........ (973) 584-4063

## 3272 Concrete products

A & A Concrete Products, Inc., 2 S. Corporate Dr., P.O. Box 108, Riverdale 07457
Pres.—Sandra L. Alway, 7 emp., *Concrete septic tanks, trench drains* ........ (973) 835-2239
Ace Crete Products, Inc., 250 Hickory Ln., Bayville 08721
Pres.—Martin E. Tanzer, 12 emp., *Manufacturer & distributor of industrial* ........ (732) 269-1400
Anchor Concrete Products, Inc. (H Q), 331 Newman Springs Rd., Bldg. 2, 3rd Fl., Ste. 236, Red Bank 07701
Pres.—John O'Neill, 20 emp., *Corporate headquarters; concrete products* ........ (732) 292-2500
Boccella Precast, LLC, 324 New Brooklyn Rd., Berlin 08009
Owner—Joseph Boccella, 10 emp., *Prestressed concrete hollow-core planks* ........ (856) 767-3861
Bradbury Burial Vault Co., Inc., 761 Lower Landing Rd., Blackwood 08012
Pres.—Lawrence A. Kenney, 23 emp., *Concrete burial vaults* ........ (856) 227-2555
Brewster Vaults & Monuments, Inc., 1017 Steeprun Rd., Millville 08332
Pres.—Joseph Brewster, 10 emp., *Concrete burial vaults* ........ (856) 785-1412
Capitol Pavers & Retaining Wall, Inc., 90 Main St., P.O. Box 3249, South Amboy 08879
Pres.—Norman Grossman, 60 emp., *Interlocking concrete pavers & retaining* ........ (732) 727-5460
Clayton & Sons, Ralph (H Q), 1355 Campus Pkwy., Neptune 07753
Pres.—William Clayton, 15 emp., *Company headquarters; ready-mixed concrete* ........ (732) 751-7600
Clayton Block Co., Inc., 194 Chestnut St., Toms River 08753
Br. Mgr.—Matthew Dingus, 20 emp., *Concrete masonry units, building supplies* ........ (732) 349-3700
Clayton Block Co., Inc., Route 9, Waretown 08758
IT Mgr.—Scott Milne, 20 emp., *Concrete masonry units, building supplies* ........ (609) 693-3000
Colas, Inc. (H Q), 163 Madison Ave., Ste. 500, Morristown 07960
Pres.—Georges Ausseil, 10 emp., *Corporate headquarters; asphalt paving* ........ (973) 290-9082
Conti Group, The (H Q), 2045 State Route 27, Edison 08817
Pres., CEO—Kurt G. Conti, 150 emp., *Company headquarters; precast concrete* ........ (732) 520-5000
Continental Cast Stone East, 400 Cooper Rd., West Berlin 08091
Pres.—Bill Russell, 50 emp., *Architectural cast stone* ........ (856) 753-4000
Cooper Wilbert Burial Vault Co., Inc., 621 E. Atlantic Ave., Barrington 08007
Pres.—Paul Cooper, 15 emp., *Corporate headquarters & concrete burial* ........ (856) 547-8405
County Concrete Corp., 50 Railroad Ave., P.O. Box F, Kenvil 07847
Pres.—John C. Crimi, 90 emp., *Corporate headquarters & concrete,* ........ (973) 584-7122
Creter Vault Corp., 417 Highway 202, Flemington 08822
Pres.—Richard E. Creter, 45 emp., *Concrete burial vaults* ........ (908) 782-7771
CST Pavers a division of Pavestone, 23 Ridge Rd., P.O. Box 2736, Branchville 07826
Pres.—William R. Magill, 57 emp., *Concrete pavers & retaining wall systems* ........ (973) 948-7193
CST Products, LLC, 345 Route 130, P.O. Box 402, Pedricktown 08067
Manager—Eric Bischoff, 20 emp., *Concrete pavers & retaining wall blocks* ........ (856) 299-5339
Di Ferraro, Inc., 28 Burgess Pl., Wayne 07470
Co-Pres.—Mario Ferraro, Jr., 25 emp., *Precast concrete products & burial* ........ (973) 694-7200
Dodson Vault Co., E., P.O. Box 966, Williamstown 08094
Owner—Ed Dodson, 2 emp., *Concrete burial vaults* ........ (856) 728-7660
Eastern Concrete Materials, Inc. (H Q), 475 Market St., 3rd Fl., Elmwood Park 07407
Pres.—Mike Gentoso, 40 emp., *Corporate headquarters; ready-mixed* ........ (201) 797-7979
Empire Blended Products, Inc., 250 Hickory Ln., Bayville 08721
Pres.—Jay Gornitzky, 31 emp., *Concrete products* ........ (732) 269-4949
Flemington Precast & Supply, LLC, 18 Allen St., Flemington 08822
Ptnr.—Jeff Hoffman, 10 emp., *Concrete precast supplies* ........ (908) 782-3246
Franklin Precast, 20 Park Dr., Franklin 07416
Pres.—Wendy Kovach, 8 emp., *Precast concrete septic tanks, seepage* ........ (973) 827-7563
G & C Fab Con, LLC, 5 Foster Ln., Bldg. A, Flemington 08822
Pres.—James C. Griffith, 41 emp., *Veterans cemeteries, including lawn* ........ (908) 782-0526
Gambale Precast, Inc., 1 Erial Rd., Clementon 08021
Pres.—Nick Gambale, Sr., 10 emp., *Precast concrete products* ........ (856) 784-3399
Garden State Precast, Inc., 1630 Wyckoff Rd., Wall Township 07719
Pres.—Kirby O'Malley, 75 emp., *Precast concrete products* ........ (732) 938-4436
Gifford & Co., Brian L., 514 Bogden Blvd., Millville 08332
Owner—Brian L. Gifford, 5 emp., *Dry mix concrete for on-site jobs &* ........ (856) 327-0011
Gillespie, Inc., Paul J., 2565 Brunetta Dr., Vineland 08360
Pres.—Donna Ruberti, 15 emp., *Precast concrete products* ........ (856) 839-0891
Granville Concrete Products, 1076 Route 10, Randolph 07869
Ptnr.—Kevin Peach, 5 emp., *Concrete septic tanks* ........ (973) 584-6653
Grinnell Concrete Pavingstones, Inc., 482 Houses Corner Rd., Sparta 07871
Ptnr.—Jason N. Cofrancesco, 45 emp., *Interlocking concrete paving stones* ........ (973) 383-9300
Harsco Corp., 1800 Lower Rd., Linden 07036
GM—Scott Wright, 25 emp., *Concrete forming & shoring* ........ (732) 396-1269
Henry Corp., E. P., 201 Park Ave., P.O. Box 615, Woodbury 08096
CEO—James C. Henry III, 150 emp., *Corporate headquarters & architectural* ........ (856) 845-6200
Hunterdon Ornamental Concrete, Inc., 440 Highway 22, Whitehouse Station 08889
Pres.—Steve Grasso, 2 emp., *Precast concrete products* ........ (908) 534-4556
J. B. & Sons Concrete Products Co., 358 New Brooklyn Rd., Berlin 08009
Owner—Joseph Boccella, 15 emp., *Precast concrete products* ........ (856) 767-4140
Jan Fence Co., Inc., 4 Industrial Rd., Pompton Plains 07444
Pres.—Robert Corrao, 15 emp., *Custom industrial, residential & security* ........ (973) 694-4055
Jersey Precast Corporation, 853 Nottingham Way, Trenton 08638
Chrm., Pres.—Mohamed Amir Ulislam, 130 emp., *Corporate headquarters & precast &* ........ (609) 689-3700
JM Lifestyles, LLC, 215 State Route 10, Ste. 3, Randolph 07869
Pres.—Michelle Radley, 6 emp., *Decorative concrete countertops, bars* ........ (973) 668-5057
Kenny Wilbert Vault Co., 40 Shades of Death Rd., Great Meadows 07838
Pres.—Bruce Kenny, 4 emp., *Concrete burial vaults* ........ (908) 637-4736
Marvic Corp./A.J.D. Stone, 2450 Iorio St., Union 07083
Pres., Marvic Corp.—Alfred J. D'Alessandro, 100 emp., *Granite, quartz, solid-surface, concrete* (908) 686-4340
Massarelli's Lawn Ornaments, 500 S. Egg Harbor Rd., Hammonton 08037
Pres.—Mario Massarelli, 100 emp., *Precast concrete & terrazzo fountains* ........ (609) 567-9700
Medford Concrete Co., 4 Tidswell Ave., P.O. Box 273, Medford 08055
GM—Bob Brick, 1 emp., *Precast concrete products, parking* ........ (609) 654-2200
Mershon Concrete, LLC, Route 130 S., P.O. Box 254, Bordentown 08505
V-P. & IT Mgr.—Patrick T. Greber, 40 emp., *Precast & ready-mixed concrete* ........ (609) 298-2150
Mid State Filigree Systems, Inc., 22 Brickyard Rd., P.O. Box 435, Cranbury 08512
Pres.—Harry Wise, 20 emp., *Precast concrete filigree wideslab* ........ (609) 448-8700
Northeast Concrete Products, LLC, 937 Burnt Meadow Rd., P.O. Box 963, Hewitt 07421
Pres.—John Vitale, 8 emp., *Concrete catch basins, tanks, lightpole* ........ (973) 728-1667
Oldcastle Precast, Inc., 1920 12th St., Williamstown 08094
Plt. Mgr.—Dennis Stevenson, 20 emp., *Concrete pipes* ........ (609) 561-3400
Peerless Concrete Products, Inc., 246 Main St., Butler 07405
Ptnr.—Phil Monaco, 40 emp., *Precast concrete products, including* ........ (973) 838-3060
Precast Mfg. Co., LLC, 187 Strykers Rd., Phillipsburg 08865
Plt. Mgr.—Vilma Delva, 30 emp., *Precast concrete products* ........ (908) 454-2122
Precast Systems, Inc., 57 Sharon Station Rd., Allentown 08501
Plt. Mgr.—Phil Potter, 25 emp., *Precast concrete products* ........ (609) 208-1987
QUIKRETE Cos., Inc, The, 22 Union Ave., Berlin 08009
Plt. Mgr.—Mark Koltura, 50 emp., *Packaged concrete, bulk mortar & grout* ........ (856) 768-6642
River Front Recycling & Aggregates, LLC, 1301 N. 26th St., Camden 08105
Owner—Aaron Cave, 80 emp., *Concrete, asphalt, dirt & wood recycling* ........ (856) 966-1100
Shared Systems Technology, Inc., 127 Salem Ave., Thorofare 08086
Pres.—Eric Swyers, 20 emp., *Concrete coatings* ........ (856) 218-7900
Sika Corporation, 201 Polito Ave., Lyndhurst 07071
Pres., CEO—Christoph Ganz, 107 emp., *Corporate headquarters & concrete materials* ........ (201) 933-8800
Smith's Concrete Products, 3504 S. West Blvd., Vineland 08360
Owner, Sales & Mktg. Mgr.—Richard S. Smith, 1 emp., *Concrete stepping stones* ........ (856) 696-3102
Stag Bros. Cast Stone, 720 Vassar Ave., Lakewood 08701
Pres.—Bill Stagliano, 10 emp., *Precast concrete & stone products* ........ (732) 363-6582
Strongwall Industries, Inc., 107 Chestnut St., Ridgewood 07450
Pres.—Nicole Kokoletsos, 12 emp., *Concrete restoration & protection products* ........ (201) 445-4633
Suburban Monument & Vault, 203 Sherman Ave., P.O. Box 2370, Newark 07114
Owner—Clyde Brooks, 6 emp., *Granite monuments & concrete burial* ........ (973) 242-7007
Trap Rock, 27 Maple Ave., Mount Holly 08060
Sales Mgr.—Michael Conti, 5 emp., *Asphalt paving compounds & concrete* ........ (609) 265-8500
Tri-State QUIKRETE, 150 Gold Mine Rd., Flanders 07836
Off. Mgr.—Sue Roach, 35 emp., *Packaged cement products* ........ (973) 347-4569
Van Dyk Trim Stone, LLC, 85 4th Ave., Haskell 07420
Pres.—David Van Dyk, 5 emp., *Cast stone* ........ (973) 831-1802
Vianini Pipe, Inc., 39 County Line Rd., Whitehouse Station 08889
Pres.—Alex Narcise, 100 emp., *Prestress, jacking & reinforced concrete* ........ (908) 534-4021
W. R. Grace & Co., 2133 85th St., North Bergen 07047
Regional Mgr.—Atom Saverse, 6 emp., *Concrete additives* ........ (201) 869-5220
Warren Materials, 703 Route 57, Stewartsville 08886
COO—James T. Haines, 23 emp., *Asphalt paving compounds & bituminous* ........ (908) 859-3333

## 3273 Concrete—ready-mixed

Action Supply, Inc., 1413 Stagecoach Rd., Ocean View 08230
Pres.—Tom Tower, 50 emp., *Corporate headquarters & manufacturer* ........ (609) 390-0663
Allied Concrete Co., Inc., 205 Franklin Ave., Rockaway 07866
Dispatcher—John Elliot, 18 emp., *Ready-mixed concrete* ........ (973) 627-6150

Anchor Concrete Products, Inc. (H Q), 331 Newman Springs Rd., Bldg. 2, 3rd Fl., Ste. 236, Red Bank 07701
Pres.—John O'Neill, 20 emp., *Corporate headquarters; concrete products* ........ (732) 292-2500
Barrett Paving Materials, Inc. (H Q), 3 Becker Farm Rd., Ste. 307, Roseland 07068
Pres.—Robert Doucet, 15 emp., *Corporate headquarters; asphalt paving* ........ (973) 533-1001
Benanti, Inc., D. F., 420 Quarry Ln., North Brunswick 08902
Pres.—Dominick Benanti, 5 emp., *Ready-mixed concrete* ........ (732) 422-3102
Clayton & Sons, LLC, Ralph, 58 Goldman Dr., Cookstown 08511
Plt. Mgr.—William Gangel, 30 emp., *Ready-mixed concrete* ........ (609) 758-6900
Clayton & Sons, Ralph, 103 Chestnut Ave., Egg Harbor Township 08234
Plt. Mgr.—Damian Haas, 18 emp., *Ready-mixed concrete* ........ (609) 383-1818
Clayton & Sons, Ralph, 125 Cox Crossing Rd., West Creek 08092
Plt. Mgr. & Dispatcher—John Pietrow, 15 emp., *Concrete block & ready-mixed concrete* ........ (609) 597-2233
Clayton Block Co., Inc., 1355 Campus Pkwy., Neptune 07753
Owner—William Clayton, Jr., 25 emp., *Corporate headquarters & ready-mixed* ........ (732) 751-7600
Clayton Block Co., Inc., 194 Chestnut St., Toms River 08753
Br. Mgr.—Matthew Dingus, 20 emp., *Concrete masonry units, building supplies* ........ (732) 349-3700
Colonial Concrete Co., 1196 McCarter Hwy., Newark 07104
Pres.—Martin Lucibello, 30 emp., *Company headquarters & ready-mixed* ........ (973) 482-1920
Colonial Concrete Co., 9301 Railroad Ave., North Bergen 07047
V-P., Br. Mgr.—Frank Rizzo, 7 emp., *Ready-mixed concrete* ........ (201) 435-9200
Concrete On Demand, Inc., 45 Edison Ave., Ste. 1, Oakland 07436
CEO—Moshe Engel, 8 emp., *Ready-mixed concrete* ........ (201) 337-0005
County Concrete Corp., 145 Ridgedale Ave., Morristown 07960
Dispatch Supv.—Bill Space, 10 emp., *Ready-mixed concrete* ........ (973) 538-3113
Eastern Concrete Materials, Inc. (H Q), 475 Market St., 3rd Fl., Elmwood Park 07407
Pres.—Mike Gentoso, 40 emp., *Corporate headquarters; ready-mixed* ........ (201) 797-7979
Erial Concrete, Inc., 965 Hickstown Rd., Sicklerville 08081
Pres.—Steve Romanowski, 15 emp., *Ready-mixed concrete* ........ (856) 784-8884
Fazzio & Sons, Inc., Frank J., 458 Elwood Ave., Pitman 08071
Pres.—Richard Fazzio, 30 emp., *Ready-mixed concrete* ........ (856) 589-3760
Hinchman & Son, Inc., Herbert J., 26 Pike Dr., Wayne 07470
Pres.—Donald Hinchman, 17 emp., *Ready-mixed concrete* ........ (973) 942-2063
Kennedy Concrete, 1969 S. East Ave., Vineland 08360
GM—Richard Jacobs, 30 emp., *Ready-mixed concrete* ........ (856) 692-8650
L & L Redi-Mix, Inc., 1939 U.S. Highway 206, Southampton 08088
Pres.—Lin Gerber, 85 emp., *Ready-mixed concrete* ........ (800) 696-2271
Mershon Concrete, LLC, Route 130 S., P.O. Box 254, Bordentown 08505
V-P. & IT Mgr.—Patrick T. Greber, 40 emp., *Precast & ready-mixed concrete* ........ (609) 298-2150
Penn Jersey Building Materials, Inc., 247 Cedar Swamp Rd., Bridgeport 08014
Br. Mgr.—Bill Rhubart, 12 emp., *Ready-mixed concrete* ........ (856) 467-0400
Penn Jersey Building Materials, Inc., 2819 Fire Rd., Egg Harbor Township 08234
CEO—Dan Quade, 20 emp., *Corporate headquarters & ready-mixed* ........ (609) 485-0068
Pierson Construction Co., Inc., R. E. (H Q), 426 Swedesboro Rd., Pilesgrove 08098
V-P.—Robert Baccala, 50 emp., *Corporate headquarters; asphalt paving* ........ (856) 769-8244
Pierson Materials Co., Inc., R. E., 860 Oak Grove Rd., P.O. Box 704, Bridgeport 08014
Sales Rep.—Fred Wietz, 20 emp., *Ready-mixed concrete* ........ (856) 467-1421
Pierson Materials Corp., R. E., 184 W. Sherman Ave., Vineland 08360
Plt. Mgr.—Geoff Warren, Jr., 10 emp., *Ready-mixed concrete* ........ (856) 696-2901
Pierson Materials, Inc., R. E., 1550 Route 38, Mount Holly 08060
Manager—Bruce Scandlin, 20 emp., *Ready-mixed concrete* ........ (609) 267-2257
Ralph Clayton & Sons, 1144 New York Ave., Trenton 08638
Dir., Qual. Control, Concrete—Matthew Savona, 15 emp., *Ready-mixed concrete* ........ (609) 695-0767
Richardson Co., J. B., 1603 N. Olden Ave., Trenton 08638
Pres.—Joe Quinn, 2 emp., *Ready-mixed concrete* ........ (609) 695-7474
S C C Concrete, 1051 River Rd., P.O. Box 47, Phillipsburg 08865
Pres., GM—Richard Cornely, 13 emp., *Ready-mixed concrete* ........ (908) 859-2172
Service Concrete Co., 173 Oak Ridge Rd., P.O. Box 235, Oak Ridge 07438
Pres., Fin. & R & D Mgr.—Anthony Dellechiaie, 34 emp., *Ready-mixed concrete* ........ (973) 697-4040
Silvi Concrete Products, Inc., 470 State Highway 33, Englishtown 07726
Plt. Mgr.—Frank King, 20 emp., *Ready-mixed concrete* ........ (267) 907-9150
Sparta Sand & Gravel Co., Inc., 33 Demarest Rd., Sparta 07871
Opers. Mgr.—Steve Russalesi, 20 emp., *Ready-mixed concrete* ........ (973) 383-4651
Tanis & Sons, Inc., Joel, 17-68 River Rd., Fair Lawn 07410
Hum. Res., IT & Plt. Mgr.—Chris Young, 38 emp., *Ready-mixed concrete* ........ (201) 796-1556
Weldon Asphalt Co., 1 New Providence Rd., Watchung 07060
GM—Robbie Roberts, 75 emp., *Crushed aggregates, hot-mixed asphalt* ........ (908) 233-9440
Weldon Materials, Inc. (H Q), 141 Central Ave., Westfield 07090
Pres., Cont.—Richard Weldon, 30 emp., *Corporate headquarters; ready-mixed* ........ (908) 233-4444

## 3275 Gypsum products

Georgia-Pacific Gypsum, LLC, 1101 S. Front St., Camden 08103
GM—Jermaine Jenkins, 20 emp., *Gypsum wallboards* ........ (856) 966-7600
National Gypsum Co., 1818 River Rd., Burlington 08016
Plt. Mgr.—Terry Peterson, 50 emp., *Gypsum wallboard* ........ (609) 499-3300

## 3281 Cut stone & stone products

A W Eurostile, 736 Route 35, Ocean 07712
Pres.—Andrea Wyman, 10 emp., *Manufacturer & distributor of marble* ........ (732) 493-1883
Abruzzi Stone & Flooring, LLC, 1641 Marlton Pike E., Cherry Hill 08034
Owner—Anthony DiGuglielmo, 10 emp., *Custom fabrication of granite & marble* ........ (856) 616-0800
ACD Custom Granite, Inc., 1304 Roller Rd., Ocean 07712
Pres.—Cynthia Schomaker, 13 emp., *Natural & engineered stone fabrication* ........ (732) 695-2400
All Granite & Marble Corp., 1 Mount Vernon St., Ste. A, Ridgefield Park 07660
Pres.—Richey Jaroslaw, 10 emp., *Corporate headquarters & marble, granite* ........ (201) 440-6779
ALPS Technologies, Inc., 500 Memorial Dr., Ste. 1, Somerset 08873
Pres.—Robert Wagner, 25 emp., *Solid-surface & granite countertops* ........ (732) 764-0777
American Monument Co., 50 Herbert Ave., Closter 07624
Pres.—Ron Boyajian, 20 emp., *Stone, natural rock, granite, brick* ........ (201) 750-1000
American Monument Co. (H Q), 479 N. Dean St., Englewood 07631
Pres.—Ron Boyajian, 3 emp., *Company headquarters; stone, natural* ........ (201) 569-4455
American Stone, Inc., 215 Route 22 W., Hillside 07205
V-P.—Steve Young, 9 emp., *Marble & granite products* ........ (973) 318-7707
Apex Marble & Granite, Inc., 998 Pompton Ave., Cedar Grove 07009
Pres.—Tom Tsatsaros, 7 emp., *Marble & granite countertops* ........ (973) 857-3655
Aphrodite Marble & Granite Co., Inc., 700 Old Shore Rd., Forked River 08731
Opers. Mgr.—Spyros Katsianis, 6 emp., *Marble & granite fabrication* ........ (609) 693-4450
Arcade Tile & Marble Co., 416 Central Ave., East Orange 07018
Pres., Plt. Mgr.—John Gallo, 5 emp., *Marble products* ........ (973) 678-4600
Art Stone Products, 113 Church St., P.O. Box 10, Newfield 08344
Pres.—Thomas Paul, 25 emp., *Cast stone products* ........ (856) 697-5895
Artistic Marble & Granite Surfaces, Inc., 269 Goffle Rd., Hawthorne 07506
Pres.—Mark Marzandarani, 22 emp., *Marble & granite countertop fabrication* ........ (973) 304-2001
Atlantic Stone II, LLC, 98 Somerset St., Garfield 07026
Ptnr.—Michele Borrielli, 4 emp., *Granite, marble & slate countertops* ........ (973) 928-1458
Atlas Marble & Granite, 44 Fadem Rd., Springfield 07081
Ptnr.—Marco Duran, 15 emp., *Granite countertops* ........ (973) 491-5454
Barre Monuments, 114 Atlantic City Blvd., Beachwood 08722
Owner—Michael Maloney, 3 emp., *Cast bronze & granite memorials* ........ (732) 240-2888
BCG Marble & Granite Co., 370 Whitesville Rd., Jackson 08527
Ptnr.—Pasquale Petrocelli, 20 emp., *Marble & granite countertops, vanities* ........ (732) 367-3788
BCG Marble & Granite Fabricators Co., Inc., 167 Sussex St., Hackensack 07601
Owner & Pres.—Giuseppe Guerini, 15 emp., *Corporate headquarters & limestone,* ........ (201) 343-8487
Beaver Run Farms, 300 Beaver Run Rd., Lafayette 07848
GM—Tim Shotmeyer, 15 emp., *Asphalt paving compounds & crushed* ........ (973) 875-5555
Bedrock Granite, Inc., 803 Shrewsbury Ave., Shrewsbury 07702
Pres.—Joe Iacono, 6 emp., *Marble & granite countertops* ........ (732) 741-0010
Burns Bros. & McCabe, Inc., 787 Tonnele Ave., Jersey City 07307
Pres.—John M. Burns, Jr., 8 emp., *Cemetery monuments* ........ (201) 795-0800
C C S Stone, 9-11 Caesar Pl., Moonachie 07074
Pres.—Don Mitnick, 25 emp., *Marble, granite, slate & limestone* ........ (201) 933-1515
Caputo International, Inc., 112 Northfield Ave., Edison 08837
Owner—Paul Caputo, 6 emp., *Marble, granite & stone slab furniture* ........ (732) 225-5777
Champion Marble & Granite, Inc., 4 Kinney Rd., Manalapan 07726
Owner—Fero Gjonbalaj, 5 emp., *Stone fabrication* ........ (732) 409-3200
Chemlime N. J., Inc. (H Q), 2350 South Ave., Scotch Plains 07076
Pres.—Daniel Fitzpatrick, 20 emp., *Corporate headquarters; industrial* ........ (908) 389-1006
Classic Marble & Tile, 11 Main St., Little Ferry 07643
Owner—Michael Timarchi, 12 emp., *Marble & granite products* ........ (201) 440-8848
Cole Bros. Marble & Granite, 892 Parvins Mill Rd., Pittsgrove 08318
Pres.—Ruth Cole, 6 emp., *Marble & granite kitchen countertops* ........ (856) 455-7989
Colossus Granite & Marble, Inc., 416 Crescent Blvd., Brooklawn 08030
Ptnr. & Pres.—Joe Franklin, 8 emp., *Custom granite & marble bathroom &* ........ (856) 742-0090
Counterfit, 1 Ironside Ct., Willingboro 08046
Pres.—Steve Daiagi, 14 emp., *Marble & granite countertops* ........ (609) 871-8888
County Concrete Corp., 50 Railroad Ave., P.O. Box F, Kenvil 07847
Pres.—John C. Crimi, 90 emp., *Corporate headquarters & concrete,* ........ (973) 584-7122
Cumberland Marble & Monument, Inc., 2858 S. West Blvd., Vineland 08360
Pres.—Paul Presgraves, Jr., 4 emp., *Graveyard monuments* ........ (856) 691-3334
Custom Wood, LLC, 400 Goldman Dr., Cream Ridge 08514
Off. Mgr.—Lisa Zucatti, 4 emp., *Kitchen & bathroom cabinets & granite* ........ (609) 758-8288
Eastern Concrete Materials, Inc., 201 Route 539, Barnegat 08005
Br. Mgr.—Tracy Davies, 6 emp., *Sand processing* ........ (609) 698-2800
Elite Stone Importers, LLC, 45 Park Rd., Tinton Falls 07724
Cust. Serv. Mgr.—Laurie Escalante, 8 emp., *Stone products, including countertops* ........ (732) 542-7900
Extech Building Materials, 100 Bogert St., Closter 07624
Br. Mgr.—Bob Lippe, 35 emp., *Custom natural stone fabrication &* ........ (201) 768-2133
Father & Son Design Center, LLC, 111 Clinton Rd., Ste. 1, Fairfield 07004
★ GM—Sal Carramusa, 4 emp., *Granite countertops* ........ (973) 575-8635
Formia Marble & Stone, Inc., 219 E. 11th Ave., Roselle 07203
Pres.—Filippo Berta, 7 emp., *Marble, granite, limestone & onyx fabrication* ........ (908) 259-0606
Gengaro Stone, LLC, 90 S. Main St., Ocean Grove 07756
Pres.—Sam Gengaro, 12 emp., *Solid-surface countertops, including* ........ (732) 776-6000
Granite Surfaces, LLC, 368 Lincoln Blvd., Middlesex 08846
Owner—Rocca Lavecchia, 5 emp., *Stone kitchen countertops, bathroom* ........ (732) 627-9200
H & S Stone, Inc., 705 Cross St., Lakewood 08701
Pres.—Nicolas Hernandez, 6 emp., *Stone fabrication* ........ (732) 364-2265
Hanson Aggregates, BMC Div., 368 New Brooklyn Rd., P.O. Box 37, Berlin 08009
Plt. Mgr.—Frank Berghof, 18 emp., *Sand & gravel processing* ........ (856) 767-3100
Hard Rock Marble & Granite, Inc., 1101 Chestnut St., Roselle 07203
CEO—N. Ruby Renjen, 12 emp., *Custom marble & granite fabrication* ........ (908) 620-9150
Harmony Sand & Gravel, Inc., 3189 Belvidere Rd., Phillipsburg 08865
Pres.—Richard L. Hummer, 24 emp., *Sand & gravel processing* ........ (908) 475-4690
House Of Granite & Marble, Inc., 1920 Swarthmore Ave., Ste. 4, Lakewood 08701
Pres.—Joel Reisman, 10 emp., *Custom fabrication of natural stone* ........ (732) 367-7211
Ilkem Marble & Granite, 2010 Springdale Rd., Ste. 200, Cherry Hill 08003
★ Owner—Mustafa Kol, 16 emp., *Granite & marble countertops* ........ (856) 433-8714
Industrial Consulting & Marketing, 20-21 Wagaraw Rd., Bldg. 38, Fair Lawn 07410
Pres.—Alfonso Bertoni, 40 emp., *Kitchen & bathroom stone countertops* ........ (973) 427-2474
Innovative Cutting Concepts, LLC, 203 Cates Rd., Egg Harbor Township 08234
Pres.—Ron Simone, 8 emp., *Marble & granite fabrication* ........ (609) 484-9960
Intelco Of Delaware Valley, 250 Harvard Ave., P.O. Box 9, Westville 08093
Pres.—Mike Wells, 120 emp., *Company headquarters & solid-surface* ........ (856) 456-6755
J & J Corp., Inc., 8607 River Rd., North Bergen 07047
Owner—Carlos Godoy, 7 emp., *Granite & marble kitchen countertops* ........ (201) 313-0900
Jersey Granite & Tile, LLC, 234 Boundary Rd., Ste. 4, Marlboro 07746
Pres.—Martin Hronchich, 8 emp., *Granite & marble countertops & vanities* ........ (732) 683-1600
Kitchen King, Inc., 1561 Route 9, Toms River 08755
Pres.—Terry Barth, 20 emp., *Quartz, granite & laminate countertops* ........ (732) 341-9660
Lincoln Marble Works, 785 Martin St., P.O. Box 111, Rahway 07065
Manager—John Szabo, 3 emp., *Marble & granite countertops* ........ (732) 381-9098
Lincoln Monument Co., Inc., 405 Orange Rd., Montclair 07042
Owner & Pres.—Ralph Rullis, Jr., 5 emp., *Burial monument engraving* ........ (973) 744-1800
Marble & Granite Fabricators, 950 Pennsylvania Ave., Trenton 08638
Owner—Andrew Podlesny, 8 emp., *Granite & marble countertops* ........ (609) 392-2792
Marble & Stone Crafters, LLC, 50 Johnson Ave., Ste. F, Hackensack 07601
Owner, Pres. & CEO—Christopher Caruso, 8 emp., *Granite & marble countertops* ........ (201) 343-2840
Marble Factory, 800 Magnolia Ave., Elizabeth 07201
Pres.—Ilda Vitorino, 12 emp., *Marble countertops, stone fabrication* ........ (908) 353-2264
Marble Systems, Inc., 610 Washington Ave., Carlstadt 07072
Manager—Serafino Aprile, 10 emp., *Natural stone fabrication, including* ........ (201) 507-0111
Marmo Enterprises, Inc., 468 Elizabeth Ave., Somerset 08873
Pres.—Matthew Partsinevelos, 2 emp., *Marble, granite, limestone, slate,* ........ (908) 486-4421
Marvic Corp./A.J.D. Stone, 2450 Iorio St., Union 07083
Pres., Marvic Corp.—Alfred J. D'Alessandro, 100 emp., *Granite, quartz, solid-surface, concrete* (908) 686-4340
Memorial Arts, Inc., 1172 E. Ridgewood Ave., Ridgewood 07450
Pres.—Suzanne Ferrie, 3 emp., *Burial monuments* ........ (201) 652-4301
Merlino Marble & Granite, Inc., 92 Route 50, Ocean View 08230
Pres.—Timothy Merlino, 2 emp., *Natural stone & solid-surface countertops* ........ (609) 624-9500
Metropole, Inc., 214 Clifton Blvd., Clifton 07011
Pres.—David Finlay, 10 emp., *Custom exterior terra cotta, granite* ........ (973) 473-2727
Monuments Are Forever, Inc., 200 E. Edgar Rd., Ste. 1-A, Linden 07036
Pres.—Andrew Cleffi, 2 emp., *Granite burial monuments & signage* ........ (908) 862-0220

Natural Stone Kitchen & Bath, 2280 U.S. Highway 130, North Brunswick 08902
Pres.—Manuel Angamarca, 3 emp., *Natural stone fabrication* .............. (732) 297-5450
New Granite & Marble, LLC, 35 8th St., Ste. 6, Passaic 07055
★ Owner—Maclej Tuniewicz, 2 emp., *Granite & marble fabrication* .............. (973) 767-6216
New Jersey Granite & Marble Corp., 50 S. Center St., Unit 3, Orange 07050
Pres.—Plauton Soreas, 6 emp., *Granite & marble countertops* .............. (973) 266-8952
New York Blackboard of NJ, Inc., 83 U.S. Highway 22, Hillside 07205
Pres.—Henry Ruggiero, 6 emp., *Markerboards, chalkboards, bulletin* .............. (973) 926-1600
North Bergen Marble & Granite Corp., 217 Palisade Ave., Cliffside Park 07010
Plt. Mgr.—Jim Markopolous, 4 emp., *Marble & granite countertops & fireplaces* .............. (201) 945-9988
Ocean Granite Marble, LLC, 140 7th Ave., Unit 9, Little Egg Harbor 08087
Ptnr.—Dustin Bodony, 4 emp., *Marble & granite fabrication & countertops* .............. (609) 296-1800
Oceana Designs, Inc., 450 Oberlin Ave. S., Lakewood 08701
Owner—George Gavallas, 20 emp., *Granite & marble countertops* .............. (732) 987-6944
Ozer International, LLC, 145 Manchester Pl., Newark 07104
Pres.—Sualp Yurteri, 25 emp., *Manufacturer of granite & marble kitchen* .............. (973) 497-5656
Paramount Fixture Corp., 175 Mount Pleasant Ave., Newark 07104
Owner & Pres.—Stephen Porcelli, 35 emp., *Custom wooden & metal store fixtures* .............. (973) 485-1585
Paterson Monuments Co., Inc., 317 Totowa Ave., Paterson 07502
Pres.—Leslie Christopher, 3 emp., *Burial monuments & engraving* .............. (973) 942-0727
Philadelphia Soapstone Co., 1001 Lower Landing Rd., Ste. 103, Blackwood 08012
Owner—Joseph McElhiney, 5 emp., *Soapstone fabrication, including slabs* .............. (856) 232-7627
Phillipsburg Marble Co., 1 Marble Hill Rd., P.O. Box 172, Phillipsburg 08865
Pres.—Robert S. Barron, 25 emp., *Architectural marble, granite, travertine* .............. (908) 859-3435
Progressive Dimensions, Inc., 44 Flint Rd., Toms River 08757
Pres.—Ed Cassidy, 10 emp., *Granite, solid-surface & laminate countertop* .............. (732) 244-0109
Quality Solid Surface, Inc., 333 Vreeland Ave., Paterson 07513
Owner—Offer Bok, 25 emp., *Fabrication of solid-surface countertops* .............. (973) 357-9770
Renaissance Marble & Granite, 107 Harmon Dr., Blackwood 08012
Pres.—Mark Hernandez, 40 emp., *Marble & granite products* .............. (856) 227-3535
Robert Young & Sons, Inc., 25 Grafton Ave., Newark 07104
Pres.—David A. Young, 5 emp., *Dimensional-cut limestone, marble &* .............. (973) 483-0451
Romano & Son, Inc., 501 Baldwin Ave., Lodi 07644
Owner—Paul Romano, 5 emp., *Granite & marble countertops & floor* .............. (973) 472-3240
Saracino Monuments, LLC, Frank, 359 Bergen Blvd., Fairview 07022
Ptnr.—Frank Saracino, 2 emp., *Granite upright monuments & markers* .............. (201) 945-1266
Shelby Caststone, 600 Jersey Ave., Gloucester City 08030
Pres.—Fredrick M. Aziack, 12 emp., *Stone products* .............. (856) 456-0668
SolidSurface Designs, Inc., 1651 Sherman Ave., Pennsauken 08110
Pres.—Matthew Baiada, 21 emp., *Solid-surface, quartz, stainless steel* .............. (856) 910-7720
Spaulding Fabricators Inc., 1136 Industrial Pkwy., Brick 08724
Pres.—Stephen Spaulding, 21 emp., *Solid-surface, granite & engineered* .............. (732) 840-4433
Stag Bros. Cast Stone, 720 Vassar Ave., Lakewood 08701
Pres.—Bill Stagliano, 10 emp., *Precast concrete & stone products* .............. (732) 363-6582
Statewide Granite & Marble, 3257 Kennedy Blvd., Jersey City 07306
GM—Linda Coviello, 7 emp., *Marble & granite countertops* .............. (201) 653-1700
Stavola Construction Materials, Inc., 810 Thompson Ave., Bound Brook 08805
Corp. Secy.—Helen Stokes, 50 emp., *Construction stone aggregates & asphalt* .............. (732) 356-7100
Stavola Construction Materials, Inc., 30 Rockaway Rd., Lebanon 08833
Plt. Supt.—Juan Berrios, 5 emp., *Crushed stone* .............. (908) 439-2800
Stone Crafters, LLC, 6084 Reega Ave., Egg Harbor Township 08234
★ Owner—Bill Millar, 15 emp., *Granite, marble & cultured quartz countertops* .............. (609) 646-0406
Stone Galaxy, 4120 Blackhorse Pike, Turnersville 08012
Mng. Ptnr.—Rey Sroka, 2 emp., *Stone fabrication, including countertops* .............. (856) 219-3450
Stone King, Inc., 900 Lincoln Blvd., Ste. 1, Middlesex 08846
Pres.—Tommy Sie, 10 emp., *Granite & marble kitchen countertops* .............. (732) 868-8687
Stone Plus Design, LLC, 21 Route 17 S., East Rutherford 07073
Owner—Roberto Palacios, 3 emp., *Stone fabrication, including kitchen* .............. (201) 438-2725
Stone Surfaces Of Central Jersey, Inc., 690 Jersey Ave., Unit 13, New Brunswick 08901
Pres.—Daniel Sakosits, 22 emp., *Granite countertops* .............. (732) 745-1727
Stone Surfaces, Inc., 890 Paterson Plank Rd., East Rutherford 07073
Pres.—Michael Sakosits, 30 emp., *Solid surface & stone countertops* .............. (201) 935-8803
Stone Tech Fabrication, 930 New York Ave., Trenton 08638
Pres.—Danny Vogia, 10 emp., *Marble & granite products* .............. (609) 984-8818
StoneShop, 670 Deer Rd., Ste. 202, Cherry Hill 08034
★ V-P.—Richard Holmes, 10 emp., *Granite, marble & engineered quartz* .............. (856) 795-8900
Suburban Monument & Vault, 203 Sherman Ave., P.O. Box 2370, Newark 07114
Owner—Clyde Brooks, 6 emp., *Granite monuments & concrete burial* .............. (973) 242-7007
Thin Stone Systems, LLC, 23 Commerce Rd., Ste. O, Fairfield 07004
CEO—Anthony Tauriello, 15 emp., *Stone cutting* .............. (973) 882-7377
Tilcon Riverdale Quarry, 125 Hamburg Tpke., Riverdale 07457
Plt. Mgr.—Bill Conklin, 50 emp., *Crushed stone* .............. (973) 835-0028
Tiles Unlimited, 1016 State Route 34, Ste. 9, Matawan 07747
Manager—Vito Mancini, 10 emp., *Stone fabrication, including marble* .............. (732) 566-3886
Top Line Co., 2131 Bethel Ave., Pennsauken 08110
Owner—Bruce MacLachlan, 50 emp., *Laminate, acrylic, marble, granite,* .............. (856) 662-6400
Top Shops, LLC, 361 W. Dewey Ave., Ste. 8, Wharton 07885
Owner—Reggie Matthews, 3 emp., *Granite & solid-surface countertops* .............. (973) 442-0050
Trap Rock Industries, Inc., Pennington Quarry, 120 Route 31 S., Pennington 08534
Plt. Opers. Mgr.—Frank Bray, 10 emp., *Crushed stone & hot asphalt mix* .............. (609) 737-3200
Tri State Stone, Inc., 111 Rome St., Ste. 2, Newark 07105
Pres.—Gene Gonsalves, 10 emp., *Stone fabrication* .............. (973) 344-7220
Tuckahoe Sand & Gravel, Inc., Route 610 & Sharp Rd., Tuckahoe 08250
Pres.—James Johnston, Jr., 15 emp., *Sand & gravel processing* .............. (609) 861-2082
U. S. Artistic Monument Co., Inc., 262 Main Ave., Clifton 07014
Pres.—Albert Manfredi, 3 emp., *Granite burial monuments* .............. (973) 777-7786
Unlimited Stone Designs, 7 McLean Blvd., Paterson 07514
Pres.—Mike Mainolfi, 4 emp., *Granite, marble & slate countertops* .............. (973) 523-2224
Urvesh Granite (USA), Inc., 1777 Route 130 S., North Brunswick 08902
Pres.—Bharat Patel, 8 emp., *Granite countertops & wooden kitchen* .............. (201) 369-3934
Van Orden Sand & Gravel, 589 W. Brook Rd., Ringwood 07456
Sales Rep.—Bucky Rodda, 12 emp., *Sand & gravel processing* .............. (973) 839-0207
W & E Baum, Inc., 89 Bannard St., Freehold 07728
CEO—Maurice Zagha, 25 emp., *Wooden, marble, metal, acrylic, glass* .............. (732) 866-1881
Weldon Materials, Inc., 181 Route 181, Lake Hopatcong 07849
V-P.—Bill Weldon, 40 emp., *Asphalt paving compounds & crushed* .............. (973) 663-1800
Whibco Of New Jersey, 377 Port Cumberland Rd., P.O. Box 456, Port Elizabeth 08348
Plt. Mgr.—Jim Workman, 30 emp., *Industrial sand & construction aggregate* .............. (856) 825-5200
White Eagle Monumental Co., Inc., 257 Ridge Rd., North Arlington 07031
Pres.—Florence Dean, 2 emp., *Burial grave monuments & sandblast* .............. (201) 991-0094
White Valley Memorials (H Q), 292 W. White Horse Pike, Berlin 08009
Owner—Al Cohlmyer, 1 emp., *Company headquarters; stone monuments* .............. (856) 767-3030
Wicki Wholesale Stone, Inc., 17 Cemetery Rd., P.O. Box 104, Great Meadows 07838
Pres.—Peter Wicki, 20 emp., *Stone fabrication* .............. (908) 637-6004
Wilkstone, LLC, 128 19th Ave., Paterson 07513
Pres.—David A. Wilkinson, 7 emp., *Marble* .............. (973) 684-5100
William B. Snelbaker & Son, 43 Cooper St., Woodbury 08096
GM—Treva Oster, 1 emp., *Stone monuments* .............. (856) 845-0634
Woodbridge Monument Factory, Inc., 10 Main St., Ste. K, Woodbridge 07095
Pres.—Adam Sprung, 6 emp., *Burial monument engraving* .............. (732) 634-1521
Workshop Stone, 281 Mount Pleasant Ave., Newark 07104
Owner—Carlos Jaramallo, 2 emp., *Marble & granite countertop fabrication* .............. (973) 230-9212

## 3291 Abrasive products

3M Co., 140 Algonquin Pkwy., Whippany 07981
Plt. Supv.—Vic Ison, 50 emp., *Diamond grinding wheels, tools & routers* .............. (973) 884-2500
Advanced Abrasives Corp., 7980 National Hwy., Pennsauken 08110
Pres.—Matthew Bees, 20 emp., *Diamond abrasives, inluding powders* .............. (856) 665-9300
Alpex Wheel Co., 29 Atwood Ave., P.O. Box 357, Tenafly 07670
MIS Mgr.—Attilo Tomasi, 4 emp., *Abrasive wheel dressers & grinding* .............. (201) 871-1700
Beacut Abrasives Corp., 788 Paterson Ave., East Rutherford 07073
Pres.—Vladimir Smilovic, 11 emp., *Industrial abrasives* .............. (973) 249-1420
Church & Dwight Co., Inc. (H Q), 500 Charles Ewing Blvd., Ewing 08628
Chrm., CEO—James Craigie, 400 emp., *Corporate headquarters; detergents,* .............. (609) 683-5900
Easy Abrasives, LLC (H Q), 16 Passaic Ave., Unit 8, Fairfield 07004
Owner—Quinn Hsu, 5 emp., *Company headquarters; carbide burs,* .............. (973) 575-7879
Garfield Industries, Inc., 62 Clinton Rd., Fairfield 07004
Pres.—Debra Gladstone, 20 emp., *Buffing & polishing wheels* .............. (973) 575-8800
Hall Co. Abrasives, William R., 901 E. Gibbsboro Rd., Lindenwold 08021
Pres.—George Aho, 30 emp., *Rubber bonded abrasives for the dental* .............. (856) 784-6700
Indasa U. S. A., Inc., 23 Madison Rd., Fairfield 07004
V-P.—Alan Zaorski, 9 emp., *Coated abrasives* .............. (800) 916-0090
Jan L, Inc., 26 Mill St., Ste. 26, Mount Holly 08060
Pres.—Bruce Levinson, 7 emp., *Hand drill dust collection systems,* .............. (609) 261-1133
Kingwood Industrial Products, Inc., 261 Main St., Unit 1 & 2, Hackettstown 07840
Pres.—Kevin Smith, 4 emp., *Audiology equipment & supplies, including* .............. (908) 852-8655
New Age Fastening Systems, Inc., 11 Enterprise Ct., Sewell 08080
Ptnr.—Stephen Swartz, Jr., 20 emp., *Stud welding equipment & blasting abrasives* .............. (856) 218-8301
New Jersey Diamond Products Co., 108 Kentucky Ave., Paterson 07503
Pres.—Mark Zambrano, 12 emp., *Diamond cutting wheels, drills & tools* .............. (973) 684-0949
Noritake Co., Inc. (H Q), 15-22 Fair Lawn Ave., Fair Lawn 07410
CEO—Satoru Shimazaki, 20 emp., *Corporate headquarters; abrasive products* .............. (201) 796-2222
Robinson Tech International Corp., 310 Fairfield Rd., Fairfield 07004
Owner—Mark Lin, 10 emp., *Abrasive supplies, including polishing* .............. (973) 287-6458
Sample Marshall Laboratories, Inc., 63 Park Ave., Lyndhurst 07071
Pres.—James Sample, 11 emp., *Diamond & CBN abrasive grinding tools* .............. (201) 933-0570
Web Industries, Inc., 5 Mars Ct., P.O. Box 237, Montville 07045
Pres.—William Burgoyne, 11 emp., *Superabrasive grinding & slicing products* .............. (973) 335-1200

## 3295 Minerals, ground or treated

Asbury Graphite Mills, Inc. (H Q), 405 Old Main St., P.O. Box 144, Asbury 08802
Chrm.—Marvin Riddle, 30 emp., *Corporate headquarters; graphite* .............. (908) 537-2155
Huber Corp., J.M. (H Q), 499 Thornall St., 8th Fl., Edison 08837
Pres., CEO—Michael Marberry, 65 emp., *Corporate headquarters; hydrocolloids* .............. (732) 549-8600
Madison Industries, Inc., 554 Waterworks Rd., Old Bridge 08857
Pres.—Bruce Bzura, 75 emp., *Zinc-based chemicals* .............. (732) 727-2225
Schundler Co., Inc., 150 Whitman Ave., Edison 08817
Admn. & Sales Mgr.—Vikki Warman, 30 emp., *Perlite & vermiculite aggregates &* .............. (732) 287-2244

## 3296 Mineral wool

Isolatek International (H Q), 41 Furnace St., Stanhope 07874
Pres., CEO—Giovanni C. Pacheco, 100 emp., *Company headquarters; spray applied* .............. (973) 347-1200
Pacor, Inc., 333 Rising Sun Rd., Bordentown 08505
Pres., CEO—Ronald Latini, 45 emp., *Corporate headquarters & thermal &* .............. (609) 324-1100
Sloan & Co., Inc., 38 Fairfield Pl., West Caldwell 07006
Pres.—Scott Casabona, 25 emp., *Architectural millwork & acoustical* .............. (973) 227-3555

## 3297 Refractories—nonclay

Bartley Crucible Refractories, 15 Muirhead Ave., P.O. Box 5464, Trenton 08638
Owner—Dan Mischel, 20 emp., *Crucibles* .............. (609) 393-0066
Kraemer Gunite, Inc., 137 Blackwood Barnsboro Rd., Sewell 08080
Pres.—Robert Kraemer, Jr., 20 emp., *Custom cast refractories, including* .............. (856) 227-8097
McNeil, Inc., 15 Marlen Dr., Robbinsville 08691
Pres.—James Schuhl, 15 emp., *Refractory materials & ceramic fiber* .............. (609) 890-7007
Nth Degree Products, LLC, 404 Laurel Ridge Rd., Hainesport 08036
CEO—Donald G. Lopata, 2 emp., *High-temperature ceramic refractories* .............. (609) 518-9447

## 3299 Mineral products—nonmetallic, nec

Accuratus Corporation, 35 Howard St., Phillipsburg 08865
Pres.—Raymond Tsao, 30 emp., *Manufacturer of advanced technical* .............. (908) 213-7070
Alpha Assocs., Inc., 145 Lehigh Ave., Lakewood 08701
Chrm., CEO—A. Louis Avallone, 100 emp., *Coated & impregnated high-temperature* .............. (732) 730-1800
California Stucco Products Corp., 85 Zabriskie St., Hackensack 07601
Pres.—Edwin D. Gorter, 10 emp., *Stucco* .............. (201) 457-1900
Classic Coves, P.O. Box 266, Garwood 07027
Pres.—Mark Wellnitz, 2 emp., *Indirect & accent cove lighting for* .............. (908) 344-1776
Crystex Composites, LLC, 125 Clifton Blvd., Clifton 07011
Pres., CEO—George Flores, 35 emp., *Machinable & moldable inorganic glass-mica* .............. (973) 779-8866
Inversand Co., 226 N. Atlantic Ave., P.O. Box 650, Clayton 08312
Pres.—Tom Carrocino, 50 emp., *Manganese greensand for municipal &* .............. (856) 881-2345
L S P Industrial Ceramics, 34 Mount Airy Village Rd., P.O. Box 302, Lambertville 08530
Pres.—Frank D. Smith, 5 emp., *Electronic & industrial ceramics* .............. (609) 397-8330
Mediterranean Stucco Corp., 111 Main St., Newark 07105
★ Pres.—Ernesto Andrade, 5 emp., *Stucco materials* .............. (973) 491-0160
Metropole, Inc., 214 Clifton Blvd., Clifton 07011
Pres.—David Finlay, 10 emp., *Custom exterior terra cotta, granite* .............. (973) 473-2727
Nth Degree Products, LLC, 404 Laurel Ridge Rd., Hainesport 08036
CEO—Donald G. Lopata, 2 emp., *High-temperature ceramic refractories* .............. (609) 518-9447
Plaque Art Creations Co., 401 S. 2nd St., Harrison 07029
Pres.—Belinda Kalthoff, 9 emp., *Plaster products* .............. (973) 482-2536
Sculpturesque, Inc., 7 Etheridge Pl., Park Ridge 07656
Owner—Catherine Schmitt, 1 emp., *Commercial & fine art sculptures &* .............. (201) 573-9150
Stone Crafters, LLC, 6084 Reega Ave., Egg Harbor Township 08234
★ Owner—Bill Millar, 15 emp., *Granite, marble & cultured quartz countertops* .............. (609) 646-0406

StoneShop, 670 Deer Rd., Ste. 202, Cherry Hill 08034
★ V-P.—Richard Holmes, 10 emp., *Granite, marble & engineered quartz* ... (856) 795-8900
United Silica Products, Inc., 3 Park Dr., Franklin 07416
Pres., CFO—Lynnmarie Kane, 20 emp., *Quartz plate, wafer carriers, process* ... (973) 209-8854

## 33 PRIMARY METAL INDUSTRIES

### 3312 Blast furnaces & steel mills

47 Industries, LLC, 59 2nd Ave., Raritan 08869
Owner—Mike Palazzo, 1 emp., *Aluminum & stainless steel fabrication* ... (908) 526-8865
A & A Ironworks, Inc., 955 Burnt Meadow Rd., Hewitt 07421
Pres.—Adam G. Muzer, 15 emp., *Ironwork & structural steel fabrication* ... (973) 728-4300
A & R Recycling Co., 1004 Union Landing Rd., P.O. Box 2440, Cinnaminson 08077
Pres.—Anthony Tognini, 14 emp., *Metal recycling* ... (856) 829-1712
A R J Custom Fabrication, Inc., 151 Taylor St., Trenton 08638
Pres.—Anthony Jones, 10 emp., *Stainless steel fabrication* ... (609) 695-6227
Airmet, Inc., 671 N. 3rd St., Newark 07107
Pres.—Stephen A. Yavorski, Sr., 6 emp., *Metal fences, gates, railings, steel* ... (973) 481-5550
Alloy Welding Co., Inc., 6-A Culnen Dr., Somerville 08876
Pres.—Leonard F. Schaffenberger, 10 emp., *Structural steel & steel fabrication* ... (908) 218-1551
Allweld Iron, 160 Culber Ave., Jersey City 07305
Owner—Jose Nedrano, 1 emp., *Steel fabrication* ... (201) 434-8750
Archer Day, 18 Mileed Way, Avenel 07001
Pres.—William DeMott, 25 emp., *Steel fabrication* ... (732) 417-0333
Atlantic Coastal Welding, Inc., 16 Butler Blvd., Bayville 08721
Pres.—John Gallo, 6 emp., *Welding & metal, aluminum & steel fabrication* ... (732) 269-1088
B & L Industrial Services, Inc., 700 Park Ave., Unit 7, Hainesport 08036
Pres.—Richard Lodwig, 4 emp., *Steel fabrication, rebuilt fans & blowers* ... (609) 386-9500
Burgess Steel Erectors Of New Jersey, LLC, 200 W. Forest Ave., P.O. Box 5629, Englewood 07631
CFO—Thomas J. Parisi, 85 emp., *Steel fabrication & ornamental metals* ... (201) 871-3500
Bush Tank Fabricators, Inc., 222 Thomas St., Newark 07114
Pres.—Thomas Horenburg, 10 emp., *Custom aluminum, steel & stainless* ... (973) 596-1121
Camden Yards Steel Co., LLC, 2500 Broadway, Drawer 14, Camden 08104
Ptnr.—Michael Amato, 25 emp., *Steel processing* ... (856) 342-7100
Canam Steel Corp., 14 Harmich Rd., South Plainfield 07080
V-P. & GM, Opers., U.S.—Tim Day, 50 emp., *Steel decks* ... (908) 561-3484
Century Fabricating Co., Inc., 84 Railroad Ave., Belford 07718
GM & R & D Mgr.—Daniel Nankenvis, 1 emp., *Steel fabrication* ... (732) 495-3200
Century Tube Corp., 22 Tannery Rd., Somerville 08876
Pres.—Dominick DeAngelo, 60 emp., *Stainless steel tubing* ... (908) 534-2001
Cornell & Co., Inc., 224 Cornell Ln., Westville 08093
Pres.—Delor Cornell, 40 emp., *Steel fabrication, erection & equipment* ... (856) 742-1900
County Glass & Metal Installers, Inc., 80 Dewitt Pl., Hackensack 07601
Pres.—Eugene Vanbert, 6 emp., *Metal, steel & aluminum fabrication* ... (201) 343-7417
Custom Steel Contractors, Inc., 17 Eastern Rd., Kearny 07032
Pres.—Dan Moran, 20 emp., *Steel fabrication* ... (973) 344-4449
D E B Maintenance, Inc., 1000 Union Landing Rd., P.O. Box 13, Riverton 08077
Pres.—Kenneth Williams, 30 emp., *Steel fabrication, tanks, vessels &* ... (856) 786-0440
D M Steel, 279 Sherman Ave., Newark 07114
Pres., CFO—Marc Ducate, 15 emp., *Steel slitting, round edging, shearing* ... (973) 732-4763
DiLauri Steel Fabricators, 5 Merrys Ln., East Hanover 07936
Pres.—Kathleen DiLauri, 2 emp., *Steel fabrication & welding job shop* ... (973) 884-2414
Doran, LLC, 599 Green Ln., Union 07083
Plt. Mgr.—Randolph Wojcik, 5 emp., *Steel fabrication & precision machining* ... (908) 289-9200
Duferco Steel, Inc. (H Q), 100 Matawan Rd., Ste. 400, Matawan 07747
Pres.—Joe Deverter, 30 emp., *Corporate headquarters; steel slabs* ... (732) 566-3130
Erasteel, Inc., 95 Fulton St., Boonton 07005
Mng. Dir.—Ken Bagady, 20 emp., *Corporate headquarters & high-speed* ... (973) 335-8400
Falcon Stainless & Alloys Corp., 39 Hewson Ave., Ste. A, Waldwick 07463
V-P.—Paul Chignola, 8 emp., *Stainless steel & alloys & open die* ... (201) 670-8300
Fitzgerald Custom Fabrication, Inc., 733 W. Bay Ave., Barnegat 08005
Pres.—Edwin Fitzgerald, 2 emp., *Steel fabrication* ... (609) 652-8899
FTI, Inc. (H Q), 8 Vreeland Rd., Florham Park 07932
V-P.—William B. Smith, 120 emp., *Corporate headquarters; gun lubricants* ... (973) 443-4200
G & J Steel & Tubing, Inc., 406 Roycefield Rd., Hillsborough 08844
Pres.—John Tursky, 45 emp., *Fabricated metal tubing* ... (908) 526-4445
G & M Welding & Fabricating, Inc., 31 W. Browning Rd., Bellmawr 08031
Pres.—George Liontas, 5 emp., *Steel & metal fabrication* ... (856) 931-0443
Garafano & Sons, Peter, 500 Marshall St., Paterson 07503
Pres.—Peter Garafano, 20 emp., *Steel fabrication* ... (973) 278-0350
Gavan Graham Electrical Products, 751 Rahway Ave., Union 07083
Pres.—Norm Cummerson, 30 emp., *Stainless steel enclosures, switch* ... (908) 729-9000
Gerdau US, Inc., Sayreville, N. Crossman Rd., P.O. Box 249, Sayreville 08872
V-P., GM—Mark Quiring, 200 emp., *Steel concrete reinforcement bars* ... (732) 721-6600
Grammer, Dempsey & Hudson Co., 212 Rome St., Newark 07105
Pres.—James Hudson, 8 emp., *Carbon, alloy, stainless & tool bar* ... (973) 589-8000
Grimmer & Sons, Inc., C. W., 75 Gilbert St. W., Tinton Falls 07701
Pres.—William D. Grimmer, 6 emp., *Steel fabrication* ... (732) 741-2189
HarMac Rebar & Steel Corp., 301 Hartle St., Sayreville 08872
Plt. Mgr.—Larry Kuzma, 15 emp., *Steel rebar fabrication* ... (732) 651-7822
Harris Structural Steel Co., Inc., 1640 New Market Ave., South Plainfield 07080
Pres.—Thomas Harris, Jr., 70 emp., *Steel fabrication* ... (732) 752-6070
Holtec International (H Q), 555 Lincoln Dr. W., Ste. 1, Marlton 08053
Pres., CEO—Kris Singh, 170 emp., *Company headquarters; steel fabrication* ... (856) 797-0900
IK Construction, Inc., 1118 E. Baltimore Ave., Linden 07036
Pres.—Ian Katwaroo, 8 emp., *Steel, ornamental iron & structural* ... (908) 925-5200
Industrial Metal, Inc., 32 Lambert Rd., Blairstown 07825
Pres.—Dan O'Hern, 8 emp., *Stainless steel equipment* ... (908) 362-0084
Industrial Services Enterprises, 192 Franklin Rd., Dover 07801
Pres.—Sante D'Emidio, 30 emp., *Structural steel fabrication* ... (973) 366-3939
Integrity Iron Works Inc., 33 Brookside Ave., P.O. Box 129, Sayreville 08872
Owner—James Zagata, 9 emp., *Steel fabrication* ... (732) 254-2200
I-Ron-X Industries, 134 Wheat Rd., Buena 08310
Pres., CFO—Paul Tomasello, 2 emp., *Wrought iron & aluminum railings, steel* ... (856) 697-3518
Jason Steel Co., Inc., 1701 Hylton Rd., Pennsauken 08110
Pers. Mgr.—Lou Cullen, 50 emp., *Steel cutting & grinding* ... (856) 663-5010
Jersey Cooperage Co., 20 River Rd., Sayreville 08872
GM, Fin. & MIS Mgr.—Michael Foglia, 19 emp., *Steel reconditioning* ... (732) 254-1765
K L M Mechanical Contractors, Inc., 109 W. Shore Ave., Dumont 07628
Pres.—Ken Loehr, 8 emp., *Sheet metal fabrication & HVAC contracting* ... (201) 385-6965
Klein Recycling, 2156 Camplain Rd., Hillsborough 08844
Pres.—Richard Santaniello, 15 emp., *Scrap metal recycling* ... (908) 722-2288
Kurth & Son, Inc., Edward, 220 Blackwood Barnsboro Rd., Sewell 08080
Pres.—Andrew Kurth, 30 emp., *Steel fabrication* ... (856) 227-8811
L & L Welding Contractors, Inc., 3 Wheeling Rd., Dayton 08810
Pres.—Frank Lagahuta, 9 emp., *Steel fabrication* ... (609) 395-1600
MacElroy Co., Inc., J. C., 91 Ethel Rd. W., Piscataway 08854
Pres.—Scott J. Spota, 30 emp., *Custom steel, stainless steel, aluminum* ... (732) 572-7100
Maltese Iron Works, Inc., John, 1453 Jersey Ave., P.O. Box 7161, North Brunswick 08902
Pres.—Laurence Danza, 18 emp., *Steel fabrication* ... (732) 249-4350
Metals USA, Plates & Shapes Group, 182 Frelinghuysen Ave., Newark 07114
GM—Thomas Creanza, 31 emp., *Steel service center, including steel* ... (973) 242-1000
Metropole, Inc., 214 Clifton Blvd., Clifton 07011
Pres.—David Finlay, 10 emp., *Custom exterior terra cotta, granite* ... (973) 473-2727
Miletta Brothers, Inc., 194 Main St., Cedarville 08311
Pres.—Joseph Miletta, Jr., 6 emp., *Steel fabrication & pipe fittings* ... (856) 447-4652
Modelsmith International, Inc., 66 Willow Ave., 2nd Fl., Hoboken 07030
Pres.—Karol Popek, 5 emp., *Steel, wood & acrylic fabrication,* ... (201) 714-9519
Mokes Steel, Inc., 280 Cox St., Roselle 07203
Pres.—Albie Mokes, 5 emp., *Steel cutting & slitting* ... (908) 241-5344
Mulberry Metal Products, Inc., 2199 Stanley Ter., Union 07083
CFO—Patricia Lynch, 100 emp., *Metal & plastic wallplates & weatherproof* ... (908) 688-8850
Newark Steel Fabricators, Inc., 104 Albert Ave., Newark 07105
Pres.—Luis Martinez, 5 emp., *Steel & ornamental iron railings &* ... (973) 344-2904
Oliver, Inc., G. J., 50 Industrial Rd., Phillipsburg 08865
CEO—John Oliver, 75 emp., *Steel fabrication & machining of pressure* ... (908) 454-9743
Pandrol USA L. P., 501 Sharptown Rd., P.O. Box 367, Bridgeport 08014
Pres.—Frank Brady, 45 emp., *Railroad joints & fasteners* ... (856) 467-3227
Park Steel & Iron Co., 82 Iron St., Toms River 08753
Plt. Mgr.—Robert Kramer, 2 emp., *Structural steel fabrication* ... (732) 349-2400
Park Steel & Iron Co. (H Q), 9 Evergreen Ave., Neptune City 07753
Pres., GM—Scott Pilling, 7 emp., *Company headquarters; structural, ornamental* ... (732) 775-7500
Passaic County Welders, Inc., 100 Parish Dr., Wayne 07470
V-P.—Robert Grimbilas, 38 emp., *Welding & structural steel, steel,* ... (973) 696-1200
Punch Products U. S. A., Inc., 2131 Felver Ct., Rahway 07065
Pres.—Michael Fishman, 40 emp., *Plastic & steel promotional travel,* ... (732) 574-1900
Radiation Systems, Inc., 455 W. Main St., Wyckoff 07481
Pres., Sales Mgr.—Richard Ver Hage, 7 emp., *Infrared ovens systems & stainless* ... (201) 891-7515
Rahway Steel, Inc., 625 Leesville Ave., P.O. Box 276, Rahway 07065
Pres.—Antonio Vasquez, 3 emp., *Steel fabrication* ... (732) 388-5300
RCC Fabricators, Inc., 2035 Highway 206, Vincentown 08088
Pres.—Alfonso Daloisio, 25 emp., *Heavy steel fabrication* ... (609) 859-9350
Richards Industries Co., 4 Fairfield Crescent, West Caldwell 07006
GM—Chuck Wampler, 20 emp., *Steel fabrication* ... (973) 575-7480
Rudco Products, Inc., 114 E. Oak Rd., Vineland 08360
Pres.—Bob Rudolph, 60 emp., *Corporate headquarters & hot-rolled* ... (856) 691-0800
Russo & Sons, Inc., Thomas, 854 Communipaw Ave., Jersey City 07304
Pres., CFO—Thomas Russo, 3 emp., *Steel fabrication* ... (201) 332-4159
Saint-Gobain Performance Plastics, 460 Milltown Rd., Bridgewater 08807
Plt. Mgr.—Massimo Caiati, 60 emp., *Flexible fluoropolymer hoses & fittings* ... (908) 218-8888
Sci-Bore, Inc., 364 Glenwood Ave., Bldg. 18-E, East Orange 07017
Pres., CFO—Nadiya Jinnah, 7 emp., *High-carbon steel wire guide nozzles* ... (973) 414-9001
Shrop's Shop, 1254 S. Route 9, Cape May Court House 08210
Owner—Bill Shropshire, 1 emp., *Steel fabrication* ... (609) 465-1640
Skyline Steel, LLC (H Q), 8 Woodhollow Rd., Ste. 102, Parsippany 07054
CEO—Laurent De Mey, 30 emp., *Company headquarters; structural steel* ... (973) 428-6100
Springfield Heating & Air Conditioning Co., Inc., 217 Sheffield St., Mountainside 07092
Pres.—Louis Gallini, 13 emp., *Steel fabrication* ... (908) 233-8400
STE Fabrication, Inc., 28 Haypress Rd., Ste. 106, Cranbury 08512
Pres.—Rick Josephson, 2 emp., *Stainless steel fabrication* ... (732) 274-0024
T & P Machine Shop, 600 Prospect Ave., Piscataway 08854
Pres.—Tony Pasquale, 3 emp., *Steel machined parts & machine shop* ... (732) 424-9141
Thompson Materials Corp., 15 Leslie Ct., Whippany 07981
GM—Ed Ries, 30 emp., *Steel rebar* ... (973) 386-1400
Timplex Corp., 1370 State Route 23, Wantage 07461
Pres.—Ron Slate, 16 emp., *Wooden trusses & light gage, cold formed* ... (973) 875-5500
Tri-Steel Fabricators, Inc., 501 Prospect St., Trenton 08618
Pres.—James Werosta, 18 emp., *Steel fabrication & erection* ... (609) 392-8660
Tube Craft Of America, 667 Lebanon Ave., Williamstown 08094
Pres.—Alexandra Taniewski, 4 emp., *Steel pipe flanges* ... (856) 629-5626
Unimet Metal Supply Co., Inc., 150 Lackawanna Ave., Parsippany 07054
Pres.—Robert Flynn, 70 emp., *Corporate headquarters & steel service* ... (973) 673-5700
Unlimited Steel Fabricators, Inc., 840 Lincoln Blvd., Middlesex 08846
Pres., GM—Richard Stokes, 2 emp., *Steel fabrication* ... (732) 356-7534
Van Grouw Welding & Fabricating, 430 W. Main St., Wyckoff 07481
Owner—Ken Vandenberg, 4 emp., *Steel fabrication* ... (201) 891-4199
VDM Metals USA, LLC, 306 Columbia Tpke., Florham Park 07932
Pres.—Tony Elfstrom, 80 emp., *Company headquarters & metal alloys* ... (973) 437-1664
Victory Iron Works, Inc., 780 Mountain Ave., Wyckoff 07481
Pres.—Teresa Edson, 6 emp., *Steel fabrication* ... (973) 427-4498
VRP Lu-Max Mfg. Co., Inc., 44 Brown Ave., Springfield 07081
Pres., R & D Mgr.—Paul Rodzak, 1 emp., *Sheet metal welding, wire forming &* ... (973) 379-5877
Westfield Sheet Metal Works, Inc., 261 Monroe Ave., P.O. Box 128, Kenilworth 07033
Pres.—Campbell Johnstone, 25 emp., *Custom stainless & carbon steel, aluminum* ... (908) 276-5500

### 3315 Steel wire & related products

Alan Baird Industries, Inc., 1 Hollywood Ave., Ste. 9, Ho-Ho-Kus 07423
Pres.—Michael Cseh, 75 emp., *Wire, mechanical cable & cable assembly* ... (201) 652-6335
Evergard Steel Corp., 1825 Pennsylvania Ave., Linden 07036
Pres.—Connie Frances Macellara, 10 emp., *Steel wire* ... (908) 925-6800
Fixturecraft Corp., 1457 Raritan Rd., Ste. 201, Clark 07066
Pres.—William P. Mooney, 3 emp., *Portable & folding wire display literature* ... (908) 272-8145
Global Wire & Cable, Inc., 61 Willet St., Bldg. S, Passaic 07055
Pres.—George Szakacs, 3 emp., *Wire & cable* ... (973) 471-1000
New Jersey Wire Cloth Co., Inc., 55 Park Slope, Clifton 07011
Pres.—John Rafanello, 7 emp., *Fine sewn, pin & brazed seams, endless* ... (973) 340-0101
Phillips Enterprises, Inc., 3600 Sunset Ave., P.O. Box 2286, Asbury Park 07712
Pres.—Joe Phillips, 7 emp., *Wire forming & metal stampings* ... (732) 493-3191
Plasma Powders & Systems, Inc., 228 Boundary Rd., Ste. 2, P.O. Box 132, Marlboro 07746
Pres.—Peter Foy, 8 emp., *Metal powders & wire & thermal spray* ... (732) 431-0992
Plasti-Clad Metal Products, 2601 Ridgewood Rd., Wall 07719
Pres.—Mark Matthews, 10 emp., *Plastic coated steel wire* ... (732) 449-2665
Wheeler Industrial Corp., 485 Lyons Ave., Irvington 07111
Chrm., Pres. & CEO—Paul Coates, 21 emp., *Corporate headquarters & copper & brass* ... (973) 926-0551

Wytech Industries, Inc., 960 E. Hazelwood Ave., Rahway 07065
CEO—Anthony J. Casalino, 105 emp., *Grinding, straightening, cutting, forming* .................... (732) 396-3900

## 3316 Cold finishing of steel shapes

Kenco Wire & Iron Products, Inc., 425 Carr Ave., Keansburg 07734
Pres.—Mary Urban, 15 emp., *Wire mesh partitions, window guards* .................... (732) 495-3000
Wytech Industries, Inc., 960 E. Hazelwood Ave., Rahway 07065
CEO—Anthony J. Casalino, 105 emp., *Grinding, straightening, cutting, forming* .................... (732) 396-3900

## 3317 Steel pipe & tubes

Century Tube Corp., 22 Tannery Rd., Somerville 08876
Pres.—Dominick DeAngelo, 60 emp., *Stainless steel tubing* .................... (908) 534-2001
Draka Specialty Tubing, 111 Chimney Rock Rd., Bridgewater 08807
Dir., Opers. & Sales—Giovanni Calimani, 60 emp., *Industrial stainless steel pressure*.......... (732) 469-5902
Kreisler Mfg. Corp., 180 Van Riper Ave., Elmwood Park 07407
Owner—Michael Stern, 150 emp., *Tube & manifold fabrication for gas* .................... (201) 791-0700
M & M International, 3619 Kennedy Rd., Ste. A, South Plainfield 07080
Owner—Min Lim, 10 emp., *Small diameter stainless steel tubing* .................... (908) 412-8300
Moretrench American Corp., 100 Stickle Ave., Rockaway 07866
Pres.—Arthur B. Corwin, 175 emp., *Pipe & structural metal fabrication* .................... (973) 627-2100
Morris Industries, Inc., 777 Route 23, P.O. Box 278, Pompton Plains 07444
CEO—Alvin Nochenson, 38 emp., *Steel pipe products, including water* .................... (973) 835-6600
RathGibson, LLC, 100 Aspen Hill Rd., North Branch 08876
V-P.—Joe Waldinger, 110 emp., *Welded stainless steel & titanium tubing* .................... (908) 218-1400
Salem Steel N.A., LLC (H Q), 80 Route 4 E., Ste. 168, Paramus 07652
★ Owner—Ronald S. Herman, 8 emp., *Company headquarters; steel pipe &* .................... (201) 843-1000
Samstubend, Inc., 31 Maryland Ave., Paterson 07503
COO—Samuel Ajadi, 13 emp., *Boiler tube fabrication & bending,* .................... (973) 278-2555
Swepco Tube, LLC, 1 Clifton Blvd., Clifton 07011
Pres.—Kenneth J. Schultz, Jr., 120 emp., *Stainless steel pipes & tubes* .................... (973) 778-3000

## 3321 Foundries—gray & ductile iron

Atlantic States Cast Iron Pipe Co., 183 Sitgreaves St., Phillipsburg 08865
V-P., GM—Dale Schmelzle, 200 emp., *Ductile iron sewer pipes* .................... (908) 454-1161
Bierman Everett Foundry Co., 133 S. 20th St., Irvington 07111
Pres.—Robert Julius, 2 emp., *Gray iron, ductile iron & aluminum* .................... (973) 373-8800
Campbell Foundry Co., 800 Bergen St., Harrison 07029
Pres.—Chris Campbell, 20 emp., *Company headquarters & manhole covers* .................... (973) 483-5480
Fairfield Industries, Inc., 827 N. 6th St., Newark 07107
Pres., Plt. Mgr.—Daniel Clover, 20 emp., *Pre-cast metal manholes & spill containers* .......... (973) 483-0100
General Foundries, Inc., 1 Progress Rd., North Brunswick 08902
Pres.—Rita J. Todani, 16 emp., *Corporate headquarters & iron castings* .................... (732) 697-9000
S H P C, Inc., 187 Christie St., P.O. Box 5328, Newark 07105
Pres. & V-P.—Paul Sacks, 20 emp., *Iron & steel castings & stampings* .................... (973) 589-5242
smALL Quantities New Jersey, Inc., 66 Ethel Rd., Edison 08817
Pres.—Harry Mathis, 50 emp., *Metal stampings* .................... (732) 248-9009
Universal Valve Co., Inc., 478 Schiller St., Elizabeth 07206
Pres., CEO—Robert Milo, 30 emp., *Valves, fittings, vapor recovery equipment* .................... (908) 351-0606

## 3322 Foundries—malleable iron

Cutting Edge Casting, Inc., 1233 W. Saint Georges Ave., Linden 07036
Pres.—Steven Filler, 30 emp., *Metal castings & stampings* .................... (908) 925-7500

## 3324 Foundries—steel investment

Alcoa, 9 Roy St., Dover 07801
GM—William Miley, 675 emp., *Aircraft turbine engines* .................... (973) 361-2310
Alloy Cast Products, Inc., 700 Swenson Dr., Kenilworth 07033
Pres.—Frank S. Panico, 15 emp., *Precision alloy castings* .................... (908) 245-2255
Atlantic Casting & Engineering, 810 Bloomfield Ave., Clifton 07012
CEO—Jim Binns, 100 emp., *Investment castings & CNC machining* .................... (973) 779-2450
Engineered Precision Casting Co., 952 Palmer Ave., Middletown 07748
Owner—Walter Dubovick, 70 emp., *Investment castings* .................... (732) 671-2424
Wheaton Co., R. W., 215 W. Clay Ave., P.O. Box 4017, Roselle Park 07204
Owner & Pres.—Christopher Kern, 10 emp., *Sand & investment castings & general* .................... (908) 241-4955

## 3325 Foundries—steel

Arm-R-Lite Door Mfg. Co., Inc., 2700 Hamilton Blvd., South Plainfield 07080
Pres.—Wilma M. Dourney, 20 emp., *Residential & commercial aluminum,* .................... (908) 754-2600
Colonial Processing, Inc., 1930 S. 6th St., Camden 08104
Pres.—Steve Gove, 33 emp., *Steel processing* .................... (856) 966-3313
Cutting Edge Casting, Inc., 1233 W. Saint Georges Ave., Linden 07036
Pres.—Steven Filler, 30 emp., *Metal castings & stampings* .................... (908) 925-7500
D & S Castings, Inc., 300 Whitehead Rd., Trenton 08619
Pres.—Deoki Sharma, 5 emp., *Metal castings* .................... (609) 689-0100
Duferco Steel, Inc. (H Q), 100 Matawan Rd., Ste. 400, Matawan 07747
Pres.—Joe Deverter, 30 emp., *Corporate headquarters; steel slabs* .................... (732) 566-3130
Falcon Stainless & Alloys Corp., 39 Hewson Ave., Ste. A, Waldwick 07463
V-P.—Paul Chignola, 8 emp., *Stainless steel & alloys & open die* .................... (201) 670-8300
Johnson Atelier, 60 Sculptors Way, Mercerville 08619
Pres.—J. Seward Johnson, Jr., 25 emp., *Metal sculpture castings* .................... (609) 890-7777
S H P C, Inc., 187 Christie St., P.O. Box 5328, Newark 07105
Pres. & V-P.—Paul Sacks, 20 emp., *Iron & steel castings & stampings* .................... (973) 589-5242

## 3334 Aluminum—primary

Frameware, Inc., 8 Audrey Pl., Fairfield 07004
Pres.—Dean DeLuccia, 16 emp., *Manufacturer & distributor of picture* .................... (973) 808-2022

## 3339 Nonferrous metals—primary, nec

Global Metals Sales Corp., 196 Inwood Ave., Montclair 07043
★ Pres.—Michael John Van Rhyn, 10 emp., *Nonferrous metals* .................... (212) 813-3100
Heraeus Precious Metals North America, LLC, 65 Euclid Ave., Newark 07105
V-P. & Site Mgr.—Alan Semko, 23 emp., *Precious metal refining & trading* .................... (973) 817-7878
Industrial Ferguson Foundry, 2365 Route 22 W., P.O. Box 531, Union 07083
Pres.—Ken Karpovich, 15 emp., *Copper, brass, bronze & aluminum castings* .................... (908) 686-8888
Metallix Refining, Inc., 59 Avenue At The Common, Ste. 201, Shrewsbury 07702
CEO—Eric Leiner, 75 emp., *Corporate headquarters & precious metals* .................... (732) 936-0050
POWER HAWK Technologies, Inc., 300 Forge Way, Ste. 2, Rockaway 07866
Pres.—William Hickerson, 16 emp., *Rescue tools & manual impact wrenches* .................... (973) 627-4646
Scientific Industries, Inc., 660 Kinderkamack Rd., Ste. 203, Oradell 07649
Prod. Mktg. Mgr.—Thomas Wright, 6 emp., *Pharmacy pilling counting & weighing* .................... (973) 473-6900

Victory White Metal Co., Inc., 129 Victoria Pl. W., Fort Lee 07024
V-P.—Steven Salomon, 3 emp., *Tin & lead alloys in bar, ingot, wire* .................... (201) 585-0747

## 3341 Secondary nonferrous metals

A & R Recycling Co., 1004 Union Landing Rd., P.O. Box 2440, Cinnaminson 08077
Pres.—Anthony Tognini, 14 emp., *Metal recycling* .................... (856) 829-1712
Canfield Technologies/Bow Electronic Solder, 1 S. Crossman Rd., Sayreville 08872
Cont.—Vito LiLoia, 45 emp., *Solder alloys & fluxes for industrial* .................... (732) 316-2100
Colantuono & Klurman Assocs., Inc., 225 Clifford St., P.O. Box 5150, Newark 07105
Pres.—Sanford Klurman, 40 emp., *Scrap metal recycling* .................... (973) 589-5445
Fortune Riverside Auto Parts, Inc., 900 Leesville Ave., P.O. Box 1589, Rahway 07065
V-P.—Simon Wong, 50 emp., *Scrap metal recycling* .................... (732) 381-3355
Kearny Smelting & Refining, Inc., 936 Harrison Ave., Ste. 5, Kearny 07032
Pres.—Francine Rothschild, 25 emp., *Brass & bronze smelting, refining &* .................... (201) 991-7276
Klein Recycling, 2156 Camplain Rd., Hillsborough 08844
Pres.—Richard Santaniello, 15 emp., *Scrap metal recycling* .................... (908) 722-2288
Matteo & Sons, Inc., James, 1692 Crown Point Rd., Thorofare 08086
Pres.—Frank Matteo, 7 emp., *Scrap metal* .................... (856) 845-0398
Metal Management Northeast, Inc., 1 Linden Ave. E., Jersey City 07305
GM—Joe Payaso, 250 emp., *Metal recycling* .................... (201) 577-3200
Vitali, Inc., Ubaldo, 188-190 Hilton Ave., Maplewood 07040
Pres.—Ubaldo Vitali, 3 emp., *Silver products* .................... (973) 763-9310
Waste Management, Inc., 107 Silvia St., Ewing 08628
Cont.—Tom Utermark, 120 emp., *Glass, scrap metal, plastic, paper,* .................... (609) 587-1500

## 3351 Copper rolling & drawing

Alpine Group, Inc., The (H Q), 1 Meadowlands Plz., Ste. 801, East Rutherford 07073
Chrm. & CEO—Steven S. Elbaum, 5 emp., *Holding company headquarters; nonilluminated*. (201) 549-4400
Amrod Corp., 305-A Craneway St., Newark 07114
Pres.—Mark Woehnker, 45 emp., *Copper rods* .................... (973) 344-2978
Fisk Alloy Wire, Inc., 10 Thomas Rd., P.O. Box 26, Hawthorne 07507
Pres.—Eric Fisk, 175 emp., *Bare & electroplated wire* .................... (973) 427-7550
Freeport-McMoran Copper & Gold, 48-94 Bayway Ave., Elizabeth 07202
Sr. Sales & Mktg. Rep.—Michael Prendergast, 125 emp., *Copper, copper alloys & extruded, drawn* (908) 558-4318
Industrial Tube Corp., 297 Valley Rd., Hillsborough 08844
Owner & Pres., IT—Lydia Imhauser, 50 emp., *Brass tubing* .................... (908) 369-3737
Little Falls Alloys, Inc., 189 Caldwell Ave., Paterson 07501
Chrm. of the Board—Vincent Jim Sacco, 30 emp., *Copper base, bare, round, flat & square* . (973) 278-1666
Phibro-Tech, Inc., 300 Frank W. Burr Blvd., Ste. 21, Glenpointe Center East, 3rd Fl., Teaneck 07666
Pres. & Sales Mgr.—Dwight Glover, 70 emp., *Corporate headquarters & copper chemicals*... (201) 329-7300
Trojan Tube Co., Yellowbrook Rd., P.O. Box 496, Farmingdale 07727
Plt. & Sales Mgr.—Garry Hupser, 16 emp., *Brass, copper, nickel & copper alloy* .................... (732) 938-5687
Wheeler Industrial Corp., 485 Lyons Ave., Irvington 07111
Chrm., Pres. & CEO—Paul Coates, 21 emp., *Corporate headquarters & copper & brass* ...... (973) 926-0551

## 3353 Aluminum sheet, plate & foil

Aleris Mfg., 838 N. Delsea Dr., Clayton 08312
Hum. Res. Mgr.—Michelle Almeida, 120 emp., *Aluminum sheet & foil* .................... (856) 881-3600

## 3354 Aluminum extruded products

Aluminum Shapes, LLC, 9000 River Rd., Delair 08110
IT Mgr.—Joe Howards, 250 emp., *Aluminum extrusions* .................... (800) 242-7512
Construction Specialties, Inc., 3 Werner Way, Lebanon 08833
Co-Chrm.—Ellen Hallock Hakes, 48 emp., *Corporate headquarters & architectural* .......... (908) 236-0800
Hoffman Extrusions, Inc., 103 1/2 Mount Tabor Way, P.O. Box 397, Ocean Grove 07756
Pres.—Carl Hoffman, 2 emp., *Aluminum & brass extrusions* .................... (732) 774-2728
Minalex Corp., 25 Coddington Rd., P.O. Box 247, Whitehouse Station 08889
Pres.—James Casey, 35 emp., *Aluminum extrusions* .................... (908) 534-4044
Rebco, Inc., 1171 Madison Ave., Ste. 1, Paterson 07503
Pres.—Tony Stolarz, 40 emp., *Commercial aluminum entrances, doors* .................... (973) 684-0200
Unique Aluminum Extrusion, LLC, 333 Cedar Ave., Ste. 6, Middlesex 08846
CFO—Selim Uzel, 20 emp., *Aluminum extrusions* .................... (732) 271-0006

## 3355 Aluminum rolling & drawing

Handi-Hut, Inc., 3 Grunwald St., Clifton 07013
Pres.—Melvin Cohen, 25 emp., *Smoking & passenger waiting shelters* .................... (973) 614-1800
State Metal Industries, Inc., 941 S. 2nd St., Camden 08103
Pres.—Yale Dorfmann, 100 emp., *Aluminum ingot & scrap aluminum* .................... (856) 964-1510

## 3356 Nonferrous rolling & drawing

Brim Electronics, Inc., 120 Home Pl., Lodi 07644
Pres.—Barry Danziger, 25 emp., *Insulated electronic wires & cables* .................... (201) 796-2886
Coining, Inc., 15 Mercedes Dr., Montvale 07645
V-P., Sales & Mktg.—Julie Scelzo, 75 emp., *Preformed solder & brazing* .................... (201) 791-4020
H. Cross Co., 150 W. Commercial Ave., Moonachie 07074
Pres.—Edward McClary, 36 emp., *Rhenium, molybdenum, tungsten, tantalum* .................... (201) 964-9380
Kaistar Research & Development, LLC, 15 Wilson Dr., Sparta 07871
Pres.—Igor Kapchenko, 4 emp., *High-purity metals, special purpose* .................... (973) 362-1487
Mac Metals, Inc., 936 Harrison Ave., CN 670, Kearny 07032
Pres.—Francine Rothschild, 34 emp., *Brass & bronze extrusions* .................... (201) 997-8001
Metalico, Inc. (H Q), 186 North Ave. E., Cranford 07016
Chrm., Pres. & CEO—Carlos E. Aguero, 12 emp., *Corporate headquarters; lead & lead*........ (908) 497-9610
Scientific Alloys Corp., 5 Troast Ct., Clifton 07011
Pres.—William Pian, 35 emp., *Solder, gold, silver & alloy spheres* .................... (973) 478-8323
Semiconductor Mfg., 5 Troast Ct., Clifton 07011
Pres.—William Pian, 54 emp., *Metal stampings, spheres & wire, including* .................... (973) 478-2880
VDM Metals USA, LLC, 306 Columbia Tpke., Florham Park 07932
Pres.—Tony Elfstrom, 80 emp., *Company headquarters & metal alloys* .................... (973) 437-1664
Victory White Metal Co., Inc., 129 Victoria Pl. W., Fort Lee 07024
V-P.—Steven Salomon, 3 emp., *Tin & lead alloys in bar, ingot, wire* .................... (201) 585-0747

## 3357 Nonferrous wiredrawing & insulating

Alcatel-Lucent (H Q), 600 Mountain Ave., Murray Hill 07974
Chrm.—Philippe Camus, 4000 emp., *Company headquarters; telecommunication* .................... (908) 582-8500
American Fibertek, Inc., 120 Belmont Dr., Somerset 08873
Pres.—Jack Fernandes, 70 emp., *Fiber-optic security system components* .................... (732) 302-0660
Antronix, Inc. (H Q), 440 Forsgate Dr., Cranbury 08512
Pres.—Danny Tang, 35 emp., *Corporate headquarters; cable television* .................... (609) 395-1390
Brim Electronics, Inc., 120 Home Pl., Lodi 07644
Pres.—Barry Danziger, 25 emp., *Insulated electronic wires & cables* .................... (201) 796-2886
C Technologies, Inc., 757 U.S. Highway 202/206, Bridgewater 08807
Pres.—Craig D. Harrison, 40 emp., *Fiber-optic cable assembly* .................... (908) 707-1009

S.I.C.

★ Indicates new listing this edition.

Chiral Photonics, Inc., 26 Chapin Rd., Unit 1104, P.O. Box 694, Pine Brook 07058
Pres.—Dan Neugroschl, 20 emp., *Ultra high-density optical I/O solutions* ........ (973) 732-0030
Chromis Fiberoptics, Inc., 6 Powderhorn Dr., Warren 07059
CEO—Whitney White, 10 emp., *Perfluorinated plastic optical fibers* ........ (732) 764-0900
Colonial Wire & Cable Of NJ, Inc., 85 National Rd., Edison 08817
Pres.—Thomas Walsh, 100 emp., *Electrical wires & cables* ........ (732) 287-1557
Compass Wire Cloth, Inc., 1942 N. Mill Rd., Vineland 08360
Pres.—Michael McGrath, 48 emp., *Vibratory hooked, pretension, aggregate* ........ (856) 853-7616
Francis Metals Co., Inc., 687 Prospect St., Ste. 430, Lakewood 08701
Pres.—Matt Deiner, 20 emp., *Armored electronic cable & commercial* ........ (732) 761-0500
Jersey Strand & Cable, Inc., 259 Center St., Phillipsburg 08865
Pres.—Al Pratt, 40 emp., *Custom & stock small & miniature ferrous* ........ (908) 213-9350
Liberty Electronics, Inc., 465 E. Main St., Denville 07834
Owner—Tom Ferrante, 4 emp., *Wire & cable & cable assemblies* ........ (973) 625-7963
Little Falls Alloys, Inc., 189 Caldwell Ave., Paterson 07501
Chrm. of the Board—Vincent Jim Sacco, 30 emp., *Copper base, bare, round, flat & square* .. (973) 278-1666
Micro-Tek Corp., P.O. Box 2134, Cinnaminson 08077
Pres.—Ricki Rogers, 12 emp., *Teflon-insulated wire* ........ (856) 829-3855
Molecu-Wire Corp., 56 Old Camplain Rd., Hillsborough 08844
Pres.—Vinod Barot, 80 emp., *Copper & insulated wires* ........ (732) 296-9473
Multimode Fiber Optics, Inc., 432 Sand Shore Rd., Unit 1, Hackettstown 07840
Pres., CFO—Roger Berkowitz, 8 emp., *Fiber-optic cables, including fiber* ........ (908) 684-5802
National Electric Wire Co., 100 Goldman Dr., Cream Ridge 08514
Pres.—Alan R. Keith, 40 emp., *Nickel chrome, nickel, flat, strip,* ........ (609) 758-3600
New Jersey Wire Cloth Co., Inc., 55 Park Slope, Clifton 07011
Pres.—John Rafanello, 7 emp., *Fine sewn, pin & brazed seams, endless* ........ (973) 340-0101
OFS Fitel, LLC, Specialty Photonics Div., 25 Schoolhouse Rd., Somerset 08873
Manager—Joann Coyne, 45 emp., *Specialty fiber-optic cables & fiber* ........ (732) 748-7400
Okonite Co., Inc., The (H Q), 102 Hilltop Rd., P.O. Box 340, Ramsey 07446
Chrm., CEO—V. A. Viggiano, 100 emp., *Corporate headquarters; electric cables* ........ (201) 825-0300
Okonite Co., The, 102 Hilltop Rd., Paterson 07513
Plt. Mgr.—Steve Nicholas, 100 emp., *Electric wire & power cables* ........ (201) 825-0300
Oxford Instruments Superconducting Technology, Inc., 600 Milik St., Carteret 07008
Pres.—Jeff Parrell, 212 emp., *Corporate headquarters & superconductor* ........ (732) 541-1300
PD-LD, Inc., 30-B Pennington-Hopewell Rd., Pennington 08534
CEO—Vladimir Ban, 60 emp., *Fiber optics, laser components & laser* ........ (609) 564-7900
Prysmian Power Cables & Systems, LLC, 5 Hollywood Ct., South Plainfield 07080
Dir.—Tony Tremonte, 15 emp., *High voltage & submarine cable systems* ........ (908) 791-2828
Ram Electronic Industries Inc., 1704 Taylors Ln., Ste. 7, Cinnaminson 08077
Pres.—Steve Misbin, 60 emp., *Audio & video cables & equipment, computer* ........ (856) 864-0999
Sigma-Netics, Inc., 2 N. Corporate Dr., Riverdale 07457
Pres.—Alan Glanzman, 30 emp., *Pressure switches & metal bellows* ........ (973) 616-6900
Surepure Chemetals, Inc., 5 Nottingham Dr., Florham Park 07932
Pres.—Barry Vegter, 8 emp., *Gold, silver & platinum wires* ........ (973) 377-4081
TE Wire & Cable, LLC, 107 5th St., Saddle Brook 07663
V-P., Sales & Mktg.—Pat Durkin, 100 emp., *Wire & cable, including thermocouple* ........ (201) 845-9400
Tielmann, Inc., D. R., 1208 State Route 34, Ste. 1, Matawan 07747
Pres.—D. R. 'Debbie' Tielmann, 5 emp., *Fiber-optic cable* ........ (732) 332-1860
Tyco Electronics Subsea Communications, LLC (H Q), 250 Industrial Way W., Eatontown 07724
Pres.—John Mitchell, 129 emp., *Divisional headquarters; underwater* ........ (732) 578-7000
U. S. Wire & Cable, Inc., 33 Queen St., Newark 07114
Pres.—David Rauch, 100 emp., *Wire, cables, cords & accessories* ........ (973) 824-5529
V-Com, 80 Little Falls Rd., Fairfield 07004
Pres.—Scott Schaefer, 25 emp., *Cable assemblies, connectors, switchers* ........ (201) 229-9800

### 3363 Aluminum die castings

Carteret Die Casting Corp., 74 Veronica Ave., P.O. Box 5610, Somerset 08875
Pres.—John W. Burk, 28 emp., *Zinc & aluminum die castings* ........ (732) 246-0070
Flemington Aluminum & Brass, Inc., 24 Junction Rd., Flemington 08822
Pres.—James Kozicki, 6 emp., *Custom aluminum & brass castings, including* ........ (908) 782-6317
Industrial Ferguson Foundry, 2365 Route 22 W., P.O. Box 531, Union 07083
Pres.—Ken Karpovich, 15 emp., *Copper, brass, bronze & aluminum castings* ........ (908) 686-8888
Premier Die Casting Co., Inc., 1177 Rahway Ave., Avenel 07001
Pres.—Leonard Cordaro, 80 emp., *Zinc & aluminum die castings* ........ (732) 634-3000

### 3364 Nonferrous die-casting, except aluminum

ABCO Die Casters, Inc., 39 Tompkins Point Rd., Newark 07114
Pres.—Joseph R. Vitollo, 70 emp., *Die casting & powder coating* ........ (973) 624-7030
Carteret Die Casting Corp., 74 Veronica Ave., P.O. Box 5610, Somerset 08875
Pres.—John W. Burk, 28 emp., *Zinc & aluminum die castings* ........ (732) 246-0070
Premier Die Casting Co., Inc., 1177 Rahway Ave., Avenel 07001
Pres.—Leonard Cordaro, 80 emp., *Zinc & aluminum die castings* ........ (732) 634-3000
Richmond Industries, Inc., 1 Chris Ct., Dayton 08810
Owner & Pres.—Keith DiGrazio, 40 emp., *Brass, bronze, manganese & aluminum* ........ (732) 355-1616
Titanium Fabrication Corp., 110 Lehigh Dr., Fairfield 07004
Pres., CEO—Brent Willey, 45 emp., *Custom titanium & reactive metal design* ........ (973) 227-5300

### 3365 Foundries—aluminum

American Aluminum Casting Co., 324 Coit St., Irvington 07111
Pres.—Robert W. Hartl, 50 emp., *Aluminum castings* ........ (973) 372-3200
American Monument Co., 50 Herbert Ave., Closter 07624
Pres.—Ron Boyajian, 20 emp., *Stone, natural rock, granite, brick* ........ (201) 750-1000
American Monument Co. (H Q), 479 N. Dean St., Englewood 07631
Pres.—Ron Boyajian, 3 emp., *Company headquarters; stone, natural* ........ (201) 569-4455
B & R Industries, Inc., 196 12th St., Piscataway 08854
Pres.—Fred Bellscheidt, 30 emp., *Aluminum castings* ........ (732) 752-3022
Bierman Everett Foundry Co., 133 S. 20th St., Irvington 07111
Pres.—Robert Julius, 2 emp., *Gray iron, ductile iron & aluminum* ........ (973) 373-8800
Biological Controls, Inc., 749 Hope Rd., Ste. A, Tinton Falls 07724
Pres.—Gary Messina, 5 emp., *Hospital infection control equipment* ........ (732) 389-8922
Bon Chef, Inc., 205 State Route 94, Lafayette 07848
Pres., R & D Mgr.—Sal Torre, 90 emp., *Flatware, chafing dishes, sandstone* ........ (973) 383-8848
Richmond Industries, Inc., 1 Chris Ct., Dayton 08810
Owner & Pres.—Keith DiGrazio, 40 emp., *Brass, bronze, manganese & aluminum* ........ (732) 355-1616
Talbot Assocs., Inc., 11 Cleveland Pl., Springfield 07081
CEO—Jeffrey Talbot, 14 emp., *Steel & aluminum castings* ........ (973) 376-9570
Tec Cast, Inc., 440 Meadow Ln., Carlstadt 07072
Pres.—Edgar Gotthold, 70 emp., *Aluminum investment castings & casting* ........ (201) 935-3885

### 3366 Copper foundries

Accurate Bushing Co., Inc./Smith Bearing Div., 443 North Ave., 1st Fl., Garwood 07027
Pres.—Peter Dubinsky, 50 emp., *Aircraft & industrial bearings, bushings* ........ (908) 789-1121
American Monument Co., 50 Herbert Ave., Closter 07624
Pres.—Ron Boyajian, 20 emp., *Stone, natural rock, granite, brick* ........ (201) 750-1000
Barre Monuments, 114 Atlantic City Blvd., Beachwood 08722
Owner—Michael Maloney, 3 emp., *Cast bronze & granite memorials* ........ (732) 240-2888
Bierman Everett Foundry Co., 133 S. 20th St., Irvington 07111
Pres.—Robert Julius, 2 emp., *Gray iron, ductile iron & aluminum* ........ (973) 373-8800
Dornan, Inc., 333 Cedarcroft Dr., Brick 08724
Pres.—Rita Dornan, 2 emp., *Brass & pewter miniature castings &* ........ (732) 295-4491
Federal Bronze Casting Industries, 9 Backus St., Newark 07105
Pres.—Doug Reichard, 42 emp., *Brass, bronze & aluminum castings &* ........ (973) 589-7575
Freeport-McMoran Copper & Gold, 48-94 Bayway Ave., Elizabeth 07202
Sr. Sales & Mktg. Rep.—Michael Prendergast, 125 emp., *Copper, copper alloys & extruded, drawn* (908) 558-4318
Industrial Ferguson Foundry, 2365 Route 22 W., P.O. Box 531, Union 07083
Pres.—Ken Karpovich, 15 emp., *Copper, brass, bronze & aluminum castings* ........ (908) 686-8888
J.R.M. Products, Inc., 701 Locust St., Keyport 07735
Pres.—Robert Wichowski, 4 emp., *American-made custom steel, stainless* ........ (732) 495-3092
Rangecraft Mfg. Co., Inc., 4-40 Banta Pl., Fair Lawn 07410
Pres.—Ramona Panus, 19 emp., *Custom-designed decorative copper,* ........ (201) 791-0440
Sculpturesque, Inc., 7 Etheridge Pl., Park Ridge 07656
Owner—Catherine Schmitt, 1 emp., *Commercial & fine art sculptures &* ........ (201) 573-9150
SRS, Inc., 74 Liberty St., P.O. Box 4277, Metuchen 08840
Pres.—Rich Blatman, 22 emp., *Stainless steel, bronze & glass guardrails* ........ (732) 548-6630

### 3369 Foundries—nonferrous, nec

Biomet, Inc., 20-01 Pollitt Dr., Fair Lawn 07410
Prodn. Mgr.—Mike Shannon, 50 emp., *Orthopedic implants alloy castings* ........ (201) 797-7300
Dornan, Inc., 333 Cedarcroft Dr., Brick 08724
Pres.—Rita Dornan, 2 emp., *Brass & pewter miniature castings &* ........ (732) 295-4491
Flemington Aluminum & Brass, Inc., 24 Junction Rd., Flemington 08822
Pres.—James Kozicki, 6 emp., *Custom aluminum & brass castings, including* ........ (908) 782-6317

### 3398 Heat treating—metal

Bennett Heat Treating & Brazing Co., Inc., 690 Ferry St., Newark 07105
Pres., CFO—David Quaglia, 40 emp., *Corporate headquarters & metal heat* ........ (973) 589-0590
Blue Blade Steel, 123 N. 8th St., P.O. Box 40, Kenilworth 07033
Pres.—Jeremiah H. Shaw, 40 emp., *High carbon, stainless & alloy strip* ........ (908) 272-2620
Bodycote, 304 Cox St., Roselle 07203
Sales Mgr.—Paul Goins, 26 emp., *Metal heat treating* ........ (908) 245-0717
Bolttech Mannings, Inc., 321 Richard Mine Rd., Ste. 300, Wharton 07885
Sales & Mktg. Mgr.—Scott Herland, 20 emp., *Heat treating, induction, hydraulic* ........ (973) 537-1576
Braddock Heat Treating Co., Inc., 123 Chimney Rock Rd., Bridgewater 08807
GM—W. J. Schultz, Jr., 20 emp., *Metal heat treating* ........ (732) 356-2906
Delphi Engineering & Contracting, Inc., 131 Blackwood Barnsboro Rd., Sewell 08080
Pres.—Nick Pjatikin, 8 emp., *Heat treating, including stress relieving* ........ (856) 228-5700
Dynaflow Engineering, 106 Egel Ave., Middlesex 08846
Pres.—Ross Block, 5 emp., *Stainless, alloy & plastic gear pumps* ........ (732) 356-9790
General Pallet, LLC, 97 River Rd., Flemington 08822
Ptnr.—Donald W. Baldwin, 7 emp., *New & reconditioned wooden, plastic* ........ (908) 238-1000
Kenney Steel Treating Corp., 100 Quincy Pl., Kearny 07032
Pres.—James Dumphy, 20 emp., *Steel brazing* ........ (201) 998-4420
Krohn Industries, Inc., 303 Veterans Blvd., P.O. Box 98, Carlstadt 07072
Pres.—Nicholas Krohn, 10 emp., *Brazing alloys* ........ (201) 933-9696
Marlo Mfg. Co., Inc., 301 Division St., Boonton 07005
Ex. V-P.—Paul Peruccio, 50 emp., *Stainless steel restaurant equipment* ........ (973) 423-0226
SICA Metal Products, 1775 Hurffville Rd., Route 41, P.O. Box 5525, Deptford 08096
Owner & Fin. Mgr.—Ralph Sica, Sr., 3 emp., *Custom stainless steel & metal fabrications* ........ (856) 227-6616
Team Industrial Services, 4 Killdeer Ct., Ste. 300, Swedesboro 08085
Br. Mgr.—Matthew Keen, 45 emp., *Metal heat treating & NDE/NDT inspections* ........ (610) 859-7800
Temperature Processing Co., Inc., 228 River Rd., North Arlington 07031
Pres.—William J. Engelhard, 10 emp., *Metal heat treating* ........ (201) 991-8000

### 3399 Primary metal products, nec

ACuPowder International, LLC, 901 Lehigh Ave., Union 07083
Tech. Serv. Mgr.—Ken Watson, 75 emp., *Nonferrous metal powders* ........ (908) 851-4500
AmerTac, Inc., 1 Route 17 S., Saddle River Executive Center, Saddle River 07458
COO—Sal Mirra, 50 emp., *Decorative metal & plastic wall plates* ........ (201) 825-0388
Ames Advanced Material, 3900 S. Clinton Ave., South Plainfield 07080
Hum. Res. Mgr.—Jennifer Quandt, 200 emp., *Precious metal powders* ........ (908) 561-1100
Atlantic Equipment Engineers, Inc., 24 Industrial Ave., P.O. Box 181, Upper Saddle River 07458
Pres., GM, Fin. & MIS Mgr.—Alan Kessler, 12 emp., *High purity metal powders & compounds*. (201) 828-9400
Glenro, Inc., 39 McBride Avenue Ext., Paterson 07501
Pres.—Gary Van Denend, 20 emp., *Industrial gas & electric infrared* ........ (973) 279-5900
Hoeganaes Corp. (H Q), 1001 Taylors Ln., Cinnaminson 08077
Pres.—Abdul Butt, 100 emp., *Corporate headquarters; iron & steel* ........ (856) 829-2220
Hoyt Corp., 520 S. Dean St., Englewood 07631
Pres.—Don Maguire, 65 emp., *Custom & standard precious metal electrical* ........ (201) 894-0707
Magnetic Metals Corp., 1900 Hayes Ave., Camden 08105
Pres.—Frank A. Raneiro, 60 emp., *Metal stampings & high-grade nickel* ........ (856) 964-7842
Metal Management Northeast, Inc., 1 Linden Ave. E., Jersey City 07305
GM—Joe Payaso, 250 emp., *Metal recycling* ........ (201) 577-3200
Plasma Powders & Systems, Inc., 228 Boundary Rd., Ste. 2, P.O. Box 132, Marlboro 07746
Pres.—Peter Foy, 8 emp., *Metal powders & wire & thermal spray* ........ (732) 431-0992
Protech Powder Coating, Inc., 21 Audrey Pl., Fairfield 07004
Cont.—Gilles Crotures, 27 emp., *Powder coatings* ........ (973) 257-0505
United States Metal Powders, Inc., 408 U.S. Highway 202, Flemington 08822
Pres., CEO—Clive Ramsey, 12 emp., *Corporate headquarters & atomized aluminum* ........ (908) 782-5454
Winter, Inc. & Co., F. W., Delaware Ave. & Elm St., Camden 08102
Pres., CEO—Friedrich W. Winter, 22 emp., *Metal & alloy powders* ........ (856) 963-7490

## 34 FABRICATED METAL PRODUCTS

### 3411 Cans—metal

Allstate Can Corp., 1 Woodhollow Rd., Parsippany 07054
Pres.—Richard D. Papera, 80 emp., *Decorative & custom metal containers* ........ (973) 560-9030
Silgan Containers Mfg. Corp., 135 National Rd., Edison 08817
Off. Mgr.—Mayson Stewart, 120 emp., *Steel cans* ........ (732) 287-0300
Stamplus Mfg., Inc., 654 W. 1st Ave., Roselle 07203
Hum. Res. & Sales Mgr.—Maureen Marhon, 21 emp., *Metal cans & covers* ........ (908) 241-8844

Wastequip, Inc., 460 New Brooklyn Rd., Williamstown 08094
Plt. Mgr.—Fred Straub, 75 emp., *Steel waste containers* .................................... (856) 629-9222

### 3412 Barrels, drums & pails—metal

BWAY Corp., 1202 Airport Rd., North Brunswick 08902
Sales Mgr.—Leslie Sammarco, 110 emp., *Metal pails*.............................................. (732) 247-6700
Industrial Drum Co., 784 New Jersey Ave., P.O. Box 586, Glassboro 08028
Owner & Pres.—Ted Demiduke, 8 emp., *Reconditioned 55-gallon steel & poly*.................... (856) 881-2000
Jones & Son, Inc., William, 238 Liberty St., Camden 08104
Pres.—John T. Williams, 23 emp., *Reconditioned steel drums, barrels,*.............................. (856) 963-1199
Kearny Steel Container Corp., 401 South St., Newark 07105
Pres.—Michael Verzaleno, 75 emp., *Reconditioned & new steel, fiber &* ............................ (973) 589-2070
Mauser USA LLC, 14 Convery Blvd., Woodbridge 07095
Plt. Mgr.—Dennis Mullin, 100 emp., *Steel drums* ........................................................ (732) 634-6000
Nelson Custom Case Co., 1014 State Route 173, Bloomsbury 08804
Owner—William A. Nelson III, 3 emp., *ATA style custom cases, including LED*..................... (908) 479-6902
Patrick J. Kelly Drums, Inc., 1810 River Ave., Camden 08105
Owner & Pres.—Patrick J. Kelly, 49 emp., *New & reconditioned industrial steel* ................... (856) 963-1795
Rahway Steel Drum Co. (H Q), 202 Elliot St., Avenel 07001
Pres.—Michael Foglia, 25 emp., *Company headquarters; steel, plastic*.............................. (732) 382-0113
Wastequip, Inc., 460 New Brooklyn Rd., Williamstown 08094
Plt. Mgr.—Fred Straub, 75 emp., *Steel waste containers* .............................................. (856) 629-9222

### 3421 Cutlery

Du-Matt Corp., 111 71st St., Guttenberg 07093
Pres.—Adolf Manttillo, 7 emp., *Wax & wax-working tools*............................................ (201) 861-4271
Energizer Personal Care, 240 Cedar Knolls Rd., Ste. 401, Cedar Knolls 07927
CFO—Thomas Kasvin, 15 emp., *Divisional headquarters & safety razors* .......................... (973) 753-3000
Hobby Blade Specialty, Inc., 725 Jerusalem Rd., Scotch Plains 07076
Pres.—Mike Torres, 3 emp., *Hunting knife blade grinding & industrial*............................. (908) 317-9306
Icicle, Inc., 341 School House Rd., Monroe Township 08831
Pres.—Richard Lamont, 2 emp., *Scissors* ..................................................................... (732) 521-4223
IDL TechniEdge, LLC, 30 Boright Ave., Kenilworth 07033
Pres., CEO—Sean Quinn, 125 emp., *Hand blades & tools, including utility* ......................... (908) 497-9818
Industrial Razor Blade Co., Inc., 575 Nassau St., Orange 07050
Owner—Frank Florey, 2 emp., *Custom blades & knives*................................................ (973) 673-4286
Master Cutlery, Inc., 700 Penhorn Ave., Secaucus 07094
Pres.—Victor Lee, 40 emp., *Cutlery* .......................................................................... (201) 271-7600
Tech Art, Inc., 12 E. 5th St., Paterson 07524
Pres.—Gerald Pfund, 5 emp., *School scissor & ruler packaging*...................................... (201) 525-0044
U. S. Blade Mfg., 90 Myrtle St., Cranford 07016
Pres.—Anthony Calenda, 75 emp., *Industrial blades*.................................................... (908) 272-2898

### 3423 Tools—hand & edge

A & J Tool Specialties, Inc., 235 Morris Ave., Summit 07901
Pres.—Aldo Curiale, 3 emp., *Cutting tools*................................................................... (908) 277-0550
Albion Engineering Co., 1250 N. Church St., Moorestown 08057
Owner—Mark Schneider, 19 emp., *Professional caulking guns & adhesive* ......................... (856) 235-6688
Armour Products, 176-180 5th Ave., Hawthorne 07506
Co-Pres.—Sydney St. James, 15 emp., *Glass etching & mirror decorating tools*.................... (973) 427-8787
Astro Tool Corp., 90 Washington Ave., Nutley 07110
Sales Mgr., Eastern—John Nosti, 2 emp., *Pneumatic, hand crimp, insertion &* ..................... (973) 661-1299
Atlas Copco North America, LLC (H Q), 7 Campus Dr., Ste. 200, Parsippany 07054
Pres., AC Holdings USA—Jim Levitt, 40 emp., *Company headquarters; industrial air* ........... (973) 397-3400
BMB Fasteners, Inc., 86 Lackawanna Ave., Ste. 208, Woodland Park 07424
Owner & Pres.—Larry Malone, 8 emp., *Screws, fasteners, bolts, nuts & washers*................. (973) 256-4010
Cementex Products, Inc., 650 Jacksonville Rd., P.O. Box 1533, Burlington 08016
Pres., CEO—Stephen H. Russo, 37 emp., *Double-insulated hand tools, related*.................... (609) 387-1040
Cobra Products, Inc., 1 Warner Ct., Swedesboro 08085
Cont.—Dick Hogan, 200 emp., *Drain-cleaning tools*...................................................... (856) 241-7700
Derma-Safe Co., LLC, 32 Juniper Rd., Wayne 07470
Owner—Paul Grosjean, 2 emp., *American-made folding utility knives*............................... (973) 839-6383
Dessau Co., Inc., Maurice, 15-01 Pollitt Dr., Fair Lawn 07410
Pres.—Richard Dessau, 25 emp., *Industrial diamond tools*............................................ (201) 791-2005
Du-Matt Corp., 111 71st St., Guttenberg 07093
Pres.—Adolf Manttillo, 7 emp., *Wax & wax-working tools*............................................ (201) 861-4271
Excel Hobby Blades Corp., 481 Getty Ave., P.O. Box 1045, Paterson 07503
Pres.—Mike Hammam, 40 emp., *Replaceable blade knives, blades &* ............................... (973) 278-4000
Fire Hooks Unlimited, 1827 Old Mill Rd., Wall 07719
CEO, R & D Mgr.—Bob Farrell, 18 emp., *Firefighting tools & equipment*............................ (732) 280-7737
Grobet File Co. Of America, LLC., 750 Washington Ave., Carlstadt 07072
Pres.—John Canzoneri, 80 emp., *Company headquarters & precision metal* ....................... (201) 939-6700
Hexacon Electric Co., 161 W. Clay Ave., Roselle Park 07204
Pres.—Kathi Johnson, 35 emp., *Soldering & branding irons & soldering*............................. (908) 245-6200
IDL TechniEdge, LLC, 30 Boright Ave., Kenilworth 07033
Pres., CEO—Sean Quinn, 125 emp., *Hand blades & tools, including utility* ......................... (908) 497-9818
Industrial Products Corp., 1 Hollywood Ave., Ste. 30, Ho-Ho-Kus 07423
Owner & Pres.—J. K. Dohner, Jr., 2 emp., *Industrial machine knives* ............................... (201) 652-5913
Mastercool, Inc., 1 Aspen Dr., Randolph 07869
Graphic Artist—Stephanie Bartell, 40 emp., *Automotive air conditioning service*................. (973) 252-9119
Metropolitan Vacuum Cleaner Co., Inc., 5 Raritan Rd., Oakland 07436
Pres.—Jules Stern, 75 emp., *Household vacuum cleaners, electric*.................................. (201) 405-2225
Nifty Products, 4 Jocama Blvd., Old Bridge 08857
Pres.—Norman Ferber, 25 emp., *Shipping room tape guns, tape & stretch*......................... (732) 591-1140
Norwolf Tool Works, Inc., 6 Sullivan St., Westwood 07675
Pres.—Steve Spirer, 5 emp., *Hand tools, hydraulic wrenches, stud* ................................ (201) 666-6655
Osborne Co., Inc., C. S., 125 Jersey St., Harrison 07029
Owner & Pres.—Jake Angell, 75 emp., *Nonelectric hand tools*......................................... (973) 483-3232
Penn Tool Co., 1776 Springfield Ave., Maplewood 07040
Owner—Gene Elson, 8 emp., *Hand tools & measuring instruments*................................. (973) 761-4343
POWER HAWK Technologies, Inc., 300 Forge Way, Ste. 2, Rockaway 07866
Pres.—William Hickerson, 16 emp., *Rescue tools & manual impact wrenches*...................... (973) 627-4646
Proedge, 167 Genessee Ave., Paterson 07503
Owner—Mike Hammam, 8 emp., *Hobby tools, blades & knives*........................................ (973) 742-3900
Ramelson Co., Inc., U. J., 165 Thomas St., Newark 07114
Pres.—John L. Ramella, 4 emp., *Woodcarving tools*..................................................... (973) 589-5422
S & G Tool Aid Corp., 43 E. Alpine St., Newark 07114
Sales Mgr., Natl.—Wayne Hutchings, 75 emp., *Automotive & auto body repair shop* ............. (973) 824-7730
Shor International Corp., 77 Fairwood Rd., Madison 07940
Pres., CFO—Peter Shor, 36 emp., *Jewelry tools & refining systems*.................................. (973) 520-8777
Tolin Design, Inc., 16 Bland St., Emerson 07630
Pres., Plt. Mgr.—Tony Suarez, 5 emp., *Aircraft tools & ground support equipment*.............. (201) 261-4455

VIS USA, LLC, 210 Meister Ave., Branchburg 08876
Pres., Fin. & MIS Mgr.—Rene Morf, 15 emp., *Power transmission & conveyor belting* ........... (908) 575-0606
W.W. Manufacturing Co., Inc., 60 Rosenhayn Ave., Bridgeton 08302
Ptnr. & Pres.—Peter Lesche, 12 emp., *Steel landscaping & nursery hand tools*.................... (856) 451-5700
Wire & Cable Fabricating Devices, 39 E. Hanover Ave., Ste. 1, Morris Plains 07950
Ptnr.—Richard Koppinger, 4 emp., *Stainless steel electrical wiring tools*.......................... (973) 290-9069

### 3425 Saw blades & handsaws

Derma-Safe Co., LLC, 32 Juniper Rd., Wayne 07470
Owner—Paul Grosjean, 2 emp., *American-made folding utility knives* ............................... (973) 839-6383
Ferrous Saw Works, 345 Lakeview Ave., Clifton 07011
Owner—Dominic Farino, Jr., 1 emp., *High-speed segmental & friction saws* ........................ (973) 513-3936
Forrest Mfg. Co., Inc., 457 River Rd., Clifton 07014
Pres.—James D. Forrest, 33 emp., *Saw blades*............................................................. (973) 473-5236
Tooling Etc., LLC, 250 Hallock Ave., Ste. C, Middlesex 08846
Pres.—Markus Jesacher, 12 emp., *Segmental, solid, circular & hot friction*........................ (732) 752-8080

### 3429 Hardware, nec

A. K. Stamping Co., Inc., 1159 Highway 22 E., Mountainside 07092
CEO—Arthur Kurz, 45 emp., *Metal stampings & circuit board brackets*............................... (908) 232-7300
A+ Products, Inc., 8 Timber Ln., Marlboro Industrial Pk., Marlboro 07746
Founder & Pres.—Mike Schreiber, 40 emp., *Corporate headquarters & custom & standard* ... (732) 866-9111
Accurate Door & Hardware, Inc., 10 W. End Rd., Totowa 07512
Pres.—Richard Cornetto, Sr., 20 emp., *Steel doors & hardware* ....................................... (973) 812-2266
Alway, Inc. (H Q), 440 U.S. Highway 202, Flemington 08822
Pres.—Terry Hubscher, 1 emp., *Corporate headquarters; metal bed sheet* .......................... (908) 788-7220
Aram, Inc., Michael, 2102 83rd St., North Bergen 07047
Pres.—Michael Wolohojis, 7 emp., *Hand-crafted metal tableware, hardware* ........................ (201) 758-2551
Art Material Service Co., Inc., 625 Joyce Kilmer Ave., New Brunswick 08901
Pres.—Joe Eichert, 50 emp., *Picture frame hardware*................................................... (732) 545-8888
AS America, Inc. (H Q), 1 Centennial Ave., P.O. Box 6820, Piscataway 08855
Pres., CEO—Jay Gould, 240 emp., *Corporate headquarters; hardware &* ............................ (732) 980-3000
Associated Pile & Fitting, 8 Wood Hollow Rd., Plz. 1, P.O. Box 5933, Parsippany 07054
Manager—Matt Scerbak, 4 emp., *Manufacturer & distributor of points*................................ (973) 773-8400
Behringer Corp., 17 Ridge Rd., Branchville 07826
Pres., GM—Ted Hinds, 40 emp., *Pipe & tube hangers, filtration products* ........................... (973) 948-0226
Brim Electronics, Inc., 120 Home Pl., Lodi 07644
Pres.—Barry Danziger, 25 emp., *Insulated electronic wires & cables* ............................... (201) 796-2886
Brown & Perkins, Inc., 1193 Route 535, P.O. Box 412, Cranbury 08512
Pres.—E. T. Comly, 16 emp., *Manufacturer & distributor of wire* ..................................... (609) 655-1150
C & G Screws Unlimited, 2150 Route 88, Brick 08724
Pres.—Sharon Petriello, 10 emp., *Screws, nuts & bolts* ................................................. (732) 892-8400
C. R. Laurence Co., Inc., 1511 Lancer Dr., Moorestown 08057
Br. Mgr.—Jason Kee, 15 emp., *Hardware for glass mirrors, displays* .................................. (856) 727-1022
Carl Stahl Sava Industries, Inc., 4 N. Corporate Dr., P.O. Box 30, Riverdale 07457
CEO—Zdenek A. Fremund, 85 emp., *Corporate headquarters & miniature* ............................ (973) 835-0882
Carpenter & Paterson, Inc., 3900 River Rd., P.O. Box 556, Pennsauken 08110
Br. Mgr.—Bob Cieslikowski, 15 emp., *Commercial & industrial pipe hangers*......................... (856) 488-1988
Carpenter & Paterson, Inc., 369 Jefferson St., Saddle Brook 07663
Br. Mgr.—Thomas Browne, 35 emp., *Metal pipe hangers, supports, struts* ........................... (973) 772-1800
Coilhose Pneumatics, 19 Kimberly Rd., East Brunswick 08816
Pres.—Marvin Aaron, 96 emp., *Company headquarters & tire gages &*................................ (732) 432-7177
Component Hardware Group, Inc., 1890 Swarthmore Ave., P.O. Box 2020, Lakewood 08701
Pres., CEO—Harry Franze, 85 emp., *Plumbing & specialty hardware & components* ............ (732) 363-4700
CorrView International, LLC, P.O. Box 8513, Landing 07850
Pres., CEO—William Duncan, 2 emp., *Metal pipe corrosion monitoring plugs* ...................... (973) 770-7764
DCI Metro, Inc., 1 Maple St., Unit 1, East Rutherford 07073
Pres.—William Mihatov, 28 emp., *Wood & metal doors & frames & hardware*........................ (201) 340-4329
Doran Sling & Assembly Corp., 1285 Central Ave., Hillside 07205
CEO—Barry Lemberg, 24 emp., *Wire rope, chain, nylon & wire rope* .................................. (908) 351-7800
East Trading West Investments LLC, 200 S. Jefferson St., Orange 07050
Owner, Pres. & CFO—M. G. Khaleeli, 6 emp., *Fabricated regulatory, warning, construction* .. (973) 678-0800
EIC Industry Group Corp. (H Q), 53 Green Pond Rd., Ste. 3, Rockaway 07866
Pres.—John Ni, 5 emp., *Corporate headquarters; custom components* ............................... (973) 983-1988
Federal Casters Corp., 785 Harrison Ave., Harrison 07029
Pres.—Charles Camella, 80 emp., *Casters* .................................................................. (973) 483-6700
Ford Atlantic Fastener Co., Inc., 341 Changebridge Rd., P.O. Box 733, Pine Brook 07058
Pres.—Anthony Innamarato, 40 emp., *Standard & custom fastners, metal stampings* ........... (973) 882-1191
Frameware, Inc., 8 Audrey Pl., Fairfield 07004
Pres.—Dean DeLuccia, 16 emp., *Manufacturer & distributor of picture* ............................... (973) 808-2022
Glentech, Inc., 46 4th St., Somerville 08876
Pres.—Scott Gordon, 15 emp., *Pipeline strainers & marine hardware*................................ (908) 685-2205
Hoboken Hearth Products, LLC, 46 Bi-State Plz., Westwood 07675
Mng. Member—Gary P. Vanderbeck, 3 emp., *Andirons* .................................................. (551) 206-3350
Imperial Weld Ring Corp., 80-88 Front St., P.O. Box 6646, Elizabeth 07206
Pres.—Calvin Sierra, 15 emp., *Precision metallic weld backing rings* .............................. (908) 354-0011
J R C Web Accessories, Inc., 46 Passaic Ave., Fairfield 07004
Chrm., Pres. & Sales Rep.—Ralph L. Ryan, 12 emp., *Pneumatic & mechanical chucks, shafts* (973) 625-3888
Ka-Lor Cubicle & Supply Co., Inc., P.O. Box 804, Fair Lawn 07410
Pres.—Dennis Brett, 21 emp., *Hospital & institutional cubicle, shower*................................ (201) 891-8077
Kelken-Gold, Inc., 550 Hartle St., Ste. C, Sayreville 08872
Pres.—Ken Ginsky, 4 emp., *Manufacturer & distributor of anchoring*.................................. (732) 416-6730
KeyValet, 15 Industrial Dr., P.O. Box 1099, Laurence Harbor 08879
Owner—Nancy Teufel, 4 emp., *Standard & specialty security locks*................................... (732) 521-1394
Metfab Metals, LLC, 560 Freeman St., Orange 07050
Pres.—James Murray, 18 emp., *Metal curtain wall parts, wall panels* ................................ (973) 675-7676
Mul-T-Lock USA, Inc., 100 Commerce Way, Ste. 2, Hackensack 07601
Pres.—Micha Kimchi, 35 emp., *High-security lock assembly*.......................................... (973) 778-3222
Northeast Lock Corp., 48 Oak St., Clifton 07014
Pres.—Kevin McCallen, 30 emp., *Lock assembly*......................................................... (973) 777-7509
Octal Corporation, 125 Galway Pl., Ste. B, Teaneck 07666
Pres.—Dani Bar-David, 20 emp., *Upgrade, retrofit & conversion kits* ................................ (201) 862-1010
Omnia Industries, Inc., 5 Cliffside Dr., P.O. Box 330, Cedar Grove 07009
Pres., CEO—Alberto R. Comini, 50 emp., *Solid brass & stainless steel latch*....................... (973) 239-7272
Pit Bull Tire Lock Corp., 205 W. Main St., 4th Fl., Somerville 08876
Pres.—Cory Marchison, 5 emp., *Tire & wheel locks for parking enforcement*....................... (888) 304-5625
Ridge Doors, 335 New Rd., P.O. Box 180, Monmouth Junction 08852
Pres., GM—Marcelle Bouvier, 5 emp., *Custom wooden garage doors & replacement* ............ (732) 329-2311
Rotor Clip Company, Inc., 187 Davidson Ave., Somerset 08873
Ptnr.—Jonathan Slass, 240 emp., *Tapered section, constant section &*............................. (732) 469-7333
S. Parker Hardware Mfg., 1 Parker Dr., P.O. Box 9882, Englewood 07631
Pres.—Charles Silberman, 25 emp., *Commercial door hardware* .................................... (201) 569-1600

S.I.C.

Schadler & Sons, Inc., John, 242 S. Parkway, P.O. Box 1068, Clifton 07014
Pres.—Herbert Johnson, 20 emp., *Large diameter fasteners* .......... (973) 777-5620
Schmidt Co., Inc., J. G., 354 U.S. Highway 22, P.O. Box 880, Green Brook 08812
Pres.—Thomas G. Schmidt, 48 emp., *Garage door hardware, including bottom* .......... (732) 563-9500
Sea Gear Marine Supply, Inc., 1144 Route 109, Cape May 08204
Owner, Pres. & CFO—Chuck Barto, 14 emp., *Wire rope & sling assembly & hardware* .......... (609) 884-2711
Shelving Depot, Inc., 419 W. Elizabeth Ave., Linden 07036
Pres.—Richard Kurland, 12 emp., *Shelving, store fixtures, metal, wooden* .......... (908) 474-8000
SOLSTICE Mfg. Co., 270 S. Main St., Ste. 102, Flemington 08822
Dir., Opers.—Chris Rawlings, 2 emp., *Ballasted solar panel mounting systems* .......... (908) 284-0096
TitanSeal, Inc., 876 N. Lenola Rd., Ste. 3-E, Moorestown 08057
Pres.—Denise Danyliw, 2 emp., *Air-purged shaft seals for industrial* .......... (856) 582-7725
Top Knobs USA, Inc., 170 Township Line Rd., Bldg. D, Hillsborough 08844
Pres.—Warren Ramsland, 35 emp., *Kitchen & bath drawer & cabinet knobs* .......... (908) 359-6174
Tower Systems, Inc.- Atlantic Towers & St. Croix Marine Products, 235 Hickory Ln., P.O. Box D, Bayville 08721
Pres.—Steve Tull, 7 emp., *Fabricated aluminum boat accessories* .......... (732) 237-8800
Tur Machine, LLC, 198 U.S. Highway 206, Ste. 5, Hillsborough 08844
Ptnr.—Zbigniew Richard Rolka, 6 emp., *General machining shop* .......... (908) 874-0235
Unicorp, Inc., 291 Cleveland St., Orange 07050
Pres.—Steven Mercadante, 40 emp., *Precision electronic component hardware* .. (973) 674-1700
Universal Tools & Mfg. Co., 115 Victory Rd., Springfield 07081
Owner, Pres. & CEO—Dorothy Principe, 30 emp., *Tooling & precision deep drawn metal* ...... (973) 379-4193
Vogelsang Fastener Corp, 1790 Swarthmore Ave., Lakewood 08701
V-P., GM—Dale Stuban, 50 emp., *Slotted, coiled & metric tension pins* .......... (732) 364-0444
W & E Sales Co., Inc., 370 Elizabeth Ave., Newark 07112
GM—R. Carr, 15 emp., *Manufacturer & wholesaler of automotive* .......... (973) 824-2000
Wheelchair Gear, 126 Cindy Dr., Egg Harbor Township 08234
Owner & Hum. Res. Mgr.—Leslie Snyder, 2 emp., *Wheelchair convenience accessories,* ...... (609) 653-6787
WingIt Innovations, LLC, 714 5th Ave., Bradley Beach 07720
Owner & Fin. Mgr.—Sal Sisto, 2 emp., *Fasteners, grab bars, shower rods &* .......... (732) 869-4466
Woodhaven Lumber & Millwork, Inc., 200 James St., P.O. Box 870, Lakewood 08701
Pres.—Alan Robinson, 152 emp., *Millwork, including decks, railings* .......... (732) 901-0030

## 3431 Metal sanitary ware

HOUZER, Inc., 2605 Kuser Rd., Hamilton 08691
Owner—Tyler Byun, 25 emp., *Corporate headquarters & stainless* .......... (609) 584-1900

## 3432 Plumbing fixture fittings & trim

B & A Flex, Inc., 34 Charlotte Dr., Bridgewater 08807
GM—Dan Souza, 14 emp., *Flexible metal hose, connectors & flow* .......... (908) 722-2808
Chatham Brass, LLC, 1253 New Market Ave., Unit D, South Plainfield 07080
Pres.—Gene Adamusik, 5 emp., *Showerheads & plumbing fixtures* .......... (908) 668-0500
Component Hardware Group, Inc., 1890 Swarthmore Ave., P.O. Box 2020, Lakewood 08701
Pres., CEO—Harry Franze, 85 emp., *Plumbing & specialty hardware & components* .......... (732) 363-4700
Danfoss Hago, Inc., 1120 Globe Ave., Mountainside 07092
GM—Rich Sthil, 110 emp., *Stainless steel spray atomizing nozzles* .......... (908) 232-8687
D'Angelo Metal Products Co., Inc., 360 Dalziel Rd., Linden 07036
Pres.—John D'Angelo, 14 emp., *Shower arms, nipples, plumbing supplies* .......... (908) 862-8220
Dason Stainless Products Co., 1773 Elizabeth Ave., Rahway 07065
Pres.—William Thompson, 9 emp., *Stainless steel pipe fittings* .......... (732) 382-7272
Jaclo Industries, 129 Dermody St., Cranford 07016
Pres.—Larry Brodey, 22 emp., *Showerheads & parts* .......... (908) 653-4433
Kissler & Co., Inc., 770 Central Blvd., Carlstadt 07072
Pres.—Barry Kissler, 75 emp., *Plumbing supplies* .......... (201) 896-9600
Knickerbocker Machine Shop, Inc., 611 Union Blvd., Totowa 07512
Pres.—John Simonelli, 70 emp., *Stainless steel pipe fittings* .......... (973) 256-1616
Lineaaqua, LLC, 2216 Hamilton Blvd., South Plainfield 07080
Pres.—Walter Mitsel, 20 emp., *Bathroom fixtures* .......... (908) 226-1199
Monarch Mfg. Works, Inc., 7249-B Browning Rd., Merchantville 08109
Pres., CEO—Harry D. Beccari, 25 emp., *Precision spray nozzles for the industrial* .......... (856) 241-1500
Selick & Bird Thermidaire, 2180 Village Rd., P.O. Box 108, Sea Girt 08750
Owner & Pres.—Lawrence Selick, 2 emp., *Steam traps & industrial supplies* .......... (732) 449-0017
Steinen Mfg. Co., Wm., 29 E. Halsey Rd., Parsippany 07054
CEO—William F. Steinen, Jr., 80 emp., *Company headquarters & industrial spray* .......... (973) 887-6400

## 3433 Heating equipment, except electric

AGF Burner, Inc., 1955 Swarthmore Ave., Unit 2, Lakewood 08701
Pres.—Christopher T. Keogh, 10 emp., *Gas, industrial, furnace, fishtail,* .......... (732) 730-8090
Aquatherm Industries, Inc., 1940 Rutgers University Blvd., Lakewood 08701
Pres., CEO—Dave Sizelove, 25 emp., *Unglazed poylmer solar thermal collectors* .......... (732) 905-9002
Carlisle Machine Works, Inc., 412 S. Wade Blvd., Bldg. 5, P.O. Box 746, Millville 08332
Pres.—Mary Dougherty, 23 emp., *Custom fabrication & machining of industrial* .......... (856) 825-0627
Corbett Industries, Inc., 39 Hewson Ave., Ste. B, P.O. Box 212, Waldwick 07463
Pres., Engrg. Mgr.—Richard J. Geier, 15 emp., *Industrial heating equipment, ovens* .......... (201) 445-6311
Diversified Heat Transfer, Inc., 439 Main Rd., Route 202, Towaco 07082
Pres.—Kenneth Kaplan, 65 emp., *Water heaters, tankless & HVAC coils* .......... (718) 386-6666
Edwards Hydronic Parts, LLC, 101 Alexander Ave., Pompton Plains 07444
Owner & Off. Mgr.—Sam Ozdemir, 5 emp., *Boiler parts, circulating pumps, zone* .......... (973) 835-7754
Energy Kinetics, Inc., 51 Molasses Hill Rd., Lebanon 08833
Pres.—Roger Marran, 45 emp., *Boilers & hot water heaters* .......... (908) 735-2066
Hayward Industries, Inc., 620 Division St., Elizabeth 07201
Chrm.—Oscar Davis, 100 emp., *Corporate headquarters & swimming pool* .......... (908) 351-5400
HTD Heat Trace, Inc., 8 Bartles Corner Rd., Unit 104, Flemington 08822
Pres.—Michael Haden, 10 emp., *Pipe tracing, tank & hopper heating* .......... (908) 788-5210
LazyMan Mfg., 616 Hardwick St., P.O. Box 327, Belvidere 07823
Pres., CFO—Brian D. Sadowski, 15 emp., *Gas barbecue grills & sheet metal fabrication* ....... (908) 475-5315
N. M. Knight Co., Inc., 1001 S. 2nd St., P.O. Box 1099, Millville 08332
Pres.—Jack Narbut, 50 emp., *Gas burners, custom machinery & polarizing* .......... (856) 327-4855
The Fireplace Place, 264 U.S. Highway 46 E., Fairfield 07004
Owner & GM—Joel Dolberg, 15 emp., *Wood, gas, pellet, electric & coal* .......... (973) 227-8540
Therma-Tech Corp., 300 Dakota St., Paterson 07503
Owner—Ben Papka, 10 emp., *Infrared heating systems* .......... (973) 345-0076
Triangle Tube Phase III, Inc., 1 Triangle Ln., Blackwood 08012
Pres., CEO—Daniel Lasserre, 50 emp., *Stainless steel hot water heating equipment* .......... (856) 228-8881
Voorheis Industries, Inc., 369 Thornden St., South Orange 07079
Co-Pres.—Steve Pozner, 4 emp., *Oil heat exchangers, burners, valve* .......... (973) 227-2446

## 3441 Structural metal—fabricated

A & A Ironworks, Inc., 955 Burnt Meadow Rd., Hewitt 07421
Pres.—Adam G. Muzer, 15 emp., *Ironwork & structural steel fabrication* .......... (973) 728-4300
Abba Metal Works, Inc., 337 River St., Paterson 07524
★ Pres.—Corrado Abbattista, 7 emp., *Structural steel fabrication & ornamental* .......... (973) 684-0808
Alberona Iron Work, Inc., 452 Scotland Rd., Orange 07050
Pres.—Tony Prioletti, 3 emp., *Ornamental ironwork & structural steel* .......... (973) 674-3375
All American Metal Fabricators, 34 Harold St., Tenafly 07670
GM—Robert Leopold, 6 emp., *Steel/metal fabrication, including* .......... (201) 567-2898
Alloy Welding Co., Inc., 6-A Culnen Dr., Somerville 08876
Pres.—Leonard F. Schaffenberger, 10 emp., *Structural steel & steel fabrication* .......... (908) 218-1551
Amerinox Processing, Inc., 2201 Mount Ephraim Ave., Bldg. 90, Camden 08104
Pres.—Seth Young, 40 emp., *Stainless steel & aluminum processing* .......... (856) 963-2200
ARD Steel Works Co., 2 Lakeview Ave., Ste. 201, Piscataway 08854
Owner—Kathryn Davisson, 10 emp., *Structural steel fabrication* .......... (732) 926-9800
Arete Development, Inc., 20 Industrial Rd., Fairfield 07004
Owner—Jonathan Ettere, 4 emp., *Structural steel fabrication* .......... (973) 244-0037
Arnold Steel Co., Inc., 79 Randolph Rd., Howell 07731
Chrm. of the Board—Felix Pflaster, 50 emp., *Structural steel fabrication & erection* .......... (732) 363-1079
Associated Anvil Iron Works, 38 Patterson Ave., Warren 07059
Pres.—Raymond Di Giambattista, 2 emp., *Structural steel fabrication* .......... (908) 647-0290
B. L. White Welding & Steel Co., Inc., 527 E. 33rd St., Paterson 07504
Pres.—Richard G. Haddad, Sr., 3 emp., *Structural steel fabrication* .......... (973) 684-4111
Bauer, Inc., Susan R., 427 Margaret King Ave., Ringwood 07456
Pres.—Susan R. Bauer, 5 emp., *Structural steel bridges for the road* .......... (973) 657-1590
Borrelli Steel Fabricators, LLC, 2800 Industrial Way, Vineland 08360
Pres.—Vincent J. Borrelli, 25 emp., *Structural steel fabrication & ironwork* .......... (856) 690-8850
BR Welding & Industrial Services, Inc., 3 Brook Rd., Howell 07731
Pres.—Brandon Reo, 20 emp., *Structural metal fabrication & welding* .......... (732) 363-8253
Canam Steel Corp., 14 Harmich Rd., South Plainfield 07080
V-P. & GM, Opers., U.S.—Tim Day, 50 emp., *Steel decks* .......... (908) 561-3484
Capital Steel Service, LLC, 82 Stokes Ave., Trenton 08638
CEO—Allen Hickman, Sr., 27 emp., *Metal service center & structural &* .......... (609) 882-6983
Capitol Steel Products, Inc., 82 Stokes Ave., P.O. Box 5063, Trenton 08638
Pres. & Fin. Mgr.—Alan Jenkins, 12 emp., *Structural steel fabrication* .......... (609) 538-9313
Central Metals, Inc., 1054 S. 2nd St., Camden 08103
Owner & Treas.—Maria Iannelli, 75 emp., *Structural steel fabrication* .......... (856) 963-5844
Conti Group, The (H Q), 2045 State Route 27, Edison 08817
Pres., CEO—Kurt G. Conti, 150 emp., *Company headquarters; precast concrete* .......... (732) 520-5000
CSI Fabricators, 15 Lexington St., Newark 07105
★ Manager—Kiran Pagarey, 7 emp., *Sheet metal fabrication, architectural* .......... (973) 344-0955
DDM Steel Construction, 3659 N. Delsea Dr., Vineland 08360
Pres.—Rich Meckenfuss, 3 emp., *Structural steel & metal fabrication* .......... (856) 794-9400
De Jong Iron Works, Inc., 223-231 Godwin Ave., Paterson 07501
Pres.—Edward De Jong, 9 emp., *Structural steel fabrication & wholesaler* .......... (973) 684-1633
Eagle Steel & Iron, LLC, 7 Garfield St., Linden 07036
Owner—Karol Kulik, 15 emp., *Structural steel fabrication & erection* .......... (908) 587-1025
F & C Professional Aluminum Railings, 1149 W. Front St., Plainfield 07063
Mng. Ptnr.—Segundo Flores, 25 emp., *Aluminum railings* .......... (908) 753-8886
Fairfield Industries, Inc., 827 N. 6th St., Newark 07107
Pres., Plt. Mgr.—Daniel Clover, 20 emp., *Pre-cast metal manholes & spill containers* .......... (973) 483-0100
Frazier Industrial Co., 91 Fairview Ave., P.O. Box F, Long Valley 07853
CEO—William Mascharka, 100 emp., *Company headquarters & structural steel* .......... (908) 876-3001
H & R Welding, LLC, 307 Drum Point Rd., Brick 08723
Ptnr.—Justin Hager, 7 emp., *Structural steel fabrication & erection* .......... (732) 920-4881
Hackensack Steel Corp., 645 Industrial Rd., Carlstadt 07072
Pres.—Tony Fasciano, 30 emp., *Structural steel stairs & railings* .......... (201) 935-0090
HarMac Rebar & Steel Corp., 301 Hartle St., Sayreville 08872
Plt. Mgr.—Larry Kuzma, 15 emp., *Steel rebar fabrication* .......... (732) 651-7822
Helidex, LLC (H Q), 186 Paterson Ave., Ste. 303, East Rutherford 07073
★ Pres.—Chawki Benteftifa, 6 emp., *Company headquarters; structural aluminum* .......... (201) 636-2546
IK Construction, Inc., 1118 E. Baltimore Ave., Linden 07036
Pres.—Ian Katwaroo, 8 emp., *Steel, ornamental iron & structural* .......... (908) 925-5200
Industrial Metal, Inc., 32 Lambert Rd., Blairstown 07825
Pres.—Dan O'Hern, 8 emp., *Stainless steel equipment* .......... (908) 362-0084
Industrial Services Enterprises, 192 Franklin Rd., Dover 07801
Pres.—Sante D'Emidio, 30 emp., *Structural steel fabrication* .......... (973) 366-3939
J. B. Welding, 2 Reynolds St., Pemberton 08068
Owner—Jerry Belsito, 1 emp., *Structural steel fabrication & welding* .......... (609) 894-9842
Jersey Tank Fabricators, Inc., 1271 New Market Ave., South Plainfield 07080
Pres.—Eric Turinsky, 30 emp., *Structural metal fabrication* .......... (908) 561-2865
JHDS, LLC, 107 Beaverbrook Rd., Ste. 3, Lincoln Park 07035
★ Ptnr.—Santosh Salvi, 15 emp., *Structural steel fabrication* .......... (973) 782-4086
Lehigh Utility Assocs., Inc., 1300 New Market Ave., P.O. Box 398, South Plainfield 07080
Pres.—William A. Butrico, 15 emp., *Aluminum & steel highway sign structures* .......... (908) 561-5252
Liberty Mechanical Contractors, Inc., 330 Raymond Blvd., Newark 07105
Pres., CFO—Frank P. Zurica, 25 emp., *Welding job shop & industrial mechanical* .......... (973) 344-6131
M & J Contracting, Inc., 85 Tracey Station, Manalapan 07726
Pres.—Doris Grillo, 3 emp., *Structural steel fabrication* .......... (732) 446-1112
Mainsource Metalfab, LLC, 59 Poinier St., Unit 61, Newark 07114
★ Owner—Eldie Lu, 20 emp., *Structural steel fabrication* .......... (973) 353-0988
Mastercraft Iron, Inc., 1111 10th Ave., Neptune 07753
Plt. Mgr.—Frank Morton, 15 emp., *Structural steel fabrication* .......... (732) 988-3113
Mitchell Welding & Iron Works, Inc., 7 Enterprise Dr., Cape May Court House 08210
Pres., CFO—William Mitchell, 8 emp., *Structural steel & metal fabrication* .......... (609) 465-7510
Moretrench American Corp., 100 Stickle Ave., Rockaway 07866
Pres.—Arthur B. Corwin, 175 emp., *Pipe & structural metal fabrication* .......... (973) 627-2100
Morsemere Ironworks, Inc., 1085 Linden Ave., Ridgefield 07657
Pres., GM, Fin., Hum. Res. & IT Mgr.—Mark Candeletti, 10 emp., *Structural steel fabrication*. (201) 941-1133
MRP, LLC, 1640 New Market Ave., South Plainfield 07080
Pres.—David Floyd, 30 emp., *Structural steel fabrication* .......... (732) 968-6061
NCS Enterprises, Inc., 300 M St., Millville 08332
Pres., Hum. Res. Mgr.—Chris Shropshire, 9 emp., *Structural steel fabrication* .......... (856) 825-3275
New Jersey Iron, Inc., 905 Patterson Rd., Jackson 08527
Pres.—Larry Karpinsky, 20 emp., *Structural iron fabrication* .......... (732) 928-7242
Newman's Ornamental Ironworks, Inc., 207 Union Ave., Brielle 08730
Pres.—Rick Newman, 20 emp., *Ornamental wrought iron* .......... (732) 223-9042
North Jersey Metal Fabricators, Inc., 130 Ryerson Ave., Ste. 107, Wayne 07470
Pres.—Bill Ecker, 7 emp., *Metal, aluminum, stainless steel &* .......... (973) 305-9830
Palmonari, Inc., J. V., 1234 Tuckahoe Rd., P.O. Box 68, Milmay 08340
Pres.—Michael Flem, 15 emp., *Structural steel fabrication* .......... (609) 476-2642
Papco Industries, Inc., 245 Pegasus Ave., Northvale 07647
Pres.—George Papailias, 20 emp., *Expansion joints* .......... (201) 767-9051
Park Steel & Iron Co., 82 Iron St., Toms River 08753
Plt. Mgr.—Robert Kramer, 2 emp., *Structural steel fabrication* .......... (732) 349-2400

Passaic County Welders, Inc., 100 Parish Dr., Wayne 07470
V-P.—Robert Grimbilas, 38 emp., *Welding & structural steel, steel,* .................... (973) 696-1200
Pearce Welding Co., LLC, 155 S. River St., Hackensack 07601
Pres.—John F. Pearce, 2 emp., *Structural steel fabrication* .................... (201) 488-0434
Perlen Steel Corp., 265 Passaic St., Newark 07104
Pres.—Richard Perlen, 13 emp., *Structural steel fabrication & distributor* .................... (973) 485-5522
Piermount Ironworks, Inc., 129 Old Turnpike Rd., Wayne 07470
Pres.—David Finucane, 15 emp., *Structural steel fabrication & erection* .................... (973) 837-1750
Portuguese Structural Steel, Inc., 255 South St., Newark 07114
Pres.—Paula Cabral, 10 emp., *Structural steel fabrication, including* .................... (973) 344-1342
Railroad Construction Company, Inc. (H Q), 75-77 Grove St., Paterson 07503
Pres.—Christopher Daloisio, 100 emp., *Corporate headquarters; heavy structural* .................... (973) 684-0362
Roof Deck, Inc., 80 Twin Rivers Dr., P.O. Box 295, Hightstown 08520
Comp., GM & Pur. Agt.—Frank LaCava, 10 emp., *Metal roof & floor decks* .................... (609) 448-6666
Schmidt Steel, J. G., 211 Central Ave., Passaic 07055
Owner—Bob Schlaier, 18 emp., *Structural steel fabrication* .................... (973) 473-4822
Single Point Precision, 429 Rockaway Valley Rd., Ste. 2300, Boonton 07005
Owner & Plt. Mgr.—Robert Pietrowicz, 1 emp., *Swiss screw machine products* .................... (973) 625-7221
Skyline Steel Fabricators, 15 Just Rd., Fairfield 07004
Pres.—Mark Malick, 17 emp., *Structural steel fabrication* .................... (973) 882-0234
South River Iron Works, LLC, 132 William St., South River 08882
Owner—Robert Peterson, 2 emp., *Structural steel fabrication* .................... (732) 257-1347
Southern New Jersey Steel, Inc, 2591 N. East Blvd., Vineland 08360
Pres.—Hugh McCaffrey, 35 emp., *Structural steel fabrication* .................... (856) 696-1612
Stateline Fabricators, LLC, 167 Bronico Way, Phillipsburg 08865
Owner—Ed Esposito, 35 emp., *Architectural & structural metal fabrication* .................... (908) 387-8800
Summit Steel Corp., 1435 Morris Ave., Union 07083
Pres., Secy.—Lila Lulinski, 10 emp., *Structural steel & ornamental iron* .................... (908) 688-8817
Super Stud Building Products, Inc., 2960 Woodbridge Ave., Edison 08837
Pres.—Ray Frobosilo, Sr., 200 emp., *Corporate headquarters & steel framing* .................... (732) 662-6200
Tamburri Assocs., 1401 Industrial Hwy., Cinnaminson 08077
Pres.—Phyllis Tamburri, 18 emp., *Steel fabrication & prefabricated steel* .................... (856) 829-4000
Triple B Fabricating, Inc., 61 Willett St., Ste. 12, Passaic 07055
Pres.—Glenn Burriello, 13 emp., *Structural steel fabrication* .................... (973) 773-2266
Truckform, Inc., 50 James St., Somerville 08876
Pres.—Jules Tishler, 4 emp., *Structural steel fabrication* .................... (908) 526-5443
Ungarini Iron Works, LLC, 56 N. Logan Ave., Trenton 08609
Owner—Kris Jackaki, 10 emp., *Ornamental ironwork & structural steel* .................... (609) 392-0540
Versatile Welding Group, LLC, 340 Cox St., Roselle 07203
Pres.—Jim Druckenmiller, 4 emp., *Stainless, structural & plate steel* .................... (908) 298-8900
Weir Welding Co., Inc., 316 12th St., P.O. Box 311, Carlstadt 07072
Pres.—Charles J. Weir, 20 emp., *Corporate headquarters & structural* .................... (201) 939-2284

## 3442 Doors, sash & trim—metal

Accurate Door & Hardware, Inc., 10 W. End Rd., Totowa 07512
Pres.—Richard Cornetto, Sr., 20 emp., *Steel doors & hardware* .................... (973) 812-2266
Acme Rolling Steel Door Corp., 1099 Linden Ave., P.O. Box 33, Ridgefield 07657
Pres.—Jeff Krautman, 17 emp., *Rolling steel service & fire doors* .................... (201) 943-7070
All Seasons Door & Window, Inc., 28 Edgeboro Rd., East Brunswick 08816
Pres., CFO—Steven Yu, 30 emp., *Vinyl & aluminum windows* .................... (732) 238-7100
American Glass Crafters, Inc., 193 Veterans Blvd., Carlstadt 07072
Pres.—Joseph Cano, 35 emp., *Frameless shower doors* .................... (201) 525-1116
Architectural Window Mfg., 359 Veterans Blvd., Rutherford 07070
V-P., Sales—Ken Thompson, 25 emp., *Aluminum & polyurethane windows* .................... (201) 939-2200
Arm-R-Lite Door Mfg. Co., Inc., 2700 Hamilton Blvd., South Plainfield 07080
Pres.—Wilma M. Dourney, 20 emp., *Residential & commercial aluminum,* .................... (908) 754-2600
Bildisco Door Mfg., Inc., 21 Central Ave., West Orange 07052
Pres.—Bruno Valente, 11 emp., *Manufacturer of wooden & metal doors* .................... (973) 673-2400
Bonded Insulation Products, 657 Union Blvd., Totowa 07512
Pres.—Harvey S. Goodman, 25 emp., *Storm doors, vinyl all-welded replacement* .................... (973) 256-2120
Capitol City Aluminum Products, 407 Rutgers Ave., Hamilton 08619
Pres.—Louis Battaglia, 5 emp., *Canvas & aluminum awnings & entries* .................... (609) 587-3653
DCI Metro, Inc., 1 Maple St., Unit 1, East Rutherford 07073
Pres.—William Mihatov, 28 emp., *Wood & metal doors & frames & hardware* .................... (201) 340-4329
Disco Aluminum, 518 South Ave., Plainfield 07060
Ptnr.—William Villane, 2 emp., *Custom window & door screens, patio* .................... (908) 754-2699
Dor-Win Mfg. Co., 109 Midland Ave., Elmwood Park 07407
Pres.—Marco Cangialosi, 40 emp., *Vinyl windows & doors & steel & fiberglass* .................... (201) 796-4300
Easco Shower Doors Co., 3 Industrial Dr., Vernon 07462
Dir., Engrg. & Opers.—Vincent Bottaro, 28 emp., *Glass & aluminum shower doors & tub* .................... (973) 209-4141
Elgen Mfg. Co., 10 Railroad Ave., Closter 07624
Pres.—David Young, 100 emp., *Flexible duct connectors, galvanized* .................... (201) 964-0008
Fast Doors, LLC, 1800 Copewood St., Camden 08103
Pres.—Al Pooner, 18 emp., *Metal storefront rolling & security* .................... (856) 966-3278
Fimbel Architectural Door Specialties, 8 Coddington Rd., Whitehouse Station 08889
Pres., Cont.—Edward Fimbel III, 50 emp., *Vinyl, composite, metal, fiberglass* .................... (908) 534-1732
Five Star Building Products, Inc., 2012 86th St., North Bergen 07047
Pres.—Daniel Politi, 15 emp., *Aluminum & vinyl doors & windows* .................... (201) 869-4181
Freedom Glass & Metal, Inc., 4 White Horse Pike, P.O. Box 868, Clementon 08021
Owner—Karen Arsenault, 20 emp., *Aluminum windows & storefronts* .................... (856) 627-3946
General Metal & Glass Co., 613 Kaighn Ave., Camden 08101
GM—Bill Tuling, 3 emp., *Glass & metal windows* .................... (856) 365-6323
Global Partners In Shielding, Inc., 90 Dayton Ave., Ste. 13, Passaic 07055
Pres.—Donald Hener, 35 emp., *Industrial EMI, RFI & X-ray shielding* .................... (973) 574-9077
Gray Overhead Door Co., 439 Third Ave., Elizabeth 07206
GM—Eddie Acosta, 5 emp., *Metal overhead garage doors* .................... (908) 355-3889
Guardrite Steel Door Corp., 81 Springdale Ave., Newark 07107
Pres.—William Santana, 4 emp., *Rolling steel doors & gates* .................... (973) 481-4424
Haydon Corp., 415 Hamberg Tpke., Bldg. D, Wayne 07470
Pres.—Doug Hillman, 65 emp., *Metal struts & baseboards* .................... (973) 904-0800
Jersey Steel Doors, Inc., 95 N. 11th St., Newark 07107
Pres.—Roland Gonzalez, 10 emp., *Steel overhead rolling doors* .................... (973) 482-4020
Joffe Lumber & Supply, Inc., 18 Burns Ave., Vineland 08360
CEO—Sol G. Joffe, 50 emp., *Wooden & vinyl windows, steel & interior* .................... (856) 825-9550
Miele Iron Works, Inc., 2340 Route 22 E., Union 07083
Pres.—Raphael Miele, 2 emp., *Steel cellar doors & railings* .................... (908) 686-0943
New Century Building Systems, Inc., 70 Sewell St., P.O. Box 775, Glassboro 08028
Pres.—Thomas Salzer, 8 emp., *Aluminum windows & glass curtain walls* .................... (856) 863-8036
Newark Wire Works, Inc., 1059 King Georges Post Rd., Ste. 103, Edison 08837
Pres.—JoAnn Spellman, 16 emp., *Architectural wire mesh panels & fabricated* .................... (732) 661-2001
Northern Architectural Systems, 111 Central Ave., Teterboro 07608
Pres.—Robert Pecorella, 149 emp., *Corporate headquarters & aluminum windows* .................... (201) 943-6400

Phil-Mar Industries, 1800 Copewood St., Camden 08103
GM—John Jones, 2 emp., *Rolling steel doors* .................... (856) 966-0931
Pioneer Industries, Inc., 171 S. Newman St., Hackensack 07601
Pres.—Mitchell Dorf, 60 emp., *Steel doors & door frames* .................... (201) 933-1900
Randall Mfg. Co., Inc., 200 Sylvan Ave., Newark 07104
Pres.—Cary Tinfow, 22 emp., *Metal & wood building products* .................... (973) 484-7600
Rebco, Inc., 1171 Madison Ave., Ste. 1, Paterson 07503
Pres.—Tony Stolarz, 40 emp., *Commercial aluminum entrances, doors* .................... (973) 684-0200
Royal Aluminum Co., Inc., 620 Market St., Newark 07105
Pres.—John Inelli, 50 emp., *Vinyl & aluminum windows & doors* .................... (973) 589-8880
Royal Prime Window Specialist, Inc., 742 Fairfield Ave., Kenilworth 07033
Pres. & IT Mgr.—Andrew Inelli, 6 emp., *High-end vinyl replacement windows* .................... (908) 354-7600
Screens & Fabricated Metals Corp., 1265 McBride Ave., P.O. Box 647, Woodland park 07424
Pres.—Mike McMillan, 50 emp., *Screen & storm doors, security screens* .................... (973) 785-1414
Screens, Inc., 130 Ryerson Ave., Ste. 219, Wayne 07470
Pres.—Robert Vorndran, 4 emp., *Aluminum window screens* .................... (973) 633-8558
Skyline Windows, LLC, 210 Park Pl. E., Wood Ridge 07075
Plt. Mgr.—Karl L. Zeyher, 83 emp., *Heavy commercial architectural aluminum* .................... (201) 531-9600
Stanley Access Technologies, LLC, 17 Marlen Dr., Ste. C, Trenton 08691
Br. Mgr.—Joe Marino, 30 emp., *Power-operated security & fire doors* .................... (609) 890-0877
Sterling Window Co., 224 21st Ave., Paterson 07501
Pres.—Joseph J. Baldino, 15 emp., *Vinyl & aluminum windows* .................... (973) 742-1900
Thermwell Products Co., Inc., 420 State Route 17, Mahwah 07430
Pres.—David B. Gerstein, 350 emp., *Weatherstripping & sealing products* .................... (201) 684-4400
Thomas Mfg., Inc., 630 Ramsey Ave., Hillside 07205
Pres.—Tom Lukowiak, 25 emp., *Commercial aluminum windows* .................... (908) 810-0030
Tri-State Building Materials Co., 65 Lodi St., Passaic 07055
Pres.—Charles Cangialosi, 18 emp., *Aluminum & vinyl windows & doors* .................... (973) 472-2377
Versatile Distributors, Inc., 80 Industrial Rd., Lodi 07644
Pres.—Joel Cuccio, 55 emp., *Vinyl windows, entry & storm doors* .................... (973) 779-1400
Vinylast, Inc., 1830 Swarthmore Ave., Lakewood 08701
Pres., GM—Steven J. Leary, 20 emp., *Aluminum & vinyl windows, doors, railings* .................... (732) 367-7200
Window Supply Corp., 5410 Kennedy Blvd., West New York 07093
Pres.—Enildo Diaz, 1 emp., *Aluminum windows* .................... (201) 392-1213

## 3443 Plate work—fabricated (boiler shops)

Ajay Metal Fabricators, Inc., 355 Dalziel Rd., Linden 07036
Pres.—Tony Zambell, 9 emp., *Steel, aluminum, stainless, copper* .................... (908) 523-0558
Allied Steel Distribution & Service Center, 118-144 Harper St., Newark 07114
Pres.—Don DeFaria, Jr., 14 emp., *Steel service center, including plate* .................... (973) 824-7347
American Galvanizing Co., Inc., 1919 R.R. 54, Folsom 08094
Pres.—John Gregor, 70 emp., *Hot dip galvanizing & value-added fabrication* .................... (609) 567-2090
American Showcase & Foodservice Equipment, Inc., 19 Commerce Rd., Unit H, Fairfield 07004
Pres.—Tony Latallade, 6 emp., *Custom fabrication & distributor of* .................... (973) 227-1277
Atlas Industrial Mfg. Co., 81 Somerset Pl., Clifton 07012
Pres.—Frank G. De Lorenzo, 36 emp., *Heat exchangers* .................... (973) 779-3970
BakerCorp., 50 Gilchris Dr., Swedesboro 08085
V-P., Div.—Jon Heslin, 19 emp., *Fiberglass & plastic liquid containment* .................... (856) 467-2677
Camac Industries, 18 Gail Ct., Sparta 07871
Pres., Opers. Mgr.—Peter Gennaro, 5 emp., *Industrial pumps, filters & heat exchangers* .................... (973) 300-5575
Corban Energy Group, 418 Falmouth Ave., Elmwood Park 07407
CEO—Daniel Chung, 15 emp., *Compressed natural gas (CNG) fueling* .................... (201) 509-8555
Crown Roll Leaf, Inc., 91 Illinois Ave., Paterson 07503
CEO—Margaret Waitts, 225 emp., *Corporate headquarters & hot stamping* .................... (973) 742-4000
CRP Industries, Inc., 35 Commerce Dr., Cranbury 08512
Off. Mgr.—Fabine Gilson, 50 emp., *Industrial housings, motors & automotive* .................... (609) 578-4100
Cryofab, Inc., 540 N. Michigan Ave., P.O. Box 485, Kenilworth 07033
Owner & Co-Pres.—Vincent J. Grillo, 49 emp., *Cryogenic equipment & accessories* .................... (908) 686-3636
D C Fabricators, Inc., 801 W. Front St., Florence 08518
Pres., CEO—Gary Butler, 130 emp., *Steam condensers, heat exchangers,* .................... (609) 499-3000
D E B Maintenance, Inc., 1000 Union Landing Rd., P.O. Box 13, Riverton 08077
Pres.—Kenneth Williams, 30 emp., *Steel fabrication, tanks, vessels &* .................... (856) 786-0440
Delta Cooling Towers, Inc., 185 U.S. Highway 206, Roxbury Township 07836
Pres.—John Flaherty, 9 emp., *Cooling towers & air strippers* .................... (973) 586-2201
Diversified Heat Transfer, Inc., 439 Main Rd., Route 202, Towaco 07082
Pres.—Kenneth Kaplan, 65 emp., *Water heaters, tankless & HVAC coils* .................... (718) 386-6666
Dusenbery Engineering Co., 309 E. Hanover Ave., P.O. Box 1001, Morristown 07962
Pres.—Philip Williams, 13 emp., *Industrial pressure vessels* .................... (973) 539-2200
Eddie Kane Steel Products, Inc. (H Q), P.O. Box 133, Spring Lake 07762
Pres.—Augustine Kane, 11 emp., *Corporate headquarters; steel service* .................... (732) 974-3339
Edwards Coils Corp., 101 Alexander Ave., Unit 6, Pompton Plains 07444
Plt. Mgr.—Mark Morabito, 9 emp., *Water-to-refrigerant heat exchangers* .................... (973) 835-2815
Flame-Cut Steel, Inc., 97 E. 2nd St., Bayonne 07002
Pres.—Ramesh Nuthi, 12 emp., *Metal service center, including plate* .................... (201) 436-9300
Fluorotherm Polymers, Inc., 333 New Rd., Ste. 1, Parsippany 07054
Pres., CEO—P. N. Shukla, 12 emp., *Immersion coil, shell & tube corrosion* .................... (973) 575-0760
Foster Wheeler Corp. (H Q), 53 Frontage Rd., P.O. Box 9000, Hampton 08827
CEO—Gary Nedelka, 500 emp., *Corporate headquarters; industrial* .................... (908) 730-4000
Garvey Corp., 208 S. Route 73, Hammonton 08037
Pres.—William J. Garvey, 80 emp., *Table top conveyors & accumulators* .................... (609) 561-2450
Group Thermo, Inc. (H Q), 137 S. Pemberton Ave., Oceanport 07757
Pres.—Adam Duch, 4 emp., *Corporate headquarters; heat exchangers* .................... (908) 757-8955
Groupe SEB USA, 2121 Eden Rd., Millville 08332
Sr. V-P., Hum. Res.—Martin Falkenberg, 210 emp., *Cookware & small appliances* .................... (856) 825-6300
Hamon Corp., 58 E. Main St., P.O. Box 1500, Somerville 08876
CEO—William P. Dillon, 100 emp., *Corporate headquarters & heat transfer* .................... (908) 685-4000
Holtec International (H Q), 555 Lincoln Dr. W., Ste. 1, Marlton 08053
Pres., CEO—Kris Singh, 170 emp., *Company headquarters; steel fabrication* .................... (856) 797-0900
Independence Cryogenic Engineering, LLC, 891 Route 9 N., P.O. Box 527, Little Egg Harbor 08087
Pres.—Susan Hughes, 16 emp., *Rebuilt cryogenic refrigeration systems* .................... (609) 294-0012
International Process Plants, 17-A Marlen Dr., Hamilton 08691
Pres.—Ron Gale, 25 emp., *Refrigeration & air conditioning equipment* .................... (609) 586-8004
Jersey Shore Steel, Inc., 636 Herman Rd., Jackson 08527
Ptnr.—Gary Loveland, 18 emp., *Sheet & plate steel fabrication* .................... (732) 833-8855
Kaplan Industries, Inc., 10 Morris Ave., Route 73, Maple Shade 08052
Dir., Opers.—Jim Johnston, 15 emp., *High & low pressure compressed gas* .................... (856) 779-8181
Leland Ltd., Inc., 2614 S. Clinton Ave., P.O. Box 466, South Plainfield 07080
Pres., CFO—Leland C. Stanford, 7 emp., *Gas cylinders* .................... (908) 561-2000
Lummus Technology, 1515 Broad St., Bloomfield 07003
Pres.—Daniel McCorthy, 400 emp., *Heat transfer equipment, including* .................... (973) 893-3000
MAC Products, Inc., 60 Pennsylvania Ave., P.O. Box 469, Kearny 07032
Pres.—Edward Russnow, 135 emp., *Electrical control panels, connectors* .................... (973) 344-0700

S.I.C.

Metalfab, Inc., 11 Prices Switch Rd., P.O. Box 9, Vernon 07462
COO—Mike Randazzo, 30 emp., Large plate steel fabrication & dry ........ (973) 764-2000
New Jersey Meter Co., 1 Hazel St., Woodland Park 07424
Pres.—Anthony Abbate, 5 emp., Dry air separators & condensate drains ........ (973) 345-6200
Oliver, Inc., G. J., 50 Industrial Rd., Phillipsburg 08865
CEO—John Oliver, 75 emp., Steel fabrication & machining of pressure ........ (908) 454-9743
Patriot Marine Fabricating, 708-4 Old Shore Rd., Forked River 08731
Pres.—Nicole Spisak, 3 emp., Aluminum work boats, marine fuel tanks ........ (609) 693-5542
Perry Products Corp., 25 Hainesport-Mount Laurel Rd., Hainesport 08036
Pres.—Gregg P. Epstein, 15 emp., Heat exchangers, including pressure ........ (609) 267-1600
Polaris Plate Heat Exchangers, 106 Apple St., Ste. 106, Tinton Falls 07724
Owner—Steve Weintraub, 4 emp., Plate heat exchangers ........ (732) 345-7188
Portable Container Services, 101 Eisenhower Pkwy., Ste. 300, Roseland 07068
GM, Sales—Christopher Gramcko, 3 emp., Steel storage & cargo containers ........ (973) 515-4721
R A S Process Equipment, 324 Meadowbrook Rd., Robbinsville 08691
Dir.—John Bonacorda, 25 emp., Heat exchangers, reactors & columns ........ (609) 371-1000
Roben Mfg. Co., Inc., 760 Vassar Ave., Lakewood 08701
Pres.—Gary R. Huhn, 32 emp., Custom nickel alloy fabrication of ........ (732) 364-6000
Sheet Metal Products, Inc., 794 N. 6th St., Newark 07107
Pres.—William F. Kovacs, 30 emp., Contract manufacturing & industrial ........ (973) 482-0450
Skripak Metal Fabricators, Inc., 170 Oberlin Ave. N., Unit 17, Lakewood 08701
Pres., CFO—John Skripak, Jr., 10 emp., Metal carts & tables, catwalks, hoods ........ (732) 364-9662
Tolan Machinery Co., Inc./Tolan Polishing Corp., 164 Franklin Ave., P.O. Box 695, Rockaway 07866
Pres.—John Tolpa, 45 emp., Stainless steel & nickel alloy pressure ........ (973) 983-7212
Utility Industries, Inc., 500 Springdale Rd., Ste. K-1, Somerdale 08083
Bus. Mgr.—John Wile, 6 emp., Conduit cable pulling devices ........ (856) 435-6969
Vacuum Sales, Inc., 51 Stone Rd., Lindenwold 08021
Pres.—James Redstreake, 20 emp., Vacuum truck tanks, street sweeper ........ (856) 627-7790
Versatile Welding Group, LLC, 340 Cox St., Roselle 07203
Pres.—Jim Druckenmiller, 4 emp., Stainless, structural & plate steel ........ (908) 298-8900
Wallace Eannace Associates, Inc., 779 Susquehanna Ave., Franklin Lakes 07417
Manager—Hank Kunkel, 20 emp., Heating specialties, including hot ........ (201) 891-9550
WECOM, Inc., 20 Warrick Ave., Glassboro 08028
Pres.—Eric C. Sprengle, Sr., 27 emp., Precision sheet metal aluminum & stainless ........ (856) 863-8400
Weil-McLain, 17000 Commerce Pkwy., Ste. B, Mount Laurel 08054
Reg. Mgr., Mid Atlantic—William Price, Jr., 11 emp., High efficiency gas & oil boilers ........ (856) 866-7400
Zvonko Stulic & Son, Inc., 21 Main St., Newark 07105
Pres.—Zvonko Stulic, 5 emp., Plate & sheet metal fabrication, welding ........ (973) 589-3773

### 3444 Sheet metal work

(MASAco) Michael Anthony Sign & Awning, Inc., 21 Randolph Ave., Avenel 07001
Pres.—Michael Bradley, 35 emp., Electric signs, including storefront ........ (732) 453-6120
47 Industries, LLC, 59 2nd Ave., Raritan 08869
Owner—Mike Palazzo, 1 emp., Aluminum & stainless steel fabrication ........ (908) 526-8865
A. B. Scantlebury Co., 112 Kings Hwy., Landing 07850
Off. Mgr.—John Spinelli, 8 emp., Sheet metal fabrication, precision ........ (973) 770-3000
Academy Fence Co., Inc., 119 N. Day St., Orange 07050
★ Owner—Lou Cavallo, 20 emp., Aluminum & wooden fencing & installation ........ (973) 674-0600
Accurate Metal Fabrication, LLC, 28 John St., East Rutherford 07073
Pres.—Stanley Patiro, 2 emp., Sheet metal fabrication ........ (201) 438-3733
Acme Model Engineering Co., 115 Victory Rd., Springfield 07081
CEO—Dorothy Principe, 30 emp., Aluminum battery holders ........ (973) 379-4193
ADM Custom Metal Fabrication, Inc., 263 Hillside Ave., Ste. 2, Nutley 07110
Pres., CEO—Andrew K. Mihal, 14 emp., Precision sheet metal & frame fabrication ........ (973) 284-0088
Air & Specialties Sheet Metal, 276 Sheffield St., Mountainside 07092
Pres.—Kim Deitrich, 15 emp., HVAC ducts & sheet metal fabrication ........ (908) 233-8306
Air Distribution Systems, Inc., 1000 Astoria Blvd., Cherry Hill 08003
Pres.—Charles Doyle, 50 emp., HVAC ducts ........ (856) 874-1100
Air Group, LLC, 1 Prince Rd., Whippany 07981
Pres.—John A. Conforti, 187 emp., Custom commercial HVAC sheet metal ........ (973) 887-5099
Airmet, Inc., 671 N. 3rd St., Newark 07107
Pres.—Stephen A. Yavorski, Sr., 6 emp., Metal fences, gates, railings, steel ........ (973) 481-5550
Airside, Inc., 246 Brighton Rd., Andover 07821
Pres.—Mario Cavellone, 10 emp., Sheet metal fabrication & HVAC ducts ........ (973) 786-6967
Airtec, Inc., 17 W. Scott Ave., P.O. Box 1181, Rahway 07065
Pres.—Joseph M. Niemczyk, Sr., 9 emp., Sheet metal fabrication, machining ........ (732) 382-3700
Ajay Metal Fabricators, Inc., 355 Dalziel Rd., Linden 07036
Pres.—Tony Zambell, 9 emp., Steel, aluminum, stainless, copper ........ (908) 523-0558
Alco Sheet Metal Fabricators, Inc., 51 Chester St., Clifton 07011
Pres.—Rick Coots, 2 emp., Sheet metal fabrication ........ (973) 772-7070
All American Metal Fabricators, 34 Harold St., Tenafly 07670
GM—Robert Leopold, 6 emp., Steel/metal fabrication, including ........ (201) 567-2898
Allied Steel Distribution & Service Center, 118-144 Harper St., Newark 07114
Pres.—Don DeFaria, Jr., 14 emp., Steel service center, including plate ........ (973) 824-7347
Alpine Metal Products, 7 Progress St., Edison 08820
V-P.—Keith Christian, 19 emp., Sheet metal fabrication ........ (908) 753-4543
Altona Blower & Sheet Metal Work, Inc., 23 N. Washington Ave., Little Ferry 07643
Pres.—Walter Martin, 8 emp., Sheet metal fabrication ........ (201) 641-3520
American Custom Fabricators, Inc., 215-A Hickory Ln., Bayville 08721
Pres.—Jacqueline Schinder, 8 emp., Structural aluminum, ornamental metal ........ (732) 237-0037
American Metal Fab & Welding, 706 7th St., Union City 07087
GM—Maher Gazawneh, 2 emp., Custom sheet metal fabrication & welding ........ (201) 295-8888
American Precision Sheet Metal Corp., 84 Baekeland Ave., Middlesex 08846
Pres.—Michael Wood, 70 emp., Sheet metal fabrication ........ (732) 356-4306
American Seamless Gutter & Leader Corp., 286 Hamburg Tpke., Riverdale 07457
Pres.—Duane Reger, 7 emp., Seamless aluminum gutters ........ (973) 838-4505
American Showcase & Foodservice Equipment, Inc., 19 Commerce Rd., Unit H, Fairfield 07004
Pres.—Tony Latallade, 6 emp., Custom fabrication & distributor of ........ (973) 227-1277
American Van Equipment, Inc., 149 Lehigh Ave., Lakewood 08701
Pres.—Charles Richter, 95 emp., Aluminum, steel & hot dipped galvanized ........ (800) 526-4743
Amerifab Corp., Inc., 196 Garibaldi Ave., Lodi 07644
Pres.—Tom Castell, 7 emp., Sheet metal fabrication ........ (973) 777-2120
Amerinox Processing, Inc., 2201 Mount Ephraim Ave., Bldg. 90, Camden 08104
Pres.—Seth Young, 40 emp., Stainless steel & aluminum processing ........ (856) 963-2200
Anello Fence, LLC, 50 State Route 23, Pequannock 07440
Pres.—Steve Anello, 4 emp., Vinyl, aluminum & wooden fencing ........ (973) 839-4100
Apollo Flags LLC, 594 Union Blvd., Totowa 07512
Ptnr.—Albert Potenzone, 4 emp., Custom, U.S., military, state, parade ........ (973) 256-8362
Architectural Metal Designs, Inc., 1505 Pineland Ave., Millville 08332
Pres.—Martin Schlembach, 20 emp., Aluminum composite wall panel systems ........ (856) 765-3000
Atlantic Air Enterprises, 856 Elston St., Rahway 07065
Pres., GM & Supv.—Darin Severino, 15 emp., HVAC ducts ........ (732) 381-4000
Atlantic Coastal Welding, Inc., 16 Butler Blvd., Bayville 08721
Pres.—John Gallo, 6 emp., Welding & metal, aluminum & steel fabrication ........ (732) 269-1088
AVCON, 1915 Swarthmore Ave., Ste. 3, Lakewood 08701
CEO—Larry Stanley, 35 emp., Structural maintenance-free thermoplastic ........ (732) 286-9496
Awning Concepts & Design, Inc., 916 Route 33, Freehold 07728
Pres.—Mark Pedersen, 8 emp., Awnings ........ (732) 462-1131
B & S Sheet Metal Co., Inc., 60 5th Ave., Hawthorne 07506
Pres.—Robert Buchmann, 14 emp., Sheet metal fabrication ........ (973) 427-3739
Babbitt Mfg. Co., Inc., 719 E. Park Ave., Vineland 08360
Pres.—Brian Gavigan, 10 emp., Sheet metal fabrication ........ (856) 692-3245
Babinec Sheet Metal Works, Inc., Joseph, 774 Martin St., Rahway 07065
CEO—Joseph T. Babinec, 50 emp., Metal fabrication of store fixtures ........ (732) 388-6600
Bayshore Metal Products, Inc., 120 Francis St., Ste. 6, Keyport 07735
Pres.—Richard Walker, 4 emp., Precision sheet metal fabrication ........ (732) 739-9260
Bills, Inc., James W., 167 Newman Springs Rd., Ste. E, Shrewsbury 07702
Pres.—James W. Bills, 2 emp., Architectural sheet metal fabrication ........ (732) 212-1009
Bluewater Welding & Fabrication, LLC, 1089 Route 47, P.O. Box 206, Dennisville 08214
Owner—Ed Myland, 6 emp., Structural aluminum fabrication ........ (609) 522-7352
Bonland Industries, Inc., 890 Towbin Ave., Lakewood 08701
Br. Mgr.—Dan Parent, 75 emp., Sheet metal fabrication ........ (732) 886-7127
Bonland Industries, Inc., 50 Newark Pompton Tpke., Wayne 07470
CEO—William Boniface, 50 emp., Corporate headquarters & sheet metal ........ (973) 694-3211
Breure Sheet Metal Co., Inc., 46 Walman Ave., Clifton 07011
Pres.—Matthew Breure, 3 emp., Sheet metal fabrication ........ (973) 772-6423
Brick Glass Co., 214 Midstreams Pl., Brick 08724
Owner—Louis Raccuglia, 6 emp., Aluminum storefronts, curtain walls ........ (732) 899-8811
Broadhurst Sheet Metal Works, 230 Warburton Ave., Hawthorne 07506
Pres.—Kristopher Lill, 8 emp., Stainless steel sheet metal fabrication ........ (973) 427-3972
Brook Metal Products, Inc., 6 Evans Terminal, Hillside 07205
Pres., Off. Mgr.—Wendy Merendino, 8 emp., Welding & sheet metal fabrication ........ (908) 355-1601
Bush Tank Fabricators, Inc., 222 Thomas St., Newark 07114
Pres.—Thomas Horenburg, 10 emp., Custom aluminum, steel & stainless ........ (973) 596-1121
C D S Sheet Metal, Inc., 1200 S. West Blvd., Ste. E, Vineland 08360
Pres.—Nick Emioholtz, 3 emp., Sheet metal fabrication ........ (856) 794-5080
C L N Designs, LLC, P.O. Box 1822, South Hackensack 07606
Ex. V-P.—John Parente, 8 emp., ADA & safety interior & exterior signs ........ (201) 939-2120
C P S Metals, Inc., 450 S. Fellowship Rd., Maple Shade 08052
Pres.—Edwin Pelczarski, 17 emp., Sheet metal fabrication ........ (856) 779-0846
CADPRO, Inc., 114 W. Atlantic Ave., Clementon 08021
Pres.—Elaine A. Bartie, 10 emp., Machined & sheet metal parts, assemblies ........ (856) 435-0050
Cambridge Sheet Metal, Inc., 14 Troy Hills Rd., Ste. 6, Whippany 07981
Owner, Pres. & GM—Jim Salvatoriello, 10 emp., Sheet metal fabrication ........ (973) 386-0788
Capitol City Aluminum Products, 407 Rutgers Ave., Hamilton 08619
Pres.—Louis Battaglia, 5 emp., Canvas & aluminum awnings & entries ........ (609) 587-3653
Carfaro Railings Company, Frank, 70 Hacklebarney Rd., Long Valley 07853
Pres.—Frank Carfaro, 1 emp., Iron & aluminum railings ........ (908) 879-7312
Center Contracting Corp., 72 Putnam St., Paterson 07524
Manager—Ralph Pecoreli, 4 emp., Sheet metal fabrication ........ (973) 523-6400
Center Metal Fabricators, Inc., 1026 Black Horse Pike, P.O. Box 29, Hammonton 08037
Pres.—Michele McDonough, 5 emp., Aluminum storefronts & windows ........ (609) 567-1808
Central Sheet Metal Fabricators, Inc., 897 South Ave., Ste. A, Middlesex 08846
Pres.—Gerard Ezyske, 45 emp., Custom sheet metal & HVAC ductwork ........ (732) 968-6100
Century Conveyor Service, Inc., 4301 S. Clinton Ave., South Plainfield 07080
Pres.—Ron Ferrara, 28 emp., Conveyors, material handling equipment ........ (908) 205-0625
Chambers Sheet Metal, Bill, 371 N. Glassboro Rd., P.O. Box 172, Woodbury Heights 08097
Owner—Bill Chambers, 3 emp., Sheet metal fabrication ........ (856) 848-4774
Ciccone Custom Railing & Manufacturing, Inc., 2002 Route 9, Toms River 08755
Pres.—Robyn Ciccone, 10 emp., All-welded custom ornamental aluminum ........ (732) 349-7071
Clark Home Supply, 205 Westfield Ave., Clark 07066
Owner—Ray Meigs, 1 emp., Aluminum awnings ........ (732) 388-5447
Clifton Metal Products Co., Inc., 41 Clifton Blvd., Clifton 07011
Pres.—Dieter Kemmerich, 14 emp., Sheet metal fabrication ........ (973) 777-6100
Coltwell Industries, Inc., 55 Winans Ave., Cranford 07016
V-P., Sales & Mktg.—Anthony Bengivenga, 15 emp., Custom & standard extruded aluminum ........ (908) 276-7600
Comfort Mechanical Corp., 420 Division St., P.O. Box 4135, Long Branch 07740
Pres.—Alexander Dohme, 15 emp., Sheet metal ductwork ........ (732) 870-2292
Computa Base Machining, Inc., 411 N. Grove St., P.O. Box 340, Berlin 08009
Pres.—Augustin Rosado, 14 emp., Fabrication & precision machining job ........ (856) 767-9517
Consolidated Steel & Aluminum Fence, 316 N. 12th St., P.O. Box 643, Kenilworth 07033
Pres.—Paul Cacicedo, 60 emp., Commercial chain-link, steel, aluminum ........ (908) 272-6262
Coronation Sheet Metal Co., Inc., 2198 Stanley Ter., Union 07083
Pres.—Joe Cafiero, 15 emp., Sheet metal fabrication ........ (908) 686-0930
County Glass & Metal Installers, Inc., 80 Dewitt Pl., Hackensack 07601
Pres.—Eugene Vanbert, 6 emp., Metal, steel & aluminum fabrication ........ (201) 343-7417
Craftsmen Railing, Inc., 3 Cass St., Keyport 07735
Pres.—Ray Cottone, 5 emp., Iron & aluminum railings ........ (732) 264-1080
Creative Metal Work, Inc., 4 Park Dr., P.O. Box 509, Franklin 07416
Pres.—Zoran Grubic, 10 emp., Sheet metal fabrication ........ (973) 823-0408
Custom Cooling Services, LLC, 99 Kingwood Stockton Rd., P.O. Box 457, Stockton 08559
★ Owner—Paul Steffanelli, 5 emp., Sheet metal fabrication, including ........ (609) 397-4448
Custom Fabricators, Inc., 400 Commerce Rd., Linden 07036
Pres.—Joseph Bonanno, 8 emp., Sheet metal fabrication & coin-operated ........ (908) 862-4244
D & M Sheet Metal Co., Inc., 430 Central Ave., East Rutherford 07073
Pres.—Mark Mihal, 15 emp., Ductwork & sheet metal fabrication ........ (201) 939-6300
D & N Machine Mfg., Inc., 334 Nicholson Rd., P.O. Box 67, Gloucester City 08030
Pres.—Robert Doble, Jr., 6 emp., Precision sheet metal fabrication ........ (856) 456-1366
D.E.B. Mfg., Inc., 850 Towbin Ave., Lakewood 08701
Pres.—Hollis T. Mueller, 12 emp., Rotary viscous dampers ........ (732) 364-7007
D'Amico Sheet Metal Works, Al, 881 Broadway, Bayonne 07002
Owner & Pres.—Al D'Amico, 1 emp., Sheet metal fabrication ........ (201) 339-1355
Dan's Heating & Air Conditioning, Inc., 1007 Eastpark Blvd., Cranbury 08512
Pres.—Daniel Isbitski, 40 emp., HVAC ducts ........ (732) 297-9162
DCI Signs & Awnings, Inc., 110 Riverside Ave., Newark 07104
Pres.—Danny Castillo, 25 emp., Interior & exterior signs & custom ........ (973) 350-0400
Dec's Metal Fabrication, LLC, 198 U.S. Highway Route 206, Bldg. 4, Ste. E, Hillsborough 08844
Owner—Adrien Dec, 3 emp., Sheet metal fabrication for HVAC applications ........ (908) 281-0283
Demand, LLC, 36 S. Adamsville Rd., Bridgewater 08807
Owner—Joseph Kafara, 16 emp., Welding, machining & custom sheet metal ........ (908) 526-2020
Dericks Sheet Metal Works Co., Inc., 631 Union Blvd., Totowa 07512
Owner & GM—Keith Dericks, 22 emp., Sheet metal fabrication ........ (973) 256-1818
Disco Aluminum, 518 South Ave., Plainfield 07060
Ptnr.—William Villane, 2 emp., Custom window & door screens, patio ........ (908) 754-2699

Diversatech, Inc., 1584 Reed Rd., Pennington 08534
Pres.—Haskel Zeloof, 5 emp., Sheet metal fabrication & machining ........ (609) 730-9668
Duct Mate, Inc., 190 Lexington Ave., Hackensack 07601
Owner & Pres.—Joseph Tasca, 7 emp., HVAC ductwork ........ (201) 488-8002
Ducts Sheet Metal, LLC, 6200 Main St., South Amboy 08879
Owner—Mike Bruce, 8 emp., Sheet metal ductwork ........ (732) 727-8781
Ductworks, Inc., 434 W. Front St., Plainfield 07060
GM & Hum. Res. Mgr.—Dianne Rocco, 10 emp., Sheet metal ductwork, including spiral ........ (908) 754-8190
Dutra Sheet Metal Co., 1940 S. West Blvd., Ste. E, Vineland 08360
Owner & Fin. Mgr.—D'lee Dutra, 11 emp., Sheet metal fabrication ........ (856) 692-8058
Edker Industries, Inc., 1401 Union Landing Rd., Cinnaminson 08077
Owner & Pres.—Tom Kerbaugh, 25 emp., Precision sheet metal fabrication, ........ (856) 786-1971
EFCO Forms, 77 Vanderburg Rd., Marlboro 07746
Sales Mgr.—Joe Capozzi, 15 emp., Concrete forms ........ (732) 308-1010
ELMCO TWO, Inc., 1045 Cambridge St., Camden 08105
Pres.—Bernhard H. Kofoet, 3 emp., Sheet metal fabrication ........ (856) 365-2244
Englert, Inc., 1200 Amboy Ave., Perth Amboy 08861
CEO—Ken Krawcheck, 100 emp., Corporate headquarters & metal roof ........ (732) 826-8614
Environmental Air Systems, 801 11th Ave., P.O. Box 508, Belmar 07719
Pres.—Glenn Brand, 10 emp., Custom HVAC ducts, including duct & ........ (732) 681-0856
Erick Industries, Inc., 837 S. 9th St., Camden 08103
Pres.—Bill Patton, 2 emp., Sheet metal skylights ........ (856) 966-2045
Essex Fence Co., 132 U.S. Highway 46, Rockaway 07866
Ptnr.—George Lenar, 17 emp., PVC vinyl, ornamental aluminum, wood ........ (973) 625-4122
EVS Metal, 1 Kenner Ct., Riverdale 07457
Ptnr. & Pres.—Scott Berkowitz, 105 emp., Company headquarters & precision sheet ........ (973) 839-4432
Falcon Industries, Inc., 371 Campus Dr., Somerset 08873
Pres.—Zig Michalski, 55 emp., Sheet metal fabrication ........ (732) 563-9889
Fiore Skylights, Inc., 210 E. Evergreen Ave., P.O. Box 160, Somerdale 08083
Pres., Div.—Richard L. Materio, 15 emp., Commercial & residential structural ........ (856) 346-0118
Foremost Mfg. Co., Inc., 941 Ball Ave., Union 07083
Pres., CEO—Herb S. Schiller, 150 emp., Aluminum lighting reflectors ........ (908) 687-4646
Franklen Sheet Metal Co., Inc., 122 S. Main St., Ocean Grove 07756
Owner & Pres.—Steven Smith, 12 emp., Roof coping sheet metal fabrication ........ (732) 988-0808
Freehold Mfg. Assembly, Inc., 86 Birch Ave., P.O. Box 269, Little Silver 07739
Pres.—Trudy Lane, 10 emp., Sheet metal fabrication ........ (732) 224-9066
G & H Sheet Metal Works, Inc., 1423 Chestnut Ave., Hillside 07205
Pres. & Proj. Mgr.—Eric Heide, 12 emp., Sheet metal fabrication ........ (973) 923-1100
Gentek Building Products, Inc., 11 Craigwood Rd., Avenel 07001
Plt. Mgr.—Bhavin Patel, 165 emp., Custom steel & aluminum coil metal ........ (732) 381-0900
Gerard Sheet Metal Fabricators, Inc., 385 Lexington Ave., East Brunswick 08816
Pres.—Betty Hogan, 30 emp., HVAC sheet metal duct work fabricating ........ (732) 257-4777
Gild, Inc., 18-02 River Rd., Ste. 5, Fair Lawn 07410
Pres.—Lev Kulek, 10 emp., Sheet metal fabrication ........ (201) 398-0030
GP Precision, Inc., 434 Sand Shore Rd., Hackettstown 07840
Pres.—W. Arthur Cubbage, 40 emp., Precision metal fabrication ........ (908) 850-1940
GTM Signs, Inc., 1298 Hurffville Rd., Deptford 08096
Ptnr.—Karl Baker, 8 emp., Signs & canvas & standing seam awnings ........ (856) 227-2333
H & H Sheet Metal & Machining, 30 White Lake Rd., Sparta 07871
Pres., CFO—Frederick Hohmann, 9 emp., Sheet metal fabrication & CNC machining ........ (973) 383-6880
Hackettstown Sheet Metal, Inc., 1 Stiger St., Hackettstown 07840
GM—Ken Nakowski, 3 emp., Sheet metal fabrication ........ (908) 852-3752
Haenssler Sheet Metal Works, Inc., 592 Hawthorne Ave., Newark 07112
Pres.—Wendy Haenssler, 12 emp., Custom sheet metal & stainless steel ........ (973) 373-6360
Halo Sheet Metal, Inc., 140 Lehigh Ave., Lakewood 08701
Pres.—Patricia Pellegrino, 40 emp., Sheet metal fabrication & installation ........ (732) 901-0080
Handi-Hut, Inc., 3 Grunwald St., Clifton 07013
Pres.—Melvin Cohen, 25 emp., Smoking & passenger waiting shelters ........ (973) 614-1800
Hays Sheet Metal, Inc., 7070 Kaighns Ave., Bldg. B, Pennsauken 08109
Pres.—Michael P. Hays, 35 emp., HVAC & fiberglass duct systems ........ (856) 662-7722
Heritage Towers, Inc., 910 Shunpike Rd., Ste. B, Cape May 08204
Owner & Pres.—Michael Seaverns, 2 emp., Custom aluminum fabrication of fishing ........ (609) 884-5999
Homiek Sheet Metal Fabrication & HVAC Supplies, Inc., 1352 Route 9, Lakewood 08701
Pres.—Edward P. Homiek, 20 emp., HVAC ducts ........ (732) 364-7644
Hotfoil-EHS, Inc., 2960 E. State Street Ext., Hamilton 08619
Pres.—Neville Richards, 35 emp., Industrial heating equipment, including ........ (609) 588-0900
Huggins Aluminum Products, 576 N. Route 73, West Berlin 08091
Ptnr.—George E. Metzler, 3 emp., Screen & fully insulated enclosures ........ (856) 767-0506
Hutchinson Industries, Inc., 460 Southard St., Trenton 08638
Pres.—Olivier Marsaly, 165 emp., Corporate headquarters & rubber & aluminum ........ (609) 394-1010
Hutchton & Simon, Inc., 140 Atlantic St., Hackensack 07601
Pres.—Dan Cubicciotti, 25 emp., Sheet metal fabrication, welding & ........ (201) 487-1033
IMCO, Inc., 858 N. Lenola Rd., Bldg. 1, Moorestown 08057
Pres.—A. Ross Davis, 40 emp., Sheet metal fabrication & precision ........ (856) 499-2214
Imperial Metal Products, Inc., 8 W. Chimney Rock Rd., Bound Brook 08805
Pres.—John Karmazyn, 5 emp., Stainless steel size reduction machinery ........ (732) 469-8181
Independent Sheet Metal Co., Inc., 233 Central Ave., Hawthorne 07506
Pres.—Ed Redenack, 25 emp., Sheet metal fabrication ........ (973) 423-1150
International Sheet Metal & Plate Mfg., Inc., 112 Veterans Memorial Dr. E., P.O. Box 5, Somerville 08876
Pres.—John Novak, 23 emp., Sheet metal fabrication ........ (908) 722-6614
International Swimming Pools, Inc., 14-C Van Dyke Ave., New Brunswick 08901
Pres.—Brad Korbel, 19 emp., Custom sheet metal fabrication, including ........ (732) 565-9229
Interstate Panel, LLC, 67 Benson Ave., Hamilton 08610
CEO—Donald Anderson, 29 emp., Metal roofing panels ........ (609) 586-4411
Interstate Welding & Mfg. Co., Inc., 1510 Village Ct., Edgewater Park 08010
Pres., CFO—Joseph N. Russomanno, 18 emp., Welding, tube, pipe & metal fabrication ........ (609) 699-6950
J & E Metal Fabricators, Inc., 1 Coan Pl., Metuchen 08840
Pres.—Mark Brazina, 25 emp., Precision sheet metal fabrication ........ (732) 548-9650
J & M Air, Inc., 189 S. Bridge St., Somerville 08876
Pres.—Michael Favreau, 12 emp., Custom galvanized & stainless steel ........ (908) 707-4040
J.R.M. Products, Inc., 701 Locust St., Keyport 07735
Pres.—Robert Wichowski, 4 emp., American-made custom steel, stainless ........ (732) 495-3092
Jantek Industries, LLC, 230 Route 70, Medford 08055
CEO—Keith Kailian, 40 emp., Windows, doors & related products for ........ (609) 654-1030
Jason Metal Products Corp., 1072 Randolph Ave., Rahway 07065
Pres.—Richard Jaszyn, 4 emp., Sheet metal fabrication ........ (732) 396-1132
Jenkins Plumbing & Heating, 103 S. Franklin, P.O. Box 509, Pleasantville 08232
Pres.—Jeffery C. Jenkins, 20 emp., Sheet metal fabrication & HVAC contracting ........ (609) 641-6262
Jersey Sheet Metal & Machine, Inc., 90 E. Dickerson St., Dover 07801
Pres.—Richard Hammond, Sr., 3 emp., Sheet metal fabrication ........ (973) 366-0101
Jersey Shore Steel, Inc., 636 Herman Rd., Jackson 08527
Ptnr.—Gary Loveland, 18 emp., Sheet & plate steel fabrication ........ (732) 833-8855
Jersey Windows & Building Supplies, 831 Broadway, Newark 07104
Store Mgr.—Will Zapata, 2 emp., Vinyl & aluminum windows & vinyl siding ........ (973) 482-3614
Jewel Precision Sheet Metal Machining, Inc., 200 Commerce Rd., Cedar Grove 07009
Pres.—Ignazio Graziano, 75 emp., Sheet metal & plastic fabrication, ........ (973) 857-5545
K L M Mechanical Contractors, Inc., 109 W. Shore Ave., Dumont 07628
Pres.—Ken Loehr, 8 emp., Sheet metal fabrication & HVAC contracting ........ (201) 385-6965
Kalis Metal Components Corp., 231 North Ave., P.O. Box 294, Garwood 07027
Hum. Res. & Off. Mgr.—Evelyn Archibald, 30 emp., Sheet metal fabrication & precision ........ (908) 789-0500
Kayden Mfg., Inc., 83-A Burlews Ct., Hackensack 07601
Owner & Pres.—Jeff Kayden, 5 emp., Vinyl swimming pool liners & sheet ........ (201) 880-9898
Kearny Sheet Metal Works, Inc., 579 Davis Ave., Kearny 07032
Pres.—Mike Smolensky, 6 emp., 24-gage to 1/4-inch sheet metal & aluminum ........ (201) 991-4745
Kendall Mfg. Co., Inc., 1366 Chews Landing Rd., Clementon 08021
Owner—James W. Strater, 3 emp., Vinyl & wooden windows & doors & retractable ........ (856) 227-2132
Kenvil Weldery & Machine, Inc., 15 Kings Pkwy., Ledgewood 07852
Pres.—Gary Magura, 3 emp., Metal fabrication & machining & welding ........ (973) 584-1729
Kiker Sheet Metal Corp., 6 S. New Rd., P.O. Box 1487, Pleasantville 08232
Pres.—Brian Kiker, 12 emp., Sheet metal fabrication ........ (609) 641-4890
Kinetron, Inc., 1416 S. Roller Rd., Ocean 07712
Pres.—Judith Gogan, 8 emp., Precision sheet metal fabrication, ........ (732) 918-7777
Kraftware Corp., 270 Cox St., Roselle 07203
Pres., CEO—Randy Grant, 22 emp., Stainless steel, polyester film & metal ........ (908) 259-8883
Krowne Metal Corp., 100 Haul Rd., Wayne 07470
Ex. V-P.—Roger Forman, 44 emp., Stainless steel bar & restaurant equipment ........ (973) 305-3300
Laursen Sheet Metal, 69 Flint Rd., Toms River 08757
Owner—Ken Laursen, 15 emp., Sheet metal fabrication ........ (732) 349-2821
LazyMan Mfg., 616 Hardwick St., P.O. Box 327, Belvidere 07823
Pres., CFO—Brian D. Sadowski, 15 emp., Gas barbecue grills & sheet metal fabrication ........ (908) 475-5315
Leary Heating & Air Conditioning, Inc., Bill, 6 Green St., Metuchen 08840
Pres.—Bill Leary, 8 emp., HVAC sheet metal fabrication ........ (732) 494-9200
Legacy Stairs & Millwork, Inc., 1000 Airport Rd., Ste. 104, Lakewood 08701
Owner—Stephen Hasse, 6 emp., Custom wooden, steel & aluminum conventional ........ (732) 905-7705
Leibrock Metal Products, Inc., 1800 Brielle Ave., Asbury Park 07712
Pres., CEO—William Vogel, 8 emp., Sheet metal fabrication ........ (732) 695-0326
Lentine Sheet Metal, Inc., 1210 E. Elizabeth Ave., Linden 07036
Pres.—John Lentine, 7 emp., Sheet metal fabrication ........ (908) 486-8974
Link Burns Mfg. Co., Inc., 253 American Way, Voorhees 08043
Pres.—Dan Zoltowski, 20 emp., Sheet metal fabrication ........ (856) 429-6844
Lloyd's Of Millville, Inc., 208 S. Wade Blvd., Millville 08332
Pres., Fin. & R & D Mgr.—Ben Lloyd, Jr., 3 emp., Canvas goods, sewing & retractable ........ (856) 825-0345
Lux Entertainment, LLC, 629 E. 19th St., Paterson 07514
Owner—Andrew Vaccaro, 3 emp., Environmentally controlled protective ........ (888) 282-8425
M C Custom Sheet Metal Fabrication, Inc., 215-E Old Egg Harbor Rd., Ste. E, West Berlin 08091
Pres.—Michael Franchi, 7 emp., Custom stock fittings for HVAC ducts ........ (856) 767-9509
MacElroy Co., Inc., J. C., 91 Ethel Rd. W., Piscataway 08854
Pres.—Scott J. Spota, 30 emp., Custom steel, stainless steel, aluminum ........ (732) 572-7100
Magic Metal Works, Inc., 40 W. Englewood Ave., Bergenfield 07621
Pres.—Vic Dabaghian, 5 emp., Precision sheet metal fabrication ........ (201) 384-8457
Marlyn Sheet Metal, Inc., 606 N. Delsea Dr., Clayton 08312
Pres.—Julius Brandt, 15 emp., HVAC sheet metal fabrication ........ (856) 863-6900
Max Gurtman & Sons, Inc., 622 Lexington Ave., Clifton 07011
Shop Mgr.—Peter Dino, 4 emp., Sheet metal fabrication ........ (973) 478-7000
Medin Corp., 11 Jackson Rd., Totowa 07512
Pres.—Jay Schainholz, 108 emp., Corporate headquarters & precision ........ (973) 779-2400
Metal Dynamix, LLC, 709 Fellowship Rd., Mount Laurel 08054
Pres.—Charles Gaw, 9 emp., Sheet metal fabrication & CNC machining ........ (856) 235-4559
Metal Masters, 630 Laurel St., Beverly 08010
Owner—Israel Gaitelband, 2 emp., Metal & stainless steel fabrication ........ (609) 332-3176
Meto Lift, Inc., 556 Commerce St., Franklin Lakes 07417
Pres.—William Rotenberry, 20 emp., Stainless steel material handling equipment ........ (201) 405-0311
Mid Jersey Building Supply, 2486 Ridgeway Blvd., Manchester 08759
Owner, Pres., CEO, GM & Off. Mgr.—Robert Jeffers, 12 emp., Aluminum patio covers, enclosures (732) 657-2000
Mid States Spiral, Inc., 1425 Grandview Ave., West Deptford 08066
CEO—Bob Seiden, 3 emp., Sheet metal fabrication & ducts ........ (215) 744-2846
Millar Sheet Metal, 39 Rizzolo Rd., Kearny 07032
Pres.—Maggie Millar, 5 emp., Sheet metal fabrication ........ (201) 997-1990
Murphy Fence Co., Inc., 507 Seashore Rd., Cape May 08204
CEO—Amy Litton, 25 emp., Wooden, PVC & aluminum fencing & PVC ........ (609) 886-1635
National Pipe Hanger Corp., 200 Campus Dr., R.R. 30, Mount Holly 08060
Pres., CEO—William McCabe, 60 emp., Corporate headquarters & metal pipe ........ (609) 261-5353
Neumann Sheet Metal, Inc., 759 North Ave., Plainfield 07062
Manager—George Kelly, 4 emp., Sheet metal fabrication & high definition ........ (908) 756-0415
New Age Metal Fabricating Co., 26 Daniel Rd., Fairfield 07004
Pres.—Mario Costa, 60 emp., Sheet metal fabrication ........ (973) 227-9107
Newark Wire Works, Inc., 1059 King Georges Post Rd., Ste. 103, Edison 08837
Pres.—JoAnn Spellman, 16 emp., Architectural wire mesh panels & fabricated ........ (732) 661-2001
Nordic Metal, LLC, 500 S. 31st St., Kenilworth 07033
Pres.—Bo L. Johansson, 8 emp., Sheet metal fabrication ........ (908) 245-8900
Nordt Precision Metal Mfg., Inc., 640 Creek Rd., Bellmawr 08031
V-P.—Dolores Nordt, 23 emp., Precision sheet metal fabrication ........ (856) 931-7444
North Jersey Metal Fabricators, Inc., 130 Ryerson Ave., Ste. 107, Wayne 07470
Pres.—Bill Ecker, 7 emp., Metal, aluminum, stainless steel & ........ (973) 305-9830
Northeast Sheet Metal, LLC, 870 Warwick Tpke., Hewitt 07421
Owner—Nicole Amado, 8 emp., Sheet metal fabrication ........ (973) 853-0500
OEG Building Materials, 395 State Route 34, Matawan 07747
Owner—Oscar Rosner, 45 emp., Metal drywall studs & steel framing ........ (732) 667-3636
Omega Metal Works, Inc., 41 Stelle Rd., Chesterfield 08515
Pres.—Ted B. Walker, 1 emp., Sheet metal fabrication & HVAC ducts ........ (609) 298-9100
P T L Sheet Metal, Inc., 70 Davies Ave., Dumont 07628
Pres.—Candice MacWilliam, 5 emp., Sheet metal fabrication ........ (201) 501-8700
Par Sheet Metal, Inc., 220 W. 1st Ave., Ste. 2, Roselle 07203
Pres.—Anthony Costa, 20 emp., Sheet metal fabrication & HVAC ducts ........ (908) 241-2477
Park Roofing & Sheet Metal Co., Inc., 427 Whitehead Ave., Ste. 1, South River 08882
Pres.—Craig Meltzer, 5 emp., Sheet metal fabrication & metal roofing ........ (732) 257-4570
Par-Metal, Inc., 29 Ewing Ave., North Arlington 07031
Pres.—John Ango, 10 emp., Steel & aluminum electronic enclosures ........ (201) 955-0800
Parr Leadburning Co., J. W., 87 Parkway, Little Falls 07424
Pres.—Gary Parr, 2 emp., Sheet metal fabrication ........ (973) 256-8093
Par-Troy Sheet Metal & Conditioning, LLC, 122 Clinton Rd., Fairfield 07004
Ptnr. & Pres.—Lino C. Rocha, 7 emp., Sheet metal fabrication & HVAC contracting ........ (973) 227-1150

F86 © Copyright 2015 Manufacturers' News, Inc. S.I.C. SECTION

Paterson Sheet Metal Works, Inc., 320 Wabash Ave., Paterson 07503
Pres.—Richard Basilicato, 4 emp., *Sheet metal fabrication* (973) 345-4182
Pemberton Fabricators, Inc., 30 Indel Ave., P.O. Box 227, Rancocas 08073
Pres.—Robert Murnane, 40 emp., *Sheet metal fabrication* (609) 267-0922
Pepco Mfg. Co., 210 E. Evergreen Ave., P.O. Box 160, Somerdale 08083
CEO—John Kennedy, 80 emp., *Company headquarters & telecommunication* (856) 783-3700
Phoenix Mfg., Inc., 1306 Brielle Ave., Ocean 07712
Pres.—Richard Sheridan, 10 emp., *PVC & aluminum railings & PVC pergolas* (732) 380-1666
Pioneer Machine & Tool Co., 425 E. Broadway, P.O. Box 8, Maple Shade 08052
Ptnr.—George Czuzak, Jr., 30 emp., *Aerospace components* (856) 779-8800
Precision Metalcrafters, Inc., 17 Filbert St., Williamstown 08094
Ptnr.—Frank Falconi, 10 emp., *Sheet metal fabrication* (856) 629-1020
Precision Parts Unlimited, Inc., 24 Patriot Crossing, Rockaway 07866
Owner & Pres.—Rose Rainone, 1 emp., *Sheet metal fabrication & precision* (973) 659-3300
Precision Shape Solutions, 243 E. Blackwell St., Dover 07801
Site Mgr.—Cory Akers, 5 emp., *Waterjet & laser cutting job shop* (973) 989-7199
Professional Environment Systems, 49 O'Brien Rd., Kearny 07032
Pres.—Percy Mentor, 15 emp., *HVAC ductwork* (201) 991-3000
Putnum Stainless Tubes, Inc., 1163 Route 22 E., Mountainside 07092
Pres.—James Schlenker, 14 emp., *Stainless steel tubing* (908) 232-9200
Quality Sheet Metal & Welding, 23 Clawson St., Piscataway 08854
Sys. Opers. Mgr.—David Doll, 13 emp., *Sheet metal fabrication & welding job* (732) 752-6300
R & L Sheet Metal Co., 3 Kulick Rd., Fairfield 07004
Pres., Shop Mgr.—Jerry Grieco, 12 emp., *Sheet metal fabrication* (973) 575-8448
R T B Fabricators, Inc., 220 Lincoln Blvd., Middlesex 08846
Owner & Pres.—Tom Gillen, 3 emp., *Aluminum, stainless steel & sheet metal* (732) 469-4127
R. K. Industries, Inc., 259 Overbrook Ave., Oakhurst 07755
★ Pres.—Richard Kuhns, 10 emp., *Aluminum gutter covers* (732) 531-1123
R.S. Phillips Steel, LLC, 128 Lake Pochung Rd., Sussex 07461
Ptnr.—Neil Phillips, 23 emp., *Steel & aluminum fabrication & erection* (973) 827-6464
Ranco Precision Sheet Metal, Inc., 40 Colorado St., P.O. Box 1101, Clifton 07014
Pres.—John C. Karpi, Sr., 9 emp., *Sheet metal fabrication & blind fasteners* (973) 472-8808
Rangecraft Mfg. Co., Inc., 4-40 Banta Pl., Fair Lawn 07410
Pres.—Ramona Panus, 19 emp., *Custom-designed decorative copper,* (201) 791-0440
Raritan Printing Plus Flags & Banners, Inc., 109 N. Feltus St., South Amboy 08879
Pres.—Joanne Corridon, 2 emp., *Stock & custom U.S. outdoor & indoor* (732) 721-2121
Ricklyn Co., Inc., 460 Route 57, Port Murray 07865
Pres., GM—Kevin J. Wauck, 6 emp., *Sheet metal fabrication* (908) 689-6770
Roof Deck, Inc., 80 Twin Rivers Dr., P.O. Box 295, Hightstown 08520
Comp., GM & Pur. Agt.—Frank LaCava, 10 emp., *Metal roof & floor decks* (609) 448-6666
Royal Seamless Corp., 1000 Airport Rd., Ste. 202, Lakewood 08701
Pres.—Barbara Kusmierczyk, 6 emp., *Aluminum & copper gutters & downspouts* (732) 901-9595
Sander Mechanical Service, Inc., 55 Columbia Rd., Ste. 1, Branchburg 08876
★ Pres.—Robert Bittel, 20 emp., *Sheet metal fabrication, including* (732) 560-0600
Schrader & Co., Inc., 188 Halsey Rd., Newton 07860
Pres.—David Lake, 10 emp., *Precision sheet metal & machined components* (973) 579-2700
Service Metal Fabricating, Inc., 10 Stickle Ave., Rockaway 07866
Ptnr.—James Moretti, 85 emp., *Corporate headquarters & sheet metal* (973) 625-8882
Shamong Mfg. Co., Inc., 33 Bunker Hill Rd., Shamong 08088
Pres.—Don Autio, 35 emp., *Sheet metal fabrication* (609) 654-2549
Sheet Metal Products, Inc., 794 N. 6th St., Newark 07107
Pres.—William F. Kovacs, 30 emp., *Contract manufacturing & industrial* (973) 482-0450
Sims Metal Management, 8-18 Noble St., Newark 07114
GM—Keith Bologno, 10 emp., *Sheet metal recycling* (973) 824-8900
Skripak Metal Fabricators, Inc., 170 Oberlin Ave. N., Unit 17, Lakewood 08701
Pres., CFO—John Skripak, Jr., 10 emp., *Metal carts & tables, catwalks, hoods* (732) 364-9662
SolidSurface Designs, Inc., 1651 Sherman Ave., Pennsauken 08110
Pres.—Matthew Baiada, 21 emp., *Solid-surface, quartz, stainless steel* (856) 910-7720
Sonrise Metal, Inc., 138 3rd Ave., Paterson 07514
Pres.—Todd Abrams, 19 emp., *Precision sheet metal fabrication &* (973) 423-4717
South Jersey Metal, Inc., 1651 Hurffville Rd., Route 41, P.O. Box 5148, Deptford 08096
Pres.—Joseph Wagner, 20 emp., *Commercial stainless steel kitchen* (856) 228-0642
Sperro Metal Products, LLC, 2 Skyline Dr., P.O. Box 397, Montville 07045
Owner—James Fernandez, 25 emp., *Sheet metal fabrication for the construction* (973) 335-2000
SRS, Inc., 74 Liberty St., P.O. Box 4277, Metuchen 08840
Pres.—Rich Blatman, 22 emp., *Stainless steel, bronze & glass guardrails* (732) 548-6630
SSM Industries, Inc., 1425 Grandview Ave., West Deptford 08066
GM—Ron Schnell, 30 emp., *Sheet metal fabrication* (856) 345-2525
Stan Catering Trucks, Inc., 15 Circle Ave., Clifton 07011
Pres.—Stanley Bednarz, 1 emp., *Sheet metal fabrication* (973) 253-0556
Stand-Out Signs, Inc., 49 W. Pond Rd., Perth Amboy 08861
Pres., Off. Mgr.—Joseph Masaruca, 3 emp., *Neon interior & exterior signs, banners* (732) 442-9399
Star Metal Products, Inc., 1125 W. Elizabeth Ave., Linden 07036
Pres., Fin., GM & R & D Mgr.—Donald Eckloff, 32 emp., *Sheet metal fabrication* (908) 474-9860
Steck, Inc., Paul C., 25 Brown Ave., Springfield 07081
Pres.—Emily S. Wantz, 8 emp., *Custom precision sheet metal fabrication* (973) 376-1830
Stefano Fence Systems, Inc., 737 New Durham Rd., Edison 08817
★ Owner—Stephen Smith, 15 emp., *Aluminum architectural metalwork &* (732) 321-5050
Stuart Mills, Inc., 25 Stillwater Rd., Newton 07860
Pres.—Stuart Mills, 6 emp., *CNC milling & turning, sheet metal* (973) 579-5717
Suburban Building Products, 1178 Lakewood Farmingdale Rd., Howell 07731
Owner—Vincent Bochario, 55 emp., *Vinyl fabrication* (732) 901-8900
Tam Metal Products, Inc., 55 Whitney Rd., Mahwah 07430
Co-Pres.—Frank Cariddi, 50 emp., *Precision sheet metal fabrication &* (201) 848-7800
Technimetal, 7 Melanie Ln., Ste. 3, East Hanover 07936
Pres.—Rich Ciatto, 6 emp., *Sheet metal fabrication* (973) 428-2881
Testrite Instrument Co., 216 S. Newman St., Hackensack 07601
Pres.—Larry Rubin, 120 emp., *Telescopic aluminum tube educational* (201) 543-0240
Toms River Sheet Metal Co., 400 Corporate Cir., Toms River 08755
Salesman—Mike Beaulieu, 23 emp., *Sheet metal fabrication & HVAC* (732) 244-2880
Total Maintenance & Service, Inc., 121 Hamburg Tpke., Bloomingdale 07403
Pres.—Dennis Palmer, Sr., 7 emp., *Sheet metal fabrication & HVAC contracting* (973) 283-0048
Tower Systems, Inc.- Atlantic Towers & St. Croix Marine Products, 235 Hickory Ln., P.O. Box D, Bayville 08721
Pres.—Steve Tull, 7 emp., *Fabricated aluminum boat accessories* (732) 237-8800
Trenton Sheet Metal, 30 Adam Ave., Trenton 08618
GM—Robert Somogyi, 25 emp., *Sheet metal fabrication* (609) 695-6328
Trolex Corp., 20 Bushes Ln., Elmwood Park 07407
Pres.—Richard Foster, 30 emp., *Ventilation duct dampers* (201) 794-8004
Tuers Aluminum, LLC, 2562 Lakewood-Allenwood Rd., Howell 07731
Ptnr.—Nick Tsoukalis, 2 emp., *Aluminum awnings* (732) 458-2031
Two Brothers Iron Works, 3709 Liberty Ave., North Bergen 07047
Proj. Mgr.—Fernando Reyes, 10 emp., *Ornamental metalwork, including interior* (201) 866-7970
Ulma Form Works, Inc., 58 5th Ave., Hawthorne 07506
Corp. Secy.—Mary Raichelson, 50 emp., *Steel concrete forms* (973) 636-2040
Unimade Metals, Inc., 115 Patterson St., Hillsdale 07642
Pres.—F. Borosch, 12 emp., *Precision sheet metal & machined products* (201) 666-7747
United Equipment & Fabricators, 175 Orange St., Newark 07103
Manager—Robert Ayars, 5 emp., *Custom plastic, fiberglass, stainless* (973) 242-2737
United Support Solutions, Inc., 134 Sand Park Rd., Cedar Grove 07009
Pres.—Joe Ostering, 80 emp., *Sheet metal fabrication, AWS & robotic* (973) 857-2298
Vee Dennis Mfg. Co., 620 Park Rd., Cherry Hill 08034
Pres.—George D. Lymper, 25 emp., *Sheet metal fabrication & machining* (856) 428-7676
VFI Fabricators, Inc., 300 Thomas Ave., Bldg. 1, Ste. 101, Williamstown 08094
Pres.—Alfred E. Fabrico, 30 emp., *Sheet metal fabrication* (856) 629-8786
Weather Tek Aluminum Corp., 123 N. Washington Ave., P.O. Box 405, Dunellen 08812
Pres.—Charlie Ponti, 15 emp., *Aluminum awnings & siding* (732) 752-0313
Weathercraft Mfg. Co., 13 Emerson Plz. E., Emerson 07630
Pres.—Salvatore Gebbia, 15 emp., *Aluminum awnings & enclosures, retractable* (201) 262-0055
WECOM, Inc., 20 Warrick Ave., Glassboro 08028
Pres.—Eric C. Sprengle, Sr., 27 emp., *Precision sheet metal aluminum & stainless* (856) 863-8400
Westfield Sheet Metal Works, Inc., 261 Monroe Ave., P.O. Box 128, Kenilworth 07033
Pres.—Campbell Johnstone, 25 emp., *Custom stainless & carbon steel, aluminum* (908) 276-5500
Wilbur Sheet Metal, Inc., 27 Ward Ave., P.O. Box 3681, Trenton 08609
Pres.—Richard Tolocka, 15 emp., *Sheet metal fabrication* (609) 393-5952
Woodroof Metal Shop, 73 Water St., Bridgeton 08302
Owner—Bob Woodroof, 2 emp., *HVAC ducts* (856) 455-1111
WP Ducts, 219 U.S. Highway 206, P.O. Box 547, Andover 07821
Pres.—William Pierce, Jr., 2 emp., *Ductwork* (973) 786-7179
Zvonko Stulic & Son, Inc., 21 Main St., Newark 07105
Pres.—Zvonko Stulic, 5 emp., *Plate & sheet metal fabrication, welding* (973) 589-3773

## 3446 Architectural metal work

A & A Ironworks, Inc., 955 Burnt Meadow Rd., Hewitt 07421
Pres.—Adam G. Muzer, 15 emp., *Ironwork & structural steel fabrication* (973) 728-4300
Abba Metal Works, Inc., 337 River St., Paterson 07524
★ Pres.—Corrado Abbattista, 7 emp., *Structural steel fabrication & ornamental* (973) 684-0808
Acme/Lingo Flagpoles, 1865 Route 206, Southampton 08088
Pres.—Jeff Lingo, 9 emp., *Tubular metal products, custom tapered* (609) 801-1897
Advanced Cutting Services, LLC, 169 E. Highland Pkwy., Roselle 07203
Owner, Pres. & Mng. Member—Bob Balchunas, 5 emp., *Ecofriendly waterjet cutting & metal* (908) 241-5332
Aeroacoustic Corp., The, 169 E. Highland Pkwy., Roselle 07203
Pres.—Margherita Kallinger, 55 emp., *Corporate headquarters & noise abatement* (908) 241-8600
Ajay Metal Fabricators, Inc., 355 Dalziel Rd., Linden 07036
Pres.—Tony Zambell, 9 emp., *Steel, aluminum, stainless, copper* (908) 523-0558
Alberona Iron Work, Inc., 452 Scotland Rd., Orange 07050
Pres.—Tony Prioletti, 3 emp., *Ornamental ironwork & structural steel* (973) 674-3375
Alenco Fence & Supply Corp., 167 Route 70, Bldg. B, Medford 08055
Owner—Chris Murphy, 10 emp., *Wooden, aluminum, chain-link & vinyl* (609) 654-6060
Alessandra Miscellaneous Metalworks, Inc., 75-B Mill St., Newton 07860
Owner—Scott Alessandra, 7 emp., *Steel stair, rail & ladder fabrication* (973) 786-6805
All Action Architectural Metal & Glass, 146 Sylvania Pl., Ste. G, South Plainfield 07080
Owner—John Quinones, 20 emp., *Architectural metalwork* (732) 738-6655
All-State Fence, Inc., 1389 Route 9 N., Howell 07731
Pres.—Scott Skrable, 8 emp., *Residential & commercial chain-link* (732) 431-4944
American Custom Fabricators, Inc., 215-A Hickory Ln., Bayville 08721
Pres.—Jacqueline Schinder, 8 emp., *Structural aluminum, ornamental metal* (732) 237-0037
American Railing Design, 191 Vineyard Rd., Edison 08817
Pres.—Andrew Martingano, 10 emp., *Commercial, residential & industrial* (732) 287-1122
Artistic Metal Works Corp., 199 7th Ave., Hawthorne 07506
V-P.—Julius Minervini, 4 emp., *Architectural & ornamental metalwork* (973) 304-0600
Artistic Railings, Inc., 500 River Dr., Garfield 07026
Pres.—Tom Zuzik, 7 emp., *Ornamental iron railings* (973) 772-8540
B & B Iron Works, 300 Coit St., Irvington 07111
Pres.—Mauro Belgiovine, 50 emp., *Architectural & ornamental ironwork* (973) 375-9000
Baldi Iron Works,Inc., 158 Belmont Ave., Belleville 07109
Pres.—Rocco Baldi, 5 emp., *Ornamental iron stairs* (973) 751-4338
Berlin Neon Sign, Inc., 326 Old White Horse Pike, Waterford Works 08089
Pres.—Tim Manna, 2 emp., *Neon signs & flagpoles* (856) 767-0525
Beta Iron Works, Inc., 31 Pasadena Ave., Lodi 07644
Owner—Aharon Elperin, 2 emp., *Architectural metalwork, including* (973) 815-2730
Blanco Assocs., Inc., J., 280 9th Ave., Unit 1, Hawthorne 07506
Pres.—Victor Ramos, 15 emp., *Pipe hangers & supports & architectural* (973) 427-0619
Bolt Welding & Iron Works, 78 Wall St., Trenton 08609
Owner—Christopher Hiltey, 5 emp., *Architectural welding* (609) 393-3993
Borrelli Steel Fabricators, LLC, 2800 Industrial Way, Vineland 08360
Pres.—Vincent J. Borrelli, 25 emp., *Structural steel fabrication & ironwork* (856) 690-8850
Brass Shop, Inc., 611 Central Ave., Westfield 07090
Pres.—Frank Giannone, 2 emp., *Rebuilt brass lighting, lamp restoration* (908) 232-2161
Capital Steel Service, LLC, 82 Stokes Ave., Trenton 08638
CEO—Allen Hickman, Sr., 27 emp., *Metal service center & structural &* (609) 882-6983
Carfaro Railings Company, Frank, 70 Hacklebarney Rd., Long Valley 07853
Pres.—Frank Carfaro, 1 emp., *Iron & aluminum railings* (908) 879-7312
Carfaro, Inc., 2075 E. State Street Ext., Trenton 08619
Pres.—Joseph Carfaro, 50 emp., *Custom & prefabricated aluminum railings* (609) 890-6600
Ciccone Custom Railing & Manufacturing, Inc., 2002 Route 9, Toms River 08755
Pres.—Robyn Ciccone, 10 emp., *All-welded custom ornamental aluminum* (732) 349-7071
City Glass Co., 282 Broadway, P.O. Box 178, Bayonne 07002
Pres.—Allan McCleod, 50 emp., *Architectural metals, glass & custom* (201) 436-8400
Clem's Ornamental Iron Works, Inc., 110 11th St., Piscataway 08854
Chrm., Pres.—Clement Carfaro III, 70 emp., *Architectural & ornamental metalwork* (732) 968-7200
Collo Ornamental Iron, Inc., 1723 Somers Point Rd., Egg Harbor Township 08234
Owner & Pres.—Jim Collo, Sr., 3 emp., *Ornamental ironwork* (609) 926-8799
Columbian Iron Works, Inc., 332 Vreeland Ave., Paterson 07513
Pres.—John Marogi, 5 emp., *Architectural ironwork* (973) 684-2303
Consolidated Steel & Aluminum Fence, 316 N. 12th St., P.O. Box 643, Kenilworth 07033
Pres.—Paul Cacicedo, 60 emp., *Commercial chain-link, steel, aluminum* (908) 272-6262
Coordinated Metals Co., Inc., 626 16th St., Carlstadt 07072
Pres.—Frank Grippi, 52 emp., *Architectural & ornamental metal fabrication* (201) 460-7280
Craftsmen Railing, Inc., 3 Cass St., Keyport 07735
Pres.—Ray Cottone, 5 emp., *Iron & aluminum railings* (732) 264-1080
CSI Fabricators, 15 Lexington St., Newark 07105
★ Manager—Kiran Pagarey, 7 emp., *Sheet metal fabrication, architectural* (973) 344-0955

Cusumano Perma-Rail Co., 213 W. Westfield Ave., Roselle Park 07204
Pres.—Jeffrey Cusumano, 15 emp., *Iron & aluminum railings & window guards*.................... (908) 245-9281
Dave's Architectural Iron, LLC, 121 McBride Ave., Ste. C, Paterson 07501
Owner—Davis Friessen, 2 emp., *Ornamental iron railings & gates*.................... (973) 523-6323
De Risi Iron Works Co., 910 Asbury Ave., Asbury Park 07712
Pres.—Santo De Risi, 2 emp., *Architectural & ornamental ironwork*.................... (732) 774-6570
Decorative Iron Works, 7383 Belmont Ave., Paterson 07522
Owner—Joseph Monga, 5 emp., *Architectural metalwork*.................... (973) 595-8517
DiPasquale Fence Co., 196 Route 9 N., Englishtown 07726
Plt. Mgr.—Henry DiPasquale, 12 emp., *Ornamental aluminum, wooden, PVC &*.................... (732) 536-0660
DMD Stairs & Rails, LLC, 370 Whitesville Rd., Ste. 8, Jackson 08527
Pres.—Douglas Diani, 20 emp., *Wooden & metal stairs & railings*.................... (732) 901-0102
Eastern Glass Resources, Inc., 770 Supor Blvd., Harrison 07029
★ Owner—Phil Phisher, 30 emp., *Insulated & tempered glass & architectural*.................... (973) 483-8411
F M B, Inc., 70 Supor Blvd., Harrison 07029
Pres.—Bradley A. Yount, 30 emp., *Metal railing fabrication*.................... (973) 485-5544
Fast Weld Co., 502 New Brunswick Ave., Phillipsburg 08865
Owner—Frank Shepherd, 1 emp., *Architectural metalwork, including*.................... (908) 213-0155
Fredon Welding & Iron Works Co., 52 State Route 15, P.O. Box 260, Lafayette 07848
Pres.—James Zylstra, 28 emp., *Ironwork & welding job shop*.................... (973) 383-6768
Hackensack Steel Corp., 645 Industrial Rd., Carlstadt 07072
Pres.—Tony Fasciano, 30 emp., *Structural steel stairs & railings*.................... (201) 935-0090
Heritage Towers, Inc., 910 Shunpike Rd., Ste. B, Cape May 08204
Owner & Pres.—Michael Seaverns, 2 emp., *Custom aluminum fabrication of fishing*.................... (609) 884-5999
IK Construction, Inc., 1118 E. Baltimore Ave., Linden 07036
Pres.—Ian Katwaroo, 8 emp., *Steel, ornamental iron & structural*.................... (908) 925-5200
International Forge, LLC, 14 Doty Rd., Haskell 07420
Pres., Sales—Michael Nestico, 7 emp., *Architectural iron railings, doors,*.................... (973) 729-0359
Interstate Architectural & Iron, Inc., 243 Laird Ave., Cliffside Park 07010
Pres.—Richard Papp, 2 emp., *Architectural metalwork*.................... (201) 941-0393
I-Ron-X Industries, 134 Wheat Rd., Buena 08310
Pres., CFO—Paul Tomasello, 2 emp., *Wrought iron & aluminum railings, steel*.................... (856) 697-3518
Kaufman Iron Works, Inc., J., 217 Godwin Ave., Paterson 07501
Pres.—Larry Kaufman, 35 emp., *Architectural ironwork, security gates*.................... (718) 991-5400
Kruysman Co., Ron, 7100 W. Buckshutem Rd., Millville 08332
Owner & Pres.—Ron Kruysman, 1 emp., *Architectural & ornamental metalwork*.................... (856) 327-0605
L M C Corp., 23 E. 23rd St., Paterson 07514
Pres.—Julian Legeard, 22 emp., *Architectural metalwork*.................... (973) 279-3573
La Forge De Style, 57 Romanelli Ave., South Hackensack 07606
Pres.—Patricia Gore, 5 emp., *Ornamental metalwork*.................... (201) 488-1955
Legacy Stairs & Millwork, Inc., 1000 Airport Rd., Ste. 104, Lakewood 08701
Owner—Stephen Hasse, 6 emp., *Custom wooden, steel & aluminum conventional*.................... (732) 905-7705
Louis Iron Works, 218 Lackawanna Ave., Newark 07103
Pres.—Louis Velasco, 2 emp., *Ornamental ironwork, including gates*.................... (973) 624-2700
M & M Welding & Steel Fabricating, 344 Essex St., P.O. Box 168, Stirling 07980
Pres.—Al Masek, 2 emp., *Architectural metalwork & general machining*.................... (908) 647-6060
Macy Custom Iron Railings Co., J., 116 River Rd., New Milford 07646
Ptnr.—John Zielen, 2 emp., *Iron railings*.................... (201) 262-4302
Majka Railing, Inc., 125 McBride Ave., Paterson 07501
Pres.—Mary Majka, 10 emp., *Aluminium railings*.................... (973) 247-7603
Mazmet, 1050 Bristol Rd., Mountainside 07092
Pres.—Dennis Maziekin, 10 emp., *Architectural metal products*.................... (908) 654-7686
Merchant & Evans, Inc., 308 Connecticut Dr., Burlington 08016
Chrm.—James R. Buck, 35 emp., *Structural & architectural metal roofing*.................... (609) 387-3033
New Jersey Stair & Rail, Inc., 746 Lloyd Rd., Matawan 07747
Pres.—Robert Barrett, 5 emp., *Wooden handrails & stairs*.................... (732) 583-8400
Newark Steel Fabricators, Inc., 104 Albert Ave., Newark 07105
Pres.—Luis Martinez, 5 emp., *Steel & ornamental iron railings &*.................... (973) 344-2904
Oceanic Metals LLC, 8555 Tonnelle Ave., Ste. 404, North Bergen 07047
Owner—Demetris Orfanos, 1 emp., *Steel, aluminum & cast iron cutting*.................... (201) 662-1192
OnGuard Fence Systems, 18 Culnen Dr., Branchburg 08876
Pres.—Thomas Chen, 30 emp., *Ornamental aluminum fencing & gates*.................... (908) 429-5522
Papp Iron Works, Inc., 950 S. 2nd St., P.O. Box 3149, Plainfield 07063
Pres.—Allan Papp, 50 emp., *Iron rails, stairways & structural*.................... (908) 731-1000
Polmar Iron Work, Inc., 673 New Brunswick Ave., Rahway 07065
Pres.—Marek Wresilo, 11 emp., *Ornamental ironwork*.................... (732) 882-0900
Post To Post, LLC, 2545 Fire Rd., Ste. 1, Egg Harbor Township 08234
★ Principal—Richard Sonsini, 7 emp., *Architectural metalwork & wooden &*.................... (609) 646-9300
R & R Stairs, Inc., 131 Wood Ave., Middlesex 08846
Pres.—Rich Kaminski, 20 emp., *Interior wooden & ornamental metal*.................... (732) 752-9400
Railco Metalcraft, Inc., 22 Park Pl., Butler 07405
Owner—Robert Williams, 3 emp., *Aluminum railings*.................... (973) 838-2822
Redyref Co., 100 Kenner Ct., Riverdale 07457
Pres.—William Pymm, 35 emp., *Touchscreen building directory, interactive*.................... (718) 784-3690
Rego Iron Co., 176 Cohawkin Rd., Clarksboro 08020
Owner—Frank Rego, 1 emp., *Wrought iron railings*.................... (856) 423-6779
Runtak Rails, LLC, 174 Kinderkamack Rd., Ste. A, Park Ridge 07656
Owner—Steve Runtak, 5 emp., *Custom architectural metalwork*.................... (201) 391-0380
S & S Mfg., Inc., 115 Fieldcrest Ave., Edison 08837
GM—Steve Silverman, 45 emp., *Aluminum & brass railings*.................... (732) 698-2400
Schtiller & Plevy, Inc., 695 S. 12th St., Newark 07103
Pres., R & D Mgr.—Lawrence Plevy, 24 emp., *Architectural metalwork & historic*.................... (973) 242-4600
Sound Management Group, 5 Ilene Ct., Bldg. 7, Unit 3, P.O. Box 6060, Hillsborough 08844
Pres.—Arthur P. Barkman, 6 emp., *Sound-masking systems, including acoustical*.................... (908) 874-7826
Stateline Fabricators, LLC, 167 Bronico Way, Phillipsburg 08865
Owner—Ed Esposito, 35 emp., *Architectural & structural metal fabrication*.................... (908) 387-8800
Stout's Metal Products, 222 Lincoln Ave., Collingswood 08108
Co-Pres.—Larry Stout, Sr., 5 emp., *Ornamental railings*.................... (856) 854-7938
Suburban Fence Co., 532 Mulberry St., Trenton 08638
Owner—Jelman S. Solomon, 20 emp., *Wooden & steel fencing & installation*.................... (609) 452-2630
Suburban Steel Craft, 22 W. 1st St., Clifton 07011
Owner & Pres.—Robert C. Feiner, 2 emp., *Railings & architectural metalwork*.................... (973) 772-3430
Summit Group II, 333 16th St., Carlstadt 07072
Pres.—Tom Klein, 5 emp., *Steel railings, ornamental iron, structural*.................... (201) 460-8888
T. S. Gates, Inc., 202 12th Ave., Paterson 07501
Pres.—Joseph Kaufman, 30 emp., *Iron gates*.................... (973) 523-7323
Tower Systems, Inc.- Atlantic Towers & St. Croix Marine Products, 235 Hickory Ln., P.O. Box D, Bayville 08721
Pres.—Steve Tull, 7 emp., *Fabricated aluminum boat accessories*.................... (732) 237-8800
Trylon Metal Works Inc., 136 Park Ave., Lyndhurst 07071
Pres.—Ralph Marchione, 15 emp., *Architectural handrails*.................... (201) 939-8282
Two Brothers Iron Works, 3709 Liberty Ave., North Bergen 07047
Proj. Mgr.—Fernando Reyes, 10 emp., *Ornamental metalwork, including interior*.................... (201) 866-7970
Ungarini Iron Works, LLC, 56 N. Logan Ave., Trenton 08609
Owner—Kris Jackaki, 10 emp., *Ornamental ironwork & structural steel*.................... (609) 392-0540
Weldall Welding & Ironworks, 115-117 S. Day St., Orange 07050
Pres.—Anthony Prioletti, 1 emp., *Ornamental iron & steel gates, fences*.................... (973) 674-8868
Weld-Done Welding, Inc., 20 Woodland Ave., Hurffville 08080
Pres.—Jeff Podesek, 15 emp., *Structural steel fabrication, metal*.................... (856) 582-7080
Willow Iron Works, 67 Pollock Ave., Jersey City 07305
Pres.—Michael Zaccaria, 7 emp., *Ornamental ironwork, including fences*.................... (201) 659-7266
Wolek's Ornamental Iron Works, 1719 H St., Route 71 W., Belmar 07719
Owner—Paul Wolek, 2 emp., *Ornamental ironwork*.................... (732) 681-5929

## 3448 Prefabricated metal buildings

Acadia Scenic, Inc., 130 Bay St., Jersey City 07302
Pres.—David Lawson, 25 emp., *Theatrical scenery buildings*.................... (201) 653-8889
Allied Specialty Group, Inc., 3114 Tonnelle Ave., North Bergen 07047
Pres.—Henry H. Bilge, 5 emp., *Aluminum composite panels systems &*.................... (201) 223-4600
American Panel Tec, 1640 New Market Ave., Bldg. 1-A, South Plainfield 07080
Pres.—John Lanzilotta, 40 emp., *Light gage steel building panels &*.................... (732) 968-0555
Architectural Metal Designs, Inc., 1505 Pineland Ave., Millville 08332
Pres.—Martin Schlembach, 20 emp., *Aluminum composite wall panel systems*.................... (856) 765-3000
BAMCO, Inc., 30 Baekeland Ave., Middlesex 08846
Pres.—Michael Biviano, 100 emp., *Architectural metal wall panels*.................... (732) 302-0889
Century Conveyor Service, Inc., 4301 S. Clinton Ave., South Plainfield 07080
Pres.—Ron Ferrara, 28 emp., *Conveyors, material handling equipment*.................... (908) 205-0625
Cooper Panels, LLC, John, 250 Maywood Ave., Ste. C, Maywood 07607
Pres.—Darby Diedrich, 6 emp., *Metal roof & wall panels*.................... (201) 487-4018
Custom Docks, Inc., 234 Route 206, Branchville 07826
Pres.—Bob Petura, 7 emp., *Aluminum boat docks*.................... (973) 948-3732
Global Partners In Shielding, Inc., 90 Dayton Ave., Ste. 13, Passaic 07055
Pres.—Donald Hener, 35 emp., *Industrial EMI, RFI & X-ray shielding*.................... (973) 574-9077
Metfab Metals, LLC, 560 Freeman St., Orange 07050
Pres.—James Murray, 18 emp., *Metal curtain wall parts, wall panels*.................... (973) 675-7676
P M C Diners, Inc., 56 Spruce St., Oakland 07436
★ Pres.—Herbert G. Enyart, 6 emp., *Prefabricated metal buildings*.................... (201) 337-6146
Pre-Fab Structures, Inc., 907 Wedgewood Way, Atco 08004
Pres.—Bill Johnson, 10 emp., *Prefabricated aluminum buildings*.................... (856) 768-4257
Tamburri Assocs., 1401 Industrial Hwy., Cinnaminson 08077
Pres.—Phyllis Tamburri, 18 emp., *Steel fabrication & prefabricated steel*.................... (856) 829-4000
Twin Modular Services, Inc., 1001 Lower Landing Rd., Ste. 607, Blackwood 08012
Pres.—Peter Broderick, 3 emp., *Prefabricated metal modular guard houses*.................... (856) 227-0057
Wel-Fab, Inc., 124 Burrs Rd., Mount Holly 08060
Chrm. of the Board & V-P.—Paul J. Elstone, Sr., 18 emp., *Steel fabrication & welding of collapsible* (609) 261-1393

## 3449 Metal work—miscellaneous, nec

Ahle Co., Inc., J. M., 190 William St., Ste. 2-D, South River 08882
Pres.—John Ahle, 29 emp., *Rebar fabrication & distributor of*.................... (732) 238-1700
Computa Base Machining, Inc., 411 N. Grove St., P.O. Box 340, Berlin 08009
Pres.—Augustin Rosado, 14 emp., *Fabrication & precision machining job*.................... (856) 767-9517
Drive-Master Co., Inc., 37 Daniel Rd. West, Fairfield 07004
Pres., CEO—Peter B. Ruprecht, 19 emp., *Wheelchair accessible vans, lifts &*.................... (973) 808-9709
Franklen Sheet Metal Co., Inc., 122 S. Main St., Ocean Grove 07756
Owner & Pres.—Steven Smith, 12 emp., *Roof coping sheet metal fabrication*.................... (732) 988-0808
HarMac Rebar & Steel Corp., 301 Hartle St., Sayreville 08872
Plt. Mgr.—Larry Kuzma, 15 emp., *Steel rebar fabrication*.................... (732) 651-7822
Haydon Corp., 415 Hamberg Tpke., Bldg. D, Wayne 07470
Pres.—Doug Hillman, 65 emp., *Metal struts & baseboards*.................... (973) 904-0800
Meadow Burke Products, 269 Commercial Ave., Palisades Park 07650
Sales Mgr., District—Don Fowler, 4 emp., *Steel reinforcing bars, wire ties &*.................... (201) 242-8989
Men Of Steel Enterprises, LLC, 4319 Route 130, Beverly 08010
Pres.—Robert Vogelbacher, 22 emp., *Rebar fabrication*.................... (877) 732-2728
Metal Management Northeast, Inc., 1 Linden Ave. E., Jersey City 07305
GM—Joe Payaso, 250 emp., *Metal recycling*.................... (201) 577-3200
Metfab Metals, LLC, 560 Freeman St., Orange 07050
Pres.—James Murray, 18 emp., *Metal curtain wall parts, wall panels*.................... (973) 675-7676
NJS Sales Corp., 2840 Mount Ephraim Ave., Camden 08104
Pres.—Lou Cirignano, 15 emp., *Rebar fabrication & distributor of*.................... (856) 619-1119
North Jersey Metal Fabricators, Inc., 130 Ryerson Ave., Ste. 107, Wayne 07470
Pres.—Bill Ecker, 7 emp., *Metal, aluminum, stainless steel &*.................... (973) 305-9830
SAS Stresssteel, Inc., 100 New Dutch Ln., Fairfield 07004
V-P., CFO—Kevin J. Dowling, 20 emp., *Rebar fabrication*.................... (973) 244-0507
Summit Group II, 333 16th St., Carlstadt 07072
Pres.—Tom Klein, 5 emp., *Steel railings, ornamental iron, structural*.................... (201) 460-8888
Tur Machine, LLC, 198 U.S. Highway 206, Ste. 5, Hillsborough 08844
Ptnr.—Zbigniew Richard Rolka, 6 emp., *General machining shop*.................... (908) 874-0235

## 3451 Screw machine products

Accurate Screw Machine Corp., 10 Audrey Pl., P.O. Box 1065, Fairfield 07004
GM—John Everett, 150 emp., *Screw machine products*.................... (973) 244-9200
Advanced Technology Group, Inc., 101 Round Hill Dr., Rockaway 07866
Chrm., Pres.—Li Yuan Tao, 35 emp., *Glass-to-metal hybrid electronic packages*.................... (973) 627-6955
Amark Industries, Inc., 18 Passaic Ave., Fairfield 07004
Pres., Qual. Assur. Mgr.—Mario Salerno, 5 emp., *High precision escomatic screw machine*. (973) 992-8900
BMB Fasteners, Inc., 86 Lackawanna Ave., Ste. 208, Woodland Park 07424
Owner & Pres.—Larry Malone, 8 emp., *Screws, fasteners, bolts, nuts & washers*.................... (973) 256-4010
Carl Stahl Sava Industries, Inc., 4 N. Corporate Dr., P.O. Box 30, Riverdale 07457
CEO—Zdenek A. Fremund, 85 emp., *Corporate headquarters & miniature*.................... (973) 835-0882
CNC Supermatic LLC, 27 Old Beach Glen Rd., Rockaway 07866
Pres.—Irene Kobrynowicz Hunter, 10 emp., *Precision machined components for the*.................... (973) 627-4433
Congruent Machining Co., Inc., 107 Maple Grange Rd., P.O. Box 888, Vernon 07462
Pres.—Jerry Caiafa, 5 emp., *Screw machine products*.................... (973) 764-6767
Cut Mark, Inc., 801 S. Church St., Ste. 6, Mount Laurel 08054
Owner—George Gibson, 7 emp., *Precision & CNC milling & turning job*.................... (856) 234-3428
D & F Screw Machine Products, Inc., 42 West St., East Hanover 07936
Pres.—David Moore, 8 emp., *Screw machine products*.................... (973) 887-1702
Deerfield Machine & Tool Co., 23 Old Beach Glen Rd., Rockaway 07866
Owner—Jeff Coughlan, 2 emp., *Screw machine products*.................... (973) 625-0505
Eastern Machining Corp., 1197 Fries Mill Rd., Franklinville 08322
Pres.—Joe Davis, 5 emp., *Swiss screw machine products & general*.................... (856) 694-3303
ESCO Precision, Inc., 71 Old Camplain Rd., Hillsborough 08844
Pres.—Samy Elkholy, 17 emp., *Screw machine products & metal stampings*.................... (908) 722-0800

S.I.C.

Ferrum Industries, Inc., 735 Commercial Ave., Carlstadt 07072
V-P.—Richard Wolfin, 10 emp., *Screw machine products* .................... (201) 935-1220
Ford Atlantic Fastener Co., Inc., 341 Changebridge Rd., P.O. Box 733, Pine Brook 07058
Pres.—Anthony Innamarato, 40 emp., *Standard & custom fastners, metal stampings*............ (973) 882-1191
Form Cut Industries, Inc., 197 Mount Pleasant Ave., Newark 07104
Pres.—Charles Alberto, 50 emp., *Precision wire forms, leads, pins,* .................... (973) 483-5154
H & H Swiss Screw Machine Products Co., Inc., 1478 Chestnut Ave., Hillside 07205
Pres.—Darryl Stacy, 55 emp., *Precision custom CNC Swiss screw machine*.................... (908) 688-6390
High Point Precision Products, 1 1st St., Sussex 07461
Pres.—Charles Stipo, 20 emp., *Swiss screw machine products* .................... (973) 875-6229
Hi-Grade Products Mfg. Co., 752 Jefferson Ave., P.O. Box 273, Kenilworth 07033
Pres.—Jeffrey Pfingst, 12 emp., *Screw machine products* .................... (908) 245-4133
Howie Mfg. Co., Inc., 1227 Mechanic St., Camden 08104
Pres.—Jo Ann Howie, 3 emp., *Screw machine products* .................... (856) 963-3560
Hudson Mfg. Co., 640 W. 1st Ave., Roselle 07203
Pres.—Albert C. Maglio, 3 emp., *Punches, die buttons & perforators*.................... (908) 241-3880
J & S Precision Co., 16 Medford Evesboro Rd., Medford 08055
Pres.—Stephen Janssen, 50 emp., *Screw machine products* .................... (609) 654-0900
Johnson & Sons, Inc., S., 1 Hardwick St., P.O. Box 66, Belvidere 07823
Pres.—Gus Johnson, 35 emp., *Screw machine products, including CNC*.................... (908) 475-2155
Johnson Engineering, Welton V., 22 N. 26th St., Kenilworth 07033
Owner & Pres.—Paul Damjanovic, 20 emp., *Screw machine products* .................... (908) 241-3100
Kearny Screw Machine Co., 554 Elm St., Kearny 07032
Owner—Otto Carchia, 1 emp., *Screw machine products* .................... (201) 998-4363
Krug Industries Inc., 65 Brown Ave., Springfield 07081
Pres.—Leslie Krug, 2 emp., *Screw machine products, including collets* .................... (973) 467-1040
Maple Machine Co., Inc., Mount Holly Industrial Commons, Unit 9, Mount Holly 08060
Pres.—Ernie Mellon, 6 emp., *Screw machine products & precision* .................... (609) 702-0975
Orion Precision Industries, Inc., 8 Veronica Ave., Somerset 08873
Pres.—John Sztankovits, 45 emp., *Precision Swiss screw machine products* .................... (732) 247-9704
Precision Specialties, 120 Greylock Ave., Belleville 07109
Pres.—Richard Pfuhler, 5 emp., *Threaded inserts for plastics, ultrasonic* .................... (973) 751-7588
Quality Swiss Screw Machine Co., Inc., 849 4th Ave., Elizabeth 07202
Foreman—Juan Monserrate, 4 emp., *Swiss screw machine products* .................... (908) 654-1881
Quality Swiss Screw Machine Co., Inc., 960 Mountain Ave., Mountainside 07092
Pres.—Andrew Cangelosi, 28 emp., *Corporate headquarters & Swiss screw* .................... (908) 654-1881
Salem Mfg. Co., 115 Roosevelt Ave., Belleville 07109
Pres., Sales Mgr.—Jerome M. Lipiec, 8 emp., *Screw machine products* .................... (973) 751-6331
Schmidt Mfg. Co., F. P., 143 Leuning St., South Hackensack 07606
Owner & Pres.—Robert Schmidt, 10 emp., *Screw machine products* .................... (201) 343-4241
Screw Machine Specialties, 50 U.S. Highway 9, Ste. 305, Morganville 07751
Dir., Sales & Mktg.—Avi Tobias, 25 emp., *Precision machined parts for OEMs,* .................... (732) 972-5400
Townsend Machine, Inc., 246 Sykesville Rd., Chesterfield 08515
Pres.—Barclay A. Townsend, 25 emp., *Screw machine products & machining* .................... (609) 298-0400
Valcar Precision Products, Inc., 22 Park Pl., Butler 07405
Pres., Fin., MIS, Opers. & R & D Mgr.—Carl Grossi, 5 emp., *Screw machine parts & CNC*..... (973) 838-7600
Well Tech, Inc., 1 Hardwick St., P.O. Box 66, Belvidere 07823
Pres.—Gustav Johnson, 30 emp., *Screw machine products*.................... (908) 475-4539
West Side Precision Machine Products, Inc., 280 Lincoln Blvd., Middlesex 08846
Pres.—David Gizzi, 5 emp., *Precision machining, including Swiss* .................... (732) 560-9006

## 3452 Bolts, nuts, rivets & washers

Advanced Fastener Industries, 130 Main St., Butler 07405
Pres.—Don Manley, 7 emp., *Industrial machinery, fasteners & cutting* .................... (973) 283-1013
Aerospace Manufacturing Corporation, 80 Van Winkle Ave., P.O. Box 3398, Wallington 07057
Pres.—Al Shafa, 26 emp., *Fasteners for the aerospace industry*.................... (973) 472-2300
Aerospace Nylok, 11 Thomas Rd. S., Hawthorne 07506
Opers. Mgr.—Hans Dorflinger, 24 emp., *Self-locking industrial fasteners*.................... (973) 427-8555
Amerifast Corp., 104 Sylvania Pl., South Plainfield 07080
Pres.—Jim Peightel, 9 emp., *Fasteners* .................... (908) 754-8989
Arrow Fastener Co., LLC, 271 Mayhill St., Saddle Brook 07663
Pres., CEO—Gary DuBoff, 650 emp., *Staplers, staples, glue guns, glues*.................... (201) 843-6900
Astro Tool & Machine Co., Inc., 810 Martin St., Rahway 07065
Pres., R & D Mgr.—Gary Price, 25 emp., *Precision machine tools, including* .................... (732) 382-2450
Captive Fastener Corp., 19 Thornton Rd., Oakland 07436
V-P., Sales—Jim Kinlin, 100 emp., *Metal fasteners* .................... (201) 337-6800
Champion Fasteners, Inc., 707 Smithville Rd., Lumberton 08048
CEO—Aldo Magazzeni, 25 emp., *Welding studs & specialty fasteners* .................... (609) 267-5222
Columbia Nut & Bolt, LLC, 50 Graphic Pl., Moonachie 07074
Pres.—William Laufer, 50 emp., *Fasteners* .................... (201) 641-7600
EZ Sockets, Inc., 5 Cornell Pkwy., Springfield 07081
Pres., CFO—Edward Werner, 25 emp., *Standard & special alloy & stainless* .................... (973) 376-5605
Ford Atlantic Fastener Co., Inc., 341 Changebridge Rd., P.O. Box 733, Pine Brook 07058
Pres.—Anthony Innamarato, 40 emp., *Standard & custom fastners, metal stampings*.................... (973) 882-1191
Form Cut Industries, Inc., 197 Mount Pleasant Ave., Newark 07104
Pres.—Charles Alberto, 50 emp., *Precision wire forms, leads, pins,* .................... (973) 483-5154
HK Metal Craft Mfg. Corp., 35 Industrial Rd., Lodi 07644
Chrm., Pres.—Joshua Hopp, 36 emp., *Metal washers & gaskets, spring washers* .................... (973) 471-7770
Industrial Rivet & Fastener Co., 200 Paris Ave., Northvale 07647
Pres.—Bill Goodman, 60 emp., *Blind, solid, semitubular, collar,* .................... (201) 750-1040
Integrity Precision Products, 7 Reuten Dr., Closter 07624
Pres.—Ken Comorau, 8 emp., *Stainless steel fasteners* .................... (201) 767-0700
Jarrdd.Co, 141 Shreve Ave., Barrington 08007
Pres.—David Farber, 6 emp., *Manufacturer & distributor of military*.................... (856) 310-0100
Kelken-Gold, Inc., 550 Hartle St., Ste. C, Sayreville 08872
Pres.—Ken Ginsky, 4 emp., *Manufacturer & distributor of anchoring* .................... (732) 416-6730
M R L Mfg. Corp., 59 Lee Ave., P.O. Box 8440, Haledon 07508
Pres.—John De Napoli, 17 emp., *Commercial nuts* .................... (973) 790-1744
ND Industries, Inc., 128 Bauer Dr., Ste. 2, Oakland 07436
GM—Bill Lang, 30 emp., *Locking elements on screws* .................... (201) 651-1500
New Jersey Rivet Co., LLC, 1785 Haddon Ave., Camden 08103
Sales Mgr., Inside—Kenneth Landgarten, 10 emp., *Semi-tubular rivets* .................... (856) 963-2237
P & R Fasteners, Inc., 325 Pierce St., Somerset 08873
Pres.—Benjamin Margulies, 60 emp., *Nuts, bolts & fasteners* .................... (732) 302-3600
Pandrol USA L. P., 501 Sharptown Rd., P.O. Box 367, Bridgeport 08014
Pres.—Frank Brady, 45 emp., *Railroad joints & fasteners*.................... (856) 467-3227
Star Stainless Screw Co., Inc. (H Q), 30 W. End Rd., Totowa 07512
Pres.—Bruce Wheeler, 100 emp., *Corporate headquarters; screws* .................... (973) 256-2300
TICO Mfg., Inc., 1044 Industrial Dr., Unit 9, West Berlin 08091
Pres.—Roger Sobradl, 9 emp., *Military, commercial & industrial fasteners*.................... (856) 767-8430
U. S. A. Tolerance Rings, 85 Route 31 N., Pennington 08534
Pres.—Al DeBlasio, 6 emp., *Tolerance rings/elastic shims for relaxation*.................... (609) 745-5000
Unicorp, Inc., 291 Cleveland St., Orange 07050
Pres.—Steven Mercadante, 40 emp., *Precision electronic component hardware* .. (973) 674-1700
Vogelsang Fastener Corp, 1790 Swarthmore Ave., Lakewood 08701
V-P., GM—Dale Stuban, 50 emp., *Slotted, coiled & metric tension pins* .................... (732) 364-0444
W & E Sales Co., Inc., 370 Elizabeth Ave., Newark 07112
GM—R. Carr, 15 emp., *Manufacturer & wholesaler of automotive* .................... (973) 824-2000
W B C Industries, Inc., 625 Central Ave., Westfield 07090
Pres.—Scott Viglianti, 20 emp., *Hook & loop fastening systems*.................... (908) 789-1234
West Side Precision Machine Products, Inc., 280 Lincoln Blvd., Middlesex 08846
Pres.—David Gizzi, 5 emp., *Precision machining, including Swiss* .................... (732) 560-9006
Wm. H. Brewster Jr., Inc., 16 Kulick Rd., Fairfield 07004
Pres.—Salvatore T. Freda, Jr., 8 emp., *Precision flat washers, shims, stampings* .................... (973) 227-1050
ZaGO Mfg. Co., Inc., 21 E. Runyon St., Newark 07114
Pres.—Harvey Rottenstrich, 24 emp., *Self-sealing fasteners, nuts, toggle* .................... (973) 643-6700

## 3462 Forgings—iron & steel

All Metals & Forge Group, LLC, 75 Lane Rd., Fairfield 07004
Pres.—Lewis A. Weiss, 39 emp., *Stainless, nickel, titanium, carbon* .................... (973) 276-5000
Bridgestate Foundry Corp., 175 Jackson Rd., Berlin 08009
Corp. Secy.—Diane Taylor, 10 emp., *Cast iron manhole frames, covers &* .................... (856) 767-0400
Cacciola Iron Works, 65 N. 9th St., Paterson 07522
Pres.—Angelo Cacciola, 4 emp., *Railings*.................... (973) 595-0854
Duferco Steel, Inc. (H Q), 100 Matawan Rd., Ste. 400, Matawan 07747
Pres.—Joe Deverter, 30 emp., *Corporate headquarters; steel slabs* .................... (732) 566-3130
Good Automatic Windlass, Inc., 357 Route 72, Barnegat 08005
Sr. V-P., GM—Thomas J. Ring, 3 emp., *Anchor windlasses for 20-foot to 55-foot*.................... (609) 698-4402
Halkias Gear & Machine Works, 14 Willow St., Bloomfield 07003
Pres., Pers. Mgr.—James Halkias, 4 emp., *Precision gears* .................... (973) 748-4901
Hal-O Mfg. Co., 137 Meeker Ave., Newark 07114
Pres.—Harold Roth, 13 emp., *Lighting components & chains* .................... (973) 824-6122
Koellmann Gear Corp., 8 Industrial Pk., Waldwick 07463
Pres.—Michael Rasovic, 15 emp., *Gear reducers*.................... (201) 447-0200
McWilliams Forge Co., 387 Franklin Ave., Rockaway 07866
Cont.—James Traynor, 80 emp., *Titanium, nickel & alloy steel closed-die* .................... (973) 627-0200
U. S. Drop Forge Corp., Highway 551, P.O. Box 131, Swedesboro 08085
Pres.—Joe Pro, 35 emp., *Steel & iron forgings* .................... (856) 467-0500

## 3463 Forgings—nonferrous

All Metals & Forge Group, LLC, 75 Lane Rd., Fairfield 07004
Pres.—Lewis A. Weiss, 39 emp., *Stainless, nickel, titanium, carbon* .................... (973) 276-5000
Titanium Fabrication Corp., 110 Lehigh Dr., Fairfield 07004
Pres., CEO—Brent Willey, 45 emp., *Custom titanium & reactive metal design*.................... (973) 227-5300

## 3465 Automotive stampings

Infor Metal & Tooling Manufacturing Corporation, 16 Commerce Rd., Cedar Grove 07009
Pres.—Charles Insel, 10 emp., *Contract metal stamping, tool & die* .................... (973) 571-9520

## 3469 Metal stampings, nec

A. K. Stamping Co., Inc., 1159 Highway 22 E., Mountainside 07092
CEO—Arthur Kurz, 45 emp., *Metal stampings & circuit board brackets*.................... (908) 232-7300
Alben Metal Products, 11 Iowa Ave., Paterson 07503
Pres., Fin. & MIS Mgr.—Al Vollaro, 4 emp., *Metal stampings & CNC machining job* .................... (973) 279-8891
American Aluminum Co. (AMALCO), 230 Sheffield St., Mountainside 07092
Pres.—Andrew Brucker, 60 emp., *Metal fabrication, including hydroforming*.................... (908) 233-3500
Array Mfg. Tech Corp., 100 Arlington Ave., Kearny 07032
Pres.—Frank Garcia, 7 emp., *Metal stampings* .................... (201) 997-1333
Basic Tool & Die Corp., 752 Ramsey Ave., Hillside 07205
Pres.—James Tollar, 4 emp., *Metal stampings & press brake dies*.................... (908) 688-9155
BeCu Manufacturing Co., Inc., 2347 Beryllium Rd., Scotch Plains 07076
Pres.—Stephan Hoeckele, 24 emp., *Precision metal stampings, including* .................... (908) 233-3343
Bel-Tech Stamping, Inc., 26 Industrial Rd., Ste. A, West Milford 07480
Pres.—Steve Baun, 7 emp., *Metal stampings*.................... (973) 728-8229
Bigelow Components Corp., 74 Diamond Rd., Springfield 07081
Owner & Pres.—C. Brett Harman, 20 emp., *Precision miniature cold-headed & stamped* ...... (973) 467-1200
Bihler Of America, Inc., 85 Industrial Dr., Phillipsburg 08865
CEO—Maxine Nordmeyer, 235 emp., *Corporate headquarters & metal stampings*.................... (908) 213-9001
Boyle Tool & Die Co., Inc., 135 Crown Point Rd., Thorofare 08086
Pres.—Thomas J. Boyle, 9 emp., *Metal stampings & tool & die job shop*.................... (856) 853-1818
C & C Metal Products Corp., 456 Nordhoff Pl., P.O. Box 7300, Englewood 07631
V-P., Secy.—Mitchell Chalfin, 50 emp., *Corporate headquarters & metal stampings* .................... (201) 569-7300
Camtec Industries, Inc., 28 Saddle Ridge Rd., Colts Neck 07722
Pres.—Anthony Mauro, 16 emp., *CNC machining job shop, including metal* .................... (732) 332-9800
Carl Stahl Sava Industries, Inc., 4 N. Corporate Dr., P.O. Box 30, Riverdale 07457
CEO—Zdenek A. Fremund, 85 emp., *Corporate headquarters & miniature* .................... (973) 835-0882
Carter Mfg. Co., Inc., 55 Anderson Ave., Moonachie 07074
Pres.—John Scholz, 30 emp., *Metal stampings* .................... (201) 935-0770
Clover Stamping Co., Inc., 60 Spruce St., Paterson 07501
Pres., Sales Mgr.—Bob Kellenberger, 10 emp., *Metal stampings & tool & die job shop* .......... (973) 278-4888
Coining Mfg., LLC, 35 Monhegen, Clifton 07013
GM—Courtney Cromley, 65 emp., *Metal stampings* .................... (973) 253-0500
Coining, Inc., 15 Mercedes Dr., Montvale 07645
V-P., Sales & Mktg.—Julie Scelzo, 75 emp., *Preformed solder & brazing* .................... (201) 791-4020
Cold Headed Fasteners, Inc., 401 Creek Rd., P.O. Box 5488, Delanco 08075
Pres., Fin., Opers. & R & D Mgr.—Charles Massey, 6 emp., *Metal fasteners* .................... (856) 461-3244
Coltwell Industries, Inc., 55 Winans Ave., Cranford 07016
V-P., Sales & Mktg.—Anthony Bengivenga, 15 emp., *Custom & standard extruded aluminum* (908) 276-7600
Co-Planar, Inc., 88 Ford Rd, P.O. Box 1115, Denville 07834
Pres.—James Cote, 28 emp., *Metal & polyester film stampings* .................... (973) 625-3500
Diamond Die Cutters & Embossers, 629 Grove St., 6th Fl., Jersey City 07310
GM—Moon Mui, 15 emp., *Die cutting, metal stamping & embossing*.................... (201) 876-8540
Durex, Inc., 5 Stahuber Ave., Union 07083
Pres., CEO—Robert Denholtz, 150 emp., *Metal stampings, sheet metal fabrication*.................... (908) 688-0800
EIC Industry Group Corp. (H Q), 53 Green Pond Rd., Ste. 3, Rockaway 07866
Pres.—John Ni, 5 emp., *Corporate headquarters; custom components* .................... (973) 983-1988
Electro Magnetic Products, Inc., 355 Crider Ave., Moorestown 08057
Pres.—Eric Mason, 40 emp., *Metal stampings, transformer & motor* .................... (856) 235-3011
Electronic Mfg. Co., 71 Newark Way, Maplewood 07040
Pres.—Martin Peterson, 25 emp., *Metal stampings & CNC turning & milling*.................... (973) 762-1300
Elray Mfg. Co., Inc., 17 Liberty St., Glassboro 08028
Pres.—Ed Stopper, 27 emp., *Metal stampings* .................... (856) 881-1936
ESCO Precision, Inc., 71 Old Camplain Rd., Hillsborough 08844
Pres.—Samy Elkholy, 17 emp., *Screw machine products & metal stampings* .................... (908) 722-0800

Excel Die Corp., 19 Grant St., Linden 07036
Pres.—Hanna Krysa, 4 emp., *Metal stamping, millwork & tool & die* ........ (908) 587-2606
F & M Machine Co., Inc., 751 Lexington Ave., Kenilworth 07033
Pres., Plt. Mgr.—Dick Rutledge, 6 emp., *Metal stamping & machining job shop* ........ (908) 245-8830
Ford Atlantic Fastener Co., Inc., 341 Changebridge Rd., P.O. Box 733, Pine Brook 07058
Pres.—Anthony Innamarato, 40 emp., *Standard & custom fastners, metal stampings* ........ (973) 882-1191
General Stamping Co., 451 E. Main St., Denville 07834
Pres.—Damon Dato, 19 emp., *Precision metal stamping* ........ (973) 627-9500
General Wire & Stamping Co., Inc., 1 Emery Ave., Unit 3, Randolph 07869
Pres.—Kenneth J. Kelly, 12 emp., *Wire forms & metal stampings* ........ (973) 366-8080
Groupe SEB USA, 2121 Eden Rd., Millville 08332
Sr. V-P., Hum. Res.—Martin Falkenberg, 210 emp., *Cookware & small appliances* ........ (856) 825-6300
H T Stamping, 19 Gardner Rd., Ste. C, Fairfield 07004
Pres.—Thomas Schall, 20 emp., *Metal stampings & tool & die job shop* ........ (973) 227-4858
Hammer Mfg. Co., Inc., 417 Commerce Rd., P.O. Box 1340, Linden 07036
Pres.—William J. Fig, 35 emp., *Metal stampings & light mechanical* ........ (908) 862-1730
Hap Engraving Ltd., 106 Windsor Way, Berkeley Heights 07922
Manager—Shane Levin, 15 emp., *Sculpture engraving, embossing, metal* ........ (201) 223-4800
Heyco Products, Inc., 1800 Industrial Way N., Toms River 08755
Pres.—Bill Jemison, Jr., 150 emp., *Plastic electrical parts, metal stampings* ........ (732) 286-4336
Highland Metal Products, Inc., 153 E. Highland Pkwy., Roselle 07203
Pres., Fin. & Sales Mgr.—Ivan Clark, 10 emp., *Metal stampings* ........ (908) 245-4848
Hillside Spinning & Stamping Co., Inc., 1060 Commerce Ave., Union 07083
Admn. Mgr.—George Thomas, 20 emp., *Metal stampings* ........ (908) 964-3080
Infor Metal & Tooling Manufacturing Corporation, 16 Commerce Rd., Cedar Grove 07009
Pres.—Charles Insel, 10 emp., *Contract metal stamping, tool & die* ........ (973) 571-9520
Interplex NAS Inc., Beta Div., 232 Pegasus Ave., Northvale 07647
Dir., Bus. Dev.—Joe Praino, 70 emp., *Metal stampings & plastic injection* ........ (201) 367-1300
J. J. Orly, Inc., 20 Commerce Dr., Ste. 128, Cranford 07016
Pres.—William Herbert, 5 emp., *Deep-drawn stainless steel, cold-rolled* ........ (908) 276-9212
J.R.M. Products, Inc., 701 Locust St., Keyport 07735
Pres.—Robert Wichowski, 4 emp., *American-made custom steel, stainless* ........ (732) 495-3092
Jan Fence Co., Inc., 4 Industrial Rd., Pompton Plains 07444
Pres.—Robert Corrao, 15 emp., *Custom industrial, residential & security* ........ (973) 694-4055
Jet Precision Metal, Inc., 7 Schoon Ave., Hawthorne 07506
Pres.—Nick DiMaggio, 37 emp., *Punching, forming, welding & precision* ........ (973) 423-4350
Jewelry Tool & Die Co., 4 Mark Rd., Ste. G, Kenilworth 07033
Owner—Peter Ehmann, 3 emp., *Jewelry, metal stampings & dies* ........ (908) 686-3500
JMK Tool, Die & Mfg. Co., Inc., 19 W. Passaic St., Rochelle Park 07662
Pres.—John Kristofich, 4 emp., *Metal stampings & tool & die job shop* ........ (201) 845-4710
Jordan Mfg., LLC, 28 Randazzo Rd., P.O. Box 226, Lafayette 07848
GM—Gary Wilson, 8 emp., *Metal stampings, tooling, CNC turning* ........ (973) 383-8363
JP Rotella Co., Inc., 20 E. Barbour St., Haledon 07508
Pres.—John Rotella, Jr., 7 emp., *Electronic components, including subassemblie* ........ (973) 942-2559
Kaupp & Sons, Inc., C. B., 6 Newark Way, Maplewood 07040
CEO—Clem Kaupp, Jr., 25 emp., *Corporate headquarters & precision* ........ (973) 761-4000
Laeger Metal Spinning Co., Inc., 1514 E. Elizabeth Ave., Linden 07036
GM—Leo Zuckerman, 5 emp., *Hydroforming & metal stampings* ........ (908) 925-5530
Loving Pets Corp., 110 Melrich Rd., Ste. 1, Cranbury 08512
Owner—Eric Abbey, 20 emp., *Natural pet treats & accessories, including* ........ (609) 655-3700
Magnetic Metals Corp., 1900 Hayes Ave., Camden 08105
Pres.—Frank A. Raneiro, 60 emp., *Metal stampings & high-grade nickel* ........ (856) 964-7842
Manutech, Inc., 29 State St., P.O.Box 758, Elmer 08318
Pres.—Edward P. Deinarowicz, 4 emp., *Metal stampings & general machining* ........ (856) 358-6136
MICRO, 140 Belmont Dr., Somerset 08873
Chrm.—Frank J. Semcer, Sr., 350 emp., *Complete medical devices & components* ........ (732) 302-0800
Minitec Corp., 158 W. Clinton St., Ste. V, Dover 07801
Owner & Pres.—Scott Mindlin, 4 emp., *Metal stampings* ........ (973) 989-1426
Monroe Tool & Die, Inc., 197 Sharp Rd., Williamstown 08094
Pres., CFO—Steven Kennedy, 8 emp., *Metal stampings & tool & die job shop* ........ (856) 629-5164
National Mfg. Co., Inc., 12 River Rd., Chatham 07928
Pres., CEO—Robert Staudinger, 190 emp., *Deep-drawn & shallow-drawn metal stampings* .. (973) 635-8846
NEAC, Inc., 526 Pacific Ave., #2202, Atlantic City 08401
Pres.—Joel H. Miller, 5 emp., *Contract manufacturing of metal & plastic* ........ (908) 903-9100
O & C Die Cutters & Finishers, 16 Andrews Dr., West Paterson 07424
Pres.—Odit Ramnarian, 20 emp., *Die cutting, foil stamping & mounting* ........ (973) 890-7778
Omega Precision Corp., 1384 Pompton Ave., Ste. 3, Cedar Grove 07009
Pres.—Lawrence Niebling, 20 emp., *Metal stampings* ........ (973) 256-3422
P D Q Electronics Components Co., Inc., 1113 Tiller Ave., Beachwood 08722
Owner, Pres. & R & D Mgr.—Thomas Blazak, 9 emp., *Metal stampings* ........ (732) 281-0025
Paramount Products, Inc., 1104 Industrial Pkwy., Brick 08724
Pres.—H. C. Vogel, 10 emp., *Custom, precision & drawn stampings* ........ (732) 458-9200
Par-Metal, Inc., 29 Ewing Ave., North Arlington 07031
Pres.—John Ango, 10 emp., *Steel & aluminum electronic enclosures* ........ (201) 955-0800
Peterson Bros. Mfg., 10 Baekeland Ave., Middlesex 08846
Pres., Mktg. Mgr.—Gary B. Lewis, 25 emp., *Metal stampings & machine products* ........ (732) 271-8240
Peterson Stamping & Mfg. Co., 75 N. Michigan Ave., P.O. Box 190, Kenilworth 07033
Pres.—Robert Olsen, Sr., 10 emp., *Metal stampings* ........ (908) 241-0900
Phillips Enterprises, Inc., 3600 Sunset Ave., P.O. Box 2286, Asbury Park 07712
Pres.—Joe Phillips, 7 emp., *Wire forming & metal stampings* ........ (732) 493-3191
ProGasket Aerospace & Automotive, LLC, 14 Doty Rd., Haskell 07420
Pres.—Mitch Prodani, 10 emp., *Metal stampings for the aerospace &* ........ (973) 831-4533
Progressive Tool & Mfg. Co., 708 Fairfield Ave., Kenilworth 07033
Pres.—Gunter Heim, 6 emp., *Metal stampings & tool & die job shop* ........ (908) 245-7010
R L R Foil Stamping, LLC, 245 4th St., Passaic 07055
Pres.—Lawrence Vincent, 10 emp., *Foil stampings* ........ (973) 778-9464
R M F Assocs., Inc., 202 Carolyn Rd., Union 07083
V-P.—Michael Rodgers, 140 emp., *Fabricated metal choke & chamber brushes* ........ (908) 687-9355
Rem Services, 310 W. 6th St., Ship Bottom 08008
Owner—Robert Mattner, 1 emp., *Name tags, trophies, small signs &* ........ (609) 494-7760
Ricci Tool & Die Co., 122 Myrtle Ave., Long Branch 07740
Pres.—John Ricci, Sr., 9 emp., *Tool & die job shop, including metal* ........ (732) 222-2777
Roseville Tool & Mfg., 22 Okner Pkwy., Livingston 07039
GM—David Miller, 30 emp., *Metal stampings & tool & die job shop* ........ (973) 992-5405
S H P C, Inc., 187 Christie St., P.O. Box 5328, Newark 07105
Pres. & V-P.—Paul Sacks, 20 emp., *Iron & steel castings & stampings* ........ (973) 589-5242
ScreenTek Mfg. Co., Inc., 220 Franklin Rd., Ste. B, Randolph 07869
Co-Pres., GM—Jay Thompson, 23 emp., *Wire & fiberglass mesh & perforated* ........ (973) 328-2121
Semiconductor Mfg., 5 Troast Ct., Clifton 07011
Pres.—William Pian, 54 emp., *Metal stampings, spheres & wire, including* ........ (973) 478-2880
Short Run Stamping Co., Inc., The, 925 E. Linden Ave., Linden 07036
Pres.—Randy Speir, 26 emp., *Corporate headquarters & custom metal* ........ (908) 862-1070

Sofield Mfg. Co., Inc., 2 Main St., Ridgefield Park 07660
Pres.—Harold Sofield, 7 emp., *Metal stampings* ........ (201) 943-1118
Sowa Corp., 223 Murray St., Newark 07114
Pres.—Adam Garstka, 4 emp., *Metal stampings* ........ (973) 297-0008
Stampex Tool&Die, Inc., 75 4th Ave., Haskell 07420
Owner—Thomas Nieshalla, 6 emp., *Precision metal stampings, including* ........ (973) 839-4040
Stamping.com, Inc., 3600 Sunset Ave., Asbury Park 07712
Owner—Charles Molnar, Jr., 3 emp., *Precision metal stampings* ........ (732) 493-4697
Stirrup Metal Products Corp., 215 Emmet St., Newark 07114
Pres.—Todd Stirrup, 20 emp., *Metal stampings & fabrication* ........ (973) 824-7086
Tekmet, LLC, 400 Myrtle Ave., Ste. A, Boonton 07005
Pres.—Richard Polese, 30 emp., *Metal stampings* ........ (973) 376-1700
Thomson Lamination Co., Inc., 504 E. Linwood Ave., Maple Shade 08052
Chrm.—Sterling A. Martin, 100 emp., *Motor laminations & assemblies, including* ........ (856) 779-8521
Topco, Inc., 107 Trumbull St., Elizabeth 07206
Pres.—Martin Gindoff, 60 emp., *Deep drawn metal stampings* ........ (908) 352-6720
Triform Products, Inc., 219 Lafayette St., Paterson 07524
Pres.—Doug Troast, 12 emp., *Powder coating & metal stampings* ........ (973) 278-2042
Tryco Tool & Mfg., Inc., 363 S. Jefferson St., Orange 07050
Owner—Art Melillo, 60 emp., *Metal stampings & dies* ........ (973) 674-6867
Universal Tools & Mfg. Co., 115 Victory Rd., Springfield 07081
Owner, Pres. & CEO—Dorothy Principe, 30 emp., *Tooling & precision deep drawn metal* ........ (973) 379-4193
Weiss-Aug Co. Inc., 220 Merry Ln., East Hanover 07936
CEO—Dieter Weissenrieder, 200 emp., *Custom insert molding, precision metal* ........ (973) 887-7600
Wellbilt Industries, 2 Maple Ave., Linden 07036
Owner & IT Mgr.—Les Zalewski, 15 emp., *Custom metal fabrication & stamping* ........ (908) 486-6002

## 3471 Plating & polishing

A & F Electroplating, Inc., 106 Ashland Ave., West Orange 07052
Pres.—Frank Chabala, 2 emp., *Electroplating* ........ (973) 736-4344
Aerocoat Source, LLC, 11 Morris Ave., Maple Shade 08052
★ Owner—Richard Creek, 15 emp., *Metal coating for aviation applications* ........ (856) 428-8145
Alcaro & Alcaro Plating Co., Inc., 112 Pine St., P.O. Box 1215, Montclair 07042
Pres.—Tony Alcaro, 20 emp., *Electroplating* ........ (973) 746-1200
All American Powder Coating, 2002 Route 9, Toms River 08755
Pres.—Robyn Ciccone, 4 emp., *Blasting & powder coating* ........ (732) 349-7001
All Bright Metal Finishing, LLC, 760 Ramsey Ave., Hillside 07205
Owner—Mario Cerva, 1 emp., *Metal finishing* ........ (908) 206-9411
All Metal Polishing & Plating, Inc., 23 George St., Newark 07105
Pres.—Ailton Lima, 10 emp., *Metal polishing, plating, powder coating* ........ (973) 589-8070
American Electroplating Co., 342 Lincoln Ave., Hawthorne 07506
Pres., V-P. & Secy-Treas.—Glenn M. Mulzet, 6 emp., *Electroplating* ........ (973) 427-2300
Andarn Electro Service, Inc., 72 Michigan Ave., Paterson 07503
Pres., CFO—Raman D. Patel, 30 emp., *Aluminum anodizing, including type* ........ (973) 523-6334
Art Metalcraft Plating Co., Inc., 529 S. 2nd St., Camden 08103
Pres.—Roger Dolente, 12 emp., *Metal plating* ........ (856) 365-0001
Automatic Plating, Inc., 3410 Jessup Rd., P.O. Box 54, West Deptford 08086
Pres.—Ralph Dreyfuss, 10 emp., *Metal finishing* ........ (856) 845-7323
B & B Electroplating Co., 559 Pennsylvania Ave., Linden 07036
Owner & Co-Pres.—Russell Thistle, 15 emp., *Electroplating, including tin, silver* ........ (908) 925-5044
B & M Finishers, Inc., 201 S. 31st St., Kenilworth 07033
Pres.—Robert Bramson, 30 emp., *Aluminum anodizing & colored & embossed* ........ (908) 241-5640
Becker Plating, Inc., 121 Highway 35 N., Neptune 07753
Pres.—Norman Becker, 2 emp., *Electroplating* ........ (732) 775-8945
BeCu Manufacturing Co., Inc., 2347 Beryllium Rd., Scotch Plains 07076
Pres.—Stephan Hoeckele, 24 emp., *Precision metal stampings, including* ........ (908) 233-3343
Brass Shop, Inc., 611 Central Ave., Westfield 07090
Pres.—Frank Giannone, 2 emp., *Rebuilt brass lighting, lamp restoration* ........ (908) 232-2161
Bridgeview Industrial Finishers, Inc., 241 Terrace Blvd., Voorhees 08043
Pres.—Nancy Wood, 9 emp., *Metal finishing, powder coating & silk* ........ (856) 768-3624
CMF Limited, Inc., 599 Ingham Ave., P.O. Box 5989, Trenton 08638
Owner & Fin. Mgr.—Jerry Donahue, 25 emp., *Full-service paint finishing, including* ........ (609) 695-3600
Cramer Plating, Inc., 4 Hoyt Ln., Belvidere 07823
Pres.—David Cramer, 25 emp., *Metal finishing* ........ (908) 453-2887
D. F. Enterprise, LLC, 3254 S. Black Horse Pike, Williamstown 08094
Owner & Pres.—Scott Richardson, 2 emp., *Industrial metal coatings, hard chrome* ........ (856) 875-1777
Dayton Grey Corp., 1008 1st Ave., Asbury Park 07712
Ptnr.—Hal Levenstein, 7 emp., *Metal finishing, powder coating, plating* ........ (732) 869-0060
Deptford Plating, Route 41 & Dein Ave., P.O. Box 5056, Deptford 08096
Lab Mgr.—Karen DeBellis, 13 emp., *Metal plating* ........ (856) 227-1144
Diamond Brite Metal Processing, 333 Cedar Ave., Ste. 1, Middlesex 08846
Pres.—George Karpus, 10 emp., *Metal polishing of pipe, strip, plate* ........ (732) 564-1164
Diamond Hard Chromium Co., Inc., 463 NJ Railroad Ave., Newark 07114
Pres.—Adolf Dobbs, 2 emp., *Hard chrome plating* ........ (973) 824-9412
Duro Plating Co., Inc., 273 Kaighns Ave., Camden 08103
Pres.—Joe Minessale, 3 emp., *Metal plating & finishing* ........ (856) 963-4967
Elkem, Inc., 443 County Rd., Cliffwood 07721
Pres.—Thomas W. Kent, 6 emp., *Gold, silver, tin, copper, nickel &* ........ (732) 566-1700
Evonik Corporation (H Q), 299 Jefferson Rd., Parsippany 07054
Pres.—John Rolando, 421 emp., *Corporate headquarters; industrial* ........ (973) 929-8000
Extreme Painting & Powder Coating, LLC, 944 Reeves Ave., Camden 08105
Pres.—Mike Pfeiffer, 8 emp., *Metal finishing & powder coating* ........ (856) 541-8733
Finas Finishing, Inc., 50 Stacy Haines Rd., Lumberton 08048
Pres.—John Fina, 8 emp., *Metal & plastic screen printing, industrial* ........ (609) 267-4836
Foley Co., 40 Pier Ln. W., Fairfield 07004
Pres.—Bill Hines, 2 emp., *Metal finishing* ........ (973) 575-8338
Galaxy Glass & Stone, 277 Fairfield Rd., P.O. Box 10154, Fairfield 07004
Pres., CEO—Eugene M. Negrin, 35 emp., *Custom & decorative architectural glass* ........ (973) 575-3440
General Magnaplate Corp., 1331 U.S. Route 1, Linden 07036
CEO & Board Chair—Candida Aversenti, 50 emp., *Corporate headquarters & industrial* ........ (908) 862-6200
Globe Plating, Inc., 220 Miller St., Newark 07114
Pres.—Michael Maykish, 6 emp., *Metal finishing & plating* ........ (973) 623-1116
Haward Corporation, 29 Porete Ave., North Arlington 07031
Pres.—Dean Ward, Jr., 42 emp., *Metal finishing, including electropolishing* ........ (201) 991-8777
Hill Cross Co., Inc., 543 56th St., P.O. Box 60, West New York 07093
Pres., CFO—Christopher C. Hammer, 8 emp., *Electroplating* ........ (201) 864-3393
Ideal Plating & Polishing Co., 681 Main St., Bldg. 39, P.O. Box 100, Belleville 07109
Pres.—Ronald Knigge, 5 emp., *Electroplating* ........ (973) 759-5559
Imperial Electro Plating, 52 Park Ave., Lyndhurst 07071
Pres.—Fred Englehardt, 20 emp., *Electroplating* ........ (201) 438-9450
Independence Plating Corp., 107 Alabama Ave., Paterson 07503
Pres., GM—Ron Knigge, 10 emp., *Plating, including anodizing & electroless* ........ (973) 523-1776

© Copyright 2015 Manufacturers' News, Inc.


Industrial Hard Chromium Co., 7 Rome St., Newark 07105
V-P.—Craig Foote, 16 emp., *Chrome plating* ... (973) 344-2265

Inrad Optics, Inc., 181 Legrand Ave., Northvale 07647
Chrm.—Jan Winston, 65 emp., *OEM custom optics, laser accessories* ... (201) 767-1910

International Micro Industries, Inc., 1951 Old Cuthbert Rd., Bldg. 404, Cherry Hill 08034
Pres., CEO—Christopher N. Angelucci, 23 emp., *Wafer electroplating & bumping & contract* (856) 616-0051

Isometric Micro Finishing Coating, 122 James St., Edison 08820
Pres.—Roy Leo, 6 emp., *Metal coating & tool & die polishing* ... (732) 906-8070

LazyMan Mfg., 616 Hardwick St., P.O. Box 327, Belvidere 07823
Pres., CFO—Brian D. Sadowski, 15 emp., *Gas barbecue grills & sheet metal fabrication* ... (908) 475-5315

Little Falls Alloys, Inc., 189 Caldwell Ave., Paterson 07501
Chrm. of the Board—Vincent Jim Sacco, 30 emp., *Copper base, bare, round, flat & square* .. (973) 278-1666

Manco Plating, Inc., 390 Park Ave., P.O. Box 7025, Newark 07107
Pres.—Luis Garcia, 12 emp., *Electroplating* ... (973) 485-6800

Mara Polishing & Plating Corp., 105-107 W. Peddie St., Newark 07112
Ptnr.—Louis Galarza, 4 emp., *Metal plating & polishing* ... (973) 242-0800

Master Metal Polishing Corp., 57 Wood St., Paterson 07520
Pres.—Jeffrey Almeyda, 15 emp., *Metal finishing, anodizing, passivation* ... (973) 684-0119

Mastercraft Electroplating, 801 Magnolia Ave., Elizabeth 07201
Owner—Desmond Naraine, 6 emp., *Vinyl record molds & electroplating* ... (908) 354-4404

Metal Cutting Corp., 89 Commerce Rd., Cedar Grove 07009
Ex. V-P.—Joshua Jablons, 65 emp., *Burr-free cut-off tight-tolerance metal* ... (973) 239-1101

Metal Graphics, Inc., 49 Empire St., Newark 07114
Pres.—Peter Parmar, 9 emp., *Metal finishing* ... (973) 242-0300

Metal Masters, 1 Lower Oak Grove Rd., Frenchtown 08825
Owner—James Sherron, 5 emp., *Production-scale & custom metal finishing* ... (908) 996-2555

Microcast Technologies Corp., 1611 W. Elizabeth Ave., Linden 07036
Pres.—Dean Fuschetti, 120 emp., *Metal plating, plastic injection molding* ... (908) 523-9503

Miller & Sons, Inc., 24 Belleville Ave., Belleville 07109
Ptnr. & V-P.—Edward Miller, 10 emp., *Electroplating, including anodizing* ... (973) 759-6445

Mold Polishing Co., Inc., 45 North Ave., P. O. Box 96, Garwood 07027
Pres.—Joseph Guerrero, 4 emp., *Mold polishing* ... (908) 518-9191

National Metal Finishings Corp., Inc., 897 South Ave., P.O. Box 486, Middlesex 08846
Pres.—Lou Fahsbender, 12 emp., *Chill rolls, including design, overlay* ... (732) 752-7770

Norton & Son, Inc., 148 E. 5th St., Bayonne 07002
V-P., Mfg.—Ed Norton III, 100 emp., *Architecural coatings* ... (201) 437-0770

P C R Technologies, Inc., 26 Chapin Rd., Unit 1111, Pine Brook 07058
Pres.—Mark Vanzini, 9 emp., *High-speed CNC machining of metals* ... (973) 882-0017

Paramount Metal Finishing Co., 1515 W. Elizabeth Ave., Linden 07036
Pres.—Michael Fuschetti, 130 emp., *Electroless nickel, bright tin, silver* ... (908) 862-0772

Polished Metals Ltd., 487 Hillside Ave., Ste. 5, Hillside 07205
V-P. & Sales Mgr.—David Lazarus, 60 emp., *Architectural & ornamental metal polishing* ... (908) 688-1188

Precision Metal Machining, Inc., 800 Central Blvd., Ste. C, Carlstadt 07072
Pres.—Pat Fanicelli, 40 emp., *General machining job shop, including* ... (201) 843-7427

Productive Industrial Finishing, 103 American Way, Voorhees 08043
Pres.—Hal Gilham, 7 emp., *Metal finishing, powder coating & painting* ... (856) 427-9646

Quality Metal Finishing Corp., 80 George St., 1st Fl., Paterson 07503
Pres.—Mark Leonardis, 25 emp., *Metal finishing* ... (973) 345-0963

Quick Strip, 1 Randolph St., Carteret 07008
Pres.—Larry Fauci, 1 emp., *Media blasting & powder coating for* ... (732) 969-3268

Redyref Co., 100 Kenner Ct., Riverdale 07457
Pres.—William Pymm, 35 emp., *Touchscreen building directory, interactive* ... (718) 784-3690

Reflective Metals, Inc., 1001 Hopewell Ave., Ocean 07712
Pres.—Joseph Lodato, 4 emp., *Architectural metal finishing & polishing* ... (732) 918-7490

Rennie Mfg. & Metal Finishing Co., Inc., 12-14 Rennie Pl., P.O. Box 285, Lodi 07644
Pres.—Alan Kessinger, 12 emp., *Metal finishing* ... (973) 773-9175

S & P Metal Finishing Corp., 185 Oakland St., Trenton 08618
Pres.—Suresh Patel, 6 emp., *Mechanical zinc, cadmium & tin plating* ... (609) 393-4833

Servometer-PMG, LLC, 501 Little Falls Rd., Cedar Grove 07009
Chrm.—Tony Penchuk, 72 emp., *Company headquarters & custom miniature* ... (973) 785-4630

Spray Coat Finishing Co., Inc., 1125 Kaighn Ave., Camden 08103
Pres.—Chris Brown, 5 emp., *Electronic component coating & furniture* ... (856) 541-0950

Stuart Steel Protection Corp., 411 Elizabeth Ave., Somerset 08873
Pres.—Gordon Stuart, 20 emp., *Corrosion control anodes & related* ... (732) 469-5544

Suffern Plating Co., 210 Garibaldi Ave., P.O. Box 755, Lodi 07644
GM—Carlos Arguello, 25 emp., *Nickel, bronze & brass plating* ... (973) 473-4404

T R B Electro Corp., 6 Morris St., P.O. Box 840, Paterson 07501
Pres., CFO—Raman D. Patel, 35 emp., *Metal plating* ... (973) 278-9014

Tolan Machinery Co., Inc./Tolan Polishing Corp., 164 Franklin Ave., P.O. Box 695, Rockaway 07866
Pres.—John Tolpa, 45 emp., *Stainless steel & nickel alloy pressure* ... (973) 983-7212

Tomken Plating Co., Inc., 625 Pear St., P.O. Box 2323, Riverton 08077
Pres.—Thomas H. Kennedy, 3 emp., *Hard chrome plating* ... (856) 829-0607

Tulenko Enterprises, LLC, 176 Franklin Ave., Rockaway 07866
Owner, Fin. & R & D Mgr.—Eric A. Tulenko, 9 emp., *Structural & architectural metal sandblasting* (973) 453-6699

United States Spray Finishing Co., Inc., 70 Blanchard St., Newark 07105
Ptnr.—Brad Newton, 9 emp., *Metal finishing* ... (973) 589-3490

United Support Solutions, Inc., 134 Sand Park Rd., Cedar Grove 07009
Pres.—Joe Ostering, 80 emp., *Sheet metal fabrication, AWS & robotic* ... (973) 857-2298

Vanguard Research Industries, 239 Saint Nicholas Ave., South Plainfield 07080
Chrm.—Harry Sica, 24 emp., *Metal electroplating* ... (908) 753-2770

## 3479 Metal coating & allied services, nec

A & A Co., Inc., 2700 S. Clinton Ave., South Plainfield 07080
Pres.—R. Stewart Brunhouse, Jr., 19 emp., *Metal, ceramic, cermet & hard face* ... (908) 561-2378

A-1 J D K Specialties, 1 Millstream Rd., Cream Ridge 08514
Owner—Gary Conk, Sr., 1 emp., *Plastic & metal trophies, plaques &* ... (732) 928-9495

Abbey/Watchung, LLC, 16 N. 26th St., Kenilworth 07033
Pres. & Member—Margaret A. Beute, 5 emp., *Film, archival & vinyl laminating,* ... (908) 241-7717

ABCO Die Casters, Inc., 39 Tompkins Point Rd., Newark 07114
Pres.—Joseph R. Vitollo, 70 emp., *Die casting & powder coating* ... (973) 624-7030

Acme Engraving Co., Inc., 19-37 Delaware Ave., P.O. Box 1657, Passaic 07055
Pres., CEO—Roy Murat, 5 emp., *Gravure & rotary engraving* ... (973) 778-0885

Acme Mfg. & Coating Co., 900 Port Reading Ave., P.O. Box 70, Port Reading 07064
Pres.—Richard Morrone, 5 emp., *Powder coating of architectural metalwork* ... (732) 541-2800

Aerocoat Source, LLC, 11 Morris Ave., Maple Shade 08052
★ Owner—Richard Creek, 15 emp., *Metal coating for aviation applications* ... (856) 428-8145

All American Powder Coating, 2002 Route 9, Toms River 08755
Pres.—Robyn Ciccone, 4 emp., *Blasting & powder coating* ... (732) 349-7001

All Metal Polishing & Plating, Inc., 23 George St., Newark 07105
Pres.—Ailton Lima, 10 emp., *Metal polishing, plating, powder coating* ... (973) 589-8070

All Nu Trophy & Screen Printing, 243 Teaneck Rd., Ridgefield Park 07660
Owner—Alan Jones, 13 emp., *Plastic & textile screen printing &* ... (201) 807-0808

All Star Awards & Trophies, Inc., 866 Haddon Ave., Collingswood 08108
Pres.—Mary Anne Sonsini, 4 emp., *Trophies & awards, including engraving* ... (856) 858-6600

All State Medal Co., Inc., 16 Adams Pl., Lodi 07644
Pres.—Richard J. Micucci, Jr., 5 emp., *Standard & laser engraving of trophies* ... (973) 458-1458

All-Star Pro Trophy, 1012 Cox Cro Rd., Ste. 10, Toms River 08755
Owner—Maryanna Forman, 1 emp., *Trophy engraving* ... (732) 364-1188

ALL-STATE LEGAL, 1 Commerce Dr., Cranford 07016
Pres., CEO—Robert H. Busch, 230 emp., *Full-color engraving & printing of* ... (908) 272-0800

Alpha Precision Mold, 8 Roselle St., Linden 07036
Owner—Hugo Daniel Santos, 3 emp., *Custom high-precision plastic molds* ... (908) 587-9090

Alpha Processing Co. Inc., 210 Delawanna Ave., P.O. Box 936, Clifton 07014
Pres.—Richard Jenny, 50 emp., *Metal products painting, powder coating* ... (973) 777-1737

American Galvanizing Co., Inc., 1919 R.R. 54, Folsom 08094
Pres.—John Gregor, 70 emp., *Hot dip galvanizing & value-added fabrication* ... (609) 567-2090

American Image, 45 W. Broad St., Bergenfield 07621
Pres.—John Paragian, 15 emp., *Engraved awards, signs, name badges* ... (201) 384-9200

Arista Trophies & Awards, 25 Portland Ave., Bergenfield 07621
Owner—David Cassens, 3 emp., *Custom & laser engraving of signs,* ... (201) 387-2165

Arrow Shed, LLC, 1 3rd Ave., Haskell 07420
V-P., Hum. Res.—Joanne Trezza, 45 emp., *Steel coating of storage units, panels* ... (973) 835-3200

Athletic Imprinters, Inc., 775 Ashbourne Ave., Lindenwold 08021
Owner, Pres. & CEO—Dennis Tallman, 2 emp., *Embroidery & heat press, tackle twill* ... (856) 346-4545

Atomic Trophies, Inc., 201 Shevchenko Ave., South Plainfield 07080
Pres.—Vijay Sha, 4 emp., *Trophy & plaque assembly, engraving* ... (732) 424-7930

Awards Trophy Co., 611 U.S. Highway 22, Hillside 07205
Owner—Ed Gallo, 5 emp., *Trophies, plaques, pins, medals & advertising* ... (908) 687-5775

B&D Marketing, Inc., 1879 Old Cuthbert Rd., Ste. 21, Cherry Hill 08034
Pres.—Marlene Epworth, 5 emp., *Custom donor recognition wall displays* ... (856) 354-2004

Bannister Co., Inc., 126 N. Main St., Milltown 08850
Pres.—Lionel E. Bannister, 4 emp., *Metal engraving & signs* ... (732) 828-1353

Bel-Art Products, Inc., 661 State Route 23, Wayne 07470
COO—Brad Mahood, 85 emp., *Corporate headquarters & laboratory* ... (973) 694-0500

Boyko's Metal Finishing Co., 100 Poinier St., Newark 07114
Pres.—John Boyko, 30 emp., *Powder coating* ... (973) 623-4254

Bridgeton Trophy & Engraving, 641 Landis Ave., Bridgeton 08302
Owner—Tom D'Agostino, 10 emp., *Engraved trophies, glass etching &* ... (856) 451-9007

Bridgeview Industrial Finishers, Inc., 241 Terrace Blvd., Voorhees 08043
Pres.—Nancy Wood, 9 emp., *Metal finishing, powder coating & silk* ... (856) 768-3624

Brown's Engraving, LLC, 12 Fort Dix Rd., Pemberton 08068
Owner—Roberta Brown, 1 emp., *Metal engraving* ... (609) 894-4443

BWAY Corporation, 6 Litho Rd., Trenton 08638
Plt. Mgr.—Mike Hutchison, 100 emp., *Lithographic printing & metal coating* ... (732) 997-4050

Cincinnati Thermal Spray East, 80 Fadem Rd., Springfield 07081
GM—Scot Crabtree, 28 emp., *Industrial pump & valve components* ... (973) 379-0003

CMF Limited, Inc., 599 Ingham Ave., P.O. Box 5989, Trenton 08638
Owner & Fin. Mgr.—Jerry Donahue, 25 emp., *Full-service paint finishing, including* ... (609) 695-3600

Concept Group, Inc., 380 Cooper Rd., West Berlin 08091
Pres.—Aarne Ried, 16 emp., *Precision vacuum brazing & CNC machining* ... (856) 767-5506

Crown Trophy Co., Inc., 86 North Ave., Garwood 07027
Pres.—Paul Todisco, 4 emp., *Custom engraving of trophies & awards* ... (908) 789-0460

Crown Trophy-River Edge, NJ, 488 Kinderkamack Rd., River Edge 07661
Owner—Chuck Hedbavny, 5 emp., *Awards, rotary & laser engraving, crystal* ... (201) 261-3933

Cumberland Engraving Service, 127 W. Broad St., Bridgeton 08302
Owner—Wayne Rizzo, 2 emp., *Trophy & plaque engraving* ... (856) 451-5052

Curtiss-Wright Corp. (H Q), 10 Waterview Blvd., 2nd Fl., Parsippany 07054
Chrm.—Martin R. Benante, 50 emp., *Corporate headquarters; flow control* ... (973) 541-3700

Custom Engraving, 29 Highland Rd., Colonia 07067
Ptnr.—John Martelle, 2 emp., *Metal trophy engraving* ... (732) 574-1901

D. F. Enterprise, LLC, 3254 S. Black Horse Pike, Williamstown 08094
Owner & Pres.—Scott Richardson, 2 emp., *Industrial metal coatings, hard chrome* ... (856) 875-1777

Dayton Grey Corp., 1008 1st Ave., Asbury Park 07712
Ptnr.—Hal Levenstein, 7 emp., *Metal finishing, powder coating, plating* ... (732) 869-0060

Deborah Sales, LLC, 109 Meeker Ave., Newark 07114
Pres.—Jacira Rei, 2 emp., *Metal imprinting, advertising specialties* ... (973) 344-8466

Du-Mor Blade Co., Inc., 1002 Union Landing Rd., Cinnaminson 08077
CEO—Elaine M. Goralski, 25 emp., *Alloy & steel machine tool blades for* ... (856) 829-9384

Engraved Images, Route 202 & Demun Pl., P.O. Box 966, Far Hills 07931
Owner—Heidi Gammon, 5 emp., *Offset & color printing & engraving* ... (908) 234-0323

Engraver's Bench & Greek Unique, Inc., 1212 Raymond Blvd., Newark 07102
Owner & Pres.—Willie J. Williams, 3 emp., *Metal, wood, plastic & glass engraving* ... (973) 297-1810

Engraving Services Of New Jersey, 804 Columbia Rd., Toms River 08753
Owner—Richard Corbo, 4 emp., *Metal engraving* ... (732) 341-0170

Extreme Painting & Powder Coating, LLC, 944 Reeves Ave., Camden 08105
Pres.—Mike Pfeiffer, 8 emp., *Metal finishing & powder coating* ... (856) 541-8733

Farrier Sporting Goods, Inc., Godwin & Crescent Aves., Wyckoff 07481
Pres.—Charles Coleman, 4 emp., *Sports & athletic equipment, footwear* ... (201) 891-9520

Finas Finishing, Inc., 50 Stacy Haines Rd., Lumberton 08048
Pres.—John Fina, 8 emp., *Metal & plastic screen printing, industrial* ... (609) 267-4836

Fischer Laser Marking, Inc., 384 Otterhole Rd., West Milford 07480
Owner & Pres.—Sharon Fischer, 4 emp., *Laser engraving & laser marking job* ... (973) 616-4696

Foster Engraving and Laser Co., 174 S. Main St., Ste. B, Hackensack 07601
Pres.—Giovanni Osorio, 5 emp., *Laser, mechanical, YAG & CO2 engraving* ... (201) 489-5979

Franklin Stamp & Sign Co., 543 Somerset St., Ste. 1, Somerset 08873
Co-Pres.—Harry Weber, Jr., 3 emp., *Rubber stamps, vinyl, plastic, color* ... (732) 846-9235

G & R Graphics, Inc., 303 Irvington Ave., South Orange 07079
Pres.—Robert Gomez, 5 emp., *Rubber stamps, embossing seals, signs* ... (973) 313-2200

Garden State Awards, 3516 John F. Kennedy Blvd., Jersey City 07307
Pres.—Michael Sky, 5 emp., *Trophy & award engraving* ... (201) 795-9420

Garden State Engraving, 126 Perrine Ave., Piscataway 08854
Owner, Fin. & MIS Mgr.—Linda S. Backovsky, 1 emp., *Engraved interior, exterior, desk &* ... (732) 463-0060

General Plastics Corp., 55 La France Ave., Bloomfield 07003
Pres.—Robert Scher, 13 emp., *Fluoropolymer coatings & liquid & powder* ... (973) 748-5500

Globe Plating, Inc., 220 Miller St., Newark 07114
Pres.—Michael Maykish, 6 emp., *Metal finishing & plating* ... (973) 623-1116

Gough Engraving & Advertising Specialties, 1745 N. Olden Avenue Ext., Ewing 08638
Owner—Kathleen Gough, 4 emp., *Brass & plastic engraving, award plaques* ... (609) 882-8700

Graphix Integrated, Inc., 971 Leonardville Rd., Atlantic Highlands 07716
Prodn. Mgr.—Alex Kreymerman, 4 emp., *Giclee printing, shadow boxes, laser* ... (732) 872-8282

Hap Engraving Ltd., 106 Windsor Way, Berkeley Heights 07922
Manager—Shane Levin, 15 emp., *Sculpture engraving, embossing, metal* ... (201) 223-4800

Haward Corporation, 29 Porete Ave., North Arlington 07031
Pres.—Dean Ward, Jr., 42 emp., *Metal finishing, including electropolishing* ... (201) 991-8777

Hero's Salute Awards Co., 1875 State Route 23, Wayne 07470
Pres.—Robert Terry, 10 emp., *Awards, trophies, signs, banners, flags* ... (973) 696-5085

IHI Ionbond, 200 Roundhill Dr., Rockaway 07866
Plt. Mgr.—Dave Neal, 25 emp., *Biocompatible hard coatings for medical* ... (973) 586-4700

Illusion Engraved, 311 Fayette St., Perth Amboy 08861
Off. Mgr.—Marien Arevallo, 2 emp., *Engraving of trophies, plaques, bronze* ... (732) 442-4488

Ironbound Trophy Center, 289 Lafayette St., Ste. A, Newark 07105
Owner—Christine Naia, 3 emp., *Trophies & plaques & acrylics, corporate* ... (973) 344-3872

Isolatek International (H Q), 41 Furnace St., Stanhope 07874
Pres., CEO—Giovanni C. Pacheco, 100 emp., *Company headquarters; spray applied* ... (973) 347-1200

Isometric Micro Finishing Coating, 122 James St., Edison 08820
Pres.—Roy Leo, 6 emp., *Metal coating & tool & die polishing* ... (732) 906-8070

J & G Enterprises, Inc., 182 High St., Nutley 07110
Principal & Manager—John Mancini, 1 emp., *Custom apparel embroidery & screen* ... (973) 667-7673

J & J Engraving, 45 Worth St., South Hackensack 07606
Owner—Joseph Polifronio, Jr., 1 emp., *Plastic & metal engraving & screen* ... (201) 342-0798

J & M Enterprises, 32 North Ave., Cedarville 08311
Owner—John Melniczuk, 2 emp., *Metal powder coating* ... (856) 447-5090

Jonart Metals, LLC, 710 New Brunswick Ave., P.O. Box 333, Rahway 07065
Owner—Garry Capaldo, 4 emp., *Handcrafted gold, palladium & platinum* ... (732) 382-0300

Jory Engravers, Inc., 23 W. Erie Ave., Rutherford 07070
GM—Gary Gagliardi, 3 emp., *Metal engraving, screen printing, metal* ... (201) 939-1546

Kefa Northeast, P.O. Box 88, Budd Lake 07828
Pres.—Regis Doucette, 10 emp., *Corrosion, thermal & anti-mold coatings* ... (201) 664-5487

L J Engraving & Signs, 409 N. Wood Ave., P.O. Box 1039, Linden 07036
Owner—Leonard Neuringer, 3 emp., *Interior & exterior signs, engraving* ... (908) 925-3510

Laser Xpressions, Inc., 3710 Route 9 S., 2nd Fl., Freehold 07728
★ Pres.—Aco Sokolovski, 14 emp., *Laser engraving of metal plaques &* ... (732) 303-9530

LazyMan Mfg., 616 Hardwick St., P.O. Box 327, Belvidere 07823
Pres., CFO—Brian D. Sadowski, 15 emp., *Gas barbecue grills & sheet metal fabrication* ... (908) 475-5315

Little Falls Trophy Co., 555 Route 46 E., P.O. Box 1050, Little Falls 07424
Ptnr. & V-P.—Ellen Riccobono, 7 emp., *Trophy engraving* ... (973) 256-5222

Main Street Awards, Inc., 55 N. Main St., P.O. Box 323, Windsor 08561
Ptnr.—Carol Whitehouse, 2 emp., *Recognition awards, trophies, plaques* ... (609) 448-6324

Majestic Optical Coatings, 152 Willow Way, Clark 07066
Owner—Jeff Decker, 2 emp., *Reflective & anti-reflective thin film* ... (732) 388-5604

Mercer Coating & Lining Co., Inc., 1410 E. Linden Ave., P.O. Box 1656, Linden 07036
CEO—R. Bussiculo, 12 emp., *Rubber linings, sandblasting & painting* ... (908) 925-5000

Merit Trophies & Engraving, Inc., 184 Main St., Hackensack 07601
V-P., GM—Jim Dolack, 5 emp., *Laser engraving of signs, plaques,* ... (201) 487-5780

Metro Bowl, 37-02 Broadway, Fair Lawn 07410
Owner—Miklos Heitler, 4 emp., *Awards & engraving* ... (201) 791-2995

Miller & Sons, Inc., 24 Belleville Ave., Belleville 07109
Ptnr. & V-P.—Edward Miller, 10 emp., *Electroplating, including anodizing* ... (973) 759-6445

Monster Coatings, Inc., 306-A Capitol St., Saddle Brook 07663
Pres.—Denise Tomahatsch, 4 emp., *Seamless industrial, decorative & waterproofi* ... (973) 983-7662

N. B. C. Engraving Co., Inc., 228 Park St., Hackensack 07601
Pres.—John Scagliotti, 4 emp., *Mechanical engraving* ... (201) 387-8011

Nash Engraving, Inc., 528 Nicholson Rd., Gloucester City 08030
Owner—M. Nash, 4 emp., *Mechanical engraving of signs, nameplates* ... (856) 456-5656

New Jersey Galvanizing & Tinning Works, Inc., 139 Haynes Ave., 1st Fl., Newark 07114
Pres., GM—Robert E. Gregory, 50 emp., *Hot dip galvanizing* ... (973) 242-3200

New Jersey Logowear, 100 McKinley Ave., Ste. 6, Manahawkin 08050
★ Ptnr.—Keith Anderson, 7 emp., *Promotional item, apparel & textile* ... (609) 597-9400

Newark Industrial Spraying, Inc., 12 Amsterdam St., Newark 07105
Pres.—Richard D. Wantz, 15 emp., *Industrial powder coating, spray painting* ... (973) 344-6855

Nicholas Galvanizing Co., 120 Duffield Ave., Jersey City 07306
Owner—Robert Gregory, 29 emp., *Galvanized steel engraving* ... (201) 795-1010

Norton & Son, Inc., 148 E. 5th St., Bayonne 07002
V-P., Mfg.—Ed Norton III, 100 emp., *Architecural coatings* ... (201) 437-0770

P C R Technologies, Inc., 26 Chapin Rd., Unit 1111, Pine Brook 07058
Pres.—Mark Vanzini, 9 emp., *High-speed CNC machining of metals* ... (973) 882-0017

Painting, Inc., 60 Luening St., South Hackensack 07606
CEO & Fin., Hum. Res. & IT Mgr.—Lee M. Bronster, 14 emp., *Metal painting & screen printing* (201) 489-6565

Parkway-Kew Corp., 2095 Excelsior Ave., North Brunswick 08902
Pres., Plt. Mgr.—Eugene E. Klein, Sr., 15 emp., *HVOF, plasma & thermal spray coatings* ... (732) 398-2100

Paul's Custom Awards & Trophy, Inc., 200 White Horse Pike, Barrington 08007
Pres.—Paul McGuigan, 8 emp., *Trophy engraving & plaques* ... (856) 547-7777

Peerless Coatings, LLC, 220-A Goffle Rd., Hawthorne 07506
GM—Joe Hyer, 45 emp., *Metal & plastic coatings* ... (973) 427-8771

Penn Metal Finishing Co., Inc., 700 Jacksonville Rd., Burlington 08016
Pres.—Louis Willa, 5 emp., *Metal painting* ... (609) 387-3400

Perry'S, 11 N. 5th Ave., Long Branch 07740
Owner, Pres., Fin. & MIS Mgr.—Carl DeCesare, 4 emp., *Metal & laser engraving, glass etching* (732) 222-5040

Picture-It, Inc., 1703 State Route 27, Edison 08817
Pres.—Roy Taetzsch, 5 emp., *Acrylic, crystal, glass & wooden awards* ... (732) 819-0420

Pioneer Metal Finishing, Inc., 2034 Coles Mill Rd., P.O. Box 387, Franklinville 08322
Pres., Fin. & R & D Mgr.—Fred Trotz, 10 emp., *Powder coating* ... (856) 694-0400

Powtek Powder Coating, Inc., 233 Dickinson St., Trenton 08638
Pres.—Fred Martucci, 6 emp., *Metal powder coating* ... (609) 394-6700

Precision Engraving II, Inc., 13 Ridgedale Ave., P.O. Box 243, East Hanover 07936
Pres.—Conrad Fiore, 3 emp., *Industrial & comercial sign, control* ... (973) 887-3350

Precision Metal Machining, Inc., 800 Central Blvd., Ste. C, Carlstadt 07072
Pres.—Pat Fanicelli, 40 emp., *General machining job shop, including* ... (201) 843-7427

Prismatix Decal, Inc., 324 Railroad Ave., Hackensack 07601
Pres., CEO—Miriam Salomon, 10 emp., *Decals, emblems, trophies & engraving* ... (201) 525-2800

Productive Industrial Finishing, 103 American Way, Voorhees 08043
Pres.—Hal Gilham, 7 emp., *Metal finishing, powder coating & painting* ... (856) 427-9646

Quick Strip, 1 Randolph St., Carteret 07008
Pres.—Larry Fauci, 1 emp., *Media blasting & powder coating for* ... (732) 969-3268

R & R Specialties, 126 Holly Dr., Rio Grande 08242
Ptnr.—Chandi Ankrum, 2 emp., *Trophies & engraving* ... (609) 886-6651

Regal Stamp & Sign Co., Inc., 240 Park Ave., P.O. Box 342, East Rutherford 07073
Owner & Pres.—Krista Brabston, 1 emp., *Rubber stamps, marking devices & signs* ... (201) 939-0400

Regen & Co., Inc., 20-21 Wagaraw Rd., Bldg. 32, Fair Lawn 07410
GM—Alan Regen, 5 emp., *Commercial printing, letterhead engraving* ... (973) 423-4236

Rem Services, 310 W. 6th St., Ship Bottom 08008
Owner—Robert Mattner, 1 emp., *Name tags, trophies, small signs &* ... (609) 494-7760

Rimex Metals (USA) Inc, 2850 Woodbridge Ave., Edison 08837
Pres.—John Horbal, 25 emp., *Metal finishes for architecture, interior* ... (732) 549-3800

SAR Industrial Finishing, Inc., 104 N. Route 73, Berlin 08009
Pres.—Ralph Mauro, 18 emp., *Industrial spray painting of machinery* ... (609) 567-2772

SDL Studio, LLC, 1591 Route 37 W., Ste. E-4, Toms River 08755
Pres.—Louis Russo, 2 emp., *Commercial, industrial & military powder* ... (732) 473-0800

Spray Coat Finishing Co., Inc., 1125 Kaighn Ave., Camden 08103
Pres.—Chris Brown, 5 emp., *Electronic component coating & furniture* ... (856) 541-0950

Spray Powders, Inc., 23 Cindly Ln., Ocean 07712
Owner—Yadu M. Patel, 2 emp., *Powder coatings* ... (732) 493-1311

Standard Tech Applied Resource, 824 South Ave., Middlesex 08846
Pres.—Carmine Spatola, 6 emp., *Wire coating* ... (732) 968-6776

Superior Powder Coating, Inc., 600 Progress St., Elizabeth 07201
Pres.—Peter Markey, 150 emp., *Metal finishing, including powder &* ... (908) 351-8707

Superior Trademark, Inc., 45 Zazzetti St., P.O. Box 35, Waldwick 07463
Pres.—Gordon McIntire, 10 emp., *Heat transfer labels, identification* ... (201) 652-1900

Thinfilms, Inc., 15 Ilene Ct., Ste. 6, Hillsborough 08844
Pres.—Arshad Mumtaz, 11 emp., *Thin film coatings* ... (908) 359-7014

Thomson Lamination Co., Inc., 504 E. Linwood Ave., Maple Shade 08052
Chrm.—Sterling A. Martin, 100 emp., *Motor laminations & assemblies, including* ... (856) 779-8521

TICO Mfg., Inc., 1044 Industrial Dr., Unit 9, West Berlin 08091
Pres.—Roger Sobradl, 9 emp., *Military, commercial & industrial fasteners* ... (856) 767-8430

Towne Technologies, Inc., 6-10 Bell Ave., P.O. Box 460, Somerville 08876
Pres., R & D Mgr.—Hercharan S. Dhillon, 16 emp., *Chemically-etched metal parts, photo* ... (908) 722-9500

Triform Products, Inc., 219 Lafayette St., Paterson 07524
Pres.—Doug Troast, 12 emp., *Powder coating & metal stampings* ... (973) 278-2042

Trophies Unlimited, 122 Fernwood Ave., Trenton 08610
Owner—Dennis Hanft, 1 emp., *Metal engraving* ... (609) 298-3544

Trophy King Of Ramsey, 503 N. Franklin Tpke., Unit 13, Ramsey 07446
GM—John Paluskiewicz, 3 emp., *Trophy assembly & engraving* ... (201) 760-6488

Trophy King, Inc., The, 309 Queen Anne Rd., Teaneck 07666
Pres.—James Walsh, 6 emp., *Corporate headquarters & trophy assembly* ... (201) 836-1482

Trybun Engraving, LLC, 706 Old Shore Rd., Ste. 3, Forked River 08731
Pres.—Robert Trybun, 3 emp., *Plastic sign engraving* ... (609) 242-3105

Tulenko Enterprises, LLC, 176 Franklin Ave., Rockaway 07866
Owner, Fin. & R & D Mgr.—Eric A. Tulenko, 9 emp., *Structural & architectural metal sandblasting* (973) 453-6699

United Support Solutions, Inc., 134 Sand Park Rd., Cedar Grove 07009
Pres.—Joe Ostering, 80 emp., *Sheet metal fabrication, AWS & robotic* ... (973) 857-2298

V & S Amboy Galvanizing, 1190 Amboy Ave., Perth Amboy 08861
Regional GM—Robert Messler, 40 emp., *Steel & iron hot dip galvanizing* ... (732) 442-7555

Vertellus Performance Materials, Inc., 40 Avenue A, Bayonne 07002
Dir., Bus.—Tom Pensak, 40 emp., *Coatings & adhesives* ... (201) 858-8810

WECOM, Inc., 20 Warrick Ave., Glassboro 08028
Pres.—Eric C. Sprengle, Sr., 27 emp., *Precision sheet metal aluminum & stainless* ... (856) 863-8400

Westside Engravers, 76 N. West Ave., Bridgeton 08302
Owner & Operator—Dianne Johnson, 1 emp., *Industrial & commercial engraving* ... (856) 455-4790

## 3482 Small arms ammunition

Lightfield Ammunition Corp., 912 Highway 33, Freehold 07728
Owner—Peter Saker, 8 emp., *Ammunition for hunting, wildlife control* ... (732) 462-9200

Metalico, Inc. (H Q), 186 North Ave. E., Cranford 07016
Chrm., Pres. & CEO—Carlos E. Aguero, 12 emp., *Corporate headquarters; lead & lead* ... (908) 497-9610

Ultimate Training Munitions, 55 Readington Rd., North Branch 08876
Opers. Mgr.—Steve Cassidy, 30 emp., *Ammunition & training blanks for small* ... (908) 725-9000

## 3483 Ammunition, except for small arms

Hawk Precision, Inc., 849 Hawks Bridge Rd., Salem 08079
Owner & Pres.—Andy Hill, 2 emp., *Hunting bullets* ... (856) 299-2800

Lightfield Ammunition Corp., 912 Highway 33, Freehold 07728
Owner—Peter Saker, 8 emp., *Ammunition for hunting, wildlife control* ... (732) 462-9200

## 3484 Small arms

Faber Precision, Inc., 198 Green Pond Rd., Unit D, Rockaway 07866
Ptnr.—Stacey Faber, 7 emp., *Firearms for individual sportsmen &* ... (973) 983-1844

Godforce Tactical, Inc., 2614-B S. Clinton Ave., South Plainfield 07080
Pres.—Leland C. Stanford, 2 emp., *Paintball guns* ... (908) 561-2021

Henry Repeating Arms Company, 59 E. 1st St., Bayonne 07002
Owner & Pres.—Anthony Imperato, 200 emp., *Company headquarters & firearms, including.* (201) 858-4400

## 3489 Ordnance & accessories, nec

Bright Lights USA, Inc., 145 Shreve Ave., Barrington 08007
Pres.—Daniel Farber, 84 emp., *Mechanical & electromechanical defense* ... (856) 546-5656

Faber Precision, Inc., 198 Green Pond Rd., Unit D, Rockaway 07866
Ptnr.—Stacey Faber, 7 emp., *Firearms for individual sportsmen &* ... (973) 983-1844

## 3491 Valves—industrial

A&M Industrial, Inc., 37 W. Cherry St., P.O. Box 1044, Rahway 07065
Pres.—Arnold Young, 100 emp., *Corporate headquarters & industrial* ... (732) 574-1111

ASCO Valve, Inc., 50 Hanover Rd., Florham Park 07932
★ Pres., Americas—John Meek, 500 emp., *Industrial valves* ... (973) 966-2000

ASCO Valve, Inc., 50-60 Hanover Rd., Florham Park 07932
Group Pres.—Jean Pierre Yaouanc, 220 emp., *Corporate headquarters & miniature* ... (973) 966-2000

Barworth Micro Valve, Inc., 673 Morris Tpke., Springfield 07081
Pres.—Robert Swatsworth, 6 emp., *Industrial gas valves* ... (973) 376-4883

Bio-Chem Fluidics, Inc., 85 Fulton St., Ste. 12, Boonton 07005
Pres.—Timothy O' Sullivan, 60 emp., *Precision fluid handling components* ... (973) 263-3001

Britten & Travel Lite Golf, E. F., 22 South Ave., P.O. Box 246, Cranford 07016
Pres.—Richard Stokes, 8 emp., *Needle valves & pressure cylinders* ... (908) 276-4800

B-Tech Valve, LLC, 200 Cinnaminson Ave., Palmyra 08065
Owner & Pres.—Charles G. Bauer, 2 emp., *Variable nozzle desuperheater valves* ... (609) 321-2205

Ceresist, Inc., 176 E. 7th St., Paterson 07524
Pres.—Dino Tsapatsaris, 14 emp., *Ceramic-lined valves, fittings & orifice* ... (973) 345-3231

Cincinnati Thermal Spray East, 80 Fadem Rd., Springfield 07081
GM—Scot Crabtree, 28 emp., *Industrial pump & valve components* ... (973) 379-0003

Eagle Flo Pumps, Inc., 306 Orient Way, Rutherford 07070
Pres.—Joseph Hamadeh, 4 emp., *Industrial pumps & valves* ... (201) 438-8595

Everlasting Valve Co., 108 Somogyi Ct., South Plainfield 07080
Pres.—Richard G. Base, 30 emp., *Boiler blowdown valves* ... (908) 769-0700

Fluidyne Corp., 9100 Collins Ave., Pennsauken 08110
Pres.—Bill Bloemker, 20 emp., *Industrial valves* ... (856) 663-1818

Fox Valve Development Corp., 85 Franklin Rd., Hamilton Business Pk., Dover 07801
Pres.—Lawrence Fox, 23 emp., *Valves, venturi eductors, ejectors* ... (973) 328-1011

G & S Valves Fittings Co., Inc., 6910 Adams St., Guttenberg 07093
Pres.—Guido Scrivanich, 9 emp., *Rebuilt valves, including repair &* ... (201) 868-8026

Gadren Machine Co., 108 Main St., P.O. Box 117, Mount Ephraim 08059
Pres.—George S. Gadren, Jr., 15 emp., *Valves & CNC machining job shop* ... (856) 456-4329

S.I.C.

**★ Indicates new listing this edition.**

GasFlo Products, Inc., 19 Industrial Rd., Fairfield 07004
Pres.—David Panetta, 40 emp., *Cylinder connections, valves, fittings* .......... (973) 276-9011
Kraissl Co., Inc., 299 Williams Ave., Hackensack 07601
Pres.—Richard C. Michel, 21 emp., *Heavy-duty industrial valves, pumps* .......... (201) 342-0008
Magnatrol Valve Corp., 67 5th Ave., Hawthorne 07506
Pres.—Raymond A. Kretschmer, Sr., 30 emp., *Corporate headquarters & industrial* .......... (973) 427-4341
Megawatt Machine Services, LLC, 417 Elizabeth Ave., Somerset 08873
Owner—Pauline Balogh, 30 emp., *Machining of severe service control* .......... (732) 805-4000
Micromat Co., 185 State Route 17, Mahwah 07430
Pres.—Erwin Eibert, 5 emp., *Safety valves* .......... (201) 529-3738
Premac, Inc., P.O. Box 9, Rahway 07065
Pres.—Eric Schenker, 15 emp., *Jet pump control valves & general machining* .......... (732) 381-7550
S & S Valve Service, Inc., 105 Liberty St., Metuchen 08840
Pres.—David Stanski, 10 emp., *Rebuilt boiler safety valves, including* .......... (732) 548-2040
Selick & Bird Thermidaire, 2180 Village Rd., P.O. Box 108, Sea Girt 08750
Owner & Pres.—Lawrence Selick, 2 emp., *Steam traps & industrial supplies* .......... (732) 449-0017
Straval Co., 21 Columbus Ave., Garfield 07026
Pres.—Ed Simin, 15 emp., *Industrial relief, back pressure &* .......... (973) 340-9955

## 3492 Fluid power valves & hose fittings

A&M Industrial, Inc., 325 Commerce Rd., Linden 07036
Ex. V-P.—David Young, 10 emp., *Manufacturer of industrial & hydraulic* .......... (908) 862-1800
ASCO Valve, Inc., 13000 Lincoln Dr. W., Ste. 106, Marlton 08053
Dir., Sales, N.E. Reg.—John Matro, 5 emp., *Pneumatic valves & fittings* .......... (856) 985-8700
B & A Flex, Inc., 34 Charlotte Dr., Bridgewater 08807
GM—Dan Souza, 14 emp., *Flexible metal hose, connectors & flow* .......... (908) 722-2808
Behringer Corp., 17 Ridge Rd., Branchville 07826
Pres., GM—Ted Hinds, 40 emp., *Pipe & tube hangers, filtration products* .......... (973) 948-0226
B-Tech Valve, LLC, 200 Cinnaminson Ave., Palmyra 08065
Owner & Pres.—Charles G. Bauer, 2 emp., *Variable nozzle desuperheater valves* .......... (609) 321-2205
Clark Cooper Div., 941 Hamilton Ave., Roebling 08554
GM—Dave Decara, 19 emp., *Standard, custom-engineered & high-pressure* .......... (856) 829-4580
Clifton Fluid Power Machinery, 295 Allwood Rd., Clifton 07012
GM—Richard Brodsky, 9 emp., *Hydraulic machinery* .......... (973) 778-3923
Convertech, Inc., 353 Richard Mine Rd., Wharton 07885
Pres.—Larry Taitel, 50 emp., *Pneumatic airshafts & printing press* .......... (973) 328-1850
Cumberland Valve, Inc., 746 Shiloh Pike, Bridgeton 08302
GM—Thomas M. Davis, 11 emp., *Hydraulic hose assemblies* .......... (856) 451-1324
Curtiss-Wright Corp. (H Q), 10 Waterview Blvd., 2nd Fl., Parsippany 07054
Chrm.—Martin R. Benante, 50 emp., *Corporate headquarters; flow control* .......... (973) 541-3700
DSO Fluid Handling Co., Inc., 300 McGaw Dr., Ste. 2, Edison 08837
V-P., GM, Bus. Dev. & Sales—Ed Clark, 15 emp., *Replacement parts for sanitary food* .......... (732) 225-9100
Emerson Instrument & Valve Services, 120 Kissel Rd., Burlington 08016
Acct. Mgr.—Mary Mallon, 30 emp., *Control valves* .......... (609) 386-5000
Exitflex USA, Inc., 254 Raritan Center Pkwy., Edison 08837
Pres.—Joseph M. Medvecky, 4 emp., *High-pressure hose, tungsten carbide* .......... (732) 512-9141
Flodyne Controls, Inc., 48 Commerce Dr., Murray Hill 07974
Pres., Adv. Mgr.—Carol Perrin, 12 emp., *Cryogenic, high-pressure & high-speed* .......... (908) 464-6200
Generant Co., Inc., 1865 Route 23 S., P.O. Box 768, Butler 07405
V-P.—Dino D'Onofrio, 140 emp., *Pressure regulating valves & instrument* .......... (973) 838-6500
Holby Valve, Inc., 24 Ferdon St., Newark 07105
V-P.—Thomas Lentine, 10 emp., *1/2-inch to 4-inch thermostatic mixing* .......... (973) 465-7400
Magnatrol Valve Corp., 67 5th Ave., Hawthorne 07506
Pres.—Raymond A. Kretschmer, Sr., 30 emp., *Corporate headquarters & industrial* .......... (973) 427-4341
Marotta Controls, Inc., 78 Boonton Ave., P.O. Box 427, Montville 07045
Pres.—Patrick Marotta, 200 emp., *High-performance & specialty motion* .......... (973) 334-7800
Micromat Co., 185 State Route 17, Mahwah 07430
Pres.—Erwin Eibert, 5 emp., *Safety valves* .......... (201) 529-3738
NResearch, Inc., 267 Fairfield Ave., West Caldwell 07006
Pres.—Akos Sule, 23 emp., *Miniature solenoid-operated PTFE isolation* .......... (973) 808-8811
Parker Hannifin Corp., 45 Route 46 E., Unit 602, P.O. Box 778, Pine Brook 07058
Application Engr.—Jamari Davis, 50 emp., *PTFE & stainless steel miniature solenoid* .......... (973) 575-4844
Plast-O-Matic Valves, Inc., 1384 Pompton Ave., Ste. 1, Cedar Grove 07009
Pres.—Tim Delorenzo, 60 emp., *Thermoplastic valves & controls for* .......... (973) 256-3000
R G I, Inc., 27 Union Valley Rd., Newfoundland 07435
Pres.—Barry Maloney, 16 emp., *CNC machining of valves, pumps & manifolds* .......... (973) 697-2624
S & S Valve Service, Inc., 105 Liberty St., Metuchen 08840
Pres.—David Stanski, 10 emp., *Rebuilt boiler safety valves, including* .......... (732) 548-2040
Teesing USA, LLC, 10 Millpond Dr., Unit 7, Lafayette 07848
Sales Acct. & Sales Mgr.—John Sparnon, 3 emp., *Quick-connect hydraulic & pneumatic* .......... (973) 383-0691
U. S. Brass & Copper, Corp., 641 E. Elizabeth Ave., P.O. Box 1052, Linden 07036
—, 10 emp., *Metal hose fittings & assemblies* .......... (908) 486-3322
Universal Valve Co., Inc., 478 Schiller St., Elizabeth 07206
Pres., CEO—Robert Milo, 30 emp., *Valves, fittings, vapor recovery equipment* .......... (908) 351-0606
Valcor Engineering Corp., 2 Lawrence Rd., Springfield 07081
Pres.—Frank Tartaglia, 240 emp., *Solenoid valves & pumps* .......... (973) 467-8400
Versa Products Co., Inc., 22 Spring Valley Rd., Paramus 07652
Pres.—Jan L. Larsson, 155 emp., *Pneumatic valves* .......... (201) 843-2400

## 3493 Springs—steel, except wire

Alfred & William, Inc., P.O. Box 364, Union 07083
Pres.—Douglas V. Suckow, 7 emp., *Steel machine springs* .......... (908) 686-3000
Atlantic Spring Co., 137 Highway 202 S., Ringoes 08551
GM—Jeff Vannatta, 80 emp., *Custom metal springs, wire forms &* .......... (908) 788-5800
Eureka Spring Co., 999 Rahway Ave., Union 07083
Pres.—Douglas Suckow, 20 emp., *Coil & flat metal springs* .......... (973) 589-4960
Jenson & Mitchell, Inc., 880 Communipaw Ave., Jersey City 07304
Pres.—Frank Mitchell, 3 emp., *Automotive springs & truck suspension* .......... (201) 332-4140
R & H Spring & Truck Repair, Inc., 4806 W. Hurley Pond Rd., Belmar 07719
Pres.—Frank Todero, Sr., 10 emp., *Rebuilt automotive & truck leaf springs* .......... (732) 681-9000

## 3494 Valves & pipe fittings

B & A Flex, Inc., 34 Charlotte Dr., Bridgewater 08807
GM—Dan Souza, 14 emp., *Flexible metal hose, connectors & flow* .......... (908) 722-2808
Blanco Assocs., Inc., J., 280 9th Ave., Unit 1, Hawthorne 07506
Pres.—Victor Ramos, 15 emp., *Pipe hangers & supports & architectural* .......... (973) 427-0619
Britten & Travel Lite Golf, E. F., 22 South Ave. W., P.O. Box 246, Cranford 07016
Pres.—Richard Stokes, 8 emp., *Needle valves & pressure cylinders* .......... (908) 276-4800
Carpenter & Paterson, Inc., 369 Jefferson St., Saddle Brook 07663
Br. Mgr.—Thomas Browne, 35 emp., *Metal pipe hangers, supports, struts* .......... (973) 772-1800
CB&I, 502-B Jersey Ave., New Brunswick 08901
Opers. Mgr.—Dan Frana, 15 emp., *Industrial pipe fittings, including* .......... (732) 435-0777
Custom Alloy Corp., 3 Washington Ave., Ste. 6, High Bridge 08829
Pres.—Adam M. Ambielli, 260 emp., *Butt-weld pipe fittings & near net* .......... (800) 453-1724
Ernst Co., Inc., John C., 21 Gail Ct., Sparta 07871
Pres.—James Wolfe, 17 emp., *Sight glasses & windows, liquid level* .......... (973) 940-1600
Esco Industrial Corp., 141 Lanza Ave., Bldg. 3-B, Garfield 07026
Hum. Res. Mgr.—Kathy Shu, 22 emp., *Pipe fittings* .......... (973) 478-5888
Euro Mechanical, Inc., 16 Industrial Ave., Fairview 07022
Pres.—Ante Pestic, 15 emp., *Rebuilt steam pipe fittings* .......... (201) 313-8050
Everlasting Valve Co., 108 Somogyi Ct., South Plainfield 07080
Pres.—Richard G. Base, 30 emp., *Boiler blowdown valves* .......... (908) 769-0700
Flodyne Controls, Inc., 48 Commerce Dr., Murray Hill 07974
Pres., Adv. Mgr.—Carol Perrin, 12 emp., *Cryogenic, high-pressure & high-speed* .......... (908) 464-6200
Fluid Filtration Corp., 102 Van Winkle Ave., Garfield 07026
Pres.—Farzad Alborzi, 10 emp., *Pipeline & cone strainers, water filters* .......... (973) 253-7070
Fox Valve Development Corp., 85 Franklin Rd., Hamilton Business Pk., Dover 07801
Pres.—Lawrence Fox, 23 emp., *Valves, venturi eductors, ejectors* .......... (973) 328-1011
Gadren Machine Co., 108 Main St., P.O. Box 117, Mount Ephraim 08059
Pres.—George S. Gadren, Jr., 15 emp., *Valves & CNC machining job shop* .......... (856) 456-4329
General Rubber Corp., 850 Washington Ave., Front, Carlstadt 07072
V-P., Sales—Kelvin Mayrina, 10 emp., *Piping & ducting expansion joints,* .......... (201) 935-1900
Holby Valve, Inc., 24 Ferdon St., Newark 07105
V-P.—Thomas Lentine, 10 emp., *1/2-inch to 4-inch thermostatic mixing* .......... (973) 465-7400
Imperial Weld Ring Corp., 80-88 Front St., P.O. Box 6646, Elizabeth 07206
Pres.—Calvin Sierra, 15 emp., *Precision metallic weld backing rings* .......... (908) 354-0011
Kaplan Industries, Inc., 10 Morris Ave., Route 73, Maple Shade 08052
Dir., Opers.—Jim Johnston, 15 emp., *High & low pressure compressed gas* .......... (856) 779-8181
Kraissl Co., Inc., 299 Williams Ave., Hackensack 07601
Pres.—Richard C. Michel, 21 emp., *Heavy-duty industrial valves, pumps* .......... (201) 342-0008
NResearch, Inc., 267 Fairfield Ave., West Caldwell 07006
Pres.—Akos Sule, 23 emp., *Miniature solenoid-operated PTFE isolation* .......... (973) 808-8811
R G I, Inc., 27 Union Valley Rd., Newfoundland 07435
Pres.—Barry Maloney, 16 emp., *CNC machining of valves, pumps & manifolds* .......... (973) 697-2624
Ramco Mfg. Co., Inc., 365 Carnegie Ave., Kenilworth 07033
Pres.—Kevin J. Nee, 25 emp., *Flanges, expansion & threaded pipe* .......... (908) 245-4500
Straval Co., 21 Columbus Ave., Garfield 07026
Pres.—Ed Simin, 15 emp., *Industrial relief, back pressure &* .......... (973) 340-9955
Taylor Forge Stainless, Inc., 22 Readington Rd., P.O. Box 610, Somerville 08876
Pres.—Mike Kearney, 100 emp., *Stainless steel pipe fittings* .......... (908) 722-1313
Universal Valve Co., Inc., 478 Schiller St., Elizabeth 07206
Pres., CEO—Robert Milo, 30 emp., *Valves, fittings, vapor recovery equipment* .......... (908) 351-0606
West Side Precision Machine Products, Inc., 280 Lincoln Blvd., Middlesex 08846
Pres.—David Gizzi, 5 emp., *Precision machining, including Swiss* .......... (732) 560-9006

## 3495 Wire springs

Murphy & Read Spring Mfg. Co., 617 W. 6th St., P.O. Box 211, Palmyra 08065
Pres.—John Seemuller, 15 emp., *Wire springs & forms, including torsion* .......... (856) 829-6887
Rotor Clip Company, Inc., 187 Davidson Ave., Somerset 08873
Ptnr.—Jonathan Slass, 240 emp., *Tapered section, constant section &* .......... (732) 469-7333
TICO Mfg., Inc., 1044 Industrial Dr., Unit 9, West Berlin 08091
Pres.—Roger Sobradl, 9 emp., *Military, commercial & industrial fasteners* .......... (856) 767-8430

## 3496 Wire products—misc. fabricated

Abate Fence, Inc., 3619 Route 23, Hamburg 07419
Pres.—Dominick Rotolo, 5 emp., *Wooden, wire, aluminum & PVC fences* .......... (973) 827-4167
Alenco Fence & Supply Corp., 167 Route 70, Bldg. B, Medford 08055
Owner—Chris Murphy, 10 emp., *Wooden, aluminum, chain-link & vinyl* .......... (609) 654-6060
All Quality Fence, 1266 Route 46, P.O. Box 85, Ledgewood 07852
Owner—John Johnson, 6 emp., *Aluminum, red & white cedar, chain-link* .......... (973) 927-0722
Allentown, Inc., 165 Route 526, Allentown 08501
CEO—Michael Coiro, Sr., 250 emp., *Stainless steel wire caging equipment* .......... (609) 259-7951
All-State Fence, Inc., 1389 Route 9 N., Howell 07731
Pres.—Scott Skrable, 8 emp., *Residential & commercial chain-link* .......... (732) 431-4944
Alpha Wire Co., 711 Lidgerwood Ave., P.O. Box 711, Elizabeth 07207
Dir., Sales—Tim Smith, 200 emp., *Divisional headquarters & cable & wire* .......... (908) 925-8000
Alpine Group, Inc., The (H Q), 1 Meadowlands Plz., Ste. 801, East Rutherford 07073
Chrm. & CEO—Steven S. Elbaum, 5 emp., *Holding company headquarters; nonilluminated* . (201) 549-4400
Amark Industries, Inc., 18 Passaic Ave., Fairfield 07004
Pres., Qual. Assur. Mgr.—Mario Salerno, 5 emp., *High precision escomatic screw machine* . (973) 992-8900
American Van Equipment, Inc., 149 Lehigh Ave., Lakewood 08701
Pres.—Charles Richter, 95 emp., *Aluminum, steel & hot dipped galvanized* .......... (800) 526-4743
Amer-Rac, LLC, 8128 River Rd., Pennsauken 08110
Pres.—Steve Shore, 10 emp., *Steel & aluminum truck & van ladder* .......... (856) 488-6210
Artistic Fence, 757 River Dr., Passaic 07055
Pres.—Steven Boggio, 20 emp., *Chain link & wooden fencing* .......... (973) 779-4540
Atlantic Spring Co., 137 Highway 202 S., Ringoes 08551
GM—Jeff Vannatta, 80 emp., *Custom metal springs, wire forms &* .......... (908) 788-5800
Belleville Wire Cloth Co., Inc., 18 Rutgers Ave., Cedar Grove 07009
Pres.—James Crowley, 35 emp., *Wire cloth, screens & filters* .......... (973) 239-0074
Bergen Cable Technology, LLC, 343 Kaplan Dr., Fairfield 07004
Pres., GM—Peter Bartholomew, 30 emp., *Mechanical wire rope cable assemblies* .......... (973) 276-9596
Blanc Display Group, The, 88 King St., Ste. 1, Dover 07801
Pres.—Didier Blanc, 100 emp., *Custom point-of-purchase displays,* .......... (973) 537-0090
Bloomex International, Inc., 295 Molnar Dr., Elmwood Park 07407
Pres.—Benjamin Laroux, 4 emp., *Low-energy electronic muscle stimulators* .......... (201) 703-9799
Brown & Perkins, Inc., 1193 Route 535, P.O. Box 412, Cranbury 08512
Pres.—E. T. Comly, 16 emp., *Manufacturer & distributor of wire* .......... (609) 655-1150
Carl Stahl Sava Industries, Inc., 4 N. Corporate Dr., P.O. Box 30, Riverdale 07457
CEO—Zdenek A. Fremund, 85 emp., *Corporate headquarters & miniature* .......... (973) 835-0882
Clip Strip Corp., 343 S. River St., Hackensack 07601
Pres.—Edward D. Spitaletta, 6 emp., *Point-of-purchase merchandise & store* .......... (201) 342-9155
Components Corp., 6 Kinsey Pl., Denville 07834
Sales Mgr., Natl.—Chris Minter, 17 emp., *Wire forms & connectors* .......... (973) 627-0290
Consolidated Steel & Aluminum Fence, 316 N. 12th St., P.O. Box 643, Kenilworth 07033
Pres.—Paul Cacicedo, 60 emp., *Commercial chain-link, steel, aluminum* .......... (908) 272-6262
Delta Fence Co., 541 Spring St., Elizabeth 07201
Owner—Carlos Milanes, 4 emp., *Wooden, vinyl & chain link fences* .......... (908) 355-9066
Display Sales, Inc., P.O. Box 115, Spotswood 08884
Pres.—Richard Nasca, 20 emp., *Display fixtures & wire racks* .......... (732) 251-8981
Donaldson Co., Inc., R. J., 1287 Glassboro Rd., Williamstown 08094
Pres.—Douglas Donaldson, 8 emp., *Wire mesh partitions & infill panels* .......... (856) 629-2737
Doran Sling & Assembly Corp., 1285 Central Ave., Hillside 07205
CEO—Barry Lemberg, 24 emp., *Wire rope, chain, nylon & wire rope* .......... (908) 351-7800

Emerson Fence, Inc., 10 Lincoln Blvd., P.O. Box 306, Emerson 07630
Pres.—Robert Skrable, Jr., 20 emp., *Manufacturer & distributor of custom* ........ (201) 265-5150
Essex Fence Co., 132 U.S. Highway 46, Rockaway 07866
Ptnr.—George Lenar, 17 emp., *PVC vinyl, ornamental aluminum, wood* ........ (973) 625-4122
E-Z Do, Inc., 40 Executive Ave., Edison 08817
Pres., CEO—Mark S. Densen, 150 emp., *Houseware products, including bath,* ........ (732) 287-8111
Fixturecraft Corp., 1457 Raritan Rd., Ste. 201, Clark 07066
Pres.—William P. Mooney, 3 emp., *Portable & folding wire display literature* ........ (908) 272-8145
General Wire & Stamping Co., Inc., 1 Emery Ave., Unit 3, Randolph 07869
Pres.—Kenneth J. Kelly, 12 emp., *Wire forms & metal stampings* ........ (973) 366-8080
Guardian Fence Co., Inc., 180 Wright St., P.O. Box 2009, Newark 07114
Pres.—Nancy Maccarelli, 20 emp., *Chain-link, wooden & vinyl fencing* ........ (973) 824-1850
Hillside Wire Cloth, Inc., 109 Roosevelt Ave., Belleville 07109
Pres.—William Messenger, 15 emp., *Stainless steel baskets & strainers* ........ (973) 751-3131
J.A.W. Products, Inc., 835 Industrial Hwy., Unit 125, Cinnaminson 08077
Pres.—Earl Weightman, 10 emp., *Manufacturer & distributor of orthodontic* ........ (856) 829-3210
J.R.M. Products, Inc., 701 Locust St., Keyport 07735
Pres.—Robert Wichowski, 4 emp., *American-made custom steel, stainless* ........ (732) 495-3092
Jan Fence Co., Inc., 4 Industrial Rd., Pompton Plains 07444
Pres.—Robert Corrao, 15 emp., *Custom industrial, residential & security* ........ (973) 694-4055
Kenco Wire & Iron Products, Inc., 425 Carr Ave., Keansburg 07734
Pres.—Mary Urban, 15 emp., *Wire mesh partitions, window guards* ........ (732) 495-3000
Main & Sons, Inc., Robert A., 555 Goffle Rd., P.O. Box 159, Wyckoff 07481
Pres., CFO & V-P., Opers.—William Main, 13 emp., *Pins & pointed wire products, including* .. (201) 447-3700
Master Wire Mfg., Inc., 1019 Black Horse Pike, Route 322, P.O. Box 328, Hammonton 08037
Pres.—Geraldine Hefferon, 16 emp., *Chain-link & PVC fencing & ornamental* ........ (609) 567-1616
Meadow Burke Products, 269 Commercial Ave., Palisades Park 07650
Sales Mgr., District—Don Fowler, 4 emp., *Steel reinforcing bars, wire ties &* ........ (201) 242-8989
Metal Textiles Corp., 970 New Durham Rd., Edison 08818
Pres.—Greg Vongas, 190 emp., *Wire mesh filtration gaskets* ........ (732) 287-0800
Modern International Corp., 145 Cliffwood Ave., Cliffwood 07721
Pres., GM—Daniel Stern, 20 emp., *Wire, steel & plastic strapping, packaging* ........ (732) 696-9100
Motion Control Technologies, Inc., 158 W. Clinton St., Ste. FF, Dover 07801
Pres.—Frank Heidinger, 10 emp., *Wire rope cable assemblies, including* ........ (973) 361-2226
Multi Tech Industries Corp., 64 S. Main St., P.O. Box 159, Marlboro 07746
Pres.—James Bernard, 11 emp., *Rotary switches, cord strain-reliefs* ........ (732) 431-0550
Murphy & Read Spring Mfg. Co., 617 W. 6th St., P.O. Box 211, Palmyra 08065
Pres.—John Seemuller, 15 emp., *Wire springs & forms, including torsion* ........ (856) 829-6887
Newark Wire Cloth Co., Inc., 160 Fornelius Ave., Clifton 07013
Pres.—Richard W. Campbell, 30 emp., *Roll & cut wire cloth & fabricated* ........ (973) 778-4478
Newark Wire Works, Inc., 1059 King Georges Post Rd., Ste. 103, Edison 08837
Pres.—JoAnn Spellman, 16 emp., *Architectural wire mesh panels & fabricated* ........ (732) 661-2001
RB & A, Inc., 350 Sparta Ave., Bldg. C, Sparta 07871
Pres.—Rod Borden, 5 emp., *Point-of-purchase, acrylic, stock &* ........ (973) 726-0830
ScreenTek Mfg. Co., Inc., 220 Franklin Rd., Ste. B, Randolph 07869
Co-Pres., GM—Jay Thompson, 23 emp., *Wire & fiberglass mesh & perforated* ........ (973) 328-2121
Sea Gear Marine Supply, Inc., 1144 Route 109, Cape May 08204
Owner, Pres. & CFO—Chuck Barto, 14 emp., *Wire rope & sling assembly & hardware* ........ (609) 884-2711
Security Fabricators, Inc., 316 N. 12th St., P.O. Box 643, Kenilworth 07033
Pres.—Paul Cacicedo, 15 emp., *Chain link fencing* ........ (908) 272-9171
Semiconductor Mfg., 5 Troast Ct., Clifton 07011
Pres.—William Pian, 54 emp., *Metal stampings, spheres & wire, including* ........ (973) 478-2880
Seminole Wire & Cable Co., 7861 Airport Hwy., Pennsauken 08109
CEO—George H. Genzel, 25 emp., *Low voltage wire & cable* ........ (856) 324-2929
Spencer Industries, Inc., 80 Holmes St., P.O. Box 128, Belleville 07109
Pres.—Martin Lawrence, 25 emp., *Corporate headquarters & military replacement* ........ (973) 751-2200
Taylor Fence Co., 1246 Route 33, Farmingdale 07727
Owner—Paul Crooks, 50 emp., *Wooden, chain-link & aluminum fencing* ........ (732) 747-5498
Tilton Rack & Basket Corp., 66 Passaic Ave., Fairfield 07004
Pres.—Joseph Tilton, 25 emp., *Industrial plating racks, fixtures* ........ (973) 226-6010
U. S. Wire & Cable, Inc., 33 Queen St., Newark 07114
Pres.—David Rauch, 100 emp., *Wire, cables, cords & accessories* ........ (973) 824-5529
Unique Wire Weaving Co., Inc., 762 Ramsey Ave., Hillside 07205
Pres.—Ken Beyer, 20 emp., *Industrial woven wire cloth & filter* ........ (908) 688-4600
VIS USA, LLC, 210 Meister Ave., Branchburg 08876
Pres., Fin. & MIS Mgr.—Rene Morf, 15 emp., *Power transmission & conveyor belting* ........ (908) 575-0606
Watson Assocs., Inc., 800 Grove Rd., Thorofare 08086
Pres.—Edward Schafer, 2 emp., *Conveyor belts & packaging equipment* ........ (856) 845-8800
Wire Cloth Mfrs., Inc., 110 Iron Mountain Rd., Mine Hill 07803
Pres.—Kathleen Hegarty, 25 emp., *Corporate headquarters & wire mesh* ........ (973) 328-1000
Wire Forming Corp. Of New Jersey, 109 Meeker Ave., Ste. 135, Newark 07114
Pres.—Donato Iannascolio, 20 emp., *Custom wire displays & four slide products* ........ (973) 824-5558
Wytech Industries, Inc., 960 E. Hazelwood Ave., Rahway 07065
CEO—Anthony J. Casalino, 105 emp., *Grinding, straightening, cutting, forming* ........ (732) 396-3900

### 3497 Metal foil & leaf

All American Graphic Arts, 763 Ramsey Ave., Hillside 07205
Owner—Ed Rodriguez, 2 emp., *Foil stamping & embossing & stationery* ........ (908) 686-1479
Anuco, Inc., 911 Charles Dr., P.O. Box 5016, Toms River 08753
Owner & GM—Robert Nugent, Jr., 15 emp., *Commercial printing & foil stamping* ........ (973) 887-9465
Crown Roll Leaf, Inc., 91 Illinois Ave., Paterson 07503
CEO—Margaret Waitts, 225 emp., *Corporate headquarters & hot stamping* ........ (973) 742-4000
Custom Converters, Inc., 115 Naylon Ave., Livingston 07039
Pres.—Mark Krause, 10 emp., *Paper, plastic film, aluminum foil* ........ (973) 994-9000
Envelopes & Printed Products, Inc., 135 Fairview Ave., Prospect Park 07508
Pres., CEO—William F. Higgins, 10 emp., *Envelope & business card printing,* ........ (973) 942-1232
Glitterex Corp., 7 Commerce Dr., Cranford 07016
Pres.—Babu Shetty, 44 emp., *Plastic & aluminum glitters* ........ (908) 272-9121
Meadowbrook Inventions, Inc., 260 Mine Brook Rd., P.O. Box 960, Bernardsville 07924
Pres.—Harold Sutton, 42 emp., *Polyester, metal & heat fusible fiber* ........ (908) 766-0606
Penny Plate, LLC (H Q), 14000 Horizon Way, Ste. 300, Mount Laurel 08054
Pres.—Paul Cobb, 12 emp., *Company headquarters; aluminum foil* ........ (856) 429-7583
Spectrum Foils, Inc., 68 Ivy Creek Dr., Little Egg Harbor 08087
Pres.—Bill Pack, 6 emp., *Hot stamping & printing foils* ........ (973) 481-0808
Unifoil Corp., 12 Daniel Rd., Ste. 101, Fairfield 07004
Pres., CEO—Joseph Funicelli, 105 emp., *Corporate headquarters & aluminum foil* ........ (973) 244-9900

### 3498 Pipe & fittings—fabricated

Capital Steel Service, LLC, 82 Stokes Ave., Trenton 08638
CEO—Allen Hickman, Sr., 27 emp., *Metal service center & structural &* ........ (609) 882-6983
Cotterman, Inc., 100 Hayes Ave., P.O. Box 278, Wenonah 08090
Pres.—William Thomas, 20 emp., *High-pressure piping & industrial welding* ........ (856) 464-6820
Custom Fab Pipe Supply Corp., 1-A Mount Vernon St., Ridgefield Park 07660
Pres.—Walt Steinel, 18 emp., *Pipe fabrication & protection* ........ (201) 343-3739
Endot Industries, Inc., 60 Green Pond Rd., Rockaway 07866
Chrm.—Gary Wellmann, 50 emp., *Corporate headquarters & HDPE plastic* ........ (973) 625-8500
Ferguson Fire & Fabrication, Inc., 151 Randolph St., Passaic 07055
Manager—Peter Braid, 40 emp., *Metal pipe & fittings fabrication* ........ (973) 614-9292
Fibrenetics, Inc., 2 Cutters Dock Rd., Woodbridge 07095
★ Owner—Herbert Segars, 10 emp., *Fiberglass tanks & metal pipe fabrication* ........ (732) 636-5670
Fluid Filtration Corp., 102 Van Winkle Ave., Garfield 07026
Pres.—Farzad Alborzi, 10 emp., *Pipeline & cone strainers, water filters* ........ (973) 253-7070
G & J Steel & Tubing, Inc., 406 Roycefield Rd., Hillsborough 08844
Pres.—John Tursky, 45 emp., *Fabricated metal tubing* ........ (908) 526-4445
GasFlo Products, Inc., 19 Industrial Rd., Fairfield 07004
Pres.—David Panetta, 40 emp., *Cylinder connections, valves, fittings* ........ (973) 276-9011
Imperial Weld Ring Corp., 80-88 Front St., P.O. Box 6646, Elizabeth 07206
Pres.—Calvin Sierra, 15 emp., *Precision metallic weld backing rings* ........ (908) 354-0011
Interstate Welding & Mfg. Co., Inc., 1510 Village Ct., Edgewater Park 08010
Pres., CFO—Joseph N. Russomanno, 18 emp., *Welding, tube, pipe & metal fabrication* ........ (609) 699-6950
JCW Rolling & Fabrication, 60 Liberty St., Metuchen 08840
★ Owner—Kenneth Greiff, 20 emp., *CNC & machining job shop & metal pipe* ........ (732) 548-7636
Jettron Products, Inc., 56 Route 10 W., P.O. Box 337, East Hanover 07936
Pres.—Ed Balzarotti, 20 emp., *High-voltage cable assemblies & precision* ........ (973) 887-0571
Kreisler Mfg. Corp., 180 Van Riper Ave., Elmwood Park 07407
Owner—Michael Stern, 150 emp., *Tube & manifold fabrication for gas* ........ (201) 791-0700
Liberty Mechanical Contractors, Inc., 330 Raymond Blvd., Newark 07105
Pres., CFO—Frank P. Zurica, 25 emp., *Welding job shop & industrial mechanical* ........ (973) 344-6131
Microtube Fabricators, Inc., 250 Lackland Dr., Middlesex 08846
Div. Mgr.—Rick Kreppel, 50 emp., *Metal medical tubing* ........ (732) 469-7420
MP Tube Works, Inc., 237 Sheffield St., Mountainside 07092
Pres.—Michael J. McGinley, 8 emp., *Tube fabrication & general machining* ........ (908) 317-2500
New World Stainless, LLC, 100 Randolph Rd., Ste. 5, Somerset 08873
Pres., CEO—Joe Zielinskie, 45 emp., *Precision welded small diameter stainless* ........ (732) 412-7170
Oceanic Metals LLC, 8555 Tonnelle Ave., Ste. 404, North Bergen 07047
Owner—Demetris Orfanos, 1 emp., *Steel, aluminum & cast iron cutting* ........ (201) 662-1192
Pipe Guards Bollards, LLC, 478 Schiller St., Elizabeth 07206
Dir., Mktg.—Joe Zulewski, 12 emp., *U-shaped pipe guards & bollards from* ........ (908) 354-2259
Piping Solutions, Inc., 81 Chimney Rock Rd., Ste. 3, Bridgewater 08807
Pres.—Ernest E. Stone III, 6 emp., *Process skid assemblies & ASME B31.1* ........ (732) 537-1009
S & W Fabricators, Inc., 100 S. Delsea Dr., Ste. 300, P.O. Box 664, Glassboro 08028
Pres.—Pattie Sebastiani, 5 emp., *Metal pipe fabrication* ........ (856) 881-8068
Sci-Bore, Inc., 364 Glenwood Ave., Bldg. 18-E, East Orange 07017
Pres., CFO—Nadiya Jinnah, 7 emp., *High-carbon steel wire guide nozzles* ........ (973) 414-9001
Standard Pipe Products, Inc., 15 North Ave., Garwood 07027
V-P.—Henry Rudorfer, 10 emp., *Carbon steel, red brass, stainless* ........ (908) 264-8284
T K L Specialty Piping, 175 Broad St., P.O. Box 5149, Phillipsburg 08865
Pres.—Thomas W. Larkin, 7 emp., *Steel pipe & adaptor nipples* ........ (908) 454-0030
Triangle Tube Phase III, Inc., 1 Triangle Ln., Blackwood 08012
Pres., CEO—Daniel Lasserre, 50 emp., *Stainless steel hot water heating equipment* ........ (856) 228-8881
Vianini Pipe, Inc., 39 County Line Rd., Whitehouse Station 08889
Pres.—Alex Narcise, 100 emp., *Prestress, jacking & reinforced concrete* ........ (908) 534-4021
Vogelsang Fastener Corp, 1790 Swarthmore Ave., Lakewood 08701
V-P., GM—Dale Stuban, 50 emp., *Slotted, coiled & metric tension pins* ........ (732) 364-0444

### 3499 Metal products—fabricated, nec

A & D Industrial & Marine Repair, 900 Port Reading Ave., Ste. B-2, Port Reading 07064
Pres.—Doug Alexander, 12 emp., *Machine shop, including rebuilt industrial* ........ (732) 541-1481
A & F Sign Company LLC, 28 E. Railway Ave., Paterson 07503
Sole Member—Frank Ferrucci, 1 emp., *Architectural, illuminated, non-illuminated* ........ (973) 278-3707
A+ Products, Inc., 8 Timber Ln., Marlboro Industrial Pk., Marlboro 07746
Founder & Pres.—Mike Schreiber, 40 emp., *Corporate headquarters & custom & standard* ... (732) 866-9111
Accent Fence, Inc., 1450 Bremen Ave., P.O. Box 656, Egg Harbor City 08215
Pres.—Greg Carnasale, 20 emp., *Wooden, metal & vinyl fences & ornamental* ........ (609) 965-6400
Accurate Forming, 24 Ames Blvd., Hamburg 07419
Pres.—Chuck Segar, 50 emp., *Metal stampings* ........ (973) 827-7155
Ace Metal Kraft Co., Inc., 815 McBride Ave., Woodland Park 07424
Pres.—Richard Zega, 9 emp., *Precision metal fabrication* ........ (973) 278-6605
Acme/Lingo Flagpoles, 1865 Route 206, Southampton 08088
Pres.—Jeff Lingo, 9 emp., *Tubular metal products, custom tapered* ........ (609) 801-1897
Action Signs & Awards, 305 N. 11th St., Millville 08332
CEO—Irene Inferrera, 2 emp., *Vinyl lettered signs, trophy engraving* ........ (856) 825-2454
Advanced Welding Service, Inc., 300 Thomas Ave., Ste. 701-1, Williamstown 08094
Pres.—Michael Hammond, 8 emp., *Welding & fabrication job shop* ........ (856) 875-2500
Airmet, Inc., 671 N. 3rd St., Newark 07107
Pres.—Stephen A. Yavorski, Sr., 6 emp., *Metal fences, gates, railings, steel* ........ (973) 481-5550
AKA, Inc., 1324 New Market Ave., South Plainfield 07080
Pres.—Michael Allocco, 6 emp., *Screen printing & embroidery, exterior* ........ (908) 753-8112
All American Metal Fabricators, 34 Harold St., Tenafly 07670
GM—Robert Leopold, 6 emp., *Steel/metal fabrication, including* ........ (201) 567-2898
All Star Awards & Trophies, Inc., 866 Haddon Ave., Collingswood 08108
Pres.—Mary Anne Sonsini, 4 emp., *Trophies & awards, including engraving* ........ (856) 858-6600
All-Star Pro & Sport Store, 642 State Route 35 N., Neptune 07753
Owner—Joe Storzieri, 2 emp., *Trophies, plaques & textile embroidery* ........ (732) 774-3444
Alway, Inc. (H Q), 440 U.S. Highway 202, Flemington 08822
Pres.—Terry Hubscher, 1 emp., *Corporate headquarters; metal bed sheet* ........ (908) 788-7220
AME Corporation, 33 Jacksonville Rd., Ste. 2, Towaco 07082
New Bus. Dev. Mgr.—Clara O'Boyle, 10 emp., *Custom rubber components, including* ........ (800) 951-0071
American Aluminum Co. (AMALCO), 230 Sheffield St., Mountainside 07092
Pres.—Andrew Brucker, 60 emp., *Metal fabrication, including hydroforming* ........ (908) 233-3500
American Van Equipment, Inc., 149 Lehigh Ave., Lakewood 08701
Pres.—Charles Richter, 95 emp., *Aluminum, steel & hot dipped galvanized* ........ (800) 526-4743
Amer-Rac, LLC, 8128 River Rd., Pennsauken 08110
Pres.—Steve Shore, 10 emp., *Steel & aluminum truck & van ladder* ........ (856) 488-6210
Anchor Optical Co., 101 E. Gloucester Pike, Barrington 08007
★ Dir., Mktg.—Kirsten Bjork Jones, 100 emp., *Commercial, experimental, specialty* ........ (856) 573-6865
Apollo Flags LLC, 594 Union Blvd., Totowa 07512
Ptnr.—Albert Potenzone, 4 emp., *Custom, U.S., military, state, parade* ........ (973) 256-8362
Aram, Inc., Michael, 2102 83rd St., North Bergen 07047
Pres.—Michael Wolohojis, 7 emp., *Hand-crafted metal tableware, hardware* ........ (201) 758-2551
Artus Corp., 201 S. Dean St., P.O. Box 511, Englewood 07631
Pres.—Raphael Levi, 40 emp., *Shims & shim stock* ........ (201) 568-1000
Astro Sign Co., 230 E. High St., Route 322, Glassboro 08028
Pres.—Christopher Painter, 16 emp., *Signs, vehicle lettering, banners,* ........ (856) 881-4300

Atlantic Coastal Welding, Inc., 16 Butler Blvd., Bayville 08721
Pres.—John Gallo, 6 emp., Welding & metal, aluminum & steel fabrication ... (732) 269-1088
Atmos Tech Industries, 1108 Pollack Ave., Ocean 07712
Mktg. Mgr.—Shaun Brower, 48 emp., Cleanroom filters, air showers, stainless ... (732) 493-8400
Atomic Trophies, Inc., 201 Shevchenko Ave., South Plainfield 07080
Pres.—Vijay Sha, 4 emp., Trophy & plaque assembly, engraving ... (732) 424-7930
Babinec Sheet Metal Works, Inc., Joseph, 774 Martin St., Rahway 07065
CEO—Joseph T. Babinec, 50 emp., Metal fabrication of store fixtures ... (732) 388-6600
Badge Company Of New Jersey, 223 Hamden Rd., P.O. Box 100, Annandale 08801
GM—Robert Marlow, 3 emp., Manufacturer & distributor of badges ... (908) 735-7700
Bird Toy Man, 197 S. Hillside Ave., Succasunna 07876
Owner—Henry E. Pedynowski, 1 emp., Wooden, plastic, acrylic, leather & ... (973) 584-0756
Bridgeton Trophy & Engraving, 641 Landis Ave., Bridgeton 08302
Owner—Tom D'Agostino, 10 emp., Engraved trophies, glass etching & ... (856) 451-9007
Burgess Steel Erectors Of New Jersey, LLC, 200 W. Forest Ave., P.O. Box 5629, Englewood 07631
CFO—Thomas J. Parisi, 85 emp., Steel fabrication & ornamental metals ... (201) 871-3500
Cain Machine, Inc., 1501 Oakland Ave., Millville 08332
Pres., GM—Douglas Cain, 6 emp., Metal parts, scientific glass machinery ... (856) 825-7225
Camtec Industries, Inc., 28 Saddle Ridge Rd., Colts Neck 07722
Pres.—Anthony Mauro, 16 emp., CNC machining job shop, including metal ... (732) 332-9800
Caporaso Sales Corp., 144 Emmet St., Newark 07114
Pres.—Nicholas F. Caporaso, 3 emp., Trophy & plaque supplies ... (973) 824-7286
Carpenter & Paterson, Inc., 369 Jefferson St., Saddle Brook 07663
Br. Mgr.—Thomas Browne, 35 emp., Metal pipe hangers, supports, struts ... (973) 772-1800
Central Safety Equipment, Inc., 300 W. Broad St., P.O. Box 250, Burlington 08016
Pres.—Mary Gordon, 30 emp., Metal machine protection parts & bellows ... (609) 386-6448
Cheney Flashing Co., LLC, 623 Prospect St., Trenton 08618
Pres.—Richard Levine, 15 emp., Metal roofing & waterproofing systems ... (609) 394-8175
Ciccone Custom Railing & Manufacturing, Inc., 2002 Route 9, Toms River 08755
Pres.—Robyn Ciccone, 10 emp., All-welded custom ornamental aluminum ... (732) 349-7071
CITYSAFE, Inc., 312 Squankum Yellowbrook Rd., Farmingdale 07727
Pres.—Karl Alizade, 7 emp., Commercial safes, vaults, strong rooms ... (732) 751-0100
Clip Strip Corp., 343 S. River St., Hackensack 07601
Pres.—Edward D. Spitaletta, 6 emp., Point-of-purchase merchandise & store ... (201) 342-9155
Coltwell Industries, Inc., 55 Winans Ave., Cranford 07016
V-P., Sales & Mktg.—Anthony Bengivenga, 15 emp., Custom & standard extruded aluminum (908) 276-7600
Computa Base Machining, Inc., 411 N. Grove St., P.O. Box 340, Berlin 08009
Pres.—Augustin Rosado, 14 emp., Fabrication & precision machining job ... (856) 767-9517
County Glass & Metal Installers, Inc., 80 Dewitt Pl., Hackensack 07601
Pres.—Eugene Vanbert, 6 emp., Metal, steel & aluminum fabrication ... (201) 343-7417
Crown Trophy, Inc., 3443 Highway 9, Freehold 07728
Pres.—Christine Sansavera, 3 emp., Trophies & awards ... (732) 462-3344
Crown Trophy-River Edge, NJ, 488 Kinderkamack Rd., River Edge 07661
Owner—Chuck Hedbavny, 5 emp., Awards, rotary & laser engraving, crystal ... (201) 261-3933
Cryofab, Inc., 540 N. Michigan Ave., P.O. Box 485, Kenilworth 07033
Owner & Co-Pres.—Vincent J. Grillo, 49 emp., Cryogenic equipment & accessories ... (908) 686-3636
Curtiss-Wright Surface Technologies, 80 Highway 4 E., Ste. 310, Paramus 07652
V-P., Cont. & Dir., Hum. Res.—David Rivellini, 31 emp., Divisional headquarters & ... (201) 843-7800
DDM Steel Construction, 3659 N. Delsea Dr., Vineland 08360
Pres.—Rich Meckenfuss, 3 emp., Structural steel & metal fabrication ... (856) 794-9400
Delva Tool & Machine Corp., 1603 Industrial Hwy., P.O. Box 2249, Cinnaminson 08077
Pres.—Stephen J. Voellinger, 90 emp., Precision machining, including low ... (856) 786-8700
Double O Mfg., 100 S. Washington Ave., Dunellen 08812
Pres., CFO—Albert J. Oslislo, 9 emp., Metal fabrication & military standard ... (732) 752-9423
Duffy, Inc., Andrew B., 322 Crown Point Rd., P.O. Box 569, Thorofare 08086
Pres.—Brian Duffy, 15 emp., Stainless steel, steel, titanium, aluminum ... (856) 845-4900
Dynamic Metals, Inc., 1713 S. 2nd St., Piscataway 08854
Pres.—Michael Wright, 60 emp., Metal fabrication ... (908) 769-5111
East Coast Steel, Inc., 317 Salina Rd., Sewell 08080
★ Owner—Jim Matthews, 20 emp., CNC & welding machining job shop ... (856) 582-6776
Eastern Sheet Metal & Plate Works, Inc., 169 E. Highland Pkwy., Roselle 07203
Sales Mgr.—John Sorber, 30 emp., Sheet metal fabrication ... (908) 241-6766
Engineered Devices Corp., 25 Bergen Tpke., Ridgefield Park 07660
Pres.—Antonio Limbardo, 15 emp., Corporate headquarters & metal fabrication ... (201) 641-2880
Ethylene Atlantic Corp., 136 Church St., P.O. Box 430, Swedesboro 08085
Pres.—Michael Johnston, 20 emp., Plastic & metal fabrication ... (856) 467-0010
Fabrite Metal, 10 Stony Brook Rd., Rockaway 07866
Owner—Robert Gilmore, 1 emp., Custom metal fabrication & precision ... (973) 714-1813
Fairfield Stamping Co., 374 Midland Ave., P.O. Box 8322, Saddle Brook 07663
Co-Pres.—Steve Orkenyi, 9 emp., Metal stampings ... (201) 791-9888
Fence Max, 6514 Black Horse Pike, Egg Harbor Township 08234
Owner & GM—Mark Amechi, 20 emp., Commercial, residential & industrial ... (609) 646-2430
Frame & Print, 778 Carver Ave., Westwood 07675
Pres., GM—Andy Kestenbaum, 5 emp., Wooden & metal picture frames & custom ... (201) 358-0404
Franklin Stamp & Sign Co., 543 Somerset St., Ste. 1, Somerset 08873
Co-Pres.—Harry Weber, Jr., 3 emp., Rubber stamps, vinyl, plastic, color ... (732) 846-9235
Freeman Products, Inc. (H Q), 71 Walsh Dr., Parsippany 07054
Ptnr.—Vincent Cariello, 25 emp., Corporate headquarters; trophy & award ... (201) 475-8888
G & M Welding & Fabricating, Inc., 31 W. Browning Rd., Bellmawr 08031
Pres.—George Liontas, 5 emp., Steel & metal fabrication ... (856) 931-0443
G M Repair, Inc., 90 Millhurst Rd., Manalapan 07726
Owner—Henry Gutzan, 1 emp., Industrial & commercial metal fabrication ... (732) 350-0304
G M Stainless, Inc., 41 Imclone Dr., Branchburg 08876
Pres.—Walter Gauer, 10 emp., Stainless steel shearing & edge conditioning ... (908) 575-1834
Garden State Foliage, LLC, 600 Central Ave., Farmingdale 07727
Ptnr.—Neil M. Roth, 20 emp., Christmas decorations, dried foliage ... (732) 751-0075
Gauer Metal Products, Inc., 175-179 N. Michigan Ave., Kenilworth 07033
CEO—Dennis J. Schultz, 40 emp., Metal storage rack frames, gravity ... (908) 241-4080
General Aviation & Electronics Mfg. Co., Inc., 30 Jersey Pl., Hackensack 07601
Pres.—John Baker, 35 emp., Precision sheet metal fabrication, ... (201) 487-1700
General Pallet, LLC, 97 River Rd., Flemington 08822
Ptnr.—Donald W. Baldwin, 7 emp., New & reconditioned wooden, plastic ... (908) 238-1000
Gentek Building Products, Inc., 11 Craigwood Rd., Avenel 07001
Plt. Mgr.—Bhavin Patel, 165 emp., Custom steel & aluminum coil metal ... (732) 381-0900
Global Partners In Shielding, Inc., 90 Dayton Ave., Ste. 13, Passaic 07055
Pres.—Donald Hener, 35 emp., Industrial EMI, RFI & X-ray shielding ... (973) 574-9077
Great Falls Metalworks, Inc., 301 E. 22nd St., Paterson 07514
CEO—J. Palombo, 15 emp., Metal fabrication ... (973) 523-6811
H & H Swiss Screw Machine Products Co., Inc., 1478 Chestnut Ave., Hillside 07205
Pres.—Darryl Stacy, 55 emp., Precision custom CNC Swiss screw machine ... (908) 688-6390
H & W Tool Co., Inc., 22 Lee Ave., Dover 07801
Pres., GM—Richard Winstead, 18 emp., Aeronautical & medical components ... (973) 366-0131
Henrich, Inc., Harold R., 300 Syracuse Ct., Lakewood 08701
Pres.—Tom Henrich, 48 emp., Metal fabrication ... (732) 370-4455
Hero's Salute Awards Co., 1875 State Route 23, Wayne 07470
Pres.—Robert Terry, 10 emp., Awards, trophies, signs, banners, flags ... (973) 696-5085
Hickok Matthews Co., 337 Main Rd., Montville 07045
Pres.—W. Schroth, 10 emp., Metal picture frames ... (973) 335-3400
Holler Metal Fabricators, Inc., 215 Liberty St., Metuchen 08840
Pres., Plt. Mgr.—Dan Holler, 7 emp., Metal fabrication ... (732) 635-9050
Holtec International (H Q), 555 Lincoln Dr. W., Ste. 1, Marlton 08053
Pres., CEO—Kris Singh, 170 emp., Company headquarters; steel fabrication ... (856) 797-0900
Horizon Sign Co., 340 Patterson Ave., Ste. C, Hamilton 08610
Owner—Thomas R. Barbieri, 1 emp., Illuminated interior & exterior signs ... (609) 586-0041
Hoyt Corp., 520 S. Dean St., Englewood 07631
Pres.—Don Maguire, 65 emp., Custom & standard precious metal electrical ... (201) 894-0707
Hun Machine Works, Inc., 51 Whittaker St., P.O. Box 189, Riverside 08075
Pres., V-P., Opers. & MIS Mgr.—Robert Kiss, 12 emp., Forgings, castings & machining job .. (856) 461-7112
Ill-Eagle Enterprises Ltd., 385 Main St., Little Falls 07424
Pres.—Darryl Sage, 44 emp., Trophies, awards & picture frames ... (973) 237-1111
Imperial Weld Ring Corp., 80-88 Front St., P.O. Box 6646, Elizabeth 07206
Pres.—Calvin Sierra, 15 emp., Precision metallic weld backing rings ... (908) 354-0011
Imprint Specialties, Inc., 601 New Broadway, Brooklawn 08030
Pres.—Francis Ferry, 5 emp., Commercial screen printing & awards ... (856) 456-2999
Industrial Welding Co., 655 Ferry St., Newark 07105
Pres.—Brian Hollfelder, 6 emp., Metal fabrication & welding job shop ... (973) 589-3100
Innovative Labeling, Inc., 12 Gloria Ln., Ste. 4, Fairfield 07004
Pres.—Cheryl Ziemba, 4 emp., Indoor & outdoor nameplates & labels ... (973) 227-4800
International Roll Forms, Inc., 8 International Ave., Sewell 08080
Pres.—Jack Vosbikian, 12 emp., Corporate headquarters & custom roll ... (856) 228-7333
International Tower Supply, 851 Bethel Ave., Pennsauken 08110
Mng. Ptnr.—Michael Moskowitz, 16 emp., Wireless infrastructure components, ... (856) 317-0005
Interstate Welding & Mfg. Co., Inc., 1510 Village Ct., Edgewater Park 08010
Pres., CFO—Joseph N. Russomanno, 18 emp., Welding, tube, pipe & metal fabrication ... (609) 699-6950
Iron Bound Metal, Inc., 238 Emmet St., Newark 07114
Pres.—John Olaya, 5 emp., General machining & fabrication job ... (973) 242-5704
Ironbound Trophy Center, 289 Lafayette St., Ste. A, Newark 07105
Owner—Christine Naia, 3 emp., Trophies & plaques & acrylics, corporate ... (973) 344-3872
I-Ron-X Industries, 134 Wheat Rd., Buena 08310
Pres., CFO—Paul Tomasello, 2 emp., Wrought iron & aluminum railings, steel ... (856) 697-3518
J & J Custom Metal Fabricators, Inc., 85 5th Ave., Ste. 17, Paterson 07524
Pres.—Jeff Wells, 3 emp., Metal fabrication ... (973) 977-9373
J & M Air, Inc., 189 S. Bridge St., Somerville 08876
Pres.—Michael Favreau, 12 emp., Custom galvanized & stainless steel ... (908) 707-4040
Jarco U. S. Casting Corp., 109 45th St., Union City 07087
Pres.—Mario A. Herrera, 35 emp., Cast metal emblems & advertising specialties ... (201) 271-0003
Jory Engravers, Inc., 23 W. Erie Ave., Rutherford 07070
GM—Gary Gagliardi, 3 emp., Metal engraving, screen printing, metal ... (201) 939-1546
JSM Co., 1052 Wayside Rd., Tinton Falls 07712
Owner—David Paraskevas, 5 emp., Precision automatic cut-off sawing, ... (732) 695-9577
Julius Machine & Tool Co., B-14 Merry Ln., East Hanover 07936
Owner & Pres.—Julius Gaida, 1 emp., Precision CNC machining, turning & ... (973) 515-8540
Kalis Metal Components Corp., 231 North Ave., P.O. Box 294, Garwood 07027
Hum. Res. & Off. Mgr.—Evelyn Archibald, 30 emp., Sheet metal fabrication & precision ... (908) 789-0500
Keller Welding Co., LLC, 22 Wantage Ave., Branchville 07826
Owner & Pres.—Jeremy Hughen, 4 emp., Fabrication & welding of steel, aluminum ... (973) 948-0046
KeyValet, 15 Industrial Dr., P.O. Box 1099, Laurence Harbor 08879
Owner—Nancy Teufel, 4 emp., Standard & specialty security locks ... (732) 521-1394
Kraftware Corp., 270 Cox St., Roselle 07203
Pres., CEO—Randy Grant, 22 emp., Stainless steel, polyester film & metal ... (908) 259-8883
Krowne Metal Corp., 100 Haul Rd., Wayne 07470
Ex. V-P.—Roger Forman, 44 emp., Stainless steel bar & restaurant equipment ... (973) 305-3300
Little Falls Trophy Co., 555 Route 46 E., P.O. Box 1050, Little Falls 07424
Ptnr. & V-P.—Ellen Riccobono, 7 emp., Trophy engraving ... (973) 256-5222
Maranatha Ceramic Tile & Marble, Inc., 253 Cookstown New Egypt Rd., Wrightstown 08562
Ptnr. & Pres.—Thomas Raab, 20 emp., Manufacturer & distributor of custom ... (609) 758-1168
Margola Corp., 232 S. Van Brunt St., Englewood 07631
Owner—Neil Chalfin, 6 emp., Manufacturer & distributor of rhinestones ... (201) 816-9500
Marshall Industrial Technologies, 529 S. Clinton Ave., Trenton 08611
Pres.—John Mako, 150 emp., Welding, metal fabrication & machining ... (609) 394-7153
Megasafe, 8 Sunrise Ave., Budd Lake 07828
Pres.—Michael J. Hookway, 20 emp., High security, jewelry, residential ... (973) 691-0382
Merit Trophies & Engraving, Inc., 184 Main St., Hackensack 07601
V-P., GM—Jim Dolack, 5 emp., Laser engraving of signs, plaques, ... (201) 487-5780
Metal Cutting Corp., 89 Commerce Rd., Cedar Grove 07009
Ex. V-P.—Joshua Jablons, 65 emp., Burr-free cut-off tight-tolerance metal ... (973) 239-1101
Metal Masters, 630 Laurel St., Beverly 08010
Owner—Israel Gaitelband, 2 emp., Metal & stainless steel fabrication ... (609) 332-3176
Metaline Products Co., Inc., 101 N. Feltus St. & 241 Raritan St., South Amboy 08879
Chrm. & CEO—August J. Zilincar III, 35 emp., Custom metal point-of-purchase displays ... (732) 721-1373
Middle Atlantic Products, Inc., 300 Fairfield Rd., Fairfield 07004
Pres. & Dir., Sales & Mktg.—Michael Baker, 490 emp., Steel audio & broadcast racks ... (973) 839-1011
Mitchell Welding & Iron Works, Inc., 7 Enterprise Dr., Cape May Court House 08210
Pres., CFO—William Mitchell, 8 emp., Structural steel & metal fabrication ... (609) 465-7510
Moreng Metal Products, 100 W. End Rd., Totowa 07512
Pres.—James R. Moreng, 100 emp., Metal products ... (973) 256-2001
Morris Tool & Machine Co., 80 Upper Hibernia Rd., Rockaway 07866
Owner & Pres.—Harry Pinand, 3 emp., Full-service precision CNC milling ... (973) 983-9209
Mozer, Inc., Theodore E., 601 W. 4th St., P.O. Box 25, Palmyra 08065
Pres.—Theodore E. Mozer, Jr., 12 emp., Metal fabrication ... (856) 829-1432
Mulberry Metal Products, Inc., 2199 Stanley Ter., Union 07083
CFO—Patricia Lynch, 100 emp., Metal & plastic wallplates & weatherproof ... (908) 688-8850
National Metal Finishings Corp., Inc., 897 South Ave., P.O. Box 486, Middlesex 08846
Pres.—Lou Fahsbender, 12 emp., Chill rolls, including design, overlay ... (732) 752-7770
NEAC, Inc., 526 Pacific Ave., #2202, Atlantic City 08401
Pres.—Joel H. Miller, 5 emp., Contract manufacturing of metal & plastic ... (908) 903-9100
Newark Wire Works, Inc., 1059 King Georges Post Rd., Ste. 103, Edison 08837
Pres.—JoAnn Spellman, 16 emp., Architectural wire mesh panels & fabricated ... (732) 661-2001
Norco, Inc., 237 South Ave., P.O. Box 186, Garwood 07027
Pres.—Michael Rosenberg, 15 emp., Lapel pins, dog tags, giant magnetic ... (908) 789-1550
Norgus Silk Screen Co., 58 Sylvan Ave., Clifton 07011
Owner & Pres.—Sanjay Thakker, 8 emp., Screen, cylindrical, digital & large-format ... (973) 365-0600
O'Brien Co., Inc., J., 40 Commerce St., Springfield 07081
Pres., CEO—Sharmay O'Brien, 20 emp., Manufacturer of lanyards, badge reels ... (973) 379-8844

Oldcastle BuildingEnvelope®, 1500 Glen Ave., Moorestown 08057
Sales Mgr.—Brian Moore, 100 emp., *Glass & metal fabrication* .... (866) 653-2278
Passaic County Welders, Inc., 100 Parish Dr., Wayne 07470
V-P.—Robert Grimbilas, 38 emp., *Welding & structural steel, steel,* .... (973) 696-1200
Patriot Marine Fabricating, 708-4 Old Shore Rd., Forked River 08731
Pres.—Nicole Spisak, 3 emp., *Aluminum work boats, marine fuel tanks* .... (609) 693-5542
Paul's Custom Awards & Trophy, Inc., 200 White Horse Pike, Barrington 08007
Pres.—Paul McGuigan, 8 emp., *Trophy engraving & plaques* .... (856) 547-7777
Pepco Mfg. Co., 210 E. Evergreen Ave., P.O. Box 160, Somerdale 08083
CEO—John Kennedy, 80 emp., *Company headquarters & telecommunication* .... (856) 783-3700
Perilstein Glass, 285 Howe Ave., P.O. Box 84, Passaic 07055
Pres.—David Perilstein, 30 emp., *Metal & glass fabrication* .... (973) 777-3610
Precision Welding, 845 Berkshire Valley Rd., Wharton 07885
Owner—Jim Stanlick, 7 emp., *Metal fabrication & welding job shop* .... (973) 366-7316
Predator Tools (H Q), 35 S. Woodruff Rd., Bridgeton 08302
Owner—Pam Lesche, 2 emp., *Company headquarters; digging tools* .... (856) 455-3790
Pride Tempered Glass Products, LLC, 2001 S. 6th St., Camden 08104
Pres.—John Galan, 10 emp., *Tempered & insulated glass & mirrors* .... (856) 365-1200
Prismatix Decal, Inc., 324 Railroad Ave., Hackensack 07601
Pres., CEO—Miriam Salomon, 10 emp., *Decals, emblems, trophies & engraving* .... (201) 525-2800
Product Identification Co., Inc., 141 Lanza Ave., Bldg. 19, Garfield 07026
Pres.—Les Weinstock, 20 emp., *Aluminum, vinyl & polyester nameplates* .... (973) 955-4747
Proof Productions, Inc., 599 Mantua Blvd., Sewell 08080
Owner & Pres.—Steve McEntee, 20 emp., *Scenic wood & metal products, including* .... (856) 442-0700
Quality Industries, Inc., 204 Getty Ave., Clifton 07011
Pres.—Andrew Ponikowski, 10 emp., *Fabrication & machining shop, including* .... (973) 478-4425
R & R Specialties, 126 Holly Dr., Rio Grande 08242
Ptnr.—Chandi Ankrum, 2 emp., *Trophies & engraving* .... (609) 886-6651
R M F Assocs., Inc., 202 Carolyn Rd., Union 07083
V-P.—Michael Rodgers, 140 emp., *Fabricated metal choke & chamber brushes* .... (908) 687-9355
R S R Food Service Equipment Corp., 6574 Delilah Rd., Egg Harbor Township 08234
Pres.—Rick Love, 3 emp., *Food processing equipment & custom* .... (609) 646-5158
R.S. Phillips Steel, LLC, 128 Lake Pochung Rd., Sussex 07461
Ptnr.—Neil Phillips, 23 emp., *Steel & aluminum fabrication & erection* .... (973) 827-6464
Rainmen U. S. A., Inc., 10 Maple St., Norwood 07648
Owner—Jeff Nanus, 200 emp., *Umbrellas, canvas bags & accessories* .... (201) 784-3244
Redyref Co., 100 Kenner Ct., Riverdale 07457
Pres.—William Pymm, 35 emp., *Touchscreen building directory, interactive* .... (718) 784-3690
Reel Parts Co., 10 Park Ave., West Orange 07052
Pres.—John Dyer, 6 emp., *Corrugated, PVC, masonite & wooden* .... (973) 731-9559
Rem Services, 310 W. 6th St., Ship Bottom 08008
Owner—Robert Mattner, 1 emp., *Name tags, trophies, small signs &* .... (609) 494-7760
Rhoads Metal Works, Inc., 1551 John Tipton Blvd., Pennsauken 08110
Pres.—William K. Rhoads, 37 emp., *Custom metal fabrication & HVAC contracting* .... (856) 486-1551
Ricci Tool & Die Co., 122 Myrtle Ave., Long Branch 07740
Pres.—John Ricci, Sr., 9 emp., *Tool & die job shop, including metal* .... (732) 222-2777
Rios Engraving, 1 Maple Ave., Morristown 07960
Owner, Plt. Opers. & Sales & Mktg. Mgr.—Rolando G. Rios, 3 emp., *Custom & laser engraving* (973) 539-5749
Robro Mfg., Inc., 288 10th Ave., Paterson 07524
Pres.—Ivan Migalko, 12 emp., *General machining job shop, including* .... (973) 279-7237
Roll Tech Industries, 55 Route 31 S., Ste. A, Pennington 08534
Pres.—John King, 26 emp., *Metal roll-formed products* .... (609) 730-9500
Romar Machine & Tool Co., 521 Commerce St., Franklin Lakes 07417
Pres.—Bob Thum, 12 emp., *Packaging machinery tube holders, fill* .... (201) 337-7111
Rummel Industries, Inc., 697 Rahway Ave., P.O. Box 1326, Union 07083
Pres.—Peter Rummel, 18 emp., *Corporate headquarters & plastic &* .... (908) 688-6600
R-Way Tooling & Metal Works, 224 S. Lincoln Ave., Vineland 08361
Cont.—Scott Sikora, 8 emp., *Steel fabrication & general machining* .... (856) 692-2218
Saracino Monuments, LLC, Frank, 359 Bergen Blvd., Fairview 07022
Ptnr.—Frank Saracino, 2 emp., *Granite upright monuments & markers* .... (201) 945-1266
Screens & Fabricated Metals Corp., 1265 McBride Ave., P.O. Box 647, Woodland park 07424
Pres.—Mike McMillan, 50 emp., *Screen & storm doors, security screens* .... (973) 785-1414
Selco Mfg. Corp., 3 Fairfield Crescent, West Caldwell 07006
Pres.—Travis Hutchinson, 55 emp., *Fabricated products for the infrastructure* .... (973) 244-1177
Selling Precision, Inc., 264 Marshall Hill Rd., West Milford 07480
Pres.—William Calcagno, 26 emp., *Hydraulic manifolds* .... (973) 728-1214
Sheet Metal Products, Inc., 794 N. 6th St., Newark 07107
Pres.—William F. Kovacs, 30 emp., *Contract manufacturing & industrial* .... (973) 482-0450
Shelving Depot, Inc., 419 W. Elizabeth Ave., Linden 07036
Pres.—Richard Kurland, 12 emp., *Shelving, store fixtures, metal, wooden* .... (908) 474-8000
SICA Metal Products, 1775 Hurffville Rd., Route 41, P.O. Box 5525, Deptford 08096
Owner & Fin. Mgr.—Ralph Sica, Sr., 3 emp., *Custom stainless steel & metal fabrications* .... (856) 227-6616
Signs By Lynn, 329 Kearny Ave., Ste. A, Kearny 07032
Owner—Lynn Oelz, 3 emp., *Commercial, residential, ADA & architectural* .... (201) 998-4273
Siloa, Inc. (H Q), 2493 Lamington Rd., Ste. C, Bedminster 07921
Pres.—Mark Bellard, 3 emp., *Corporate headquarters; plastic & metal* .... (908) 234-9040
Springfield Metal Products Co., 8 Commerce St., Springfield 07081
Pres.—John D. Sommer, 10 emp., *Metal fabrication* .... (973) 379-4600
Staloff Bros., 22 Lewis Ave., Jersey City 07306
Ptnr.—Glenn Brownsteim, 3 emp., *Architectural metal fabrication* .... (201) 653-6479
Stewart-Morris, Inc., 71 Kings Rd., Madison 07940
Pres.—John W. Morris, 6 emp., *Awards, gifts, flags & promotional* .... (973) 822-2777
Stirrup Metal Products Corp., 215 Emmet St., Newark 07114
Pres.—Todd Stirrup, 20 emp., *Metal stampings & fabrication* .... (973) 824-7086
Support Systems Specialties, Inc., 25 Ridge Rd., P.O. Box 269, South Plainfield 07080
Owner—Joseph Belardo, 13 emp., *Custom metal fabrication* .... (908) 510-4349
Swenson Welding & Fabrication, Bill, 707 W. Duerer St., Egg Harbor City 08215
Pres.—Bill Swenson, 3 emp., *Metal fabrication & welding job shop* .... (609) 653-1177
T J's Sportwide Trophy & Awards, 236 S. Salem St., Randolph 07869
Pres.—Joe Balzarotti, 10 emp., *Awards, trophies, plaques, ribbons,* .... (973) 989-8775
Technical Name Plate Corp., 92 1st St., Passaic 07055
Pres.—Perla Navarro, 20 emp., *Metal, vinyl, polyester film, plastic* .... (973) 773-4256
Todd Architectural Models, 54 Mountainview Rd., P.O. Box 1002, Chatham 07928
Pres.—Douglas Pitney, 7 emp., *Wooden, plastic & metal architectural* .... (973) 507-4072
TORNQVIST, 29 Hanes Dr., Wayne 07470
Off. Mgr.—Adam Mosciszko, 22 emp., *Metal fabrication, laser cutting &* .... (973) 686-5999
Town Line Trophies, 2 Amberfield Dr., Delran 08075
Ptnr. & Off. Mgr.—Nancy Hagmaier, 3 emp., *Trophies, plaques, bronze castings,* .... (856) 461-0540
Tropar Mfg. Co., Inc., 5 Vreeland Rd., Florham Park 07932
Pres.—Peter E. Ilaria, 60 emp., *Corporate headquarters & plaques, clocks* .... (973) 822-2400
Trophy King Of Ramsey, 503 N. Franklin Tpke., Unit 13, Ramsey 07446
GM—John Paluskiewicz, 3 emp., *Trophy assembly & engraving* .... (201) 760-6488
Trophy King, Inc., The, 309 Queen Anne Rd., Teaneck 07666
Pres.—James Walsh, 6 emp., *Corporate headquarters & trophy assembly* .... (201) 836-1482
Tur Machine, LLC, 198 U.S. Highway 206, Ste. 5, Hillsborough 08844
Ptnr.—Zbigniew Richard Rolka, 6 emp., *General machining shop* .... (908) 874-0235
Unique Metal Products Co., Inc., 17 W. Scott Ave., P.O. Box 1181, Rahway 07065
Pres.—Joseph S. Niemczyk, 16 emp., *Metal products, fabrication, laser* .... (732) 388-1888
V & R Design Co., 941 State St., Perth Amboy 08861
Owner—Victor Carollo, 6 emp., *Metal fabrication* .... (732) 442-9249
Vandermolen Corp., 119 Dorsa Ave., Livingston 07039
Pres.—Aldo H. Vandermolen, 3 emp., *Electric indoor & outdoor insect control* .... (973) 992-8506
Versabar Corp., 100 Maltese Dr., Totowa 07512
Chrm., Pres.—William E. Taylor, 12 emp., *Metal framing systems* .... (973) 279-8400
Vo-Toys, Inc., 400 S. 5th St., Harrison 07029
Pres.—Arthur Hirschberg, 125 emp., *Pet accessories & products, including* .... (973) 484-0088
W & E Baum, Inc., 89 Bannard St., Freehold 07728
CEO—Maurice Zagha, 25 emp., *Wooden, marble, metal, acrylic, glass* .... (732) 866-1881
Ware Industries, Inc., 400 Metuchen Rd., South Plainfield 07080
Vice Chairwoman—Ottavia McLaughlin, 350 emp., *Corporate headquarters & steel framing* . (908) 757-9000
Weld-Done Welding, Inc., 20 Woodland Ave., Hurffville 08080
Pres.—Jeff Podesek, 15 emp., *Structural steel fabrication, metal* .... (856) 582-7080
Wellbilt Industries, 2 Maple Ave., Linden 07036
Owner & IT Mgr.—Les Zalewski, 15 emp., *Custom metal fabrication & stamping* .... (908) 486-6002
West Hudson Industries, 1687 Saint Georges Ave., Rahway 07065
Pres.—Les Moshinsky, 4 emp., *Metal & plastic engraving & laminating* .... (732) 381-6800
Westfield Sheet Metal Works, Inc., 261 Monroe Ave., P.O. Box 128, Kenilworth 07033
Pres.—Campbell Johnstone, 25 emp., *Custom stainless & carbon steel, aluminum* .... (908) 276-5500
Wine Products, Inc., 2416 Highway 35, Ste. B, Manasquan 08736
Pres.—John Kuntz, 2 emp., *Wooden & metal wine racks* .... (732) 528-5222
Z I Parts Co., 215 Cristiani St., Cranford 07016
Owner—Zbigniew Bielen, 1 emp., *Metal fabrication & machining job shop* .... (908) 241-0109

## 35 INDUSTRIAL MACHINERY & EQUIPMENT

### 3511 Turbines & turbine generator sets

ABB Inc., Business Unit Turbocharger, 1460 Livingston Ave., P.O. Box 6005, North Brunswick 08902
Pres.—Chuck Noddin, 12 emp., *Rebuilt turbochargers* .... (732) 932-6000
Conhagen, Inc., Alfred (H Q), 2035 Lincoln Hwy., Edison Sq. W., Ste. 3003, Edison 08817
Pres.—Alfred Conhagen, Jr., 5 emp., *Corporate headquarters; pump parts,* .... (732) 287-4565
E-Harvest Systems (H Q), 424 Little Brook Rd., Glen Gardner 08826
Owner—Robert Klein, 2 emp., *Company headquarters; hydroelectric* .... (908) 832-0400
MAN Diesel & Turbo, 2 Amboy Ave., Bldg. 2, Woodbridge 07095
GM—Angel Colon Perez, 22 emp., *Divisional headquarters & rebuilt rotating* .... (732) 582-8200
Princeton Power Systems, Inc., 3175 Princeton Pike, Ste. C, Lawrenceville 08648
Co-Founder & Ex. CSO—Darren Hammell, 48 emp., *Electric power converting equipment* ... (609) 955-5390
PSEG Power, 749 Cliff Rd., Sewaren 07077
Off. Mgr.—Carmen Esteves, 80 emp., *Gas & steam turbines, electric turbines* .... (732) 750-2062
Siemens Energy, Inc., 840 Nottingham Way, Trenton 08638
V-P.—Ken Win, 200 emp., *Industrial turbines & compressors,* .... (609) 890-5000
Van Hydraulics, 643 Sayre Ave., Perth Amboy 08861
GM—Steve Roberts, 30 emp., *Rebuilt cylinders, pumps, motors, valves* .... (732) 442-5500

### 3519 Engines—internal combustion, nec

American Crankshaft Grinding Co., Inc., 851-861 Fairmount Ave., Elizabeth 07201
Owner—Tony DiCosmo, 3 emp., *Rebuilt engines & automotive machine* .... (908) 352-5558
Arrow Machine Co., 117 Norfolk St., Newark 07103
Owner & Corp. Pres.—George Ambandos, 6 emp., *Rebuilt engines* .... (973) 642-2430
Atlantic Detroit Diesel-Allison, LLC, 169 Old New Brunswick Rd., Piscataway 08854
Off. Admn.—Elaine Loss, 50 emp., *Rebuilt diesel engines & transmission* .... (732) 752-7100
Cast Technology, Inc., 161 West St., South Plainfield 07080
Pres.—Kenneth Shilay, 7 emp., *Rebuilt engines & distributor of bearings* .... (908) 753-5155
Coates International Ltd., 2100 Highway 34 & Ridgewood Rd., Wall 07719
Pres., CEO—George J. Coates, 14 emp., *Spherical rotary valve system for internal* .... (732) 449-7717
D & F Performance, 417 N. Grove St., Berlin 08009
Ptnr.—David R. Thornton, Sr., 2 emp., *Rebuilt performance engines & distributor* .... (856) 767-4095
Garden State Diesel, 97 Foster Rd., Ste. 4, Moorestown 08057
Owner & GM—Rich Carragher, 8 emp., *Rebuilt diesel engine fuel injection* .... (856) 914-9797
Houpert Truck Service, 115 Atlantic Ave., P.O. Box 8, Berlin 08009
Owner—Deborah Baccellieri, 11 emp., *Rebuilt diesel engines & truck service* .... (856) 767-0145
Jackson Racing Engines, Inc., Henry, 787 Route 537, Cream Ridge 08514
Pres.—Henry Jackson, 2 emp., *Automotive racing engines* .... (609) 758-7476
Jetek Enterprises, LLC, 4329 Atlantic Brigantine Blvd., Brigantine 08203
★ Owner—Ronnie Walker, 3 emp., *Rebuilt marine engines* .... (609) 266-4700
Johnson & Towers, Inc., 2021 Briggs Rd., P.O. Box 4000, Mount Laurel 08054
Chrm.—Walter Johnson III, 75 emp., *Corporate headquarters & rebuilt truck* .... (856) 234-6990
K & K Automotive, Inc., 979 Main Ave., Passaic 07055
Pres., GM—Abraham Hazin, 6 emp., *Rebuilt automotive & marine engines* .... (973) 777-2235
Kraft Power Corp., 241 W. Parkway, Pompton Plains 07444
V-P.—Chris Stemper, 30 emp., *Manufacturer of combined heat & power* .... (973) 835-9800
L E C Electronics, Inc., 814 Warsaw Ave., Blackwood 08012
Pres.—Elsie Lewis, 5 emp., *Marine after-cooler systems* .... (856) 227-3953
Lake Small Engine Repair, LLC, 283 Cedar Grove Ln., Somerset 08873
Owner—Patti Lake, 2 emp., *Rebuilt small engines* .... (732) 873-9047
LRB Performance Machine Co., 22-B Lasinski Rd., Franklin 07416
Owner—Lou Bengivenni, 3 emp., *High performance & racing engines,* .... (973) 209-7770
Manley Performance Products, Inc., 1960 Swarthmore Ave., Lakewood 08701
Pres.—Henry Manley, 115 emp., *High-performance internal engine components* .... (732) 905-3366
Medford Speed & Machine, Inc., 132 Red Lion Rd., Southampton 08088
Pres.—Gerald Glenn, 2 emp., *Rebuilt engines* .... (609) 801-0808
Melton Sales & Service, Inc., 511 Elbow Ln., Burlington 08016
V-P., Prodn.—Chris Robles, 85 emp., *Remanufactured diesel engines, drive* .... (609) 699-4800
Shoemaker's Automotive Machine, 176 Kings Hwy., Cape May Court House 08210
Owner—Doug Shoemaker, 1 emp., *Rebuilt automotive engines* .... (609) 624-0847
SLP Specialty Vehicles, Inc., 1501 Industrial Way N., Toms River 08755
Pres.—Ed Hamburger, 12 emp., *Supercharged specialty vehicles, high* .... (732) 240-3696

### 3523 Farm machinery & equipment

Chick Master International, Inc. (H Q), 25 Rockwood Pl., Ste. 335, Englewood 07631
Pres.—Robert Holzer, 9 emp., *Corporate headquarters; poultry incubators* .... (201) 871-8810
Delmhorst Instrument Co., 51 Indian Ln. E., Towaco 07082
Pres., CEO—Thomas Laurenzi, 24 emp., *Hand-held moisture testing instruments* .... (973) 334-2557
Metalfab, Inc., 11 Prices Switch Rd., P.O. Box 9, Vernon 07462
COO—Mike Randazzo, 30 emp., *Large plate steel fabrication & dry* .... (973) 764-2000

S.I.C.

Monarch Mfg. Works, Inc., 7249-B Browning Rd., Merchantville 08109
Pres., CEO—Harry D. Beccari, 25 emp., *Precision spray nozzles for the industrial* ........ (856) 241-1500

### 3524 Lawn & garden equipment

Monarch Mfg. Works, Inc., 7249-B Browning Rd., Merchantville 08109
Pres., CEO—Harry D. Beccari, 25 emp., *Precision spray nozzles for the industrial* ........ (856) 241-1500
Reinco, Inc., 520 North Ave., Plainfield 07060
Pres.—Erich W. Reinecker, 11 emp., *Power mulchers for landscape construction* ........ (908) 755-0921
Snow Joe, LLC, 86 Executive Ave., Edison 08817
Pres.—Joe Cohen, 25 emp., *Lawn & garden equipment, including* ........ (866) 766-9563
Vandermolen Corp., 119 Dorsa Ave., Livingston 07039
Pres.—Aldo H. Vandermolen, 3 emp., *Electric indoor & outdoor insect control* ........ (973) 992-8506
W.W. Manufacturing Co., Inc., 60 Rosenhayn Ave., Bridgeton 08302
Ptnr. & Pres.—Peter Lesche, 12 emp., *Steel landscaping & nursery hand tools* ........ (856) 451-5700

### 3531 Construction machinery

Franklin Miller, Inc., 60 Okner Pkwy., P.O. Box 070663, Livingston 07039
V-P., Sales—Dave Schuppe, 35 emp., *Size reduction processors for wet/dry* ........ (973) 535-9200
Hainesport Tool & Maintenance, 1924 Ark Rd., Hainesport 08036
Owner & Pres.—Gary Zwick, 18 emp., *Rebuilt machine tools & earth moving* ........ (609) 261-0016
International Process Equipment Co., 9300 Route 130 N., Pennsauken 08110
Pres.—Ronald C. Miller, 20 emp., *Pulverizers & grinders* ........ (856) 665-4007
Jescraft, 201 W. Fort Lee Rd., Bogota 07603
Pres., CFO—Michael Brown, 10 emp., *Construction job site material handling* ........ (201) 488-4545
Long Reach High Reach, LLC, 890 E. Rte. 70, Ste. B, Marlton 08053
Owner—Percy Ransome, 6 emp., *Construction equipment attachments,* ........ (856) 797-6999
Marindus Co., Inc, P.O. Box 663, Englewood 07631
Pres.—Jim Bartis, 10 emp., *Concrete surface preparation equipment* ........ (201) 567-8383
Modi Systems, Inc., 88 S. State St., Hackensack 07601
V-P., GM—Theresa Esposito, 10 emp., *Roofing torches* ........ (201) 525-0775
Triple D Enterprises, Inc., 135 Eayrestown Rd., Southampton 08088
Pres.—Douglas Melegari, 8 emp., *Underground horizontal directional* ........ (609) 859-3000

### 3532 Mining machinery

Enviro-Clear Co., Inc., 152 Cregar Rd., High Bridge 08829
Pres.—C. Meyer, 19 emp., *Liquid/solid clarifiers, thickeners* ........ (908) 638-5507
International Process Equipment Co., 9300 Route 130 N., Pennsauken 08110
Pres.—Ronald C. Miller, 20 emp., *Pulverizers & grinders* ........ (856) 665-4007
National Environmental Service Co. (H Q), 7 Hampshire Dr., Mendham 07945
Pres.—Mark Kestner, 2 emp., *Company headquarters; high-pressure* ........ (973) 543-4586
National Environmental Services Co., 700 Grand Ave., Hackettstown 07840
CFO—Paul Kestner, 6 emp., *High-pressure water spray dust control* ........ (908) 813-1195
Pallmann Industries, Inc., 820 Bloomfield Ave., Clifton 07012
GM—Rolf Gren, 12 emp., *Pulverizing & granulating machines* ........ (973) 471-1450
Rema Tip Top/North America, Inc. (H Q), 119 Rockland Ave., Northvale 07647
Pres.—Olafur Gunnarsson, 25 emp., *Corporate headquarters; rubber, epoxy* ........ (201) 768-8100

### 3533 Oil & gas field machinery

Atlas Copco North America, LLC (H Q), 7 Campus Dr., Ste. 200, Parsippany 07054
Pres., AC Holdings USA—Jim Levitt, 40 emp., *Company headquarters; industrial air* ........ (973) 397-3400
GEA Mechanical Equipment US, Inc., 100 Fairway Ct., Northvale 07647
Pres.—Michael J. Vick, 175 emp., *Corporate headquarters & centrifuges* ........ (201) 767-3900
Glentech, Inc., 46 4th St., Somerville 08876
Pres.—Scott Gordon, 15 emp., *Pipeline strainers & marine hardware* ........ (908) 685-2205

### 3534 Elevators & moving stairways

Elevator Doors, Inc./Elevator Cabs, Inc., 15 Jane St., Paterson 07522
Pres.—Paul Pedretti, 100 emp., *New elevator cabs & elevator entrances* ........ (973) 790-9100
Elevator Products Corp., 100 Dermarest Dr., Wayne 07470
Mfg. Mgr.—Eudoro Perez, 85 emp., *Elevator components* ........ (973) 341-8000
Elevator Technology Corp., 337 Market St., Paterson 07501
Pres.—Shlomo Tagjer, 5 emp., *Elevator replacement parts* ........ (973) 523-7760
Florlift Of New Jersey, Inc., 19 Gardner Rd., Ste. M, Fairfield 07004
Pres.—Casper Vivona, Jr., 22 emp., *Hydraulic invalid lifts & elevators* ........ (973) 484-1717
Fujitec America Inc., New York Region, 215 Entin Rd., Clifton 07014
Opers. Mgr.—Joseph Smith, 100 emp., *Elevators & escalators* ........ (973) 330-0100
North American Elevator, Inc., 609 W. Elizabeth Ave., Linden 07036
Pres.—Tommy Curran, 20 emp., *Elevators* ........ (908) 523-1234
Princeton Power Systems, Inc., 3175 Princeton Pike, Ste. C, Lawrenceville 08648
Co-Founder & Ex. CSO—Darren Hammell, 48 emp., *Electric power converting equipment* ........ (609) 955-5390
Regency Elevator Products, 870 Mount Prospect Ave., Newark 07104
V-P.—Jack Guarino, 20 emp., *Elevator cars, fixtures & fronts* ........ (973) 481-1400
Schindler Elevator Corp., 840 N. Lenola Rd., Ste. 4, Moorestown 08057
Site Mgr.—Kyle Rainwater, 20 emp., *Escalators & elevators* ........ (856) 234-2220
Schindler Elevator Corp. (H Q), 20 Whippany Rd., Morristown 07960
Chrm.—Alfred N. Schindler, 240 emp., *Corporate headquarters; elevators,* ........ (973) 397-6500
Woerner Machine & Tool Co., 700 Grand Ave., Bldg. 7, Hackettstown 07840
Pres., Fin., MIS & R & D Mgr.—Edgar W. Woerner, 2 emp., *Elevator & escalator parts* ........ (908) 979-0042

### 3535 Conveyors & conveying equipment

Aero Mfg Co., 310 Allwood Rd., P.O. Box 1250, Clifton 07012
Pres.—Wayne Phillips, 100 emp., *Stainless steel foodservice, material* ........ (973) 473-5300
Automated Flexible Conveyors, Inc., 55 Walman Ave., 2nd Fl., Clifton 07011
Pres.—Kevin Devaney, 20 emp., *Spiral feeder conveyors, dump clean* ........ (973) 340-1695
BEUMER Corporation, 800 Apgar Dr., Somerset 08873
Pres., CEO—Thomas Dahlstein, 175 emp., *Conveying, loading, palletizing & packaging* ........ (732) 893-2800
Caddy Corp., 509 Sharptown Rd., P.O. Box 345, Bridgeport 08014
Owner—Craig Cohen, 40 emp., *Conveyor systems* ........ (856) 467-4222
Century Conveyor Service, Inc., 4301 S. Clinton Ave., South Plainfield 07080
Pres.—Ron Ferrara, 28 emp., *Conveyors, material handling equipment* ........ (908) 205-0625
Conveyors By North American, 156 Huron Ave., Clifton 07013
Pres.—Gloria J. Kolodziej, 3 emp., *Gravity conveyors* ........ (973) 777-6600
Coperion K-Tron Pitman, Inc., 590 Woodbury Glassboro Rd., Sewell 08080
CFO, GM—Robert E. Wisniewski, 100 emp., *Corporate headquarters & feeding &* ........ (856) 589-0500
D A S Installations, Inc., 176 Saddle River Rd., Bldg. D, Garfield 07026
Pres.—Louis Skvarca, 10 emp., *Belt conveyors* ........ (973) 473-6858
DYNA-Veyor, Inc., 10 Hudson St., Newark 07103
Pres., CEO—Steve Ayre, 18 emp., *Plastic conveyor chains, belting, sprockets* ........ (973) 484-1119
ECS, LLC, 1827 U.S. Highway 9, Howell 07731
Owner—Virginia Sena, 15 emp., *Conveyors & truck loaders* ........ (732) 462-5530
Equipment Erectors, Inc., 110 Garden St., Somerset 08873
Pres.—George Anderson, 43 emp., *Conveyors* ........ (732) 846-1212
Flow-Turn, Inc., 1050 Commerce Ave., Ste. 1, Union 07083
Pres.—Hermann Miedel, 19 emp., *Belt curve conveyors* ........ (908) 687-3225
Garvey Corp., 208 S. Route 73, Hammonton 08037
Pres.—William J. Garvey, 80 emp., *Table top conveyors & accumulators* ........ (609) 561-2450
Intelligrated, 265 Davidson Ave., Ste. 219, Somerset 08873
V-P., Opers., Eastern Rep.—Eric Palotas, 34 emp., *Conveyors, sortation, automated storage* (732) 302-2590
Keneco, Inc., 123 N. 8th St., P.O. Box 121, Kenilworth 07033
Pres.—William Van Loan, 3 emp., *Gravity flow racks* ........ (908) 241-3700
Kinesys Automation, Inc., 5 Fir Ct., Unit 3, Oakland 07436
Pres.—Diana Manoussakis, 8 emp., *Packaging, conveying, filling, capping* ........ (201) 337-5000
Lamson Airtubes, LLC, 10 Millpond Dr., Unit 4, Lafayette 07848
CEO—Scott Begraft, 10 emp., *Pneumatic tube conveyor systems* ........ (973) 300-4267
Lazar Technologies, Inc., 39 Evergreen St., Hazlet 07730
Pres.—Carlos Gaviria, 9 emp., *Bottle capping equipment, inspection* ........ (732) 739-9622
Lynn Mechanical Contractors, 1810 Rowland St., Riverton 08077
Machinist—Tim Hossler, 10 emp., *Conveyors* ........ (856) 829-1717
Metalfab, Inc., 11 Prices Switch Rd., P.O. Box 9, Vernon 07462
COO—Mike Randazzo, 30 emp., *Large plate steel fabrication & dry* ........ (973) 764-2000
Mulhern Belting, Inc., 148 Bauer Dr., P.O. Box 620, Oakland 07436
CEO—Patrick Mulhern, 45 emp., *Corporate headquarters & conveyor belting* ........ (201) 337-5700
Nedco Conveyor Technology Co., 967 Lehigh Ave., Union 07083
Pres.—Curtis Tarlton, 40 emp., *Conveyors & bucket elevators* ........ (908) 964-9400
Precision Automation Company, Inc., 1841 Old Cuthbert Rd., Cherry Hill 08034
Pres., CEO—G. Frederick Rexon, Jr., 50 emp., *Automation, conveyor, control & complete* ........ (856) 428-7400
Sandvik Process Systems, LLC, 21 Campus Rd., Totowa 07512
Pres.—Robert Stivale, 30 emp., *Conveyor systems* ........ (973) 790-1600
Sparks Belting Co., 5 Spielman Rd., Fairfield 07004
Region Mgr.—David Engelhard, 18 emp., *Industrial conveyor belting* ........ (973) 227-4100
Tec Installations, Inc., 375 E. 22nd St., Paterson 07514
Pres.—Scott Crance, 10 emp., *Conveyor systems* ........ (973) 684-0503
Teledynamics, LLC, 45 Indian Ln. E., Ste. 1, Towaco 07082
Pres., CFO—Eric J. Witt, 20 emp., *Conveyors & conveying equipment* ........ (973) 248-3360
UNEX Manufacturing, Inc., 50 Progress Pl., Jackson 08527
Pres.—Brian Neuwirth, 65 emp., *Carton flow track & material handling* ........ (732) 928-2800
Vac-U-Max, 69 William St., Belleville 07109
Pres., CEO—Stevens P. Pendleton, 50 emp., *Industrial vacuum cleaners & pneumatic* ........ (973) 759-4600
W & H Systems, Inc., 120 Asia Pl., Carlstadt 07072
Pres.—Don Betman, 75 emp., *Automated material handling systems* ........ (201) 933-7840
White Conveyors, Inc., 10 Boright Ave., Kenilworth 07033
Ex. V-P.—Mark Speckhart, 100 emp., *Garment conveyors for dry cleaners,* ........ (800) 524-0273

### 3536 Hoists, cranes & monorails

Breeze-Eastern Corp., 35 Melanie Ln., Whippany 07981
Pres.—Brad Peterson, 200 emp., *Aerospace rescue hoists & winches,* ........ (973) 602-1001
Butco, Inc., 2009 Route 130 N., Burlington 08016
Pres., CFO & Webmaster—Peter Senin, 3 emp., *Portable tripod & tube hoists, parts* ........ (800) 872-8055
Maximum Material Handling, LLC, 750 Edwards Rd., Parsippany 07054
★ Pres.—Michael Dal Bon, Jr., 6 emp., *Material handling equipment, including* ........ (973) 227-1227
Permadur Industries, Inc., 186 U.S. Highway 206 S., Hillsborough 08844
Pres.—William A. Schneider, 63 emp., *Hoists, cranes, table & vehicle lifts* ........ (908) 359-9767
SISSCO Material Handling, 186 Route 206 S., Hillsborough 08844
Pres.—William Schneider, Sr., 49 emp., *Hoists, cranes, jib cranes & monorails* ........ (908) 359-9767
St. Croix Marine Products, Inc., 235 Hickory Ln., Bayville 08721
Pres.—Steve Tull, 6 emp., *Sail & power boat removable & rotating* ........ (732) 237-8800

### 3537 Trucks & tractors—industrial

Ajay Metal Fabricators, Inc., 355 Dalziel Rd., Linden 07036
Pres.—Tony Zambell, 9 emp., *Steel, aluminum, stainless, copper* ........ (908) 523-0558
Century Conveyor Service, Inc., 4301 S. Clinton Ave., South Plainfield 07080
Pres.—Ron Ferrara, 28 emp., *Conveyors, material handling equipment* ........ (908) 205-0625
Crown Lift Trucks, 104 Bauer Dr., Oakland 07436
Br. Mgr.—Paul Almeida, 80 emp., *New & rebuilt material handlings lift* ........ (201) 337-1211
Crown Lift Trucks, Inc., 680 River Dr., Elmwood Park 07407
Manager—Paul Meda, 20 emp., *Material handling equipment, including* ........ (845) 753-5868
D & D Trailers, Inc., 100 Lexington Ave., Trenton 08618
Pres.—G. D. Reside, 6 emp., *Utility trailers* ........ (609) 771-0001
Electro Lift, Inc., 204 Sargeant Ave., Clifton 07013
Pres.—David Erenstoft, 30 emp., *Material handling equipment* ........ (973) 471-0204
Essex Rise, 4 Fairfield Crescent, West Caldwell 07006
CEO—C. Wampler, 10 emp., *Material handling systems, including* ........ (973) 575-7483
Hilman Rollers, 12 Timber Ln., P.O. Box 45, Marlboro 07746
Pres., CEO—Jeff Hill, 70 emp., *Roller dollies for moving very heavy* ........ (732) 462-6277
HTD Heat Trace, Inc., 8 Bartles Corner Rd., Unit 104, Flemington 08822
Pres.—Michael Haden, 10 emp., *Pipe tracing, tank & hopper heating* ........ (908) 788-5210
Jescraft, 201 W. Fort Lee Rd., Bogota 07603
Pres., CFO—Michael Brown, 10 emp., *Construction job site material handling* ........ (201) 488-4545
Middlesex Industrial Sales, Inc., 522 New Brunswick Ave., Fords 08863
Pres.—Michael Amendola, 3 emp., *Material handling equipment & air compressors* ........ (732) 738-0537
Raymond Of NJ, LLC, 1000 Brighton St., Union 07083
Owner—Cliff Sneyers, 135 emp., *Lift trucks & replacement parts* ........ (908) 624-9570
Rent-Rite Lift Truck Services, 73 Green Pond Rd., P.O. Box 349, Rockaway 07866
★ Owner—Paul Warren, 10 emp., *Rebuilt forklifts* ........ (973) 586-4477
Saturn Overhead Equipment, LLC, 100 Apgar Dr., Somerset 08873
Pres.—Steve Gordon, 20 emp., *Material handling equipment* ........ (732) 560-7210
Skripak Metal Fabricators, Inc., 170 Oberlin Ave. N., Unit 17, Lakewood 08701
Pres., CFO—John Skripak, Jr., 10 emp., *Metal carts & tables, catwalks, hoods* ........ (732) 364-9662
UNEX Manufacturing, Inc., 50 Progress Pl., Jackson 08527
Pres.—Brian Neuwirth, 65 emp., *Carton flow track & material handling* ........ (732) 928-2800
Vibra Screw, Inc., 755 Union Blvd., Totowa 07512
Pres.—Eugene R. Wahl, 50 emp., *Bulk material handling equipment* ........ (973) 256-7410
W & H Systems, Inc., 120 Asia Pl., Carlstadt 07072
Pres.—Don Betman, 75 emp., *Automated material handling systems* ........ (201) 933-7840
Warwick Mfg. & Equipment Co., LLC, 1112 12th St., North Brunswick 08902
Mng. Dir.—Greg Pantchenko, 3 emp., *Food, packaging, chemical, cosmetic* ........ (732) 729-0400

### 3541 Machine tools, metal cutting types

Accurate Diamond Tool Corp., 1 Palisade Ave., Emerson 07630
Pres.—Daniel Michael, 25 emp., *Diamond dressing tools, diamond/CBN* ........ (201) 265-8868
Advanced Fastener Industries, 130 Main St., Butler 07405
Pres.—Don Manley, 7 emp., *Industrial machinery, fasteners & cutting* ........ (973) 283-1013
Aloris Tool Technology Co., Inc., 397-407 Getty Ave., Clifton 07011
Pres.—Richard Roslowski, 25 emp., *Quick-change tooling, cutting tools* ........ (973) 772-1201

Altech Abrasives Services, 130 Ryerson Ave., Ste. 103, Wayne 07470
Owner & Pres.—Kemper Smith, 1 emp., *Metal cutting* ... (973) 305-1922
Astro Tool & Machine Co., Inc., 810 Martin St., Rahway 07065
Pres., R & D Mgr.—Gary Price, 25 emp., *Precision machine tools, including* ... (732) 382-2450
AutoDrill, LLC, 50 Division Ave., Ste. 18, Millington 07946
Ptnr.—Joe Agro, Sr., 6 emp., *Manufacturer & distributor of automatic* ... (908) 542-0244
Bruderer Machinery, Inc., 1200 Hendricks Cswy., Ridgefield 07657
Pres.—Alois J. Rupp, 30 emp., *Corporate headquarters & high speed* ... (201) 941-2121
Century Engineering Co., Inc., 4 Orono St., Clifton 07013
Pres.—Edward Haracz, 15 emp., *Deburring & glass washer machinery* ... (973) 779-3900
Clover Co., Inc., F. G., 40 Stickle Ave., Rockaway 07866
Ptnr. & Off. Mgr.—Cindy Just, 3 emp., *Metal spinning & hydroforming* ... (973) 625-1811
E & J Machine And Tool, LLC, 12 Orben Dr., Unit 1, Landing 07850
Owner—Edmund Kiss, 5 emp., *CNC lathe & milling job shop, including* ... (973) 810-2312
Everite Machine Products Co., 6995 Airport Highway Ln., Pennsauken 08110
Pres., CFO—Bruce Mergenthal, 26 emp., *Electrolytic & electrochemical grinding* ... (856) 330-6700
Fecken-Kirfel America, Inc., 6 Leighton Pl., Ste. 1, Mahwah 07430
Bookkeeper—Laurie Weis, 9 emp., *Foam & plastic cutting blades* ... (201) 891-5530
Ferrous Saw Works, 345 Lakeview Ave., Clifton 07011
Owner—Dominic Farino, Jr., 1 emp., *High-speed segmental & friction saws* ... (973) 513-3936
Glebar Co., 527 Commerce St., P.O. Box 623, Franklin Lakes 07417
Chrm.—Frederick Schumacher, 63 emp., *Centerless grinding machines* ... (201) 337-1500
Jersey Machine Tool Repairing & Rebuilding Co., 1275 Bloomfield Ave., Bldg. 2, Unit 10, Fairfield 07004
Owner—John Csiszar, 3 emp., *Rebuilt machine tools* ... (973) 575-1044
Jet Industrial Electronics Corp., 104 Ridge Rd., Oak Ridge 07438
Pres.—John Boyce, 25 emp., *Roller grinding machinery & CNC machining* ... (973) 697-2300
Komo Machine, Inc., 1 Komo Dr., Lakewood 08701
Pres.—Mike Kolibas, 40 emp., *High speed CNC routing machining centers* ... (732) 719-6222
Nasa Machine Tools, Inc., 1-B Frassetto Way, Lincoln Park 07035
Pres.—Bob DeGeorge, 25 emp., *Precision & CNC machine tools* ... (973) 633-5200
National Steel Rule Co., Inc., 750 Commerce Rd., Linden 07036
Pres.—Eddie Mucci, Jr., 90 emp., *Industrial cutting blades* ... (908) 862-3366
Ridge Carbide Tool Co., 595 New York Ave., P.O. Box 497, Lyndhurst 07071
Pres. & Shpg. Mgr.—John Ferrie, 8 emp., *Carbide cutting tools* ... (201) 438-8777
Royal Masters Grinders, Inc., 143 Bauer Dr., P.O Box 630, Oakland 07436
Pres.—John Memmelaar, 48 emp., *Centerless grinding machines* ... (201) 337-8500
Sandvik, Inc. (H Q), 1702 Nevins Rd., P.O. Box 428, Fair Lawn 07410
Pres., Market Area Americas—Eduardo Martin, 200 emp., *Corporate headquarters; cutting tools* . (201) 794-5000
Tool Shop, Inc., 335 Chestnut Ave., P.O. Box 36, West Berlin 08091
Pres.—Paul Bruninghaus, 9 emp., *Screw machine cutting tools, including* ... (856) 767-8077
Tri State Perfection Knife Grinding, 3 S. Gold Dr., Robbinsville 08691
Owner—Chris Albanese, 8 emp., *Shear blades & brake dies sharpening* ... (609) 890-4989
Triple-T Cutting Tools, Inc., 135 Edgewood Ave., West Berlin 08091
Pres.—Steve Thomas, 14 emp., *Cutting tools for the metal & plastic* ... (856) 768-0800
Ultimate Spinning & Turning Corp., 9 Willow St., Moonachie 07074
Pres.—Mike Novack, 12 emp., *Metal, stainless steel & brass spinning* ... (201) 372-9740

## 3542 Machine tools, metal forming types

Bruderer Machinery, Inc., 1200 Hendricks Cswy., Ridgefield 07657
Pres.—Alois J. Rupp, 30 emp., *Corporate headquarters & high speed* ... (201) 941-2121
C & S Machinery Rebuilding Corp., 636 E. 19th St., Paterson 07514
Pres.—Cosmo Scardino, 4 emp., *Rebuilt metal coating machinery* ... (973) 742-7302
Hainesport Tool & Maintenance, 1924 Ark Rd., Hainesport 08036
Owner & Pres.—Gary Zwick, 18 emp., *Rebuilt machine tools & earth moving* ... (609) 261-0016
Jersey Machine Tool Repairing & Rebuilding Co., 1275 Bloomfield Ave., Bldg. 2, Unit 10, Fairfield 07004
Owner—John Csiszar, 3 emp., *Rebuilt machine tools* ... (973) 575-1044
Komo Machine, Inc., 1 Komo Dr., Lakewood 08701
Pres.—Mike Kolibas, 40 emp., *High speed CNC routing machining centers* ... (732) 719-6222
RANDCASTLE Extrusion Systems, Inc., 220 Little Falls Rd., Unit 6, Cedar Grove 07009
Pres.—Keith Luker, 5 emp., *Bench & floor screw extrusion machinery* ... (973) 239-1150
Teknics Industries, Inc., 170 Beaver Brook Rd., Lincoln Park 07035
Pres.—Bruce Robertson, 24 emp., *Industrial automation & heavy truck* ... (973) 633-7575
TRUMPF Photonics, Inc., 2601 US Route 130 S., Cranbury 08512
Mng. Dir.—Georg Treusch, 150 emp., *High-power semiconductor lasers, RF* ... (609) 925-8200
Vansco, Inc., 138-B Cannonball Rd., Pompton Lakes 07442
Pres.—Everett Van Steenberghe, 2 emp., *Hot stamping equipment* ... (973) 835-8423

## 3543 Patterns—industrial

Advanced Molding Concepts, 329 Wilson Ave., Aberdeen 07747
Owner—Mike Guglielmo, 6 emp., *Custom prototypes & precision machining* ... (732) 390-8366
Alpha Precision Mold, 8 Roselle St., Linden 07036
Owner—Hugo Daniel Santos, 3 emp., *Custom high-precision plastic molds* ... (908) 587-9090
Belco Technologies Corp., 9 Entin Rd., Parsippany 07054
Pres.—Kevin Gilman, 55 emp., *Air pollution control systems* ... (973) 884-4700
Best Cast, 822 Kinderkamack Rd., River Edge 07661
Pres.—Zsombar Antal, 15 emp., *High-resolution three-dimensionally* ... (201) 225-1750
Biztech, Inc., 3155 Route 10, Ste. 202, Denville 07834
Pres.—Louis Bizzarro, 7 emp., *Prototypes* ... (973) 361-7666
Brown Tool & Machine Co., Inc., Rosemont Raven Rock Rd., P.O. Box 142, Rosemont 08556
Pres.—Alan Brown, 2 emp., *Industrial & medical prototypes & architectur* ... (609) 397-1751
Consolidated Prototypes, Inc., 5 Oechsner Ct., Berkeley Heights 07922
Pres.—Jack Horner, 1 emp., *Industrial prototypes* ... (908) 464-6261
Elena Consultants, 1175 Globe Ave., P.O. Box 1339, Mountainside 07092
Owner—Karen Miller, 10 emp., *Industrial prototypes* ... (908) 654-8309
Fredon Development Industries, 393 State Route 94 S., Newton 07860
Pres.—Jerry Wildrick, 11 emp., *Plastic custom component prototype* ... (973) 383-7576
GAC Model Making, LLC, 1879 Old Cuthbert Rd., Unit 38, Cherry Hill 08034
Ptnr.—Patricia Christoffersen, 2 emp., *2D & 3D interactive models for product* ... (856) 857-9848
GPR Co., Inc., 22 Daniel Rd., Fairfield 07004
Pres.—George Verhoest, 40 emp., *Production machining & contract manufacturing* ... (973) 227-6160
Harry Shaw Model Maker Inc., 401 Stokes Rd., Shamong 08088
Pres.—John Kerby, 11 emp., *Industrial prototypes* ... (609) 268-0647
I D J, Inc., 121 Mechanic St., Boonton 07005
Pres.—Julian Pop, 1 emp., *Industrial prototypes* ... (973) 334-1517
Inner Spaces Lighting And Design, LLC, 98 Copley Ave., Teaneck 07666
GM—Scott Usher, 2 emp., *Custom LED & halogen lighting fixtures* ... (201) 692-0702
International Tool & Mfg., Inc., 30 Sherwood Ln., Ste. 10, Fairfield 07004
Owner & Pres.—Susan Brock, 10 emp., *Precision machining job shop, including* ... (973) 227-6767
J S Tool, LLC, 187 Wescott Dr., Ste. D, Rahway 07065
Pres.—John Skurzynski, 2 emp., *Tool & die job shop, including fixtures* ... (732) 815-1382

Jet Industrial Electronics Corp., 104 Ridge Rd., Oak Ridge 07438
Pres.—John Boyce, 25 emp., *Roller grinding machinery & CNC machining* ... (973) 697-2300
Modelsmith International, Inc., 66 Willow Ave., 2nd Fl., Hoboken 07030
Pres.—Karol Popek, 5 emp., *Steel, wood & acrylic fabrication,* ... (201) 714-9519
Ponte Model Makers, Tom, 25 Pine St., Ste. 2, Rockaway 07866
Pres.—Michale F. Leone, 5 emp., *Industrial prototypes, point-of-purchase* ... (973) 627-5906
Precise Components & Tool Design, Inc., 10 Clifton Blvd., Unit A-4, Clifton 07011
Pres.—Harry Benedikt, 7 emp., *Industrial prototypes & precision machining* ... (973) 928-2928
Precise Machine & Tool, Inc., 369 Knickerbocker Ave., Paterson 07503
Owner, Pres., Fin., Opers. & R & D Mgr.—Fatih Civi, 3 emp., *CNC machining & prototype*..... (201) 790-3320
Product Development Assocs., LLC, 12 Say Dr., East Hanover 07936
Pres.—Stefan Bloom, 3 emp., *Industrial prototypes & models* ... (973) 267-0033
Qualecon Machine, 235 Stateline Rd., Sussex 07461
Owner—Ken Robertson, 1 emp., *Industrial prototypes* ... (973) 875-4144
Ramsey Model Design, David A., P.O. Box 87, Clarksburg 08510
Owner—David A. Ramsey, 1 emp., *Models & prototypes* ... (609) 259-6757
Rapid Models & Prototypes, Inc., 1311 Marlkress Rd., Cherry Hill 08003
Ptnr. & Pres.—Angela A. Pizzo, 6 emp., *Rapid prototyping, CAD design & digitized* ... (856) 933-2929
Rock-Tenn Co., 15 Garner Rd., Fairfield 07004
Off. Mgr.—Ashley Shiminsky, 40 emp., *Paperboard & corrugated display prototypes* ... (973) 594-6000
Screens & Fabricated Metals Corp., 1265 McBride Ave., P.O. Box 647, Woodland park 07424
Pres.—Mike McMillan, 50 emp., *Screen & storm doors, security screens* ... (973) 785-1414
Sure Design, 5027 Industrial Rd., Unit 3, Farmingdale 07727
Ptnr.—Ken Thomas, 11 emp., *Printed circuit board assemblies &* ... (732) 919-3066
Ultimate Tool & Mfg. Co., 360-A Carnegie Ave., Kenilworth 07033
Owner, GM & Plt. Mgr.—Paul Plante, 5 emp., *Tool & die & CNC machining job shop* ... (908) 241-4575
West Pattern Works, Inc., 124 S. Main St., Cranbury 08512
Pres.—Douglas Trendell, 15 emp., *Foundry patterns* ... (609) 443-6241

## 3544 Dies, tools, jigs & fixtures—special

3M Co., 140 Algonquin Pkwy., Whippany 07981
Plt. Supv.—Vic Ison, 50 emp., *Diamond grinding wheels, tools & routers* ... (973) 884-2500
A & F Tool, 930 Magnolia Ave., Elizabeth 07201
GM—Fernando Paramo, 6 emp., *Tool & die & general machining job* ... (973) 262-1792
AB Precision Co., 1506 E. Elizabeth Ave., Linden 07036
Pres.—Puzant Duznatian, 2 emp., *Plastic injection molds & tool & die* ... (908) 925-1356
Accurate Machine & Tool Co., 135 W. Clay Ave., P.O. Box 187, Roselle Park 07204
Pres.—Jerry Tiehl, 5 emp., *Tool & die job shop* ... (908) 245-5545
Accurate Mold, Inc., 900 Chestnut Ave., Somerdale 08083
Opers. Mgr.—Gary McCloskey, 8 emp., *Injection molds for the plastics industry* ... (856) 784-8484
Ace Steel Rule Die Co., 251 Atsion Rd., Medford 08055
Ptnr.—Joe Schoel, 2 emp., *Steel rule dies* ... (609) 654-4161
Advance Tool & Die, Inc., 1401 Bremen Ave., Egg Harbor City 08215
Pres., GM & Opers. Mgr.—Robert C. Sullivan, 2 emp., *Plastic injection molds & dies & plastic* (856) 854-6329
Advanced Molding Concepts, 329 Wilson Ave., Aberdeen 07747
Owner—Mike Guglielmo, 6 emp., *Custom prototypes & precision machining* ... (732) 390-8366
Aljay Tool & Die Corp., 1213 Kennedy Blvd., Manville 08835
Pres.—Albert Fischer, Sr., 4 emp., *Tool & die job shop* ... (908) 722-2403
Aloris Tool Technology Co., Inc., 397-407 Getty Ave., Clifton 07011
Pres.—Richard Roslowski, 25 emp., *Quick-change tooling, cutting tools* ... (973) 772-1201
Alpha Precision Mold, 8 Roselle St., Linden 07036
Owner—Hugo Daniel Santos, 3 emp., *Custom high-precision plastic molds* ... (908) 587-9090
Altech Machine & Tool, Inc., 230 Bank St., Ste. 1, Midland Park 07432
Pres., Hum. Res. Mgr.—Ismael Sierra, 5 emp., *Tool & die & CNC machining job shop* ... (201) 652-4409
Artmark Mold & Tool Corp., 742 Paterson Ave., East Rutherford 07073
Pres.—Ted Ura, 7 emp., *Tool & molds* ... (201) 935-3377
Atlas Recording Machines Corp., 2140 Bridge Ave., Point Pleasant 08742
Pres.—Anthony Hopcroft, 5 emp., *Punches & carbide drilling tools* ... (732) 295-3663
Automated Tapping Systems, Inc., 22 Davos Rd., Brick 08724
Pres.—William R. Pfister, 10 emp., *In-die tapping units* ... (732) 899-2282
Barcus Co., Inc., Edgar C., Route 45 & Park Ave., P.O. Box 128, Westville 08093
Pres.—Leo Laskowski, 17 emp., *Steel rule dies* ... (856) 456-0204
Basic Tool & Die Corp., 752 Ramsey Ave., Hillside 07205
Pres.—James Tollar, 4 emp., *Metal stampings & press brake dies* ... (908) 688-9155
Big 3 Precision Mold Services, 30 Gorton Rd., Millville 08332
Plt. Mgr.—Joe Klaudi, 50 emp., *Injection blow molds & injection stretch* ... (856) 293-1400
Bihler Of America, Inc., 85 Industrial Dr., Phillipsburg 08865
CEO—Maxine Nordmeyer, 235 emp., *Corporate headquarters & metal stampings* ... (908) 213-9001
Bilt-Rite Tool & Die Co., Inc., 29 Montesano Rd., Fairfield 07004
Pres., Fin., MIS & R & D Mgr.—Dennis George, 12 emp., *Tool & die job shop* ... (973) 227-2882
Bodine Tool & Machine Co., Inc., 1273 N. Church St., Ste. 103, Moorestown 08057
Pres.—William Lauth, 30 emp., *Tool & die job shop* ... (856) 234-7800
Bowman Tool, 147 Pinebrook Rd., Englishtown 07726
Owner—Paul Bowman, 1 emp., *Molds & tool & die job shop* ... (732) 786-0770
Boyle Tool & Die Co., Inc., 135 Crown Point Rd., Thorofare 08086
Pres.—Thomas J. Boyle, 9 emp., *Metal stampings & tool & die job shop* ... (856) 853-1818
C & C Tool & Machine Co., LLC, 38 W. Scott St., P.O. Box 407, Riverside 08075
Pres., GM—Frank Canduci, 11 emp., *CNC machining & tool & die job shop* ... (856) 461-6090
C & C Tool Co., LLC, 216 U.S. Highway 206, Ste. 2, Hillsborough 08844
Owner & Pres.—Steven A. Calello, 4 emp., *Plastic injection molds for the plastic* ... (908) 431-0330
C & K Punch & Screw Machine Products, 160 Hobart St., Hackensack 07601
Pres., GM—Don Kuder, 8 emp., *Punches for steel rule dies & precision* ... (201) 343-6750
Camac Industries, 18 Gail Ct., Sparta 07871
Pres., Opers. Mgr.—Peter Gennaro, 5 emp., *Industrial pumps, filters & heat exchangers* ... (973) 300-5575
Charles G.G. Schmidt & Co., Inc., 301 W. Grand Ave., Montvale 07645
Pres.—Richard I. Paul, 20 emp., *Woodworking machinery, knives, cutters* ... (201) 391-5300
CK Manufacturing, Inc., 8 Gardner Rd., Fairfield 07004
Pres.—Richard Cafaro, 20 emp., *Plastic injection molds & molding* ... (973) 808-3500
Clover Stamping Co., Inc., 60 Spruce St., Paterson 07501
Pres., Sales Mgr.—Bob Kellenberger, 10 emp., *Metal stampings & tool & die job shop* ... (973) 278-4888
Comet Tool Co., Inc., 651 Lambs Rd., Pitman 08071
Pres.—Frank Maatje, 80 emp., *Plastic injection molds & plastic molded* ... (856) 256-1070
Container Graphics Corp., 3535 Highway 66, Parkway 100, Bldg. 2, Neptune 07753
Site Mgr.—Dominick Georgiano, 13 emp., *Flat & rotary laser cutting dies* ... (732) 922-1180
D C Metric Tool, Inc., 11 Mathews Ave., Riverdale 07457
Pres.—Djordje Cakmak, 2 emp., *Architectural millwork & machining* ... (973) 838-7590
Danielle Die Cut Products, Inc., 238 Lindbergh Pl., Paterson 07503
Pres.—Danny Dibetitto, 20 emp., *Steel rule dies & die cutting of paper* ... (973) 278-3000
Day Tool & Mfg., Inc., 6 Carman Ln., P.O. Box 466, Whitehouse 08888
Pres.—John J. Callahan III, 19 emp., *Custom machines, precision tooling,* ... (908) 439-3800
Diamond Die Cutters & Embossers, 629 Grove St., 6th Fl., Jersey City 07310
GM—Moon Mui, 15 emp., *Die cutting, metal stamping & embossing* ... (201) 876-8540

S.I.C.

Die Tech, LLC, 58 McKinley St., Hackensack 07601
Pres.—James Galbreath, 15 emp., *Steel rule dies* (201) 343-8324
Drew-Wal Machine & Tool Corp., 76 Monroe St., Little Ferry 07643
Pres.—Andrew J. Kovach, 4 emp., *General machining & tool & die job* (201) 641-3887
Dura-Carb, Inc., 204 Chamberlain Rd., P.O. Box 407, Oak Ridge 07438
Pres.—Donald Biermeister, 10 emp., *Carbide die components* (973) 697-6665
Durex, Inc., 5 Stahuber Ave., Union 07083
Pres., CEO—Robert Denholtz, 150 emp., *Metal stampings, sheet metal fabrication* (908) 688-0800
Ebco Tool Co., 8-B Great Meadow Ln., East Hanover 07936
Owner & GM—Edward Brown, 1 emp., *Tool & die job shop* (973) 887-5255
Exactal Tool & Die Ltd., Inc., 3586 Kennedy Rd., South Plainfield 07080
Pres.—Scott Kaese, 1 emp., *Tool & die job shop* (908) 561-1177
Excel Die Corp., 19 Grant St., Linden 07036
Pres.—Hanna Krysa, 4 emp., *Metal stamping, millwork & tool & die* (908) 587-2606
F & G Tool & Die, Inc., 195 Sumner Ave., Kenilworth 07033
CEO—Carl Friedrich, 10 emp., *Stamping dies & CNC machining job shop* (908) 241-5880
F G H Systems, Inc., 10 Prospect Pl., Denville 07834
Pres.—Frank Hohmann, 22 emp., *Tool & die job shop* (973) 625-8114
Fancort Industries, Inc., 31 Fairfield Pl., West Caldwell 07006
Pres., CEO & MIS Mgr.—Ronald J. Corey, 20 emp., *Electronic production racks & fixtures* (973) 575-0610
Fram Trak Industries, Inc., 205 Hallock Ave., Middlesex 08846
Pres., CEO—Al Santelli, Sr., 50 emp., *Custom & stock plastic extrusions &* (732) 424-8400
Fredon Development Industries, 393 State Route 94 S., Newton 07860
Pres.—Jerry Wildrick, 11 emp., *Plastic custom component prototype* (973) 383-7576
G L Tool & Mfg. Co., Inc., 26 Okner Pkwy., Livingston 07039
Pres.—Gerhard Liepold, 12 emp., *Tool & die job shop* (973) 740-0001
Garden State Precision, Inc., 510 Church St., Ridgefield 07657
Pres.—Joseph D. Molino, 9 emp., *Tool & die job shop* (201) 945-6410
Geiger Tool & Mfg. Co., Inc., 50 Liberty St., Passaic 07055
Pres., CEO—Joseph Szczesny, 21 emp., *Precision machining & tool & die job* (973) 777-2136
General Tool Specialties, Inc., 284 Sunnymead Rd., Hillsborough 08844
Pres.—John Domici, 13 emp., *Plastic molds* (908) 874-3040
Golden Rule, Inc., 7150 N. Park Dr., Ste. 620, Pennsauken 08109
Manager—Neil Miller, 2 emp., *Steel rule dies* (856) 663-3074
H T Stamping, 19 Gardner Rd., Ste. C, Fairfield 07004
Pres.—Thomas Schall, 20 emp., *Metal stampings & tool & die job shop* (973) 227-4858
Hammonton Mold Co., Inc., 4171 S. Black Horse Pike, Williamstown 08094
Pres.—Steve Domazet, 16 emp., *Injection blow molds & stretch blow* (856) 728-9112
Hansen Machine & Tool Co., Inc., 27 Walnut Ave., Clark 07066
Pres.—Robert Hansen, 3 emp., *Tooling & machining of parts for the* (732) 340-0466
Hoffman Precision Plastics, Inc., 548 Almonesson Rd., P.O. Box 338, Blackwood 08012
Pres.—Robert J. Hoffman, Sr., 8 emp., *Custom plastic injection molding &* (856) 228-3550
Hofmann Tool & Die Corp., 356 Route 17 N., Upper Saddle River 07458
Pres.—Charlie S. Franco, 6 emp., *Tool & die job shop* (201) 327-0226
Honeyware, Inc., 244 Dukes St., Kearny 07032
Chrm. & CEO—Tony Sheng, 60 emp., *Plastic injection molding, tooling* (201) 997-5900
Horizon Tool & Mold, Inc., 56 Paterson Ave., Newton 07860
Co-Pres.—Don Van De Moere, 2 emp., *Molds & tool & die job shop* (973) 300-0393
Howell Precision Tool Co., 415 Cranberry Rd., Farmingdale 07727
Owner & Pres.—David Hanrahan, 5 emp., *Close tolerance CNC milling, turning* (732) 919-7300
Hudson Mfg. Co., 640 W. 1st Ave., Roselle 07203
Pres.—Albert C. Maglio, 3 emp., *Punches, die buttons & perforators* (908) 241-3880
Hydratight Operations, 12 Worlds Fair Dr., Ste. A, Somerset 08873
IT Mgr.—Wes Harris, 21 emp., *Custom hydraulic & electronic torque* (732) 271-4100
Industrial Machine Corp., 44 Lehigh Ave., Paterson 07503
Pres.—Sam Szewczyk, 14 emp., *Parts, tools & general machining job* (973) 345-1800
Infor Metal & Tooling Manufacturing Corporation, 16 Commerce Rd., Cedar Grove 07009
Pres.—Charles Insel, 10 emp., *Contract metal stamping, tool & die* (973) 571-9520
Isometric Micro Finishing Coating, 122 James St., Edison 08820
Pres.—Roy Leo, 6 emp., *Metal coating & tool & die polishing* (732) 906-8070
J & J Marine, 1596 Hurffville Rd., Sewell 08096
Pres.—Jim Clauss, 38 emp., *Tool & die & machining job shop* (856) 228-4744
J S Tool, LLC, 187 Wescott Dr., Ste. D, Rahway 07065
Pres.—John Skurzynski, 2 emp., *Tool & die job shop, including fixtures* (732) 815-1382
JMK Tool, Die & Mfg. Co., Inc., 19 W. Passaic St., Rochelle Park 07662
Pres.—John Kristofich, 4 emp., *Metal stampings & tool & die job shop* (201) 845-4710
Jordan Mfg., LLC, 28 Randazzo Rd., P.O. Box 226, Lafayette 07848
GM—Gary Wilson, 8 emp., *Metal stampings, tooling, CNC turning* (973) 383-8363
Kessler Steel Rule Die, Inc., 1004 Industrial Dr., Ste. 10, West Berlin 08091
Pres.—Dennis Kessler, 6 emp., *Steel rule dies* (856) 767-0231
Komo Machine, Inc., 1 Komo Dr., Lakewood 08701
Pres.—Mike Kolibas, 40 emp., *High speed CNC routing machining centers* (732) 719-6222
L & Z Tool & Engineering, Inc., 1691 U.S. Highway 22, Watchung 07069
Pres., CEO, CFO—Thomas LaMarca, 35 emp., *Injection molding tools* (908) 322-2220
Lasercam, Inc., 1039 Hoyt Ave., Ridgefield 07657
Pres.—David Shapiro, 40 emp., *Corporate headquarters & steel rule* (201) 941-1262
Lawrence Mold and Tool Corp., 1412 Ohio Ave., Lawrenceville 08648
Owner—George Lesenskyj, 25 emp., *Plastic injection molding & tool &* (609) 392-5422
Leco Plastics, Inc., 130 Gamewell St., Hackensack 07601
Pres.—Barry Schwartz, 9 emp., *Plastic extrusions & molding* (201) 343-3330
Liberty Machine Tool & Die, Inc., 903 E. Elizabeth Ave., Linden 07036
Co-Pres.—Michael Elzahr, 2 emp., *Tool & die & general machining job* (908) 925-0300
Life Of The Party, LLC, 832 Ridgewood Ave., Ste. 4, North Brunswick 08902
Pres.—Carole Krinsky, 15 emp., *Plastic candy & craft molds* (732) 828-0886
Lincoln Mold & Die Corp., 225 E. 1st Ave., Roselle 07203
Pres.—Edward Drozd, 50 emp., *Plastic injection molds & tool & die* (908) 241-3344
Linden Mold & Tool Corp., 155 Wescott Dr., P.O. Box C, Rahway 07065
Pres.—Vincent Illuzzi, 43 emp., *Plastic injection molds* (732) 381-1411
M & G Tool & Die Co., 936 Harrison Ave., Kearny 07032
Owner—Giovanni Millocca, 4 emp., *Tool & die job shop* (201) 997-0506
Machine Corp., E. B., 320 Richard Mine Rd., Wharton 07885
Pres.—Emil Boller, 3 emp., *Mold, grinding, tool, die & CNC machining* (973) 442-7729
Mark/Trece, Inc., 160 Algonquin Pkwy., Whippany 07981
GM—Paul Rachanow, 30 emp., *Corrugated & flexographic printing* (973) 884-1005
Marlton Pike Precision, LLC, 728 Beechwood Ave., Cherry Hill 08002
Pres.—Antonio Sala, 18 emp., *Precision machined parts, fixtures,* (856) 665-1900
Master Craft Steel Rule Die, 84 Bell St., Orange 07050
Owner—Bruno Nieves, 1 emp., *Steel rule dies for corrugated box* (973) 674-7662
Mastercraft Electroplating, 801 Magnolia Ave., Elizabeth 07201
Owner—Desmond Naraine, 6 emp., *Vinyl record molds & electroplating* (908) 354-4404
Mercer Machine & Tool Products, 332 Darcy Ave., Trenton 08629
Pres.—Tom Erni, 5 emp., *General machining & tool & die job* (609) 587-1106
MMC Steel Rule Dies, 864 New Brunswick Ave., Piscataway 08854
Owner—Marcello Cabrera, 1 emp., *Steel rule dies* (973) 760-3286
Monroe Tool & Die, Inc., 197 Sharp Rd., Williamstown 08094
Pres., CFO—Steven Kennedy, 8 emp., *Metal stampings & tool & die job shop* (856) 629-5164
MS Tool Co., Inc., 500 S. 31st St., Kenilworth 07033
Owner—Eberhard Schweitzer, 2 emp., *Tool & die job shop* (908) 245-7989
National Equipment Co., 342 Squankum Yellowbrook Rd., P.O. Box 674, Farmingdale 07727
Pres.—Mauro R. Raccuglia, 4 emp., *Rebuilt production pipe & bolt threading* (732) 938-5084
Nelson, Inc., Louis A., 224 Glenwood Ave., Bloomfield 07003
Pres., MIS Mgr.—David Sibilia, 12 emp., *Thermoforming, metal tooling, prototypes* (973) 743-7404
New Jersey Precision Technologies, Inc., 1081 Bristol Rd., Mountainside 07092
Pres., Sales Mgr.—Bob Tarantino, 45 emp., *Wire & ram EDM & small hole drilling*
Newark Mold & Tool, Inc., 147 New Jersey Railroad Ave., Newark 07104
Pres., Hum. Res. & IT Mgr.—Joe Cerejo, 2 emp., *Injection molds & tooling for the plastic* (973) 578-2881
Newton T & M Corp., 119 Fredon Springdale Rd., Newton 07860
Pres., Plt. Mgr.—Ralph Meola, 8 emp., *Plastic injection molding & molds* (973) 383-1232
Nymar Mfg. Co., Inc., 215 State Route 10 E., Randolph 07869
Pres.—Gerald Hughes, 10 emp., *Plastic blow mold tooling* (973) 366-7265
O K Tool & Die Co., 603 Bluebell Rd., Williamstown 08094
Pres.—Kenneth Ostapovich, 15 emp., *Plastic products & tool & die job shop* (856) 629-5757
Olympic EDM & Waterjet, Inc., 20 Kiel Ave., Butler 07405
Owner & Pres.—Don Ferrante, 8 emp., *Wire EDM, waterjet & tool & die shop* (973) 492-0664
Omega Tool Die, 8 International Ave., Sewell 08080
Pres.—Jack Vosbikian, 8 emp., *Tool & die job shop* (856) 232-1015
Oxbow Tool & Die Corp., 44 Fremont Ter., Oak Ridge 07438
Pres.—John G. Tulp, 1 emp., *Precision & CNC tool & die machining* (973) 697-6647
P & J Machine Co., 261 Crosskeys Rd., P.O. Box 178, Berlin 08009
Owner—John Pepe, 3 emp., *CNC & conventional machining & tooling* (856) 767-8441
P M Z Tool, Inc., 321 Warren Ave., Stirling 07980
Pres.—Paul Zuzokz, 6 emp., *Tool & die job shop* (908) 647-2125
Pahco Machine, Inc., 572 Whitehead Rd., Ste. 101, Trenton 08619
GM—Pete Horvath, 3 emp., *Tool & die & general machining job* (609) 587-1188
Perfectone Mold Co., 277 New York Ave., Jersey City 07307
Pres., Engr.—Lawrence Taub, 5 emp., *Rubber dental molds for making wax* (201) 798-5353
Peterson Steel Rule Die Corp., 35 Broad St., Carlstadt 07072
Pres.—Leonard Esposito, 10 emp., *Steel rule dies, die cutting & finishing* (201) 935-6180
Precise Tool & Mold Co., Inc., 240 E. Lackland Dr., Middlesex 08846
Pres.—George Peppe, Sr., 20 emp., *Plastic injection molds* (732) 469-3062
Precision Ball Specialties, Inc., 1451 Glassboro Rd., Williamstown 08094
Off. & Sales Mgr.—Carol Symanski, 3 emp., *Ball bearing cages* (856) 881-5646
Precision Forms, Inc., 97 Decker Rd., Butler 07405
Pres., Hum. Res. & IT Mgr.—William Sulski, 36 emp., *Long & short run production machining* (973) 838-3800
Precision Saw & Tool Corp., 56 Colfax Ave., Clifton 07013
Pres.—James Montesano, 10 emp., *Tool & die job shop* (973) 773-7302
Precision Steel Rule Die, 400 Benigno Blvd., Rear, Bellmawr 08031
Owner—Michael Sheahan, 3 emp., *Flat steel rule cutting dies for gasket* (856) 931-2548
Preferred Plastics Corp., 6512 Park Ave., Pennsauken 08109
Co-Pres., Fin. Mgr.—Joseph Flood, 6 emp., *Plastic injection molds & dies, including* (856) 662-6250
Prentco Co., 952 Koehl Ave., Union 07083
Owner—Chris Steinberg, 9 emp., *Investment casting molds & tools* (908) 687-9518
Product Identification Co., Inc., 141 Lanza Ave., Bldg. 19, Garfield 07026
Pres.—Les Weinstock, 20 emp., *Aluminum, vinyl & polyester nameplates* (973) 955-4747
Progressive Tool & Mfg. Co., 708 Fairfield Ave., Kenilworth 07033
Pres.—Gunter Heim, 6 emp., *Metal stampings & tool & die job shop* (908) 245-7010
R L Tool & Die Co., 739 Fairfield Ave., Kenilworth 07033
Owner & Pres.—Dennis Heucke, 3 emp., *Precision tooling of medical products* (908) 245-7710
R. & M. Mold Mfg. Co., LLC, 1022 Route 173 E., P.O. Box 578, Bloomsbury 08804
Owner & Pres.—John A. Roser, Jr., 4 emp., *Metal injection, plastic & die-cast* (908) 479-4444
RANDCASTLE Extrusion Systems, Inc., 220 Little Falls Rd., Unit 6, Cedar Grove 07009
Pres.—Keith Luker, 5 emp., *Bench & floor screw extrusion machinery* (973) 239-1150
Redkeys Dies, Inc., 1307 Market St., Gloucester City 08030
Pres., CEO—Morgan F. Reichner, 6 emp., *Steel rule, copper foil stamping &* (856) 456-7890
Republic Mold & Tool Co., Inc., 109 Bradford Ave., Linden 07036
Pres.—Werner Brandl, 2 emp., *Plastic injection molds* (908) 862-3344
Rex Tool & Mfg. Co., 544 E. Elizabeth Ave., P.O. Box 1423, Linden 07036
Pres.—John Haydu, 3 emp., *Tool & die job shop* (908) 925-2727
Ricci Tool & Die Co., 122 Myrtle Ave., Long Branch 07740
Pres.—John Ricci, Sr., 9 emp., *Tool & die job shop, including metal* (732) 222-2777
Roselle Tool & Die Co., 135 W. Clay Ave., P.O. Box 103, Roselle Park 07204
Pres.—George Kaminski, 6 emp., *Tool & die job shop* (908) 245-3133
Roseville Tool & Mfg., 22 Okner Pkwy., Livingston 07039
GM—David Miller, 30 emp., *Metal stampings & tool & die job shop* (973) 992-5405
Rotech Tool & Mold Co., Inc., 824 Fairfield Ave., Kenilworth 07033
Pres.—Terry Leschinski, 7 emp., *Plastic injection molds, including* (908) 241-9669
Rule One, Inc., 68 E. Centre St., Nutley 07110
Pres.—Roger Emil, 3 emp., *Steel rule cutting dies & die cutting* (973) 661-4563
Saturn Tool & Die, Inc., 1064 Commerce Ave., Union 07083
Pres.—Robert Wilson, 3 emp., *CNC machining & tool & die job shop* (908) 964-0504
Schneider & Marquard, Inc., 112 Phil Hardin Rd., P.O. Box 39, Newton 07860
Pres.—Michael J. O'Shea, 22 emp., *Retaining rings & tool & die job shop* (973) 383-2200
Seajay Mfg. Co., 9 Memorial Dr., Ste. 1, Neptune 07753
Pres.—Jeffrey Finn, 8 emp., *Plastic bottle molds & industrial molds* (732) 774-0900
Sedtek, Inc., 113 Meadow St., Hackensack 07601
Pres., R & D Mgr.—Gerald Danker, 15 emp., *Metal bar soap molds, rubber products* (201) 489-4040
Seibert Machine & Tool, Inc., 4405 S. Clinton Ave., South Plainfield 07080
Pres.—George G. Seibert, 3 emp., *General machining & tool & die job* (908) 754-0774
Sine-Tru Tool Co., Inc., 238 Boundry Rd., Marlboro 07746
Pres.—Ken Klawunn, 6 emp., *Rebuilt industrial tooling, knives* (732) 591-1100
Smith Steel Rule Die, Michael, 2479 S. Main Rd., Vineland 08360
Owner—Michael Smith, 1 emp., *Steel rule dies* (856) 692-5510
Smith Tool & Mfg., R. G., 245 South St., Newark 07114
Pres.—Edgar Blaus, Jr., 9 emp., *General machining & tool & die job* (973) 344-1395
South Jersey Precision Tool & Mold, Inc., 4375 S. Lincoln Ave., Vineland 08361
Pres.—Victor Rone, 16 emp., *Plastic injection molds* (856) 327-0500
Spec Steel Rule Dies, Inc., 92 N. Main St., Bldg. 1-B, P.O. Box 33, Windsor 08561
Pres., R & D Mgr.—John Nagy, 24 emp., *Steel rule dies & rubber printing plates* (609) 443-9200
Stampex Tool&Die, Inc., 75 4th Ave., Haskell 07420
Owner—Thomas Nieshalla, 6 emp., *Precision metal stampings, including* (973) 839-4040
Summit Tool Co., Inc., 719 23rd St., Union City 07087
Pres.—Paul Cairoli, 3 emp., *Machining job shop* (201) 867-8600
Supreme Steel Rule Dies, Inc., 985 Madison Ave., Paterson 07501
Pres.—Federico Espinal, 2 emp., *Flat steel rule cutting dies* (973) 345-9474

TAF Tooling, LLC, 1100 E. Linden Ave., Linden 07036
Owner—Hector Aboal, 3 emp., *Molds for vacuum thermoforming applications* ........ (908) 474-0294
Tec Cast, Inc., 440 Meadow Ln., Carlstadt 07072
Pres.—Edgar Gotthold, 70 emp., *Aluminum investment castings & casting* ........ (201) 935-3885
Thal Precision Industries, Inc., 19-A Walnut Ave., Clark 07066
Pres.—Jim Thal, 10 emp., *Injection mold fabrication, CNC & wire* ........ (732) 381-6106
Thomson Lamination Co., Inc., 504 E. Linwood Ave., Maple Shade 08052
Chrm.—Sterling A. Martin, 100 emp., *Motor laminations & assemblies, including* ........ (856) 779-8521
Titan Technologies International, Inc., 222 Getty Ave., Clifton 07011
★ Chrm.—John J. Staudinger, 20 emp., *Hydraulic, pneumatic & electric industrial* ........ (973) 928-5222
Totowa Precision Tooling, Inc., 500 Riverview Dr., Totowa 07512
Pres.—George Bondarenko, 9 emp., *Medical instruments & CNC machining* ........ (973) 256-2283
Tri State Perfection Knife Grinding, 3 S. Gold Dr., Robbinsville 08691
Owner—Chris Albanese, 8 emp., *Shear blades & brake dies sharpening* ........ (609) 890-4989
Triad Tool Co., 9 Commerce St., Branchburg 08876
Pres., CEO—Eric Wichelhaus, 45 emp., *Aerospace, medical & communication* ........ (908) 534-1784
Tryco Tool & Mfg., Inc., 363 S. Jefferson St., Orange 07050
Owner—Art Melillo, 60 emp., *Metal stampings & dies* ........ (973) 674-6867
Ultimate Tool & Mfg. Co., 360-A Carnegie Ave., Kenilworth 07033
Owner, GM & Plt. Mgr.—Paul Plante, 5 emp., *Tool & die & CNC machining job shop* ........ (908) 241-4575
Ultra Punch & Die Corp., 8 N. Main St., P.O. Box 353, Boonton 07005
GM & Fin. Mgr.—Joseph Hogh, Sr., 12 emp., *Carbide & steel punches & die bushings* ........ (973) 335-3200
Union Tool & Mold Co., 220 Rutgers St., Maplewood 07040
Pres.—Robert Arrighi, 30 emp., *Plastic molds & metal dies* ........ (973) 763-6611
United Die Co., Inc., 199 Devon Ter., Kearny 07032
Pres.—Jim Kontra, 30 emp., *Tungsten carbide, steel & ceramic tooling* ........ (201) 997-0250
United National Machine Tool, Inc., 2404 Sylon Blvd., P.O. Box 608, Hainesport 08036
Pres.—Robert Donahue, 14 emp., *Rotary tooling* ........ (609) 265-2269
Unity Graphics & Engraving/Unity Steel Rule Die, 210 S. Van Brunt St., P.O. Box 88, Englewood 07631
Ptnr.—Diane Iamartino, 50 emp., *Rubber printing, plate engraving &* ........ (201) 569-6400
Universal Mold & Tool, Inc., 1200 S. West Blvd., Bldg. 4, Vineland 08360
Ptnr., GM, Hum. Res., IT & Plt. Mgr.—David Rainear, 18 emp., *Molds & tooling* ........ (856) 563-0488
Universal Tools & Mfg. Co., 115 Victory Rd., Springfield 07081
Owner, Pres. & CEO—Dorothy Principe, 30 emp., *Tooling & precision deep drawn metal* ........ (973) 379-4193
Vantage Tool & Mfg., 223 Stirling Rd., Warren 07059
Pres.—Stephen Heinle, 3 emp., *Tool & die job shop, including general* ........ (908) 647-1010
Verden Tool & Mfg., LLC, 121 E. Blackwell St., Dover 07801
Pres., Member & R & D Mgr.—Robert Denzer, 2 emp., *Tool & die job shop* ........ (973) 366-7510
Viz Mold & Die Ltd., 210 Industrial Pkwy., Northvale 07647
Pres.—Dimitrios Lymberis, 5 emp., *Plastic injection molds, tools & dies* ........ (201) 784-8383
Zimmer Machinery Systems, 19 Springcroft Rd., Far Hills 07931
Owner—Theodore Zimmer, 1 emp., *Tool & die & precision machining job* ........ (908) 234-2560
Zin-Tech, 1416 Union Ave., Pennsauken 08110
Pres.—Joe Zingaro, 20 emp., *Steel rule dies* ........ (856) 661-0900

## 3545 Machine tool accessories

Accurate Diamond Tool Corp., 1 Palisade Ave., Emerson 07630
Pres.—Daniel Michael, 25 emp., *Diamond dressing tools, diamond/CBN* ........ (201) 265-8868
Aloris Tool Technology Co., Inc., 397-407 Getty Ave., Clifton 07011
Pres.—Richard Roslowski, 25 emp., *Quick-change tooling, cutting tools* ........ (973) 772-1201
American Machine Tool Repair, 12 Middlebury Blvd., Randolph 07869
Pres.—Alex Karoly, Jr., 8 emp., *Rebuilt production machinery, including* ........ (973) 927-0820
Armstrong & Sons, Inc., 2335 Highway 34, Manasquan 08736
Pres.—Linda Pietsch, 3 emp., *Tube cutting tools for replacing thin* ........ (732) 223-1555
Atlas Recording Machines Corp., 2140 Bridge Ave., Point Pleasant 08742
Pres.—Anthony Hopcroft, 5 emp., *Punches & carbide drilling tools* ........ (732) 295-3663
B & S Tool & Cutter Service, Inc., 99 John St., Hackensack 07601
Pres.—Fred Lindenau, 7 emp., *Cutting tools & sharpening, including* ........ (201) 488-3545
Barnett Machine Tool Corp., 401 Supor Blvd., P.O. Box 189, Harrison 07029
Pres.—Antonio Ferreira, 24 emp., *Precision machine tools & general machining* ........ (973) 482-6222
Blanchette Tool & Gage Mfg., 845 Bloomfield Ave., P.O. Box 1270, Clifton 07012
Pres.—R. Blanchette Garvey, 8 emp., *Visual gage comparators & dimensional* ........ (973) 471-2100
BMB Fasteners, Inc., 86 Lackawanna Ave., Ste. 208, Woodland Park 07424
Owner & Pres.—Larry Malone, 8 emp., *Screws, fasteners, bolts, nuts & washers* ........ (973) 256-4010
CDS Corp., 27 Wilson Dr., Unit C, Sparta 07871
Pres.—Robert Zarbua, 25 emp., *Cam actuated mechanical drives & machinery* ........ (973) 300-0090
Daven Industries, Inc., 55 Dwight Pl., Fairfield 07004
Pres.—Lou Lever, 30 emp., *Shafts, chucks, safety chucks, winders* ........ (973) 808-8848
Du-Mor Blade Co., Inc., 1002 Union Landing Rd., Cinnaminson 08077
CEO—Elaine M. Goralski, 25 emp., *Alloy & steel machine tool blades for* ........ (856) 829-9384
General Polygon Systems, Inc., 203 Peterson St., Millville 08332
Owner & Pres.—Joseph Pitassi, 11 emp., *Machined polygon profiles for precision* ........ (856) 825-3300
Heller Co., E. P., 21-25 Samson Ave., P.O. Box 26, Madison 07940
Chrm., CEO—Eugene Heller, 25 emp., *Solid carbide cutting & pneumatic tools* ........ (973) 377-2878
Hutchinson Co., William T., 453 Lehigh Ave., Union 07083
Pres.—Dean Roth, 12 emp., *Drill & reamer blanks, punches, core* ........ (908) 688-0533
Hydratight Operations, 12 Worlds Fair Dr., Ste. A, Somerset 08873
IT Mgr.—Wes Harris, 21 emp., *Custom hydraulic & electronic torque* ........ (732) 271-4100
Marlton Pike Precision, LLC, 728 Beechwood Ave., Cherry Hill 08002
Pres.—Antonio Sala, 18 emp., *Precision machined parts, fixtures,* ........ (856) 665-1900
Penn Tool Co., 1776 Springfield Ave., Maplewood 07040
Owner—Gene Elson, 8 emp., *Hand tools & measuring instruments* ........ (973) 761-4343
Precision Specialties, 120 Greylock Ave., Belleville 07109
Pres.—Richard Pfuhler, 5 emp., *Threaded inserts for plastics, ultrasonic* ........ (973) 751-7588
Pro Machine Co., 5 Sicomac Rd., Haledon 07508
★ Owner—Eddie Demetro, 18 emp., *Rebuilt gear boxes, pumps & shear blades* ........ (973) 855-9935
Tool Shop, Inc., 335 Chestnut Ave., P.O. Box 36, West Berlin 08091
Pres.—Paul Bruninghaus, 9 emp., *Screw machine cutting tools, including* ........ (856) 767-8077
V & L Machine Tool Co., Inc., 30 Sherwood Ln., Ste. 11, Fairfield 07004
Pres.—Michael Sollitto, 5 emp., *Precision machine parts* ........ (973) 808-5858
Vozeh Equipment Corp., 509 Commerce St., Franklin Lakes 07417
Owner—Karen Vozeh, 55 emp., *Industrial & medical cutting tools* ........ (201) 337-4212

## 3546 Power-driven handtools

Alpha Professional Tools (H Q), 103 Bauer Dr., Oakland 07436
Pres.—Nao Takahashi, 25 emp., *Company headquarters; power hand tools* ........ (800) 648-7229
Astro Tool Corp., 90 Washington Ave., Nutley 07110
Sales Mgr., Eastern—John Nosti, 2 emp., *Pneumatic, hand crimp, insertion &* ........ (973) 661-1299
Croft Tool, Inc., 2144 Bridge Ave., Point Pleasant Boro 08742
Owner—Anthony Hopcroft, 5 emp., *Power-driven hand tools* ........ (732) 899-4885
Demountable Concepts, Inc., 200 Acorn Rd., Glassboro 08028
Pres.—Rustin Casswav, 35 emp., *Demountable truck body systems & equipment* ........ (856) 863-0900
Eggers Sails, Inc., John, 7076 Route 35, South Amboy 08879
CEO—John Eggers, 3 emp., *Sails & riggers* ........ (732) 721-4667
Fire Hooks Unlimited, 1827 Old Mill Rd., Wall 07719
CEO, R & D Mgr.—Bob Farrell, 18 emp., *Firefighting tools & equipment* ........ (732) 280-7737
Pfingst & Co., Inc., 105 Snyder Rd., P.O. Box 377, South Plainfield 07080
Pres.—Karl Pfingst, 10 emp., *Manufacturer & distributor of precision* ........ (908) 561-6400
S & G Tool Aid Corp., 43 E. Alpine St., Newark 07114
Sales Mgr., Natl.—Wayne Hutchings, 75 emp., *Automotive & auto body repair shop* ........ (973) 824-7730
Titan Technologies International, Inc., 222 Getty Ave., Clifton 07011
★ Chrm.—John J. Staudinger, 20 emp., *Hydraulic, pneumatic & electric industrial* ........ (973) 928-5222
W.W. Manufacturing Co., Inc., 60 Rosenhayn Ave., Bridgeton 08302
Ptnr. & Pres.—Peter Lesche, 12 emp., *Steel landscaping & nursery hand tools* ........ (856) 451-5700

## 3547 Rolling mill machinery

Pedrick Tool & Machine Co., 1518 Bannard St., P.O. Box 190, Riverton 08077
Pres.—Ralph M. Scott, 10 emp., *Bending machines for pipes, tubes,* ........ (856) 829-8900

## 3548 Welding apparatus

C N I Ceramics Nozzles, Inc., 23 Commerce Rd., Ste. L, Fairfield 07004
Pres.—Thomas M. Calandrillo, 6 emp., *Welding equipment* ........ (973) 276-1535
DCC Corporation, 7250 Westfield Ave., Ste. B, Pennsauken 08110
Pres.—Joseph Marshall, 6 emp., *Thermocouple welders for the production* ........ (856) 662-7272
ElectroHeat Induction, 9 Spruce St., Jersey City 07306
★ Proj. Engr.—Charlie Parsana, 10 emp., *Induction heating & melting equipment* ........ (908) 494-0726
Hotfoil-EHS, Inc., 2960 E. State Street Ext., Hamilton 08619
Pres.—Neville Richards, 35 emp., *Industrial heating equipment, including* ........ (609) 588-0900
International Welding Technologies, Inc., 2650 Egg Harbor Rd., Lindenwold 08021
GM—Neil Wilkinson, 10 emp., *Manufacturer & wholesaler of welding* ........ (856) 435-8004
Interstate Welding & Mfg. Co., Inc., 1510 Village Ct., Edgewater Park 08010
Pres., CFO—Joseph N. Russomanno, 18 emp., *Welding, tube, pipe & metal fabrication* ........ (609) 699-6950
New Age Fastening Systems, Inc., 11 Enterprise Ct., Sewell 08080
Ptnr.—Stephen Swartz, Jr., 20 emp., *Stud welding equipment & blasting abrasives* ........ (856) 218-8301
Orgo-Thermit, Inc., 3500 Colonial Dr. N., Manchester 08759
Pres.—Dave Randolph, 30 emp., *Aluminothermic welding products, kits* ........ (732) 657-5781
Praxair, 515 E. Edgar Rd., Linden 07036
Opers. Mgr.—Mike Anuszeniski, 2 emp., *Welding equipment & specialty gases* ........ (908) 862-7200
Pyroptics, Inc., 2015 Columbus Rd., Burlington 08016
Pres.—Stephen Boyle, 5 emp., *Stud welding equipment* ........ (609) 386-6930
Resistance Welding Solutions, Inc., 1090 Lousons Rd., Union 07083
CEO—Gregory W. Labelle, 20 emp., *Resistance welding equipment, including* ........ (908) 964-9100
Wikstrom Machines, Inc., 412 Summit Ave., Perth Amboy 08861
Pres.—Walter Geslak, 10 emp., *Resistance welding machinery* ........ (732) 826-4800

## 3549 Metalworking machinery, nec

APW Company, 5 Astro Pl., Ste. B, Rockaway 07866
Owner & Pres.—Jason Kellenberger, 10 emp., *Standard & custom electromagnets &* ........ (973) 627-0643
Falls Products, Inc., 220 Franklin Rd., 1st Fl., Randolph 07869
Pres.—David Vander May, 2 emp., *Deburring machinery* ........ (973) 537-6464
Lever Mfg. Corp., 420 State Route 17, Mahwah 07430
Ex. V-P.—William M. Corbett, 25 emp., *Slitting machinery for tapes, foams* ........ (201) 684-4400
New Jersey Wire Stitching Machine Co., 1841 Old Cuthbert Rd., Cherry Hill 08034
GM & Qual. Assur. Mgr.—Mike Menaquale, 50 emp., *Wire stitching machinery* ........ (856) 428-7400
Niehoff Endex North America, Inc., 1 Mallard Ct., Swedesboro 08085
Pres.—Robert Wild, 35 emp., *Nonferrous wire processing machinery* ........ (856) 467-4884
Resistance Welding Solutions, Inc., 1090 Lousons Rd., Union 07083
CEO—Gregory W. Labelle, 20 emp., *Resistance welding equipment, including* ........ (908) 964-9100
Weber & Scher Mfg. Co., Inc., 1231 US Highway 22 E., P.O. Box 366, Lebanon 08833
Chrm., CEO—J. William Scher, 35 emp., *Machinery & equipment for the manufacturing* ........ (908) 236-8484

## 3552 Textile machinery

2 For 1 Machinery Group, The, 30 N. Pine Ave., Maple Shade 08052
Pres.—Wayne Bancroft, 4 emp., *Remanufactured spindle machinery &* ........ (856) 321-0474
A B C Machinery Corp., 712-1 Old Shore Rd., P.O. Box 1212, Forked River 08731
Prodn. Mgr.—Barry Cerino, 6 emp., *Textile machinery parts* ........ (609) 971-0990
Baxter Corp., The, 511 Commerce St., P.O. Box 645, Franklin Lakes 07417
Pres.—George Bowen, 5 emp., *Textile patterns & machinery, loom* ........ (201) 337-1212
C & S Machine, Inc., 22 Commerce Rd., Ste. Q, Fairfield 07004
Plt. & Sales Mgr.—Ron Woods, 4 emp., *Textile & converting machinery* ........ (973) 882-1097
Chandler Machine Co., Inc., 400 Veterans Blvd., Carlstadt 07072
V-P., Opers.—Michael Feit, 10 emp., *Industrial hand-operated & electrical* ........ (212) 741-2474
Clinton Industries, Inc., 207 Redneck Ave., Little Ferry 07643
COO—Larry Paricio, 15 emp., *Industrial sewing machine motors &* ........ (201) 440-0400
Heights USA, Inc., 1445 Lower Ferry Rd., Ewing 08618
Opers. Mgr.—Tim Philburn, 12 emp., *Lithographic & flexographic printing* ........ (609) 530-1300
Kay Machine Co., 130 Cannonball Rd., Pompton Lakes 07442
Pres., Hum. Res. Mgr.—George Kaiser, 1 emp., *Textile machinery rollers* ........ (973) 839-4404
M & P Machinery, 1500 Main Ave., Ste. 31, Clifton 07011
Ptnr.—Marian Szuba, 2 emp., *Rebuilt textile machinery & repair* ........ (973) 253-1004
MRI International, 44-50 Clinton St., Newton 07860
Pres.—William Foltyn, 7 emp., *Sensitizers for the offset lithographic* ........ (973) 383-3645
New Era Converting Machinery, 235 Route 20, Paterson 07504
CEO—Frank P. Lembo, 60 emp., *Coating, laminating, unwinding & winding* ........ (201) 670-4848

## 3553 Woodworking machinery

Charles G.G. Schmidt & Co., Inc., 301 W. Grand Ave., Montvale 07645
Pres.—Richard I. Paul, 20 emp., *Woodworking machinery, knives, cutters* ........ (201) 391-5300
Colwood Electronics, Inc., 44 Main St., Farmingdale 07727
Pres.—Richard Colaguori, 4 emp., *Wood burning tools* ........ (732) 938-5556

## 3554 Paper industries machinery

Catbridge Machinery, LLC, 222 New Rd., Ste. 1, Parsippany 07054
Pres.—Michael Pappas, 40 emp., *Paper converting machinery, including* ........ (973) 808-0029
Colter & Peterson, Inc., 414 E. 16th St., Paterson 07514
Pres.—Bruce Peterson, 40 emp., *Corporate headquarters & paper cutter* ........ (973) 684-0901
Euler Industries, Inc., 464 Old Tappan Rd., Old Tappan 07675
Owner & Pres.—Friedrich Euler, 5 emp., *Pulp mill tools* ........ (201) 666-9523
International Converting Machinery, Inc., 45 Camelot Dr., West Milford 07480
Pres., Sales & Mktg. Mgr.—Ted Gusek, Sr., 2 emp., *Converting machinery* ........ (973) 728-2600
Phoenix Machine, 4 Gold Mine Rd., Flanders 07836
Pres.—Michael Coulson, 20 emp., *New & rebuilt paper & film converting* ........ (973) 691-8029

Potdevin Machine Co., 26 Fairfield Pl., West Caldwell 07006
Pres.—Robert S. Potdevin, 15 emp., *Gluing equipment* ........ (201) 288-1941
Wagner Industries, Inc., 51 Sparta Rd., Stanhope 07874
Pres.—William Wagner, 11 emp., *Paper converting equipment that unwinds* ........ (973) 347-0800
Woodward Jogger Aerators, Inc., 45 Carlton Ave., East Rutherford 07073
Pres.—John Scillieri, 20 emp., *Paper & paperboard aerators* ........ (201) 933-6800

## 3555 Printing trades machinery

Ackley Machine Corp., 1273 N. Church St., Ste. 106, Moorestown 08057
Pres.—Michael Ackley, 32 emp., *Printing machinery* ........ (856) 234-3626
Allison Systems Corp., 220 Adams St., Riverside 08075
Pres.—Eve Allison, 15 emp., *Precision doctor blades for gravure* ........ (856) 461-9111
Andrus Screen Printing, LLC, 1915 Church Ave., Scotch Plains 07076
Pres., GM & Sales Mgr.—Jules Andrus, 1 emp., *Photo screens* ........ (908) 322-4299
Atlantic Zeiser, Inc., 15 Patton Dr., West Caldwell 07006
Pres., CEO—Thomas Coco, 40 emp., *High resolution drop-on-demand inkjet* ........ (973) 228-0800
Bell-Mark Sales Co., Inc., 331 Changebridge Rd., P.O. Box 2007, Pine Brook 07058
Pres.—John Marozzi, 30 emp., *Code-dating & in-line printing equipment* ........ (973) 882-0202
Benton Graphics, Inc., 3 Industrial Dr., Trenton 08619
Owner—Mary A. Benton, 28 emp., *White & blue carbon steel, stainless* ........ (609) 587-4000
Beta Screen Corp., 707 Commercial Ave., Carlstadt 07072
Pres.—Arnold Serchuk, 9 emp., *Microscopes, prepress quality control* ........ (201) 939-2400
Chesnut Engineering, Inc., W. R., 14 Spielman Rd., Fairfield 07004
Pres.—Richard Chesnut, 10 emp., *Gravure & flexographic printing presses* ........ (973) 227-6995
Cohen Printing & Invitation, 500 Cedar Ln., Teaneck 07666
Owner—Ruth Cohen, 5 emp., *Electronic prepress printing* ........ (201) 287-0343
Colex Imaging, Inc., 55-57 Bushes Ln., Elmwood Park 07407
Pres.—Werner Waden, 26 emp., *Manufacturer & distributor of wide-format* ........ (201) 265-5670
Continental Roller Co., Inc., 75 Arlington Ave., Kearny 07032
Owner—Carmine Bruzzesi, 6 emp., *Printing rollers for sheetfeed & web* ........ (201) 997-7999
Cronite Co., Inc., 120 E. Halsey Rd., P.O. Box 6330, Parsippany 07054
Pres.—Robert Steffens, 15 emp., *Etching & engraving equipment & supplies* ........ (973) 887-7900
Diversified Graphic Machinery, 230 Highway 35, Red Bank 07701
Pres.—Michael DeBard, 10 emp., *Cold foil systems & hot foil stamping* ........ (732) 933-4865
Gottscho Printing Systems, Inc., 335 Chambers Brook Rd., Branchburg 08876
Aftersales Mgr.—Paulette Katz, 5 emp., *Printing & code marking machines &* ........ (908) 688-2400
Graphic Equipment Corp., 55 Wester Ave., Metuchen 08840
Pres.—Karl Kuehnrich, 55 emp., *Printing press rewinders, machinery* ........ (732) 494-5350
Gulton, Inc., 116 Corporate Blvd., Ste. A, South Plainfield 07080
Pres.—Om Srivastava, 20 emp., *Barcode & lottery ticket thermal printing* ........ (908) 791-4622
Hary Mfg., Inc., 24 Cokesbury Rd., Lebanon 08833
Pres.—Paul Hary, 12 emp., *Fully automated screen & stencil printing* ........ (908) 722-7100
Heights USA, Inc., 1445 Lower Ferry Rd., Ewing 08618
Opers. Mgr.—Tim Philburn, 12 emp., *Lithographic & flexographic printing* ........ (609) 530-1300
Innolutions, Inc., 92 N. Main St., P.O. Box 384, Windsor 08561
Pres.—Manny Patel, 9 emp., *Electronic printing press controls* ........ (609) 490-9799
Interchange Equipment, Inc., 90 Dayton Ave., Ste. 200, Passaic 07055
Pres.—Marc Herrmann, 15 emp., *Manufacturer & distributor of printing* ........ (973) 473-5005
J R C Web Accessories, Inc., 46 Passaic Ave., Fairfield 07004
Chrm., Pres. & Sales Rep.—Ralph L. Ryan, 12 emp., *Pneumatic & mechanical chucks, shafts* (973) 625-3888
Jessup, Inc., Charles, 177 Smith St., Keasbey 08832
Pres.—Jay Jessup, 6 emp., *OEM manual screen printing equipment* ........ (732) 324-0430
Kompac Technologies, LLC, 7 Commerce St., Ste. 1, Somerville 08876
Pres.—Thomas Hayes, 25 emp., *UV & aqueous coating & curing, automatic* ........ (908) 534-8411
Marko Engraving & Art Corp., 439 Fairview Ave., Fairview 07022
Pres.—Marko Melnitchenko, 20 emp., *Photo polymer printing plates* ........ (201) 945-6555
Midlan Corp., 3 Bohnert Pl., Waldwick 07463
Pres., GM—Jacob Van Dyke, 10 emp., *Printing press ink dryers* ........ (201) 445-4405
Mosstype Corp., 150 Franklin Tpke., Waldwick 07463
GM—Edgar Coscolluela, 20 emp., *Flexographic equipment & supplies* ........ (201) 444-8000
On Demand Machinery, LLC, 150 Broadway, Elizabeth 07206
Co-Pres.—John Jacobson, Sr., 16 emp., *Bookbinding machinery* ........ (908) 351-6906
Pamarco Technologies, Inc., 235 E. 11th Ave., Roselle 07203
Pres.—Terry Ford, 30 emp., *Corporate headquarters & printing press* ........ (908) 241-1200
PanPac, LLC, 212 N. Virginia Ave., Carneys Point 08069
Owner—Rahul Kaushik, 14 emp., *Rebuilt offset printing & postpress* ........ (856) 376-3576
Polytype America Corp., 10 Industrial Ave., Mahwah 07430
Pres., CEO—Peter Andrich, 25 emp., *Digital grand-format printers & dry* ........ (201) 995-1000
Printers' Service, Inc., 26 Blanchard St., Newark 07105
Chrm.—Richard B. Liroff, 100 emp., *Corporate headquarters & pressroom* ........ (973) 589-7800
Schaefer, Inc., Ernest, 731 Lehigh Ave., Union 07083
Pres.—Ernest Schaefer III, 6 emp., *Zinc & brass type for hot foil stamping* ........ (908) 964-1280
Van Dam Machine Corp., 81-B Walsh Dr., Parsippany 07054
Cont., Fin. & MIS Mgr.—Kim Filippone, 20 emp., *Plastic printing machinery* ........ (973) 257-7050
West Essex Graphics, Inc., 305 Fairfield Ave., Fairfield 07004
Co-Pres.—Don Alldian, 35 emp., *Offset spot coating plates & digital* ........ (973) 227-2400

## 3556 Food products machinery

Aero Mfg Co., 310 Allwood Rd., P.O. Box 1250, Clifton 07012
Pres.—Wayne Phillips, 100 emp., *Stainless steel foodservice, material* ........ (973) 473-5300
Alex Machine Shop, Inc., 267 Livingston St., P.O. Box 268, Northvale 07647
Pres.—Alex Aleksich, 5 emp., *General machining job shop & food products* ........ (201) 768-9110
Allen Steel Co., 202 High St., Leesburg 08327
Pres.—James P. Allen III, 5 emp., *Commercial fishing boats & food processing* ........ (856) 785-1171
American Showcase & Foodservice Equipment, Inc., 19 Commerce Rd., Unit H, Fairfield 07004
Pres.—Tony Latallade, 6 emp., *Custom fabrication & distributor of* ........ (973) 227-1277
AM-MAC, Inc., 311 Route 46 W., Fairfield 07004
Owner—Judith Spritzer, 12 emp., *Food preparation equipment* ........ (973) 575-7567
Armfield, Inc., 9 Trenton Lakewood Rd., Ste. 2, Millstone Township 08510
GM, U.S.—Mike Di Leo, 8 emp., *Laboratory equipment for engineering* ........ (609) 208-2800
Bridge Rotary Machine Co., LLC, 614 Kennedy St., P.O. Box 45, Palmyra 08065
Opers. Mgr.—Nickolas Cimino, 30 emp., *Food processing machinery* ........ (856) 829-3110
Buhler Inc, 40 Whitney Rd., Mahwah 07430
Pres.—Steve Jacobson, 15 emp., *Processing equipment for the chemical* ........ (201) 847-0600
Coastal Imports, Inc., 31 Mulberry Ct., Unit B, Brielle 08730
Pres.—Patricia Lusk, 2 emp., *New & used baking & restaurant equipment* ........ (732) 223-4356
Custom Sales & Service, Inc., 275 S. 2nd Rd., P.O. Box 635, Hammonton 08037
Pres.—William Sikora, 50 emp., *Food carts, trailers & trucks* ........ (609) 561-6900
Edhard Corp., 279 Blau Rd., Hackettstown 07840
Pres.—Edgar Bars, 27 emp., *Liquid & viscous product filling &* ........ (908) 850-8444
Etta Controls, Inc., 31 Belgrade Ter., West Orange 07052
Pres.—Paul Rametta, 6 emp., *Control panels, system integrators,* ........ (973) 731-6552
Excalibur Bagel & Bakery Equipment, Inc., 4-01 Banta Pl., Fair Lawn 07410
Pres.—Richard Zinn, 14 emp., *Bagel & artisan bread making equipment* ........ (201) 797-2788
Excellent Bakery Equipment Co., 315 Fairfield Rd., Fairfield 07004
Pres.—Karin Seruga, 15 emp., *Manufacturer & distributor of bakery* ........ (973) 244-1664
Foodline Piping Products Co., 225 Edgewood Ave., West Berlin 08091
Pres.—Daniel Diadul, 7 emp., *Aluminum piping & tank UV systems for* ........ (856) 767-1177
GEA Mechanical Equipment US, Inc., 100 Fairway Ct., Northvale 07647
Pres.—Michael J. Vick, 175 emp., *Corporate headquarters & centrifuges* ........ (201) 767-3900
Glen Mills Inc., 220 Delawanna Ave., Clifton 07014
Pres.—Peter Kendall, 10 emp., *Distributor of sample preparation laboratory* ........ (973) 777-0777
Gray Star, Inc., 200 Valley Rd., Ste. 200, Mount Arlington 07856
Pres.—Martin Stein, 4 emp., *Food irradiation equipment* ........ (973) 398-3331
Gusmer Enterprises, Inc. (H Q), 1165 Globe Ave., Mountainside 07092
Pres.—Marla G. Jeffrey, 18 emp., *Corporate headquarters; beverage production* ........ (908) 301-1811
Hill Machine, Inc., 295 Governor St., Paterson 07501
Pres.—John Poulos, 5 emp., *Food mixers* ........ (973) 684-2808
Hockmeyer Equipment Corp., 610 Supor Blvd., Ste. 1, Harrison 07029
Cont.—Maureen Jetter, 4 emp., *Grinding & dispersion equipment & industrial* ........ (973) 482-0225
J T D Sales, LLC (H Q), 71 Bloomfield Ave., Newark 07104
Pres., CEO—Michael Fortanascio, 5 emp., *Company headquarters; meat slicing* ........ (973) 482-5070
Jaygo, Inc., 7 Emery Ave., Randolph 07869
Pres.—Jason Hayday, 11 emp., *Industrial process equipment, including* ........ (908) 688-3600
Key International, Inc., 4 Corporate Dr., Cranbury 08512
CEO—Valerie R. Ianieri, 20 emp., *Food & pharmaceutical processing &* ........ (609) 619-3685
Kuhl Corp., 39 Kuhl Rd., P.O. Box 26, Flemington 08822
CEO—Kevin H. Kuhl, 60 emp., *Washers, dryers, coolers & filters* ........ (908) 782-5696
Linker Machines, 20 Pine St., Rockaway 07866
Pres.—Jean Hebrank, 10 emp., *Food processing equipment* ........ (973) 983-0001
M B C Food Machinery Corp., 78 McKinley St., Hackensack 07601
Pres.—John Battaglia, 7 emp., *Food processing equipment* ........ (201) 489-7000
Magna Industries, Inc., 1825 Swarthmore Ave., Ste. 1, Lakewood 08701
Pres.—Walter Ostrowicki, 27 emp., *Bakery equipment, including baking,* ........ (732) 905-0957
Marlo Mfg. Co., Inc., 301 Division St., Boonton 07005
Ex. V-P.—Paul Peruccio, 50 emp., *Stainless steel restaurant equipment* ........ (973) 423-0226
Nitta Casings Inc., 141 Southside Ave., Bridgewater 08807
Pres., CEO—Rod Moore, 192 emp., *Edible collagen sausage casings & collagen* ........ (908) 218-4400
Patty-O-Matic, Inc., Route 547, P.O. Box 404, Farmingdale 07727
Pres.—Bernard Miles, 12 emp., *Food processing equipment* ........ (732) 938-2757
R S R Food Service Equipment Corp., 6574 Delilah Rd., Egg Harbor Township 08234
Pres.—Rick Love, 3 emp., *Food processing equipment & custom* ........ (609) 646-5158
Revent, Inc., 100 Ethel Rd. W., Piscataway 08854
Chrm.—Tor Bolin, 35 emp., *Commercial electric & gas ovens* ........ (732) 777-9433
T & A Metal Products, Inc., 1671 Hurffville Rd., P.O. Box 1805, Deptford 08096
Pres.—Nick Demarco, 6 emp., *Stainless steel kitchen equipment* ........ (856) 227-1700
T M U, Inc., 910 Shunpike Rd., Cape May 08204
Owner & Pres.—Robert Bartle, 10 emp., *Food processing machinery, precision* ........ (609) 884-7656
Techno Design, Inc., 11 Erie St., Front, Garfield 07026
Pres., CFO—Ruben A. Diaz, 4 emp., *Food processing machinery* ........ (973) 478-0930
Traycon Manufacturing Company, 555 Barell Ave., Carlstadt 07072
Pres.—Al Cialone, 25 emp., *Food & tray handling conveyor systems* ........ (201) 939-5555
Warwick Mfg. & Equipment Co., LLC, 1112 12th St., North Brunswick 08902
Mng. Dir.—Greg Pantchenko, 3 emp., *Food, packaging, chemical, cosmetic* ........ (732) 729-0400
Winter Scale & Equipment, 20-A Kulick Rd., Fairfield 07004
Pres.—John Winter, 25 emp., *Food processing equipment* ........ (888) 808-3611
Witte Co., Inc., The, 507 Route 31 S., P.O. Box 47, Washington 07882
Pres.—Richard Witte, 40 emp., *Continuous drying, cooling & separating* ........ (908) 689-6500
Wyssmont Co., Inc., 1470 Bergen Blvd., Fort Lee 07024
Pres.—Ed Weisselberg, 25 emp., *Drying equipment, feeders & lumpbreakers* ........ (201) 947-4600

## 3559 Machinery—special industry, nec

Acrison, Inc., 20 Empire Blvd., Moonachie 07074
Dir., Mktg.—John T. Shaw, 140 emp., *Volumetric & weight-loss feeders &* ........ (201) 440-8300
Advanced Process Technology, Inc., 200 Egel Ave., Middlesex 08846
Pres.—Henry Phillips, 15 emp., *Processing equipment* ........ (732) 356-4438
Advanced Specialty Gas Equipment, 241 Lackland Dr., Middlesex 08846
GM—Jackie Flatky, 15 emp., *High-purity specialty gas equipment* ........ (732) 271-9300
Alfa Machine Co., Inc., 2154 Highway 130 N., Monmouth Junction 08852
Pres.—Louis Pall, 4 emp., *Holography equipment, including special* ........ (732) 821-0044
Amano McGann, 140 Harrison Ave., Roseland 07068
GM—Jim Newcomer, 15 emp., *Pay stations & computer software for* ........ (973) 618-4050
American Custom Hydraulics, Inc., 33 Roosevelt Ave., Belleville 07109
Owner—Jean Zachar, 28 emp., *Rebuilt hydraulic equipment & machines* ........ (973) 751-1440
Applied Engineering, Corp., 232 Palisade Ave., Garfield 07026
Pres.—Andre Savin, 5 emp., *Manufacturer & distributor of custom* ........ (973) 772-6022
ARDE Barinco, Inc., 875 Washington Ave., Carlstadt 07072
Engrg. & Sales Mgr.—Roy Scott, 4 emp., *Mixing equipment, high-shear rotor* ........ (201) 768-6070
Atlantic Coast Crushers, Inc., 128 Market St., Kenilworth 07033
Pres.—Jack Paddock, 10 emp., *Industrial particle size reduction* ........ (908) 259-9292
Autobar Systems Corp., 1 Meridian Rd., Eatontown 07724
Pres.—Donald E. Ullery, Jr., 5 emp., *Liquor bottle dispensers & control* ........ (732) 922-3355
Automated Business Products, Inc. (H Q), 50 Clinton Pl., Mail Slot 1, Hackensack 07601
Pres.—Robert Mahalik, 9 emp., *Corporate headquarters; money & document* ........ (201) 489-1440
Automated Flexible Conveyors, Inc., 55 Walman Ave., 2nd Fl., Clifton 07011
Pres.—Kevin Devaney, 20 emp., *Spiral feeder conveyors, dump clean* ........ (973) 340-1695
AZCO Corp., 26 Just Rd., Fairfield 07004
Pres.—Andrew Zucaro, 30 emp., *Machinery for feeding, cutting, inserting* ........ (973) 439-1428
Brabender® Instruments, C. W., 50 E. Wesley St., P.O. Box 2127, South Hackensack 07606
Pres.—Richard F. Thoma, 30 emp., *Industrial laboratory testing instruments* ........ (201) 343-8425
Buhler Inc, 40 Whitney Rd., Mahwah 07430
Pres.—Steve Jacobson, 15 emp., *Processing equipment for the chemical* ........ (201) 847-0600
Butensky Services Co., Inc., 3380 Route 22, P.O. Box 5020, Somerville 08876
Pres.—Bryan Butensky, 50 emp., *Rebuilt & refurbished electromechanical* ........ (908) 707-0912
Camatron Sewing Machine, Inc., 42 Bergenwood Rd., Ste. A, Fairview 07022
Pres.—Robert Ross, 7 emp., *Manufacturer & distributor of specialized* ........ (201) 941-5116
Capus Automation Services, Inc., 856 Highway 206, Hillsborough 08844
Pres.—Joseph B. Vautier, 4 emp., *Automated material, storage & retrieval* ........ (908) 281-0227
Carteret Coding, Inc., 1431 Raritan Rd., Clark 07066
Pres.—Charles Vill, 6 emp., *Date & lot coding systems for the packaging* ........ (732) 574-0900
Cartridge Actuated Devices, Inc. (H Q), 51 Dwight Pl., Fairfield 07004
Pres.—John Grant, 40 emp., *Corporate headquarters; pyrotechnic* ........ (973) 575-1312
Cavalla, Inc., 111 Union St., Hackensack 07601
Pres.—Arthur Pisani, 18 emp., *Equipment for manufacturing & packaging* ........ (201) 343-3338

© Copyright 2015 Manufacturers' News, Inc.


Century Engineering Co., Inc., 4 Orono St., Clifton 07013
Pres.—Edward Haracz, 15 emp., *Deburring & glass washer machinery* ........ (973) 779-3900
Chem Flowtronics, Inc., 195 Paterson Ave., Little Falls 07424
Pres., CEO—Kevin Mooney, 10 emp., *Pharmaceutical, biotechnical & chemical* ........ (973) 785-0001
Cire Technologies, Inc., 251 Boulevard, Mountain Lakes 07046
Pres.—Eric Becht, 3 emp., *Industrial dryers for the converting* ........ (973) 402-8301
Clover Co., Inc., F. G., 40 Stickle Ave., Rockaway 07866
Ptnr. & Off. Mgr.—Cindy Just, 3 emp., *Metal spinning & hydroforming* ........ (973) 625-1811
Computa Base Machining, Inc., 411 N. Grove St., P.O. Box 340, Berlin 08009
Pres.—Augustin Rosado, 14 emp., *Fabrication & precision machining job* ........ (856) 767-9517
Consolidated Sewing Machine Corp., 400 Veterans Blvd., Carlstadt 07072
Pres.—Murray Feit, 29 emp., *Corporate headquarters & industrial* ........ (212) 741-7788
Coperion Corp., 663 E. Crescent Ave., Ramsey 07446
V-P., CFO—Thomas Hummel, 110 emp., *Corporate headquarters & plastic &* ........ (201) 327-6300
Cornell Machine Co., The, 45 Brown Ave., Springfield 07081
Pres.—Martin C. Huska, 10 emp., *Mechanical vacuum deaerators, defoamers* ........ (973) 379-6860
CTC International, Inc., 11 York Ave., West Caldwell 07006
Pres.—Erwin Herbert, 25 emp., *Automation equipment, including lap* ........ (973) 228-2300
D R Technology, Inc., 73 South St., Freehold 07728
Pres., CFO—Richard Schwartz, 7 emp., *Pollution control scrubbers* ........ (732) 780-4664
Dalemark Industries, Inc., 575 Prospect St., Ste. 211, Lakewood 08701
GM—Michael DelliGatti, 10 emp., *Industrial coding, labeling & imprinting* ........ (732) 367-3100
Dantco Mixers Corp., 9 Oak St., Paterson 07501
Pres.—Michael D'Antuono, 5 emp., *Pharmaceutical & chemical processing* ........ (973) 278-8776
Davis-Standard, LLC, 220 Davidson Ave., Ste. 401, Somerset 08873
V-P., Blown Film—Rick Keller, 130 emp., *Converting & extrusion systems for* ........ (908) 722-6000
Day Tool & Mfg., Inc., 6 Carman Ln., P.O. Box 466, Whitehouse 08888
Pres.—John J. Callahan III, 19 emp., *Custom machines, precision tooling,* ........ (908) 439-3800
De Dietrich U. S. A., Inc. (H Q), 244 Sheffield St., Mountainside 07092
Pres.—Don Doell, 30 emp., *Corporate headquarters; glass lining* ........ (908) 317-2585
Deborah Sales, LLC, 109 Meeker Ave., Newark 07114
Pres.—Jacira Rei, 2 emp., *Metal imprinting, advertising specialties* ........ (973) 344-8466
Denton Vacuum, LLC, 1259 N. Church St., Bldg. 3, Moorestown 08057
Chrm.—Peter Denton, 45 emp., *Vacuum thin film coating deposition* ........ (856) 439-9100
Designmecha, Inc., 73 Race St., Nutley 07110
Pres.—Joseph Kinney, 3 emp., *Ultrasonic nanocrystal surface modification* ........ (973) 493-8146
Ekato Corp., 48 Spruce St., Oakland 07436
V-P., Hum. Res. & IT Mgr.—Don Rowen, 20 emp., *Fluid mixing systems, mixers, agitators* ........ (201) 825-4684
Emabond Solutions, LLC, 49 Walnut St., Ste. 2, Norwood 07648
V-P., Sales—Steve Chookazian, 18 emp., *Plastic bonding machinery* ........ (201) 767-7400
Energy Beams, Inc., 185 Hamburg Tpke., Bloomingdale 07403
Pres.—John Richard, 16 emp., *CNC & precision machining job shop* ........ (973) 838-3037
Enviro-Clear Co., Inc., 152 Cregar Rd., High Bridge 08829
Pres.—C. Meyer, 19 emp., *Liquid/solid clarifiers, thickeners* ........ (908) 638-5507
ESG, LLC, 3 Gold Mine Rd., Flanders 07836
Pres.—Vincent LoConte, 6 emp., *Foil stamping machinery for the printing* ........ (973) 691-8517
Everite Machine Products Co., 6995 Airport Highway Ln., Pennsauken 08110
Pres., CFO—Bruce Mergenthal, 26 emp., *Electrolytic & electrochemical grinding* ........ (856) 330-6700
Excelsior Medical Corp., 1933 Heck Ave., Neptune 07753
CEO—Steve Thornton, 400 emp., *Pharmaceutical pumps* ........ (732) 776-7525
Fisnar, Inc., 19-C Chapin Rd. Ste. 307, Pine Brook 07058
Pres.—Vladimir Siroky, 40 emp., *Adhesive dispensing equipment* ........ (973) 646-5044
Galvanotech, 330-A Dalziel Rd., Linden 07036
Pres.—Gerry Volkov, 12 emp., *Electroplating equipment* ........ (908) 241-3900
General Carbon Corporation, 33 Paterson St., Paterson 07501
Pres.—Robert Muller, 20 emp., *Activated carbon & related filtration* ........ (973) 523-2223
General Machine Co. Of New Jersey, 301 Smalley Ave., Middlesex 08846
Chrm.—John Muench, 30 emp., *Industrial laboratory, portable production* ........ (732) 752-7900
Glatt Air Techniques, Inc., 20 Spear Rd., Ramsey 07446
Ex. V-P., Sales—John Carey, 140 emp., *Pharmaceutical processing machinery* ........ (201) 825-8700
Glenbrook Technologies, Inc., 11 Emery Ave., Randolph 07869
Pres.—Gil Zweig, 18 emp., *X-ray inspection equipment, accessories* ........ (973) 361-8866
Hickory Industries, Inc., 4900 W. Side Ave., North Bergen 07047
Pres.—Steven Amroti, 30 emp., *Rotisseries, pizza ovens, warmers &* ........ (201) 223-0050
High Technology Corp., 144 South St., Hackensack 07601
V-P., Sales—Aline Alroy, 20 emp., *Plastics machinery* ........ (201) 488-0010
Hoffman/New Yorker, Inc. (H Q), 46 Clinton Pl., Hackensack 07601
V-P.—Terry Rothlisberger, 10 emp., *Corporate headquarters; steam finishing* ........ (201) 488-1800
Hosokawa Micron Powder Systems, 10 Chatham Rd., Summit 07901
V-P.—Rob Voorhees, 50 emp., *Company headquarters & powder processing* ........ (908) 273-6360
Hunter Products, Inc., 792 Partridge Dr., P.O. Box 6795, Bridgewater 08807
Pres.—Phyllis Zelnick, 18 emp., *Ultra-compact electroplating pens &* ........ (908) 526-8440
Imperial Sewing Machine Co., Inc., 584 S. 21st St., Irvington 07111
Pres.—Philip Pantusco, 6 emp., *Industrial sewing machines, including* ........ (973) 374-3405
Intelligrated, 265 Davidson Ave., Ste. 219, Somerset 08873
V-P., Opers., Eastern Reg.—Eric Palotas, 34 emp., *Conveyors, sortation, automated storage.* (732) 302-2590
International Micro Industries, Inc., 1951 Old Cuthbert Rd., Bldg. 404, Cherry Hill 08034
Pres., CEO—Christopher N. Angelucci, 23 emp., *Wafer electroplating & bumping & contract* (856) 616-0051
J R Engineering & Machine Corp., 663 Ramsey Ave., Hillside 07205
Pres., CEO—F. Joseph Kilroy, 15 emp., *Rebuilt centrifugal pump parts & machining* ........ (908) 810-6300
Jaygo, Inc., 7 Emery Ave., Randolph 07869
Pres.—Jason Hayday, 11 emp., *Industrial process equipment, including* ........ (908) 688-3600
Jersey Metalworks, LLC, 1022 Hamilton St., Ste. A, Somerset 08873
Pres.—Ray Ferrari, 4 emp., *Custom machinery* ........ (732) 565-1313
Jesse J. Heap & Sons, Inc., 576 S. 21st St., Irvington 07111
Pres.—Jesse Heap, 8 emp., *Industrial sewing machine attachments* ........ (973) 372-1559
Jet Pulverizer Co., Inc., 1255 N. Church St., Moorestown 08057
Pres.—Ed Fay, 30 emp., *Jet pulverizers, including jet energy* ........ (856) 235-5554
Jomar Corp., 115 E. Parkway Dr., Egg Harbor Township 08234
Ex. Admn.—Chris Acquaviva, 34 emp., *Plastic injection blow molding machinery* ........ (609) 646-8000
Kahle Automation, 89 Headquarters Plz., Ste. 355, Morristown 07960
Pres.—Julie Logothetis, 10 emp., *Assembly machinery for pharmaceutical* ........ (973) 993-1850
Kautex Machines, Inc., 201 Chambers Brook Rd., P.O. Box 5329, North Branch 08876
V-P., Sales, North America—Chuck Flammer, 20 emp., *Plastic extrusion blow molding machinery* (908) 252-9350
Koch Modular Process Systems, LLC, 45 Eisenhower Dr., Ste. 350, Paramus 07652
Pres.—George Schlowsky, 60 emp., *Preassembled modular mass transfer* ........ (201) 368-2929
Kraemer Koating, Inc., 1925 Swarthmore Ave., Lakewood 08701
Pres. & Software Techn.—Paul Kraemer, 5 emp., *Research machinery coating equipment* ........ (732) 886-6315
Kuntz Co., Inc., R. T., 5146 W. Hurley Pond Rd., P.O. Box 476, Farmingdale 07727
Owner & Pres.—Rod Kuntz, 7 emp., *Manufacturer & distributor of resin* ........ (732) 751-1770
Leneta Co., Inc., 15 Whitney Rd., Mahwah 07430
Pres.—Dan Schaeffer, 115 emp., *Paint test charts & draw down equipment* ........ (201) 847-9300
Lummus Technology, 1515 Broad St., Bloomfield 07003
Pres.—Daniel McCorthy, 400 emp., *Heat transfer equipment, including* ........ (973) 893-3000
Marindus Co., Inc, P.O. Box 663, Englewood 07631
Pres.—Jim Bartis, 10 emp., *Concrete surface preparation equipment* ........ (201) 567-8383
Medical Packaging, Inc., 470 Route 31, P.O. Box 500, Ringoes 08551
CEO—Andy Bartels, 20 emp., *Pharmacy oral solids & liquid packaging* ........ (609) 466-8991
Mendel Co. (H Q), 12-C Great Meadow Ln., East Hanover 07936
Pres.—Barry Fox, 1 emp., *Company headquarters; pharmaceutical* ........ (973) 599-1300
Meto Lift, Inc., 556 Commerce St., Franklin Lakes 07417
Pres.—William Rotenberry, 20 emp., *Stainless steel material handling equipment* ........ (201) 405-0311
Milspray, LLC, 845 Towbin Ave., Lakewood 08701
Pres., CEO—Brian Feser, 40 emp., *Mil-spec paint, renewable energy, corrosion* ........ (732) 886-2223
Modular Packaging Systems, Inc., 6 Aspen Dr., Randolph 07869
Pres.—Clifford Smith, 13 emp., *Modular packaging equipment & systems* ........ (973) 970-9393
N. M. Knight Co., Inc., 1001 S. 2nd St., P.O. Box 1099, Millville 08332
Pres.—Jack Narbut, 50 emp., *Gas burners, custom machinery & polarizing* ........ (856) 327-4855
Nanonex Corp., 1 Deerpark Dr., Ste. O, Monmouth Junction 08852
Chrm. & Founder—Stephen Y. Chou, 30 emp., *Nano/microstructure manufacturing equipment* (732) 355-1600
National Equipment Co., 342 Squankum Yellowbrook Rd., P.O. Box 674, Farmingdale 07727
Pres.—Mauro R. Raccuglia, 4 emp., *Rebuilt production pipe & bolt threading* ........ (732) 938-5084
N-C Carpet Binding & Equipment Corp., 858 Summer Ave., Newark 07104
Pres., CEO & Principal, Sales & Mktg.—Mel Maher, 14 emp., *Machinery for the carpeting* ........ (973) 481-3500
New Brunswick Plating, Inc., 1010 Jersey Ave., New Brunswick 08901
Pres.—Anthony Melchione, 52 emp., *Metal finishing* ........ (732) 545-6522
New York Sewing Machine, Inc., 8555 Tonnelle Ave., Unit 301, North Bergen 07047
Pres.—Sheldon Rothstein, 5 emp., *Manufacturer & distributor of sewing* ........ (201) 809-2009
Newark Caplan Sewing Machine, Inc., 858 Summer Ave., Newark 07104
Pres., CEO, CFO, Principal & MIS Mgr.—Mel Maher, Sr., 14 emp., *Industrial sewing machinery* (973) 481-4400
Pedrick Tool & Machine Co., 1518 Bannard St., P.O. Box 190, Riverton 08077
Pres.—Ralph M. Scott, 10 emp., *Bending machines for pipes, tubes,* ........ (856) 829-8900
Polytype America Corp., 10 Industrial Ave., Mahwah 07430
Pres., CEO—Peter Andrich, 25 emp., *Digital grand-format printers & dry* ........ (201) 995-1000
Precious Metals Processing Consultants, Inc., 430 Bergen Blvd., Palisades Park 07650
Pres.—Randy Epner, 4 emp., *Electrolytic metal recovery equipment* ........ (201) 944-8053
Precision Automation Company, Inc., 1841 Old Cuthbert Rd., Cherry Hill 08034
Pres., CEO—G. Frederick Rexon, Jr., 50 emp., *Automation, conveyor, control & complete* ........ (856) 428-7400
Progressive-Ruesch Machine Co., LLC, 21 Van Natta Dr., Ringwood 07456
CEO—Stephen Honczarenko, 17 emp., *Industrial machinery for the metal,* ........ (973) 962-7700
Quartz Technology, Inc., 1355 Plymouth Rd., Bridgewater 08807
Pres.—Lothar Jung, 2 emp., *Quartz processing machinery* ........ (908) 526-6362
Ramco Equipment Corp., 32 Montgomery St., Hillside 07205
Owner & Pres.—Fred Randall, 20 emp., *Industrial parts washers & parts washers* ........ (908) 687-6700
Rame-Hart, Inc., 5 Emery Ave., Ste. 1, Randolph 07869
Pres., CEO—Ken Christiansen, 25 emp., *Egg harvesting & inoculating machines* ........ (973) 335-0560
RANDCASTLE Extrusion Systems, Inc., 220 Little Falls Rd., Unit 6, Cedar Grove 07009
Pres.—Keith Luker, 5 emp., *Bench & floor screw extrusion machinery* ........ (973) 239-1150
RecycleTech Corp., 418 Falmouth Ave., Elmwood Park 07407
Pres.—Dan Chung, 15 emp., *Assembly of EPS (expanded polystyrene)* ........ (201) 475-5000
Reliable Rubber & Plastic Machinery Co., 2008 Union Tpke., North Bergen 07047
Pres.—Helga Liccardo, 40 emp., *Processing machinery for the rubber* ........ (201) 865-1073
Remington Industries, Inc., Cordes Machine Div., 269 Sheffield St., Mountainside 07092
Plt. Mgr.—Doug West, 120 emp., *Stair building equipment for wood stair* ........ (908) 233-2600
Resec Systems, LLC, 93 S. Railroad Ave., Ste. A, Bergenfield 07621
Owner—Bob Schulkin, 4 emp., *Automated high-speed inspection & sorting* ........ (201) 384-6960
Royal Sovereign International, Inc., 2 Volvo Dr., Rockleigh 07647
Chrm.—T. K. Lim, 40 emp., *Desktop & wide-format lamination &* ........ (201) 750-1020
Royle Systems Group, LLC, 111 Bauer Dr., Ste. 2, Oakland 07436
Pres.—Greg Ramsey, 30 emp., *Rubber & plastic extrusion equipment* ........ (201) 644-0345
Rudolph Technologies, Inc., 1 Rudolph Rd., P.O. Box 1000, Flanders 07836
Chrm., CEO—Paul F. McLaughlin, 25 emp., *Corporate headquarters & semiconductor* ........ (973) 691-1300
Servolift, LLC, 35 Righter Rd., Randolph 07869
Pres.—Marc Kaufman, 29 emp., *Pharmaceuticals handling & processing* ........ (973) 442-7878
Sonar Products, Inc., 609-611 Industrial Rd., Carlstadt 07072
Pres.—Mark Newman, 18 emp., *Pharmaceutical processing equipment* ........ (201) 729-1116
Spadix Technologies, Inc., 110 Egel Ave., Middlesex 08846
Pres.—Albert Simone, 10 emp., *Automation machinery* ........ (732) 356-6906
Spiral Binding Co., Inc., 1 Maltese Dr., Totowa 07512
Pres.—Robert Roth, 150 emp., *Corporate headquarters & binding, laminating* ........ (973) 256-0666
Tech Products Co., Inc., 300 Greenwood Ave., Midland Park 07432
Owner—Robert White, 10 emp., *Precision machinery job shop & pharmaceutical* ........ (201) 444-7777
Themac, Inc., 405 Railroad Ave., P.O. Box 44, East Rutherford 07073
Pres.—Joseph Cremona, 7 emp., *Tool post grinding machines* ........ (201) 438-2313
Trico Poly Systems, LLC, 60 Brown Ave., Springfield 07081
Ptnr.—Kenneth J. Plis, 10 emp., *Polyurethane & epoxy processing machinery* ........ (973) 376-7770
Triple-T Cutting Tools, Inc., 135 Edgewood Ave., West Berlin 08091
Pres.—Steve Thomas, 14 emp., *Cutting tools for the metal & plastic* ........ (856) 768-0800
Ulysses Machine Co., 41 Lancelot Ln., Mount Laurel 08054
Owner—Ulysses Xenophontos, 2 emp., *Rope twisting, wire braider & ballistic* ........ (856) 979-3674
Valeur Corp., Oilco U. S. A. Div., 596 Ridge Rd., P.O. Box 226, Monmouth Junction 08852
Pres.—R. C. Slawinski, Jr., 10 emp., *Liquid handling systems* ........ (732) 329-4666
Vandermolen Corp., 119 Dorsa Ave., Livingston 07039
Pres.—Aldo H. Vandermolen, 3 emp., *Electric indoor & outdoor insect control* ........ (973) 992-8506
Veeco Instruments, Inc., 145 Belmont Dr., Somerset 08873
Sr. V-P., GM—Jim Jenson, 115 emp., *Metal organic chemical vapor deposition* ........ (732) 560-5300
Vytran, LLC, 1400 Campus Dr., Morganville 07751
Pres., CEO—Ed Connor, 50 emp., *Precision fiber splicing & glass processing* ........ (732) 972-2880
Witte Co., Inc., The, 507 Route 31 S., P.O. Box 47, Washington 07882
Pres.—Richard Witte, 40 emp., *Continuous drying, cooling & separating* ........ (908) 689-6500
Wyssmont Co., Inc., 1470 Bergen Blvd., Fort Lee 07024
Pres.—Ed Weisselberg, 25 emp., *Drying equipment, feeders & lumpbreakers* ........ (201) 947-4600
Zenith Ultrasonics, 85 Oak St., P.O. Box 412, Norwood 07648
Pres., Sales & Mktg. Mgr.—Michael Pedzy, 15 emp., *Ultrasonic cleaning equipment, including* (201) 767-1332

## 3561 Pumps & pumping equipment

A & D Industrial & Marine Repair, 900 Port Reading Ave., Ste. B-2, Port Reading 07064
Pres.—Doug Alexander, 12 emp., *Machine shop, including rebuilt industrial* ........ (732) 541-1481
All Mechanical Services, Inc., 430 High St., P.O. Box 110, Perth Amboy 08862
Pres., Hum. Res. Mgr.—Greg Huhn, 5 emp., *Rebuilt pumps & motors* ........ (732) 442-8292
Allied Pump Corporation, 1109 Grand Ave., Bldg. 5, North Bergen 07047
Pres.—Benjamin Miller, 15 emp., *Manufacturer & distributor of boiler* ........ (201) 798-3277
Arcadia Equipment, Inc., 140 Lawrence St., Hackensack 07601
Pres.—Doug White, 12 emp., *Pump systems for the pharmaceutical* ........ (201) 342-3308

S.I.C.

Bio-Chem Fluidics, Inc., 85 Fulton St., Ste. 12, Boonton 07005
Pres.—Timothy O' Sullivan, 60 emp., *Precision fluid handling components* ............ (973) 263-3001
Camac Industries, 18 Gail Ct., Sparta 07871
Pres., Opers. Mgr.—Peter Gennaro, 5 emp., *Industrial pumps, filters & heat exchangers* ........ (973) 300-5575
Carter Pump, 326 S. Dean St., Englewood 07631
Pres., CEO—Kevin Powers, 31 emp., *Company headquarters & plunger & diaphragm* .......... (201) 568-9798
Chase Machine Co., Inc., 127 Park Ave., P.O. Box 148, Lyndhurst 07071
Pres.—Donald Lascola, 13 emp., *Industrial pump parts for the water* ............ (201) 438-2218
Cincinnati Thermal Spray East, 80 Fadem Rd., Springfield 07081
GM—Scot Crabtree, 28 emp., *Industrial pump & valve components* ............ (973) 379-0003
ClearDrain, 219 Saint Mihiel Dr., Riverside 08075
Mng. Dir.—Frank A. Chille, Jr., 10 emp., *Self-adjusting, self-cleaning, self-defrostin* ............ (856) 461-0091
Conhagen, Inc., Alfred (H Q), 2035 Lincoln Hwy., Edison Sq. W., Ste. 3003, Edison 08817
Pres.—Alfred Conhagen, Jr., 5 emp., *Corporate headquarters; pump parts,* ............ (732) 287-4565
Croll-Reynolds, 90 Hollister Rd., Teterboro 07608
Br. Mgr.—A. Patel, 4 emp., *Steam ejectors for industrial process* ............ (201) 288-9282
Deltronics Corp., 224 Bogden Blvd., P.O. Box 446, Millville 08332
Pres.—Bob Hignutt, 12 emp., *Rebuilt sewage pumps* ............ (856) 825-8200
DSO Fluid Handling Co., Inc., 300 McGaw Dr., Ste. 2, Edison 08837
V-P., GM, Bus. Dev. & Sales—Ed Clark, 15 emp., *Replacement parts for sanitary food* ............ (732) 225-9100
Dynaflow Engineering, 106 Egel Ave., Middlesex 08846
Pres.—Ross Block, 5 emp., *Stainless, alloy & plastic gear pumps* ............ (732) 356-9790
Eagle Flo Pumps, Inc., 306 Orient Way, Rutherford 07070
Pres.—Joseph Hamadeh, 4 emp., *Industrial pumps & valves* ............ (201) 438-8595
Etta Controls, Inc., 31 Belgrade Ter., West Orange 07052
Pres.—Paul Rametta, 6 emp., *Control panels, system integrators,* ............ (973) 731-6552
Flowserve Corp., 142 Clinton Rd., Fairfield 07004
Plt. Mgr.—M. Patel, 25 emp., *Rebuilt pumps* ............ (973) 227-4565
Frontline Industries, Inc., 990 Chancellor Ave., Irvington 07111
Pres.—Alfredo Ciotola, 15 emp., *Custom mechanical seals, flexible shaft* ............ (973) 373-7211
Godwin, a Xylem brand, 84 Floodgate Rd., Bridgeport 08014
Pres. & Sr. V-P., Dewatering—Colin Sabol, 260 emp., *Company headquarters & automatic self-priming* (856) 467-3636
Hayward Industries, Inc., 620 Division St., Elizabeth 07201
Chrm.—Oscar Davis, 100 emp., *Corporate headquarters & swimming pool* ............ (908) 351-5400
J R Engineering & Machine Corp., 663 Ramsey Ave., Hillside 07205
Pres., CEO—F. Joseph Kilroy, 15 emp., *Rebuilt centrifugal pump parts & machining* ............ (908) 810-6300
Kraissl Co., Inc., 299 Williams Ave., Hackensack 07601
Pres.—Richard C. Michel, 21 emp., *Heavy-duty industrial valves, pumps* ............ (201) 342-0008
Layne Christensen Co., 719 Mount Holly Rd., Beverly 08010
Hum. Res. Mgr.—Michelle Ryan, 10 emp., *Rebuilt water pumps* ............ (609) 877-2700
Leistritz Corp., 165 Chestnut St., Allendale 07401
Pres.—Sven Olson, 18 emp., *Industrial pumps* ............ (201) 934-8262
Liquiflo Equipment Co., Inc., 443 North Ave., Ste. 2, Garwood 07027
Pres.—Richard Picut, 30 emp., *Centrifugal & external gear pumps* ............ (908) 518-0777
Mid-Atlantic Engine Supply, Route 130 S. & Pennsauken St., P.O. Box 2270, Cinnaminson 08077
V-P., Treas. & Cont.—Chuck Cook, 15 emp., *Marine & industrial diesel engines* ............ (856) 829-7798
Mobile Power International, LLC, 1010 Old Egg Harbor Rd., Voorhees 08043
Owner—Anthony F. Amorosia, 12 emp., *Contract manufacturing & metal fabrication* ............ (856) 784-3195
Parker Hannifin Corp., 45 Route 46 E., Unit 602, P.O. Box 778, Pine Brook 07058
Application Engr.—Jamari Davis, 50 emp., *PTFE & stainless steel miniature solenoid* ............ (973) 575-4844
Pro Machine Co., 5 Sicomac Rd., Haledon 07508
★ Owner—Eddie Demetro, 18 emp., *Rebuilt gear boxes, pumps & shear blades* .... (973) 855-9935
PSEG Power, 749 Cliff Rd., Sewaren 07077
Off. Mgr.—Carmen Esteves, 80 emp., *Gas & steam turbines, electric turbines* ............ (732) 750-2062
Pul-A Pump Corp., 29 Paradise Trl., P.O. Box 155, Stockholm 07460
Pres., CEO—Robert A. Wilbert, 2 emp., *Water pump hoists, pullers & pushers* ............ (973) 697-2008
R G I, Inc., 27 Union Valley Rd., Newfoundland 07435
Pres.—Barry Maloney, 16 emp., *CNC machining of valves, pumps & manifolds* ............ (973) 697-2624
Reid Plumbing Products, LLC, 371 Route 31 N., Hopewell 08525
Owner—John Reid, 7 emp., *Well management equipment for maintaining* ........ (609) 466-1785
SC Engineering Co., Inc., 115 Stryker Ln., Bldg. 4, Hillsborough 08844
Pres.—Tom Arias, 7 emp., *Vertical turbine pumps, pumping equipment* ............ (908) 874-5955
Sims Pump Valve Co., Inc., 1314 Park Ave., P.O. Box 3338, Hoboken 07030
Pres.—John A. Kozel, 22 emp., *Structural composite pumps & pump parts* ............ (201) 792-0600
Smith Brothers Services, LLC, 3212 State Route 94, Ste. 9, Franklin 07416
Owner—Charles Smith, 1 emp., *Rebuilt snowplow pumps, snowplow pump* ............ (973) 209-7569
Sulzer Pumps (U.S.), Inc., 621 Haron Dr., P.O. Box 487, Bridgeport 08014
Serv. Ctr. Mgr.—Ginny Johnston, 25 emp., *Industrial centrifugal pumps* ............ (856) 467-2400
Tri-State Pump, Inc., 5044 Industrial Rd., Ste. C, Farmingdale 07727
Co-Pres.—Mike Caringi, 10 emp., *Industrial pumps* ............ (732) 223-3222
Vanton Pump & Equipment Corp., 201 Sweetland Ave., Hillside 07205
Ex. V-P.—Larry Lewis, 50 emp., *Nonmetallic chemical pumps* ............ (908) 688-4216
Wire Equipment Mfg. Co., Inc., 319 Birch Hollow Dr., Bordentown 08505
Pres.—Christine Stone-Quinn, 1 emp., *Molten metal centrifugal pumps* ............ (609) 499-4411

## 3562 Bearings—ball & roller

Accurate Bronze Bearing Co., 64 Illinois Ave., Paterson 07503
Pres., Secy-Treas.—Roger R. Zito, 5 emp., *Custom bronze bearings & machine parts* ............ (973) 345-2304
DGB Bearing & Technology, 700 Mid Atlantic Pkwy., P.O. Box 189, Thorofare 08086
Pres.—Ken Walker, 250 emp., *Bearings* ............ (856) 848-3200
Emmco Development Corp., 243 Belmont Dr., Somerset 08873
Pres.—Patrick Ryan, 25 emp., *Sub-miniature ball bearings* ............ (732) 469-6464
Fortuna Enterprise USA, Inc., 235 Country Club Dr., Moorestown 08057
Pres.—Huichuan C. Liao, 2 emp., *Casters* ............ (856) 778-7588
King Engine Bearings, 371 Little Falls Rd., Ste. 5, Cedar Grove 07009
Owner & Pres.—Dalila Michel, 15 emp., *Engine bearings* ............ (973) 857-0705
Precision Ball Specialties, Inc., 1451 Glassboro Rd., Williamstown 08094
Off. & Sales Mgr.—Carol Symanski, 3 emp., *Ball bearing cages* ............ (856) 881-5646
RBC Bearings, Inc., 400 Sullivan Way, West Trenton 08628
Plt. Mgr.—Deval Glover, 125 emp., *Standard & custom engineered bearings* ............ (609) 882-5050
Rollon Corp., 101 Bilby Rd., Ste. B, Hackettstown 07840
Cont.—Shelly Connolly, 25 emp., *Linear bearings, actuators & linear* ............ (973) 300-5492
Saint-Gobain Performance Plastics, 150 Dey Rd., Wayne 07470
Sales Mgr., Global—William O. Textores, 250 emp., *Plastic film & maintenance-free bearings* (973) 696-4700

## 3563 Compressors—air & gas

Aavolyn Corp., 207 Bogden Blvd., P.O. Box 1097, Millville 08332
Pres.—Lynn Farrell, 32 emp., *Compressor replacement parts, including* ............ (856) 327-8040
Air Center, Inc., 270 Monroe Ave., Kenilworth 07033
Pres.—Matthew W. Ruggiero, 15 emp., *Rebuilt air compressors* ............ (908) 276-1992
ARMCO Compressor Products Corp., 2042 46th St., North Bergen 07047
Pres.—Ara Zadourian, 11 emp., *Air & process compressor components* ............ (201) 866-6766
Atlas Copco North America, LLC (H Q), 7 Campus Dr., Ste. 200, Parsippany 07054
Pres., AC Holdings USA—Jim Levitt, 40 emp., *Company headquarters; industrial air* ............ (973) 397-3400
Corban Energy Group, 418 Falmouth Ave., Elmwood Park 07407
CEO—Daniel Chung, 15 emp., *Compressed natural gas (CNG) fueling* ............ (201) 509-8555
EMSE Corp., 10 Plog Rd., Unit 1, Fairfield 07004
Pres.—Alex Rothenberg, 10 emp., *Medical vacuum pumps & compressors* ............ (973) 227-9221
Evey Engineering Co., LLC, 158 Weymouth Rd., Vineland 08360
Pres.—Donald Callahan, 2 emp., *Rebuilt vacuum pumps, blowers & systems* ............ (856) 692-6705
International Compressor Co., Inc., 361 Jelliff Ave., Newark 07108
Pres.—Clarence Wilson, 7 emp., *Rebuilt air compressors & distributor* ............ (973) 824-7170
KNF Neuberger, Inc., 2 Black Forest Rd., Trenton 08691
Cont.—Gary Frank, 105 emp., *Industrial pumps & compressors* ............ (609) 890-8600
Middlesex Industrial Sales, Inc., 522 New Brunswick Ave., Fords 08863
Pres.—Michael Amendola, 3 emp., *Material handling equipment & air compressors* ............ (732) 738-0537
Parenta & Sons Enterprises, Inc., 85 Fulton St., Unit 9-B, Boonton 07005
Pres.—Joseph Parenta, 15 emp., *Remanufactured compressed gas equipment* ............ (973) 334-9266
Technology General Corp. (H Q), 12 Cork Hill Rd., Franklin 07416
Sales Mgr.—Diane Olsen, 5 emp., *Corporate headquarters; electric &* ............ (973) 827-4143
Trillium, Inc., 3627 Route 23 S., Hamburg 07419
Pres.—Al Citarella, 20 emp., *Industrial rotary piston vacuum pumps* ............ (973) 827-1661

## 3564 Blowers & fans

Aer-X-Dust Corp., P.O. Box 93, Tennent 07763
Pres.—Guy D. Cusumano, 5 emp., *Landfill biogas skid systems, including* ............ (732) 946-9462
Air Clean Co., Inc., 1135 Chestnut St., Elizabeth 07201
Pres.—Alex Drucker, 8 emp., *Air pollution control equipment* ............ (908) 355-1515
Atmos Tech Industries, 1108 Pollack Ave., Ocean 07712
Mktg. Mgr.—Shaun Brower, 48 emp., *Cleanroom filters, air showers, stainless* ............ (732) 493-8400
B & L Industrial Services, Inc., 700 Park Ave., Unit 7, Hainesport 08036
Pres.—Richard Lodwig, 4 emp., *Steel fabrication, rebuilt fans & blowers* ............ (609) 386-9500
Belco Technologies Corp., 9 Entin Rd., Parsippany 07054
Pres.—Kevin Gilman, 55 emp., *Air pollution control systems* ............ (973) 884-4700
BioAir Solutions, LLC, 110 Kresson-Gibbsboro Rd., Ste. 303, Voorhees 08043
Owner—Louis D. Leroux, 35 emp., *Biological odor control filter systems* ............ (856) 258-6969
Bioclimatic Air Systems, 600 Delran Pkwy., Ste. D, Delran 08075
CEO—Stephen Zitin, 22 emp., *Air purification equipment* ............ (856) 764-4300
Biological Controls, Inc., 749 Hope Rd., Eatontown 07724
★ Owner—Gary Messina, 5 emp., *Air purification systems* ............ (732) 542-5822
Biological Controls, Inc., 749 Hope Rd., Ste. A, Tinton Falls 07724
Pres.—Gary Messina, 5 emp., *Hospital infection control equipment* ............ (732) 389-8922
Bionomic Industries, Inc., 777 Corporate Dr., Mahwah 07430
Pres.—John Enhoffer, 12 emp., *Air pollution control equipment* ............ (201) 529-1094
Building Performance Equipment, Inc., 80 Broadway, Ste. 101, Hillsdale 07642
CEO—Klas Haglid, 10 emp., *High-efficiency energy recovery ventilation* ............ (201) 722-1414
C D M Dust Control Of New Jersey, 15-17 S. 7th Ave., Long Branch 07740
Pres.—Robert G. Koenig, 11 emp., *Dust control systems* ............ (732) 222-3694
Camfil USA, Inc., 1 N. Corporate Dr., Riverdale 07457
Pres.—Armando Brunetti, 150 emp., *Corporate headquarters & air filtration* ............ (973) 616-7300
CleanZones, LLC, 640 Herman Rd., Ste. 2, Jackson 08527
Pres.—David McClelland, 10 emp., *Air filtration equipment for the cleanroom* ............ (732) 534-5590
Columbia Filters, Inc., 255 Highland Cross, Rutherford 07070
Pres.—Nick Pizzone, 10 emp., *Air conditioning filters* ............ (201) 438-3883
Connell Industries, Inc., 13 Fairfield Ave., West Caldwell 07006
Pres.—Vincent DiGangi, 5 emp., *Industrial automation systems & equipment* ............ (877) 926-6635
CSM Worldwide, Inc., 1100 Globe Ave., Mountainside 07092
CEO—Atul Shah, 20 emp., *Air pollution control equipment* ............ (908) 233-2882
Drytech, Inc., 54 Wrightstown Cookstown Rd., P.O. Box 249, Cookstown 08511
Pres., Fin. & R & D Mgr.—Tony Jones, 24 emp., *Cartridge dehydrators, moisture management* (609) 758-1794
Electric Fan Engineering Co., 8 Crown Plz., Unit 105, Hazlet 07730
Pres.—Roger Clemente, 5 emp., *Electric & hydraulic fan cooling systems* ............ (732) 203-0320
Glocon, Inc. (Swifter Fans), 3-1 Luger Rd., Denville 07834
V-P.—Arjun Agarwal, 5 emp., *Industrial axial fiberglass fans for* ............ (973) 463-7300
Hamon Corp., 58 E. Main St., P.O. Box 1500, Somerville 08876
CEO—William P. Dillon, 100 emp., *Corporate headquarters & heat transfer* ............ (908) 685-4000
L M Air Technology, Inc., 1467 Pinewood St., Rahway 07065
Pres.—Peter Daniele, 40 emp., *Hardwall & softwall cleanrooms & lab* ............ (732) 381-8200
Mainstream Custom Air Handling Units, 47 Russo Pl., Berkeley Heights 07922
Member & Hum. Res. Mgr.—Derrick Markham, 50 emp., *Industrial air-handling units for the .* (908) 931-1010
Micro-Air, Inc., 124 Route 526, Allentown 08501
Pres.—Andrew Spaziani, 20 emp., *Electronic controls & environmental* ............ (609) 259-2636
Mitsubishi Hitachi Power Systems America - Energy & Environment, 645 Martinsville Rd., Basking Ridge 07920
Pres., CEO—Hank E. Bartoli, 150 emp., *Industrial air filtration systems* ............ (908) 605-2800
Plymovent Corporation (H Q), 115 Melrich Rd., Ste. 2, Cranbury 08512
Dir.—Jens Schlueter, 20 emp., *Corporate headquarters; indoor pollution* ............ (609) 395-3500
Smith Filter Corp., 16 Van Dyke Ave., New Brunswick 08901
Plt. Mgr.—Wiley Hargrove III, 28 emp., *Permanent & disposable building ventilation* ............ (732) 745-2600
Spartan Air Purification, 150 Cooper Rd., Ste. E-14, West Berlin 08091
Owner—Dan Fitzpatrick, 3 emp., *Air purification systems* ............ (856) 768-2929
Sternvent, 5 Stahuber Ave., Union 07083
Pres.—Robert Denholtz, 20 emp., *Dust collection systems used for industrial* ............ (908) 688-0807
Summit Filter Corporation, 20 Milltown Rd., P.O. Box 427, Union 07083
Pres.—James K. Shahidi, 30 emp., *Industrial fabric filter, pleated,* ............ (908) 687-3500
United Blower Co., Inc., 22 Westbrook Dr., Morganville 07751
Pres.—Howard Spitzer, 3 emp., *Food safe pressure & explosion-proof* ............ (201) 601-5700
Vitaire Corp., 141 Lanza Ave., 4th Fl., Garfield 07026
Pres.—Peter Vayda, 6 emp., *HEPA air purification units for allergy* ............ (973) 473-2244

## 3565 Packaging machinery

A T Information Products, Inc., 575 Corporate Dr., Mahwah 07430
Pres.—Joseph Traut, 9 emp., *Inkjet printing & labeling systems* ............ (201) 529-0202
Action Packaging Automation, Inc., 15 Oscar Dr., P.O. Box 190, Roosevelt 08555
Sales Mgr.—John Wojnicki, 12 emp., *Packaging machinery, including automatic* ............ (609) 448-9210
Advantage Packaging Technologies, LLC, P.O. Box 301, Carlstadt 07072
Ptnr.—Glenn Rice, 4 emp., *Packaging machinery* ............ (201) 832-1858
Am Jet Enterprises, 11 1/2 Elm St., Rockaway 07866
Pres.—Andrew Chop, 3 emp., *Filling & assembly machines* ............ (973) 627-5690
Applied Engineering, Corp., 232 Palisade Ave., Garfield 07026
Pres.—Andre Savin, 5 emp., *Manufacturer & distributor of custom* ............ (973) 772-6022
AZCO Corp., 26 Just Rd., Fairfield 07004
Pres.—Andrew Zucaro, 30 emp., *Machinery for feeding, cutting, inserting* ............ (973) 439-1428

B.D. Briggs, 31 Richboynton Rd., Dover 07801
Pres.—Ray Michael Gudelanis, 20 emp., *Custom packaging machinery* (973) 989-1950
CAMPAK, Inc., 119 Naylon Ave., Livingston 07039
CEO—Thomas Miller, 11 emp., *Packaging equipment* (973) 597-1414
Cavalla, Inc., 111 Union St., Hackensack 07601
Pres.—Arthur Pisani, 18 emp., *Equipment for manufacturing & packaging* (201) 343-3338
Clements Industries, Inc., 50 Ruta Ct., South Hackensack 07606
Pres.—Alan Clements, 12 emp., *Manual & semiautomatic twist-tie machines* (201) 440-5500
Cozzoli Machine Co., 50 Schoolhouse Rd., Somerset 08873
Pres.—Joan Rooney, 100 emp., *Packaging machinery* (732) 564-0400
Dalemark Industries, Inc., 575 Prospect St., Ste. 211, Lakewood 08701
GM—Michael DelliGatti, 10 emp., *Industrial coding, labeling & imprinting* (732) 367-3100
Deitz Co., Inc., 1750 Highway 34, P.O. Box 1108, Wall 07719
Pres.—John Deitz, 18 emp., *Pharmaceutical & vitamin bottle filling* (732) 681-0200
Edhard Corp., 279 Blau Rd., Hackettstown 07840
Pres.—Edgar Bars, 27 emp., *Liquid & viscous product filling &* (908) 850-8444
F & L Machinery & Design, Inc., 48 Commerce St., Springfield 07081
Pres.—Fred Villaverde, 9 emp., *Packaging machinery* (973) 218-6216
F P Developments, Inc., 402 S. Main St., Williamstown 08094
Pres.—Fred Pfleger, 32 emp., *Pharmaceuticals & industrial packaging* (856) 875-7100
Global Packaging Machinery, Inc., 36 Peel St., Paterson 07524
Owner & Dir., Engrg.—Michael Kurdyla, 5 emp., *Cartoning & material handling machinery* (973) 279-2300
Greener Corp., 4 Helmly St., Bayville 08721
V-P.—Matthew Wojtech, 24 emp., *Parts for packaging machinery* (732) 341-3880
Harland America, 1803 Underwood Blvd., Delran 08075
Pres.—Jim Potter, 10 emp., *Pressure sensitive labeling equipment* (856) 764-9622
Heisler Industries, Inc., 224 Passaic Ave., Fairfield 07004
Pres.—Richard A. Heisler, 38 emp., *Packaging machines, automation & system* (973) 227-6300
Hunter Mfg. Services, Inc., 19 Just Rd., Fairfield 07004
Owner & Pres.—Kenneth C. Hunter, 12 emp., *CNC machining of pharmaceutical packaging* (973) 365-5880
Id Technology, 48 Spruce St., Oakland 07436
V-P., GM—Jack Roe, 25 emp., *Pressure sensitive labeling machinery* (888) 405-4574
Industrial Automation Systems Engineering Co., Inc., 161 Industrial Pkwy., Unit 6, Branchburg 08876
Pres., R & D Mgr.—Michael D'Egidio, 20 emp., *Robotic packaging machinery* (908) 218-1104
Integrated Packaging Systems, 3 Luger Rd., Ste. 5, Denville 07834
Ptnr. & Pres.—Robert W. Fields, 10 emp., *Packaging equipment for the pharmaceutical* (973) 664-0020
International Paper Co., 33 Phoenix Dr., Thorofare 08086
Cont.—Richard Scott, 175 emp., *Corrugated boxes & point-of-purchase* (856) 853-7000
JG Machine Works, 2182 State Route 35, Holmdel 07733
GM—Donald Nelson, 4 emp., *Packaging machinery* (732) 203-2077
Jo-De Machine Co., Inc., 43 Ethel Ave., Hawthorne 07506
Pres.—Joseph D'Angelo, 4 emp., *Packaging machinery* (973) 427-9555
Key International, Inc., 4 Corporate Dr., Cranbury 08512
CEO—Valerie R. Ianieri, 20 emp., *Food & pharmaceutical processing &* (609) 619-3685
Key-Pak Machines By Luciano Packaging Technologies, Inc, 29 County Line Rd., Somerville 08876
Pres., MIS Mgr.—Larry Luciano, 10 emp., *Custom form, fill & seal machinery,* (908) 722-3222
Kinesys Automation, Inc., 5 Fir Ct., Unit 3, Oakland 07436
Pres.—Diana Manoussakis, 8 emp., *Packaging, conveying, filling, capping* (201) 337-5000
Lazar Technologies, Inc., 39 Evergreen St., Hazlet 07730
Pres.—Carlos Gaviria, 9 emp., *Bottle capping equipment, inspection* (732) 739-9622
Modular Packaging Systems, Inc., 6 Aspen Dr., Randolph 07869
Pres.—Clifford Smith, 13 emp., *Modular packaging equipment & systems* (973) 970-9393
Monroe Machine & Design, Inc., 566 Buckelew Ave., Monroe Township 08831
Pres.—Susan Kovacs, 5 emp., *Packaging & automation machinery, including* (732) 521-3434
National Shrinkwrap, 6220 U.S. Highway 9, Howell 07731
Owner & Pres.—Art Marko, 2 emp., *Shrink-wrapping machinery & film* (732) 942-4554
Norwalt Design, Inc., 961 Route 10 E., Bldg. 2-A, Randolph 07869
Br. Mgr.—Michael Seidel, 45 emp., *Packaging machinery* (973) 927-3200
Oystar USA, Inc., 523 Raritan Centre S.W., Edison 08837
IT Mgr.—Brian McNamara, 47 emp., *Packaging machinery* (732) 343-7600
Packaging Consultants Assocs., 7300 N. Crescent Blvd., Unit 14, Pennsauken 08110
Cust. Serv. Mgr.—Lorraine Dischert, 10 emp., *Film equipment packaging* (856) 488-0277
Packaging Machinery & Equipment Co., 181 Watson Ave., West Orange 07052
Corp. Secy.—Mary E. Cameron, 5 emp., *Packaging machinery* (973) 325-2418
Per-Fil Industries, Inc., 407 Adams St., P.O. Box 9, Riverside 08075
Pres., CFO—Shari Becker, 25 emp., *Auger filling equipment for powder,* (856) 461-5700
PMC Industries, 275 Hudson St., Hackensack 07601
Pres.—Kazmier Wysocki, 25 emp., *Special screw capping machines & plug* (201) 342-3684
Prodo-Pak Corp., 77 Commerce St., P.O. Box 363, Garfield 07026
Pres.—John Mueller, 25 emp., *Automatic form/fill/seal packaging* (973) 772-4500
Romar Machine & Tool Co., 521 Commerce St., Franklin Lakes 07417
Pres.—Bob Thum, 12 emp., *Packaging machinery tube holders, fill* (201) 337-7111
Scandia Packaging Machinery Co., 15 Industrial Rd., Fairfield 07004
Pres.—Wilhelm B. Bronander III, 35 emp., *Packaging machinery for overwrapping* (973) 473-6100
Seal Spout Corp., 50 Allen Rd., P.O. Box 74, Liberty Corner 07938
Prodn. Mgr.—Frank Lombardo, 12 emp., *Packaging machinery* (908) 647-1900
Solbern, 8 Kulick Rd., Fairfield 07004
Pres.—Tom Berger, 35 emp., *Food processing equipment* (973) 227-3030
Stiles Enterprises, Inc., 114 Beach St., P.O. Box 92, Rockaway 07866
Pres.—Richard Stiles, 15 emp., *Manufacturer & distributor of packaging* (973) 625-9660
Systech Solutions, Inc., 2540 U.S. Highway 130, Ste. 128, Cranbury 08512
Pres., CEO—Robert DeJean, 100 emp., *Packaging systems for the pharmaceutical* (609) 395-8400
Torpac, Inc., 333 U.S. Highway 46, Fairfield 07004
Pres.—Raj Tahil, 10 emp., *Custom & large-size two-piece empty* (973) 244-1125
Uhlmann Packaging Systems, 44 Indian Ln. E., Towaco 07082
Pres.—Andy Stobbe, 75 emp., *Packaging machinery* (973) 402-8855
Warwick Mfg. & Equipment Co., LLC, 1112 12th St., North Brunswick 08902
Mng. Dir.—Greg Pantchenko, 3 emp., *Food, packaging, chemical, cosmetic* (732) 729-0400
Watson Assocs., Inc., 800 Grove Rd., Thorofare 08086
Pres.—Edward Schafer, 2 emp., *Conveyor belts & packaging equipment* (856) 845-8800
Wrapade Packaging Systems, LLC, 27 Law Dr., Ste. B, Fairfield 07004
Pres.—Bill Beattie, 16 emp., *Vertical & horizontal four side seal* (973) 773-6150

## 3566 Speed changers, drives & gears

Acme Gear Co., Inc., 130 W. Forest Ave., P.O. Box 779, Englewood 07631
Pres.—Joseph Gelles, 100 emp., *Gear machining job shop* (201) 568-2245
Andantex U.S.A., Inc., 1705 Valley Rd., Ocean 07712
Pres.—Michael G. Munn, 20 emp., *Right-angle gearboxes, servo worm &* (732) 493-2812
Apex Gear & Machine Co., 938 Lake St., Newark 07104
Pres.—Steve Ciocci, 6 emp., *Precision gears, racks & grinding,* (973) 482-5542
Electronic Drives & Controls, Inc., 17 Eastmans Rd., Parsippany 07054
Pres.—Henry Dillard III, 26 emp., *Electronic drives & controls systems* (973) 428-0500
Intech Corp., 250 Herbert Ave., Closter 07624
Pres.—Georg Bartosch, 7 emp., *Self-lubricating plastic non-hygroscopic* (201) 767-8066
Koll Machine & Tool Co., Frank G., 390 Warburton Pl., P.O. Box 464, Long Branch 07740
Owner—Richard Koll, 3 emp., *Model boat radio controls, gearboxes* (732) 870-2966
M J H Gear & Tool Co., Inc., 15 Maple St., Norwood 07648
Pres.—John M. Halkias, 3 emp., *Precision gears* (212) 246-3800
Pro Machine Co., 5 Sicomac Rd., Haledon 07508
★ Owner—Eddie Demetro, 18 emp., *Rebuilt gear boxes, pumps & shear blades* (973) 855-9935
SC Engineering Co., Inc., 115 Stryker Ln., Bldg. 4, Hillsborough 08844
Pres.—Tom Arias, 7 emp., *Vertical turbine pumps, pumping equipment* (908) 874-5955
SEW-Eurodrive, Inc., 2107 High Hill Rd., P.O. Box 481, Bridgeport 08014
Opers. Mgr.—Scott Bansky, 55 emp., *Motors & drives assembly* (856) 467-2277
State Tool Gear Co., Inc., 211 Camden St., Newark 07103
Pres.—Michael Insabella, 14 emp., *Gears & gear cutting* (973) 642-6181
Walter Machine Co., Inc., The, 84-98 Cambridge Ave., P.O. Box 7700, Jersey City 07307
Pres.—Don Chatrnuck, 40 emp., *Gear drives* (201) 656-5654

## 3567 Furnaces & ovens—industrial

ABP Induction, LLC, 1460 Livingston Ave., North Brunswick 08902
V-P., Melting Foundry Div.—David Decker, 22 emp., *Induction melting furnaces for foundry* (732) 932-6400
CM Furnace, Inc., 103 Dewey St., Bloomfield 07003
Pres.—David Neill, 46 emp., *High-temperature electric batch & continuous* (973) 338-6500
Consarc Corp., 100 Indel Ave., P.O. Box 156, Rancocas 08073
Pres.—William J. Marino, 109 emp., *Vacuum & controlled atmosphere melting* (609) 267-8000
Corbett Industries, Inc., 39 Hewson Ave., Ste. B, P.O. Box 212, Waldwick 07463
Pres., Engrg. Mgr.—Richard J. Geier, 15 emp., *Industrial heating equipment, ovens* (201) 445-6311
ECCO High Frequency, 2360 Hamburg Tpke., Wayne 07470
Pres.—Richard E. Sullivan, 8 emp., *Induction heating & melting equipment* (973) 248-3366
ElectroHeat Induction, 9 Spruce St., Jersey City 07306
★ Proj. Engr.—Charlie Parsana, 10 emp., *Induction heating & melting equipment* (908) 494-0726
Elnik Systems, LLC, 107 Commerce Rd., Cedar Grove 07009
Pres.—Claus Joens, 35 emp., *Sintering furnaces & debinding ovens* (973) 239-6066
FCS Fluidaire Cleaning Services, Inc., 11 Industrial Dr., New Brunswick 08901
V-P., Sales—Robert P. Lasky, 30 emp., *Thermal fluidized bed cleaning equipment* (732) 964-1700
Gas Drying, Inc., 355 W. Dewey Ave., P.O. Box 504, Wharton 07885
Pres.—Gary Behrens, 15 emp., *Industrial compressed air & gas dryers* (973) 361-2212
Glenro, Inc., 39 McBride Avenue Ext., Paterson 07501
Pres.—Gary Van Denend, 20 emp., *Industrial gas & electric infrared* (973) 279-5900
H E D International, Inc., 449 Route 31, P.O. Box 246, Ringoes 08551
Pres.—James Dennis, 9 emp., *Furnaces & kilns* (609) 466-1900
Hankin Environmental Systems, Inc., 1 Harvard Way, Ste. 6, P.O. Box 5759, Hillsborough 08844
Pres.—David Chou, 12 emp., *Multiple hearth industrial & municipal* (908) 722-9595
Hotfoil-EHS, Inc., 2960 E. State Street Ext., Hamilton 08619
Pres.—Neville Richards, 35 emp., *Industrial heating equipment, including* (609) 588-0900
Inductotherm Corp., 10 Indel Ave., P.O. Box 157, Rancocas 08073
Pres.—Satyen N. Prabhu, 200 emp., *Corporate headquarters & metal induction* (609) 267-9000
Kinetics Infrared, 40 Pier Ln. W., Fairfield 07004
Pres.—Chris Hines, 6 emp., *Industrial electric infrared quartz* (973) 575-5332
L & L Kiln Mfg. Co., Inc., 505 Sharptown Rd., Swedesboro 08085
Pres.—Stephen J. Lewicki, 15 emp., *Ceramic kilns for potters, schools,* (856) 294-0077
Marsden, Inc., 6800 Westfield Ave., Pennsauken 08110
Pres., CEO—Gerard J. Lucidi, 15 emp., *Gas infrared emitters & systems* (856) 663-2227
Pennington Furnace Supply, Inc., 6 Brookside Ave., Pennington 08534
Pres.—Mark Blackwell, 3 emp., *Channel induction furnaces* (609) 737-2500
Procedyne Corp., 11 Industrial Dr., New Brunswick 08901
Pres., COO—Thomas Parr, 35 emp., *High-temperature industrial & heat* (732) 249-8347
PV/T, Inc., 100 Indel Ave., P.O. Box 156, Rancocas 08073
Pres., CFO—Brett Wenger, 4 emp., *Aluminum, copper, nickel, stainless* (609) 267-3933
R Welding, 97 Main St., Waretown 08758
Owner—Risden Russell, 2 emp., *Commercial & industrial desiccate dehumidifie* (609) 971-6017
Radiant Energy Systems, Inc., 175 N. Ethel Ave., Hawthorne 07506
Sales & Mktg. Coord.—Jim Margiotta, 20 emp., *Custom electrical & gas-fired infrared* (973) 423-5220
Radiation Systems, Inc., 455 W. Main St., Wyckoff 07481
Pres., Sales Mgr.—Richard Ver Hage, 7 emp., *Infrared ovens systems & stainless* (201) 891-7515
RDO Induction LLC, 2170 State Route 57 W., Washington 07882
CEO & Principal—Robert Okner, 4 emp., *Induction heating, melting & casting* (908) 835-7222
Solar Products, Inc., 228 Wanaque Ave., Pompton Lakes 07442
Pres.—Mike Sirotnak, 30 emp., *Industrial heating units* (973) 835-6581
Thermal Innovations Corp., 2220 Landmark Pl., Ste. 1, Manasquan 08736
Pres.—Nicholas Fusilli, 4 emp., *Infrared, convection & ultraviolet* (732) 223-1812
T-M Vacuum Products, Inc., 630 S. Warrington Ave., Cinnaminson 08077
Pres.—Fred Stuffer, 35 emp., *Furnaces, ovens, environmental chambers* (856) 829-2000
Waage Electric, Inc., 720 Colfax Ave., P.O. Box 337, Kenilworth 07033
Pres., R & D Mgr.—Marc Waage, 6 emp., *Commercial & industrial electric heating* (908) 245-9363
Wyssmont Co., Inc., 1470 Bergen Blvd., Fort Lee 07024
Pres.—Ed Weisselberg, 25 emp., *Drying equipment, feeders & lumpbreakers* (201) 947-4600

## 3568 Power transmission equipment

Accurate Bushing Co., Inc./Smith Bearing Div., 443 North Ave., 1st Fl., Garwood 07027
Pres.—Peter Dubinsky, 50 emp., *Aircraft & industrial bearings, bushings* (908) 789-1121
Amscot Structural Products Corp., 241 E. Blackwell St., Dover 07801
Pres. & IT Mgr.—Peter Somogyi, 22 emp., *Structural slide bearings* (973) 989-8800
Atlanta Drive Systems, Inc., 1775 State Route 34, Ste. D-10, Farmingdale 07727
V-P.—Brad Donmoyer, 4 emp., *Rack & pinion drive systems* (732) 282-0480
BCC (U.S.A.) Inc., 143 Ethel Rd. W., Piscataway 08854
Dir. & GM—Marquis Yeh, 10 emp., *Split pillow block bearing housings* (732) 572-5450
Daven Industries, Inc., 55 Dwight Pl., Fairfield 07004
Pres.—Lou Lever, 30 emp., *Shafts, chucks, safety chucks, winders* (973) 808-8848
DYNA-Veyor, Inc., 10 Hudson St., Newark 07103
Pres., CEO—Steve Ayre, 18 emp., *Plastic conveyor chains, belting, sprockets* (973) 484-1119
EIC Industry Group Corp. (H Q), 53 Green Pond Rd., Ste. 3, Rockaway 07866
Pres.—John Ni, 5 emp., *Corporate headquarters; custom components* (973) 983-1988
Electrical Motor Repair Co., 809 E. State St., Trenton 08609
Pres.—Paul Doran, 30 emp., *Couplings for elevator hoist motors* (609) 392-6149
Electroid Co., 45 Fadem Rd., Springfield 07081
Pres.—Stephen Etter, 90 emp., *Custom electromagnetic clutches, brakes* (973) 467-8100
Lee Linear, 727 South Ave., Piscataway 08854
Pres.—Glen Michalske, 45 emp., *Linear motion products, including linear* (732) 752-5200
S G Mfg. Corp., 15 Oliver St., Metuchen 08840
Foreman—George Roma, 4 emp., *Nuclear submarine universal joints* (732) 494-6520

S.I.C.

★ **Indicates new listing this edition.**

F104 © Copyright 2015 Manufacturers' News, Inc. S.I.C. SECTION

S.S. White Technologies, Inc., 151 Old New Brunswick Rd., Piscataway 08854
Pres., CEO—Rahul Shukla, 180 emp., Flexible shafts for surgical tools, (732) 474-1700

## 3569 Machinery—general industrial, nec

ABOX Automation Corp., 2 Frassetto Way, Unit 2, Lincoln Park 07035
Mng. Ptnr.—Steve Kanthan, 4 emp., Precision feeding, cutting & dispensing (973) 659-9611
Action Packaging Automation, Inc., 15 Oscar Dr., P.O. Box 190, Roosevelt 08555
Sales Mgr.—John Wojnicki, 12 emp., Packaging machinery, including automatic (609) 448-9210
Admiral Filter Co., 18 Green Pond Rd., Unit 3, Rockaway 07866
Plt. Mgr.—Bruce Kristiansen, 10 emp., Oily water separators & filters (973) 948-3252
Advanced Industrial Technology, 640 Cambridge Rd., Paramus 07652
Pres.—T. S. Wang, 12 emp., Pollution control equipment (201) 265-1414
Alfa Production Systems, 522 Boulevard, Westfield 07090
V-P., Sales—Charles Holhea, 19 emp., Automation machinery (908) 654-0255
Allied Group, Inc., 5 Coldhill Rd., Bldg. 19, P.O. Box 209, Mendham 07945
Pres.—Ed Thomas, 24 emp., Coalescing filters, mist eliminators (973) 543-5404
Ameridia, 20 Worlds Fair Dr., Ste. F, Somerset 08873
V-P.—Daniel H. Bar, 4 emp., Industrial electrodialysis modules (732) 805-4001
Applied Engineering, Corp., 232 Palisade Ave., Garfield 07026
Pres.—Andre Savin, 5 emp., Manufacturer & distributor of custom (973) 772-6022
AZCO Corp., 26 Just Rd., Fairfield 07004
Pres.—Andrew Zucaro, 30 emp., Machinery for feeding, cutting, inserting (973) 439-1428
BEUMER Corporation, 800 Apgar Dr., Somerset 08873
Pres., CEO—Thomas Dahlstein, 175 emp., Conveying, loading, palletizing & packaging (732) 893-2800
Boomerang Systems, Inc., 30-A Vreeland Rd., Ste. 150, Florham Park 07932
CEO—Mark R. Patterson, 8 emp., Corporate headquarters & automated (973) 538-1194
Butensky Services Co., Inc., 3380 Route 22, P.O. Box 5020, Somerville 08876
Pres.—Bryan Butensky, 50 emp., Rebuilt & refurbished electromechanical (908) 707-0912
Capitol Fire Protection Co., Inc., 56 N. Logan Ave., Trenton 08609
Pres.—Charles S. Parkerson, 8 emp., Automatic fire sprinkler systems & (609) 393-3936
Carlisle Machine Works, Inc., 412 S. Wade Blvd., Bldg. 5, P.O. Box 746, Millville 08332
Pres.—Mary Dougherty, 23 emp., Custom fabrication & machining of industrial (856) 825-0627
Clawson Machine, Div. Of Technology General Corp., 12 Cork Hill Rd., Franklin 07416
Pres., Div.—Ryan Barbulescu, 5 emp., Commercial & industrial ice crushers (973) 827-8209
Clifton Fluid Power Machinery, 295 Allwood Rd., Clifton 07012
GM—Richard Brodsky, 9 emp., Hydraulic machinery (973) 778-3923
Connell Industries, Inc., 13 Fairfield Ave., West Caldwell 07006
Pres.—Vincent DiGangi, 5 emp., Industrial automation systems & equipment (877) 926-6635
Croll-Reynolds (H Q), 6 Campus Dr., Parsippany 07054
Pres.—Samuel Croll, 25 emp., Company headquarters; industrial process (908) 232-4200
CryoVation, LLC, 9-B Mary Way, Hainesport 08036
Pres.—Ric Boyd, 25 emp., Gas cylinder filling systems (609) 914-4792
CTC International, Inc., 11 York Ave., West Caldwell 07006
Pres.—Erwin Herbert, 25 emp., Automation equipment, including lap (973) 228-2300
Davis-Standard, LLC, 220 Davidson Ave., Ste. 401, Somerset 08873
V-P., Blown Film—Rick Keller, 130 emp., Converting & extrusion systems for (908) 722-6000
Eastern Automation Systems, 1151 New Jersey Route 33, P.O. Box 2394, Farmingdale 07727
Pres.—Scott Bellows, 3 emp., Custom automated machinery (732) 938-2002
Eaton Filtration, LLC, 44 Apple St., Tinton Falls 07724
Pres.—Rick Jacobs, 100 emp., Filtration systems (732) 767-4200
Edmund Optics, Inc., 101 E. Gloucester Pike, Barrington 08007
Chrm., CEO—Robert Edmund, 165 emp., Corporate headquarters & optical lens (856) 547-3488
Energy Options, LLC, 256 Campus Dr., Edison 08837
Pres.—Bradley Freeman, 43 emp., Automated HVAC systems & security monitoring (732) 512-9100
FCS Fluidaire Cleaning Services, Inc., 11 Industrial Dr., New Brunswick 08901
V-P., Sales—Robert P. Lasky, 30 emp., Thermal fluidized bed cleaning equipment (732) 964-1700
Fire Hooks Unlimited, 1827 Old Mill Rd., Wall 07719
CEO, R & D Mgr.—Bob Farrell, 18 emp., Firefighting tools & equipment (732) 280-7737
Fluid Filtration Corp., 102 Van Winkle Ave., Garfield 07026
Pres.—Farzad Alborzi, 10 emp., Pipeline & cone strainers, water filters (973) 253-7070
Fluitec International (H Q), 333 Washington St., Ste. 201, Jersey City 07302
Pres., CEO—Frank Magnotti, 50 emp., Company headquarters; lubricant conditioning (201) 946-4584
Franklin Miller, Inc., 60 Okner Pkwy., P.O. Box 070663, Livingston 07039
V-P., Sales—Dave Schuppe, 35 emp., Size reduction processors for wet/dry (973) 535-9200
GEA Mechanical Equipment US, Inc., 100 Fairway Ct., Northvale 07647
Pres.—Michael J. Vick, 175 emp., Corporate headquarters & centrifuges (201) 767-3900
Glen Mills Inc., 220 Delawanna Ave., Clifton 07014
Pres.—Peter Kendall, 10 emp., Distributor of sample preparation laboratory (973) 777-0777
Hangsterfer's Laboratories, Inc., 175 Ogden Rd., Mantua 08051
CEO—Ann Jones, 40 emp., Metal working lubricants & coolants (856) 468-0216
HAYNES Corp., 6 Carman Ln., P.O. Box 467, Whitehouse 08888
Pres.—Steve Haynes, 7 emp., Custom automation machinery for the (908) 439-4600
Heinkel Filtering Systems, Inc., 520 Sharptown Rd., Swedesboro 08085
Pres.—Alan Ferraro, 10 emp., Centrifuges, dryers, mixers, filtration (856) 467-3399
Heisler Industries, Inc., 224 Passaic Ave., Fairfield 07004
Pres.—Richard A. Heisler, 38 emp., Packaging machines, automation & system (973) 227-6300
Heller Industries, Inc., 4 Vreeland Rd., Ste. 1, Florham Park 07932
CEO—David Heller, 45 emp., Reflow soldering ovens (973) 377-6800
Hudson Robotics, Inc., 10 Stern Ave., Springfield 07081
Pres.—Philip Farrelly, 10 emp., Life science research laboratory robots (973) 376-7400
Imperial Metal Products, Inc., 8 W. Chimney Rock Rd., Bound Brook 08805
Pres.—John Karmazyn, 5 emp., Stainless steel size reduction machinery (732) 469-8181
Industrial Filters Co., Inc., 9 Industrial Rd., Fairfield 07004
Pres.—Steven Donker, 7 emp., Industrial water filters (973) 575-0533
Intelligrated, 265 Davidson Ave., Ste. 219, Somerset 08873
V-P., Opers., Eastern Reg.—Eric Palotas, 34 emp., Conveyors, sortation, automated storage. (732) 302-2590
Jessup, Inc., Charles, 177 Smith St., Keasbey 08832
Pres.—Jay Jessup, 6 emp., OEM manual screen printing equipment (732) 324-0430
Kason Corp., 67-71 E. Willow St., Millburn 07041
Pres.—Henry Alamzad, 40 emp., Screening & processing equipment & (973) 467-8140
Komo Machine, Inc., 1 Komo Dr., Lakewood 08701
Pres.—Mike Kolibas, 40 emp., High speed CNC routing machining centers (732) 719-6222
Leak Detection Associates, Inc., 3003 N. Mill Rd., Vineland 08360
CEO—Darrell Morrow, 4 emp., Turnkey helium leak detectors & systems (856) 405-6636
Library Automation Technologies, 2 E. Atlantic Ave., Somerdale 08083
CEO—Oleg Boyarsky, 15 emp., Library patron self-check-in & self-checkout (856) 566-4121
Liquiflo, Inc., 7 Wilpert Rd., Bridgewater 08807
Pres.—Brian Atherton, 3 emp., Fluid handling filters & pumps (732) 271-4600
LRC Associates, Inc., 328 S. 2nd St., Millville 08332
Pres.—Lawrence R. Clements, 35 emp., Custom & engineered production automation (215) 244-1150
Mega Pumps, L. P., 611 Industrial Way W., Eatontown 07724
Pres.—Lucyna Silberstein, 53 emp., Cosmetic dispensing systems (732) 578-9100
Metalfab, Inc., 11 Prices Switch Rd., P.O. Box 9, Vernon 07462
COO—Mike Randazzo, 30 emp., Large plate steel fabrication & dry (973) 764-2000
Monick Mfg. Corp., 2619 Route 206, Mount Holly 08060
Pres.—Monte Hauser, 5 emp., Machine parts & welding job shop (609) 267-0777
Monroe Machine & Design, Inc., 566 Buckelew Ave., Monroe Township 08831
Pres.—Susan Kovacs, 5 emp., Packaging & automation machinery, including (732) 521-3434
Neill Supply Co., Inc., 700 Schuyler Ave., Lyndhurst 07071
Pres.—Robert Moss, 60 emp., Manufacturer of fire sprinklers & distributor (201) 939-1100
New Jersey Meter Co., 1 Hazel St., Woodland Park 07424
Pres.—Anthony Abbate, 5 emp., Dry air separators & condensate drains (973) 345-6200
Nova Systems, 246 Cozy Lake Rd., Oak Ridge 07438
Owner—Bob Deutsch, 3 emp., Custom control systems & equipment (973) 697-3281
Pace Packaging Corp., 3 Sperry Rd., Fairfield 07004
Pres.—Kenneth Regula, 48 emp., Automatic plastic bottle unscrambling (973) 227-1040
Process Components, 301 John Wall Rd., Monroe Township 08831
Pres.—David Zimmerman, 8 emp., High purity flow components (732) 786-1500
Rails Co., 101 Newark Way, Maplewood 07040
Chrm., Pres. & CEO—G. N. Burwell, 35 emp., Railroad heaters, controls & lubrication (973) 763-4320
RDO Induction LLC, 2170 State Route 57 W., Washington 07882
CEO & Principal—Robert Okner, 4 emp., Induction heating, melting & casting (908) 835-7222
Reel Parts Co., 10 Park Ave., West Orange 07052
Pres.—John Dyer, 6 emp., Corrugated, PVC, masonite & wooden (973) 731-9559
Renewable BioSystems, LLC, 20 Spielman Rd., Fairfield 07004
CEO—Peter Behrle, 15 emp., Organic oil extraction machinery for (973) 769-0600
Resec Systems, LLC, 93 S. Railroad Ave., Ste. A, Bergenfield 07621
Owner—Bob Schulkin, 4 emp., Automated high-speed inspection & sorting (201) 384-6960
Resource Systems, Inc., 7 Merry Ln., East Hanover 07936
Pres.—Leonard R. Rubin, 3 emp., Industrial gas & palladium-alloy hydrogen (973) 884-0650
Robotunits, Inc., 5 Chris Ct., Ste. G, Dayton 08810
Pres.—Juergen Roth, 15 emp., Modular automation system, including (732) 438-0500
Simple Solutions Distribution, LLC (H Q), 6 Jacobs Rd., West Milford 07480
Ptnr. & Mktg. Mgr.—Andrew McGibbon, 2 emp., Company headquarters; odor control (973) 846-7817
ST Robotics, 103 Carnagie Ctr., Ste. 300, Princeton 08540
Owner—David Sands, 5 emp., Industrial equipment handling robots (609) 584-7522
Summit International Filtration Systems, 500 W. Main St., Ste. 10, Wyckoff 07481
Pres.—Charles Cole III, 6 emp., Filtration equipment for separation (201) 847-2370
T M Industries, Inc., 729 Route 625 S., Hampton 08827
Pres., CFO—Gerda A. Tietje, 8 emp., Automatic grease lubricators (908) 730-7674
Technical Fabricators, Inc., 203 Wood Ave., Ste. A, Middlesex 08846
Ptnr.—Keith Ball, 10 emp., Industrial filters (732) 469-7373
Technology General Corp. (H Q), 12 Cork Hill Rd., Franklin 07416
Sales Mgr.—Diane Olsen, 5 emp., Corporate headquarters; electric & (973) 827-4143
Tyco (H Q), 9 Roszel Rd., Princeton 08540
CEO—George Oliver, 350 emp., Company headquarters; security & fire (609) 720-4200
Ultra Clean Technologies Corp., 1274 Highway 77, Bridgeton 08302
Sales Mgr., North America—Steve Roath, 100 emp., Pneumatic cleaning & sealing systems (856) 451-2176
UNEX Corp., 333 Route 17 N., Mahwah 07430
CEO—John Junkers, 80 emp., Hydraulic tools & bolting systems (201) 512-9500
Universal Filters, Inc., 1207 Main St., Asbury Park 07712
Pres., Fin. & MIS Mgr.—Jerrold D. Kolton, 15 emp., Liquid filter bags (732) 774-8555
W & H Systems, Inc., 120 Asia Pl., Carlstadt 07072
Pres.—Don Betman, 75 emp., Automated material handling systems (201) 933-7840

## 3571 Electronic computers

AAEON Electronics, Inc. (H Q), 11 Crown Plz., Ste. 208, Hazlet 07730
Pres.—Yuhmin Hwang, 20 emp., Corporate headquarters; single board (732) 203-9300
Alphatec Computer Communications, 41 Merchant St., Newark 07105
Owner—Viton Nascimendo, 2 emp., Computers (973) 344-8736
American Ink Jet Systems, Inc., 34 Chestnut St., Emerson 07630
Pres.—Stephen Saltman, 5 emp., Manufacturer of inkjet inks, bulk ink (201) 263-9177
BIG Client, LLC, 1 Industrial Way W., Bldg. E, Eatontown 07724
CEO—Ben H. Zehavi, 30 emp., Thin client terminal computer & point-of-sale (732) 918-8221
Blue Sage Software, 35 Lord William Penn Dr., Morristown 07960
Pres.—Roger Moyers, 10 emp., Computer systems (973) 366-1900
Casio America, Inc. (H Q), 570 Mount Pleasant Ave., Dover 07801
Chrm.—Shigenori Itoh, 180 emp., Corporate headquarters; computers & (973) 361-5400
Comp-Solutions & Services, 621 N. Delsea Dr., Clayton 08312
Pres.—Robert Errera, 8 emp., Computer parts (856) 863-1137
Computerist, Inc., 15 Smull Ave., Ste. A, Caldwell 07006
Pres.—Anthony Camilleri, 5 emp., Rebuilt computers & computer network (973) 226-0100
DAX Systems, Inc., 343 New Rd., Ste. 4, Parsippany 07054
Pres.—Ernie Kaminaris, 6 emp., Computer servers (973) 227-8111
Dialogic Corp., 1515 State Route 10 E., Parsippany 07054
Hum. Res. Mgr.—Ester Zohn, 120 emp., Computers & computer parts (973) 967-6000
Dialogic, Inc. (H Q), 4 Gatehall Dr., Parsippany 07054
★ Pres., CEO—Kevin Cook, 100 emp., Corporate headquarters; telecommunications (800) 755-4444
Dynamic Decisions, Inc., 2709 Hamilton Blvd., South Plainfield 07080
Pres.—Alan Fan, 5 emp., Computer systems, including servers (908) 755-5000
Electronic Marine Systems, 800 Ferndale Pl., Rahway 07065
Pres., GM—Thomas J. Priola, 25 emp., Control, monitoring & tank gaging systems (732) 382-4344
Franklin Electronic Publishers, Inc., 8 Terri Ln., Burlington 08016
Pres., CEO—Barry Lipsky, 30 emp., Electronic language learning handheld (609) 386-2500
Global Business Dimensions Inc., 220 W. Parkway, Ste. 8, Pompton Plains 07444
Pres., CEO—Sanjay Prasad, 25 emp., Manufacturer & distributor of personal (973) 831-5866
I & E Co., 150 Main St., Ogdensburg 07439
Pres.—Joseph Trobert, 12 emp., Touchscreen kiosks (973) 579-0009
I T O X, LLC, 15 Corporate Pl. S., Ste. 201, Piscataway 08854
Ex. Sales Mgr.—Nancie Frank, 25 emp., Computers & motherboards (732) 390-2815
J W S Computers, Inc., 20 S. Main, Lambertville 08530
Ptnr.—Jeff Sailer, 7 emp., Computers (908) 730-6628
Masstar, 18 Heritage Rd., Eatontown 07724
Owner—Charles Massa, 2 emp., Computer network systems integration (732) 542-8004
Network Access Systems, 19 Isaac Dr., Dayton 08810
Pres.—Bruce Lin, 7 emp., Computer assembly (732) 355-9770
Panurgy OEM, 701 Ford Rd., Rockaway 07866
Pres.—Rick Levinson, 135 emp., Contract electronics, computer hardware (973) 625-4056
PlanITROI Inc, 100-10 Ford Rd., Denville 07834
Pres., CEO—Paul Baum, 60 emp., Rebuilt computers (973) 664-0700
R T I, Inc., 401 Hasbrouck Blvd., Oradell 07649
Owner & Pres.—Richard Tashjian, 10 emp., Computers, software development & radiation (201) 261-5852
Raritan Computer, Inc., 400 Cottontail Ln., Somerset 08873
Chrm., CEO—Ching-I Hsu, 150 emp., Data center infrastructure management (732) 764-8886

Sony Electronics, Inc., 1 Sony Dr., Park Ridge 07656
Facility Mgr.—Phillip D'Anna, 300 emp., *Consumer & professional audio & video* ........ (201) 930-1000
Storage Engine, Inc., 1 Sheila Dr., Eatontown 07724
Pres., CEO—Gregg M. Azcuy, 25 emp., *Computer data storage servers* ........ (732) 747-6995
Telegence Corp., 383 Kings Hwy. N., Ste. B-1, Cherry Hill 08034
Owner—Mansour Kabirian, 5 emp., *Business & operational support systems* ........ (856) 755-1717
Touch Dynamic, Inc., 17 Camptown Rd., Irvington 07111
Pres.—Craig Paritz, 30 emp., *Book-size PCs & touch-screen flat-panel* ........ (732) 382-5701

## 3572 Computer storage devices

API Technologies Corp., 120 Corporate Blvd., South Plainfield 07080
Dir., Opers.—Peter Paulson, 20 emp., *Remote device administration products* ........ (908) 546-3900

## 3575 Computer terminals

Sakar International, Inc. (H Q), 195 Carter Dr., Edison 08817
CEO—Charles Saka, 75 emp., *Corporate headquarters; consumer electronics* ........ (732) 248-1306

## 3577 Computer peripheral equipment

AAEON Electronics, Inc. (H Q), 11 Crown Plz., Ste. 208, Hazlet 07730
Pres.—Yuhmin Hwang, 20 emp., *Corporate headquarters; single board* ........ (732) 203-9300
Accuview, Inc., 40-C Cotters Ln., Ste. F, East Brunswick 08816
Pres.—David H. Wu, 10 emp., *Flat panel LCD monitors & touchscreens* ........ (201) 440-2225
Arch Crown, Inc., 460 Hillside Ave., Ste. 1, Hillside 07205
CEO—Norman Liebman, 32 emp., *Tags & labels, including die cutting* ........ (973) 731-6300
Atlas Desk & Office Equipment Corp., 185-193 Central Ave., 2nd Fl., Newark 07103
Pres.—Mark Parra, 12 emp., *Office furniture & equipment* ........ (973) 242-8989
Aurora Multimedia Corp., 205 Commercial Ct., Morganville 07751
CEO—Paul Harris, 30 emp., *Audio visual processors, controls &* ........ (732) 591-5800
Comp-Solutions & Services, 621 N. Delsea Dr., Clayton 08312
Pres.—Robert Errera, 8 emp., *Computer parts* ........ (856) 863-1137
Dataram Corp., 777 Alexander Rd., Princeton 08540
Pres.—John Freeman, 50 emp., *Corporate headquarters & computer memory* ........ (609) 799-0071
Depot America, Inc., 1495 Highway 34, Farmingdale 07727
Pres.—Eric Martin, 200 emp., *Computer printer parts* ........ (732) 919-0209
Dtrovision, LLC, 535 E. Crescent Ave., Ste. 1, Ramsey 07446
Pres.—Minsoo Park, 15 emp., *Professional & consumer digital A/V* ........ (201) 488-3232
EMS Aviation, 121 Whittendale Dr., Ste. A, Moorestown 08057
V-P., Opers.—John Serazio, 100 emp., *Computer peripherals & components for* ........ (856) 234-5020
Futuretech Systems, Inc., 515 Plainfield Ave., Ste. 101, Edison 08817
Pres.—Perry NeJappa, 7 emp., *Document management systems* ........ (732) 777-7355
Humanscale Corp., 220 Circle Dr. N., Piscataway 08854
Sr. V-P., Mktg.—Chris Gibson, 200 emp., *Sustainable, high-performance ergonomic* ........ (732) 537-2944
Index Security, Inc. (H Q), 500 Parker Ave., Ste. G, Deal 07723
Pres.—Ezra Hedaya, 2 emp., *Corporate headquarters; biometric fingerprint* ........ (732) 531-9209
Kessler Ellis Products Co., Inc., 10 Industrial Way E., Ste. 6, Eatontown 07724
CEO—Corson Ellis III, 50 emp., *Flowmeters, counting devices, timers* ........ (732) 935-1320
Koamtac, Inc., 116 Village Blvd., Ste. 305, Princeton 08540
Pres.—Hanjin Lee, 10 emp., *Programmable wireless data exchanging* ........ (609) 256-4700
Kyocera Document Solutions America, Inc. (H Q), 225 Sand Rd., Fairfield 07004
Pres.—Norihiko Ina, 200 emp., *Corporate headquarters; office machines* ........ (973) 808-8444
Masstar, 18 Heritage Rd., Eatontown 07724
Owner—Charles Massa, 2 emp., *Computer network systems integration* ........ (732) 542-8004
MICROS Retail Systems, Inc., 1500 Harbor Blvd., Ste. 2, Weehawken 07086
Pres.—Lubodar Olesnycky, 108 emp., *Point-of-sale software development* ........ (201) 866-1000
Oki Data Americas, Inc., 2000 Bishops Gate Blvd., Mount Laurel 08054
Pres., CEO—Masahiko Morioka, 350 emp., *Digital color & monochrome printers* ........ (856) 235-2600
Rack Design Group Inc. / BarCodeAmerica.com, 81 Clinton Rd., Fairfield 07004
Pres.—Robert Rack, 10 emp., *Manufacturer & distributor of custom* ........ (973) 377-8182
RAD Data Communications, Inc., 900 Corporate Dr., Ste. 1, Mahwah 07430
Pres.—Uri Zilberman, 55 emp., *Network communication equipment for* ........ (201) 529-1100
Samsung Electronics America, Inc., 85 Challenger Rd., Ridgefield Park 07660
V-P., Bus. Dev.—Thomas Rhee, 300 emp., *Electronic components, including mobile* ........ (201) 229-4000
Sensigraphics, Inc., 105 W. Park Dr., Mount Laurel 08054
Pres.—Harold Gilham, 30 emp., *Custom membrane switches, keypads,* ........ (856) 853-9100
Sony Electronics, Inc., 1 Sony Dr., Park Ridge 07656
Facility Mgr.—Phillip D'Anna, 300 emp., *Consumer & professional audio & video* ........ (201) 930-1000
Symbology Enterprises, Inc., 185 Industrial Pkwy., Ste. H, Somerville 08876
V-P.—Tom McInerney, 8 emp., *Bar coding equipment, including bar* ........ (908) 725-1699
TBC Partners, LLC, 743 Alexander Rd., Ste. 15, Princeton 08540
Pres., CEO—David Anderson, 15 emp., *Company headquarters & miniature touchscreen* ........ (855) 937-6466
Touch Dynamic, Inc., 17 Camptown Rd., Irvington 07111
Pres.—Craig Paritz, 30 emp., *Book-size PCs & touch-screen flat-panel* ........ (732) 382-5701
Xceedium, Inc., 30 Montgomery St., Ste. 1020, Jersey City 07302
CFO—Rick Rose, 50 emp., *All-in-one computer network hardened* ........ (201) 536-1000
ZK Software (H Q), 201 Circle Dr. N., Ste. 116, Piscataway 08854
CEO—Jaimin Shah, 25 emp., *Company headquarters; facial & fingerprint* ........ (732) 412-6007

## 3578 Calculating & accounting equipment

Automated Business Products, Inc. (H Q), 50 Clinton Pl., Mail Slot 1, Hackensack 07601
Pres.—Robert Mahalik, 9 emp., *Corporate headquarters; money & document* .... (201) 489-1440
Comtrex Systems Corp., 1247 N. Church St., Ste. 7, Moorestown 08057
Pres.—Jeffrey Rice, 13 emp., *Computer cash registers* ........ (856) 778-0090
Heartland Payment Systems, Inc. (H Q), 90 Nassau St., 2nd Fl., Princeton 08542
CEO—Robert O. Carr, 25 emp., *Corporate headquarters; electronic* ........ (609) 683-3831
Lacey Cash Registers & Business Machines Co., 2180 Llewellyn Pkwy., P.O. Box 1151, Forked River 08731
★ Owner—Gene D'Alessandro, 2 emp., *Rebuilt electronic cash registers* ........ (609) 971-9494
Lane Bond Traders, 27 Cedar Lake Rd., Denville 07834
Owner—William Peer, 2 emp., *Bond calculating devices & trading* ........ (973) 586-2720
Myron Corp., 205 Maywood Ave., Maywood 07607
CEO—Jim Adler, 450 emp., *Imprinted personalized business gifts* ........ (201) 843-6464

## 3579 Office machines, nec

Amano USA Holdings, Inc., 140 Harrison Ave., Roseland 07068
Pres., CEO—Masamiki Konno, 60 emp., *Corporate headquarters & time clocks* ........ (973) 403-1900
Avante International Technology, Inc., 70 Washington Rd., Princeton 08540
★ Pres.—Kevin Chung, 20 emp., *Voting equipment & RFID monitoring* ........ (609) 799-8896
Bonney-Vehslage Tool Co., 3 Dundar Rd., Springfield 07081
Pres.—Ramsey Vehslage, 5 emp., *Metal ticket punchers* ........ (973) 589-6975
Brother International Corporation, 200 Crossing Blvd., Bridgewater 08807
Chrm.—Tadashi Ishiguro, 350 emp., *Corporate headquarters & office machinery* ........ (908) 704-1700
Elmendorf Office Supply , Inc., 3201 Bridge Ave., Ste. 1, Point Pleasant Beach 08742
Pres.—Laurie Sairhurst, 2 emp., *Rebuilt typewriters & office equipment* ........ (732) 295-8700
OPEX Corporation, 305 Commerce Dr., Moorestown 08057
Pres., CEO—Dave Stevens, 400 emp., *Incoming & outgoing mail processing* ........ (856) 727-1100
Pike & Co., Inc., E. W., 2149 Price St., Rahway 07065
Pres.—Emil Sudzina, 2 emp., *Illuminated magnifying instruments* ........ (732) 396-0002
Royal Sovereign International, Inc., 2 Volvo Dr., Rockleigh 07647
Chrm.—T. K. Lim, 40 emp., *Desktop & wide-format lamination &* ........ (201) 750-1020
Swintec East (H Q), 320 W. Commercial Ave., Moonachie 07074
Pres.—Dominic Vespia, 10 emp., *Company headquarters; typewriters,* ........ (201) 935-0115
Widmer Time Recorder Co., Inc., 228 Park St., Hackensack 07601
Pres.—Robert J. Widmer, 25 emp., *Time recorders, including time clocks* ........ (201) 489-3810

## 3581 Vending machines—automatic

Autobar Systems Corp., 1 Meridian Rd., Eatontown 07724
Pres.—Donald E. Ullery, Jr., 5 emp., *Liquor bottle dispensers & control* ........ (732) 922-3355
Betti Industries, Inc., H., 303 Patterson Plank Rd., Carlstadt 07072
Chrm., CEO—Peter Betti, 140 emp., *Corporate headquarters & rebuilt vending* ........ (201) 438-1300
Custom Fabricators, Inc., 400 Commerce Rd., Linden 07036
Pres.—Joseph Bonanno, 8 emp., *Sheet metal fabrication & coin-operated* ........ (908) 862-4244
Ellenby Technologies, Inc., 412 Grandview Ave., Woodbury Heights 08097
CEO—Bob Dobbins, 53 emp., *Contract electronic manufacturing of* ........ (856) 848-2020
P & E Technologies, Inc., 5140 W. Hurley Pond Rd., Farmingdale 07727
Pres.—Phil Cornick, 12 emp., *Video games & vending machines* ........ (732) 751-1515

## 3582 Laundry equipment—commercial

Fairfield Laundry Machinery, 5 Montesano Rd., Fairfield 07004
Pres., GM—Raymond Hall, 20 emp., *Commercial laundry machines* ........ (973) 575-4330
Hoffman/New Yorker, Inc. (H Q), 46 Clinton Pl., Hackensack 07601
V-P.—Terry Rothlisberger, 10 emp., *Corporate headquarters; steam finishing* ........ (201) 488-1800
Multimatic, 162 Veterans Dr., P.O. Box 156, Northvale 07647
COO—Ron Velli, 10 emp., *Dry cleaning machines* ........ (201) 767-9660
Tingue, Brown & Co. (H Q), 535 N. Midland Ave., Saddle Brook 07663
Pres., CEO—David Tingue, 20 emp., *Company headquarters; laundry bags* ........ (201) 796-4490
White Conveyors, Inc., 10 Boright Ave., Kenilworth 07033
Ex. V-P.—Mark Speckhart, 100 emp., *Garment conveyors for dry cleaners,* ........ (800) 524-0273

## 3585 Refrigeration & heating equipment

Alternative Air & Store Fixtures, 3-C Mary Way, Hainesport 08036
Ptnr.—James Lunstead, 6 emp., *Refrigerated & dry custom & standard* ........ (609) 261-5870
Arcticcoolers, Inc., 135 Gaither Dr., Ste. A, Mount Laurel 08054
Pres.—Andrew Pearl, 15 emp., *Water coolers* ........ (856) 231-0262
Atomizing Systems Inc., 1 Hollywood Ave., Ste. 1, Ho-Ho-Kus 07423
Pres., CEO—Michael V. Elkas, 16 emp., *Patented ruby-orifice, non-wearing* ........ (201) 447-1222
Bush Refrigeration, 1700 Admiral Wilson Blvd., Pennsauken 08109
Pres.—Alex Bush, 20 emp., *Refrigeration systems, including walk-in* ........ (856) 963-1800
Butensky Services Co., Inc., 3380 Route 22, P.O. Box 5020, Somerville 08876
Pres.—Bryan Butensky, 50 emp., *Rebuilt & refurbished electromechanical* ........ (908) 707-0912
CALMAC, 3-00 Banta Pl., Fair Lawn 07410
CEO—Mark M. MacCracken, 40 emp., *Ice storage & ice rink equipment, including* ........ (201) 797-1511
Electro Impulse Laboratory, Inc., 1805 Route 33, Neptune 07753
Pres.—Mark Rubin, 41 emp., *Custom closed-loop cooling systems* ........ (732) 776-5800
Encur, Inc., 200 Division St., P.O. Box 92, Keyport 07735
Pres.—Mark M. Curcio, 7 emp., *Induction heating equipment* ........ (732) 264-2098
Foster Wheeler Corp. (H Q), 53 Frontage Rd., P.O. Box 9000, Hampton 08827
CEO—Gary Nedelka, 500 emp., *Corporate headquarters; industrial* ........ (908) 730-4000
Honeywell HBS, 534 Fellowship Rd., Mount Laurel 08054
GM—Ed Neary, 50 emp., *Heating & air conditioning equipment* ........ (856) 437-1832
Hussmann Corp., 3001 Irwin Rd., Ste. D, Mount Laurel 08054
Reg. Sales Mgr., Northeast—Tony Saggiomo, 10 emp., *Stationary refrigeration equipment* .... (856) 793-7050
Independence Cryogenic Engineering, LLC, 891 Route 9 N., P.O. Box 527, Little Egg Harbor 08087
Pres.—Susan Hughes, 16 emp., *Rebuilt cryogenic refrigeration systems* ........ (609) 294-0012
International Process Plants, 17-A Marlen Dr., Hamilton 08691
Pres.—Ron Gale, 25 emp., *Refrigeration & air conditioning equipment* ........ (609) 586-8004
Kohlder Mfg., Inc., 1001 Line St., Camden 08103
V-P.—Jeffery Kerber, 6 emp., *Commercial refrigeration* ........ (856) 342-8398
Kooltronic, Inc., 30 Pennington-Hopewell Rd., P.O. Box 240, Pennington 08534
Chrm.—G. Freedman, 150 emp., *Air conditioners for electronic enclosures* ........ (609) 466-3400
Micro-Air, Inc., 124 Route 526, Allentown 08501
Pres.—Andrew Spaziani, 20 emp., *Electronic controls & environmental* ........ (609) 259-2636
Migali Industries, Inc., 516 Lansdowne Ave., Camden 08104
Pres.—Ernest Migali, 15 emp., *Commercial refrigerators & freezers* ........ (856) 963-3600
Sealed Unit Parts Co., Inc., 2230 Landmark Pl., P.O. Box 21, Allenwood 08720
Pres., CEO—Christopher Mancuso, 95 emp., *Air conditioning & refrigeration parts* ........ (732) 223-6644
SISCO Mfg. Co., Inc., 7930 National Hwy., Pennsauken 08110
Principal—Paul Schulte, 12 emp., *HVAC components, including pressure* ........ (856) 486-7550
Stamm International Corp. (H Q), 1530 Palisade Ave., P.O. Box 1929, Fort Lee 07024
Pres.—Arthur Stamm, 2 emp., *Holding company headquarters; commercial* ........ (201) 947-1700
Task U. S. A., 3 Cass St., Keyport 07735
V-P.—Tom Saporita, 20 emp., *Commercial air conditioners* ........ (732) 739-0377
Technology General Corp. (H Q), 12 Cork Hill Rd., Franklin 07416
Sales Mgr.—Diane Olsen, 5 emp., *Corporate headquarters; electric &* ........ (973) 827-4143
Trane Co., 2231 E. State St., Trenton 08619
V-P., Plt.—Andy Stevenson, 715 emp., *Commercial air conditioners & furnaces* ........ (609) 587-3400
Trane, Inc. (H Q), 1 Centennial Ave., P.O. Box 6820, Piscataway 08855
V-P., Compliance & Deputy Gen. Counsel—Allan Tananbaum, 400 emp., *Corporate headquarters; automotive* ........ (732) 652-7100
Troy Hills Mfg., Inc., 2 Como Ct., P.O. Box 98, Towaco 07082
Pres.—Leif W. Melgaard, 6 emp., *Ice cream freezer lids* ........ (973) 263-1885
Victory Refrigeration, 110 Woodcrest Rd., Cherry Hill 08003
Pres.—Richard Babboni, 180 emp., *Commercial refrigerators & freezers* ........ (856) 428-4200

## 3586 Measuring & dispensing pumps

Corban Energy Group, 418 Falmouth Ave., Elmwood Park 07407
CEO—Daniel Chung, 15 emp., *Compressed natural gas (CNG) fueling* ........ (201) 509-8555

## 3589 Service industry machinery, nec

Acrison, Inc., 20 Empire Blvd., Moonachie 07074
Dir., Mktg.—John T. Shaw, 140 emp., *Volumetric & weight-loss feeders &* ........ (201) 440-8300
American Water Works Co., Inc. (H Q), 1025 Laurel Oak Rd., Voorhees 08043
Pres., CEO—Susan Story, 300 emp., *Corporate headquarters; wastewater* ........ (856) 346-8200

★ Indicates new listing this edition.

Aqua Products, Inc., 25 Rutgers Ave., Cedar Grove 07009
Pres.—Tomer Porat, 200 emp., *Robotic swimming pool cleaners for* ........ (973) 857-2700
Arrow Steel, Inc., 629 E. 19th St., Paterson 07514
Pres.—Mario Ferraro, 8 emp., *Trash compactors* ........ (973) 523-1122
Azzota Corp., 178 Franklin Rd., Randolph 07869
GM—Geoff Darling, 10 emp., *Corporate headquarters & laboratory* ........ (877) 649-2746
Bon Chef, Inc., 205 State Route 94, Lafayette 07848
Pres., R & D Mgr.—Sal Torre, 90 emp., *Flatware, chafing dishes, sandstone* ........ (973) 383-8848
Budd Built In Vacuum Cleaners, 445 W. Main St., Wyckoff 07481
Pres.—William Schwartz, 25 emp., *Industrial & household central vacuum* ........ (201) 891-3010
C S L Water Quality, Inc., 156 Mount Bethel Rd., P.O. Box 4246, Warren 07059
Pres.—John V. Truglio, 7 emp., *Water treatment chemicals, filters,* ........ (908) 647-1400
Chemquip Corp., 258-262 Atlantic St., Paterson 07503
Pres.—Igor Ostrer, 10 emp., *Chemical feed systems* ........ (973) 684-3009
Clayton Assocs., Inc., 1650 Oak St., Lakewood 08701
Pres., MIS Mgr.—James Clayton, 20 emp., *Automotive & industrial brake washing* ........ (732) 363-2100
Consolidated Chemex Corp., 235 Jersey Ave., New Brunswick 08901
Pres.—Walter M. Geslak, 18 emp., *Pressure washers & cleaning chemicals* ........ (732) 828-7676
Corrective Hydraulics, 731 Birch St., P.O. Box 850, Boonton 07005
Pres.—Eugene Mini, 8 emp., *Hydraulics, including compactor, baler* ........ (973) 334-3792
Creative Industrial Kitchens, 8 Leo Pl., Wayne 07470
Owner—Tom Walsh, 20 emp., *Stainless steel food service equipment* ........ (973) 633-0420
D.W.L International Trading Co., 65 Industrial Rd., Lodi 07644
Pres., CEO—David Li, 150 emp., *Company headquarters & restaurant supplies* ........ (973) 916-9958
Dynatec Systems, Inc., 360 Connecticut Dr., Burlington 08016
Pres.—Thomas Doherty, 15 emp., *Wastewater treatment equipment* ........ (609) 387-0330
ECOTEC, Inc., 1944 E. Elmer Rd., Vineland 08361
Pres., R & D Mgr.—Larry Mitchell, 6 emp., *Ecologically sensitive water treatment* ........ (856) 205-9283
Edhard Corp., 279 Blau Rd., Hackettstown 07840
Pres.—Edgar Bars, 27 emp., *Liquid & viscous product filling &* ........ (908) 850-8444
Elgee Mfg. Co., 225 Stirling Rd., Warren 07059
Pres.—Stephen Heinle, 6 emp., *Industrial power vacuums & sweepers* ........ (908) 647-4100
Energy Recycling Co., LLC, 409 Joyce Kilmer Ave., New Brunswick 08901
Pres.—Larry Schrager, 5 emp., *Wheeled metal recycling & janitorial* ........ (732) 545-6619
Enpro, Inc., 1401 U.S. Highway 22, P.O. Box 418, Lebanon 08833
Pres.—Vincent R. Cioffi, 15 emp., *Deaerators for the power industry* ........ (908) 236-2137
Evoqua Water Technologies, 624 Evans St., Elizabeth 07201
★ Br. Mgr.—Brian Frank, 15 emp., *Wastewater treatment equipment* ........ (908) 353-7230
Filtrex, Inc., 450 Hamburg Tpke., Wayne 07470
Pres.—Kenneth A. Bergstrom, 8 emp., *Swimming pool filters* ........ (973) 595-0400
Fin-Tek Ozone, 6 Leo Pl., Wayne 07470
Pres., Fin., MIS & R & D Mgr.—Donald Finnegan, 10 emp., *Water purifying ozone generators &* (973) 628-2988
Firehawk Industries, LLC, 309 N. Willow St., Trenton 08618
Pres.—Cary Wische, 3 emp., *High-pressure cleaning equipment, including* ........ (609) 393-0007
Fleetwash, Inc. (H Q), 26 Law Dr., Unit E, Fairfield 07004
Co-Founder, Pres. & CEO—Vito DeGiovanni, 100 emp., *Corporate headquarters; sanitation* . (800) 847-3735
Fluid Filtration Corp., 102 Van Winkle Ave., Garfield 07026
Pres.—Farzad Alborzi, 10 emp., *Pipeline & cone strainers, water filters* ........ (973) 253-7070
Glasco UV, LLC, 126 Christie Ave., Ste. 1, Mahwah 07430
Pres.—Julie Donnellan, 7 emp., *Ultraviolet water disinfection equipment* ........ (201) 934-3348
Graco Manufacturing, 500 University Ct., Blackwood 08012
Hum. Res. Mgr.—Todd McGovern, 60 emp., *Manufacturer & distributor of aftermarket* ........ (856) 228-1800
Graver Water Systems, LLC, 675 Central Ave., Ste. 3, New Providence 07974
Pres.—Michael O'Brien, 35 emp., *Water & wastewater treatment equipment* ........ (908) 516-1400
Hafco Foundry, Inc., 301 Greenwood Ave., Front, Midland Park 07432
Pres.—Michael Fornaci, 6 emp., *Heavy-duty industrial vacuum cleaners* ........ (201) 447-0433
Hickory Industries, Inc., 4900 W. Side Ave., North Bergen 07047
Pres.—Steven Amroti, 30 emp., *Rotisseries, pizza ovens, warmers &* ........ (201) 223-0050
Hoffman/New Yorker, Inc. (H Q), 46 Clinton Pl., Hackensack 07601
V-P.—Terry Rothlisberger, 10 emp., *Corporate headquarters; steam finishing* ........ (201) 488-1800
Hungerford & Terry, Inc., 226 N. Atlantic Ave., P.O. Box 650, Clayton 08312
Pres. & V-P., Opers.—Thomas J. Carrocino, 50 emp., *Water treatment equipment for iron,* ..... (856) 881-3200
Industrial Environmental, 176 W. Westfield Ave., Elizabeth 07201
Opers. Mgr.—Frank Volpe, 5 emp., *Sanitation control systems & pressure* ........ (908) 241-3830
JDV Equipment Corp., 1 Princeton Ave., Dover 07801
Pres.—Robert T. Abbott, 8 emp., *Water & wastewater treatment equipment* ........ (973) 366-6556
Jersey Chemicals, Inc., 775 River St., P.O. Box 542, Paterson 07524
Pres.—David Paulen, 10 emp., *Swimming pool chemicals & pool related* ........ (973) 523-3736
Komline-Sanderson Engineering, 12 Holland Ave., Peapack 07977
Pres.—Russell M. Komline, 100 emp., *Process/production filtration, drying* ........ (908) 234-1000
Liquid Solids Separation Corp., 25 Arrow Rd., Ramsey 07446
Pres.—David Painter, 35 emp., *Industrial filtration equipment* ........ (201) 236-4833
Membranes International, Inc., 219 Margaret King Ave., P.O. Box 219, Ringwood 07456
Ptnr.—Dwight Loren, 3 emp., *Ion exchange membranes for the water* ........ (973) 998-5530
Mercer International, Inc., 39 W. Main St., P.O. Box 540, Mendham 07945
Pres.—David Goding, 10 emp., *Custom oil/water separators, including* ........ (973) 543-9000
Mercury Floor Machines, Inc., 110 S. Van Brunt St., Englewood 07631
Pres.—Bill Allen, 15 emp., *Commercial floor cleaning equipment* ........ (201) 568-4606
Milspray, LLC, 845 Towbin Ave., Lakewood 08701
Pres., CEO—Brian Feser, 40 emp., *Mil-spec paint, renewable energy, corrosion* ........ (732) 886-2223
Mobile Power International, LLC, 1010 Old Egg Harbor Rd., Voorhees 08043
Owner—Anthony F. Amorosia, 12 emp., *Contract manufacturing & metal fabrication* ........ (856) 784-3195
Nephros, Inc., 41 Grand Ave., Ste. 201, River Edge 07661
Chrm.—James S. Scibetta, 6 emp., *Hemodiafiltration systems for the end-stage* ........ (201) 343-5202
Orival Water Filters, 213 S. Van Brunt St., Englewood 07631
Pres.—Reuven Schwartz, 10 emp., *Automatic self-cleaning line pressure* ........ (201) 568-3311
Ozonia North America, LLC, 600 Willow Tree Rd., Leonia 07605
CEO—Anthony Dusovic, 50 emp., *Water & wastewater treatment equipment* ........ (201) 676-2525
Premier Compaction Systems, 264 Lackawanna Ave., Woodland Park 07424
Pres.—Robert Frustaci, 25 emp., *Refuse compactors & containers, recycling* ........ (973) 305-6646
Pure H2O Technologies, Inc., 211 Warren St., Ste. 318, Newark 07103
CEO—John Edwards, 20 emp., *Water treatment & purification equipment* ........ (973) 622-0440
Repco, Inc., 6 Eves Dr., Marlton 08053
Pres. & Fin. Mgr.—Ann Braytenbah, 11 emp., *Replacement electrical contacts, coils* ........ (800) 822-9190
Resistance Welding Solutions, Inc., 1090 Lousons Rd., Union 07083
CEO—Gregory W. Labelle, 20 emp., *Resistance welding equipment, including* ........ (908) 964-9100
R-S Restaurant Equipment Mfg. Corp., 40 Camptown Rd., Maplewood 07040
Off. Mgr.—Andrew Lee, 14 emp., *Restaurant equipment* ........ (973) 375-3388
S & G Tool Aid Corp., 43 E. Alpine St., Newark 07114
Sales Mgr., Natl.—Wayne Hutchings, 75 emp., *Automotive & auto body repair shop* ........ (973) 824-7730
Siemens Industry, Inc., Water Technologies, 2 Milltown Ct., Union 07083
Area Mgr.—Mark Kelly, 100 emp., *Water purification & anti-corrosion* ........ (908) 851-2277
Siemens Industry, Inc., Water Technologies, 1901 W. Garden Rd., Vineland 08360
V-P., GM—Guy Chadwell, 180 emp., *Water treatment equipment* ........ (856) 507-9000
SmartPool, Inc., 687 Prospect St., Ste. 460, Lakewood 08701
Pres.—Lewis Dubrofsky, 20 emp., *Robotic swimming pool cleaners* ........ (732) 730-9880
Stain-Less Water Filters, LLC, 51 Munion Field Rd., P.O. Box 219, New Gretna 08224
Owner—Jill Pennella, 2 emp., *Portable water softeners & filters* ........ (609) 296-2564
Terriss Consolidated Industries, 807 Summerfield Ave., P.O. Box 110, Asbury Park 07712
V-P.—Edward J. Della Zanna, 15 emp., *Eco-friendly scientific instruments* ........ (732) 988-0909
Trident Ionic, Inc., 19 Olsen Dr., Warren 07059
Pres.—Carol Fitzgerald, 2 emp., *Water treatment systems* ........ (908) 647-4329
Turnkey Solutions, Inc., 45 Whitney Rd., Mahwah 07430
Pres.—David Lyman, 9 emp., *Industrial wastewater treatment equipment* ........ (201) 848-7676
Vac-U-Max, 69 William St., Belleville 07109
Pres., CEO—Stevens P. Pendleton, 50 emp., *Industrial vacuum cleaners & pneumatic* ........ (973) 759-4600
Veolia Water Solutions & Technologies North America, Inc., 6981 N. Park Dr., Ste. 600, Pennsauken 08109
V-P., Opers.—Bill O'Donnell, 40 emp., *Industrial wastewater treatment plants* ........ (856) 438-1776
WaterDoctor, Inc., 1030-C Campus Dr., Morganville 07751
Pres.—Joe Lee, 9 emp., *Water purification equipment* ........ (732) 972-4510

## 3592 Carburetors, pistons, rings & valves

Coates International Ltd., 2100 Highway 34 & Ridgewood Rd., Wall 07719
Pres., CEO—George J. Coates, 14 emp., *Spherical rotary valve system for internal* ........ (732) 449-7717
Manley Performance Products, Inc., 1960 Swarthmore Ave., Lakewood 08701
Pres.—Henry Manley, 115 emp., *High-performance internal engine components* ........ (732) 905-3366
Marotta Controls, Inc., 78 Boonton Ave., P.O. Box 427, Montville 07045
Pres.—Patrick Marotta, 200 emp., *High-performance & specialty motion* ........ (973) 334-7800
Screw Machine Specialties, 50 U.S. Highway 9, Ste. 305, Morganville 07751
Dir., Sales & Mktg.—Avi Tobias, 25 emp., *Precision machined parts for OEMs,* ........ (732) 972-5400

## 3593 Fluid power cylinders & actuators

Complete Hydraulic Works, Inc., 140 Greenwood Ave., Midland Park 07432
Pres.—Daniel J. Fano, 5 emp., *Hydraulic systems* ........ (201) 444-7877
Convertech, Inc., 353 Richard Mine Rd., Wharton 07885
Pres.—Larry Taitel, 50 emp., *Pneumatic airshafts & printing press* ........ (973) 328-1850
Delta Sales Co., Inc., 1355 State Route 23, Butler 07405
Pres., Fin. & MIS Mgr.—Robert Infante, 2 emp., *Hydraulic & pneumatic cylinders & rotary* ..... (973) 838-0371
Industrial Hydraulics & Rubber, LLC, 458 Atlantic Ave., Camden 08104
GM—Michael Donahue, 7 emp., *Rebuilt hydraulic cylinders & machining* ........ (856) 966-2600
Lehigh Fluid Power, Inc., 1413 Route 179, Lambertville 08530
Pres.—Frank McGonigle, 30 emp., *Custom & standard NFPA-styled hydraulic* ........ (609) 397-3487
Moran Power Dynamics, 263 Route 537 E., Colts Neck 07722
Pres.—Edward Moran, 6 emp., *Seat actuators* ........ (732) 544-8443
Pamarco Global Graphics, Imaging Div., 1 Roto Ave., Palmyra 08065
Pres.—John Burgess, 20 emp., *Metal cylinders engraving* ........ (856) 829-4585
R A M Hydraulics, 215 B. Hickory Ln., P.O. Box 416, Bayville 08721
Pres.—Michael Mattei, 7 emp., *Hydraulic cylinders* ........ (732) 237-0904

## 3594 Fluid power pumps & motors

American Custom Hydraulics, Inc., 33 Roosevelt Ave., Belleville 07109
Owner—Jean Zachar, 28 emp., *Rebuilt hydraulic equipment & machines* ........ (973) 751-1440
Bogue Systems, Inc., 100 Pennsylvania Ave., Paterson 07503
Pres.—Anthony Sabatino, 44 emp., *Electric motor battery chargers, elevator* ........ (973) 523-2200
Corrective Hydraulics, 731 Birch St., P.O. Box 850, Boonton 07005
Pres.—Eugene Mini, 8 emp., *Hydraulics, including compactor, baler* ........ (973) 334-3792
Grimco Presses Co., 65 1st Ave., Paterson 07514
Pres.—David Grimaldi, 5 emp., *Hydraulic & pneumatic presses* ........ (973) 345-0660
KNF Neuberger, Inc., 2 Black Forest Rd., Trenton 08691
Cont.—Gary Frank, 105 emp., *Industrial pumps & compressors* ........ (609) 890-8600
Neptune Products, Inc., 353 E. Blackwell St., P.O. Drawer 829, Dover 07801
Pres.—Richard Schroeder, 5 emp., *Laboratory gas & air vacuum pumps* ........ (973) 366-8200

## 3596 Scales & balances, except laboratory

Key-Pak Machines By Luciano Packaging Technologies, Inc, 29 County Line Rd., Somerville 08876
Pres., MIS Mgr.—Larry Luciano, 10 emp., *Custom form, fill & seal machinery,* ........ (908) 722-3222
Scientific Industries, Inc., 660 Kinderkamack Rd., Ste. 203, Oradell 07649
Prod. Mktg. Mgr.—Thomas Wright, 6 emp., *Pharmacy pilling counting & weighing* ........ (973) 473-6900
Sterling Home Products, Inc., 127 U.S. Highway 206, Ste. 22, Hamilton 08610
V-P., Fin., MIS & Opers.—Roger DeAngelis, 4 emp., *Bathroom, kitchen, parcel, postal &* ....... (609) 585-8941

## 3599 Industrial machinery, nec

3D Medical Mfg., Inc., 7145 Colonial Ln., Pennsauken 08109
V-P., Mfg.—Anthony Jenkowski, 60 emp., *CNC & Swiss screw turning & milling* ........ (856) 486-9600
A & D Industrial & Marine Repair, 900 Port Reading Ave., Ste. B-2, Port Reading 07064
Pres.—Doug Alexander, 12 emp., *Machine shop, including rebuilt industrial* ........ (732) 541-1481
A & F Tool, 930 Magnolia Ave., Elizabeth 07201
GM—Fernando Paramo, 6 emp., *Tool & die & general machining job* ........ (973) 262-1792
A G Machine & Tool Co., 147 E. 1st Ave., Roselle 07203
Pres.—Gregory Aiello, 5 emp., *Precision machining job shop* ........ (908) 241-3205
A M A Centerless Grinding, Inc., 88-C Cannonball Rd., P.O. Box 14, Pompton Lakes 07442
Pres.—John Memmelaar, 6 emp., *Centerless grinding* ........ (973) 835-2919
A. B. Scantlebury Co., 112 Kings Hwy., Landing 07850
Off. Mgr.—John Spinelli, 8 emp., *Sheet metal fabrication, precision* ........ (973) 770-3000
Abba Metal Works, Inc., 337 River St., Paterson 07524
★ Pres.—Corrado Abbattista, 7 emp., *Structural steel fabrication & ornamental* ........ (973) 684-0808
ABCO Metal, LLC, 138 3rd Ave., Paterson 07514
Pres. & Sales Mgr.—Todd Abrams, 25 emp., *Precision machining job shop* ........ (973) 772-8160
Able Gear & Machine Co., 91 Stickle Ave., Rockaway 07866
Owner—Robert Hebrank, 3 emp., *General machining job shop, including* ........ (973) 983-8055
Accelerated CNC, LLC, 2500 S. Clinton Ave., Ste. A, South Plainfield 07080
Pres.—John Kologe, 6 emp., *CNC machining job shop* ........ (908) 561-8875
Accurate Machine, LLC., 27 Arneytown Chesterfield Rd., Allentown 08501
Pres.—Tony Scharko, 5 emp., *Machined parts, low to high volume,* ........ (609) 758-1381
Actioneering Mfg. Engineers, 30 Plane St., Bldg. 12, P.O. Box 333, Boonton 07005
Owner—Nick Debald, 6 emp., *Precision machining job shop* ........ (973) 299-1999
ADM Custom Metal Fabrication, Inc., 263 Hillside Ave., Ste. 2, Nutley 07110
Pres., CEO—Andrew K. Mihal, 14 emp., *Precision sheet metal & frame fabrication* ........ (973) 284-0088
Advance Machine, Inc., 531 Pennsylvania Ave., Linden 07036
Pres.—Richard Walano, Sr., 7 emp., *Precision machining job shop* ........ (908) 486-7244
Advanced Cutting Services, LLC, 169 E. Highland Pkwy., Roselle 07203
Owner, Pres. & Mng. Member—Bob Balchunas, 5 emp., *Ecofriendly waterjet cutting & metal* (908) 241-5332

Advanced Fastener Industries, 130 Main St., Butler 07405
Pres.—Don Manley, 7 emp., *Industrial machinery, fasteners & cutting* ........ (973) 283-1013
Advanced Molding Concepts, 329 Wilson Ave., Aberdeen 07747
Owner—Mike Guglielmo, 6 emp., *Custom prototypes & precision machining* ........ (732) 390-8366
Advanced Precision, Inc., 15 Wilson Dr., Sparta 07871
Pres.—Vincent Fay, 20 emp., *Precision wire EDM job shop* ........ (973) 383-2296
Advanced Welding Service, Inc., 300 Thomas Ave., Ste. 701-1, Williamstown 08094
Pres.—Michael Hammond, 8 emp., *Welding & fabrication job shop* ........ (856) 875-2500
Advantage EDM, 38 Main St., Route 206, Andover 07821
Pres.—Alex Gilsenan, 20 emp., *Electrical discharge machining job* ........ (973) 786-0177
Aero Products Co., 19-21 N. 8th St., Belleville 07109
Pres.—David Bucci, 20 emp., *General machining job shop* ........ (973) 759-0959
Aerospace Precision Mfg. Co., Inc., 6 Hinchman Ave., Denville 07834
Pres.—Emile Ayli, 4 emp., *Precision machining job shop* ........ (973) 625-2100
Airmet, Inc., 671 N. 3rd St., Newark 07107
Pres.—Stephen A. Yavorski, Sr., 6 emp., *Metal fences, gates, railings, steel* ........ (973) 481-5550
Alben Metal Products, 11 Iowa Ave., Paterson 07503
Pres., Fin. & MIS Mgr.—Al Vollaro, 4 emp., *Metal stampings & CNC machining job* ........ (973) 279-8891
Alessandra Miscellaneous Metalworks, Inc., 75-B Mill St., Newton 07860
Owner—Scott Alessandra, 7 emp., *Steel stair, rail & ladder fabrication* ........ (973) 786-6805
Alex Machine Shop, Inc., 267 Livingston St., P.O. Box 268, Northvale 07647
Pres.—Alex Aleksich, 5 emp., *General machining job shop & food products* ...... (201) 768-9110
Alfa Machine Co., Inc., 2154 Highway 130 N., Monmouth Junction 08852
Pres.—Louis Pall, 4 emp., *Holography equipment, including special* ........ (732) 821-0044
All American Metal Fabricators, 34 Harold St., Tenafly 07670
GM—Robert Leopold, 6 emp., *Steel/metal fabrication, including* ........ (201) 567-2898
All Tool Company, Inc., 899 Rahway Ave., Union 07083
Pres.—John A. Vinciguerra, 13 emp., *Precision machining job shop* ........ (908) 687-3636
Allgrind Plastics, Inc., 6 Vliet Farm Rd., Asbury 08802
Pres., Fin. & R & D Mgr.—Bill Willoughby, 13 emp., *Custom grinding, granulating, pulverizing* (908) 479-4400
Allied Steel Distribution & Service Center, 118-144 Harper St., Newark 07114
Pres.—Don DeFaria, Jr., 14 emp., *Steel service center, including plate* ........ (973) 824-7347
Almark Tool & Mfg. Co., Inc., 27 South Ave., P.O. Box 189, Garwood 07027
Pres.—Mark Bowman, 10 emp., *Custom machined parts, including CNC* ........ (908) 789-2440
Alpha Lehigh Tool & Machine Co., Inc., 41 Industrial Rd., Alpha 08865
Pres.—William S. Green, 42 emp., *Precision machining job shop* ........ (908) 454-6481
Altech Machine & Tool, Inc., 230 Bank St., Ste. 1, Midland Park 07432
Pres., Hum. Res. Mgr.—Ismael Sierra, 5 emp., *Tool & die & CNC machining job shop* ........ (201) 652-4409
Am Jet Enterprises, 11 1/2 Elm St., Rockaway 07866
Pres.—Andrew Chop, 3 emp., *Filling & assembly machines* ........ (973) 627-5690
American Machine Specialties, Inc., 51 Bergenline Ave., Westwood 07675
Pres.—Norman Illian, 10 emp., *General machining job shop* ........ (201) 664-2100
American Machine Tool Repair, 12 Middlebury Blvd., Randolph 07869
Pres.—Alex Karoly, Jr., 8 emp., *Rebuilt production machinery, including* ........ (973) 927-0820
American Machining Co., LLC, 110 Harmon Dr., Blackwood 08012
★ Owner—Bill Ehsign, 5 emp., *CNC & wire EDM machining job shop* ........ (856) 245-7801
American Metal Fab & Welding, 706 7th St., Union City 07087
GM—Maher Gazawneh, 2 emp., *Custom sheet metal fabrication & welding* ........ (201) 295-8888
American Products Co., Inc., 610 Rahway Ave., Union 07083
Pres.—Chris Walsh, 78 emp., *Corporate headquarters & precision* ........ (908) 687-4100
Ameritech Precision Machining Co., 425 N. Grove St., Unit 3-A, Berlin 08009
Owner—Joseph Speyerer, 2 emp., *Precision machining job shop* ........ (856) 767-1660
Amex Tool Co., Inc., 4 Fox Hill Ln., Asbury 08802
Pres.—Hubert Stria, 10 emp., *Precision tool & die job shop* ........ (908) 735-5176
Anderson Machine Co., 109 Stryker Ln., Unit 10, Hillsborough 08844
Ptnr.—John Anderson, 3 emp., *General machining job shop* ........ (908) 281-7153
Apex Gear & Machine Co., 938 Lake St., Newark 07104
Pres.—Steve Ciocci, 6 emp., *Precision gears, racks & grinding,* ........ (973) 482-5542
Apostolico Machine, 144 Linwood Ave., Paterson 07502
Owner—Aniello Apostolico, 1 emp., *Precision & general machining job shop* ........ (973) 790-3351
Applied Surface Technologies, 15 Hawthorne Dr., New Providence 07974
Owner—Robert Sherman, 1 emp., *Carbon dioxide snow cleaning equipment* ........ (908) 464-6675
Arch Custom Mfg Inc, 1215 S. 6th St., Camden 08104
Pres. & Fin. Mgr.—Donald Blair, 4 emp., *Precision machining job shop* ........ (856) 966-3835
Arias Machine Tool & Die Co., 645 Atlantic Ave., Perth Amboy 08861
Pres.—Joseph Arias, 2 emp., *General machining & welding job shop* ........ (732) 442-2398
Aries Precision Tool, Inc., 300 State Route 17, Ste. H, Mahwah 07430
Pres.—Stephen Bachman, 6 emp., *Precision machining & CNC turning &* ........ (201) 252-8550
Arlington Machine & Tool Co., 90 New Dutch Ln., Fairfield 07004
CEO—Susan Blanck, 90 emp., *Contract close tolerance precision* ........ (973) 276-1377
Atlantic Casting & Engineering, 810 Bloomfield Ave., Clifton 07012
CEO—Jim Binns, 100 emp., *Investment castings & CNC machining* ........ (973) 779-2450
Atlantic Coastal Welding, Inc., 16 Butler Blvd., Bayville 08721
Pres.—John Gallo, 6 emp., *Welding & metal, aluminum & steel fabrication* ........ (732) 269-1088
Atlantic Precision Technology, LLC, 432 Quarry Ln., North Brunswick 08902
CEO—Richard Slacum, 5 emp., *Precision machining job shop* ........ (732) 648-7786
Atlas Consolidated Machine Corp., 53 Bleeker St., Paterson 07524
Pres.—Walter Wozney, 2 emp., *General machining job shop* ........ (973) 684-5803
Atlas Welders & Fabricators Corp., 2505 S. Clinton Ave., South Plainfield 07080
Pres.—Ronald Eodice, 3 emp., *Welding job shop* ........ (908) 561-1144
Automatic Machine Products, 56 Paterson Ave., Newton 07860
Owner—Don Schanstra, 5 emp., *General machining job shop* ........ (973) 383-9929
AW Machinery, LLC, 7 Just Rd., Fairfield 07004
Ptnr. & Pres.—Nestor E. Gener, 16 emp., *Industrial equipment & integrated systems* ........ (973) 882-3223
AZCO Corp., 26 Just Rd., Fairfield 07004
Pres.—Andrew Zucaro, 30 emp., *Machinery for feeding, cutting, inserting* ........ (973) 439-1428
Aztech Mfg., LLC, 147 W. Hampton St., Pemberton 08068
Pres., GM—Dan Murphy, 3 emp., *Precision machining job shop* ........ (609) 726-1212
B & A Flex, Inc., 34 Charlotte Dr., Bridgewater 08807
GM—Dan Souza, 14 emp., *Flexible metal hose, connectors & flow* ........ (908) 722-2808
B & B Ultra-Sonic, Inc., 10 E. Main St., High Bridge 08829
Pres.—Richard N. Baumann, 10 emp., *General machining job shop* ........ (908) 638-5775
B & C Machine Co., Inc., 22 Lasinski Rd., Franklin 07416
Pres.—Robert Van Dyke, 5 emp., *Precision machining job shop* ........ (973) 823-1120
B & L Precision Grinding Corp., 7-B Ivy St., Pompton Lakes 07442
Pres.—Lonnie Petersen, 2 emp., *Centerless grinding* ........ (973) 839-4141
B & M Grinding Co., 50 Brown Ave., Springfield 07081
Ptnr.—Fred Grosso, 2 emp., *Internal & external metal grinding* ........ (973) 564-7648
B & M Machine Co., Inc., 67-69 Greylock Ave., Belleville 07109
Pres.—Richard Bing, 18 emp., *Contract machine work & precision machining* ........ (973) 751-0789
B P Machine Co., Inc., 10 American Way, Spotswood 08884
Pres.—Robert Provell, 5 emp., *General machining job shop* ........ (732) 251-0449

Bach Tool Precision, Inc., 51 Executive Pkwy., Ringwood 07456
Pres.—Richard Ebersbach, 5 emp., *Precision machining of metal components* ........ (973) 962-6224
Barnett Machine Tool Corp., 401 Supor Blvd., P.O. Box 189, Harrison 07029
Pres.—Antonio Ferreira, 24 emp., *Precision machine tools & general machining* ........ (973) 482-6222
Bauer Precision, Inc., 174 Kinderkamack Rd., Ste. D, Park Ridge 07656
Owner & Pres.—Peter Bauer, 4 emp., *Precision machining job shop, including* ........ (201) 307-0369
BBK Machining, Inc., 429 Garrison Rd., Elmer 08318
Pres.—Edward Suess, 2 emp., *General machining job shop* ........ (856) 358-8864
BCS Machine & Mfg. Corp., 3575 Kennedy Rd., South Plainfield 07080
Pres.—Sal Capparelli, 10 emp., *CNC & general machining job shop, including* ........ (908) 561-1656
BeCu Manufacturing Co., Inc., 2347 Beryllium Rd., Scotch Plains 07076
Pres.—Stephan Hoeckele, 24 emp., *Precision metal stampings, including* ........ (908) 233-3343
Bergen Metal Products, Inc., 120 Brighton Rd., Ste. 5, Clifton 07012
Pres.—John Mottola, 10 emp., *Precision metal parts* ........ (973) 249-1500
Berkshire Machine, Inc., 390 Route 15 S., Wharton 07885
Pres.—Gerald Munsterer, 2 emp., *General machining job shop* ........ (973) 366-7710
Bertot Industries, Inc., 23 Malcolm St., Ste. 1, Morristown 07960
Pres.—Harold Jelonnek, 10 emp., *General machining job shop* ........ (973) 267-0006
Betar, Inc., 100 Randolph Rd., Ste. 4, Somerset 08873
Pres.—John M. Lohse, 17 emp., *General machining job shop, including* ........ (908) 359-4200
Bigelow Components Corp., 74 Diamond Rd., Springfield 07081
Owner & Pres.—C. Brett Harman, 20 emp., *Precision miniature cold-headed & stamped* ...... (973) 467-1200
Bill Martin Machine, LLC, 56 Paterson Ave., Ste. 112, Newton 07860
Owner—Bill Martin, 1 emp., *CNC machining job shop* ........ (973) 300-5052
Bisaga, Inc., 212 Ashland Ave., Somerdale 08083
Pres.—Robert E. Bisaga, 11 emp., *General machining job shop for the* ........ (856) 784-7966
Biwal Mfg. Co., Inc., 48 Industrial St. W., Clifton 07012
Pres.—Joseph J. Mrocka, 22 emp., *General machining job shop* ........ (973) 778-0105
Blue Chip Industries, Inc., 50 Old Camplain Rd., Hillsborough 08844
Pres.—Carl Imhoff, 1 emp., *General machining job shop* ........ (908) 704-1466
Blue Chip Technology, 267 Richwood Rd., P.O. Box 287, Richwood 08074
Owner—Frank J. Winters, 10 emp., *General machining job shop* ........ (856) 881-3133
BR Welding & Industrial Services, Inc., 3 Brook Rd., Howell 07731
Pres.—Brandon Reo, 20 emp., *Structural metal fabrication & welding* ........ (732) 363-8253
Bralen, LLC, 236 U.S. Highway 206 N., Branchville 07826
Plt. Mgr.—E. J. Syphers, 4 emp., *General machining job shop* ........ (973) 948-6575
Bright Machinery Mfg. Group, Inc., 239 Lindbergh Pl., Bldg. 2-A, Paterson 07503
Owner—Fred Gull, 2 emp., *Machined parts & general machining* ........ (973) 345-7405
Brodie System, Inc., 1539 W. Elizabeth Ave., Linden 07036
Opers. Mgr.—John Farrell, 15 emp., *General machining job shop* ........ (908) 862-8620
Brook Metal Products, Inc., 6 Evans Terminal, Hillside 07205
Pres., Off. Mgr.—Wendy Merendino, 8 emp., *Welding & sheet metal fabrication* ........ (908) 355-1601
Brown Tool & Machine Co., Inc., Rosemont Raven Rock Rd., P.O. Box 142, Rosemont 08556
Pres.—Alan Brown, 2 emp., *Industrial & medical prototypes & architectur* ........ (609) 397-1751
Buhler Inc, 40 Whitney Rd., Mahwah 07430
Pres.—Steve Jacobson, 15 emp., *Processing equipment for the chemical* ........ (201) 847-0600
Butensky Services Co., Inc., 3380 Route 22, P.O. Box 5020, Somerville 08876
Pres.—Bryan Butensky, 50 emp., *Rebuilt & refurbished electromechanical* ........ (908) 707-0912
C & C Tool & Machine Co., LLC, 38 W. Scott St., P.O. Box 407, Riverside 08075
Pres., GM—Frank Canduci, 11 emp., *CNC machining & tool & die job shop* ........ (856) 461-6090
C & K Punch & Screw Machine Products, 160 Hobart St., Hackensack 07601
Pres., GM—Don Kuder, 8 emp., *Punches for steel rule dies & precision* ........ (201) 343-6750
C & L Machining Co., 110 S. New Broadway, P.O. Box 167, Brooklawn 08030
Pres.—George Cohen, 6 emp., *General machining, welding & gear cutting* ........ (856) 456-1932
C & S Precision Products, LLC, 22 Park Pl., Butler 07405
Member—Leonard Marion, 4 emp., *Machine parts & CNC machining job shop* ........ (973) 838-3644
C & S Tool Co., Inc., 304 Ridgedale Ave., East Hanover 07936
Pres.—Robert Sadowski, 7 emp., *Precision machining job shop* ........ (973) 887-6865
C. J.'s Tool Mfg., Inc., 620 Route 168, Turnersville 08012
Pres.—Charles Corbett, 7 emp., *General machining job shop* ........ (856) 227-7342
C.A.M.E. Machine & Metal Works, Inc., 181 Pacific Ave., Jersey City 07304
Pres.—Ciro Medina, 4 emp., *Machining job shop, including general* ........ (201) 309-0005
CADPRO, Inc., 114 W. Atlantic Ave., Clementon 08021
Pres.—Elaine A. Bartie, 10 emp., *Machined & sheet metal parts, assemblies* ........ (856) 435-0050
Cain Machine, Inc., 1501 Oakland Ave., Millville 08332
Pres., GM—Douglas Cain, 6 emp., *Metal parts, scientific glass machinery* ........ (856) 825-7225
Camtec Industries, Inc., 28 Saddle Ridge Rd., Colts Neck 07722
Pres.—Anthony Mauro, 16 emp., *CNC machining job shop, including metal* ........ (732) 332-9800
Carlen Machine Co., 1275 Bloomfield Ave., Bldg. 10, Door 89, Fairfield 07004
Owner—Carmine Zecca, 1 emp., *General machining job shop* ........ (973) 808-1441
Carlisle Machine Works, Inc., 412 S. Wade Blvd., Bldg. 5, P.O. Box 746, Millville 08332
Pres.—Mary Dougherty, 23 emp., *Custom fabrication & machining of industrial* ........ (856) 825-0627
Cartco, Inc., 621 Grape St., Hammonton 08037
Owner—Carl Tillstrom, 50 emp., *General machining job shop* ........ (978) 692-7070
Central Metal Fabricators, Inc., 300 Central Ave., Farmingdale 07727
Pres.—Frank Cris, 20 emp., *Precision machined components & assemblies* ........ (732) 938-6900
Chamberlain's VACU-Blast Sales, 1200 Bannard St., P.O. Box 225, Cinnaminson 08077
Pres.—Mike Cataline, Jr., 7 emp., *Manufacturer of abrasive blasting equipment* ........ (856) 829-6444
Charles Machine Shop Service, Rob, 24 Rake Rd., Flemington 08822
Owner—Rob Charles, 1 emp., *General machining job shop* ........ (908) 806-8512
Class Tool Co., 2500 S. Clinton Ave., P.O. Box 286, South Plainfield 07080
Owner & Pres.—John Nagy, 1 emp., *Machining job shop* ........ (908) 561-6633
ClearDrain, 219 Saint Mihiel Dr., Riverside 08075
Mng. Dir.—Frank A. Chille, Jr., 10 emp., *Self-adjusting, self-cleaning, self-defrostin* ........ (856) 461-0091
Clover Stamping Co., Inc., 60 Spruce St., Paterson 07501
Pres., Sales Mgr.—Bob Kellenberger, 10 emp., *Metal stampings & tool & die job shop* ........ (973) 278-4888
CMI-Promex, Inc., 7 Benjamin Green Rd., Pedricktown 08067
Pres.—Wayne Ligato, 20 emp., *Commercial machining, engineered thermoplasti* ........ (856) 351-1000
CNC Supermatic LLC, 27 Old Beach Glen Rd., Rockaway 07866
Pres.—Irene Kobrynowicz Hunter, 10 emp., *Precision machined components for the* ........ (973) 627-4433
Collinear Machine & Design, 7 Wilson Dr., Sparta 07871
Pres.—John Sangiacomo, 9 emp., *Precision machining job shop* ........ (973) 300-1681
Columbia Machine, 1 N. Riverview Ave., Columbia 07832
Owner—Alex Curtis, 1 emp., *CNC machining job shop* ........ (908) 475-4057
Components & Controls, Inc., 495 Washington Ave., P.O. Box 437, Carlstadt 07072
Pres., CEO—Jerry Orlando, 21 emp., *Flexible metal & TFE hoses & industrial* ........ (201) 438-9190
Concept Group, Inc., 380 Cooper Rd., West Berlin 08091
Pres.—Aarne Ried, 16 emp., *Precision vacuum brazing & CNC machining* ........ (856) 767-5506
Conti Group, The (H Q), 2045 State Route 27, Edison 08817
Pres., CEO—Kurt G. Conti, 150 emp., *Company headquarters; precast concrete* ........ (732) 520-5000
Cotterman, Inc., 100 Hayes Ave., P.O. Box 278, Wenonah 08090
Pres.—William Thomas, 20 emp., *High-pressure piping & industrial welding* ........ (856) 464-6820

S.I.C.

★ **Indicates new listing this edition.**

Creative Industries, 1409 Astor St., P.O. Box 313, South Plainfield 07080
Pres.—Arthur Kopacc, 14 emp., *Plastic injection molds & machining* ........ (908) 561-5600
Creative Machining Systems, Inc., 124 Youngs Rd., Mercerville 08619
Co-Pres., CEO—Victor Scharko, 15 emp., *Precision machining job shop* ........ (609) 586-3932
Creter, Inc., Philip, 20 Monroe St., Union 07083
Pres.—Doris Logan, 4 emp., *Precision & CNC machining job shop* ........ (908) 686-2910
Crown Precision Corp., 61 Willet St., Ste. 13, Passaic 07055
Owner & Pres.—Todd W. Evans, 4 emp., *Precision machined components for the* ........ (973) 470-0097
CSI Fabricators, 15 Lexington St., Newark 07105
★ Manager—Kiran Pagarey, 7 emp., *Sheet metal fabrication, architectural* ........ (973) 344-0955
Custom Cut Metal Products, Inc., 7 Daniel Rd. E., Fairfield 07004
V-P.—Gerhard Muller, 18 emp., *Precision machining of stainless steel* ........ (973) 808-6803
Cut Mark, Inc., 801 S. Church St., Ste. 6, Mount Laurel 08054
Owner—George Gibson, 7 emp., *Precision & CNC milling & turning job* ........ (856) 234-3428
Cutting Techniques, Inc., 651 Industrial Rd., Carlstadt 07072
Pres.—Ron Radomski, 6 emp., *General machining job shop, including* ........ (201) 438-2222
D & G Precision, 709 Louis Ave., Linden 07036
Owner—Jesse Lesniak, 2 emp., *Precision machining job shop* ........ (908) 925-1578
D & H Cutoff Co., Inc., 412-I Trimmer Rd., Bldg. 11, Califon 07830
Ptnr. & Pres.—Art W. DeSaules, Jr., 9 emp., *Precision abrasive cutting* ........ (908) 454-4961
D & W Diesel, 423 County Rd., Cliffwood 07721
Opers. Mgr.—Craig Marcurano, 40 emp., *Rebuilt automotive generators, starters* ........ (732) 566-4970
D C Metric Tool, Inc., 11 Mathews Ave., Riverdale 07457
Pres.—Djordje Cakmak, 2 emp., *Architectural millwork & machining* ........ (973) 838-7590
D E B Maintenance, Inc., 1000 Union Landing Rd., P.O. Box 13, Riverton 08077
Pres.—Kenneth Williams, 30 emp., *Steel fabrication, tanks, vessels &* ........ (856) 786-0440
D. F. Enterprise, LLC, 3254 S. Black Horse Pike, Williamstown 08094
Owner & Pres.—Scott Richardson, 2 emp., *Industrial metal coatings, hard chrome* ........ (856) 875-1777
Davis-Standard, LLC, 220 Davidson Ave., Ste. 401, Somerset 08873
V-P., Blown Film—Rick Keller, 130 emp., *Converting & extrusion systems for* ........ (908) 722-6000
Day Tool & Mfg., Inc., 6 Carman Ln., P.O. Box 466, Whitehouse 08888
Pres.—John J. Callahan III, 19 emp., *Custom machines, precision tooling,* ........ (908) 439-3800
DCM Industries LLC, 50 S. Center St., Unit 8, Orange 07050
Owner—Dave Myers, 5 emp., *General machining job shop* ........ (973) 675-3200
Defined Pro Machining, LLC, 105 W. Dewey Ave., Ste. 205, Wharton 07885
Owner & Mng. Member—Henrietta Fidler, 5 emp., *CNC machining job shop, including CNC* . (973) 941-2430
DeJohn Machine Co., 2 Elm St., Garfield 07026
V-P., Fin.—Gino DiGiovanni, 4 emp., *Precision & general machining job shop* ........ (973) 478-1144
Delta Machine Works, Inc., 257 Division Ave., Carlstadt 07072
Pres., R & D Mgr.—Michael Alpos, 3 emp., *General machining job shop* ........ (201) 935-7474
Demand, LLC, 36 S. Adamsville Rd., Bridgewater 08807
Owner—Joseph Kafara, 16 emp., *Welding, machining & custom sheet metal* ........ (908) 526-2020
Dependable Machining & Stone Co., 53 Weaverville Rd., Freehold 07728
Owner—Frank Minervini, 3 emp., *Precision machining job shop* ........ (732) 462-0262
DeWalt Mfg. Co., Inc., 88 W. Cohawkin Rd., Clarksboro 08020
Pres.—Roger Dewalt, 7 emp., *Precision & waterjet machining job* ........ (856) 423-1207
Deza Machine & Tool Co., 938 E. 19th St., Paterson 07501
Owner—Antiono Defabrizio, 1 emp., *General machining job shop* ........ (973) 278-6654
Diamond Machine Co., Inc., 30 N. Valley Rd., P.O. Box 420, Roosevelt 08555
Pres.—George Pall, 4 emp., *General machining job shop* ........ (609) 490-8940
Dicar, Inc., 10 Bloomfield Ave., P.O. Box 643, Pine Brook 07058
Pres.—Steve Warl, 150 emp., *Corporate headquarters & replacement* ........ (973) 575-1174
Die-Tech, Inc., 677 Amwell Rd., Hillsborough 08844
Pres.—Joe Welches, 2 emp., *Precision machining job shop* ........ (908) 369-6756
DIHCO, Inc., 612 E. Crescent Ave., Upper Saddle River 07458
Pres.—Peter Diamantes, 4 emp., *General machining job shop* ........ (201) 327-0518
DiLauri Steel Fabricators, 5 Merrys Ln., East Hanover 07936
Pres.—Kathleen DiLauri, 2 emp., *Steel fabrication & welding job shop* ........ (973) 884-2414
Diversatech, Inc., 1584 Reed Rd., Pennington 08534
Pres.—Haskel Zeloof, 5 emp., *Sheet metal fabrication & machining* ........ (609) 730-9668
Diversified Machine, LLC, 15 American Way, Ste. 12, Spotswood 08884
Pres.—Greg Kopitskie, 1 emp., *General machining job shop* ........ (732) 251-6600
Diversitech, Inc., 18 Hamburg Tpke., Riverdale 07457
V-P.—Linda Weinacker, 28 emp., *Precision machining job shop* ........ (973) 835-2900
Doran, LLC, 599 Green Ln., Union 07083
Plt. Mgr.—Randolph Wojcik, 5 emp., *Steel fabrication & precision machining* ........ (908) 289-9200
Double O Mfg., 100 S. Washington Ave., Dunellen 08812
Pres., CFO—Albert J. Oslislo, 9 emp., *Metal fabrication & military standard* ........ (732) 752-9423
Drew-Wal Machine & Tool Corp., 76 Monroe St., Little Ferry 07643
Pres.—Andrew J. Kovach, 4 emp., *General machining & tool & die job* ........ (201) 641-3887
Drytech, Inc., 54 Wrightstown Cookstown Rd., P.O. Box 249, Cookstown 08511
Pres., Fin. & R & D Mgr.—Tony Jones, 24 emp., *Cartridge dehydrators, moisture management* (609) 758-1794
Duffy, Inc., Andrew B., 322 Crown Point Rd., P.O. Box 569, Thorofare 08086
Pres.—Brian Duffy, 15 emp., *Stainless steel, steel, titanium, aluminum* ........ (856) 845-4900
Dunn Fabrication, 8470 Remington Ave., Pennsauken 08110
★ Owner—Evan Dunn, 1 emp., *Automotive machining job shop* ........ (856) 486-3866
Dynametric Tool Co., 27 Somerset Pl., Clifton 07012
Pres.—Frank Csapo, 4 emp., *Precision machining job shop* ........ (973) 471-8009
Dynamic Machining, Inc., 876 N. Lenola Rd., Ste. 9-A, Moorestown 08057
Pres.—Harold Budman, 25 emp., *Precision machining job shop* ........ (856) 273-9830
E & J Machine And Tool, LLC, 12 Orben Dr., Unit 1, Landing 07850
Owner—Edmund Kiss, 5 emp., *CNC lathe & milling job shop, including* ........ (973) 810-2312
East Coast Steel, Inc., 317 Salina Rd., Sewell 08080
★ Owner—Jim Matthews, 20 emp., *CNC & welding machining job shop* ........ (856) 582-6776
Eastern Machining Corp., 1197 Fries Mill Rd., Franklinville 08322
Pres.—Joe Davis, 5 emp., *Swiss screw machine products & general* ........ (856) 694-3303
Eclipse Mfg., LLC, 438 Lanza Ave., Garfield 07026
Owner—Ziggy Nieradka, 4 emp., *Industrial machine parts, CNC machining* ........ (973) 340-9939
Eddie Kane Steel Products, Inc. (H Q), P.O. Box 133, Spring Lake 07762
Pres.—Augustine Kane, 11 emp., *Corporate headquarters; steel service* ........ (732) 974-3339
Edison Machine, 25 Liberty St., Metuchen 08840
Ptnr.—Joshua Leo, 10 emp., *General machining job shop* ........ (732) 494-5011
Ed-Mar Industries, Inc., 11 Ray Pl., Fairfield 07004
Pres.—Edward Puchalski, 4 emp., *General machining job shop & packaging* ........ (973) 808-9205
Edston Mfg. Co., Inc., 321 Warren Ave., Stirling 07980
Pres., CFO—Paul Zuzozk, 2 emp., *General machining job shop* ........ (908) 647-0116
ELC America Corp., 235-B Hickory Ln., Bayville 08721
Pres.—Edmund Cassella, 8 emp., *Precision & general machining job shop* ........ (732) 269-5274
Electronic Mfg. Co., 71 Newark Way, Maplewood 07040
Pres.—Martin Peterson, 25 emp., *Metal stampings & CNC turning & milling* ........ (973) 762-1300
Elite Tool, Inc., 1640 New Market Ave., P.O. Box 853, South Plainfield 07080
Owner & Pres.—Stan Kravetsky, 3 emp., *Precision machining job shop* ........ (732) 424-1126
Elmi Machine & Tool Co., Inc., 1275 Bloomfield Ave., Bldg. 5, Unit 2-B, Fairfield 07004
Pres.—Victor Vitencz, 3 emp., *General machining job shop* ........ (973) 882-1277
EMMC Co., 1 Nicola Pl., Belleville 07109
Pres.—Byshek Gasior, 3 emp., *General machining, fabricating & welding* ........ (973) 751-0100
Engineering Dynamics, LLC, 429 Rockaway Valley Rd., Ste. 1300, Boonton 07005
Owner—Richard G. Spitzlei, 2 emp., *General & CNC machining job shop* ........ (973) 794-4500
Evans Machine & Tool Co., 410 Summit Ave., Perth Amboy 08861
Pres.—Thomas S. Geslak, 10 emp., *General machining job shop* ........ (732) 442-1144
Exacta V & H Corp., 107 Whittendale Dr., Moorestown 08057
Pres.—Wayne Hubler, 9 emp., *General machining job shop* ........ (856) 235-7379
Experimental Machine & Tool, 114 Pulaski Rd., Whitehouse Station 08889
Pres.—John Nieliwodski, 4 emp., *General machining job shop* ........ (908) 534-4725
Extruders International, Inc., 181 W. Clay Ave., Roselle Park 07204
Pres.—Stanley Dickerson, 2 emp., *Machine parts* ........ (908) 241-7750
Exxcel Welding Corp., 14 Brookhill Rd., Pittstown 08867
Owner—Castor Rosocha, 1 emp., *Welding job shop* ........ (908) 735-0000
F & A Machine Co., Inc., 133 Lincoln Blvd., Middlesex 08846
Pres.—Frank Adami, 3 emp., *General machining job shop* ........ (732) 356-5777
F & M Machine Co., Inc., 751 Lexington Ave., Kenilworth 07033
Pres., Plt. Mgr.—Dick Rutledge, 6 emp., *Metal stamping & machining job shop* ........ (908) 245-8830
F & R Grinding, Inc., 138 County Road 513, Frenchtown 08825
Pres.—Ron Nicolato, 15 emp., *Centerless grinding* ........ (908) 996-0440
Fabrite Metal, 10 Stony Brook Rd., Rockaway 07866
Owner—Robert Gilmore, 1 emp., *Custom metal fabrication & precision* ........ (973) 714-1813
Famcam, Inc., 3 Eastmans Rd., Parsippany 07054
Pres.—Samir Aboulhosn, 10 emp., *General machining job shop* ........ (973) 319-3033
Fano Machine & Tool Co., 20 Passaic St., Garfield 07026
Pres.—Tony Cristofano, 2 emp., *General machining job shop* ........ (973) 773-9353
Farmer Co., Arthur E., 47 Frazier St., Trenton 08618
Owner—Edward C. Farmer, 2 emp., *General machining job shop* ........ (609) 392-8722
Fazzio Machine & Steel, 3278 Glassboro Cross Keys Rd., P.O. Box 232, Glassboro 08028
Pres.—Phil Fazzio, 6 emp., *General machining job shop & distributor* ........ (856) 881-2832
Ferrite Welding Products, Inc., 31 S. Passaic Ave., Chatham 07928
Pres.—Kevin Bukata, 5 emp., *Welding alloys & accessories* ........ (973) 377-6636
Ferry Machine Corp., 75 Industrial Ave., Little Ferry 07643
Pres., MIS & R & D Mgr.—Louis Ferretti, 30 emp., *Precision military & medical machining* .... (201) 641-9191
FIMS Mfg. Corp., 8 Allerman Rd., Oakland 07436
Pres., CFO—Sergio Facchini, 20 emp., *Machine parts, including CNC milling* ........ (201) 845-7088
Fischer Laser Marking, Inc., 384 Otterhole Rd., West Milford 07480
Owner & Pres.—Sharon Fischer, 4 emp., *Laser engraving & laser marking job* ........ (973) 616-4696
Fischl Machine & Tool Co., 79 Clinton Rd., Fairfield 07004
Pres.—Rudolph Fischl, 3 emp., *General machining job shop* ........ (973) 227-0767
Flame-Cut Steel, Inc., 97 E. 2nd St., Bayonne 07002
Pres.—Ramesh Nuthi, 12 emp., *Metal service center, including plate* ........ (201) 436-9300
Fluets Corp., 260 Pennsylvania Ave., Hillside 07205
Pres.—Ray Fluet, 30 emp., *Precision machining job shop* ........ (908) 353-5229
Foremost Machine Builders, Inc., 23 Spielman Rd., Fairfield 07004
Pres.—Marlena Heydenreich, 45 emp., *Machine parts for the plastic industry* ........ (973) 227-0700
Form, Fit & Function, LLC, 25 McLean Blvd., Paterson 07514
Owner—Odilo Vazquez, 20 emp., *Precision machining job shop* ........ (973) 442-2290
Forthmann Machines, Inc., 1495 MacArthur Blvd., Mahwah 07430
Pres.—James Beezer, 50 emp., *Label cutting machines* ........ (201) 818-1221
Frederiks Machine & Tool, Inc., 99 Kingwood Stockton Rd., P.O. Box 247, Rosemont 08556
Pres.—Peter Frederiks, 5 emp., *Hydraulic fittings & general machining* ........ (609) 397-4991
Fredon Welding & Iron Works Co., 52 State Route 15, P.O. Box 260, Lafayette 07848
Pres.—James Zylstra, 28 emp., *Ironwork & welding job shop* ........ (973) 383-6768
Frieri A Machine Tool Co., Inc., 1112 Belmont Ave., South Plainfield 07080
Pres.—Andrew Frieri, 6 emp., *General machining job shop* ........ (908) 753-7555
G & B Machine, Inc., 35 N. Middaugh St., Ste. 2-B, Somerville 08876
Pres.—Gary Boccadutre, 6 emp., *CNC machining job shop* ........ (908) 722-7940
G A F Machine Tool Co., Inc., 39 Maple Pl., P.O. Box 18, Keyport 07735
Pres.—George Fernandez, 6 emp., *Precision & CNC machining job shop* ........ (732) 264-8717
G B Industries II, Inc., 341 Margaret King Ave., Ringwood 07456
Pres., CFO—Gerard Barrere, 7 emp., *Precision machining, including Swiss-type* ........ (973) 728-5900
G. Cotter Enterprises, Inc., 48 Brown Ave., Springfield 07081
Pres.—Jerry Cotter, 13 emp., *Micro & laser micro welding job shop* ........ (973) 376-5840
Gadren Machine Co., 108 Main St., P.O. Box 117, Mount Ephraim 08059
Pres.—George S. Gadren, Jr., 15 emp., *Valves & CNC machining job shop* ........ (856) 456-4329
Galaxy II, Inc., 235 Jersey Ave., Unit A, New Brunswick 08901
Pres.—Earl Creighton, 5 emp., *Precision machining job shop* ........ (732) 828-2686
Galicia Metal, Inc., 573 E. 19th St., Paterson 07514
Pres.—John Martinez, 2 emp., *General machining job shop* ........ (973) 278-1058
Galow Co., Inc., H., 15 Maple St., Norwood 07648
Pres.—Michael Galow, 45 emp., *Precision machine parts, including* ........ (201) 768-0547
Garvey Precision Machine, Inc., 19 Ironside Ct., Willingboro 08046
Pres.—Joseph Corr, 22 emp., *Precision machining job shop* ........ (609) 835-4900
Gauer Metal Products, Inc., 175-179 N. Michigan Ave., Kenilworth 07033
CEO—Dennis J. Schultz, 40 emp., *Metal storage rack frames, gravity* ........ (908) 241-4080
Gaum, Inc., 1080 Route 130, P.O. Box 485, Robbinsville 08691
Pres.—Robert Gaum, 50 emp., *Custom industrial machinery & machine* ........ (609) 586-0132
GEA Mechanical Equipment US, Inc., 100 Fairway Ct., Northvale 07647
Pres.—Michael J. Vick, 175 emp., *Corporate headquarters & centrifuges* ........ (201) 767-3900
Geiger Tool & Mfg. Co., Inc., 50 Liberty St., Passaic 07055
Pres., CEO—Joseph Szczesny, 21 emp., *Precision machining & tool & die job* ........ (973) 777-2136
General Machine & Experimental Works, 117 Gertrude Ave., Paramus 07652
Pres.—Paul Oelkrug, 5 emp., *Packaging components & general machining* ........ (201) 843-9035
General Machine Kraft, Inc., 216 Broad St., Phillipsburg 08865
Pres.—Eugene Cancelliera, 10 emp., *Close tolerance high production & CNC* ........ (908) 454-5955
Gibson, Inc., George, 801 S. Church St., Ste. 6, Mount Laurel 08054
Pres.—George Gibson, 3 emp., *General machining job shop* ........ (856) 234-5502
Global Packaging Machinery, Inc., 36 Peel St., Paterson 07524
Owner & Dir., Engrg.—Michael Kurdyla, 5 emp., *Cartoning & material handling machinery* ..... (973) 279-2300
Globe Industries Corp., 48 Industrial St. W., Clifton 07012
Pres.—Mark Melillo, 7 emp., *Precision machining job shop* ........ (973) 992-8990
Gluefast Co., Inc., 3535 State Route 66, Ste. 1, Neptune 07753
Pres.—Lester Mallet, 10 emp., *Glue & gluing equipment for the packaging* ........ (732) 918-4600
GMI, 599 State St., Perth Amboy 08861
Pres.—Christopher Grimes, 10 emp., *Precision machining job shop* ........ (732) 442-4572
Good Automatic Windlass, Inc., 357 Route 72, Barnegat 08005
Sr. V-P., GM—Thomas J. Ring, 3 emp., *Anchor windlasses for 20-foot to 55-foot* ........ (609) 698-4402
Gorsky, Inc., E., 33 South Ave., Fanwood 07023
Pres. & Manager—Bill Gorsky, 5 emp., *Machine parts fabrication* ........ (908) 322-8580

GPR Co., Inc., 22 Daniel Rd., Fairfield 07004
Pres.—George Verhoest, 40 emp., *Production machining & contract manufacturing* .......... (973) 227-6160
Grammer, Dempsey & Hudson Co., 212 Rome St., Newark 07105
Pres.—James Hudson, 8 emp., *Carbon, alloy, stainless & tool bar* .......... (973) 589-8000
Grand Equipment Of America, 267 Livingston St., Northvale 07647
Pres.—Neil White, 21 emp., *Company headquarters & dairy equipment* .......... (201) 784-1101
Great Notch Industries, Inc., 140 Liberty St., Hackensack 07601
Pres.—Paul Galinski, 2 emp., *Precision machining job shop* .......... (201) 343-8110
Guerard Co., J. D., 43 Old Washington Crossing Rd., Titusville 08560
Owner—John Guerard, 1 emp., *Precision machining job shop* .......... (609) 737-8892
H & H Sheet Metal & Machining, 30 White Lake Rd., Sparta 07871
Pres., CFO—Frederick Hohmann, 9 emp., *Sheet metal fabrication & CNC machining* .......... (973) 383-6880
H & H Swiss Screw Machine Products Co., Inc., 1478 Chestnut Ave., Hillside 07205
Pres.—Darryl Stacy, 55 emp., *Precision custom CNC Swiss screw machine* .......... (908) 688-6390
H E K Machine, Inc., 785 State St., Ste. 2, Perth Amboy 08861
Pres., GM, Pur. & Sales & Mktg. Mgr.—Mike Kurth, 2 emp., *General machining job shop* .......... (732) 442-8672
H P Performance, Inc., 8 Industrial Pkwy., Ringwood 07456
Pres.—Frank Patricola, 6 emp., *General machining job shop* .......... (973) 962-0800
H.P. Machine Shop, Inc., 415 Oxford St., Vineland 08360
Pres.—John Petyan, 9 emp., *Machining of plastics, stainless steel* .......... (856) 692-1192
Haledon Auto Parts, 269 Haledon Ave., Haledon 07508
Pres., Hum. Res. & IT Mgr.—Howard T. Wilson, 23 emp., *Automotive machine shop & distributor* (973) 595-8200
Hamelin Products, Inc., 1616 Highway 77, P.O. Box 153, Deerfield Street 08313
Pres.—Don S. Kolbe, 14 emp., *General machining job shop, including* .......... (856) 451-2935
Hansen Machine & Tool Co., Inc., 27 Walnut Ave., Clark 07066
Pres.—Robert Hansen, 3 emp., *Tooling & machining of parts for the* .......... (732) 340-0466
Harley Tool & Machine, Inc., 24 McDermott Pl., Bergenfield 07621
Owner & Pres.—Robert Harley, 4 emp., *CNC & general machining job shop* .......... (201) 244-8899
Harout Tool & Machine Corp., 9-11 Dyatt Pl., Hackensack 07601
Pres.—Harry Terjanian, 3 emp., *General machining job shop* .......... (201) 646-0664
Harrison Machine & Tool, Inc., 21 Lexington Ave., Trenton 08618
Pres.—Steve Harrison, 7 emp., *Precision machining job shop* .......... (609) 883-0800
Head Masters, Inc., 263 Route 46 W., Saddle Brook 07663
Pres.—Leon Touloughian, 8 emp., *General machining job shop* .......... (201) 843-6666
Heads Up Industries, 132 Van Liew Ave., Ste. 4, Milltown 08850
Owner—Wayne Celko, 1 emp., *General machining & welding job shop* .......... (732) 846-3388
Henry Machine Shop, Inc., 345 Market St., Kenilworth 07033
Pres.—Henry Lee, 6 emp., *Precision CNC machine shop* .......... (908) 925-2218
Hercules Welding & Machine Co., 616 5th St., Palmyra 08065
Pres.—Edward Beddall, 2 emp., *General machining job shop* .......... (856) 829-1820
High Precision Machine Shop, LLC, 1275 Bloomfield Ave., Ste. 63, Fairfield 07004
Pres.—Peter Mitas, 6 emp., *Precision machining job shop* .......... (973) 227-5110
Hobby Blade Specialty, Inc., 725 Jerusalem Rd., Scotch Plains 07076
Pres.—Mike Torres, 3 emp., *Hunting knife blade grinding & industrial* .......... (908) 317-9306
Hone-A-Matic Tool & Cutter Co., 187 Wescott Dr., Rahway 07065
Chrm.—Anthony R. La Mastra, 2 emp., *Tooling job shop* .......... (732) 382-6000
Howell Precision Tool Co., 415 Cranberry Rd., Farmingdale 07727
Owner & Pres.—David Hanrahan, 5 emp., *Close tolerance CNC milling, turning* .......... (732) 919-7300
Hummel Machine & Tool Co., 580 Davis Ave., Kearny 07032
Mfg. Mgr.—Edward Evans, 15 emp., *CNC machining job shop* .......... (201) 991-5200
Hun Machine Works, Inc., 51 Whittaker St., P.O. Box 189, Riverside 08075
Pres., V-P., Opers. & MIS Mgr.—Robert Kiss, 12 emp., *Forgings, castings & machining job* .. (856) 461-7112
Hunter Mfg. Services, Inc., 19 Just Rd., Fairfield 07004
Owner & Pres.—Kenneth C. Hunter, 12 emp., *CNC machining of pharmaceutical packaging* (973) 365-5880
Hutchton & Simon, Inc., 140 Atlantic St., Hackensack 07601
Pres.—Dan Cubicciotti, 25 emp., *Sheet metal fabrication, welding &* .......... (201) 487-1033
Hy-Tech Metal Works, Inc., 1252 South Ave., Plainfield 07062
Pres.—Julius Nagy, 2 emp., *General machining job shop* .......... (908) 757-6754
I C Machine, Inc., 199 U.S. Highway 46, Budd Lake 07828
Pres.—Ioan Comsulea, 2 emp., *Precision machining job shop* .......... (973) 252-7083
IK Construction, Inc., 1118 E. Baltimore Ave., Linden 07036
Pres.—Ian Katwaroo, 8 emp., *Steel, ornamental iron & structural* .......... (908) 925-5200
IMCO, Inc., 858 N. Lenola Rd., Bldg. 1, Moorestown 08057
Pres.—A. Ross Davis, 40 emp., *Sheet metal fabrication & precision* .......... (856) 499-2214
Imperial Machine & Tool Co., 8 W. Crisman Rd., Columbia 07832
Owner—Christian Joest, 35 emp., *Contract manufacturing & CNC machining* .......... (908) 496-8100
Imperial Metal Products, Inc., 8 W. Chimney Rock Rd., Bound Brook 08805
Pres.—John Karmazyn, 5 emp., *Stainless steel size reduction machinery* .......... (732) 469-8181
Indemax, Inc., 1 Industrial Dr., Vernon 07462
Chrm.—A. Infurna, 18 emp., *Glue machine parts* .......... (973) 209-2424
Independent Machine Co., 2 Stewart Pl., Fairfield 07004
Pres.—Jack Santa Lucia, 20 emp., *Industrial machinery* .......... (973) 882-0060
Industrial Hydraulics & Rubber, LLC, 458 Atlantic Ave., Camden 08104
GM—Michael Donahue, 7 emp., *Rebuilt hydraulic cylinders & machining* .......... (856) 966-2600
Industrial Machine & Engineering Co., 1807 W. Elizabeth Ave., Linden 07036
Owner—Valerie Peti, 10 emp., *General machining job shop* .......... (908) 862-8874
Industrial Machine Corp., 44 Lehigh Ave., Paterson 07503
Pres.—Sam Szewczyk, 14 emp., *Parts, tools & general machining job* .......... (973) 345-1800
Industrial Welding Co., 655 Ferry St., Newark 07105
Pres.—Brian Hollfelder, 6 emp., *Metal fabrication & welding job shop* .......... (973) 589-3100
Innovative Mfg., Inc., 198 U.S. Highway 206, Ste. 4, Hillsborough 08844
Owner—Kevin Lovell, 17 emp., *General machining job shop* .......... (908) 904-1884
International Tool & Machine, LLC, 446 Hillside Ave., Hillside 07205
Pres.—Chris Hoeker, 5 emp., *Precision machining job shop* .......... (908) 687-5580
International Tool & Mfg., Inc., 30 Sherwood Ln., Ste. 10, Fairfield 07004
Owner & Pres.—Susan Brock, 10 emp., *Precision machining job shop, including* .......... (973) 227-6767
Inventors Shop, The, 800 Industrial Hwy., Cinnaminson 08077
Off. Mgr.—Maryann Merritt, 30 emp., *General machining job shop* .......... (856) 303-8787
Iron Bound Metal, Inc., 238 Emmet St., Newark 07114
Pres.—John Olaya, 5 emp., *General machining & fabrication job* .......... (973) 242-5704
Ironbound Welding, Inc., 156 Walnut St., Newark 07105
Pres.—Louis Tamasco, 2 emp., *Welding job shop* .......... (973) 589-3128
I-Ron-X Industries, 134 Wheat Rd., Buena 08310
Pres., CFO—Paul Tomasello, 2 emp., *Wrought iron & aluminum railings, steel* .......... (856) 697-3518
J & D Tool, LLC, 5 Grant St., Linden 07036
Owner—James Didyoung, 2 emp., *General machining job shop* .......... (908) 486-5353
J & J Marine, 1596 Hurffville Rd., Sewell 08096
Pres.—Jim Clauss, 38 emp., *Tool & die & machining job shop* .......... (856) 228-4744
J & M Air, Inc., 189 S. Bridge St., Somerville 08876
Pres.—Michael Favreau, 12 emp., *Custom galvanized & stainless steel* .......... (908) 707-4040
J & M Mfg., Inc., 54 Main St., P.O. Box 43, High Bridge 08829
CEO—John Gargas, 10 emp., *Precision machining job shop* .......... (908) 638-6727
J & M Precision Enterprises, Inc., 8103 River Rd., Pennsauken 08110
Pres.—Marty Moskat, 2 emp., *Precision jig, OD & ID grinding & micro* .......... (856) 661-9595
J A Machine & Tool Co., Inc., 84 Herbert Ave., Closter 07624
Pres.—Andrew Petrinic, 12 emp., *Precision aircraft components & general* .......... (201) 767-1308
J M C Tool & Mfg. Co., 845 Fairfield Ave., Kenilworth 07033
Pres.—Charles Giamo, 8 emp., *Precision & CNC machining job shop* .......... (908) 241-8950
J M Machine Co., LLC, 5 Central Ave., Ste. 2, P.O. Box 1863, Clifton 07011
Owner—Jerry Mazur, 2 emp., *General machining job shop* .......... (973) 253-2188
J M T Design, Inc., 914 Route 33, Fairfield Industrial Pk., Freehold 07728
Pres.—Jerry Wojciehowski, 3 emp., *Precision machine parts, including* .......... (732) 409-6661
J N R Machine & Tool, 12 Ilene Ct., Bldg. 12, Unit 2, Hillsborough 08844
Pres.—John Radecsky, 2 emp., *Precision machining job shop* .......... (908) 281-6603
J S Tool, LLC, 187 Wescott Dr., Ste. D, Rahway 07065
Pres.—John Skurzynski, 2 emp., *Tool & die job shop, including fixtures* .......... (732) 815-1382
J. B. Welding, 2 Reynolds St., Pemberton 08068
Owner—Jerry Belsito, 1 emp., *Structural steel fabrication & welding* .......... (609) 894-9842
J.B.A.T., Inc., 28 Coles Ave., Cherry Hill 08002
Pres.—John Schallenhammer, 22 emp., *Precision machining job shop* .......... (856) 667-7307
J.D. Machine Parts, Inc., 158 W. Weymouth Rd., Vineland 08360
Pres.—Joseph Di Mento, 18 emp., *Custom CNC machine parts & fabrication* .......... (856) 691-8430
Jarco Industries, Inc., 1803 Union Valley Rd., West Milford 07480
Pres.—Steve Jarvis, 5 emp., *Precision machining job shop* .......... (973) 728-5012
JCW Rolling & Fabrication, 60 Liberty St., Metuchen 08840
★ Owner—Kenneth Greiff, 20 emp., *CNC & machining job shop & metal pipe* .......... (732) 548-7636
Jersey Metalworks, LLC, 1022 Hamilton St., Ste. A, Somerset 08873
Pres.—Ray Ferrari, 4 emp., *Custom machinery* .......... (732) 565-1313
Jet Industrial Electronics Corp., 104 Ridge Rd., Oak Ridge 07438
Pres.—John Boyce, 25 emp., *Roller grinding machinery & CNC machining* .......... (973) 697-2300
Jet Pulverizer Co., Inc., 1255 N. Church St., Moorestown 08057
Pres.—Ed Fay, 30 emp., *Jet pulverizers, including jet energy* .......... (856) 235-5554
Jewel Precision Sheet Metal Machining, Inc., 200 Commerce Rd., Cedar Grove 07009
Pres.—Ignazio Graziano, 75 emp., *Sheet metal & plastic fabrication,* .......... (973) 857-5545
Jo Bella Machine Mfg., 232 Washington Ave., Carteret 07008
Owner—Izabella Skrzypko, 4 emp., *General machining job shop* .......... (732) 541-7076
JOCO Precision, Inc., 333 Dalziel Rd., Linden 07036
Co-Pres.—Peter Korcusko, 6 emp., *Precision grinding* .......... (908) 862-1611
Joyrei Enterprises, Inc., 3143 Bordentown Ave., Parlin 08859
GM—Jeff Reising, 6 emp., *General machining job shop* .......... (732) 727-0742
JSM Co., 1052 Wayside Rd., Tinton Falls 07712
Owner—David Paraskevas, 5 emp., *Precision automatic cut-off sawing,* .......... (732) 695-9577
Julius Machine & Tool Co., B-14 Merry Ln., East Hanover 07936
Owner & Pres.—Julius Gaida, 1 emp., *Precision CNC machining, turning &* .......... (973) 515-8540
K & R Precision Machining, 54 S. Front St., Bergenfield 07621
Pres.—Rick Penser, 5 emp., *Precision machining job shop* .......... (201) 385-8855
K D Industries, Inc., 18 Falstrom Ct., Passaic 07055
Pres.—Chris D'Alessandro, 34 emp., *General machining job shop* .......... (973) 594-4800
K G M Precision Corp., 1875 Route 206, Southampton 08088
Pres.—Kenneth Mikle, 8 emp., *Precision machining job shop* .......... (609) 801-0210
K H Machine Works, 4322 Grand Ave., North Bergen 07047
Pres.—Shereelynn Koehler, 5 emp., *General machining job shop* .......... (201) 867-2338
K T S Machine Shop, 60 Bushes Ln., Elmwood Park 07407
Owner—Stanley Darszcz, 2 emp., *CNC & precision machining job shop* .......... (201) 791-2228
Kaupp & Sons, Inc., C. B., 6 Newark Way, Maplewood 07040
CEO—Clem Kaupp, Jr., 25 emp., *Corporate headquarters & precision* .......... (973) 761-4000
Kearny Sheet Metal Works, Inc., 579 Davis Ave., Kearny 07032
Pres.—Mike Smolensky, 6 emp., *24-gage to 1/4-inch sheet metal & aluminum* .......... (201) 991-4745
Keller Welding Co., LLC, 22 Wantage Ave., Branchville 07826
Owner & Pres.—Jeremy Hughen, 4 emp., *Fabrication & welding of steel, aluminum* .......... (973) 948-0046
Kelles, Inc., 20 Hoiles Dr., Kenilworth 07033
Pres., CEO—Michael J. Patrick, 14 emp., *General machining job shop* .......... (908) 241-9300
Kenvil Weldery & Machine, Inc., 15 Kings Pkwy., Ledgewood 07852
Pres.—Gary Magura, 3 emp., *Metal fabrication & machining & welding* .......... (973) 584-1729
Kern & Szalai Machine, LLC, 351 Crider Ave., Moorestown 08057
Pres.—Erwin Vermes, 45 emp., *CNC machining job shop, including production* .......... (856) 802-1500
KeyValet, 15 Industrial Dr., P.O. Box 1099, Laurence Harbor 08879
Owner—Nancy Teufel, 4 emp., *Standard & specialty security locks* .......... (732) 521-1394
Kinnery Metal, 11 Exchange Pl., Passaic 07055
Owner—Naresh Chaudhari, 3 emp., *CNC machining job shop* .......... (973) 473-4664
KPMC, Inc., 113 Walters Ave., Trenton 08638
Pres.—Don Hoven, 15 emp., *General machining job shop* .......... (609) 538-1100
Kramer Industries, Inc., 140 Ethel Rd. W., Ste. U, Piscataway 08854
Sales Mgr.—Steve Schneider, 10 emp., *Industrial machinery* .......... (732) 650-9599
KWG Industries, LLC, 330 Roycefield Rd., Unit B, Hillsborough 08844
Pres., CEO—Kurt W. Grimm, 15 emp., *Manufacturer of precision machined* .......... (908) 218-8900
L & M Machine & Tool Co., Inc., 105 Lehigh Ave., Paterson 07503
Pres.—Manny Morone, 10 emp., *General machining job shop* .......... (973) 523-5288
L M C Precision, Inc., 91 Rome St., Ste. 93, Newark 07105
Pres.—Manuel Lobo, 12 emp., *CNC machining job shop* .......... (973) 522-0005
L.C. Machine Shop, Inc., 249 S. White Horse Pike, Berlin 08009
Pres.—George Kelling, 10 emp., *General machining job shop* .......... (856) 767-1111
Labern Machine Products, 3388 Highway 22 W., Branchburg 08876
Pres.—Larry Remaly, 17 emp., *CNC machining* .......... (908) 722-1970
Lattimer USA, 3603 N. Mill Rd., Vineland 08360
Pres., GM—Steve Abernathy, 36 emp., *Precision CNC milling & turning, assembly* .......... (856) 691-2203
Lee Linear, 727 South Ave., Piscataway 08854
Pres.—Glen Michalske, 45 emp., *Linear motion products, including linear* .......... (732) 752-5200
Legend Machine & Grinding, LLC, 36 S. Adamsville Rd., Somerville 08876
GM—Eric Butler, 15 emp., *General machining & grinding job shop* .......... (908) 685-1100
Lehigh Precision Co., Inc., P.O. Box 214, Elizabeth 07207
Owner & Pres.—Mark Biederman, 5 emp., *General machining of aircraft components* .......... (908) 351-6600
Lentron Corp., 24 Ironia Rd., Flanders 07836
Off. Mgr.—Anna Klett, 20 emp., *General machining & assembly job shop* .......... (973) 252-9668
Liberty Machine Tool & Die, Inc., 903 E. Elizabeth Ave., Linden 07036
Co-Pres.—Michael Elzahr, 2 emp., *Tool & die & general machining job* .......... (908) 925-0300
Liberty Mechanical Contractors, Inc., 330 Raymond Blvd., Newark 07105
Pres., CFO—Frank P. Zurica, 25 emp., *Welding job shop & industrial mechanical* .......... (973) 344-6131
Livingston & W, Inc., 973-B New Durham Rd., Edison 08817
Pres.—Scott James, 4 emp., *CNC & general machining job shop* .......... (732) 287-5790
LMK Waterjet, 835 Fairfield Ave., Kenilworth 07033
Pres.—Herbert J. Olbrich, 2 emp., *Contract & custom waterjet cutting* .......... (908) 241-8113

S.I.C.

**★ Indicates new listing this edition.**

LRB Performance Machine Co., 22-B Lasinski Rd., Franklin 07416
Owner—Lou Bengivenni, 3 emp., *High performance & racing engines,* ........ (973) 209-7770
Lucas & Son, H. N., 211 Carriage Ln., Delran 08075
Pres.—Steve Lloyd, 12 emp., *General machining job shop* ........ (856) 764-2400
LUSO Machine, Inc., 29 Avenue C, Newark 07114
Pres.—Adriano Remelgado, 8 emp., *Machine parts* ........ (973) 242-1717
M & D Precision Centerless Grinding, Inc., 120 Kossuth St., Riverside 08075
Pres.—David R. Speegle, 6 emp., *Precision centerless grinding job shop* ........ (856) 764-1616
M & F Machine Works, 243-245 Custer Ave., Jersey City 07305
Owner—Alexander Salazar, 3 emp., *General machining job shop* ........ (201) 433-4085
M & M Grinding, LLC, 132 Lewis St., Eatontown 07724
Owner & Pres.—John M. Dietz III, 3 emp., *Cylindrical grinding job shop* ........ (732) 542-1157
M & M Welding & Steel Fabricating, 344 Essex St., P.O. Box 168, Stirling 07980
Pres.—Al Masek, 2 emp., *Architectural metalwork & general machining* ........ (908) 647-6060
M & S Machine & Tool Corp., 108 Maryland Ave., Paterson 07503
Pres.—Nazim Sulejmanovski, 20 emp., *General machining job shop* ........ (973) 345-5847
M J H Gear & Tool Co., Inc., 15 Maple St., Norwood 07648
Pres.—John M. Halkias, 3 emp., *Precision gears* ........ (212) 246-3800
MAC Products, Inc., 60 Pennsylvania Ave., P.O. Box 469, Kearny 07032
Pres.—Edward Russnow, 135 emp., *Electrical control panels, connectors* ........ (973) 344-0700
Machine Corp., E. B., 320 Richard Mine Rd., Wharton 07885
Pres.—Emil Boller, 3 emp., *Mold, grinding, tool, die & CNC machining* ........ (973) 442-7729
Machine Parts, Inc., 17 Ferdon St., Newark 07105
Pres.—Ricardo Cruz, 7 emp., *CNC machining job shop* ........ (973) 491-5444
Machine Plus, Inc., 97 4th Ave., Haskell 07420
Pres.—Ford Robbins, 7 emp., *Precision machine parts* ........ (973) 839-8884
Machine Shop At Engine Specialties, The, 203 Carriage Ln., Delran 08075
GM—Scott Woodington, 7 emp., *Automotive machining job shop* ........ (856) 764-8701
Machine Tech, 3125 Woodbridge Ave., Ste. 4, Edison 08837
Owner—Gordon Scala, 4 emp., *Precision & CNC machining job shop* ........ (732) 738-6810
Mag Signs, Inc., 1208-F Columbus Rd., Burlington 08016
★ Owner—Bob Persichetti, 12 emp., *Interior & exterior signs & welding* ........ (609) 747-9600
MAN Diesel & Turbo, 2 Amboy Ave., Bldg. 2, Woodbridge 07095
GM—Angel Colon Perez, 22 emp., *Divisional headquarters & rebuilt rotating* ...... (732) 582-8200
Manutech, Inc., 29 State St., P.O.Box 758, Elmer 08318
Pres.—Edward P. Deinarowicz, 4 emp., *Metal stampings & general machining* ........ (856) 358-6136
Maple Machine Co., Inc., Mount Holly Industrial Commons, Unit 9, Mount Holly 08060
Pres.—Ernie Mellon, 6 emp., *Screw machine products & precision* ........ (609) 702-0975
Mark I Industries, Inc., 910 Shunpike Rd., Cape May 08204
Owner—Robert Bartle, 15 emp., *General machining job shop* ........ (609) 884-0051
Marlton Pike Precision, LLC, 728 Beechwood Ave., Cherry Hill 08002
Pres.—Antonio Sala, 18 emp., *Precision machined parts, fixtures,* ........ (856) 665-1900
Marshall Industrial Technologies, 529 S. Clinton Ave., Trenton 08611
Pres.—John Mako, 150 emp., *Welding, metal fabrication & machining* ........ (609) 394-7153
Martin Sprocket & Gear, Inc., 7 Highpoint Dr., Wayne 07470
Dist. Mgr.—Rick Bongiorno, 6 emp., *General machining job shop* ........ (973) 633-5700
Master Tool Corp., 342 Squankum Yellowbrook Rd., P.O. Box 7, Farmingdale 07727
Pres.—Tom Di Donato, 4 emp., *General machining job shop* ........ (732) 919-1010
Mastercool, Inc., 1 Aspen Dr., Randolph 07869
Graphic Artist—Stephanie Bartell, 40 emp., *Automotive air conditioning service* ........ (973) 252-9119
Maxflight Corp., 1 Executive Dr., Toms River 08755
CEO—Frank McClintic, 20 emp., *Amusement rides & simulators* ........ (732) 281-2007
Maza & Maza Welding, 28 Mulock Pl., Harrison 07029
Owner—Luis Maza, 2 emp., *Welding job shop* ........ (973) 481-4441
MDI Mfg., Inc., 100 Syracuse Ct., Lakewood 08701
Pres.—Mark Daugherty, 24 emp., *Precision machining job shop* ........ (732) 994-5599
Mechanical Components Corp., 145 Yellowbrook Rd., Farmingdale 07727
Owner & Pres.—Doel Burgos, 4 emp., *General machining job shop* ........ (732) 938-3737
Mechanical Precision, Inc., 11 Hopewell Ave., Flemington 08822
Pres.—Wallace Cullen, Jr., 54 emp., *Precision machining, including CNC* ........ (908) 782-2511
Mechanitron Corp., 310 W. 1st Ave., Roselle 07203
Pres.—Dave Newman, 3 emp., *Thread grinding & general machining* ........ (908) 620-1001
Megawatt Machine Services, LLC, 417 Elizabeth Ave., Somerset 08873
Owner—Pauline Balogh, 30 emp., *Machining of severe service control* ........ (732) 805-4000
Mercer Machine & Tool Products, 332 Darcy Ave., Trenton 08629
Pres.—Tom Erni, 5 emp., *General machining & tool & die job* ........ (609) 587-1106
Metal Components, 92 Maryland Ave., Paterson 07503
Pres.—Frank Mottola, 35 emp., *Precision machining job shop* ........ (973) 247-1204
Metal Dynamix, LLC, 709 Fellowship Rd., Mount Laurel 08054
Pres.—Charles Gaw, 9 emp., *Sheet metal fabrication & CNC machining* ........ (856) 235-4559
Metallo Gasket Co., Inc., 16 Bethany St., New Brunswick 08901
Pres., CEO—Frederick Haleluk, 10 emp., *Gaskets, shims, washers, raschig rings* ........ (732) 545-7223
Metem Corp., 700 Parsippany Rd., Parsippany 07054
Chrm.—Duval Goldthwaite, 180 emp., *Corporate headquarters & general machining* ........ (973) 887-6635
Mid-Lantic Precision, Inc., 940 Market St., Gloucester City 08030
Pres.—Lauri Wilke, 15 emp., *General, precision & CNC machining* ........ (856) 456-3810
Midway Machine Product Corp., 763-A Railroad Ave., P.O. Box 129, Florence 08518
Pres.—William Greene, 10 emp., *General machining job shop* ........ (609) 499-4377
Millson Precision Machining, 145 11th St., Piscataway 08854
Pres.—Bryan Miller, 3 emp., *Precision machining job shop* ........ (732) 424-1700
Mini Precision Devices, Inc., 615 Pennsylvania Ave., Elizabeth 07201
Pres.—Tony Neto, 11 emp., *General machining job shop* ........ (908) 351-7423
Mira Plastics Co., Inc., 1 Mira Ave., Fredon Twp., P. O. Box 399, Newton 07860
Pres.—Anthony Miragliotta, 25 emp., *Thermoplastic injection molding, hot* ........ (973) 383-6380
Mnemonics, Inc., P.O. Box 877, Mount Laurel 08054
Pres.—Michael Negin, 4 emp., *Computer-automated proofreading, machine* ........ (856) 234-0970
Modern Metric Machine, 101 Nicholson Rd., Audubon 08106
Owner & Pres.—Paul Volkwine, 6 emp., *General machining job shop* ........ (856) 547-4044
Mola Iron Works, 61 Patterson Ave., Hoboken 07030
Owner—Tony Mola, 3 emp., *Welding job shop* ........ (201) 963-3485
Monarch Mfg. Works, Inc., 7249-B Browning Rd., Merchantville 08109
Pres., CEO—Harry D. Beccari, 25 emp., *Precision spray nozzles for the industrial* ........ (856) 241-1500
Monarch Moor Whips, 1104 Tiller Ave., Beachwood 08722
Pres. & Fin. Mgr.—Donald Brushaber, 3 emp., *Marine machining job shop* ........ (732) 244-4584
Monick Mfg. Corp., 2619 Route 206, Mount Holly 08060
Pres.—Monte Hauser, 5 emp., *Machine parts & welding job shop* ........ (609) 267-0777
Morris Tool & Machine Co., 80 Upper Hibernia Rd., Rockaway 07866
Owner & Pres.—Harry Pinand, 3 emp., *Full-service precision CNC milling* ........ (973) 983-9209
MP Tube Works, Inc., 237 Sheffield St., Mountainside 07092
Pres.—Michael J. McGinley, 8 emp., *Tube fabrication & general machining* ........ (908) 317-2500
MSD Precision, 300 Thomas Ave., Bldg. 6, Williamstown 08094
Owner—Mark Dejong, 3 emp., *Precision machining job shop* ........ (856) 262-8142

N & J Machine Products Corp., 52 Bruen St., Newark 07105
Pres.—Nino Pereira, 5 emp., *General machining job shop* ........ (973) 589-0031
N. B. & Sons, LLC, 402 E. Wheat Rd., Vineland 08360
Pres.—Maria Berezin, 6 emp., *Precision machined parts, including* ........ (856) 692-6191
National Precision Tool Co., Inc., 24 Sherwood Ln., Fairfield 07004
Pres., Fin., MIS & R & D Mgr.—Leon Roitburg, 20 emp., *Precision machining job shop* ........ (973) 227-5005
NEAC, Inc., 526 Pacific Ave., #2202, Atlantic City 08401
Pres.—Joel H. Miller, 5 emp., *Contract manufacturing of metal & plastic* ........ (908) 903-9100
Nelson, Inc., Louis A., 224 Glenwood Ave., Bloomfield 07003
Pres., MIS Mgr.—David Sibilia, 12 emp., *Thermoforming, metal tooling, prototypes* ........ (973) 743-7404
Neumann Sheet Metal, Inc., 759 North Ave., Plainfield 07062
Manager—George Kelly, 4 emp., *Sheet metal fabrication & high definition* ........ (908) 756-0415
Neuweiler, Inc., Karl H., 23 Russo Pl., Berkeley Heights 07922
Pres.—Dan Neuweiler, Sr., 10 emp., *Machine parts* ........ (908) 464-6532
New Jersey Machine & Tool Co., 257 Houses Corner Rd., Lafayette 07848
Pres.—Tom Hegyi, 1 emp., *General machining job shop* ........ (973) 383-6102
New Jersey Precision Technologies, Inc., 1081 Bristol Rd., Mountainside 07092
Pres., Sales Mgr.—Bob Tarantino, 45 emp., *Wire & ram EDM & small hole drilling* ........
New Jersey Rivet Co., LLC, 1785 Haddon Ave., Camden 08103
Sales Mgr., Inside—Kenneth Landgarten, 10 emp., *Semi-tubular rivets* ........ (856) 963-2237
Newark Welding Co., 47 Morris Ave., Newark 07103
Owner—Richard Dellatorre, 1 emp., *Welding job shop* ........ (973) 642-6479
Nodeco Machine Service, 5 Wayside Ln., Lebanon 08833
Owner—Richard Nodes, 1 emp., *CNC machining job shop* ........ (908) 236-7996
Nova Precision Products, Inc., 160 Franklin Ave., Rockaway 07866
Pres.—Robert Suhoski, 20 emp., *Precision CNC machining* ........ (973) 625-1586
Nowak, Inc., 17 Robert St., Ste. B-5, Wharton 07885
Pres., CEO—Mark Nowak, 15 emp., *Precision machining job shop, including* ........ (973) 366-7208
O M P Technologies, Inc., 24-H Commerce Rd., Fairfield 07004
V-P.—Kanhan Hsiao, 15 emp., *CNC machining job shop* ........ (973) 808-5543
O.K. Tool Corp., 1233 North Ave., Plainfield 07062
Pres.—Eric Kiesel, 6 emp., *General machining job shop* ........ (908) 561-9920
Oceanic Metals LLC, 8555 Tonnelle Ave., Ste. 404, North Bergen 07047
Owner—Demetris Orfanos, 1 emp., *Steel, aluminum & cast iron cutting* ........ (201) 662-1192
Oliver, Inc., G. J., 50 Industrial Rd., Phillipsburg 08865
CEO—John Oliver, 75 emp., *Steel fabrication & machining of pressure* ........ (908) 454-9743
Olsen Machine, LLC, 2504 Route 73, Cinnaminson 08077
Pres.—David Olsen, 3 emp., *Machine parts* ........ (856) 662-2121
Olympic EDM & Waterjet, Inc., 20 Kiel Ave., Butler 07405
Owner & Pres.—Don Ferrante, 8 emp., *Wire EDM, waterjet & tool & die shop* ........ (973) 492-0664
Orgo-Thermit, Inc., 3500 Colonial Dr. N., Manchester 08759
Pres.—Dave Randolph, 30 emp., *Aluminothermic welding products, kits* ........ (732) 657-5781
P & J Machine Co., 261 Crosskeys Rd., P.O. Box 178, Berlin 08009
Owner—John Pepe, 3 emp., *CNC & conventional machining & tooling* ........ (856) 767-8441
P C R Technologies, Inc., 26 Chapin Rd., Unit 1111, Pine Brook 07058
Pres.—Mark Vanzini, 9 emp., *High-speed CNC machining of metals* ........ (973) 882-0017
Pabst Enterprises Equipment Co., Inc., 676 Pennsylvania Ave., Elizabeth 07201
Pres.—David Bechtold, 20 emp., *Sheet metal fabrication & CNC & general* ........ (908) 353-2880
Pahco Machine, Inc., 572 Whitehead Rd., Ste. 101, Trenton 08619
GM—Pete Horvath, 3 emp., *Tool & die & general machining job* ........ (609) 587-1188
Paragon Steel & Tool Co., Inc., 339 Bergen Ave., Kearny 07032
Pres.—William Fisher, 3 emp., *Tool sharpening* ........ (201) 997-1676
Parkway-Kew Corp., 2095 Excelsior Ave., North Brunswick 08902
Pres., Plt. Mgr.—Eugene E. Klein, Sr., 15 emp., *HVOF, plasma & thermal spray coatings* ........ (732) 398-2100
Parlin Precision Products, Inc., 999 Route 9, Parlin 08859
Pres.—Lee White, 3 emp., *Precision machining job shop* ........ (732) 727-6111
Parsell's Welding, Inc., 354 Route 580, Blawenburg 08504
Owner—Art Parsell, 1 emp., *Welding job shop* ........ (609) 466-1930
Passaic County Welders, Inc., 100 Parish Dr., Wayne 07470
V-P.—Robert Grimbilas, 38 emp., *Welding & structural steel, steel,* ........ (973) 696-1200
Peterson Bros. Mfg., 10 Baekeland Ave., Middlesex 08846
Pres., Mktg. Mgr.—Gary B. Lewis, 25 emp., *Metal stampings & machine products* ........ (732) 271-8240
Phelps Mfg., LLC, 567 Brass Castle Rd., Oxford 07863
Pres.—Fred Phelps, 4 emp., *Precision machining job shop* ........ (908) 453-2288
Phoenix Precision, Inc., 2963 Route 23, Newfoundland 07435
Pres.—Edward F. Wolos III, 12 emp., *Precision machining job shop* ........ (973) 208-8877
Phoenix Tool & Machine, Inc., 1044 Industrial Dr., Unit 5, West Berlin 08091
Pres.—John Dusak, 6 emp., *General machining job shop* ........ (856) 753-5565
Picut Manufacturing Company, Inc., 140 Mount Bethel Rd., Warren 07059
Pres.—Frederick Picut, 98 emp., *Corporate headquarters & general machining* ........ (908) 754-1333
Pine Hill Machine Shop & Welding, 44 W. 3rd Ave., Pine Hill 08021
Ptnr.—Lisa Schaefer, 2 emp., *General machining & welding job shop* ........ (856) 783-9842
PK Precision Machining, Inc., 7 Mathews Ave., Riverdale 07457
Ptnr.—Kenneth Androvich, Jr., 3 emp., *Precision machining job shop, including* ........ (973) 925-2020
Plainfield Welders, 1130 North Ave., Plainfield 07062
Pres.—Gerry Ventriglia, 2 emp., *Welding job shop* ........ (908) 755-6263
Polo Machine, Inc., 223 Banta Ave., P.O. Box 403, Garfield 07026
Pres.—John Pszeniczny, 5 emp., *General machining job shop* ........ (973) 340-9984
Povinelli & Sons, Inc., M., 318 9th St., Fairview 07022
Pres.—Matthew Povinelli, 6 emp., *Sharpening of professional cutlery* ........ (201) 943-0039
Precise Components & Tool Design, Inc., 10 Clifton Blvd., Unit A-4, Clifton 07011
Pres.—Harry Benedikt, 7 emp., *Industrial prototypes & precision machining* ........ (973) 928-2928
Precise Machine & Tool, Inc., 369 Knickerbocker Ave., Paterson 07503
Owner, Pres., Fin., Opers. & R & D Mgr.—Fatih Civi, 3 emp., *CNC machining & prototype* ........ (201) 790-3320
Precision Automation Company, Inc., 1841 Old Cuthbert Rd., Cherry Hill 08034
Pres., CEO—G. Frederick Rexon, Jr., 50 emp., *Automation, conveyor, control & complete* ........ (856) 428-7400
Precision Forms, Inc., 97 Decker Rd., Butler 07405
Pres., Hum. Res. & IT Mgr.—William Sulski, 36 emp., *Long & short run production machining* (973) 838-3800
Precision Machined Products, LLC, 24 Kulick Rd., Fairfield 07004
Owner, Pres. & CFO—Kevin Blide, 4 emp., *General machining, TIG welding, CNC* ........ (973) 227-9538
Precision Metal Machining, Inc., 800 Central Blvd., Ste. C, Carlstadt 07072
Pres.—Pat Fanicelli, 40 emp., *General machining job shop, including* ........ (201) 843-7427
Precision Numerical Technology, Inc., 31 Ardsley Pl., Morganville 07751
Pres.—Carol Barfield, 3 emp., *Precision machining job shop* ........ (732) 591-4884
Precision Parts Unlimited, Inc., 24 Patriot Crossing, Rockaway 07866
Owner & Pres.—Rose Rainone, 1 emp., *Sheet metal fabrication & precision* ........ (973) 659-3300
Precision Rollers, Inc., 155 Cooper Rd., West Berlin 08091
Pres.—Louis Marquez, 2 emp., *General machining job shop* ........ (856) 768-7696
Precision Specialists Machine, LLC, 1004 Industrial Dr., Ste. 5, West Berlin 08091
Pres., CEO—Richard Bottoni, 12 emp., *CNC machining, assembly & finishing* ........ (856) 768-5990
Precision Tool & Engineering, Inc., 123 Florence Ave., Trenton 08618
Pres.—Tom Harter, 1 emp., *Precision machining job shop* ........ (609) 882-9223

Precision Welding, 845 Berkshire Valley Rd., Wharton 07885
Owner—Jim Stanlick, 7 emp., *Metal fabrication & welding job shop* ........ (973) 366-7316
Predator Tools (H Q), 35 S. Woodruff Rd., Bridgeton 08302
Owner—Pam Lesche, 2 emp., *Company headquarters; digging tools* ........ (856) 455-3790
Premac, Inc., P.O. Box 9, Rahway 07065
Pres.—Eric Schenker, 15 emp., *Jet pump control valves & general machining* ........ (732) 381-7550
Pro Machine Co., 5 Sicomac Rd., Haledon 07508
★ Owner—Eddie Demetro, 18 emp., *Rebuilt gear boxes, pumps & shear blades* .... (973) 855-9935
Progress Machine Shop, Inc., 41 Kentucky Ave., Paterson 07503
Owner—Tony Markovski, 7 emp., *General machining job shop* ........ (973) 278-4999
Progressive Machine Co., 293 Hudson St., Hackensack 07601
Pres.—Peter Wysocki, 6 emp., *Machining job shop* ........ (201) 342-3636
Progressive-Ruesch Machine Co., LLC, 21 Van Natta Dr., Ringwood 07456
CEO—Stephen Honczarenko, 17 emp., *Industrial machinery for the metal,* ........ (973) 962-7700
Projects, Inc., 310 Orange St., Millville 08332
Pres.—Anees Hanna, 6 emp., *Rebuilt injection molding machines* ........ (856) 825-7312
Pulcin Machine, 13 Cedar Ln., Bordentown 08505
Owner—Paul Mara, 1 emp., *General machining job shop* ........ (609) 387-3060
Purves Marine Works, 197 Main St., West Creek 08092
Co-Pres.—Chester Purves, 2 emp., *General machining job shop* ........ (609) 296-1263
Qualiturn Corp., 205 Columbus Ave., Roselle 07203
Pres.—Heinz Teska, 3 emp., *Precision machine parts* ........ (908) 241-4909
Quality Industries, Inc., 204 Getty Ave., Clifton 07011
Pres.—Andrew Ponikowski, 10 emp., *Fabrication & machining shop, including* ........ (973) 478-4425
Quality Sheet Metal & Welding, 23 Clawson St., Piscataway 08854
Sys. Opers. Mgr.—David Doll, 13 emp., *Sheet metal fabrication & welding job* ........ (732) 752-6300
Quincas Corp., 112 East Ave., Unit 7-A, Hackettstown 07840
Pres.—Bill DeMarco, 3 emp., *CNC & general machining job shop, including* ........ (908) 850-3914
R G I, Inc., 27 Union Valley Rd., Newfoundland 07435
Pres.—Barry Maloney, 16 emp., *CNC machining of valves, pumps & manifolds* ........ (973) 697-2624
R Welding, 97 Main St., Waretown 08758
Owner—Risden Russell, 2 emp., *Commercial & industrial desiccate dehumidifie* ........ (609) 971-6017
Rabell Precision, Inc., 8 Queen Anne Rd., Bogota 07603
Pres., GM—John Rabell, 2 emp., *Precision machining job shop* ........ (201) 473-7373
Radco Enterprises, Inc., 734 Oxford St., Vineland 08360
Pres.—Ralph Laragione, 1 emp., *General machining job shop* ........ (856) 691-3125
Rako Machine Products, Inc., 845 Monmouth Rd., Cream Ridge 08514
Owner—John Vanderduys, 6 emp., *Prototypes & CNC machining job shop* ........ (609) 758-1200
Raue Screw Machine Product Co., 173 Oak Ridge Rd., P.O. Box 207, Oak Ridge 07438
Pres.—Carl Raue, 3 emp., *Precision machining job shop* ........ (973) 697-7500
Rawco, Inc., 452 Route 513, Califon 07830
Pres.—Jeff Riley, 7 emp., *CNC turning, milling & machining job* ........ (908) 832-7700
Raz Performance Machine, 247 Harding Hwy., Vineland 08360
Ptnr.—Raymond Zieger, 2 emp., *Rebuilt automotive motors & machining* ........ (856) 697-4275
Rehtek Machine Co., 135 Monroe St., Passaic 07055
Pres., MIS Mgr.—Stephen K. Reh, 10 emp., *Precision machining of electronics* ........ (973) 365-2101
Remington Industries, Inc., Cordes Machine Div., 269 Sheffield St., Mountainside 07092
Plt. Mgr.—Doug West, 120 emp., *Stair building equipment for wood stair* ........ (908) 233-2600
Renewable BioSystems, LLC, 20 Spielman Rd., Fairfield 07004
CEO—Peter Behrle, 15 emp., *Organic oil extraction machinery for* ........ (973) 769-0600
Reuther Engineering & Machining Co., Inc., 126 S. 14th St., Newark 07107
Owner—Ken Rys, 24 emp., *General machining job shop* ........ (973) 485-5800
Ricci Tool & Die Co., 122 Myrtle Ave., Long Branch 07740
Pres.—John Ricci, Sr., 9 emp., *Tool & die job shop, including metal* ........ (732) 222-2777
Ridge Precision Products Inc., 288 U.S. Highway 46, Ste. D, Dover 07801
Pres., Sales & Mktg. Mgr.—Mark Leone, 10 emp., *Precision machining job shop* ........ (973) 361-3508
RJD Machine Products, Inc., 1424 Heath Ave., Ewing 08638
Pres.—Richard Roslowski, 11 emp., *Precision machining job shop* ........ (609) 392-1515
Robro Mfg., Inc., 288 10th Ave., Paterson 07524
Pres.—Ivan Migalko, 12 emp., *General machining job shop, including* ........ (973) 279-7237
Romar Machine & Tool Co., 521 Commerce St., Franklin Lakes 07417
Pres.—Bob Thum, 12 emp., *Packaging machinery tube holders, fill* ........ (201) 337-7111
Ronald-Mark Assocs., Inc., 150 N. Summit Ave., P.O. Box 355, Pitman 08071
GM—Lawrence Wolfe, 26 emp., *Precision plastic size reduction &* ........ (856) 582-6766
Rosco, Inc., 55 South Ave., P.O. Box 184, Garwood 07027
Pres.—John Burton, 6 emp., *Precision & CNC machining job shop* ........ (908) 789-1020
Ruggieri Precision Machine, LLC, 1404 Route 179, Lambertville 08530
Owner—John Ruggieri, 5 emp., *General machining job shop* ........ (609) 397-4378
Ruoff & Sons, Inc., 1030 Rose Ave., P.O. Box 320, Runnemede 08078
Pres.—Steve Ruoff, 25 emp., *Metal machine parts* ........ (856) 931-2064
R-Way Tooling & Metal Works, 224 S. Lincoln Ave., Vineland 08361
Cont.—Scott Sikora, 8 emp., *Steel fabrication & general machining* ........ (856) 692-2218
Ryan Industrial Service, Inc., 80 Freneau Ave., Matawan 07747
Pres.—Chris Ryan, 3 emp., *General machining job shop* ........ (732) 566-9538
S & S Precision, 2205 Sherman Ave., Pennsauken 08110
Ptnr.—Walter Smith, 12 emp., *Precision grinding, boring & general* ........ (856) 662-0006
S S Tool & Mfg. Co., Inc., 1 Garfield St., Linden 07036
Pres.—Steven Kanyo, 6 emp., *Precision machining job shop* ........ (908) 486-5497
Safety-Kleen Systems, Inc., 1200 Sylvan St., Linden 07036
Facility Mgr.—Andrea Martone, 50 emp., *Industrial recycling* ........ (908) 862-2000
Sandik Mfg., Inc., 100 8th St., Bldg. 33-A, Passaic 07055
Pres.—Girish Shah, 5 emp., *General machining job shop* ........ (973) 779-0707
Sarlo Tool & Machine Co., 62 Suburban Blvd., Delran 08075
Pres.—Chris Sarlo, 14 emp., *General machining job shop* ........ (856) 461-3206
Saturn Tool & Die, Inc., 1064 Commerce Ave., Union 07083
Pres.—Robert Wilson, 3 emp., *CNC machining & tool & die job shop* ........ (908) 964-0504
Schall Mfg., Inc., 3501 Rose Ave., Ocean 07712
Pres.—Martin Schall, 5 emp., *General machining job shop* ........ (732) 918-8800
Schrader & Co., Inc., 188 Halsey Rd., Newton 07860
Pres.—David Lake, 10 emp., *Precision sheet metal & machined components* ........ (973) 579-2700
Seajay Mfg. Co., 9 Memorial Dr., Ste. 1, Neptune 07753
Pres.—Jeffrey Finn, 8 emp., *Plastic bottle molds & industrial molds* ........ (732) 774-0900
Sedtek, Inc., 113 Meadow St., Hackensack 07601
Pres., R & D Mgr.—Gerald Danker, 15 emp., *Metal bar soap molds, rubber products* ........ (201) 489-4040
Seibert Machine & Tool, Inc., 4405 S. Clinton Ave., South Plainfield 07080
Pres.—George G. Seibert, 3 emp., *General machining & tool & die job* ........ (908) 754-0774
Select Machine Tool, Inc., 19 Thompson Ave., Mount Ephraim 08059
Pres.—Jay Brad, 7 emp., *Precision machining job shop* ........ (856) 933-2100
Service Machine Co., 311 Lincoln Blvd., Middlesex 08846
Pres.—Peter Delia, 4 emp., *General machining job shop* ........ (732) 356-9021
Servometer-PMG, LLC, 501 Little Falls Rd., Cedar Grove 07009
Chrm.—Tony Penchuk, 72 emp., *Company headquarters & custom miniature* ........ (973) 785-4630

Severna Operations, Inc., 3 Eastmans Rd., Parsippany 07054
Pres.—Samir Aboulhosn, 20 emp., *Custom precision machined parts & fluoropolym* ........ (973) 503-1600
Shore Precision Mfg., Inc., 1000 Industrial Way N., Unit D, Toms River 08755
Pres.—Wayne Cornwell, 8 emp., *Precision machining job shop* ........ (732) 914-0949
Sigma Design Company, 200 Pond Ave., Middlesex 08846
Pres.—Gerard J. Lynch, 10 emp., *Contract manufacturing & assembly of* ........ (732) 629-7555
Sigma Engineering & Consulting Assocs., 220 Lincoln Blvd., Middlesex 08846
Pres.—Robert P. Bruno, 10 emp., *General machining job shop* ........ (732) 356-3046
Sine-Tru Tool Co., Inc., 238 Boundry Rd., Marlboro 07746
Pres.—Ken Klawunn, 6 emp., *Rebuilt industrial tooling, knives* ........ (732) 591-1100
Sliker Machine Werkes, LLC, 2 Maple St., P.O. Box 53, South River 08882
Pres.—Barbara Sliker, 2 emp., *Precision machining job shop* ........ (732) 238-0331
Smith Tool & Mfg., R. G., 245 South St., Newark 07114
Pres.—Edgar Blaus, Jr., 9 emp., *General machining & tool & die job* ........ (973) 344-1395
Snyder Machine Co., 214 Sunnymead Rd., Hillsborough 08844
Owner—Eric Snyder, 1 emp., *General machining job shop* ........ (908) 359-2745
Sonrise Metal, Inc., 138 3rd Ave., Paterson 07514
Pres.—Todd Abrams, 19 emp., *Precision sheet metal fabrication &* ........ (973) 423-4717
Spectrum Tool, 56 Paterson Ave., Newton 07860
Pres., CFO—Steve Denison, 3 emp., *General machining job shop* ........ (973) 579-0087
Spencer Industries, Inc., 80 Holmes St., P.O. Box 128, Belleville 07109
Pres.—Martin Lawrence, 25 emp., *Corporate headquarters & military replacement* ........ (973) 751-2200
Stanton Precision Products, LLC, 10 Park Pl., Bldg. 4, Butler 07405
Member—Sean Stanton, 7 emp., *Screw machine job shop, including .060-inch* ........ (973) 838-6951
Stapling Machine Co., LLC, 41 Pine St., Rockaway 07866
Pres., Fin. Mgr.—Douglas Halkenhauser, 5 emp., *Machine parts* ........ (973) 627-4400
Star-Glo Industries, LLC, 2 Carlton Ave., East Rutherford 07073
Pres.—Edward Peterhoff, 90 emp., *Swiss machining & rubber molding for* ........ (201) 939-6162
State Tool Gear Co., Inc., 211 Camden St., Newark 07103
Pres.—Michael Insabella, 14 emp., *Gears & gear cutting* ........ (973) 642-6181
State Welding, 5 Industry Ct., Ewing 08638
★ Owner—Donald Petrescu, 4 emp., *Welding & general machining job shop* ........ (609) 882-3288
Steck, Inc., Paul C., 25 Brown Ave., Springfield 07081
Pres.—Emily S. Wantz, 8 emp., *Custom precision sheet metal fabrication* ........ (973) 376-1830
Steimling & Son, Inc.-Machinist, 7 Nickel Ave., Sayreville 08872
Pres.—Linda Steimling, 10 emp., *General machining job shop for large* ........ (732) 613-1550
Stelron Cam Co., 1495 MacArthur Blvd., Mahwah 07430
Ptnr.—James Beezer, 85 emp., *Manufacturing machinery components,* ........ (201) 529-5450
Stetz Machine Shop, John, 17 Highway 36, Middletown 07748
Owner—John Stetz, 7 emp., *Aerospace machining job shop* ........ (732) 495-0847
Stollen Machine & Tool Co., Inc., 761 Lexington Ave., Kenilworth 07033
Pres., Fin. & R & D Mgr.—Douglas Stollen, 5 emp., *CNC machining job shop* ........ (908) 241-0622
Stuart Mills, Inc., 25 Stillwater Rd., Newton 07860
Pres.—Stuart Mills, 6 emp., *CNC milling & turning, sheet metal* ........ (973) 579-5717
Sumatic Co., Inc., 102 Dewitt St., P.O. Box 435, Garfield 07026
Pres.—Michel A. Sunier, 5 emp., *Screw machine products* ........ (973) 772-1288
Summit Tool Co., Inc., 719 23rd St., Union City 07087
Pres.—Paul Cairoli, 3 emp., *Machining job shop* ........ (201) 867-8600
Superior Tool & Mfg. Co., Inc., 42 Columbia Rd., Branchburg 08876
Pres.—Ed Braunig, 10 emp., *Precision machining, including CNC* ........ (908) 526-9011
Swenson Welding & Fabrication, Bill, 707 W. Duerer St., Egg Harbor City 08215
Pres.—Bill Swenson, 3 emp., *Metal fabrication & welding job shop* ........ (609) 653-1177
T & P Machine Shop, 600 Prospect Ave., Piscataway 08854
Pres.—Tony Pasquale, 3 emp., *Steel machined parts & machine shop* ........ (732) 424-9141
T M U, Inc., 910 Shunpike Rd., Cape May 08204
Owner & Pres.—Robert Bartle, 10 emp., *Food processing machinery, precision* ........ (609) 884-7656
T N R Tool & Machine Co., 2 Coddington Ave., North Plainfield 07060
Owner—Rudy Romani, Sr., 3 emp., *Precision machining job shop* ........ (908) 754-4010
T P S Machining, 204 E. Main St., Manasquan 08736
Pres.—Ken C. Ludwig, 3 emp., *General machining job shop* ........ (732) 223-9305
Tam Metal Products, Inc., 55 Whitney Rd., Mahwah 07430
Co-Pres.—Frank Cariddi, 50 emp., *Precision sheet metal fabrication &* ........ (201) 848-7800
Taurus Precision, Inc., 129 Paterson Ave., Little Falls 07424
Pres.—Michael Jakubas, 18 emp., *Precision machining of medical & defense* ........ (973) 785-9254
Techline Extrusion Systems, 89 4th Ave., Haskell 07420
Ptnr.—Wilma Norman, 15 emp., *Extrusion machinery* ........ (973) 831-0317
Technatron, Inc., 78 Route 173 W., Ste. 9, Hampton 08827
Pres.—Jose Medeiros, 5 emp., *CNC & precision machining job shop* ........ (908) 238-1122
Technology General Corp. (H Q), 12 Cork Hill Rd., Franklin 07416
Sales Mgr.—Diane Olsen, 5 emp., *Corporate headquarters; electric &* ........ (973) 827-4143
Teknics Industries, Inc., 170 Beaver Brook Rd., Lincoln Park 07035
Pres.—Bruce Robertson, 24 emp., *Industrial automation & heavy truck* ........ (973) 633-7575
Telemark CNC, LLC, 429 Rockaway Valley Rd., Bldg. 2200, Boonton 07005
Owner—William Hovey, 5 emp., *Precision Swiss CNC machining of stainless* ........ (973) 794-4857
Thal Precision Industries, Inc., 19-A Walnut Ave., Clark 07066
Pres.—Jim Thal, 10 emp., *Injection mold fabrication, CNC & wire* ........ (732) 381-6106
Tim's Automotive Machine Shop, 1760 Highway 37 E., Toms River 08753
Owner—Timothy Hall, 1 emp., *Automotive machining job shop* ........ (732) 573-0600
Titan Technologies International, Inc., 222 Getty Ave., Clifton 07011
★ Chrm.—John J. Staudinger, 20 emp., *Hydraulic, pneumatic & electric industrial* ........ (973) 928-5222
TJK Machine, LLC, 870 E. Elmer Rd., Vineland 08360
Owner—Nancy Parkin, 4 emp., *General machining job shop* ........ (856) 691-7811
Tomcel Machine, Inc., 86 Lackawanna Ave., West Paterson 07424
Pres.—Rick Foy, 2 emp., *General machining job shop* ........ (973) 256-8257
Tooling Etc., LLC, 250 Hallock Ave., Ste. C, Middlesex 08846
Pres.—Markus Jesacher, 12 emp., *Segmental, solid, circular & hot friction* ........ (732) 752-8080
TORNQVIST, 29 Hanes Dr., Wayne 07470
Off. Mgr.—Adam Mosciszko, 22 emp., *Metal fabrication, laser cutting &* ........ (973) 686-5999
Toth Inc., 6970 Central Hwy., Pennsauken 08109
V-P.—Theodore Toth, Jr., 48 emp., *Precision machining & assembly of machined* ........ (856) 662-8700
Town & Country Plastics, Inc., P.O. Box 269, Morganville 07751
Pres., Sales Mgr.—Harold Marmel, 18 emp., *Plastic pollution control & chemically* ........ (732) 780-5300
Townsend Machine, Inc., 246 Sykesville Rd., Chesterfield 08515
Pres.—Barclay A. Townsend, 25 emp., *Screw machine products & machining* ........ (609) 298-0400
Tracer Tool & Machine Co., Inc., 32 Iron Horse Rd., Oakland 07436
Pres.—D. Lindsay Conner, 22 emp., *Precision & CNC machining, milling* ........ (201) 337-6184
Transstar Truck Body Welding Co., Inc., 514 Route 513, P.O. Box 226, Califon 07830
Pres.—Dominick Tranquilli, 5 emp., *Truck bodies & welding job shop* ........ (908) 832-2688
Trend Machine, Inc., 793 Martin St., P.O. Box 218, Rahway 07065
Pres.—Bill Joseph, 3 emp., *Packaging machinery parts, machined* ........ (732) 382-4170
Tri Phase Tool Co., 2345 Route 9, Ste. 10, Toms River 08755
Owner & GM—Robert J. Fischer, 3 emp., *General machining job shop, including* ........ (732) 370-4737

S.I.C.

Triad Tool Co., 9 Commerce St., Branchburg 08876
Pres., CEO—Eric Wichelhaus, 45 emp., *Aerospace, medical & communication* .................... (908) 534-1784
Triangle Automatic, Inc., 105 W. Dewey Ave., Ste. 305, Wharton 07885
★ Manager—Viggy Rosa, 3 emp., *General machining job shop* .............................. (973) 625-3830
Triple S Industries, 1108 E. Linden Ave., P.O. Box 1293, Linden 07036
Pres.—Robert Schulte, 10 emp., *General machining job shop* .............................. (908) 862-0110
Tru Mfg., Inc., 40 Oak St., Norwood 07648
Pres.—Paul Mastropietro, 12 emp., *Precision machining job shop* .............................. (201) 768-4050
Tulenko Enterprises, LLC, 176 Franklin Ave., Rockaway 07866
Owner, Fin. & R & D Mgr.—Eric A. Tulenko, 9 emp., *Structural & architectural metal sandblasting* (973) 453-6699
Tur Machine, LLC, 198 U.S. Highway 206, Ste. 5, Hillsborough 08844
Ptnr.—Zbigniew Richard Rolka, 6 emp., *General machining shop* .............................. (908) 874-0235
Ultimate Spinning & Turning Corp., 9 Willow St., Moonachie 07074
Pres.—Mike Novack, 12 emp., *Metal, stainless steel & brass spinning* .............................. (201) 372-9740
Ultimate Tool & Mfg. Co., 360-A Carnegie Ave., Kenilworth 07033
Owner, GM & Plt. Mgr.—Paul Plante, 5 emp., *Tool & die & CNC machining job shop* .............. (908) 241-4575
Unilite Co., Inc., 151 River Rd., Nutley 07110
Pres.—Mario Foti, 9 emp., *Electronic devices & machining job* .............................. (973) 667-1674
Unimade Metals, Inc., 115 Patterson St., Hillsdale 07642
Pres.—F. Borosch, 12 emp., *Precision sheet metal & machined products* .............................. (201) 666-7747
Unique Metal Products Co., Inc., 17 W. Scott Ave., P.O. Box 1181, Rahway 07065
Pres.—Joseph S. Niemczyk, 16 emp., *Metal products, fabrication, laser* .............................. (732) 388-1888
Unique Systems, Inc., 4 Saddle Rd., Cedar Knolls 07927
Pres.—Olof A. Eriksen, 20 emp., *Machined replacement parts & assemblies* .............................. (973) 455-0440
United Equipment & Fabricators, 175 Orange St., Newark 07103
Manager—Robert Ayars, 5 emp., *Custom plastic, fiberglass, stainless* .............................. (973) 242-2737
United Motor Parts, Inc., 1130 Teaneck Rd., Teaneck 07666
★ Owner—Alan Gladstein, 20 emp., *General machining job shop for the* .............................. (201) 837-6760
United National Machine Tool, Inc., 2404 Sylon Blvd., P.O. Box 608, Hainesport 08036
Pres.—Robert Donahue, 14 emp., *Rotary tooling* .............................. (609) 265-2269
United Support Solutions, Inc., 134 Sand Park Rd., Cedar Grove 07009
Pres.—Joe Ostering, 80 emp., *Sheet metal fabrication, AWS & robotic* .............................. (973) 857-2298
Universal Metalcraft, Inc., 24 Burgess Pl., Wayne 07470
Pres.—Eric Wenstrom, 25 emp., *General & precision machining job shop* .............................. (973) 345-3284
Utility Tool Co., 15 Orange St., Bloomfield 07003
Pres., Fin., MIS & R & D Mgr.—Tony Nigro, 2 emp., *Precision machining job shop* .............. (973) 743-8010
V & L Machine Tool Co., Inc., 30 Sherwood Ln., Ste. 11, Fairfield 07004
Pres.—Michael Sollitto, 5 emp., *Precision machine parts* .............................. (973) 808-5858
V E P Manufacturing Inc., 575 S. Hope Chapel Rd., Jackson 08527
Pres., CFO—Robert Pfluger, 22 emp., *Precision CNC machining job shop* .............................. (732) 657-0666
V H Machine Tool Co., 29 Smith Ave., Fair Lawn 07410
Owner—Dennis Van Houten, 1 emp., *Machine parts* .............................. (973) 427-8666
Vahl, Inc., 34 Kennedy Blvd., East Brunswick 08816
Pres.—Henry G. Dieken, 40 emp., *Precision machining job shop* .............................. (718) 492-6655
Valle Precision Machine Co., Inc., 58 Myrtle Ave., Passaic 07055
Pres.—Louis Valle, 6 emp., *Machine parts* .............................. (973) 773-3037
Van Hydraulics, 643 Sayre Ave., Perth Amboy 08861
GM—Steve Roberts, 30 emp., *Rebuilt cylinders, pumps, motors, valves* .............................. (732) 442-5500
Vector Precision Machining, Inc., 1558 Janvier Rd., Williamstown 08094
Pres.—Pawel Les, 5 emp., *Precision machining job shop* .............................. (856) 740-5131
Vee Dennis Mfg. Co., 620 Park Rd., Cherry Hill 08034
Pres.—George D. Lymper, 25 emp., *Sheet metal fabrication & machining* .............................. (856) 428-7676
Vermes Machine Co., Inc., 351 Crider Ave., Moorestown 08057
Ptnr.—Mike Vermes, 50 emp., *CNC machining job shop* .............................. (856) 642-9300
Versatile Welding Group, LLC, 340 Cox St., Roselle 07203
Pres.—Jim Druckenmiller, 4 emp., *Stainless, structural & plate steel* .............................. (908) 298-8900
Vertol Machine, 15 Burns Ave., Vineland 08360
Owner—James Vertolli, 1 emp., *General machining of custom & contract* .............................. (856) 327-2489
Viking Yachting Center, Inc., 5724 N. Route 9, New Gretna 08224
★ GM—Eugene R. McCann, 3 emp., *General machining job shop for fiberglass* .............................. (609) 296-2388
Vin-Law Machine & Tool Co., Inc., 3 Kulick Rd., P.O. Box 10950, Fairfield 07004
Pres.—Vincent Cirelli, Sr., 5 emp., *General machining job shop* .............................. (973) 227-5100
VRP Lu-Max Mfg. Co., Inc., 44 Brown Ave., Springfield 07081
Pres., R & D Mgr.—Paul Rodzak, 1 emp., *Sheet metal welding, wire forming &* .............................. (973) 379-5877
Warren Mfg. Corp., 23 Bloomfield Ave., Pine Brook 07058
Pres.—Frank Petrus, 3 emp., *Precision machining job shop* .............................. (973) 227-4220
WECOM, Inc., 20 Warrick Ave., Glassboro 08028
Pres.—Eric C. Sprengle, Sr., 27 emp., *Precision sheet metal aluminum & stainless* .............. (856) 863-8400
Weldall Welding & Ironworks, 115-117 S. Day St., Orange 07050
Pres.—Anthony Prioletti, 1 emp., *Ornamental iron & steel gates, fences* .............................. (973) 674-8868
Weldon Machine & Boring, Inc., 134 Wood Ave., Middlesex 08846
Pres.—Weldon Brantley, 3 emp., *General machining job shop* .............................. (732) 356-1887
Wel-Fab, Inc., 124 Burrs Rd., Mount Holly 08060
Chrm. of the Board & V-P.—Paul J. Elstone, Sr., 18 emp., *Steel fabrication & welding of collapsible* (609) 261-1393
Wellbilt Industries, 2 Maple Ave., Linden 07036
Owner & IT Mgr.—Les Zalewski, 15 emp., *Custom metal fabrication & stamping* .............................. (908) 486-6002
Werko Machine Co., Inc., 9200 Collins Ave., Pennsauken 08110
Pres.—Robert Mueller, Sr., 10 emp., *Industrial machinery* .............................. (856) 662-0669
West Machine Works, Inc., 101 Liberty St., Metuchen 08840
Pres.—Jan Van Hoesen, 8 emp., *Precision machining job shop* .............................. (732) 549-2183
West Side Precision Machine Products, Inc., 280 Lincoln Blvd., Middlesex 08846
Pres.—David Gizzi, 5 emp., *Precision machining, including Swiss* .............................. (732) 560-9006
Weston Machine, 161 11th St., Piscataway 08854
Owner—Charlie Weston, 1 emp., *Automotive machining job shop* .............................. (732) 752-2711
Wheaton Co., R. W., 215 W. Clay Ave., P.O. Box 4017, Roselle Park 07204
Owner & Pres.—Christopher Kern, 10 emp., *Sand & investment castings & general* .............................. (908) 241-4955
White Marine, Inc., 500 Division St., Perth Amboy 08861
Owner—Jennifer Billand, 50 emp., *Precision machine parts* .............................. (732) 826-4491
Whitehouse Machine, LLC, 3585 U.S. Highway 22 E., Somerville 08876
Pres.—Matthew Kessel, 2 emp., *General machining job shop, including* .............................. (908) 534-4722
Wilson Reconditioning & Design Co., LLC, 117 S. Rutherford Ave., Franklin 07416
Pres.—Tim Wilson, 4 emp., *Rebuilt tag finishing machinery* .............................. (973) 823-6317
Win-Tech Precision Products, Inc., 5 Littell Rd., East Hanover 07936
Owner—Pravin Patel, 6 emp., *CNC milling, turning, mechanical assembly* .............................. (973) 887-8727
Woodbridge Machine & Tool Co., Inc., 259 Bergen St., Woodbridge 07095
Pres.—Steve Sepa, 7 emp., *Precision machining job shop* .............................. (732) 634-0179
Wortmann Machine Works, Inc., E., 50 Hollister Rd., P.O. Box 1657, Teterboro 07608
GM & Sales Mgr.—Brett Rogers, 10 emp., *Fabrication & general machining job* .............................. (201) 288-1654
Xevee Corp., 27 Montgomery St., P. O. Box 5277, Hillside 07205
Pres.—Zev Sluzak, 4 emp., *Welding job shop* .............................. (908) 964-0444
Z & R Cutter Service, Inc., 50 Division Ave., Ste. 21, Millington 07946
Owner—Dennis Zetterstrom, 2 emp., *General machining & grinding job shop* .............................. (908) 647-6757
Z I Parts Co., 215 Cristiani St., Cranford 07016
Owner—Zbigniew Bielen, 1 emp., *Metal fabrication & machining job shop* .............................. (908) 241-0109
Zala Machine Co., Inc., 109 Stryker Ln., Ste. 11, Hillsborough 08844
Owner & Pres.—Stanley Zala, 15 emp., *Medium & large machining, including* .............................. (908) 431-9106
Zenex Precision Products Corp., 69 George St., Paterson 07503
Pres.—Zenon Wrowski, 6 emp., *Precision machining job shop* .............................. (973) 523-6910
Zenith Precision, Inc., 536 Paterson Ave., East Rutherford 07073
Pres.—Matt de Gennaro, 10 emp., *Precision & CNC machining, including* .............................. (201) 933-8640
Zero Tolerance Machine, 1650 Glassboro Rd., Williamstown 08094
Ptnr.—Kenneth Homeyer, 2 emp., *Military & aircraft machine parts* .............................. (856) 881-9072
Ziezer Tool Co., Inc., 960 Koehl Ave., Union 07083
Pres.—Ron Ziezer, 3 emp., *Precision machine parts* .............................. (908) 686-1332
Zimmer Machinery Systems, 19 Springcroft Rd., Far Hills 07931
Owner—Theodore Zimmer, 1 emp., *Tool & die & precision machining job* .............................. (908) 234-2560

## 36 ELECTRONIC & OTHER ELECTRIC EQUIPMENT

### 3612 Transformers

A C Transformer Corp., 89 Madison St., Newark 07105
Pres.—Robert Giangrande, 6 emp., *Electrical & specialty transformers* .............................. (973) 589-8574
American Modular Power Solution, 429 Rockaway Rd., Bldg. 10, Boonton 07005
Pres. & Sales Mgr.—Greg Lowndes, 6 emp., *Modular electrical substations* .............................. (973) 588-4026
Bey Electronics Corp., 39 Kentucky Ave., Paterson 07503
GM & Fin. Mgr.—Rena Nuss, 12 emp., *Electronic transformers* .............................. (973) 225-9494
Bogue Systems, Inc., 100 Pennsylvania Ave., Paterson 07503
Pres.—Anthony Sabatino, 44 emp., *Electric motor battery chargers, elevator* .............................. (973) 523-2200
Coates International Ltd., 2100 Highway 34 & Ridgewood Rd., Wall 07719
Pres., CEO—George J. Coates, 14 emp., *Spherical rotary valve system for internal* .............................. (732) 449-7717
Electromech, Inc., 624 Swan St., Ramsey 07446
V-P., Engrg.—Solomon Ezra, 25 emp., *Transformers & power supplies* .............................. (201) 934-3456
G & S Motor Equipment Co., 1800 Harrison Ave., P.O. Box 493, Kearny 07032
Pres.—Gabor Newmark, 55 emp., *Rebuilt electrical transformers & oil-filled* .............................. (201) 998-9244
Galaxy Transformer & Magnetics, LLC, 386 Cooper Rd., West Berlin 08091
Owner—James Curry, 12 emp., *Electrical & high frequency transformers* .............................. (856) 753-4546
Glassman High Voltage, Inc., 124 W. Main St., P.O. Box 317, High Bridge 08829
Owner—Sanford H. Glassman, 70 emp., *High voltage power supplies* .............................. (908) 638-3800
Glen Magnetics, Inc., 1165 3rd Ave., Alpha 08865
Pres.—John DiSarro, 35 emp., *Electric transformers* .............................. (908) 454-3717
Hitran Corp., 362 Highway 31, Flemington 08822
Pur. Mgr.—Deb Frey, 80 emp., *Transformers* .............................. (908) 782-5525
Hotfoil-EHS, Inc., 2960 E. State Street Ext., Hamilton 08619
Pres.—Neville Richards, 35 emp., *Industrial heating equipment, including* .............................. (609) 588-0900
J A M B Industries, 336 Rockaway Valley Rd., Boonton 07005
Owner—Alexander Budlin, 3 emp., *Current transformers* .............................. (973) 263-9295
Magnetic & Transformer Technologies Corp., 653 Sayre Ave., Perth Amboy 08861
Pres.—Samir Fattohi, 5 emp., *Custom energy-saving single-phase &* .............................. (609) 371-1258
Magnetic & Transformer Technologies Corp. (H Q), 7 Tanager Ln., Robbinsville 08691
Pres.—Samir Fattohi, 5 emp., *Corporate headquarters; single & three-phase* .............................. (609) 371-1258
NWL, Inc., 312 Rising Sun Rd., Bordentown 08505
Pres., CEO—David Seitz, 150 emp., *Corporate headquarters & transformers* .............................. (609) 298-7300
Pioneer Power Solutions, Inc. (H Q), 400 Kelby St., 9th Fl., Fort Lee 07024
Chrm. & CEO—Nathan J. Mazurek, 10 emp., *Corporate headquarters; liquid-filled* .............................. (212) 867-0700
Power Magne-Tech Corp., 653 Sayre Ave., Perth Amboy 08861
Pres., GM—Leon Zelcer, 20 emp., *Transformers* .............................. (732) 826-4700
Power Magnetics, Inc., 377 Reservoir St., Trenton 08618
Pres.—Carl Bannwart, 26 emp., *Transformers, reactors & inductors* .............................. (609) 695-1170
Princeton Power Systems, Inc., 3175 Princeton Pike, Ste. C, Lawrenceville 08648
Co-Founder & Ex. CSO—Darren Hammell, 48 emp., *Electric power converting equipment* ... (609) 955-5390
Zero Surge, Inc., 889 State Route 12, Ste. 2, Frenchtown 08825
Pres.—Jack Harford, 10 emp., *Power line surge suppressors* .............................. (908) 996-7700

### 3613 Switchgear & switchboard apparatus

Advanced Industrial Controls Corp., 10 County Line Rd., Ste. 30, Somerville 08876
Pres.—Douglas K. Morrison, 6 emp., *Industrial control systems, including* .............................. (908) 725-7575
Applied Resource Corp., 105 W. Dewey Ave., Ste. 311, Wharton 07885
Pres.—Mark Colello, 22 emp., *Aerospace components & switches, including* .............................. (973) 328-3882
AW Machinery, LLC, 7 Just Rd., Fairfield 07004
Ptnr. & Pres.—Nestor E. Gener, 16 emp., *Industrial equipment & integrated systems* .............. (973) 882-3223
Barantec, Inc., 777 Passaic Ave., Ste. 345, Clifton 07012
Pres.—Hillel Mordkowicz, 10 emp., *Standard & custom touch metal piezo* .............................. (973) 779-8774
Bel Fuse, Inc. (H Q), 206 Van Vorst St., Jersey City 07302
Pres., CEO—Daniel Bernstein, 22 emp., *Corporate headquarters; electronic* .............................. (201) 432-0463
Buchmann Control Panels Mfg., Inc., 5-18 Banta Pl., Fair Lawn 07410
Owner—Red Buchman, 5 emp., *Control panels* .............................. (201) 791-3161
Control & Power Systems, Inc., 17 Spielman Rd., Fairfield 07004
Pres.—D. Shevich, 36 emp., *Control & information systems integration* .............................. (973) 575-3300
Custom Heliarc Welding & Machine, Inc., 49 Decatur St., P.O. Box 232, Columbia 07832
Pres.—Michael D. Gannon, 11 emp., *High voltage bus bar assemblies & connectors* .............. (908) 496-8190
Dantco Mixers Corp., 9 Oak St., Paterson 07501
Pres.—Michael D'Antuono, 5 emp., *Pharmaceutical & chemical processing* .............................. (973) 278-8776
East Coast Panelboard, Inc., 101 Tornillo Way, Tinton Falls 07712
Pres.—Salvatore Rinaldi III, 24 emp., *Electrical controls, switchboards &* .............................. (732) 739-6400
Eaton Corp., Electrical Div., 96 Stemmers Ln., Westampton 08060
Plt. Mgr.—Nick Kluf, 15 emp., *Electrical panel boards* .............................. (609) 835-4230
Etta Controls, Inc., 31 Belgrade Ter., West Orange 07052
Pres.—Paul Rametta, 6 emp., *Control panels, system integrators,* .............................. (973) 731-6552
FMDK Technologies, Inc., 63 Ramapo Valley Rd., Lobby 4, Mahwah 07430
Pres.—Frank Gallo, 4 emp., *Electronic control system spare parts* .............................. (201) 828-9822
Howman Assocs., Inc., 12 Garden St., Edison 08817
Pres.—Howard Rood, 8 emp., *Electrical control panels* .............................. (732) 985-7474
Instrumentation Design & Service Co., 256 Bearfort Rd., West Milford 07480
Pres.—Jerry Oselador, 2 emp., *Instrument panels* .............................. (973) 728-3748
Kraus & Naimer, Inc., 760 New Brunswick Rd., Somerset 08873
Pres.—Joachim L. Naimer, 40 emp., *Corporate headquarters & electric switches* .............................. (732) 560-1240
Lincoln Electric Products Co., Inc., 947 Lehigh Ave., Union 07083
CEO—Bruce Leff, 30 emp., *Electrical control panels & switchgears* .............................. (908) 688-2900
MAC Products, Inc., 60 Pennsylvania Ave., P.O. Box 469, Kearny 07032
Pres.—Edward Russnow, 135 emp., *Electrical control panels, connectors* .............................. (973) 344-0700
Mercury Commercial Electronics, 2 Henderson Dr., Ste. B, Caldwell 07006
Pres.—Tony Pospishil, 80 emp., *Commercial electronics, including RF/microwav* .............................. (973) 244-1040
Mid State Controls, Inc., 8 Crown Plz., Ste. 102, Hazlet 07730
Opers. & R & D Mgr.—Robert Rosko, 7 emp., *Electric control panels* .............................. (732) 335-0500

Norsal Distribution Assocs., 150 Cregar Rd., High Bridge 08829
Owner—Norma Moscato, 10 emp., *Custom switchgear, switchboard & motor* ... (908) 638-8900
Olson Motor & Control Co., Inc., 100 Old Camplain Rd., Hillsborough 08844
Pres.—William Olson, 15 emp., *Custom electrical panels & enclosures* ... (908) 231-1500
P K M Panel Systems Corp., 43 Ferry St., P.O. Box 272, South River 08882
Pres.—Wallace Toto, 15 emp., *Control panels* ... (732) 238-6760
R & J Control, Inc., 58 Harding Ave., Dover 07801
Pres., MIS Mgr.—Robert Berry, 20 emp., *Rebuilt diesel & gas generators & automatic* ... (973) 328-6880
Snap Action, Inc., 1260 Route 22 W., Mountainside 07092
GM—Doreen Dauria, 25 emp., *Circuit breakers* ... (908) 654-4380
Symcon, Inc., 47 Cedar Ln., West Milford 07480
Pres.—Stella Scilingo, 6 emp., *Electromechanical assemblies* ... (201) 967-7378
Trek Connect, 120 Mount Holly Bypass, Lumberton 08048
Dir.—Craig Jacobs, 30 emp., *Cable & harness assemblies & switching* ... (856) 608-0901
Vehicle Safety Mfg., LLC, 408 Central Ave., Newark 07107
Pres.—Ernest Scherler, 52 emp., *Heavy-duty vehicle safety & lighting* ... (973) 643-3000

## 3621 Motors & generators

Aerosource, Inc., 390 Campus Dr., Somerset 08873
V-P., GM—Robert A. Rist, 42 emp., *DC10, KC10, MD10, MD11 & KC-390 air-driven* ... (732) 469-9300
All Mechanical Services, Inc., 430 High St., P.O. Box 110, Perth Amboy 08862
Pres., Hum. Res. Mgr.—Greg Huhn, 5 emp., *Rebuilt pumps & motors* ... (732) 442-8292
Atlantic Kenmark Electric, Inc., 11 Ewing Ave., North Arlington 07031
Pres., Fin., MIS & R & D Mgr.—Salvatore Gaccione, 15 emp., *Rebuilt electric motors* ... (201) 991-2117
Bauer Gear Motor, LLC, 31 Schoolhouse Rd., Somerset 08873
Opers. Mgr.—Steven Blazek, 12 emp., *Electric gear motors* ... (732) 469-8770
Cobra Power Systems, Inc., 8 America Way, Spotswood 08884
Owner—Doug Cohen, 7 emp., *Power generation trailer, control &* ... (908) 486-1800
CRP Industries, Inc., 35 Commerce Dr., Cranbury 08512
Off. Mgr.—Fabine Gilson, 50 emp., *Industrial housings, motors & automotive* ... (609) 578-4100
D Electric Motors, Inc., 94 W. Sherman Ave., Vineland 08360
Pres., CFO—Anthony Desiere, 15 emp., *Rebuilt electric motors* ... (856) 696-5959
Eagle Engineering & Automation, Inc., 2111 Herbertsville Rd., P.O. Box 924, Point Pleasant 08742
Pres.—Maura Ryan, 11 emp., *Electric motor controls* ... (732) 899-2292
EIC Industry Group Corp. (H Q), 53 Green Pond Rd., Ste. 3, Rockaway 07866
Pres.—John Ni, 5 emp., *Corporate headquarters; custom components* ... (973) 983-1988
Electrical Motor Repair Co., 809 E. State St., Trenton 08609
Pres.—Paul Doran, 30 emp., *Couplings for elevator hoist motors* ... (609) 392-6149
Electro-Miniatures Corp., 68 W. Commercial Ave., Moonachie 07074
Pres.—Mark Pollack, 70 emp., *Electrical slip rings & slip ring assemblies* ... (201) 460-0510
Electro-Steam Generator Corp., 50 Indel Ave., P.O. Box 438, Rancocas 08073
Pres.—Bob Murnane, 10 emp., *Stationary & portable electric & indirect* ... (609) 288-9071
ENER-G Rudox, Inc., 765 State Route 17 N., P.O. Box 467, Carlstadt 07072
Pres.—Ryan Goodman, 40 emp., *Diesel & natural gas generator sets* ... (201) 438-0111
Fin-Tek Ozone, 6 Leo Pl., Wayne 07470
Pres., Fin., MIS & R & D Mgr.—Donald Finnegan, 10 emp., *Water purifying ozone generators &* (973) 628-2988
Globtek, Inc., 186 Veterans Dr., Northvale 07647
CEO—Anna Kaplan, 65 emp., *Manufacturer & distributor of power* ... (201) 784-1000
Hansome Energy Systems, Inc., 365 Dalziel Rd., Linden 07036
Chrm.—Al Reposi, 32 emp., *Electric motors* ... (908) 862-9044
Hydro-Mechanical Systems, Inc., 1030 Delsea Dr., P.O. Box 87, Westville 08093
Pres.—Howard Rosenbloom, 17 emp., *Hydrostatic motors & electric & diesel* ... (856) 848-8888
Innovative Power Solutions, LLC, 373 South St., Eatontown 07724
CEO—Eli Libermann, 40 emp., *Generators* ... (732) 544-1075
JNT Technical Services, Inc., 85 Industrial Ave., Little Ferry 07643
Pres.—Glenn F. Jorgensen, 20 emp., *Power plant equipment* ... (201) 641-2130
Kraft Power Corp., 241 W. Parkway, Pompton Plains 07444
V-P.—Chris Stemper, 30 emp., *Manufacturer of combined heat & power* ... (973) 835-9800
Lockwood's Electric Motor Service, Inc., 2239 Nottingham Way, Trenton 08619
Pres.—Richard L. Dey, 35 emp., *Rebuilt electric motors* ... (609) 587-2333
Melton Sales & Service, Inc., 511 Elbow Ln., Burlington 08016
V-P., Prodn.—Chris Robles, 85 emp., *Remanufactured diesel engines, drive* ... (609) 699-4800
Mid-Atlantic Engine Supply, Route 130 S. & Pennsauken St., P.O. Box 2270, Cinnaminson 08077
V-P., Treas. & Cont.—Chuck Cook, 15 emp., *Marine & industrial diesel engines* ... (856) 829-7798
Mid-Eastern Industries Div, Technology Dynamics, Inc, 100 School St., Bergenfield 07621
V-P., GM—Daniel R. Ellenback, 110 emp., *Linear power supplies & DC power systems* ... (201) 385-0500
Mobile Power International, LLC, 1010 Old Egg Harbor Rd., Voorhees 08043
Owner—Anthony F. Amorosia, 12 emp., *Contract manufacturing & metal fabrication* ... (856) 784-3195
Motion Systems Corp., 600 Industrial Way W., Eatontown 07724
Pres.—William Wolf, 80 emp., *Electromechanical actuators & gear* ... (732) 222-1800
Ocean Power Technologies, Inc., 1590 Reed Rd., Pennington 08534
Interim CEO—David Keller, 29 emp., *Ocean wave power electricity converters* ... (609) 730-0400
Panasonic Corp. Of North America (H Q), 2 River Front Plz., Newark 07102
Chrm., CEO—Joseph M. Taylor, 800 emp., *Corporate headquarters; electric motors* ... (201) 348-7500
PHT Aerospace, LLC, 230 West Pkwy., Ste. 2, Pompton Plains 07444
Dir., Opers.—Joseph Wall, 30 emp., *Electric motors & components for aerospace* ... (973) 831-1230
Polytron Devices, Inc., 295-303 River St., Paterson 07524
Pres.—Nancy Metzger, 25 emp., *Power supplies* ... (973) 345-5885
Power Pool Plus, Inc., 7 Edge Rd., Alpha 08865
V-P., GM—Brent Kephart, 18 emp., *Manufacturer & distributor of power* ... (908) 454-1124
R & J Control, Inc., 58 Harding Ave., Dover 07801
Pres., MIS Mgr.—Robert Berry, 20 emp., *Rebuilt diesel & gas generators & automatic* ... (973) 328-6880
Reliable Electric Motor Repair, Inc., 19 California Ave., Paterson 07503
GM—Ken Maulfair, 15 emp., *Rebuilt electric motors & distributor* ... (973) 278-8122
Seren I.P.S., Inc., 1670 Gallagher Dr., Vineland 08360
Pres.—Lawrence Hooper, 45 emp., *Radio frequency power supplies* ... (856) 205-1131
Somfy Systems, Inc., 121 Herrod Blvd., Dayton 08810
CEO—Michael Lee, 80 emp., *Specialized motors & electronic controls* ... (609) 395-1300
Steamist, Inc., 25 E. Union Ave., East Rutherford 07073
Pres.—J. Noll, 40 emp., *Steam generators for residential &* ... (201) 933-5800
Stewart & Stevenson Power Products, LLC, ADDA Div., 33 Gregg St., Lodi 07644
Serv. Mgr.—Scott Brandstetter, 200 emp., *Gas open, weatherproof, sound-attenuated* ... (201) 291-8415
Stonite Coil Corp., 476 Route 156, P.O. Box 11036, Yardville 08620
Pres.—William Engel, 25 emp., *Electronic coils* ... (609) 585-6600
Technology Dynamics, Inc., 100 School St., Bergenfield 07621
Pres.—Aron Levy, 90 emp., *Switching power supplies & DC-DC converters* ... (201) 385-0500
Tremont Co., Inc., I. W., 18 Utter Ave., Hawthorne 07506
Pres.—Sal Averso, 25 emp., *Packaging converters* ... (973) 427-3800
Universal Electric Motor Service, Inc., 131 S. Newman St., Hackensack 07601
Pres.—Stephen Stagg, 35 emp., *Rebuilt electric motors* ... (201) 968-1000

Walther Electric Corp., F., 12 Worlds Fair Dr., Ste. F, Somerset 08873
GM—Ray Stark, 10 emp., *Electrical plug & receptacle devices* ... (732) 537-9201

## 3624 Carbon & graphite products

Asbury Graphite Mills, Inc. (H Q), 405 Old Main St., P.O. Box 144, Asbury 08802
Chrm.—Marvin Riddle, 30 emp., *Corporate headquarters; graphite* ... (908) 537-2155
Bar-Lo Carbon Products, Inc., 31 W. Daniel Rd., P.O. Box 10031, Fairfield 07004
Owner—Mohammed Yasin, 32 emp., *Graphite products, crucibles, jigs,* ... (973) 227-2717
BASF Fuel Cell, Inc., 39 Veronica Ave., Somerset 08873
V-P., Dir., Sales—Emory Decastro, 45 emp., *Membrane electrode assemblies, low-temperatur* (732) 545-5100
General Carbon Corporation, 33 Paterson St., Paterson 07501
Pres.—Robert Muller, 20 emp., *Activated carbon & related filtration* ... (973) 523-2223
Mersen USA BN Corp., 400 Myrtle Ave., Boonton 07005
Pres.—Didier Muller, 120 emp., *Corporate headquarters & carbon electrical* ... (973) 334-0700

## 3625 Relays & industrial controls

Acrison, Inc., 20 Empire Blvd., Moonachie 07074
Dir., Mktg.—John T. Shaw, 140 emp., *Volumetric & weight-loss feeders &* ... (201) 440-8300
Alliance Technologies Group, Inc., 3 Luger Rd., Ste. 4, Denville 07834
CEO—Phillip William Depalma, 6 emp., *Contract manufacturing of mechanical* ... (973) 664-1151
American Teletimer Corp., 1167 Globe Ave., Mountainside 07092
Pres.—Joel Rosenzweig, 3 emp., *Horse race timing equipment* ... (908) 654-4200
Amperite Co., 4201 Tonnelle Ave., Ste. 6, North Bergen 07047
V-P., Admn. & Sales & Hum. Res. Mgr.—Judith Johnson, 20 emp., *Time delay relays, flashers* (201) 864-9503
APW Company, 5 Astro Pl., Ste. B, Rockaway 07866
Owner & Pres.—Jason Kellenberger, 10 emp., *Standard & custom electromagnets &* ... (973) 627-0643
Artisan Controls Corp., 111 Canfield Ave., Ste. B-15-18, Randolph 07869
Pres.—John D. Murray, 30 emp., *Industrial controls & timers* ... (973) 598-9400
ASCO Power Technologies, L.P. (H Q), 50 Hanover Rd., Florham Park 07932
Pres.—Armand J. Visioli, 300 emp., *Divisional headquarters; automatic* ... (800) 800-2726
Automation & Control, Inc., 1491 Lancer Dr., Moorestown 08057
Pres.—Ron Iannacone, 30 emp., *Custom industrial automation control* ... (856) 234-2300
Barantec, Inc., 777 Passaic Ave., Ste. 345, Clifton 07012
Pres.—Hillel Mordkowicz, 10 emp., *Standard & custom touch metal piezo* ... (973) 779-8774
Circonix Technologies, LLC, 29 Executive Pkwy., Ringwood 07456
Pres.—Andre Icso, 10 emp., *Film & paper control systems* ... (973) 962-6160
Connell Industries, Inc., 13 Fairfield Ave., West Caldwell 07006
Pres.—Vincent DiGangi, 5 emp., *Industrial automation systems & equipment* ... (877) 926-6635
Control & Power Systems, Inc., 17 Spielman Rd., Fairfield 07004
Pres.—D. Shevich, 36 emp., *Control & information systems integration* ... (973) 575-3300
Crestron Electronics, Inc., 15 Volvo Dr., Rockleigh 07647
Ex. V-P.—Randy Klein, 3000 emp., *Control systems, multimedia distribution* ... (201) 767-3400
CTI Motor Drives, Inc., 105 Jackson St., South River 08882
Pres.—John Micheli, 18 emp., *Electronic control systems for the* ... (732) 613-8390
Dataprobe, Inc., 1-B Pearl Ct., Allendale 07401
Pres.—David Weiss, 15 emp., *Electronic equipment, including remote* ... (201) 934-9944
Dialight Corporation (H Q), 1501 State Highway 34 S., Farmingdale 07727
CEO—Roy Burton, 85 emp., *Corporate headquarters; solid-state* ... (732) 919-3119
DigiVac Co., 105-B Church St., Matawan 07747
Pres.—Timothy Collins, 14 emp., *Vacuum instrumentation & scientific* ... (732) 765-0900
Eagle Engineering & Automation, Inc., 2111 Herbertsville Rd., P.O. Box 924, Point Pleasant 08742
Pres.—Maura Ryan, 11 emp., *Electric motor controls* ... (732) 899-2292
East Coast Panelboard, Inc., 101 Tornillo Way, Tinton Falls 07712
Pres.—Salvatore Rinaldi III, 24 emp., *Electrical controls, switchboards &* ... (732) 739-6400
Electronic Drives & Controls, Inc., 17 Eastmans Rd., Parsippany 07054
Pres.—Henry Dillard III, 26 emp., *Electronic drives & controls systems* ... (973) 428-0500
Electronic Power Designs, Inc., 132 Union Ave., Bloomingdale 07403
Pres.—Gregory J. Brown, 15 emp., *Gaseous piping skids & industrial control* ... (973) 838-7055
Electronic Technology, Inc., 511 Lyons Ave., Irvington 07111
Pres.—Victor Mohl, 80 emp., *Electronic controls & computers* ... (973) 371-5160
Electronika For Industry, Inc., 3599 Route 46, Parsippany 07054
Pres.—Witold Tarnawski, 9 emp., *Industrial controls* ... (973) 575-4994
Ellis Kuhnke Controls, Inc., 132 Lewis St., Unit A-2, Eatontown 07724
Pres.—Howard J. Boyce, 8 emp., *Manufacturer & distributor of pneumatic* ... (732) 291-3334
Emergency Transfer Controls, Inc., 251 Nuthatch Ct., Three Bridges 08887
V-P.—Joseph Ragland, 2 emp., *Industrial controllers for automatic* ... (908) 782-1794
Fargo Controls, Inc., P.O. Box 539, Eatontown 07724
Pres.—E. Fargo, 5 emp., *Proximity sensors, counters, timers* ... (732) 389-3376
FMDK Technologies, Inc., 63 Ramapo Valley Rd., Lobby 4, Mahwah 07430
Pres.—Frank Gallo, 4 emp., *Electronic control system spare parts* ... (201) 828-9822
H A Z Laboratories, 39 Hartmans Corner Rd., Washington 07882
Pres.—Henry Zajac, 15 emp., *Industrial controls* ... (908) 453-3300
Howman Electronics, Route 22 E., Salem Industrial Pk., Whitehouse 08888
Owner & Pres.—Salvatore Treppiccione, 15 emp., *Industrial controls* ... (908) 534-2247
Innolutions, Inc., 92 N. Main St., P.O. Box 384, Windsor 08561
Pres.—Manny Patel, 9 emp., *Electronic printing press controls* ... (609) 490-9799
Instrumentation Technology Systems, Inc., 205 E. Inman Ave., Rahway 07065
Co-Pres., Fin. Mgr.—Anna Sadowska, 6 emp., *Water treatment plant control systems* ... (732) 388-0866
Nova Systems, 246 Cozy Lake Rd., Oak Ridge 07438
Owner—Bob Deutsch, 3 emp., *Custom control systems & equipment* ... (973) 697-3281
Philips Lighting North America, 200 Franklin Square Dr., Somerset 08873
Pres., Phillips Lighting N. America—Bruno Biasiotta, 300 emp., *Company headquarters & light* (732) 563-3000
Plast-O-Matic Valves, Inc., 1384 Pompton Ave., Ste. 1, Cedar Grove 07009
Pres.—Tim Delorenzo, 60 emp., *Thermoplastic valves & controls for* ... (973) 256-3000
Powertronic, Inc., 3092 Shafto Rd., Unit 7, Tinton Falls 07753
Pres.—David Emery, 4 emp., *Industrial control panels for commercial* ... (732) 643-1500
Precision Multiple Controls, Inc., 33 Greenwood Ave., Midland Park 07432
Pres.—Peter Zecher, 50 emp., *Industrial timers, low-voltage & defrost* ... (201) 444-0600
Rockwell Automation, Inc., 165 Fieldcrest Ave., Raritan Ctr., Edison 08837
Regional Mgr.—Werny Castro, 15 emp., *AC & DC variable-speed drives* ... (732) 225-1360
Sico Systems Control, Inc., 1263 Ringwood Ave., Haskell 07420
Pres., CFO—Gary Sigal, 6 emp., *System integration & industrial controls* ... (973) 831-9110
Somfy Systems, Inc., 121 Herrod Blvd., Dayton 08810
CEO—Michael Lee, 80 emp., *Specialized motors & electronic controls* ... (609) 395-1300
Symcon, Inc., 47 Cedar Ln., West Milford 07480
Pres.—Stella Scilingo, 6 emp., *Electromechanical assemblies* ... (201) 967-7378
Thomas Instrumentation, Inc. (H Q), 133 Landing Rd., Cape May Court House 08210
CEO & Engr.—Cassandra Gluyas, 16 emp., *Corporate headquarters; custom microcontrolle* (609) 624-2630
Vehicle Safety Mfg., LLC, 408 Central Ave., Newark 07107
Pres.—Ernest Scherler, 52 emp., *Heavy-duty vehicle safety & lighting* ... (973) 643-3000

S.I.C.

Vibration Isolation Co., 225 Grand St., Paterson 07501
Pres.—Doug Bennett, 10 emp., *Vibration isolators* .......... (973) 345-8282

## 3629 Electrical industrial apparatus, nec

Almetek Industries, Inc., 2 Joy Dr., Hackettstown 07840
CEO—Lori McMahon, 75 emp., *Metal & polyethelene safety signs,* .......... (908) 850-9700
Avionic Instruments, LLC, 1414 Randolph Ave., P.O. Box 498, Avenel 07001
Opers. Mgr.—Tony Gatta, 180 emp., *Power conversion products, including* .......... (732) 388-3500
Data Technologies, Inc., 224 N. Pegasus Ave., Ste. A, Northvale 07647
Chrm.—Rachel Peleg, 10 emp., *Battery chargers* .......... (201) 784-3225
Haier America Trading, LLC (H Q), 1800 Valley Rd., Wayne 07470
Pres.—Shariff Kan, 100 emp., *Company headquarters; appliances &* .......... (973) 617-1800
Magna-Power Electronics, 39 Royal Rd., Flemington 08822
Pres.—Ira Pitel, 90 emp., *DC power supplies* .......... (908) 237-2200
Marine Electric Systems, Inc., 80 Wesley St., South Hackensack 07606
Pres.—H. Epstein, 20 emp., *Electronic measurement systems, alarm* .......... (201) 531-8600
Mobile Power, Inc., 392 Watters Rd., Hackettstown 07840
Pres.—Paul Mitchell, 5 emp., *Mobile heavy output alternators & current* .......... (908) 852-3117
Plasmatic Systems, Inc., 1327 Aaron Rd., North Brunswick 08902
Pres.—Aaron Ribner, 1 emp., *Electronics plasma cleaning equipment* .......... (732) 297-9107
Symcon, Inc., 47 Cedar Ln., West Milford 07480
Pres.—Stella Scilingo, 6 emp., *Electromechanical assemblies* .......... (201) 967-7378

## 3631 Cooking equipment—household

M M T C, Inc., 12 Roszel Rd., Ste. A-203, Princeton 08540
Pres.—Fred Sterzer, 3 emp., *Microwave equipment engineering* .......... (609) 520-9699
Maverick Industries, Inc., 94 Mayfield Ave., Edison 08837
Pres.—Edward Mackin, 10 emp., *Specialty kitchen & barbecue appliances* .......... (732) 417-9666

## 3632 Refrigerators & freezers—household

Aspen Mfg. Co., Inc., 703 Van Rossum Ave., Unit 5, Beverly 08010
Pres.—John DeFulgentis, 10 emp., *Residential washer, dryer, refrigerator* .......... (609) 871-6400
Gem Refrigerator Co., Inc., 176 Blvd. Route 50, Mays Landing 08330
Plt. Mgr.—Tony Iacono, 17 emp., *Refrigerators & freezers for pharmacies* .......... (609) 625-2500

## 3633 Laundry equipment—household

Aspen Mfg. Co., Inc., 703 Van Rossum Ave., Unit 5, Beverly 08010
Pres.—John DeFulgentis, 10 emp., *Residential washer, dryer, refrigerator* .......... (609) 871-6400

## 3634 Electric housewares & fans

Drytech, Inc., 54 Wrightstown Cookstown Rd., P.O. Box 249, Cookstown 08511
Pres., Fin. & R & D Mgr.—Tony Jones, 24 emp., *Cartridge dehydrators, moisture management* (609) 758-1794
HealthTools, LLC (H Q), 681 Lawlins Rd., Unit 70, Wyckoff 07481
Member—William T. Geronimo, 3 emp., *Company headquarters; kitchen & bathroom* .......... (201) 465-4381
Maverick Industries, Inc., 94 Mayfield Ave., Edison 08837
Pres.—Edward Mackin, 10 emp., *Specialty kitchen & barbecue appliances* .......... (732) 417-9666
Monitor Products, Inc., 7-A Marlen Dr., Robbinsville 08691
V-P.—Koji Isayama, 6 emp., *Electric heating systems for homes* .......... (609) 584-0505
Samsung Electronics America, Inc., 85 Challenger Rd., Ridgefield Park 07660
V-P., Bus. Dev.—Thomas Rhee, 300 emp., *Electronic components, including mobile* .......... (201) 229-4000
Sharp Electronics Corp. (H Q), 1 Sharp Plz., Mahwah 07430
Chrm., CEO—Toshiyuki Osawa, 900 emp., *Corporate headquarters; microwave ovens* .......... (201) 529-8200
Ulanet Co., George, 413-415 Market St., Newark 07105
Pres.—Jon Ulanet, 9 emp., *Heating elements, including immersion* .......... (973) 589-4876

## 3635 Vacuum cleaners—household

Budd Built In Vacuum Cleaners, 445 W. Main St., Wyckoff 07481
Pres.—William Schwartz, 25 emp., *Industrial & household central vacuum* .......... (201) 891-3010
Metropolitan Vacuum Cleaner Co., Inc., 5 Raritan Rd., Oakland 07436
Pres.—Jules Stern, 75 emp., *Household vacuum cleaners, electric* .......... (201) 405-2225

## 3639 Appliances—household, nec

HYSO, LLC, 430 Gotham Pkwy., 2nd Fl., Carlstadt 07072
★ Owner—Simon Sassoon, 6 emp., *Odor control & air freshening devices* .......... (201) 635-9555
Kansai Special American Machine Corp., 1 Madison St., Ste. F-11, East Rutherford 07073
Pres.—Hideo Koge, 5 emp., *Industrial sewing machines & parts* .......... (973) 470-8321
Multi-Pak Corp., 180 Atlantic St., Hackensack 07601
Chrm.—Neil Cavanaugh, 25 emp., *Trash compactors, including repair* .......... (201) 342-7474
New York Sewing Machine, Inc., 8555 Tonnelle Ave., Unit 301, North Bergen 07047
Pres.—Sheldon Rothstein, 5 emp., *Manufacturer & distributor of sewing* .......... (201) 809-2009
Sewmatic Attachments, 39 E. Hanover Ave., Morris Plains 07950
Owner—Richard Rivera, 15 emp., *Industrial sewing machine attachments* .......... (973) 290-9174
Sharp Electronics Corp. (H Q), 1 Sharp Plz., Mahwah 07430
Chrm., CEO—Toshiyuki Osawa, 900 emp., *Corporate headquarters; microwave ovens* .......... (201) 529-8200
Stony Brook Sew & Vacuums, Inc., 191 U.S. Highway 130, Bordentown 08505
★ Owner—Howard Anderson, 10 emp., *Rebuilt sewing machines & vacuum cleaners* .......... (609) 372-4018
Wastequip, 1031 Hickstown Rd., Sicklerville 08081
Pres.—Joe Futcher, 100 emp., *Waste-handling equipment* .......... (856) 784-5500

## 3641 Lamps—electric

Bliss Electrical Supply Co., 207 South St., Elizabeth 07202
Owner & CEO—Vincent Cicio, 7 emp., *Fluorescent indoor & outdoor lighting* .......... (908) 289-9719
E G L Co., Inc., 100 Industrial Rd., Berkeley Heights 07922
Pres.—Harold Cortese, 100 emp., *Neon & LED sign lights & components* .......... (908) 508-1111
Hanovia Specialty Lighting LLC, 6 Evans St., Fairfield 07004
Ptnr.—Jeffrey S. Andrews, 20 emp., *Exposure & UV curing equipment* .......... (973) 651-5510
Lumenarc, Inc., 37 Fairfield Pl., West Caldwell 07006
Pres.—Harminder Bhalla, 12 emp., *Manufacturer of high-intensity discharge* .......... (973) 227-8048
Martek Industries, Inc., 600 Deer Rd., Ste. 8, Cherry Hill 08034
Pres.—Robert Anzalone, 3 emp., *Miniature light bulbs* .......... (856) 427-9411
Philips Lighting North America, 200 Franklin Square Dr., Somerset 08873
Pres., Phillips Lighting N. America—Bruno Biasiotta, 300 emp., *Company headquarters & light* (732) 563-3000
Radiant Thermal Products Co., 640 W. 1st Ave., Roselle 07203
Pres.—Albert C. Maglio, 30 emp., *Laboratory industrial process electrodes* .......... (908) 241-7700
TCS Technologies, Inc., 430 Sand Shore Rd., Unit 1, Hackettstown 07840
Pres.—Gerard Fitzgerald, 12 emp., *Ultraviolet lamps for digital inkjet* .......... (908) 852-7555
Unique Lighting, LLC, 555 7th St., Somers Point 08244
Owner—James Fox, 1 emp., *Low-voltage light bulbs & decorative* .......... (609) 926-8966

## 3643 Current-carrying wiring devices

American Fittings Corp., 17-10 Willow St., Fair Lawn 07410
Pres.—Allen Fischbein, 50 emp., *Electrical fittings* .......... (201) 664-0027
Andrex, Inc., 101 Bilby Rd., Ste. E, Hackettstown 07840
Pres.—William T. Pote, 20 emp., *Brass, nickel & stainless steel flexible* .......... (908) 852-4377
Archtech Electronics Corp., 117 Docks Corner Rd., Ste. A, Dayton 08810
Owner—Peggy Foung, 36 emp., *Fiber-optic & copper networking cable* .......... (732) 355-1288
Armel Electronics, Inc., 1601 75th St., North Bergen 07047
Pres.—Edward D. Johnsen, 19 emp., *Electronic components for military* .......... (201) 869-4300
Buhl Electric, Inc., 80 Little Falls Rd., Fairfield 07004
Pres.—Sheldon Goldstein, 16 emp., *LED lighting products, including lighting* .......... (201) 296-0600
Connector Products, Inc., 1300 John Tipton Blvd., Pennsauken 08110
Pres.—Nick Polidori, 22 emp., *Electrical connector terminals* .......... (856) 829-9190
Control Products, 280 Ridgedale Ave., East Hanover 07936
V-P.—Mac Stuhler, 55 emp., *Waterproof & thermal switches & linear* .......... (973) 887-9400
Custom Heliarc Welding & Machine, Inc., 49 Decatur St., P.O. Box 232, Columbia 07832
Pres.—Michael D. Gannon, 11 emp., *High voltage bus bar assemblies & connectors* .......... (908) 496-8190
East-West Service Co., Inc., 2 Marlen Dr., Hamilton 08691
Owner—Avinash C. Diwan, 17 emp., *Exit signs, emergency lights & power* .......... (609) 631-9000
Elgen Mfg. Co., 10 Railroad Ave., Closter 07624
Pres.—David Young, 100 emp., *Flexible duct connectors, galvanized* .......... (201) 964-0008
Flexco Microwave, Inc., 17 Karville Rd., P.O. Box 115, Port Murray 07865
Pres., R & D Mgr.—William T. Pote, 40 emp., *Electronic cable & connectors* .......... (908) 835-1720
Globtek, Inc., 186 Veterans Dr., Northvale 07647
CEO—Anna Kaplan, 65 emp., *Manufacturer & distributor of power* .......... (201) 784-1000
Hofer Machine & Tool Co., Inc., 126 Linda Vista Ave., North Haledon 07508
Pres.—Alan P. Hofer, 19 emp., *Electrical cable connectors* .......... (973) 427-1195
J. Jeb Products, LLC, 10 Cutler Ave., P.O. Box 40, Westville 08093
Pres.—Jack Sukala, 2 emp., *120 volt connectors for engine pre-heaters* .......... (856) 845-4455
Lighting Prevention Systems, Inc., 154 Cooper Rd., Unit 1201, P.O. Box 353, West Berlin 08091
Pres.—Ian Fawthrop, 10 emp., *Lightning protection products, grounding* .......... (856) 767-7806
Lightning Prevention Systems, Inc., 154 Cooper Rd., Ste. 1201, West Berlin 08091
CEO—Patricia McLaughlin, 10 emp., *Lightning protection equipment for* .......... (856) 767-7209
MAC Products, Inc., 60 Pennsylvania Ave., P.O. Box 469, Kearny 07032
Pres.—Edward Russnow, 135 emp., *Electrical control panels, connectors* .......... (973) 344-0700
Mennekes Electronics, Inc., 277 Fairfield Rd., Fairfield 07004
Pres.—Walter Mennekes, 20 emp., *Electronics equipment, including wiring* .......... (973) 882-8333
Mitronix, Inc., 239 Old Tappan Rd., Old Tappan 07675
Pres.—Jeffrey Weinstein, 3 emp., *Custom lamp holders & light sockets* .......... (201) 263-0063
Multi Tech Industries Corp., 64 S. Main St., P.O. Box 159, Marlboro 07746
Pres.—James Bernard, 11 emp., *Rotary switches, cord strain-reliefs* .......... (732) 431-0550
Pressure Controls, Inc., 406 Courtlandt St., Belleville 07109
Plt. Mgr.—Paul Emmarco, 26 emp., *Pressure switches, flow switches &* .......... (973) 751-5002
Princetel, Inc., 2560 E. State Street Ext., Hamilton 08619
Pres.—Barry Zhang, 40 emp., *Fiber-optic rotary joints, electrical* .......... (609) 588-8801
Richards Mfg., 517 Lyons Ave., Irvington 07111
Ptnr. & Pres.—Joseph Bier, 150 emp., *Electric cable connectors* .......... (973) 371-1771
Robert Technologies, Inc., 37 Main St., South River 08882
Pres.—Barry Greenberg, 30 emp., *Electrical connectors for military,* .......... (732) 254-6389
Thomas & Betts Corp., Elastimold Div., 1 Esna Pk., Hackettstown 07840
GM—Allan Bordstrom, 300 emp., *High-voltage underground connectors* .......... (908) 852-1122
Walther Electric Corp., F., 12 Worlds Fair Dr., Ste. F, Somerset 08873
GM—Ray Stark, 10 emp., *Electrical plug & receptacle devices* .......... (732) 537-9201
Warren Lightning Rod Co., 2 Richey Ave., Collingswood 08107
Pres.—Stephen Humeniuk, 24 emp., *UL96A & NFPA 780 lightning protection* .......... (856) 854-7000
Weber & Scher Mfg. Co., Inc., 1231 US Highway 22 E., P.O. Box 366, Lebanon 08833
Chrm., CEO—J. William Scher, 35 emp., *Machinery & equipment for the manufacturing* .......... (908) 236-8484

## 3644 Wiring devices—non-current carrying

American Fittings Corp., 17-10 Willow St., Fair Lawn 07410
Pres.—Allen Fischbein, 50 emp., *Electrical fittings* .......... (201) 664-0027
Endot Industries, Inc., 60 Green Pond Rd., Rockaway 07866
Chrm.—Gary Wellmann, 50 emp., *Corporate headquarters & HDPE plastic* .......... (973) 625-8500
FRP Corp., 15 Hoskier Rd., South Orange 07079
Pres.—Alan M. Tarnow, 11 emp., *Custom molded fiberglass protection* .......... (973) 763-5496
Multi Tech Industries Corp., 64 S. Main St., P.O. Box 159, Marlboro 07746
Pres.—James Bernard, 11 emp., *Rotary switches, cord strain-reliefs* .......... (732) 431-0550
Stevens Products, Inc., 128 N. Park St., East Orange 07017
Pres., CFO—Ross S. Stevens, Jr., 30 emp., *Electrical insulation* .......... (973) 672-2140

## 3645 Lighting fixtures—residential

Adam Metal Products, 7 Orben Dr., P.O. Box 450, Ledgewood 07852
Pres.—Raymond B. Bentley, 50 emp., *Commercial & residential lighting fixtures* .......... (973) 770-1100
American Brass & Crystal, Inc., 835 Lehigh Ave., Union 07083
Pres.—Ross Kirsh, 32 emp., *Cast & crystal chandeliers* .......... (908) 688-8611
Bliss Electrical Supply Co., 207 South St., Elizabeth 07202
Owner & CEO—Vincent Cicio, 7 emp., *Fluorescent indoor & outdoor lighting* .......... (908) 289-9719
Cast Lighting, LLC, 1120-A Goffle Rd., Hawthorne 07506
★ Owner—David Beausoleil, 4 emp., *Lighting fixtures & transformers for* .......... (973) 423-2303
Fabbian USA Corp., 161 Dwight Pl., Fairfield 07004
Owner—Renato Fabbian, 6 emp., *Residential & commercial decorative* .......... (973) 882-3824
Feldman Stained Glass, 401 Halladay St., Jersey City 07304
Proprietor—Larry A. Feldman, 3 emp., *Custom stained glass windows, skylights* .......... (201) 434-2887
Gemini Cut Glass Co., Inc., 4 E. Forest Ave., Englewood 07631
Pres.—Eric Zelwian, 7 emp., *Custom chandeliers, sconces & lighting* .......... (201) 568-7722
Genie House, Inc., 139 Red Lion Rd., P.O. Box 2478, Vincentown 08088
Pres.—Lloyd Williams, Jr., 22 emp., *Residential & commercial lighting fixtures* .......... (609) 859-0600
Illuminating Experiences, LLC, 625 Jersey Ave., Unit 7, New Brunswick 08901
Owner—Claire Vitale, 10 emp., *Commercial & residential lighting fixtures* .......... (732) 745-5858
Inner Spaces Lighting And Design, LLC, 98 Copley Ave., Teaneck 07666
GM—Scott Usher, 2 emp., *Custom LED & halogen lighting fixtures* .......... (201) 692-0702
It's Exciting Lighting, LLC, 1270 Glen Ave., Moorestown 08057
CEO—John Murphy, 8 emp., *Battery operated wireless wall sconces* .......... (856) 727-5200
Jay-Bee Lamp & Shade Co., Inc., 33 Hoover Ave., Passaic 07055
Pres., Pers. Mgr.—Robert Schurman, 4 emp., *Lampshades & lamps* .......... (973) 473-1569
Lum Tech Lighting, Inc., 201 Commerce Dr., Ste. 5, Moorestown 08057
★ Owner—Joseph Ma, 10 emp., *Lighting supplies, including incandescent* .......... (856) 234-2211
Mercury Lighting Products Co., 20 Audrey Pl., Fairfield 07004
Ptnr. & Opers. Mgr.—Brian Cunningham, 130 emp., *Commercial & residential lighting fixtures* . (973) 244-9444
New Brunswick Lamp Shade Co., 7 Terminal Rd., New Brunswick 08901
CEO—Paul Zankel, 20 emp., *Lampshades* .......... (732) 545-0377
Philips Lighting North America, 200 Franklin Square Dr., Somerset 08873
Pres., Phillips Lighting N. America—Bruno Biasiotta, 300 emp., *Company headquarters & light* (732) 563-3000
Reggiani Lighting USA, Inc., 372 Starke Rd., Carlstadt 07072
Pres.—John Savoretti, 19 emp., *HID, low-voltage & fluorescent lighting* .......... (201) 372-1717

Specialty Lighting Industries, Inc., 1306 Doris Ave., Ocean 07712
Pres.—Ben Salomon, 25 emp., *Commercial & residential lighting equipment* (732) 517-0800

Starfire Lighting, Inc., 7 Donna Dr., Wood Ridge 07075
Pres., Fin. & GM—Zachary Gomes, 55 emp., *Commercial & residential linear & recessed* (201) 438-9540

Tektite Industries, Inc., 309 N. Clinton Ave., Trenton 08638
Pres.—Scott Mele, 9 emp., *LED flashlights & replacement bulbs* (609) 656-0600

## 3646 Lighting fixtures—commercial

Adam Metal Products, 7 Orben Dr., P.O. Box 450, Ledgewood 07852
Pres.—Raymond B. Bentley, 50 emp., *Commercial & residential lighting fixtures* (973) 770-1100

Amerlux, LLC, 178 Bauer Dr., Oakland 07436
Chrm.—Frank P. Diassi, 250 emp., *Company headquarters & architectural* (973) 882-5010

Belfer Group, 10 Ruckle Ave., Farmingdale 07727
Pres.—Bruce Belfer, 47 emp., *Lighting fixtures* (732) 493-2666

Bernhard-Link Theatrical, LLC, 815 Fairview Ave., Ste. 11, Fairview 07022
Bus. Mgr.—Ruthie Burman, 18 emp., *Custom theatrical staging, scenery* (201) 943-4190

Bliss Electrical Supply Co., 207 South St., Elizabeth 07202
Owner & CEO—Vincent Cicio, 7 emp., *Fluorescent indoor & outdoor lighting* (908) 289-9719

Cast Lighting, LLC, 1120-A Goffle Rd., Hawthorne 07506
★ Owner—David Beausoleil, 4 emp., *Lighting fixtures & transformers for* (973) 423-2303

Compact Fluorescent Systems, 3 Adams St., Belvidere 07823
Chrm.—Dory Broyer, 3 emp., *Industrial lighting fixtures* (973) 729-5262

Coronet, Inc., 77 Wood St., Paterson 07524
Pres.—Ronald Osur, 24 emp., *Fluorescent light fixtures* (973) 345-7660

Dazian Fabrics, LLC, 18 Central Blvd., South Hackensack 07606
Chrm.—Milt Wolfson, 40 emp., *Textiles, fabricated items & LED scenic* (201) 549-1000

Design Plan Lighting, Inc., 79 Trenton Ave., Frenchtown 08825
V-P.—Richard Klapper, 20 emp., *Lighting fixtures* (908) 996-7710

Fabbian USA Corp., 161 Dwight Pl., Fairfield 07004
Owner—Renato Fabbian, 6 emp., *Residential & commercial decorative* (973) 882-3824

Gemini Cut Glass Co., Inc., 4 E. Forest Ave., Englewood 07631
Pres.—Eric Zelwian, 7 emp., *Custom chandeliers, sconces & lighting* (201) 568-7722

Genie House, Inc., 139 Red Lion Rd., P.O. Box 2478, Vincentown 08088
Pres.—Lloyd Williams, Jr., 22 emp., *Residential & commercial lighting fixtures* (609) 859-0600

Glass Dynamics, LLC, 2662 Hance Bridge Rd., Vineland 08361
CEO & Head of Opers.—Kimberlie Lawson, 9 emp., *Custom & precision glass fabrication* (856) 205-1530

Hal-O Mfg. Co., 137 Meeker Ave., Newark 07114
Pres.—Harold Roth, 13 emp., *Lighting components & chains* (973) 824-6122

Illuminating Experiences, LLC, 625 Jersey Ave., Unit 7, New Brunswick 08901
Owner—Claire Vitale, 10 emp., *Commercial & residential lighting fixtures* (732) 745-5858

Kurt Versen Inc, 10 Charles St., Westwood 07675
V-P., Opers. & Sales—Nancy Stathes, 130 emp., *Commercial lighting fixtures* (201) 664-8200

Lucid Lighting, LLC, 811 Rosemont Ringoes Rd., Stockton 08559
Pres.—Robert Wallace, 1 emp., *Residential & commercial lighting fixtures* (609) 649-0596

Lum Tech Lighting, Inc., 201 Commerce Dr., Ste. 5, Moorestown 08057
★ Owner—Joseph Ma, 10 emp., *Lighting supplies, including incandescent* (856) 234-2211

Lumenarc, Inc., 37 Fairfield Pl., West Caldwell 07006
Pres.—Harminder Bhalla, 12 emp., *Manufacturer of high-intensity discharge* (973) 227-8048

Luminaire Lighting Corp., 5 Sutton Pl., Edison 08817
Ptnr.—Joe Lipson, 10 emp., *Industrial lighting fixtures* (732) 549-0056

M K S, Inc., 7 N. Industrial Blvd., Bridgeton 08302
Pres.—Kennneth Brattlie, 13 emp., *Electroluminescent lamps, membrane* (856) 451-5545

Mark Architectural Lighting, 3 Kilmer Rd., Edison 08817
Pres.—Tim O'Brien, 120 emp., *Commercial lighting fixtures* (732) 985-2600

Mercury Lighting Products Co., 20 Audrey Pl., Fairfield 07004
Ptnr. & Opers. Mgr.—Brian Cunningham, 130 emp., *Commercial & residential lighting fixtures* (973) 244-9444

Natale Machine & Tool Co., Inc., 339 13th St., Carlstadt 07072
Co-Pres.—Lynn Natale, 6 emp., *Portable, permanent, industrial & marine* (201) 933-5500

National Lighting Co., Inc., 522 Cortlandt St., Belleville 07109
Pres.—Warren Siegel, 30 emp., *Commercial lighting fixtures* (973) 751-1600

New Horizon Lighting, Inc., 632 Cedar Swamp Rd., Jackson 08527
Pres.—Michael Stoddard, 15 emp., *Energy-efficient light fixtures for* (732) 833-8086

Night Canyon, Inc., The, 1475 Park Ave., Alpha 08865
Pres.—Mark Smith, 20 emp., *Movie theatre projectors, speakers,* (908) 454-6344

North American Illumination Co., 79 Commerce St., Garfield 07026
Co-Pres.—Paul Goldberg, 16 emp., *Commercial lighting fixtures* (973) 478-4700

Oceanic Electrical Mfg. Co., 248-256 3rd St., Elizabeth 07206
Pres.—Hank Barnes, 15 emp., *Marine lighting fixtures* (908) 355-1900

Philips Lighting North America, 200 Franklin Square Dr., Somerset 08873
Pres., Phillips Lighting N. America—Bruno Biasiotta, 300 emp., *Company headquarters & light* (732) 563-3000

Picasso Lighting Industries, LLC, 46 Sellers St., Kearny 07032
Owner—Boris Bregman, 20 emp., *LED, recessed, suspended, surface mount* (201) 246-8188

R L E Industries, LLC, 35 Kulick Rd., Fairfield 07004
CEO—Scott Koenig, 40 emp., *Lighting fixtures* (973) 276-1444

Sea Gull Lighting Products, LLC., 301 W. Washington St., P.O. Box 329, Riverside 08075
Pres.—Matt Vooris, 600 emp., *Lighting fixtures* (856) 764-0500

Specialty Lighting Industries, Inc., 1306 Doris Ave., Ocean 07712
Pres.—Ben Salomon, 25 emp., *Commercial & residential lighting equipment* (732) 517-0800

Starfire Lighting, Inc., 7 Donna Dr., Wood Ridge 07075
Pres., Fin. & GM—Zachary Gomes, 55 emp., *Commercial & residential linear & recessed* (201) 438-9540

Tektite Industries, Inc., 309 N. Clinton Ave., Trenton 08638
Pres.—Scott Mele, 9 emp., *LED flashlights & replacement bulbs* (609) 656-0600

Unique Lighting, LLC, 555 7th St., Somers Point 08244
Owner—James Fox, 1 emp., *Low-voltage light bulbs & decorative* (609) 926-8966

Vision Lighting, Inc., 48 N. 2nd St., Paterson 07522
Pres.—Barry Mabery, 10 emp., *Lighting fixtures for sports, commercial* (973) 720-1200

Voigt Lighting, 79 Commerce St., Garfield 07026
Pres.—Paul Goldberg, 18 emp., *Commercial & industrial lighting fixtures* (973) 928-2252

Zumtobel Lighting, Inc., 17-09 Zink Pl., Unit 7, Fair Lawn 07410
V-P.—Wolfgang Egger, 25 emp., *Commercial lighting fixtures* (973) 340-8900

## 3647 Lighting equipment—vehicular

Dialight Corporation (H Q), 1501 State Highway 34 S., Farmingdale 07727
CEO—Roy Burton, 85 emp., *Corporate headquarters; solid-state* (732) 919-3119

Natale Machine & Tool Co., Inc., 339 13th St., Carlstadt 07072
Co-Pres.—Lynn Natale, 6 emp., *Portable, permanent, industrial & marine* (201) 933-5500

Reggiani Lighting USA, Inc., 372 Starke Rd., Carlstadt 07072
Pres.—John Savoretti, 19 emp., *HID, low-voltage & fluorescent lighting* (201) 372-1717

StreetGlow, Inc. (H Q), 57 Oak St., Norwood 07648
Pres., CEO, CFO & COO—Jack Panzarella, 5 emp., *Corporate headquarters; automotive* (973) 709-9000

Vehicle Safety Mfg., LLC, 408 Central Ave., Newark 07107
Pres.—Ernest Scherler, 52 emp., *Heavy-duty vehicle safety & lighting* (973) 643-3000

## 3648 Lighting equipment

Ameral International, Inc., 7 Railroad Ln., Brooklawn 08030
Pres.—Louis Grieco, 15 emp., *Custom cable & wire harness assemblies* (856) 456-9000

American Railing Design, 191 Vineyard Rd., Edison 08817
Pres.—Andrew Martingano, 10 emp., *Commercial, residential & industrial* (732) 287-1122

Bernhard-Link Theatrical, LLC, 815 Fairview Ave., Ste. 11, Fairview 07022
Bus. Mgr.—Ruthie Burman, 18 emp., *Custom theatrical staging, scenery* (201) 943-4190

Big Eye Lamp, Inc., 870 Route 530, Ste. 2, Whiting 08759
Pres.—William J. O'Hara, 6 emp., *High intensity magnifying lamps* (732) 557-9400

Bliss Electrical Supply Co., 207 South St., Elizabeth 07202
Owner & CEO—Vincent Cicio, 7 emp., *Fluorescent indoor & outdoor lighting* (908) 289-9719

BML Blackbird Theatrical Services, Inc., 1 Aquarium Dr., Secaucus 07094
CEO—Elliot Krowe, 80 emp., *Staging, lighting, audio, rigging &* (201) 617-8900

Bright Ideas USA, LLC, 890 Morris Ave., Lakewood 08701
Mng. Member & GM—Deena Leiman, 4 emp., *Company headquarters & safety & nighttime* (732) 886-8865

Carpenter Emergency Lighting, Inc., 2 Marlen Dr., Hamilton 08691
Owner—Avinash C. Diwan, 30 emp., *Emergency lighting & exit signs* (609) 689-3090

City Theatrical, Inc., 475 Barell Ave., Carlstadt 07072
Pres.—Gary Fails, 34 emp., *Theatrical lighting accessories* (201) 549-1160

Dialight Corporation (H Q), 1501 State Highway 34 S., Farmingdale 07727
CEO—Roy Burton, 85 emp., *Corporate headquarters; solid-state* (732) 919-3119

East-West Service Co., Inc., 2 Marlen Dr., Hamilton 08691
Owner—Avinash C. Diwan, 17 emp., *Exit signs, emergency lights & power* (609) 631-9000

Frezzolini Electronics, Inc., 7 Valley St., Hawthorne 07506
Pres.—James Crawford, 15 emp., *Professional portable powered lighting* (973) 427-1160

Gemini DJ & Pro Audio, 107 Trumbull St., Ste. F-8, Elizabeth 07206
CEO—Artie Cabasso, 18 emp., *Disc jockey & pro audio gear* (732) 346-0061

Lordon, Inc., 453 Route 46, Ste. 1-A, Hackettstown 07840
Pres.—Donna Quagliana, 5 emp., *Reflective traffic sign panels & strips* (908) 813-1143

Lumitron Corp., Inc., 35 Russo Pl., Berkeley Heights 07922
Pres.—Harry Chassie, 19 emp., *Aerospace lighting components, including* (908) 273-8998

Musco Sports Lighting, LLC, 5146 W. Hurley Pond Rd., Farmingdale 07727
Dist. Sales Mgr.—Dan Shalloo, 2 emp., *Sports lighting equipment* (732) 751-9114

Natale Machine & Tool Co., Inc., 339 13th St., Carlstadt 07072
Co-Pres.—Lynn Natale, 6 emp., *Portable, permanent, industrial & marine* (201) 933-5500

Picasso Lighting Industries, LLC, 46 Sellers St., Kearny 07032
Owner—Boris Bregman, 20 emp., *LED, recessed, suspended, surface mount* (201) 246-8188

Precision Multiple Controls, Inc., 33 Greenwood Ave., Midland Park 07432
Pres.—Peter Zecher, 50 emp., *Industrial timers, low-voltage & defrost* (201) 444-0600

PRG Light, Inc., 915 Secaucus Ave., Secaucus 07094
Sr. V-P.—Jim Lehner, 100 emp., *Theatrical lighting equipment* (201) 758-4000

Princeton Tec, 5198 Route 130 N., Bordentown 08505
Pres.—Arthur W. Stephens, 110 emp., *Company headquarters & flashlights* (609) 298-9331

R & R Plastics, Inc., 62-70 Myrtle Ave., Passaic 07055
Pres., CFO—R. Russell Corona, 12 emp., *Lighting diffusers & replacement plastics* (973) 365-8083

RAB Lighting, Inc., 170 Ludlow Ave., Northvale 07647
CEO—Ross Barna, 100 emp., *Outdoor commercial & residential lighting* (201) 784-8600

Rambusch Company, 160 Cornelison Ave., Jersey City 07304
Chrm.—Martin V. Rambusch, 43 emp., *Standard & custom lighting fixtures* (201) 333-2525

Raritan Printing Plus Flags & Banners, Inc., 109 N. Feltus St., South Amboy 08879
Pres.—Joanne Corridon, 2 emp., *Stock & custom U.S. outdoor & indoor* (732) 721-2121

Smartlite, LLC, 25 Madison Ave., Clifton 07011
Manager—Gabor Lederer, 7 emp., *Battery-operated electric votive &* (973) 470-9400

Tektite Industries, Inc., 309 N. Clinton Ave., Trenton 08638
Pres.—Scott Mele, 9 emp., *LED flashlights & replacement bulbs* (609) 656-0600

Teledex, Inc. (H Q), 1 Atlas St., Kenilworth 07033
Owner & CEO—Mei Nogochi, 6 emp., *Corporate headquarters; LED lighting* (908) 964-8109

Unilux, Inc., 59 5th St., Saddle Brook 07663
Pres.—Michael Simonis, 45 emp., *Strobe lights for surface inspection* (201) 712-1266

Vision Lighting, Inc., 48 N. 2nd St., Paterson 07522
Pres.—Barry Mabery, 10 emp., *Lighting fixtures for sports, commercial* (973) 720-1200

Wattlots, LLC, 1932 Long Hill Rd., Millington 07946
Founder & CEO—William E. S. Kaufman, 5 emp., *Solar-generated parking lot canopy* (908) 626-1555

## 3651 Audio & video equipment—household

A. V. Bluebook, 80 Little Falls Rd., Fairfield 07004
Sales Mgr., Natl.—Stephen Marino, 1 emp., *Electronic audiovisual equipment &* (800) 631-0868

Adcomm, Inc., 89 Leuning St., 1st Fl., South Hackensack 07606
Pres.—Allen Cohen, 100 emp., *Amplifiers for telecommunications* (201) 342-6349

APB-DynaSonics, Inc., 20 W. End Rd., Totowa 07512
GM—Peter Patel, 9 emp., *High-performance analog mixing consoles* (973) 785-1101

Apogee Sound International, LLC, 50 Spring St., Ramsey 07446
V-P., Accts., Natl.—David Chambers, 75 emp., *Amplifiers, speakers & processors* (201) 995-2001

Applied Microphone Technology, 104 Hillside Rd., Sparta 07871
Owner—Martin Taglione, 5 emp., *Microphones* (973) 729-9333

Aurora Multimedia Corp., 205 Commercial Ct., Morganville 07751
CEO—Paul Harris, 30 emp., *Audio visual processors, controls &* (732) 591-5800

Azden Corp., 200 Valley Rd., Ste. 101, Mount Arlington 07856
★ CEO—Motonori Sato, 10 emp., *Wireless microphone systems, powered* (973) 810-3070

CVE, Inc., 5 N. Corporate Dr., Riverdale 07457
Pres.—Kyu T. Cho, 100 emp., *Rebuilt consumer electronics, including* (201) 770-0005

D&M Holdings US, Inc. (H Q), 100 Corporate Dr., Mahwah 07430
CEO—Jim Caudill, 100 emp., *Holding company headquarters; home* (201) 762-6500

Digitize, Inc., 158 Edison Rd., Lake Hopatcong 07849
Pres.—Abraham Brecher, 18 emp., *Proprietary, ETL listed, FM approved* (973) 663-1011

Dtrovision, LLC, 535 E. Crescent Ave., Ste. 1, Ramsey 07446
Pres.—Minsoo Park, 15 emp., *Professional & consumer digital A/V* (201) 488-3232

ECSI International, Inc., 790 Bloomfield Ave., Bldg. C-1, Clifton 07012
Pres., CEO—Arthur Birch, 24 emp., *Infrared perimeter & intrusion detection* (973) 574-8555

Empirical Labs, Inc., 41 N. Beverwyck Rd., Lake Hiawatha 07034
Pres.—David Derr, 7 emp., *Professional audio processing equipment* (973) 541-9446

Euphonic Audio, Inc., 18 Newtown Blvd., Robbinsville 08691
Pres.—Larry Ullman, 4 emp., *Bass guitar amplifiers & speaker cabinets* (888) 894-3790

FSR, Inc., 244 Bergen Blvd., West Paterson 07424
Chrm.—William Fitzsimmons, 80 emp., *Signal management & infrastructure* (973) 785-4347

Fuchs Audio Technology, LLC, 407 Getty Ave., 2nd Fl., Clifton 07011
Pres.—Annette Fuchs, 10 emp., *Tube guitar & bass amplifiers, speaker* (973) 772-4420

Gemini DJ & Pro Audio, 107 Trumbull St., Ste. F-8, Elizabeth 07206
CEO—Artie Cabasso, 18 emp., *Disc jockey & pro audio gear* (732) 346-0061

Kramer Electronics USA, Inc./Sierra Video Systems (H Q), 6 State Route 173 W., Clinton 08809
Pres.—David Bright, 53 emp., *Corporate headquarters; manufacturer* ........ (908) 735-0018
LG Electronics USA, Inc. (H Q), 1000 Sylvan Ave., Englewood Cliffs 07632
Co-Pres., CEO—William Cho, 500 emp., *Corporate headquarters; computer, home* ........ (201) 816-2000
Oklahoma Sound Corp., 149 Entin Rd., Clifton 07014
V-P., Fin.—Barry Stauber, 30 emp., *Electronic sound systems* ........ (973) 594-9000
Onkyo USA Corp. (H Q), 18 Park Way, Upper Saddle River 07458
Pres.—Hiroshi Izutani, 40 emp., *Corporate headquarters; home theater* ........ (201) 785-2600
Panasonic Corp. Of North America (H Q), 2 River Front Plz., Newark 07102
Chrm., CEO—Joseph M. Taylor, 800 emp., *Corporate headquarters; electric motors* ........ (201) 348-7500
Pendulum Audio Systems, Inc., P.O. Box 339, Gillette 07933
Pres.—Gregory Gualtieri, 10 emp., *Professional vacuum tube recording* ........ (908) 665-9333
Phoenix Systems, LLC, 39 Morningside Ave., North Haledon 07508
Owner—Andrew Vaccaro, 5 emp., *Audiovisual equipment & systems for* ........ (201) 857-3901
S D I Technologies, Inc., 1299 Main St., Rahway 07065
CEO—Ezra Ashkenazi, 70 emp., *Home audio devices* ........ (877) 895-8324
Samsung Electronics America, Inc., 85 Challenger Rd., Ridgefield Park 07660
V-P., Bus. Dev.—Thomas Rhee, 300 emp., *Electronic components, including mobile* ........ (201) 229-4000
Sharp Electronics Corp. (H Q), 1 Sharp Plz., Mahwah 07430
Chrm., CEO—Toshiyuki Osawa, 900 emp., *Corporate headquarters; microwave ovens* ........ (201) 529-8200
Sound Environments, LLC, 1133 Industrial Pkwy., Ste. E, Brick 08724
Pres.—Michael S. Conacchio, 4 emp., *Custom high power nightclub, commercial* ........ (732) 840-6600
Systems Design Technology, P.O. Box 547, West Long Branch 07764
Pres.—Felix 'Phil' Foggia, 1 emp., *Sound, video & communications systems* ........ (732) 571-4547
Tech 21 USA, Inc., 790 Bloomfield Ave., Ste. B-1, Clifton 07012
Pres.—Andrew Barta, 20 emp., *Electric guitar & bass amplifiers,* ........ (973) 777-6996
Vanderbilt Industries, 2 Cranberry Rd., Parsippany 07054
Pres.—Mitchell Kane, 75 emp., *Computer controlled building security* ........ (973) 316-3900
VCOM International Multi-Media Corp., 80 Little Falls Rd., Fairfield 07004
Pres., CEO—Sheldon Goldstein, 22 emp., *Corporate headquarters & manufacturer* ........ (201) 229-4270
VPI Industries, Inc., 77 Cliffwood Ave., Ste. 3-B, Cliffwood 07721
Ptnr. & Co-Pres.—Mathew Weisfeld, 10 emp., *Audio turntables, tonearms, record* ........ (732) 583-6895
Zaxcom, Inc., 230 West Pkwy., Unit 9, Pompton Plains 07444
Pres.—Glenn Sanders, 10 emp., *Professional audio gear for the television* ........ (973) 835-5000

## 3652 Records & tapes—prerecorded

Audio Dynamix, Inc., 170 Coolidge Ave., Englewood 07631
Pres.—Rich Gayed, 15 emp., *CD & DVD duplication* ........ (201) 567-5488
Disc Makers, 7905 N. Route 130, Pennsauken 08110
Chrm.—Morris Ballen, 500 emp., *CD & DVD replication & packaging* ........ (856) 663-9030
Learning Ally, 20 Roszel Rd., Princeton 08540
Pres., CEO—Andrew Friedman, 100 emp., *Company headquarters & audio book production* (609) 452-0606
Mardee Co., Inc., 242 Saint Nicholas Ave., South Plainfield 07080
Pres.—Mariano D. Santis, 10 emp., *DVD & CD replication & duplication* ........ (908) 753-4343
Oasis Recording, Inc., 7905 N. Crescent Blvd., Delair 08110
Pres.—Micah Solomon, 10 emp., *Compact disc duplication* ........ (888) 296-2747

## 3661 Telephone & telegraph apparatus

A. V. Bluebook, 80 Little Falls Rd., Fairfield 07004
Sales Mgr., Natl.—Stephen Marino, 1 emp., *Electronic audiovisual equipment &* ........ (800) 631-0868
Alcatel-Lucent (H Q), 600 Mountain Ave., Murray Hill 07974
Chrm.—Phillippe Camus, 4000 emp., *Company headquarters; telecommunication* ........ (908) 582-8500
Breaker Group, Inc., The, 32-34 Mill St., Mount Holly 08060
Pres.—Tony Minervini, 14 emp., *Computer integrated systems, including* ........ (609) 267-1330
Comtron, Inc., 391 State Route 33 E., Englishtown 07726
Pres.—Gunther Wackerman, 14 emp., *Electromechanical devices, cellular* ........ (732) 446-7571
CVE, Inc., 5 N. Corporate Dr., Riverdale 07457
Pres.—Kyu T. Cho, 100 emp., *Rebuilt consumer electronics, including* ........ (201) 770-0005
Dialogic, Inc. (H Q), 4 Gatehall Dr., Parsippany 07054
★ Pres., CEO—Kevin Cook, 100 emp., *Corporate headquarters; telecommunications* ........ (800) 755-4444
I T I Electronics, Inc., 32 Stonewall Dr., Livingston 07039
Pres.—Robert Stein, 2 emp., *Telecommunications equipment* ........ (973) 890-7888
Iniven, A Div. Of Conolog Corp., 5 Columbia Rd., Somerville 08876
CEO—Micheal Horn, 12 emp., *Teleprotection, telemetry & multiplexing* ........ (908) 722-8081
InPhot, Inc., 3490 W. Route 1, Princeton 08540
Pres.—Krishna Linga, 3 emp., *Telecommunication equipment components* ........ (609) 750-0992
Netquest Corp., 523 Fellowship Rd., Ste. 205, Mount Laurel 08054
CEO—Jesse Price, 20 emp., *High speed broadband optical & copper* ........ (856) 866-0505
NICE Systems, Inc. (H Q), 461 From Rd., Paramus 07652
Pres., Americans—Barak Eilam, 180 emp., *Corporate headquarters; telephones* ........ (201) 964-2600
Packetstorm Communications, Inc., 20 Meridian Rd., Eatontown 07724
Pres.—Bill Luthy, 10 emp., *Internet protocol network emulators* ........ (732) 544-2434
Parwan Electronics Corp., 1230 State Route 34, Aberdeen 07747
Pres.—Suraj Tschand, 25 emp., *Telecom systems, including calling* ........ (732) 290-1900
Science Dynamics Corp., 7150 N. Park Dr., Ste. 500, Pennsauken 08109
Pres.—Paul Burgess, 12 emp., *Commercial call management systems,* ........ (856) 910-1166
Shore Microsystems, Inc., 45 Memorial Pkwy., Long Branch 07740
Pres.—Gordon Elam, 10 emp., *Computer networking redundant Ethernet* ........ (732) 870-0800
Sonetronics, Inc., 1718 State Route 71, P.O. Box L, Belmar 07719
Pres.—Gary Kuskin, 85 emp., *Military communications equipment,* ........ (732) 681-5016
Star Dynamic Corp., 100 Outwater Ln., Garfield 07026
Pres.—Maria Vecchiotti, 60 emp., *Military telecommunications equipment* ........ (973) 340-3883
Telecom Assistance Group, Inc., 150 Cooper Rd., Ste. F-15, West Berlin 08091
V-P.—Murray Kaplan, 30 emp., *Telecommunications testing equipment* ........ (856) 753-8585
TX Technology Corp., 100 Ford Rd., Unit 100-18, Denville 07834
GM—Donald Black, 15 emp., *Control monitoring systems, sensors* ........ (973) 442-7500
Voicecom Plus, Inc., 63 Ramapo Valley Rd., Ste. 201-A, Mahwah 07430
★ Owner—Tina Lyding, 20 emp., *Rebuilt voice & communications telephone* ........ (201) 760-2260
Walk The Technology Solution, 9000 Commerce Pkwy., Ste. H, Mount Laurel 08054
V-P., Engrg. & IT Mgr.—Marty Roselli, 30 emp., *Data communications equipment* ........ (856) 222-0643

## 3663 Radio & TV communications equipment

Accuview, Inc., 40-C Cotters Ln., Ste. F, East Brunswick 08816
Pres.—David H. Wu, 10 emp., *Flat panel LCD monitors & touchscreens* ........ (201) 440-2225
Adcomm, Inc., 89 Leuning St., 1st Fl., South Hackensack 07606
Pres.—Allen Cohen, 100 emp., *Amplifiers for telecommunications* ........ (201) 342-6349
Aeroflex Control Components, Inc., 40 Industrial Way E., Eatontown 07724
Cont.—Jim Ebessen, 100 emp., *Radio frequency & microwave components* ........ (732) 460-0212
Alphion Corp., 196 Princeton Hightstown Rd., Bldg. 1-A, 2nd Fl., Princeton Junction 08550
Chrm., Pres. & CEO—Bharat P. Dave, 20 emp., *GPON-based optical network access products* . (609) 936-9001
ATI Audio, 154 Cooper Road S-902, West Berlin 08091
Pres.—David Day, 12 emp., *Broadcast audio equipment* ........ (856) 719-9900
Avida, Inc., 174-B Kinderkamack Rd., P.O. Box 2, Park Ridge 07656
Pres.—Eric Kruegle, 5 emp., *Security surveillance equipment for* ........ (201) 802-0749
B & G International, Inc., 1085 Morris Ave., Union 07083
Pres., CEO—Chet Kolton, 30 emp., *Printed & die-cut plastic tags & hangers* ........ (973) 824-0334
Berkeley Varitronics Systems, Inc., 255 Liberty St., Metuchen 08840
Pres., CEO—Scott N. Schober, 30 emp., *Wireless telecommunications test equipment* ........ (732) 548-3737
Blonder Tongue Laboratories, Inc., 1 Jake Brown Rd., P.O. Box 1000, Old Bridge 08857
CEO—James Luksch, 150 emp., *Corporate headquarters & electronic* ........ (732) 679-4000
Bogen Communications, Inc., 50 Spring St., Ste. 1, Ramsey 07446
Pres.—Michael Fleischer, 85 emp., *Telecommunications peripherals & sound* ........ (201) 934-8500
B-Tron Corp., 154 Cooper Rd., Ste. 1203, West Berlin 08091
Pres., Fin. & GM—Walter Kiss, 4 emp., *CCTV & access control power supplies* ........ (856) 719-8485
Cellebrite USA Corp., 7 Campus Dr., Ste. 210, Parsippany 07054
CEO—Jim Grady, 40 emp., *Mobile interceptor communications equipment* ........ (201) 848-8552
Communication Devices, Inc., 85 Fulton St., Unit 2, Boonton 07005
Pres.—Tadhg Kelly, 12 emp., *Data encryption & security devices* ........ (973) 334-1980
Conolog Corp., 5 Columbia Rd., Somerville 08876
CEO—Michael Horn, 12 emp., *Telemetering & teleprotection communication* ........ (908) 722-8081
DAQ Electronics, LLC, 262 Old New Brunswick Rd., Ste. B, Piscataway 08854
V-P., Sales & Mktg.—James W. Recchia, 28 emp., *Telemetering & security equipment* ........ (732) 981-0050
Digitize, Inc., 158 Edison Rd., Lake Hopatcong 07849
Pres.—Abraham Brecher, 18 emp., *Proprietary, ETL listed, FM approved* ........ (973) 663-1011
East Coast Security Products, 53 Green Pond Rd., Ste. 1, Rockaway 07866
Pres.—William R. Vogt, 11 emp., *Security control equipment* ........ (973) 625-3277
Electro Impulse Laboratory, Inc., 1805 Route 33, Neptune 07753
Pres.—Mark Rubin, 41 emp., *Custom closed-loop cooling systems* ........ (732) 776-5800
Electromagnetic Technologies, 50 Intervale Rd., Unit 15, Boonton 07005
CEO—John Howard, 40 emp., *Radar & antenna microwave couplers,* ........ (973) 394-1719
Eventide, Inc., 1 Alsan Way, Little Ferry 07643
Bookkeeper—Phyllis Wasserman, 70 emp., *Broadcasting equipment* ........ (201) 641-1200
EXELIS, Inc., 77 River Rd., Clifton 07014
Pres.—Rich Sorelle, 1150 emp., *Aircraft self-protection, communications* ........ (973) 284-0123
Fiber-Span, 3434 U.S. Highway 22, Ste. 120, Branchburg 08876
CEO—Hal Halpern, 15 emp., *RF ON FIBER(R) communication network* ........ (908) 253-9080
Frezzolini Electronics, Inc., 7 Valley St., Hawthorne 07506
Pres.—James Crawford, 15 emp., *Professional portable powered lighting* ........ (973) 427-1160
Gamco Industries, Inc., 7 Walnut Ave., Clark 07066
Pres.—Fred Whiting, 25 emp., *Cable television filters* ........ (732) 381-0700
G-O-Metric, Inc., 215 Ash St., Delanco 08075
Pres.—Paul Manion, 6 emp., *EMI & RFI honeycomb ventilation panels* ........ (856) 461-8080
GuardTrax, LLC, 11 Commerce Dr., Lobby, Cranford 07016
CEO—Rich Pekmezian, 8 emp., *Handheld GPS & wireless tracking devices* ........ (908) 272-0114
Haier America Trading, LLC (H Q), 1800 Valley Rd., Wayne 07470
Pres.—Shariff Kan, 100 emp., *Company headquarters; appliances &* ........ (973) 617-1800
Hamilton Buhl, 80 Little Falls Rd., Fairfield 07004
V-P.—Madeline Piccone, 19 emp., *Technology & AV equipment for educational* ........ (201) 229-9800
Infinova, 51 Stouts Ln., Monmouth Junction 08852
Pres.—Jeffrey Liu, 20 emp., *Megapixel, IP & analog surveillance* ........ (732) 355-9100
Iniven, A Div. Of Conolog Corp., 5 Columbia Rd., Somerville 08876
CEO—Micheal Horn, 12 emp., *Teleprotection, telemetry & multiplexing* ........ (908) 722-8081
INSTOCK Wireless Components, Inc., 50 Intervale Rd., Ste. 15, Boonton 07005
Pres.—Mike Davo, 10 emp., *RF microwave power dividers, combiners* ........ (973) 335-6550
Integrated Microwave Technologies, LLC, 200 International Dr., Mount Olive 07828
CFO—Robert Chiarulli, 80 emp., *Digital microwave video equipment &* ........ (908) 852-3700
Intelligent Security Systems, 1480 U.S. Highway 9 N., Ste. 202, Woodbridge 07095
CFO—Boris Kalk, 180 emp., *Analytic software development & security* ........ (732) 855-1111
International Tower Supply, 851 Bethel Ave., Pennsauken 08110
Mng. Ptnr.—Michael Moskowitz, 16 emp., *Wireless infrastructure components,* ........ (856) 317-0005
LG Electronics USA, Inc. (H Q), 1000 Sylvan Ave., Englewood Cliffs 07632
Co-Pres., CEO—William Cho, 500 emp., *Corporate headquarters; computer, home* ........ (201) 816-2000
Linearizer Technology, Inc., 3 Nami Ln., Ste. 9-C, Hamilton 08619
Pres.—Allen Katz, 75 emp., *Amplifier distortion control modules* ........ (609) 584-8424
LiveU, Inc., 2 University Plz., Ste. 505, Hackensack 07601
★ Pres.—Avichai Cohen, 60 emp., *Portable video equipment & software* ........ (201) 742-5229
LTS / LT Security Inc. (H Q), 109 W. Park Dr., Ste. C, Mount Laurel 08054
Pres.—Wing Pang, 32 emp., *Corporate headquarters; full-line professiona* ........ (856) 780-9888
Mikros Systems Corp., 707 Alexander Rd., Princeton 08540
Pres.—Thomas Meaney, 25 emp., *Wireless communication systems* ........ (609) 987-1513
Millimeter Wave Technology, 90 Dayton Ave., Ste. 6-E, Passaic 07055
Pres.—Michael Katz, 10 emp., *Waterproof composite microwave & millimeter* ........ (845) 369-7808
Mizco International, Inc. (H Q), 80 Essex Ave. E., Avenel 07001
Pres., CEO—Albert Mizrahi, 50 emp., *Corporate headquarters; cell phone* ........ (732) 912-2000
MYAT, Inc., 360 Franklin Tpke., Mahwah 07430
Pres.—Philip Cindrich, 25 emp., *Electronic transmission equipment* ........ (201) 684-0100
New Jersey Microsystems, Inc., 211 Warren St., Ste. 31, Newark 07103
Pres.—Frederick D. Chichester, 12 emp., *RFID tags & sensor systems* ........ (973) 297-1450
OnPATH Technologies, 100 Mount Holly Bypass, Lumberton 08048
Founder—Peter Dougherty, 90 emp., *Data communications hardware & software* ........ (609) 518-4100
ORBCOMM, Inc. (H Q), 395 W. Passaic St., Ste. 325, Rochelle Park 07662
CEO—Marc J. Eisenberg, 50 emp., *Corporate headquarters; wireless networks* ........ (703) 433-6300
PatchAmp, Inc., 20 E. Kennedy St., Hackensack 07601
Pres.—Virginia Connors, 7 emp., *Prewired video & audio distribution* ........ (201) 457-1504
Polytron Devices, Inc., 295-303 River St., Paterson 07524
Pres.—Nancy Metzger, 25 emp., *Power supplies* ........ (973) 345-5885
Pro-Comm, Inc., 1105 Industrial Pkwy., Brick 08724
Pres.—Sheryl J. Visone, 11 emp., *High-power, UHF, L-band, S-band, C-band* ........ (732) 206-0660
Pulsar Microwave Corp., 48 Industrial St. W., Clifton 07012
Pres.—Charles Bobroski, 25 emp., *Microwave components & subsystems* ........ (973) 779-6262
QEI Corp., 1 Airport Dr., P.O. Box 805, Williamstown 08094
Pres.—Jay Osselburn, 10 emp., *Analog radio broadcasting transmitters* ........ (856) 728-2020
R T I, Inc., 401 Hasbrouck Blvd., Oradell 07649
Owner & Pres.—Richard Tashjian, 10 emp., *Computers, software development & radiation* ... (201) 261-5852
Radio Systems Design, Inc., 601 Heron Dr., Logan Township 08085
Pres.—Daniel Braverman, 15 emp., *Radio broadcasting equipment* ........ (856) 467-8000
RC Repair, 526 Doremus Ave., Glen Rock 07452
Owner—John Deneke, 2 emp., *Rebuilt radio control systems* ........ (201) 445-0361
RF Products, Inc., 1500 Davis St., Camden 08103
Pres.—Robert M. Minke, 38 emp., *Radio frequency distribution systems* ........ (856) 365-5500
SightLogix, Inc., 745 Alexander Rd., Ste. 5 & 6, Princeton 08540
Founder, Pres. & CEO—John Romanovich, 23 emp., *Thermal outdoor video analytics cameras* (609) 951-0008
Telegenix, Inc., 71 Indel Ave., P.O. Box 577, Rancocas 08073
Pres.—Joseph Miller, 14 emp., *Custom & contract voice communications* ........ (609) 265-3910

Telemetrics, Inc., 6 Leighton Pl., Ste. 4, Mahwah 07430
Pres. & V-P.—Anthony Cuomo, 29 emp., *Robotic television camera systems* .......... (201) 848-9818
Telescript, International LLC, 55 Walnut St., Ste. 101-A, Norwood 07648
Ptnr.—Christopher O'Brien, 12 emp., *Teleprompter systems* .......... (201) 767-6733
Verrex Corp., 1130 Route 22, Mountainside 07092
Pres.—Thomas Berry, Jr., 70 emp., *Corporate audiovisual & conferencing* .......... (908) 232-7000
Virtual Management Services Corp., 242 Atlantic City Blvd., Ste. 12, Bayville 08721
Owner—Jason Gonzalez, 5 emp., *Video surveillance equipment, including* .......... (732) 281-1350
Wide Band Systems, Inc., 389 Franklin Ave., Rockaway 07866
Pres.—Frank Padula, 15 emp., *Military communication systems, including* .......... (973) 586-6500
Wireworks Corp., 380 Hillside Ave., Hillside 07205
Pres.—Gerald Krulewicz, 20 emp., *Audio & video cable systems* .......... (908) 686-7400

## 3669 Communications equipment, nec

Acuative (H Q), 30 Two Bridges Rd., Ste. 240, Fairfield 07004
Pres., CEO—Vince Sciarra, 40 emp., *Company headquarters; telecommunication* .......... (973) 227-8040
Aesys, Inc., 27 Bland St., Emerson 07630
CFO—Evelyn McGregor, 5 emp., *Pure LED signs for transit, coach &* .......... (201) 871-3223
Alison Control, Inc., 35 Daniel Rd. W., Fairfield 07004
Pres.—Gene E. Benzenberg, 20 emp., *Fire detectors, fire detection control* .......... (973) 575-7100
Alphion Corp., 196 Princeton Hightstown Rd., Bldg. 1-A, 2nd Fl., Princeton Junction 08550
Chrm., Pres. & CEO—Bharat P. Dave, 20 emp., *GPON-based optical network access products* . (609) 936-9001
American Fibertek, Inc., 120 Belmont Dr., Somerset 08873
Pres.—Jack Fernandes, 70 emp., *Fiber-optic security system components* .......... (732) 302-0660
Archtech Electronics Corp., 117 Docks Corner Rd., Ste. A, Dayton 08810
Owner—Peggy Foung, 36 emp., *Fiber-optic & copper networking cable* .......... (732) 355-1288
ASCO Power Technologies, L.P. (H Q), 50 Hanover Rd., Florham Park 07932
Pres.—Armand J. Visioli, 300 emp., *Divisional headquarters; automatic* .......... (800) 800-2726
Avaya, Inc. (H Q), 211 Mount Airy Rd., Basking Ridge 07920
Pres., CEO—Kevin Kennedy, 2000 emp., *Corporate headquarters; business communicatio* .. (908) 953-6000
Berkeley Varitronics Systems, Inc., 255 Liberty St., Metuchen 08840
Pres., CEO—Scott N. Schober, 30 emp., *Wireless telecommunications test equipment* .......... (732) 548-3737
Checkpoint Systems, Inc. (H Q), 101 Wolf Dr., P.O. Box 188, Thorofare 08086
★ Pres., Shrink Mgmt. Sols.—Farrokh Abadi, 200 emp., *Corporate headquarters; advanced shrink* (856) 848-1800
Conolog Corp., 5 Columbia Rd., Somerville 08876
CEO—Michael Horn, 12 emp., *Telemetering & teleprotection communication* .......... (908) 722-8081
Cooper Notification, 273 Branchport Ave., Long Branch 07740
Pres.—Scott Hearn, 350 emp., *Fire alarm signals & voice systems* .......... (732) 222-6880
COTE-L Industries, Inc., 1542 Jefferson St., Teaneck 07666
CEO—Avi Aviner, 6 emp., *Safety, polyurethane, epoxy, waterproofing* .......... (201) 836-0733
DAQ Electronics, LLC, 262 Old New Brunswick Rd., Ste. B, Piscataway 08854
V-P., Sales & Mktg.—James W. Recchia, 28 emp., *Telemetering & security equipment* .......... (732) 981-0050
Dialogic, Inc. (H Q), 4 Gatehall Dr., Parsippany 07054
★ Pres., CEO—Kevin Cook, 100 emp., *Corporate headquarters; telecommunications* .......... (800) 755-4444
Digitize, Inc., 158 Edison Rd., Lake Hopatcong 07849
Pres.—Abraham Brecher, 18 emp., *Proprietary, ETL listed, FM approved* .......... (973) 663-1011
East Coast Security Products, 53 Green Pond Rd., Ste. 1, Rockaway 07866
Pres.—William R. Vogt, 11 emp., *Security control equipment* .......... (973) 625-3277
EXELIS, Inc., 77 River Rd., Clifton 07014
Pres.—Rich Sorelle, 1150 emp., *Aircraft self-protection, communications* .......... (973) 284-0123
Frezzolini Electronics, Inc., 7 Valley St., Hawthorne 07506
Pres.—James Crawford, 15 emp., *Professional portable powered lighting* .......... (973) 427-1160
FSR, Inc., 244 Bergen Blvd., West Paterson 07424
Chrm.—William Fitzsimmons, 80 emp., *Signal management & infrastructure* .......... (973) 785-4347
G-Way Microwave, 38 Leuning St., South Hackensack 07606
Pres.—Greg David, 19 emp., *Cellular communication tower components* .......... (201) 343-6388
Hamilton Buhl, 80 Little Falls Rd., Fairfield 07004
V-P.—Madeline Piccone, 19 emp., *Technology & AV equipment for educational* .......... (201) 229-9800
I.D. Systems, Inc., 123 Tice Blvd., Ste. 101, Woodcliff Lake 07677
Chrm., Pres. & CEO—Kenneth S. Ehrman, 100 emp., *Wireless systems integration & software* (201) 996-9000
Infinova, 51 Stouts Ln., Monmouth Junction 08852
Pres.—Jeffrey Liu, 20 emp., *Megapixel, IP & analog surveillance* .......... (732) 355-9100
Iniven, A Div. Of Conolog Corp., 5 Columbia Rd., Somerville 08876
CEO—Micheal Horn, 12 emp., *Teleprotection, telemetry & multiplexing* .......... (908) 722-8081
INSTOCK Wireless Components, Inc., 50 Intervale Rd., Ste. 15, Boonton 07005
Pres.—Mike Davo, 10 emp., *RF microwave power dividers, combiners* .......... (973) 335-6550
IPC Systems, Inc. (H Q), Harborside Financial Ctr., 3 2nd St., Plz. 10, 15th Fl., Jersey City 07311
CEO—Neil Barua, 130 emp., *Corporate headquarters; telephone systems* .......... (201) 253-2000
Ketec, Inc., 1256 N. Church St., Ste. A, Moorestown 08057
Pres.—George Kaltner, 14 emp., *Theft-prevention tags & detection systems* .......... (856) 778-4343
L-3 Communications Corp., 1 Federal St., Camden 08102
Pres.—Dave Micha, 700 emp., *Communications systems* .......... (856) 338-3000
Lee Electric, Inc., 309-11 51st St., P.O. Box 238, West New York 07093
Pres., GM—Andrew Abramowitz, 5 emp., *Electric locks* .......... (201) 866-3656
Masi Electronics, Don, 25 Walden Pl., West Caldwell 07006
Owner—Don Masi, 5 emp., *Security systems, including intercoms* .......... (973) 618-6288
Moniteur Devices, Inc., 36 Commerce Rd., Cedar Grove 07009
Pres.—John Unoski, 15 emp., *Valve position transmitters, indicators* .......... (973) 857-1600
National Protective Systems, 1 Meridian Rd., Eatontown 07724
V-P., Mfg.—Donald E. Ullery, Jr., 7 emp., *Portable personal & stationary equipment* .......... (732) 922-3609
Nistica, Inc., 745 U.S. Highway 202-206, Ste. 201, Bridgewater 08807
Founder—Jefferson Wagener, 55 emp., *Fiber-optic components* .......... (908) 707-9500
Nuvico, Inc., 53 Smith St., Englewood 07631
CEO—I. J. Choi, 20 emp., *IP surveillance closed-circuit television* .......... (201) 541-1605
Parwan Electronics Corp., 1230 State Route 34, Aberdeen 07747
Pres.—Suraj Tschand, 25 emp., *Telecom systems, including calling* .......... (732) 290-1900
Pem All Fire Extinguisher Corp., 39-A Myrtle St., P.O. Box 586, Cranford 07016
Pres.—Tom Moskaluk, 15 emp., *Fire extinguishers & suppression systems* .......... (908) 276-0211
Protection One, Inc., 50 Williams Pkwy., Ste. L, East Hanover 07936
GM—Frank Benna, 18 emp., *Burglar alarm, fire alarm, CCTV & access* .......... (973) 227-3421
Radiant Communications Corp., 5001 Hadley Rd., P.O. Box 867, South Plainfield 07080
Pres.—Thomas Lewis, 60 emp., *IP media & fiber-optic communications* .......... (908) 757-7444
RF Products, Inc., 1500 Davis St., Camden 08103
Pres.—Robert M. Minke, 38 emp., *Radio frequency distribution systems* .......... (856) 365-5500
Siemens Infrastructure & Cities, Building Technologies, 8 Fernwood Rd., Florham Park 07932
V-P., Div.—Robert Suermann, 250 emp., *Fire protection systems* .......... (973) 593-2600
SL Industries, Inc. (H Q), 520 Fellowship Rd., Ste. A-114, Mount Laurel 08054
Pres., CEO—William T. Fejes, Jr., 10 emp., *Corporate headquarters; power electronics* .......... (856) 727-1500
Sonetronics, Inc., 1718 State Route 71, P.O. Box L, Belmar 07719
Pres.—Gary Kuskin, 85 emp., *Military communications equipment,* .......... (732) 681-5016
Stanley Access Technologies, LLC, 17 Marlen Dr., Ste. C, Trenton 08691
Br. Mgr.—Joe Marino, 30 emp., *Power-operated security & fire doors* .......... (609) 890-0877
Sycamore Networks, Inc., 100 Century Pkwy, Ste. 120, Mount Laurel 08054
Opers. Mgr.—Joan Gianiotis, 110 emp., *Communications equipment* .......... (856) 359-9301
Systems Sales Corp., 1345 Campus Pkwy., Neptune 07753
Pres.—John Ventrella, 20 emp., *Fire alarm systems* .......... (732) 751-0600
Teknicom Sales Co., 470 Commercial Ave., Palisades Park 07650
Pres.—Don Duthaler, 9 emp., *Elevator hands-free telephone & intercom* .......... (201) 327-4500
Telegenix, Inc., 71 Indel Ave., P.O. Box 577, Rancocas 08073
Pres.—Joseph Miller, 14 emp., *Custom & contract voice communications* .......... (609) 265-3910
TomPat Technologies, Inc., 28 Muller Pl., Little Falls 07424
Pres.—Peter Chin, 9 emp., *Factory automation, safety & consumer* .......... (973) 785-1118
Tyco (H Q), 9 Roszel Rd., Princeton 08540
CEO—George Oliver, 350 emp., *Company headquarters; security & fire* .......... (609) 720-4200
Verint Systems, Inc., 9 Polito Ave., 9th Fl., Lyndhurst 07071
Off. Admn.—Sasha Matthews, 50 emp., *Voice recording & archiving systems* .......... (201) 559-3788
Voxware, Inc., 300 American Metro Blvd., Ste. 155, Hamilton 08619
Pres., CEO—Keith Phillips, 30 emp., *Voice-recognition systems, including* .......... (609) 514-4100

## 3671 Electron tubes

Amherst Scientific, LLC, 112 Kings Hwy., Landing 07850
Pres.—Chris Grant, 6 emp., *Cooled photomultiplier vacuum tube* .......... (973) 770-7772
Industrial Electronic Devices, Inc., 8 Bartles Corner Rd., Bldg. 101, Flemington 08822
Pres.—Jerry Kalajian, 5 emp., *Open frame, enclosed & watertight industrial* .......... (908) 806-2255
Kaistar Research & Development, LLC, 15 Wilson Dr., Sparta 07871
Pres.—Igor Kapchenko, 4 emp., *High-purity metals, special purpose* .......... (973) 362-1487
Linear Photonics, LLC, 3 Nami Ln., Ste. 7-C, Hamilton 08619
Pres.—Allen Katz, 10 emp., *Fiber-optic detectors, receivers, photonics* .......... (609) 584-5747
Schlumberger-Princeton Technology Center, 20 Wallace Rd., Princeton Junction 08550
Pers. Mgr.—Henrietta Ayewoh, 40 emp., *Ceramic & glass photomultiplier tubes* .......... (609) 799-1000
Troy-Onic, Inc., 90 Dell Ave., P.O. Box 494, Kenvil 07847
Pres.—Mike Murphy, 20 emp., *Electron tubes* .......... (973) 584-6830
Union City Filament Corp., 1039-A Hoyt Ave., P.O. Box 777, Ridgefield 07657
CEO—Joseph E. Celia III, 30 emp., *Electronic components* .......... (201) 945-3366

## 3672 Printed circuit boards

Access Control Group, LLC, 2555 U.S. Highway 130 S., Ste. 2, Cranbury 08512
Pres.—Arun Patel, 25 emp., *Electronic assembly, wiring harnesses* .......... (908) 789-8700
Altior, 444 Route 35 S., Bldg. B, Eatontown 07724
Pres., CEO—Ramana Jampala, 55 emp., *Computer hardware protocol acceleration* .......... (732) 440-1280
Anta Electric, Inc., 32 Richboynton Rd., Dover 07801
Owner & Hum. Res. Mgr.—Tanya Khazen, 40 emp., *Printed circuit board & wire harness* .......... (973) 366-2222
Applicad, Inc., 5029 Industrial Rd., Farmingdale 07727
Pres., CFO—John MacMillan, 30 emp., *Printed circuit board design & assembly* .......... (732) 751-2555
Argus International, 424 Route 31 N., P.O. Box 559, Ringoes 08551
Pres.—B. J. Costello, 35 emp., *Printed circuit board manufacturing* .......... (609) 466-1677
AudioCodes, Inc., 27 Worlds Fair Dr., 1st Fl., Somerset 08873
V-P., Call Recording Prod.—Ron Romanchik, 80 emp., *Corporate headquarters & recording,* (732) 469-0880
C & C Jetronic, Inc., 126 Evergreen Rd., New Egypt 08533
Pres.—Cheng J. Chiang, 3 emp., *Electronic contract manufacturing of* .......... (609) 758-3553
Ccard, Inc., 17 Belleterre Dr., Manalapan 07726
Pres.—Chris Cardinale, 6 emp., *Electronic cable assemblies & printed* .......... (732) 303-8264
Circuit Reproduction Co., Inc., 219 Hergesell Ave., Maywood 07607
Pres.—Paul Kabaria, 11 emp., *Printed circuit boards* .......... (201) 712-9292
Circuit Tech Assembly, LLC, 341 New Albany Rd., Ste. 130, Moorestown 08057
Pres.—Bill Sherlock, Jr., 12 emp., *Contract electronic manufacturing services* .......... (856) 231-0777
Circuits Sales, 104 Alissa Dr., Toms River 08753
Owner—Thomas Solosky, 1 emp., *Printed circuit boards, including custom* .......... (732) 255-1325
Cygnus, LLC, 510 E. 41st St., Paterson 07504
Ptnr.—Gabriela Naydenov, 50 emp., *Contract electronic manufacturing of* .......... (973) 523-0668
Delta Circuits, Inc., 26 Spielman Rd., Fairfield 07004
Pres.—Pravin Bhuva, 30 emp., *Printed circuit boards* .......... (973) 575-3000
Doralex, Inc., 403 Saint Mihiel Dr., Riverside 08075
Pres.—Alexander Hwang, 6 emp., *Printed circuit boards, including circuits* .......... (856) 764-0694
Douglas Electrical Components, Inc., 5 Middlebury Blvd., Randolph 07869
Pres.—Edward Douglas, 76 emp., *Hermetically sealed electrical & fiber-optic* .......... (973) 627-8230
E C Tronics, Inc., 855 Industrial Hwy., Unit 5, Riverton 08077
Pres.—Edwin L. Willard, 15 emp., *Electronic cables & printed circuit* .......... (856) 829-7161
Flextron Systems, 85 Nicholson Rd., Gloucester City 08030
Pres.—Ish Chauhan, 11 emp., *Printed circuit boards & flexible printed* .......... (856) 742-0550
GAB Electronic Services, LLC, 1703 Industrial Hwy., Unit 8, Cinnaminson 08077
Pres.—Greg Bogle, 20 emp., *Printed circuit board assembly* .......... (856) 786-0108
Galaxy Circuits, Inc., 100 Somogyi Ct., South Plainfield 07080
Pres.—Navin Patel, 10 emp., *Printed circuit boards* .......... (908) 822-1400
Gray Contract Assembly, 102 Columbia Ave., Pitman 08071
Owner—William Gray, 4 emp., *Cable assemblies & printed circuit* .......... (856) 589-3263
JRE Incorporated, 22 Fairfield Pl., West Caldwell 07006
Pres.—James Tuscano, 35 emp., *Printed circuit board assemblies, including* .......... (973) 808-0055
K-Tron Electronics, 590 Woodbury Glassboro Rd., Sewell 08080
GM—Keith E. Kressley, 35 emp., *Electronic contract manufacturing,* .......... (856) 232-2300
MB Mfg., Inc., 1 Gwinup Rd., Blairstown 07825
Owner & Pres.—Mark Beesley, 7 emp., *Adjustable wave solder pallets & selective* .......... (908) 362-5588
Micro Logic, Inc., 31 Industrial Ave., Ste. 6, Mahwah 07430
CEO—Jim Lewis, 17 emp., *Corporate headquarters & printed circuit* .......... (201) 962-7512
Multiforce Systems Corp., 101 Wall St., Princeton 08540
V-P., Sales—Keith Griesinger, 19 emp., *Automated fuel management systems that* .......... (609) 683-4242
Omega Circuits & Engineering Corp., 8 Terminal Rd., New Brunswick 08901
Pres.—James C. Genes, Jr., 24 emp., *Printed circuit boards* .......... (732) 246-1661
Patriot American Solutions, LLC, 5 Astro Pl., Rockaway 07866
Pres.—William O'Connor, 50 emp., *Electronic contract manufacturing* .......... (973) 586-2717
PNC, Inc., 115 E. Centre St., Nutley 07110
Pres.—Sam Sangani, 80 emp., *Printed circuit boards & assemblies* .......... (973) 284-1600
PPI-Time Zero, Inc., 11 Madison Rd., Fairfield 07004
Chrm., Pres.—Dana Pittman, 150 emp., *Printed circuit board assemblies, sub-assembl* .......... (973) 278-6500
Precision Graphics, Inc., 21 County Line Rd., Somerville 08876
Pres.—Marybeth Weissman, 48 emp., *Printed circuit boards, including thru-hole* .......... (908) 707-8880
Precision Products Co., 219 Hergesell Ave., Maywood 07607
Pres.—Amit Kabaria, 15 emp., *Printed circuit boards* .......... (201) 712-5757
R & D Circuits, 3601 S. Clinton Ave., South Plainfield 07080
Pres.—Jim Russell, 125 emp., *Company headquarters & printed circuit* .......... (732) 549-4554
Reliance Electronics, Inc., 20 W. End Rd., Totowa 07512
Pres.—Peter Patel, 30 emp., *Printed circuit boards* .......... (973) 237-0400
Rockwood Holdings, Inc. (H Q), 100 Overlook Ctr., 1st Fl., Princeton 08540
Chrm.—Seifi Ghasemi, 35 emp., *Corporate headquarters; specialty chemicals* .......... (609) 514-0300

S.I.C.

SAK Technologies, Inc., 134 Gaston Ave., Garfield 07026
Pres.—Steven Karras, 20 emp., *Electronic contract manufacturing,* ........ (973) 340-8300
Shore P C, 3 Meridian Rd., Eatontown 07724
Owner & V-P.—David Rose, 20 emp., *Printed circuit boards assemblies* ........ (732) 380-0590
Sure Design, 5027 Industrial Rd., Unit 3, Farmingdale 07727
Ptnr.—Ken Thomas, 11 emp., *Printed circuit board assemblies &* ........ (732) 919-3066
SWEMCO, 1215 N. Church St., Moorestown 08057
Pres., COO—Richard P. Szczepkowski, 90 emp., *Contract manufacturing of printed circuit* ... (856) 222-9900
Technical Aids, Inc., 219 S. 18th St., East Orange 07018
Pres.—Alan Fenton, 12 emp., *Printed circuit boards, cables & wire* ........ (973) 674-1082
Technobox, Inc., 154 Cooper Rd., Ste. 901, West Berlin 08091
Pres.—Joseph Norris, 8 emp., *Printed circuit cards & boards & design* ........ (856) 809-2306
Thomas Instrumentation, Inc., 118 Kings Hwy., Cape May Court House 08210
CEO—Cassandra Gluyas, 11 emp., *Electronic circuit board assembly for* ........ (609) 624-7777
Thomas Instrumentation, Inc. (H Q), 133 Landing Rd., Cape May Court House 08210
CEO & Engr.—Cassandra Gluyas, 16 emp., *Corporate headquarters; custom microcontrolle* (609) 624-2630
Ventronics, Inc., 346 Monroe Ave., P.O. Box 142, Kenilworth 07033
Pres.—Joseph C. Venerus, 19 emp., *Transformers, inductors, chokes, coils* ........ (908) 272-9262

## 3674 Semiconductors & related devices

Advanced Solar Products, Inc. (H Q), 270 S. Main St., Ste. 203, Flemington 08822
Pres., CEO—Lyle Rawlings, 27 emp., *Corporate headquarters; commercial* ........ (908) 751-5818
America Semiconductor, LLC, 2810 Morris Ave., Ste. 204, Union 07083
★ Manager—Don Schroeder, 10 emp., *Semiconductors* ........ (908) 810-7364
American Microsemiconductor, Inc., 133 Kings Rd., P.O. Box 104, Madison 07940
Pres.—William Foley, 15 emp., *Semiconductors & devices* ........ (973) 377-9566
Anadigics, Inc., 141 Mount Bethel Rd., Warren 07059
Plt. Mgr.—Henry Ostrowski, 550 emp., *Radio frequency integrated circuits* ........ (908) 668-5000
Anchor Optical Co., 101 E. Gloucester Pike, Barrington 08007
★ Dir., Mktg.—Kirsten Bjork Jones, 100 emp., *Commercial, experimental, specialty* ........ (856) 573-6865
Applied Optronics, 111 Corporate Blvd., Bldg. J, South Plainfield 07080
GM—Victor Yantovsky, 15 emp., *Laser diodes* ........ (908) 753-6300
Archcon Technology, 5000 Hadley Rd., South Plainfield 07080
V-P., Sales—Arun Kumar, 150 emp., *Photonics* ........ (908) 757-8817
Chiral Photonics, Inc., 26 Chapin Rd., Unit 1104, P.O. Box 694, Pine Brook 07058
Pres.—Dan Neugroschl, 20 emp., *Ultra high-density optical I/O solutions* ........ (973) 732-0030
Dean Technology, Inc., 5027 Industrial Rd., Unit 4, P.O. Box 848, Farmingdale 07727
Pres., Opers. Mgr.—Craig Dean, 10 emp., *Corporate headquarters & high-voltage* ........ (732) 938-4499
Digitron Electronic Corp., 144 Market St., Kenilworth 07033
Pres.—Joe Schwartz, 9 emp., *Semiconductors & diodes* ........ (908) 245-7200
Discovery Semiconductors, Inc., 119 Silvia St., Ewing 08628
Pres.—Abhay Joshi, 20 emp., *Semiconductors* ........ (609) 434-1311
H. G. Schaevitz LLC, 102 Commerce Dr., Ste. 8, Moorestown 08057
CEO—Harold Schaevitz, 14 emp., *Industrial position, linear & rotary* ........ (856) 727-0250
Hybrid-Tek, Inc., 9 Trenton Lakewood Rd., Ste. 1, Clarksburg 08510
IT Mgr.—Michael Murphy, 14 emp., *Electronic thick film hybrids & assemblies* ........ (609) 259-3355
II-VI Advanced Materials, 20 Chapin Rd., Ste. 1007, P.O. Box 840, Pine Brook 07058
GM—Tom Anderson, 40 emp., *Silicon carbide wafers* ........ (973) 227-1551
Ikanos Communications, Inc., 100 Schultz Dr., Red Bank 07701
Dir., Opers.—Larry Hicks, 100 emp., *Computer chips* ........ (732) 345-7500
Innovative Photonic Solutions, 4250 U.S. Highway 1, Ste. 1, Monmouth Junction 08852
Pres.—John Connolly, 20 emp., *High-technology wavelength-stabilized* ........ (732) 355-9300
Intense-US, 1200 Airport Rd., Ste. A, North Brunswick 08902
Dir., Mktg.—Kevin Laughlin, 40 emp., *Semiconductor lasers* ........ (732) 249-2228
International Crystal Laboratories, 11 Erie St., Ste. 2, Garfield 07026
Pres.—Theresa Herpst, 20 emp., *Optical lenses, lasers & spectroscopic* ........ (973) 478-8944
Intersil Corp., 440 U.S. Highway 22 E., Ste. 100, Bridgewater 08807
GM—Paul S. Ferrazza, 24 emp., *High-performance analog semiconductors* ........ (908) 685-6000
IQE RF, LLC, 265 Davidson Ave., Ste. 141, Somerset 08873
GM—Alex Ceruzzi, 68 emp., *Semiconductor wafer products for wireless* ........ (732) 271-5990
ISOWAVE, 64 Harding Ave., Dover 07801
Pres., CEO—Stuart Samuelson, 15 emp., *Optical isolators* ........ (973) 328-7000
MEC TECH, Inc., 2200 Industrial Way S., Toms River 08755
Pres.—Richard Kulkaski, 30 emp., *Plastic injection molding & semiconductor* ........ (732) 505-0308
Mobile Power International, LLC, 1010 Old Egg Harbor Rd., Voorhees 08043
Owner—Anthony F. Amorosia, 12 emp., *Contract manufacturing & metal fabrication* ........ (856) 784-3195
Nanonex Corp., 1 Deerpark Dr., Ste. O, Monmouth Junction 08852
Chrm. & Founder—Stephen Y. Chou, 30 emp., *Nano/microstructure manufacturing equipment* (732) 355-1600
Natcore Technology, Inc. (H Q), 87 Maple Ave., Red Bank 07701
Chrm., Dir.—Brien Lundin, 5 emp., *Corporate headquarters; photovoltaic* ........ (732) 576-8800
NTE Electronics, Inc., 44 Farrand St., Bloomfield 07003
Owner—Andrew Licari, 72 emp., *Semiconductor components* ........ (973) 748-5089
OSI Laser Diode, Inc., 4 Olsen Ave., Edison 08820
GM—Rollin Ball, 50 emp., *Semiconductor lasers & telecommunication* ........ (732) 549-9001
Petra System, 1 Cragwood Rd., Ste. 303, South Plainfield 07080
Pres.—Steve Rhoades, 70 emp., *Utility-grade smart-grid interactive* ........ (908) 462-5200
PNY Technologies, Inc., 100 Jefferson Rd., Parsippany 07054
Pres.—Gadi Cohen, 200 emp., *Video & flash cards & memory chips* ........ (973) 515-9700
PowerTech, 0-02 Fair Lawn Ave., Fair Lawn 07410
Mng. Ptnr.—Marty Lanning, 9 emp., *High-power NPN silicon transistors* ........ (201) 791-5050
Princeton Lightwave, Inc., 2555 U.S. Highway 130, Ste. 1, Cranbury 08512
CEO—Mark Itzler, 40 emp., *Photon counting, dual band cameras,* ........ (609) 495-2600
Riber, Inc., 15 Liberty St., Metuchen 08840
Off. Mgr.—Karima Javios, 5 emp., *Semiconductor equipment* ........ (732) 603-0680
Rockwood Holdings, Inc. (H Q), 100 Overlook Ctr., 1st Fl., Princeton 08540
Chrm.—Seifi Ghasemi, 35 emp., *Corporate headquarters; specialty chemicals* ........ (609) 514-0300
Sonali Energees USA, LLC (H Q), 409 Grand Ave., Ste. 3, Englewood 07631
Pres., CEO—Pankaj Desai, 100 emp., *Company headquarters; photovoltaic* ........ (201) 297-1177
Sony Electronics, Inc., 1 Sony Dr., Park Ridge 07656
Facility Mgr.—Phillip D'Anna, 300 emp., *Consumer & professional audio & video* ........ (201) 930-1000
Space Power Electronics, Inc., 493 Westhill Rd., Glen Gardner 08826
Pres.—Ross J. Alestra, 20 emp., *Semiconductors* ........ (908) 689-6547
TDI Power, 36 Newburgh Rd., Hackettstown 07840
CEO—James Feely, 225 emp., *High technology power conversion products* ........ (908) 850-5088
Teesing USA, LLC, 10 Millpond Dr., Unit 7, Lafayette 07848
Sales Acct. & Sales Mgr.—John Sparnon, 3 emp., *Quick-connect hydraulic & pneumatic* ........ (973) 383-0691
Thorlabs, Inc., 56 Sparta Ave., Newton 07860
Pres., CEO—Alex Cable, 850 emp., *Corporate headquarters & optomechanical* ........ (973) 300-3000
UTC Aerospace Systems-ISR Systems (Sensors Unlimited, Inc.), 330 Carter Rd., Ste. 100, Princeton 08540
Dir., Sales & Mktg.—Robert Struthers, 48 emp., *Infrared sensors & cameras* ........ (609) 520-0610
Violin Memory, Inc., 33 Wood Ave. S., 3rd Fl., Iselin 08830
Off. Mgr.—Mary Martis, 57 emp., *Semiconductor devices* ........ (650) 396-1492
Wattlots, LLC, 1932 Long Hill Rd., Millington 07946
Founder & CEO—William E. S. Kaufman, 5 emp., *Solar-generated parking lot canopy* ........ (908) 626-1555

## 3675 Electronic capacitors

Electronic Concepts, Inc., 526 Industrial Way W., Eatontown 07724
Pres., CEO—Bernard Lavene, 150 emp., *Corporate headquarters & electronic* ........ (732) 542-7880
Metuchen Capacitors, Inc., 2139 Highway 35, Ste. 2, P.O. Box 399, Holmdel 07733
Pres.—Gary Ficsor, 26 emp., *Manufacturer & distributor high-voltage* ........ (732) 888-9700

## 3676 Electronic resistors

Metuchen Capacitors, Inc., 2139 Highway 35, Ste. 2, P.O. Box 399, Holmdel 07733
Pres.—Gary Ficsor, 26 emp., *Manufacturer & distributor high-voltage* ........ (732) 888-9700
Microelettrica-USA, LLC, 4 Middlebury Blvd., Ste. 12, Randolph 07869
CFO—Raffaele diBartolomeo, 15 emp., *Electronic components for industrial* ........ (973) 598-0806
Microwave Consulting Corp., 150 Railroad Ave., Paterson 07501
Pres.—Scott Warner, 4 emp., *Microwave equipment, including directional* ........ (973) 523-6700

## 3677 Electronic coils & transformers

AFP Transformers Corp., 206 Talmadge Rd., Edison 08817
Pres.—Greg Bongas, 75 emp., *Electrical cast coil, dry-type, control* ........ (732) 248-0305
APW Company, 5 Astro Pl., Ste. B, Rockaway 07866
Owner & Pres.—Jason Kellenberger, 10 emp., *Standard & custom electromagnets &* ........ (973) 627-0643
Bey Electronics Corp., 39 Kentucky Ave., Paterson 07503
GM & Fin. Mgr.—Rena Nuss, 12 emp., *Electronic transformers* ........ (973) 225-9494
C & C Jetronic, Inc., 126 Evergreen Rd., New Egypt 08533
Pres.—Cheng J. Chiang, 3 emp., *Electronic contract manufacturing of* ........ (609) 758-3553
Electronic Transformer Corp., 460 Totowa Ave., Paterson 07522
Pres.—Daniel Cezar, 45 emp., *Transformers* ........ (973) 942-2222
H I D Systems, Inc., 27 Brookfield Dr., Sparta 07871
Co-Pres.—Shannon Lesko, 10 emp., *Transformers & electric power supplies* ........ (973) 383-8535
Hunterdon Transformer Co., 75 Industrial Rd., Alpha 08865
Pres.—Mark Brock, 100 emp., *Company headquarters & transformers* ........ (908) 454-2400
Mech-Tronics, 100 Campus Dr., Mount Holly 08060
Pres.—Peter Reed, 7 emp., *Custom electronic transformers & inductors* ........ (609) 267-0680
Stonite Coil Corp., 476 Route 156, P.O. Box 11036, Yardville 08620
Pres.—William Engel, 25 emp., *Electronic coils* ........ (609) 585-6600
Torelco, Inc., 55 Industrial Dr., Alpha 08865
Pres.—Matt Peterson, 15 emp., *Transformers, inductors & reactors* ........ (908) 387-0814
Ventronics, Inc., 346 Monroe Ave., P.O. Box 142, Kenilworth 07033
Pres.—Joseph C. Venerus, 19 emp., *Transformers, inductors, chokes, coils* ........ (908) 272-9262

## 3678 Electronic connectors

Archtech Electronics Corp., 117 Docks Corner Rd., Ste. A, Dayton 08810
Owner—Peggy Foung, 36 emp., *Fiber-optic & copper networking cable* ........ (732) 355-1288
Central Components Mfg., LLC (H Q), 440 Lincoln Blvd., Middlesex 08846
Pres.—Marion Weldon, 20 emp., *Company headquarters; electronic connectors* ........ (732) 469-5720
Connector Technology, Inc., 5 Walter E. Foran Blvd., Ste. 4005, Flemington 08822
Cont.—Judith Angiuoli, 10 emp., *Electronic interconnect systems for* ........ (732) 745-2880
Da-Green Electronics, Inc., 37 Main St., P.O. Box 486, South River 08882
Pres.—Barry Greenberg, 33 emp., *Electronic, electrical & military connectors* ........ (732) 254-2735
Flexco Microwave, Inc., 17 Karville Rd., P.O. Box 115, Port Murray 07865
Pres., R & D Mgr.—William T. Pote, 40 emp., *Electronic cable & connectors* ........ (908) 835-1720
J. Jeb Products, LLC, 10 Cutler Ave., P.O. Box 40, Westville 08093
Pres.—Jack Sukala, 2 emp., *120 volt connectors for engine pre-heaters* ........ (856) 845-4455
Lapp USA, 29 Hanover Rd., Florham Park 07932
Pres.—Marc Mackin, 150 emp., *Company headquarters & rectangular,* ........ (973) 660-9700
Metuchen Capacitors, Inc., 2139 Highway 35, Ste. 2, P.O. Box 399, Holmdel 07733
Pres.—Gary Ficsor, 26 emp., *Manufacturer & distributor high-voltage* ........ (732) 888-9700
Powell Electronics, Inc., 200 Commodore Dr., Logan Township 08085
Pres.—E. J. Schilling, 150 emp., *Corporate headquarters & distributor* ........ (856) 241-8000
Princetel, Inc., 2560 E. State Street Ext., Hamilton 08619
Pres.—Barry Zhang, 40 emp., *Fiber-optic rotary joints, electrical* ........ (609) 588-8801
Quadrangle Products, 28 Harrison Ave., Bldg. 16-D, Englishtown 07726
Pres.—Michael Levine, 31 emp., *Custom cable assemblies for interfacing* ........ (732) 792-1234
Ventronics, Inc., 346 Monroe Ave., P.O. Box 142, Kenilworth 07033
Pres.—Joseph C. Venerus, 19 emp., *Transformers, inductors, chokes, coils* ........ (908) 272-9262
Volta Corp., 11 Industrial Dr., P.O. Box 1027, Laurence Harbor 08879
Acctg. Mgr.—James Brown, 10 emp., *Electrical connectors* ........ (732) 583-3300

## 3679 Electronic components, nec

A. B. Scantlebury Co., 112 Kings Hwy., Landing 07850
Off. Mgr.—John Spinelli, 8 emp., *Sheet metal fabrication, precision* ........ (973) 770-3000
Access Control Group, LLC, 2555 U.S. Highway 130 S., Ste. 2, Cranbury 08512
Pres.—Arun Patel, 25 emp., *Electronic assembly, wiring harnesses* ........ (908) 789-8700
Ace Electronics, Inc., 235 Liberty St., Metuchen 08840
Pres.—Ed Divila, 65 emp., *Corporate headquarters & cable assemblies* ........ (732) 603-9800
Advanced Technology Group, Inc., 101 Round Hill Dr., Rockaway 07866
Chrm., Pres.—Li Yuan Tao, 35 emp., *Glass-to-metal hybrid electronic packages* ........ (973) 627-6955
Aeroflex Control Components, Inc., 40 Industrial Way E., Eatontown 07724
Cont.—Jim Ebessen, 100 emp., *Radio frequency & microwave components* ........ (732) 460-0212
Ameral International, Inc., 7 Railroad Ln., Brooklawn 08030
Pres.—Louis Grieco, 15 emp., *Custom cable & wire harness assemblies* ........ (856) 456-9000
American Autowire, 150 Heller Pl., Bellmawr 08031
Pres.—Michael Manning, 67 emp., *Wiring harnesses, kits & accessories* ........ (856) 933-0801
American Fibertek, Inc., 120 Belmont Dr., Somerset 08873
Pres.—Jack Fernandes, 70 emp., *Fiber-optic security system components* ........ (732) 302-0660
American Radar Components, Inc., 39 Front St., Denville 07834
Pres., CEO—John Maluk, Jr., 8 emp., *Microwave components* ........ (973) 627-5530
Ametek Glasseal, Inc., 485 Oberlin Ave. S., Lakewood 08701
Hum. Res. Mgr.—Emma Tardiff, 160 emp., *Hermetic seals* ........ (732) 370-9100
Amperite Co., 4201 Tonnelle Ave., Ste. 6, North Bergen 07047
V-P., Admn. & Sales & Hum. Res. Mgr.—Judith Johnson, 20 emp., *Time delay relays, flashers* (201) 864-9503
Anatech Electronics, Inc., 70 Outwater Ln., Ste. 3, P.O. Box 2217, Garfield 07026
V-P., Sales & Mktg.—Sam Benzacar, 30 emp., *Electronic components & filters* ........ (973) 772-4242
Andrex, Inc., 101 Bilby Rd., Ste. E, Hackettstown 07840
Pres.—William T. Pote, 20 emp., *Brass, nickel & stainless steel flexible* ........ (908) 852-4377
Anta Electric, Inc., 32 Richboynton Rd., Dover 07801
Owner & Hum. Res. Mgr.—Tanya Khazen, 40 emp., *Printed circuit board & wire harness* ........ (973) 366-2222
Antron Technologies, Inc., 40 Brunswick Ave., Ste. 104, Edison 08817
Pres.—Sing Hung, 5 emp., *Power supplies* ........ (732) 205-0415

AOS Thermal Compounds, LLC, 22 Meridian Rd., Ste. 6, Eatontown 07724
Pres., CEO—John Ziemski, 12 emp., *Heat sink compounds & thermal interface* .......... (732) 389-5514
Applied Resource Corp., 105 W. Dewey Ave., Ste. 311, Wharton 07885
Pres.—Mark Colello, 22 emp., *Aerospace components & switches, including* .......... (973) 328-3882
Aqua Products, Inc., 25 Rutgers Ave., Cedar Grove 07009
Pres.—Tomer Porat, 200 emp., *Robotic swimming pool cleaners for* .......... (973) 857-2700
Archtech Electronics Corp., 117 Docks Corner Rd., Ste. A, Dayton 08810
Owner—Peggy Foung, 36 emp., *Fiber-optic & copper networking cable* .......... (732) 355-1288
Argus International, 424 Route 31 N., P.O. Box 559, Ringoes 08551
Pres.—B. J. Costello, 35 emp., *Printed circuit board manufacturing* .......... (609) 466-1677
Armel Electronics, Inc., 1601 75th St., North Bergen 07047
Pres.—Edward D. Johnsen, 19 emp., *Electronic components for military* .......... (201) 869-4300
Ascentta, Inc., 370 Campus Drive, Ste. 105, Somerset 08873
Dir. & Cust. Serv. Mgr.—Jennifer Ke, 7 emp., *Fiber-optic isolator, circulator &* .......... (732) 868-1766
ASCO Power Technologies, Inc., 5000 Sagemore Dr., Ste. 200, Marlton 08053
Opers. Mgr.—Jeff Dunn, 10 emp., *Backup power equipment* .......... (856) 810-9600
ASCO Power Technologies, L.P. (H Q), 50 Hanover Rd., Florham Park 07932
Pres.—Armand J. Visioli, 300 emp., *Divisional headquarters; automatic* .......... (800) 800-2726
Astro Sign Co., 230 E. High St., Route 322, Glassboro 08028
Pres.—Christopher Painter, 16 emp., *Signs, vehicle lettering, banners,* .......... (856) 881-4300
Astrolab, Inc., 4 Powderhorn Dr., Warren 07059
GM—Stephen J. Toma, 46 emp., *Microwave components* .......... (732) 560-3800
Avante International Technology, Inc., 70 Washington Rd., Princeton 08540
★ Pres.—Kevin Chung, 20 emp., *Voting equipment & RFID monitoring* .......... (609) 799-8896
Ballantine Laboratories, Inc., 312 Old Allerton Rd., Annandale 08801
Pres.—Russell McAdoo, 6 emp., *Electronic test & measurement equipment* .......... (908) 713-7742
Bel Fuse, Inc. (H Q), 206 Van Vorst St., Jersey City 07302
Pres., CEO—Daniel Bernstein, 22 emp., *Corporate headquarters; electronic* .......... (201) 432-0463
Blitz Safe Of America, Inc., 33 Honeck St., Englewood 07631
Pres.—Ira Marlowe, 15 emp., *Automobile stereos* .......... (201) 569-5000
Bomar Crystal Co., 201 Blackford Ave., P.O. Box 10, Middlesex 08846
Off. & Sales Mgr.—Minnie Lirio, 10 emp., *Electronic components, including quartz* .......... (732) 356-7787
Canare Corp. Of America, 45 Commerce Way, Unit C, Totowa 07512
CEO—Kazuo Urata, 30 emp., *Cables, connectors & fiber-optic links* .......... (973) 837-0070
Cardinal Components, Inc., 145 U.S. Highway 46 W., Wayne Interchange I, Wayne 07470
Pres.—Carl E. Fabend, 15 emp., *Standard & custom quartz crystals,* .......... (973) 785-1333
Casio America, Inc. (H Q), 570 Mount Pleasant Ave., Dover 07801
Chrm.—Shigenori Itoh, 180 emp., *Corporate headquarters; computers &* .......... (973) 361-5400
Castle Industries, Inc., 120 Sylvan Ave., Ste. 107, Englewood Cliffs 07632
Pres.—Artie Schloss, 20 emp., *Electrical components & contract assembly* .......... (201) 585-8400
Ccard, Inc., 17 Belleterre Dr., Manalapan 07726
Pres.—Chris Cardinale, 6 emp., *Electronic cable assemblies & printed* .......... (732) 303-8264
Celco, Inc., 14 Industrial Ave., 3rd Fl., Mahwah 07430
V-P.—John Constantine, Jr., 3 emp., *Corporate headquarters & electronic* .......... (201) 327-1123
Circuit Tech Assembly, LLC, 341 New Albany Rd., Ste. 130, Moorestown 08057
Pres.—Bill Sherlock, Jr., 12 emp., *Contract electronic manufacturing services* .......... (856) 231-0777
Clantech, Inc., 198 Highway 206 S., Hillsborough 08844
GM—David Gracie, 2 emp., *Electronic components & equipment* .......... (908) 281-7667
Compex Corp., 439 Commerce Ln., Ste. 1, West Berlin 08091
Pres.—David Gordon, 45 emp., *Electronic components* .......... (856) 335-2277
Components Corp., 6 Kinsey Pl., Denville 07834
Sales Mgr., Natl.—Chris Minter, 17 emp., *Wire forms & connectors* .......... (973) 627-0290
Computer Crafts, Inc., 57 Thomas Rd., Hawthorne 07506
Pres.—Donald Harkins, 80 emp., *Computer cable assemblies* .......... (973) 423-3500
Comtron, Inc., 391 State Route 33 E., Englishtown 07726
Pres.—Gunther Wackerman, 14 emp., *Electromechanical devices, cellular* .......... (732) 446-7571
Comus International, Inc., 454 Allwood Rd., Clifton 07012
Pres., CEO—Robert P. Romano, 80 emp., *Tilt, tip-over, float & reed switches* .......... (973) 777-6900
Consolidated Steel & Aluminum Fence, 316 N. 12th St., P.O. Box 643, Kenilworth 07033
Pres.—Paul Cacicedo, 60 emp., *Commercial chain-link, steel, aluminum* .......... (908) 272-6262
Conta-Clip, Inc., 400 Apgar Dr., Ste. D, P.O. Box 6510, Somerset 08873
Pres.—Rudolph Abraham, 6 emp., *Electronic terminal blocks* .......... (732) 564-0705
Control Products, 280 Ridgedale Ave., East Hanover 07936
V-P.—Mac Stuhler, 55 emp., *Waterproof & thermal switches & linear* .......... (973) 887-9400
COTE-L Industries, Inc., 1542 Jefferson St., Teaneck 07666
CEO—Avi Aviner, 6 emp., *Safety, polyurethane, epoxy, waterproofing* .......... (201) 836-0733
Cryofab, Inc., 540 N. Michigan Ave., P.O. Box 485, Kenilworth 07033
Owner & Co-Pres.—Vincent J. Grillo, 49 emp., *Cryogenic equipment & accessories* .......... (908) 686-3636
Cryogenic Equipment & Repair Co., Inc. (Cerco), 3143 Bordentown Ave., Bldg. 4, Parlin 08859
Pres.—Catherine Helmer, 5 emp., *New & refurbished cryogenic equipment* .......... (732) 727-1555
Custom Cable Crafters, Inc., 1830 Gallagher Dr., Ste. 103, Vineland 08360
Pres., CEO—Robert A. Nestor, 10 emp., *Cable assemblies* .......... (856) 696-3151
Daburn Electronics & Cable, Inc., 44 Richboynton Rd., Dover 07801
Pres., CEO—Ed Flaherty, 29 emp., *Electronic wire, cable, heat shrinkable* .......... (973) 328-3200
Data Access Datapatch, Inc., 40 Eisenhower Dr., Ste. 101, Paramus 07652
Pres.—Mark Barbalat, 65 emp., *Computer cables* .......... (201) 843-5468
Data Delay Devices, Inc., 3 Mount Prospect Ave., Clifton 07013
Pres.—Nino Lupi, 8 emp., *Electronic components, timing devices* .......... (973) 773-2299
Database Access Systems, Inc., 60 Midvale Rd., Ste. 206, P.O. Box 126, Mountain Lakes 07046
Pres., CEO—Michael Palazzi, 4 emp., *Fiber-optic network cards & switches* .......... (973) 335-0800
Dataprobe, Inc., 1-B Pearl Ct., Allendale 07401
Pres.—David Weiss, 15 emp., *Electronic equipment, including remote* .......... (201) 934-9944
Delaire U. S. A., Inc., 1913 Atlantic Ave., Ste. R-1, Manasquan 08736
Pres.—Lorraine Hallock, 20 emp., *Custom RF & fiber optic cable assemblies* .......... (732) 528-4520
Deltronic Crystal Industries, 60 Harding Ave., Dover 07801
Pres.—Stuart Samuelson, 20 emp., *Laser crystals for optoelectronic materials* .......... (973) 328-7000
Dewey Electronics Corp., 27 Muller Rd., Oakland 07436
Pres., CEO—John H. D. Dewey, 30 emp., *Electronic components, 2kW diesel generator* .......... (201) 337-4700
Dialight Corporation (H Q), 1501 State Highway 34 S., Farmingdale 07727
CEO—Roy Burton, 85 emp., *Corporate headquarters; solid-state* .......... (732) 919-3119
Douglas Electrical Components, Inc., 5 Middlebury Blvd., Randolph 07869
Pres.—Edward Douglas, 76 emp., *Hermetically sealed electrical & fiber-optic* .......... (973) 627-8230
E C Tronics, Inc., 855 Industrial Hwy., Unit 5, Riverton 08077
Pres.—Edwin L. Willard, 15 emp., *Electronic cables & printed circuit* .......... (856) 829-7161
Edgewater Mfg. Co., Inc., 17-10 Willow St., Fair Lawn 07410
V-P., Opers.—Rachell Fischbein, 12 emp., *Electrical fittings* .......... (201) 664-0022
Electro Impulse Laboratory, Inc., 1805 Route 33, Neptune 07753
Pres.—Mark Rubin, 41 emp., *Custom closed-loop cooling systems* .......... (732) 776-5800
Electromotive, Inc., 55 Brown Ave., Springfield 07081
Pres.—Thomas Barta, 10 emp., *Electrical solenoids* .......... (973) 564-8809
Electronic Subassemblies, Inc., 1541 New Brooklyn Rd., Sicklerville 08081
V-P., GM—James J. Cunningham, 30 emp., *Cable, wire harness, electro & mechanical* .......... (856) 629-2492

Elemco Building Controls, 14 Ilene Ct., Bldg. 11, Unit 1, Hillsborough 08844
Pres.—Joe Wozniak, 8 emp., *Mechanical HVAC, process automation* .......... (908) 281-2201
Ellenby Technologies, Inc., 412 Grandview Ave., Woodbury Heights 08097
CEO—Bob Dobbins, 53 emp., *Contract electronic manufacturing of* .......... (856) 848-2020
Excel Display Corp., 100 Jersey Ave., Ste. A206, New Brunswick 08901
Pres., CFO & GM—Tom K. Shih, 5 emp., *Electronic components, including liquid* .......... (732) 246-3728
Fancort Industries, Inc., 31 Fairfield Pl., West Caldwell 07006
Pres., CEO & MIS Mgr.—Ronald J. Corey, 20 emp., *Electronic production racks & fixtures* .......... (973) 575-0610
FibroLAN, Inc., 350 W. Passaic St., Ste. 23, Rochelle Park 07662
V-P., Sales—Paul Ellett, 40 emp., *Layer 2 access switches & single channel* .......... (201) 843-1626
FMDK Technologies, Inc., 63 Ramapo Valley Rd., Lobby 4, Mahwah 07430
Pres.—Frank Gallo, 4 emp., *Electronic control system spare parts* .......... (201) 828-9822
Francis Metals Co., Inc., 687 Prospect St., Ste. 430, Lakewood 08701
Pres.—Matt Deiner, 20 emp., *Armored electronic cable & commercial* .......... (732) 761-0500
FRC Electrical Industries, 705 Central Ave., New Providence 07974
Sales & Mktg. Mgr.—Dennis King, 50 emp., *Hermetic seals* .......... (908) 464-3200
Frezzolini Electronics, Inc., 7 Valley St., Hawthorne 07506
Pres.—James Crawford, 15 emp., *Professional portable powered lighting* .......... (973) 427-1160
FSR, Inc., 244 Bergen Blvd., West Paterson 07424
Chrm.—William Fitzsimmons, 80 emp., *Signal management & infrastructure* .......... (973) 785-4347
FUJIFILM U.S.A., Inc., 1100 King Georges Post Rd., Edison 08837
Facility Mgr.—Theresa Collins, 60 emp., *Professional & consumer films, cameras* .......... (732) 857-3000
Fujipoly America Corp., 900 Milik St., P.O. Box 119, Carteret 07008
Pres.—Frank Hobler, 30 emp., *Silicon rubber electronic components* .......... (732) 969-0100
Future Electronics Corp., 959 Route 46 E., Ste. 303, Parsippany Pl, Parsippany 07054
Dir. & GM—Tom Tosco, 10 emp., *Electronic components* .......... (973) 299-0400
G T Microwave, Inc., 2 Emery Ave., Ste. 2, Randolph 07869
Pres. & Chief Engr.—George Apsley, 23 emp., *Microwave components & electrical devices* .. (973) 361-5700
Garan Electronics, Inc., 223 Stirling Rd., Unit C, Warren 07059
Mng. Ptnr.—Robert Mills, 10 emp., *Plastic electronic hardware, including* .......... (908) 484-7100
GAW Associates, Inc., 670 Deer Rd., Unit A, Cherry Hill 08034
Pres.—Kathleen Gaw-Betz, 10 emp., *Electronic cabinets/racks, custom cable* .......... (856) 608-1428
General Electronic Enterprises, Inc., 132 W. Main St., Rahway 07065
Pres.—William Piegari, 12 emp., *Perimeter electric & hydronic heating* .......... (732) 381-1144
General Reliance Corp., 88 Ford Rd., Ste. 20, Denville 07834
Pres.—Christopher Schmidt, 29 emp., *Complex electronic molded cable assemblies* .......... (973) 361-1400
Gray Contract Assembly, 102 Columbia Ave., Pitman 08071
Owner—William Gray, 4 emp., *Cable assemblies & printed circuit* .......... (856) 589-3263
Greetingtap, LLC, 832 Spicer Ave., South Plainfield 07080
★ Owner—Kadeer Beg, 6 emp., *Personalizable video greeting cards* .......... (347) 731-4263
H A Z Laboratories, 39 Hartmans Corner Rd., Washington 07882
Pres.—Henry Zajac, 15 emp., *Industrial controls* .......... (908) 453-3300
H I D Systems, Inc., 27 Brookfield Dr., Sparta 07871
Co-Pres.—Shannon Lesko, 10 emp., *Transformers & electric power supplies* .......... (973) 383-8535
Hamilton Buhl, 80 Little Falls Rd., Fairfield 07004
V-P.—Madeline Piccone, 19 emp., *Technology & AV equipment for educational* .......... (201) 229-9800
Harrison Electro Mechanical Corp., 1607 Coach St., Rahway 07065
Pres. & Sys. Engr.—William A. Piegari, 13 emp., *HVAC DDC control systems & commercial* .. (732) 382-6008
Harrison Seal Corp., 1201 Kennedy Blvd., Manville 08835
Pres.—Jack Argento, 4 emp., *Hermetic seals* .......... (908) 722-3322
Industrial Electronic Devices, Inc., 8 Bartles Corner Rd., Bldg. 101, Flemington 08822
Pres.—Jerry Kalajian, 5 emp., *Open frame, enclosed & watertight industrial* .......... (908) 806-2255
Innodyne Engineering, 1711 Ginesi Dr., Unit 2, Freehold 07728
GM—Jim Mort, 5 emp., *Electronic components & wires* .......... (646) 240-0200
Integrated Microwave Technologies, LLC, 200 International Dr., Mount Olive 07828
CFO—Robert Chiarulli, 80 emp., *Digital microwave video equipment &* .......... (908) 852-3700
International Tower Supply, 851 Bethel Ave., Pennsauken 08110
Mng. Ptnr.—Michael Moskowitz, 16 emp., *Wireless infrastructure components,* .......... (856) 317-0005
J M L Computer Products, Inc., 9 Wheelwright Ln., Cherry Hill 08003
Pres.—John McLaughlin, 10 emp., *Computer cable assembly* .......... (856) 753-8500
Jerome Industries Corp., 730 Division St., Elizabeth 07201
Graphic Designer—Ben Ahhi, 100 emp., *Custom & military grade low leakage* .......... (908) 353-5700
Jersey Microwave, LLC, 230 U.S. Highway 206, Ste. 407, Flanders 07836
Pres.—Thanh Nguyen, 28 emp., *Microwave components, including receivers* .......... (908) 684-2390
Jersey Strand & Cable, Inc., 259 Center St., Phillipsburg 08865
Pres.—Al Pratt, 40 emp., *Custom & stock small & miniature ferrous* .......... (908) 213-9350
Jettron Products, Inc., 56 Route 10 W., P.O. Box 337, East Hanover 07936
Pres.—Ed Balzarotti, 20 emp., *High-voltage cable assemblies & precision* .......... (973) 887-0571
Johanson Mfg. Corp., 301 Rockaway Valley Rd., Boonton 07005
Pres., CEO—Nancy Johanson, 60 emp., *Electronic components, including trimmer* .......... (973) 334-2676
JP Rotella Co., Inc., 20 E. Barbour St., Haledon 07508
Pres.—John Rotella, Jr., 7 emp., *Electronic components, including subassemblie* .......... (973) 942-2559
JRE Incorporated, 22 Fairfield Pl., West Caldwell 07006
Pres.—James Tuscano, 35 emp., *Printed circuit board assemblies, including* .......... (973) 808-0055
K R Electronics, Inc., 91 Avenel St., Avenel 07001
Pres.—Charles Kiall, 13 emp., *Electronic filters* .......... (732) 636-1900
Key Joy USA, LLC, 3 Kellogg Ct., Ste. 12, Edison 08817
★ Regional Mgr.—Jerry Huang, 15 emp., *Computer cable assemblies & wire harnesses* .......... (732) 339-0450
Kinetics Industries, Inc., 140 Stokes Ave., Ewing 08638
Pres.—Ronald Secrest, 30 emp., *Power rectifiers & field excitation* .......... (609) 883-9700
Kratos-CTI, 9 Whippany Rd., Bldg. A-1, Whippany 07981
Dir., Qual. Control—Art Alexander, 70 emp., *Oscillators & synthesizers* .......... (973) 884-2580
LC Engineers, Inc., 1471 Pinewood St., Rahway 07065
Pres. & IT Mgr.—Suresh Kapoor, 10 emp., *Contract commercial electronic, production* .......... (732) 340-9190
Liberty Electronics, 465 Route 53, Denville 07834
Pres.—Thomas Ferrante, 4 emp., *Voice & data products* .......... (973) 625-7966
Liberty Electronics, Inc., 465 E. Main St., Denville 07834
Owner—Tom Ferrante, 4 emp., *Wire & cable & cable assemblies* .......... (973) 625-7963
Linear Photonics, LLC, 3 Nami Ln., Ste. 7-C, Hamilton 08619
Pres.—Allen Katz, 10 emp., *Fiber-optic detectors, receivers, photonics* .......... (609) 584-5747
Lingraphicare America, Inc., 103 Carnegie Ctr., Ste. 204, Princeton 08540
CEO—Andrew Gomory, 25 emp., *Electronic interface communication* .......... (609) 275-1300
Link Computer Graphics, Inc., 17-A Daniel Rd., Fairfield 07004
Pres.—Hung-Wei Yeh, 10 emp., *Digital storage oscilloscopes, logic* .......... (973) 808-8990
Lockheed Martin, 199 Borton Landing Rd., Rm. 108-108, P.O. Box 1027, Moorestown 08057
V-P., GM—Jeff Bantle, 4500 emp., *Electronic components* .......... (856) 722-4100
Lux Entertainment, LLC, 629 E. 19th St., Paterson 07514
Owner—Andrew Vaccaro, 3 emp., *Environmentally controlled protective* .......... (888) 282-8425
Macro Sensors, 7300 Route 130 N., Bldg. 22, Pennsauken 08110
Sales & Mktg. Mgr.—Eileen Otto, 30 emp., *LVDT based position sensors & support* .......... (856) 662-8000
Mars International, Inc., 60 Kingsbridge Rd., Piscataway 08854
CEO—Charles Engelstein, 50 emp., *Electronic component assemblies* .......... (908) 233-0044

S.I.C.

★ **Indicates new listing this edition.**

Masi Electronics, Don, 25 Walden Pl., West Caldwell 07006
Owner—Don Masi, 5 emp., *Security systems, including intercoms* .................. (973) 618-6288
Mayfair Technology, LLC, 66 Witherspoon St., Princeton 08542
Member & GM—James Furey, 10 emp., *Single-use pressure sensors* .................. (609) 802-1262
Meca Electronics, Inc., 459 E. Main St., Denville 07834
Pres.—William C. Davo, 45 emp., *RF/microwave components, including* .................. (973) 625-0661
Medco West, 25-21 Di Carolis Ct., Hackensack 07601
V-P., Sales—Don Hahn, 25 emp., *Contract electronic, through-hole,* .................. (201) 457-9260
MEGA Electronics, Inc., 4-B Jules Ln., New Brunswick 08901
Pres.—Elfie Schwarzinger, 15 emp., *Power supplies, including AC/DC & DC/DC* .................. (732) 249-2656
Mercury Commercial Electronics, 2 Henderson Dr., Ste. B, Caldwell 07006
Pres.—Tony Pospishil, 80 emp., *Commercial electronics, including RF/microwav* .................. (973) 244-1040
Merrimac Industries, Inc., 41 Fairfield Pl., West Caldwell 07006
V-P., COO—Reynold K. Green, 120 emp., *Electronic components* .................. (973) 575-1300
Microelettrica-USA, LLC, 4 Middlebury Blvd., Ste. 12, Randolph 07869
CFO—Raffaele diBartolomeo, 15 emp., *Electronic components for industrial* .................. (973) 598-0806
Microlab/FXR, 25 Eastmans Rd., Parsippany 07054
Dir., Field Sales—Rand Skopas, 120 emp., *Passive wireless electronic components* .................. (973) 386-9696
Microwave Consulting Corp., 150 Railroad Ave., Paterson 07501
Pres.—Scott Warner, 4 emp., *Microwave equipment, including directional* .................. (973) 523-6700
Mid-Eastern Industries Div, Technology Dynamics, Inc, 100 School St., Bergenfield 07621
V-P., GM—Daniel R. Ellenback, 110 emp., *Linear power supplies & DC power systems* .................. (201) 385-0500
MISTRAS Group, Inc., 195 Clarksville Rd., Princeton Junction 08550
Chrm., CEO—Sotirios Vahaviolos, 150 emp., *Nondestructive ultrasonic & acoustic* .................. (609) 716-4100
Molecu-Wire Corp., 1215 Kennedy Blvd., Manville 08835
★ Pres., CEO—Vinod K. Barot, 12 emp., *Wire & cable harness assemblies, including* .................. (908) 429-0300
Motek Industries, LLC, 250 Park Ave., Teaneck 07666
Pres.—Ruth Hacohen, 12 emp., *Contract electronic manufacturing for* .................. (201) 836-4167
Motion Control Technologies, Inc., 158 W. Clinton St., Ste. FF, Dover 07801
Pres.—Frank Heidinger, 10 emp., *Wire rope cable assemblies, including* .................. (973) 361-2226
National Communication, Inc., 69 Washington St., West Orange 07052
Pres., Hum. Res. Mgr.—Andrew Brooke, 17 emp., *Cable assemblies* .................. (973) 325-3151
Omega Shielding Products, Inc., 9 Emery Ave., Randolph 07869
Pres.—Leon Komsa, 9 emp., *EMI & RFI electronic shielding* .................. (973) 366-0080
Oxford Instruments Superconducting Technology, Inc., 600 Milik St., Carteret 07008
Pres.—Jeff Parrell, 212 emp., *Corporate headquarters & superconductor* .................. (732) 541-1300
Paige Electric Co. L. P., 1160 Springfield Rd., P.O. Box 368, Union 07083
Pres.—Louis Grotta, 40 emp., *Company headquarters & electronic &* .................. (908) 687-7810
Palmer Electronics, Inc., 156 Belmont Ave., Garfield 07026
Pres.—Victor R. Palmeri, 4 emp., *Custom adaptors, connectors, heads,* .................. (973) 772-5900
Panasonic Corp. Of North America (H Q), 2 River Front Plz., Newark 07102
Chrm., CEO—Joseph M. Taylor, 800 emp., *Corporate headquarters; electric motors* .................. (201) 348-7500
Panasonic Industrial Devices Sales Co. Of America (H Q), 2 River Front Plz., 7th Fl., Newark 07102
Cont.—Kane Inoue, 180 emp., *Company headquarters; electronic components* .................. (908) 464-3550
Panel Components & Systems, Inc., 149 Main St., Stanhope 07874
★ Owner—Tanja Lewit, 10 emp., *Electrical components, including transformers* .................. (973) 448-9400
Panurgy OEM, 701 Ford Rd., Rockaway 07866
Pres.—Rick Levinson, 135 emp., *Contract electronics, computer hardware* .................. (973) 625-4056
Paramount Products, Inc., 1104 Industrial Pkwy., Brick 08724
Pres.—H. C. Vogel, 10 emp., *Custom, precision & drawn stampings* .................. (732) 458-9200
Park Plus, Inc., 480 Main Ave., Ste. 1, Wallington 07057
CEO—Ronald Astrup, 9 emp., *Valet parking equipment & high density* .................. (973) 574-8020
Parker Chomerics, 135 Bryant Ave., Cranford 07016
Regional Mgr.—Eric Krohto, 50 emp., *Electronic & magnetic interference* .................. (908) 272-5500
Pendulum Audio Systems, Inc., P.O. Box 339, Gillette 07933
Pres.—Gregory Gualtieri, 10 emp., *Professional vacuum tube recording* .................. (908) 665-9333
Phillips Scientific, 31 Industrial Ave., Ste. 1, Mahwah 07430
Pres.—Thomas Phillips, 15 emp., *Data acquisition electronics* .................. (201) 934-8015
Powerspec, Inc., 1 Linsley Pl., Metuchen 08840
★ Manager—Peter Elkoury, 7 emp., *Contract manufacturing & assembly of* .................. (732) 494-9490
PPI-Time Zero, Inc., 11 Madison Rd., Fairfield 07004
Chrm., Pres.—Dana Pittman, 150 emp., *Printed circuit board assemblies, sub-assembl* .................. (973) 278-6500
Pressure Controls, Inc., 406 Courtlandt St., Belleville 07109
Plt. Mgr.—Paul Emmarco, 26 emp., *Pressure switches, flow switches &* .................. (973) 751-5002
Princetel, Inc., 2560 E. State Street Ext., Hamilton 08619
Pres.—Barry Zhang, 40 emp., *Fiber-optic rotary joints, electrical* .................. (609) 588-8801
Princeton Microwave Technology, 5 Nami Ln., Trenton 08619
Co-Pres.—Amarjit Kaur, 13 emp., *Microwave components* .................. (609) 586-8140
Protection One, Inc., 50 Williams Pkwy., Ste. L, East Hanover 07936
GM—Frank Benna, 18 emp., *Burglar alarm, fire alarm, CCTV & access* .................. (973) 227-3421
Quadrangle Products, 28 Harrison Ave., Bldg. 16-D, Englishtown 07726
Pres.—Michael Levine, 31 emp., *Custom cable assemblies for interfacing* .................. (732) 792-1234
R F L Electronics, Inc., 353 Powerville Rd., Boonton 07005
Pres.—Tony King, 110 emp., *Electronic communication & relaying* .................. (973) 334-3100
R S Microwave Co., Inc., 22 Park Pl., P.O. Box 273, Butler 07405
Pres.—Richard V. Snyder, 49 emp., *Microwave filters multiplexers & subassemblie* .................. (973) 492-1207
Radiant Communications Corp., 5001 Hadley Rd., P.O. Box 867, South Plainfield 07080
Pres.—Thomas Lewis, 60 emp., *IP media & fiber-optic communications* .................. (908) 757-7444
Ram Electronic Industries Inc., 1704 Taylors Ln., Ste. 7, Cinnaminson 08077
Pres.—Steve Misbin, 60 emp., *Audio & video cables & equipment, computer* .................. (856) 864-0999
Raritan Computer, Inc., 400 Cottontail Ln., Somerset 08873
Chrm., CEO—Ching-I Hsu, 150 emp., *Data center infrastructure management* .................. (732) 764-8886
Rectico, Inc., 12 Gloria Ln., Unit 1, Fairfield 07004
Pres.—Scott Sandler, 10 emp., *Crating, corrugated boxes & contract* .................. (973) 575-0009
Redkoh Industries, Inc., 300 Valley Rd., Hillsborough 08844
Pres.—Paul Ford, 23 emp., *Electronic pollution control components* .................. (908) 369-1590
Reflex Analytical Corporation, 643 Albert Pl., Ridgewood 07450
V-P., Hum. Res. & IT Mgr.—Tony Jacobini, 5 emp., *Spectroscopy accessories & photonic* .................. (201) 444-8958
Repco, Inc., 6 Eves Dr., Marlton 08053
Pres. & Fin. Mgr.—Ann Braytenbah, 11 emp., *Replacement electrical contacts, coils* .................. (800) 822-9190
Riber, Inc., 15 Liberty St., Metuchen 08840
Off. Mgr.—Karima Javios, 5 emp., *Semiconductor equipment* .................. (732) 603-0680
Richards Mfg., 517 Lyons Ave., Irvington 07111
Ptnr. & Pres.—Joseph Bier, 150 emp., *Electric cable connectors* .................. (973) 371-1771
Robodyssey Systems, LLC, 20 Quimby Ave., Trenton 08610
Pres.—David Peins, 2 emp., *Educational systems for teaching practical* .................. (609) 585-8535
SAK Technologies, Inc., 134 Gaston Ave., Garfield 07026
Pres.—Steven Karras, 20 emp., *Electronic contract manufacturing,* .................. (973) 340-8300
Samsung Electronics America, Inc., 85 Challenger Rd., Ridgefield Park 07660
V-P., Bus. Dev.—Thomas Rhee, 300 emp., *Electronic components, including mobile* .................. (201) 229-4000
Schaffner EMC, Inc., 52 Mayfield Ave., Edison 08837
Pres.—Ken Bellero, 17 emp., *Electronic components* .................. (732) 225-9533
Schneider Electric, 2001 Highway 46, Ste. 402, Parsippany 07054
Opers. Mgr.—Ashish Sawardekar, 30 emp., *Electrical distribution, control &* .................. (973) 263-6100
Sensigraphics, Inc., 105 W. Park Dr., Mount Laurel 08054
Pres.—Harold Gilham, 30 emp., *Custom membrane switches, keypads,* .................. (856) 853-9100
Silver Cloud Mfg. Co., 525 Orange St., Millville 08332
V-P., Sales & Mktg.—Robert Cowperthwait, 50 emp., *Display filters, lenses, EMI/RFI shielding* (856) 825-8900
Somfy Systems, Inc., 121 Herrod Blvd., Dayton 08810
CEO—Michael Lee, 80 emp., *Specialized motors & electronic controls* .................. (609) 395-1300
Sony Electronics, Inc., 1 Sony Dr., Park Ridge 07656
Facility Mgr.—Phillip D'Anna, 300 emp., *Consumer & professional audio & video* .................. (201) 930-1000
SPEM Corp., 403 Bell St., Piscataway 08854
Pres.—Satish Patel, 9 emp., *Contract manufacturing of electronic* .................. (732) 356-3366
Spencer Industries, Inc., 80 Holmes St., P.O. Box 128, Belleville 07109
Pres.—Martin Lawrence, 25 emp., *Corporate headquarters & military replacement* .................. (973) 751-2200
Stanley Access Technologies, LLC, 17 Marlen Dr., Ste. C, Trenton 08691
Br. Mgr.—Joe Marino, 30 emp., *Power-operated security & fire doors* .................. (609) 890-0877
Swatch Group (U.S.), Inc. (H Q), 1200 Harbor Blvd., 7th Fl., Weehawken 07086
Pres.—Caroline Faivet, 125 emp., *Corporate headquarters; pulsed laser/sources* .................. (201) 271-1400
Symcon, Inc., 47 Cedar Ln., West Milford 07480
Pres.—Stella Scilingo, 6 emp., *Electromechanical assemblies* .................. (201) 967-7378
Synergy Microwave Corp., 201 McLean Blvd., Paterson 07504
Pres.—Meta Rhode, 90 emp., *Microwave components, including swtiches* .................. (973) 881-8800
Syscom Tech, 1537 Glen Ave., Moorestown 08057
Owner—Peter Aninnos, 60 emp., *Wire harness & cable assemblies* .................. (856) 642-7661
T & E Industries, Inc., 215 Watchung Ave., Orange 07050
Pres.—Edward McEntee, 48 emp., *Electronic components & glass-to-metal* .................. (973) 672-5454
T/Mac, Inc., 100 Jersey Ave., Bldg. D-6, New Brunswick 08901
Pres.—Marvin Wurtzelman, 10 emp., *Radio frequency & microwave power amplifiers* .................. (732) 247-0022
Taylor Microwave, Inc., 48 Industrial W., Clifton 07012
Pres.—Breni Saftre, 8 emp., *Industrial microwave components* .................. (973) 890-7763
TBT Group, Inc., 191 Heller Pl., Bellmawr 08031
Plt. Mgr.—Elias Medina, 4 emp., *Customized piezoelectric materials* .................. (856) 753-4500
TDK-Lambda, Inc., 405 Essex Rd., Neptune 07753
Pres.—Pascal Chausson, 165 emp., *Power supplies* .................. (732) 922-9300
Tech 21 USA, Inc., 790 Bloomfield Ave., Ste. B-1, Clifton 07012
Pres.—Andrew Barta, 20 emp., *Electric guitar & bass amplifiers,* .................. (973) 777-6996
Techflex, 29 Brookfield Dr., Sparta 07871
Pres.—William Dermody III, 25 emp., *Advanced braided sleeving & related* .................. (973) 300-9242
Technical Aids, Inc., 219 S. 18th St., East Orange 07018
Pres.—Alan Fenton, 12 emp., *Printed circuit boards, cables & wire* .................. (973) 674-1082
Technical Systems Group, Inc., 28 Muller Pl., Little Falls 07424
Pres.—Peter Y. Chin, 7 emp., *Custom factory automation, safety &* .................. (973) 785-1118
Technobox, Inc., 154 Cooper Rd., Ste. 901, West Berlin 08091
Pres.—Joseph Norris, 8 emp., *Printed circuit cards & boards & design* .................. (856) 809-2306
Technology Dynamics, Inc., 100 School St., Bergenfield 07621
Pres.—Aron Levy, 90 emp., *Switching power supplies & DC-DC converters* .................. (201) 385-0500
Telegenix, Inc., 71 Indel Ave., P.O. Box 577, Rancocas 08073
Pres.—Joseph Miller, 14 emp., *Custom & contract voice communications* .................. (609) 265-3910
Thosani, Inc., 150 Cooper Rd., Ste. E-12, West Berlin 08091
Pres., Treas.—Jitendra Thosani, 5 emp., *Wire harness & cable assemblies* .................. (856) 753-9000
TICO Mfg., Inc., 1044 Industrial Dr., Unit 9, West Berlin 08091
Pres.—Roger Sobradl, 9 emp., *Military, commercial & industrial fasteners* .................. (856) 767-8430
Toth Inc., 6970 Central Hwy., Pennsauken 08109
V-P.—Theodore Toth, Jr., 48 emp., *Precision machining & assembly of machined* .................. (856) 662-8700
Trek Connect, 120 Mount Holly Bypass, Lumberton 08048
Dir.—Craig Jacobs, 30 emp., *Cable & harness assemblies & switching* .................. (856) 608-0901
Unicorp, Inc., 291 Cleveland St., Orange 07050
Pres.—Steven Mercadante, 40 emp., *Precision electronic component hardware* .. (973) 674-1700
Union City Filament Corp., 1039-A Hoyt Ave., P.O. Box 777, Ridgefield 07657
CEO—Joseph E. Celia III, 30 emp., *Electronic components* .................. (201) 945-3366
United Silica Products, Inc., 3 Park Dr., Franklin 07416
Pres., CFO—Lynnmarie Kane, 20 emp., *Quartz plate, wafer carriers, process* .................. (973) 209-8854
UTE Microwave, Inc., 3500 Sunset Ave., Ste. D-1, Ocean 07712
Pres.—L. Nilson, 20 emp., *High-powered microwave ferrite & low-powered* ...... (732) 922-1009
UTZ, LLC, 4 Peckman Rd., Little Falls 07424
Plt. Mgr.—Jonah Bilotta, 25 emp., *Wire mesh thick film screens, laser* .................. (973) 339-1100
V G Controls, Inc., 11 Butternut Dr., Vernon 07462
Pres.—V. Gelman, 10 emp., *Electronic systems* .................. (973) 764-6500
Valconn Electronics, Inc., 909 Rahway Ave., Union 07083
Pres.—Joel Cohn, 20 emp., *Custom cable assemblies & electronic* .................. (908) 687-1600
Vanderbilt Industries, 2 Cranberry Rd., Parsippany 07054
Pres.—Mitchell Kane, 75 emp., *Computer controlled building security* .................. (973) 316-3900
V-Com, 80 Little Falls Rd., Fairfield 07004
Pres.—Scott Schaefer, 25 emp., *Cable assemblies, connectors, switchers* .................. (201) 229-9800
Ventronics, Inc., 346 Monroe Ave., P.O. Box 142, Kenilworth 07033
Pres.—Joseph C. Venerus, 19 emp., *Transformers, inductors, chokes, coils* ......... (908) 272-9262
VIP Industries, Inc., 90 Brighton Rd., Clifton 07012
Pres.—John Sonatore, 50 emp., *Wire harnesses, coaxial cable & electromechan* .................. (973) 472-7500
Waveline, Inc., 160 Passaic Ave., Fairfield 07004
Pres.—James McGregor, 30 emp., *Waveguide components & test equipment* .................. (973) 808-9113
West Electronics, Inc., 5 Terri Ln., Ste. 15, P.O. Box 366, Burlington 08016
Pres.—Bradford Brainard, 20 emp., *Guided missile power controls, communication* .................. (609) 387-4300
Win-Tech Precision Products, Inc., 5 Littell Rd., East Hanover 07936
Owner—Pravin Patel, 6 emp., *CNC milling, turning, mechanical assembly* .................. (973) 887-8727
Y.C. Cable East, Inc., 240 Circle Dr. N., Piscataway 08854
Pres.—James Hsu, 30 emp., *Custom & medical cable assemblies,* .................. (732) 868-0800

## 3691 Batteries—storage

Cardinal Components, Inc., 145 U.S. Highway 46 W., Wayne Interchange I, Wayne 07470
Pres.—Carl E. Fabend, 15 emp., *Standard & custom quartz crystals,* .................. (973) 785-1333
Eos Energy Storage, LLC, 214 Fernwood Ave., Bldg. B, Edison 08837
CEO—Michael Oster, 30 emp., *Zinc-air battery system for the electric* .................. (732) 225-8400
Hoppecke Batterys, Inc., 1960 Old Cuthbert Rd., Ste. 130, Cherry Hill 08034
V-P.—Larry Meisner, 15 emp., *Lead-acid batteries* .................. (856) 616-0032

## 3692 Batteries—primary, dry & wet

Cardinal Components, Inc., 145 U.S. Highway 46 W., Wayne Interchange I, Wayne 07470
Pres.—Carl E. Fabend, 15 emp., *Standard & custom quartz crystals,* .................. (973) 785-1333

Eos Energy Storage, LLC, 214 Fernwood Ave., Bldg. B, Edison 08837
CEO—Michael Oster, 30 emp., *Zinc-air battery system for the electric* .... (732) 225-8400

### 3694 Engine electrical equipment

Coates International Ltd., 2100 Highway 34 & Ridgewood Rd., Wall 07719
Pres., CEO—George J. Coates, 14 emp., *Spherical rotary valve system for internal* .... (732) 449-7717
D & W Diesel, 423 County Rd., Cliffwood 07721
Opers. Mgr.—Craig Marcurano, 40 emp., *Rebuilt automotive generators, starters* .... (732) 566-4970
Hydro-Mechanical Systems, Inc., 1030 Delsea Dr., P.O. Box 87, Westville 08093
Pres.—Howard Rosenbloom, 17 emp., *Hydrostatic motors & electric & diesel* .... (856) 848-8888
J & R Rebuilders, Inc., 330 Washington Ave., Laurel Springs 08021
Pres.—Robert Visconti, 1 emp., *Rebuilt alternators & starters* .... (856) 627-1414
Middlesex Armature Service, 1155 Saint Georges Ave., Colonia 07067
Owner—Kenneth Pittman, 8 emp., *Rebuilt automotive starters & alternators* .... (732) 634-3779
Mobile Power, Inc., 392 Watters Rd., Hackettstown 07840
Pres.—Paul Mitchell, 5 emp., *Mobile heavy output alternators & current* .... (908) 852-3117
Morris Magnetos, Inc., 103 Washington St., Morristown 07960
Pres.—David Shaw, 4 emp., *Motorcycle magnetos* .... (973) 540-9171
Quality Rebuilders, 617 Broadway, Long Branch 07740
Owner—Manuel Azevedo, 1 emp., *Rebuilt automotive starters & alternators* .... (732) 222-9100
Rudy's & Vitor's V. A. S. Co., Inc., 521 W. Hazelwood Ave., P.O. Box 1544, Rahway 07065
Pres.—Vitor Soares, 8 emp., *Rebuilt alternators & starters* .... (732) 388-0334
Swanson Assocs., P.O. Box 151, Wayne 07470
Owner—Kent Swanson, 2 emp., *Model airplane glow plugs & igniters* .... (973) 984-5930

### 3695 Magnetic & optical recording media

Franklin Electronic Publishers, Inc., 8 Terri Ln., Burlington 08016
Pres., CEO—Barry Lipsky, 30 emp., *Electronic language learning handheld* .... (609) 386-2500
PMC Group, Inc. (H Q), 1288 Route 73, Mount Laurel 08054
Pres., COO—Debtash Chakrabarti, 35 emp., *Corporate headquarters; industrial* .... (856) 533-1866
Post Office Digital, Inc., 33 Hilliard Ave., Edgewater 07020
Pres.—Achille Raspantini, 10 emp., *DVD & media replication & production* .... (201) 945-8119
Synergem, 2323 Randolph Ave., Avenel 07001
Chrm.—Thomas DeMaeyer, 14 emp., *CD & DVD duplication/replication &* .... (732) 225-0001

### 3699 Electrical equipment & supplies, nec

Adapter Technologies, Inc., 154 Cooper Rd., Unit 1303, West Berlin 08091
Pres., Plt. Mgr.—John Miller, 6 emp., *Electronic connectors & assemblies* .... (856) 767-3930
Ameral International, Inc., 7 Railroad Ln., Brooklawn 08030
Pres.—Louis Grieco, 15 emp., *Custom cable & wire harness assemblies* .... (856) 456-9000
Avida, Inc., 174-B Kinderkamack Rd., P.O. Box 2, Park Ridge 07656
Pres.—Eric Kruegle, 5 emp., *Security surveillance equipment for* .... (201) 802-0749
Crest Ultrasonics Corp., 10 Grumman Ave., P.O. Box 7266, Trenton 08628
Pres.—Michael Goodson, 50 emp., *Corporate headquarters & ultrasonic* .... (609) 883-4000
Environmental Services Group/Green Power, 151 Sparta Stanhope Rd., Hopatcong 07843
CEO—August D'Angelo, 15 emp., *Environmentally friendly cleaners,* .... (201) 569-2020
Eonsmoke, LLC (H Q), 1500 Main Ave., Ste. 2, Clifton 07011
CFO—Gregory Grishayev, 7 emp., *Company headquarters; electronic cigarettes* .... (800) 616-3711
Fastpulse Technology, Inc., 220 Midland Ave., Saddle Brook 07663
Chrm., Pres.—Robert Goldstein, 15 emp., *Electro-optical instruments for lasers* .... (973) 478-5757
Festo Didactic Inc., 1710 Highway 34, P.O. Box 686, Farmingdale 07727
CFO—Ralf Hermkens, 54 emp., *Electronic educational training systems* .... (732) 938-2000
GAW Associates, Inc., 670 Deer Rd., Unit A, Cherry Hill 08034
Pres.—Kathleen Gaw-Betz, 10 emp., *Electronic cabinets/racks, custom cable* .... (856) 608-1428
Haas Laser Technologies, Inc., 37 Ironia Rd., Flanders 07836
Pres.—Gilbert J. Haas, 14 emp., *Industrial laser systems, laser beam* .... (973) 598-1150
Hoyt Corp., 520 S. Dean St., Englewood 07631
Pres.—Don Maguire, 65 emp., *Custom & standard precious metal electrical* .... (201) 894-0707
Innovative Photonic Solutions, 4250 U.S. Highway 1, Ste. 1, Monmouth Junction 08852
Pres.—John Connolly, 20 emp., *High-technology wavelength-stabilized* .... (732) 355-9300
International Cord Sets, Inc., 6 Spielman Rd., Fairfield 07004
Pres.—Dieter Baars, 18 emp., *Manufacturer of international cord* .... (973) 227-2118
Intertek Laboratories, Inc., 340 Union St., Stirling 07980
Pres., GM, Bus. & Fin. Mgr.—Mary Labella, 15 emp., *Automatic test equipment & electronic* . (908) 903-1800
Jewel Precision Sheet Metal Machining, Inc., 200 Commerce Rd., Cedar Grove 07009
Pres.—Ignazio Graziano, 75 emp., *Sheet metal & plastic fabrication,* .... (973) 857-5545
Kidde Fire Trainers, LLC, 17 Philips Pkwy., Montvale 07645
Pres., CEO—Rob Lane, 65 emp., *Firefighter training simulator systems* .... (201) 300-8100
L & R Mfg. Co., Inc., 577 Elm St., P.O. Box 607, Kearny 07032
Pres.—Robert J. Lazarus, 100 emp., *Manufacturer & distributor of ultrasonic* .... (201) 991-5330
Laser Energetics, Inc., 3535 Quakerbridge Rd., Ste. 700, Mercerville 08619
Founder, Pres. & CEO—Robert D. Battis, 12 emp., *Industrial lasers* .... (609) 587-8250
Maxflight Corp., 1 Executive Dr., Toms River 08755
CEO—Frank McClintic, 20 emp., *Amusement rides & simulators* .... (732) 281-2007
MJG Technologies, Inc., 832 Camden Ave., Blackwood 08012
Pres.—Jeff Genzel, 3 emp., *Manufacturer of electric matches, igniters* .... (856) 228-6118
Mulberry Metal Products, Inc., 2199 Stanley Ter., Union 07083
CFO—Patricia Lynch, 100 emp., *Metal & plastic wallplates & weatherproof* .... (908) 688-8850
Napoleon/Lynx, 25 Empire Blvd., South Hackensack 07606
GM—Max Godoy, 10 emp., *Overhead door openers* .... (973) 278-5588
Pacific Coast Systems, LLC, 4 Fox Hill Ln., Asbury 08802
Pres.—James Mork, 5 emp., *Military simulation & training equipment* .... (908) 735-9955
Power Dynamics, Inc., 145 Algonquin Pkwy., Whippany 07981
CEO—James Papianni, 178 emp., *Electrical equipment, including IEC* .... (973) 560-0019
PRC Laser, 350 N. Frontage Rd., Landing 07850
Pres.—James G. Rickert, 60 emp., *Industrial lasers* .... (973) 347-0100
Precision Filaments, 17 Bannard St., Ste. 30, Freehold 07728
Pres.—Robert McLean, 5 emp., *CRT filaments* .... (732) 462-3755
Pro-Comm, Inc., 1105 Industrial Pkwy., Brick 08724
Pres.—Sheryl J. Visone, 11 emp., *High-power, UHF, L-band, S-band, C-band* .... (732) 206-0660
Resistance Welding Solutions, Inc., 1090 Lousons Rd., Union 07083
CEO—Gregory W. Labelle, 20 emp., *Resistance welding equipment, including* .... (908) 964-9100
Schneider Electric, 2001 Highway 46, Ste. 402, Parsippany 07054
Opers. Mgr.—Ashish Sawardekar, 30 emp., *Electrical distribution, control &* .... (973) 263-6100
Service Metal Fabricating, Inc., 10 Stickle Ave., Rockaway 07866
Ptnr.—James Moretti, 85 emp., *Corporate headquarters & sheet metal* .... (973) 625-8882
Swanson Assocs., P.O. Box 151, Wayne 07470
Owner—Kent Swanson, 2 emp., *Model airplane glow plugs & igniters* .... (973) 984-5930
Swatch Group (U.S.), Inc. (H Q), 1200 Harbor Blvd., 7th Fl., Weehawken 07086
Pres.—Caroline Faivet, 125 emp., *Corporate headquarters; pulsed laser/sources* .... (201) 271-1400
TRUMPF Photonics, Inc., 2601 US Route 130 S., Cranbury 08512
Mng. Dir.—Georg Treusch, 150 emp., *High-power semiconductor lasers, RF* .... (609) 925-8200

U.S. Laser Corp., 825 Windham Ct. N., Ste. 2, Wyckoff 07481
Pres., CFO—Robert Regna, 17 emp., *10-watt to 2500-watt YAG, fiber & Vanadate* .... (201) 848-9200
Vandermolen Corp., 119 Dorsa Ave., Livingston 07039
Pres.—Aldo H. Vandermolen, 3 emp., *Electric indoor & outdoor insect control* .... (973) 992-8506

## 37 TRANSPORTATION EQUIPMENT

### 3711 Motor vehicles & car bodies

BMW Of North America, LLC (H Q), 300 Chestnut Ridge Rd., Woodcliff Lake 07677
Chrm., CEO—Ludwig Willisch, 1000 emp., *Company headquarters; automobiles,* .... (201) 307-4000
First Priority Emergency Vehicles, Inc., 2444 Ridgeway Blvd., Bldg. 500, Manchester 08759
Pres.—Robert J. Freeman, 47 emp., *Manufacturer & distributor of emergency* .... (732) 657-1104
Gambardella Racing & Performance, Inc., 1999 S. Black Horse Pike, Williamstown 08094
Pres., Shop Mgr.—Tony Gambardella, 3 emp., *Race car bodies & components* .... (856) 728-1869
Octal Corporation, 125 Galway Pl., Ste. B, Teaneck 07666
Pres.—Dani Bar-David, 20 emp., *Upgrade, retrofit & conversion kits* .... (201) 862-1010
Odyssey Specialty Vehicles, 317 Richard Mine Rd., Wharton 07885
CEO—Daniel Huang, 30 emp., *First response EMS, Fire Chief & command* .... (973) 328-2667
PL Custom Body & Equipment Co., 2201 Atlantic Ave., Manasquan 08736
Chrm., CEO—Jean S. Smock, 140 emp., *Ambulances, heavy rescue vehicles &* .... (732) 223-1411
Sirchie Finger Print Labs, Inc., Vehicle Div., 612 Gravelly Hollow Rd., P.O. Box 789, Medford 08055
CEO—Anthony A. Saggiomo, 35 emp., *Crime scene investigation & forensic* .... (609) 654-0777
SLP Specialty Vehicles, Inc., 1501 Industrial Way N., Toms River 08755
Pres.—Ed Hamburger, 12 emp., *Supercharged specialty vehicles, high* .... (732) 240-3696
Subaru Of America, Inc. (H Q), 2235 Route 70 W., Subaru Plz., Cherry Hill 08002
Chrm. & CEO—Tomomi Nakamura, 450 emp., *Corporate headquarters; automobiles* .... (856) 488-8500
T E O Fabrications, Inc., 95 Maple Grange Rd., P.O. Box 232, Vernon 07462
Pres.—Robert Hearn, 6 emp., *Race cars & components* .... (973) 764-5500
Ward LaFrance, Inc., 37 W. Broad St., Paulsboro 08066
Pres.—Jon Burzichelli, 5 emp., *Fire trucks* .... (609) 922-8383

### 3713 Truck & bus bodies

Barrier Enterprises, Inc., 175 Stanhope Sparta Rd., Andover 07821
CEO—Thomas Stiffen, 4 emp., *Rebuilt truck & bus bodies* .... (973) 770-3983
BMW Of North America, LLC (H Q), 300 Chestnut Ridge Rd., Woodcliff Lake 07677
Chrm., CEO—Ludwig Willisch, 1000 emp., *Company headquarters; automobiles,* .... (201) 307-4000
Cliffside Body Corp., 130 Broad Ave., P.O. Box 206, Fairview 07022
Pres.—Edward Greenwald, 30 emp., *Truck bodies & equipment, snow plows* .... (201) 945-3970
Demountable Concepts, Inc., 200 Acorn Rd., Glassboro 08028
Pres.—Rustin Cassway, 35 emp., *Demountable truck body systems & equipment* .... (856) 863-0900
Fleet Equipment Corp. (H Q), 567 Commerce St., Franklin Lakes 07417
Pres.—Rick Pearson, 30 emp., *Corporate headquarters; steel & aluminum* .... (201) 337-7332
Funs Truck'N & Mobility, 255 Route 46 W., Saddle Brook 07663
Pres.—Allen Ackerman, 7 emp., *Handicapped van conversions* .... (973) 546-1900
Heller Truck Body Corp., 138 U.S. Highway 22, Hillside 07205
Pres., CEO—Darryl Novak, 3 emp., *Custom aluminum & fiberglass reinforced* .... (973) 923-9200
Highway Body Works, Inc., 8600 Tonnelle Ave., North Bergen 07047
Pres.—Raymond Koeppel, 8 emp., *Rebuilt truck bodies* .... (201) 869-0900
Holman Enterprises, Inc. (H Q), 244 E. Kings Hwy., Maple Shade 08052
Chrm.—Joseph Holman, 30 emp., *Corporate headquarters; truck bodies* .... (856) 663-5200
Jack Doheny Companies, Inc., 15 Taylor Rd., Ste. 1, Wharton 07885
★ GM—Ty Rose, 40 emp., *Pump trucks, vacuum trucks & sewer* .... (973) 659-0061
Norcia Corp., 451 Black Horse Ln., North Brunswick 08902
Pres.—Pat Norcia, 8 emp., *Truck bodies & equipment* .... (732) 297-1101
Omaha Standard, 572 Whitehead Rd., Trenton 08619
V-P., Operation—Danny Anthony, 50 emp., *Truck bodies for the waste, recycling* .... (609) 588-5400
SLP Specialty Vehicles, Inc., 1501 Industrial Way N., Toms River 08755
Pres.—Ed Hamburger, 12 emp., *Supercharged specialty vehicles, high* .... (732) 240-3696
Smith Brothers Services, LLC, 3212 State Route 94, Ste. 9, Franklin 07416
Owner—Charles Smith, 1 emp., *Rebuilt snowplow pumps, snowplow pump* .... (973) 209-7569
Suburban Caps, Inc., 899 State Route 18, Old Bridge 08857
★ Principal—Scott Kidd, 2 emp., *Truck caps & accessories* .... (732) 251-4383
Transstar Truck Body Welding Co., Inc., 514 Route 513, P.O. Box 226, Califon 07830
Pres.—Dominick Tranquilli, 5 emp., *Truck bodies & welding job shop* .... (908) 832-2688
Van-Con, Inc., 123 William St., Middlesex 08846
Pres.—James Anderson, 18 emp., *School buses* .... (732) 356-8484
Vending Truck, Inc., 5 Litchfield Rd., East Brunswick 08816
CEO—Howard Seasonwein, 20 emp., *Custom new & used vending food trucks* .... (732) 969-5400
Wiegers, Inc., 181 Fornelius Ave., Clifton 07013
Pres. & Parts Mgr.—Ernest Wiegers, 10 emp., *Manufacturer & distributor of custom-built* .... (973) 778-8607

### 3714 Motor vehicle parts & accessories

American Crankshaft Grinding Co., Inc., 851-861 Fairmount Ave., Elizabeth 07201
Owner—Tony DiCosmo, 3 emp., *Rebuilt engines & automotive machine* .... (908) 352-5558
American Hose & Hydraulics, Inc., 700 21st Ave., Paterson 07513
CIO—Graham Page, 100 emp., *Corporate headquarters & truck parts* .... (973) 684-3225
Atlantic Detroit Diesel-Allison, LLC, 169 Old New Brunswick Rd., Piscataway 08854
Off. Admn.—Elaine Loss, 50 emp., *Rebuilt diesel engines & transmission* .... (732) 752-7100
Auto Cool Radiator Service, 10 Terhune Pl., Hackensack 07601
Owner—Tom Meek, 15 emp., *Rebuilt automotive & truck radiators* .... (201) 343-3099
Auto Sun Roof, Inc. (H Q), 1305 Industrial Hwy., P.O. Box 2321, Cinnaminson 08077
Pres.—Richard W. Jones, 30 emp., *Corporate headquarters; car sunroof* .... (856) 786-0600
Automotive Rentals, Inc., 4001 Leadenhall Rd., P.O. Box 5039, Mount Laurel 08054
Pres.—Carl Ortell, 900 emp., *Corporate headquarters & truck bodies* .... (856) 778-1500
Bristol-Donald Co., Inc., 50 Roanoke Ave., Newark 07105
Pres.—Robert Greeley, Jr., 25 emp., *Truck equipment* .... (973) 589-2640
Ceralli Competition Engines, Inc., 395 E. 18th St., Paterson 07524
Owner & Pres.—Bill Ceralli, 1 emp., *Rebuilt automotive engines* .... (973) 742-4972
Clayton Assocs., Inc., 1650 Oak St., Lakewood 08701
Pres., MIS Mgr.—James Clayton, 20 emp., *Automotive & industrial brake washing* .... (732) 363-2100
Clear Plus Windshield Wipers, 100 Outwater Ln., Garfield 07026
Owner—Raj Chawla, 10 emp., *Windshield wipers* .... (973) 546-8800
ClearDrain, 219 Saint Mihiel Dr., Riverside 08075
Mng. Dir.—Frank A. Chille, Jr., 10 emp., *Self-adjusting, self-cleaning, self-defrostin* .... (856) 461-0091
Coates Precision Engineering Ltd., 2100 Highway 34 & Ridgewood Rd., Wall 07719
Pres.—George Coates, 15 emp., *Automotive engines, including industrial* .... (732) 449-7717
Coilhose Pneumatics, 19 Kimberly Rd., East Brunswick 08816
Pres.—Marvin Aaron, 96 emp., *Company headquarters & tire gages &* .... (732) 432-7177
Custom Auto Radiator, Inc., 441 S. Main St., Route 9, Forked River 08731
Pres.—Charles Monjoy, 4 emp., *Automotive radiators* .... (609) 242-9700
D&M Holdings US, Inc. (H Q), 100 Corporate Dr., Mahwah 07430
CEO—Jim Caudill, 100 emp., *Holding company headquarters; home* .... (201) 762-6500

Drive Line Service Of New Jersey, Inc., 622 U.S. Highway 46, Clifton 07013
Pres.—Emmett Acocella, 3 emp., *Automotive drive shafts*........ (973) 473-7900
Drive-Master Co., Inc., 37 Daniel Rd. West, Fairfield 07004
Pres., CEO—Peter B. Ruprecht, 19 emp., *Wheelchair accessible vans, lifts &*........ (973) 808-9709
Dunbar Mfg., LLC, 2400 Egg Harbor Rd., Lindenwold 08021
Owner—Sheila Santarpio, 2 emp., *Truck-mounted cranes & hydrostatic*........ (856) 346-0666
E.W.E. Auto Seat Cover Co., 8431 Kennedy Blvd., North Bergen 07047
Pres.—Walter Somick, 3 emp., *Leather, fabric & vinyl automotive*........ (201) 869-6470
East Performance Exhaust, 1050 U.S. Highway 22, Bldg. B, Lebanon 08833
Pres.—Steve Babinsky, 3 emp., *Automotive exhaust systems*........ (908) 236-2820
Electroid Co., 45 Fadem Rd., Springfield 07081
Pres.—Stephen Etter, 90 emp., *Custom electromagnetic clutches, brakes*........ (973) 467-8100
Felco Products, LLC, 18 Furler St., Totowa 07512
Pres.—Joe Geronimo, 5 emp., *Automotive parts, accessories & filters*........ (973) 890-7979
Filtration Solutions, Inc., 432 Sand Shore Rd., Ste. 8, Hackettstown 07840
Pres.—Chang Jen, 5 emp., *Fuel, oil, wastewater treatment & aqueous*........ (908) 684-4000
Garden State Diesel, 97 Foster Rd., Ste. 4, Moorestown 08057
Owner & GM—Rich Carragher, 8 emp., *Rebuilt diesel engine fuel injection*........ (856) 914-9797
Gnutti Carlo, 140 Ludlow Ave., Northvale 07647
CFO—Renato Bampa, 120 emp., *Company-headquarters & automotive parts*........ (201) 768-8200
Gren Machinery Co., 70 School House Rd., Somerset 08873
CEO—Gianfei Han, 7 emp., *Automotive brake pads, rotors & shoes*........ (732) 356-5118
Haledon Auto Parts, 269 Haledon Ave., Haledon 07508
Pres., Hum. Res. & IT Mgr.—Howard T. Wilson, 23 emp., *Automotive machine shop & distributor* (973) 595-8200
Hi-Per Tech Brake Products, Inc., 100 Delsea Dr., P.O. Box 770, Glassboro 08028
Pres.—Michael Carmolingo, 20 emp., *Vehicle brakes*........ (856) 881-0900
Hutchinson Industries, Inc., 460 Southard St., Trenton 08638
Pres.—Olivier Marsaly, 165 emp., *Corporate headquarters & rubber & aluminum*........ (609) 394-1010
Industrial Brake & Clutch Exchange, 2 U.S. Highway 9, Ste. 4, Morganville 07751
Pres.—Chris Makrilos, 3 emp., *Industrial & automotive clutches &*........ (732) 970-0090
J & J Radiator Shop, 71 St. Mihiel Dr., Delran 08075
Owner—Joe Zeisweiss, 1 emp., *Rebuilt automotive radiators*........ (856) 461-3533
Jackson Racing Engines, Inc., Henry, 787 Route 537, Cream Ridge 08514
Pres.—Henry Jackson, 2 emp., *Automotive racing engines*........ (609) 758-7476
JDM Engineering, 60 Jerseyville Ave., Freehold 07728
Owner—James P. D'Amore, 13 emp., *Iron, steel & aluminum automotive performance*........ (732) 780-0770
Jenson & Mitchell, Inc., 880 Communipaw Ave., Jersey City 07304
Pres.—Frank Mitchell, 3 emp., *Automotive springs & truck suspension*........ (201) 332-4140
Jesel, Inc., 1985 Cedar Bridge Ave., Ste. 2, Lakewood 08701
Pres.—Dan Jesel, 50 emp., *Race car engine parts*........ (732) 901-1800
JJ Products, Inc., 133 Mountain Ave., West Caldwell 07006
Pres.—Jim Bocchini, 3 emp., *Automobile arm rests & accessories*........ (973) 228-3460
Johnson & Towers, Inc., 2021 Briggs Rd., P.O. Box 4000, Mount Laurel 08054
Chrm.—Walter Johnson III, 75 emp., *Corporate headquarters & rebuilt truck*........ (856) 234-6990
Kisthardt Auto Products, LLC, 354 4th St., Ewing 08638
Pres., Fin., MIS & R & D Mgr.—Kevin Burke, 4 emp., *Upholstered automobile seats, convertible* (609) 434-0700
Last Chance Rebuilt Corp., 340 W. 1st Ave., Roselle 07203
Owner—Navneep Singh, 5 emp., *Rebuilt automotive parts*........ (908) 245-4421
LRB Performance Machine Co., 22-B Lasinski Rd., Franklin 07416
Owner—Lou Bengivenni, 3 emp., *High performance & racing engines,*........ (973) 209-7770
Machine Shop At Engine Specialties, The, 203 Carriage Ln., Delran 08075
GM—Scott Woodington, 7 emp., *Automotive machining job shop*........ (856) 764-8701
Manley Performance Products, Inc., 1960 Swarthmore Ave., Lakewood 08701
Pres.—Henry Manley, 115 emp., *High-performance internal engine components*........ (732) 905-3366
Melton Sales & Service, Inc., 511 Elbow Ln., Burlington 08016
V-P., Prodn.—Chris Robles, 85 emp., *Remanufactured diesel engines, drive*........ (609) 699-4800
Midland Radiator Service Co., 420 Midland Ave., Garfield 07026
Pres.—Tom Peraino, 8 emp., *Rebuilt heavy-duty truck radiators*........ (973) 340-0533
Mr. Drive Shaft, 5134-A Hurley Pond Rd., Farmingdale 07727
Owner & MIS Mgr.—William Everson, 2 emp., *Automotive drive shafts*........ (732) 938-4118
Neptune Auto Supply, Inc., 51 TFH Plz., Neptune City 07753
Chrm.—John Giganti, 20 emp., *Automotive hydraulic & air conditioning*........ (732) 774-0002
Octal Corporation, 125 Galway Pl., Ste. B, Teaneck 07666
Pres.—Dani Bar-David, 20 emp., *Upgrade, retrofit & conversion kits*........ (201) 862-1010
Odyssey Specialty Vehicles, 317 Richard Mine Rd., Wharton 07885
CEO—Daniel Huang, 30 emp., *First response EMS, Fire Chief & command*........ (973) 328-2667
Olde Granddad Industries, 1 Market St., Passaic 07055
Owner—Mike Kostak, 10 emp., *Automotive mats, air fresheners & accessories*........ (201) 997-1899
Part-Rite, Inc., 19 Butler Ave., Bayville 08721
Manager—Mark Buglio, 12 emp., *Rebuilt automotive torque converters*........ (732) 269-5000
Phoenix Friction Products, Inc., 276-278 Lincoln Blvd., Middlesex 08846
Pres.—Lou Rivieccio, 10 emp., *Automotive, truck & all-terrain vehicle*........ (732) 667-7937
Pro-Motion Engines, LLC, 2 Great Meadow Ln., Apt. B, East Hanover 07936
Owner—Larry Lempicki, 2 emp., *High-performance engines, including*........ (973) 884-5936
Quality Rebuilders, Inc., 969 Market St., Paterson 07513
Pres.—Zecky Cohen, 7 emp., *Car & truck front axles*........ (973) 523-8800
Radaire Distributors, Inc., 1318 Segart Ave., Sea Girt 08750
Pres.—Eric Bomenblit, 8 emp., *Automotive transmissions & rebuilt*........ (732) 282-1144
Raz Performance Machine, 247 Harding Hwy., Vineland 08360
Ptnr.—Raymond Zieger, 2 emp., *Rebuilt automotive motors & machining*........ (856) 697-4275
Rebuilt Parts Co., 7929 River Rd., Pennsauken 08110
GM—Henry Matznick, 15 emp., *Front wheel axles, drive shafts & driveline*........ (856) 662-3252
Shadow Racing & Hobby Products, Inc., 70 1st Ave., Paterson 07514
Owner & Pres.—Robert DeBois, 2 emp., *Race car shocks, weight jackers & set-up*........ (973) 684-7270
Shoemaker's Automotive Machine, 176 Kings Hwy., Cape May Court House 08210
Owner—Doug Shoemaker, 1 emp., *Rebuilt automotive engines*........ (609) 624-0847
SLP Specialty Vehicles, Inc., 1501 Industrial Way N., Toms River 08755
Pres.—Ed Hamburger, 12 emp., *Supercharged specialty vehicles, high*........ (732) 240-3696
Stef's Performance Products, 693 Cross St., Lakewood 08701
Pres.—Joe Stefanacci, 22 emp., *Race car oil system components*........ (732) 367-8700
StreetGlow, Inc. (H Q), 57 Oak St., Norwood 07648
Pres., CEO, CFO & COO—Jack Panzarella, 5 emp., *Corporate headquarters; automotive*........ (973) 709-9000
T E O Fabrications, Inc., 95 Maple Grange Rd., P.O. Box 232, Vernon 07462
Pres.—Robert Hearn, 6 emp., *Race cars & components*........ (973) 764-5500
Tim's Automotive Machine Shop, 1760 Highway 37 E., Toms River 08753
Owner—Timothy Hall, 1 emp., *Automotive machining job shop*........ (732) 573-0600
Trane, Inc. (H Q), 1 Centennial Ave., P.O. Box 6820, Piscataway 08855
V-P., Compliance & Deputy Gen. Counsel—Allan Tananbaum, 400 emp., *Corporate headquarters; automotive*........ (732) 652-7100
TransAxle, LLC, 2501 Route 73 S., P.O. Box 2306, Cinnaminson 08077
CEO—Dave Olsen, 70 emp., *Company headquarters & rebuilt truck*........ (856) 665-4445
Truck Parts Specialists, 150 Central Ave., Teterboro 07608
GM—Rich Toskonka, 12 emp., *Rebuilt transmissions*........ (201) 288-9333

United Motor Parts, Inc., 1130 Teaneck Rd., Teaneck 07666
★ Owner—Alan Gladstein, 20 emp., *General machining job shop for the*........ (201) 837-6760
Weston Machine, 161 11th St., Piscataway 08854
Owner—Charlie Weston, 1 emp., *Automotive machining job shop*........ (732) 752-2711
Wiegers, Inc., 181 Fornelius Ave., Clifton 07013
Pres. & Parts Mgr.—Ernest Wiegers, 10 emp., *Manufacturer & distributor of custom-built*........ (973) 778-8607

## 3715 Truck trailers

A B Jersey Trailer Corp., 100 Kresson Gibbsboro Rd., Voorhees 08043
Secy-Treas.—Christine Barnabie, 1 emp., *Flatbed trailers*........ (856) 784-7766
Drive-Master Co., Inc., 37 Daniel Rd. West, Fairfield 07004
Pres., CEO—Peter B. Ruprecht, 19 emp., *Wheelchair accessible vans, lifts &*........ (973) 808-9709
Dunn Fabrication, 8470 Remington Ave., Pennsauken 08110
★ Owner—Evan Dunn, 1 emp., *Automotive machining job shop*........ (856) 486-3866
Green Trailers, Inc., Stephan L., 74 Squankum Yellowbrook Rd., Farmingdale 07727
Pres., Fin. & MIS Mgr.—Stephan L. Green, 7 emp., *Equipment & flatbed trailers*........ (732) 938-5663
Hercules Enterprises, LLC, 321 Valley Rd., Hillsborough 08844
Pres.—Karl Massaro, 65 emp., *Steel container chassis for the trucking*........ (908) 369-0000
Odyssey Specialty Vehicles, 317 Richard Mine Rd., Wharton 07885
CEO—Daniel Huang, 30 emp., *First response EMS, Fire Chief & command*........ (973) 328-2667
Shafer Bros. Trailers, 38 Martin Ave., Pittsgrove 08318
Owner—Richard Shafer, 4 emp., *Flatbed & tri-axle trailers*........ (856) 358-3483
Vanco U. S. A., LLC, 1170 Florence Rd., Bordentown 08505
Chrm., CFO—James Massaro, 4 emp., *Dry freight trailers & truck bodies*........ (609) 499-4141

## 3716 Motor homes

Bornmann's RV, 131 Delsea Dr. S., Glassboro 08028
Owner—Eugene Bornmann, 4 emp., *Recreational vehicle conversions &*........ (856) 881-7979
Drive-Master Co., Inc., 37 Daniel Rd. West, Fairfield 07004
Pres., CEO—Peter B. Ruprecht, 19 emp., *Wheelchair accessible vans, lifts &*........ (973) 808-9709

## 3721 Aircraft

Dassault Falcon Jet Corp. (H Q), Teterboro Airport, 200 Riser Rd., Little Ferry 07643
Pres., CEO—John Rosanvallon, 420 emp., *Corporate headquarters; aircraft, including*........ (201) 440-6700

## 3724 Aircraft engines & engine parts

Aerosource, Inc., 390 Campus Dr., Somerset 08873
V-P., GM—Robert A. Rist, 42 emp., *DC10, KC10, MD10, MD11 & KC-390 air-driven*........ (732) 469-9300
Alcoa, 9 Roy St., Dover 07801
GM—William Miley, 675 emp., *Aircraft turbine engines*........ (973) 361-2310

## 3728 Aircraft parts & equipment

Aeronautical Instrument & Radio, Inc., 234 Garibaldi Ave., Lodi 07644
Pres.—Wilfrid Burke, 28 emp., *Aircraft equipment*........ (973) 473-0034
Aeropanel Corp., 661 Myrtle Ave., Boonton 07005
V-P., GM—Jack Miller, 22 emp., *Illuminated aircraft control & information*........ (973) 335-9636
Aerosource, Inc., 390 Campus Dr., Somerset 08873
V-P., GM—Robert A. Rist, 42 emp., *DC10, KC10, MD10, MD11 & KC-390 air-driven*........ (732) 469-9300
Alpine Corp., 42 Bergenline Ave., Westwood 07675
V-P.—Thomas Wanner, 10 emp., *Aerospace components*........ (201) 666-0959
Avionix Corp., 35 Ruta Ct., South Hackensack 07606
Pres.—Carmelo Scordo, 15 emp., *Flight instruments & electromechanical*........ (201) 343-1550
Breeze-Eastern Corp., 35 Melanie Ln., Whippany 07981
Pres.—Brad Peterson, 200 emp., *Aerospace rescue hoists & winches,*........ (973) 602-1001
Consolidated Instrument, Avionics & Radio Sales & Service, 510 Industrial Ave., Teterboro 07608
Pres.—Eric Johannessen, 15 emp., *Repair of aircraft instruments, avionics*........ (201) 288-1189
Export Consultants Corp., 250 Lackland Dr., Ste. 6, P.O. Box 308, Middlesex 08846
Pres.—Mary Ann Althausen, 7 emp., *Aircraft parts*........ (732) 469-0700
Ferry Machine Corp., 75 Industrial Ave., Little Ferry 07643
Pres., MIS & R & D Mgr.—Louis Ferretti, 30 emp., *Precision military & medical machining*........ (201) 641-9191
H & W Tool Co., Inc., 22 Lee Ave., Dover 07801
Pres., GM—Richard Winstead, 18 emp., *Aeronautical & medical components*........ (973) 366-0131
Hunter Mfg. Services, Inc., 19 Just Rd., Fairfield 07004
Owner & Pres.—Kenneth C. Hunter, 12 emp., *CNC machining of pharmaceutical packaging* (973) 365-5880
J A Machine & Tool Co., Inc., 84 Herbert Ave., Closter 07624
Pres.—Andrew Petrinic, 12 emp., *Precision aircraft components & general*........ (201) 767-1308
Lehigh Precision Co., Inc., P.O. Box 214, Elizabeth 07207
Owner & Pres.—Mark Biederman, 5 emp., *General machining of aircraft components*........ (908) 351-6600
Marotta Controls, Inc., 78 Boonton Ave., P.O. Box 427, Montville 07045
Pres.—Patrick Marotta, 200 emp., *High-performance & specialty motion*........ (973) 334-7800
Moser Jewel Co., 518 Route 57, Phillipsburg 08865
CEO—Sharon Duffield, 10 emp., *Micro-precision components, instrument*........ (908) 454-1155
Oavco Ltd., LLC, 103 Carnegie Ctr., Princeton 08540
★ Member—Mark Stuart, 20 emp., *Aircraft bearings*........ (609) 454-5340
Panasonic Corp. Of North America (H Q), 2 River Front Plz., Newark 07102
Chrm., CEO—Joseph M. Taylor, 800 emp., *Corporate headquarters; electric motors*........ (201) 348-7500
Panelcraft, Inc., 105 W. Dewey Ave., Bldg. C, Unit 16, Wharton 07885
Pres.—Frank Brown, 10 emp., *Aircraft instrument panels*........ (973) 895-2700
PHT Aerospace, LLC, 230 West Pkwy., Ste. 2, Pompton Plains 07444
Dir., Opers.—Joseph Wall, 30 emp., *Electric motors & components for aerospace*........ (973) 831-1230
Pioneer Machine & Tool Co., 425 E. Broadway, P.O. Box 8, Maple Shade 08052
Ptnr.—George Czuzak, Jr., 30 emp., *Aerospace components*........ (856) 779-8800
Stetz Machine Shop, John, 17 Highway 36, Middletown 07748
Owner—John Stetz, 7 emp., *Aerospace machining job shop*........ (732) 495-0847
Sun Dial & Panel Corp., 2 Daniel Rd., Fairfield 07004
Chrm., Pres. & CEO—Roger J. Lokker, 15 emp., *Aircraft components, including edgelit*........ (973) 226-4334
Transmission Technology Corp., 1 High Mountain Trl., Lincoln Park 07035
Pres.—Dezi Folenta, 1 emp., *Helicopter & marine vessel transmission*........ (973) 305-3600
Vulcan Tool Co., Inc., 1080-C Garden State Rd., Union 07083
Pres.—Anton Heldmann, 20 emp., *Aerospace components*........ (908) 686-0550
Zodiac Arresting Systems America - Logan, 2239 High Hill Rd., Swedesboro 08085
Pres.—G. Kent Thompson, 120 emp., *Military & commercial aircraft arresting*........ (856) 241-8620

## 3731 Ship building & repairing

Bayonne Dry-Dock & Repair, Inc., Military Ocean Terminal Dock Yard, P.O. Box 240, Bayonne 07002
Pres.—Mike Cranston, 20 emp., *Rebuilt ships*........ (201) 823-9295
Cherubini Yachts, LLC, 51 Norman Ave., Riverside 08075
Pres.—David Cherubini, 5 emp., *Semi-custom mahogany, teak & fiberglass*........ (856) 764-5319
Dorchester Shipyard, Inc., 13 Front St., P.O. Box 600, Dorchester 08316
Pres.—John Kelleher, 16 emp., *Shipbuilding & repairs*........ (856) 785-8040
Jersey Cape Yachts, 2143 River Rd., Egg Harbor City 08215
Pres.—Wayne Puglise, 40 emp., *Custom sportfishing yachts & marine*........ (609) 965-8650

TF Yachts, LLC, 801 Philadelphia Ave., P.O. Box 702, Egg Harbor City 08215
Pres.—Ira Trocki, 25 emp., *Pleasure & sport fishing yachts & boats* (609) 965-2300
Union Dry Dock & Repair Co., Inc., 901 Sinatra Dr., P.O. Box M-1539, Hoboken 07030
Pres.—Robert J. Burke, 75 emp., *Marine dry-docking & barge & vessel* (201) 792-9090
Viking Yacht Co., 5738 U.S. Highway 9 N., P.O. Box 308, New Gretna 08224
Co-Pres., CEO—Patrick Healey, 750 emp., *Yachts* (609) 296-6000

## 3732 Boat building & repairing

Allen Steel Co., 202 High St., Leesburg 08327
Pres.—James P. Allen III, 5 emp., *Commercial fishing boats & food processing* (856) 785-1171
Cherubini Yachts, LLC, 51 Norman Ave., Riverside 08075
Pres.—David Cherubini, 5 emp., *Semi-custom mahogany, teak & fiberglass* (856) 764-5319
Commercial Water Sports, Inc., 28 Clermont Dr., Cape May Court House 08210
Pres.—Rob Guarini, 5 emp., *Custom commercial fiberglass 31-foot* (609) 624-3404
Egg Harbor Yachts, 801 Philadelphia Ave., Egg Harbor City 08215
Owner—Ira Trocki, 20 emp., *33 feet-52 feet convertible, motor* (609) 965-2300
Forsberg's Boat Works, Inc., 1692 W. End Dr., Point Pleasant Boro 08742
Pres.—Nils Forsberg, 4 emp., *Boats* (732) 892-4246
Gordon's Marine Service, 454 S. Green St., Tuckerton 08087
Owner—Gordon Ford, 1 emp., *Rebuilt boats* (609) 296-5817
Grant Boat Works, 120 Lakeside Dr., Ste. E, P.O. Box 597, Forked River 08731
Owner—Gregory Grant, 2 emp., *Rebuilt boats* (609) 971-1075
Henriques Yachts, Inc., 198 Hilton Ave., Bayville 08721
CEO—Manuel Costa, 7 emp., *Sportsfishing boats* (732) 269-1180
Master Shipwrights, Inc., 25 W. Highland Ave., P.O. Box 273, Atlantic Highlands 07716
Pres.—Hans MiKaitis, 1 emp., *Shipbuilding* (732) 872-7500
Ocean Rockets, Inc., 5 Mosquito Landing Rd., Tuckahoe 08250
Owner—John Yank, 30 emp., *Commercial speedboats* (609) 628-4445
Ocean Yachts, Inc., 2713 Green Bank Rd., Egg Harbor City 08215
Pres.—John Leek III, 30 emp., *Fishing & cruising boats* (609) 965-4616
Out Island Sport Yachts, Inc., 107 Edgewood Ave., West Berlin 08091
Pres.—Scott Jastrzembski, 6 emp., *Manufacturer of custom-built fiberglass* (609) 861-4000
Patriot Marine Fabricating, 708-4 Old Shore Rd., Forked River 08731
Pres.—Nicole Spisak, 3 emp., *Aluminum work boats, marine fuel tanks* (609) 693-5542
Roseman's Boat Yard & Charter, 5 Roseman Ln., Cape May 08204
Ptnr.—Joan Roseman, 2 emp., *Rebuilt boats* (609) 884-3370
TF Yachts, LLC, 801 Philadelphia Ave., P.O. Box 702, Egg Harbor City 08215
Pres.—Ira Trocki, 25 emp., *Pleasure & sport fishing yachts & boats* (609) 965-2300
Transmission Technology Corp., 1 High Mountain Trl., Lincoln Park 07035
Pres.—Dezi Folenta, 1 emp., *Helicopter & marine vessel transmission* (973) 305-3600
True World Group, LLC (H Q), 24 Link Dr., Rockleigh 07647
CFO—Tom Ino, 10 emp., *Company headquarters; fiberglass boats* (201) 750-0024
Viking Marine Products, Inc., 1160 State St., Ste. 17, Perth Amboy 08861
Pres.—Kurt Grimsgaard, 8 emp., *Tug boat & barge fenders, docks & piers* (732) 826-4559
Viking Yacht Co., 5738 U.S. Highway 9 N., P.O. Box 308, New Gretna 08224
Co-Pres., CEO—Patrick Healey, 750 emp., *Yachts* (609) 296-6000
Viking Yachting Center, Inc., 5724 N. Route 9, New Gretna 08224
★ GM—Eugene R. McCann, 3 emp., *General machining job shop for fiberglass* (609) 296-2388
Yank Marine, Inc., Mosquito Landing Rd., P.O. Box 569, Tuckahoe 08250
Pres.—John C. Yank III, 50 emp., *Corporate headquarters & boats* (609) 628-2928

## 3743 Railroad equipment

Great American Trolley Co. (H Q), 821 Shunpike Rd., Cape May 08204
Pres.—Richard Adelizzi, 50 emp., *Company headquarters; trackless trolleys* (609) 884-0450
Rails Co., 101 Newark Way, Maplewood 07040
Chrm., Pres. & CEO—G. N. Burwell, 35 emp., *Railroad heaters, controls & lubrication* (973) 763-4320

## 3751 Motorcycles, bicycles & parts

American Railing Design, 191 Vineyard Rd., Edison 08817
Pres.—Andrew Martingano, 10 emp., *Commercial, residential & industrial* (732) 287-1122
BMW Of North America, LLC (H Q), 300 Chestnut Ridge Rd., Woodcliff Lake 07677
Chrm., CEO—Ludwig Willisch, 1000 emp., *Company headquarters; automobiles,* (201) 307-4000
Van Dessel Sports, LLC, 15 W. Main St., Ste. 2, Mendham 07945
Pres.—Edwin Bull, 2 emp., *Bicycles* (973) 543-2599

## 3764 Space propulsion units & parts

Arde, Inc., 875 Washington Ave., Carlstadt 07072
GM—Kirk Sneddon, 60 emp., *Corporate headquarters & guided missiles* (201) 784-9880
Bright Lights USA, Inc., 145 Shreve Ave., Barrington 08007
Pres.—Daniel Farber, 84 emp., *Mechanical & electromechanical defense* (856) 546-5656
Whippany Actuation System, 110 Algonquin Pkwy., Whippany 07981
Accts. Payable Supv.—Mary Hubert, 225 emp., *Aerospace parts* (973) 428-9898

## 3769 Space vehicle equipment, nec

L-3 Communications Corp., Space & Navigation Systems, 450 Clark Dr., Budd Lake 07828
Pres., Div.—Ted Trzesniowski, 260 emp., *Inertial instruments & integrated fire* (973) 446-4000
Marotta Controls, Inc., 78 Boonton Ave., P.O. Box 427, Montville 07045
Pres.—Patrick Marotta, 200 emp., *High-performance & specialty motion* (973) 334-7800

## 3795 Tanks & tank components

Octal Corporation, 125 Galway Pl., Ste. B, Teaneck 07666
Pres.—Dani Bar-David, 20 emp., *Upgrade, retrofit & conversion kits* (201) 862-1010
Plastics Consulting & Mfg. Co., 1431 Ferry Ave., Camden 08104
Pres.—Steven Schwartz, 20 emp., *Tetrafluoroethylene, flouropolymer* (856) 963-7700

## 3799 Transportation equipment, nec

Custom Sales & Service, Inc., 275 S. 2nd Rd., P.O. Box 635, Hammonton 08037
Pres.—William Sikora, 50 emp., *Food carts, trailers & trucks* (609) 561-6900
Hoyt Corp., 520 S. Dean St., Englewood 07631
Pres.—Don Maguire, 65 emp., *Custom & standard precious metal electrical* (201) 894-0707
Sealion Metal Fabricators, Inc., 776 Creek Rd., Bellmawr 08031
Pres., MIS Mgr.—Louis D'Orazio, 10 emp., *Boat trailers* (856) 933-3914

# 38 INSTRUMENTS & RELATED PRODUCTS

## 3812 Search & navigation equipment

Advanced Orientation Systems, Inc., 2525 E. Brunswick Ave., Ste. 205, Linden 07036
Pres., Fin. & Opers. Mgr.—Marty Berger, 9 emp., *Electrolytic tilt sensors, inclinometers* (908) 474-9595
Avionix Corp., 35 Ruta Ct., South Hackensack 07606
Pres.—Carmelo Scordo, 15 emp., *Flight instruments & electromechanical* (201) 343-1550
Electromagnetic Technologies, 50 Intervale Rd., Unit 15, Boonton 07005
CEO—John Howard, 40 emp., *Radar & antenna microwave couplers,* (973) 394-1719
EXELIS, Inc., 77 River Rd., Clifton 07014
Pres.—Rich Sorelle, 1150 emp., *Aircraft self-protection, communications* (973) 284-0123
General Dynamics Advanced Information Systems, 7-9 Vreeland Rd., Florham Park 07932
Br. Mgr.—John Incera, 25 emp., *Information systems for the aerospace* (973) 514-4000
Kearfott Corporation, Guidance & Navigation Div., 1150 McBride Ave., Little Falls 07424
Pres.—Craig Scott, 200 emp., *Corporate headquarters & inertial guidance* (973) 785-6000
L-3 Communications Corp., Space & Navigation Systems, 450 Clark Dr., Budd Lake 07828
Pres., Div.—Ted Trzesniowski, 260 emp., *Inertial instruments & integrated fire* (973) 446-4000
Malwin Electronics Corp., 52 E. 22nd St., Paterson 07514
Pres.—G. Weber, 10 emp., *Simulated flight instruments* (973) 881-1500
Moser Jewel Co., 518 Route 57, Phillipsburg 08865
CEO—Sharon Duffield, 10 emp., *Micro-precision components, instrument* (908) 454-1155
Pro-Comm, Inc., 1105 Industrial Pkwy., Brick 08724
Pres.—Sheryl J. Visone, 11 emp., *High-power, UHF, L-band, S-band, C-band* (732) 206-0660

## 3821 Laboratory apparatus & furniture

3M Co., 500 U.S. Highway 202 N., Flemington 08822
Plt. Mgr.—Bob Silbernagel, 250 emp., *Sterilization monitoring devices* (908) 788-4000
Ace Glass, Inc., 1430 N. West Blvd., Vineland 08360
Pres., CEO—Richard Kramme, 80 emp., *Scientific glassware & laboratory equipment* (856) 692-3333
Analytical Sales & Services, Inc., 237 W. Parkway, Ste. 1, Pompton Plains 07444
Pres.—David A. Isom, 11 emp., *Manufacturer & distributor of laboratory* (973) 616-0700
Arrow Engineering Co., 260 Pennsylvania Ave., Hillside 07205
Pres.—Raymond Fluet, 20 emp., *Laboratory equipment, including laboratory* (908) 353-5233
Azzota Corp., 178 Franklin Rd., Randolph 07869
GM—Geoff Darling, 10 emp., *Corporate headquarters & laboratory* (877) 649-2746
Bel-Art Products, Inc., 661 State Route 23, Wayne 07470
COO—Brad Mahood, 85 emp., *Corporate headquarters & laboratory* (973) 694-0500
Bellco Glass, Inc., 340 Edrudo Rd., Vineland 08360
Pres.—Steven J. Harker, 77 emp., *Biological glassware & equipment* (856) 691-1075
Benchmark Scientific, Inc., 116 Corporate Blvd., South Plainfield 07080
Pres.—Walter Demsia, 10 emp., *Laboratory equipment & supplies, including* (908) 222-1712
Blickman, Inc., 500 U.S. Highway 46, Clifton 07011
Pres.—Rob Freedman, 85 emp., *Stainless steel & chrome hospital furniture* (973) 330-0557
CleanZones, LLC, 640 Herman Rd., Ste. 2, Jackson 08527
Pres.—David McClelland, 10 emp., *Air filtration equipment for the cleanroom* (732) 534-5590
Denton Vacuum, LLC, 1259 N. Church St., Bldg. 3, Moorestown 08057
Chrm.—Peter Denton, 45 emp., *Vacuum thin film coating deposition* (856) 439-9100
Design Of Tomorrow, Inc., 24 Sherwood Ln., Fairfield 07004
Pres., GM—David Roitburg, 15 emp., *Casework & millwork for schools & laboratorie* (973) 227-5676
Evex Global, 857 State Rd., Princeton 08540
Pres.—Claudio Tarquinio, 15 emp., *Scientific instrumentation for nanotechnology* (408) 907-2994
GE Healthcare LifeSciences, 800 Centennial Ave., P.O. Box 1327, Piscataway 08855
GM, Comml. Americas—Eric Roman, 1000 emp., *Biotechnology testing equipment* (732) 457-8000
Glen Mills Inc., 220 Delawanna Ave., Clifton 07014
Pres.—Peter Kendall, 10 emp., *Distributor of sample preparation laboratory* (973) 777-0777
Globe Scientific, Inc., 610 Winters Ave., Paramus 07652
Pres.—Milton Diamond, 45 emp., *Laboratory plastic ware, glassware* (201) 599-1400
Hamilton Bell Co., Inc., 30 Craig Rd., Montvale 07645
GM—Linda Luciano, 7 emp., *Laboratory centrifuges* (201) 391-4100
Heinkel Filtering Systems, Inc., 520 Sharptown Rd., Swedesboro 08085
Pres.—Alan Ferraro, 10 emp., *Centrifuges, dryers, mixers, filtration* (856) 467-3399
International Crystal Laboratories, 11 Erie St., Ste. 2, Garfield 07026
Pres.—Theresa Herpst, 20 emp., *Optical lenses, lasers & spectroscopic* (973) 478-8944
Kingwood Industrial Products, Inc., 261 Main St., Unit 1 & 2, Hackettstown 07840
Pres.—Kevin Smith, 4 emp., *Audiology equipment & supplies, including* (908) 852-8655
L M Air Technology, Inc., 1467 Pinewood St., Rahway 07065
Pres.—Peter Daniele, 40 emp., *Hardwall & softwall cleanrooms & lab* (732) 381-8200
New Era Enterprises, Inc., 208 N. West Blvd., Rear, Newfield 08344
Pres.—Frank Bosco, 7 emp., *Scientific glassware* (856) 794-2005
Ohaus Corp., 7 Campus Dr., Ste. 310, Parsippany 07054
Pres.—Ted Xia, 100 emp., *Analytical & precision balances & scales* (973) 377-9000
Omnitek, Inc., 20 Newburgh Rd., Hackettstown 07840
Pres.—Forrest Vander Vliet, 12 emp., *Organic & inorganic photoconductors* (908) 852-8500
OPS Diagnostics, LLC, 291 U.S. Highway 22 E., Bldg. 6, Lebanon 08833
Pres.—David Burden, 3 emp., *Laboratory equipment & reagent prototyping* (908) 253-3444
Perma Pure, LLC, 8 Executive Dr., Toms River 08755
Pres.—Richard Curran, 56 emp., *Laboratory & environmental gas analyzing* (732) 244-0010
Primary Systems, Inc., 30 State Route 18, Ste. 1, Old Bridge 08857
Pres.—Eric Alter, 15 emp., *Automation control & information systems* (732) 679-2200
Scientific Industries, Inc., 660 Kinderkamack Rd., Ste. 203, Oradell 07649
Prod. Mktg. Mgr.—Thomas Wright, 6 emp., *Pharmacy pilling counting & weighing* (973) 473-6900
Scientific Machine, 700 Cedar Ave., P.O. Box 67, Middlesex 08846
Pres.—Elizabeth Landau Lawrence, 25 emp., *PTFE laboratory ware & accessories,* (732) 356-1553
Spex Forensics, 203 Norcross Ave., Metuchen 08840
★ GM—Lisa Petro, 3 emp., *Forensic laboratory equipment* (732) 549-7144
Terriss Consolidated Industries, 807 Summerfield Ave., P.O. Box 110, Asbury Park 07712
V-P.—Edward J. Della Zanna, 15 emp., *Eco-friendly scientific instruments* (732) 988-0909
Troemner, LLC, Henry, 201 Wolf Dr., P.O. Box 87, Thorofare 08086
Pres.—Wilbert Abele, 100 emp., *Precision weights, laboratory equipment* (856) 686-1600
Uehling Instrument Co., 473 Getty Ave., Paterson 07503
Pres.—Richard Pavan, 20 emp., *Liquid level & panel mounted gages,* (973) 742-8710
United Products & Instruments, Inc. (H Q), 182 Ridge Rd., Ste. E, Dayton 08810
Pres.—Albert Chang, 10 emp., *Corporate headquarters; laboratory* (732) 274-1155
Wilmad-LabGlass, 1172 N. West Blvd., Vineland 08360
Dir., Sales & Mktg.—Doug Grady, 133 emp., *Divisional headquarters & precision* (856) 691-3200

## 3822 Environmental controls

Alpha Automation, Inc., 127 Walters Ave., Trenton 08638
Pres., Bus. Mgr.—Paul Bamburak, 3 emp., *Industrial controls testing equipment* (609) 882-0366
Ammark Corp., 230 W. Parkway, Ste. 12, Pompton Plains 07444
Pres.—John T. Ford, 4 emp., *Electric & nonelectric hydronic valves* (973) 616-2555
Crown Engineering Corp., 550 Squankum Yellowbrook Rd., Howell 07731
Pres.—Michael J. Palmer, 20 emp., *Electrodes, flame rods, igniters &* (732) 938-3600
Datatest, Inc., 300 Valley Rd., Hillsborough 08844
Pres.—Paul Ford, 25 emp., *Air pollution & combustion monitoring* (908) 369-1590
Elemco Building Controls, 14 Ilene Ct., Bldg. 11, Unit 1, Hillsborough 08844
Pres.—Joe Wozniak, 8 emp., *Mechanical HVAC, process automation* (908) 281-2201
EWC Controls, Inc., 385 State Route 33, Manalapan 07726
Pres.—Mike Reilly, 53 emp., *HVAC controls & zoning systems for* (732) 446-3110
Flow Safe, Inc., 30 Broad St., Denville 07834
COO—Eileen Klees, 6 emp., *Air flow control products assembly* (973) 627-8553

S.I.C.

General Electronic Enterprises, Inc., 132 W. Main St., Rahway 07065
Pres.—William Piegari, 12 emp., *Perimeter electric & hydronic heating* .......... (732) 381-1144
Harrison Electro Mechanical Corp., 1607 Coach St., Rahway 07065
Pres. & Sys. Engr.—William A. Piegari, 13 emp., *HVAC DDC control systems & commercial* .. (732) 382-6008
Heat-Timer Corp., 20 New Dutch Ln., Fairfield 07004
Pres.—Michael Pitonyak, 50 emp., *Heat timer controls* .......... (973) 575-4004
Honeywell International, Inc. (H Q), 101 Columbia Rd., Morristown 07962
Chrm., CEO—David M. Cote, 1500 emp., *Corporate headquarters; control & energy* .......... (973) 455-2000
Istec Corp., 5 Park Lake Rd., Ste. 6, Sparta 07871
Pres.—Peter Johnson, 6 emp., *Flow & BTU meters & control valves* .......... (973) 383-9888
Lux Products Corp. (H Q), 6000 Commerce Pkwy., Ste. I, Mount Laurel 08054
Pres.—Paul Balon, 23 emp., *Corporate headquarters; thermostats* .......... (856) 234-7905
Micro-Air, Inc., 124 Route 526, Allentown 08501
Pres.—Andrew Spaziani, 20 emp., *Electronic controls & environmental* .......... (609) 259-2636
Ulanet Co., George, 413-415 Market St., Newark 07105
Pres.—Jon Ulanet, 9 emp., *Heating elements, including immersion* .......... (973) 589-4876
Westwood Products, Inc., 330 William St., P.O. Box 610, South River 08882
Pres.—Pat DiNicola, 35 emp., *Oil burner igniters & filters, combustion* .......... (732) 651-7700
Zytron Control Products, Inc., 20 Lexington Ave., Trenton 08618
Pres., Fin., MIS & R & D Mgr.—John Wilkinson, 25 emp., *Temperature & process controls & sensors*. (609) 771-0101

## 3823 Process control instruments

A.K. De Rama Industrial Control Systems, Inc., 253 Sheffield St., Mountainside 07092
Pres.—Antonio K. De Rama, 12 emp., *Industrial control systems* .......... (908) 789-1600
American Gas & Chemical Co., 220 Pegasus Ave., Northvale 07647
Pres.—Gerald Anderson, 75 emp., *Leak detectors, gas monitors & detection* .......... (201) 767-7300
Analytical Sales & Services, Inc., 237 W. Parkway, Ste. 1, Pompton Plains 07444
Pres.—David A. Isom, 11 emp., *Manufacturer & distributor of laboratory* .......... (973) 616-0700
BGS, Inc., 910 E. County Line Rd., Ste. 101, Lakewood 08701
★ CEO—Elkana Tombak, 15 emp., *Boiler controls* .......... (732) 442-5000
Burling Instruments, Inc., 16 River Rd., P.O. Box 298, Chatham 07928
Pres., GM—Harry Bentas, 10 emp., *Temperature controls* .......... (973) 635-9481
C & F Burner Co., 39 River Rd., P.O. Box 7189, North Arlington 07031
Pres.—Elizabeth Dunn, 34 emp., *Heating controls for boilers & water* .......... (201) 998-8083
CEA Instrument, Inc., 160 Tillman St., Westwood 07675
V-P., Sales & Mktg.—Steven Adelman, 4 emp., *Portable & wall-mounted hazardous &* .......... (201) 967-5660
CG Automation Solutions USA, 60 Fadem Rd., Springfield 07081
Pres.—Normand N. Lavoie, 55 emp., *Supervisory control & data acquisition* .......... (973) 379-7400
Chemetall, 675 Central Ave., New Providence 07974
Pres., CEO—Ron Felber, 100 emp., *Company headquarters & surface treatment* .......... (908) 464-6900
Chromatic Control, LLC (H Q), 63 Fox Trail Rd., P.O. Box 374, Sparta 07871
Owner—Steve Rotyliano, 2 emp., *Company headquarters; electro-optical* .......... (973) 944-3996
Control Instruments Corp., 25 Law Dr., Fairfield 07004
Dir., Sales—Debra Hall, 35 emp., *Gas detection systems* .......... (973) 575-9114
Crestron Electronics, Inc., 15 Volvo Dr., Rockleigh 07647
Ex. V-P.—Randy Klein, 3000 emp., *Control systems, multimedia distribution* .......... (201) 767-3400
Ernst Co., Inc., John C., 21 Gail Ct., Sparta 07871
Pres.—James Wolfe, 17 emp., *Sight glasses & windows, liquid level* .......... (973) 940-1600
Fleetwash, Inc. (H Q), 26 Law Dr., Unit E, Fairfield 07004
Co-Founder, Pres. & CEO—Vito DeGiovanni, 100 emp., *Corporate headquarters; sanitation* . (800) 847-3735
Fluitec International (H Q), 333 Washington St., Ste. 201, Jersey City 07302
Pres., CEO—Frank Magnotti, 50 emp., *Company headquarters; lubricant conditioning* .......... (201) 946-4584
Hudson Robotics, Inc., 10 Stern Ave., Springfield 07081
Pres.—Philip Farrelly, 10 emp., *Life science research laboratory robots* .......... (973) 376-7400
Istec Corp., 5 Park Lake Rd., Ste. 6, Sparta 07871
Pres.—Peter Johnson, 6 emp., *Flow & BTU meters & control valves* .......... (973) 383-9888
Lux Products Corp. (H Q), 6000 Commerce Pkwy., Ste. I, Mount Laurel 08054
Pres.—Paul Balon, 23 emp., *Corporate headquarters; thermostats* .......... (856) 234-7905
Marine Electric Systems, Inc., 80 Wesley St., South Hackensack 07606
Pres.—H. Epstein, 20 emp., *Electronic measurement systems, alarm* .......... (201) 531-8600
Mechanical Ingenuity Corp., 61 Riordan Pl., Shrewsbury 07702
CEO—Peter Manning, 15 emp., *Control & monitoring systems, including* .......... (732) 842-8889
Monitoring Solutions, Inc., 78 Route 173, Ste. 7, Hampton 08827
Pres.—Mike Sroka, 25 emp., *Corporate headquarters & emissions* .......... (908) 713-0172
Multiforce Systems Corp., 101 Wall St., Princeton 08540
V-P., Sales—Keith Griesinger, 19 emp., *Automated fuel management systems that* .......... (609) 683-4242
Onyx Valve Co., 835 Industrial Hwy., Ste. 4, Cinnaminson 08077
Owner—David Gardellin, 20 emp., *Industrial pinch valves & pressure* .......... (856) 829-2888
Orycon Control Technology, Inc., 3407 Rose Ave., Ocean 07712
Pres. & GM, Hum. Res.—Sal Benenati, 20 emp., *Plastics working hot runner systems* .......... (732) 922-2400
Papailias Co., Inc., J. G., 245 Pegasus Ave., Northvale 07647
Pres., Cont.—George Papailias, 40 emp., *Variable process control equipment* .......... (201) 767-4027
Princeton Power Systems, Inc., 3175 Princeton Pike, Ste. C, Lawrenceville 08648
Co-Founder & Ex. CSO—Darren Hammell, 48 emp., *Electric power converting equipment*.... (609) 955-5390
Process Components, 301 John Wall Rd., Monroe Township 08831
Pres.—David Zimmerman, 8 emp., *High purity flow components* .......... (732) 786-1500
Radiant Thermal Products Co., 640 W. 1st Ave., Roselle 07203
Pres.—Albert C. Maglio, 30 emp., *Laboratory industrial process electrodes* .......... (908) 241-7700
Rees Scientific Corp., 1007 Whitehead Road Ext., Trenton 08638
Pres., CEO—Rees Thomas, 125 emp., *Environmental monitoring, integrated* .......... (609) 530-1055
Schaedler Quinzel, Inc. (H Q), 1259 U.S. Highway 46, Ste. 4, Parsippany 07054
Pres.—John N. Schaedler, 2 emp., *Corporate headquarters; polymer-based* .......... (973) 263-4949
Sensor Scientific, Inc., 6 Kingsbridge Rd., Fairfield 07004
Pres.—G. Robert Brinley, 22 emp., *Thermistors, RTD's & custom sensor* .......... (973) 227-7790
Simple Step, LLC, 12 W. Owassa Tpke., Newton 07860
Pres.—Charles Grenz, 10 emp., *Motion controllers for the automation* .......... (973) 948-2938
Smith Brothers Services, LLC, 3212 State Route 94, Ste. 9, Franklin 07416
Owner—Charles Smith, 1 emp., *Rebuilt snowplow pumps, snowplow pump* .......... (973) 209-7569
Thermo Systems, LLC (H Q), 84 Twin Rivers Dr., East Windsor 08520
Ptnr.—Greg Smith, 50 emp., *Company headquarters; direct digital* .......... (609) 371-3300
TIP Industries, Inc., 340 W. Broad St., Burlington 08016
Owner, CEO & GM—Daniel E. Farnan, 10 emp., *Temperature sensors, alarm systems,* .......... (609) 239-1900
Tymac Controls Corp., 432 U.S. Highway 206, Ste. C, Montague 07827
Pres., CEO—John Mickowski, 25 emp., *Process sensors & control instruments* .......... (973) 293-3339
West Electronics, Inc., 5 Terri Ln., Ste. 15, P.O. Box 366, Burlington 08016
Pres.—Bradford Brainard, 20 emp., *Guided missile power controls, communication* .......... (609) 387-4300
Wyssmont Co., Inc., 1470 Bergen Blvd., Fort Lee 07024
Pres.—Ed Weisselberg, 25 emp., *Drying equipment, feeders & lumpbreakers* .......... (201) 947-4600

## 3824 Fluid meters & counting devices

Advanced Marine Technology, 12 Crown Plz., Unit 204, Hazlet 07730
Pres., GM—Anatoly Nemiroski, 7 emp., *Oil content meters* .......... (732) 888-8248
Blanchette Tool & Gage Mfg., 845 Bloomfield Ave., P.O. Box 1270, Clifton 07012
Pres.—R. Blanchette Garvey, 8 emp., *Visual gage comparators & dimensional* .......... (973) 471-2100
Blend-Rite Industries, Inc., 585 Forest St., Unit 4, Orange 07050
Pres.—Milt Westrich, 15 emp., *Water meters* .......... (973) 395-3889
Edhard Corp., 279 Blau Rd., Hackettstown 07840
Pres.—Edgar Bars, 27 emp., *Liquid & viscous product filling &* .......... (908) 850-8444
Ellis Kuhnke Controls, Inc., 132 Lewis St., Unit A-2, Eatontown 07724
Pres.—Howard J. Boyce, 8 emp., *Manufacturer & distributor of pneumatic* .......... (732) 291-3334
Ernst Co., Inc., John C., 21 Gail Ct., Sparta 07871
Pres.—James Wolfe, 17 emp., *Sight glasses & windows, liquid level* .......... (973) 940-1600
Fargo Controls, Inc., P.O. Box 539, Eatontown 07724
Pres.—E. Fargo, 5 emp., *Proximity sensors, counters, timers* .......... (732) 389-3376
Kessler Ellis Products Co., Inc., 10 Industrial Way E., Ste. 6, Eatontown 07724
CEO—Corson Ellis III, 50 emp., *Flowmeters, counting devices, timers* .......... (732) 935-1320
Matrix Controls Co., Inc., 330 Elizabeth Ave., Somerset 08873
Pres.—Brad Lindemann, 14 emp., *Production tracking, monitoring & scheduling* .......... (732) 469-5551
Multiforce Systems Corp., 101 Wall St., Princeton 08540
V-P., Sales—Keith Griesinger, 19 emp., *Automated fuel management systems that* .......... (609) 683-4242
Parkeon, Inc., 40 Twosome Dr., Ste. 7, Moorestown 08057
Pres., N. Amer.—Chris Octon, 40 emp., *On & off integrated street parking* .......... (856) 234-8000
Seaboard Instrument Co., Inc., 4 N. 1st St., Pleasantville 08232
Pres., Opers. Mgr.—Thomas J. Higbee, Sr., 6 emp., *Vibrating reed tachometers & frequency* (609) 641-5300
TIP Industries, Inc., 340 W. Broad St., Burlington 08016
Owner, CEO & GM—Daniel E. Farnan, 10 emp., *Temperature sensors, alarm systems,* .......... (609) 239-1900

## 3825 Electricity measuring instruments

ABC Digital Electronics, Inc., 44 Country Squire Rd., Old Tappan 07675
Pres.—C. H. Wu, 3 emp., *Production line electrical/electronic* .......... (201) 666-6888
Advanced Orientation Systems, Inc., 2525 E. Brunswick Ave., Ste. 205, Linden 07036
Pres., Fin. & Opers. Mgr.—Marty Berger, 9 emp., *Electrolytic tilt sensors, inclinometers* .......... (908) 474-9595
BTECH, Inc., 10 Astro Pl., Rockaway 07866
CEO—Manfred R. Laidig, 30 emp., *Stationary battery monitors, systems* .......... (973) 983-1120
Byram Laboratories, Inc., 1 Columbia Rd., Branchburg 08876
Pres.—Monte J. Prince, 24 emp., *Automatic meter reading systems, including* .......... (908) 252-0852
CG Automation Solutions USA, 60 Fadem Rd., Springfield 07081
Pres.—Normand N. Lavoie, 55 emp., *Supervisory control & data acquisition* .......... (973) 379-7400
D B M Corp., Inc., 32-A Spruce St., Oakland 07436
Pres.—Dale Sybnor, 15 emp., *Wireless communication radio frequency* .......... (201) 677-0008
Dranetz Technologies, 1000 New Durham Rd., Edison 08818
Pres.—Bob Hart, 50 emp., *Company headquarters & electrical power* .......... (732) 287-3680
DSPCon, 380 Foothill Rd., Ste. 101, Bridgewater 08807
Dir., Engrg.—Clarke Ryan, 30 emp., *Data acquisition & test-end measurement* .......... (908) 722-5656
Electro Impulse Laboratory, Inc., 1805 Route 33, Neptune 07753
Pres.—Mark Rubin, 41 emp., *Custom closed-loop cooling systems* .......... (732) 776-5800
Empire Telecommunications, Inc., 15 S. Van Brunt St., Englewood 07631
Pres.—Sid Kaplan, 12 emp., *Electronic testing equipment* .......... (201) 569-3339
In-Phase Technologies, Inc., 401 Bordentown Hedding Rd., Bldg. 4, Ste. A, Bordentown 08505
Pres.—Ed MacMullen, 30 emp., *Electronic test equipment* .......... (609) 298-9555
Intertek Laboratories, Inc., 340 Union St., Stirling 07980
Pres., GM, Bus. & Fin. Mgr.—Mary Labella, 15 emp., *Automatic test equipment & electronic* (908) 903-1800
InterTest, Inc., 303 State Route 94, Columbia 07832
Pres.—William Habermann, 40 emp., *Specialized vision products, remote* .......... (908) 496-8008
Link Computer Graphics, Inc., 17-A Daniel Rd., Fairfield 07004
Pres.—Hung-Wei Yeh, 10 emp., *Digital storage oscilloscopes, logic* .......... (973) 808-8990
Linseis, Inc., 109 N. Gold Dr., Robbinsville 08691
Pres.—Claus Linseis, 6 emp., *Thermal & thermal conductivity analyzers* .......... (609) 223-2070
Matrix Test Equipment, Inc., 200 Wood Ave., Middlesex 08846
Sales Mgr.—Charles Kouzoujian, 10 emp., *Cable television test equipment & distortion* .......... (732) 469-9510
Pentek, Inc., 1 Park Way, 2nd Fl., Upper Saddle River 07458
Pres.—Dan Shamah, 55 emp., *Digital signal processing, software* .......... (201) 818-5900
Photon Technology International, 3880 Park Ave., Edison 08820
Chrm., Pres. & CEO—Charles G. Marianik, 15 emp., *Fluorescence instrumentation for industry* (732) 494-8660
Powercomm Solutions, LLC, 15 Minneakoning Rd., Ste. 311, Flemington 08822
★ Manager—Raymond Fella, 5 emp., *Instrumentation products for the electric* .......... (908) 806-7025
Quantem Corp., 1457 Lower Ferry Rd., Trenton 08618
CEO—Chris Bromberg, 20 emp., *Thermostats & temperature controls* .......... (609) 883-9191
R F VII, Inc., 1041 Glassboro Rd., Bldg. 6, Williamstown 08094
Pres., Treas.—Kelly Barber, 13 emp., *Radio frequency plasma generators,* .......... (856) 875-2121
Satec, Inc. (H Q), 10 Milltown Ct., Union 07083
Pres.—Edwin Hoinowski, 16 emp., *Corporate headquarters; power meters* .......... (908) 686-9510
Sensor Products, Inc., 300 Madison Ave., Ste. 100, Madison 07940
Off. Mgr.—Evan Worthing, 25 emp., *Tactile pressure sensors* .......... (973) 884-1755
Signalcrafters Tech, Inc., 57 Eagle Rock Ave., East Hanover 07936
Pres., Mfg. Mgr.—Al Vnencak, 6 emp., *Frequency selective volt, impedance* .......... (973) 781-0880
Spirent Communications PLC, 541 Industrial Way W., Eatontown 07724
V-P., Fin.—Steve Clark, 150 emp., *Telecommunication testing equipment* .......... (732) 544-8700
Tel-Instrument Electronics Corp., 1 Branca Rd., East Rutherford 07073
CEO—Jeffrey O'Hara, 58 emp., *Avionic test equipment* .......... (201) 933-1600
V. Tech Instruments, Inc., 171 Burns Ave., Lodi 07644
Pres.—Jaw Wu, 5 emp., *Portable electronic spectrum analyzers* .......... (973) 546-7635
Wireless Telecom Group, Inc., 25 Eastmans Rd., Parsippany 07054
Pres., CEO—Paul Genova, 95 emp., *Wireless communication test & measurement* .......... (973) 386-9696
Woyshner Service Co., Inc., 813 Edgewood Ave., Riverside 08075
Owner—William Woyshner, 3 emp., *Calibration volume chambers assembly* .......... (856) 461-9196

## 3826 Analytical instruments

Abbott Point Of Care, 400 College Rd. E., Princeton 08540
Div. V-P., R & D—Michael P. Zelin, 350 emp., *Hand-held portable digital blood sample* .......... (609) 454-9000
Advanced Imaging Assocs., Inc., 190 Munsonhurst Rd., Ste. 6, Franklin 07416
Pres.—Clifford Barker, 6 emp., *Non-medical magnetic resonance imaging* .......... (973) 823-8999
Airscan, Inc., 291 Route 22 E., Ste. 12, Lebanon 08833
Pres., CEO—Stephen Shoemaker, 8 emp., *Gas monitors for OSHA compliance* .......... (908) 823-9425
Assem-Pak, Inc., 1649 Castpa Pl., Vineland 08360
Pres.—Don Bayer, 140 emp., *Analytical instruments for the pharmaceutical* .......... (856) 692-3355
Aviv Biomedical, Inc., 750 Vassar Ave., Lakewood 08701
Pres.—Jack Aviv, 14 emp., *Scientific & clinical instruments* .......... (732) 370-1300
Azzota Corp., 178 Franklin Rd., Randolph 07869
GM—Geoff Darling, 10 emp., *Corporate headquarters & laboratory* .......... (877) 649-2746
Biometallics, Inc., 37 Station Dr., Princeton Junction 08550
Pres.—Christa Kuehn, 12 emp., *Diagnostic veterinary test kits & microplate* .......... (609) 275-0133
BioTillion, LLC, 30 Vreeland Dr., Ste. 7, Skillman 08558
Owner—Hanan Davidowitz, 3 emp., *RFID vial reading systems for biotechnology* .......... (609) 454-3523

Cargille Laboratories, 55 Commerce Rd., Cedar Grove 07009
Pres., Tech.—William J. Sacher, 22 emp., *Refractive index & sink-float standards* ........ (973) 239-6633
Distek, Inc., 121 N. Center Dr., North Brunswick 08902
Pres.—Gerald Brinker, 63 emp., *Pharmaceutical testing instruments* ........ (732) 422-7585
ECI Technology, Inc., 60 Gordon Dr., Totowa 07512
Pres., CEO—Marianna Rabinovitch, 85 emp., *Chemical management systems & analyzers* ... (973) 890-1114
ES Industries, 701 S. Route 73, West Berlin 08091
Pres., Sales Mgr.—David Kohler, 9 emp., *Laboratory chromatographic instruments* ........ (856) 753-8400
Eurotek, Inc., Carlton Street 61, Unit 2, Rumson 07760
Pres.—Jack Ross, 5 emp., *Medical & scientific equipment* ........ (732) 224-1300
Evex Global, 857 State Rd., Princeton 08540
Pres.—Claudio Tarquinio, 15 emp., *Scientific instrumentation for nanotechnology* ........ (408) 907-2994
GE Healthcare LifeSciences, 800 Centennial Ave., P.O. Box 1327, Piscataway 08855
GM, Comml. Americas—Eric Roman, 1000 emp., *Biotechnology testing equipment* ........ (732) 457-8000
Hematechnologies, Inc., 291 U.S. Highway 22, Ste. 12, Lebanon 08833
Pres.—Stephen M. Shoemaker, 4 emp., *Medical laboratory instruments* ........ (908) 823-9430
HORIBA Scientific, 3880 Park Ave., Edison 08820
Pres.—Steve Slutter, 130 emp., *Analytical instruments for scientific* ........ (732) 494-8660
Hosokawa Micron Powder Systems, 10 Chatham Rd., Summit 07901
V-P.—Rob Voorhees, 50 emp., *Company headquarters & powder processing* ........ (908) 273-6360
International Crystal Laboratories, 11 Erie St., Ste. 2, Garfield 07026
Pres.—Theresa Herpst, 20 emp., *Optical lenses, lasers & spectroscopic* ........ (973) 478-8944
Koslow Scientific Co., 172 Walkers Ln., Englewood 07631
Pres.—Wolfgang Koslow, 30 emp., *Metal analyzing kits* ........ (201) 541-9100
Light Age, Inc., 500 Apgar Dr., Ste. 1, Somerset 08873
CEO—Donald F. Heller, 50 emp., *Lasers* ........ (732) 563-0600
Link Computer Graphics, Inc., 17-A Daniel Rd., Fairfield 07004
Pres.—Hung-Wei Yeh, 10 emp., *Digital storage oscilloscopes, logic* ........ (973) 808-8990
Linseis, Inc., 109 N. Gold Dr., Robbinsville 08691
Pres.—Claus Linseis, 6 emp., *Thermal & thermal conductivity analyzers* ........ (609) 223-2070
Little Joe Industries, 10 Ilene Ct., Ste. 4, Hillsborough 08844
Owner—Michael Engel, 4 emp., *Ink testing equipment* ........ (908) 359-5213
Logan Instruments Corp., 19 Schoolhouse Rd., Ste. C, Somerset 08873
Pres.—Luke Lee, 12 emp., *Pharmaceutical testing instruments* ........ (732) 302-9888
Marsden, Inc., 6800 Westfield Ave., Pennsauken 08110
Pres., CEO—Gerard J. Lucidi, 15 emp., *Gas infrared emitters & systems* ........ (856) 663-2227
Microdata Instrument, Inc., 1207 Hogan Dr., South Plainfield 07080
GM—George Cai, 5 emp., *Laboratory instruments, including microinject* ........ (908) 222-1717
MicroSurfaces, Inc., 1 W. Forest Ave., Englewood 07631
Pres.—Athena Guo, 6 emp., *Protein microarrays* ........ (201) 408-5596
Norell, Inc., 314 Arbor Ave., P.O. Box 307, Landisville 08326
Pres.—Greg Norell, 20 emp., *Test tubes* ........ (856) 697-0020
Norland Products, Inc., 2540 Route 130, Ste. 100, Cranbury 08512
Pres.—Eric Norland, 20 emp., *Interferometric microscopes for profiling* ........ (609) 395-1966
Ortho-Clinical Diagnostics, Inc. (H Q), 1001 U.S. Highway 202, P.O. Box 350, Raritan 08869
Chrm., CEO—Martin Madaus, 750 emp., *Corporate headquarters; donor screening* ........ (908) 218-1300
Princeton BioMeditech Corp., 4242 U.S. Highway 1, Monmouth Junction 08852
Pres.—Jemo Kang, 70 emp., *One-step advanced rapid diagnostic* ........ (732) 274-1000
Princeton Chromatography, Inc., 1206 Cranbury-S. River Rd., Cranbury 08512
Pres., CFO—Linda Caldwell, 7 emp., *Chromatographic columns & bonded-phase* ........ (609) 860-1803
Princeton Instruments, 3660 Quakerbridge Rd., Trenton 08619
Pres.—William Asher, 60 emp., *High-performance CCD, ICCD, EMCCD &* ........ (609) 587-9797
Rame-Hart, Inc., 5 Emery Ave., Ste. 1, Randolph 07869
Pres., CEO—Ken Christiansen, 25 emp., *Egg harvesting & inoculating machines* ........ (973) 335-0560
Resource Systems, Inc., 7 Merry Ln., East Hanover 07936
Pres.—Leonard R. Rubin, 3 emp., *Industrial gas & palladium-alloy hydrogen* ........ (973) 884-0650
Rudolph Instruments, Inc., 400 Morris Ave., Ste. 120, Denville 07834
Pres.—Kumar Utukuri, 5 emp., *Laboratory analytical instruments,* ........ (973) 983-6700
Rudolph Research Analytical, 55 Newburgh Rd., Hackettstown 07840
Pres., Mktg. Mgr.—Richard C. Spainer, 55 emp., *Automatic polarimeters, refractometers* ........ (973) 584-1558
Siemens Healthcare Diagnostics, Inc., 62 Flanders Bartley Rd., Flanders 07836
Head of R & D—David Stein, 450 emp., *Blood & urine immunoassay systems for* ........ (973) 927-2828
Sigma Design Company, 200 Pond Ave., Middlesex 08846
Pres.—Gerard J. Lynch, 10 emp., *Contract manufacturing & assembly of* ........ (732) 629-7555
Sonntek, Inc., 125 Pleasant Ave., Upper Saddle River 07458
Pres.—David Keller, 7 emp., *Chromatographic research instruments* ........ (201) 236-9300
Spark Holland, Inc., 816 Delsea Dr. N., Glassboro 08028
★ Pres.—John Crutchfield, 4 emp., *Analytical instruments for laboratories* ........ (609) 799-7250
SPEX CertiPrep, Inc., 203 Norcross Ave., Metuchen 08840
Chrm.—Neil Stein, 80 emp., *Organic & inorganic certified reference* ........ (732) 549-7144
Spex Forensics, 203 Norcross Ave., Metuchen 08840
★ GM—Lisa Petro, 3 emp., *Forensic laboratory equipment* ........ (732) 549-7144
Techne, Inc., 3 Terri Ln., Ste. 10, Burlington 08016
Pres., Hum. Res. Mgr.—Peter Lucas, 13 emp., *Manufacturer & distributor of temperature* ........ (609) 589-2560
Temptime Corp., 116 The American Rd., Morris Plains 07950
★ Pres.—Renaat Van den Hooff, 70 emp., *Non-reversible temperature indicators* ........ (973) 984-6000
Tess-Com, Inc., 400 South Ave., Ste. 11, Middlesex 08846
V-P., GM—David Colonna, 10 emp., *Gas analyzers & continuous emission* ........ (732) 560-8100
Thorlabs, Inc., 56 Sparta Ave., Newton 07860
Pres., CEO—Alex Cable, 850 emp., *Corporate headquarters & optomechanical* ........ (973) 300-3000
Trace Environmental Systems, Inc., 7 Park Lake Rd., Unit 9, Sparta 07871
CEO—David Martin, 5 emp., *Air quality monitors* ........ (973) 383-3550
Uehling Instrument Co., 473 Getty Ave., Paterson 07503
Pres.—Richard Pavan, 20 emp., *Liquid level & panel mounted gages,* ........ (973) 742-8710
Waltron, Bull & Roberts, LLC, 50 Tannery Rd., P.O. Box 70, Whitehouse 08888
Chrm.—John M. Walsh III, 12 emp., *Analytical instruments for ultra pure* ........ (908) 534-5100

## 3827 Optical instruments & lenses

Anchor Optical Co., 101 E. Gloucester Pike, Barrington 08007
★ Dir., Mktg.—Kirsten Bjork Jones, 100 emp., *Commercial, experimental, specialty* ........ (856) 573-6865
Azzota Corp., 178 Franklin Rd., Randolph 07869
GM—Geoff Darling, 10 emp., *Corporate headquarters & laboratory* ........ (877) 649-2746
Chiral Photonics, Inc., 26 Chapin Rd., Unit 1104, P.O. Box 694, Pine Brook 07058
Pres.—Dan Neugroschl, 20 emp., *Ultra high-density optical I/O solutions* ........ (973) 732-0030
Coherent Advanced Crystal Group, 31 Farinella Dr., East Hanover 07936
GM—Dominic Loiacono, 60 emp., *Optical crystals* ........ (973) 240-6800
Datacolor, 5 Princess Rd., Lawrenceville 08648
Pres., CEO—Albert Busch, 120 emp., *Spectrophotometers, software, instruments* ........ (609) 924-2189
Dynasil Corp. Of America, 385 Cooper Rd., West Berlin 08091
V-P., Sales & Mktg. & GM—Bruce Leonetti, 16 emp., *Precision fused silica &* ........ (856) 767-4600
ECSI International, Inc., 790 Bloomfield Ave., Bldg. C-1, Clifton 07012
Pres., CEO—Arthur Birch, 24 emp., *Infrared perimeter & intrusion detection* ........ (973) 574-8555
Edmund Optics, Inc., 101 E. Gloucester Pike, Barrington 08007
Chrm., CEO—Robert Edmund, 165 emp., *Corporate headquarters & optical lens* ........ (856) 547-3488
Esco Optics, 1 Tideland Rd., P.O. Box 308, Oak Ridge 07438
Pres.—Lee Steneken, 33 emp., *American-made custom & standard optical* ........ (973) 697-3700
Fastpulse Technology, Inc., 220 Midland Ave., Saddle Brook 07663
Chrm., Pres.—Robert Goldstein, 15 emp., *Electro-optical instruments for lasers* ........ (973) 478-5757
Inrad Optics, Inc., 181 Legrand Ave., Northvale 07647
Chrm.—Jan Winston, 65 emp., *OEM custom optics, laser accessories* ........ (201) 767-1910
International Crystal Laboratories, 11 Erie St., Ste. 2, Garfield 07026
Pres.—Theresa Herpst, 20 emp., *Optical lenses, lasers & spectroscopic* ........ (973) 478-8944
M H Optical Supplies, Inc., 128 Leuning St., South Hackensack 07606
Pres.—Mitchell Hirsch, 25 emp., *Corporate headquarters & optical lenses* ........ (201) 489-1110
Phillips Safety Products, Inc., 123 Lincoln Blvd., Middlesex 08846
Pres.—Robert Phillips, 10 emp., *Lead glass windows, glass etching,* ........ (732) 356-1493
Pike & Co., Inc., E. W., 2149 Price St., Rahway 07065
Pres.—Emil Sudzina, 2 emp., *Illuminated magnifying instruments* ........ (732) 396-0002
Princeton Instruments, 3660 Quakerbridge Rd., Trenton 08619
Pres.—William Asher, 60 emp., *High-performance CCD, ICCD, EMCCD &* ........ (609) 587-9797
Rame-Hart Instrument Co., LLC, 19 Route 10 E., Ste. 11, Succasunna 07876
Principal—Carl Clegg, 5 emp., *Goniometers* ........ (973) 448-0305
Reflex Analytical Corporation, 643 Albert Pl., Ridgewood 07450
V-P., Hum. Res. & IT Mgr.—Tony Jacobini, 5 emp., *Spectroscopy accessories & photonic* ........ (201) 444-8958
Shanghai Optics, Inc. (H Q), 17 Brant Ave., Ste. 6, Clark 07066
★ V-P., Sales & Mktg.—Joanna Lee, 7 emp., *Corporate headquarters; lens design* ........ (732) 321-6915
Sofradir EC, Inc., 373 U.S. Highway 46, Ste. E, Fairfield 07004
Pres.—Frank Vallese, 42 emp., *Uncooled & cooled infrared & thermography* ........ (973) 882-0211
Spectro Analytical Instruments, Inc., 91 McKee Dr., Mahwah 07430
V-P., Sales & Mktg.—Tom Blumer, 20 emp., *Emission spectrometers* ........ (201) 642-3000
Tech-Optics International, 600 Deer Rd., Cherry Hill 08034
Dir., Sales & GM—Lisa Wassmer, 10 emp., *Hand & stand magnifiers, loupes & binoculars* ........ (856) 795-8585
Thorlabs, Inc., 56 Sparta Ave., Newton 07860
Pres., CEO—Alex Cable, 850 emp., *Corporate headquarters & optomechanical* ........ (973) 300-3000
TRUMPF Photonics, Inc., 2601 US Route 130 S., Cranbury 08512
Mng. Dir.—Georg Treusch, 150 emp., *High-power semiconductor lasers, RF* ........ (609) 925-8200
Village Opticians, 550 Route 530, Whiting 08759
Owner & Optician—Joel C. Wolf, 4 emp., *Optical lens grinding* ........ (732) 350-1900

## 3829 Measuring & controlling devices, nec

A Mat Control Technologies, LLC, 70 Mount Bethel Rd., Warren 07059
Pres.—Jens Waale, 2 emp., *Programmable smokehouse process controllers* ........ (908) 756-1699
A&M Industrial, Inc., 325 Commerce Rd., Linden 07036
Ex. V-P.—David Young, 10 emp., *Manufacturer of industrial & hydraulic* ........ (908) 862-1800
ABC Digital Electronics, Inc., 44 Country Squire Rd., Old Tappan 07675
Pres.—C. H. Wu, 3 emp., *Production line electrical/electronic* ........ (201) 666-6888
Alison Control, Inc., 35 Daniel Rd. W., Fairfield 07004
Pres.—Gene E. Benzenberg, 20 emp., *Fire detectors, fire detection control* ........ (973) 575-7100
American Sensor Technologies, Inc., 450 Clark Dr., Ste. 4, Budd Lake 07828
Pres., CEO—Richard Tasker, 90 emp., *Corporate headquarters & industrial* ........ (973) 448-1901
Analytical Measurements, 22 Mountain View Dr., Chester 07930
Pres., CEO—W. Richard Adey, 5 emp., *pH & ORP instrumentation* ........ (908) 955-7170
Auto Clear, LLC, 2 Gardner Rd., Fairfield 07004
Pres., CEO—Brad Conway, 80 emp., *Hand-held, desktop, vehicle & walk-through* ........ (973) 276-6161
Berkeley Varitronics Systems, Inc., 255 Liberty St., Metuchen 08840
Pres., CEO—Scott N. Schober, 30 emp., *Wireless telecommunications test equipment* ........ (732) 548-3737
Blanchette Tool & Gage Mfg., 845 Bloomfield Ave., P.O. Box 1270, Clifton 07012
Pres.—R. Blanchette Garvey, 8 emp., *Visual gage comparators & dimensional* ........ (973) 471-2100
Brabender® Instruments, C. W., 50 E. Wesley St., P.O. Box 2127, South Hackensack 07606
Pres.—Richard F. Thoma, 30 emp., *Industrial laboratory testing instruments* ........ (201) 343-8425
Brewer Assocs., 400 Apgar Dr., Unit G, Somerset 08873
Pres.—Thomas Flack, 25 emp., *Engineering, architectural, sign making* ........ (732) 564-9070
Burling Instruments, Inc., 16 River Rd., P.O. Box 298, Chatham 07928
Pres., GM—Harry Bentas, 10 emp., *Temperature controls* ........ (973) 635-9481
Comus International, Inc., 454 Allwood Rd., Clifton 07012
Pres., CEO—Robert P. Romano, 80 emp., *Tilt, tip-over, float & reed switches* ........ (973) 777-6900
Connell Industries, Inc., 13 Fairfield Ave., West Caldwell 07006
Pres.—Vincent DiGangi, 5 emp., *Industrial automation systems & equipment* ........ (877) 926-6635
CorrView International, LLC, P.O. Box 8513, Landing 07850
Pres., CEO—William Duncan, 2 emp., *Metal pipe corrosion monitoring plugs* ........ (973) 770-7764
Datatest, Inc., 300 Valley Rd., Hillsborough 08844
Pres.—Paul Ford, 25 emp., *Air pollution & combustion monitoring* ........ (908) 369-1590
DEK-TRON International Corp., 244 E. 3rd St., Plainfield 07060
GM & Test Engr.—Mark Tsvet, 25 emp., *Materials testing instruments for the* ........ (908) 226-1777
Delmhorst Instrument Co., 51 Indian Ln. E., Towaco 07082
Pres., CEO—Thomas Laurenzi, 24 emp., *Hand-held moisture testing instruments* ........ (973) 334-2557
DigiVac Co., 105-B Church St., Matawan 07747
Pres.—Timothy Collins, 14 emp., *Vacuum instrumentation & scientific* ........ (732) 765-0900
Diopsys, Inc., 16 Chapin Rd., Ste. 912, P.O. Box 672, Pine Brook 07058
Pres., CEO—Joseph Fontanetta, 22 emp., *Visual evoked potential (VEP) vision* ........ (973) 244-0622
Electronic Measuring Devices, Inc., 15 Mill Rd., Flanders 07836
COO—Klaus Ulbrich, 1 emp., *Analog coordinate measuring systems* ........ (973) 691-4755
Ellenby Technologies, Inc., 412 Grandview Ave., Woodbury Heights 08097
CEO—Bob Dobbins, 53 emp., *Contract electronic manufacturing of* ........ (856) 848-2020
Ernst Co., Inc., John C., 21 Gail Ct., Sparta 07871
Pres.—James Wolfe, 17 emp., *Sight glasses & windows, liquid level* ........ (973) 940-1600
Ernst Flow Industries, 116 Main St., Farmingdale 07727
Sales Supv.—Susan Shanahan, 14 emp., *gages & flow indicators* ........ (732) 938-5641
Flemington Instrument Co., Inc., 55 Sandra Rd., P.O. Box 298, Ringoes 08551
Pres.—Ralph Migliaccio, 40 emp., *Measurement & display instruments &* ........ (908) 782-4229
Gerin Corp., 1109 7th Ave., Neptune 07753
Pres.—Robert N. Gerin, 10 emp., *Oil testing equipment* ........ (732) 774-3256
Instrument Specialties Co., Inc., 661 Myrtle Ave., Boonton 07005
GM—Jack Miller, 19 emp., *Aircraft engine monitoring instruments* ........ (973) 335-2136
Instru-Met Corp., 931 Lehigh Ave., Union 07083
Pres.—Paul Metzger, 8 emp., *Tensile strength testing machines* ........ (908) 851-0700
inTEST Corp., 804 E. Gate Dr., Ste. 200, Mount Laurel 08054
Ex. Chrm.—Alyn Holt, 50 emp., *Corporate headquarters & semiconductor* ........ (856) 505-8800
Kershaw Instrumentation, LLC, 517 Auburn Ave., P.O. Box 163, Swedesboro 08085
Pres.—Dean Kershaw, 5 emp., *Ink testing equipment* ........ (856) 467-5482
Kulite Semiconductor Products, Inc., 1 Willow Tree Rd., Leonia 07605
Chrm. of the Board & CEO—Nora Kurtz, 750 emp., *Miniature high frequency* ........ (201) 461-0900
Lawler Mfg. Corp., 7 Kilmer Ct., Edison 08817
Pres., CFO—Mark Cekada, 15 emp., *Fuels & lubricants testing equipment* ........ (732) 777-2040

S.I.C.

Leneta Co., Inc., 15 Whitney Rd., Mahwah 07430
Pres.—Dan Schaeffer, 115 emp., *Paint test charts & draw down equipment* (201) 847-9300
Link Computer Graphics, Inc., 17-A Daniel Rd., Fairfield 07004
Pres.—Hung-Wei Yeh, 10 emp., *Digital storage oscilloscopes, logic* (973) 808-8990
Macro Sensors, 7300 Route 130 N., Bldg. 22, Pennsauken 08110
Sales & Mktg. Mgr.—Eileen Otto, 30 emp., *LVDT based position sensors & support* (856) 662-8000
Matrix Controls Co., Inc., 330 Elizabeth Ave., Somerset 08873
Pres.—Brad Lindemann, 14 emp., *Production tracking, monitoring & scheduling* (732) 469-5551
Mayfair Technology, LLC, 66 Witherspoon St., Princeton 08542
Member & GM—James Furey, 10 emp., *Single-use pressure sensors* (609) 802-1262
Mesa Laboratories, Inc., 10 Park Pl., Ste. 3, Butler 07405
Dir., Opers.—Brian Roberts, 22 emp., *Portable primary gas flow measurement* (973) 492-8400
Metricon Corp., 12 N. Main St., P.O. Box 63, Pennington 08534
Pres.—John H. Jackson, 7 emp., *Film thickness measuring instruments* (609) 737-1052
MISTRAS Group, Inc., 195 Clarksville Rd., Princeton Junction 08550
Chrm., CEO—Sotirios Vahaviolos, 150 emp., *Nondestructive ultrasonic & acoustic* (609) 716-4100
New Jersey Microsystems, Inc., 211 Warren St., Ste. 31, Newark 07103
Pres.—Frederick D. Chichester, 12 emp., *RFID tags & sensor systems* (973) 297-1450
Nuclear Diagnostic Products, Inc., 101 Round Hill Dr., Rockaway 07866
★ Pres.—Wayne Wong, 12 emp., *Radiopharmaceuticals* (973) 664-9696
Ohaus Corp., 7 Campus Dr., Ste. 310, Parsippany 07054
Pres.—Ted Xia, 100 emp., *Analytical & precision balances & scales* (973) 377-9000
Operations Technology, Inc., 30 Lambert Rd., P.O. Box 408, Blairstown 07825
Pres.—Richard B. Amon, 14 emp., *Inspection & measurement instruments* (908) 362-6200
Orpak USA, 100 1st St., Ste. 200, Hackensack 07601
Pres.—Shlomo Slotwiner, 10 emp., *Fuel management systems* (201) 441-9820
Park Plus, Inc., 480 Main Ave., Ste. 1, Wallington 07057
CEO—Ronald Astrup, 9 emp., *Valet parking equipment & high density* (973) 574-8020
Perma Pure, LLC, 8 Executive Dr., Toms River 08755
Pres.—Richard Curran, 56 emp., *Laboratory & environmental gas analyzing* (732) 244-0010
Phillips Scientific, 31 Industrial Ave., Ste. 1, Mahwah 07430
Pres.—Thomas Phillips, 15 emp., *Data acquisition electronics* (201) 934-8015
Powercomm Solutions, LLC, 15 Minneakoning Rd., Ste. 311, Flemington 08822
★ Manager—Raymond Fella, 5 emp., *Instrumentation products for the electric* (908) 806-7025
PRIMME Co., Inc., 42 Columbia Rd., Branchburg 08876
Pres.—Ed Braunig, 9 emp., *Ink & coatings testing equipment &* (908) 231-9490
Princeton Instruments, 3660 Quakerbridge Rd., Trenton 08619
Pres.—William Asher, 60 emp., *High-performance CCD, ICCD, EMCCD &* (609) 587-9797
Pro-Comm, Inc., 1105 Industrial Pkwy., Brick 08724
Pres.—Sheryl J. Visone, 11 emp., *High-power, UHF, L-band, S-band, C-band* (732) 206-0660
PulseTor, LLC, 1580 Reed Rd., Ste. C-2, Pennington 08534
Chief Technical Officer—Richard Mott, 5 emp., *Silicon drift detection devices* (609) 303-0578
Pyrometer Instrument Co., Inc., 92 N. Main St., Bldg. 18-D, P.O. Box 479, Windsor 08561
CEO—David Crozier, 6 emp., *Precision infrared thermometers with* (609) 443-5522
Quantem Corp., 1457 Lower Ferry Rd., Trenton 08618
CEO—Chris Bromberg, 20 emp., *Thermostats & temperature controls* (609) 883-9191
Refinery Systems, A Div. Of Core Lab, 11 Princess Rd., Lawrenceville 08648
GM—Craig Tournay, 12 emp., *Octane/cetane, CFR engine testing equipment...* (609) 896-2673
Resec Systems, LLC, 93 S. Railroad Ave., Ste. A, Bergenfield 07621
Owner—Bob Schulkin, 4 emp., *Automated high-speed inspection & sorting* (201) 384-6960
Scientific Instrument Services, Inc., 1027 Old York Rd., Ringoes 08551
Pres.—John Manura, 30 emp., *Mass spectrometers, vacuum systems,* (908) 788-5550
Seaboard Instrument Co., Inc., 4 N. 1st St., Pleasantville 08232
Pres., Opers. Mgr.—Thomas J. Higbee, Sr., 6 emp., *Vibrating reed tachometers & frequency* (609) 641-5300
Sensor Products, Inc., 300 Madison Ave., Ste. 100, Madison 07940
Off. Mgr.—Evan Worthing, 25 emp., *Tactile pressure sensors* (973) 884-1755
Sigma-Netics, Inc., 2 N. Corporate Dr., Riverdale 07457
Pres.—Alan Glanzman, 30 emp., *Pressure switches & metal bellows* (973) 616-6900
Spectrex, Inc., 218 Little Falls Rd., Unit 7, Cedar Grove 07009
Pres.—Eric Zinn, 14 emp., *Open-path (line of sight) gas detection* (973) 239-8398
Superior Signal Company LLC, 178 W. Greystone Rd., Old Bridge 08857
Pres.—James A. Kovacs, 20 emp., *Ultrasonic leak detectors & smoke generators* (732) 251-0800
T A C Technical Instrument Corp., 21 W. Piper Ave., Trenton-Mercer Airport, West Trenton 08628
Pres.—Frederick Beck, 15 emp., *Ultrasonic inspection machinery* (609) 882-2894
Techne, Inc., 3 Terri Ln., Ste. 10, Burlington 08016
Pres., Hum. Res. Mgr.—Peter Lucas, 13 emp., *Manufacturer & distributor of temperature* (609) 589-2560
Technical Products Co., 264 Park Ave., Caldwell 07006
Chrm.—Donald Meserlian, 2 emp., *Floor & footwear friction testers,* (973) 228-2258
Temperature Humidity Instruments LLC, 235 Main St., Ste. 281, Madison 07940
Pres.—Richard Bettle, 5 emp., *Temperature & humidity indicators &* (908) 354-8236
Terriss Consolidated Industries, 807 Summerfield Ave., P.O. Box 110, Asbury Park 07712
V-P.—Edward J. Della Zanna, 15 emp., *Eco-friendly scientific instruments* (732) 988-0909
Tess-Com, Inc., 400 South Ave., Ste. 11, Middlesex 08846
V-P., GM—David Colonna, 10 emp., *Gas analyzers & continuous emission* (732) 560-8100
Thomas Scientific, Inc. (H Q), 1654 High Hill Rd., Interstate 295, P.O. Box 99, Swedesboro 08085
Chrm.—Robert Patterson, 82 emp., *Corporate headquarters; water, soil* (856) 467-2000
Thorlabs, Inc., 56 Sparta Ave., Newton 07860
Pres., CEO—Alex Cable, 850 emp., *Corporate headquarters & optomechanical* (973) 300-3000
Thwing-Albert Instrument Company, 14 W. Collings Ave., West Berlin 08091
Pres.—Joseph W. Raab, 50 emp., *Testing equipment to measure physical* (856) 767-1000
TIP Industries, Inc., 340 W. Broad St., Burlington 08016
Owner, CEO & GM—Daniel E. Farnan, 10 emp., *Temperature sensors, alarm systems,* (609) 239-1900
Troemner, LLC, Henry, 201 Wolf Dr., P.O. Box 87, Thorofare 08086
Pres.—Wilbert Abele, 100 emp., *Precision weights, laboratory equipment* (856) 686-1600
TX Technology Corp., 100 Ford Rd., Unit 100-18, Denville 07834
GM—Donald Black, 15 emp., *Control monitoring systems, sensors* (973) 442-7500
Tyco (H Q), 9 Roszel Rd., Princeton 08540
CEO—George Oliver, 350 emp., *Company headquarters; security & fire* (609) 720-4200
Ulysses Machine Co., 41 Lancelot Ln., Mount Laurel 08054
Owner—Ulysses Xenophontos, 2 emp., *Rope twisting, wire braider & ballistic* (856) 979-3674
VMC Group, The, 113 Main St., P.O. Box 270, Bloomingdale 07403
Chrm.—Richard Berger, 110 emp., *Company headquarters & vibration isolation* (973) 838-1780
Westlock Controls Corp., 280 N. Midland Ave., Ste. 258, Saddle Brook 07663
Cont.—Pete Mooney, 100 emp., *Industrial valve monitors & controls* (201) 794-7650
Willrich Precision Instrument, Inc., 80 Broadway, Cresskill 07626
Pres.—George Chitos, 10 emp., *Measuring instrumentation* (201) 567-1411
Zytron Control Products, Inc., 20 Lexington Ave., Trenton 08618
Pres., Fin., MIS & R & D Mgr.—John Wilkinson, 25 emp., *Temperature & process controls & sensors.* (609) 771-0101

### 3841 Surgical & medical instruments

3D Biotek, LLC, 1 Ilene Ct., Hillsborough 08844
CEO—Qing Liu, 3 emp., *3D in-vitro cell culture scaffolds* (732) 729-6270
3M Co., 500 U.S. Highway 202 N., Flemington 08822
Plt. Mgr.—Bob Silbernagel, 250 emp., *Sterilization monitoring devices* (908) 788-4000
Abbott Point Of Care, 400 College Rd. E., Princeton 08540
Div. V-P., R & D—Michael P. Zelin, 350 emp., *Hand-held portable digital blood sample* (609) 454-9000
ABSCO, Inc., 101 Eisenhower Pkwy., Ste. 402, Roseland 07068
Pres., CEO—Peter Carr, 3 emp., *Proprietary bone cement, cement mixing* (973) 635-9040
Alfa Wassermann, Inc., 4 Henderson Dr., West Caldwell 07006
CEO—Ira Nordlicht, 100 emp., *Medical laboratory instruments* (973) 882-8630
Alkaline Corp., 20 Meridian Rd., Eatontown 07724
Pres.—Isadore Bale, 5 emp., *Disposable allergy test needles* (732) 531-7830
Alto Development Corp., 5206 Asbury Rd., P.O. Box 758, Farmingdale 07727
Pres.—Tim Wojciechowicz, 75 emp., *Surgical supplies, including electrosurgical* (732) 938-2266
American Bionostica, Inc., 510 Heron Dr., Ste. 203, Swedesboro 08085
Pres.—Rick Thompson, 10 emp., *Rapid immunochromatographic tests for* (856) 467-7070
Antares Pharma, Inc., 100 Princeton S. Corporate Ctr., Ste. 300, Ewing 08628
Pres., CEO—Eamonn P. Hobbs, 30 emp., *Corporate headquarters & needle-free* (609) 359-3020
Automated Medical Products Co., 440 Cliff Rd., Sewaren 07077
CEO—Jerry M. Brown, 8 emp., *Fine stainless steel single arm & double-arm* (732) 602-7717
Aviv Biomedical, Inc., 750 Vassar Ave., Lakewood 08701
Pres.—Jack Aviv, 14 emp., *Scientific & clinical instruments* (732) 370-1300
Becton, Dickinson & Co. (H Q), 1 Becton Dr., Franklin Lakes 07417
Ex. Chrm.—Edward J. Ludwig, 1400 emp., *Company headquarters; medical equipment* (201) 847-6800
Bio Compression Systems, Inc., 120 W. Commercial Ave., Moonachie 07074
CEO, Sales Mgr.—Robert G. Freidenrich, 15 emp., *Medical equipment* (201) 939-0716
Biological Controls, Inc., 749 Hope Rd., Ste. A, Tinton Falls 07724
Pres.—Gary Messina, 5 emp., *Hospital infection control equipment* (732) 389-8922
BioMediCon, 30 E. Central Ave., Moorestown 08057
Pres., GM & Opers. Mgr.—Mark Singer, 19 emp., *Hospital operating room & procedure* (856) 778-1880
BioMedtrix, LLC, 50 Intervale Rd., Ste. 5, Boonton 07005
Member—Joseph Pych, 8 emp., *Veterinary orthopedic implants* (973) 331-7800
Biometallics, Inc., 37 Station Dr., Princeton Junction 08550
Pres.—Christa Kuehn, 12 emp., *Diagnostic veterinary test kits & microplate* (609) 275-0133
Biosearch Medical Products, Inc., 35 Industrial Pkwy., Branchburg 08876
Pres., CEO & V-P.—Manfred F. Dyck, 50 emp., *Biocompatible hydrophilic polymer coatings* (908) 722-5000
Bipore, Inc., 31 Industrial Pkwy., Northvale 07647
Pres.—Durmus Koch, 50 emp., *Plastic medical devices* (201) 767-1993
Burpee Material Technology, LLC, 15 Christopher Way, Eatontown 07724
★ CEO—Janet Burpee, 70 emp., *Medical devices, including catheters* (732) 544-8900
Buxton Biomedical, Inc. (H Q), 15-A Melanie Ln., Unit 7, East Hanover 07936
Pres.—Ed Schussler, 5 emp., *Corporate headquarters; surgical instruments* (973) 560-4848
C.R. Bard, Inc. (H Q), 730 Central Ave., New Providence 07974
Chrm., CEO—Timothy M. Ring, 300 emp., *Corporate headquarters; vascular, urology* (908) 277-8000
Cantel Medical Corp. (H Q), 150 Clove Rd., 9th Fl., Little Falls 07424
Chrm.—Charles M. Diker, 23 emp., *Corporate headquarters; dialysis equipment* (973) 890-7220
Capintec, Inc., 6 Arrow Rd., Ste. 101, Ramsey 07446
CEO—John Viscovic, 26 emp., *Corporate headquarters & radiation* (201) 825-9500
Case Medical, Inc., 19 Empire Blvd., South Hackensack 07606
CEO—Marcia A. Frieze, 60 emp., *Medical sterilization trays & cases* (201) 313-1999
Catheter Robotics, Inc., 500 International Dr., Ste. 255, Budd Lake 07828
Pres.—David A. Jenkins, 8 emp., *Remote catheter systems for cardiac* (973) 691-2000
CH Technologies, Inc., 263 Center Ave., Ste. 2, Westwood 07675
Pres. & Chief Scientist—Rudolph J. Jaeger, 3 emp., *Medical research inhalation exposure ...* (201) 666-2335
Cross Medical Specialties, Inc., 450 Andbro Dr., Unit 7, Pitman 08071
Pres.—Rita Lopes, 15 emp., *Rebuilt medical equipment & instruments* (856) 589-3288
Davol, Inc., 1822 Underwood Blvd., Delran 08075
Plt. Mgr.—Jose Nunez, 13 emp., *Medical textiles* (856) 764-8158
Diagnostic Specialties, 4 Leonard St., Metuchen 08840
Pres., MIS Mgr.—Praful Raja, 6 emp., *Medical diagnostic test kits, including* (732) 549-4011
Diopsys, Inc., 16 Chapin Rd., Ste. 912, P.O. Box 672, Pine Brook 07058
Pres., CEO—Joseph Fontanetta, 22 emp., *Visual evoked potential (VEP) vision* (973) 244-0622
DMG America, LLC, 242 S. Dean St., Englewood 07631
Pres.—George Wolfe, 25 emp., *Dental materials* (201) 894-5505
Eastmed Enterprises, Inc., 11 Brandywine Dr., Marlton 08053
Pres.—Supti M. Putatunda, 4 emp., *Corporate headquarters & surgical instruments* (856) 797-0131
Elcam Medical, Inc., 2 University Plz., Ste. 620, Hackensack 07601
Pres.—Amir Halperin, 6 emp., *OEM disposable medical devices for* (201) 457-1120
Endo Optiks, Inc., 39 Sycamore Ave., Little Silver 07739
Founder—Martin Uram, 6 emp., *Ophthalmic laser & endoscopy instruments* (732) 530-6762
Endo Pharmaceutical, Inc., 8 Clarke Dr., Cranbury 08512
Hum. Res. Coord.—Brooke Reeder, 27 emp., *Drug delivery devices* (609) 409-9010
Engineered Medical Solutions Co., LLC, 85 Industrial Rd., Bldg. B, Phillipsburg 08865
Pres.—Maxine Nordmeyer, 5 emp., *Hand-held adjustable surgical lights* (908) 329-9123
Eurotek, Inc., Carlton Street 61, Unit 2, Rumson 07760
Pres.—Jack Ross, 5 emp., *Medical & scientific equipment* (732) 224-1300
Flowonix, 500 International Dr., Ste. 200, Budd Lake 07828
★ Pres.—Steve Adler, 20 emp., *Medical devices, including implantable* (973) 426-9229
Gerresheimer Glass, Inc., 91 W. Forest Grove Rd., Vineland 08360
Cont.—Bill Miskelly, 180 emp., *Glass vials & pharmaceutical, biotech* (856) 507-5600
Gore & Assocs., Inc., W. L., 1746 State Route 34 N., Wall Township 07727
IT & MIS Mgr.—Andy Marotta, 160 emp., *Disposable medical devices* (732) 681-7070
G-U Tek, Inc., 266 King George Rd., Ste. B-2, Warren 07059
Pres.—Anthony Solazzo, 5 emp., *Medical devices* (908) 626-0012
IDL TechniEdge, LLC, 30 Boright Ave., Kenilworth 07033
Pres., CEO—Sean Quinn, 125 emp., *Hand blades & tools, including utility* (908) 497-9818
Immunostics, Inc., 3505 Sunset Ave., Ocean 07712
Pres.—Kenneth Kupits, 30 emp., *Medical diagnostic kits* (732) 918-0770
Impact Instrumentation, Inc., 27 Fairfield Pl., West Caldwell 07006
Pres.—L. Sherman, 165 emp., *Portable ventilators, automatic resuscitators* (973) 882-1212
Jan L, Inc., 26 Mill St., Ste. 26, Mount Holly 08060
Pres.—Bruce Levinson, 7 emp., *Hand drill dust collection systems,* (609) 261-1133
Ka-Lor Cubicle & Supply Co., Inc., P.O. Box 804, Fair Lawn 07410
Pres.—Dennis Brett, 21 emp., *Hospital & institutional cubicle, shower* (201) 891-8077
Katena Products, Inc., 4 Stewart Ct., Denville 07834
CEO—William Friedberg, 25 emp., *Eye surgery instruments* (973) 989-1600
KayPENTAX, 3 Paragon Dr., Montvale 07645
Pres.—David Woods, 50 emp., *Medical instruments* (973) 628-6200
L & R Mfg. Co., Inc., 577 Elm St., P.O. Box 607, Kearny 07032
Pres.—Robert J. Lazarus, 100 emp., *Manufacturer & distributor of ultrasonic* (201) 991-5330
Mada Medical Products, Inc., 625 Washington Ave., Carlstadt 07072
Pres.—Jeffrey Adam, 35 emp., *Medical respiratory equipment* (201) 460-0454
Manasquan Sight Saver Optical, 1407 W. Atlantic Ave., Manasquan 08736
Owner—Bruce Ziegler, 6 emp., *Prescription eyeglasses* (732) 223-4242

Martin Tool Co., Inc., 60 Route 15 S., Wharton 07885
Pres., Hum. Res. Mgr.—Louis Martin, 12 emp., *Medical devices* ............ (973) 361-9212
Maxter Corp. (H Q), 51 Edgemont Ln., Willingboro 08046
Pres.—John Mughal, 4 emp., *Corporate headquarters; surgical instruments* ...... (609) 877-9700
MedConnection, LLC, 65 Howard St., Phillipsburg 08865
Pres.—Robert K. Kolonia, 10 emp., *Plastic injection-molded medical supplies* ............ (908) 213-7012
Medical Indicators, Inc., 16 Thomas J. Rhodes Industrial Dr., Hamilton 08619
V-P., GM—Paul Baker, 50 emp., *Custom promotional single-use, reusable* ............ (609) 737-1600
Medrecon, Inc., 257 South Ave., Garwood 07027
Pres., CEO—Gary P. Sitcer, 8 emp., *New & rebuilt OR & surgical tables* ............ (908) 789-2050
Merton Tech, LLC, 168 Central Ave., Rochelle Park 07662
Ptnr. & Pres.—Antonio Gil, 6 emp., *Contract manufacturing of medical instruments* ............ (201) 881-0555
MICRO, 140 Belmont Dr., Somerset 08873
Chrm.—Frank J. Semcer, Sr., 350 emp., *Complete medical devices & components* ............ (732) 302-0800
Milestone Scientific, Inc. (H Q), 220 S. Orange Ave., Ste. 102, Livingston 07039
Chrm.—Leslie Bernhard, 10 emp., *Corporate headquarters; computer-controlled* ............ (973) 535-2717
Nephros, Inc., 41 Grand Ave., Ste. 201, River Edge 07661
Chrm.—James S. Scibetta, 6 emp., *Hemodiafiltration systems for the end-stage* ............ (201) 343-5202
Neurotron Medical, 800 Silvia St., West Trenton 08628
Owner—Jack Guldalian, 10 emp., *Diagnostic & electrotherapy medical* ............ (609) 896-3444
New Jersey Precision Technologies, Inc., 1081 Bristol Rd., Mountainside 07092
Pres., Sales Mgr.—Bob Tarantino, 45 emp., *Wire & ram EDM & small hole drilling* ............
NEXT Medical Products, 45 Columbia Rd., Branchburg 08876
★ Dir., Cust. Serv.—John Buday, 6 emp., *Ultrasound scanning gels & medical* ............ (800) 458-4254
North American Sterilization & Packaging Company, Inc., 19 Park Dr., Franklin 07416
Chief Operating Officer—Larry Partika, 50 emp., *Contract manufacturing of medical devices* (973) 209-4388
Northeast Medical Systems Corp., 901 Beechwood Ave., Cherry Hill 08002
Pres.—Joseph Conte, 5 emp., *Medical products* ............ (856) 910-8111
Omnimed, Inc., 800 Glen Ave., Moorestown 08057
Pres.—Steve Heffernen, 30 emp., *Medical products, including privacy* ............ (856) 359-2231
P A K Mfg., Inc., 704 S. 21st St., Irvington 07111
Pres.—Alex Even-Esh, 38 emp., *Surgical instruments* ............ (973) 372-1090
Peace Medical, Inc., 50 S. Center St., Ste. 11, Orange 07050
Pres.—Tim Fegan, 12 emp., *Respiratory machines, including filtration* ............ (973) 672-2120
Philips Respironics, 200 Franklin Square Dr., Somerset 08873
Pres.—Frans van Houten, 50 emp., *Inhalers, inhaler components & nebulizers* ............ (732) 563-3400
Phillips Precision, Inc., 7 Paul Kohner Pl., Elmwood Park 07407
Owner—Francis Phillips, 200 emp., *Orthopedic implants & instrumentation* ............ (201) 797-8820
Phil-Lu, Inc., 1206 Herbert Ave., Ocean 07712
Pres.—Lucille Petillo, 3 emp., *Custom spinal, ophthalmic, microsurgical* ............ (732) 531-6338
Physitemp Instruments, Inc., 154 Huron Ave., Clifton 07013
Pres.—Ronald Feller, 19 emp., *Medical temperature measurement & control* ............ (973) 779-5577
Princeton BioMeditech Corp., 4242 U.S. Highway 1, Monmouth Junction 08852
Pres.—Jemo Kang, 70 emp., *One-step advanced rapid diagnostic* ............ (732) 274-1000
Quantum Concepts, Inc., 24 River Rd., Ste. 12, Bogota 07603
Pres.—Paul Viola, 12 emp., *Medical instruments* ............ (201) 343-2008
Robbins Instruments, Inc., 2 N. Passaic Ave., P.O. Box 441, Chatham 07928
Pres.—George Mulvaney, 5 emp., *Surgical instruments, including medical* ............ (973) 635-8972
Scimedx Corp., 53 Richboynton Rd., Dover 07801
Pres.—Thomas L. Britten, 25 emp., *Medical diagnostic test kits* ............ (973) 625-8822
Sigma Design Company, 200 Pond Ave., Middlesex 08846
Pres.—Gerard J. Lynch, 10 emp., *Contract manufacturing & assembly of* ............ (732) 629-7555
Terumo Medical Corp. (H Q), 2101 Cottontail Ln., Somerset 08873
Pres., CEO—H. Arase, 120 emp., *Corporate headquarters; blood collection* ............ (732) 302-4900
Thoramet Surgical Products, Inc., 301 Route 17-N, Ste. 800, Rutherford 07070
CEO—Peter J. Scranton, 2 emp., *Surgical instruments* ............ (973) 399-7792
Topcon Medical Systems, Inc., 111 Bauer Dr., Oakland 07436
Pres., CEO—Dave Mudrick, 133 emp., *Medical diagnostic equipment, including* ............ (201) 599-5100
Totowa Precision Tooling, Inc., 500 Riverview Dr., Totowa 07512
Pres.—George Bondarenko, 9 emp., *Medical instruments & CNC machining* ............ (973) 256-2283
Triangle Mfg., 116 Pleasant Ave., Upper Saddle River 07458
Pres.—Dax Strohmeyer, 165 emp., *Medical devices, including implants* ............ (201) 825-1212
Tronex International, Inc., 300 International Dr., Mount Olive 07828
Pres., CEO—Donald L. Chu, 69 emp., *Advanced medical, hospital health &* ............ (973) 335-2888
Vention Medical, 6 Century Rd., South Plainfield 07080
Pres.—Dan Croteau, 140 emp., *Injection molded medical devices* ............ (908) 561-0717
Vozeh Equipment Corp., 509 Commerce St., Franklin Lakes 07417
Owner—Karen Vozeh, 55 emp., *Industrial & medical cutting tools* ............ (201) 337-4212

## 3842 Surgical appliances & supplies

ABSCO, Inc., 101 Eisenhower Pkwy., Ste. 402, Roseland 07068
Pres., CEO—Peter Carr, 3 emp., *Proprietary bone cement, cement mixing* ............ (973) 635-9040
Achilles Prosthetics & Orthotics, LLC, 503 N. Franklin Tpke., Ste. 12, Ramsey 07446
Pres.—Peter R. Buffington, 3 emp., *Custom braces, prosthetics & orthotics* ............ (201) 785-9944
Active Controls, LLC, 597 Mantua Blvd., Sewell 08080
CEO—Mike Flowers, 7 emp., *Power wheelchair controls, components* ............ (856) 669-0940
Aetrex Worldwide, Inc., 414 Alfred Ave., Teaneck 07666
Chrm.—Richard Schwartz, 140 emp., *Footwear, orthotics, foot health aids* ............ (201) 833-2700
Allied Op, 810 Hooper Ave., Toms River 08753
Pres.—Joshua Schenkman, 3 emp., *Prosthetics & orthotics* ............ (732) 341-9191
Allied Orthotics & Prosthetics, 813 E. Gate Dr., Ste. A, Mount Laurel 08054
Ex. V-P.—Howard Brand, 14 emp., *Orthotic & prosthetic devices, including* ............ (856) 273-6400
AlliedOP, 1527 Route 27, Somerset 08873
Ex. V-P.—Howard Brand, 2 emp., *Orthotic & prosthetic appliances &* ............ (732) 545-2885
AlliedOP, Inc., 1 Emery Ave., Ste. 1, Randolph 07869
Pres.—Joshua Schenkman, 8 emp., *Corporate headquarters & orthopedic* ............ (973) 328-3340
AlliedOP, Inc., 579 Goffle Rd., Wyckoff 07481
Practitioner—Michael Rebarber, 5 emp., *Orthopedic braces & prosthesis* ............ (201) 444-7750
Angel Medical Systems, Inc., 1163 Shrewsbury Ave., Ste. E, Shrewsbury 07702
CEO—David Fischell, 50 emp., *Implantable cardiac monitors & alert* ............ (732) 542-5551
Armac Assocs., 71 Passaic Ave., Florham Park 07932
★ Owner—Herb Etzold, 20 emp., *Orthopedic devices* ............ (888) 422-3044
Artegraft, Inc., 220 N. Center Dr., North Brunswick 08902
Pres., CEO—Richard A. Gibson, 18 emp., *Vascular grafts & thrombectomy devices* ............ (732) 422-8333
Atlantic Prosthetic & Orthotic Services, Inc., 199 New Rd., Ste. 56, Linwood 08221
Pres.—Rich Kathrins, 5 emp., *Custom prosthetic & orthotic devices* ............ (609) 927-6330
Bernafon, LLC, 2501 Cottontail Ln., Somerset 08873
Pres.—Joe Lugara, 20 emp., *Acrylic hearing aids* ............ (732) 560-9996
Bestwork Industries For The Blind, Inc., 1940 Almay Ave., Ste. 200, Cherry Hill 08003
Pres.—Belinda Moore, 100 emp., *Fabric safety vests, work aprons, tool* ............ (856) 939-5220
BioMediCon, 30 E. Central Ave., Moorestown 08057
Pres., GM & Opers. Mgr.—Mark Singer, 19 emp., *Hospital operating room & procedure* ............ (856) 778-1880

Biomet, Inc., 20-01 Pollitt Dr., Fair Lawn 07410
Prodn. Mgr.—Mike Shannon, 50 emp., *Orthopedic implants alloy castings* ............ (201) 797-7300
Bright Ideas USA, LLC, 890 Morris Ave., Lakewood 08701
Mng. Member & GM—Deena Leiman, 4 emp., *Company headquarters & safety & nighttime* . (732) 886-8865
Cantel Medical Corp. (H Q), 150 Clove Rd., 9th Fl., Little Falls 07424
Chrm.—Charles M. Diker, 23 emp., *Corporate headquarters; dialysis equipment* ............ (973) 890-7220
Carlascio Inc. Orthotics, Prosthetic, Custom Shoes, 283 Grove St., Jersey City 07302
Owner—Louis Carlascio, 11 emp., *Custom handmade orthotics, prosthetics* ............ (201) 333-8716
Cenogenics Corp., 100 Route 520, P.O. Box 308, Morganville 07751
Pres.—Michael Katz, 15 emp., *Contract medical stool, blood, urinalysis* ............ (732) 536-6457
CircuLite, Inc., 250 Pehle Ave., Ste. 403, Saddle Brook 07663
Pres., CEO—Paul Southworth, 20 emp., *Implantable blood pumps & cardiovascular* ............ (201) 543-2430
Cocco Enterprises, Inc., 333 Chambers St., Trenton 08609
V-P.—Cynthia Minelli, 15 emp., *Orthotic & prosthetic devices* ............ (609) 393-5939
Comfort Concepts, Inc., 501 Broad Ave., Ste. 7, Ridgefield 07657
Ptnr.—Robert Mass, 16 emp., *Manufacturer & distributor of reusable* ............ (201) 941-6700
Custom Spine, Inc. (H Q), 9 Campus Dr., Parsippany 07054
CEO—Mahmoud Abdelgany, 16 emp., *Corporate headquarters; spinal implants* .. (973) 808-0019
DDS, Inc., 100 Commerce Way, Ste. 5, Hackensack 07601
Sr. V-P.—Paul Kim, 10 emp., *Spinal & neck braces* ............ (888) 495-7440
Diabetic & Athletic Foot Center, LLC, Cedarwood Plz., 226 Route 37, Toms River 08753
Owner—Dan Dalsey, 10 emp., *Orthotics & prosthetics appliances* ............ (732) 281-3134
EBI, 399 Jefferson Rd., Parsippany 07054
Pres.—Adam Johnson, 300 emp., *Athletic knee braces* ............ (973) 299-9300
Edge Orthotics, Inc., 209 Pierson Ave., Edison 08837
Owner & Pres.—James C. Bauman, 5 emp., *Orthotics & prosthetics* ............ (732) 549-3343
Elcam Medical, Inc., 2 University Plz., Ste. 620, Hackensack 07601
Pres.—Amir Halperin, 6 emp., *OEM disposable medical devices for* ............ (201) 457-1120
Engineered Silicone Products, LLC, 75 Mill St., Ste. 2, Newton 07860
Opers. Mgr.—Lynn Haberman, 5 emp., *Silicone medical devices, including* ............ (973) 300-5120
England Orthopedics, Inc., 1002 Commons Way, Toms River 08755
Pres.—Frank Scarnati, 4 emp., *Orthopedic, orthotic & prosthetic devices* ............ (732) 286-4444
Ethicon, Inc., 737 U.S. Highway 22 W., P.O. Box 151, Somerville 08876
Pres., Wound Mgmt.—Daniel Wildman, 1300 emp., *Corporate headquarters & surgical sutures* (908) 218-0707
Extremity Medical, LLC, 300 Interpace Pkwy., Ste. 410, Parsippany 07054
Pres., CEO—James Gannoe, 20 emp., *Orthopedic implants* ............ (973) 588-8980
Ferry Machine Corp., 75 Industrial Ave., Little Ferry 07643
Pres., MIS & R & D Mgr.—Louis Ferretti, 30 emp., *Precision military & medical machining* .... (201) 641-9191
Garden State Dental Prosthetics, Inc., 805 4th Ave., Asbury Park 07712
Pres.—Michael A. Dipersio, 4 emp., *Full & partial dentures, night guards* ............ (732) 922-6650
Garden State Orthopaedic Center, Inc., 9 Post Rd., Ste. OP-1, Oakland 07436
Pres.—Louis J. Haberman, 3 emp., *Corporate headquarters & orthopedic* ............ (201) 337-5566
Garden State Orthopedic, Inc., 95 Mount Kemble Ave., Morristown 07960
Off. Mgr.—Jennifer Cordileone, 5 emp., *Orthopedic, orthotic & prosthetic appliances* ............ (973) 538-4948
Gemtor, Inc., 1 Johnson Ave., Matawan 07747
Pres.—Craig Neustater, 30 emp., *Safety, fall protection & confined-space* ............ (732) 583-6200
Global Partners In Shielding, Inc., 90 Dayton Ave., Ste. 13, Passaic 07055
Pres.—Donald Hener, 35 emp., *Industrial EMI, RFI & X-ray shielding* ............ (973) 574-9077
Greiner & Sons, Inc., L. J., 63-69 Dan Forth Ave., Paterson 07501
Pres.—Lothar Greiner, 4 emp., *Artificial eyes* ............ (973) 977-9441
Griffin Care, LLC, 80 Manheim Ave., Bridgeton 08302
CEO—Mark Naim, 80 emp., *Absorbent disposable incontinence products* ............ (856) 455-6870
Hanger Clinic, 210 New Rd., Ste. 7, Linwood 08221
GM—Brian Kleiberg, 4 emp., *Prosthetics & orthotics* ............ (609) 653-8323
Hanger Prosthetics & Orthotics, Inc., 265 Fernwood Ave., Edison 08837
Practice Mgr.—Robert Austin, 6 emp., *Prosthetic & orthotic appliances, including* ............ (732) 417-0480
Hanger Prosthetics & Orthotics, Inc., 5100 Belmore Blvd., Farmingdale 07727
GM—Brian Kleiberg, 8 emp., *Orthotic & prosthetic appliances* ............ (732) 919-7774
Hanger Prosthetics & Orthotics, Inc., 59 Main St., Ste. 111, West Orange 07052
Clinic Mgr.—Jenny Adase, 12 emp., *Prosthetic & orthopedic appliances* ............ (973) 736-0628
Hausmann Industries, Inc., 130 Union St., Northvale 07647
CEO—David Hausmann, 100 emp., *American-made healthcare products,* ............ (201) 767-0255
Integra LifeSciences Corp., 105 Morgan Ln., Plainsboro 08536
Dir., Sales Opers.—Scott Lewkowitz, 1200 emp., *Artificial skin & medical kits* ............ (609) 275-2700
Integra LifeSciences Corp., 311 Enterprise Dr., Plainsboro 08536
Ex. Chrm.—Stuart M. Essig, 400 emp., *Corporate headquarters & artificial* ............ (609) 275-0500
J. C. Orthopedic, Inc., 1680 Highway 88, Brick 08724
Pres., CEO—Frank Digeronimo, 6 emp., *Artifical limbs & braces* ............ (732) 458-7900
Jefferson Prosthetics & Orthotics, 120 Prospect St., South Orange 07079
Pres.—Simon Chang, 4 emp., *Prosthetics & orthotics* ............ (973) 762-0780
Johnson & Johnson (H Q), 1 Johnson & Johnson Plz., New Brunswick 08933
Worldwide Chrm., Consumer Div.—Jesse Wu, 900 emp., *Company headquarters; surgical* .. (732) 524-0400
Ken-Mar Machine & Mfg., 477 E. 30th St., Paterson 07504
V-P. & Hum. Res. Mgr.—Ken Walder, 25 emp., *Medical implants* ............ (973) 278-5827
Kingwood Industrial Products, Inc., 261 Main St., Unit 1 & 2, Hackettstown 07840
Pres.—Kevin Smith, 4 emp., *Audiology equipment & supplies, including* ............ (908) 852-8655
Laboratory Diagnostics Co., Inc., 100 Route 520, P.O. Box 160, Morganville 07751
Pres.—Michael Katz, 15 emp., *Medical diagnostic test kits, including* ............ (732) 536-6300
Lawall & Son, Inc., Harry J., 3071 E. Chestnut Ave., Ste. C-9, Vineland 08361
★ Manager—Harry Lawall, 7 emp., *Orthotics & prosthetics* ............ (856) 691-7764
Levy & Rappel, Inc., 339 10th St., Saddle Brook 07663
Pres.—David Kramer, 22 emp., *Custom foot orthotics, ankle/foot orthotics* ............ (973) 478-6511
LifeCell Corp., 1 Millennium Way, Branchburg 08876
V-P., Qual., Regulatory & Tissue Svcs.—Frances Harrison, 900 emp., *Acellular dermal matrix for* (908) 947-1100
Maddak Inc., 661 State Route 23, Wayne 07470
COO—Brad Mahood, 100 emp., *Corporate headquarters & home healthcare* ............ (973) 628-7600
Manfredi Orthotic & Prosthetic Affiliates, LLC, 749 Hope Rd., Eatontown 07724
Pres.—Robert Manfredi, 8 emp., *Orthopedic, orthotic & prosthetic appliances* ............ (732) 380-0366
Maquet Cardiovascular, LLC, 45 Barbour Pond Dr., Wayne 07470
Pres., CEO—Peter Hinchcliffe, 500 emp., *Company headquarters & surgical vascular* ............ (973) 709-7000
Merton Tech, LLC, 168 Central Ave., Rochelle Park 07662
Ptnr. & Pres.—Antonio Gil, 6 emp., *Contract manufacturing of medical instruments* ............ (201) 881-0555
Modern Limb & Brace Co., 916 Somerset St., Watchung 07069
Owner, Pres. & CFO—Horst Oertel, 6 emp., *Company headquarters & prosthetics* ............ (908) 757-2702
New Jersey Precision Technologies, Inc., 1081 Bristol Rd., Mountainside 07092
Pres., Sales Mgr.—Bob Tarantino, 45 emp., *Wire & ram EDM & small hole drilling* ............
NEXT Medical Products, 45 Columbia Rd., Branchburg 08876
★ Dir., Cust. Serv.—John Buday, 6 emp., *Ultrasound scanning gels & medical* ............ (800) 458-4254
Next Step Orthopedics, Inc., 331 Main St., West Orange 07052
Ptnr.—Michael Moschella, 4 emp., *Orthopedic, orthotic & prosthetic appliances* ............ (973) 736-2244
North American Sterilization & Packaging Company, Inc., 19 Park Dr., Franklin 07416
Chief Operating Officer—Larry Partika, 50 emp., *Contract manufacturing of medical devices* (973) 209-4388

S.I.C.

North Jersey Prosthetics & Orthotics, 39 Broad Ave., Palisades Park 07650
Ptnr. & Pres.—Anthony Marano, 4 emp., *Orthopedic, orthotic & prosthetic appliances* (201) 943-4448
Nouveau Prosthetics & Orthotics, 984 State Route 36, Hazlet 07730
Pres.—Stuart Weiner, 10 emp., *Prosthetic & orthotic appliances* (732) 739-0888
O. R. Comfort, LLC, 28 Appleton Rd., Glen Ridge 07028
Pres., GM—Henry Marguet, 4 emp., *Inflatable cushions & positioning devices* (973) 239-1950
Oertel Orthopedics, Inc., 2095 U.S. Highway 22 W., Union 07083
Off. Mgr.—N. Oertel, 6 emp., *Artificial limbs & braces* (908) 688-1818
Ortho Remedy, Inc., The, 522 Anderson Ave., Cliffside Park 07010
Pres.—Thomas Velenti, 7 emp., *Orthotics & prosthetics* (201) 943-3900
Ortho-Dynamics, Inc., 210 E. 16th St., Paterson 07524
Pres.—Steve Tushingham, 18 emp., *Custom orthotics & non-prescription* (973) 742-4390
Orthofeet, Inc., 152-A Veterans Dr., Northvale 07647
Pres.—Aaron Bar, 20 emp., *Custom orthotics & therapeutic shoes* (201) 767-6224
Orthologix, LLC, 2301 E. Evesham Rd., Ste. 303, Voorhees 08043
Principal—Eileen Levis, 25 emp., *Orthotics & prosthetics* (856) 651-1510
Ossur Americas, Inc., 1414 Metropolitan Ave., Paulsboro 08066
Dir., Dist. Ctr.—Axel Bjornsson, 100 emp., *Cervical collars* (856) 345-6000
Oticon, Inc., 580 Howard Ave., Somerset 08873
Pres.—Peer Lauritsen, 460 emp., *Corporate headquarters & hearing aids* (732) 560-1220
Pacon Mfg., Corp., 400 Pierce St., Somerset 08873
Pres.—Michael Shannon, 200 emp., *Nonwoven disposable medical towels,* (732) 764-9070
PeaPodz, LLC, 79 S. Central Ave., Ramsey 07446
Owner—Shelley Doherty, 1 emp., *Cold therapy ice packs* (201) 362-8883
Phillips Precision, Inc., 7 Paul Kohner Pl., Elmwood Park 07407
Owner—Francis Phillips, 200 emp., *Orthopedic implants & instrumentation* (201) 797-8820
Phil-Lu, Inc., 1206 Herbert Ave., Ocean 07712
Pres.—Lucille Petillo, 3 emp., *Custom spinal, ophthalmic, microsurgical* (732) 531-6338
Precision Orthotic Lab International, 1595 Imperial Way, West Deptford 08066
Pres.—Aaron Adams, 18 emp., *Orthopedic foot appliances* (856) 848-6226
Precision Shoe Brace & Limb, LLC, 618 W. Elizabeth Ave., P.O. Box 1213, Linden 07036
Pres.—Paul Goodman, 8 emp., *Artificial limbs & orthotic braces* (908) 523-0026
Precision Technology, Inc., 50 Maple St., P.O. Box 422, Norwood 07648
Pres., CEO—Ira Housman, 40 emp., *Plastic components for orthopedic body* (201) 767-1600
Pro-Fit Prosthetic & Orthotic, LLC, 215 Edgewood Ave., West Berlin 08091
Owner—Tom Dalsey, 27 emp., *Comprehensive prosthetics & orthotics* (856) 809-9910
Prosthetic Orthotic Solutions International, 100 Brick Rd., Ste. 315, Marlton 08053
Manager—Kevin Towers, 5 emp., *Prosthetics* (856) 810-7900
Redfield Corp., 336 W. Passaic St., Rochelle Park 07662
CEO—Andrew Gould, 5 emp., *Infrared coagulation systems* (201) 845-3990
Rinko Orthopedic Appliances, Inc., 2509 Broadway, Fair Lawn 07410
Pres.—Stephen Rinko, 6 emp., *Orthotic & prosthetic appliances, including* (201) 796-3121
S.S. White Technologies, Inc., 151 Old New Brunswick Rd., Piscataway 08854
Pres., CEO—Rahul Shukla, 180 emp., *Flexible shafts for surgical tools,* (732) 474-1700
Siemens Hearing Instruments, Inc., 10 Constitution Ave., P.O. Box 1397, Piscataway 08855
Acting CEO & V-P., Global CRM—Scott Davis, 450 emp., *Divisional headquarters & hearing aids* (732) 562-6600
Silipos, Inc., 4 Brighton Rd., Ste. 320, Clifton 07012
★ Pres., CEO—Bob Kuhn, 8 emp., *Corporate headquarters & orthopedic* (973) 928-5900
Somerset Prosthetic & Orthotics, Inc., 56 W. Union Ave., Bound Brook 08805
Pres.—Glen Honcharik, 2 emp., *Custom & off-the-shelf orthopedic bracing* (732) 560-2830
Stryker Corp., 2 Pearl Ct., Allendale 07401
IT Mgr.—James Anastasio, 180 emp., *Orthopaedic beds for spinal cord patients* (201) 760-8000
Stryker Orthopaedics, 325 Corporate Dr., Mahwah 07430
Group Pres.—David Floyd, 1300 emp., *Divisional headquarters & orthopedic* (201) 831-5000
Swiss Orthopedic Co., Inc., 188 Highway 206, Hillsborough 08844
Pres.—Peter Seitz, 4 emp., *Artificial limbs & braces* (908) 874-5522
Technidyne Corp., 2190 Route 9, Ste. 9, Toms River 08755
Pres.—Frank Jehn, 3 emp., *Veterinary scales & transport & lift* (732) 363-1055
Temptime Corp., 116 The American Rd., Morris Plains 07950
★ Pres.—Renaat Van den Hooff, 70 emp., *Non-reversible temperature indicators* (973) 984-6000
ThermaFreeze Products Corp. (H Q), 107 Maple Grange Rd., Vernon 07462
Pres.—Sahin Atlas, 3 emp., *Corporate headquarters; reusable ice* (877) 777-8397
Top Safety Products Co., 160 Meister Ave., Ste. 16, Branchburg 08876
Pres., CEO, Fin. & R & D Mgr.—Gerald P. Kutsop, 15 emp., *First aid kits* (908) 707-8680
Total Control Orthotic Lab, 14 W. Front St., Florence 08518
Pres.—Dominic Ciccone, Jr., 4 emp., *Prosthetics & orthotics* (609) 499-2200
Tronex International, Inc., 300 International Dr., Mount Olive 07828
Pres., CEO—Donald L. Chu, 69 emp., *Advanced medical, hospital health &* (973) 335-2888
Tyber Medical, LLC (H Q), 89 Headquarters Plz. N., Ste. 1464, Morristown 07960
Pres., CEO—Jeff Tyber, 12 emp., *Company headquarters; orthopedic implants* (866) 761-0933
Ultimate Training Munitions, 55 Readington Rd., North Branch 08876
Opers. Mgr.—Steve Cassidy, 30 emp., *Ammunition & training blanks for small* (908) 725-9000
V L V Assocs., Inc., 30-C Ridgedale Ave., East Hanover 07936
Pres., Mfg. Mgr.—Michael J. Vaillancourt, 30 emp., *Medical devices* (973) 428-2884
Vital Signs, A CareFusion Co., 20 Campus Rd., Totowa 07512
Corp. Cont.—Daria Hennessey, 300 emp., *Divisional headquarters & anesthesia* (973) 956-5300
Vozeh Equipment Corp., 509 Commerce St., Franklin Lakes 07417
Owner—Karen Vozeh, 55 emp., *Industrial & medical cutting tools* (201) 337-4212
Water-Jel Technologies, 50 Broad St., Carlstadt 07072
CFO—John McAndris, 80 emp., *Sterile burn dressings, fire blankets* (201) 507-8300
Westcon Orthopedics, Inc., 4 Craig Rd., Neshanic Station 08853
Chrm.—Patti Merwin, 4 emp., *Orthopedic products & surgical devices* (908) 806-8981
WingIt Innovations, LLC, 714 5th Ave., Bradley Beach 07720
Owner & Fin. Mgr.—Sal Sisto, 2 emp., *Fasteners, grab bars, shower rods &* (732) 869-4466
Zimmer Trabecular Metal Technology, 10 Pomerov Rd., Parsippany 07054
Dir., Prod. Dev.—Scott Cron, 50 emp., *Surgical joint replacement implants* (973) 576-0032
Zimmer Tri-State, Inc., 1001 Briggs Rd., Ste. 275, Mount Laurel 08054
Opers. Mgr.—Stan Smoyer, 60 emp., *Orthopedic joint implants* (856) 778-8300

## 3843 Dental equipment & supplies

Acteon, Inc., 124 Gaither Dr., Ste. 140, Mount Laurel 08054
V-P., COO—Tim Long, 25 emp., *Electronic dental equipment & supplies* (856) 222-9988
Amory A & E Campian Dental Art, Inc., 803 Main St., Ste. 2, Toms River 08753
★ Owner—Daniel Campian, 4 emp., *Dental prosthetics* (732) 240-0323
Andon Brush Co., Inc., 1 Merrit Ave., Little Falls 07424
Pres., GM—Robert Newell, 15 emp., *Dental, pharmaceutical, cosmetic, commercial* (973) 256-6611
Dental Models & Designs, Inc., 20 Passaic St., Ste. 3, Garfield 07026
Pres., Hum. Res.—David Lauchheimer, 5 emp., *Dental models* (973) 472-8009
E M Orthodontic Labs, Inc., 6 Lafayette Pl., P.O. Box 112, Waldwick 07463
Pres.—Paul Macz, 7 emp., *Orthodontic retainers* (201) 652-4411
Essential Dental Systems, Inc., 89 Leuning St., Ste. 2, South Hackensack 07606
Pres.—Barry Lee Musikant, 40 emp., *Dental & endodontic instruments* (201) 487-9090
Fields, Inc., Samuel H., 197 Union St., Hackensack 07601
V-P.—Robert Fields, 25 emp., *Dental prosthetics* (201) 343-4626
George Taub Products, 277 New York Ave., Jersey City 07307
Owner, Pres. & Fin. Mgr.—Lawrence Taub, 6 emp., *Dental coatings & stains for acrylic* (201) 798-5353
Hall Co. Abrasives, William R., 901 E. Gibbsboro Rd., Lindenwold 08021
Pres.—George Aho, 30 emp., *Rubber bonded abrasives for the dental* (856) 784-6700
Handler Mfg. Co., Inc., 612 North Ave. E., Westfield 07090
CEO—William A. Lehman, 40 emp., *Dentists' metal processing equipment* (908) 233-7796
Helm Dental, Inc., 111 Troast St., Hackensack 07601
Ptnr. & Pres.—Albert Helm, 4 emp., *Dentures* (201) 342-2915
Integrated Laminate Systems, 1301 Industrial Hwy., Riverton 08077
Pres.—Chris Sparacio, 45 emp., *Plastic laminate dental cabinets* (856) 786-6500
Ivoclar Vivadent Mfg., Inc., 500 Memorial Dr., Somerset 08873
IT Mgr.—Rich Mccann, 120 emp., *Dental products* (732) 563-4755
J.A.W. Products, Inc., 835 Industrial Hwy., Unit 125, Cinnaminson 08077
Pres.—Earl Weightman, 10 emp., *Manufacturer & distributor of orthodontic* (856) 829-3210
Keystone Industries, 616 Hollywood Ave., Cherry Hill 08002
CEO—Fred Robinson, 130 emp., *Company headquarters & dental abrasives* (856) 663-4700
Lincoln Dental Supply, Inc., 616 Hollywood Ave., Cherry Hill 08002
Chrm. of the Board—Fred Robinson, 100 emp., *Dental supplies, including denture* (856) 488-1333
M T I Precision Products, LLC, 730 Airport Rd., Lakewood 08701
Ptnr.—Joe DeLuca, 12 emp., *Dental handpieces, including nose cones* (732) 905-7440
Malin Corp., James S., 3 Victoria Ln., Ringwood 07456
Pres.—James Malin, 3 emp., *Prosthetic teeth* (973) 831-9135
MEND Tech, Inc., 38 Irving Pl., Garfield 07026
Pres.—Eli Kaadan, 5 emp., *Dental laboratory equipment* (973) 340-9212
Napco Cabinets, Inc., 6938 Westfield Ave., Pennsauken 08110
Pres., Sales Mgr.—William Cocchi, 1 emp., *Dental & doctor's office laminate cabinets* (856) 665-0253
Natural Dental Studios, Inc., 216 U.S. Highway 206, Ste. 23, Hillsborough 08844
Pres.—Charles Palmieri, 5 emp., *Dental restoration products* (908) 281-0089
Newark Dental Pemco, 35 Stern Ave., P.O. Box 249, Springfield 07081
Owner—Lawrence Balfour, 55 emp., *Dental cabinets* (973) 564-9622
Palisades Dental, LLC, 111 Cedar Ln., P.O. Box 5419, Englewood 07631
Cust. Serv. Rep.—Robin Rinker, 15 emp., *Dental drills* (201) 569-0050
Perfectone Mold Co., 277 New York Ave., Jersey City 07307
Pres., Engr.—Lawrence Taub, 5 emp., *Rubber dental molds for making wax* (201) 798-5353
Pfingst & Co., Inc., 105 Snyder Rd., P.O. Box 377, South Plainfield 07080
Pres.—Karl Pfingst, 10 emp., *Manufacturer & distributor of precision* (908) 561-6400
Ross Co., Inc., Frank B., 970 New Brunswick Ave., Ste. H, Rahway 07065
Pres.—Larry Powell, 5 emp., *Natural & synthetic waxes, including* (732) 669-0810
SS White Burs, Inc., 1145 Towbin Ave., Lakewood 08701
Pres.—Tom Gallop, 250 emp., *Carbide dental burs* (800) 535-2877
Takara Belmont U. S. A., Inc., 101 Belmont Dr., Somerset 08873
Pres.—Karataka Yashikawa, 80 emp., *Corporate headquarters & beauty, spa* (732) 469-5000
Titan Implants, Inc., 18 Columbia Ave., Bergenfield 07621
Pres., Hum. Res. Mgr.—Cyril Chen, 5 emp., *Dental implants, attachments & accessories* (201) 439-0027
Viscot Medical, LLC, 32 West St., P.O. Box 351, East Hanover 07936
Pres.—Gary J. Pieringer, 25 emp., *Disposable medical, surgical & dental* (973) 887-9273

## 3844 X-ray apparatus & tubes

A Walsh Imaging, Inc., 55 Cannonball Rd., Pompton Lakes 07442
Pres.—Patrick Walsh, 30 emp., *X-ray machines, digital equipment &* (973) 616-7100
Auto Clear, LLC, 2 Gardner Rd., Fairfield 07004
Pres., CEO—Brad Conway, 80 emp., *Hand-held, desktop, vehicle & walk-through* (973) 276-6161
Gray Star, Inc., 200 Valley Rd., Ste. 200, Mount Arlington 07856
Pres.—Martin Stein, 4 emp., *Food irradiation equipment* (973) 398-3331
Kodex Inc., 160 Park Ave., Ste. 1, Nutley 07110
Pres., CEO, CFO—Donna Korkala, 5 emp., *Digital x-ray imaging systems for industrial* (973) 235-0606
Swissray International, Inc. (H Q), 31 Gordon Rd., Piscataway 08854
★ Chrm.—Alex Rosenzweig, 15 emp., *Corporate headquarters; digital x-ray* (908) 353-0971

## 3845 Electromedical equipment

ADM Tronics Unlimited, Inc., 224 Pegasus Ave., Northvale 07647
Pres.—Andre DiMino, 14 emp., *Contract manufacturing of medical electronic* (201) 767-6040
Baeta Corp., 1 Bridge Plz., Ste. 275, Fort Lee 07024
CEO—Len Pushkantser, 5 emp., *Electronic hand-held health improvement* (201) 471-0988
Bloomex International, Inc., 295 Molnar Dr., Elmwood Park 07407
Pres.—Benjamin Laroux, 4 emp., *Low-energy electronic muscle stimulators* (201) 703-9799
Capintec, Inc., 6 Arrow Rd., Ste. 101, Ramsey 07446
CEO—John Viscovic, 26 emp., *Corporate headquarters & radiation* (201) 825-9500
Clinical Image Retrieval, Inc., 376 Lafayette Rd., Ste. 202, P.O. Box 899, Sparta 07871
Pres.—Douglas D. Haas, 4 emp., *Electromedical portable walkway systems* (973) 862-6151
CytoTherm, 110 Sewell Ave., Trenton 08610
Pres.—Roman Kuzyk, 6 emp., *Digitally-controlled dry & conventional* (609) 396-1456
Diagnostix Plus, Inc., 197 Cedar Ln., Ste. 1, Teaneck 07666
Founder, Pres. & CEO—Don Bogutski, 6 emp., *Remanufactured nuclear medicine imaging* . (201) 530-5505
Fuji Film Medical Systems U.S.A., Inc., 10 Highpoint Dr., Wayne 07470
Pres.—Keiichi Nagata, 65 emp., *Corporate headquarters & endoscopic* (973) 633-5600
General Devices, 1000 River St., Ridgefield 07657
Pres.—Curt Bashford, 18 emp., *EMS information, telemedicine, communication* (201) 313-7075
JACE Systems, Inc., 5 Rockhill Rd., Ste. 2, Cherry Hill 08003
Pres., CEO—Thomas Zieser, 15 emp., *Electrotherapy & continuous passive* (800) 800-4276
Maquet, 15 Law Dr., Fairfield 07004
Dir., IT—Shen Lu, 200 emp., *Medical devices* (973) 244-6100
Mednet Healthcare Technologies, Inc., 275 Phillips Blvd., Ewing 08618
Sales Mgr.—Janice Hardell, 50 emp., *Ambulatory cardiac monitors & electromedical* (609) 671-1790
Medtronic, Inc., 300 Interpace Pkwy., Parsippany 07054
V-P.—Thomas Conlin, 40 emp., *Implantable cardioverter defibrillators* (516) 222-2848
MICRO, 140 Belmont Dr., Somerset 08873
Chrm.—Frank J. Semcer, Sr., 350 emp., *Complete medical devices & components* (732) 302-0800
Mindray North America, 800 MacArthur Blvd., Mahwah 07430
Dir., Opers.—George Soloman, 200 emp., *Patient monitoring devices* (201) 995-8000
Nephros, Inc., 41 Grand Ave., Ste. 201, River Edge 07661
Chrm.—James S. Scibetta, 6 emp., *Hemodiafiltration systems for the end-stage* (201) 343-5202
Neurotron Medical, 800 Silvia St., West Trenton 08628
Owner—Jack Guldalian, 10 emp., *Diagnostic & electrotherapy medical* (609) 896-3444
Nexcore Technology, Inc., 150 Hopper Ave., Waldwick 07463
Pres.—Milton Frank, 35 emp., *Endoscopic light sources, fluid monitoring* (201) 968-9400
Parker Laboratories, Inc., 286 Eldridge Rd., Fairfield 07004
Pres.—Neal Buchalter, 50 emp., *Ultrasound lotions, gels & medical* (973) 276-9500
PENTAX Of America, Inc., 3 Paragon Dr., Ste. 1, Montvale 07645
Pres.—David Woods, 180 emp., *Corporate headquarters & medical endoscopes* (201) 571-2300

Scivanta Medical Corp. (H Q), 215 Morris Ave., Spring Lake 07762
CEO—David R. LaVance, 2 emp., *Corporate headquarters; minimally invasive* ... (732) 282-1055
Sterling Medical Devices, 17 Legion Pl., Rochelle Park 07662
V-P., Engrg.—Bruce Swope, 50 emp., *Medical device software development* ... (201) 227-7569
VectraCor, Inc., 785 Totowa Rd., Ste. 100, Totowa 07512
Pres., CEO—Brad S. Schreck, 8 emp., *Patented cardiology equipment, including* ... (973) 904-0444

## 3851 Ophthalmic goods

Charmant Group, Inc., 400 American Rd., Morris Plains 07950
Pres.—Harry Aida, 60 emp., *Eyeglasses* ... (973) 538-1511
Eagle Eyewear, Inc. (H Q), P.O. Box 486, Whitehouse 08888
Pres.—William Marfuggi, 2 emp., *Corporate headquarters; eyeglass frames* ... (908) 236-9300
Essilor Laboratories, 5 Powderhorn Dr., Warren 07059
GM—Debra Case, 14 emp., *Eyeglass lenses* ... (732) 563-9884
I-See Optical Laboratories, Inc., 44 W. Church St., Blackwood 08012
Pres.—Michael Palkovicz, 20 emp., *Eyeglass lenses* ... (856) 227-9300
Kennedy Opticians, 552 Boulevard, Kenilworth 07033
Owner—James Kennedy, 3 emp., *Optic lens grinding & contact lenses* ... (908) 276-2020
LeGrand Assocs., 214 W. Main St., Ste. 102, Moorestown 08057
Pres.—Joseph LeGrand, 3 emp., *Artificial eyes* ... (800) 273-8565
Lens Co., Inc., 700 Route 46 W., Unit 7, Clifton 07013
COO, Hum. Res. Mgr.—Prasad Umarye, 4 emp., *Glass lenses* ... (973) 546-0866
Lens Mode, Inc., 150 Main St., Ste. 1, Millburn 07041
Pres.—Daniel Strulowitz, 5 emp., *Contact lenses* ... (973) 467-2000
Liberty Sport, Inc., 107 Fairfield Rd., Fairfield 07004
Pres.—Anthony DiChiara, 30 emp., *Protective sports eyewear* ... (973) 882-0986
Mancine Optical Co., 2910 Route 130, Ste. 1, Delran 08075
Pres.—Joseph Mancine, 20 emp., *Prescription safety glasses & specialty* ... (856) 764-0200
Marfori Family Eye Care, 20 Brick Plz., Brick 08723
Owner—Michelle Marfori, 3 emp., *Eyeglasses* ... (732) 920-1775
Motif Industries, Inc., 8 Commerce Rd., Fairfield 07004
Pres.—Al Elkay, 28 emp., *Ophthalmic products, including lens* ... (973) 575-1800
Optical Insight, LLC, 778 Highway 1, North Brunswick 08902
Owner—Joseph Grodman, 2 emp., *Eyeglasses* ... (732) 828-3937
Pearle Vision, Inc., 1278 Hooper Ave., Toms River 08753
GM & Sales Mgr.—Ed Santos, 20 emp., *Eyeglasses* ... (732) 505-0533
Schreiber, Inc., Earle C., 1 Bethany Rd., Bldg. 1, Ste. 13, Hazlet 07730
Pres.—Margery Schreiber Wright, 4 emp., *Artificial eyes* ... (732) 335-1424
Seiko Optical Products Of America, Inc. (H Q), 575 Corporate Dr., Ste. 205, Mahwah 07430
Pres.—Yoshito Kataoka, 50 emp., *Divisional headquarters; optical lenses* ... (201) 529-9099
Sheridan Optical Co., Inc., 108 Clinton Ave., Pitman 08071
Pres.—Edward F. Sheridan, 20 emp., *Eyeglass lenses* ... (856) 582-0963
Special Optics Manufacture & Design, Inc., 315 Richard Mine Rd., Wharton 07885
Cont.—Tom Young, 18 emp., *Laser optic lenses* ... (973) 366-7289
Switch Vision, 103 Fairfield Rd., Fairfield 07004
Owner—Anthony Dichiara, 60 emp., *Magnetic interchangeable optical lenses* ... (973) 582-2304
Tech-Optics International, 600 Deer Rd., Cherry Hill 08034
Dir., Sales & GM—Lisa Wassmer, 10 emp., *Hand & stand magnifiers, loupes & binoculars* ... (856) 795-8585
The Lifestyle Company, Inc., 6 Paragon Way, Ste. 112, Freehold 07728
Pres., CEO—Tom Seidner, 4 emp., *Plastic for contact lenses & contact* ... (732) 303-7849
Value Eyewear, Inc., 1454 Main Ave., Clifton 07011
Pres.—Richard Weiss, 15 emp., *Eyeglass & sunglass frames* ... (973) 478-6500
VIP Optical Laboratories, Inc., 325 Dalziel Rd., Linden 07036
Owner—Richard Robbins, 10 emp., *Optical lens grinding* ... (908) 523-1422

## 3861 Photographic equipment & supplies

Acteon, Inc., 124 Gaither Dr., Ste. 140, Mount Laurel 08054
V-P., COO—Tim Long, 25 emp., *Electronic dental equipment & supplies* ... (856) 222-9988
Automatic Transfer, Inc., 2 Industrial Rd., Phillipsburg 08865
★ Pres.—Alfred W. La Costa, 4 emp., *Sublimation toner & heat transfer paper* ... (908) 213-2830
Avida, Inc., 174-B Kinderkamack Rd., P.O. Box 2, Park Ridge 07656
Pres.—Eric Kruegle, 5 emp., *Security surveillance equipment for* ... (201) 802-0749
Cartridge Renewal Systems, 13 Glendale Dr., Englishtown 07726
Ptnr.—Jacklyn Berman, 2 emp., *Remanufactured toner cartridges* ... (732) 845-9497
Cartridge World Oakhurst, 1815 State Route 35, Oakhurst 07755
Owner—Joe Betesh, 2 emp., *Remanufactured inkjet & toner printer* ... (732) 531-4232
Coda, Inc., 30 Industrial Ave., Mahwah 07430
Pres.—Lee Coda, 30 emp., *Laminating equipment & graphic finishing* ... (201) 825-7400
Diagnostic Services, Inc., 220 Mountain Ave., Middlesex 08846
Pres.—Mike Molner, 4 emp., *New & rebuilt overhead & rail-mounted* ... (732) 271-9199
Dyna-Lite, Inc., 1050 Commerce Ave., Union 07083
Pres., GM—Peter Poremba, 18 emp., *Photographic lighting equipment* ... (908) 687-8800
Falcon Safety Products, Inc., 25 Imclone Dr., P.O. Box 1299, Branchburg 08876
Pres.—Phil Lapin, 60 emp., *Compressed gas computer cleaning products* ... (908) 707-4900
Flexo Craft Prints, Inc., 1000 1st St., Harrison 07029
Pres.—Mendel Klein, 15 emp., *Gift wrap printing, heat transfer paper* ... (973) 482-7200
FUJIFILM U.S.A., Inc., 1100 King Georges Post Rd., Edison 08837
Facility Mgr.—Theresa Collins, 60 emp., *Professional & consumer films, cameras* ... (732) 857-3000
Hamilton Buhl, 80 Little Falls Rd., Fairfield 07004
V-P.—Madeline Piccone, 19 emp., *Technology & AV equipment for educational* ... (201) 229-9800
Hammer Too, LLC, 2576-B U.S. Highway 22 E., Union 07083
★ Mng. Member—Alexander Martello, 4 emp., *Remanufactured toner cartridges* ... (908) 688-5601
Konica Minolta Business Solutions U. S. A., Inc. (H Q), 100 Williams Dr., Ramsey 07446
Chrm., CEO—Toshimitsu 'Tom' Taiko, 400 emp., *Corporate headquarters; production* ... (201) 825-4000
Kyocera Document Solutions America, Inc. (H Q), 225 Sand Rd., Fairfield 07004
Pres.—Norihiko Ina, 200 emp., *Corporate headquarters; office machines* ... (973) 808-8444
L-3 Communications Mobile-Vision, Inc., 90 Fanny Rd., Boonton 07005
Pres.—Leo Lorenzetti, 70 emp., *Police car video systems* ... (973) 263-1090
Laser Save, 843 State Route 33, Ste. 11, Freehold 07728
Pres.—Alan D. Yoss, 18 emp., *Remanufactured compatible color & monochrome* ... (732) 431-3339
Long Valley Equipment, 165 Fairview Ave., Long Valley 07853
Owner—Doug Underdahl, 6 emp., *Photographic equipment* ... (908) 876-1022
MRI International, 44-50 Clinton St., Newton 07860
Pres.—William Foltyn, 7 emp., *Sensitizers for the offset lithographic* ... (973) 383-3645
Night Canyon, Inc., The, 1475 Park Ave., Alpha 08865
Pres.—Mark Smith, 20 emp., *Movie theatre projectors, speakers,* ... (908) 454-6344
Oki Data Americas, Inc., 2000 Bishops Gate Blvd., Mount Laurel 08054
Pres., CEO—Masahiko Morioka, 350 emp., *Digital color & monochrome printers* ... (856) 235-2600
Oxberry, LLC, 180 Broad St., Carlstadt 07072
Secy., Corp. Counsel—Anna Ferraro, 1 emp., *Cameras & film scanners* ... (201) 935-3000
Petitts Ink Corp., 1745 State Route 10, Ste. 4, Morris Plains 07950
CEO—Kathleen Petitt, 3 emp., *Remanufactured inkjet & laser toner* ... (973) 984-2400
Pioneer Research Co., 97 Foster Rd., Ste. 5, Moorestown 08057
Pres.—W. Harms, 40 emp., *Underwater cameras & photographic equipment* ... (856) 866-9191
Sakar International, Inc. (H Q), 195 Carter Dr., Edison 08817
CEO—Charles Saka, 75 emp., *Corporate headquarters; consumer electronics* ... (732) 248-1306
Sofradir EC, Inc., 373 U.S. Highway 46, Ste. E, Fairfield 07004
Pres.—Frank Vallese, 42 emp., *Uncooled & cooled infrared & thermography* ... (973) 882-0211
Towne Technologies, Inc., 6-10 Bell Ave., P.O. Box 460, Somerville 08876
Pres., R & D Mgr.—Hercharan S. Dhillon, 16 emp., *Chemically-etched metal parts, photo* ... (908) 722-9500
Turbon Group, 4350 Haddonfield Rd., Ste. 300, Pennsauken 08109
CEO—Al Deluca, 100 emp., *Laser toner cartridges* ... (856) 665-6650
VCOM International Multi-Media Corp., 80 Little Falls Rd., Fairfield 07004
Pres., CEO—Sheldon Goldstein, 22 emp., *Corporate headquarters & manufacturer* ... (201) 229-4270
Vision Research, Inc., 100 Dey Rd., Wayne 07470
V-P., Bus. Unit & GM—Jay Stepleton, 100 emp., *Corporate headquarters & high-speed* ... (973) 696-4500
Zeta Products, Inc., 1060 Garden State Rd., Union 07083
Pres.—Michael Naso, 4 emp., *Film cartridges & microfilm storage* ... (908) 688-0440

## 3873 Watches, clocks, watchcases & parts

Acon Watch Crown Co., 260 Division Ave., P.O. Box 800, Garfield 07026
Owner—Arnold K. Cohen, 8 emp., *Watch & watch band parts, including* ... (973) 546-8585
Arcadian Clock Co., 189 North Ave. E., Cranford 07016
Owner—David Munro, 1 emp., *Precision regulator clocks* ... (908) 276-0276
Garrett Clocks, 35 N. Middaugh St., Unit 3-C, Somerville 08876
Owner & Founder—Garrett Moore, 4 emp., *World, time zone & international clock* ... (908) 231-9231
Movado Group, Inc., 650 From Rd., 3rd Fl., Paramus 07652
Chrm., Pres.—G. Grinberg, 300 emp., *Manufacturer & distributor of watches* ... (201) 267-8000
Myron Corp., 205 Maywood Ave., Maywood 07607
CEO—Jim Adler, 450 emp., *Imprinted personalized business gifts* ... (201) 843-6464
SEIKO Corp. Of America (H Q), 1111 MacArthur Blvd., Mahwah 07430
Pres., CEO—Yoshikatsu Kawada, 150 emp., *Corporate headquarters; watches & clocks* ... (201) 529-5730
Sterling Home Products, Inc., 127 U.S. Highway 206, Ste. 22, Hamilton 08610
V-P., Fin., MIS & Opers.—Roger DeAngelis, 4 emp., *Bathroom, kitchen, parcel, postal &* ... (609) 585-8941
Tropar Mfg. Co., Inc., 5 Vreeland Rd., Florham Park 07932
Pres.—Peter E. Ilaria, 60 emp., *Corporate headquarters & plaques, clocks* ... (973) 822-2400

# 39 MISCELLANEOUS MANUFACTURING INDUSTRIES

## 3911 Jewelry, precious metal

925ny, 200 Middlesex Tpke., Ste. 202, Iselin 08830
★ Pres.—John LaBarbera, 5 emp., *Sterling silver jewelry* ... (732) 404-4400
Aabhushan Exports Private Ltd., 155 Wood Ave., Edison 08820
Manager—Rachna Bhalla, 5 emp., *Precious metal jewlery* ... (732) 516-0800
Aires Jewelry Co., 3 Harrison Ave., Morris Plains 07950
Pres.—Ronald W. Arends, 8 emp., *Gold, silver & platinum jewelry* ... (973) 292-0950
Ann Carol Designs, Inc., 333 Mountain Ave., Bound Brook 08805
Pres.—Janet Schroeder, 2 emp., *Custom handcrafted contemporary sterling* ... (732) 469-7552
Aydin Jewelry, Inc., 885 Route 17 S., Ramsey 07446
Pres.—Rick Aydin, 2 emp., *Precious metal jewelry* ... (201) 818-1002
Ayesha Studio & Gallery, 21 N. Dean St., Englewood 07631
Owner—Ayesha Mayadas, 2 emp., *Gold jewelry, including earrings, brooches* ... (201) 503-0073
Barrasso & Blasi, Inc., 1581 Springfield Ave., Maplewood 07040
Pres.—Robert Blasi, 3 emp., *Precious metal jewelry & pins* ... (973) 761-0595
Best Cast, 822 Kinderkamack Rd., River Edge 07661
Pres.—Zsombar Antal, 15 emp., *High-resolution three-dimensionally* ... (201) 225-1750
Bhamra Chain Mfg. Co., 1020 Springfield Rd., Union City 07087
Ptnr. & Pres.—Ajit Bhamra, 3 emp., *Precious & base metal chains for the* ... (908) 686-4555
Big Apple Jewelry Mfg., 62 Railroad Ave., East Rutherford 07073
Pres.—Albert Sirazi, 7 emp., *Custom-designed gold, sterling silver* ... (201) 531-1600
Calbar, LLC, 307 Bergen Ave., Kearny 07032
Pres.—Vincent J. Caldaro, 5 emp., *Gold & silver jewelry, including casting* ... (201) 246-1555
Calima Jewels, 215 Glen Ridge Ave., Montclair 07042
Owner—George Lugo, 2 emp., *Precious metal jewelry* ... (973) 746-2976
Callahan Jewelers, Inc., 86 Vervalen St., Closter 07624
★ Owner—Brian Callahan, 7 emp., *Precious metal jewelry, including diamond* ... (201) 768-6136
Castor Jewelry, 13 N. Union St., Lambertville 08530
Ptnr.—Tom Castor, 3 emp., *Precious metal jewelry* ... (609) 397-0809
Chavez Jewelry, Marie, 642 Bloomfield Ave., Verona 07044
Owner—Marie Chavez, 5 emp., *Precious metal jewelry, including gold* ... (973) 337-8551
Church & Co., 2121 Whitesville Rd., Toms River 08755
Owner—David Hopkinson, 6 emp., *Precious metal jewelry* ... (732) 363-4949
Cinco Star, LLC, 2 Karnell Ct., Edison 08820
Owner—Vin Zaveri, 5 emp., *Fine jewelry* ... (732) 744-1617
Corbo Jewelers, Inc., 1055 Bloomfield Ave., Clifton 07012
Pres.—Steven Corbo, 10 emp., *Jewelry, diamonds, color stones & watches* ... (973) 777-1635
Donsky Designs, 3851 Boardwalk, Apt. 2405, Atlantic City 08401
Owner—David Donsky, 2 emp., *Custom jewelry, including watches,* ... (609) 345-4445
Eli Jewels, Inc., 14 Wyckoff Ave., Ramsey 07446
Pres.—Simon Makhlouf, 4 emp., *Precious metal jewelry* ... (201) 291-4200
Fisher Co., Inc., Robert, 280 Sheffield St., Mountainside 07092
Pres.—David Roth, 3 emp., *Fine handmade 14K gold & silver jewelry* ... (908) 928-0002
Gary's Gem Garden, 404 Route 70 E., Cherry Hill 08034
Owner—Gary Weinstein, 3 emp., *Precious & semiprecious gems & metal* ... (856) 795-5077
Goldstein Setting Co Inc /TA DanMar Jewelers, 2464 Morris Ave., Union 07083
Pres.—Joseph Goldstein, 5 emp., *Gemstone & diamond setting* ... (908) 964-1034
Guida Setting Co., 124 E. Main St., Denville 07834
Owner—William D. Guida, 4 emp., *Precious & semiprecious jewelry* ... (973) 625-1225
Harris Kenya Gem Co., Tom, 6504 Ventnor Ave., Ventnor City 08406
Owner—Tom Harris, 2 emp., *Precious metal, gold & diamond jewelry* ... (609) 823-3315
I Did It Metal Art, Inc., 53 Gables Way, Jackson 08527
Owner—Dale Pilling, 1 emp., *Precious metal jewelry* ... (732) 866-8481
Ilie's Eternally Flawless, 275 E. State Route 4, Paramus 07652
Owner—Yves Ilie, 2 emp., *Precious metal jewelry* ... (201) 487-1991
Jeweler's Gallery Corp., 9 W. Main St., Mendham 07945
Pres., GM—Robert West, 3 emp., *Precious metal jewelry* ... (973) 543-6117
Jewelry Arts Mfg., Inc., 1701 Summit Ave., Union City 07087
Pres.—Alberto Tapia, 50 emp., *Precious metal jewelry* ... (201) 864-5188
Jewelry Design Gallery, Inc., 357 U.S. Highway 9, Ste. 18, Englishtown 07726
★ Manager—Drew Cowit, 4 emp., *Precious metal jewelry, including gold* ... (732) 536-1184
Jewelry Tool & Die Co., 4 Mark Rd., Ste. G, Kenilworth 07033
Owner—Peter Ehmann, 3 emp., *Jewelry, metal stampings & dies* ... (908) 686-3500
Jocely, Inc., 280 Sheffield St., Mountainside 07092
Pres.—David Connolly, 35 emp., *Precious metal jewelry* ... (800) 526-4597

S.I.C.

Jonart Metals, LLC, 710 New Brunswick Ave., P.O. Box 333, Rahway 07065
Owner—Garry Capaldo, 4 emp., *Handcrafted gold, palladium & platinum* ..... (732) 382-0300
Jost Brothers, Inc., 295 Jost Dr., Oxford 07863
Pres.—Charlie Jost, 4 emp., *Custom handmade gold & silver jewelry* ..... (908) 453-2266
Kay, Inc., Scott, 780 Palisape Ave., Teaneck 07666
Pres.—Scott Kay, 40 emp., *Precious metal jewelry* ..... (201) 287-0100
Kornspan Jewelry, Inc., 1131 W. Saint Georges Ave., Linden 07036
Co-Pres.—Albert Kornspan, 3 emp., *Gold, platinum & diamond jewelry* ..... (908) 925-1101
Lamar Diamond Jewelry Corp., 5600 John F. Kennedy Blvd., Ste. 109, West New York 07093
Pres.—Lisette George, 2 emp., *Precious metal jewelry* ..... (201) 863-8683
Le Monde Deluxe, 232 White Horse Pike, Collingswood 08107
Owner—Pete D'Amico, 7 emp., *Precious metal jewelry* ..... (856) 854-5440
Nadri Jewelry Group, 2 Executive Dr., Ste. 500, Fort Lee 07024
Owner—Young Choy, 20 emp., *Precioius metal jewelry* ..... (201) 585-0088
NEI Group, Inc., 44 Burlews Ct., Hackensack 07601
Pres.—John Nanasi, 40 emp., *Corporate headquarters & gold jewelry* ..... (201) 488-5858
Novell Enterprises, Inc., 2100 Felver Ct., Rahway 07065
Pres.—Victor Novogrodsky, 70 emp., *Precious metal jewelry* ..... (732) 428-8300
Pacicco & Co. Jewelers, 331 Broad Ave., Leonia 07605
Pres.—Robert Pacicco, 5 emp., *Precious metal jewelry* ..... (201) 947-1106
Paglia & Son, Inc., D., 280 Sheffield St., Mountainside 07092
Pres.—Daniel Paglia, 4 emp., *Ladies' jewelry* ..... (908) 654-5999
Provost Square Assocs., 6 Provost Sq., Caldwell 07006
Pres.—Barbara Mamchur, 5 emp., *Class rings* ..... (973) 403-8755
S & R Designs, Inc., 36 W. Route 70, Ste. 213, Marlton 08053
Pres.—Steve Billig, 2 emp., *Precious metal jewelry* ..... (856) 985-0303
Salkin's Jewel Case, Inc., 3585 Highway 9, South Freehold Shopping Ctr., Freehold 07728
Pres.—Eric Salkin, 7 emp., *Diamond, gold, silver & platinum jewelry* ..... (732) 462-3311
Samuel, Inc., 60 W. Englewood, Bergenfield 07621
Pres.—Steve Samuel, 20 emp., *Precious metal jewelry* ..... (201) 439-1555
Silver Stones International, LLC, 902 E. County Line Rd., Ste. 200, Lakewood 08701
Off. Mgr.—Cindy Kallus, 10 emp., *Silver jewelry* ..... (732) 886-0011
SJA Jewelry, Inc., 44 Burlews Ct., Hackensack 07601
Bookkeeper—Roseann Bonito, 40 emp., *Precious metal jewelry* ..... (201) 837-0990
Ski Jewelers Co., 299 Route 22, Green Brook 08812
Pres.—Joseph Sulovski, 6 emp., *Precious metal jewelry* ..... (732) 752-6446
Star Creation, Inc. (H Q), 1506 Stelton Rd., Piscataway 08854
Pres., Hum. Res. Mgr.—Kavita Khandelwal, 5 emp., *Corporate headquarters; gemstone jewelry* (732) 819-7070
Studio Feifish, Llc, 54 Ironia Rd., Randolph 07869
★ Owner—Wenlee Fei, 2 emp., *Cast silver jewelry, including bracelets* ..... (973) 303-3287
Tomorrow's Heirlooms Handcrafted Gemstone Jewelry, 2 Chambers St., Princeton 08542
Ptnr.—John Miller, 2 emp., *Handcrafted gemstone jewelry* ..... (609) 921-9440
Trimarco Jewelers, Inc., 1847-1849 Springfield Ave., Maplewood 07040
GM—Ken Trimarco, 4 emp., *Precious metal jewelry* ..... (973) 762-7380
Ultimate Trading Corp., 4 Just Rd., Fairfield 07004
Pres.—Todd Knichel, 60 emp., *Manufacturer & distributor of fine* ..... (973) 228-7700
Vincent & Co., Inc., J., 420 Route 34, Ste. 301, P.O. Box 448, Colts Neck 07722
Pres.—Joseph V. Brando, 3 emp., *Precious metal jewelry* ..... (732) 256-4410

## 3914 Silverware & plated ware

Bob's Trophy, 6 Hamilton St., Montvale 07645
Owner—Mitch Cumstein, 3 emp., *Trophies & plaques* ..... (201) 391-3790
Cambridge Silversmiths Ltd. (H Q), 30 Hook Mountain Rd., P.O. Box 625, Pine Brook 07058
Pres.—Roger Freeman, 90 emp., *Company headquarters; stainless steel* ..... (973) 227-4400
D.W.L International Trading Co., 65 Industrial Rd., Lodi 07644
Pres., CEO—David Li, 150 emp., *Company headquarters & restaurant supplies* ..... (973) 916-9958
Freeman Products, Inc. (H Q), 71 Walsh Dr., Parsippany 07054
Ptnr.—Vincent Cariello, 25 emp., *Corporate headquarters; trophy & award* ..... (201) 475-8888
Hampton Forge, Ltd., 442 State Route 35, Eatontown 07724
Pres.—Felix Amar, 30 emp., *Flatware & cutlery* ..... (732) 389-5507
Joseph Castings, Inc., 25 Brook Ave., Maywood 07607
Off. Mgr.—Paul Low, 15 emp., *Jewelry castings* ..... (201) 712-0717
Solmor Mfg. Co., Inc., 164 Emmet St., Newark 07114
Pres.—Robert Ulmer, 5 emp., *Earring findings* ..... (973) 824-7203
Stay Focused Marketing, 157 Veterans Dr., Northvale 07647
Pres.—Marvin Levy, 5 emp., *Titanium & ceramic knives* ..... (201) 750-5050
Summit Brass & Bronze Works, Inc., 112 71st St., Guttenberg 07093
Pres.—Robert Francin, 4 emp., *Brass & bronze ecclesiastical ware* ..... (201) 861-2080

## 3915 Jewelers' materials & lapidary work

Big Apple Jewelry Mfg., 62 Railroad Ave., East Rutherford 07073
Pres.—Albert Sirazi, 7 emp., *Custom-designed gold, sterling silver* ..... (201) 531-1600
C & C Metal Products Corp., 456 Nordhoff Pl., P.O. Box 7300, Englewood 07631
V-P., Secy.—Mitchell Chalfin, 50 emp., *Corporate headquarters & metal stampings* ..... (201) 569-7300
Creations By Stefano, Inc., 1261 Paterson Plank Rd., Secaucus 07094
Pres.—Stefano Simone, 2 emp., *Jewelry* ..... (201) 863-5806
Gary's Gem Garden, 404 Route 70 E., Cherry Hill 08034
Owner—Gary Weinstein, 3 emp., *Precious & semiprecious gems & metal* ..... (856) 795-5077
GlassRoots, Inc., 10 Bleeker St., Newark 07102
Dir., Hum. Res.—Katie Witzig, 20 emp., *Glass jewelry, beadmaking & mosaics* ..... (973) 353-9555
Grassmann-Blake, Inc., 58 E. Willow St., Millburn 07041
Pres.—Richard Blake, 25 emp., *Precious metal jewelry clasps* ..... (973) 379-6170
Metal City Findings Co., 456 Nordhoff Pl., P.O. Box 7300, Englewood 07631
Pres.—Gerald Nathel, 40 emp., *Costume jewelry findings & metal stamping* ..... (201) 569-7300
Tessler & Weiss, Inc., 2389 Vauxhall Rd., P.O. Box 3414, Union 07083
Pres.—Mark Tessler, 155 emp., *Jewelry findings* ..... (908) 686-0513
Victor's Three-D, Inc., 25 Brook Ave., Maywood 07607
Pres., GM—Robert Hess, 100 emp., *High-precision, die-struck jewelry* ..... (201) 845-4433

## 3931 Musical instruments

D R Handmade Strings, Inc., 7 Palisade Ave., Emerson 07630
Pres.—Mark Dronge, 35 emp., *Guitar strings* ..... (201) 599-0100
Fuchs Audio Technology, LLC, 407 Getty Ave., 2nd Fl., Clifton 07011
Pres.—Annette Fuchs, 10 emp., *Tube guitar & bass amplifiers, speaker* ..... (973) 772-4420
Jan-Mar Industries, 568 Hillsdale, P.O. Box 314, Hillsdale 07642
Pres.—Mark Biddelman, 1 emp., *Musical instrument accessories* ..... (201) 664-3930
Kratos-CTI, 9 Whippany Rd., Bldg. A-1, Whippany 07981
Dir., Qual. Control—Art Alexander, 70 emp., *Oscillators & synthesizers* ..... (973) 884-2580
Kratt Pitch Pipe Co., Wm, 40 Lafayette Pl., Kenilworth 07033
Plt. Mgr.—Robert McNamara, 7 emp., *Musical pitch pipes* ..... (908) 709-8901
Latin Percussion, Inc., 160 Belmont Ave., Garfield 07026
Creative Dir.—Heidi Linsalata Schaeffer, 25 emp., *Percussion instruments* ..... (973) 330-9103
Malletech, LLC, 1107 11th Ave., Neptune 07753
CEO—Leigh H. Stevens, 15 emp., *Keyboard percussion instruments, marimbas* (732) 774-0011
McNally Instruments, LLC, 11 Longview Rd., Rockaway 07866
Ptnr.—Robert McNally, 2 emp., *Strumsticks* ..... (973) 983-9153
Peragallo Pipe Organ Co., 306 Buffalo Ave., Paterson 07503
CEO—John Peragallo, 15 emp., *Handcrafted pipe organs* ..... (973) 684-3414
Tech 21 USA, Inc., 790 Bloomfield Ave., Ste. B-1, Clifton 07012
Pres.—Andrew Barta, 20 emp., *Electric guitar & bass amplifiers,* ..... (973) 777-6996
Trek II Products, Inc., 570 Jersey Ave., New Brunswick 08901
Pres.—Michael Smokowicz, 10 emp., *Musical instruments* ..... (732) 214-9200
Vintage Vibe ltd., 114 Beach St., Bldg. 5, Ground Fl., Rockaway 07866
Owner—Chris Carroll, 8 emp., *Piano parts for vintage electric pianos* ..... (973) 989-2178

## 3942 Dolls & stuffed toys

Chriselles Dolls, 216 Hillbrook Dr., River Edge 07661
Principal—Diane King, 1 emp., *Costumes for dolls* ..... (201) 488-1905
H M S Monaco, Inc., 629 Grove St., 5th Fl., Jersey City 07310
Pres., CEO—Ira Erstling, 40 emp., *Costume jewelry, stuffed toys & novelties* ..... (201) 533-0007
Kids Of America Corp., 103 Route 46 W., Fairfield 07004
Owner—Stephen Chan, 5 emp., *Plush toys* ..... (973) 808-8242
New Adventures, LLC (H Q), 6 Deforest Ave., Ste. 7, East Hanover 07936
Ptnr.—Beth Reiling, 5 emp., *Company headquarters; toys & dolls* ..... (973) 884-8887
Oshko International Corp., 115 Riverbend Dr., North Brunswick 08902
Pres.—Michael Oh, 1 emp., *Stuffed animals* ..... (732) 821-8222
Peek-A-Boo Toys, 9040 Pensauken Hwy., Pennsauken 08110
Owner—Ari Ohnona, 20 emp., *Plush toys, including teddy bears for* ..... (856) 317-9100
Pride Products, Inc., 5 Slater Dr., Elizabeth 07206
Pres.—Joseph Yen, 23 emp., *Contract assembly of toys* ..... (908) 353-6800
Rauhauser's Candy, 721 Asbury Ave., Ocean City 08226
Owner—Rodney Blomdahl, 10 emp., *Chocolate candy, tinware & stuffed* ..... (609) 399-1465
Reeves International, Inc., 14 Industrial Rd., Pequannock 07440
Pres.—Anthony Fleischmann, 50 emp., *Corporate headquarters & manufacturer* ..... (973) 694-5006
Tiffanees Toys, Inc., 601 Nassau St., Ste. 593, North Brunswick 08902
Pres.—Mirta D'Amaro, 13 emp., *Stuffed toys, pet beds, pillow cushions* ..... (732) 828-6333
TMP International, Inc., 15 Hamburg Tpke., Bloomingdale 07403
V-P., Prod.—Ed Frank, 25 emp., *Highly detailed toy models of musicians* ..... (973) 838-7072

## 3944 Games, toys & children's vehicles

Beta Craft, Inc., 2682 Route 130, P.O. Box 536, Cranbury 08512
Pres.—Arthur Hasselbach, 2 emp., *Pinewood derby kits & supplies & orchid* ..... (609) 655-1940
Bucci Management Co., Inc., 603 N. 1st Rd., Hammonton 08037
Pres.—Guy Bucci, 1 emp., *Children's games & marbles* ..... (609) 561-1888
Dively Models, Inc., Bob, 540 Hudson St., Hackensack 07601
Pres.—William Stevick, 1 emp., *Scale model airplane kits, including* ..... (201) 310-2340
D'Lite Products, Inc., 540 Ravine Ct., Wyckoff 07481
Pres.—Bill Hennessy, 10 emp., *Magic & novelty products* ..... (201) 444-0822
Endless Games, Inc., 35 Main St., Ste. B, Matawan 07747
Pres.—Michael Gasser, 5 emp., *Family board games* ..... (732) 414-2213
Geebee Marketing, Inc., 300 Raritan Ave., 2nd Fl., Highland Park 08904
Pres.—Robert N. Kersey, 4 emp., *Games & puzzles* ..... (732) 777-6033
Model Rectifier Corp., 80 Newfield Ave., P.O. Box 6312, Edison 08837
Pres.—Frank Ritota, 30 emp., *Hobby & toy products & remote control* ..... (732) 225-2100
Moose Mountain Marketing, Inc. (H Q), 8 Wood Hollow Rd., Ste. 302, Parsippany 07054
Pres.—Ronald Lokos, 10 emp., *Corporate headquarters; toys (mfg.* ..... (973) 884-8900
New Adventures, LLC (H Q), 6 Deforest Ave., Ste. 7, East Hanover 07936
Ptnr.—Beth Reiling, 5 emp., *Company headquarters; toys & dolls* ..... (973) 884-8887
P & E Technologies, Inc., 5140 W. Hurley Pond Rd., Farmingdale 07727
Pres.—Phil Cornick, 12 emp., *Video games & vending machines* ..... (732) 751-1515
Panline USA, Inc., 251 Union St., Northvale 07647
Pres.—Fred Keeler, 66 emp., *Juvenile toys, including bathtub play* ..... (201) 750-8010
Park Sales, P.O. Box 586, Point Pleasant Beach 08742
Owner—Dennis Vitkauskis, 1 emp., *Boardwalk games* ..... (732) 899-0684
Prime Time Toys, LLC, P.O. Box 256, Pompton Lakes 07442
V-P., Opers. & Manager—Mark Milano, 2 emp., *Water & flying toys & games* ..... (973) 839-5711
Reeves International, Inc., 14 Industrial Rd., Pequannock 07440
Pres.—Anthony Fleischmann, 50 emp., *Corporate headquarters & manufacturer* ..... (973) 694-5006
Reeves International, Inc., 34 Owens Dr., Wayne 07470
Prodn. Mgr.—Bill Rausch, 100 emp., *Model horses* ..... (973) 956-9555
Shooting Star, Inc., 2500 Plainfield Ave., Scotch Plains 07076
Pres.—Fred Andreae, Sr., 2 emp., *Shooting gallery gun & water games* ..... (908) 789-2500
Smart Gear, LLC, 82 Norwood Ave., Ste. 2, Deal 07723
CEO—Sam Cohen, 30 emp., *Environmentally friendly educational* ..... (732) 663-0000
Tucker International, LLC, 200 W. Somerdale Rd., Ste. B, Voorhees 08043
Pres.—Michael J. Goldman, 5 emp., *Children's toys & games* ..... (856) 216-1333
Wish Factory, Inc., The, 21 Church St., Ste. 2, Montclair 07042
Owner—Scott Bachrach, 13 emp., *Children's toys* ..... (973) 744-3131

## 3949 Sporting & athletic goods, nec

Akadema, Inc., 140 5th Ave., Hawthorne 07506
CEO—Joe Gilligan, 21 emp., *Baseball & softball equipment for professiona* ..... (973) 304-1470
American Teletimer Corp., 1167 Globe Ave., Mountainside 07092
Pres.—Joel Rosenzweig, 3 emp., *Horse race timing equipment* ..... (908) 654-4200
Aqua Clear Tackle, P.O. Box 8454, Turnersville 08012
Ptnr., Pres. & Sales & Mktg. Mgr.—Mike Hanson, 3 emp., *Fishing tackles & rigs* ..... (609) 861-1088
Aurorae (H Q), 46 N. Central Ave., Ramsey 07446
Pres., CEO—Dennis Ingui, 2 emp., *Company headquarters; yoga mats, accessories* ..... (551) 579-4003
Best Billiards, 393 Pittstown Rd., Pittstown 08867
Owner & Sole Proprietor—Charles Jacobi, 1 emp., *Custom pool, shuffleboard & game tables* (908) 730-0933
Blue Gauntlet Fencing Gear, Inc., 280 N. Midland Ave., Bldg. W, Saddle Brook 07663
Pres.—Jing X. Chen, 15 emp., *Fencing sport equipment* ..... (201) 797-3332
CDK Industry, LLC, 900 Haddonfield Rd., Cherry Hill 08002
Pres., GM—James Walford, 3 emp., *Horse racing equipment & embroidery* ..... (856) 488-5456
Century Sports, 1715 Oak St., Ste. 1, Lakewood 08701
Opers. Mgr.—Sandy Hunt, 20 emp., *Tennis court equipment, gymnasium padding* ..... (732) 905-4422
Crown Products, Inc., 1302 Roller Rd., Ocean 07712
Pres., GM—Joseph Tagliareni, 25 emp., *Promotional golf accessories* ..... (732) 493-0022
Dolphin Industries Ltd., 2141 River Rd., P.O. Box 344, Egg Harbor City 08215
Pres.—Antonio Pacheco, 9 emp., *Fiberglass swimming pools* ..... (609) 965-5188
Enor Corp., 245 Livingston St., Northvale 07647
CEO—Steven Udwin, 100 emp., *Sporting goods for children* ..... (201) 750-1680
Fairway Products Co., 265 Garden Rd., P.O. Box 611, Elmer 08318
Pres.—Edward Carman, 4 emp., *Golf course equipment, including fairway* ..... (856) 358-6016

Folsom Corp. (H Q), 43 McKee Dr., Ste. 1, P.O. Box 6660, Mahwah 07430
Pres., CEO—Robert Feldscott, 20 emp., *Corporate headquarters; sport fishing* ........ (201) 529-3550
Godforce Tactical, Inc., 2614-B S. Clinton Ave., South Plainfield 07080
Pres.—Leland C. Stanford, 2 emp., *Paintball guns*........ (908) 561-2021
Harris Miniature Golf Courses, Inc., 141 W. Burk Ave., Wildwood 08260
Pres.—Richard Lahey, 15 emp., *Miniature golf course construction*........ (609) 522-4200
Har-Tru Sports, 1715 Oak St., Ste. 1, Lakewood 08701
Dir., Sales—Tracy Lynch, 30 emp., *Netting products & knitted industrial*........ (434) 295-6167
Hayward Industries, Inc., 620 Division St., Elizabeth 07201
Chrm.—Oscar Davis, 100 emp., *Corporate headquarters & swimming pool*........ (908) 351-5400
Imperial Billiards Corp., 2 Sandy Ln., Hardwick 07825
Pres.—Valerio Vindici, 3 emp., *Billiard & poker tables*........ (908) 459-4825
International Riding Helmets, Inc., 21 Industrial Dr., Old Bridge Township, Keyport 07735
Pres., GM—Frank Plastino, 10 emp., *Equestrian helmets*........ (732) 290-3000
Landice, Inc., 111 Canfield Ave., Unit A-1, Randolph 07869
Pres.—Greg Savetierie, 30 emp., *Treadmills & elliptical trainers for*........ (973) 927-9010
Liberty Sport, Inc., 107 Fairfield Rd., Fairfield 07004
Pres.—Anthony DiChiara, 30 emp., *Protective sports eyewear*........ (973) 882-0986
MegaStrike, Inc., 331 Fairfield Rd., Ste. B-1, Freehold 07728
★ Owner—Robert Uhrig, 4 emp., *Fishing lures*........ (732) 780-7383
Newbold, Inc., 200 Egel Ave., Middlesex 08846
Pres.—Henry A. Phillips, 5 emp., *Polymer handgun & pistol targets*........ (732) 469-5654
Pegasus Products, Inc., 19 Readington Rd., Somerville 08876
Pres.—Frank Patel, 30 emp., *Swimming pool & tank liners*........ (908) 707-1122
Rockwood Corp. / Speedwell Targets, 410 Clermont Ter., Ste. D, Union 07083
Pres.—Michael Panos, 4 emp., *Qualification, military, NRA competition*........ (908) 355-8600
Sportstar, 19 Thomas St., South River 08882
GM—Mike Shannon, 4 emp., *Sports uniforms*........ (732) 254-9214
Standard Merchandising Co. (H Q), 1125 Wright Ave., Camden 08103
Pres., CFO—Jeff Tarnoff, 50 emp., *Company headquarters; men's & women's*........ (856) 964-9700
Swim 'N Play, Inc., 313 Regina Ave., Rahway 07065
Pres.—Ray Ventrice, 35 emp., *Aboveground swimming pools & accesories*........ (732) 574-1500
T G Mfg., Inc., 299 Old Forks Rd., Hammonton 08037
Pres.—Tom Garvey, 15 emp., *Overhead mounted aluminum big game*........ (609) 561-0022
TechnoGym U. S. A. Corp., 700 U.S. Highway 46 E., Fairfield 07004
★ CEO—Federico Foli, 40 emp., *Commercial fitness equipment*........ (206) 623-1488
XO Athletic Co., 911 Springfield Rd., Union 07083
CEO—Michael T. Landi, 10 emp., *Athletic protection products, including*........ (908) 964-1242

## 3951 Pens & mechanical pencils

Bankers Pen Co., Inc., 141 Lanza Rd., Garfield 07026
Pres.—Richard Danziger, 30 emp., *Promotional pens, pencils, key tags*........ (718) 768-7107
Cra-Z-Art, 1578 Sussex Tpke., Bldg. 5, Randolph 07869
CEO—Nellie Mahabir, 30 emp., *Company headquarters & arts & crafts*........ (973) 543-2037
Myron Corp., 205 Maywood Ave., Maywood 07607
CEO—Jim Adler, 450 emp., *Imprinted personalized business gifts*........ (201) 843-6464
Private Label Products, Inc., 20-21 Wagaraw Rd., Bldg. 34, Fair Lawn 07410
Off. Mgr.—David Naor, 12 emp., *Specialty writing instruments*........ (201) 791-1177
Rosa Pen Corp., 155 Park Ave., Ste. 101, Lyndhurst 07071
Owner & Pres.—Anthony J. Rosa, 5 emp., *Custom manufacturing of bent chiropractic*........ (201) 939-1112

## 3952 Lead pencils & art goods

Brewer Assocs., 400 Apgar Dr., Unit G, Somerset 08873
Pres.—Thomas Flack, 25 emp., *Engineering, architectural, sign making*........ (732) 564-9070
Chavant, Inc., 5043 Industrial Rd., Farmingdale 07727
Pres.—Jack North, 10 emp., *Clay, including modeling, hard styling*........ (732) 751-0003
Cra-Z-Art, 1578 Sussex Tpke., Bldg. 5, Randolph 07869
CEO—Nellie Mahabir, 30 emp., *Company headquarters & arts & crafts*........ (973) 543-2037
Daler-Rowney U. S. A., Ltd., 7 Corporate Dr., Cranbury 08512
Pres., Sales Mgr.—Andrew Daler, 25 emp., *Fine art materials*........ (609) 655-5252
General Pencil Co., 67 Fleet St., Jersey City 07306
Chrm.—James S. Weissenborn, 42 emp., *Wooden-cased art & school pencils &*........ (201) 653-5351
Hygloss Products, Inc., 45 Hathaway St., Wallington 07057
Pres.—Moshe Neurath, 30 emp., *Arts & crafts products for teachers*........ (973) 458-1700
Rich Art Color Co., Inc., 202 Pegasus Ave., Northvale 07647
Pres.—Marc Jennings, 15 emp., *Washable & non-washable paints & decorative*........ (201) 767-0009
Sculpture House, Inc., 405 Skillman Rd., P.O. Box 69, Skillman 08558
Pres., CEO—Bruner Barrie, 11 emp., *Corporate headquarters & clay products*........ (609) 466-2986
Tri-Chem, Inc., 681 Main St., Ste. 27, Belleville 07109
Pres.—Jitu Patel, 4 emp., *Water-based craft paints*........ (973) 751-9200

## 3953 Marking devices

A A A Stamp & Seal Mfg. Co., 361 N. Midland Ave., Saddle Brook 07663
Owner—Robert Goldman, 4 emp., *Rubber stamps & engraved plastic signs*........ (201) 796-1500
A B Stamp, 10 Mill Pine Dr., Lafayette 07848
Pres.—Fred Thornton, 3 emp., *Interior & exterior signs, rubber stamps*........ (973) 383-1683
A To Z Rubber Stamps, 617 Oradell Ave., Oradell 07649
Manager—Linda Shaffer, 2 emp., *Rubber stamps, seals & marking devices*........ (201) 265-9595
Acme Rubber Stamp Works, 6 Burnett Ave., Maplewood 07040
Pres.—Lori Bierman, 3 emp., *Rubber stamps & seals*........ (973) 761-7146
American Marking Systems, Inc., 1015 Paulison Ave., Clifton 07011
Pres.—John Collins, 30 emp., *Corporate headquarters & custom office*........ (973) 478-5600
Anchor Rubber Stamp & Printing, Inc., 339 Herbertsville Rd., Brick 08724
Pres.—Thomas McTague, 3 emp., *Rubber stamps, marking devices & embossers*........ (732) 583-6578
Arro-Mark Co., LLC, 158 W. Forest Ave., Englewood 07631
Ptnr.—Stephanie Pappageorge, 22 emp., *Metal, paint, permanent ink, refillable*........ (201) 567-4112
Bantle's Banners & Signs, 213 Clements Bridge Rd., Barrington 08007
Owner—Janice Bantle, 3 emp., *Street, door, window & magnetic vehicle*........ (856) 546-1112
BCT-NY/NJ, 11 Industrial Ave., Upper Saddle River 07458
Pres., GM—Douglas Negrin, 10 emp., *Rubber stamps & offset printing of*........ (201) 236-0088
Classic Marking Products, Inc., 10 Millpond Dr., Unit 9, Lafayette 07848
Pres.—Fred Thornton, Sr., 9 emp., *Rubber stamps, markers, signs & promotional*........ (973) 383-2223
Digital Design, Inc., 67 Sand Park Rd., Cedar Grove 07009
Pres., CEO—Ed Gerri, 30 emp., *Inkjet coding & marking systems*........ (973) 857-0901
Franklin Stamp & Sign Co., 543 Somerset St., Ste. 1, Somerset 08873
Co-Pres.—Harry Weber, Jr., 3 emp., *Rubber stamps, vinyl, plastic, color*........ (732) 846-9235
G & R Graphics, Inc., 303 Irvington Ave., South Orange 07079
Pres.—Robert Gomez, 5 emp., *Rubber stamps, embossing seals, signs*........ (973) 313-2200
Mackey's Print Xpress, 1107 7th Ave., Neptune 07753
Owner & Pres.—Ron Mackey, 3 emp., *Single, multicolor offset & digital*........ (732) 775-1730
Magic Printing Corp., 386 Avenel St., Avenel 07001
Pres.—Steven Glassman, 20 emp., *Business card & stationery printing*........ (732) 726-0620
Metal Etching Technology Assocs., Inc., 140 Mount Holly Bypass, Unit 10, Lumberton 08048
Pres.—Ting Shi, 20 emp., *Solder paste stencils*........ (609) 261-2670
Newark Stamp & Die Works, Inc., 35 Verona Ave., Newark 07104
Pres.—Bruce McNab, 9 emp., *Rubber & metal stamps*........ (973) 485-7111
Oraton Rubber Stamp Co., Inc., 407 Route 94, Columbia 07832
Plt. Mgr.—Vicky Finelli, 30 emp., *Rubber stamps*........ (908) 496-4161
Paterson Stamp Works, 1015 Paulison Ave., Clifton 07011
Pres.—John Collins, 17 emp., *Custom office & ID products, including*........ (973) 478-5600
PNC, Inc., 115 E. Centre St., Nutley 07110
Pres.—Sam Sangani, 80 emp., *Printed circuit boards & assemblies*........ (973) 284-1600
R. B.'s Rubber Stamp, Inc., 551 W. Side Ave., Jersey City 07304
Pres.—Leila Bahadur, 2 emp., *Rubber stamps, marking devices, signs*........ (201) 547-9955
Ranger Industries, Inc., 15 Park Rd., Tinton Falls 07724
Dir., Sales—Alain Avrillon, 62 emp., *Ink, pads & embossing powders*........ (732) 389-1101
Regal Stamp & Sign Co., Inc., 240 Park Ave., P.O. Box 342, East Rutherford 07073
Owner & Pres.—Krista Brabston, 1 emp., *Rubber stamps, marking devices & signs*........ (201) 939-0400
Rubber Stamp Man, LLC, 1236 Route 166, Ste. 140, Toms River 08753
GM—Robert Pyott, 3 emp., *Custom rubber stamps*........ (732) 557-0275
Shachihata, Inc., U. S. A., 525 Oberlin Ave. S., Lakewood 08701
GM—Young Sin Park, 30 emp., *Rubber stamps & engraved signs*........ (732) 370-4770
Trodat USA, 48 Hellar Pk., Somerset 08873
V-P., Sales—Chris Boyle, 42 emp., *Self-inking marking devices, notaryseals*........ (732) 529-8500

## 3955 Carbon paper & inked ribbons

Antistatic Industries, A Div. of ADM Tronics, Inc., 224 Pegasus Ave., Northvale 07647
Pres., CEO—Andre DiMino, 15 emp., *Static dissipative products, including*........ (201) 767-6040
Care Plus NJ, Inc., 185 6th Ave., Paterson 07524
Manager—John Maisto, 10 emp., *Remanufactured inkjet cartridges*........ (973) 553-1954
Cartridge World New Providence, LLC, 1310 Springfield Ave., New Providence 07974
Owner—John T. Figueiredo, 3 emp., *Rebuilt ink cartridges*........ (908) 771-9696
Cartridge World Oakhurst, 1815 State Route 35, Oakhurst 07755
Owner—Joe Betesh, 2 emp., *Remanufactured inkjet & toner printer*........ (732) 531-4232
Cartridge World Of Wayne, LLC, 1055 Hamburg Tpke., Wayne 07470
Owner—Rosemarie Peluso, 4 emp., *Eco-friendly remanufactured printer*........ (973) 696-2880
Pengad, Inc., 55 Oak St., P.O. Box 99, Bayonne 07002
Pres.—Thomas S. Pierson, 20 emp., *Corporate headquarters & printed report*........ (201) 436-5625
Petitts Ink Corp., 1745 State Route 10, Ste. 4, Morris Plains 07950
CEO—Kathleen Petitt, 3 emp., *Remanufactured inkjet & laser toner*........ (973) 984-2400

## 3961 Jewelry—costume

American Image, 45 W. Broad St., Bergenfield 07621
Pres.—John Paragian, 15 emp., *Engraved awards, signs, name badges*........ (201) 384-9200
Atlas Fashions, 148 Tices Ln., East Brunswick 08816
Owner—Seo Shim, 7 emp., *Costume jewelry*........ (732) 254-6090
David Aubrey, Inc, 186 Griffith St., Jersey City 07307
Pres.—Jennifer Arago, 25 emp., *Costume jewelry*........ (201) 653-2200
E F Design Ltd., 600 Harbor Blvd., Unit 1022, Weehawken 07086
Chrm.—Robert Fuhrman, 4 emp., *Patented jewelry accessories, including*........ (201) 319-9075
GlassRoots, Inc., 10 Bleeker St., Newark 07102
Dir., Hum. Res.—Katie Witzig, 20 emp., *Glass jewelry, beadmaking & mosaics*........ (973) 353-9555
H M S Monaco, Inc., 629 Grove St., 5th Fl., Jersey City 07310
Pres., CEO—Ira Erstling, 40 emp., *Costume jewelry, stuffed toys & novelties*........ (201) 533-0007
InBeau, Inc., 101 W. Palisade, Englewood 07631
Owner—Simon Yang, 7 emp., *Costume jewelry, including necklaces*........ (201) 227-8875
Kole Design, LLC, 35 Cedar Ct., Freehold 07728
Owner—Terri Kolodny, 5 emp., *Novelty & costume jewelry*........ (732) 252-9365
Lieberfarb, Inc., 2100 Felver Ct., Rahway 07065
Pres.—Mark Schonwetter, 80 emp., *Costume jewelry*........ (973) 676-9090
Making Waves, Inc., 1916 Old Cuthbert Rd., Ste. B-20, Cherry Hill 08034
Pres.—Francine Keller, 4 emp., *Costume jewelry*........ (856) 795-9311
Norco, Inc., 237 South Ave., P.O. Box 186, Garwood 07027
Pres.—Michael Rosenberg, 15 emp., *Lapel pins, dog tags, giant magnetic*........ (908) 789-1550
Oori Trading, Inc., 230 Union St., P.O. Box 154, Northvale 07647
CEO—Ku Tae Yi, 15 emp., *Corporate headquarters & costume jewelry*........ (201) 367-3030
Panline USA, Inc., 251 Union St., Northvale 07647
Pres.—Fred Keeler, 66 emp., *Juvenile toys, including bathtub play*........ (201) 750-8010
Perfect Pearl Co., Inc., 100 State St., Moonachie 07074
Pres.—Albert Spitzer, 40 emp., *Costume jewelry*........ (201) 705-5200
San Marel Designs, Inc., 98 U.S. Highway 46, Ste. 10, Budd Lake 07828
CEO—Doug Landon, 8 emp., *Precious metal jewelry & wholesaler*........ (973) 426-9554

## 3965 Fasteners, buttons, needles & pins

Allary Corp. (H Q), 2204 Morris Ave., Ste. 209, Union 07083
Pres.—Alan Sorrell, 14 emp., *Corporate headquarters; sewing notions*........ (908) 851-0077
BMB Fasteners, Inc., 86 Lackawanna Ave., Ste. 208, Woodland Park 07424
Owner & Pres.—Larry Malone, 8 emp., *Screws, fasteners, bolts, nuts & washers*........ (973) 256-4010
C & C Metal Products Corp., 456 Nordhoff Pl., P.O. Box 7300, Englewood 07631
V-P., Secy.—Mitchell Chalfin, 50 emp., *Corporate headquarters & metal stampings*........ (201) 569-7300
Eagle Button Co., Inc., 700-76 Broadway, Westwood 07675
Pres.—Arthur Simon, 25 emp., *Designer buttons for apparel*........ (201) 652-4063
FASTENation, Inc., 120 Brighton Rd., Ste. 2, Clifton 07012
Owner & CEO—Jayne Petak, 22 emp., *Manufacturer & distributor of hook-*........ (973) 591-1277
Form Cut Industries, Inc., 197 Mount Pleasant Ave., Newark 07104
Pres.—Charles Alberto, 50 emp., *Precision wire forms, leads, pins,*........ (973) 483-5154
J K A Specialties Mfg., Inc., 157 Eayrestown Rd., Southampton 08088
Pres.—James Young, 5 emp., *Printing of buttons, vinyl decals,*........ (609) 859-2090
Kane-M, Inc., 1 Madison St., Ste. F-9, East Rutherford 07073
Pres.—Masato Yamakawa, 4 emp., *Clothing snaps & fasteners*........ (973) 777-2797
Main & Sons, Inc., Robert A., 555 Goffle Rd., P.O. Box 159, Wyckoff 07481
Pres., CFO & V-P., Opers.—William Main, 13 emp., *Pins & printed wire products, including*. (201) 447-3700
Micron Fastener, Inc., 85-99 Hazel St., Paterson 07503
Pres., CEO—Cilek Seker, 8 emp., *Buttons, grommets, dies, jean accessories*........ (973) 278-4100
Nu-Style Embroidery & Button Co., Inc., 5212 Polk St., West New York 07093
Pres.—Jay Rosner, 5 emp., *Apparel buttons, belts, neckties, lace*........ (201) 864-1808
Nu-Style Embroidery & Trimming, 5212 Polk St., West New York 07093
Pres.—Sam Rosner, 2 emp., *Embroidery & lace covered buttons &*........ (201) 864-1808
Royal Slide Sales Co., Inc., 42 Hepworth Pl., Garfield 07026
V-P.—Lewis Neuman, 15 emp., *Home furnishings packaging bags, cosmetics*........ (973) 777-1177
Snapco Mfg. Corp., 140 Central Ave., Hillside 07205
Chrm., Pres., CFO & R & D Mgr.—Jeffrey G. Spitz, 25 emp., *Snap, fastener tape, eyelets, grommets* (973) 282-0300

Yale Hook & Eye Co., Inc., 33 Race St., Hillside 07205
Pres.—Ann Roseman, 15 emp., Hooks, eye & snap fastener tapes ... (973) 824-1440

## 3991 Brooms & brushes

Andon Brush Co., Inc., 1 Merrit Ave., Little Falls 07424
Pres., GM—Robert Newell, 15 emp., Dental, pharmaceutical, cosmetic, commercial ... (973) 256-6611
Custom Brush Co. Inc., 1933 Owl Ct., Cherry Hill 08003
Pres., Fin. & MIS Mgr.—Robin Reisman, 3 emp., Industrial brushes for the pharmaceutical ... (856) 354-1673
Elder & Jenks Co., 148 E. 5th St., Bayonne 07002
V-P.—Mike Norton, 40 emp., Paint brushes & rollers ... (201) 437-0770
Green & Son, Inc., Charles E., 625 3rd St., Newark 07107
Pres.—John V. Green III, 40 emp., Metal paint brush ferrules & paint ... (973) 485-3630
Industrial Brush Co., Inc., 105 Clinton Rd., Fairfield 07004
V-P., Sales—Scott Enchelmaier, 25 emp., Industrial brushes ... (973) 575-0455
Jenkins & Sons, Inc., M. W., 444 Pompton Ave., P.O. Box 303, Cedar Grove 07009
Pres. & V-P., Sales—Craig Sigler, 7 emp., Industrial brushes ... (973) 239-5150
Johnson & Johnson Consumer Companies, Inc. (H Q), 199 Grandview Rd., Skillman 08558
Chrm., Co. Group—Roberto Marques, 1100 emp., Corporate headquarters; baby, skin, ... (908) 874-1000
Keystone Plastics, Inc., 3451 S. Clinton Ave., South Plainfield 07080
Pres., CFO—Marvin Naftal, 70 emp., Streetsweeper broom units & broom bristles ... (908) 561-1300
Manufacturers' Brush Corp., 69 King St., Dover 07801
Pres.—Richard Draudt, 5 emp., Industrial & commercial brushes ... (973) 882-6966
Muralo Co., Inc., 148 E. 5th St., Bayonne 07002
Pres.—James F. Norton, 50 emp., Corporate headquarters & paints, brushes ... (201) 437-0770
Newark Brush Company, 1 Silver Ct., Springfield 07081
Pres.—Jeremy Glick, 22 emp., Industrial brushes & sweeper brooms ... (973) 376-1000
Quickie Mfg. Corp. (H Q), 1150 Taylors Ln., P.O. Box 156, Cinnaminson 08077
Ex. V-P., Engrg.—Jace Weaver, 70 emp., Corporate headquarters; cleaning products ... (856) 829-7900
Silver Brush Ltd., 92 N. Main St., Bldg. 18-E, P.O. Box 414, Windsor 08561
Pres.—Deirdra Silver, 5 emp., Brushes for arts & crafts & beauty ... (609) 443-4900
Supply Plus, Inc., 155 Sherman Ave., Paterson 07502
V-P.—Samuel Neustein, Jr., 35 emp., Household cleaning products, sponges ... (973) 782-5930
The Fifty/Fifty Group, Inc, 343 S. River St., Hackensack 07601
Chrm. of the Board—Edward D. Spitaletta, 25 emp., Mop, broom & brush assemblies ... (201) 343-1243
Trim Brush Co., Inc., 22 Littell Rd., East Hanover 07936
CEO & Dir.—Diane Carton, 5 emp., Scrubbing brushes ... (973) 887-2525
Ward & Sons, Inc., J. B., 1434 Route 565, Wantage 07461
Pres.—Ed Boscia, 4 emp., Industrial brushes ... (973) 827-4600

## 3993 Signs & advertising specialties

(MASAco) Michael Anthony Sign & Awning, Inc., 21 Randolph Ave., Avenel 07001
Pres.—Michael Bradley, 35 emp., Electric signs, including storefront ... (732) 453-6120
1 Stop Wraps, LLC, 1525 Prospect St., Ste. 602, Lakewood 08701
Owner & Pres.—Frank Mele, 4 emp., Signs & large-format digital printing ... (732) 363-7800
10-31, Inc., 2 W. Crisman Rd., Columbia 07832
Pres.—William Stender, 24 emp., Custom wooden, plastic & glass artwork ... (908) 496-4946
419 Neon, LLC, 364 Glenwood Ave., East Orange 07017
Owner & Off. Mgr.—Roger Borg, 2 emp., Custom neon signs & lighting ... (732) 324-2445
A & F Sign Company LLC, 28 E. Railway Ave., Paterson 07503
Sole Member—Frank Ferrucci, 1 emp., Architectural, illuminated, non-illuminated ... (973) 278-3707
A A A Stamp & Seal Mfg. Co., 361 N. Midland Ave., Saddle Brook 07663
Owner—Robert Goldman, 4 emp., Rubber stamps & engraved plastic signs ... (201) 796-1500
A B Stamp, 10 Mill Pine Dr., Lafayette 07848
Pres.—Fred Thornton, 3 emp., Interior & exterior signs, rubber stamps ... (973) 383-1683
A C Display Studios, Inc., 2715 Arctic Ave., Atlantic City 08401
Off. Mgr.—Jackie Boyd, 6 emp., Interior & exterior signs ... (609) 345-0814
A-Affordable Sign.Com, 1053 Madison Hill Rd., Rahway 07065
GM—Jim Miggioze, 12 emp., Custom signs & vinyl lettering ... (732) 287-0446
ABC SignSystems, Inc., 7970 National Hwy., P.O. Box 622, Pennsauken 08110
Pres.—Stephen Trifletti, 20 emp., Interior & exterior signs ... (856) 665-0950
Abco Signs, 7300 N. Crescent Blvd., Ste. 11, Pennsauken 08110
Pres.—Howard Gaston, 2 emp., Interior & exterior signs ... (856) 663-6001
ABS Sign Co., Inc., 3008 Park Blvd., Wildwood 08260
Pres.—Randy Hentges, 6 emp., Interior & exterior signs ... (609) 522-6833
Ace Neon Factory, LLC, 2101 Grier Ave., Linden 07036
Pres.—Scott Fedor, 3 emp., Custom neon signs & neon sign repair ... (908) 486-6366
Ace Sign Co., Inc., 419 Summit Ave., Perth Amboy 08861
Pres.—Philip Smith, 9 emp., Interior & exterior signs, channel ... (732) 826-3858
ACL Equipment Corp., 257 E. Northfield Rd., P.O. Box 620, Livingston 07039
Pres.—Martin Reinfeld, 3 emp., Interior signs & assembly ... (973) 740-9800
Action Sign Co., Inc., 217 Ewan Rd., Mullica Hill 08062
Pres.—John V. Secatore, 4 emp., Interior & exterior signs ... (856) 478-0404
Action Signs & Awards, 305 N. 11th St., Millville 08332
CEO—Irene Inferrera, 2 emp., Vinyl lettered signs, trophy engraving ... (856) 825-2454
Acu-Data Business Products, Inc., 1572 State Route 23, Ste. D, Butler 07405
Pres.—Gerald J. Vinci, 2 emp., Business forms, advertising specialties ... (973) 838-5678
Adco Signs Of New Jersey, Inc., 57 Westfield Ave., Elizabeth 07208
Owner—Clara D. Molski, 40 emp., Interior dimensional, silkscreen & ... (908) 965-2112
Adpro Imprints, Inc., 3411 Rose Ave., Ocean 07712
Pres.—Peter L. Demaree, Jr., 5 emp., Textile screen printing, embroidery ... (732) 493-8555
ADV Promos & More, LLC, 12 Baltusrol St., Hamilton Square 08690
Owner—Andrea M. Anepete, 1 emp., Custom printed promotional products ... (609) 587-7500
Advantage Signs, Flags & Banners/ Country Crossings, 130 Newton Sparta Rd., Newton 07860
Owner—Glenn Gerard, 1 emp., Interior & exterior signs & banners ... (973) 579-3880
Ad-Venture Graphics, Inc., 46 Main St., Succasunna 07876
Pres.—Ray Vanderhoof, 3 emp., Interior & exterior signs, exhibits ... (973) 927-0951
Agin Signs & Design, Route 1 S., Monmouth Junction 08852
Owner—Rick Agin, 2 emp., Interior & exterior signs ... (732) 297-9007
AKA, Inc., 1324 New Market Ave., South Plainfield 07080
Pres.—Michael Allocco, 6 emp., Screen printing & embroidery, exterior ... (908) 753-8112
All Signs Direct, LLC, 38 Washington St., West Orange 07052
Pres.—Rick Iannuzzelli, 7 emp., Interior & exterior signs ... (973) 736-7446
Allegra Princeton, 12 Stults Rd., Ste. 100, Dayton 08810
CEO—David Kovacs, 30 emp., Printing, digital archiving, finishing & mailing service ... (609) 771-4000
Allen Signs, 600 Martin Luther King Ave., Pleasantville 08232
Owner—Jose Allen, 1 emp., Interior & exterior signs ... (609) 645-9268
Alliance Sign Co., Inc., 37 Grove St., Passaic 07055
Owner—Daniel Casabona, 30 emp., Custom signs ... (973) 458-0900
Allied Environmental Signage, 556 Industrial Way W., Eatontown 07724
Pres.—Kevin White, 24 emp., Interior & exterior vinyl signs ... (732) 578-1818
Almetek Industries, Inc., 2 Joy Dr., Hackettstown 07840
CEO—Lori McMahon, 75 emp., Metal & polyethelene safety signs, ... (908) 850-9700
Alpak Display Group, 575 N. Midland Ave., Saddle Brook 07663
V-P., POP Sales—Jason Taub, 30 emp., Corrugated point-of-purchase displays ... (201) 797-1411
Alpha 1 Studio, Inc., 3 Linda Ln., Ste. A, Southampton 08088
Pres., Fin., MIS & R & D Mgr.—Ray E. Witthauer, 6 emp., Interior & exterior sandblasted, wooden ... (609) 859-2200
AlphaGraphics of Mahwah, 1 Lethbridge Plz., Route 17 N., Mahwah 07430
Pres.—John Chrisostomou, 6 emp., Digital, direct mail & business printing ... (201) 327-2200
Alpine Group, Inc., The (H Q), 1 Meadowlands Plz., Ste. 801, East Rutherford 07073
Chrm. & CEO—Steven S. Elbaum, 5 emp., Holding company headquarters; nonilluminated ... (201) 549-4400
Alternative Air & Store Fixtures, 3-C Mary Way, Hainesport 08036
Ptnr.—James Lunstead, 6 emp., Refrigerated & dry custom & standard ... (609) 261-5870
American Display, 291 Route 22 E, Bldg. 8, P.O. Box 244, Whitehouse 08888
Pres.—Keith La Rue, 9 emp., ADA, Braille, corporate wall, office ... (908) 534-2700
American Graphic Systems, Inc., 39-26 Broadway, Fair Lawn 07410
Pres.—Stan Schechter, 5 emp., Offset printing & signs ... (201) 796-0666
American Image, 45 W. Broad St., Bergenfield 07621
Pres.—John Paragian, 15 emp., Engraved awards, signs, name badges ... (201) 384-9200
American Marking Systems, Inc., 1015 Paulison Ave., Clifton 07011
Pres.—John Collins, 30 emp., Corporate headquarters & custom office ... (973) 478-5600
American Plastic Co., 2137 Highway 1, Rahway 07065
Owner—Stephen Korstein, 3 emp., Plastic sign letters & numbers ... (732) 388-1601
American Screen Printing, 272 Kent Ave., Wayne 07470
Pres.—Howard Bischoff, 1 emp., Textile screen printing & signs ... (973) 471-0206
American Woodcarving, LLC, 1123 State Route 23, Ste. 6, Wayne 07470
Pres.—Mike Holst, 7 emp., Signs, displays & awnings & custom ... (973) 835-8510
Anchor Rubber Stamp & Printing, Inc., 339 Herbertsville Rd., Brick 08724
Pres.—Thomas McTague, 3 emp., Rubber stamps, marking devices & embossers ... (732) 583-6578
Apollo Sign Co., Inc., 835 Midland Ave., Garfield 07026
Pres.—Valerie Vegliante, 5 emp., Trade show, neon & magnetic interior ... (973) 772-7446
Apple Exhibits, 730 Grand Ave., Unit 1-A, Ridgefield 07657
Owner—Young Park, 10 emp., Trade show exhibits & booths & custom ... (201) 943-2775
Applied Image, Inc., 800 Business Park Dr., Freehold 07728
Pres.—Allen Shanosky, 20 emp., Large-format graphic printing & environmental ... (732) 410-2444
Aquarian What's Your Sign, LLC, 37 Newtons Corner Rd., Howell 07731
Owner—Bill McCarrick, 2 emp., Vinyl signs ... (732) 206-0726
Arista Trophies & Awards, 25 Portland Ave., Bergenfield 07621
Owner—David Cassens, 3 emp., Custom & laser engraving of signs, ... (201) 387-2165
Ariston Multimedia, LLC, 94 Valley Rd., Clifton 07013
★ Owner—Bernard Williams, 4 emp., Commercial printing, t-shirt screen ... (973) 553-2727
Arizona Signs & Truck Lettering, 3121 Route 73 S., Maple Shade 08052
Owner—Jeffrey Chudoff, 5 emp., Vinyl interior & exterior signs, lettering ... (856) 482-2288
Art D'Mensions, Inc., 1998 Scotch Plains Route 22, Scotch Plains 07076
Pres.—Bernice Mattos, 2 emp., Interior & exterior signs ... (908) 322-8488
Art Graphics, 54 Delsea Dr. N., Glassboro 08028
Ptnr.—Art Dorn, 3 emp., Textile screen printing, embroidery ... (856) 881-5029
Art Guild, Inc., 300 Wolf Dr., West Deptford 08086
Pres.—Doug Zegel, 210 emp., Corporate headquarters & trade show ... (856) 853-7500
Artcraft Sign Studio, Inc., 738 W. Branch Ave., Pine Hill 08021
Pres., CFO, MIS Mgr.—Arthur Elkins, 5 emp., Dimensional, sandblasted, carved, interior ... (856) 783-8008
Artisan Digital, Inc., 21 Fadem Rd., Unit 1, Springfield 07081
★ Owner—Kevin Hunt, 8 emp., Commercial printing & interior & exterior ... (973) 379-2788
Astro Sign Co., 230 E. High St., Route 322, Glassboro 08028
Pres.—Christopher Painter, 16 emp., Signs, vehicle lettering, banners, ... (856) 881-4300
Atlas Flasher & Supply Co., Inc., 430 Swedesboro Ave., P.O. Box 488, Mickleton 08056
CEO—Karenanne Brown, 40 emp., Corporate headquarters & traffic control ... (856) 423-3333
Aura Badge Co., 264 Clayton Ave., Monroeville 08343
Owner & IT Mgr.—Phil Barbaro, 70 emp., Promotional & identification products ... (856) 881-9026
Auto Graphix, 56 Edsel Dr., Sussex 07461
Owner—Mike Paul, 1 emp., Interior & exterior signs & truck lettering ... (973) 492-1300
Awards Trophy Co., 611 U.S. Highway 22, Hillside 07205
Owner—Ed Gallo, 5 emp., Trophies, plaques, pins, medals & advertising ... (908) 687-5775
Ayr Graphics & Printing, Inc., 320 Chestnut St., Roselle Park 07204
Pres.—Carl Gamba, 8 emp., Offset, color & digital printing & ... (908) 241-8118
Aztec Graphics, Inc., 420 Whitehead Rd., Trenton 08619
Pres.—Ronald Balerno, 15 emp., Screenprinted & embroidered sportswear ... (609) 587-1000
B & J Sign Service, 971 Landis Ave., Pittsgrove 08318
Owner & Pres.—Warren Jillson, 1 emp., Boat & truck lettering ... (856) 455-3636
Bankers Pen Co., Inc., 141 Lanza Rd., Garfield 07026
Pres.—Richard Danziger, 30 emp., Promotional pens, pencils, key tags ... (718) 768-7107
Banner Design, 600 N. Union Ave., P.O. Box 5343, Hillside 07205
Sales Mgr.—Bill Levy, 40 emp., Graphic & industrial design, signs, ... (908) 687-5335
Bannister Co., Inc., 126 N. Main St., Milltown 08850
Pres.—Lionel E. Bannister, 4 emp., Metal engraving & signs ... (732) 828-1353
Bantle's Banners & Signs, 213 Clements Bridge Rd., Barrington 08007
Owner—Janice Bantle, 3 emp., Street, door, window & magnetic vehicle ... (856) 546-1112
BCS Machine & Mfg. Corp., 3575 Kennedy Rd., South Plainfield 07080
Pres.—Sal Capparelli, 10 emp., CNC & general machining job shop, including ... (908) 561-1656
Bell Signs, 3125 Woodbridge Ave., Ste. 5-C, Edison 08837
Ptnr.—Stephen Bell, 2 emp., Sandblasted, carved & site interior ... (732) 738-0010
Bergen Screen Printing, Inc., 255 W. Broadway, Paterson 07522
Pres.—Uday Patel, 5 emp., Screen & wide-format digital printing ... (973) 595-1222
Bergen Sign Co., Inc., 161 E. Railway Ave., Paterson 07503
Pres.—Tom Schneider, 20 emp., Interior & exterior signs ... (973) 742-7755
Berlin Neon Sign, Inc., 326 Old White Horse Pike, Waterford Works 08089
Pres.—Tim Manna, 2 emp., Neon signs & flagpoles ... (856) 767-0525
Bilcar Signs, 2131 Morris Ave., Union 07083
Co-Pres.—Carlo Filipelli, 2 emp., Interior & exterior signs ... (908) 687-3777
Blanc Industries, Inc., 88 King St., Dover 07801
Pres.—Didier Blanc, 60 emp., Corporate headquarters & point-of-purchase ... (973) 678-1200
Blue Dog Graphics, 222 River St., Hackensack 07601
Pres.—Donald Perlman, 5 emp., Printing & promotional products ... (201) 343-3343
Blue Parachute, 263 Amboy Ave., Ste. 1, Metuchen 08840
Pres.—David Friedberg, 4 emp., Commercial printing, large-format signage ... (732) 767-1320
Bob's Signs Co., 1918 Englishtown Rd., P.O. Box 15, Old Bridge 08857
Owner—Robert Miller, 3 emp., Interior & exterior signs ... (732) 521-4554
Bon-Jour Group, LLC, 1100 Blanch Ave., Norwood 07648
Owner & Pres.—Michael Tchertchian, 17 emp., Embroidery & screen printing of promotional . (201) 646-1070
Bono Signs & Designs, LLC, 1 Beamer Rd., Sussex 07461
Owner—Larry Bono, 1 emp., Interior & exterior signs ... (973) 875-5488
Bright Signs, LLC, 2626 County Road 516, Old Bridge 08857
Owner—Ho Yung Yun, 2 emp., Magnetic & commercial signs & vinyl ... (732) 679-7440
Brimar Industries, Inc., 64 Outwater Ln., 3rd Fl., P.O. Box 467, Garfield 07026
Pres.—Brian Costello, 60 emp., Printed identification labels, decals ... (973) 340-7889

Broadway Signs, Inc., 1029 Ocean Rd., Point Pleasant 08742
Pres.—Joe Mulani, 2 emp., *Interior & exterior vinyl signs* .................... (732) 892-6334
Brunswick Sign & Exhibit Corp., 1510 Jersey Ave., North Brunswick 08902
GM—Bruce Talan, 4 emp., *Interior & exterior vinyl & neon signs* .................... (732) 246-2500
Brussian Strokes Sign Co., 15-A Melanie Ln., Ste. 3-A, East Hanover 07936
Owner—David Gersham, 3 emp., *Trade show, interior & exterior signs* .................... (973) 515-5151
Bry-Pat Advertising Specialty & Signs, Tennent Rd., Route 79, P.O. Box 369, Morganville 07751
Owner—Gary Birne, 4 emp., *Custom interior & exterior signs* .................... (732) 591-0999
Budget Printing, LLC, 70 Westfield Ave., Clark 07066
Owner & Pres.—Robert Borg, 6 emp., *Full-color digital, offset & screen* .................... (732) 574-1330
Budget Signs, 8 Caroline Ave., Clifton 07011
Owner—Sandy Glogiewicz, 1 emp., *Truck lettering* .................... (973) 340-2086
Butler Sign Company, 582 Fairfield Rd., Wayne 07470
Pres.—John J. Janis, Jr., 19 emp., *ADA, architectural, changeable letter* .................... (973) 633-5757
C & C Signs & Banners, 812 Forepeak Dr., Forked River 08731
★ Owner—Paul Colucci, 1 emp., *Interior & exterior signs & vinyl lettering* .................... (609) 693-4667
C C & D Capital Contracting & Design, Inc., 640 North Ave., Plainfield 07060
Pres.—Don Finley, 45 emp., *Point-of-purchase displays & custom* .................... (908) 561-8411
C L N Designs, LLC, P.O. Box 1822, South Hackensack 07606
Ex. V-P.—John Parente, 8 emp., *ADA & safety interior & exterior signs* .................... (201) 939-2120
C N R Products Co., 74 Portland Ave., Bergenfield 07621
Owner & Sales Mgr.—Peter Rebsch, 5 emp., *Architectural commercial signs* .................... (201) 384-7003
CAD SIGNS, 169 Lodi St., Hackensack 07601
Pres.—Alex Galiano, 30 emp., *Signs, banners, vinyl letters & graphics* .................... (201) 267-0457
Carl Sign, LLC, 1200 Madison Ave., Paterson 07503
Owner—Jim Reilly, 2 emp., *Truck lettering & interior & exterior* .................... (973) 340-0210
Carpenter Emergency Lighting, Inc., 2 Marlen Dr., Hamilton 08691
Owner—Avinash C. Diwan, 30 emp., *Emergency lighting & exit signs* .................... (609) 689-3090
Casabona Signs, LLC, 37 Grove St., Passaic 07055
Owner—Daniel Casabona, 2 emp., *Custom signs* .................... (201) 325-8711
CBS Outdoor, 185 Highway 46, Fairfield 07004
V-P., East Reg.—George Gross, 60 emp., *Billboards & signs* .................... (973) 575-6900
CBS Outdoor, 1245 Towbin Ave., Lakewood 08701
Opers. Supv.—Bill Fredricks, 25 emp., *Advertising billboards* .................... (732) 901-1100
Central Art & Engineering, Inc., 500 Goldman Dr., P.O. Box 289, Cream Ridge 08514
Pres., Hum. Res. Mgr.—John Makkay, 8 emp., *Custom plastic fabrication & cutting* .................... (609) 758-5922
Cheshire Studio, Inc., 261 Main St., 2nd Fl., Ledgewood 07852
Pres.—Jack Hurdes, 2 emp., *Commercial printing, advertising specialties* .................... (973) 240-7360
Choice Signs, 3407 Rose Ave., Ste. 3, Ocean 07712
V-P., Opers.—Daniel Kowalski, 3 emp., *ADA braille, vinyl & magnetic interior* .................... (732) 493-1644
Classic Marking Products, Inc., 10 Millpond Dr., Unit 9, Lafayette 07848
Pres.—Fred Thornton, Sr., 9 emp., *Rubber stamps, markers, signs & promotional* .................... (973) 383-2223
Classic Signs, 3651 S. Clinton, South Plainfield 07080
Owner—John Mazzeo, 2 emp., *Neon & vinyl interior & exterior signs* .................... (908) 668-8248
Color Optics By Arcade, Inc., 40 Green Pond Rd., Rockaway 07866
CEO—Joe Cicci, 58 emp., *Paperboard & visual packaging & commercial* .................... (973) 664-3100
Colorcraft Sign Co., 400 Magnolia St., Beverly 08010
Owner—Steve Molnar, 8 emp., *Full-color graphics, vinyl, vehicle* .................... (609) 386-1115
Colorcraft, Inc., 1506 Beaver Dam Rd., Point Pleasant Boro 08742
Owner & Pres.—Leonard W. Thomas, 4 emp., *Banners, signs, decals & posters* .................... (732) 892-6639
Coloredge, 190 Jony Dr., Carlstadt 07072
Dir.—Tony Chester, 50 emp., *Large-format printing & visual displays* .................... (201) 716-5200
Commerce Sign Solutions, LLC, 540 Cranbury Rd., Ste. 334, East Brunswick 08816
Owner—Linda Harrington, 1 emp., *ADA & architectural signs, banners,* .................... (732) 238-7000
Compass Signs, LLC, 1 Market Yard, Freehold 07728
Owner—Jeff Cherchia, 4 emp., *Trade show & fleet graphics, interior* .................... (732) 294-7977
Concept Printing, Inc., 160 Woodbine St., Ste. 2, Bergenfield 07621
Pres.—Kerry Monahan-Gaughan, 6 emp., *Offset & screen printing, embroidery* .................... (201) 387-6000
Copyshop Office Supply & Repro Center, 921 U.S. Highway 9, South Amboy 08879
Owner—Scott Restiano, Jr., 3 emp., *Full-service, digital & large-format* .................... (732) 721-5700
COTE-L Industries, Inc., 1542 Jefferson St., Teaneck 07666
CEO—Avi Aviner, 6 emp., *Safety, polyurethane, epoxy, waterproofing* .................... (201) 836-0733
Creating Your Design, LLC, 45 Wood St., Paterson 07524
Owner—David Batiz, 10 emp., *Trade show exhibits, commercial & retail* .................... (973) 357-1080
Creative Design Plus, 1634 E. Elizabeth Ave., Linden 07036
GM—Ping Larrabee, 8 emp., *Commercial printing, advertising specialties* .................... (732) 287-3336
Crown Products, Inc., 1302 Roller Rd., Ocean 07712
Pres., GM—Joseph Tagliareni, 25 emp., *Promotional golf accessories* .................... (732) 493-0022
Crown Trophy-River Edge, NJ, 488 Kinderkamack Rd., River Edge 07661
Owner—Chuck Hedbavny, 5 emp., *Awards, rotary & laser engraving, crystal* .................... (201) 261-3933
Csonka Cigar Requisites, Inc. (H Q), 407 Blue Spring Rd., Princeton 08540
Pres., CEO—Michael Chunko, 40 emp., *Corporate headquarters; custom promotional* .................... (609) 514-2766
Cueva's Signs, 853 Bayway Cir., Elizabeth 07201
Owner—Jose Miguel Cueva, 2 emp., *Vinyl lettered signs* .................... (908) 820-5744
Curtis Sign Design, 640 Herman Rd., Ste. 1, Jackson 08527
Pres.—Ed Kronenthal, 2 emp., *Nonelectric signs* .................... (732) 928-9494
Custom Lettering, 3031 Belvidere Rd., Phillipsburg 08865
Owner—Al Pisani, 1 emp., *Vinyl, plastic & wooden interior &* .................... (908) 454-4140
D and S Designs, P.O. Box 1707, Bridgeton 08302
Owner—Sandra L. Rodriguez, 2 emp., *Custom screen printing & embroidery* .................... (856) 451-0954
D P J Signs, 245 E. Inman Ave., Rahway 07065
Pres.—Derrick Dehoyo, 4 emp., *Interior & exterior signs* .................... (732) 499-8600
Danor Signs, LLC, 47 Central Ave., Passaic 07055
Pres.—Daniel Ovido, 1 emp., *Neon, interior & exterior signs* .................... (973) 471-2897
Datascan Graphics, Inc., 55 Madison Ave., Ste. 400, Morristown 07960
★ Pres.—Roy House, 25 emp., *Point-of-purchase displays* .................... (973) 543-4800
Davis Sign Systems, 65 Harrison St., Boonton 07005
Pres.—Elaine Davis, 3 emp., *Signs* .................... (973) 394-9909
DCI Signs & Awnings, Inc., 110 Riverside Ave., Newark 07104
Pres.—Danny Castillo, 25 emp., *Interior & exterior signs & custom* .................... (973) 350-0400
Deborah Sales, LLC, 109 Meeker Ave., Newark 07114
Pres.—Jacira Rei, 2 emp., *Metal imprinting, advertising specialties* .................... (973) 344-8466
Del Sol Signs, 119 New Jersey Railroad Ave., Newark 07105
Owner—Jose DelSol, 2 emp., *Interior & exterior signs & vinyl lettering* .................... (973) 589-8655
Delcrest Sign Co., Inc., 1202 Haddonfield-Berlin Rd., Ste. 1, Voorhees 08043
Owner—Willy Johnson, 4 emp., *Vinyl & neon signs* .................... (856) 768-5552
D'Elia Sign Co., 32 W. Fort Lee Rd., Bogota 07603
Owner—Nicholas D'Elia, 2 emp., *Interior & exterior signs* .................... (201) 342-7231
Design A Sign, Inc., 745 Lehigh Ave., Ste. 3, Union 07083
Owner & Pres.—William T. Meehan, Jr., 1 emp., *Development, neon, carved gold leaf* .................... (908) 656-0822
Design Display Group, Inc., 105 Amor Ave., Carlstadt 07072
Pres., CEO—Andrew Freedman, 150 emp., *Custom point-of-purchase displays &* .................... (201) 438-6000

Design Production, Inc., 9 Industrial Pk., Waldwick 07463
Pres.—Thomas Murphy, 25 emp., *Point-of-purchase displays* .................... (201) 447-5656
Designer Sign Systems, LLC, 352 Washington Ave., Carlstadt 07072
Ptnr.—Danijel Farkas, 11 emp., *Healthcare, educational, corporate,* .................... (201) 939-5577
Designs By James, 892 N. Delsea Dr., Vineland 08360
Pres.—James Crescenzo, 3 emp., *Interior & exterior signs, screen printing* .................... (856) 692-1316
Detail Model & Machine, 61 Woodstown Rd., Mullica Hill 08062
Owner—David Rose, 4 emp., *Training & trade show models & trade* .................... (856) 223-0184
Dialogic, Inc. (H Q), 4 Gatehall Dr., Parsippany 07054
★ Pres., CEO—Kevin Cook, 100 emp., *Corporate headquarters; telecommunications* .................... (800) 755-4444
Digital Arts Imaging, LLC, 105 State Route 31, Ste. 10, Flemington 08822
Pres.—Robert Vernon, 5 emp., *Digital printing of signages, banners* .................... (908) 237-4646
DMR Sign Systems, 215 State Route 10, Ste. 1-A, Randolph 07869
Pres.—Andrew Tunkel, 4 emp., *Interior signs for the healthcare industry* .................... (973) 361-1829
Dohrman Printing Co., Inc., 445 Industrial Rd., Carlstadt 07072
Pres., Fin., MIS & R & D Mgr.—Kenny Bell, 6 emp., *Commercial offset 1-6 color, digital* .................... (201) 933-0346
Dover Signs Mfg. & Graphics, Inc., 1471 Sussex Tpke., Randolph 07869
Pres.—Nanette Holder, 3 emp., *Interior & exterior vinyl signs* .................... (973) 366-2229
East Trading West Investments LLC, 200 S. Jefferson St., Orange 07050
Owner, Pres. & CFO—M. G. Khaleeli, 6 emp., *Fabricated regulatory, warning, construction* .. (973) 678-0800
Eastern Sign Co., 3011 Ocean Heights Ave., Ste. B, Egg Harbor Township 08234
Ptnr.—Michael Franklin, 5 emp., *Interior & exterior signs & banners* .................... (609) 927-0885
Eastern Sign Tech, LLC, 112 Connecticut Dr., P.O. Box 564, Burlington 08016
Pres.—John Dunphy, 40 emp., *Architectural signage & LED displays* .................... (609) 261-2805
East-West Service Co., Inc., 2 Marlen Dr., Hamilton 08691
Owner—Avinash C. Diwan, 17 emp., *Exit signs, emergency lights & power* .................... (609) 631-9000
Educational Information & Resource Center, 107 Gilbreth Pkwy., Mullica Hill 08062
Ex. Dir.—Charles Ivory, 70 emp., *Vinyl lettering & education-related* .................... (856) 582-7000
Empire Designs, Inc., 7 Main St., Englishtown 07726
Pres.—Kathleen T. Bien, 1 emp., *Embroidery, screen printing, promotional* .................... (732) 446-6447
Empro Products Co., Inc., 47 Montgomery St., Belleville 07109
Pres.—Darsh Mehta, 10 emp., *Interior & exterior signs* .................... (973) 279-1010
Exhibit Co., Inc., The, 239 Old New Brunswick Rd., Piscataway 08854
Pres.—Frank Geraci, 25 emp., *Custom & portable trade show exhibits* .................... (732) 465-1070
ExhibitCraft, Inc., 22 Riverview Dr., Ste. 103, Wayne 07470
Pres.—Scott Walode, 15 emp., *Customized trade show exhibits, show* .................... (973) 686-9393
Express Tag & Label Co., 52 N. Main St., Marlboro 07746
Owner—Gerald Tomaselli, 4 emp., *Printed labels & tags, postcards &* .................... (718) 965-1400
F & M Expressions Unlimited, 211 Island Rd., Mahwah 07430
Pres., CEO—Frank Flanagan, 100 emp., *Heat transfer & decal printing* .................... (201) 512-3338
Fantastic Signs Co., 351 Shrewsbury Ave., Red Bank 07701
Pres.—John Oakley, 2 emp., *Interior & exterior vinyl signs* .................... (732) 747-7763
FASTSIGNS®, 485 Route 1 S., Crossroads Plz., Edison 08817
Owner—Sharad Patel, 2 emp., *Interior & exterior signs* .................... (732) 985-1166
FASTSIGNS®, 906 Greentree Sq., Route 73 N., Marlton 08053
Pres.—Kevin Rose, 8 emp., *Interior & exterior signs* .................... (856) 985-8730
FASTSIGNS®, 407 Sette Dr., Paramus 07652
Owner—Glenn Lanzl, 3 emp., *Interior & exterior signs* .................... (201) 587-8444
FASTSIGNS®, 105 Sherman Ave., Raritan 08869
Owner—Tony DiRoma, 3 emp., *Wood & metal interior & exterior signs* .................... (908) 231-0306
FASTSIGNS®, 255 State Route 3, Secaucus 07094
Pres.—Elizabeth Selbach, 7 emp., *Yard, interior & exterior signs, banners* .................... (201) 902-8640
FASTSIGNS®, 2290 Route 22 E., Union 07083
Pres., Fin. & R & D Mgr.—Mark Favaloro, 20 emp., *Interior & exterior neon & vinyl signs* .................... (908) 810-1400
FedEx Office & Print Center, 1 Quality Way, Iselin 08830
Off. Mgr.—Kathleen Murray, 4 emp., *Commercial & instant printing, signs* .................... (732) 636-3580
Fiber Optic Systems, Inc., P.O. Box 62, Whitehouse Station 08889
Pres.—Cyr A. Ryan, 6 emp., *Fiber-optic displays, exhibits & advertising* .................... (908) 534-5500
Finas Finishing, Inc., 50 Stacy Haines Rd., Lumberton 08048
Pres.—John Fina, 8 emp., *Metal & plastic screen printing, industrial* .................... (609) 267-4836
Forrest Signs, 281 Greenwood Ave., Midland Park 07432
Owner—Norman Forrest, 1 emp., *Interior & exterior signs* .................... (201) 670-7760
Franklin Stamp & Sign Co., 543 Somerset St., Ste. 1, Somerset 08873
Co-Pres.—Harry Weber, Jr., 3 emp., *Rubber stamps, vinyl, plastic, color* .................... (732) 846-9235
Freedom Glass & Metal, Inc., 4 White Horse Pike, P.O. Box 868, Clementon 08021
Owner—Karen Arsenault, 20 emp., *Aluminum windows & storefronts* .................... (856) 627-3946
Future Signs, 19 Bowhill Ave., Trenton 08610
Pres.—Rich Rutzler, 5 emp., *Electric & nonelectric signs* .................... (609) 695-6263
G & G Signs, Inc., 323 2nd Ave., Lyndhurst 07071
Pres.—Joe Garofalo, 2 emp., *Interior & exterior signs* .................... (201) 939-4099
Gail's Lettering & Design, 24 Beaver Ave., Annandale 08801
Pres.—Gail Kugelman, 2 emp., *Interior & exterior signs & truck lettering* .................... (908) 735-4628
Garden State Highway Products, Inc., 1740 E. Oak Rd., Vineland 08361
Pres.—Sharon Green, 48 emp., *Manufacturer of traffic, street, specialty* .................... (856) 692-7572
Garden State Sign Co., 4880 U.S. Highway 9, Howell 07731
Pres.—Joseph E. Ervin, 7 emp., *Interior & exterior signs, electronic* .................... (732) 363-7645
General Sign Co., Inc., 105 Chestnut Ave., West Berlin 08091
Pres.—Steve Brocco, 6 emp., *Interior & exterior signs* .................... (856) 753-3535
Girtain Sign Co., 1765 Route 9, Toms River 08755
Ptnr.—Andy Girtain, 20 emp., *Interior & exterior signs* .................... (732) 349-8499
Gotham Group, The, 202 W. Parkway Dr., Ste. 2, Egg Harbor Township 08234
Pres.—Qiang Wang, 16 emp., *Large-format digital displays, specialty* .................... (609) 645-2211
Gough Engraving & Advertising Specialties, 1745 N. Olden Avenue Ext., Ewing 08638
Owner—Kathleen Gough, 4 emp., *Brass & plastic engraving, award plaques* .................... (609) 882-8700
Grand Displays, Inc., 12 Empire Blvd., Moonachie 07074
Pres.—Susan Ostreicher, 60 emp., *Paper die cutting & displays* .................... (201) 994-1500
Graphic Image, Inc., 445 Route 46, Hackettstown 07840
Pres.—Claudia Ehrgott, 4 emp., *Commercial printing, signs, posters* .................... (908) 852-7007
Graphic Marketing Group, 7 Kingsbridge Rd., Ste. 2, Fairfield 07004
Pres.—David Greene, 2 emp., *Commercial printing & vehicle wraps* .................... (973) 276-7901
Graphic Presentation Systems, Inc., 262 Old New Brunswick Rd., Ste. F, Piscataway 08854
Pres., Treas.—Kevin J. Keizer, 15 emp., *Trade show displays* .................... (732) 981-1120
Graphic Solutions & Signs, LLC, 82 Burlews Ct., Hackensack 07601
★ Member—Felipe Alarcon, 18 emp., *Interior & exterior signs & vinyl lettering* .................... (201) 343-7446
Graphix One, LLC, 725 Lincoln Blvd., Middlesex 08846
Ptnr.—Jeff Yingling, 3 emp., *Commercial, screen & offset printing* .................... (732) 560-4700
Gregory Signs, LLC, 1453 Springfield Ave., P.O. Box 671, Maplewood 07040
Ptnr.—Gregory Rabinovich, 2 emp., *Interior & exterior signs* .................... (973) 761-0165
Griffin Sign Co., Inc., 464 N. Randolph Ave., Cinnaminson 08077
Pres.—Michelle Angerame, 50 emp., *Traffic highway signage* .................... (856) 786-8517
GTM Signs, Inc., 1298 Hurffville Rd., Deptford 08096
Ptnr.—Karl Baker, 8 emp., *Signs & canvas & standing seam awnings* .................... (856) 227-2333

S.I.C.

**★ Indicates new listing this edition.**

Hank's Signs, 793 Jersey Pl., Paramus 07652
Owner—Hank Emr, 2 emp., *Interior & exterior signs* .......... (201) 652-5979
Hathaway Plastics, Inc., 911 Springfield Rd., Union 07083
Pres.—Robert Daniel, 3 emp., *Plastic molded point-of-purchase displays* .......... (908) 688-9494
Hawk Graphics, Inc., 1248 Sussex Tpke., Ste. C-9, Randolph 07869
Pres.—Nick Battaglino, 20 emp., *Commercial offset, digital color &* .......... (973) 895-5569
HE Designs & Awnings, 75 Rutgers St., Belleville 07109
Pres.—Kevin Horan, 4 emp., *Signs, vehicle graphics & banners* .......... (973) 751-0030
Hero's Salute Awards Co., 1875 State Route 23, Wayne 07470
Pres.—Robert Terry, 10 emp., *Awards, trophies, signs, banners, flags* .......... (973) 696-5085
Hillman Graphic Products, P.O. Box 5233, Somerset 08875
Owner—Marty Hillman, 4 emp., *Commercial offset & digital printing* .......... (201) 487-6900
Holding Sign Design, E. R., 2 N. Black Horse Pike, Blackwood 08012
Owner—Roxanne Holding, 2 emp., *Interior & exterior signs* .......... (856) 227-1570
Horizon Sign Co., 340 Patterson Ave., Ste. C, Hamilton 08610
Owner—Thomas R. Barbieri, 1 emp., *Illuminated interior & exterior signs* .......... (609) 586-0041
House Printing, LLC, 311 Kearny Ave., Kearny 07032
★ Owner—Juan Calva, 1 emp., *T-shirt screen printing & embroidery* .......... (201) 772-5988
Hoyt Signs, 2825 Belvidere Rd., Phillipsburg 08865
Owner & Pres.—Scott Hoyt, 1 emp., *Interior & exterior signs* .......... (908) 859-3768
Hub Sign Crane Corp., 67 Wood Ave., Englishtown 07726
Principal—Chris Barber, 5 emp., *Neon & vinyl signs* .......... (732) 252-9090
Hudson Awning & Sign Co., Inc., 27 Cottage St., Bayonne 07002
Pres.—Edward Burak, 35 emp., *Lightweight fabric & membrane structures* .......... (201) 339-7171
Hurricane Signs, 103 Main St., Bloomingdale 07403
Owner—Ronald Kelemen, 3 emp., *Metal, acrylic & magnetic business* .......... (973) 838-3373
Hygrade Business Group, Inc., 232 Entin Rd., P.O. Box 1099, Clifton 07014
Pres., CEO—Victor Albetta, 40 emp., *Offset, digital & color printing of* .......... (973) 249-6700
Iken Media, LLC, 70 Triangle Blvd., Carlstadt 07072
★ Owner—David Eichen, 5 emp., *Commercial printing & interior & exterior* .......... (201) 372-0800
Image Makers Printing, Copy & Sign Center, 1581 State Route 23, Wayne 07470
Pres.—Gino Nuzzo, 5 emp., *High-speed color printing, blueprinting* .......... (973) 633-1771
Image Signs and More, LLC, 2906 N. Centre St., Pennsauken 08109
Owner—Boris Rubin, 2 emp., *Vehicle lettering & graphics & custom* .......... (856) 665-1890
Impact Displays Group, LLC, 310 13th St., Carlstadt 07072
★ CEO—Gill Horowitz, 32 emp., *Point-of-purchase displays* .......... (212) 842-1800
Impressive Printing, Inc., 313 10th St., Carlstadt 07072
Pres.—Robert Egan, 2 emp., *Commercial, full-color & large-format* .......... (201) 933-1650
Infinite Manufacturing Group, Inc., 171 Coit St., Irvington 07111
Founder & CEO—Bernard Alloysius, 20 emp., *Indoor & outdoor architectural signage* .......... (973) 649-9950
INKit Design N' Print LLC, 644 Cross St., Unit 2, Lakewood 08701
Pres.—Aaron Dembinsky, 6 emp., *Interior & exterior signs & banners* .......... (732) 363-8098
Insign, Inc., 1937 Olney Ave., Cherry Hill 08003
Pres.—Samuel Miner, 30 emp., *Vinyl signs* .......... (856) 424-1161
J K A Specialties Mfg., Inc., 157 Eayrestown Rd., Southampton 08088
Pres.—James Young, 5 emp., *Printing of buttons, vinyl decals,* .......... (609) 859-2090
J T Graphics, 34 Mt. Ephraim Ave., Mount Ephraim 08059
Owner & GM—John Thompson, 1 emp., *Interior & exterior signs & lettering* .......... (856) 931-3548
Jarco U. S. Casting Corp., 109 45th St., Union City 07087
Pres.—Mario A. Herrera, 35 emp., *Cast metal emblems & advertising specialties* .......... (201) 271-0003
JB Signs, 23 Dorchester Dr., P.O. Box 454, East Brunswick 08816
Owner—Leigh Baumann, 1 emp., *Signs, magnets, banners & window, boat* .......... (732) 613-3700
JD Graphics, Inc., 6 Richardson Ct., Marlboro 07746
Pres., Fin. & MIS Mgr.—Jay Davis, 3 emp., *Interior & exterior signs* .......... (732) 972-7790
Jefferson Printing Service, 184 Jefferson St., Newark 07105
★ Pres.—Julio DePaula, 10 emp., *Commercial printing, signage & vehicle* .......... (973) 491-0019
Jencks Signs Corp., 50 Division Ave., Ste. 14, Millington 07946
Pres.—Barry Herman Jencks, 5 emp., *Interior & exterior signs* .......... (908) 542-1400
JerseyCarts, LLC, 6 Whiskey Ln., Flemington 08822
Owner—Greg Merrigan, 1 emp., *Golf carts, vinyl banners & signs* .......... (908) 806-6400
Jim's Signs, 1400 Rahway Ave., Ste. 3, Avenel 07001
Owner & Pres.—Jim Petrocy, 10 emp., *Plastic & reflective safety, ADA, room* .......... (732) 381-8700
K & J Accessories, Inc., 25 Ridgewood Rd., Clifton 07012
Pres.—Karen Dicky, 2 emp., *Electric scoreboards* .......... (973) 777-6741
Kevin's Sign Co., 1212 Bridgeboro Rd., Edgewater Park 08010
Owner—Kevin Liebner, 1 emp., *Interior & exterior signs* .......... (609) 871-2385
Keystone Printing, Inc., 21-C E. Madison Ave., Dumont 07628
Pres.—Janice Worner, 4 emp., *Digital offset printing, typesetting* .......... (201) 387-7252
KNA Graphics, Inc., 303 N. 14th St., Kenilworth 07033
Pres.—Kamal Assad, 6 emp., *Wide-format digital printing, light* .......... (908) 272-4232
Kraftwork Custom Design, 1837 S. Broad St., Hamilton 08610
Owner—Michael K. Sylvester, 4 emp., *Dimensional, carved, gold, neon, channel* .......... (609) 848-0578
L & M Architectural Graphics, Inc., 20 Montesano Rd., Fairfield 07004
Pres.—Justin Lorenzo, 15 emp., *Interior & exterior signs & environmental* .......... (973) 575-7665
L J Engraving & Signs, 409 N. Wood Ave., P.O. Box 1039, Linden 07036
Owner—Leonard Neuringer, 3 emp., *Interior & exterior signs, engraving* .......... (908) 925-3510
Lane Signs, 34 Central Ave., Toms River 08753
GM—John Lane, 1 emp., *Vinyl signs* .......... (732) 349-1904
Library Automation Technologies, 2 E. Atlantic Ave., Somerdale 08083
CEO—Oleg Boyarsky, 15 emp., *Library patron self-check-in & self-checkout* .......... (856) 566-4121
Life A Stitch, 37 Jackson Ave., Carteret 07008
★ Owner—Ray Malivuk, 2 emp., *Embroidery, t-shirt screen printing* .......... (732) 969-0232
Lincoln Signs & Awnings, Inc., 895 Estate St., Perth Amboy 08861
Pres.—Julio Hernandez, 9 emp., *Interior & exterior signs & awnings* .......... (732) 442-3151
Lines & Letters DESIGNS, 1386 Mount Vernon Rd., Bridgewater 08807
Owner & Pres.—Brian Schofield, 2 emp., *Interior & exterior signs* .......... (732) 563-0909
Lobello Arts Corp., 50 Route 10 W., East Hanover 07936
Owner & Manager—Matt Lobello, 5 emp., *Interior & exterior signs* .......... (973) 887-6700
Lordon, Inc., 453 Route 46, Ste. 1-A, Hackettstown 07840
Pres.—Donna Quagliana, 5 emp., *Reflective traffic sign panels & strips* .......... (908) 813-1143
LouMarc Signs, 178 Route 206, Hillsborough 08844
Pres.—Larry Gliozzi, 6 emp., *Interior & exterior signs, including* .......... (908) 575-4000
Loveline Industries, Inc., 90 Dayton Ave., Ste. 33, Passaic 07055
Pres.—Morton Goldstein, 15 emp., *Hi-visibility safety clothing, including* .......... (973) 928-3427
Lynch Exhibits, 7 Campus Dr., Burlington 08016
Pres.—Michael Carrozza, 110 emp., *Trade show displays* .......... (609) 387-1600
Mackey's Print Xpress, 1107 7th Ave., Neptune 07753
Owner & Pres.—Ron Mackey, 3 emp., *Single, multicolor offset & digital* .......... (732) 775-1730
Madison Line, The, 40 Commerce St., Springfield 07081
Pres., CEO—Sheamus O'Brien, 10 emp., *Manufacturer & distributor of promotional* .......... (973) 379-1108
Mag Signs, Inc., 1208-F Columbus Rd., Burlington 08016
★ Owner—Bob Persichetti, 12 emp., *Interior & exterior signs & welding* .......... (609) 747-9600
Majestic Signs, 951 Teaneck Rd., Teaneck 07666
Owner—Robert Hamburg, 2 emp., *Interior & exterior neon, vinyl & plastic* .......... (201) 837-8104
Manhattan Signs, Inc., 130 Beckwith Ave., Paterson 07503
CEO—Anthony Decrescenzo, 13 emp., *Interior & exterior signs, including* .......... (973) 278-3603
Mantua Sign & Lighting, 550 Bridgeton Pike, Ste. 5, Mantua 08051
★ Owner—Jay Glaser, 3 emp., *Interior & exterior signs, channel* .......... (856) 415-0022
Mark-O-Lite Sign Co., 1420 U.S. Highway 9, Howell 07731
Pres., Sales Mgr.—Howard Mark, 5 emp., *Interior & exterior signs* .......... (732) 462-8530
Mashal Signs Co., Inc., 568 55th St., West New York 07093
Owner & CEO—Alai Mashal, 6 emp., *Custom signs & awnings* .......... (201) 348-8500
Master Printing Co., P.O. Box 9609, Elizabeth 07202
Pres.—Bill DePaolo, 3 emp., *Offset printing, graphics & copywriting* .......... (908) 351-1568
Matthews Engravers, Edward R., 61 S. State St., Hackensack 07601
Owner & Engraver—Nick Lontemuro, 1 emp., *Engraved interior & exterior signs* .......... (201) 342-4644
MC Signs, 231 West Ave., Ocean City 08226
Owner—Mark Crego, 10 emp., *Interior & exterior signs & vinyl lettering* .......... (609) 399-7446
McLain Studios, Inc., 1203 Main St., Asbury Park 07712
Pres.—Jim McLain, 2 emp., *Yard, political campaign, real estate* .......... (732) 775-0271
Meadowlands Signs, 58 State Route 17, Hasbrouck Heights 07604
★ Owner—Jose Fuentes, 4 emp., *Interior & exterior signs & canvas* .......... (201) 426-0420
Mega Media Concepts Ltd., 286 Houses Corner Rd., Sparta 07871
Pres.—Amy Pink, 4 emp., *Large-format digital eco-friendly printing* .......... (973) 919-5661
Merchant Street Printer, LLC, 107 E. Atlantic Ave., Audubon 08106
Owner—Charlotte Skeggs, 4 emp., *Offset printing & advertising specialties* .......... (856) 547-1991
Merit Trophies & Engraving, Inc., 184 Main St., Hackensack 07601
V-P., GM—Jim Dolack, 5 emp., *Laser engraving of signs, plaques,* .......... (201) 487-5780
Metaline Products Co., Inc., 101 N. Feltus St. & 241 Raritan St., South Amboy 08879
Chrm. & CEO—August J. Zilincar III, 35 emp., *Custom metal point-of-purchase displays* .......... (732) 721-1373
Metro Signs, 410 Downs Dr., P.O. Box 865, Cherry Hill 08003
Owner—Richard Lees, 3 emp., *Signs* .......... (856) 428-9050
Michael's Commercial Signs, 629 62nd St., Ste. 31, West New York 07093
Mng. Ptnr. & Pres.—Ruben Gonzalez, 4 emp., *Interior & exterior signs, bus & truck* .......... (201) 868-7166
Minuteman Press, 1 Trenton Ave., Clifton 07011
Principal—Joseph Mulligan, 18 emp., *Offset & digital printing, promotional* .......... (973) 894-1500
Minuteman Press, 23-51 Fair Lawn Ave., Fair Lawn 07410
Pres., CEO—Mitch Palin, 4 emp., *Full-color & instant printing & graphic* .......... (201) 791-0550
Minuteman Press, 19 Sheridan Ave., Ho-Ho-Kus 07423
Member—Suzanne Seise, 3 emp., *Digital, offset & high-speed printing* .......... (201) 444-0236
Minuteman Press Of Dover, 25 Pine St., Ste. 10, Rockaway 07866
Pres., R & D Mgr.—Andy Krauser, 2 emp., *Offset & digital & color instant printing* .......... (973) 625-5800
Minuteman Press of Livingston, LLC, 47 E. Northfield Rd., Livingston 07039
Pres.—Bhuman Patel, 2 emp., *Instant printing, signs, banners &* .......... (973) 992-3136
Minuteman Press, Inc./Windsor Graphics, 2100 Nottingham Way, Hamilton 08619
Owner—Anthony Loffredo, 4 emp., *Offset, screen & digital color printing* .......... (609) 586-3838
MJ Corporate Sales, Inc., 109 W. Park Dr., Unit B, Mount Laurel 08054
★ Owner—John Dikmak, 25 emp., *Apparel screen printing & embroidery* .......... (856) 778-0055
MJG Screen Printing & Embroidery, 24 Commerce Rd., Ste. K, Fairfield 07004
Owner—Michael Garamella, 4 emp., *T-shirt screen printing & embroidery* .......... (973) 575-8877
Morris Forms Corp., 5 Saddle Rd., Cedar Knolls 07927
Pres.—Carl Badenhausen, 5 emp., *Color, offset & digital printing of* .......... (973) 829-1200
Morris Sign Co., 30 Troy Rd., Whippany 07981
Pres.—Michael Hoehn, 9 emp., *Interior & exterior signs* .......... (973) 386-1755
Mr. J's Xcaliber Corp., 39 Dundee Ave., Paterson 07503
Ptnr.—Julian Braet, 3 emp., *Interior & exterior signs* .......... (973) 278-1611
Mr. Quick Sign, 30 Dairy St., Midland Park 07432
Pres.—Trena Greenfield, 3 emp., *Vinyl interior & exterior signs* .......... (201) 670-1690
Mr. Sign, Inc., 319 Bound Brook Rd., Middlesex 08846
Pres.—Ron Gengoult, 3 emp., *Interior & exterior signs* .......... (732) 560-0606
Nassau Communications, Inc., 115 N. Gold Dr., Robbinsville 08691
Pres.—Ken Fisher, 7 emp., *Commercial & digital printing & promotional* .......... (908) 625-8512
NEMA Associates, Inc., 57 Bruen St., Newark 07105
Pres., CEO—Juan Carlos Lopez, 14 emp., *Full-service digital, large-format,* .......... (973) 274-0052
Nemec Sign Co., 114 Route 31, Flemington 08822
Pres., GM—Bill Nemec, 1 emp., *Interior & exterior signs* .......... (908) 782-3175
Neverending Neon, 91 Dell Glen Ave., Lodi 07644
Owner & Pres.—Mark Provenzano, 1 emp., *Neon interior & exterior signs, LED* .......... (973) 772-4840
Newton Printing & Embroidery, 75 Main St., Franklin 07416
Owner—Frank Newton, 10 emp., *Promotional & corporate branding products* .......... (973) 827-2006
Newton Trophy & Sport Center, 1-3 Milk St., Bldg. 3, Branchville 07826
Pres.—Linda Moran, 5 emp., *Textile screen printing, embroidery* .......... (973) 948-0613
Next Day Signs & Banners, Inc., 300 Route 17, Paramus 07652
Pres.—Robert Ryan, 3 emp., *Interior & exterior vinyl signs* .......... (201) 986-1960
Nickel Artistic Services, LLC, 39 U.S. Highway 46, Rockaway 07866
Mng. Member—Bryan Nickel, 4 emp., *Interior & exterior signs & banners* .......... (973) 627-0390
Norco, Inc., 237 South Ave., P.O. Box 186, Garwood 07027
Pres.—Michael Rosenberg, 15 emp., *Lapel pins, dog tags, giant magnetic* .......... (908) 789-1550
Norman Dee Associates, 31 N. Sovereign Ave., Atlantic City 08401
Owner—Norman Dee Grossman, 2 emp., *Interior & exterior signs* .......... (609) 348-5777
Norman's Glass & Auto Services, Inc., 4482 Route 130 S., Burlington 08016
Pres.—John Farfalla, 10 emp., *Automotive, residential & commercial* .......... (609) 386-7100
Novel Box Co. Ltd., 825 Lehigh Ave., Union 07083
Owner & Pres.—Moishe Sternhill, 50 emp., *Manufacturer & distributor of jewelry* .......... (908) 686-7772
Nunn & Son Custom Lettering, 10 Harding Dr., Brick 08724
Pres.—James Nunn, 1 emp., *Interior & exterior signs, banners,* .......... (732) 899-9682
NW Sign Industries, Inc., 360 Crider Ave., Moorestown 08057
Chrm. & CEO—Ronald Brodie, 60 emp., *Corporate headquarters & interior &* .......... (856) 802-1677
O. Co Imprints, LLC, 58 W. Bergen Pl., P.O. Box 8249, Red Bank 07701
Owner—Olivia Conklin, 3 emp., *Screen printed & embroidered garments* .......... (732) 530-3202
Omega Specialty Products, LLC, 2511 Fire Rd., Ste. B-6, Egg Harbor Township 08234
V-P.—Walt Vayo, 9 emp., *Interior & exterior signage* .......... (609) 383-8835
One Stop Printing, LLC, 135 Kearny Ave., Ste. B, Kearny 07032
Owner—Darwin Yamuca, 2 emp., *Commercial printing, t-shirt screen* .......... (201) 991-3320
On-Line Sign, 2 Sheffield Rd., East Windsor 08520
Pres.—Bernard Lerner, 3 emp., *Interior & exterior signs & banners* .......... (609) 443-1704
Painton Studios, Inc., 299 U.S. Highway 22, Ste. 21, Green Brook 08812
Pres.—Lisa J. Secula, 3 emp., *4-color digital printing, signage,* .......... (732) 302-0200
Parker3d, 1325 Terrill Rd., Scotch Plains 07076
Pres.—Richard Parker, 100 emp., *Custom interactive & traditional holiday* .......... (908) 322-5552
Parrish Sign Co., Inc., 2242 S. Delsea Dr., Vineland 08360
Pres.—Charles Parrish, 9 emp., *Full color, digitally printed, lighted* .......... (856) 696-4040
Paterson Stamp Works, 1015 Paulison Ave., Clifton 07011
Pres.—John Collins, 17 emp., *Custom office & ID products, including* .......... (973) 478-5600

Pecata Enterprises, Inc., 18 Market St., Paterson 07501
Pres.—Roger Glickman, 80 emp., *Table linens & printed banners* ............ (973) 523-5866
Pendergast Signs, 566 Charlestown Rd., Hampton 08827
Pres.—Thomas Pendergast, 4 emp., *Carved, gold leafed, sandblasted &* ............ (908) 735-9295
Penn Jersey Weekend Directionals, 208 W. Clinton Ave., Oaklyn 08107
Owner—Ann Marie Bauman, 10 emp., *Signs, including weekend directional* ............ (856) 858-8888
Peoplevision, Inc., 311 E. 1st Ave., Bldg. A, Roselle 07203
Pres.—Wayne Sullivant, 5 emp., *Plastic museum exhibits* ............ (973) 509-2056
Peter J. Morley LLC, 21 Village Ct., Hazlet 07730
Pres.—Pete Morley, 3 emp., *Business printing & promotional products* ............ (732) 264-0010
Philadelphia Sign Co., 707 W. Spring Garden St., Palmyra 08065
Pres.—Bob Mehmet, 300 emp., *Signs & vinyl lettering* ............ (856) 829-1460
Phil's Sign Shop, 55 Cutters Dock Rd., Woodbridge 07095
Owner—Peter Starlin, 2 emp., *Wooden, plastic & aluminum interior* ............ (732) 726-1555
Photo Art Stencil & Sign Corp., 701 17th Ave., P.O. Box 127, Lake Como 07719
Pres.—Frederick J. Tanis, 2 emp., *Industrial & yard signs & screen printing* ............ (732) 681-7300
Precision Sign Works, LLC, 82 Richter Rd., Tabernacle 08088
Owner—Victor Gorin, 3 emp., *Exterior, carved, site & yard signs* ............ (609) 702-9700
Pride Products Distributors, LLC, 673 Morris Ave., Ste. 2, Springfield 07081
Pres., CEO—Andrew Nadel, 7 emp., *Promotional product printing* ............ (973) 564-6300
Princeton Printer, 150 Nassau St., Princeton 08542
CEO—Bill Howard, 6 emp., *Digital, instant & large-format color* ............ (609) 924-4630
Print Group, Inc., The, 24 E. Wesley St., South Hackensack 07606
Ptnr.—Martin Bender, 15 emp., *Digital & offset commercial printing* ............ (201) 487-4400
Print Tech Ltd., 49 Fadem Rd., Springfield 07081
Ptnr.—Russell Evans, 35 emp., *Company headquarters & digital printing* ............ (908) 232-2287
Printing & Signs Express, Inc., 634 Wyckoff Ave., Mahwah 07430
Pres.—Joe Busto, 4 emp., *Interior & exterior signs* ............ (201) 368-1255
Printmasters, 1108 Goffle Rd., Hawthorne 07506
Pres.—Paula Cornett, 4 emp., *Business printing, graphics & design* ............ (973) 427-6598
Pro Signs, 296 S. Main St., Phillipsburg 08865
Pres.—Frank Geraghty, 3 emp., *Interior & exterior signs* ............ (908) 454-4888
Proforma Unlimited Marketing Expressions, 36 Keswick Ave., Ewing 08638
Ptnr.—Susan Barosko, 3 emp., *Commercial printing, stationery & promotional* ............ (609) 882-0112
Project Sign, 282 Irvington Rd., South Orange 07079
Pres., MIS Mgr.—Larry Aufiero, 3 emp., *Interior & exterior signs* ............ (973) 763-1959
Props, Displays & Interiors, Inc., 45 Glenwood Pl., East Orange 07017
Pres., GM—Stephen Sebbane, 10 emp., *Retail displays, cabinets & woodworking* ............ (862) 704-6463
Pyramid Imprints, 28 N. Washington Ave., Bergenfield 07621
Owner—Eleanor Garcia, 2 emp., *Commercial screen printing, textile* ............ (201) 384-0336
Quality Concepts, Inc., 730 Marne Hwy., Moorestown 08057
Ptnr. & V-P., Sales & Mktg.—Michael Santori, 15 emp., *Commercial printing & promotional items* (856) 235-0909
Quality Printing, 1181 E. Landis Ave., Ste. 3, Vineland 08360
Ptnr.—Jerry Dondero, 2 emp., *Printing, advertising specialty products* ............ (856) 691-7577
R. B.'s Rubber Stamp, Inc., 551 W. Side Ave., Jersey City 07304
Pres.—Leila Bahadur, 2 emp., *Rubber stamps, marking devices, signs* ............ (201) 547-9955
Rand Diversified, 3 Ethel Rd., Ste. 301, Edison 08817
Chrm.—Jack Wuensch, 40 emp., *Company headquarters & point-of-purchase* ............ (732) 287-2525
Raritan Valley Printing Co., 7 Sheephill Cir., Branchburg 08876
Ptnr. & Pres.—Arthur E. Fritz, 3 emp., *Commercial printing, signs & banners* ............ (908) 725-4140
Ray's Reproductions, Inc., 39 Bland St., Emerson 07630
Pres.—Ray Stuart, 5 emp., *Digital, offset, large-format & instant* ............ (201) 666-5650
Red Feather Marketing Group, 332 Main St., Madison 07940
Ptnr.—Steve Becker, 7 emp., *Advertising specialties, including* ............ (973) 966-1399
Regn Sign Studio, Inc., 42 Main St., Bradley Beach 07720
Pres., CEO—Lori Regn, 3 emp., *Interior & exterior signs* ............ (732) 988-3595
Rem Services, 310 W. 6th St., Ship Bottom 08008
Owner—Robert Mattner, 1 emp., *Name tags, trophies, small signs &* ............ (609) 494-7760
Rex Sign Co., 60 Steiner Ave., Neptune City 07753
Pres.—Jacqueline Janocha, 8 emp., *Signs* ............ (732) 774-1377
Riedel Sign Co., Inc., 15 Warren St., Little Ferry 07643
Pres.—William C. Riedel, 5 emp., *Interior & exterior signs, vehicle* ............ (201) 641-9121
Riverside Prints LLC, 11 Lawrence Cir., Middletown 07748
Pres., CEO—Howard Kirschner, 2 emp., *Large-format digital & offset printing* ............ (732) 671-8222
Rose Signs, 13 Route 206 S., Branchville 07826
Owner—Rosemarie Devries, 2 emp., *Interior & exterior signs* ............ (973) 948-0501
Royce Signworks, Inc., 226 DeSoto Pl., Cliffside Park 07010
Pres.—Richard Curasco, 1 emp., *Interior & exterior signs, truck lettering* ............ (201) 945-5536
Rozano Signs, 1005 County Road 523, Flemington 08822
Owner—Paul Rozano, 2 emp., *Vinyl & hand lettered signs* ............ (908) 788-5042
Rubber Stamp Engraving, 386 Avenel St., Avenel 07001
Owner & Pres.—Steven Glassman, 15 emp., *Plastic engraving, interior & exterior* ............ (732) 726-5664
Rudy Di Signs & Displays, 169 N. Dean St., Englewood 07631
Owner—Ralph DiPasquale, 1 emp., *Interior & exterior signs* ............ (201) 568-6160
Rutherford Signright Co., 769 Morton St., East Rutherford 07073
Pres.—Steven Hanley, 7 emp., *Vinyl, neon, wooden, graphic & plastic* ............ (201) 935-1511
S & M Press, Inc., 169 Semel Ave., Ste. 2, Garfield 07026
Owner—Maxine Bing, 11 emp., *Commercial printing, promotional items* ............ (973) 778-4405
Safeguard, 1253 Springfield Ave., Ste. 258, New Providence 07974
Pres.—Anthony 'Tony' De Paola, 1 emp., *Offset printing, vinyl signs & advertising* ............ (973) 887-9500
Sandoval Graphics & Printing, 9 Minnetonka Rd., Somerdale 08083
Mng. Ptnr.—Tony Sandoval, 6 emp., *Commercial, offset & digital printing* ............ (856) 435-7320
Select Services, 500 Morris Ave., Ste. 116, Springfield 07081
Owner—David Hunter, 5 emp., *Printing, direct mail service, promotional* ............ (973) 467-8860
Service Apex, 564-A Union Ave., Bridgewater 08807
★ Pres.—Ken Griggs, 10 emp., *Commercial printing, t-shirt screen* ............ (732) 560-2222
Service Apex, 299 U.S. Highway 22, Green Brook 08812
Owner—Ken Griggs, 6 emp., *Digital commercial printing, signs,* ............ (732) 424-1616
Shachihata, Inc., U. S. A., 525 Oberlin Ave. S., Lakewood 08701
GM—Young Sin Park, 30 emp., *Rubber stamps & engraved signs* ............ (732) 370-4770
Shore Sign & Banner, 1214 Route 37 E., Toms River 08753
Owner—Phillip Wagner, 2 emp., *Signs, including neon & electric signs* ............ (732) 270-6020
Showcase Graphics, LLC, 33 E. Main St., Ste. 4, Moorestown 08057
Owner—Debra Marsdale, 3 emp., *Commercial & digital printing of packaging* ............ (856) 722-5400
Sign Boy, LLC, 370 N. Glassboro Rd., Woodbury Heights 08097
Pres.—Scott Phillip, 1 emp., *Interior & exterior signs* ............ (856) 384-2937
Sign Concepts, 33 Broad St., Toms River 08753
Owner—Walter Myers, 1 emp., *Handcrafted, vinyl, non-vinyl & painted* ............ (732) 341-7624
Sign Crew, 1426 Union Ave., Pennsauken 08110
Pres.—Joe Crew, 5 emp., *Custom signage, including light box* ............ (856) 665-3676
Sign Effectz, 800 New Brunswick Ave., Ste. 7, Rahway 07065
Owner & Pres.—Brian Snyder, 1 emp., *Signs, banners, decal printing, apparel* ............ (732) 388-7446
Sign Maker, 1005 Union Ave., Union Beach 07735
Owner—Nancy McCarthy, 1 emp., *Interior & exterior vinyl, paper, plexiglass* ............ (732) 739-4800
Sign On, Inc., 149 Washington Ave., Apt. A, Dumont 07628
Pres.—Manohar G. Massand, 4 emp., *Interior & exterior signs, banners* ............ (201) 384-7714
Sign Tech, 361 South Ave. E., Westfield 07090
GM—Gary Alessio, 30 emp., *Interior & exterior signs* ............ (908) 232-2287
Sign Up Signs, LLC, 649 Atlantic City Blvd., Unit 2, Beachwood 08722
Ptnr. & Mng. Member—Larry Snover, 2 emp., *Interior & exterior signs, vinyl banners* ............ (732) 240-6025
Signal Sign Co., 105 Dorsa Ave., Livingston 07039
Mng. Member—Bruce J. Fish, 12 emp., *Architectural interior & exterior signs* ............ (973) 535-9277
Signarama, 655 S. White Horse Pike, Hammonton 08037
Owner—Richard Matteo, 3 emp., *Illuminated & non-illuminated full-color* ............ (609) 878-3375
Signarama, 349 U.S. Highway 9, Ste. 6, Manalapan 07726
Ptnr. & Pres.—Jackie Barber, 4 emp., *Full-service commercial & residential* ............ (732) 536-7575
Sign-A-Rama, 4000 Route 130, Ste. 25, Delran 08075
Owner—Joann Davis, 4 emp., *Interior & exterior signs* ............ (856) 764-9777
Sign-A-Rama, 400 Fairfield Rd., Ste. 5, Fairfield 07004
Owner & Mng. Member—Eric Bleezarde, 7 emp., *Interior & exterior architectural signs* ............ (973) 227-6363
Sign-A-Rama, 1459 Highway 38, P.O. Box 360, Hainesport 08036
Owner—Gary Kuffer, 4 emp., *Interior & exterior, ADA & project* ............ (609) 702-1444
Sign-A-Rama, 32 S. Main St., Manville 08835
Pres.—Deepak Changrani, 2 emp., *Vinyl, lawn & carved signs, banners* ............ (908) 203-8005
Sign-A-Rama, 166 Ridgedale Ave., Morristown 07962
Owner—David Fan, 4 emp., *Interior & exterior signs* ............ (973) 605-8313
Sign-A-Rama, 1030 U.S. Highway 22, North Plainfield 07060
Owner & Pres.—Paul Janulis, 2 emp., *Interior & exterior signs, banners,* ............ (908) 561-4167
Sign-A-Rama, 1633 Stelton Rd., Piscataway 08854
Owner & Mng. Member—Matthew Rabinowitz, 6 emp., *Interior & exterior signs* ............ (732) 819-8844
Sign-A-Rama, 34 S. White Horse Pike, Somerdale 08083
Owner—Jennifer Gray, 4 emp., *Interior, exterior & illuminated signs* ............ (856) 627-5352
Sign-A-Rama Ledgewood, 244 Main St., Ledgewood 07852
Pres., Sales—Michael Grivalsky, 6 emp., *Electric signs, monuments & specialty* ............ (973) 584-9301
Sign-A-Rama, Inc., 379 Main St., Hackensack 07601
Pres.—Michael Fried, 3 emp., *Interior & exterior signs & vinyl sign* ............ (201) 489-6969
SignArt Graphix, 177 Stanhope Sparta Rd., Andover 07821
Pres.—Diane Lounsbery, 11 emp., *Interior & exterior signs* ............ (973) 770-4500
Signature Sign, 31 Milaystown Rd., Cream Ridge 08514
Owner—Michele Long, 5 emp., *Interior & exterior signs* ............ (609) 351-2231
Signdesign, LLC, 206 Lake Ave., P.O. Box 892, Island Heights 08732
Pres.—Stephan Mueller, 1 emp., *Nonelectric signs* ............ (732) 929-3700
SignPros, 1215 Black Horse Pike, Glendora 08029
Owner & Pres.—Nick Kappatos, 18 emp., *LED channel letters, illuminated sign* ............ (856) 939-1099
Signright, Inc., 76 Ashland Ave., West Orange 07052
Ptnr.—Stephen Hanley, 8 emp., *Interior & exterior signs* ............ (973) 731-8882
Signs & Custom Metal, Inc., 62 Monitor St., Jersey City 07304
Pres.—Shan Kumar, 10 emp., *Custom architectural signs* ............ (201) 200-0110
Signs & Graphix, 433 Bloomfield Ave., Caldwell 07006
Owner—Eric Sterru, 1 emp., *Big format interior, exterior & job* ............ (973) 226-8392
Signs & Lines Printing, 242 Gibbsboro Rd., Lindenwold 08021
Owner, Hum. Res. & IT Mgr.—Dan Krug, 2 emp., *Vinyl letter signs & textile screen* ............ (856) 784-0400
Signs By Blohm, Inc., 230 River Rd., New Milford 07646
Pres.—Wayne Blohm, 4 emp., *Carved, sandblasted, plastic, metal* ............ (201) 262-3172
Signs By Lynn, 329 Kearny Ave., Ste. A, Kearny 07032
Owner—Lynn Oelz, 3 emp., *Commercial, residential, ADA & architectural* ............ (201) 998-4273
Signs By Raymond, 626 Route 88, Point Pleasant 08742
Owner—Raymond Lamonica, 1 emp., *Interior & exterior signs* ............ (732) 840-7793
Signs By Tomorrow, 326 U.S. Highway 22, Ste. 8-B, Green Brook 08812
Owner—Rajesh Patel, 4 emp., *Interior & exterior, trade show, architectura* ............ (732) 424-9785
Signs By Tomorrow, 1108 Goffle Rd., Ste. 1, Hawthorne 07506
Owner—Joe Sevean, 2 emp., *Interior & exterior signs* ............ (973) 423-4600
Signs By Tomorrow, 825 Highway 1 S., Ste. 6, Iselin 08830
Pres.—Rajeev Krishna, 7 emp., *Interior & exterior signs* ............ (732) 602-7878
Signs For Today, 173 Upper Hibernia Rd., Rockaway 07866
Owner & Pres.—Bradley O'Connor, 4 emp., *Carved wood & electric exterior signs* ............ (973) 983-2530
Signs Of 2000, 421 Broad St., Clifton 07011
GM—Ray Salem, 10 emp., *Interior & exterior signs & awnings* ............ (973) 253-1333
Signs Of Security, Inc., 64 Outwater Ln., 2nd Fl., P.O. Box 468, Garfield 07026
Pres.—Brian Costello, 60 emp., *Burglar & security interior & exterior* ............ (973) 340-8404
Signs Of Sense, 79 Bassett Hwy., Dover 07801
Owner & Pres.—Scott Rothbart, 3 emp., *Full-color interior & exterior signs* ............ (973) 361-0037
Signs Of The Times By Beutel & Sons, 81 Park Ave., Park Ridge 07656
Owner—George Beutel, 2 emp., *Vinyl interior & exterior signs & lettering* ............ (201) 391-8444
Signs Sealed & Delivered, Inc., 121 Main St., Bradley Beach 07720
Co-Pres.—Peter Schulle, 3 emp., *Interior & exterior signs, vinyl lettering* ............ (732) 775-7227
Signs Unlimited, Inc., 601 Hessian Ave., National Park 08063
Pres.—Cecilia B. Chinai, 4 emp., *Interior & exterior signs, name & photo* ............ (856) 848-4942
Sir Speedy, 897 Rancocas Rd., Westampton 08060
GM—Joseph Barlam, 4 emp., *Offset printing, including color, instant* ............ (609) 267-1232
Sir Speedy Printing And Marketing Services, 5505 Route 130 N., Pennsauken 08110
Pres.—Francis V. Gavin, Jr., 5 emp., *Digital color & offset printing, signs* ............ (856) 488-1480
Sir Speedy Printing and Marketing Services, 1032 Stelton Rd., Piscataway 08854
Pres., Fin. & GM—Mark Yanofsky, 4 emp., *High-speed full-color digital & offset* ............ (732) 981-9011
Sir Speedy Printing Center, 122 Ridge Rd., Lyndhurst 07071
Dir.—Tom Penisch, 5 emp., *Full-color digital, traditional offset* ............ (201) 896-2727
Sir Speedy Printing Center, 300 S. Lenola Rd., Ste. 22, Maple Shade 08052
Pres.—Dennis Marks, 8 emp., *Offset, single, multicolor & color* ............ (856) 866-0588
Skyline Graphic Management, 601 Adams St., P.O. Box 6147, Hoboken 07030
Owner—Al Festa, 2 emp., *Interior & exterior vinyl signs* ............ (201) 798-1919
Skyline Graphics Design, 11 Skyline Lake Dr., Ringwood 07456
Pres.—Scott White, 4 emp., *Offset, digital & digital full-color* ............ (973) 839-3329
Sonntag Graphics, Eric, 93 John E. Busch Ave., Somerset 08873
Owner—Eric J. Sonntag, 2 emp., *Interior & exterior signs, including* ............ (732) 828-5200
Sonoco CorrFlex, LLC, Heritage Plaza II, 1st Fl., 65 Harristown Rd., Glen Rock 07452
Mktg. Svcs. Mgr.—Debra Koch, 18 emp., *Display signs, graphic design & packaging* ............ (201) 612-4008
Spectrum Neon, Inc., 9130-B Pennsauken Hwy., Pennsauken 08110
Pres.—Teresa Simone, 3 emp., *Neon signs* ............ (856) 317-9223
Speed Pro Imaging Of Piscataway, 56 Ethel Rd. W., Ste. 14, Piscataway 08854
Owner—R. Scott Schoner, 3 emp., *Large-format digital printing & banners* ............ (732) 662-9860
Speedpro Imaging, 52 E. Centre St., Ste. 3-B, Nutley 07110
Pres.—Doug Nixon, 4 emp., *Large-format graphic printing, including* ............ (973) 542-8384
Spruce Run Printing, 2005 Route 31, Clinton 08809
Ptnr.—Tom Kowal, 3 emp., *Offset printing & binding of banners* ............ (908) 638-6464

S.I.C.

★ **Indicates new listing this edition.**

SSI Creative Group, 20 E. Clementon Rd., Ste. 203-N, Gibbsboro 08026
Pres.—Chuck Jacques, 70 emp., *Interior & exterior signs* ........ (856) 663-2292
Stand-Out Signs, Inc., 49 W. Pond Rd., Perth Amboy 08861
Pres., Off. Mgr.—Joseph Masaruca, 3 emp., *Neon interior & exterior signs, banners* ........ (732) 442-9399
Stewart-Morris, Inc., 71 Kings Rd., Madison 07940
Pres.—John W. Morris, 6 emp., *Awards, gifts, flags & promotional* ........ (973) 822-2777
Stone Graphics Co., Inc., 5020 Industrial Rd., Farmingdale 07727
Pres.—Raymond C. Stone, 6 emp., *Screen printing, large-format digital* ........ (732) 919-1111
Stone Mountain Printing, 74 Main St., Ste. 1, Woodbridge 07095
Pres.—Steve Steinberg, 8 emp., *Commercial & digital printing, graphic* ........ (732) 634-4444
Storkdelivery.Com, 232 Webster Ave., Lyndhurst 07071
Owner—Dennis Mazza, 2 emp., *Lawn signs, wooden exterior signs,* ........ (201) 933-7721
Strive Group, LLC, The, 160 Chubb Ave., Ste. 101, Lyndhurst 07071
Owner—Jeff Schuoski, 50 emp., *Point-of-purchase displays* ........ (973) 893-1300
Stuyvesant Press, Inc., 119 Coit St., Irvington 07111
Pres., CEO—Michael Roesch, 10 emp., *Offset, commercial, digital, color* ........ (973) 399-3880
Suburban Sign Mfg., LLC, 210 Marion Ave., Linden 07036
Pres.—Thomas Testa, 18 emp., *Wholesale interior & exterior signs* ........ (908) 862-7222
Sun Neon Sign & Electric Co., 6701-B Rudderow Ave., Pennsauken 08109
Pres.—Stuart Rosner, 1 emp., *Interior & exterior signs* ........ (856) 663-7667
Superior Graphics & Signs, Inc., 576 Casino Dr., Howell 07731
Pres.—Ken Barnaby, 3 emp., *Car & boat vinyl decals & commercial* ........ (732) 625-0101
Suzie Mac Specialties, Inc., 12-B Connery Ct., East Brunswick 08816
Pres.—Suzanne MacDougall, 9 emp., *Custom & screenprinted photoluminescent* ........ (732) 238-3500
Sweet Sign Systems, Inc., 9 Davison Ave., Ste. 4, Jamesburg 08831
Pres., CEO & CFO—Richard Dawson, 5 emp., *Architectural interior & exterior signs* ........ (732) 521-9300
Swift Print Solutions, LLC, 405 Front St., Belvidere 07823
Owner—Linda Swift, 4 emp., *Commercial, screen & instant printing* ........ (908) 475-1374
Szabo Signs, 1108 Neck Rd., Burlington 08016
Pres.—Joe Szabo, Jr., 1 emp., *Interior & exterior signs, lettering* ........ (609) 387-7213
T J's Sportwide Trophy & Awards, 236 S. Salem St., Randolph 07869
Pres.—Joe Balzarotti, 10 emp., *Awards, trophies, plaques, ribbons,* ........ (973) 989-8775
Tally Display Corp., 19 Gardner Rd., Ste. A, Fairfield 07004
Pres.—Steve Rose, 5 emp., *LED, full-color & moving message signs* ........ (973) 777-7760
TLC Sign & Banner, Inc., 188 Walnut St., Toms River 08753
Owner—Tim Snover, 17 emp., *Interior & exterior signs & banners* ........ (732) 244-4225
Tooker Sign Service, 1439 Route 539, P.O. Box 1129, Tuckerton 08087
Owner—Jeff Tooker, 1 emp., *Plastic, metal, electric, nonelectric* ........ (609) 296-1000
Totally T Shirts & More, 201 W. Hampton St., Pemberton 08068
Owner—Tony Miralglia, 5 emp., *T-shirt screen printing, embroidery* ........ (609) 894-0011
Tradewin Sign, LLC, 699 Challenger Way, Unit D-7, Forked River 08731
Owner—Darren Gibson, 2 emp., *Signs, including neon & vinyl signs* ........ (609) 488-5961
Traffic Safety & Equipment Co., 457 State Route 17, Mahwah 07430
Pres.—Peter J. Simpson, 9 emp., *Interior & exterior signs & vinyl lettering* ........ (201) 327-6050
Tri-Plex Business Products, Inc / Graphic Solutions, 400 Morris Ave., Ste. 220, Denville 07834
Pres.—Walter Lapham, 9 emp., *Digital color, commercial, offset,* ........ (973) 627-5388
Universal Valve Co., Inc., 478 Schiller St., Elizabeth 07206
Pres., CEO—Robert Milo, 30 emp., *Valves, fittings, vapor recovery equipment* ........ (908) 351-0606
Urban Sign & Crane, Inc., 527 E. Chestnut Ave., P.O. Box 640, Vineland 08360
Pres.—Seth Davis, 12 emp., *Interior & exterior signs* ........ (856) 691-8388
US Sign & Lighting Service, LLC, 105 Dorsa Ave., Wayne 07470
GM—John Kelley, 7 emp., *Interior & exterior signs* ........ (973) 305-8900
Vigg Designs, LLC, 584 Park Ave., Freehold 07728
Owner—John Vigg, 5 emp., *Interior & exterior signs* ........ (732) 683-9400
Visual Graphic Systems, Inc., 330 Washington Ave., Carlstadt 07072
Chrm.—Don Healy, 155 emp., *Custom eco-friendly interior & exterior* ........ (201) 528-2700
Vital Signs, 50 Bedford Rd., Mahwah 07430
Pres.—David Treadwell, 3 emp., *Interior & exterior signs* ........ (201) 723-8488
Vitale Signs, 2204 Elizabeth Ave., Rahway 07065
Pres.—Joe Vitale, 5 emp., *Interior & exterior signs, truck lettering* ........ (732) 388-8401
Walter's Signs, 159 W. White Horse Pike, Berlin 08009
Owner—Walter Schmitz, 2 emp., *Interior & exterior signs, commercial* ........ (856) 210-6324
Welter & Kreutz Printing Co., 51 Worth St., P.O. Box 1834, South Hackensack 07606
Pres.—Robert W. Kreutz, 6 emp., *Commercial printing, promotional materials* ........ (201) 489-9098
Zeek's Tees, 515 Highway 36, Belford 07718
Owner—Frank Zechman, 6 emp., *Textile embroidery, screen & digital* ........ (732) 291-2700
Zienowicz Signs, 202 E. Canal St., Trenton 08609
Owner—George Zienowicz, 3 emp., *Interior & exterior signs* ........ (609) 393-4068

## 3996 Floor coverings—hard surface

Congoleum Corp., 3500 Quakerbridge Rd., P.O. Box 3127, Mercerville 08619
Pres., CEO—Robert Moran, 354 emp., *Corporate headquarters & resilient* ........ (609) 584-3000
Congoleum Corp., Plt. 2, 3500 Quakerbridge Rd., P.O. Box 3127, Mercerville 08619
Plt. Mgr.—Wayne Neville, Sr., 200 emp., *Vinyl laminate floor coverings* ........ (609) 584-3000
Evertile Flooring Co., Inc., 127 Frelinghuysen Ave., Newark 07114
Owner & Pres.—Nigel Mandel, 8 emp., *PVC flooring tiles* ........ (973) 242-7474
Mannington Mills, Inc., 75 Mannington Mills Rd., P.O. Box 30, Salem 08079
Chrm. of the Board—Keith Campbell, 600 emp., *Corporate headquarters & residential* ........ (856) 935-3000
Sika Corporation, 201 Polito Ave., Lyndhurst 07071
Pres., CEO—Christoph Ganz, 107 emp., *Corporate headquarters & concrete materials* ........ (201) 933-8800

## 3999 Manufacturing industries, nec

Abilities Of Northwest Jersey, Inc., 264 Route 31 N., P.O. Box 251, Washington 07882
CEO—Cindy Wildermuth, 300 emp., *Contract packaging/fulfillment, including* ........ (908) 689-1118
AG Peters & Son, Inc., 1025 N. Black Horse Pike, Runnemede 08078
Pres.—Diane Lansberry, 7 emp., *Burial dresses & funeral supplies* ........ (856) 931-7476
Airborne Systems North America Of New Jersey, Inc., 5800 Magnolia Ave., Pennsauken 08109
Sr. V-P., Cust. Bus., N. America—Elizabeth Johnson, 125 emp., *Corporate headquarters & military ram-air* (856) 663-1275
Ana Design Corp., 1 Ott St., Trenton 08638
Pres., R & D Mgr.—Lauren Polito, 6 emp., *Candles* ........ (609) 394-0300
Apparel Distribution, Inc., 45 Saw Mill Pond Rd., Edison 08817
V-P.—Robert Shaw, 75 emp., *Apparel label sewing, pick ticket,* ........ (732) 287-1110
Aromatic Innovations, 600 Hartle St., Sayreville 08872
★ Owner—Golam Bhuiyan, 2 emp., *Fragrances, including perfumes, personal* ........ (732) 967-6346
Aurorae (H Q), 46 N. Central Ave., Ramsey 07446
Pres., CEO—Dennis Ingui, 2 emp., *Company headquarters; yoga mats, accessories* ........ (551) 579-4003
Bernhard-Link Theatrical, LLC, 815 Fairview Ave., Ste. 11, Fairview 07022
Bus. Mgr.—Ruthie Burman, 18 emp., *Custom theatrical staging, scenery* ........ (201) 943-4190
Beta Craft, Inc., 2682 Route 130, P.O. Box 536, Cranbury 08512
Pres.—Arthur Hasselbach, 2 emp., *Pinewood derby kits & supplies & orchid* ........ (609) 655-1940
Betti Industries, Inc., H., 303 Patterson Plank Rd., Carlstadt 07072
Chrm., CEO—Peter Betti, 140 emp., *Corporate headquarters & rebuilt vending* ........ (201) 438-1300

Brisar Industries, Inc., 150 E. 7th St., Paterson 07524
Pres.—Mark Cohen, 45 emp., *Pharmaceutical, cosmetic, R.F. & blister* ........ (973) 278-2500
Candle Artisans, Inc., 253 E. Washington Ave., P.O. Box 190, Washington 07882
Pres.—Robert D. Rumfield, 20 emp., *Paraffin wax candles* ........ (908) 689-2000
Cellunet Mfg. Co., Inc., 460 Veterans Dr., Burlington 08016
Pres.—John Titone, 11 emp., *Nylon hair nets* ........ (609) 386-3361
Century Service Affiliates, Inc., 22 Mercer St., Ste. 1, Paterson 07524
Chrm.—Steven Holland, 29 emp., *Carrying case interiors* ........ (973) 742-8118
Cerbaco Ltd., 809 Harrison St., Frenchtown 08825
Pres.—Alan Flash, 20 emp., *Nonmetallic weld backings* ........ (908) 996-1333
Coastal Amusements, Inc., 1950 Swarthmore Ave., Lakewood 08701
Pres.—Lenny Dean, 35 emp., *Corporate headquarters & coin operated* ........ (732) 905-6662
Confection Collection, 6754 Route 9, Howell 07731
Owner—Sarah Cywiak, 3 emp., *Chocolates, nuts, dried fruit, candy* ........ (732) 905-3039
Creating Your Design, LLC, 45 Wood St., Paterson 07524
Owner—David Batiz, 10 emp., *Trade show exhibits, commercial & retail* ........ (973) 357-1080
Csonka Cigar Requisites, Inc. (H Q), 407 Blue Spring Rd., Princeton 08540
Pres., CEO—Michael Chunko, 40 emp., *Corporate headquarters; custom promotional* ........ (609) 514-2766
De Meo Brothers., Inc., 2 Brigton Ave., Passaic 07055
Sales Mgr.—Shayna Dowek, 9 emp., *Human hair goods, wigs, weaves & related* ........ (973) 778-8100
Design Assistance Corp., 3 Killdeer Ct., Ste. 301, P.O. Box 215, Swedesboro 08085
Pres.—Glenn Woerner, 25 emp., *Training devices for mechanical, electrical* ........ (856) 241-9500
Detail Model & Machine, 61 Woodstown Rd., Mullica Hill 08062
Owner—David Rose, 4 emp., *Training & trade show models & trade* ........ (856) 223-0184
Dolan Creation, Inc., 255 Squankum Rd., P.O. Box 693, Farmingdale 07727
Pres.—Douglas Dolan, 5 emp., *Refrigerator magnets, framed pictures* ........ (732) 938-6656
Dura Tape International, 2816 Morris Ave., Ste. 21, Union 07083
Pres., Fin. & R & D Mgr.—Lee Goldman, 11 emp., *Water-activated & fiberglass mesh joint* ........ (908) 687-8273
E&M Gold Beekeepers, LLC, 113 Hope Rd., Tinton Falls 07724
Ptnr.—Mary Kosenski, 2 emp., *All-natural honey & honey & beeswax-based* ........ (732) 542-6528
EnvironMolds, LLC, 18 Bank St., Ste. 1, Summit 07901
Owner—Ed McCormick, 10 emp., *Molding & casting kits for fine art* ........ (908) 273-5401
Fab Dog, Inc., 160 Gregg St., Unit 7, Lodi 07644
COO—Michael Becher, 5 emp., *Dog accessories* ........ (973) 472-5555
Frankford Umbrellas, 824 E. Gate Dr., Mount Laurel 08054
Pres.—Marc Kaufer, 15 emp., *Patio & beach umbrellas & chaise lounges* ........ (856) 222-4134
G R Office Products, Inc., 11 Kentucky Ave., Paterson 07503
Pres.—Bernardo Guterman, 2 emp., *Floor mats, fabric-wrapped tackboards* ........ (973) 345-2769
GAC Model Making, LLC, 1879 Old Cuthbert Rd., Unit 38, Cherry Hill 08034
Ptnr.—Patricia Christoffersen, 2 emp., *2D & 3D interactive models for product* ........ (856) 857-9848
Galleria Enterprises, Inc., 300-3 State Route 17 S., Ste. E, Lodi 07644
Ptnr. & CEO—Joe Simeone, 7 emp., *Folding & stick umbrellas & canvas* ........ (646) 416-6683
Garden State Foliage, LLC, 600 Central Ave., Farmingdale 07727
Ptnr.—Neil M. Roth, 20 emp., *Christmas decorations, dried foliage* ........ (732) 751-0075
Gloucester City Box Works, LLC, 775 Charles St., Gloucester City 08030
Pres.—Kathy White, 9 emp., *Contract packaging* ........ (856) 456-9032
H M S Monaco, Inc., 629 Grove St., 5th Fl., Jersey City 07310
Pres., CEO—Ira Erstling, 40 emp., *Costume jewelry, stuffed toys & novelties* ........ (201) 533-0007
Hartz Mountain Corp., The, 400 Plaza Dr., Secaucus 07094
Div. V-P., Mktg.—Adam Coacher, 250 emp., *Corporate headquarters & animal health* ........ (201) 271-4800
Ho-Ho-Kus, Inc., 189-201 Lyon St., Paterson 07524
Sales Mgr.—Steve Sucharski, 50 emp., *Aerospace products* ........ (973) 278-2274
Hygloss Products, Inc., 45 Hathaway St., Wallington 07057
Pres.—Moshe Neurath, 30 emp., *Arts & crafts products for teachers* ........ (973) 458-1700
Image Systems For Business, 22 Worlds Fair Dr., Ste. E, Somerset 08873
Pres.—Arthur Schwartz, 30 emp., *Rebuilt fax copiers & faxes* ........ (732) 302-1500
Jan L, Inc., 26 Mill St., Ste. 26, Mount Holly 08060
Pres.—Bruce Levinson, 7 emp., *Hand drill dust collection systems,* ........ (609) 261-1133
Jersey Jack Pinball, Inc., 1645 Oak St., Lakewood 08701
Pres., CEO—Jack Guarnieri, 60 emp., *Coin-operated pinball arcade games* ........ (732) 364-9900
Jodhpuri, Inc., 260-A Walsh Dr., Parsippany 07054
Pres., CEO—L. C. Mehta, 90 emp., *Custom & private label home fragrance* ........ (973) 299-7009
Lentron Corp., 24 Ironia Rd., Flanders 07836
Off. Mgr.—Anna Klett, 20 emp., *General machining & assembly job shop* ........ (973) 252-9668
Little House Candles, 20 Province Line Rd., New Egypt 08533
Owner—Jennifer Ingalls, 5 emp., *Scented candles* ........ (609) 758-2996
LittleGifts, Inc. (H Q), 600 Meadowlands Pkwy., Ste. 131, Secaucus 07094
CEO—Rishi Gupta, 12 emp., *Corporate headquarters; pet-themed* ........ (212) 868-2559
Look Of Love International (H Q), 1795-B Route 27 S., Edison 08817
Pres.—Robert A. Anzivino, 15 emp., *Company headquarters; women's hairpieces* ........ (908) 687-9502
Mercer Occupational Training, 600 New York Ave., Trenton 08638
Ex. Dir.—Steven Cook, 150 emp., *Contract assembly* ........ (609) 393-2483
Miller & Sons, Inc., I. V., 15 Cindy Ln., Ocean 07712
Pres., CFO—George H. Miller, 18 emp., *Metallizing of plastic packaging components* ........ (732) 493-4040
Miniature Folding, Inc., 14 Wenzel St., Elmwood Park 07407
Pres.—Christopher Taliercio, Sr., 25 emp., *Contract miniature folding of pharmaceutical* ........ (201) 773-6477
Mirrotek International, LLC, 90 Dayton Ave., Bldg. 1-F, Passaic 07055
Pres.—Joe Bezzy, 45 emp., *Decorative & dressing mirrors, home* ........ (973) 472-1400
Monter Lite Co., Inc., 560 Lincoln Blvd., Ste. 2, Middlesex 08846
V-P.—Jerry Lin, 10 emp., *Manufacturer & wholesaler of handmade* ........ (732) 748-1288
MP Technologies, LLC (H Q), 345 Claremont Ave., Ste. 26, Montclair 07042
Chrm.—John Mahdessian, 15 emp., *Company headquarters; pocket stain* ........ (646) 366-1155
Mystic Timber, LLC, 95 Youmans Ave., Washington 07882
★ Principal—Bruce Jorgensen, 4 emp., *Wooden smoking accessories, including* ........ (908) 223-7878
National Christmas Products, 2 Commerce Dr., Cranford 07016
Pres., CEO—Joseph A. Puleo, 35 emp., *Artificial Christmas trees & related* ........ (908) 709-4141
Nylabone Products, 1 TFH Plz., 3rd & Union Ave., P.O. Box 427, Neptune City 07753
Ex. V-P.—Mark E. Johnson, 250 emp., *Pet chew toys & pet book publishing* ........ (732) 988-8400
O'Brien Co., Inc., J., 40 Commerce St., Springfield 07081
Pres., CEO—Sharmay O'Brien, 20 emp., *Manufacturer of lanyards, badge reels* ........ (973) 379-8844
Occupational Training Center, 215 W. White Horse Pike, Berlin 08009
Ex. Dir.—Loret McClain, 35 emp., *Contract assembly & packaging, including* ........ (856) 768-0845
One Stop Packaging, LLC, 71-B Kingsland Ave., Clifton 07014
Opers. Mgr.—Jason Werba, 2 emp., *Contract packaging, including poly* ........ (973) 272-0170
Pafa Training Center, Inc., 1301 W. Forest Grove Rd., Bldg. 3-C, Vineland 08360
Pres., CEO, COO—Michelle Vernamonti, 70 emp., *Contract assembly* ........ (856) 696-1414
Panline USA, Inc., 251 Union St., Northvale 07647
Pres.—Fred Keeler, 66 emp., *Juvenile toys, including bathtub play* ........ (201) 750-8010
Peerless Umbrella Co., Inc., 427 Ferry St., Newark 07105
Pres.—Gene Moscowitz, 120 emp., *Manufacturer & distributor of umbrellas* ........ (973) 578-4900
Radii, Inc., 66 Willow Ave., 3rd Fl., Hoboken 07030
Pres.—Ed Wood, 12 emp., *Architectural models* ........ (201) 420-4700

Ramsey Model Design, David A., P.O. Box 87, Clarksburg 08510
Owner—David A. Ramsey, 1 emp., *Models & prototypes* ........ (609) 259-6757
Raritan Engineering Co., Inc., 530 Orange St., Millville 08332
Pres.—Arthur J. Bretnall, Jr., 20 emp., *Corporate headquarters & pleasure boats* ........ (856) 825-4900
Raritan Valley Workshop, 9 Terminal Rd., New Brunswick 08901
Plt. Mgr.—Andy Scisorek, 250 emp., *Contract packaging & assembly* ........ (732) 828-8080
Reed-Lane, Inc., 359 Newark Pompton Tpke., Wayne 07470
Pres.—Patricia Elvin, 175 emp., *Contract assembly & packaging for the* ........ (973) 709-1090
Robalo Enterprises, 104 New Era Dr., South Plainfield 07080
Owner—Albert Dilello, 45 emp., *Contract packaging & assembly* ........ (908) 753-1075
Robessa Enterprises, Inc., 1030 Delsea Dr., P.O. Box 72, Westville 08093
Owner—William Green, 10 emp., *Corrugated boxes & contract packaging* ........ (856) 251-0055
Rose Brand, Inc., 4 Emerson Ln., Secaucus 07094
Pres.—George Jacobstein, 197 emp., *Curtains, draperies, backdrops, fabrics* ........ (201) 809-1730
S. Frankford & Sons, Inc., 110 Gaither Dr., Mount Laurel 08054
Pres.—Mark Kaufer, 6 emp., *Umbrellas, including commercial-grade* ........ (856) 222-4134
Sandpiper Embroidery, Inc., 5905 New Jersey Ave., Wildwood Crest 08260
Owner—Virginia Fineberg, 3 emp., *Embroidery products, designs & supplies* ........ (609) 522-4560
Sigma Design Company, 200 Pond Ave., Middlesex 08846
Pres.—Gerard J. Lynch, 10 emp., *Contract manufacturing & assembly of* ........ (732) 629-7555
Smartplay International, Inc., 1550 Bridgeboro Rd., Edgewater Park 08010
Pres.—David Michaud, 23 emp., *Custom lottery number drawing machines* ........ (609) 880-1860
Star Soap & Candle, LLC, 300 Industrial Ave., Ridgefield Park 07660
Pres.—Stanley Gurewitsch, 200 emp., *Candles* ........ (201) 690-9090
Sunset Florist, LLC, 470 Bergen Blvd., Ridgefield 07657
Pres.—Harry Khorozin, 4 emp., *Artificial flowers* ........ (201) 941-5411
Sweet Success, 14 Ellison Rd., Watchung 07069
Pres.—Stella Testa, 2 emp., *All-occasion, fruit & gourmet, corporate* ........ (908) 561-2997
Telmark Packaging Corp., 30 Freneau Ave., Ste. 2-B, Matawan 07747
Pres.—Eric Ludwig, 8 emp., *Contract formulation, manufacturing* ........ (732) 739-9100
USA Tealight, LLC, 4 Craigwood Rd., Avenel 07001
★ Pres.—Michael Zohar, 15 emp., *Tealight candles* ........ (732) 943-2408
Vikolya Corp., 140 Ethel Rd. W., Unit J, Piscataway 08854
Owner—Mike Bahet, 6 emp., *Jewelry boxes, stands & organizers* ........ (732) 529-5540
Vo-Toys, Inc., 400 S. 5th St., Harrison 07029
Pres.—Arthur Hirschberg, 125 emp., *Pet accessories & products, including* ........ (973) 484-0088
Water-Jel Technologies, 50 Broad St., Carlstadt 07072
CFO—John McAndris, 80 emp., *Sterile burn dressings, fire blankets* ........ (201) 507-8300
Weiss & Sons, Inc., I., 815 Fairview Ave., Ste. 10, Fairview 07022
Pres.—David Rosenberg, 33 emp., *Theatrical draperies & rigging equipment* ........ (201) 402-6500
Wick It, LLC, 1 Gregory Ave., Passaic 07055
Owner—Joe Blythe, 7 emp., *Candle wicks & wick clip assemblies* ........ (973) 249-2970

## 50 WHOLESALER TRADE—DURABLE GOODS

### 5012 Automobiles & other motor vehicles

Equipment Sales & Service, 152 Floyd Ave., Bloomfield 07003
Owner—Dan DePalma, 8 emp., *Wholesaler of tow trucks & recovery* ........ (973) 743-7516
First Priority Emergency Vehicles, Inc., 2444 Ridgeway Blvd., Bldg. 500, Manchester 08759
Pres.—Robert J. Freeman, 47 emp., *Manufacturer & distributor of emergency* ........ (732) 657-1104
Jaguar Land Rover North America, 555 MacArthur Blvd., Mahwah 07430
Pres.—Andy Goss, 250 emp., *Distributor of automobiles* ........ (201) 818-8500
Liftec, Inc., 124 Sylvania Pl., South Plainfield 07080
Pres.—Stephen Panek, 50 emp., *Distributor of industrial forklift* ........ (908) 769-0034
Mid-Atlantic Truck Center, Inc., 525 W. Linden Ave., Linden 07036
GM—Fred Berger, 48 emp., *Distributor of flatbeds, custom semi* ........ (908) 862-8181
United Scrap Iron & Metal Co., 124 Wood St., Paterson 07524
Manager—John Lewer, 15 emp., *Wholesaler of recycled metal & iron* ........ (973) 279-1683
Utility Trailer Sales Of New Jersey, 589 Nassau St., North Brunswick 08902
Pres.—Larry Dwyer, Sr., 16 emp., *Distributor of new & used trailers* ........ (732) 745-1222
Vic Gerard Golf Cars, 281 Squankum Rd., Farmingdale 07727
Pres.—William Lynch, 23 emp., *Distributor of golf cars & utility* ........ (732) 938-4464
Wiegers, Inc., 181 Fornelius Ave., Clifton 07013
Pres. & Parts Mgr.—Ernest Wiegers, 10 emp., *Manufacturer & distributor of custom-built* ........ (973) 778-8607

### 5013 Motor vehicle supplies & new parts

ABS Brake Systems Ltd., 445 Godwin Ave., Midland Park 07432
Pres., CEO—Ronald P. Torriani, 5 emp., *Company headquarters & wholesaler of* ........ (201) 689-6893
Ace Auto Salvage, 34 Stover Ave., Kearny 07032
Owner—Frances Reilly, 2 emp., *Wholesaler of rebuilt & used automotive* ........ (201) 997-6178
Auto King Parts & Supplies, 67 E. Railroad Ave., Jamesburg 08831
Owner—Joseph Donnelly, 10 emp., *Distributor of automotive parts & supplies* ........ (732) 521-0474
Autopart International, Inc., 260 Hudson St., Hackensack 07601
Br. Mgr.—John Lopez, 2 emp., *Distributor of automotive parts* ........ (201) 488-4187
Autopart International, Inc., 1773 Pine Ave., Unit A, Vineland 08360
Br. Mgr.—Dana Kidd, 10 emp., *Wholesaler of aftermarket automotive* ........ (856) 405-0346
BK Classic Auto Glass, LLC, 441 Cortlandt St., Belleville 07109
Owner—Robert Kent, 1 emp., *Distributor of classic automotive glass* ........ (973) 759-1485
D & F Performance, 417 N. Grove St., Berlin 08009
Ptnr.—David R. Thornton, Sr., 2 emp., *Rebuilt performance engines & distributor* ........ (856) 767-4095
Dreyco, Inc., 263 Veterans Blvd., Carlstadt 07072
Pres.—Michael Borghard, 15 emp., *Distributor of automotive parts, tools* ........ (201) 896-9000
Elizabeth Truck Center, 878 North Ave., Elizabeth 07201
Pres.—Steven Pesce, 30 emp., *Distributor of truck parts* ........ (908) 355-8800
Equipment Sales & Service, 152 Floyd Ave., Bloomfield 07003
Owner—Dan DePalma, 8 emp., *Wholesaler of tow trucks & recovery* ........ (973) 743-7516
FinishMaster, Inc., 700 Garfield Ave., Jersey City 07305
GM—Cliff White, 4 emp., *Distributor of automotive paints &* ........ (201) 435-1555
Haledon Auto Parts, 269 Haledon Ave., Haledon 07508
Pres., Hum. Res. & IT Mgr.—Howard T. Wilson, 23 emp., *Automotive machine shop & distributor* (973) 595-8200
Interstate Battery System Of America, Inc., 408 Commerce Ln., West Berlin 08091
GM—Robert Marshall, 8 emp., *Wholesaler of batteries, including* ........ (856) 767-3903
Johnson & Towers, Inc., 2701 Fire Rd., Egg Harbor Township 08234
Dir., Bus. Dev.—Paul Apple, 20 emp., *Distributor of diesel truck & marine* ........ (609) 272-1415
K. S. I. Trading Corp., 100 Wade Ave., Ste. A, South Plainfield 07080
Owner—Wayne Jan, 75 emp., *Corporate headquarters & wholesaler* ........ (908) 668-1380
Kumar & Kumar, Inc., 57 Denise Dr., Edison 08820
Pres.—Ashish Sood, 5 emp., *Distributor of machined forging & casting* ........ (732) 322-0435
Model Electronics, Inc., 615 E. Crescent Ave., Ramsey 07446
V-P.—Thomas Churchill, 55 emp., *Distributor of OEM automotive electronics* ........ (201) 961-6200
Modern Technologies Group, Inc., 3 Reeves Station Rd., Medford 08055
Pres.—Ric Cohen, 30 emp., *Corporate headquarters & distributor* ........ (609) 714-8900
National Parts Supply Co., Inc., 56 State Route 31, Flemington 08822
Store Mgr.—Barry Higgins, 20 emp., *Distributor of automotive parts, including* ........ (908) 782-3530
National Parts Supply Co., Inc., 535 Milltown Rd., North Brunswick 08902
Owner—John Salasko, 100 emp., *Corporate headquarters & wholesaler* ........ (732) 247-5171
Ogura Industrial Corp., 100 Randolph Rd., 2nd Fl., Somerset 08873
Pres.—Frank Flemming, 15 emp., *Corporate headquarters & wholesaler* ........ (732) 271-7361
P & A Auto Parts, Inc., 396 Midland Ave., Garfield 07026
Br. Mgr.—Louis Doto, 10 emp., *Distributor of automotive parts* ........ (973) 405-6068
P & A Auto Parts, Inc., 530 River St., Hackensack 07601
Pres., CFO—Joe Cupoli, 30 emp., *Corporate headquarters & distributor* ........ (201) 843-7156
Part-Rite, Inc., 19 Butler Ave., Bayville 08721
Manager—Mark Buglio, 12 emp., *Rebuilt automotive torque converters* ........ (732) 269-5000
Parts Distributors, LLC, 901 N. Lenola Rd., P.O. Box 832, Moorestown 08057
Hum. Rels. Mgr.—Denise Esposito, 200 emp., *Distributor of automotive parts* ........ (856) 778-1400
Precision Fasteners, Inc., 24 Worlds Fair Dr., Ste. D, Somerset 08873
V-P., CEO—Bill Miicke, 6 emp., *Distributor of fasteners for the automotive* ........ (732) 627-0032
Ransome International, 2320 High Hill Rd., Logan Township 08085
GM—Brian Walsh, 20 emp., *Wholesaler of truck parts* ........ (856) 241-8890
Runnemede Truck Refrigeration, 320 Borelli Blvd., Paulsboro 08066
Pres.—Robert Hyndman, 10 emp., *Wholesaler of truck refrigeration &* ........ (856) 423-4400
Stewart & Stevenson Power Products, LLC- ADDA Div., 180 Route 17 S., P.O. Box 950, Lodi 07644
CEO—John F. Farmer, 90 emp., *Company headquarters & distributor* ........ (201) 489-5800
Strauss Discount Auto, 7-C Brick Plant Rd., South River 08882
Pres., COO—Joe Catalano, 150 emp., *Company headquarters & distributor* ........ (732) 390-9000
Suburban Auto Seat Co., Inc., 35 Industrial Rd., Lodi 07644
Pres.—Amy Winfield, 13 emp., *Distributor of aftermarket replacement* ........ (973) 778-9227
TransAxle Corp., 540 Huyler St., South Hackensack 07606
GM—Ralph Guavagno, 12 emp., *Distributor of transmission parts* ........ (201) 440-1911
TRC, 1700 Sherman Ave., Pennsauken 08110
★ Manager—Keith Loura, 20 emp., *Wholesaler of automatic transmissions* ........ (856) 910-7979
Utility Trailer Sales Of New Jersey, 589 Nassau St., North Brunswick 08902
Pres.—Larry Dwyer, Sr., 16 emp., *Distributor of new & used trailers* ........ (732) 745-1222
W & E Sales Co., Inc., 370 Elizabeth Ave., Newark 07112
GM—R. Carr, 15 emp., *Manufacturer & wholesaler of automotive* ........ (973) 824-2000
Wiegers, Inc., 181 Fornelius Ave., Clifton 07013
Pres. & Parts Mgr.—Ernest Wiegers, 10 emp., *Manufacturer & distributor of custom-built* ........ (973) 778-8607
Worldwide Parts & Accessories Corp., 300 Herrod Blvd., Dayton 08810
Mktg. Progs. Mgr.—Sherry Blake, 90 emp., *Distributor of automotive parts* ........ (732) 230-5000

### 5014 Tires & tubes

Casings Of NJ, Inc., 711 Ramsey Ave., Hillside 07205
Br. Mgr.—Bill Evans, 30 emp., *Wholesaler of recycled tires* ........ (908) 851-7766
Eastern Lift Truck Co., Inc., 549 E. Linwood Ave., Route 73 N., P.O. Box 307, Maple Shade 08052
Pres.—Mike Pruitt, 370 emp., *Corporate headquarters & distributor* ........ (856) 779-8880
Haledon Auto Parts, 269 Haledon Ave., Haledon 07508
Pres., Hum. Res. & IT Mgr.—Howard T. Wilson, 23 emp., *Automotive machine shop & distributor* (973) 595-8200
Mercury Tire Co., Inc., 1 Fairfield Rd., Caldwell 07006
Pres.—James Gilroy, 15 emp., *Distributor of tires* ........ (973) 785-0080
Reliable Tire Distributors, Inc., 805 N. Black Horse Pike, P.O. Box 39, Blackwood 08012
CEO—Mike Betz, 60 emp., *Corporate headquarters & distributor* ........ (856) 232-0700

### 5015 Motor vehicle parts, used

Ace Auto Salvage, 34 Stover Ave., Kearny 07032
Owner—Frances Reilly, 2 emp., *Wholesaler of rebuilt & used automotive* ........ (201) 997-6178
Knopf Automotive, LLC, 93 Shrewsbury Ave., Apt. 1, Red Bank 07701
Ptnr.—Marshall Knopf, 20 emp., *Company headquarters & wholesaler of* ........ (732) 212-0444
Taylor Auto Parts, 222 Pacific St., Newark 07114
Pres.—Frederick Taylor, 3 emp., *Wholesaler of used automotive parts* ........ (973) 465-4345

### 5021 Furniture

ABC Supply, 41 N. Pearl St., Bridgeton 08302
Br. Mgr.—Patrick Torinese, 4 emp., *Distributor of vinyl, aluminum, wood* ........ (856) 455-4888
Archer Plastics, Inc., 1510 Jesse Bridge Rd., Elmer 08318
Pres.—Steve Archer, 5 emp., *Wholesaler of modern & collectible* ........ (856) 692-0242
Business Furniture, Inc., 133 Rahway Ave., Elizabeth 07202
CEO—Paul Gold, 35 emp., *Corporate headquarters & wholesaler* ........ (908) 355-3400
Business Furniture, Inc., 10 Lanidex Plz. W., Ste. 202, Parsippany 07054
Pres., CEO—Dan Morley, 35 emp., *Distributor of office furniture, including* ........ (973) 503-0730
Creative Displays & Designs, Inc., 349 Essex Rd., Neptune 07753
Pres.—Danette Bussey, 22 emp., *Wholesaler of home dÉcor products,* ........ (732) 918-8010
Dream On Me Industries, Inc., 125 Helen St., South Plainfield 07080
Pres.—Mark Severe, 40 emp., *Manufacturer of baby mattresses & wholesaler* ........ (908) 791-0555
Environmental Site Furnishings, 700 Goldman Dr., Cream Ridge 08514
Dir., Sales, Natl.—Kevin Mahoney, 10 emp., *Distributor of outdoor public site* ........ (281) 975-1776
Garden Oaks Garden Center, 1921 U.S. Highway 22, Bound Brook 08805
Owner—Madeline Wenz, 20 emp., *Full-line distributor of outdoor, lawn* ........ (732) 356-7333
Glenwood Office Furniture II, Inc., 561 U.S. Highway 22, Hillside 07205
Owner & V-P.—Ravi Uppal, 7 emp., *Distributor of new & used commercial-grade* ........ (908) 687-3770
National Public Seating Corp., 149 Entin Rd., Clifton 07014
Pres., Dir., Sales—Barry Stauber, 80 emp., *Distributor of upholstered & plastic* ........ (973) 594-1100
Restaurant Depot, LLC, 1050 Thomas Busch Memorial Hwy., Pennsauken 08110
GM—Paul Jensen, 75 emp., *Wholesaler of general line groceries* ........ (856) 488-4288
United Stationers Supply Co., 100 Liberty Way, Cranbury 08512
Br. Mgr.—Wayne Scott, 100 emp., *Wholesaler of office equipment, furniture* ........ (609) 619-4000

### 5023 Home furnishings

A D S Sale Co., Inc., 1010 Campus Dr., Morganville 07751
Pres.—Marshall Summer, 21 emp., *Distributor of hotel products, including* ........ (732) 591-0500
Alan Schatzberg & Assoc., Inc., 45 Ruta Ct., South Hackensack 07606
Pres., GM—Alan Schatzberg, 12 emp., *Manufacturer & distributor of custom* ........ (201) 440-8855
Atlantic City Shade Shop, Inc., 500 Tilton Rd., P.O. Box 217, Northfield 08225
Owner, MIS Mgr. & Chief Engr.—Howard Markman, 16 emp., *Manufacturer & distributor of pleated* (609) 641-8700
Bai Lar Interior Services, Inc., 554 New Brunswick Ave., Fords 08863
Pres.—James E. Quinn, 5 emp., *Manufacturer & distributor of commercial* ........ (732) 738-0350
Bloomfield Drapery Co., Inc., 948 Paterson Ave., East Rutherford 07073
Pres.—Steve Gold, 15 emp., *Manufacturer & distributor of theatrical* ........ (973) 777-3566
C & M Shade Corp., 53 Dwight Pl., Fairfield 07004
Pres.—Allen Francus, 13 emp., *Manufacturer & distributor of motorized* ........ (201) 807-1200
CAC International, 30 Camptown Rd., Maplewood 07040
Owner—Kevin Deng, 10 emp., *Wholesaler of chinaware* ........ (973) 371-4300
Classic Tile, Inc., 325 Pine St., P.O. Box 1066, Elizabeth 07207
Pres.—Leah Glucroft, 25 emp., *Distributor of floor coverings, including* ........ (908) 289-8400

S.I.C.

★ **Indicates new listing this edition.**

Fishman Flooring Solutions, 621 Chapel Ave. E., Ste. A, Cherry Hill 08034
GM—Jason Edwards, 4 emp., *Distributor of floor coverings & installation*.......... (856) 857-1141
General Floor Industries, 190 Benigno Blvd., Bellmawr 08031
Pres.—David Cometz, 85 emp., *Company headquarters & wholesaler of*.......... (856) 931-0012
General Floor, Inc., 2 Pin Oak Ln., Cherry Hill 08003
Br. Mgr.—David Garro, 3 emp., *Wholesaler of carpet, laminate, hardwood*.......... (856) 424-0111
General Floor, Inc., 777 New Durham Rd., Edison 08817
Br. Mgr.—Raul Corrales, 4 emp., *Wholesaler of carpet, laminate, hardwood*.......... (732) 603-6100
General Floor, Inc., 125 Market St., Kenilworth 07033
Br. Mgr.—Marcio Nescia, 4 emp., *Wholesaler of carpet, laminate, hardwood*.......... (908) 241-4888
General Floor, Inc., 815 Hylton Rd., Pennsauken 08110
Manager—Rob Roark, 3 emp., *Wholesaler of carpet, laminate, hardwood*.......... (856) 663-4750
Harbor Linen, LLC (H Q), 2 Foster Ave., Gibbsboro 08026
Chrm.—Earl Waxman, 100 emp., *Company headquarters; manufacturer*.......... (856) 435-2000
Home Essentials, Inc., 1 Terminal Way, Avenel 07001
Off. Mgr.—Rashad Hassan, 10 emp., *Distributor of textile home furnishings*.......... (732) 388-4008
International Mercantile Agencies, Inc., 18 Home News Row, New Brunswick 08901
Pres.—Aman Kapur, 10 emp., *Wholesaler of imported decorative home*.......... (732) 246-3900
Johnson's Appliances & Bedding, 930 Asbury Ave., P.O. Box 95, Ocean City 08226
Pres. & Dir., Opers. & Sales—Don Johnson, 30 emp., *Company headquarters & wholesaler of* (609) 399-1598
Johnson's Appliances & Bedding, 2510 New York Ave., Wildwood 08260
GM—Jerry Stroh, 3 emp., *Wholesaler of household appliances*.......... (609) 522-1421
Kay Window Fashions, Inc., 271 2nd St., Saddle Brook 07663
Ptnr.—Sol Kleinstein, 12 emp., *Manufacturer & distributor of draperies*.......... (862) 591-1555
Matting World, P.O. Box 43, Beverly 08010
Ptnr.—Marialynn Patalano, 3 emp., *Distributor of mats & janitorial supplies*.......... (609) 641-4747
Michael Halebian & Co., Inc., 557 Washington Ave., Carlstadt 07072
Pres.—Michael Halebian, Jr., 50 emp., *Distributor of floor coverings & related*.......... (201) 935-3535
Momeni, Inc., 60 Broad St., Carlstadt 07072
Pres.—Reza Momeni, 35 emp., *Corporate headquarters & distributor*.......... (212) 532-9577
Nikko Ceramics, Inc., 815 Fairview Ave., Ste. 9, Fairview 07022
Pres.—Kenji Anzai, 11 emp., *Distributor of chinaware*.......... (201) 840-5200
Restaurant Depot, LLC, 1050 Thomas Busch Memorial Hwy., Pennsauken 08110
GM—Paul Jensen, 75 emp., *Wholesaler of general line groceries*.......... (856) 488-4288
Town & Country Linen Corp., 475 Oberlin Ave. S., Lakewood 08701
V-P., Cust. Serv. & Dist.—Susan Keingarsky, 32 emp., *Distributor of domestic & imported*.......... (732) 364-2000

## 5031 Lumber, plywood, millwork & wood panels

A-Able Fence Builders, 28 Lakeside Ave., West Orange 07052
Owner—William Byrne, 10 emp., *Wholesaler & installer of wooden &*.......... (973) 325-1900
ABC Supply Co., Inc., 5004 Route 130, Riverside 08075
Br. Mgr.—Ray Coxe, 5 emp., *Wholesaler of roofing, siding, windows*.......... (856) 461-5252
ABC Supply Co., Inc., Bradco Div., 45 Samworth Rd., Clifton 07012
Br. Mgr.—Greg Anderson, 10 emp., *Distributor of roofing materials, signs*.......... (973) 777-3663
ABC Supply Co., Inc., Bradco Div., 725 W. Delilah Rd., Pleasantville 08232
Sales Mgr.—Mark Morrison, 13 emp., *Distributor of residential & commercial*.......... (609) 484-9100
ABC Supply Co., Inc., Bradco Div., 301 Brunswick Ave., Trenton 08618
Br. Mgr.—Richard Mattson, 10 emp., *Distributor of building materials,*.......... (609) 393-7000
Allied Building Products Corp., 15 E. Union Ave., East Rutherford 07073
Chrm.—Michael Lynch, 200 emp., *Corporate headquarters & wholesaler*.......... (201) 507-8400
Allied Building Products Corp., 850 Flora St., Elizabeth 07201
Br. Mgr.—Thomas Meola, 10 emp., *Distributor of building materials &*.......... (908) 820-9790
Allied Building Products Corp., 406 State Route 23 N., Franklin 07416
Br. Mgr.—Jerome Newman, 12 emp., *Distributor of building materials &*.......... (973) 827-4113
Allied Building Products Corp., 27-33 Franklin Tpke., Mahwah 07430
Br. Mgr.—John Rogan, 10 emp., *Distributor of building materials &*.......... (201) 529-3300
Allied Building Products Corp., 320 W. Water St., Toms River 08753
Br. Mgr.—Gary Finn, 10 emp., *Distributor of building materials &*.......... (732) 341-4767
Allied Building Products Corp., 595 Union Blvd., Totowa 07512
Br. Mgr.—Robert Gall, 10 emp., *Distributor of building materials &*.......... (973) 790-5500
Allied Building Products Corp., 2065 State Route 34, Wall Township 07719
Br. Mgr.—Gary Finn, 5 emp., *Distributor of building materials &*.......... (732) 449-3355
Amarr Garage Doors, 12 Coddington Rd., Whitehouse Station 08889
Matls. Mgr.—Victor Vergalito, 50 emp., *Distributor of steel garage doors*.......... (908) 534-4112
American Fence Co., 326 U.S. Highway 46, Saddle Brook 07663
Owner—Piero Mosca, 10 emp., *Wholesaler of wooden, metal, aluminum*.......... (973) 546-4373
Arzee Supply, 1905 Swarthmore Ave., Lakewood 08701
Br. Mgr.—Paul Maslanek, 20 emp., *Distributor of building materials &*.......... (201) 935-0800
Arzee Supply Corp. Of New Jersey, 15 E. Frederick Pl., Cedar Knolls 07927
Br. Mgr.—Ed Jacobus, 48 emp., *Distributor of building materials &*.......... (973) 267-1576
Arzee Supply Corp. Of New Jersey, 450 York St., Elizabeth 07201
Sales Mgr.—John Esteves, 7 emp., *Distributor of building materials &*.......... (908) 820-3700
Atlantic Window & Door, Inc., 1608 Dubac Rd., Wall Township 07719
Pres.—Mark Daly, 5 emp., *Distributor of home improvement products*.......... (732) 793-2452
Bath Connection, The, 183 Millburn Ave., Millburn 07041
Br. Mgr.—Nancy Malchi, 7 emp., *Wholesaler of bathroom accessories,*.......... (973) 467-7888
Bayonne Plumbing Supply, Inc., 250 Avenue E, Bayonne 07002
Ptnr.—Richard Epstein, 6 emp., *Corporate headquarters & wholesaler*.......... (201) 339-8000
Boro Sawmill & Timber Co., Inc., 139 Ryerson Ave., Wayne 07470
Pres.—Gregory Sussek, 11 emp., *Manufacturer & wholesaler of construction*.......... (973) 832-4607
Burlington County Overhead Door Co., Inc., 444 Logan Ave., P.O. Box 127, Burlington 08016
Br. Mgr.—Tom Ballard, 10 emp., *Distributor of hollow metal overhead*.......... (609) 387-9092
Classic Tile, Inc., 325 Pine St., P.O. Box 1066, Elizabeth 07207
Pres.—Leah Glucroft, 25 emp., *Distributor of floor coverings, including*.......... (908) 289-8400
Commercial Hardware, Inc., 5 Perina Blvd., Cherry Hill 08003
CEO—Victor Palladino, 50 emp., *Corporate headquarters & distributor*.......... (856) 810-0600
Designer Source, Inc., 2139 State Route 35, Holmdel 07733
Ptnr.—Laura Beglin, 6 emp., *Distributor of architectural mouldings*.......... (732) 264-7775
Door Jockey, Inc., 915 18th Ave., Wall 07719
Pres.—Ken Karmazyn, 3 emp., *Distributor of pedestrian automatic*.......... (732) 942-6099
Dreyer's Lumber & Hardware, Inc., 348 Elberon Blvd., Oakhurst 07755
★ Owner—Walter Dreyer, 4 emp., *Lumber processing & millwork & distributor*.......... (732) 531-0220
Dubell Lumber Co., 731 Cuthbert Blvd., Cherry Hill 08002
Br. Mgr.—Jim Eaise, 20 emp., *Wholesaler of building materials &*.......... (856) 665-9100
Dubell Lumber Co., 148 Route 70 E., P.O. Box 1449, Medford 08055
Owner—Gene DiMediao, 35 emp., *Company headquarters & wholesaler of*.......... (609) 654-4143
Emerson Fence, Inc., 10 Lincoln Blvd., P.O. Box 306, Emerson 07630
Pres.—Robert Skrable, Jr., 20 emp., *Manufacturer & distributor of custom*.......... (201) 265-5150
Empire Lumber & Millwork Co., 377 Frelinghuysen Ave., Newark 07114
Chrm.—Ira Kent, 35 emp., *Architectural millwork, dimension lumber*.......... (973) 242-2700
Environmental Site Furnishings, 700 Goldman Dr., Cream Ridge 08514
Dir., Sales, Natl.—Kevin Mahoney, 10 emp., *Distributor of outdoor public site*.......... (281) 975-1776
Fessenden Hall, Inc., 1050 Sherman Ave., Pennsauken 08110
Pres.—Edward Birdsall, 120 emp., *Corporate headquarters & distributor*.......... (856) 665-2210
Garfield Lumber & Millwork Co., 260 Lanza Ave., Garfield 07026
Pres., CFO—Ray Sowa, 20 emp., *Distributor of lumber, millwork, hardware*.......... (973) 478-2160
General Floor Industries, 190 Benigno Blvd., Bellmawr 08031
Pres.—David Cometz, 85 emp., *Company headquarters & wholesaler of*.......... (856) 931-0012
General Floor, Inc., 2 Pin Oak Ln., Cherry Hill 08003
Br. Mgr.—David Garro, 3 emp., *Wholesaler of carpet, laminate, hardwood*.......... (856) 424-0111
General Floor, Inc., 777 New Durham Rd., Edison 08817
Br. Mgr.—Raul Corrales, 4 emp., *Wholesaler of carpet, laminate, hardwood*.......... (732) 603-6100
General Floor, Inc., 125 Market St., Kenilworth 07033
Br. Mgr.—Marcio Nescia, 4 emp., *Wholesaler of carpet, laminate, hardwood*.......... (908) 241-4888
General Floor, Inc., 815 Hylton Rd., Pennsauken 08110
Manager—Rob Roark, 3 emp., *Wholesaler of carpet, laminate, hardwood*.......... (856) 663-4750
Heath Lumber Co., 1580 N. Olden Avenue Ext., Ewing 08638
Pres.—Gary Patricelli, 30 emp., *Distributor of building materials &*.......... (609) 392-1166
Kelly, Inc., Myles F., 43-57 Harrison Ave., Harrison 07029
Pres.—Jeff Kelly, 20 emp., *Corporate headquarters & distributor*.......... (973) 481-0600
Kelly, Inc., Myles F., 210 W. Westfield Ave., Roselle Park 07204
GM—Michael Oroake, 9 emp., *Distributor of residential & commercial*.......... (908) 245-7296
Kuiken Brothers Commercial, 485 River Dr., Garfield 07026
Store Mgr.—Kenneth Kuiken, 25 emp., *Distributor of drywall, studs, acoustical*.......... (973) 772-0044
Kuiken Brothers Company, Inc., 145 Lake Ave., Midland Park 07432
Dir., Mktg.—Ryan Mulkeen, 70 emp., *Wholesaler of lumber*.......... (201) 652-1000
Kuiken Brothers Company, Inc., 31 State Route 10 E., Succasunna 07876
Store Mgr.—Marc Gattuso, 25 emp., *Distributor of residential & commercial*.......... (973) 584-2444
L & W Supply Corp., 126 Route 94, Blairstown 07825
Br. Mgr.—Tony Amadales, 5 emp., *Distributor of building materials,*.......... (908) 362-6103
Majestic Fence Co., Inc., 6839 US Highway 9, Howell 07731
Pres.—Ken Gorlin, 10 emp., *Distributor of residential & commercial*.......... (732) 363-8181
MarJam Supply Co., 6 International Way, Newark 07114
Sales Rep.—Steve Hartler, 60 emp., *Distributor of building materials,*.......... (973) 491-6030
MarJam Supply Co., 615 W. Delilah Rd., Pleasantville 08232
Br. Mgr.—Steve Rios, 15 emp., *Wholesaler of building materials, paint*.......... (609) 407-1234
Masda Corp., 22 Troy Rd., P.O. Box D, Whippany 07981
GM—Dan Darche, 8 emp., *Distributor of fireplaces, kitchen*.......... (973) 386-1100
Michael Halebian & Co., Inc., 557 Washington Ave., Carlstadt 07072
Pres.—Michael Halebian, Jr., 50 emp., *Distributor of floor coverings & related*.......... (201) 935-3535
Mid-State Lumber Corp., 200 Industrial Pkwy., Branchburg 08876
Ptnr. & V-P., Sales & Mktg.—Kenneth Bernstein, 50 emp., *Corporate headquarters & wholesaler* (908) 725-4900
Morak, Inc., 3 Janice Dr., Hackettstown 07840
Owner—Thomas Byrnes, 4 emp., *Distributor of windows & doors*.......... (973) 527-7470
Outwater Plastics/Industries, Inc., 24 River Rd., P.O. Box 500, Bogota 07603
Pres.—Peter Kessler, 125 emp., *Corporate headquarters & distributor*.......... (201) 498-8750
Plywood & Door Mfrs. Corp. (H Q), 1435 Morris Ave., 3rd Fl., P.O. Box 1212, Union 07083
Pres.—Juhani Haikala, 7 emp., *Corporate headquarters; wholesaler*.......... (908) 687-7890
PrimeSource Building Products, Inc., 20 Van Dyke Ave, New Brunswick 08901
GM—Scott Simmel, 30 emp., *Distributor of building materials,*.......... (732) 296-0600
Rugby ABP Corp., 60 Joseph St., Moonachie 07074
Regional Mgr.—Arsenio Alvarez, 20 emp., *Wholesaler of industrial building materials*.......... (201) 807-9701
Tri State Hardware, Inc., 5 Perina Blvd., Cherry Hill 08003
Pres.—Rose Palladino, 6 emp., *Distributor of architectural doors,*.......... (856) 810-0990
Tri-County Building Supplies, Inc., 14 Reading Ave., Cape May Court House 08210
Br. Mgr.—Gary Rousseau, 20 emp., *Distributor of building supplies, including*.......... (609) 465-5021
Tri-County Building Supplies, Inc., 1001 Doughty Rd., Pleasantville 08232
Pres.—Stephen Gross, 30 emp., *Corporate headquarters & distributor*.......... (609) 646-0950
Tulnoy Lumber, Inc., 9-D Raskulinecz Rd., Carteret 07008
Br. Mgr.—Tony Ginese, 25 emp., *Wholesaler of lumber*.......... (732) 634-4000
Urban Millwork & Supply Corp., 90 2nd Ave., Paterson 07514
Pres.—Brett Stundel, 1 emp., *Wholesaler of wooden doors*.......... (973) 278-7072
Woodhaven Lumber & Millwork, Inc., 725 E. Bay Ave., Manahawkin 08050
Br. Mgr.—John Cadanatre, 15 emp., *Distributor of lumber, windows, doors*.......... (609) 597-1118

## 5032 Brick, stone & related construction materials

A W Eurostile, 736 Route 35, Ocean 07712
Pres.—Andrea Wyman, 10 emp., *Manufacturer & distributor of marble*.......... (732) 493-1883
Ace Crete Products, Inc., 250 Hickory Ln., Bayville 08721
Pres.—Martin E. Tanzer, 12 emp., *Manufacturer & distributor of industrial*.......... (732) 269-1400
Action Supply, Inc., 1413 Stagecoach Rd., Ocean View 08230
Pres.—Tom Tower, 50 emp., *Corporate headquarters & manufacturer*.......... (609) 390-0663
ATAK Trucking, Inc., 1341 Route 34, Matawan 07747
Pres.—Sharon Torocco, 2 emp., *Wholesaler of building materials, including*.......... (917) 912-2900
Athenia Mason Supply, Inc., 72 Mina Ave., Clifton 07011
V-P.—Ken Kievit, 20 emp., *Distributor of masonry supplies*.......... (973) 253-0570
Brida Stone, Inc., 555 Mullica Hill Rd., Glassboro 08028
Owner—Anthony Brida, 15 emp., *Wholesaler of natural stone & landscape*.......... (856) 881-1700
Classic Ceramic Tile, Inc., 272 State Route 18, Ste. 3, East Brunswick 08816
Manager—Chris Martins, 4 emp., *Wholesaler of ceramic tile & stone*.......... (732) 390-7700
Classic Tile, Inc., 325 Pine St., P.O. Box 1066, Elizabeth 07207
Pres.—Leah Glucroft, 25 emp., *Distributor of floor coverings, including*.......... (908) 289-8400
DAL-Tile Corporation, 1250 Valley Brook Ave., Lyndhurst 07071
Stone Mgr.—Peter Chomyszak, 15 emp., *Distributor of ceramic, porcelain &*.......... (201) 729-0203
DAL-Tile Sales Service Center 186, 2030 Springdale Rd., Ste. 100, Cherry Hill 08003
Manager—John Huff, 9 emp., *Distributor of porcelain & ceramic*.......... (856) 489-3335
Designer Source, Inc., 2139 State Route 35, Holmdel 07733
Ptnr.—Laura Beglin, 6 emp., *Distributor of architectural mouldings*.......... (732) 264-7775
Dubell Lumber Co., 731 Cuthbert Blvd., Cherry Hill 08002
Br. Mgr.—Jim Eaise, 20 emp., *Wholesaler of building materials &*.......... (856) 665-9100
E & B Distributors, Inc., 400 Route 22 E., Bridgewater 08807
Pres.—Brian Skowronek, 12 emp., *Distributor of plumbing & heating supplies*.......... (732) 469-2266
Earle Asphalt Company, 1800 Route 34, Bldg. 2, Ste. 205, Wall 07719
Pres.—Walter R. Earle II, 25 emp., *Company headquarters & distributor*.......... (732) 308-1113
Extech Building Materials, 100 Bogert St., Closter 07624
Br. Mgr.—Bob Lippe, 35 emp., *Custom natural stone fabrication &*.......... (201) 768-2133
Extech Building Materials, Inc., 385 Asbury Rd., Farmingdale 07727
Manager—Bob Lippe, 7 emp., *Distributor of masonry materials &*.......... (732) 919-3340
Extech Building Materials, Inc., 61-89 Ave. K, Newark 07105
Pres.—Timothy Feury, 50 emp., *Distributor of brick, stone, construction*.......... (973) 274-3340
Garden State Tile Distributors, Inc., 1290 Route 130, Dayton 08810
Off. Mgr.—Jill France, 20 emp., *Distributor of floor tile*.......... (732) 329-0860
Garden State Tile Distributors, Inc., 267 Route 46 W., Dover 07801
Opers. Mgr.—Mark Nielsen, 4 emp., *Distributor of ceramic, porcelain &*.......... (973) 366-5035

Garden State Tile Distributors, Inc., 472 E. Westfield Ave., Roselle Park 07204
Br. & Opers. Mgr.—Anna Petrosky, 10 emp., *Distributor of wall & floor tiles* ........ (908) 241-4900
Garden State Tile Distributors, Inc., 790 S. Route 73, West Berlin 08091
GM—Nancy Scanlan, 15 emp., *Distributor of ceramic floor tile* ........ (856) 753-0300
Garden State Tile Distributors, Inc. (H Q), 5001 Industrial Rd., Farmingdale 07727
Pres.—Stephen Fischer, 20 emp., *Corporate headquarters; distributor* ........ (732) 938-6675
Haddonstone (USA) Ltd., 201 Heller Pl., Bellmawr 08031
V-P.—Myla Policarpo, 8 emp., *Distributor of fine cast limestone* ........ (856) 931-7011
Hanson Aggregates Better Materials Corp., 1401 Route 610, Woodbine 08270
Plt. Mgr.—Al Lorenzo, 12 emp., *Distributor of commercial sand & gravel* ........ (856) 447-4294
High Bridge Stone Co., Inc., 187 Marsh St., Newark 07114
Chrm.—John Bitow, 10 emp., *Wholesaler of Indian Belgian block* ........ (973) 344-5522
Ideal Tile Importing Co., Inc., 2232 Route 9 S., Howell 07731
Pres.—Mario Grillo, 11 emp., *Distributor of floor & wall tiles* ........ (732) 308-1008
Klinges, Inc., Charles A., 790 S. Mill Rd., Absecon 08201
Co-Pres.—Bob Klinges, Sr., 3 emp., *Distributor of ceramic, granite & marble* ........ (609) 641-7755
Lotus Exim International, Inc., 16 Leliarts Ln., Elmwood Park 07407
Pres.—Rajendra Kankariya, 15 emp., *Wholesaler of granite & marble* ........ (201) 475-2810
M & N Boychuk Stone Co., Inc., 360 U.S. Highway 22, P.O. Box 133, Springfield 07081
Pres.—Marshall Maudsley, 5 emp., *Distributor of natural stone, flagstone* ........ (973) 376-1333
M S International, Inc., 36 Brunswick Ave., Edison 08817
Br. Mgr.—Kirit Shah, 15 emp., *Distributor of natural stone, including* ........ (732) 650-1815
Medford Cedar Products, Inc., 59 Old Red Lion Rd., Vincentown 08088
Pres.—Albin E. Scheibner, 7 emp., *Manufacturer of cedar garden structures* ........ (609) 859-1400
Midlantic Supply, LLC, 8000 Midlantic Dr., Ste. 200-N., P.O. Box 506, Mount Laurel 08054
Owner—Diane Disanto, 5 emp., *Distributor of waterworks & sewer equipment* ........ (856) 813-5014
National Tile & Mosaic, 175 Moonachie Rd., Moonachie 07074
Pres.—Leila Mehrnia, 3 emp., *Wholesaler of limestone, stone & marble* ........ (201) 807-9800
Pierson Materials, Inc., R. E., 151 Industrial Dr., Williamstown 08094
Asst. Treas.—Joe Huffner, 10 emp., *Distributor of ready-mixed concrete* ........ (856) 740-2400
Riverdale Environmental Recycling, 1 Riverdale Rd., Riverdale 07457
Pres.—Andrew Flockard, 20 emp., *Manufacturer of mulch, compost & soil* ........ (973) 616-6654
Rocket Building Supply Co., Inc., 13 Hewson Ave., Waldwick 07463
Pres.—Ron Durante, 5 emp., *Distributor of building supplies, including* ........ (201) 652-8884
Tri-County Building Supplies, Inc., 211 Stites & Railroad Aves., Cape May Court House 08210
GM—Gary Rouseau, 14 emp., *Wholesaler of roofing, siding & sheet* ........ (609) 465-7839

## 5033 Roofing, siding & insulation materials

ABC Supply, 41 N. Pearl St., Bridgeton 08302
Br. Mgr.—Patrick Torinese, 4 emp., *Distributor of vinyl, aluminum, wood* ........ (856) 455-4888
ABC Supply Co., Inc., 5004 Route 130, Riverside 08075
Br. Mgr.—Ray Coxe, 5 emp., *Wholesaler of roofing, siding, windows* ........ (856) 461-5252
ABC Supply Co., Inc., Bradco Div., 45 Samworth Rd., Clifton 07012
Br. Mgr.—Greg Anderson, 10 emp., *Distributor of roofing materials, signs* ........ (973) 777-3663
ABC Supply Co., Inc., Bradco Div., 691 New Hampshire Ave., Lakewood 08701
Dir., Sales—Larry Gelber, 50 emp., *Distributor of roofing materials, including* ........ (732) 905-9355
ABC Supply Co., Inc., Bradco Div., 725 W. Delilah Rd., Pleasantville 08232
Sales Mgr.—Mark Morrison, 13 emp., *Distributor of residential & commercial* ........ (609) 484-9100
ABC Supply Co., Inc., Bradco Div., 301 Brunswick Ave., Trenton 08618
Br. Mgr.—Richard Mattson, 10 emp., *Distributor of building materials,* ........ (609) 393-7000
Allied Building Products Corp., 11 Cadillac Rd., Box 1838, Burlington 08016
Br. Mgr.—Bill Oratello, 15 emp., *Distributor of residential & commercial* ........ (609) 386-5500
Allied Building Products Corp., 15 E. Union Ave., East Rutherford 07073
Chrm.—Michael Lynch, 200 emp., *Corporate headquarters & wholesaler* ........ (201) 507-8400
Allied Building Products Corp., 850 Flora St., Elizabeth 07201
Br. Mgr.—Thomas Meola, 10 emp., *Distributor of building materials &* ........ (908) 820-9790
Allied Building Products Corp., 406 State Route 23 N., Franklin 07416
Br. Mgr.—Jerome Newman, 12 emp., *Distributor of building materials &* ........ (973) 827-4113
Allied Building Products Corp., 27-33 Franklin Tpke., Mahwah 07430
Br. Mgr.—John Rogan, 10 emp., *Distributor of building materials &* ........ (201) 529-3300
Allied Building Products Corp., 27 Kentucky Ave., Paterson 07503
Br. Mgr.—Adam Carten, 5 emp., *Distributor of building materials,* ........ (973) 357-1600
Allied Building Products Corp., 320 W. Water St., Toms River 08753
Br. Mgr.—Gary Finn, 10 emp., *Distributor of building materials &* ........ (732) 341-4767
Allied Building Products Corp., 595 Union Blvd., Totowa 07512
Br. Mgr.—Robert Gall, 10 emp., *Distributor of building materials &* ........ (973) 790-5500
Allied Building Products Corp., 2065 State Route 34, Wall Township 07719
Br. Mgr.—Gary Finn, 5 emp., *Distributor of building materials &* ........ (732) 449-3355
Arzee Supply, 1905 Swarthmore Ave., Lakewood 08701
Br. Mgr.—Paul Maslanek, 20 emp., *Distributor of building materials &* ........ (201) 935-0800
Arzee Supply Corp. Of New Jersey, 15 E. Frederick Pl., Cedar Knolls 07927
Br. Mgr.—Ed Jacobus, 48 emp., *Distributor of building materials &* ........ (973) 267-1576
Arzee Supply Corp. Of New Jersey, 450 York St., Elizabeth 07201
Sales Mgr.—John Esteves, 7 emp., *Distributor of building materials &* ........ (908) 820-3700
Atlantic Window & Door, Inc., 1608 Dubac Rd., Wall Township 07719
Pres.—Mark Daly, 5 emp., *Distributor of home improvement products* ........ (732) 793-2452
Extech Building Materials, Inc., 61-89 Ave. K, Newark 07105
Pres.—Timothy Feury, 50 emp., *Distributor of brick, stone, construction* ........ (973) 274-3340
Johns Manville, 437 North Grove St., Berlin 08009
Hum. Res. Mgr.—Joe Catania, 14 emp., *Distributor of fiberglass* ........ (856) 768-7000
Kelly, Inc., Myles F., 43-57 Harrison Ave., Harrison 07029
Pres.—Jeff Kelly, 20 emp., *Corporate headquarters & distributor* ........ (973) 481-0600
Kelly, Inc., Myles F., 210 W. Westfield Ave., Roselle Park 07204
GM—Michael Oroake, 9 emp., *Distributor of residential & commercial* ........ (908) 245-7296
Kuiken Brothers Company, Inc., 31 State Route 10 E., Succasunna 07876
Store Mgr.—Marc Gattuso, 25 emp., *Distributor of residential & commercial* ........ (973) 584-2444
L & W Supply Corp., 126 Route 94, Blairstown 07825
Br. Mgr.—Tony Amadales, 5 emp., *Distributor of building materials,* ........ (908) 362-6103
MarJam Supply Co., 6 International Way, Newark 07114
Sales Rep.—Steve Hartler, 60 emp., *Distributor of building materials,* ........ (973) 491-6030
MarJam Supply Co., 615 W. Delilah Rd., Pleasantville 08232
Br. Mgr.—Steve Rios, 15 emp., *Wholesaler of building materials, paint* ........ (609) 407-1234
PrimeSource Building Products, Inc., 20 Van Dyke Ave, New Brunswick 08901
GM—Scott Simmel, 30 emp., *Distributor of building materials,* ........ (732) 296-0600
Tri-County Building Supplies, Inc., 14 Reading Ave., Cape May Court House 08210
Br. Mgr.—Gary Rousseau, 20 emp., *Distributor of building supplies, including* ........ (609) 465-5021
Tri-County Building Supplies, Inc., 211 Stites & Railroad Aves., Cape May Court House 08210
GM—Gary Rouseau, 14 emp., *Wholesaler of roofing, siding & sheet* ........ (609) 465-7839
Tri-County Building Supplies, Inc., 1001 Doughty Rd., Pleasantville 08232
Pres.—Stephen Gross, 30 emp., *Corporate headquarters & distributor* ........ (609) 646-0950

## 5039 Construction materials, nec

A. H. Harris & Sons, Inc., 160 Fairfield Rd., Fairfield 07004
GM—Dennis Orozco, 10 emp., *Distributor of construction equipment* ........ (973) 227-1600
A-Able Fence Builders, 28 Lakeside Ave., West Orange 07052
Owner—William Byrne, 10 emp., *Wholesaler & installer of wooden &* ........ (973) 325-1900
Ahle Co., Inc., J. M., 190 William St., Ste. 2-D, South River 08882
Pres.—John Ahle, 29 emp., *Rebar fabrication & distributor of* ........ (732) 238-1700
American Fence Co., 326 U.S. Highway 46, Saddle Brook 07663
Owner—Piero Mosca, 10 emp., *Wholesaler of wooden, metal, aluminum* ........ (973) 546-4373
Bendheim, 61 Willett St., Bldg. PP, Passaic 07055
Pres.—Robert Jason, 50 emp., *Distributor of specialty & decorative* ........ (973) 471-1733
Innovative Glass & Mirror, Inc., 15 Chambersbridge Rd., Lakewood 08701
Pres.—Dave Panebianco, 4 emp., *Distributor of architectural glass* ........ (732) 961-2267
Mabey Inc., 218 N. Randolphville Rd., Piscataway 08854
Depot Mgr.—Aaron Lee, 13 emp., *Distributor of structural steel components* ........ (732) 752-6600
Majestic Fence Co., Inc., 6839 US Highway 9, Howell 07731
Pres.—Ken Gorlin, 10 emp., *Distributor of residential & commercial* ........ (732) 363-8181
Modern Fence & Construction, LLC, 1527 Livingston Ave., North Brunswick 08902
Pres.—Kenneth Walewski, 3 emp., *Manufacturer & wholesaler of PVC &* ........ (732) 238-5588
Modern Technologies Group, Inc., 3 Reeves Station Rd., Medford 08055
Pres.—Ric Cohen, 30 emp., *Corporate headquarters & distributor* ........ (609) 714-8900
Williams Scotsman, Inc., 35 Ford Ln., Kearny 07032
GM—Greg Downing, 100 emp., *Wholesaler of modular buildings, mobile* ........ (973) 589-1234

## 5043 Photographic equipment & supplies

Cartridge World Oakhurst, 1815 State Route 35, Oakhurst 07755
Owner—Joe Betesh, 2 emp., *Remanufactured inkjet & toner printer* ........ (732) 531-4232
Electronic Measurement Laboratories, Inc., 668 Easton Ave., Somerset 08873
Owner—Richard J. Pleconis, 4 emp., *Distributor of industrial gas detectors* ........ (732) 846-4029
Gill Assocs. Identification Systems, LLC, 2025 Hamburg Tpke., Ste. M, Wayne 07470
Owner & Member—Dave Gill, 6 emp., *Distributor of photo identification* ........ (973) 835-5456
Micron Optics, 14 Ridgedale Ave., Ste. 125, Cedar Knolls 07927
Pres.—Peter Burboeck, 7 emp., *Distributor of microscopes, cameras* ........ (973) 267-5047
QLT.com, 238 Boundary Rd., Unit 304, Marlboro 07746
Owner—Ken Kendes, 25 emp., *Distributor of photographic heat transfer* ........ (732) 431-0740
RPL Supplies, Inc., 141 Lanza Ave., Bldg. 3-A, Garfield 07026
★ Pres.—Michael Kaminski, 18 emp., *Wholesaler of printing equipment &* ........ (973) 767-0880

## 5044 Office equipment

Addressing Machine Supply, 1290 Central Ave., Hillside 07205
Pres.—Herbert Singe, 13 emp., *Distributor of new, refurbished & pre-owned* ........ (908) 289-7900
Advanced Business Machines Co., 230 Randolph Rd., Freehold 07728
Owner—J. Respler, 4 emp., *Wholesaler of office equipment, printers* ........ (732) 431-1464
Allister Business Systems, Inc., 205 E. 1st Ave., Roselle 07203
Pres.—David Offenberg, 30 emp., *Distributor of office equipment, including* ........ (732) 972-8400
AMERICAN Time Recorder, 2661 Brunetta Dr., Vineland 08360
Sales & Serv. Mgr.—Bryan Presgraves, 1 emp., *Distributor of computerized time clocks* ........ (856) 691-7976
Asset Recovery Specialists, Inc., 3 Killdeer Ct., Ste. 303, Swedesboro 08085
Br. Mgr.—Joe Gonnella, 7 emp., *Wholesaler of used computers, computer* ........ (856) 467-9822
Atlantic Time Systems, 112 N. 8th St., Vineland 08360
Pres., CEO—Norton D. Fern, 3 emp., *Distributor of PC-based & Internet* ........ (856) 692-9594
Cartridge World, 830 Franklin Ave., Franklin Lakes 07417
Pres.—Jeffrey W. Bier, 3 emp., *Distributor of ink & toner cartridges* ........ (201) 891-0990
Cartridge World Of Wayne, LLC, 1055 Hamburg Tpke., Wayne 07470
Owner—Rosemarie Peluso, 4 emp., *Eco-friendly remanufactured printer* ........ (973) 696-2880
Computerist, Inc., 15 Smull Ave., Ste. A, Caldwell 07006
Pres.—Anthony Camilleri, 5 emp., *Rebuilt computers & computer network* ........ (973) 226-0100
Dornisch Enterprises, Inc., 112 Cromwell Ct., Woodbury 08096
Pres.—Edward C. Dornisch, 3 emp., *Distributor of commercial & residential* ........ (856) 863-1225
Equipment Solutions Corp., 622 State Route 10, Ste. 20, Whippany 07981
Pres., GM—Bret Schwerdt, 4 emp., *Distributor of mailing, packaging &* ........ (973) 887-9277
General Reproduction Products, 23 McKee Dr., Mahwah 07430
Owner—Wayne Alexander, 13 emp., *Wholesaler of large-format copiers* ........ (201) 934-0027
Integrated Document Technologies, 1 Cardinal Dr., Little Falls 07424
Ptnr. & Treas.—Gerard Perillo, 20 emp., *Distributor of office equipment, including* ........ (973) 237-1200
Laser Save, 843 State Route 33, Ste. 11, Freehold 07728
Pres.—Alan D. Yoss, 18 emp., *Remanufactured compatible color & monochrome* ........ (732) 431-3339
Neopost, Inc., 2 Ridgedale Ave., 1st Fl., Cedar Knolls 07927
GM—Steven Kaplan, 40 emp., *Distributor of postage & folding machines* ........ (973) 647-6700
Ronstan Paper & Packaging, 72 James Way, Eatontown 07724
Pres.—William F. LaMorte, 12 emp., *Distributor of industrial & personal* ........ (732) 389-1040
Superior Office Systems, Inc., 19 Gross Ave., Edison 08837
Pres.—Phil Blank, 50 emp., *Distributor of office equipment, including* ........ (732) 738-0093
Time Systems International, Inc., 142 S. Van Brunt St., Englewood 07631
Pres.—Samuel Gleich, 20 emp., *Corporate headquarters & distributor* ........ (973) 472-2202
United Stationers Supply Co., 100 Liberty Way, Cranbury 08512
Br. Mgr.—Wayne Scott, 100 emp., *Wholesaler of office equipment, furniture* ........ (609) 619-4000

## 5045 Computers, peripherals & software

Advanced Business Machines Co., 230 Randolph Rd., Freehold 07728
Owner—J. Respler, 4 emp., *Wholesaler of office equipment, printers* ........ (732) 431-1464
Advanced Recovery, Inc., 50 Grafton Ave., Newark 07104
Pres., GM—Mark Rea, 15 emp., *Wholesaler of used electronic & computer* ........ (973) 485-9100
Allister Business Systems, Inc., 205 E. 1st Ave., Roselle 07203
Pres.—David Offenberg, 30 emp., *Distributor of office equipment, including* ........ (732) 972-8400
Asset Recovery Specialists, Inc., 3 Killdeer Ct., Ste. 303, Swedesboro 08085
Br. Mgr.—Joe Gonnella, 7 emp., *Wholesaler of used computers, computer* ........ (856) 467-9822
BarCodeAmerica.com, 144 Shunpike Rd., P.O. Box 506, Madison 07940
Pres.—Robert W. Rack, 10 emp., *Systems integration & distributor of* ........ (973) 377-8182
Computer Wholesalers, Inc., 715 Willow Grove St., Ste. 5, Hackettstown 07840
Pres.—Ivan Somyk, 25 emp., *Wholesaler of computer equipment &* ........ (908) 684-0802
Computerist, Inc., 15 Smull Ave., Ste. A, Caldwell 07006
Pres.—Anthony Camilleri, 5 emp., *Rebuilt computers & computer network* ........ (973) 226-0100
Global Business Dimensions Inc., 220 W. Parkway, Ste. 8, Pompton Plains 07444
Pres., CEO—Sanjay Prasad, 25 emp., *Manufacturer & distributor of personal* ........ (973) 831-5866
HyperTech, Inc., 279 Central Ave., Ste. B, Metuchen 08840
Pres.—Ann Hsu, 10 emp., *Computer network systems integration* ........ (732) 635-1755
InduKey North America, LLC, 329 Moore Ave., Leonia 07605
Pres.—Roland Weimer, 2 emp., *Distributor of industrial, medical* ........ (877) 588-2172



★ Indicates new listing this edition.

Innovative Marking Systems, Inc., 105 Forest Rd., Fanwood 07023
Owner—Harry Fattenyatz, 5 emp., *Distributor of marking, labeling &* ..... (908) 322-2900
Interactive Computer Center, Inc., 482 Brick Blvd., Brick 08723
Owner—Steve Byrnes, 10 emp., *Distributor of computer software* ..... (732) 477-5800
Lucille Maud Corp., 513 N. Olden Ave., Trenton 08638
Pres.—Louis Muirhead, 8 emp., *Computer systems integration & distributor* ..... (609) 393-7555
O'Brien Co., Inc., J., 40 Commerce St., Springfield 07081
Pres., CEO—Sharmay O'Brien, 20 emp., *Manufacturer of lanyards, badge reels* ..... (973) 379-8844
Princeton Computer Support, Inc., 3490 U.S. Highway 1, Ste. 15-E, Princeton 08540
Pres.—Kathleen Sneedse, 7 emp., *Distributor of IT network servers &* ..... (609) 520-0770
Rack Design Group Inc. / BarCodeAmerica.com, 81 Clinton Rd., Fairfield 07004
Pres.—Robert Rack, 10 emp., *Manufacturer & distributor of custom* ..... (973) 377-8182
SHI International Corp., 290 Davidson Ave., Somerset 08873
Chrm., CEO—Leo Koguan, 1100 emp., *Wholesaler of computer hardware & software* ..... (732) 477-6479
Superior Office Systems, Inc., 19 Gross Ave., Edison 08837
Pres.—Phil Blank, 50 emp., *Distributor of office equipment, including* ..... (732) 738-0093
Thanks For Being Green, LLC, 5070-B Central Hwy., Merchantville 08109
★ Pres.—John Martorano, Jr., 10 emp., *Distributor of parts reclaimed from* ..... (856) 333-0991
Worldwide Supply, LLC, 1 Park Dr., Franklin 07416
Mng. Ptnr.—Jay Van Orden, 30 emp., *Wholesaler of new, excess, secondary* ..... (973) 823-6400

## 5046 Commercial equipment, nec

American Hanger & Fixture Corp., 687 Lehigh Ave., Union 07083
Pres.—Phillip Steinhardt, 6 emp., *Distributor of garment hangers, clothing* ..... (908) 687-1776
American Showcase & Foodservice Equipment, Inc., 19 Commerce Rd., Unit H, Fairfield 07004
Pres.—Tony Latallade, 6 emp., *Custom fabrication & distributor of* ..... (973) 227-1277
Beisler America, LLC, 1841 E. Elizabeth Ave., P.O. Box 1683, Linden 07036
Pres.—Ron Liang, 5 emp., *Distributor of industrial & commercial* ..... (908) 925-4040
Belleville Scale & Balance, LLC, 50 S. Center St., Orange 07050
Ptnr. & Pres.—Thomas Rockhill, 22 emp., *Distributor of industrial, truck &* ..... (973) 759-4487
Chef's Corner, 178 U.S. Highway 206, Ste. B, Flanders 07836
Store Mgr.—Theresa Berntsen, 5 emp., *Wholesaler of restaurant & institutional* ..... (973) 691-1500
Coldstat Refrigeration, 60 Eisenhower Dr., Paramus 07652
Owner & Pres.—Ion Sarkisian, 15 emp., *Wholesaler of commercial refrigeration* ..... (201) 599-1200
Dreyco, Inc., 263 Veterans Blvd., Carlstadt 07072
Pres.—Michael Borghard, 15 emp., *Distributor of automotive parts, tools* ..... (201) 896-9000
Equipment Solutions Corp., 622 State Route 10, Ste. 20, Whippany 07981
Pres., GM—Bret Schwerdt, 4 emp., *Distributor of mailing, packaging &* ..... (973) 887-9277
Erika Record, LLC, 37 Atlantic Way, Clifton 07012
GM—Max Oehler, 10 emp., *Wholesaler of commercial baking equipment* ..... (973) 614-8500
Excellent Bakery Equipment Co., 315 Fairfield Rd., Fairfield 07004
Pres.—Karin Seruga, 15 emp., *Manufacturer & distributor of bakery* ..... (973) 244-1664
E-Z Edge, Inc., 6119 Adams St., West New York 07093
★ Owner—Michael Maffei, 4 emp., *Distributor of food processing equipment* ..... (201) 295-1171
K C S Metal Products, Inc., 415 Ferry St., Newark 07105
Pres.—Carmen Khuu, 5 emp., *Wholesaler of wire shelving* ..... (973) 578-2688
Luca Laundry Equipment, Inc., 1500 W. Blancke St., Linden 07036
V-P., Reg.—Richard R. Luca, 14 emp., *Distributor of commercial & industrial* ..... (908) 862-2200
M&J Frank, Inc., 29 Eagle Rock Ave., East Hanover 07936
Pres.—Andrew Becker, 13 emp., *Wholesaler of foodservice & restaurant* ..... (973) 887-1040
New Brunswick Saw Service, Inc., 400 Lincoln Blvd., Middlesex 08846
Pres.—Michael Schaefer, 20 emp., *Distributor of meat processing equipment* ..... (908) 755-2366
Oberg & Lindquist Corp., 671 Broadway, Westwood 07675
Pres.—John Oberg, 50 emp., *Distributor of industrial, residential* ..... (201) 664-1300
PC Tan, Inc., 1040 Wilt Ave., Ridgefield 07657
Pres.—Susan Miller, 35 emp., *Corporate headquarters & distributor* ..... (201) 943-6100
Restaurant Depot, LLC, 1050 Thomas Busch Memorial Hwy., Pennsauken 08110
GM—Paul Jensen, 75 emp., *Wholesaler of general line groceries* ..... (856) 488-4288
RONDO Inc. USA, 51 Joseph St., Moonachie 07074
Pres.—Jerry Murphy, 15 emp., *Distributor of commercial & industrial* ..... (201) 229-9700
Sanzo Ltd., 35 Munsee Dr., Cranford 07016
Owner & Pres.—Carol Sanzo, 5 emp., *Wholesaler of industrial, commercial* ..... (908) 276-6654
Savco Restaurant Equipment, Inc., 600 Main St., Paterson 07503
Owner—Sam Scorpo, 7 emp., *Distributor of new & used restaurant* ..... (973) 523-4464
Styles Mfg. Co., Inc., A. E., 416 Richmond Ave., P.O. Box 1306, Point Pleasant Beach 08742
Pres.—John Criscuolo, 15 emp., *Manufacturer of car wash detergents* ..... (732) 899-0872
WMS Gaming, Inc., 2511 Fire Rd., Ste. A-10, Egg Harbor Township 08234
GM—David Rifkin, 20 emp., *Distributor of slot machines* ..... (609) 569-0100

## 5047 Medical & hospital equipment & supplies

Apria Healthcare, Inc., 1 Frassetto Way, Ste. F, Lincoln Park 07035
Br. Mgr.—Rosemary Berkowitz, 30 emp., *Distributor of durable medical equipment* ..... (973) 305-0099
Apria Healthcare, Inc., 118 Burrs Rd., Ste. C, Mount Holly 08060
Br. Mgr.—Christopher Lange, 50 emp., *Distributor of medical equipment &* ..... (609) 265-2190
Bailey Packaging Co., Inc., 217 Prospect Ave., Ste. 8-3B, Cranford 07016
Pres.—Vincent Bailey, 3 emp., *Distributor of packaging materials,* ..... (908) 759-0991
Cenmed Enterprises, 121 Jersey Ave., New Brunswick 08901
Sales Mgr.—Rizwan Chaudhry, 12 emp., *Manufacturer of diagnostic drug tests* ..... (732) 447-1100
Cobalt Medical Supply, Inc., 4 Haul Rd., Wayne 07470
Opers. Mgr.—Tamar Rees, 15 emp., *Distributor of medical equipment &* ..... (973) 305-0730
Diagnostix Plus, Inc., 197 Cedar Ln., Ste. 1, Teaneck 07666
Founder, Pres. & CEO—Don Bogutski, 6 emp., *Remanufactured nuclear medicine imaging* . (201) 530-5505
DRG International, Inc., 841 Mountain Ave., Springfield 07081
Pres., CEO—Cyril E. Geacintov, 25 emp., *Distributor of diagnostic kits* ..... (973) 564-7555
Fortrad Instruments, LLC, 8 Franklin Rd., Mendham 07945
Pres.—Karl H. Grohn, 2 emp., *Distributor of hand-held ophthalmic* ..... (973) 543-2371
GlobePharma, Inc., 2-B Janine Pl., New Brunswick 08901
Pres.—Sanni Raju, 10 emp., *Wholesaler of pharmaceutical solid* ..... (732) 296-9700
Hanger Prosthetics & Orthotics, 201 White Horse Rd. E., Voorhees 08043
Br. Mgr.—Dennise Dehaven, 3 emp., *Distributor of prosthetics & orthopedic* ..... (856) 309-0709
Independent Imaging, 1819 Underwood Blvd., Unit 1, Delran 08075
Owner & Hum. Res. Mgr.—John Thomas Walsh, 10 emp., *Distributor of medical imaging equipment* (856) 764-9729
Jefferson Medical & Imaging, Inc., 5470 Berkshire Valley Rd., P.O. Box 254, Oak Ridge 07438
Pres., CEO—Susan E. Kurylo, 15 emp., *Distributor of medical imaging equipment* ..... (973) 697-5077
Lymphedema Products, LLC, 750 State Route 34, Ste. 7, Matawan 07747
Owner & COO—Max Salas, 5 emp., *Distributor of medical supplies, including* ..... (732) 290-2888
M. O. Industries, Inc., 9 Whippany Rd., Bldg. B1-2, Whippany 07981
Pres.—Alex Maier, 6 emp., *Distributor of pharmaceutical handling* ..... (973) 386-9228
Matrix Distributors, Inc., 110 Tices Ln., Ste. 5-B, East Brunswick 08816
Ptnr.—Seth Grumet, 50 emp., *Corporate headquarters & distributor* ..... (732) 698-9991
McKesson Medical-Surgical, 1130 Commerce Blvd., Swedesboro 08085
Dist. Mgr.—Dan Castro, 140 emp., *Distributor of medical supplies* ..... (856) 241-1709
Medrecon, Inc., 257 South Ave., Garwood 07027
Pres., CEO—Gary P. Sitcer, 8 emp., *New & rebuilt OR & surgical tables* ..... (908) 789-2050
Med-X International, Inc., 20 Foster St., Bergenfield 07621
Pres.—Gary Malajian, 3 emp., *Distributor of medical supplies* ..... (201) 387-8556
Med-X-Ray Co., Inc., 356 Glenwood Ave., East Orange 07017
Pres.—Anthony Irwin, 6 emp., *Distributor of x-ray imaging equipment* ..... (973) 673-8822
Midwest Medical Supply Company, LLC, 200 Seaview Dr., Secaucus 07094
GM—Kevin McDonald, 11 emp., *Distributor of surgical & medical supplies* ..... (201) 223-4602
Other Orthodontic Co., Inc., 22 Gail Ct., Sparta 07871
Pres.—Jon Bergeron, 9 emp., *Manufacturer of commercial wooden cabinets* ..... (973) 383-8662
Owens & Minor, Inc., 1220 Forest Pkwy., Paulsboro 08066
Reg. V-P.—Mike Nugent, 55 emp., *Distributor of medical & surgical supplies* ..... (856) 423-9900
PSS/World Medical, Inc., 208 Passaic Ave., Ste. 2, Fairfield 07004
GM—Jason Bennett, 50 emp., *Distributor of medical supplies, equipment* ..... (973) 775-8600
Sullivan Dental Products, Inc., 45 U.S. Highway 46, Montville 07058
Manager—George Khoury, 60 emp., *Distributor of dental, medical & veterinarian* ..... (973) 227-3533

## 5048 Ophthalmic goods

Lab-Tech, Inc., 103 Stonehurst Ct., Northvale 07647
Pres., CEO—Michael Pildes, 8 emp., *Distributor of ophthalmic lenses &* ..... (201) 784-1093
Nassau Lens Co., Inc., 160 LeGrand Ave., Northvale 07647
Pres.—Maureen Cavanaugh, 50 emp., *Corporate headquarters & distributor* ..... (201) 767-8033
Safilo USA, Inc. (H Q), 801 Jefferson Rd., Parsippany 07054
Pres., COO—Ross Brown Lee, 350 emp., *Corporate headquarters; distributor* ..... (973) 952-2800

## 5049 Professional equipment & supplies, nec

Across International, LLC, 111 Dorsa Ave., Livingston 07039
★ Member—Rentian Huang, 5 emp., *Distributor of laboratory equipment* ..... (888) 988-0899
Alltest Instruments, 500 Central Ave., Farmingdale 07727
Pres.—Nathan Nelson, 18 emp., *Distributor of testing equipment, including* ..... (732) 919-3339
Analytical Sales & Services, Inc., 237 W. Parkway, Ste. 1, Pompton Plains 07444
Pres.—David A. Isom, 11 emp., *Manufacturer & distributor of laboratory* ..... (973) 616-0700
Bailey Packaging Co., Inc., 217 Prospect Ave., Ste. 8-3B, Cranford 07016
Pres.—Vincent Bailey, 3 emp., *Distributor of packaging materials,* ..... (908) 759-0991
Belair Instrument Co., Inc., 36 Commerce St., P.O. Box 619, Springfield 07081
Pres.—David Patterson, 32 emp., *Wholesaler of laboratory equipment* ..... (973) 912-8900
Blake Industries, Inc., 660 Jerusalem Rd., Scotch Plains 07076
Pres.—Dave Rognlie, 10 emp., *Distributor of scientific instruments* ..... (908) 233-7240
Colex Imaging, Inc., 55-57 Bushes Ln., Elmwood Park 07407
Pres.—Werner Waden, 26 emp., *Manufacturer & distributor of wide-format* ..... (201) 265-5670
Durawear Glove & Safety, Inc., 30 Royal Rd., Ste. 4, Flemington 08822
Pres.—William Archipoli, 5 emp., *Distributor of industrial safety equipment* ..... (908) 284-0776
Enviropore, Inc., P.O. Box 443, Lumberton 08048
Pres.—Tom Bintliff, 5 emp., *Distributor of industrial environmental* ..... (609) 261-1588
Friedrich & Dimmock, Inc., 2127 Wheaton Ave., P.O. Box 230, Millville 08332
CEO—Joseph A. Plumbo, 45 emp., *Manufacturer of precision glass & quartz* ..... (856) 825-0305
Glen Mills Inc., 220 Delawanna Ave., Clifton 07014
Pres.—Peter Kendall, 10 emp., *Distributor of sample preparation laboratory* ..... (973) 777-0777
IBF Corp., 44 Plauderville Ave., Garfield 07026
Sr. V-P.—Amauri Augusto, 28 emp., *Distributor of graphic arts equipment* ..... (973) 546-0055
J & H Berge, Inc., 4111 S. Clinton Ave., South Plainfield 07080
Pres.—Steven N. Krupp, 17 emp., *Distributor of laboratory supplies* ..... (908) 561-1234
Labnet International, Inc., 31 Mayfield Ave., Edison 08837
Pres.—Gerry Cooney, 40 emp., *Distributor of laboratory centrifuges* ..... (732) 417-0700
Metro America Sales, Inc., 137 South Ave., Fanwood 07023
Pres.—Harold Nevins, 3 emp., *Wholesaler of jewelry machinery, tools* ..... (908) 490-0001
Micron Optics, 14 Ridgedale Ave., Ste. 125, Cedar Knolls 07927
Pres.—Peter Burboeck, 7 emp., *Distributor of microscopes, cameras* ..... (973) 267-5047
Mingolo Precision Products, Inc., 174 S. Main St., Ste. 1, Hackensack 07601
Pres.—Louis Mingolo, 22 emp., *Wholesaler of surveying equipment &* ..... (201) 488-6300
Oberg & Lindquist Corp., 671 Broadway, Westwood 07675
Pres.—John Oberg, 50 emp., *Distributor of industrial, residential* ..... (201) 664-1300
PC Tan, Inc., 1040 Wilt Ave., Ridgefield 07657
Pres.—Susan Miller, 35 emp., *Corporate headquarters & distributor* ..... (201) 943-6100
Pfingst & Co., Inc., 105 Snyder Rd., P.O. Box 377, South Plainfield 07080
Pres.—Karl Pfingst, 10 emp., *Manufacturer & distributor of precision* ..... (908) 561-6400
R.A.H. Carpet Supplies, Inc., 80 Willow St., East Rutherford 07073
Owner—Robert Holzberg, 9 emp., *Distributor of carpet laying equipment* ..... (973) 778-4759

## 5051 Metal service centers & offices

A. H. Harris & Sons, Inc., 160 Fairfield Rd., Fairfield 07004
GM—Dennis Orozco, 10 emp., *Distributor of construction equipment* ..... (973) 227-1600
All Metals & Forge Group, LLC, 75 Lane Rd., Fairfield 07004
Pres.—Lewis A. Weiss, 39 emp., *Stainless, nickel, titanium, carbon* ..... (973) 276-5000
Allied Steel Distribution & Service Center, 118-144 Harper St., Newark 07114
Pres.—Don DeFaria, Jr., 14 emp., *Steel service center, including plate* ..... (973) 824-7347
Atlantic Track & Turnout Co., 270 Broad St., P.O. Box 1589, Bloomfield 07003
Owner—Peter Hughes, 15 emp., *Company headquarters & distributor* ..... (973) 748-5885
Atlas Bronze, 445 Bunting Ave., Trenton 08611
Owner & Pres.—Tom Smith, 25 emp., *Distributor of nonferrous metals, including* ..... (609) 599-1402
AZCO Steel Co., 1641 New Market Ave., South Plainfield 07080
Pres.—David Maslin, 30 emp., *Wholesaler of steel* ..... (908) 754-8700
Baosteel America, Inc., 85 Chestnut Ridge Rd., Ste. 210, Montvale 07645
★ Pres.—Ye Meng, 25 emp., *Metal service center* ..... (201) 307-3355
Benedict-Miller, LLC, 123 N. 8th St., Kenilworth 07033
Pres.—Jerry Shaw, 40 emp., *Wholesaler of aircraft sheet & plate* ..... (908) 497-1477
BSTC Group, Inc., 135 Kinnelon Rd., Rm. 201, Kinnelon 07405
Pres.—Andrew Berardinelli, 4 emp., *Distributor of nails* ..... (973) 492-5220
Canuso, Inc., Louis P., 401 Crown Point Rd., P.O. Box 501, Thorofare 08086
Owner—Joseph Canuso, 65 emp., *Wholesaler of pipe, valves, fittings* ..... (856) 845-2700
Capital Steel Service, LLC, 82 Stokes Ave., Trenton 08638
CEO—Allen Hickman, Sr., 27 emp., *Metal service center & structural &* ..... (609) 882-6983
Carpathian Industries, LLC, 51 Newark St., Ste. 508, Hoboken 07030
Owner & Pres.—Paul Lichstein, 9 emp., *Wholesaler of plastic & metal parts* ..... (201) 798-8883
Certified Steel Co., 199 Whitehead Rd., Hamilton 08619
CFO—Dante Germano, 82 emp., *Full-line steel service center, including* ..... (609) 890-7000
Certified Steel Company (H Q), 1333 Brunswick Ave., Ste. 200, Lawrenceville 08648
CEO—Sydney Sussman, 25 emp., *Company headquarters; steel service* ..... (609) 396-7600
De Jong Iron Works, Inc., 223-231 Godwin Ave., Paterson 07501
Pres.—Edward De Jong, 9 emp., *Structural steel fabrication & wholesaler* ..... (973) 684-1633
Dodson Global, Inc., 27 Cotters Ln., East Brunswick 08816
Br. Mgr.—Allen Goodrich, 7 emp., *Distributor of pipes & fittings* ..... (732) 238-7001

Eddie Kane Steel Products, Inc., 450 Southard St., Trenton 08638
★ Sales Rep.—Joe Kane, 10 emp., *Steel service center* ........ (609) 392-1161
Eddie Kane Steel Products, Inc. (H Q), P.O. Box 133, Spring Lake 07762
Pres.—Augustine Kane, 11 emp., *Corporate headquarters; steel service* ........ (732) 974-3339
Empire Resources, 1 Parker Plz., Fort Lee 07024
Pres., CEO—Nathan Kahn, 50 emp., *Distributor of semifinished aluminum* ........ (201) 944-2200
Fagan, Inc., Ed, 769 Susquehanna Ave., Franklin Lakes 07417
Pres.—Edward Fagan, 20 emp., *Distributor of specialty metals & alloys* ........ (201) 891-4003
Fazzio Machine & Steel, 3278 Glassboro Cross Keys Rd., P.O. Box 232, Glassboro 08028
Pres.—Phil Fazzio, 6 emp., *General machining job shop & distributor* ........ (856) 881-2832
Ferguson Enterprises, Inc., 190 Oberlin Ave. N., Lakewood 08701
GM—Jim Golini, 100 emp., *Wholesaler of industrial pipe & valves* ........ (732) 905-1000
Flame-Cut Steel, Inc., 97 E. 2nd St., Bayonne 07002
Pres.—Ramesh Nuthi, 12 emp., *Metal service center, including plate* ........ (201) 436-9300
George A. Mathewson Co., 9-11 Foundry St., Newark 07105
Pres.—Dave Czachur, 2 emp., *Wholesaler of bearings & power transmission* ........ (973) 344-0081
Gerber Metal Supply Co., 2 Boundary Rd., Somerville 08876
CEO—Glenn Gerber, 46 emp., *Steel service center, including sheets* ........ (908) 823-9150
Grammer, Dempsey & Hudson Co., 212 Rome St., Newark 07105
Pres.—James Hudson, 8 emp., *Carbon, alloy, stainless & tool bar* ........ (973) 589-8000
Hose Shop, Inc., The, 100 New England Ave., Ste. 2, Piscataway 08854
Owner & GM—Thomas Peterson, 13 emp., *Wholesaler of hydraulic & industrial* ........ (732) 562-1000
IBOCO Corp., 26 Northfield Ave., Edison 08837
Pres.—Larry M. Darst, 12 emp., *Distributor of wire duct, din rail* ........ (732) 417-0066
ICC Cable Corp., 2125 Center Ave., Ste. 401, Fort Lee 07024
Pres.—Jang Kim, 6 emp., *Distributor of cable & wire, including* ........ (201) 482-5750
Independent Metal Sales, Inc., Park & Delaware Aves., Hainesport Industrial Pk., P.O. Box 17, Hainesport 08036
Pres.—Edward Kligerman, 17 emp., *Steel service center* ........ (609) 261-8090
International Wire Co., 27-E Kearney St., Bridgewater 08807
GM—Mike Lee, 15 emp., *Distributor of steel products, including* ........ (732) 968-8122
Jen-Cyn Enterprises, Inc., 407 Atlantic Ave., Camden 08104
Pres.—Carol Clements, 45 emp., *Wholesaler of galvanized & coated metal* ........ (856) 541-7400
Kennedy Cos., The, 8000 Midlantic Dr., Ste. 200-N, Mount Laurel 08054
Pres., Hum. Res. Mgr.—Robert Kennedy, Jr., 20 emp., *Company headquarters & distributor* (856) 813-5000
Kessler Industries, Inc., 500 Green St., Woodbridge 07095
Pres.—Neil Kessler, 65 emp., *Distributor of steel & PVC pipe, copper* ........ (973) 684-2130
KOPO International, Inc., 100 Village Ct., Ste. 202, Hazlet 07730
Pres., CEO—Stephen Cucih, 3 emp., *Distributor of steel* ........ (732) 203-1505
KWG Industries, LLC, 330 Roycefield Rd., Unit B, Hillsborough 08844
Pres., CEO—Kurt W. Grimm, 15 emp., *Manufacturer of precision machined* ........ (908) 218-8900
Mabey Inc., 218 N. Randolphville Rd., Piscataway 08854
Depot Mgr.—Aaron Lee, 13 emp., *Distributor of structural steel components* ........ (732) 752-6600
Madsen & Howell, Inc., 500 Market St., Ste. 1, Perth Amboy 08861
Pres.—Peter Madsen, 50 emp., *Distributor of industrial equipment* ........ (732) 826-4000
McNICHOLS Co., 2 Home News Row, New Brunswick 08901
GM—Mike Davidson, 28 emp., *Metal service center, including perforated* ........ (732) 509-3092
Metal Associates, Inc., 230 W. Parkway, Unit 3-2, Pompton Plains 07444
Pres.—Charles Bareijsza, 10 emp., *Distributor of brass, copper, stainless* ........ (973) 835-8480
Metal Stock, 471 Southard St., Trenton 08638
Pres.—Morris Mann, 15 emp., *Distributor of steel sheets* ........ (609) 394-1129
Metals USA, Plates & Shapes Group, 182 Frelinghuysen Ave., Newark 07114
GM—Thomas Creanza, 31 emp., *Steel service center, including steel* ........ (973) 242-1000
Midlantic Metals, 2201 Mount Ephraim Ave., Ste. 90, Camden 08104
Pres.—Dean Sharon, 5 emp., *Distributor of stainless steel flat* ........ (856) 963-2822
Midlantic Supply, LLC, 8000 Midlantic Dr., Ste. 200-N., P.O. Box 506, Mount Laurel 08054
Owner—Diane Disanto, 5 emp., *Distributor of waterworks & sewer equipment* ........ (856) 813-5014
Minerais U. S., LLC, 105 Raider Blvd., Ste. 104, Hillsborough 08844
CEO—Tom Mayrides, 13 emp., *Distributor of metal alloys* ........ (908) 874-7666
MJG Technologies, Inc., 832 Camden Ave., Blackwood 08012
Pres.—Jeff Genzel, 3 emp., *Manufacturer of electric matches, igniters* ........ (856) 228-6118
National Electronic Alloys, Inc., 3 Fir Ct., Oakland 07436
Pres.—Richard Geoffrion, 20 emp., *Metal service center* ........ (201) 337-9400
Neill Supply Co., Inc., 700 Schuyler Ave., Lyndhurst 07071
Pres.—Robert Moss, 60 emp., *Manufacturer of fire sprinklers & distributor* ........ (201) 939-1100
Newark Steel & Ornamental Supply, 41-43 Frelinghuysen Ave., Newark 07114
Owner—Jose Martinez, 8 emp., *Wholesaler of hot-rolled steel supplies* ........ (973) 424-9790
NJS Sales Corp., 2840 Mount Ephraim Ave., Camden 08104
Pres.—Lou Cirignano, 15 emp., *Rebar fabrication & distributor of* ........ (856) 619-1119
Numax, Inc., 7251-B Browning Rd., Pennsauken 08109
Sales Mgr.—Gary Mullins, 3 emp., *Distributor of construction supplies* ........ (856) 910-0088
O'Neal Flat Rolled Metals, 1 Fitzgerald Ave., Monroe Township 08831
GM—Jeff Katz, 34 emp., *Steel service center, including stainless* ........ (609) 395-7007
Perlen Steel Corp., 265 Passaic St., Newark 07104
Pres.—Richard Perlen, 13 emp., *Structural steel fabrication & distributor* ........ (973) 485-5522
Rahway Electric Supply, Inc., 1684 Essex St., Rahway 07065
Br. Mgr.—Clara Garcia, 10 emp., *Distributor of electrical supplies,* ........ (732) 381-6060
Rancocas Metals Corp., 35 Indel Ave., P.O. Box 223, Rancocas 08073
Pres.—Robert W. Hitchon, 25 emp., *Metal service center, including aluminum* ........ (609) 267-4120
Rebuth Metal Services, 2262 Stocker Ln., P.O. Box 488, Scotch Plains 07076
Owner—Michael J. Rebuth, 10 emp., *Wholesaler of steel & aluminum* ........ (908) 889-6400
RM Metals, 50 Cragwood Rd., South Plainfield 07080
V-P.—Snehal 'Sam' Desai, 5 emp., *Distributor of primary & secondary* ........ (908) 222-1500
Samson Metal Service, 2604 Route 130 N., Cranbury 08512
Pres.—Jacques Capelluto, 19 emp., *Distributor of steel, metal & plastics* ........ (609) 655-0777
SIGMA Corp. (H Q), 700 Goldman Dr., P.O. Box 300, Cream Ridge 08514
Chrm., CEO—Jim McGivern, 90 emp., *Corporate headquarters; distributor* ........ (609) 758-0800
Stulz Sickles Steel Co., 929 Julia St., Elizabeth 07201
Pres.—Philip DeStasio, 30 emp., *Wholesaler of steel products & steel* ........ (800) 351-1776
Summit Stainless Steel, LLC, 2001 Elizabeth St., North Brunswick 08902
Pres.—Frank Tairaue, 25 emp., *Wholesaler of stainless steel* ........ (732) 297-9505
Taurus International, Inc., 275 N. Franklin Tpke., Ste. 3, Ramsey 07446
Owner—William Coleman, 12 emp., *Distributor of forgings, castings &* ........ (201) 825-2420
ThyssenKrupp Materials NA Copper & Brass Sales Div., 800 Arlington Blvd., Ste. C, Swedesboro 08085
Sales Mgr.—Robert Davis, 40 emp., *Metal service center* ........ (610) 586-1800
Titanium Fabrication Corp., 110 Lehigh Dr., Fairfield 07004
Pres., CEO—Brent Willey, 45 emp., *Custom titanium & reactive metal design* ........ (973) 227-5300
Titanium Industries, Inc., 18 Green Pond Rd., Rockaway 07866
Pres., COO—Brett Paddock, 50 emp., *Corporate headquarters & wholesaler* ........ (973) 983-1185
TW Metals, Inc., 27 Engelhard Dr., Monroe Township 08831
V-P.—Bill Schmit, 100 emp., *Distributor of specialty metals* ........ (609) 655-4120
UER Metals, Inc., 235 Saint Nicholas Ave., P.O. Box 407, South Plainfield 07080
Off. Admn.—Marge Reedy, 25 emp., *Steel service center* ........ (908) 561-5800
Unimet Metal Supply Co., Inc., 150 Lackawanna Ave., Parsippany 07054
Pres.—Robert Flynn, 70 emp., *Corporate headquarters & steel service* ........ (973) 673-5700
World Wide Metric, Inc., 37 Readington Rd., P.O. Box 5267, Branchburg 08876
CEO—George Contos, 16 emp., *Corporate headquarters & distributor* ........ (732) 247-2300

## 5052 Coal & other minerals & ores

Modern Group Ltd., 75 New St., Edison 08837
Br. Mgr., Forklifts—Jerry Hagen, 25 emp., *Distributor of construction, industrial* ........ (800) 846-5840

## 5063 Electrical apparatus & wiring supplies

A.C.T. Lighting, Inc., 122 John St., Hackensack 07601
V-P., Sales—Brian Dowd, 20 emp., *Distributor of lighting fixtures* ........ (201) 996-0884
Accredited Lock Supply, 1161 Paterson Plank Rd., Secaucus 07094
CEO—Ron Weaver, 45 emp., *Distributor of locks, door & decorative* ........ (201) 865-5015
Ace Janitorial Supply, Inc., 164 Franklin Tpke., Ste. 2, Mahwah 07430
Pres.—H. Mike Timpone, 4 emp., *Distributor of janitorial & electrical* ........ (201) 529-1750
Ademco Distribution, Inc., 1000 Lincoln Dr. E., Unit 4, Marlton 08053
Sales Mgr.—Marion Longaker, 10 emp., *Distributor of security products, including* ........ (856) 985-9050
Allied Electronics, Inc., 197 State Hwy. N-18, East Brunswick 08816
Off. Mgr.—Stan Duvall, 5 emp., *Distributor of electrical equipment* ........ (732) 846-4271
American Distributors, Inc., 2 Emery Ave., Ste. 1, Randolph 07869
Pres.—David Beck, 35 emp., *Corporate headquarters & distributor* ........ (973) 328-1181
American Paper & Supply Co., LLC, 10 Industrial Rd., P.O. Box 346, Carlstadt 07072
Owner—Larry Shapiro, 45 emp., *Distributor of maintenance/janitorial* ........ (201) 939-4200
Ardom Bearing Group, 1000 Bennett Blvd., Ste. 7, Lakewood 08701
Owner & Pres.—Dominick Commesso, 5 emp., *Company headquarters & wholesaler of* ........ (732) 370-2310
Armor Metals & Recycling, 8300 National Hwy., Ste. 2, Pennsauken 08110
Mng. Ptnr.—Frank Lobascio, 10 emp., *Wholesaler of scrap metals & parts* ........ (856) 665-5715
Bath Connection, The, 183 Millburn Ave., Millburn 07041
Br. Mgr.—Nancy Malchi, 7 emp., *Wholesaler of bathroom accessories,* ........ (973) 467-7888
Bayonne Plumbing Supply, Inc., 250 Avenue E, Bayonne 07002
Ptnr.—Richard Epstein, 6 emp., *Corporate headquarters & wholesaler* ........ (201) 339-8000
Billows Electric Supply Co., Inc., 301 N. New Rd., Pleasantville 08232
Br. Mgr.—John Dittess, 30 emp., *Distributor of electrical equipment* ........ (609) 345-6154
Billows Electric Supply Co., Inc., 1719 Nottingham Way, Trenton 08619
Br. Mgr.—Paul Greig, 12 emp., *Distributor of electrical supplies* ........ (609) 890-2822
Billows Electric Supply Co., Inc., 3901 New Jersey Ave., Wildwood 08260
Manager—Fran Dwestefano, 5 emp., *Distributor of electrical supplies,* ........ (609) 522-7736
Caola & Co., 2 Crossroads Dr., P.O. Box 8772, Hamilton 08691
CEO—John Caola, 18 emp., *Wholesaler of locks & electronic security* ........ (609) 890-7331
Chiswick Electric Co., Inc., 40 Brown Ave., Springfield 07081
V-P.—Charlie Chiswick, 15 emp., *Distributor of new AC & DC electric* ........ (973) 824-9600
Colonial Commercial Corp., 275 Wagaraw Rd., Hawthorne 07506
Chrm.—Michael Goldman, 50 emp., *Corporate headquarters & distributor* ........ (973) 427-8224
Colonial Electric Supply Co., The, 1143 S. Route 9, Cape May Court House 08210
Br. Mgr.—Chris Brunetti, *Distributor of electrical equipment* ........ (609) 465-7144
Colonial Electric Supply Co., The, 469 S. White Horse Pike, Hammonton 08037
Br. Mgr.—Fred Snyder, 6 emp., *Distributor of electrical equipment* ........ (609) 704-9950
Colonial Electric Supply Co., The, 701 W. Delilah Rd., Pleasantville 08232
Br. Mgr.—Walt Brunetti, 10 emp., *Distributor of electrical equipment* ........ (609) 645-8110
Colonial Electric Supply Co., The, 64 W. Landis Ave., Vineland 08360
Br. Mgr.—Mike Farside, 6 emp., *Distributor of electrical equipment* ........ (856) 462-6300
Cooper Electric Supply Co., 17 Route 206 S., Unit 3, Augusta 07822
Manager—Dean Cosentino, 4 emp., *Distributor of electrical equipment* ........ (973) 940-8905
Cooper Electric Supply Co., 72 N. Washington Ave., Bergenfield 07621
Sales Mgr., Inside—Gabe Ferrari, 20 emp., *Distributor of electrical supplies,* ........ (201) 385-7777
Cooper Electric Supply Co., 933 Cedarbridge Ave., Brick 08723
Br. Mgr.—Gary Wilson, 15 emp., *Distributor of electrical equipment* ........ (732) 920-3130
Cooper Electric Supply Co., 2727 Fire Rd., Egg Harbor Township 08234
Br. Mgr.—Jim Deangelis, 10 emp., *Distributor of electrical equipment* ........ (609) 833-2115
Cooper Electric Supply Co., 217 Broad Ave., Fairview 07022
Br. Mgr.—Brian Bertsch, 10 emp., *Distributor of electrical equipment* ........ (201) 945-5900
Cooper Electric Supply Co., 19 Royal Rd., Flemington 08822
Br. Mgr.—Jim Stevens, 15 emp., *Distributor of electrical equipment* ........ (908) 782-3200
Cooper Electric Supply Co., 3477 U.S. Highway 9, Freehold 07728
Br. Mgr.—Tania Rodriguez, 12 emp., *Distributor of electrical equipment* ........ (732) 462-2424
Cooper Electric Supply Co., 1521 John F. Kennedy Blvd., Jersey City 07305
Br. Mgr.—Scott MacDonald, 8 emp., *Distributor of electrical equipment* ........ (201) 434-8575
Cooper Electric Supply Co., 1805 Lower Rd., Linden 07036
Br. Mgr.—Anthony Merola, 10 emp., *Distributor of electrical equipment* ........ (732) 340-0346
Cooper Electric Supply Co., 317 E. Bay Ave., Manahawkin 08050
Br. Mgr.—Bruce Whitley, 3 emp., *Distributor of commercial, industrial* ........ (609) 978-4666
Cooper Electric Supply Co., 666 State Route 35, Middletown 07748
Br. Mgr.—Chris Schuman, 5 emp., *Distributor of electrical equipment* ........ (732) 671-5000
Cooper Electric Supply Co., 1 Matrix Dr., Monroe 08831
Pres.—Mike Dudas, 160 emp., *Company headquarters & distributor* ........ (732) 747-2233
Cooper Electric Supply Co., 225 Stockton St., Phillipsburg 08865
Br. Mgr.—Clint Ramsberger, 5 emp., *Distributor of electrical equipment* ........ (908) 454-8500
Cooper Electric Supply Co., 412 W. 2nd St., Plainfield 07060
Br. Mgr.—Bob Gaydos, 9 emp., *Distributor of electrical equipment* ........ (908) 756-4090
Cooper Electric Supply Co., 1251 Metropolitan Ave., West Deptford 08066
Lighting Mgr.—Kate Bell, 7 emp., *Distributor of electrical equipment* ........ (856) 853-9922
Cooper Electric Supply Corp., 444 Route 46 E., Fairfield 07004
Br. Mgr.—Randy Montgomery, 12 emp., *Distributor of electrical equipment* ........ (973) 278-8400
Cuny & Guerber, Inc., 2100 Kerrigan Ave., P.O. Box 1192, Union City 07087
Pres.—David B. Matthews, Jr., 35 emp., *Industrial automation systems integration* ........ (201) 617-5800
Electronic Measurement Laboratories, Inc., 668 Easton Ave., Somerset 08873
Owner—Richard J. Pleconis, 4 emp., *Distributor of industrial gas detectors* ........ (732) 846-4029
Estrin Calabrese Sales Agency, 17 S. Main St., Ste. 3, Manville 08835
Pres.—Michael Estrin, 7 emp., *Distributor of commercial & residential* ........ (908) 722-9980
Farmer Electrical Supply, 16 Littell Rd., East Hanover 07936
Owner—Sam Farmer, 5 emp., *Wholesaler of electrical equipment* ........ (973) 887-0510
Federal Pacific Equipment, Inc., 1133 Industrial Pkwy., Ste. A, Brick 08724
Pres., Hum. Res. Mgr.—John Cifrodella, 3 emp., *Wholesaler of electric circuit breakers* ........ (732) 840-4800
Filter Technologies, Inc., 45 Stouts Ln., Unit 3, Monmouth Junction 08852
Dir.—Peter Wojnarowicz, 5 emp., *Distributor of industrial water & air* ........ (732) 329-2500
Fox Electric Supply Co., Inc., 1 Dodge Dr., West Caldwell 07006
Pres.—Bruce Fox, 30 emp., *Wholesaler of electrical supplies,* ........ (973) 227-4151
Fuseco, Inc., 86 Lackawanna Ave., Ste. 240, Woodland Park 07424
Br. Mgr.—Bill Engel, 5 emp., *Distributor of fuses, fuse blocks &* ........ (973) 894-3727

S.I.C.

Gaffney-Kroese Supply Corp., 50 Randolph Rd., Somerset 08873
Pres.—Christopher Kroese, 75 emp., *Corporate headquarters & distributor* ... (732) 885-9000
Gexpro, 522 Pedricktown Rd., Swedesboro 08085
Opers. Mgr.—Matt Brickner, 22 emp., *Wholesaler of electrical & lighting* ... (856) 241-4700
Globtek, Inc., 186 Veterans Dr., Northvale 07647
CEO—Anna Kaplan, 65 emp., *Manufacturer & distributor of power* ... (201) 784-1000
Graybar Electric Co., Inc., 105 E. Crest Ave., Ste. 207, Edison 08837
Br. Mgr.—Scott Kennedy, 60 emp., *Distributor of electrical supplies,* ... (973) 404-5555
Griffith Electric Supply Co., Inc., 4-W Chimney Rock Rd., Bridgewater 08807
Br. Mgr.—Paul Mauro, 6 emp., *Wholesaler of switches, boxes, panels* ... (908) 203-1601
Griffith Electric Supply Co., Inc., 5 2nd St., Trenton 08611
Pres.—William Goodwin, 50 emp., *Corporate headquarters & wholesaler* ... (609) 695-6121
IBOCO Corp., 26 Northfield Ave., Edison 08837
Pres.—Larry M. Darst, 12 emp., *Distributor of wire duct, din rail* ... (732) 417-0066
ICC Cable Corp., 2125 Center Ave., Ste. 401, Fort Lee 07024
Pres.—Jang Kim, 6 emp., *Distributor of cable & wire, including* ... (201) 482-5750
Interline Brands, Inc. (H Q), 804 Eastgate Dr., Ste. 100, Mount Laurel 08054
V-P., Hum. Res.—Annette Ricciuti, 250 emp., *Divisional headquarters; distributor* ... (856) 439-1222
International Compressor Co., Inc., 361 Jelliff Ave., Newark 07108
Pres.—Clarence Wilson, 7 emp., *Rebuilt air compressors & distributor* ... (973) 824-7170
International Cord Sets, Inc., 6 Spielman Rd., Fairfield 07004
Pres.—Dieter Baars, 18 emp., *Manufacturer of international cord* ... (973) 227-2118
Interstate Battery System Of America, Inc., 408 Commerce Ln., West Berlin 08091
GM—Robert Marshall, 8 emp., *Wholesaler of batteries, including* ... (856) 767-3903
KALDOR Emergency Lights, LLC, 19 Vanderburg Rd., Marlboro 07746
Owner—Ilana Gases, 5 emp., *Distributor of automotive emergency* ... (732) 780-6707
Longo Electrical-Mechanical, 1 Harry Shupe Blvd., Wharton 07885
Owner—Joseph J. Longo, 100 emp., *Wholesaler of motors, pumps, switchgears* ... (973) 537-0400
Lumenarc, Inc., 37 Fairfield Pl., West Caldwell 07006
Pres.—Harminder Bhalla, 12 emp., *Manufacturer of high-intensity discharge* ... (973) 227-8048
Main Electric Supply Co., Inc., 24 Public Rd., P.O. Box 7323, Monroe Township 08831
Pres.—Perry Sablosky, 35 emp., *Distributor of electrical supplies* ... (609) 860-8500
Metuchen Capacitors, Inc., 2139 Highway 35, Ste. 2, P.O. Box 399, Holmdel 07733
Pres.—Gary Ficsor, 26 emp., *Manufacturer & distributor high-voltage* ... (732) 888-9700
Monarch Electric Co., Inc., 1 Dodge Dr., West Caldwell 07006
Pres.—Greg Griswald, 150 emp., *Wholesaler of electrical supplies* ... (973) 227-4151
Monarch Electric Supply Co., 1527 Livingston Ave., North Brunswick 08902
Manager—Fred Brutko, 5 emp., *Distributor of electrical supplies* ... (732) 249-1616
Norstat, Inc., 300 Round Hill Dr., Ste. 4, Rockaway 07866
CEO—Vincent M. Orrico, 15 emp., *Master distributor of safety & automation* ... (973) 586-2500
Northeast Industrial, LLC, 661 Route 9, Cape May 08204
Pres., GM—Donald Carter, 2 emp., *Distributor of hydraulic, marine, industrial* ... (609) 884-3510
Outwater Plastics/Industries, Inc., 24 River Rd., P.O. Box 500, Bogota 07603
Pres.—Peter Kessler, 125 emp., *Corporate headquarters & distributor* ... (201) 498-8750
PBM Supply Co., Inc., 88 Cannonball Rd., P.O. Box 351, Pompton Lakes 07442
Pres.—Robert Fox, 3 emp., *Distributor of power transmission products* ... (973) 839-0050
Philips Luminaries NA, 2345 Vauxhall Rd., P.O. Box 129, Union 07083
Dir., Supply Group—James Lewis, 35 emp., *Wholesaler of commercial & industrial* ... (908) 964-7000
Rahway Electric Supply, Inc., 1684 Essex St., Rahway 07065
Br. Mgr.—Clara Garcia, 10 emp., *Distributor of electrical supplies,* ... (732) 381-6060
Reliable Electric Motor Repair, Inc., 19 California Ave., Paterson 07503
GM—Ken Maulfair, 15 emp., *Rebuilt electric motors & distributor* ... (973) 278-8122
Richards Co., 437 Boulevard, P.O. Box 199, Elmwood Park 07407
V-P., Opers. & CEO—Dan J. Kleinrock, 10 emp., *Distributor of industrial equipment* ... (201) 797-6300
Rides4U, Inc., 221 Evans Way, Ste. E, Somerville 08876
★ Owner—Len Soled, 5 emp., *Distributor of amusement equipment* ... (908) 526-8009
RSR Electronics, Inc., 900 Hart St., Rahway 07065
Pres.—Eli Rosenbaum, 47 emp., *Distributor of electrical & electronic* ... (732) 381-8777
Rumsey Electric Co., 311 N. Clinton Ave., Trenton 08638
Regional Mgr.—Frank Pypcznski, 15 emp., *Distributor of electrical supplies,* ... (609) 989-9400
Seashore Supply Of Wildwood, 306 Wildwood Ave., Wildwood 08260
Br. Mgr.—Mark Tilsner, 3 emp., *Distributor of plumbing, HVAC & electrical* ... (609) 522-1491
Service Lamp Corp., 112 Route 73, Voorhees 08043
Owner—Mark Kushner, 12 emp., *Distributor of commercial, industrial* ... (856) 768-0404
Single Source Technologies, 30 Chapin Rd., Ste. 1208, P.O. Box 655, Pine Brook 07058
Pres.—Nick Casbar, 10 emp., *Company headquarters & wholesaler of* ... (973) 227-6601
Star Micronics America, Inc. (H Q), 1150 King Georges Post Rd., Edison 08837
Pres.—B. Aoki, 60 emp., *Corporate headquarters; distributor* ... (732) 623-5500
Swift Electrical Supply Co., Inc., 100 Hollister Rd., Teterboro 07608
Pres.—August Sodora, Jr., 56 emp., *Corporate headquarters & distributor* ... (201) 462-0900
Tekris Power Electronics, Inc., 1675 State Route 34, Farmingdale 07727
Pres.—Chris Hanrahan, 2 emp., *Distributor of inverters & generators* ... (732) 938-4996
Total Machine Solutions, Inc., 16 Spielman Rd., Fairfield 07004
Whse. Mgr.—Joe Vasquez, 7 emp., *Distributor of electrical & mechanical* ... (973) 244-0017
Turtle & Hughes, Inc., 188 Foothill Rd., Bridgewater 08807
Ex. V-P., Br. Mgr.—Rick Reffler, 100 emp., *Distributor of electrical & industrial* ... (732) 560-5575
Turtle & Hughes, Inc., 1900 Lower Rd., Linden 07036
Chrm.—Suzanne T. Millard, 150 emp., *Corporate headquarters & distributor* ... (732) 574-3600
U.S. Tech, Inc., P.O. Box 152, Franklin Lakes 07417
Pres.—Jeff Lerner, 5 emp., *Distributor of uninterruptible power* ... (800) 783-8187
United Electric Supply Co., 1150 W. Garden Rd., Vineland 08360
Br. Mgr.—Jim Petka, 7 emp., *Wholesaler of electrical supplies,* ... (856) 691-6668
V.S. Systematics, Inc., 300 S. Michigan Ave., 1st Fl., Kenilworth 07033
Owner—Sarah Esteves, 3 emp., *Wholesaler of industrial automation* ... (908) 241-5110
VCOM International Multi-Media Corp., 80 Little Falls Rd., Fairfield 07004
Pres., CEO—Sheldon Goldstein, 22 emp., *Corporate headquarters & manufacturer* ... (201) 229-4270
W. W. Grainger, Inc., 308 Allwood Rd., Clifton 07012
Br. Mgr.—Kevin Wojcicki, 20 emp., *Wholesaler of commercial & industrial* ... (973) 777-7700
W. W. Grainger, Inc., 55 Jackson Dr., Cranford 07016
Br. Mgr.—Michael Crupe, 10 emp., *Wholesaler of electrical & janitorial* ... (908) 272-7156
Wayne Electrical Supply Co., 255 W. Parkway, Pompton Plains 07444
CEO—Ryan Schmitt, 15 emp., *Distributor of electrical supplies,* ... (973) 839-6500
Willier Electric Motor Repair Co., Inc., 1 Linden Ave., P.O. Box 98, Gibbsboro 08026
Pres.—Don Willier, Sr., 30 emp., *Corporate headquarters & wholesaler* ... (856) 627-3535

## 5064 Electrical appliances, TV & radios

D&M Holdings US, Inc. (H Q), 100 Corporate Dr., Mahwah 07430
CEO—Jim Caudill, 100 emp., *Holding company headquarters; home* ... (201) 762-6500
Eastern Marketing Corp., 24 Eisenhower Pkwy., Roseland 07068
Pres.—Martin Friedman, 25 emp., *Distributor of luxury kitchen appliances* ... (973) 403-8900
Gotham Sales Co., 302 Main St., Millburn 07041
Pres.—Daniel Schwartzstein, 8 emp., *Distributor of household appliances* ... (973) 912-8412
Interline Brands, Inc. (H Q), 804 Eastgate Dr., Ste. 100, Mount Laurel 08054
V-P., Hum. Res.—Annette Ricciuti, 250 emp., *Divisional headquarters; distributor* ... (856) 439-1222
Johnson's Appliances & Bedding, 930 Asbury Ave., P.O. Box 95, Ocean City 08226
Pres. & Dir., Opers. & Sales—Don Johnson, 30 emp., *Company headquarters & wholesaler of* (609) 399-1598
Johnson's Appliances & Bedding, 2510 New York Ave., Wildwood 08260
GM—Jerry Stroh, 3 emp., *Wholesaler of household appliances* ... (609) 522-1421
Karl's Appliance, LLC, 65 Passaic Ave., Fairfield 07004
Pres.—Dan Schwartz, 45 emp., *Wholesaler of household appliances,* ... (973) 227-1777
Kraft Power Corp., 241 W. Parkway, Pompton Plains 07444
V-P.—Chris Stemper, 30 emp., *Manufacturer of combined heat & power* ... (973) 835-9800
Marcone Supplies, 870 Boulevard, Ste. 4, Kenilworth 07033
Br. Mgr.—Denin Burke, 5 emp., *Wholesaler of appliance parts* ... (973) 371-8800
Marcone Supply, 180 Main St., Hackensack 07601
Sales Rep.—Gaston Hinton, 10 emp., *Wholesaler of appliance parts* ... (201) 489-6444
Musical Distributors Group, LLC, 9 Mars Ct., Unit C-3, Boonton 07005
Pres.—Steven Savvides, 12 emp., *Distributor of audio equipment, including* ... (973) 335-7888
New York Sewing Machine, Inc., 8555 Tonnelle Ave., Unit 301, North Bergen 07047
Pres.—Sheldon Rothstein, 5 emp., *Manufacturer & distributor of sewing* ... (201) 809-2009
Oberg & Lindquist Corp., 671 Broadway, Westwood 07675
Pres.—John Oberg, 50 emp., *Distributor of industrial, residential* ... (201) 664-1300
Tri-ed/Northern Video Distribution, 7 Corporate Dr., Ste. 2, Cranbury 08512
Reg. Dir.—Steve Chilimidos, 20 emp., *Distributor of security, network video* ... (609) 860-0708
VCOM International Multi-Media Corp., 80 Little Falls Rd., Fairfield 07004
Pres., CEO—Sheldon Goldstein, 22 emp., *Corporate headquarters & manufacturer* ... (201) 229-4270

## 5065 Electronic parts & equipment, nec

Accredited Lock Supply, 1161 Paterson Plank Rd., Secaucus 07094
CEO—Ron Weaver, 45 emp., *Distributor of locks, door & decorative* ... (201) 865-5015
Advanced Business Machines Co., 230 Randolph Rd., Freehold 07728
Owner—J. Respler, 4 emp., *Wholesaler of office equipment, printers* ... (732) 431-1464
Advanced Recovery, Inc., 50 Grafton Ave., Newark 07104
Pres., GM—Mark Rea, 15 emp., *Wholesaler of used electronic & computer* ... (973) 485-9100
Allister Business Systems, Inc., 205 E. 1st Ave., Roselle 07203
Pres.—David Offenberg, 30 emp., *Distributor of office equipment, including* ... (732) 972-8400
ARCO, INC., 300 State Route 17, Unit K, Mahwah 07430
CEO—Adil Ansari, 25 emp., *Distributor of memory products & supply* ... (201) 828-9808
Axis, Inc., 210 Meister Ave., Somerville 08876
Sales Mgr.—Gary Eliasson, 22 emp., *Distributor of electronic industrial* ... (908) 429-0090
BarCodeAmerica.com, 144 Shunpike Rd., P.O. Box 506, Madison 07940
Pres.—Robert W. Rack, 10 emp., *Systems integration & distributor of* ... (973) 377-8182
Caola & Co., 2 Crossroads Dr., P.O. Box 8772, Hamilton 08691
CEO—John Caola, 18 emp., *Wholesaler of locks & electronic security* ... (609) 890-7331
Central Connectors, Inc., 4 Bridge Plaza Dr., Ste. 1, Manalapan 07726
Owner & Pres.—Maureen Ledbetter, 3 emp., *Distributor of electronic connectors* ... (732) 972-3456
Communications Supply Corp., 104 Sunfield Ave., Edison 08837
Br. Mgr.—Bill Dalton, 30 emp., *Wholesaler of communication equipment* ... (732) 346-1550
Cuny & Guerber, Inc., 2100 Kerrigan Ave., P.O. Box 1192, Union City 07087
Pres.—David B. Matthews, Jr., 35 emp., *Industrial automation systems integration* ... (201) 617-5800
GCE Market, Inc., 1001 Lower Landing Rd., Ste. 307, Blackwood 08012
CEO & Dir., Sales—Jaydeep Patel, *Corporate headquarters & wholesaler* ... (856) 401-8900
Heerema Co., 200 6th Ave., Hawthorne 07506
Pres.—William C. Heerema, 25 emp., *Wholesaler of industrial pumps, refrigeration* ... (973) 423-0505
Heraeus Sensor Technology USA, 1901 U.S. Highway 130, North Brunswick 08902
GM—Douglas Joy, 6 emp., *Distributor of platinum RTD temperature* ... (732) 940-4400
Interstate Connecting Components, Inc., 120 Mount Holly Byp., Lumberton 08048
Pres.—Scott Jacobs, 60 emp., *Distributor of industrial, military-spec.* ... (856) 722-5535
Jessup, Inc., Charles M., 177 Smith St., Keasbey 08832
Pres., CEO & CFO—Charles M. Jessup, 9 emp., *Distributor of commercial & textile* ... (732) 324-0430
Kramer Electronics USA, Inc./Sierra Video Systems (H Q), 6 State Route 173 W., Clinton 08809
Pres.—David Bright, 53 emp., *Corporate headquarters; manufacturer* ... (908) 735-0018
Lantek Corporation, 29 Brookfield Dr., Sparta 07871
GM—Frank Cervino, 20 emp., *Distributor of electronic components* ... (973) 579-8100
Micron Optics, 14 Ridgedale Ave., Ste. 125, Cedar Knolls 07927
Pres.—Peter Burboeck, 7 emp., *Distributor of microscopes, cameras* ... (973) 267-5047
Model Electronics, Inc., 615 E. Crescent Ave., Ramsey 07446
V-P.—Thomas Churchill, 55 emp., *Distributor of OEM automotive electronics* ... (201) 961-6200
Modern Technologies Group, Inc., 3 Reeves Station Rd., Medford 08055
Pres.—Ric Cohen, 30 emp., *Corporate headquarters & distributor* ... (609) 714-8900
New Jersey Semiconductor Products, Inc., 20 Stern Ave., Springfield 07081
Pres.—Robert Hildebrandt, 60 emp., *Distributor of semiconductor products* ... (973) 376-2922
Powell Electronics, Inc., 200 Commodore Dr., Logan Township 08085
Pres.—E. J. Schilling, 150 emp., *Corporate headquarters & distributor* ... (856) 241-8000
PTC Electronics, Inc., 45 Whitney Rd., Ste. B-9, Mahwah 07430
Pres.—Alan Kicks, 7 emp., *Distributor of electronic weighing,* ... (201) 847-0500
Rack Design Group Inc. / BarCodeAmerica.com, 81 Clinton Rd., Fairfield 07004
Pres.—Robert Rack, 10 emp., *Manufacturer & distributor of custom* ... (973) 377-8182
Relay Specialties, Inc., 17 Raritan Rd., P.O. Box 7000, Oakland 07436
Pres.—Barry Sauer, 35 emp., *Wholesaler of electromechanical & electronic* ... (201) 337-1000
Robert McKeown Co., Inc., 111 Chambers Brook Rd., Branchburg 08876
Pres.—Lindsey McKeown, 25 emp., *Distributor of engineered specialty* ... (908) 218-9000
RSR Electronics, Inc., 900 Hart St., Rahway 07065
Pres.—Eli Rosenbaum, 47 emp., *Distributor of electrical & electronic* ... (732) 381-8777
Sims Metal Management, 1511 Calhoun St., Trenton 08638
GM—Juan Mezza, 15 emp., *Wholesaler of recycled steel & parts* ... (609) 396-0880
Solid State, Inc., 46 Farrand St., Bloomfield 07003
Pres.—Andrew Licari, 60 emp., *Distributor of electronic components* ... (973) 429-8700
Star Micronics America, Inc. (H Q), 1150 King Georges Post Rd., Edison 08837
Pres.—B. Aoki, 60 emp., *Corporate headquarters; distributor* ... (732) 623-5500
Superior Office Systems, Inc., 19 Gross Ave., Edison 08837
Pres.—Phil Blank, 50 emp., *Distributor of office equipment, including* ... (732) 738-0093
Teleco Business Telephone Systems, 1883 State Route 27, Edison 08817
★ V-P. & Hum. Res. Mgr.—Andrew Taub, 15 emp., *Distributor of business telephone systems* ... (732) 777-7990
Thanks For Being Green, LLC, 5070-B Central Hwy., Merchantville 08109
★ Pres.—John Martorano, Jr., 10 emp., *Distributor of parts reclaimed from* ... (856) 333-0991
Tri-ed/Northern Video Distribution, 7 Corporate Dr., Ste. 2, Cranbury 08512
Reg. Dir.—Steve Chilimidos, 20 emp., *Distributor of security, network video* ... (609) 860-0708
Washington Professional Systems, Inc., 109 Gaither Dr., Ste. 301, Mount Laurel 08054
Br. Mgr.—Joe Hondros, 4 emp., *Distributor of audiovisual equipment* ... (856) 273-8688

Worldwide Supply, LLC, 1 Park Dr., Franklin 07416
Mng. Ptnr.—Jay Van Orden, 30 emp., *Wholesaler of new, excess, secondary* (973) 823-6400

## 5072 Hardware

A. H. Harris & Sons, Inc., 160 Fairfield Rd., Fairfield 07004
GM—Dennis Orozco, 10 emp., *Distributor of construction equipment* (973) 227-1600
ABC Supply Co., Inc., Bradco Div., 691 New Hampshire Ave., Lakewood 08701
Dir., Sales—Larry Gelber, 50 emp., *Distributor of roofing materials, including* (732) 905-9355
Accredited Lock Supply, 1161 Paterson Plank Rd., Secaucus 07094
CEO—Ron Weaver, 45 emp., *Distributor of locks, door & decorative* (201) 865-5015
Accurate Precision Fasteners Corp., 20 Honeck St., Englewood 07631
Pres.—Michael Jacobs, 25 emp., *Distributor of aerospace fasteners* (201) 567-9700
Associated Pile & Fitting, 8 Wood Hollow Rd., Plz. 1, P.O. Box 5933, Parsippany 07054
Manager—Matt Scerbak, 4 emp., *Manufacturer & distributor of points* (973) 773-8400
B/E Consumables Management, 650 From Rd., Paramus 07652
Pres.—Robert Marchetti, 50 emp., *Distributor of aerospace fasteners* (201) 265-8770
Bildisco Door Mfg., Inc., 21 Central Ave., West Orange 07052
Pres.—Bruno Valente, 11 emp., *Manufacturer of wooden & metal doors* (973) 673-2400
Caola & Co., 2 Crossroads Dr., P.O. Box 8772, Hamilton 08691
CEO—John Caola, 18 emp., *Wholesaler of locks & electronic security* (609) 890-7331
Commercial Hardware, Inc., 5 Perina Blvd., Cherry Hill 08003
CEO—Victor Palladino, 50 emp., *Corporate headquarters & distributor* (856) 810-0600
Continental-Aero (H Q), 530 Bergen St., P.O. Box 354, Harrison 07029
Pres.—William Giddins, 6 emp., *Company headquarters; distributor of* (973) 481-3000
Couse & Bolten Co., 90 South St., Dock 5, Newark 07114
Owner, CEO & COO—Michael Nelson, 7 emp., *Manufacturer & distributor of hydraulic* (973) 344-6330
Dreyer's Lumber & Hardware, Inc., 348 Elberon Blvd., Oakhurst 07755
★ Owner—Walter Dreyer, 4 emp., *Lumber processing & millwork & distributor* (732) 531-0220
Dubell Lumber Co., 731 Cuthbert Blvd., Cherry Hill 08002
Br. Mgr.—Jim Eaise, 20 emp., *Wholesaler of building materials &* (856) 665-9100
Dubell Lumber Co., 148 Route 70 E., P.O. Box 1449, Medford 08055
Owner—Gene DiMediao, 35 emp., *Company headquarters & wholesaler of* (609) 654-4143
Empire Lumber & Millwork Co., 377 Frelinghuysen Ave., Newark 07114
Chrm.—Ira Kent, 35 emp., *Architectural millwork, dimension lumber* (973) 242-2700
Enfasco, 1675 Hylton Rd., Pennsauken 08110
Pres.—Frank Bailey, 20 emp., *Distributor of commercial & military* (856) 662-7660
Fastbolt Corp., 200 Louis St., South Hackensack 07606
Pres.—Albert Zaukas, 50 emp., *Corporate headquarters & distributor* (201) 440-9100
Fastenal Co., 1115 N. New Rd., Absecon 08201
GM—Wayne Winn, 3 emp., *Wholesaler of fasteners, safety equipment* (609) 813-2356
Fastenal Co., 421 Route 73 & Cushman Ave., Unit 11, Berlin 08009
Br. Mgr.—David Gabrielski, 1 emp., *Wholesaler of fasteners, safety equipment* (856) 768-3657
Fastenal Co., 921 Route 130 N., Burlington 08016
GM—Tom Petruzzi, 3 emp., *Wholesaler of fasteners, safety equipment* (609) 239-3016
Fastenal Co., 33 Route 17 S., East Rutherford 07073
Br. Mgr.—Mike Scrobel, 5 emp., *Wholesaler of fasteners, safety equipment* (201) 804-2228
Fastenal Co., 22 Meridian Rd., Unit 2, Eatontown 07724
Br. Mgr.—Jan Humphrey, 3 emp., *Wholesaler of fasteners, safety equipment* (732) 542-7533
Fastenal Co., 55 Carter Dr., Edison 08817
Br. & Sales Mgr., Inside—Harrison Jennings, 5 emp., *Wholesaler of fasteners, tools, abrasives* (732) 777-1029
Fastenal Co., 68-A Clinton Rd., Fairfield 07004
Br. Mgr.—Joe Bourlier, 4 emp., *Wholesaler of fasteners, safety equipment* (973) 244-0540
Fastenal Co., 186 Gold Mine Rd., Unit 1, Flanders 07836
Br. Mgr.—Matthew Cohen, 5 emp., *Wholesaler of fasteners, safety equipment* (973) 691-0547
Fastenal Co., 316 Black Horse Pike, Unit C, Glendora 08029
Store Mgr.—Blake Phillips, 4 emp., *Wholesaler of fasteners, safety equipment* (856) 939-2500
Fastenal Co., 1026 W. Elizabeth Ave., Unit 2, Linden 07036
Br. Mgr.—Alex Klinga, 3 emp., *Wholesaler of fasteners, safety equipment* (908) 862-8880
Fastenal Co., 550 Lincoln Blvd., Middlesex 08846
Store Mgr.—Derek Dandy, 5 emp., *Wholesaler of fasteners, safety equipment* (732) 748-0140
Fastenal Co., 987 Jersey Ave., Ste. C, New Brunswick 08901
Br. Mgr.—Mike Kane, 3 emp., *Wholesaler of fasteners, safety equipment* (732) 246-0248
Fastenal Co., 443 Madison Ave., Paterson 07524
Sales Rep., Inside—Joe Bresett, 3 emp., *Wholesaler of fasteners, safety equipment* (973) 278-5509
Fastenal Co., 1163 Route 130, Robbinsville 08691
Br. Mgr.—William Strobel, 3 emp., *Wholesaler of fasteners, safety equipment* (609) 259-4290
Fastenal Co., 500 Hartle St., Ste. D, Sayreville 08872
Manager—Dan Divine, 2 emp., *Wholesaler of industrial fasteners,* (732) 254-1117
Fastenal Co., 1875 N. Olden Ave., Trenton 08638
Store Mgr.—Chris Varlaro, 4 emp., *Wholesaler of fasteners, safety equipment* (609) 530-0456
Fastenal Co., 53 S. Jefferson Rd., Ste. K, Whippany 07981
Br. Mgr.—Jason Smith, 3 emp., *Wholesaler of fasteners, safety equipment* (973) 428-3300
Ford Fasteners, Inc., 110 S. Newman St., Hackensack 07601
CEO—Christopher Cellary, 10 emp., *Distributor of industrial, self-drilling* (201) 487-3151
Franzen International, Inc., 23 Birch St., Ste. 1, Midland Park 07432
Pres.—Michaela Franzen, 3 emp., *Distributor of firearm security products* (201) 405-2228
Garfield Lumber & Millwork Co., 260 Lanza Ave., Garfield 07026
Pres., CFO—Ray Sowa, 20 emp., *Distributor of lumber, millwork, hardware* (973) 478-2160
Gotham Sales Co., 302 Main St., Millburn 07041
Pres.—Daniel Schwartzstein, 8 emp., *Distributor of household appliances* (973) 912-8412
Grabber Northeast, 1125 Thomas Busch Memorial Hwy., Pennsauken 08110
Br. Mgr.—Val Anesti, 7 emp., *Distributor of construction equipment* (856) 662-2525
HBC Home & Hardware, 324-A Half Acre Rd., Cranbury 08512
CEO—Donald C. Devine, 170 emp., *Company headquarters & wholesaler of* (609) 860-9990
Heath Lumber Co., 1580 N. Olden Avenue Ext., Ewing 08638
Pres.—Gary Patricelli, 30 emp., *Distributor of building materials &* (609) 392-1166
Kanebridge Corp., 153 Bauer Dr., Oakland 07436
Pres.—Joseph McGrath, 45 emp., *Corporate headquarters & distributor* (201) 337-3200
Kelken-Gold, Inc., 550 Hartle St., Ste. C, Sayreville 08872
Pres.—Ken Ginsky, 4 emp., *Manufacturer & distributor of anchoring* (732) 416-6730
Klingelhofer Corp., 165 Mill Ln., Mountainside 07092
Pres.—Al Klingelhofer, 11 emp., *Distributor of metal sawing, deburring* (908) 232-7200
Kuiken Brothers Commercial, 485 River Dr., Garfield 07026
Store Mgr.—Kenneth Kuiken, 25 emp., *Distributor of drywall, studs, acoustical* (973) 772-0044
Kuiken Brothers Company, Inc., 31 State Route 10 E., Succasunna 07876
Store Mgr.—Marc Gattuso, 25 emp., *Distributor of residential & commercial* (973) 584-2444
Lifetime Brands, Inc., Distribution Center, 12 Applegate Dr., Robbinsville 08691
Opers. Mgr.—John McCranor, 240 emp., *Wholesaler of household cutlery, kitchen* (609) 208-1500
Machine Shop Discount Supply, P.O. Box 16, Little Ferry 07643
Pres.—Hy Ash, 15 emp., *Distributor of cutting & measuring* (201) 518-8472
MarJam Supply Co., 615 W. Delilah Rd., Pleasantville 08232
Br. Mgr.—Steve Rios, 15 emp., *Wholesaler of building materials, paint* (609) 407-1234
Melfast, Inc., 18 Passaic Ave., Unit 4-5, Fairfield 07004
Pres.—Larry Melone, 20 emp., *Distributor of inch & metric steel,* (973) 227-0045
Moe Distributors, Inc., 55 Abbett Ave., Morristown 07960
V-P.—Jeff Doremus, 7 emp., *Distributor of decorative bathroom* (973) 539-8200
Muenz Engineered Sales Co., 21 Chatham Rd., Summit 07901
CEO—Jeff O'Sullivan, 16 emp., *Distributor of abrasives, cutting &* (908) 273-6755
Norstat, Inc., 300 Round Hill Dr., Ste. 4, Rockaway 07866
CEO—Vincent M. Orrico, 15 emp., *Master distributor of safety & automation* (973) 586-2500
Numax, Inc., 7251-B Browning Rd., Pennsauken 08109
Sales Mgr.—Gary Mullins, 3 emp., *Distributor of construction supplies* (856) 910-0088
Porteous Fastener Co., Inc., 1000 Amboy Ave., Ste. 1, Perth Amboy 08861
Region Mgr.—Jessica Roche, 23 emp., *Distributor of fasteners* (732) 376-8420
Precision Fasteners, Inc., 24 Worlds Fair Dr., Ste. D, Somerset 08873
V-P., CEO—Bill Miicke, 6 emp., *Distributor of fasteners for the automotive* (732) 627-0032
PrimeSource Building Products, Inc., 20 Van Dyke Ave, New Brunswick 08901
GM—Scott Simmel, 30 emp., *Distributor of building materials,* (732) 296-0600
Rugby ABP Corp., 60 Joseph St., Moonachie 07074
Regional Mgr.—Arsenio Alvarez, 20 emp., *Wholesaler of industrial building materials* (201) 807-9701
Scientific Models, Inc., 340 Snyder Ave., Berkeley Heights 07922
★ Owner—John Frisoli, 20 emp., *Distributor of tools & hardware, including* (908) 464-7070
Shallcross Bolt & Specialties Co., 1 McCandless St., Linden 07036
Owner & Pres.—Jeff Kaden, 25 emp., *Distributor of steel, steel plated,* (908) 925-4700
Stauff Corp., 7 William Demarest Pl., Waldwick 07463
Pres.—Peter Anderton, 25 emp., *Corporate headquarters & wholesaler* (201) 444-7800
Syntex Group, Inc., 1838 Downs Ave., Clementon 08021
Pres.—Eric Ezeiruaku, 5 emp., *Distributor of industrial machinery* (856) 566-0058
Tri State Hardware, Inc., 5 Perina Blvd., Cherry Hill 08003
Pres.—Rose Palladino, 6 emp., *Distributor of architectural doors,* (856) 810-0990
W & E Sales Co., Inc., 370 Elizabeth Ave., Newark 07112
GM—R. Carr, 15 emp., *Manufacturer & wholesaler of automotive* (973) 824-2000
W. W. Grainger, Inc., 308 Allwood Rd., Clifton 07012
Br. Mgr.—Kevin Wojcicki, 20 emp., *Wholesaler of commercial & industrial* (973) 777-7700
Wurth International Trading America, 91 Grant St., Ramsey 07446
CEO—Esther Jakob, 7 emp., *Company headquarters & distributor* (201) 995-1111

## 5074 Plumbing & hydronic heating equipment & supplies

Aaron & Co., 30 Turner Pl., Piscataway 08854
Pres.—Barry Portnoy, 100 emp., *Wholesaler of plumbing & HVAC supplies* (732) 752-8200
Bergen Industrial Supply A division of F.W. Webb, 30 Stefanic Ave., Elmwood Park 07407
GM—Tim Vandenburgh, 65 emp., *Distributor of plumbing supplies* (201) 796-2600
Blackman Plumbing Supply Co., Inc., 270 Route 17 S., Mahwah 07430
Br. Mgr.—Randy Gillies, 30 emp., *Distributor of plumbing, heating &* (201) 529-5500
Brent Material Co., 325 Columbia Tpke., Ste. 308, Florham Park 07932
Pres.—Linda Gardner, 12 emp., *Distributor of construction material* (973) 325-3030
Canuso, Inc., Louis P., 401 Crown Point Rd., P.O. Box 501, Thorofare 08086
Owner—Joseph Canuso, 65 emp., *Wholesaler of pipe, valves, fittings* (856) 845-2700
Colonial Commercial Corp., 275 Wagaraw Rd., Hawthorne 07506
Chrm.—Michael Goldman, 50 emp., *Corporate headquarters & distributor* (973) 427-8224
Dodson Global, Inc., 27 Cotters Ln., East Brunswick 08816
Br. Mgr.—Allen Goodrich, 7 emp., *Distributor of pipes & fittings* (732) 238-7001
E & B Distributors, Inc., 400 Route 22 E., Bridgewater 08807
Pres.—Brian Skowronek, 12 emp., *Distributor of plumbing & heating supplies* (732) 469-2266
East Brunswick Supply, Inc., 413 State Route 18, East Brunswick 08816
V-P.—Charles T. Lyons, Jr., 11 emp., *Wholesaler of plumbing & HVAC supplies* (732) 254-1015
Ferguson Enterprises, 835 Bloomfield Ave., Clifton 07012
Br. Mgr.—Joseph Proctor, 8 emp., *Wholesaler of industrial plumbing supplies* (973) 614-9464
Ferguson Enterprises, Inc., 401 Main St., Avon By The Sea 07717
Br. Mgr.—David Hulse, 10 emp., *Distributor of plumbing & heating supplies* (732) 775-5270
Ferguson Enterprises, Inc., 830 Route 22, Bridgewater 08807
Br. Mgr.—Roger White, 10 emp., *Wholesaler of plumbing & heating supplies* (908) 725-0666
Ferguson Enterprises, Inc., 2531 Tilton Rd., Egg Harbor Township 08234
Br. Mgr.—Kyle Lawton, 4 emp., *Distributor of plumbing supplies, including* (609) 485-2266
Ferguson Enterprises, Inc., 369 Anderson Ave., Fairview 07022
Br. Mgr.—Richard Aquimo, 4 emp., *Distributor of HVAC & plumbing supplies* (201) 945-3080
Ferguson Enterprises, Inc., 737 S. Main St., Forked River 08731
Br. Mgr.—Anthony D'Cone, 8 emp., *Distributor of plumbing & HVAC equipment* (609) 693-0077
Ferguson Enterprises, Inc., 1 Colony Rd., Jersey City 07305
Br. Mgr.—Chad Leland, 20 emp., *Distributor of plumbing & heating supplies* (201) 369-5120
Ferguson Enterprises, Inc., 190 Oberlin Ave. N., Lakewood 08701
GM—Jim Golini, 100 emp., *Wholesaler of industrial pipe & valves* (732) 905-1000
Ferguson Enterprises, Inc., 444 Livingston St., Norwood 07648
Br. Mgr.—Kerry Hampton, 10 emp., *Distributor of plumbing supplies, including* (201) 768-6080
Ferguson Enterprises, Inc., 16 Arrow Rd., Ramsey 07446
Br. Mgr.—Josh Reiter, 15 emp., *Wholesaler of plumbing pipes & valves* (201) 236-3111
Ferguson Enterprises, Inc., 207 Cooper Rd., Red Bank 07701
Br. Mgr.—Thomas McManus, 20 emp., *Distributor of plumbing & HVAC equipment* (732) 530-7200
Ferguson Enterprises, Inc., 404 Route 31 N., Ringoes 08551
Br. Mgr.—Graham Vidal, 9 emp., *Distributor of plumbing & HVAC equipment* (609) 466-5445
Ferguson Enterprises, Inc., 100 U.S. Highway 46, Rockaway 07866
Sales Mgr.—James Cobb, 13 emp., *Distributor of plumbing supplies, including* (973) 983-1177
General Plumbing Supply, Inc., 980 New Durham Rd., Edison 08817
Pres.—Bruce Tucker, 50 emp., *Distributor of HVAC & plumbing equipment* (732) 248-1000
Gotham Sales Co., 302 Main St., Millburn 07041
Pres.—Daniel Schwartzstein, 8 emp., *Distributor of household appliances* (973) 912-8412
Grant Supply Co., Inc., 901 Joyce Kilmer Ave., North Brunswick 08902
Pres.—Bill Stanbach, 55 emp., *Corporate headquarters & distributor* (732) 545-1018
Grant Supply Co., Inc., 755 W. Delilah Rd., Pleasantville 08232
Br. Mgr.—Tim O'Connell, 15 emp., *Distributor of plumbing supplies* (609) 641-1114
Grove Supply, Inc., 1818 Rowland St., Cinnaminson 08077
Br. Mgr.—Tim Thompson, 7 emp., *Wholesaler of HVAC & kitchen & bathroom* (856) 303-2310
Grove Supply, Inc., 3801 Park Blvd., Wildwood 08260
Br. Mgr.—Bud Fox, 5 emp., *Wholesaler of HVAC & plumbing equipment* (609) 522-1449
HBC Home & Hardware, 324-A Half Acre Rd., Cranbury 08512
CEO—Donald C. Devine, 170 emp., *Company headquarters & wholesaler of* (609) 860-9990
Industrial Combustion Associates Inc., 20 Worlds Fair Dr., Ste. C, Somerset 08873
Pres., Inside Sales—Nancy Peles-Hufnagel, 11 emp., *Distributor of industrial & commercial* (732) 271-0300
Interline Brands, Inc. (H Q), 804 Eastgate Dr., Ste. 100, Mount Laurel 08054
V-P., Hum. Res.—Annette Ricciuti, 250 emp., *Divisional headquarters; distributor* (856) 439-1222
Masda Corp., 22 Troy Rd., P.O. Box D, Whippany 07981
GM—Dan Darche, 8 emp., *Distributor of fireplaces, kitchen* (973) 386-1100
Mid Atlantic Pump & Equipment Co., 228 N. Route 73, Berlin 08009
Pres.—Dennis Zepp, 10 emp., *Wholesaler of industrial, commercial* (856) 768-3880

Moe Distributors, Inc., 55 Abbett Ave., Morristown 07960
V-P.—Jeff Doremus, 7 emp., *Distributor of decorative bathroom* ........ (973) 539-8200
Neill Supply Co., Inc., 700 Schuyler Ave., Lyndhurst 07071
Pres.—Robert Moss, 60 emp., *Manufacturer of fire sprinklers & distributor* ........ (201) 939-1100
New Jersey Plumbing, Heating & Industrial Supply, LLC, 91 Newark Way, Maplewood 07040
Ptnr.—Jim Buggy, 5 emp., *Wholesaler of plumbing supplies, including* ........ (973) 761-4567
Nutley Heating & Cooling Supply Co., 5016 Industrial Rd., Wall Township 07727
Manager—Craig Soden, 6 emp., *Distributor of HVAC equipment, boilers* ........ (732) 919-1933
Nutley Heating & Cooling Supply Co., Inc., 50 Page Rd., Clifton 07012
Pres.—Rick Cancelosi, 45 emp., *Corporate headquarters & distributor* ........ (973) 470-8844
Palermo Supply, 1819 Central Ave., Ship Bottom 08008
Br. Mgr.—Bill Pugh, 5 emp., *Distributor of industrial plumbing* ........ (609) 494-0343
Park Pumps & Controls, Inc., 950 Mount Holly Rd., Ste. B, Edgewater Park 08010
Owner—Calvin Stevenson, 5 emp., *Distributor of sewage & wastewater* ........ (609) 871-0944
Penn Supply, Inc., 618 E. State St., Trenton 08609
Owner—Ronald Vernon, 10 emp., *Wholesaler of plumbing & heating equipment* ........ (609) 394-1151
Perrotti Sales, 19 Woodside Ln., Flemington 08822
Owner—Ray Perrotti, 4 emp., *Wholesaler of plumbing supplies* ........ (908) 806-8899
Robert-James Sales, Inc., 9 Corporate Dr., P.O. Box B, Cranbury 08512
Br. Mgr.—Erin Motter, 10 emp., *Distributor of stainless steel pipes* ........ (609) 860-0900
Rugby ABP Corp., 60 Joseph St., Moonachie 07074
Regional Mgr.—Arsenio Alvarez, 20 emp., *Wholesaler of industrial building materials* ........ (201) 807-9701
Sanzo Ltd., 35 Munsee Dr., Cranford 07016
Owner & Pres.—Carol Sanzo, 5 emp., *Wholesaler of industrial, commercial* ........ (908) 276-6654
Seashore Supply Of Wildwood, 306 Wildwood Ave., Wildwood 08260
Br. Mgr.—Mark Tilsner, 3 emp., *Distributor of plumbing, HVAC & electrical* ........ (609) 522-1491
Weinstein Supply Co., 3187 Fire Rd., Egg Harbor Township 08234
Br. Mgr.—Kevin Mooney, 12 emp., *Wholesaler of plumbing & heating supplies* ........ (609) 677-0666
Weinstein Supply Co., 4019 S. Main Rd., Vineland 08360
Dir., Hum. Res.—Mary Melson, 4 emp., *Wholesaler of plumbing & heating equipment* ........ (856) 825-1460
Weinstein Supply Corp., 1687 Haddon Ave., Camden 08103
Profit Center Mgr.—Christopher Conte, 12 emp., *Wholesaler of plumbing, heating & air* ........ (856) 964-1700

## 5075 Warm air heating & air conditioning

ABCO Refrigeration Supply Corp., 395 N. 14th St., Kenilworth 07033
Opers. Mgr.—John Canetti, 5 emp., *Distributor of air conditioning systems* ........ (908) 931-0700
Air Purifiers, Inc., 1 Pine St., Rockaway 07866
Pres.—John Di Rezze, 12 emp., *Distributor of pollution control systems* ........ (973) 586-3988
Airmatic Compressor Systems, Inc., 700 Washington Ave., Carlstadt 07072
Pres.—William N. Vowteras, 30 emp., *Distributor of air compressors, compressed* ........ (201) 342-1300
Alabaster Supply, Inc., 2317 South St., Toms River 08753
Pres.—Steven Pereira, 2 emp., *Wholesaler of replacement heating parts* ........ (732) 330-9242
Analytical Sales & Services, Inc., 237 W. Parkway, Ste. 1, Pompton Plains 07444
Pres.—David A. Isom, 11 emp., *Manufacturer & distributor of laboratory* ........ (973) 616-0700
Blackman Plumbing Supply Co., Inc., 270 Route 17 S., Mahwah 07430
Br. Mgr.—Randy Gillies, 30 emp., *Distributor of plumbing, heating &* ........ (201) 529-5500
Colonial Commercial Corp., 275 Wagaraw Rd., Hawthorne 07506
Chrm.—Michael Goldman, 50 emp., *Corporate headquarters & distributor* ........ (973) 427-8224
Dunphey-Smith Co., 30 Progress St., Union 07083
V-P.—Thomas McCreesh, Jr., 12 emp., *Distributor of heating & air conditioning* ........ (908) 687-6292
East Brunswick Supply, Inc., 413 State Route 18, East Brunswick 08816
V-P.—Charles T. Lyons, Jr., 11 emp., *Wholesaler of plumbing & HVAC supplies* ........ (732) 254-1015
Enterprise HVAC Supply, 701 Main St., Belleville 07109
Ptnr.—Humberto Gonzalez, 6 emp., *Distributor of HVAC products, machinery* ........ (973) 759-6900
Ferguson Enterprises, Inc., 737 S. Main St., Forked River 08731
Br. Mgr.—Anthony D'Cone, 8 emp., *Distributor of plumbing & HVAC equipment* ........ (609) 693-0077
Ferguson Enterprises, Inc., 207 Cooper Rd., Red Bank 07701
Br. Mgr.—Thomas McManus, 20 emp., *Distributor of plumbing & HVAC equipment* ........ (732) 530-7200
Ferguson Enterprises, Inc., 404 Route 31 N., Ringoes 08551
Br. Mgr.—Graham Vidal, 9 emp., *Distributor of plumbing & HVAC equipment* ........ (609) 466-5445
General Plumbing Supply, Inc., 980 New Durham Rd., Edison 08817
Pres.—Bruce Tucker, 50 emp., *Distributor of HVAC & plumbing equipment* ........ (732) 248-1000
Grove Supply, Inc., 1818 Rowland St., Cinnaminson 08077
Br. Mgr.—Tim Thompson, 7 emp., *Wholesaler of HVAC & kitchen & bathroom* ........ (856) 303-2310
Grove Supply, Inc., 3801 Park Blvd., Wildwood 08260
Br. Mgr.—Bud Fox, 5 emp., *Wholesaler of HVAC & plumbing equipment* ........ (609) 522-1449
Harvey Industries, Inc., Sid, 159 E. 1st Ave., Roselle 07203
Br. Mgr.—Don Kucza, 5 emp., *Wholesaler of HVAC equipment* ........ (908) 245-8688
Harvey Industries, Inc., Sid, 1684 5th St., Trenton 08638
Sales Mgr.—Lew Benchoff, 8 emp., *Distributor of HVAC equipment* ........ (609) 882-1766
Hudson Heating Wholesaler, Inc., 1109 Grand Ave., Ste. 1, North Bergen 07047
Pres.—Chris Connell, 12 emp., *Distributor of HVAC supplies* ........ (201) 348-6700
Interline Brands, Inc. (H Q), 804 Eastgate Dr., Ste. 100, Mount Laurel 08054
V-P., Hum. Res.—Annette Ricciuti, 250 emp., *Divisional headquarters; distributor* ........ (856) 439-1222
Lyon, Conklin & Co., Inc., 1165 Thomas Busch Memorial Hwy., Pennsauken 08110
Br. Mgr., Satellite—Chris Long, 5 emp., *Distributor of HVAC equipment & supplies* ........ (856) 488-0191
Nutley Heating & Cooling Supply Co., Inc., 50 Page Rd., Clifton 07012
Pres.—Rick Cancelosi, 45 emp., *Corporate headquarters & distributor* ........ (973) 470-8844
Penn Supply, Inc., 618 E. State St., Trenton 08609
Owner—Ronald Vernon, 10 emp., *Wholesaler of plumbing & heating equipment* ........ (609) 394-1151
R. E. Michel Co., Inc., 895 Towbin Ave., Lakewood 08701
Manager—John Manning, 3 emp., *Wholesaler of heating & air conditioning* ........ (732) 886-3592
R. E. Michel Co., Inc., 262 Old New Brunswick Rd., Piscataway 08854
Br. Mgr.—Ivan Childres, 6 emp., *Distributor of heating, air conditioning* ........ (732) 465-9700
Seashore Supply Of Wildwood, 306 Wildwood Ave., Wildwood 08260
Br. Mgr.—Mark Tilsner, 3 emp., *Distributor of plumbing, HVAC & electrical* ........ (609) 522-1491
United Supply Co., Inc., 7 Chris Ct., Ste. A, Dayton 08810
Br. Mgr.—Kevin Horn, 6 emp., *Distributor of HVAC systems & accessories* ........ (732) 329-6301
United Supply Co., Inc., 457 W. End Ave., Plainfield 07060
CEO—Steve Kantor, 20 emp., *Corporate headquarters & distributor* ........ (908) 757-3232
Weinstein Supply Corp., 1687 Haddon Ave., Camden 08103
Profit Center Mgr.—Christopher Conte, 12 emp., *Wholesaler of plumbing, heating & air* ........ (856) 964-1700
Z & Z Holding Co Inc, 370 Market St., P.O. Box 239, Kenilworth 07033
Pres.—Robert Zimmermann, 57 emp., *Wholesaler of HVAC/R equipment & supplies* ........ (908) 298-1212

## 5078 Refrigeration equipment & supplies

Beverage Distribution Center, Inc., 8275 Route 130, Pennsauken 08110
Pres., CFO—Walt Wilkinson, 700 emp., *Corporate headquarters & manufacturer* ........ (856) 665-6200
Bridy Sales & Leasing Co., Inc., 115 Madison Ave., Paterson 07524
Owner—Ralph Bridy, 16 emp., *Distributor of beverage dispensers* ........ (973) 345-4311
Chef's Corner, 178 U.S. Highway 206, Ste. B, Flanders 07836
Store Mgr.—Theresa Berntsen, 5 emp., *Wholesaler of restaurant & institutional* ........ (973) 691-1500
Coldstat Refrigeration, 60 Eisenhower Dr., Paramus 07652
Owner & Pres.—Ion Sarkisian, 15 emp., *Wholesaler of commercial refrigeration* ........ (201) 599-1200
Heerema Co., 200 6th Ave., Hawthorne 07506
Pres.—William C. Heerema, 25 emp., *Wholesaler of industrial pumps, refrigeration* ........ (973) 423-0505
Karl's Appliance, LLC, 65 Passaic Ave., Fairfield 07004
Pres.—Dan Schwartz, 45 emp., *Wholesaler of household appliances,* ........ (973) 227-1777
M&J Frank, Inc., 29 Eagle Rock Ave., East Hanover 07936
Pres.—Andrew Becker, 13 emp., *Wholesaler of foodservice & restaurant* ........ (973) 887-1040
R. E. Michel Co., Inc., 262 Old New Brunswick Rd., Piscataway 08854
Br. Mgr.—Ivan Childres, 6 emp., *Distributor of heating, air conditioning* ........ (732) 465-9700
Z & Z Holding Co Inc, 370 Market St., P.O. Box 239, Kenilworth 07033
Pres.—Robert Zimmermann, 57 emp., *Wholesaler of HVAC/R equipment & supplies* ........ (908) 298-1212

## 5082 Construction & mining machinery & equipment

A. H. Harris & Sons, Inc., 160 Fairfield Rd., Fairfield 07004
GM—Dennis Orozco, 10 emp., *Distributor of construction equipment* ........ (973) 227-1600
Action Lift Trucks, Inc., 35 Avenue C, Newark 07114
Owner—Sid Litvack, 5 emp., *Distributor of forklift trucks* ........ (973) 589-2320
Binder Machinery Co., Inc., 201 N. Route 73, Winslow 08095
Pres.—Alan Binder, 20 emp., *Distributor of heavy construction equipment* ........ (856) 767-5900
Extech Building Materials, Inc., 61-89 Ave. K, Newark 07105
Pres.—Timothy Feury, 50 emp., *Distributor of brick, stone, construction* ........ (973) 274-3340
Hoffman Equipment, Inc., 300 S. Randolphville Rd., Piscataway 08854
Pres., CEO—Timothy Watters, 50 emp., *Corporate headquarters & wholesaler* ........ (732) 752-3600
Hoffman Equipment, Inc., 2610 S. Black Horse Pike, Williamstown 08094
Opers. Mgr.—Jeff Pauls, 5 emp., *Distributor of construction cranes* ........ (856) 875-0036
Jesco, Inc., 118 Saint Nicholas Ave., South Plainfield 07080
Founder & Chrm.—Lou Robustelli, 50 emp., *Corporate headquarters & distributor* ........ (908) 821-1400
L & W Supply Corp., 1351 Route 37 W., Toms River 08755
Br. Mgr.—Bob Jordan, 20 emp., *Distributor of building materials &* ........ (732) 341-3737
Mabey Inc., 218 N. Randolphville Rd., Piscataway 08854
Depot Mgr.—Aaron Lee, 13 emp., *Distributor of structural steel components* ........ (732) 752-6600
Macro Equipment Co., 205 Hartford Rd., Route 38, Mount Laurel 08054
Owner & Pres.—Paul J. Panarello, 7 emp., *Distributor of outdoor power equipment* ........ (856) 235-4235
Modern Group Ltd., 112-128 Route 17 N., Hasbrouck Heights 07604
Br. Mgr.—Joe Frassa, 35 emp., *Wholesaler of industrial machinery* ........ (201) 288-1441

## 5083 Farm & garden machinery & equipment

Arett Sales Corp., 9285 Commerce Hwy., Pennsauken 08110
Pres.—Lindsey Chesbrough, 100 emp., *Corporate headquarters & distributor* ........ (856) 751-1224
Brida Stone, Inc., 555 Mullica Hill Rd., Glassboro 08028
Owner—Anthony Brida, 15 emp., *Wholesaler of natural stone & landscape* ........ (856) 881-1700
Gotham Sales Co., 302 Main St., Millburn 07041
Pres.—Daniel Schwartzstein, 8 emp., *Distributor of household appliances* ........ (973) 912-8412
Keehn Power Products, 132 Johnson Ave., Hackensack 07601
★ Owner—Charles Keehn, 20 emp., *Distributor of lawn & garden power* ........ (201) 489-4454
Macro Equipment Co., 205 Hartford Rd., Route 38, Mount Laurel 08054
Owner & Pres.—Paul J. Panarello, 7 emp., *Distributor of outdoor power equipment* ........ (856) 235-4235
Rodio Tractor Sales, Inc., 717 White Horse Pike, Hammonton 08037
Pres.—Butch Rodio, 10 emp., *Distributor of agricultural equipment* ........ (609) 561-0141

## 5084 Industrial machinery & equipment

A&M Industrial, Inc., 325 Commerce Rd., Linden 07036
Ex. V-P.—David Young, 10 emp., *Manufacturer of industrial & hydraulic* ........ (908) 862-1800
ABCO Systems, Inc., 15 Willet St., Ste. 4, Bloomfield 07003
Pres.—Seth Weisberg, 12 emp., *Distributor of industrial handling* ........ (201) 507-0999
AC Compacting, LLC, 1577 Livingston Ave., P.O. Box 7266, North Brunswick 08902
Pres.—Paul Schaa, 10 emp., *Distributor of pharmaceutical processing* ........ (732) 249-6900
Advanced Filtration Co., 25-A Arnold Blvd., P.O. Box 324, Howell 07731
Pres.—John Woods, 3 emp., *Distributor of water, air, gas, fuel* ........ (732) 901-6676
Air & Gas Technologies, Inc., 42 Industrial Dr., Keyport 07735
Pres.—Vince Tomasso, 18 emp., *Wholesaler of industrial air & breathing* ........ (732) 566-7227
Airgas East, Inc., 121 Stanley Ave., Bellmawr 08031
GM—Joe Sergi, 2 emp., *Distributor of welding equipment &* ........ (856) 931-0900
Airgas East, Inc., 2 Beckwith Ave., Paterson 07503
Br. Mgr.—Pete Miteiko, 2 emp., *Distributor of welding equipment, supplies* ........ (973) 742-2211
Airgas East, Inc., 490 Stelton Rd., Piscataway 08854
Administrator—Terry Dalessio, 40 emp., *Wholesaler of welding supplies & industrial* ........ (732) 752-4500
Airgas East, Inc., 1750 Gallagher Dr., Vineland 08360
Accts. Mgr.—Joe Gernaloff, 4 emp., *Wholesaler of welding equipment & supplies* ........ (856) 692-7734
Airmatic Compressor Systems, Inc., 700 Washington Ave., Carlstadt 07072
Pres.—William N. Vowteras, 30 emp., *Distributor of air compressors, compressed* ........ (201) 342-1300
Allied Building Products Corp., 15 E. Union Ave., East Rutherford 07073
Chrm.—Michael Lynch, 200 emp., *Corporate headquarters & wholesaler* ........ (201) 507-8400
Allied Pump Corporation, 1109 Grand Ave., Bldg. 5, North Bergen 07047
Pres.—Benjamin Miller, 15 emp., *Manufacturer & distributor of boiler* ........ (201) 798-3277
American Machinery Liquidators, Inc., P.O. Box 6995, East Brunswick 08816
Pres.—Marc Gallanter, 2 emp., *Distributor of new & used toolroom* ........ (732) 390-0006
Applied Engineering, Corp., 232 Palisade Ave., Garfield 07026
Pres.—Andre Savin, 5 emp., *Manufacturer & distributor of custom* ........ (973) 772-6022
Applied Industrial Technologies, Inc., 24-C Worlds Fair Dr., Somerset 08873
GM—Glenn Casey, 5 emp., *Wholesaler of industrial equipment* ........ (732) 356-0522
ARAMSCO, 1480 Grandview Ave., P.O. Box 29, Thorofare 08086
Pres.—Rich Salerno, 65 emp., *Company headquarters & distributor* ........ (856) 686-7700
Ardom Bearing Group, 1000 Bennett Blvd., Ste. 7, Lakewood 08701
Owner & Pres.—Dominick Commesso, 5 emp., *Company headquarters & wholesaler of* ........ (732) 370-2310
Arlington Machine & Tool Co., 90 New Dutch Ln., Fairfield 07004
CEO—Susan Blanck, 90 emp., *Contract close tolerance precision* ........ (973) 276-1377
Atlas Welding Supply Co., Inc., 808 Brook Rd., Lakewood 08701
Corp. Secy.—Dina Pincus, 7 emp., *Distributor of welding equipment &* ........ (732) 363-1148
AutoDrill, LLC, 50 Division Ave., Ste. 18, Millington 07946
Ptnr.—Joe Agro, Sr., 6 emp., *Manufacturer & distributor of automatic* ........ (908) 542-0244
Automation Sales Co., 226 Beacon Hill Rd., Califon 07830
Pres.—James Powell, 7 emp., *Distributor of automation machinery* ........ (908) 832-7040
Avery Filter Co., Inc., 99 Kinderkamack Rd., Ste. 209, Westwood 07675
Pres.—Quentin Avery, 4 emp., *Distributor of filter paper, filter* ........ (201) 666-9664
Awisco Corp., 24 Lakeside Ave., West Orange 07052
Br. Mgr.—Abel Marriott, 6 emp., *Wholesaler of welding equipment, industrial* ........ (973) 736-0200
Awisco West Milford, LLC, 26 Industrial Rd., West Milford 07480
Br. Mgr.—Andrew Cullen, 8 emp., *Distributor of welding, industrial* ........ (973) 728-9008
Axis, Inc., 210 Meister Ave., Somerville 08876
Sales Mgr.—Gary Eliasson, 22 emp., *Distributor of electronic industrial* ........ (908) 429-0090

B & B Supply Corp., 40 Arnot St., Unit 14, Lodi 07644
Pres.—Slobodan Ristovic, 5 emp., *Wholesaler of machine cutting tools* ............ (201) 313-9021
Bacon & Graham, Inc., 34 E. 25th St., Paterson 07514
Pres.—Craig Bacon, 30 emp., *Wholesaler of packaging, shipping,* ............ (973) 684-1488
Barclay Brand Ferdon, 2401 S. Clinton Ave., P.O. Box 341, South Plainfield 07080
Dir., Mktg.—Catherine Kenvin, 50 emp., *Distributor of material handling &* ............ (908) 561-2100
Bass, Inc., Rudolf, 45 Halladay St., Jersey City 07304
Pres.—Richard H. Bass, 4 emp., *Distributor of industrial woodworking* ............ (201) 433-3800
Beisler America, LLC, 1841 E. Elizabeth Ave., P.O. Box 1683, Linden 07036
Pres.—Ron Liang, 5 emp., *Distributor of industrial & commercial* ............ (908) 925-4040
Belleville Scale & Balance, LLC, 50 S. Center St., Orange 07050
Ptnr. & Pres.—Thomas Rockhill, 22 emp., *Distributor of industrial, truck &* ............ (973) 759-4487
Bergen County Motor & Tool Co., 17-16 River Rd., Fair Lawn 07410
Pres.—David Rink, 4 emp., *Distributor of power tools & accessories* ............ (201) 796-3006
BlackHawk Industrial, Atlantic Tool Systems Div., 170 5th Ave., Hawthorne 07506
GM—J. F. Montague, 8 emp., *Wholesaler of pneumatic tools, abrasives* ............ (973) 238-0009
Boro Supply Co., Inc., 2-21 Banta Pl., P.O. Box 1034, Fair Lawn 07410
Pres.—Stanley Romanek, 7 emp., *Wholesaler of machinery, equipment* ............ (201) 794-3111
Bottcher America Corp., 88 Ford Rd., Ste. 8, Denville 07834
Sr. Sales Mgr.—Steve Foulds, 18 emp., *Distributor of printing press rollers* ............ (973) 664-1241
Camatron Sewing Machine, Inc., 42 Bergenwood Rd., Ste. A, Fairview 07022
Pres.—Robert Ross, 7 emp., *Manufacturer & distributor of specialized* ............ (201) 941-5116
Cangro Transmission Co. Of New Jersey, 295 Crooks Ave., Clifton 07011
Br. Mgr.—Michael Thompson, 10 emp., *Distributor of industrial power transmission* ............ (973) 772-7662
Cavagna North America, Inc., 50 Napoleon Ct., Somerset 08873
Pres.—Richard Darche, 25 emp., *Distributor of compressed propane,* ............ (732) 469-2100
Central Forklift, Inc., 415 Bell St., Piscataway 08854
Pres., GM—Robert Salimbene, 7 emp., *Distributor of new & used forklifts* ............ (732) 805-9494
Classic Printers & Converters, 140 Ethel Rd. W., Ste. K, Piscataway 08854
Pres., CEO—Sat Khurana, 9 emp., *Manufacturer of custom printed & plain* ............ (732) 985-1100
Comairco Equipment, Inc., 17 Progress St., Edison 08820
Sales Mgr.—Dave George, 12 emp., *Wholesaler of air & gas compressors* ............ (732) 331-1100
Conveyor Systems & Components, 21 Norman Ave., P.O. Box 343, Delran 08075
GM & Sales Mgr.—Thomas McLarney, 4 emp., *Distributor of conveyors & conveying* ............ (856) 461-8084
Cuny & Guerber, Inc., 2100 Kerrigan Ave., P.O. Box 1192, Union City 07087
Pres.—David B. Matthews, Jr., 35 emp., *Industrial automation systems integration* ............ (201) 617-5800
Cutter, Drill & Machine, Inc., 175 Ramtown Greenville Rd., Unit 701, Howell 07731
Pres.—Michael C. Tellier, 4 emp., *Distributor of water pipeline tapping* ............ (732) 206-1112
D & F Performance, 417 N. Grove St., Berlin 08009
Ptnr.—David R. Thornton, Sr., 2 emp., *Rebuilt performance engines & distributor* ............ (856) 767-4095
Devco Corp., 131 Morristown Rd., Bldg. B, Basking Ridge 07920
GM—Bill Durnan, 7 emp., *Distributor of lubrication equipment* ............ (908) 630-0005
Diamond Enterprise Group, 321 Snyder Ave., Berkeley Heights 07922
Owner—Robert Mornan, 9 emp., *Wholesaler of laminating equipment* ............ (908) 771-6777
Dynaclear Packaging / Pro Pack, Inc., 500 W. Main St., Wyckoff 07481
Chrm., CEO—Peter Quercia, 12 emp., *Full-service distributor of custom* ............ (201) 337-1001
Eastern Lift Truck Co., Inc., 549 E. Linwood Ave., Route 73 N., P.O. Box 307, Maple Shade 08052
Pres.—Mike Pruitt, 370 emp., *Corporate headquarters & distributor* ............ (856) 779-8880
EDI Distributors, Inc., 20 Lakeside Ave., P.O. Box 501, Cherry Hill 08003
Pres.—Skip Markowitz, 3 emp., *Wholesaler of custom high-pressure* ............ (856) 429-2580
Electric Forklift Repair Corp., 837 Somerset St., P.O. Box 1126, Somerset 08875
Co-Pres., CEO—Raul Pretto, 15 emp., *Distributor of electric & propane forklifts* ............ (732) 249-7757
Electronic Measurement Laboratories, Inc., 668 Easton Ave., Somerset 08873
Owner—Richard J. Pleconis, 4 emp., *Distributor of industrial gas detectors* ............ (732) 846-4029
Elkay Products Co., Inc., 35 Brown Ave., P.O. Box 149, Springfield 07081
Pres.—Steven Piller, 10 emp., *Manufacturer of quilted van pads &* ............ (973) 376-7550
Ellis Kuhnke Controls, Inc., 132 Lewis St., Unit A-2, Eatontown 07724
Pres.—Howard J. Boyce, 8 emp., *Manufacturer & distributor of pneumatic* ............ (732) 291-3334
Engine Distributors, Inc., 400 University Ct., Blackwood 08012
Pres.—Glenn Cummings, 40 emp., *Corporate headquarters & distributor* ............ (856) 228-7298
Enviropore, Inc., P.O. Box 443, Lumberton 08048
Pres.—Tom Bintliff, 5 emp., *Distributor of industrial environmental* ............ (609) 261-1588
Equipment Xchange, LLC, 309 Columbia Rd., Hammonton 08037
Ptnr.—Scott Tarzy, 8 emp., *Wholesaler of used processing equipment* ............ (609) 561-0500
Executive Binding Systems, Inc., 330 Franklin Tpke., Mahwah 07430
CFO—Bob Kronenberger, 6 emp., *Distributor of document binding equipment* ............ (201) 642-0011
F & H Supply, Inc, 1315 Route 77, P.O. Box 379, Bridgeton 08302
V-P.—Harry Swistunow, 5 emp., *Wholesaler of industrial equipment* ............ (856) 451-7080
FallProof Systems LLC, 61 2nd Ave., Trenton 08619
Ptnr.—W. Burke Sinclair, 10 emp., *Distributor of fall protection equipment* ............ (609) 325-5555
Fastenal Co., 1115 N. New Rd., Absecon 08201
GM—Wayne Winn, 3 emp., *Wholesaler of fasteners, safety equipment* ............ (609) 813-2356
Fastenal Co., 421 Route 73 & Cushman Ave., Unit 11, Berlin 08009
Br. Mgr.—David Gabrielski, 1 emp., *Wholesaler of fasteners, safety equipment* ............ (856) 768-3657
Fastenal Co., 921 Route 130 N., Burlington 08016
GM—Tom Petruzzi, 3 emp., *Wholesaler of fasteners, safety equipment* ............ (609) 239-3016
Fastenal Co., 33 Route 17 S., East Rutherford 07073
Br. Mgr.—Mike Scrobel, 5 emp., *Wholesaler of fasteners, safety equipment* ............ (201) 804-2228
Fastenal Co., 22 Meridian Rd., Unit 2, Eatontown 07724
Br. Mgr.—Jan Humphrey, 3 emp., *Wholesaler of fasteners, safety equipment* ............ (732) 542-7533
Fastenal Co., 55 Carter Dr., Edison 08817
Br. & Sales Mgr., Inside—Harrison Jennings, 5 emp., *Wholesaler of fasteners, tools, abrasives* (732) 777-1029
Fastenal Co., 68-A Clinton Rd., Fairfield 07004
Br. Mgr.—Joe Bourlier, 4 emp., *Wholesaler of fasteners, safety equipment* ............ (973) 244-0540
Fastenal Co., 186 Gold Mine Rd., Unit 1, Flanders 07836
Br. Mgr.—Matthew Cohen, 5 emp., *Wholesaler of fasteners, safety equipment* ............ (973) 691-0547
Fastenal Co., 316 Black Horse Pike, Unit C, Glendora 08029
Store Mgr.—Blake Phillips, 4 emp., *Wholesaler of fasteners, safety equipment* ............ (856) 939-2500
Fastenal Co., 1026 W. Elizabeth Ave., Unit 2, Linden 07036
Br. Mgr.—Alex Klinga, 3 emp., *Wholesaler of fasteners, safety equipment* ............ (908) 862-8880
Fastenal Co., 550 Lincoln Blvd., Middlesex 08846
Store Mgr.—Derek Dandy, 5 emp., *Wholesaler of fasteners, safety equipment* ............ (732) 748-0140
Fastenal Co., 987 Jersey Ave., Ste. C, New Brunswick 08901
Br. Mgr.—Mike Kane, 3 emp., *Wholesaler of fasteners, safety equipment* ............ (732) 246-0248
Fastenal Co., 443 Madison Ave., Paterson 07524
Sales Rep., Inside—Joe Bresett, 3 emp., *Wholesaler of fasteners, safety equipment* ............ (973) 278-5509
Fastenal Co., 1163 Route 130, Robbinsville 08691
Br. Mgr.—William Strobel, 3 emp., *Wholesaler of fasteners, safety equipment* ............ (609) 259-4290
Fastenal Co., 1875 N. Olden Ave., Trenton 08638
Store Mgr.—Chris Varlaro, 4 emp., *Wholesaler of fasteners, safety equipment* ............ (609) 530-0456
Fastenal Co., 53 S. Jefferson Rd., Ste. K, Whippany 07981
Br. Mgr.—Jason Smith, 3 emp., *Wholesaler of fasteners, safety equipment* ............ (973) 428-3300
Forklift Headquarter, LLC, 975 Joyce Kilmer Ave., North Brunswick 08902
Pres.—Mark Gabel, 1 emp., *Distributor of used forklifts & racking* ............ (732) 821-1413
Gaffney-Kroese Supply Corp., 50 Randolph Rd., Somerset 08873
Pres.—Christopher Kroese, 75 emp., *Corporate headquarters & distributor* ............ (732) 885-9000
GAMS Power Tools & Supplies, Inc., 133-135 Schuyler Ave., Kearny 07032
Pres.—Margaret Servidio, 5 emp., *Distributor of contractor's tools &* ............ (201) 955-0222
Garden State Engine & Equipment Co., Inc., 3509 U.S. Highway 22, Branchburg 08876
GM—John Meyer, 15 emp., *Distributor of truck-mounted cranes* ............ (908) 534-5444
George A. Mathewson Co., 9-11 Foundry St., Newark 07105
Pres.—Dave Czachur, 2 emp., *Wholesaler of bearings & power transmission* ............ (973) 344-0081
GlobePharma, Inc., 2-B Janine Pl., New Brunswick 08901
Pres.—Sanni Raju, 10 emp., *Wholesaler of pharmaceutical solid* ............ (732) 296-9700
GTS-Welco, 425 Avenue P, Newark 07105
Chrm. of the Board—Robert D'Alessandro, 100 emp., *Wholesaler of welding equipment & supplies* (973) 589-7895
Harrison Equipment Corp., 500 Essex St., Harrison 07029
Owner—Robert Koones, 11 emp., *Distributor of welding & compaction* ............ (973) 485-1448
Hayes Pump, Inc., 295 Fairfield Ave., Fairfield 07004
Ex. V-P.—Joseph F. Larkin, Sr., 22 emp., *Distributor of pumps & parts, including* ............ (973) 808-0606
Heerema Co., 200 6th Ave., Hawthorne 07506
Pres.—William C. Heerema, 25 emp., *Wholesaler of industrial pumps, refrigeration* ............ (973) 423-0505
Houser Welding Supply Co., Inc., 12-14 E. Main St., Somerville 08876
Pres.—David Houser, 5 emp., *Wholesaler of welding equipment, supplies* ............ (908) 526-7777
Indexing Technologies, Inc., 37 Orchard St., Ramsey 07446
Pres.—Mike Bickham, 10 emp., *Wholesaler of machine tools, including* ............ (201) 934-6333
Industrial Controls Distributors, LLC, 17 Christopher Way, Eatontown 07724
Pres.—Joe Eichelberger, 55 emp., *Company headquarters & distributor* ............ (732) 918-9000
Industrial Welding Supply, Inc., 999 Airport Rd., Ste. 1, Lakewood 08701
Pres.—Jim Cusick, 4 emp., *Distributor of welding equipment &* ............ (732) 367-7100
Industrial Welding Supply, Inc., 4 Val St., Sayreville 08872
Pres.—Jim Cusick, 21 emp., *Corporate headquarters & distributor* ............ (732) 721-1150
Interchange Equipment, Inc., 90 Dayton Ave., Ste. 200, Passaic 07055
Pres.—Marc Herrmann, 15 emp., *Manufacturer & distributor of printing* ............ (973) 473-5005
International Compressor Co., Inc., 361 Jelliff Ave., Newark 07108
Pres.—Clarence Wilson, 7 emp., *Rebuilt air compressors & distributor* ............ (973) 824-7170
International Welding Technologies, Inc., 2650 Egg Harbor Rd., Lindenwold 08021
GM—Neil Wilkinson, 10 emp., *Manufacturer & wholesaler of welding* ............ (856) 435-8004
J & J Industrial Supply, Inc., 113 E. Centre St., P.O. Box 110174, Nutley 07110
Pres.—Joe Damore, Sr., 7 emp., *Wholesaler of industrial equipment* ............ (973) 235-0100
Jersey Diesel, 487 Main St., Dorchester 08316
GM—Bette Jeanyank, 4 emp., *Distributor of diesel engines* ............ (856) 785-8810
Jesco, Inc., 118 Saint Nicholas Ave., South Plainfield 07080
Founder & Chrm.—Lou Robustelli, 50 emp., *Corporate headquarters & distributor* ............ (908) 821-1400
Jessup, Inc., Charles M., 177 Smith St., Keasbey 08832
Pres., CEO & CFO—Charles M. Jessup, 9 emp., *Distributor of commercial & textile* ............ (732) 324-0430
Jet Line Products, Inc., 55 Jacobus Ave., Kearny 07032
Pur. Agt.—Laura Meola, 20 emp., *Corporate headquarters & distributor* ............ (973) 690-2999
Johnson & Towers, Inc., 2701 Fire Rd., Egg Harbor Township 08234
Dir., Bus. Dev.—Paul Apple, 20 emp., *Distributor of diesel truck & marine* ............ (609) 272-1415
Johnson & Towers, Inc., 2021 Briggs Rd., P.O. Box 4000, Mount Laurel 08054
Chrm.—Walter Johnson III, 75 emp., *Corporate headquarters & rebuilt truck* ............ (856) 234-6990
Kaman Industrial Technologies Corp., 502 Bloy St., Hillside 07205
GM—John Marra, 8 emp., *Distributor of industrial equipment* ............ (908) 687-0004
Kaman Industrial Technologies Corp., 195 Borelli Rd., Paulsboro 08066
Br. Mgr.—Robert Widen, 5 emp., *Wholesaler of industrial equipment* ............ (856) 227-7000
Kaman Industrial Technologies Corp., 195 Borrelli Blvd., Ste. B, Paulsboro 08066
Team Leader—Mark Pancoast, 10 emp., *Distributor of industrial equipment* ............ (856) 284-7400
Kemperle, Inc., Albert, 626 E. Elizabeth Ave., Linden 07036
Br. Mgr.—Terry Gardner, 20 emp., *Wholesaler of automotive body shop* ............ (908) 925-6133
Klingelhofer Corp., 165 Mill Ln., Mountainside 07092
Pres.—Al Klingelhofer, 11 emp., *Distributor of metal sawing, deburring* ............ (908) 232-7200
Kraft Power Corp., 241 W. Parkway, Pompton Plains 07444
V-P.—Chris Stemper, 30 emp., *Manufacturer of combined heat & power* ............ (973) 835-9800
Kuntz Co., Inc., R. T., 5146 W. Hurley Pond Rd., P.O. Box 476, Farmingdale 07727
Owner & Pres.—Rod Kuntz, 7 emp., *Manufacturer & distributor of resin* ............ (732) 751-1770
L & R Mfg. Co., Inc., 577 Elm St., P.O. Box 607, Kearny 07032
Pres.—Robert J. Lazarus, 100 emp., *Manufacturer & distributor of ultrasonic* ............ (201) 991-5330
Liberty Welding Supply, Inc., 187 W. Fort Lee Rd., Bogota 07603
Pres.—Robert Safranek, 2 emp., *Distributor of new & warranted used* ............ (973) 923-2900
Liftec, Inc., 124 Sylvania Pl., South Plainfield 07080
Pres.—Stephen Panek, 50 emp., *Distributor of industrial forklift* ............ (908) 769-0034
Longo Electrical-Mechanical, 1 Harry Shupe Blvd., Wharton 07885
Owner—Joseph J. Longo, 100 emp., *Wholesaler of motors, pumps, switchgears* ............ (973) 537-0400
M C Machinery Systems, Inc., 16 Chapin Rd., P.O. Box 405, Pine Brook 07058
V-P.—Nick Giannotte, 9 emp., *Wholesaler of industrial machinery* ............ (973) 244-1501
Machine Shop Discount Supply, P.O. Box 16, Little Ferry 07643
Pres.—Hy Ash, 15 emp., *Distributor of cutting & measuring* ............ (201) 518-8472
Mack Boring & Parts Co., 2365 U.S. Highway 22 W., P.O. Box 3116, Union 07083
Chrm.—Ned McGovern, 55 emp., *Company headquarters & full service* ............ (908) 964-0700
Madsen & Howell, Inc., 500 Market St., Ste. 1, Perth Amboy 08861
Pres.—Peter Madsen, 50 emp., *Distributor of industrial equipment* ............ (732) 826-4000
Marchesini Packaging Machinery, 43 Fairfield Pl., West Caldwell 07006
GM—Anna Marie Bellina, 18 emp., *Wholesaler of packaging machinery &* ............ (973) 575-7445
Maruka U.S.A., Inc., 45 Route 46 E., Ste. 610, P.O. Box 747, Pine Brook 07058
Pres.—Gary Lowery, 35 emp., *Corporate headquarters & distributor* ............ (973) 487-3800
Material Handling Supply, Inc., 1 Old Salem Rd., Brooklawn 08030
Pres.—Andrew Levin, 110 emp., *Wholesaler of material handling equipment* ............ (856) 541-1290
MBO America, 4 E. Stow Rd., Ste. 12, Marlton 08053
Pres., CEO—Frank Bahmer, 20 emp., *Distributor of printing industry machinery* ............ (609) 267-2900
McIntosh Controls Corp., 218 Little Falls Rd., Unit 1, Cedar Grove 07009
Pres.—Harold Mattesky, 9 emp., *Distributor of level, flow, pressure* ............ (973) 433-4700
McJunkin Red Man Corporation, 305 Center Ave., Waterford Works 08089
Br. Mgr.—Tim Fish, 4 emp., *Distributor of oilfield equipment,* ............ (856) 753-7690
Mel-Pak Equipment Co., 649 U.S. Highway 206, Ste. 9-303, Hillsborough 08844
Pres., GM—Mike Mellone, 2 emp., *Wholesaler of packaging machinery &* ............ (201) 825-2624
Metro Hydraulic Jack Co., 1271 McCarter Hwy., P.O. Box 9410, Newark 07104
Pres.—Michael Storch, 17 emp., *Distributor of jacks, cylinders, pumps* ............ (973) 350-0111
Metro Industrial Supply, Inc., 200 Charles St., Garfield 07026
Pres.—Richard Dino, 5 emp., *Wholesaler of industrial equipment* ............ (973) 546-5660
MG America, Inc., 31 Kulick Rd., Fairfield 07004
Pres.—Fabio Trippodo, 20 emp., *Wholesaler of packaging machinery,* ............ (973) 808-8185
MHE, Inc., 47 Atlantic Ave., Long Branch 07740
Pres., GM—Dave Stickle, 4 emp., *Wholesaler of material handling equipment* ............ (732) 571-6112

S.I.C.

Mid Atlantic Pump & Equipment Co., 228 N. Route 73, Berlin 08009
Pres.—Dennis Zepp, 10 emp., *Wholesaler of industrial, commercial* ........ (856) 768-3880

Mid-Atlantic CNC, Inc., 260 Evans Way, Branchburg 08876
Ptnr. & V-P.—Richard Knof, 25 emp., *Corporate headquarters & wholesaler* ........ (908) 809-1100

Midlantic Supply, LLC, 8000 Midlantic Dr., Ste. 200-N., P.O. Box 506, Mount Laurel 08054
Owner—Diane Disanto, 5 emp., *Distributor of waterworks & sewer equipment* ........ (856) 813-5014

Modern Group Ltd., 75 New St., Edison 08837
Br. Mgr., Forklifts—Jerry Hagen, 25 emp., *Distributor of construction, industrial* ........ (800) 846-5840

Modern Group Ltd., 112-128 Route 17 N., Hasbrouck Heights 07604
Br. Mgr.—Joe Frassa, 35 emp., *Wholesaler of industrial machinery* ........ (201) 288-1441

MSC Industrial Supply Co., 105 Newfield Ave., Ste. E, Edison 08837
Mktg. Mgr.—David Bothe, 15 emp., *Wholesaler of industrial equipment* ........ (732) 512-9555

Muenz Engineered Sales Co., 21 Chatham Rd., Summit 07901
CEO—Jeff O'Sullivan, 16 emp., *Distributor of abrasives, cutting &* ........ (908) 273-6755

Mulcare Pipeline Solutions, 9 Mars Ct., Ste. C-4, Boonton 07005
Pres.—Robert Engdahl, 15 emp., *Distributor of natural gas distribution* ........ (973) 335-4800

National Equipment Co., 342 Squankum Yellowbrook Rd., P.O. Box 674, Farmingdale 07727
Pres.—Mauro R. Raccuglia, 4 emp., *Rebuilt production pipe & bolt threading* ........ (732) 938-5084

National Public Seating Corp., 149 Entin Rd., Clifton 07014
Pres., Dir., Sales—Barry Stauber, 80 emp., *Distributor of upholstered & plastic* ........ (973) 594-1100

New York Sewing Machine, Inc., 8555 Tonnelle Ave., Unit 301, North Bergen 07047
Pres.—Sheldon Rothstein, 5 emp., *Manufacturer & distributor of sewing* ........ (201) 809-2009

Northeast Industrial, LLC, 661 Route 9, Cape May 08204
Pres., GM—Donald Carter, 2 emp., *Distributor of hydraulic, marine, industrial* ........ (609) 884-3510

NRG Energy, Inc. (H Q), 211 Carnegie Ctr., Princeton 08540
Pres., CEO—David Crane, 340 emp., *Corporate headquarters; diverse energy* ........ (609) 524-4500

Nutley Heating & Cooling Supply Co., Inc., 50 Page Rd., Clifton 07012
Pres.—Rick Cancelosi, 45 emp., *Corporate headquarters & distributor* ........ (973) 470-8844

P & A Crane & Hoist Co., 369 Reuter Ave., Elizabeth 07202
Pres.—Manny Pego, 2 emp., *Distributor of cranes* ........ (908) 527-6990

PAC Tool & Supply Co., Inc., 420 Paterson Ave., P.O. Box 7482, East Rutherford 07073
Pres. & Sales Mgr.—Mike Pacala, 3 emp., *Distributor of industrial metalworking* ........ (201) 933-8550

PBM Supply Co., Inc., 88 Cannonball Rd., P.O. Box 351, Pompton Lakes 07442
Pres.—Robert Fox, 3 emp., *Distributor of power transmission products* ........ (973) 839-0050

Pipeline Supply Co., 203 Egel Ave., Middlesex 08846
COO—James Westerman, 10 emp., *Distributor of pipeline equipment,* ........ (732) 560-1509

Plate Concepts, Inc., 1221 U.S. Highway 22, Ste. 3, Lebanon 08833
Pres.—James Gooch, 10 emp., *Wholesaler of plate heat exchangers* ........ (908) 236-9570

Power Pool Plus, Inc., 7 Edge Rd., Alpha 08865
V-P., GM—Brent Kephart, 18 emp., *Manufacturer & distributor of power* ........ (908) 454-1124

Preferred Plastics & Packaging Co., Inc., 681 Main St., Ste. 42, Belleville 07109
Pres.—Randolph Swickle, 30 emp., *Distributor of packaging materials* ........ (973) 759-1510

Printers Parts Store, 82 Herman St., East Rutherford 07073
Pres.—Barbara Pignato, 4 emp., *Wholesaler of replacement parts, rollers* ........ (201) 935-9595

Pro-Motion Industries, LLC, 102 Allied Pkwy., Sicklerville 08081
Owner—Kelly Cone, 12 emp., *Wholesaler of labeling equipment &* ........ (856) 809-0040

Pro-Pac Services, Inc., 15 Van Natta Dr., Ringwood 07456
Pres.—Brian Douglas, 12 emp., *Wholesaler of vacuum packaging machinery* ........ (973) 962-8080

Proven Technology, Inc., 5 Woodshire Way, Hillsborough 08844
Pres.—Robert Slawska, 5 emp., *Wholesaler of plastics machinery &* ........ (908) 359-7888

Quality Discount Press Parts & Equipment, Inc., 6088 Reega Ave., Egg Harbor Township 08234
Pres.—Jeff Ludwig, 20 emp., *Wholesaler of new & used printing equipment* ........ (609) 646-2212

R & H Spring & Truck Repair, Inc., 4806 W. Hurley Pond Rd., Belmar 07719
Pres.—Frank Todero, Sr., 10 emp., *Rebuilt automotive & truck leaf springs* ........ (732) 681-9000

R.P. Machine, LLC, 906 Stillwater Rd., P.O. Box 144, Stillwater 07875
Owner—Randall Pobutkiewicz, 6 emp., *Distributor of new & used sheet metal* ........ (973) 383-8994

Richards Co., 437 Boulevard, P.O. Box 199, Elmwood Park 07407
V-P., Opers. & CEO—Dan J. Kleinrock, 10 emp., *Distributor of industrial equipment* ........ (201) 797-6300

RONDO Inc. USA, 51 Joseph St., Moonachie 07074
Pres.—Jerry Murphy, 15 emp., *Distributor of commercial & industrial* ........ (201) 229-9700

Safety-Kleen Systems, Inc., 116 Skyline Dr., South Plainfield 07080
Manager—Thomas Colligan, 100 emp., *Distributor of used industrial parts* ........ (908) 791-9600

Safway Atlantic, LLC, 700 Commercial Ave., Carlstadt 07072
Pres.—Greg Karas, 20 emp., *Wholesaler of supported & suspended* ........ (201) 636-5500

Salomon Bros. Equipment Co., Inc., P.O. Box 43, Cranford 07016
Pres.—David R. Salomon, 4 emp., *Distributor of waste & recycling equipment* ........ (908) 931-9311

Sanzo Ltd., 35 Munsee Dr., Cranford 07016
Owner & Pres.—Carol Sanzo, 5 emp., *Wholesaler of industrial, commercial* ........ (908) 276-6654

Scales Industrial Technologies, Inc of NJ, 185 Lackawanna Ave., Woodland Park 07424
GM—Rich Hohn, 45 emp., *Distributor of air & gas compressors* ........ (973) 890-1010

Scientific Models, Inc., 340 Snyder Ave., Berkeley Heights 07922
★ Owner—John Frisoli, 20 emp., *Distributor of tools & hardware, including* ........ (908) 464-7070

Shingle & Gibb Company, 845 Lancer Dr., Moorestown 08057
Pres.—Drew Pfleger, 25 emp., *Company headquarters & distributor* ........ (856) 234-8500

SOS Gases, Inc., 1100 Harrison Ave., Kearny 07032
Pres.—Steve Defillipps, Sr., 23 emp., *Distributor of industrial & specialty* ........ (201) 998-7800

South Jersey Welding Supply Co., 496 Route 38 E., Maple Shade 08052
Pres.—Robert Thornton, Jr., 35 emp., *Company headquarters & wholesaler of* ........ (856) 778-4440

South Jersey Welding Supply Co., 94 W. Forest Grove Rd., Vineland 08360
Owner—Robert Thorton, Jr., 15 emp., *Distributor of welding equipment &* ........ (856) 691-9659

Stewart & Stevenson Power Products, LLC- ADDA Div., 180 Route 17 S., P.O. Box 950, Lodi 07644
CEO—John F. Farmer, 90 emp., *Company headquarters & distributor* ........ (201) 489-5800

Stiles Enterprises, Inc., 114 Beach St., P.O. Box 92, Rockaway 07866
Pres.—Richard Stiles, 15 emp., *Manufacturer & distributor of packaging* ........ (973) 625-9660

Structured Materials Industries, Inc., 201 Circle Dr. N., Unit 102-103, Piscataway 08854
Pres., CEO—Gary Tompa, 15 emp., *Distributor of MOCVD, PECVD, CVD &* ........ (732) 302-9274

Syntex Group, Inc., 1838 Downs Ave., Clementon 08021
Pres.—Eric Ezeiruaku, 5 emp., *Distributor of industrial machinery* ........ (856) 566-0058

T & B Specialties, Inc., 479 Wright Debow Rd., Jackson 08527
Pres.—Thomas E. Barchie, 3 emp., *Wholesaler of industrial equipment* ........ (732) 928-4500

Tarantin Industries, 86 Vanderveer Rd., Freehold 07728
Pres., CEO—Thomas Tarantin, 25 emp., *Company headquarters & distributor* ........ (732) 780-9340

Tool-Krib Supply Co. (H Q), 787 Passaic Ave., P.O. Box 6064, West Caldwell 07006
GM—Bob Nichols, 11 emp., *Company headquarters; wholesaler of* ........ (973) 808-4550

Total Machine Solutions, Inc., 16 Spielman Rd., Fairfield 07004
Whse. Mgr.—Joe Vasquez, 7 emp., *Distributor of electrical & mechanical* ........ (973) 244-0017

Trico Lift, Inc., 418 Southgate Ct., Mickleton 08056
★ Br. Mgr.—Chuck Turner, 100 emp., *Distributor of industrial lifts, including* ........ (800) 468-7426

Trico Lift, Inc. (H Q), 1101 Wheaton Ave., Millville 08332
Pres.—Ken Pustizzi, 25 emp., *Corporate headquarters; distributor* ........ (856) 776-2350

Turtle & Hughes, Inc., 188 Foothill Rd., Bridgewater 08807
Ex. V-P., Br. Mgr.—Rick Reffler, 100 emp., *Distributor of electrical & industrial* ........ (732) 560-5575

UAC Packaging, LLC, 330 Roycefield Rd., Unit C, Hillsborough 08844
Pres.—Charles Bernius, 10 emp., *Distributor of automatic capping machinery* ........ (908) 595-6890

V.S. Systematics, Inc., 300 S. Michigan Ave., 1st Fl., Kenilworth 07033
Owner—Sarah Esteves, 3 emp., *Wholesaler of industrial automation* ........ (908) 241-5110

Valley National Gases, WV LLC, 201 Crown Point Rd., West Deptford 08086
GM—Wendy Hughes, 10 emp., *Distributor of welding supplies, including* ........ (856) 848-7321

Van Air & Hydraulics, Inc., 612 E. Woodlawn Ave., Maple Shade 08052
GM—Barb Fox, 10 emp., *Distributor of industrial motion control* ........ (856) 779-7300

W. W. Grainger, Inc., 308 Allwood Rd., Clifton 07012
Br. Mgr.—Kevin Wojcicki, 20 emp., *Wholesaler of commercial & industrial* ........ (973) 777-7700

W. W. Grainger, Inc., 560-596 Bercik St., Ste. 1, Elizabeth 07201
GM—Phil Circelli, 12 emp., *Wholesaler of industrial equipment* ........ (908) 787-1952

W. W. Grainger, Inc., 277 Route 46 W., Fairfield 07004
Br. Mgr.—Damian Czirjak, 10 emp., *Wholesaler of industrial equipment* ........ (973) 227-7220

W. W. Grainger, Inc., 819 E. Gate Dr., Mount Laurel 08054
GM—Ron Schomo, 15 emp., *Wholesaler of industrial equipment* ........ (856) 234-8550

W. W. Grainger, Inc., 1585 N. Olden Ave., Trenton 08638
Br. Mgr.—Patricia James, 10 emp., *Distributor of industrial equipment* ........ (609) 394-2620

Water Resources New Jersey, LLC, 1609 Route 206, P.O. Box 2172, Tabernacle 08088
Owner—S. Cocco, 6 emp., *Distributor of water treatment equipment* ........ (609) 268-7965

WENCO Machinery Corp., 355 Margaret King Ave., Ringwood 07456
Pres.—Will Schouten, 6 emp., *Wholesaler of metal stamping & fabricating* ........ (973) 657-9660

xpedx, 261 River Rd., Clifton 07014
CFO—Jeffrey Patterson, 120 emp., *Distributor of paper, packaging materials* ........ (973) 405-2310

Yecies, Inc., Herman W., 11 Roosevelt Ave., P.O. Box 6186, West Orange 07052
Pres.—Roberta Yecies, 3 emp., *Wholesaler of industrial equipment* ........ (973) 736-7362

## 5085 Industrial supplies

ABCO Systems, Inc., 15 Willet St., Ste. 4, Bloomfield 07003
Pres.—Seth Weisberg, 12 emp., *Distributor of industrial handling* ........ (201) 507-0999

Advanced Filtration Co., 25-A Arnold Blvd., P.O. Box 324, Howell 07731
Pres.—John Woods, 3 emp., *Distributor of water, air, gas, fuel* ........ (732) 901-6676

Airgas East, Inc., 121 Stanley Ave., Bellmawr 08031
GM—Joe Sergi, 2 emp., *Distributor of welding equipment &* ........ (856) 931-0900

Airgas East, Inc., 2 Beckwith Ave., Paterson 07503
Br. Mgr.—Pete Miteiko, 2 emp., *Distributor of welding equipment, supplies* ........ (973) 742-2211

Airgas East, Inc., 1750 Gallagher Dr., Vineland 08360
Accts. Mgr.—Joe Gernaloff, 4 emp., *Wholesaler of welding equipment & supplies* ........ (856) 692-7734

American Filter & Tank Co., Inc., 231 Greenwood Ave., Ste. 2, Midland Park 07432
Owner & Pres.—John Spanedda, 3 emp., *Distributor of spray nozzles & air* ........ (201) 857-5056

Andler South Corp., 102 E. Parkway Dr., Egg Harbor Township 08234
Pres.—Richard Mclaughlin, 12 emp., *Distributor of plastic & glass containers* ........ (609) 485-2000

Applied Industrial Technologies, Inc., 24-C Worlds Fair Dr., Somerset 08873
GM—Glenn Casey, 5 emp., *Wholesaler of industrial equipment* ........ (732) 356-0522

ARAMSCO, 1480 Grandview Ave., P.O. Box 29, Thorofare 08086
Pres.—Rich Salerno, 65 emp., *Company headquarters & distributor* ........ (856) 686-7700

Ardom Bearing Group, 3377 S. Clinton Ave., Unit 15, South Plainfield 07080
GM—Mark A. Commesso, 2 emp., *Distributor of bearings, motors, reducers* ........ (908) 755-3000

Associated Plastics, Inc., 179 E. Inman Ave., Rahway 07065
Pres.—Richard W. Fisher, 3 emp., *Distributor of plastic pull straps,* ........ (732) 574-2800

AST Bearings, LLC, 115 Main Rd., Montville 07045
Pres.—Mike Pelehach, 60 emp., *Distributor of ball bearings & related* ........ (973) 335-2230

Atlantic Coast Container Brokerage & Sales, Inc., 906 Oak Tree Rd., Ste. P, South Plainfield 07080
Pres.—Lillian Skov-Nissen, 3 emp., *Wholesaler of new & used ISO cargo* ........ (908) 755-2898

Atlas Welding Supply Co., Inc., 808 Brook Rd., Lakewood 08701
Corp. Secy.—Dina Pincus, 7 emp., *Distributor of welding equipment &* ........ (732) 363-1148

Avery Filter Co., Inc., 99 Kinderkamack Rd., Ste. 209, Westwood 07675
Pres.—Quentin Avery, 4 emp., *Distributor of filter paper, filter* ........ (201) 666-9664

Awisco Corp., 24 Lakeside Ave., West Orange 07052
Br. Mgr.—Abel Marriott, 6 emp., *Wholesaler of welding equipment, industrial* ........ (973) 736-0200

Awisco West Milford, LLC, 26 Industrial Rd., West Milford 07480
Br. Mgr.—Andrew Cullen, 8 emp., *Distributor of welding, industrial* ........ (973) 728-9008

Axis, Inc., 210 Meister Ave., Somerville 08876
Sales Mgr.—Gary Eliasson, 22 emp., *Distributor of electronic industrial* ........ (908) 429-0090

Bacon & Graham, Inc., 34 E. 25th St., Paterson 07514
Pres.—Craig Bacon, 30 emp., *Wholesaler of packaging, shipping,* ........ (973) 684-1488

Bearing Depot & Supply, Inc., 819 Lincoln Blvd., Ste. 1, Middlesex 08846
Pres.—Donna Hardgrove, 5 emp., *Distributor of metric & inch ceramic* ........ (732) 563-2225

Benchmark, Cane Farm, Bldg. 7, P.O. Box 214, Rosemont 08556
Owner—Mair La Touche, 3 emp., *Distributor of brass display & museum* ........ (609) 397-1131

Berlin Packaging, LLC, 2050 Center Ave., Ste. 400, Fort Lee 07024
V-P., Reg.—Jonathan Rabinowitz, 20 emp., *Distributor of packaging materials,* ........ (201) 947-7744

Berliss Bearing Co., 644 W. Mount Pleasant Ave., P.O. Box 45, Livingston 07039
Pres.—Darin Vogt, 20 emp., *Distributor of roller bearings* ........ (973) 992-4242

BlackHawk Industrial, Atlantic Tool Systems Div., 170 5th Ave., Hawthorne 07506
GM—J. F. Montague, 8 emp., *Wholesaler of pneumatic tools, abrasives* ........ (973) 238-0009

Boneham Metal Products, Inc., 327 N. 14th St., Kenilworth 07033
Assoc. V-P.—Doreen Guenther, 7 emp., *Wholesaler of bushings & dowel pins* ........ (908) 272-1200

Brown & Perkins, Inc., 1193 Route 535, P.O. Box 412, Cranbury 08512
Pres.—E. T. Comly, 16 emp., *Manufacturer & distributor of wire* ........ (609) 655-1150

Cangro Transmission Co. Of New Jersey, 295 Crooks Ave., Clifton 07011
Br. Mgr.—Michael Thompson, 10 emp., *Distributor of industrial power transmission* ........ (973) 772-7662

Cast Technology, Inc., 161 West St., South Plainfield 07080
Pres.—Kenneth Shilay, 7 emp., *Rebuilt engines & distributor of bearings* ........ (908) 753-5155

Cavagna North America, Inc., 50 Napoleon Ct., Somerset 08873
Pres.—Richard Darche, 25 emp., *Distributor of compressed propane,* ........ (732) 469-2100

CermSource, Inc, 25 Kimberly Rd., Unit A, P.O. Box 6026, East Brunswick 08816
Mktg. Mgr.—Philip Kent, 10 emp., *Wholesaler of refractories, including* ........ (732) 257-5002

Certified Products Co., 269 Kearney Ave., Jersey City 07305
Owner—Cosimo Ferretti, 15 emp., *Distributor of hose assemblies & lubricants* ........ (201) 433-0013

Chalmers & Kubeck, Inc., 8 Jules Ln., New Brunswick 08901
Sales Mgr.—Jim Heuer, 25 emp., *Distributor of pump, turbine, gearbox* ........ (732) 993-1251

Chamberlain's VACU-Blast Sales, 1200 Bannard St., P.O. Box 225, Cinnaminson 08077
Pres.—Mike Cataline, Jr., 7 emp., *Manufacturer of abrasive blasting equipment* ........ (856) 829-6444

Combined Supply Co., LLC, 640 S. Broad St., P.O. Box 9192, Elizabeth 07202
Pres., GM—Patrick O'Grady III, 2 emp., *Distributor of industrial hoses & fittings* ........ (908) 353-8888

Concord Paper Mfg., Inc., 375 Sylvan Ave., Ste. 23, Englewood Cliffs 07632
Dir., Sales & Mktg.—Donna Parker, 4 emp., *Shipping boxes & folding cartons, printing* ........ (201) 567-2529

Consolidated Bearings Company, 10 Wing Dr., Cedar Knolls 07927
Pres.—Glenn R. Kuskin, 30 emp., *Company headquarters & distributor* ........ (973) 539-8300

Corporate Graphic Solutions, Inc., 11 W. Passaic St., Rochelle Park 07662
CEO—Harvey Ginsberg, 2 emp., *Commercial printing & distributor of* ........ (201) 556-0700

Couse & Bolten Co., 90 South St., Dock 5, Newark 07114
Owner, CEO & COO—Michael Nelson, 7 emp., *Manufacturer & distributor of hydraulic* ........ (973) 344-6330
CPR Container, 94 Ford Rd., Ste. 5, Denville 07834
Owner—Nick Foglia, 5 emp., *Wholesaler of plastic & steel packaging* ........ (973) 625-0664
Cutter, Drill & Machine, Inc., 175 Ramtown Greenville Rd., Unit 701, Howell 07731
Pres.—Michael C. Tellier, 4 emp., *Distributor of water pipeline tapping* ........ (732) 206-1112
Delta Tool & Polishing Supplies Co., Inc., 45 North Ave., P.O. Box 169, Garwood 07027
Pres.—Jose Santos, 3 emp., *Distributor of mold polishing supplies* ........ (908) 518-7600
Diamond Enterprise Group, 321 Snyder Ave., Berkeley Heights 07922
Owner—Robert Mornan, 9 emp., *Wholesaler of laminating equipment* ........ (908) 771-6777
Duva, Inc., James, 66-B Columbia Rd., Branchburg 08876
Pres.—James Duva, 8 emp., *Wholesaler of pipe, hose & fittings* ........ (908) 526-1222
Elkay Products Co., Inc., 35 Brown Ave., P.O. Box 149, Springfield 07081
Pres.—Steven Piller, 10 emp., *Manufacturer of quilted van pads &* ........ (973) 376-7550
Ellis Kuhnke Controls, Inc., 132 Lewis St., Unit A-2, Eatontown 07724
Pres.—Howard J. Boyce, 8 emp., *Manufacturer & distributor of pneumatic* ........ (732) 291-3334
Extech Building Materials, Inc., 385 Asbury Rd., Farmingdale 07727
Manager—Bob Lippe, 7 emp., *Distributor of masonry materials &* ........ (732) 919-3340
Extech Building Materials, Inc., 61-89 Ave. K, Newark 07105
Pres.—Timothy Feury, 50 emp., *Distributor of brick, stone, construction* ........ (973) 274-3340
F & H Supply, Inc, 1315 Route 77, P.O. Box 379, Bridgeton 08302
V-P.—Harry Swistunow, 5 emp., *Wholesaler of industrial equipment* ........ (856) 451-7080
Fastenal Co., 1115 N. New Rd., Absecon 08201
GM—Wayne Winn, 3 emp., *Wholesaler of fasteners, safety equipment* ........ (609) 813-2356
Fastenal Co., 921 Route 130 N., Burlington 08016
GM—Tom Petruzzi, 3 emp., *Wholesaler of fasteners, safety equipment* ........ (609) 239-3016
Fastenal Co., 186 Gold Mine Rd., Unit 1, Flanders 07836
Br. Mgr.—Matthew Cohen, 5 emp., *Wholesaler of fasteners, safety equipment* ........ (973) 691-0547
Fastenal Co., 1026 W. Elizabeth Ave., Unit 2, Linden 07036
Br. Mgr.—Alex Klinga, 3 emp., *Wholesaler of fasteners, safety equipment* ........ (908) 862-8880
Fastenal Co., 987 Jersey Ave., Ste. C, New Brunswick 08901
Br. Mgr.—Mike Kane, 3 emp., *Wholesaler of fasteners, safety equipment* ........ (732) 246-0248
Fastenal Co., 1875 N. Olden Ave., Trenton 08638
Store Mgr.—Chris Varlaro, 4 emp., *Wholesaler of fasteners, safety equipment* ........ (609) 530-0456
Fastenal Co., 53 S. Jefferson Rd., Ste. K, Whippany 07981
Br. Mgr.—Jason Smith, 3 emp., *Wholesaler of fasteners, safety equipment* ........ (973) 428-3300
FCX Performance, Inc., 333 Route 46 W., Ste. 130, Fairfield 07004
Br. Mgr.—John Ramey, 10 emp., *Distributor of automated valves for* ........ (973) 575-8350
Filter Technologies, Inc., 45 Stouts Ln., Unit 3, Monmouth Junction 08852
Dir.—Peter Wojnarowicz, 5 emp., *Distributor of industrial water & air* ........ (732) 329-2500
Frank Winne & Son, Inc., 521 Fellowship Rd., Ste. 115, Mount Laurel 08054
Pres.—Doug Coath, 25 emp., *Wholesaler of rope, tape, twine, safety* ........ (931) 212-3720
Gaffney-Kroese Supply Corp., 50 Randolph Rd., Somerset 08873
Pres.—Christopher Kroese, 75 emp., *Corporate headquarters & distributor* ........ (732) 885-9000
GAMS Power Tools & Supplies, Inc., 133-135 Schuyler Ave., Kearny 07032
Pres.—Margaret Servidio, 5 emp., *Distributor of contractor's tools &* ........ (201) 955-0222
Garden State Highway Products, Inc., 1740 E. Oak Rd., Vineland 08361
Pres.—Sharon Green, 48 emp., *Manufacturer of traffic, street, specialty* ........ (856) 692-7572
Goyen Valve Corp., 1195 Airport Rd., Lakewood 08701
Pres.—Steven O'Neill, 15 emp., *Distributor of dust collector pilot* ........ (732) 364-7800
GTS-Welco, 425 Avenue P, Newark 07105
Chrm. of the Board—Robert D'Alessandro, 100 emp., *Wholesaler of welding equipment & supplies* (973) 589-7895
Hart Industries, Inc., 135 Crown Rd., Thorofare 08086
GM—Steve Shera, 5 emp., *Wholesaler of rubber & plastic hose* ........ (856) 686-1455
Hayes Pump, Inc., 295 Fairfield Ave., Fairfield 07004
Ex. V-P.—Joseph F. Larkin, Sr., 22 emp., *Distributor of pumps & parts, including* ........ (973) 808-0606
HBC Home & Hardware, 324-A Half Acre Rd., Cranbury 08512
CEO—Donald C. Devine, 170 emp., *Company headquarters & wholesaler of* ........ (609) 860-9990
HD Supply Water Works, Inc., 228 Williamstown Rd., Berlin 08009
GM—Rusty Miller, 8 emp., *Distributor of waterworks valves, hydrants* ........ (856) 753-5566
HKK Chain Corp. Of America, 9 Riverside Dr., P.O. Box 604, Pine Brook 07058
Pres., COO—Ted Kawamoto, 20 emp., *Corporate headquarters & wholesaler* ........ (973) 575-7860
Hose Shop, Inc., The, 100 New England Ave., Ste. 2, Piscataway 08854
Owner & GM—Thomas Peterson, 13 emp., *Wholesaler of hydraulic & industrial* ........ (732) 562-1000
Houser Welding Supply Co., Inc., 12-14 E. Main St., Somerville 08876
Pres.—David Houser, 5 emp., *Wholesaler of welding equipment, supplies* ........ (908) 526-7777
IKO International, Inc., 91 Walsh Dr., Parsippany 07054
Pres.—Dan Sugihara, 10 emp., *Corporate headquarters & wholesaler* ........ (973) 402-0254
Indexing Technologies, Inc., 37 Orchard St., Ramsey 07446
Pres.—Mike Bickham, 10 emp., *Wholesaler of machine tools, including* ........ (201) 934-6333
Industrial Instrumentation Services, Inc., 1400 Rahway Ave., Ste. 4, Avenel 07001
Pres.—William Ball, 21 emp., *Distributor of industrial instrumentation* ........ (732) 815-9090
International Welding Technologies, Inc., 2650 Egg Harbor Rd., Lindenwold 08021
GM—Neil Wilkinson, 10 emp., *Manufacturer & wholesaler of welding* ........ (856) 435-8004
J & J Industrial Supply, Inc., 113 E. Centre St., P.O. Box 110174, Nutley 07110
Pres.—Joe Damore, Sr., 7 emp., *Wholesaler of industrial equipment* ........ (973) 235-0100
Kaman Industrial Technologies Corp., 502 Bloy St., Hillside 07205
GM—John Marra, 8 emp., *Distributor of industrial equipment* ........ (908) 687-0004
Kaman Industrial Technologies Corp., 195 Borelli Rd., Paulsboro 08066
Br. Mgr.—Robert Widen, 5 emp., *Wholesaler of industrial equipment* ........ (856) 227-7000
Kaman Industrial Technologies Corp., 195 Borrelli Blvd., Ste. B, Paulsboro 08066
Team Leader—Mark Pancoast, 10 emp., *Distributor of industrial equipment* ........ (856) 284-7400
Kavon Filter Products Co., Inc., 5022 Industrial Rd., P.O. Box 1166, Wall Township 07719
V-P., Sales & Mktg.—Douglas Von Bulow, 20 emp., *Manufacturer & distributor of industrial* .... (732) 938-3135
Keith Industries, Inc., 248 Astor St., Newark 07114
Pres.—Jay Weiss, 50 emp., *Distributor of plastic, steel & fibre* ........ (973) 642-3332
Kelken-Gold, Inc., 550 Hartle St., Ste. C, Sayreville 08872
Pres.—Ken Ginsky, 4 emp., *Manufacturer & distributor of anchoring* ........ (732) 416-6730
KTK Corp., 65 Midvale Rd., Edison 08817
Pres.—Joseph Kapler, 5 emp., *Distributor of steel, fiber & plastic* ........ (732) 985-0447
Levine Packaging Supply Corp., 400 U.S. Highway 46 E., Fairfield 07004
V-P.—L. Levine, 20 emp., *Manufacturer of corrugated boxes &* ........ (973) 575-3383
Lewis-Goetz & Co., Inc., 1571 Grandview Ave., Paulsboro 08066
Opers. Mgr.—Ron Bianchi, 18 emp., *Distributor of hoses, couplings & related* ........ (856) 579-1421
Liberty Welding Supply, Inc., 187 W. Fort Lee Rd., Bogota 07603
Pres.—Robert Safranek, 2 emp., *Distributor of new & warranted used* ........ (973) 923-2900
MacAuley, Inc., James R., 1 Industrial Dr., P.O. Box 704, Waterford Works 08089
Pres.—George MacAuley, 2 emp., *Wholesaler of plastic pails & plastic* ........ (856) 767-3474
Machine Shop Discount Supply, P.O. Box 16, Little Ferry 07643
Pres.—Hy Ash, 15 emp., *Distributor of cutting & measuring* ........ (201) 518-8472
Madsen & Howell, Inc., 500 Market St., Ste. 1, Perth Amboy 08861
Pres.—Peter Madsen, 50 emp., *Distributor of industrial equipment* ........ (732) 826-4000
Marchesini Packaging Machinery, 43 Fairfield Pl., West Caldwell 07006
GM—Anna Marie Bellina, 18 emp., *Wholesaler of packaging machinery &* ........ (973) 575-7445
Maruka U.S.A., Inc., 45 Route 46 E., Ste. 610, P.O. Box 747, Pine Brook 07058
Pres.—Gary Lowery, 35 emp., *Corporate headquarters & distributor* ........ (973) 487-3800
McJunkin Red Man Corporation, 305 Center Ave., Waterford Works 08089
Br. Mgr.—Tim Fish, 4 emp., *Distributor of oilfield equipment,* ........ (856) 753-7690
McMaster-Carr Supply Co., 200 New Canton Way, Robbinsville 08691
Br. Mgr.—Michael Bostancic, 180 emp., *Distributor of industrial supplies* ........ (609) 259-8900
Metro Industrial Supply, Inc., 200 Charles St., Garfield 07026
Pres.—Richard Dino, 5 emp., *Wholesaler of industrial equipment* ........ (973) 546-5660
Midlantic Supply, LLC, 8000 Midlantic Dr., Ste. 200-N., P.O. Box 506, Mount Laurel 08054
Owner—Diane Disanto, 5 emp., *Distributor of waterworks & sewer equipment* ........ (856) 813-5014
Motion Industries, Inc., 141 Market St., Ste. 8, Kenilworth 07033
Br. Mgr.—John Velit, 20 emp., *Distributor of industrial maintenance* ........ (908) 241-1047
Motion Industries, Inc., 12-D Jules Ln., New Brunswick 08901
Br. Mgr.—John Velit, 5 emp., *Distributor of industrial maintenance* ........ (732) 828-8711
Motion Industries, Inc., 600 Hollister Rd., Teterboro 07608
Br. Mgr.—John Kondel, 9 emp., *Distributor of industrial maintenance* ........ (201) 288-8111
Motion Industries, Inc., 9A S. Gold Dr., Trenton 08691
Br. Mgr.—John Velit, 18 emp., *Distributor of industrial maintenance* ........ (609) 588-0555
MSC Industrial Supply Co., 105 Newfield Ave., Ste. E, Edison 08837
Mktg. Mgr.—David Bothe, 15 emp., *Wholesaler of industrial equipment* ........ (732) 512-9555
Mulcare Pipeline Solutions, 9 Mars Ct., Ste. C-4, Boonton 07005
Pres.—Robert Engdahl, 15 emp., *Distributor of natural gas distribution* ........ (973) 335-4800
Neill Supply Co., Inc., 700 Schuyler Ave., Lyndhurst 07071
Pres.—Robert Moss, 60 emp., *Manufacturer of fire sprinklers & distributor* ........ (201) 939-1100
PAC Tool & Supply Co., Inc., 420 Paterson Ave., P.O. Box 7482, East Rutherford 07073
Pres. & Sales Mgr.—Mike Pacala, 3 emp., *Distributor of industrial metalworking* ........ (201) 933-8550
Pallet Express, Inc., 70 Caroline Ave., Clifton 07011
Pres., GM—Lenny Driesse, 7 emp., *Distributor of wooden pallets* ........ (973) 633-5858
PBM Supply Co., Inc., 88 Cannonball Rd., P.O. Box 351, Pompton Lakes 07442
Pres.—Robert Fox, 3 emp., *Distributor of power transmission products* ........ (973) 839-0050
Pioneer Bearing Corp., 623 Eagle Rock Ave., Ste. 135, West Orange 07052
Pres.—Kenneth Abeles, 1 emp., *Distributor of commercial & industrial* ........ (973) 325-9095
Quality Electric Motor Service, Inc., 396 State Route 18, East Brunswick 08816
Pres., GM—Michael Quaglietta, Sr., 3 emp., *Distributor of new & rebuilt electric* ........ (732) 257-6655
Quality Seals, Inc., 2444 Morris Ave., Ste. 201, Union 07083
GM—Steve Patterson, 3 emp., *Distributor of rubber & plastic products* ........ (908) 206-0410
R.P. Machine, LLC, 906 Stillwater Rd., P.O. Box 144, Stillwater 07875
Owner—Randall Pobutkiewicz, 6 emp., *Distributor of new & used sheet metal* ........ (973) 383-8994
Richards Co., 437 Boulevard, P.O. Box 199, Elmwood Park 07407
V-P., Opers. & CEO—Dan J. Kleinrock, 10 emp., *Distributor of industrial equipment* ........ (201) 797-6300
Robert-James Sales, Inc., 9 Corporate Dr., P.O. Box B, Cranbury 08512
Br. Mgr.—Erin Motter, 10 emp., *Distributor of stainless steel pipes* ........ (609) 860-0900
RS Rubber Corp., 55 Paterson Ave., P.O. Box 3400, Wallington 07057
GM—Bob Busch, 10 emp., *Manufacturer & distributor of industrial* ........ (973) 777-2200
S & S Valve Service, Inc., 105 Liberty St., Metuchen 08840
Pres.—David Stanski, 10 emp., *Rebuilt boiler safety valves, including* ........ (732) 548-2040
Scientific Laboratory Supplies, Inc., 1401 Wade Blvd., Millville 08332
Dir.—Cliff Hitchner, 12 emp., *Distributor of glass & plastic containers* ........ (856) 327-4410
Sea Box, Inc., 700 Union Landing Rd., 1 Sea Box Dr., Cinnaminson 08077
V-P., Sales—Nick Catanzariti, 49 emp., *Wholesaler of new & used steel ISO* ........ (856) 303-1101
Seashore Supply Of Wildwood, 306 Wildwood Ave., Wildwood 08260
Br. Mgr.—Mark Tilsner, 3 emp., *Distributor of plumbing, HVAC & electrical* ........ (609) 522-1491
Shingle & Gibb Company, 845 Lancer Dr., Moorestown 08057
Pres.—Drew Pfleger, 25 emp., *Company headquarters & distributor* ........ (856) 234-8500
South Jersey Welding Supply Co., 496 Route 38 E., Maple Shade 08052
Pres.—Robert Thornton, Jr., 35 emp., *Company headquarters & wholesaler of* ........ (856) 778-4440
South Jersey Welding Supply Co., 94 W. Forest Grove Rd., Vineland 08360
Owner—Robert Thorton, Jr., 15 emp., *Distributor of welding equipment &* ........ (856) 691-9659
Stauff Corp., 7 William Demarest Pl., Waldwick 07463
Pres.—Peter Anderton, 25 emp., *Corporate headquarters & wholesaler* ........ (201) 444-7800
Stiles Enterprises, Inc., 114 Beach St., P.O. Box 92, Rockaway 07866
Pres.—Richard Stiles, 15 emp., *Manufacturer & distributor of packaging* ........ (973) 625-9660
Supply Source, 64 Oak Ave., Tenafly 07670
Pres.—Fred Keen, 2 emp., *Distributor of office reprographic* ........ (201) 735-0232
T & B Specialties, Inc., 479 Wright Debow Rd., Jackson 08527
Pres.—Thomas E. Barchie, 3 emp., *Wholesaler of industrial equipment* ........ (732) 928-4500
Tarantin Industries, 86 Vanderveer Rd., Freehold 07728
Pres., CEO—Thomas Tarantin, 25 emp., *Company headquarters & distributor* ........ (732) 780-9340
The Liner Co., Inc., 7 Meadows Run Dr., Colts Neck 07722
Owner & Pres.—Carol Hartwell, 2 emp., *Distributor of HDPE, PVC, geocomposite* ........ (732) 761-0700
Trico Hose & Gasket Corp., 700-2 Challenger Way, Lacey Business Pk., Forked River 08731
Owner—Adrian Seitz, 4 emp., *Manufacturer of rubber gaskets & seals* ........ (609) 693-5301
TricorBraun, 250 Pehle Ave., Ste. 100, Saddle Brook 07663
Br. & Sales Mgr.—Scott Danheiser, 70 emp., *Distributor of plastic & glass bottles* ........ (201) 556-4800
Tunnel Barrel & Drum Co., Inc., 85 Triangle Blvd., Carlstadt 07072
Pres.—Anthony Urcioli, 20 emp., *Reconditioned fiber & plastic drums* ........ (201) 933-1444
Turtle & Hughes, Inc., 188 Foothill Rd., Bridgewater 08807
Ex. V-P., Br. Mgr.—Rick Reffler, 100 emp., *Distributor of electrical & industrial* ........ (732) 560-5575
Valley National Gases, WV LLC, 201 Crown Point Rd., West Deptford 08086
GM—Wendy Hughes, 10 emp., *Distributor of welding supplies, including* ........ (856) 848-7321
W&O Supply, Inc., 7 W. Baltimore Ave., Linden 07036
★ Regional Mgr.—Bill Duffy, 5 emp., *Distributor of marine piping, valves* ........ (908) 486-5338
W. W. Grainger, Inc., 560-596 Bercik St., Ste. 1, Elizabeth 07201
GM—Phil Circelli, 12 emp., *Wholesaler of industrial equipment* ........ (908) 787-1952
W. W. Grainger, Inc., 277 Route 46 W., Fairfield 07004
Br. Mgr.—Damian Czirjak, 10 emp., *Wholesaler of industrial equipment* ........ (973) 227-7220
W. W. Grainger, Inc., 819 E. Gate Dr., Mount Laurel 08054
GM—Ron Schomo, 15 emp., *Wholesaler of industrial equipment* ........ (856) 234-8550
W. W. Grainger, Inc., 1585 N. Olden Ave., Trenton 08638
Br. Mgr.—Patricia James, 10 emp., *Distributor of industrial equipment* ........ (609) 394-2620
Weinstein Supply Corp., 1687 Haddon Ave., Camden 08103
Profit Center Mgr.—Christopher Conte, 12 emp., *Wholesaler of plumbing, heating & air* ........ (856) 964-1700
World Wide Metric, Inc., 37 Readington Rd., P.O. Box 5267, Branchburg 08876
CEO—George Contos, 16 emp., *Corporate headquarters & distributor* ........ (732) 247-2300
xpedx, 261 River Rd., Clifton 07014
Br. & Div. Mgr.—John Ransone, 50 emp., *Distributor of printing paper & graphics* ........ (973) 405-2300

S.I.C.

★ **Indicates new listing this edition.**

Yecies, Inc., Herman W., 11 Roosevelt Ave., P.O. Box 6186, West Orange 07052
Pres.—Roberta Yecies, 3 emp., *Wholesaler of industrial equipment* ..... (973) 736-7362

## 5087 Service establishment equipment

Advantage Vacuum LLC, 110 South Ave., Ste. A, Garwood 07027
Owner—Alan Schwartz, 5 emp., *Distributor of commercial vacuum cleaners* ..... (908) 228-5629
Amsan Eagle Maintenance Supply, 80 Twin Bridge Dr., Pennsauken 08110
Br. Mgr.—Candy Chapman, 55 emp., *Distributor of janitorial supplies,* ..... (856) 317-9500
Belleville Scale & Balance, LLC, 50 S. Center St., Orange 07050
Ptnr. & Pres.—Thomas Rockhill, 22 emp., *Distributor of industrial, truck &* ..... (973) 759-4487
Bunzl New Jersey, Inc., 27 Distribution Way, Monmouth Junction 08852
GM—Mike Schilling, 30 emp., *Distributor of paper bags & janitorial* ..... (732) 821-7000
Cintas Fire Protection, 1705 U.S. Route 46 W., Ledgewood 07852
Off. Mgr.—Paula Cincotta, 30 emp., *Distributor of fire extinguishers &* ..... (973) 347-3901
Coldstat Refrigeration, 60 Eisenhower Dr., Paramus 07652
Owner & Pres.—Ion Sarkisian, 15 emp., *Wholesaler of commercial refrigeration* ..... (201) 599-1200
D.W.L International Trading Co., 65 Industrial Rd., Lodi 07644
Pres., CEO—David Li, 150 emp., *Company headquarters & restaurant supplies* ..... (973) 916-9958
Dade Paper Co., 120 Tices Ln., East Brunswick 08816
V-P., Opers.—Mark Rogers, 20 emp., *Distributor of janitorial supplies,* ..... (732) 254-3100
De Pasquale Salon Systems, Inc., 21-21 Broadway, Fair Lawn 07410
Pres.—Joe Mastalia, 100 emp., *Distributor of beauty salon supplies* ..... (201) 797-9101
Dreyco, Inc., 263 Veterans Blvd., Carlstadt 07072
Pres.—Michael Borghard, 15 emp., *Distributor of automotive parts, tools* ..... (201) 896-9000
Equipment Marketers, 100 Melrose Ave., Cherry Hill 08003
Owner—Dick LaMaina, 15 emp., *Distributor of commercial laundry equipment* ..... (856) 428-3355
Excellent Bakery Equipment Co., 315 Fairfield Rd., Fairfield 07004
Pres.—Karin Seruga, 15 emp., *Manufacturer & distributor of bakery* ..... (973) 244-1664
Franklin Machine Products, Inc., 101 Mount Holly By Pass, Lumberton 08048
Owner & Pres.—Joe Grato, 150 emp., *Distributor of food service parts &* ..... (609) 267-3700
Graco Manufacturing, 500 University Ct., Blackwood 08012
Hum. Res. Mgr.—Todd McGovern, 60 emp., *Manufacturer & distributor of aftermarket* ..... (856) 228-1800
Jersey Paper Plus, Inc., 600 Federal Blvd., Carteret 07008
Pres.—Steven Tabak, 50 emp., *Distributor of janitorial paper products* ..... (732) 750-1900
Kennedy Cos., The, 8000 Midlantic Dr., Ste. 200-N, Mount Laurel 08054
Pres., Hum. Res. Mgr.—Robert Kennedy, Jr., 20 emp., *Company headquarters & distributor* (856) 813-5000
Luca Laundry Equipment, Inc., 1500 W. Blancke St., Linden 07036
V-P., Reg.—Richard R. Luca, 14 emp., *Distributor of commercial & industrial* ..... (908) 862-2200
Matting World, P.O. Box 43, Beverly 08010
Ptnr.—Marialynn Patalano, 3 emp., *Distributor of mats & janitorial supplies* ..... (609) 641-4747
Oberg & Lindquist Corp., 671 Broadway, Westwood 07675
Pres.—John Oberg, 50 emp., *Distributor of industrial, residential* ..... (201) 664-1300
PC Tan, Inc., 1040 Wilt Ave., Ridgefield 07657
Pres.—Susan Miller, 35 emp., *Corporate headquarters & distributor* ..... (201) 943-6100
Pine Environmental Services, LLC, 92 N. Main St., Bldg. 20, Windsor 08561
Ptnr.—Angelo Pinheiro, 60 emp., *Company headquarters & distributor* ..... (609) 371-9663
Pressure King, Inc., 231 Herbert Ave., Ste. 1, Closter 07624
CEO—Harry McCormick, 2 emp., *Distributor of commercial & industrial* ..... (201) 768-1911
Rides4U, Inc., 221 Evans Way, Ste. E, Somerville 08876
★ Owner—Len Soled, 5 emp., *Distributor of amusement equipment* ..... (908) 526-8009
Schofield Co., Inc., George, 831 E. Main St., Bridgewater 08807
Pres.—Bill Newell, 34 emp., *Corporate headquarters & distributor* ..... (732) 356-0858
Stickel Packaging Supply, 1991 Rutgers University Blvd., Lakewood Industrial Pk., Lakewood 08701
Founder—Hal Stickel, 31 emp., *Wholesaler of packaging, janitorial* ..... (732) 905-2811
Supplyone, Inc., 1200 Madison Ave., Paterson 07503
Pres.—Jerry Vitelli, 60 emp., *Distributor of corrugated boxes & janitorial* ..... (718) 392-7400
SYSCO Food Services Of Metro New York, LLC, 20 Theodore Conrad Dr., Jersey City 07305
Pres.—Phillip Lahm, 530 emp., *Wholesaler of general line groceries* ..... (201) 433-2000
W. W. Grainger, Inc., 55 Jackson Dr., Cranford 07016
Br. Mgr.—Michael Crupe, 10 emp., *Wholesaler of electrical & janitorial* ..... (908) 272-7156

## 5088 Transportation equipment & supplies

American Filter & Tank Co., Inc., 231 Greenwood Ave., Ste. 2, Midland Park 07432
Owner & Pres.—John Spanedda, 3 emp., *Distributor of spray nozzles & air* ..... (201) 857-5056
Atlantic Coast Container Brokerage & Sales, Inc., 906 Oak Tree Rd., Ste. P, South Plainfield 07080
Pres.—Lillian Skov-Nissen, 3 emp., *Wholesaler of new & used ISO cargo* ..... (908) 755-2898
Atlantic Track & Turnout Co., 270 Broad St., P.O. Box 1589, Bloomfield 07003
Owner—Peter Hughes, 15 emp., *Company headquarters & distributor* ..... (973) 748-5885
Multipower International, Inc., 7 Woodshire Ter., P.O. Box 197, Towaco 07082
Pres.—Qiang Ge, 7 emp., *Wholesaler of narrow & standard gage* ..... (973) 727-0327
Out Island Sport Yachts, Inc., 107 Edgewood Ave., West Berlin 08091
Pres.—Scott Jastrzembski, 6 emp., *Manufacturer of custom-built fiberglass* ..... (609) 861-4000
Runnemede Truck Refrigeration, 320 Borelli Blvd., Paulsboro 08066
Pres.—Robert Hyndman, 10 emp., *Wholesaler of truck refrigeration &* ..... (856) 423-4400

## 5091 Sporting & recreational goods & supplies

CAP Barbell, Inc., 625 Rahway Ave., Union 07083
Owner—Isabel Tseng, 23 emp., *Distributor of exercise equipment,* ..... (908) 624-1133
Environmental Site Furnishings, 700 Goldman Dr., Cream Ridge 08514
Dir., Sales, Natl.—Kevin Mahoney, 10 emp., *Distributor of outdoor public site* ..... (281) 975-1776
Heritage Surf & Sport, Inc., 3700 Landis Ave., Sea Isle City 08243
Pres.—Barbara Heritage, 9 emp., *Distributor of surfboards & sportswear* ..... (609) 263-3033
Jet Line Products, Inc., 55 Jacobus Ave., Kearny 07032
Pur. Agt.—Laura Meola, 20 emp., *Corporate headquarters & distributor* ..... (973) 690-2999
Joannou Cycle Co., Inc., G., 151 Ludlow Ave., Northvale 07647
CEO—Carine Joannou, 100 emp., *Corporate headquarters & wholesaler* ..... (201) 768-9050
Kent International Inc., 60 E. Halsey Rd., Parsippany 07054
CEO—Arnold Kamler, 70 emp., *Wholesaler of bicycles & accessories* ..... (973) 434-8181
SCP Distributors, LLC, 1985 Rutgers University Blvd., Ste. A, Lakewood 08701
Br. Mgr.—Jeff Delmastero, 7 emp., *Distributor of swimming pools, spas* ..... (732) 730-1451
Superior Pool Products, LLC, 200 Freeway Dr., Ste. 2, Blackwood 08012
Br. Mgr.—Russel Bacon, 12 emp., *Distributor of swimming pool products* ..... (856) 232-7774

## 5092 Toys & hobby goods & supplies

Carrera Of America, Inc., 2 Corporate Dr., Ste. D, Cranbury 08512
Pres.—Edward Gershowitz, 12 emp., *Wholesaler of electronic toy cars,* ..... (609) 409-8510
Daron Worldwide Trading, Inc., 24 Stewart Pl., Ste. 4, Fairfield 07004
Pres.—Ronald Marx, 29 emp., *Wholesaler of aviation, cruise ship* ..... (973) 882-0035
Garden State Fireworks, Inc., 383 Carlton Rd., P.O. Box 403, Millington 07946
V-P.—August Nunzio Santore, 24 emp., *Manufacturer & distributor of fireworks* ..... (908) 647-1086
International Playthings LLC, 75D Lackawanna Ave., Parsippany 07054
CEO—Michael Varda, 30 emp., *Wholesaler of children's toys & games* ..... (973) 316-2500
Reeves International, Inc., 14 Industrial Rd., Pequannock 07440
Pres.—Anthony Fleischmann, 50 emp., *Corporate headquarters & manufacturer* ..... (973) 694-5006
Y & W International, Inc., 16 Edgeboro Rd., Unit 5, East Brunswick 08816
Pres.—Yun Shun Yang, 5 emp., *Wholesaler of toy, novelties, die cast* ..... (732) 390-7722

## 5093 Scrap & waste materials

A & A Iron & Metal Co., LLC, 2006 40th St., North Bergen 07047
Member—Robert Albericci, 7 emp., *Wholesaler of recycled scrap metals* ..... (201) 865-1370
Abbey Metal Corp., 59 Grand St., Moonachie 07074
Pres.—Burton G. Zuckerman, 10 emp., *Wholesaler of nonferrous, high temperature* ..... (201) 438-0330
Abington Reldan Metals, LLC, 396-402 Whitehead Ave., South River 08882
GM—Kathleen Whitaker, 9 emp., *Wholesaler of precious metal scrap* ..... (732) 238-8550
Advanced Metal Processing NJ, LLC, 326 S. Wade Blvd., Millville 08332
Br. Mgr.—Patricia Campbell, 20 emp., *Wholesaler of scrap metals* ..... (856) 327-0048
Advanced Recovery, Inc., 50 Grafton Ave., Newark 07104
Pres., GM—Mark Rea, 15 emp., *Wholesaler of used electronic & computer* ..... (973) 485-9100
All American Recycling Corp., 2 Hope St., Jersey City 07307
Pres.—Vincent M. Ponte, 137 emp., *Paper & plastic recycling, including* ..... (201) 656-3363
American Auto Salvage & Recycling, Inc., 3113 Route 50, Mays Landing 08330
Pres.—Joe Silipena, 45 emp., *Wholesaler of scrap metals* ..... (609) 965-2900
American Iron & Metal International, LLC, 301 S. 12th St., P.O. Box 965, Millville 08332
Mng. Member—Lori A. Winterbottom, 40 emp., *Wholesaler of scrap metals* ..... (856) 825-2950
Armor Metals & Recycling, 8300 National Hwy., Ste. 2, Pennsauken 08110
Mng. Ptnr.—Frank Lobascio, 10 emp., *Wholesaler of scrap metals & parts* ..... (856) 665-5715
Atlantic Coast Fibers, LLC, 101 7th St., Passaic 07055
Owner—Chris Riviello, 100 emp., *Wholesaler of recycled paper & commercial* ..... (973) 614-9600
Bayshore Recycling Corp., 75 Crows Mill Rd., P.O. Box 290, Keasbey 08832
Pres.—Valerie Montecalvo, 160 emp., *Wholesaler of recycled concrete, asphalt* ..... (732) 738-6000
Cali Carting, Inc., 450 Bergen Ave., P.O. Box 440, Kearny 07032
Owner—John Cali, 10 emp., *Wholesaler of recycled scrap plastic* ..... (201) 991-5400
Camden Iron & Metal, Inc., 143 Harding Ave., Bellmawr 08031
Pres., CEO—Joseph Balzano, 38 emp., *Corporate headquarters & wholesaler* ..... (856) 365-7500
Casings Of NJ, Inc., 711 Ramsey Ave., Hillside 07205
Br. Mgr.—Bill Evans, 30 emp., *Wholesaler of recycled tires* ..... (908) 851-7766
Chinook Sciences, LLC (H Q), 20 Commerce Dr., Ste. 350, Cranford 07016
Co-Founder, Chrm. & CEO—Rifat Chalabi, 15 emp., *Company headquarters; wholesaler of* . (908) 272-5091
Container Recyclers-Camden, Inc., 267 Jefferson St., Camden 08104
Owner & Hum. Res. Mgr.—Ron Fogel, Jr., 30 emp., *Wholesaler of recycled shipping containers* (856) 963-5200
Cooper Alloy Corp., 201 Sweetland Ave., Hillside 07205
Pres.—Stuart Cooper, 15 emp., *Wholesaler of scrap metal* ..... (908) 688-4216
Electrum, Inc., 827 Martin St., Rahway 07065
Pres.—Jack Douglas, 15 emp., *Wholesaler of eco-friendly recycled* ..... (732) 396-1616
Empire Recycling, Inc., 3 New York Ave., P.O. Box 17398, Jersey City 07307
Pres., GM—Gary Giordano, 35 emp., *Wholesaler of scrap paper for the recycling* ..... (732) 393-0200
Excel Plastics Recycling, Inc., 996 Belleville Tpke., Kearny 07032
Owner—Brian Chen, 20 emp., *Wholesaler of recycled plastic materials* ..... (201) 991-2500
Fairfield Pallet Co., Inc., 282 Rockville Rd., P.O. Box 361, Fairton 08320
Pres.—Michael Smith, 50 emp., *Mulch & wholesaler of rebuilt wooden* ..... (856) 455-7999
Faith Group Co. (H Q), 195 Route 9, Ste. 205, Manalapan 07726
Pres.—Yong Liu, 15 emp., *Company headquarters; wholesaler of* ..... (732) 431-1326
FCR Camden, Inc., 2201 Mt. Ephraim Ave., Bldg. 10-A, Camden 08104
Pres.—Shawn Duffy, 35 emp., *Wholesaler of recycled plastics, paper* ..... (856) 342-7503
Federal Metals & Alloys, 4216 S. Clinton Ave., South Plainfield 07080
V-P.—Mark Scoda, 18 emp., *Wholesaler of nonferrous, nickel alloys* ..... (908) 756-0900
Fortune Plastic & Metal, Inc., 20 Carbon Pl., Jersey City 07035
CEO—Norman Ng, 40 emp., *Corporate headquarters & wholesaler* ..... (201) 333-3339
Freedom Metals, LLC, 960 Frelinghuysen Ave., Newark 07114
Ptnr.—Peter Bartolomeo, 5 emp., *Wholesaler of nonferrous scrap metals* ..... (973) 242-2119
H & C Metals, Inc., 91 Malvern St., P.O. Box 5150, Newark 07105
Pres.—Frank Colantuono, 15 emp., *Wholesaler of scrap metal* ..... (973) 589-7778
IESI Recycling Corp. (H Q), 1099 Wall St. W., Ste. 250, Lyndhurst 07071
V-P. & Reg. Mgr.—Ed Apuzzi, 15 emp., *Divisional headquarters; wholesaler* ..... (201) 443-3000
J & J Metals Trading, LLC, 26 Edie Dr., Marlboro 07746
Manager—Ralph Borenstein, 2 emp., *Wholesaler of recycled nonferrous metals* ..... (732) 617-0500
JFD Associates, Inc., 15 Railroad Ave., Farmingdale 07727
Pres.—Andrea Holt, 17 emp., *Wholesaler of recycled paper & cardboard* ..... (732) 751-9041
K & J Scrap Metal, Inc., 609 25th St., Union City 07087
Pres.—Kevin Istok, 3 emp., *Wholesaler of scrap metals* ..... (201) 348-3368
K-C International, LLC, 1608 Route 88, Ste. 301, Brick 08724
CEO—Frank Crowley, 30 emp., *Wholesaler of recycled paper, plastic* ..... (732) 202-9500
Lion Metals, Inc., 2460 Lemoine Ave., Ste. 400-B, Fort Lee 07024
Owner—Bob Blum, 3 emp., *Wholesaler of scrap metals* ..... (201) 585-9191
Lorco Petroleum Services, 450 S. Front St., Elizabeth 07202
Pres.—John Lionetti, 150 emp., *Wholesaler of recycled residual & used* ..... (908) 820-8800
M & A Recycling, 65 Old Camplain Rd., Hillsborough 08844
Owner—Jake Fiedler, 10 emp., *Wholesaler of recycled scrap metals* ..... (908) 218-9191
Materials Reclaim Industries, 409 Joyce Kilmer Ave., Ste. 3, New Brunswick 08901
Pres.—Ted Kasternakis, 4 emp., *Wholesaler of recycled industrial &* ..... (732) 979-3479
Mercer Group International, Inc., 1519 Calhoun St., P.O. Box 5626, Trenton 08638
Pres.—Mario Mazza, 40 emp., *Wholesaler of recycled concrete, asphalt* ..... (609) 393-4834
Mid County Paper Stock, Inc., 235 Brighton Rd., P.O. Box 624, Andover 07821
Pres.—James Koukoulas, 10 emp., *Wholesaler of recycled paper* ..... (973) 786-7499
Park Stein, Inc., 613 Route 46 E., P.O. Box 2399, Clifton 07013
Pres.—Steve Tendler, 28 emp., *Wholesaler of recycled scrap metal* ..... (973) 340-3535
Plastic Services, Inc., 200 Pacific Ave., Jersey City 07304
Pres.—Jeff Turner, 20 emp., *Plastic reprocessing & wholesaler of* ..... (201) 200-1200
Puggi Class B Recycling, A. J., 6150 Mill Rd., Egg Harbor Township 08234
Pres.—A. J. Puggi, 10 emp., *Wholesaler of recycled scrap paper,* ..... (609) 926-6991
Ragonese & Sons, Inc., Patsy, 331 Adams St., Newark 07105
Pres.—Gerald Ragonese, Jr., 20 emp., *Wholesaler of shredded recycled paper* ..... (973) 344-7411
RecycleTech Corp., 418 Falmouth Ave., Elmwood Park 07407
Pres.—Dan Chung, 15 emp., *Assembly of EPS (expanded polystyrene)* ..... (201) 475-5000
River Road Recycling Inc., 450 37th St., P.O. Box 302, Pennsauken 08110
Owner—Christopher Wang, 15 emp., *Wholesaler of ferrous & nonferrous* ..... (856) 661-0770
Rover & Son Iron & Steel Co., F., 516 Central Ave., Harrison 07029
Pres.—John Rover, 10 emp., *Wholesaler of recycled iron & metal* ..... (973) 484-7668
Safety-Kleen Systems, Inc., 123 Red Lion Rd., Vincentown 08088
Manager—Keith Wilson, 25 emp., *Wholesaler of recycled oils & solvents* ..... (609) 859-2049
Schroth, Inc., Emil A., Yellowbrook Rd. & Copper Ave., Howell 07731
Pres.—Emil A. Schroth, Jr., 15 emp., *Wholesaler of copper & aluminum* ..... (732) 938-5015
Sims Metal Management, 1511 Calhoun St., Trenton 08638
GM—Juan Mezza, 15 emp., *Wholesaler of recycled steel & parts* ..... (609) 396-0880

Specialty Disposal Services, Inc., 115 Route 46, Bldg. E-37-38, Mountain Lakes 07046
Opers. Mgr.—Stephen Nesteriak, 50 emp., *Wholesaler of recycled cardboard, plastic* .......... (973) 402-9246
Supreme Asset Management & Recovery, Inc., 1950 Rutgers University Blvd., Lakewood 08701
Pres.—Albert Boufarah, 35 emp., *Corporate headquarters & distributor* .......... (732) 370-4100
Taylor Auto Parts, 222 Pacific St., Newark 07114
Pres.—Frederick Taylor, 3 emp., *Wholesaler of used automotive parts* .......... (973) 465-4345
Trinity Recycling Of New Jersey, 116 Iron Mountain Rd., Mine Hill 07803
V-P.—John Mroz, 10 emp., *Wholesaler of recycled newspaper, cardboard* .......... (973) 366-9199
Unichem Industries, Inc., 1 Bayberry Close, Piscataway 08854
Pres.—Kishore Sanghvi, 2 emp., *Wholesaler of ferrous & nonferrous* .......... (732) 463-8442
United Scrap Iron & Metal Co., 124 Wood St., Paterson 07524
Manager—John Lewer, 15 emp., *Wholesaler of recycled metal & iron* .......... (973) 279-1683
Veolia Environmental Services, 27-33 Iowa Ave., Paterson 07503
Br. Mgr.—Nydia Patino, *Wholesaler of recycled aluminum, metal* .......... (973) 742-6789
Vinch Recycling, Inc., 1607 N. Olden Ave., P.O. Box 55300, Trenton 08638
Pres.—Joseph Vinch, 8 emp., *Wholesaler of recycled concrete, asphalt* .......... (609) 393-0200
Vish Corp., 200 State Route 17, Ste. 200-A, Mahwah 07430
Pres.—Mahesh T. Kukreja, 20 emp., *Wholesaler of recycled scrap metal,* .......... (201) 529-2900
Wade Environmental Industries, 382 Jackson Rd., Atco 08004
Pres.—Andrew Wade, 5 emp., *Wholesaler of recycled metal scrap* .......... (856) 767-2760
Win Laboratories, Ltd., 182 Ridge Rd., Ste. D, Dayton 08810
Owner—Jimmy Wu, 7 emp., *Wholesaler of recycled electronic scrap* .......... (732) 355-1355

## 5094 Jewelry, watches & precious stones & metals

D.W.L International Trading Co., 65 Industrial Rd., Lodi 07644
Pres., CEO—David Li, 150 emp., *Company headquarters & restaurant supplies* .......... (973) 916-9958
Devon Trading Corp., 5 Fairfield Rd., Caldwell 07006
Pres.—Fran Orzech, 22 emp., *Distributor of religious items, including* .......... (973) 812-9190
Metro America Sales, Inc., 137 South Ave., Fanwood 07023
Pres.—Harold Nevins, 3 emp., *Wholesaler of jewelry machinery, tools* .......... (908) 490-0001
Movado Group, Inc., 650 From Rd., 3rd Fl., Paramus 07652
Chrm., Pres.—G. Grinberg, 300 emp., *Manufacturer & distributor of watches* .......... (201) 267-8000
Royal Deluxe Accessories, LLC, 2563 Brunswick Ave., Bldg. O, Linden 07036
Pres.—Elliot Zeitoune, 18 emp., *Wholesaler of costume jewelry, ladies'* .......... (908) 523-0550
Supreme Asset Management & Recovery, Inc., 1950 Rutgers University Blvd., Lakewood 08701
Pres.—Albert Boufarah, 35 emp., *Corporate headquarters & distributor* .......... (732) 370-4100
Ultimate Trading Corp., 4 Just Rd., Fairfield 07004
Pres.—Todd Knichel, 60 emp., *Manufacturer & distributor of fine* .......... (973) 228-7700

## 5099 Durable goods, nec

ABC Supply Co., Inc., Bradco Div., 45 Samworth Rd., Clifton 07012
Br. Mgr.—Greg Anderson, 10 emp., *Distributor of roofing materials, signs* .......... (973) 777-3663
All Hands Fire Equipment, LLC, 7 3rd Ave., Neptune City 07753
Ptnr. & Pres.—Don Colarusso, 4 emp., *Wholesaler of firefighting equipment* .......... (732) 502-8060
Amerex Corp., 128 Bauer Dr., Ste. 4, Oakland 07436
V-P., Sales, NJ & NY & Br. Mgr.—Jack Miller, 5 emp., *Distributor of hand portable & wheeled* (201) 337-1616
AMERICAN Time Recorder, 2661 Brunetta Dr., Vineland 08360
Sales & Serv. Mgr.—Bryan Presgraves, 1 emp., *Distributor of computerized time clocks* .......... (856) 691-7976
Annin Flagmakers, 105 Eisenhower Pkwy., Ste. 203, Roseland 07068
Pres.—Carter Beard, 65 emp., *Company headquarters & wholesaler of* .......... (973) 228-9400
Badge Company Of New Jersey, 223 Hamden Rd., P.O. Box 100, Annandale 08801
GM—Robert Marlow, 3 emp., *Manufacturer & distributor of badges* .......... (908) 735-7700
Cintas Fire Protection, 1705 U.S. Route 46 W., Ledgewood 07852
Off. Mgr.—Paula Cincotta, 30 emp., *Distributor of fire extinguishers &* .......... (973) 347-3901
Escadaus Magnetics, 2 Wood Glen Way, Boonton 07005
V-P.—Henry Kuo, 4 emp., *Distributor of magnets & magnetic components* .......... (973) 335-8888
Garden Oaks Garden Center, 1921 U.S. Highway 22, Bound Brook 08805
Owner—Madeline Wenz, 20 emp., *Full-line distributor of outdoor, lawn* .......... (732) 356-7333
Hannecke Display Systems, Inc., 91 Fulton St., Unit 4, Boonton 07005
Pres.—Cuno VonOlhausen, 7 emp., *Distributor of display systems* .......... (973) 335-0434
International Mercantile Agencies, Inc., 18 Home News Row, New Brunswick 08901
Pres.—Aman Kapur, 10 emp., *Wholesaler of imported decorative home* .......... (732) 246-3900
Pfingst & Co., Inc., 105 Snyder Rd., P.O. Box 377, South Plainfield 07080
Pres.—Karl Pfingst, 10 emp., *Manufacturer & distributor of precision* .......... (908) 561-6400
Randa Luggage Co., 200 Broadacres Dr., 2nd Fl., Bloomfield 07003
Pres.—Terry Tackett, 50 emp., *Distributor of luggage* .......... (973) 873-9050
Royce Leather, 501 Penhorn Ave., Ste. 9, Secaucus 07094
Owner—Kathy Bauer, 14 emp., *Distributor of leather luggage, briefcases* .......... (201) 330-7720
Structured Materials Industries, Inc., 201 Circle Dr. N., Unit 102-103, Piscataway 08854
Pres., CEO—Gary Tompa, 15 emp., *Distributor of MOCVD, PECVD, CVD &* .......... (732) 302-9274
Time Systems International, Inc., 142 S. Van Brunt St., Englewood 07631
Pres.—Samuel Gleich, 20 emp., *Corporate headquarters & distributor* .......... (973) 472-2202
Tube Light Co., Inc. (H Q), 300 Park St., Moonachie 07074
Pres.—Leon Jaffe, 180 emp., *Corporate headquarters; distributor* .......... (201) 641-6660

# 51 WHOLESALE TRADE—NONDURABLE GOODS

## 5111 Printing & writing paper

Ariva Distribution, Inc., 1705 Suckle Hwy., Pennsauken 08110
V-P., GM—Ray Radomicki, 50 emp., *Wholesaler of printing paper & packaging* .......... (856) 488-0800
U.S. Pulp & Paper Corp., 1930 Marlton Pike E., Ste. N-73, Cherry Hill 08003
Pres.—Arnold Cohen, 20 emp., *Paper converting & distributor of packaging* .......... (856) 489-3500
xpedx, 261 River Rd., Clifton 07014
CFO—Jeffrey Patterson, 120 emp., *Distributor of paper, packaging materials* .......... (973) 405-2310
xpedx, 261 River Rd., Clifton 07014
Br. & Div. Mgr.—John Ransone, 50 emp., *Distributor of printing paper & graphics* .......... (973) 405-2300
xpedx LLC A veritiv Company, 1200 Highland Dr., Ste. 1-B, Westampton 08060
GM—Terence M. Sheehy, 98 emp., *Distributor of printing & writing paper* .......... (609) 518-9700

## 5112 Stationery & office supplies

Action Office Supplies, Inc., 687 Prospect St., Ste. 480, Lakewood 08701
Pres.—Sonny Arora, 21 emp., *Commercial printing & distributor of* .......... (732) 534-3000
ALL-STATE LEGAL, 1 Commerce Dr., Cranford 07016
Pres., CEO—Robert H. Busch, 230 emp., *Full-color engraving & printing of* .......... (908) 272-0800
Cartridge World, 830 Franklin Ave., Franklin Lakes 07417
Pres.—Jeffrey W. Bier, 3 emp., *Distributor of ink & toner cartridges* .......... (201) 891-0990
Cartridge World Of Wayne, LLC, 1055 Hamburg Tpke., Wayne 07470
Owner—Rosemarie Peluso, 4 emp., *Eco-friendly remanufactured printer* .......... (973) 696-2880
Laser Save, 843 State Route 33, Ste. 11, Freehold 07728
Pres.—Alan D. Yoss, 18 emp., *Remanufactured compatible color & monochrome* .......... (732) 431-3339
Lucille Maud Corp., 513 N. Olden Ave., Trenton 08638
Pres.—Louis Muirhead, 8 emp., *Computer systems integration & distributor* .......... (609) 393-7555
Metro Tag & Label, Inc., 25 E. Spring Valley Ave., Ste. 200, Maywood 07607
Pres.—Phil Glassman, 3 emp., *Commercial offset & digital printing* .......... (201) 845-4747
O'Brien Co., Inc., J., 40 Commerce St., Springfield 07081
Pres., CEO—Sharmay O'Brien, 20 emp., *Manufacturer of lanyards, badge reels* .......... (973) 379-8844
Office Depot Business Solution Div. Of New Jersey, 4 Brighton Rd., Clifton 07012
Dir., Sales—Steve Cimilluca, 150 emp., *Promotional & commercial printing &* .......... (973) 594-3000
QLT.com, 238 Boundary Rd., Unit 304, Marlboro 07746
Owner—Ken Kendes, 25 emp., *Distributor of photographic heat transfer* .......... (732) 431-0740
Quality Repro Centers, Inc., 296 Route 46 E., P.O. Box 111, Elmwood Park 07407
Pres.—Joe DiGiaimo, 6 emp., *Commercial & digital color printing* .......... (201) 794-3905
Ronstan Paper & Packaging, 72 James Way, Eatontown 07724
Pres.—William F. LaMorte, 12 emp., *Distributor of industrial & personal* .......... (732) 389-1040
Supply Source, 64 Oak Ave., Tenafly 07670
Pres.—Fred Keen, 2 emp., *Distributor of office reprographic* .......... (201) 735-0232
United Stationers Supply Co., 100 Liberty Way, Cranbury 08512
Br. Mgr.—Wayne Scott, 100 emp., *Wholesaler of office equipment, furniture* .......... (609) 619-4000

## 5113 Industrial & personal service paper

Ace Janitorial Supply, Inc., 164 Franklin Tpke., Ste. 2, Mahwah 07430
Pres.—H. Mike Timpone, 4 emp., *Distributor of janitorial & electrical* .......... (201) 529-1750
Advantage Vacuum LLC, 110 South Ave., Ste. A, Garwood 07027
Owner—Alan Schwartz, 5 emp., *Distributor of commercial vacuum cleaners* .......... (908) 228-5629
American Paper & Supply Co., LLC, 10 Industrial Rd., P.O. Box 346, Carlstadt 07072
Owner—Larry Shapiro, 45 emp., *Distributor of maintenance/janitorial* .......... (201) 939-4200
Ariva Distribution, Inc., 1705 Suckle Hwy., Pennsauken 08110
V-P., GM—Ray Radomicki, 50 emp., *Wholesaler of printing paper & packaging* .......... (856) 488-0800
Bacon & Graham, Inc., 34 E. 25th St., Paterson 07514
Pres.—Craig Bacon, 30 emp., *Wholesaler of packaging, shipping,* .......... (973) 684-1488
Bag Factory, Inc., The, 726 N. Stiles St., Linden 07036
★ Owner—Charlie Klein, 4 emp., *Distributor of bingo bags, papers,* .......... (908) 925-7122
Bailey Packaging Co., Inc., 217 Prospect Ave., Ste. 8-3B, Cranford 07016
Pres.—Vincent Bailey, 3 emp., *Distributor of packaging materials,* .......... (908) 759-0991
Bunzl New Jersey, Inc., 27 Distribution Way, Monmouth Junction 08852
GM—Mike Schilling, 30 emp., *Distributor of paper bags & janitorial* .......... (732) 821-7000
Childcare Supply Co. Inc., 77 Pension Rd., Ste. 13, Englishtown 07726
Sales Mgr.—Shari Schwartz, 10 emp., *Distributor of child care items, including* .......... (732) 786-9888
Concord Paper Mfg., Inc., 375 Sylvan Ave., Ste. 23, Englewood Cliffs 07632
Dir., Sales & Mktg.—Donna Parker, 4 emp., *Shipping boxes & folding cartons, printing* .......... (201) 567-2529
Corman Bag Co., 7 Evergreen Pl., Sparta 07871
Manager—John Walsh, 1 emp., *Wholesaler of packaging materials* .......... (973) 729-2816
Corporate Graphic Solutions, Inc., 11 W. Passaic St., Rochelle Park 07662
CEO—Harvey Ginsberg, 2 emp., *Commercial printing & distributor of* .......... (201) 556-0700
CPR Container, 94 Ford Rd., Ste. 5, Denville 07834
Owner—Nick Foglia, 5 emp., *Wholesaler of plastic & steel packaging* .......... (973) 625-0664
Crystalware, 601 Prospect St., Lakewood 08701
★ Ptnr.—Nisson Kugler, 50 emp., *Distributor of disposable plastic cutlery* .......... (732) 367-4444
Dade Paper Co., 120 Tices Ln., East Brunswick 08816
V-P., Opers.—Mark Rogers, 20 emp., *Distributor of janitorial supplies,* .......... (732) 254-3100
Driscoll Foods, 174 Delawanna Ave., Clifton 07014
Pres.—Tim Driscoll, 300 emp., *Distributor of foodservice products* .......... (973) 672-9400
Enterprise Corrugated Container, LLC, 575 N. Midland Ave., P.O. Box 857, Saddle Brook 07663
Sales Mgr.—James Breit, 40 emp., *Distributor of corrugated boxes* .......... (201) 797-7200
Hillside Paper Products, Inc., 20 Butler St., Elizabeth 07206
Pres.—Alan Lerner, 7 emp., *Distributor of corrugated boxes* .......... (908) 352-3300
Jersey Paper Plus, Inc., 600 Federal Blvd., Carteret 07008
Pres.—Steven Tabak, 50 emp., *Distributor of janitorial paper products* .......... (732) 750-1900
Levine Packaging Supply Corp., 400 U.S. Highway 46 E., Fairfield 07004
V-P.—L. Levine, 20 emp., *Manufacturer of corrugated boxes &* .......... (973) 575-3383
Mainetti USA, Inc., 300 Mac Ln., Keasbey 08832
Pres., Mainetti Americas—Roberto Peruzzo, 30 emp., *Corporate headquarters & distributor* . (201) 215-2900
Maintape, Inc., 1 Capital Dr., Ste. 101, Bldg. 1, Cranbury 08512
Pres.—Karen Olsen, 100 emp., *Manufacturer & distributor of adhesive-backed* .......... (609) 395-1704
Marchesini Packaging Machinery, 43 Fairfield Pl., West Caldwell 07006
GM—Anna Marie Bellina, 18 emp., *Wholesaler of packaging machinery &* .......... (973) 575-7445
Novel Box Co. Ltd., 825 Lehigh Ave., Union 07083
Owner & Pres.—Moishe Sternhill, 50 emp., *Manufacturer & distributor of jewelry* .......... (908) 686-7772
Plus Packaging, Inc., 10 Mount Pleasant Rd., Morristown 07960
Pres.—Lee Dornfeld, 6 emp., *Distributor of corrugated boxes for* .......... (973) 538-2216
Preferred Plastics & Packaging Co., Inc., 681 Main St., Ste. 42, Belleville 07109
Pres.—Randolph Swickle, 30 emp., *Distributor of packaging materials* .......... (973) 759-1510
Ronstan Paper & Packaging, 72 James Way, Eatontown 07724
Pres.—William F. LaMorte, 12 emp., *Distributor of industrial & personal* .......... (732) 389-1040
Stephen Gould Corporation, 35 S. Jefferson Rd., Whippany 07981
Pres., CEO—Michael Golden, 110 emp., *Corporate headquarters & packaging* .......... (973) 428-1510
Stickel Packaging Supply, 1991 Rutgers University Blvd., Lakewood Industrial Pk., Lakewood 08701
Founder—Hal Stickel, 31 emp., *Wholesaler of packaging, janitorial* .......... (732) 905-2811
Supplyone, Inc., 1200 Madison Ave., Paterson 07503
Pres.—Jerry Vitelli, 60 emp., *Distributor of corrugated boxes & janitorial* .......... (718) 392-7400
TricorBraun, 250 Pehle Ave., Ste. 100, Saddle Brook 07663
Br. & Sales Mgr.—Scott Danheiser, 70 emp., *Distributor of plastic & glass bottles* .......... (201) 556-4800
Victory Packaging, Inc., 8 Corn Rd., Ste. 2, Dayton 08810
Pres.—Robert Egan, 75 emp., *Distributor of packaging materials,* .......... (732) 274-1745
xpedx, 261 River Rd., Clifton 07014
CFO—Jeffrey Patterson, 120 emp., *Distributor of paper, packaging materials* .......... (973) 405-2310
xpedx LLC A veritiv Company, 1200 Highland Dr., Ste. 1-B, Westampton 08060
GM—Terence M. Sheehy, 98 emp., *Distributor of printing & writing paper* .......... (609) 518-9700

## 5122 Drugs, proprietaries & sundries

A D S Sale Co., Inc., 1010 Campus Dr., Morganville 07751
Pres.—Marshall Summer, 21 emp., *Distributor of hotel products, including* .......... (732) 591-0500
ABRAZIL, LLC, 1 Jacques Ave., Kendall Park 08824
Owner—Tony Chuang, 4 emp., *Wholesaler of dietary supplements,* .......... (732) 658-5191
Bio-Medical Products Corp., 10 Halstead Rd., Mendham 07945
Manager—John G. Geppert, 2 emp., *Distributor of medical products for* .......... (973) 543-7434
Caremark Rx, Inc., 180 Passaic Ave., Ste. 5, Fairfield 07004
GM—Ed Ochoa, 20 emp., *Distributor of medical pharmaceuticals* .......... (973) 461-1550
Cenmed Enterprises, 121 Jersey Ave., New Brunswick 08901
Sales Mgr.—Rizwan Chaudhry, 12 emp., *Manufacturer of diagnostic drug tests* .......... (732) 447-1100
Childcare Supply Co. Inc., 77 Pension Rd., Ste. 13, Englishtown 07726
Sales Mgr.—Shari Schwartz, 10 emp., *Distributor of child care items, including* .......... (732) 786-9888
Cosmetic Essence, Inc., 1248 S. River Rd., Cranbury 08512
GM—Gaetano Losito, 40 emp., *Distributor of personal care supplies* .......... (609) 395-1271

S.I.C.

De Pasquale Salon Systems, Inc., 21-21 Broadway, Fair Lawn 07410
Pres.—Joe Mastalia, 100 emp., Distributor of beauty salon supplies ........ (201) 797-9101
Distinctive Promotions, Inc., 268 U.S. Highway 206, Ste. 404, Flanders 07836
Pres.—Lois Patrick, 10 emp., Distributor of advertising promotional ........ (973) 584-6800
EC Hair Import, Inc., 99 Murray Hill Pkwy., Ste. B, East Rutherford 07073
Pres.—Peter Lee, 4 emp., Wholesaler of hair care supplies ........ (201) 933-8071
Emiliani Enterprises, 600 Green Ln., Union 07083
CEO—Don Emiliani, 200 emp., Distributor of beauty care products ........ (908) 964-6340
Essential Amenities, Inc., 208 Passaic Ave., Ste. 1, Fairfield 07004
Pres.—Mike Ware, 25 emp., Distributor of personal amenities, ........ (973) 882-8441
Glenmark Generics Inc., USA, 750 Corporate Dr., Mahwah 07430
Pres., CEO—Terry Coughlin, 50 emp., Distributor of generic pharmaceuticals ........ (201) 684-8000
International Beauty Products, 26 Chapin Rd., Ste. 1108, P.O. Box 708, Pine Brook 07058
Pres.—Henry Cho, 11 emp., Distributor of beauty salon products ........ (973) 575-6400
Marcor Development Corp., 341 Michele Pl., Carlstadt 07072
Pres.—Tom Tchang, 12 emp., Distributor of bulk food ingredients ........ (201) 935-2111
Matrix Distributors, Inc., 110 Tices Ln., Ste. 5-B, East Brunswick 08816
Ptnr.—Seth Grumet, 50 emp., Corporate headquarters & distributor ........ (732) 698-9991
McKesson Corp., 400 Delran Pkwy., Delran 08075
Dir., Opers.—Dan Montreuil, 200 emp., Wholesaler of pharmaceuticals ........ (856) 461-7800
Olla Beauty Supply, Inc., 10 New Maple Ave., Unit 301-A, P.O. Box 898, Pine Brook 07058
V-P.—May Chroney, 100 emp., Distributor of ethnic hair care & beauty ........ (973) 575-5260
PC Tan, Inc., 1040 Wilt Ave., Ridgefield 07657
Pres.—Susan Miller, 35 emp., Corporate headquarters & distributor ........ (201) 943-6100
PSS/World Medical, Inc., 208 Passaic Ave., Ste. 2, Fairfield 07004
GM—Jason Bennett, 50 emp., Distributor of medical supplies, equipment ........ (973) 775-8600
SST Corp., 635 Brighton Rd., Clifton 07012
Pres.—D. Gary Vassallo, 36 emp., Distributor of pharmaceutical ingredients ........ (973) 473-4300
Thomas & Co., Inc., P. L., 119 Headquarters Plz., Morristown 07960
Pres.—Paul M. Flowerman, 18 emp., Distributor of vitamins, minerals & ........ (973) 984-0900
TRI-K Industries, Inc., 2 Stewart Ct., P.O. Box 10, Denville 07834
Pres.—Subhas Sen, 30 emp., Corporate headquarters & distributor ........ (973) 298-8850
Windmill Health Products, LLC, 6 Henderson Dr., Caldwell 07006
Pres.—Howard Munk, 45 emp., Manufacturer & distributor of vitamin ........ (973) 575-6591
Xerimis Inc., 102 Executive Dr., Moorestown 08057
CEO—Carol Sue Bernardo, 100 emp., Custom primary & secondary clinical ........ (856) 727-9940
Y, Inc., 20-21 Wagaraw Rd., Bldg. 32, Fair Lawn 07410
Pres.—Dong Jin Yoon, 4 emp., Manufacturer & distributor of professional ........ (201) 773-8425

## 5131 Piece goods & notions

Annin Flagmakers, 105 Eisenhower Pkwy., Ste. 203, Roseland 07068
Pres.—Carter Beard, 65 emp., Company headquarters & wholesaler of ........ (973) 228-9400
Associated Fabrics Corp., 15-01 Pollitt Dr., Ste. 7, Fair Lawn 07410
Pres.—Martin Markowitz, 6 emp., Fabric converting & distributor of ........ (800) 232-4077
Cottage Lace & Ribbon Co., 21 TFH Plaza Union & 3rd Ave., Neptune 07753
Pres.—Shahid Waseem, 2 emp., Manufacturer of wired ribbons & distributor ........ (732) 776-9353
Grey Owl Indian Craft Sales Corp., 15 Meridian Rd., Ste. 5, Eatontown 07724
Pres.—Jim Feldman, 2 emp., Distributor of Native American crafts ........ (732) 389-4626
Royal Lace Co., Inc., 902 E. Hazelwood Ave., Rahway 07065
★ Pres.—Moises Guttman, 25 emp., Manufacturer of knitted lace & wholesaler ........ (718) 495-9327
Ste-Lar Textiles, Inc., 1301 Marlton Pike W., Cherry Hill 08002
Pres.—Steven Bronstein, 5 emp., Corporate headquarters & distributor ........ (856) 429-2245
Stylex Imports & Export Co., Inc., 425 Paterson Ave., East Rutherford 07073
Owner—Yogendra Chokshi, 1 emp., Wholesaler of imported India silk fabric ........ (201) 964-1900
Tri Vantage, LLC, 16 Worlds Fair Dr., Somerset 08873
Br. Mgr.—John Caporaso, 20 emp., Distributor of industrial & marine ........ (732) 868-8400

## 5136 Men's & boys' clothing

A-1 Uniforms, Inc., 721 Broadway, Camden 08103
Pres.—Ralph Ishack, 3 emp., Manufacturer & wholesaler of custom ........ (856) 963-7680
All Hands Fire Equipment, LLC, 7 3rd Ave., Neptune City 07753
Ptnr. & Pres.—Don Colarusso, 4 emp., Wholesaler of firefighting equipment ........ (732) 502-8060
Ambassador Uniform Group, Inc., 289 Highway 33 E., Manalapan 07726
Pres.—Allan Behm, 8 emp., Manufacturer & wholesaler of service ........ (732) 792-1111
Asia Trading, 390 Nye Ave., Irvington 07111
Pres.—Meir Frei, 20 emp., Manufacturer & distributor of security ........ (973) 577-1300
Durawear Glove & Safety, Inc., 30 Royal Rd., Ste. 4, Flemington 08822
Pres.—William Archipoli, 5 emp., Distributor of industrial safety equipment ........ (908) 284-0776
Franco Apparel Group, 231 Docks Corner Rd., Dayton 08810
V-P., Dist.—Ronnie Blazer, 5 emp., Distributor of children's clothing ........ (732) 438-5170
G & K Services, Inc., 137 Ralph St., Belleville 07109
Plt. Mgr.—Joseph E. Sherwood, 70 emp., Distributor of general purpose & government ........ (973) 751-0464
Harbor Linen, LLC (H Q), 2 Foster Ave., Gibbsboro 08026
Chrm.—Earl Waxman, 100 emp., Company headquarters; manufacturer ........ (856) 435-2000
Heritage Surf & Sport, Inc., 3700 Landis Ave., Sea Isle City 08243
Pres.—Barbara Heritage, 9 emp., Distributor of surfboards & sportswear ........ (609) 263-3033
Latico Leather, 321 Palmer Rd., Ste. A, Denville 07834
Owner—Paul Schreiber, 10 emp., Distributor of women's & men's leather ........ (973) 442-9622
Peerless Umbrella Co., Inc., 427 Ferry St., Newark 07105
Pres.—Gene Moscowitz, 120 emp., Manufacturer & distributor of umbrellas ........ (973) 578-4900
Rimmel Rogers, Inc., 250 Passaic St., Newark 07104
Pres.—Manoj Doshi, 7 emp., Contract packaging & distributor of ........ (201) 998-4700
Scaasis Originals, Inc./Oceanic Trading Co., 1006 11th Ave., Neptune 07753
CEO—Neil Saada, 20 emp., Wholesaler of souvenirs, novelties ........ (732) 775-7474
Strong Wear, LLC, 191 The Plaza Ave., Teaneck 07666
Owner—Gilbert Ortiz, 3 emp., Distributor of work & school uniforms ........ (201) 837-7830
Westport Corp., 331 Changebridge Rd., P.O. Box 2002, Pine Brook 07058
CEO—Richard Florin, 120 emp., Distributor of leather & synthetic ........ (973) 575-0110

## 5137 Women's, children's & infants' clothing

A-1 Uniforms, Inc., 721 Broadway, Camden 08103
Pres.—Ralph Ishack, 3 emp., Manufacturer & wholesaler of custom ........ (856) 963-7680
Ambassador Uniform Group, Inc., 289 Highway 33 E., Manalapan 07726
Pres.—Allan Behm, 8 emp., Manufacturer & wholesaler of service ........ (732) 792-1111
Asia Trading, 390 Nye Ave., Irvington 07111
Pres.—Meir Frei, 20 emp., Manufacturer & distributor of security ........ (973) 577-1300
Durawear Glove & Safety, Inc., 30 Royal Rd., Ste. 4, Flemington 08822
Pres.—William Archipoli, 5 emp., Distributor of industrial safety equipment ........ (908) 284-0776
Franco Apparel Group, 231 Docks Corner Rd., Dayton 08810
V-P., Dist.—Ronnie Blazer, 5 emp., Distributor of children's clothing ........ (732) 438-5170
G & K Services, Inc., 137 Ralph St., Belleville 07109
Plt. Mgr.—Joseph E. Sherwood, 70 emp., Distributor of general purpose & government ........ (973) 751-0464
Gordon Mills Mfg., Inc. (H Q), 68 Sherwood Dr., Morristown 07960
Pres.—Bernard Factor, 3 emp., Corporate headquarters; manufacturer ........ (973) 359-1080
Heritage Surf & Sport, Inc., 3700 Landis Ave., Sea Isle City 08243
Pres.—Barbara Heritage, 9 emp., Distributor of surfboards & sportswear ........ (609) 263-3033
Jump Apparel, 350 Secaucus Rd., Secaucus 07094
Manager—Michael Giaella, 100 emp., Distributor of women's clothing ........ (201) 558-9191
Latico Leather, 321 Palmer Rd., Ste. A, Denville 07834
Owner—Paul Schreiber, 10 emp., Distributor of women's & men's leather ........ (973) 442-9622
Rimmel Rogers, Inc., 250 Passaic St., Newark 07104
Pres.—Manoj Doshi, 7 emp., Contract packaging & distributor of ........ (201) 998-4700
San Marel Designs, Inc., 98 U.S. Highway 46, Ste. 10, Budd Lake 07828
CEO—Doug Landon, 8 emp., Precious metal jewelry & wholesaler ........ (973) 426-9554
Scaasis Originals, Inc./Oceanic Trading Co., 1006 11th Ave., Neptune 07753
CEO—Neil Saada, 20 emp., Wholesaler of souvenirs, novelties ........ (732) 775-7474
Strong Wear, LLC, 191 The Plaza Ave., Teaneck 07666
Owner—Gilbert Ortiz, 3 emp., Distributor of work & school uniforms ........ (201) 837-7830
Westport Corp., 331 Changebridge Rd., P.O. Box 2002, Pine Brook 07058
CEO—Richard Florin, 120 emp., Distributor of leather & synthetic ........ (973) 575-0110

## 5139 Footwear

All Hands Fire Equipment, LLC, 7 3rd Ave., Neptune City 07753
Ptnr. & Pres.—Don Colarusso, 4 emp., Wholesaler of firefighting equipment ........ (732) 502-8060
Gordon Mills Mfg., Inc. (H Q), 68 Sherwood Dr., Morristown 07960
Pres.—Bernard Factor, 3 emp., Corporate headquarters; manufacturer ........ (973) 359-1080
Josmo Shoes, Inc., 601 59th St., West New York 07093
Owner—Sam Esquenazi, 100 emp., Wholesaler of children's shoes ........ (201) 617-1477
Royal Deluxe Accessories, LLC, 2563 Brunswick Ave., Bldg. O, Linden 07036
Pres.—Elliot Zeitoune, 18 emp., Wholesaler of costume jewelry, ladies' ........ (908) 523-0550

## 5141 Groceries, general line

Atalanta Corporation, 1 Atalanta Plz., Elizabeth 07206
Chrm., CEO—George Gellert, 150 emp., Corporate headquarters & distributor ........ (908) 351-8000
Driscoll Foods, 174 Delawanna Ave., Clifton 07014
Pres.—Tim Driscoll, 300 emp., Distributor of foodservice products ........ (973) 672-9400
Ferraro Foods, Inc., 287 S. Randolphville Rd., Piscataway 08854
Pres.—Michael Giammarino, 34 emp., Corporate headquarters & distributor ........ (732) 424-3400
Foods Galore, Inc., 9246 Commerce Hwy., Pennsauken 08110
Pres.—Morton Waxler, 90 emp., Wholesaler of food, dairy & meat products ........ (856) 488-1112
Jetro Cash & Carry, Inc., 1 Amity St., Jersey City 07304
GM—Tom Desciscio, 50 emp., Wholesaler of general line groceries ........ (201) 434-4334
JFC International, Inc., 55 Wildcat Way, Linden 07036
Br. Mgr.—Shoso Ota, 60 emp., Wholesaler of packaged Japanese foods ........ (908) 525-4400
KeyImpact Sales & Systems, Inc., 95 Connecticut Dr., Burlington 08016
CEO—Daniel T. Cassidy, 75 emp., Corporate headquarters & wholesaler ........ (609) 265-8300
La Fe Foods, Inc., 230 Moonachie Ave., Moonachie 07074
Pres.—Juan Carlos Pena, 85 emp., Distributor of groceries from the Caribbean ........ (201) 329-6260
McLane Burlington, 600 Commerce Dr., Burlington 08016
Dir., Opers.—Don Lenc, 150 emp., Distributor of general line groceries ........ (609) 239-5000
McLane New Jersey, 742 Courses Landing Rd., Carneys Point 08069
Pres.—Jim Tidmore, 413 emp., Distributor of general line groceries ........ (856) 351-6200
Mivila Corp., 226 Getty Ave., Paterson 07503
Pres.—Ted Laoudis, 10 emp., Corporate headquarters & distributor ........ (973) 278-4148
Nishimoto Trading Co. Ltd., 602 Washington Ave., Carlstadt 07072
Br. Mgr.—Pat Suguki, 120 emp., Distributor of general line Asian food ........ (201) 804-1600
Restaurant Depot, LLC, 1050 Thomas Busch Memorial Hwy., Pennsauken 08110
GM—Paul Jensen, 75 emp., Wholesaler of general line groceries ........ (856) 488-4288
Roma Food Enterprises, Inc., 1 Roma Blvd., Piscataway 08854
Pres.—Jim Palazzo, 100 emp., Distributor of Italian & Italian-American ........ (732) 463-7662
Roma Of Mid-Atlantic, 301 Heron Dr., Swedesboro 08085
Pres.—Ken Wineland, 100 emp., Distributor of Italian & Italian-American ........ (856) 467-8100
SYSCO Food Services Of Metro New York, LLC, 20 Theodore Conrad Dr., Jersey City 07305
Pres.—Phillip Lahm, 530 emp., Wholesaler of general line groceries ........ (201) 433-2000
US Foods, Inc., 1051 Amboy Ave., Perth Amboy 08861
Pres., Div.—Charles Gannon, 550 emp., Distributor of general line groceries ........ (732) 934-3400

## 5142 Packaged frozen foods

Azuma Foods International, Inc., 20 Murray Hill Pkwy., Ste. 130, East Rutherford 07073
Br. Mgr.—Yoshi Sugiura, 10 emp., Distributor of fresh & frozen seafood ........ (201) 372-1112
Camerican International, 45 Eisenhower Dr., Ste. 310, Paramus 07652
Pres.—Lawrence Abramson, 40 emp., Distributor of imported packaged & ........ (201) 587-0101
La Fe Foods, Inc., 230 Moonachie Ave., Moonachie 07074
Pres.—Juan Carlos Pena, 85 emp., Distributor of groceries from the Caribbean ........ (201) 329-6260
Performance Food Group-AFI Foodservice, 1 Ikea Dr., Elizabeth 07207
CEO—Chuck Cuomo, 450 emp., Distributor of food products to restaurants ........ (908) 629-1800
Roma Food Enterprises, Inc., 1 Roma Blvd., Piscataway 08854
Pres.—Jim Palazzo, 100 emp., Distributor of Italian & Italian-American ........ (732) 463-7662
US Foods, Inc., 1051 Amboy Ave., Perth Amboy 08861
Pres., Div.—Charles Gannon, 550 emp., Distributor of general line groceries ........ (732) 934-3400

## 5143 Dairy products, except dried or canned

Albert's Organics, Inc., 200 Eagle Ct., P.O. Box 624, Bridgeport 08014
Pres.—Scott Dennis, 150 emp., Corporate headquarters & distributor ........ (856) 241-9090
Atalanta Corporation, 1 Atalanta Plz., Elizabeth 07206
Chrm., CEO—George Gellert, 150 emp., Corporate headquarters & distributor ........ (908) 351-8000
Cumberland Dairy, Inc., 899 Landis Ave., P.O. Box 308, Rosenhayn 08352
Pres.—Carmine Catalana IV, 55 emp., Corporate headquarters & distributor ........ (856) 451-1300
DCI Cheese Co., 861 Washington Ave., Carlstadt 07072
Pres.—Kevin Therauilt, 30 emp., Distributor of traditional, organic ........ (201) 807-0999
Finlandia Cheese, Inc., 2001 U.S. Highway 46, Ste. 303, Parsippany 07054
Pres.—Chris Franco, 15 emp., Distributor of cheese ........ (973) 316-6699
Foods Galore, Inc., 9246 Commerce Hwy., Pennsauken 08110
Pres.—Morton Waxler, 90 emp., Wholesaler of food, dairy & meat products ........ (856) 488-1112
Haddon House Food Products, Inc., 433 Oak Glen Rd., Howell 07731
Opers. Mgr.—Ken Wilkinson, 225 emp., Distributor of gourmet, frozen, ethnic ........ (732) 367-7901
Haddon House Food Products, Inc. (H Q), 250 Old Marlton Pike, Medford 08055
CEO—David Anderson, 30 emp., Corporate headquarters; distributor ........ (609) 654-7901
Hunter Walton & Co., Inc., 120 Circle Dr. N., Piscataway 08854
CEO—Peter Love, 10 emp., Distributor of dairy products, including ........ (732) 805-0808
La Fe Foods, Inc., 230 Moonachie Ave., Moonachie 07074
Pres.—Juan Carlos Pena, 85 emp., Distributor of groceries from the Caribbean ........ (201) 329-6260
Malincho Inc, 2545 Fire Rd., Ste. 3, Egg Harbor Township 08234
Ptnr.—Vladimir Natchev, 6 emp., Distributor of European food products ........ (609) 677-6090

MCT Dairies, Inc., 15 Bleeker St., Millburn 07041
Pres., CEO—Kenneth Meyers, 11 emp., *Corporate headquarters & wholesaler* ...................... (973) 258-9600
Panza & Sons, Ltd., A., 141 Fieldcrest Ave., Edison 08837
Pres.—Vito Panza, 70 emp., *Stocking distributor of ice cream mixes* ...................... (732) 225-1314
Roma Food Enterprises, Inc., 1 Roma Blvd., Piscataway 08854
Pres.—Jim Palazzo, 100 emp., *Distributor of Italian & Italian-American* ...................... (732) 463-7662
Schratter Foods, Inc. (H Q), 333 Fairfield Rd., Fairfield 07004
Pres., CEO—Alain J. Voss, 34 emp., *Corporate headquarters; distributor* ...................... (973) 575-3226
Wakefern Food Corp. (H Q), 5000 Riverside Dr., Keasbey 08832
Chrm., CEO—Joseph S. Colalillo, 400 emp., *Corporate headquarters; distributor* ...................... (732) 906-5932

## 5145 Confectionery

Delaware Valley Wholesale Florist, Inc., 520 Mantua Blvd., Sewell 08080
Chrm.—John R. Wilkins, 50 emp., *Corporate headquarters & wholesaler* ...................... (856) 468-7000
Malincho Inc, 2545 Fire Rd., Ste. 3, Egg Harbor Township 08234
Ptnr.—Vladimir Natchev, 6 emp., *Distributor of European food products* ...................... (609) 677-6090

## 5146 Fish & seafoods

Atlantic Capes Fisheries, Inc., 985 Ocean Dr., Cape May 08204
Pres.—Daniel Cohen, 50 emp., *Distributor of scallops & related seafoods* ...................... (609) 884-3000
Azuma Foods International, Inc., 20 Murray Hill Pkwy., Ste. 130, East Rutherford 07073
Br. Mgr.—Yoshi Sugiura, 10 emp., *Distributor of fresh & frozen seafood* ...................... (201) 372-1112
Bay Treasure Seafood, LLC, 2002 Lakewood Rd., Unit 4, Toms River 08755
Member—Stephen Miller, 10 emp., *Distributor of seafood* ...................... (732) 240-3474
Driscoll Foods, 174 Delawanna Ave., Clifton 07014
Pres.—Tim Driscoll, 300 emp., *Distributor of foodservice products* ...................... (973) 672-9400
Fishermans Dock Co-Op, 57 Channel Dr., P.O. Box 1314, Point Pleasant Beach 08742
Pres.—John Cole, 10 emp., *Wholesaler of seafood, including fish* ...................... (732) 899-1872
Foods Galore, Inc., 9246 Commerce Hwy., Pennsauken 08110
Pres.—Morton Waxler, 90 emp., *Wholesaler of food, dairy & meat products* ...................... (856) 488-1112
JFC International, Inc., 55 Wildcat Way, Linden 07036
Br. Mgr.—Shoso Ota, 60 emp., *Wholesaler of packaged Japanese foods* ...................... (908) 525-4400
Kontos Foods, Inc., 100 6th Ave., P.O. Box 628, Paterson 07544
Pres.—Evris Kontos, 150 emp., *Manufacturer of authentic ethnic hand-stretch* ...................... (973) 278-2800
Mary Ellen Maryland Crabmeat Co., Inc., 2613 Fire Rd., Egg Harbor Township 08234
Pres.—Audrey Jenkins, 8 emp., *Distributor of fresh, pasteurized,* ...................... (609) 645-0161
Roma Of Mid-Atlantic, 301 Heron Dr., Swedesboro 08085
Pres.—Ken Wineland, 100 emp., *Distributor of Italian & Italian-American* ...................... (856) 467-8100
True World Foods, LLC, 32-34 Papetti Plz., Elizabeth 07206
Hum. Res. Mgr.—Eve Roberts, 55 emp., *Wholesaler of fresh & frozen seafood* ...................... (908) 351-1400
Viking Village, Inc., 19th St. & Bayview Ave., P.O. Box 458, Barnegat Light 08006
Pres.—Louis Puskas, Jr., 15 emp., *Distributor of fresh fish & seafood* ...................... (609) 494-0113

## 5147 Meats & meat products

Atalanta Corporation, 1 Atalanta Plz., Elizabeth 07206
Chrm., CEO—George Gellert, 150 emp., *Corporate headquarters & distributor* ...................... (908) 351-8000
Buckhead Beef Co., 220 Raritan Ctr., P.O. Box 6988, Edison 08837
GM—Glenn Ermoian, 104 emp., *Distributor of meat, including beef* ...................... (732) 661-4900
Driscoll Foods, 174 Delawanna Ave., Clifton 07014
Pres.—Tim Driscoll, 300 emp., *Distributor of foodservice products* ...................... (973) 672-9400
Foods Galore, Inc., 9246 Commerce Hwy., Pennsauken 08110
Pres.—Morton Waxler, 90 emp., *Wholesaler of food, dairy & meat products* ...................... (856) 488-1112
Kontos Foods, Inc., 100 6th Ave., P.O. Box 628, Paterson 07544
Pres.—Evris Kontos, 150 emp., *Manufacturer of authentic ethnic hand-stretch* ...................... (973) 278-2800
Red Square Foods, Inc., 62 Berry St., Somerset 08873
Pres.—Boris Rappaport, 15 emp., *Manufacturer & distributor of deli* ...................... (732) 846-0190
Roma Food Enterprises, Inc., 1 Roma Blvd., Piscataway 08854
Pres.—Jim Palazzo, 100 emp., *Distributor of Italian & Italian-American* ...................... (732) 463-7662

## 5148 Fresh fruits & vegetables

ACB Produce, Inc., 135-137 Pacific St., Newark 07105
Pres.—Anibal Bota, 7 emp., *Wholesaler of fruits & vegetables* ...................... (973) 522-1141
Albert's Organics, Inc., 200 Eagle Ct., P.O. Box 624, Bridgeport 08014
Pres.—Scott Dennis, 150 emp., *Corporate headquarters & distributor* ...................... (856) 241-9090
Capespan North America, 701 N. Broadway., Ste. 102, Gloucester City 08030
Dir., Opers. & Sales—Stephen Stackhouse, 13 emp., *Distributor of fruit* ...................... (856) 742-0242
Custom Pak, Inc., 800 Grove Rd., Thorofare 08086
GM & Plt. Mgr.—Don Martin, 300 emp., *Wholesaler of produce* ...................... (856) 384-4980
Delaware Valley Wholesale Florist, Inc., 520 Mantua Blvd., Sewell 08080
Chrm.—John R. Wilkins, 50 emp., *Corporate headquarters & wholesaler* ...................... (856) 468-7000
Donio, Inc., Frank, 692 N. Egg Harbor Rd., P.O. Box 529, Hammonton 08037
Pres.—David F. Arena, 120 emp., *Distributor of fresh fruits & vegetables* ...................... (609) 561-2466
New York Produce, Inc., 125 Seaview Dr., Secaucus 07094
Off. Mgr.—Ari Sanemeterio, 90 emp., *Distributor of produce* ...................... (201) 223-0909
Performance Food Group-AFI Foodservice, 1 Ikea Dr., Elizabeth 07207
CEO—Chuck Cuomo, 450 emp., *Distributor of food products to restaurants* ...................... (908) 629-1800
Riviera Produce Corp., 205 Jackson St., P.O. Box 6065, Englewood 07631
Pres.—Ben Friedman, 100 emp., *Wholesaler of fresh fruit & vegetables* ...................... (201) 227-7105

## 5149 Groceries & related products, nec

AMD Special Oil, LLC, 90 N. Franklin Tpke., Ramsey 07446
Pres.—Donald Griego, 7 emp., *Distributor of edible oils* ...................... (201) 327-0642
Apple Food Sales Co., Inc., 117 Fort Lee Rd., Ste. B-7, Leonia 07605
Pres.—Jill Bush, 15 emp., *Distributor of Italian food products* ...................... (201) 592-0277
BakeMark USA, LLC, 1815 Route 130 N., Burlington 08016
GM—Anthony Lotito, 50 emp., *Distributor of baking ingredients,* ...................... (609) 747-9000
Caffe Borbone USA, 19 Commerce Rd., Ste. G, Fairfield 07004
Pres.—Antonio Amato, 8 emp., *Espresso coffee packing & distributor* ...................... (973) 227-7799
Camerican International, 45 Eisenhower Dr., Ste. 310, Paramus 07652
Pres.—Lawrence Abramson, 40 emp., *Distributor of imported packaged &* ...................... (201) 587-0101
Cumberland Dairy, Inc., 899 Landis Ave., P.O. Box 308, Rosenhayn 08352
Pres.—Carmine Catalana IV, 55 emp., *Corporate headquarters & distributor* ...................... (856) 451-1300
Delaware Valley Wholesale Florist, Inc., 520 Mantua Blvd., Sewell 08080
Chrm.—John R. Wilkins, 50 emp., *Corporate headquarters & wholesaler* ...................... (856) 468-7000
Edesia Oil, LLC, 225 County Road 522, Unit B, Englishtown 07726
★ Owner—Joseph Calcagno, 10 emp., *Distributor of edible oils, including* ...................... (732) 851-7979
Elixens America, Inc., 1443 Pinewood St., Rahway 07065
Pres.—Adam Roman, 3 emp., *Distributor of organic essential oils* ...................... (732) 388-3555
Franklin Farms East, Inc., 111 W. Washington Ave., Washington 07882
Pres.—Donald L. Riggs, 14 emp., *Wholesaler of nonfat dry milks & whey* ...................... (908) 835-0016
Haddon House Food Products, Inc., 433 Oak Glen Rd., Howell 07731
Opers. Mgr.—Ken Wilkinson, 225 emp., *Distributor of gourmet, frozen, ethnic* ...................... (732) 367-7901
Haddon House Food Products, Inc. (H Q), 250 Old Marlton Pike, Medford 08055
CEO—David Anderson, 30 emp., *Corporate headquarters; distributor* ...................... (609) 654-7901
High Grade Beverage, 891 Georges Rd., Monmouth Junction 08852
Corp. V-P.—Guy Battaglia, 150 emp., *Company headquarters & distributor* ...................... (732) 821-7600
High Grade Beverage, 86 Canfield Ave., Randolph 07869
Corp. V-P.—George Policastro, 100 emp., *Distributor of beverages, including* ...................... (973) 927-1400
J.D. Beverage Co., 10 Richards St., Newark 07105
Pres.—Joe D'Orazio, 12 emp., *Wholesaler of nonalcoholic beverages* ...................... (973) 344-8149
JFC International, Inc., 55 Wildcat Way, Linden 07036
Br. Mgr.—Shoso Ota, 60 emp., *Wholesaler of packaged Japanese foods* ...................... (908) 525-4400
Kaffe Magnum Opus, 500 S. Wade Blvd., Millville 08332
Pres., CEO—Bob Johnson, 18 emp., *Wholesaler of coffee* ...................... (856) 327-9962
Kontos Foods, Inc., 100 6th Ave., P.O. Box 628, Paterson 07544
Pres.—Evris Kontos, 150 emp., *Manufacturer of authentic ethnic hand-stretch* ...................... (973) 278-2800
Malincho Inc, 2545 Fire Rd., Ste. 3, Egg Harbor Township 08234
Ptnr.—Vladimir Natchev, 6 emp., *Distributor of European food products* ...................... (609) 677-6090
Mary Ellen Maryland Crabmeat Co., Inc., 2613 Fire Rd., Egg Harbor Township 08234
Pres.—Audrey Jenkins, 8 emp., *Distributor of fresh, pasteurized,* ...................... (609) 645-0161
Mitsui Foods, Inc., 35 Maple St., Norwood 07648
Pres., CEO—Tom Osada, 60 emp., *Manufacturer of frozen pasta products* ...................... (201) 750-0500
Monkey Joe's Big Nut Co., 205 N. White Horse Pike, Laurel Springs 08021
Owner—Joe Bush, 18 emp., *Wholesaler of dried fruits & salted* ...................... (856) 627-4600
Oilmatic Systems, LLC, 155 Smith St., P.O. Box 185, Keasbey 08832
Acct. Mgr.—Deena Allora, 20 emp., *Distributor of bulk cooking oil systems* ...................... (732) 324-9890
Oliveri & Sons, Inc., A., 4401 Dell Ave., P.O. Box 88, North Bergen 07047
Ptnr.—Iggy DePalma, 12 emp., *Wholesaler of baking flour & ingredients* ...................... (201) 319-9112
Puratos Corp., 945 Sherman Ave., Pennsauken 08110
Sales Mgr.—George Rodier, 50 emp., *Distributor of bakery ingredients* ...................... (856) 661-3112
Samuel Elliott, Inc., 1818 Bannard St., Riverton 08077
Pres.—Mary Bossen, 20 emp., *Wholesaler of organic green tea* ...................... (856) 773-6000
Summit Import Corp., 100 Summit Pl., Jersey City 07305
Pres., CEO—Whiting Wu, 80 emp., *Distributor of Asian food products,* ...................... (201) 985-9800

## 5159 Farm products, raw materials, nec

Monkey Joe's Big Nut Co., 205 N. White Horse Pike, Laurel Springs 08021
Owner—Joe Bush, 18 emp., *Wholesaler of dried fruits & salted* ...................... (856) 627-4600

## 5162 Plastic materials & basic forms & shapes

Associated Plastics, Inc., 179 E. Inman Ave., Rahway 07065
Pres.—Richard W. Fisher, 3 emp., *Distributor of plastic pull straps,* ...................... (732) 574-2800
Bailey Packaging Co., Inc., 217 Prospect Ave., Ste. 8-3B, Cranford 07016
Pres.—Vincent Bailey, 3 emp., *Distributor of packaging materials,* ...................... (908) 759-0991
Campbell Foundry, Materials Div., 630 S. Hope Chapel Rd., Jackson 08527
Br. Mgr.—Leon Theodorou, 5 emp., *Wholesaler of PVC, HDPE, RCP, CMP &* ...................... (732) 408-1111
Carpathian Industries, LLC, 51 Newark St., Ste. 508, Hoboken 07030
Owner & Pres.—Paul Lichstein, 9 emp., *Wholesaler of plastic & metal parts* ...................... (201) 798-8883
Claude Bamberger Molding Compounds Corp., 111 Paterson Plank Rd., P.O. Box 67, Carlstadt 07072
Pres.—Claude Bamberger, 7 emp., *Manufacturer & distributor of purging* ...................... (201) 933-6262
Complete Plastic Distributors, Inc., 778 Carver Ave., Westwood 07675
Owner—Andy Kestenbaum, 5 emp., *Plastic fabrication & distributor of* ...................... (201) 666-8600
Dynaclear Packaging / Pro Pack, Inc., 500 W. Main St., Wyckoff 07481
Chrm., CEO—Peter Quercia, 12 emp., *Full-service distributor of custom* ...................... (201) 337-1001
Emco Industrial Plastics, Inc., 99 Commerce Rd., P.O. Box 2503, Cedar Grove 07009
Pres.—William Egner, 75 emp., *Plastic fabrication & distributor of* ...................... (973) 559-5610
Hart Industries, Inc., 135 Crown Rd., Thorofare 08086
GM—Steve Shera, 5 emp., *Wholesaler of rubber & plastic hose* ...................... (856) 686-1455
Labnet International, Inc., 31 Mayfield Ave., Edison 08837
Pres.—Gerry Cooney, 40 emp., *Distributor of laboratory centrifuges* ...................... (732) 417-0700
MacAuley, Inc., James R., 1 Industrial Dr., P.O. Box 704, Waterford Works 08089
Pres.—George MacAuley, 2 emp., *Wholesaler of plastic pails & plastic* ...................... (856) 767-3474
Medford Silicones, Inc., P.O. Box 2072, Medford 08055
Owner & Pres.—Eric Ley, 2 emp., *Wholesaler of silicone resins* ...................... (609) 953-1092
Michael Halebian & Co., Inc., 557 Washington Ave., Carlstadt 07072
Pres.—Michael Halebian, Jr., 50 emp., *Distributor of floor coverings & related* ...................... (201) 935-3535
Outwater Plastics/Industries, Inc., 24 River Rd., P.O. Box 500, Bogota 07603
Pres.—Peter Kessler, 125 emp., *Corporate headquarters & distributor* ...................... (201) 498-8750
Preferred Plastics & Packaging Co., Inc., 681 Main St., Ste. 42, Belleville 07109
Pres.—Randolph Swickle, 30 emp., *Distributor of packaging materials* ...................... (973) 759-1510
Pro Plastics, Inc., 1190 Sylvan St., P.O. Box 1489, Linden 07036
Pres.—George Sievewright, 12 emp., *Manufacturer of custom plastic parts* ...................... (908) 925-5555
Quality Seals, Inc., 2444 Morris Ave., Ste. 201, Union 07083
GM—Steve Patterson, 3 emp., *Distributor of rubber & plastic products* ...................... (908) 206-0410
Robert McKeown Co., Inc., 111 Chambers Brook Rd., Branchburg 08876
Pres.—Lindsey McKeown, 25 emp., *Distributor of engineered specialty* ...................... (908) 218-9000
Ryan Herco Flow Solutions Corp., 50 Tannery Rd., Reading Industrial Ctr., Bldg. 3, Somerville 08876
Dist. Sales Mgr.—John Matonis, 25 emp., *Distributor of plastic products* ...................... (908) 534-6111
Stuart Mills, Inc., 25 Stillwater Rd., Newton 07860
Pres.—Stuart Mills, 6 emp., *CNC milling & turning, sheet metal* ...................... (973) 579-5717
T & T Marketing, Inc., P.O. Box 120, Allamuchy 07820
Pres., CEO—Tom Jordan, 23 emp., *Distributor of PVC, TPE, TPU, FEP,* ...................... (973) 426-0453
The Liner Co., Inc., 7 Meadows Run Dr., Colts Neck 07722
Owner & Pres.—Carol Hartwell, 2 emp., *Distributor of HDPE, PVC, geocomposite* ...................... (732) 761-0700
Victory Packaging, Inc., 8 Corn Rd., Ste. 2, Dayton 08810
Pres.—Robert Egan, 75 emp., *Distributor of packaging materials,* ...................... (732) 274-1745

## 5169 Chemicals & allied products, nec

Ace Janitorial Supply, Inc., 164 Franklin Tpke., Ste. 2, Mahwah 07430
Pres.—H. Mike Timpone, 4 emp., *Distributor of janitorial & electrical* ...................... (201) 529-1750
Advantage Vacuum LLC, 110 South Ave., Ste. A, Garwood 07027
Owner—Alan Schwartz, 5 emp., *Distributor of commercial vacuum cleaners* ...................... (908) 228-5629
Air Products & Chemicals, Inc., 405 State Route 33, Englishtown 07726
Br. Mgr.—Ellen Hammer, 13 emp., *Distributor of industrial chemicals* ...................... (732) 446-5676
Airgas East, Inc., 2 Beckwith Ave., Paterson 07503
Br. Mgr.—Pete Miteiko, 2 emp., *Distributor of welding equipment, supplies* ...................... (973) 742-2211
Airgas East, Inc., 490 Stelton Rd., Piscataway 08854
Administrator—Terry Dalessio, 40 emp., *Wholesaler of welding supplies & industrial* ...................... (732) 752-4500
Airgas Retail Solutions, 270 U.S. Highway 9, Manalapan 07726
Opers. Mgr.—Christine Zrebiec, 12 emp., *Wholesaler of compressed helium & carbon* ...................... (732) 431-0288
Airmatic Compressor Systems, Inc., 700 Washington Ave., Carlstadt 07072
Pres.—William N. Vowteras, 30 emp., *Distributor of air compressors, compressed* ...................... (201) 342-1300
Allied Building Products Corp., 27 Kentucky Ave., Paterson 07503
Br. Mgr.—Adam Carten, 5 emp., *Distributor of building materials,* ...................... (973) 357-1600

S.I.C.

★ Indicates new listing this edition.

American Paper & Supply Co., LLC, 10 Industrial Rd., P.O. Box 346, Carlstadt 07072
Owner—Larry Shapiro, 45 emp., *Distributor of maintenance/janitorial* ............ (201) 939-4200
Apria Healthcare, Inc., 1 Frassetto Way, Ste. F, Lincoln Park 07035
Br. Mgr.—Rosemary Berkowitz, 30 emp., *Distributor of durable medical equipment* ............ (973) 305-0099
ARAMSCO, 1480 Grandview Ave., P.O. Box 29, Thorofare 08086
Pres.—Rich Salerno, 65 emp., *Company headquarters & distributor* ............ (856) 686-7700
Arden Sales, 128 14th St., Lakewood 08701
Owner—Charles Saltz, 1 emp., *Distributor of cleaning supplies* ............ (732) 730-1418
Atlas Welding Supply Co., Inc., 808 Brook Rd., Lakewood 08701
Corp. Secy.—Dina Pincus, 7 emp., *Distributor of welding equipment &* ............ (732) 363-1148
Awisco Corp., 24 Lakeside Ave., West Orange 07052
Br. Mgr.—Abel Marriott, 6 emp., *Wholesaler of welding equipment, industrial* ............ (973) 736-0200
Awisco West Milford, LLC, 26 Industrial Rd., West Milford 07480
Br. Mgr.—Andrew Cullen, 8 emp., *Distributor of welding, industrial* ............ (973) 728-9008
Bacon & Graham, Inc., 34 E. 25th St., Paterson 07514
Pres.—Craig Bacon, 30 emp., *Wholesaler of packaging, shipping,* ............ (973) 684-1488
Banner Chemical Corp., 111 Hill St., Orange 07050
Pres.—David Herman, 10 emp., *Manufacturer & distributor of sanitary* ............ (973) 676-2900
Bearing Depot & Supply, Inc., 819 Lincoln Blvd., Ste. 1, Middlesex 08846
Pres.—Donna Hardgrove, 5 emp., *Distributor of metric & inch ceramic* ............ (732) 563-2225
Belair Instrument Co., Inc., 36 Commerce St., P.O. Box 619, Springfield 07081
Pres.—David Patterson, 32 emp., *Wholesaler of laboratory equipment* ............ (973) 912-8900
Berje Inc., 700 Blair Rd., Carteret 07008
CEO—Kim Bleimann, 100 emp., *Corporate headquarters & distributor* ............ (973) 748-8980
Bio-Ox International, Inc., 140 Ethel Rd. W., Ste. U, Piscataway 08854
Owner—Steven Schneider, 10 emp., *Distributor of cleaning compounds* ............ (732) 650-9779
Bunzl New Jersey, Inc., 27 Distribution Way, Monmouth Junction 08852
GM—Mike Schilling, 30 emp., *Distributor of paper bags & janitorial* ............ (732) 821-7000
Cal-Chlor Corp., 141 Baekeland Ave., Piscataway 08854
Plt. Mgr.—Mike Scelsa, 25 emp., *Distributor of dry calcium chloride* ............ (732) 271-3500
Certified Products Co., 269 Kearney Ave., Jersey City 07305
Owner—Cosimo Ferretti, 15 emp., *Distributor of hose assemblies & lubricants* ............ (201) 433-0013
Childcare Supply Co. Inc., 77 Pension Rd., Ste. 13, Englishtown 07726
Sales Mgr.—Shari Schwartz, 10 emp., *Distributor of child care items, including* ............ (732) 786-9888
Dreyco, Inc., 263 Veterans Blvd., Carlstadt 07072
Pres.—Michael Borghard, 15 emp., *Distributor of automotive parts, tools* ............ (201) 896-9000
Fastenal Co., 500 Hartle St., Ste. D, Sayreville 08872
Manager—Dan Divine, 2 emp., *Wholesaler of industrial fasteners,* ............ (732) 254-1117
Grabber Northeast, 1125 Thomas Busch Memorial Hwy., Pennsauken 08110
Br. Mgr.—Val Anesti, 7 emp., *Distributor of construction equipment* ............ (856) 662-2525
Heath Lumber Co., 1580 N. Olden Avenue Ext., Ewing 08638
Pres.—Gary Patricelli, 30 emp., *Distributor of building materials &* ............ (609) 392-1166
Hisco, Inc., 55 Veronica Ave., Somerset 08873
Br. Mgr.—Greg Smith, 10 emp., *Distributor of industrial chemicals* ............ (732) 745-2828
Industrial Welding Supply, Inc., 4 Val St., Sayreville 08872
Pres.—Jim Cusick, 21 emp., *Corporate headquarters & distributor* ............ (732) 721-1150
Kenseal Construction Products Corp., 799 Edwards Rd., Parsippany 07054
Cont.—Charles J. Meyers, 20 emp., *Distributor of sealants, concrete admixtures* ............ (973) 287-5858
Marcor Development Corp., 341 Michele Pl., Carlstadt 07072
Pres.—Tom Tchang, 12 emp., *Distributor of bulk food ingredients* ............ (201) 935-2111
Michael Halebian & Co., Inc., 557 Washington Ave., Carlstadt 07072
Pres.—Michael Halebian, Jr., 50 emp., *Distributor of floor coverings & related* ............ (201) 935-3535
Parts Cleaning Technologies, LLC, 835 Industrial Hwy., Ste. 1, Cinnaminson 08077
GM—Derrick Fatzinger, 5 emp., *Wholesaler of chemicals, including* ............ (856) 786-8686
Praxair, Inc., 554 Shell Rd., Penns Grove 08069
Ex. V-P.—Paul Bilek, 10 emp., *Distributor of propane & oxygen gases* ............ (856) 299-3500
PrimeSource Building Products, Inc., 20 Van Dyke Ave, New Brunswick 08901
GM—Scott Simmel, 30 emp., *Distributor of building materials,* ............ (732) 296-0600
Protameen Chemicals, Inc., 375 Minnisink Rd., Totowa 07512
Pres.—Emanuel Balsamides, Sr., 30 emp., *Distributor of chemicals & personal* ............ (973) 256-4374
Ronstan Paper & Packaging, 72 James Way, Eatontown 07724
Pres.—William F. LaMorte, 12 emp., *Distributor of industrial & personal* ............ (732) 389-1040
Rugby ABP Corp., 60 Joseph St., Moonachie 07074
Regional Mgr.—Arsenio Alvarez, 20 emp., *Wholesaler of industrial building materials* ............ (201) 807-9701
Safety-Kleen Systems, Inc., 116 Skyline Dr., South Plainfield 07080
Manager—Thomas Colligan, 100 emp., *Distributor of used industrial parts* ............ (908) 791-9600
Seidler Chemical & Supply Co., 537 Raymond Blvd., Newark 07105
Pres.—Richard Seidler, 18 emp., *Distributor of specialty & industrial* ............ (973) 465-1122
Signature Marketing & Mfg., 301 Wagaraw Rd., Hawthorne 07506
Owner & Pres.—Michael Assile, 6 emp., *Manufacturer & wholesaler of adhesives* ............ (973) 427-3700
South Jersey Welding Supply Co., 94 W. Forest Grove Rd., Vineland 08360
Owner—Robert Thorton, Jr., 15 emp., *Distributor of welding equipment &* ............ (856) 691-9659
SST Corp., 635 Brighton Rd., Clifton 07012
Pres.—D. Gary Vassallo, 36 emp., *Distributor of pharmaceutical ingredients* ............ (973) 473-4300
Stevens Industries, Inc., 39 Avenue C, P.O. Box 8, Bayonne 07002
Pres.—William Rubenstein, 15 emp., *Distributor of lubricants, corrosion* ............ (201) 437-6500
Styles Mfg. Co., Inc., A. E., 416 Richmond Ave., P.O. Box 1306, Point Pleasant Beach 08742
Pres.—John Criscuolo, 15 emp., *Manufacturer of car wash detergents* ............ (732) 899-0872
Thermo Fisher Scientific Inc., 1 Reagent Ln., Fair Lawn 07410
V-P., Global Sales & Mktg.—Duane Talhouk, 360 emp., *Wholesaler of chemicals for pharmaceutical* (201) 796-7100
Unichem Industries, Inc., 1 Bayberry Close, Piscataway 08854
Pres.—Kishore Sanghvi, 2 emp., *Wholesaler of ferrous & nonferrous* ............ (732) 463-8442
Universal Chemicals Inc., 100 N. Hackensack Ave., Kearny 07032
Pres.—Jerry Kaplan, 10 emp., *Distributor of water treatment & swimming* ............ (973) 589-1525
Universal Preserv-A-Chem, Inc., 60 Jiffy Rd., Somerset 08873
Chrm.—Herbert Ravitz, 25 emp., *Distributor of chemicals, fine chemicals* ............ (732) 568-1266
Valley National Gases, WV LLC, 201 Crown Point Rd., West Deptford 08086
GM—Wendy Hughes, 10 emp., *Distributor of welding supplies, including* ............ (856) 848-7321
Veckridge Chemical Co., Inc., 60 Central Ave., Kearny 07032
Pres.—Mark Veca, 20 emp., *Wholesaler of industrial chemicals* ............ (973) 344-1818
W. W. Grainger, Inc., 308 Allwood Rd., Clifton 07012
Br. Mgr.—Kevin Wojcicki, 20 emp., *Wholesaler of commercial & industrial* ............ (973) 777-7700
Wurth International Trading America, 91 Grant St., Ramsey 07446
CEO—Esther Jakob, 7 emp., *Company headquarters & distributor* ............ (201) 995-1111

## 5172 Petroleum products

Airgas, Inc., 5 Iron Horse Rd., Oakland 07436
Facility Mgr.—Larry Myers, 20 emp., *Wholesaler of propane gas* ............ (201) 337-5891
BlackHawk Industrial, Atlantic Tool Systems Div., 170 5th Ave., Hawthorne 07506
GM—J. F. Montague, 8 emp., *Wholesaler of pneumatic tools, abrasives* ............ (973) 238-0009
BP Lubricants USA, Inc., 1500 Valley Rd., Wayne 07470
Pres.—Marcia Brand, 250 emp., *Corporate headquarters & distributor* ............ (973) 633-2200
Ferrell's Oil Service, 26 E. Mill St., P.O. Box 130, Pedricktown 08067
Pres.—William Ferrell, Jr., 2 emp., *Distributor of home heating oil* ............ (856) 299-0500
Hess Corp., 123 Derousse Ave., Pennsauken 08110
Terminal Supt.—Brian Clark, 17 emp., *Distributor of petroleum, including* ............ (856) 663-5111
Lorco Petroleum Services, 450 S. Front St., Elizabeth 07202
Pres.—John Lionetti, 150 emp., *Wholesaler of recycled residual & used* ............ (908) 820-8800
Muenz Engineered Sales Co., 21 Chatham Rd., Summit 07901
CEO—Jeff O'Sullivan, 16 emp., *Distributor of abrasives, cutting &* ............ (908) 273-6755
Nustar Energy L. P., 7 N. Delaware St., Paulsboro 08066
Terminal Mgr.—Russel Wright, 6 emp., *Distributor of gasoline, crude oil,* ............ (856) 224-8903
Praxair, Inc., 554 Shell Rd., Penns Grove 08069
Ex. V-P.—Paul Bilek, 10 emp., *Distributor of propane & oxygen gases* ............ (856) 299-3500
Propane Power Corporation, a Div. of Suburban Propane, 915 Delancy St., Newark 07105
Manager—Tom Raulinavich, 40 emp., *Distributor of propane gas* ............ (973) 589-3030
Sonneborn, LLC, 600 Parsippany Rd., Ste. 100, Parsippany 07054
CEO—Paul Raymond, 12 emp., *Company headquarters & manufacturer* ............ (201) 760-2940
SOS Gases, Inc., 1100 Harrison Ave., Kearny 07032
Pres.—Steve Defillipps, Sr., 23 emp., *Distributor of industrial & specialty* ............ (201) 998-7800
Stevens Industries, Inc., 39 Avenue C, P.O. Box 8, Bayonne 07002
Pres.—William Rubenstein, 15 emp., *Distributor of lubricants, corrosion* ............ (201) 437-6500
Suburban Propane Partners, L.P. (H Q), 240 Route 10 W., P.O. Box 206, Whippany 07981
CEO—Michael Dunn, 300 emp., *Company headquarters; distributor of* ............ (973) 887-5300
Supreme Energy, Inc., 532 Freeman St., Orange 07050
Pres.—Deborah Fineman, 100 emp., *Distributor of heating oil for commercial* ............ (973) 678-1800
Taylor Oil Co., Inc., 77 2nd St., P.O. Box 974, Somerville 08876
Pres.—Rick Workman, 20 emp., *Corporate headquarters & distributor* ............ (908) 725-7737
TC Petroleum, 575 Prospect St., Ste. 264, Lakewood 08701
Pres.—Dennis Schurgin, 5 emp., *Wholesaler of lubricants* ............ (732) 367-2116

## 5181 Beer & ale

Allied Beverage Group, LLC, 600 Washington Ave., P.O. Box 838, Carlstadt 07072
Co-Chrm.—Eric M. Perlmutter, 500 emp., *Company headquarters & distributor* ............ (201) 842-6200
Federal Wine & Liquor Co., 1 Central Ave., Mount Laurel 08054
Opers. Mgr.—John Longa, 150 emp., *Distributor of wine, liquor & beer* ............ (856) 234-3200
High Grade Beverage, 891 Georges Rd., Monmouth Junction 08852
Corp. V-P.—Guy Battaglia, 150 emp., *Company headquarters & distributor* ............ (732) 821-7600
High Grade Beverage, 86 Canfield Ave., Randolph 07869
Corp. V-P.—George Policastro, 100 emp., *Distributor of beverages, including* ............ (973) 927-1400
Shore Point Distributing Co., 100 Shore Point Dr., Freehold 07728
Pres.—James Annarella, 210 emp., *Distributor of beer* ............ (732) 308-3334

## 5182 Wine & distilled alcoholic beverages

Aidil Wines & Liquors, 574 Ferry St., Newark 07105
GM—Pedro Carvalho, 15 emp., *Distributor of wine* ............ (973) 712-0950
Allied Beverage Group, LLC, 600 Washington Ave., P.O. Box 838, Carlstadt 07072
Co-Chrm.—Eric M. Perlmutter, 500 emp., *Company headquarters & distributor* ............ (201) 842-6200
Allied Beverage Group, LLC, 901 Plesant Valley Ave., P.O. Box 5090, Mount Laurel 08054
V-P.—Ed Feldman, 50 emp., *Wholesaler of wine* ............ (856) 234-4111
American Estates Wines, Inc., 19 Hillside Ave., Summit 07901
Pres.—George Galey, 7 emp., *Distributor of wines* ............ (908) 273-5060
Crown Jewel Importers & Marketing Corp., 140 Sylvan Ave., Ste. 109, Englewood Cliffs 07632
★ Pres.—Zach Klein, 5 emp., *Distributor of wines* ............ (201) 461-3900
Dozortsev & Sons Enterprises, 411-415 John St., Elizabeth 07202
Owner—Eugene Dozortsev, 6 emp., *Distributor of imported & exported* ............ (908) 353-1234
Federal Wine & Liquor Co., 56 Hackensack Ave., P.O. Box 519, Kearny 07032
Pres.—Richard Leventhal, 40 emp., *Company headquarters & distributor* ............ (973) 624-6444
Federal Wine & Liquor Co., 1 Central Ave., Mount Laurel 08054
Opers. Mgr.—John Longa, 150 emp., *Distributor of wine, liquor & beer* ............ (856) 234-3200
Laird & Co., Inc., 1 Laird Rd., Eatontown 07724
Pres.—Larrie Laird, 40 emp., *Corporate headquarters & manufacturer* ............ (732) 542-0312
Opici Winery, Inc., 25 DeBoer Dr., Glen Rock 07452
Pres.—Dina Opici, 120 emp., *Corporate headquarters & distributor* ............ (201) 689-1200
R & R Marketing, LLC, 2900 E. State Street Ext., Trenton 08619
GM—Jerry DeAngelo, 100 emp., *Distributor of wine & liquors* ............ (609) 587-6103
R & R Marketing, LLC, 10 Patton Dr., West Caldwell 07006
Pres.—Jon Maslin, 200 emp., *Company headquarters & distributor* ............ (973) 228-5100
Winebow, Inc., 75 Chestnut Ridge Rd., Ste. 1, Montvale 07645
Founder & Chrm.—Leonardo LoCascio, 100 emp., *Corporate headquarters & distributor* ...... (201) 445-0620

## 5191 Farm supplies

Growmark FS, LLC, 55 Silver Lake Rd., Bridgeton 08302
Plt. Mgr.—Rick Hatz, 15 emp., *Distributor of agricultural pesticides* ............ (856) 455-7688

## 5192 Books, periodicals & newspapers

Devon Trading Corp., 5 Fairfield Rd., Caldwell 07006
Pres.—Fran Orzech, 22 emp., *Distributor of religious items, including* ............ (973) 812-9190
Hudson News Distributors, LLC, 5903 W. Side Ave., North Bergen 07047
Corp. V-P., IS—David Blish, 645 emp., *Company headquarters & distributor* ............ (201) 867-3600
Mundo Esoterico dist inc, 6207 Madison St., West New York 07093
GM—Beder Marina, 1 emp., *Wholesaler of religious goods, including* ............ (201) 766-4084

## 5193 Flower, nursery stock & florists' supplies

Brick Wholesale Flower Market, 570 Mantoloking Rd., Brick 08723
Pres., GM—Nancy Petrellese, 5 emp., *Distributor of fresh-cut flowers &* ............ (732) 477-6765
Creative Displays & Designs, Inc., 349 Essex Rd., Neptune 07753
Pres.—Danette Bussey, 22 emp., *Wholesaler of home dÉcor products,* ............ (732) 918-8010
Delaware Valley Wholesale Florist, Inc., 520 Mantua Blvd., Sewell 08080
Chrm.—John R. Wilkins, 50 emp., *Corporate headquarters & wholesaler* ............ (856) 468-7000
Kube-Pak Corp., 194 Route 526, Allentown 08501
Pres.—William Swanekamp, 110 emp., *Wholesaler of greenhouse plants, including* ............ (609) 259-3114
Pennock Co., 7135 Colonial Ln., Pennsauken 08109
Pres.—Robert P. Billings, 60 emp., *Company headquarters & wholesaler of* ............ (215) 492-7900
Sunshine Bouquet Co., 3 Chris Ct., Ste. A, P.O. Box 892, Dayton 08810
Owner—John Simko, 50 emp., *Wholesaler of flowers & floral arrangements* ............ (732) 274-2900

## 5194 Tobacco & tobacco products

M & M Wholesale, 66 Market St., Saddle Brook 07663
Owner—Hema Papaiya, 13 emp., *Wholesaler of tobacco products* ............ (201) 368-0770
United Candy & Tobacco Co., 7408 Tonnelle Ave., North Bergen 07047
Pres.—Joseph Choi, 10 emp., *Wholesaler of cigarettes* ............ (201) 943-8675

Zucca, Inc., L. J., 760 S. Delsea Dr., P.O. Box 1447, Vineland 08362
Pres.—Louis Zucca, Jr., 70 emp., Corporate headquarters & wholesaler (856) 692-7425

### 5198 Paints, varnishes & supplies

BlackHawk Industrial, Atlantic Tool Systems Div., 170 5th Ave., Hawthorne 07506
GM—J. F. Montague, 8 emp., Wholesaler of pneumatic tools, abrasives (973) 238-0009
Brenntag Specialties, Inc., 1000 Coolidge St., South Plainfield 07080
Pres.—Steve Brauer, 50 emp., Divisional headquarters & wholesaler (908) 561-6100
FinishMaster, Inc., 700 Garfield Ave., Jersey City 07305
GM—Cliff White, 4 emp., Distributor of automotive paints & (201) 435-1555
HBC Home & Hardware, 324-A Half Acre Rd., Cranbury 08512
CEO—Donald C. Devine, 170 emp., Company headquarters & wholesaler of (609) 860-9990
Kemperle, Inc., Albert, 626 E. Elizabeth Ave., Linden 07036
Br. Mgr.—Terry Gardner, 20 emp., Wholesaler of automotive body shop (908) 925-6133
Kenseal Construction Products Corp., 799 Edwards Rd., Parsippany 07054
Cont.—Charles J. Meyers, 20 emp., Distributor of sealants, concrete admixtures (973) 287-5858
MarJam Supply Co., 615 W. Delilah Rd., Pleasantville 08232
Br. Mgr.—Steve Rios, 15 emp., Wholesaler of building materials, paint (609) 407-1234
Stevens Industries, Inc., 39 Avenue C, P.O. Box 8, Bayonne 07002
Pres.—William Rubenstein, 15 emp., Distributor of lubricants, corrosion (201) 437-6500

### 5199 Nondurable goods, nec

ABRAZIL, LLC, 1 Jacques Ave., Kendall Park 08824
Owner—Tony Chuang, 4 emp., Wholesaler of dietary supplements, (732) 658-5191
Accuratus Corporation, 35 Howard St., Phillipsburg 08865
Pres.—Raymond Tsao, 30 emp., Manufacturer of advanced technical (908) 213-7070
Acme International Enterprises, Inc., 400 Lyster Ave., Saddle Brook 07663
CEO—Fred Reffsin, 65 emp., Distributor of kitchen & household (973) 416-0400
Affordable Offset Printing, Inc., 809 Hylton Rd., Ste. 11, Pennsauken 08110
Pres.—Gary Coates, 4 emp., Offset & digital printing, electronic (856) 661-0722
Agfa Corp., 400 Heller Park Ct., Dayton 08810
CEO—Anthony P. Crupi, 100 emp., Corporate headquarters & distributor (973) 812-0400
Arctic Glacier, Inc., 2 Johnson Dr., Raritan 08869
Asst. Dist. Mgr.—Mike Janner, 8 emp., Distributor of cubed ice (908) 231-0100
Artique, Inc., P.O. Box 44, Midland Park 07432
GM—Jack Reeman, 12 emp., Wholesaler of handmade seasonal gift (201) 444-8989
Blackwell Assocs., Inc., 15 Kimberly Rd., East Brunswick 08816
GM, Opers. & Whse. Mgr.—John Johnson, 65 emp., Wholesaler of imported holiday decoration. (732) 238-8000
CDI Group, Inc., 1135 W. Elizabeth Ave., Linden 07036
CEO—Jordan Ruddy, 20 emp., Manufacturer of custom modular trade (908) 862-1493
Central Pet, 301 Island Rd., Mahwah 07430
Pres.—Neill Hines, 50 emp., Distributor of pet supplies (201) 529-5050
Childcare Supply Co. Inc., 77 Pension Rd., Ste. 13, Englishtown 07726
Sales Mgr.—Shari Schwartz, 10 emp., Distributor of child care items, including (732) 786-9888
Comfort Concepts, Inc., 501 Broad Ave., Ste. 7, Ridgefield 07657
Ptnr.—Robert Mass, 16 emp., Manufacturer & distributor of reusable (201) 941-6700
Dani Leather USA, Inc., 37 Ironia Rd., Ste. 2, Flanders 07836
Sales Mgr.—Mike Belluzzi, 5 emp., Distributor of Italian leather for (973) 598-0890
Devon Trading Corp., 5 Fairfield Rd., Caldwell 07006
Pres.—Fran Orzech, 22 emp., Distributor of religious items, including (973) 812-9190
Distinctive Promotions, Inc., 268 U.S. Highway 206, Ste. 404, Flanders 07836
Pres.—Lois Patrick, 10 emp., Distributor of advertising promotional (973) 584-6800
Dream On Me Industries, Inc., 125 Helen St., South Plainfield 07080
Pres.—Mark Severe, 40 emp., Manufacturer of baby mattresses & wholesaler (908) 791-0555
Elixens America, Inc., 1443 Pinewood St., Rahway 07065
Pres.—Adam Roman, 3 emp., Distributor of organic essential oils (732) 388-3555
Garden Oaks Garden Center, 1921 U.S. Highway 22, Bound Brook 08805
Owner—Madeline Wenz, 20 emp., Full-line distributor of outdoor, lawn (732) 356-7333
Geographia Map Co., Inc., 75 Moore St., Hackensack 07601
Pres.—Israel Polak, 15 emp., Publisher & distributor of maps (201) 488-4411
Grey Owl Indian Craft Sales Corp., 15 Meridian Rd., Ste. 5, Eatontown 07724
Pres.—Jim Feldman, 2 emp., Distributor of Native American crafts (732) 389-4626
Madison Line, The, 40 Commerce St., Springfield 07081
Pres., CEO—Sheamus O'Brien, 10 emp., Manufacturer & distributor of promotional (973) 379-1108
Monter Lite Co., Inc., 560 Lincoln Blvd., Ste. 2, Middlesex 08846
V-P.—Jerry Lin, 10 emp., Manufacturer & wholesaler of handmade (732) 748-1288
Mundo Esoterico dist inc, 6207 Madison St., West New York 07093
GM—Beder Marina, 1 emp., Wholesaler of religious goods, including (201) 766-4084
Peerless Umbrella Co., Inc., 427 Ferry St., Newark 07105
Pres.—Gene Moscowitz, 120 emp., Manufacturer & distributor of umbrellas (973) 578-4900
Rizzo Fine Arts Inc., Nicholas F., 32 Watchung Ave., Chatham 07928
Pres.—Nicholas F. Rizzo, 10 emp., Wholesaler of fine artwork, mirrors (973) 635-7278
Roma Moulding, Inc., 115 Northfield Ave., Edison 08837
Manager—Barry Zimmerman, 15 emp., Distributor of picture frame moulding (732) 346-0999
Royal Deluxe Accessories, LLC, 2563 Brunswick Ave., Bldg. O, Linden 07036
Pres.—Elliot Zeitoune, 18 emp., Wholesaler of costume jewelry, ladies' (908) 523-0550
Royce Leather, 501 Penhorn Ave., Ste. 9, Secaucus 07094
Owner—Kathy Bauer, 14 emp., Distributor of leather luggage, briefcases (201) 330-7720
S & R Sales, Inc., 1 Sandart Plz., Jackson 08527
Pres.—Stu Pancer, 12 emp., Distributor of sand & candle art & (732) 905-0278
Scaasis Originals, Inc./Oceanic Trading Co., 1006 11th Ave., Neptune 07753
CEO—Neil Saada, 20 emp., Wholesaler of souvenirs, novelties (732) 775-7474
South Jersey Wiping Cloth, 314 Rosewood Ave., Vineland 08360
Owner—Dennis Koons, 1 emp., Distributor of wiping cloths (856) 696-0129
Southern Ocean Marine Sportswear, 79 S. Main St., Ste. 2, Barnegat 08005
Owner—Sherry Haferbier, 4 emp., Manufacturer of embroidered & screen-printed (609) 698-8868
Stanley Foam Rubber Corp., 14 Orchard St., Wallington 07057
Pres.—Burt Alkes, 7 emp., Distributor of polyurethane foam, upholstery (973) 778-1660
Tees & Novelties, Inc., P.O. Box 2059, Garfield 07026
Pres.—Sandy Ehrlich, 6 emp., Distributor of embroidered patches (973) 574-7591
Tube Light Co., Inc. (H Q), 300 Park St., Moonachie 07074
Pres.—Leon Jaffe, 180 emp., Corporate headquarters; distributor (201) 641-6660
William Usdan & Sons LLC, 140 Little St., Belleville 07109
Pres.—Simon Markman, 5 emp., Paper & fabric converting & distributor (973) 844-9988

## 73 BUSINESS SERVICES

### 7372 Prepackaged software

A3 Technology, Inc., 311 S. New York Rd., Redding Office Pk., Ste. 36, Absecon 08205
Pres., CEO—Karen Vargas, 90 emp., Computer software development & integrated (609) 652-7933
Abacus Systems, Inc., 10 County Road 639, Sussex 07461
Pres.—David Dipietro, 3 emp., Computer software development (973) 875-9900
Acsis, Inc., 9 E. Stow Rd., Ste. D, Marlton 08053
CEO—Jeremy Coote, 60 emp., Cloud-based software development for (856) 673-3000
Advanced Technology Corp., 79 N. Franklin Tpke., Ste. 103, Ramsey 07446
Pres.—Joseph Bove, 7 emp., Software development for the veterinary (201) 934-7127
Aergo Solutions, Inc., 33 Wood Ave. S., 5th Fl., Iselin 08830
Pres.—Michael Fetteducati, 12 emp., Software development (732) 321-1500
Alanda Software, 391 George St., New Brunswick 08901
Founder & Pres.—Dean Rossi, 20 emp., Software development (201) 386-2007
Albridge Solutions, Inc., 1009 Lenox Dr., Bldg. 4, Ste. 204, Lawrenceville 08648
CEO—John Brett, 230 emp., Computer network systems integration (609) 620-5800
ALK Technologies, Inc., 457 N. Harrison St., Princeton 08540
CTO—Mike Bodden, 125 emp., Transportation & logistics software (609) 683-0220
Altech Star, Inc., 4365 U.S. Highway 1, Ste. 205, Princeton 08540
Dir., Opers.—Jeya Lell, 35 emp., Web-enterprise software development (609) 520-9000
Altibase, Inc., 1 Bridge Plz. N., Fort Lee 07024
★ CEO—Chris Chung, 10 emp., Downloable in-memory database management (888) 837-7333
American Ink Jet Systems, Inc., 34 Chestnut St., Emerson 07630
Pres.—Stephen Saltman, 5 emp., Manufacturer of inkjet inks, bulk ink (201) 263-9177
Amerinex Applied Imaging, Inc., P.O. Box 6473, Monroe Township 08831
Pres.—Richard Kretschmann, 8 emp., Two dimensional & three dimesional (609) 944-8855
API Technologies Corp., 120 Corporate Blvd., South Plainfield 07080
Dir., Opers.—Peter Paulson, 20 emp., Remote device administration products (908) 546-3900
AS Software, Inc., 560 Sylvan Ave., Ste. 2052, Englewood Cliffs 07632
Pres.—Ari Sandman, 21 emp., Medical ultrasound reporting & image (201) 541-1900
Aumtech, Inc., 710 Old Bridge Tpke., East Brunswick 08816
Ex. V-P., COO—Tom Porter, 30 emp., Software development, including VoiceXml (732) 254-1875
AuthentiDate Holding Corp., 300 Connell Dr., 5th Fl., Berkeley Heights 07922
Pres., CEO—O'Connell Benjamin, 32 emp., Healthcare IT & SaaS workflow software (908) 787-1700
Automation & Control, Inc., 1491 Lancer Dr., Moorestown 08057
Pres.—Ron Iannacone, 30 emp., Custom industrial automation control (856) 234-2300
Axletree Solutions, Inc., 2 King Arthur Ct., Lakeside W., Ste. A-1, North Brunswick 08902
Pres.—Mohan Murali, 15 emp., Bank communication & treasury automation (732) 296-0001
AXS-ONE, Inc., 301 Route 17, Ste. 11, Rutherford 07070
Pres., CEO—William Lyons, 150 emp., Email archiving software development (201) 935-3400
Aztec Software Assoc., Inc., 51 Commerce St., 2nd Fl., Springfield 07081
CEO—Jonathan Blitt, 13 emp., Basic skills remediation, academic, (973) 258-0011
BIO-key International, Inc. (H Q), 3349 Highway 138, Bldg. A, Ste.E, Wall 07719
Pres., CEO—Michael W. DePasquale, 10 emp., Corporate headquarters; fingerprint-based (732) 359-1100
BlackStratus, 1551 S. Washington Ave., Ste. 401, Piscataway 08854
Pres., CEO—Dale Cline, 70 emp., Security information management software (732) 393-6000
Blue Planet Solutions, Inc., 116 Millburn Ave., Ste.108, Millburn 07041
Co-Pres.—Avinash Kulkarni, 30 emp., IT recruiting & consulting software (973) 597-4555
Boston Technologies, Inc., 610 E. Landis Ave., Vineland 08360
Pres.—David E. Boston, 5 emp., Behavioral healthcare software development (856) 692-4958
Burgiss Group, LLC, The, 111 River St., Ste. 10, Hoboken 07030
Pres.—James M. Kocis, 80 emp., Company headquarters & private equity (201) 427-9600
Business Power, Inc., 39 Hunt Ave., Ste. C, Stratford 08084
Pres., CEO—Ken Baysal, 9 emp., Business management software development (856) 783-7390
Buyers Laboratory LLC, 20 Railroad Ave., Hackensack 07601
CEO—Gerry Stoia, 40 emp., Newsletter & test report publishing (201) 488-0404
CADCAM-E.Com, Inc., 2115 Linwood Ave., Ste. 313, Fort Lee 07024
CEO—Kumar Rajan, 250 emp., CAD & MCAD engineering platform & file (201) 503-1881
CAMO Software, 1 Woodbridge Ctr., Ste. 319, Woodbridge 07095
Accts. Mgr.—John Chartier, 4 emp., Multivariate analysis software development (732) 726-9200
Case Medical, Inc., 19 Empire Blvd., South Hackensack 07606
CEO—Marcia A. Frieze, 60 emp., Medical sterilization trays & cases (201) 313-1999
CAST, Inc. (H Q), 11 Stonewall Ct., Woodcliff Lake 07677
Pres.—Hal Barbour, 50 emp., Corporate headquarters; semiconductor (201) 391-8300
Chemspeed, Inc., 113 N. Center Dr., North Brunswick 08902
★ GM—Mark Meyers, 10 emp., Automated workflow application software (732) 329-1225
Chenoa Information Service, Inc., 10 Parsonage Rd., Ste. 312, Edison 08837
V-P.—Niku Trivedi, 20 emp., Financial service & healthcare forms (732) 549-6800
coAction, 50 Kildee Rd., Belle Mead 08502
Pres.—Jagdish Talreja, 20 emp., Invoicing, collections & customer risk (888) 682-3050
Cognizant Technology Solutions, 500 Frank W. Burr Blvd., Teaneck 07666
Vice Chrm.—Lakshmi Narayanan, 250 emp., Company headquarters & marketing & (201) 801-0233
CommVault Systems, Inc., 2 Crescrent Pl., P.O. Box 900, Oceanport 07757
Pres., CEO—N. Robert Hammer, 800 emp., Data & information management software (732) 870-4000
Compliance Educational Systems, Inc., P.O. Box 669, Marlton 08053
Pres.—Christine Castile, 5 emp., Regular & special education management (856) 793-0137
Computer Square, Inc., 330 Mac Ln., Keasbey 08832
★ Pres., CEO—Chen C. Yeh, 33 emp., Web-based e-government software development (732) 346-0200
Cover-All Technologies, Inc., 412 Mount Kemble Ave., Ste. 110-C, Morristown 07960
Pres., CEO—Manishy Shah, 50 emp., Policy administration, data capture (973) 461-5200
Data Communique, Inc., 65 Challenger Rd., 4th Fl., Ridgefield Park 07660
CEO—Richard Plotka, 45 emp., Content management & document workflow (201) 508-6000
Datamatics Management Services, Inc., 330 New Brunswick Ave., Fords 08863
Chrm.—Norman C. Heinle, Jr., 20 emp., Time & attendance, employee tracking (732) 738-9600
Delphus, Inc., 152 Speedwell Ave., Morristown 07960
Owner & Pres.—Hans Levenbach, 8 emp., Demand forecasting & order replenishment (973) 267-9269
Desktop Alert, Inc., 346 Main St., Chatham 07928
Founder & Chief R & D Officer—Howard Ryan, 5 emp., IP-based emergency notication (973) 727-0066
Dillistone Systems, Inc., 50 Harrison St., Ste. 201-A, Hoboken 07030
★ Pres.—Jason Starr, 10 emp., Prepackaged software development (201) 653-0013
Direct Computer Resources, Inc., 120 Birch Rd., Franklin Lakes 07417
Pres., CEO—Joe Buonomo, 3 emp., Prepackaged software for data masking (201) 848-0018
Drawbase Software, 1099 Wall St. W., Ste. 269, Lyndhurst 07071
Pres., CEO—Evan Kontos, 10 emp., Integrated workplace management software (973) 927-6814
DVTel, Inc., 65 Challenger Rd., Ste. 2, Ridgefield Park 07660
Pres., CEO—Yoav Stern, 40 emp., IP-based physical security system development (201) 368-9700
ec2 Software Solutions, 400 Apgar Dr., Ste. I, Somerset 08873
CEO—Scott Nelson, 50 emp., Nuclear medicine & radiopharmacy management (732) 356-0070
Edmunds & Assocs., 301-A Tilton Rd., Northfield 08225
Pres.—Bob Edmunds, 30 emp., Financial, accounting & billing software (609) 645-7333
Electronic Measuring Devices, Inc., 15 Mill Rd., Flanders 07836
COO—Klaus Ulbrich, 1 emp., Analog coordinate measuring systems (973) 691-4755
Elevate HR, Inc., 1055 Parsippany Blvd., Ste. 511, Parsippany 07054
★ Pres.—David M. Erickson, 20 emp., Human capital management (HCM) software (973) 917-3230
Ellkay, LLC, 259 Seddle Ln., 3rd Fl., Teaneck 07666
Pres.—Kamao Patel, 11 emp., Software development (201) 791-0606
Empirical Labs, Inc., 41 N. Beverwyck Rd., Lake Hiawatha 07034
Pres.—David Derr, 7 emp., Professional audio processing equipment (973) 541-9446



★ Indicates new listing this edition.

Ericsson, Inc., 1 Ericsson Dr., Piscataway 08854
Sr. Prod. Mgr.—Zach Gilstein, 2000 emp., *Software-defined networking (SDN) software* ........ (732) 699-2000
Evex Global, 857 State Rd., Princeton 08540
Pres.—Claudio Tarquinio, 15 emp., *Scientific instrumentation for nanotechnology* .......... (408) 907-2994
EXP, Inc., 285 Davidson Ave., Somerset 08873
Pres.—Sreedhar Velicheti, 3 emp., *Environment, health & safety (QEHS)* .......... (732) 626-3700
eZCom Software, Inc., 25 Rockwood Pl., Ste. 420, Englewood 07631
CEO—Carol Weidner, 28 emp., *EDI software development for manufacturers* .......... (201) 883-1900
FemtoTek, Inc., 865 Lower Ferry Rd., Ste. B-9, Ewing 08628
Pres.—David Edwards, 5 emp., *High-performance test & instrumentation* .......... (609) 406-9680
Folded Structures Co., LLC, 1142-A Old York Rd., Ringoes 08551
Pres.—Daniel Kling, 3 emp., *Mathematical folding software development* .......... (908) 237-1955
General Dynamics Advanced Information Systems, 7-9 Vreeland Rd., Florham Park 07932
Br. Mgr.—John Incera, 25 emp., *Information systems for the aerospace* .......... (973) 514-4000
GL Consulting, Inc., 1000 Plaza Three, Jersey City 07311
Sr. V-P.—Roger Elwell, 45 emp., *General ledger database software development* .......... (201) 451-9121
Global Business Dimensions Inc., 220 W. Parkway, Ste. 8, Pompton Plains 07444
Pres., CEO—Sanjay Prasad, 25 emp., *Manufacturer & distributor of personal* .......... (973) 831-5866
Glowpoint, Inc., 430 Mountain Ave., Ste. 301, Murray Hill 07974
Pres., CEO—Joe Laezza, 80 emp., *Cloud-managed SaaS software development* .......... (973) 855-3411
GrayHair Software, Inc., 124 Gaither Dr., Ste. 160, Mount Laurel 08054
Pres.—Cameron Bellamy, 35 emp., *Direct mail production, preparation* .......... (856) 727-9372
Grumium Labs, 4400 U.S. 9, Ste. 1000, Freehold 07728
Pres.—Regina Chitto, 28 emp., *Custom software development for the* .......... (732) 562-0001
GTBM, 351 Paterson Ave., East Rutherford 07073
CEO—Richard Picolli, 21 emp., *Real-time database search & communications* .......... (201) 935-5090
Halberd Match Corp., 1230 Parkway Ave., Ste. 306, Trenton 08628
CEO—Michael Shutt, 6 emp., *Advanced image recognition & acquisition* .......... (609) 882-7000
Health Care Software, Inc., 1350 Campus Pkwy., Neptune 07753
Pres.—Tom Fahey, 50 emp., *Computer software development & system* .......... (732) 938-5600
HealthTronics, Inc., 354 Eisenhower Pkwy., Ste. 2150, Livingston 07039
Ex. V-P., Sales & Mktg.—Lawrence G. Drappi, 22 emp., *Interoperable EHR software development* (973) 994-3220
High Speed Video, 19 Spear Rd., Ste. 104, Ramsey 07446
CEO—Michael Maresca, 8 emp., *Enterprise-grade video communications* .......... (201) 327-6801
Hudson Robotics, Inc., 10 Stern Ave., Springfield 07081
Pres.—Philip Farrelly, 10 emp., *Life science research laboratory robots* .......... (973) 376-7400
HumanConcepts, 1031 Route 22, Ste. 303, Bridgewater 08807
Off. Mgr.—Patricia Wilder, 40 emp., *Software development* .......... (908) 231-0204
I.D. Systems, Inc., 123 Tice Blvd., Ste. 101, Woodcliff Lake 07677
Chrm., Pres. & CEO—Kenneth S. Ehrman, 100 emp., *Wireless systems integration & software* (201) 996-9000
INFINITT North America, Inc., 755 Memorial Pkwy., Ste. 304, Phillipsburg 08865
Pres., CEO—David Smarro, 45 emp., *Medical imaging visualization & management* .......... (908) 387-6960
INFOLynx, Inc., 500 Frank W. Burr Blvd., Ste. 14, Teaneck 07666
Pres.—Raymond Zoltowski, 5 emp., *Financial transaction data software* .......... (201) 569-9085
Informatica Corp., 309 Fellowship Rd., Mount Laurel 08054
GM—Scott Seifried, 15 emp., *Data integration software development* .......... (856) 642-4080
Infragistics, Inc., 2 Commerce Dr., Cranbury 08512
Pres., CEO—Dean Guida, 150 emp., *Digital presentation software development* .......... (609) 448-2000
Innovative Software Solutions, Inc. (H Q), 3000 S. Lenola Rd., Maple Shade 08052
Ptnr.—Steve Webb, 90 emp., *Corporate headquarters; software development* .......... (856) 910-9190
Insurance Services Office, Inc., 545 Washington Blvd., Jersey City 07310
Chrm.—Frank J. Coyne, 1200 emp., *Risk evaluation & management software* .......... (201) 469-2000
Integrated Business Systems, Inc., 999 Riverview Dr., Ste. 280, Totowa 07512
Pres.—Michael Mullin, 25 emp., *Property management & accounting software* .......... (973) 575-4950
Integrated Media Management, LLC, 330 Dalziel Rd., Linden 07036
Pres.—Charles Klein, 60 emp., *Document management software development* .......... (908) 862-6600
Intellect Technologies, Inc., 4301 U.S. Highway 1, Ste. 120, Monmouth Junction 08852
★ Dir., Global Sales—John LeDuc, 20 emp., *Prepackaged software development* .......... (609) 454-3170
Intelligent Security Systems, 1480 U.S. Highway 9 N., Ste. 202, Woodbridge 07095
CFO—Boris Kalk, 180 emp., *Analytic software development & security* .......... (732) 855-1111
Intelligrated, 265 Davidson Ave., Ste. 219, Somerset 08873
V-P., Opers., Eastern Reg.—Eric Palotas, 34 emp., *Conveyors, sortation, automated storage*. (732) 302-2590
Ipacesetters, 135 Chestnut Ridge Rd., Ste. 2, Montvale 07645
Pres., CEO—Tim Searcy, 25 emp., *Marketing & subscription fulfillment* .......... (201) 391-1500
IPKeys Technologies, 1 Industrial Way W., Ste. E-1, Eatontown 07724
Pres.—Mark Pappas, 117 emp., *Computer & network systems integration* .......... (732) 389-4702
iSpeech, 211 Warren St., Newark 07103
Founder & CEO—Heath Ahrens, 30 emp., *Speech recognition software development* .......... (917) 338-7723
Jersey Cow Software Co., Inc., 3031 State Route 27, Ste. A, Franklin Park 08823
Pres.—Bob Wickenden, 4 emp., *Educational software development* .......... (732) 422-0101
Judy Lynn Software, Inc., 278 Dunhams Corner Rd., P.O. Box 373, East Brunswick 08816
Pres.—Elliot Pludwinski, 2 emp., *Downloadable switch software development* .......... (732) 390-8845
K & A Industries, Inc., 51 Cragwood Rd., Ste. 204, South Plainfield 07080
Pres.—George Keelty, 8 emp., *Identification badges, identity management* .......... (908) 226-7000
Knorr Assocs., Inc., 10 Park Pl., P.O. Box 400, Butler 07405
Pres.—Norman Dotti, 10 emp., *Environmental & health & safety management* .......... (973) 492-8500
L. S. Software Systems, Inc., 419 12th St., Lakewood 08701
Pres.—Adele Yoffe, 6 emp., *Jewelry pricing calculation & inventory* .......... (732) 367-7164
LabVantage Solutions, Inc., 265 Davidson Ave., Somerset 08873
Pres.—Peter Bailey, 50 emp., *Laboratory information management software* .......... (908) 707-4100
Lagniappe Health Acquisition Co., 34 Maple Ave., Ste. 102, P.O. Box 727, Pine Brook 07058
Qual. Assur. Analyst—Joe Pinto, 47 emp., *Pharmacy management software development* .... (973) 256-7633
Lane Bond Traders, 27 Cedar Lake Rd., Denville 07834
Owner—William Peer, 2 emp., *Bond calculating devices & trading* .......... (973) 586-2720
Library Automation Technologies, 2 E. Atlantic Ave., Somerdale 08083
CEO—Oleg Boyarsky, 15 emp., *Library patron self-check-in & self-checkout* .......... (856) 566-4121
Life Systems, Inc., 75 E. Main St., Rockaway 07866
Pres.—Paul Bindell, 4 emp., *Electronic health record (EHR) systems* .......... (973) 625-3716
LOG-NET, Inc., 230 Half Mile Rd., 3rd Fl., Red Bank 07701
Pres., CEO—John Motley, 40 emp., *Supply chain software development* .......... (732) 758-6800
Lumeta Corporation, 300 Atrium Dr., Ste. 302, Somerset 08873
★ CEO—Pat Donnellan, 25 emp., *SaaS software development* .......... (732) 357-3500
Macrosoft, Inc., 2 Sylvan Way, Parsippany 07054
CEO—Ronald Mueller, 120 emp., *Software development* .......... (973) 889-0500
Maestro Technolgies, Inc., 510 Thornall St., Ste. 375, Edison 08837
Mng. Dir.—Kamal S. Bathla, 54 emp., *Software development & computer & network* .......... (908) 458-8600
Magestic Systems, Inc., 205 Fairview Ave., Westwood 07675
Dir., Bus. Dev.—Massimiliano Moruzzi, 15 emp., *Nesting software development for CNC* ...... (201) 263-0090
Magnum Technologies, Inc., 95 Mount Bethel Rd., Warren 07059
Pres.—Raj Subramanian, 60 emp., *Enterprise content managment & planning* .......... (908) 546-7950
Marketing Advertising Promotions, Inc., 4 Edison Pl., Fairfield 07004
Pres.—John Litwinka, 15 emp., *Medical coding & billing software development* .......... (973) 575-5656

Markov Processes International, LLC, 25 Deforest Ave., Ste. 102, Summit 07901
Chrm.—Michael Markov, 36 emp., *Financial research & reporting software* .......... (908) 608-1558
Masstar, 18 Heritage Rd., Eatontown 07724
Owner—Charles Massa, 2 emp., *Computer network systems integration* .......... (732) 542-8004
Med A-Z.Net, LLC, 37 Station Dr., Ste. 1-E, Princeton Junction 08550
CIO—Vasu S. Iyengar, 9 emp., *Healthcare software development* .......... (609) 716-6991
MentisSoft, Inc., 347 Plainfield Ave., Ste. 104, Edison 08817
V-P.—Jeevesh Murthy, 3 emp., *Software development for retail, healthcare* .......... (732) 568-4715
MICROS Retail Systems, Inc., 1500 Harbor Blvd., Ste. 2, Weehawken 07086
Pres.—Lubodar Olesnycky, 108 emp., *Point-of-sale software development* .......... (201) 866-1000
Millennium Systems International, 28 Eastmans Rd., Parsippany 07054
Founder & CEO—John Harms, 60 emp., *Beauty industry software development* .......... (973) 402-9500
Moofwd, Inc., 103 Carnegie Ctr., Ste. 209, Princeton 08540
Founder & Chrm.—Sunil Mehta, 10 emp., *Mobile application software development* .......... (855) 266-6393
Multiforce Systems Corp., 101 Wall St., Princeton 08540
V-P., Sales—Keith Griesinger, 19 emp., *Automated fuel management systems that* .......... (609) 683-4242
Nandvarik Systems, 190 Lewis St., Rahway 07065
COO—R. Nandvarik, 3 emp., *Sales & marketing software development* .......... (732) 306-9999
Ness Technologies, Inc., 300 Frank W. Burr Blvd., Teaneck 07666
Dir., Mktg.—Douglas Mow, 50 emp., *Life science & pharmaceuticals software* .......... (201) 488-7222
Netcom Systems, Inc., 200 Metroplex Dr., Edison 08817
Pres.—Niten Ved, 20 emp., *Software development* .......... (732) 393-6100
Netquest Corp., 523 Fellowship Rd., Ste. 205, Mount Laurel 08054
CEO—Jesse Price, 20 emp., *High speed broadband optical & copper* .......... (856) 866-0505
NetWrix Corp., 12 N. State Route 17, Ste. 104, Paramus 07652
Pres., CEO—Michael Fimin, 12 emp., *Change reporting, auditing & identity* .......... (201) 490-8840
Niksun, Inc., 100 Nassau Park Blvd., 3rd Fl., Princeton 08540
CEO—Parag Pruthi, 100 emp., *Network monitoring software development* .......... (609) 936-9999
Nxlevel Solutions, 57 Hamilton Ave., Ste. 303, Hopewell 08525
Pres.—Robert Christensen, 15 emp., *E-learning software development* .......... (609) 466-2828
Objectif Lune, LLC, 300 Broadacres Dr., 4th Fl., Bloomfield 07003
Pres.—Howard Silverstein, 15 emp., *Transactional document & business form* .......... (973) 780-0100
Oli Systems, Inc., 240 Cedar Knolls Rd., Ste. 301, Cedar Knolls 07927
CEO—Marshall Rafal, 20 emp., *Software development* .......... (973) 539-4996
OmniComm Systems, Inc., 1100 Cornwall Rd., Ste. 111, Monmouth Junction 08852
Ex. V-P., Opers. & Svcs.—Ken Light, 20 emp., *eClinical software development for* .......... (732) 960-2820
One Source Solutions, 3 industrial Ct., Ste. 3, Freehold 07728
Hum. Res. & IT Mgr.—Timothy O'Handley, 12 emp., *Point-of-sale, inventory control &* .......... (732) 536-0702
OnPATH Technologies, 100 Mount Holly Bypass, Lumberton 08048
Founder—Peter Dougherty, 90 emp., *Data communications hardware & software* .......... (609) 518-4100
Oracle Corp., 330 Fellowship Rd., Ste. 100, Mount Laurel 08054
Facility Mgr.—Scott Goldberg, 20 emp., *Software development* .......... (856) 359-2999
Palayekar Cos., Inc., 101 Interchange Plz., Ste. 105, Cranbury 08512
Pres.—Supriya Palayekar, 49 emp., *Software consulting & development* .......... (609) 426-0564
Pegasystems, Inc., 111 Town Square Pl., Jersey City 07310
Pres., CEO—James Hemmer, 30 emp., *Mobile platform software development* .......... (201) 239-2300
Princeton Payment Solutions, 501 Forrestal Rd., Ste. 324, Princeton 08540
CEO—Kevin M. McGuire, 20 emp., *Credit card payment processing & encryption* .......... (609) 919-0700
Purchasingnet, Inc., 125 Half Mile Rd., Red Bank 07701
Pres., CEO—Tim McEneny, 40 emp., *Software development* .......... (732) 212-1500
QAD, Inc., 10000 Midlantic Dr., Ste. 100 W., Mount Laurel 08054
Hum. Res. Bus. Ptnr.—Stephanie Derman, 140 emp., *Warehouse management system software* (856) 273-1717
QED Financial Systems, Inc., 10000 Sagemore Dr., Ste. 10201, Marlton 08053
★ CEO—Joseph Potesta, 30 emp., *Prepackaged software development* .......... (856) 797-1200
Quality Attributes Software, 1 Pelican Dr., Ste. 6, Bayville 08721
Ex. V-P.—Ken Echevarria, 8 emp., *Facility data management software development* .......... (732) 504-2200
Quality Software Systems, Inc., 80 Cottontail Ln., Ste. 105, Somerset 08873
Pres.—Edward Troianello, 40 emp., *Warehouse & transportation management* .......... (732) 805-0400
Quest Diagnostics (H Q), 3 Giralda Farms, Madison 07940
Non-Exec. Chrm.—Daniel C. Stanzione, 300 emp., *Company headquarters; healthcare medical* (973) 520-2700
R T I, Inc., 401 Hasbrouck Blvd., Oradell 07649
Owner & Pres.—Richard Tashjian, 10 emp., *Computers, software development & radiation* ... (201) 261-5852
Ramco Systems Corp., 3150 U.S. Highway 1, Ste. 130, Lawrence Township 08648
CEO—Virender Agarwal, 30 emp., *Software development & implementation* .......... (609) 620-4871
Raritan Computer, Inc., 400 Cottontail Ln., Somerset 08873
Chrm., CEO—Ching-I Hsu, 150 emp., *Data center infrastructure management* .......... (732) 764-8886
Red Oak Software, Inc., 115 U.S. Highway 46, Ste. F-1000, Mountain Lakes 07046
Pres., CEO—George Cummings, 5 emp., *Enterprise software development* .......... (973) 316-6064
Relational Architects, 33 Newark St., Ste. 3-A, Hoboken 07030
Mng. Dir.—Max Gartner, 30 emp., *Software development* .......... (201) 420-0400
Revelation Technologies, Inc., 99 Kinderkamack Rd., Ste. 109, Westwood 07675
Pres.—Michael Ruane, 17 emp., *Software development & office automation* .......... (201) 594-1422
RightAnswers, Inc., 333 Thornall St., Ste. 703, Edison 08837
Pres., CEO—Jeff Weinstein, 50 emp., *Software development* .......... (732) 396-9010
Robertson Piper Software Group, Inc. (H Q), 1500 Cardinal Dr., Chatham 07928
CEO—Doug Robertson, *Holding company headquarters; pharmacy* .......... (973) 435-3640
R-Squared Services & Solutions, Inc., 12 Dean Ct., Princeton Junction 08550
CEO—Michael D. Bell, 70 emp., *Compliance software development for* .......... (866) 522-8558
SaaShr, 3040 U.S. Highway 22, Ste. 200, Somerville 08876
Dir., Prod. Mgmt.—Chad Brennaman, 50 emp., *Workforce management SaaS software* ....... (908) 722-9952
SAI Global, Inc., 101 Morgan Ln., Ste. 301, Plainsboro 08536
Pres.—Tim Whipple, 75 emp., *Corporate headquarters & compliance* .......... (609) 955-5100
Sawhney Systems, Inc., 777 Alexander Rd., Ste. 204, Princeton 08540
CEO—Jai Sawhney, 10 emp., *Personal financial planning software* .......... (609) 987-5000
Simtronics Corp., 50 Birch Ave., Ste. 100, P.O. Box 38, Little Silver 07739
Pres.—Thomas Judge, 25 emp., *Prepackaged software development, including* .......... (732) 747-0322
SiMX Corp., 196 Princeton-Hightstown Rd., Bldg. 2-A, Princeton Junction 08550
Pres.—Vladimir Bernstein, 6 emp., *Data extraction & conversion software* .......... (609) 750-9345
Skila, A Sela2 Co., 201 Littleton Rd., 2nd Fl., Morris Plains 07950
CEO—Kilian Weiss, 25 emp., *Pharmaceutical software development* .......... (973) 889-1300
Slingo, Inc., 411 Hackensack Ave., 8th Fl., Hackensack 07601
Founder—Sal Faloiglia, 18 emp., *Online casual game software development* .......... (201) 489-6727
Sovereign Technology Corporation, 2200 River Rd., Unit A, Point Pleasant Boro 08742
Pres., CEO—William Robinson, 15 emp., *Real-time asset & personnel management* .......... (732) 298-8104
Spacemaster, Inc., 855 Bloomfield Ave., Glen Ridge 07028
Pres.—Raphael Badagliacca, 15 emp., *Software development* .......... (973) 429-1155
Spirent Communications, Inc., 211 Mount Airy Rd., Basking Ridge 07920
CEO—Kevin Kennedy, 40 emp., *Internet & video conferencing software* .......... (908) 953-6000
SQN Banking Systems, Inc., 65 Indel Ave., P.O. Box 423, Rancocas 08073
Pres.—Joseph Uhland, Jr., 30 emp., *Fraud detection software development* .......... (609) 261-5500
Sterling Medical Devices, 17 Legion Pl., Rochelle Park 07662
V-P., Engrg.—Bruce Swope, 50 emp., *Medical device software development* .......... (201) 227-7569

Sterling System LLC, 22 Meridian Rd., Unit 10, Edison 08820
Pres. & Dir.—Sejal Dasondi, 5 emp., Software development................................ (732) 452-1881
StrikeForce Technologies, Inc., 1090 King Georges Post Rd., Ste. 603, Edison 08837
CEO—Mark Kay, 7 emp., Identity protection software development ................. (732) 661-9641
SumTotal Systems, LLC, 600 Parsippany Rd., Parsippany 07054
CFO—Jeff Laborde, 200 emp., Workforce management software development ...................... (973) 364-0480
Syncsort, Inc., 50 Tice Blvd., Ste. 250, Woodcliff Lake 07677
CEO—Lonnie Jaffe, 10 emp., Downloadable data integration & data ................................ (201) 930-9700
Systems House, Inc., The, 1033 U.S. Highway 46, Clifton 07013
Pres.—Seymour Fertig, 20 emp., Cloud or in-house ERP systems for medical ........................ (973) 777-8050
Thetica Systems, Inc., 145 13th St., Cresskill 07626
★ CEO—Ariel Yankilevich, 3 emp., Computer systems integration & prepackaged ........................ (201) 399-7800
Timecruiser Computing Corp., 9 Law Dr., Ste. 2, Fairfield 07004
Pres.—Anthony Ma, 25 emp., Prepackaged communications software .............. (973) 244-7856
United ERP, LLC, 2460 Lemoine Ave., Ste. 503, Fort Lee 07024
Owner, Member, Hum. Res. & IT Mgr.—Judith Fisher, 11 emp., Computer integrated systems (201) 567-6315
Universal Business Systems, Inc., 185 Industrial Pkwy., Ste. J, Somerville 08876
Pres.—Christofer Raffo, 25 emp., ERP software for business, financial ................................. (908) 725-8899
uReach Technologies, Inc., 2137 State Highway 35, 1st Fl., Holmdel 07733
CEO & Dir.—David Ittner, 45 emp., Prepackaged software development for ........................ (732) 335-5400
Vanderbilt Industries, 2 Cranberry Rd., Parsippany 07054
Pres.—Mitchell Kane, 75 emp., Computer controlled building security ................................ (973) 316-3900
Ventraq, Inc., 817 E. Gate Dr., Ste. 101, Mount Laurel 08054
Dir., Opers., N. American—Bruce Kasian, 40 emp., Telecommunication billing mediation....... (856) 866-1000
Viamente, Inc., 3600 State Route 66, Ste. 400, Neptune 07753
Pres.—Chris Sullens, 1 emp., Cloud-based SaaS software development ................................ (732) 686-7843
Visual Retail Plus, Inc., 540 Hudson St., 4th Fl., Hackensack 07601
Owner—Dafna Halevy, 11 emp., Point-of-sale & inventory management ................................ (201) 678-9888
Vitech Systems Group, Inc., 111 Wood Ave. S., Iselin 08830
Pres.—Frank Vitiello, 80 emp., Insurance, investment & benefit administratio ........................ (646) 344-5282
vSplash Techlabs, Inc. (H Q), 1050 Wall St. W., Ste. 630, Lyndhurst 07071
★ Pres.—Umesh Tibrewal, 27 emp., Corporate headquarters; internet-based ........................ (201) 355-0066
WellCare Today, LLC, 89 Headquarters Plz., Ste. 1461, Morristown 07960
Pres.—Dan Ferrara, 10 emp., Healthcare mobile phone application.................................... (866) 656-1188
World Software Corp., 266 Harristown Rd., Ste. 201, Glen Rock 07452
Dir.—Julie Camporini, 25 emp., Prepackaged document management software ..................... (201) 444-3228
Xybion Medical Systems, 201 Littleton Rd., Morris Plains 07950
CEO—Pradip K. Banerjee, 50 emp., Toxicology & pathology data management .. (973) 538-5111

## 7373 Computer integrated systems design

A3 Technology, Inc., 311 S. New York Rd., Redding Office Pk., Ste. 36, Absecon 08205
Pres., CEO—Karen Vargas, 90 emp., Computer software development & integrated............. (609) 652-7933
AccessIT Group, Inc., 115 Route 46 W., Bldg. E, Ste. 35, Mountain Lakes 07046
CEO—Joe Luciano, 10 emp., Computer security integrated systems..................................... (973) 316-6016
Activu, 301 Round Hill Dr., Rockaway 07866
CEO—Paul Noble, 60 emp., Computer systems integration, including ................................. (973) 366-5550
Admiral Integration, Inc., 1001 Marlton Pike W., Cherry Hill 08002
Owner & Pres.—Katiusca McEntee, 8 emp., Computer network integration, including........... (856) 429-6700
AgileAccess™, LLC, 23 Londonderry Dr., Flemington 08822
Founder & CTO—Syed Ahmed, 3 emp., Hardware system integration for the........................ (908) 788-7740
All Covered, 100 Dobbs Ln., Ste. 208, Cherry Hill 08034
Pres.—Anthony Calabrese, 25 emp., Computer LAN, WAN & internet integrated ..................... (856) 795-7330
All Star Identification, 400 Morris Ave., Ste. 241, Denville 07834
★ Owner—Art Evans, 15 emp., Computer systems integration ................................ (973) 625-4100
Amdocs, Inc., 34 Exchange Pl., Jersey City 07311
★ Dir.—Amy McLean, 8 emp., Computer systems integration, including ............... (201) 631-3200
Automated Control Concepts, Inc., 3535 State Route 66, Ste. 14, Neptune 07753
Pres.—Michael Blechman, 40 emp., Systems integration services, including ........................ (732) 922-6611
Automation & Control, Inc., 1491 Lancer Dr., Moorestown 08057
Pres.—Ron Iannacone, 30 emp., Custom industrial automation control .................................. (856) 234-2300
Aventa Systems, LLC, 40 Arnot St., Unit 7, Lodi 07644
Member—Felix Gorohovsky, 3 emp., Computer network system integration .......................... (973) 246-4853
Avid Communications, Inc., 27 Bluebird Ct., P.O. Box 2481, Flemington 08822
Pres.—Thomas Chen, 4 emp., Computer network system integration.................................... (973) 625-7350
Azzurro Group, LLC, 100 Stonehurst Ct., Northvale 07647
CEO—Frank Luperella, 15 emp., Broadcast system integration ........................... (201) 767-0850
BarCodeAmerica.com, 144 Shunpike Rd., P.O. Box 506, Madison 07940
Pres.—Robert W. Rack, 10 emp., Systems integration & distributor of................................. (973) 377-8182
Bauman's Computer Solutions, 192 Route 130, Bordentown 08505
Owner & IT Mgr.—Henry Bauman, 1 emp., Computer network systems integration ................ (609) 920-0121
BIG Client, LLC, 1 Industrial Way W., Bldg. E, Eatontown 07724
CEO—Ben H. Zehavi, 30 emp., Thin client terminal computer & point-of-sale......................... (732) 918-8221
Bluenog Corp., 285 Davidson Ave., Ste. 306, Somerset 08873
CEO—Sastry Taravai, 13 emp., Computer network system integration ................................. (732) 584-2340
Breaker Group, Inc., The, 32-34 Mill St., Mount Holly 08060
Pres.—Tony Minervini, 14 emp., Computer integrated systems, including ............................. (609) 267-1330
CCSI Group, The, 1351 Morris Ave., P.O. Box 3554, Union 07083
Owner—Doug Rotoly, 10 emp., Business infrastructure computer integrated ......................... (908) 686-6464
Comport Consulting Corp., 78 Orchard St., Ramsey 07446
Pres. & IT Mgr.—Jack Margossian, 20 emp., Computer network system integration .............. (201) 236-0505
Compunite Computers, Inc., 39 U.S. Highway 46, Ste. 803, P.O. Box 3, Pine Brook 07058
Owner & Pres.—Steve Ferman, 15 emp., Computer network system integration .................... (973) 227-6008
Computer Ease, LLC, 153 Newark Pompton Tpke., Ste. A, Little Falls 07424
Owner—Matt Aquino, 5 emp., Computer networrk systems integration.................................. (973) 812-6626
Computerist, Inc., 15 Smull Ave., Ste. A, Caldwell 07006
Pres.—Anthony Camilleri, 5 emp., Rebuilt computers & computer network ........................... (973) 226-0100
Computrs, Inc., 294 Wanaque Ave., Pompton Lakes 07442
Pres.—Ken Freedman, 4 emp., Computer network systems integration ................................ (973) 248-9500
ComTec Systems, Inc., 2658 N. West Blvd., Vineland 08360
Owner—Michael Vertolli, 35 emp., Computer & telephone system integration........................ (856) 691-5111
Comtel Global Services, LLC, 105 Newfield Ave., Ste. K, Edison 08837
Pres., CEO—Yossi Teichman, 17 emp., Computer network system integration ....................... (732) 225-3055
Control & Power Systems, Inc., 17 Spielman Rd., Fairfield 07004
Pres.—D. Shevich, 36 emp., Control & information systems integration................................. (973) 575-3300
CoreMatrix Systems, 125 Half Mile Rd., Ste. 200, Red Bank 07701
Co-Founder & Pres.—Frank McMahon, 75 emp., Computer network systems integration ....... (732) 332-1931
Corente, Inc., 758 Route 18, Ste. 110, East Brunswick 08816
Pres.—James Zucco, 35 emp., Computer network systems integration ................................ (732) 254-0210
CPI USA Inc., 6 Doreen Ct., Edison 08820
Founder & CEO—Isha Advani, 4 emp., Computer network system integration ....................... (732) 494-0007
Cuny & Guerber, Inc., 2100 Kerrigan Ave., P.O. Box 1192, Union City 07087
Pres.—David B. Matthews, Jr., 35 emp., Industrial automation systems integration ................. (201) 617-5800

DBM Of America, Inc., 295 U.S. Highway 22 E., Ste. 104, Whitehouse Station 08889
Pres.—David Wesner, 3 emp., Computer network system integration..................................... (908) 534-1665
Deloitte, 3 2nd St., Harborside Plaza 10, Ste. 300, Jersey City 07311
Co-Founder & COO—Samuel Goldman, 120 emp., Business process & technology computer (212) 937-8200
Dematic Corp., 150 Allen Rd., Ste. 102, Basking Ridge 07920
GM—Tom Dancer, 25 emp., Material handling systems integration .................. (908) 991-9900
DialConnection, LLC, 1040 Route 73 S., Berlin 08009
Pres.—Michael Vesper, 10 emp., Computer network system integration ................................. (856) 753-6620
Digital Surroundings, LLC, 11 Princess Rd., Ste. E, Lawrence Township 08648
Pres.—Chris D. Erdman, 10 emp., Commercial & residential audio/visual ............................... (609) 912-1800
Dorado Systems, LLC, 8 Kings Hwy. E., Haddonfield 08033
Dir.—Michael Matt, 4 emp., Healthcare EDI system integration, ........................................... (856) 354-0048
DynTek Services, Inc., 1120 Route 73, Ste. 100, Mount Laurel 08054
Sr. Dist. Mgr.—Orlando Lima, 10 emp., Advanced networking & IP communications ............ (856) 834-1100
E*Pro, Inc., 1000 U.S. Highway 9 N., Ste. 303, Woodbridge 07095
★ Pres.—Sadeesh Venugopal, 12 emp., Computer network system integration ........................ (732) 283-0499
Edgesys, Inc., 411 State Route 17, Ste. 310, Hasbrouck Heights 07604
CEO—Emanuell James, 15 emp., Business process outsourcing & knowledge...................... (201) 727-1663
Emtec, Inc., 11 Diamond Rd., Springfield 07081
Chrm., Pres. & CEO—Dinesh R. Desai, 65 emp., Corporate headquarters & computer network (973) 376-4242
Energy Options, LLC, 256 Campus Dr., Edison 08837
Pres.—Bradley Freeman, 43 emp., Automated HVAC systems & security monitoring............. (732) 512-9100
EPS Corporation, 78 Apple St., Tinton Falls 07724
Chrm., CEO—Francesco A. Musorrafiti, 52 emp., Computer integrated systems, including ... (732) 747-8277
eSystems, Inc., 4390 U.S. Highway 1, Ste. 301, Princeton 08540
Pres.—Ashish Mukherji, 50 emp., Computer network systems integration............................... (609) 945-7437
Etta Controls, Inc., 31 Belgrade Ter., West Orange 07052
Pres.—Paul Rametta, 6 emp., Control panels, system integrators,........................................ (973) 731-6552
GMB (USA), Inc., 190 Veterans Dr., Ste. B, Northvale 07647
Pres.—Bryant Kang, 23 emp., Systems integration for the shipbuilding ............. (201) 768-3577
Health Care Software, Inc., 1350 Campus Pkwy., Neptune 07753
Pres.—Tom Fahey, 50 emp., Computer software development & system ............................ (732) 938-5600
Heisler Industries, Inc., 224 Passaic Ave., Fairfield 07004
Pres.—Richard A. Heisler, 38 emp., Packaging machines, automation & system .................. (973) 227-6300
HyperTech, Inc., 279 Central Ave., Ste. B, Metuchen 08840
Pres.—Ann Hsu, 10 emp., Computer network systems integration ....................................... (732) 635-1755
I.D. Systems, Inc., 123 Tice Blvd., Ste. 101, Woodcliff Lake 07677
Chrm., Pres. & CEO—Kenneth S. Ehrman, 100 emp., Wireless systems integration & software (201) 996-9000
ID-Tech Solutions, Inc., 505 E. County Line Rd., Lakewood 08701
Pres.—Isaac Deutsch, 25 emp., Computer network system integration ................................. (718) 408-9199
Innovative Network Solutions, 29 Cove Rd., Hopatcong 07843
Pres.—Garry Manz, 5 emp., Computer network system integration ....................................... (973) 299-8800
INS Technologies, P.O. Box 615, Nutley 07110
Pres.—Steve Melillo, 10 emp., Computer telephone network integrated ................................ (973) 808-6400
Integrated Micro Systems, Inc., 74 Lee Ave., Haledon 07508
★ Pres.—Jeffery Durante, 6 emp., Computer network system integration................................ (973) 904-9700
Intuitive Technology Partners, 102 Serpentine Dr., Morganville 07751
★ Pres.—Jay Modh, 48 emp., Computer network system integration..................... (201) 993-7799
IPKeys Technologies, 1 Industrial Way W., Ste. E-1, Eatontown 07724
Pres.—Mark Pappas, 117 emp., Computer & network systems integration ............................ (732) 389-4702
IT America, Inc., 100 Metroplex Dr., Ste. 207, Edison 08817
V-P.—Praveen Thadakamalla, 2 emp., Computer business operations management............. (732) 985-5100
IT Management, 195 Browertown Rd., Ste. 2, Little Falls 07424
Owner—Marc Caruso, 1 emp., Computer network system integration ................................... (973) 389-1200
K & A Industries, Inc., 51 Cragwood Rd., Ste. 204, South Plainfield 07080
Pres.—George Keelty, 8 emp., Identification badges, identity management ......................... (908) 226-7000
Kaizen Technologies, Inc., 1 State Route 27, Ste. 10, Edison 08820
Pres.—Ashok Krish, 72 emp., CAD engineering computer integrated.................................... (732) 452-9555
Kavayah Solutions, Inc., 5 Independence Way, Ste. 360, Princeton 08540
Pres.—Vivek Casula, 18 emp., Computer network systems integration ................................ (609) 919-9797
Living Intelligent, Inc., 70 Oak St., Ste. 103, Norwood 07648
CEO—Mitchell Arthur, 8 emp., Computer, communications & audiovisual............................. (201) 784-0500
Lucid Technologies, LLC, 231 Clarksville Rd., Princeton Junction 08550
Mng. Member—Bharath Khambadkone, 13 emp., Computer network systems integration...... (609) 277-4138
Lucille Maud Corp., 513 N. Olden Ave., Trenton 08638
Pres.—Louis Muirhead, 8 emp., Computer systems integration & distributor......................... (609) 393-7555
Maestro Technolgies, Inc., 510 Thornall St., Ste. 375, Edison 08837
Mng. Dir.—Kamal S. Bathla, 54 emp., Software development & computer & network........... (908) 458-8600
Masstar, 18 Heritage Rd., Eatontown 07724
Owner—Charles Massa, 2 emp., Computer network systems integration .............................. (732) 542-8004
Mazzanti, Inc., 701 Grand St., Hoboken 07030
Owner & Pres.—Carl Mazzanti, 14 emp., Computer network systems integration ................. (201) 360-4400
Navitend, 23 U.S. Highway 206, Stanhope 07874
Pres.—Frank Ableson, 10 emp., Bar coding & inventory & field service ................................ (973) 448-0070
NetQ Multimedia, 919 State Route 33, Ste. 52, Freehold 07728
★ Owner—Rich Tillman, 4 emp., Computer network system integration.................................. (732) 833-9300
Networking Technologies & Integration, 50 Boright Ave., Kenilworth 07033
Pres.—John Azzinaro, 10 emp., Computer network system integration.................................. (908) 276-1200
New Jersey Business Systems, Inc., 7-C Marlen Dr., Trenton 08691
V-P.—Michael Bolling, 20 emp., LAN & wireless computer integrated ................................. (609) 587-5500
NIC Group, The, 1130 U.S. Highway 202, Ste. E-6, Raritan 08869
Pres.—Michael Skomba, 9 emp., Computer network systems integration ........... (908) 253-8106
Olmec Systems, Inc., 255 W. Main St., Denville 07834
Ptnr., Pres. & CEO—Chris Forte, 10 emp., Computer network system integration................. (973) 586-6590
One Source Solutions, 3 industrial Ct., Ste. 3, Freehold 07728
Hum. Res. & IT Mgr.—Timothy O'Handley, 12 emp., Point-of-sale, inventory control & ......... (732) 536-0702
ORBCOMM, Inc. (H Q), 395 W. Passaic St., Ste. 325, Rochelle Park 07662
CEO—Marc J. Eisenberg, 50 emp., Corporate headquarters; wireless networks .................... (703) 433-6300
P & M Computers, Inc., 97 Oakdene Ave., P.O. Box 270, Cliffside Park 07010
★ Pres., CTO—Francis Poeta, 6 emp., Computer systems integration, including..................... (201) 943-0353
PeggNet Computers, LLC, 4 E. Main St., Ste. 3, Mendham 07945
Pres.—Christopher McManus, 10 emp., Computer network system integration ...................... (973) 543-1222
Phoenix Systems, LLC, 39 Morningside Ave., North Haledon 07508
Owner—Andrew Vaccaro, 5 emp., Audiovisual equipment & systems for............................... (201) 857-3901
Praxis Data Systems, Inc., 4 Foster Ave., Ste. B & C, Gibbsboro 08026
★ V-P.—Harry Srolovitz, 17 emp., Computer systems integration, including........................... (856) 679-2256
Precision Automation Company, Inc., 1841 Old Cuthbert Rd., Cherry Hill 08034
Pres., CEO—G. Frederick Rexon, Jr., 50 emp., Automation, conveyor, control & complete..... (856) 428-7400
Promedia Technology Services, Inc., 535 U.S. Highway 46, Little Falls 07424
Pres.—Gene Murphy, 50 emp., Computer network system integration.................................. (973) 253-7600
Quality Software Systems, Inc., 80 Cottontail Ln., Ste. 105, Somerset 08873
Pres.—Edward Troianello, 40 emp., Warehouse & transportation management ..................... (732) 805-0400

S.I.C.

© Copyright 2015 Manufacturers' News, Inc.

R A C Systems Corp., 1-B Glimpsewood Ln., Morristown 07960
★ Pres.——Walter Rodriguez, 2 emp., *Computer systems integration, including* ........................... (973) 292-3200
Radiant Systems, Inc., 107 Corporate Blvd., Ste. B, South Plainfield 07080
Pres.——Venu Myneni, 365 emp., *Computer systems integration & consulting* ........................... (908) 668-1080
Reliance Global Services, Inc., 50 Cragwood Rd., Ste. 100, South Plainfield 07080
Pres.——Reddy Palvai, 40 emp., *Computer integrated systems for enterprise* ........................... (908) 769-1271
Ripen Interactive, LLC, 117 Rockingham Row, Princeton 08540
Owner——Michael Tudor, 30 emp., *Computer network system integration* ........................... (609) 520-8820
RSA Associates, 812 County Road 579, Flemington 08822
Pres.——Robert Alparone, 4 emp., *Computer network systems integration* ........................... (908) 806-4681
Sarnoff Corp., 201 Washington Rd., Princeton 08540
Corp. Comm. Mgr.——Lou Ann Hodges, 430 emp., *Electronic, biomedical, information* ........... (609) 734-2000
Secure Technology Integration Group, Ltd., 15 Schneider Rd., Allendale 07401
Pres.——Richard Shinnick, 19 emp., *Computer network system integration* ........................... (201) 825-1255
Shaman Systems, Inc., 402 Main St., Ste. 100-330, Metuchen 08840
Pres.——Ketan Shah, 6 emp., *Computer network systems integration* ........................... (908) 429-0542
Sirius Technology LLC, 1 Hollywood Ave., Ste. 19-A, Ho-Ho-Kus 07423
CEO——David Dadian, 10 emp., *Computer network system integration* ........................... (201) 493-1414
Sita Corp., 347 Elizabeth Ave., Ste. 200, Somerset 08873
Pres., CEO——Ramgopal Reddy, 30 emp., *Computer network systems integration* ................... (732) 906-7806
StarTrak Information Technologies, LLC, 395 W. Passaic St., Ste. 325, Rochelle Park 07662
V-P., Sales——Chris MacDonald, 25 emp., *Wireless GPS & remote monitoring &* ........................... (703) 433-6300
Strategic Products & Services, LLC, 300 Littleton Rd., 2nd Fl., Parsippany 07054
Chrm. of the Board, Pres. & CEO——John Poole, 126 emp., *IT & telephone systems integration,.* (888) 777-7280
Sunhillo Corp., 444 Kelly Dr., West Berlin 08091
Pres.——David Whitman, 40 emp., *Legacy platform data transport & data* ........................... (856) 767-7676
Systems House, Inc., The, 1033 U.S. Highway 46, Clifton 07013
Pres.——Seymour Fertig, 20 emp., *Cloud or in-house ERP systems for medical* ........................... (973) 777-8050
Targeted Technologies, LLC, 1735 Hooper Ave., Ste. 2, Toms River 08753
Ptnr.——Michael Schlachter, 7 emp., *Computer network system integration* ........................... (732) 255-9005
Tech Support, Inc., 23 Pawnee Ave., Rockaway 07866
Pres.——Charlie Calabrese, 11 emp., *Telephone call center computer integrated* ........................... (973) 627-8870
Technovision, Inc., 1119 Raritan Rd., Ste. 2, Clark 07066
Hum. Res. Mgr.——Vanitha Vasudevan, 20 emp., *Computer systems integration* ........................... (732) 381-0200
Thetica Systems, Inc., 145 13th St., Cresskill 07626
★ CEO——Ariel Yankilevich, 3 emp., *Computer systems integration & prepackaged* ........................... (201) 399-7800
Trident Computer Resources, Inc., 151 Industrial Way E., Ste. A-3, Eatontown 07724
Pres.——Scott Swain, 35 emp., *Computer network system integration* ........................... (732) 544-9333
United ERP, LLC, 2460 Lemoine Ave., Ste. 503, Fort Lee 07024
Owner, Member, Hum. Res. & IT Mgr.——Judith Fisher, 11 emp., *Computer integrated systems* (201) 567-6315
US Logic, LLC, 2885 E. State Street Ext., Hamilton 08619
Pres. & Member Mgr.——Seth Jackson, 17 emp., *Computer network systems integration* ......... (609) 530-0005
Vanderbilt Industries, 2 Cranberry Rd., Parsippany 07054
Pres.——Mitchell Kane, 75 emp., *Computer controlled building security* ........................... (973) 316-3900
Veraciti, Inc., 1044 Route 23, Ste. 102, Wayne 07470
Pres. & IT Mgr.——Frank Altieri, 7 emp., *Computer network & wireless security* ........................... (973) 887-8660
Verrex Corp., 1130 Route 22, Mountainside 07092
Pres.——Thomas Berry, Jr., 70 emp., *Corporate audiovisual & conferencing* ........................... (908) 232-7000
Western Scientific Computers, Inc., 28 W. Shore Rd., Mountain Lakes 07046
Pres.——Joe Lutz, 14 emp., *Systems integration for CAD/CAM* ........................... (973) 263-9311
XTreme Technologies Group, LLC, 135 Gaither Dr., Ste. F, Mount Laurel 08054
Owner——Louis Passareola, 20 emp., *Network systems integration & custom* ........................... (856) 273-7800

# PARENT COMPANY SECTION

This section indexes alphabetically each parent company (headquarters, divisional headquarters or home office) of the state's manufacturers, processors, wholesalers or distributors. The parent company is indicated in bold type, followed by its division, subsidiary or affiliate profiled in this publication. It is not intended to indicate that this is the full scope of the operations of the parent company.

PARENT COMPANY

**3D MEDICAL MANUFACTURING, INC.**
1006 W. 15th St., Riviera Beach FL 33404 . . . . . . . . . . . . . . . . . . . . . . . . (561) 842-7175
Pres.—James Davis, Jr.; Ex. V.P.—Joe Davis; V.P., Engrg.—Eddie Pena;
   Comp.—George Taylor
3D Medical Mfg., Inc., 7145 Colonial Ln., Pennsauken, 08109 . . . . . . . . . . . . . (856) 486-9600

**3M CO.**
3M Center, St. Paul MN 55144 . . . . . . . . . . . . . . . . . . . . . . . . . . . . . . . (651) 733-1110
Chrm., Pres. & CEO—Inge Thulin; Sr. V.P., R & D & CTO—Ashish Khandpur;
   Sr. V.P., CFO—Nicholas Gangestad;
   Sr. V.P., Corp. Comms. & Enterprise Svcs.—Ian F. Hardgrove;
   Sr. V.P., Supply Chain—Paul A. Keel; Ex. V.P., Intl. Opers.—H. C. Shin;
   Ex. V.P., Healthcare—Joaquin Delgado; Ex. V.P., Indl. Svcs.—Michael F. Roman;
   Ex. V.P., Electrical—Michael Kelly; Sales & Mktg. Mgr., Natl.—Clint Hinze
3M Co., 500 U.S. Highway 202 N., Flemington, 08822 . . . . . . . . . . . . . . . . (908) 788-4000
3M Co., 140 Algonquin Pkwy., Whippany, 07981 . . . . . . . . . . . . . . . . . . . (973) 884-2500

**A TASTE OF OLIVE, LLC**
26 S. High St., West Chester PA 19382 . . . . . . . . . . . . . . . . . . . . . . . . . . (610) 429-0292
CEO—Kimber Schladwier; GM—Kate Schroeder
A Taste Of Olive, LLC, 106 Kings Hwy. E., Ste. A, Haddonfield, 08033 . . . . . . . . (856) 795-0043

**A&M INDUSTRIAL, INC.**
37 W. Cherry St., P.O. Box 1044, Rahway NJ 07065 . . . . . . . . . . . . . . . . . (732) 574-1111
Pres.—Arnold Young; Ex. V.P.—David Young; Ex. Dir., Bus. Dev.—Kevin Rosenthal;
   Dir., Opers.—Tom Richards
A&M Industrial, Inc., 325 Commerce Rd., Linden, 07036 . . . . . . . . . . . . . . . (908) 862-1800

**A.C.T. LIGHTING, INC.**
5308 Derry Ave., Unit R, Agoura Hills CA 91301 . . . . . . . . . . . . . . . . . . . (818) 707-0884
Pres., CEO—Bob Gordon; V.P., Tech. Serv.—Mario Collazo; V.P., Lighting—George Masek;
   Dir., Software Dev.—Will Murphy
A.C.T. Lighting, Inc., 122 John St., Hackensack, 07601 . . . . . . . . . . . . . . . . (201) 996-0884

**A.H. HARRIS & SONS, INC.**
433 S. Main St., Ste. 202, West Hartford CT 06110 . . . . . . . . . . . . . . . . . . (860) 216-9500
Cont.—Jennifer Desjardins; Dir., Mktg.—Sally Harris; Dir., Hum. Res.—Vance Harris
A. H. Harris & Sons, Inc., 160 Fairfield Rd., Fairfield, 07004 . . . . . . . . . . . . . (973) 227-1600

**ABB INC.**
12040 Regency Pkwy., Ste. 200, Cary NC 27518 . . . . . . . . . . . . . . . . . . . (919) 856-2360
Pres., CEO—Gregory Scheu; Sr. V.P., Hum. Res.—Charlene Binder;
   Reg. Treas.—Daniel Hagmann; Reg. Dir., Comms. & Media Rels.—Mary Flieller;
   Dir., Inv. Rels.—John Chironna; Mktg. Comms. Mgr.—Barry Dillon;
   Off. Mgr.—Michael Edwards
ABB Inc., Business Unit Turbocharger,
   1460 Livingston Ave., P.O. Box 6005, North Brunswick, 08902 . . . . . . . . . . (732) 932-6000

**ABBOTT LABORATORIES**
100 Abbott Park Rd., Abbott Park IL 60064 . . . . . . . . . . . . . . . . . . . . . . . (847) 937-6100
Chrm., CEO—Miles D. White; Ex. V.P., Fin. & CFO—Thomas Freyman;
   Sr. V.P., Established Prods. Div.—Michael Warmuth; Sr. V.P., Diagnostics—Brian Blaser;
   V.P., Global Engrg.—Corliss Murray; Dir., Bus. Hum. Res.—William Lee
Abbott Point of Care, 400 College Rd. E., Princeton, 08540 . . . . . . . . . . . . . . (609) 454-9000

**ABC SUPPLY CO., INC.**
1 ABC Pkwy., P.O. Box 838, Beloit WI 53511 . . . . . . . . . . . . . . . . . . . . . (608) 362-7777
Founder & Chrm.—Diane Hendricks; Pres., CEO—David Luck;
   Ex. V.P., Chief Operating Officer—Kevin Rozolis; V.P., CIO—Kathy Murray;
   V.P., Chief Legal Officer—Karl W. Leo; V.P., Chief Admn. Officer—Todd Buehl;
   CFO & Treas.—Kendra Story; V.P., Div. Opers. & Strategic Bus. Units—Kevin Hendricks;
   V.P., Mfg. Opers.—Brad Money; V.P., Assoc. Svcs. & Hum. Res.—Lisa Indgjer;
   V.P., Natl. Bus. Dev.—Brent Fox; V.P., Corp. Dev.—Kim Hendricks;
   Dir., Bus. Intelligence & Mktg.—Mike Schwarz; Adv. Mgr.—Jeff Garrow
ABC Supply Co., Inc., 5004 Route 130, Riverside, 08075 . . . . . . . . . . . . . . . (856) 461-5252
ABC Supply Co., Inc., Bradco Div., 45 Samworth Rd., Clifton, 07012 . . . . . . . . (973) 777-3663
ABC Supply Co., Inc., Bradco Div., 691 New Hampshire Ave., Lakewood, 08701 . (732) 905-9355
ABC Supply Co., Inc., Bradco Div., 725 W. Delilah Rd., Pleasantville, 08232 . . . (609) 484-9100
ABC Supply Co., Inc., Bradco Div., 301 Brunswick Ave., Trenton, 08618 . . . . . . (609) 393-7000

**ABCO REFRIGERATION SUPPLY CORP.**
49-70 31st St., Long Island City NY 11101 . . . . . . . . . . . . . . . . . . . . . . . (718) 937-9000
CEO—Michael Senter; Pres.—Jon Gottlieb; Cont.—Scott Strumps;
   Mktg. Mgr.—Michelle Zellman; Hum. Res. Mgr.—Elsy Taylor
ABCO Refrigeration Supply Corp., 399 N. 14th St., Kenilworth, 07033 . . . . . . . (908) 931-0700

**ABINGTON RELDAN METALS, LLC**
550 Old Bordentown Rd., Fairless Hills PA 19030 . . . . . . . . . . . . . . . . . . . (267) 316-2000
Pres.—Howard Steinberg; Cont.—Mike Randolph
Abington Reldan Metals, LLC, 396-402 Whitehead Ave., South River, 08882 . . . . (732) 238-8550

**ACCUCOLOR, LLC**
771 Shrewsbury Ave., Ste. B, Shrewsbury NJ 07702 . . . . . . . . . . . . . . . . . (732) 741-4594
Owner—Robert LaBella
Jamm Litho, Inc., 185 Broadway, Long Branch, 07740 . . . . . . . . . . . . . . . . (732) 870-1999
Jamm Printing, 108 W. Sylvania Ave., Neptune, 07753 . . . . . . . . . . . . . . . . (732) 502-0110

**ACTAVIS, INC.**
Morris Corporate Ctr. 3, 400 Interpace Pkwy., Parsippany NJ 07054 . . . . . . . . (862) 261-7000
Ex. Chrm. of the Board—Paul M. Bisaro; Pres., CEO—Brenton L. Saunders;
   COO—Bob Stewart; CFO, Global—R. Todd Joyce; Chief Hum. Res. Officer—Karen Ling;
   Chief Comms. Officer—Charles M. Mayr; Chief Legal Officer, Global—Bob Bailey;
   Ex. V.P., Comml.—Bil Meury;
   Ex. V.P., Comml., N. American Generic & Intl.—David Buchen;
   V.P., Inv. Rels.—Lisa DeFrancesco; Ex. Dir., Corp. Comms.—Steve Sost
Actavis Elizabeth, LLC, 200 Elmora Ave., Elizabeth, 07202 . . . . . . . . . . . . . (908) 527-9100
Warner Chilcott, 100 Enterprise Dr., Ste. 280, Rockaway, 07866 . . . . . . . . . . (973) 442-3200

**ACTION SUPPLY, INC.**
1413 Stagecoach Rd., Ocean View NJ 08230 . . . . . . . . . . . . . . . . . . . . . (609) 390-0663
Pres.—Tom Tower; Sales Mgr.—George Smith
Kennedy Concrete, 1969 S. East Ave., Vineland, 08360 . . . . . . . . . . . . . . . (856) 692-8650

**ACTUANT CORP.**
N86W12500 Westbrook Xing, Menomonee Falls WI 53051 . . . . . . . . . . . . . (262) 293-1500
Pres., CEO—Mark Goldstein; Ex. V.P., CFO—Andy Lempereur;
   Ex. V.P., Hum. Res., Global—Sheri Grissom; Ex. V.P., Engineered Sols.—Bill Blackmore;
   Ex. V.P., Energy Segment—Brian Kobylinski; Ex. V.P., Bus. Dev.—Ted Wozniak;
   Ex. V.P.—Gustav Boel; Treas.—Terry Braatz; Asst. Treas.—Sandy Bugbee;
   Corp. Cont.—Matt Pauli; Leader—Karen Bauer
Hydratight Operations, 12 Worlds Fair Dr., Ste. A, Somerset, 08873 . . . . . . . . (732) 271-4100

**ACUITY BRANDS LIGHTING, INC.**
1400 Laster Rd., Conyers GA 30012 . . . . . . . . . . . . . . . . . . . . . . . . . . . (770) 922-9000
COO—Mark A. Black; Sr. V.P., Hum. Res.—Joe Jackson; V.P., Mktg.—David Grimm
Mark Architectural Lighting, 3 Kilmer Rd., Edison, 08817 . . . . . . . . . . . . . . . (732) 985-2600

**ADEMCO DISTRIBUTION, INC.**
263 Old Country Rd., Melville NY 11747 . . . . . . . . . . . . . . . . . . . . . . . . . (631) 692-1000
Pres.—Michael Flink; CIO—Bob McManus; V.P., Sales—Jon Sullivan;
   Hum. Res. Mgr.—Thomas Pucci
Ademco Distribution, Inc., 1000 Lincoln Dr. E., Unit 4, Marlton, 08053 . . . . . . . (856) 985-9050

**ADLER, INC., KURT S.**
7 W. 34th St., Ste. 100, New York NY 10001 . . . . . . . . . . . . . . . . . . . . . . (212) 924-0900
Co-Pres.—Howard Adler; Co-Pres.—Clifford Adler; CFO & Cont.—Karen Adler;
   V.P.—Lou Benjamin
Blackwell Assocs., Inc., 15 Kimberly Rd., East Brunswick, 08816 . . . . . . . . . . (732) 238-8000

**ADVANCED DRAINAGE SYSTEMS, INC.**
4640 Trueman Blvd., Hilliard OH 43026 . . . . . . . . . . . . . . . . . . . . . . . . . . (614) 658-0050
Pres.—Joseph Chlapaty; CFO—Mark Sturgeon; Cont.—Richard Martorano;
   Mktg. Mgr.—Tori Durlauf; IT Mgr.—Eric Reo
Advanced Drainage Systems, Inc., 300 Progress Ct., Logan Township, 08085 . . . (856) 467-4779

**ADVANCED SOLAR PRODUCTS, INC.**
270 S. Main St., Ste. 203, Flemington NJ 08822 . . . . . . . . . . . . . . . . . . . . (908) 751-5818
Pres., CEO—Lyle Rawlings; V.P., COO—Edward Seliga; Dir., Opers.—Katie Hallock
SOLSTICE Mfg. Co., 270 S. Main St., Ste. 102, Flemington, 08822 . . . . . . . . . (908) 284-0096

**ADVANSTAR COMMUNICATIONS, INC.**
2501 Colorado Ave., Ste. 280, Santa Monica CA 90404 . . . . . . . . . . . . . . . (310) 857-7500
Pres., CEO—Joseph Loggia; Ex. V.P., Corp. Dev.—Eric Lisman;
   Ex. V.P., Exhibitions—Tony Calanca; V.P., Gen. Counsel—Ward Hewins;
   V.P., Hum. Res.—Nancy Nugent
Advanstar Communications, Inc., 485 U.S. Highway 1 S., Ste. 200, Iselin, 08830 . (732) 346-3000

**AEROFLEX, INC.**
35 S. Service Rd., P.O. Box 6022, Plainview NY 11803 . . . . . . . . . . . . . . . . (516) 694-6700
Pres.—Leonard Borow; CFO—John Adamovich; V.P., Mfg.—Carl Caruso;
   V.P., Corp. Dev. & Inv. Rels.—Andrew Kaminsky; Treas.—Charles Badlato
Aeroflex Control Components, Inc., 40 Industrial Way E., Eatontown, 07724 . . . . (732) 460-0212

**AEROJET ROCKETDYNE, INC.**
8900 DeSoto Ave., Canoga Park CA 91304 . . . . . . . . . . . . . . . . . . . . . . (818) 586-1000
V.P., Enterprise Opers.—Tom Cadwell; V.P. & Prog. Mgr.—John Vilja;
   Dir., Comms.—Erin Dick; Prog. Mgr., RS-68—Dan Adamski;
   Prog. Mgr., RS-27A Engines—Elizabeth Jones
Arde, Inc., 875 Washington Ave., Carlstadt, 07072 . . . . . . . . . . . . . . . . . . (201) 784-9880

**AEROPRES CORP.**
1324 N. Hearne Ave., Ste. 200, Shreveport LA 71107 . . . . . . . . . . . . . . . . (318) 221-6282
CEO—Ken Odom; Pres., COO—Bob Wilkie; CFO—Chris Rey;
   V.P., Sales & Mktg.—Joe Bowen; V.P., Opers.—James McKeever;
   V.P., Hum. Res.—Amy Crisler; V.P., Technical Svcs.—Mark Rivers;
   Dir., Sales—Tony Jackson; Sales Mgr., Regional—Brad Nash;
   Sales Mgr., Cylinder—Cathy Johnston
Aeropres Corp., 318 Valley Rd., Hillsborough, 08844 . . . . . . . . . . . . . . . . . (908) 722-2571

**AGFA CORP.**
611 River Dr., Elmwood Park NJ 07407 . . . . . . . . . . . . . . . . . . . . . . . . . (201) 440-0111
Pres.—Peter Wilkens; CFO—Gunther Mertens; IT Mgr.—Joe Milici;
   Mktg. Comm. Mgr.—Lois Catala
Agfa Corp., 400 Heller Park Ct., Dayton, 08810 . . . . . . . . . . . . . . . . . . . . (973) 812-0400

**AIR LIQUIDE AMERICA L.P.**
2700 Post Oak Blvd., Ste. 1800, Houston TX 77056 . . . . . . . . . . . . . . . . . (713) 624-8000
Pres., CEO—Kim Denny; CFO—Rick Hallett; CIO—Ravi Waran;
   Sr. V.P., Bus. Dev.—Johnnye J. Wozniak; Sr. V.P.—Woody Garman;
   Facility Mgr.—Brian Keene
Air Liquide America L.P., A-Line Rd., P.O. Box 155, Gibbstown, 08027 . . . . . . . (856) 423-5220
Voltaix, LLC (H Q), 3121 U.S. Highway 22, P.O. Box 5357, Branchburg, 08876 . . (908) 231-9060

G2 © Copyright 2015 Manufacturers' News, Inc. PARENT COMPANY SECTION

**AIR LIQUIDE AMERICA SPECIALTY GASES, LLC**
**6141 Easton Rd., P.O. Box 310, Plumsteadville PA 18949 ................ (215) 766-8860**
**Pres.—Steve Dziak; Chief Technical Officer—Stephen Miller;**
**Dir., Mktg. Comm.—Robert Jefferys; Dir., Specialty Gases—Sarah Herbert;**
**Mktg. Proj. Mgr.—Michele Haurin**
Advanced Specialty Gas Equipment, 241 Lackland Dr., Middlesex, 08846 ...... (732) 271-9300
Air Liquide America Specialty Gases, LLC,
2330 Hamilton Blvd., South Plainfield, 07080 .......................... (908) 754-7700

**AIR PRODUCTS & CHEMICALS, INC.**
**7201 Hamilton Blvd., Allentown PA 18195 ............................ (610) 481-4911**
**Chrm., Pres. & COO—John McGlade; Sr. V-P., CFO—M. Scott Crocco;**
**V-P., Energy, Gen. Svcs., Matls. & Chief Proc. Officer—Wilbur Mok;**
**Secy., Chief Governance Officer—Mary T. Afflerbach;**
**V-P., Treas. & Chief Risk Officer—George Bitto;**
**V-P., Gen. Counsel & Chief Admn. Officer—John Stanley;**
**V-P., IT & CIO—Kevin B. Michaelis; Sr. V-P., Supply Chain—Corning Painter;**
**Sr. V-P., Supply Chain—Patricia Mattimore; V-P., Global Engrg. & Mfg.—Tom Mutchler;**
**V-P., Global Opers.—Richard Boocock; V-P., Hum. Res.—Jennifer L. Grant;**
**V-P. & GM, N. American Merchant Gases—Nelson Squires;**
**V-P., Env. Health, Qual. & Safety & Corp. Chief Engr.—Joseph M. Pietrantonio;**
**V-P., Electronics Assets Mgmt. & Supply Chain—Pat Loughlin;**
**V-P., Energy Bus.—David J. Taylor; V-P., Taxes—Charles G. Stinner;**
**Dir., Inv. Rels.—Simon R. Moore; Dir., Global Bus.—Ed Kiczek;**
**Dir., LNG—Jim Solomon, Jr.**
Air Products & Chemicals, Inc., 405 State Route 33, Englishtown, 07726 ....... (732) 446-5676

**AIRGAS EAST, INC.**
**27 Northwestern Dr., Salem NH 03079 ............................. (603) 890-4600**
**Pres.—Tony Simonetta; V-P., GM—Adam Beck; Dir., Hum. Res.—Tony Natale;**
**Sales Mgr.—Gary Smith; IT Mgr.—Eric Webb**
Airgas East, Inc., 121 Stanley Ave., Bellmawr, 08031 ...................... (856) 931-0900
Airgas East, Inc., 270 Benigno Blvd., Bellmawr, 08031 ..................... (856) 933-0544
Airgas East, Inc., 1-D Frassetto Way, Lincoln Park, 07035 .................. (973) 633-9666
Airgas East, Inc., 2 Beckwith Ave., Paterson, 07503 ...................... (973) 742-2211
Airgas East, Inc., 490 Stelton Rd., Piscataway, 08854 ..................... (732) 752-4500
Airgas East, Inc., 1750 Gallagher Dr., Vineland, 08360 .................... (856) 692-7734

**AIRGAS, INC.**
**259 N. Radnor Chester Rd., Ste. 100, Radnor PA 19087 ................. (610) 687-5253**
**Ex. Chrm.—Peter McCausland; Pres., CEO—Michael Molinini;**
**Sr. V-P., CFO—Robert M. McLaughlin; Sr. V-P., CIO—Robert A. Dougherty;**
**Sr. V-P., Gen. Counsel—Robert H. Young, Jr.; Sr. V-P., Hum. Res.—Pamela Claypool;**
**Sr. V-P., Corp. Dev.—Leslie J. Graff; Sr. V-P., Dist.—Andy Cichocki;**
**V-P., Mktg. Comm.—Doug Sherman; Dir., Corp. Comm. & Inv. Rels.—Barry Strzelec**
Airgas, Inc., 5 Iron Horse Rd., Oakland, 07436 ........................... (201) 337-5891
Airgas Specialty Gases, 600 Union Landing Rd., Riverton, 08077 ............ (856) 829-7878
Airgas Retail Solutions, 270 U.S. Highway 9, Manalapan, 07726 ............. (732) 431-0288

**AKORN, INC.**
**1925 W. Field Ct., Ste. 300, Lake Forest IL 60045 ..................... (847) 279-6100**
**Chrm., CEO—Raj Rai; CFO—Timothy Dick; COO—Bruce Kutinsky;**
**Sr. V-P., Acct. Mgmt.—John Sabat; Sr. V-P., New Bus. Dev.—Sean Brynjelsen;**
**Sr. V-P., Reg. Affs.—Sam Boddapati; Hum. Res. Mgr.—Renee Wolf**
Akorn, Inc., 72 Veronica Ave., Somerset, 08873 ........................... (732) 846-8066

**ALCOA, INC.**
**390 Park Ave., 12th Fl., New York NY 10022 ........................... (212) 836-2600**
**Chrm. & CEO—Klaus Kleinfeld; CFO—Bill Oplinger; V-P., Treas.—Peter Hung;**
**V-P., Fin., N. American Rolled Prods.—Matthew Garth; V-P.—Kay Meggers;**
**Dir., Inv. Rels.—Roy Harvey; Compliance Officer—Audrey Strauss**
Alcoa, 9 Roy St., Dover, 07801 .......................................... (973) 361-2310

**ALERIS INTERNATIONAL, INC.**
**25825 Science Park Dr., Ste. 400, Beachwood OH 44122 ................ (216) 910-3400**
**Chrm., CEO—Steve Demetriou; Pres., Rolled Prods. N. America & Ex. V-P.—Alan Dick;**
**Ex. V-P., CFO—Sean Stack; Sr. V-P., Cont.—Scott McKinley;**
**Ex. V-P., Gen. Counsel—Christopher R. Clegg;**
**V-P., Sales & Mktg., Rolled Prods. N. America—Stephen Stone;**
**V-P., Hum. Res.—Melissa Olmstead; V-P., Risk Mgmt., Global—Kelly Thomas;**
**V-P., Comm.—Kristen M. Bihary;**
**V-P., Fin., Aleris Rolled Prods., N. America—Mike Keown;**
**V-P., Aleris Americas Metals Proc.—Ted Lehman; Mktg. Comm. Mgr.—Catherine Balzer**
Aleris Mfg., 838 N. Delsea Dr., Clayton, 08312 ........................... (856) 881-3600

**ALFA LAVAL, INC.**
**5400 International Trade Dr., Richmond VA 23231 ..................... (804) 222-5300**
**Pres., CEO—John Atanasio; Sr. V-P., Process Tech.—John Piazza;**
**V-P., Hum. Res.—Amy Hartley; V-P., Serv.—Jeff Sharbaugh;**
**V-P., Comms.—Chip Bresette; Gen. Counsel—Bill Connolly**
DSO Fluid Handling Co., Inc., 300 McGaw Dr., Ste. 2, Edison, 08837 ......... (732) 225-9100

**ALLIANCE VINYL WINDOW CO., INC.**
**301 Crescent Blvd., Mount Ephraim NJ 08059 ........................ (856) 456-4954**
**Pres., GM & Sales Mgr.—Jeff Hersh; Maint. Mgr.—Jim Pierce**
ABC Supply, 41 N. Pearl St., Bridgeton, 08302 ........................... (856) 455-4888

**ALLIED BEVERAGE GROUP, LLC**
**600 Washington Ave., P.O. Box 838, Carlstadt NJ 07072 ................ (201) 842-6200**
**Co-Chrm.—Eric M. Perlmutter; CIO—Brian Margolies; V-P., Hum. Res.—Jolynn Kawoczka**
Allied Beverage Group, LLC,
901 Plesant Valley Ave., P.O. Box 5090, Mount Laurel, 08054 .............. (856) 234-4111

**ALLIED BUILDING PRODUCTS CORP.**
**15 E. Union Ave., East Rutherford NJ 07073 .......................... (201) 507-8400**
**Chrm.—Michael Lynch; CEO—Bob Feury, Jr.; V-P., IT—Allen Amtel; V-P., Fin.—Frank Furia**
Allied Building Products Corp., 11 Cadillac Rd., Box 1838, Burlington, 08016 .... (609) 386-5500
Allied Building Products Corp., 850 Flora St., Elizabeth, 07201 ............. (908) 820-9790
Allied Building Products Corp., 406 State Route 23 N., Franklin, 07416 ........ (973) 827-4113
Allied Building Products Corp., 27-33 Franklin Tpke., Mahwah, 07430 .......... (201) 529-3300
Allied Building Products Corp., 27 Kentucky Ave., Paterson, 07503 ............ (973) 357-1600
Allied Building Products Corp., 320 W. Water St., Toms River, 08753 .......... (732) 341-4767
Allied Building Products Corp., 2065 State Route 34, Wall Township, 07719 ..... (732) 449-3355

**ALLIED BUILDING PRODUCTS CORP.—(cont.)**
Arzee Supply, 1905 Swarthmore Ave., Lakewood, 08701 ...................... (201) 935-0800
Arzee Supply Corp. Of New Jersey, 15 E. Frederick Pl., Cedar Knolls, 07927 .... (973) 267-1576
Arzee Supply Corp. Of New Jersey, 450 York St., Elizabeth, 07201 ........... (908) 820-3700
Allied Building Products Corp., 595 Union Blvd., Totowa, 07512 .............. (973) 790-5500

**ALLIED ELECTRONICS, INC.**
**7151 Jack Newell Blvd. S., P.O. Box 2325, Fort Worth TX 76118 ........... (817) 595-3500**
**Pres.—Lee Davidson; CFO—Ken Kempker; V-P., Sales—Mark Simon;**
**V-P., Mktg.—Scott McLendon; Dir., Hum. Res.—Susan Overcash**
Allied Electronics, Inc., 197 State Hwy. N-18, East Brunswick, 08816 .......... (732) 846-4271

**ALLIEDOP, INC.**
**1 Emery Ave., Ste. 1, Randolph NJ 07869 ............................ (973) 328-3340**
**Pres.—Joshua Schenkman**
AlliedOP, 1527 Route 27, Somerset, 08873 ............................... (732) 545-2885
AlliedOP, Inc., 579 Goffle Rd., Wyckoff, 07481 ........................... (201) 444-7750

**ALL-STATE FENCE, INC.**
**1389 Highway 9 N., Howell NJ 07731 ................................ (732) 431-4944**
**Pres.—Scott Skrable**
All-State Fence, Inc., 1389 Route 9 N., Howell, 07731 ...................... (732) 431-4944

**ALPHA INDUSTRIES CORP.**
**P.O. Box 808, Lyndhurst NJ 07071 ................................... (201) 933-6000**
**CEO—Alfred Teo; CFO—John Reier; Hum. Res. Mgr.—Debra Barbour**
Beta Plastics Corp., 120 Amor Ave., Carlstadt, 07072 ...................... (201) 933-1400
Omega Plastics Corp.,
Page & Schuyler Ave., Bldg. 3, P.O. Box 808, Lyndhurst, 07071 ............ (201) 933-5353
Sigma Plastics Group (H Q),
Page & Schuyler Aves., Bldg. 5, P.O. Box 808, Lyndhurst, 07071 ........... (201) 933-6000
Southeastern Plastics Corp., 15 Home News Row, New Brunswick, 08901 ...... (732) 846-8500

**ALPHAGRAPHICS PRINTSHOPS OF THE FUTURE**
**15720 N. Greenway Hayden Loop, Ste. 4, Scottsdale AZ 85260 ........... (480) 991-1636**
**Owner—Cash Bestor; Prod. Mgr.—Adam Duffy; Manager—Steve Petrie**
AlphaGraphics Printshops, 68 White St., Red Bank, 07701 ................. (732) 758-0095

**ALTRA INDUSTRIAL MOTION, INC.**
**300 Granite St., Ste. 201, Braintree MA 02184 ........................ (781) 917-0600**
**Pres.—Carl Christianson; V-P., Legal Counsel—Glenn Deegan; Cont.—Todd Patriacca**
Bauer Gear Motor, LLC, 31 Schoolhouse Rd., Somerset, 08873 .............. (732) 469-8770

**AMANO USA HOLDINGS, INC.**
**140 Harrison Ave., Roseland NJ 07068 ............................... (973) 403-1900**
**Pres., CEO—Masamiki Konno; Dir., Hum. Res.—Pat Pearson;**
**Global Sys. Mgr.—Hiro Araseki**
Amano McGann, 140 Harrison Ave., Roseland, 07068 ...................... (973) 618-4050

**AMARR GARAGE DOORS**
**165 Carriage Ct., Winston-Salem NC 27105 ........................... (336) 744-5100**
**Vice Chrm.—Richard Brenner; Pres., CEO—Jeff Mick; V-P., CFO—Richard Sears;**
**CIO—Steve Crawford; V-P., Sales—Lyle Simons; V-P., Supply Chain—Matt Hukill;**
**V-P., Process Improvement—Shawn O'Brien; Hum. Res. Mgr.—Terri Workman**
Amarr Garage Doors, 12 Coddington Rd., Whitehouse Station, 08889 ......... (908) 534-4112

**AMCOR FLEXIBLES, INC.**
**1919 S. Butterfield Rd., Mundelein IL 60060 .......................... (847) 362-9000**
**V-P., Hum. Res.—Steve Slesnick; V-P., Tech.—Bob Biasi; V-P., Med. Cluster—Tony King;**
**Cont., Fin. Mgr.—Fred Anhalt; MIS Mgr.—Tom Hicks; Bus. Dev. Mgr.—Christine Schaefer**
Amcor Flexibles, Inc., 220 Shreve St., Mount Holly, 08060 .................. (609) 267-5900

**AMCOR RIGID PLASTICS**
**10521 S. Highway M-52, Manchester MI 48158 ......................... (734) 428-9741**
**Pres.—Michael Schmitt; V-P., GM, Beverage Div.—Larry Weber;**
**V-P., GM, Food Div.—Michael Curia; V-P., Hum. Res.—Mike Bieringer;**
**Sr. Dir., Hum. Res.—Denise Hansen; Hum. Res. Mgr.—Barbara Kerr**
Amcor Rigid Plastics, 625 Sharp St., Millville, 08332 ...................... (856) 327-1540

**AMDOCS, INC.**
**1390 Timberlake Manor Pkwy., Chesterfield MO 63017 ................... (314) 212-7000**
**Chrm.—Bruce Anderson; Pres., CEO—Eli Gelman; V-P., IT—Golan Remi**
Amdocs, Inc., 34 Exchange Pl., Jersey City, 07311 ........................ (201) 631-3200

**AMEREX CORP.**
**7595 Gadsden Hwy., P.O. Box 81, Trussville AL 35173 ................... (205) 655-3271**
**Pres.—Dennis Kennedy; V-P., Sales, Intl.—Mayra Diaz; V-P., Sales—Andy Halasz;**
**V-P., Prodn.—Vick Modic; V-P., Adv. & Mktg.—Mike Champion;**
**V-P., Hum. Res.—Chris Thomas; V-P., Fin.—Brian Justinger;**
**V-P., Engrg.—Fred Goodnight**
Amerex Corp., 128 Bauer Dr., Ste. 4, Oakland, 07436 ...................... (201) 337-1616

**AMERICAN ASPHALT CO., INC.**
**116 Main St., West Collingswood Heights NJ 08059 ..................... (856) 456-2899**
**Pres., CEO—Robert M. Brown; COO—Joseph R. Ford; V-P., Sales & Mktg.—Dave Sulkin;**
**V-P., Construction—Robert Moncrief; Cont.—Karen Ioven; Dir., Mktg.—Maryann Busler**
American Asphalt Company, Inc., 1701 River Rd., Burlington, 08016 .......... (856) 456-2899

**AMERICAN BILTRITE, INC.**
**57 River St., Ste. 302, Wellesley MA 02481 ........................... (781) 237-6655**
**Pres.—Richard Marcus; V-P., CFO—Howard Feist; Ex. V-P.—William Marcus;**
**Hum. Res. Mgr.—Adelle Muller**
American Biltrite, Inc., 105 Whittendale Dr., Moorestown, 08057 ............ (856) 778-0700

**AMERICAN MARKING SYSTEMS, INC.**
**1015 Paulison Ave., Clifton NJ 07011 ................................ (973) 478-5600**
**Pres.—John Collins; Cont.—John Newberger; Sales & Mktg. Mgr.—Ronald Cochran**
Paterson Stamp Works, 1015 Paulison Ave., Clifton, 07011 .................. (973) 478-5600

**AMERICAN MONUMENT CO.**
**479 N. Dean St., Englewood NJ 07631 ................................ (201) 569-4455**
**Pres.—Ron Boyajian; V-P.—Greg Boyajian**
American Monument Co., 50 Herbert Ave., Closter, 07624 .................. (201) 750-1000

**AMERICAN PAPER PRODUCTS**
**1722 Sumneytown Pike, P.O. Box 412, Kulpsville PA 19443 ................ (215) 362-8582**
**Pres.—Ramon C. Gerber; V-P., Sales—David Perelman**
American Tube & Paper, 80 Furler St., Totowa, 07512 ..................... (973) 256-3600

**AMERICAN SENSOR TECHNOLOGIES, INC.**
**450 Clark Dr., Ste. 4, Budd Lake NJ 07828 .......... (973) 448-1901**
**Pres., CEO—Richard Tasker; V-P., CFO—Michael Eldredge; V-P., Bus. Dev.—Karmjit Sidhu; Sales & Mktg. Mgr.—Samuel Franzblau; Mktg. Mgr.—Greg Montrose**
Macro Sensors, 7300 Route 130 N., Bldg. 22, Pennsauken, 08110 .......... (856) 662-8000

**AMETEK, INC.**
**1100 Cassatt Rd., Berwyn PA 19312 .......... (610) 647-2121**
**Chrm., CEO—Frank Hermance; Co-Pres.—John Weslie Hardin; Co-Pres.—Timothy N. Jones; Co-Pres.—David A. Zapico; CFO—Bob Mandos; V-P., CIO—Kenneth C. Weirman; Sr. V-P., Comp. & Treas.—William J. Burke; Sr. V-P., GM—Tom Marecic; Sr. V-P., Hum. Res.—Gregory J. Kelble; Pub. Rels. Mgr.—Jim McKinley**
Ametek Glasseal, Inc., 485 Oberlin Ave. S., Lakewood, 08701 .......... (732) 370-9100
Coining, Inc., 15 Mercedes Dr., Montvale, 07645 .......... (201) 791-4020
Spectro Analytical Instruments, Inc., 91 McKee Dr., Mahwah, 07430 .......... (201) 642-3000
Vision Research, Inc., 100 Dey Rd., Wayne, 07470 .......... (973) 696-4500

**AMNEAL PHARMACEUTICALS, LLC**
**400 Crossing Blvd., 3rd Fl., Bridgewater NJ 08807 .......... (908) 947-3120**
**Chrm., Co-CEO—Chirag Patel; Sr. V-P., Opers.—Sanjiv Patel; Sr. V-P., Global Opers. & Strategy—Joseph Todisco**
Amneal Pharmaceuticals, LLC, 47 Colonial Dr., Piscataway, 08854 .......... (732) 645-3030

**AMSAN FLORIDA**
**3031 N. Andrews Ave. Ext., Pompano Beach FL 33064 .......... (954) 972-1700**
**Pres., Div.—James Cusick; Sales Mgr.—Michael Dinnen; Hum. Res. Mgr.—Gladys Marin**
Amsan Eagle Maintenance Supply, 80 Twin Bridge Dr., Pennsauken, 08110 ..... (856) 317-9500

**ANCHOR GLASS CONTAINER CORP.**
**401 E. Jackson St., Ste. 2800, Tampa FL 33602 .......... (813) 884-0000**
**Pres., CEO—Jim Fredlake; Chief Comml. Officer—Alex Robertson; V-P., Sales—Tom Wieclaw; V-P., Mfg.—Gene Gavin; Cont.—Jerry Jurik**
Ardagh Group, 83 Griffith St., Salem, 08079 .......... (856) 935-4000

**ANDERSEN CORP.**
**100 4th Ave. N., Bayport MN 55003 .......... (651) 264-5150**
**Chrm., Pres. & CEO—Jay Lund; Sr. V-P., CFO—Philip Donaldson; Sr. V-P., CAO—Mary Carter; V-P., Hum. Res.—Nancy Merritt; V-P., Enterprise Fin.—Keith Olson; Dir., Comm.—Laurie Bauer**
Silver Line Building Products, LLC, 1 Silver Line Dr., P.O. Box 6029, North Brunswick, 08902 .......... (732) 435-1000

**ANDLER PACKAGING GROUP**
**376 3rd St., P.O. Box 499125, Everett MA 02149 .......... (617) 387-5700**
**Pres.—Arnold Andler; IT Mgr.—Richard Lewin; Accts. Payable Mgr.—Lisa Syngajewski**
Andler South Corp., 102 E. Parkway Dr., Egg Harbor Township, 08234 .......... (609) 485-2000

**ANHEUSER-BUSCH INBEV WORLDWIDE, INC.**
**1 Busch Pl., St. Louis MO 63118 .......... (314) 577-2000**
**Pres.—David A. Peacock; Pres., Busch Entertainment Group—Jim Atchison; Zone Pres., N. America—Luis Fernando Edmond; V-P., Zone Gen. Counsel—Gary L. Rutledge; V-P., Corp. Affs.—James Villeneuve; V-P., Sales—Evan Athanas; V-P., Natl. Retail Sales—Chris Williams; V-P., Retail & Brand Mktg.—Dan Hoffmann; V-P., Entertainment, Media & Sports Mktg.—Mark Wright; V-P., Fin.—David Almeida; V-P., Budweiser—Rob McCarthy; V-P., People—James G. Brickey; V-P., Innovations—Pat McGauley; V-P., Insights—Linda Tucker; V-P., Mktg. Sols.—Julia Mize; V-P., Bus. & Dev., Wholesale—Don Johnson; V-P., Bus. Svcs. & Info.—Odilon Queiroz; V-P., Supply—Peter J. Kraemer; V-P., Proc.—Thomas J. Adamitis; V-P., Logistics—Pablo Gonzalez**
Anheuser-Busch Cos., Inc., 200 U.S. Highway 1 & 9, Newark, 07114 .......... (973) 645-7700

**API TECHNOLOGIES CORP.**
**4705 S. Apopka Vineland Rd., Ste. 210, Orlando FL 32819 .......... (855) 294-3800**
**Pres., CEO—Bel Lazar; CFO—Phil Rehkemper**
API Technologies Corp., 120 Corporate Blvd., South Plainfield, 07080 .......... (908) 546-3900

**APPLIED INDUSTRIAL TECHNOLOGIES, INC.**
**1 Applied Plz., Cleveland OH 44115 .......... (216) 426-4000**
**Chrm., CEO—Dave Pugh; Pres., COO—Ben Mondics; V-P., CFO & Fin.—Mark Eisele; V-P., IT—Lonny Lawrence; V-P., Hum. Res.—Barb Emery**
Applied Industrial Technologies, Inc., 24-C Worlds Fair Dr., Somerset, 08873 ... (732) 356-0522

**APRIA HEALTHCARE, INC.**
**26220 Enterprise Ct., Lake Forest CA 92630 .......... (949) 639-2000**
**CEO—Norman C. Payson; Pres., COO—Jim Gallas; CFO—Chris A. Karkenny; Ex. V-P., CIO—Douglas Rutledge; Sr. V-P., Mktg.—Jonathan Zalk; Ex. V-P., Sales—Gregory Scofield; Ex. V-P., Hum. Res.—Howard Derman; Ex. V-P., Govt. Rels., Inv. Svcs. Compliance—Lisa Getson; Ex. V-P., Revenue Mgmt.—Robin Barton; Ex. V-P.—Robert Holcombe**
Apria Healthcare, Inc., 1 Frassetto Way, Ste. F, Lincoln Park, 07035 .......... (973) 305-0099
Apria Healthcare, Inc., 118 Burrs Rd., Ste. C, Mount Holly, 08060 .......... (609) 265-2190

**AQUA SYSTEMS, INC.**
**Exeter Rd., P.O. Box 181, Hampton Falls NH 03844 .......... (603) 778-8796**
**Pres.—Ernest M. Cherry, Jr.**
Edwards Coils Corp., 101 Alexander Ave., Unit 6, Pompton Plains, 07444 ....... (973) 835-2815

**ARC DOCUMENT SOLUTIONS, INC.**
**1981 N. Broadway, Ste. 385, Walnut Creek CA 94596 .......... (925) 949-5100**
**Chrm., Pres. & CEO—Kumarakulasingam Suriyakumar; CFO—John Toth; Chief Operating Officer—Dilantha 'Dilo' Wijesuriya; CTO—Rahul Roy; V-P., Fin. & CAO—Jorge Avalos; Ex. V-P., Sales, N. America—Patrick Welch; V-P., Corp. Comms. & Inv. Rels.—David Stickney; Dir., Mktg., Worldwide—Scott Sipherd; Dir., Hum. Res.—Laura Williams**
ARC Document Solutions, 844 Fairfield Ave., Kenilworth, 07033 .......... (973) 372-5200

**ARCADE MARKETING, INC.**
**1700 Broadway, Ste. 2500, New York NY 10019 .......... (212) 541-2600**
**Sr. V-P., Bus. Dev. & Sales & Mktg.—Diane Crecca; V-P., Sales Admn.—Paul S. Pearl; Admn. Mgr.—Yvette Stewart**
Color Optics By Arcade, Inc., 40 Green Pond Rd., Rockaway, 07866 .......... (973) 664-3100

**ARCTIC GLACIER U. S .A., INC.**
**1654 Marthaler Ln., West St. Paul MN 55118 .......... (651) 455-0410**
**Regional GM—Robert Nikolai; Plt. Mgr.—Chris Cook; Qual. Assur. Mgr.—Chris Green; Dist. Mgr.—Curt Larson**
Arctic Glacier, Inc., 2 Johnson Dr., Raritan, 08869 .......... (908) 231-0100

**ARDE, INC.**
**875 Washington Ave., Carlstadt NJ 07072 .......... (201) 784-9880**
**GM—Kirk Sneddon**
ARDE Barinco, Inc., 875 Washington Ave., Carlstadt, 07072 .......... (201) 768-6070

**ARDOM BEARING GROUP**
**1000 Bennett Blvd., Ste. 7, Lakewood NJ 08701 .......... (732) 370-2310**
**Owner & Pres.—Dominick Commesso**
Ardom Bearing Group, 3377 S. Clinton Ave., Unit 15, South Plainfield, 07080 ... (908) 755-3000

**ARIVA DISTRIBUTION, INC.**
**50 E. River Center Blvd., Ste. 500, Covington KY 41011 .......... (859) 292-5000**
**Pres.—Mark Ushpol; V-P., USA—Mark Matthews; V-P., Hum. Res.—Cindy Witterstaetter; Dir., IT—Scott Alexander**
Ariva Distribution, Inc., 1705 Suckle Hwy., Pennsauken, 08110 .......... (856) 488-0800

**ARIZONA BEVERAGES USA, LLC**
**60 Crossways Park Dr. W., Ste. 400, Woodbury NY 11797 .......... (516) 812-0300**
**Ptnr. & Creative Dir.—Wesley Vultaggio; Ptnr. & Dir., Brand Dev.—Spencer Vultaggio; Chrm.—Don Vultaggio; CEO—David Menashi; CFO—Pat Catalina; Ex. V-P., Sales & Mktg.—Rob Marciano; V-P., Facilities—John Posillico; V-P., Opers.—Tom Deluca; Dir., Sales & Mktg.—Doreen Higney; Dir., Comms. & Mktg.—Jennifer Smith**
Maplewood Beverage Packers, LLC, 45 Camptown Rd., Maplewood, 07040 .... (973) 416-4582

**ARNOLD FURNITURE MFRS., INC.**
**400 Coit St., Irvington NJ 07111 .......... (973) 399-0505**
**Pres.—Julius Arnold; Sr. V-P.—Glenn Arnold; GM—Mark Lipka; Special Projs. Mgr.—Barbara Arnold**
Arnold Desks, Inc., 1409 Chestnut Ave., P.O. Box 842, Hillside, 07205 .......... (908) 686-5656
Arnold Kolax Furniture, Inc., 146 Coit St., Irvington, 07111 .......... (973) 375-3344

**ARROW SHED, LLC**
**1101 N. 4th St., Breese IL 62230 .......... (618) 526-4546**
**Plt. Opers. Mgr.—Steve Weilbacher; Hum. Res. & Pers. Mgr.—Beth Fischer; Hum. Res. Coord.—Cathy Wood**
Arrow Shed, LLC, 1 3rd Ave., Haskell, 07420 .......... (973) 835-3200

**ART GUILD, INC.**
**300 Wolf Dr., West Deptford NJ 08086 .......... (856) 853-7500**
**Pres.—Doug Zegel; Proj. Mgr.—Rich Clark; Proj. Mgr.—Desiree Williams; Pur. Agt.—Brian Moore**
SYMA Systems, Inc., 300 Wolf Dr., West Deptford, 08086 .......... (856) 686-4190

**ARYZTA LA BREA BAKERY, INC.**
**15963 Strathern St., Van Nuys CA 91406 .......... (818) 742-4242**
**Pres., CEO—John Yamin**
Aryzta/La Brea Bakery, 11 Technology Dr., Swedesboro, 08085 .......... (856) 417-8100

**ASBURY PARK PRESS, INC.**
**3600 Highway 66, P.O. Box 1550, Neptune NJ 07754 .......... (732) 922-6000**
**Pres., Publisher—Thomas M. Donovan; V-P., Editor—Hollis Townes; V-P., IT—Wayne Peragallo; V-P., Hum. Res.—Kathy Abatemarco; V-P., Fin.—Kevin Huff; V-P., Prod.—Jack Roth; V-P., Circ.—Jane Pettigrew; Dir. & Mktg. Mgr.—Gina Longo**
Asbury Park Press, 3600 Highway 66, Neptune, 07753 .......... (732) 922-6000

**ASCO POWER TECHNOLOGIES, L.P.**
**50 Hanover Rd., Florham Park NJ 07932 .......... (800) 800-2726**
**Pres.—Armand J. Visioli; V-P., Sales & Mktg.—Donald Blackman; V-P., Opers.—Mike Quinn; V-P., Serv.—Allan Dunster; V-P., Intl.—Amir Abouhasm; V-P., Engrg.—Daniel Scheffer**
ASCO Power Technologies, Inc., 5000 Sagemore Dr., Ste. 200, Marlton, 08053 . (856) 810-9600

**ASCO VALVE, INC.**
**50-60 Hanover Rd., Florham Park NJ 07932 .......... (973) 966-2000**
**Group Pres.—Jean Pierre Yaouanc; Ex. V-P., Sales & Mktg., Americas—Robert W. Kemple, Jr.; V-P., Hum. Res.—Christopher Walsh; Corp. Secy.—Mary Ann Kranz; Dir., IT—Horst Braumann; Mktg. Comm. Mgr.—Kristen Walker**
ASCO Valve, Inc., 50 Hanover Rd., Florham Park, 07932 .......... (973) 966-2000
ASCO Valve, Inc., 13000 Lincoln Dr. W., Ste. 106, Marlton, 08053 .......... (856) 985-8700

**ASHLAND, INC.**
**50 E. RiverCenter Blvd., Covington KY 41012 .......... (859) 815-3333**
**Chrm., CEO—James J. O'Brien; Sr. V-P., CFO—Kevin Willis; Sr. V-P., Gen. Counsel—Peter Ganz; V-P., Comm. & Hum. Res.—Susan Esler; Dir., Inv. Rels.—David A. Neuberger; Pur. Mgr.—David Noll; IT Mgr.—Robert Williams**
Ashland, Inc., 116 Summit Ave., Chatham, 07928 .......... (973) 635-1551
Ashland, Inc., International Specialty Products (H Q), 56 Livingston Ave., Ste. 400, Roseland, 07068 .......... (973) 533-5400

**ASHLAND, INC.**
**500 Hercules Rd., Wilmington DE 19808 .......... (302) 995-3000**
**Pres. & V-P., Ashland Spec. Ingredients—John E. Panichella; V-P., CIO—Anne T. Schumann; —Mike Hassman**
Ashland Aqualon, Inc., 50 S. Minnisink Ave., Parlin, 08859 .......... (732) 254-1234

**ASSA, INC.**
**110 Sargent Dr., New Haven CT 06511 .......... (203) 603-5958**
**Pres., CEO—Thanasis Molokotos; Dir., Sales & Mktg.—Richard Eisen; Sales Mgr., Western—Lance Berger; Opers. Mgr.—Al Leites; Hum. Res. Mgr.—Jack Dwyer; Cust. Serv. Mgr.—Edmond Dorne; Pur. Agt.—Steve Heltke**
Mul-T-Lock USA, Inc., 100 Commerce Way, Ste. 2, Hackensack, 07601 .......... (973) 778-3222

**ASSEMBLIES UNLIMITED, INC.**
**143 Covington Dr., Bloomingdale IL 60108 .......... (630) 980-0200**
**Pres.—Randy Shaw; CFO—Kimberly Vorhees; Sales Mgr.—Jim DeKosta; Cust. Serv. Mgr.—Michele Butler; Sales Coord., Inside—Justin Dickert; Sales Coord., Inside—Les Shaw**
Assemblies Unlimited, Inc., 530 N. Michigan Ave., Kenilworth, 07033 .......... (877) 273-6259

**ASSET RECOVERY SPECIALISTS, INC.**
9707 Aero Dr., San Diego CA 92123 . . . . . . . . . . . . . . . . (858) 277-7555
Ptnr.—Dean Baker; CEO—Randy Dillon; Hum. Res. Mgr.—Dulce Martinez
Asset Recovery Specialists, Inc., 3 Killdeer Ct., Ste. 303, Swedesboro, 08085 . . . (856) 467-9822

**ASTRO TOOL CORP.**
21615 S.W. Tualatin Valley Hwy., Beaverton OR 97006 . . . . . . . . . . . . . . (503) 642-9853
Pres.—James Vargo; GM—Mike Barnes
Astro Tool Corp., 90 Washington Ave., Nutley, 07110 . . . . . . . . . . . (973) 661-1299

**ASTRODYNE CORP.**
375 Forbes Blvd., Mansfield MA 02048 . . . . . . . . . . . . . . . . . . (508) 964-6300
Pres., CEO—Peter Kaczmarek; Secy-Treas.—James Herlihy; Sales Mgr.—Eric Kessler;
Pur. Mgr.—Christine Sargo; IT Mgr.—David Lee; Qual. Control Mgr.—James Clifford
Jerome Industries Corp., 730 Division St., Elizabeth, 07201 . . . . . . . . . . (908) 353-5700

**ASTRONAUTICS CORP. OF AMERICA**
4115 N. Teutonia Ave., Milwaukee WI 53209 . . . . . . . . . . . . . . . (414) 449-4000
Chrm., CEO—Ronald E. Zelazo; Pres.—Chad Cundiff; CFO—Stephen Givant;
V-P., Secy., Admn.—Holly Russek; V-P., Matls., Dir., IT & Opers. Mgr.—Joe Potts;
V-P., Engrg.—Greg Burton; V-P., Bus. Dev.—Dan Wade; Pur. Mgr.—Ron Reitz
Kearfott Corporation, Guidance & Navigation Div.,
1150 McBride Ave., Little Falls, 07424 . . . . . . . . . . . . . . . (973) 785-6000

**ATCO RUBBER PRODUCTS, INC.**
7101 Atco Dr., Fort Worth TX 76118 . . . . . . . . . . . . . . . . . . (817) 595-2894
Chrm., Pres. & CEO—Ramesh Bhatia; CFO—Randel Calaway;
V-P., Sales—Samuel Kirkland; V-P., Mfg.—Larry Cox; V-P., Opers.—Paul Evans;
V-P., Hum. Res.—Bill Lightsey; Dir., Engrg.—Bill McReynolds;
Dir., Tech. Svcs.—Ralph Koerber
ATCO Rubber Products, Inc., 1480 N. West Blvd., Vineland, 08360 . . . . . . . . . (856) 794-3393

**ATLANTIC COAST CONTAINER BROKERAGE & SALES, INC.**
520 Water Garden Ct., Irmo SC 29063 . . . . . . . . . . . . . . . . . (803) 749-6061
Pres.—Jim Neal
Atlantic Coast Container Brokerage & Sales, Inc.,
906 Oak Tree Rd., Ste. P, South Plainfield, 07080 . . . . . . . . . (908) 755-2898

**AUTOPART INTERNATIONAL, INC.**
192 Mansfield Ave., Norton MA 02766 . . . . . . . . . . . . . . . . . (781) 784-1111
Founder—Steve Patkin; CEO—Roger Patkin; CFO—Thomas O'Reilly;
Integrated Dist. Chief, Opers. Div.—Brian Vautrin
Autopart International, Inc., 260 Hudson St., Hackensack, 07601 . . . . . . . . (201) 488-4187
Autopart International, Inc., 1773 Pine Ave., Unit A, Vineland, 08360 . . . . . . . (856) 405-0346

**AVANTI**
1580 Corporate Parkway Blvd., Clarksville TN 37040 . . . . . . . . . . . (931) 542-1039
Pres.—Gregory Day
Avanti, 2650 U.S. Highway 130., Ste. I, Cranbury, 08512 . . . . . . . . . . (609) 655-5333

**AWISCO NEW YORK CORP.**
5515 43rd St., Maspeth NY 11378 . . . . . . . . . . . . . . . . . . (718) 786-7788
Pres.—Lloyd Robinson; V-P., Opers.—Felim O'Malley; V-P., Sales & Mktg.—Victor Fuhrman
Awisco Corp., 24 Lakeside Ave., West Orange, 07052 . . . . . . . . . (973) 736-0200
Awisco West Milford, LLC, 26 Industrial Rd., West Milford, 07480 . . . . . . . . (973) 728-9008

**AZUMA FOODS INTERNATIONAL, INC. U.S.A.**
20201 Mack St., Hayward CA 94545 . . . . . . . . . . . . . . . . . (510) 782-1112
Chrm.—Toshinobu Azuma; Pres.—Takahiro Tamura; Mktg. Mgr.—Lawrence Sato
Azuma Foods International, Inc.,
20 Murray Hill Pkwy., Ste. 130, East Rutherford, 07073 . . . . . . . . . . (201) 372-1112

**B & G FOODS, INC.**
4 Gatehall Dr., Ste. 110, Parsippany NJ 07054 . . . . . . . . . . . . . . (973) 401-6500
Pres.—David Wenner; CFO—Robert Cantwell; Ex. V-P., Sales—Vanessa Maskal;
Ex. V-P., Opers.—Bill Herbes; V-P., Hum. Res.—Andy Chosso;
V-P., Qual. Control—William Wright; V-P., Dist.—Chris Bauman; Dir., IT—Steve DePaul;
Dir., Fin.—Amy Chiovari
Violet Packing, 123 Railroad Ave., Williamstown, 08094 . . . . . . . . . (856) 629-7428

**B. BRAUN MEDICAL, INC.**
824 12th Ave., Bethlehem PA 18018 . . . . . . . . . . . . . . . . . (610) 691-5400
Chrm. & CEO, Americas—Caroll Neubauer; Sr. V-P., CFO—Bruce A. Heugel;
Sr. V-P., Hum. Res.—Chris Donigan; V-P., IT—Scott Fehnco
Central Admixture Pharmacy Services, 160 W. Forest Ave., Englewood, 07631 . . (201) 541-0080

**B/E AEROSPACE, INC.**
1400 Corporate Center Way, Wellington FL 33414 . . . . . . . . . . . . (561) 791-5000
Chrm., CEO—Amin Khoury; Pres., COO—Werner Lieberherr; CFO—Tom McCaffrey;
V-P., Fin. & Treas.—Eric Wesch; V-P., Fin. & Cont.—Stephen Swisher
B/E Consumables Management, 650 From Rd., Paramus, 07652 . . . . . . . . (201) 265-8770

**BAKEMARK USA, LLC**
7351 Crider Ave., Pico Rivera CA 90660 . . . . . . . . . . . . . . . . (562) 949-1054
Pres., CEO—Jim Parker; CFO—Refugio Reynoso;
V-P., Mktg. & Natl. Acct. Sales—Rik Bennett; Dir., Sales—Dave Smith;
Hum. Res. Mgr.—Christine Salazar
BakeMark USA, LLC, 1815 Route 130 N., Burlington, 08016 . . . . . . . . (609) 747-9000

**BAKERCORP.**
3020 Old Ranch Pkwy., Ste. 220, Seal Beach CA 90740 . . . . . . . . . (562) 430-6262
CEO—Brian Livingston; CFO—Jim Leonetti; Chief Hum. Res. Officer—Beth Ganem;
Ex. V-P.—Mark Pugh; V-P., Sales & Mktg.—Paul Cummins; Gen. Counsel—Amy Paul;
Treas.—Tim Labuda; IT Mgr.—Larry Shelton
BakerCorp., 50 Gilchris Dr., Swedesboro, 08085 . . . . . . . . . . . (856) 467-2677

**BARRY CALLEBAUT USA, LLC**
600 W. Chicago Ave., Ste. 860, Chicago IL 60654 . . . . . . . . . . . . (312) 496-7300
Pres., CEO—Dave Johnson; CFO—James G. Hagedorn; CIO—Steve Vandamme;
V-P., Opers.—Ken Cotich; Tech. Mgr.—Bart Goetmaeckers
Barry Callebaut USA, LLC, 1500 Suckle Hwy., Pennsauken, 08110 . . . . . . . . (856) 663-2260

**BASF CORPORATION**
100 Park Ave., Florham Park NJ 07932 . . . . . . . . . . . . . . . . (973) 245-6000
Chrm., CEO—Hans Engel; Pres., Ex. V-P. & CFO—Andre Becker;
Pres. & Ex. V-P., Cust. & Market Dev.—Beate Ehle;
Pres. & Ex. V-P., Catalysts Div.—Kenneth Lane;
Sr. V-P., Gen. Counsel & CCO—Matthew Lepore;
V-P., Chief Comms. Officer—Robin Rotenberg; Sr. V-P., Hum. Res.—Judy Zagorski;
Corp. Media Rels. Mgr.—Kelley P. White
BASF Corp., 2 Pleasant View Ave., Washington, 07882 . . . . . . . . . . (908) 689-7540
BASF Corporation, Catalysts Div.,
25 Middlesex-Essex Tpke., P.O. Box 770, Iselin, 08830 . . . . . . . . (732) 205-5000
BASF Fuel Cell, Inc., 39 Veronica Ave., Somerset, 08873 . . . . . . . . . (732) 545-5100

**BA-TAMPTE PICKLE PRODUCTS, INC.**
77 Brooklyn Terminal Market, Brooklyn NY 11236 . . . . . . . . . . . . (718) 251-2100
Pres.—Barry Silberstein; V-P.—Scott Silberstein
Ba-Tampte Pickle Products, Inc., 2660 Main Rd., Franklinville, 08322 . . . . . . (856) 697-9815

**BAY STATE MILLING CO.**
100 Congress St., Quincy MA 02169 . . . . . . . . . . . . . . . . . (617) 328-4400
Chrm. of the Board—Bernard Rothwell III; CEO—Brian Rothwell;
Pres., COO—Peter Levangie; V-P., Fin.—Bill Quigley; Dir., Hum. Res.—Val Hawkes;
IT Mgr.—Kim Yaworsky
Bay State Milling Co., 404 Getty Ave., Clifton, 07011 . . . . . . . . . . . (973) 772-1000

**BAYER HEALTHCARE**
100 Global View Dr., Warrendale PA 15086 . . . . . . . . . . . . . . (412) 767-2400
Ex. Dir., Hum. Res.—Karen Zelenski; Dir., Opers.—Joe Kridgen;
Comm. Mgr.—Alicia Cafardi; Head of Interventional & Radiology—Samuel Liang
Bayer Healthcare, Consumer Care Div.,
100 Bayer Blvd., P.O. Box 915, Whippany, 07962 . . . . . . . . . . (862) 404-3000

**BAYER MATERIALSCIENCE, LLC**
100 Bayer Rd., Ste. 4, Pittsburgh PA 15205 . . . . . . . . . . . . . . (412) 777-2000
Pres.—Gerald MacCleary; Gen. Counsel & Secy.—Lars Benecke
Bayer HealthCare Pharmaceuticals (H Q), 100 Bayer Blvd., Whippany, 07981 . . . (862) 404-3000

**BAYONNE PLUMBING SUPPLY, INC.**
250 Avenue E, Bayonne NJ 07002 . . . . . . . . . . . . . . . . . . (201) 339-8000
Ptnr.—Richard Epstein; Ptnr.—Chris Bayonne
New Jersey Plumbing, Heating & Industrial Supply, LLC,
91 Newark Way, Maplewood, 07040 . . . . . . . . . . . . . . . (973) 761-4567
Bath Connection, The, 183 Millburn Ave., Millburn, 07041 . . . . . . . . . (973) 467-7888

**BCG MARBLE & GRANITE FABRICATORS CO., INC.**
167 Sussex St., Hackensack NJ 07601 . . . . . . . . . . . . . . . . (201) 343-8487
Owner & Pres.—Giuseppe Guerini
BCG Marble & Granite Co., 370 Whitesville Rd., Jackson, 08527 . . . . . . . . (732) 367-3788

**BELDEN INC.**
1 N. Brentwood Blvd., 15th Fl., St. Louis MO 63105 . . . . . . . . . . . (314) 854-8000
Pres., CEO—John Stroup; Sr. V-P., Fin., CAO & CFO—Henk Derkson;
Sr. V-P., Gen. Counsel & Secy.—Kevin Bloomfield; Dir., Outbound Mktg.—Eric Ehlers;
Mktg. Comms. Mgr.—Michelle Foster
Alpha Wire Co., 711 Lidgerwood Ave., P.O. Box 711, Elizabeth, 07207 . . . . . . (908) 925-8000

**BENJAMIN MOORE & CO.**
101 Paragon Dr., Montvale NJ 07645 . . . . . . . . . . . . . . . . . (201) 573-9600
CEO—Mike Searles; Sr. V-P., Opers.—Barry Chadwick; V-P., Gen. Counsel—Mark Boyland;
V-P., Mfg.—Ken Marino; V-P., Mktg.—Nick Harris; V-P., Fin.—Robert Pettel;
Dir., Corp. Comm.—Kimberlee Bradshaw; Comms. Mgr.—Kelly Sinatra
Benjamin Moore & Co., 134 Lister Ave., Newark, 07105 . . . . . . . . . . (973) 344-1200

**BERKSHIRE HATHAWAY, INC.**
3555 Farnam St., Ste. 1440, Omaha NE 68131 . . . . . . . . . . . . . (402) 346-1400
Chrm., CEO—Warren E. Buffett; Vice Chrm.—Charles T. Munger;
V-P., Treas., CFO—Marc D. Hamburg
Benjamin Moore & Co. (H Q), 101 Paragon Dr., Montvale, 07645 . . . . . . . . (201) 573-9600
Graver Water Systems, LLC, 675 Central Ave., Ste. 3, New Providence, 07974 . . (908) 516-1400

**BERLIN PACKAGING, LLC**
525 W. Monroe St., Ste. 1400, Chicago IL 60661 . . . . . . . . . . . . (312) 876-9292
Chrm., CEO—Andrew T. Berlin; CIO—Paul Roche;
V-P., Admn. & Mktg. Svcs.—Carole Branchetti; V-P., Hum. Res.—Jim Sollenberger;
V-P., Fin.—Neil Schwab; V-P., Design & Innovation—Scott Jost
Berlin Packaging, LLC, 2050 Center Ave., Ste. 400, Fort Lee, 07024 . . . . . . . (201) 947-7744

**BERRY PLASTICS CORP.**
101 Oakley St., Evansville IN 47710 . . . . . . . . . . . . . . . . . (812) 424-2904
CEO—Jonathan Rich; Pres., Rigid Open Top—William Norman; Ex. V-P., CFO—Mark Miles;
Ex. V-P., CIO—Mark Freeman; Ex. V-P., Opers.—Rodgers Greenawalt;
Ex. V-P., Pur., Global—Scott Farmer; Ex. V-P., Hum. Res.—Ed Stratton;
Ex. V-P., Strategic Corp. Dev.—Brett Bauer; Ex. V-P., Prod. Dev.—David Jochem;
Corp. Traf. Mgr.—Julie Jacobs
Berry Plastics, 34 Engelhard Dr., Monroe Township, 08831 . . . . . . . . . (609) 655-4600
Berry Plastics, Inc., 190 Strykers Rd., Phillipsburg, 08865 . . . . . . . . . (908) 454-0900

**BEVERAGE DISTRIBUTION CENTER, INC.**
8275 Route 130, Pennsauken NJ 08110 . . . . . . . . . . . . . . . . (856) 665-6200
Pres., CFO—Walt Wilkinson; V-P., Opers.—George Heinhold; Dir., Hum. Res.—June Raufer
Pepsi-Cola & National Brand Beverages Ltd.,
8191 N. U.S. Route 130, Pennsauken, 08110 . . . . . . . . . . . (856) 665-6200

**BEVERAGE MEDIA GROUP, INC.**
152 Madison Ave., New York NY 10016 . . . . . . . . . . . . . . . . (212) 571-3232
Chrm., CEO & Publisher—William Slone; Pres.—Michael Roth; COO—Jason Glasser;
V-P.—Jody Slone-Spitalnik; Sales & Mktg. Mgr.—Estie Wartenberg;
Sales Mgr., Promotional Prod.—Jessica Roszkowiak; Circ. Mgr.—Sylvia Prince
Beverage Media Group, Inc., 2444 Morris Ave., Ste. 318, Union, 07083 . . . . . . (908) 964-5060

© Copyright 2015 Manufacturers' News, Inc.




**BIG 3 PRECISION PRODUCTS**
**2923 Wabash Ave., P.O. Box A, Centralia IL 62801 .................. (618) 533-3251**
**Pres., CEO—Alan J. Scheidt; CFO—Susan Niepoetter; GM—Mike Marz;**
**Plt. Mgr.—Scott Gibson; Pur. Mgr., Rack Div.—Ward Pickett;**
**Pur. Mgr., Mold Div.—Rob Niepoetter; Hum. Res. Mgr.—Teresa Hayden;**
**Asst. Plt. Mgr., Tools—Bryan McIntosh**
Big 3 Precision Mold Services, 30 Gorton Rd., Millville, 08332 .............. (856) 293-1400

**BIHLER OF AMERICA, INC.**
**85 Industrial Dr., Phillipsburg NJ 08865 .................. (908) 213-9001**
**CEO—Maxine Nordmeyer; Pres.—Mathias Bihler;**
**Dir., Technical & Engrg. & Sales Mgr.—Max Linder; IT Mgr.—Martin Peverly;**
**Hum. Res. Mgr.—Luz Rivera**
Ultimate Training Munitions, 55 Readington Rd., North Branch, 08876 ......... (908) 725-9000

**BILLOWS ELECTRIC SUPPLY CO., INC.**
**9100 State Rd., Philadelphia PA 19136 .................. (215) 332-9700**
**Pres.—Jeff Billow; CFO—Scott Pressler; V-P., Vendor Rels.—David Lowenstein;**
**Cont.—Pat Tomaro**
Billows Electric Supply Co., Inc., 301 N. New Rd., Pleasantville, 08232 ........ (609) 345-6154
Billows Electric Supply Co., Inc., 1719 Nottingham Way, Trenton, 08619 ....... (609) 890-2822
Billows Electric Supply Co., Inc., 3901 New Jersey Ave., Wildwood, 08260 ...... (609) 522-7736

**BINDI NORTH AMERICA, INC.**
**630 Belleville Tpke., Kearny NJ 07032 .................. (973) 812-8118**
**Pres., CEO—Attilio Bindi; Dir., Operation—Christopher Klemensowicz;**
**Hum. Res. Mgr.—Kelly Cespebes; Sales & Mktg. Coord.—Belda Apolinario**
Bindi North America, Inc., 507 Main St., Belleville, 07109 .................. (973) 751-1754

**BIOMET, INC.**
**56 E. Bell Dr., Warsaw IN 46582 .................. (574) 267-6639**
**Pres., CEO—Jeffrey R. Binder; Sr. V-P., CFO—Daniel P. Florin;**
**Sr. V-P., Hum. Res., Global—Peggy Taylor; Dir., Inv. Rels.—Barbara A. Goslee**
Biomet, Inc., 20-01 Pollitt Dr., Fair Lawn, 07410 .................. (201) 797-7300
EBI, 399 Jefferson Rd., Parsippany, 07054 .................. (973) 299-9300

**BLACK CAR NEWS**
**714 Crestbrook Ave., Cherry Hill NJ 08003 .................. (856) 751-0656**
**Publisher—Neil Weiss**
Black Car News, 420 Inverness Rd., Williamstown, 08094 .................. (856) 262-2368

**BLACKMAN PLUMBING SUPPLY CO., INC.**
**900 Sylvan Ave., Bayport NY 11705 .................. (631) 823-4300**
**Area Mgr., East—Sean Mulderig**
Blackman Plumbing Supply Co., Inc., 270 Route 17 S., Mahwah, 07430 ........ (201) 529-5500

**BLACKSTONE GROUP L. P., THE**
**345 Park Ave., New York NY 10154 .................. (212) 583-5000**
**Chrm., CEO—Stephen A. Schwarzman; Vice Chrm.—Tomilson J. Hill;**
**Pres.—Hamilton E. James; Sr. Mng. Dir.—Neil Simpkins; Media Mgr.—Heather Lucania**
Catalent Pharma Solutions, Inc. (H Q), 14 Schoolhouse Rd., Somerset, 08873 .. (732) 537-6200
Pinnacle Foods Group, LLC (H Q), 121 Woodcrest Rd., Cherry Hill, 08003 ..... (856) 969-7100

**BLINDS TO GO, INC.**
**101 E. State Route 4, Paramus NJ 07652 .................. (732) 321-5000**
**CEO—Nkere Udofia; IT Mgr.—Hitesh Barot; Store Mgr.—Sheryl Antonio**
Blinds To Go, Inc., 1800 Cedar Bridge Ave., Lakewood, 08701 .................. (732) 901-2001

**BLUEKNIGHT ENERGY PARTNERS L. P.**
**6120 Yale Ave., Ste. 500, Tulsa OK 74136 .................. (918) 237-4000**
**CEO—Mark Hurley; Secy., CFO—Alex G. Stallings; COO—Jeffrey Speer;**
**CAO—James R. Griffin**
Blueknight Energy Partners L. P.,
King & Jersey St., P.O. Box 31, Gloucester City, 08030 .................. (856) 456-6673

**BNP MEDIA, INC.**
**2401 W. Big Beaver Rd., Ste. 700, Troy MI 48084 .................. (248) 362-3700**
**Owner & CEO—Tagg Henderson; Bus. Editor, Walls & Ceilings Magazine—John Hall;**
**Dir., Hum. Res.—Marlene Witthoft; Dir., Corp. Strategy—Rita Foumia;**
**Publisher—Randy Green; Payroll Mgr.—Andrea Camp; IS Dev. Mgr.—Christine Wyatt**
BNP Media, Inc., 210 E. State Route 4, Ste. 203, Paramus, 07652 ............ (201) 291-9001

**BODYCOTE THERMAL PROCESSING, INC.**
**12700 Park Central Dr., Ste. 700, Dallas TX 75251 .................. (214) 904-2420**
**V-P., Cont.—Fred Pelletier; V-P., Shared Svcs.—Stephanie Edgar;**
**Dir., Info. Svcs. & IT Mgr.—Dan Collins**
Bodycote, 304 Cox St., Roselle, 07203 .................. (908) 245-0717

**BOLTTECH MANNINGS, INC.**
**501 Mosside Blvd., North Versailles PA 15137 .................. (724) 872-4873**
**CEO—Ed Komoski; CFO—Adam Kassab; Ex. V-P.—Brian Knopp; Ex. V-P.—Harry Knopp;**
**Qual. Assur. Mgr.—Rob Gerlach**
Bolttech Mannings, Inc., 321 Richard Mine Rd., Ste. 300, Wharton, 07885 ...... (973) 537-1576

**BONLAND INDUSTRIES, INC.**
**50 Newark Pompton Tpke., Wayne NJ 07470 .................. (973) 694-3211**
**CEO—William Boniface; Pres.—Andrew Boniface; Admn. Mgr.—Laurie Hughes;**
**Hum. Res. Mgr.—Holly Reger**
Bonland Industries, Inc., 890 Towbin Ave., Lakewood, 08701 .................. (732) 886-7127

**BORDEN DAIRY CO.**
**8750 N. Central Expy., Ste. 400, Dallas TX 75231 .................. (214) 526-1687**
**CEO—Arquimedes Celis; V-P., Strategic Plng.—Farouk Salim;**
**V-P., Supply Chain—Nucci Cerioli**
Farmland Dairies, 520 Main Ave., P.O. Box 3340, Wallington, 07057 .......... (973) 777-2500

**BOSTIK, INC.**
**11320 W. Watertown Plank Rd., Wauwatosa WI 53226 .................. (414) 774-2250**
**Pres., CEO—Robert Marquette; V-P., CFO—Jeffrey Goldberg; Dir., IT—Jim Kremel;**
**Dir., Hum. Res.—Chuck Whaley; Mktg. Comms. Mgr.—Chris Eichman**
Bostik, Inc., 2000 Nolte Dr., West Deptford, 08066 .................. (856) 848-8669

**BOTTCHER AMERICA CORPORATION**
**4600 Mercedes Dr., Belcamp MD 21017 .................. (410) 273-7000**
**Pres.—David Dinsmore; V-P., Sales—Charles Hands; V-P.—Wayne Porter;**
**MIS Mgr.—Sharon Sexton; Hum. Res. Mgr.—Nancy Pushkin**
Bottcher America Corp., 88 Ford Rd., Ste. 8, Denville, 07834 .................. (973) 664-1241

**BP AMERICA, INC.**
**501 Westlake Park Blvd., Houston TX 77079 .................. (281) 366-2000**
**CEO—Robert Dudley; CFO—Brian Gilvary; COO, Prodn.—Bernard Looney;**
**Ex. V-P., Safety & Operational Risk—Bob Fryar;**
**Ex. V-P., Corp. Bus. Activities—Katrina Landis; Group Gen. Counsel—Rupert Bondy**
BP Lubricants USA, Inc., 1500 Valley Rd., Wayne, 07470 .................. (973) 633-2200

**BRADDOCK METALLURGICAL, INC.**
**400 Fentress Blvd., Daytona Beach FL 32114 .................. (386) 267-0955**
**CEO—Steve Braddock; Pres. & Metallurgical Engr.—George Gieger; CFO—Cynthia Earl;**
**Plt. Mgr.—Jeff Young; Off. Mgr.—Dee Wood; Qual. Control Mgr.—Paul Alexander**
Braddock Heat Treating Co., Inc., 123 Chimney Rock Rd., Bridgewater, 08807 .. (732) 356-2906

**BRADY WORLDWIDE, INC.**
**6555 W. Good Hope Rd., Milwaukee WI 53223 .................. (414) 358-6600**
**Interim CEO & CFO—Tom Felmer; V-P., CIO—Bentley Curren;**
**V-P., R & D & CTO—Robert Tatterson; Sr. V-P., Hum. Res.—Helena Nelligan;**
**V-P., Opers.—Lee Marks; Dir., Corp. Comm.—Carole Herbstreit;**
**Dir., Inv. Rels.—Aaron Pearce**
SPC Sorbent Products Co., Inc., 645 Howard Ave., Somerset, 08873 ......... (732) 302-0080

**BRENNTAG NORTH AMERICA, INC.**
**5083 Pottsville Pike, Reading PA 19605 .................. (610) 926-6100**
**CEO—William A. Fidler; Pres., COO—Markus Klahn; Ex. V-P., CFO—H. Ed Boyadjian;**
**Sr. V-P., Opers.—David Garner; Ex. V-P., Comml.—Tom Corcoran;**
**Ex. V-P.—Anthony J. Gerace; V-P., Global Accts. & Dir., Govt. Affs.—Robert Moser, Jr;**
**V-P., IT—Todd Stewart; Dir., Sales & Sourcing—Michael DelliCompagni;**
**Dir., Hum. Res.—Mark Andriate; Mktg. & Plng. Mgr.—Barbara Nothstein**
Brenntag Specialties, Inc., 1000 Coolidge St., South Plainfield, 07080 ......... (908) 561-6100

**BRICK-WALL CORP.**
**25 1st Ave., Ste. 200, Atlantic Highlands NJ 07716 .................. (732) 787-0226**
**Pres.—Lawrence Hesse; CFO—Larry Mulcahy**
Brick-Wall Corp., 2215 Lacey Rd., Forked River, 08731 .................. (609) 693-6223

**BRIDOR, INC.**
**1370 Graham-Bell St., Boucherville, Quebec, Canada, J4B 6H5, .......... (450) 641-1265**
**Pres., CEO—Bob Wallace**
Bridor USA, 2260 Industrial Way, Vineland, 08360 .................. (856) 691-8000

**BRIGGS HEALTHCARE**
**7300 Westown Pkwy., Ste. 100, West Des Moines IA 50266 .................. (515) 327-6400**
**Sr. V-P., CFO—Tom Young; Sr. V-P., Sales—Jeff Pigott; V-P., Mktg.—Jeff Kane;**
**Dir., Mfg.—John Milburn; Dir., Bus. Info. Svcs.—DeeAnn Drew;**
**Hum. Res. Mgr.—Deb Nordaas**
Omnimed, Inc., 800 Glen Ave., Moorestown, 08057 .................. (856) 359-2231

**BRISTOL-MYERS SQUIBB COMPANY**
**345 Park Ave., New York NY 10154 .................. (212) 546-4000**
**Chrm.—James Cornelius; CEO—Lamberto Andreotti;**
**Chief Compliance & Ethics Officer—Anne Nielsen; Gen. Counsel & Secy.—Sandra Leung**
Bristol-Myers Squibb Company, 777 Scudders Mill Rd., Plainsboro, 08536 ..... (609) 897-2000

**BROAD STREET MEDIA, LLC**
**2512 Metropolitan Dr., Trevose PA 19053 .................. (215) 355-9009**
**Publisher—Perry Corsetti; Editor—Tom Waring; Sales Mgr.—Michelle McDevitt;**
**Bus. Mgr.—Kat Wamser; Circ. Mgr.—Pearl Harta**
New Jersey Media Group, 11 Melanie Ln., Unit 22-A, East Hanover, 07936 ..... (973) 434-8888
Broad Street Media, 53 Haddonfield Rd., Ste. 306, Cherry Hill, 08002 ......... (856) 779-3800

**BUHLER INC.**
**13105 12th Ave. N., Plymouth MN 55441 .................. (763) 847-9900**
**Pres.—Rene Steiner; V-P., Fin. & CFO—Markus Nikles;**
**V-P., Logistics & Mfg.—Duane Hiltner; Hum. Res. Mgr.—Ellen Bies;**
**Cust. Serv. Mgr.—Alan Fischer; Comml. Mgr.—Steven Romer**
Buhler Inc, 40 Whitney Rd., Mahwah, 07430 .................. (201) 847-0600

**BUMBLE BEE FOODS, LLC**
**280 10th Ave., San Diego CA 92101 .................. (858) 715-4000**
**Pres., CEO—Christopher Lischewski; Ex. V-P., CFO—Kent McNeil; COO—Jan Tharp;**
**CIO—Anthony Costa; V-P., Hum. Res.—Patrick Menke; Cust. Serv. Mgr.—Lori Carter**
Snow's, 994 Ocean Dr., Cape May, 08204 .................. (609) 884-0440

**BUNGE NORTH AMERICA, INC.**
**11720 Borman Dr., St. Louis MO 63146 .................. (314) 292-2000**
**CEO—Todd Bastean; CFO—George Allard; Sr. V-P., Gen. Counsel—David Kabbes;**
**V-P., GM, Grain—Matt Gibson; Cont.—John Sabourin; Dir., Mktg.—Bill McCullough**
Bunge North America, Inc., 125 Sanford Ave., Kearny, 07032 .................. (201) 467-0200

**BUNZL USA, INC.**
**One City Place Dr., Ste. 200, St. Louis MO 63141 .................. (314) 997-5959**
**CEO—Patrick Larmon; Sr. V-P., Fin.—Jane Jennewein; V-P., IT—Jim Schulz;**
**Cont.—Lonny White; Sr. Dir., Hum. Res.—Gene Perry**
Bunzl New Jersey, Inc., 27 Distribution Way, Monmouth Junction, 08852 ....... (732) 821-7000

**BUSHWICK METALS, LLC**
**560 N. Washington Ave., Bridgeport CT 06604 .................. (203) 576-1800**
**Pres., CEO—Rick Perlen; V-P., Sales—Howard Schreer; Mktg. Mgr.—John Homer;**
**Hum. Res. Mgr.—Sue Cannone**
AZCO Steel Co., 1641 New Market Ave., South Plainfield, 07080 ............ (908) 754-8700

**BUSINESS FURNITURE, INC.**
**133 Rahway Ave., Elizabeth NJ 07202 .................. (908) 355-3400**
**CEO—Paul Gold; CFO—John Trotter; V-P., Opers.—John McClendon; Principal—Eric Gold;**
**Hum. Res. Mgr.—Linda D'Adamo**
Business Furniture, Inc., 10 Lanidex Plz. W., Ste. 202, Parsippany, 07054 ...... (973) 503-0730

**BWAY CORPORATION**
**8607 Roberts Dr., Ste. 250, P.O. Box 2210, Atlanta GA 30350 ............ (770) 645-4800**
**Pres., CEO—Ken Roessler; Ex. V-P., CFO—Michael B. Clauer; V-P., Mktg.—Bob Coleman;**
**Mktg. & Plng. Mgr.—John Heck; Hum. Res. Mgr.—Jennifer Armbruster**
BWAY Corp., 1202 Airport Rd., North Brunswick, 08902 .................. (732) 247-6700
North America Packaging Corp. (NAMPAC), 7 Wheeling Rd., Dayton, 08810 .... (732) 997-4100
BWAY Corporation, 6 Litho Rd., Trenton, 08638 .................. (732) 997-4050

© Copyright 2015 Manufacturers' News, Inc.


**C & C METAL PRODUCTS CORP.**
**456 Nordhoff Pl., P.O. Box 7300, Englewood NJ 07631 .................. (201) 569-7300**
**V-P., Secy.—Mitchell Chalfin; V-P., Pur.—Neal Liber; V-P.—Matthew Nathel;**
**V-P.—Michael Nathel; Dir.—Daniel Nathel**
Metal City Findings Co., 456 Nordhoff Pl., P.O. Box 7300, Englewood, 07631 .... (201) 569-7300

**C. R. LAURENCE CO., INC.**
**2503 E. Vernon Ave., Los Angeles CA 90058 .......................... (323) 588-1281**
**CEO—Don Friese, Sr.; Pres.—Lloyd Talbert; Ex. V-P.—Don Friese, Jr.;**
**V-P., Sales—Paul Daniels; V-P., Mfg.—Patrick Devine; V-P., Mktg.—Greg Rewers;**
**V-P., Engrg.—Gary Sprague; Dir., Hum. Res. & Qual. Assur. Mgr.—Carlos Lemus;**
**Pur. Mgr.—Darren Scott**
C. R. Laurence Co., Inc., 1511 Lancer Dr., Moorestown, 08057 .............. (856) 727-1022

**C.R. BARD, INC.**
**730 Central Ave., New Providence NJ 07974 .......................... (908) 277-8000**
**Chrm., CEO—Timothy M. Ring; Pres., COO—John H. Weiland;**
**Sr. V-P., CFO—Christopher S. Holland; V-P., Gen. Counsel & Secy.—Sam Khichi;**
**V-P., Hum. Res.—Bronwen K. Kelly; Group V-P.—Timothy P. Collins;**
**Group V-P.—Brian P. Kelly; Group V-P.—Sharon M. Alterio;**
**Mktg. Progs. Mgr.—Jacqueline Ference**
Davol, Inc., 1822 Underwood Blvd., Delran, 08075 .......................... (856) 764-8158

**CAL-CHLOR CORP.**
**627 Jefferson St., Lafayette LA 70501 ................................ (337) 264-1449**
**Owner & CEO—Mark S. Hanna; Pres.—Todd Trahan; CFO, Secy-Treas.—Ken Matthews**
Cal-Chlor Corp., 141 Baekeland Ave., Piscataway, 08854 .................... (732) 271-3500

**CALKINS MEDIA, INC.**
**8400 N. Bristol Pike, Levittown PA 19057 ............................ (215) 949-4000**
**Pres., Publisher—Michael Jameson; CFO—Mike White; Ex. Editor—Patricia Walker;**
**Cont.—Tim Weaver; Dir., Mktg. & Promotion Mgr.—Tracy Meyer; Dir., Adv.—Deanna Fox;**
**Dir., Circ.—William Lobecker; Facility Mgr.—Jack Keyburn**
Burlington County Times, Inc., 4284 Route 130, Willingboro, 08046 ........... (609) 871-8000

**CAMPBELL FOUNDRY CO.**
**800 Bergen St., Harrison NJ 07029 .................................. (973) 483-5480**
**Pres.—Chris Campbell; V-P., Secy.—John R. Campbell III; V-P., Treas.—Greg Campbell;**
**Cont.—John Burguillos**
Campbell Foundry, Materials Div., 630 S. Hope Chapel Rd., Jackson, 08527 .... (732) 408-1111

**CAMPBELL SOUP CO.**
**1 Campbell Pl., Camden NJ 08103 .................................... (856) 342-4800**
**Chrm.—Paul Charron; CEO—Denise M. Morrison; Sr. V-P., CFO—Craig Owens;**
**Sr. V-P., CIO—Joseph Spagnoletti; Dir., Hum. Res.—Pauline Ashworth;**
**Hum. Res. Mgr.—Bob Morrisey**
Campbell Soup Supply Co., 3500 S. Clinton Ave., South Plainfield, 07080 ...... (908) 561-1660
Ecce Panis, 3-B Brick Plant Rd., East Brunswick, 08816 ..................... (732) 254-1770

**CANAM STEEL CORP.**
**4010 Clay St., P.O. Box 285, Point Of Rocks MD 21777 .................. (301) 874-5141**
**Pres.—Sam Blatchford; V-P., Cont.—Mary Gordon; GM—Michel Cyr;**
**MIS Mgr.—Charles Adams; Hum. Res. Mgr.—Rose Davis; Contracts Mgr.—Kim Neuman**
Canam Steel Corp., 14 Harmich Rd., South Plainfield, 07080 ................. (908) 561-3484

**CANDELA CORP.**
**530 Boston Post Rd., Wayland MA 01778 .............................. (508) 358-7400**
**Pres., CEO & Dir.—Shimon Eckhuce; V-P., Sales—Brian Hayes;**
**V-P., Research—Jay Bhawalker; Dir., Facilities—Karl Meincke;**
**Dir., Comm. & Mktg.—Cherri Lucas; Dir., Hum. Res.—Gayl Lange;**
**Sales Mgr., N. America—Colleen Hennessey**
Applied Optronics, 111 Corporate Blvd., Bldg. J, South Plainfield, 07080 ....... (908) 753-6300

**CANGRO INDUSTRIES, INC.**
**495 Smith St., Farmingdale NY 11735 ................................ (631) 454-9000**
**Pres.—Victor Cangro**
Cangro Transmission Co. Of New Jersey, 295 Crooks Ave., Clifton, 07011 ...... (973) 772-7662

**CAPESPAN NORTH AMERICA**
**301-6700 CH Cote-De-Liesse, Saint-Laurant, QC, Canada H4T 2B5, ........ (514) 739-9181**
**CFO—Howard Freedman; V-P., Sales & Mktg.—Paul Marier**
Capespan North America, 701 N. Broadway., Ste. 102, Gloucester City, 08030 .. (856) 742-0242

**CAREFUSION CORP.**
**3750 Torrey View Ct., San Diego CA 92130 ............................ (858) 617-2000**
**Chrm., CEO—Kieran Gallahue; Pres.—Tom Leonard;**
**Sr. V-P., Channel & Portfolio Dev.—Jason Strohm;**
**Sr. V-P., Med., Qual. & Regulatory Affs.—Don Abbey;**
**Ex. V-P., Hum. Res.—Mike Paoulucci**
Vital Signs, A CareFusion Co., 20 Campus Rd., Totowa, 07512 .............. (973) 956-5300

**CARL STAHL SAVA INDUSTRIES, INC.**
**4 N. Corporate Dr., P.O. Box 30, Riverdale NJ 07457 .................... (973) 835-0882**
**CEO—Zdenek A. Fremund; Pres.—Marc E. Alterman; V-P., Sales—Bruce R. Staubitz;**
**V-P., Opers.—Jack Mass; V-P., Engrg.—Greg Soja; Mfg. Mgr.—Ron Paras;**
**Pur. Mgr.—Jerry Picazio; Fin. Mgr.—Ralph Engelhardt;**
**Qual. Assur. Mgr.—Thomas Moore**
Jordan Mfg., LLC, 28 Randazzo Rd., P.O. Box 226, Lafayette, 07848 .......... (973) 383-8363

**CARLYLE GROUP, THE**
**1001 Pennsylvania Ave. N.W., Washington, DC MD 20004 ............... (202) 347-2626**
**Co-Founder & Chrm.—Daniel A. D'Aniello; Co-Founder & Co-CEO—William E. Conway, Jr.;**
**Co-Founder & Co-CEO—David M. Rubenstein;**
**Chief Compliance Officer—Catherine Ziobro; Dir., Global Comm.—Christopher Ullman**
Ortho-Clinical Diagnostics, Inc. (H Q),
1001 U.S. Highway 202, P.O. Box 350, Raritan, 08869 .................... (908) 218-1300

**CARPENTER & PATERSON, INC.**
**225 Merrimac St., Woburn MA 01801 .................................. (781) 935-7036**
**Chrm.—Donald Paterson; Pres.—David Lynch; Cont.—Kathleen Tawa**
Carpenter & Paterson, Inc., 3900 River Rd., P.O. Box 556, Pennsauken, 08110 .. (856) 488-1988
Carpenter & Paterson, Inc., 369 Jefferson St., Saddle Brook, 07663 ........... (973) 772-1800

**CARRINGTON CO., LLC**
**7 Reuten Dr., Closter NJ 07624 ..................................... (800) 505-9546**
**CEO—Debbie Shandel; Pres.—Brad Miller**
Carrington Tea, LLC, 7 Reuten Dr., P.O. Box 102, Closter, 07624 ............. (201) 261-5517

**CARTRIDGE ACTUATED DEVICES, INC.**
**51 Dwight Pl., Fairfield NJ 07004 ................................... (973) 575-1312**
**Pres.—John Grant; Dir., Sales—Patrick M. Goudie;**
**Admn. & Cust. Serv. Mgr.—Patty Kietrys; Hum. Res. Mgr.—Elizabeth Stichling**
Cartridge Actuated Devices, Inc., 40 Old Indian Spring Rd., Andover, 07821 .... (973) 347-2281

**CASINGS, INC.**
**169 Maple Ave., Catskill NY 12414 ................................... (518) 943-9404**
**Pres.—Richard Evans; Opers. Mgr.—William Evans; Manager—James Sabrizilo**
Casings Of NJ, Inc., 711 Ramsey Ave., Hillside, 07205 ...................... (908) 851-7766

**CATAMARAN MEDIA CO., LLC**
**507 S. Shore Rd., Marmora NJ 08223 ................................. (609) 624-8900**
**Publisher—Rick Travers; Pres.—Curt Travers; Editor—James Fitzpatrick;**
**Editor—Bill Barlow; Comp.—John Cavaretti; Adv. & Sales Mgr.—Steve Mehl**
Catamaran Media Co., LLC, 3120 Fire Rd., Egg Harbor Township, 08234 ...... (609) 266-1860
Catamaran Media Co., LLC, 3120 Fire Rd., Egg Harbor Township, 08234 ...... (609) 383-8994

**CATELLI BROS. VEAL & LAMB, INC.**
**50 Ferry Ave., Collingswood NJ 08103 ................................ (856) 869-9293**
**Pres.—Anthony Catelli; V-P., Opers.—Tom Thomson; Dir., Food Serv.—Louis Licht;**
**Cust. Serv. Mgr.—Jack Womack**
Catelli Bros. Veal & Lamb, Inc., 776 Broad St., Shrewsbury, 07702 ........... (732) 741-3687

**CB&I**
**4171 Essen Ln., Baton Rouge LA 70809 ............................... (225) 932-2500**
**V-P., Global Comms. & Mktg.—Gentry Brann; Dir., Construction—Bryan Vollmer;**
**Proj. Mgr., Controls—Jason Jordan**
CB&I, 502-B Jersey Ave., New Brunswick, 08901 ............................ (732) 435-0777

**CB&I, INC.**
**2103 Research Forest Dr., The Woodlands TX 77380 ..................... (832) 513-1800**
**Pres., CEO—Philip K. Asherman; Ex. V-P., CFO—Ronald Ballschmiede;**
**V-P., Corp. Planning—Christine Thoms; Sr. Dir., Global Mktg.—Bruce Steimle**
Lummus Technology, 1515 Broad St., Bloomfield, 07003 ..................... (973) 893-3000

**CBS OUTDOOR AMERICAS, INC.**
**405 Lexington Ave., New York NY 10174 ............................... (212) 297-6400**
**CEO—Jeremy Male; Ex. V-P., CFO—Donald R. Shassian; Ex. V-P., CMO—Jodi Senese;**
**Ex. V-P., U.S., CAO & CFO—Raymond Nowak; Ex. V-P., Real Estate—John Clements;**
**Dir., Reg. Opers.—Roger Willis**
CBS Outdoor, 185 Highway 46, Fairfield, 07004 ............................ (973) 575-6900
CBS Outdoor, 1245 Towbin Ave., Lakewood, 08701 .......................... (732) 901-1100

**CCL INDUSTRIES CORP.**
**161 Worcester St., Ste. 502, Boston MA 02218 ......................... (508) 872-4511**
**Pres., CEO—Geoffrey Martin; Sr. V-P., CFO—Sean Washchuk;**
**Sr. V-P., Admn., Fin. & IT—Lalitha Vaidyanathan;**
**Sr. V-P., Gen. Counsel & Secy.—Bohdan I. Sirota;**
**V-P., Env. Mgmt. & Safety—Susan V. Snelgrove**
CCL Label, Inc., 120 Stockton St., Hightstown, 08520 ....................... (609) 443-3700
CCL Label, Inc., 104 N. Gold Dr., Robbinsville, 08691 ...................... (609) 586-1332

**CENTIV SERVICES, LLC**
**233 S. Wacker Dr., Ste. 4400, Chicago IL 60606 ....................... (312) 235-5700**
**Pres.—John Larkin; Ex. V-P.—Dave Wilson; Acctg. Mgr.—Matt Lash**
Graphic Express Menu Co., Inc., 200 Clifton Blvd., Ste. 6, Clifton, 07011 ....... (973) 685-0022

**CENTRAL GARDEN & PET CO.**
**1340 Treat Blvd., Ste. 600, Walnut Creek CA 94597 ..................... (925) 948-4000**
**Chrm.—William E. Brown; Pres., CEO—John Rannelli; Ex. V-P., CFO—Lori Varlas;**
**Sr. V-P., Supply Chain—Paul Hibbert; V-P., Hum. Res.—Marilyn Leahy**
Central Pet, 301 Island Rd., Mahwah, 07430 .............................. (201) 529-5050
Nylabone Products,
1 TFH Plz., 3rd & Union Ave., P.O. Box 427, Neptune City, 07753 ........... (732) 988-8400

**CENTRAL INK CORP.**
**1100 Harvester Rd., West Chicago IL 60185 ............................ (630) 231-6500**
**Pres.—Gregg Dahleen; V-P., Sales & Mktg.—John Pieranunziki;**
**V-P., Opers.—Doug Anderson; Cont. & Hum. Res. Mgr.—Mary Frentz**
Central Ink Corp., 2085 Center Square Rd., Unit A, Swedesboro, 08085 ....... (856) 467-5562

**CENVEO, INC.**
**200 1st Stamford Pl., Stamford CT 06902 .............................. (203) 595-3000**
**Chrm., CEO—Robert G. Burton, Sr.; Pres.—Rob G. Burton, Jr.;**
**Pres., Envelope Group—Mark S. Hiltwein; CFO—Scott Goodwin;**
**V-P., Legal Affs.—Ian Scheinmann**
Cenveo, Inc., 25 Linden Ave. E., Jersey City, 07305 ........................ (201) 434-2100

**CERTIFIED STEEL COMPANY**
**1333 Brunswick Ave., Ste. 200, Lawrenceville NJ 08648 ................. (609) 396-7600**
**CEO—Sydney Sussman; Pres.—Diane Kane; Cont.—Jo Ellen Boyd;**
**IT Mgr.—Michael Ciesialka; Hum. Res. Mgr.—Kathy Finch**
Certified Steel Co., 199 Whitehead Rd., Hamilton, 08619 .................... (609) 890-7000

**CETEK, INC.**
**19 Commerce St., Poughkeepsie NY 12603 .............................. (845) 452-3510**
**Chrm., Pres.—Fayiz Hilal**
Hybrid-Tek, Inc., 9 Trenton Lakewood Rd., Ste. 1, Clarksburg, 08510 .......... (609) 259-3355

**CHALMERS & KUBECK, INC.**
**150 Commerce Dr., P.O. Box 2447, Aston PA 19014 ....................... (610) 494-4300**
**Pres.—Dennis Kubeck; Cont.—Gary H. Powers; GM & Sales Mgr.—Jim Moore;**
**IT Mgr.—Don Ritter**
Chalmers & Kubeck, Inc., 8 Jules Ln., New Brunswick, 08901 ............... (732) 993-1251

**CHAMPION WINDOW MANUFACTURING & SUPPLY CO., LLC**
**12121 Champion Way, Cincinnati OH 45241 ............................ (513) 346-4600**
**CEO—James Mishler; Plt. Opers. Mgr.—Danny Nichols; MIS Mgr.—George Price;**
**Off. Mgr.—Carol Pharo**
Champion Window Of Pennsauken, 8400 Remington Ave., Ste. B, Pennsauken, 08110 . (856) 662-3400

**CHANEL, INC.**
**9 W. 57th St., 44th Fl., New York NY 10019 ........................... (212) 688-5055**
**Chrm.—Alain Wertheimer; Vice Chrm.—Arie Kopelman;**
**Ex. V-P., Beauty & Fragrance—Christine Dagousset**
Chanel, Inc., 876 Centennial Ave., Piscataway, 08854 ...................... (732) 885-5500

PARENT COMPANY

**CHARMER SUNBELT GROUP, THE**
60 E. 42nd St., Ste. 1915, New York NY 10165 ............... **(212) 699-7000**
Vice Chrm. & CEO—Charley Merinoff; Ex. V.P., CFO—Gene Luciana;
Ex. V.P., Hum. Res.—Ann Giambusso; Ex. V.P., Capability Dev.—Joe Davolio;
V.P., Natl. Accts.—Gerald L. Baxter
R & R Marketing, LLC, 10 Patton Dr., West Caldwell, 07006 ............(973) 228-5100

**CHASEN & SONS, INC., M.**
123 S. 20th St., Irvington NJ 07111 ............................. **(973) 589-8700**
Pres., CEO—Alan Schachman; V.P.—David Schachman
Chasen & Sons, Inc., M., 117 S. 20th St., Irvington, 07111 ........(973) 374-8956

**CHEMTRADE CHEMICAL, LLC**
90 E. Halsey Rd., 3rd Fl., Parsippany NJ 07054 ................ **(973) 515-0900**
Pres., CEO—William Redmond; CFO—Doug Grierson; Bus. & Mktg. Mgr.—Lisa Brownlee
Chemtrade, 330 Doremus Ave., Newark, 07105 ....................(973) 589-5300
General Chemical Corp., 235 Snyder Ave., Berkeley Heights, 07922 ....(908) 464-1500

**CHEMTRADE LOGISTICS, INC.**
155 Gordon Baker Rd., Ste. 300, Toronto, Ontario, Canada M2H 3N5, ..... **(416) 496-5856**
Pres., CEO—Mark Davis; V.P., Sales—Leon Aarts; V.P., Mktg.—Douglas Cadwell;
V.P., Mfg.—Tab McCullough; V.P., Hum. Res.—Maryann Romano
Chemtrade Chemical, LLC, 90 E. Halsey Rd., 3rd Fl., Parsippany, 07054 ......(973) 515-0900

**CHEMTURA CORP.**
1818 Market St., Ste. 3700, Philadelphia PA 19103 .................... **(215) 446-3911**
Chrm., Pres. & CEO—Craig Rogerson;
Group Pres., Engineered & Performance Indl. Prods. & Ex. V.P.—Chet H. Cross;
Sr. V.P., Hum. Res. & Support Svcs.—Alan H. Swiech;
V.P., EHS&S, Reg. Affs. & Mfg. Excellence—Thomas Strang
Anderol, Inc., 215 Merry Ln., East Hanover, 07936. ...............(973) 887-7410
Chemtura Corp., 1000 Convery Blvd., Perth Amboy, 08861 ...........(732) 826-6600
Chemtura Corp., Hatco Div., 1020 King George Post Rd., Fords, 08863 .......(732) 738-1000

**CHESAPEAKE PHARMACEUTICAL PACKAGING COMPANY, LLC**
325 Duffy Ave., Hicksville NY 11801 ........................... **(516) 277-8600**
V.P., Sales & Mktg.—Christopher Cassidy; V.P., Qual. Assur.—Curt Taylor;
V.P., Cust. Rels.—Rosemarie Torrisi; Dir., Strategic Dev.—Robin S. Henfling;
Plt. Mgr.—Mike Greenberg; Hum. Res. Mgr.—Brenda Cabrera
Chesapeake Pharmaceutical & Healthcare Packaging,
6 Commerce Rd., Fairfield, 07004 ...............................(973) 808-8000

**CHINOOK SCIENCES, LLC**
20 Commerce Dr., Ste. 350, Cranford NJ 07016. ................ **(908) 272-5091**
Co-Founder, Chrm. & CEO—Rifat Chalabi; Co-Founder & V.P., Admn.—Fanli Meng;
Co-Founder & V.P., R & D—Harry Perry; Gen. Counsel—Zachary M. Barth;
Sr. Dir., Fin.—Richard Galinkin; Dir., Bus. Dev.—Kenneth Foladare
Advanced Metal Processing NJ, LLC, 326 S. Wade Blvd., Millville, 08332 ......(856) 327-0048

**CHURCH & DWIGHT CO., INC.**
500 Charles Ewing Blvd., Ewing NJ 08628 .................... **(609) 683-5900**
Chrm., CEO—James Craigie; V.P., CFO & Fin.—Matthew T. Farrell;
V.P., Gen. Counsel—Patrick DeMaynagies; V.P., Sales—Lou Tursi;
V.P., Global Opers.—Mark Conish; V.P., Mktg.—Bruce Fleming
Church & Dwight Co., Inc., 326 Half Acre Rd., Cranbury, 08512 ............(609) 655-6000
Church & Dwight Co., Inc., 800 Airport Rd., Lakewood, 08701 ............(732) 730-3100

**CINCINNATI THERMAL SPRAY, INC.**
5901 Creek Rd., Cincinnati OH 45242 ........................... **(513) 793-0670**
Pres.—Dan Classen; V.P., Fin.—Tom Dagenback; Sales Mgr.—Bill Walsh;
Mfg. Mgr.—Sheldon Sparks; MIS Mgr.—Steve Wilson; Hum. Res. Mgr.—Sharyn Brunetti;
Engrg. Mgr.—Kirk Fick; Qual. Control Mgr.—Mark Dobrowski
Cincinnati Thermal Spray East, 80 Fadem Rd., Springfield, 07081 ........(973) 379-0003

**CINTAS CORP.**
6800 Cintas Blvd., Mason OH 45040 ........................... **(513) 459-1200**
Founder & Chrm. Emeritus—Richard T. Farmer; Chrm. of the Board—Robert J. Kohlhepp;
CEO—Scott D. Farmer; Pres., COO—J. Phillip Holloman; Sr. V.P., CFO—William Gale;
V.P., Govt. Affs. & Chief Compliance Officer—Greg Hart;
Sr. V.P., Global Supply Chain—David Wheeler; V.P., Treas.—Mike Hansen;
Gen. Counsel & Secy.—Thomas Frooman; Corp. Comms. Mgr.—Gini Verbesselt
Cintas Fire Protection, 1705 U.S. Route 46 W., Ledgewood, 07852 ........(973) 347-3901

**CLAYTON & SONS, RALPH**
1355 Campus Pkwy., Neptune NJ 07753 ...................... **(732) 751-7600**
Pres.—William Clayton; V.P.—Douglas Clayton; V.P.—Dan Clayton; V.P.—Casey Clayton;
Dir., Tech. Svcs., Qual. Control—Matthew Savona;
Gen. Sales Mgr.—Joseph M. Scaramuzzo
Clayton & Sons, Ralph, 103 Chestnut Ave., Egg Harbor Township, 08234 ......(609) 383-1818
Clayton & Sons, Ralph, 125 Cox Crossing Rd., West Creek, 08092 ........(609) 597-2233

**CLAYTON BLOCK CO., INC.**
1355 Campus Pkwy., Neptune NJ 07753 ...................... **(732) 751-7600**
Owner—William Clayton, Jr.; V.P.—Douglas Clayton; V.P.—Casey Clayton;
V.P.—Dan Clayton; Dir., Mktg.—Kathy Roe; Gen. Sales Mgr.—Joseph M. Scaramuzzo;
Hum. Res. Mgr.—Wayne Tart
Clayton Block Co., Inc., 1601 18th Ave., Belmar, 07719 ...............(732) 681-1414
Clayton Block Co., Inc., 1025 Route 1 S., Edison, 08837 ...............(732) 549-1234
Clayton Block Co., Inc., 225 Throckmorton St., Freehold, 07728 ..........(732) 462-1860
Clayton Block Co., Inc, 2 Porete Ave., North Arlington, 07031 ...........(201) 955-6292
Clayton Block Co., Inc., 194 Chestnut St., Toms River, 08753 ...........(732) 349-3700
Clayton Block Co., Inc., Route 9, Waretown, 08758 .................(609) 693-3000
Clayton & Sons, LLC, Ralph, 58 Goldman Dr., Cookstown, 08511 .........(609) 758-6900
Ralph Clayton & Sons, 1144 New York Ave., Trenton, 08638 ............(609) 695-0767

**CLEMENT PAPPAS & COMPANY, INC.**
1 Collins Dr., Ste. 200, Carneys Point NJ 08069 ............... **(856) 455-1000**
CEO—Mark McNeil; Hum. Res. Bus. Ptnr.—Krystal Reid;
Chief Administrative Officer—Dimitri Pappas; Sr. V.P., Sales—Bob Crawford;
Sr. V.P., Mktg.—Patricia Nicolino
Clement Pappas & Company, Inc., 1045 Parsonage Rd., Seabrook, 08302 ......(856) 455-1001

**CLONDALKIN PHARMA & HEALTHCARE**
1072 Boulder Rd., Greensboro NC 27409 ........................ **(336) 292-4555**
CEO—David Lennon; V.P., Sales & Mktg.—Kevin Kenjarski; V.P., Opers.—Jim Franklin;
V.P., Tech.—Dave Brown; V.P., Qual. Assur.—Shannon Walker; Dir., Proc.—David Belez;
Hum. Res. Mgr.—Keisha Chapman
Clondalkin Pharma & Healthcare, 1224 N. Church St., Moorestown, 08057 ..... (856) 439-1700

**COCKPIT USA, INC.**
15 W. 39th St., 12th Fl., New York NY 10018 ................... **(212) 575-1616**
Pres.—Jeffrey Clyman; Ex. V.P., Secy.—Jacky Clyman; IT Mgr.—Steward Schuman;
Hum. Res. Mgr.—Lydia Yap
Cockpit USA, Inc., 725 New Point Rd., Elizabeth, 07201 .................(908) 558-9704

**COHERENT, INC.**
5100 Patrick Henry Dr., Santa Clara CA 95054 .................. **(408) 764-4000**
Pres., CEO—John R. Ambroseo; Ex. V.P., CFO—Helene Simonet;
Ex. V.P., CTO—Luis Spinelli; Ex. V.P., Gen. Counsel—Bret DiMarco;
Ex. V.P., Global Bus. Opers.—Mark Sobey; V.P., Hum. Res.—Mark Rakic;
GM—Larry DiBattista; Sr. Mktg. Comm. Proj. Mgr.—Rhonda Albrecht;
MarComm Mgr.—Rosemarie Smith-Wood
Coherent Advanced Crystal Group, 31 Farinella Dr., East Hanover, 07936 ......(973) 240-6800

**COLGATE-PALMOLIVE CO.**
300 Park Ave., New York NY 10022 ........................... **(212) 310-2000**
Pres., CEO—Ian M. Cook; CFO—Dennis Hickey;
Sr. V.P., Chief Legal Officer & Secy.—Andrew D. Hendry; V.P., Sales—Taylor Gordy;
V.P., Global Hum. Res.—Daniel Marcili
Colgate-Palmolive Co., 400 Elbow Ln., Burlington, 08016. ..............(609) 239-2000
Colgate-Palmolive Co., 191 E. Hanover Ave., Morristown, 07960 ..........(973) 630-1500

**COLLAGEN MATRIX, INC.**
15 Thornton Rd., Oakland NJ 07436. .......................... **(201) 405-1477**
Pres., CEO—Shu-Tung Li; V.P., COO—Debbie Yuen; V.P., CRO—Peggy Hansen;
Cont.—Keith Westpy; Sr. Sales & Mktg. Mgr.—Margo Lane;
Sr. Pur. Mgr. & Cust. Serv. Admn.—Liesa DeNardo
Collagen Matrix, Inc., 509 Commerce St., Franklin, 07417 ...............(201) 405-1477

**COLONIAL CONCRETE CO.**
1196 McCarter Hwy., Newark NJ 07104. ....................... **(973) 482-1920**
Pres.—Martin Lucibello; Dir., Comms. & Tech.—Jerry Jansen;
Dir., Qual. Control—John Serro; Sales Mgr.—Richard Shoop;
Plt. Opers. Mgr.—James Bizarro
Colonial Concrete Co., 9301 Railroad Ave., North Bergen, 07047. ..........(201) 435-9200

**COLONIAL ELECTRIC SUPPLY CO., THE**
201 W. Church Rd., King of Prussia PA 19406 .................. **(610) 312-8100**
Pres.—Steven P. Bellwoar; CFO—Andrew Pedlow; CTO—Jay Bellwoar;
Ex. V.P., Sales—Peter Bellwoar; V.P., Hum. Res.—Joseph Perri;
Sales Mgr., Inside—Robert Steinhauer; Pur. Mgr.—Scott O'Hara;
Fin. Svcs. Mgr.—Pat Glover
Colonial Electric Supply Co., The, 1143 S. Route 9, Cape May Court House, 08210 . (609) 465-7144
Colonial Electric Supply Co., The, 469 S. White Horse Pike, Hammonton, 08037 .(609) 704-9950
Colonial Electric Supply Co., The, 701 W. Delilah Rd., Pleasantville, 08232 .....(609) 645-8110
Colonial Electric Supply Co., The, 64 W. Landis Ave., Vineland, 08360 .......(856) 462-6300

**COLOREDGE VISUAL**
127 W. 30th St., 8th Fl., New York NY 10001 .................. **(212) 594-4800**
Chrm.—Terry Tevis; Pres., CEO—Jeb Ball; CFO—Sharon Koh;
V.P., Sales, East Coast—Lisa Frey; Cont.—Chris Barbaro; Sales Mgr.—Jim Bonventura;
Hum. Res. Mgr.—Krisna Basdeo
Coloredge, 190 Jony Dr., Carlstadt, 07072. ......................(201) 716-5200

**COMAIRCO EQUIPMENT LTD.**
5525 Ernest Cormier, Laval, Quebec, Canada, H7C 2S9, ............. **(450) 665-8780**
Pres.—Roland Nadeau
Comairco Equipment, Inc., 17 Progress St., Edison, 08820 ...............(732) 331-1100

**COMMAND WEB FAMILY OF COMPANIES**
100 Castle Rd., Secaucus NJ 07094. .......................... **(201) 863-8100**
Pres.—Andrew Merson; Ex. V.P.—Steven Merson; Dir., Hum. Res.—Alexandra Llano
Bind-Rite Robbinsville, 1 Applegate Dr., Robbinsville, 08691 .............(609) 208-1917

**COMMERCIAL HARDWARE, INC.**
5 Perina Blvd., Cherry Hill NJ 08003 .......................... **(856) 810-0600**
CEO—Victor Palladino; Pres.—John D. DelCollo; V.P., Fin. & CFO—Dennis Barag;
Collections Mgr.—Jenny Embaby
Tri State Hardware, Inc., 5 Perina Blvd., Cherry Hill, 08003 ..............(856) 810-0990

**COMMUNICATIONS SUPPLY CORP.**
200 E. Lies Rd., Carol Stream IL 60188 ........................ **(630) 221-6400**
CFO—Matt Zimmerman; V.P., Sales & Mktg.—Frank LaPlante; V.P., Opers.—Bob Bessler;
Br. Mgr.—John Marsden; Mktg. Mgr.—Stephanie Rembiszewski;
Hum. Res. Mgr.—David Aldriege; Mktg. Comms. Mgr.—Sharon Wrobel
Communications Supply Corp., 104 Sunfield Ave., Edison, 08837 ...........(732) 346-1550

**CONAGRA FOODS, INC.**
1 ConAgra Dr., Omaha NE 68102 ............................. **(402) 240-4000**
CEO—Gary Rodkin; Pres., Conagra Food Sales—Doug Knudsen;
Pres., Comml.—Paul Maass; Ex. V.P., CFO—John Gehring; Ex. V.P., CMO—Joan Chow;
Sr. V.P., Chief Counsel—Leo A. Knowles;
Ex. V.P., Gen. Counsel & Secy.—Colleen Batcheler; V.P., Corp. Comm.—Teresa Paulson;
V.P., Facilities & Real Estate—Jim Doyle; V.P., Inv. Rels.—Chris W. Klinefelter
ConAgra Food Ingredients, 6 Santa Fe Way, Cranbury, 08512 .............(609) 409-6200

**CONGOLEUM CORP.**
3500 Quakerbridge Rd., P.O. Box 3127, Mercerville NJ 08619 ....... **(609) 584-3000**
Pres., CEO—Robert Moran; Sr. V.P., Sales & Mktg.—Dennis Jarosz;
Sr. V.P., Opers.—Dan Garson; Sr. V.P., Admn.—Tom Sciortino; V.P., Mfg.—Greg Guynn;
Dir., IT—Ron Duchesneau; Dir., Hum. Res.—Robert Ingram
Congoleum Corp., Plt. 2,
3500 Quakerbridge Rd., P.O. Box 3127, Mercerville, 08619 .............(609) 584-3000

**CONSOLIDATED CONTAINER COMPANY**
**3101 Towercreek Pkwy. S.E., Ste. 300, Atlanta GA 30339 ................ (678) 742-4600**
**Pres., CEO—Jeffrey Greene; CFO—Richard Sehring;**
**Sr. V-P. & GM, Dairy/Water Group—Rob Zimmerman**
Consolidated Container Co., 28-36 Slater Dr., Elizabeth, 07206 .............. (908) 351-7919
Consolidated Container Co., LLC, 4 Pleasant Hill Rd., Monroe Township, 08831 . (609) 655-0855

**CONTAINER GRAPHICS CORP.**
**114 Edinburgh Dr. S., Ste. 104, Cary NC 27511 ........................ (919) 481-4200**
**CEO—Neil Saunders; Pres.—James Alexander; CFO—Jeffrey Manning;**
**V-P., Engrg.—James Smithwick**
Container Graphics Corp., 3535 Highway 66, Parkway 100, Bldg. 2, Neptune, 07753 . (732) 922-1180

**CONTINENTAL CAST STONE MFG., INC.**
**22001 W. 83rd St., Shawnee KS 66227 .............................. (913) 422-7575**
**Pres.—Dennis McBride; Region Mgr.—Chris Giesken; Opers. Mgr.—Jay Barnickol;**
**Hum. Res. Mgr.—Amy Thomas**
Continental Cast Stone East, 400 Cooper Rd., West Berlin, 08091 ............ (856) 753-4000

**COOPER ELECTRIC SUPPLY CO.**
**1 Matrix Dr., Monroe NJ 08831 .................................... (732) 747-2233**
**Pres.—Mike Dudas; Ex. V-P.—David Cooper; Corp. V-P.—Ronald Reffler;**
**Dir., Pur.—Jim Walsh; Corp. Cred. Mgr.—Diane Beresford; Regional Mgr.—Tom Brady;**
**Mktg. Mgr.—Linda Maia-Lopes; Hum. Res. Mgr.—Georgia Nicolaou**
Cooper Electric Supply Co., 17 Route 206 S., Unit 3, Augusta, 07822 ......... (973) 940-8905
Cooper Electric Supply Co., 72 N. Washington Ave., Bergenfield, 07621 ....... (201) 385-7777
Cooper Electric Supply Co., 933 Cedarbridge Ave., Brick, 08723 ............. (732) 920-3130
Cooper Electric Supply Co., 2727 Fire Rd., Egg Harbor Township, 08234 ....... (609) 833-2115
Cooper Electric Supply Co., 217 Broad Ave., Fairview, 07022 ................ (201) 945-5900
Cooper Electric Supply Co., 19 Royal Rd., Flemington, 08822 ................ (908) 782-3200
Cooper Electric Supply Co., 3477 U.S. Highway 9, Freehold, 07728 ........... (732) 462-2424
Cooper Electric Supply Co., 1521 John F. Kennedy Blvd., Jersey City, 07305 .... (201) 434-8575
Cooper Electric Supply Co., 1805 Lower Rd., Linden, 07036 ................ (732) 340-0346
Cooper Electric Supply Co., 317 E. Bay Ave., Manahawkin, 08050 ............ (609) 978-4666
Cooper Electric Supply Co., 666 State Route 35, Middletown, 07748 .......... (732) 671-5000
Cooper Electric Supply Co., 225 Stockton St., Phillipsburg, 08865 ........... (908) 454-8500
Cooper Electric Supply Co., 412 W. 2nd St., Plainfield, 07060 .............. (908) 756-4090
Cooper Electric Supply Co., 1251 Metropolitan Ave., West Deptford, 08066 ..... (856) 853-9922
Cooper Electric Supply Corp., 444 Route 46 E., Fairfield, 07004 ............. (973) 278-8400

**COOPER INDUSTRIES, INC.**
**600 Travis St., Ste. 5800, Houston TX 77002 ........................ (713) 209-8400**
**Chrm., Pres. & CEO—Kirk Hachigian;**
**Sr. V-P., Gen. Counsel & Chief Compliance Officer—Bruce Taten;**
**V-P., Cont. & CAO—Rick L. Johnson; V-P., Hum. Res.—Heath B. Monesmith;**
**V-P., Bus. Dev.—Mark Doheny; Dir., Mktg.—Rob Taylor**
Cooper Notification, 273 Branchport Ave., Long Branch, 07740 .............. (732) 222-6880

**COOPERSURGICAL, INC.**
**75 Corporate Dr., Trumbull CT 06611 ............................. (203) 601-5200**
**CEO—Paul Remmel; Sales Mgr.—Richard Fox; Cust. Serv. Mgr.—Chris Lentocha**
Origio, Inc., 77 Elbo Ln., Mount Laurel, 08054 .......................... (856) 762-2000

**COPERION K-TRON PITMAN, INC.**
**590 Woodbury Glassboro Rd., Sewell NJ 08080 ....................... (856) 589-0500**
**CFO, GM—Robert E. Wisniewski; V-P., Global Mktg.—Robert Barnett;**
**Dir., Sales—John Winski; Dir., WW Qual.—Jirina Ramescu; Mktg. Mgr.—Nora Ashmen;**
**Bus. Dev. Mgr., Chemicals & Plastics—Jaime Gomez;**
**Bus. Dev. Mgr., Food & Pharmaceutical—Sharon Nowak**
K-Tron Electronics, 590 Woodbury Glassboro Rd., Sewell, 08080 ............. (856) 232-2300

**CORBION**
**7905 Quivira Rd., Lenexa KS 66215 ................................ (913) 890-5500**
**Pres., CEO—William McGowan; V-P., Natl. Acct. Sales—Gary Schmidt;**
**V-P., Sales, Bakery—Mark Woodman; V-P., Sales, Indl.—William Gambel;**
**V-P., Opers.—Nick Blawat; V-P., Bus. Dev. & Mktg.—Mary Bentley;**
**V-P., Hum. Res.—Brett Woodson; V-P., R & D—Larry Skogerson**
Corbion Caravan, 100 Adams Dr., Totowa, 07512 ......................... (973) 256-8886

**CORE LABORATORIES, INC.**
**6316 Windfern St., Houston TX 77040 ............................... (713) 328-2673**
**Pres.—David Demshur; CFO—Richard L. Bergmark; COO—Monty L. Davis;**
**V-P., Hum. Res.—Gwen Schreffler**
Refinery Systems, A Div. Of Core Lab, 11 Princess Rd., Lawrenceville, 08648 ... (609) 896-2673

**CORIANT AMERICA, INC.**
**220 Mill Rd., Chelmsford MA 01824 ................................ (978) 250-2900**
**V-P., Admn. & Gen. Counsel—Mike Reardon; V-P., Corp. Mktg.—Scott Larson;**
**V-P., Sales, N. America—Rich Moulder; V-P., Engrg.—Christopher Riello;**
**Opers. Mgr., Hum. Res.—Cathie Bolduc**
Sycamore Networks, Inc., 100 Century Pkwy, Ste. 120, Mount Laurel, 08054 .... (856) 359-9301

**CORMAN BAG CO.**
**32 Arlington St., P.O. Box 505649, Chelsea MA 02150 .................. (617) 884-7600**
**Pres.—Julie Corman**
Corman Bag Co., 7 Evergreen Pl., Sparta, 07871 ......................... (973) 729-2816

**CORNING, INC.**
**1 Riverfront Plz., Corning NY 14831 ............................... (607) 974-9000**
**Chrm., CEO—Wendell P. Weeks; Vice Chrm., CFO—James B. Flaws;**
**Ex. V-P., CTO—David Morris; Ex. V-P., Chief Admn. Officer—Kirk P. Gregg;**
**Sr. V-P., Corp. Dev. & Strategy—Lawrence D. McRae;**
**Sr. V-P., Gen. Counsel—Lewis Steverson; V-P., GM—Richard Eglen;**
**V-P., Engrg. & Mfg.—Robert B. Brown; V-P., Corp. Comm.—Daniel Collins;**
**Dir., Tech.—Paul M. Then**
Labnet International, Inc., 31 Mayfield Ave., Edison, 08837 ................ (732) 417-0700

**COSMETIC ESSENCE, INC.**
**2182 Route 35 S., Holmdel NJ 07733 ................................ (732) 888-7788**
**Pres., CEO—Peter Martin; CFO—Tom Nelson; Sr. V-P., Global Sales & Mktg.—Matt Heuer;**
**Sr. V-P., Hum. Res.—Brian Laperriere; IT Mgr.—Rick Hopkins;**
**Accts. Payable Mgr.—Jeannine Callahan**
Cosmetic Essence, Inc., 1248 S. River Rd., Cranbury, 08512 ................ (609) 395-1271
Cosmetic Essence, Inc., 50 Clearview Rd., Edison, 08837 .................. (732) 225-2031
Cosmetic Essence, Inc., 1135 Pleasantview Ter. W., Ridgefield, 07657 ......... (201) 941-9800

**COUNTY CONCRETE CORP.**
**50 Railroad Ave., P.O. Box F, Kenvil NJ 07847 ....................... (973) 584-7122**
**Pres.—John C. Crimi; Ex. V-P.—Peter Crimi; V-P., Sales—John Post; V-P.—Ron Sutton;**
**Cont.—Sam DeSteno; Dir., Hum. Res.—John Skelly; Maint. Mgr., Fleet—Ed Gaffney**
County Concrete Corp., 145 Ridgedale Ave., Morristown, 07960 ............. (973) 538-3113

**COURIER CORP.**
**15 Wellman Ave., North Chelmsford MA 01863 ........................ (978) 251-6000**
**Chrm., CEO—James F. Conway III; Sr. V-P., CFO—Peter Folger; CIO—David LaFauci;**
**V-P., Sales—Peter Conway; V-P., Mktg.—Peter Tobin; V-P., Hum. Res.—Diana Sawyer**
Courier Corp., 1 International Blvd., Ste. 400, Mahwah, 07495 .............. (201) 934-7100
Research & Education Assn., 61 Ethel Rd. W., Piscataway, 08854 ............ (732) 819-8880

**COX INDUSTRIES, INC.**
**860 Cannon Bridge Rd. S.W., Orangeburg SC 29115 .................... (803) 534-7467**
**Pres., CEO—R. Michael Johnson; CFO—Phil Tetterton; CAO—Matt Yaun;**
**V-P., Sales, Residential—Brandt Mitchell; V-P., Sales, Intl.—Brian Hayson;**
**Dir., Plt. Opers.—Greg B. Campbell; Dir., IT—Bill Howerton;**
**Dir., Hum. Res.—Pam Bedenbaugh; Sr. Sales Mgr., Support—Kenneth C. Panitt**
Cox Industries, 1517 Route 38 W., P.O. Box 507, Hainesport, 08036 .......... (609) 267-4700

**CRAFTMASTER PRINTING, INC.**
**2024 Corlies Ave., Neptune NJ 07753 ............................... (732) 775-0011**
**Pres.—Curtis Baumgartner**
Craftmaster Printing, Inc., 3 Main St., New Egypt, 08533 .................. (609) 758-5990

**CRANE CO.**
**100 1st Stamford Pl., 4th Fl., Stamford CT 06902 ..................... (203) 363-7300**
**Chrm.—Robert Evans; Pres. & COO, Fluid Handling—Tom Perlitz;**
**V-P., Treas.—Andrew Krawitt; Dir., Corp. Comm. & Inv. Rels.—Richard Koch**
Merrimac Industries, Inc., 41 Fairfield Pl., West Caldwell, 07006 ............ (973) 575-1300

**CROLL-REYNOLDS**
**6 Campus Dr., Parsippany NJ 07054 ................................ (908) 232-4200**
**Pres.—Samuel Croll**
Croll-Reynolds, 90 Hollister Rd., Teterboro, 07608 ....................... (201) 288-9282

**CROP PRODUCTION SERVICES, INC.**
**3005 Rocky Mountain Ave., Loveland CO 80538 ....................... (970) 685-3300**
**Pres., CEO—Richard Gearheard; V-P., Hum. Res.—Kent McDaniel; V-P., Fin.—Tony Engel;**
**Sr. Dir., IT—Connie Herschbach; Dir., Hum. Res.—Susan Guthman**
Crop Production Services, Inc., 127 Perryville Rd., Pittstown, 08867 .......... (908) 735-5545

**CROSSFIELD PRODUCTS CORP**
**3000 E. Harcourt St., Rancho Dominguez CA 90221 ..................... (310) 886-9100**
**Pres., CEO—Brad Watt; CFO—David Johnson; Ex. V-P.—Ron Borum;**
**V-P.—Steven C. Schroeder**
Crossfield Products Corp., 140 Valley Rd., Roselle Park, 07204 ............. (908) 245-2800

**CROWN EQUIPMENT CORP.**
**44 S. Washington St., New Bremen OH 45869 ......................... (419) 629-2311**
**Chrm. Emeritus—James F. Dicke; Chrm., CEO—James F. Dicke II;**
**Pres.—James F. Dicke III; V-P., CFO—Kent W. Spille; Sr. V-P.—Tim Quellhorst;**
**Sr. V-P.—John G. Maxa; Sr. V-P.—Jim Mozer; Sr. V-P.—James Ellis; Sr. V-P.—John Tate;**
**Sr. V-P.—Dave Besser; V-P.—David Beddow; Dir., Hum. Res.—Pete Falk**
Crown Lift Trucks, 104 Bauer Dr., Oakland, 07436 ....................... (201) 337-1211
Crown Lift Trucks, Inc., 680 River Dr., Elmwood Park, 07407 .............. (845) 753-5868

**CUMBERLAND DAIRY, INC.**
**899 Landis Ave., P.O. Box 308, Rosenhayn NJ 08352 ................... (856) 451-1300**
**Pres.—Carmine Catalana IV; CFO—John Cowan; V-P., Sales—David Catalana**
Cumberland Dairy, Inc., 80 Edward Ave., Bridgeton, 08302 ................. (856) 451-1300

**CURBELL PLASTICS, INC.**
**7 Cobham Dr., Orchard Park NY 14127 ............................. (716) 667-3377**
**Pres.—Sam Martin; CFO—Arthur Weibel; Dir., Mktg.—Tracy Schiedel;**
**Dir., IT—Phil Otminski; Dir., Bus. Dev.—Keith Hechtel**
Curbell, Inc., Plastics Div., 844 N. Lenola Rd., Ste. 6, Moorestown, 08057 ...... (856) 778-1100

**CURTISS-WRIGHT CORP.**
**10 Waterview Blvd., 2nd Fl., Parsippany NJ 07054 ..................... (973) 541-3700**
**Chrm.—Martin R. Benante; CEO—David Adams; V-P., CFO—Glenn Tynan;**
**V-P., Gen. Counsel & Secy.—Paul Ferdenzi;**
**V-P., Hum. Res. & Assoc. Gen. Counsel—Joanne Karimi;**
**Hum. Res. Mgr.—Janine O'Rourke; Off. Mgr.—Jane Winter**
Curtiss-Wright Surface Technologies, 80 Highway 4 E., Ste. 310, Paramus, 07652 . (201) 843-7800

**CUSTOM BUILDING PRODUCTS, INC.**
**13001 Seal Beach Blvd., Ste. 200, Seal Beach CA 90740 ................. (562) 598-8808**
**Sr. V-P., Bus. Affs.—Thomas R. Peck II; Ex. V-P.—Dean Leffler; IT Mgr.—Michael Shaw**
Custom Building Products, Inc., 2115 High Hill Rd., Logan Township, 08085 .... (856) 467-9226

**CVS/CAREMARK CORP.**
**1 CVS Dr., Woonsocket RI 02895 ................................... (401) 765-1500**
**Pres., CEO—Larry J. Merlo; Pres., CVS/Pharmacy & Ex. V-P.—Mark Crosby;**
**Sr. V-P., CMO—Rob Price; Sr. V-P., CIO—Stephen J. Gold;**
**Sr. V-P., Chief Hum. Res. Officer—Lisa Bisaccia;**
**Sr. V-P., Fin., CAO & Cont.—Eva Boratto;**
**Ex. V-P., Chief Medical Officer—Troyen M. Brennan; Ex. V-P., CFO—David Denton;**
**Ex. V-P., Gen. Counsel—Thomaș M. Moriarty; V-P., Corp. Comms.—Carolyn Castel;**
**Chief Medical Officer & Chief Scientific Officer—William Shrank**
Caremark Rx, Inc., 180 Passaic Ave., Ste. 5, Fairfield, 07004 .............. (973) 461-1550

**DAILY NEWS L. P.**
**4 New York Plz., 6th Fl., New York NY 10004 ........................ (212) 210-2100**
**Chrm., Publisher—Mort Zuckerman; Sr. V-P., Mktg.—Christine Curtin;**
**Sr. V-P., Adv.—John Polizano; Sr. V-P., Admn. Svcs. & Hum. Res.—Jeff Zomper;**
**Editor-in-Chief—Colin Myler**
New York Daily News, 125 Theodore Conrad Dr., Jersey City, 07305 .......... (201) 946-6000

PARENT COMPANY

**DAL-TILE CORPORATION**
7834 C. F. Hawn Fwy., Dallas TX 75217 . . . . . . . . . . . . . . . . . . . . . . **(214) 398-1411**
Pres.—John Turner, Jr.; CFO—Michael F. McGlothin; Sr. V.-P., Mfg. Opers.—David S. Baran;
   Sr. V.-P., Mktg.—Jim Fanning; Sr. V.-P., Daltile SBU—John Cousins;
   V.-P., Hum. Res.—Troy Closson; V.-P., American Olean SBU—Jon Shedlosky;
   Sr. Digital Mktg. Mgr.—Nathalie Baier; Mktg. Proj. Mgr.—Matt Lewis
DAL-Tile Corporation, 1250 Valley Brook Ave., Lyndhurst, 07071 . . . . . . . . . . (201) 729-0203
DAL-Tile Sales Service Center 186,
   2030 Springdale Rd., Ste. 100, Cherry Hill, 08003 . . . . . . . . . . . . (856) 489-3335

**DANFOSS, INC.**
11655 Crossroads Cir., Baltimore MD 21220 . . . . . . . . . . . . . . . . . . . . . **(410) 931-8250**
Pres., N. Amer.—John Galyen; Dir., Sales—Brian Davis; Dir., Sales—Joel Eggert;
   Dir., Sales—Michael Strouboulis; Dir., Sales—Stephen Gugliotta;
   Mktg. Mgr.—Jason Paquette
Danfoss Hago, Inc., 1120 Globe Ave., Mountainside, 07092 . . . . . . . . . . (908) 232-8687

**DARLING INGREDIENTS, INC.**
251 O'Connor Ridge Blvd., Ste. 300, Irving TX 75038 . . . . . . . . . . . . . . **(972) 717-0300**
Chrm., CEO—Randall C. Stuewe; Ex. V.-P., Admn. & Fin.—John Muse;
   Treas.—Brad Phillips; Dir., Commodity Exports—Brian Schultz;
   Corp. Comm. Mgr.—Carla Simons; Sales Mgr.—Brian Griffin;
   Mktg. Mgr.—Mitch Kilanowski
Darling Ingredients, Inc., 825 Wilson Ave., Newark, 07105 . . . . . . . . . . (973) 465-1900

**DASH PRINTING, INC.**
153 W. 27th St., New York NY 10001 . . . . . . . . . . . . . . . . . . . . . . . . **(212) 643-8534**
Pres.—David Ashendorf; Dir., Mktg.—Rachel Feiner
Dash Printing, Inc., 52 Woodbine St., Ste. 3, Bergenfield, 07621 . . . . . . . (201) 338-2561

**DAVIS-STANDARD, LLC**
1 Extrusion Dr., Pawcatuck CT 06379 . . . . . . . . . . . . . . . . . . . . . . . **(860) 599-1010**
Co-Pres., CEO—Robert Preston; Co-Pres., Extrusion—James Murphy;
   CFO—Michael Pisch; Ex. V.-P.—Ernie Plasse; Dir., Hum. Res.—Michael Bontempo;
   Pur. Mgr.—Paul Loranger
Circonix Technologies, LLC, 29 Executive Pkwy., Ringwood, 07456 . . . . . . (973) 962-6160
Davis-Standard, LLC, 220 Davidson Ave., Ste. 401, Somerset, 08873 . . . . . . . (908) 722-6000

**DCI CHEESE CO.**
3018 Helsan Dr., Richfield WI 53076 . . . . . . . . . . . . . . . . . . . . . . . **(262) 677-3407**
V.-P., Sales—Dominique Delugeau; Dir., Supply Chain—Doug Bissing;
   Procurement Mgr.—Kim Schwartzmiller
DCI Cheese Co., 861 Washington Ave., Carlstadt, 07072 . . . . . . . . . . . . (201) 807-0999

**DELAWARE VALLEY BOX & LUMBER CO.**
2651 E. State St. Ext., Trenton NJ 08619 . . . . . . . . . . . . . . . . . . . . . **(609) 890-2900**
Pres.—Charles C. Gould
Delaware Valley Box & Lumber Co., 14 Austin Ave., Glendora, 08029 . . . . . . . (856) 939-1900

**DELTECH CORP.**
11911 Scenic Hwy., Baton Rouge LA 70807 . . . . . . . . . . . . . . . . . . . **(225) 775-0150**
Chrm., Pres.—Robert Elefante; V.-P., GM—Tom LeBlanc; Cont.—Steve Hartmann;
   EHS & Security Mgr.—Hunters Howes
Deltech Resin Co., 49 Rutherford St., Newark, 07105 . . . . . . . . . . . . . . (973) 589-0880

**DELUXE CORP.**
3680 Victoria St. N., Shoreview MN 55126 . . . . . . . . . . . . . . . . . . . . **(651) 483-7111**
CEO—Lee Schram; Sr. V.-P., CFO—Terry Peterson; Sr. V.-P., CIO—Mike Mathews;
   Chief Acctg. Officer, V.-P. & Cont.—Jeff Bata;
   Sr. V.-P., Secy., Gen. Counsel—Anthony C. Scarfone;
   Sr. V.-P., Hum. Res.—Julie Loosbrock; Sr. V.-P., Small Bus. Svcs.—Malcolm McRoberts;
   V.-P., Enterprise Brand—Laura Radewald
Deluxe Mfg. Operations, Inc., 105 U.S. Highway 46, Mountain Lakes, 07046 . . . . (973) 334-8000

**DEMATIC CORP.**
507 Plymouth Ave. N.E., Grand Rapids MI 49505 . . . . . . . . . . . . . . . . **(616) 913-7700**
Pres., CEO—John Baysore; Sr. V.-P., Opers.—David Berghorn;
   Sr. V.-P., Cust. Serv.—Timothy Wolf; Sr. V.-P., Supply Chain—Katie Russell;
   Sr. V.-P., Integrated Sys.—Mike Khodl; Ex. V.-P., Sales & Mktg.—Robert F. Bork;
   Ex. V.-P., Integrated Sys.—David Bartley; Ex. V.-P., Mech. Sols. & SAIT—Jeffrey Moss;
   V.-P., Sol. Dev.—Michael Kohdl
Dematic Corp., 150 Allen Rd., Ste. 102, Basking Ridge, 07920 . . . . . . . . . . (908) 991-9900

**DIALOGIC, INC.**
4 Gatehall Dr., Parsippany NJ 07054 . . . . . . . . . . . . . . . . . . . . . . . **(800) 755-4444**
Pres., CEO—Kevin Cook; Ex. V.-P., CFO—Bob Dennerlein;
   Sr. V.-P., Worldwide Sales—Bill Crank; Sr. V.-P., Opers. & Prod. Dev.—Kevin Gould;
   Sr. V.-P., Hum. Res.—Rosanna Sargent
Dialogic Corp., 1515 State Route 10 E., Parsippany, 07054 . . . . . . . . . . . . (973) 967-6000

**DICAR, INC.**
10 Bloomfield Ave., P.O. Box 643, Pine Brook NJ 07058 . . . . . . . . . . . . **(973) 575-1174**
Pres.—Steve Warl; V.-P., Cont.—Thomas Curcio; Hum. Res. Mgr.—Loretta Resz;
   Safety Mgr.—Ira Sanders; Tech. Mgr.—Raymond So; Pur. Agt.—Jim Johnson
Dicar, Inc., 5 Bader Rd., Pine Brook, 07058 . . . . . . . . . . . . . . . . . . . (973) 575-4220

**DIGITAL FIRST MEDIA**
448 Lincoln Hwy., Fairless Hills PA 19030 . . . . . . . . . . . . . . . . . . . . **(215) 504-4200**
Chrm., CEO—John Paton; CFO—Barbara Bennett; CIO—Arturo Duran;
   V.-P., Fin.—Gary Struening; V.-P., Content—Jon Cooper
Central Record Corp., The,
   32 S. Main St., Ste. A, P.O. Box 1027, Medford, 08055 . . . . . . . . . . (609) 654-9221
Journal Register Co., The, 32 S. Main St., Ste. A, Medford, 08055 . . . . . . (609) 654-5000
Trentonian, The, 600 Perry St., Trenton, 08618 . . . . . . . . . . . . . . . . . (609) 989-7800

**DINASO STATEN ISLAND, LLC**
520 Industrial Loop, Staten Island NY 10309 . . . . . . . . . . . . . . . . . . **(718) 559-5855**
Pres.—John DiNaso
DiNaso Building Supplies, 133 Ocean Ave., Lakewood, 08701 . . . . . . . . . . (732) 886-6666

**DIOCESE OF CAMDEN**
631 Market St., Camden NJ 08102 . . . . . . . . . . . . . . . . . . . . . . . . . **(856) 756-7900**
Publisher—Reverend Dennis Sullivan; Dir., Comms.—Peter Feurerhard
Catholic Star Herald, 15 N. 7th St., Camden, 08102 . . . . . . . . . . . . . . . (856) 583-6142

**DIOCESE OF PATERSON**
777 Valley Rd., Clifton NJ 07013 . . . . . . . . . . . . . . . . . . . . . . . . . **(973) 777-8818**
Publisher—Bishop Arthur Joseph Serratelli
Beacon Publishing Co., Inc., 775 Valley Rd., Clifton, 07013 . . . . . . . . . . (973) 279-8845

**DITECH GROUP**
630 Loucks Mill Rd., Ste. 8, York PA 17403 . . . . . . . . . . . . . . . . . . . **(717) 846-6002**
Pres.—Jim Osmolinski
Zin-Tech, 1416 Union Ave., Pennsauken, 08110 . . . . . . . . . . . . . . . . . (856) 661-0900

**DODSON GLOBAL, INC.**
5650 E. Ponce De Leon Ave., Stone Mountain GA 30083 . . . . . . . . . . . . **(404) 363-8900**
Pres.—Bob Elliott; Pur. Mgr.—Rodney Fulmer; Fin. & Off. Mgr.—Tim Henderson
Dodson Global, Inc., 27 Cotters Ln., East Brunswick, 08816 . . . . . . . . . . (732) 238-7001

**DOW CHEMICAL CO., THE**
2030 Dow Ctr., Midland MI 48674 . . . . . . . . . . . . . . . . . . . . . . . . . **(989) 636-1000**
Chrm., Pres. & CEO—Andrew Liveris; Pres., Polyurethane—Glenn Wright;
   CIO—David E. Kepler; Ex. V.-P., CFO—William H. Weideman;
   V.-P., CTO—William F. Banholzer;
   Ex. V.-P., Basic Plastics & Chemicals, Mfg. & Engrg.—Carol Williams;
   Ex. V.-P., Aviation, Corp. Affs. & Hum. Res.—Gregory Freiwald;
   V.-P., Cont.—Ron Edmonds; V.-P., Inv. Rels.—Doug May
Dow Chemical Co., The, 1500 John Tipton Blvd., Pennsauken, 08110 . . . . . . (856) 910-4900
Lightscape Materials, Inc., 201 Washington Rd., Princeton, 08540 . . . . . . . (609) 734-2227

**DOW JONES & CO., INC.**
1211 Avenue of the Americas, 8th Fl., New York NY 10036 . . . . . . . . . . . **(212) 416-2000**
Pres., CEO—William Lewis; CFO—Anna Sedgley; Sr. V.-P., CCO—Paula Keve;
   Sr. V.-P., Hum. Res.—Mark Musgrave; Sr. V.-P., Special Proj.—Ian Weston;
   Ex. V.-P., Gen. Counsel—Mark Jackson;
   Editor-In-Chief, DJ & Mng. Editor, WSJ—Gerard Baker;
   Sales & Mktg. Mgr.—Jennifer H. Hall
Dow Jones & Co., Inc., 4300 N. Route 1, Monmouth Junction, 08852 . . . . . . . (609) 520-4000

**DPT LABORATORIES LTD.**
318 McCullough Ave., P.O. Box 1659, San Antonio TX 78215 . . . . . . . . . **(210) 476-8100**
Pres., CEO—Paul Johnson; CFO—Glenn Kues; Ex. V.-P., Gen. Counsel—Mark Mitchell;
   V.-P., Sales & Mktg.—Paul Joseph; V.-P., Hum. Res.—Rick Bentzinger;
   Sr. Dir., Bus. Dev.—J. J. Feik; Dir., Hum. Res.—Ernie Serrato
DPT Lakewood, LLC, 1200 Paco Way, Bldg. 19, Lakewood, 08701 . . . . . . (732) 367-9000

**DR PEPPER SNAPPLE GROUP, INC.**
5301 Legacy Dr., Plano TX 75024 . . . . . . . . . . . . . . . . . . . . . . . . . **(972) 673-7000**
CFO—Marty M. Ellen
Dr Pepper Snapple Group, Inc., 1200 Milik St., Carteret, 07008 . . . . . . . . (732) 969-1600
Yoo-Hoo Chocolate Beverage Corp., 600 Commercial Ave., Carlstadt, 07072 . . . . (201) 933-0070

**DSM PHARMACEUTICAL PRODUCTS, INC.**
45 Waterview Blvd., Parsippany NJ 07054 . . . . . . . . . . . . . . . . . . . . **(973) 257-1063**
Pres., CEO—Alexander Wessels; Pres. & Bus. Unit Dir., Biologics—Karen King;
   Pres., Group Protection—Hugh Welsh; Sr. V.-P., Hum. Res.—Stan Veltman;
   V.-P., Mktg. & Strategy—Paul Sidhu; Dir., Comms. & Mktg.—Guy Tiene;
   Bldg. Mgr.—Catherine Dooney
DSM Nutritional Products, Inc., 206 Macks Island Dr., Belvidere, 07823 . . . . . . (908) 475-5300

**DUBELL LUMBER CO.**
148 Route 70 E., P.O. Box 1449, Medford NJ 08055 . . . . . . . . . . . . . . . **(609) 654-4143**
Owner—Gene DiMediao; GM—Carmen Chappine; Sales Mgr.—John Cusick;
   Hum. Res. Mgr.—Pam Shepard
Dubell Lumber Co., 102 S. Route 73, Cedar Brook, 08018 . . . . . . . . . . . (609) 567-2467
Dubell Lumber Co., 731 Cuthbert Blvd., Cherry Hill, 08002 . . . . . . . . . . (856) 665-9100

**DUN-RITE SAND & GRAVEL CO., INC.**
573 E. Grant Ave., Vineland NJ 08360 . . . . . . . . . . . . . . . . . . . . . . **(856) 692-2520**
Pres.—Peter Galetto; Off. Mgr.—Fay Platania
Dun-Rite Sand & Gravel Co., Inc., 3765 Mays Landing Rd., Vineland, 08361 . . . . (856) 825-9900

**DURAAMEN ENGINEERED PRODUCTS, INC.**
116 W. 23rd St., 5th Fl., New York NY 10011 . . . . . . . . . . . . . . . . . . . **(212) 386-7609**
Owner & Pres.—Victor Pachade; Hum. Res. Mgr.—Amy Pachade
Duraamen Engineered Products, Inc., 457 Frelinghuysen Ave., Newark, 07114 . . (973) 230-1301

**DURO BAG MFG. CO.**
7600 Empire Dr., Florence KY 41042 . . . . . . . . . . . . . . . . . . . . . . . **(859) 581-8200**
Chrm., Pres. & CEO—Charles L. Shor; COO—Don Breen;
   Ex. V.-P., Sales, Standard Prods. Div.—Jim Eaton; Dir., Hum. Res.—Lisa Gasper
Duro Bag Mfg. Co., 750 Dowd Ave., Elizabeth, 07201 . . . . . . . . . . . . . (908) 351-2400

**DYNASIL CORP. OF AMERICA**
44 Hunt St., Watertown MA 02472 . . . . . . . . . . . . . . . . . . . . . . . . . **(617) 668-6855**
Chrm., Pres. & Interim CEO—Peter Sulick; CFO—Thomas C. Leonard;
   Corp. Secy.—Patricia Kehe; Hum. Res. Mgr.—Rebecca Johnson
Dynasil Corp. Of America, 385 Cooper Rd., West Berlin, 08091 . . . . . . . . (856) 767-4600

**DYNTEK, INC.**
4440 Von Karman Ave., Ste. 200, Newport Beach CA 92660 . . . . . . . . . . **(949) 271-6700**
CEO—Ron Ben-Yishay; CFO—Karen Rosenberger; CTO—Steve Struthers;
   V.-P., Sales & Mktg.—Linda Ford; Dir., Training—Jeff Brambir;
   Hum. Res. Mgr.—Angel Hermes
DynTek Services, Inc., 1120 Route 73, Ste. 100, Mount Laurel, 08054 . . . . . . (856) 834-1100

**DYSON, DYSON & DUNN, INC.**
566 Chestnut St., Ste. 7, Winnetka IL 60093 . . . . . . . . . . . . . . . . . . . **(847) 441-5517**
Pres.—Peter Dyson; Principal—Barbara B. Dyson
Grobet File Co. Of America, LLC, 750 Washington Ave., Carlstadt, 07072 . . . . . . (201) 939-6700

**E & T PLASTICS MFG. CO., INC.**
4545 37th St., Long Island City NY 11101 . . . . . . . . . . . . . . . . . . . . **(718) 729-6226**
Pres.—Gary Thal; V.-P., Sales & Mktg.—Greg Gillen; V.-P., Opers.—Mark Elowsky
E & T Plastics, 824 E. Gate Dr., Ste. E, Mount Laurel, 08054 . . . . . . . . . (856) 787-0900

**E. I. DU PONT DE NEMOURS & CO.**
**1007 Market St., Wilmington DE 19898 .............................. (302) 774-1000**
**Chrm., CEO—Ellen Kullman; Pres., Health & Nutrition—Craig F. Binetti;**
**Pres., Bldg. Innovations—Timothy P. McCann;**
**Pres., Dupont Packaging & Indl. Polymers—William J. Harvey;**
**Pres., DuPont Crop Protection—Rik Miller;**
**Pres., Performance Polymers—Patrick Lindner;**
**Pres., DuPont Sustainable Risk—James R. Weigand;**
**Ex. V-P., CFO—Nicholas C. Fanandakis;**
**Ex. V-P., Chief Innovation Officer—Thomas M. Connelly, Jr.;**
**V-P., IT & CIO—Phuong Tram;**
**V-P., Env., Health & Safety & Chief Sustainability Officer—Linda J. Fisher;**
**V-P., Logistics & Sourcing & Chief Proc. Officer—Shelly Stewart, Jr.;**
**Sr. V-P. & Gen. Counsel—Stacy L. Fox;**
**Sr. V-P., Engrg. & Integrated Opers.—Gary W. Spitzer;**
**Sr. V-P., Hum. Res.—Benito Cachinero-Sanchez;**
**Sr. V-P., Indl. Biosciences, Performance Polymers & Packaging—James C. Collins, Jr.;**
**Sr. V-P., Bus. Process Simplification & Corp. Productivity—Richard C. Olson;**
**Sr. V-P., Bldg. Innovations, Protection Tech. & Sustainable Sols.—Matthew Trerotola;**
**Ex. V-P.—James C. Borel; Ex. V-P.**
Belco Technologies Corp., 9 Entin Rd., Parsippany, 07054.................. (973) 884-4700
E. I. du Pont de Nemours & Co., Chambers Works Plt.,
67 Canal St., Deepwater, 08023 .................................... (856) 299-5000

**EARLE ASPHALT COMPANY**
**1800 Route 34, Bldg. 2, Ste. 205, Wall NJ 07719.................. (732) 308-1113**
**Pres.—Walter R. Earle II; V-P.—Thomas J. Earle; Hum. Res. Mgr.—Darlene Rasmussen**
Walter R. Earle Corporation, 655 S. Hope Chapel Rd., Jackson, 08527 ........ (732) 657-8551

**EARTH FRIENDLY PRODUCTS**
**111 S. Rohlwing Rd., Addison IL 60101 ............................. (630) 595-1900**
**CEO—E. Van Vlahakis; Pres.—John Vlahakis; V-P., Admn., Fin. & MIS—Gladys Beber;**
**V-P.—Kelly Vlahakis; GM—Mike Marrese; Hum. Res. Mgr.—Jennifer DelBocchio**
Earth Friendly Products, Inc., 380 Chestnut St., Norwood, 07648............ (201) 750-7701

**EARTHCOLOR, INC.**
**249 Pomeroy Rd., P.O. Box 169, Parsippany NJ 07054 .................. (973) 884-1300**
**CEO—Robert Kashan; V-P., IT—William Chillin; V-P., Fin.—Nat Modugno;**
**Dir., Mktg.—Karen Missud; Dir., Hum. Res.—Alan Liebeskind**
EarthColor, 345 Walsh Dr., Parsippany, 07054.............................. (973) 884-1300
EarthDigital, 77 Moonachie Ave., Moonachie, 07074 ....................... (551) 497-5400

**EAST COAST TILE IMPORTS, INC.**
**8 Stony Brook St., P.O. Box 909, Ludlow MA 01056 .................... (413) 583-4246**
**Pres.—Robert Rose; V-P., CFO—Bill Dupuis; IT Mgr.—Stacey Anair;**
**Import Mgr.—Donna Napolitan**
Classic Ceramic Tile, Inc., 272 State Route 18, Ste. 3, East Brunswick, 08816... (732) 390-7700

**EASTER SEALS NEW JERSEY**
**9 Terminal Rd., New Brunswick NJ 08901........................... (732) 257-6662**
**CEO—Brian Fitzgerald; COO—Charles Perry; Dir., Mktg.—Vanessa Holden;**
**IT Mgr.—Curt Butler; Bus. Dev. Mgr.—Colleen Ward**
Easter Seal Society Of New Jersey, 133 Main St., Franklin, 07416 ........... (973) 827-9066
Raritan Valley Workshop, 9 Terminal Rd., New Brunswick, 08901............. (732) 828-8080

**EASTERN CONCRETE MATERIALS, INC.**
**475 Market St., 3rd Fl., Elmwood Park NJ 07407....................... (201) 797-7979**
**Pres.—Mike Gentoso; Dir., IT—Robert Osbahr; Sales Mgr.—Gary Graziano;**
**Opers. Mgr.—Louis Petrollo; Hum. Res. Mgr.—Patricia Kotlowski;**
**Qual. Control Mgr.—Paul DeRosa**
Eastern Concrete Materials, Inc., 201 Route 539, Barnegat, 08005 .......... (609) 698-2800
Eastern Concrete Materials, Inc., 1 Railroad Ave., Glen Gardner, 08826........ (908) 537-2135
Eastern Concrete Materials, Inc., 3620 Route 23 N., Hamburg, 07419 ......... (973) 827-7625

**EASTERN LIFT TRUCK CO., INC.**
**10 Grumbacher Rd., York PA 17406.................................. (717) 764-1161**
**Pres.—Michael Pruitt; GM—Luke Gross; Sales Mgr.—Brad Stein;**
**Sales Mgr., Aftermarket—Jason Thompson; Br. Mgr.—Matt Harman;**
**Mktg. Mgr.—Michael Edmonds; Hum. Res. Mgr.—Esther Lehman**
Eastern Lift Truck Co., Inc.,
549 E. Linwood Ave., Route 73 N., P.O. Box 307, Maple Shade, 08052 ....... (856) 779-8880

**EATON CORP.**
**1000 Eaton Blvd., Cleveland OH 44122.............................. (216) 523-5000**
**Chrm., Pres. & CEO—Alexander M. Cutler; Vice Chrm., CFO—Richard N. Fearon;**
**Vice Chrm. & COO, Electrical Group—Thomas S. Gross;**
**Vice Chrm. & COO, Indl. Group—Craig Arnold; Sr. V-P., Cont.—Billie K. Rawot;**
**Sr. V-P., Taxes—John S. Mitchell; Sr. V-P., Inv. Rels.—Don Bullock;**
**Ex. V-P., Gen. Counsel—Mark M. McGuire; Ex. V-P., Eaton Bus. Sys.—Uday Yadav;**
**Dir., Comms., Indl. Sector—Kelly Jasko**
Eaton Filtration, LLC, 44 Apple St., Tinton Falls, 07724 ..................... (732) 767-4200

**EATON CORP., ELECTRICAL DIV.**
**8609 6 Forks Rd., Raleigh NC 27615 ................................ (919) 870-3000**
**V-P., Cont., Power Sys. Div.—Richard Nicholas; V-P., GM—Brian Brickhouse;**
**Mktg. Mgr.—Kristin Somers; Cred. Mgr.—Linda Hight**
Eaton Corp., Electrical Div., 96 Stemmers Ln., Westampton, 08060 ........... (609) 835-4230

**EDDIE KANE STEEL PRODUCTS, INC.**
**P.O. Box 133, Spring Lake NJ 07762 ................................. (732) 974-3339**
**Pres.—Augustine Kane**
Eddie Kane Steel Products, Inc., 450 Southard St., Trenton, 08638 ........... (609) 392-1161

**EDMUND OPTICS, INC.**
**101 E. Gloucester Pike, Barrington NJ 08007 ......................... (856) 547-3488**
**Chrm., CEO—Robert Edmund; CFO—Jason Mulliner; COO—Samuel Sadoulet;**
**V-P., Global Sales—Thomas Kessler; V-P., Opers.—Susan O'Keefe;**
**V-P., Mktg.—Marisa Edmund; Sr. Dir., Hum. Res.—Susan Tunney;**
**Dir., Mktg. Comms.—Kirsten Bjork-Jones; Database Dev. Mgr.—Jeff Harvey**
Anchor Optical Co., 101 E. Gloucester Pike, Barrington, 08007 .............. (856) 573-6865

**EFCO CORP.**
**1800 N.E. Broadway Ave., Des Moines IA 50313 ....................... (515) 266-1141**
**Chrm., CEO—Al Jennings; Ex. V-P.—Curt Bennethum; Adv. Mgr.—Cathy Howell;**
**Hum. Res. Mgr.—Tracy Kierry**
EFCO Forms, 77 Vanderburg Rd., Marlboro, 07746 ......................... (732) 308-1010

**ELECTRICAL WHOLESALERS, INC.**
**51 Homestead Ave., Hartford CT 06120............................... (860) 522-3232**
**Pres.—John Reznick; Mktg. Mgr.—Mark Osak; IT Mgr.—Jeff Shovak;**
**Hum. Res. Mgr.—Nadra Morgan**
Fox Electric Supply Co., Inc., 1 Dodge Dr., West Caldwell, 07006 ............ (973) 227-4151
Monarch Electric Co., Inc., 1 Dodge Dr., West Caldwell, 07006 .............. (973) 227-4151

**ELEMENTIS SPECIALTIES, INC.**
**469 Old Trenton Rd., East Windsor NJ 08512 ......................... (609) 443-2000**
**Pres.—Greg McClatchy; V-P., Global Supply Chain—Gustavo Araujo; V-P., Fin.—Joe Budd;**
**Dir., Mktg.—Clare Doyle; Dir., Bus., Coatings—Dave Brown;**
**Dir., Global R & D—Ken Smith; Dir., Global Oilfield & Lubrication—Jim Foley;**
**Mktg. Mgr.—Eric Post; Tech. Mgr.—Homer Jamasbi**
Elementis Specialties, Inc., 400 Claremont Ave., Jersey City, 07304 .......... (201) 395-5108

**ELI LILLY**
**440 Route 22 E., Bridgewater NJ 08807 .............................. (908) 541-8100**
**V-P., Global Qual.—Carole Beer; Assoc. V-P., Corp. Comms.—Tracy Henrikson;**
**Sr. Dir., Portfolio Mktg., Oncology—Kim Aldridge;**
**Assoc. Dir., Learning Tech.—Bob Guglielman**
Eli Lilly & Co., 33 ImClone Dr., Branchburg, 08876 ........................ (908) 541-8100

**ELI LILLY & CO.**
**Lilly Corporate Ctr., Indianapolis IN 46285 ........................... (317) 276-2000**
**Chrm., Pres. & CEO—John C. Lechleiter; Pres., Lilly Oncology & Sr. V-P.—Susan Mahony;**
**Pres., Lilly Research Lab & Ex. V-P.—Jan M. Lundberg; Pres., Lilly USA—Alex M. Azar II;**
**Pres., Mfg. Opers.—Maria Crowe; Pres., Diabetes & Sr. V-P.—Enrique Conterno;**
**Sr. V-P., CFO—Derica W. Rice; Sr. V-P., CMO—Rob Brown; V-P., IT & CIO—Michael Heim;**
**Sr. V-P., Gen. Counsel—Michael J. Harrington;**
**Sr. V-P., Diversity & Hum. Res.—Stephen F. Fry;**
**Sr. V-P., Corp. Affs. & Comms.—Bart Peterson; Sr. V-P., Global Qual.—Fionnuala Walsh;**
**Sr. Dir., Mktg.—Karen Wurster; Dir., Mktg.—Amy Chafin;**
**Dir., Mktg., Mens Health—Erica Hardy; Dir., Innovation—Joseph Holman**
Eli Lilly (H Q), 440 Route 22 E., Bridgewater, 08807 ....................... (908) 541-8100

**EMERALD PERFORMANCE MATERIALS, LLC**
**2020 Front St., Ste. 100, Cuyahoga Falls OH 44221..................... (330) 916-6700**
**Pres., CFO—Candace M. Wagner; V-P., Bus. Dev. & Mktg. Svcs.—Julie O. Vaughn;**
**V-P., IT—Chris O'Neill; V-P., Hum. Res.—Thomas J. Nelson;**
**V-P., Corp. Cont.—Becky L. Watson; V-P., Proc.—Robert Culp**
CVC Thermoset Specialties, Inc., 844 N. Lenola Rd., Ste. 1, Moorestown, 08057 . (856) 533-3000

**EMERSON ELECTRIC CO.**
**8000 W. Florissant Ave., Bldg. AA, P.O. Box 4100, St. Louis MO 63136 ..... (314) 553-2000**
**Chrm., CEO—David Farr; Pres., COO—Edward Monser; Sr. V-P., CTO—R. D. Ledford;**
**Ex. V-P., CFO—Frank Dellaquila; Ex. V-P., Secy. & Gen. Counsel—Frank Steeves;**
**Sr. Ex. V-P.—Charles A. Peters; Sr. V-P., Hum. Res. & Emp. Rels.—Mike Rohrat;**
**Sr. V-P., Dev.—J. D. Switzer; Sr. V-P., Organization & Plng.—P. E. McKnight;**
**Ex. V-P.—Jay Geldmacher; Ex. V-P.—D. Scott Barbour; Ex. V-P.—Mark Bulanda;**
**Ex. V-P.—James J. Lindeman; Ex. V-P.—Patrick J. Sly; Ex. V-P.—Steven A. Sonnenberg;**
**V-P., Fin.—S. C. Roemer**
ASCO Power Technologies, L.P. (H Q), 50 Hanover Rd., Florham Park, 07932... (800) 800-2726
ASCO Valve, Inc., 50-60 Hanover Rd., Florham Park, 07932 .................. (973) 966-2000

**EMI INDUSTRIES, LLC**
**1316 Tech Blvd., Tampa FL 33619 ................................... (813) 626-3166**
**Pres., GM—Allen Harvill; CFO—Karl Herold; V-P., Sales & Mktg.—Eric Johnson;**
**Proj. Mgr.—Rafael Abreu**
Marlo Mfg. Co., Inc., 301 Division St., Boonton, 07005...................... (973) 423-0226

**ENDO PHARMACEUTICALS, INC.**
**1400 Atwater Dr., Malvern PA 19355.................................. (484) 216-0000**
**Pres., CEO—Rajiv De Silva; Chief Compliance Officer—Jon Smollen;**
**Ex. V-P., Chief Legal Officer—Caroline B. Manogue;**
**Sr. V-P., Hum. Res.—Larry Cunningham; Ex. V-P., R & D—Ivan Gergel;**
**V-P., Corp. Affs.—Blaine Davis**
Endo Pharmaceutical, Inc., 8 Clarke Dr., Cranbury, 08512.................... (609) 409-9010

**ENERGIZER HOLDINGS, INC.**
**533 Maryville University Dr., St. Louis MO 63141 ...................... (314) 985-2000**
**CEO—Ward Klein; Pres., Household Prods. Div.—Alan Hoskins;**
**Pres., Personal Care Div.—David Hatfield; Ex. V-P., CFO—Daniel J. Sescleifer;**
**V-P., Inv. Rels.—Jacqueline E. Burwitz**
Energizer Personal Care, 240 Cedar Knolls Rd., Ste. 401, Cedar Knolls, 07927.. (973) 753-3000

**ENESCO, LLC**
**225 Windsor Dr., Itasca IL 60143 .................................... (630) 875-5300**
**CEO—Thomas G. Bowles; CFO—Theodore Eischeid; Sr. V-P., Sales, U.S.—Michael Griffith**
Our Name Is Mud, 15 Potter St., Ste. 1, Haddonfield, 08033 ................. (856) 375-2098

**ENPRO INDUSTRIES, INC.**
**5605 Carnegie Blvd., Ste. 500, Charlotte NC 28209..................... (704) 731-1500**
**Pres., CEO—Steve Macadam; Sr. V-P., CFO—Alexander W. Pease;**
**V-P., Gen. Counsel—Robert S. McLean; V-P., Treasury & Tax—David S. Burnett;**
**V-P., Dev. & Plng.—J. Milton Childress; Dir., Corp. Comm. & Inv. Rels.—Daniel Grgurich**
DGB Bearing & Technology,
700 Mid Atlantic Pkwy., P.O. Box 189, Thorofare, 08086 .................... (856) 848-3200

**ENSINGER, INC.**
**365 Meadowlands Blvd., Washington PA 15301......................... (724) 746-6050**
**CFO—Bob Racchini; V-P., GM—Chris Ranallo; V-P.—Lawrence G. Resavage;**
**Sales Mgr., Natl.—Ken Pitchok; MIS Mgr.—John Hill**
Hyde Co., A. L., 1 Main St., P.O. Box 62, Grenloch, 08032.................... (856) 227-0500

**EPIC MANAGEMENT, INC.**
**136 11th St., Ste. 1, Piscataway NJ 08854 ............................ (732) 752-6100**
**CEO—Robert Epifano, Jr.; Pres.—John Epifano; Sr. V-P.—Joel G. Lizotte;**
**IT Mgr.—Miguel Alayon**
Epic Millwork, 1022 Hamilton St., Ste. G, Somerset, 08873.................. (732) 296-0273

PARENT COMPANY

## EPOCH TIMES INTERNATIONAL, INC.
**229 W. 28th St., 5th Fl., New York NY 10001** .................. **(212) 239-2808**
Publisher—John Tang; COO—Du Xiao Hua; Editor—John Nania; Dir., Adv.—Amir Talai
New Jersey Epoch Times, 50 Cragwood Rd., South Plainfield, 07080 ........ (908) 548-8380

## ERICSSON, INC.
**6300 Legacy Dr., Plano TX 75024** ........................... **(972) 583-0000**
Pres., CEO—Angel Ruiz; V.-P., CFO—Per Lofgren; V.-P., Hum. Res.—Gunjan Aggarwal;
  Dir., Comm.—Jimmy Duvall
Ericsson, Inc., 1 Ericsson Dr., Piscataway, 08854 .................... (732) 699-2000

## ESSILOR OF AMERICA, INC.
**13515 N. Stemmons Fwy., Dallas TX 75234** .................. **(214) 496-4000**
Pres.—John Carrier; Ex. V.-P., Admn. & Fin. & CFO—Kevin A. Rupp;
  V.-P., GM, Essilor Retail Group—Steve Nussbaumer; V.-P., Strategic Accts.—Bill Clove;
  V.-P., Mktg.—Carl Bracy; V.-P., Hum. Res.—Steve Cunningham;
  Corp. Comms. Mgr.—Kristan Zeilan
Essilor Laboratories, 5 Powderhorn Dr., Warren, 07059 .................... (732) 563-9884

## EVOQUA WATER TECHNOLOGIES
**4800 North Point Pkwy., Ste. 250, Alpharetta GA 30005** .............. **(978) 614-7111**
Interim CEO—Gary Cappeline; V.-P., Global Sales—Ursula Boehm;
  V.-P., Indl. Bus.—Rodney Aulick; V.-P., Municipal Bus.—Malcolm Kinnaird;
  V.-P., Svcs.—Brent Hillier; Dir., Info. Tech.—Dennis Strom
Evoqua Water Technologies, 624 Evans St., Elizabeth, 07201 ............... (908) 353-7230
Siemens Industry, Inc., Water Technologies,
  20 Murray Hill Pkwy., Ste. 140, East Rutherford, 07073 ............. (201) 531-9338
Siemens Industry, Inc., Water Technologies, 2 Milltown Ct., Union, 07083 ...... (908) 851-2277
Siemens Industry, Inc., Water Technologies, 1901 W. Garden Rd., Vineland, 08360 . (856) 507-9000

## EXTECH BUILDING MATERIALS
**43-87 Vernon Blvd., Long Island City NY 11101** ............... **(718) 786-2288**
Br. Mgr.—Tom Miczko; Pur. Mgr.—Randy Ramtahal; Asst. Br. Mgr.—Patrick Navaine
Extech Building Materials, 100 Bogert St., Closter, 07624 .................... (201) 768-2133
Extech Building Materials, Inc., 385 Asbury Rd., Farmingdale, 07727 ......... (732) 919-3340
Extech Building Materials, Inc., 61-89 Ave. K, Newark, 07105 ................. (973) 274-3340

## EXXONMOBIL CORP.
**5959 Las Colinas Blvd., Irving TX 75039** .................... **(972) 444-1000**
Chrm., CEO—Rex Tillerson; Sr. V.-P.—Michael Dolan; V.-P., Cont.—Pat Mulva;
  V.-P., Hum. Res.—Malcolm Farrant
Exxon Mobil Corp., 1001 Billingsport Rd., Paulsboro, 08066 ................. (856) 224-5000

## FASTENAL CO.
**2001 Theurer Blvd., Winona MN 55987** ..................... **(507) 454-5374**
Chrm.—Robert Kierlin; CEO—Willard Oberton; CFO—Daniel Florness;
  V.-P., Sales—Nicholas J. Lundquist; V.-P., IT—Ashok Singh;
  Sales Mgr., Outside—Adam Williams; Mfg. Mgr.—Tim Borkowsky;
  Pur. Mgr.—Scott Kemp; Hum. Res. Mgr.—Renee Wisecup
Fastenal Co., 1115 N. New Rd., Absecon, 08201 .................... (609) 813-2356
Fastenal Co., 421 Route 73 & Cushman Ave., Unit 11, Berlin, 08009 ...... (856) 768-3657
Fastenal Co., 921 Route 130 N., Burlington, 08016 .................... (609) 239-3016
Fastenal Co., 33 Route 17 S., East Rutherford, 07073 ................. (201) 804-2228
Fastenal Co., 22 Meridian Rd., Unit 2, Eatontown, 07724 .............. (732) 542-7533
Fastenal Co., 55 Carter Dr., Edison, 08817 .......................... (732) 777-1029
Fastenal Co., 68-A Clinton Rd., Fairfield, 07004 ..................... (973) 244-0540
Fastenal Co., 186 Gold Mine Rd., Unit 1, Flanders, 07836 ............. (973) 691-0547
Fastenal Co., 316 Black Horse Pike, Unit C, Glendora, 08029 .......... (856) 939-2500
Fastenal Co., 1026 W. Elizabeth Ave., Unit 2, Linden, 07036 .......... (908) 862-8880
Fastenal Co., 550 Lincoln Blvd., Middlesex, 08846 ................... (732) 748-0140
Fastenal Co., 987 Jersey Ave., Ste. C, New Brunswick, 08901 .......... (732) 246-0248
Fastenal Co., 443 Madison Ave., Paterson, 07524 .................... (973) 278-5509
Fastenal Co., 1163 Route 130, Robbinsville, 08691 .................. (609) 259-4290
Fastenal Co., 500 Hartle St., Ste. D, Sayreville, 08872 ............... (732) 254-1117
Fastenal Co., 1875 N. Olden Ave., Trenton, 08638 ................... (609) 530-0456
Fastenal Co., 53 S. Jefferson Rd., Ste. K, Whippany, 07981 ........... (973) 428-3300

## FCX PERFORMANCE, INC.
**3000 E. 14th Ave., Columbus OH 43219** ..................... **(614) 253-1996**
Owner—Charles Simon; CFO—Charles Hale; CIO—Russ Frazee; V.-P.—Donald Simon;
  Acctg. Mgr.—Rick Binkley
FCX Performance, Inc., 333 Route 46 W., Ste. 130, Fairfield, 07004 ..... (973) 575-8350

## FEDERAL WINE & LIQUOR CO.
**56 Hackensack Ave., P.O. Box 519, Kearny NJ 07032** ............... **(973) 624-6444**
Pres.—Richard Leventhal
Federal Wine & Liquor Co., 1 Central Ave., Mount Laurel, 08054 ............ (856) 234-3200

## FEDEX OFFICE & PRINT SERVICES, INC.
**13155 Noel Rd., Ste. 1600, Dallas TX 75240** .................. **(214) 550-7000**
Pres., CEO—Brian D. Philips; CFO—Leslie Benners;
  Dir., Mktg. & Prod. Dev.—Randall Scarborough; Hum. Res. Mgr.—Leslie Perez
FedEx Office & Print Center, 1160 Marlton Pike E., Cherry Hill, 08034 ....... (856) 427-0099
FedEx Office & Print Center, 212 State Route 18, East Brunswick, 08816 ...... (732) 249-9222
FedEx Office & Print Center, 1 Quality Way, Iselin, 08830 ............... (732) 636-3580
FedEx Office & Print Center, 1211 Route 73, Mount Laurel, 08054 .......... (856) 273-5959
FedEx Office & Print Center, 450 Tilton Rd., Northfield, 08225 ........... (609) 569-8100
FedEx Office & Print Center, 315 N. Route 17, Paramus, 07652 ........... (201) 599-0031
FedEx Office & Print Center, Highway 1 & 731 Nassau, Princeton, 08540 .... (609) 799-2863
FedEx Office & Print Center, 559 N. Franklin Tpke., Ramsey, 07446 ........ (201) 818-1623
FedEx Office & Print Center, 399 Highway 28, Raritan, 08869 ............ (908) 575-1221
FedEx Office & Print Center, 55 U.S. Highway 22 E., Springfield, 07081 ..... (973) 376-3966
FedEx Office Commercial Press, 450 W. 1st Ave., P.O. Box 379, Roselle, 07203 . (908) 245-4400

## FENDER MUSICAL INSTRUMENTS CORP.
**17600 N. Perimeter Dr., Ste. 100, Scottsdale AZ 85255** .................. **(480) 596-9690**
Interim CEO—Scott Gilbertson; CFO—Jim Broenen; CFO—Mark Van Vleet;
  CIO—Michael Spandau; Pub. Rels. Mgr.—Jason Farrell
Latin Percussion, Inc., 160 Belmont Ave., Garfield, 07026 ............. (973) 330-9103

## FERGUSON ENTERPRISES
**2750 S. Towne Ave., Pomona CA 91766** ............... **(909) 517-3085**
Hum. Res. Mgr.—Randy Cross; Bus. Dev. Mgr.—John Potter;
  Prod. Serv. Mgr.—Crystal Duran
Ferguson Fire & Fabrication, Inc., 151 Randolph St., Passaic, 07055 ........ (973) 614-9292

## FERGUSON ENTERPRISES, INC.
**12500 Jefferson Ave., Newport News VA 23602** ..................... **(757) 874-7795**
CEO—Frank Roach; CFO—Dave Keltner; COO—Kevin Murphy; Sr. V.-P.—Steven Roznowski;
  Pub. Rels. Mgr.—Christine Dwyer
Ferguson Enterprises, 835 Bloomfield Ave., Clifton, 07012 ................. (973) 614-9464
Ferguson Enterprises, Inc., 401 Main St., Avon By The Sea, 07717 .......... (732) 775-5270
Ferguson Enterprises, Inc., 830 Route 22, Bridgewater, 08807 ............. (908) 725-0666
Ferguson Enterprises, Inc., 2531 Tilton Rd., Egg Harbor Township, 08234 ..... (609) 485-2266
Ferguson Enterprises, Inc., 369 Anderson Ave., Fairview, 07022 ........... (201) 945-3080
Ferguson Enterprises, Inc., 737 S. Main St., Forked River, 08731 .......... (609) 693-0077
Ferguson Enterprises, Inc., 1 Colony Rd., Jersey City, 07305 ............. (201) 369-5120
Ferguson Enterprises, Inc., 190 Oberlin Ave. N., Lakewood, 08701 ......... (732) 905-1000
Ferguson Enterprises, Inc., 444 Livingston St., Norwood, 07648 .......... (201) 768-6080
Ferguson Enterprises, Inc., 16 Arrow Rd., Ramsey, 07446 .............. (201) 236-3111
Ferguson Enterprises, Inc., 207 Cooper Rd., Red Bank, 07701 ........... (732) 530-7200
Ferguson Enterprises, Inc., 404 Route 31 N., Ringoes, 08551 ........... (609) 466-5445
Ferguson Enterprises, Inc., 100 U.S. Highway 46, Rockaway, 07866 ....... (973) 983-1177
Lyon, Conklin & Co., Inc., 1165 Thomas Busch Memorial Hwy., Pennsauken, 08110 . (856) 488-0191
Palermo Supply, 1819 Central Ave., Ship Bottom, 08008 ............... (609) 494-0343

## FERRO CORP.
**6060 Parkland Blvd., Mayfield Heights OH 44124** ..................... **(216) 875-5600**
Pres., CEO—Peter T. Thomas; V.-P., CFO—Jeffrey Rutherford;
  V.-P., Gen. Counsel & Secy.—Mark H. Duesenberg; V.-P., Hum. Res.—Ann E. Killian;
  Treas. & Dir., Inv. Rels.—John Bingle; Dir., Corp. Comms.—Mary Abood
Ames Advanced Material, 3900 S. Clinton Ave., South Plainfield, 07080 ....... (908) 561-1100
Ferro Corp., Delaware River Plt.,
  170 U.S. Route 130 S., P.O. Box 309, Bridgeport, 08014 .................... (856) 467-8216
Ferro Corp., 54 Kellogg Ct., Edison, 08817 ......................... (732) 287-1930

## FIELDBROOK FOODS CORP.
**1 Ice Cream Dr., P.O. Box 1318, Dunkirk NY 14048** ..................... **(716) 366-5400**
Pres., CEO—Ken Johnson; Ex. V.-P., Sales & Mktg.—Jim Masood;
  V.-P., Pur.—Bob Griewisch; V.-P., Fin.—Ronald Odebralski; Dir., IT—Jim Carlson;
  Dir., Logistics—Jack Fuhrman; Plt. Mgr.—Kevin Grismore;
  Hum. Res. Mgr.—Colleen Hutchinson
Mister Cookie Face, LLC, 1989 Rutgers University Blvd., Lakewood, 08701 ..... (732) 370-5533

## FILTER RESEARCH CORP.
**1270 Clearmont St. N.E., Unit 5, Palm Bay FL 32905** ..................... **(321) 676-3300**
Pres.—Ahmed Hady; Prodn. Mgr.—Syed Hady; Cust. Serv. & Hum. Res. Mgr.—Carla Moffitt
FRC Electrical Industries, 705 Central Ave., New Providence, 07974 ......... (908) 464-3200

## FINISHMASTER, INC.
**115 W. Washington St., Ste. 700 South, Indianapolis IN 46204** ........... **(317) 237-3678**
Pres.—Steve Arndt; Dir., IT—Tom Smith
FinishMaster, Inc., 700 Garfield Ave., Jersey City, 07305 ............... (201) 435-1555

## FINNERAN ASSOCS., J. G.
**3600 Reilly Ct., Vineland NJ 08360** ..................... **(856) 696-3605**
CEO—Jerry Finneran; Pres.—Jo Finneran; Sr. V.-P.—Sandy F. Hitchner;
  V.-P., Global Sales & Mktg.—Janet F. Cohen;
  Sales & Mktg. Mgr., Domestic—Dawn C. Nelson; Prodn. Mgr.—Damon Hitchner;
  Pur. Mgr.—Steve McKishen; Hum. Res. Mgr.—Michelle Zenchuk;
  Engrg. & R & D Mgr.—Randy Eccles; Qual. Assur. Mgr.—Sharon Bruno
Scientific Laboratory Supplies, Inc., 1401 Wade Blvd., Millville, 08332 ........ (856) 327-4410

## FIREFREEZE WORLDWIDE, INC.
**272 Highway 46, Rockaway NJ 07866** ..................... **(973) 627-0722**
Pres.—Eveline Giessler
Firefreeze Worldwide, Inc., 429 Rockaway Valley Rd., Boonton, 07005 ....... (973) 394-1335

## FIRMENICH, INC.
**250 Plainsboro Rd., Plainsboro NJ 08536** ..................... **(609) 452-1000**
Pres., N. Amer.—David Shipman; V.-P., Admn. & Fin.—Douglas Lucht;
  V.-P., Hum. Res.—Raymond Collins; Hum. Res. Proj. Mgr.—Wendy Bruzzese
Firmenich, Inc., 150 Firmenich Way, Newark, 07114 ..................... (973) 589-3443

## FISHMAN & SON, INC., L.
**6301 E. Lombard St., Baltimore MD 21224** ..................... **(410) 633-2500**
Pres.—Robert Wagner; Sales Mgr., Regional—Bill Mabeus; IT Mgr.—Steve Ruoff;
  Hum. Res. Mgr.—John Kart; Cust. Serv. Mgr.—Mary Henritz
Fishman Flooring Solutions, 621 Chapel Ave. E., Ste. A, Cherry Hill, 08034 .... (856) 857-1141

## FLEETWASH, INC.
**26 Law Dr., Unit E, Fairfield NJ 07004** ..................... **(800) 847-3735**
Co-Founder, Pres. & CEO—Vito DeGiovanni; CFO—Robert McDonald;
  CAO—Loraine Matarazzo; V.-P.—Philip DeStafano; Env. Mgr.—Jim DiCarlo
Industrial Environmental, 176 W. Westfield Ave., Elizabeth, 07201 .......... (908) 241-3830

## FLEXMASTER CANADA LTD.
**20 E. Pearce St., Richmond Hill, Ontario, Canada, L4B 1B7,** ............... **(905) 731-9411**
Pres.—Ian Donnelly
Novaflex Industries, Inc., 1024 Industrial Dr., West Berlin, 08091 .......... (856) 768-2275

## FLINT GROUP
**14909 N. Beck Rd., Plymouth MI 48170** ..................... **(734) 781-4600**
Pres., GM, N. America—Bill Miller; V.-P., Hum. Res., N. American Div.—Bruce Harrison;
  V.-P., Treas.—Michelle Domas; Dir., Mktg.—Kim Stone
Flint Group, 6 Corn Rd., Dayton, 08810 ............................ (732) 329-4627

## FLOWSERVE CORP.
**5215 N. O'Connor Blvd., Ste. 2300, Irving TX 75039** .................. **(972) 443-6500**
Pres., CEO—Mark Blinn; CFO—Michael Taff; Sr. V.-P., Hum. Res. & IT—Mark Dailey
Flowserve Corp., 401 Heron Dr., P.O. Box 563, Bridgeport, 08014 .......... (856) 241-7800
Flowserve Corp., 142 Clinton Rd., Fairfield, 07004 .................... (973) 227-4565

## FLUIDRA USA, LLC
**8525 Mallory Rd., Jacksonville FL 32220** ..................... **(904) 378-0999**
Pres., CEO—Steve De Bever; Cont.—Janice Hague; Bus. Dev. Mgr.—Paul Terminello
Aqua Products, Inc., 25 Rutgers Ave., Cedar Grove, 07009 ............... (973) 857-2700

**FORBO SIEGLING, LLC**
12201 Vanstory Dr., Huntersville NC 28078 . . . . . . . . . . . . . . . . . . . . . . (704) 948-0800
Pres.—Wayne Hoffman; V.P., Sales—John Casali;
Dir., Opers., N. America—Chris Flannigan; Dir., Fin. & Controlling—Norm Nelson;
Food Segment Mgr., Americas—Rich Grantham;
Segment Mgr., P/P, IP, RM, Textiles—Paul McGuire;
Prolink Prod. Mgr., Americas—Flemming Frederiksen; Mktg. Comms. Mgr.—Kitty Spence
Forbo Siegling, LLC, 130 Coolidge Ave., Englewood, 07631 . . . . . . . . . . . . . . (201) 567-6100

**FORTUNE PLASTIC & METAL, INC.**
20 Carbon Pl., Jersey City NJ 07035 . . . . . . . . . . . . . . . . . . . . . . . . (201) 333-3339
CEO—Norman Ng; V.P.—Victor Ng
Fortune Riverside Auto Parts, Inc.,
900 Leesville Ave., P.O. Box 1589, Rahway, 07065 . . . . . . . . . . . . . . (732) 381-3355

**FRAGRANCE RESOURCES, INC.**
620 Route 3 W., Clifton NJ 07014 . . . . . . . . . . . . . . . . . . . . . . . . . (973) 777-2979
Mktg. Mgr.—Michael Simpson
Fragrance Resources, Inc., 275 Clark St., P.O. Box 110, Keyport, 07735 . . . . . . . . (732) 264-6767

**FRANCO APPAREL GROUP**
1407 Broadway, 30th Fl., New York NY 10018 . . . . . . . . . . . . . . . . . . . (212) 967-7272
Pres.—Ike Franco; CFO—Joanne Guglielmo; V.P., Sales—Allen Franco;
Sales Mgr.—Melissa Lippman
Franco Apparel Group, 231 Docks Corner Rd., Dayton, 08810 . . . . . . . . . . . . . (732) 438-5170

**FREEPORT-MCMORAN INC.**
333 N. Central Ave., Phoenix AZ 85004 . . . . . . . . . . . . . . . . . . . . . . (602) 366-8100
Chrm.—James Moffet; Pres., CEO—Richard Adkerson; Pres., FM Americas—Harry Conger;
CFO & Treas.—Kathleen Quirk; Chief Admn. Officer—Mike Arnold;
Dir., Ext. Comms.—Eric Kinneberg
Freeport-McMoran Copper & Gold, 48-94 Bayway Ave., Elizabeth, 07202 . . . . . . (908) 558-4318

**FRIEND SKOLER & CO., INC.**
160 Pehle Ave., Ste. 303, Saddle Brook NJ 07663 . . . . . . . . . . . . . . . . . (201) 712-0075
CFO & Dir., Portfolio Mgmt.—Gregory P. Sullivan; Mng. Dir.—Alexander A. Friend;
Mng. Dir.—Steven F. Skoler; Dir.—Cheryl Moss
Madan Plastics, Inc., 108 N. Union Ave., Ste. 3, Cranford, 07016 . . . . . . . . . . (908) 276-8484

**FRONTLINE MEDICAL COMMUNICATIONS, INC.**
7 Century Dr., Ste. 302, Parsippany NJ 07054 . . . . . . . . . . . . . . . . . . . (973) 206-3434
Chrm.—Stephen Stoneburn; Pres., CEO, Clinical Content Div.—Marcy Holeton;
CEO, Med. News Div.—Alan J. Imhoff; Dir., Mfg. Svcs.—Mike Wendt;
Dir., Hum. Res. & Opers.—Carolyn Caccavelli; IT Mgr.—Tim Riley
Frontline Medical Communications, Inc., 7 Century Dr., Parsippany, 07054 . . . . . (973) 290-8200

**FUJIFILM HOLDINGS AMERICA CORP.**
200 Summit Lake Dr., Valhalla NY 10595 . . . . . . . . . . . . . . . . . . . . . (914) 789-8100
Pres.—Shigeru Sano; V.P., Gen. Counsel & Secy.—Judy Melillo;
V.P. & GM, Imaging Div.—Manny Almeida; V.P., IT—Joseph Arnett;
V.P., Admn. & Fin.—Bill Meacham; V.P., Hum. Res.—Mike Prutting;
V.P., Corp. Comms.—Joan C. Rutherford; Community Rels. Mgr.—Lori Franco
FUJIFILM U.S.A., Inc., 1100 King Georges Post Rd., Edison, 08837 . . . . . . . . . (732) 857-3000

**FUJITEC AMERICA, INC.**
7258 Innovation Way, Mason OH 45040 . . . . . . . . . . . . . . . . . . . . . . (513) 932-8000
Pres.—Katsuji Okuda; CFO—Ray Gibson; Mktg. Mgr.—K. C. DeBra
Fujitec America Inc., New York Region, 215 Entin Rd., Clifton, 07014 . . . . . . . (973) 330-0100

**FULLER CO., H.B.**
1200 Willow Lake Blvd., St. Paul MN 55110 . . . . . . . . . . . . . . . . . . . . (651) 236-5900
Pres., CEO—James Owens; Sr. V.P., CFO—James Giertz; Sr. V.P., Market Dev.—Pat Trippel;
Sr. V.P., Americas, Adhesives—Traci Jensen; Sr. V.P., EMEA—Steven Kenny;
V.P., Gen. Counsel & Secy.—Timothy Keenan; V.P., Treas.—Cheryl Reinitz;
V.P., Corp. Cont.—Robert Martsching; V.P., Hum. Res.—Ann Parriott;
Dir., Corp. Comms. & Pub. Rels.—Kimberlee Sinclair
Fuller Construction Products, Inc., H.B., 59 Brunswick Ave., Edison, 08817 . . . . . (732) 287-8330

**FUSECO INC.**
10553 Olympic Dr., Ste. 101, Dallas TX 75220 . . . . . . . . . . . . . . . . . . (214) 357-6676
Pres.—Pat Hare; Sales & Mktg. Mgr.—Sterling Mays
Fuseco, Inc., 86 Lackawanna Ave., Ste. 240, Woodland Park, 07424 . . . . . . . . (973) 894-3727

**FUTURE ELECTRONICS CORP.**
237 Hymus Blvd., Pointe-Claire, Quebec H9R 5C7, Canada, . . . . . . . . . . . . (514) 694-7710
Pres., CEO—Robert Miller; COO—E. Stephen Segal; CFO—Pierre Giulbault
Future Electronics Corp.,
959 Route 46 E., Ste. 303, Parsippany Pl, Parsippany, 07054 . . . . . . . . . . . (973) 299-0400

**FXI, INC.**
1400 N. Providence Rd., Ste. 2000, Media PA 19063 . . . . . . . . . . . . . . . . (610) 744-2300
Pres., CEO—John Cowles; Ex. V.P., CFO—Harold J. Earley;
Sr. V.P., Legal—Andrew R. Prusky; —Donald W. Phillips; Corp. Cont.—Darryl Dunn
F X I, Foamex Innovations Div., 13 Manor Rd., East Rutherford, 07073 . . . . . . . (201) 933-8540

**G & K SERVICES, INC.**
5995 Opus Pkwy., Ste. 500, Minnetonka MN 55343 . . . . . . . . . . . . . . . . (952) 912-5500
Chrm. of the Board—Lenny Pippin; Pres., CEO—Doug Milroy;
Ex. V.P., CFO—Jeffery Wright; Sr. V.P., Hum. Res.—Randy Ross;
V.P., Sales & Mktg.—Dave Euson
G & K Services, Inc., 137 Ralph St., Belleville, 07109 . . . . . . . . . . . . . . . (973) 751-0464

**G.J. CHEMICAL CO., INC.**
40 Veronica Ave., Somerset NJ 08873 . . . . . . . . . . . . . . . . . . . . . . (973) 589-1450
Pres.—Diana Colonna; V.P., Sales—Tim Fenstemaker; Cont.—Wendell Wenger
G.J. Chemical Co., Inc., 128 Doremus Ave., Newark, 07105 . . . . . . . . . . . . . (973) 589-4176

**GALLUS BIOPHARMACEUTICALS, LLC**
4766 LaGuardia Dr., St. Louis MO 63134 . . . . . . . . . . . . . . . . . . . . . (314) 426-5000
Founder & CFO—Steven H. Kasok; Dir., Hum. Res.—Rebecca Schoklee;
Sr. Mktg. Mgr.—Claire Ruzicka
Gallus BioPharmaceuticals New Jersey, LLC, 201 College Rd. E., Princeton, 08540 . (609) 919-3300

**GANNETT CO., INC.**
7950 Jones Branch Dr., McLean VA 22107 . . . . . . . . . . . . . . . . . . . . (703) 854-6000
Chrm.—Marjorie Magner; Pres., CEO—Gracia Martore; CFO—Victoria Harker;
Sr. V.P., Gen. Counsel & Secy.—Todd Mayman; V.P., IT—Mark Morneau;
V.P., Dev. & Plng.—Daniel S. Ehrman, Jr.; V.P., Taxes—Sally Clurman;
V.P., Corp. Comms.—Jeremy Gaines; V.P., Inv. Rels.—Jeffrey Heinz
Asbury Park Press, Inc. (H Q), 3600 Highway 66, P.O. Box 1550, Neptune, 07754 . (732) 922-6000
Courier News, 92 E. Main St., Ste. 202, Somerville, 08876 . . . . . . . . . . . . (908) 722-8800
Courier-Post Newspaper, 301 Cuthbert Rd., Cherry Hill, 08002 . . . . . . . . . . (856) 663-6000
Daily Journal, The, 891 E. Oak Rd., Vineland, 08360. . . . . . . . . . . . . . . . (856) 691-5000
Hammonton News & Atlantic County Newspaper Group,
115 12th St., Hammonton, 08037 . . . . . . . . . . . . . . . . . . . . . . . . (609) 561-2300
Home News Tribune, 92 E. Main St., Somerville, 08876 . . . . . . . . . . . . . . (908) 722-8800

**GARDEN STATE ORTHOPAEDIC CENTER, INC.**
9 Post Rd., Ste. OP-1, Oakland NJ 07436 . . . . . . . . . . . . . . . . . . . . . (201) 337-5566
Pres.—Louis J. Haberman
Garden State Orthopedic, Inc., 95 Mount Kemble Ave., Morristown, 07960 . . . . . (973) 538-4948

**GARDEN STATE TILE DISTRIBUTORS, INC.**
5001 Industrial Rd., Farmingdale NJ 07727 . . . . . . . . . . . . . . . . . . . . (732) 938-6675
Pres.—Stephen Fischer; V.P., Sales—Robert A. Fischer; IT Mgr.—Jose Rodriguez;
Inventory Mgr.—Janet Bruno
Garden State Tile Distributors, Inc., 1290 Route 130, Dayton, 08810 . . . . . . . . (732) 329-0860
Garden State Tile Distributors, Inc., 267 Route 46 W., Dover, 07801 . . . . . . . . (973) 366-5035
Garden State Tile Distributors, Inc.,
472 E. Westfield Ave., Roselle Park, 07204 . . . . . . . . . . . . . . . . . . . (908) 241-4900
Garden State Tile Distributors, Inc., 790 S. Route 73, West Berlin, 08091 . . . . . (856) 753-0300

**GARELICK FARMS, LLC**
1199 W. Central St., Franklin MA 02038 . . . . . . . . . . . . . . . . . . . . . (508) 528-9000
V.P., Opers.—Rick Over; Cont.—Sue Hayward; Dir., Sales—Dave Flannery;
Dir., Sales—Frank Kyger; Dir., Hum. Res.—Scott Cran; GM—Tom Davis;
Plt. Mgr.—Cleland Cochrane; Hum. Res. Mgr.—Steve Coughlin
Tuscan Dairy, Inc., 117 Cumberland Blvd., Burlington, 08016 . . . . . . . . . . . (609) 499-2600

**GARON PRODUCTS, INC.**
2430 Route 34, Ste. B-12, Manasquan NJ 08736 . . . . . . . . . . . . . . . . . (732) 223-2500
Pres.—Arthur Crowley; V.P., Mktg.—Tara Crowley; V.P., New Bus. Dev.—John Crowley;
Cust. Serv. Exec.—Pamela Weir
Garon Products, Inc., 256 Maxim Rd., Howell, 07731 . . . . . . . . . . . . . . . (732) 828-6400

**GARRATT-CALLAHAN CO.**
50 Ingold Rd., Burlingame CA 94010 . . . . . . . . . . . . . . . . . . . . . . . (650) 697-5811
Pres.—Jeffrey L. Garratt; Dir., Hum. Res.—Lia Maafu; Reg. Mgr., Western—Vance Ruberg;
Mktg. Mgr.—Manny Charkoloff; IT Mgr.—Ryan Benner
Garratt-Callahan Co., 306 Talmadge Rd., Edison, 08817 . . . . . . . . . . . . . . (732) 287-2200

**GE AVIATION SYSTEMS, LLC**
1 Neumann Way, Cincinnati OH 45215 . . . . . . . . . . . . . . . . . . . . . . (513) 243-2000
Pres., CEO—David L. Joyce; V.P., GM, Sales—Kevin McAllister;
V.P., GM, Supply Chain—Colleen Athans; V.P., Hum. Res.—Raghu Krishnamoorthy;
Sr. Leader, Exec. & Mktg. Comms.—Janet Flaherty
Whippany Actuation System, 110 Algonquin Pkwy., Whippany, 07981 . . . . . . . (973) 428-9898

**GE HEALTHCARE**
3000 N. Grandview Blvd., Waukesha WI 53188 . . . . . . . . . . . . . . . . . . (262) 544-3011
Dir., Comm.—Tracy Doyle; GM, Opers. & Sourcing—Ralph Strosin
GE Healthcare, 900 Durham Ave., South Plainfield, 07080 . . . . . . . . . . . . . (908) 757-0500
GE Healthcare LifeSciences,
800 Centennial Ave., P.O. Box 1327, Piscataway, 08855 . . . . . . . . . . . . . (732) 457-8000

**GENBAND, INC.**
2801 Network Blvd., Ste. 300, Frisco TX 75034 . . . . . . . . . . . . . . . . . . (972) 521-5800
CEO—David Walsh; IT Mgr.—Don Rawley; Hum. Res. Mgr.—Robin Wright
uReach Technologies, Inc., 2137 State Highway 35, 1st Fl., Holmdel, 07733 . . . . (732) 335-5400
Ventraq, Inc., 817 E. Gate Dr., Ste. 101, Mount Laurel, 08054 . . . . . . . . . . . (856) 866-1000

**GENERAL DYNAMICS CORP.**
2941 Fairview Park Dr., Ste. 100, Falls Church VA 22042 . . . . . . . . . . . . . (703) 876-3000
Pres.—John P. Casey; Sr. V.P., CFO—L. Hugh Redd;
Sr. V.P., Asia-Pacific Reg.—Leda M. L. Chong;
Sr. V.P., Admn. & Hum. Res.—Walter M. Oliver; Sr. V.P., Engrg.—Kevin J. Poitras;
V.P., Treas.—David H. Fogg; V.P., Cont.—Kimberly Kuryea;
V.P., Comm. & Govt. Rels.—Kendell Pease; Staff V.P., Inv. Rels.—Amy Gilliland;
Staff V.P., Comm.—Rob Doolittle; V.P., Cybersecurity Svcs.—Mike Buratowski;
Chief Cyber Svcs. Strategist—Jim Jaeger
General Dynamics Advanced Information Systems,
7-9 Vreeland Rd., Florham Park, 07932 . . . . . . . . . . . . . . . . . . . . . (973) 514-4000

**GENERAL FLOOR INDUSTRIES**
190 Benigno Blvd., Bellmawr NJ 08031 . . . . . . . . . . . . . . . . . . . . . . (856) 931-0012
Pres.—David Cometz; V.P.—Michael Cometz; Corp. Secy.—Sonia Cometz
General Floor, Inc., 2 Pin Oak Ln., Cherry Hill, 08003 . . . . . . . . . . . . . . . (856) 424-0111
General Floor, Inc., 777 New Durham Rd., Edison, 08817 . . . . . . . . . . . . . (732) 603-6100
General Floor, Inc., 125 Market St., Kenilworth, 07033 . . . . . . . . . . . . . . (908) 241-4888
General Floor, Inc., 815 Hylton Rd., Pennsauken, 08110 . . . . . . . . . . . . . . (856) 663-4750

**GENERAL MILLS, INC.**
1 General Mills Blvd., Minneapolis MN 55426 . . . . . . . . . . . . . . . . . . . (763) 764-7600
Chrm. & CEO—Ken Powell; Ex. V.P., CFO—Don Mulligan; CMO—Mark Addicks;
Ex. V.P., Gen. Counsel & Chief Compliance & Risk Mgmt. Officer & Secy.—Rick Palmore;
Sr. V.P., Global Strategy Growth & Mktg. Innovations—Y. Marc Belton;
Sr. V.P., Hum. Res., Global—Michael L. Davis;
Sr. V.P., External Rels.—Kimberly A. Nelson; V.P., Global Comm.—Thomas Forsythe
General Mills Progresso, 500 W. Elmer Rd., Vineland, 08360. . . . . . . . . . . . (856) 691-1565

**GENERAL RUBBER CORP.**
2201 E. Ganley Rd., Tucson AZ 85706 . . . . . . . . . . . . . . . . . . . . . . (520) 889-2979
Pres.—Lloyd Aanonsen; V.P.—Amy Hammarstrom; Plt. Mgr.—Wade Craddock;
Admn. Mgr.—Jodi Booker
General Rubber Corp., 850 Washington Ave., Front, Carlstadt, 07072 . . . . . . . (201) 935-1900

**GENERATION BRANDS, LLC**
7400 Linder Ave., Skokie IL 60077 . . . . . . . . . . . . . . . . . . **(847) 410-4400**
Chrm. of the Board—Joe Higgins; CEO—Josh Weiss; Ex. V.-P., CFO—Blake Bonyko;
V.-P., Mktg.—Tiscia Eicher; V.-P., Engrg.—Kevin Fagan; Pub. Rels. Mgr.—Sherry Bale
Sea Gull Lighting Products, LLC.,
301 W. Washington St., P.O. Box 329, Riverside, 08075 . . . . . . (856) 764-0500

**GENTEK BUILDING PRODUCTS, INC.**
3773 State Rd., Cuyahoga Falls OH 44223 . . . . . . . . . . . . . . **(330) 929-1811**
V.-P., Sales—Dennis Thompson; V.-P., Mktg.—Bob Schindler;
Dir., Cust. & Warranty Svcs.—Dana Mason
Gentek Building Products, Inc., 11 Craigwood Rd., Avenel, 07001 . . . (732) 381-0900

**GENZYME CORP.**
500 Kendall St., Cambridge MA 02142 . . . . . . . . . . . . . . . . **(617) 252-7500**
Pres., CEO—David Meeker; CFO—Mark Esteva; Sr. V.-P., Hum. Res.—Jayne M. Ganslier
Genzyme Corp., Biosurgery Div., 1125 Pleasant View Ter., Ridgefield, 07657 . . (201) 945-9550

**GEO SPECIALTY CHEMICALS, INC.**
340 Mathers Rd., Ambler PA 19002 . . . . . . . . . . . . . . . . . **(215) 773-9280**
Pres.—Kenneth Ghazey; Hum. Res. Mgr.—Michelle McLendon; Off. Mgr.—Terry Dick;
Cust. Serv. Rep.—Rita Wenrich
GEO Specialty Chemicals, Inc., 1st & Essex St., Harrison, 07029 . . . . (973) 484-8400

**GEORGIA-PACIFIC, LLC**
133 Peachtree St. N.E., Atlanta GA 30303 . . . . . . . . . . . . . . **(404) 652-4000**
Pres., CEO—James Hannan;
Pres., Packaging & Ex. V.-P., Georgia-Pacific—Christian Fischer;
Pres., Containerboard & Kraft—Brandon Bennett; Pres., Gypsum—Brent Paugh;
Sr. V.-P., CFO—Tyler Woolson; Sr. V.-P., Gen. Counsel & Pub. Sector—Tye Darland;
Sr. V.-P., Opers. Excellence—Wes Jones; Sr. V.-P., Bus. Dev. & Strategy—David Park;
Ex. V.-P., Global Consumer Prods.—Kathy Walters;
V.-P., Comm. & Corp. Mktg.—Sheila Weidman; Comm. Mgr.—Karen Kohl
Georgia Pacific, Inc., 623 Riegelsville Rd., Milford, 08848 . . . . . . (908) 995-2228
Georgia-Pacific Gypsum, LLC, 1101 S. Front St., Camden, 08103 . . . . (856) 966-7600

**GERDAU AMERISTEEL US, INC.**
4221 W. Boy Scout Blvd., Ste. 600, Tampa FL 33607 . . . . . . . . **(813) 286-8383**
Pres., CEO—Guilherme Johannpeter; V.-P., Hum. Res.—Carl Czarnic;
V.-P., Fin.—Rodrigo Souza
Gerdau US, Inc., Sayreville, N. Crossman Rd., P.O. Box 249, Sayreville, 08872 . (732) 721-6600

**GERRESHEIMER GLASS, INC.**
537 Crystal Ave., Vineland NJ 08360 . . . . . . . . . . . . . . . . **(856) 692-3600**
CFO—Chris Bouffard; Ex. V.-P., Tubular Glass Tubing—John McDermott;
V.-P., Hum. Res.—Susan Kinnon
Gerresheimer Glass, Inc., 91 W. Forest Grove Rd., Vineland, 08360 . . . (856) 507-5600
Gerresheimer, Inc., 1300 Wheaton Ave., Millville, 08332 . . . . . . . (856) 506-0501

**GEXPRO**
1000 Bridgeport Ave., 5th Fl., Shelton CT 06484 . . . . . . . . . . **(203) 925-2400**
CEO—Jim Hibberd; V.-P., Global Accts.—Bill Hoyt; Manager—Susan Reynolds
Gexpro, 522 Pedricktown Rd., Swedesboro, 08085 . . . . . . . . . (856) 241-4700

**GIVAUDAN FLAVORS CORP.**
1199 Edison Dr., Cincinnati OH 45216 . . . . . . . . . . . . . . . . **(513) 948-8000**
Pres., The Americas—Louie D'Amico; V.-P., Mktg.—John Masters;
V.-P., Hum. Res.—Bob Sherwood; Dir., Comms.—Jeff Peppet;
Head of N. American Opers.—Markus Brunnschweiler
Givaudan Flavors Corp., 245 Merry Ln., East Hanover, 07936 . . . . . (973) 386-9800
Givaudan Fragrances Corp., 300 Waterloo Valley Rd., Mount Olive, 07828 . . . (973) 448-6500

**GLASGOW, INC.**
104 Willow Grove Ave., P.O. Box 1089, Glenside PA 19038 . . . . . . **(215) 884-8800**
Pres.—Bruce Rambo; Mktg. Mgr.—Steven Combs; Cred. Mgr.—Aileen Gibson
National Paving Co., Inc., 148 Williamstown Rd., P.O. Box 5, Berlin, 08009 . . . (856) 767-1950

**GOLD & REISS CORP.**
2392 Nostrand Ave., Brooklyn NY 11210 . . . . . . . . . . . . . . . **(718) 680-2600**
Pres., CEO—Shimon Eidlisz; Dir., Hum. Res.—Anschel Itzkowitz
Kentucky Cabinet Corp., 601 Lehigh Ave., Union, 07083 . . . . . . . (347) 452-5797

**GOLDEN OIL HOLDING CORP.**
2000 Bering Dr., Ste. 255, Houston TX 77057 . . . . . . . . . . . . **(713) 626-1110**
Pres.—Ralph McElvenny
Instrument Specialties Co., Inc., 661 Myrtle Ave., Boonton, 07005 . . . . (973) 335-2136

**GOLDEN RULE, INC.**
1282-A Surfside Industrial Pk., Myrtle Beach SC 29575 . . . . . . . **(843) 232-9092**
Pres.—John Liberto
Golden Rule, Inc., 7150 N. Park Dr., Ste. 620, Pennsauken, 08109 . . . (856) 663-3074

**GORDON TERMINAL SERVICE CO. OF PENNSYLVANIA**
1000 Agnes St., P.O. Box 313, McKees Rocks PA 15136 . . . . . . . **(412) 331-9410**
Pres., Sales & Mktg. Mgr.—R. M. Gordon, Jr.; V.-P., Treas.—Thomas P. Gordon;
Plt. Mgr.—Tim Fiedler; Hum. Res. Mgr.—Tim Gordon
Gordon Terminal Service Co. Of New Jersey, Inc.,
2 Hook Rd., P.O. Box 143, Bayonne, 07002 . . . . . . . . . . . . (201) 437-8300

**GORE & ASSOCS., INC., W. L.**
555 Paper Mill Rd., Newark DE 19711 . . . . . . . . . . . . . . . . **(302) 738-4880**
Pres., CEO—Terri Kelly; CFO—Paul Kaniefski; Hum. Res. Leader—Mary Tilley
Gore & Assocs., Inc., W. L., 1746 State Route 34 N., Wall Township, 07727 . . . (732) 681-7070

**GOURMET FOODS, INC.**
2910 E. Harcourt St., Rancho Dominguez CA 90221 . . . . . . . . . **(310) 632-3300**
Pres., CEO—Heinz Naef; CFO—Gary David; Pur. Mgr.—Chandra Williams;
Hum. Res. Mgr.—Gabriella Diaz
Gourmet Foods, Inc., 25 Andrews Dr., Woodland Park, 07424 . . . . . (973) 237-1776

**GOYA FOODS, INC.**
100 Seaview Dr., Secaucus NJ 07094 . . . . . . . . . . . . . . . . **(201) 348-4900**
Pres.—Robert Unanue; Sr. V.-P.—Joseph Perez; Ex. V.-P.—Peter J. Unanue;
V.-P., Sales & Mktg.—Conrad O. Colon; V.-P., Sales—Luis Tejada;
V.-P., MIS—Dave Kinkela; Dir., Hum. Res.—Tony Rico; Dir., Fin.—Miguel Lugo;
Dir., Pub. Rels.—Rafael Toro
Goya Foods, Inc., 650 New County Rd., Secaucus, 07094 . . . . . . . (201) 865-3470

**GRABBER CONSTRUCTION PRODUCTS, INC.**
20 W. Main Street Ct., Ste. 200, Alpine UT 84004 . . . . . . . . . . **(801) 492-3880**
V.-P., CFO—Roland Snyder; Dir., Mktg.—Bevan Wulfenstein;
Pur. Mgr., Intl.—Scott Henderson
Grabber Northeast, 1125 Thomas Busch Memorial Hwy., Pennsauken, 08110 . . . (856) 662-2525

**GRAHAM PACKAGING CO. L. P.**
2401 Pleasant Valley Rd., York PA 17402 . . . . . . . . . . . . . . **(717) 849-8500**
CEO—Malcolm Bundy; CFO—Michael Graham; V.-P., Global Hum. Res.—Sheldon Thorpe
Graham Packaging Co. L. P., 600 5th St., Belvidere, 07823 . . . . . . (908) 475-2181

**GRAHAM PARTNERS, INC.**
3811 W. Chester Pike, Bldg. 2, Ste. 200, Newtown Square PA 19073 . . . . . . **(610) 408-0500**
CEO—Anthony J. Folino III; Cont.—Elizabeth Haerling;
Sr. Mng. Principal—Steven C. Graham; Mng. Principal—Christopher A. Lawler;
Mng. Principal—Joseph G. May; Mng. Principal—William P. McKee, Jr.;
Mng. Principal—Christina W. Morin; Mng. Principal—Robert A. Newbold
TransAxle, LLC, 2501 Route 73 S., P.O. Box 2306, Cinnaminson, 08077 . . . . (856) 665-4445

**GRANT & SONS, INC., WILLIAM**
200 Park Ave. S., Ste. 1218, New York NY 10003 . . . . . . . . . . **(212) 246-1760**
Pres.—Simon Hunt; IT Mgr.—Ray Focht; Hum. Res. Mgr.—Tom Green
Grant & Sons, Inc., William, 130 Fieldcrest Ave., Edison, 08837 . . . . (732) 225-9000

**GRANT SUPPLY CO., INC.**
901 Joyce Kilmer Ave., North Brunswick NJ 08902 . . . . . . . . . **(732) 545-1018**
Pres.—Bill Stanbach; V.-P.—Joseph Nastus; Hum. Res. Mgr.—Grace Desantis
Grant Supply Co., Inc., 755 W. Delilah Rd., Pleasantville, 08232 . . . . (609) 641-1114

**GRAPHIC PACKAGING HOLDING COMPANY**
1500 Riveredge Pkwy. N.W., Atlanta GA 30328 . . . . . . . . . . . **(770) 240-7200**
Pres., CEO—David Scheible; CFO—Daniel Blount;
V.-P., Corp. Hum. Res. & Talent Mgmt.—Jacinta Carter
Graphic Packaging International, Inc.,
4100 New Brunswick Ave., Piscataway, 08854 . . . . . . . . . . . (732) 424-2100

**GRAVER TECHNOLOGIES, LLC**
200 Lake Dr., Newark DE 19702 . . . . . . . . . . . . . . . . . . **(302) 731-1700**
Pres., CEO—John McPeak; V.-P., Mktg.—Mark Koster; V.-P., Fin.—Sharon Gotta
Graver Technologies, LLC, 72 Lockwood St., Newark, 07105 . . . . . . (973) 690-5290

**GRAYBAR ELECTRIC CO., INC.**
34 N. Meramec Ave., St. Louis MO 63105 . . . . . . . . . . . . . . **(314) 573-9200**
Chrm., Pres. & CEO—Robert Reynolds, Jr.; Sr. V.-P., CFO—Beatty D'Alessandro;
Ex. V.-P., Sales & Mktg. & COO—Kathleen M. Mazzarella; V.-P., CIO—Scott Clifford;
Sr. V.-P., U.S. Bus.—Robert C. Lyons; V.-P., Treas.—Jon Reed; V.-P., Sales—Steve Stone;
V.-P., Mktg.—Bill Mansfield; V.-P.—Bob Siegel;
Dir., Corp. & Mktg. Comm.—Carrie Johnson
Graybar Electric Co., Inc., 105 E. Crest Ave., Ste. 207, Edison, 08837 . . . (973) 404-5555

**GREATER MEDIA, INC.**
35 Braintree Hill Pk., Ste. 300, Braintree MA 02184 . . . . . . . . . **(781) 348-8600**
Chrm., CEO—Peter H. Smyth; V.-P., CFO—Edward R. Nolan, Jr.;
V.-P., Gen. Counsel—Ellen J. Rubin; V.-P., Corp. Comm.—Heidi A. Raphael;
Corp. Cont.—Joseph McKevitz; Dir., IT—Edward McCormack
Greater Media Newspapers, 198 Route 9 N., P.O. Box 950, Manalapan, 07726 . . (732) 358-5200

**GREIF, INC.**
425 Winter Rd., Delaware OH 43015 . . . . . . . . . . . . . . . . . **(740) 549-6000**
Pres., CEO—David B. Fischer; Group Pres.—Addison Kilibarda;
Group Pres.—Tim Bergwall; COO—Peter Watson; CIO—Doug Lingrel;
Sr. V.-P., People Svcs. & Talent Dev.—Karen Lane;
Ex. V.-P., Gen. Counsel & Secy.—Gary Martz;
V.-P., Comms. & Chief Sustainability Officer—Scott Griffin;
V.-P., Global Comms.—Deb Strohmaier
Greif, Inc., 200 Rike Dr., Millstone Township, 08535 . . . . . . . . . (609) 448-5300

**GRIFF PAPER & FILM**
275 Lower Morrisville Rd., Levittown PA 19054 . . . . . . . . . . . **(215) 428-1075**
V.-P.—John Phinn; GM—Todd Phinn; Bus. Dev. & Sales Mgr.—Alex Phinn;
IT Mgr.—Jason Hoverson
Griff Decorative Films Ltd., 700 Vassar Ave., Lakewood, 08701 . . . . . (732) 367-2166

**GRIFFITH ELECTRIC SUPPLY CO., INC.**
5 2nd St., Trenton NJ 08611 . . . . . . . . . . . . . . . . . . . . **(609) 695-6121**
Pres.—William Goodwin; V.-P., Sales & Mktg.—Ronald A. Lim;
V.-P., Opers. & Whse. Mgr.—Crystal Simmons; V.-P., Pur.—Ron Kaccmarek;
Dir., Admn.—Sue Adams
Griffith Electric Supply Co., Inc., 4-W Chimney Rock Rd., Bridgewater, 08807 . . (908) 203-1601

**GROVE SUPPLY, INC.**
106 Steamboat Dr., P.O. Box 3029, Warminster PA 18974 . . . . . . **(215) 672-8666**
Owner—Carl Wolfe; Cont.—Bob Hamilton; Sales Mgr.—Clem Ciocca
Grove Supply, Inc., 1818 Rowland St., Cinnaminson, 08077 . . . . . . (856) 303-2310
Grove Supply, Inc., 3801 Park Blvd., Wildwood, 08260 . . . . . . . . (609) 522-1449

**GROWMARK FS, LLC**
308 N.E. Front St., Milford DE 19963 . . . . . . . . . . . . . . . . **(302) 422-3002**
CFO—Jeff Price; V.-P., Eastern Retail Opers.—Steve Buckalew;
Sales & Mktg. Mgr.—Denis Shaffer; Opers. & Proc. Mgr.—Norman Hamstead;
Cred. Mgr.—Joseph Koch; Accts. Payable Mgr.—Mike MacCoy
Growmark FS, LLC, 60 Lehigh Ave., P.O. Box 116, Bloomsbury, 08804 . . . (908) 479-4500
Growmark FS, LLC, 55 Silver Lake Rd., Bridgeton, 08302 . . . . . . . (856) 455-7688

**GTS-WELCO**
5275 Tilghman St., Allentown PA 18104 . . . . . . . . . . . . . . . **(610) 398-2211**
Pres., CEO—Bryan Gentry; CFO—Mike Masha; Dir., Pur.—Michael Caron
GTS-Welco, 425 Avenue P, Newark, 07105 . . . . . . . . . . . . . (973) 589-7895
Praxair, 515 E. Edgar Rd., Linden, 07036 . . . . . . . . . . . . . . (908) 862-7200

**GULBRANDSEN TECHNOLOGIES, INC.**
2 Main St., P.O. Box 5523, Clinton NJ 08809 . . . . . . . . . . . . **(908) 735-5458**
Founder & CEO—Donald Gulbrandsen; Pres.—David Drollinger; Cont.—Ray Jankowski;
Hum. Res. Mgr. & Mktg. Rep.—Rosa Lessa; Team Leader—Rose Bredael
Gulbrandsen Technologies, Inc., 1 Riverside Way, Phillipsburg, 08865 . . . (908) 238-2030

**H & U, INC.**
**1933 Colburn St., Honolulu HI 96819 ................ (808) 841-5808**
**Pres.—Hidehito Uki; V-P., GM—Takao Morioka; V-P., Fin.—Keiko Uki**
H & U, Inc., 375 North St., Ste. O, Teterboro, 07608 ................ (201) 530-1100

**HADDON HOUSE FOOD PRODUCTS, INC.**
**250 Old Marlton Pike, Medford NJ 08055 ................ (609) 654-7901**
**CEO—David Anderson; CFO—Dave Landis; Ex. V-P.—David Anderson, Jr.; V-P., Investor Svcs.—Donna Nelson**
Haddon House Food Products, Inc., 433 Oak Glen Rd., Howell, 07731 ........ (732) 367-7901

**HADDONSTONE (USA) LTD.**
**32207 United Ave., Pueblo CO 81001 ................ (719) 948-4554**
**Pres.—David West; Cont.—Robert Tcshida**
Haddonstone (USA) Ltd., 201 Heller Pl., Bellmawr, 08031 ................ (856) 931-7011

**HAIN CELESTIAL GROUP, INC., THE**
**1111 Marcus Ave., Bldg. 1, New Hyde Park NY 11042 ................ (516) 587-5000**
**Chrm., Pres. & CEO—Irwin D. Simon; Sr. V-P., Chief Growth Officer—Ellen B. Deutsch; Sr. V-P., Special Proj.—Benjamin Brecher; V-P., Hum. Res.—Charmaine Cook; V-P., Inv. Rels.—Mary Celeste Anthes; V-P.—Jeff Goldberg; Pur. Mgr.—Randy Sias**
Hain Celestial Group, Inc., The, 50 Knickerbocker Rd., Moonachie, 07074 ...... (201) 935-4500

**HAINES & KIBBLEHOUSE, INC.**
**2052 Lucon Rd., P.O. Box 196, Skippack PA 19474 ................ (610) 584-8500**
**Pres.—Scott Haines; COO—Jim Haines; V-P., Secy.—Jack Kibblehouse; Mktg. & Pub. Affs. Mgr.—Tony Jeremiah; Hum. Res. Mgr.—Rodney Grass; Pub. Affs. Mgr.—Anthony T. Jeremias**
Warren Materials, 703 Route 57, Stewartsville, 08886 ................ (908) 859-3333

**HAJOCA CORP.**
**127 Coulter Ave., Ardmore PA 19003 ................ (610) 649-1430**
**Chrm.—Richard Klau; Pres.—Rick Fantham; V-P., Fin.—Christopher Pappo; Dir., Vendor Rels.—Roy Pitts; Admn. Svcs. Mgr.—Bikki Bevelhymer**
Weinstein Supply Co., 3187 Fire Rd., Egg Harbor Township, 08234 .......... (609) 677-0666
Weinstein Supply Co., 4019 S. Main Rd., Vineland, 08360 ................ (856) 825-1460
Weinstein Supply Corp., 1687 Haddon Ave., Camden, 08103 ................ (856) 964-1700

**HALMA HOLDINGS, INC.**
**11500 Northlake Dr., Ste. 306, Cincinnati OH 45249 ................ (513) 772-5501**
**Benefits Mgr.—Carrie Bishop; Pub. Rels. Mgr.—Lisa Wallner**
Bio-Chem Fluidics, Inc., 85 Fulton St., Ste. 12, Boonton, 07005 ................ (973) 263-3001
Fiberguide Industries, Inc., 1 Bay St., Stirling, 07980 ................ (908) 647-6601
Perma Pure, LLC, 8 Executive Dr., Toms River, 08755 ................ (732) 244-0010

**HANDY & HARMAN LTD.**
**1133 Westchester Ave., Ste. N-222, White Plains NY 10604 ................ (914) 461-1300**
**Chrm.—Warren G. Lichtenstein; Chrm.—Jack Howard; Pres., CEO, Handy & Harman—Jeff Szoboda; Sr. V-P., CFO—James F. McCabe, Jr.; V-P., Treas.—Ted Yerdan; V-P., Hum. Res.—Peter J. Marciniak; Gen. Counsel & Secy.—Michael MacManus; Cont.—Douglas Woodworth; Asst. Cont.—Susan C. Handler**
Microtube Fabricators, Inc., 250 Lackland Dr., Middlesex, 08846 ................ (732) 469-7420

**HANESBRANDS, INC.**
**1000 E. Hanes Mill Rd., Winston-Salem NC 27105 ................ (336) 519-8080**
**Chrm., CEO—Richard Noll; Pres., Outerwear—John Marsh; Pres., Innerwear—W. Howard Upchurch, Jr.; Ex. V-P., CCO—Joan Reynolds; COO—Gerald Evans; Ex. V-P., Gen. Counsel & Secy.—Joia M. Johnson; Ex. V-P., Hum. Res.—Elizabeth Burger; V-P., Corp. Social Responsiblity—Chris Fox**
Maidenform Brands, Inc., 485 U.S. Highway 1 S., Bldg. F, Iselin, 08830 ........ (732) 621-2500

**HANGER, INC.**
**10910 Domain Dr., Ste. 300, Austin TX 78758 ................ (512) 777-3800**
**Chrm.—Tom Cooper; Pres., CEO—Vinit K. Asar; CFO—George E. McHenry; CIO—Walt Meffert; Chief Hum. Res. Officer—Drew Morton; V-P., Sales & Mktg.—Jim Reichmann; Dir., Mktg.—Daryl Williams**
Hanger Clinic, 210 New Rd., Ste. 7, Linwood, 08221 ................ (609) 653-8323
Hanger Prosthetics & Orthotics, 201 White Horse Rd. E., Voorhees, 08043 ..... (856) 309-0709
Hanger Prosthetics & Orthotics, Inc., 265 Fernwood Ave., Edison, 08837 ....... (732) 417-0480
Hanger Prosthetics & Orthotics, Inc., 5100 Belmore Blvd., Farmingdale, 07727 . . (732) 919-7774
Hanger Prosthetics & Orthotics, Inc., 59 Main St., Ste. 111, West Orange, 07052 . (973) 736-0628

**HANOVER FOODS CORP.**
**1486 York St., P.O. Box 334, Hanover PA 17331 ................ (717) 632-6000**
**Chrm.—John A. Warehime; CEO—Jeff Warehime; Pres.—Andrew Warehime; CFO—David Shaqfed; V-P., Sales, Food Serv.—Daniel Schuchart, Jr.; V-P., Retail Branded Sales—Jim Kelly; V-P., Opers., Canning—David Still; V-P., Opers., Frozen—Carl Anderson; V-P., Hum. Res.—Patricia Townsend; V-P., Qual. Assur. & R & D—Timothy Mechler; Treas.—Steve Robertson**
Aunt Kitty's Foods, Inc., 270 N. Mill Rd., Vineland, 08360 ................ (856) 691-2100

**HARBOR LINEN, LLC**
**2 Foster Ave., Gibbsboro NJ 08026 ................ (856) 435-2000**
**Chrm.—Earl Waxman; V-P., Opers.—Ronald Brazzo; Cont.—Jim Malloy; Hum. Res. Mgr.—Michelle O'Donald**
Superior Drapery Co. & Harbor Linen Co, 2 Foster Ave., Gibbsboro, 08026 ..... (856) 435-2000

**HARMAC REBAR & STEEL CORP.**
**103 Cornshop Rd., P.O. Box 142, Fryeburg ME 04037 ................ (207) 935-3531**
**Pres.—Gary MacFarlane; Ex. V-P.—Pat Maillett; GM—Amos Maillett**
HarMac Rebar & Steel Corp., 301 Hartle St., Sayreville, 08872 ................ (732) 651-7822

**HARRIS FREEMAN & CO., INC.**
**3110 E. Miraloma Ave., Anaheim CA 92806 ................ (714) 765-1190**
**Owner—Anil Shah; Pres., CEO, Harris Tea—Chirayu Borooah; V-P., Harris Spice Div.—Peter Shah; Opers. Mgr.—Anil Vyas**
Harris Tea Co., 344 New Albany Rd., Moorestown, 08057 ................ (856) 793-0290

**HARSCO CORP.**
**350 Poplar Church Rd., Camp Hill PA 17011 ................ (717) 763-7064**
**Pres., CEO—Patrick Decker; Sr. V-P., CFO—F. Nicholas Grasberger III; V-P., Gen. Counsel & Secy.—A. Verona Dorch; Sr. Dir., Corp. Comm.—Kenneth Julian**
Harsco Corp., 1800 Lower Rd., Linden, 07036 ................ (732) 396-1269

**HART INDUSTRIES, INC.**
**931 Jeanette St., Middletown OH 45044 ................ (513) 422-3639**
**Pres.—Roger K. Hart; Treas.—Christopher Hart**
Hart Industries, Inc., 135 Crown Rd., Thorofare, 08086 ................ (856) 686-1455

**HAR-TRU SPORTS CORP.**
**2200 Old Ivy Rd., Ste. 100, Charlottesville VA 22903 ................ (434) 295-6167**
**GM—Pat Hanssen; Sales Mgr.—Ed Montecalvo**
Har-Tru Sports, 1715 Oak St., Ste. 1, Lakewood, 08701 ................ (434) 295-6167

**HARVEY INDUSTRIES, INC., SID**
**605 Locust St., Garden City NY 11530 ................ (516) 745-9200**
**Pres.—Sid Harvey; Sr. V-P., CFO—Russell TumSuden; Sr. V-P., Sales & Mktg.—John Rynecki; Sr. V-P., Mfg.—Jim Otto; Sr. V-P., Opers. Bus. Dev.—Jack DeCotiis; Ex. V-P.—David Harvey; V-P., Pur.—Rich Carbonaro; MIS Mgr.—Lynda O'Brien**
Harvey Industries, Inc., Sid, 159 E. 1st Ave., Roselle, 07203 ................ (908) 245-8688
Harvey Industries, Inc., Sid, 1684 5th St., Trenton, 08638 ................ (609) 882-1766

**HAYES PUMP, INC.**
**66 Old Powder Mill Rd., Concord MA 01742 ................ (978) 369-8800**
**Pres., CEO—Eric Zadravec; CFO—Elvis Cabral; V-P., Sales—James Crowley; V-P., Engrg.—Robert Simonds; IT Mgr.—Jason Marquis**
Hayes Pump, Inc., 295 Fairfield Ave., Fairfield, 07004 ................ (973) 808-0606

**HD SUPPLY WATERWORKS, INC.**
**1820 Metcalf Ave., Thomasville GA 31792 ................ (229) 226-1433**
**CEO—Jerry Webb; Pres.—Steve LeClair; CFO—Don Clayton; IT Mgr.—Neil Brinson**
HD Supply Water Works, Inc., 228 Williamstown Rd., Berlin, 08009 ........... (856) 753-5566

**HEALTHTRONICS, INC.**
**9825 Spectrum Dr., Bldg. 3, Austin TX 78717 ................ (512) 328-2892**
**Pres.—Russell Newman; Dir., Comms. & Mktg.—John Eberts**
HealthTronics, Inc., 354 Eisenhower Pkwy., Ste. 2150, Livingston, 07039 ...... (973) 994-3220

**HEALTHY FOOD BRANDS, LLC**
**74 Mall Dr., Commack NY 11725 ................ (631) 543-9600**
**CFO—Norman Gross; Plt. Mgr.—Robert Howitt**
Healthy Food Brands, LLC, 122 Quentin Ave., New Brunswick, 08901 .......... (212) 444-9909

**HEARTHSIDE FOOD SOLUTIONS, LLC**
**3250 Lacey Rd., Ste. 200, Downers Grove IL 60515 ................ (630) 967-3600**
**CEO—Rich Scalise; CFO—James Wojciechowski; CIO—Bob Burchfield; V-P., GM—Jim Downers; V-P., Sales & Mktg.—Brian McNamara; V-P., Mktg.—Roy Jasper; V-P., Hum. Res.—Steve England; V-P., Supply Chain—Dwayne Hughes**
Quality Bakery Products Of New Jersey, Inc., 24 Ironside Ct., Willingboro, 08046 ................ (609) 871-7393

**HEILIND ELECTRONICS, INC.**
**58 Jonspin Rd., Wilmington MA 01887 ................ (978) 657-4870**
**Pres.—Robert Clapp; CFO—Ugo Passerelli; V-P., Prod.—Alan Clapp; Hum. Res. Mgr.—Carol Boisvert**
Interstate Connecting Components, Inc., 120 Mount Holly Byp., Lumberton, 08048 . (856) 722-5535

**HEMISPHERX BIOPHARMA, INC.**
**1617 John F. Kennedy Blvd., Ste. 660, Philadelphia PA 19103 ............ (215) 988-0080**
**Chrm., CEO—William Carter; Ex. Vice Chrm., Gen. Counsel & Secy.—Thomas K. Equels; Off. Mgr.—Annmarie Coverly**
Hemispherx Biopharma, Inc., 783 Jersey Ave., New Brunswick, 08901 ........ (732) 249-3250

**HENRY SCHEIN, INC.**
**135 Duryea Rd., Melville NY 11747 ................ (631) 843-5500**
**Chrm., CEO—Stanley M. Bergman; Pres., COO—James P. Breslawski; Corp. Sr. V-P., Chief Compliance Officer—Leonard David; Sr. V-P., CTO—James A. Harding; Sr. V-P., Chief Merchandising Officer—Michael Racioppi; Ex. V-P., CFO—Steven Paladino; Ex. V-P., Chief Admn. Officer—Gerald A. Benjamin; Ex. V-P., Chief Strategic Officer—Mark E. Mlotek; V-P., Corp. Comm.—Susan Vassallo; V-P., Global Comm.—Gerard K. Meuchner; Corp. Comms. Mgr.—Angela Ruggiero**
Sullivan Dental Products, Inc., 45 U.S. Highway 46, Montville, 07058 .......... (973) 227-3533

**HERAEUS, INC.**
**540 Madison Ave., 16th Fl., New York NY 10022 ................ (212) 752-2705**
**Pres.—Yuri Rozenfeld; V-P., Hum. Res.—Terry Corcoran; V-P., Fin.—Artin Janian**
Heraeus Precious Metals North America, LLC, 65 Euclid Ave., Newark, 07105 . . (973) 817-7878

**HERITAGE BAG CO.**
**1648 Diplomat Dr., Carrollton TX 75006 ................ (972) 241-5525**
**Pres.—Carl Allen, Jr.; Sr. V-P., Sales & Mktg.—Scott Hoeft; V-P., Sales—Tim Rechner; V-P., Accts., Natl.—Sam Miller; Plt. Mgr.—Bob Seidl; Hum. Res. Mgr.—Linda Bidding; Maint. Mgr.—Fernando Fernandez; Cust. Serv. Mgr.—Shannon Holt**
Heritage Bag Co., Inc., 2321 High Hill Rd., Swedesboro, 08085 ................ (856) 467-2247

**HESS CORP.**
**1185 Avenue of the Americas, 40th Fl., New York NY 10036 ............ (212) 997-8500**
**Chrm. of the Board & CEO—John B. Hess; Sr. V-P. & CEO, Hess LNG—R. Gordon Shearer; Sr. V-P., CFO—John P. Rielly; V-P., Chief Risk Officer—Jonathan C. Stein; Sr. V-P., Hum. Res.—Mykel Ziolo; Sr. V-P., Corp. Dev. & Fin.—John J. Scelfo; V-P., Cont.—Kevin B. Wilcox**
Hess Corp., 2800 U.S. Highway 1, North Brunswick, 08902 ................ (732) 940-3705
Hess Corp., 123 Derousse Ave., Pennsauken, 08110 ................ (856) 663-5111
Hess Corp., 1 Hess Plz., Woodbridge, 07095 ................ (732) 750-6000

**HIGH GRADE BEVERAGE**
**891 Georges Rd., Monmouth Junction NJ 08852 ................ (732) 821-7600**
**Corp. V-P.—Guy Battaglia; V-P., Corp. Fin.—Herbert J. Schloss; Corp. Cont.—Jeffrey Epstein; Dir., Hum. Res.—William Calcagno; Opers. Mgr.—John Morra**
High Grade Beverage, 86 Canfield Ave., Randolph, 07869 ................ (973) 927-1400

**HILLENBRAND, INC.**
**1 Batesville Blvd., Batesville IN 47006 ................ (812) 934-7000**
**Pres., CEO—Kenneth A. Camp; CFO—Cynthia L. Lucchese; V-P., Cont. & CAO—Elizabeth E. Dreyer; V-P., Treas.—Ted Haddad, Jr.; V-P., Lean Bus.—Jan M. Santerre; Corp. Cont.—Elaine Brouillette**
Coperion Corp., 663 E. Crescent Ave., Ramsey, 07446 ................ (201) 327-6300
Coperion K-Tron Pitman, Inc., 590 Woodbury Glassboro Rd., Sewell, 08080 .... (856) 589-0500

© Copyright 2015 Manufacturers' News, Inc.



**HIPPOGRAPHICS, INC.**
**9100 Pennsauken Hwy., Pennsauken NJ 08110 ........ (856) 662-9111**
**Owner & Pres.—Larry Weiss**
CRW Graphics, Inc., 9100 Pennsauken Hwy., Pennsauken, 08110 ........ (856) 662-9111

**HISCO, INC.**
**6650 Concord Park Dr., Houston TX 77040 ........ (713) 934-1600**
**Pres.—Bob Dill; Ex. V-P., Sales & Mktg.—Paul Gill; IT Mgr.—Daniel Porres; Hum. Res. Mgr.—Priscilla Everett; Manager—Tommy O'Connor**
Hisco, Inc., 55 Veronica Ave., Somerset, 08873 ........ (732) 745-2828

**HITACHI AMERICA LTD.**
**50 Prospect Ave., Tarrytown NY 10591 ........ (914) 332-5800**
**Chrm.—Takashi Hatchoji; Pres., CEO—Kenji Nakamura; CFO—T. Tsujiura; Dir., Branding & Corp. Comms.—Lauren E. Raguzin**
Mitsubishi Hitachi Power Systems America - Energy & Environment, 645 Martinsville Rd., Basking Ridge, 07920 ........ (908) 605-2800

**HOFFMAN EQUIPMENT, INC.**
**300 S. Randolphville Rd., Piscataway NJ 08854 ........ (732) 752-3600**
**Pres., CEO—Timothy Watters; CFO & Hum. Res. Mgr.—Eric Shumaker; Sr. V-P., Sales & Mktg.—Mike Anderson; Acct. Mgr.—Bryan Bloyd; Cred. Mgr.—Simone Hines; Parts Mgr.—Kathy Gould; Rental Mgr.—Janine Labor**
Hoffman Equipment, Inc., 2610 S. Black Horse Pike, Williamstown, 08094 ........ (856) 875-0036

**HOLCIM (US), INC.**
**24 Crosby Dr., Bedford MA 01730 ........ (781) 647-2501**
**Pres., CEO—Filiberto Ruiz; Sr. V-P., CFO—Richard Reinhart; Sr. V-P., Gen. Counsel & Secy.—Jay Tangney; Sr. V-P., Sales & Mktg.—Norm Jagger; Sr. V-P., Hum. Res.—Alyse Martinelli**
Holcim U.S., 595 Morgan Blvd., Camden, 08104 ........ (856) 964-2555

**HOLMAN ENTERPRISES, INC.**
**244 E. Kings Hwy., Maple Shade NJ 08052 ........ (856) 663-5200**
**Chrm.—Joseph Holman; V-P., Dealership Opers.—William Cariss; Hum. Res. Mgr.—Brandon Renous**
Automotive Rentals, Inc., 4001 Leadenhall Rd., P.O. Box 5039, Mount Laurel, 08054 ........ (856) 778-1500

**HONEYWELL AEROSPACE**
**1944 E. Sky Harbor Cir. N., Phoenix AZ 85034 ........ (602) 436-2311**
**Pres., CEO—Tim Mahoney; CFO—Kevin Moriarty; CIO—Dave Jarvis; CTO—Bob Smith; V-P., Mktg. & Prod. Mgmt.—Carl Esposito; V-P., Hum. Res.—Chris Clason; V-P., Airbus—Justin Ryan**
EMS Aviation, 121 Whittendale Dr., Ste. A, Moorestown, 08057 ........ (856) 234-5020

**HONEYWELL INTERNATIONAL, INC.**
**101 Columbia Rd., Morristown NJ 07962 ........ (973) 455-2000**
**Chrm., CEO—David M. Cote; Pres., CEO, Performance Matls. & Technologies—Andreas Kramvis; Pres., Trans. Sys.—Terrence Hahn; Sr. V-P., CFO—David J. Anderson; Sr. V-P., Gen. Counsel—Kate Adams; Sr. V-P., Hum. Res.—Mark James; V-P., Chief Mktg. & Strategy Officer—Rhonda Germany; V-P., Info. Sys.—Michael Lang; V-P., Inv. Rels.—Elena Doom; Dir., New Bus. Dev. & Strategy—Phil Wojcik; Weatherization Prods. & Svcs. Bus. Mgr.—Bryan Magnus**
Honeywell HBS, 534 Fellowship Rd., Mount Laurel, 08054 ........ (856) 437-1832

**HORIBA INSTRUMENTS, INC.**
**2890 John R. Rd., Troy MI 48083 ........ (248) 689-9000**
**CMO—Bill Foskett; GM—Ken Mitera; Sales Mgr.—Rick Egglesteon; Hum. Res. Mgr.—Joann Brodbeck; Cust. Serv. Mgr.—Kevin Ksaiser**
HORIBA Scientific, 3880 Park Ave., Edison, 08820 ........ (732) 494-8660

**HOUGHTON CHEMICAL CORP.**
**52 Cambridge St., P.O. Box 307, Allston MA 02134 ........ (617) 254-1010**
**Pres., CEO, CFO—Bruce E. Houghton; V-P., Plt.—Joseph A. Lima; V-P., Admn.—Deborah J. Gavin; V-P., Fin.—H. Patricia Kincade; MIS Mgr.—Ronald McGilvray; Bus. Mgr., Antifreeze—Sol B. Sandperl**
Houghton Chemical Corp., 30 Amor Ave., Carlstadt, 07072 ........ (800) 777-2466

**HOUSE FOODS AMERICA CORP.**
**7351 Orangewood Ave., Garden Grove CA 92841 ........ (714) 901-4350**
**Sales Mgr.—Paul Eastman; New Acct. Mgmt. & Sales Mgr.—Shunzo Horikawa; Hum. Res. Mgr.—Chiemi Mitsuyama; Consumer Affs. Mgr.—Noriko Tsuiji**
House Foods America Corp., 801 Randolph Rd., Somerset, 08873 ........ (732) 537-9500

**HUBBELL LIGHTING, INC.**
**701 Millennium Blvd., Greenville SC 29607 ........ (864) 678-1000**
**Pres.—Scott Muse; V-P., Sales—Bruce Bittner; V-P., Hum. Res.—Steve Nail; V-P., Fin.—Rob Stamper; Cont.—August Spencer; Dir., Mktg. Svcs.—Ken Beale; Hum. Res. Mgr.—George Fajardo**
Kurt Versen Inc, 10 Charles St., Westwood, 07675 ........ (201) 664-8200

**HUMANSCALE CORPORATION**
**11 E. 26th St., 8th Fl., New York NY 10010 ........ (212) 725-4749**
**CEO—Bob King; V-P., Fin.—Michele Gerards; Dir., Hum. Res.—Bruny Carlo**
Humanscale Corp., 220 Circle Dr. N., Piscataway, 08854 ........ (732) 537-2944

**HUNTERDON TRANSFORMER CO.**
**75 Industrial Rd., Alpha NJ 08865 ........ (908) 454-2400**
**Pres.—Mark Brock; V-P., Treas.—Peter Droelle; V-P., Sales & Mktg.—Carol Liotta; V-P., Engrg. & Sales—Richard McCabe; Hum. Res. Mgr.—Theresa Mack**
Torelco, Inc., 55 Industrial Dr., Alpha, 08865 ........ (908) 387-0814

**HUSSMANN CORP.**
**12999 Saint Charles Rock Rd., Bridgeton MO 63044 ........ (314) 291-2000**
**Pres.—Dennis Gipson; V-P., Mktg.—Mike Higgins; V-P., Hum. Res.—Scott Mannis; V-P., Fin.—Tim Figge; Dir., Mktg. Comm.—Steve Hagler**
Hussmann Corp., 3001 Irwin Rd., Ste. D, Mount Laurel, 08054 ........ (856) 793-7050

**ICC INDUSTRIES, INC.**
**460 Park Ave., 7th Fl., New York NY 10022 ........ (212) 521-1700**
**Chrm., CEO—John J. Farber; Pres., Mfg. Group, V-P., CFO & COO—Blaise Sarcone; V-P., Treas.—Susan Abinder; MIS Mgr.—Steve Savard**
Frutarom USA, Inc., 9500 Railroad Ave., North Bergen, 07047 ........ (201) 861-9500

**IESI CORP.**
**2301 Eagle Pkwy., Ste. 200, Fort Worth TX 76177 ........ (817) 632-4000**
**Pres., CEO—Joe Quarin; COO—Kevin Walbridge; V-P., Sales—Colin Wittke; V-P., Acquisitions—Dan Pio; Dir., Hum. Res.—Joyce Stock; Dir., Comm. & Pub. Rels.—Donna Higgins**
IESI Recycling Corp. (H Q), 1099 Wall St. W., Ste. 250, Lyndhurst, 07071 ........ (201) 443-3000

**IFCO SYSTEMS NORTH AMERICA, INC.**
**13100 N.W. Fwy., Ste. 500, Houston TX 77040 ........ (713) 332-6145**
**Pres.—David S. Russell; Sr. V-P., CFO—Rich Hamlin; Dir., Hum. Res.—Keith Hancock**
IFCO Systems, 320 Dulty's Ln., P.O. Box 1333, Burlington, 08016 ........ (609) 386-5200

**IHI IONBOND, LLC**
**1823 E. Whitcomb Ave., Madison Heights MI 48071 ........ (248) 398-9100**
**CEO—Joe Haggerty; Pres., N. America—Ton Hurkmans; CFO, N. America—Tim Hopman; Hum. Res. Mgr.—Theresa Krieger**
IHI Ionbond, 200 Roundhill Dr., Rockaway, 07866 ........ (973) 586-4700

**II-VI INCORPORATED**
**375 Saxonburg Blvd., Saxonburg PA 16056 ........ (724) 352-4455**
**Chrm. of the Board—Carl J. Johnson; Pres., CEO—Francis J. Kramer; Treas., CFO—Craig Creaturo; V-P., COO & GM, Compound Semiconductor Group—Vincent Mattera; V-P., Govt. & Military—James Martinelli; GM, Infrared Optics—Mark West**
II-VI Advanced Materials, 20 Chapin Rd., Ste. 1007, P.O. Box 840, Pine Brook, 07058 ........ (973) 227-1551

**IKANOS COMMUNICATIONS, INC.**
**47669 Fremont Blvd., Fremont CA 94538 ........ (510) 979-0400**
**Pres., CEO—Omid Tahernia; Sr. V-P., CTO—Debajyoti Pal; V-P., Fin. & CFO—Dennis Bencala; V-P., Opers.—Bob Dunnigan; V-P., Mktg.—Kourosh Amiri; V-P., Hum. Res., Worldwide—Jim Murphy; V-P., Worldwide Engrg.—Syrus Ziai**
Ikanos Communications, Inc., 100 Schultz Dr., Red Bank, 07701 ........ (732) 345-7500

**ILLINOIS TOOL WORKS, INC.**
**3600 W. Lake Ave., Glenview IL 60026 ........ (847) 724-7500**
**Non-Exec. Chrm.—Robert S. Morrison; Vice Chrm.—David Parry; Pres., CEO—E. Scott Santi; Sr. V-P., CFO—Michael M. Larsen; Sr. V-P., CHRO—Marie K. 'Katie' Lawler; Ex. V-P., Global Welding Bus.—Sundaram Nagarajan; V-P., Intellectual Property—Mark Croll; V-P., Govt. Rels.—Michael J. Lynch**
ITW Covid Security Group, 32 Commerce Dr., Ste. 1, Cranbury, 08512 ........ (609) 395-5600
ITW Professional Brands, 1295 Towbin Ave., Lakewood, 08701 ........ (732) 363-9281
ITW Thielex, 95 Commerce Dr., Somerset, 08873 ........ (732) 873-5500
Signode Packaging Group, 151 Fabyan Pl., Newark, 07112 ........ (800) 235-4066
Truck Parts Specialists, 150 Central Ave., Teterboro, 07608 ........ (201) 288-9333

**INDUCTOTHERM CORP.**
**10 Indel Ave., P.O. Box 157, Rancocas NJ 08073 ........ (609) 267-9000**
**Pres.—Satyen N. Prabhu; Sr. V-P., Sales & Serv.—Joseph T. Belsh; V-P., Admn. & Treas.—Ted Baugh; Dir., Opers.—Rajul Patel; Hum. Res. Mgr.—Georga Smith**
PV/T, Inc., 100 Indel Ave., P.O. Box 156, Rancocas, 08073 ........ (609) 267-3933
Consarc Corp., 100 Indel Ave., P.O. Box 156, Rancocas, 08073 ........ (609) 267-8000
Electro-Steam Generator Corp., 50 Indel Ave., P.O. Box 438, Rancocas, 08073 ........ (609) 288-9071
Jomar Corp., 115 E. Parkway Dr., Egg Harbor Township, 08234 ........ (609) 646-8000
Rancocas Metals Corp., 35 Indel Ave., P.O. Box 223, Rancocas, 08073 ........ (609) 267-4120
Telegenix, Inc., 71 Indel Ave., P.O. Box 577, Rancocas, 08073 ........ (609) 265-3910

**INDUSTRIAL WELDING SUPPLY, INC.**
**4 Val St., Sayreville NJ 08872 ........ (732) 721-1150**
**Pres.—Jim Cusick; V-P.—Scott Cusick; Secy-Treas.—Linda Cusick**
Industrial Welding Supply, Inc., 999 Airport Rd., Ste. 1, Lakewood, 08701 ........ (732) 367-7100

**INFORMATICA CORP.**
**2100 Seaport Blvd., Redwood City CA 94063 ........ (650) 385-5000**
**CEO—Sohaib Abbasi; Ex. V-P., CAO & CFO—Earl E. Fry; Ex. V-P., CTO—James Markarian; Ex. V-P., CPO—Girish Pancha; Ex. V-P., Chief Hum. Res. Officer—Jo Stoner**
Informatica Corp., 309 Fellowship Rd., Mount Laurel, 08054 ........ (856) 642-4080

**INGERSOLL-RAND CO. LTD.**
**800-E Beaty St., Davidson NC 28036 ........ (704) 655-4000**
**Chrm., Pres. & CEO—Michael Lamach; Sr. V-P., CFO—Sue Carter; V-P., Cont.—Richard Weller; Dir., Ext. Comm.—Misty Zelent; Hum. Res. Mgr.—Dan Hawkins**
Trane, Inc. (H Q), 1 Centennial Ave., P.O. Box 6820, Piscataway, 08855 ........ (732) 652-7100

**INGREDION INC.**
**5 Westbrook Corp. Ctr., Ste. 500, P.O. Box 7100, Westchester IL 60154 ........ (708) 551-2600**
**Chrm., Pres. & CEO—Ilene Gordon; V-P., CFO—Jack Fortnum; V-P., Hum. Res.—Diane Frisch; V-P., Inv. Rels. & Dir., Corp. Comms.—Aaron Hoffman**
Ingredion Incorporated (H Q), 10 Finderne Ave., Ste. C, Bridgewater, 08807 ........ (908) 685-5555

**INNERWORKINGS, INC.**
**600 W. Chicago Ave., Ste. 850, Chicago IL 60654 ........ (312) 642-3700**
**Pres., CEO—Eric D. Belcher; CFO—Joseph Busky; CTO—Neil Graver; COO—John Eisel; Gen. Counsel—Ron Provenzano**
InnerWorkings, Inc., 7 Joanna Ct., Ste. H, East Brunswick, 08816 ........ (732) 651-8822

**INTEGRA LIFESCIENCES CORP.**
**311 Enterprise Dr., Plainsboro NJ 08536 ........ (609) 275-0500**
**Ex. Chrm.—Stuart M. Essig; Pres., CEO & Dir.—Peter Arduini; Corp. V-P. & Pres., Instruments—Debbi Leonetti; Corp. V-P. & Pres., Extremity Reconstruction—Robert D. Paltridge; Pres., Intl. & Corp. V-P.—Dan Reyvers; Corp. V-P. & Pres., Neurosurgery—Robert T. Davis, Jr.; Corp. V-P. & Pres., Global Spine & Orthobiotics & Head of Strategic Dev.—Brian Larkin; Pres., U.S. Spine—Kirt Stephenson; Ex. V-P., Admn. & Fin. & CFO—John B. Henneman III; Chief Scientific Officer—Simon J. Archibald; CIO—Robert Perrett;**

G16 © Copyright 2015 Manufacturers' News, Inc. PARENT COMPANY SECTION

**INTEGRA LIFESCIENCES CORP.—(cont.)**
**Corp. V-P., Global Opers. & Supply Chain—John Mooradian;**
**Sr. V-P., Global Opers.—James Oti;**
**Sr. V-P., Admn., Gen. Counsel & Secy.—Richard D. Gorelick;**
**Sr. V-P., Corp. Dev.—Maria Platsis;**
**Corp. V-P., Admn., Gen. Counsel & Secy.—Judith E. O'Grady;**
**Sr. V-P., Global Supply Chain—John Bostjancic;**
**Corp. V-P., Global Qual. Assur.—Joseph Vinhais; V-P., Treas.—Nora Brennan;**
**V-P., Corp. Cont.—Jerry Corbin**
Integra LifeSciences Corp., 105 Morgan Ln., Plainsboro, 08536 ............. (609) 275-2700

**INTEK PLASTICS, INC.**
**1000 Spiral Blvd., Hastings MN 55033 ............................. (651) 437-7700**
**Pres.—Mike Kinning; Chief Opers. Officer—Steve Glienke; Key Acct. Mgr.—Colleen Berg**
Intek Plastics, Inc., 150 5th Ave., Hawthorne, 07506 ...................... (973) 427-7331

**INTELLIGRATED, INC.**
**7901 Innovation Way, Mason OH 45040 .............................. (513) 701-7300**
**CEO—Chris Cole; Pres., COO—Jim McCarthy; CFO—Ed Puisis;**
**Sr. V-P., Sales & Mktg.—Jim McKnight**
Intelligrated, 265 Davidson Ave., Ste. 219, Somerset, 08873 ............... (732) 302-2590

**INTERLINE BRANDS, INC.**
**701 San Marco Blvd., Jacksonville FL 32207 ........................ (904) 421-1400**
**Chrm., CEO—Michael Grebe; Pres., COO—Ken Sweder; CFO—Fred Pensotti;**
**CAO & Corp. Cont.—David C. Serrano; CIO—Lucretia Doblado;**
**Mktg. Mgr.—Ramesh Bulusu**
Interline Brands, Inc. (H Q), 804 Eastgate Dr., Ste. 100, Mount Laurel, 08054 ... (856) 439-1222

**INTERNATIONAL DATA GROUP**
**1 Exeter Plz., 15th Fl., Boston MA 02116 ............................ (617) 534-1200**
**Chrm. of the Board of Dirs., IDG—Walter Boyd;**
**CEO, IDG Comms., Worldwide—Michael Friedenberg; Dir., Corp. Comm.—Susanna Hinds**
International Data Group, 650 From Rd., Ste. 558, Paramus, 07652 .......... (201) 634-2300

**INTERNATIONAL FLAVORS & FRAGRANCES, INC.**
**521 W. 57th St., New York NY 10019 ............................... (212) 765-5500**
**Chrm., CEO—Doug Tough; CFO—Kevin Berryman;**
**Sr. V-P., Gen. Counsel & Secy.—Anne Chwat; V-P., Hum. Res.—Angelica Cantlon**
International Flavors & Fragrances, Inc., 150 Docks Corner Rd., Dayton, 08810 .. (732) 329-4600
International Flavors & Fragrances, Inc., 600 Highway 36, Hazlet, 07730 ...... (732) 264-4500

**INTERNATIONAL FOAM PRODUCTS, INC.**
**10530 Westlake Dr., Charlotte NC 28273 ............................ (704) 588-0080**
**Pres.—Steven Sklow; V-P.—Jennifer Garis**
International Foam Products, Inc., P.O. Box 545, Stanhope, 07874 ........... (201) 909-0950

**INTERNATIONAL PAINT, LLC**
**6001 Antoine Dr., Houston TX 77091 ................................ (713) 682-1711**
**V-P., Sales—Chris Tierney; V-P., Opers.—Rick Preciado; Comp.—Jeff Danhert;**
**Dir., Prod. Mktg.—Dave Maurere; IT Mgr.—Krista Harman**
International Paint, LLC, 2270 Morris Ave., Union, 07083 .................. (908) 686-1300

**INTERNATIONAL PAPER CO.**
**6400 Poplar Ave., Memphis TN 38197 ............................... (901) 419-9000**
**Chrm., CEO—Mark Sutton; Sr. V-P., CFO—Carol Roberts;**
**Sr. V-P., Indl. Packaging—Timothy S. Nicholls;**
**Sr. V-P., Container, Americas—William Hoel;**
**Sr. V-P., N.A., Papers, Pulp & Consumer Pkg.—W. Michael Amick, Jr.;**
**V-P., E H S & S—David Kiser; V-P., Sustainability—Teri Shanahan;**
**V-P., Global Sourcing—David Liebetreu; Board Dir.—Christopher E. Kubasik;**
**Dir., Comms.—Patty Neuhoff; Dir., Pub. Rels.—Tom Ryan;**
**Sr. Comms. Mgr., Indl. Packaging—Richard Ouellette; Mktg. Mgr.—Beth McKeithen;**
**Sr. Graphic Designer—Michael Baldwin**
International Paper Co., 100 E. Gloucester Pike, Barrington, 08007 .......... (856) 546-7000
International Paper Co., 370 Benigno Blvd., Bellmawr, 08031 ................ (856) 931-8000
International Paper Co., 101 Ford Ave., Milltown, 08850 .................... (732) 828-1700
International Paper Co., 140 Summerhill Rd., Spotswood, 08884 ............. (732) 251-2000
International Paper Co., 33 Phoenix Dr., Thorofare, 08086 .................. (856) 853-7000
Shorewood Digital Design & Development Center, 1 Kero Rd., Carlstadt, 07072 .. (201) 372-3900

**INTERPLEX INDUSTRIES, INC.**
**14-34 110th St., Ste., 301, College Point NY 11356 .................. (718) 961-6212**
**Chrm., CEO—Jack Seidler; CFO—Irving Klein; Ex. V-P., Opers.—Steve Feinstein**
Interplex NAS Inc., Beta Div., 232 Pegasus Ave., Northvale, 07647 ........... (201) 367-1300

**INTERSIL CORP.**
**1001 Murphy Ranch Rd., Milpitas CA 95035 .......................... (408) 546-3300**
**CEO—Dave Bell; CFO—Jonathan Kennedy; V-P., Opers.—Mark Hobaugh;**
**V-P., Hum. Res.—Vern Kelly**
Intersil Corp., 440 U.S. Highway 22 E., Ste. 100, Bridgewater, 08807 .......... (908) 685-6000

**INTERSTATE BATTERY SYSTEM OF AMERICA, INC.**
**12770 Merit Dr., Ste. 400, Dallas TX 75251 .......................... (972) 991-1444**
**Chrm.—Norm Miller; Pres., CEO—Carlos Sepulveda; CFO—Lisa Huntsberry;**
**Dir., Dev. & Franchising—Jim Eades**
Interstate Battery System Of America, Inc.,
408 Commerce Ln., West Berlin, 08091 .................................. (856) 767-3903

**INTERSTATE RESOURCES, INC.**
**1300 Wilson Blvd., Ste. 1075, Arlington VA 22209 ..................... (703) 243-3355**
**Pres.—Jim Morgan; CFO—Pierre Khattar; V-P., Hum. Res.—Susan Newman;**
**IT Mgr.—Jerry Clark**
Interstate Container Brunswick, LLC, 501 Finnegan Ln., North Brunswick, 08902 . (732) 821-8100

**ISE AMERICA, INC.**
**33335 Galena Sassafras Rd., P.O. Box 267, Galena MD 21635 ............ (410) 755-6300**
**Pres.—Hikonobo Ise; CFO—Denise Ford; V-P., COO—Greg Clanton; V-P.—Doug Wicker**
I S E Farms, Inc., 110 Goodspring Rd., P.O. Box 567, Broadway, 08808 ........ (908) 454-4148

**ISLAND CONTAINER CORP.**
**44 Island Container Plz., Wyandanch NY 11798 ........................ (631) 253-4400**
**Pres.—Edward Berkowitz; V-P.—Gary Berkowitz; GM—Michael Scudiero**
Alpak Display Group, 575 N. Midland Ave., Saddle Brook, 07663 ............. (201) 797-1411
Enterprise Corrugated Container, LLC,
575 N. Midland Ave., P.O. Box 857, Saddle Brook, 07663 ................... (201) 797-7200

**IVC INDUSTRIES, INC.**
**500 Halls Mill Rd., Freehold NJ 07728 .............................. (732) 308-3000**
**Pres., CEO—Steven Dai; V-P., Mktg.—Steve Rosenman; Hum. Res. Mgr.—Jill Stambler**
Intergel Vitamin Co., 191 40th St., Irvington, 07111 ........................ (973) 371-4400

**J & J SNACK FOODS CORP.**
**6000 Central Hwy., Pennsauken NJ 08109 ............................ (856) 665-9534**
**Pres., CEO—Gerald Shreiber; CFO—Dennis G. Moore; Sr. V-P., COO—Robert M. Radano;**
**Sr. V-P., Sales—Robert Pape; V-P., Hum. Res.—Harry Fronjian;**
**Mktg. Mgr.—Amanda Osorio**
Federal Pretzel Baking Co., 300 Eagle Ct., P.O. Box 257, Bridgeport, 08014 ..... (215) 467-0505
J & J Snack Foods Corp., 361 Benigno Blvd., Ste. A, Bellmawr, 08031 ......... (856) 933-3597
Uptown Bakeries/J & J Snack Foods,
300 Eagle Ct., P.O. Box 257, Bridgeport, 08014 ........................... (856) 467-9552

**J. M. FRY COMPANY, INC.**
**4329 Eubank Rd., P.O. Box 7719, Henrico VA 23231 ................... (804) 236-8100**
**Ptnr. & Pres.—Robert A. Hodges; Ptnr. & V-P.—Bill J. Hodges;**
**Ptnr. & V-P.—James Hodges; Cont.—Darrell Anderson;**
**Dir., Qual. Control, Laboratory—Michael Varnier; Dir., Tech.—William Watson;**
**Plt. Mgr.—George Durocher; Off. Mgr.—Margaret Hodges**
J.M. Fry Co., Inc., 124 Tices Ln., Ste. A, East Brunswick, 08816 ............. (732) 238-1060

**JABAT, INC.**
**715 N. West St., P.O. Box 38, Olney IL 62450 ........................ (618) 392-3010**
**V-P., Sales—Aaron Ackman; V-P., Opers. & GM—Rod Michels; V-P., Mktg.—Tom Simmering;**
**V-P., Fin.—Rita Kman; Plt. Mgr.—Beth Price; Engrg. Mgr.—Matt Craig**
Jabat, Inc., K., 342 Highway 22 W., Green Brook, 08812 .................... (732) 469-8177

**JACK DOHENY COMPANIES, INC.**
**777 Doheny Dr., P.O. Box 609, Northville MI 48167 .................... (248) 349-0904**
**CEO—Jack Doheny; Pres.—Dan Weber; V-P., CFO—Andrew Kirk; Sr. V-P.—Gary Mapes;**
**V-P.—Kay Doheny Snyder; Sales & Mktg. Mgr., Inside—Mike Renner;**
**IT Mgr.—Chris Gravlin**
Jack Doheny Companies, Inc., 15 Taylor Rd., Ste. 1, Wharton, 07885 ......... (973) 659-0061

**JACOBUS PHARMACEUTICAL CO., INC.**
**37 Cleveland Ln., Princeton NJ 08540 ............................... (609) 921-7447**
**Ptnr.—David Jacobus; Ptnr.—Laura Jacobus; Site Mgr.—Rich Pursell**
Jacobus Pharmaceutical Co., Inc., P.O. Box 5290, Princeton, 08540 .......... (609) 799-8221

**JAMES CO., THE TOM**
**263 Seaboard Ln., Franklin TN 37067 ............................... (615) 771-1122**
**CEO—Sergio Casalena; Pres.—Todd Browne; CFO—Phil Williams;**
**Hum. Res. Mgr.—Diane Nichols**
Individualized Shirts, Inc., 581 Cortland St., Perth Amboy, 08861 ............ (732) 826-8400

**JAMES D. MORRISSEY, INC.**
**9119 Frankford Ave., Philadelphia PA 19114 ......................... (215) 333-8000**
**Pres.—James Morrissey; V-P.—Joseph Morrissey; Corp. Secy.—Alice Morrissey;**
**Treas.—R. Scott Barcusky**
Ward Sand & Materials, 223 Sooy Place Rd., Vincentown, 08088 ............ (609) 859-2860

**JARDEN CORP.**
**1800 N. Military Trl., Boca Raton FL 33431 .......................... (561) 447-2520**
**Co-Founder, Vice Chrm., Pres. & CFO—Ian G. H. Ashken; CEO—James E. Lillie**
Quickie Mfg. Corp. (H Q), 1150 Taylors Ln., P.O. Box 156, Cinnaminson, 08077 .. (856) 829-7900

**JDS UNIPHASE CORP.**
**430 N. McCarthy Blvd., Milpitas CA 95035 ........................... (408) 546-5000**
**Pres., CEO—Thomas Waechter; Pres., Comms. Test & Measurement—David Heard;**
**Sr. V-P., Comms. Test & Measurement—Tom Smith; V-P., Hum. Res.—Brett Hooper;**
**Global Comp., Facilities—Robert Ule**
JDSU, 2 Applegate Dr., Robbinsville, 08691 .............................. (609) 632-0800

**JFC INTERNATIONAL, INC.**
**7101 E. Slauson Ave., Los Angeles CA 90040 ......................... (323) 721-6100**
**Pres.—Hiroyuki Enomoto; Treas.—Masnori Takenako; Pur. Mgr.—Masakazu Kaneda;**
**Hum. Res. Mgr.—Margaret Thurman**
JFC International, Inc., 55 Wildcat Way, Linden, 07036 ..................... (908) 525-4400

**JOHN CRANE, INC.**
**6400 W. Oakton St., Morton Grove IL 60053 .......................... (847) 967-2400**
**Pres.—Duncan Gillis; V-P., Sales—Andrew Forrest; V-P., Hum. Res.—Barbara Turk;**
**Dir., Prod. Line, Gas Seals—Simon Outhwaite;**
**Dir., Prod. Line, Bearings—Morched Medhioub; Mfg. Mgr.—Dan Schaumbeck;**
**Aftermarket Mgr., Gas Seal—Mark Daniel**
John Crane, Inc., 301 Berkeley Dr., Swedesboro, 08085 .................... (856) 241-3507
U.S. Seal Mfg., 400 Apgar Dr., Ste. A, Somerset, 08873 .................... (732) 667-1100

**JOHNS MANVILLE**
**717 17th St., Denver CO 80202 ..................................... (303) 978-2000**
**Pres., CEO—Mary K. Rhinehart; V-P., Hum. Res.—Scott Simmons;**
**Dir., Capital Projs.—Todd McCollough; Corp. Comm. Mgr.—Melody Dunbar**
Johns Manville, 437 North Grove St., Berlin, 08009 ........................ (856) 768-7000
Johns Manville, 1000 Liddle Ave., Edison, 08837 .......................... (732) 225-9190

**JOHNSON & JOHNSON**
**1 Johnson & Johnson Plz., New Brunswick NJ 08933 .................... (732) 524-0400**
**Worldwide Chrm., Consumer Div.—Jesse Wu; CEO—Alex Gorsky;**
**V-P., Fin. & CFO—Dominic J. Caruso; V-P., Inv. Rels.—Louise Mehrotra**
Ethicon, Inc., 737 U.S. Highway 22 W., P.O. Box 151, Somerville, 08876 ....... (908) 218-0707
Janssen Pharmaceuticals, Inc.,
1125 Trenton-Harbourton Rd., P.O. Box 200, Titusville, 08560 ............... (908) 218-6000
Janssen Research & Development, LLC, A Div. of Johnson & Johnson,
920 U.S. Highway 202, P.O. Box 300, Raritan, 08869 ....................... (908) 704-4000
Johnson & Johnson Consumer Companies, Inc. (H Q),
199 Grandview Rd., Skillman, 08558 .................................... (908) 874-1000

© Copyright 2015 Manufacturers' News, Inc.




**JOHNSON & TOWERS, INC.**
**2021 Briggs Rd., P.O. Box 4000, Mount Laurel NJ 08054 ................ (856) 234-6990**
**Chrm.—Walter Johnson III; GM—Bob Shomo, Jr.; Hum. Res. Mgr.—Shelley Hink**
Johnson & Towers, Inc., 2701 Fire Rd., Egg Harbor Township, 08234 .......... (609) 272-1415

**JOHNSON MATTHEY, INC.**
**456 Devon Park Dr., P.O. Box 19087, Wayne PA 19087 .................... (610) 341-8300**
**Pres., N. America—William F. Clauhs; Dir., IT—Mark O'Neil;**
**Dir., Hum. Res., Regional—Bernie Brady; Dir., Fin.—Scott Delorefice;**
**Dir., Comml.—Kevin Donegan**
INTERCAT, Inc. (H Q), 2399 Highway 34, Ste. C-1, Manasquan, 08736 ........ (732) 223-4644
Johnson Matthey, Inc., 2001 Nolte Dr., West Deptford, 08066 ................ (856) 384-7000
Johnson Matthey Pharmaceutical Materials, 2003 Nolte Dr., Paulsboro, 08066 ... (856) 384-7001

**JOHNSON'S APPLIANCES & BEDDING**
**930 Asbury Ave., P.O. Box 95, Ocean City NJ 08226 .................... (609) 399-1598**
**Pres. & Dir., Opers. & Sales—Don Johnson**
Johnson's Appliances & Bedding, 2510 New York Ave., Wildwood, 08260 ...... (609) 522-1421

**JOHNSTONE SUPPLY, INC.**
**11632 N.E. Ainsworth Cir., Portland OR 97220 ...................... (503) 419-9100**
**Pres., CEO—DeWight Wallace; CFO—Julie Schultz; V-P., Sales & Mktg.—Andrew Verey;**
**V-P., Comm.—Janet McCreary; V-P., Prod. Dev.—Steve Porter;**
**V-P., Org. Dev.—Johanna Glode**
Z & Z Holding Co Inc, 370 Market St., P.O. Box 239, Kenilworth, 07033 ........ (908) 298-1212

**JOSTENS, INC.**
**3601 Minnesota Dr., Ste. 400, Minneapolis MN 55435 .................. (952) 830-3300**
**Pres., CEO—Chuck Mooty; CIO—Scott Henkel; Sr. V-P., CFO—James Simpson;**
**Hum. Res. Mgr.—Suzanne Martz**
Jostens, Inc., 86 Roseville Rd., Andover, 07821 ........................... (973) 584-5843

**JOURNAL MULTIMEDIA**
**1500 Paxton St., 3rd Fl., Harrisburg PA 17104 ........................ (717) 236-4300**
**CEO—David Schankweiler; Pres.—Larry Kluger; Editor—Hope Stephan;**
**Sales Mgr.—Shaun McCoach; Prodn. Mgr.—Chad Pickard;**
**Mktg. Mgr.—Beth Feltenberger; Bus. Mgr.—Donna Schankweiler;**
**Circ. Mgr.—Criss Kerkendall**
NJBIZ, 220 Davidson Ave., Ste. 302, Somerset, 08873 ...................... (732) 246-7677

**JUMP APPAREL**
**1400 Broadway, Ste. 201, New York NY 10018 ......................... (212) 869-3300**
**CEO—Glenn Schlossberg; Pres., Sales—Richard Silverstein;**
**Pres., Prod.—Terry Freedman; IT Mgr.—Ray Sitorus; Hum. Res. Mgr.—Yaury Rueda;**
**Fin. Mgr.—Patrick Corrigan**
Jump Apparel, 350 Secaucus Rd., Secaucus, 07094 ......................... (201) 558-9191

**KAMAN INDUSTRIAL TECHNOLOGIES CORP.**
**1 Vision Way, Bloomfield CT 06002 ................................. (860) 687-5000**
**Pres., Div.—Steve Smidler; V-P., Hum. Res.—Carmen Rivera;**
**V-P., Mktg. & Serv.—David Mayer; Sr. Mktg. Comms. Mgr.—Arti Patel**
Kaman Industrial Technologies Corp., 502 Bloy St., Hillside, 07205 ........... (908) 687-0004
Kaman Industrial Technologies Corp., 195 Borelli Rd., Paulsboro, 08066 ....... (856) 227-7000
Kaman Industrial Technologies Corp.,
195 Borrelli Blvd., Ste. B, Paulsboro, 08066 ............................ (856) 284-7400

**KAPSTONE PAPER AND PACKAGING CORP.**
**1101 Skokie Blvd., Ste. 300, Northbrook IL 60062 ..................... (847) 239-8800**
**Chrm., CEO—Roger W. Stone; Pres.—Matthew Kaplan; V-P., GM—Tim Keneally;**
**Dir., Hum. Res.—Irina Feldman**
Kampack, Inc., 100 Frontage Rd., Newark, 07114 ........................... (973) 589-7400

**KARCHER NORTH AMERICA**
**750 W. Hampden Ave., Ste. 400, Englewood CO 80110 .................. (303) 738-2400**
**CEO—Hannes Saeubert; CFO—Thomas Brendel; CTO—Bill Ott;**
**V-P., Hum. Res.—Donita Gardner**
Graco Manufacturing, 500 University Ct., Blackwood, 08012 .................. (856) 228-1800

**KAY PRINTING CO.**
**220 Entin Rd., Clifton NJ 07014 ................................... (973) 330-3000**
**Ptnr. & Pres.—Richard Kirschenbaum; Ptnr. & V-P.—Charlie Tuminello;**
**V-P., Sales—Steven Tuminello; V-P.—Michael Costello; V-P.—Jeffrey Kirschenbaum;**
**Cont.—Robert Generale; Sales Mgr.—Myron Kowal**
JDS Graphics, Inc., 220 Entin Rd., Clifton, 07014 .......................... (973) 330-3300

**KAYDON CORP.**
**2723 S. State St., Ste. 300, Ann Arbor MI 48104 ...................... (734) 747-7025**
**Pres., CEO—James O'Leary; CIO—Greg Billingsley**
Canfield Technologies/Bow Electronic Solder,
1 S. Crossman Rd., Sayreville, 08872 ................................... (732) 316-2100

**KB DESIGN GROUP, INC.**
**113 W. Jersey Ave., Pitman NJ 08071 ................................ (856) 589-3110**
**Owner & Pres.—Ben Bonaccorso**
KB Acrylics, Inc., I-295 Industrial Ctr., Bldg. B, Box 47, Westville, 08093 ....... (856) 589-3110

**KELLOGG CO.**
**1 Kellogg Sq., Battle Creek MI 49017 ............................... (269) 961-2000**
**Chrm., CEO—John A. Bryant; Sr. V-P., CFO—Ron Dissinger;**
**Sr. V-P., Chief Growth Officer—Paul Norman; Sr. V-P., Hum. Res.—Sammie Long;**
**Treas.—Joel Vander Kooi; Inv. Rels. Mgr.—Ellen Leithold**
Kellogg Co., 322 S. Egg Harbor Rd., Hammonton, 08037 ..................... (609) 567-2300

**KELLY, INC., MYLES F.**
**43-57 Harrison Ave., Harrison NJ 07029 .............................. (973) 481-0600**
**Pres.—Jeff Kelly**
Kelly, Inc., Myles F., 210 W. Westfield Ave., Roselle Park, 07204 ............. (908) 245-7296

**KEMPERLE, INC., ALBERT**
**176 New Hwy., Amityville NY 11701 ................................. (631) 842-5300**
**Pres.—Albert Kemperle**
Kemperle, Inc., Albert, 626 E. Elizabeth Ave., Linden, 07036 ................. (908) 925-6133

**KENSEAL CONSTRUCTION PRODUCTS CORP.**
**2960 Washington Blvd., Baltimore MD 21230 .......................... (410) 646-5801**
**Pres.—Paul McKinnell; IT Mgr.—Amy Missel; Hum. Res. Mgr.—Aaron Smith;**
**Sales Rep.—Kevin Kulisiewicz**
Kenseal Construction Products Corp., 799 Edwards Rd., Parsippany, 07054 .... (973) 287-5858

**KERRY, INC.**
**3400 Millington Rd., Beloit WI 53511 ............................... (608) 363-1200**
**Pres., CEO—Gerry Behan; CFO—Olivia Nelligan; CMO—Andy Royston;**
**CTO—Khaled Zitoun; Chief Food Safety & Quality Officer—Marie Tanner;**
**Sr. V-P., Opers.—Michael Leahy; V-P., Hum. Res.—Lynn Holt;**
**Dir., Mktg. Comms.—Alexandra Rice**
Kerry Ingredients, 26 Minneakoning Rd., Flemington, 08822 ................. (908) 782-4919
Kerry Ingredients & Flavors, 160 Terminal Ave., Clark, 07066 ................ (732) 882-0202

**KIRKER ENTERPRISES, INC.**
**55 E. 6th St., Paterson NJ 07524 ................................... (973) 754-9000**
**CEO—Jeffrey S. Hersh; Pres.—Jeff Kirson; Hum. Res. Mgr.—Ivy Ho;**
**Pur. Agt.—Patty LaPenter**
Tevco Enterprises, Inc., 110 Pomponio Ave., South Plainfield, 07080 .......... (908) 754-7306

**KLINGES, INC., CHARLES A.**
**410 Swedeland Rd., King Of Prussia PA 19406 ........................ (610) 279-2700**
**Pres.—Edward Klinges; Cont.—Kathy Kirk**
Klinges, Inc., Charles A., 790 S. Mill Rd., Absecon, 08201 .................. (609) 641-7755

**KNF CORP.**
**734 W. Penn Pike, Ste. 1, Tamaqua PA 18252 ......................... (570) 386-3550**
**CEO—Philip J. Carcara; GM—Lee Eikszta; Opers. Mgr.—Ken Kochol;**
**Maint. Mgr.—David Gilbert**
KNF Flexpak Corporation., 44 Howell St., Jersey City, 07306 ............... (201) 656-4012

**KOLMAR LABORATORIES, INC.**
**20 W. King St., P.O. Box 1111, Port Jervis NY 12771 .................. (845) 856-5311**
**Pres., CEO—Robert Edmonds; V-P., Sales & Mktg.—Jullie Strasser;**
**V-P., Opers. & Technologies—Chris Baker; Dir., Tech. Svcs.—Jeff Swaine;**
**Dir., Qual.—Liam Jablesnik; Comms. & Mktg. Mgr.—Amy Skellett**
Acupac Packaging, Inc., 55 Ramapo Valley Rd., Mahwah, 07430 ............. (201) 529-3434

**KOP-COAT, INC.**
**436 7th Ave., Ste. 1850, Pittsburgh PA 15219 ........................ (412) 227-2700**
**Pres.—Richard Kelly**
Kop-Coat, Inc., 36 Pine St., Rockaway, 07866 ............................. (973) 625-3100

**KRAFT POWER CORP.**
**199 Wildwood Ave., Woburn MA 01801 ............................... (781) 938-9100**
**Pres.—Owen Duffy; Dir., Sales—Dave Barstow; IT Mgr.—Brian Donahoe**
Kraft Power Corp., 241 W. Parkway, Pompton Plains, 07444 .................. (973) 835-9800

**KRATOS-NEW ENGLAND**
**10 Sonar Dr., Woburn MA 01801 .................................... (781) 729-9450**
**Pres., Div.—Richard F. Poirier; IT Mgr.—Dan Haynes; Off. Mgr.—Denise Giles;**
**Sales Admn.—Ligia Couto; Sales Admn.—Adria Lombardini**
Kratos-CTI, 9 Whippany Rd., Bldg. A-1, Whippany, 07981 .................... (973) 884-2580

**KRONOS, INC.**
**297 Billerica Rd., Chelmsford MA 01824 ............................. (978) 250-9800**
**CEO—Aron Ain; Sr. V-P., CMO—James Kizielewicz; CFO—Mark Julien;**
**Chief Administrative Officer—Charles Dickson; Chief People Officer—David Almeda;**
**Chief Prod. Officer—Jim Welch; Sr. V-P., Global Svcs.—Christopher Todd;**
**V-P., Cust. Support—Dennis Cameron; Dir., Mfg. Opers.—Howard Prescott**
SaaShr, 3040 U.S. Highway 22, Ste. 200, Somerville, 08876 .................. (908) 722-9952

**KUIKEN BROTHERS COMPANY, INC.**
**6-02 Fair Lawn Ave., P.O. Box 1040, Fair Lawn NJ 07410 ................ (201) 796-2082**
**Pres.—Douglas Kuiken; Cont.—Tom Tubridy; Plt. Mgr.—Phil Cerne;**
**Hum. Res. Mgr.—Debbie Steyling**
Kuiken Brothers Commercial, 485 River Dr., Garfield, 07026 ................ (973) 772-0044
Kuiken Brothers Company, Inc., 145 Lake Ave., Midland Park, 07432 .......... (201) 652-1000
Kuiken Brothers Company, Inc., 31 State Route 10 E., Succasunna, 07876 ..... (973) 584-2444
Kuiken Brothers Company, Inc., 175 Route 23, Wantage, 07461 ............... (973) 875-5106

**KYOCERA DOCUMENT SOLUTIONS AMERICA, INC.**
**225 Sand Rd., Fairfield NJ 07004 .................................. (973) 808-8444**
**Pres.—Norihiko Ina; Sr. V-P., Sales—Ed Bialecki; V-P., Mktg.—Peter Hendrick;**
**V-P., Hum. Res.—Gary Bonomolo; Hum. Res. Mgr.—Kerri Fiore**
Allister Business Systems, Inc., 205 E. 1st Ave., Roselle, 07203 ............. (732) 972-8400

**L & W SUPPLY CORP.**
**550 W. Adams St., Chicago IL 60661 ................................ (312) 436-4000**
**Pres., CEO—Brendan J. Deely; Sr. V-P., Opers. & Sales—Rob Waterhouse;**
**V-P., Mktg.—Jake Gress; Dir., Hum. Res.—Cassandra Nelson**
L & W Supply Corp., 1351 Route 37 W., Toms River, 08755 .................. (732) 341-3737
L & W Supply Corp., 126 Route 94, Blairstown, 07825 ...................... (908) 362-6103

**L-3 COMMUNICATIONS CORP.**
**600 3rd Ave., 34th Fl., New York NY 10016 .......................... (212) 697-1111**
**Chrm., CEO—Michael T. Strianese; V-P., CIO—Vince Taylor; Sr. V-P., Secy.—Steven Post;**
**V-P., Treas.—Steve Souza; V-P., Hum. Res.—John Hill**
L-3 Communications Corp., 1 Federal St., Camden, 08102 .................. (856) 338-3000
L-3 Communications Corp., Space & Navigation Systems,
450 Clark Dr., Budd Lake, 07828 ........................................ (973) 446-4000
L-3 Communications Mobile-Vision, Inc., 90 Fanny Rd., Boonton, 07005 ....... (973) 263-1090

**LABEL GRAPHICS MFG., INC.**
**175 Paterson Ave., Little Falls NJ 07424 ............................ (973) 890-5665**
**Pres.—Thomas Silvano; V-P.—Denise Silvano; GM—Ali Kahn; Pur. Mgr.—Jake Ritz**
Label Graphics Mfg., 315 Fairfield Rd., Unit 1, Fairfield, 07004 .............. (973) 890-5665

**LAIRD PLASTICS, INC.**
**6800 Broken Sound Pkwy., Ste. 150, Boca Raton FL 33487 ............... (561) 443-9100**
**CEO—Mark Kramer; CFO—Willy Figueras; V-P., Opers. & Sales—Peter Edelstein;**
**V-P., Pur.—Gerry Burnett; Dir., Corp. Dev.—Mark Steele**
Laird Plastics, Inc., 135 Fieldcrest Ave., Ste. 135-F, Edison, 08837 .......... (732) 593-2777

**LARSON-JUHL, LLC**
**3900 Steve Reynolds Blvd., Norcross GA 30093 ........................ (770) 279-5200**
**Pres., CEO—Drew Van Pelt; Pres., N. America—Dave Calhoun;**
**Sr. V-P., Fin. & CFO—R. Bradley Goodson; Sr. V-P., Mfg., U.S. & Canada—Jim McCoy;**
**V-P., Corp. Identity—Lynn Fey**
Larson-Juhl, LLC, 165 Clinton Rd., Caldwell, 07006 ........................ (973) 439-1801

**LASSONDE INDUSTRIES, INC.**
　755 Principale St., Rougemont, Quebec, Canada, J0L 1M0,.......... **(866) 552-7643**
　Chrm. of the Board & CEO—Pierre-Paul Lassonde; COO—Jean Gattuso
Clement Pappas & Company, Inc. (H Q),
　1 Collins Dr., Ste. 200, Carneys Point, 08069.................... (856) 455-1000

**LAYNE CHRISTENSEN CO.**
　1800 Hughes Landing Blvd., The Woodlands TX 77380.......... **(281) 475-2600**
　Pres., CEO—Michael Caliel;
　　Sr. V.-P., Gen. Counsel, Secy. & Hum. Res. Mgr.—Steven F. Crooke;
　　Sr. V.-P., Fin.—Jim Easter
Layne Christensen Co., 719 Mount Holly Rd., Beverly, 08010......... (609) 877-2700

**LEGGETT & PLATT, INC.**
　1 Leggett Rd., P.O. Box 757, Carthage MO 64836................. **(417) 358-8131**
　Chrm. & CEO—David S. Haffner; Vice Chrm.—Richard Fisher;
　Pres., COO—Karl G. Glassman; Ex. V.-P., CFO—Matthew Flanigan;
　Sr. V.-P., Hum. Res.—John Moore; Sr. V.-P., Gen. Counsel & Secy.—Scott Douglas;
　Treas.—Sheri Mossbeck; V.-P., Cont.—William S. Weil; V.-P., IT—Michael Blinzler;
　Staff V.-P., Inv. Rels.—Susan McCoy
Edison Foam Processing Corp., 157 Helen St., South Plainfield, 07080....... (732) 225-2440

**LEGRAND ASSOCS.**
　1601 Walnut St., Ste. 616, Philadelphia PA 19102................. **(215) 496-1307**
　Pres.—Joseph A. LeGrand, Jr.; Off. Mgr.—Maddie Vazquez
LeGrand Assocs., 214 W. Main St., Ste. 102, Moorestown, 08057........... (800) 273-8565

**LEGRAND NORTH AMERICA**
　60 Woodlawn St., West Hartford CT 06110................. **(860) 233-6251**
　Ex. V.-P., Market Dev. & Sales—John Hoffman; V.-P., GM—Brian DiBella;
　V.-P., Opers.—Jim Pilon; V.-P., Hum. Res.—Bernie Urbina;
　Dir., Comms. & Mktg.—Don Torrant; Pur. Mgr.—Bryan Kachur
Middle Atlantic Products, Inc., 300 Fairfield Rd., Fairfield, 07004........... (973) 839-1011

**LEHIGH HANSON, INC.**
　300 E. John Carpenter Fwy., Ste. 1645, Irving TX 75062................. **(972) 653-5500**
　Pres., CEO—Daniel Harrington; Pres., Regional—Jon Morrish; V.-P., Sales—Stan Dacus;
　V.-P., Hum. Res.—Van Waldrop; V.-P., Sustainability—Lori Tiesenthaler;
　Dir., Hum. Res.—Keith Bechly; Dir., Mktg. Subdivs.—Heather Meiner;
　Dir., Comms.—Jeff Sieg
Hanson Aggregate BMC, 1101 Railroad Ave., Newport, 08345.......... (856) 447-4294
Hanson Aggregates Better Materials Corp., 1401 Route 610, Woodbine, 08270.. (856) 447-4294
Hanson Aggregates, BMC Div., 368 New Brooklyn Rd., P.O. Box 37, Berlin, 08009.. (856) 767-3100
Hanson Aggregates North America, 311 Unexpected Rd., Buena, 08310...... (856) 697-1616
Lehigh Cement Co., 66 Demarest Rd., Sparta, 07871................ (973) 579-2111

**LENAPE PRODUCTS, INC.**
　600 Plum St., Trenton NJ 08638................. **(609) 394-5376**
　Pres.—Stephen M. Bielawski
Easco Shower Doors Co., 3 Industrial Dr., Vernon, 07462.................. (973) 209-4141

**LEVEL FOUR ORTHOTICS & PROSTHETICS, INC.**
　2530 Empire Dr., P.O. Box 24905, Winston-Salem NC 27114.............. **(336) 397-2165**
　Pres.—Richard Gingras; Dir., Contracting—Vikki Shoaf;
　　Hum. Res. & IT Mgr.—Lela McDonald
Cocco Enterprises, Inc., 333 Chambers St., Trenton, 08609................ (609) 393-5939

**LEWIS-GOETZ & CO., INC.**
　650 Washington Rd., Ste. 500, P.O. Box 895, Pittsburgh PA 15228......... **(412) 341-7100**
　Chrm.—David R. Goetz, Sr.; Pres., CEO—Jeff Crane; COO & Gen. Counsel—G. Randy Fox;
　Ex. V.-P., Opers.—Scott Johnson; Prodn. Mgr.—Randy Smith
Lewis-Goetz & Co., Inc., 1571 Grandview Ave., Paulsboro, 08066........... (856) 579-1421

**LIDESTRI FOODS, INC.**
　815 Whitney Rd. W., Fairport NY 14450................. **(585) 377-7700**
　Owner & CEO—Giovanni LiDestri; Pres.—John Vetere; Sr. V.-P.—Donna Yanicky;
　V.-P., Sales—James 'Jimmy' Rinaldi; V.-P., Mfg.—Anthony Ciulla;
　V.-P., Hum. Res.—Sharon Blake; V.-P., Bus. Dev. & Contract Mfg.—Alan Davis;
　V.-P., Proc.—Mary Beth Hall; Corp. Dir., Hum. Res.—Jane Oca
LiDestri Foods, Inc., 1550 John Tipton Blvd., Pennsauken, 08110........... (856) 662-1800

**LIFEGAS, LLC**
　6600 Peachtree Dunwoody Rd., Embassy Row 400, Ste. 300, Atlanta GA 30328. **(866) 543-3427**
　Pres.—Mike Walsh; Dir., Sales & Mktg.—Kenth Drott; Dir., Opers.—Greg Reppar;
　Hum. Res. Mgr.—Claudia Unchima
LifeGas, LLC, 174 Ridge Rd., Ste. A, Dayton, 08810.................. (866) 543-3427

**LIFETIME BRANDS, INC.**
　1000 Stewart Ave., Garden City NY 11530................. **(516) 683-6000**
　Chrm., Pres. & CEO—Jeffrey Siegel; COO—Ronald Shiftan; CFO—Laurence Winoker;
　Sr. V.-P., CIO—John Impellizeri; Ex. V.-P., Sales—Evan Miller;
　V.-P., Hum. Res.—Jacqueline Fagan; Gen. Counsel & Secy.—Sara Shindel
Lifetime Brands, Inc., Distribution Center,
　12 Applegate Dr., Robbinsville, 08691.................. (609) 208-1500

**LINDE NORTH AMERICA, INC.**
　575 Mountain Ave., New Providence NJ 07974................. **(908) 464-8100**
　Pres.—Patrick F. Murphy; V.-P., Gen. Counsel—Mark Weller; V.-P., Supply—Ken Flessner;
　V.-P., Energy Sols.—Earl Lawson; V.-P., Corp. Comm.—Peter Gavigan;
　V.-P., Electronics & Markets—Cliff Caldwell;
　Head of Hum. Res., Americas—Peter Vermeulen; Mktg. Support Mgr.—Janice Lamb
Linde Gas North America, LLC, 1 Greenwich St., Ste. 200, Stewartsville, 08886. (800) 755-9277

**LINK THEORY HOLDINGS (US), INC.**
　38 Gansevoort St., New York NY 10014................. **(212) 300-0800**
　Pres., Co-CEO—Andrew Rosen; CFO—Yoram Arieven; Secy.-Treas.—Hidetsugu Onishi;
　Hum. Res. Mgr.—Pam Meany; Pub. Rels. Mgr.—Juliana Simmons
Link Theory, 165 Polito Ave., Lyndhurst, 07071.................. (201) 728-5700

**LIPMAN**
　315 New Market Rd. E., Immokalee FL 34142................. **(239) 657-4421**
　CEO—Kent Shoemaker; COO—Darren P. Micelle; GM—Marc Danner; IT Mgr.—Dave King;
　Hum. Res. Mgr.—John Martinez
Colace Co., LLC, Thomas, 800 Grove Rd., Thorofare, 08086........... (856) 384-4980
Custom Pak, Inc., 800 Grove Rd., Thorofare, 08086.................. (856) 384-4980

**LIPO CHEMICALS, INC.**
　207 19th Ave., Paterson NJ 07504................. **(973) 345-8600**
　Ex. V.-P.—Conrad Kempinska; V.-P., Global Mktg.—Nancy Clements;
　　Dir., Sales, N. America—Michael Lotito
Lipo Chemicals, Inc., 1515 W. Blancke St., Linden, 07036................ (973) 926-0331

**LOCKHEED MARTIN CORP.**
　6801 Rockledge Dr., Bethesda MD 20817................. **(301) 897-6000**
　Chrm., Pres. & CEO—Marilyn A. Hewson; Sr. V.-P., CTO—Ray O. Johnson;
　V.-P., CFO—Bruce L. Tanner; Sr. V.-P., Gen. Counsel—Maryanne R. Lavan;
　Sr. V.-P., Bus. Dev. & Corp. Strategy—Patrick M. Dewar;
　Ex. V.-P., Info. Sys. & Global Sols.—Sondra L. Barbour;
　Corp. Officer & V.-P., Internal Audit—Lisa Callahan; Dir., Media Rels.—Jennifer Allen
Lockheed Martin,
　199 Borton Landing Rd., Rm. 108-108, P.O. Box 1027, Moorestown, 08057.... (856) 722-4100

**LOLLYTOGS, LTD.**
　100 W. 33rd St., Ste. 1012, New York NY 10001................. **(212) 502-6000**
　Pres.—Richard Sutton; CFO—Larry Daparis; Ex. V.-P., Sales—Stephen Asher;
　V.-P., Opers.—Abe Kassin
LT Apparel Group, 301 Herrod Blvd., P.O. Box 1001, Dayton, 08810........... (732) 438-5500

**LONZA, INC.**
　90 Boroline Rd., Allendale NJ 07401................. **(201) 316-9200**
　Pres.—Jeanne Thoma; Gen. Counsel—Scott Waldman; Cont.—Andy Hoy;
　Pur. Mgr.—Robert Williams; Hum. Res. Mgr.—Terry Krezmer;
　Mktg. Comms. Mgr., Global—Donna Weinstock
Lonza, Inc., 70 Tyler Pl., South Plainfield, 07080.................. (908) 561-5200

**L'OREAL U S A, INC.**
　575 5th Ave., New York NY 10017................. **(212) 818-1500**
　Pres., CEO—Frederic Roze; Pres., L'Oreal Paris Div.—Karen T. Fondu;
　CFO—Alexandre Pagliano; Sr. V.-P., Hum. Res.—Sarah Hibberson;
　Sr. V.-P., R & D—Eric Bone; Ex. V.-P., Corp. Affs.—Rebecca Caruso;
　Ex. V.-P., Bus. Dev. & Ext. Fin. Rels.—Roger Dolden; Dir., Hum. Res.—Alda Garcia
L'Oreal U S A, Inc., 222 Terminal Ave., Clark, 07066................ (732) 499-2838
L'Oreal U S A, Inc., 81 New England Ave., Piscataway, 08854........... (732) 562-5000

**LOTITO FOODS, INC./MRS. MAZZULA FOODS**
　240 Carter Dr., Edison NJ 08817................. **(732) 248-0222**
　Pres.—Christopher Lotito; Cont.—Greg Natchez; Prodn. Mgr.—Patricia Sanchez;
　IT Mgr.—Carol LoPinto; Procurement Mgr.—Stephen LoPinto
Lotito Foods, Inc., 510 E. 35th St., Paterson, 07504.................. (973) 684-2900

**LUBRIZOL ADVANCED MATERIALS, INC.**
　9911 Brecksville Rd., Brecksville OH 44141................. **(216) 447-5000**
　Pres.—Eric M. Schnur; V.-P., CFO—Brian Pitts; Dir., Comm.—Judy Makowski
Lubrizol Advanced Materials, Inc., 76 Porcupine Rd., Pedricktown, 08067...... (856) 351-2100

**LUBRIZOL CORP.**
　29400 Lakeland Blvd., Wickliffe OH 44092................. **(440) 943-4200**
　Chrm., Pres. & CEO—James L. Hambrick; Corp. V.-P., CFO—Brian A. Valentine;
　Corp. V.-P., Gen. Counsel & Chief Ethics Officer—Suzanne F. Day;
　Corp. V.-P., Hum. Res.—Andrew B. Penega;
　Corp. V.-P., Corp. Strategy, Comms. & Dev.—Gregory D. Taylor;
　Corp. V.-P., R & D—Robert Graf
Lubrizol Advanced Materials, Inc., 1 Industrial W., Clifton, 07012........... (973) 471-1300

**LUXOTTICA RETAIL NORTH AMERICA, INC.**
　4000 Luxottica Pl., Mason OH 45040................. **(513) 765-6000**
　Sr. V.-P., GM—Michael Hansen; Sr. V.-P., Hum. Res.—Jack Roddy; V.-P., Sales—Mike Elvitsky;
　V.-P., Mktg.—Kathy Drury; Sr. Dir., E-Commerce—Maureen Klosterman;
　Dir., Mktg., Lenscrafters—Kelly Uihlein
Pearle Vision, Inc., 1278 Hooper Ave., Toms River, 08753........... (732) 505-0533

**LYONDELLBASELL INDUSTRIES**
　LyondellBasell Tower, 1221 McKinney St., Ste. 300, Houston TX 77010..... **(713) 652-7200**
　CEO—Jim Gallogly; Sr. V.-P., CFO—Karyn Ovelmen;
　Sr. V.-P., Strategic Plng. & Transactions—Sergey Vasnetsov;
　V.-P., Hum. Res.—Jackie Wolf; V.-P., Inv. Rels.—Doug Pike;
　Dir., Corp. Comm.—Stan Sehested
LyondellBasell Industries, 340 Meadow Rd., Edison, 08817................ (732) 777-2272
LyondellBasell Industries, 300 Doremus Ave., Newark, 07105........... (973) 578-2200

**M & F WORLDWIDE CORP.**
　35 E. 62nd St., New York NY 10065................. **(212) 572-8600**
　Pres., CEO—Barry F. Schwartz; Ex. V.-P., CFO—Paul G. Savas;
　Ex. V.-P., Corp. Comms. & Ext. Affs.—Christine M. Taylor
Mafco Worldwide Corp., 300 Jefferson St., Camden, 08104........... (856) 964-8840

**M C MACHINERY SYSTEMS, INC., MITSUBISHI E D M/LASER DIV.**
　1500 Michael Dr., Wood Dale IL 60191................. **(630) 860-4210**
　Pres., CEO—J. Oguichi; CFO—T. Wada; Sr. Hum. Res. Mgr.—Carol Lincoln;
　Mktg. Mgr.—Pat Simon; IT Mgr.—Randy Smith
M C Machinery Systems, Inc., 16 Chapin Rd., P.O. Box 405, Pine Brook, 07058. (973) 244-1501

**MABEY, INC.**
　6770 Dorsey Rd., Elkridge MD 21075................. **(410) 379-2800**
　Pres., CEO—Bob Aylward; Sr. V.-P., Sales—Jennifer Stiles; V.-P., Strategy—Eric Wohlust;
　Hum. Res. Mgr.—Vicky Guyer
Mabey Inc., 218 N. Randolphville Rd., Piscataway, 08854.................. (732) 752-6600

**MADDAK INC.**
　661 State Route 23, Wayne NJ 07470................. **(973) 628-7600**
　COO—Brad Mahood; Ex. V.-P.—Mary Seto; Dir., MIS—Israel Engle;
　Dir., Prod. Dev.—Kathleen Hanek; Mktg. Mgr.—Susan Tulanowski;
　Hum. Res. Mgr.—Lucie Zembruski; Cust. Serv. Rep.—Cathy Jacovelli
Bel-Art Products, Inc., 661 State Route 23, Wayne, 07470................ (973) 694-0500

**MADISON DEARBORN PARTNERS, LLC**
　70 W. Madison St., Ste. 4600, Chicago IL 60602................. **(312) 895-1000**
　Chrm.—John Canning; Co-CEO—Paul Finnegan; Co-CEO—Samuel Mencoff;
　Hum. Res. Mgr.—Mary DeSilva
Ikaria, Inc. (H Q), 53 Frontage Rd., P.O. Box 9001, Hampton, 08827........ (908) 238-6600

**MAGGIO DATA FORMS PRINTING LTD.**
**1735 Express Dr. N., Hauppauge NY 11788 .......... (631) 348-0343**
**Pres.—Robert Maggio; V-P. & Hum. Res. Mgr.—James Maggio; Cred. Mgr.—Cathy Smith**
Maggio Data Forms Printing Ltd., 171 Heller Pl., Bellmawr, 08031 .......... (856) 931-7805

**MAGNATROL VALVE CORP.**
**67 5th Ave., Hawthorne NJ 07506 .......... (973) 427-4341**
**Pres.—Raymond A. Kretschmer, Sr.; COO, Opers. Mgr.—David Kretschmer; Cont., Fin. & Hum. Res. Mgr.—Bob Malzacher; GM—David DeCara; Adv., Sales & Mktg. Mgr.—David J. Calafiore; Sales Mgr.—Raymond Kretschmer, Jr.; Cred. Mgr.—Dot Stierli**
Clark Cooper Div., 941 Hamilton Ave., Roebling, 08554 .......... (856) 829-4580

**MAGNETIC & TRANSFORMER TECHNOLOGIES CORP.**
**7 Tanager Ln., Robbinsville NJ 08691 .......... (609) 371-1258**
**Pres.—Samir Fattohi**
Magnetic & Transformer Technologies Corp., 653 Sayre Ave., Perth Amboy, 08861 .. (609) 371-1258

**MAGNETIC TICKET & LABEL CORP.**
**8719 Diplomacy Row, Dallas TX 75247 .......... (214) 634-8600**
**Pres.—Pete Pyhrr; V-P.—Barb Fulenwider; Sales Mgr.—Stan Welker; Hum. Res. Mgr.—Kaylin Phillips; Manager—Denita Given**
Magnetic Ticket & Label Corp., 151 Cortlandt St., Belleville, 07109 .......... (973) 759-6500

**MAKINO, INC.**
**7680 Innovation Way, P.O. Box 8003, Mason OH 45040 .......... (513) 573-7200**
**Pres., CEO—Donald Lane; V-P., Sales—Robert J. Henry; V-P., Cust. Support—Thomas Slager; MIS Mgr.—Chris Vonohain; Hum. Res. Mgr.—Stephanie Breneman; Maint. Mgr.—Joe Belcuore; R & D Mgr.—Billy Grobe; Pur. Agt.—Anthony Pennisi**
Single Source Technologies,
30 Chapin Rd., Ste. 1208, P.O. Box 655, Pine Brook, 07058 .......... (973) 227-6601

**MALT PRODUCTS CORP.**
**88 Market St., P.O. Box 898, Saddle Brook NJ 07663 .......... (201) 845-4420**
**Pres.—Ronald Targan; V-P.—Joe Hickenbottom**
Malt Products Corp., 121 E. Hunter Ave., Maywood, 07607 .......... (201) 845-9106

**MANISCHEWITZ CO., THE**
**80 Avenue K, Newark NJ 07105 .......... (201) 553-1100**
**Pres.—Mark Weinstein; CFO—Tom Keogh; V-P., Sales—Kevin O'Brien; V-P., Pur.—Yossi Ostreicher; V-P., Admn. & Hum. Res.—Beatrice Scotti; Opers. Mgr.—Randall Copeland; Consumer Affs. Mgr.—Deborah Ross**
R.A.B. Food Group, LLC, 80 Avenue K, Newark, 07105 .......... (201) 553-1100

**MAPEI CORP.**
**1144 E. Newport Center Dr., Deerfield Beach FL 33442 .......... (954) 246-8888**
**Pres., CEO—Luigi DiGeso; CFO—John Zimmerman; Dir., Hum. Res.—Vickie Brint; Opers. Mgr.—Mark Sheffer; Mktg. Mgr.—Steven Day; IT Mgr.—Tieneke Rosestam; Env. Health & Safety Mgr.—Ernie Perez**
MAPEI Corp., Off White Head Ave., P.O. Box 105, South River, 08882 .......... (732) 254-8001

**MAQUET CARDIOVASCULAR, LLC**
**45 Barbour Pond Dr., Wayne NJ 07470 .......... (973) 709-7000**
**Pres., CEO—Peter Hinchliffe; Pres., Cardiopulmonary & CEO—Wolfgang Rencken; CFO—Gerhard Mayer; Ex. V-P., Global Sales & Mktg.—John Saavedra; V-P., Mktg.—Brad Cilley; MIS Mgr.—Richard Tartini; Hum. Res. Mgr.—Beverly Walker**
Maquet, 15 Law Dr., Fairfield, 07004 .......... (973) 244-6100

**MARCONE APPLIANCE PARTS CENTER**
**1 City Place Dr., Ste. 400, St. Louis MO 63141 .......... (314) 993-9196**
**CEO—Mitchell Markow; Pres., COO—Jim Souers; Sr. V-P.—Dave Cook**
Marcone Supplies, 870 Boulevard, Ste. 4, Kenilworth, 07033 .......... (973) 371-8800
Marcone Supply, 180 Main St., Hackensack, 07601 .......... (201) 489-6444

**MARJAM SUPPLY CO.**
**885 Conklin St., Farmingdale NY 11735 .......... (631) 249-4900**
**Pres.—Mark Buller; COO—Carmen Arguelles; Cred. Mgr.—Gabriel Iosefson**
MarJam Supply Co., 6 International Way, Newark, 07114 .......... (973) 491-6030
MarJam Supply Co., 615 W. Delilah Rd., Pleasantville, 08232 .......... (609) 407-1234

**MARK/TRECE, INC.**
**2001 Stockton Rd., Joppa MD 21085 .......... (410) 879-0060**
**Pres.—Richard Godfrey, Sr.; CFO & Hum. Res. Mgr.—Sandra Godfrey**
Mark/Trece, Inc., 160 Algonquin Pkwy., Whippany, 07981 .......... (973) 884-1005

**MARMON GROUP, LLC, THE**
**181 W. Madison St., 26th Fl., Chicago IL 60602 .......... (312) 372-9500**
**Pres., CEO—Frank Ptak; Pres., Div.—Henry J. West; Sr. V-P., CFO—Robert K. Lorch; Sr. V-P., Gen. Counsel & Secy.—Robert W. Webb; V-P., Taxes—James D. Angus; Dir., Comms.—David Dees**
Aerospace Nylok, 11 Thomas Rd. S., Hawthorne, 07506 .......... (973) 427-8555
TE Wire & Cable, LLC, 107 5th St., Saddle Brook, 07663 .......... (201) 845-9400

**MARS, INCORPORATED**
**6885 Elm St., McLean VA 22101 .......... (703) 821-4900**
**Chrm.—John Franklyn Mars; Pres.—Paul S. Michaels; Chief Science Officer & Dir., Biomedical Bus. Unit—Harold Schmitz**
Mars Chocolate North America, 800 High St., Hackettstown, 07840 .......... (908) 852-1000

**MARTIN SPROCKET & GEAR, INC.**
**3100 Sprocket Dr., P.O. Box 91588, Arlington TX 76015 .......... (817) 258-3000**
**Chrm., CEO—Joe R. Martin; Pres.—Reid Martin; V-P., Sales & Mktg.—Paul Taylor; V-P., IT—Bill Willis**
Martin Sprocket & Gear, Inc., 7 Highpoint Dr., Wayne, 07470 .......... (973) 633-5700

**MASCO CORP.**
**21001 Van Born Rd., Taylor MI 48180 .......... (313) 274-7400**
**Chrm. of the Board—Verne G. Istock; Chrm. of the Board—Dennis Archer; Pres., CEO—Keith J. Allman; V-P., CFO & Treas.—John Sznewajs; V-P., Chief Hum. Res. Officer—Renee Straber; V-P., Gen. Counsel & Secy.—Kenneth Cole; Dir., Corp. Comm.—Susan Sabo**
Arrow Fastener Co., LLC, 271 Mayhill St., Saddle Brook, 07663 .......... (201) 843-6900
Cobra Products, Inc., 1 Warner Ct., Swedesboro, 08085 .......... (856) 241-7700

**MATCHLESS METAL POLISH CO.**
**840 W. 49th Pl., Chicago IL 60609 .......... (773) 924-1515**
**Chrm., CEO—Frank Ungari; CFO & Hum. Res. Mgr.—Gary Slonski; V-P., Opers.—John Denman**
Matchless United Co., 801 E. Linden Ave., Linden, 07036 .......... (908) 862-7300

**MATHESON TRI-GAS, INC.**
**6500 Rockside Rd., Ste. 220, Independence OH 44131 .......... (216) 573-9909**
**Sr. V-P.—Roland Ostrowski; V-P.—Mark Blakley; Dir., Hum. Res.—Mike Patton**
Valley National Gases, WV LLC, 201 Crown Point Rd., West Deptford, 08086 ... (856) 848-7321

**MAUSER USA LLC**
**35 Cotters Ln., Ste. C, East Brunswick NJ 08816 .......... (732) 353-7000**
**Pres., CEO—Jeff Simmonds; V-P., Fin. & Treas.—Elizabeth Miller; V-P., Sales & Mktg.—Anthony Piersanti; Dir., Hum. Res.—Ellen Sherman; Dir., Regulatory Affs. & Tech.—Christopher Lind; Assoc. Dir., Financial Reporting—Len DePinto; Plt. Controller—Brian Baughjmann**
Mauser USA LLC, 14 Convery Blvd., Woodbridge, 07095 .......... (732) 634-6000

**MCCAIN FOODS USA, INC.**
**2275 Cabot Dr., Lisle IL 60532 .......... (630) 955-0400**
**CEO, The Americas—Frank Van Schaayk; Pres.—Frank Finn; V-P., CFO—Randy Myles**
McCain Foods USA, Inc., 11 Gregg St., Lodi, 07644 .......... (201) 368-0600

**MCGRAW-HILL FINANCIAL, INC.**
**1221 Avenue of the Americas, 49th Fl., New York NY 10020 .......... (212) 512-2000**
**Chrm., Pres. & CEO—Harold McGraw III; V-P., Group Publisher, McGraw-Hill Construction—James McGraw IV; Pres., McGraw-Hill Professional—Phil Ruppel; Pres., McGraw-Hill Construction—Keith Fox; Pres., Media—Glenn S. Goldberg; Pres., Aviation Week—Gregory Hamilton; Ex. V-P., CFO—Robert J. Bahash; Ex. V-P., Gen. Counsel—Kenneth M. Vittor; Ex. V-P., Hum. Res.—John Bersford; Ex. V-P., Global Strategy—Charles L. Teschner, Jr.; V-P., Corp. Affs.—Eileen Gabriele; V-P., Diversity & Inclusion—Terri Austin; Hum. Res. Mgr.—Aine McGrath**
McGraw-Hill Construction, 148 Princeton Hightstown Rd., Hightstown, 08520 ... (800) 393-6343

**MCKESSON CORP.**
**1 Post St., San Francisco CA 94104 .......... (415) 983-8300**
**Chrm., Pres. & CEO—John H. Hammergren; Ex. V-P., CFO—James Beer; Ex. V-P., Hum. Res.—Jorge Figueredo; V-P., Brand & Corp. Comms.—Andy Burtis**
McKesson Corp., 400 Delran Pkwy., Delran, 08075 .......... (856) 461-7800

**MCKESSON MEDICAL-SURGICAL**
**8741 Landmark Rd., Richmond VA 23228 .......... (804) 264-7500**
**Pres., Div.—Stanton McComb; CFO—Todd Baldanzi; Sr. V-P., Mktg. & Supplier Mgmt.—Joan Eliasek; Creative Svcs. Mgr.—Eve Ghiold**
McKesson Medical-Surgical, 1130 Commerce Blvd., Swedesboro, 08085 .......... (856) 241-1709

**MCLANE COMPANY, INC., FOODSERVICE DIVISION**
**2085 Midway Rd., Carrollton TX 75006 .......... (972) 364-2000**
**Pres., Div.—Tom Zatina; Reg. V-P.—Mike Shirey; V-P., Sales & Mktg.—Susan Adzick; V-P., Bus. Dev.—Scott Siers**
McLane Burlington, 600 Commerce Dr., Burlington, 08016 .......... (609) 239-5000

**MCLANE COMPANY, INC., GROCERY DIV.**
**6101 N.W. H. K. Dodgen Loop, Temple TX 76504 .......... (254) 771-7500**
**Pres.—Mike Youngblood; V-P., Sales & Mktg.—Stuart Clark; V-P., Reg.—Tony Frankenberger; IT Mgr.—Ken Watts; Hum. Res. Mgr.—Terri Marlatt**
McLane New Jersey, 742 Courses Landing Rd., Carneys Point, 08069 .......... (856) 351-6200

**MCMASTER-CARR SUPPLY CO.**
**600 N. County Line Rd., Elmhurst IL 60126 .......... (630) 834-9600**
**Pres.—Bob Delaney; GM & Opers. Mgr.—Seth Epstein; Order Fulfillment Mgr.—Katie Harrison**
McMaster-Carr Supply Co., 200 New Canton Way, Robbinsville, 08691 .......... (609) 259-8900

**MCNICHOLS CO.**
**2502 N. Rocky Point Dr., Ste. 750, Tampa FL 33607 .......... (813) 282-3828**
**Chrm. & CEO—Gene McNichols; Pres.—Scott M. McNichols; CFO—Craig Stein; Ex. V-P., Sales—Dave Brenneman**
McNICHOLS Co., 2 Home News Row, New Brunswick, 08901 .......... (732) 509-3092

**MCWANE, INC.**
**2900 Highway 280 S., Ste. 300, Birmingham AL 35223 .......... (205) 414-3100**
**Pres.—Ruffner Page; CFO—Charlie Nowlin; Dir., IT—Rod Reisner**
Atlantic States Cast Iron Pipe Co., 183 Sitgreaves St., Phillipsburg, 08865 ..... (908) 454-1161

**MEADOW BURKE PRODUCTS**
**2835 Overpass Rd., Tampa FL 33619 .......... (813) 248-1944**
**Pres.—Jan Olsen; V-P., Engrg.—Mike Recker; Bus. Dev. Mgr.—Lance Osborne**
Meadow Burke Products, 269 Commercial Ave., Palisades Park, 07650 .......... (201) 242-8989

**MECCA & SONS TRUCKING CORP.**
**580 Luis Munoz Marin Blvd., Jersey City NJ 07310 .......... (201) 792-5866**
**Pres.—Helen Mecca; CFO—Sandy Anest; Sales Mgr.—Paul Kish**
Cocoa Processing Corp., 650 Ramsey Ave., Hillside, 07205 .......... (201) 792-5866

**MEDCO MANUFACTURING CO.**
**190 Rodeo Dr., Brentwood NY 11717 .......... (631) 667-9699**
**Pres.—Guy Intoci; Hum. Res. Mgr.—Sheryl Sickles**
Medco West, 25-21 Di Carolis Ct., Hackensack, 07601 .......... (201) 457-9260

**MEDPLAST, INC.**
**405 W. Geneva Dr., Tempe AZ 85282 .......... (480) 968-6653**
**CEO—Harold Faig; Corp. Cont.—Dawn McCardle; Asst. Cont.—Kathleen Schell; IT Mgr.—Dan Streufert; Hum. Res. Mgr.—Sylvia Lechuga; Hum. Res. Mgr.—Tom Bledsoe; Matls. Mgr.—Leslie Washburn**
MedPlast Group, 225 Old Egg Harbor Rd., West Berlin, 08091 .......... (856) 753-7600

**MEDTRONIC, INC.**
**710 Medtronic Pkwy., Minneapolis MN 55432 .......... (763) 514-4000**
**CEO—Omar Ishrak; Pres., Surgical Tech. & Sr. V-P.—Mark Fletcher; Group Pres., Restorative Therapies & Ex. V-P.—Christopher J. O'Connell; Ex. V-P., CFO—Gary Ellis; Sr. V-P., Medicine & Tech.—Stephen Oesterle**
Medtronic, Inc., 300 Interpace Pkwy., Parsippany, 07054 .......... (516) 222-2848
TYRX, Inc., 1 Deer Park Dr., Ste. G, Monmouth Junction, 08852 .......... (732) 246-8676

G20 © Copyright 2015 Manufacturers' News, Inc. PARENT COMPANY SECTION

**MEESE ORBITRON DUNNE CO.**
**4920 State Rd., Ashtabula OH 44004 . . . . . (440) 998-1202**
**Pres.—Robert W. Dunne, Jr.; GM—William Dunne; Hum. Res. Mgr.—Jennifer Lemponen**
Meese Orbitron Dunne Co., 535 N. Midland Ave., Saddle Brook, 07663 . . . . . (201) 796-4667

**MENASHA PACKAGING COMPANY, LLC**
**350 N. Clark St., Ste. 300, Chicago IL 60654 . . . . . (312) 880-4620**
**Group V-P.—Annette Groenink; Sr. Dir., Design & Sales—Jim Ghere;**
**Dir., Fin.—Patrick Lauscher; Dir., Continuous Improvement & Qual.—Pam Horine**
Strive Group, LLC, The, 160 Chubb Ave., Ste. 101, Lyndhurst, 07071 . . . . . (973) 893-1300

**MERCK & CO., INC.**
**1 Merck Dr., P.O. Box 100, Whitehouse Station NJ 08889 . . . . . (908) 423-1000**
**Chrm. & CEO—Kenneth C. Frazier;**
**Pres., Global Human Health & Ex. V-P.—Adam H. Schechter;**
**Pres., Mfg. Div. & Ex. V-P.—William A. Deese;**
**Pres., Merck Consumer Care & Ex. V-P.—Bridgette P. Heller;**
**Pres., Merck Animal Health & Ex. V-P.—Richard R. DeLuca, Jr.;**
**Pres., Merck Research Labs & Ex. V-P.—Roger Perlmutter;**
**Ex. V-P., CFO—Robert M. Davis; Ex. V-P., CIO—Clark Golestani;**
**Ex. V-P., Chief Medical Officer—Michael Rosenblatt;**
**Ex. V-P., Chief Strategy Officer—Cuong Viet Do;**
**Ex. V-P., Chief Compliance & Ethics Officer—Michael J. Holston;**
**Sr. V-P., U.S. Reg.—James Mackey; Sr. V-P., Inv. Rels.—Joseph Romanelli;**
**Ex. V-P., Gen. Counsel—Bruce N. Kuhlik; Ex. V-P., Hum. Res.—Mirian M. Graddick-Weir;**
**Ex. Dir., MMD Global Comms.—Kyra Lindemann**
Merck & Co., Inc., 2000 Galloping Hill Rd., Kenilworth, 07033 . . . . . (908) 298-4000
Merck & Co., Inc., 126 E. Lincoln Ave., P.O. Box 2000, Rahway, 07065 . . . . . (732) 594-4000

**MERCURY SYSTEMS, INC.**
**201 Riverneck Rd., Chelmsford MA 01824 . . . . . (978) 256-1300**
**Pres., CEO—Mark Aslett; Pres., Mercury Comml. Electronics—Didier Thibaud;**
**V-P., Gen. Counsel & Secy.—Gerry Haines; V-P., Sales—Brian Hoerl;**
**Dir., Corp. Comm. & Mktg.—Bob McGrail**
Mercury Commercial Electronics, 2 Henderson Dr., Ste. B, Caldwell, 07006 . . . . . (973) 244-1040

**MERIAL LTD.**
**3239 Satellite Blvd., Duluth GA 30096 . . . . . (678) 638-3000**
**Sr. V-P., Bus. Dev.—Kristen Kilgos; V-P., Admn. & Facilities—Steven Tanner;**
**V-P.—Robert Nordgren**
Merial Ltd., 631 U.S. Highway 1, North Brunswick, 08902 . . . . . (732) 729-5700

**MERRILL CORP.**
**1 Merrill Cir., St. Paul MN 55108 . . . . . (651) 646-4501**
**CEO—John Castro; Pres., COO—Rick Atterbury; CFO—Robert Nazarian;**
**CAO—Brenda Vale; V-P., Mktg.—John Lundgren; Gen. Counsel—Lisa Bilcik;**
**Dir., Mktg.—Nancy Moeller; Hum. Res. Mgr.—Michelle Carlson**
Merrill Corp., 649 Rahway Ave., Union, 07083 . . . . . (908) 688-5757

**MESA LABORATORIES, INC.**
**12100 W. 6th Ave., Lakewood CO 80228 . . . . . (303) 987-8000**
**Chrm.—Luke R. Schmieder; Pres., CEO—John Sullivan;**
**V-P., CFO, Fin. & Secy.—John Sakys; V-P., CMO—Glenn Adriance;**
**Dir., Pur.—Gary Alcala; Prodn. Mgr. & Opers. Supv.—Rex Trout;**
**Plt. Opers. Mgr.—Bryan Leo; IT Mgr.—Jason Metcalfe; Cust. Serv. Mgr.—Loretta Baca**
Mesa Laboratories, Inc., 10 Park Pl., Ste. 3, Butler, 07405 . . . . . (973) 492-8400

**METALS USA, INC.**
**2400 E. Commercial Blvd., Ste. 905, Fort Lauderdale FL 33308 . . . . . (954) 202-4000**
**Chrm., Pres. & CEO—C. Lourenco Goncalves; Sr. V-P., CIO—Hugh Gray;**
**Sr. V-P., Chief Legal Officer—William A. Smith II; Sr. V-P., CFO—Robert C. McPherson III;**
**Sr. V-P., Bus. Dev.—Keith Koci; V-P., Corp. Cont.—Dan Henneke;**
**V-P., Hum. Res.—Joe Stewart**
Metals USA, Plates & Shapes Group, 182 Frelinghuysen Ave., Newark, 07114 . . . (973) 242-1000

**METTLER-TOLEDO, LLC**
**1900 Polaris Pkwy., Columbus OH 43240 . . . . . (614) 438-4511**
**GM, N. Amer.—Alton Hills; GM, Retail—Gregory Sears; Hum. Res. Mgr.—Alexis Street;**
**Media Rels. & Mktg. Events Mgr.—Shana Wheeler**
Ohaus Corp., 7 Campus Dr., Ste. 310, Parsippany, 07054 . . . . . (973) 377-9000

**MICHAEL FOODS, INC.**
**301 Carlson Pkwy., Ste. 400, Minnetonka MN 55305 . . . . . (952) 258-4000**
**Pres., CEO—Jim Dwyer; CFO—Mark Westphal; IT Mgr.—Matt Scheck**
Michael Foods, Inc., 847 North Ave., Elizabeth, 07201 . . . . . (908) 282-7140
Papetti's Hygrade Egg Products, Inc., 877 North Ave. E., Elizabeth, 07201 . . . . . (908) 282-7140

**MIDOCEAN PARTNERS**
**320 Park Ave., Ste.1600, New York NY 10022 . . . . . (212) 497-1400**
**Chrm.—Robert Miller; CFO & Mng. Dir.—Andrew Spring; COO—Deborah Hodges**
Agilex Flavors & Fragrances, Inc., 140 Centennial Ave., Piscataway, 08854 . . . . . (732) 393-7300

**MIDWEST MEDICAL SUPPLY CO., LLC**
**13400 Lakefront Dr., Earth City MO 63045 . . . . . (314) 291-2900**
**Pres., CEO—Gary Reeve; Sr. V-P., Bus. Sys.—Dan Rieman; Ex. V-P.—Tom Harris;**
**V-P., GM—Ed Warren; V-P., Sales, Primary Care—Lou Carfello;**
**V-P., Bus. Dev. & Mktg.—Tony Gadzinski; V-P., Corp. Dev. & Mktg.—Tom Tenhula;**
**V-P., Fin.—John Kastberg; V-P., Strategic Plng.—Gene Byerly;**
**V-P., Logistics—Bernie Thien; V-P., Extended Care—Kelly Hart;**
**V-P., Acute Care & Specialty—Rich Hawkins; Dir., Mktg.—Judy Boc;**
**Dir., IT—Dale Behlmann; Hum. Res. Mgr.—Regina Frye**
Midwest Medical Supply Company, LLC, 200 Seaview Dr., Secaucus, 07094 . . . . . (201) 223-4602

**MILLWOOD, INC.**
**3708 International Blvd., Vienna OH 44473 . . . . . (330) 393-4400**
**Ptnr. & CEO—Steve Miller; Ptnr. & Pres.—Lionel Trebilcock;**
**Ptnr. & Ex. V-P.—Ron Ringness; CFO—Craig Gretter; V-P., Opers.—Brad Arnold;**
**V-P., Natl. Accts.—Keith Countryman; Dir., Reg. Sales—Doug Gaier;**
**GM, Liberty Technologies—Kirk Ambrose; Strategic Sourcing Mgr.—Don Smith;**
**Strategic Sourcing Mgr.—Lee Evans**
Millwood, Inc., 7 Brick Plant Rd., Ste. C, South River, 08882 . . . . . (732) 967-8818

**MITSUI & CO. U. S. A., INC.**
**200 Park Ave., 36th Fl., New York NY 10166 . . . . . (212) 878-4000**
**Pres., CEO—Motomu Takahashi; Sr. V-P., Hum. Res.—Steve Menzer; V-P.—Eric Campbell;**
**Treas.—Anthony Pensabene; GM, Hum. Res.—Masaya Watanabe**
Mitsui Foods, Inc., 35 Maple St., Norwood, 07648 . . . . . (201) 750-0500

**MODERN GROUP LTD.**
**2501 Durham Rd., Bristol PA 19007 . . . . . (215) 943-9100**
**Chrm. of the Board—George Wilkinson; Pres., COO—Paul Farrell; CFO—Steve Seminack;**
**Sr. V-P., Legal—Tom Callahan; IT Mgr.—John Barilar**
Modern Group Ltd., 75 New St., Edison, 08837 . . . . . (800) 846-5840
Modern Group Ltd., 112-128 Route 17 N., Hasbrouck Heights, 07604 . . . . . (201) 288-1441

**MODERN LIMB & BRACE CO.**
**916 Somerset St., Watchung NJ 07069 . . . . . (908) 757-2702**
**Owner, Pres. & CFO—Horst Oertel**
Oertel Orthopedics, Inc., 2095 U.S. Highway 22 W., Union, 07083 . . . . . (908) 688-1818

**MONARCH COLOR CORP.**
**5327 Brookshire Blvd., Charlotte NC 28216 . . . . . (704) 394-4626**
**Pres.—Greg West; V-P., Opers.—Jerry Woodall; V-P., Fin.—Ralph Petros;**
**IT Mgr.—Tom Ledane; Hum. Res. & Payroll Mgr.—Debbie Brown; Pur. Agt.—Diana Fritz**
Monarch Color Corp., 7247 Browning Rd., Pennsauken, 08109 . . . . . (856) 662-0432

**MONDELEZ INTERNATIONAL, INC.**
**3 Parkway N., Deerfield IL 60015 . . . . . (847) 943-4000**
**Chrm., CEO—Irene B. Rosenfeld; Ex. V-P., CFO—David A. Brearton;**
**Ex. V-P., Hum. Res.—Karen May; Ex. V-P., Strategy—Tracey Belcourt**
Mondelez International, Inc., 22-11 State Route 208, Fair Lawn, 07410 . . . . . (201) 794-4000

**MONDI AKROSIL, LLC**
**7201 108th St., Pleasant Prairie WI 53158 . . . . . (262) 997-3000**
**V-P., GM—Steven J. Hutter; V-P., Comml. Dev.—Martin McDonough;**
**Fin. Mgr.—Brad Hettlinger**
Tekkote Corp., 580 Willow Tree Rd., Leonia, 07605 . . . . . (201) 585-8875

**MORGAN TECHNICAL CERAMICS**
**2425 Whipple Rd., Hayward CA 94544 . . . . . (510) 491-1100**
**Pres.—John Stang; Pur. Mgr. & Agt.—Jose Pena; Hum. Res. Mgr.—Angie Galvin**
Morgan Advanced Ceramics, Inc., 26 Madison Rd., Fairfield, 07004 . . . . . (973) 227-8877

**MORINAGA AMERICA, INC.**
**18552 MacArthur Blvd., Ste. 360, Irvine CA 92612 . . . . . (949) 732-1155**
**CEO—Masao Hoshino; COO—Teruhiro Kawabe; CFO—Tomohiko Nakatogawa**
Morinaga America, Inc., 400 Kelby St., 14th Fl., Fort Lee, 07024 . . . . . (201) 947-0408

**MORO CORP.**
**994 Old Eagle School Rd., Ste. 1000, Wayne PA 19087 . . . . . (484) 367-0300**
**Pres.—David W. Menard; Ex. V-P.—Lawrence J. Corr**
Ahle Co., Inc., J. M., 190 William St., Ste. 2-D, South River, 08882 . . . . . (732) 238-1700

**MORRE-TEC INDUSTRIES, INC.**
**1 Gary Rd., Union NJ 07083 . . . . . (908) 688-9009**
**Pres.—Leonard Glass; GM—Aaron Kopstick; Plt. Mgr.—John Tierney;**
**Import & Export Mgr.—Frimma Messer**
Extracts & Ingredients Ltd., Div. Of MORRE-TEC Industries, Inc.,
1 Gary Rd., Union, 07083 . . . . . (908) 688-9009
Jedco Adhesives Co., Div. Of Morre-Tec Industries, Inc.,
1 Gary Rd., Union, 07083 . . . . . (908) 688-9009

**MORTON SALT, INC.**
**123 N. Wacker Dr., 26th Fl., Chicago IL 60606 . . . . . (312) 807-2000**
**CEO—Christin Herrrmann; V-P., Sales & Mktg.—Shayn Wallace; V-P., Opers.—Jim Vincent;**
**V-P., Hum. Res.—Matthew Beliveau; Gen. Counsel—Mary E. Doohan;**
**Dir., IT—Penny St. Peter**
Morton Salt, Inc., 920 High St., Perth Amboy, 08861 . . . . . (732) 826-3595

**MOTION INDUSTRIES, INC.**
**1605 Alton Rd., Birmingham AL 35210 . . . . . (205) 951-1154**
**CEO—William J. Stevens; Pres., COO, U.S.—Tim Breen;**
**Sr. V-P., Mktg. & Strategic Plng.—Randy Breaux;**
**Ex. V-P., Admn. & Fin.—G. Harold Dunaway; Brand & Creative Mgr.—Amanda Bergen**
AST Bearings, LLC, 115 Main Rd., Montville, 07045 . . . . . (973) 335-2230
Motion Industries, Inc., 141 Market St., Ste. 8, Kenilworth, 07033 . . . . . (908) 241-1047
Motion Industries, Inc., 12-D Jules Ln., New Brunswick, 08901 . . . . . (732) 828-8711
Motion Industries, Inc., 600 Hollister Rd., Teterboro, 07608 . . . . . (201) 288-8111
Motion Industries, Inc., 9A S. Gold Dr., Trenton, 08691 . . . . . (609) 588-0555

**MRC GLOBAL, INC.**
**2 Houston Ctr., 909 Fannin St., Ste. 3100, Houston TX 77010 . . . . . (713) 655-1005**
**Chrm., Pres. & CEO—Andrew Lane; Ex. V-P., CFO—Jim E. Braun;**
**Ex. V-P., Secy.—Dan Churay; Sr. V-P., Opers., N. America—Scott Hutchinson;**
**Sr. V-P., Bus. Dev.—Rory Isaac; Sr. V-P., Energy Tubular Prods.—Jim Dionisio;**
**Sr. V-P., Reg., Europe—Steinar Aasland;**
**Sr. V-P., Asia Pacific & Middle East—John Bowhay;**
**Sr. V-P., Fittings, Flanges & Valves—Gary Ittner**
McJunkin Red Man Corporation, 305 Center Ave., Waterford Works, 08089 . . . . . (856) 753-7690

**MS INTERNATIONAL, INC.**
**2095 N. Batavia St., Orange CA 92865 . . . . . (714) 685-7500**
**Pres.—Manu Shah; Sr. V-P.—Sanjay Sanghvi; Cont.—Neha Mehta;**
**Hum. Res. Mgr.—Maylin Conner**
M S International, Inc., 36 Brunswick Ave., Edison, 08817 . . . . . (732) 650-1815

**MSC INDUSTRIAL DIRECT CO., INC.**
**75 Maxess Rd., Melville NY 11747 . . . . . (516) 812-2000**
**Chrm. of the Board—Mitchell Jacobson; Pres., CEO—Erik Gershwind;**
**Sr. V-P., CIO—Charles Bonomo; Ex. V-P., CFO—Jeffrey Kaczka;**
**Sr. V-P., Gen. Counsel & Secy.—Steve Armstrong; Ex. V-P., Sales—Tom Cox;**
**Ex. V-P., Global Supply Chain—Douglas Jones**
MSC Industrial Supply Co., 105 Newfield Ave., Ste. E, Edison, 08837 . . . . . (732) 512-9555

**MULTI-PLASTICS, INC.**
**7770 N. Central Dr., Lewis Center OH 43035 . . . . . (740) 548-4894**
**Pres.—John Parsio, Sr.; V-P., Mfg.—Steve Parsio; Mktg. Mgr.—Cheryl Cautill**
Multi Plastics Extrusions, 30 Production Way, Avenel, 07001 . . . . . (732) 388-2300
Multi-Plastics, Inc., 210 Commodore Dr., Swedesboro, 08085 . . . . . (856) 241-9014

PARENT COMPANY

**MURALO CO., INC.**
148 E. 5th St., Bayonne NJ 07002 . . . . . . . . . . . . . . . . . . . . . . (201) 437-0770
Pres.—James F. Norton; CFO—Charles P. Lee, Jr.; Sales Mgr.—Peter Seaborg;
Pur. Mgr.—Kathy Santella; Hum. Res. Mgr.—Stephanie Fisk
Elder & Jenks Co., 148 E. 5th St., Bayonne, 07002 . . . . . . . . . . . . (201) 437-0770
Norton & Son, Inc., 148 E. 5th St., Bayonne, 07002 . . . . . . . . . . . (201) 437-0770

**MUSCO SPORTS LIGHTING, LLC**
100 1st Ave. W., P.O. Box 808, Oskaloosa IA 52577 . . . . . . . . . . (641) 673-0411
Co-Founder & CEO—Joe P. Crookham; Co-Founder—Myron Gordin;
Dir., IS & GM—Brett Nelson
Musco Sports Lighting, LLC, 5146 W. Hurley Pond Rd., Farmingdale, 07727 . . (732) 751-9114

**MW INDUSTRIES, INC.**
9501 Technology Blvd., Ste. 401, Rosemont IL 60018 . . . . . . . . . . (847) 349-5780
Pres., CEO—Bill Marcum; CFO—Chet Kwasniak; Ex. V.-P., Sales—Scott Solomon;
V.-P., Mktg.—Robert Jack; V.-P., Hum. Res.—Jim Thompson
Accurate Screw Machine Corp., 10 Audrey Pl., P.O. Box 1065, Fairfield, 07004 . . (973) 244-9200
Atlantic Spring Co., 137 Highway 202 S., Ringoes, 08551 . . . . . . . (908) 788-5800

**NAPOLEON/LYNX**
111 Weires Dr., P.O. Box 160, Archbold OH 43502 . . . . . . . . . . (419) 445-1010
Pres.—Doris Schram; Cont.—Fritz Grieser; Sales & Mktg. Mgr.—Steve Nofziger;
Plt. Mgr.—Mike Sharpe; Hum. Res. Mgr.—Mary Hoops; Chief Engr.—E. J. Horst
Napoleon/Lynx, 25 Empire Blvd., South Hackensack, 07606 . . . . . . (973) 278-5588

**NATIONAL CASEIN CO.**
601 W. 80th St., Chicago IL 60620 . . . . . . . . . . . . . . . . . . . . . (773) 846-7300
Pres.—Hope T. Cook; MIS Mgr.—Leonel Jensen;
Regulatory & Safety Mgr.—Roger Quackenbush; Pur. Agt.—Ed Laurence
National Casein Of New Jersey, 401 Martha's Ln., P.O. Box 226, Riverton, 08077 . (856) 829-1880

**NATIONAL ENVIRONMENTAL SERVICE CO.**
7 Hampshire Dr., Mendham NJ 07945 . . . . . . . . . . . . . . . . . . . (973) 543-4586
Pres.—Mark Kestner; CFO—Paul Kestner
National Environmental Services Co., 700 Grand Ave., Hackettstown, 07840 . . . . (908) 813-1195

**NATIONAL FLAG & DISPLAY CO., INC.**
22 W. 21st St., Basement Level, New York NY 10010 . . . . . . . . . . (212) 462-4000
Pres.—Howard Siegel; V.-P., Sales—Bill Lindsay; Off. Mgr.—Steven Bowman;
Proj. Mgr. & Graphic Designer—Bruce Cohen; Qual. Control Mgr.—Sofia Lai
Metro Flag Co., 353 Richard Mine Rd., Unit 100, Wharton, 07885 . . . . . . . . . . (973) 366-1776

**NATIONAL GYPSUM CO.**
2001 Rexford Rd., Charlotte NC 28211 . . . . . . . . . . . . . . . . . . (704) 365-7300
Pres.—Tom Nelson; Sr. V.-P., Mfg.—John Coris; V.-P., Sales & Mktg.—John Mixon;
Dir., Corp. Comms.—Nancy Spurlock; Dir., Mktg.—Jay Watt;
Mktg. Mgr.—Renee Cieslikowski
National Gypsum Co., 1818 River Rd., Burlington, 08016 . . . . . . . . (609) 499-3300

**NATIONAL PAINT INDUSTRIES**
1999 Elizabeth St., North Brunswick NJ 08902 . . . . . . . . . . . . . (732) 821-3200
Co-Pres.—Michael Schnurr; Co-Pres.—Donald Schnurr; V.-P., Sales—Bruce Bernard;
Hum. Res. Mgr.—Sandy Lipesky
Talon Paint Products, Inc., 1999 Elizabeth St., North Brunswick, 08902 . . . . . . (732) 821-3200

**NATIONAL PARTS SUPPLY CO., INC.**
535 Milltown Rd., North Brunswick NJ 08902 . . . . . . . . . . . . . . (732) 247-5171
Owner—John Salasko; Comp.—Joe Mesquite; Sales Mgr.—John Warren;
IT Mgr.—Pete Garcia
National Parts Supply Co., Inc., 56 State Route 31, Flemington, 08822 . . . . . . (908) 782-3530

**NATURE'S CHOICE CORP.**
482 Houses Corner Rd., Sparta NJ 07871 . . . . . . . . . . . . . . . . (201) 333-5244
Pres.—Nicholas Vene; Ex. V.-P.—Matthew Vastano; Hum. Res. Mgr.—Carmen Rodriguez
Nature's Choice Corp., 40 Foul Rift Rd., Belvidere, 07823 . . . . . . . . . . . . . . . (908) 475-1804

**NAVISTAR INTERNATIONAL CORP.**
2701 Navistar Dr., Lisle IL 60532 . . . . . . . . . . . . . . . . . . . . . (331) 332-5000
Non-Exec. Chrm.—James H. Keyes; Pres., CEO—Troy Clarke;
Pres., Opers.—Persio V. Lisboa; Pres., Parts & Truck—Bill Kozek;
Ex. V.-P., CFO—Walter G. Borst;
Sr. V.-P., Gen. Counsel & Chief Ethics Officer—Steven Covey;
Chief Ethics Officer, Gen. Counsel & Secy.—Greg Elliott; Sr. V.-P., Treas.—James Moran;
Sr. V.-P., Plng. & Strategy & Pres., Global & Specialty Bus.—Eric Tech;
V.-P., Govt. Rels.—Patrick Charbonneau; Dir., Labor Rels.—Barry Morris
Ransome International, 2320 High Hill Rd., Logan Township, 08085 . . . . . . . . (856) 241-8890

**NAZDAR CO.**
8501 Hedge Lane Ter., Shawnee KS 66227 . . . . . . . . . . . . . . . (913) 422-1888
Pres.—Michael Fox; V.-P., Cont.—Tom Mulvenon; V.-P., Sales, Intl.—Jim Davidson;
V.-P., Dist. & Opers.—Gary Blair; V.-P., IT—Chris Davis; Dir., Mktg. Comms.—Jay Tharp
Nazdar Co., 7055 Central Hwy., Pennsauken, 08109 . . . . . . . . . . . (856) 663-7878

**NBCUNIVERSAL MEDIA, LLC**
30 Rockefeller Plaza, New York NY 10112 . . . . . . . . . . . . . . . . (212) 664-4444
CEO—Stephen B. Burke
iVillage, Inc., 900 Sylvan Ave., Englewood Cliffs, 07632 . . . . . . . . (212) 664-4444

**NCH CORP.**
2727 Chemsearch Blvd., Irving TX 75062 . . . . . . . . . . . . . . . . (972) 438-0211
Pres., GM—Lester Levy; Ex. V.-P.—Walter Levy; V.-P., Opers.—Michael Benton
NCH Corp., 34 Stouts Ln., P.O. Box 25, Monmouth Junction, 08852 . . . . . . . . (732) 329-8111

**ND INDUSTRIES, INC.**
1000 N. Crooks Rd., Clawson MI 48017 . . . . . . . . . . . . . . . . . (248) 288-0000
Pres.—Richard M. Wallace; CFO & Dir., Hum. Res.—Bonnie Stanke;
Sr. V.-P.—Michael Garafalo; MIS Mgr.—Joe Gutowski; R & D Mgr.—Jim Barr
ND Industries, Inc., 128 Bauer Dr., Ste. 2, Oakland, 07436 . . . . . . . (201) 651-1500

**NEI GROUP, INC.**
44 Burlews Ct., Hackensack NJ 07601 . . . . . . . . . . . . . . . . . . (201) 488-5858
Pres.—John Nanasi; GM—Andy Kardos; Sales Mgr.—Ernie Reinitz
SJA Jewelry, Inc., 44 Burlews Ct., Hackensack, 07601 . . . . . . . . . (201) 837-0990

**NEOPOST USA, INC.**
478 Wheelers Farms Rd., Milford CT 06461 . . . . . . . . . . . . . . . (203) 301-3400
Pres., CEO—Dennis LeStrange; CFO—Fabrice Assous; Ex. V.-P.—Christopher M. O'Brien;
V.-P., Hum. Res.—Marie Mann; Mktg. Mgr.—Kathy Rabinoff
Neopost, Inc., 2 Ridgedale Ave., 1st Fl., Cedar Knolls, 07927 . . . . . . (973) 647-6700

**NEOSTEM, INC.**
420 Lexington Ave., Ste. 350, New York NY 10170 . . . . . . . . . . . (212) 584-4180
Chrm., CEO—Robin L. Smith; CFO—Larry A. May; V.-P., Gen. Counsel—Catherine M. Vaczy
Progenitor Cell Therapy, LLC, 4 Pearl Ct., Ste. C, Allendale, 07401 . . . (201) 883-5300

**NESTLE USA, INC.**
800 N. Brand Blvd., Glendale CA 91203 . . . . . . . . . . . . . . . . . (818) 549-6000
Chrm., CEO—Paul Grimwood; Pres., Sales—Tom Smith; CIO—Kimberly Lund;
Sr. V.-P., Mfg. & Tech.—Allan McIntosh; Sr. V.-P., Hum. Res.—Judy Cascapera
Nestle' USA, Inc., Beverage Div., 61 Jerseyville Ave., Freehold, 07728 . . (732) 462-1300

**NESTLE' WATERS NORTH AMERICA, INC.**
900 Long Ridge Rd., Bldg. 2, Stamford CT 06902 . . . . . . . . . . . (203) 531-4100
Pres., CEO—Tim Brown; Ex. V.-P., Retail Opers.—Mike Pengue;
Ex. V.-P., Hum. Res.—Mike Swinton; Dir., Media Rels.—Jane Lazgin
Nestle Waters North America, Inc., 111 Thomas McGovern Dr., Jersey City, 07305. (201) 451-4000

**NEW JERSEY BUSINESS & INDUSTRY ASSN.**
10 W. Lafayette St., Trenton NJ 08608 . . . . . . . . . . . . . . . . . . (609) 393-7707
Pres.—Michele N. Siekerka; Sr. V.-P., Govt. Affs.—Melanie Willoughby;
V.-P., Admn. & Treas.—Julia Stoller; V.-P., Mktg.—Michele Glassburg;
V.-P., Health & Legal Affs.—Christine Stearns;
V.-P., Energy, Env. & Fed. Affs.—Sara Bluhm; Asst. V.-P., Comm.—Steve Wilson
New Jersey Business Magazine, 310 Passaic Ave., Ste. 201, Fairfield, 07004 . . . (973) 882-5004

**NEW JERSEY PULVERIZING CO., INC.**
4 Rita St., Syosset NY 11791 . . . . . . . . . . . . . . . . . . . . . . . (516) 921-9595
Pres.—Martin Tanzer
Ace Crete Products, Inc., 250 Hickory Ln., Bayville, 08721 . . . . . . . . (732) 269-1400
Empire Blended Products, Inc., 250 Hickory Ln., Bayville, 08721 . . . . . (732) 269-4949

**NEW WINCUP HOLDINGS, INC.**
4640 Lewis Rd., Stone Mountain GA 30083 . . . . . . . . . . . . . . . (770) 493-8568
Pres., CEO—Jack Brucker; CIO—Lawrence Perkins; Sr. V.-P., CFO—Dan Fischer;
Sr. V.-P., Sales & Mktg.—Michael Winters; V.-P., Fin.—Kim Knotts;
V.-P., Corp. Treas.—Evan Hardin; Dir., Mktg.—Mark Meranda;
Dir., Cust. Serv.—Cheryl Comfort
WinCup, 190 Liberty St., Metuchen, 08840 . . . . . . . . . . . . . . . (732) 494-1999

**NEW YORK PRODUCE, INC.**
511 Barry St., Bronx NY 10474 . . . . . . . . . . . . . . . . . . . . . . (718) 585-1041
Owner—Elio Valdivia; GM—Ari San Emeterio; Sales Mgr.—Marian Pena
New York Produce, Inc., 125 Seaview Dr., Secaucus, 07094 . . . . . . . (201) 223-0909

**NEWARK GROUP, INC., THE**
20 Jackson Dr., Cranford NJ 07016 . . . . . . . . . . . . . . . . . . . . (908) 276-4000
Pres., CEO—Frank Papa; CFO—Gregg Kam; Sr. V.-P., Hum. Res.—Manny Silva;
V.-P., Gen. Counsel—David Ascher; IT Mgr.—Tom Ritter
Newark Group, Inc., The, 60 Lockwood St., Newark, 07105 . . . . . . . (973) 465-3900

**NEWARK MORNING LEDGER CO.**
1 Star Ledger Plz., Newark NJ 07102 . . . . . . . . . . . . . . . . . . . (973) 392-4141
Publisher—Rich Vezza; Dir., Mktg.—Robert C. Provost; Dir., IT—Pat Riccio;
Dir., Circ.—Dennis Carletta; Opers. Mgr.—Steve Leotsakos
Star Ledger, 26 Riverside Dr., Pine Brook, 07058 . . . . . . . . . . . . (973) 882-6120

**NEWLY WEDS FOODS, INC.**
4140 W. Fullerton Ave., Chicago IL 60639 . . . . . . . . . . . . . . . . (773) 489-7000
Pres.—Charles T. Angell; V.-P., Gen. Counsel—J. J. Seely; V.-P., Mfg.—Mike D. Hopp;
V.-P., Pur.—Leo Culligan; V.-P., Fin.—Brian Johnson; Pers. Mgr.—Tanya Luna;
Mktg. Svcs. Mgr.—Rich Zenor
Continental Seasoning, Inc., 1700 Palisade Ave., P.O. Box 629, Teaneck, 07666 . (201) 837-6111

**NISHIMOTO TRADING CO. LTD.**
13409 Orden Dr., Santa Fe Springs CA 90670 . . . . . . . . . . . . . . (562) 802-1900
Pres.—Robert Susaki; Cont.—Iris Miyazato; IT Mgr.—Masanori Tabata;
Hum. Res. Mgr.—Lisa Tanaka; Asst. Br. Mgr.—Taka Taniguchi
Nishimoto Trading Co. Ltd., 602 Washington Ave., Carlstadt, 07072 . . . . . . . . (201) 804-1600

**NITTO DENKO AMERICA, INC.**
48500 Fremont Blvd., Fremont CA 94538 . . . . . . . . . . . . . . . . (510) 445-5400
V.-P.—Eiji Hayashi; GM, Opers.—Robin Andrew; MIS Mgr.—Mark Sakamoto;
Hum. Res. Mgr.—Stacie Knoph
Nitto Denko America Automotive, Inc., 1990 Rutgers Blvd., Lakewood, 08701 . . (732) 901-7905

**NJN PUBLISHING, INC.**
8 Minneakoning Rd., Flemington NJ 08822 . . . . . . . . . . . . . . . . (908) 782-4747
Publisher—Joe Gioioso; V.-P., Adv.—Al Kratzer; Ex. Editor—Craig Turpin;
Cont.—Pamela Cahalan; Dir., Circ.—Judith Morgan; IT Mgr.—Robert Bell;
Hum. Res. Mgr.—Sherry Ferello
NJN Publishing Independent Press, Inc., 309 South St., New Providence, 07974 . (908) 464-1025

**NOMADIC DISPLAY**
5617 Industrial Dr., Ste. E, Springfield VA 22151 . . . . . . . . . . . . (703) 866-9200
Pres.—Patricia Goeke; Sr. V.-P., Sales & Mktg.—Gwen Parsons; Ex. Dir.—Douglas Turpin;
Hum. Res. Mgr.—Karen Chace
Nomadic Display, 4-6 Just Rd., Fairfield, 07004 . . . . . . . . . . . . . (862) 210-8120

**NORMISKA CORP.**
109 Ridley Blvd., Toronto, Canada M5M 3L8, . . . . . . . . . . . . . . (519) 780-0955
Pres., CEO—Craig McKean
Schundler Co., 150 Whitman Ave., Edison, 08817 . . . . . . . . . . . . (732) 287-2244

**NORTH JERSEY MEDIA GROUP, INC.**
1 Garret Mountain Plz., P.O. Box 471, Woodland Park NJ 07424 . . . . (973) 569-7000
Chrm. of the Board—Malcolm A. Borg; Pres.—Stephen A. Borg;
CFO—Thomas G. Heffernan; V.-P., Gen. Counsel—Jennifer A. Borg;
V.-P., Editor—Martin Gottlieb; V.-P., Circ. & Mfg.—Robert Konig;
V.-P., Hum. Res.—Susan Beard; V.-P., Internet Tech.—Yuri Demidov;
Dir., Sales, Corp. & Natl.—Richard Colandrea; Dir., Mktg.—Maggie Grande
Community Newspapers & Magazines Of North Jersey Media Group,
1 Garret Mountain Plz., P.O. Box 471, Woodland Park, 07424 . . . . . . (973) 569-7000

**NORTH JERSEY MEDIA GROUP, INC.—(cont.)**
Franklin Lakes Oakland, 41 Oak St., Ridgewood, 07450 .................... (201) 612-5415
Record, The, 1 Garret Mountain Plz., P.O. Box 471, Woodland Park, 07424 ..... (973) 569-7770
North Jersey Media Group Inc., 100 Commons Way, Rockaway, 07866 ........ (973) 586-8000
South Bergenite, 9 Lincoln Ave., Rutherford, 07070 ........................ (201) 933-1166
Verona-Cedar Grove Times, 130 Valley Rd., Montclair, 07042 ............... (973) 233-5048
WayneToday, 1 Garret Mountain Plz., P.O. Box 471, Woodland Park, 07424 ..... (973) 569-7393

**NORTHEAST FOODS, INC.**
**601 S. Caroline St., Baltimore MD 21231 ............................ (410) 558-3050**
**Pres., CEO—Bill Paterakis; V-P., Hum. Res.—Don Mann; V-P., Trans.—Chuck Paterakis; Dir., Cust. Serv.—Stacey Nilson; Pur. Mgr.—Jessica Rohe**
Automatic Rolls Of New Jersey, Inc., 1 Gourmet Ln., Edison, 08837 ........... (732) 549-2243

**NOVARTIS FINANCE CORP.**
**230 Park Ave., 21st Fl., New York NY 10169 .......................... (212) 307-1122**
**Pres.—Andrew Wyss; CFO—Helen Boudreau; Dir., Media Rels.—Julie Masow; Head of Hum. Res.—MaryLynn Sauro**
Novartis Pharmaceuticals Corp. (H Q), 1 Health Plz., East Hanover, 07936 ..... (862) 778-8300

**NOVARTIS PHARMACEUTICALS CORP.**
**1 Health Plz., East Hanover NJ 07936 ............................... (862) 778-8300**
**Pres.—Christi Shaw; Head of U.S. Med. & Chief Scientific Officer—Cathryn M. Clary; V-P. & Chief Admn. & Fin. Officer—Meryl Zausner; V-P., Chief Compliance Officer—Cynthia Cetani; V-P. & Head of Hum. Res.—Caryn Parlavecchio; V-P., Gen. Counsel—Thomas Kendris; V-P., Head of Diversity & Inclusion—Rhonda Crichlow; V-P., Head of Integrated Hospital Care Bus. Unit—Carol Lynch; V-P., Head of Mngd. Mkts., Mkt. Access, Primary Care & Estab. Meds.—Gregory Oakes; V-P. & Head of Multiple Sclerosis Bus. Unit—Dagmar Rosa-Bjorkeson; V-P., Head of Critical Care Bus. Unit—Jesus Leal; V-P., Pub. Affs.—Kevin T. Rigby; V-P., Comms.—Anna Frable**
Sandoz, Inc. (H Q), 506 Carnegie Ctr., Ste. 400, Princeton, 08540 ............ (609) 627-8500

**NRI**
**44 W. 18th St., 2nd Fl., New York NY 10011 .......................... (212) 366-7000**
**Pres.—Douglas Magid; CTO—More McCormack; V-P., Sales—Russell Genest; V-P., Opers.—Dan Gabrich; Dir., Mktg.—Anca Munteanu; Hum. Res. Mgr.—Lori DeHart**
Rethink Color, a division of NRI, 3175 Princeton Pike, Lawrenceville, 08648..... (609) 896-4100
National Reprographics, Inc., 3175 Princeton Pike, Lawrenceville, 08648 ....... (609) 896-4100

**NUCOR CORP.**
**1915 Rexford Rd., Ste. 400, Charlotte NC 28211 ....................... (704) 366-7000**
**Chrm., Pres. & CEO—John Ferriola; Ex. V-P., CFO, Treas.—James D. Frias; Ex. V-P., Bar Prods.—James R. Darsey; Ex. V-P.—R. Joseph Stratman; Ex. V-P.—Hamilton Lott, Jr.; Ex. V-P.—Ladd R. Hall; Hum. Res. Mgr.—Donovan Marks; Inv. Rels. Mgr.—Greg Lucas**
Skyline Steel, LLC (H Q), 8 Woodhollow Rd., Ste. 102, Parsippany, 07054...... (973) 428-6100

**NUMAX, INC.**
**1073 Route 94, Ste. 11, New Windsor NY 12553 ....................... (845) 674-9060**
**Owner—Ron Hunkapillar**
Numax, Inc., 7251-B Browning Rd., Pennsauken, 08109 .................. (856) 910-0088

**NUSTAR ENERGY L. P.**
**19003 W. Interstate 10, San Antonio TX 78257 ......................... (210) 918-2000**
**Chrm.—Bill Greehey; CEO—Brad Barron; Ex. V-P., CFO—Tom Shoaf; Sr. V-P., Gen. Counsel & Secy., Corp. & Comml. Law—Amy Perry; Sr. V-P. & Gen. Counsel, Litigation, Regulatory & Env.—Karen Thompson; V-P., Cont.—Jorge Del Alamo**
Nustar Energy L. P., 7 N. Delaware St., Paulsboro, 08066 .................. (856) 224-8903

**NUTLEY HEATING & COOLING SUPPLY CO., INC.**
**50 Page Rd., Clifton NJ 07012 ...................................... (973) 470-8844**
**Pres.—Rick Cancelosi; V-P.—Susan Cancelosi; Pur. Mgr.—Joe Servidio; Cred. Mgr.—Karen Oliver**
Nutley Heating & Cooling Supply Co., 5016 Industrial Rd., Wall Township, 07727 . (732) 919-1933

**OCEAN SPRAY CRANBERRIES, INC.**
**1 Ocean Spray Dr., Middleboro MA 02349 ............................. (508) 946-1000**
**Pres., CEO—Randy Papadellis; CFO—Rick Lees; Sr. V-P., COO—Ken Romanzi; V-P., Hum. Res.—Jane Borkowski; V-P., Global Ptnrs.—Larry Martin; Cont.—Jon Cowell; Dir., Corp. Comms.—Cindy Taccini; Corp. Comms. Mgr.—Kellyanne Dignan**
Ocean Spray Cranberries, Inc., 104 E. Park St., Bordentown, 08505 .......... (609) 298-0905

**OFFICE DEPOT, INC.**
**6600 N. Military Trl., Boca Raton FL 33496 ........................... (561) 438-4800**
**Chrm., CEO—Roland Smith; Pres., N. Amer.—Mike Cosby; Pres., Intl. & Ex. V-P.—Steve Schmidt; Ex. V-P., CFO—Stephen Hare; Ex. V-P., Chief Legal Officer—Elisa Garcia; Ex. V-P., Chief People Officer—Michael Allison; Ex. V-P., Chief Strategy Officer—Juliet Johansson; V-P., Inv. Rels.—Michael Steele**
Office Depot Business Solution Div. Of New Jersey,
4 Brighton Rd., Clifton, 07012 ........................................ (973) 594-3000

**OFS FITEL, LLC**
**2000 Northeast Expy., Norcross GA 30071 ............................ (770) 798-2000**
**Chrm., CEO—Tim Murray; CTO—David DiGiovanni; CFO & Treas.—Ashish Gandhi; Sr. V-P., Hum. Res.—Stephanie Y. Street; V-P., Global Sales & Mktg.—Pierre Marty; Dir., Branding & Mktg.—Michael Fortin; Dir., Pub. Rels.—Sherry Salyer**
OFS Fitel, LLC, Specialty Photonics Div., 25 Schoolhouse Rd., Somerset, 08873 . (732) 748-7400

**OKONITE CO., INC., THE**
**102 Hilltop Rd., P.O. Box 340, Ramsey NJ 07446 ....................... (201) 825-0300**
**Chrm., CEO—V. A. Viggiano; Pres., COO—Alfred Coppola; CFO—Dave Sokira; V-P., Sales & Mktg.—Bruce Sellers; V-P., Mfg.—John Silver; Dir., Adv.—Robert Seltsam; MIS Mgr.—Bill Blowers**
Okonite Co., The, 102 Hilltop Rd., Paterson, 07513 ...................... (201) 825-0300

**OLDCASTLE BUILDINGENVELOPE®**
**5005 LBJ Fwy., Ste. 1050, Dallas TX 75244 ........................... (214) 273-3400**
**CEO—Ted Hathaway; CFO—Kevin Watson; V-P., Legal—Mollie Hines**
Oldcastle BuildingEnvelope®, 1500 Glen Ave., Moorestown, 08057 .......... (866) 653-2278

**OLDCASTLE PRECAST, INC.**
**1002 15th St. S.W., Ste. 110, Auburn WA 98001 ........................ (253) 833-2777**
**Pres., Enclosures Div.—George Heusel; CFO—Eric Farinha; Cont.—James Hunsaker**
Oldcastle Precast, Inc., 1920 12th St., Williamstown, 08094 ................ (609) 561-3400

**OLDCASTLE, INC.**
**900 Ashwood Pkwy., Ste. 600, Atlanta GA 30338 ....................... (770) 804-3363**
**CEO—Mark Towe; CFO—Michael O'Driscoll; Ex. V-P.—Mark Schack; Dir., Strategic Plng.—Tom Conroy; IT Mgr.—Josh Griffin; Hum. Res. Mgr.—Cindy Reeves-Durdun**
Allied Building Products Corp., 15 E. Union Ave., East Rutherford, 07073 ...... (201) 507-8400
Anchor Concrete Products, Inc. (H Q),
331 Newman Springs Rd., Bldg. 2, 3rd Fl., Ste. 236, Red Bank, 07701 ....... (732) 292-2500

**OLE HANSEN & SON, INC.**
**523 S. Leipzig Ave., P.O. Box 1020, Cologne NJ 08213 ................. (609) 965-3700**
**Chrm.—Roger B. Hansen; Pres., CEO—David Goddard; CFO & Corp. Treas.—Michael Lentz**
Ole Hansen & Sons, Inc., 100 Old Port Republic Rd., Absecon, 08205 ........ (609) 652-5666

**OLYMPIC CONTROLS CORP.**
**1250 Crispin Dr., Elgin IL 60123 .................................... (847) 742-3566**
**Pres.—Albano Andreini; V-P., Sales & Mktg.—David Armon; V-P., Opers.—John Scandora; Pur. Mgr.—Randall Henson; IT Mgr.—Bob Andreini; Hum. Res. Mgr.—Jennifer Lund; Qual. Assur. Mgr.—Gerald Berger**
Amperite Co., 4201 Tonnelle Ave., Ste. 6, North Bergen, 07047 ............. (201) 864-9503

**OM GROUP, INC.**
**950 Main Ave., Ste. 1300, Cleveland OH 44113 ........................ (216) 781-0083**
**Chrm., CEO—Joseph M. Scaminace; CFO—Christopher M. Hix; V-P., Hum. Res.—Michael Johnson; V-P., Bus. Dev. & Investor Rels.—Greg Griffith; Dir., Inv. Rels.—Rob Pearce**
OMG Electronic Chemicals, LLC,
400 Corporate Ct., Ste. A, South Plainfield, 07080 ...................... (908) 222-5800

**OMAHA WORLD-HERALD CO.**
**1314 Douglas St., Omaha NE 68102 .................................. (402) 444-1000**
**Pres., CEO & Publisher—Terry Kroeger; Sr. V-P., CFO—Duane Polodna; Sr. V-P., COO—Doug Hiemstra; CIO & Dir., IT—Phil Tomek; V-P., Adv.—Dave Storey; Ex. Editor—Mike Reilly; Dir., Hum. Res.—Roshelle Campbell; Dir., Comm.—Joel Long; Dir., Circ.—Dennis Cronin**
World Media Enterprises, Inc., 1000 W. Washington Ave., Pleasantville, 08232 .. (609) 272-7000

**OMNICOMM SYSTEMS, INC.**
**2101 W. Commercial Blvd., Ste. 3500, Fort Lauderdale FL 33309 .......... (954) 473-1254**
**Chrm., CTO—Randall G. Smith; CEO & Dir.—Cornelis F. Wit; Pres., COO—Stephen E. Johnson; CFO—Thomas Vickers; Sr. V-P., Opers.—John Fontenault; Ex. V-P., Transformation Dept.—Ken Light; Dir., IT—Hal Flynt**
OmniComm Systems, Inc., 1100 Cornwall Rd., Ste. 111, Monmouth Junction, 08852 . (732) 960-2820

**ONE EQUITY PARTNERS, LLC**
**320 Park Ave., 18th Fl., New York NY 10022 .......................... (212) 277-1500**
**Ptnr.—Brad Coppens; Chrm. & Mng. Dir.—Dick Cashin; CFO—Katy Bryan**
Sonneborn, LLC, 600 Parsippany Rd., Ste. 100, Parsippany, 07054 ........... (201) 760-2940

**O'NEAL STEEL, INC.**
**744 41st St. N., Birmingham AL 35222 ............................... (205) 599-8000**
**Regional V-P.—Gary Gray; Mktg. Mgr.—Henley Smith**
O'Neal Flat Rolled Metals, 1 Fitzgerald Ave., Monroe Township, 08831 ........ (609) 395-7007

**ORACLE CORP.**
**500 Oracle Pkwy., Redwood City CA 94065 ........................... (650) 506-7000**
**Vice Chrm.—Jeff Henley; Ex. Chrm.—Larry Ellison; CEO—Safra Catz; CEO—Mark Hurd; CMO—Judith Sim; Sr. V-P., Gen. Counsel & Secy.—Dorian Daley; Ex. V-P., Server Tech.—Charles Rozwat; Corp. Comms. Mgr.—Kimberly Pineda**
Oracle Corp., 330 Fellowship Rd., Ste. 100, Mount Laurel, 08054 ............ (856) 359-2999

**ORBCOMM, INC.**
**395 W. Passaic St., Ste. 325, Rochelle Park NJ 07662 .................. (703) 433-6300**
**CEO—Marc J. Eisenberg; CFO—Robert G. Costantini; Ex. V-P., Sales & Mktg.—Patrick Shay; Ex. V-P., Opers. & Tech.—John J. Stolte, Jr.; Ex. V-P., Prod. Dev.—Craig Malone; Gen. Counsel—Christian G. LeBrun**
StarTrak Information Technologies, LLC,
395 W. Passaic St., Ste. 325, Rochelle Park, 07662 ...................... (703) 433-6300

**OSI SYSTEMS, INC.**
**12525 Chadron Ave., Hawthorne CA 90250 ............................ (310) 978-0516**
**CEO—Deepak Chopra; CFO—Alan Edrick; CIO—Mohinder Chopra; Ex. V-P., Gen. Counsel—Victor Sze; V-P., GM—Peter C. Williamson; V-P. & Hum. Res. Mgr.—Heather Zammit; Corp. Dir., Fin. Plng.—Jack Wallace**
OSI Laser Diode, Inc., 4 Olsen Ave., Edison, 08820 ...................... (732) 549-9001

**OSSUR AMERICAS, INC.**
**27051 Towne Centre Dr., Ste. 100, Foothill Ranch CA 92610 ............. (949) 382-3883**
**Ex. V-P.—Olafur Gylfason; V-P., Hum. Res.—Pamela James; Dir., Cust. Serv. & Sales, Inside—Brandon Echols; IT Mgr.—Shannon Hungerford**
Ossur Americas, Inc., 1414 Metropolitan Ave., Paulsboro, 08066 ............. (856) 345-6000

**OVERHEAD DOOR CORP.**
**2501 S. State Highway 121 Bus., Ste. 200, Lewisville TX 75067 ........... (469) 549-7100**
**Pres., CEO—Dennis Stone; Pres., ASD—Kelly Terry; Pres., Todco—Joe Owen; CIO—Larry Freed; Sr. V-P., Sales & Mktg.—Preston Bowen; V-P., Gen. Counsel—Bill Schochet; V-P., Hum. Res.—Ken Mahlke; Hum. Res. Mgr.—Sandy Denton**
Burlington County Overhead Door Co., Inc.,
444 Logan Ave., P.O. Box 127, Burlington, 08016 ........................ (609) 387-9092

**OWENS & MINOR, INC.**
**9120 Lockwood Blvd., Mechanicsville VA 23116 ........................ (804) 723-7000**
**Chrm.—G. Gilmer Minor III; Pres., CEO—Craig R. Smith; CIO—Rick Mears; Sr. V-P., CFO—Jim Bierman; Sr. V-P., Hum. Res.—Erika Davis; Dir., Opers.—John O'Bryant; Dir., Hum. Res.—Will Angus; Dir., Investor Comm.—Trudi Allcott; Dir., First Impressions—Marjorie Ray**
Owens & Minor, Inc., 1220 Forest Pkwy., Paulsboro, 08066 ................. (856) 423-9900

 © Copyright 2015 Manufacturers' News, Inc. 



**OWENS CORNING**
**1 Owens Corning Pkwy., Toledo OH 43659 .......... (419) 248-8000**
**Chrm., CEO—Michael H. Thaman; Group Pres., Bldg. Matls.—Chuck Dana; Sr. V-P., CFO—Michael C. McMurray; V-P., CIO—Steve Zerby; V-P., CSO—Frank O'Brien-Bernini; V-P., Cont.—Kelly J. Schmidt; V-P., Corp. Dev.—Harry Shaw; V-P., Inv. Rels.—Thierry Denis; Dir., Hum. Res., Asphalt & Roofing—Tony Justice; Dir., Sustainability—Gale Tedhams; Mktg. Mgr., Asphalt & Roofing—Sue Burkett**
Owens Corning, 1249 Newark Tpke., Kearny, 07032 .......... (201) 998-5666

**OXFORD INSTRUMENTS AMERICA, INC.**
**300 Baker Ave., Ste. 150, Concord MA 01742 .......... (978) 369-9933**
**V-P., Sales—Chris Horvath; V-P., Fin.—Chris Frazer; IT Mgr.—Ian Springer; Hum. Res. Mgr.—Sandra Kindlan; Cred. Mgr.—Pat Capadanno; Cust. Serv. Rep.—Lindsey Baldwin**
Oxford Instruments Superconducting Technology, Inc., 600 Milik St., Carteret, 07008 .......... (732) 541-1300

**OXYVINYLS L. P.**
**5005 LBJ Fwy., Ste. 2200, Dallas TX 75244 .......... (972) 720-7488**
**Sr. V-P., Bus. Analysis—Eric Wynia; Dir., Sales—Jason Welch**
OxyVinyls, P.O. Box 411, Pedricktown, 08067 .......... (856) 299-8498

**P & A AUTO PARTS, INC.**
**530 River St., Hackensack NJ 07601 .......... (201) 843-7156**
**Pres., CFO—Joe Cupoli; Sales Mgr.—Russell Guarciello; Opers. Mgr.—Michael Agnello**
P & A Auto Parts, Inc., 396 Midland Ave., Garfield, 07026 .......... (973) 405-6068

**PACKAGING CORP. OF AMERICA**
**1955 W. Field Ct., Lake Forest IL 60045 .......... (847) 482-3000**
**Chrm.—Paul T. Stecko; CEO—Mark Kowlzan; Sr. V-P., CFO—Richard B. West; Sr. V-P., Sales & Mktg.—Tom Hassfurther; Mktg. Mgr.—Tina Matheis**
Packaging Corp. Of America, Cranbury Creative Design Center, 8 E. Stow Rd., Ste. 100, Marlton, 08053 .......... (856) 596-5020

**PALMETTO ADHESIVES CO.**
**112 Guess St., Greenville SC 29605 .......... (864) 232-8865**
**Pres.—Tom Wilson; CFO—Tim Wilson; Plt. Mgr.—Ronnie Cook; Cred. Mgr.—Nance Brown**
Palmetto Adhesives Co., Inc., 1785 Burlington Rd., Bridgeton, 08302 .......... (856) 451-0405

**PAMARCO TECHNOLOGIES, INC.**
**235 E. 11th Ave., Roselle NJ 07203 .......... (908) 241-1200**
**Pres.—Terry Ford; CFO—Kim Parada; V-P., Sales, Natl.—John Rastetter; Hum. Res. Mgr.—Angela Grieco**
Pamarco Global Graphics, Imaging Div., 1 Roto Ave., Palmyra, 08065 .......... (856) 829-4585

**PANERA BREAD CO., INC.**
**3630 S. Geyer Rd., Ste. 100, Sunset Hills MO 63127 .......... (314) 984-1000**
**Ex. Chrm. of the Board—Ronald M. Shaich; Pres., CEO—William W. Moreton; COO—Charles Chapman III; Sr. V-P., Chief Legal Officer & Gen. Counsel—Scott Blair; Sr. V-P., Chief Concept Officer—Scott Davis; Sr. V-P., Chief People Officer—Rebecca Fine; Sr. V-P., CIO—Thomas Kish; Sr. V-P., Chief Franchise Officer—Michael Kupstas; Sr. V-P., Chief Dev. Officer—Michael Nolan; Sr. V-P., CMO—Michael Simon; Sr. V-P., Chief Co. & Joint Venture Opers. Officer—William H. Simpson; Ex. V-P., Co-COO—Cedric Vanzura**
Panera Bread Co., LLC, 5 E. Evans St., Fairfield, 07004 .......... (973) 276-0250

**PAR PHARMACEUTICAL COS., INC.**
**300 Tice Blvd., Woodcliff Lake NJ 07677 .......... (201) 802-4000**
**CEO—Paul Campanelli; Pres.—Thomas Haughey; Ex. V-P., CFO—Michael A. Tropiano; Sr. V-P., Hum. Res.—Steve Montalto**
Strativa Pharmaceuticals (H Q), 300 Tice Blvd., Woodcliff Lake, 07677 .......... (201) 802-4000

**PARIS ART LABEL CO., INC.**
**217 River Ave., Patchogue NY 11772 .......... (631) 467-2300**
**Pres.—Ronald J. Tarantino, Sr.; V-P., Sales—Ronald Tarantino, Jr.; Sales Mgr.—Jonathan Tarantino; Dir., Engrg. & Tech.—Ronen Gilat**
Princeton Label Co., 1226 U.S. Highway 130, Robbinsville, 08691 .......... (609) 490-0800

**PARK STEEL & IRON CO.**
**9 Evergreen Ave., Neptune City NJ 07753 .......... (732) 775-7500**
**Pres., GM—Scott Pilling; Off. Mgr.—Elan Palmer**
Park Steel & Iron Co., 82 Iron St., Toms River, 08753 .......... (732) 349-2400

**PARKER HANNIFIN CORPORATION**
**6035 Parkland Blvd., Cleveland OH 44124 .......... (216) 896-3000**
**Chrm., Pres. & CEO—Donald E. Washkewicz; Pres., Seal Group & V-P.—Andy Ross; Pres., Aerospace Group—Roger Sherrard; Pres., Automation Group—Michael Chung; Ex. V-P., Admn. & Fin. & CFO—Jon P. Marten; Ex. V-P. & Operating Officer—Lee C. Banks; Ex. V-P. & Operating Officer—Thomas L. Williams; V-P., Hum. Res.—Daniel S. Serbin; V-P., Comms. & Ext. Affs.—Christopher Farage; V-P., Treas.—Pamela Huggins; Mktg. Mgr.—Steve Erickson**
Parker Chomerics, 135 Bryant Ave., Cranford, 07016 .......... (908) 272-5500
Parker Hannifin Corp., 45 Route 46 E., Unit 602, P.O. Box 778, Pine Brook, 07058 .......... (973) 575-4844

**PARTS CLEANING TECHNOLOGIES, LLC**
**26400 Capitol, Redford MI 48239 .......... (313) 952-2646**
**Pres.—David Crandell**
Parts Cleaning Technologies, LLC, 835 Industrial Hwy., Ste. 1, Cinnaminson, 08077 .......... (856) 786-8686

**PATRIARCH PARTNERS, LLC**
**1 Broadway, 10th Fl., New York NY 10004 .......... (212) 825-0550**
**CEO & Principal—Lynn Tilton; Mng. Dir., Engrg. & Mfg. Platform—John Harrington; Hum. Res. Mgr.—Joanne Celauro**
Acme International Enterprises, Inc., 400 Lyster Ave., Saddle Brook, 07663 .......... (973) 416-0400
Dana Classic Fragrances, Inc. (H Q), 400 Lyster Ave., Saddle Brook, 07663 .......... (201) 881-8550

**PAZERA ASSOCS., INC.**
**121 Edwards Ave., Calverton NY 11933 .......... (631) 727-2258**
**Ptnr.—Peter Pazera**
Pazera Cabinets Door, 3160 Bordentown Ave., Old Bridge, 08857 .......... (732) 727-1600

**PBF ENERGY PARTNERS L. P.**
**1 Sylvan Way, Parsippany NJ 07054 .......... (973) 455-7500**
**Chrm.—Thomas O'Malley; CEO—Thomas J. Nimbley; Pres.—Michael D. Gayda; CFO—Eric Young; Sr. V-P., Gen. Counsel & Secy.—Jeffrey Dill; Ex. V-P.—Mathew Lucey; Dir., Inv. Rels.—Colin Murray; Dir., Compensation—Wendy Ho Tai**
Paulsboro Refining Co., 800 Billingsport Rd., Paulsboro, 08066 .......... (856) 224-6000

**PEARSON EDUCATION, INC.**
**1 Lake St., Upper Saddle River NJ 07458 .......... (201) 236-7000**
**CEO—Marjorie Scardino; Ex. V-P., CFO & COO—George Warner; Sr. V-P., Comm.—Wendy Spiegel; Ex. V-P., Opers.—John LaVacca; Ex. V-P., Hum. Res.—Angela Schwers**
Pearson Technology, 200 Old Tappan Rd., Old Tappan, 07675 .......... (201) 767-5000

**PEGASYSTEMS, INC.**
**1 Rogers St., Cambridge MA 02142 .......... (617) 866-6000**
**Chrm., CEO—Alan Trefler; Sr. V-P., Global Sales—Leon Trefler; Sr. V-P., Engrg.—Mike Pyle; V-P., Gen. Counsel—Shawn Hoyt; V-P., Corp. Dev.—Max Mayer; V-P., Global Svcs.—Douglas Kra**
Pegasystems, Inc., 111 Town Square Pl., Jersey City, 07310 .......... (201) 239-2300

**PELLA CORP.**
**102 Main St., Pella IA 50219 .......... (641) 621-1000**
**Chrm.—Charles Farver; Vice Chrm.—Adam Farver; Pres., CEO—Patrick Meyer; Sr. Group V-P., Cust. Serv., Natl. Acct. Sales, Prod. Dev. & Qual.—Denny Van Zanten; V-P., Cust. Support & Mktg.—Elaine Sagers; V-P., Hum. Res.—Karen Peterson; Dir., Opers.—Brian Kingery; Corp. Pub. Rels. Mgr.—Kathy Krafka Harkema; Sr. Residential Strategic Mktg. Mgr.—Matt Kiernan**
Pella Windows & Doors, 4 Dedrick Pl., West Caldwell, 07006 .......... (973) 575-0200

**PENETONE CORP.**
**1000 Herrontown Rd., Ste. 2, Princeton NJ 08540 .......... (609) 921-0501**
**Pres.—Elwood Phares**
Penetone Corp., 700 Gotham Pkwy., Ste. 2, Carlstadt, 07072 .......... (201) 567-3000

**PENN COLOR, INC.**
**400 Old Dublin Pike, Doylestown PA 18901 .......... (215) 345-6550**
**Pres., CEO—Kevin S. Putnam; CFO—David Hill; V-P., Sales & Mktg.—Tom Farrell; Cont.—David Loeffler; IT Mgr.—Chris Driscoll; Hum. Res. Mgr.—Dana Deardoff**
Penn Color, Inc., 30 Kohner Pl., Elmwood Park, 07407 .......... (201) 791-5100

**PENN JERSEY BUILDING MATERIALS, INC.**
**2819 Fire Rd., Egg Harbor Township NJ 08234 .......... (609) 485-0068**
**CEO—Dan Quade; CFO—William Sutton**
Penn Jersey Building Materials, Inc., 247 Cedar Swamp Rd., Bridgeport, 08014 . (856) 467-0400

**PENTAX OF AMERICA, INC.**
**3 Paragon Dr., Ste. 1, Montvale NJ 07645 .......... (201) 571-2300**
**Pres.—David Woods; Ex. V-P.—Gene Merente; V-P., Hum. Res.—Adrienna Messina; Hum. Res. Mgr.—Chris Casteline**
KayPENTAX, 3 Paragon Dr., Montvale, 07645 .......... (973) 628-6200

**PEPCO MFG. CO.**
**210 E. Evergreen Ave., P.O. Box 160, Somerdale NJ 08083 .......... (856) 783-3700**
**CEO—John Kennedy; Pres.—Frank A. Reiss; CFO—Beverly Winter; COO—Edward Miller; V-P.—Richard Materio**
Fiore Skylights, Inc., 210 E. Evergreen Ave., P.O. Box 160, Somerdale, 08083 ... (856) 346-0118

**PEPSI BEVERAGES COMPANY**
**1 Pepsi Way, Somers NY 10589 .......... (914) 767-6000**
**CEO—Al Carey; CFO—Cynthia Swanson; CPO—Linda Reddy**
Pepsi Beverages Company, 2200 New Brunswick Ave., Piscataway, 08854 ..... (732) 424-3000

**PEPSICO, INC.**
**700 Anderson Hill Rd., Purchase NY 10577 .......... (914) 253-2000**
**Chrm. of the Board & CEO—Indra Nooyi; Vice Chrm., PepsiCo & CEO, PepsiCo Intl.—Michael D. White; CEO, PepsiCo Foods—John Compton; CFO—Hugh F. Johnston; CMO—Jill Beraud; Chief Scientific Officer—Mehmood Khan; Chief Diversity & Inclusion Officer—Ronald C. Parker; Sr. V-P., Chief Proc. Officer—Mitch Adamek; Chief Design Officer—Mauro Porcini; Sr. V-P., Govt. Affs., Gen. Counsel & Secy.—Larry D. Thompson; Sr. V-P., Treas.—Lionel L. Nowell III; Sr. V-P., Comm.—Jim Wilkinson; Ex. V-P., Hum. Res.—Cynthia M. Trudell; Sr. Dir., Comms.—Aurora Gonzalez; Board Dir.—George Buckley; Global Innovation Officer—Margey Schelling**
Beverage Distribution Center, Inc., 8275 Route 130, Pennsauken, 08110 .......... (856) 665-6200

**PERFECT FINISHING, INC.**
**40 Webro Rd., Clifton NJ 07012 .......... (973) 472-7400**
**Co-Pres.—Bruce Flaim; Co-Pres.—Hank Ruggiero; Cont.—Elyse Stone**
Glue-Fold, Inc., Div. Of Perfect Finishing, Inc., 40 Webro Rd., Clifton, 07012 .... (973) 575-8400

**PERFORMANCE FOOD GROUP, INC.**
**12500 W. Creek Pkwy., Richmond VA 23238 .......... (804) 484-7700**
**Pres., CEO—George Holm; Sr. V-P., CFO—Bob Evans; Dir. & Hum. Res. Mgr.—Nancy Rooke**
Performance Food Group-AFI Foodservice, 1 Ikea Dr., Elizabeth, 07207 ....... (908) 629-1800

**PHARMACHEM LABORATORIES, INC.**
**265 Harrison Ave., Kearny NJ 07032 .......... (201) 246-1000**
**Pres.—Dave Holmes; V-P., GM—Colin MacIntyre; V-P., Sales—Paul Borrell; Treas.—Andrea Bauer; Dir., New Prod. Dev.—Mitch Skop; IT Mgr.—Marco Lipps; Hum. Res. & Payroll Mgr.—Maritere Velazquez**
MPT Delivery Systems, Inc., 95 Prince St., Paterson, 07501 .......... (973) 279-4132
Pharmachem Laboratories, Inc., 130 Wesley St., South Hackensack, 07606 . (201) 343-3611

**PHARMEDIUM SERVICES, LLC**
**150 N. Field Dr., Ste. 350, Lake Forest IL 60045 .......... (847) 457-2300**
**CEO—William R. Spalding; Pres.—Rich Kruzynski; CFO—Matthew Anderson; V-P., Sales—Jennifer Adams; V-P., Cust. Serv. & Sales Opers.—Todd A. Lesser; V-P., Bus. Dev. & Mktg.—Amy Langan; V-P., Field Opers. & Supply Chain—Tim Cosentino; Dir., Hum. Res.—Nancy Brandt**
PharMEDium, 43 Distribution Blvd., Edison, 08817 .......... (732) 287-8655

**PHIBRO ANIMAL HEALTH CORP.**
**300 Frank W. Burr Blvd., Stn. 21, Glenpointe Center East, 3rd Fl., Teaneck NJ 07666 . (201) 329-7300**
**Chrm.—Jack Bendheim; CEO—Gerald Carlson; CIO—Gary Fling; CFO—Richard Johnson; Sr. V-P., Hum. Res.—Dan Welch; V-P., Pur.—Milton Hamburger; Dir., Sales, Natl. Specialty Chemicals—Mark Chamberlin; Dir., Opers.—Shari Seidman; Global Dir., R & D, Ethanol Performance Sols.—Dennis Bayrock; Tech. Mgr., Specialty Chemicals—Michael Pollock**
Phibro-Tech, Inc., 300 Frank W. Burr Blvd., Ste. 21, Glenpointe Center East, 3rd Fl., Teaneck, 07666 . (201) 329-7300

**PHILIPS LIFELINE**
**111 Lawrence St., Framingham MA 01702 ............................ (508) 988-1000**
**Cont.—Sheryl B. Sigrist; Sr. Dir., IT—Marcia Conrad-Miller; Dir., Sales, Corp. Accts.—Linda Schertzer; Hum. Res. Mgr.—Karen Gosselin**
Philips Lighting North America, 200 Franklin Square Dr., Somerset, 08873 ..... (732) 563-3000

**PHILIPS LIGHTING NORTH AMERICA**
**200 Franklin Square Dr., Somerset NJ 08873 ......................... (732) 563-3000**
**Pres., Phillips Lighting N. America—Bruno Biasiotta; CFO—Raoul Gatzen; V-P., Mktg., Lighting N.A.—Ted Simpson; V-P., Hum. Res.—Cathy Cubberly; GM, Light Sources & Electronics—Ed Crawford; Internal Comms. Mgr.—Rico Scardelletti**
Philips Luminaries NA, 2345 Vauxhall Rd., P.O. Box 129, Union, 07083 ........ (908) 964-7000

**PHILIPS RESPIRONICS**
**1010 Murry Ridge Ln., Murrysville PA 15668 ......................... (724) 387-5200**
**CEO—Brent Shafer; Dir., Mktg. Comm.—Maryellen Bizzack**
Philips Respironics, 200 Franklin Square Dr., Somerset, 08873 ............. (732) 563-3400

**PHILLIPS 66 CO.**
**3010 Briarpark Dr., Houston TX 77042............................... (281) 293-6000**
**Chrm., CEO—Greg C. Garland; Ex. V-P., Fin. & CFO—Greg G. Maxwell; Sr. V-P., Hum. Res.—Chantal Veevaete; Sr. V-P., Govt. Affs.—Philip D. Brady; Sr. V-P., Corp. Affs., Inv. Rels. & Strategy—C. C. Reasor; Ex. V-P., Legal, Gen. Counsel & Secy.—Paula Johnson; Ex. V-P., Refining—Lawrence M. Ziemba**
Phillips 66 Bayway Refinery, 1400 Park Ave., Linden, 07036 ............... (908) 523-5000

**PHYSIOTHERAPY ASSOCS., INC.**
**855 Springdale Dr., Ste. 200, Exton PA 19341........................ (610) 644-7824**
**Pres., CEO—Andrew DeVoe; CIO—David Valcik; Ex. V-P., Gen. Counsel & Secy.—Janna King; Dir., Hum. Res.—Laurie Lampie**
Prosthetic Orthotic Solutions International, 100 Brick Rd., Ste. 315, Marlton, 08053 ........................ (856) 810-7900

**PICUT MANUFACTURING COMPANY, INC.**
**140 Mount Bethel Rd., Warren NJ 07059............................ (908) 754-1333**
**Pres.—Frederick Picut; CFO—Ray Mattes; V-P.—Richard Picut; V-P.—Russell Picut; Cont.—Cheryl Lloyd; GM—Dan Scagliozzi; Hum. Res. Mgr.—Chris Hardgrove**
American Products Co., Inc., 610 Rahway Ave., Union, 07083 ............... (908) 687-4100

**PIERSON CONSTRUCTION CO., INC., R. E.**
**426 Swedesboro Rd., Pilesgrove NJ 08098............................ (856) 769-8244**
**V-P.—Robert Baccala; Cont.—Cherri Coles; Hum. Res. Mgr.—Donna Brady**
Pierson Materials Co., Inc., R. E., 860 Oak Grove Rd., P.O. Box 704, Bridgeport, 08014 .................... (856) 467-1421
Pierson Materials Corp., R. E., 184 W. Sherman Ave., Vineland, 08360 ........ (856) 696-2901
Pierson Materials Inc., R. E., 860 Oak Grove Rd., P.O. Box 704, Bridgeport, 08014 .................... (856) 467-4199
Pierson Materials, Inc., R. E., 1550 Route 38, Mount Holly, 08060 ............ (609) 267-2257
Pierson Materials, Inc., R. E., 151 Industrial Dr., Williamstown, 08094 ......... (856) 740-2400

**PILOT CHEMICAL COMPANY**
**2744 E. Kemper Rd., Cincinnati OH 45241 ........................... (513) 326-0600**
**Market Research Mgr.—Kenny Potter; CEO—Paul Morrisroe; Pres., COO—Pam Butcher; CFO—Dave Waizmann; V-P., Engrg. & Mfg.—Ken Eckroth; V-P., Bus. Svcs. & Tech.—Sue Leslie; V-P., Comml.—Glynn Goertzen; Dir., Admn. & Hum. Res.—Catherine Ochterski; Sales Mgr., Natl.—Robert Rechtin**
Pilot Chemical Co., 267 Homestead Ave., Avenel, 07001 .................. (732) 634-6613

**PMC, INC.**
**12243 Branford St., Sun Valley CA 91352 ........................... (818) 896-1101**
**Pres.—Gary Kamins; CFO—T. C. Cheong; Treas.—Peter Gamboa; Cont.—David Keller; IT Mgr.—Jim Bauer; Hum. Res. Mgr.—Wanda Bakshafar**
General Plastics Corp., 55 La France Ave., Bloomfield, 07003 ................ (973) 748-5500
Komo Machine, Inc., 1 Komo Dr., Lakewood, 08701 ......................... (732) 719-6222

**POCHET OF AMERICA, INC.**
**415 Hamburg Tpke., Ste. 2, Wayne NJ 07470 ......................... (973) 942-4923**
**Pres.—Borislav Zivkovic; Cont.—Maha Sambamurthy; Dir., Sales—Olivier Trevidic; Dir., Indl. Opers.—Jonathan Clark**
Qualipac America Corp., 1 Garret Mountain Plz., 5th Fl., West Paterson, 07424 . . (973) 389-7730

**POLYAIR INTER PACK, INC.**
**330 Humberline Dr., Toronto, Ontario, Canada M9W 1R5, ............... (416) 679-6600**
**CEO—Gary Tessitore**
Polyair North East, 495 Meadow Ln., Carlstadt, 07072..................... (201) 804-1700

**POLYONE CORP.**
**33587 Walker Rd., Avon Lake OH 44012 ............................. (440) 930-1000**
**Ex. Chrm.—Steve Newlin; Pres., CEO—Robert Patterson; Pres., Global Specialty Engineered Matls.—Craig Nikrant; Pres., Global Color, Additives & Inks & Sr. V-P.—John Van Hulle; Pres., Performance Prods. & Sols. & Sr. V-P.—Michael A. Garratt; Sr. V-P., Hum. Res. & CIO—Ken Smith; Sr. V-P., Dist.—Mark Crist; V-P., Treas.—Daniel J. O'Bryon; V-P., Inv. Rels. & Plng.—Isaac DeLuca; V-P., Global Key Acct. Mgmt.—Kurt Schuering; Dir., Global Mktg.—Larry Johnson; Dir., Global Mktg. Comms.—David Honeycutt**
Poly One Corp., 297 Ferry St., Newark, 07105............................ (973) 522-2800

**POOL CORPORATION**
**109 Northpark Blvd., Ste. 400, Covington LA 70433 .................... (985) 892-5521**
**Pres., CEO—Manuel Perez de la Mesa; V-P., CFO—Mark W. Joslin; CAO—Melanie M. Housey; V-P., Opers.—Stephen C. Nelson; Group V-P.—Kenneth G. St. Romain; Group V-P.—A. David Cook; Gen. Counsel & Secy.—Jennifer M. Neil; GM, Prod. Mgmt., Sales & Mktg.—Donna Williams**
SCP Distributors, LLC, 1985 Rutgers University Blvd., Ste. A, Lakewood, 08701 . (732) 730-1451
Superior Pool Products, LLC, 200 Freeway Dr., Ste. 2, Blackwood, 08012 ...... (856) 232-7774

**PORTEOUS FASTENER CO., INC.**
**12801 Leffingwell Ave., Santa Fe Springs CA 90670 .................... (310) 549-9180**
**Pres.—Barry Porteous; Ex. V-P., Sales & COO—Bob Porteous; V-P., Pur.—Bruce Darling; IT Mgr.—Tom White; Hum. Res. Mgr.—Kristine Castillo; Payroll Mgr.—Mary Kay Mueller; Whse. Mgr.—Bret Swan**
Porteous Fastener Co., Inc., 1000 Amboy Ave., Ste. 1, Perth Amboy, 08861 .... (732) 376-8420

**POTTERS INDUSTRIES, INC.**
**300 Lindenwood Dr., Malvern PA 19355.............................. (610) 651-4700**
**Sales Mgr., Natl.—Kevin Goforth; Opers. Mgr.—Jim Hayward**
Potters Industries, Inc., 600 Industrial Rd., Carlstadt, 07072 ............... (201) 460-0666

**PPG AEROSPACE**
**12780 San Fernando Rd., Sylmar CA 91342........................... (818) 362-6711**
**Pres.—Barry Gillespie; Global Dir., Aerospace Mfg. & Qual.—Ted Bonneau; Dir., Hum. Res., Global—John Machin; Global Dir., Fin. Serv.—Ralph Dyba; Comms. & Mktg. Mgr.—Audrey Fujimoto**
PRC-DeSoto International, Inc., 823 E. Gate Dr., Unit 4, Mount Laurel, 08054. . . (856) 234-1600

**PQ CORPORATION**
**300 Lindenwood Dr., Malvern PA 19355.............................. (610) 651-4200**
**Chrm., CEO—Michael Boyce; CFO—Alan McIlroy; V-P., IT—Billy Whalen; V-P., Hum. Res.—Kevin Doran; Pur. Mgr.—Karl Kramer**
P Q Corp., 2 Paddock St., Avenel, 07001.................................. (732) 750-9040

**PRAXAIR, INC.**
**39 Old Ridgebury Rd., Danbury CT 06810 ............................ (203) 837-2000**
**Chrm., Pres. & CEO—Stephen F. Angel; Ex. V-P., CFO—James S. Sawyer; CIO—Marc Franciosa; Sr. V-P., Gen. Counsel & Secy.—Jim Breedlove; Sr. V-P.—Scott Telesz; V-P., Cont.—Elizabeth H. Hirsch; V-P., Global Opers. Excellence & Dev.—Murray G. Covello; V-P., Mergers & Acquisitions—Richard L. Steinseifer; Dir., Inv. Rels.—Kelcey Hoyt**
Praxair, Inc., 554 Shell Rd., Penns Grove, 08069.......................... (856) 299-3500
Praxair, Inc., Rairatan Bay, Plt. 907, 60 Crows Mill Rd., Keasbey, 08832........ (732) 738-4150

**PRECAST CONCRETE SALES CO.**
**123 Route 303, P.O. Box 516, Valley Cottage NY 10989 ................ (845) 268-4949**
**Pres., CEO—Greg Fisher; V-P., Sales—Bruce Rose; Cont.—Jay Dellolio; Opers. Mgr.—Jose Estevez**
Precast Mfg. Co., LLC, 187 Strykers Rd., Phillipsburg, 08865................ (908) 454-2122

**PRECISION AUTOMATION COMPANY, INC.**
**1841 Old Cuthbert Rd., Cherry Hill NJ 08034.......................... (856) 428-7400**
**Pres., CEO—G. Frederick Rexon, Jr.; V-P., COO—Daniel Pomponio; V-P. & Dir., Conveyor Sys. Div.—Mark Petri; Dir., Sales & Mktg.—Gerry Renzi; GM & Qual. Assur. Mgr.—Michael Menaquale**
New Jersey Wire Stitching Machine Co., 1841 Old Cuthbert Rd., Cherry Hill, 08034 .................................. (856) 428-7400

**PRECISION CASTPARTS CORP.**
**4650 S.W. MacAdam Ave., Ste. 300, Portland OR 97239 ................. (503) 946-4800**
**Chrm., CEO—Mark Donegan; CFO—Shawn Hagel; V-P., CIO—Byron Gaddis; V-P., Inv. Rels.—Jay Khetani; Hum. Res. Mgr.—Brian Keegan**
McWilliams Forge Co., 387 Franklin Ave., Rockaway, 07866 ................ (973) 627-0200

**PRESIDENT CONTAINER GROUP**
**200 W. Commercial Ave., Moonachie NJ 07074 ......................... (201) 933-7500**
**Pres.—Marvin Grossbard; Sr. V-P.—Richard Grossbard; V-P., Sales—John Kasztan; V-P., Prodn.—Joe Restifo; V-P., Opers.—Richard Goldberg; V-P.—Larry Grossbard; IT Mgr.—Trevor Smith**
Tech-Pak, Inc., 100 Blum, P.O. Box 51, Wood Ridge, 07075.................. (201) 935-3800

**PRIDE SOLVENTS & CHEMICAL CO.**
**6 Long Island Ave., Holtsville NY 11742............................. (631) 758-0200**
**Pres.—Arthur Dhom; V-P., Sales—James Stipicevic; Opers. Mgr.—Dave Sticht; IT Mgr.—Vincent Chan; Fin. Mgr.—Gary Kludt**
Pride Solvents & Chemical Co., 211 Randolph Ave., Avenel, 07001 ........... (732) 499-0125

**PRIMESOURCE BUILDING PRODUCTS, INC.**
**1321 Greenway Dr., Irving TX 75038 ............................... (972) 999-8500**
**Co-CEO—Mona Zinman; CFO—Jerry Kegley; Cont.—Melody Keener**
PrimeSource Building Products, Inc., 20 Van Dyke Ave, New Brunswick, 08901 . . (732) 296-0600

**PRIMEX PLASTICS CORP.**
**1235 N. F St., Richmond IN 47374 .................................. (765) 966-7774**
**Pres.—Mike Cramer; V-P., Sales & Mktg.—Tim Schultz; V-P., Opers.—Gus Finet; Dir., Hum. Res.—Darin Dubbs; Dir., Fin.—Rob Houseman; GM—Jeff Longsworth; Hum. Res. Mgr.—Shannon Davis**
O'Neil Color & Compounding Corp., 61 River Dr., Garfield, 07026 ............ (973) 777-8999
Primex Plastics Corp., 65 River Dr., Garfield, 07026 ...................... (973) 470-8000

**PRINCETON TEC**
**5198 Route 130 N., Bordentown NJ 08505 ............................ (609) 298-9331**
**Pres.—Arthur W. Stephens; Dir., Sales & Sales Mgr., Natl.—David Cozzone; Opers. & Prodn. Mgr.—Debra Safranko; IT Mgr.—Rich Shenowski; Hum. Res. Mgr.—Laura Papp**
Princeton Tec, 110 Collings Ave., West Berlin, 08091....................... (609) 298-9331

**PRINT TECH LTD.**
**49 Fadem Rd., Springfield NJ 07081 ................................ (908) 232-2287**
**Ptnr.—Russell Evans; Ptnr.—Gary Alessio**
Sign Tech, 361 South Ave. E., Westfield, 07090............................ (908) 232-2287

**PRO MACH, INC.**
6279 Tri Ridge Blvd., Ste. 410, Loveland OH 45140. . . . . . . . . . . . . . . . . . . (513) 831-8778
Pres., CEO—Mark Anderson; CFO—William Schult; V.-P., Bus. Dev. & Mktg.—John Eklung;
V.-P., IT—Thomas Scheper; V.-P., Hum. Res.—Patrick Mohan; Corp. Cont.—Darryl Baer
Id Technology, 48 Spruce St., Oakland, 07436 . . . . . . . . . . . . . . . . . . . . . . . (888) 405-4574

**PROBUILD HOLDINGS, INC.**
7595 Technology Way, Ste. 500, Denver CO 80237 . . . . . . . . . . . . . . . . . . (303) 262-8500
CEO—Rob Marchbank; Sr. V.-P., IT & CIO—Karin Catton; Sr. V.-P., Hum. Res.—Steve Bloom;
Sr. V.-P., Supply Chain—Paul Dodge; Ex. V.-P., Supply Chain & Tech.—Don Riley;
Dir., Emp. Rels.—Debbie Duran
ProBuild Co., LLC, 817 Eastgate Dr., Ste. 101, Mount Laurel, 08054 . . . . . . . . (856) 505-1100
ProBuild Co., LLC, 210 Williamstown Rd., Berlin, 08009 . . . . . . . . . . . . . . . (856) 767-3153

**PROCTER & GAMBLE CO., THE**
1 Procter & Gamble Plz., Cincinnati OH 45202 . . . . . . . . . . . . . . . . . . . . (513) 983-1100
Chrm., Pres. & CEO—Alan 'A.G.' Lafley; Board Chrm.—Valerie Shepphard;
Vice Chair, Global Opers.—Werner Geissler; Group Pres., N. America—Melanie Healey;
Global Pres., Baby, Feminine & Family Care—Martin Riant; CFO—Jon R. Moeller;
Chief Legal Officer & Secy.—Deborah Platt Majoras;
V.-P., Global Sustainability—Len Sauers;
Dir., Mktg., N. American Hair Care—Kevin Crociata; Dir., Mktg., Pampers—John Brase;
Global Brand Bldg. Officer—Marc Pritchard
Procter & Gamble Mfg. Co., 100 Essex Ave. E., Avenel, 07001 . . . . . . . . . . . . (732) 602-4500

**PRODUCTION RESOURCE GROUP, LLC**
539 Temple Hill Rd., New Windsor NY 12553 . . . . . . . . . . . . . . . . . . . . . (845) 567-5700
Ex. V.-P., Chief Admn. Officer—Nicole Cano-Schwiebert; V.-P., Fin. & CAO—Tom Minganelli;
CFO & Chief of Asset Strategy—Scott Hansen; V.-P.—Orestes Mihaly;
Hum. Res. Mgr.—Carol Sager; Pur. Agt.—Dan Easterly
PRG Light, Inc., 915 Secaucus Ave., Secaucus, 07094 . . . . . . . . . . . . . . . . (201) 758-4000

**PROMOTION IN MOTION COS., INC., THE**
25 Commerce Dr., Allendale NJ 07401 . . . . . . . . . . . . . . . . . . . . . . . . . . (201) 784-5800
Pres., CEO—Michael Rosenberg; COO—Basant Dwivedi; CFO—Robert Purcell;
Ex. V.-P., Sales—Jeff Brown; V.-P., Mktg.—Josh Shapiro; Dir.—IT—Robert Lascar
PIM Brands, LLC, 500 Pierce St., Somerset, 08873 . . . . . . . . . . . . . . . . . . (732) 560-8300

**PROQUEST, LLC**
789 E. Eisenhower Pkwy., P.O. Box 1346, Ann Arbor MI 48108 . . . . . . . . . . (734) 761-4700
CEO—Kurt Sanford; CFO—Jonathan Collins; Sr. V.-P., Global Sales—Tony Rummans;
Sr. V.-P., Cust. Care & Mktg.—Lynda James-Gilboe;
V.-P., Content Opers.—Neal McCormick; Gen. Counsel—Kevin Norris
R. R. Bowker, 630 Central Ave., New Providence, 07974 . . . . . . . . . . . . . . . (908) 795-3500

**PROTECH CHEMICALS LTD.**
7600 Henri Bourassa West, Montreal, Quebec, Canada H4S 1W3, . . . . . . . . (514) 745-0200
Mng. Ptnr.—David Ades
Protech Powder Coating, Inc., 21 Audrey Pl., Fairfield, 07004 . . . . . . . . . . . (973) 257-0505

**PROTECTION ONE ALARM MONITORING, INC.**
1035 N. 3rd St., Ste. 101, Lawrence KS 66044 . . . . . . . . . . . . . . . . . . . . (785) 856-5500
Pres., CEO & CMO—Tim Whall; Ex. V.-P., CFO—Dan Bresingham;
COO & Dir., Mktg.—Jamie S. Haenggi; Sr. V.-P., Cust. Opers.—Joseph Sanchez;
V.-P., Hum. Res.—Betsy Scott; Mktg. Mgr.—Madelyn Wagner;
Hum. Res. & Info. Svcs. Mgr.—Michelle Munoz
Protection One, Inc., 50 Williams Pkwy., Ste. L, East Hanover, 07936 . . . . . . (973) 227-3421

**PRUDENT PUBLISHING CO.**
65 Challenger Rd., Ridgefield Park NJ 07660 . . . . . . . . . . . . . . . . . . . . . (201) 641-7900
Chrm.—Alan Solow; Pres.—Allen Greenwald; CMO—H. L. DeVore;
IT Mgr.—Juan Carlos Pinzon; Hum. Res. Mgr.—Yuhen Abreu
Prudent Publishing Co., 400 N. Frontage Rd., Landing, 07850 . . . . . . . . . . . (973) 347-4554

**PSS WORLD MEDICAL, INC.**
4345 Southpoint Blvd., Jacksonville FL 32216 . . . . . . . . . . . . . . . . . . . . . (904) 332-3000
CEO—Gary Corless; V.-P., CFO—David M. Bronson; Ex. V.-P., CMO—John Sasen, Sr.;
V.-P., Compliance—Andy Woods
PSS/World Medical, Inc., 208 Passaic Ave., Ste. 2, Fairfield, 07004 . . . . . . . (973) 775-8600

**PURATOS CORP.**
1941 Old Cuthbert Rd., Cherry Hill NJ 08034 . . . . . . . . . . . . . . . . . . . . . (856) 428-4300
Pres., U.S.—Frederic Duvauchelle; V.-P., Sales—Michael Simone;
V.-P., Sales—Matt Crumpton; V.-P., Opers. & Pur.—Brent Laurin;
V.-P., Fin. & IT—Marinela Maritescu; V.-P., Hum. Res.—Robert Donegan;
Reg. Dir., Americas—Karel Zimmermann; Dir., Export, N. America—Pat Pilla;
Comms. & Mktg. Mgr.—Kathryn Power
Puratos Corp., 945 Sherman Ave., Pennsauken, 08110 . . . . . . . . . . . . . . . . (856) 661-3112

**PURDUE PHARMA L. P.**
201 Tresser Blvd., Stamford CT 06901 . . . . . . . . . . . . . . . . . . . . . . . . . (203) 588-8000
Pres., CEO—Mark Timney; Sr. V.-P., Hum. Res.—David E. Long;
V.-P., Pub. Affs. & State Govt.—Alan Must; V.-P., Corp. Affs. & Comms.—Raul Damas;
Sr. Dir., Pub. Affs.—James W. Heins
P. F. Laboratories, Inc., 700 Union Blvd., Totowa, 07512 . . . . . . . . . . . . . . (973) 256-3100

**PYROTECNICO**
299 Wilson Rd., P.O. Box 149, New Castle PA 16103 . . . . . . . . . . . . . . . . . (724) 652-9555
Pres., CEO—Stephen Vitale; V.-P., GM & Opers.—Michael J. Fox;
Pers. Mgr.—Joseph Mitchell
Pyrotechnic Industries, Inc., 1640 Garden Rd., Vineland, 08360 . . . . . . . . . . (856) 697-1023

**Q. E. P. CO., INC.**
1001 Broken Sound Pkwy. N.W., Ste. A, Boca Raton FL 33487 . . . . . . . . . . (561) 994-5550
CEO—Lewis Gould; Pres.—Leonard Gould; CFO—Richard Brooke; COO—Herbert Maertl;
Sr. V.-P. & Gen. Counsel—Lawrence Levine; Sr. V.-P., Mktg.—Jamie Clingan;
Corp. Cont.—Mike Miller
Boiardi Products Corp., 453 Main St., Ste. 4, Little Falls, 07424 . . . . . . . . . (973) 256-1100

**QAD, INC.**
100 Innovation Pl., Santa Barbara CA 93108 . . . . . . . . . . . . . . . . . . . . . (805) 566-6000
Chrm., Pres.—Pamela M. Lopker; CEO—Karl F. Lopker; CIO—Leif Petersen;
CTO—Tony J. Winter; CMO—Gordon Fleming; CFO—Daniel Lender;
Chief People Officer—Kaye Swanson; Sr. V.-P., CAO & Cont.—Kara Bellamy;
Sr. V.-P., Treas.—John Neale; Sr. V.-P., Global Strategy & N. America—Lisa Pope;
Sr. V.-P., Global Svcs.—Anton Chilton; Sr. V.-P., R & D—Bill Keese;
V.-P., Industry & Prod. Mktg.—Phil Friedman; V.-P.—Charlie Eggerding
QAD, Inc., 10000 Midlantic Dr., Ste. 100 W., Mount Laurel, 08054 . . . . . . . . . (856) 273-1717

**QUAD/GRAPHICS, INC.**
N61W23044 Harry's Way, Sussex WI 53089 . . . . . . . . . . . . . . . . . . . . . (414) 566-6000
Chrm., Pres. & CEO—Joel Quadracci; Pres., Dist. & Logistics—Dave Riebe;
Ex. V.-P., CFO—John Fowler; Ex. V.-P., Client Svcs. & Sales—Dave Blais;
Ex. V.-P., Mfg.—Tom Frankowski; V.-P., Gen. Counsel—Andy Schiesl;
V.-P., Treas.—Kelly Vanderboom; V.-P., Hum. Res.—Nancy Ott;
V.-P., Info. Sys. & Infrastructure—Steve Jaeger; V.-P., Press—Tim Sands;
V.-P., Cust. Serv.—Ron Nash; Dir., Postal Affs.—Joseph E. Schick;
Dir., Corp. Comm.—Claire Ho; Corp. Co-Mail Sols. Mgr.—Steve Jost;
GM—Tim Ohnmacht
Quad/Graphics, Inc., 28 Engelhard Dr., Monroe Township, 08831 . . . . . . . . . (609) 495-1200

**QUADRIGA ART, INC.**
30 E. 33rd St., 10th Fl., New York NY 10016 . . . . . . . . . . . . . . . . . . . . . (212) 685-0751
Chrm., CEO—Mark Schulhof; Pres.—Thomas B. Schulhof;
V.-P., Intl. Mfg. & Plng.—Judy Costello
Quadriga Art, Inc., 825 Hylton Rd., Pennsauken, 08110 . . . . . . . . . . . . . . . (856) 663-2500

**QUALITY SWISS SCREW MACHINE CO., INC.**
960 Mountain Ave., Mountainside NJ 07092 . . . . . . . . . . . . . . . . . . . . . (908) 654-1881
Pres.—Andrew Cangelosi; Prodn. Mgr.—Todd Luetters;
Hum. Res. Mgr.—Isabella Cangelosi
Quality Swiss Screw Machine Co., Inc., 849 4th Ave., Elizabeth, 07202 . . . . . (908) 654-1881

**QUEST DIAGNOSTICS**
3 Giralda Farms, Madison NJ 07940 . . . . . . . . . . . . . . . . . . . . . . . . . . (973) 520-2700
Non-Exec. Chrm.—Daniel C. Stanzione; Pres., CEO—Stephen H. Rusckowski;
Sr. V.-P., Chief Med. Officer—Jon R. Cohen;
Sr. V.-P., Chief Legal Counsel—Michael Prevoznik; V.-P., Corp. Comms.—Gary Samuels;
Ex. Dir., Investor Rels.—Kathleen Valentine
Enterix, Inc., 236 Fernwood Ave., Edison, 08837 . . . . . . . . . . . . . . . . . . . (732) 429-1899

**QUIKIE PRINT & COPY SHOPS**
703 Broad St., Shrewsbury NJ 07702 . . . . . . . . . . . . . . . . . . . . . . . . . (732) 933-1010
Pres.—Francine Goldstein; Corp. Secy.—Gerald Goldstein; Manager—Allen Dougherty
Quikie Print & Copy Shop, 827 W. Park, Ocean, 07712 . . . . . . . . . . . . . . . (732) 531-8860
QP2000, LLC, 827 W. Park Ave., Ocean, 07712. . . . . . . . . . . . . . . . . . . . (732) 531-8860

**QUIKRETE COS., INC., THE**
3490 Piedmont Rd., Ste. 1300, Atlanta GA 30305 . . . . . . . . . . . . . . . . . . (404) 634-9100
Pres.—J. E. Winchester, Jr.; Ex. V.-P., Sales—Dennis W. Winchester;
Ex. V.-P.—J. O. Winchester; V.-P., Acctg.—Will Magill; Hum. Res. Mgr.—Mark Malcahy;
Pur. Agt.—Mike Tomiko
CST Pavers a division of Pavestone,
23 Ridge Rd., P.O. Box 2736, Branchville, 07826 . . . . . . . . . . . . . . . . . . (973) 948-7193
QUIKRETE Cos., Inc, The, 22 Union Ave., Berlin, 08009 . . . . . . . . . . . . . . . (856) 768-6642
Tri-State QUIKRETE, 150 Gold Mine Rd., Flanders, 07836 . . . . . . . . . . . . . (973) 347-4569

**QUINCY NEWSPAPERS, INC.**
130 S. 5th St., Quincy IL 62301 . . . . . . . . . . . . . . . . . . . . . . . . . . . . . (217) 223-5100
Pres., CEO—Ralph M. Oakley; CFO—Brad Eaton; Ex. Editor & GM—Ron Wallace;
Dir., IT—Michael Funk; Dir., Hum. Res.—Jena Schulz;
Dir., Newspapers & New Media—Mary Winters; Dir., Engrg.—Brady Dreasler;
Dir., Broadcast News—Dennis Kendall
New Jersey Herald, The, 2 Spring St., P.O. Box 10, Newton, 07860 . . . . . . . . (973) 383-1500

**R & R MARKETING, LLC**
10 Patton Dr., West Caldwell NJ 07006 . . . . . . . . . . . . . . . . . . . . . . . . (973) 228-5100
Pres.—Jon Maslin; V.-P., Opers.—Doug Siegel; V.-P., Fin.—Dennis M. Portsmore
R & R Marketing, LLC, 2900 E. State Street Ext., Trenton, 08619 . . . . . . . . . (609) 587-6103

**R TAPE CORPORATION**
6 Ingersoll Rd., South Plainfield NJ 07080 . . . . . . . . . . . . . . . . . . . . . . (908) 753-5570
Pres., CEO—Paul Charapata; CFO—Tom Kennedy; Cont.—Tim Riener;
Sales Mgr., Inside—Laurie Richard; Hum. Res. Mgr.—Kristy Ninemin;
Export Mgr.—Wendy Miller
CET Films, Inc., 1650 Corporate Rd. W., Lakewood, 08701 . . . . . . . . . . . . . (732) 367-5511

**R. E. MICHEL CO., INC.**
1 R. E. Michel Dr., Glen Burnie MD 21060 . . . . . . . . . . . . . . . . . . . . . . . (410) 760-4000
Pres.—J. W. Michel; Ex. V.-P., CFO—Ron Miller; V.-P., Sales—Glen Baker;
V.-P., Opers.—Gene Winters; V.-P., Mktg.—J. V. Michel, Jr.;
Dir., Hum. Res.—Sherry Atkinson; Dir., Dist.—J. V. Michel III
R. E. Michel Co., Inc., 895 Towbin Ave., Lakewood, 08701 . . . . . . . . . . . . . (732) 886-3592
R. E. Michel Co., Inc., 262 Old New Brunswick Rd., Piscataway, 08854 . . . . . . (732) 465-9700

**R. R. DONNELLEY & SONS CO.**
111 S. Wacker Dr., 36th Fl., Chicago IL 60606 . . . . . . . . . . . . . . . . . . . . (312) 326-8000
Pres., CEO—Thomas Quinlan III; Ex. V.-P., CFO—Daniel Leib;
V.-P., Hum. Res.—Scott Bigelow; V.-P., Inv. Rels.—Dave Gardella
R. R. Donnelley & Sons Co., 215 County Ave., Secaucus, 07094 . . . . . . . . . . (201) 271-1000
R. R. Donnelley & Sons Co., 5 Henderson Dr., West Caldwell, 07006 . . . . . . . (973) 882-7000

**RAILING DYNAMICS, INC.**
135 Steelmanville Rd., Egg Harbor Township NJ 08234 . . . . . . . . . . . . . . . (609) 601-1300
Pres.—Chris Terrels; V.-P. & Dir., Fin.—Jon Gronow; Dir., Sales, Natl.—Jay Penney;
Mktg. Comm. Mgr.—Carol Lyn Groce
Railing Dynamics, Inc., 1201 N. 10th St., Millville, 08332 . . . . . . . . . . . . . . (856) 327-1698

**RAILROAD CONSTRUCTION COMPANY, INC.**
75-77 Grove St., Paterson NJ 07503 . . . . . . . . . . . . . . . . . . . . . . . . . . (973) 684-0362
Pres.—Christopher Daloisio; V.-P. & Secy.—James A. Daloisio;
Dir., Hum. Res.—Mary Daloisio
RCC Fabricators, Inc., 2035 Highway 206, Vincentown, 08088 . . . . . . . . . . . (609) 859-9350

PARENT COMPANY

**RANBAXY, INC.**
600 College Rd. E., Ste. 2100, Princeton NJ 08540 . . . . . . . . . . . . . . . . (609) 720-9200
V.-P., Hum. Res.—Bernard Brothman; V.-P., Comm. & Govt. Affs.—Charles Caprariello
OHM Laboratories, Inc., 14 Terminal Rd., New Brunswick, 08901 . . . . . . . . . . . . (732) 514-4380
OHM Laboratories, Inc.,
1385 Livingston Ave., P.O. Box 7397, North Brunswick, 08902 . . . . . . . . . . . . (732) 418-2235

**RANDA CORP.**
417 5th Ave., 11th Fl., New York NY 10016 . . . . . . . . . . . . . . . . . . . . (212) 768-8800
Pres., CEO—Jeffrey Spiegel; Sr. V.-P., Merchandising—John Kammeier;
V.-P., Sales—Judy Person
Randa Luggage Co., 200 Broadacres Dr., 2nd Fl., Bloomfield, 07003 . . . . . . . . . (973) 873-9050

**RATHGIBSON, LLC**
2505 Foster Ave., Janesville WI 53545 . . . . . . . . . . . . . . . . . . . . . (608) 754-2222
V.-P., GM—John Fortin; Dir., Process & Prod. Dev.—Dave O'Donnell;
Qual. Assur. Mgr.—Mike Aston
RathGibson, LLC, 100 Aspen Hill Rd., North Branch, 08876. . . . . . . . . . . . . . (908) 218-1400

**RBC BEARINGS, INC.**
One Tribology Ctr., 102 Willenbrock Rd., Oxford CT 06478 . . . . . . . . . . . (203) 267-7001
Pres., CEO—Michael J. Hartnett; V.-P., CFO—Daniel A. Bergeron;
Gen. Counsel & Secy.—Thomas J. Williams; Corp. Cont.—Thomas M. Burigo
RBC Bearings, Inc., 400 Sullivan Way, West Trenton, 08628 . . . . . . . . . . . . (609) 882-5050

**READY PAC PRODUCE, INC.**
4401 Foxdale Ave., Irwindale CA 91706 . . . . . . . . . . . . . . . . . . . . . (626) 856-8686
Chrm., CEO—Michael Solomon; Ex. V.-P., Sales & Mktg.—Michael Celani;
V.-P., Hum. Res.—Renee Atwood; Plt. Opers. Mgr.—Santiago Pacheco;
Hum. Res. Mgr.—Virginia Sandoval
Ready Pac, 101 Arlington Blvd., Swedesboro, 08085 . . . . . . . . . . . . . . (856) 241-0900
Ready Pac Produce, Inc., 700 Railroad Ave., P.O. Box 6, Florence, 08518 . . . . . . (609) 499-1900

**RECKITT BENCKISER, INC.**
399 Interpace Pkwy., P.O. Box 225, Parsippany NJ 07054. . . . . . . . . . . . . (973) 404-2600
Pres., Frenchs Food Prod.—Elliott Penner; Ex. V.-P., N. America—Rob de Groot;
V.-P., Hum. Res.—Beverly Wilen; GM, Household Prod. Sales—Anthony Jenkinson;
GM, Household Prod. Mktg.—Alexander Iacik
Reckitt Benckiser, LLC,
799 U.S. Highway 206, P.O. Box 5817, Hillsborough, 08844 . . . . . . . . . . (908) 533-2000

**RECONSERVE, INC.**
2811 Wilshire Blvd., Ste. 410, Santa Monica CA 90403 . . . . . . . . . . . . . . (310) 458-1574
CEO—Meyer Luskin; V.-P., CFO—Rudy Alvarez; Sr. V.-P.—David Luskin;
Ex. V.-P., Admn. & Fin.—Rida Hamed
ReConserve, Inc., 1250 Amboy Ave., Perth Amboy, 08861 . . . . . . . . . . . . (732) 826-4240

**RECORDER PUBLISHING CO.**
17-19 Morristown Rd., P.O. Box 687, Bernardsville NJ 07924 . . . . . . . . . . . (908) 766-3900
Ptnr.—Stephen W. Parker; Ptnr.—Elizabeth K. Parker; Editor—Charlie Zavalick;
Dir., Adv.—Jerry O'Donnell
Recorder Newspaper Co., 530 E. Main St., P.O. Box 600, Chester, 07930 . . . . . (908) 766-3900

**REED ELSEVIER, INC.**
125 Park Ave., 23rd Fl., New York NY 10017 . . . . . . . . . . . . . . . . . (212) 309-8100
CEO—Marl Kelsey; Pres.—Nick Luff;
V.-P., Emerging Voice Technologies & Global Comms.—Jim Webb;
Dir., Corp. Affs.—Youngsuk Chi
LexisNexis Martindale-Hubell, 121 Chanlon Rd., New Providence, 07974 . . . . . . (908) 464-6800

**REEDY INTERNATIONAL CORP.**
9301-A Forsythe Park Dr., Charlotte NC 28273 . . . . . . . . . . . . . . . . (980) 819-6930
Owner & CFO—Anne Marie Reedy; Pres., CEO—Peter Schroeck; V.-P., Opers.—Elena Miller;
V.-P., Global Bus.—Bryan Burgess; V.-P., Fin.—Kristen Reedy;
Sales Mgr., Tech.—Lee Hollar
Reedy International Corp., 25 E. Front St., Ste. 200, Keyport, 07735 . . . . . . . . (732) 264-1777

**REEVES INTERNATIONAL, INC.**
14 Industrial Rd., Pequannock NJ 07440 . . . . . . . . . . . . . . . . . . . (973) 694-5006
Pres.—Anthony Fleischmann; CFO—Arthur Minnocci;
V.-P., Mktg. & Prod. Dev.—Stephanie Macejko; V.-P., Comms.—Kathleen Fallon;
Dir., Sales, Specialty Toy Sales—Bob LaRocca; Dir., Proc.—Jeffrey Uhrig;
Sales Mgr., Natl.—Edward Dean; IT Mgr.—Lisa Raimondo
Reeves International, Inc., 34 Owens Dr., Wayne, 07470 . . . . . . . . . . . . . (973) 956-9555

**RESOLV CORPORATION**
237 Worthen Rd. E., Lexington MA 02421 . . . . . . . . . . . . . . . . . . . (973) 676-5141
Pres., Hum. Res. & Pur. Mgr.—Syed Ali Rizvi; V.-P., Pub. Affs.—Mohammad Afzal;
Cont.—James R. Ross; Sales & Serv. Mgr.—Sanjay Rao; Mktg. Mgr.—Sid Rogers;
Off. Mgr.—S. Parveen; Logistics Mgr.—Sohail Mustafa; Shpg. Mgr.—Ian Ramos;
Qual. Control Mgr.—D. Dill
Resolv Corporation, 410 Division St., Elizabeth, 07201 . . . . . . . . . . . . . (973) 676-5141

**RESTAURANT DEPOT, LLC**
1524 132nd St., College Point NY 11356 . . . . . . . . . . . . . . . . . . . (718) 762-8700
CEO—Stanley Fleishman; Pres.—Richard Kirschner; CFO—Bryan Emmert;
Mktg. Mgr.—Doug Klein; Hum. Res. Mgr.—Shez Darden
Jetro Cash & Carry, Inc., 1 Amity St., Jersey City, 07304 . . . . . . . . . . . . (201) 434-4334
Restaurant Depot, LLC, 1050 Thomas Busch Memorial Hwy., Pennsauken, 08110. . (856) 488-4288

**RESTEK CORP.**
110 Benner Cir., Bellefonte PA 16823 . . . . . . . . . . . . . . . . . . . . . (814) 353-1300
Pres. & Head Coach—Bryan Wolcot; Dir., Hum. Res.—Tina Welch;
IT Mgr.—Vlad Safyanovsky; R & D Mgr.—Valerie Strohm; Pur. Agt.—Jim Steyers;
Cust. Serv. Rep.—Lauren Brooks; Technical Writer—Naomi Lovallo
Glastron, Inc., 510 N. West Blvd., Vineland, 08360 . . . . . . . . . . . . . . . (856) 692-0500

**REVIEW PUBLISHING L. P.**
1617 JFK Blvd., Ste. 1005, Philadelphia PA 19103 . . . . . . . . . . . . . . . (215) 563-7400
Chrm., COO—Anthony Clifton; V.-P., Cont. & Hum. Res. Mgr.—James Stokes;
Cont. & Hum. Res. Mgr.—Ginger Monte; Chief Operating Mgr.—John Gallo
Atlantic City Weekly, L. P.,
Bayport 1, 8025 Black Horse Pike, Ste. 3, Pleasantville, 08232 . . . . . . . . (609) 646-4848

**REX LUMBER CO.**
840 Main St., Acton MA 01720 . . . . . . . . . . . . . . . . . . . . . . . . (978) 263-0055
Pres.—Craig Forester; COO—A. Ledyard Smith; Dir., Pur.—Andy Godzinski;
Dir., Fin.—Mark Bronstein; Sales Mgr.—Tom Murray; Hum. Res. Mgr.—Irene Flannery;
Traf. Mgr.—William Rivera
Rex Lumber Co., 1 Station St., P.O. Box 1776, Englishtown, 07726 . . . . . . . . (732) 446-4200

**REXAM, INC.**
4201 Congress St., Ste. 340, Charlotte NC 28209 . . . . . . . . . . . . . . . (704) 551-1500
V.-P., Hum. Res., Shared Svcs.—Ken Hicks; Treas.—Clint Turlin; Cont.—Judy Graham
Rexam Healthcare Packaging, Inc., 14-B Brass Castle Rd., Washington, 07882. . (908) 689-1660

**RG GROUP**
650 N. State St., York PA 17403 . . . . . . . . . . . . . . . . . . . . . . . (717) 846-9300
CEO—Randall Gross; Pres., COO—Rich Freeh; Ex. V.-P., Field Sales—Dennis Ohme;
V.-P., Mfg.—Ed Stum; V.-P., Instrumentation—Rick Miller;
V.-P., Indl. Connectors & Dir., Mktg.—Jeff Gunnet; Dir., Opers.—Donna Benner;
Cust. Sales & Serv. Mgr.—Tracy Hedgepeth
Van Air & Hydraulics, Inc., 612 E. Woodlawn Ave., Maple Shade, 08052 . . . . . . (856) 779-7300

**RICH PRODUCTS CORP.**
1 Robert Rich Way, Buffalo NY 14213 . . . . . . . . . . . . . . . . . . . . . (716) 878-8000
Chrm.—Robert E. Rich, Jr.; Vice Chrm.—Mindy Rich; Pres., CEO—William Gisel;
Pres., U.S. & Canada—Ray Burke; Ex. V.-P., COO—Richard Ferranti;
Ex. V.-P., CFO—Jim Deuschele; V.-P., Comm.—Dwight Graham
Mother's Kitchen, Inc., 499 Veterans Dr., Burlington, 08016 . . . . . . . . . . . (609) 589-3033
Rich Products, 1910 Gallagher Dr., Vineland, 08360 . . . . . . . . . . . . . . (856) 696-5600

**RING CONTAINER TECHNOLOGIES, INC.**
1 Industrial Park, Oakland TN 38060 . . . . . . . . . . . . . . . . . . . . . (901) 465-6333
Chrm.—Carl Ring; CFO—Tim Whealen; Ex. V.-P., Sales & Mktg.—Jeff Ullrich;
Ex. V.-P., Opers.—Scott Wuerfel; V.-P., Hum. Res.—Michelle Redmond;
V.-P., Logistics & Pur.—David Hollis; Cust. Serv. Mgr.—Jenne Lindley
Ring Container Technologies, 50 Fadem Rd., Ste. 1, Springfield, 07081 . . . . . . (973) 258-0707

**RIVERSIDE ACQUISITION GROUP, LLC**
365 New Albany Rd., Moorestown NJ 08057 . . . . . . . . . . . . . . . . . . (856) 802-1900
Pres.—Cliff McDuggle; CFO—Scott Mangan; COO—Russ Stewart; Cont.—Joan Rose
Com-Pak, Inc., 365 New Albany Rd., Moorestown, 08057 . . . . . . . . . . . . (856) 802-1900

**RIVERSIDE PARTNERS, LLC**
Terminal Tower, 50 Public Sq., 29th Fl., Cleveland OH 44113 . . . . . . . . . . (216) 344-1040
Co-CEO—Bela Szigethy; Co-CEO—Stewart Kohl; V.-P.—Sarah Roth; V.-P.—Brian Sauer;
Mktg. Mgr.—Graham Hearns
Water-Jel Technologies, 50 Broad St., Carlstadt, 07072 . . . . . . . . . . . . . (201) 507-8300

**ROBERT-JAMES SALES, INC.**
2585 Walden Ave., Buffalo NY 14225 . . . . . . . . . . . . . . . . . . . . . (716) 651-6000
Ptnr.—Jim Bokor, Sr.; Ptnr.—Bob Glidden, Jr.; Pres.—Jim Bokor, Jr.;
V.-P., Fin.—Joe McIntosh; Sales Mgr., Natl.—Jeff Parrish
Robert-James Sales, Inc., 9 Corporate Dr., P.O. Box B, Cranbury, 08512 . . . . . (609) 860-0900

**ROBERTSON PIPER SOFTWARE GROUP, INC.**
1500 Cardinal Dr., Chatham NJ 07928 . . . . . . . . . . . . . . . . . . . . . (973) 435-3640
CEO—Doug Robertson; CFO—Tad Piper; V.-P., Bus. Dev.—Kevin Kogler
Lagniappe Health Acquisition Co.,
34 Maple Ave., Ste. 102, P.O. Box 727, Pine Brook, 07058 . . . . . . . . . . (973) 256-7633

**ROCHE HOLDINGS, INC.**
1 DNA Way S., South San Francisco CA 94080 . . . . . . . . . . . . . . . . . (650) 225-1000
CEO—Ian T. Clark; Ex. V.-P., Research—Richard Scheller; Cont.—Robert Andreatta;
Dir., Hum. Res.—Denise Smith-Hams; Dir., Inv. Rels.—Thomas K. Larsen
Roche Nutley, 340 Kingsland St., Nutley, 07110 . . . . . . . . . . . . . . . . (973) 235-5000

**ROCHE MOLECULAR DIAGNOSTICS**
4300 Hacienda Dr., Pleasanton CA 94588 . . . . . . . . . . . . . . . . . . . (925) 730-8000
Pres.—Paul Brown; V.-P., Regulatory Affs.—Angela Tucker; V.-P., Comms.—Bob Purcell
Roche Molecular Systems, Inc., 1080 U.S. Highway 202 S., Branchburg, 08876. . (908) 253-7200

**ROCKLAND BAKERY, INC.**
94 Demarest Mill Rd. W., Nanuet NY 10954 . . . . . . . . . . . . . . . . . . (845) 623-5800
Pres.—Salvatore Battaglia; V.-P.—Philip Battaglia; Dir., Sales—Mike Battaglia;
Hum. Res. Mgr.—Ashley Samsalomd; Accts. Payable Mgr.—Norm Sears
R. P. Baking Co., 840 Jersey St., Harrison, 07029 . . . . . . . . . . . . . . . (973) 483-3374

**ROCKLINE INDUSTRIES, INC.**
4343 S. Taylor Dr., Sheboygan WI 53081 . . . . . . . . . . . . . . . . . . . (920) 452-3004
Pres.—Randy Rudolph; Sr. V.-P., Sales & Mktg.—Ron Kerscher; V.-P., Mfg.—Dan Joslyn;
V.-P., Hum. Res.—Kirk Engholt; Dir., IT—Craig Albert
Rockline Industries, Inc., 1 Kramer Dr., P.O. Box 189, Montville, 07045 . . . . . . (973) 257-9346

**ROCK-TENN CO.**
504 Thrasher St., Norcross GA 30071 . . . . . . . . . . . . . . . . . . . . . (770) 448-2193
Chrm.—G. Stephen Felker; CEO—Steven C. Voorhees;
Pres., Pkg. Sols.—Michael C. Kiepura; Pres., Paper Sols.—James B. Porter III;
Ex. V.-P., CFO—Ward H. Dickson; CAO—A. Stephen Meadows;
Ex. V.-P., Gen. Counsel & Secy.—Robert B. McIntosh;
Ex. V.-P., Hum. Res.—Jennifer Graham-Johnson; Dir., Corp. Comms.—Robin Keegan;
Corp. Comms. Mgr.—Kelly Fowler
Graph Corr, LLC, 4 Corn Rd., Dayton, 08810 . . . . . . . . . . . . . . . . . (732) 355-0088
Rock-Tenn Co., 1 Corn Rd., P.O. Box 440, Dayton, 08810 . . . . . . . . . . . (732) 274-2500
Rock-Tenn Co., 15 Garner Rd., Fairfield, 07004 . . . . . . . . . . . . . . . . (973) 594-6000
Rock-Tenn Co., 2013 McCarter Hwy., Newark, 07104 . . . . . . . . . . . . . (973) 268-4938

**ROCKWELL AUTOMATION, INC.**
1201 S. 2nd St., Milwaukee WI 53204 . . . . . . . . . . . . . . . . . . . . . (414) 382-2000
Chrm., CEO—Keith Nosbusch; Sr. V.-P., CFO—Theodore Crandall;
Sr. V.-P., Gen. Counsel & Secy.—Douglas Hagerman; Sr. V.-P., Hum. Res.—Susan Schmitt;
Sr. V.-P., Engrg. & Opers. Svcs.—Marty Thomas; Dir., Ext. Comm.—John Bernaden
Rockwell Automation, Inc., 165 Fieldcrest Ave., Raritan Ctr., Edison, 08837. . . . (732) 225-1360

**ROFIN-SINAR, INC.**
40984 Concept Dr., Plymouth MI 48170 . . . . . . . . . . . . . . . . . . . . (734) 455-5400
Pres., COO—Louis Molnar; Cont., Secy.—Cindy Denis; Sales Mgr., Macro—Scott Mabie
PRC Laser, 350 N. Frontage Rd., Landing, 07850 . . . . . . . . . . . . . . . (973) 347-0100

PARENT COMPANY

**ROMA MOULDING, INC.**
360 Hanlan Rd., Woodbridge, Ontario, Canada L4L 8V6, .............. **(905) 850-1500**
   Pres.—John Garei
Roma Moulding, Inc., 115 Northfield Ave., Edison, 08837 ................. (732) 346-0999

**RONALD-MARK ASSOCS., INC.**
1227 Central Ave., P.O. Box 776, Hillside NJ 07205 ............... **(908) 558-0011**
   Pres., CEO—Les Satz; V-P., PVC Film & Supported Fabrics—Charles Riotto;
     V-P., Trading—Ron Satz; V-P.—Michael Satz
Ronald-Mark Assocs., Inc., 150 N. Summit Ave., P.O. Box 355, Pitman, 08071 ... (856) 582-6766

**ROPER INDUSTRIES, INC.**
6901 Professional Pkwy. E., Ste. 200, Sarasota FL 34240 ............ **(941) 556-2601**
   Chrm., Pres. & CEO—Brian D. Jellison; CFO—John Humphrey;
     V-P., Gen. Counsel & Secy.—David B. Liner; V-P., Cont.—Paul J. Soni;
     V-P., Hum. Res.—Greg Anderson
Princeton Instruments, 3660 Quakerbridge Rd., Trenton, 08619 ............... (609) 587-9797

**ROSENBERGER OF NORTH AMERICA, LLC**
309 Colonial Dr., P.O. Box 309, Akron PA 17501 .................. **(717) 859-8900**
   Pres.—Steven Sacco; Hum. Res. Mgr.—Sally Eby; Logistics Mgr.—Maria Mitton;
     Qual. Assur. Mgr.—Roy Stowe; Pur. Agt.—Betty Zazwirsky
Toth Inc., 6970 Central Hwy., Pennsauken, 08109 ............... (856) 662-8700

**ROTONDI & SONS, INC., S.**
3 Watchung Ave., Chatham NJ 07928 ...................... **(973) 635-7799**
   Pres., CEO—Angelo Rotondi; CFO, Sales Mgr.—John Canace;
     Hum. Res. Mgr.—Mike Rotondi
Rotondi & Sons, Inc., S., 139 Reeder Rd., Phillipsburg, 08865 ............... (908) 475-1916

**ROYAL ADHESIVES & SEALANTS, LLC**
2001 W. Washington St., South Bend IN 46628 .................. **(574) 246-5000**
   Chrm., CEO—Ted Clark; CFO—Gary Stenke; V-P., Sales & Mktg.—Steve Zens;
     V-P., Opers.—Randy Greenlee; MIS Mgr.—Bernie Cunningham;
     Hum. Res. Mgr.—Patty Myers; Qual. Assur. Mgr.—Dave Thompson
Royal Adhesive, Inc., 48 Burgess Pl., Wayne, 07470 ............... (973) 694-0845

**ROYCE ASSOCS., L. P.**
35 Carlton Ave., East Rutherford NJ 07073 ............... **(201) 438-5200**
   Pres.—Jay Royce
Royce Assocs., L. P., 28-36 Paterson St., Paterson, 07501 ............... (973) 279-0400

**R-PAC INTERNATIONAL CORP.**
132 W. 36th St., 7th Fl., New York NY 10018 ............... **(212) 465-1818**
   Chrm.—Daniel Teitelbaum; Pres., CEO—Michael Teitelbaum;
     Pres., Intl. & COO—Matt Matsuo; Ex. V-P., Mfg. & Opers.—Frank Schatz
R-Pac International Corp., 69 Kingsland Ave., Marino Plz. 1, Clifton, 07014 ... (973) 916-1600

**RPM INTERNATIONAL, INC.**
2628 Pearl Rd., Medina OH 44256 ............... **(330) 273-5090**
   Chrm., CEO—Frank C. Sullivan; Pres., COO—Ronald Rice; V-P., CFO—Russell Gordon;
     V-P., Fin. & Cont.—Keith Smiley; V-P., Corp. Benefits & Risk Mgmt.—Janeen Kastner;
     Dir., IT—Matt Franklin; Inv. Rels. Mgr.—Kathie Rogers
Stonhard, A Div. Of StonCor Group,
   1000 E. Park Ave., P.O. Box 308, Maple Shade, 08052 ................. (856) 779-7500

**RSL, INC.**
3092 English Creek Ave., Egg Harbor Township NJ 08234 ............... **(609) 484-1600**
   Pres.—Ron Lewkowitz; V-P.—Kevin Kavanaugh; Opers. Mgr.—Steve Nixon, Sr.
RSL, Inc., 3049 Fernwood Ave., Egg Harbor Township, 08234 ............... (609) 645-9770

**RTS PACKAGING, LLC**
504 Thrasher St., Norcross GA 30071 ...................... **(770) 448-2244**
   CEO—Dick Steed; Pres.—Alan Bosma; Admn. Mgr.—Sandra Boyett
RTS Packaging, LLC, 869 State Highway 12, Frenchtown, 08825 ........... (908) 782-0505

**RUGBY IPD CORP.**
10 Ferry St., Ste. 427-A, Concord NH 03301 ............... **(603) 369-6004**
   Pres.—David Hughes; Corp. Cont.—Ann Stroehlein; Supply Chain Mgr.—Jim Trusiani
Rugby ABP Corp., 60 Joseph St., Moonachie, 07074 ..................... (201) 807-9701

**RUMSEY ELECTRIC CO.**
15 Colwell Ln., Conshohocken PA 19428 ............... **(610) 832-9000**
   Pres., CEO—Gerald M. Lihota; V-P., Secy.-Treas., CFO—Scott M. Cutler;
     V-P., Opers.—Larry Haggerty; Dir., Mktg.—Jill Michener; IT Mgr.—Matt Prior
Rumsey Electric Co., 311 N. Clinton Ave., Trenton, 08638 ............... (609) 989-9400

**RUST-OLEUM CORP.**
11 E. Hawthorn Pkwy., Vernon Hills IL 60061 ...................... **(847) 367-7700**
   Pres.—Tom Reed; CFO—Don Harmeyer; V-P., Sales, Intl.—Kurt Hardy;
     V-P., Opers.—Bill Whiting; V-P., Hum. Res.—Steve Gillman; V-P., Corp. Dev.—Neal Barry;
     Dir., Sales, Intl.—John Simons; Dir., Mktg.—Jim Stinner
Rust-Oleum Corp., 480 Frelinghuysen Ave., Newark, 07114 ............... (732) 469-8100
Rust-Oleum Corp., ZINSSER Brands, 173 Belmont Dr., Somerset, 08873 ...... (732) 469-8100

**RYAN HERCO FLOW SOLUTIONS CORP.**
3010 N. San Fernando Blvd., Burbank CA 91504 ............... **(818) 841-1141**
   Pres., CEO—David Patterson; CFO—Michael Koch; V-P., Sales & Mktg.—Randy Beckwith;
     V-P., Opers.—Carol Thompson; Dir., Bus. Dev.—Rod Grin
Ryan Herco Flow Solutions Corp.,
   50 Tannery Rd., Reading Industrial Ctr., Bldg. 3, Somerville, 08876 ......... (908) 534-6111

**S S M INDUSTRIES, INC.**
3401 Grand Ave., Pittsburgh PA 15225 ...................... **(412) 777-5100**
   Pres.—Thomas Szymczak; V-P., Sales & Mktg.—Leo C. Monaghan;
     Secy.-Treas.—Lawrence E. Gorman; Shop Mgr.—Karl Limmer;
     Pur. Agt.—Bill Reichenecker
Mid States Spiral, Inc., 1425 Grandview Ave., West Deptford, 08066 ......... (215) 744-2846
SSM Industries, Inc., 1425 Grandview Ave., West Deptford, 08066 ........... (856) 345-2525

**SABA SOFTWARE, INC.**
2400 Bridge Pkwy., Redwood City CA 94065 ...................... **(650) 581-2500**
   Pres., CEO—Shawn Farschi; Sr. V-P., Client Success Opers.—Amar Dhaliwal;
     Ex. V-P., Gen. Counsel—Peter Williams; V-P., People—Gina Cruse;
     Sr. Dir., Mktg. Progs.—Ann Heuser
HumanConcepts, 1031 Route 22, Ste. 303, Bridgewater, 08807 ............... (908) 231-0204

---

**SAFEGUARD BUSINESS SYSTEMS, INC.**
8585 N. Stemmons Fwy., Ste. 600-N, Dallas TX 75247 ................... **(214) 905-3935**
   Pres.—J. J. Sorrenti; Ex. Dir., Channel Mktg.—Mark Roggenkamp; IT Mgr.—Terry Robison;
     Cust. Serv. Mgr.—Linda Limon
Safeguard, 1253 Springfield Ave., Ste. 258, New Providence, 07974 ......... (973) 887-9500

**SAFER HOLDING CORP.**
1875 McCarter Hwy., Newark NJ 07104 ...................... **(973) 482-6400**
   Pres., CEO—Albert Safer; CFO—Richard Wachsman; COO—Niso Barokas;
     Plt. Mgr.—Ami Inbal
Markbilt Technical Fabrics Corp., 1875 McCarter Hwy., Newark, 07104 ....... (973) 482-6400
Meadows Knitting Corp., 1875 McCarter Hwy., Newark, 07104. .............. (973) 482-6400

**SAFETY-KLEEN SYSTEMS, INC.**
2600 N. Central Expy., Richardson TX 75080 ............... **(972) 265-2000**
   Pres.—Jerry Correll; Sr. V-P., Chief Compliance Officer—Virgil 'Chip' Duffie;
     Sr. Dir., Corp. Compliance & Hum. Res.—Connie Kopp
Safety-Kleen Systems, Inc., 1200 Sylvan St., Linden, 07036 ............... (908) 862-2000
Safety-Kleen Systems, Inc., 116 Skyline Dr., South Plainfield, 07080 .......... (908) 791-9600
Safety-Kleen Systems, Inc., 123 Red Lion Rd., Vincentown, 08088 .......... (609) 859-2049

**SAFRAN USA, INC.**
2300 Clarendon Blvd., Ste. 607, Arlington VA 22201 ............... **(703) 351-9898**
   Pres., CEO—Peter Lengyel; Sr. V-P., External Affs.—Read Vandewater;
     Dir., Mktg. Comms.—Michelle Lyle; Dir., Pub. Affs.—Allison McKay
Aerosource, Inc., 390 Campus Dr., Somerset, 08873 ............... (732) 469-9300

**SAFWAY GROUP HOLDING, LLC**
N19W24200 Riverwood Dr., Ste. 200, Waukesha WI 53188 ............... **(262) 523-6500**
   Pres., CEO—William Hayes; Ex. V-P., CFO—Jim Walters;
     Sr. V-P., Acquisitions & Corp. Dev.—Chris Wells;
     Sr. V-P., Indl. Svcs. & Natl. Accts.—Marty McGee; V-P., Gen. Counsel—Curt Paulsen
Safway Atlantic, LLC, 700 Commercial Ave., Carlstadt, 07072 ............... (201) 636-5500

**SAI GLOBAL, INC.**
101 Morgan Ln., Ste. 301, Plainsboro NJ 08536 ...................... **(609) 955-5100**
   Pres.—Tim Whipple; Mktg. Mgr.—Michael Orrick; IT Mgr.—Mark Taylor;
     Hum. Res. Mgr.—Pam Kohen
SAI Global Ltd., 210 State Route 4 E., Paramus, 07652 ............... (201) 986-1131

**SAINT-GOBAIN PERFORMANCE PLASTICS**
1199 S. Chillicothe Rd., Aurora OH 44202 ...................... **(216) 245-0529**
   Pres.—Tom Kinisky; V-P.—Marco-Antonio Corrales; Dir., Hum. Res.—Cindy Baldwin;
     Dir., Innovation—Kim Saville
Saint-Gobain Performance Plastics, 460 Milltown Rd., Bridgewater, 08807 ..... (908) 218-8888
Saint-Gobain Performance Plastics, 210 Harmony Rd., Mickleton, 08056 ..... (856) 423-6630
Saint-Gobain Performance Plastics, 150 Dey Rd., Wayne, 07470 ............. (973) 696-4700

**SANDVIK, INC.**
1702 Nevins Rd., P.O. Box 428, Fair Lawn NJ 07410 ............... **(201) 794-5000**
   Pres., Market Area Americas—Eduardo Martin;
     Mktg. Comms. Mgr., Market Area Americas—Ester Codina;
     Mktg. Comms. Mgr., Market Area Americas—Debby Oliveri
Sandvik Process Systems, LLC, 21 Campus Rd., Totowa, 07512 ............. (973) 790-1600

**SCALES INDUSTRIAL TECHNOLOGIES, INC.**
110 Voice Rd., Carle Place NY 11514 ...................... **(516) 248-9096**
   Pres.—William Scales; CFO, GM—Manny Cafiero; V-P.—Peter Scales;
     Plt. Mgr.—Robert Guthy, Jr.; Hum. Res. Mgr.—Tina Hanaway
Scales Industrial Technologies, Inc of NJ,
   185 Lackawanna Ave., Woodland Park, 07424 ............... (973) 890-1010

**SCHAFF PIANO SUPPLY CO.**
451 Oakwood Rd., Lake Zurich IL 60047 ...................... **(847) 438-4556**
   Owner—Herb Johnson; Pres.—Rob Johnson; Cont.—Grace Ordakowski
Schadler & Sons, Inc., John, 242 S. Parkway, P.O. Box 1068, Clifton, 07014 ... (973) 777-5620

**SCHINDLER ELEVATOR CORP.**
20 Whippany Rd., Morristown NJ 07960 ...................... **(973) 397-6500**
   Chrm.—Alfred N. Schindler; CEO—Jakob Zueger; Corp. Comms. Mgr.—Kathy Rucki;
     Dist. Mgr.—Jeremiah Heller
Elevator Products Corp., 100 Dermarest Dr., Wayne, 07470 ............... (973) 341-8000
Schindler Elevator Corp., 840 N. Lenola Rd., Ste. 4, Moorestown, 08057 ...... (856) 234-2220

**SCHLUMBERGER LTD.**
5599 San Felipe St., Ste. 1700, Houston TX 77056 ............... **(713) 513-2000**
   Chrm., CEO—Andrew Gould; CFO—Simon Ayat; V-P., Inv. Rels.—Simon Farrant;
     V-P., Taxes—Mark Danton
Schlumberger-Princeton Technology Center,
   20 Wallace Rd., Princeton Junction, 08550 ............... (609) 799-1000

**SCHNEIDER ELECTRIC USA, INC.**
1415 S. Roselle Rd., Palatine IL 60067 ...................... **(847) 397-2600**
   Pres., CEO, N. America—Laurent Vernerny; Sr. V-P., Admn. & Hum. Res.—George Powers;
     Sr. V-P., Energy Sols.—James Potach; Sr. V-P., Supply Chain—Ted Klee;
     Sr. V-P., Bus. Dev. & Strategy—Holly Benz; V-P., Press Rels., N. America—Martin Hanna
Schneider Electric, 2001 Highway 46, Ste. 402, Parsippany, 07054 ........... (973) 263-6100

**SCHRATTER FOODS, INC.**
333 Fairfield Rd., Fairfield NJ 07004 ...................... **(973) 575-3226**
   Pres., CEO—Alain J. Voss
Cognati Cheese Co., Inc., 205 Moonachie Rd., 2nd Fl., Moonachie, 07074 ...... (201) 807-9100

**SCHULZ ELECTRIC COMPANY, THE**
30 Gando Dr., New Haven CT 06513 ...................... **(203) 562-5811**
   Pres.—Robert Davis; V-P., Shop Opers.—Dominic Cleveland;
     V-P., Controls—Joseph Kowerdovich; V-P., Field Svcs.—John Wilonski;
     Cont.—Calef Davis; Mktg. Mgr.—Tina Romandetti
Reliable Electric Motor Repair, Inc., 19 California Ave., Paterson, 07503 ....... (973) 278-8122

**SCHWEITZER-MAUDUIT INTERNATIONAL**
**100 N. Point Ctr. E., Ste. 600, Alpharetta GA 30022 .................... (770) 569-4200**
**Chrm., CEO—Frederic Villoutreix; Pres., Americas & V-P., LIP Opers.—Wilfred A. Martinez; COO—Stephen Dunmead; Ex. V-P., CFO—Jeffrey Cook; Ex. V-P., Paper, Global—Patrick DeLuca; Ex. V-P., Reconstituted Tobacco—Michel Fievez; V-P., Hum. Res.—Vera M. Arthur; Cont.—Robert Cardin**
Schweitzer-Mauduit International, Inc., 85 Main St., Spotswood, 08884 ........ (732) 723-6100

**SEABRA GROUP**
**574 Ferry St., Newark NJ 07105 .................... (973) 491-0399**
**Pres.—Antonio Seabra; IT Mgr.—Pedro Cardoso**
Aidil Wines & Liquors, 574 Ferry St., Newark, 07105 .................... (973) 712-0950
Corte Provisions, 574 Ferry St., Newark, 07105 .................... (973) 712-0970

**SEALED AIR CORP.**
**200 Riverfront Blvd., 3rd Fl., Elmwood Park NJ 07407 .................. (201) 791-7600**
**Pres., CEO—Jerome Peribere; Sr. V-P., CFO—Carol Lowe; Dir., Inv. Rels.—Lori Chaitman; Hum. Res. Mgr.—Norman Finch; Benefits Mgr.—Tony Meola**
CPI Packaging, Inc., 50 Jiffy Rd., Somerset, 08873 .................... (732) 431-3500
Sealed Air Corp., 301 Mayhill St., Saddle Brook, 07663 .................... (201) 712-7000

**SEALY, INC.**
**1 Office Parkway Rd., Trinity NC 27370 .................... (336) 861-3500**
**CEO—Larry Rogers; Sr. V-P., CMO—Jodi Allen; Sr. V-P., Opers.—G. Michael Hoffman; Sr. V-P., Hum. Res.—Carmen Dabiero; Ex. V-P., Sales—Lewis Bachicha**
Sealy Mattress Co. Of New Jersey, 697 River St., Paterson, 07524 ............ (973) 345-8800

**SEIKO CORP. OF AMERICA**
**1111 MacArthur Blvd., Mahwah NJ 07430 .................... (201) 529-5730**
**Pres., CEO—Yoshikatsu Kawada; Sr. V-P., Sales & Mktg.—Martin Gormley; Sr. V-P., Corp. Opers. & Plng.—Nozomu Oshima**
Seiko Optical Products Of America, Inc. (H Q), 575 Corporate Dr., Ste. 205, Mahwah, 07430 .................... (201) 529-9099

**SENSIENT TECHNOLOGIES CORP.**
**777 E. Wisconsin Ave., Ste. 1100, Milwaukee WI 53202 .................. (414) 271-6755**
**Chrm.—Kenneth P. Manning; Pres., CEO—Paul Manning; Sr. V-P., CFO—Richard Hobbs; V-P., CAO—Jeffrey Makal; Sr. V-P., Gen. Counsel & Secy.—John Hammond; V-P., Treas.—John Collopy; V-P., Admn.—Stephen J. Rolfs; V-P., Hum. Res.—Christopher Daniels; Cont.—Richard Malin**
Sensient Cosmetic & Pharmaceutical Technologies, 107 Wade Ave., South Plainfield, 07080 .................... (908) 757-4500

**SERVICE METAL FABRICATING, INC.**
**10 Stickle Ave., Rockaway NJ 07866 .................... (973) 625-8882**
**Ptnr.—James Moretti; Ptnr.—Joseph Morretti, Jr.; Opers. Mgr.—Dave Lewin**
Precision Shape Solutions, 243 E. Blackwell St., Dover, 07801 .............. (973) 989-7199

**SEW-EURODRIVE, INC.**
**1275 Old Spartanburg Hwy., P.O. Box 518, Lyman SC 29365 ............ (864) 439-7537**
**Owner & CEO—Juergen Blickle; V-P.—Christopher Blickle; Cont.—Erica Mosely; Prodn. Mgr.—Carl Hinze; Engrg. & Mktg. Mgr.—Tom Cappel; IT Mgr.—Virginia Benintende; Pers. Mgr.—Edie Bacome; Cust. Serv. Mgr.—Mike Thompson**
SEW-Eurodrive, Inc., 2107 High Hill Rd., P.O. Box 481, Bridgeport, 08014 ...... (856) 467-2277

**SHACHIHATA, INC.**
**20775 S. Western Ave., Ste. 105, Torrance CA 90501 .................... (310) 530-4445**
**Pres.—Bob Ally; Sr. Trade Mktg. Mgr.—Christine Wiederkehr; Hum. Res. Mgr.—Wendy Ramirez**
Shachihata, Inc., U. S. A., 525 Oberlin Ave. S., Lakewood, 08701 ............ (732) 370-4770

**SHERWIN-WILLIAMS CO., THE**
**101 W. Prospect Ave., Cleveland OH 44115 .................... (216) 566-2000**
**Chrm., CEO—Christopher M. Connor; Pres., COO—John G. Morikis; Sr. V-P., CFO—Sean P. Hennessy; Sr. V-P., Sales & Mktg.—George Diver; Sr. V-P., Hum. Res.—Thomas E. Hopkins; Sr. V-P., Corp. Comms. & Pub. Affs.—Robert J. Wells; Sr. V-P., Dev. & Plng.—Steven J. Oberfeld; V-P., Treas.—Jeff Miklich; V-P., Cont.—Al Mistysyn; V-P., Natl. Accts.—Mark Henderson; V-P., Mktg., Chemical Coatings—Dennis Karnstein; V-P., Auditing—Mark J. Dvoroznak; V-P., Global Innovation—Max Lewis; Dir., Corp. Comm. & Inv. Rels.—Mike Conway**
Sherwin-Williams Co., The, 6 Currie Ave., Wallington, 07057 ................ (201) 933-3800
Sherwin-Williams Co., The, Woodcare Products Div. (H Q), 10 Mountainview Rd., Upper Saddle River, 07458 .................... (201) 818-7500

**SHISEIDO AMERICA, INC.**
**900 3rd Ave., 15th Fl., New York NY 10022 .................... (212) 805-2300**
**CEO—Heidi Manheimer; V-P., Sales—Rita Mangan; Hum. Res. Mgr.—Tarika Ward**
Davlyn Industries, Inc., 7 Fitzgerald Ave., Monroe Township, 08831 .......... (609) 860-5100
Shiseido America, Inc., 366 Princeton Hightstown Rd., East Windsor, 08520 . . . (609) 371-5800

**SIEMENS CORPORATION**
**527 Madison Ave., 8th Fl., New York NY 10022 .................... (212) 258-4000**
**Pres., CEO—Eric Spiegel; CFO—Klaus P. Stegemann; Sr. V-P., Gen. Counsel & Secy.—E. Robert Lupone**
Siemens Hearing Instruments, Inc., 10 Constitution Ave., P.O. Box 1397, Piscataway, 08855 .................... (732) 562-6600

**SIEMENS ENERGY, INC.**
**4400 N. Alafaya Trl., Orlando FL 32826 .................... (407) 736-2000**
**Pres., CEO—Randy Zwirn; CEO, Serv. Renewables Bus. Unit—Tim Holt; V-P., Fin.—Steve Conner; Dir., Hum. Res.—Lee Vickers; IT Mgr.—Richard Visnor**
Siemens Energy, Inc., 840 Nottingham Way, Trenton, 08638 .................... (609) 890-5000

**SIEMENS HEALTHCARE DIAGNOSTICS, INC.**
**1717 Deerfield Rd., Ste. 1, Deerfield IL 60015 .................... (847) 267-5300**
**CEO—Micahel Reitermann; CEO, Health Sciences—John Glaser; Sr. V-P., CFO—John Duffey; Sr. V-P., CIO—David Edelstein; Sr. V-P., Hum. Res.—Anthonie Goudemond; Sr. V-P., Strategy Comm.—Nancy Krejsa**
Siemens Healthcare Diagnostics, Inc., 62 Flanders Bartley Rd., Flanders, 07836 . (973) 927-2828

**SIEMENS INFRASTRUCTURE & CITIES, BUILDING TECHNOLOGIES**
**1000 Deerfield Pkwy., Buffalo Grove IL 60089 .................... (847) 215-1000**
**Pres., CEO, Siemens Bldg. Technologies Div.—Matthias Rebellius; V-P., Hum. Res.—Jennifer Olmstead; V-P., Control & Prods. Sys.—Richard Lattanzi**
Siemens Infrastructure & Cities, Building Technologies, 8 Fernwood Rd., Florham Park, 07932 .................... (973) 593-2600

**SIGMA CORP.**
**700 Goldman Dr., P.O. Box 300, Cream Ridge NJ 08514 .................. (609) 758-0800**
**Chrm., CEO—Jim McGivern; Pres.—Larry Rybacki; CFO—Jeff Marcus; V-P.—Mitchell Rona; V-P.—S. Bhattacharji; Hum. Res. Mgr.—Dave Press**
Environmental Site Furnishings, 700 Goldman Dr., Cream Ridge, 08514 ....... (281) 975-1776

**SIGMA PLASTICS GROUP**
**Page & Schuyler Aves., Bldg. 5, P.O. Box 808, Lyndhurst NJ 07071 ........ (201) 933-6000**
**Ex. V-P.—Alan Teo; Pur. Mgr., Resin—Lisa Muccilo; Hum. Res. Mgr.—Debra Barbour**
Sigma Stretch Film, Page Ave., Bldg. 5 & 8, P.O. Box 808, Lyndhurst, 07071 .... (201) 507-9100

**SILGAN CONTAINERS, LLC**
**21800 Oxnard St., Ste. 600, Woodland Hills CA 91367 .................. (818) 710-3700**
**Pres.—Thomas Snyder; Sr. V-P., Sales & Mktg.—Rick Brewer; Sr. V-P., Opers.—John Moores; V-P., Hum. Res.—Tony Cost; V-P., Fin.—Joseph Heaney**
Silgan Containers Mfg. Corp., 135 National Rd., Edison, 08817 ............... (732) 287-0300

**SILVER LINE BUILDING PRODUCTS, LLC**
**1 Silver Line Dr., P.O. Box 6029, North Brunswick NJ 08902 ............... (732) 435-1000**
**V-P., Sales—Al Worthing; V-P., Mktg.—Andrew Karr; Dir., Engr.—Andrew Obst; Mktg. Mgr.—Sharon Gifford**
Custom Craft Plastics, 100 King Arthurs Ct., P.O. Box 6029, North Brunswick, 08902 ............ (732) 843-3000

**SILVI CONCRETE PRODUCTS, INC.**
**355 Newbold Rd., Fairless Hills PA 19030 .................... (215) 295-0777**
**Co-Pres.—Larry Silvi; Co-Pres.—John L. Silvi; CFO—Mike Matalavage; V-P., Sales & Mktg.—Toby Rich**
Silvi Concrete Products, Inc., 470 State Highway 33, Englishtown, 07726 ...... (267) 907-9150

**SIMMONS FOODS, INC.**
**601 N. Hico St., P.O. Box 430, Siloam Springs AR 72761 ................ (479) 524-8151**
**Chrm.—Mark Simmons; CEO—Todd Simmons; Pres., Poultry Opers. & COO—Gary Murphy; Pres., Pet Food & COO—David Jackson; Ex. V-P., CFO—Mark Wiens; Sr. V-P., Hum. Res.—Dan Houston; V-P., Sales—Chip Miller; Dir., IT—Stacy Smith**
Menu Foods, Inc., 9130 Griffith Morgan Ln., Pennsauken, 08110 ............. (856) 662-7412

**SIMS METAL MANAGEMENT**
**16 W. 22nd St., 10th Fl., New York NY 10010 .................... (212) 604-0710**
**Group CEO—Galdino Claro; Pres., N. Amer.—Robert Kelman; Comm. Mgr.—Dawn Miner**
Metal Management Northeast, Inc., 1 Linden Ave. E., Jersey City, 07305 ...... (201) 577-3200
Sims Metal Management, 8-18 Noble St., Newark, 07114 .................. (973) 824-8900
Sims Metal Management, 1511 Calhoun St., Trenton, 08638 ................ (609) 396-0880

**SINCLAIR & RUSH, INC.**
**123 Manufacturers Dr., Arnold MO 63010 .................... (636) 282-6800**
**Pres., CEO—Brad Philip; Dir., Sales & Mktg.—Jeff Barket; Sales Mgr., Natl.—Don Daut; Mktg. Coord.—MaryLou Pudlowski**
VisiPak, a Sinclair & Rush Company, 640 Dell Rd., Ste. 1, P.O. Box 0188, Carlstadt, 07072 .................... (800) 949-1141

**SIRCHIE FINGER PRINT LABS, INC.**
**100 Hunter Pl., Bldg. 1, P.O. Box 639, Youngsville NC 27596 ............. (919) 554-2244**
**Pres., COO—Dwight Hallman; CFO—Jason Wimmer; Dir., Mfg. & Supply, Domestic—Jason Emerline; Sales Mgr.—Wes Bunting; Mfg. Mgr.—Terry Keaton; Hum. Res. Mgr.—Catrina Brown**
Sirchie Finger Print Labs, Inc., Vehicle Div., 612 Gravelly Hollow Rd., P.O. Box 789, Medford, 08055 .................... (609) 654-0777

**SKYLINE STEEL, LLC**
**8 Woodhollow Rd., Ste. 102, Parsippany NJ 07054 .................... (973) 428-6100**
**CEO—Laurent De Mey; CFO—Judith Gorog; Sales Opers. Mgr.—Holly Dwyer**
Associated Pile & Fitting, 8 Wood Hollow Rd., Plz. 1, P.O. Box 5933, Parsippany, 07054 ............. (973) 773-8400

**SKYLINE WINDOWS, LLC**
**220 E. 138th St., Bronx NY 10451 .................... (212) 491-3000**
**CEO—Steven Kraus; Pres.—Richard C. Apfel; COO—Jeff Schiller; V-P., Hum. Res.—Philippe Gouamba**
Skyline Windows, LLC, 210 Park Pl. E., Wood Ridge, 07075 ................ (201) 531-9600

**SL INDUSTRIES, INC.**
**520 Fellowship Rd., Ste. A-114, Mount Laurel NJ 08054 .................. (856) 727-1500**
**Pres., CEO—William T. Fejes, Jr.; CFO, Secy-Treas.—Louis J. Belardi; Dir., Hum. Res.—Maryann Cassidy**
R F L Electronics, Inc., 353 Powerville Rd., Boonton, 07005 ............... (973) 334-3100

**SMITH FILTER CORP.**
**5000 41st St., Moline IL 61265 .................... (309) 764-8324**
**Co-Pres.—Jana Lecander; Co-Pres.—Sharilyn Solis; V-P.—Jim Solis; Engrg. Mgr.—Gary Melton**
Smith Filter Corp., 16 Van Dyke Ave., New Brunswick, 08901 ................ (732) 745-2600

**SNYDER'S-LANCE, INC.**
**8600 South Blvd., Charlotte NC 28273 .................... (704) 554-1421**
**Pres., CEO—Carl Lee, Jr.; Pres., Distribution—Ed Good; Sr. V-P., Shared Svcs. & CIO—Nikhil Sawant; Sr. V-P., CHRO—Kevin Henry; Ex. V-P., CFO—Rick Puckett; Sr. V-P., Sales, East—Daniel Morgan; Sr. V-P., Sales, W.—Frank Schuster; Sr. V-P., Supply Chain—Pat McInerney; V-P., Corp. Cont.—Margaret Wicklund; V-P., Strategic Initiatives—Mark Carter**
The Snack Factory, LLC., 11 Tamarack Cir., Skillman, 08558 ............... (609) 683-5400

**SOLVAY AMERICA, INC.**
**3333 Richmond Ave., Houston TX 77098 .................... (713) 525-6500**
**Pres. & Dir., Fin.—Mike Lacey; V-P., Comm. & Hum. Res.—William Barnes; V-P.—Mark Looney; Qual. Mgr.—Sarah Seaman; R & D Mgr.—Alastair McNeillie; Comms. Supv.—Suggie Casey**
Solvay U. S. A., Inc., 8 Cedar Brook Dr., CN-7500, Cranbury, 08512 .......... (609) 860-4000

**SONEPAR USA**
**510 Walnut St., Ste. 400, Philadelphia PA 19106 ........ (215) 399-5900**
**Pres., CEO—David G. Gabriel; CFO—Kathy Rusko;**
**Ex. V-P., Bus. Dev. & Mktg.—Jay Bricker; Dir., Comms.—Maria Venezia**
Cooper Electric Supply Co., 1 Matrix Dr., Monroe, 08831 ........ (732) 747-2233

**SONOCO**
**1 N. 2nd St., Hartsville SC 29550 ........ (843) 383-7000**
**Ex. Chrm.—Harris E. DeLoach, Jr.; Pres., CEO—M. Jack Sanders;**
**V-P., CFO—Barry L. Saunders;**
**Sr. V-P., Global Indl. Prod. & Protective Sols.—John M. Colyer;**
**Sr. V-P., Global Consumer Packaging & Svcs.—Rob Tiede;**
**Sr. V-P., Primary Matls.—Marty F. Pignone; V-P., Hum. Res.—Allan H. McLeland;**
**V-P., Corp. Affs. & Inv. Rels.—Roger Schrum; V-P., Protective Sols.—Vicki Arthur;**
**Group V-P., Paper, Tubes & Cores, N. America—Rodger D. Fuller;**
**Group V-P., Global Rigid Paper & Plastics—Howard Coker;**
**Div. V-P., GM, Indl. Bus. Segment—Carl Kraus;**
**Div. V-P., Mfg. & Protective Sols.—Ron O'Neal; Corp. Comms. Mgr.—Joyce Beasley**
Sonoco CorrFlex, LLC,
Heritage Plaza II, 1st Fl., 65 Harristow, Glen Rock, 07452 ........ (201) 612-4008
Sonoco Products Co., 5 Stults Rd., Dayton, 08810 ........ (609) 655-0300

**SONY ELECTRONICS, INC.**
**16530 Via Esprillo, San Diego CA 92127 ........ (858) 942-2400**
**Non-Exec. Chrm.—Phil Molyneux; Pres.—Michael Fasulo;**
**Ex. V-P., Gen. Counsel—Michael T. Williams; V-P., Corp. Comms.—John Dolak;**
**Sr. Pub. Rels. Mgr.—Yolanda Hunt-Boes**
Sony Electronics, Inc., 1 Sony Dr., Park Ridge, 07656 ........ (201) 930-1000

**SOUTH JERSEY WELDING SUPPLY CO.**
**496 Route 38 E., Maple Shade NJ 08052 ........ (856) 778-4440**
**Pres.—Robert Thornton, Jr.; V-P.—David Thornton**
South Jersey Welding Supply Co., 94 W. Forest Grove Rd., Vineland, 08360 .... (856) 691-9659

**SOUTH STATE MATERIALS, LLC**
**202 Reeves Rd., P.O. Box 68, Bridgeton NJ 08302 ........ (856) 451-5300**
**Pres.—Chester Ottinger, Jr.; V-P.—Tim Larson; Cont.—Anthony Suppa;**
**Accts. Payable Mgr.—Robin Mitchell**
South State, Inc., 1340 Glassboro Rd., Williamstown, 08094 ........ (856) 881-6030

**SP INDUSTRIES, INC.**
**935 Mearns Rd., Warminster PA 18974 ........ (215) 672-7800**
**Pres., CEO—William E. Downs; CFO—Michael F. Bonner; Dir., Mfg.—Cynthia Reiter;**
**Plt. Mgr.—Ron Petersen; Hum. Res. Mgr.—Kim Smith**
Maddak Inc., 661 State Route 23, Wayne, 07470 ........ (973) 628-7600
Wilmad-LabGlass, 1172 N. West Blvd., Vineland, 08360 ........ (856) 691-3200

**SPARKS BELTING CO., INC.**
**3800 Stahl Dr. S.E., Grand Rapids MI 49546 ........ (616) 949-2750**
**V-P., Sales—Bruce Dieleman; V-P., Opers.—John Grasmeyer; V-P., Fin.—Martha Couturier;**
**Cont.—Kerri Hubers; Dir., IT—Todd Brower; R & D Mgr.—Dave Vanderwood;**
**Matls. Mgr.—Eric Johnson**
Sparks Belting Co., 5 Spielman Rd., Fairfield, 07004 ........ (973) 227-4100

**SPECTRUM CHEMICAL MFG. CORP.**
**14422 S. San Pedro St., Gardena CA 90248 ........ (310) 516-8000**
**Chrm.—Paul Burg; Pres.—Prem Jain; CFO—Steve Toigo; Dir., IT—Srinath Yardalagga;**
**GM—Mark Hurd**
Spectrum Chemical Mfg. Corp., 769 Jersey Ave., New Brunswick, 08901 ....... (732) 214-1300

**SPIRENT COMMUNICATIONS, INC.**
**26750 Agoura Rd., Calabasas CA 91302 ........ (818) 676-2300**
**CFO & COO—Eric Hutchinson; V-P., Bus. Dev. & Mktg.—Jeff Schmitz; Dir., IT—Ed Nakam**
Spirent Communications, Inc., 211 Mount Airy Rd., Basking Ridge, 07920 ...... (908) 953-6000
Spirent Communications PLC, 541 Industrial Way W., Eatontown, 07724 ....... (732) 544-8700

**SPX CORPORATION**
**13320 Ballantyne Corporate Pl., Charlotte NC 28277 ........ (704) 752-4400**
**Chrm., Pres. & CEO—Christopher J. Kearney;**
**Pres., Asia Pacific & Ex. V-P., Global Bus. Sys.—Robert B. Foreman;**
**Segment Pres., Flow Tech.—Marc Michael;**
**Segment Pres., Indl. Prods. & Svcs. & Test & Measurement—Dave Kowalski;**
**Ex. V-P., CFO—Jeremy Smeltser; CIO—Kevin Eamigh; V-P., Hum. Res.—Jane Ballard;**
**V-P., Bus. Dev., Mergers & Acquisitions—Mike Whitted; Dir., Inv. Rels.—Ryan Taylor;**
**Comm. Mgr.—Jennifer H. Epstein**
Weil-McLain, 17000 Commerce Pkwy., Ste. B, Mount Laurel, 08054 ........ (856) 866-7400

**SRI INTERNATIONAL**
**333 Ravenswood Ave., Menlo Park CA 94025 ........ (650) 859-2000**
**Pres., CEO—Bill Jeffrey; Sr. V-P., CFO—Luther Lau;**
**V-P., Bus. & Legal Affs. & Gen. Counsel—Richard Abramson;**
**V-P., Corp. Comm. & Mktg.—Alice R. Resnick; V-P., Hum. Res.—Jean E. Tooker;**
**V-P., Engrg. & Sys.—John W. Prausa; V-P., Computing & Info. Sciences—William Mark;**
**V-P., Strategic Affs.—Norman Winarsky; V-P., Biosciences—Walter Moos;**
**Dir., Formulations R & D—Gita Shankar**
Sarnoff Corp., 201 Washington Rd., Princeton, 08540 ........ (609) 734-2000

**STANLEY ACCESS TECHNOLOGIES, LLC**
**65 Scott Swamp Rd., Farmington CT 06032 ........ (860) 677-2861**
**Pres.—Frank Luke; Dir., Mfg. Opers. & Pur.—Costas Drakatos;**
**Dir., Hum. Res.—Vanessa Bradford; Dir., Prod.—Vito Spinelli;**
**Dir., Innovation & Tech.—John Nurse; Engrg. Mgr.—Dean Negrelli**
Stanley Access Technologies, LLC, 17 Marlen Dr., Ste. C, Trenton, 08691 ...... (609) 890-0877

**STAPLES, INC.**
**500 Staples Dr., Framingham MA 01702 ........ (508) 253-5000**
**Chrm., CEO—Ronald L. Sargent; Vice Chrm., CFO—John J. Mahoney;**
**Pres., COO—Michael Miles; Pres., U.S. Stores—Demos Parneros;**
**Pres., N. American Delivery—Joseph G. Doody;**
**Sr. V-P., Gen. Counsel—Cynthia L. Pevehouse; Sr. V-P., Corp. Cont.—Christine Komola;**
**Sr. V-P., Staples Bus. Delivery—Steven Bussberg; Ex. V-P., Real Estate—John K. Barton;**
**Ex. V-P., Staples Contract—Jay Baitler; Ex. V-P.—Brian T. Light;**
**V-P., Env. Affs.—Mark Buckley; Pub. Rels. Mgr.—Owen Davis**
Staples Contract Digital Copy Services, 258 Fernwood Ave., Edison, 08837 .... (732) 346-1377

**STATEN ISLAND PUBLICATIONS, INC.**
**950 W. Fingerboard Rd., Staten Island NY 10305 ........ (718) 981-1234**
**Publisher—Caroline Diamond-Harrison; Editor—Brian Laline; Comp.—Arthur Silverstein;**
**Dir., IT & Prodn.—John Giustiniani; Dir., Adv.—Gary V. Cognetta;**
**Adv. Mgr., Online—Frank Cianciotta**
Newark Morning Ledger Co., 1 Star Ledger Plz., Newark, 07102 ........ (973) 392-4141
News Of Cumberland County, The, 93 5th St., Salem, 08079 ........ (856) 451-1000
South Jersey Times, 93 5th St., Salem, 08079 ........ (856) 935-1500
Times Of Trenton, 413 River View Plz., Trenton, 08611 ........ (609) 989-5454

**STAVOLA CONTRACTING CO., INC.**
**175 Drift Rd., Tinton Falls NJ 07724 ........ (732) 542-2328**
**Pres.—Joseph Stavola; Corp. Secy.—James Stavola, Jr.; Sales Mgr.—Tony Monsalud;**
**IT Mgr.—Jim Bean; Hum. Res. Mgr.—Dominique Goode; Off. Mgr.—Karen Dunn**
Stavola Construction Materials, Inc., 810 Thompson Ave., Bound Brook, 08805 .. (732) 356-7100
Stavola Construction Materials, Inc., 30 Rockaway Rd., Lebanon, 08833 ....... (908) 439-2800
Stavola Contracting Co., Inc., 120 Old Bergen Mill Rd., Englishtown, 07726 .... (732) 542-2328

**STEEL'S FUDGE, INC.**
**2719 Boardwalk, Atlantic City NJ 08401 ........ (609) 345-4051**
**Pres.—George Steel; Manager—Steve Plettner**
Steel's Fudge, Inc., 1000 Boardwalk, Ocean City, 08226 ........ (609) 398-2383
Steel's Fudge, Inc., 1928 E. Riverside Dr., Atlantic City, 08401 ........ (609) 345-4051

**STEELSTRAN INDUSTRIES, INC.**
**35 Mileed Way, P.O. Box 30, Avenel NJ 07001 ........ (732) 574-0700**
**CEO—Peter Gronbeck; Pres.—Susan Gronbeck; COO—Arthur Jeronimo;**
**V-P.—Thomas Burns**
AISCO, 35 Mileed Way, P.O. Box 30, Avenel, 07001 ........ (732) 574-3233

**STEPAN CO.**
**22 W. Frontage Rd., Northfield IL 60093 ........ (847) 446-7500**
**Chrm.—F. Quinn Stepan; Pres., CEO—F. Quinn Stepan, Jr.; V-P., CIO—Scott D. Beamer;**
**V-P., Gen. Counsel—H. Edward Wynn; V-P., GM, Surfactants—John V. Venegoni;**
**V-P., GM, Polymers—Arthur Mergner; V-P., Hum. Res.—Greg Servatius;**
**V-P., R & D—Frank Pacholec; V-P., Supply Chain—Scott Mason;**
**V-P., Proc.—Kyle Montgomery**
Stepan Co., 220 4th St., Fieldsboro, 08505 ........ (609) 298-1222
Stepan Co., 100 W. Hunter Ave., Maywood, 07607 ........ (201) 845-3030

**STEWART & STEVENSON POWER PRODUCTS, LLC- ADDA DIV.**
**180 Route 17 S., P.O. Box 950, Lodi NJ 07644 ........ (201) 489-5800**
**CEO—John F. Farmer; Sr. V-P.—Timothy E. Meade; Sr. V-P.—Michael McGovern;**
**V-P., Admn.—Megan Hollberg**
Stewart & Stevenson Power Products, LLC, ADDA Div., 33 Gregg St., Lodi, 07644 . (201) 291-8415
Atlantic Detroit Diesel-Allison, LLC,
169 Old New Brunswick Rd., Piscataway, 08854 ........ (732) 752-7100

**STEWART & STEVENSON, LLC**
**1000 Louisiana St., Ste. 5900, Houston TX 77002 ........ (713) 751-2700**
**Vice Chrm. of the Board—Robert Hargrave; CEO—John Simmons; CFO—Michael Kirksey;**
**V-P., Sales & Mktg., Dist. Segment—Dennis Weisgerber; V-P., Hum. Res.—Terry Hatcher**
Stewart & Stevenson Power Products, LLC- ADDA Div.,
180 Route 17 S., P.O. Box 950, Lodi, 07644 ........ (201) 489-5800

**STONE INDUSTRIES, INC.**
**400-402 Central Ave., Haledon NJ 07508 ........ (973) 595-6250**
**Chairwoman & CEO—Janet Braen; Pres.—Scott Braen; CFO—Rob Kranznoski;**
**V-P., Sales & Mktg.—Thomas Lynch; V-P., Hum. Res.—Samantha Braen;**
**IT Mgr.—Ray Scott**
Van Orden Sand & Gravel, 589 W. Brook Rd., Ringwood, 07456 ........ (973) 839-0207

**STONE, INC., A. E.**
**1435 Doughty Rd., Egg Harbor Township NJ 08234 ........ (609) 641-2781**
**CEO—Thomas K. Ritter; Pres. & IT Mgr.—Steven C. Kurtz; Fin. Cont.—Kellie Macom;**
**Plt. Mgr.—Stanley Iwanowski; Hum. Res. Mgr.—Tracey Mitchell;**
**Qual. Control Mgr.—Keith Sterling; Maint. Mgr.—Michael Dear**
Winslow Hot Mix, LLC, 784 Piney Hollow Rd., Hammonton, 08037 ........ (609) 561-2100

**STONHARD, A DIV. OF STONCOR GROUP**
**1000 E. Park Ave., P.O. Box 308, Maple Shade NJ 08052 ........ (856) 779-7500**
**Pres.—David Reif; V-P., Mktg., Intl.—Peggy Fynan; V-P., R & D—Fred Gelfant;**
**V-P., Prod. Dev.—Mike Jewell; Dir., Dev. & Training—Mike Galie; Dir.—Rick Neill;**
**Mktg. Mgr.—Kendall Ellis**
Epoplex, 1000 E. Park Ave., P.O. Box 308, Maple Shade, 08052 ........ (856) 667-8399

**STRUCTURAL GROUP, INC.**
**7455 New Ridge Rd., Ste. T, Hanover MD 21076 ........ (410) 850-7000**
**CEO—Peter Emmons; Pres.—Scott Greenhaus; IT Mgr.—Jason Kasch**
Shared Systems Technology, Inc., 127 Salem Ave., Thorofare, 08086 ........ (856) 218-7900

**STRYKER CORPORATION**
**2825 Airview Blvd., Portage MI 49002 ........ (269) 385-2600**
**Pres., CEO—Kevin Lobo; V-P., Secy.—Dean H. Bergy; IT Mgr.—Jeff Hutchison**
Stryker Orthopaedics, 325 Corporate Dr., Mahwah, 07430 ........ (201) 831-5000
Stryker Corp., 2 Pearl Ct., Allendale, 07401 ........ (201) 760-8000

**SUBURBAN GLASS & MIRROR, INC.**
**231 Herbert Ave., Closter NJ 07624 ........ (201) 768-9586**
**Pres.—Wayne Gangeri; V-P.—Jeffrey Gangeri; IT Mgr.—Matt Gangeri;**
**Off. Mgr.—Christa Farrell**
Suburban Glass & Mirror, Inc., 418 S. Broad St., Ridgewood, 07450 ........ (201) 447-0440

**SUBURBAN PROPANE PARTNERS, L.P.**
**240 Route 10 W., P.O. Box 206, Whippany NJ 07981 ........ (973) 887-5300**
**CEO—Michael Dunn; CFO—Michael Stivala; CAO—Michael A. Kuglin;**
**V-P., Operational Support & Analysis—Mark Wienberg;**
**Sr. V-P., Admn.—Michael Keating; V-P., Gen. Counsel—Paul E. Abel;**
**Dir., IS—Dale Amabile**
Propane Power Corporation, a Div. of Suburban Propane,
915 Delancy St., Newark, 07105 ........ (973) 589-3030

**SULZER PUMPS (U.S.), INC.**
**200 S.W. Market St., Ste. 400, Portland OR 97201 .......... (503) 205-3600**
**V-P., Sales & Mktg.—Fernando Bermudez; V-P., Fin.—Philippe Dewitz;**
**V-P., Proj. Mgmt.—Jack Feinstein; V-P., Cust. Support Svcs.—Dennis Barton;**
**Mktg. Mgr., Americas—Harinath Tirumal**
Sulzer Pumps (U.S.), Inc., 621 Haron Dr., P.O. Box 487, Bridgeport, 08014 ...... (856) 467-2400

**SUMTOTAL SYSTEMS, INC.**
**2850 N.W. 43rd St., Ste. 150, Gainesville FL 32606 .......... (352) 264-2800**
**V-P., Hum. Res.—Richard Oyen; GM—Hardeep Gulagi;**
**Sr. Technical Support Mgr.—Arun Kumar**
SumTotal Systems, LLC, 600 Parsippany Rd., Parsippany, 07054 .......... (973) 364-0480

**SUN CAPITAL PARTNERS, INC.**
**5200 Town Center Cir., Ste. 600, Boca Raton FL 33486 .......... (561) 394-0550**
**Co-CEO—Rodger R. Krouse; Co-CEO—Marc J. Leder; CFO & Mng. Dir.—Kevin J. Calhoun;**
**Mng. Dir. & Group CFO, Opers.—Lynn R. Skillen;**
**Mng. Dir. & Group CFO, Opers.—Mark Brody; Sr. V-P.—Mark A. Hajduch;**
**Dir.—Luis Henriquez**
AS America, Inc. (H Q), 1 Centennial Ave., P.O. Box 6820, Piscataway, 08855 ... (732) 980-3000

**SUN CHEMICAL CORP.**
**35 Waterview Blvd., Ste. 100, Parsippany NJ 07054 .......... (973) 404-6000**
**Pres., CEO—Rudi Lenz; Pres., N. American Inks—Charles Murray;**
**Sr. V-P., Chief Administrative Officer—John McKeown;**
**Chief Proc. Officer—Edward Pruitt; CFO—Gerry Brady;**
**Gen. Counsel & Secy.—James R. Van Horn;**
**V-P., Prod. Mgmt. & Publication Ink—Dennis Sweet**
K V K U. S. A., Inc., 19-A Home News Row, New Brunswick, 08901 .......... (732) 846-2355
Sun Chemical Corp., 631 Central Ave., Carlstadt, 07072 .......... (201) 933-4500
Sun Chemical Corp., 390 Central Ave., East Rutherford, 07073 .......... (201) 438-4041
US Ink Corp. (H Q), 631 Central Ave., Carlstadt, 07072 .......... (201) 935-8666

**SUNBELT CORP.**
**2120 Burkett Rd., Rock Hill SC 29730 .......... (803) 329-9787**
**CEO & CFO—Larry French; Co-Pres.—Matt Weinschuetz; Co-Pres.—Al Zimin, Sr.;**
**Plt. Mgr.—Scott Alford; Hum. Res. Mgr.—Gwen Pittman; Whse. Mgr.—Danny Thompson**
Sunbelt Corp., 63 Atwood Pl., Wayne, 07470 .......... (803) 329-9787

**SUNNY DELIGHT BEVERAGES CO.**
**10300 Alliance Rd., Ste. 500, Cincinnati OH 45242 .......... (513) 483-3300**
**Chrm.—True Knowles; Pres., CEO—William B. Cyr; Sr. V-P., CFO—William Schumacher;**
**Acctg. Mgr.—Trevor Crossen; Corp. Hum. Res. Leader—Jennifer Phelps**
Sunny Delight Beverages Co., 10 Corn Rd., Dayton, 08810 .......... (732) 329-2391

**SUPER LAUNDRY EQUIPMENT CORP.**
**234 Crossways Park Dr., Woodbury NY 11797 .......... (516) 678-4404**
**V-P., Reg.—Charles Prato; V-P., Area—Michael Mastorides**
Luca Laundry Equipment, Inc., 1500 W. Blancke St., Linden, 07036 .......... (908) 862-2200

**SUPERIOR PRINTING INK CO., INC.**
**100 North St., Teterboro NJ 07608 .......... (201) 478-5600**
**Chrm., Pres. & CEO—Jeffrey Simons; CFO—Harold Rubin; COO—James La Rocca;**
**Ex. V-P.—Stanley Hittman; Corp. Cont.—Peter Nunez; Dir., Mfg. Svcs.—Dan Shevkun;**
**Dir., Corp. Pur.—Judith Zuckerman; Dir., Hum. Res.—Robert Volante;**
**Cred. Mgr.—Ken Hurkala**
Superior Printing Ink Co., Inc., 666 E. Linwood Ave., Maple Shade, 08052 ...... (856) 482-9066

**SUPPLY TECHNOLOGIES, LLC**
**6065 Parkland Blvd., Cleveland OH 44124 .......... (440) 947-2100**
**Dir., Matls.—Michelle Vranker; Opers. Mgr.—Paul Campagna;**
**Reg. Qual. Mgr.—Linda Burton; Application & Dev. Mgr.—Todd Soppitt**
Columbia Nut & Bolt, LLC, 50 Graphic Pl., Moonachie, 07074 .......... (201) 641-7600

**SUPPLYONE, INC.**
**20 N. Waterloo Rd., Ste. 200, Devon PA 19333 .......... (484) 582-5005**
**Pres., CEO—William T. Leith; V-P., Mktg.—Gary Bourdon; Cont.—Michelle Kane**
Supplyone, Inc., 1200 Madison Ave., Paterson, 07503 .......... (718) 392-7400
SupplyOne, Inc., 1090 Thomas Busch Memorial Hwy., Pennsauken, 08110 ...... (856) 727-1010

**SWIFT CO., INC., JOHN S.**
**999 Commerce Ct., P.O. Box 5529, Buffalo Grove IL 60089 .......... (847) 465-3300**
**Chrm.—John S. Swift; Sr. V-P., Opers.—Deane Fraser; Hum. Res. Mgr.—Rich Habenicht**
Swift Co., Inc., John S., 375 North St., Unit N, Teterboro, 07608 .......... (201) 678-3232

**SWISHER HYGIENE, INC.**
**4725 Piedmont Row Dr., Ste. 400, Charlotte NC 28210 .......... (704) 364-7707**
**Pres., CEO—William Pierce; CAO & Cont.—Linda Wilson-Ingram; CFO—Bill Nanovsky;**
**COO—Blake Thompson; V-P., Sales & Training—Melissa Frankling;**
**V-P., Corp. Accts. & Dist.—Jeff Rhodes; Dir., Comms. & Mktg.—Erin Peiffer**
Swisher Hygiene Inc., 1805 Lower Rd., Linden, 07036 .......... (800) 221-0806

**SYMRISE, INC.**
**300 North St., Teterboro NJ 07608 .......... (201) 288-3200**
**CEO—Heinz-Jurgen Bertram; V-P., Hum. Res.—Margaret Castello**
Symrise, Inc., 180 Industrial Pkwy., Branchburg, 08876 .......... (908) 429-6946
Symrise Purescents, 1715 Oak St., Ste. 3, Lakewood, 08701 .......... (732) 922-2520

**SYSCO CORP.**
**1390 Enclave Pkwy., Houston TX 77077 .......... (281) 584-1390**
**Pres., CEO—William J. DeLaney III; Ex. V-P., CFO—R. Chris Kreidler; CTO—Wayne Shurts;**
**Sr. V-P., Sales—Scott Sonnemaker; Sr. V-P., Specialty Co.—Chuck Staes;**
**Sr. V-P., Food Serv. N.—Joel Grade; Dir., Comms.—Wendy Olson**
Buckhead Beef Co., 220 Raritan Ctr., P.O. Box 6988, Edison, 08837 .......... (732) 661-4900
SYSCO Food Services Of Metro New York, LLC,
20 Theodore Conrad Dr., Jersey City, 07305 .......... (201) 433-2000
Sysco Guest Supply (H Q),
4301 Highway 1, P.O. Box 902, Monmouth Junction, 08852 .......... (609) 514-9696

**SYSCO GUEST SUPPLY**
**4301 Highway 1, P.O. Box 902, Monmouth Junction NJ 08852 .......... (609) 514-9696**
**Pres., COO—Paul T. Xenis; V-P., CFO—Michael Louro; Dir., Mktg.—Kathy Hatrak;**
**Hum. Res. Mgr.—Barbara Moran**
Guest Packaging, LLC, 414 E. Inman Ave., Rahway, 07065 .......... (732) 382-7270

**T. A. SYSTEMS, INC.**
**1842 Rochester Industrial Dr., Rochester Hills MI 48309 .......... (248) 656-5150**
**Pres.—Tim Gale; V-P.—Kirk Brunssen; Cont.—Patricia Angerilli; Acct. Mgr.—Holly Dolphin**
Emabond Solutions, LLC, 49 Walnut St., Ste. 2, Norwood, 07648 .......... (201) 767-7400

**TAKASAGO INTERNATIONAL CORP.**
**4 Volvo Dr., P.O. Box 932, Rockleigh NJ 07647 .......... (201) 767-9001**
**Pres.—Hasiya Fujiwara; V-P. & GM, Flavor Div.—Brian Buck; V-P.—Bill Bushman;**
**Cont.—Vee Ferrara; Dir., IT—Menno Poutsma; Plt. Mgr.—Dana Drevitson;**
**Hum. Res. Mgr.—Donna Mattis**
Takasago International Corp., 267 Union St., Northvale, 07647 .......... (201) 767-9001

**TAYLOR CORP.**
**1725 Roe Crest Dr., North Mankato MN 56003 .......... (507) 625-2828**
**Chrm. of the Board, Pres. & CEO—Glen Taylor; CIO—Jeff Eccles; CAO—Greg Jackson;**
**CFO—Tom Johnson; CSO—Todd Alexander**
Oraton Rubber Stamp Co., Inc., 407 Route 94, Columbia, 07832 .......... (908) 496-4161

**TBT GROUP, INC.**
**267 5th Ave., Ste. B-103, New York NY 10016 .......... (212) 685-1839**
**CEO—Dan DeClement; Dir., Sales—Joshua Sharon; Dir., Mfg.—Eric Weiss**
TBT Group, Inc., 191 Heller Pl., Bellmawr, 08031 .......... (856) 753-4500

**TDK-LAMBDA AMERICAS, INC.**
**3055 Del Sol Blvd., San Diego CA 92154 .......... (619) 575-4400**
**V-P., Mktg.—David Norton; Facilities Mgr.—Russell Shankle;**
**Hum. Res. Mgr.—Lynette De los Santos**
TDK-Lambda, Inc., 405 Essex Rd., Neptune, 07753 .......... (732) 922-9300

**TE CONNECTIVITY**
**1050 Westlakes Dr., Berwyn PA 19312 .......... (610) 893-9800**
**CEO—Thomas J. Lynch; Pres., Channel & Cust. Experience—Joan Wainwright;**
**Ex. V-P., CTO—Robert Shaddock; CFO—Robert Hau;**
**Sr. V-P., Comms. & Mktg.—Amy Shaw; Sr. V-P., Hum. Res., Global—Jane Leipold;**
**Ex. V-P., Gen. Counsel—John Jenkins; Sr. Ext. Comms. Mgr.—Jane Crawford**
Tyco Electronics Subsea Communications, LLC (H Q),
250 Industrial Way W., Eatontown, 07724 .......... (732) 578-7000

**TEAM INDUSTRIAL SERVICES**
**13131 Dairy Ashford, Ste. 600, Sugar Land TX 77478 .......... (281) 331-6154**
**Chrm., CEO—Phil Hawk; Sr. V-P., CFO—Ted Owen; COO—Pete Wallace;**
**Sr. V-P., Admn. & Law—Andre C. Bouchard; Sr. V-P.—Pat Kearns;**
**V-P., Hum. Res.—Mark Hinderliter; Cont.—Rob Baker; Dir., IT—Guy Thomas;**
**Dir., Hum. Res.—Doug Frankhouse; Mktg. Mgr.—Jason Box**
Team Industrial Services, 4 Killdeer Ct., Ste. 300, Swedesboro, 08085 ........ (610) 859-7800

**TECHNOLOGY GENERAL CORP.**
**12 Cork Hill Rd., Franklin NJ 07416 .......... (973) 827-4143**
**Sales Mgr.—Diane Olsen; Opers. Mgr.—Jeff Fletcher**
Clawson Machine, Div. Of Technology General Corp.,
12 Cork Hill Rd., Franklin, 07416 .......... (973) 827-8209

**TEKKOTE CORP.**
**580 Willow Tree Rd., Leonia NJ 07605 .......... (201) 585-8875**
**Dir., Fin.—Ron Saia; GM—Paul Ortiz; Hum. Res. Mgr.—Beth Arp**
Mondi, 1100 Slocum Ave., Ridgefield, 07657 .......... (201) 585-8875

**TEKNI-PLEX, INC.**
**1150 1st Ave., Ste. 500, King of Prussia PA 19406 .......... (484) 690-1520**
**Pres., CEO—Paul Young; CFO—Glenn Fish; Sr. V-P., Gen. Counsel—Dave Waksman;**
**V-P., Proc.—Kirk Rumsey**
Colorite, A Tekni-Plex Co., 101 Railroad Ave., Ridgefield, 07657 .......... (201) 941-2900
Tekni-Plex, Inc., 201 Industrial Pkwy., Somerville, 08876 .......... (908) 722-4800
Tri-Seal, 112 Church St., Flemington, 08822 .......... (908) 782-4000

**TENSION CORPORATION**
**819 E. 19th St., Kansas City MO 64108 .......... (816) 471-3800**
**Chrm.—Bert Berkley; Pres., CEO—Bill Berkley; V-P., Mfg. & COO—Bob Broadbear;**
**V-P., Sales—Susan Christie; V-P., Strategic Accts.—Andy Weed;**
**Secy-Treas.—Dick Berkley; Dir., Mktg.—Karen Loggia; Dir., Corp. Pur.—Tom Brackhahn;**
**Dir., Hum. Res.—Melissa Kent; MIS Mgr.—Brad Bradley**
Tension Envelope Corp., 19 Wesley St., South Hackensack, 07606 .......... (201) 487-1880

**TESS-COM, INC.**
**507 Saint Clair Ave., P.O. Box 600, Clairton PA 15025 .......... (412) 233-5782**
**Pres., GM—Louis Colonna; Off. Mgr.—John Skodak**
Tess-Com, Inc., 400 South Ave., Ste. 11, Middlesex, 08846 .......... (732) 560-8100

**TETRA PAK, INC.**
**3300 Airport Rd., Denton TX 76207 .......... (940) 565-8800**
**Pres.—Michael Zacka; V-P., Mktg. & Prod. Mgmt.—Suley Maratoglu;**
**Hum. Res. Mgr.—Pamelyn Woodard; Comms. Mgr.—Giovanna Lemos**
Novembal U. S. A., A Tetra Pak Co., 3 Greek Ln., Edison, 08817 .......... (732) 287-4949

**TEVA PHARMACEUTICALS USA, INC.**
**1090 Horsham Rd., P.O. Box 1090, North Wales PA 19454 .......... (215) 591-3000**
**Pres., CEO—Allan Oberman; CFO—Kobi Altman; V-P., Hum. Res.—Leslie Billow;**
**V-P., Corp. Comm.—Denise Bradley; Dir., Engrg. & Facilities—Steve Middlebrooks**
Teva Pharmaceuticals U.S.A., Inc., 8-10 Gloria Ln., Fairfield, 07004 .......... (973) 575-2775

**TEXPACK, INC.**
**1001 S. Brickell Bay Dr., Ste. 1710, Miami FL 33131 .......... (305) 358-9696**
**Pres., CEO—Jose Luis Artiga; V-P., Engrg.—Manuel Gonzalez; V-P., Fin.—Joaquin Vinas;**
**V-P., Paper—Fernando Martinez**
Lamitech, Inc., 322 Half-Acre Rd., Cranbury, 08512 .......... (609) 860-8037

**THERMO FISHER SCIENTIFIC, INC.**
**81 Wyman St., P.O. Box 9046, Waltham MA 02451 .......... (781) 622-1000**
**Pres., CEO—Marc N. Casper; Sr. V-P., CFO—Peter M. Wilver;**
**Sr. V-P. & Gen. Counsel—Seth H. Hoogasian; Sr. V-P., Hum. Res.—Sue Rice;**
**Sr. V-P., Global Bus. Svcs.—Alex G. Stachtiaris;**
**V-P., Cust. Experience & Mktg.—William McMahon;**
**V-P., Corp. Comms. & Pub. Rels.—Karen A. Kirkwood;**
**V-P., Inv. Rels.—Kenneth J. Apicerno; Dir., Corp. Comms.—Ron O'Brien**
Thermo Fisher Scientific, 755 U.S. Highway 202, Bridgewater, 08807 .......... (908) 526-1800
Thermo Fisher Scientific Inc., 1 Reagent Ln., Fair Lawn, 07410 .......... (201) 796-7100

**THERMOPLASTIC PROCESSES, INC.**
**21649 Cedar Creek Ave., Georgetown DE 19947 .......... (302) 855-0139**
**Pres.—D. Brooke Kinney; V-P., Acctg. & Admn. Opers.—Betty Adkins; GM—Joe Raborn; Sales Mgr.—Bary Voshell; Traf. Mgr.—Sandy Shannon**
Thermoplastic Processes, 1268 Valley Rd., P.O. Box 124, Stirling, 07980 ....... (888) 554-6400

**THOMAS & BETTS CORP.**
**8155 T & B Blvd., Memphis TN 38125 .......... (901) 252-5000**
**CEO & Reg. Div. Mgr., N. America—Charles Treadway; Sr. V-P., Cont.—David Alyea; Sr. V-P., Hum. Res.—Peggy Gann**
Thomas & Betts Corp., Elastimold Div., 1 Esna Pk., Hackettstown, 07840 ...... (908) 852-1122

**THOMAS & SKINNER, INC.**
**1120 E. 23rd St., Indianapolis IN 46205 .......... (317) 923-2501**
**Pres., CEO & Plt. Mgr.—Vernon A. Detlef; V-P., CFO & Treas.—Neil Moehring; Engrg. & Safety Mgr.—Gary Ullom; Cred. Mgr.—Diana Ernsting**
Ceramic Magnetics, Inc., 16 Law Dr., Fairfield, 07004 .......... (973) 227-4222

**THOMAS INSTRUMENTATION, INC.**
**133 Landing Rd., Cape May Court House NJ 08210 .......... (609) 624-2630**
**CEO & Engr.—Cassandra Gluyas; Pres. & Engrg. Supv.—Thomas Gluyas; CFO—Jan Gluyas**
Thomas Instrumentation, Inc., 118 Kings Hwy., Cape May Court House, 08210 .. (609) 624-7777

**THOMSON REUTERS HOLDINGS, INC.**
**3 Times Sq., New York NY 10036 .......... (646) 223-4000**
**CEO—James C. Smith; Pres., Reuters Media—Susan Taylor Martin; Ex. V-P., CTO—James Powell; Chief People Officer—Peter Warwick; Ex. V-P., Gen. Counsel—Deirdre Stanley; Corp. Affs. Mgr.—David Girardin**
Thomson Reuters Corp., 492 River Rd., Nutley, 07110 .......... (973) 662-3070

**THYSSENKRUPP MATERIALS NA, INC.**
**22355 W. 11 Mile Rd., Southfield MI 48033 .......... (248) 233-5600**
**Chrm.—Joachim Limberg; Pres., CEO—Hans J. Hoss; CFO—Norbert Goertz**
ThyssenKrupp Materials NA Copper & Brass Sales Div.,
800 Arlington Blvd., Ste. C, Swedesboro, 08085 .......... (610) 586-1800

**TIGHE PUBLISHING SERVICES, INC.**
**1700 W. Irving Park Rd., Ste. 210, Chicago IL 60613 .......... (773) 281-9100**
**Pres.—Suzanne Tighe; V-P., Opers.—Kevin Tighe; Dir., Editorial—Sue Evans**
Tighe Publishing Services, Inc., 788 Morris Tpke., Ste. 100, Short Hills, 07078 .. (973) 379-7770

**TILCON NEW YORK INC.**
**162 Old Mill Rd., West Nyack NY 10994 .......... (845) 358-4500**
**Pres., Div.—John Cooney, Jr.; COO—Bill Poole; V-P., IT—Niall O'Gara; V-P., Construction—Paul Taphorn; Cont.—Charlie Brassell; Gen. Sales Mgr.—Robert Diccianni**
Tilcon Riverdale Quarry, 125 Hamburg Tpke., Riverdale, 07457 .......... (973) 835-0028
Tilcon, Inc., Oxford Quarry, 193 Mount Pisgah Ave., P.O. Box 120, Oxford, 07863 . (908) 453-4141
Tilcon Totowa Asphalt, 859 Riverview Dr., Totowa, 07512 .......... (973) 256-8300
Tilcon New York, Inc., 625 Mount Hope Rd., Wharton, 07885 .......... (973) 366-7741

**TIMBAR PACKAGING & DISPLAY**
**148 Penn St., Hanover PA 17331 .......... (717) 632-4727**
**Pres., CEO—Matthew Heleva; CFO—Rick Fritz; CIO—Barry G. Cline; Sr. V-P., Opers.—Bill Thom**
TimBar Corp., 15-01 Pollitt Dr., Unit 9, Fair Lawn, 07410 .......... (201) 568-7300

**TIME SYSTEMS INTERNATIONAL, INC.**
**142 S. Van Brunt St., Englewood NJ 07631 .......... (973) 472-2202**
**Pres.—Samuel Gleich; Off. Mgr.—Debbi Greenfield**
AMERICAN Time Recorder, 2661 Brunetta Dr., Vineland, 08360 .......... (856) 691-7976

**TOTAL MACHINE SOLUTIONS, INC.**
**79 Express St., Ste. A, P.O. Box 799, Plainview NY 11803 .......... (516) 942-5125**
**Pres.—Marvin Goldman; V-P.—Kevin Orloski; Off. Mgr.—Christina Doner; Whse. Mgr.—James Fuoco**
Total Machine Solutions, Inc., 16 Spielman Rd., Fairfield, 07004 .......... (973) 244-0017

**TOWNSEND FARMS, INC.**
**23400 N.E. Townsend Way, Fairview OR 97024 .......... (503) 666-1780**
**Pres.—Mike Townsend; CFO—Kerry Rea; Plt. Mgr.—Alan Keith**
Townsend Farms, Inc., 3501 S. East Blvd., Vineland, 08360 .......... (856) 825-5240

**TOYO INK AMERICA**
**5360 Commerce Ave., Moorpark CA 93021 .......... (805) 378-0033**
**GM—Terrill Newkirk; Prodn. Mgr.—Tony Magana**
Toyo Ink America, 4301 New Brunswick Ave., Ste. A, South Plainfield, 07080 .... (732) 752-5660

**TOYO INK AMERICA, LLC**
**1225 N. Michael Dr., Wood Dale IL 60191 .......... (630) 930-5100**
**Chrm., CEO—Hideki 'Jeff' Okaichi; Pres., COO—John Copeland; V-P., Sales—Michael Keegan; Treas.—Jane Krasner; Corp. Sales & Mktg. Mgr.—Masa Nagatsubo; Pur. Mgr.—Robert Wichtendahl**
Toyo Ink America, LLC, 30 Murray Hill Pkwy., Ste. 100, East Rutherford, 07073 .. (201) 804-0616

**TRANE COMMERCIAL SYSTEMS**
**3600 Pammel Creek Rd., La Crosse WI 54601 .......... (608) 787-2000**
**CEO—Herbert Henkel; CFO—Brian Harrison; Plt. Mgr.—Jeff Helgesen**
Trane Co., 2231 E. State St., Trenton, 08619 .......... (609) 587-3400

**TRANSAXLE, LLC**
**2501 Route 73 S., P.O. Box 2306, Cinnaminson NJ 08077 .......... (856) 665-4445**
**CEO—Dave Olsen; CFO—David Gordan; GM—John Ferry; GM, Off Hwy. Hydraulic Div.—John Malley; IT Mgr.—Jason Matkowsky**
TransAxle Corp., 540 Huyler St., South Hackensack, 07606 .......... (201) 440-1911
TRC, 1700 Sherman Ave., Pennsauken, 08110 .......... (856) 910-7979

**TRANSDIGM, INC.**
**1301 E. 9th St., Cleveland OH 44114 .......... (216) 706-2960**
**Chrm., CEO—W. Nicholas Howley; Pres., Chief Operating Officer—Raymond F. Laubenthal; Ex. V-P., CFO & Secy.—Gregory Rufus; Ex. V-P.—Robert S. Henderson**
Airborne Systems North America Of New Jersey, Inc.,
5800 Magnolia Ave., Pennsauken, 08109 .......... (856) 663-1275

**TRAP ROCK IND., LLC**
**4415 Route 27, P.O. Box 419, Kingston NJ 08528 .......... (609) 924-0300**
**Pres.—Wiliam H. Stavola; V-P.—Michael Crowley; Sales Mgr.—Michael Conti; Plt. Opers. Mgr.—Gilbert Girard; Hum. Res. Mgr.—Jerry Myers; Cred. Mgr.—Gloria Morgan**
Sta-Seal, Inc., 5205 Route 130 S., Bordentown, 08505 .......... (609) 924-0300
Trap Rock, 27 Maple Ave., Mount Holly, 08060 .......... (609) 265-8500
Trap Rock Industries, Foot of Crows Mill Rd., Keasbey, 08832 .......... (732) 738-4222
Trap Rock Industries, Inc., Pennington Quarry,
120 Route 31 S., Pennington, 08534 .......... (609) 737-3200

**TRI VANTAGE, LLC**
**2937 W. 25th St., Cleveland OH 44113 .......... (216) 696-2820**
**Br. Mgr.—Phil Franz; Acctg. Mgr.—Mark Nicoletti; Traf. Mgr.—Kim Churang**
Tri Vantage, LLC, 16 Worlds Fair Dr., Somerset, 08873 .......... (732) 868-8400

**TRICO LIFT, INC.**
**1101 Wheaton Ave., Millville NJ 08332 .......... (856) 776-2350**
**Pres.—Ken Pustizzi; Cont.—Stephan Cattle; Dir., Mktg.—Terry Cardenter; IT Mgr.—Bob McClellan; Hum. Res. Mgr.—Andrea Jaworski; Dispatch Mgr.—Micki McCue**
Trico Lift, Inc., 418 Southgate Ct., Mickleton, 08056 .......... (800) 468-7426

**TRICORBRAUN, INC.**
**620 W. Germantown Pike, Ste. 460, Plymouth Meeting PA 19462 .......... (484) 534-5900**
**Whse. Mgr.—Dave Armstrong**
TricorBraun, 250 Pehle Ave., Ste. 100, Saddle Brook, 07663 .......... (201) 556-4800

**TRI-COUNTY BUILDING SUPPLIES, INC.**
**1001 Doughty Rd., Pleasantville NJ 08232 .......... (609) 646-0950**
**Pres.—Stephen Gross; Cont.—Bob Watts; GM—Pat Finnerty**
Tri-County Building Supplies, Inc.,
14 Reading Ave., Cape May Court House, 08210 .......... (609) 465-5021
Tri-County Building Supplies, Inc.,
211 Stites & Railroad Aves., Cape May Court House, 08210 .......... (609) 465-7839

**TRI-ED DISTRIBUTION, INC.**
**135 Crossways Park Dr., Ste. 101, Woodbury NY 11797 .......... (516) 941-2800**
**Pres., CEO—Steve Roth; COO—Pat Comunale; Sr. V-P., Mktg.—James Rothstein; V-P., Secy-Treas.—Jason Roth; Asst. Cont.—Ken Bocamazo**
Tri-ed/Northern Video Distribution, 7 Corporate Dr., Ste. 2, Cranbury, 08512 .... (609) 860-0708

**TRIMBLE NAVIGATION LTD.**
**935 Stewart Dr., P.O. Box 3642, Sunnyvale CA 94085 .......... (408) 481-8000**
**Pres., CEO—Steven W. Berglund; V-P., Gen. Counsel—James Kirkland; V-P., Geospatial Div.—Erik Arvesen; V-P., Hum. Res.—Mary K. Strangis; V-P.—Bryn Fosburgh; GM, Embedded Prod. Div.—Steve Ruff**
ALK Technologies, Inc., 457 N. Harrison St., Princeton, 08540 .......... (609) 683-0220

**TROPHY KING, INC., THE**
**309 Queen Anne Rd., Teaneck NJ 07666 .......... (201) 836-1482**
**Pres.—James Walsh; Prodn. Mgr.—Terrence Crotty; Manager—Bobby Schuvert; Engraver—Kevin Johnson**
Trophy King Of Ramsey, 503 N. Franklin Tpke., Unit 13, Ramsey, 07446 ....... (201) 760-6488

**TROY CORP.**
**8 Vreeland Rd., Florham Park NJ 07932 .......... (973) 443-4200**
**Chrm., CEO—Daryl Smith; V-P., Mktg.—David E. Faherty; V-P., Admn. & Govt. Rels.—Alexander Gerardo; V-P., Hum. Res.—Robert Chance; V-P., Dev.—Donald Shaw**
FTI, Inc. (H Q), 8 Vreeland Rd., Florham Park, 07932 .......... (973) 443-4200
Troy Chemicals, 1 Avenue L, Newark, 07105 .......... (973) 589-2500

**TRUE WORLD GROUP, LLC**
**24 Link Dr., Rockleigh NJ 07647 .......... (201) 750-0024**
**CFO—Tom Ino; Cont.—Ikue Saito; Hum. Res. Mgr.—Mike Korutio**
Crystal World, Inc., 89 Leuning St., Ste. A-2, South Hackensack, 07606 ....... (201) 488-0909
True World Foods, LLC, 32-34 Papetti Plz., Elizabeth, 07206 .......... (908) 351-1400

**TRUMPF, INC.**
**111 Hyde Rd., Farmington CT 06032 .......... (860) 255-6000**
**Pres., CEO—Lars Gruenert; V-P., Sales & Mktg.—Burke Doar; V-P., Fin.—Doug Devnew; V-P., Cust. Serv.—Kevin Domingue**
TRUMPF Photonics, Inc., 2601 US Route 130 S., Cranbury, 08512 .......... (609) 925-8200

**TULNOY LUMBER, INC.**
**1620 Webster Ave., Bronx NY 10457 .......... (718) 583-3434**
**Pres., GM—Steven Tulchin; Off. Mgr.—Lori Zwier**
Tulnoy Lumber, Inc., 9-D Raskulinecz Rd., Carteret, 07008 .......... (732) 634-4000

**TURTLE & HUGHES, INC.**
**1900 Lower Rd., Linden NJ 07036 .......... (732) 574-3600**
**Chrm.—Suzanne T. Millard; Pres.—Jayne Millard; CFO—Trevor Barnett; Opers. Mgr.—Chuck Noll; Hum. Res. Mgr.—Lucy Liana**
Turtle & Hughes, Inc., 188 Foothill Rd., Bridgewater, 08807 .......... (732) 560-5575

**TW METALS, INC.**
**760 Constitution Dr., Ste. 204, P.O. Box 644, Exton PA 19341 .......... (610) 458-1300**
**Pres., CEO—Jack Elrod; V-P., Sales & Mktg.—Bob Mraz; V-P., Hum. Res.—Pat Wilson**
TW Metals, Inc., 27 Engelhard Dr., Monroe Township, 08831 .......... (609) 655-4120

**TYCO**
**9 Roszel Rd., Princeton NJ 08540 .......... (609) 720-4200**
**CEO—George Oliver; Ex. V-P., CFO—Arun Nayar; COO—Brian McDonald; Sr. V-P., CIO—John Repko; Sr. V-P., Chief Proc. Officer—Vivek Kamath; Ex. V-P., Gen. Counsel—Judith Reinsdorf; Ex. V-P., Hum. Res.—Larry Costello; V-P., Global Comms.—Steve Wasdick; Comms. Mgr.—Jaqueline Davis**
Goyen Valve Corp., 1195 Airport Rd., Lakewood, 08701 .......... (732) 364-7800
Westlock Controls Corp., 280 N. Midland Ave., Ste. 258, Saddle Brook, 07663 .. (201) 794-7650

**U. S. CONCRETE, INC.**
**331 N. Main St., Euless TX 76039 .......... (817) 835-4105**
**Pres., CEO—William J. Sandbrook; Ex. V-P., CFO—Kevin Kohutek; Sr. V-P., Opers. & Special Projs.—Terry Green; V-P., Gen. Counsel—Paul Jolas; V-P., Sales & Mktg.—Wallace Johnson; V-P., Hum. Res.—Gary J. Konnie; Dir., IT—Darnell Streat**
Eastern Concrete Materials, Inc. (H Q),
475 Market St., 3rd Fl., Elmwood Park, 07407 .......... (201) 797-7979

© Copyright 2015 Manufacturers' News, Inc.


**U.S. SILICA COMPANY**
**8490 Progress Dr., Ste. 300, Frederick MD 21701 .................... (301) 682-0600**
**Pres., CEO—Bryan Shinn; V-P., CFO—Don Merril;**
**V-P., Chief Operating Officer—Mike Winkler;**
**V-P., Chief Admn. Officer—Adam Yoxtheimer; V-P., Talent Mgmt. & CHRO—Dave Murry;**
**Gen. Counsel & Secy.—Christine Marshall; V-P., Supply Chain—Jason Tedrow;**
**V-P., Strategic Plng.—Brad Casper**
U.S. Silica Co., 9035 Noble St., P.O. Box 254, Mauricetown, 08329 .......... (856) 785-0720

**UFP TECHNOLOGIES, INC.**
**172 E. Main St., Georgetown MA 01833 .................... (800) 372-3172**
**Chrm. of the Board, Pres. & CEO—Jeffrey Bailly; V-P., Treas. & CFO—Ronald Lataille;**
**V-P., Sales & Mktg.—Mitch C. Rock; V-P., Prod. Dev.—Daniel Shaw, Jr.;**
**Mktg. Comm. Mgr.—Tom Fitzgerald**
UFP Technologies, Inc., 1 Johnson Dr., Raritan, 08869 .................. (800) 372-3172

**UNICOR FEDERAL PRISON INDUSTRIES, INC.**
**320 1st St. N.W., Washington, DC MD 20534 .................... (202) 305-3500**
**CEO—Charles Samuels; Cont.—Ray Wiley; Asst. Dir.—Mary M. Mitchell;**
**IT Mgr.—Sharad Tilak; Prog. Mgr.—Mark Gustafson; Mgmt. Analyst—Natalie Davison**
Unicor Federal Prison Industries, Inc.,
5835 Doughboy Loop, P.O. Box 38, Fort Dix, 08640 .................... (609) 723-1100

**UNIFOIL CORP.**
**12 Daniel Rd., Ste. 101, Fairfield NJ 07004 .................... (973) 244-9900**
**Pres., CEO—Joseph Funicelli; V-P., CFO—William Mulrooney; R & D Mgr.—Bob Gallino**
Unifoil Corp., 12 Vanil Rd. E., Fairfield, 07004 .................... (973) 244-9900

**UNI-SELECT USA, INC.**
**20 Hazelwood Dr., Ste. 100, Amherst NY 14228 .................... (716) 531-9200**
**CEO—Jim Buzzard; V-P., Admn. & IT—Bob Buzzard; Hum. Res. Mgr.—Shelly Whitt**
Parts Distributors, LLC, 901 N. Lenola Rd., P.O. Box 832, Moorestown, 08057 . . . (856) 778-1400

**UNITED CAPITAL CORP.**
**9 Park Pl., 4th Fl., Great Neck NY 11021 .................... (516) 466-6464**
**Chrm., Pres. & CEO—Attilio F. Petrocelli; CFO—Anthony Miceli; V-P.—Michael T. Lamoretti;**
**V-P.—Michael J. Weinbaum; Corp. Cont.—Gary Rosenberg**
AFP Transformers Corp., 206 Talmadge Rd., Edison, 08817 .................. (732) 248-0305
Metal Textiles Corp., 970 New Durham Rd., Edison, 08818 .................. (732) 287-0800

**UNITED ELECTRIC SUPPLY CO.**
**10 Bellecor Dr., New Castle DE 19720 .................... (800) 322-3374**
**CEO—George Vorwick; CFO—Rich Stagliano;**
**V-P., Delaware Valley Sales Reg.—Pat Melvin; V-P., Hum. Res.—Gayle Davis;**
**V-P., Vendor Rels.—Rick Freebery; Dir., Mktg.—Lou Salvadori**
United Electric Supply Co., 1150 W. Garden Rd., Vineland, 08360 .......... (856) 691-6668

**UNITED NATURAL FOODS, INC.**
**313 Iron Horse Way, Providence RI 02908 .................... (401) 528-8634**
**CEO—Steven Spinner; Pres.—Richard Youngman; CFO—Mark Shamber; CIO—Eric Dorne;**
**Sr. V-P., Chief Hum. Res. & Sustainability Officer—Tom Dziki;**
**Sr. V-P., Dist.—Sean Griffin; Cont.—Lisa N'Chonon**
Albert's Organics, Inc., 200 Eagle Ct., P.O. Box 624, Bridgeport, 08014 ........ (856) 241-9090
Woodstock Farms Mfg., 96 Executive Ave., Edison, 08817 .................. (732) 650-9905

**UNITED REFRIGERATION, INC.**
**11401 Roosevelt Blvd., Philadelphia PA 19154 .................... (215) 698-9100**
**V-P., CFO—Nicholas V. Hope; Dir., Mktg.—Chris Bock; Hum. Res. Mgr.—Barbara Keenan**
National Refrigerants, Inc., 661 Kenyon Ave., Bridgeton, 08302 .......... (856) 455-4555

**UNITED STATIONERS, INC.**
**1 Parkway North Blvd., Ste. 100, Deerfield IL 60015 .................... (847) 627-7000**
**Pres., CEO—P. Cody Phipps; Pres., Opers. & Logistics Serv.—Timothy P. Connolly;**
**Sr. V-P., CFO—Todd Shelton; V-P., Cont. & CAO—Kenneth M. Nickel;**
**Sr. V-P., Gen. Counsel & Secy.—Eric Blanchard;**
**Sr. V-P., Inventory Mgmt.—Ronald C. Berg; Dir., Hum. Res.—Maureen West;**
**Sr. Mgr., Comm. & Pub. Rels.—Michael Chazin**
United Stationers Supply Co., 100 Liberty Way, Cranbury, 08512 .......... (609) 619-4000

**UNITED SUPPLY CO., INC.**
**457 W. End Ave., Plainfield NJ 07060 .................... (908) 757-3232**
**CEO—Steve Kantor; Pres.—Lynn Campagna; GM—Fred Tamberelli; IT Mgr.—Jack So;**
**Hum. Res. Mgr.—Sue Stockinger; Showroom Mgr.—Aaron Cacchione**
United Supply Co., Inc., 7 Chris Ct., Ste. A, Dayton, 08810 .................. (732) 329-6301

**UNIVERSAL FOREST PRODUCTS, INC.**
**2801 E. Beltline Ave. N.E., Grand Rapids MI 49525 .................... (616) 364-6161**
**Chrm.—William Currie; CEO—Matthew J. Missad; Pres., COO—Patrick Webster;**
**CFO—Mike Cole; Ex. V-P., Sales—Don James;**
**Ex. V-P., Eastern Div., North—Patrick Benton;**
**Ex. V-P., Eastern Div., South—Jonathan West; Ex. V-P., Opers.—Bob Coleman;**
**Ex. V-P., Mktg.—C. Scott Greene; Dir., Corp. Comms.—Lynn Afendoulis**
UFP Berlin, LLC, 159 Jackson Rd., Berlin, 08009 .................... (856) 767-0043

**US ELECTRICAL SERVICES, INC.**
**151 Walnut St., Hartford CT 06120 .................... (860) 522-3232**
**CFO—Darlene Crouch; Dir., IT—Alice Brown**
Monarch Electric Supply Co., 1527 Livingston Ave., North Brunswick, 08902 . . . . (732) 249-1616
Rahway Electric Supply, Inc., 1684 Essex St., Rahway, 07065 .............. (732) 381-6060

**US FOODS, INC.**
**9399 W. Higgins Rd., Ste. 500, Rosemont IL 60018 .................... (847) 720-8000**
**CEO—John Lederer; CIO—Keith Rohland; Chief Hum. Res. Officer—Dave Esler;**
**Cont.—Dirk Locascio; Sr. Dir., Corp. Comms.—Michelle Calcagni;**
**Dir., Hum. Res.—Mary Ellen Spedale**
US Foods, Inc., 1051 Amboy Ave., Perth Amboy, 08861 .................. (732) 934-3400

**US INK CORP.**
**631 Central Ave., Carlstadt NJ 07072 .................... (201) 935-8666**
**Pres.—Michael Dodd; V-P., Sales—John Corcoran; Dir., Hum. Res.—David Benson;**
**Mktg. Mgr.—Todd Wheeler**
US Ink Corp., 390 Central Ave., East Rutherford, 07073 .................. (201) 438-4041

**USG CORP.**
**550 W. Adams St., Chicago IL 60661 .................... (312) 436-4000**
**Chrm., Pres. & CEO—James S. Metcalf; Ex. V-P., CFO—Matthew F. Hilzinger;**
**Sr. V-P., Hum. Res.—Brian Cook; Ex. V-P., Gen. Counsel—Stanley Ferguson;**
**Ex. V-P., Mfg.—Dominic A. Dannessa; Dir., Corp. Comm.—Bob Williams;**
**Hum. Res. Mgr.—Jose Vega**
USG Corp., Port Reading Plt., 300 Markley St., Port Reading, 07064 ......... (732) 636-7900

**UTC AEROSPACE SYSTEMS, ISR & PROPELLER SYSTEMS**
**7 Technology Park Dr., Westford MA 01886 .................... (978) 303-6700**
**Pres.—Thomas Bergeron; V-P., GM—Andrew Chrostowski; Dir., Bus. Dev.—Tom Breen**
UTC Aerospace Systems-ISR Systems (Sensors Unlimited, Inc.),
330 Carter Rd., Ste. 100, Princeton, 08540 .................... (609) 520-0610

**VALHI, INC.**
**5430 LBJ Fwy., Ste. 1700, Dallas TX 75240 .................... (972) 233-1700**
**Chrm.—Harold Simmons; Pres., CEO—Steve Watson; V-P., CFO—Bobby O'Brien;**
**Sr. V-P.—William Lindquist; Corp. Secy.—A. Andrew R. Louis**
Kronos Worldwide, Inc., 5 Cedarbrook Dr., Ste. 2, Cranbury, 08512 .......... (609) 860-6200

**VALID USA, INC.**
**1011 Warrenville Rd., Ste. 450, Lisle IL 60532 .................... (630) 852-5600**
**V-P., Opers.—Daniel Impieri; Dir., Hum. Res.—Gail Peterson; IT Mgr.—Rubin Mendez;**
**Hum. Res. Mgr.—Karen McCormick; Qual. Assur. Mgr.—Dana Titus**
Valid USA, Inc., 800 Montrose Ave., South Plainfield, 07080 .............. (908) 668-0999

**VANTAGE OLEOCHEMICALS, INC.**
**4650 S. Racine Ave., Chicago IL 60609 .................... (773) 376-9000**
**CFO—Helen Scott; COO—Noel Beavis; Hum. Res. Mgr.—Barry Rosenthal;**
**Cust. Serv. Mgr.—Maureen Melnik**
Lipo Chemicals, Inc., 207 19th Ave., Paterson, 07504 .................. (973) 345-8600

**VCOM INTERNATIONAL MULTI-MEDIA CORP.**
**80 Little Falls Rd., Fairfield NJ 07004 .................... (201) 229-4270**
**Pres., CEO—Sheldon Goldstein; Sales Mgr., Natl.—Stephen P. Marino;**
**Cred. Mgr.—Eileen Graper; Pur. Agt.—Ronnie Turner; Pur. Agt.—Charlie Mena**
A. V. Bluebook, 80 Little Falls Rd., Fairfield, 07004 .................. (800) 631-0868
Buhl Electric, Inc., 80 Little Falls Rd., Fairfield, 07004 .................. (201) 296-0600
V-Com, 80 Little Falls Rd., Fairfield, 07004 .................. (201) 229-9800
Hamilton Buhl, 80 Little Falls Rd., Fairfield, 07004 .................. (201) 229-9800

**VEECO INSTRUMENTS INC.**
**1 Terminal Dr., Plainview NY 11803 .................... (516) 677-0200**
**CEO—John Peeler; Ex. V-P., CFO—David Glass; Sr. V-P., Corp. Comms.—Debra Wasser;**
**Sr. V-P., Fin.—John Kiernan; Ex. V-P., Sales—Peter Collingwood;**
**Facility Mgr.—David Albert**
Veeco Instruments, Inc., 145 Belmont Dr., Somerset, 08873 .................. (732) 560-5300

**VEOLIA ENVIRONMENTAL SERVICES NORTH AMERICA CORP.**
**200 E. Randolph St., Ste. 7900, Chicago IL 60601 .................... (312) 552-2800**
**CEO—Terry Mah; Pres.—Jim Bell; Ex. V-P., CFO—Jason Salgo;**
**V-P., Comm. & Sales & Mktg.—Curtis Mabry; Dir., Comms. & Mktg.—Denisse Ike**
Veolia Environmental Services, 27-33 Iowa Ave., Paterson, 07503 .......... (973) 742-6789
Veolia ES Technical Solutions, LLC, 125 Factory Ln., Middlesex, 08846 ....... (732) 469-5100

**VEOLIA WATER NORTH AMERICA**
**200 E. Randolph Dr., Ste. 7900, Chicago IL 60601 .................... (312) 552-2800**
**Pres., CEO—Terry Mah; Ex. V-P., Hum. Res.—Augie Schulke; Gen. Counsel—Eric Robben;**
**Media Rels. Mgr.—Scott Edwards**
Veolia Water Solutions & Technologies North America, Inc.,
6981 N. Park Dr., Ste. 600, Pennsauken, 08109 .................... (856) 438-1776

**VERINT SYSTEMS, INC.**
**330 S. Service Rd., Ste. 108, Melville NY 11747 .................... (631) 962-9600**
**Pres., CEO—Dan Bodner; Pres., Americas—Elan Moriah; CFO—Doug Robinson;**
**V-P., Mktg.—Ryan Hollenbeck**
Verint Systems, Inc., 9 Polito Ave., 9th Fl., Lyndhurst, 07071 .............. (201) 559-3788

**VERISK ANALYTICS, INC.**
**545 Washington Blvd., Jersey City NJ 07310 .................... (201) 469-2000**
**Pres., CEO—Scott G. Stephenson; Ex. V-P., CFO—Mark V. Anquillare**
Insurance Services Office, Inc., 545 Washington Blvd., Jersey City, 07310 ...... (201) 469-2000

**VERITIV CORP.**
**6285 Tri Ridge Blvd., Loveland OH 45140 .................... (513) 965-2900**
**Pres.—Mary Laschinger; Ex. V-P., Sales & Mktg.—Steve Bowden;**
**Ex. V-P., E. Reg.—James Connelly; Ex. V-P., W. Reg.—W. Michael Amick, Jr.;**
**Ex. V-P., Opers.—John Biscanti; V-P., GM, Sallfeld & xpedx, Stores Div.—Carol Butler;**
**V-P., Mktg., Print—Cara Tanner; V-P., Fin.—Walter Klein; Dir., IT—Peggy Scott;**
**Comms. Mgr.—Lisa Jonas; Bus. Comm. Mgr.—Stephanie Mangini**
xpedx, 261 River Rd., Clifton, 07014 .................... (973) 405-2310
xpedx, 261 River Rd., Clifton, 07014 .................... (973) 405-2300
xpedx LLC A veritiv Company, 1200 Highland Dr., Ste. 1-B, Westampton, 08060 . (609) 518-9700

**VERMONT STORE FIXTURE CORP.**
**1566 Route 7, Danby VT 05739 .................... (802) 293-5126**
**Pres.—D. R. Sherman; V-P., Sales—Kevin Murphy; Pur. Mgr.—Corinna Reymond**
Vermont Store Fixture Corporation, 265 Greenwood Ave., Midland Park, 07432 . . (201) 652-3401

**VERNON CO., THE**
**1 Promotion Pl., P.O. Box 600, Newton IA 50208 .................... (641) 792-9000**
**Chrm., CEO—William F. Vernon; Pres., COO—Chris Vernon;**
**Sr. V-P., Opers.—Brad Lundquist; V-P., Sales & Mktg.—David Regan;**
**V-P., Fin.—Joe Stocker; Dir., IT—Chris Lanagan; Industry Rels. Mgr.—Andrea Smith;**
**Pur. Agt.—Deb Sloan**
Vernon Display Graphics, 145 Commerce Rd., Carlstadt, 07072 .............. (201) 935-7117

**VERTELLUS SPECIALTIES, INC.**
**201 N. Illinois St., Ste. 1800, Indianapolis IN 46204 .................... (317) 247-8141**
**Pres., CEO—Richard Preziotti; CFO—Philip Gillespie;**
**V-P., Global Opers. & Supply Chain—John Washuta; Cont.—Scott Dearing**
Vertellus Performance Materials, Inc., 40 Avenue A, Bayonne, 07002 .......... (201) 858-8810

**VICTORY PACKAGING, INC.**
**3555 Timmons Ln., Ste. 1440, Houston TX 77027 .................... (713) 961-3299**
**CEO—Ben Samuels; V-P., Opers.—Fred Brown; V-P., Pur. & Supply Chain—John Kaiser**
Victory Packaging, Inc., 8 Corn Rd., Ste. 2, Dayton, 08810 .................. (732) 274-1745

© Copyright 2015 Manufacturers' News, Inc.


**VICTORY WHITE METAL CO., INC.**
**3027 E. 55th St., Cleveland OH 44127 .............................. (216) 271-1400**
**Co-Pres.—Alex Stanwick; V-P.—Bill Clarke; Sales Mgr.—Donna Shubert**
Victory White Metal Co., Inc., 129 Victoria Pl. W., Fort Lee, 07024 ........... (201) 585-0747

**VIOLIN MEMORY, INC.**
**4555 Great America Pkwy., Santa Clara CA 95054 .................... (650) 396-1500**
**Co-Founder & CTO—Jon Bennett; Pres., CEO—Kevin DeNuccio; Sr. V-P., CMO—Eric Herzog; CFO—Corey Sindelar; Sr. V-P., Opers.—Ebrahim Abbasi; Sr. V-P., Global Field Opers.—Tom Mitchell; Sr. V-P., Prod. Mgmt.—Said Ouissal; Gen. Counsel—Gary Lloyd**
Violin Memory, Inc., 33 Wood Ave. S., 3rd Fl., Iselin, 08830 ................ (650) 396-1492

**VIRGINIA AMERICAN INDUSTRIES, INC.**
**710 Hospital St., Richmond VA 23219 .............................. (804) 644-2611**
**Pres.—Jerry Dawson; V-P., GM, Construction—Les Dixon; V-P., Sales—Johnny Moss; Comp.—Clay Foster**
American Galvanizing Co., Inc., 1919 R.R. 54, Folsom, 08094 .............. (609) 567-2090

**VISTAR CORP.**
**12650 E. Arapahoe Rd., Bldg. D, Centennial CO 80112 ................. (303) 662-7100**
**Pres., CEO—Patrick T. Hagerty; V-P., Sales & Mktg.—Terry Touchton; V-P., Hum. Res.—Eric Cremer; V-P., Retail—Bob Beck; V-P., Strategic Dev.—Jeff Fischer; V-P., Fin.—Patrick Hatcher; V-P., Merchandising—Ann Reidy; Dir., Hum. Res.—K. P. Pastorini**
Roma Food Enterprises, Inc., 1 Roma Blvd., Piscataway, 08854............. (732) 463-7662
Roma Of Mid-Atlantic, 301 Heron Dr., Swedesboro, 08085 ................. (856) 467-8100

**VITECH SYSTEMS GROUP, INC.**
**401 Park Ave. S., New York NY 10016 .............................. (212) 868-0900**
**Pres.—Frank Vitiello; V-P.—Jamie Vitiello; V-P.—Chris Lodge**
Vitech Systems Group, Inc., 111 Wood Ave. S., Iselin, 08830 ............... (646) 344-5282

**VOIGT & SCHWEITZER, LLC**
**987 Buckeye Park Rd., Columbus OH 43207 .......................... (614) 449-8281**
**Pres.—Brian Miller; V-P. & Dir., Sales & Mktg.—Terry Wolfe; Cont.—Troy Gaerke; Hum. Res. Mgr.—Tammy Kinsey**
V & S Amboy Galvanizing, 1190 Amboy Ave., Perth Amboy, 08861 ........... (732) 442-7555

**VON ROLL USA, INC.**
**200 Von Roll Dr., Schenectady NY 12306 ........................... (518) 344-7100**
**GM—Jon Roberts; Sales Mgr.—Jim Danze**
Dolph Co., John C., 320 New Rd., Monmouth Junction, 08852 ............... (732) 329-2333

**W&O SUPPLY, INC.**
**2677 Port Industrial Dr., Jacksonville FL 32226 ...................... (904) 354-3800**
**Pres., CEO—Michael Hume; V-P., Opers., E. Coast & W. Coast—Michael Page; V-P., Opers.—Michael Mickle; Dir., Comms. & Mktg.—Kimberly Hegg; Hum. Res. Mgr.—Lori Ulrich**
W&O Supply, Inc., 7 W. Baltimore Ave., Linden, 07036..................... (908) 486-5338

**W. R. GRACE & CO.**
**7500 Grace Dr., Columbia MD 21044 ............................... (410) 531-4000**
**Chrm., CEO—Fred Festa; Pres., Grace Davison & COO—Greg Poling; Sr. V-P., CFO—Hudson La Force; Chief Hum. Res. Officer—Pamela Wagoner; V-P., Gen. Counsel & Secy.—Mark Shelnitz; V-P., Pub. & Reg. Affs.—William Corcoran; Dir., Corp. Comm.—Mike Jones; Comms. Mgr.—Carla Beumont**
W. R. Grace & Co., 2133 85th St., North Bergen, 07047.................... (201) 869-5220

**W. W. GRAINGER, INC.**
**100 Grainger Pkwy., Lake Forest IL 60045 .......................... (847) 535-1000**
**Chrm., Pres. & CEO—James T. Ryan; Group Pres., Americas & Sr. V-P.—Court Carruthers; Sr. V-P. & Group Pres., Global Supply Chain & Intl.—D. G. McPherson; Sr. V-P., CIO—Michael Ali; Sr. V-P., CFO—Ronald L. Jadin; Sr. V-P., Chief People Officer—Joseph High; Sr. V-P., Gen. Counsel—John L. Howard; Sr. V-P., Comms. & Inv. Rels.—Laura Brown; V-P., GM—Deb Oler; Sr. Dir., Inv. Rels.—William Chapman; —Michael Ferreter**
W. W. Grainger, Inc., 308 Allwood Rd., Clifton, 07012..................... (973) 777-7700
W. W. Grainger, Inc., 55 Jackson Dr., Cranford, 07016 .................... (908) 272-7156
W. W. Grainger, Inc., 560-596 Bercik St., Ste. 1, Elizabeth, 07201 ........... (908) 787-1952
W. W. Grainger, Inc., 277 Route 46 W., Fairfield, 07004 ................... (973) 227-7220
W. W. Grainger, Inc., 819 E. Gate Dr., Mount Laurel, 08054 ................ (856) 234-8550
W. W. Grainger, Inc., 1585 N. Olden Ave., Trenton, 08638 ................. (609) 394-2620

**WACOAL AMERICA, INC.**
**136 Madison Ave., 14th Fl., New York NY 10016 ...................... (212) 532-6100**
**Pres., Co-CEO—Robert J. Vitale; V-P., Sales—Robb Irby; V-P., Mgmt. Info. Svcs.—Cathryn Hondros; V-P., Fin. & Cont.—La-Rome Talley; Dir., Hum. Res.—Mary Beth McCreadie**
Wacoal America, Inc., 1 Wacoal Plz., Lyndhurst, 07071 ................... (201) 933-8400

**WAKEFERN FOOD CORP.**
**5000 Riverside Dr., Keasbey NJ 08832 ............................. (732) 906-5932**
**Chrm., CEO—Joseph S. Colalillo; Pres., COO—Joe Sheridan; CFO—Doug Wille; Sr. V-P., Perishables—Bill Mayo; Sr. V-P., Non-Perishable—Chris Lane; Sr. V-P.—Jeff Reagan; V-P., eCommerce—Cheryl Williams; V-P., Consumer & Corp. Comms.—Karen Meleta**
Readington Farms, Inc., 12 Mill Rd., P.O. Box 164, Whitehouse, 08888 ........ (908) 534-2121

**WALPOLE WOODWORKERS, INC.**
**767 East St., P.O. Box 151, Walpole MA 02081 ....................... (508) 668-2800**
**Pres.—Louis Maglio, Jr.; V-P., Opers.—Sid Tildsley; Treas.—James Loer, Jr.; IT Mgr.—Sam DeForest; Hum. Res. Mgr.—Janet Conroy; Payroll Benefits Mgr.—Chris Bridges**
Walpole Woodworkers, Inc., 540 Tabor Rd., Morris Plains, 07950............. (973) 539-3555

**WASHINGTON PROFESSIONAL SYSTEMS, INC.**
**11242 Grandview Ave., Wheaton MD 20902........................... (301) 942-6800**
**Pres.—Robert Levin; V-P.—Greg Lukens; V-P.—Alan Levin**
Washington Professional Systems, Inc.,
109 Gaither Dr., Ste. 301, Mount Laurel, 08054 ......................... (856) 273-8688

**WASTE MANAGEMENT, INC.**
**1001 Fannin St., Ste. 4000, Houston TX 77002 ....................... (713) 512-6200**
**Pres., CEO—David Steiner; Sr. V-P., Corp. Opers. & Pres., Div.—Puneet Bahsin; Sr. V-P., Chief Legal Officer—Barry Caldwell; Sr. V-P., Field Opers.—John Morris, Jr.; Sr. V-P., Hum. Res.—Mark Schwartz; Sr. V-P., Gen. Consul—Rick Wittenbraker; V-P., Renewable Energy—Paul Pabor; Corp. Secy.—Linda Smith; Dir., Supply Chain—Christian Pierce**
Waste Management, Inc., 107 Silvia St., Ewing, 08628 .................... (609) 587-1500

**WASTEQUIP, INC.**
**6525 Morrison Blvd., Ste. 300, Charlotte NC 28211 .................... (704) 366-7140**
**CEO, COO—Martin Bryant; Pres., Tech. Div.—Mark Taylor; Pres., Parts Div.—Robert Munroe; CFO—Steve Svetik; Sr. V-P., Gen. Counsel—Richard Sedory**
Wastequip, 1031 Hickstown Rd., Sicklerville, 08081....................... (856) 784-5500
Wastequip, Inc., 460 New Brooklyn Rd., Williamstown, 08094 ............... (856) 629-9222

**WEATHERFORD INTERNATIONAL LTD.**
**2000 Saint James Pl., Houston TX 77056 ........................... (713) 836-4000**
**Chrm., Pres. & CEO—Bernard Duroc-Danner; CFO—Karen David-Green; V-P., Mktg.—Kelly Lawrence**
Bilfinger Water Technologies, 708 Challenger Way, Forked River, 08731 ....... (609) 693-9434

**WELDON MATERIALS, INC.**
**141 Central Ave., Westfield NJ 07090 .............................. (908) 233-4444**
**Pres., Cont.—Richard Weldon; V-P.—William Weldon; Hum. Res. Mgr.—Eileen Mooney**
Weldon Asphalt Co., 1100 Harrison Ave., Kearny, 07032 ................... (201) 991-3200
Weldon Asphalt Co., 311 W. Main St., Rockaway, 07866 ................... (973) 627-7500
Weldon Asphalt Co., 1 Eisenhower Pkwy., Roseland, 07068 ................. (973) 228-7473
Weldon Asphalt Co., 1 New Providence Rd., Watchung, 07060 ............... (908) 233-9440
Weldon Asphalt Corp., 2000 Marshes Dock Rd., Linden, 07036.............. (908) 862-0646
Weldon Materials, Inc., 181 Route 181, Lake Hopatcong, 07849 ............. (973) 663-1800

**WHIBCO, INC.**
**87 E. Commerce St., Bridgeton NJ 08302 ........................... (856) 455-9200**
**Pres.—Wade R. Sjogren; Ex. V-P.—Walter Sjogren; Cont.—Bill Simcox; Asst. Cont.—Betty Whitelan; Dir., Admn. & MIS—Richard Bertonaczi**
Whibco Of New Jersey,
377 Port Cumberland Rd., P.O. Box 456, Port Elizabeth, 08348 ............ (856) 825-5200

**WHITE VALLEY MEMORIALS**
**292 W. White Horse Pike, Berlin NJ 08009............................ (856) 767-3030**
**Owner—Al Cohlmyer**
William B. Snelbaker & Son, 43 Cooper St., Woodbury, 08096............... (856) 845-0634

**WHITEWAVE FOODS CO.**
**12002 Airport Way, Broomfield CO 80021 ........................... (303) 635-4000**
**Pres.—Blaine McPeak; Sr. V-P., Canada & Plant-Based Beverages—Craig Shiesley; V-P., IT—Steve Liedtke; V-P., Hum. Rels.—Tommy Zanetich; V-P., Govt. & Indl. Rels.—Kelly Shea; V-P., Comms.—Molly Keveney; Corp. Comms. Mgr.—Luana Hancock**
WhiteWave Foods Co., 70 Rosenhayn Ave., Bridgeton, 08302 ............... (856) 459-3890

**WHITLOCK PACKAGING CORP.**
**6655 S. Lewis Ave., Ste. 105, Tulsa OK 74136 ........................ (918) 524-4029**
**Chrm. & Founder—Jerry D. Whitlock; CEO—David M. Moller; V-P., Corp. Cont.—Keith Bishop; V-P., Sales, CEB/Private Label—Bill Towler; V-P., Hum. Res.—Ted Smith; V-P., Bus. Dev.—Mike Guidry**
Whitlock Packaging Corp., 92 N. Main St., Wharton, 07885 ................. (973) 361-9794

**WICKS GROUP OF COS., LLC, THE**
**400 Park Ave., Ste. 1210, New York NY 10022 ........................ (212) 838-2100**
**Co-Founder & Mng. Ptnr.—Craig Klosk; Mng. Ptnr.—Matthew Gormly III; Mng. Ptnr.—Daniel Black; Mng. Ptnr.—Daniel Kortick; Opers. Mgr.—Andreia Santos**
North Star Travel Media, LLC (H Q), 100 Lighting Way, 2nd Fl., Secaucus, 07094. (201) 902-2000

**WILLIAMS SCOTSMAN, INC.**
**901 S. Bond St., Ste. 600, Baltimore MD 21231 ....................... (410) 931-6000**
**Chrm. of the Board—Gerald Holthaus; Pres., CEO—John Mark; CFO—Tom Koster; V-P., Mktg.—Lin Snyder; Cont.—Michelle Cunningham; Dir., Hum. Res.—Lisa Potis**
Williams Scotsman, Inc., 35 Ford Ln., Kearny, 07032...................... (973) 589-1234

**WMS INDUSTRIES, INC.**
**800 S. Northpoint Blvd., Waukegan IL 60085 ......................... (847) 785-3000**
**Pres., COO—Kenneth Lochiatto; CFO, Gaming & Chief Integration Officer—Scott D. Schweinfurth; CTO, Enterprise—Steven W. Beason; Chief Revenue Officer—Brooks Pierce; Sr. V-P., Prod. Dev.—Frederick M. Gabbard**
WMS Gaming, Inc., 2511 Fire Rd., Ste. A-10, Egg Harbor Township, 08234..... (609) 569-0100

**WOODHAVEN LUMBER & MILLWORK, INC.**
**200 James St., P.O. Box 870, Lakewood NJ 08701...................... (732) 901-0030**
**Pres.—Alan Robinson; V-P.—David Robinson; Cont.—Peter Lavin; Dir., Mktg.—Tom London**
Woodhaven Lumber & Millwork, Inc., 725 E. Bay Ave., Manahawkin, 08050..... (609) 597-1118

**WORLD JOURNAL**
**141-07 20th Ave., 2nd Fl., Whitestone NY 11357 ...................... (718) 746-8889**
**Pres.—Jan Young; Editor—Tai Sheng Won; IT Mgr.—James Lee; Acctg. Mgr.—Alice Chiang; Hum. Res. Mgr.—Salina Wu; Acct. Svcs. Mgr.—Rose Hsiung; Asst. Hum. Res. Mgr.—Pauline Cheng**
World Journal, Inc., 41-A Bridge St., Metuchen, 08840 .................... (732) 632-8890

**WORLDPAC, INC.**
**37137 Hickory St., Newark CA 94560 ............................... (510) 742-8900**
**Pres., CEO—Robert Cushing; Ex. V-P.—Mike Hellweg; Ex. V-P.—Steve Sharp; V-P., Sales—David Heine; V-P., Opers.—Patrick Healy; V-P., Mktg.—Mario Recchia; V-P., Pur.—Hans Wulff; V-P., Fin.—Steve Hoeven; V-P.—Susan Grass; V-P.—Peter Klotz**
Worldwide Parts & Accessories Corp., 300 Herrod Blvd., Dayton, 08810 ....... (732) 230-5000

**X-RITE, INC.**
**4300 44th St. S.E., Grand Rapids MI 49512 ......................... (616) 803-2100**
**Pres.—Ron Voigt; CFO—Jeffrey McKee; CIO—John Meighan; V-P., Hum. Res.—Tony Stohlmeyer; Plt. Mgr.—Roger Offringa**
Pantone LLC, 590 Commerce Blvd., Carlstadt, 07072 ...................... (201) 935-5500

© Copyright 2015 Manufacturers' News, Inc.

**XYLEM, INC.**
1 International Pl., Rye Brook NY 10573 . . . . . . . . . . . . . . . . . . . . . . . . . . . . . (914) 323-5700
  Pres., CEO—Patrick Decker; Pres., Dewatering, Xylem, Inc.—Colin R. Sabol;
    Sr. V.-P., CFO—Mike Speetzen; Sr. V.-P., Chief Hum. Res. Officer—Robyn Mingle;
    Sr. V.-P., Chief Comms. Officer—Angela A. Buonocore
Godwin, a Xylem brand, 84 Floodgate Rd., Bridgeport, 08014 . . . . . . . . . . . . . . (856) 467-3636

**YANK MARINE, INC.**
Mosquito Landing Rd., P.O. Box 569, Tuckahoe NJ 08250 . . . . . . . . . . . . . . (609) 628-2928
  Pres.—John C. Yank III; Mng. Member—Bette Jean Yank;
    Accts. Rec. & Hum. Res. Mgr.—Kellie Hartman
Jersey Diesel, 487 Main St., Dorchester, 08316 . . . . . . . . . . . . . . . . . . . . . . (856) 785-8810

**ZEUS INDUSTRIAL PRODUCTS, INC.**
620 Magnolia St., Orangeburg SC 29115 . . . . . . . . . . . . . . . . . . . . . . . . . . . (803) 268-9500
  CEO—John Worley; Pres.—John Winarchick;
    Sr. V.-P., Sales & Mktg., Global—Alan Andrews; V.-P., Sales & Mktg.—Bob Jennings;
    V.-P., Research & Strategic Dev.—Bob Ballard; V.-P., Engineered Extrusions—Rob Hall;
    Corp. Dir., Mktg.—Alvin Caughman; Dir., Hum. Res.—Bryan Hamrick;
    Corp. R & D Mgr.—Bruce Anneaux; Adv. Mgr.—Laura Young
Zeus Industrial Products, Inc., 134 Chubb Way, Branchburg, 08876 . . . . . . . . . . (908) 526-6500

**ZIEGLER CHEMICAL & MINERAL CORP.**
600 Prospect Ave., Piscataway NJ 08854 . . . . . . . . . . . . . . . . . . . . . . . . . (732) 752-4111
  Pres., Hum. Res. Mgr.—Chip Ziegler
Ziegler Chemical & Mineral Corp., 600 Prospect Ave., Bldg. A, Piscataway, 08854 . (732) 752-4111

**ZIMMER HOLDINGS, INC.**
345 E. Main St., Warsaw IN 46580 . . . . . . . . . . . . . . . . . . . . . . . . . . . . . . (574) 267-6131
  Pres., CEO—David Dvorak; Pres., Reconstructive—Jeff McCaulley;
    Ex. V.-P., Fin. & CFO—James Crines; V.-P., Fin., CAO & Corp. Cont.—Derek M. Davis
Zimmer Trabecular Metal Technology, 10 Pomerov Rd., Parsippany, 07054 . . . . . (973) 576-0032
Zimmer Tri-State, Inc., 1001 Briggs Rd., Ste. 275, Mount Laurel, 08054 . . . . . . . . (856) 778-8300

**ZODIAC AEROSPACE, INC.**
5701 Bolsa Ave., Huntington Beach CA 92647 . . . . . . . . . . . . . . . . . . . . . . (714) 934-0000
  Pres., CEO—Jude Dozor; CFO—John Maglione; V.-P., Hum. Res.—Rochelle Konyha;
    Matls. Mgr.—Gabriel Ward; Application Dev. Mgr.—Jonas English
Zodiac Arresting Systems America - Logan, 2239 High Hill Rd., Swedesboro, 08085 . (856) 241-8620

# America's Premiere Industrial Search Engine!

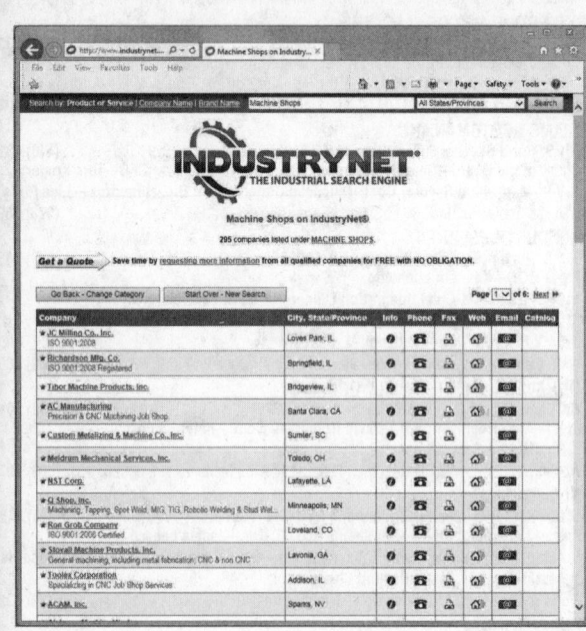

THE INDUSTRIAL SEARCH ENGINE

## mni's Industrial Search Engine

Allows decision makers to shop for products & industrial services among the 430,000 companies in MNI's database of U.S. manufacturers & suppliers. This is the guide to *"who makes it,"* *"who does it,"* and *"who supplies it!"*

## Absolutely free to users!

## No registration, hassle or obligation!

## *IndustryNet.com*

# COUNTY MARKETING BREAKDOWN SECTION

## NEW JERSEY CITIES, TOWNS AND VILLAGES BY COUNTIES

This section is a list of the state divided by counties. Under
each county name are the names of cities within that county.

### Atlantic County
Absecon
Atlantic City
Batsto
Brigantine
Buena
Cologne
Dorothy
Egg Harbor City
Egg Harbor Township
Elwood
Estell Manor
Folsom
Galloway
Hammonton
Landisville
Leeds Point
Linwood
Longport
Margate City
Mays Landing
Milmay
Minotola
Mizpah
Newtonville
Northfield
Oceanville
Pleasantville
Pomona
Port Republic
Richland
Somers Point
Ventnor City

### Bergen County
Allendale
Alpine
Bergenfield
Bogota
Carlstadt
Cliffside Park
Closter
Cresskill
Demarest
Dumont
East Rutherford
Edgewater
Elmwood Park
Emerson
Englewood
Englewood Cliffs
Fair Lawn
Fairview
Fort Lee
Franklin Lakes
Garfield
Glen Rock
Hackensack
Harrington Park
Hasbrouck Heights
Haworth
Hillsdale
Ho-Ho-Kus
Leonia
Little Ferry
Lodi
Lyndhurst
Mahwah
Maywood
Midland Park
Montvale
Moonachie
New Milford
North Arlington
Northvale
Norwood
Oakland
Old Tappan
Oradell
Palisade
Palisades Park
Paramus
Park Ridge

Ramsey
Ridgefield
Ridgefield Park
Ridgewood
River Edge
River Vale
Rochelle Park
Rockleigh
Rutherford
Saddle Brook
Saddle River
South Hackensack
Teaneck
Tenafly
Teterboro
Township of
  Washington
Upper Saddle River
Waldwick
Wallington
Westwood
Wood Ridge
Woodcliff Lake
Wyckoff

### Burlington County
Beverly
Birmingham
Bordentown
Browns Mills
Burlington
Chatsworth
Chesterfield
Cinnaminson
Clermont
Columbus
Cookstown
Crosswicks
Delanco
Delran
Eastampton
Eastampton Township
Edgewater Park
Fieldsboro
Florence
Fort Dix
Hainesport
Jobstown
Juliustown
Lumberton
Maple Shade
Marlton
Medford
Medford Lakes
Moorestown
Mount Holly
Mount Laurel
New Gretna
New Lisbon
Palmyra
Pemberton
Rancocas
Riverside
Riverton
Roebling
Shamong
Southampton
Tabernacle
Vincentown
Westampton
Willingboro
Wrightstown

### Camden County
Atco
Audubon
Barrington
Bellmawr
Berlin
Blackwood
Brooklawn
Camden
Cedar Brook

Cherry Hill
Clementon
Collingswood
Delair
Erial
Gibbsboro
Glendora
Gloucester City
Haddon Heights
Haddon Township
Haddonfield
Kirkwood
Laurel Springs
Lawnside
Lindenwold
Magnolia
Merchantville
Mount Ephraim
Oaklyn
Pennsauken
Pine Hill
Runnemede
Sicklerville
Somerdale
Stratford
Turnersville
Voorhees
Waterford Works
West Berlin
West Collingswood
  Heights
Westmont
Winslow

### Cape May County
Avalon
Cape May
Cape May Court
  House
Cape May Point
Dennisville
Goshen
Green Creek
Marmora
North Cape May
North Wildwood
Ocean City
Ocean View
Rio Grande
Sea Isle City
South Dennis
South Seaville
Stone Harbor
Strathmere
Tuckahoe
Villas
West Cape May
Whitesboro
Wildwood
Wildwood Crest
Woodbine

### Cumberland County
Bridgeton
Cedarville
Deerfield Street
Delmont
Dividing Creek
Dorchester
Fairton
Fortescue
Greenwich
Heislerville
Leesburg
Mauricetown
Millville
Newport
Port Elizabeth
Port Norris
Rosenhayn
Seabrook
Shiloh
Vineland

### Essex County
Belleville
Bloomfield
Caldwell
Cedar Grove
East Orange
Essex Fells
Fairfield
Glen Ridge
Irvington
Livingston
Maplewood
Millburn
Montclair
Newark
North Caldwell
Nutley
Orange
Roseland
Short Hills
South Livingston
South Orange
Upper Montclair
Verona
West Caldwell
West Orange

### Gloucester County
Blackwood Terrace
Bridgeport
Clarksboro
Clayton
Deptford
Ewan
Franklinville
Gibbstown
Glassboro
Grenloch
Harrisonville
Hurffville
Logan Township
Malaga
Mantua
Mickleton
Mount Royal
Mullica Hill
National Park
Newfield
Paulsboro
Pilesgrove
Pitman
Richwood
Sewell
Swedesboro
Thorofare
Wenonah
West Deptford
Westville
Williamstown
Woodbury
Woodbury Heights
Woolwich Township

### Hudson County
Bayonne
East Newark
Guttenberg
Harrison
Hoboken
Jersey City
Kearny
North Bergen
Secaucus
Union City
Weehawken
West New York

### Hunterdon County
Annandale
Baptistown
Bloomsbury
Blue Anchor

Califon
Clinton
Flemington
Frenchtown
Glen Gardner
Hampton
High Bridge
Lambertville
Lebanon
Little York
Milford
Oldwick
Pittstown
Pottersville
Quakertown
Readington
Ringoes
Rosemont
Sergeantsville
Stanton
Stockton
Three Bridges
Whitehouse
Whitehouse Station

### Mercer County
East Windsor
Ewing
Hamilton
Hamilton Square
Hamilton Township
Hightstown
Hopewell
Lawrence Township
Lawrenceville
Mercerville
Pennington
Princeton
Princeton Junction
Robbinsville
Titusville
Trenton
West Trenton
West Windsor
Windsor
Yardville

### Middlesex County
Avenel
Carteret
Colonia
Cranbury
Dayton
Dunellen
East Brunswick
Edison
Fords
Green Brook
Helmetta
Highland Park
Hopelawn
Iselin
Jamesburg
Keasbey
Kendall Park
Laurence Harbor
Metuchen
Middlesex
Milltown
Monmouth Junction
Monroe
Monroe Township
New Brunswick
North Brunswick
Old Bridge
Parlin
Perth Amboy
Piscataway
Plainsboro
Port Reading
Sayreville
Sewaren
South Amboy

South Plainfield
South River
Spotswood
Woodbridge

### Monmouth County
Aberdeen
Adelphia
Allenhurst
Allentown
Allenwood
Asbury Park
Atlantic Highlands
Avon by the Sea
Belford
Belmar
Bradley Beach
Brielle
Clarksburg
Cliffwood
Colts Neck
Cream Ridge
Deal
Eatontown
Englishtown
Fair Haven
Farmingdale
Fort Monmouth
Freehold
Hazlet
Highlands
Holmdel
Howell
Imlaystown
Keansburg
Keyport
Lake Como
Leonardo
Lincroft
Little Silver
Long Branch
Manalapan
Manasquan
Marlboro
Matawan
Middletown
Millstone Township
Monmouth Beach
Morganville
Navesink
Neptune
Neptune City
New Monmouth
Oakhurst
Ocean
Ocean Grove
Oceanport
Perrineville
Port Monmouth
Red Bank
Roosevelt
Rumson
Sea Bright
Sea Girt
Shrewsbury
Spring Lake
Suburban
Tennent
Tinton Falls
Union Beach
Wall
Wall Township
Wanamassa
West Long Branch
Wickatunk

### Morris County
Boonton
Brookside
Budd Lake
Butler
Cedar Knolls
Chatham

Chester
Convent Station
Denville
Dover
East Hanover
Flanders
Florham Park
Gillette
Green Village
Hibernia
Ironia
Kenvil
Kinnelon
Lake Hiawatha
Lake Hopatcong
Landing
Ledgewood
Lincoln Park
Long Valley
Madison
Mendham
Millington
Mine Hill
Montville
Morris Plains
Morristown
Mount Arlington
Mount Freedom
Mount Olive
Mount Tabor
Mountain Lakes
Netcong
New Vernon
Parsippany
Pequannock
Picatinny Arsenal
Pine Brook
Pompton Plains
Randolph
Riverdale
Rockaway
Roxbury Township
Schooleys Mountain
Stirling
Succasunna
Towaco
Wharton
Whippany

## Ocean County

Barnegat
Barnegat Light
Bay Head
Bayville
Beach Haven
Beachwood
Brick
Forked River
Harvey Cedars
Island Heights
Jackson
Lakehurst
Lakewood
Lanoka Harbor
Lavallette
Little Egg Harbor
Little Egg Harbor
  Township
Long Beach Township
Manahawkin
Manchester
Mantoloking
New Egypt
Normandy Beach
Ocean Gate
Pine Beach
Point Pleasant
Point Pleasant Beach
Point Pleasant Boro
Seaside Heights
Seaside Park
Ship Bottom
Stafford TWP
Surf City
Toms River
Tuckerton
Waretown
West Creek
Whiting

## Passaic County

Bloomingdale
Clifton
Haledon
Haskell
Hawthorne
Hewitt
Little Falls
Milton
Newfoundland
North Haledon
Oak Ridge
Passaic
Paterson
Pompton Lakes
Prospect Park
Ringwood
Totowa
Wanaque
Wayne
West Milford
West Paterson

## Salem County

Alloway
Carneys Point
Deepwater
Elmer
Hancocks Bridge
Monroeville
Norma
Pedricktown
Penns Grove
Pennsville
Pittsgrove
Quinton
Salem
Woodstown

## Somerset County

Basking Ridge
Bedminster
Belle Mead
Bernardsville
Blawenburg
Bound Brook
Branchburg
Bridgewater
Far Hills
Flagtown
Franklin Park
Gladstone
Hillsborough
Kingston
Liberty Corner
Lyons
Manville
Martinsville
Neshanic Station
North Branch
Peapack
Pluckemin
Raritan
Rocky Hill
Skillman
Somerset
Somerville
South Bound Brook
Warren
Zarephath

## Sussex County

Andover
Augusta
Branchville
Franklin
Fredon Township
Glasser
Glenwood
Greendell
Hamburg
Highland Lakes
Hopatcong
Lafayette
Layton
McAfee
Middleville
Montague
Newton

Ogdensburg
Sparta
Stanhope
Stillwater
Stockholm
Sussex
Swartswood
Tranquility
Vernon
Wallpack Center
Wantage

## Union County

Berkeley Heights
Clark
Cranford
Elizabeth
Fanwood
Garwood
Hillside
Kenilworth
Linden
Mountainside
Murray Hill
New Providence
North Plainfield
Plainfield
Rahway
Roselle
Roselle Park
Scotch Plains
Springfield
Summit
Union
Vauxhall
Watchung
Westfield
Woodland Park

## Warren County

Allamuchy
Alpha
Asbury
Belvidere
Blairstown
Broadway
Buttzville
Changewater
Columbia
Delaware
Great Meadows
Hackettstown
Hardwick
Hope
Johnsonburg
Oxford
Pattenburg
Phillipsburg
Port Murray
Stewartsville
Vienna
Washington

# 5-YEAR GROWTH PATTERN CHART BY CITY

| City | County & area of state where located | | 2011 | 2012 | 2013 | 2014 | 2015 | City | County & area of state where located | | 2011 | 2012 | 2013 | 2014 | 2015 |
|---|---|---|---|---|---|---|---|---|---|---|---|---|---|---|---|
| Aberdeen | Monmouth | N.E. | 1 | 1 | 2 | 2 | 2 | Clark | Union | N.E. | 22 | 20 | 19 | 16 | 17 |
| Absecon | Atlantic | S.E. | 7 | 6 | 6 | 7 | 7 | Clarksboro | Gloucester | S.W. | 3 | 2 | 2 | 2 | 2 |
| Allamuchy | Warren | N.W. | — | — | — | — | 1 | Clarksburg | Monmouth | N.E. | 4 | 2 | 2 | 2 | 2 |
| Allendale | Bergen | N.E. | 8 | 9 | 10 | 10 | 10 | Clayton | Gloucester | S.W. | 7 | 7 | 7 | 7 | 6 |
| Allentown | Monmouth | N.E. | 12 | 12 | 12 | 12 | 9 | Clementon | Camden | S.W. | 5 | 5 | 6 | 6 | 6 |
| Allenwood | Monmouth | N.E. | 2 | 3 | 3 | 4 | 4 | Clermont | Burlington | S.E. | 1 | 1 | 1 | — | — |
| Alpha | Warren | N.W. | 11 | 10 | 10 | 9 | 8 | Cliffside Park | Bergen | N.E. | 6 | 6 | 6 | 6 | 6 |
| Andover | Sussex | N.W. | 13 | 13 | 14 | 14 | 12 | Cliffwood | Monmouth | N.E. | 5 | 4 | 4 | 4 | 4 |
| Annandale | Hunterdon | N.W. | 4 | 4 | 4 | 4 | 3 | Clifton | Passaic | N.E. | 200 | 199 | 197 | 189 | 179 |
| Asbury | Warren | N.W. | 4 | 4 | 4 | 4 | 4 | Clinton | Hunterdon | N.W. | 7 | 5 | 4 | 6 | 4 |
| Asbury Park | Monmouth | N.E. | 21 | 22 | 21 | 19 | 17 | Closter | Bergen | N.E. | 14 | 14 | 12 | 13 | 14 |
| Atco | Camden | S.W. | 5 | 5 | 5 | 4 | 4 | Collingswood | Camden | N.E. | 8 | 8 | 9 | 8 | 8 |
| Atlantic City | Atlantic | S.E. | 14 | 14 | 14 | 14 | 13 | Cologne | Atlantic | S.E. | 2 | 2 | 2 | 2 | 2 |
| Atlantic Highlands | Monmouth | N.E. | 9 | 8 | 9 | 7 | 7 | Colonia | Middlesex | N.E. | 2 | 1 | 2 | 2 | 2 |
| Audubon | Camden | S.W. | 6 | 5 | 5 | 5 | 5 | Colts Neck | Monmouth | N.E. | 8 | 7 | 8 | 6 | 6 |
| Augusta | Sussex | N.W. | 3 | 3 | 2 | 3 | 2 | Columbia | Warren | N.W. | 7 | 7 | 7 | 7 | 7 |
| Avenel | Middlesex | N.E. | 34 | 35 | 34 | 37 | 31 | Columbus | Burlington | S.E. | 2 | 2 | 2 | 2 | 3 |
| Avon by the Sea | Monmouth | N.E. | 3 | 3 | 3 | 3 | 3 | Cookstown | Burlington | S.E. | 2 | 2 | 2 | 3 | 2 |
| Barnegat | Ocean | S.E. | 4 | 4 | 3 | 4 | 5 | Cranbury | Middlesex | N.E. | 54 | 55 | 54 | 56 | 51 |
| Barnegat Light | Ocean | S.E. | 2 | 2 | 1 | 1 | 1 | Cranford | Union | N.E. | 38 | 37 | 35 | 36 | 34 |
| Barrington | Camden | S.W. | 12 | 12 | 11 | 11 | 12 | Cream Ridge | Monmouth | N.E. | 8 | 8 | 8 | 9 | 10 |
| Basking Ridge | Somerset | N.E. | 9 | 8 | 8 | 10 | 9 | Cresskill | Bergen | N.E. | 6 | 5 | 4 | 3 | 5 |
| Bay Head | Ocean | S.E. | 1 | 1 | 1 | 1 | 1 | Dayton | Middlesex | N.E. | 39 | 41 | 41 | 39 | 38 |
| Bayonne | Hudson | N.E. | 39 | 39 | 41 | 38 | 32 | Deal | Monmouth | N.E. | 2 | 2 | 2 | 2 | 2 |
| Bayville | Ocean | S.E. | 16 | 15 | 17 | 18 | 17 | Deepwater | Salem | S.W. | 1 | 1 | 1 | 1 | 1 |
| Beach Haven | Ocean | S.E. | 1 | 1 | 1 | — | — | Deerfield Street | Cumberland | S.W. | 2 | 1 | 1 | 1 | 1 |
| Beachwood | Ocean | S.E. | 6 | 6 | 6 | 6 | 5 | Delair | Camden | S.W. | 4 | 4 | 3 | 2 | 2 |
| Bedminster | Somerset | N.E. | 3 | 4 | 6 | 8 | 3 | Delanco | Burlington | S.E. | 7 | 7 | 6 | 6 | 6 |
| Belford | Monmouth | N.E. | 3 | 3 | 3 | 3 | 4 | Delmont | Cumberland | S.W. | 1 | 1 | 1 | 1 | 1 |
| Belle Mead | Somerset | N.E. | 1 | 1 | 1 | 1 | 1 | Delran | Burlington | S.E. | 15 | 15 | 16 | 16 | 16 |
| Belleville | Essex | N.E. | 58 | 55 | 57 | 55 | 50 | Dennisville | Cape May | S.E. | — | 1 | 1 | 1 | 1 |
| Bellmawr | Camden | S.W. | 24 | 23 | 23 | 21 | 22 | Denville | Morris | N.W. | 30 | 30 | 33 | 35 | 32 |
| Belmar | Monmouth | N.E. | 16 | 14 | 12 | 12 | 11 | Deptford | Gloucester | S.W. | 8 | 8 | 8 | 8 | 8 |
| Belvidere | Warren | N.W. | 12 | 12 | 12 | 13 | 13 | Dorchester | Cumberland | S.W. | 1 | 1 | 2 | 2 | 2 |
| Bergenfield | Bergen | N.E. | 32 | 30 | 30 | 28 | 25 | Dorothy | Atlantic | S.E. | 1 | 1 | 1 | 1 | 2 |
| Berkeley Heights | Union | N.E. | 16 | 16 | 16 | 16 | 15 | Dover | Morris | N.W. | 51 | 47 | 45 | 43 | 36 |
| Berlin | Camden | S.W. | 34 | 34 | 35 | 34 | 33 | Dumont | Bergen | N.E. | 9 | 7 | 6 | 6 | 6 |
| Bernardsville | Somerset | N.E. | 7 | 7 | 6 | 6 | 7 | Dunellen | Middlesex | N.E. | 11 | 8 | 8 | 8 | 8 |
| Beverly | Burlington | S.E. | 16 | 16 | 13 | 14 | 15 | East Brunswick | Middlesex | N.E. | 56 | 55 | 52 | 49 | 43 |
| Birmingham | Burlington | S.E. | 2 | 2 | 2 | 2 | 1 | East Hanover | Morris | N.W. | 56 | 52 | 50 | 46 | 42 |
| Blackwood | Camden | S.W. | 24 | 19 | 18 | 19 | 18 | East Orange | Essex | N.E. | 24 | 25 | 21 | 21 | 21 |
| Blairstown | Warren | N.W. | 10 | 9 | 8 | 7 | 6 | East Rutherford | Bergen | N.E. | 63 | 59 | 59 | 56 | 53 |
| Blawenburg | Somerset | N.E. | — | — | 1 | 1 | 1 | East Windsor | Mercer | N.E. | 5 | 6 | 8 | 8 | 8 |
| Bloomfield | Essex | N.E. | 40 | 39 | 36 | 34 | 30 | Eastampton | Burlington | S.E. | 1 | 2 | 1 | 2 | 1 |
| Bloomingdale | Passaic | N.E. | 6 | 6 | 7 | 7 | 7 | Eastampton Township | Burlington | S.E. | 1 | — | — | — | — |
| Bloomsbury | Hunterdon | N.W. | 5 | 5 | 5 | 5 | 5 | Eatontown | Monmouth | N.E. | 38 | 35 | 38 | 42 | 43 |
| Blue Anchor | Hunterdon | N.W. | — | — | — | 1 | 1 | Edgewater | Bergen | N.E. | 12 | 11 | 12 | 7 | 7 |
| Bogota | Bergen | N.E. | 7 | 7 | 8 | 9 | 8 | Edgewater Park | Burlington | S.E. | 2 | 2 | 3 | 3 | 4 |
| Boonton | Morris | N.W. | 47 | 47 | 47 | 44 | 40 | Edison | Middlesex | N.E. | 163 | 166 | 170 | 162 | 145 |
| Bordentown | Burlington | S.E. | 15 | 16 | 17 | 17 | 14 | Egg Harbor City | Atlantic | S.E. | 17 | 17 | 18 | 18 | 15 |
| Bound Brook | Somerset | N.E. | 12 | 13 | 12 | 10 | 8 | Egg Harbor Township | Atlantic | S.E. | 37 | 37 | 36 | 36 | 36 |
| Bradley Beach | Monmouth | N.E. | 6 | 5 | 6 | 5 | 5 | Elizabeth | Union | N.E. | 95 | 95 | 92 | 88 | 82 |
| Branchburg | Somerset | N.E. | 32 | 31 | 35 | 38 | 38 | Elmer | Salem | S.W. | 7 | 7 | 6 | 5 | 5 |
| Branchville | Sussex | N.W. | 10 | 10 | 9 | 8 | 9 | Elmwood Park | Bergen | N.E. | 34 | 37 | 35 | 35 | 33 |
| Brick | Ocean | S.E. | 33 | 32 | 34 | 33 | 30 | Elwood | Atlantic | S.E. | 1 | 1 | 1 | 1 | 1 |
| Bridgeport | Gloucester | S.W. | 16 | 16 | 15 | 15 | 14 | Emerson | Bergen | N.E. | 9 | 9 | 11 | 11 | 10 |
| Bridgeton | Cumberland | S.W. | 35 | 33 | 32 | 34 | 34 | Englewood | Bergen | N.E. | 68 | 69 | 68 | 68 | 65 |
| Bridgewater | Somerset | N.E. | 39 | 39 | 40 | 38 | 36 | Englewood Cliffs | Bergen | N.E. | 20 | 20 | 19 | 20 | 16 |
| Brielle | Monmouth | N.E. | 3 | 2 | 2 | 3 | 3 | Englishtown | Monmouth | N.E. | 24 | 19 | 21 | 20 | 22 |
| Brigantine | Atlantic | S.E. | 1 | 1 | — | — | 1 | Erial | Camden | S.W. | 1 | 1 | 1 | 1 | 1 |
| Broadway | Warren | N.W. | 2 | 1 | 1 | 1 | 1 | Estell Manor | Atlantic | S.E. | 1 | 1 | — | — | — |
| Brooklawn | Camden | S.W. | 5 | 5 | 5 | 5 | 5 | Ewing | Mercer | N.E. | 23 | 23 | 23 | 25 | 25 |
| Budd Lake | Morris | N.W. | 8 | 8 | 10 | 8 | 8 | Fair Haven | Monmouth | N.E. | 1 | 1 | 1 | 1 | — |
| Buena | Atlantic | S.E. | 7 | 7 | 7 | 6 | 6 | Fair Lawn | Bergen | N.E. | 51 | 52 | 53 | 54 | 47 |
| Burlington | Burlington | S.E. | 53 | 51 | 51 | 52 | 51 | Fairfield | Essex | N.E. | 230 | 227 | 218 | 223 | 212 |
| Butler | Morris | N.W. | 31 | 30 | 30 | 30 | 28 | Fairton | Cumberland | S.W. | 2 | 2 | 2 | 2 | 2 |
| Caldwell | Essex | N.E. | 11 | 10 | 8 | 11 | 10 | Fairview | Bergen | N.E. | 26 | 27 | 26 | 25 | 25 |
| Califon | Hunterdon | N.W. | 7 | 8 | 8 | 8 | 7 | Fanwood | Union | N.E. | 6 | 4 | 4 | 4 | 4 |
| Camden | Camden | S.W. | 76 | 68 | 63 | 59 | 57 | Far Hills | Somerset | N.E. | 4 | 3 | 2 | 2 | 2 |
| Cape May | Cape May | S.E. | 17 | 18 | 18 | 17 | 17 | Farmingdale | Monmouth | N.E. | 60 | 56 | 56 | 56 | 52 |
| Cape May Court House | Cape May | S.E. | 16 | 15 | 13 | 13 | 14 | Fieldsboro | Burlington | S.E. | 1 | 1 | 1 | 1 | 1 |
| Carlstadt | Bergen | N.E. | 132 | 129 | 128 | 126 | 112 | Flanders | Morris | N.W. | 23 | 21 | 21 | 19 | 17 |
| Carneys Point | Salem | S.W. | 5 | 5 | 5 | 5 | 4 | Flemington | Hunterdon | N.W. | 47 | 45 | 47 | 50 | 49 |
| Carteret | Middlesex | N.E. | 22 | 22 | 18 | 15 | 12 | Florence | Burlington | S.E. | 6 | 6 | 6 | 6 | 6 |
| Cedar Brook | Camden | S.W. | 1 | 1 | 1 | 1 | 1 | Florham Park | Morris | N.W. | 17 | 19 | 18 | 17 | 20 |
| Cedar Grove | Essex | N.E. | 35 | 33 | 32 | 33 | 29 | Folsom | Atlantic | S.E. | 2 | 1 | 1 | 1 | 1 |
| Cedar Knolls | Morris | N.W. | 19 | 17 | 16 | 17 | 14 | Fords | Middlesex | N.E. | 8 | 7 | 7 | 7 | 5 |
| Cedarville | Cumberland | S.W. | 4 | 4 | 3 | 3 | 3 | Forked River | Ocean | S.E. | 20 | 20 | 19 | 19 | 19 |
| Chatham | Morris | N.W. | 14 | 12 | 12 | 13 | 15 | Fort Dix | Burlington | S.E. | 1 | 1 | 1 | 1 | 1 |
| Chatsworth | Burlington | S.E. | 1 | — | 1 | 1 | — | Fort Lee | Bergen | N.E. | 24 | 25 | 25 | 26 | 25 |
| Cherry Hill | Camden | S.W. | 93 | 88 | 86 | 88 | 82 | Franklin | Sussex | N.W. | 25 | 22 | 22 | 20 | 17 |
| Chester | Morris | N.W. | 5 | 6 | 6 | 6 | 4 | Franklin Lakes | Bergen | N.E. | 20 | 19 | 17 | 16 | 16 |
| Chesterfield | Burlington | South | 2 | 3 | 3 | 3 | 2 | Franklin Park | Somerset | N.E. | 1 | 1 | 1 | 1 | 1 |
| Cinnaminson | Burlington | S.E. | 46 | 41 | 40 | 37 | 33 | Franklinville | Gloucester | S.W. | 6 | 5 | 5 | 4 | 5 |

© Copyright 2015 Manufacturers' News, Inc.

| City | County & area of state where located | | 2011 | 2012 | 2013 | 2014 | 2015 |
|---|---|---|---|---|---|---|---|
| Freehold | Monmouth | N.E. | 47 | 44 | 45 | 47 | 51 |
| Frenchtown | Hunterdon | N.W. | 10 | 10 | 9 | 8 | 7 |
| Galloway | Atlantic | S.E. | 1 | — | — | — | — |
| Garfield | Bergen | N.E. | 75 | 74 | 70 | 71 | 67 |
| Garwood | Union | N.E. | 22 | 19 | 19 | 19 | 19 |
| Gibbsboro | Camden | S.W. | 4 | 4 | 4 | 5 | 6 |
| Gibbstown | Gloucester | S.W. | 3 | 3 | 2 | 2 | 2 |
| Gillette | Morris | N.W. | 3 | 3 | 3 | 2 | 2 |
| Glassboro | Gloucester | S.W. | 19 | 19 | 19 | 19 | 18 |
| Glen Gardner | Hunterdon | N.W. | 3 | 3 | 3 | 3 | 3 |
| Glen Ridge | Essex | N.E. | 3 | 2 | 2 | 2 | 2 |
| Glen Rock | Bergen | N.E. | 9 | 11 | 11 | 11 | 7 |
| Glendora | Camden | S.W. | 5 | 5 | 5 | 4 | 3 |
| Gloucester City | Camden | S.W. | 18 | 19 | 18 | 16 | 15 |
| Great Meadows | Warren | N.W. | 3 | 3 | 3 | 3 | 3 |
| Green Brook | Middlesex | N.E. | 9 | 8 | 7 | 7 | 8 |
| Green Village | Morris | N.W. | 1 | 1 | 1 | 1 | 1 |
| Grenloch | Gloucester | S.W. | 1 | 1 | 1 | 1 | 1 |
| Guttenberg | Hudson | N.E. | 7 | 6 | 5 | 5 | 5 |
| Hackensack | Bergen | N.E. | 137 | 137 | 130 | 119 | 114 |
| Hackettstown | Warren | N.W. | 37 | 35 | 34 | 37 | 34 |
| Haddon Heights | Camden | S.W. | 2 | 3 | 3 | 2 | 2 |
| Haddon Township | Camden | S.W. | — | — | — | — | 1 |
| Haddonfield | Camden | S.W. | 5 | 5 | 5 | 8 | 8 |
| Hainesport | Burlington | S.E. | 14 | 14 | 14 | 13 | 14 |
| Haledon | Passaic | N.E. | 9 | 9 | 9 | 8 | 9 |
| Hamburg | Sussex | N.W. | 9 | 10 | 9 | 10 | 9 |
| Hamilton | Mercer | N.E. | 24 | 25 | 26 | 27 | 28 |
| Hamilton Square | Mercer | N.E. | 1 | 1 | 1 | 2 | 2 |
| Hamilton Township | Mercer | N.E. | 1 | 1 | 1 | 2 | 2 |
| Hammonton | Atlantic | S.E. | 32 | 38 | 37 | 32 | 29 |
| Hampton | Hunterdon | N.W. | 10 | 9 | 10 | 8 | 8 |
| Hardwick | Warren | N.W. | 1 | 1 | 1 | 1 | 1 |
| Harrington Park | Bergen | N.E. | 2 | 2 | 2 | 1 | 2 |
| Harrison | Hudson | N.E. | 25 | 25 | 26 | 26 | 21 |
| Hasbrouck Heights | Bergen | N.E. | 9 | 8 | 8 | 8 | 7 |
| Haskell | Passaic | N.E. | 13 | 12 | 12 | 11 | 12 |
| Haworth | Bergen | N.E. | — | — | 1 | 1 | 1 |
| Hawthorne | Passaic | N.E. | 58 | 56 | 56 | 53 | 50 |
| Hazlet | Monmouth | N.E. | 13 | 13 | 13 | 12 | 13 |
| Heislerville | Cumberland | S.W. | 1 | — | — | — | — |
| Hewitt | Passaic | N.E. | 11 | 10 | 10 | 8 | 9 |
| High Bridge | Hunterdon | N.W. | 6 | 6 | 6 | 6 | 6 |
| Highland Park | Middlesex | N.E. | 5 | 4 | 3 | 3 | 3 |
| Highlands | Monmouth | N.E. | 1 | 1 | 1 | 1 | 1 |
| Hightstown | Mercer | N.E. | 13 | 10 | 8 | 9 | 9 |
| Hillsborough | Somerset | N.E. | 71 | 68 | 65 | 63 | 61 |
| Hillsdale | Bergen | N.E. | 9 | 9 | 7 | 5 | 5 |
| Hillside | Union | N.E. | 72 | 71 | 70 | 67 | 58 |
| Hoboken | Hudson | N.E. | 34 | 34 | 27 | 26 | 23 |
| Ho-Ho-Kus | Bergen | N.E. | 7 | 7 | 7 | 8 | 7 |
| Holmdel | Monmouth | N.E. | 6 | 6 | 7 | 7 | 6 |
| Hopatcong | Sussex | N.W. | 2 | 2 | 2 | 1 | 2 |
| Hope | Warren | N.W. | 1 | 1 | 1 | 1 | 1 |
| Hopelawn | Middlesex | N.E. | 1 | 1 | 1 | 1 | 1 |
| Hopewell | Mercer | N.E. | 4 | 5 | 4 | 5 | 5 |
| Howell | Monmouth | N.E. | 36 | 35 | 33 | 37 | 36 |
| Hurffville | Gloucester | S.W. | 2 | 2 | 2 | 2 | 1 |
| Imlaystown | Monmouth | N.E. | 1 | — | — | — | — |
| Irvington | Essex | N.E. | 46 | 43 | 41 | 38 | 32 |
| Iselin | Middlesex | N.E. | 15 | 15 | 15 | 14 | 18 |
| Island Heights | Ocean | S.E. | 3 | 3 | 3 | 2 | 2 |
| Jackson | Ocean | S.E. | 25 | 26 | 26 | 23 | 20 |
| Jamesburg | Middlesex | N.E. | 8 | 6 | 6 | 4 | 4 |
| Jersey City | Hudson | N.E. | 155 | 151 | 140 | 130 | 107 |
| Johnsonburg | Warren | N.W. | 1 | 1 | 1 | 1 | 1 |
| Keansburg | Monmouth | N.E. | 3 | 4 | 4 | 4 | 3 |
| Kearny | Hudson | N.E. | 72 | 75 | 75 | 70 | 63 |
| Keasbey | Middlesex | N.E. | 7 | 8 | 8 | 8 | 10 |
| Kendall Park | Middlesex | N.E. | 2 | 2 | 2 | 2 | 2 |
| Kenilworth | Union | N.E. | 88 | 89 | 87 | 83 | 80 |
| Kenvil | Morris | N.W. | 3 | 3 | 3 | 3 | 3 |
| Keyport | Monmouth | N.E. | 22 | 22 | 21 | 20 | 17 |
| Kingston | Somerset | N.E. | 2 | 2 | 2 | 3 | 2 |
| Kinnelon | Morris | N.W. | 5 | 5 | 5 | 5 | 3 |
| Lafayette | Sussex | N.W. | 10 | 9 | 9 | 10 | 10 |
| Lake Como | Monmouth | N.E. | 1 | 1 | 1 | 1 | 1 |
| Lake Hiawatha | Morris | N.W. | 7 | 7 | 5 | 5 | 3 |
| Lake Hopatcong | Morris | N.W. | 12 | 12 | 9 | 6 | 9 |
| Lakehurst | Ocean | S.E. | 2 | 1 | 1 | 1 | 1 |
| Lakewood | Ocean | S.E. | 132 | 133 | 130 | 125 | 125 |
| Lambertville | Hunterdon | N.W. | 10 | 11 | 11 | 9 | 8 |
| Landing | Morris | N.W. | 6 | 6 | 5 | 6 | 7 |
| Landisville | Atlantic | S.E. | 2 | 2 | 2 | 2 | 2 |
| Laurel Springs | Camden | S.W. | 3 | 2 | 2 | 2 | 3 |
| Laurence Harbor | Middlesex | N.E. | 3 | 3 | 3 | 3 | 2 |
| Lavallette | Ocean | S.E. | 3 | 4 | 4 | 4 | 2 |
| Lawrence Township | Mercer | N.E. | — | — | — | 3 | 3 |
| Lawrenceville | Mercer | N.E. | 15 | 16 | 17 | 15 | 14 |
| Lebanon | Hunterdon | N.W. | 18 | 19 | 19 | 22 | 21 |
| Ledgewood | Morris | N.W. | 8 | 8 | 10 | 9 | 8 |
| Leesburg | Cumberland | S.W. | 1 | 1 | 1 | 1 | 1 |
| Leonardo | Monmouth | N.E. | 2 | 1 | 1 | 1 | 1 |
| Leonia | Bergen | N.E. | 7 | 8 | 8 | 7 | 7 |
| Liberty Corner | Somerset | N.E. | 2 | 2 | 2 | 2 | 2 |
| Lincoln Park | Morris | N.W. | 12 | 12 | 12 | 11 | 12 |
| Lincroft | Monmouth | N.E. | 2 | 2 | 2 | 1 | 1 |
| Linden | Union | N.E. | 138 | 133 | 131 | 129 | 120 |
| Lindenwold | Camden | S.W. | 8 | 8 | 8 | 8 | 8 |
| Linwood | Atlantic | S.E. | 4 | 4 | 4 | 4 | 4 |
| Little Egg Harbor | Ocean | S.E. | 3 | 5 | 3 | 3 | 3 |
| Little Egg Harbor Township | Ocean | S.E. | 1 | 2 | 1 | — | — |
| Little Falls | Passaic | N.E. | 30 | 25 | 25 | 28 | 24 |
| Little Ferry | Bergen | N.E. | 28 | 22 | 22 | 17 | 16 |
| Little Silver | Monmouth | N.E. | 3 | 5 | 5 | 4 | 4 |
| Livingston | Essex | N.E. | 27 | 28 | 27 | 24 | 23 |
| Lodi | Bergen | N.E. | 46 | 45 | 46 | 46 | 41 |
| Logan Township | Gloucester | S.W. | 5 | 5 | 6 | 7 | 7 |
| Long Branch | Monmouth | N.E. | 21 | 21 | 21 | 22 | 19 |
| Long Valley | Morris | N.W. | 4 | 4 | 4 | 5 | 7 |
| Longport | Atlantic | S.E. | 1 | 1 | 1 | 1 | 1 |
| Lumberton | Burlington | S.E. | 13 | 16 | 16 | 15 | 13 |
| Lyndhurst | Bergen | N.E. | 39 | 40 | 39 | 36 | 35 |
| Madison | Morris | N.W. | 9 | 9 | 10 | 12 | 12 |
| Magnolia | Camden | S.W. | 2 | 2 | 2 | 2 | 1 |
| Mahwah | Bergen | N.E. | 58 | 61 | 60 | 63 | 64 |
| Malaga | Gloucester | S.W. | 1 | 1 | 1 | 1 | 1 |
| Manahawkin | Ocean | S.E. | 9 | 8 | 7 | 7 | 8 |
| Manalapan | Monmouth | N.E. | 18 | 20 | 21 | 20 | 18 |
| Manasquan | Monmouth | N.E. | 25 | 24 | 22 | 21 | 17 |
| Manchester | Ocean | S.E. | 6 | 5 | 4 | 4 | 4 |
| Mantoloking | Ocean | S.E. | 1 | 1 | 1 | 1 | 1 |
| Mantua | Gloucester | S.W. | 3 | 3 | 3 | 3 | 4 |
| Manville | Somerset | N.E. | 6 | 5 | 5 | 5 | 6 |
| Maple Shade | Burlington | S.E. | 23 | 22 | 22 | 22 | 22 |
| Maplewood | Essex | N.E. | 26 | 22 | 22 | 22 | 20 |
| Marlboro | Monmouth | N.E. | 16 | 17 | 18 | 18 | 16 |
| Marlton | Burlington | S.E. | 28 | 28 | 28 | 26 | 22 |
| Marmora | Cape May | S.E. | 1 | 1 | 1 | 2 | 2 |
| Martinsville | Somerset | N.E. | 3 | 3 | 2 | — | 1 |
| Matawan | Monmouth | N.E. | 23 | 20 | 19 | 19 | 19 |
| Mauricetown | Cumberland | S.W. | 1 | 1 | 1 | 1 | 1 |
| Mays Landing | Atlantic | S.E. | 9 | 9 | 9 | 7 | 8 |
| Maywood | Bergen | N.E. | 19 | 19 | 19 | 19 | 17 |
| Medford | Burlington | S.E. | 24 | 21 | 22 | 21 | 20 |
| Medford Lakes | Burlington | S.E. | 1 | 1 | 1 | 1 | 1 |
| Mendham | Morris | N.W. | 7 | 7 | 6 | 8 | 9 |
| Mercerville | Mercer | N.E. | 8 | 8 | 8 | 8 | 8 |
| Merchantville | Camden | S.W. | 6 | 6 | 4 | 5 | 6 |
| Metuchen | Middlesex | N.E. | 30 | 31 | 32 | 34 | 37 |
| Mickleton | Gloucester | S.W. | 3 | 3 | 3 | 4 | 5 |
| Middlesex | Middlesex | N.E. | 86 | 80 | 80 | 77 | 72 |
| Middletown | Monmouth | N.E. | 9 | 6 | 6 | 6 | 6 |
| Midland Park | Bergen | N.E. | 24 | 23 | 25 | 23 | 22 |
| Milford | Hunterdon | N.W. | 4 | 4 | 4 | 4 | 3 |
| Millburn | Essex | N.E. | 10 | 9 | 10 | 10 | 9 |
| Millington | Morris | N.W. | 9 | 9 | 9 | 8 | 7 |
| Millstone Township | Monmouth | N.E. | — | — | — | 1 | 2 |
| Milltown | Middlesex | N.E. | 6 | 6 | 7 | 6 | 6 |
| Millville | Cumberland | S.W. | 45 | 46 | 48 | 47 | 46 |
| Milmay | Atlantic | S.E. | 2 | 2 | 2 | 2 | 1 |
| Mine Hill | Morris | N.W. | 4 | 4 | 4 | 3 | 3 |
| Mizpah | Atlantic | S.E. | 1 | 1 | 1 | 1 | — |
| Monmouth Junction | Middlesex | N.E. | 28 | 27 | 28 | 27 | 27 |
| Monroe | Middlesex | N.E. | 3 | 3 | 5 | 5 | 5 |
| Monroe Township | Middlesex | N.E. | 18 | 17 | 18 | 19 | 16 |
| Monroeville | Salem | S.W. | 2 | 2 | 2 | 2 | 3 |
| Montague | Sussex | N.W. | 4 | 3 | 4 | 4 | 3 |
| Montclair | Essex | N.E. | 18 | 16 | 16 | 16 | 14 |
| Montvale | Bergen | N.E. | 16 | 18 | 18 | 18 | 18 |
| Montville | Morris | N.W. | 11 | 12 | 12 | 13 | 11 |
| Moonachie | Bergen | N.E. | 56 | 59 | 56 | 54 | 47 |
| Moorestown | Burlington | S.E. | 67 | 62 | 63 | 67 | 60 |
| Morganville | Monmouth | N.E. | 15 | 15 | 15 | 14 | 16 |
| Morris Plains | Morris | N.W. | 13 | 12 | 13 | 12 | 13 |
| Morristown | Morris | N.W. | 44 | 42 | 40 | 38 | 39 |
| Mount Arlington | Morris | N.W. | 1 | 1 | 1 | 1 | 2 |
| Mount Ephraim | Camden | S.W. | 7 | 7 | 7 | 5 | 5 |
| Mount Freedom | Morris | N.W. | 2 | 2 | 2 | 3 | 3 |
| Mount Holly | Burlington | S.E. | 20 | 21 | 23 | 19 | 16 |
| Mount Laurel | Burlington | S.E. | 61 | 65 | 68 | 67 | 63 |
| Mount Olive | Morris | N.W. | 1 | 2 | 2 | 2 | 4 |
| Mount Royal | Gloucester | S.W. | 1 | 1 | 1 | 1 | 1 |
| Mount Tabor | Morris | N.W. | 1 | 1 | 1 | 1 | 1 |

| City | County & area of state where located | | 2011 | 2012 | 2013 | 2014 | 2015 |
|---|---|---|---|---|---|---|---|
| Mountain Lakes | Morris | N.W. | 12 | 10 | 10 | 9 | 9 |
| Mountainside | Union | N.E. | 37 | 35 | 32 | 32 | 30 |
| Mullica Hill | Gloucester | S.W. | 3 | 3 | 4 | 5 | 4 |
| Murray Hill | Union | N.E. | 4 | 5 | 4 | 5 | 5 |
| National Park | Gloucester | S.W. | 1 | 1 | 1 | 1 | 1 |
| Neptune | Monmouth | N.E. | 39 | 38 | 39 | 37 | 35 |
| Neptune City | Monmouth | N.E. | 5 | 5 | 5 | 5 | 6 |
| Neshanic Station | Somerset | N.E. | 1 | 1 | 1 | 1 | 1 |
| Netcong | Morris | N.W. | 4 | 2 | — | — | — |
| New Brunswick | Middlesex | N.E. | 66 | 65 | 67 | 64 | 58 |
| New Egypt | Ocean | S.E. | 5 | 4 | 4 | 4 | 3 |
| New Gretna | Burlington | S.E. | 3 | 3 | 2 | 2 | 3 |
| New Milford | Bergen | N.E. | 3 | 3 | 3 | 3 | 4 |
| New Providence | Union | N.E. | 15 | 15 | 18 | 16 | 16 |
| New Vernon | Morris | N.W. | 1 | 1 | 1 | 1 | — |
| Newark | Essex | N.E. | 322 | 310 | 303 | 289 | 281 |
| Newfield | Gloucester | S.W. | 10 | 10 | 7 | 5 | 3 |
| Newfoundland | Passaic | N.E. | 6 | 6 | 6 | 6 | 4 |
| Newport | Cumberland | S.W. | 2 | 2 | 1 | 2 | 2 |
| Newton | Sussex | N.W. | 33 | 30 | 31 | 32 | 29 |
| Norma | Salem | S.W. | 1 | 1 | 1 | 1 | 1 |
| North Arlington | Bergen | N.E. | 13 | 15 | 15 | 13 | 11 |
| North Bergen | Hudson | N.E. | 63 | 59 | 57 | 53 | 48 |
| North Branch | Somerset | N.E. | 7 | 6 | 5 | 5 | 5 |
| North Brunswick | Middlesex | N.E. | 48 | 50 | 53 | 50 | 51 |
| North Caldwell | Essex | N.E. | 1 | 1 | 1 | 1 | 2 |
| North Haledon | Passaic | N.E. | 2 | 2 | 2 | 2 | 2 |
| North Plainfield | Union | N.E. | 6 | 5 | 5 | 5 | 4 |
| Northfield | Atlantic | S.E. | 6 | 5 | 5 | 5 | 3 |
| Northvale | Bergen | N.E. | 46 | 43 | 42 | 43 | 38 |
| Norwood | Bergen | N.E. | 26 | 24 | 24 | 21 | 22 |
| Nutley | Essex | N.E. | 25 | 24 | 23 | 20 | 20 |
| Oak Ridge | Passaic | N.E. | 9 | 9 | 9 | 8 | 10 |
| Oakhurst | Monmouth | N.E. | 6 | 4 | 4 | 6 | 7 |
| Oakland | Bergen | N.E. | 38 | 35 | 34 | 32 | 29 |
| Oaklyn | Camden | S.W. | 2 | 3 | 2 | 3 | 3 |
| Ocean | Monmouth | N.E. | 29 | 29 | 28 | 28 | 23 |
| Ocean City | Cape May | S.E. | 9 | 9 | 10 | 10 | 10 |
| Ocean Grove | Monmouth | N.E. | 3 | 3 | 3 | 3 | 4 |
| Ocean View | Cape May | S.E. | 4 | 5 | 6 | 5 | 4 |
| Oceanport | Monmouth | N.E. | 2 | 2 | 4 | 4 | 5 |
| Oceanville | Atlantic | S.E. | — | — | — | 1 | 1 |
| Ogdensburg | Sussex | N.W. | 3 | 3 | 4 | 2 | 2 |
| Old Bridge | Middlesex | N.E. | 19 | 20 | 18 | 16 | 17 |
| Old Tappan | Bergen | N.E. | 6 | 6 | 6 | 6 | 6 |
| Oldwick | Hunterdon | N.W. | 1 | 1 | 1 | 1 | 1 |
| Oradell | Bergen | N.E. | 7 | 7 | 9 | 10 | 10 |
| Orange | Essex | N.E. | 28 | 25 | 27 | 26 | 26 |
| Oxford | Warren | N.W. | 3 | 3 | 4 | 4 | 3 |
| Palisades Park | Bergen | N.E. | 14 | 12 | 12 | 11 | 9 |
| Palmyra | Burlington | S.W. | 11 | 10 | 10 | 10 | 8 |
| Paramus | Bergen | N.E. | 37 | 39 | 41 | 40 | 34 |
| Park Ridge | Bergen | N.E. | 9 | 9 | 10 | 10 | 9 |
| Parlin | Middlesex | N.E. | 7 | 6 | 6 | 6 | 6 |
| Parsippany | Morris | N.W. | 78 | 83 | 92 | 89 | 87 |
| Passaic | Passaic | N.E. | 92 | 90 | 85 | 81 | 76 |
| Paterson | Passaic | N.E. | 276 | 264 | 254 | 246 | 237 |
| Paulsboro | Gloucester | S.W. | 20 | 21 | 19 | 18 | 18 |
| Peapack | Somerset | N.E. | 1 | 1 | 1 | 1 | 1 |
| Pedricktown | Salem | S.W. | 5 | 5 | 5 | 6 | 7 |
| Pemberton | Burlington | S.E. | 2 | 2 | 3 | 4 | 4 |
| Pennington | Mercer | N.E. | 20 | 18 | 19 | 17 | 16 |
| Penns Grove | Salem | S.W. | 3 | 1 | 1 | 1 | 1 |
| Pennsauken | Camden | S.W. | 130 | 128 | 128 | 132 | 122 |
| Pennsville | Salem | S.W. | 1 | 1 | 1 | 1 | 2 |
| Pequannock | Morris | N.W. | 7 | 6 | 4 | 4 | 3 |
| Perrineville | Monmouth | N.E. | 2 | 2 | 2 | 1 | 1 |
| Perth Amboy | Middlesex | N.E. | 46 | 47 | 45 | 42 | 36 |
| Phillipsburg | Warren | N.W. | 44 | 43 | 42 | 39 | 35 |
| Pilesgrove | Gloucester | S.W. | 2 | 2 | 2 | 1 | 1 |
| Pine Beach | Ocean | S.E. | 1 | 1 | 1 | 1 | 1 |
| Pine Brook | Morris | N.W. | 25 | 23 | 26 | 30 | 30 |
| Pine Hill | Camden | S.W. | 4 | 4 | 4 | 3 | 3 |
| Piscataway | Middlesex | N.E. | 98 | 94 | 92 | 96 | 97 |
| Pitman | Gloucester | S.W. | 18 | 13 | 13 | 11 | 8 |
| Pittsgrove | Salem | | 5 | 5 | 5 | 5 | 5 |
| Pittstown | Hunterdon | N.W. | 4 | 4 | 4 | 4 | 3 |
| Plainfield | Union | N.E. | 29 | 29 | 28 | 28 | 24 |
| Plainsboro | Middlesex | N.E. | 8 | 9 | 8 | 9 | 7 |
| Pleasantville | Atlantic | S.E. | 29 | 30 | 29 | 25 | 24 |
| Pluckemin | Somerset | N.E. | 1 | 1 | 1 | 1 | 1 |
| Point Pleasant | Ocean | S.E. | 9 | 9 | 9 | 9 | 9 |
| Point Pleasant Beach | Ocean | S.E. | 15 | 14 | 12 | 11 | 9 |
| Point Pleasant Boro | Ocean | S.E. | 3 | 4 | 4 | 5 | 6 |
| Pomona | Atlantic | S.E. | 2 | 2 | 1 | 1 | 1 |
| Pompton Lakes | Passaic | N.E. | 11 | 10 | 10 | 13 | 14 |
| Pompton Plains | Morris | N.W. | 21 | 21 | 21 | 19 | 18 |
| Port Elizabeth | Cumberland | S.W. | 1 | 1 | 1 | 1 | 1 |
| Port Monmouth | Monmouth | N.E. | 1 | 1 | 1 | 1 | 1 |
| Port Murray | Warren | N.W. | 5 | 4 | 4 | 4 | 4 |
| Port Norris | Cumberland | S.W. | 4 | 3 | 3 | 3 | 4 |
| Port Reading | Middlesex | N.E. | 6 | 7 | 7 | 8 | 6 |
| Port Republic | Atlantic | S.E. | 1 | 1 | 1 | 1 | 1 |
| Princeton | Mercer | N.E. | 63 | 68 | 70 | 73 | 69 |
| Princeton Junction | Mercer | N.E. | 9 | 9 | 12 | 11 | 12 |
| Prospect Park | Passaic | N.E. | 3 | 3 | 3 | 3 | 3 |
| Quakertown | Hunterdon | N.W. | 1 | 1 | 1 | 1 | 1 |
| Rahway | Union | N.E. | 64 | 65 | 67 | 67 | 66 |
| Ramsey | Bergen | N.E. | 31 | 32 | 33 | 35 | 31 |
| Rancocas | Burlington | S.E. | 8 | 8 | 8 | 8 | 8 |
| Randolph | Morris | N.W. | 43 | 45 | 44 | 41 | 41 |
| Raritan | Somerset | N.E. | 13 | 15 | 14 | 13 | 13 |
| Readington | Hunterdon | N.W. | 1 | 2 | 1 | — | — |
| Red Bank | Monmouth | N.E. | 26 | 29 | 28 | 26 | 28 |
| Richwood | Gloucester | S.W. | 1 | 1 | 1 | 1 | 1 |
| Ridgefield | Bergen | N.E. | 34 | 33 | 34 | 35 | 30 |
| Ridgefield Park | Bergen | N.E. | 19 | 20 | 17 | 17 | 18 |
| Ridgewood | Bergen | N.E. | 11 | 11 | 11 | 12 | 12 |
| Ringoes | Hunterdon | N.W. | 12 | 12 | 12 | 12 | 12 |
| Ringwood | Passaic | N.E. | 17 | 17 | 17 | 17 | 15 |
| Rio Grande | Cape May | S.E. | 7 | 6 | 7 | 6 | 6 |
| River Edge | Bergen | N.E. | 7 | 7 | 7 | 8 | 8 |
| River Vale | Bergen | N.E. | 1 | 1 | 1 | 1 | 1 |
| Riverdale | Morris | N.W. | 14 | 14 | 16 | 15 | 16 |
| Riverside | Burlington | S.E. | 24 | 21 | 20 | 17 | 15 |
| Riverton | Burlington | S.E. | 16 | 16 | 14 | 13 | 11 |
| Robbinsville | Mercer | N.E. | 21 | 23 | 22 | 23 | 21 |
| Rochelle Park | Bergen | N.E. | 14 | 12 | 11 | 13 | 12 |
| Rockaway | Morris | N.W. | 73 | 71 | 72 | 76 | 76 |
| Rockleigh | Bergen | N.E. | 5 | 8 | 7 | 7 | 6 |
| Rocky Hill | Somerset | N.E. | 1 | 1 | 1 | 1 | 1 |
| Roebling | Burlington | S.E. | — | — | — | — | 1 |
| Roosevelt | Monmouth | N.E. | 3 | 3 | 3 | 3 | 3 |
| Roseland | Essex | N.E. | 12 | 11 | 10 | 10 | 12 |
| Roselle | Union | N.E. | 43 | 45 | 43 | 41 | 37 |
| Roselle Park | Union | N.E. | 20 | 18 | 18 | 17 | 16 |
| Rosemont | Hunterdon | N.W. | 4 | 4 | 3 | 3 | 3 |
| Rosenhayn | Cumberland | S.W. | 5 | 5 | 5 | 5 | 5 |
| Roxbury Township | Morris | N.W. | — | — | — | 1 | 1 |
| Rumson | Monmouth | N.E. | 4 | 3 | 3 | 3 | 2 |
| Runnemede | Camden | S.W. | 8 | 7 | 8 | 7 | 7 |
| Rutherford | Bergen | N.E. | 13 | 16 | 14 | 13 | 11 |
| Saddle Brook | Bergen | N.E. | 49 | 55 | 53 | 51 | 48 |
| Saddle River | Bergen | N.E. | 4 | 4 | 4 | 4 | 5 |
| Salem | Salem | S.W. | 8 | 8 | 10 | 7 | 6 |
| Sayreville | Middlesex | N.E. | 19 | 20 | 21 | 20 | 19 |
| Scotch Plains | Union | N.E. | 17 | 17 | 17 | 18 | 17 |
| Sea Bright | Monmouth | N.E. | 3 | 2 | 2 | 1 | — |
| Sea Girt | Monmouth | N.E. | 2 | 2 | 2 | 3 | 2 |
| Sea Isle City | Cape May | S.E. | 2 | 2 | 2 | 2 | 2 |
| Seabrook | Cumberland | S.W. | 2 | 2 | 2 | 2 | 2 |
| Secaucus | Hudson | N.E. | 39 | 38 | 38 | 32 | 32 |
| Sewaren | Middlesex | N.E. | 2 | 2 | 2 | 2 | 2 |
| Sewell | Gloucester | S.W. | 17 | 15 | 14 | 17 | 18 |
| Shamong | Burlington | S.E. | 6 | 6 | 5 | 3 | 3 |
| Ship Bottom | Ocean | S.E. | 3 | 3 | 2 | 2 | 2 |
| Short Hills | Essex | N.E. | 4 | 3 | 2 | 2 | 3 |
| Shrewsbury | Monmouth | N.E. | 13 | 15 | 17 | 16 | 14 |
| Sicklerville | Camden | S.W. | 11 | 9 | 8 | 7 | 5 |
| Skillman | Somerset | N.E. | 5 | 5 | 6 | 6 | 5 |
| Somerdale | Camden | S.W. | 10 | 10 | 10 | 11 | 12 |
| Somers Point | Atlantic | S.E. | 7 | 7 | 5 | 3 | 3 |
| Somerset | Somerset | N.E. | 102 | 108 | 113 | 114 | 110 |
| Somerville | Somerset | N.E. | 59 | 55 | 54 | 50 | 51 |
| South Amboy | Middlesex | N.E. | 12 | 13 | 11 | 11 | 11 |
| South Bound Brook | Somerset | N.E. | 1 | 1 | 1 | 1 | 1 |
| South Hackensack | Bergen | N.E. | 58 | 61 | 58 | 47 | 41 |
| South Orange | Essex | N.E. | 5 | 5 | 7 | 7 | 7 |
| South Plainfield | Middlesex | N.E. | 133 | 134 | 136 | 124 | 116 |
| South River | Middlesex | N.E. | 22 | 23 | 21 | 21 | 19 |
| Southampton | Burlington | S.E. | 9 | 9 | 9 | 9 | 9 |
| Sparta | Sussex | N.W. | 31 | 37 | 36 | 34 | 34 |
| Spotswood | Middlesex | N.E. | 7 | 6 | 6 | 7 | 6 |
| Spring Lake | Monmouth | N.E. | 4 | 3 | 3 | 3 | 4 |
| Springfield | Union | N.E. | 51 | 51 | 55 | 55 | 52 |
| Stafford TWP | Ocean | S.E. | 51 | 51 | 55 | 55 | 52 |
| Stanhope | Sussex | N.W. | 9 | 9 | 9 | 9 | 10 |
| Stewartsville | Warren | N.W. | 3 | 3 | 3 | 3 | 3 |
| Stillwater | Sussex | N.W. | 2 | 2 | 2 | 2 | 2 |
| Stirling | Morris | N.W. | 11 | 10 | 8 | 8 | 8 |
| Stockholm | Sussex | N.W. | 2 | 2 | 2 | 2 | 1 |
| Stockton | Hunterdon | N.W. | 2 | 2 | 3 | 3 | 4 |
| Stratford | Camden | S.W. | 2 | 2 | 2 | 2 | 2 |
| Succasunna | Morris | N.W. | 10 | 9 | 10 | 9 | 10 |

| City | County & area of state where located | | 2011 | 2012 | 2013 | 2014 | 2015 |
|---|---|---|---|---|---|---|---|
| Summit | Union | N.E. | 14 | 16 | 16 | 16 | 12 |
| Surf City | Ocean | S.E. | 1 | 1 | 1 | 1 | 1 |
| Sussex | Sussex | N.W. | 11 | 11 | 11 | 10 | 10 |
| Swedesboro | Gloucester | S.W. | 35 | 38 | 36 | 36 | 30 |
| Tabernacle | Burlington | S.E. | 5 | 5 | 5 | 5 | 3 |
| Teaneck | Bergen | N.E. | 32 | 36 | 39 | 35 | 30 |
| Tenafly | Bergen | N.E. | 11 | 9 | 7 | 7 | 5 |
| Tennent | Monmouth | N.E. | 3 | 2 | 2 | 2 | 2 |
| Teterboro | Bergen | N.E. | 17 | 17 | 17 | 22 | 21 |
| Thorofare | Gloucester | S.W. | 19 | 18 | 19 | 17 | 16 |
| Three Bridges | Hunterdon | N.W. | 2 | 2 | 2 | 1 | 1 |
| Tinton Falls | Monmouth | N.E. | 18 | 19 | 17 | 19 | 19 |
| Titusville | Mercer | N.E. | 4 | 3 | 4 | 3 | 3 |
| Toms River | Ocean | S.E. | 66 | 65 | 58 | 57 | 57 |
| Totowa | Passaic | N.E. | 47 | 48 | 50 | 48 | 46 |
| Towaco | Morris | N.W. | 13 | 13 | 12 | 13 | 11 |
| Trenton | Mercer | N.E. | 193 | 183 | 175 | 162 | 140 |
| Tuckahoe | Cape May | S.E. | 3 | 4 | 4 | 3 | 3 |
| Tuckerton | Ocean | S.E. | 3 | 2 | 4 | 4 | 5 |
| Turnersville | Camden | S.W. | 8 | 7 | 6 | 6 | 6 |
| Union | Union | N.E. | 115 | 110 | 111 | 103 | 96 |
| Union Beach | Monmouth | N.E. | 3 | 3 | 3 | 1 | 1 |
| Union City | Hudson | N.E. | 27 | 25 | 25 | 27 | 24 |
| Upper Montclair | Essex | N.E. | — | 1 | 1 | 1 | 1 |
| Upper Saddle River | Bergen | N.E. | 14 | 15 | 15 | 13 | 13 |
| Vauxhall | Union | N.E. | 2 | 2 | 2 | 1 | — |
| Ventnor City | Atlantic | S.E. | 3 | 3 | 3 | 4 | 4 |
| Vernon | Sussex | N.W. | 9 | 8 | 8 | 7 | 7 |
| Verona | Essex | N.E. | 11 | 10 | 10 | 7 | 7 |
| Villas | Cape May | S.E. | 1 | 1 | 1 | 1 | 1 |
| Vincentown | Burlington | S.E. | 7 | 7 | 6 | 6 | 6 |
| Vineland | Cumberland | S.W. | 113 | 116 | 117 | 117 | 113 |
| Voorhees | Camden | S.W. | 16 | 16 | 17 | 18 | 19 |
| Waldwick | Bergen | N.E. | 19 | 19 | 17 | 17 | 16 |
| Wall | Monmouth | N.E. | 16 | 15 | 16 | 15 | 15 |
| Wall Township | Monmouth | N.E. | 10 | 11 | 9 | 9 | 8 |
| Wallington | Bergen | N.E. | 19 | 17 | 14 | 13 | 14 |
| Wanamassa | Monmouth | N.E. | 1 | 1 | — | — | — |
| Wanaque | Passaic | N.E. | 2 | 2 | 2 | 2 | 1 |
| Wantage | Sussex | N.W. | 2 | 2 | 2 | 3 | 4 |
| Waretown | Ocean | S.E. | 3 | 3 | 3 | 3 | 2 |
| Warren | Somerset | N.E. | 19 | 20 | 21 | 23 | 23 |
| Washington | Warren | N.W. | 16 | 17 | 16 | 15 | 16 |
| Watchung | Union | N.E. | 7 | 7 | 7 | 7 | 6 |
| Waterford Works | Camden | S.W. | 4 | 4 | 3 | 3 | 3 |
| Wayne | Passaic | N.E. | 90 | 82 | 80 | 76 | 71 |
| Weehawken | Hudson | N.E. | 6 | 6 | 6 | 6 | 6 |
| Wenonah | Gloucester | S.W. | 3 | 3 | 3 | 3 | 3 |
| West Berlin | Camden | S.W. | 55 | 54 | 49 | 50 | 49 |
| West Caldwell | Essex | N.E. | 39 | 40 | 39 | 39 | 37 |
| West Cape May | Cape May | S.E. | 2 | 2 | 2 | 1 | 1 |
| West Collingswood Heights | Camden | S.W. | 1 | 1 | 1 | 1 | 1 |
| West Creek | Ocean | S.E. | 10 | 9 | 8 | 7 | 6 |
| West Deptford | Gloucester | S.W. | 9 | 14 | 16 | 17 | 17 |
| West Long Branch | Monmouth | N.E. | 9 | 9 | 10 | 10 | 9 |
| West Milford | Passaic | N.E. | 13 | 13 | 12 | 9 | 9 |
| West New York | Hudson | N.E. | 25 | 25 | 24 | 23 | 24 |
| West Orange | Essex | N.E. | 27 | 28 | 29 | 25 | 22 |
| West Paterson | Passaic | N.E. | 17 | 10 | 6 | 6 | 4 |
| West Trenton | Mercer | N.E. | 2 | 3 | 3 | 3 | 3 |
| West Windsor | Mercer | N.E. | 2 | 1 | 1 | — | — |
| Westampton | Burlington | S.E. | 6 | 6 | 6 | 6 | 6 |
| Westfield | Union | N.E. | 12 | 13 | 13 | 13 | 12 |
| Westmont | Camden | S.W. | 1 | 1 | 1 | 1 | 1 |
| Westville | Gloucester | S.W. | 16 | 16 | 17 | 13 | 13 |
| Westwood | Bergen | N.E. | 30 | 29 | 27 | 24 | 20 |
| Wharton | Morris | N.W. | 26 | 26 | 26 | 24 | 27 |
| Whippany | Morris | N.W. | 30 | 30 | 28 | 29 | 25 |
| Whitehouse | Hunterdon | N.W. | 8 | 8 | 7 | 8 | 8 |
| Whitehouse Station | Hunterdon | N.W. | 11 | 11 | 11 | 12 | 11 |
| Whiting | Ocean | S.E. | 3 | 2 | 2 | 3 | 3 |
| Wildwood | Cape May | S.E. | 11 | 10 | 11 | 11 | 9 |
| Wildwood Crest | Cape May | S.E. | 1 | 2 | 2 | 2 | 2 |
| Williamstown | Gloucester | S.W. | 34 | 32 | 34 | 36 | 33 |
| Willingboro | Burlington | S.E. | 6 | 6 | 6 | 6 | 6 |
| Windsor | Mercer | N.E. | 9 | 8 | 8 | 8 | 9 |
| Winslow | Camden | S.W. | 2 | 2 | 2 | 2 | 2 |
| Wood Ridge | Bergen | N.E. | 10 | 9 | 10 | 9 | 7 |
| Woodbine | Cape May | S.E. | 4 | 4 | 4 | 4 | 3 |
| Woodbridge | Middlesex | N.E. | 17 | 18 | 19 | 16 | 17 |
| Woodbury | Gloucester | S.W. | 19 | 14 | 13 | 14 | 15 |
| Woodbury Heights | Gloucester | S.W. | 6 | 7 | 7 | 6 | 5 |
| Woodcliff Lake | Bergen | N.E. | 7 | 6 | 8 | 9 | 8 |
| Woodland Park | Union | N.E. | 11 | 16 | 21 | 19 | 18 |
| Woodstown | Salem | S.W. | 4 | 4 | 3 | 3 | 3 |
| Woolwich Township | Gloucester | S.W. | 4 | 4 | 4 | 4 | 4 |
| Wrightstown | Burlington | S.E. | 3 | 2 | 2 | 2 | 2 |
| Wyckoff | Bergen | N.E. | 26 | 27 | 25 | 24 | 20 |
| Yardville | Mercer | N.E. | 4 | 4 | 3 | 2 | 1 |

# 5-YEAR GROWTH PATTERN CHART BY COUNTY

The chart below indicates the number of manufacturing, processing and wholesale or distribution facilities profiled in the state over the last five years for all counties in the state.

| COUNTY | 2011 | 2012 | 2013 | 2014 | 2015 |
|---|---|---|---|---|---|
| Atlantic | 190 | 193 | 186 | 175 | 165 |
| Bergen | 1712 | 1715 | 1683 | 1631 | 1509 |
| Burlington | 531 | 519 | 518 | 507 | 472 |
| Camden | 612 | 587 | 571 | 568 | 549 |
| Cape May | 78 | 80 | 82 | 78 | 75 |
| Cumberland | 220 | 219 | 220 | 222 | 218 |
| Essex | 1002 | 967 | 942 | 916 | 870 |
| Gloucester | 295 | 288 | 285 | 281 | 265 |
| Hudson | 492 | 483 | 464 | 436 | 385 |
| Hunterdon | 177 | 176 | 175 | 179 | 169 |
| Mercer | 420 | 414 | 412 | 404 | 376 |
| Middlesex | 1119 | 1114 | 1112 | 1076 | 1013 |
| Monmouth | 692 | 664 | 669 | 664 | 642 |
| Morris | 831 | 815 | 814 | 800 | 774 |
| Ocean | 390 | 386 | 370 | 359 | 348 |
| Passaic | 912 | 873 | 852 | 821 | 782 |
| Salem | 42 | 40 | 40 | 37 | 38 |
| Somerset | 402 | 401 | 406 | 404 | 390 |
| Sussex | 178 | 176 | 176 | 171 | 163 |
| Union | 944 | 933 | 930 | 901 | 840 |
| Warren | 159 | 153 | 150 | 149 | 141 |

# 5-YEAR GROWTH PATTERN CHART BY INDUSTRY

The chart below indicates the number of manufacturing, processing and wholesale or distribution facilities profiled in the state over the last five years by industry.

| | 2011 | 2012 | 2013 | 2014 | 2015 |
|---|---|---|---|---|---|
| Metal mining | — | — | — | — | — |
| Coal mining | 2 | 2 | 1 | 1 | 1 |
| Oil and gas extraction | 6 | 6 | 6 | 7 | 10 |
| Nonmetallic minerals, except fuels | 20 | 20 | 18 | 22 | 26 |
| Food | 595 | 593 | 595 | 595 | 600 |
| Tobacco | 1 | 1 | 2 | 2 | 2 |
| Textiles | 106 | 103 | 98 | 96 | 97 |
| Apparel & Fabric Products | 530 | 513 | 507 | 501 | 504 |
| Lumber & Wood Products | 375 | 360 | 355 | 337 | 326 |
| Furniture & Fixtures | 237 | 230 | 226 | 217 | 216 |
| Paper & Allied Products | 266 | 266 | 263 | 258 | 254 |
| Printing & Publishing | 1328 | 1245 | 1195 | 1232 | 1265 |
| Chemicals | 734 | 744 | 762 | 766 | 755 |
| Petroleum & Fuel Products | 77 | 79 | 81 | 78 | 74 |
| Rubber & Plastic Products | 521 | 513 | 511 | 506 | 496 |
| Leather Goods | 30 | 28 | 27 | 26 | 25 |
| Stone, Glass & Concrete | 396 | 390 | 381 | 377 | 364 |
| Primary Metals | 211 | 210 | 201 | 192 | 185 |
| Metal Fabricating | 1051 | 1025 | 1005 | 978 | 944 |
| Industrial Machinery & Eqpt. | 1313 | 1280 | 1249 | 1225 | 1196 |
| Electrical & Electronic Eqpt. | 606 | 593 | 589 | 584 | 583 |
| Transportation Eqpt. | 151 | 144 | 141 | 137 | 134 |
| Measuring Devices | 468 | 469 | 463 | 461 | 460 |
| Misc. Manufacturing | 569 | 544 | 525 | 524 | 507 |
| Wholesale trade—durable goods | 1199 | 1198 | 1198 | 1048 | 718 |
| Wholesale trade—nondurable goods | 453 | 466 | 457 | 367 | 196 |
| Mfg. Allied Business Services | 149 | 170 | 194 | 235 | 238 |

# New Jersey
## By Sections and Counties

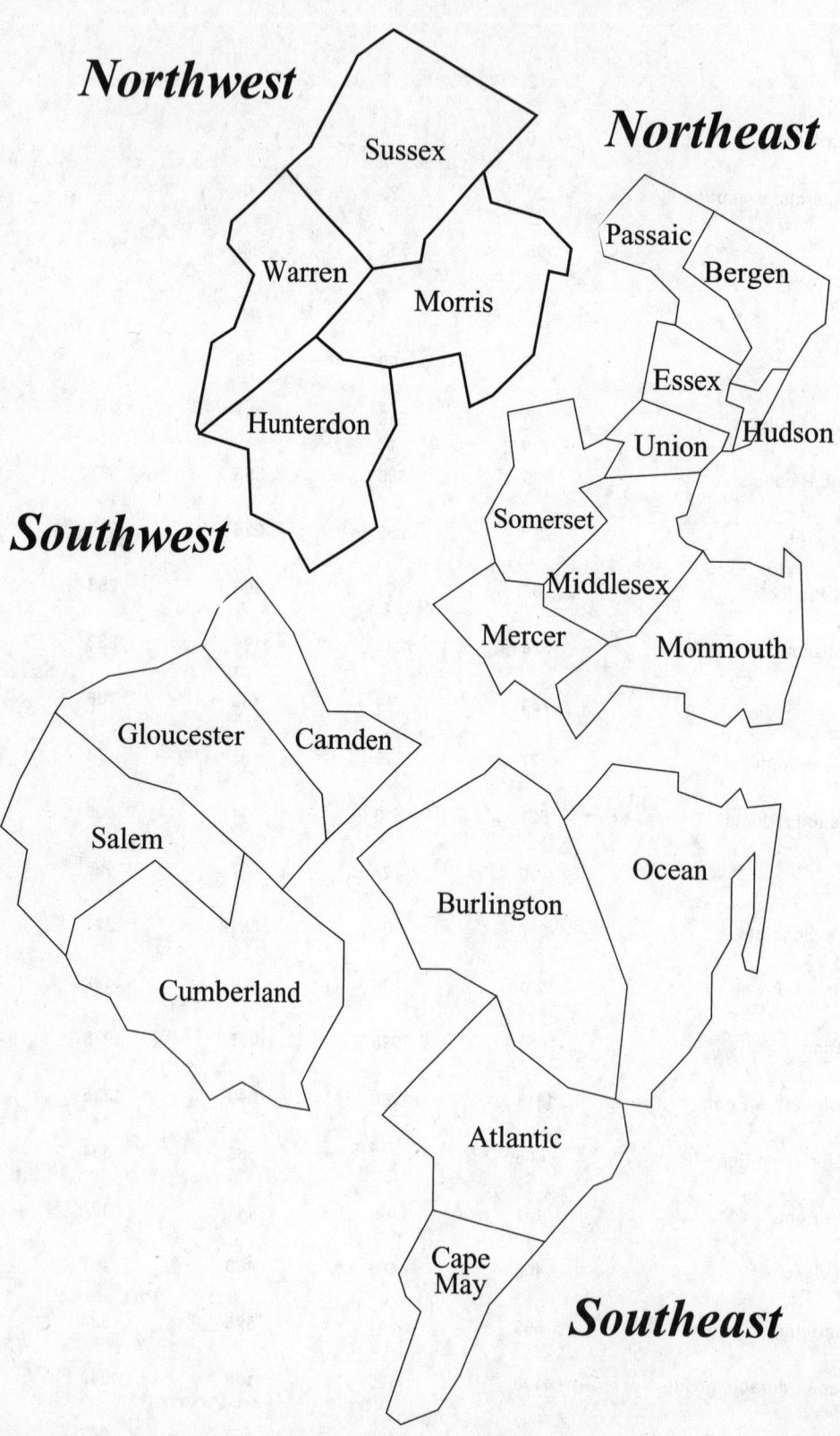

Northwest

Northeast

Sussex

Passaic

Bergen

Warren

Morris

Essex

Union

Hudson

Hunterdon

Southwest

Somerset

Middlesex

Mercer

Monmouth

Gloucester

Camden

Salem

Ocean

Burlington

Cumberland

Atlantic

Cape May

Southeast